Hoover's Handbook of

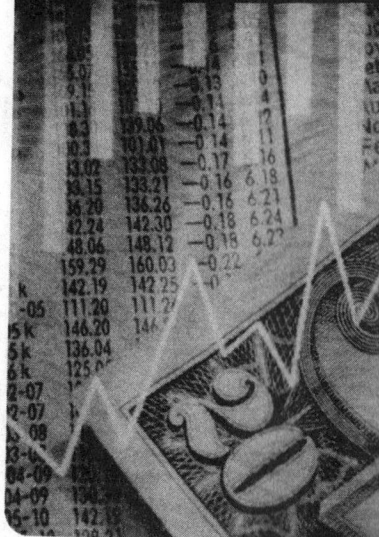

American Business

2018

A D&B COMPANY

Austin, Texas

Hoover's Handbook of American Business 2018 is intended to provide readers with accurate and authoritative information about the enterprises covered in it. Hoover's researched all companies and organizations profiled, and in many cases contacted them directly so that companies represented could provide information. The information contained herein is as accurate as we could reasonably make it. In many cases we have relied on third-party material that we believe to be trustworthy, but were unable to independently verify. We do not warrant that the book is absolutely accurate or without error. Readers should not rely on any information contained herein in instances where such reliance might cause financial loss. The publisher, the editors, and their data suppliers specifically disclaim all warranties, including the implied warranties of merchantability and fitness for a specific purpose. This book is sold with the understanding that neither the publisher, the editors, nor any content contributors are engaged in providing investment, financial, accounting, legal, or other professional advice.

The financial data (Historical Financials sections) in this book are from a variety of sources. Mergent Inc., provided selected data for the Historical Financials sections of publicly traded companies. For private companies and for historical information on public companies prior to their becoming public, we obtained information directly from the companies or from trade sources deemed to be reliable. Hoover's, Inc., is solely responsible for the presentation of all data.

Many of the names of products and services mentioned in this book are the trademarks or service marks of the companies manufacturing or selling them and are subject to protection under US law. Space has not permitted us to indicate which names are subject to such protection, and readers are advised to consult with the owners of such marks regarding their use. Hoover's is a trademark of Hoover's, Inc.

A D&B COMPANY

10 9 8 7 6 5 4 3 2 1

Publishers Cataloging-in-Publication Data
Hoover's Handbook of American Business 2018
    Includes indexes.
    ISBN: 978-1-68200-725-9
    ISSN 1055-7202
    1. Business enterprises — Directories. 2. Corporations — Directories.
HF3010 3387

U.S. AND WORLD BOOK SALES
Mergent Inc.
580 Kingsley Park Drive
Fort Mill, SC
29715
Phone: 800-342-5647
e-mail: orders@mergent.com
Web: www.mergentbusinesspress.com

Mergent Inc.

Executive Managing Director: John Pedernales

Managing Director of Print Products and Publisher: Thomas Wecera

Managing Director of Relationship Management: Chris Henry

Director of Print Products: Charlot Volny

Director of Data: Mohamed Hanif

Quality Assurance Editor: Wayne Arnold

Production Research Assistant: Davie Christna

Data Manager: Jason Horvat

MERGENT CUSTOMER SERVICE
Support and Fulfillment Manager: Melanie Horvat

ABOUT MERGENT INC.

For over 100 years, Mergent, Inc. has been a leading provider of business and financial information on public and private companies globally. Mergent is known to be a trusted partner to corporate and financial institutions, as well as to academic and public libraries. Today we continue to build on a century of experience by transforming data into knowledge and combining our expertise with the latest technology to create new global data and analytical solutions for our clients. With advanced data collection services, cloud-based applications, desktop analytics and print products, Mergent and its subsidiaries provide solutions from top down economic and demographic information, to detailed equity and debt fundamental analysis. We incorporate value added tools such as quantitative Smart Beta equity research and tools for portfolio building and measurement. Based in the U.S., Mergent maintains a strong global presence, with offices in New York, Charlotte, San Diego, London, Tokyo, Kuching and Melbourne. Mergent, Inc. is a member of the London Stock Exchange plc group of companies. The Mergent business forms part of LSEG's Information Services Division, which includes FTSE Russell, a global leader in indexes.

Abbreviations

AFL-CIO – American Federation of Labor and Congress of Industrial Organizations

AMA – American Medical Association

AMEX – American Stock Exchange

ARM – adjustable-rate mortgage

ASP – application services provider

ATM – asynchronous transfer mode

ATM – automated teller machine

CAD/CAM – computer-aided design/computer-aided manufacturing

CD-ROM – compact disc – read-only memory

CD-R – CD-recordable

CEO – chief executive officer

CFO – chief financial officer

CMOS – complementary metal oxide silicon

COO – chief operating officer

DAT – digital audiotape

DOD – Department of Defense

DOE – Department of Energy

DOS – disk operating system

DOT – Department of Transportation

DRAM – dynamic random-access memory

DSL – digital subscriber line

DVD – digital versatile disc/digital video disc

DVD-R – DVD-recordable

EPA – Environmental Protection Agency

EPROM – erasable programmable read-only memory

EPS – earnings per share

ESOP – employee stock ownership plan

EU – European Union

EVP – executive vice president

FCC – Federal Communications Commission

FDA – Food and Drug Administration

FDIC – Federal Deposit Insurance Corporation

FTC – Federal Trade Commission

FTP – file transfer protocol

GATT – General Agreement on Tariffs and Trade

GDP – gross domestic product

HMO – health maintenance organization

HR – human resources

HTML – hypertext markup language

ICC – Interstate Commerce Commission

IPO – initial public offering

IRS – Internal Revenue Service

ISP – Internet service provider

kWh – kilowatt-hour

LAN – local-area network

LBO – leveraged buyout

LCD – liquid crystal display

LNG – liquefied natural gas

LP – limited partnership

Ltd. – limited

mips – millions of instructions per second

MW – megawatt

NAFTA – North American Free Trade Agreement

NASA – National Aeronautics and Space Administration

NASDAQ – National Association of Securities Dealers Automated Quotations

NATO – North Atlantic Treaty Organization

NYSE – New York Stock Exchange

OCR – optical character recognition

OECD – Organization for Economic Cooperation and Development

OEM – original equipment manufacturer

OPEC – Organization of Petroleum Exporting Countries

OS – operating system

OSHA – Occupational Safety and Health Administration

OTC – over-the-counter

PBX – private branch exchange

PCMCIA – Personal Computer Memory Card International Association

P/E – price to earnings ratio

RAID – redundant array of independent disks

RAM – random-access memory

R&D – research and development

RBOC – regional Bell operating company

RISC – reduced instruction set computer

REIT – real estate investment trust

ROA – return on assets

ROE – return on equity

ROI – return on investment

ROM – read-only memory

S&L – savings and loan

SCSI – Small Computer System Interface

SEC – Securities and Exchange Commission

SEVP – senior executive vice president

SIC – Standard Industrial Classification

SOC – system on a chip

SVP – senior vice president

USB – universal serial bus

VAR – value-added reseller

VAT – value-added tax

VC – venture capitalist

VoIP – Voice over Internet Protocol

VP – vice president

WAN – wide-area network

WWW – World Wide Web

Contents

Companies Profiled vi

About *Hoover's Handbook of American Business 2018* xi

Using Hoover's Handbooks xii

A List-Lover's Compendium 1a

The Companies.. 1

The Indexes 945

    Index of Companies by Headquarters Location 947

    Index of Company Executives 955

List of Lists

HOOVER'S RANKINGS

The 300 Largest Companies by Sales in *Hoover's
Handbook of American Business 2018* 2a–3a

The Most Profitable Companies in *Hoover's
Handbook of American Business 2018* 4a–5a

The 300 Largest Employers in *Hoover's
Handbook of American Business 2018* 6a–7a

Mergent Top 500 Global Corp. by Revenues...................8a

Companies Profiled

1st Source Corp..........1
3m Co..........1
A-mark Precious Metals, Inc...........3
Abbott Laboratories..........4
Abbvie Inc...........5
Abm Industries, Inc..........7
Access Group, Inc...........8
Ace Hardware Corporation..........8
Activision Blizzard, Inc...........9
Adobe Systems Inc..........10
Advance Auto Parts Inc..........11
Advocate Health Care Network..........13
Aecom..........14
Aerotek, Inc...........15
Aes Corp...........16
Aetna Inc...........17
Aflac Inc...........19
Agco Corp...........20
Agsouth Farm Credit Aca..........21
Aimco Properties, L.p...........21
Air Products & Chemicals Inc..........21
Ak Steel Holding Corp...........23
Alabama Power Co..........24
Alaska Air Group, Inc...........25
Alaska Permanent Fund Corporation..........26
Alcoa Corporation..........27
Alerus Financial Corp..........27
Alfred P. Sloan Foundation..........27
Allegany Corp...........27
Allegiance Bancshares Inc..........28
Allegis Group, Inc...........28
Alliance Data Systems Corp...........29
Allstate Corp...........30
Ally Financial Inc..........32
Alphabet Inc..........33
Altria Inc..........34
Altior Inc...........34
Altria Group Inc..........35
Amazon.com Inc..........36
Ambac Financial Group, Inc...........38
Ameren Corp..........39
American Airlines Group Inc..........41
American Balanced Fund, Inc...........41
American Electric Power Company, Inc...........42
American Equity Investment Life
   Holding Co..........43
American Express Co...........44
American Financial Group Inc..........46
American International Group Inc..........47
American National Bankshares, Inc.
   (Danville, Va)..........47
American National Insurance Co.
   (Galveston, Tx)..........48
American Tire Distributors Holdings, Inc. 50
American Tower Corp (new)..........50
Ameriprise Financial Inc..........52
Ameris Bancorp..........53
Amerisafe Inc..........54
Amerisourcebergen Corp...........55
Amgen Inc..........56
Amphenol Corp...........58
Amtrust Financial Services Inc..........59
Anadarko Petroleum Corp..........60
Analog Devices Inc..........62
Andeavor..........63
Anixter International Inc..........64
Annaly Capital Management Inc..........65
Anthem Inc...........65
Apache Corp..........67
Apple Hospitality Reit, Inc...........68
Apple Inc...........69
Applied Materials, Inc...........70
Aramark..........71
Archer Daniels Midland Co...........73
Arconic Inc..........75
Arrow Electronics, Inc...........76
Arrow Financial Corp...........77
Asbury Automotive Group Inc..........77
Ascena Retail Group Inc..........78

Ascension Health Alliance..........79
Associated Banc-corp..........80
Associated Wholesale Grocers, Inc...........81
Assurant Inc..........82
At&t Inc..........83
Athene Annuity & Life Assurance
   Company..........85
Atlantic Capital Bancshares Inc..........85
Autoliv Inc..........85
Automatic Data Processing Inc...........87
Autonation, Inc...........88
Autozone, Inc...........89
Avangrid Inc..........91
Avery Dennison Corp..........91
Avis Budget Group Inc..........92
Avnet Inc..........93
Avon Products, Inc...........95
Baker Hughes, A Ge Company..........95
Ball Corp..........96
Banc Of California Inc..........97
Bancfirst Corp. (oklahoma City, Okla)..........98
Bancorpsouth Bank (tupelo, Ms)..........99
Bank Of America Corp...........100
Bank Of Hawaii Corp...........102
Bank Of Marin Bancorp..........104
Bank Of New York Mellon Corp...........104
Bank Of The Ozarks Inc (new)..........106
Bankfinancial Corp..........108
Bankunited Inc..........109
Bankwell Financial Group Inc..........110
Banner Corp...........110
Banner Health..........111
Bar Harbor Bankshares..........112
Battelle Memorial Institute..........113
Battelle Memorial Institute Inc..........113
Baxter International Inc..........114
Bb&t Corp...........116
Bcb Bancorp Inc..........118
Bear State Financial Inc..........118
Becton, Dickinson & Co...........119
Bed, Bath & Beyond, Inc...........120
Beneficial Bancorp Inc..........121
Berkley (wr) Corp...........121
Berkshire Hathaway Inc...........122
Berkshire Hills Bancorp Inc..........124
Berry Global Group Inc..........125
Best Buy Inc..........126
Big Lots, Inc...........127
Biogen Inc..........128
Biourja Trading, Llc..........130
Blackrock Inc..........130
Blackstone Group Lp (the)..........132
Blue Hills Bancorp Inc..........134
Board Of Education Of City Of Chicago..........134
Boeing Co. (the)..........134
Bofi Holding, Inc...........136
Bok Financial Corp..........137
Booz Allen Hamilton Holding Corp...........138
Borgwarner Inc..........139
Boston Private Financial Holdings, Inc...141
Boston Scientific Corp...........142
Bridge Bancorp, Inc.
   (bridgehampton, Ny)..........143
Brighthouse Financial Inc..........143
Brighthouse Life Insurance Co - Insurance
   Products..........143
Bristol-myers Squibb Co...........143
Brixmor Llc..........145
Brookdale Senior Living Inc..........145
Brookline Bancorp Inc (de)..........147
Bryn Mawr Bank Corp..........147
Bsb Bancorp Inc. (md)..........148
Builders Firstsource Inc..........149
Burlington Northern & Santa Fe Railway
   Co. (the)..........150
Burlington Stores Inc..........151
Byline Bancorp Inc..........152
Cadence Bancorporation..........152
Calpine Corp..........152

Cambridge Bancorp..........153
Camden National Corp. (me)..........154
Campbell Soup Co...........155
Candid Color Systems, Inc...........156
Capital City Bank Group, Inc...........156
Capital One Financial Corp...........157
Capitol Federal Financial Inc..........159
Cardinal Health, Inc...........160
Carmax Inc..........162
Carolina Financial Corp (new)..........163
Carter Bank & Trust (martinsville, Va)..........163
Casey's General Stores, Inc...........163
Cass Information Systems Inc..........164
Caterpillar Inc..........165
Cathay General Bancorp..........166
Catholic Health Initiatives..........167
Cbre Group Inc..........169
Cbs Corp..........171
Cbtx Inc..........172
Cdw Corp..........173
Celanese Corp (de)..........173
Celgene Corp..........174
Centene Corp...........175
Centerpoint Energy, Inc...........177
Centerstate Bank Corp..........178
Central Pacific Financial Corp...........179
Century Bancorp, Inc...........180
Centurylink Inc..........181
Cerner Corp...........182
Cfj Properties Llc..........183
Cgb Enterprises, Inc...........183
Ch2m Hill Companies, Ltd...........184
Chalmette Refining, L.l.c...........186
Charles And Lynn Schusterman Family
   Foundation..........186
Charter Communications Inc (new)..........186
Charter Financial Corp (md)..........187
Chemical Financial Corp..........187
Chemours Co (the)..........188
Chemung Financial Corp..........188
Chesapeake Energy Corp...........188
Chevron Corporation..........189
Chevron Phillips Chemical Company Llc 191
Christian Brothers Investment
   Services, Inc...........192
Chs Inc..........192
Chugach Government Solutions, Llc..........194
Cigna Corp...........194
Cim Commercial Trust Corp..........195
Cincinnati Financial Corp...........196
Cintas Corporation..........197
Cisco Systems Inc..........198
Cit Group Inc..........200
Citigroup Inc..........202
Citizens Financial Group Inc (new)..........205
Citizens, Inc. (austin, Tx)..........206
City Holding Co...........207
Clorox Co (the)..........208
Cms Energy Corp..........209
Cna Financial Corp..........210
Cnb Financial Corp. (clearfield, Pa)..........211
Cno Financial Group Inc..........212
Coastal Federal Credit Union..........213
Cobank Acb..........213
Cobiz Financial Inc..........214
Coca-cola Co (the)..........215
Codorus Valley Bancorp, Inc...........217
Cognizant Technology Solutions Corp. ...217
Colgate-palmolive Co...........219
Colorado Housing And Finance
   Authority..........220
Columbia Banking System Inc..........220
Comcast Corp..........221
Comenity Bank..........223
Comerica, Inc...........223
Commerce Bancshares Inc..........225
Commercial Metals Co...........227
Commscope Holding Co., Inc...........227
Community Bank System, Inc...........228

Companies Profiled (continued)

Community Health Systems, Inc. 229
Community Trust Bancorp, Inc. 230
Communitybank Of Texas National
   Association 231
Conagra Brands Inc 231
Conduent Inc 233
Connectone Bancorp Inc (new) 233
Conocophillips 234
Consolidated Edison Co. Of New York,
   Inc. 234
Consolidated Edison Inc 235
Consolidated Grain & Barge Company 236
Constellation Brands Inc 236
Consumers Energy Co. 237
Core Mark Holding Co Inc 238
Corning Inc 239
Costco Wholesale Corp 240
Coty, Inc. 241
Crown Holdings Inc 243
Csra Inc 244
Csx Corp 245
Cullen/frost Bankers, Inc. 246
Cummins, Inc. 247
Customers Bancorp Inc 248
Cvb Financial Corp. 249
Cvr Energy Inc 250
Cvs Health Corporation 251
Dairy Farmers Of America, Inc. 253
Dana Inc 254
Danaher Corp 255
Darden Restaurants, Inc. 256
Davita Inc 257
Dean Foods Co. 259
Deere & Co. 260
Dell Technologies Inc 261
Delta Air Lines Inc (de) 262
Devon Energy Corp. 263
Dick's Sporting Goods, Inc. 264
Dignity Health 265
Dillard's Inc. 266
Dime Community Bancshares, Inc 268
Discover Financial Services 269
Discovery Communications Inc 270
Dish Network Corp. 271
Disney (walt) Co. (the) 272
Dividend Capital Diversified
   Property Fund Inc. 274
Dollar General Corp 275
Dollar Tree Inc 276
Dominion Energy Inc (new) 277
Domtar Corp 278
Donegal Group Inc. 279
Donnelley (rr) & Sons Company 279
Dover Corp 280
Dowdupont Inc. 281
Dr Pepper Snapple Group Inc 281
Dte Electric Company 283
Dte Energy Co 283
Duke Energy Carolinas Llc 284
Duke Energy Corp. 285
Duke University 286
Dxc Technology Co 287
E*trade Financial Corp. 287
Eagle Bancorp Inc (md) 288
East Boston Saving Bank 289
East West Bancorp, Inc 289
Eastman Chemical Co. 290
Ebay Inc. 292
Ecolab Inc. 293
Edison International 295
Educational Funding Of The South, Inc. ..296
Electronic Arts, Inc. 296
Emc Insurance Group Inc. 297
Emcor Group, Inc. 298
Emerson Electric Co. 299
Employers Holdings Inc 300
Energy Transfer Equity Lp 301
Energy Transfer Partners Lp (new) 302
Entergy Corp 303
Enterprise Bancorp, Inc. (ma) 305

Enterprise Financial Services Corp 305
Enterprise Products Partners L.p. 306
Eog Resources, Inc. 308
Equity Bancshares Inc 309
Erie Indemnity Co. 309
Essa Bancorp Inc 310
Essendant Inc 310
Essex Portfolio, L.p. 312
Eversource Energy 312
Exchange Bank (santa Rosa, Ca) 313
Exelon Corp 314
Exelon Generation Co Llc 315
Expedia Inc 316
Expeditors International Of
   Washington, Inc. 317
Express Scripts Holding Co 318
Exxon Mobil Corp 319
Facebook Inc 321
Fannie Mae 321
Farm Credit Illinois, Aca 323
Farm Credit Of The Virginias Aca 323
Farm Credit Services Of America, Pca 323
Farm Credit West 323
Farmers & Merchants Bancorp (lodi, Ca) 323
Farmers & Merchants Bank Of
   Long Beach (ca) 324
Farmers Capital Bank Corp. 324
Farmers National Banc Corp.
   (canfield,oh) 324
Fb Financial Corp. 325
Fbl Financial Group Inc 325
Fcb Financial Holdings Inc 326
Federal Agricultural Mortgage Corp 326
Federal Home Loan Bank New York 327
Federal Home Loan Bank Of Atlanta 328
Federal Home Loan Bank Of Chicago 328
Federal Home Loan Bank Of Cincinnati ..328
Federal Home Loan Bank Of Dallas 328
Federal Home Loan Bank Of
   Des Moines 329
Federal Home Loan Bank Of San
   Francisco 329
Federal-mogul Holdings Llc 329
Fedex Corp. 329
Fidelity National Financial Inc 331
Fidelity National Information Services
   Inc. 333
Fidelity Southern Corp 334
Fifth Third Bancorp (cincinnati, Oh) 335
Financial Institutions Inc. 338
First American Financial Corp 338
First Bancorp 340
First Bancorp (nc) 341
First Bancorp Inc (me) 341
First Busey Corp. 342
First Business Financial Services, Inc. 343
First Citizens Bancshares Inc (nc) 344
First Citizens Bancshares, Inc.
   (dyersburg, Tn) 345
First Commonwealth Financial Corp
   (indiana, Pa) 345
First Community Bancshares, Inc. (nv) ...346
First Connecticut Bancorp Inc (md) 347
First Data Corp (new) 347
First Defiance Financial Corp. 348
First Financial Bancorp (oh) 349
First Financial Bankshares, Inc. 350
First Financial Corp. (in) 351
First Foundation Inc 351
First Guaranty Bancshares, Inc. 352
First Hawaiian Inc. 352
First Horizon National Corp 352
First Internet Bancorp 353
First Interstate Bancsystem Inc 354
First Merchants Corp 354
First Mid-illinois Bancshares Inc 355
First Midwest Bancorp, Inc. (naperville,
   Il) 356
First National Bank Alaska 357
First Of Long Island Corp 357

First Republic Bank (san Francisco, Ca) ..358
Firstenergy Corp 359
Fiserv Inc. 360
Flagstar Bancorp, Inc. 362
Florida Power & Light Co. 363
Florida Power Corp. 363
Fluor Corp. 364
Flushing Financial Corp. 366
Fnb Corp 367
Foot Locker, Inc. 368
Ford Motor Co. (de) 369
Fortive Corp 370
Fortune Brands Home & Security, Inc. ...371
Franklin Financial Network Inc 372
Franklin Resources, Inc. 372
Freddie Mac 373
Freeport-mcmoran Inc 374
Frontier Communications Corp 375
Fulton Financial Corp. (pa) 376
Gallagher (arthur J.) & Co. 377
Gamestop Corp. 378
General Dynamics Corp 379
General Electric Co 381
General Mills, Inc. 382
General Motors Co 384
Genesis Healthcare Inc 386
Genuine Parts Co. 387
Genworth Financial, Inc. (holding Co) 388
Georgia Power Co. 389
German American Bancorp Inc 390
Gilead Sciences Inc 390
Glacier Bancorp, Inc. 392
Global Partners Lp 393
Goldman Sachs Group Inc. 394
Goodyear Tire & Rubber Co. 396
Grainger (w.w.) Inc. 397
Graybar Electric Co., Inc. 398
Great Southern Bancorp, Inc. 399
Great West Life & Annuity
   Insurance Co - Insurance Products......400
Great Western Bancorp Inc 401
Green Bancorp Inc 401
Group 1 Automotive, Inc. 401
Growmark, Inc. 402
Guaranty Bancorp (de) 403
Guaranty Bancshares Inc 404
Halliburton Company 404
Hancock Holding Co. 406
Hanesbrands Inc 406
Hanmi Financial Corp. 407
Hanover Insurance Group Inc 408
Harborone Bancorp Inc 410
Harley-davidson Inc 410
Harris Corp. 411
Hartford Financial Services Group Inc. ...412
Hartford Life Insurance Co 414
Hasbro, Inc. 414
Hca Healthcare Inc 415
Hd Supply Holdings Inc 417
Healthpartners, Inc. 419
Heartland Financial Usa, Inc.
   (dubuque, Ia) 419
Heritage Commerce Corp 420
Heritage Financial Corp. (wa) 420
Hershey Company (the) 421
Hertz Global Holdings Inc (new) 422
Hess Corp 423
Hewlett Packard Enterprise Co 424
Hill/ahern Fire Protection, Llc 425
Hills Bancorporation 425
Hilton Worldwide Holdings Inc 426
Hingham Institution For Savings 427
Hollyfrontier Corp. 428
Home Bancorp Inc 429
Home Bancshares Inc 429
Home Depot Inc 430
Home Properties, Limited Partnership 432
Homestreet Inc 432
Hometown America Management Corp. ..433
Hometrust Bancshares Inc. 433

Companies Profiled (continued)

Honeywell International Inc....433
Hope Bancorp Inc....435
Horace Mann Educators Corp....435
Horizon Bancorp (michigan City, In)....436
Hormel Foods Corp....436
Horton (dr) Inc....438
Host Hotels & Resorts Inc....439
Houchens Industries, Inc....441
Hp Inc....441
Hrg Group Inc....443
Hsbc Finance Corp....444
Hsbc Usa, Inc....444
Humana Inc....445
Hunt (j.b.) Transport Services, Inc....447
Huntington Bancshares Inc....448
Huntington Ingalls Industries, Inc....450
Huntsman Corp....451
Hy-vee, Inc....452
Iberiabank Corp....453
Icahn Enterprises Lp....455
Iheartmedia Inc....456
Illinois Tool Works, Inc....457
Independent Bank Corp (ma)....458
Independent Bank Corporation (ionia, Mi)....459
Independent Bank Group Inc....460
Infinity Property & Casualty Corp....460
Ingredion Inc....461
Insight Enterprises Inc....462
Intel Corp....464
Intercontinental Exchange Inc....466
Intermountain Health Care Inc....467
International Bancshares Corp....468
International Business Machines Corp....469
International Paper Co....471
Interpublic Group Of Companies Inc....473
Intl Fcstone Inc....473
Intuit Inc....475
Investors Bancorp Inc (new)....476
Iowa Finance Authority....477
Iowa Student Loan Liquidity Corporation....477
Iqvia Holdings Inc....477
Irc Retail Centers Llc....479
Isabella Bank Corp....479
Jabil Inc....480
Jacobs Engineering Group, Inc....481
Jetblue Airways Corp....482
Johns Hopkins University....483
Johnson & Johnson....484
Jones Financial Companies Lllp....485
Jones Lang Lasalle Inc....485
Jpmorgan Chase & Co....487
Juniper Networks Inc....489
Kaiser Foundation Hospitals Inc....491
Kansas City Life Insurance Co (kansas City, Mo)....491
Kearny Financial Corp (md)....492
Kellogg Co....492
Kelly Services, Inc....494
Kemper Corp (de)....495
Keycorp....496
Kiewit Corporation....498
Kilroy Realty, L.p....498
Kimberly-clark Corp....498
Kinder Morgan Inc....499
Kindred Healthcare Inc....501
Knights Of Columbus....502
Kohl's Corp....503
Kraft Heinz Co (the)....505
Kroger Co (the)....506
L Brands, Inc....508
L3 Technologies Inc....509
Laboratory Corporation Of America Holdings....509
Lakeland Bancorp, Inc....510
Lakeland Financial Corp....511
Lam Research Corp....512
Las Vegas Sands Corp....513
Lauder (estee) Cos., Inc. (the)....514
Lear Corp....514
Legacytexas Financial Group Inc....515
Leidos Holdings Inc....516
Leidos, Inc....517
Lendingclub Corp....517
Lennar Corp....518
Leucadia National Corp....519
Levi Strauss & Co....520
Liberty Interactive Corp....523
Liberty Media Corp (de)....525
Lifepoint Health Inc....526
Lilly (eli) & Co....527
Limetree Bay Terminals Llc....529
Lincoln National Corp....529
Lithia Motors Inc....531
Live Nation Entertainment Inc....532
Live Oak Bancshares Inc....533
Lkq Corp....533
Lockheed Martin Corp....534
Loews Corp....535
Lord Baltimore Capital Corporation....536
Lowe's Companies Inc....536
Lukoil Pan Americas, Llc....538
M & T Bank Corp....538
Macatawa Bank Corp....539
Mack-cali Realty, L. P....540
Macy's Inc....540
Magellan Health Inc....540
Maine State Housing Authority....541
Mainsource Financial Group Inc....542
Manpowergroup....542
Marathon Oil Corp....543
Marathon Petroleum Corp....546
Markel Corp (holding Co)....545
Marquette National Corp (il)....547
Marriott International, Inc....547
Marsh & Mclennan Companies Inc....549
Masco Corp....551
Massachusetts Housing Finance Agency Property Acquisition And Disposition Corporation....552
Mastec Inc. (fl)....553
Mastercard Inc....554
Mattel Inc....556
Mb Financial Inc....557
Mbia Inc....559
Mccormick & Co Inc....560
Mcdonald's Corp....561
Mckesson Corp....562
Mercantile Bank Corp....564
Merchants Bancorp (indiana)....564
Merck & Co Inc....565
Mercury General Corp....566
Meridian Bancorp Inc....567
Merrick Bank Corporation....568
Merrill Lynch Life Insurance Co - Insurance Products....568
Meta Financial Group Inc....568
Metlife Inc....569
Metropolitan Transportation Authority....571
Mgic Investment Corp. (wi)....571
Mgm Resorts International....572
Michaels Companies Inc....573
Micron Technology Inc....574
Microsoft Corporation....575
Midland States Bancorp Inc....576
Midsouth Bancorp, Inc....577
Midwestone Financial Group, Inc....578
Missouri Higher Education Loan Authority....579
Modern Woodmen Of America....579
Mohawk Industries, Inc....580
Molina Healthcare Inc....581
Molson Coors Brewing Co....582
Mondelez International Inc....583
Monogram Residential Trust, Inc....584
Monsanto Co....584
Morgan Stanley....586
Mosaic Co (the)....587
Motorola Solutions Inc....588
Murphy Usa Inc....589
Mutualfirst Financial Inc....590
Nasb Financial Inc....590
National Bank Holdings Corp....591
National Commerce Corp....591
National General Holdings Corp....592
National Oilwell Varco Inc....592
National Western Life Group Inc....594
Navient Corp....594
Navigators Group Inc (the)....595
Navistar International Corp....596
Nbt Bancorp. Inc....597
Ncl Corporation Ltd....598
Ncr Corp....599
Neiman Marcus Group Ltd Llc....600
Nelnet Inc....600
Netapp, Inc....601
Netflix Inc....602
New Jersey Housing And Mortgage Finance Agency....603
New York Community Bancorp Inc....603
New York Community Trust And Community Funds Inc....605
New York Presbyterian Hospital Weill Cornell University Medical Center....605
New York State Catholic Health Plan Inc....605
New York University....606
New York University....606
Newell Brands Inc....607
Newmont Mining Corp (holding Co)....608
News Corp (new)....610
Nextera Energy Inc....611
Ngl Energy Partners Lp....612
Nicolet Bankshares Inc....613
Nielsen Holdings Plc....614
Nielsen Holdings Plc....614
Nike Inc....614
Nordstrom, Inc....616
Norfolk Southern Corp....617
Northern Trust Corp....619
Northfield Bancorp Inc (de)....621
Northrim Banccorp Inc....621
Northrop Grumman Corp....622
Northwest Bancshares, Inc. (md)....623
Northwest Farm Credit Services....624
Nrg Energy Inc....624
Nucor Corp....625
Nvidia Corp....627
Nvr Inc....628
O'reilly Automotive, Inc....629
Occidental Petroleum Corp....631
Oceanfirst Financial Corp....632
Office Depot, Inc....633
Old Line Bancshares Inc....634
Old National Bancorp (evansville, In)....634
Old Republic International Corp....636
Old Second Bancorp., Inc. (aurora, Ill.)....637
Olin Corp....637
Omnicom Group, Inc....638
Oneamerica Financial Partners, Inc....640
Onemain Holdings Inc....640
Oneok Inc....641
Opus Bank (irvine, Ca)....642
Oracle Corp....642
Oritani Financial Corp (de)....644
Oshkosh Corp (new)....645
Owens & Minor, Inc....646
Owens Corning....647
Owens-illinois, Inc....648
Paccar Inc....649
Pacific Premier Bancorp Inc....650
Pacificorp....650
Packaging Corp Of America....651
Pacwest Bancorp....652
Park National Corp (newark, Oh)....653
Parker Hannifin Corp....653
Partners Healthcare System, Inc....655
Patterson Companies Inc....656
Paypal Holdings Inc....657
Pbf Energy Inc....657
Peabody Energy Corp (new)....658
Peapack-gladstone Financial Corp....659

Companies Profiled (continued)

Penney (j.c.) Co.,inc. (holding Co.) 660
Pennsylvania Housing Finance Agency....661
Pennymac Financial Services Inc............662
Penske Automotive Group Inc 662
People's United Financial Inc 663
People's Utah Bancorp 665
Peoples Bancorp, Inc. (marietta, Oh) 665
Peoples Financial Services Corp.............666
Pepsico Inc 667
Performance Food Group Co 669
Peter Kiewit Sons', Inc. 669
Pfizer Inc 670
Pg&e Corp (holding Co) 673
Philip Morris International Inc 673
Phillips 66 674
Phillips Edison - Arc Shopping Center Reit
      Inc 675
Pilgrims Pride Corp. 676
Pinnacle Financial Partners Inc 677
Placid Holding Company 678
Placid Refining Company Llc 678
Plains All American Pipeline Lp 679
Plains Gp Holdings Lp 679
Pnc Financial Services Group (the).........680
Polaris Industries Inc 681
Popular Inc. 682
Post Holdings Inc 683
Powershares Db Commodity Index
      Tracking Fund 684
Ppg Industries Inc 684
Ppl Corp 685
Praxair Inc 687
Preferred Bank (los Angeles, Ca) 688
Priceline Group Inc (the) 688
Primerica Inc 690
Principal Financial Group Inc 690
Proassurance Corp 691
Procter & Gamble Company (the)...........692
Progressive Corp. (oh) 694
Prospect Capital Corporation 695
Prosperity Bancshares Inc. 696
Protective Life Insurance Co 697
Provident Financial Services Inc.............697
Prudential Annuities Life Assurance
      Corp 698
Prudential Financial, Inc. 699
Public Service Enterprise Group Inc........700
Publix Super Markets, Inc. 701
Pultegroup Inc 703
Pvh Corp 704
Qcr Holdings Inc 706
Qualcomm Inc 706
Quanta Services, Inc. 708
Quest Diagnostics, Inc. 709
Qvc, Inc. 710
Qwest Corp 711
R. Directional Drilling & Underground
      Technology, Inc. 711
Racetrac Petroleum, Inc. 711
Radian Group, Inc. 711
Ralph Lauren Corp 712
Raymond James Financial, Inc. 714
Raytheon Co. 716
Realogy Group Llc 717
Realogy Holdings Corp 718
Redwood Credit Union 719
Regeneron Pharmaceuticals, Inc. 719
Regents Of The University Of Michigan ...720
Regions Financial Corp...........................721
Reinsurance Group Of America, Inc........723
Reliance Steel & Aluminum Co. 724
Renasant Corp 726
Republic Bancorp, Inc. (ky) 726
Republic First Bancorp, Inc. 727
Republic Services Inc 728
Rexford Industrial Realty, Inc. 729
Rite Aid Corp 730
Riversource Life Insurance Co 731
Rli Corp. 732
Robert Bosch Llc 733
Robert Half International Inc. 734

Robert W. Baird & Co. Incorporated 734
Robinson (c.h.) Worldwide, Inc. 736
Rockwell Automation, Inc. 737
Rockwell Collins Inc 738
Ross Stores, Inc. 740
Rpm International Inc (de) 741
Ryder System, Inc. 742
Ryman Hospitality Properties, Inc. 743
S & T Bancorp Inc (indiana, Pa) 744
S&p Global Inc 745
Safety Insurance Group, Inc. 746
Saint Thomas Health Services, Inc. 747
Salesforce.com Inc 747
Sandy Spring Bancorp Inc 749
Sanmina Corp 749
Santander Consumer Usa Holdings Inc ...751
Santander Holdings Usa Inc. 751
Schein (henry) Inc 752
Schwab (charles) Corp (the) 753
Seaboard Corp..755
Seacoast Banking Corp. Of Florida.........756
Sealed Air Corp......................................757
Sears Holdings Corp 758
Securities Investor Protection
      Corporation 759
Selective Insurance Group Inc 760
Sempra Energy 761
Sentara Healthcare 762
Servisfirst Bancshares Inc 763
Sherwin-williams Co (the).......................764
Shi International Corp. 765
Si Financial Group Inc (md) 766
Sierra Bancorp 766
Signature Bank (new York, Ny) 767
Simmons First National Corp. 768
Simon Property Group, Inc. 769
Sirius Xm Holdings Inc 771
Sl Green Operating Partnership, L.p........771
Slm Corp. 771
Smucker (j.m.) Co. 773
Solstice Holdings Inc. 774
Sonic Automotive, Inc. 774
Sonoco Products Co. 775
South State Corp.....................................776
Southern California Edison Co.................777
Southern Company (the) 778
Southern Copper Corp. 778
Southern Missouri Bancorp, Inc. 779
Southside Bancshares, Inc. 779
Southwest Airlines Co. 780
Spartannash Co. 780
Spectrum Brands Holdings Inc 782
Spectrum Health Systems, Inc. 783
Spirit Aerosystems Holdings Inc 783
Springleaf Finance Corporation 784
Sprint Corp (new) 784
St. Joseph Health System 785
Stanley Black & Decker Inc 785
Starbucks Corp.......................................786
State Auto Financial Corp.......................788
State Bank Financial Corp 789
State Of California 790
State Of New York Mortgage Agency........790
State Of Oklahoma 790
State Of Rhode Island 790
State Of Rhode Island And Providence
      Plantations 790
State Of Texas 791
State Street Corp....................................791
State University Of New York 793
Statoil Marketing & Trading (us) Inc.......793
Steel Dynamics Inc. 793
Sterling Bancorp (de).............................794
Stifel Financial Corp 795
Stock Yards Bancorp Inc.........................796
Stryker Corp...796
Summit Financial Group Inc 798
Sunoco Lp 798
Suntrust Banks Inc 798
Suny College At Cortland 800
Supervalu Inc 800

Sutter Health..802
Svb Financial Group 803
Synchrony Financial 804
Synnex Corp 804
Synovus Financial Corp. 806
Sysco Corp...807
T Rowe Price Group Inc. 809
T-mobile Us Inc 810
Targa Resources Corp 811
Target Corp 812
Tcf Financial Corp. 814
Tech Data Corp. 815
Telco Intercontinental Corp 816
Telephone & Data Systems Inc 816
Tenaska Marketing Ventures 817
Tenet Healthcare Corp. 817
Tenneco Inc. 819
Tennessee Valley Authority......................820
Territorial Bancorp Inc 821
Tesla Inc 822
Texas A&m Foundation 823
Texas Capital Bancshares Inc 823
Texas Instruments Inc. 824
Textron Inc 825
Tfs Financial Corp. 827
The Bancorp Inc 827
The Charlotte-mecklenburg Hospital
      Authority 828
The Cleveland Foundation........................828
The Ford Foundation 828
The Gap Inc 829
The Irvine James Foundation 830
The Pennsylvania State University 830
The Priddy Foundation 831
The Scoular Company 831
The Turner Corporation 832
The Whiting-turner Contracting
      Company 833
The William Penn Foundation 835
Thermo Fisher Scientific Inc....................835
Thor Industries, Inc. 836
Time Warner Inc 837
Tjx Companies, Inc. 839
Toll Brothers Inc. 840
Tompkins Financial Corp 842
Torchmark Corp......................................843
Townebank 844
Toyota Motor Credit Corp. 844
Tpg Specialty Lending Inc 845
Tractor Supply Co. 845
Trammo, Inc. 846
Travelcenters Of America Llc 847
Travelers Companies Inc (the) 848
Treehouse Foods Inc...............................850
Trico Bancshares (chico, Ca) 851
Trinity Industries, Inc. 852
Tristate Capital Holdings, Inc..................853
Triumph Bancorp Inc 853
Trustco Bank Corp. (n.y.) 853
Trustmark Corp......................................854
Turner Construction Company Inc..........855
Tutor Perini Corp. 856
Twenty-first Century Fox Inc 857
Tyson Foods Inc 859
U.s. Venture, Inc. 860
Ugi Corp...861
Ulta Beauty Inc.......................................862
Umb Financial Corp. 862
Umpqua Holdings Corp 864
Under Armour Inc 865
Union Bank And Trust Company..............866
Union Bankshares Corp (new) 866
Union Pacific Corp 867
United Bankshares Inc 868
United Community Banks Inc
      (blairsville, Ga) 869
United Community Financial Corp. (oh) .870
United Continental Holdings Inc 871
United Financial Bancorp Inc (new) 872
United Fire Group, Inc. 872
United Natural Foods Inc.........................873

Companies Profiled (continued)

United Parcel Service Inc....................874
United Rentals Inc.............................876
United States Steel Corp. 877
United Technologies Corp 878
Unitedhealth Group Inc 880
Univar Inc..881
Universal Health Services, Inc.............882
University Of Texas At Tyler................883
University Of Texas System.................883
Univest Corp. Of Pennsylvania
    (souderton)..................................884
Unum Group 885
Upmc Presbyterian Shadyside 887
Us Bancorp (de)................................887
Us Foods Holding Corp 889
Utah Housing Corporation 889
Valero Energy Corp............................889
Valley National Bancorp (nj)...............891
Veritiv Corp......................................892
Verizon Communications Inc................892
Vf Corp..894
Viacom Inc.......................................895
Virginia Electric & Power Co................897
Virginia Housing Development
    Authority.....................................897
Virtu Financial Llc 898

Visa Inc...898
Voya Financial Inc..............................899
Wakefern Food Corp. 899
Walgreens Boots Alliance Inc 900
Walmart Inc......................................902
Washington Federal Inc.......................904
Washington Trust Bancorp, Inc. 905
Waste Management, Inc. (de) 906
Waterstone Financial Inc (md)..............907
Webster Financial Corp (waterbury,
    Conn)..907
Wec Energy Group Inc........................908
Wegmans Food Markets, Inc. 910
Wellcare Health Plans Inc....................910
Wells Fargo & Co. 912
Wesbanco Inc....................................912
Wesco International, Inc......................913
West Bancorporation, Inc....................914
Westamerica Bancorporation 915
Western Alliance Bancorporation...........916
Western Digital Corp 917
Western New England Bancorp Inc.........918
Western Union Co 918
Westlake Chemical Corp......................919
Westrock Co 920
Weyerhaeuser Co...............................921

Whirlpool Corp..................................922
Williams Cos Inc (the) 923
Williams Partners Lp (new) 924
Williams Sonoma Inc..........................924
Wilson Bank Holding Co......................925
Windstream Holdings Inc.....................925
Wintrust Financial Corp (il) 927
World Fuel Services Corp. 928
World Wide Technology Holding Co.,
    Inc. 929
World Wide Technology, Inc. 930
Wsfs Financial Corp 930
Wyndham Worldwide Corp....................931
Xcel Energy Inc.................................932
Xerox Corp.......................................933
Xpo Logistics, Inc..............................936
Yosemite Farm Credit, Aca 937
Yrc Worldwide Inc..............................937
Yum China Holdings Inc 938
Yum! Brands Inc 938
Zen-noh Grain Corporation 939
Zimmer Biomet Holdings Inc................939
Zions Bancorporation 941
Zoetis Inc..942

About Hoover's Handbook of American Business 2018

In these tough economic times, it pays to have all the facts, whether you're making business, financial, or employment decisions. When you need information about companies, *Hoover's Handbook of American Business* is the place to turn for answers. Throughout its history, it has stood as one of America's respected sources of business information, packed with the information you need.

We at Hoover's Business Press pledge we will continue our work to add more value to this already valuable resource. So search away for the business information you need to make the important decisions facing you. Leave the fact-finding and digging and the sorting and sifting to the editors at Hoover's.

Hoover's Handbook of American Business is the first of our four-title series of handbooks that covers, literally, the world of business. The series is available as an indexed set, and also includes *Hoover's Handbook of World Business, Hoover's Handbook of Private Companies,* and *Hoover's Handbook of Emerging Companies*. This series brings you information on the biggest, fastest-growing, and most influential enterprises in the world.

HOOVER'S ONLINE FOR BUSINESS NEEDS

In addition to the 2,550 companies featured in our handbooks, comprehensive coverage of more than 40,000 business enterprises is available in electronic format on the Mergent website. Our goal is to provide one site that offers authoritative, updated intelligence on US and global companies, industries, and the people who shape them. Hoover's has partnered with other prestigious business information and service providers to bring you all the right business information, services, and links in one place.

We welcome the recognition we have received as a provider of high-quality company information — online, electronically, and in print — and continue to look for ways to make our products more available and more useful to you.

We believe that anyone who buys from, sells to, invests in, lends to, competes with, interviews with, or works for a company should know all there is to know about that enterprise. Taken together, this book and the other Hoover's products and resources represent the most complete source of basic corporate information readily available to the general public.

This latest version of *Hoover's Handbook of American Business* contains, as always, profiles of the largest and most influential companies in the United States. Each of the companies profiled here was chosen because of its important role in American business. For more details on how these companies were selected, see the section titled "Using Hoover's Handbooks."

HOW TO USE THIS BOOK

This book has four sections:

1. "Using Hoover's Handbooks" describes the contents of our profiles and explains the ways in which we gather and compile our data.

2. "A List-Lover's Compendium" contains lists of the largest, smallest, best, most, and other superlatives related to companies involved in American business.

3. The company profiles section makes up the largest and most important part of the book — 750 profiles of major US enterprises.

4. Three indexes complete the book. The first sorts companies by industry groups, the second by headquarters location. The third index is a list of all the executives found in the Executives section of each company profile.

Using Hoover's Handbooks

SELECTION OF THE COMPANIES PROFILED

The 750 enterprises profiled in this book include the largest and most influential companies in America. Among them are:

- more than 710 publicly held companies, from 3M to Zions Bancorporation
- more than 30 large private enterprises (such as Cargill and Mars)
- several mutual and cooperative organizations (such as State Farm and Ace Hardware)
- a selection of other enterprises (such as Kaiser Foundation Health Plan, the US Postal Service, and the Tennessee Valley Authority) that we believe are sufficiently large and influential enough to warrant inclusion.

In selecting these companies, our foremost question was "What companies will our readers be most interested in?" Our goal was to answer as many questions as we could in one book — in effect, trying to anticipate your curiosity. This approach resulted in four general selection criteria for including companies in the book:

1. Size. The 500 or so largest American companies, measured by sales and by number of employees, are included in the book. In general, these companies have sales in excess of $2 billion, and they are the ones you will have heard of and the ones you will want to know about. These are the companies at the top of the *FORTUNE*, *Forbes*, and *Business Week* lists. We have made sure to include the top private companies in this number.

2. Growth. We believe that relatively few readers will be going to work for, or investing in, the railroad industry. Therefore, only a few railroads are in the book. On the other hand, we have included a number of technology firms, as well as companies that provide medical products and services — pharmaceutical and biotech companies, health care insurers, and medical device makers.

3. Visibility. Most readers will have heard of the Hilton Worldwide and Harley-Davidson companies. Their service or consumer natures make them household names, even though they are not among the corporate giants in terms of sales and employment.

4. Breadth of coverage. To show the diversity of economic activity, we've included, among others, a professional sports team, one ranch, the Big Four accounting firms, and one of the largest law firms in the US. We feel that these businesses are important enough to enjoy at least "token" representation. While we might not emphasize certain industries, the industry leaders are present.

ORGANIZATION

The profiles are presented in alphabetical order. This alphabetization is generally word by word, which means that Legg Mason precedes Leggett & Platt. You will find the commonly used name of the enterprise at the beginning of the profile; the full, legal name is found in the Locations section. If a company name is also a person's name, like Walt Disney, it will be alphabetized under the first name; if the company name starts with initials, like J. C. Penney or H.J. Heinz, look for it under the combined initials (in the above examples, JC and HJ, respectively). Basic financial data is listed under the heading Historical Financials; also included is the exchange on which the company's stock is traded if it is public, the ticker symbol used by the stock exchange, and the company's fiscal year-end.

The annual financial information contained in the profiles is current through fiscal year-ends occurring as late as May 2014. We have included certain nonfinancial developments, such as officer changes, through September 2014.

OVERVIEW

In the first section of the profile, we have tried to give a thumbnail description of the company and what it does. The description will usually include information on the company's strategy, reputation, and ownership. We recommend that you read this section first.

HISTORY

This extended section, included for almost all companies in the book, reflects our belief that every enterprise is the sum of its history and that you have to know where you came from in order to know where you are going. While some companies have limited historical awareness, we think the vast majority of the enterprises in this book have colorful backgrounds. We have tried to focus on the people who made the enterprises what they are today. We have found these histories to be full of twists and ironies; they make fascinating reading.

EXECUTIVES

Here we list the names of the people who run the company, insofar as space allows. In the case of public companies, we have shown the ages and total compensation of key officers. In some cases the published data is for the previous year although the company has announced promotions or retirements since year-end. Total compensation is the sum of salary, bonus, and the value of any other benefits, such as stock options or deferred compensation.

Although companies are free to structure their management titles any way they please, most modern corporations follow standard practices. The ultimate power in any corporation lies with the shareholders, who elect a board of directors, usually including officers or "insiders" as well as individuals from outside the company. The chief officer, the person on whose desk the buck stops, is usually called the chief executive officer (CEO). Often, he or she is also the chairman of the board.

As corporate management has become more complex, it is common for the CEO to have a "right-hand person" who oversees the day-to-day operations of the company, allowing the CEO plenty of time to focus on strategy and long-term issues. This right-hand person is usually designated the chief operating officer (COO) and is often the president of the company. In other cases one person is both chairman and president.

A multitude of other titles exists, including chief financial officer (CFO), chief administrative officer, and vice chairman. We have always tried to include the CFO, the chief legal officer, and the chief human resources or personnel officer. Our best advice is that officers' pay levels are clear indicators of who the board of directors thinks are the most important members of the management team.

The people named in the Executives section are indexed at the back of the book.

The Executives section also includes the name of the company's auditing (accounting) firm, where available.

LOCATIONS

Here we include the company's full legal name and its headquarters, street address, telephone and fax numbers, and Web site, as available. The back of the book includes an index of companies by headquarters locations.

In some cases we have also included information on the geographic distribution of the company's business, including sales and profit data. Note that these profit numbers, like those in the Products/Operations section below, are usually operating or pretax profits rather than net profits. Operating profits are generally those before financing costs (interest income and payments) and before taxes, which are considered costs attributable to the whole company rather than to one division or part of the world. For this reason the net income figures (in the Historical Financials section) are usually much lower, since they are after interest and taxes. Pretax profits are after interest but before taxes.

Headquarters for companies that are incorporated in Bermuda, but whose operational headquarters are in the US, are listed under their US address.

PRODUCTS/OPERATIONS

This section lists as many of the company's products, services, brand names, divisions, subsidiaries, and joint ventures as we could fit. We have tried to include all its major lines and all familiar brand names. The nature of this section varies by company and the amount of information available. If the company publishes sales and profit information by type of business, we have included it.

COMPETITORS

In this section we have listed companies that compete with the profiled company. This feature is included as a quick way to locate similar companies and compare them. The universe of competitors includes all public companies and all private companies with sales in excess of $500 million. In a few instances we have identified smaller private companies as key competitors.

HISTORICAL FINANCIALS

Here we have tried to present as much data about each enterprise's financial performance as we could compile in the allocated space. The information varies somewhat from industry to industry and is less complete in the case of private companies that do not release data (although we have always tried to provide annual sales and employment). There are a few industries, venture capital and investment banking, for example, for which revenue numbers are unavailable as a rule.

The following information is generally present.

A 5-year table, with relevant annualized compound growth rates, covers:
- Sales — fiscal year sales (year-end assets for most financial companies)
- Net income — fiscal year net income (before accounting changes)
- Net profit margin — fiscal year net income as a percent of sales (as a percent of assets for most financial firms)
- Employees — fiscal year-end or average number of employees
- Stock price — the fiscal year close
- P/E — high and low price/earnings ratio
- Earnings per share — fiscal year earnings per share (EPS)
- Dividends per share — fiscal year dividends per share
- Book value per share — fiscal year-end book value (common shareholders' equity per share)

The information on the number of employees is intended to aid the reader interested in knowing whether a company has a long-term trend of increasing or decreasing employment. As far as we know, we are the only company that publishes this information in print format.

The numbers on the left in each row of the Historical Financials section give the month and the year in which the company's fiscal year actually ends. Thus, a company with a March 31, 2017, year-end is shown as 3/17.

In addition, we have provided in graph form a stock price history for most public companies. The graphs, covering up to five years, show the range of trading between the high and the low price, as well as the closing price for each fiscal year. Generally, for private companies, we have graphed net income, or, if that is unavailable, sales.

Key year-end statistics in this section generally show the financial strength of the enterprise, including:

- Debt ratio (long-term debt as a percent of shareholders' equity)
- Return on equity (net income divided by the average of beginning and ending common shareholders' equity)
- Cash and cash equivalents
- Current ratio (ratio of current assets to current liabilities)
- Total long-term debt (including capital lease obligations)
- Number of shares of common stock outstanding
- Dividend yield (fiscal year dividends per share divided by the fiscal year-end closing stock price)
- Dividend payout (fiscal year dividends divided by fiscal year EPS)
- Market value at fiscal year-end (fiscal year-end closing stock price multiplied by fiscal year-end number of shares outstanding)

Per share data has been adjusted for stock splits. The data for public companies has been provided to us by Mergent Inc. Other public company information was compiled by Hoover's, which takes full responsibility for the content of this section.

In the case of private companies that do not publicly disclose financial information, we usually did not have access to such standardized data. We have gathered estimates of sales and other statistics from numerous sources.

Hoover's Handbook of

American Business

A List-Lover's Compendium

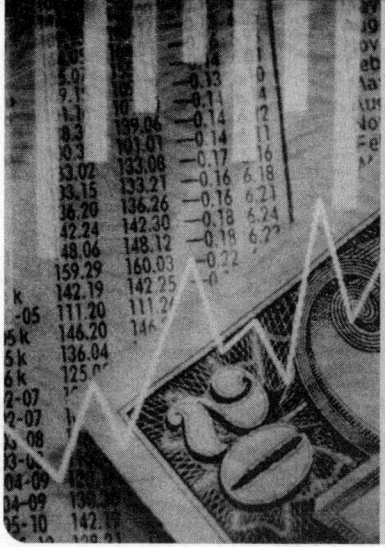

The 300 Largest Companies by Sales in
Hoover's Handbook of American Business 2018

Rank	Company	Sales ($ mil.)	Rank	Company	Sales ($ mil.)	Rank	Company	Sales ($ mil.)
1	Walmart Inc	$485,873	60	Cisco Systems Inc	$48,005	119	U.S. Bancorp (DE)	$22,744
2	Apple Inc	$229,234	61	Caterpillar Inc.	$45,462	120	Duke Energy Corp	$22,743
3	Exxon Mobil Corp	$226,094	62	Coca-Cola Co (The)	$41,863	121	AFLAC Inc.	$22,559
4	Berkshire Hathaway Inc	$223,604	63	Charter Communications Inc (	$41,581	122	Starbucks Corp.	$22,387
5	UnitedHealth Group Inc	$201,159	64	HCA Healthcare Inc	$41,490	123	Qualcomm Inc	$22,291
6	McKesson Corp	$198,533	65	Facebook Inc	$40,653	124	Sears Holdings Corp	$22,138
7	CVS Health Corp	$184,765	66	Centene Corp	$40,607	125	Dollar General Corp	$21,987
8	Amazon.com Inc	$177,866	67	T-Mobile US Inc	$40,604	126	AutoNation, Inc.	$21,535
9	AT&T Inc	$163,786	68	Honeywell International Inc	$40,534	127	Whirlpool Corp	$21,253
10	Ford Motor Co. (DE)	$156,776	69	American Airlines Group Inc	$40,180	128	Union Pacific Corp	$21,240
11	AmerisourceBergen Corp.	$153,144	70	Merck & Co Inc	$39,807	129	Eli Lilly & Co	$21,222
12	General Motors Co	$145,588	71	Cigna Corp	$39,668	130	Southwest Airlines Co	$21,171
13	Cardinal Health, Inc.	$129,976	72	Delta Air Lines Inc (DE)	$39,639	131	International Paper Co	$21,079
14	Costco Wholesale Corp	$129,025	73	Best Buy Inc	$39,403	132	Bristol-Myers Squibb Co.	$20,776
15	Verizon Communications Inc	$125,980	74	Tyson Foods Inc	$38,260	133	Dollar Tree Inc	$20,719
16	General Electric Co	$123,693	75	Morgan Stanley	$37,949	134	Halliburton Company	$20,620
17	Walgreens Boots Alliance Inc	$118,214	76	Oracle Corp	$37,728	135	Lear Corp.	$20,467
18	Kroger Co (The)	$115,337	77	Goldman Sachs Group Inc	$37,712	136	Cummins, Inc.	$20,428
19	Chevron Corporation	$114,472	78	Energy Transfer Equity LP	$37,504	137	Micron Technology Inc.	$20,322
20	Alphabet Inc	$110,855	79	United Continental Holdings	$36,556	138	Plains GP Holdings LP	$20,182
21	Fannie Mae	$107,162	80	Allstate Corp.	$36,534	139	Plains All American Pipeline	$20,182
22	JPMorgan Chase & Co	$105,486	81	American Express Co.	$35,583	140	Penske Automotive Group Inc	$20,119
23	Express Scripts Holding Co	$100,288	82	NIKE Inc	$34,350	141	ManpowerGroup	$19,654
24	Home Depot Inc	$94,595	83	Publix Super Markets, Inc.	$34,274	142	Tenet Healthcare Corp.	$19,621
25	Wells Fargo & Co.	$94,176	84	Exelon Corp	$33,531	143	Burlington Northern & Santa F	$19,278
26	Bank of America Corp.	$93,662	85	Sprint Corp (New)	$33,347	144	Western Digital Corp	$19,093
27	Boeing Co.	$93,392	86	TJX Companies, Inc.	$33,184	145	Jabil Inc	$19,063
28	Microsoft Corporation	$89,950	87	Rite Aid Corp.	$32,845	146	Fluor Corp.	$19,037
29	Phillips 66	$85,777	88	CHS Inc	$31,935	147	Kohl's Corp.	$18,686
30	Anthem Inc	$84,863	89	3M Co	$31,657	148	Community Health Systems, In	$18,438
31	Comcast Corp	$84,526	90	General Dynamics Corp	$30,973	149	Visa Inc	$18,358
32	Citigroup Inc	$82,386	91	Gilead Sciences Inc	$30,390	150	Hartford Financial Services	$18,300
33	International Business Machi	$79,919	92	Deere & Co.	$29,738	151	Thermo Fisher Scientific Inc	$18,274
34	Philip Morris International	$78,098	93	INTL FCStone Inc.	$29,382	152	Kimberly-Clark Corp.	$18,259
35	Valero Energy Corp	$75,659	94	Time Warner Inc	$29,318	153	AECOM	$18,203
36	Johnson & Johnson	$71,890	95	Travelers Companies Inc (The	$28,902	154	DXC Technology Co	$18,112
37	Target Corp	$69,495	96	Hewlett Packard Enterprise C	$28,871	155	Molina Healthcare Inc	$17,782
38	Freddie Mac	$65,665	97	21st Century Fox Inc	$28,500	156	Exelon Generation Co LLC	$17,751
39	Procter & Gamble Co (The)	$65,058	98	AbbVie Inc	$28,216	157	CenturyLink Inc	$17,470
40	Lowe's Companies Inc	$65,017	99	Capital One Financial Corp	$27,519	158	Avnet Inc	$17,440
41	PepsiCo Inc	$63,525	100	Abbott Laboratories	$27,390	159	NextEra Energy Inc	$17,195
42	Metlife Inc	$63,476	101	World Fuel Services Corp.	$27,016	160	PG&E Corp (Holding Co)	$17,135
43	Marathon Petroleum Corp.	$63,364	102	Arrow Electronics, Inc.	$26,813	161	Synnex Corp	$17,046
44	Aetna Inc.	$63,155	103	Tech Data Corp.	$26,235	162	Paccar Inc.	$17,033
45	Intel Corp	$62,761	104	Kraft Heinz Co (The)	$26,232	163	Danaher Corp	$16,882
46	DuPont Inc	$62,484	105	Mondelez International Inc	$25,896	164	Performance Food Group Co	$16,762
47	Dell Technologies Inc	$61,642	106	Northrop Grumman Corp	$25,803	165	PNC Financial Services Group	$16,423
48	United Parcel Service Inc	$60,906	107	Macy's Inc	$25,778	166	American Electric Power Co.,	$16,380
49	Archer Daniels Midland Co.	$60,828	108	Altria Group Inc	$25,744	167	Icahn Enterprises LP	$16,348
50	FedEx Corp	$60,319	109	Raytheon Co.	$25,348	168	Nucor Corp.	$16,208
51	United Technologies Corp	$59,837	110	McDonald's Corp	$24,622	169	PBF Energy Inc	$15,920
52	Prudential Financial, Inc.	$59,689	111	Andeavor	$24,582	170	Carmax Inc.	$15,875
53	Sysco Corp	$55,371	112	ConocoPhillips	$24,360	171	Sunoco LP	$15,698
54	Disney (Walt) Co. (The)	$55,137	113	Progressive Corp. (OH)	$23,441	172	Bank of New York Mellon Corp	$15,674
55	Humana, Inc.	$54,379	114	Enterprise Products Partners	$23,022	173	General Mills, Inc.	$15,620
56	Pfizer Inc	$52,824	115	Southern Co.	$19,896	174	Gap Inc	$15,516
57	HP Inc	$52,056	116	US Foods Holding Corp	$22,919	175	Colgate-Palmolive Co.	$15,454
58	Lockheed Martin Corp	$51,048	117	Marriott International, Inc.	$22,894	176	XPO Logistics, Inc.	$15,381
59	American International Group	$49,520	118	Amgen Inc	$22,849	177	Goodyear Tire & Rubber Co.	$15,377
						178	Genuine Parts Co.	$15,340

Rank	Company	Sales ($ mil.)
179	Omnicom Group, Inc.	$15,274
180	Emerson Electric Co.	$15,264
181	Synchrony Financial	$15,122
182	Dish Network Corp	$15,095
183	WestRock Co	$14,860
184	Freeport-McMoRan Inc	$14,830
185	Nordstrom, Inc.	$14,757
186	PPG Industries Inc	$14,750
187	DaVita Inc	$14,745
188	Monsanto Co	$14,640
189	Aramark	$14,604
190	FirstEnergy Corp	$14,562
191	Applied Materials, Inc.	$14,537
192	Core Mark Holding Co Inc	$14,529
193	Waste Management, Inc. (DE)	$14,485
194	Illinois Tool Works, Inc.	$14,314
195	WellCare Health Plans Inc	$14,237
196	Principal Financial Group In	$14,093
197	DR Horton Inc	$14,091
198	CDW Corp	$13,982
199	Textron Inc	$13,788
200	Loews Corp.	$13,735
201	Kinder Morgan Inc.	$13,705
202	AES Corp.	$13,586
203	Cognizant Technology Solutio	$13,487
204	Texas Instruments, Inc.	$13,370
205	Lincoln National Corp.	$13,330
206	Baker Hughes A GE Co	$13,269
207	Newell Brands Inc	$13,264
208	Viacom Inc	$13,263
209	Parker-Hannifin Corp	$12,029
210	Marsh & McLennan Companies I	$13,211
211	CBS Corp	$13,166
212	Ecolab Inc	$13,153
213	Robinson (C.H.) Worldwide, I	$13,144
214	PayPal Holdings Inc	$13,094
215	CBRE Group Inc	$13,072
216	NGL Energy Partners LP	$13,022
217	Kellogg Co	$13,014
218	Celgene Corp	$13,003
219	Ross Stores, Inc.	$12,867
220	Lennar Corp	$12,646
221	DTE Energy Co	$12,607
222	L Brands, Inc	$12,574
223	Penney (J.C.) Co.,Inc. (Hold	$12,547
224	Mastercard Inc	$12,497
225	Supervalu Inc	$12,480
226	Stryker Corp	$12,444
227	Arconic Inc	$12,394
228	Automatic Data Processing In	$12,380
229	NRG Energy Inc	$12,351
230	Biogen Inc	$12,274
231	Bed, Bath & Beyond, Inc.	$12,216
232	Devon Energy Corp.	$12,197
233	Becton Dickinson And Co	$12,093
234	Consolidated Edison Inc	$12,075
235	VF Corp.	$12,019
236	Anadarko Petroleum Corp	$11,908
237	Edison International	$11,869
238	Sherwin-Williams Co (The)	$11,856
239	Southern California Edison C	$11,830
240	Lauder (Estee) Cos., Inc. (T	$11,824
241	Dominion Energy Inc (New)	$11,737
242	Ameriprise Financial Inc	$11,696
243	Netflix Inc	$11,693
244	Murphy USA Inc	$11,595
245	First Data Corp (New)	$11,584
246	Henry Schein Inc	$11,572
247	BB&T Corp.	$11,538
248	Reinsurance Group of America	$11,522
249	Las Vegas Sands Corp	$11,410
250	CSX Corp	$11,408
251	Stanley Black & Decker Inc	$11,407
252	BlackRock Inc	$11,155
253	Xcel Energy Inc	$11,107
254	Unum Group	$11,047
255	Office Depot, Inc.	$11,021
256	Toyota Motor Credit Corp.	$11,020
257	Florida Power & Light Co.	$10,895
258	AutoZone, Inc.	$10,889
259	Group 1 Automotive, Inc.	$10,888
260	Entergy Corp. (New)	$10,846
261	Voya Financial Inc	$10,782
262	Xerox Corp	$10,771
263	Santander Holdings USA Inc.	$10,745
264	Priceline Group Inc (The)	$10,743
265	Tennessee Valley Authority	$10,739
266	Ally Financial Inc	$9,835
267	BorgWarner Inc	$9,799
268	Liberty Interactive Corp	$10,647
269	State Street Corp.	$10,635
270	Norfolk Southern Corp.	$10,551
271	HollyFrontier Corp	$10,536
272	Praxair Inc	$10,534
273	L3 Technologies Inc	$10,511
274	Discover Financial Services	$10,497
275	Occidental Petroleum Corp	$10,398
276	United States Steel Corp.	$10,261
277	Liberty Interactive Corp – Q	$10,219
278	Liberty Interactive Corp – Q	$10,219
279	Sempra Energy	$10,183
280	Consolidated Edison Co. of N	$10,165
281	Baxter International Inc	$10,163
282	Grainger (W.W.), Inc.	$10,137
283	Autoliv Inc.	$10,074
284	Leucadia National Corp.	$10,063
285	Expedia Inc	$10,060
286	Jacobs Engineering Group, In	$10,023
287	Universal Health Services, I	$9,766
288	Sonic Automotive, Inc.	$9,732
289	Owens & Minor, Inc. (New)	$9,723
290	Huntsman Corp	$9,657
291	LabCorp	$9,642
292	Advance Auto Parts Inc	$9,568
293	eBay Inc.	$9,567
294	Fidelity National Financial	$9,554
295	MGM Resorts International	$9,455
296	Corning Inc	$9,390
297	Republic Services Inc	$9,388
298	CNA Financial Corp	$9,366
299	Alcoa Corporation	$9,318
300	United Natural Foods Inc.	$9,274

The 300 Most Profitable Companies in
Hoover's Handbook of American Business 2018

Rank	Company	Net Income ($ mil.)
1	Apple Inc	$48,351
2	JPMorgan Chase & Co	$24,733
3	Berkshire Hathaway Inc	$24,074
4	Comcast Corp	$22,714
5	Wells Fargo & Co.	$21,938
6	Microsoft Corporation	$21,204
7	Bank of America Corp.	$17,906
8	Johnson & Johnson	$16,540
9	Facebook Inc	$15,934
10	Procter & Gamble Co (The)	$15,326
11	Citigroup Inc	$14,912
12	Altria Group Inc	$14,239
13	Walmart Inc	$13,643
14	Gilead Sciences Inc	$13,501
15	Verizon Communications Inc	$13,127
16	AT&T Inc	$12,976
17	Alphabet Inc	$12,662
18	Fannie Mae	$12,313
19	International Business Machi	$11,872
20	Kraft Heinz Co (The)	$10,999
21	Union Pacific Corp	$10,712
22	UnitedHealth Group Inc	$10,558
23	Charter Communications Inc (	$9,895
24	Cisco Systems Inc	$9,609
25	Intel Corp	$9,601
26	Oracle Corp	$9,335
27	Disney (Walt) Co. (The)	$8,980
28	General Electric Co	$8,831
29	Boeing Co.	$8,197
30	Home Depot Inc	$7,957
31	Prudential Financial, Inc.	$7,863
32	Exxon Mobil Corp	$7,840
33	Freddie Mac	$7,815
34	Ford Motor Co. (DE)	$7,602
35	Goldman Sachs Group Inc	$7,398
36	Pfizer Inc	$7,215
37	Visa Inc	$6,699
38	CVS Health Corp	$6,622
39	Coca-Cola Co (The)	$6,527
40	Philip Morris International	$6,035
41	Morgan Stanley	$5,979
42	U.S. Bancorp (DE)	$5,888
43	CSX Corp	$5,471
44	Norfolk Southern Corp.	$5,404
45	NextEra Energy Inc	$5,378
46	AbbVie Inc	$5,309
47	Micron Technology Inc.	$5,089
48	McKesson Corp	$5,070
49	Baxter International Inc	$4,965
50	3M Co	$4,858
51	PepsiCo Inc	$4,857
52	McDonald's Corp	$4,687
53	United Technologies Corp	$4,552
54	T-Mobile US Inc	$4,536
55	ERP Operating L.P.	$4,464
56	Delta Air Lines Inc (DE)	$4,373
57	Equity Residential	$4,292
58	Burlington Northern & Santa F	$4,260
59	NIKE Inc	$4,240
60	Walgreens Boots Alliance Inc	$4,078
61	Time Warner Inc	$3,926
62	Merck & Co Inc	$3,920
63	Mastercard Inc	$3,915
64	PNC Financial Services Group	$3,903
65	Exelon Corp	$3,770
66	Capital One Financial Corp	$3,751
67	Corning Inc	$3,695
68	Texas Instruments, Inc.	$3,595
69	Bank of New York Mellon Corp	$3,547
70	Southwest Airlines Co	$3,488
71	Applied Materials, Inc.	$3,434
72	United Parcel Service Inc	$3,431
73	Express Scripts Holding Co	$3,404
74	BlackRock Inc	$3,172
75	Lowe's Companies Inc	$3,093
76	Amazon.com Inc	$3,033
77	Ford Motor Credit Company LL	$3,007
78	Air Products & Chemicals Inc	$3,000
79	FedEx Corp	$2,997
80	21st Century Fox Inc	$2,952
81	Celgene Corp	$2,940
82	Mondelez International Inc	$2,922
83	General Dynamics Corp	$2,912
84	HCA Healthcare Inc	$2,890
85	Starbucks Corp.	$2,885
86	Eli Lilly & Co	$2,738
87	Target Corp	$2,737
88	American Express Co.	$2,736
89	Costco Wholesale Corp	$2,679
90	American Airlines Group Inc	$2,676
91	AFLAC Inc.	$2,659
92	Danaher Corp	$2,554
93	Biogen Inc	$2,539
94	HP Inc	$2,526
95	Intercontinental Exchange In	$2,514
96	Enterprise Products Partners	$2,513
97	Southern Co.	$2,493
98	Anthem Inc	$2,470
99	Qualcomm Inc	$2,466
100	BB&T Corp.	$2,426
101	Discover Financial Services	$2,393
102	Principal Financial Group In	$2,310
103	TJX Companies, Inc.	$2,298
104	Liberty Expedia Holdings Inc	$2,292
105	Valero Energy Corp	$2,289
106	Kimberly-Clark Corp.	$2,278
107	Aetna Inc.	$2,271
108	United Continental Holdings	$2,263
109	Monsanto Co	$2,260
110	Synchrony Financial	$2,251
111	Energy XXI Gulf Coast Inc	$2,248
112	Deere & Co.	$2,159
113	Duke Energy Corp	$2,152
114	State Street Corp.	$2,143
115	Priceline Group Inc (The)	$2,135
116	Dominion Energy Inc (New)	$2,123
117	Travelers Companies Inc (The	$2,056
118	Liberty Broadband Corp	$2,034
119	Publix Super Markets, Inc.	$2,026
120	Raytheon Co.	$2,024
121	Colgate-Palmolive Co.	$2,024
122	Thermo Fisher Scientific Inc	$2,022
123	Northrop Grumman Corp	$2,015
124	Lockheed Martin Corp	$2,002
125	Amgen Inc	$1,979
126	Molson Coors Brewing Co.	$1,976
127	Kroger Co (The)	$1,975
128	Waste Management, Inc. (DE)	$1,949
129	PPL Corp	$1,902
130	Charles Schwab Corp	$1,889
131	SunTrust Banks Inc	$1,878
132	Allstate Corp.	$1,877
133	Viacom Inc	$1,874
134	Cigna Corp	$1,867
135	Simon Property Group, Inc.	$1,839
136	PayPal Holdings Inc	$1,795
137	Tyson Foods Inc	$1,774
138	Marsh & McLennan Companies I	$1,768
139	Automatic Data Processing In	$1,733
140	Florida Power & Light Co.	$1,727
141	Lam Research Corp	$1,698
142	Franklin Resources, Inc.	$1,697
143	Adobe Systems Inc	$1,694
144	Illinois Tool Works, Inc.	$1,687
145	Las Vegas Sands Corp	$1,670
146	NVIDIA Corp	$1,666
147	PG&E Corp (Holding Co)	$1,660
148	General Mills, Inc.	$1,658
149	Honeywell International Inc	$1,655
150	Duke Realty Corp	$1,634
151	Yum! Brands Inc	$1,619
152	Archer Daniels Midland Co.	$1,595
153	PPG Industries Inc	$1,591
154	Fifth Third Bancorp (Cincinn	$1,564
155	Phillips 66	$1,555
156	Cognizant Technology Solutio	$1,553
157	Constellation Brands Inc	$1,535
158	CME Group Inc	$1,534
159	Emerson Electric Co.	$1,518
160	EQT Corp	$1,509
161	Praxair Inc	$1,500
162	Southern California Edison C	$1,499
163	T Rowe Price Group, Inc.	$1,498
164	S&P Global Inc	$1,496
165	DowDuPont Inc	$1,460
166	Public Storage	$1,454
167	Dish Network Corp	$1,450
168	Annaly Capital Management In	$1,434
169	Marriott International, Inc.	$1,372
170	Sempra Energy	$1,371
171	Ventas Inc	$1,356
172	Georgia Power Co	$1,347
173	United Rentals Inc	$1,346
174	M & T Bank Corp	$1,315
175	Ameriprise Financial Inc	$1,314
176	Lear Corp.	$1,313
177	Edison International	$1,311
178	GGP Inc	$1,288

SOURCE: MERGENT INC., DATABASE, AUGUST 2017

Rank	Company	Net Income ($ mil.)	Rank	Company	Net Income ($ mil.)	Rank	Company	Net Income ($ mil.)
179	Cardinal Health, Inc.	$1,288	220	AvalonBay Communities, Inc.	$1,034	261	Amphenol Corp.	$823
180	AutoZone, Inc.	$1,281	221	Alaska Air Group, Inc.	$1,034	262	Camden Property Trust	$820
181	Ciena Corp	$1,262	222	Northern Trust Corp	$1,033	263	Paychex Inc	$817
182	CBS Corp	$1,261	223	Progressive Corp. (OH)	$1,031	264	Dover Corp	$812
183	Hilton Worldwide Holdings In	$1,259	224	Stryker Corp	$1,020	265	Lennar Corp	$810
184	Dollar General Corp	$1,251	225	Skyworks Solutions, Inc.	$1,010	266	Magellan Midstream Partners	$803
185	Lauder (Estee) Cos., Inc. (T	$1,249	226	Bristol-Myers Squibb Co.	$1,007	267	MetLife Inc	$800
186	Consolidated Edison Inc	$1,245	227	Cummins, Inc.	$999	268	Nucor Corp.	$796
187	Prologis LP	$1,244	228	Energy Transfer Equity LP	$995	269	KeyCorp	$791
188	Liberty Interactive Corp	$1,235	229	Parker-Hannifin Corp	$983	270	Wells Fargo Real Estate Inve	$784
189	Ecolab Inc	$1,230	230	Intuit Inc	$971	271	Southern Copper Corp	$777
190	Best Buy Inc	$1,228	231	Electronic Arts	$967	272	CA Inc	$775
191	Virginia Electric & Power Co	$1,218	232	Activision Blizzard, Inc.	$966	273	Santander Consumer USA Holdi	$766
192	Prologis Inc	$1,210	233	Stanley Black & Decker Inc	$965	274	Pacificorp	$763
193	Regeneron Pharmaceuticals, I	$1,199	234	Textron Inc	$962	275	Host Hotels & Resorts Inc	$762
194	Discovery Communications Inc	$1,194	235	Kansas City Southern	$962	276	Liberty Ventures Com (New)	$762
195	Lincoln National Corp.	$1,192	236	American Tower Corp (New)	$956	277	Liberty Ventures Com Ser B (	$762
196	Huntington Bancshares Inc	$1,186	237	Eversource Energy	$942	278	JetBlue Airways Corp	$759
197	Marathon Petroleum Corp.	$1,174	238	WEC Energy Group Inc	$940	279	Hologic Inc	$756
198	Duke Energy Carolinas LLC	$1,166	239	Unum Group	$931	280	Caterpillar Inc.	$754
199	Loews Corp.	$1,164	240	Mohawk Industries, Inc.	$930	281	Jones Financial Companies LL	$746
200	Regions Financial Corp	$1,163	241	Fiserv Inc	$930	282	Comerica, Inc.	$743
201	Spectra Energy Partners LP	$1,161	242	KLA-Tencor Corp.	$926	283	Andeavor	$734
202	L Brands, Inc	$1,158	243	Vornado Realty L.P.	$907	284	LabCorp	$732
203	Sysco Corp	$1,143	244	International Paper Co	$904	285	Analog Devices Inc	$727
204	DTE Energy Co	$1,134	245	Dollar Tree Inc	$896	286	Plains All American Pipeline	$726
205	Sherwin-Williams Co (The)	$1,133	246	Hartford Financial Services	$896	287	Hershey Company (The)	$720
206	Xcel Energy Inc	$1,123	247	Public Service Enterprise Gr	$887	288	United Therapeutics Corp	$714
207	Ross Stores, Inc.	$1,118	248	Campbell Soup Co.	$887	289	Monster Beverage Corp (New)	$713
208	MGM Resorts International	$1,101	249	DaVita Inc	$880	290	Federal Home Loan Bank Of Sa	$712
209	Becton Dickinson And Co	$1,100	250	Fortive Corp	$872	291	L3 Technologies Inc	$710
210	Omnicom Group, Inc.	$1,088	251	TD Ameritrade Holding Corp	$872	292	WestRock Co	$708
211	Qwest Corp	$1,085	252	Cerner Corp.	$867	293	Energy Transfer Partners LP	$705
212	Welltower Inc	$1,078	253	Zoetis Inc	$864	294	Rockwell Collins Inc	$705
213	VF Corp.	$1,074	254	CNA Financial Corp	$859	295	Universal Health Services, I	$702
214	Ally Financial Inc	$1,067	255	Eastman Chemical Co	$854	296	Reinsurance Group of America	$701
215	Consolidated Edison Co. of N	$1,056	256	Dr Pepper Snapple Group Inc	$847	297	Clorox Co (The)	$701
216	Citizens Financial Group Inc	$1,045	257	Hormel Foods Corp.	$847	298	Kellogg Co	$694
217	Blackstone Group LP	$1,039	258	Celanese Corp (DE)	$843	299	Harley-Davidson Inc	$692
218	DR Horton Inc	$1,038	259	Alabama Power Co	$839	300	Genuine Parts Co.	$687
219	O'Reilly Automotive, Inc.	$1,038	260	Rockwell Automation, Inc.	$826			

The 300 Largest Employers in
Hoover's Handbook of American Business 2018

Rank	Company	Employees	Rank	Company	Employees	Rank	Company	Employees
1	Walmart Inc	2,300,000	60	Tyson Foods Inc	122,000	119	HanesBrands Inc	67,200
2	Amazon.com Inc	566,000	61	Dollar General Corp	121,000	120	Sysco Corp	66,500
3	Kelly Services, Inc.	507,500	62	Community Health Systems, In	120,000	121	Hewlett Packard Enterprise C	66,000
4	Kroger Co (The)	443,000	63	Barrett Business Services, I	115,746	122	Envision Healthcare Corp	65,200
5	United Parcel Service Inc	434,000	64	Synnex Corp	113,600	123	Bed, Bath & Beyond, Inc.	65,000
6	Yum China Holdings Inc	420,000	65	DXC Technology Co	112,900	124	Laureate Education Inc	65,000
7	Home Depot Inc	406,000	66	Penney (J.C.) Co.,Inc. (Hold	106,000	125	Raytheon Co.	64,000
8	International Business Machi	380,300	67	Intel Corp	102,700	126	Goodyear Tire & Rubber Co.	64,000
9	McDonald's Corp	375,000	68	Coca-Cola Co (The)	100,300	127	Ascena Retail Group Inc	64,000
10	Berkshire Hathaway Inc	367,700	69	Kindred Healthcare Inc	100,100	128	Danaher Corp	62,000
11	Walgreens Boots Alliance Inc	345,000	70	Lockheed Martin Corp	100,000	129	Amphenol Corp.	62,000
12	Target Corp	323,000	71	Abbott Laboratories	99,000	130	Fluor Corp.	61,551
13	General Electric Co	295,000	72	General Dynamics Corp	98,600	131	Brinks Co (The)	60,700
14	Lowe's Companies Inc	290,000	73	Caterpillar Inc.	98,400	132	Deere & Co.	60,476
15	Starbucks Corp.	277,000	74	DowDuPont Inc	98,000	133	Marsh & McLennan Companies I	60,000
16	Wells Fargo & Co.	269,100	75	Pfizer Inc	96,500	134	Cummins, Inc.	58,600
17	AT&T Inc	268,000	76	Conduent Inc	96,000	135	MetLife Inc	58,000
18	PepsiCo Inc	263,000	77	Procter & Gamble Co (The)	95,000	136	Automatic Data Processing In	58,000
19	UnitedHealth Group Inc	260,800	78	XPO Logistics, Inc.	95,000	137	Brinker International, Inc.	57,906
20	Aramark	260,500	79	Charter Communications Inc (	94,800	138	Parker-Hannifin Corp	56,690
21	Cognizant Technology Solutio	260,200	80	L Brands, Inc	93,600	139	Southwest Airlines Co	56,100
22	CVS Health Corp	246,000	81	Whirlpool Corp	92,000	140	On Assignment, Inc.	55,880
23	JPMorgan Chase & Co	243,355	82	3M Co	91,536	141	Sykes Enterprises, Inc.	55,525
24	HCA Healthcare Inc	241,000	83	Icahn Enterprises LP	90,960	142	Morgan Stanley	55,311
25	TJX Companies, Inc.	235,000	84	Mondelez International Inc	90,000	143	Fidelity National Financial	55,219
26	Half Robert International In	231,400	85	Yum! Brands Inc	90,000	144	Chevron Corporation	55,200
27	Costco Wholesale Corp	231,000	86	United Continental Holdings	88,000	145	American Express Co.	55,000
28	Citigroup Inc	219,000	87	Rite Aid Corp.	87,000	146	International Paper Co	55,000
29	Bank of America Corp.	208,000	88	AECOM	87,000	147	Halliburton Company	55,000
30	United Technologies Corp	205,000	89	AutoZone, Inc.	87,000	148	Thermo Fisher Scientific Inc	55,000
31	Ford Motor Co. (DE)	202,000	90	Delta Air Lines Inc (DE)	84,000	149	Fidelity National Informatio	55,000
32	Disney (Walt) Co. (The)	199,000	91	Genesis Healthcare Inc	82,000	150	Jacobs Engineering Group, In	54,700
33	Publix Super Markets, Inc.	191,000	92	Philip Morris International	80,600	151	Humana, Inc.	54,200
34	General Motors Co	180,000	93	Alphabet Inc	80,110	152	Stanley Black & Decker Inc	54,023
35	Darden Restaurants, Inc. (Un	178,729	94	Ross Stores, Inc.	78,600	153	RMR Group Inc (The)	53,475
36	Marriott International, Inc.	177,000	95	McKesson Corp	78,000	154	Newell Brands Inc	53,400
37	Dollar Tree Inc	176,800	96	Brookdale Senior Living Inc	77,600	155	Anthem Inc	53,000
38	Jabil Inc	170,000	97	Omnicom Group, Inc.	77,300	156	Texas Roadhouse Inc	52,500
39	FedEx Corp	169,000	98	Jones Lang LaSalle Inc	77,300	157	PNC Financial Services Group	52,006
40	Lear Corp.	165,000	99	Emerson Electric Co.	76,500	158	Bank of New York Mellon Corp	52,000
41	Comcast Corp	164,000	100	Universal Health Services, I	75,325	159	LabCorp	52,000
42	Hilton Worldwide Holdings In	163,000	101	CBRE Group Inc	75,000	160	T-Mobile US Inc	51,000
43	Verizon Communications Inc	160,900	102	O'Reilly Automotive, Inc.	74,715	161	Foot Locker, Inc.	50,168
44	Macy's Inc	148,300	103	NIKE Inc	74,400	162	Illinois Tool Works, Inc.	50,000
45	Boeing Co.	140,800	104	Advance Auto Parts Inc	74,000	163	IQVIA Holdings Inc	50,000
46	Sears Holdings Corp	140,000	105	Cracker Barrel Old Country S	73,000	164	Michaels Companies Inc	50,000
47	ABM Industries, Inc.	140,000	106	Cisco Systems Inc	72,900	165	American International Group	49,800
48	Dell Technologies Inc	138,000	107	Nordstrom, Inc.	72,500	166	Interpublic Group of Compani	49,800
49	Oracle Corp	138,000	108	U.S. Bancorp (DE)	71,191	167	Prudential Financial, Inc.	49,705
50	Kohl's Corp.	138,000	109	Exxon Mobil Corp	71,100	168	Aetna Inc.	49,500
51	Gap Inc	135,000	110	DaVita Inc	70,300	169	HP Inc	49,000
52	Honeywell International Inc	131,000	111	Autoliv Inc.	70,300	170	Las Vegas Sands Corp	49,000
53	Tenet Healthcare Corp.	130,000	112	Northrop Grumman Corp	70,000	171	Healthcare Services Group In	48,900
54	Convergys Corp	130,000	113	VF Corp.	69,000	172	Baxter International Inc	48,000
55	Johnson & Johnson	126,400	114	MGM Resorts International	69,000	173	TTEC Holdings Inc	48,000
56	Best Buy Inc	125,000	115	Chipotle Mexican Grill Inc	68,890	174	Ecolab Inc	47,565
57	Microsoft Corporation	124,000	116	Merck & Co Inc	68,000	175	Capital One Financial Corp	47,300
58	Apple Inc	123,000	117	Western Digital Corp	68,000	176	PPG Industries Inc	47,200
59	American Airlines Group Inc	122,300	118	GameStop Corp	68,000	177	Sanmina Corp	47,000
						178	LifePoint Health Inc	47,000

SOURCE: MERGENT INC., DATABASE, AUGUST 2017

Rank	Company	Employees	Rank	Company	Employees	Rank	Company	Employees
179	Six Flags Entertainment Corp	47,000	220	Mohawk Industries, Inc.	37,800	261	Freeport–McMoRan Inc	30,000
180	Lauder (Estee) Cos., Inc. (T	46,000	221	Wyndham Worldwide Corp	37,800	262	Avis Budget Group Inc	30,000
181	Cedar Fair LP	45,600	222	Xerox Corp	37,600	263	Cooper–Standard Holdings Inc	30,000
182	Hyatt Hotels Corp	45,000	223	BB&T Corp.	37,500	264	Texas Instruments, Inc.	29,865
183	WestRock Co	44,800	224	Kellogg Co	37,369	265	United States Steel Corp.	29,800
184	PVH Corp	44,500	225	Huntington Ingalls Industrie	37,000	266	Sally Beauty Holdings Inc	29,475
185	Marathon Petroleum Corp.	44,460	226	Textron Inc	36,000	267	Red Robin Gourmet Burgers In	29,293
186	RR Donnelley & Sons Company	44,360	227	Hertz Global Holdings Inc (N	36,000	268	BG Staffing Inc	29,291
187	Allstate Corp.	43,500	228	Colgate–Palmolive Co.	35,900	269	AbbVie Inc	29,000
188	Quest Diagnostics, Inc.	43,000	229	Big Lots, Inc.	35,100	270	Supervalu Inc	29,000
189	Jones Financial Companies LL	43,000	230	Casey's General Stores, Inc.	35,014	271	BorgWarner Inc	29,000
190	Abercrombie & Fitch Co	43,000	231	Exelon Corp	34,621	272	Boston Scientific Corp.	29,000
191	Sherwin–Williams Co (The)	42,550	232	Ryder System, Inc.	34,500	273	Dover Corp	29,000
192	LKQ Corp	42,500	233	Goldman Sachs Group Inc	34,400	274	Rockwell Collins Inc	29,000
193	Waste Management, Inc. (DE)	42,300	234	Command Center Inc	34,219	275	Duke Energy Corp	28,798
194	Kimberly–Clark Corp.	42,000	235	Micron Technology Inc.	34,100	276	TTM Technologies Inc	28,360
195	Cintas Corp	42,000	236	Baker Hughes A GE Co	34,000	277	Frontier Communications Corp	28,300
196	Union Pacific Corp	41,992	237	Qualcomm Inc	33,800	278	Williams Sonoma Inc	28,300
197	Eli Lilly & Co	41,975	238	State Street Corp.	33,783	279	AMERCO	28,300
198	Becton Dickinson And Co	41,933	239	NCR Corp.	33,500	280	Quanta Services, Inc.	28,100
199	Arconic Inc	41,500	240	Vail Resorts Inc	33,500	281	Sprint Corp (New)	28,000
200	Select Medical Holdings Corp	41,500	241	Stryker Corp	33,000	282	ManpowerGroup	28,000
201	AMC Entertainment Holdings I	41,373	242	Republic Services Inc	33,000	283	Encompass Health Corp	27,968
202	Cigna Corp	41,000	243	Southern Co.	32,020	284	Amkor Technology Inc.	27,900
203	Burlington Northern & Santa F	41,000	244	Leidos Holdings Inc	32,000	285	KBR Inc	27,500
204	Regis Corp.	41,000	245	Mattel Inc	32,000	286	Genesco Inc.	27,200
205	Corning Inc	40,700	246	YRC Worldwide Inc	32,000	287	Norfolk Southern Corp.	27,110
206	Dick's Sporting Goods, Inc	40,500	247	ON Semiconductor Corp	32,000	288	Gallagher (Arthur J.) & Co.	26,800
207	Cardinal Health, Inc.	40,400	248	National Oilwell Varco Inc	31,889	289	Civitas Solutions Inc	26,700
208	Acadia Healthcare Company In	40,400	249	Ulta Beauty Inc	31,800	290	Owens–Illinois, Inc.	26,500
209	CenturyLink Inc	40,000	250	Progressive Corp. (OH)	31,721	291	Praxair Inc	26,498
210	Genuine Parts Co.	40,000	251	Archer Daniels Midland Co.	31,300	292	Avon Products, Inc.	26,400
211	Dillard's Inc.	40,000	252	Bright Horizons Family Solut	31,200	293	AutoNation, Inc.	26,000
212	Burlington Stores Inc	40,000	253	Tenneco Inc	31,000	294	News Corp (New)	26,000
213	Pilgrims Pride Corp.	39,600	254	EMCOR Group, Inc.	31,000	295	Masco Corp.	26,000
214	Kraft Heinz Co (The)	39,000	255	Caesars Entertainment Corp	31,000	296	Tractor Supply Co.	26,000
215	Cheesecake Factory Inc. (The	38,800	256	Energy Transfer Equity LP	30,992	297	Cerner Corp.	26,000
216	American Eagle Outfitters, I	38,700	257	Travelers Companies Inc (The	30,800	298	Barnes & Noble Inc	26,000
217	General Mills, Inc.	38,000	258	Centene Corp	30,500	299	ExlService Holdings Inc	26,000
218	Office Depot, Inc.	38,000	259	Dana Inc	30,100	300	Express Scripts Holding Co	25,600
219	L3 Technologies Inc	38,000	260	Tesla Inc	30,025			

The Mergent 500 Largest Global Corporations (By Revenues)

Rank	Company	Sales ($ mil.)	Rank	Company	Sales ($ mil))	Rank	Company	Sales ($ mil.)
1	Walmart Inc	$485,873	68	Anthem Inc	$84,863	135	ArcelorMittal SA	$56,791
2	Cementos Bio-Bio S.A. (Chile)	$289,960	69	Comcast Corp	$84,526	136	Unilever N.V.	$55,659
3	China Petroleum & Chemical C	$278,066	70	Carrefour S.A.	$83,176	137	Unilever Plc (United Kingdom	$55,659
4	Toyota Motor Corp	$246,830	71	Citigroup Inc	$82,386	138	Sysco Corp	$55,371
5	Royal Dutch Shell Plc	$240,033	72	Hitachi, Ltd.	$81,947	139	Disney (Walt) Co. (The)	$55,137
6	PetroChina Co Ltd	$232,847	73	Rosneft Oil Co OJSC (Moscow)	$81,460	140	Telefonica SA	$54,944
7	Volkswagen A.G. (Germany, Fe	$229,409	74	Petroleo Brasileiro SA	$81,405	141	Dai-ichi Life Holdings Inc	$54,820
8	Apple Inc	$229,234	75	International Business Machi	$79,919	142	Humana, Inc.	$54,379
9	Exxon Mobil Corp	$226,094	76	SoftBank Group Corp	$79,611	143	Renault S.A. (France)	$54,107
10	Berkshire Hathaway Inc	$223,604	77	Banco Santander SA	$78,943	144	Pfizer Inc	$52,824
11	Oil and Natural Gas Corp. Lt	$209,464	78	China Life Insurance Co Ltd	$78,720	145	Wesfarmers Ltd.	$52,589
12	UnitedHealth Group Inc	$201,159	79	Philip Morris International	$78,098	146	Koninklijke Ahold Delhaize N	$52,472
13	McKesson Corp	$198,533	80	Hyundai Motor Co., Ltd.	$77,953	147	Reliance Industries Ltd	$52,369
14	BP PLC	$185,474	81	HSBC Holdings Plc	$77,683	148	JBS S.A.	$52,349
15	CVS Health Corp	$184,765	82	Bosch (Robert) GmbH (Germany	$77,216	149	Mexican Petroleum	$52,174
16	Amazon.com Inc	$177,866	83	Deutsche Telekom AG	$77,180	150	HP Inc	$52,056
17	Samsung Electronics Co Ltd	$168,032	84	Credit Agricole SA	$77,124	151	Seven & i Holdings Co. Ltd.	$51,987
18	AT&T Inc	$163,786	85	Japan Post Insurance Co Ltd	$76,015	152	Toyota Tsusho Corp	$51,852
19	Daimler AG	$161,826	86	Valero Energy Corp	$75,659	153	Roche Holding AG	$51,710
20	Ford Motor Co. (DE)	$156,776	87	EDF Trading Ltd	$75,182	154	Lockheed Martin Corp	$51,048
21	AmerisourceBergen Corp.	$153,144	88	Electricite de France	$75,182	155	Vodafone Group Plc	$50,889
22	Glencore PLC	$152,948	89	Enel SpA	$74,537	156	China Telecom Corp Ltd	$50,732
23	Industrial and Commercial Ba	$145,803	90	Aeon Co. Ltd. (Japan)	$73,140	157	Korea Electric Power Corp KE	$50,102
24	General Motors Co	$145,588	91	Itau Unibanco Holding S.A.	$72,986	158	American International Group	$49,520
25	Hon Hai Precision Industry C	$134,728	92	Johnson & Johnson	$71,890	159	Novartis AG Basel	$49,436
26	Cardinal Health, Inc.	$129,976	93	Engie SA	$71,170	160	Bayer AG	$49,383
27	China Construction Bank Corp	$129,253	94	Indian Oil Corporation	$70,561	161	AEGON N.V.	$49,034
28	Costco Wholesale Corp	$129,025	95	Airbus SE	$70,302	162	ThyssenKrupp AG	$48,969
29	AXA S.A.	$128,209	96	Tesco PLC	$70,173	163	ING Groep NV	$48,558
30	Total SA	$127,925	97	Target Corp	$69,495	164	Rewe-Zentral AG (Germany, Fed	$48,219
31	Verizon Communications Inc	$125,980	98	Aviva Plc (United Kingdom)	$68,017	165	PTT Public Co Ltd.	$48,019
32	Honda Motor Co., Ltd.	$125,209	99	Sony Corp	$68,004	166	Cisco Systems Inc	$48,005
33	General Electric Co	$123,693	100	Deutscher Sparkassen-und Giro	$67,936	167	Tokyo Electric Power Company	$47,920
34	Japan Post Holdings Co Ltd	$119,193	101	Zurich Insurance Group AG	$67,245	168	MS&AD Insurance Group Holdin	$47,226
35	Walgreens Boots Alliance Inc	$118,214	102	Societe Generale	$66,115	169	America Movil SAB de CV	$47,141
36	Fiat Chrysler Automobiles NV	$117,222	103	CITIC Ltd	$65,761	170	Noble Group Ltd	$46,528
37	Kroger Co (The)	$115,337	104	Panasonic Corp	$65,682	171	Manulife Financial Corp.	$46,523
38	Chevron Corporation	$114,472	105	Freddie Mac	$65,665	172	Tokio Marine Holdings Inc	$46,180
39	Agricultural Bank of China	$112,195	106	Nippon Life Insurance Co.	$65,664	173	LG Electronics Inc	$46,087
40	Alphabet Inc	$110,855	107	Ceconomy AG	$65,212	174	State Bank of India	$46,050
41	SAIC Motor Corp Ltd	$108,930	108	Procter & Gamble Co (The)	$65,058	175	RWE AG	$46,026
42	Bank of China Ltd	$108,913	109	Lowe's Companies Inc	$65,017	176	Sberbank Russia	$45,942
43	Fannie Mae	$107,162	110	Munich Re Group	$64,594	177	Statoil ASA	$45,873
44	Allianz SE	$106,319	111	Marubeni Corp.	$63,760	178	Deutsche Bahn AG	$45,718
45	Ping An Insurance (Group) Co	$105,792	112	PepsiCo Inc	$63,525	179	CNP Assurances S.A.	$45,651
46	JPMorgan Chase & Co	$105,486	113	MetLife Inc	$63,476	180	Anheuser Busch InBev SA/NV	$45,517
47	Nissan Motor Co., Ltd.	$104,824	114	Marathon Petroleum Corp.	$63,364	181	Caterpillar Inc.	$45,462
48	BNP Paribas (France)	$104,756	115	Aetna Inc.	$63,155	182	Banco Bilbao Vizcaya Argenta	$44,453
49	China Mobile Limited	$102,018	116	JXTG Holdings Inc	$62,832	183	Toshiba Corp	$44,354
50	Nippon Telegraph & Telephone	$101,881	117	Intel Corp	$62,761	184	POSCO (South Korea)	$44,186
51	Express Scripts Holding Co	$100,288	118	AUDI AG	$62,632	185	Kia Motors Corp. (South Kore	$43,878
52	PJSC Gazprom	$99,857	119	DowDuPont Inc	$62,484	186	Swiss Re AG	$43,786
53	Bayerische Motoren Werke AG	$99,425	120	China Communications Constru	$62,174	187	ITOCHU Corp (Japan)	$43,275
54	Siemens AG (Germany)	$98,120	121	Dell Technologies Inc	$61,642	188	Deutsche Bank AG	$43,230
55	Legal & General Group PLC (U	$95,913	122	Banco do Brasil S.A.	$61,521	189	Orange	$43,156
56	Home Depot Inc	$94,595	123	United Parcel Service Inc	$60,906	190	Lenovo Group Ltd	$43,035
57	Wells Fargo & Co.	$94,176	124	Archer Daniels Midland Co.	$60,828	191	Continental AG (Germany, Fed	$42,816
58	Bank of America Corp.	$93,662	125	BASF SE	$60,766	192	Bunge Ltd.	$42,679
59	Boeing Co.	$93,392	126	Deutsche Post AG	$60,538	193	KDDI Corp	$42,468
60	China Railway Group Ltd	$92,648	127	FedEx Corp	$60,319	194	Woolworths Group Ltd	$42,135
61	China Railway Construction C	$90,628	128	ENI S.p.A.	$59,861	195	Coca-Cola Co (The)	$41,863
62	Microsoft Corporation	$89,950	129	United Technologies Corp	$59,837	196	Charter Communications Inc (	$41,581
63	Assicurazioni Generali S.p.A	$88,841	130	Prudential Financial, Inc.	$59,689	197	HCA Healthcare Inc	$41,490
64	Prudential Plc	$88,600	131	Lloyds Banking Group Plc	$59,432	198	Nippon Steel & Sumitomo Meta	$41,437
65	Nestle SA	$88,207	132	Banco Bradesco SA	$58,104	199	Wilmar International Ltd	$41,402
66	Phillips 66	$85,777	133	Mitsubishi Corp	$57,472	200	Compagnie de Saint-Gobain	$41,310
67	PJSC Lukoil	$85,364	134	Peugeot SA	$57,049			

The Mergent 500 Largest Global Corporations (By Revenues)

Rank	Company	Sales ($ mil.)
201	NTT DoCoMo Inc	$41,004
202	Tata Motors Ltd	$40,963
203	Vinci SA	$40,912
204	E.ON SE	$40,873
205	Facebook Inc	$40,653
206	Centene Corp	$40,607
207	T-Mobile US Inc	$40,604
208	Honeywell International Inc	$40,534
209	Imperial Brands PLC	$40,504
210	Denso Corp. (Japan)	$40,491
211	Fujitsu Ltd	$40,335
212	American Airlines Group Inc	$40,180
213	Mitsubishi UFJ Financial Gro	$39,973
214	Merck & Co Inc	$39,807
215	LVMH Moet Hennessy Louis Vui	$39,704
216	Cigna Corp	$39,668
217	Delta Air Lines Inc (DE)	$39,639
218	China Unicom (Hong Kong) Ltd	$39,487
219	China United Network Communi	$39,486
220	Finatis SA	$39,448
221	Fonciere Euris SA	$39,447
222	Best Buy Inc	$39,403
223	Manufacturers Life Insurance	$39,365
224	Royal Bank of Canada (Montre	$39,257
225	Hanwha Corp	$39,222
226	Mitsui & Co., Ltd.	$39,031
227	Rallye S.A. Neuilly-Sur-Sein	$38,840
228	BHP Billiton Plc	$38,285
229	BHP Billiton Ltd.	$38,285
230	Tyson Foods Inc	$38,260
231	Sumitomo Life Insurance Co.	$38,087
232	Casino Guichard Perrachon S.	$38,043
233	Morgan Stanley	$37,949
234	Mitsubishi Electric Corp.	$37,911
235	Alimentation Couche-Tard Inc	$37,905
236	Oracle Corp	$37,728
237	Goldman Sachs Group Inc	$37,712
238	Power Corp. of Canada	$37,568
239	Energy Transfer Equity LP	$37,504
240	JD.com, Inc.	$37,460
241	Sinopharm Group Co., Ltd.	$37,210
242	Jardine Matheson Holdings Ltd	$37,051
243	Accenture plc	$36,765
244	Repsol S.A.	$36,764
245	Sanofi	$36,648
246	United Continental Holdings	$36,556
247	Allstate Corp.	$36,534
248	Magna International Inc	$36,445
249	Power Financial Corp	$36,377
250	Sumitomo Mitsui Financial Gr	$36,323
251	SSE PLC	$36,252
252	Pegatron Corp	$35,785
253	Sumitomo Corp.	$35,749
254	Shanghai Jinfeng Investment C	$35,628
255	George Weston Ltd	$35,617
256	American Express Co.	$35,583
257	NATIXIS SA	$35,518
258	Toronto Dominion Bank	$35,482
259	A.P. Moller – Maersk A/S	$35,464
260	Saudi Basic Industries Corp –	$35,415
261	UBS Group AG	$35,103
262	Intesa Sanpaolo S.P.A.	$35,097
263	Mitsubishi Heavy Industries	$35,007
264	Meiji Yasuda Life Insurance	$34,662
265	China Vanke Co Ltd	$34,631
266	Loblaw Companies Ltd	$34,419
267	Great-West Lifeco Inc	$34,416
268	NIKE Inc	$34,350
269	GlaxoSmithKline Plc	$34,307
270	Publix Super Markets, Inc.	$34,274
271	Barclays Bank Plc	$34,271
272	ACS Actividades de Construcc	$34,243
273	Barclays PLC	$34,133
274	Commonwealth Bank of Austral	$33,917
275	ABB Ltd	$33,828
276	Rio Tinto Ltd	$33,781
277	Rio Tinto Plc (United Kingdo	$33,781
278	Bouygues S.A.	$33,683
279	Exelon Corp	$33,531
280	Lufthansa AG (Germany, Fed.	$33,530
281	Talanx AG	$33,515
282	CK Hutchison Holdings Ltd	$33,508
283	Sprint Corp (New)	$33,347
284	Centrica Plc	$33,339
285	Volvo AB	$33,307
286	TJX Companies, Inc.	$33,184
287	SK Innovation Co Ltd	$32,897
288	Hongkong And Shanghai Bankin	$32,847
289	Rite Aid Corp.	$32,845
290	Hyundai Heavy Industries Co	$32,727
291	CHS Inc	$31,935
292	Aisin Seiki Co Ltd	$31,864
293	Hyundai Mobis Co Ltd (South	$31,849
294	J.Sainsbury PLC	$31,841
295	Banque Federative du Credit M	$31,749
296	3M Co	$31,657
297	China Pacific Insurance (Gro	$31,620
298	Metallurgical Corp China Ltd	$31,618
299	Chubb Ltd	$31,469
300	Daiwa House Industry Co Ltd	$31,419
301	DZ Bank AG Deutsche Zentral–	$31,125
302	Fresenius SE & Co KGaA	$31,118
303	General Dynamics Corp	$30,973
304	Iberdrola SA	$30,848
305	Schlumberger Ltd	$30,664
306	China Evergrande Group	$30,450
307	Gilead Sciences Inc	$30,390
308	Compass Group PLC (United Ki	$30,221
309	Sompo Holdings Inc	$30,216
310	Mitsubishi Chemical Holdings	$30,195
311	Johnson Controls Internation	$30,172
312	Banco Santander Brasil SA	$30,086
313	BT Group Plc	$30,040
314	Zhejiang Material Industrial	$29,834
315	Subaru Corp	$29,748
316	Deere & Co.	$29,738
317	Medtronic PLC	$29,710
318	JFE Holdings Inc	$29,596
319	Jardine Strategic Holdings L	$29,552
320	Westpac Banking Corp	$29,407
321	INTL FCStone Inc.	$29,382
322	Time Warner Inc	$29,318
323	Taiwan Semiconductor Manufac	$29,300
324	LyondellBasell Industries NV	$29,183
325	Jiangxi Copper Co., Ltd.	$29,134
326	Canon, Inc.	$29,082
327	Travelers Companies Inc (The	$28,902
328	Hewlett Packard Enterprise C	$28,871
329	Bharat Petroleum Corporation	$28,790
330	Mazda Motor Corp. (Japan)	$28,749
331	CRH Plc	$28,619
332	Hindustan Petroleum Corporation	$28,540
333	Idemitsu Kosan Co Ltd	$28,534
334	Bridgestone Corp. (Japan)	$28,531
335	21st Century Fox Inc	$28,500
336	Suzuki Motor Corp.	$28,348
337	AbbVie Inc	$28,216
338	AIA Group Ltd.	$28,191
339	Bank Nova Scotia Halifax	$28,059
340	Quanta Computer Inc	$27,633
341	Unicredit SpA	$27,559
342	Samsung Life Insurance Co Lt	$27,531
343	Capital One Financial Corp	$27,519
344	Vale SA	$27,488
345	Medipal Holdings Corp	$27,405
346	Abbott Laboratories	$27,390
347	L'Oreal S.A.	$27,281
348	Australia & New Zealand Bank	$27,058
349	World Fuel Services Corp.	$27,016
350	Kansai Electric Power Co., I	$26,933
351	Arrow Electronics, Inc.	$26,813
352	Baoshan Iron & Steel Co Ltd	$26,744
353	LafargeHolcim	$26,431
354	China Shenhua Energy Co., Lt	$26,372
355	Tech Data Corp.	$26,325
356	Air France-KLM	$26,234
357	Kraft Heinz Co (The)	$26,232
358	Schneider Electric SE	$26,073
359	Mondelez International Inc	$25,896
360	Royal Philips NV	$25,886
361	Northrop Grumman Corp	$25,803
362	Macy's Inc	$25,778
363	East Japan Railway Co.	$25,766
364	Veolia Environnement	$25,753
365	Altria Group Inc	$25,744
366	Wal-Mart de Mexico S.A.B. de	$25,730
367	Lloyds Bank plc	$25,710
368	Enbridge Inc	$25,645
369	Raytheon Co.	$25,348
370	National Australia Bank Ltd.	$25,274
371	Gazprom Neft PJSC	$25,242
372	Sumitomo Electric Industries	$25,173
373	Industria De Diseno Textil I	$25,053
374	Nokia Corp	$24,934
375	CNH Industrial NV	$24,872
376	McDonald's Corp	$24,622
377	Andeavor	$24,582
378	Lotte Shopping Co Ltd	$24,577
379	Telefonaktiebolaget LM Erics	$24,558
380	Ericsson	$24,558
381	Gas Natural SDG, S.A.	$24,480
382	Brookfield Asset Management	$24,411
383	ConocoPhillips	$24,360
384	Orix Corp. (Japan)	$23,997
385	Adecco Group AG	$23,977
386	Flex Ltd	$23,863
387	NEC Corp	$23,836
388	International Consolidated A	$23,828
389	Ultrapar Participacoes SA	$23,767
390	Compal Electronics Inc	$23,702
391	Mapfre SA	$23,443
392	Progressive Corp. (OH)	$23,441
393	Samsung C&T Corp (New)	$23,392
394	HSBC Bank Plc (United Kingdo	$23,360
395	SAP SE	$23,295
396	Chubu Electric Power Co., In	$23,286
397	Danone	$23,170
398	ANZ National Bank Ltd	$23,058
399	Standard Life Aberdeen PLC	$23,039
400	Enterprise Products Partners	$23,022

Rank	Company	Sales ($ mil.)	Rank	Company	Sales ($ mil.)	Rank	Company	Sales ($ mil.)
401	AstraZeneca Plc	$23,002	434	Dollar General Corp	$21,987	466	ENBW Energie Baden-Wuertte	$20,593
402	Koc Holdings AS	$20,104	435	Heineken Holding NV (Netherl	$21,954	467	Lear Corp.	$20,467
403	Endesa S.A.	$20,040	436	Heineken NV (Netherlands)	$21,954	468	Morrison (Wm.) Supermarkets	$20,453
404	Suncor Energy Inc	$20,011	437	TUI AG	$21,899	469	Cummins, Inc.	$20,428
405	Liberty Global plc	$20,009	438	BAE Systems Plc	$21,884	470	Wistron Corp	$20,398
406	Telstra Corp., Ltd.	$19,987	439	Tencent Holdings Ltd.	$21,880	471	Adidas AG	$20,369
407	Ferguson PLC	$19,972	440	Bank of Montreal (Quebec)	$21,862	472	OMV AG (Austria)	$20,336
408	Credit Suisse Group AG	$19,966	441	Randstad Holding N.V.	$21,840	473	Micron Technology Inc.	$20,322
409	CJ Corp (Korea)	$19,939	442	Mitsubishi Shokuhin Co., Ltd	$21,568	474	Imperial Oil Ltd	$20,297
410	Volvo Car Corp. (Sweden)	$19,932	443	AutoNation, Inc.	$21,535	475	Plains GP Holdings LP	$20,182
411	Southern Co.	$19,896	444	WH Group Ltd	$21,534	476	Plains All American Pipeline	$20,182
412	Alibaba Group Holding Ltd	$22,980	445	China Taiping Insurance Hold	$21,470	477	Penske Automotive Group Inc	$20,119
413	US Foods Holding Corp	$22,919	446	Suning Appliance Co., Ltd.	$21,397	478	R&V Versicherungsgruppe (Germ	$19,783
414	Marriott International, Inc.	$22,894	447	Anglo American Plc (United K	$21,378	479	Henkel AG & Co KGAA	$19,760
415	Amgen Inc	$22,849	448	Whirlpool Corp	$21,253	480	Faurecia	$19,756
416	Alfresa Holdings Corp Tokyo	$22,824	449	Union Pacific Corp	$21,240	481	Eaton Ltd (United Kingdom)	$19,747
417	U.S. Bancorp (DE)	$22,744	450	Eli Lilly & Co	$21,222	482	Eaton Corp plc	$19,747
418	Duke Energy Corp	$22,743	451	Sun Life Financial Inc	$21,202	483	Standard Chartered Bank (Tha	$19,679
419	United Arab Emirates (United	$22,734	452	Southwest Airlines Co	$21,171	484	Standard Chartered Plc	$19,679
420	Old Mutual Plc	$22,690	453	China Overseas Land & Invest	$21,158	485	ManpowerGroup	$19,654
421	Christian Dior SE	$22,635	454	Cnooc Ltd.	$21,096	486	Tenet Healthcare Corp.	$19,621
422	AFLAC Inc.	$22,559	455	Telecom Italia SpA	$21,091	487	Royal Bank of Scotland Group	$19,615
423	Sodexo	$22,542	456	International Paper Co	$21,079	488	Merro Pharmaceutical Co Ltd	$19,502
424	ONEX Corp (Canada)	$22,523	457	Hennes & Mauritz AB	$21,008	489	Great-West Life Assurance Co	$19,483
425	Starbucks Corp.	$22,387	458	JSC VTB Bank	$20,981	490	Swiss Life Holding AG	$19,360
426	Teva Pharmaceutical Industri	$22,385	459	Hochtief AG	$20,923	491	L'Air Liquide S.A.	$19,332
427	Qualcomm Inc	$22,291	460	Associated British Foods Plc	$20,839	492	Fomento Economico Mexicano,	$19,308
428	Poly Real Estate Group Co.,	$22,289	461	Bristol-Myers Squibb Co.	$20,776	493	Burlington Northern & Santa F	$19,278
429	Sears Holdings Corp	$22,138	462	FUJIFILM Holdings Corp	$20,769	494	Shanghai Construction Group	$19,248
430	Compagnie Generale des Etabl	$22,075	463	Aluminum Corp of China Ltd.	$20,747	495	Western Digital Corp	$19,093
431	LG Display Co Ltd	$22,062	464	Dollar Tree Inc	$20,719	496	Jabil Inc	$19,063
432	McKesson Europe AG	$22,056	465	Halliburton Company	$20,620	497	Fluor Corp.	$19,037
433	Country Garden Holdings Co.,	$22,046				498	Suzuken Co Ltd	$19,029
						499	PKN Orlen SA	$19,019
						500	Royal Bank of Scotland plc	$19,001

Hoover's Handbook of
American Business

The Companies

1st Source Corp

Need a bank? Don't give it a 2nd thought. Contact 1st Source Corporation parent of 1st Source Bank which provides commercial and consumer banking services through nearly 80 branches in northern Indiana and southwestern Michigan. The bank offers deposit accounts; business agricultural and consumer loans; residential and commercial mortgages; credit cards; and trust services. Its specialty finance group provides financing for aircraft automobile fleets trucks and construction and environmental equipment through about two-dozen offices nationwide; such loans account for nearly half of 1st Source's portfolio.

Operations

The firm operates nearly 80 banking center locations across Indiana and Michigan. 1st Source's Specialty Finance Group boasts more than 20 locations that offer specialized financing for new and used private and cargo aircraft automobiles and light trucks for leasing and rental agencies medium and heavy duty trucks and construction and environmental equipment.

Geographic Reach

Indiana-based 1st Source serves customers across 17 counties in Michigan and its home state.

Sales and Marketing

To keep its name in front of existing and potential customers 1st Source spends millions on advertising. In fiscal 2013 the firm spent about $4.9 million on ads up from 2012's $4.2 million.

Financial Performance

Fiscal 2013's revenue slipped some 2% — or $6.5 million — to $256.8 million from $263.3 million in 2012. 1st Source points to both a drop in mortgage banking income due to lower loan production volumes and a decrease in investment securities for the overall decline. During the reporting period net income increased some 11% to $54.9 million vs. 2012's $49.6 million thanks to drops in interest and non-interest expenses. Cash flow decreased to $86.9 million as compared to $93.2 million in 2012 due in part to a decline in interest receivables and asset changes.

Strategy

The company offers mutual funds through an agreement with Wasatch Advisors which has owned its 1st Source Monogram family of funds (now the Wasatch - 1st Source Funds) since 2008. Bank subsidiary 1st Source Insurance sells corporate and personal property/casualty coverage and group and individual life and health insurance.

1st Source has expanded its aircraft leasing business which accounts for the largest portion of its specialty finance activities into Brazil and Mexico and may be looking to expand into other selected markets in South America.

EXECUTIVES

Chairman and CEO, Christopher J. (Chris) Murphy, age 70, $726,923 total compensation

EVP Administration Secretary and General Counsel, John B. Griffith, age 59, $328,429 total compensation

EVP CFO and Treasurer, Andrea G. Short, age 54, $275,769 total compensation

President 1st Source Bank, James R. Seitz, age 64, $325,010 total compensation

SVP and Chief Credit Officer 1st Source Bank, Jeffrey L. Buhr, $226,565 total compensation

President 1st Source Insurance, John Ball

Vice President, John Lutz

Assistant Vice President Lease Accounting Manager, Joe Malinowski

Vice President Business Banking, Cecile A Weir

Auditors: BKD LLP

LOCATIONS

HQ: 1st Source Corp
100 North Michigan Street, South Bend, IN 46601
Phone: 574 235-2000
Web: www.1stsource.com

PRODUCTS/OPERATIONS

2016 Sales

	$ mil.	% of total
Interest		
Loans & leases	175	63
Investment securities taxable	11	4
Investment securities tax-exempt	2	1
Other	1	-
Non-interest		
Trust fees	19	7
Equipment rental income	9	3
Service charges on deposits accounts	25	9
Debit card income	10	4
Mortgage banking income	4	2
Insurance commissions	5	2
Gains (losses) on investment securities available-for-sale	1	1
Other	12	4
Total	**280**	**100**

Selected Subsidiaries

1st Source Bank
   1st Source Commercial Aircraft Leasing
   1st Source Corporation Investment Advisors Inc.
   1st Source Insurance Inc.
   1st Source Specialty Finance Inc.
   Michigan Transportation Finance Corporation
   SFG Aircraft Inc.
   SFG Equipment Leasing Corporation I
1st Source Funding LLC
1st Source Intermediate Holding LLC
1st Source Leasing Inc.
1st Source Master Trust

COMPETITORS

Bank of America	MainSource Financial
Fifth Third	Old National Bancorp
Huntington Bancshares	PNC Financial
JPMorgan Chase	U.S. Bancorp
KeyCorp	Wells Fargo

HISTORICAL FINANCIALS

Company Type: Public

Income Statement

FYE: December 31

	ASSETS ($ mil.)	NET INCOME ($ mil.)	INCOME AS % OF ASSETS	EMPLOYEES
12/16	5,486	57	1.1%	1,150
12/15	5,187	57	1.1%	1,150
12/14	4,829	58	1.2%	1,100
12/13	4,722	54	1.2%	1,100
12/12	4,550	49	1.1%	1,180
Annual Growth	**4.8%**	**3.9%**	**—**	**(0.6%)**

2016 Year-End Financials

Debt ratio: 1.46%
Return on equity: 8.75%
Cash ($ mil.): 108
Current ratio: —
Long-term debt ($ mil.): —

No. of shares (mil.): 25
Dividends
  Yield: 0.0%
  Payout: 32.4%
Market value ($ mil.): 1,156

	STOCK PRICE ($) FY Close	P/E High/Low		PER SHARE ($) Earnings	Dividends	Book Value
12/16	44.66	20	12	2.22	0.72	26.00
12/15	30.87	16	13	2.17	0.67	24.75
12/14	34.31	16	13	2.17	0.65	23.41
12/13	31.94	16	11	2.03	0.62	21.88
12/12	22.09	14	11	1.84	0.60	20.95
Annual Growth	**19.2%**	**—**	**—**	**4.9%**	**4.7%**	**5.5%**

3M Co

Loath to be stuck on one thing 3M makes everything from tape to high-tech security gear. The diversified company makes products through five operating segments: Industrial; Safety and Graphics; Electronics and Energy; Health Care; and Consumer. Well-known brands include Post-it notes Scotch tapes Scotchgard fabric protectors Scotch-Brite scouring pads and Filtrete home air filters. 3M sells products directly to users and through numerous wholesalers retailers distributors and dealers worldwide.

HISTORY

Five businessmen in Two Harbors Minnesota founded Minnesota Mining and Manufacturing (3M) in 1902 to sell corundum to grinding-wheel manufacturers. The company soon needed to raise working capital. Co-founder John Dwan offered his friend Edgar Ober 60% of 3M's stock. Ober persuaded Lucius Ordway VP of a plumbing business to help underwrite 3M. In 1905 the two took over the company and moved it to Duluth.

In 1907 future CEO William McKnight joined 3M as a bookkeeper. Three years later the plant moved to St. Paul. The board of directors declared a dividend to shareholders in the last quarter of 1916 and 3M hasn't missed a dividend since. The next two products 3M developed — Scotch-brand masking tape (1925) and Scotch-brand cellophane tape (1930) — assured its future.

McKnight introduced one of the first employee pension plans in 1931 and in the late 1940s he implemented a vertical management structure. 3M introduced the first commercially viable magnetic recording tape in 1947.

In 1950 after a decade of work and $1 million in development costs 3M employee Carl Miller completed the Thermo-Fax copying machine which was the foundation of 3M's duplicating division.

Products in the 1960s included 3M's dry-silver microfilm photographic products carbonless papers overhead projection systems and medical and dental products. The company moved into pharmaceuticals radiology energy control and office markets in the 1970s and 1980s.

A 3M scientist developed Post-it Notes (1980) because he wanted to attach page markers to his church hymnal. Recalling that a colleague had developed an adhesive that wasn't very sticky he brushed some on paper and began a product line that now generates hundreds of millions of dollars each year.

In 1990 the company bought sponge maker O-Cel-O. But not all of its inventions have brought 3M good news. In 1995 along with fellow silicone breast-implant makers Baxter International and Bristol-Myers Squibb it agreed to settle thousands of personal-injury claims related to implants. The companies paid an average of $26000 per claim.

3M spun off its low-profit imaging and data-storage businesses in 1996 as Imation Corp. and closed its audiotape and videotape businesses. The next year 3M sold its National Advertising billboard business to Infinity Outdoor for $1 billion and its Media Network unit (a printer of advertising inserts) to Time Warner.

The company created the 3M Nexcare brand for its line of first-aid and home health products in 1998. To regain earnings growth 3M closed about 10% of its plants in the US and abroad; it also discontinued unprofitable product lines. The next year 3M sold its heart-surgery-equipment health care unit to Japan's Terumo and its Eastern Heights

Bank subsidiary to Norwest Bank of Minnesota. It also bought out Hoechst AG's 46% stake in Dyneon LLC a fluorine elastomer joint venture between the two companies.

3M bought Polaroid's Technical Polarizer and Display Films business and a controlling stake in Germany-based Quante AG (telecom systems) in 2000. In addition the company decided to halt the manufacture of many of its Scotchgard-brand repellent products due to research revealing that one of the compounds (perfluorooctane sulfonate) used in the manufacturing process is "persistent and pervasive" in the environment and in people's bloodstreams. As 2000 drew to a close 3M named GE executive James McNerney to succeed L. D. DeSimone as its chairman and CEO. With the sale of Eastern Heights and several health care businesses (including its cardiovascular systems unit) 3M was rewarded with its second-best financial performance in 14 years.

3M then bought Robinson Nugent (electronic connectors) and MicroTouch Systems (touch screens) in 2001. It also announced plans to cut 6000 jobs and authorized a stock buy-back program of up to $2.5 billion.

The company changed its legal name from Minnesota Mining and Manufacturing Company to 3M Company that year. Also in 2002 3M restructured its business segments around end uses rather than products or raw materials. So the Health Care segment encompassed everything from transdermal skin patches to software for hospital coding and classification. Similarly the Consumer and Office Business unit became responsible for Post-its O-Cel-O sponges wood-finishing materials and air conditioner filters. By the end of that year the company had cut more than 8500 jobs 11% of its total workforce.

Nevertheless a strong year in 2003 emboldened the company to look to expand. 3M closed a deal to buy fellow Minnesota resident HighJump Software a maker of supply chain software for businesses in February 2004. CEO McNerney left 3M in 2005 to join Boeing in the same capacity and was replaced by George Buckley formerly of the Brunswick Corporation.

That year the company made a billion-dollar acquisition of liquid filtration producer CUNO. 3M's own filtration products business — primarily air filters — amounted to more than $1 billion in annual sales before the deal and the deal added nearly half that. (3M eventually changed CUNO's name to 3M Purification.)

The company signaled a new strategic direction in 2006 when it broke up its pharmaceutical unit along geographic lines and sold it in pieces. In total 3M got $2.1 billion for the sale of its pharmaceutical operations. The next year it sold HighJump Software. High-tech venture capital firm Battery Ventures bought HighJump to set it up as a standalone company.

The company then ran through another string of acquisitions in 2007 buying companies such as Unifam Lingualcare Innovative Paper Technologies and Diamond Productions.

Its 2008 acquisition of protection products maker Aearo Technologies helped 3M's sales growth in the area of safety security and protection services. It added to the unit with the purchase (through its 3M Canada subsidiary) of Toronto-based MTI PolyFab which makes thermal and acoustic insulation for aerospace products. 3M also capitalized on its purchase of Beiersdorf subsidiary Futuro which makes medical products such as wraps elastic bandages and compression hosiery.

3M made two moves into the high-tech security field in 2010. The company acquired Cogent Inc. for $943 million. Known as Cogent Systems the firm provides finger palm face and iris biometric systems for governments law enforcement agencies and commercial enterprises. 3M also acquired Attenti Ltd. an Israeli manufacturer of people-tracking technology for $230 million. Attenti makes remote monitoring devices to track people awaiting trial or on probation as well as for eldercare facilities to monitor patient safety.

The company expanded its consumer and office business line in 2010 by acquiring a majority stake in Japanese company A-One the top office label brand in Asia and the second-largest label business worldwide. It also acquired Alpha Beta Enterprise a manufacturer of box sealing tape and masking tape headquartered in Taiwan. Both acquisitions will expand 3M's presence in the global packaging market.

Also in 2010 3M acquired J.R. Phoenix Ltd. a manufacturer of hand hygiene and skin care products for health care and professional use. The majority of J.R. Phoenix products are sold under the Laura Line brand in Canada. The deal expanded 3M's line of hand hygiene skin care products to the healthcare market in Canada. The company also acquired UK-based Dailys Ltd. a global supplier of non-woven disposable chemical protective coveralls for industrial use.

The company made several acquisitions in 2010 including Minnesota-based Arizant which manufactures forced-air warming garments designed to prevent hypothermia in surgical settings a growing international market estimated at some $1 billion per year.

3M completed nine acquisitions in 2011 that totaled $649 million including the do-it-yourself unit and professional division of France's GPI Group a manufacturer and marketer of home improvement products such as tapes hooks insulation and floor protection products. The deal boosts 3M's presence in Western Europe. It also added to its growing Industrial and Transportation segment by acquiring a majority stake in Switzerland-based Winterthur Technology Group an international supplier of precision grinding technologies that makes grinding tools used in the aircraft automotive industrial and steel industries.

Back in the US it acquired Florida-based Nida-Core a manufacturer of structural honeycomb core and fiber-reinforced foam core materials and Nida-Core's French affiliate Structiso SARL. The acquisition allows 3M's Engineered Products and Solutions department to build on its composite and engineered materials product portfolio.

In a related deal in 2012 3M acquired Maryland-based CodeRyte which provides clinical natural language processing (NLP) technology and computer-assisted coding for healthcare outpatient providers. Terms of the sale were not disclosed. 3M will apply CodeRyte's NLP technology to its new 3M 360 Encompass system used by its 3M Health Information Systems division for clinical documentation and coding workflows. More than 5000 hospitals worldwide use 3M's coding for patient data for measurement and reimbursement purposes. The 3M system also addresses data problems resulting from health care reform requirements.

In 2012 the company brought Inge Thulman in as CEO who altered 3M's acquisition strategy to target fewer larger companies. In the ive years after his appointment 3M spent $5.8 billion on nine businesses versus $4.8 billion on 70 businesses in the five years prior to Thulman's appointment.

In an effort to broaden its global presence in office education and consumer products in 2012 3M acquired the Office and Consumer Products business of Avery Dennison Corp. for $550 million.

Continuing a quest for technology buys on 2012 3M acquired the Federal Signal Technologies Group (FSTech) from Federal Signal Corp. for $110 million in cash. FSTech focuses on hardware and software services for the $3 billion electronic tolling industry. The business also complements offerings from 3M's Traffic Safety Systems Division.

Growing its ceramics portfolio in 2012 it also bought advanced technical ceramics producer Ceradyne for $860 million. The deal adds Ceradyne's advanced ceramics technologies portfolio to its own diversified product line.

In 2013 the company and China-based Hunan Reshine New Material Company signed a patent license agreement to expand the use of nickel manganese and cobalt in lithium ion batteries (in growing demand in consumer electronics automotive and other markets).

In 2014 3M formed partnership with US-China Clean Energy Research Center Building Energy Efficiency Consortium under which 3M participates in research on building efficiency strategies tools and practices in areas such as building envelope technologies and integration of new construction materials for increasing energy efficiency.

In a move aimed at bringing greater economic efficiencies to Premier's more than 100000 health care provider members in 2014 the company reached a group purchasing agreement with health care alliance company Premier Inc. for multiple catheter securement and stability products. The new agreement allows them to take advantage of special pricing and terms pre-negotiated by Premier.

EXECUTIVES

EVp Health Care Business, Brad T Sauer

EVP Safety and Graphics, Frank R. Little, age 56

Chairman President and CEO, Inge G. Thulin, age 64, $1,483,929 total compensation

EVP Consumer, Joaquin Delgado, age 57, $629,074 total compensation

Vice Chair and EVP, Hak Cheol (H.C.) Shin, age 60, $765,496 total compensation

EVP International Operations, Julie L. Bushman, age 55, $599,029 total compensation

SVP Business Transformation Americas, James L. (Jim) Bauman, age 57

EVP and COO, Michael F. Roman, age 57, $747,022 total compensation

SVP and CFO, Nicholas C. Gangestad, age 52, $681,551 total compensation

EVP Health Care, Michael G. Vale, age 51, $633,302 total compensation

EVP Electronics and Energy Business Group, Ashish K. Khandpur, age 49

SVP Business Development and Marketing and Sales, Jon T. Lindekugel, age 53

SVP Business Transformation and Information Technology, Eric Hammes

Senior Vice President Supply Chain, Christopher D Holmes

National Sales Manager, Jim Stevens

National Sales Manager and Operations Manager, Nick Dan

National Account Manager, Deann Rutledge

Vice President Research and Development 3m Infection Prevention Division, Ann Meitz

Vice President New Market Development, Patrick Hiner

Vice President Finance and Human Resources, Philip Hanson

Information Technology Sales Vice President, Dave Herington

National Sales Manager, Gina Kuehn

Vice President Human Resources, Kathleen Rossette

National Sales Manager, Jay Reese

Vice President, Jacques Dumonteil

Vice President of Quality, Dan Tenney

Vice President of Finance, Mary Cannon

Vice President of Business Development, Richard Nimer
Vice President, Paul Acito
Vice President, David Schwedler
Regional Sales Vice President, Robert McDonald
National Account Manager, Pat Kinate
National Account Manager, Christian Rudeen
Vice President Mobile Interactive Solutions Division, Mark Colin
Vice President, Jim Walsh
Sales Vice President, Erin Douglass
Vice President, Patrick Moran
National Sales Manager, Timothy Mogck
Vice President Investor Relations and Corporate Communications, Dan Mcintyre
Vice President Technical Services and Information Technology, Ronen Shraga
Vice President Of Marketing, Sharon Cohen
Vice President and General Manager Corrosion Protection Products, Paiul Acito
Vice President Customer Service, Angel Zimmerman
Vice President Research and Development, James Sax
National Account Manager, Sherry Knollmaier
Vice President Controller, Dave Meline
Vice President of Research Devt, Gary Silvers
Vice President Management Executive, Kevin Higgins
Vice President Research and Development 3m Drug Delivery Systems, Steven Wick
Vice President of Technology, Witold Witwicki
Vice President, Gayle Schueller
Vice President Of Finance, Gerardo Pereyra
National Account Manager, Bart Rasmussen
Vice President, Christina Kim
Senior Management (Senior Vice President General Manager Director), Mark Sutton
Vice President Research and Development, Betty Mei
Vice President and General Manager, John Riccardi
Vice President Of Sales, Jill Cherbow
Vice President, Brian Spiewak
Finance Vice President, Tom Pepinski
Vice President Quality and Safety, Molly Wallace
National Sales Manager, Chris Decolli
Vice President Environmental Health and Safety Operations, Jean Sweeney
National Sales Manager, Scott McConnell
Vice President Global Marketing 3M Unitek Orthodontic Products, Marcello Napol
Executive Vice President International Operations, Hak Shin
Vice President, Gerry Erickson
Vice President Cio, Ernie Park
Executive Vice President Global Human Resources, Anthony Jackson
Vice President of Quality Drug Delivery Systems Division, Will Donovan
National Account Manager, Chris Theobald
Vice President And General Manager Automotive Afte, Laino Richard
Senior Vice President Operations Redmond, A Dubner
Vice President of Business Development, Jack Driessen
National Account Manager, MIKE ZIELINSKI
Vice President Supply Chain Operations, Norman Clason
Vice President Operations, Joe LaPlante
Vice President and General Manager, Erik Aunan
Vice President, Mariann Birk
National Sales Manager, Andrew Petrone
Vice President Investor Relations and Treasurer, Matt Ginter
Board Member, Ken Brown
Auditors: PricewaterhouseCoopers LLP

LOCATIONS

HQ: 3M Co
3M Center, St. Paul, MN 55144
Phone: 651 733-1110   **Fax:** 651 733-9973
Web: www.3M.com

2016 Sales

	$ mil.	% of total
United States	12,188	41
Asia Pacific	8,847	29
Europe Middle East and Africa	6,163	20
Latin America and Canada	2,901	10
Other Unallocated	10	-
Total	**30,109**	**100**

PRODUCTS/OPERATIONS

2016 Sales

	$ mil.	% of total
Industrial	10,313	33
Safety and Graphics	5,660	18
Health Care	5,527	18
Electronics and Energy	4,826	16
Consumer	4,482	15
Corporate and unallocated	9	-
Eliminations	(708)	-
Total	**30,109**	**100**

Selected Segments and Products

Industrial and Transportation
  Automotive aftermarket products
  Automotive products
  Closures for disposable diapers
  Coated and nonwoven abrasives
  Films
  Filtration products
  Specialty adhesives
  Tapes
Health Care
  Dental products
  Drug delivery systems
  Health information systems
  Infection prevention
  Medical and surgical supplies
  Microbiology products
  Skin health products
Safety Security and Protection
  Commercial cleaning products
  Consumer safety products
  Corrosion protection products
  Floor matting
  Occupational health and safety products
  Safety and security products
  Track and trace products
Consumer and Office
  Carpet and fabric protectors
  Commercial cleaning products
  Fabric protectors (Scotchgard)
  High-performance cloth (Scotch-Brite)
  Home-improvement products
  Repositionable notes (Post-it)
  Scour pads (Scotch-Brite)
  Sponges (O-Cel-O)
  Tape (Scotch)
Display and Graphics
  Commercial graphics systems
  Optical films for electronic display
  Specialty film and media products
  Traffic control materials
Electro and Communications
  Insulating and splicing products for electronics
  telecommunications and electrical industries
  Packaging and interconnection devices

COMPETITORS

ACCO Brands	Henkel
BASF SE	Honeywell
Bayer AG	International
Beiersdorf	Illinois Tool Works
Bostik	Johnson & Johnson
Carlisle Companies	Kimberly-Clark
Corning	RPM International
Danaher	Ricoh Company
DuPont	S.C. Johnson
GE	Sealed Air Corp.
H.B. Fuller	Sika

HISTORICAL FINANCIALS

Company Type: Public

Income Statement

FYE: December 31

	REVENUE ($ mil.)	NET INCOME ($ mil.)	NET PROFIT MARGIN	EMPLOYEES
12/17	31,657	4,858	15.3%	91,536
12/16	30,109	5,050	16.8%	91,584
12/15	30,274	4,833	16.0%	89,446
12/14	31,821	4,956	15.6%	89,800
12/13	30,871	4,659	15.1%	88,667
Annual Growth	0.6%	1.1%	—	0.8%

2017 Year-End Financials

Debt ratio: 36.88%
Return on equity: 44.44%
Cash ($ mil.): 3,053
Current ratio: 1.86
Long-term debt ($ mil.): 12,156
No. of shares (mil.): 594
Dividends
  Yield: 0.0%
  Payout: 59.2%
Market value ($ mil.): 140,018

	STOCK PRICE ($) FY Close	P/E High/Low		PER SHARE ($) Earnings	Dividends	Book Value
12/17	235.37	30	21	7.93	4.70	19.44
12/16	178.57	22	16	8.16	4.44	17.26
12/15	150.64	22	18	7.58	4.10	19.21
12/14	164.32	22	16	7.49	3.42	20.64
12/13	140.25	20	14	6.72	2.54	26.39
Annual Growth	13.8%	—	—	4.2%	16.6%	(7.4%)

A-Mark Precious Metals, Inc

Auditors: Grant Thornton LLP

LOCATIONS

HQ: A-Mark Precious Metals, Inc
2121 Rosecrans Ave., Suite 6300, El Segundo, CA 90245
Phone: 310 587-1477
Web: www.amark.com

HISTORICAL FINANCIALS

Company Type: Public

Income Statement

FYE: June 30

	REVENUE ($ mil.)	NET INCOME ($ mil.)	NET PROFIT MARGIN	EMPLOYEES
06/17	6,989	7	0.1%	127
06/16	6,784	9	0.1%	83
06/15	6,070	7	0.1%	52
06/14	5,979	8	0.1%	55
06/13	7,247	12	0.2%	31
Annual Growth	(0.9%)	(13.3%)	—	42.3%

2017 Year-End Financials

Debt ratio: 37.72%
Return on equity: 10.66%
Cash ($ mil.): 13
Current ratio: 1.11
Long-term debt ($ mil.): —
No. of shares (mil.): 7
Dividends
  Yield: 1.8%
  Payout: 30.0%
Market value ($ mil.): 115

STOCK PRICE ($)	P/E	PER SHARE ($)		
FY Close	High/Low	Earnings	Dividends	Book Value
06/17	16.39	21 15	1.00	0.30	9.90
06/16	16.18	17 8	1.30	0.24	9.02
06/15	10.47	12 9	1.00	0.10	8.02
06/14	11.16	13 10	1.09	0.00	7.10
Annual Growth	10.1%	— —	(2.1%)	—	8.6%

Abbott Laboratories

With activities ranging from filling baby bottles to making generic medications Abbott Laboratories is a top health care products manufacturer. Its nutritional products division makes such well-known brands as Similac infant formula and the Ensure line of nutrition supplements while its drug division sells branded generic medicines (such as antibiotics and gastroenterology medicines) in international markets. The company also makes diagnostic instruments (including tests and assays) vascular medical devices such as its Xience drug-eluting stents and the FreeStyle diabetes care line as well as eye care products. The company acquired medical device maker St. Jude Medical for $23.6 billion in early 2017.

Operations

Abbott operates in five segments: Nutritional Products (the largest accounting for some 35% of sales) which makes adult and pediatric nutritional items; Diagnostic (nearly 25% of sales) which makes tests diagnostic products and data management systems for labs; Established Pharmaceutical Products (nearly 20%) the branded generics arm; Vascular (about 15%) which makes devices for coronary endovascular and structural heart procedures; and Other (some 10%) which includes Abbott's Diabetes Dare operations.

Geographic Reach

Abbott has plants in Argentina Brazil Chile Colombia Costa Rica China Canada Germany India Ireland Mexico the Netherlands Pakistan Peru Puerto Rico Russia Spain Singapore Sweden the UK and the US.

The company's products are sold in more than 150 countries. Abbott earns more than 30% of its revenues in the domestic market some 50% in emerging markets (especially Brazil China India and Russia) and around 20% in non-US developed markets (including Canada Western Europe Japan New Zealand and Australia).

Sales and Marketing

Abbott conducts distribution operations both from its own distribution centers and through third-party partners. Established pharmaceutical and nutritional customers include health care organizations wholesalers pharmacies retailers government agencies and third-party distribution entities. Diagnostic and vascular products are sold to blood banks hospitals and other health care facilities physicians plasma protein therapeutic companies government agencies alternative testing sites and commercial laboratories.

Financial Performance

Abbott's revenues declined significantly in 2013 as a result of the spinoff of AbbVie and the loss of that unit's income. It has held steady since then and in 2016 it rose 2% to $20.9 billion. This was driven by modest increases in the Established Pharmaceuticals Diagnostics and Vascular segments but offset by a decline in the Nutritionals segment.

Net income had been in alignment with revenue but nearly doubled in 2015 when the company sold its non-US developed markets specialty and branded generics pharmaceuticals business and its animals business. In 2016 net income dropped 68% to $1.4 billion. The negative impact of foreign exchange rates plus a steep reduction in net earnings from discontinued operations drove that decline.

Despite that drop in net income Abbott's cash flow from operations rose 8% to $3.2 billion in 2016. Leading factors contributing to that increase included the impact of currency devaluation and an adjustment in an investment in Mylan.

Strategy

Abbott has a diverse set of operations and it has lined up strategies specific to its different segments. In the Nutritionals segment the company is focused on R&D activities in the pediatric adult and performance nutrition fields. It has a number of products in development which it expects to launch over the next few years.

The Diagnostic segment is focused on commercializing its blood screening immunoassay clinical chemistry and hematology systems as well as various assays and management solutions. It also has molecular in vitro diagnostic products and systems under development. To boost its point-of-care diagnostics offerings Abbott acquired Alere for $5.8 billion in 2017. Alere makes tests for cancers cardiovascular disease and infections such as HIV and malaria among others.

In the Established Pharmaceuticals segment Abbott is working to build portfolios of branded generic medicines for emerging markets. It focuses on building country-specific portfolios to best meet the needs of each nation. The company has more than 400 projects under development. Among its key brands are Creon Duphaston and Influvac.

The Vascular segment has several projects in its pipeline ranging from its MitraClip device for the treatment of mitral regurgitation and its Portico transcatheter heart valve and delivery system to its Supera self-expanding nitinol stent system and next-generation Xience products.

In the Other segment diabetes care remains an area of focus. Its FreeStyle Libre Flash (approved in Europe in 2014 and in the US in mid-2017) is the first continuous glucose monitoring system that doesn't require a fingerstick.

In 2015 Abbott sold its non-US developed markets specialty and branded generics operations to Mylan. The sale included a portfolio of more than 100 pharmaceutical products in markets including Europe Japan Canada Australia and New Zealand; upon closing of the deal Abbott received a 21% stake in the combined company. The company also sold its animal health business to Zoetis in early 2015. Furthering its focus on cardiovascular and diagnostic operations Abbott sold its Abbott Medical Optics subsidiary to Johnson & Johnson for $4.3 billion in early 2017.

Mergers and Acquisitions

In 2015 Abbott bought the rest of Tendyne Holdings it didn't already own for $225 million; it also invested in Cephea Valve Technologies. Both of those medical device firm acquisitions boosted Abbott's portfolio of mitral valve replacement therapies.

The following year Abbott announced a major deal to further grow its line of heart-related devices. It agreed to buy St. Jude Medical which makes such products as heart catheters and defibrillators in a deal valued at $23.6 billion. The combination of the two firms which closed in early 2017 created one of the world's largest makers of cardiovascular devices.

Also in 2017 Abbott acquired Alere which makes a range of diagnostic health tests. That transaction was valued at $5.3 billion.

HISTORY

Dr. Wallace Abbott started making his dosimetric granule (a pill that supplied uniform quantities of drugs) at his home outside Chicago in 1888. Aggressive marketing earned Abbott the American Medical Association's criticism though much of the medical profession supported him.

During WWI Abbott scientists synthesized anesthetics previously available only from Germany. Abbott improved its research capacity in 1922 by buying Dermatological Research Laboratories; in 1928 it bought John T. Milliken and its well-trained sales force. Abbott went public in 1929.

Salesman DeWitt Clough became president in 1933. International operations began in the mid-1930s with branches in Argentina Brazil Cuba Mexico and the UK.

Abbott was integral to the WWII effort; the US made only 28 pounds of penicillin in 1943 before the company began to ratchet up production. Consumer infant and nutritional products (such as Selsun Blue shampoo Murine eye drops and Similac formula) joined the roster in the 1960s. The FDA banned Abbott's artificial sweetener Sucaryl in 1970 saying it might be carcinogenic and in 1971 millions of intravenous solutions were recalled following contamination deaths.

Robert Schoellhorn became CEO in 1979; profits increased but research and development was cut. In the 1980s Abbott began selling Japanese-developed pharmaceuticals in the US.

EXECUTIVES

SVP and Chief Marketing and External Affairs Officer, Elaine R. Leavenworth, age 59

Vice President Diagnostic Commercial Operations Europe Africa and Middle East, Jaime Contreras

Chairman and CEO, Miles D. White, age 61, $1,900,000 total compensation

EVP Human Resources, Stephen R. (Steve) Fussell, age 60, $454,689 total compensation

EVP Ventures, John M. Capek, age 55, $675,000 total compensation

EVP Nutritional Products, Heather L. Mason, age 57

SVP and Group President Cardiovascular and Neuromodulation, Eric S. Fain, age 56

EVP Medical Devices, Robert B. Ford, age 43

EVP Diagnostic Products, Brian J. Blaser, age 52, $692,057 total compensation

EVP General Counsel and Secretary, Hubert L. Allen, age 51, $650,000 total compensation

SVP Finance and CFO, Brian B. Yoor, age 47, $584,231 total compensation

SVP U.S. Nutrition, Roger M. Bird, age 60

SVP Abbott Vascular, Deepak Nath, age 44

SVP Established Pharmaceuticals Latin America, Daniel Salvadori, age 38

SVP Diabetes Care, Jared L. Watkin, age 49

EVP Established Pharmaceuticals Emerging Markets, Andrew H. Lane, age 46

President Cardiovascular and Neuromodulation, Michael T. (Mike) Rousseau, age 61

SVP International Nutrition, Joseph (Joe) Manning, age 48

Senior Non IT Management Chief Executive Officer Chief Financial Officer Vice President Directo, Randi Pickens

Divisional Vice President Pharma Research And Development, Leanna Walther

Senior Vice President, Ann Long

Divisional Vice President, Andy Brookes

Medical Director, Thomas Podsadecki

Senior Vice President Central Region, Pamela Switalski

Evp Corporate Development, Richard W Ashley, age 74

Divisional Vice President, Brian Wentworth

Senior Vice President, Maureen Snider
Vice President Sales Training And Development, Randee Stelman
Group Vice President, Tiffany Cincotta
Division Vice President Pediatric Commercial Operations, Rich Schaefer
Vice President Marketing And Human Resources, Jennifer Pestikas
Medical Director, Roger Trinh
Medical Director, Gwendolyn Janssen
Area Treasurer, Quintin Noble
Auditors: Ernst & Young LLP

LOCATIONS

HQ: Abbott Laboratories
100 Abbott Park Road, Abbott Park, IL 60064-6400
Phone: 224 667-6100
Web: www.abbott.com

2016 Sales

	$ mil.	% of total
US	6,486	31
China	1,728	8
India	1,114	5
Germany	1,044	5
Japan	924	4
The Netherlands	830	4
Switzerland	766	4
Russia	554	3
Vietnam	434	2
Colombia	424	2
Brazil	410	2
Canada	408	2
United Kingdom	377	2
Italy	365	2
Other countries	4,989	24
Total	**20,853**	**100**

PRODUCTS/OPERATIONS

2016 Sales

	$ mil.	% of total
Nutritionals	6,899	33
Diagnostics	4,813	23
Established pharmaceuticals	3,859	19
Vascular	2,896	14
Other	2,386	11
Total	**20,853**	**100**

Selected Products

Nutritional
Alimentum (infant formula)
EAS nutritional brands
AdvantEdge (nutritional supplements)
Myoplex (nutritional supplements)
Ensure (adult nutrition)
Freego (enteral pump)
Glucerna (nutritional beverage for diabetics)
Isomil (soy-based infant formula)
Jevity (liquid food for enteral feeding)
NeoSure (infant formula)
Osmolite
Pedialyte (pediatric electrolyte solution)
PediaSure (children's nutrition)
Similac (infant formula)
Zone Perfect (nutritional bars)
Established Pharmaceuticals (branded generics)
Creon (pancreatic enzyme replacement therapy)
Duphaston (progesterone deficiency)
Klacid (macrolide antibiotic)
Diagnostic
Abbott PRISM (high-volume blood-screening system)
ARCHITECT (clinical chemistry system)
AxSYM (clinical chemistry system)
Cell-Dyn (hematology systems and reagents)
Diagnostic and screening assays
Informatics and automation solutions for lab use
i-STAT (blood analyzer)
m2000 (instrument that detects and measures infectious agents)
Vysis (genomic-based tests)
PathVysion (breast cancer diagnostic test)
UroVysion (bladder cancer)
Medical Devices (former vascular division)
Absorb (vascular scaffold)
Acculink/Accunet (carotid stent)

Asahi (coronary guidewires licensed from Asahi Intecc)
Hi-Torque Balance Middleweight (coronary guidewire licensed from Asahi Intecc)
MitraClip (valve repair)
Multi-Link 8 Multi-Link Mini Vision and Multi-Link Vision (coronary metallic stents)
Perclose (vessel closure)
StarClose (vessel closure)
Trek (balloon dilation)
Xience V Xience nano and Xience Prime (drug-eluting stents)
Voyager (balloon dilation)

COMPETITORS

Allergan plc	Mannatech
AstraZeneca	Mead Johnson
Bard	Merck
Baxter International	Mylan
Bayer AG	NBTY
Becton Dickinson	Nature's Sunshine
Boston Scientific	Nestlé
Cordis	Perrigo
Danone	Roche Holding
Dr. Reddy's	Sandoz International
GNC	GmbH
GlaxoSmithKline	Schiff Nutrition
Heinz	International
Herbalife Ltd.	Sun Pharmaceutical
Johnson & Johnson	Teva
LifeScan	

HISTORICAL FINANCIALS

Company Type: Public

Income Statement

FYE: December 31

	REVENUE ($ mil.)	NET INCOME ($ mil.)	NET PROFIT MARGIN	EMPLOYEES
12/17	27,390	477	1.7%	99,000
12/16	20,853	1,400	6.7%	75,000
12/15	20,405	4,423	21.7%	74,000
12/14	20,247	2,284	11.3%	77,000
12/13	21,848	2,576	11.8%	69,000
Annual Growth	5.8%	(34.4%)	—	9.4%

2017 Year-End Financials

Debt ratio: 36.62%
Return on equity: 1.85%
Cash ($ mil.): 9,407
Current ratio: 2.26
Long-term debt ($ mil.): 27,210

No. of shares (mil.): 1,743
Dividends
Yield: 0.0%
Payout: 392.5%
Market value ($ mil.): 99,507

	STOCK PRICE ($) FY Close	P/E High/Low		PER SHARE ($)		
				Earnings	Dividends	Book Value
12/17	57.07	213	145	0.27	1.06	17.72
12/16	38.41	48	39	0.94	1.04	13.94
12/15	44.91	17	13	2.92	0.96	14.40
12/14	45.02	31	24	1.49	0.88	14.27
12/13	38.33	40	20	1.62	0.56	16.26
Annual Growth	10.5%	—	—	(36.1%)	17.3%	2.2%

AbbVie Inc

AbbVie is vying for dominance in the world of medications. The firm discovers develops and commercializes both biopharmaceutical and small molecule drugs with a focus on autoimmune diseases hepatitis C HIV and other ailments. Its primary product is Humira best known as a rheumatoid arthritis drug; it accounts for more than 60% of AbbVie's sales. Other key products include cancer treatment Imbruvica and hepatitis C drug Viekira.

The firm has seven facilities making products that are available in more than 170 countries. After the expiration of Humira's compound patent protection in late 2016 the R&D firm is looking for the next big thing.

Operations

AbbVie's products focus on treating conditions such as chronic autoimmune diseases (including rheumatoid arthritis psoriasis and Crohn's disease) hepatitis C HIV endometriosis thyroid disease Parkinson's disease low testosterone and complications from chronic kidney disease and cystic fibrosis. The company has a pipeline of promising new medications in clinical development that covers such areas as oncology neurology and women's health.

The company has a number of partnerships with other pharmaceuticals to develop new treatments. Partners include C2N Diagnostics (Alzheimer's disease) Calico Life Sciences (age-related diseases) and Infinity Pharmaceuticals (cancer).

In addition to its portfolio of existing and developmental drugs AbbVie's operations include its global R&D apparatus focused on small molecule drugs and biologics and its sales marketing and distribution network delivering its products to more than 170 countries.

Geographic Reach

AbbVie collects more than 60% of its sales from the US. Key foreign markets include Brazil Canada France Germany Italy Japan the Netherlands Spain and the UK. The company also has R&D facilities in Germany and China and has a goal of expanding in emerging markets.

The company has four R&D facilities in the US (located in Abbott Park Illinois; Chicago; Redwood City California; and Worcester Massachusetts).

Sales and Marketing

AbbVie markets its products to managed care providers including health maintenance organizations (HMOs) and pharmacy benefit managers (PBMs) hospitals and government agencies (including the US Department of Veterans Affairs and the Department of Defense). Its pharmaceutical products are primarily distributed in the US through independent wholesalers; to a lesser extent it also sells them directly to pharmacies and patients. Internationally AbbVie principally markets to payors physicians and state regulatory bodies.

In 2016 three wholesale distributors — McKesson Cardinal Health and AmerisourceBergen— accounted for practically all of the company's sales in the US.

AbbVie spent $764 million on advertising in 2016 up from $704 million in 2014 and $665 million in 2014.

Financial Performance

Despite facing a number of patent expirations AbbView has seen steady growth since its 2013 spin-off from Abbott. In 2016 revenue grew 12% to $25.6 billion as sales of Humira remained strong both in the US and abroad (thanks largely to its approval for new indications). Two drugs cancer treatment Imbruvica and leukemia treatment Viekira have topped $1 billion in sales within the past couple of years. Other products that have performed well include Synthroid and Creon.

After declining in 2013 and 2014 net income rebounded by 190% to $5.1 billion in 2015. It rose another 16% to $6 billion in 2016 thanks to the growth in revenue.

Cash flow from operations (which has been erratic) fell 7% to $7 billion in 2016. This was largely due to income tax payments as well as the company's voluntary contributions to benefit plans.

Strategy

As AbbVie faced the patent expirations of many of its top sellers between 2011 and 2016 (Aluvia TriCor Niaspan Humira) having a strong R&D focus is key to AbbVie's continued success. It has more than 50 candidates in the pipeline including treatments in immunology oncology neuroscience hepatitis C chronic kidney disease and women's health. If any one of those reaches the market the risky development process will pay off for the research pharmaceuticals company. The company plans to keep adding to its pipeline through strategic licensing deals and partnerships.

The company is also considering acquisitions to boost its drug development stockpile. In a major move to boost its drug pipeline AbbVie bought Pharmacyclics which markets the promising cancer medication Imbruvica for $21 billion in 2015. The following year it acquired Stemcentrx which is developing potential blockbuster Rova-T for small cell lung cancer for $5.8 billion. The purchases should help lighten AbbVie's dependence on Humira and other key treatments.

In 2015 the company purchased a rare pediatric disease priority review voucher (or PRV giving it the option to speed up the FDA's review process) for $350 million from United Therapeutics. That hefty price speaks to AbbVie's need to get more blockbusters on the market soon. The company plans to use the PRV for an existing product in development.

It's also willing to collaborate to develop new drugs. To that end in 2016 it collaborated with Boehringer Ingelheim to develop and commercialize a phase 3 psoriasis treatment.

In mid-2017 the FDA approved AbbVie's hepatitis C treatment Mavyret which should challenge such pricier drugs as Gilead Science's Epclusa and Vosevi. Other new products include hepatitis C regimen Viekira Pak (launched in the US in late 2014) and Viekirax/Exviera (launched in Europe in early 2015).

AbbVie is also concentrating on boosting sales of Humira by expanding its share of the market and its presence in underserved markets. In 2015 Humira was given European approval for the treatment of severe chronic plaque psoriasis for children and adolescents.

However Humira could soon see competition in Europe which approved a third biosimilar version of the drug in mid-2017. AbbVie's basic patent is set to expire in Europe in October 2018.

Mergers and Acquisitions

To pump up its oncology pipeline AbbVie paid $21 billion for Pharmacyclics (which makes cancer treatments including Imbruvica) in 2015. The following year it acquired Stemcentrx which has four early-stage cancer treatments and the late-stage Rova-T treatment for small-cell lung cancer in clinical testing for $5.8 billion.

Company Background

The biopharmaceutical research company was spun off from its former parent health care products maker Abbott Labs in 2013.

EXECUTIVES

Chairman and CEO, Richard A. (Rick) Gonzalez, age 63, $1,600,000 total compensation

EVP External Affairs General Counsel and Corporate Secretary, Laura J. Schumacher, age 54, $979,369 total compensation

EVP Commercial Operations, Carlos Alban, age 54, $888,461 total compensation

EVP and CFO, William J. Chase, age 49, $979,369 total compensation

President Pharmacyclics, Wulff-Erik von Borcke

SVP Operations, Azita Saleki-Gerhardt, age 54

EVP Research and Development and Chief Scientific Officer, Michael E. Severino, age 51, $960,969 total compensation

EVP and Chief Strategy Officer, Henry O. Gosebruch, $894,523 total compensation

VP and Chief Ethics and Compliance Officer, Karen Hale

Vice President, Sean Mcewen

Vice President Human Resources Operations, Leanna Walther

National Sales Manager Immunology, Bryan Drummond

Vice President Immunology Clinical Development, John Medich

Associate Medical Director, Roger Trinh

Vice President Finance, Kevin Buckbee

Senior Vice President Training Coordinator, Reynaldo Ortiz

National Sales Manager, Teresa Stotts

National Sales Manager, Marie Glenn

VP Supply Chain, Chris Mlynek

Vice President Director Discovery Research, Steven Elmore

Vice President, Matt J Williams

DVP Immunology Research, Lisa Olson

National Sales Manager, Randee Stelman

Vice President of Sales and Marketing, Taymar Hartman

Medical Director, Boris Renjifo

Vice President Med Safety Evaluation, Linda Scarazzini

Geschaeftsfuehrer And Vice President DPD, Friedrich Richter

Area Vice President, Alberto Colzi

Associate Medical Director Latinoamrica, Leandro Castillo

Medical Director, Damian Gruca

Medical Director, Manuel Uribe-Granja

Vice President Latin America, Santiago Luque

Vice President US Endocrinology, Marianne Sutcliffe

Vice President, Tracie Haas

Vice President Japan Asia Pacific, Esteban Plata

Vice President Discovery Neuroscience Pa, James Summers

Senior Vice President Biologic Prod Superintendent, Eidamarie Ruiz

Vice President Global Purchasing, Terry Simmons

Medical Director, Ana Lacerda

Associate Medical Director, Jalaja Potluri

Vice President Pharmaceutical Development, Scott Brun

Medical Director, Simonne Lens

Medical Director, Eduardo Ribeiro

Senior Vice President Quality Assurance Superintendent, Elba Maldonado

Vice President and Treasurer, Amarendra Duvvur

Associate Medical Director, Just Genius

Vice President Clinical Program Development, Kathryn R King

Vice President Global Medical Affairs Oncology, Dany Habr

MEDICAL DIRECTOR, Anjla Sood

Medical Director, Sandra Bloch

Vice President and Distinguished Research Fellow Discovery Chemistry and Technology, Steven Djuric

Vice President Head of Business Development Acquisitions, Jay Stamatis

Treasurer (Western Europe and Pacific Asia), Brian Turner

Area Treasurer, Cindy Lee

Vice President Assistant Treasurer, Tabetha Skarbek

Auditors: Ernst & Young LLP

LOCATIONS

HQ: AbbVie Inc
1 North Waukegan Road, North Chicago, IL 60064-6400
Phone: 847 932-7900
Web: www.abbvie.com

2015 Sales

	$ mil.	% of total
US	13,561	59
Germany	1,082	5
UK	688	3
Spain	618	3
Japan	599	3
France	597	3
Canada	551	2
Italy	452	2
Brazil	376	2
The Netherlands	334	1
Rest of the world	4,001	17
Total	**22,859**	**100**

PRODUCTS/OPERATIONS

2015 Sales

	$ mil.	% of total
Humira	14,012	61
Viekira	1,639	7
Lupron	826	4
Imbruvica	754	3
Creon	632	3
Synagis	740	3
Synthroid	755	3
Kaletra	700	3
AndroGel	694	3
Sevoflurane	474	2
Duodopa	231	1
Dyslipidemia products	179	1
Other	1,223	6
Total	**22,859**	**100**

COMPETITORS

Amgen	Merck
AstraZeneca	Novartis
Bayer AG	Pfizer
Bristol-Myers Squibb	Roche Holding
Eli Lilly	Sanofi
GlaxoSmithKline	Teva
Johnson & Johnson	

HISTORICAL FINANCIALS

Company Type: Public

Income Statement

FYE: December 31

	REVENUE ($ mil.)	NET INCOME ($ mil.)	NET PROFIT MARGIN	EMPLOYEES
12/17	28,216	5,309	18.8%	29,000
12/16	25,638	5,953	23.2%	30,000
12/15	22,859	5,144	22.5%	28,000
12/14	19,960	1,774	8.9%	26,000
12/13	18,790	4,128	22.0%	25,000
Annual Growth	**10.7%**	**6.5%**	**—**	**3.8%**

2017 Year-End Financials

Debt ratio: 52.79%
Return on equity: 109.09%
Cash ($ mil.): 9,303
Current ratio: 1.28
Long-term debt ($ mil.): 30,953
No. of shares (mil.): 1,592
Dividends
　Yield: 0.0%
　Payout: 77.5%
Market value ($ mil.): 153,975

	STOCK PRICE ($) FY Close	P/E High/Low		PER SHARE ($) Earnings	Dividends	Book Value
12/17	96.71	30	18	3.30	2.56	3.20
12/16	62.62	18	14	3.63	2.28	2.91
12/15	59.24	23	15	3.13	2.02	2.45
12/14	65.44	63	42	1.10	1.66	1.09
12/13	52.81	21	13	2.56	1.60	2.83
Annual Growth	**16.3%**	**—**	**—**	**6.6%**	**12.5%**	**3.1%**

ABM Industries, Inc.

Many businesses hope to clean up but diversified facilities services contractor ABM counts on it. The company primarily offers janitorial services to owners and operators of office buildings hospitals manufacturing plants schools shopping centers and transportation facilities throughout the US UK Canada Puerto Rico the UAE and Saudi Arabia. Through other units ABM maintains mechanical electrical and plumbing systems. Its Ampco System Parking operates more than 2000 parking lots and garages mainly at airports across 41 states while ABM Security Services provides security officers and security systems monitoring services.

Operations

ABM operates in five reportable segments: Janitorial Facility Services Parking Building & Energy Solutions and Other (which includes its Air Serv business). The company's Janitorial segment is its largest segment and it accounts for about 55% of ABM's revenue. ABM is in the middle of a strategic transformation that will result in changes to its reportable segments in 2017.

Geographic Reach

ABM has locations throughout the US UK Puerto Rico Canada the UAE and Saudi Arabia. The US accounts for about 95% of revenue.

Sales and Marketing

ABM sells its services directly in client locations which enable to provide full range of solutions through intra-company sales referrals multi-service sales and national account sales. Its sales and marketing efforts are conducted by corporate subsidiary regional branch and district offices. The company serves some 20000 clients.

ABM spent $2.1 million on advertising expenses in fiscal 2016 down from $2.8 million and $6.8 million in fiscal 2015 and 2014 respectively.

Financial Performance

ABM reported revenue of $5.14 billion for fiscal 2016. The company's revenue increased by $246.9 million or 5% during fiscal 2016 as compared to the prior fiscal period. The increase in revenue was primarily attributable to organic growth within our the Janitorial and Parking segments contract expansion within the company's Air Serv U.S. operations combined with higher technical services revenues within the Building & Energy Solutions segment. ABM also grought in $101.9 million of incremental revenues from acquisitions.

ABM's net income was $57 million in fiscal 2016. That was a decrease compared to the company's net income of $76.3 million the prior fiscal year mainly caused by impairment losses.

ABM ended fiscal 2016 with $83 million in cash flow from operations. That was a decrease compared to the company's operating cash flow at the end of 2015 ($145.3 million) mainly due to increased operating expenses along with changes in trade accounts payable along with other accrued liabilities and insurance claims. The company's operating expenses increased by $213.4 million or 4.8% during fiscal 2016 as compared to fiscal 2015.

Strategy

Like other conglomerates in the business services sector ABM has grown mainly by acquiring local and regional operating companies and their client rosters. ABM generates cost savings by centralizing many business functions such as marketing sales and accounting.

The company's 2020 Vision strategic transformation initiative is intended to differentiate ABM in the marketplace. ABM's transformation initiative includes plans to accelerate revenue growth for certain industry groups and beneficial cost savings through the realignment of ABM's business operations to better support specific industries. ABM hopes the 2020 Vision plan will improve the effectiveness of its risk management and safety programs solidify the strategic direction of its government services business and improve its overall operating and financial performance.

Mergers and Acquisitions

In a sweeping move to expand ABM agreed to acquire rival GCA Services Group (GCA) for $1.25 billion in cash and stock in mid-2017. The purchase will fortify ABM's own core facility services offerings and enhance its presence in the education market and commercial sector. ABM also expects to achieve a significant revenue surge of $1.1 billion; of this amount about $600 million will reside within the education industry group and the remaining $500 million will be allocated to other key industry groups.

In 2016 ABM acquired Mechanical Solutions Inc. a provider of specialized HVAC chiller and plumbing services and OFJ Connections Ltd a provider of transportation services in the UK for $12 million and $6.3 million respectively. Also in 2016 the company acquired BRBIBR Limited for $16.1 million.

HISTORY

Morris Rosenberg invested $4.50 in a bucket and cleaning tools and began cleaning San Francisco storefront windows in 1909. Later that year he purchased Chicago Window Cleaning for $300 and armed with new supplies and a Ford Model T began offering annual cleaning contracts. He changed the company's name to American Building Maintenance in 1913 to emphasize its broadening services. By 1920 the company had established three west coast offices and it became the first contractor to clean a major college campus when it signed an agreement with Stanford University in 1921.

The company added cleaning supplies to its offerings in 1927 with the acquisition of Easterday Janitorial Supply Company and continued to grow even during the Great Depression by providing cleaning services cheaper than its clients could provide for themselves. ABM expanded to the East Coast in 1932. Morris Rosenberg died in 1935 leaving the company to his oldest son Theodore who bought electrical services company Alta Electric the following year. During WWII ABM cleaned Navy ships and wired amphibious vehicles called Water Buffaloes. By the end of the war it operated 17 offices in the US and Canada.

Now called American Building Maintenance Industries the company went public in 1962 with Theodore serving as chairman and younger brother Sydney as CEO. To diversify its services ABM Industries stepped up its acquisition pace in the late 1960s buying Ampco Auto Parks (1967 parking facilities) Commercial Air Conditioning (1968 equipment maintenance) and General Elevator Corporation (1969 elevator maintenance and repair).

ABM Industries continued to expand its business into diverse services and regions through a three-decade buying spree. In 1981 the company combined its air-conditioning elevator lighting and energy services into American Technical Services Company (Amtech) to better focus on the high-growth tech and energy businesses. A management-led buyout of the company failed in 1990 on opposition from the Rosenberg brothers. Although ABM Industries' president stepped down and several lawsuits were filed following the aborted LBO the company continued to post impressive sales and profit numbers.

The company shortened its name to ABM Industries in 1994 the same year William Steele was named CEO. Sydney Rosenberg retired as chairman in 1997 marking the end of family control. The following year the company formed a Facility Services division to provide one-stop shopping for all of its services. It moved into landscaping services in 1999 with the purchase of Commercial Landscape Systems. The following year Steele stepped down as CEO and Henrik Slipsager a former executive of Dutch services giant ISS was tapped as the company's new chief.

In 2001 ABM sold off its Easterday Janitorial Supply subsidiary to AmSan West. ABM acquired six companies in 2001 and 2002 including Lakeside Building Maintenance a large Midwestern janitorial contractor. In 2003 the company sold its Amtech Elevator Services to Otis Elevator Company for $112 million. Two years later the company sold its CommAir Mechanical Services unit to Carrier Corp.

In 2005 ABM sold the last of its mechanical operations divesting its water treatment business to San Joaquin Chemicals. ABM made one of the biggest deals in its history in 2007 when it obtained rival facility services company OneSource Services paying about $390 million. The operations of OneSource including more than 10000 commercial accounts in the US Canada and Puerto Rico were integrated into those of ABM Janitorial throughout 2008.

In order to focus on its core operations in late 2008 the company sold the operating assets of its Amtech Lighting Services business to a unit of OSRAM SYLVANIA for about $34 million. ABM acquired several companies in 2009 and 2010 including Diversco and The Linc Group. It also snatched up several cleaning and engineering businesses — Control Building Services Control Engineering Services and TTF Assets — located primarily in New Jersey and New York. Collectively these businesses generate annual revenues of about $50 million and cater to the commercial institutional and pharmaceutical industries.

EXECUTIVES

President and CEO, Scott Salmirs, age 55, $793,333 total compensation

EVP and CFO, D. Anthony Scaglione, age 44, $466,666 total compensation

EVP and President Business and Industry, Rene Jacobsen

EVP and COO, Scott Giacobbe, age 54

Vice President and Deputy General Counsel, Miranda Tolar

Vice President Safety, Duong HO

Vice President of Franchise Support, Kelli Daley

Vice President and General Manager, Bruce Wright

Senior Vice President of Operations, Michael Tolliver

Vice President, Bill Francis

Vice President, AL Smith

Vice President of Sales and Marketing, Menno Enters

Vice President Middle Atlantic Region, David Monroe

Vice President And Deputy General Counsel, Lanesha T Anderson

Vice President Sales andamp; National Accounts, Eric Kirchhoefer

National Account Manager, Dan Kampmeyer

Chairman, Sudhakar Kesavan, age 63

Auditors: KPMG LLP

LOCATIONS

HQ: ABM Industries, Inc.
One Liberty Plaza, 7th Floor, New York, NY 10006
Phone: 212 297-0200
Web: www.abm.com

2016 Sales

	$ mil.	% of total
United States	4,845	94
All other countries	299	6
Total	**5,144**	**100**

PRODUCTS/OPERATIONS

2016 Sales

	$ mil.	% of total
Janitorial	2,768	54
Parking	666	13
Facility Services	597	12
Building & Energy Solutions	643	12
Other	469	9
Total	**5,144**	**100**

Selected Services

Electrical & lighting
Energy
Engineering
Facility services
HVAC & mechanical
Janitorial
Landscape & golf
Maintenance & repair
Parking & transportation
Security

COMPETITORS

ARAMARK	Menzies Aviation
AlliedBarton Security	Mercury Air Group
Comfort Systems USA	PrimeFlight
EMCOR	SP Plus
Guardsmark	ServiceMaster
Healthcare Services	Siemens AG
IAP Worldwide Services	Sodexo USA
ICTS International	Temco Service
ISS A/S	Industries
Impark	

HISTORICAL FINANCIALS

Company Type: Public

Income Statement

FYE: October 31

	REVENUE ($ mil.)	NET INCOME ($ mil.)	NET PROFIT MARGIN	EMPLOYEES
10/17	5,453	3	0.1%	140,000
10/16	5,144	57	1.1%	110,000
10/15	4,897	76	1.6%	120,000
10/14	5,032	75	1.5%	118,000
10/13	4,809	72	1.5%	110,000
Annual Growth	**3.2%**	**(52.2%)**	**—**	**6.2%**

2017 Year-End Financials

Debt ratio: 30.90%	No. of shares (mil.): 65
Return on equity: 0.32%	Dividends
Cash ($ mil.): 62	Yield: 1.6%
Current ratio: 1.63	Payout: 251.8%
Long-term debt ($ mil.): 1,161	Market value ($ mil.): 2,749

	STOCK PRICE ($) FY Close	P/E High/Low	PER SHARE ($) Earnings	Dividends	Book Value
10/17	41.97	640546	0.07	0.68	21.00
10/16	39.08	40 26	1.01	0.66	17.52
10/15	28.40	25 20	1.33	0.64	17.96
10/14	27.64	22 18	1.32	0.62	17.40
10/13	27.51	22 14	1.30	0.60	16.54
Annual Growth	**11.1%**	**— —**	**(51.8%)**	**3.2%**	**6.2%**

ACCESS GROUP, INC.

Auditors: GRANT THORNTON LLP
PHILADELPH

LOCATIONS

HQ: ACCESS GROUP, INC.
  10 N HIGH ST FL 4, WEST CHESTER, PA 193803014
Phone: 484 653-3300
Web: WWW.ACCESSGROUP.ORG

COMPETITORS

Bank of America	First Marblehead
College Loan	JPMorgan Chase
Corporation	Nelnet
Discover	Sallie Mae

HISTORICAL FINANCIALS

Company Type: Private

Income Statement

FYE: March 31

	ASSETS ($ mil.)	NET INCOME ($ mil.)	INCOME AS % OF ASSETS	EMPLOYEES
03/16	5,056	16	0.3%	60
03/11	8,767	58	0.7%	—
03/10	10,316	(0)	—	—
Annual Growth	**(11.2%)**	**—**	**—**	**—**

2016 Year-End Financials

Debt ratio: —	
Return on equity: 15.10%	Dividends
Cash ($ mil.): 16	Yield: —
Current ratio: —	Payout: —
Long-term debt ($ mil.): —	Market value ($ mil.): —

ACE HARDWARE CORPORATION

In an age of big-box home improvement centers (Home Depot Lowes) wholesaler Ace makes the case for the local hardware store. By sales it is the #1 hardware cooperative in the US ahead of Do It Best. Ace dealer-owners operate more than 95% of the 4800 Ace Hardware-branded stores home centers and lumber and building materials locations selling more than 75000 products across all 50 US states and about 70 other countries. Stores range in size from small urban shops to large rural locations. From about 15 warehouses Ace distributes such products as electrical and plumbing supplies garden equipment hand tools housewares and power tools. Ace was founded in 1924 by a group of Chicago hardware store owners.

HISTORY

A group of Chicago-area hardware dealers — William Stauber Richard Hesse Gern Lindquist and Oscar Fisher — decided in 1924 to pool their hardware buying and promotional costs. In 1928 the group incorporated as Ace Stores named in honor of the superior WWI fliers dubbed aces. Hesse became president the following year retaining that position for the next 44 years. The com-

pany also opened its first warehouse in 1929 and by 1933 it had 38 dealers.

The organization had 133 dealers in seven states by 1949. In 1953 Ace began to allow dealers to buy stock in the company through the Ace Perpetuation Plan. During the 1960s Ace expanded into the South and West and by 1969 it had opened distribution centers in Georgia and California — its first such facilities outside Chicago. In 1968 it opened its first international store in Guam.

By the early 1970s the do-it-yourself market began to surge as inflation pushed up plumber and electrician fees. As the market grew large home center chains gobbled up market share from independent dealers such as those franchised through Ace. In response Ace and its dealers became a part of a growing trend in the hardware industry — cooperatives.

Hesse sold the company to its dealers in 1973 for $6 million (less than half its book value) and the following year Ace began operating as a cooperative. Hesse stepped down in 1973. In 1976 the dealers took full control when the company's first Board of Dealer-Directors was elected.

After signing up a number of dealers in the eastern US Ace had dealers in all 50 states by 1979. The co-op opened a plant to make paint in Matteson Illinois in 1984. By 1985 Ace had reached $1 billion in sales and had initiated its Store of the Future Program allowing dealers to borrow up to $200000 to upgrade their stores and conduct market analyses. Former head coach John Madden of the National Football League's Oakland Raiders signed on as Ace's mouthpiece in 1988.

A year later the co-op began to test ACENET a computer network that allowed Ace dealers to check inventory send and receive e-mail make special purchase requests and keep up with prices on commodity items such as lumber. In 1990 Ace established an International Division to handle its overseas stores. (It had been exporting products since 1975.) EVP and COO David Hodnik became president in 1995. That year the co-op added a net of 67 stores including a three-store chain in Russia. Expanding further internationally Ace signed a five-year joint-supply agreement in 1996 with Canadian lumber and hardware retailer Beaver Lumber. Hodnik added CEO to his title in 1996.

Ace fell further behind its old rival True Value in 1997 when ServiStar Coast to Coast and True Value merged to form TruServ (renamed True Value in 2005) a hardware giant that operated more than 10000 outlets at the completion of the merger.

Late in 1997 Ace launched an expansion program in Canada. (The co-op already operated distribution centers in Ontario and Calgary.) In 1999 Ace merged its lumber and building materials division with Builder Marts of America to form a dealer-owned buying group to supply about 2700 retailers. Ace gained 208 member outlet stores in 2000 but saw 279 member outlets terminated. The next year it gained 220 but lost 255.

Sodisco-Howden bought all the shares of Ace Hardware Canada in February 2003. To better serve international members Ace opened its first international buying office in Hong Kong in April 2004.

In all the company added 131 new stores in 2005. That year after 33 years with the company David F. Hodnik retired as president and CEO of Ace Hardware. He was succeeded by COO Ray A. Griffith.

In 2007 Griffith sent a letter to Ace's retailers saying the company was considering changing from a cooperative to a traditional corporation to become more competitive and to better fuel growth. Shortly after the company announced an accounting shortfall of about $150 million or nearly half of its equity which was uncovered while Ace prepared to convert formats. The error turned out to be an accident by a mid-level employee.

In 2009 Ace launched Aisle411 a free product-location service that can be accessed via phone similar to dialing for information. The company launched the service after learning that shoppers who were unable to find a product either left (about 20% of the time) or asked store associates for assistance (about 60%) which created a high demand for staff attention. Dedicated to pleasing its shoppers Ace was ranked "Highest in Customer Satisfaction among Home Improvement Stores" by J.D. Power and Associates in 2007 2008 and 2009.

In mid-2010 the hardware store chain became the first retailer — outside of Sears and Kmart stores — to sell Craftsman brand tools.

In January 2011 the company reorganized its international division into a stand-alone entity: Ace Hardware International Holdings. Ace Hardware owns about 78% of the newly-created entity.

In December 2012 Ace exited the paint manufacturing business with the sale of its paint manufacturing division including two paint manufacturing plants near Chicago to Valspar Corp. for about $45 million. Under the terms of the sale Valspar will continue to make and supply Ace-branded paint under a long-term supply agreement. Also it will supply a comprehensive line of Valspar-branded paints to Ace retail stores.

EXECUTIVES

President and CEO, John S. Venhuizen, age 47
VP Information Technology and CIO, Karen Fedyszyn
EVP CFO and Chief Risk Officer, Bill Guzik
Vice President General Counsel and Secretary, Howard Japlon
Chairman, Jim Ackroyd

LOCATIONS

HQ: ACE HARDWARE CORPORATION
  2200 KENSINGTON CT, OAK BROOK, IL 605232100
Phone: 866 681-1836
Web: WWW.ACEHARDWAREINTL.COM

PRODUCTS/OPERATIONS

2014 Sales

	$ mil.	% of total
Wholesale Revenues	4,466	95
Retail Revenues	233	5
Total	**4,700**	**100**

Selected Services

Assembly
Automotive chip key cutting
Blade sharpening
Glass & Acrylic sheet cutting
Glass Repair
Hunting/Fishing license
In-store lock servicing

SELECTED BRANDS

ACCO BRANDS
ACE
ACME
ADANAC
BIG BEN
BILCO
EUREKA
EVEREADY

COMPETITORS

84 Lumber
Akzo Nobel
BMC Stock

McCoy Corp.
Menard
Northern Tool

Costco Wholesale
Do it Best
Fastenal
Grossman's
Home Depot
Kmart
Lowe's

Orgill
Sears
Sutherland Lumber
True Value
United Hardware
Distributing
Wal-Mart

HISTORICAL FINANCIALS

Company Type: Private

Income Statement

FYE: January 2

	REVENUE ($ mil.)	NET INCOME ($ mil.)	NET PROFIT MARGIN	EMPLOYEES
01/16	5,045	156	3.1%	4,500
01/15*	4,700	141	3.0%	—
12/13	4,154	105	2.5%	—
12/12	3,840	82	2.1%	—
Annual Growth	9.5%	23.9%	—	—

*Fiscal year change

2016 Year-End Financials

Debt ratio: ——
Return on equity: 3.10%
Cash ($ mil.): 11
Current ratio: 0.50
Long-term debt ($ mil.): —

Dividends
  Yield: —
  Payout: —
  Market value ($ mil.): —

Activision Blizzard, Inc.

Activision Blizzard answers the Call of Duty to make video games that millions of users play for billions of hours. The company is the biggest producer of video games including some of the most durable franchises: World of Warcraft Guitar Hero Candy Crush and of course Call of Duty. Newer blockbuster titles are Overwatch and Skylanders. Users play Activision Blizzard?s games on PCs game consoles and mobile devices. The company also creates games based on licensed properties from Marvel DreamWorks Animation and EON Production. Activision Blizzard is expanding its theater of operations to games products and service for TV movies toys and a professional esports league.

Operations

Activision Blizzard operates in three segments: Activision Blizzard and King.

Activision which accounts for about a third of revenue produces the company?s signature Call of Duty franchise a first-person shooter game for console and PCs; Destiny an online shared-world shooter game for console; and Skylanders a children?s-oriented game primarily for consoles. The segment has more than 50 million monthly active users.

Blizzard about 40% of revenue produces another high-profile game World of Warcraft a subscription-based massive multi-player online role-playing game (MMORPG) for the PC as well as StarCraft a real-time strategy game for the PC and Overwatch a team-based first-person shooter game PC and console platforms. Blizzard?s monthly active user count exceeds 40 million

King about a quarter of revenue develops PC and mobile games that include Candy Crush Farm Heroes Pet Rescue and Bubble Witch. The segment rules the company?s roost for monthly active users with 355 million.

Activision Blizzard?s other operations are Major League Gaming the company?s esports business; Activision Blizzard Studios which develops film

and TV programming based on the company?s games; Activision Blizzard Distribution which are operations in Europe that provide warehousing logistics and sales distribution services.

Geographic Reach

Activision Blizzard gets more than half of its revenue from the Americas about a third from Europe and the rest from the Asia/Pacific region. The company has about 100 offices in some 20 countries around the world. Overall the company has players in about every country. The company notes that Candy Crush is played on all continents including Antarctica.

Sales and Marketing

Activision Blizzard markets its games on multiple platforms including social media such as Facebook Twitter and YouTube online advertising print and broadcast advertising direct response and product sampling. The company delivers content through retail channels or digital downloads including subscriptions full-game sales and in-game purchases as well as licenses of software to third-party or related-party companies that distribute Blizzard products. Advertising expenses have risen in recent years.

Financial Performance

Activision Blizzard?s revenue jumped more than 40% in 2016 to $6.6 billion (a company record) from 2015 thanks to its acquisition of King Digital Media and its online games such Candy Crush. In recent years its revenue has ranged from $4.2 billion to $4.8 billion. The company?s revenue can be cyclical depending on the timing of releases of new games and sequels.

In 2016 Candy Crush sales helped drive revenue higher as did sales from Overwatch a new team-based first-person shooter game released in May 2016 and Call of Duty: Black Ops III which was released in late 2015. Games that posted lower sales for the year were Destiny Skylanders Imaginators (released in late 2016) and the Diablo franchise. The biggest surge in revenue came from digital in-game sales which more than doubled to $3.8 billion year-to-year thanks to King?s mobile games as well as Overwatch and World of Warcraft. In-game purchases accounted for more than half of Activision Blizzard's revenue.

Activision Blizzard posted a $966 million profit in 2016 an 8% increase from 2015. Most of the company?s costs rose in 2016 as a result of the King acquisition. Expenses ate up about 80% of revenue for the year up from about 70% in 2015.

Cash generated by operations jumped to $2.2 billion in 2016 compared to $1.2 billion in 2015. The stronger cash flow resulted from higher net income in 2016 adjustments to net income for non-cash charges associated with the amortization of the acquired intangibles in the King deal higher stock compensation expense due to converted awards for King employees and other costs related to debt-related activities.

Strategy

Part of Activision Blizzard's strategy is the same as it ever was: Develop blockbuster games and issue sequels that people play for hours and hours. The Call of Duty and World of Warcraft franchises have produced steady streams of income for the company. The acquisition of King Digital has already proved lucrative with the King games providing billions of dollars of in-game sales to Activision Blizzard. The acquisition also significantly increased the company's presence on mobile devices and social media platforms. The added revenue also put Activision Blizzard on the Fortune 500 at No. 406.

Games produce a lot of revenue but Activision Blizzard sees opportunities for more sales in game-related ventures. The company's biggest move comes in esports where users play each other while spectators watch. Activision Blizzard organizes and broadcasts tournaments for players of Call of Duty Hearthstone StarCraft and Heroes of the Storm. In order to show these games the company bought Major League Gaming (MLG) a team-based esports venture in 2015.

Activision Blizzard is going a step further and organizing a league for its Overwatch game one of the company?s fastest growing properties. It reached 30 million players and $1 billion in revenue within a year of its release. The league is one of several emerging organizations based on video games as a spectator sport. The Overwatch league has attracted high-profile investors such as Robert Kraft owner of the New England Patriots who has put money into the Boston franchise. Activision Blizzard has ambitions to create professional a esports league that rivals the NFL and professional sports leagues.

In other beyond-game activity a movie based on Call of Duty is due out by 2018. On the small screen ABC viewers could watch live-action Candy Crush competition in the summer of 2017 and Skylandershas spawned an animated series on Netflix and a line of toys.

In another revenue-producing initiative Activision Blizzard is proceeding with selling advertising within the King digital games. After testing the concept in 2016 the company reported that users play more rounds of a game spend more time in the game and report a better game experience with advertising. Early advertisers have included Nestle Visa and Fox Entertainment. After more testing in 2017 the company plans to roll out a full-scale advertising program in 2018.

Mergers and Acquisitions

With its $5.9 billion purchase of King Digital Entertainment Activision Blizzard is putting its money where people play games: on mobile devices. King developed the popular Candy Crush game but other efforts such as Farm Heroes and Pet Rescue haven't been as successful. Mobile games are growing faster than console or PC-based games and some such as Candy Crush reach a female demographic. Competitors in the mobile game arena include Zynga maker of Farmville and Rovio the creator of Angry Birds.

In December 2015 Activision Blizzard got into the live gaming business with its acquisition of Major League Gaming (MLG) for $46 million. MLG stream game competitions that it organizes as they happen.

EXECUTIVES

CEO, Robert A. (Bobby) Kotick, age 54, $2,375,858 total compensation

CFO, Spencer Neumann, age 47

CEO Activision, Eric Hirshberg, age 49, $961,677 total compensation

President and CEO Blizzard Entertainment, Michael (Mike) Morhaime, age 49, $957,378 total compensation

President and CEO Consumer Products Division, Timothy J. (Tim) Kilpin, age 57

Chief Customer Officer, Brian Hodous, age 53, $533,365 total compensation

Chief Corporate Officer, Dennis Durkin, age 46, $787,185 total compensation

CEO King Digital Entertainment, Riccardo Zacconi, age 48, $415,928 total compensation

President and CEO Major League Gaming (MLG), Pete Vlastelica

President and COO, Collister (Coddy) Johnson, age 40

Vice President, Linda Howard

Vice President of Operations, Denise Walsh

Vice President Infrastructure And Operations, Pmp Archer

Vice President Financial Services, Shiro Lewis

Vice President of Marketing, Lori Davis

Vice President of Operations, Marcus Sanford

Vice President of Marketing, Laura Lombardi

Vice President of Marketing, Byron Beede

Chairman, Brian G. Kelly, age 54

CFO Activision Publishing, Thomas Tippl, age 51

Auditors: PricewaterhouseCoopers LLP

LOCATIONS

HQ: Activision Blizzard, Inc.
   3100 Ocean Park Boulevard, Santa Monica, CA 90405
Phone: 310 255-2000
Web: www.activisionblizzard.com

2016 Sales

	$ mil.	% of total
Americas	3,423	52
Europe Middle East and Africa	2,221	34
Asia Pacific	964	14
Total	**6,608**	**100**

PRODUCTS/OPERATIONS

2016 Sales

	$ mil.	% of total
Blizzard	2,428	37
Activision	2,220	34
King	1,586	24
Other segments	365	5
Net effect from recognition (deferral) of deferred net revenues and related cost of revenues	(9)	-
Total	**6,608**	**100**

2016 Sales

	$ mil.	% of total
Console	2,453	37
PC	2,124	32
Mobile and ancillary	1,674	25
Other	357	6
Total	**6,608**	**100**

2016 Sales

	$ mil.	% of total
Subscription licensing and other revenues	4,412	67
Product sales	2,196	33
Total	**6,608**	**100**

COMPETITORS

Capcom	SEGA
Disney Interactive Studios	Sony
	Square Enix
Electronic Arts	Take-Two
Konami	Tencent
Lucasfilm Entertainment	Turbine Inc.
	Ubisoft
Microsoft	Valve Corporation
Namco Limited	ZeniMax Media
Nintendo	Zynga
Rovio Entertainment	

HISTORICAL FINANCIALS

Company Type: Public

Income Statement

FYE: December 31

	REVENUE ($ mil.)	NET INCOME ($ mil.)	NET PROFIT MARGIN	EMPLOYEES
12/16	6,608	966	14.6%	9,600
12/15	4,664	892	19.1%	7,300
12/14	4,408	835	18.9%	6,800
12/13	4,583	1,010	22.0%	6,900
12/12	4,856	1,149	23.7%	6,700
Annual Growth	**8.0%**	**(4.2%)**	**—**	**9.4%**

2016 Year-End Financials

Debt ratio: 28.00%
Return on equity: 11.21%
Cash ($ mil.): 3,245
Current ratio: 1.82
Long-term debt ($ mil.): 4,887

No. of shares (mil.): 745
Dividends
   Yield: 0.0%
   Payout: 20.3%
Market value ($ mil.): 26,920

	STOCK PRICE ($) FY Close	P/E High/Low	PER SHARE ($) Earnings	PER SHARE ($) Dividends	PER SHARE ($) Book Value
12/16	36.11	35 22	1.28	0.26	12.23
12/15	38.71	33 15	1.19	0.23	10.98
12/14	20.15	21 15	1.13	0.20	10.02
12/13	17.83	19 11	0.95	0.19	9.41
12/12	10.62	13 10	1.01	0.18	10.18
Annual Growth	**35.8%**	**— —**	**6.1%**	**9.6%**	**4.7%**

Adobe Systems Inc

Adobe Systems is the house that desktop publishing software built and now it helps customers create distribute and manage digital content from the cloud. One of the top publishing software providers it has been known for brands such as Acrobat Photoshop Flash and Dreamweaver. Adobe serves customers such as content creators and web application developers with its digital media products and marketers advertisers publishers and others with its digital marketing business. A long-time publisher of traditional software packages Adobe is moving its products to cloud-based versions. Subscriptions account for about 80% of revenue. Customers in the US generate about 60% of sales.

Operations

Adobe's digital media segment (about two-thirds of revenue) includes products such as Flash Photoshop and Illustrator. Its digital marketing segment (30% of revenue) includes a host of tools for creating managing and measuring digital advertising and marketing initiatives. The print and publishing unit (less than 5% of revenue) includes authoring and publishing software and tools.

Geographic Reach

The US is Adobe's largest market representing about 60% of revenue. The EMEA (Europe Middle East and Africa) region generates nearly 30% of revenue and the Asia-Pacific region led by Japan contributes about 15%.

Sales and Marketing

Adobe sells directly and through distributors resellers systems integrators and retailers. In addition it licenses its technology to hardware manufacturers for integration into their products.

Financial Performance

Adobe Systems posted robust increases in revenue and profit in 2016 compared to 2015

Revenue jumped 22% to $5.8 billion on higher sales in Digital Media driven by demand for its creative offerings (up nearly 40%) and in Digital Revenue fueled by a 20% increase in Adobe Marketing Cloud revenue from rising adoption of Adobe Experience Manager.

An 42% increase in subscription revenue across Adobe?s offerings propelled net income to about $1.2 billion in 2016 an 86% rise from 2015.

Cash flow from rose to $2.2 billion in 2016 increased from about $1.5 billion in 2015 on the strength of higher net income and an increase in deferred revenue.

Strategy

Adobe Systems? charge into the cloud and a subscription-based business model has paid off for the company. It has reported rising revenue and net income for the past three years and driven its profit margin to nearly 20% in 2016 from about 6% in 2014.

Just about every product in Adobe?s stock has the word cloud in it. The company has added digital marketing applications and services to its digital media offerings which has raised subscriptions to account for three-quarters of revenue from two-thirds of revenue in 2015. Its applications also are made to use and view on mobile devices.

The Adobe Experience Manager product which helps customers organize create and manage the delivery of creative assets and other content across digital marketing channels has been a hit with customers according to the company. Increasing adoption of AEM was one of the drivers of the company?s 2016 revenue increase.

Mergers and Acquisitions

In 2017 Adobe Systems bought the SkyBox technology assets from Mettle a developer 360-degree and virtual reality software. The Skybox tools are designed for post-production in Adobe Premiere Pro CC and Adobe After Effects CC and complement Adobe Creative Cloud?s 360/VR cinematic production technology. Adobe integrated SkyBox plugin functionality into subsequent releases of Premiere Pro and After Effects.

In 2016 Adobe bought TubeMogul for $540 million. With TubeMogul on board Adobe could offer more video marketing options to its customers.

In May 2016 Adobe acquired Livefyre a privately-held content curation and audience engagement company. Livefyre will be part of Adobe Experience Manager and integrated across Adobe Marketing Cloud to make user-generated content available across all digital marketing solutions.

To further expand its product offerings in 2014 Adobe purchased the privately-held stock-photography website company Fotolia for roughly $800 million. The acquisition will allow Adobe to obtain a market exchange with over 34 million stock images and videos and sell them to its Creative Cloud customers on one cloud-based software platform.

HISTORY

When Charles Geschke hired John Warnock as chief scientist for Xerox's new graphics and imaging lab he set the stage for one of the world's largest software makers. While at the Xerox lab the pair developed the PostScript computer language which tells printers how to reproduce digitized images on paper. When Xerox refused to market it the duo left that company and started Adobe (named after a creek near their homes in San Jose California) in 1982.

EXECUTIVES

EVP and General Manager Digital Media, Bryan Lamkin, age 56, $568,590 total compensation

EVP and Chief Marketing Officer, Ann Lewnes, age 55

EVP General Counsel and Corporate Secretary, Michael A. (Mike) Dillon, age 58

EVP and CFO, Mark S. Garrett, age 59, $698,977 total compensation

Chairman President and CEO, Shantanu Narayen, age 53, $1,010,260 total compensation

EVP Customer and Employee Experience, Donna Morris, age 49

EVP Worldwide Field Operations, Matthew A. (Matt) Thompson, age 59, $673,720 total compensation

EVP and General Manager Digital Marketing, Bradley (Brad) Rencher, age 43, $573,514 total compensation

EVP and CTO, Abhay Parasnis, age 42, $183,583 total compensation

Vice President Americas Marketing, Bridget Perry

Vice President Licensing and Associate General Counsel, Joe Ramirez

Senior Vice President Worldwide Sales and Field Operations, Matt Thompson

Vice President Strategic Planning and Business Development, Marianne Deaton

Vice President Customer Care, Lambert Walsh

Vice President Manager Director, Angelica Pina

Vice President Product Management, Bill Ingram

Auditors: KPMG LLP

LOCATIONS

HQ: Adobe Systems Inc
345 Park Avenue, San Jose, CA 95110-2704
Phone: 408 536-6000
Web: www.adobe.com

2016 Sales

	$ mil.	% of total
Americas:		
United States	3,087	53
Other	312	5
Europe Middle East & Africa	1,619	28
APAC:		
Japan	401	7
Other	433	7
Total	**5,854**	**100**

PRODUCTS/OPERATIONS

2016 Sales

	$ mil.	% of total
Digital Media	3,941	67
Digital Marketing	1,736	30
Print and Publishing	176	3
Total	**5,854**	**100**

2016 Sales

	$ mil.	% of total
Subscription	4,584	78
Product	800	14
Services and support	469	8
Total	**5,854**	**100**

Selected Products

Digital media
Acrobat (PDF management)
Audition (audio editing)
Dreamweaver (software development)
Flash (Internet application and video creation)
Illustrator (graphic artwork creation)
Photoshop
Premiere (video editing)
Digital marketing
AudienceManager
Connect (enterprise collaboration and communication)
CRX (enterprise content management)
DataWarehouse
Scene7 (merchandising system)
Print and publishing
Authorware (tutorial creation)
Font Folio
PageMaker (document creation and page layout)
RoboHelp (help system creation)
Shockwave (media player)

COMPETITORS

ACD Systems	Monotype
Apple Inc.	Nexaweb
ArcSoft	Nikon
Autodesk	Nuance Communications
Avid Technology	Oracle
Bare Bones Software	Pegasystems
Box Inc.	Quark
Canon	RealNetworks
Citrix Systems	Rovi
Corel	SAS Institute
Coremetrics	Sony
Dell	TIBCO Software
Eastman Kodak	Ultimus
Google	Webtrends
HP	Xara
IBM	Yahoo!
Microsoft	Zinio Systems

HISTORICAL FINANCIALS

Company Type: Public

Income Statement

FYE: December 1

	REVENUE ($ mil.)	NET INCOME ($ mil.)	NET PROFIT MARGIN	EMPLOYEES
12/17	7,301	1,693	23.2%	17,973
12/16*	5,854	1,168	20.0%	15,706
11/15	4,795	629	13.1%	13,893
11/14	4,147	268	6.5%	12,499
11/13	4,055	289	7.2%	11,847
Annual Growth	**15.8%**	**55.5%**	**—**	**11.0%**

*Fiscal year change

2017 Year-End Financials

Debt ratio: 12.94%
Return on equity: 21.39%
Cash ($ mil.): 2,306
Current ratio: 2.05
Long-term debt ($ mil.): 1,881
No. of shares (mil.): 491
Dividends
Yield: —
Payout: —
Market value ($ mil.): 88,191

	STOCK PRICE ($) FY Close	P/E High/Low		PER SHARE ($) Earnings	Dividends	Book Value
12/17	179.52	54	30	3.38	0.00	17.22
12/16*	99.73	47	31	2.32	0.00	15.02
11/15	92.17	73	55	1.24	0.00	14.06
11/14	73.68	136	100	0.53	0.00	13.62
11/13	56.78	99	59	0.56	0.00	13.55
Annual Growth	**33.3%**	**—**		**56.7%**	**—**	**6.2%**

*Fiscal year change

Advance Auto Parts Inc

Advance Auto Parts (AAP) has taken the lead in the race to become the #1 provider of automotive aftermarket parts in North America. Serving both the do-it-yourself (DIY) and professional installer markets AAP operates nearly 5200 stores under the Advance Auto Parts Autopart International (AI) Carquest and Worldpac banners in the US and Canada. Its stores carry brand-name replacement parts batteries maintenance items and automotive chemicals for individual car and truck owners. AAP's Carquest AI and Worldpac stores cater to commercial customers including garages service stations and auto dealers.

Operations

Advance Auto Part's parts and batteries account for more than 65% of its total product sales. The rest of its sales come from accessories and chemicals (about 20%) engine maintenance (nearly 15%) and other products.

Among the brands there are roughly 4275 stores under the Advance Auto Parts banner over 600 stores under the Carquest banner more than 125 Worldpac stores and some 185 stores operating under the Autopart International brand. In addition the company serves some 1250 independently-owned Carquest branded stores.

Geographic Reach

Roanoake Virginia-based Advance Auto Parts has stores in all 50 states as well as Puerto Rico the US Virgin Islands and Canada. Florida is the company's largest market with about 535 stores. North Carolina New York Ohio Texas Pennsylvania and Georgia are also major markets for Advance Auto Parts each home to more than 250 stores. The independently owned Carquest stores are also found in Mexico the Bahamas Turks and Caicos the British Virgin Islands and certain Pacific Islands.

Sales and Marketing

Advance Auto Parts builds its marketing and advertising campaigns around radio television direct marketing mobile and social media and local in-store marketing. Its "Speed Perks" customer loyalty campaign targets core DIY customers and emphasizes service.

The company serves professional and DIY customers. It delivers wares to branch locations of its professional customers' businesses including garages auto dealers and service stations. DIY customers are reached through its owned stores and it also sells online and offers click-and-collect services. Professional sales account for 60% of total sales.

Financial Performance

Advance Auto Part's revenue fell for a second consecutive year in fiscal 2016 falling 2% to $9.6 billion. The decrease was mostly down to lower same store sales and store closures — it shuttered a net 104 stores in the year.

Net income fell 3% to $459.6 million as higher supply chain costs relating to significant increases in inventoryimpacted on profitability. Lower net income weighed on cash from operations which fell $188.8 million to $500.9 million as did a decrease in accounts payable.

Strategy

Advance Auto Parts (AAP) acquired General Parts International in 2014 to transform the business from a pure-play DIY retailer to a combination DIY and "do-it-for-me" retailer. However three years later and the integration is still ongoing with a number of the +1000 acquired stores yet to be consolidated into AAP's existing store network. As such AAP lags its competitors on a number of key metrics (such as operating margin productivity and inventory management) but as consolidation continues and the company invests further in its supply chain performance is improving. The company aims to generate $500 million in productivity into 2022.

Company Background

Founded as Advance Stores Company in 1929 AAP was a general merchandise retailer until the '80s. From there the company shifted its focus to automotive parts retailing targeting DIY customers.

In 2014 AAP acquired General Parts International (GPI) for about $2.1 billion — creating the largest automotive aftermarket parts provider in North America with $9 billion-plus in annual sales. GPI a privately-held distributor and supplier of original equipment and aftermarket replacement parts to commercial markets owned the CARQUEST and WORLDPAC brands. The deal added 1233 Carquest stores 103 Worldpac branches in 45 states and Canada and the business of nearly 1400 independently-owned Carquest stores to AAP's network.

EXECUTIVES

Vice President Finance, Kevin Quinn
President and CEO, Thomas R. (Tom) Greco, age 58, $803,852 total compensation
SVP E-Commerce, Scott Bauhofer
President Â– Northern Division, Maria Ayres
President Southern Division, David McCartney
President Western Division, Mike Pack
President Autopart International, Michael Creedon
EVP Commercial, Robert B. (Bob) Cushing, age 63, $453,910 total compensation
President CARQUEST Canada, Steve Gushie
EVP General Counsel and Secretary, Tammy M. Finley, age 50, $400,005 total compensation
SVP and CIO, James A. (Andy) Paisley
SVP and Chief Marketing Officer, Walter Scott

EVP and CFO, Thomas B. (Tom) Okray, age 54, $86,540 total compensation
SVP Supply Chain, Todd Greener
EVP Supply Chain Strategy and Transformation, Leslie Keating
SVP Professional Business, Al Wheeler
Vice President Systems Development, Donna Justiss
Assistant Vice President Strategic Store Systems, Craig Anderman
Vice President Information Technology, David Jones
Vice President Internal Audit, Tom Belt
Vice President Self Service Purchasing, Kim Buskirk
Senior Vice President sales, Troy Downing
Vice President Distribution Operations, Jason Howes
Regional Vice President, Frank Miller
National Sales Manager, Chad Schnitz
Regional Vice President, Ernesto Valderrama
Senior Vice President Chief Informatio, Jim Upchurch
Vice President, Warren Shatzer
Senior Vice President and Chief Inform, Angela Kessler
Vice President of Human Resources, Kathy Gillis
Vice President Information Technology, Greg Anderson
Vice President Store Development, Jim Germann
Regional Vice President of Sales and Operations, Chris McCollum
Vice President Design and Development Real Estate, Tom Drapac
Vice President of Operations, Bob Lingsch
Vice President Commercial eCommerce and Store Online, Walt Scott
Executive Vice President Merchandising And Marketing, David Mueller
Senior Vice President Team Member Excellence, Carl Hauch
Vice President Commercial Marketing, Chris Rowe
Vice President Information Technology, Mark Patterson
Vice President Business Development, William Alexander
Commercial Vice President, Mark Zuanich
Regional Vice President, Mike Molnar
Regional Vice President, Mike Byrd
Vice President Strategic Accounts, Todd Sanders
Regional Vice President Midwest Region, Mike Hoye
SVP Human Resources, Natalie Rothman
Vice President Store Operations Support, Don Kohlbeck
Regional Vice President, Michael Cooper
Vice President Commercial Sales Operations, Casey Brannigan
Vice President Professional Sales, Richard Merchant
Vice President, Ken Bush
Regional Vice President Sales and Operations, Lee Dixon
Vice President Chief Transformation Officer, Nicole Jefferies
Chairman, Jeffrey C. Smith
Auditors: DELOITTE & TOUCHE LLP

LOCATIONS

HQ: Advance Auto Parts Inc
    5008 Airport Road, Roanoke, VA 24012
Phone: 540 362-4911
Web: www.AdvanceAutoParts.com

PRODUCTS/OPERATIONS

2016 Product Group

	% of total
Parts and Batteries	66
Accessories and Chemicals	19
Engine Maintenance	14
Other	1
Total	**100**

SELECTED PRODUCTS

PARTS & BATTERIES
Batteries and battery accessories
Belts and hoses
Brakes and brake pads
Chassis parts
Climate control parts
Clutches and drive shafts
Engines and engine parts
Exhaust systems and parts
Hub assemblies
Ignition components and wire
Radiators and cooling parts
Starters and alternators
Steering and alignment parts

ACCESSORIES & CHEMICALS
AC chemicals and accessories
Air fresheners
Antifreeze and washer fluid
Electrical wire and fuses
Electronics
Floor mats seat covers and interior accessories
Hand and specialty tools
Lighting
Performance parts
Sealants adhesives and compounds
Tire repair accessories
Vent shades mirrors and exterior accessories
Washes waxes and cleaning supplies
Wiper blades

ENGINE MAINTENANCE
Air filters
Fuel and oil additives
Fuel filters
Grease and lubricants
Motor Oil
Oil filters
Part cleaners and treatments
Transmission fluid

Selected Brands
Bosch
Castrol
Dayco
Denso
Gates
Monroe
Moog
Prestone
Purolator
Trico
Wagner

COMPETITORS

AutoZone	Sears
Fisher Auto Parts	Somerset Tire Service
Genuine Parts	U.S. Auto Parts
Keystone Automotive	Uni-Select
Operations	VIP
O'Reilly Automotive	Wal-Mart
Pep Boys	Whitney Automotive
Replacement Parts	Group

HISTORICAL FINANCIALS

Company Type: Public

Income Statement

FYE: December 31

	REVENUE ($ mil.)	NET INCOME ($ mil.)	NET PROFIT MARGIN	EMPLOYEES
12/16*	9,567	459	4.8%	74,000
01/16	9,737	473	4.9%	73,000
01/15	9,843	493	5.0%	73,000
12/13	6,493	391	6.0%	71,867
12/12	6,205	387	6.2%	55,000
Annual Growth	11.4%	4.3%	—	7.7%

*Fiscal year change

2016 Year-End Financials

Debt ratio: 12.55%
Return on equity: 17.14%
Cash ($ mil.): 135
Current ratio: 1.41
Long-term debt ($ mil.): 1,042

No. of shares (mil.): 73
Dividends
  Yield: 0.0%
  Payout: 3.8%
Market value ($ mil.): 12,472

	STOCK PRICE ($) FY Close	P/E High/Low	PER SHARE ($) Earnings	Dividends	Book Value
12/16*	169.12	28 22	6.20	0.24	39.54
01/16	150.51	31 22	6.40	0.24	33.56
01/15	158.56	24 16	6.71	0.24	27.41
12/13	109.92	21 13	5.32	0.24	20.82
12/12	71.51	17 12	5.22	0.24	16.50
Annual Growth	24.0%	—	4.4%	(0.0%)	24.4%

*Fiscal year change

ADVOCATE HEALTH CARE NETWORK

Advocating wellness in Chicagoland from Palos Heights to Palatine Advocate Health Care is a not-for-profit integrated health care network with more than 250 care sites serving the Chicago and surrounding areas. Advocate's operations include about a dozen acute and specialty care hospitals (including Christ Medical Center Hope Children's Hospital Advocate BroMenn Medical Center and Lutheran General Hospital) with more than 3550 beds as well as community health clinics and home health care and hospice services. The health system includes the largest physician network of primary care physicians specialists and sub-specialists in the state. Advocate Health plans to merge with Wisconsin-based Aurora Health Care.

Operations

Along with providing the full spectrum of health care services Advocate Health has a clinical laboratory joint venture ACL Laboratories with Aurora Health Care. ACL provides analytical and diagnostic testing services for both companies' facilities.

With more than 35000 associates the company is one of the largest employers in the Chicago area. Its staff includes 6300 affiliated physicians and more than 10000 nurses.

The system has teaching affiliations with area medical schools such as the University of Illinois at Chicago and the University of Chicago Pritzker School of Medicine. Its three major teaching hospitals — Christ Medical Center Illinois Masonic Medical Center and Lutheran General Hospital — train 600 residents and fellows per year and provide more than 1600 medical student rotations annually

Geographic Reach

Advocate Health operates more than 250 care sites serving Chicago and surrounding areas. Physician group Advocate Medical Group part of Advocate Health has more than 1200 physicians and specialists; it operates in more than 300 neighborhood-based practices that are located throughout Chicagoland and Bloomington and Normal Indiana.

Financial Performance

In 2014 Advocate Health's revenue increased 6% to $5.2 billion (over $4.9 billion in 2013); a 7% increase in patient service revenues and a 6% increase in capitation revenues primarily drove that growth but the increases were partially offset by declines in other operating revenues.

Strategy

Advocate Health has grown through a series of acquisitions; recent purchases have included central Illinois health network BroMenn Healthcare System the 280-bed Condell Medical Center the Midwest Physician Group (now part of the Advocate Medical Group division) and Sherman Health Systems.

The system also expands its presence through partnerships. In 2014 it launched a clinical affiliation with Silver Cross Hospital boosting its Advocate Physicians' Partners (APP) organization's clinical integration program. As part of the partnership Silver Cross Hospital was clinically integrated with APP and Advocate Health (but it stopped short of becoming part of the system itself).

In 2017 Advocate Health dropped its plans to merge with NorthShore University Health System another Illinois hospital operator. The combination would have created a 16-hospital market leader in Chicago's North Shore area. The merger was blocked by the FTC which claimed that it would harm consumers by raising prices and lowering health care quality.

Later that year Advocate Health and Wisconsin-based Aurora Health Care agreed to combined forces. The merged company to be named Advocate Aurora Health Care will operate 27 hospitals and more than 500 care sites; it will serve nearly 3 million patient annually. The two companies already have a working relationship through their ACL Laboratories joint venture.

Company Background

Advocate Health was formed in 1995 by the United Church of Christ and the Evangelical Lutheran Church in America.

EXECUTIVES

EVP and Chief Medical Officer; President Advocate Physician Partners, Lee B. Sacks
SVP CFO Treasurer, Dominic J. Nakis
President Advocate Condell Medical Center, Ann Errichetti
President Advocate Good Shepherd Hospital, Karen A. Lambert
President Advocate Home Health Services, Denise M. Keefe
President Advocate Physician Partners, Martin F. (Marty) Manning, age 62
President Advocate Medical Group, James R. Dan
President recognized associates, John Bruss
SVP and Chief Marketing Officer, Kelly Jo Golson
President Dreyer Clinic, Donna Copper
President ACL Laboratories, Barbara Bigler
COO, Dana Gilbert
Vice President Human Resources Operations, Robin Fell
Vice President Physician and Ambulatory Services, Lois Elia
Vice President Advocate Operating System, Alex Andrade
Vice President of Clinical Effectiveness, Debra Oconnor

Senior Vice President and General Counsel, Earl Barnes
Medical Director, Martin Doot
Medical Director, Alvia Siddiqui
Managing Director, Nimit Aggarwal
Vice President of Finance and Ambulatory Division, Neil Beck
Advocate Medical Group Interim Vice President Operations South Region, Amy Place
Director of Pharmacy, William Forslev
Medical Director Cardiology, Patrick Fenner
VP GLOBAL APPLICATIONS, Jennifer Steinman
Pharmacy Manager, Paul Miller
Vice President Research, William Summerfelt
Vice President Operations, Karen Moore
Vice President Cardiovascular Service Line, Dawn Imburgia
Vice President Professional Arrangements Professional Arrangements, Peg Stone
Medical Director of Women and Childrens Services, Julie Ms
Auditors: ERNST & YOUNG LLP CHICAGO IL

LOCATIONS

HQ: ADVOCATE HEALTH CARE NETWORK
3075 HIGHLAND PKWY FL 6, DOWNERS GROVE, IL 605155563
Phone: 630 572-9393
Web: WWW.ADVOCATEHEALTH.COM

PRODUCTS/OPERATIONS

Selected Locations

Advocate BroMenn Medical Center (Normal Illinois) - 221 beds
Advocate Christ Medical Center (Oak Lawn Illinois) - 695 beds
Advocate Condell Medical Center (Libertyville Illinois) - 281 beds
Advocate Good Samaritan Hospital (Downers Grove Illinois) -340 beds
Advocate Eureka Hospital (Eureka Illinois)- 25 beds
Advocate Good Shepherd Hospital (Barrington Illinois) - 183 beds
AdvoAdvocate Hope Children's Hospital (Oak Lawn Illinois)
Advocate Illinois Masonic Medical Center (Chicago Illinois) -408 beds
Advocate Lutheran General Hospital (Park Ridge Illinois) - 639 beds
Advocate Sherman Hospital (ElginIllinois)- 225 beds
Advocate South Suburban Hospital (Hazel Crest Illinois) - 284 beds
Advocate Trinity Hospital (Chicago Illinois) - 250 beds

COMPETITORS

Alexian Brothers Health System
Central DuPage Hospital
Children's Hopsital of Chicago
Covenant Ministries
Elmhurst Memorial Healthcare
Gottlieb Memorial Hospital
HCA
Hospital Sisters Health System
KishHealth
Loyola University Health System

Mercy Hospital and Medical Center
NorthShore University HealthSystem
Northwest Community Healthcare
Northwestern Lake Forest Hospital
Northwestern Memorial HealthCare
Pronger Smith
Rush System for Health
SSM Health Care
Silver Cross Hospital
Sinai Health System
University of Chicago Medical Center

HISTORICAL FINANCIALS

Company Type: Private

Income Statement

FYE: December 31

	REVENUE ($ mil.)	NET INCOME ($ mil.)	NET PROFIT MARGIN	EMPLOYEES
12/15	5,392	60	1.1%	25,000
12/06	3,268	286	8.8%	—
12/05	2,973	140	4.7%	—
Annual Growth	6.1%	(8.1%)	—	—

2015 Year-End Financials

Debt ratio: ——
Return on equity: 1.10%
Cash ($ mil.): 203
Current ratio: 0.60
Long-term debt ($ mil.): —

Dividends
Yield: —
Payout: —
Market value ($ mil.): —

AECOM

AECOM is one of the world's top engineering and design groups. The company provides planning consulting and construction management services for civil and infrastructure construction to government and private clients in some 150 countries. The company also provides facilities management and maintenance logistics IT services and systems integration services. AECOM projects include the Mall of Oman (scheduled to open in 2019) the Hyderabad Metro Rail in India Mercedes-Benz Stadium (future home of the Atlanta Falcons) and New York City's Second Avenue Subway. AECOM generates more than a quarter of its sales outside the US.

Operations

AECOM operates through four business segments: Design and Consulting Services (DCS) Construction Services (CS) Management Services (MS) and AECOM Capital.

DCS is the largest segment generating more than 40% of the company's total revenue and consists of planning consulting architectural and engineering design services. CS includes construction for buildings energy infrastructure and industrial facilities and accounts for about 40% of sales. MS at about 20% of revenue includes AECOM's facilities management and maintenance training logistics consulting technical assistance and systems integration and IT services.

The company invests in real estate infrastructure projects and public/private partnerships through AECOM Capital.

Geographic Reach

Based in California AECOM serves clients in about 150 countries. The company generates more than 70% of its revenue from the US about 10% from Europe and just less than 20% together from the Asia-Pacific region Canada and other areas.

It has primary office locations in the US as well as in Australia Hong Kong Russia the United Arab Emirates and the UK.

Sales and Marketing

AECOM serves several sectors such as transportation facilities environmental energy water and government.

AECOM's revenue is split roughly half-and-half between private sector clients and government entities. Of the government entities contracts half are direct contracts with US federal government agencies (Departments of Defense Energy Justice and Homeland Security) and half are state and local governments as well as foreign governments.

Financial Performance

After a breakout year in fiscal 2015 (ended September) which saw revenue more than double due to the acquisition of URS Corporation AECOM reported a 3% drop in sales to $17.4 billion in fiscal 2016. Sales rebounded in fiscal 2017 rising 5% to $18.2 billion on strong performance from the Construction Services segment. Construction of new sports arenas in the Americas and a high-rise residential project in New York City added about $700 million in increased revenue and the acquisition of Shimmick Construction added another $220 million. Those gains were partially offset by small declines in both the Design and Consulting Services and the Management Services segments.

AECOM's net income skyrocketed in fiscal 2017 jumping more than 250% to about $340 million on much lower acquisition and integration expenses as compared to fiscal years 2016 and 2015 ($39 million compared to $214 million and $398 million respectively). Cash from operations fell to nearly $700 million in fiscal 2017 from $814 million the prior year on the timing of receipts and payments of working capital as well as a $60 million cash payment related to a settled federal lawsuit.

Strategy

AECOM believes that its diversification is key to growth. It has diversified end markets funding (50:50 private/public) and capabilities during its transition from solely engineering design to construction and then ultimately operations and maintenance. The company plans to leverage this diversification to win contracts and grow its customer base amid a time of increased infrastructure focus in Washington DC and across the country.

Infrastructure is truly a major target for the company which is boosting its expertise in that area through internal investment (including the creation of a federal contracting division) and acquisitions (including the 2017 purchase of Shimmick). In addition in mid-2017 the company announced plans to hire some 3000 workers to support its infrastructure operations in the US and the rest of the North America.

The company is already a leader in "mega projects" worth more than $1 billion; current projects that fit that description include Hudson Yards in New York City and the Los Angeles Rams stadium.

Although AECOM's acquisition spending in 2017 and 2016 has been miniscule compared to the billions it paid for USR Corp in late 2014 growth by acquisition remains a large part of the company's strategy as it works to cement its leadership position in existing markets and enter new ones.

Mergers and Acquisitions

AECOM paid about $165 million in 2017 for heavy civil construction company Shimmick which operates primarily in California and the western US. The purchase complements AECOM's North American offerings and better positions it to take advantage of upcoming infrastructure projects particularly in the western US.

The previous year AECOM acquired the outstanding 50% interest in Alberta-based FT Services Limited. The acquisition strengthens the company's oil and gas business by further diversifying its end market exposure.

EXECUTIVES

Vice President Leasing, David B Kilpatrick
Chief Executive AECOM Capital, John T. Livingston
President Major Pursuits, Frederick W. (Fred) Werner, age 64, $661,540 total compensation
SVP and Chief Marketing and Communications Officer, Heather Rim
Chairman and CEO, Michael S. (Mike) Burke, age 53, $1,276,928 total compensation
Group President Construction Services, Daniel P. McQuade, age 57
EVP and General Counsel, Carla J. Christofferson, age 49
Group President Design and Consulting Services Americas, Steve Morriss
President Technical and Operational Services, Randall A. (Randy) Wotring, age 60, $705,389 total compensation
EVP and CFO, W. Troy Rudd, age 53, $528,851 total compensation
EVP and Chief Human Resources Officer, Mary E. Finch, age 47
Chief Executive Europe the Middle East India and Africa (EMIA), Lara Poloni
Senior Vice President, Stephen Polechronis
Vice President, Jim Dray
Associate Vice President, Jim Daniel
Vice Presidenthuman Resources, Pam Hoebener
Associate Vice President, Harley Hanson
Vice President, Alan R Eckman
Vice President Technology, Dev Paul
Associate Vice President, Brett Canimore
Vice President and LACCD Program Director, Terri Mestas
Senior Vice President Programs, David Wall
Vice President, Don Hagen
Associate Vice President, David Husson
Vice President, Tim Green
Senior Vice President, Kevin Cornish
Assistant Vice President Casualty, Andy Shepard
Vice President, Will Wright
Senior Vice President Total Rewards, Marc Buchsbaum
Vice President, Juli Binaco
Executive Vice President, Robert Seibert
Vice President And Director of Circulation, Paul Kareth
Senior Vice President, Charles Manning
Vice President, Robert Kleinman
Vice President, Gregory Yates
Associate Vice President, John Glowacki
Associate Vice President, James Gast
Senior Vice President, Stephen Engblom
Assistant Vice President Technical Director, Richard Silos
Vice President, James Kaczor
Vice President of Technology, Andrew Schleppi
Associate Vice President, Robert Joseph
Associate Vice President, Paul Berkowitz
Vice President, Abbas Sarmad
Vice President, Christopher McDermott
Vice President Client Service Manager, Pedro Hernandez
First Vice President, Andy Bachman
Executive Vice President, Rob Blackman
Executive Vice President And General Counsel, Judy Herman
Vice President Of Operations, Rae Loui
Associate Vice President, William Norquist
Vice President Technical Services, Jeff Brier
Senior Vice President Business Development, Neal Greeley
Vice President Global Integrated Delivery Manager, Patrick Reily
Vice President Operations, John Sartorius
ASSOCIATE Vice President Operations Manager, Michael Adams
ASSOCIATE Vice President Project Management, Peng Zhao
Vice President Project Manager, Randy Kirschner
Vice President Growth Strategy, John Rhoads
Vice President, Shaoling Zhao
Senior Vice President Operations, D Linford
Vice President Operations, Robert Wallace
Associate Vice President, Guy Frearson

Vice President Talent Acquisition, Mike Dadey
Vice President Program Director, Dan Levy
Vice President, Richard Blagg
Associate Vice President, Alan Jefts
Vice President Operations And, Brad White
Vice President Cei Business Line Manager, Larry Sauls
Associate Vice President, John Holmes
Vice President and Senior Counsel, Chris Kane
Associate Vice President Project Director, Khan Rahman
Senior Vice President, Steve Woolwine
Senior Vice President Operations, Danny Syhre
Vice President, Dan Shumaker.
Executive Vice President, Rebecca Nolan
Senior Vice President, Eric Reid
Vice President of Business Development, Troy Hoberg
Senior Vice President, Kurt Stahl
Vice President, Robert Feille
Senior Vice President, Carl Valentino
Senior Vice President, Louis Tucciarone
Vice President, Jack Fager
Vice President Operations Manager, Sujan Punyamurthula
Department Head, Kevin Dill
Vice President, Scott Moorhouse
Senior Vice President National Director Surface Transportation, Albert Bast
Vice President of Business Development, Rick Randall
Vice President Marketing and Business Dev, James Daly
Vice President Business Development, Brian Hinkley
Vice President Marketing and Business Development, Carol Papillo
Sr.Vice President, Tim Siegel
Vice President Design Engineering Department Manager, Dwayne Deutscher
Regional Vice President, Kevin Jeansonne
Vice President, Joseph Sacco
Associate Vice President, Lee Wolochuk
Associate Vice President, John Q Wong
Vice President, John Kouchoukos
Vice President Human Resources, Johnie Brown
ASSOCIATE Vice President Project Management, Frances H Boettcher
Vice President Field Operations, William Racky
Vice President Business Development and Marketing, Jonas Klingspor
Senior Vice President Southeast Regional Business Line Leader, Elisabeth Bernitt
Vice President Field Operations, Sid Perkins
Associate Vice President, Alastair MacGregor
Executive Vice President Global Accounts, Siva Dhamotharan
Senior Vice President, Denise Casalino
Vice President, Marcos Diaz-Gonzalez
Vice President, James Karl
Vice President Contract Admin, Tony Esposito
Vice President, Thomas Loomis
Associate Vice President, Andres Garcia
Senior Vice President, Gareth Middleton
Vice President, Bob Turley
Executive Vice President and General Manager, Jill Bruning
Senior Vice President, Jeff Rosenstein
Vice President, Chris Morante
Senior Vice President Power, Greg Brown
Senior Vice President and Global P3 Leader, Karl Reichelt
Vice President of Business Development, Glen Rector
Vice Chairman, Daniel R. (Dan) Tishman, age 62
Advisory Board Member, Antonio Santoro
Auditors: Ernst & Young LLP

LOCATIONS

HQ: AECOM
1999 Avenue of the Stars, Suite 2600, Los Angeles, CA 90067
Phone: 213 593-8000
Web: www.aecom.com

2017 Sales

	$ mil.	% of total
US	13,042	72
Europe	1,870	10
Asia/Pacific	1,353	8
Canada	1,160	6
Other foreign countries	778	4
Total	**18,203**	**100**

PRODUCTS/OPERATIONS

Selected Services
Architecture & Design
Construction
Decommissioning & Closure
Engineering
Environmental Services
International Development
IT & Cybersecurity
Operations & Maintenance
Planning & Consulting
Program Management/Construction Management
Risk Management & Resilience
Specialized Services
  Cities Solutions
  Equity Investment
  Fabrication
  Process Technologies
  Public/Private Partnerships
Technical Services

COMPETITORS

Amec Foster Wheeler	MWH Global
Bechtel	Parsons Brinckerhoff
Black & Veatch	Parsons Corporation
CH2M HILL	STV
EMCOR	Skidmore Owings
Fluor	Stantec
Henkels & McCoy	Terracon
Jacobs Engineering	Tetra Tech
KBR	Tutor Perini
Louis Berger	

HISTORICAL FINANCIALS

Company Type: Public

Income Statement

FYE: September 30

	REVENUE ($ mil.)	NET INCOME ($ mil.)	NET PROFIT MARGIN	EMPLOYEES
09/17	18,203	339	1.9%	87,000
09/16	17,410	96	0.6%	87,000
09/15	17,989	(154)	—	92,000
09/14	8,356	229	2.8%	43,300
09/13	8,153	239	2.9%	45,500
Annual Growth	22.2%	9.1%	—	17.6%

2017 Year-End Financials

Debt ratio: 26.70%
Return on equity: 9.22%
Cash ($ mil.): 802
Current ratio: 1.20
Long-term debt ($ mil.): 3,702
No. of shares (mil.): 157
Dividends
  Yield: —
  Payout: —
Market value ($ mil.): 5,799

	STOCK PRICE ($) FY Close	P/E High/Low	PER SHARE ($) Earnings	Dividends	Book Value
09/17	36.81	18 12	2.13	0.00	25.37
09/16	29.73	58 37	0.62	0.00	21.88
09/15	27.51	— —	(1.04)	0.00	22.53
09/14	33.75	16 12	2.33	0.00	22.61
09/13	31.27	15 8	2.35	0.00	21.05
Annual Growth	4.2%	— —	(2.4%)	—	4.8%

AEROTEK, INC.

Aerotek a unit of staffing powerhouse Allegis Group offers commercial and technical staffing services throughout North America. Through several divisions Aerotek staffs workers such as engineers mechanics scientists and technical professionals as well as administrative staff members general laborers and tradespeople. The company also provides training and support services. Along with aerospace auto and engineering companies Aerotek's clients include companies from the construction energy manufacturing health care and finance industries.

Geographic Reach

Aerotek is headquartered in Hanover Maryland. The company has office locations in Asia Australia Europe and North America. Aerotek also operates a network of more than 250 non-franchised offices.

Sales and Marketing

Aerotek serves a wide variety of industries including the accounting construction engineering financial services government and public administration health care manufacturing and pharmaceutical industries among others. The company serves more than 18000 clients and 300000 contract employees every year.

Strategy

Aerotek has expanded its operations over the years through organic growth and acquisitions especially in niche markets such as the biotechnology health care clinical research chemical and plastics sectors. Despite the economic downturn demand within these industries has been consistent along with engineering giving Aerotek some continuity during the recession. Aerotek has also widened its client focus to include the niche market of minority and woman-owned companies.

EXECUTIVES

VP Technical and Professional Services, Mark Cooper
President, Todd M. Mohr
CFO, Thomas B. (Tom) Kelly
SVP Operations, John Flanigan
Regional VP Northeast, John Rudy
Regional VP Midwest, Marty Schager
Regional VP Central, Mike Hansen
Regional VP West, Tony Bartolucci
Regional VP Northwest, Brooks Wells
VP Canada, Bryan Toffey
Regional VP Southwest, Brad Kennedy
Regional VP Mid-Atlantic, Jeff Colvin
Regional VP Southeast, Greg Jones
Senior Vice President And Project Director, Lori Clanton
Auditors: PRICEWATERHOUSECOOPERS LLP B

LOCATIONS

HQ: AEROTEK, INC.
7301 PARKWAY DR, HANOVER, MD 210761159
Phone: 410 694-5100

PRODUCTS/OPERATIONS

INDUSTRIES SERVED
Accounting
Administrative & Support Services
Aerospace Aviation & Defense
Architecture & Design
Automotive
Construction
Customer Service
Energy & Utilities
Engineering

Environmental
Financial Services
Government & Public Administration
Healthcare
Manufacturing
Pharmaceutical
Sciences
Warehouse & Distribution

COMPETITORS

AMN Healthcare	MSX International
Adecco	ManpowerGroup
Bryant Bureau	On Assignment
CDI	Pinnacle Staffing
COMFORCE	Randstad Holding
Kelly Services	Robert Half
Kforce	

HISTORICAL FINANCIALS

Company Type: Private

Income Statement

FYE: December 31

	REVENUE ($ mil.)	NET INCOME ($ mil.)	NET PROFIT MARGIN	EMPLOYEES
12/15	5,492	0	—	4,200
12/14	5,353	0	—	—
12/13	5,268	0	—	—
12/12	5,119	307	6.0%	—
Annual Growth	2.4%	—	—	—

2015 Year-End Financials

Debt ratio: —
Return on equity: —
Cash ($ mil.): 14
Current ratio: 3.40
Long-term debt ($ mil.): —

Dividends
Yield: —
Payout: —
Market value ($ mil.): —

AES Corp.

The AES Corp. is a leading independent power producer. The company has interests in about 110 generation facilities in more than 15 countries throughout the Americas Asia Africa Europe and the Middle East. AES sells electricity to utilities and other energy marketers through wholesale contracts or on the spot market. AES also sells power directly to customers worldwide through stakes in distribution utilities mainly in Latin America and the US.

HISTORY

Applied Energy Services (AES) was founded in 1981 three years after passage of the Public Utilities Regulation Policies Act which enabled small power firms to enter electric generation markets formerly dominated by utility monopolies. Co-founders Roger Sant and Dennis Bakke who had served in President Nixon's Federal Energy Administration saw that an independent power producer (IPP) could make money by generating cheap power in large volumes to sell to large power consumers and utilities.

AES set about building massive cogeneration plants (producing both steam and electricity) in 1983. The first plant Deepwater went into operation near Houston in 1986. By 1989 AES had three plants on line and it then opened plants in Connecticut and Oklahoma. In 1991 the company formally renamed AES went public but one plant's falsified emissions reports caused AES's stock to plummet in 1992.

Facing environmental groups' opposition to new power plant construction and an overall glut in the US power market AES bought interests in two Northern Ireland plants in 1992 and began expanding into Latin America in 1993. Also in 1993 AES set up a separately traded subsidiary AES China Generating Co. to focus on Chinese development projects. AES won a plant development contract with the Puerto Rico Electric Power Authority (1994) and a bid to privatize an Argentine hydrothermal company (1995).

In 1996 AES began adding stakes in electric utility and distribution companies to its portfolio including interests in formerly state-owned Brazilian electric utilities Light-Servi §os de Eletricidade (1996) and CEMIG (1997); one Brazilian and two Argentine distribution companies (1997); and a distribution company in El Salvador (1998).

AES almost doubled its revenues after buying Destec Energy's international operations from NGC (now Dynegy) in 1997. By the next year prospects in international markets were dimming so AES turned to the US market again. It bought three California plants from Edison International and arranged for The Williams Companies to supply natural gas to the facilities and market the electricity generated. AES also won a bid to buy six plants from New York State Electric & Gas (now Energy East) affiliate NGE.

Also in 1998 despite black days in many world markets AES bought 90% of Argentine electric distribution company Edelap and a 45% stake in state-owned Orissa Power Generation in India. Its moves paid off: AES posted a 70% gain in sales that year.

It bought CILCORP an Illinois utility holding company in an $886 million deal in 1999. Boosting its presence in the UK AES bought the Drax power station a 3960-MW coal-fired plant from National Power. It also bought a majority stake in Brazilian data transmission company Eletronet from Brazil's government-owned utility ELETROBR S. In 2000 AES increased its interests in Brazilian power distributors. It also gained a 73% stake (later expanded to 87%) in Venezuelan electric utility Grupo EDC in a $1.5 billion hostile takeover.

The next year AES bought IPALCO the parent of Indianapolis Power & Light in a $3 billion deal. Also in 2001 AES acquired the outstanding shares of Chilean generation company Gener in which it previously held a 60% stake.

That year AES moved to take control of CANTV Venezuela's #1 telecom company. Through Grupo EDC which already owned 6.9% of CANTV AES offered to buy 43.2% of the company. But AES withdrew the offer after the CANTV board rejected it. (AES sold Grupo EDC's stake in CANTV the following year.) AES also sold some generation assets in Argentina to TOTAL FINA ELF (now TOTAL) for about $370 million.

In 2002 AES sold its 24% interest in Light Servi §os de Eletricidade (Light) to Electricit © de France (EDF) in exchange for a 20% stake in Brazilian utility Eletropaulo (increasing its stake in Eletropaulo to 70%). In that same year the company sold its retail energy marketing unit (AES NewEnergy) to Constellation Energy Group for $240 million and its CILCORP subsidiary which holds utility Central Illinois Light to Ameren.

In 2007 the company acquired two 230 MW petroleum coke-fired power generation facilities in Tamuin Mexico for $611 million. It also bought a 51% stake in Turkish power generator IC ICTAS Energy Group.

AES has faced controversy in Brazil where an unstable power market has caused the company to default on debts incurred from its purchases of stakes in local utilities (as well as bankrupt telecom firm Eletronet) in recent years. To restructure its debt with Banco Nacional de Desenvolvimento

Economico e Social (BNDES) AES completed a deal in 2007 in which the firm's interests in AES Eletropaulo AES Uruguaiana AES Tiete and AES Sul was placed into a new holding company (Brasiliana Energia). AES owns 50.1% of that company while BNDES holds 49.9%.

To raise cash in 2008 and 2009 AES sold the AES Ekibastuz power plant and Maikuben coal mine in Kazakhstan to Kazakhmys (renamed KAZ Minerals) for $1.1 billion.

In 2008 the company boosted it assets in the Philippines acquiring the 660 MW Masinloc coal-fired power plant in Barangay Bula for $930 million.

EXECUTIVES

EVP and CFO, Thomas M. (Tom) O'Flynn, age 57, $683,000 total compensation
CEO, Andr ©s R. Gluski, age 60, $1,165,000 total compensation
EVP General Counsel and Corporate Secretary, Brian A. Miller, age 51, $585,000 total compensation
VP Integrated Utilities Dominican Republic, Julian Nebreda
SVP Technology and Services and CIO, Elizabeth Hackenson, age 56, $433,000 total compensation
SVP and COO, Bernerd Da Santos, $456,000 total compensation
President Asia Strategic Business Unit (SBU), Marty Crotty
President Europe Strategic Business Unit (SBU), Mark Green
President Mexico Central America and the Caribbean (MCAC) Strategic Business Unit (SBU), Manuel P ©rez Dubuc
President US Strategic Business Unit (SBU), Ken Zagzebski
President and COO, Patrick Moran
Vice President Global Operations Support, Evaristo Leonardi
Vice President AES Global Insurance Company, Andrew Baillie
Vice President and Chief Tax Officer, Margaret Tigre
Vice President Internal Audit and Advisory Services, Sarah Blake
Vice President, Ruben Saavedra
Vice President Finanzas, Rosa Alvarado
Vice President, Robert Mill
Vice President (Human Resources), Paritosh Mishra
Vice President, Brett Galura
Vice President Portfolio Management, Rick Sturges
Vice President, Mohammad Al Qudah
Vice President Channel Strategy and Global Business Development, Ismario Gonzalez
Vice President Business Development United States and Canada, Charles Vaughan
Vice President, Vincent Mathis
Chairman, Charles O. Rossotti, age 77
Board Member, Carlos Quiroz
Auditors: Ernst & Young LLP

LOCATIONS

HQ: AES Corp.
4300 Wilson Boulevard, Arlington, VA 22203
Phone: 703 522-1315   **Fax:** 703 528-4510
Web: www.aes.com

2016 Sales

	$ mil.	% of total
Brazil SBU	3,755	28
US SBU	3,429	25
Andes SBU	2,506	18
MCAC SBU	2,172	16
Europe SBU	918	7
Asia SBU	752	5
Corporate and Other	77	1
Intersegment eliminations	(23)	-
Total	**13,586**	**100**

2016 Sales

	$ mil.	% of total
Brazil	3,755	28
US	3,489	26
Chile	1,707	13
Dominican Republic	614	5
El salvador	601	4
Colombia	437	3
Philippines	401	3
Argentina	359	3
Mexico	342	3
Vietnam	340	3
United Kingdom	337	2
Bulgaria	334	2
Panama	312	2
Puerto Rico	301	1
Jordan	136	1
Kazakhstan	103	1
Sri Lanka	10	1
Other countries	8	-
Total	**13,586**	**100**

PRODUCTS/OPERATIONS

2016 Sales

	$ mil.	% of total
Regulated	6,629	49
Non-regulated	6,957	51
Total	**13,586**	**100**

Selected Electric Utilities and Distribution Companies

AES CLESA (electric utility El Salvador)
AES Edelap (electric utility Argentina)
AES Eden (electric utility Argentina)
AES Edes (electric utility Argentina)
AES Gener (electric generation Chile)
AES India Private Ltd.
AES SeaWest Inc.
Brasiliana Energia
  AES Sul Distribuidora Gaucha de Energia SA (AES Sul electric utility Brazil)
  AES Tiete (power generation Brazil)
  AES Uruguaiana (power generation Brazil)
  Eletropaulo Metropolitana Eletricidade de São Paulo S.A. (AES Electropaulo electric distribution Brazil)
CAESS (electric utility El Salvador)
Companhia Energé;tica de Minas Gerais (CEMIG Brazil)
DPL (electric utility US)
EEO (electric utility El Salvador)
IC ICTAS Energy Group (power generation Turkey)
IPALCO Enterprises Inc. (holding company)

COMPETITORS

Alliant Energy	Enterprise Products
Berkshire Hathaway Energy	Exelon
	Huadian Power
Bonneville Power	IBERDROLA
CMS Energy	Indeck Energy
CPFL Energia	International Power
Calpine	NRG Energy
CenterPoint Energy	NextEra Energy
Duke Energy	Nicor Gas
Dynegy	PG&E Corporation
E.ON UK	Public Service
Edison International	Enterprise Group
Endesa S.A.	Sempra Energy
Energias de Portugal	Siemens AG
Energy Future	Tractebel Engineering
Enersis	Xcel Energy
Entergy	

HISTORICAL FINANCIALS
Company Type: Public

Income Statement
FYE: December 31

	REVENUE ($ mil.)	NET INCOME ($ mil.)	NET PROFIT MARGIN	EMPLOYEES
12/16	13,586	(1,130)	—	
12/15	14,963	306	2.0%	21,000
12/14	17,146	769	4.5%	18,500
12/13	15,891	114	0.7%	22,000
12/12	18,141	(912)	—	25,000
Annual Growth	**(7.0%)**	—	—	—

2016 Year-End Financials

Debt ratio: 56.65%
Return on equity: (-31.03%)
Cash ($ mil.): 1,305
Current ratio: 1.22
Long-term debt ($ mil.): 19,160

No. of shares (mil.): 659
Dividends
Yield: 0.0%
Payout: —
Market value ($ mil.): 7,660

	STOCK PRICE ($) FY Close	P/E High/Low	Earnings	Dividends	Book Value
12/16	11.62	— —	(1.71)	0.44	5.42
12/15	9.57	31 20	0.44	0.40	5.53
12/14	13.77	15 12	1.06	0.20	6.18
12/13	14.51	102 71	0.15	0.16	6.10
12/12	10.70	— —	(1.21)	0.04	6.24
Annual Growth	**2.1%**		—	**82.1%**	**(3.5%)**

Aetna Inc.

Life death health or injury — Aetna's got an insurance policy to cover it. The company one of the largest health insurers in the US also offers life and disability insurance as well as retirement savings products. Its health care division offers HMO PPO point of service (POS) health savings account (HSA) and traditional indemnity coverage along with dental vision behavioral health and Medicare and Medicaid plans to groups and individuals. The health care segment covers some 23 million medical members. Aetna's group insurance segment (which it is selling to The Hartford) sells life and disability insurance nationwide and its large case pensions segment offers pensions annuities and other retirement savings products.In what would be the largest health insurance deal in history retail pharmacy giant CVS plans to buy Aetna for $69 billion.

HISTORY

Hartford Connecticut businessman and judge Eliphalet Bulkeley started Connecticut Mutual Life Insurance in 1846. Agents gained control of the firm the following year. Undeterred Bulkeley and a group of Hartford businessmen founded Aetna Life Insurance in 1853 as a spinoff of Aetna Fire Insurance. Among its offerings was coverage for slaves a practice for which the company apologized in 2000.

A nationwide agency network fueled early growth at Aetna which expanded in the 1860s by offering a participating life policy returning dividends to policyholders based on investment earnings. (This let Aetna compete with mutual life insurers.) In 1868 Aetna became the first firm to offer renewable term life policies.

Eliphalet's son Morgan became president in 1879. Aetna moved into accident (1891) health (1899) workers' compensation (1902) and auto

and other property insurance (1907) during his 43-year tenure. He served as Hartford mayor Connecticut governor and US senator all the while leading Aetna.

By 1920 the company sold marine insurance and by 1922 it was the US's largest multiline insurer. Aetna overexpanded its nonlife lines (particularly autos) during the 1920s threatening its solvency. It survived the Depression by restricting underwriting and rebuilding reserves.

After WWII the firm expanded into group life health and accident insurance. In 1967 it reorganized into holding company Aetna Life and Casualty.

The 1960s 1970s and 1980s were go-go years: The company added lines and bought and sold everything from an oil services firm to commercial real estate. The boom period led to a bust and a 1991 reorganization in which Aetna eliminated 8000 jobs withdrew from such lines as auto insurance and sold its profitable American Reinsurance.

To take advantage of the boom in retirement savings in 1995 it got permission to set up bank AE Trust to act as a pension trustee.

With its health care business accounting for some 60% of sales by 1995 the company restructured in the late 1990s. Aetna sold its property/casualty behavioral managed care (1997) and individual life insurance (1998) businesses. It then expanded overseas and bought U.S. Healthcare and New York Life's NYLCare managed health business (1998).

Controversy marred 1998. Contract terms — including a "gag" clause against discussing uncovered treatments — prompted 400 Texas doctors to leave its system; defections followed in Kentucky and West Virginia. Consumers balked over Aetna's refusal to cover some treatments including experimental procedures and advanced fertility treatments. One group sued for false advertising.

EXECUTIVES

EVP Law and Regulatory Affairs and General Counsel, Thomas J. (Tom) Sabatino, age 58, $502,871 total compensation
Senior Vice President and Chief Investment Officer, Tim Holt
Executive Vice President Commercial Business, Frank Mccauley
EVP Consumer Health and Services, Gary W. Loveman, age 56, $796,935 total compensation
EVP Enterprise Strategy, Rick M. Jelinek
EVP Corporate Affairs, Steven B. Kelmar
Chairman and CEO, Mark T. Bertolini, age 60, $1,141,762 total compensation
EVP Operations and Technology, Margaret M. (Meg) McCarthy, age 63, $627,960 total compensation
EVP CFO and Chief Enterprise Risk Officer, Shawn M. Guertin, age 53, $796,935 total compensation
EVP and Chief Human Resources Officer, Thomas W. (Tom) Weidenkopf
EVP and Chief Medical Officer, Harold L. Paz, age 62
EVP Aetna International, Richard di Benedetto
President, Karen S. Lynch, age 54, $919,483 total compensation
EVP Government Services, Francis S. (Fran) Soistman, age 60, $675,287 total compensation
Assistant Vice President, Marilyn J Stoudt
Vice President Enterprise Solutions Product Engineering, Loren Jenkins
Vice President of Sales and Service, Janice C Washeleski
Vice President of Public Policy for Government Affairs, Christina Nyquist
National Account Manager, Douglas Schoener
Vice President Network, Karen Chotiner
Vice President, Stacy Patrick

Senior Vice President Of Product And Marketing, Curtis Carik

Vice President Client Management, Sue Helke

Vice President Sales, Tina Ortega

Vice President of Business Development, Debbie Dexter

Vice President Head of Product Marketing, Karen Weinseiss

Vice President and Controller and Chief Accounting Officer, Rajana Parmeswar

Vice President Workforce Planning, Melissa Cummings

Vice President, John Stockton

Vice President Sales and Marketing for National Accounts, Sheryl Burke

Assistant Vice President Public Relations, Cynthia Michener

Vice President of Business Development, Miguel Centeno

Senior Vice President and Executive Director New York Market, David Kobus

Director Executive Vice President and Chief Financial Officer, Jennifer S Shick

Regional Vice President Bh, Mark Hartinger

Vice President, Amy Burgoyne

National Account Manager, Nancy Shinn

Vice President Business Development, Randy Solomon

Vice President And Chief Medicare Counse, Alicia Palmer

Medical Director, Terry Golash

Vice President, Michael Hoss

Vice President Integration and Implementation, Laura Gargano

Assistant Vice President Network, Cecilia Moseler

Vice President Client Management National Accounts, Michael Fusaro

Vice President Investor Relations, Joseph Krocheski

Vice President Of Information Technology Goverment Programs And Projects, James Atkin

Regional Vice President of Business Development, Taira A Green-Kelley

Vice President and Owner, Lisa A Sandoval

Medical Director National Accounts Dedicated Units, John Schaller

Senior Vice President Of Medicaid Business Development, Donna Checkett

Vice President, Noreen Giannini

Regional Vice President Public and Labor Segment, Stuart MacDonald

Vice President NCO, Michael Gannon

SVP, Art Lynch

Vice President and Counsel, Iovino Charlie

Medical Director, Richard Grassy

Sales Vice President, Frank Binetti

Vice President, Betty Assapimonwait

VP Operations, Ava Reinstein

VP Strategy and Distribution, David Goodrich

National Accounts Manager, Linda Reid

Vice President And Head Labor Sector Business, Karen Moran

Sales Vice President, John Russo

Vice President Client Management, Jacqueline McCaffrey

Vice President Human Resources, Alison Rogers-McCoy

Senior Vice President of Emerging Businesses and Strategic Initiatives, Steve Doyle

Vice President of Sales and Service, Greg Haley

Regional Vice President, Jan Stallmeyer

Vice President Sales and Service, John Gialamas

Medical Director, Clinton Clapp

Vice President of Sales and Service at Aetna, Troy McClaren

Director Of Pharmacy Western Region, Friedmann Yrena

Senior Vice President Strategy And Operations, Michelle Copenhaver

Senior Vice President and Deputy General Counsel, Charles Klippel

Regional Vice President Sales, Rassi Christina

Senior Vice President, Sandra Paskiewicz

Vice President Controller and Chief Accounting Officer, Sharon Virag

Vice President Chief Financial Officer National Accounts, Heather Mackie

Network Vice President, Thomas Nasby

Vice President Sales And Client Management National Accounts, Dina Segro-nogueira

Vice President Group Insurance Dental and Vision, Michael Barski

Sales Vice President, Brian Katits

Sales Vice President, Leigh Hull

Vice President Health Services, Lee Reilly

VP Pharmacy Contracting, Debra Keena

Vice President Actuarial and Underwriting (National Accounts), Andy Hiles

Vice President Executive Financial Advisor, Ron Pearsall

Vice President, William Casazza

Vice President Marketing, Ramon Soto

Evice President And General Counsel For Regulatory Affairs, Edward Shaw

Vice President and Controller, Richard C Alves

Vice President Sales and Service, David Lasaracino

Vice President, Reinaldo Toro

Medical Director, Frank DiTirro

Regional Vice President Sales, Erich Twachtman

Vice President of Pharmaceutical Contracting and Vendor Management, Michael Rothrock

National Account Sales Vice President, Jim Milligan

Vice President Of Sales And Services, Pete Diniaco

Vice President Sales And Services, Dave Lasaracino

Vice President Sales And Service, Bradley Fischer

Senior Vice President Corporate Communications, John R Bolton

Medical Director National Medical Policy and Operations, Paul Aitken

Medical Director, Lela Mayers

Medical Director, Davelyn Eaves

Medical Director, Meera Atkins

Vice President of Health Services, Esther Watson

Medical Director National Accounts at Aetna, Omo Olurin

Vice President, Neil Van

Vice President Network Management, Melissa Tangen

Vice President of Operations, James Ricciuti

Vice President and Chief Architect, Claus Jensen

Vice President, Denise Southall

Vice President and Product Head, Dan Clark

Medical Director, Farrell Johnson

Vice President And Head Of Sales And Marketing, Elizabeth Winsor

VP Network Management, Tim Giess

Vice President, Donna Esposito

Medical Director, Cheryl Woodson

Vice President, Diane Lopes

Medical Director, Linda Ladesich

Medical Director, Maria Diaz

Medical Director, Art Sippo

Medical Director, William Sippo

Individual Business Development and Service Vice President, Don Van

Medical Director Southeast Region (Georgia Louisiana Alabama Mississippi), Anthony Grieco

Medical Director Florida, Darwin Caraballo

Vice President and Head of Digital Products, Firdaus Bhathena

Vice President and Head of Product and Solutions Management, Justin Steinman

Medical Director, Gail Croall

Vice President Sales and Service, Tim Matthews

National Account Manager, Jeanie Sims

Sales Vice President West Region Aetna Behavorial Health Resource for Living, Lauren Rizzo

National Account Manager, Adam Shafnisky

VP IT, Ron Cordova

Sales Vice President, Mark Tucker

Medical Director for South Florida, Angela Burrafato

Sales Vice President Public and Labor, Branson Cobb

Regional Vice President Midwest Region, George Pelekanos

Vice President Finance and Treasurer, David Buda

Board Treasurer, Sheila M Jaskowiak

Assistant Treasurer, Eric Trafton

Assistant Treasurer Head Of Corporate Finance And Strat, Grant Jones

Board Member, Joseph Newhouse

Board Member, Cheryl Parmelee

Auditors: KPMG LLP

LOCATIONS

HQ: Aetna Inc.
151 Farmington Avenue, Hartford, CT 06156
Phone: 860 273-0123
Web: www.aetna.com

PRODUCTS/OPERATIONS

2016 Sales

	$ mil.	% of total
Health care	54,116	86
Other Premium	2,182	3
Fees & other	5,861	9
Net invest income	910	1
Net realization capital loss	86	1
Total	**63,155**	**100**

Selected Products and Services

Behavioral and Mental Health Plans
Dental Plans
Disability Insurance
Health Expense Funds
Life Insurance
Medicaid
Medical Plans
Medicare
Pharmacy
Student Health
Support Programs
Vision Plans
Wellness Programs and Discounts

COMPETITORS

AMERIGROUP	Humana
Anthem	Independence Blue
Blue Cross	Cross
CIGNA	Kaiser Foundation
Centene	Health Plan
Chubb Limited	Magellan Health
HCSC	Molina Healthcare
Health Net	UnitedHealth Group
HealthSpring	WellCare Health Plans
Highmark	

HISTORICAL FINANCIALS

Company Type: Public

Income Statement

FYE: December 31

	ASSETS ($ mil.)	NET INCOME ($ mil.)	INCOME AS % OF ASSETS	EMPLOYEES
12/16	69,146	2,271	3.3%	49,500
12/15	53,424	2,390	4.5%	50,100
12/14	53,402	2,040	3.8%	48,800
12/13	49,871	1,913	3.8%	48,600
12/12	41,494	1,657	4.0%	35,000
Annual Growth	**13.6%**	**8.2%**	**—**	**9.1%**

2016 Year-End Financials

Debt ratio: 29.88%	No. of shares (mil.): 351
Return on equity: 13.32%	Dividends
Cash ($ mil.): 17,996	Yield: 0.0%
Current ratio: —	Payout: 15.6%
Long-term debt ($ mil.): —	Market value ($ mil.): 43,614

	STOCK PRICE ($)	P/E	PER SHARE ($)		
	FY Close	High/Low	Earnings	Dividends	Book Value
12/16	124.01	21 15	6.41	1.00	50.84
12/15	108.12	19 13	6.78	1.00	46.11
12/14	88.83	16 11	5.68	0.90	41.40
12/13	68.59	13 8	5.33	0.80	38.72
12/12	46.31	10 7	4.81	0.70	31.76
Annual Growth	27.9%	— —	7.4%	9.3%	12.5%

AFLAC Inc

To soften the financial stresses during periods of disability or illness Aflac sells supplemental health and life insurance policies including coverage for accidents intensive care dental vision and disability as well as for specific conditions (primarily cancer) and general life policies. It is a leading supplier of supplemental insurance in the US and is an industry leader in Japan's life and cancer insurance markets. Aflac which is marketed through — and is an acronym for — American Family Life Assurance Company sells policies that pay cash benefits for hospital confinement emergency treatment and medical appliances.

Operations

Aflac operates through two reportable segments — Aflac Japan and Aflac U.S. The firm acts as a management company overseeing the operations of its subsidiaries by providing management services and making capital available. Its principal business is supplemental health and life insurance which is marketed and administered through its subsidiary American Family Life Assurance Company of Columbus (Aflac) which operates in the US and as a branch in Japan (Aflac Japan). Aflac individual and group insurance products help provide protection to more than 50 million people around the world.

Geographic Reach

Despite its US roots Aflac makes about 70% of its insurance sales in Japan where its policies fill in gaps not covered by the national health insurance system. Aflac has a presence in all 50 US states (the US accounts for more than 25% of revenue) and in Puerto Rico and the Virgin Islands.

Sales and Marketing

In Japan Aflac primarily sells through an independent corporate agency system in which corporations form subsidiaries to sell Aflac insurance to their employees. The company also sells through banks and post offices and it has opened retail shops where consumers can purchase directly from sales associates.

By the end of 2016 the company had agreements to sell its products with 372 banks approximately 90% of the total number of banks in Japan. Banks contributed nearly 10% of Aflac Japan's new annualized premium sales that year.

In the US Aflac sells mainly at the workplace with employers deducting premiums from paychecks through sales associates of its Continental American Insurance Company subsidiary (known as Aflac Group Insurance). Building on its strong brand recognition — due largely to the company's popular TV ads featuring a valiant spokes-duck — Aflac has invested in its US business by adding more sales associates and expanding its distribution to include independent insurance brokers.

Aflac's extensive distribution network includes about 12100 sales agencies with some 108000 licensed sales associates. In 2016 the company recruited approximately 200 new sales agencies. Independent corporate and individual agencies contribute nearly half of new annualized premium sales each year.

The company's advertising costs in 2016 were $224 million compared to $211 million in 2015 and $229 million in 2014.

Financial Performance

Aflac saw steady revenue declines from 2012 until 2016 when revenue rose 8% to $22.6 billion. This was largely due to an increase in net premiums across all geographies. In Japan cancer and medical insurance product sales increased 5% and the introduction of a new income support insurance product (which targets young to middle-aged customers) should secure new clients for the long term. Health insurance premiums gained 9% that year while life insurance premiums gained 11%.

The higher revenue boosted net income which had fallen over the past two years. In 2016 net income rebounded 5% to $2.7 billion.

Cash flow from operations has generally fallen over the past five years. It declined 12% to $6 billion in 2016 as a result of an increase in deferred policy acquisition costs and other negative adjustments to cash provided by operations.

Strategy

Aflac is focusing on improving and expanding its distribution network and product development processes and on improving its customer service activities. As part of its US strategy the company aims to grow and enhance the effectiveness of its US sales team. In 2015 Aflac launched a new critical illness plan Critical Care Protection which provides a range of coverage options as well as new benefits for heart conditions.

In Japan where Aflac already covers about 25% of all households the company has created new health and life insurance products to attract even more customers. In addition to standard life insurance it has child endowment products that pay out part of the benefit when the child enters high school and then functions like an annuity for four years during college. In 2016 the company launched a new income support insurance product which provides support when a sickness keeps customers from working long-term.That profduct targets younger customers which the company hopes to keep with different products as they age. And to boost distribution Aflac Japan and Japan Post Holdings have an alliance which has boosted the number of postal outlets offering Aflac's cancer products from 1000 to more than 20000.

HISTORY

American Family Life Assurance Company (AFLAC) was founded in Columbus Georgia in 1955 by brothers John Paul and William Amos to sell life health and accident insurance. Competition was fierce and the little company did poorly. With AFLAC nearing bankruptcy the brothers looked for a niche.

The polio scares of the 1940s and 1950s had spawned insurance coverage written especially against that disease; the Amos brothers (whose father was a cancer victim) took a cue from that concept and decided to sell cancer insurance. In 1958 they introduced the world's first cancer-expense policy. It was a hit and by 1959 the company had written nearly a million dollars in premiums and expanded across state lines.

The enterprise grew quickly during the 1960s especially after developing its cluster-selling approach in the workplace where employers were usually willing to make payroll deductions for premiums. By 1971 the company was operating in 42 states.

While visiting the World's Fair in Osaka in 1970 John Amos decided to market supplemental cancer coverage to the Japanese whose national health care plan left them exposed to considerable expense from cancer treatment. After four years the company finally won approval to sell in Japan since the policies did not threaten existing markets and because the Amoses found notable backers in the insurance and medical industries. AFLAC became one of the first US insurance companies to enter the Japanese market and it enjoyed an eight-year monopoly on the cancer market. Back in the US in 1973 AFLAC organized a holding company and began buying television stations in the South and Midwest.

The 1980s were marked by US and state government inquiries into dread disease insurance. Critics said such policies were a poor value because they were relatively expensive and covered only one disease. However the inquiries led nowhere and demand for such insurance increased bringing new competition. In the 1980s AFLAC's scales tilted: US growth slowed while business grew in Japan which soon accounted for most of the company's sales.

EXECUTIVES

EVP Treasurer and Head of Corporate Finance and Development, Kenneth S. (Ken) Janke, age 59
President, Kriss Cloninger, age 69, $975,000 total compensation
Chairman and CEO, Daniel P. (Dan) Amos, age 65, $1,441,100 total compensation
EVP and CFO, Frederick J. (Fred) Crawford, age 53, $700,000 total compensation
President Aflac International; Chairman Aflac Japan, Charles D. Lake, age 56, $333,333 total compensation
EVP and General Counsel, Audrey Boone Tillman, age 52
President Aflac, Paul S. Amos, age 42, $700,000 total compensation
President Aflac U.S., Teresa L. White, age 51
SVP and Chief Marketing Officer, Gail A. Galuppo, age 53
SVP Business Services; President and CEO Communicorp, Eric B. Seldon
EVP and Global Chief Investment Officer, Eric M. Kirsch, age 56, $593,800 total compensation
Managing Director and Global Head of Credit Global Investments, Bradley E. Dyslin
SVP and CIO, Julia K. Davis
Managing Director and Head of Global Investments and Corporate IT, J. Pete Kelso
EVP Global Chief Risk Officer and Chief Actuary, J. Todd Daniels, age 46
Senior Managing Director and Global Head Macro Investment Strategy Quantitative Research and Trading Global Investments, Timothy (Chip) Stevens
Managing Director and Chief Investment Officer Global Investments, Teresa Q. McTague
President Aflac Corporate Ventures, Nadeem G. Khan
Executive Vice President and Chief Financial Officer, Rob Moran
VICE PRESIDENT TRADE OPERATIONS, Evan Philippopoulos
Executive Vice President, Ken Janke
Second Vice President, Maki Hishikawa
SENIOR VICE PRESIDENT OF INTERNAL OPERATIONS, Virgil R Miller
SECOND VICE PRESIDENT SHAREHOLDER SERVICES, Patricia A Bell
EXECUTIVE VICE PRESIDENT, Kenneth S Janke
ASSISTANT VICE PRESIDENT SENIOR TECH AND DESKTOP SUPP, Jack Chong
VICE PRESIDENT ENTERPRISE ARCHITECTURE, Joe Parsons
Vice President Chief People Officer, Brenda Mullins
Auditors: KPMG LLP

LOCATIONS

HQ: AFLAC Inc
1932 Wynnton Road, Columbus, GA 31999
Phone: 706 323-3431   **Fax:** 706 596-3488
Web: www.aflac.com

PRODUCTS/OPERATIONS

2016 Sales

	$ mil.	% of total
Aflac Japan	16,131	71
Aflac US	6,167	27
Corporate	284	1
Other business	275	1
Other non-operating income	109	-
Adjustments	(407)	-
Total	**22,559**	**100**

2016 Sales

	$ mil.	% of total
Net premiums principally supplemental health insurance	19,225	85
Net investment income	3,278	14
Other income	179	1
Realized investment gains (losses)	(123)	-
Total	**22,559**	**100**

COMPETITORS

American Fidelity
  Assurance Company
American National
  Insurance
Asahi Mutual Life
CNO Financial
Colonial Life &
  Accident

Meiji Yasuda Life
MetLife
Nippon Life Insurance
Taiyo Life
Torchmark
Unum Group

HISTORICAL FINANCIALS

Company Type: Public

Income Statement   FYE: December 31

	ASSETS ($ mil.)	NET INCOME ($ mil.)	INCOME AS % OF ASSETS	EMPLOYEES
12/16	129,819	2,659	2.0%	10,212
12/15	118,296	2,533	2.1%	9,915
12/14	119,767	2,951	2.5%	9,525
12/13	121,307	3,158	2.6%	9,141
12/12	131,094	2,866	2.2%	8,965
Annual Growth	(0.2%)	(1.9%)	—	3.3%

2016 Year-End Financials

Debt ratio: 4.13%
Return on equity: 13.89%
Cash ($ mil.): 4,859
Current ratio: —
Long-term debt ($ mil.): —

No. of shares (mil.): 405
Dividends
  Yield: 0.0%
  Payout: 25.8%
Market value ($ mil.): 28,244

	STOCK PRICE ($) FY Close	P/E High/Low		PER SHARE ($) Earnings	Dividends	Book Value
12/16	69.60	11	9	6.42	1.66	50.47
12/15	59.90	11	9	5.85	1.58	41.73
12/14	61.09	10	9	6.50	1.50	41.47
12/13	66.80	10	7	6.76	1.42	31.82
12/12	53.12	9	6	6.11	1.34	34.16
Annual Growth	7.0%	—	—	1.2%	5.5%	10.3%

AGCO Corp.

AGCO makes tractors combines hay and forage tools sprayers grain storage and protein production systems seeding and tillage implements and replacement parts for agricultural end uses. It sells through a global network of some 3000 dealers and distributors spanning more than 150 countries. It also builds diesel engines gears and generators through its AGCO Sisu Power unit. Core brands include Massey Ferguson GSI Challenger Valtra (Finland-based) and Fendt (Germany). The company offers financing services to retail customers and dealers via a venture with Dutch company Rabobank .

Operations

AGCO sells a full range of agricultural equipment including tractors combines self-propelled sprayers hay tools forage equipment seeding and tillage equipment implements and grain storage and protein production systems.

Tractors accounts for more than 55% of its total sales while replacement parts generates over 15%.

Geographic Reach

AGCO has manufacturing locations in US France Italy Finland Germany Austria Denmark Brazil and China. It manufactures and assembles its products in 47 locations worldwide including seven locations where the company operates joint ventures. The EMEA region is its largest market representing about 55% of net sales.

Sales and Marketing

AGCO distributes its products primarily through a network of 3000 independent dealers and distributors who are responsible for retail sales to the equipment's end user in addition to after-sales service and support of the equipment. Distributors also sell its products through a network of dealers supported by the distributor. Sales are not dependent on any specific dealer distributor or group of dealers.

Financial Performance

AGCO's revenues dipped 1% from $7.47 billion in 2015 to $7.41 billion in 2016 its lowest total in five years. This was primarily due to softer global market conditions and the unfavorable impact of currency translations driven by the weakening of the euro and the Brazilian real.On the flip side additional revenue from acquisitions generated growth of about 2% during 2016.

Profits also plunged 39% from $264 million in 2015 to $160 million in 2016 mainly due to decreased production levels and a weaker product mix. In addition AGCO's cash flow from operations has fluctuated over the years; after rising in 2015 cash flow decreased in 2016 mainly due to an increase in inventories.

Strategy

The company is targeting China Africa and Russia as areas for growth and is expanding its use of component suppliers in these markets. In addition it continues to focus on developing technologically advanced equipment to solve the myriad challenges facing farmers such as population growth changing diets and scarcity of land.

Adhering to this strategy AGCO in 2017 announced plans to further develop its Challenger farm machinery business in Africa by integrating it with Fendt AGCO?s partner brand that manufactures agriculture tractors and machines. Challenger is AGCO?s core brand in Africa the Asia-Pacific and North and South America.

Mergers and Acquisitions

Strategic acquisitions have supported AGCO's international growth. In 2016 AGCO obtained Denmark-based Cimbria Holdings Limited (Cimbria) for approximately $338 million. Cimbria is a manufacturer of products and equipment for the processing handling and storage of seed and grain and the deal enhanced the company?s market position in the European grain handling and storage industry.

Also in 2016 AGCO picked up Italy-based Tecno Poultry Equipment S.p.A for approximately $64 million. Tecno manufactures and supplies poultry housing and related products including egg collection equipment and trolley feeding systems. The transaction further strengthened AGCO's position in the commercial egg business and expanded its global product portfolio and distribution network.

HISTORY

In 1861 American Edward Allis purchased the bankrupt Reliance Works a leading Milwaukee-based manufacturer of sawmills and flour-milling equipment. Under shrewd management The Reliance Works of Edward P. Allis & Co. weathered financial troubles - bankruptcy in the Panic of 1873 — but managed to renegotiate its debt and recover. By the time Allis died in 1889 Reliance Works employed some 1500 workers.

The company branched into different areas of manufacturing in the late 19th century and by the 20th century the Edward P. Allis Co. (as it was then known) was the world leader in steam engines. In 1901 the company merged with another manufacturing giant Fraser & Chalmers to form the Allis-Chalmers Company. In the 1920s and 1930s Allis-Chalmers entered the farm equipment market.

Although overshadowed by John Deere and International Harvester (IH) Allis-Chalmers made key contributions to the industry — the first rubber-tired tractor (1932) and the All-Crop harvester. Allis-Chalmers spun off its farm equipment business in the 1950s and phased out several unrelated products. The company with its orange-colored tractors expanded and prospered from the 1940s through the early 1970s. Then the chafing farm economy of the late 1970s and early 1980s hurt Allis-Chalmers' sales.

After layoffs and a plant shutdown in 1984 the company was purchased in 1985 by German machinery maker Klockner-Humboldt-Deutz (KHD) who moved the company (renamed Deutz-Allis) to Georgia. In the mid-1980s low food prices hurt farmers and low demand hurt the equipment market. KHD was never able to bring profits up to a satisfactory level and in 1990 the German firm sold the unit to the US management in a buyout led by Robert Ratliff. Ratliff believed the company could succeed by acquiring belly-up equipment makers turning them around and competing on price. It was renamed AGCO in 1991.

EXECUTIVES

SVP and CFO, Andrew H. (Andy) Beck, age 53, $530,000 total compensation
SVP; General Manager Asia/Pacific and Africa, Gary L. Collar, age 60, $480,000 total compensation
Chairman President and CEO, Martin H. Richenhagen, age 64, $1,345,575 total compensation
SVP; General Manager Americas, Robert B. Crain, age 57, $306,667 total compensation
SVP and Chief Supply Chain Officer, Hans-Bernd Veltmaat, age 62, $575,000 total compensation
SVP; General Manager Europe and Middle East, Rob Smith, age 51, $566,512 total compensation
Svp Global Grain & Protein, Tom Welke
Senior Vice President Global Harvesting Advanced Technology, Eric Hansotia
Vice President General Counsel, Debra Kuper
Vice President Product Line, Matt Rushing
Vice President Global Purchasing and Materials, Josip Tomasevic
Vice President Finance, Brian Zydel
Senior Vice President, Norman Boyd
Senior Vice President Human Resources, Lucinda Smith
Vice President Finance, Frederic Devienne
Vice President and General Manager Harvesting Eame Chief Executive Officer Laverda S.p.A., Francesco Quaranta

National Sales Manager, Martin Mills
Vice President Distribution Development, Alistair
 Mclelland
Senior Vice President Engineering, Helmut Endres
Auditors: KPMG LLP

LOCATIONS

HQ: AGCO Corp.
 4205 River Green Parkway, Duluth, GA 30096
Phone: 770 813-9200
Web: www.agcocorp.com

2016 Sales

	$ mil.	% of total
Europe/Africa/Middle East	4,206	57
North America	1,807	24
South America	917	12
Asia/Pacific	479	7
Total	**7,410**	**100**

2016 Sales

	$ mil.	% of total
United States	1,404	19
Other Europe	1,127	15
Germany	891	12
South America	898	12
France	746	10
Finland and Scandinavia	677	9
United Kingdom and Ireland	440	6
Canada	286	4
Middle East and Africa	321	4
Asia	266	4
Australia and New Zealand	212	3
Mexico Central America and Caribbean	135	2
Total	**7,410**	**100**

PRODUCTS/OPERATIONS

2016 Sales

	$ mil.	% of total
Tractors	4,225	57
Replacement parts	1,211	16
Grain storage and protein production systems	892	12
Other machinery	521	7
Combines	302	4
Application equipment	257	4
Total	**7,410**	**100**

Selected Products

Application equipment
Combine Harvesters
Grounds care
Hay and forage
Implements attachments and material handling
Power generation
Seeding and tillage
Tractors

COMPETITORS

Buhler Industries	Komatsu
CNH Industrial	Kubota
Caterpillar	Mahindra
Deere	Toro Company

HISTORICAL FINANCIALS

Company Type: Public

Income Statement

	REVENUE ($ mil.)	NET INCOME ($ mil.)	NET PROFIT MARGIN	EMPLOYEES
12/16	7,410	160	2.2%	19,800
12/15	7,467	266	3.6%	19,600
12/14	9,723	410	4.2%	20,800
12/13	10,786	597	5.5%	22,100
12/12	9,962	522	5.2%	20,300
Annual Growth	**(7.1%)**	**(25.6%)**	**—**	**(0.6%)**

FYE: December 31

2016 Year-End Financials

Debt ratio: 23.65%
Return on equity: 5.69%
Cash ($ mil.): 429
Current ratio: 1.48
Long-term debt ($ mil.): 1,610

No. of shares (mil.): 79
Dividends
 Yield: 0.0%
 Payout: 26.5%
Market value ($ mil.): 4,598

	STOCK PRICE ($) FY Close	P/E High/Low		PER SHARE ($) Earnings	Dividends	Book Value
12/16	57.86	31	22	1.96	0.52	34.93
12/15	45.39	19	14	3.06	0.48	33.86
12/14	45.20	13	10	4.36	0.44	38.68
12/13	59.19	10	8	6.01	0.40	41.19
12/12	49.12	10	7	5.30	0.00	35.79
Annual Growth	**4.2%**	**—**	**—**	**(22.0%)**	**—**	**(0.6%)**

AGSOUTH FARM CREDIT ACA

Auditors: PRICEWATERHOUSEC-
OOPERS LLP FO

LOCATIONS

HQ: AGSOUTH FARM CREDIT ACA
 26 S MAIN ST, STATESBORO, GA 304585256
Phone: 912 764-9091

HISTORICAL FINANCIALS

Company Type: Private

Income Statement

FYE: December 31

	ASSETS ($ mil.)	NET INCOME ($ mil.)	INCOME AS % OF ASSETS	EMPLOYEES
12/15	1,651	39	2.4%	226
12/14	1,594	49	3.1%	—
12/13	1,594	49	3.1%	—
12/12	1,583	42	2.7%	—
Annual Growth	**1.4%**	**(2.1%)**	**—**	**—**

2015 Year-End Financials

Debt ratio: ——
Return on equity: 34.60%
Cash ($ mil.): 4
Current ratio: —
Long-term debt ($ mil.): —

Dividends
 Yield: —
 Payout: —
Market value ($ mil.): —

AIMCO PROPERTIES, L.P.

AIMCO Properties' aim is true. The company is the operating arm of multifamily real estate giant Apartment Investment and Management Company (AIMCO) which owns and/or manages some 500 apartment properties (with nearly 94000 individual units) throughout the US. AIMCO Properties holds most of AIMCO's assets and manages its day-to-day operations including property management and asset management. Its portfolio includes suburban apartment communities urban high-rise properties and government-subsidized affordable housing properties. Investment management operations include management of its own portfolio as well as services for affiliated partnerships. AIMCO controls more than 90% of AIMCO Properties.

EXECUTIVES

Board Member, Cara M Nelson
Auditors: ERNST & YOUNG LLP DENVER COL

LOCATIONS

HQ: AIMCO PROPERTIES, L.P.
 4582 S ULSTER ST STE 1100, DENVER, CO
802372662
Phone: 303 757-8101

COMPETITORS

AMLI Residential	Home Properties
Alliance Residential	LEDIC
Berkshire Income	Simpson Housing
Realty	Trammell Crow
Camden Property	Residential
Education Realty	Transcontinental
Equity Residential	Realty

HISTORICAL FINANCIALS

Company Type: Private

Income Statement

FYE: December 31

	ASSETS ($ mil.)	NET INCOME ($ mil.)	INCOME AS % OF ASSETS	EMPLOYEES
12/16	6,232	483	7.8%	15,301
12/15	6,144	271	4.4%	—
12/14	6,097	356	5.8%	—
12/13	6,079	237	3.9%	—
Annual Growth	**0.8%**	**26.7%**	**—**	**—**

2016 Year-End Financials

Debt ratio: ——
Return on equity: 48.50%
Cash ($ mil.): 61
Current ratio: —
Long-term debt ($ mil.): —

Dividends
 Yield: —
 Payout: —
Market value ($ mil.): —

Air Products & Chemicals Inc

Air Products and Chemicals has built a solid business out of gasses and liquids. The company produces and distributes atmospheric process and specialty gases in the US and across the world. It is a leading hydrogen supplier and also provides helium nitrogen argon and carbon dioxide among other gases. Air Products and Chemicals which generates more than half its revenue outside the Americas also provides related equipment and services (air separation hydrocarbon recovery natural gas liquefaction etc.) to customers in the energy electronics chemicals metals and manufacturing industries.

HISTORY

In the early 1900s Leonard Pool the son of a boilermaker began selling oxygen to industrial users. By the time he was 30 he was district manager for Compressed Industrial Gases. In the late 1930s Pool hired engineer Frank Pavlis to help him design a cheaper more efficient oxygen generator. In 1940 they had the design and Pool established Air Products in Detroit (initially sharing space with the cadavers collected by his brother who was starting a mortuary science college). The company was based on a simple breakthrough concept: the provision of on-site gases. Instead of delivering oxygen in cylinders Pool proposed to build oxygen-generating facilities near large-volume gas users and then lease them reducing distribution costs.

Although industrialists encouraged Pool to pursue his ideas few orders were forthcoming and the company faced financial crisis. The outbreak of WWII got the company out of difficulty as the US military became a major customer. During the war the company moved to Chattanooga Tennessee for the available labor.

The end of the war brought with it another downturn as demand dried up. By waiting at the Weirton Steel plant until a contract was signed Pool won a contract for three on-site generators. Weirton was nearly the company's only customer. Pool relocated the company to Allentown Pennsylvania to be closer to the Northeast's industrial market where he could secure more contracts with steel companies.

The Cold War and the launching of the Sputnik satellite in 1957 propelled the company's growth. Convinced that Soviet rockets were powered by liquid hydrogen the US government asked Air Products to supply it with the volatile fuel. The company entered the overseas market that year through a joint venture with Butterley (UK) to which it licensed its cryogenic processes and equipment. The company went public in 1961 and formed a subsidiary in Belgium in 1964.

Air Products diversified into chemicals when it bought Houdry Process (chemicals and chemical-plant maintenance 1962) and Airco's chemicals and plastics operations in the 1970s. The company continued to diversify in the mid-1980s as it built large-scale plants for its environmental- and energy-systems business and added Anchor Chemical and the industrial chemicals unit of Abbott Labs.

In 1995 and 1996 Air Products expanded into China and other countries by winning 20 contracts with semiconductor makers. It bought Carburos Metálicos Spain's #1 industrial gas supplier in 1996. To focus on its core gas and chemical lines the company shed most of its environmental- and energy-systems business.

Expanding further in Europe Air Products bought the methylamines and derivatives unit of UK-based Imperial Chemical Industries (ICI) in 1997. The company sold its remaining interest in American Ref-Fuel (a waste-to-energy US operation).

In 1998 Air Products bought Solkatronic Chemicals and opened a methylamines plant in Florida to complement its ICI purchase. To further target semiconductor makers it formed Air Products Electronic Chemicals and allied with AlliedSignal Chemical (now part of Honeywell International).

The next year Air Products and France's L'Air Liquide agreed to buy and break up BOC Group. European Union regulators initially approved the deal but in 2000 the companies shelved the plan when other regulatory issues arose. Also in 2000 Air Products sold its polyvinyl alcohol business to Celanese for about $326 million. The company boosted its European presence in 2001 with the acquisition of Messer Griesheim's (Germany) respiratory home-care business and 50% of AGA's Netherlands industrial gases operations.

Air Products was hurt by the slowdown in manufacturing primarily in the electronics and steel industries which are major customers for gases. Its chemical revenues also were hurt by pressure on pricing. To improve profits the company initiated cost cuts including job cuts (about 10% of its employees) and divestitures such as its US packaged gas business.

The company broadened its health care operations in late 2002 by acquiring American Homecare Supply. It appeared briefly that Air Products wanted to devote a great deal of attention to the health care business. The company had created its Air Products Healthcare unit in 1999 and expanded it greatly three years later with the acquisition of American Homecare Supply. Air Products proceeded to add to the division through subsequent acquisitions; however the US portion of the business never performed to the company's expectations and Air Products sold the domestic operations of the health care unit in 2008 and 2009.

It also decided to divest its chemicals operations in the latter half of the decade. Those operations included the production of catalysts surfactants and intermediates derived from vinyl acetate monomer (VAM) all of which it sold in 2008. Air Products had sold its amines business to chemical company Taminco in 2006. The company's polymers operations which were run through a joint venture with Wacker-Chemie called Air Products Polymers were divested in 2008. The company sold most of its holdings in the JV to Wacker for $265 million though two facilities that had belonged to the joint venture were sold to Ashland Performance Materials.

In 2007 Air Products made a small but strategic move into Eastern Europe. The company took advantage of Linde's selloff of some BOC assets after the German company bought BOC in 2006. Air Products acquired the Polish Gazy SP for just under $500 million with the hopes of moving into the Central and Eastern European markets to take advantage of the migration of manufacturing to the region.

In 2010 the company made a major bid to buy rival Airgas but it was rejected. The Airgas board considered the $5.1 billion offer too low. Air Products extended its tender offer to Airgas stockholders several times making its "best and final offer" of $70 a share in December 2010. Airgas also rejected that offer.

In late 2012 Air Products opened an advanced gas applications laboratory in Shanghai to support the increasing needs in high-growth markets in China across Asia.

In addition to growing organically the company has been divesting operations to focus on its higher growth operations and to pursue strategic acquisitions. By early 2012 the company began divesting units to focus on more profitable operations. It sold its homecare business in continental Europe (which supplied oxygen and infusion treatments in Belgium France Germany Portugal and Spain) to Germany's Linde for $750 million. The company also began evaluating its homecare assets in Argentina Brazil Ireland and the UK.

With more money in its coffers from divestments in 2012 the company acquired Germany-based ROVI Cosmetics International which develops delivery systems for the personal care industry in Europe. The unit is now part of the company's Performance Materials division. To extend its Latin American footprint Air Products in 2012 acquired a 67% stake in Indura S.A. an industrial gas company in Chile for $884 million.

Expanding its portfolio of industrial gases offerings in North America to include liquid carbon dioxide in 2013 Air Products acquired EPCO Carbon Dioxide Products Inc. a privately-held Louisiana-based producer and marketer of liquid carbon dioxide.

EXECUTIVES

Chairman President and CEO, Seifi Ghasemi, age 71, $1,200,000 total compensation
EVP Industrial Gases, Corning F. Painter, age 56, $573,077 total compensation
VP Northern Continent and Packaged Gases (Air Products Europe), Ivo Bols
President Industrial Gases Asia, Wilbur W. Mok, age 57
President Industrial Gases Middle East India Egypt and Turkey, Richard Boocock
SVP and CFO, M. Scott Crocco, age 54, $581,923 total compensation
President Industrial Gases Americas, Marie Ffolkes
EVP Materials Technologies, Guillermo Novo, age 56, $465,000 total compensation
President China Industrial Gases, Choon Seong Saw
VP and CIO, Alyssa A. Budraitis
President Air Products Korea, Kyo Yung (K Y) Kim
President Air Products San Fu, Eugene Y. C. Lu
President Southeast Asia Industrial Gases, Alex Tan
Auditors: KPMG LLP

LOCATIONS

HQ: Air Products & Chemicals Inc
7201 Hamilton Boulevard, Allentown, PA 18195-1501
Phone: 610 481-4911　　　**Fax:** 610 481-5900
Web: www.airproducts.com

2017 Sales

	$ mil.	% of total
US	2,886	35
Europe/Middle East	2,478	30
Asia (Excluding China & India)	849	11
China	1,143	14
Other (Canada Latin America India)	829	10
Total	**8,187**	**100**

PRODUCTS/OPERATIONS

2017 Sales

	% of total
Industrial Gases- Americas	44
Industrial Gases- EMEA	22
Industrial Gases- Asia	24
Industrial Gases- Global	9
Corporate and other	1
Total	**100**

Selected Products and Services

Industrial Gases
　Argon
　Carbon dioxide
　Carbon monoxide
　Helium
　Hydrogen
　Nitrogen
　Oxygen
　Synthesis gas
Equipment and Services
　Air-pollution control systems
　Air-separation equipment
　Hydrogen-purification equipment
　Natural gas-liquefaction equipment

COMPETITORS

Airgas	Messer Group
Iwatani International	Praxair
L'Air Liquide	Taiyo Nippon Sanso
Matheson Tri-Gas	The Linde Group

HISTORICAL FINANCIALS

Company Type: Public

Income Statement

FYE: September 30

	REVENUE ($ mil.)	NET INCOME ($ mil.)	NET PROFIT MARGIN	EMPLOYEES
09/17	8,187	3,000	36.6%	15,300
09/16	9,524	631	6.6%	18,600
09/15	9,894	1,277	12.9%	19,700
09/14	10,439	991	9.5%	21,200
09/13	10,180	994	9.8%	21,600
Annual Growth	(5.3%)	31.8%	—	(8.3%)

2017 Year-End Financials

Debt ratio: 21.46%
Return on equity: 34.96%
Cash ($ mil.): 3,273
Current ratio: 2.36
Long-term debt ($ mil.): 3,402

No. of shares (mil.): 218
Dividends
Yield: 0.0%
Payout: 26.5%
Market value ($ mil.): 33,018

	STOCK PRICE ($) FY Close	P/E High/Low		PER SHARE ($) Earnings	Dividends	Book Value
09/17	151.22	11	10	13.65	3.62	46.19
09/16	150.34	54	40	2.89	3.34	32.57
09/15	127.58	27	20	5.88	3.20	33.66
09/14	130.18	29	22	4.61	3.02	34.49
09/13	106.57	23	16	4.68	2.77	33.35
Annual Growth	9.1%	—	—	30.7%	6.9%	8.5%

AK Steel Holding Corp.

Automobile sales help AK Steel's business keep rolling though it also has operations in the infrastructure and manufacturing industries. The company manufactures carbon stainless and electrical steel. It sells hot- and cold-rolled carbon steel to construction companies steel distributors and service centers and automotive and industrial machinery producers. AK Steel also sells cold-rolled and aluminum-coated stainless steel to automakers. The company produces electrical steels (iron-silicon alloys with unique magnetic properties) for makers of power transmission and distribution equipment.

Operations

AK Steel operates on a consolidated integrated basis in order to use the most appropriate equipment and facilities for the production of each product. The company?s carbon products account for about two-thirds of revenue followed by stainless and electrical products about 30% and tubular the remainder.

Its major subsidiaries include AK Tube LLC AK Coal Resources Inc and Magnetation LLC. AK Tube produces carbon and stainless electric resistance welded tubular steel products for truck automotive and other markets.

It produces flat-rolled value-added carbon steels including premium-quality coated cold-rolled and hot-rolled carbon steel products and specialty stainless and electrical steels that are sold in sheet and strip form as well as carbon and stainless steel that is finished into welded steel tubing.

It also works through joint ventures to share costs. Its Magnetation LLC joint venture with Magnetation Inc. uses advanced magnetic separation technology to recover iron ore from existing stockpiles of previously-mined material.

In addition AK Steel indirectly owns 50% of Vicksmetal/Armco Associates a joint venture with Sumitomo unit Vicksmetal Company. The joint venture slits electrical steel primarily for AK Steel and for third parties.

Geographic Reach

AK Steel is based in West Chester Ohio and operates eight steel plants two coke plants and two tube manufacturing plants across Indiana Kentucky Michigan Ohio Pennsylvania and West Virginia and a tube plant in Mexico. The company also operates subsidiaries in the UK the Netherlands Italy France Germany and other countries. US is the largest market accounting for about 90% of revenue.

Sales and Marketing

AK Steel sells a major portion of its flat-rolled carbon steel products and stainless steel products to US automotive manufacturers and to distributors service centers and converters. It sells electrical steel products (in the US and globally) to manufacturers of power transmission and distribution transformers and electrical motors and generators to the infrastructure and manufacturing customers.

The automotive industry accounted for about two-thirds of the company's sales with Ford and Fiat Chrysler among its biggest customers. Other major markets are distributors and converters about 20% and infrastructure and manufacturing about 15%.

AK Steel ships about 70% of its flat-rolled steel products to contract customers with the balance to customers in the spot market at prevailing prices at the time of sale.

Financial Performance

In 2016 AK Steel's sales fell below the $6 billion mark reached (and then some) in 2015 to about $5.8 billion a 12% year-to-year drop. The company posted lower revenue in all its product lines led by carbon which slumped about 15%. Sales also were lower in the US and internationally. AK Steel received lower pricing in its automotive contracts in 2016.

While revenue fell the company?s net loss improved to about $7.8 million in 2016 from a loss of about $509 million in 2015. The 2016 loss included several charges including several related to pensions and the termination of a Magnetation pellet offtake agreement.

Cash from operating activities totaled about $304 for 2016 an improvement from about $200 million in 2015. The 2016 figure included some $80 million generated by subsidiary SunCoke Middletown (in which AK Steel has an interest) and which only it can use.

Strategy

The steel industry has been consolidating for years as market leaders snap up troubled companies. AK Steel has maintained its independence in part because of it's a leading supplier of high-grade niche products such as components of stainless steel exhaust systems for carmakers.

The company?s 2017 purchase of Precision Partners Holding Co. for about $360 million gets it deeper into automotive market. Based in Canada Precision supplies auto parts that meet the industry?s requirements for lighter vehicles. It has eight plants in Ontario Kentucky and Alabama. Precision specializes in the design and engineering of tooling and die making and the stamping of complex hard-to-manufacture automotive components.

In 2016 AK Steel took several actions financially that strengthened its balance sheet and provided room to maneuver financially in investing in research and development as well as acquisitions. The company moved in to its new Research and Innovation Center in Middletown Ohio in 2016. The facility includes pilot lines and operational simulators for developing new products and services.

The company also pulled away from selling steel on the spot market where prices are volatile and have low margins.

Mergers and Acquisitions

AK Steel bought Precision Partners Holding Co. for about $360 million in 2017 to move deeper into supplying steel to the automotive industry.

HISTORY

George Verity who was in the roofing business in Cincinnati around the turn of the century often had trouble getting sheet metal so in 1900 he founded his own steel company American Rolling Mill. His first plant in Middletown Ohio was followed by a second production facility 11 years later in Ashland Kentucky. Plant superintendent John Tytus whose family was in paper milling applied those rolling techniques to make American Rolling Mill's steel more uniform in thickness.

In 1926 Columbia Steel developed a process to overcome several production problems inherent in the Tytus method and in 1930 American Rolling Mill bought Columbia Steel. The company changed its name to Armco Steel in 1948.

Armco began diversifying in the 1950s and continued diversifying until the early 1980s. Subsidiaries were involved in coal oil and gas-drilling equipment and insurance and financial services among other things. In 1978 the company changed its name to Armco Inc.

Armco began shedding subsidiaries in the early 1980s. Sales and market share increased as the company approached the billion-dollar mark at the end of the decade. In 1989 Armco formed Armco Steel Company with Japan's Kawasaki Steel Corporation.

The company's sales reached $1.3 billion in 1991 though the high operating expenses in the steel industry of the 1990s kept profits low. Armco began looking outside the company for help and in 1992 it persuaded retired steel executive Tom Graham to head the company. Graham brought with him another industry veteran Richard Wardrop who would succeed Graham as CEO in 1995. After evaluating the company's holdings the two divested more than 10 subsidiaries and divisions. Armco also worked on improving quality and customer service with special emphasis placed on timely delivery.

In 1994 Armco's limited partnership with Kawasaki was altered and AK Steel Holding Corporation was formed with AK Steel Corporation as its main subsidiary and the Middletown and Ashland plants as its production base. The holding company went public the same year raising more than $650 million enabling the company to pay off its debt.

AK Steel Holding moved its headquarters to Middletown Ohio in 1995. Despite many naysayers Graham then pushed a plan to build a state-of-the-art $1.1 billion steel production facility. Many doubted the wisdom of going into long-term debt so soon after coming out of the hole — especially when a similar facility had produced lackluster results for Inland Steel. Graham stuck by his plant and in 1997 ground was broken on the facility in Spencer County near Rockport Indiana (Rockport Works). Graham retired that year and Wardrop took over as chairman.

In 1998 the company opened its Rockport Works cold-rolling mill and began operating a hot-dip galvanizing and galvannealing line. The next year AK Steel bought former parent Armco for $842 million. AK Steel acquired welded steel tubing maker Alpha Tube Corporation (renamed AK Tube LLC) in 2001. In late 2001 the company took a charge of $194 million for losses in its pension fund which had been battered by a weak stock market and lowered interest rates.

AK Steel sold its Sawhill Tubular Division to John Maneely Company (Collingswood NJ) for roughly $50 million in 2002.

AK Steel offered to purchase National Steel which was operating under Chapter 11 bankruptcy protection. However AK Steel's bid was trumped in 2003 by one from U.S. Steel that included a ratified labor agreement with the United Steelworkers of America. AK Steel also lost out in an effort to acquire Rouge Industries (later Severstal North America).

Chairman and CEO Wardrop and president John Hritz left their posts in September 2003. CFO James Wainscott was named president and CEO and Robert Jenkins became chairman. (Wainscott succeeded Jenkins as chairman in January 2006.)

In an effort to reduce its debt AK Steel in 2004 sold its Douglas Dynamics unit a maker of snow and ice removal equipment for $260 million and its Greens Port Industrial Park a 600-acre development in Houston for $75 million.

In 2007 the company moved its corporate headquarters to West Chester Ohio.

EXECUTIVES

VP Research and Development, Eric Petersen
VP Finance and CFO, Jaime Vasquez, age 56
CEO, Roger K. Newport, age 52, $579,551 total compensation
President and COO, Kirk W. Reich, age 49, $479,551 total compensation
VP Engineering Raw Materials and Energy, Maurice A. Reed, age 54
VP Operations, Keith Howell
Executive Vice President Of Information Technology, Steve Boston
Senior Vice President of Human Resources, Larry Zizzo
Vice President Ppd, Jim Landon
Chairman, James A. Thomson, age 73
Auditors: Ernst & Young LLP

LOCATIONS

HQ: AK Steel Holding Corp.
9227 Centre Pointe Drive, West Chester, OH 45069
Phone: 513 425-5000   **Fax:** 513 425-5220
Web: www.aksteel.com

2016 Sales

	$ mil.	% of total
United States	5,226	89
Foreign countries	655	11
Total	**5,882**	**100**

PRODUCTS/OPERATIONS

2016 Sales (by Market)

	% of total
Automotive	66
Distributors & converters	18
Infrastructure & manufacturing	16
Total	**100**

2016 Sales (by product)

	$ mil.	% of total
Carbon steel	4,014	68
Stainless & electrical steel	1,654	29
Tubular steel	193	3
Other	20	0
Total	**5,882**	**100**

Carbon Steels

Carbon Steels
Alumized
Coil coated products
Cold rolled
Electrogalvanized
Enameling products
Hot dip galvanized
Hot dip galvannealed
Hot rolled
Ultalume®;
Stainless Steels

Austentic
Duplex Alloy
Ferritic
Martensitic
Precipitation hardening
Electrical Steels
Nonoriented
Oriented
TRAN-COR®; H
Antimicrobial Coated Steels

COMPETITORS

ArcelorMittal USA	Steel Dynamics
Dofasco	Union Electric Steel
Ferralloy	United States Steel
Kobe Steel USA	Worthington Industries
Nucor	

HISTORICAL FINANCIALS

Company Type: Public

Income Statement

FYE: December 31

	REVENUE ($ mil.)	NET INCOME ($ mil.)	NET PROFIT MARGIN	EMPLOYEES
12/16	5,882	(7)	—	8,500
12/15	6,692	(509)	—	8,500
12/14	6,505	(96)	—	8,000
12/13	5,570	(46)	—	6,400
12/12	5,933	(1,027)	—	6,400
Annual Growth	**(0.2%)**	**—**	**—**	**7.4%**

2016 Year-End Financials

Debt ratio: 45.01%
Return on equity: ***.***.**%
Cash ($ mil.): 173
Current ratio: 2.11
Long-term debt ($ mil.): 1,816

No. of shares (mil.): 314
Dividends
  Yield: —
  Payout: —
Market value ($ mil.): 3,208

	STOCK PRICE ($) FY Close	P/E High/Low	PER SHARE ($) Earnings	Dividends	Book Value
12/16	10.21	— —	(0.03)	0.00	(0.87)
12/15	2.24	— —	(2.86)	0.00	(5.50)
12/14	5.94	— —	(0.65)	0.00	(2.78)
12/13	8.20	— —	(0.34)	0.00	(1.62)
12/12	4.60	— —	(9.06)	0.15	(3.72)
Annual Growth	**22.1%**	**— —**	**—**	**—**	**—**

Alabama Power Co

Alabama Power powers up Southern Rockers and many others in the heart of Dixie. The Southern Company subsidiary provides electricity to 1.4 million residential and business customers in a 44500 sq. ml. service area in Alabama. The utility operates more than 83000 miles of power lines and it has nuclear hydroelectric and fossil-fueled power plant interests that give it a generating capacity of more than 12000 MW. Alabama Power sells wholesale power to more than 15 municipal and rural distribution utilities; it also provides steam transmission (used for heating and cooling buildings) in downtown Birmingham Alabama and sells electric appliances (such as thermostats ovens and washing machines).

Operations

Alabama Power owns coal reserves near its Plant Gorgas power plant and uses the output of coal from the reserves in its generating plants.

It has cogeneration contracts with 12 industrial customers and purchased 151 million KWHs from these companies in 2013.

SEGCO (a public utility company jointly owned by Alabama Power and sister company Georgia Power) owns electric generating units with a capacity of 1019 MW at Plant Gaston on the Coosa River near Wilsonville Alabama. Alabama Power owns 92% ownership in Plant Miller Units 1 and 2 which have a total capacity of 1320 MW.

Geographic Reach

The company sells electricity at retail in 400 Alabama cities and towns (including Anniston Birmingham Gadsden Mobile Montgomery and Tuscaloosa) as well as in rural areas and at wholesale to 14 municipally-owned electric distribution systems 11 of which are served indirectly through sales to Alabama Municipal Electric Authority and two rural distributing cooperative associations.

Financial Performance

The company reported a 2% increase in revenues in 2013 primarily due to higher retail revenues and wholesale revenues from affiliates partially offset by the wholesale revenues from non-affiliates.

Retail revenues increased due to favorable weather (which pushed up demand) higher fuel revenues and increased revenues associated with a new plant; partially offset by a drop in revenues related to net investments related to the certification of one of its newer plants. That year its wholesale revenues from sales to affiliates grew due to an increase in energy sales fueled by higher energy prices partially offset by a lower capacity revenues.

Wholesale revenues from sales to non-affiliates decreased as a result of a drop in capacity revenues and a decline in revenues from energy sales.

The company's net income was almost flat in 2013 as the increase in revenues was offset by higher fuel expenses (an 11% increase in the average cost of KWHs generated by natural gas and a 10% increase in KWHs generated by coal).

Net cash provided from operating activities increased by $538 million in 2013 primarily due to changes in timing of fossil fuel stock purchases and payment of accounts payable and the collection of fuel cost recovery revenues.

Strategy

An active player in the larger community in 2014 Alabama Power and B.A.S.S. (a fishing association) signed an agreement to enhance and maintain sport-fishing resources on the 11 lakes managed by Alabama Power.

Growing its green energy portfolio in 2013 Alabama Power partnered with City of Montgomery to set up electric vehicle charging station. In the same vein in 2012 the company received approval from the state Public Service Commission to purchase more electricity from midwestern wind projects. It agreed to buy 202 MW of power from a Oklahoma wind park being developed by TradeWind Energy and which is expected to commence operations in 2014. It also agreed to a 202 MW deal with TradeWind Energy's Buffalo Dunes Wind Project in Kansas.

Company Background

In 2011 Alabama Power completed a six-year $1.7 billion clean air project that called for the installation of scrubbers (air pollution control devices) at all seven of its largest coal fired plants in Alabama. By 2010 six scrubbers were in operation at four power plants in Jefferson Shelby Walker and Mobile counties.

In 2009 Alabama Power began exploring the possibility of generating power by burning wood and other renewable fuels at one of its coal-fired plants in response to government regulations calling for lower carbon emissions. In 2010 the company teamed up with The Westervelt Company agreeing to buy biomass-fuel (waste wood material) from the timber company.

LOCATIONS

HQ: Alabama Power Co
   600 North 18th Street, Birmingham, AL 35203
Phone: 205 257-1000
Web: www.alapower.com

PRODUCTS/OPERATIONS

2016 Sales

	$ mil.	% of total
Retail		
Residential	2,322	39
Commercial	1,627	27
Industrial	1,416	24
Other retail	(43)	—
Wholesale	352	6
Other	215	4
Total	**5,889**	**100**

COMPETITORS

AEP	Entergy
AES	Ferrellgas Partners
Alagasco	NextEra Energy
Duke Energy	Sempra Energy

HISTORICAL FINANCIALS

Company Type: Public

Income Statement

FYE: December 31

	REVENUE ($ mil.)	NET INCOME ($ mil.)	NET PROFIT MARGIN	EMPLOYEES
12/16	5,889	839	14.2%	6,805
12/15	5,768	811	14.1%	6,986
12/14	5,942	800	13.5%	6,935
12/13	5,618	751	13.4%	6,896
12/12	5,520	743	13.5%	6,778
Annual Growth	1.6%	3.1%	—	0.1%

2016 Year-End Financials

Debt ratio: 31.52%	No. of shares (mil.): 30
Return on equity: 13.00%	Dividends
Cash ($ mil.): 420	Yield: —
Current ratio: 0.95	Payout: 93.0%
Long-term debt ($ mil.): 6,535	Market value ($ mil.): —

Alaska Air Group, Inc.

Alaska Air Group operates through subsidiaries Alaska Airlines Horizon Air and Virgin America. It flies more than 40 million passengers to more than 120 destinations with an average of 1200 daily flights in the US (mainly western states including Alaska and Hawaii) Canada and Mexico. The group's primary hub is Seattle (accounting for almost two-thirds of passengers) but it also flies out of key markets such as Portland Oregon; Los Angeles; and Anchorage Alaska. Alaska Airlines has a fleet of about 155 Boeing 737 jets. Horizon Air operates more than 50 Bombardier Q400 turboprops.Alaska Air Group in late 2016 achieved growth through the purchase of Virgin America for $2.6 billion.

Operations
Accounting for 85% of revenue the passenger segment's Alaska line is divided into Alaska Mainline (78%) which makes flights with average stage lengths that are more than 1200 miles and Alaska Regional (15%) for shorter distances. Airline Horizon sells all of its capacity to Alaska under a capacity purchase agreement. In a given year Mainline operations carry 25 million revenue passengers while regional operations which includes Horizon transport more than 9 million revenue passengers mainly in Washington Oregon Idaho and California.

Newly acquired Virgin America competes as a low-fare carrier and attempts to separate itself from rivals by providing first-class service and an assortment of in-flight entertainment options. Combined Alaska Air and Virgin America offer almost 290 daily flights to 52 destinations from California including 113 daily nonstop flights to 32 destinations from three Bay Area airports and more than 100 daily nonstop flights to 37 destinations from four Los Angeles area airports.

As its name implies Alaska Air Group transports more passengers between Alaska and the US mainland than any other airline. Besides its own flights the passenger segment provides passenger service through contracts with SkyWest Airlines and Peninsula Airways. Carrying about 4% of all US domestic passenger traffic the segment also includes such non-ticket revenue as reservations fees ticket change fees and charges for baggage service.

Freight and mail account for 2% of revenue. The Other segment around 15% of revenue includes the Mileage Plan on-board food and beverages commissions from car and hotel vendors and travel insurance. The Mileage Plan awards miles for flights on Alaska Horizon and partner airlines and sells miles to third parties.

Geographic Reach
Alaska Air Group serves more than 120 cities through an expansive network in Alaska the contiguous 48 states Hawaii Canada and Mexico. The company leases operations training and aircraft maintenance facilities in Portland and Spokane as well as line maintenance stations in Boise Bellingham Eugene San Jose Medford Redmond Seattle and Spokane. It also leases call center facilities in Phoenix and Boise.

Sales and Marketing
Alaska Air's airline tickets are distributed through the airline's website and through traditional and online travel agencies that use global distribution systems to obtain their fare and inventory data from airlines and reservation call centers located in Phoenix; Kent Washington; and Boise Idaho.

The company has increased its investment in advertising year-over-year; in 2016 the company spent $61 million on advertising compared to $55 million in 2015.

Financial Performance
Alaska Air has achieved unprecedented growth over the years with revenues rising 6% to peak at a record-setting $5.9 billion in 2016. The historic growth was fueled by a 6% increase in mainline passenger capacity by new routes the addition of seats to the existing fleet and the delivery of 10 737-900ERs.

Alaska Air also experienced a 17% spike in sales from its Other segment in 2016. This was fueled by a 30% bump in Mileage Plan sales due to increased miles sold and improved compensation terms with its Mileage Plan affinity credit card partner.

The company's net income however declined 4% from $848 million in 2015 to $814 million in 2016 mainly due to the addition of merger-related costs. In addition its operating cash flow declined from $1.58 billion to 2015 to $1.39 billion in 2016.

Strategy
Alaska Air is primarily focused on the successful integration of Virgin America into its own operations. The company has stated that the merger with Virgin America should be completed during 2017 to 2019 and that it's likely 2019 is when the company would enjoy a full annual efficiency benefit.

Mergers and Acquisitions
In a noteworthy move within the US airline industry Alaska Air Group in late 2016 acquired Virgin America for $2.6 billion. The company expects the deal to boost its annual revenue by 27% and to add to its earnings within the transaction's first year. The combination also created the fifth-largest US airline by traffic replacing JetBlue which formerly held that spot.

The Virgin America acquisition helped Alaska Air Group to better serve West Coast travelers. Virgin America also provides a platform for Alaska Air's low-fare growth as well as enhanced international partnerships. Additionally the deal provides an opportunity to grow and improve the company's loyalty program while gaining access to constrained gates particularly on the East Coast.

HISTORY

Pilot Mac McGee started McGee Airways in 1932 to fly cargo between Anchorage and Bristol Bay Alaska. He joined other local operators in 1937 to form Star Air Lines which began airmail service between Fairbanks and Bethel in 1938. In 1944 a year after buying three small airlines Star adopted the name Alaska Airlines.

The company expanded to include freight service to Africa and Australia in 1950. This expansion coupled with the seasonal nature of the airline's business caused losses in the early 1970s. Developer Bruce Kennedy gained control of the board turning the firm around by the end of 1973. But the Civil Aeronautics Board forced the carrier to drop service to northwestern Alaska in 1975 and by 1978 it served only 10 Alaskan cities and Seattle.

Kennedy became CEO the next year. The 1978 Airline Deregulation Act allowed Alaska Air to move into new areas as well as regain the routes it had lost. By 1982 it was the largest airline flying between Alaska and the lower 48 states.

In 1985 the airline reorganized forming Alaska Air Group as its holding company. The next year Alaska Air Group bought Jet America Airlines (expanding its routes eastward to Chicago St. Louis and Dallas) and Seattle-based Horizon Air Industries (which served 30 Northwest cities). When competition in the East and Midwest cut profits in 1987 Kennedy shut down Jet America to focus on West Coast operations.

To counterbalance summer traffic to Alaska the airline began service to two Mexican resorts in 1988. Fuel prices and sluggish traffic hurt 1990 earnings but Alaska Air Group stayed in the black unlike many other carriers. Kennedy retired as chairman and CEO in 1991.

That year the airline began service to Canada and seasonal flights to two Russian cities. Neil Bergt's MarkAir airline declared war cutting fares and horning in on Alaska Air Group's territory. Alaska Air Group's profits were slashed and MarkAir went into bankruptcy.

Alaska Air extended Russian flights to year-round in 1994. The airline began service to Vancouver in 1996. That year it became the first major US carrier to use the GPS satellite navigation system. In 1997 it added service to more than a dozen new cities but halted service to Russia because of that country's economic woes in 1998.

Alaska Air Group and Dutch airline KLM agreed to a marketing alliance in 1998 that included reciprocal frequent-flier programs and code-sharing and in 1999 it added code-sharing agreements with several major airlines including American and Continental. Alaska Airlines developed an online check-in system a first among US carriers.

In 2000 an Alaska Airlines MD-83 crashed into the Pacific Ocean near Los Angeles killing all 88 people on board. A federal investigation of Alaska Airlines' maintenance practices found deficiencies but the FAA eventually accepted the airline's plan to tighten safety standards.

Like most carriers in the latter part of 2001 Alaska Airlines cut back its flights as a result of reduced demand after the September 11 terrorist attacks. As demand slowly returned in 2002 Alaska Airlines began to add new destinations and increase the number of flights on some established routes.

In its biggest deal ever Alaska Air Group in late 2016 acquired Virgin America for $2.6 billion.

EXECUTIVES

Vice President Information and Technology Alaska Airlines, Kris Kutchera
EVP Finance and CFO; EVP Finance and CFO Alaska Airlines, Bradley D. (Brad) Tilden, age 56, $487,600 total compensation
President and CEO Horizon Air Industries Inc., Gary L. Beck
SVP Communications and External Affairs, Joseph A. (Joe) Sprague, $303,846 total compensation

EVP Finance and CFO, Brandon S. Pedersen, age 50, $390,769 total compensation
EVP and Chief Commercial Officer Alaska Airlines, Andrew R. Harrison, age 46, $383,077 total compensation
President and COO Alaska Airlines, Benito (Ben) Minicucci, age 50, $426,923 total compensation
COO Horizon Air Industries Inc., Constance Von Muehlen
Vice President Of Marketing, Jimmy Johnson
Assistant To The Executive Vice President Finance And Chief Financial Officer, Lorraine Hurt
Auditors: KPMG LLP

LOCATIONS

HQ: Alaska Air Group, Inc.
19300 International Boulevard, Seattle, WA 98188
Phone: 206 392-5040
Web: www.alaskaair.com

PRODUCTS/OPERATIONS

2016 Sales

	$ mil.	% of total
Passenger Revenue — Mainline	4,098	69
Passenger Revenue — Regional	908	15
Freight & mail	108	2
Other	817	14
Total	**5,931**	**100**

2016 Sales

	$ mil.	% of total
Alaska		
Mainline	4,940	78
Regional	987	15
Horizon	428	7
Consolidating	(424)	-
Total	**5,931**	**100**

Selected Products and Services

Accessible services
Baggage
Book a Shipment
Children traveling alone
Customer of size
Delayed baggage
Emergency exit row
General Air Freight
GoldStreak®; Package Express
Infants and children
Price a Shipment
Priority Air Freight
Rate charts and surcharges
Sports equipment
Ticket receipt
Track a Shipment
Transporting firearms
Traveling with pets

COMPETITORS

Aeromexico	JetBlue
Air Canada	Mesa Air
Allegiant Travel	SkyWest
American Airlines	Southwest Airlines
Group	United Continental
Delta Air Lines	WestJet
Hawaiian Holdings	

HISTORICAL FINANCIALS

Company Type: Public

Income Statement

FYE: December 31

	REVENUE ($ mil.)	NET INCOME ($ mil.)	NET PROFIT MARGIN	EMPLOYEES
12/17	7,933	1,034	13.0%	23,156
12/16	5,931	814	13.7%	19,112
12/15	5,598	848	15.1%	15,143
12/14	5,368	605	11.3%	13,952
12/13	5,156	508	9.9%	13,177
Annual Growth	**11.4%**	**19.4%**	**—**	**15.1%**

2017 Year-End Financials

Debt ratio: 23.92%	No. of shares (mil.): 123
Return on equity: 31.09%	Dividends
Cash ($ mil.): 194	Yield: 0.0%
Current ratio: 0.79	Payout: 14.3%
Long-term debt ($ mil.): 2,262	Market value ($ mil.): 9,046

	STOCK PRICE ($) FY Close	P/E High/Low		PER SHARE ($) Earnings	Dividends	Book Value
12/17	73.51	12	7	8.35	1.20	30.24
12/16	88.73	14	8	6.54	1.10	23.77
12/15	80.51	13	9	6.56	0.80	19.26
12/14	59.76	22	9	4.42	0.50	16.18
12/13	73.37	22	12	3.58	0.20	14.76
Annual Growth	**0.0%**	**—**	**—**	**23.6%**	**56.5%**	**19.6%**

ALASKA PERMANENT FUND CORPORATION

Auditors: KPMG LLP ANCHORAGE AK

LOCATIONS

HQ: ALASKA PERMANENT FUND CORPORATION
801 W 10TH ST STE 302, JUNEAU, AK 998011878
Phone: 907 796-1500
Web: WWW.APFC.ORG

HISTORICAL FINANCIALS

Company Type: Private

Income Statement

FYE: June 30

	ASSETS ($ mil.)	NET INCOME ($ mil.)	INCOME AS % OF ASSETS	EMPLOYEES
06/16	55,346	(30)	—	50
06/15	55,900	1,586	2.8%	—
06/14	54,614	6,360	11.6%	—
06/13	49,797	4,520	9.1%	—
Annual Growth	**3.6%**	**—**	**—**	**—**

Alcoa Corporation

LOCATIONS

HQ: Alcoa Corporation
201 Isabella Street, Pittsburgh, PA 15212-5858
Phone: 412 315-2900
Web: www.alcoa.com

HISTORICAL FINANCIALS

Company Type: Public

Income Statement

FYE: December 31

	REVENUE ($ mil.)	NET INCOME ($ mil.)	NET PROFIT MARGIN	EMPLOYEES
12/16	9,318	(400)	—	14,000
12/15	11,199	(863)	—	16,000
12/14	13,147	(256)	—	—
12/13	12,573	(2,909)	—	—
Annual Growth	(9.5%)	—	—	—

2016 Year-End Financials

Debt ratio: 8.63%
Return on equity: (-5.28%)
Cash ($ mil.): 853
Current ratio: 1.13
Long-term debt ($ mil.): 1,424
No. of shares (mil.): 182
Dividends
Yield: —
Payout: —
Market value ($ mil.): 5,137

	STOCK PRICE ($) FY Close	P/E High/Low		PER SHARE ($) Earnings	Dividends	Book Value
12/16	28.08	—	—	(2.19)	0.00	30.91
12/15	0.00	—	—	(0.00)	0.00	(0.00)
Annual Growth	—			—	—	—

Alerus Financial Corp

EXECUTIVES

Senior Vice President, Mike Winkel
President; Chief Executive Officer Chairman Director, Randy Newman
Vice President Purchasing, Scott Harter
Auditors: CliftonLarsonAllen LLP

LOCATIONS

HQ: Alerus Financial Corp
401 Demers Avenue, Grand Forks, ND 58021
Phone: 701 795-3200   **Fax:** 701 795-3378
Web: www.alerusfinancial.com

HISTORICAL FINANCIALS

Company Type: Public

Income Statement

FYE: December 31

	ASSETS ($ mil.)	NET INCOME ($ mil.)	INCOME AS % OF ASSETS	EMPLOYEES
12/16	2,050	14	0.7%	—
12/15	1,744	16	0.9%	—
12/14	1,488	20	1.4%	—
12/13	1,380	20	1.5%	584
12/12	1,322	17	1.4%	—
Annual Growth	11.6%	(5.9%)	—	—

2016 Year-End Financials

Debt ratio: 2.87%
Return on equity: 7.96%
Cash ($ mil.): 207
Current ratio: —
Long-term debt ($ mil.): —
No. of shares (mil.): 13
Dividends
Yield: 0.0%
Payout: 44.0%
Market value ($ mil.): 230

	STOCK PRICE ($) FY Close	P/E High/Low		PER SHARE ($) Earnings	Dividends	Book Value
12/16	17.00	19	16	1.00	0.44	12.47
12/15	18.90	17	15	1.17	0.42	13.61
12/14	19.75	42	14	1.44	0.38	(0.00)
12/13	51.00	35	21	1.46	0.34	11.21
12/12	31.00	47	20	1.29	0.31	10.49
Annual Growth	(13.9%)	—	—	(6.2%)	8.9%	4.4%

ALFRED P. SLOAN FOUNDATION

Auditors: KPMG PEAT MARWICK LLP

LOCATIONS

HQ: ALFRED P. SLOAN FOUNDATION
45 ROCKEFELLER PLZ # 2200, NEW YORK, NY 101110217
Phone: 212 649-1649
Web: WWW.SLOAN.ORG

HISTORICAL FINANCIALS

Company Type: Private

Income Statement

FYE: December 31

	ASSETS ($ mil.)	NET INCOME ($ mil.)	INCOME AS % OF ASSETS	EMPLOYEES
12/14	1,875	(2)	—	25
12/13	1,278	(7)	—	—
12/06	1,807	219	12.1%	—
12/05	1,581	0	—	—
Annual Growth	1.9%	—	—	—

2014 Year-End Financials

Debt ratio: —
Return on equity: (-2.00%)
Cash ($ mil.): 1
Current ratio: —
Long-term debt ($ mil.): —
Dividends
Yield: —
Payout: —
Market value ($ mil.): —

Alleghany Corp.

Alleghany is a holding company with a focus on property/casualty reinsurance and insurance. Its subsidiaries include Transatlantic Holdings (TransRe) which offers property/casualty reinsurance (risk coverage for insurers) globally through Transatlantic Reinsurance Fair American and Trans Re Zurich. It also issues specialty property/casualty insurance policies through RSUI Group and CapSpecialty. Targeting small and midsized US firms CapSpecialty underwrites specialty lines including commercial property fidelity surety and professional lines. Alleghany's offerings are marketed in the US and abroad.

HISTORY

Alleghany was formed in 1929 by Clevelanders Mantis and Oris Van Sweringen as a pyramid railroad holding company. It collapsed in 1934 and after passing through several hands it was bought in 1937 by speculator Robert Young with backing from Woolworth heir Allan Kirby.

Young resurrected the company's Chesapeake and Ohio railroad but another holding Missouri Pacific Railroad (Mo-Pac) failed to thrive and Young embarked on a 40-year struggle to maximize Mo-Pac's value. Young focused on railroads even as the industry declined but he also made other investments including a chunk of IDS (which became the US's largest mutual fund company) and real estate. He also trimmed company holdings from nearly 70 to about 10. By the time Young committed suicide in 1958 Alleghany was in trouble and Kirby who had always kept to the shadows took over.

In his first three years at the helm Kirby fought a takeover attempt by Abraham Sonnabend and a proxy fight with investors John and Clint Murchison. After being ousted briefly in 1961 Kirby re-emerged in control of the company. Allan suffered a stroke in 1965 and his son Fred Morgan "F. M." Kirby II took over.

In 1966 the company sold its interest in the New York Central railroad (bought in 1945) and eight years later finally emerged from the Mo-Pac mess with about $42 million in cash and some stock. Alleghany used the cash to buy metal fabricating company MSL Industries and the rest of IDS.

Fred Kirby's mantra was flexibility and in 1984 he sold IDS to American Express for a then-flabbergasting $800 million including a pile of stock. Kirby used these proceeds to buy Chicago Title & Trust the same year. Two years later he liquidated the old Alleghany and reincorporated Alleghany Financial CT&T's parent as Alleghany Corporation.

Kirby used the cash from the American Express deal to buy and then spin off a construction company. Other purchases followed in the 1990s including more title operations a California thrift and in 1991 Celite which produced filtration materials. This line was expanded the next year with the purchase of Harborlite. After several purchases in direct insurance (quickly flipped for a profit) in 1993 Alleghany bought Underwriters Re.

In 1994 and 1995 the company bought up shares of Burlington Northern Railroad which merged with Santa Fe in 1995.

In the 1990s CT&T lost market share through industry consolidation so in 1998 Alleghany spun off CT&T's title operations (later acquired by Fidelity National Financial). The next year hit by a down market in reinsurance Alleghany agreed to sell Underwriters Re to Swiss Reinsurance keeping its hand in the market via Alleghany Underwriting Holdings Ltd. (AUL).

In 1999 the company bulked up its asset management operations through acquisitions and in 2000 its industrial fastener business Heads & Threads International bought Acktion's Reynold's Fasteners unit. In 2001 Alleghany sold Lloyd's reinsurer Alleghany Underwriting to Bermuda-based Talbot Holdings and Dutch bank ABN Amro bought the company's asset management business.

The company built up its insurance operations with the purchase of Resurgens Specialty Underwriting (RSUI Group) a subsidiary of British insurance powerhouse Royal & Sun Alliance. It also expanded insurance operations with the 2004 acquisitions of Capitol Transamerica and Darwin National Assurance Company (formerly known as U.S. AEGIS Energy Insurance Company) later renamed as Darwin Professional Underwriters. In early 2006 it took Darwin through an initial public offering and used the funds to reduce its equity interest while retaining majority ownership. (Alleghany's 55% stake in Darwin was sold to Allied World Assurance in 2008.)

While Alleghany collected insurance firms it shed other operations. The company sold Heads & Threads to a management-led investors group in 2004. In 2005 it sold its World Minerals subsidiary (diatomite production) to the US branch of Imerys in a deal valued at about $217 million.

Hurricane Katrina took a serious bite out of profits in 2005. In response Alleghany Insurance Holdings created AIHL Re a reinsurance subsidiary to provide reinsurance directly to RSUI while RSUI worked to reduce its exposure and increased its prices on property insurance. Once the reinsurance market settled down AIHL Re was allowed to go dormant in 2008.

During the quieter 2006 and 2007 hurricane seasons Alleghany found it still had an appetite for insurance providers. The company plunked down $120 million in cash to purchase 33% of monoline homeowners insurance provider Homesite Group in 2006 and spent $198 million to acquire Employers Direct in 2007.

Alleghany held 55% of Darwin Professional Underwriters a specialty property/casualty insurance writer but in 2008 sold it to Allied World Assurance for approximately $300 million.

F. M. Kirby retired as chairman at the end of 2006. His brother Allan Kirby retired from the board in 2010 leaving Jefferson Kirby F. M.'s son as the last family member on the board as directors. F. M. died at the age of 91 in early 2011.

Transatlantic Holdings caught Alleghany's eye and in early 2012 the company paid some $3.4 billion for the long-tail reinsurer. The deal's announcement in late 2011 ended a months-long buyout battle for Transatlantic.

EXECUTIVES

Chairman and CEO CapSpecialty Inc. (f/k/a Capitol Transamerica Corporation), Stephen J. Sills, age 68

Chairman Alleghany Capital Corporation, Udi Toledano, age 67

President and CEO, Weston M. Hicks, age 61, $1,000,000 total compensation

President and CEO Alleghany Properties, David J. Bugatto, age 52

President and CEO Transatlantic Holdings Inc., Michael C. (Mike) Sapnar, age 50

Chairman President and CEO Pacific Compensation Corporation, Janet D. (Jan) Frank, age 66

SVP Head of Fixed Income and Treasurer, Roger B. Gorham, age 54, $600,000 total compensation

SVP General Counsel and Secretary, Christopher K. Dalrymple, age 49, $650,000 total compensation

Chairman and CEO RSUI Group Inc., David E. (Dave) Leonard

SVP and CFO, John L. (Jack) Sennott, age 51, $650,000 total compensation

EVP, Joseph P. Brandon, age 58, $825,000 total compensation

President and CEO Alleghany Capital Corporation, David Van Geyzel

VP Finance and Chief Risk Officer, Kerry J. Jacobs

Vice President, Jeff Kirby

Assistant Vice President Accounting, Natalie Anbinder

Chairman, Jefferson W. Kirby, age 55

Auditors: Ernst &Young LLP

LOCATIONS

HQ: Alleghany Corp.
1411 Broadway, 34th Floor, New York, NY 10018
Phone: 212 752-1356
Web: www.alleghany.com

PRODUCTS/OPERATIONS

2016 Revenues

	$ mil.	% of total
Reinsurance		
Casualty & Other	2,677	44
Property	1,168	19
Insurance		
RSUI Group	754	12
Cap Specialty	237	4
Pacific Comp	138	2
Net investment income	438	7
Net realized Capital gains	63	1
Other income	653	11
Total	**6,131**	**100**

2016 Sales

	% of total
Net premium earned	81
Net investment income	7
Net realized capital gains	1
Other	11
Total	**100**

Selected operating companies

Alleghany Capital Corporation
Alleghany Properties LLC
Capitol Transamerica Corporation
Pacific Compensation Corporation
Roundwood Asset Management LLC
RSUI Group Inc.
Transatlantic Holdings Inc.

COMPETITORS

AIG	PartnerRe
CNA Surety	Reinsurance Group of
California Casualty	America
Everest Re	RenaissanceRe
General Re	State Compensation
Hannover Re	Insurance Fund
Liberty Mutual Agency	State Farm
Munich Re Group	Swiss Re
Nationwide	Travelers Companies
OdysseyRe	Unico American
Ohio Casualty	

HISTORICAL FINANCIALS
Company Type: Public

Income Statement
FYE: December 31

	ASSETS ($ mil.)	NET INCOME ($ mil.)	INCOME AS % OF ASSETS	EMPLOYEES
12/16	23,756	456	1.9%	3,420
12/15	22,846	560	2.5%	3,135
12/14	23,489	679	2.9%	2,067
12/13	23,361	628	2.7%	1,985
12/12	22,807	702	3.1%	1,506
Annual Growth	**1.0%**	**(10.2%)**	**—**	**22.8%**

2016 Year-End Financials

Debt ratio: 6.22%
Return on equity: 5.88%
Cash ($ mil.): 594
Current ratio: —
Long-term debt ($ mil.): —
No. of shares (mil.): 15
Dividends
  Yield: —
  Payout: —
Market value ($ mil.): 9,371

	STOCK PRICE ($) FY Close	P/E High/Low	PER SHARE ($) Earnings	Dividends	Book Value
12/16	608.12	21 15	29.59	0.00	515.24
12/15	477.93	15 13	35.13	0.00	486.02
12/14	463.50	12 9	41.40	0.00	465.51
12/13	399.96	11 9	37.44	0.00	412.96
12/12	335.42	8 6	45.48	0.00	379.13
Annual Growth	**16.0%**	**— —**	**(10.2%)**	**—**	**8.0%**

Allegiance Bancshares Inc

Auditors: Crowe Horwath LLP

LOCATIONS

HQ: Allegiance Bancshares Inc
8847 West Sam Houston Parkway N., Suite 200, Houston, TX 77040
Phone: 281 894-3200
Web: www.allegiancebank.com

HISTORICAL FINANCIALS
Company Type: Public

Income Statement
FYE: December 31

	ASSETS ($ mil.)	NET INCOME ($ mil.)	INCOME AS % OF ASSETS	EMPLOYEES
12/16	2,450	22	0.9%	327
12/15	2,084	15	0.8%	310
12/14	1,280	9	0.7%	304
12/13	1,164	6	0.6%	—
Annual Growth	**28.1%**	**49.5%**	**—**	**—**

2016 Year-End Financials

Debt ratio: 8.56%
Return on equity: 8.47%
Cash ($ mil.): 142
Current ratio: —
Long-term debt ($ mil.): —
No. of shares (mil.): 12
Dividends
  Yield: —
  Payout: —
Market value ($ mil.): 468

	STOCK PRICE ($) FY Close	P/E High/Low	PER SHARE ($) Earnings	Dividends	Book Value
12/16	36.15	21 9	1.75	0.00	21.59
12/15	23.65	18 15	1.43	0.00	20.17
12/14	0.00	— —	1.26	0.00	17.62
Annual Growth	**—**	**— —**	**11.6%**	**—**	**7.0%**

ALLEGIS GROUP, INC.

Allegis Group is one of the world's largest staffing and recruitment firms. Among its group of staffing companies are Aerotek (engineering automotive and scientific professionals) Stephen James Associates (recruitment for accounting financial and cash management positions) and TEKsystems (information technology staffing and consulting). Other Allegis Group units include sales support outsourcer MarketSource. Allegis Group operates through more than 500 offices worldwide. Chairman Jim Davis helped found the company (originally known as Aerotek) in 1983 to provide contract engineering personnel to two clients in the aerospace industry.

Operations

Allegis Group has more than 12000 internal employees including 3000 dedicated recruiters and 130000 contract employees working with customers around the world.

Geographic Reach

Allegis Group's corporate headquarters are located in Hanover Maryland. Outside of the US the company has operations in Canada Europe the Middle East the Pacific Rim Puerto Rico and the UK.

Financial Performance

Allegis Group averages about $11 billion in annual revenue.

Strategy

Allegis Group has expanded its geographical footprint and improved its position in specialist staffing markets through the use of acquisitions. The company's specialized staffing firms cater to various industries.

Mergers and Acquisitions

In 2016 Allegis Group acquired Switzerland-based staffing recruiting and services organization The Stamford Group. The deal increased Allegis Group's global footprint and strengthened its European presence.

EXECUTIVES

CFO, Paul J. Bowie
President, Andy Hilger
Chairman, James C. (Jim) Davis
Auditors: PRICEWATERHOUSECOOPERS LLP BA

LOCATIONS

HQ: ALLEGIS GROUP, INC.
7301 PARKWAY DR, HANOVER, MD 210761159
Phone: 410 579-3000
Web: WWW.AEROTEK.COM

PRODUCTS/OPERATIONS

Selected Subsidiaries
Aerotek
  Aerotek Automotive
  Aerotek Aviation LLC
  Aerotek Canada
  Aerotek CE
  Aerotek Commercial Staffing
  Aerotek E&E
  Aerotek Energy Services
  Aerotek Germany
  Aerotek Netherlands
  Aerotek Professional Services
  Aerotek Scientific LLC
  Aerotek United Kingdom
Allegis Group Canada
Allegis Group Europe
Allegis Group India
Allegis Group Services
InSearch Worldwide
Major Lindsey & Africa
MarketSource Inc
Stephen James Associates
TEKsystems
  TEKsystems Canada
  TEKsystems Germany
  TEKsystems Netherlands
  TEKsystems United Kingdom

COMPETITORS

ASG Renaissance	Kelly Services
Adecco	Korn/Ferry
CDI	ManpowerGroup
Curran Partners	RDL Corporation
ExecuNet	Randstad Holding
Heidrick & Struggles	Robert Half
Horton International	Snelling Staffing
Innovative Management	Volt Information
Solutions Group	

HISTORICAL FINANCIALS
Company Type: Private

Income Statement
FYE: December 31

	REVENUE ($ mil.)	NET INCOME ($ mil.)	NET PROFIT MARGIN	EMPLOYEES
12/15	11,222	0	—	85,000
12/14	10,827	0	—	—
12/13	10,440	0	—	—
12/12	9,544	0	—	—
Annual Growth	5.5%	—	—	—

2015 Year-End Financials

Debt ratio: ——
Return on equity: —
Cash ($ mil.): 390
Current ratio: 2.50
Long-term debt ($ mil.): —

Dividends
Yield: —
Payout: —
Market value ($ mil.): —

Alliance Data Systems Corp.

Alliance Data Systems provides private-label credit card financing and processing and database and direct marketing services to more than 1500 companies. In a given year it holds the credit for approximately $15 billion in card balances. Its client base includes retailers like J. Crew Pottery Barn and Victoria's Secret as well as banks (Bank of America) grocery and drugstore chains gas stations and hospitality media and pharmaceutical companies. The company also develops and operates customer loyalty programs such as its Canadian-focused AIR MILES program. Additionally it performs database marketing digital analytics and strategic consulting services.

Operations

Alliance Data Systems operates three main business segments: Card Services Epsilon and LoyaltyOne.

Card Services generates roughly half of the company?s revenue by operating private label and co-branded credit card accounts for leading retailers. The retailers achieve a degree of brand loyalty and Alliance gathers customer information and buying habits with which it helps the retailer more precisely target customers for future sales opportunities. The segment manages more than 160 credit card programs whose consumer membership exceeds 40 million accounts. Alliance provides the credit behind the cards processes sales transactions and helps its clients leverage card branding to drive consumer loyalty.

The Epsilon segment serves roughly 1400 clients in industries such as financial services insurance media & entertainment automotive retail and hospitality. It gathers consumer data largely through its loyalty programs and credit card transactions then analyzes it to design client-customized digital and direct mail marketing programs. The segment generates about 30% of total company revenue.

LoyaltyOne accounts for some 20% of revenue. The segment gathers customer information through its loyalty programs to help Alliance clients design and implement marketing programs. It operates one of Canada?s largest loyalty programs AIR MILES through which consumers earn miles as they shop at more than 170 brand name retailers. The BrandLoyalty program offers similar objectives for grocers primarily in Europe and Asia with a growing presence in North America.

Broadly speaking Alliance Data Systems generates 80% of revenue from finance charges database marketing fees and direct marketing services.

Geographic Reach

The US accounts for about 80% of Alliance Data Systems? revenue a share that has increased in recent years as Canada?s share has decreased. The company is growing in EMEA and Asia Pacific.

Alliance has more than a dozen facilities in the US including its corporate headquarters in Plano Texas a large facility in Columbus Ohio and offices in Texas Illinois and Idaho among others. Its LoyaltyOne segment operates in Canada and The Netherlands. The company?s only other international facility is an Epsilon office in Bengaluru India.

Sales and Marketing

Although significant revenue is generated by card-carrying consumers Alliance?s key customers are name brand retail outlets. It is through the likes of L Brands (owner of Victoria's Secret and Bath & Body Works) and Ascena Retail Group (Lane Bryant Dress Barn) that Alliance issues new cards grows its consumer base and mines data essential to the Epsilon segment. The company typically enters into multi-year contracts with such retail partners. To manage loan loss risk from its credit card account holders Alliance targets retail brands that appeal to middle and upper-class consumers and intentionally avoids issuing cards to sub-prime borrowers.

Its 10 largest clients account for roughly 35% of total revenue. The LoyaltyOne business counts Bank of Montreal and Canada-based grocer Sobeys as its largest clients together representing 30% of segment revenue.

The company operates in a highly competitive market contending with marketing services companies credit card issuers and data processing companies as well as with the in-house staffs of current and potential clients.

Financial Performance

Although 2016 profitability slipped Alliance?s revenues and profits have more than doubled since 2011 as consumers? usage of reward programs and credit/debit cards has ballooned.

The company?s revenue increased 4% to $1.83 billion in 2016. Epsilon segment revenue was steady while Card Services grew 26% (to $988 million) due to higher finance charges as strong cardholder spending and new client signups drove higher average credit card and loan receivables balances. LoyaltyOne?s contribution to revenue slipped by $242 million due to a new law in Ontario Canada that triggered a one-time recalculation of Alliance?s air miles asset valuation.

Despite higher revenue net income fell 14% to $516 million in 2016. The decrease stemmed from higher interest expenses a growth in loan loss provisions and an increase in operations costs.

Cash at the end of 2016 was $1.9 billion an increase of nearly $700 million which came from $2.6 billion of cash provided by financing activities (primarily borrowings issuance) and $2.1 billion from operating activities both offset by a $4.1 billion usage by investing activities (in part from purchasing $1.0 billion of credit card portfolios).

Strategy

Alliance?s strategy includes growing its Card Services customer base shifting Epsilon?s product mix towards targeted direct marketing and shoring up LoyaltyOne following the impact of an Ontario Canada law change.

With credit and debit card usage driving Alliance?s financial performance the company continues to seek co-branded partnerships with a variety of retailers to grow its borrower base. During 2016 for example it signed a long-term agreement to provide branded credit card programs to Boscov's Department Store (the largest family-owned department chain in the US) clothing retailer Forever 21 and luxury home furnishings shop Restoration Hardware.

Following industry shifts Alliance is trending away from mass marketing (ex. direct mailings) and moving towards direct personalized efforts made possible by mining data from its huge consumer base and applying data analytics to design targeted ads. In recent years it experienced a time-to-market inhibitor and cost competition that impeded sales. It is addressing these problems with renewed focus on its less-customized (and less expensive) technology offerings and redirecting some of its focus into the mid-market space and into digital marketing.

The LoyaltyOne business was hit hard in 2016 with a law change in the province of Ontario Canada that rescinded the company?s 5-year expiration of loyalty points. Assuming other provinces would follow Alliance took the step to change its valuation model and accepted a more than $200 million hit to revenue. The segment continues to lower its expenses to match the drop in revenue and is expanding the geographic reach of its BrandLoyalty program to counteract the Canadian impact.

Company Background

Alliance Data Systems was formed by the 1996 acquisition by Welsh Carson Anderson & Stowe of J.C. Penney's transaction services business and L Brands' credit card bank operation Comenity Bank (formerly World Financial Network Bank which is now a subsidiary of the company.

EXECUTIVES

EVP and CFO, Charles L. Horn, age 56, $627,000 total compensation
President and CEO, Edward J. (Ed) Heffernan, age 54, $1,114,000 total compensation
EVP; President LoyaltyOne, Bryan A. Pearson, age 54, $459,895 total compensation
EVP; President Epsilon, Bryan J. Kennedy, age 48, $602,500 total compensation
EVP; President Retail Credit Services, Melisa A. Miller, age 58, $602,500 total compensation
Senior Vice President Treasurer, Brian Gore
Vice President Corporate Human Resources, Calvin Hilton
Vice President Client Sales, Gwen Mannarino
Senior Vice President Tax, Jeffrey Fair
Vice President Corporate Development, Jeff Chesnut
Vice President of Information Technology and Operations, Mike Rosello
Vice President Risk Management, Thomas Giancola
Chairman, Robert A. Minicucci, age 64
Auditors: Deloitte & Touche LLP

LOCATIONS

HQ: Alliance Data Systems Corp.
7500 Dallas Parkway, Suite 700, Plano, TX 75024
Phone: 214 494-3000
Web: www.alliancedata.com

PRODUCTS/OPERATIONS

2016 Sales By Segment

	$ mil.	% of total
Card Services	3,675	51
Epsilon	2,155	30
LoyaltyOne	1,337	19
Corporate & other	0	-
Adjustments	(30.3)	-
Total	**7,138**	**100**

2016 Sales

	$ mil.	% of total
Finance charges net	3,639	51
Marketing services	2,019	28
Redemption	993	14
Transaction	278	4
Other revenue	206	3
Total	**7,138**	**100**

2016 Sales

	$ mil.	% of total
United States	5,730	80
Canada	706	10
Europe Middle East and Africa	537	8
Asia Pacific	154	2
Other	9	0
Total	**7,138**	**100**

Selected Products and Services

Epsilon
  Marketing Services
  Agency services
  Database design & management
  Data services
  Analytical services
  Traditional & digital communications
LoyaltyOne
  AIR MILES Reward program
  Loyalty services
  Customer analytics
  Creative services
Private Label Services & Credit
  Receivables Financing
  Underwriting & risk management
  Receivables funding
  Processing Services
  New account processing
  Bill processing
  Remittance processing
  Customer care
  Marketing Services

COMPETITORS

ATCO I-Tek	Discover
Affinion Group	Maritz
American Express	PGi
Capital One	Payment Processing
Chockstone	Total System Services

HISTORICAL FINANCIALS

Company Type: Public

Income Statement

FYE: December 31

	REVENUE ($ mil.)	NET INCOME ($ mil.)	NET PROFIT MARGIN	EMPLOYEES
12/16	7,138	515	7.2%	17,000
12/15	6,439	596	9.3%	16,000
12/14	5,302	506	9.5%	15,000
12/13	4,319	496	11.5%	12,000
12/12	3,641	422	11.6%	10,700
Annual Growth	**18.3%**	**5.1%**	**—**	**12.3%**

2016 Year-End Financials

Debt ratio: 49.22%
Return on equity: 28.05%
Cash ($ mil.): 1,859
Current ratio: 2.12
Long-term debt ($ mil.): 10,103

No. of shares (mil.): 57
Dividends
  Yield: 0.0%
  Payout: 7.0%
Market value ($ mil.): 13,116

	STOCK PRICE ($) FY Close	P/E High/Low	PER SHARE ($) Earnings	Dividends	Book Value
12/16	228.50	38 24	7.34	0.52	28.89
12/15	276.57	35 28	8.85	0.00	33.02
12/14	286.05	34 27	7.87	0.00	37.55
12/13	262.93	26 14	7.42	0.00	16.60
12/12	144.76	18 12	6.58	0.00	10.65
Annual Growth	**12.1%**	**— —**	**2.8%**	**—**	**28.3%**

Allstate Corp.

Ya gotta hand it to Allstate: The "good hands" company has managed to work its way towards the top of the property/casualty insurance pile. The company is the second-largest personal lines insurer in the US just behind rival State Farm. Its Allstate Protection segment sells auto homeowners and other property/casualty insurance products in Canada and the US. Allstate Financial provides life insurance through subsidiaries including Allstate Life and American Heritage Life. It also provides investment products targeting affluent and middle-income consumers. Allstate Motor Club provides emergency road service.

Operations

Allstate operates through four segments: Allstate Protection Allstate Financial Discontinued Lines and Coverages and Corporate and Other.

The Allstate Protection segment's property and liability businesses — which cover about 16 million households — account for more than 85% of Allstate's total premiums. Most of the segment's sales come from traditional auto and homeowners policies. In addition to traditional property/casualty policies Allstate sells specialty products including coverage for motorcycle and boat owners renters and landlords and mobile home dwellers. It also provides roadside assistance as well as auto protection and service coverage sold through dealerships. Commercial products are geared towards small business owners.

Subsidiaries Esurance (auto insurance) Encompass (package policies) and Answer Financial (agency sales) operate online and have a combined customer base of close to 840000 and growing.

All of the company's life insurance annuities and banking services operate through Allstate Financial. While these sales account for approximately 10% of the company's total revenue Allstate primarily considers them to be useful for deepening relationships with Allstate Protection customers.

The Discontinued Lines and Coverages segment includes results from coverage Allstate no longer writes and run-off businesses.

Geographic Reach

Allstate's largest property/casualty markets are California Florida New York and Texas. The company operates throughout the US and in Puerto Rico the US Virgin Islands Guam and Canada. It operates from some 1240 administrative claims handling data processing and other facilities in North America. It also leases properties in Northern Ireland (three) India (two) and London.

Sales and Marketing

Allstate maintains a network of about 10400 exclusive agencies which sell its Allstate-branded insurance products through approximately 24000 licensed sales professionals. It also offers these products and Encompass-branded products through some 2200 independent agencies that are primarily located in rural areas of the US.

Allstate Financial products are sold through exclusive agencies (and approximately 1000 exclusive specialists) and 6000 workplace enrolling independent agents. Other products are sold through financial representatives online and over the phone.

To better compete with its faster-growing direct-to-consumer competitors Progressive and GEICO Allstate has been expanding its marketing efforts to reach younger consumers who like to compare and purchase insurance online.

In 2016 Allstate spend $11.2 million on advertising versus $12.6 million in 2015.

Financial Performance

Allstate's revenue has grown modestly over the past five years; it rose 2% to $36.5 billion in 2016. This gain was largely driven by a 3% or $1 billion increase in property and liability insurance premiums.

However net income took its second fall in 2016 declining 14% to $1.9 billion as operating costs and expenses increased. Property and liability claims and claims expenses rose 6% to $22.2 billion that year.

Despite the lower net income cash flow from operations rose 10% to $4 billion. Positive changes in income taxes and policy benefits helped boost the company's cash flow.

Strategy

Allstate is focused on growing its number of insurance policies in force increasing premiums maintaining profitability in the auto segment and increasing returns in the homeowners and annuity segments. It is also focused on proactively managing its investments modernizing its operating model and building long-term growth platforms. To grow policy sales the company is enhancing its independent agency network (especially in targeted geographic areas) sales support organization and online sales platforms. It is also working to increase cross-sales of voluntary benefit products through its exclusive agents as well as to form new strategic alliances and develop new product offerings. Subsidiary Esurance is expanding both by adding new complementary products and by launching its products in new geographical locations. At the same time Allstate is working to reduce its operational costs.

The company is continuing to invest in automotive telematics or wireless device technologies that track drivers' habits through which it can provide more accurate policy pricing.

Catastrophe management is also a key part of the company's stability. To limit its exposure to catastrophic claims in the face of increasing severe weather events in recent years Allstate has quit writing new homeowners policies in some coastal areas including California and Florida that are vulnerable to hurricane wind storms and earthquakes. In 2016 the company began writing a limited number of homeowner policies in certain areas of California. And while it still renews existing homeowners policies in California the company tweaked its underwriting to reduce exposure to claims for fires following earthquakes.

Mergers and Acquisitions

In early 2017 Allstate acquired rapidly growing consumer protection plan provider SquareTrade which specializes in extended warranties for electronics devices. The $1.4 billion deal expanded Allstate's consumer-focused offerings adding some 25 million protection plans.

HISTORY

Allstate traces its origins to a friendly game of bridge played in 1930 on a Chicago-area commuter train by Sears president Robert Wood and a friend insurance broker Carl Odell. The insurance man suggested Sears sell auto insurance through the mail. Wood liked the idea financed the company and in 1931 put Odell in charge (that hand of bridge must have shown Wood that Odell was no dummy). The company was named Allstate after one of Sears' tire brands. Allstate was born just as Sears was beginning its push into retailing and Allstate went with it selling insurance out of all the new Sears stores.

Growth was slow during the Depression and WWII but the postwar boom was a gold mine for both Sears and Allstate. Suburban development made cars a necessity; 1950s prudence necessitated car insurance; and Sears made it easy to buy the insurance at their stores and increasingly at freestanding agencies.

In the late 1950s Allstate added home and other property/casualty insurance lines. It also went into life insurance — in-force policies zoomed from zero to $1 billion in six years the industry's fastest growth ever.

Sears formed Allstate Enterprises in 1960 as an umbrella for all its noninsurance operations. In 1970 that firm bought its first savings and loan (S&L). The insurer continued to acquire other S&Ls and to add subsidiaries throughout the 1970s and 1980s.

This strategy dovetailed with Sears' strategy which was to become a diversified financial services company. In 1985 Sears introduced the Discover Card through Allstate's Greenwood Trust Company. However by the late 1980s it was obvious Sears would never be a financial services giant. Moreover it was losing so much in retailing that by 1987 Allstate was the major contributor to corporate net income. Sears began to dismantle its financial empire in the 1990s.

Allstate also suffered from a backlash against high insurance rates. When Massachusetts instituted no-fault insurance in 1989 Allstate stopped writing new auto insurance there. Later the company had to refund $110 million to customers to settle a suit with California over rate rollbacks required by 1988's Proposition 103.

Allstate went public in 1993 when Sears sold about 20% of its stake. That year it began reducing its operations in Florida to protect itself against high losses from hurricanes. Two years later the retailer sold its remaining interest to its shareholders. Also in 1995 Allstate sold 70% of PMI its mortgage insurance unit to the public.

EXECUTIVES

Senior Vice President Marketing, Robert Apatoff
Vice President, Sari Macrie
Vice President Auditing, Kathleen Swain
Chairman President and CEO The Allstate Corporation and Allstate Insurance Company, Thomas J. Wilson, age 59, $1,200,000 total compensation
Senior Vice President, Bryan Anderson
EVP Marketing Innovation and Corporate Relations Allstate Insurance, Sanjay Gupta, age 49
President The Allstate Corporation and Allstate Life Insurance, Matthew E. (Matt) Winter, age 61, $820,673 total compensation
President Allstate Financial, Mary Jane B. Fortin, $632,752 total compensation
President Service Businesses, Don Civgin, age 56, $776,885 total compensation
EVP Product Integration and Management, W. Guy Hill
EVP Product Operations Allstate Insurance, Steven P. Sorenson, age 53
EVP Brand Operations Allstate Insurance, Thomas M. Troy
EVP Technology and Strategic Ventures, Suren Gupta, age 55, $537,404 total compensation
President West Territory Allstate Personal Lines, Thomas F. Clarkson
President East Territory, David Prendergast
President Allstate Personal Lines, Glenn T. Shapiro
EVP Allstate Brand Distribution Allstate Insurance Company (AIC), Katherine (Kathy) Mabe
Vice Chairman The Allstate Corporation and Allstate Insurance Company, Steven E. (Steve) Shebik, age 60, $770,673 total compensation
EVP General Counsel and Secretary Allstate Corp and Allstate Insurance Company (AIC), Susan L. Lees, age 59
EVP Allstate Personal Lines Business Transformation, Brian R. Bohaty
EVP Human Resources, Harriet K. Harty, age 50

EVP and Chief Investment Officer; President Allstate Investments, John Dugenske
EVP and CFO The Allstate Corporation and Allstate Insurance Company, Mario Rizzo
Field Vice President Midwest Region, Alice Byrne
Vice President Technology and Operations The Allstate Corpor, Butch Necastro
Senior Vice President Of Claims, Mark Mcgillivray
Department Head, Paul Schutt
Vice President Of Product And Pricing, Keith Green
Assistant Vice President, Steve King
Vice President Regional Marketing, Kurt Winter
Assistant Vice President And Chief Actuary, Errol Cramer
Vice President and Assistant General Counsel, William Vainisi
Senior Vice President Corporate Relations, Stacy Sharpe
Senior Vice President, Kelly Noll
Associate Vice President Claims, Erik Kiehn
Vice President Human Resources, Joseph Testor
Vice President, Scott Harris
Vice President Human Resources, Amy Mills
Vice President Investor Relations, Robert Block
Assistant Vice President Claims, James Murray
Vice President Marketing And Business, Patrick Rogers
Vice President, Wayne Kullman
Assistant Vice President claims, Christine Sullivan
Vice President Director Manager, Carl Majeski
Assistant Vice President human Resources compensation, Vernessa Davis
Vice President Product Technology, Daniel Butch Necastro
Assistant Vice President Claims, Pam Overton
Assistant Vice President, Kerry Flack
Vice President Relationship Management, Vince Sommer
Vice President, Heather Vangrevenhof
Vice President And Senior Key Account Manager, Stephen Lipker
Assistant Vice President Strategic Initiatives Management Office, Kimberly Purdy
Assistant Vice President P CCSO, Marcie Molek
Assistant Vice President Allstate Marketing Customer Communication Division, Richard Heneberry
Vice President Talent Acquisition, Cathy Winn
Vice President, Robert Transon
Senior Vice President and Group Chief Information Officer, Peter Logothetis
Vice President Business Development, Jerry Lamparski
Assistant Vice President and Assistant Treasurer, Karen Duffy
Vice President Human Resources, Bridgette Moore
Vice President, Elizabeth Smith
Vice President National Accounts, William Prince
Assistant Vice President Finance, Kevin Corbett
Vice President Risk Assesment, Bob Roberts
Vice President Vehicle Product Management, Dave Border
Vice President Relationship Management, Jody Lemmon
Vice President, Angela Booles
Vice President Information Technology Testing and Release Management, Opal Perry
Vice President, Steve Miller
Assistant Vice President and Assistant General Counsel, Steve Ihm
Vice President Manager Director, Bob Halter
Senior Vice President Aic (Corporate Relations And Interim Chief Marketing Officer), Joan Walker
Vice President Director Manager, Howard Gurvitz
Assistant Vice President Talent Acquisition, Tom Hall
Vice President, Patty VanLammeren
Vice President, Shane O'Brien

Floridian Executive Vice President, George Grawe
Executive Vice President Human Resources, Liz Oppenhuis
Vice President Finance, Michael Kasper
Afvp, Brian Walsh
Vice President Sol, David Dickson
Vice President Finance, Joy Sweet
Vice President and Chief Financial Officer Information Technology and Operations, Michael Scardina
Vice President CIO, Mike Boyle
Vice President Tax, Karen Gardner
Senior Vice President Secretary General Counsel and Director, Michael Velotta
Senior Vice President, Jeff McRae
Vice President Human Resources, Joan Naughton-Gerdes
Vice President, Kathy Smith
Vice President, Monika Wirtz
Vice President Information Technology Group, James Baum
Assistant Vice President Financial Resource Admin., Mike Scardina
Assistant Vice President Allstate Marketing Customer Experience, Jessica Rivera
Assistant Vice President Excess and Surplus Lines, John Moran
Senior Vice President Customer Fulfillment and Underwriting, John Rugel
Vice President and CIO, Kamal Natarajan
Vice President, Patti Lenseth
Vice President of Private Client Services, Luke Doebele
Vice President of Operations, Rodney Nail
Vice President and Assistant Treasurer, Stephanie Neely
National Account Manager, Kim Dewhurst
Senior Vice President Marketing, Gannon Jones
Vice President Business Development, David Burgis
Vice President Eastern Territory, Daniel Hebel
Vice President of Sales, Joe Hallberg
Regional Vice President Life Wholesaling, Ryan Nichols
Board Member, Lisa Jennings
Board Member and Mentor, Justin Eggar
Treasurer, James W Jonske
Treasurer, Deborah Marcus
Treasurer, Michelle Ackerman
Treasurer, Bill Mann
secretary, Lisa Love
Secretary, Christina Zarate
secretary, Debi Gaudiosi
Secretary, Rachel Oldham
Auditors: Deloitte & Touche LLP

LOCATIONS

HQ: Allstate Corp.
2775 Sanders Road, Northbrook, IL 60062
Phone: 847 402-5000
Web: www.allstate.com

PRODUCTS/OPERATIONS

2016 Revenues

	$ mil.	% of total
Property/liability		
Auto	21,264	58
Homeowners	7,257	20
Other personal lines	1,700	5
Commercial lines	506	1
Other business lines	580	2
Others	1,260	3
Allstate Financial	3,928	11
Corporate & other	39	-
Total	**36,534**	**100**

Selected Subsidiaries

Allstate Insurance Company of Canada
Allstate Life Insurance Company
Allstate Motor Club

American Heritage Life Insurance Company
Encompass Insurance Company
Esurance Insurance Company
Kennett Capital Inc.
Northbrook Indemnity Company
Pafco Insurance Company (Canada)
Sterling Collision Centers Inc.

COMPETITORS

Farmers Group	Prudential
GEICO	State Farm
Hanover Insurance	The Hartford
Liberty Mutual	Torchmark
MetLife	Travelers Companies
Nationwide	USAA
Progressive Corporation	

HISTORICAL FINANCIALS

Company Type: Public

Income Statement

FYE: December 31

	ASSETS ($ mil.)	NET INCOME ($ mil.)	INCOME AS % OF ASSETS	EMPLOYEES
12/16	108,610	1,877	1.7%	43,500
12/15	104,656	2,171	2.1%	41,600
12/14	108,533	2,850	2.6%	40,200
12/13	123,520	2,280	1.8%	39,400
12/12	126,947	2,306	1.8%	38,600
Annual Growth	**(3.8%)**	**(5.0%)**	**—**	**3.0%**

2016 Year-End Financials

Debt ratio: 5.84%
Return on equity: 9.22%
Cash ($ mil.): 436
Current ratio: —
Long-term debt ($ mil.): —
No. of shares (mil.): 366
Dividends
Yield: 0.0%
Payout: 28.2%
Market value ($ mil.): 27,128

	STOCK PRICE ($) FY Close	P/E High/Low	Earnings	Dividends	Book Value
12/16	74.12	16 12	4.67	1.32	56.21
12/15	62.09	14 11	5.05	1.20	52.56
12/14	70.25	11 8	6.27	1.12	53.36
12/13	54.54	11 8	4.81	1.00	47.84
12/12	40.17	9 6	4.68	0.88	42.96
Annual Growth	**16.5%**	**— —**	**(0.1%)**	**10.7%**	**6.9%**

Ally Financial Inc

Ally Financial wants to be your friend in the financing business. Ally operates branchless online-only retail bank Ally Bank which offers deposit mortgage (through Ally Home) and credit card products. Ally also provides auto financing for 18000 auto dealerships (mostly GM and Chrysler) and their customers. Ally Financial offers financing services for large- and mid-market companies through Ally Corporate Finance. Formerly known as GMAC and once majority-owned by US taxpayers following a federal bailout in 2008 Ally Financial went public in 2014.

Operations

Ally Financial carries more than $163 billion in assets. The company operates four business segments: Automotive Finance Insurance Mortgage and Corporate Finance.

Automotive Finance is Ally?s biggest earner at some 75% of sales. The segment provides auto financing to consumers and auto dealers. Insurance the next biggest at 20% of sales offers consumer finance protection and insurance products through its automotive dealer channel. It also sells commercial insurance directly to dealers.

The Mortgage segment accounting for a few percent of sales manages a held-for-investment consumer mortgage portfolio and bulk purchases high-quality jumbo loans. It has does limited direct mortgage originations through LenderLive a third-part fulfilment partner.

Corporate Finance offers senior secured lever-aged cash flow and asset-based loans to US-based middle market companies; its sales are in the low single-digits of Ally?s total revenue.

Geographic Reach

Ally Financial focuses almost entirely on the US. It has corporate offices in Detroit; New York City; and Charlotte North Carolina and additional offices in Chicago; Dallas; Pittsburgh Pennsylvania; Duluth Georgia; and Jacksonville Florida. While Ally Bank is headquartered in Midvale Utah the subsidiary is an online direct bank that doesn't have branches.It operates in Texas California Florida Pennsylvania Illinois Georgia North Carolina Ohio New York and Michigan.

Sales and Marketing

Ally Financial and its subsidiaries serve 5.6 million consumers and 18000 auto dealers. Some of its top clients include General Motors and Chrysler .

Ally's insurance operations sells its consumer financial and insurance products primarily through the automotive dealer channel while commercial insurance products are sold to dealers. As a direct bank Ally Bank raises deposit funds via its internet telephone mobile and mail channels. Its 1.2 million-strong customer base continues to grow and its customer satisfaction score has reliably exceeded 90%.

Financial Performance

In fiscal 2016 (ended December) revenue increased 3% to $9.8 billion as a $92 million decrease in financing revenue was more than offset by a $388 increase in other income. The increase in other income reflected the absence of a $357 million extinguishment of debt incurred in the previous year.

Net income fell 17% to $1.1 billion due to a $392 million profit on discontinued operations the previous year. On a comparable basis net income was up $214 million due mostly to higher net revenue.

Cash from operating activities reduced 10% to $4.6 billion due to a $0.6 billion increase in cash outflows from other assets and a $0.4 billion decrease in loss on extinguishment of debt.

Strategy

Ally Financial is motivated to offer its customers the most convenient and well-rounded mobile banking service on the market. To allow its customers access to brokerage services in 2016 Ally acquired TradeKing. TradeKing is a discount online brokerage firm that allowed the individual user to buy and sell stocks bonds and mutual funds. TradeKing was rebranded as Ally Invest in 2017 and integrated into Ally?s web platform.

Additionally Ally launched Ally Home a direct-to-consumer mortgage offering in December 2016. The product further fleshed out its online banking service. Unlike Ally Bank?s other products Ally Home?s customers have access to a team of experts in the shape of the Ally Home Team.

Mergers and Acquisitions

In June 2016 Ally expanded into online brokerage after buying digital wealth management and broker-dealer TradeKing Group for $275 million. TradeKing had some $4.5 billion in client assets at the time.

Company Background

In February 2013 Ally sold its Canadian auto finance business to Royal Bank of Canada. A few months later it sold its Mexican insurance business ABA Seguros to ACE for $865 million. In October it sold its business in Europe and Latin America as well as a joint venture in China to GM Financial for $611 million. Also in 2013 it sold its business lending operations to Walter Investment Management Corp. completed the sales of agency mortgage servicing rights (MSRs) to Ocwen Financial Corp. and Quicken Loans Inc. and exited the correspondent lending channel.

Ally Financial was founded as a subsidiary of General Motors in 1919. It was owned by GM until 2006 when the automaker sold a 51% stake in the company to the Cerberus Capital Management investment group for some $7 billion.

EXECUTIVES

President Auto Finance, Timothy M. (Tim) Russi, age 54, $541,800 total compensation
CIO, Michael Baresich
CEO and Director, Jeffrey J. (JB) Brown, age 43, $1,000,000 total compensation
President and CEO Ally Commercial Finance LLC, William (Bill) Hall
President Consumer and Commercial Banking Products, Diane Morais, age 51, $550,000 total compensation
CFO, Christopher A. Halmy, age 48, $600,000 total compensation
President Ally Insurance, Douglas Timmerman
Chief Risk Officer, David Shevsky, age 55, $500,000 total compensation
Executive Vice President Organizational Effectiveness, Renee Otjen
Senior Vice President Offshore, Joe Glick
Vice President Alliance Sales, Mark Manzo
Senior Vice President Commercial Finance, Ricky Mims
Senior Vice President and Manager Business Aircraft Group Commercial Finance, Tad Herrin
Vice President, Jim Farmer
Senior Vice President Business Analytics, Tom Elkins
Chairman, Franklin W. (Fritz) Hobbs, age 69
Corporate Treasurer, Bradley Brown
Auditors: Deloitte & Touche LLP

LOCATIONS

HQ: Ally Financial Inc
Ally Detroit Center, 500 Woodward Avenue, Floor 10, Detroit, MI 48226
Phone: 866 710-4623
Web: www.ally.com

PRODUCTS/OPERATIONS

2016 sales

	$ mil.	% of total
Financing revenue and other interest income	8,305	84
Insurance premiums and service revenue earned	945	10
Gain on mortgage and automotive loans net	11	—
Other gain on investments net	185	2
Other income	394	4
Loss on extinguishment of debt	(5)	—
Total	**9,835**	**100**

2016 Sales

	% of total
Automotive Finance	73
Insurance	20
Corporate Finance	3
Mortgage Finance	2
Corporate and Other	2
Total	**100**

Selected Operations

Automotive
  Commercial finance
  Consumer finance
  Dealer inventory insurance

Extended service contracts
Loan servicing
Vehicle remarketing services
Corporate
  Asset-based lending
  Health capital
  Resort finance
  Structured finance
Mortgage
  Loan servicing
  Residential mortage loans
  Other lending

COMPETITORS

Bank of America
Citigroup
Ford Motor Credit
Mercedes-Benz Credit
Mercedes-Benz Financial Services USA
Mitsubishi Motors Credit of America
Toyota Motor Credit
Volkswagen Financial Services

HISTORICAL FINANCIALS

Company Type: Public

Income Statement

FYE: December 31

	ASSETS ($ mil.)	NET INCOME ($ mil.)	INCOME AS % OF ASSETS	EMPLOYEES
12/16	163,728	1,067	0.7%	7,600
12/15	158,581	1,289	0.8%	7,100
12/14	151,828	1,150	0.8%	6,900
12/13	151,167	361	0.2%	7,100
12/12	182,347	1,196	0.7%	10,600
Annual Growth	**(2.7%)**	**(2.8%)**	**—**	**(8.0%)**

2016 Year-End Financials

Debt ratio: 35.27%
Return on equity: 7.95%
Cash ($ mil.): 5,934
Current ratio: —
Long-term debt ($ mil.): —
No. of shares (mil.): 467
Dividends
  Yield: 0.0%
  Payout: 7.4%
Market value ($ mil.): 8,882

	STOCK PRICE ($) FY Close	P/E High/Low		PER SHARE ($) Earnings	Dividends	Book Value
12/16	19.02	9	7	2.15	0.16	28.52
12/15	18.64	—	—	(2.66)	0.00	27.88
12/14	23.62	4727	11	1.83	0.00	32.07
Annual Growth	**(5.3%)**	**—**	**—**	**4.1%**	**—**	**(2.9%)**

Alphabet Inc

If you don't know what the term Google means there's a leading Internet search engine you can use to find out. Google offers targeted search results from billions of Web pages. Results are based on a proprietary algorithm; its technology for ranking Web pages is called PageRank. The firm generates revenue through ad sales. Advertisers deliver relevant ads targeted to search queries or Web content. The Google Network is a network of third-party customers that use Google's ad programs to deliver relevant ads to their own sites. In October 2015 Google formally became part — and by far the biggest part — of the Alphabet Inc. holding company.

Operations

Because the technology industry demands constant innovation Google has been nothing short of relentless in its efforts to develop or acquire new services and products in order to stay ahead of such rivals as Yahoo! and Microsoft. Since its founding as search engine the company has branched out to provide Web portal services such as Webmail (Gmail) blogging (Blogger) photo sharing (Picasa) interactive maps (Google Maps) and Web browsing (Google Chrome).

In addition its Android operating system is a platform for mobile and tablet products; Google has also released an Android smart phone. The company sells digital content such as apps music and movies through Google Play Store (formerly called Android Market). Google subsidiaries include YouTube and DoubleClick.

Despite this plethora of diverse offerings Google's lead in Internet search is still fueled by its advertising system comprised of its AdWords and AdSense products (90% of its revenue stemmed from advertising in fiscal 2015). Customers of AdWords seek to drive traffic from Google to their sites and generate leads. Advertisers bid on keywords and have their ads appear as links on the right-hand column of Google's search results page under the sponsored links heading.

Through AdSense for Search Google powers the search capabilities of other publishers' websites and search engines product. With AdSense for Content Google delivers ads to a publisher's website that are targeted to the content on the publisher's site and the publisher shares in the revenue generated when readers click on the ads. AdSense customers are publishers of third-party websites that comprise the Google AdSense Network. The AdSense Network includes many small websites but has also attracted several big players in online publishing and e-commerce including AOL Ask.com and NYTimes.com.

Geographic Reach

In order to face its international rivals head on Google operates from more than 70 offices in about 40 countries. International domains include Google.ba Google.dm Google.nr Google.co.jp and Google.ca and the Google interface is available in more than 100 languages. However the US accounted for 46% of the company's revenue during fiscal 2015.

Financial Performance

Google has historically reported year-over-year revenue and net income growth and fiscal 2015 was no different. Its revenues climbed from $66 billion in fiscal 2014 to a record-setting $74.9 billion in fiscal 2015. The company's net income also surged 13% from $14.4 billion in fiscal 2014 to reach a milestone $16.3 billion in fiscal 2015.

The historic growth for 2015 was attributed to the increase in advertising revenues generated by Google websites Google Network Members' websites and hardware product sales. The growth in advertising revenue was fueled by a 16% spike in Google website revenue as a result of increases in mobile search due to ongoing improvements in ad formats as well as growth in YouTube video advertising across TrueView and Google Preferred.

Google's cash flow from operations has also significantly increased year-over-year. Its cash flow in fiscal 2015 increased to $26 billion compared to $22.4 billion in 2014. The spike was mainly due to the company's higher net income and changes in working capital.

Strategy

In order to enter new markets and maintain a portfolio of innovative offerings Google is continuing its strategy of investment in innovation and new product development.

Mergers and Acquisitions

During fiscal 2015 Google paid $380.2 million to acquire bebop Technologies Inc. (bebop) a London-based company with a cloud-based development platform focused on enterprise applications.

HISTORY

Google is the product of two computer science grad students Sergey Brin and Larry Page who met in 1995 at Stanford University where they studied methods of searching and organizing large datasets. They discovered a formula to rank the order of random search results by relevancy and in 1997 they adopted the name Google to their findings. In 1998 the two presented their discovery at the World Wide Web Conference and by 1999 they had raised almost $30 million in funding from private investors venture capital firms and Stanford University. Later that year the Google site was launched.

Brin and Page hired tech industry veteran Eric Schmidt (former CTO at Sun Microsystems and former CEO of Novell) in 2001 as Google's CEO. Brin previously the company's chairman adopted the role of president of technology and Page previously CEO of Google became president of product. Also in 2001 Google launched AdWords its search-based advertising service. The following year the company launched another advertising service the context-based AdSense.

In 2004 the company entered the social networking sphere with the launch of its Orkut product which allows users (by invitation only) to search and connect with one another through online networks of friends. Later that year the once highly secretive company went public in one of the most anticipated IPOs ever raising $1.6 billion.

In October 2015 Google became a subsidiary of Alphabet Inc.

EXECUTIVES

SVP Products Google Inc., Sundar Pichai, age 45
SVP and CFO Alphabet Inc. and Google Inc., Ruth M. Porat, age 60
President Enterprise Sales, Tariq M. Shaukat, age 44
VP and CEO Google Israel, Meir Brand
Senior Vice President Business Operations, Shona Brown
Senior Vice President, Belvia Sharp
Vice President Human Resources, Amy Buchen
Senior Vice President Global Operations, Dan Zhang
Vice President Real Estate and Workplace Services, Christopher Coleman
Vice President and General Counsel, Joanna Flint
Vice President Keepin Information Technology Real, Luke Mahe
Vice President and General Counsel, Mike Walker
Vice President Product Management EMEA and Latin America, Mario Queiroz
Vice President S, Amit Singh
Board Member, Marc Ellenbogen
Board Member, Jonathan Cranmer
Assistant Treasurer, Tony Altobelli
Treasurer, Alex Kwok
Auditors: Ernst & Young LLP

LOCATIONS

HQ: Alphabet Inc
1600 Amphitheatre Parkway, Mountain View, CA 94043
Phone: 650 253-0000
Web: www.abc.xyz

PRODUCTS/OPERATIONS

Selected Products & Advertising Platforms
AdWords
DoubleClick Digital Marketing
Google Analytics
Google Consumer Surveys
Google Display Network
Google for Retail
Google+ for Brands
YouTube

COMPETITORS

AOL	MSN
Apple Inc.	Myspace
Ask.com	NetEase
Baidu	SINA
Blucora	Shopping.com
CityGrid Media	Shopzilla
Conversant	Sohu.com
Daum Communications	Twitter
Facebook	Yahoo!
LiveJournal	craigslist
LookSmart	

HISTORICAL FINANCIALS

Company Type: Public

Income Statement

FYE: December 31

	REVENUE ($ mil.)	NET INCOME ($ mil.)	NET PROFIT MARGIN	EMPLOYEES
12/17	110,855	12,662	11.4%	80,110
12/16	90,272	19,478	21.6%	72,053
12/15	74,989	16,348	21.8%	61,814
12/14	66,001	14,444	21.9%	53,600
12/13	59,825	12,920	21.6%	47,756
Annual Growth	16.7%	(0.5%)	—	13.8%

2017 Year-End Financials

Debt ratio: 2.01%
Return on equity: 8.69%
Cash ($ mil.): 10,715
Current ratio: 5.14
Long-term debt ($ mil.): 3,969
No. of shares (mil.): 694
Dividends
 Yield: —
 Payout: —
Market value ($ mil.): 731,884

	STOCK PRICE ($) FY Close	P/E High/Low	Earnings	Dividends	Book Value
12/17	1,053.40	59 44	18.00	0.00	219.50
12/16	792.45	30 24	27.85	0.00	201.12
12/15	778.01	33 21	23.59	0.00	175.07
12/14	530.66	57 23	21.02	0.00	153.64
12/13	1,120.71	58 36	19.07	0.00	129.99
Annual Growth	(1.5%)	— —	(1.4%)	—	14.0%

Altaba Inc

EXECUTIVES

Chairman, Alfred J. (Fred) Amoroso, age 66
Co-Founder and Chief Yahoo!, David Filo, age 49
Chairman, Maynard G. Webb Jr., age 61
VP and Managing Director Yahoo! EMEA, Christophe Parcot, age 45
EVP Technology Organization, David E. Dibble, age 54
SVP Advertising Technology, Scott Burke
President CEO and Director, Marissa Mayer
SVP APAC Region, Rose Tsou, age 51
SVP Communication Products, Jeff Bonforte
SVP Global Media and Commerce Yahoo!, Mickie Rosen
COO, Henrique De Castro
Chief Marketing Officer, Kathy Savitt
CFO, Kenneth (Ken) Goldman
General Counsel and Secretary, Ron Bell
SVP Mobile and Emerging Products, Adam Cahan
EVP People and Development, Jacqueline D Reses
SVP Platforms, Jay Rossiter
SVP Search Products, Laurie Mann
SVP Homepage & Verticals, Mike Kerns
Director, David W. Kenny, age 53
Director, Maynard G. Webb Jr., age 59
Director, Thomas E. McInerney, age 73

Director, Peter Liguori, age 55
Director, Brad D. Smith, age 51
Director, Michael J. Wolf, age 53
President CEO and Director, Marissa Mayer
Director, Daniel S. Loeb, age 52
Director, Susan (Sue) James, age 69
Director, Harry J. Wilson, age 43
Auditors: PricewaterhouseCoopers LLP

LOCATIONS

HQ: Altaba Inc
140 East 45th St. 15th Floor, New York, NY 10017
Phone: 646 679-2000
Web: www.altaba.com

COMPETITORS

24/7 Real Media	Facebook
AOL	Google
About.com	LookSmart
Amazon.com	MSN
Apple Inc.	Myspace
Ask.com	RealNetworks
Blucora	Twitter
CBS Interactive	Vertro
CityGrid Media	craigslist
Daum Communications	eBay
Disney Online	

HISTORICAL FINANCIALS

Company Type: Public

Income Statement

FYE: December 31

	REVENUE ($ mil.)	NET INCOME ($ mil.)	NET PROFIT MARGIN	EMPLOYEES
12/16	5,169	(214)	—	9,100
12/15	4,968	(4,359)	—	11,260
12/14	4,618	7,521	162.9%	12,500
12/13	4,680	1,366	29.2%	12,200
12/12	4,986	3,945	79.1%	11,700
Annual Growth	0.9%	—	—	(6.1%)

2016 Year-End Financials

Debt ratio: 2.70%
Return on equity: (-0.71%)
Cash ($ mil.): 1,119
Current ratio: 6.31
Long-term debt ($ mil.): 1,299
No. of shares (mil.): 955
Dividends
 Yield: —
 Payout: —
Market value ($ mil.): 36,942

	STOCK PRICE ($) FY Close	P/E High/Low	Earnings	Dividends	Book Value
12/16	38.67	— —	(0.23)	0.00	32.50
12/15	33.26	— —	(4.64)	0.00	30.71
12/14	50.51	7 4	7.45	0.00	41.35
12/13	40.44	31 15	1.26	0.00	12.89
12/12	19.90	6 4	3.28	0.00	13.06
Annual Growth	18.1%	— —	—	—	25.6%

ALTICOR INC.

At the core of Alticor there's Amway. Holding company Alticor operates direct-selling giant Amway International and North American Web sales affiliate Amway Corp. which does business as Amway Global. Its Access Business Group offers manufacturing and distribution services primarily catering to the Amway units but also to contract clients. Outside the direct-sales realm Alticor Corporate Enterprises operates resort management firm Amway Hotel and health diagnostics developer Interleukin Genetics. Formed in 2000 Alticor is owned by Amway's founders the DeVos and Van Andel families.

Operations

Alticor is the parent company to Amway Access Business Group LLC and Alticor Corporate Enterprises.

Collectively through its network of businesses Alticor serves more than 100 countries and territories worldwide. The company offers consumer products and business opportunities not available elsewhere. Its services include product development manufacturing and logistics. Besides Alticor's Amway Hotel and Interleukin Genetics businesses the company operates several other unique entities. Its Metagenics unit a global life sciences company focuses on reversing chronic illness and on improving health through nutrition. Fulton Innovation another subsidiary is a technology licensing company. Its KinDex Therapeutics unit concentrates on the discovery of molecules associated with chronic disease.

In 2016 Alticor sold upscale cosmetics maker Gurwitch Products (known for its Laura Mercier and ReVive brands) to cosmetics maker Shiseido Americas Corporation.

Geographic Reach

Based in Ada Michigan Alticor's headquarters spans more than 1 million sq. ft. The company owns or manages manufacturing and distribution facilities worldwide. It boasts manufacturing facilities in the US China Vietnam and India and oversees organically-certified farms in the US Mexico and Brazil for growing food supplements. Alticor's distribution facilities are located in North America Europe and the Far East.

Sales and Marketing

Amway boasts more than 3 million independent distributors worldwide. China has become its largest market.It's a well-known multi-level marketer and direct seller of household personal care nutrition and cleaning items. The company also peddles the products of other companies worldwide in more than 80 markets.

Financial Performance

While privately-owned Alticor doesn't report its results Amway reported global sales of $10.8 billion in 2014 down from $12 billion in 2013.

Strategy

The company's success depends on setting up Independent Business Owners (IBOs) to sell its name-brand products but more importantly build its network. The company has been accused of focusing on new IBO recruitment rather than on selling and developing new products or services. Although individuals are required to pay a membership fee Amway asserts that they can then buy its products and sell them at a 20% to 25% markup. IBOs that recruit get a cut from the sales made by those members.

The direct-selling business model is popular; Amway reaches across North America and Europe. Its focus however is increasingly on Asia's fertile market. Sales from its Amway China and India units are anticipated to jump by double-digits as consumers increase retail spending. The company deepens its presence by outsourcing its manufacturing operations to third parties in the Asia/Pacific region as well as by aligning its product design and branding around their cultures.

To this end Amway is investing $335 million in manufacturing and research and development expansion. The initiative involves upgrading four factories in the US building a new manufacturing facility in India and adding second sites in both China and Vietnam. In 2013 Amway broke ground on a new $95-million production plant in Tamil Nadu India set for completion in 2015. Its second plant in China will be located in Guangzhou; the $75-million facility is slated for completion by 2016.

Alticor continues to invest in its supply chain manufacturing and scientific resources to ensure distributors have access to products when and where they need them.

Mergers and Acquisitions

In 2015 Alticor purchased energy drink brand XS Energy which the company says has $150 million in sales in nearly 40 global markets. XS Energy creator David Vanderveen is a former Amway salesman.

EXECUTIVES

President, Doug DeVos
Vice President, Richard Holwill
Senior Vice President Internal, Michael Duong
Executive Vice President Sales, Glenn Armstrong
Vice President Logistics, Ken Davis
Chairman, Steve Van Andel

LOCATIONS

HQ: ALTICOR INC.
7575 FULTON ST E, ADA, MI 493550001
Phone: 616 787-1000
Web: WWW.ALTICOR.COM

PRODUCTS/OPERATIONS

Selected Operations
Access Business Group LLC
Alticor Corporate Enterprises
 Amway Hotel Corp.
 Fulton Innovation
 Interleukin Genetics
 KinDex Therapeutics
 Metagenics
Amway
 Amway International
 Amway Corp.

COMPETITORS

Avon	Kao
Bath & Body Works	L'Or©al
BeautiControl	MacAndrews & Forbes
Bluestem Brands	Mary Kay
Brown-Forman	Melaleuca
CCL Industries	Newell Brands
Clorox	Nikken
Colgate-Palmolive	Nu Skin
Daiei	PFSweb
Est©e Lauder	Procter & Gamble
Forever Living	S.C. Johnson
GNC	Shaklee
Henkel	Tupperware Brands
Johnson & Johnson	

HISTORICAL FINANCIALS

Company Type: Private

Income Statement

FYE: December 31

	REVENUE ($ mil.)	NET INCOME ($ mil.)	NET PROFIT MARGIN	EMPLOYEES
12/15	9,459	0	—	14,000
12/14	10,804	0	—	
12/13	11,754	0	—	
12/12	11,338	0	—	
Annual Growth	(5.9%)	—	—	

2015 Year-End Financials

Debt ratio: ——
Return on equity: —
Cash ($ mil.): 1,300
Current ratio: 0.70
Long-term debt ($ mil.): —

Dividends
 Yield: —
 Payout: —
Market value ($ mil.): —

Altria Group Inc

The house the Marlboro Man built Altria Group owns the largest cigarette company in the US. Altria operates through subsidiary Philip Morris USA which sells Marlboro — the world's #1-selling cigarette brand. Controlling about half of the US tobacco market Altria manufactures cigarettes under the Parliament Virginia Slims and Basic brands among many others. Altria however has diversified from solely a cigarette maker to a purveyor of cigars and pipe tobacco through John Middleton Co.; smokeless tobacco products through UST; and wine through Ste. Michelle Wine Estates. Another subsidiary Philip Morris Capital Corp. holds a group of finance leases. Altria also owns a 10% stake in brewing giant AB InBev.

HISTORY

Philip Morris opened his London tobacco store in 1847 and by 1854 was making his own cigarettes. Morris died in 1873 and his heirs sold the firm to William Thomson just before the turn of the century. Thomson introduced his company's cigarettes to the US in 1902. American investors bought the rights to leading Philip Morris brands in 1919 and in 1925 the new company Philip Morris & Co. introduced Marlboro which targeted women smokers and produced modest sales.

When the firm's larger competitors raised their prices in 1930 Philip Morris Companies countered by introducing inexpensive cigarettes that caught on with Depression-weary consumers. By 1936 it was the fourth-biggest cigarette maker.

The firm acquired Benson & Hedges in 1954. It signed ad agency Leo Burnett which promptly initiated the Marlboro Man campaign. Under Joseph Cullman (who became president in 1957) Philip Morris experienced tremendous growth overseas. After dipping to sixth place among US tobacco companies in 1960 it rebounded at home thanks to Marlboro's growing popularity among men (Marlboro became the #1 cigarette brand in the world in 1972).

In 1970 Philip Morris bought the nation's seventh-largest brewer Miller Brewing and with aggressive marketing it vaulted to #2 among US beer makers by 1980. To protect itself against a shrinking US tobacco market in 1985 Philip Morris paid $5.6 billion for General Foods (Kool-Aid Post Stove Top). In 1988 it bought Kraft (Miracle Whip Velveeta). The next year Philip Morris joined Kraft with General Foods.

In 1994 Australian Geoffrey Bible became CEO. By late 1998 the company and its rivals had settled tobacco litigation with most states agreeing to pay about $250 billion over 25 years to receive protection from further state suits.

In 1999 Philip Morris bought three cigarette brands (L&M Chesterfield and Lark) from the Brooke Group. The US government filed a massive lawsuit against Big Tobacco and Philip Morris admitted — no kidding — that smoking increases the risk of getting cancer and other illnesses.

In 2000 Philip Morris vowed to appeal after a state court awarded $74 billion in punitive damages to Florida smokers. The court later ruled that Philip Morris Lorillard and the Liggett Group would pay at least $709 million in the case regardless of the outcome but would not have to pay damages until after the appeals are resolved. A Los Angeles jury awarded Richard Boeken $3 billion in punitive damages. The company appealed even after Boeken later agreed to reduced damages of $100 million. (Boeken died in 2002.)

In December 2000 Philip Morris completed its purchase of Nabisco Holdings for $18.9 billion. In June 2001 Philip Morris spun off Kraft Foods in what was the second-largest IPO in US history; it retained an 84% stake in the company and 97% of the voting rights.

In April 2002 CFO Louis Camilleri succeeded Bible as CEO; in September Camilleri became chairman upon Bible's retirement. In July 2002 Philip Morris sold Miller Brewing to South African Breweries for $5.6 billion ($3.6 billion in SAB stock and the assumption of $2 billion in Miller debt) in July 2002.

In the ongoing saga of tobacco-related litigation Philip Morris said it would appeal an October 2002 verdict by a California jury that ordered the company to pay $28 billion in punitive damages the most ever in an individual tobacco liability lawsuit (later reduced to $28 million). In January 2003 Philip Morris changed its name to Altria Group in an effort to distance itself from its tobacco litigation. In April a Florida appeals court threw out the state's multibillion-dollar judgment (made in 2000) against Philip Morris USA and four other US tobacco companies stating that thousands of Florida smokers could not lump their complaints together in a single case.

In March 2003 Philip Morris USA lost an Illinois lawsuit which claimed the company's use of the word "light" was misleading and violated Illinois consumer fraud laws. The judge ordered Philip Morris USA to pay damages of $10 billion and post a $12 billion bond. The Illinois Supreme Court has lowered the bond to $7 billion and agreed to hear Philip Morris USA's appeal of the original verdict.

In 2005 Altria purchased a $4.8 billion stake in Indonesia's third-largest tobacco firm PT Hanjaya Mandala Sampoerna which makes kreteks or clove cigarettes. Also in 2005 the company formed a long-term alliance with China National Tobacco Corp.

In mid-2006 Altria unseated Roger Deromedi from Kraft's top spot and appointed Irene Rosenfeld to head the company. The executive realignment was part of Altria's plan to spin off Kraft. Deromedi a 28-year Kraft veteran had been under fire for the unit's stale sales since taking over as sole CEO in 2003. Rosenfeld spent more than 20 years at Kraft and exited the firm in mid-2003 as president of Kraft Foods North America. The former chairman and CEO of Frito-Lay Rosenfeld is known for her integration expertise as well as restructuring and turning around companies.

In March 2007 Altria completed the spinoff of Kraft Foods to Altria shareholders. Also in 2007 Altria bought US cigar maker John Middleton from privately held Bradford Holdings. Based in Pennsylvania John Middleton specializes in machine-made cigars — most notably the Black & Mild brand. The deal was valued at $2.2 billion. A year later in March 2008 Altria spun off its Philip Morris International arm also to shareholders and moved its headquarters from New York City's Park Avenue to Richmond Virginia to be closer to its bread and butter operations. (As part of the move Altria in late 2007 agreed to sell the headquarters that has housed the firm since 1982 to a unit of privately held Global Holdings for some $525 million. Altria relocated about 100 of its about 500 employees in the move from New York City to Richmond.)

In January 2009 the company purchased smokeless tobacco maker UST as well as its wine business. The $11 billion deal gave Altria a significant foothold in the US smokeless tobacco market garnering popular brands Copenhagen and Skoal into Altria's fold. Following the acquisition Altria consolidated the sales forces of UST's U.S. Smokeless Tobacco brands and Philip Morris USA and

relocated U.S. Smokeless Tobacco Company to Richmond Virginia. Altria has since launched a new versions of certain brands designed to compete with value-priced brands such as Reynolds American's Grizzly and Swedish Match AB's Timber Wolf.

In June 2009 the passage of the Family Smoking and Tobacco Control Act by the US Congress gave the U.S. Food and Drug Administration unprecedented authority to regulate tobacco products including the authority to regulate marketing ban candy flavorings and reduce nicotine in tobacco products.

EXECUTIVES

Chairman President and CEO, Martin J. (Marty) Barrington, age 64, $1,408,333 total compensation
President and CEO Ste. Michelle Wine Estates, Theodor P. (Ted) Baseler, age 63
SVP Research Development and Regulatory Affairs and Chief Innovation Officer, James E. (Jim) Dillard, $530,833 total compensation
President and CEO Altria Group Distribution, Craig A. Johnson, age 65, $901,667 total compensation
EVP Strategy and Business Development, Howard A. Willard, age 54, $833,333 total compensation
President and CEO U.S. Smokeless Tobacco, Brian W. Quigley
CFO, William F. (Billy) Gifford, age 47, $640,833 total compensation
EVP and General Counsel, Denise F. Keane, age 66, $938,500 total compensation
President and CEO Philip Morris USA, Clifford B. (Cliff) Fleet
President Nu Mark, Jody L. Begley
VP and CIO, Daniel C. Cornell
Auditors: PricewaterhouseCoopers LLP

LOCATIONS

HQ: Altria Group Inc
   6601 West Broad Street, Richmond, VA 23230
Phone: 804 274-2200
Web: www.altria.com

PRODUCTS/OPERATIONS

2015 Income

	% of total
Smokeable products	90
Smokeless products	7
Wine	3
All other	-
Total	**100**

Selected Subsidiaries

F.W. Rickard Seeds Inc.
Green Smoke Inc.
International Wine & Spirits Ltd.
John Middleton Co.
Philip Morris Capital Corp.
Philip Morris USA Inc.
Stag's Leap Wine Cellars LLC
Ste. Michelle Wine Estates Ltd.
U.S. Smokeless Tobacco Co. LLC
UST LLC

COMPETITORS

Altadis	Loews
Anheuser-Busch	Molson Coors
Anheuser-Busch InBev	North Atlantic Trading
British American	Ravenswood Winery
Tobacco	Reynolds American
Constellation Brands	Sebastiani Vineyards
E. & J. Gallo	Swedish Match
Heineken	Treasury Wine Estates
Imperial Brands	Vector Group
Japan Tobacco	

HISTORICAL FINANCIALS

Company Type: Public

Income Statement

FYE: December 31

	REVENUE ($ mil.)	NET INCOME ($ mil.)	NET PROFIT MARGIN	EMPLOYEES
12/16	25,744	14,239	55.3%	8,300
12/15	25,434	5,241	20.6%	8,800
12/14	24,522	5,070	20.7%	9,000
12/13	24,466	4,535	18.5%	9,000
12/12	24,618	4,180	17.0%	9,100
Annual Growth	**1.1%**	**35.9%**	**—**	**(2.3%)**

2016 Year-End Financials

Debt ratio: 30.22%
Return on equity: 181.47%
Cash ($ mil.): 4,569
Current ratio: 0.98
Long-term debt ($ mil.): 13,881
No. of shares (mil.): 1,943
Dividends
Yield: 0.0%
Payout: 32.2%
Market value ($ mil.): 131,404

	STOCK PRICE ($) FY Close	P/E High/Low		PER SHARE ($) Earnings	Dividends	Book Value
12/16	67.62	10	8	7.28	2.35	6.57
12/15	58.21	23	18	2.67	2.17	1.47
12/14	49.27	20	13	2.56	2.00	1.53
12/13	38.39	17	14	2.26	1.84	2.07
12/12	31.44	18	14	2.06	1.70	1.58
Annual Growth	**21.1%**	**—**	**—**	**37.1%**	**8.4%**	**42.9%**

Amazon.com Inc

Amazon.com began as Earth's biggest bookstore but has become Earth's biggest everything store. Its website still offers millions of books as well as other media home furnishings clothing pet supplies office products and hundreds of other product categories (with items often ordered and delivered the same day). The company is also the dominant cloud services provider an influential entertainment company through its video operations (it produced 2017 Oscar-nominated Manchester-by-the-Sea) a force to be reckoned with in grocery with its ownership of natural foods chain Whole Foods and a leader in digital personal assistant devices with Alexa and its Echo product line.

HISTORY

Jeff Bezos was researching the Internet in the early 1990s for hedge fund D.E. Shaw. He realized that book sales would be a perfect fit with e-commerce because book distributors already kept meticulous electronic lists. Bezos who as a teen had dreamed of entrepreneurship in outer space took the idea to Shaw. The company passed on the idea but Bezos ran with it trekking cross country to Seattle (close to a facility owned by major book distributor Ingram) and typing up a business plan along the way.

Bezos founded Amazon.com in 1994. After months of preparation he launched a website in July 1995 (Douglas Hofstadter's Fluid Concepts and Creative Analogies was its first sale); it had sales of $20000 a week by September. Bezos and his team kept working with the site pioneering features that now seem mundane such as one-click shopping customer reviews and e-mail order verification.

Amazon went public in 1997. Moves to cement the Amazon.com brand included becoming the sole book retailer on AOL's website and Netscape's commercial channel.

In 1998 the company launched its online music and video stores and it began to sell toys and electronics. Amazon also expanded its European reach with the purchases of online booksellers in the UK and Germany and it acquired the Internet Movie Database. Bezos also expanded the company's base of online services buying Junglee (comparison shopping) and PlanetAll (address book calendar reminders).

By midyear Amazon.com had attracted so much attention that its market capitalization equaled the combined values of profitable bricks-and-mortar rivals Barnes & Noble and Borders Group even though their combined sales were far greater than the upstart's. Late that year Amazon formed a promotional link with Hoover's publisher of this profile.

After raising $1.25 billion in a bond offering early in 1999 Amazon.com began a spending spree with deals to buy all or part of several dotcoms. However some have since been sold (HomeGrocer.com) and others have gone out of business or bankrupt — Pets.com living.com (furniture). It also bought the catalog businesses of Back to Basics and Tool Crib of the North.

Amazon.com began conducting online auctions in early 1999 and partnered with venerable auction house Sotheby's. Also that year Amazon added distribution facilities including one each in England and Germany.

In 2000 the company inked a 10-year deal with Toysrus.com to set up a co-branded toy and video game store. (The partnership came to a bitter end in 2006 after Toys "R" Us sued Amazon.com when it began selling toys from other companies.) Also that year Amazon.com added foreign-language sites for France and Japan.

In 2001 Amazon cut 15% of its workforce as part of a restructuring plan that also forced a $150 million charge. That year the company also made a deal with Borders to provide inventory fulfillment content and customer service for borders.com. As part of a deal to expand their marketing partnership AOL invested $100 million in Amazon.com in 2001. Later that year Amazon purchased some assets from Egghead.com (which filed for Chapter 11 in August) and relaunched the site.

In 2002 the firm introduced clothing sales featuring hundreds of retailers including names such as The Gap Nordstrom and Lands' End. Amazon.com received accreditation from ICANN (the Internet Corporation for Assigned Names and Numbers) as an Internet domain name registrar becoming one of about 160 entities permitted to register Internet addresses.

The company launched its Search Inside the Book feature in 2003. The tool allows customers to search the text inside books for more relevant search returns. At launch the search feature covered more than 120000 books from over 190 publishers. Amazon expanded into China in 2004 with the purchase of Joyo.com. (It renamed the unit Joyo Amazon in 2007.)

In 2005 Amazon launched Amazon Prime a two-day shipping service for an annual fee of $79.

Amazon.com began testing the online dry grocery waters in 2006. It launched the Amazon Fresh delivery service for the Seattle area a year later to include perishables.

The company acquired shopping site Shopbop.com in 2006 boosting its apparel offerings. Also that year IBM filed a pair of patent infringement lawsuits alleging that Amazon.com has been violating at least five of its patents — including technologies that govern how the online retailer handles product recommendations and displays advertising — for about four years. In 2007 the

two companies settled the litigation and signed a long-term patent cross-license agreement.

The Internet bookseller in November 2007 introduced the Kindle an electronic portable book reader. The launch Amazon's first foray into the tech hardware market is aimed at kindling demand for electronic books.

Also in 2007 Amazon launched Endless.com which sells shoes and accessories; Askville.com where users can solicit answers from others on the site; and the Amazon MP3 site which offers digital music free of copyright restrictions. In addition Amazon acquired audiobook publisher Brilliance Audio.

Amazon stayed focused on entertainment in 2008. The company launched Amazon Video On Demand a service that gives customers the option to stream or download ad-free digital movies and TV shows on Macs or PCs. It also purchased AbeBooks an online retailer of more than 110 million primarily used rare and out-of-print books as well as Shelfari a social-networking site for booklovers. Additionally Amazon.com sold its UK and German online DVD rental services to Internet movie-rental company LOVEFiLM International in exchange for stock. The deal gave Amazon about a 40% stake in LOVEFiLM.

Shopping was also at the top of Amazon's list in 2008. In May the company invested in The Talk Market a user-generated TV Shopping Channel. In June Amazon launched an online office supplies store and sewed up the acquisition of the online fabrics retailer Fabrics.com.

In June 2009 Amazon agreed to pay Toys "R" Us$51 million to settle a dispute dating back to 2004. The settlement was related to a partnership that gave the toy seller exclusive rights to supply some of the toys on Amazon's site. In November Amazon completed its $888 million acquisition of shoe e-tailer Zappos.com — the #1 online shoe and apparel retailer. (Besides footwear and clothing Zappos also sells handbags housewares and beauty products.) The purchase allowed Amazon to boost its sales and expand its products portfolio by leveraging Zappos' widely recognized customer service expertise.

In mid-2010 Amazon acquired Woot Inc. a pioneer in the deal-of-the-day genre of online retailing. While neither Amazon or Woot would disclose the selling price reports valued the deal at about $110 million in cash.

In January 2011 Amazon completed its move to a new corporate headquarters in Seattle's South Lake Union neighborhood. Amazon also made several acquisitions that year. The company acquired the remaining shares it didn't already own in LOVEFiLM International. It purchased a pair of UK companies: online book seller The Book Depository and digital agency Pushbutton (later folding the operation into its Amazon Development Centre in London). The behemoth also picked up voice-to-text startup Yap based in Charlotte North Carolina that year.

Kiva Systems which Amazon bought in 2012 was purchased to provide the firm with a boost in automation capabilities. Amazon picked up some former talent including Amazon ex Dave Schappell when it bought online education marketplace Teachstreet and shuttered the site in 2012. Acquiring England's Evi and its namesake cloudbased Artificial Intelligence expertise in 2012 offered Amazon a leg up in answer engine technology.

To extend the reach of its Kindle range Amazon in 2013 acquired Poland's IVONA Software. Months after being bought by Amazon in 2013 social cataloging company Goodreads announced it had amassed some 20 million members. In 2013 Amazon also purchased electrowetting display panel expert Liquavista from Samsung Electronics

which had held the company for fewer than three years.

Investments in 2014 include acquiring the .buy domain for nearly $4.6 million. Besides the domain purchase Amazon has been focused on games. It acquired Silent Hill: Homecoming video game developer Double Helix Games based in Irvine California. Its newest release Strider is available on five platforms. Amazon also bought cloud-based digital comics platform ComiXology in 2014. In late 2014 Amazon purchased game-streaming site Twitch which boasted 55 million monthly active users after talks with Google turned to anti-trust concerns.

EXECUTIVES

Vice President Kindle Content, Russell Grandinetti
CEO Worldwide Consumer Business, Jeffrey A. (Jeff) Wilke, age 51, $175,000 total compensation
Chairman President and CEO, Jeffrey P. (Jeff) Bezos, age 54, $81,840 total compensation
CEO Amazon Web Services, Andrew R. (Andy) Jassy, age 50, $175,000 total compensation
SVP and CFO, Brian T. Olsavsky, $160,000 total compensation
Vice President Seller Applications Technology, Paul Kotas
Vice President Home Improvements, John Witham
Vice President, Seth Dallaire
Vice President Investor Relations, Tim Stone
Vice President AD Platform, Tim Craycroft
Vice President of Information Technology Infrastructure, Tom Killalea
Vice President Information Technology, Yvette Bohanan
Vice President Of Legal Retail Team, Amber Beckman
Vice President Human Resources Kindle, John Olsen
Vice President Worldwide Discovery, Kim Rachmeler
Vice President E Commerce Platform Services, Gene Pope
Vice President Content Acquisition And I, David Naggar
Vice President Information Technology, Kathryn Giorgianni
Vice President Corporate Sales Development, Robert Saltzman
Senior Vice President, Jeffrey Blackburn
Vice President of Legal Retail Team, Michael Kawachi
Vice President Visual Search and Mobile Innovation, Gautam Bhargava
MVP Program Security Officer, Rachel Lopez
Vice President And Distinguished Engineer, Jim Roskind
Vice President, Ashish Thaker
Vice President, Carmine Arabia
Vice President Public Policy, Monique Meche
AVP8 Senior HRA, Sandy Motyleski
Vice President Supply Chain and Procurement, Jens Gruenkemeier
Vice President, Adrian Cockcroft
Vice President, Jasper Cheung
Vice President Iot, Dirk Didascalou
Vice President Voice and Nui Shopping, Assaf Ronen
Senior Vice President, Steve Kessel
Vice President People Operations, Ardine Williams
Assistant Treasurer, Tara Thiara
Treasurer, Tony Masone
Auditors: Ernst & Young LLP

LOCATIONS

HQ: Amazon.com Inc
410 Terry Avenue North, Seattle, WA 98109-5210
Phone: 206 266-1000   **Fax:** 206 266-1821
Web: www.amazon.com

2017 Sales

	$ mil.	% of total
North America	106,110	60
International	54,297	30
AWS	17,459	10
Total	**177,866**	**100**

2017 Sales

	$ mil.	% of total
United States	120,486	68
International		
Germany	16,951	9
Japan	11,907	7
United Kingdom	11,372	6
Other countries	17,150	10
Total	**177,866**	**100**

PRODUCTS/OPERATIONS

2017 Sales

	$ mil.	% of total
Online stores	108,354	61
Retail third-party seller services	31,881	18
AWS	17,459	10
Retail subscription services	9,721	5
Physical stores	5,798	3
Other	4,653	3
Total	**177,866**	**100**

2017 Sales

	$ mil.	% of total
Product	118,573	67
Services	59,293	33
Total	**177,866**	**100**

Selected Departments

Apparel shoes and jewelry
Books
  Books
  Kindle e-books
  Textbooks
  Magazines
Computers and office
  Computers and accessories
  Computer components
  Office products and supplies
  PC games
  Software
Digital downloads
  Amazon shorts
  Game downloads
  Kindle Store
  MP3 downloads
Electronics
  Audio TV and home theater
  Camera photo and video
  Car electronics and GPS
  Cell phones and service
  Home appliances
  MP3 and media players
  Musical instruments
  Video games
Grocery health and beauty
  Beauty
  Diapers
  Gourmet food
  Grocery
  Health and personal care
  Natural and organic
Home and garden
  Bedding and bath
  Furniture and decor
  Home appliances
  Home improvement
  Kitchen and dining
  Patio lawn and garden
  Pet supplies
  Sewing craft and hobby
  Vacuums and storage
Kindle
  Books

Blogs
Magazines
Newspapers
Movies music and games
  Blu-ray
  Movies and TV
  Music
  Musical instruments
  Video games
  Video On Demand
Sports and outdoors
  Action sports
  Camping and hiking
  Cycling
  Exercise and fitness
  Fan gear
  Golf
  Team sports
Tools auto and industrial
  Automotive
  Home improvement
  Industrial and scientific
  Lighting and electrical
  Motorcycle and ATV
  Outdoor power equipment
  Plumbing fixtures
  Power and hand tools
Toys kids and baby
  Apparel (kids and baby)
  Baby
  Books
  Movies
  Music
  Software
  Toys and games
  Video games

Selected Operations

A9.com (search technology development)
Amazon.ca (Canada)
Amazon.cn (China)
Amazon.de (Germany)
Amazon.fr (France)
Amazon.co.jp (Japan)
Amazon.co.uk (UK)
Audible (audiobooks and other recorded content)
Endless (shoes and handbags)
Internet Movie Database (IMDb)
IVONA Software
Joyo (China)
LOVEFiLM International Ltd.
Whole Foods Market (grocery stores)
Woot.com (US)
Zappos.com (US)

COMPETITORS

Albertsons	JD.com
Alibaba Group	Kering
Apple Inc.	Kroger
AutoNation	Lowe's
AutoZone	Macy's
Barnes & Noble	Michaels Companies
Bed Bath & Beyond	Microsoft
Best Buy	Netflix
Big Lots	Office Depot
Buy.com	Overstock.com
CDW	Peapod LLC
Costco Wholesale	Safeway
DSW	Sears
Dollar General	Shoe Carnival
Dollar Tree	Sprouts
Family Dollar Stores	Staples
Finish Line	TJX Companies
Foot Locker	Target Corporation
GameStop	The Gap
Google	Toys "R" Us
HSN	Trader Joe's
Home Depot	Wal-Mart
IAC	Wayfair
J. C. Penney	eBay

HISTORICAL FINANCIALS
Company Type: Public

Income Statement

FYE: December 31

	REVENUE ($ mil.)	NET INCOME ($ mil.)	NET PROFIT MARGIN	EMPLOYEES
12/17	177,866	3,033	1.7%	566,000
12/16	135,987	2,371	1.7%	341,400
12/15	107,006	596	0.6%	230,800
12/14	88,988	(241)	—	154,100
12/13	74,452	274	0.4%	117,300
Annual Growth	**24.3%**	**82.4%**	**—**	**48.2%**

2017 Year-End Financials

Debt ratio: 28.88%
Return on equity: 12.91%
Cash ($ mil.): 30,986
Current ratio: 1.04
Long-term debt ($ mil.): 37,926

No. of shares (mil.): 484
Dividends
  Yield: —
  Payout: —
Market value ($ mil.): 566,023

	STOCK PRICE ($) FY Close	P/E High/Low		Earnings	PER SHARE ($) Dividends	Book Value
12/17	1,169.47	189	119	6.15	0.00	57.25
12/16	749.87	169	96	4.90	0.00	40.43
12/15	675.89	542	224	1.25	0.00	28.42
12/14	310.35	—	—	(0.52)	0.00	23.10
12/13	398.79	674	414	0.59	0.00	21.23
Annual Growth	**30.9%**	**—**	**—**	**79.7%**	**—**	**28.1%**

Ambac Financial Group, Inc.

Ambac has scaled back in a major way. Holding company Ambac Financial operates through subsidiaries including its flagship unit Ambac Assurance Everspan Financial Guarantee and Ambac Assurance UK. The businesses offered financial guarantees and related services to customers around the world. Ambac Assurance guaranteed public finance and structured finance obligations but it has stopped offering new business and placed its existing business in run-off (meaning it still accepts premium payments due on existing policies and pays out claims as it can).

Operations

In addition to its core financial guarantee offerings in better days Ambac also insured infrastructure and utility finance deals internationally. Its Ambac Financial Services unit offered interest rate swaps credit swaps and investment management primarily to states and municipal authorities tied to their bond financing. These operations are also in run-off through means including transaction terminations settlements and scheduled contract amortizations.

How did a once-solid municipal bond insurer fall so hard? Along with other US bond insurers including FGIC and MBIA the US subprime mortgage meltdown knocked the wind out of Ambac. Its financial guarantee business fizzled and the company began to post heavy losses. Meanwhile Ambac's portfolio bulged with collateralized debt obligations (CDOs) of asset-backed securities — the financial equivalent of a sack of rotten potatoes once the credit markets turned sour.

Geographic Reach

Ambac's run-off operations primarily bring in revenues from the US market which accounts for three-fourths of revenues. The company also has international operations (also in runoff) in markets including the UK (some 20% of revenues) Australia Austria Germany and Italy.

Financial Performance

Ambac's run-off (existing account) insurance operations brought in some $644 million in revenues in 2015 nearly doubling that of 2014. Those improved earnings marked a turnaround after a couple of years of declining revenues; they were a result of increased premiums earned lower losses on derivatives and a gain on extinguishment of debt.

Net income has remained relatively flat for the past few years and in 2015 rose a modest 2% to $492 million. That was thanks to the higher revenue but partially offset by goodwill impairment charges incurred in 2014.

After reporting an operating cash outflow of $971 million in 2014 Ambac had an inflow of operating cash totaling $87.5 million in 2015 as it has lower losses and loss expenses.

Strategy

Ambac is hoping to diversify its business and has its sights set on either buying or developing new operations. It is interested in such activities as advisory services asset management and even insurance. In late 2015 the group launched a residential property investment program.

HISTORY

Mortgage Guaranty Insurance Corporation (MGIC) in 1971 founded American Municipal Bond Assurance Corporation (Ambac Indemnity) in Milwaukee. That year Ambac wrote the very first municipal bond insurance policy — for a bond to fund a medical building and a sewage treatment facility in Juneau Alaska. New York City's 1975 moratorium on debt payments helped make the new product more attractive. The company wrote the first insurance policies for mutual funds (1977) and secondary market municipal bonds (1983). In 1981 Ambac moved to New York; four years later it became a Citibank subsidiary. It went public in 1991.

In 1995 Ambac and rival MBIA allied to offer bond insurance overseas. Two years later the company formed a UK subsidiary to serve Europe. In recognition of the growing market the joint venture was amended in 2000 to provide for individual operations by the two partners in Europe though they continued to reinsure each other there and to work jointly in Japan. Ambac went on a buying spree in 1996 and 1997 buying the investment advisory and broker dealer operations of Cadre and Construction Loan Insurance (renamed Connie Lee Holdings) a guarantor of college bonds and hospital infrastructure bonds.

In 1998 as Ambac lost share in the US municipal bond market because it declined to cut premiums the company began concentrating on asset-backed securities and international bonds. Two years later Ambac entered the Japanese market through a joint venture with Yasuda Fire & Marine.

In late 2010 after missing a scheduled interest payment and failing to reach an agreement for a prepackaged bankruptcy proceeding with its creditors the company voluntarily filed for Chapter 11 bankruptcy protection. Through the filing Ambac hoped to restructure more than $1.6 billion in outstanding debt. The company also haggled with the IRS over $700 million in allegedly improper tax refunds received between 2003 and 2008.

The bankruptcy court approved a plan of reorganization for Ambac in 2012 and the plan went into effect the following year.

EXECUTIVES

Senior Managing Director Chief Accounting Officer and Controller, Robert B. Eisman, age 49, $500,000 total compensation
President and CEO Ambac Financial Group and Ambac Assurance Corporation, Claude L. LeBlanc, age 52
Senior Managing Director CFO and Treasurer, David Trick, age 46, $770,000 total compensation
President CEO and Director, Nader Tavakoli, age 58, $1,800,000 total compensation
Senior Managing Director and General Counsel, Stephen M. Ksenak, age 51, $525,000 total compensation
Senior Managing Director Restructuring and Corporate Development, David Barranco, age 46
Senior Managing Director CIO and Chief Administrative Office, Michael Reilly, age 60
Assistant Vice President, John Ng
Assistant Vice President Business Applications and Support, Sarbah Arthur
First Vice President, Patrick Mccormick
Vice President, Robert Tyrrell
Assistant Vice President Financial Control, Shannon Kelly
VP and Manager, Aaron Liao
First Vice President, Art Heffner
First Vice President, Ronaldo Contreras
Assistant Vice President and Closing Coordinator, Yolanda Ortiz
First Vice President and Assistant General Counsel, Juan Roman
Vice President, Hartmut Ott
First Vice President Structured Real Estate, Gregory Mayer
Vice President, Gary Stein
First Vice President, Sunil Rao
First Vice President, David Holloway
First Vice President, Joan Allman
Assistant Vice President Risk Operations, Pranay Nadkarni
Assistant Vice President, Linda Crocitto
Vice President Senior Vice President Finance Director, Thomas Staskowski
Assistant Vice President Finance, Chris Dudonis
First Vice President, Tracy Pridgen
Vice President Financial Planning and Analysis, Robyn Leong
Assistant Vice President in Technology, Venka Korsapati
Assistant Vice President Payroll, Yanira Vergara
Vice President Information Technology, David Murelli
First Vice President Housing Group, Kelly Wimmer
First Vice President Credit Risk Management, Robert Bose
First Vice President, Yuliang LI
Vice President Finance Systems, Alan Lefton
Vice President Information Technology, Alan Leung
Fvp, Pat Mccormick
First Vice President, Linda Ebrahim
First Vice President, Sulexan Chery
Chairman, Jeffrey S. Stein
Auditors: KPMG LLP

LOCATIONS

HQ: Ambac Financial Group, Inc.
One State Street Plaza, New York, NY 10004
Phone: 212 658-7470

2015 Permiums by Geographic

	% of total
United States	73
United Kingdom	22
Other international	5
Total	**100**

PRODUCTS/OPERATIONS

2015 Net Premiums

	% of total
Accelerated earnings	44
Public Finance	31
International Finance	14
Structured Finance	11
Total	**100**

2015 Sales

	% of total
Net premiums earned	44
Total	37
Net realized investment gains	8
Net change in fair value of credit derivatives	6
Income (loss) on variable interest entities	4
Other income	1
Net other-than-temporary impairment losses recognized in earnings	-
Derivative products	-
Total	**100**

Selected Services

Adversely Classified Credit
Amendment Waiver and Consen
Credit Risk Management (CRM)
International Finance Insured Portfolio
U.S. Public Finance Insured Portfolio
U.S. Structured Finance

COMPETITORS

Assured Guaranty   MBIA
FGIC

HISTORICAL FINANCIALS

Company Type: Public

Income Statement

FYE: December 31

	ASSETS ($ mil.)	NET INCOME ($ mil.)	INCOME AS % OF ASSETS	EMPLOYEES
12/16	22,635	74	0.3%	154
12/15	23,728	493	2.1%	171
12/14	25,159	484	1.9%	188
12/13*	27,106	505	1.9%	212
04/13	0	3,349	—	—
Annual Growth	—	(61.3%)	—	—

*Fiscal year change

2016 Year-End Financials

Debt ratio: 54.21%
Return on equity: 4.39%
Cash ($ mil.): 91
Current ratio: —
Long-term debt ($ mil.): —

No. of shares (mil.): 45
Dividends
  Yield: —
  Payout: —
Market value ($ mil.): 1,016

	STOCK PRICE ($) FY Close	P/E High/Low		PER SHARE ($) Earnings	Dividends	Book Value
12/16	22.50	16	7	1.64	0.00	37.94
12/15	14.09	3	1	10.72	0.00	37.41
12/14	24.50	3	2	10.31	0.00	31.09
12/13*	24.56	2	1	10.91	0.00	15.62
Annual Growth	(2.2%)	—	—	(37.7%)	—	24.8%

*Fiscal year change

Ameren Corp

Ameren provides the power that lights much of Illinois and Missouri. The holding company distributes electricity to 2.4 million customers and natural gas to 900000 customers through regulated utility subsidiaries Union Electric (which does business as Ameren Missouri) and Ameren Ilinois.

Ameren has generating capacity of about 10000 MW of primarily coal-fired power most of which is owned by Ameren Missouri. Ameren supplements its customers? electricity needs by purchasing additional electricity from third parties.

HISTORY

More than 30 St. Louis companies had built a chaotic grid of generators and power lines throughout the city by 1900. Two years later many of them merged into the Union Company which attracted national notice when it lit the St. Louis World's Fair in the first broad demonstration of electricity's power. In 1913 the company by then named Union Electric (UE) began buying electricity from an Iowa dam 150 miles away — the greatest distance power had ever been transmitted in such quantity.

UE pushed into rural Missouri and began buying and building fossil-fuel plants. Despite a slowdown during the Depression UE built Bagnell Dam on Missouri's Osage River in the early 1930s to gather power for a hydroelectric plant. At the onset of WWII construction began on new plants with larger generators and lower production costs; however demand for electricity lagged. In the late 1940s UE compensated by joining a "power pool" a system of utilities with interconnected transmission lines that shared electricity.

Growth in the 1950s came from acquisitions including Missouri Power & Light (1950) and Missouri Edison (1954). During the 1960s and 1970s UE built five new plants including the Labadie plant (2300 MW) one of the largest coal-fired plants in the US.

UE began producing nuclear energy in 1984 at its Callaway nuke. High costs and the expenses of a scrapped second plant caused UE to battle the Missouri Public Service Commission throughout the 1980s for rate increases.

Charles Mueller became president in 1993 and CEO one year later. He oversaw continued staff reductions and cost cutting through the 1990s in an increasingly competitive market. In 1997 UE expanded into Illinois through its purchase of CIPSCO which owned utility Central Illinois Public Service Company (CIPS).

CIPS began as a Mattoon Illinois streetcar company in the early 1900s. The firm bought Mattoon's electric power plant in 1904 and began growing its power business buying small electric companies in the 1920s and 1930s. CIPS built five generating units in the 1940s and 1950s and became part-owner (along with UE) of Electric Energy Inc. which built a power plant on the Ohio River. The company bought Illinois Electric and Gas Company in the 1960s and the state's Gas Utilities in the 1980s. To prepare for competition under deregulation CIPS created holding company CIPSCO in the 1990s to diversify.

UE's purchase of CIPSCO expanded its geographic scope and the new company was named Ameren in 1997 to reflect its American energy focus. The next year the company committed to adding generating capacity through several natural gas-fired combustion turbines. It joined nine other utilities to form the Midwest Independent System Operator to manage their transmission needs.

In 1999 Ameren bought a 245-mile railroad line between St. Louis and Kansas City to help the area's economic development. Looking for new opportunities in deregulated energy markets the company purchased Data & Metering Specialties.

In 2000 Ameren created subsidiary AmerenEnergy Generating to operate its nonregulated power plants and affiliate AmerenEnergy Marketing to sell the generating facilities' power. When deregulation took effect in Illinois in 2002 the company transferred AmerenCIPS' power plants to AmerenEnergy Generating. In 2003 Ameren acquired CILCORP the holding company for electric and gas utility Central Illinois Light (now operating as AmerenCILCO) from independent power producer AES in a $1.4 billion deal. To further expand its utility operations Ameren acquired power and gas utility Illinois Power from Dynegy in a $2.3 billion deal in 2004. As part of the agreement Ameren gained Dynegy's 20% stake in power generator Electric Energy in which Ameren already held a 60% stake.

In 2007 Ameren subsidiary AmerenUE moved into wind power operations by contracting to buy 100 MW of wind power from Horizon Wind Energy's Rail Splitter Wind Farm located near Delavan Illinois.

In 2010 the company combined AmerenIP AmerenCIPS and AmerenCILCO into one entity Ameren Illinois in order to streamline operations and reduce confusion among customers. The three Illinois utilities have operated as a single business since 2004 and deliver energy to more than 1100 communities. Ameren Illinois also operates some 21400 miles of natural gas distribution and transmission lines.

Ameren's overall revenues decreased by 9% in 2012 due to a 24% drop Merchant Generation sales caused by lower market prices and a sales contract in 2011 that was not supplied in 2012. Ameren Illinois' revenues dropped by 10% due to lower wholesale distribution revenues primarily due to lower demand and the recognition of a reserve for revenues subject to a refund which dropped revenues by $6 million. Ameren Missouri's revenues declined by only 3% due to reduced purchased power expenses as a result of a FERC-ordered refund which helped to improve margins.

The company reported a net loss of $974 million in 2012 (a whopping 288% drop compared to 2011) due to lower sales and higher operating expenses as well as an increase in impairment and other charges.

Ameren opened a waste-to-energy plant in 2012.

In 2012 Ameren Missouri entered into an agreement with Westinghouse Electric to exclusively support Westinghouse's application for the Department of Energy's Small Modular Reactors investment funds of up to $452 million.

In order to focus on its regulated operations and offload a number of older an expensive-to-maintain coal-fired plants in 2013 Ameren sold its merchant generation business Ameren Energy Resources to an affiliate of Dynegy. Dynegy's subsidiary Illinois Power Holdings bought Ameren Energy Resources (and its subsidiaries Ameren Energy Generating Company AmerenEnergy Resources Generating Company and Ameren Energy Marketing Company). The deal is expected to generate about $900 million in cash and savings for Ameren.

It also agreed to sell three merchant gas-fired energy centers which were not part of the Dynegy transaction to a special purpose entity affiliated with and formed by Rockland Capital.

To leverage abundant natural gas supplies and low wholesale costs in 2013 Ameren Illinois outlined details of a legislative proposal to accelerate the modernization of Illinois' aging natural gas delivery infrastructure.

The company also opened its first hydroelectric center in the state in 2013.

In 2013 Ameren Illinois opened a $3.3 million testing facility to facilitate research and development of smart grid technologies and support the state's economic development and job creation goals.

EXECUTIVES

Vice President UE Ameren Services, Dennis Weisenborn
SVP Finance Ameren AmerenUE AmerenCIPS Ameren Services AmerenEnergy Generating and AmerenEnergy Fuels and Services, Warner L. Baxter, age 56, $1,040,000 total compensation
EVP and CFO, Martin J. Lyons, age 50, $640,000 total compensation
Chairman and President Ameren Illinois, Richard J. Mark, age 62, $490,000 total compensation
Chairman and President Ameren Missouri, Michael L. Moehn, age 48, $512,000 total compensation
VP Strategic Initiatives Ameren Services, Shawn E. Schukar, age 53
SVP and CIO Ameren Services, Mary P. Heger
Senior Vice President Corporate Planning And Business Risk Management, Mark Birk
Senior Vice President General Counsel and Secretary, Steven R Sullivan
Auditors: PricewaterhouseCoopers LLP

LOCATIONS

HQ: Ameren Corp
   1901 Chouteau Avenue, St. Louis, MO 63103
Phone: 314 621-3222
Web: www.ameren.com

PRODUCTS/OPERATIONS

2016 Sales

	$ mil.	% of total
Ameren Missouri	3,469	57
Ameren Illinois Electric Distribution	1,545	26
Ameren Illinois Natural Gas	753	12
Ameren Transmission	309	5
Total	**6,076**	**100**

2016 Sales

	$ mil.	% of total
Electric	5,196	86
Gas	880	14
Total	**6,076**	**100**

COMPETITORS

AES	Exelon
Alliant Energy	Great Plains Energy
Atmos Energy	Midwest Generation
Commonwealth Edison	Nicor Gas
Empire District Electric	Southern Union

HISTORICAL FINANCIALS

Company Type: Public

Income Statement

FYE: December 31

	REVENUE ($ mil.)	NET INCOME ($ mil.)	NET PROFIT MARGIN	EMPLOYEES
12/16	6,076	653	10.7%	8,629
12/15	6,098	630	10.3%	8,527
12/14	6,053	586	9.7%	8,527
12/13	5,838	289	5.0%	8,527
12/12	6,828	(974)	—	9,097
Annual Growth	**(2.9%)**	**—**		**(1.3%)**

2016 Year-End Financials

Debt ratio: 31.72%	No. of shares (mil.): 242
Return on equity: 9.27%	Dividends
Cash ($ mil.): 9	Yield: 0.0%
Current ratio: 0.60	Payout: 63.9%
Long-term debt ($ mil.): 6,595	Market value ($ mil.): 12,727

STOCK PRICE ($)		P/E		PER SHARE ($)		
	FY Close	High/Low		Earnings	Dividends	Book Value
12/16	52.46	20	16	2.68	1.72	29.28
12/15	43.23	18	14	2.59	1.66	28.63
12/14	46.13	20	15	2.40	1.61	27.67
12/13	36.16	31	26	1.18	1.60	26.97
12/12	30.72	—	—	(4.01)	1.60	27.27
Annual Growth	14.3%	—	—	—	1.8%	1.8%

American Airlines Group Inc

American Airlines Group (AAG) is one of the largest airlines in the world. After merging with US Airways in late 2013 the combined airline company together with its third-party regional carriers including Air Wisconsin Chautauqua ExpressJet Mesa Republic and SkyWest operates nearly 6700 daily flights to roughly 350 destinations in more than 50 countries. American and US Airways operate 930 mainline jets and regional subsidiaries and third-party regional carriers operate nearly 600 regional jets. AAG extends its geographic reach through code-sharing arrangements and is part of the oneworld Alliance.

Operations

Following the truism that you have to spend money to make money AMR ordered 460 single-aisle jets — 200 Boeing 737s and 260 Airbus A320s for delivery between 2013 and 2022; it is the largest aircraft order in history. The new aircraft are designed for fuel efficiency and should save in operating costs. (During 2016 the company took delivery of 55 mainline aircraft and retired 71 older legacy mainline aircraft.)

Geographic Reach

AAG has primary hubs in Charlotte (North Carolina) Chicago Dallas/Fort Worth Los Angeles Miami New York Philadelphia Phoenix and Washington DC. It provides international service to Australia Canada Europe the Middle East New Zealand Central and South America and Asia.

Sales and Marketing

AAG sells its tickets through several distribution channels including its website (www.aa.com) reservations centers and third-party distribution channels. It spent $116 million on advertisements in 2016.

Financial Performance

AAG has posted two straight years of revenue declines with revenues dipping 2% from almost $41 billion in 2015 to $40 billion in 2016. The slight dip in revenue for 2016 was attributed to a decline in mainline and regional passenger revenues that were driven by lower yields fueled by competitive capacity growth. The carrier also experienced macroeconomic softness outside of the US and foreign currency weakness.

AAG's net income nosedived by 65% from $7.6 billion in 2015 to $2.7 billion in 2016. The massive drop was mainly due to the absence of a special $3 billion non-cash tax benefit it incurred the previous year. In addition cash flow increased from $6.2 billion in 2015 to $6.5 billion 2016 driven by additional payments received related to its new co-branded credit card agreements that became effective in the third quarter of 2016.

Strategy

AAG is adding new aircraft and new service into markets which cater to a wide breadth of industries - entertainment banking and finance energy technology and manufacturing. This includes direct service to all of American's hubs with the most nonstop flights from LAX to New York (JFK); Dallas/Fort Worth; Miami; Philadelphia; Washington DC (DCA); Phoenix; and Charlotte North Carolina.

The company is also planning significant investments in modernizing its fleet and integrating the American and US Airways businesses. The company has set aside $18 billion in planned aggregate expenditures for aircraft purchase commitments and certain engines on a consolidated basis for years 2016-2020.

AAG in mid-2017 made a significant move to expand internationally with the announcement of a $200 million equity investment in China Southern Airlines. The two major carriers expect to begin codeshare and interline agreements that will grant customers access to additional destinations in China as well as North and South America. AAG customers will be able to access nearly 40 destinations beyond Beijing and more than 30 destinations beyond Shanghai.

HISTORY

In 1929 Sherman Fairchild created a New York City holding company called the Aviation Corporation (AVCO) combining some 85 small airlines in 1930 to create American Airways. In 1934 the company had its first dose of financial trouble after the government suspended private airmail for months. Corporate raider E. L. Cord took over and named the company American Airlines.

In late 2013 AMR merged with rival US Airways in a mega deal worth $11 billion. The milestone transaction created the world's largest airline. The combined entity kept the American Airlines name and is led by former US Airways CEO Doug Parker.

EXECUTIVES

EVP Corporate Affairs, Stephen L. (Steve) Johnson, age 60, $600,936 total compensation
Chairman and CEO, W. Douglas (Doug) Parker, age 55, $1 total compensation
EVP People and Communications, Elise R. Eberwein, age 51
EVP and CFO, Derek J. Kerr, age 52, $600,936 total compensation
President, Robert D. Isom, age 53, $641,306 total compensation
EVP and CIO, Maya Leibman, age 52, $600,936 total compensation
VP Corporate Development and Treasurer American Airlines, Beverly K. Goulet, age 62
Auditors: KPMG LLP

LOCATIONS

HQ: American Airlines Group Inc
4333 Amon Carter Blvd., Fort Worth, TX 76155
Phone: 817 963-1234   **Fax:** 817 967-9641
Web: www.aa.com

2016 Sales

	$ mil.	% of total
DOT Domestic	28,620	71
DOT Latin America	4,995	12
DOT Atlantic	4,769	12
DOT Pacific	1,796	5
Total	40,180	100

Selected Hub Locations

Chicago (O'Hare)
Dallas/Fort Worth (DFW)
Los Angeles
Miami
New York City

PRODUCTS/OPERATIONS

2016 Sales

	$ mil.	% of total
Mainline Passenger	27,909	69
Regional passenger	6,670	17
Cargo	700	2
Other	4,901	12
Total	40,180	100

COMPETITORS

Air France-KLM	Lufthansa
AirTran Airways	Mesa Air
Alaska Air	SkyWest
China Southern Airlines	Southwest Airlines
	Spirit Airlines
Delta Air Lines	UPS
FedEx	United Air Lines
Frontier Airlines	United Continental
Greyhound	Virgin Atlantic
Hawaiian Holdings	Airways
JetBlue	

HISTORICAL FINANCIALS

Company Type: Public

Income Statement

FYE: December 31

	REVENUE ($ mil.)	NET INCOME ($ mil.)	NET PROFIT MARGIN	EMPLOYEES
12/16	40,180	2,676	6.7%	122,300
12/15	40,990	7,610	18.6%	118,500
12/14	42,650	2,882	6.8%	113,300
12/13	26,743	(1,834)	—	110,400
12/12	24,855	(1,876)	—	77,750
Annual Growth	12.8%	—		12.0%

2016 Year-End Financials

Debt ratio: 47.48%	No. of shares (mil.): 507
Return on equity: 56.66%	Dividends
Cash ($ mil.): 960	Yield: 0.0%
Current ratio: 0.74	Payout: 8.3%
Long-term debt ($ mil.): 22,489	Market value ($ mil.): 23,686

STOCK PRICE ($)		P/E		PER SHARE ($)		
	FY Close	High/Low		Earnings	Dividends	Book Value
12/16	46.69	10	5	4.81	0.40	7.46
12/15	42.35	5	3	11.07	0.40	9.02
12/14	53.63	13	6	3.93	0.20	2.90
12/13	25.25	—	—	(11.25)	0.00	(10.46)
12/12	0.80	—	—	(14.99)	0.00	(63.78)
Annual Growth	176.8%	—	—	—	—	—

AMERICAN BALANCED FUND, INC.

Auditors: DELOITTE & TOUCHE LLP

LOCATIONS

HQ: AMERICAN BALANCED FUND, INC.
1 MARKET, SAN FRANCISCO, CA 941051596
Phone: 707 864-3945

HISTORICAL FINANCIALS

Company Type: Private

Income Statement

FYE: December 31

	ASSETS ($ mil.)	NET INCOME ($ mil.)	INCOME AS % OF ASSETS	EMPLOYEES
12/15	87,394	4,903	5.6%	9
12/00	6,203	832	13.4%	—
12/99	5,996	218	3.6%	—
Annual Growth	18.2%	21.4%	—	—

2015 Year-End Financials

Debt ratio: ——
Return on equity: 367.30%
Cash ($ mil.): 0
Current ratio: —
Long-term debt ($ mil.): —

Dividends
Yield: —
Payout: —
Market value ($ mil.): —

American Electric Power Company, Inc.

American Electric Power (AEP) takes its slice of the US power pie out of Middle America with markets in Ohio Michigan and Indiana. The holding company is one of the largest power generators and distributors in the US. AEP owns the nation's largest electricity transmission system a network of more than 40000 miles. It also has 224000 miles of distribution lines. Its electric utilities have 5.4 million customers in 11 states and have about 26000 MW of largely coal-fired generating capacity although it is adding renewable sources to its generation portfolio. AEP is a top wholesale energy company; it markets electricity in the US.

HISTORY

In 1906 Richard Breed Sidney Mitchell and Henry Doherty set up American Gas & Electric (AG&E) in New York to buy 23 utilities from Philadelphia's Electric Company of America. With properties in seven northeastern US states AG&E began acquiring and merging small electric properties creating the predecessors of Ohio Power (1911) Kentucky Power (1919) and Appalachian Power (1926). AG&E also bought the predecessor of Indiana Michigan Power (1925).

By 1926 the company was operating in Indiana Kentucky Michigan Ohio Virginia and West Virginia. In 1935 AG&E engineer Philip Sporn later known as the Henry Ford of power introduced his high-voltage high-velocity circuit breaker. AG&E picked up Kingsport Power in 1938.

Becoming president in 1947 Sporn began an ambitious building program that continued through the 1960s. Plants designed by AG&E (renamed American Electric Power in 1958) were among the world's most efficient and electric rates stayed 25%-38% below the national average.

AEP bought Michigan Power in 1967 six years after Donald Cook succeeded Sporn as president. Cook who refused to attach scrubbers to the smokestacks of coal-fired plants was criticized in the early 1970s by environmental protesters. AEP's first nuclear plant named in Cook's honor went on line in Michigan in 1975. He retired in 1976.

The firm moved from New York to Columbus Ohio in 1980 after buying what is now Columbus Southern Power (formed in 1883). It set up AEP Generating in 1982 to provide power to its electric utilities.

AEP began converting its second nuke Zimmer to coal in 1984. In 1992 AEP finally began installing scrubbers at its coal-fired Gavin plant in Ohio after being ordered to comply with the Clean Air Act. It also cleaned up its image by planting millions of trees in 1996.

The company formed AEP Communications after Congress passed the Telecommunications Act of 1996. The next year AEP jumped into the UK's deregulated electric market; AEP and New Century Energies (now Xcel Energy) bought Yorkshire Electricity (later Yorkshire Power Group) for $2.8 billion. However a $109 million UK windfall tax on the transaction — and increased wholesale competition — hurt AEP's bottom line.

As the normally staid electric industry succumbed to merger mania AEP agreed in 1997 to buy Central and South West (CSW) of Texas in a $6.6 billion deal. AEP's sales would nearly double and CSW was to bring its own UK utility SEEBOARD and other overseas holdings.

In 1998 AEP bought a 20% stake in Pacific Hydro an Australian power producer and CitiPower an Australian electric distribution company. AEP also bought Equitable Resources' Louisiana natural gas midstream operations including an intrastate pipeline. In 1999 China's Pushan Power Plant (70%-owned by AEP) began operations. Environmental concerns resurfaced that year when the EPA sued the utility alleging its old coal-powered plants which had been grandfathered from the Clean Air Act had been quietly upgraded to extend their lives.

Regulators approved the company's acquisition of CSW in 2000 but AEP had to agree to relinquish control of its 22000 miles of transmission lines to an independent operator. The CSW deal closed later that year. (However the SEC's approval of the deal was challenged by a federal appeals court in 2002.)

AEP sold its 50% stake in Yorkshire Power Group to Innogy (now RWE npower) in 2001; it also purchased Houston Pipe Line Co. (which it later sold in early 2005) from Enron for $727 million. AEP became one of the largest US barge operators that year when it bought MEMCO Barge Line from Progress Energy. It also purchased two UK coal-fired power plants (4000 MW) from Edison Mission Energy a subsidiary of Edison International in a $960 million deal.

In 2002 AEP sold its UK utility SEEBOARD to Electricit © de France in a $2.2 billion deal; it also sold its Australian utility CitiPower to a consortium led by Cheung Kong Infrastructure and Hongkong Electric for $855 million. The following year the company sold two of its competitive Texas retail electric providers (WTU Retail Energy and CPL Retail Energy) to UK utility Centrica. It also divested its power plant development subsidiary AEP Pro Serv and its stakes in telecom firms C3 Communications and AFN.

The company sold two UK power plants to Scottish and Southern Energy for $456 million in 2004 and it sold a 50% stake in a third UK plant to Scottish Power in a $210 million deal. AEP also sold four independent power plants in Florida and Colorado to Bear Stearns for $156 million that year.

In 2006 the company sold its Plaquemine cogeneration plant to Dow Chemical for $64 million. Also that year it formed a joint venture company with MidAmerican Energy Holdings to build and own new electric transmission assets within the Electric Reliability Council of Texas.

AEP settled an eight-year lawsuit with the US government in 2007 and agreed to pay more than $4.6 billion to reduce hazardous air pollution from 16 coal-burning power plants.

In 2011 the company reached a $425 million settlement covering all claims with BOA and Enron related to their purchase of Houston Pipeline Company from Enron in 2001.

Growing its retail business in the US in 2012 AEP acquired Chicago-based Blue Star Energy and its independent retail electric supplier BlueStar Energy Solutions. The company has about 23000 customer accounts. The deal also gives AEP the opportunity to hedge the output of its soon-to-be unregulated Ohio power generation.

By the end of 2012 AEP was operating 310 MW of wind power facilities and had about 180 MW of long-term purchase power agreements for wind power.

In 2013 AEP received the regulatory go-ahead to separate its AEP Ohio-owned generation assets from its Ohio distribution and transmission operations and complete transfer of that generation to AEP's competitive generation company (AEP Generation Resources) and regulated affiliates Appalachian Power and Kentucky Power.

To create a more customer friendly service in 2013 AEP launched a new enhanced version of its website at aepenergy.com. optimized for mobile devices.

EXECUTIVES

EVP and Chief Administrative Officer, Lana L. Hillebrand, age 57, $490,680 total compensation
Vice Chairman, Robert P. (Bob) Powers, age 63, $723,773 total compensation
President and COO Southwestern Electric Power, Venita McCellon-Allen, age 58, $410,919 total compensation
VP Corporate Communications; President American Electric Power Foundation, Dale E. Heydlauff, age 57
EVP External Affairs, Charles R. Patton, age 58
SVP Portfolio Management and Optimization, Charles E. (Chuck) Zebula, age 57, $446,310 total compensation
President and COO AEP Ohio, Julie Sloat, age 44
EVP and CFO, Brian X. Tierney, age 50, $730,800 total compensation
President and COO Public Service Company of Oklahoma, J. Stuart Solomon, age 55
Chairman President and CEO, Nicholas K. (Nick) Akins, age 57, $1,325,077 total compensation
EVP General Counsel and Secretary, David M. Feinberg, age 48, $615,354 total compensation
EVP Generation, Mark C. McCullough, age 57
EVP Utilities, Paul Chodak, age 53
EVP AEP Transmission and President and COO AEP Transmission Holding Company (AEPTHCO), Lisa M. Barton, age 51, $532,039 total compensation
President and COO Kentucky Power, Matthew J. Satterwhite, age 44
President and COO Indiana Michigan Power, Toby L. Thomas
President and COO Appalachian Power, Chris T. Beam
President and COO AEP Texas, Judith Talavera
Vice President Operations, Jonathan Dickerman
Vice President Taxes, William Scott
VICE PRESIDENT, Floyd Nickerson
Senior Vice President Strategic Initiatives and Chief Risk Officer, Stephan Haynes
Vice President Information Technology, Lance Sogan
Senior Vice President, Jeffrey Cross
NATIONAL ACCOUNT MANAGER, James B Clark
Auditors: Deloitte & Touche LLP

LOCATIONS

HQ: American Electric Power Company, Inc.
1 Riverside Plaza, Columbus, OH 43215-2373
Phone: 614 716-1000 **Fax:** 614 223-1823
Web: www.aep.com

PRODUCTS/OPERATIONS

2016 sales

	$ mil.	% of total
Vertically integrated utilities	9,012	55
Transmission and distribution utilities	4,328	26
Generation and marketing	2,858	18
AEP transmission holdco	141	1
Corporation and others	39	-
Total	**16,380**	**100**

Selected Subsidiaries

AEP Energy Services Inc. (energy marketing and trading)
AEP Generating Co. (electricity generator marketer)
AEP Retail Energy (retail energy marketing in deregulated territories)
AEP Texas Central Company (formerly Central Power and Light electric utility)
AEP Texas North Company (formerly West Texas Utilities electric utility)
AEP Towers (wireless communications towers)
Appalachian Power Company (electric utility)
Columbus Southern Power Company (electric utility)
Indiana Michigan Power Company (electric utility)
Kentucky Power Company (electric utility)
Kingsport Power Company (electric utility)
Ohio Power Company (electric utility)
Public Service Company of Oklahoma (electric utility)
Southwestern Electric Power Company (electric utility)
Wheeling Power Company (electric utility)
Utility Distribution/Customer Service Divisions
AEP Ohio (handles distribution customer service and external affairs functions for Columbus Southern Power Company Ohio Power Company and Wheeling Power Company)
AEP Texas (handles distribution customer service and external affairs functions for AEP Texas Central Company and AEP Texas North Company)
Appalachian Power (handles distribution customer service and external affairs functions for Appalachian Power Company and Kingsport Power Company)
Indiana Michigan Power (handles distribution customer service and external affairs functions for Indiana Michigan Power Company)
Kentucky Power (handles distribution customer service and external affairs functions for Kentucky Power Company)
Public Service Company of Oklahoma (handles distribution customer service and external affairs functions for Public Service Company of Oklahoma)
Southwestern Electric Power Company (handles distribution customer service and external affairs functions for Southwestern Electric Power Company)

COMPETITORS

BP	Energy Future
CMS Energy	Entergy
Calpine	Exelon
CenterPoint Energy	FirstEnergy
Constellation Energy Group	NiSource
	PG&E Corporation
DTE	Sempra Energy
Delmarva Power	Southern Company
Dominion Energy	TVA
Duke Energy	Xcel Energy
Dynegy	

HISTORICAL FINANCIALS

Company Type: Public

Income Statement

FYE: December 31

	REVENUE ($ mil.)	NET INCOME ($ mil.)	NET PROFIT MARGIN	EMPLOYEES
12/16	16,380	610	3.7%	17,634
12/15	16,453	2,047	12.4%	17,405
12/14	17,020	1,634	9.6%	18,529
12/13	15,357	1,480	9.6%	18,521
12/12	14,945	1,259	8.4%	18,513
Annual Growth	**2.3%**	**(16.5%)**	**—**	**(1.2%)**

2016 Year-End Financials

Debt ratio: 34.62%
Return on equity: 3.45%
Cash ($ mil.): 622
Current ratio: 0.64
Long-term debt ($ mil.): 17,378
No. of shares (mil.): 491
Dividends
Yield: 0.0%
Payout: 183.0%
Market value ($ mil.): 30,958

	STOCK PRICE ($) FY Close	P/E High/Low	PER SHARE ($) Earnings	Dividends	Book Value
12/16	62.96	57 46	1.24	2.27	35.38
12/15	58.27	15 13	4.17	2.15	36.44
12/14	60.72	19 14	3.34	2.03	34.37
12/13	46.74	17 14	3.04	1.95	32.98
12/12	42.68	17 14	2.60	1.88	31.37
Annual Growth	**10.2%**	**— —**	**(16.9%)**	**4.8%**	**3.1%**

American Equity Investment Life Holding Co

American Equity Investment Life Holding (American Equity Life) helps middle-income investors plan for a cushier retirement. The company issues and administers fixed-rate and indexed annuities through subsidiaries American Equity Investment Life Insurance Eagle Life Insurance Company and American Equity Investment Life Insurance Company of New York. Licensed in 50 states and the District of Columbia the company sells its products through about 35000 independent agents and 35 national marketing associations. American Equity Life targets individuals between the ages of 45 and 75. The company also offers a variety of whole term and universal life insurance products.

Geographic Reach

Though American Equity Life is licensed in all fifty US states five big states bring in the bulk of its business. California Florida Illinois Pennsylvania and Texas together account for around 35% of American Equity Life's premiums.

Sales and Marketing

American Equity Life sells its products through 35 national marketing associations covering about 35000 independent agents.

Financial Performance

After spiking 63% in 2013 American Equity Life's revenue declined the following two years. In 2015 revenue dropped 30% to $1.5 billion despite growth in premiums and net investment earnings. The decline was largely due to changes in fair values of derivatives as a result of loss on option expirations. Net income which has been fluctuating

over the past few years rose 74% to $220 million in 2015. This was due to a decrease in index product benefit expenses as well as a change in the fair value of embedded derivatives from fixed index annuities.

Cash flow from operations has followed revenue's trend as of late; it fell 29% to $505 million in 2015 as more cash was used for accrued investment income and income taxes.

Strategy

American Equity Life is working to increase sales in core service territories by enhancing its relationships with regional independent agents and introducing new products.

As the US population ages American Equity Life also hopes to take advantage of the growing demand for fixed index annuity products. To that end in 2015 the company launched a new fixed indexed annuity series the Choice Series.

In 2016 the US Department of Labor announced new regulations that tighten standards for the sale of fixed-index annuities — key products for American Equity Life. The conflict of interest fiduciary ruling is intended to minimize advisers selling high-fee products that may not be in customers' best interests; it also favors the sales of fixed-index annuities by broker-dealers and banks over independent agents. American Equity Life's Eagle Life unit operates with a network of broker-dealers banks and investment advisors which should help the company as it navigates the new rule.

EXECUTIVES

Chairman President and CEO, John M. Matovina, age 62, $727,500 total compensation
SVP and National Marketing Director American Equity Life, Ronald J. (Ron) Grensteiner, age 54, $510,000 total compensation
EVP and Chief Investment Officer, Jeffrey D. (Jeff) Lorenzen, age 51, $445,000 total compensation
CFO and Treasurer, Ted M. Johnson, age 47, $500,000 total compensation
EVP and COO, Bruce D. Cheek
EVP General Counsel and Corporate Secretary, Renee D. Montz, age 45, $356,250 total compensation
Assistant Vice President Andndash; Technical Services, Kevin Seuferer
Assistant Vice President Commercial Mortgage Administration, Loryssa L Rippey
Assistant Vice President QA, Dennis Young
Senior Vice President and Chief Human Resources Officer, Jennifer Bryant
Auditors: KPMG LLP

LOCATIONS

HQ: American Equity Investment Life Holding Co
6000 Westown Parkway, West Des Moines, IA 50266
Phone: 515 221-0002
Web: www.american-equity.com

PRODUCTS/OPERATIONS

2015 Sales

	$ mil.	% of total
Net investment income	1,692	90
Annuity product charges	136	7
Premiums	36	2
Net realized gains on investments	10	1
Net OTTI losses	(19.5)	-
Change in fair value of derivatives	(336.1)	-
Total	**1,518**	**100**

COMPETITORS

Allianz Life	National Western
Aviva	Nationwide
FBL Financial	Northwestern Mutual
Fidelity & Guaranty	Presidential Life

Life	Prudential
Great American Life	Sammons Financial
Integrity Life	Security Benefit Group
Midland National Life	The Hartford

HISTORICAL FINANCIALS

Company Type: Public

Income Statement

FYE: December 31

	ASSETS ($ mil.)	NET INCOME ($ mil.)	INCOME AS % OF ASSETS	EMPLOYEES
12/16	56,053	83	0.1%	530
12/15	49,041	219	0.4%	490
12/14	43,989	126	0.3%	418
12/13	39,621	253	0.6%	416
12/12	35,133	57	0.2%	388
Annual Growth	12.4%	9.5%	—	8.1%

2016 Year-End Financials

Debt ratio: 1.31%	No. of shares (mil.): 88
Return on equity: 3.92%	Dividends
Cash ($ mil.): 791	Yield: 0.0%
Current ratio: —	Payout: 24.7%
Long-term debt ($ mil.): —	Market value ($ mil.): 1,984

	STOCK PRICE ($) FY Close	P/E High/Low		PER SHARE ($) Earnings	Dividends	Book Value
12/16	22.54	25	13	0.97	0.24	26.04
12/15	24.03	11	8	2.72	0.22	23.90
12/14	29.19	17	12	1.58	0.20	28.13
12/13	26.38	7	3	3.38	0.18	19.63
12/12	12.21	14	11	0.89	0.15	27.86
Annual Growth	16.6%	—	—	2.2%	12.5%	(1.7%)

American Express Co.

American Express makes money even if you do leave home without it. Best known for its charge cards and revolving credit cards the company is also one of the world's largest providers of travel services. And yes the company still issues traveler's checks. Its travel agency operations have thousands of locations worldwide and its Travelers Cheque Group is the world's largest issuer of traveler's checks. Still the company's charge and credit cards are its bread and butter; American Express boasts $160 billion in assets and $1 trillion in annual billed business and has about 110 million cards in circulation in 140-plus countries. It?s longtime CEO Kenneth Chenault announced his retirement in late-2017.

HISTORY

In 1850 Henry Wells and his two main competitors combined their delivery services to form American Express. When directors refused to expand to California in 1852 Wells and executive William Fargo formed Wells Fargo while remaining at American Express.

American Express merged with Merchants Union Express in 1868 and developed a money order to compete with the government's postal money order. Fargo's difficulty in cashing letters of credit in Europe led to the offering of Travelers Cheques in 1891.

In WWI the US government nationalized and consolidated all express delivery services compensating the owners. After the war American Express incorporated as an overseas freight and financial services and exchange provider (the freight operation was sold in 1970). In 1958 the company introduced the American Express charge card. It bought Fireman's Fund American Insurance (sold gradually between 1985 and 1989) and Equitable Securities in 1968.

James Robinson CEO from 1977 to 1993 hoped to turn American Express into a financial services supermarket. The company bought brokerage Shearson Loeb Rhoades in 1981 and investment banker Lehman Brothers in 1984 among others. In 1987 it introduced Optima a revolving credit card to compete with MasterCard and Visa. It had no experience in underwriting credit cards though and was badly burned by losses.

Most of the financial units were combined as Shearson Lehman Brothers. But the financial services supermarket never came to fruition and losses in this area brought a steep drop in earnings in the early 1990s. Harvey Golub was brought in as CEO in 1993 to restore stability.

The company sold its brokerage operations as Shearson (to Travelers now Citigroup) and spun off investment banking as Lehman Brothers in 1994. In late 1996 it teamed with Advanta Corp. to allow Advanta Visa and MasterCard holders to earn points in the American Express Membership Rewards program. The move sparked a lawsuit from Visa and MasterCard which prohibit their member banks from doing business with American Express. That set off a spate of lawsuits culminating in the US Justice Department filing an antitrust suit against Visa and MasterCard. A federal judge sided with the Justice Department in 2001 but Visa and MasterCard appealed.

In 1997 Kenneth Chenault became president and COO putting him in line to succeed Golub.

Online banking service Membership B@nking was launched in 1999. That year American Express invested in Ticketmaster (the ticketing giant that merged with Live Nation Entertainment in 2010). In 2000 the company established a headquarters in Beijing to develop business in China. Also that year American Express bought more than 4500 ATMs from Electronic Data Systems (now HP Enterprise Services) making it a leading US operator of ATMs.

In 2001 Chenault replaced Golub as chairman and CEO. American Express was hit hard that year by bad investments in below-investment grade bonds by its money-management unit which shaved about $1 billion from earnings. Adding to its woes the company's employees at its New York City headquarters across the street from the World Trade Center were displaced by the 2001 terrorist attacks; its headquarters reopened in May 2002.

To grow its corporate travel management business Amex acquired Rosenbluth International a leading global travel management company with corporate travel operations in 15 countries in 2003. When Rosenbluth was fully integrated into the organization in mid-2004 American Express announced a relaunch of its corporate travel organization renamed American Express Business Travel.

American Express underwent a mild shakeup in late 2004 when it cut 2.5% of its workforce in a restructuring that included the company's business travel operations. The restructuring also included the sale of the company's banking operations in Bangladesh Egypt Luxembourg and Pakistan and the relocation of some finance operations. On a brighter note the company that year announced a milestone agreement with Industrial and Commercial Bank of China (ICBC) one of the biggest banks in China to issue the first American Express-branded credit cards in that country.

To focus on its travel and credit card operations the company in 2005 spun off Ameriprise Financial (formerly American Express Financial Advisors) a provider of insurance mutual funds investment advice and brokerage and asset management services. Toward that same end American Express sold its Tax and Business Services division to H&R Block and its UK-based American Express Financial Services Europe to TD Waterhouse (now part of TD AMERITRADE). Also in 2005 the company sold its equipment leasing business to Key Equipment Finance.

In 2007 the company's business travel division bought the rest of Farrington American Express Travel Services Limited it didn't already own. The travel management company had been a joint venture with Farrington Travel. The move was part of American Express's global expansion push especially in the Asia-Pacific region.

The company discontinued its Travelers Cheque card that year after determining that customers preferred paper travelers checks over a stored-value card. However sales of the travelers checks continued to decline in 2007 affected by the rising use of ATMs among other factors.

Also in 2007 American Express reached a $2.5 billion settlement with Visa and other defendants including JPMorgan Chase Capital One U.S. Bancorp and Wells Fargo dropping them from the lawsuit that alleged the companies conspired to block American Express from the bank-issued card business in the US. The following year it reached a $1.8 billion settlement with Mastercard the final remaining defendant in the suit.

American Express sold the international operations of American Express Bank to Stanchart in 2008.

American Express became a banking holding company in 2009. As a result it received some $3.4 billion from the Troubled Asset Relief Fund (TARP) early that year; it repaid the debt within months.

EXECUTIVES

EVP and CIO, Marc D. Gordon, age 56

EVP and CFO, Jeffrey C. (Jeff) Campbell, age 56, $1,000,000 total compensation

Chairman and CEO, Stephen J. (Steve) Squeri, age 58, $1,350,000 total compensation

EVP and General Counsel, Laureen E. Seeger, age 55, $800,000 total compensation

President Credit Risk & Information Management, Ashwini (Ash) Gupta, age 64

President Global Consumer Services Group, Douglas E. Buckminster, age 57, $700,000 total compensation

President Global Network and International Consumer Services, James P. Bush, age 58

President Global Merchant Services and Loyalty, Anr © Williams, age 51

President Global Risk & Compliance and Chief Risk Officer, Paul D. Fabara, age 51

EVP Corporate Affairs and Communications, Michael J. OÂ'Neill, age 63

Executive Vice President Corporate Affairs and Communications, Michael O'Neill

Executive Vice President Merchant Services Americas, Ed Jay

Vice President and General Manager, Vincent Campana

Vice President Human Resources American Express, Kent Price

Vice President Human Resources, Julie Pope

Vice President Network Capacity and Performance, Donald Harris

Corporate Officer Executive Vice President, Jim Bush

Vice President Marketing, Kathleen King

Senior Management (Senior Vice President General Manager Director), Boriana Tchobanova

Vice President Information Technology, Bo Gorham

Vice President assurance Services leader, Gary Pollack

Vice President, Anderson Lee

Vice President, Nigel Greenwood

Vice President Network Management, Karen Czack

Vice President and Senior Counsel, Adrian Villaraos

Vice President Director, Gloria Ochalek

Vice President IPD Project Information technology, Mike La Rooy

Vice President Information Technology Audit, Diane Gullickson

Vice President GSM Americas And Global Strategy, Gaurav Saxena

Senior Vice President Financial Services, Mei Chan

Senior Vice President Of Finance, Sharon Kensington

Vice President Network Management, Karen Schmidt

Senior Vice President Human Resources Relationship Leader and Head of Talent, Gaby Giglio

Senior Vice President, Penny Frank

Vice President and General Manager Client Solutions, Howard Fulton

Vice President B2B Solution Development, Andrew Jamison

Vice President Advertising and Global Agency Management, Eddie Hill

Vice President Of Human Resources Uk And Ireland, Chris Lamb

Vice President Marketing, Colin Kennedy

Vice President Data Center 2015 Program, Jason Hall

Senior Vice President investment Operations, Peter Anderson

Vice President Client Management, Larry Restiano

National Account Manager, Elizabeth Scullin

Senior Vice President and General Manager Small Business Customer Acquisition, David Rabkin

Vice President Global Service Management And Delivery, Vic Verma

Vice President Marketing Development, Trang Dinh

Vice President, Kathleen Haggerty

Director of Nursing, Karen Diprofio

Executive Vice President Human Resources, Manu Narang

Vice President And General Manager, Debra Davies

Vice President Marketing, Tatyana Zlotsky

Vice President Business and Vendor Management Global Infrastructure and Workplace Technology, Sabra Mannan

Vice President, Guillermo Rabiela

Vice President Social Marketing Innovation, Phil Wilson

Vice President New Product Development, Dave Cronin

Senior Vice President, John Stack

Vice President Head of Acquisition and Business Development, Lisandro Delfino

Vice President Product Development, Dave Pereira

Vice President Implementation and Operations, Frank Holbrook

Vice President Business Insights and Digital Capabilities, Amit Parmar

Vice President Field Channel Marketing, Katya Skorik

Vice President and Senior Counsel, Wayne Thomson

Senior Vice President Marketing Services, Christina Crawford

Vice President Risk Management, Ravi Varma

Vice President Network Management, Brandy Williams

Vice President Finance Manda Controller, Dylan Haverty-Stacke

Vice President Finance, Avi Beinhacker

Vice President Technology American Express Bank Te, Marc Brown

Vice President Mergers and Acquisitions Technologies, Bob Morgan

Vice President Network Capacity and Performance, David Harris

Vice President Finance for Commerce Innovation, Dominic Paniccia

Vice President Marketing, Elizabeth Curtis

Vice President Network Management, Tim Williams

Vice President, Rahul Dutta

Vice President and Senior Counsel, Emily Goodman Binick

Vice President Strategic Technology Relationships, Janice King

VICE PRESIDENT, STEPHEN FERRIS

Vice President Facilities, Samuel Brick

Vice President Compliance and Ethics, Glenn Jarvis

Vice President Strategy, Daniel Jeffery

Vice President and Senior Counsel, Tori Chami

Vice President, Laura Waters

Vice President Fraud Risk Strategy, Irfan Tareen

Vice President Business Partner Human Resources, Patricia Huska

Vice President International, Eric Kocher

Vice President Marketing And Product, Opeyemi Oluwole

Vice President, Barbara Bock

Vice President Of Regulatory Strategy, Christine Olson

Vice President Regulatory Affairs, Victor Gold

Vice President, John Dolfin

Vice President, Jarrod Fagan

VICE PRESIDENT, JIM TOBIN

Vice President Loyalty Analytics, Justin Maynard

Vice President Operations, John Koslow

Vice President, Richard Glynn

Vice President, Smriti Sinha

Vice President Of Co Brand Finance, Ian Woolley

Vice President and Controller, Lawrence Belmonte

Vice President Digital Acquisition, John Dotto

Vice President Marketing, Rita Byrne

Vice President Government Relations, Sean Peterson

Vice President Compliance, Nitish Pandey

Vice President, Leah Schweller

General Auditor Senior Vice President, Julie Scammahorn

Vice President New Business Partnerships B2B, Mark Moncher

VICE PRESIDENT, TAMMY YEE

Vice President General Tax Counsel, Joe Gagliano

Vice President of Human Resources, Kim Seymour

Vice President and Controller, Larry Belmonte

Vice President Corporate Comptrollers Office, Elaine McDonnell

Vice President Human Resources, Madelyn Marino

Vice President Basel Implementation, James Zhou

Vice President Application Development Serve Prepaid, Sachin Joshi

Vice President Technologies Communications, Gerilyn Cammaroto

Vice President and General Manager Global Client Group, Lisa Skiptunis

Senior Vice President, Joseph Quagliata

Vice President Global Privacy, Katharina Kopp

Vice President Online Consumer Travel, Christopher Besendorfer

Vice President of Customer Experience Insights and Analytics, Tanuj Suri

Vice President Customer Experience, Todd Schemm

Vice President, Laura Fink

Vice President of Consumer and Small Business Services Technologies, Miles Farrel

Foreign Exchange Vice President, Helen Grace

Global Network Services Senior Vice President and North America Head, William Stredwick

Vice President of Social Media and Communications, Brad Minor

VICE PRESIDENT GLOBAL DIVERSITY and INCLUSION, DIANNE CAMPBELL

Todd Fennell Vice President Security Assurance

Greg Huff Vice President Application Security, Teri Drapeau

Vice President Global Accounting Policy, Aulene Wessel

Vice President Human Resources, Steve Squeri

Vice President, Srinivas Dasari

Vice President Business Development, Ashok Paul

Vice President Data Center Infrastructure, Fred Jordan

Vice President Open Commercial, Richard Prescott

Vice President, Susan Evers

Vice President Software Engineering and Chief Architect, Mark Morawski

Vice President State Government Affairs, Steve Lemson

Vice President LFO of Technology Infrastructure, Julie Bush

Vice President, Hans Fleming

Vice President Lifestyle Partnerships, Noah Prawer

Vice President Information Systems, John Husted-Sherman

Vice President And Senior Counsel, Brett Kaplicer

Vice President of Acquisition, Danielle Crop

Vice President Global Business Development, Ton Maanicus

Vice President Marketing, Steven Davis

Vice President Human Resources, Stephanie Ahern

Vice President Network Strategy, Anthony Devane

Vice President Pricing And Business, Jason Wynn

Senior Vice President And General Manager Head Of Service Delivery Emea American Express Business T, Suzan Kereere

Vice President International Lending and New Product Development, Brett Noel

Vice President Information Security, Beverly Effendi

Vice President Technologies Finance, Phil Konort

Auditors: PricewaterhouseCoopers LLP

LOCATIONS

HQ: American Express Co.
200 Vesey Street, New York, NY 10285
Phone: 212 640-2000   **Fax:** 212 640-0404
Web: www.americanexpress.com

2016 Sales

	% of total
United States	74
Europe the Middle East and Africa (EMEA)	10
Japan Asia/Pacific and Australia (JAPA)	9
Latin America Canada and the Caribbean (LACC)	7
Total	**100**

PRODUCTS/OPERATIONS

2016 Sales

	$ mil.	% of total
Non-interest		
Discount revenue	18,680	56
Net card fees	2,886	9
Other commissions & fees	2,753	8
Other	2,029	6
Interest		
Loans including fees	7,205	21
Interest & dividends on investment securities	131	—
Deposits with banks & other	139	—
Total	**33,823**	**100**

2016 Sales by Segment

	% of total
U.S. Consumer Services (USCS)	39
Global Commercial Services (GCS)	30
International Consumer and Network Services (ICNS)	17
Global Merchant Services (GMS)	14
Total	**100**

HISTORICAL FINANCIALS

Company Type: Public

Income Statement

FYE: December 31

	ASSETS ($ mil.)	NET INCOME ($ mil.)	INCOME AS % OF ASSETS	EMPLOYEES
12/17	181,159	2,736	1.5%	55,000
12/16	158,893	5,408	3.4%	56,400
12/15	161,184	5,163	3.2%	54,800
12/14	159,103	5,885	3.7%	54,000
12/13	153,375	5,359	3.5%	62,800
Annual Growth	4.3%	(15.5%)	—	(3.3%)

2017 Year-End Financials

Debt ratio: 30.80%	No. of shares (mil.): 859
Return on equity: 14.13%	Dividends
Cash ($ mil.): 32,927	Yield: 0.0%
Current ratio: —	Payout: 44.1%
Long-term debt ($ mil.): —	Market value ($ mil.): 85,307

	STOCK PRICE ($) FY Close	P/E High/Low	Earnings	PER SHARE ($) Dividends	Book Value
12/17	99.31	33 25	2.97	1.31	21.22
12/16	74.08	13 9	5.65	1.19	22.68
12/15	69.55	18 13	5.05	1.10	21.33
12/14	93.04	17 14	5.56	0.98	20.21
12/13	90.73	18 12	4.88	0.86	18.32
Annual Growth	2.3%	—	(11.7%)	11.1%	3.7%

American Financial Group Inc

American Financial Group (AFG) insures American businessmen in pursuit of the Great American Dream. Through the Great American Insurance Group of companies and its flagship Great American Insurance Company AFG offers commercial property/casualty insurance with a focus on specialties such as workers' compensation professional liability ocean and inland marine and multiperil crop insurance. The company also provides surety coverage for contractors and risk management services. For individuals and employers AFG provides a wide range of annuity policies through its Great American Financial Resources Inc. (GAFRI) subsidiary.

Operations

AFG operates through two primary segments — Property and Casualty Insurance and Annuity— and two smaller segments — Run-Off Long-Term Care and Life and Other (which includes holding company costs).

The Property and Casualty Insurance segment is the largest accounting for more than 70% of AFG's annual revenues. Its operations are divided into more than 30 businesses including property and transportation (marine crops and commercial auto) specialty casualty (professional excess and surplus workers' compensation and general liabilities) and specialty financial (fidelity and surety lend/lease risk management).

In the Annuities segment (which accounts for about a quarter of total revenue) GAFRI offers fixed rate and indexed annuity products through underwriting companies Great American Life Insurance and Annuity Investors Life Insurance.

Geographic Reach

AFG's largest markets include California Illinois Texas New York and Florida. The company has more than 100 locations throughout North America and Europe.

Sales and Marketing

AFG primarily markets its insurance policies through a nationwide network of independent agents and brokers although a small number are written through employee agents. Annuity products are marketed through a retail network of approximately 55 national marketing organizations managing general agents financial advisors and independent brokers.

The company's customers include Wells Fargo BB&T PNC Financial Services LPL Financial and Regions Financial.

Financial Performance

AFG's revenue which has grown over the past five years increased 6% to $6.5 billion in 2015.Net earned property/causualty premiums rose 2% (largely due to an increase in property and transportation business) and net investment income rose 4% but those gains were partially offset by a decline in net earned life accident and health premiums.

Net income which had been on the decline jumped 84% to a record $649 million in 2016. Leading factors in that jump were decreases in life accident and health benefits paid out and in provisions for income taxes.

Cash flow from operations dipped 15% to $1.2 billion that year due to changes in reinsurance and other assets and in managed investment entities' assets and liabilities.

Strategy

Like all property/casualty insurers AFG seeks to balance out calm and catastrophe by operating on long-term income cycles where years of profits balance out years of increased claims. The company sees opportunity in such areas as workers' compensation and commercial auto coverage and it has worked to build its operations both organically and through acquisitions.

In terms of annuities AFG is focused on fixed and indexed products and has steered away from offering variable annuities and other types of offerings where it doesn't have a competitive advantage.

To focus on core operations the company has sold off supplemental benefits and other units. In 2015 it sold the entities that held its runoff long-term care policies to HC2 Holdings for approximately $15 million.In 2016 the company sold its struggling Neon (formerly Marketform) medical malpractice operations which provided coverage in 30 countries (primarily in Australia Italy and the UK).

Mergers and Acquisitions

AFG expands its property/casualty operations through acquisitions in existing and new markets such as medical malpractice and workers' compensation. In mid-2016 the company acquired the rest of transportation-focused National Interstate Corporation it didn't already own for $320 million.

HISTORY

When his father became ill in the mid-1930s Carl Lindner Jr. dropped out of high school to take over his family's dairy business. He built it into a large ice-cream store chain called United Dairy Farmers. Lindner branched out in 1955 with Henthy Realty and in 1959 he bought three savings and loans. The next year Lindner changed the company's name to American Financial Corp. (AFC). He took it public in 1961 using the proceeds to buy United Liberty Life Insurance (1963) and Provident Bank (1966).

Lindner also formed the American Financial Leasing & Services Company in 1968 to lease airplanes computers and other equipment. In 1969 the company acquired Phoenix developer Rubenstein Construction and renamed it American Continental. AFC bought several life casualty and mortgage insurance firms in the 1970s including National General parent of Great American Insurance Group later the core of AFC's insurance segment. The company also moved into publishing by buying 95% of the Cincinnati Enquirer paperback publisher Bantam Books and hardback publisher Grosset & Dunlap.

But the publishing interests soon went back on the block as Lindner concentrated on insurance which was then suffering from an industry-wide slowdown. In addition to selling the Enquirer AFC spun off American Continental in 1976. American Continental's president was Charles Keating who had joined AFC in 1972 and whose brother published the Enquirer. Keating (who was later jailed released then eventually pleaded guilty in connection with the failure of Lincoln Savings) underwent an SEC investigation during part of his time at AFC for alleged improprieties at Provident Bank. The bank was spun off in 1980.

Lindner took AFC private in 1981. That year following a strategy of bottom-feeding the firm began building its interest in the non-railroad assets of Penn Central the former railroad that had emerged from bankruptcy as an industrial manufacturer. Later that decade AFC increased its ownership in United Brands (later renamed Chiquita Brands International) from 29% to 45%. Lindner installed himself as CEO and reversed that company's losses. In 1987 AFC acquired a TV company Taft Communications (renamed Great American Communications) entailing a heavy debt load. To reduce its debt AFC trimmed its holdings including Circle K Hunter S&L and an interest in Scripps Howard Broadcasting.

Great American Communications went bankrupt in 1992 and emerged the next year as Citicasters Inc. (sold 1996). In 1995 Lindner created American Financial Group to effect the merger of AFC and Premier Underwriters of which he owned 42%. The result was American Financial Group (AFG).

AFG's results in the 1990s were uneven and it typically did not make an underwriting profit. In 2003 the insurer kept operating expenses down (partly by merging two of its holding company subsidiaries into AFG) and swung to a profit even though premium revenue was down.

The company shed some commercial lines to concentrate on its property/casualty and life and annuities businesses. To refine its mix AFG transferred Atlanta Casualty Company Infinity Insurance Company Leader Insurance Company and Windsor Insurance Company into 40%-owned Infinity Property and Casualty which went public in 2003. In 2004 the business exchanged its stake in Provident Financial Group for a holding in National City Corporation.

Founder and chairman Carl Lindner retired as CEO in 2005 and died in 2011. No one was named to replace him as chairman but two of his sons Carl Lindner III and Craig Lindner carried on as co-CEOs.

EXECUTIVES

Vice President and Controller, Robert H Ruffing
Co-President Co-CEO and Director, S. Craig
Lindner, age 62, $1,150,000 total compensation
Co-President Co-CEO and Director, Carl H.
Lindner, age 64, $1,150,000 total compensation
EVP and CFO, Joseph E. (Jeff) Consolino, age 50,
$868,269 total compensation
SVP and Chief Administrative Officer, Michelle A.
(Shelly) Gillis, age 48, $332,315 total compensation
SVP and General Counsel, Vito C. Peraino, age 61,
$565,962 total compensation
**Divisional Senior Vice President Product
Management Property and Inland Marine
Division GAIC,** Julie Kadnar
**Divisional Senior Vice President Executive
Liability Division GAIC,** Thomas Siebers
Vice President Of Benefits, Spencer Stooksbury
**Associate Vice President Infrastructure and
Operations,** James Niehaus
Vice President and Assistant General Counsel,
Mark A Weiss
Senior Vice President, Chester Eng
Executive Vice President, Alicia Yoo
**Divisional Vice President Great American
International Division GAIC,** Julian Bartlett
**Divisional Vice President Loss Prevention Ocean
Marine Division GAIC,** Edward Wilmot
Divisional Senior Vice President GAIC, Veronika
Willard
**Divisional Senior Vice President Specialty Excess
and Surplus Division Great American Insurance
Group,** Brian Sloan
**Divisional Vice President Ocean Marine Division
West Regional Office GAIC,** Thomas Nager
Divisional Assistant Vice President, Helen Lally
**Divisional Vice President Excess Liability
Division GAIC,** Christopher Bright
**Divisional Vice President Marketing Trucking
Division GAIC,** Tim Clinton
**Divisional Senior Vice President Ocean Marine
East Regional Office GAIC,** Forrest Downing
**Divisional Senior Vice President Occupational
Accident Trucking Division Great American
Insurance Group,** Mary Ford
**Divisional Vice President Underwriting and
Regional Manager Midwest Environmental
Division GAIC,** Patrick Mahoney
Auditors: Ernst & Young LLP

LOCATIONS

HQ: American Financial Group Inc
301 East Fourth Street, Cincinnati, OH 45202
Phone: 513 579-2121
Web: www.afginc.com

PRODUCTS/OPERATIONS

2016 Sales

	$ mil.	% of total
Property/casualty	4,697	72
Annuity	1,459	23
Run-off long term care & life	49	1
Consolidated MIEs	151	2
Holding Co. other and unallocated	89	1
Non-core reclass	53	1
Total	**6,498**	**100**

2016 Sales

	% of total
California	14
Florida	10
New York	7
Texas	6
Illinois	5
Georgia	3
Missouri	3
New Jersey	3
Pennsylvania	3
North Carolina	2
Iowa	2

Kansas	2
Michigan	2
Arizona	2
Indiana	2
Other	34
Total	**100**

Selected Subsidiaries

Property/Casualty
  American Empire Surplus Lines Insurance Company
  Great American Insurance Company
  Mid-Continent Casualty Company
  National Interstate Insurance Company
  Republic Indemnity Company of America
Annuities and Life Insurance
  Great American Financial Resources Inc. (GAFRI)
  Annuity Investors Life Insurance
  Great American Life Insurance Company
Real estate investments
  Charleston Harbor Resort and Marina
  Mountain View Grand Resort
  Sailfish Marina and Resort
  Skipjack Cove Yachting Resort and Bay Bridge Marina

COMPETITORS

AIG	Midland National Life
Allianz	Munich Re Group
Allstate	Mutual of Omaha
Arch Capital	National Western
Aviva	Pacific Life
CNA Financial	RLI
Chubb Limited	The Hartford
Cincinnati Financial	Tokio Marine
HCC Insurance	Travelers Companies
Jackson National Life	W. R. Berkley
LSW	XL Group plc
Liberty Mutual	Zenith National
Markel	Zurich Insurance Group
MetLife	

HISTORICAL FINANCIALS

Company Type: Public

Income Statement

FYE: December 31

	ASSETS ($ mil.)	NET INCOME ($ mil.)	INCOME AS % OF ASSETS	EMPLOYEES
12/16	55,072	649	1.2%	400
12/15	49,859	352	0.7%	400
12/14	47,535	452	1.0%	7,200
12/13	42,087	471	1.1%	6,300
12/12	39,171	488	1.2%	6,100
Annual Growth	**8.9%**	**7.4%**	**—**	**(49.4%)**

2016 Year-End Financials

Debt ratio: 2.33%
Return on equity: 13.61%
Cash ($ mil.): 2,107
Current ratio: —
Long-term debt ($ mil.): —

No. of shares (mil.): 86
Dividends
  Yield: 0.0%
  Payout: 29.3%
Market value ($ mil.): 7,660

	STOCK PRICE ($) FY Close	P/E High/Low		PER SHARE ($) Earnings	Dividends	Book Value
12/16	88.12	12	9	7.33	2.15	56.55
12/15	72.08	19	14	3.94	2.03	52.50
12/14	60.72	12	10	4.97	1.91	55.63
12/13	57.72	11	7	5.16	1.81	51.38
12/12	39.52	8	7	5.09	0.97	51.45
Annual Growth	**22.2%**	**—**	**—**	**9.5%**	**22.1%**	**2.4%**

American International Group Inc

Auditors: PricewaterhouseCoopers LLP

LOCATIONS

HQ: American International Group Inc
175 Water Street, New York, NY 10038
Phone: 212 770-7000
Web: www.aig.com

HISTORICAL FINANCIALS

Company Type: Public

Income Statement

FYE: December 31

	ASSETS ($ mil.)	NET INCOME ($ mil.)	INCOME AS % OF ASSETS	EMPLOYEES
12/17	498,301	(6,084)	—	49,800
12/16	498,264	(849)	—	56,400
12/15	496,943	2,196	0.4%	66,400
12/14	515,581	7,529	1.5%	65,000
12/13	541,329	9,085	1.7%	64,000
Annual Growth	**(2.0%)**	**—**	**—**	**(6.1%)**

2017 Year-End Financials

Debt ratio: 6.35%
Return on equity: (-8.60%)
Cash ($ mil.): 2,362
Current ratio: —
Long-term debt ($ mil.): —

No. of shares (mil.): 899
Dividends
  Yield: 0.0%
  Payout: —
Market value ($ mil.): 53,565

	STOCK PRICE ($) FY Close	P/E High/Low		PER SHARE ($) Earnings	Dividends	Book Value
12/17	59.58	—	—	(6.54)	1.28	72.49
12/16	65.31	—	—	(0.78)	1.28	76.66
12/15	61.97	38	29	1.65	0.81	75.10
12/14	56.01	11	9	5.20	0.50	77.69
12/13	51.05	8	6	6.13	0.20	68.62
Annual Growth	**3.9%**			**—**	**59.1%**	**1.4%**

American National Bankshares, Inc. (Danville, VA)

American National Bankshares with total assets of around $1.5 billion is the holding company for American National Bank and Trust. Founded in 1909 the bank operates some 25 branches that serve southern and central Virginia and north central North Carolina. Operating through two segments — Community Banking and Trust and Investment Services — it offers checking and savings accounts CDs IRAs and insurance. Lending activities primarily consist of real estate loans: Commercial mortgages account for about 40% of its loan portfolio while residential mortgages bring in another 20%. American National Bankshares' trust and investment services division manages nearly $610 million in assets.

Operations

American National Bankshares operates through two segments: Community Banking which accounts for more than 80% of the company's total revenue and offers deposit accounts and loans to individuals and small and middle-market businesses; and Trust and Investment Services which provides estate planning trust account administration investment management and retail brokerage services.

The bank makes more than 80% of its revenue from interest income. About 68% of its total revenue came from loan interest during 2015 while another 13% came from interest income on investment securities. The rest of its revenue came from trust fees (6% of revenue) deposit account service charges (3%) mortgage banking income (2%) brokerage fees (1%) and other miscellaneous income sources.

Geographic Reach

Danville Virginia-based American National Bankshares has 25 branches mostly in southern Virginia and in North Carolina (including in Alamance and Guilford Counties). It also has two loan production offices in Roanoke Virginia and Raleigh North Carolina.

Sales and Marketing

American National Bankshares has been cutting back on its advertising and marketing spend in recent years. It spent $356000 on advertising and marketing in 2015 up from $453000 and $607000 in 2014 and 2013 respectively.

Financial Performance

The bank group has struggled to consistently grow its revenues and profits over the past several years despite steadily increasing loan business mostly due to shrinking interest margins on loans stemming from the low-interest environment.

American National had a breakthrough year in 2015 however as its revenue jumped 17% to $68.46 million almost entirely thanks to its acquisition of MainStreet BankShares which boosted its loan and other interest-earning assets by double digits and increased its non-interest income by 19% with newly acquired deposit and other fee related income.

Double-digit revenue growth in 2015 drove the group's net income up 18% to $15.04 million. The bank's operating cash levels climbed 16% to $19.26 million for the year thanks to the boost in cash-denominated earnings.

Strategy

American National Bankshares grows its branch reach as well as its loan and deposit business by opening new branch locations or by buying other branches or banks.

The bank continues to have the largest deposit market share in the Dannville Virginia metro area boasting a 32.8% market share in the region as of mid-2015. It also had the second-largest market share in Pittsylvania County Virginia with a 21.1% share.

Mergers and Acquisitions

In January 2015 American National expanded into Roanoke Virginia after purchasing $164 million-asset MainStreet BankShares Inc. for a total purchase price of $24.2 million. The deal added $122 million in new loan assets $137 million in deposits and three Franklin Bank branches in Franklin County and the Smith Mountain Lake area.

Company Background

In 2011 American National acquired bank holding company MidCarolina Financial expanding its presence in North Carolina specifically in both Alamance and Guilford counties.

EXECUTIVES

EVP and CFO, William W. Traynham, age 60, $211,232 total compensation

President and CEO, Jeffrey V. Haley, age 56, $240,000 total compensation

EVP; EVP and Chief Administrative Officer American National Bank and Trust, Dabney T. P. (Dexter) Gilliam, age 61, $124,544 total compensation

SVP and Chief Credit Officer American National Bank and Trust, R. Helm Dobbins, age 65, $139,570 total compensation

Executive Vice President President - Alamance Region, Charles T. Canaday, age 56

EVP; EVP and Chief Banking Officer American National Bank and Trust, H. Gregg Strader

Executive Vice President Chief Banking Officer, Gregg Strader

Chairman, Charles H. (Charlie) Majors, age 71

Board Member, Ronda Penn

Auditors: Yount, Hyde & Barbour, P.C.

LOCATIONS

HQ: American National Bankshares, Inc. (Danville, VA)
628 Main Street, Danville, VA 24541
Phone: 434 792-5111
Web: www.amnb.com

PRODUCTS/OPERATIONS

2015 Sales

	$ mil.	% of total
Interest and Dividend Income		
Interest and fees on loans	46	69
Taxable	4	6
Tax-exempt	3	5
Other	0	1
Non-interest income		
Trust fees	3	7
Service charges on deposit accounts	2	3
Other fees and commissions	2	3
Other	4	6
Total	**68**	**100**

Selected Subsidiaries

American National Bank and Trust Company
AMNB Statutory Trust I A Delaware Statutory Trust
MidCarolina Trust I A Delaware Statutory Trust
MidCarolina Trust II A Delaware Statutory Trust

Selected Services

Business Banking
  Cash Management
  Checking
  Loans
  Savings
Personal Banking
  Checking
  Loans
  Savings
Insurance
  Business
  Personal

COMPETITORS

BB&T	First Citizens
Bank of America	BancShares
First Century	NewBridge Bancorp
Bankshares	

HISTORICAL FINANCIALS

Company Type: Public

Income Statement

FYE: December 31

	ASSETS ($ mil.)	NET INCOME ($ mil.)	INCOME AS % OF ASSETS	EMPLOYEES
12/16	1,678	16	1.0%	320
12/15	1,547	15	1.0%	303
12/14	1,346	12	0.9%	284
12/13	1,307	15	1.2%	290
12/12	1,283	16	1.2%	307
Annual Growth	6.9%	0.5%	—	1.0%

2016 Year-End Financials

Debt ratio: 2.25%	No. of shares (mil.): 8
Return on equity: 8.14%	Dividends
Cash ($ mil.): 53	Yield: 0.0%
Current ratio: —	Payout: 50.7%
Long-term debt ($ mil.): —	Market value ($ mil.): 300

	STOCK PRICE ($) FY Close	P/E High/Low		PER SHARE ($) Earnings	Dividends	Book Value
12/16	34.80	19	12	1.89	0.96	23.37
12/15	25.61	15	12	1.73	0.93	22.95
12/14	24.81	16	13	1.62	0.92	22.07
12/13	26.25	14	10	2.00	0.92	21.23
12/12	20.19	12	9	2.04	0.92	20.80
Annual Growth	14.6%	—	—	(1.9%)	1.1%	2.9%

American National Insurance Co. (Galveston, TX)

True to its name American National Insurance Company offers agricultural commercial and personal property/casualty insurance as well as life insurance annuities supplemental health credit and other types of insurance throughout the US Puerto Rico and other territories. It subsidiaries include Garden State Life Insurance Standard Life and Accident Insurance and Farm Family Holdings. American National markets its products through independent and career agents broker-dealers employee benefit advisors financial representatives and managing general underwriters.

Operations

American National operates in five segments: Life (including whole term universal indexed and variable life insurance) Annuity (fixed indexed and variable annuity products) Health (Medicare Supplement stop-loss credit disability insurance) Property/Casualty (personal and commercial coverage) and Corporate and Other (income from investments not related to the insurance segments as well as non-insurance operations).

While the company considers its Life and Annuity segments to be its main focus it earns more of its premiums from property/casualty insurance. Together both groups make up about half of the company's total revenues; altogether premiums account for more than 60% of revenues. Investment income accounts for about 30% of sales.

American National has more than $100 billion in life insurance in-force.

Geographic Reach

American National is licensed to conduct business in all states except New York. Business is conducted in New York by American National Life Insurance Company of New York.

The company serves about 6 million customers throughout the US and in Puerto Rico.

Sales and Marketing

American National markets life insurance and annuities through Independent Marketing Group (IMG) which utilizes independent agents serving middle-income and wealthy clients. IMG markets policies through financial institutions employee benefits organizations broker-dealers marketing organizations and independent agents and brokers. It also sells life insurance using direct mail internet and telemarketing campaigns. The company's Career Sales and Service Division primarily serves the middle-income market (life annuities and health coverage) though exclusive employee agents. The group's Health segment serves middle-income seniors self-insured employers and individuals and performs marketing through independent agents and managing general underwriters.

Financial Performance

American National's revenues have hovered around $3 billion for the past five years. In 2016 revenue rose 7% to $3.2 billion. This increase was driven by gains in property/casualty annuity and life premiums (but partially offset by a decline in accident and health premiums). Other policy revenues including mortality charges and earned policy service fees and net investment income also trended upward that year.

Despite the higher revenue net income— which has declined since 2013— fell another 26% to $181 million in 2016. The company's rising expenses cut into its bottom line; life and annuity policyholder benefits and property/casualty claims incurred all increased that year. Additionally a negative change in deferred policy acquisition costs impacted profits.

Cash flow from operations fell 32% to $379.5 million in 2015; it recovered slightly the following year rising 6% to $401.6 million. Among the factors leading to the improvement were changes in current taxes and in prepaid reinsurance premiums.

Strategy

In its quest to be a leading financial products and services company American National aims to maintain the conservative business practices it has upheld for more than a century including controlling risk factors in its growth and investment strategies. The company looks to maintain strong finances through profitable growth primarily by investing in its distribution channels expanding into new geographic markets attracting and training employees and enhancing marketing programs.

As Baby Boomers reach retirement age the company expects that two of its core segments life insurance and annuities will continue to see growth. Its size and financial strength provide it with the ability to introduce new products to this demographic to remain competitive.

In the health insurance sector American National is working to expand in the work site market; however it remains cautious as the future of the Affordable Care Act remains in question.

Another key strategy is improving its use of technology to improve its operating efficiencies and the services it offers its customers. The company is committed to providing exemplary customer service and to offering innovative diversified and competitively priced products to meet the needs of its policyholders and agents.

American National also occasionally grows by acquiring like-minded businesses. It occasionally exits businesses after reassessing its exposure.

Company Background

American National was founded by Galveston businessman W. L. Moody in 1905. The Moody Foundation a charitable trust controlled by W L. Moody descendant Robert Moody and his family and the Moody National Bank together own about 70% of the company.

Based in hurricane-prone Galveston Texas American National knows first-hand the importance of property/casualty insurance and how to evaluate risk. The company withdrew from writing some policies along the Atlantic and Gulf coasts in 2005 and in 2008 it moved its claims processing facilities further inland to San Antonio.

American National launched the American National Life Insurance Company of New York in 2010.

EXECUTIVES

EVP Independent Marketing Group, David A. Behrens, age 54, $532,569 total compensation
Chairman President and CEO, James E. Pozzi, age 66, $918,847 total compensation
EVP CFO Treasurer and Multiple Line (ML) and Property and Casualty (P&C) Operations, Timothy A. Walsh, age 55, $400,400 total compensation
EVP Career Sales and Service Division, Hoyt J. Strickland, age 60, $375,353 total compensation
Vice President of Operations, Dan Williams
Vice President Broker Dealer Marketing, Steven Dobbe
National Sales Manager, Mike Sawdey
Assistant Vice President Life Insurance, Sharon Garner
Vice President Special Markets, Mark Walker
National Sales Manager, Sam Castello
National Sales Manager, Kendra Kelly
Vice President of Product Development, Kara Phillips
Vice President, Sabrina Bermudez
Assistant Vice President Advanced Sales and Priority Markets, Walter Rudecki
National Sales Manager, Michael Kresl
Vice President and Health Actuary, William Watson
National Sales Manager, Cliff McConville
Assistant Vice President Director of Advanced Life Sales, Wayne J Cucco
Assistant Vice President And Assistant Actuary, Michael Shumate
National Sales Manager, Ed Ferrin
National Sales Manager, J Taylor
Senior Vice President Securities Investments, Gordon Dixon
Vice President Marketing, Debie Knowles
Assistant Vice President Data Communications Messaging (Its), Jimmy Watson
National Sales Manager, Jason Weaver
Assistant Vice President And Director Telecommunications, James McEniry
Vice President, Bob Schefft
Assistant Vice President and Associate Medical Director, John White
Assistant Vice President Director Life Marketing Sales Director, Clu Jon O'Neal
National Sales Manager, Thomas Granata
Senior Vice President Of Human Reources, Bruce Lepard
Assistant Vice President, Trish Boudreaux
Senior Vice President Corporate Digital Officer, Bernard Svp
Auditors: KPMG LLP

LOCATIONS

HQ: American National Insurance Co. (Galveston, TX)
One Moody Plaza, Galveston, TX 77550-7999
Phone: 409 763-4661   **Fax:** 409 766-6502
Web: www.anico.com

PRODUCTS/OPERATIONS

2016 Revenue

	$ mil.	% of total
Premiums		
Property/casualty	1,253	39
Life	319	10
Annuity	248	8
Accident and Health	175	5
Net investment income	860	27
Other policy revenues	306	9
Realized investment gains	46	1
Other income	35	1
Other-than-temporary impairments	(17.7)	-
Total	**3,228**	**100**

Selected Subsidiaries

American National Life Insurance Company of Texas (ANTEX)
American National Life Insurance Company of New York
American National Property and Casualty Company (ANPAC)
ANICO Financial Services Inc.
Farm Family Casualty Insurance Company
Farm Family Life Insurance Company
Garden State Life Insurance Company
Pacific Property and Casualty Company
Standard Life and Accident Insurance Company
United Farm Family Insurance Company

COMPETITORS

Allstate	Nationwide
American Financial Group	New York Life
	Penn Mutual
CNO Financial	Prudential
Farmers Group	State Farm
Mutual of Omaha	Torchmark
National Western	USAA

HISTORICAL FINANCIALS

Company Type: Public

Income Statement

FYE: December 31

	ASSETS ($ mil.)	NET INCOME ($ mil.)	INCOME AS % OF ASSETS	EMPLOYEES
12/16	24,533	181	0.7%	4,597
12/15	23,746	242	1.0%	4,736
12/14	23,552	247	1.0%	3,138
12/13	23,324	268	1.2%	3,078
12/12	23,107	191	0.8%	3,075
Annual Growth	**1.5%**	**(1.3%)**	**—**	**10.6%**

2016 Year-End Financials

Debt ratio: 0.55%	No. of shares (mil.): 26
Return on equity: 3.97%	Dividends
Cash ($ mil.): 289	Yield: 0.0%
Current ratio: —	Payout: 48.5%
Long-term debt ($ mil.): —	Market value ($ mil.): 3,354

	STOCK PRICE ($) FY Close	P/E High/Low		PER SHARE ($) Earnings	Dividends	Book Value
12/16	124.61	19	14	6.71	3.26	172.85
12/15	102.27	13	10	9.02	3.14	165.55
12/14	114.26	13	11	9.18	3.08	164.94
12/13	114.54	12	7	9.97	3.08	155.81
12/12	68.29	10	9	7.11	3.08	142.63
Annual Growth	**16.2%**	**—**	**—**	**(1.4%)**	**1.4%**	**4.9%**

AMERICAN TIRE DISTRIBUTORS HOLDINGS, INC.

Business for American Tire Distributors Holdings starts where the rubber meets the road. The company through its American Tire Distributors (ATD) unit is one of the largest independent tire wholesalers in the North America. Its offerings include flagship brands Bridgestone Continental Goodyear Pirelli and Michelin as well as budget brands and private-label tires. ATD also markets custom wheels and tire service equipment. Its network of 140-plus distribution centers serve independent tire dealers retail chains and auto service centers in more than 40 US states and now Canada. The company is owned by private equity firm TPG Capital.

Operations

Beyond tires which account for about 98% of ATD's total sales the company also distributes wheels and other automotive products. Its brands include Cruiser Alloy Drifz O.E. Performance and Racing which are made a numerous manufacturers. The company also sells lower-priced tires under the brands Capitol and Negotiator.

Passenger & Light Truck Tire sales contributed about 83% to the company's total revenue in fiscal 2015 (ended January 3) with medium truck farm vehicles and specialty tire sales making up the remainder.

Geographic Reach

North Carolina-based American Tire Distributors Holdings rings up about 87% of its sales in the US. Canada accounts for the remainder. The company has nearly 120 distribution centers across some 43 US states and 24 distribution centers in Canada.

Sales and Marketing

ATD sells tires to local regional and national independent tire retailers which are located in the US primarily in the Southeastern Mid-Atlantic regions as well as the Midwest Northeast Southwest and West Coast. Other customers include mass merchandisers warehouse clubs tire-manufacturer-owned stores automotive dealerships and web-based markets.

The company's main suppliers for tires are Bridgestone Continental Goodyear and Michelin from whom it bought more than 55% of its tire products in 2014. Other top suppliers include Hankook Kumho Nexen Nitto and Pirelli.

Financial Performance

ATD's sales have been rising at a healthy clip over the past few years swelling from $3 billion in FY2011 to more than $5 billion in the latest fiscal year. The company's bottom line however has slipped into heavy losses in recent years due to thin operating margins and large (and growing) interest expenses stemming from its long-term debt.

The company's net sales jumped by 31% to $5 billion in fiscal 2015 (ended January 3) thanks to a combination of new distribution centers as well as from added business from slew of wholesale-retail distribution center acquisitions made in 2014 and 2013. Additionally comparable unit tire sales also grew thanks to stronger sales unit environment and because of the fiscal year period adjustment that added four selling days to the fiscal year.

Despite higher revenue in FY2015 ATD suffered a net loss of $94.6 million — its deepest loss in three years. The company's losses worsened considerably from the prior year's $6.4 billion loss mostly as its interest expenses ballooned by an additional $51.3 million compared to the prior year as it borrowed more for acquisitions and because its selling general and administrative costs increased after making those acquisitions. ATD's operating cash levels declined sharply to $31.7 million for the year mostly due to the large decline in cash earnings.

Strategy

ATD plans to grow steadily over the years by opening or selectively acquiring distribution outlets in new and under-served markets particularly in Canada. Before making a slew of acquisitions throughout 2014 to expand its presence in select US markets and Canada the company in 2013 opened distribution centers in Chattanooga Tennessee; Manchester New Hampshire; Missouri City Texas; Albany New York; and West Palm Beach Florida.

The tire wholesaler entered Canada in late 2012 and has been strengthening its presence there through acquisitions ever since.

Mergers and Acquisitions

During 2014 American Tire Distributors and its subsidiaries made several acquisitions to expand its market reach. That year the company acquired wholesale tire distributor Regional Tire Distributor operations in Langley Vernon Victoria Calgary and Edmonton in Canada. It also purchased Canada-based wholesalers Trail Tire Distributors and Extreme Wheel Distributors as well as Canadian wholesale and retail tire businesses Kirks Tire Ltd and Kipling Tire Co.

Also in 2014 the company purchased Hercules Tire Holdings including its Hercules Tire & Rubber Company subsidiary 15 distribution centers in the US six distribution centers in Canada and one warehouse in northern China. The acquisition strengthened ATD's presence in the major markets of California Texas Florida and Canada.

ATD's 2014 acquisition of wholesale-retail distributor Terry's Tire Town Holdings and subsidiaries added 10 US distribution centers spanning from Virginia to Maine and in Ohio expanding its market reach in those regions while aligning distribution centers nicely with ATD's recently opened centers in the Northeast and Ohio.

ATD in November 2012 acquired Triwest Trading (Canada) Ltd. (dba TriCan Tire Distributors or TriCan for short). TriCan is a wholesale distributor of tires tire parts tire accessories and related equipment in Canada with 15 distribution centers nationwide. The purchase marked ATD's entry into Canada.

EXECUTIVES

EVP General Counsel and Secretary, J. Michael (Mike) Gaither, age 64, $400,000 total compensation
EVP and CFO, Jason T. Yaudes, age 43, $400,000 total compensation
President and CEO, Stuart Schuette
EVP Product Strategy and Supply, Jason Shannon
Senior Vice President Proprietary Brands, Joshua Simpson
Regional Vice President, John Reid
Senior Vice President Supply Chain, Mark Chandler
Vice President Supply Chain, Randy Arthur
Assistant Treasurer, Chris Ravenberg
Auditors: PRICEWATERHOUSECOOPERS LLP CH

LOCATIONS

HQ: AMERICAN TIRE DISTRIBUTORS HOLDINGS, INC. 12200 HERBERT WAYNE CT # 150, HUNTERSVILLE, NC 280786335
Phone: 704 992-2000
Web: WWW.ATD-US.COM

2014 Sales

	% of total
US	87
Canada	13
Total	**100**

PRODUCTS/OPERATIONS

2014 Sales by Product

	% of total
Passenger & light truck tires	83
Medium trucks farm vehicles & other specialty tires	17
Total	**100**

2014 Sales

	% of total
Tires	98
Tire supplies tools custom wheels & accessories	2
Total	**100**

Brands

Brands
Capitol®; tires
Negotiator®; tires
Regul®; tires
Dynatrac®; tires
Cruiseralloy®; custom wheels
Drifz®; custom wheels
ICW®; custom wheels
Pacer®; custom wheels
O.E. Performance®; custom wheels

Selected Products

Equipment tools and supplies (valve stems auto lifts)
Tires
Wheel covers
Wheel Wizard (computer program allowing customers to virtually see wheel types on their vehicle)

COMPETITORS

Dealer Tire	Tire Distribution
TBC	Systems
TCI Tire Centers	Wal-Mart

HISTORICAL FINANCIALS

Company Type: Private

Income Statement

FYE: January 3

	REVENUE ($ mil.)	NET INCOME ($ mil.)	NET PROFIT MARGIN	EMPLOYEES
01/15*	5,030	(94)	—	500
12/13	3,839	(6)	—	
12/12	3,455	(14)	—	
12/11	3,050	0	0.0%	
Annual Growth	**18.1%**	—	—	

*Fiscal year change

2015 Year-End Financials

Debt ratio: —
Return on equity: (-1.90%)
Cash ($ mil.) 35
Current ratio: 0.50
Long-term debt ($ mil.): —
Dividends
Yield: —
Payout: —
Market value ($ mil.): —

American Tower Corp (New)

Growth in wireless communications is taking American Tower to new heights. The company rents space on towers and rooftop antenna systems to wireless carriers and radio and TV broadcasters who use the infrastructure to enable their services. It operates about 40000 wireless towers in the US some 57000 in India and roughly 43000 throughout the rest of the world. Its portfolio additionally includes approximately 800 Distributed Antenna System networks used mainly for indoor communications (malls casinos etc.). American Tower also offers tower-related services such as site acquisition structural analysis to determine support for additional equipment and zoning and permitting management services.

Operations

American Tower's primary business is the leasing of antenna space on multi-tenant communications sites. It provides the service to wireless providers radio and television broadcast companies wireless data providers government agencies and municipalities and tenants from several other industries.

The company operates five business segments mostly based in regions where it leases its property. The US Property segment is its largest and accounts for nearly 60% of revenue. The three other geographic segments include Latin America Property EMEA Property and Asia Property. The Services segment which generates only 1% of revenue acquires sites and offers zoning and permitting services and structural analysis to support its site leasing businesses.

Geographic Reach

Boston MA-headquartered American Tower operates it corporate functions in the US and runs distributed operations in its non-US markets. The company produces most of its revenue in the US. However the company is pursuing frequent geographic expansions and the percentage of non-US activity is rising. Almost 15% of revenue comes from India 9% originates in Brazil and just less than 6% comes from Mexico. The communications firm also operates in a variety of countries in EMEA (Germany Ghana Nigeria S. Africa Uganda) and in Latin America (Argentina Chile Colombia Costa Rica and Peru).

Sales and Marketing

American Tower's top four tenants generate most of its total revenue: about 20% from AT&T Mobility some 15% from Verizon Wireless a little more than 10% from Sprint and about 10% from T-Mobile. Other top tenants include Tata Airtel Idea Cellular Telefonica Nextel International Telecom Italia MTN Group Limited and Vodafone.

Financial Performance

American Tower experienced explosive growth in both revenue and net income over the past several years. Between 2010 and 2016 revenue and net income averaged a near-20% increase each year as consumer demand for wireless products rose around the world.

In 2016 revenue rose more than 21% year-over-year to $5.8 billion. Across all geographies American Tower saw growth in new sites and growth in additional leases on existing sites. More than half of the year?s revenue increase originated in Asia which saw $341 million generated by new sites primarily as the result of the company?s 2016 Viom acquisition. Other notable site increases came from Airtel in Nigeria and Verizon in the US. New leases on existing sites contributed more than $175 million of revenue growth in 2016.

Net income shot up 40% to $956 million in 2016 compared to 2015?s $685 million due to increased revenue and a multi-point drop in operating expense margin.

Cash grew by $466 million in 2016 to end the year with $787 million in the coffers. Uses of cash included $2.1 billion and $100 million for investing and financing activities respectively. They were more than offset by contributions from operating activities which included net income and a $1.5 billion reconciliation for depreciation & amortization.

Strategy

Wireless communication is growing rapidly throughout the world due to increased demand for new customers wanting to connect (such as in emerging markets) and for existing customers wanting more bandwidth at higher speeds. American Tower wants to capitalize on this trend by expanding its property footprint and making the most out of the property and towers it already owns and operates. It intends to achieve this with geographic expansion opportunistic acquisition of additional towers and maximizing occupancy of its existing towers.

As evidenced by the increasing revenue share coming from non-US sources American Tower is expanding more rapidly overseas than at home. Its recent acquisition of Viom Networks more than tripled its number of towers in India. A follow-on purchase in late 2017 added 20000 more communication sites to its India portfolio bringing its total to more than 70000 sites. Its ATC Europe segment plunged into the French market in 2017 with the acquisition of 2400 wireless towers. Additionally the company purchased in 2016 about 900 towers across a variety of countries.

The costs of increasing tenant occupancy on existing sites is noticeably less than acquiring a new site and erecting new towers. The company has a global average of approximately 1.9 tenants per tower and hopes to increase that rate through targeted sales and marketing activities. It believes that towers that are at or near capacity can be upgraded or augmented to meet future tenant demand with relatively modest capital investment.

Mergers and Acquisitions

In late 2017 ATC India agreed to purchase for $1.2 billion approximately 20000 communication sites in India from two firms Vodafone and Idea Cellular.

In early 2017 ATC Europe a 51%/49% joint venture between ATC and Netherlands-based PGGM spent approximately $750 million to acquire FPS Towers an owner and operator of 2400 wireless tower sites in France.

In 2016 American Tower purchased a 51% controlling interest for $1.1 billion in Viom Networks Ltd a telecommunications infrastructure company that owns and operates about 42000 wireless towers and 200 indoor distributed antenna system (DAS) networks in India. Viom was renamed to ATC Telecom Infrastructure Private Ltd and is part of ATC?s Asia geographic region.

During 2015 the company purchased for $1.1 billion a total of 25368 communications sites (with 3235 build-to-suits) including some 4700 communications sites in Nigeria from Bharti Airtel. In that same year it acquired another nearly 11500 wireless communication sites from Verizon Communications for about $5.05 billion.

EXECUTIVES

EVP and CFO, Thomas A. (Tom) Bartlett, age 58, $750,000 total compensation
Chairman President and CEO, James D. (Jim) Taiclet, age 56, $1,100,000 total compensation
EVP International Operations; President Latin America and EMEA, William H. (Hal) Hess, age 54, $650,000 total compensation
EVP and President US Tower, Steven C. Marshall, age 56, $650,000 total compensation
EVP; President Asia, Amit Sharma, age 57
EVP Chief Administrative Officer General Counsel and Secretary, Edmund (Ed) DiSanto, age 65, $600,000 total compensation
CEO Europe Middle East and Africa, Leah C. Stearns
Chairman ATC Europe, Stephen Harris
Auditors: Deloitte & Touche LLP

LOCATIONS

HQ: American Tower Corp (New)
116 Huntington Avenue, Boston, MA 02116
Phone: 617 375-7500
Web: www.americantower.com

2016 Sales

	$ mil.	% of total
US	3,442	60
India	827	14
Brazil	506	9
Mexico	331	6
Nigeria	215	4
Ghana	116	2
Germany	60	1
South Africa	80	1
Uganda	57	1
Chile	33	1
Colombia	79	1
Argentina	1	-
Costa Rica	19	-
Peru	15	-
Total	**5,785**	**100**

PRODUCTS/OPERATIONS

2016 Sales

	$ mil.	% of total
Property	5,713	99
Services	72	1
Total	**5,785**	**100**

COMPETITORS

Crown Castle International	SBA Communications
LCC International	VelociTel
Microwave Transmission Systems	

HISTORICAL FINANCIALS

Company Type: Public

Income Statement

FYE: December 31

	REVENUE ($ mil.)	NET INCOME ($ mil.)	NET PROFIT MARGIN	EMPLOYEES
12/16	5,785	956	16.5%	4,507
12/15	4,771	685	14.4%	3,371
12/14	4,100	824	20.1%	2,974
12/13	3,361	551	16.4%	2,716
12/12	2,875	637	22.2%	2,432
Annual Growth	**19.1%**	**10.7%**	**—**	**16.7%**

2016 Year-End Financials

Debt ratio: 60.02%
Return on equity: 14.22%
Cash ($ mil.): 787
Current ratio: 1.04
Long-term debt ($ mil.): 18,294
No. of shares (mil.): 427
Dividends
  Yield: 0.0%
  Payout: 109.6%
Market value ($ mil.): 45,136

	STOCK PRICE ($) FY Close	P/E High/Low		PER SHARE ($) Earnings	Dividends	Book Value
12/16	105.68	59	42	1.98	2.17	15.84
12/15	96.95	73	61	1.41	1.81	15.69
12/14	98.85	52	39	2.00	1.40	9.97
12/13	79.82	60	49	1.38	1.10	8.95
12/12	77.27	48	37	1.60	0.90	9.04
Annual Growth	**8.1%**	**—**		**5.5%**	**24.6%**	**15.0%**

Ameriprise Financial Inc

Ameriprise Financial provides a variety of financial products including mutual funds savings plans annuities personal trust services and insurance products. It does so through its various brands and affiliates — which include Ameriprise Financial Services Columbia Management and RiverSource. Ameriprise manages some $800 billion in assets for more than 2 million individual institutional and small business clients primarily in the US with a growing international presence. It markets and administers its products primarily through a network of some 10000 financial advisors. Founded in 1894 Ameriprise Financial was spun off from American Express in 2005.

Operations

Ameriprise operates four main segments: Advice & Wealth Management Asset Management Annuities and Protection.

Its Advice & Wealth Management segment includes 2000 employee advisors and 7700 independent franchises. Together they provide financial planning advice and brokerage services primarily to the firm?s US retail clients. The segment generates about 35% of revenue.

Asset Management (25% of revenue) offers investment management and products to retail high-net-worth and institutional clients globally. It does so through Columbia Management in the US and Threadneedle internationally. Columbia manages just under 140 funds (mutual funds ETFs etc.) and about 70 variable insurance trust funds (VIT Funds) in the US while Threadneedle manages some 180 funds outside the US.

The Annuities segment provides variable and fixed annuity products to individual clients via Ameriprise?s RiverSource subsidiary. The fourth segment Protection offers Ameriprise clients insurance products including life disability income and property casualty. Each of these two segments provides about 20% of net revenue.

Geographic Reach

Ameriprise Financial and its affiliates are headquartered in Minneapolis Minnesota. Other primary offices are in New York City Boston and London. The US is by far its largest market generating more than 90% of the firm's revenue and possessing approximately 90% of its long-lived assets.

Sales and Marketing

Ameriprise?s customers are varied ranging from individuals to universities to corporations. It employs a variety of methods to market and sell to this diverse group. The company?s primary retail clients come from the ?mass affluent consumer? segment which controls almost half of all investable assets in the US. The firm markets to them through its financial advisor network and its website. Ameriprise tends to the non-retail segment (institutional & high-net-worth individuals) by nurturing direct relationships with entities such as university endowments pension plans sovereign wealth funds and foundations.

Financial Performance

Thanks to appreciating financial markets and a growing investor base Ameriprise Financial's asset-based fees have led it to consistent revenue and profit growth over the past several years. Since the Great Recession of 2008-2009 revenues have steadily climbed from a low of $7 billion to more recent amounts near $12 billion. Net income followed a similar albeit more varied trend with a loss of $36 million in 2008 followed by years of $1 billion earnings appreciating to $2 billion in 2014 before settling lower in recent years.

The 2016 results saw the company's revenue dip 4% to $11.7 billion the second year of low percentage decline caused mostly by a decrease in fees (management financial advice distribution performance) net investment income and other revenue. A decrease in average assets under management (AUM) of $28 billion (4%) contributed to the lower fees.

Net income in 2016 was $1.3 billion a 22% drop compared to 2015 due primarily to lower revenues and increased expenses for benefits claims losses and settlements.

The change to cash and cash equivalents in 2016 was negligible decreasing a mere $40 million leaving the year-end total at $2.4 billion. While cash generated by operating activities was just under $2 billion investing and financing efforts depleted cash by $800 million and $1.1 billion respectively.

Strategy

Ameriprise?s long-term strategy involves a portfolio shift to pursue high growth areas in Advice & Wealth Management and Asset Management. It also has a near-term tactical strategy to target two key segments: individuals with $100000 or more in investable assets and high-net-worth people and institutional investors.

Between 2010 and 2016 the financial firm orchestrated a shift in assets under management which altered the mix of its pretax operating earnings from one heavily weighted towards Protection & Annuities (55% in 2010) to one almost equally balanced across its segments.

Its advisor network is crucial to growing and maintaining its base of individuals with $100000 or more in assets. The network model is one of a relationship-based direct sales organization in which the company makes considerable investment in technology training and support in addition to a plethora of financial products (mutual funds annuities life insurance). Occasionally Ameriprise adds to its network through acquisition which it did in 2016 with the purchase of Emerging Global Advisors and in 2017 with the purchase of Investment Professionals Inc.

The high-net-worth and institutional client segment is global in scale and therefore requires an approach that is not reliant on the advisor network. Instead Ameriprise offers a broad spectrum of investment advice and products through third parties and its Columbia Threadneedle subsidiary. Global geographic expansion innovations to investment solutions and delivering competitive investment performance are key to growing the fees and commissions received for this segment?s fundamental metric assets under management (AUM).

EXECUTIVES

Chairman and CEO, James M. (Jim) Cracchiolo, age 58, $1,025,000 total compensation
CEO Global Asset Management, William F. (Ted) Truscott, age 56, $675,000 total compensation
EVP and CFO, Walter S. Berman, age 75, $675,000 total compensation
EVP Human Resources, Kelli A. Hunter, age 56
President Advice and Wealth Management Products and Service Delivery, Joseph E. (Joe) Sweeney, age 56, $550,000 total compensation
Chief Strategy Officer; President Insurance and Annuities, John R. Woerner, age 48
EVP Marketing Corporate Communications and Community Relations, Deirdre D. McGraw, age 47
COO; President Advice & Wealth Management Business Development, Neal Maglaque
EVP and CIO, Randy Kupper
EVP and Global Chief Investment Officer, Colin Moore, $475,000 total compensation
EVP Ameriprise Franchise Group, Bill Williams
EVP Ameriprise Advisor Group, Pat O'Connell
EVP and General Counsel, Karen Wilson Thissen
Senior Vice President, Gumer Alvero
Vice President Operations, George Tsafaridis
Vice President, William Emptage
Vice President and Chief Counsel, Heather Klaas Melloh
Vice President Human Resources, Karen Dekker
Field Vice President, Homer Smith
Vice President Underwriting and Chief Underwriter, Thor Holmgren
Vice President Financial Applications Support Controllership, John Mead
Vice President Appointed Actuary, Stephen Blaske
Vice President External Products Group, Tracy Anderson
Vice President Investment Research Group, Lyle Schonberger
Senior Vice President of Consumer Marketing, Marie O'Neill
Regional Vice President, Tara Eisenbeis
Vice President Wholesaling operations, Mike Kirchner
Vice President Technical Advisory Group, Michael Mattox
Vice President, Jayme Cleghorn
Vice President Marketing, Linda Moriarty
Vice President ??? Field Strategy, Stephen Ehele
Vice President of Sales and Marketing, Stephanie Rustad
Vice President, Steven Good
Field Vice President, Todd Orton
Vice President Human Resources Services, Jay Rasula
Regional Vice President, Phillip Buckner
Vice President And Group Counsel, Lisa Lewis
Financial Advisor Associate Vice President, Peter Smith
Vice President, Lori Arrell
Senior Vice President Enterprise Implementation and Operational Risk Assessment, Jeninne McGee
Vice President Compliance, Jeff Soderstrom
Vice President Risk Management Owned Assets, David Berger
Vice President, Paul Major
Vice President=CLR Project Management Office, Mike Greene
Vice President Underwriting, Tom Botsford
Vice President, Chip Pierron
Vice President General Manager Managed Products, Greg Nordmeyer
Vice President Architecture, Tom Esselman
Vice President and Group Counsel, Christopher Long
Vice President And General Manager External Products, Frank Mccarthy
Vice President Information Technology, Clarissa C Ramos
Vice President Compensation Human Resources, Jason Williams
Vice President Human Resources Program, Kristi Kooda-Chizek
Vice President Insurance Marketing, Thomas Maki
Vice President Workforce Strategy and Planning, Penny Meier
Vice President Financial Planning, Marcy Keckler
Vice President and Chief Compliance Of, Nicole Smith
Vice President, Gerard Smyth
Vice President and Group Counsel, Christopher Petersen
Vice President and Group Counsel, Kurt Johansen
RVP Retirement Plans, Matthew Miller
Vice President and Head Of Advice and Wealth Management Operations, Manish Ganatra
Vice President Financial Advisor, Paul Hoghaug
Vice President Sales, LeAnn M Thomas
Vice President Training And Development, Lamont Boykins

Vice President Of Technical Department,
Jacqueline Glockner
Vice President Clearing Operations, Michael Pszybylski
Vice President, Nate Pugliese
Vice President, Jason Miller
Associate Vice President Financial Advisor, David Williams
Executive Vice President, Patrick O'Connell
Senior Regional Vice President Insurance West, Bj Seastone
Vice President, Daniel Masiello
Financial Advisor Associate Vice President, Evan Dankner
Vice President And Financial Advisor, Edward Moran
Vice President Communications, Adrienne Nestor
Vice President, Nicolo Manlapaz
Associate Vice President, James Sams
Vice President, Russ Zorn
Financial Advisor Associate Vice President, Barbara Black
Financial Advisor Associate Vice President, Tim Harrison
Vice President Derivative and Product Risk, Manuel Balsera
Financial Advisor Associate Vice President, Jeffrey Rippon
Financial Advisor Associate Vice President, Harish Dang
Vice President Financial Advisor, Raymond Bolleia
Vice President Investment Advisor, Christine Pall
Financial Advisor Associate Vice President, Randall Kronour
Divisional Vice President, Michael DeLorenzo
Associate Vice President of Finance, Brian Mccabe
Senior Vice President, Eddy Augsten
Financial Advisor Associate Vice President, Jeremy Kitamura
Senior Vice President Financial Advisor, Bob Marmor
Associate Vice President, Bob Dennis
Vice President, Pradeep Gokhale
Vice President, Jeff Tarter
Associate Vice President Investments, John Stella
Associate Vice President, Michael Carboni
Associate Vice President, Karen Hartley
Vice President, Richard Cfp
Vice President, Christopher Grella
Vice President Financial Planner, James Dickie
Vice President Quantitative Strategies, Philip Jones
Financial Advisor: Vice President, Amy Boyle
Vice President and Investment Officer, Josh Waterman
FRANCHISE REGION VICE PRESIDENT, Barry Stockdale
ASSOCIATE VICE PRESIDENT, Wendy Risse
VICE PRESIDENT, James J Obrien
Financial Advisor Associate Vice President, Jonathan Steinman
Financial Advisor Associate Vice President, Greg Trost
Vice President Flight Operations and Chief Pilot, Steve Kozlow
Vice President, William Callahan
Vice President of Client Services, Lauren Silva
Vice President Certified Financial Planner, Jennifer Theissing
Financial Advisor Associate Vice President, Chad Meisner
Associate Vice President, Andrew Tabaczuk
Field Vice President, Ken Franklin
Regional Vice President Northwest, Jamie Frisone
Associate Vice President Financial Advisor, Carl Fazio
Associate Vice President of Investments, Dawn Williams
Associate Vice President, Paul Donas
Regional Vice President, Tim McClurg

Vice President Federal Government Affairs, Elizabeth Varley
Regional Vice President, John Berg
Financial Advisor Associate Vice President, Mike Quinn
Franchise Field Vice President Pacific Northwest, George Varones
Vice President I and A PMO, Abir Roy
Auditors: PricewaterhouseCoopers LLP

LOCATIONS

HQ: Ameriprise Financial Inc
1099 Ameriprise Financial Center, Minneapolis, MN 55474
Phone: 612 671-3131
Web: www.ameriprise.com

PRODUCTS/OPERATIONS

2016 Sales

	% of total
Advice & Wealth Management	39
Asset Management	23
Annuities	19
Protection	19
Total	**100**

2016 Sales

	$ mil.	% of total
Management and financial advice fees	5,778	49
Distribution fees	1,795	15
Net investment income	1,576	13
Premiums	1,491	13
Other revenues	1,095	9
Banking and deposit interest expense	(39)	-
Total	**11,696**	**100**

PRODUCTS & SERVICES
Cash Cards & Lending
Financial Planning
Insurance & Annuities
Investments
Personal Trust Services

Selected Subsidiaries and Affiliates
American Enterprise Investment Services Inc.
Ameriprise Financial Services Inc.
Ameriprise Certificate Company
Ameriprise Trust Company
Columbia Management Investment Advisers LLC
Columbia Management Investment Distributors Inc.
IDS Property Casualty Insurance Company
J. & W. Seligman & Co. Incorporated
RiverSource Distributors Inc.
RiverSource Life Insurance Co. of New York
Threadneedle Asset Management Holdings

Selected Brands
Ameriprise Financial®;
Columbia Management®;
RiverSource®;

COMPETITORS

AXA Financial	MassMutual
Allstate	Merrill Lynch
Bank of America	MetLife
Bank of New York Mellon	Nationwide Financial
Calamos Asset Management	New York Life
Capital Group	Northwestern Mutual
Charles Schwab	PNC Financial
Citigroup	Primerica
FMR	Principal Financial
First Eagle Investment Mangement	Prudential
John Hancock Financial Services	Regions Financial
Lincoln Financial Group	State Street
	TIAA
	U.S. Bancorp

HISTORICAL FINANCIALS
Company Type: Public

Income Statement
FYE: December 31

	REVENUE ($ mil.)	NET INCOME ($ mil.)	NET PROFIT MARGIN	EMPLOYEES
12/16	11,696	1,314	11.2%	13,000
12/15	12,170	1,562	12.8%	13,000
12/14	12,268	1,619	13.2%	12,209
12/13	11,199	1,334	11.9%	12,039
12/12	10,217	1,029	10.1%	12,235
Annual Growth	3.4%	6.3%	—	1.5%

2016 Year-End Financials

Debt ratio: 3.89%	No. of shares (mil.): 154
Return on equity: 19.40%	Dividends
Cash ($ mil.): 2,486	Yield: 0.0%
Current ratio: 0.65	Payout: 37.3%
Long-term debt ($ mil.): 5,236	Market value ($ mil.): 17,169

	STOCK PRICE ($) FY Close	P/E High/Low		PER SHARE ($) Earnings	Dividends	Book Value
12/16	110.94	15	10	7.81	2.92	40.66
12/15	106.42	16	12	8.48	2.59	42.20
12/14	132.25	16	12	8.30	2.26	44.37
12/13	115.05	17	10	6.44	2.01	42.64
12/12	62.63	14	10	4.62	1.43	44.58
Annual Growth	15.4%	—	—	14.0%	19.5%	(2.3%)

Ameris Bancorp

Ameris Bancorp enjoys the financial climate of the Deep South. It is the holding company of Ameris Bank which holds roughly $3.6 billion in assets and serves retail and consumer customers through more than 75 full-service and mortgage branches in Alabama Georgia South Carolina and northern Florida. In addition to its standard banking products and services the bank also provides treasury services mortgage and refinancing solutions and investment services through an agreement with Raymond James Financial. Loans secured by commercial real estate accounted for approximately 45% of the company's loan portfolio while 1-4 family residential and construction & land development mortgages accounted for nearly a quarter and about 10% respectively.

Operations

Like most banks Ameris earns the vast majority of its recurring revenue (71.5%) from interest income from loans. Nearly 80% of these loans are made up of commercial real estate 1-4 family residential and construction & land development loans. The remaining 20% are from a mix of commercial multi-family residential and consumer loans (home improvement home equity personal lines of credit auto loans and student loans).

Traditional banking products (deposit accounts) and services along with investment products and services (which primarily earn income from fees and commissions) made up about 28% of the bank's annual sales in fiscal 2013.

Sales and Marketing

Through an acquisition-oriented growth strategy Ameris seeks to grow its brand and presence in the markets it currently serves in Georgia Alabama Florida and South Carolina as well as in neighboring communities. In addition the bank expects its community-oriented philosophy will help strengthen existing customer relations and attract new customers.

The company spent $1.62 million on advertising and public relations in Fiscal Year 2013 just under the $1.622 million it spent in 2012 and more than double the $722000 it spent in 2011. The company increased its advertising spending by $900000 during 2012 to support its revenue and growth- strategies during the year.

Financial Performance

Ameris carried $3.67 billion in total assets as of December 31 2013. Loans made up $2.5 billion (approximately 68.9% of total assets). The bank also reported carrying $3 billion in deposits.

Ameris' net revenue dipped in fiscal 2013 declining 5% to $163 million from its high of $172 million in 2012 mostly from an $11.3 million dip in non-interest revenue. But this dip in non-interest revenue is primarily because the bank recorded a large gain of $20 million from acquisitions in 2012. When excluding this acquisition gain from 2012's revenues and thanks to $6.1 million revenue increase in mortgage banking activity management reports that total non-interest income actually increased $8.7 million in 2013 compared to 2012. A decline in interest-earning loan assets from $2.47 billion in 2013 compared to $2.5 billion in 2012 also played a role in the dip in net revenues.

Thanks to aggressive acquisitions and despite revenue decreasing net income jumped a whopping 43% to $20 million in 2013 from $14 million in 2012. This is only slightly below the bank's net income high of $21 million in 2011. It's most notable acquisition of Prosperity Bank increased Ameris' total assets by $744.9 million and added $449.7 million in loans to its interest-earning loan portfolio. Adding to the extra income from new loans Ameris collected higher net interest margins on all of its loans which increased to 4.74% in 2013 from 4.60% in 2012.

Strategy

Ameris plans to continue using its community banking philosophy to lessen its risk and identify prime local lending markets. Management reports that by encouraging a personalized service experience and building deeper customer relationships the bank has already grown a "substantial" base of low-cost core deposits (which pad the bank's reserves and lessen financial risk). And between its bench of experienced decision makers and lenders operating in a "decentralized" structure (which differentiates Ameris from mega banks) and its deep familiarity with local markets management believes the bank can better identify prime growth markets (for lending and bank services) with managed risk in the years ahead.

Mergers and Acquisitions

Integral to the bank's growth strategy Ameris has aggressively acquired banks to broaden its reach into its primary southern markets.

Ameris Bancorp purchased Jacksonville Bancorp and its eight branches more than doubling its branch network in Jacksonville Illinois to 14 branches.

Company Background

In addition to acquiring several troubled and failing banks with help from the FDIC Ameris merged with Prosperity Bank in 2013 which broadened its reach into Florida through Prosperity's branches in St. Augustine Jacksonville Panama City Lynn Haven Palatka and Ormand Beach.

Georgia's economy was one of the hardest hit in the US during the recession and Ameris has taken advantage of the plethora of banks seized by regulators in the state. Since 2009 the company has acquired about 10 failed banks in Georgia though FDIC-assisted transactions adding some 20 branches to its network. Ameris also snagged the failed First Bank of Jacksonville in Florida which had two locations.

EXECUTIVES

Chief Banking Executive Ameris Bancorp and Ameris Bank, Andrew B. (Andy) Cheney, age 67, $400,000 total compensation
EVP and Chief Credit Officer, Jon S. Edwards, age 55, $260,000 total compensation
EVP Chief Administrative Officer and Corporate Secretary, Cindi H. Lewis, age 63, $90,333 total compensation
President and CEO, Edwin W. (Ed) Hortman, age 63, $625,000 total compensation
EVP and Banking Group President Ameris Bancorp and President Ameris Bank, Lawton E. Bassett
EVP CFO and COO, Dennis J. Zember, age 47, $320,000 total compensation
EVP and Chief Risk Officer, Stephen A. Melton, $275,000 total compensation
EVP and Chief Banking Officer, James A. LaHaise
Assistant Vice President, Ann Dunn
Senior Vice president and Business Banker, Scott Sylvester
Senior Vice President, Rob Kowkabany
Senior Vice President Commercial Banking, Alan Eubanks
Vice President of Residential Mortgage, Greg Seabaugh
Vice President Mortgage Sales Manager, Jason Fralix
Executive Vice President and Chief Information Officer, Joe Kissel
Vice President Mortgage Sales Manager, Marlene Buhler
Vice President Credit Portfolio Manager, Clark Robeson
Chairman, Daniel B. Jeter, age 65
Auditors: Crowe Horwath LLP

LOCATIONS

HQ: Ameris Bancorp
310 First Street S.E., Moultrie, GA 31768
Phone: 229 890-1111
Web: www.amerisbank.com

PRODUCTS/OPERATIONS

2016 sales chart

	$ mil.	% of total
Interest income:		
Interest and fees on loans	218	64
Interest on taxable securities	17	5
Interest on nontaxable securities	1	-
Interest on deposits in other banks	0	-
Interest on federal funds sold	-	-
Non Interest income:		
Service charges on deposit accounts	42	13
Mortgage banking activity	48	14
Other service charges commissions and fees	3	1
Net gains on sales of securities	-	-
Gain on sale of SBA loans	3	1
Other noninterest income	7	2
Total	**344**	**100**

2016 sales chart

	% of total
Banking Division	91
Retail Mortgage Division	5
Warehouse Lending Division	3
SBA Division	1
Total	**100**

Selected Acquisitions

American United Bank
Central Bank of Georgia
Darby Bank & Trust
First Bank of Jacksonville
High Trust Bank
Montgomery Bank & Trust
One Georgia Bank
Satilla Community Bank
Tifton Banking Company
United Security Bank

COMPETITORS

BBVA Compass Bancshares	First South Bancorp (NC)
Bank of America	Regions Financial
Capital City Bank	Southwest Georgia
Colony Bankcorp	Financial
Community Capital Bancshares	SunTrust
	Thomasville Bancshares

HISTORICAL FINANCIALS

Company Type: Public

Income Statement — FYE: December 31

	ASSETS ($ mil.)	NET INCOME ($ mil.)	INCOME AS % OF ASSETS	EMPLOYEES
12/16	6,892	72	1.0%	1,298
12/15	5,588	40	0.7%	1,304
12/14	4,037	38	1.0%	1,027
12/13	3,667	20	0.5%	984
12/12	3,019	14	0.5%	866
Annual Growth	**22.9%**	**49.5%**	**—**	**10.6%**

2016 Year-End Financials

Debt ratio: 1.81%
Return on equity: 12.38%
Cash ($ mil.): 198
Current ratio: —
Long-term debt ($ mil.): —
No. of shares (mil.): 34
Dividends
  Yield: 0.0%
  Payout: 14.4%
Market value ($ mil.): 1,523

	STOCK PRICE ($) FY Close	P/E High/Low		PER SHARE ($) Earnings	Dividends	Book Value
12/16	43.60	23	12	2.08	0.30	18.51
12/15	33.99	27	18	1.27	0.20	15.98
12/14	25.64	18	13	1.46	0.15	13.67
12/13	21.11	28	16	0.75	0.00	12.62
12/12	12.49	29	22	0.46	0.00	11.72
Annual Growth	**36.7%**	**—**	**—**	**45.8%**	**—**	**12.1%**

Amerisafe Inc

AMERISAFE has what it takes to insure roughnecks and truckers. AMERISAFE specializes in providing workers' compensation insurance for businesses in hazardous industries including agriculture manufacturing construction logging and sawmill oil and gas maritime and trucking. Through its subsidiaries American Interstate Insurance Silver Oak Casualty and American Interstate Insurance of Texas the company writes coverage for more than 7900 employers (mainly small and midsized firms). In addition AMERISAFE offers worksite safety reviews loss prevention and claims management services. AMERISAFE sells its products in more than 30 states and the District of Columbia.

Geographic Reach

AMERISAFE's largest markets are Louisiana Georgia and Pennsylvania with each accounting for roughly 10% of its gross premiums written.

Sales and Marketing

The company sells its products through more than 3100 independent agents as well as through its Amerisafe General Agency.

Financial Performance

Like all workers' compensation providers AMERISAFE saw its revenues drop during the economic recession for the simplest reason: when employers trim their workforces they need less workers' compensation coverage.

However the company's revenue has been increasing year-over-year since 2010. It reported $356.3 million in revenue for fiscal 2013 up from $321.2 million in revenue for fiscal 2012 and $280.7 million in revenue for fiscal 2011.

AMERISAFE's net income has also been trending up across recent fiscal years. The company netted more than $43 million in fiscal 2013 after reporting a net income of about $29 million for fiscal 2012 and $24 million for fiscal 2011.

The company's cash flow remains strong. It had almost $50 million more on hand at the end of fiscal 2013 than it did at the close of fiscal 2012.

Strategy

AMERISAFE's strategy for growth is based on managing its capital and focusing on its underwriting profitability. It hopes to increase its book value and produce favorable returns by maintaining rate levels that are in balance with the risks it underwrites improving its risk selection and pricing and reducing the frequency and severity of claims through workplace safety reviews medical cost containment and rapid closing of claims. Additionally the company is looking to increase market penetration in the states where it operates as well as seek opportunities in the 12 other states and the US Virgin Islands where it licensed.

Another key element of the company's strategy is to capitalize on its information technology tools. These include its GEAUX underwriting and agency management system and ICAMS its customized operational system which together with the analytical data warehouse that ICAMS feeds improve its ability to select risk write profitable business and administer billing claims and audit functions more cost-effectively.

EXECUTIVES

President and COO, G. Janelle Frost, age 47, $370,833 total compensation
EVP and Chief Risk Officer, Vincent J. Gagliano, age 44, $202,000 total compensation
Vice President Treasurer, Angela Lannen
SENIOR VICE PRESIDENT, Kathryn Rowan
Vice President Sales Northeast Region, Ed Ennis
Vice President, Martin Rozboril
Senior Vice President Sales Marketing, David Morton
Vice President Sales Midwest Region, Mark Burger
Vice President Of Sales, Martha Mcleod
Chairman, Jared A. Morris, age 41
Auditors: Ernst & Young LLP

LOCATIONS

HQ: Amerisafe Inc
2301 Highway 190 West, DeRidder, LA 70634
Phone: 337 463-9052
Web: www.amerisafe.com

PRODUCTS/OPERATIONS

2016 Sales

	$ mil.	% of total
Net premiums earned	368	93
Net investment income	28	7
Fee and other income	0	—
Net realized gains (losses) on investments	(0.5)	—
Loss on disposal of assets	(0.001)	—
Total	**396**	**100**

COMPETITORS

ACSTAR	McM Corporation
Baldwin & Lyons	Nationwide
Bituminous Insurance Companies	SeaBright Insurance
Farm Family Holdings	W. R. Berkley
	Zenith National

HISTORICAL FINANCIALS

Company Type: Public

Income Statement

FYE: December 31

	ASSETS ($ mil.)	NET INCOME ($ mil.)	INCOME AS % OF ASSETS	EMPLOYEES
12/16	1,518	77	5.1%	439
12/15	1,502	70	4.7%	451
12/14	1,457	53	3.7%	445
12/13	1,329	43	3.3%	437
12/12	1,220	29	2.4%	429
Annual Growth	**5.6%**	**27.6%**	**—**	**0.6%**

2016 Year-End Financials

Debt ratio: —
Return on equity: 17.06%
Cash ($ mil.): 58
Current ratio: —
Long-term debt ($ mil.): —

No. of shares (mil.): 19
Dividends
Yield: 0.0%
Payout: 98.0%
Market value ($ mil.): 1,199

	STOCK PRICE ($) FY Close	P/E High/Low	PER SHARE ($) Earnings	Dividends	Book Value
12/16	62.35	16 12	4.05	3.97	23.72
12/15	50.90	15 11	3.69	3.60	23.73
12/14	42.36	15 12	2.84	1.98	23.65
12/13	42.24	19 11	2.32	0.32	22.41
12/12	27.25	17 14	1.58	0.00	20.88
Annual Growth	**23.0%**	**—**	**26.5%**	**—**	**3.2%**

AmerisourceBergen Corp.

AmerisourceBergen is the source for many of North America's pharmacies and health care providers. The distribution company serves as a go-between for drug makers and the pharmacies doctors' offices hospitals and other health care providers that dispense drugs. Operating primarily in the US it distributes generic branded and over-the-counter pharmaceuticals as well as some medical supplies and other products using its network of more than two dozen facilities. Its specialty distribution unit focuses on sensitive and complex biopharmaceuticals. Other operations include pharmaceutical packaging. AmerisourceBergen also provides commercialization and consulting services to its customers.

Operations

AmerisourceBergen operates through an alphabet soup of subsidiaries. Its main operating segment — Pharmaceutical Distribution Services — consists of its drug and specialty drug distribution businesses and the AmerisourceBergen Consulting Services (ABCS) unit. The company's remaining revenues (classified under the "Other" segment) come from the World Courier (specialty logistics) and MWI Animal Health units.

Its primary distribution business — which accounts for more than 95% of total revenue — offers a full range of generic and brand-name pharmaceuticals over-the-counter products and home health care supplies and equipment. It also delivers specialty drugs for particular diseases (especially cancer) directly to the doctors who administer them.The segment distributes plasma and other blood products injectable pharmaceuticals and vaccines.

The company's consulting services business helps retailers and manufacturers coordinate marketing programs to successfully launch new biotech drugs and increase sales of existing drugs. ABCS also provides sales tracking and logistics support as well as research field staffing co-pay assistance programs and risk mitigation services. In addition the division provides group purchasing merchandising and managed care services to independent and hospital-based pharmacies.

MWI sells pharmaceuticals vaccines diagnostics parasiticides micro-feed ingredients and related products for pets and production animals.

Altogether AmerisourceBergen distributes more than 1.5 million products.

Geographic Reach

AmerisourceBergen operates more than 25 distribution centers throughout the US and has more than 150 offices in more than 50 countries worldwide. Its products are distributed to more than 15000 retail pharmacies and more than 50000 health care facilities.

Sales and Marketing

AmerisourceBergen serves customers including hospitals and health systems retail and mail order pharmacies medical clinics and long-term care facilities throughout North America. The company's two largest customers Walgreens Boots Alliance and Express Scripts account for some 30% and 15% of total revenue respectively.Its top 10 customers account for some two-thirds of revenue.

Each of the company's businesses have independent sales and marketing personnel who specialize in their respective offerings.

AmerisourceBergen also has a corporate marketing group for branding and broad-scale initiatives.

Financial Performance

AmerisourceBergen's revenue has been increasing for the last five years. In fiscal 2017 (ended September) it rose 4% to $153.1 billion as both the Pharmaceutical Distribution Services and Other segments had higher sales. Pharmaceutical Distribution Services increased 4% due to factors including market growth in the retail segment strong performance of oncology products and a thriving third-party logistics business. The Other segment increased 10% thanks to growth in the MWI business.

Although revenue has been steadily rising net income has been rather turbulent. After rising significantly in fiscal 2016 net income fell 74% to $364.5 million in fiscal 2017. This decline was driven by increases in certain operating expenses as well as in income tax expenses.

The lower net income led cash flow from operations to decline 53% to $1.5 billion that year.

Strategy

AmerisourceBergen's mission is to help its customers reduce health care expenses increase channel efficiencies and improve the quality of patient outcomes.It is focused on expanding its pharmaceutical distribution business including its growing specialty pharmaceuticals operations by investing in its network. The company is opening a new $45 million distribution center in Indiana for example. It has also invested in new IT platforms to enhance its warehouses.

Additionally the company is growing its services offerings to manufacturers; these services include marketing product data reporting and logistical support. In this line of business the firm recently expanded into Switzerland now the base of its global manufacturer relations operations.

AmerisourceBergen is also investing in growth of its World Courier and MWI Animal Health units. World Courier provides specialty transportation and logistics for the biopharmaceutical industry and is key to the company's expansion beyond North America. In addition to distributing animal health products MWI provides services such as an e-commerce system technology management systems equipment procurement consultation and educational seminars.

The company benefits from forming large supply agreements with key clients and factors such as competitive pressures and industry consolidation can occasionally hamper (or assist) the company's growth efforts in this area.

AmerisourceBergen occasionally divests noncore operations to focus on key areas of growth. To supplement organic growth the company also makes selective acquisitions

Mergers and Acquisitions

Acquisitions have helped AmerisourceBergen expand its reach to new customer segments and geographic markets.In early 2018 the company acquired private drug wholesaler H. D. Smith for $815 million. H. D. Smith operates 10 distribution centers throughout the US.

In 2016 MWI acquired St. Francis Group the UK's largest animal health buying group. The acquisition expanded AmerisourceBergen and MWI's global footprint in the animal health space and also positioned MWI to better support independent veterinary practices internationally.That deal followed the 2015 acquisition of MWI Veterinary Supply.

Also in 2015 AmerisourceBergen paid $2.7 billion for PharMEDium Healthcare in a move to expand its compounded drug distribution operations.

HISTORY

In 1977 Cleveland millionaire and horse racing enthusiast Tinkham Veale went into the drug wholesaling business. His company Alco Standard (now IKON Office Solutions) already owned chemical electrical metallurgical and mining companies but by the late 1970s the company was pursuing a strategy of zeroing in on various types of distribution businesses.

Alco's first drug wholesaler purchase was The Drug House (Delaware and Pennsylvania); the next was Duff Brothers (Tennessee). The company then bought further wholesalers in the South East and Midwest. Its modus operandi was to buy small well-run companies for cash and Alco stock and leave the incumbent management in charge.

By the early 1980s Alco was the US's third-largest wholesale drug distributor and growing quickly (28% between 1983 and 1988) at a time of mass consolidation in the industry (the number of wholesalers dropped by half between 1980 and 1992). In 1985 Alco Standard spun off its drug distribution operations as Alco Health Services retaining 60% ownership.

Alco Health boosted its sales above $1 billion mostly via acquisitions and expanded product lines. The company offered marketing and promotional help to its independent pharmacy customers (which were beleaguered by the growth of national discounters) and also targeted hospitals nursing homes and clinics.

The US was in the midst of its LBO frenzy in 1988 but an Alco management group failed in its attempt. Rival McKesson then tried to acquire Alco Health but that deal fell through for antitrust reasons. Later in 1988 management turned for backing to Citicorp Venture Capital in another buyout attempt. This time the move succeeded and a new holding company Alco Health Distribution was formed.

Alco Health went public as AmeriSource Health in 1995. Throughout the next year AmeriSource made a series of acquisitions to move into related areas including inventory management technology drugstore pharmaceutical supplies and disease-management services for pharmacies.

In 1997 McKesson once again made an offer to buy AmeriSource this time for $2.4 billion while two other major wholesale distributors Cardinal Health and Bergen Brunswig reached a similar pact. The deals were scrapped in 1998 when the Federal Trade Commission voted against both pacts and a federal judge supported that decision.

In 2013 AmerisourceBergen signed a 10-year agreement to supply Walgreen Boots Alliance.

EXECUTIVES

Chairman President and CEO, Steven H. Collis, age 56, $1,234,231 total compensation

EVP and CFO, Tim G. Guttman, age 58, $706,539 total compensation

EVP and Chief Marketing Officer, Gina K. Clark, age 60

EVP and Chief Legal & Business Officer, John G. Chou, age 61, $621,231 total compensation

Group President Pharmaceutical Distribution and Strategic Global Sourcing, James F. (Jim) Cleary, age 54

EVP and President Health Systems Physician Practices and Strategic Health Solutions, Peyton R. Howell, age 50

EVP and CIO, Dale Danilewitz, age 55

EVP; President AmerisourceBergen Drug, Robert P. Mauch, age 50, $593,077 total compensation

EVP and Chief Human Resources Officer, Kathy H. Gaddes, age 54

EVP Strategy and Development, Sun Park, age 41

Vice President Government Accounts, Kent Rischar

Vice President Professional Services, Kathryn Uchida

Vice President Of Strategic Accounts, Matt Johnson

Vice President Global Sourcing Operations, Barbara Miller

Vice President Health Systems Sales, Michael Haddad

Vice President Financial Processes, Brian Mangiaracina

Vice President Supply Chain Solutions, Wesley Jones

Executive Assistant To Senior Vice President Chief Human Resources Officer And Chief Information Officer, Kelly Jakeman

Vice President Strategic Accounts, Steve Iampietro

Senior Vice President Of Marketing, Thomas Connolly

Sales Vice President, Catherine Carminati

Senior Vice President Sales And Corporate Services, Brian Ansay

Auditors: Ernst & Young LLP

LOCATIONS

HQ: AmerisourceBergen Corp.
1300 Morris Drive, Chesterbrook, PA 19087-5594
Phone: 610 727-7000 **Fax:** 610 647-0141
Web: www.amerisourcebergen.com

PRODUCTS/OPERATIONS

2017 Sales by Segment

	$ mil.	% of total
Pharmaceutical Distribution Services	147,453	96
Other	5,747	4
Adjustments	(57.5)	-
Total	153,143	100

COMPETITORS

Allergan plc	Medline Industries
BioScrip	Owens & Minor
Cardinal Health	PSS World Medical
Express Scripts	Quality King
FFF Enterprises	Roadnet
Henry Schein	UPS
McKesson	US Oncology

Company Type: Public

Income Statement   FYE: September 30

	REVENUE ($ mil.)	NET INCOME ($ mil.)	NET PROFIT MARGIN	EMPLOYEES
09/17	153,143	364	0.2%	20,000
09/16	146,849	1,427	1.0%	19,000
09/15	135,961	(134)	—	17,500
09/14	119,569	276	0.2%	14,000
09/13	87,959	433	0.5%	13,000
Annual Growth	14.9%	(4.3%)		11.4%

2017 Year-End Financials

Debt ratio: 10.74%	No. of shares (mil.): 217
Return on equity: 17.38%	Dividends
Cash ($ mil.): 2,435	Yield: 0.0%
Current ratio: 0.91	Payout: 89.0%
Long-term debt ($ mil.): 3,781	Market value ($ mil.): 18,039

	STOCK PRICE ($) FY Close	P/E High/Low	PER SHARE ($) Earnings	Dividends	Book Value
09/17	82.75	58 41	1.64	1.46	9.47
09/16	80.78	16 11	6.32	1.36	9.68
09/15	94.99	— —	(0.62)	1.16	3.06
09/14	77.30	64 50	1.17	0.94	8.82
09/13	61.10	33 21	1.84	0.84	10.09
Annual Growth	7.9%	— —	(2.8%)	14.8%	(1.6%)

Amgen Inc

Amgen is among the biggest of the biotechs. The company uses cellular biology and medicinal chemistry to target cancers kidney ailments inflammatory disorders and metabolic diseases. Its top protein-based therapeutic products include Neulasta and Neupogen (both used as anti-infectives in cancer patients) Aranesp and Epogen (used to fight anemia in chronic kidney disease and cancer patients) and Enbrel for rheumatoid arthritis. In addition Amgen has extensive drug research and development programs. Its products are marketed in approximately 100 countries to doctors hospitals pharmacies and other health care providers.

HISTORY

Amgen was formed as Applied Molecular Genetics in 1980 by a group of scientists and venture capitalists to develop health care products based on molecular biology. George Rathmann a VP at Abbott Laboratories and researcher at UCLA became the company's CEO and first employee. Rathmann decided to develop a few potentially profitable products rather than conduct research. The company initially raised $19 million.

Amgen operated close to bankruptcy until 1983 when company scientist Fu-Kuen Lin cloned the human protein erythropoietin (EPO) which stimulates the body's red blood cell production. Amgen went public that year. It formed a joint venture with Kirin Brewery in 1984 to develop and market EPO. The two firms also collaborated on recombinant human granulocyte colony stimulating factor (G-CSF later called Neupogen) a protein that stimulates the immune system.

Amgen joined Johnson & Johnson subsidiary Ortho Pharmaceutical (later Ortho-McNeil Pharmaceutical) in a marketing alliance in 1985 and created a tie with Roche in 1988. Fortunes soared in 1989 when the FDA approved Epogen (the brand name of EPO) for anemia. (It is most commonly used to counter side effects of kidney dialysis.)

In 1991 Amgen received approval to market Neupogen to chemotherapy patients. A federal court ruling also gave it a US monopoly for EPO. The following year Amgen won another dispute forcing a competitor to renounce its US patents for G-CSF.

As the company grew it needed to transform itself from startup to going concern; to do so Amgen hired MCI veteran Kevin Sharer as president in 1992. Neupogen's usage was expanded in 1993 to include treatment of severe chronic neutropenia (low white-blood-cell count).

In 1993 Amgen became the first American biotech to gain a foothold in China through an agreement with Kirin Pharmaceuticals to sell Neupogen (under the name Gran) and Epogen there. The purchase of Synergen in 1994 added another research facility accelerating the pace of and increasing the number of products in research and clinical trials.

Although Amgen had two proven sellers in Epogen and Neupogen its growth lay in its pipeline. In 1997 Amgen and partner Regeneron Pharmaceuticals reported the failure of human trials for a drug to treat Lou Gehrig's disease. Still its new drug Stemgen for breast cancer patients undergoing chemotherapy was recommended for approval by an FDA advisory committee in 1998.

Amgen had to swallow a couple of tough legal pills in 1998. First a dispute with J&J over Amgen's 1985 licensing agreement with Ortho Pharmaceutical ended when an arbiter ordered Amgen to pay about $200 million. Later that year however Amgen won a legal battle with J&J over the rights to a promising anemia drug.

Work on its product pipeline continued in 1999: Amgen ended development of obesity and Parkinson's disease drugs after clinical trials produced discouraging results while it began human tests with partner Guilford Pharmaceuticals on a drug designed to regenerate damaged nerve cells in the brains of Parkinson's disease patients. (Guildford and Amgen ended the collaboration in 2001.)

In 2000 the firm resumed its battle to keep its stranglehold on the Epogen market: It sued Transkaryotic Therapies and Aventis (later Sanofi-Aventis) for alleged patent violations over its Epogen product in both the US and the UK. Although it initially won its case in the UK that verdict was overturned in 2002 making Amgen vulnerable to competition before Epogen's patents expire in 2004. That year it won EU and US approval for Aranesp an updated version of Epogen; Amgen in 2002 teamed with former J&J marketing partner Fresenius to sell Aranesp in Germany and take some market share away from J&J. Meanwhile an arbitration committee found J&J had breached its contract with Amgen when it sold Procrit to the dialysis market which Amgen had reserved for itself in their 1985 licensing deal.

In 2003 the company bought leukemia and rheumatoid arthritis drugs maker Immunex. As part of the FTC's blessing on the $10.3 billion union Amgen and Immunex licensed some technologies to encourage competition. Merck Serono gained access to Enbrel data and Regeneron Pharmaceuticals licensed some interleukin inhibitor rights.

The next year Amgen spent $1.3 billion to purchase the remaining 79% of cancer treatment technology maker Tularik that it did not already own.

EXECUTIVES

SVP US Commercial Operations, Laura Hamill

EVP Full Potential Initiatives, Brian M. McNamee, age 61
SVP Global Marketing and Commercial Development, Suzanne Blaug
EVP Global Commercial Operations, Anthony C. (Tony) Hooper, age 62, $1,031,788 total compensation
SVP General Counsel and Secretary, Jonathan P. Graham, age 56, $916,789 total compensation
EVP and CFO, David W. Meline, age 59, $946,733 total compensation
SVP Global Business Services, Michael A. Kelly, age 60, $511,757 total compensation
EVP Research and Development, Sean E. Harper, age 54, $946,246 total compensation
Chairman and CEO, Robert A. (Bob) Bradway, age 55, $1,531,731 total compensation
SVP Global Medical and Chief Medical Officer, Paul R. Eisenberg
SVP and Head European Region, Corinne Le Goff
EVP Operations, Esteban Santos
Vice President, Brian Kotzin
Vice President, Patricia Turney
VP Human Resources, John Oakes
Vice President, Alison Moore
Vice President Sales Cardiovascular Specialty and Bone Business Units, Shannon Sullivan
First Vice President Wealth Management, Saket Malhotra
Vice President Research and Development, Mingqiang Zhang
Vice President Marketing, Richard Paulson
Vice President and Construction, Pascale Samama
Vice President Environmental Affairs, Deron Johnson
Vice President Finance, Anton Rabushka
Vice President Corporate Communications, Janeen Hererra
Vice President and General Manager Cardiovascular and Inflamation Business Units, Vanessa Broadhurst
Vice President Sales, Scott Van Houten
Senior Vice President Translational Sciences, David Reese
Vice President, Sharon Stoddard
Vice President and Chief Accounting Officer, George Revelle
VP Supply Chain, Rayne Waller
Senior Vice President;Business Control Executive, Claudia Turecek
Medical Director, Vladimir Hanes
Vice President Finance and Treasurer, Mary Lehmann
Finance Vice President, Tonya Cheng
Vice President, Martin Zagari
Vice President General Manager Germany, Roland Wandeler
National Sales Manager, Mike Ellis
Vice President Business Development, William Erb
Associate Medical Director Medical Affairs, Mark Rutstein
Vice President Sales, John Snowden
Vice President Global Line Head Pharmacokinetics And Drug Metabolism, Guy Padbury
Vice President Corporate Accounts, Aston William
Vice President Of Pre Clinical Research, David Balaban
Vice President General Manager France, Jean Monin
Vice President of Engineering, Carletto Pardo
Vice President General Manager Us Bone Health Bu, Ken Keller
Administrative Coordinate Government Relations, Janice Vasquez
Seniorvice President Of Manufacturing, Madhu Balachandran
Senior Vice President, Steven K Galson
Vice President Operations, Martin Vantrieste

Senior Vice President Results Delivery Office, Annalisa Pizzarello
Vice President, Carol Whiting
Vice President Finance, Andreas Bierl
Medical Director, Christopher Depre
Vice President Commercial Transformation, James Cain
Senior Vice President, Gilles Marrache
Vice President Regional General Manager, Penny Wan
Vice President Regional Medical, Tony Hoos
Executive Vice President Global Commercial Operations, Tony Hooper
Medical Director, Ted Okerson
Medical Director, Bassem Abws
Pharmd, Kamran Mahramzadeh
Medical Director, Sarachaga Max
Medical Director Phd, Neeraja Balachander
Senior Management (Senior Vice President General Manager Director), Minnie Chou
Vice President Worldwide Compliance and Business Ethics, Nancy Grygiel
Vice President Strategy, Mike Nohaile
Vice President Oncology and Inflammation Discovery Research, Flavius Martin
Vice President Amgen Global Safety, Isma Benattia
Junior RPh Vice President Global Advocacy Relations, Thomas Croce
Board Member, Elena Molina
Board Member, Erich Durchschlag
Board Member, Marcus Schulte
Treasurer, Loretta Joseph
Board of Directors, Jonie Anderson
Auditors: Ernst & Young LLP

LOCATIONS

HQ: Amgen Inc
One Amgen Center Drive, Thousand Oaks, CA 91320-1799
Phone: 805 447-1000   **Fax:** 805 447-1010
Web: www.amgen.com

2016 Sales

	$ mil.	% of total
United States	18,326	80
Rest of the world	4,665	20
Total	**22,991**	**100**

Selected Locations

Algeria
Australia
Austria
Belgium
Brazil
Bulgaria
Canada
China
Colombia
Croatia
Czech Republic
Denmark
Egypt
Estonia Japan
Finland
France
Germany
Greece
Hong Kong
Hungary
Iceland
India
Ireland
Italy
Latvia
Lithuania
Luxembourg
Mexico
Netherlands
Norway
Poland
Portugal
Romania
Russia
Saudi Arabia
Slovakia

Slovenia
South Africa
Spain
Sweden
Switzerland
Turkey
United Arab Emirates
United Kingdom
United States

PRODUCTS/OPERATIONS

2016 Sales

	$ mil.	% of total
Product sales	21,892	95
Other revenues	1,099	5
Total	**22,991**	**100**

2016 Sales

	$ mil.	% of total
ENBREL	5,965	26
Neulasta	4,648	20
Aranesp	2,093	9
Prolia	1,635	7
Sensipar/Mimpara	1,582	7
XGEVA	1,529	7
EPOGEN	1,282	6
NEUPOGEN	765	3
KYPROLIS	692	3
Vectibix	611	3
Nplate	584	2
Repatha	141	1
BLINCYTO	155	0
Other	250	1
Other revenues	1,099	5
Total	**22,991**	**100**

Top Selling Products

Neupogen/Neulasta (chemotherapy-induced neutropenia - low white blood cells and cancer-related infections)
Enbrel (rheumatoid arthritis psoriasis)
Aranesp (chemotherapy-induced anemia and chronic renal failure anemia sustained duration Epogen)
Epogen (anemia in chronic renal failure)
Sensipar/Mimpara (also known as Mimpara chronic kidney disease)
Xgeva (to prevent bone fractures)
Vectibix (monoclonal antibody for colorectal cancer)
Nplate (romiplostim for autoimmune bleeding disorder ITP or immune thrombocytopenic purpura)
Prolia (postmenopausal osteoporosis)

COMPETITORS

AbbVie	Johnson & Johnson
Abbott Labs	Merck
Affymax	Merck KGaA
Apotex	Millennium: The Takeda
AstraZeneca	Oncology Company
Bayer HealthCare Pharmaceuticals Inc.	Nektar Therapeutics
	Novartis
Bristol-Myers Squibb	Pfizer
Celgene	Roche Holding
Chugai	Sanofi
Eli Lilly	Shire
Fresenius Medical Care	Takeda Pharmaceutical
Genentech	Teva
GlaxoSmithKline	UCB
Hospira	

HISTORICAL FINANCIALS

Company Type: Public

Income Statement

FYE: December 31

	REVENUE ($ mil.)	NET INCOME ($ mil.)	NET PROFIT MARGIN	EMPLOYEES
12/17	22,849	1,979	8.7%	20,800
12/16	22,991	7,722	33.6%	19,200
12/15	21,662	6,939	32.0%	17,900
12/14	20,063	5,158	25.7%	17,900
12/13	18,676	5,081	27.2%	20,000
Annual Growth	**5.2%**	**(21.0%)**	**—**	**1.0%**

2017 Year-End Financials

Debt ratio: 44.20%	No. of shares (mil.): 722
Return on equity: 7.18%	Dividends
Cash ($ mil.): 3,800	Yield: 0.0%
Current ratio: 5.49	Payout: 171.0%
Long-term debt ($ mil.): 34,190	Market value ($ mil.): 125,591

	STOCK PRICE ($) FY Close	P/E High/Low	PER SHARE ($) Earnings	Dividends	Book Value
12/17	173.90	70 56	2.69	4.60	34.95
12/16	146.21	17 13	10.24	4.00	40.47
12/15	162.33	19 14	9.06	3.16	37.25
12/14	159.29	25 16	6.70	2.44	33.90
12/13	114.08	18 12	6.64	1.88	29.28
Annual Growth	**11.1%**	**— —**	**(20.2%)**	**25.1%**	**4.5%**

Amphenol Corp.

A connected world needs connections at the basic level: from component to component and from device to device. That's where Amphenol Corp. comes in. The company is a leading manufacturer of connector and interconnect products for the communications industrial automotive aerospace and military markets. Amphenol's interconnect products are used to conduct electrical and optical signals in computers wired and wireless communications networking equipment vehicles aircraft and spacecraft and energy applications. Amphenol also makes high-speed and specialized coaxial cable. With customers in about 70 countries more than 70% of its sales come from outside the US.

Operations

Amphenol's Interconnect Products and Assemblies segment accounts for 95% of sales with Cable Products and Solutions segment accounting for the rest. The cable group makes cables and components for the broadband communications and information technology markets.

In terms of markets information technology and data communications accounts for about 20% of revenue followed by mobile devices about 15%; automotive less than 10%; military and mobile networks about 10% each and broadband communications and commercial aerospace about 5% each.

The company handles its own manufacturing with facilities in low-cost manufacturing areas and near customers.

Geographic Reach

Amphenol has 400 locations — manufacturing facilities warehouses and offices — in more than 20 countries around the world with about 400. The US and China each account for about 30% of Amphenol's sales. The company doesn't break down sales to other countries.

Sales and Marketing

Amphenol's products are sold in more than 10000 customer locations worldwide (one customer can have components sent to multiple manufacturing locations). Its products are sold directly to original equipment manufacturers (OEMs) electronics manufacturing services (EMS) firms original design manufacturers (ODMs) cable system operators and IT companies. The company also selles through manufacturers' representatives and distributors which account for about 15% of revenue.

About half of Amphenol's sales are to the communications industry including information technology and data communication wireless communications and broadband communications companies.

Financial Performance

Amphenol has been on a seven-year run of revenue and net income gains. In 2016 revenue jumped 13% to $6.3 billion from in 2015.

Higher sales came from information technology and data communications industrial automotive mobile networks and military markets abetted by acquisitions. The FCI acquisition reverberated through several product areas boosting sales in information technology data communications industrial and mobile networks. Sources of sales strength were products for data centers automotive applications and factory automation. On the down side sales in mobile devices and commercial aerospace markets slipped in 2016.

The FCI acquisition help raised net income 8% in 2016 but it also raised the company?s acquisition costs for the year.

Cash flow from operations was about $1.1 billion in 2016 compared to about $1 billion in 2015. Higher net income higher non-cash charges related to the FCI acquisition and a decrease in the components of working capital were responsible for the increase.

Strategy

The 2016 acquisition of FCI is emblematic of Amphenol?s strategy. Amphenol slotted FCI?s products into several of its product areas strengthening the company?s focus on a diverse balanced portfolio. None of the company?s lines of products account for more than about 20% of revenue. FCI was Amphenol?s biggest acquisition at $1.2 billion and contributed about 7% of revenue in its first year. Other recent acquisitions added complementary products to Amphenol?s industrial automotive IT and data communications and broadband markets.

Amphenol has been willing to buy what is doesn't have in-house making more than 20 acquisitions in the past five years.

The company also has embraced geographic diversity. China and the US are its biggest country markets and international revenue not counting China provides about 40% of the total. Amphenol sites manufacturing facilities globally especially in low-cost areas.

Mergers and Acquisitions

In 2017 Amphenol bought Phitek Systems Limited a New Zealand-based provider of interconnects for in-flight entertainment systems in commercial aircraft. The acquisition adds to Amphenol?s line of products used throughout airplanes.

In 2016 Amphenol closed the acquisition of FCI Electronics a maker of interconnect products for $1.2 billion. The addition of FCI expands Amphenol products as well as its markets. Other 2016 acquisitions included Auxel Custom Cable SGX Sensortech and All Systems Broadband.

Company Background

Amphenol was founded in 1932 to make sockets to plug vacuum tubes into radios. Its first customer was RCA.

EXECUTIVES

SVP and Group General Manager IT and Communications Products Division, Richard E. (Rick) Schneider, age 59, $490,000 total compensation
President CEO and Director, Richard A. (Adam) Norwitt, age 48, $1,061,000 total compensation
SVP and Group General Manager Military and Aerospace Operations Group, Luc Walter, age 58, $560,000 total compensation
SVP and CFO, Craig A. Lampo, age 47, $450,000 total compensation

SVP and Group General Manager Worldwide RF and Microwave Products, Zachary W. Raley, age 48, $500,000 total compensation

VP and Group General Manager Global Interconnect Systems Group, Jean-Luc Gavelle, age 57

VP and Group General Manager Automotive and Sensor Products division, John Treanor, age 59

VP and Group General Manager Industrial Products Group, Martin W. Booker, age 58

VP and Group General Manager IT Communications Products Group, William J. Doherty, age 58

VP and General Manager Mobile Consumer Products Group, Yaobin (Richard) Gu

Chairman, Martin H. Loeffler, age 73

Vice President Secretary and General Counsel, Edward Wetmore

Assistant Treasurer, Howard Wardlow

Auditors: Deloitte & Touche LLP

LOCATIONS

HQ: Amphenol Corp.
358 Hall Avenue, Wallingford, CT 06492
Phone: 203 265-8900   **Fax:** 203 265-8746
Web: www.amphenol.com

2016 Sales

	$ mil.	% of total
US	1,740	28
China	1,865	30
Other countries	2,680	42
Total	**6,286**	**100**

PRODUCTS/OPERATIONS

2016 Sales

	$ mil.	% of total
Interconnect products & assemblies	5,922	94
Cable products	364	6
Total	**6,286**	**100**

Selected Brands

Amphenol
Kai Jack
Matrix
Pyle-National
Sine
Socapex
Spectra-Strip
Times Fiber
Tuchel

Selected Products

Interconnect products
  Automotive interconnect systems
  CATV interconnects
  Data/telecom connectors
  Fiber-optic connectors and systems
  Filter connectors
  Flexible circuit interconnects
  High-performance connectors
  Industrial power connectors
  Radio-frequency coaxial connectors
  Smart card connectors
Cable products
  Electronic cable
  Engineered cable assemblies
  Times Fiber coaxial cable
  Wireless cable products
Other
  Mobile and portable antennas

COMPETITORS

3M	Molex
ARRIS	Northrop Grumman
AVX	Panduit
Alcatel-Lucent	Radiall
CommScope	Sensata
Corning	Smiths Group
Delphi Automotive	Spirent
Systems	Sumitomo Electric
FCI	TE Connectivity

Hirose Electric	TT electronics
Hon Hai	Telect
Huber + Suhner Inc.	Thomas & Betts
Japan Aviation	Tri-Star Electronics
Electronics Industry	International
Methode Electronics	Yazaki

HISTORICAL FINANCIALS

Company Type: Public

Income Statement

FYE: December 31

	REVENUE ($ mil.)	NET INCOME ($ mil.)	NET PROFIT MARGIN	EMPLOYEES
12/16	6,286	822	13.1%	62,000
12/15	5,568	763	13.7%	50,700
12/14	5,345	709	13.3%	50,700
12/13	4,614	635	13.8%	44,500
12/12	4,292	555	12.9%	41,600
Annual Growth	**10.0%**	**10.3%**	**—**	**10.5%**

2016 Year-End Financials

Debt ratio: 35.43%
Return on equity: 23.74%
Cash ($ mil.): 1,034
Current ratio: 2.20
Long-term debt ($ mil.): 2,635

No. of shares (mil.): 308
Dividends
  Yield: 0.0%
  Payout: 22.2%
Market value ($ mil.): 20,718

	STOCK PRICE ($) FY Close	P/E High/Low	PER SHARE ($) Earnings	Dividends	Book Value
12/16	67.20	26 17	2.61	0.58	11.92
12/15	52.23	24 20	2.41	0.53	10.51
12/14	53.81	47 20	2.21	0.45	9.38
12/13	89.18	44 32	1.96	0.31	9.04
12/12	64.70	38 27	1.70	0.21	7.60
Annual Growth	**1.0%**	**— —**	**11.4%**	**28.9%**	**11.9%**

AmTrust Financial Services Inc

Insurance holding company AmTrust Financial Services likes a mix of businesses on its plate. Its subsidiaries offer a range of commercial property/casualty insurance products for small and midsized customers including workers' compensation products auto and general liability workplace and agricultural coverage and extended service and warranty coverage of consumer and commercial goods. It also provides a small amount of personal auto reinsurance. AmTrust operates in Bermuda Ireland the UK and the US and distributes its products through brokers agents and claims administrators. Customers include restaurants retailers physicians' offices auto and electronics manufacturers and trucking operations.

Operations

AmTrust's revenue comes primarily from premium income from its largest three segments: Small Commercial Business which provides workers' compensation to small businesses (40% of revenue); Specialty Risk and Extended Warranty which offers coverage for consumer products and specialty coverage (about 30%); and Specialty Program which includes workers' compensation general and corporate auto liability and other insurance products (more than 15%). The remainder of revenue comes primarily from services and fees as well as investment income.

Geographic Reach

AmTrust sells insurance products in all 50 US states the District of Columbia and Puerto Rico as well as parts of Europe and the Caribbean. Its largest market is the US which brings in more than half of all revenue; Bermuda where one of its reinsurers is located brings in 35% of revenue. In total the company operates in more than 200 countries through 25 international locations.

AmTrust also provides third-party adminstrator services (claims handling and call center services) for the consumer products and automotive industries in the US Canada Europe and Asia.

Sales and Marketing

AmTrust distributes its products via a network of more than 9500 retail and wholesale agents. Unaffiliated third parties sell its small commercial business and specialty risk and extended warranty products. AmTrust also partners with wholesale agents and claims administrators.

Industries served include retail wholesale service artisan contracting hospitality and trucking.

Financial Performance

As a result of an aggressive acquisition strategy AmTrust has seen steadily increasing revenue over the last five years. Revenue increased 17% to a record $5.5 billion in 2016 as premium service and fee and interest income all rose. Numerous significant acquisitions made that year (including ANV Holding B.V. Nationale Borg First Nationwide and Republic Group) boosted revenues for the company. In terms of segments the Small Commercial Business and Specialty Risk and Extended Warranty segments saw growth (due primarily to acquisitions made) while the Specialty Program segment remained flat.

Net income had also been on the rise for the past few years but in 2016 it fell 18% to $411 million. This was largely due to increased loss and loss adjustment expenses as well as acquisition costs and losses from foreign currency rates. Cash flow from operations fell for the second year in a row dropping 7% to $916.7 million due to changes in prepaid expenses and related factors.

Strategy

Key to AmTrust's overall business strategy is focusing on lower hazard businesses with low-severity claims. For example the largest segment Small Commercial Business targets small niche workers' compensation exposure in low-danger occupations.

Another strategy is to diversify its portfolio by both business line and geography. The company has been busily buying up other insurance and warranty companies ramping up its acquisition activities in the past couple of years. In 2016 alone it completed 10 acquisitions including ANB Holding Republic Group and Nationale Borg.

With all of the purchases it has made in the decade since it's gone public the company has grown to a size where it can now capitalize on its existing operations and expand organically. Cross-selling opportunities is just one way AmTrust intends to pursue this growth. AmTrust also works to establish new distribution partnerships hiring new specialty lines underwriters and developing new client relationships.

The company has always invested in its technology infrastructure to remain operationally efficient. Because of this it can leverage its tremendous set of data to find new opportunities and inform decision-making. The company developed and services a personal lines policy management system for National General Holdings; it now plans to sell the system to National General for $200 million. And by 2018 it should complete the implementation of a financial automation system.

Mergers and Acquisitions

AmTrust has been able to expand its product offerings and geographic reach through acquisitions of smaller competitors though it approaches its purchases with a conservative eye avoiding huge financial investments. In 2017 the company acquired AmeriHealth Casualty Insurance from Independence Health Group for $92.8 million.

In 2016 AmTrust bought specialty insurer ANV Holding B.V. from Ontario Teachers' Pension Plan for $203 million. As part of the deal AmTrust will replace Ontario Teachers' support of the ANV funds on Lloyd's building its presence in the Lloyd's of London market. The company also acquired Texas-based property/casualty insurer Republic Group for $233 million that year. In addition it bought the European mortgage insurance business of Genworth Financial for $54.5 million as well as Dutch surety and trade credit insurer Nationale Borg for $180 million. Smaller deals in 2016 included the purchases of First Nationwide Title Agency Total Program ManagementArc Legal Assistance and Assure Space.

AmTrust bought Wells Fargo's Warranty Solutions business in 2015 for $152 million. Warranty Solutions underwrites vehicle service contracts and auto-related finance and insurance products to dealerships around the nation; the purchase expanded AmTrust's existing vehicle warranty operations and added new fees and service revenue. Also that year the company's North America segment acquired the crop insurance operations of The Climate Corporation a division of Monsanto. Other deals that year included the acquisitions of CorePointe a Michigan-based property/casualty firm serving car dealers and auto repair shops; TMI Solutions a warranty and consumer protection coverage provider; and Oryx Insurance Brokerage which serves the construction industry in upstate New York.

EXECUTIVES

President CEO and Director, Barry D. Zyskind, age 46, $975,000 total compensation
EVP U.S. Commercial Lines, Michael J. Saxon, age 59, $726,923 total compensation
EVP and COO, Christopher M. Longo, age 44, $664,423 total compensation
CEO AmTrust International Limited, Max G. Caviet, age 64, $677,875 total compensation
EVP and Chief Legal Officer, David H. Saks, age 50, $550,000 total compensation
EVP and CFO, Adam Karkowsky, age 42, $550,000 total compensation
SVP and CIO, Ariel Gorelik
Assistant Vice President of Loss Control, Gordon Celliers
National Sales Manager, Matthew Craven
Vice President and Head Information Risk Management, Sheryl Skolnik
Assistant Vice President Of Finance, Lindsay Santos
Vice President, Hilly Gross
Vice President Finance, Stephen W Brandt
Vice President Business Applications, Michael Frampton
Assistant Vice President Of Operations, Gina Bilak
Vice President Strategic Development, Zachary Wolf
Vice President Mobile Products, Don Cunningham
Assistant Vice President Sales, Lauren Dunnigan
Executive Vice President Systems Innovation, Brian Fullerton
Vice President Of Sales, Bruce Caldwell
Vice President Sales, Dennis Tebon
Senior Vice President Marketing, Scott Roe
Vice President Finance, Mark D Murphy
Vice President, Pam Beaulieu
Senior Vice President, Joel Alligood
Vice President Claims, Lynda Barry
Regional Vice President, John Allen
Vice President Business Development, Richard Rodriguez

Assistant Vice President Finance, Christina Stone
Assistant Vice President. Information Technology, David Filley
Vice President, James Bell
Assistant Vice President Information Technology, Chris Harwood
Assistant Vice President Insurance Business Consultant Finance, Tom Harding
Vice President Corporate Underwriting, Michael LeSchack
Assistant Vice President, Michael Kantor
Vice President, Mark Adams
Vice President of Underwriting, Mary Enkler
Senior Vice President, Gene Mason
AVP Operations, Jinat Rahman
Vice President of Underwriting, Scott Stevens
Vice President Business Integration, Debra Hochman
Senior Vice President and Chief Underwriting Counsel, Felice Shapiro
Senior Vice President First Nationwide Title, Christopher Suozzi
Vice President National Agency Representative Amtrust Title Insurance Company An Amtrust Financial Services Company, Frank Laisch
Vice President and Senior Underwriter, Jesse Iadanza
Assistant Vice President Professional Lines, Cynthia Yousef
Assistant Vice President, Michael Ehrhardt
Senior Vice President, Christopher Donnelly
Assistant Vice President, Joe Nuss
Senior Vice President, James Cosolito
Auditors: KPMG LLP

LOCATIONS

HQ: AmTrust Financial Services Inc
59 Maiden Lane, 43rd Floor, New York, NY 10038
Phone: 212 220-7120
Web: www.amtrustgroup.com

2016 Sales

	$ mil.	% of total
US	2,756	51
Bermuda	1,742	32
Other countries	951	17
Total	**5,450**	**100**

PRODUCTS/OPERATIONS

2016 Sales

	$ mil.	% of total
Small commercial business	2,203	40
Specialty risk & extended warranty	1,543	28
Specialty program	920	17
Service & fee income	538	10
Net investment income	208	4
Net gain on investments	36	1
Total	**5,450**	**100**

Selected Acquisitions

COMPETITORS

AIG	Liberty Mutual
Allianz Insurance	National Indemnity
Amica Mutual	Company
Bankers Financial	The Hartford
Berkshire Hathaway	Travelers Companies
FCCI	

HISTORICAL FINANCIALS

Company Type: Public

Income Statement

FYE: December 31

	ASSETS ($ mil.)	NET INCOME ($ mil.)	INCOME AS % OF ASSETS	EMPLOYEES
12/16	22,614	410	1.8%	8,000
12/15	17,111	503	2.9%	6,200
12/14	13,847	447	3.2%	5,100
12/13	11,257	290	2.6%	3,238
12/12	7,417	177	2.4%	2,100
Annual Growth	**32.1%**	**23.3%**	**—**	**39.7%**

2016 Year-End Financials

Debt ratio: 6.20%
Return on equity: 13.27%
Cash ($ mil.): 567
Current ratio: —
Long-term debt ($ mil.): —

No. of shares (mil.): 170
Dividends
　Yield: 0.0%
　Payout: 30.7%
Market value ($ mil.): 4,669

	STOCK PRICE ($) FY Close	P/E High/Low	Earnings	Dividends	Book Value
12/16	27.38	29　11	2.08	0.64	19.17
12/15	61.58	25　17	2.80	0.55	16.54
12/14	56.25	20　11	2.73	0.43	13.10
12/13	32.69	23　15	1.84	0.27	9.69
12/12	28.69	25　18	1.17	0.17	7.74
Annual Growth	**(1.2%)**	**—　—**	**15.5%**	**39.4%**	**25.5%**

Anadarko Petroleum Corp

Anadarko Petroleum has ventured beyond its original area of operation — the Anadarko Basin — to explore for develop produce and market oil natural gas natural gas liquids and related products worldwide. The company boasts reported proved reserves (90% of which is located in the US) of 1.7 billion barrels of oil equivalent. Additional assets include coal trona (natural soda ash) and other minerals. Anadarko operates a handful of gas-gathering systems in the Mid-Continent. Internationally the company has substantial oil and gas interests in Algeria. It also has holdings in Brazil Mozambique and West Africa.

Operations

Anadarko operates three segments: Oil and Gas Midstream and Marketing.

The Oil and Gas segment explores for and produces oil natural gas and NGLs (natural gas liquids). Its properties in the US consist of some 12700 wells (and 3500 nonoperated wells) across in DJ Basin in Colorado; Delaware Basin Eagleford and Eaglebine in Texas; Greater Natural Buttes in Utah; Greater Green River Basin in Wyoming; and Marcellus in Pennsylvania. It also has operations in Lousiana and Kansas. Internationally in Algeria the company works Blocks 404 and 208 in the Sahara Desert where it has a 24.5% stake; the offshore West Cape Three Points block and Deepwater Tano Block in Ghana; and Offshore Area 1 in Mozambique.

The Marketing segment brings in nearly 45% of sales and actively manages Anadarko's worldwide oil natural gas and NGLs sales minimizing market-related shut-ins maximizing realized prices and managing credit risk exposure.

Accounting for over 5% of sales the Midstream segment aids the oil and gas segment by conducting gas gathering processing transportation and produced-water disposal. It has 34 gathering systems and 72 processing and treating facilities.

Geographic Reach

Texas-based Anadarko's assets include US onshore resource plays in the Rocky Mountains area the southern US and the Appalachian basin. It is one of the largest independent producers in the deepwater Gulf of Mexico and has production and exploration activities worldwide including high-potential basins located in Alaska Algeria Brazil C´te d'Ivoire Ghana Kenya Mozambique New Zealand and other countries.

The US is Anadarko's largest market and accounts for more than 80% of the company's total revenue. Algeria is its primary non-US territory at nearly 15% of sales; other countries account for the remainder.

Sales and Marketing

Anadarko sells crude oil and natural gas via a range of contractual agreements including indexed fixed-price and cost-escalation-based agreements. Most of the company's US oil condensate and NGLs production is sold under contracts.

The company's oil is primarily sold to marketers gatherers and refiners. Natural gas is sold mainly to interstate and intrastate natural gas pipelines direct end-users industrial users local distribution companies and natural gas marketers.

Anadarko is contractually committed to deliver nearly 900 billion cu. ft. of natural gas to various US customers through 2031. It also delivers some 10 million barrels of oil to ports in Algeria and Ghana.

Financial Performance

Weak international oil and natural gas prices have put a huge dent in Anadarko's revenue since 2014.

In fiscal 2016 sales fell a further 10% to $8.4 billion as overall oil production volumes remained steady while prices fell further. Natural gas prices likewise fell as did production. On the upside the company recorded an $88 million improvement in NGLs (natural gas liquids) sales and a $68 million increase in gathering processing and marketing. The latter related to higher gas and NGLs volumes at the DJ Basin and DBM Complex.

Anadarko posted its third consecutive net loss in 2016 as gas prices remained below the break-even point and it suffered hefty write-downs of its producing assets values. In fiscal 2016 the company reduced its net loss to $3.1 billion due to lower impairment charges and layoffs.

Cash from operations was considerably higher in 2016 than 2015 at $3.0 billion versus a cash outflow of $1.9 billion. The improvement relates to the $5.2 billion settlement Anadarko paid in 2015 for environmental damages. Aside from this item operating cash flow benefited from a $881 million tax refund.

Strategy

To cope with revenue falls and heavy losses Anadarko has been selling off $4 billion of assets including in its US Onshore Marcellus and Eagle Ford oil and gas assets as well as its interest in Springfield Pipeline. It also sold shares in Western Gas Equity Partners. Additionally in 2016 Anadarko reduced capital expenditure by 44% laid off 17% of its workforce carried out layoffs and reduced dividends.

The extra liquidity offered by the sales will allow Anadarko to develop its higher margin properties such as Delaware Basin in Texas and DJ Basin in Colorado as well as its deepwater assets in the Gulf of Mexico — it made a major Gulf acquisition in 2016. With gas prices having risen somewhat since 2016 the company has more scope for capital expenditure. It ramped up its capital program to

$4.7 billion 80% of which will be put towards its US onshore upstream and midstream activities and in the Gulf of Mexico.

Mergers and Acquisitions

In 2016 Anadarko acquired the deepwater Gulf of Mexico assets of Freeport McMoRan Oil & Gas for $2 billion.

In 2015 Anadarko made a bid to acquire Apache which was rebuffed.

HISTORY

In 1959 the Panhandle Eastern Pipe Line Company set up Anadarko (named after the Anadarko Basin) to carry out its gas exploration and production activities. The new company was also formed to take advantage of a ruling by the Federal Power Commission (now the Federal Energy Regulatory Commission) to set lower price ceilings for producing properties owned by pipeline companies.

The company grew rapidly during the early 1960s largely because of its gas-rich namesake. It bought Ambassador Oil of Fort Worth Texas in 1965 — adding interests in 19 states in the US and Canada. The firm also relocated from Kansas to Fort Worth.

Anadarko began offshore exploration in the Gulf of Mexico in 1970 and focused there early in the decade. After moving to Houston in 1974 Anadarko increased its oil exploration activities when the energy crisis led to higher gas prices. A deal with Amoco (now part of BP) led to major finds on Matagorda Island off the Texas coast in the early 1980s.

To realize shareholder value Panhandle spun off Anadarko in 1986 — separating transmission from production. At the time more than 90% of Anadarko's reserves were natural gas. The next year Anadarko made new discoveries in Canada.

Low domestic natural gas prices led Anadarko overseas. It signed a production-sharing agreement with Algeria's national oil and gas firm SONATRACH in 1989. The deal covered 5.1 million acres in the Sahara. Two years later Anadarko began operating in the South China Sea and in Alaska's North Slope.

Back home the company spent $190 million in 1992 for properties in West Texas and in 1993 Anadarko began divesting noncore assets. Along with some of its partners the company also discovered oil in the Mahogany Field offshore Louisiana. Production from Mahogany began in 1996.

In 1997 Anadarko added exploration acreage in the North Atlantic and Tunisia.

Anadarko expanded its presence in western Canada in 2001 by buying Berkley Petroleum for more than $1 billion in cash and assumed debt.

Expanding its presence and asset base in the lucrative resource plays in the Rocky Mountains and the deepwater Gulf of Mexico in 2006 Anadarko acquired midstream operator Western Gas and fellow explorer Kerr-McGee for about $26 billion.

In 2013 Anadarko agreed to sell 10% of its property off the shores of Mozambique to Oil and Natural Gas Corp. Ltd. for $2.64 billion.

That year it acquired a number of US oil and gas assets for about $500 million.

EXECUTIVES

EVP Law and Chief Administrative Officer, Robert K. (Bobby) Reeves, age 59, $700,000 total compensation

Chairman President and CEO, R. A. (Al) Walker, age 59, $1,300,000 total compensation

EVP Operations, Darrell E. Hollek, age 59

EVP Finance and Chief Financial Officer, Robert G. (Bob) Gwin, age 53, $750,000 total compensation

EVP International and Deepwater Exploration, Ernest A. Leyendecker, age 56, $473,654 total compensation

EVP Global LNG, Mitchell W. (Mitch) Ingram, age 54, $625,000 total compensation

VP Operations, Daniel Brown

Vice President, Philip Peacock

Vice President In Charge of Drain Information Technology, Larry Hutson

Finance Vice President, Dustin David

Executive Vice President Exploration, Ernie Leyendecker

Sr.Vice President, Norm Benson

Vice President Human Resources, Joe Mongrain

Auditors: KPMG LLP

LOCATIONS

HQ: Anadarko Petroleum Corp
1201 Lake Robbins Drive, The Woodlands, TX 77380-1046
Phone: 832 636-1000
Web: www.anadarko.com

Sales by Geography

	% of total
United States	83
Algeria	13
Other International	4
Total	**100**

PRODUCTS/OPERATIONS

Sales by Segment

	% of total
Oil and Gas Exploration & Production	50
Marketing	43
Midstream	7
Total	**100**

Sales by Products

	$ mil.	% of total
Oil sales	4,668	55
Natural-gas sales	1,564	19
Gathering processing and marketing sales	1,294	15
Natural-gas liquids sales	921	11
Gains (losses) on divestitures and other net	(578)	-
Total	**7,869**	**100**

COMPETITORS

Adams Resources	Exxon Mobil
Apache	Hunt Consolidated
BP	Jones Energy
Cabot Oil & Gas	Key Energy
Chesapeake Energy	National Fuel Gas
Chevron	Noble Energy
Cimarex	Pioneer Natural
ConocoPhillips	Resources
Devon Energy	Royal Dutch Shell
EOG	

HISTORICAL FINANCIALS

Company Type: Public

Income Statement

FYE: December 31

	REVENUE ($ mil.)	NET INCOME ($ mil.)	NET PROFIT MARGIN	EMPLOYEES
12/17	11,908	(456)	—	4,400
12/16	7,869	(3,071)	—	4,500
12/15	8,698	(6,692)	—	5,800
12/14	18,470	(1,750)	—	6,100
12/13	14,581	801	5.5%	5,700
Annual Growth	**(4.9%)**	**—**	**—**	**(6.3%)**

2017 Year-End Financials

Debt ratio: 37.28%		No. of shares (mil.): 530	
Return on equity: (-3.98%)		Dividends	
Cash ($ mil.): 4,553		Yield: 0.0%	
Current ratio: 1.73		Payout: —	
Long-term debt ($ mil.): 15,547		Market value ($ mil.): 28,472	

	STOCK PRICE ($)	P/E	PER SHARE ($)		
	FY Close	High/Low	Earnings	Dividends	Book Value
12/17	53.64	— —	(0.85)	0.20	20.15
12/16	69.73	— —	(5.90)	0.20	22.16
12/15	48.58	— —	(13.18)	1.08	25.22
12/14	82.50	— —	(3.47)	0.99	38.94
12/13	79.32	62 47	1.58	0.54	43.39
Annual Growth (17.4%)	(9.3%)	— —		—(22.0%)	

Analog Devices Inc

If the world is turning digital Analog Devices is paving the way. Its linear integrated circuits (ICs) translate real-world phenomena such as pressure temperature and sound into digital signals. It's a leading maker of linear IC as well as mixed-signal analog integrated circuits and digital ICs. Its line of 22000 devices includes converters amplifiers power management products and digital signal processors (DSPs). ADI's chip designs are used in industrial process controls medical and scientific instruments communications gear computers automobiles and consumer electronics. Its chips operate in high-tech goods from more than 100000 companies. Customers outside the US account for most of the company's sales.

Operations

ADI's industrial segment accounts for about 45% of sales followed by ICs for communications applications with about 20% of sales automotive at more than 15% and consumer at about 20%.

The company makes some of its IC products and outsources some 60% of production to third-party manufacturers primarily Taiwan Semiconductor Manufacturing Company. ADI's wafer fab facilities are in Wilmington Massachusetts and Limerick Ireland. The company operates test facilities in the Philippines and uses third-party subcontractors for assembly and testing.

Geographic Reach

The US is ADI's single biggest market accounting for about 40% of sales followed by China with more than 15% and Japan less than 10%. Customers in Europe account for a bit less than 30% of ADI's revenue. Headquartered in Norwood Massachusetts the company has facilities in the US the Philippines Ireland India and China.

Sales and Marketing

Although more than 50% of the company's sales are made through distributors ADI also sells through direct sales offices and sales representatives worldwide and via its website. Apple the company's biggest customer accounts for about an eighth of revenue while the 20 largest customers account for about 40% of revenue.

Financial Performance

ADI's 2016 (ended October) revenue of $3.4 billion hardly budged from 2015 but profit and cash flow from operations increased year-to-year.

The automotive market and China kept ADI from a revenue retreat. The company reported a 3% automotive increase from automakers' demand for ADI powertrain advanced driver assistance systems and infotainment products. The sales of chips for consumer applications fell on lower demand for portable devices. In China where sales rose 13% in 2016 ADI saw rising demand for automotive as well as industrial and communications products.

ADI kept expenses under control in 2016 allowing it to post a $862 million a 24% increase from 2015. The company spent more on research and development but reduced slightly its selling general and administrative expenses. It also had a lower tax bill in 2016.

Cash flow from operations came in at $1.3 billion in 2016 from more than $900 million in 2015. The increase came from a decrease in inventory and an increase in accounts receivable.

Strategy

ADI which marked its 50th anniversary in 2015 is in the midst of a transition to broaden its product line and its markets. Since 2009 the company has invested $4 billion in research and development with most of the money going toward products for the industrial automotive and communications infrastructure markets. The company is trying to develop a more varied mix of customers and diminish its dependence on consumer-oriented customers such as Apple (12% of revenue in 2016). The automotive emphasis is already paying off as the sector produced the company's notable revenue gain in 2016. ADI's products find homes throughout vehicles especially in the electronics required for self-driving vehicles.

The nearly $15 billion Linear Technology acquisition which closed in 2017 is another major step in ADI's transformation. ADI and Linear combine to grab top-two market share across the analog market in data convertors power management amplifiers interface and high performance RF and microwave. ADI expects the combination to achieve about $150 million in manufacturing and operating expense synergies. ADI has made smaller acquisitions to provide more capabilities that provide additional value to its customers. Transactions have brought board technologies for internet of things applications cloud security and LIDAR.

ADI also has taken steps to tighten its operating processes to save money and increase cash flow. A tighter inventory management program reduced inventory by $36 million (9%) in 2016.

Mergers and Acquisitions

Analog Devices agreed to buy OneTree Microdevices for an undisclosed amount in March 2017. OneTree is a fabless semiconductor company with a GaAs and GaN amplifier portfolio for cable TV and fiber-to-the-home applications. The acquisition extends Analog's product lineup to those uses.

ADI concluded its acquisition of Linear Technology also a maker of analog ICs for about $15 billion in 2017. While both companies produce analog devices their product mixes are complementary executives said. The acquisition should expand ADI's possible market from $8 billion to $14 billion. Linear posted profit of about $494 million on $1.4 billion in revenue in 2016 (ended June).

In 2016 ADI acquired SNAP Sensor SA a privately held company that specializes in vision sensing technologies. The acquisition advances ADI's leadership position in sensing and signal processing and build upon platform-level internet of things products such as ADI's Blackfin Low Power Imaging Platform.

ADI also made acquisitions concentrated in autonomous vehicles. ADI acquired Innovasic a developer of Ehternet technology that allows for deterministic real-time communication; the cyber security products of Sypris which can provide customers with sensor-to-cloud security products; and technology from Vescent Photonics that should help ADI develop a solid state scanning LIDAR system that complements its RADAR-based ADAS products.

ADI acquired Hittite Microwave Corporation in 2014 for $2.4 billion. Adding Hittite technologies strengthens ADI's capabilities in RF microwave and millimeter wave applications for developing products for industrial healthcare aerospace and defense automotive safety and communications infrastructure applications.

EXECUTIVES

President and CEO, Vincent T. Roche, age 57, $827,692 total compensation
SVP Global Operations and Technology, Joseph (John) Hassett, age 59
SVP and CTO, Peter Real, age 57, $376,008 total compensation
SVP Communications and Automotive Business Group, Rick D. Hess, age 63, $519,231 total compensation
SVP Worldwide Sales and Digital Marketing, Martin Cotter, age 52
SVP Finance and CFO, Prashanth Mahendra-Rajah, age 47
Vice President International, Thomas Wessel
Vice President Finance and Supply Chain, Jim Mollica
Chairman, Ray Stata, age 83
Auditors: Ernst & Young LLP

LOCATIONS

HQ: Analog Devices Inc
One Technology Way, Norwood, MA 02062-9106
Phone: 781 329-4700
Web: www.analog.com

2016 Sales

	% of total
United States	38
Rest of North and South America	3
Europe	27
Japan	8
China	17
Rest of Asia	7
Total	**100**

PRODUCTS/OPERATIONS

2016 Sales

	% of total
Industrial	44
Automotive	16
Consumer	20
Communications	20
Total	**100**

COMPETITORS

Analogic	Microchip Technology
Cirrus Logic	Microsemi
Conexant Systems	NXP Semiconductors
Custom Sensors &	ON Semiconductor
Technologies	Qualcomm CDMA
DENSO	ROHM
DSP Group	Robert Bosch
Fairchild	STMicroelectronics
Semiconductor	Semtech
Infineon Technologies	Silicon Image
Integrated Device	Silicon Labs
Technology	Siliconix
Intersil	Skyworks
Linear Technology	Texas Instruments
Marvell Technology	
Maxim Integrated	
Products	

HISTORICAL FINANCIALS

Company Type: Public

Income Statement

FYE: October 28

	REVENUE ($ mil.)	NET INCOME ($ mil.)	NET PROFIT MARGIN	EMPLOYEES
10/17	5,107	727	14.2%	15,300
10/16	3,421	861	25.2%	10,000
10/15*	3,435	696	20.3%	9,700
11/14	2,864	629	22.0%	9,600
11/13	2,633	673	25.6%	9,100
Annual Growth	18.0%	1.9%	—	13.9%

*Fiscal year change

2017 Year-End Financials

Debt ratio: 37.14%
Return on equity: 9.52%
Cash ($ mil.): 1,047
Current ratio: 1.47
Long-term debt ($ mil.): 7,551

No. of shares (mil.): 368
Dividends
Yield: 0.0%
Payout: 85.5%
Market value ($ mil.): 33,623

	STOCK PRICE ($) FY Close	P/E High/Low	PER SHARE ($) Earnings	Dividends	Book Value
10/17	91.21	44 30	2.07	1.77	27.57
10/16	63.53	23 18	2.76	1.66	16.76
10/15*	60.12	31 22	2.20	1.57	16.26
11/14	49.62	28 21	1.98	1.45	15.29
11/13	49.68	23 18	2.14	1.32	15.24
Annual Growth	16.4%	—	(0.8%)	7.6%	16.0%

*Fiscal year change

Andeavor

Andeavor Corporation does its best to turn crude oil into something useful for its customers. The independent oil refiner and marketer operates seven US refineries that produce nearly 900000 barrels per day of gasoline jet fuel diesel fuel fuel oil liquid asphalt and other fuel products. It has refineries in Alaska California (two) North Dakota (two) Utah and Washington. Andeavor markets fuel to nearly 25000 branded retail gas stations (including Shell and USA Gasoline brands) primarily in Alaska and the Western US. It owns 36% of Andeavor Logistics LP (ALLP). In 2017 Andeavor (then called Tresoro) acquired all segments of Western Refining except its logistics arm in a $6.4 billion deal. The combined Tesoro-Western company changed its name to Andeavor.

Operations

Andeavor has three operating segments: Refining Andeavor Logistics (ALLP) and Marketing.

Refining generates more than 55% of sales and operates seven petroleum refineries which manufacture gasoline and gasoline blendstocks jet fuel diesel fuel residual fuel oil and other refined petroleum products.

Andeavor's marketing segment sells transportation fuels through branded businesses such as ARCO Shell Exxon Mobil USA Gasoline Rebel Thrift and Tesoro. Consisting of nearly 2500 retail gas stations the segment generates nearly 40% of Andeavor's sales.

The Logistics businesses owns crude oil and natural gas gathering assets natural gas processing and crude oil and refined products terminalling transportation and storage assets acquired from Andeavor and third parties. Its gathering operation consists of crude oil natural gas and produced water gathering systems in the North Dakota Williston Basin/Bakken Shale area and the Uinta Vermillion and greater Green River basins. It accounts for less than 5% of revenue.

Geographic Reach

San Antonio Texas-based Andeavor serves customers in Alaska and 16 states in the Western US. Its supply and distribution operations include bulk terminals in Anchorage Alaska; Boise Idaho Burley Idaho; Port Angeles Washington; Salt Lake City Utah; Stockton California; and Vancouver Washington.

Sales and Marketing

Andeavor sells its refined products to its marketing segment through terminal facilities and other locations and exports to non-US markets. It sells gasoline through its network of branded retail stations as well as on an unbranded or wholesale and bulk basis.

Its branded operations include transportation fuel sales through retail stations and agreements with third-party dealers and distributors (jobber/dealers). Its unbranded or wholesale business includes volumes sold through agreements with third-party dealers.

Financial Performance

The downturn in the oil price has put a severe dent in Andeavor's revenue. In fiscal 2016 (while it was still Tesoro) net revenue fell a further 14% to $24.6 billion. The fall was primarily a result of lower average selling prices over the year.

Net income also fell sharply down 49% to $860 million due to lower revenue and weak margins in the refining business.

Cash from operates fell 39% to $1.3 billion due to lower net income plus a $676 million change in the lower cost of market adjustment.

Strategy

Andeavor's strategy is in large part based on making acquisitions that will diversify its operations and improve profitability. For instance in 2016 it acquired Virent a company with expertise in developing lower-carbon renewable energy and serve to lower compliance costs with federal fuel standards. It also acquired the 20000 barrel per day Dickinson refinery in North Dakota and in 2017 it completed the major acquisition of Western Refining which will take its annual output to above 1 million barrels per day.

To finance its capital expenditure programs the company sometimes makes strategic divestitures often to its logistics business. In 2015 it sold its storage and pipeline assets in Los Angeles for $500 million.

Mergers and Acquisitions

In 2017 Andeavor (then Tesoro) acquired all segments of Western Refining except its logistics arm in a $6.4 billion deal. Subsequently the company was renamed as Andeavor. The acquisition takes the company's output capacity to over 1 million barrels per day.

In 2016 Tesoro acquired Great Northern Midstream a crude oil logistics provider which owns and operates crude oil pipeline gathering system transportation storage and rail loading facilities in the Williston Basin of North Dakota. The acquisition includes the 97-mile BakkenLink crude oil pipeline which connects to several third-party gathering systems; and a proprietary 28-mile gathering system in the core of the Bakken supported by acreage dedication.

HISTORY

Founded by Robert West in 1964 as a spinoff of petroleum producer Texstar Tesoro Petroleum was hamstrung by debt from the get-go. In 1968 West merged Tesoro with Intex Oil and Sioux Oil to invigorate its financial standing.

Reborn the company constructed an Alaska refinery and began a 10-year stretch of petroleum-related acquisitions usually at bargain prices including almost half of the oil operations of British Petroleum (BP) in Trinidad which became

Trinidad-Tesoro Petroleum. By 1973 earnings had quintupled.

In 1975 Tesoro paid $83 million for about a third of Commonwealth Oil Refining Company (Corco) a troubled Puerto Rican oil refiner one-and-a-half times its size. Debt soon was troubling Tesoro again and the company divested many of its holdings including refineries in Montana and Wyoming. Corco declared bankruptcy in 1978. That year Tesoro was hit with tax penalties and revealed it had bribed officials in foreign countries.

The company fought takeover attempts and bankruptcy in the 1980s and sold its half of Trinidad-Tesoro in 1985. In the 1990s it expanded its natural gas operations and returned to profitability.

In 1998 Tesoro bought a refinery and 32 retail outlets in Hawaii from an affiliate of BHP and a refinery in Washington from an affiliate of Shell. To concentrate on its downstream businesses the company in 1999 sold its exploration and production operations in the US (to EEX for $215 million) and in Bolivia (to BG for about $100 million).

To raise cash to invest in US mainland businesses in 2013 Tesoro completed the sale of Tesoro Hawaii for $539 million.

In 2013 Tesoro bought BP's Southern California refining and marketing assets including the 266000 barrels-per-day Carson refinery and 800 dealer-operated gas stations for more than $2.5 billion.

EXECUTIVES

EVP and CFO, Steven M. (Steve) Sterin, age 46, $761,250 total compensation
EVP General Counsel and Secretary, Kim K. W. Rucker, age 50, $640,865 total compensation
President Tesoro Logistics GP, Phillip M. Anderson
Chairman President and CEO, Gregory J. (Greg) Goff, age 60, $1,600,000 total compensation
SVP Refining, Brian Coffman
EVP Operations, Cynthia (CJ) Warner, age 58, $647,596 total compensation
EVP Operations, Keith M. Casey, age 50, $706,635 total compensation
SVP Marketing, Michael J. Morrison
Auditors: Ernst & Young LLP

LOCATIONS

HQ: Andeavor
19100 Ridgewood Pkwy., San Antonio, TX 78259-1828
Phone: 210 626-6000
Web: www.tsocorp.com

PRODUCTS/OPERATIONS

2016 Sales

	$ mil.	% of total
Refining		
Refined products	21,213	54
Crude oil resales & other	1,043	3
Tesoro Logistics LP		
Gathering	339	1
Processing	276	1
Terminalling and transportation	605	2
Marketing		
Fuel	15,405	39
Other non-fuel	85	0
Adjustments	(14384)	-
Total	24,582	100

Selected Products

Asphalt
Calcined coke
Diesel fuel
Gasoline and Gasoline blend stocks
Heavy fuel oils
Jet fuel
Liquefied petroleum gas
Petroleum coke
Residual fuel oil

HISTORICAL FINANCIALS

Company Type: Public

Income Statement
FYE: December 31

	REVENUE ($ mil.)	NET INCOME ($ mil.)	NET PROFIT MARGIN	EMPLOYEES
12/16	24,582	734	3.0%	6,300
12/15	28,711	1,540	5.4%	6,000
12/14	40,633	843	2.1%	5,600
12/13	37,601	412	1.1%	7,000
12/12	32,974	743	2.3%	5,700
Annual Growth	(7.1%)	(0.3%)	—	2.5%

2016 Year-End Financials

Debt ratio: 33.99%	No. of shares (mil.): 116
Return on equity: 13.71%	Dividends
Cash ($ mil.): 3,295	Yield: 0.0%
Current ratio: 2.09	Payout: 34.3%
Long-term debt ($ mil.): 6,468	Market value ($ mil.): 10,223

	STOCK PRICE ($) FY Close	P/E High/Low		PER SHARE ($) Earnings	Dividends	Book Value
12/16	87.45	17	11	6.12	2.10	46.75
12/15	105.37	9	5	12.36	1.85	43.66
12/14	74.35	12	7	6.44	1.10	35.64
12/13	58.50	21	13	3.00	0.90	32.64
12/12	44.05	8	4	5.25	0.27	30.77
Annual Growth	18.7%	—	—	3.9%	67.0%	11.0%

Anixter International Inc

Anixter International is a distributor of communication products used to connect voice video data and security systems. It sells 400000-plus products including electrical and electronic wire cable and security system components to some 150000 customers in a host of industries. Anixter operates primarily through three segments: Network & Security Solutions Electrical & Electronic Solutions and Utility Power Solutions. It operates from about 320 warehouses and sales centers in 50 countries. Although Anixter gets its products from thousands of suppliers almost one-quarter come from just five companies.

Operations

Anixter operates through three distinct segments: Network & Security Solutions (NSS) Electrical & Electronic Solutions (EES) and Utility Power Solutions (UPS).

NSS (almost 55% of net sales) offers a variety of products that run the gamut between copper and fiber optic cable and connectivity products to video surveillance and cable management equipment.

EES (30%) offers several product lines of electrical and electronic wire and cable industrial communication and control products industrial Ethernet switches and voice and data cable.

UPS (nearly 15%) supplies electrical transmission and distribution products power plant maintenance and repair and operations supplies to the utilities and electrical markets. It also sells smart-grid products conductors transformers and switches.

Geographic Reach

Anixter's distribution network consists of 320 locations in 50 countries with 9 million sq. ft. of space. This total includes around 15 regional distribution centers 45 local distribution centers 190 service centers and almost 70 branch locations. It also has roughly 80 sales offices worldwide. North America accounts for about 85% of its revenue.

Sales and Marketing

More than two dozen industries are represented among Anixter customers — markets such as education government health care manufacturing retail and transportation. Anixter also serves contractors and integrators who install and maintain communications networks and data centers. International national regional and local OEMs number among Anixter's customers as well procuring wire cable fasteners and other small components to help finish the manufacturing of their own products typically with short lead times.

Anixter's distribution network consists of 320 locations in 50 countries. It also has roughly 80 sales offices worldwide.

Financial Performance

Anixter's revenues soared from 2015 to 2016 mainly due to more than $1 billion in additional revenue posted from its Power Solutions acquisitions. The company also recognized 4% growth from its NSS segment due to stronger demand within the North American and EMEA regions.

Its profits declined marginally from 2015 to 2016 mainly due to a slight loss from discontinued operations and a bump in operating expenses.

Cash flow from operations increased sharply from 2015 to 2016 mainly as a result of improved working capital efficiency and a surge in cash from accounts payable for more than $100 million.

Strategy

In 2015 the company sold its fasteners segment to American Industrial Partners a middle-market private equity firm for $380 million in cash. The proceeds of the sale were utilized for paying down debt and extending its acquisition strategy. The sale also enhanced the company's focus on its other core segments.

Using part of these proceeds Anixter in late 2015 acquired the Power Solutions business belonging to HD Supply Holdings for $825 million in cash. The business distributed electrical transmission and distribution products power plant MRO supplies and smart-grid products and also arranges materials management and procurement outsourcing for the power generation and distribution industries.Due in part to the capabilities created by the combined businesses Anixter in 2016 was awarded a $750 million five-year contract serving one of the largest investor-owned utilities in the country. The contract is the largest in Anixter?s history.

After recognizing significant revenue growth mostly in North America as a result of the Power Solutions acquisition Anixter is looking to expand its combined operations internationally and has growth initiatives underway in Mexico and the UK which will further leverage its North American product portfolio.

HISTORY

Anixter International was founded in 1957 by two brothers Alan and Bill Anixter along with a small group of employees in Evanston Illinois. The company was known as Anixter Brothers at the time and it supplied distributors and wholesalers looking for an alternative to buying wire and cable in bulk quantities directly from manufacturers. The company went public on the American Stock Exchange in 1967. Anixter became an international company when Anixter United Kingdom was formed in 1972.

EXECUTIVES

EVP and CFO, Theodore A. (Ted) Dosch, age 57, $595,000 total compensation
EVP Human Resources, Rodney A. Smith, age 59, $300,000 total compensation
EVP General Counsel and Corporate Secretary, Justin C. Choi, age 51, $455,000 total compensation
CEO and Director, Robert J. (Bob) Eck, age 58, $980,000 total compensation
President and COO, William A. (Bill) Galvin, age 54, $525,000 total compensation
EVP Operations, William A. (Bill) Standish, age 62, $455,000 total compensation
EVP Electrical and Electronic Solutions, Robert M. (Bob) Graham, age 49
EVP and CIO, Scott Ramsbottom, age 43
SVP International Network and Security Solutions, William C. Geary, age 47
Vice President Marketing, Scott Quinton
Chairman, Samuel Zell, age 75
Auditors: Ernst & Young LLP

LOCATIONS

HQ: Anixter International Inc
2301 Patriot Blvd., Glenview, IL 60026
Phone: 224 521-8000
Web: www.anixter.com

2016 Sales

	$ mil.	% of total
North America	6,385	84
EMEA	570	7
Emerging Markets	668	9
Total	**7,623**	**100**

PRODUCTS/OPERATIONS

2016 Sales

	$ mil.	% of total
NSS	4,084	54
EES	2,103	28
UPS	1,436	18
Total	**7,623**	**100**

Selected Products and Services

Products
- Electrical wire and cable (power cable)
- Electronic wire and cable (coax)
- Fasteners and connectors ("C" class)
- Industrial networking communications
- Network cabling (copper and fiber)
- Networking wireless and voice electronics
- Security (video surveillance access control)

Supply chain services
- Database tracking
- Deployment
- Inventory management
- Logistics
- Product enhancement and packaging
- Sourcing

COMPETITORS

Arrow Electronics	Rexel
Avnet	ScanSource
Belden	Tech Data
Fastenal	W.W. Grainger
General Cable	WESCO International
HWC	Watsco
MSC Industrial Direct	

HISTORICAL FINANCIALS

Company Type: Public

Income Statement

FYE: December 30

	REVENUE ($ mil.)	NET INCOME ($ mil.)	NET PROFIT MARGIN	EMPLOYEES
12/16*	7,622	120	1.6%	8,900
01/16	6,190	127	2.1%	8,700
01/15	6,445	194	3.0%	9,100
01/14	6,226	200	3.2%	8,200
12/12	6,253	124	2.0%	8,300
Annual Growth	5.1%	(0.9%)	—	1.8%

*Fiscal year change

2016 Year-End Financials

Debt ratio: 33.68%
Return on equity: 9.78%
Cash ($ mil.): 115
Current ratio: 2.13
Long-term debt ($ mil.): 1,378

No. of shares (mil.): 33
Dividends
  Yield: —
  Payout: —
Market value ($ mil.): 2,710

	STOCK PRICE ($) FY Close	P/E High/Low		PER SHARE ($) Earnings	Dividends	Book Value
12/16*	81.05	23	11	3.59	0.00	38.64
01/16	60.39	23	15	3.81	0.00	35.44
01/15	88.18	18	13	5.84	0.00	34.19
01/14	89.61	15	11	6.04	5.00	31.27
12/12	62.64	19	13	3.69	4.50	29.81
Annual Growth	6.7%	—	—	(0.7%)	—	6.7%

*Fiscal year change

Annaly Capital Management Inc

A real estate investment trust (REIT) Annaly Capital Management invests in and finances residential and commercial assets. It primarily manages a portfolio of mortgage-backed securities including mortgage pass-through certificates collateralized mortgage obligations and agency callable debentures. Commencing operations in 1997 the firm typically invests in high-quality securities issued or guaranteed by the likes of Freddie Mac Fannie Mae and Ginnie Mae and backed by single-family residential mortgages. More than 95% of Annaly's assets are agency mortgage-backed securities which carry an implied AAA rating. The firm is externally managed by Annaly Management Company LLC.

Operations

Annaly invests through four primary groups: Agency Residential Credit Commercial Real Estate and Middle Market Lending. The Agency group primarily invests in agency mortgage-backed securities and related derivatives. The Residential Credit group invests in non-agency mortgage-backed assets within securitized products and residential mortgage loan markets. Commercial Real Estate writes and invests in commercial mortgage loans securities and related assets and Middle Market Lending provides customized debt financing to middle-market businesses.

Financial Performance

Annaly's revenue and profits had been trending upward until 2014 when the REIT suffered a loss of $115 million; this was primarily driven by nearly $950 million in unrealized losses on interest rate swaps for the year. Revenue rebounded the fol-

lowing year and more than doubled to reach $2.3 billion in 2016. A steep decline in realized losses on interest rate swaps plus unrealized gains on interest rate swaps led to that year's improved performance.

Like revenue net income has been climbing since 2014 (when the company lost a net $842.3 million). In 2016 the REIT's higher revenue led net income to rise more than 200% to $1.4 billion.

The company's cash flow from operations has been fluctuating greatly over the past few years. It rose to $6.9 billion in 2016 (compared to an operating outflow of $3.2 billion in 2015) thanks to the higher net income and after adjusting its earnings for non-cash items (mostly related to proceeds from repurchase agreements of RCap investments).

Strategy

Annaly makes its money based on the interest rate spread: When interest rates go down Annaly's returns tend to go up. It does this by borrowing short-term loans which typically carry lower interest rates and using that money to invest in mortgage-backed securities which typically carry higher rates. As such the troubled economy actually benefited the REIT as lowered short-term interest rates translated into higher interest income.

However in an environment where the Federal Reserve has carried out interest rate hikes Annaly's strategy of earning income from the spread could be threatened. With rate hikes expected to continue the REIT is increasingly focusing on gains from its credit assets investment portfolio which are tied to long-term rates.

In addition to funding purchases of mortgage-backed securities through short-term repurchase agreements Annaly raises investment funds through equity and debt offerings. It seeks to minimize prepayment risk by structuring a diversified portfolio with a variety of prepayment characteristics and through other means; it also increases the size of its balance sheet when opportunities are likely to allow growth in earnings per share.

In mid-2017 Annaly agreed to sell Pingora Holdings (acquired the previous year with the purchase of Hatteras Financial) to Bayview Asset Management. Pingora is a specialized asset manager focused on investing in mortgage servicing rights and servicing residential mortgages.

Mergers and Acquisitions

In July 2016 Annaly acquired North Carolina-based Hatteras Financial Corp for $1.5 billion. The deal expanded and diversified Annaly's portfolio which was made up of mostly fixed-rate mortgage-backed securities by adding Hatteras' portfolio of mostly adjustable-rate mortgage-backed securities.

EXECUTIVES

CFO, Glenn A. Votek, age 58, $91,346 total compensation
Chairman President and CEO, Kevin G. Keyes, age 49, $375,000 total compensation
Chief Legal Officer, Anthony C. Green
Chief Investment Officer, David L. Finkelstein, age 44
Chief Credit Officer, Timothy P. Coffey, age 43
Auditors: Ernst & Young LLP

LOCATIONS

HQ: Annaly Capital Management Inc
1211 Avenue of the Americas, New York, NY 10036
Phone: 212 696-0100   **Fax:** 212 696-9809
Web: www.annaly.com

PRODUCTS/OPERATIONS

Selected Subsidiaries

Fixed Income Discount Advisory Company Delaware corporation
RCap Securities Inc. Maryland corporation
FIDAC Housing Cycle Fund LLC Delaware limited liability company
FHC Master Fund Ltd. a Cayman Islands exempted company (wholly owned subsidiary of FIDAC Housing Cycle Fund LLC)
Shannon Funding LLC Delaware limited liability company
Charlesfort Capital Management LLC Delaware limited liability company
FIDAC FSI LLC Delaware limited liability company
CXS Acquisition Corporation a Maryland corporation

COMPETITORS

AG Mortgage Investment Trust
Capstead Mortgage
Drive Shack
Impac Mortgage Holdings
Institutional Financial Markets
JAVELIN Mortgage
MFA Financial
Redwood Trust
iStar Financial Inc

HISTORICAL FINANCIALS

Company Type: Public

Income Statement

FYE: December 31

	ASSETS ($ mil.)	NET INCOME ($ mil.)	INCOME AS % OF ASSETS	EMPLOYEES
12/16	87,905	1,433	1.6%	189
12/15	75,190	466	0.6%	149
12/14	88,355	(842)	—	25
12/13	81,922	3,729	4.6%	48
12/12	133,452	1,735	1.3%	147
Annual Growth	(9.9%)	(4.7%)	—	6.5%

2016 Year-End Financials

Debt ratio: 8.95%
Return on equity: 11.69%
Cash ($ mil.): 1,539
Current ratio: —
Long-term debt ($ mil.): —

No. of shares (mil.): 1,018
Dividends
  Yield: 0.3%
  Payout: 227.9%
Market value ($ mil.): 10,159

	STOCK PRICE ($) FY Close	P/E High/Low		PER SHARE ($) Earnings	Dividends	Book Value
12/16	9.97	8	6	1.39	3.17	12.33
12/15	9.38	26	22	0.42	1.20	12.71
12/14	10.81	—	—	(0.96)	1.20	14.06
12/13	9.97	4	3	3.74	1.50	13.09
12/12	14.04	10	8	1.71	2.05	16.81
Annual Growth	(8.2%)	—	—	(5.0%)	11.5%	(7.4%)

Anthem Inc

Health benefits provider Anthem through a number of subsidiaries provides health coverage to around 40 million members in the US. One of the nation?s largest health insurers Anthem is a Blue Cross and Blue Shield Association licensee in more than a dozen states (where it operates as Anthem Empire and BCBS) and provides plans under the Unicare Amerigroup and CareMore names in other states. Plans include PPO HMO indemnity and hybrid plans offered to employers individuals and Medicare and Medicaid recipients. Anthem also provides administrative services to self-insured groups as well as specialty insurance.

In 2017 a federal judge blocked the planned merger between Anthem and rival Cigna.

Operations

Anthem operates through three reportable segments: Government Business Commercial and Specialty Business and Other.

The Government Business segment offers Medicare and Medicaid Services including Medicare Advantage and Medicare Part D as well as National Government Services and services related to Blue Cross and Blue Shield's Federal Employee Program. That segment accounts for around 55% of Anthem?s total revenue.

The Commercial and Specialty Business segment provides fully insured health products managed care services such as claims processing and underwriting and specialty products including dental vision life and disability coverage. It accounts for nearly half of Anthem's revenues.

Anthem's specialty products include dental vision long-term care workers' compensation and group life and disability insurance. Through several of its subsidiaries Anthem also performs claims processing fraud prevention cost-control benefits management and other administrative tasks for government-run Medicare plans other insurance firms and employer groups.

Altogether the company serves around 75 million customers.

Geographic Reach

Anthem is headquartered in Indiana and through its various operations is licensed to conduct insurance operations in all 50 states. It serves Blue Cross customers in Colorado Connecticut Georgia Indiana Kentucky Maine Missouri Nevada New Hampshire New York Ohio South Carolina Virginia and Wisconsin.

Subsidiary Unicare sells group and individual health coverage in geographic areas where Anthem is not a Blue Cross licensee. The company's AMERIGROUP subsidiary which provides health insurance for public programs operates in Florida Georgia Iowa Kansas Louisiana Maryland Nevada New Jersey New Mexico New York Tennessee Texas and Washington. Simply Healthcare (acquired in early 2015) provides managed care services for Medicaid and Medicare recipients in Florida.

Despite its expansion into other business areas in recent years Anthem's Blue-focused expansion efforts in past decades have kept Blue-branded health coverage at the core of its business. Many of the company's Blue subsidiaries operate under the name Anthem Blue Cross Blue Shield.

Sales and Marketing

Anthem markets most of its products through a network of independent agents and brokers. The exception comes with the company's national account and large employer-focused products which are sold by an in-house sales force customer-hired consultants and independent brokers. The company is working to increase online promotional and sales interaction with both consumers and brokers.

Advertising expenses totaled $246.2 million in 2016 down from $313.5 million in 2015 and $337 million in 2014.

Financial Performance

Anthem has posted several years of steady incremental revenue growth including in 2016 when revenue rose 7% to $84.9 billion. That increase was largely due to higher sales of managed care products in the Government Business segment as well as growth in the Commercial and Specialty Business segment. However these gains were partially offset by a decline in the Government Business segment?s administrative fees business.

Net income for Anthem had also been on the rise for years but took a modest dip in the past couple of years. In 2016 net income dropped 3.5% to $2.5 billion due to a number of factors including transactional expenses related to the plan to acquire Cigna higher interest expenses and lower investment earnings.

Cash flow from operations dropped for the first time in five years in 2016 falling 22% to $3.2 billion on an increase in claims payments (due to higher membership numbers).

Strategy

Overall Anthem hopes to get bigger through acquisitions (including its planned purchase of Cigna) in combination with organic expansion (such as adding new members in existing markets).

Covering the Medicare market is a significant part of Anthem's growth strategy: The company anticipates more than 1 million Baby Boomers will become eligible for Medicare every year between 2011 and 2030 in all of Anthem's Blue-branded states and it is beefing up its Medicare offerings and expanding into new service territories to prepare for the change.

To cope with the changes brought about by health care reform Anthem has made some changes to the way it does business. For example it has expanded into areas such as online health insurance exchanges and raised its premium rates in certain market segments (individuals and local groups).

Mergers and Acquisitions

In early 2018 Anthem acquired Medicare Advantage firm America's 1st Choice which operates under the Freedom Health and Optimum brands in Florida and the America's 1st Choice brand in South Carolina. With that purchase Anthem's Medicare and Medicaid plans serve more than 780000 customers in Florida.

In what would have amounted to a huge industry-reshaping deal Anthem agreed to acquire competitor Cigna for some $48 billion in 2015. The combined health insurance behemoth would serve some 53 million customers and generate sales of about $115 billion. However in early 2017 a federal judge blocked the merger just weeks after a similar planned merger between Aetna and Humana was halted.

HISTORY

Anthem's earliest predecessor prepaid hospital plan Blue Cross of Indiana was founded in 1944. Unlike other Blues Blue Cross of Indiana never received tax advantages or mandated discounts so it competed as a private insurer. Within two years it had 100000 members; by 1970 there were nearly 2 million.

Blue Shield of Indiana another Anthem precursor also grew rapidly after its 1946 formation as a mutual insurance company to cover doctors' services. The two organizations shared expenses and jointly managed the state's Medicare and Medicaid programs.

The 1970s and early 1980s were difficult as Indiana's economy stagnated and health insurance competition increased. In 1982 the joint operation restructured adding new management and service policies to improve its performance.

Following the 1982 merger of the national Blue Cross and Blue Shield organizations the Indiana Blues merged in 1985 as Associated Insurance Companies. The next year the company moved outside Indiana began diversifying to help insulate itself from such industry changes as the shift to managed care and renamed itself Associated Group to reflect a broader focus.

By 1990 Associated Group had more than 25 operating units with nationwide offerings including health insurance HMO services life insurance insurance brokerage financial services and software and services for the insurance industry.

The group grew throughout the mid-1990s buying health insurer Southeastern Mutual Insurance (including Kentucky Blue Cross and Blue Shield) in 1992 diversified insurer Federal Kemper (a Kemper Corporation subsidiary) in 1993 and Seattle-based property/casualty brokerage Pettit-Morry in 1994. That year it entered the health care delivery market with the creation of American Health Network.

In 1995 the company merged with Ohio Blues licensee Community Mutual and took the Anthem name. Merger-related charges caused a loss that year.

Anthem bounced back the next year thanks to cost-cutting and customers switching to its more profitable managed care plans. Anthem divested its individual life insurance and annuity business and its Anthem Financial subsidiaries. Its 1996 deal to buy Blue Cross and Blue Shield of New Jersey fell apart in 1997 because of New Jersey Blue's charitable status. Anthem did manage to buy Blue Cross and Blue Shield of Connecticut that year.

Anthem in 1997 sold four property/casualty insurance subsidiaries to Vesta Insurance Group. It bought the remainder of its Acordia property/casualty unit (workers' compensation) then sold Acordia's brokerage operations. That year Anthem was involved in court battles regarding the Blue mergers in Kentucky as well as in Connecticut where litigants feared a rise in their premiums. Expenses related to merging Blues organizations contributed to a loss that year.

Anthem shed the rest of its noncore operations in 1998 selling subsidiary Anthem Health and Life Insurance Company to Canadian insurer Great-West Life Assurance. Its proposed purchase of Blue Cross and Blue Shield of Maine (which it acquired in 2000) and merger with the Blues in Rhode Island were met with outcries similar to those that dogged earlier pairings.

Larry Glasscock was appointed president and CEO of the company in 1999. Under Glasscock's leadership Anthem aggressively expanded through mergers and acquisitions. It bought Blues plans in Colorado Nevada and New Hampshire in 1999 and finalized the acquisition of Maine's Blue plan in 2000.

In 2001 it became a publicly traded company and sold its military insurance business to Humana. In the next couple of years it snapped up Virginia-based Trigon Healthcare and a Wisconsin Blue plan.

And in 2004 Anthem made its biggest leap yet deciding to merge with WellPoint Health Networks in a deal that would make it the nation's largest health insurer. After the merger — which added Blue plans in California Georgia Missouri and Wisconsin — Anthem changed its name to WellPoint.

EXECUTIVES

Executive Vice President Clinical Health Policy and Chief Medical Officer, Samuel Nussbaum

EVP and Chief Administrative Officer, Gloria M. McCarthy, age 64, $699,999 total compensation

President CEO and Director, Gail K. Boudreaux

EVP and CFO, John E. Gallina, age 57, $623,918 total compensation

EVP and President Government Business, Peter D. Haytaian, age 47, $740,371 total compensation

EVP and General Counsel, Thomas C. Zielinski, age 66

President Commercial Plan, Brian T. Griffin, age 58, $740,368 total compensation

EVP and Chief Clinical Officer, Craig E. Samitt, age 52

President Medicare East Region, Tomas Orozco

President Life and Disability, Greg Poulakos

President Specialty, Nicholas L. Brecker

Senior Vice President; President and Chief Executive Officer Anthem National Accounts, John Langenus

Vice President Information Technology, Bryan Bearden

Executive Vice President Chief Human Resources Officer, Jose Tomas

Assistant Vice President Information Technology Project Management Office, Sheri Coyner

Regional Vice President of Internal Audit, Robin Rosenblum

Regional Vice President and Medical Director, Tony Linares

Vice President, Renee Hunter

Regional Vice President, Wallace Adamson

Assistant Vice President Customer Relations Department, Pamela Martin

Regional Vice President Group Pricing, Keith Passwater

Vice President of Customer Support, John M Murphy

Staff Vice President Investment Programs, Vince Scher

Executive Vice President and President and Chief Executive Officer Commercial and Specialty Busines, Ken Goulet

Vice President, Stephen Schlegel

Vice President Marketing, James Jackson

Medical Director Senior Markets, Joseph Fox

Staff Vice President Business Continuation, Steve Labrique

Vice President Enterprise Execution, Saurabh Tandon

Vice President and Chief Operating Officer Pharmacy Services, Deepti Jain

Regional Vice President Indiana Group Underwriting, Matt Winders

Vice President and Chief Security Officer, Greg Wurm

Chairman, Joseph R. Swedish, age 65

Auditors: Ernst & Young LLP

LOCATIONS

HQ: Anthem Inc
120 Monument Circle, Indianapolis, IN 46204-4903
Phone: 317 488-6000
Web: www.antheminc.com

PRODUCTS/OPERATIONS

2016 Premiums

	% of total
Commercial & specialty business	46
Government business	53
Other	1
Total	**100**

2016 Sales

	% of total
Premiums	93
Administrative fee	6
Other revenue	-
Net investment income	1
Net realized gains on investments	-
Other	-
Total	**100**

Selected Operations

Blue-licensed subsidiaries
 Anthem Blue Cross (California)
 Anthem Blue Cross and Blue Shield (Colorado
 Connecticut Kentucky Indiana Maine Missouri Nevada
 New Hampshire Ohio Virginia Wisconsin)
 Blue Cross Blue Shield of Georgia
 Empire Blue Cross Blue Shield (New York)
Non-Blue Cross Subsidiaries and Affiliates
 AIM Specialty Health (benefits management)
 American Imaging Management (Diagnostic imaging)
 Anthem Life Insurance (life and accident)
 Anthem Workers' Compensation
 CareMore (Medicare Advantage and special needs plans)

DeCare Dental (Dental benefit management)
HealthCore (Clinical research)
HealthLink (Administrative services)
Golden West Dental & Vision (Dental/vision California)
Meridian Resource Company (Cost containment)
National Government Services (Administration of government contracts)
Resolution Health (Cost containment)
TrustSolutions (Fraud prevention)
UniCare (Health care plans)

COMPETITORS

Aetna
Assurant
CIGNA
ConnectiCare
Coventry Health Care
Delta Dental Plans
HCSC
Harvard Pilgrim
Health Net
Humana
Kaiser Foundation Health Plan
Medical Mutual
MetLife
Molina Healthcare
Southern California Permanente Medical Group
UnitedHealth Group
WellCare Health Plans

HISTORICAL FINANCIALS

Company Type: Public

Income Statement

FYE: December 31

	REVENUE ($ mil.)	NET INCOME ($ mil.)	NET PROFIT MARGIN	EMPLOYEES
12/16	84,863	2,469	2.9%	53,000
12/15	79,156	2,560	3.2%	53,000
12/14	73,874	2,569	3.5%	51,500
12/13	71,023	2,489	3.5%	48,200
12/12	61,711	2,655	4.3%	43,500
Annual Growth	**8.3%**	**(1.8%)**	**—**	**5.1%**

2016 Year-End Financials

Debt ratio: 24.16%
Return on equity: 10.23%
Cash ($ mil.): 4,075
Current ratio: 1.61
Long-term debt ($ mil.): 14,358
No. of shares (mil.): 263
Dividends
 Yield: 0.0%
 Payout: 28.2%
Market value ($ mil.): 37,919

	STOCK PRICE ($) FY Close	P/E High/Low		PER SHARE ($) Earnings	Dividends	Book Value
12/16	143.77	16	12	9.21	2.60	95.17
12/15	139.44	18	13	9.38	2.50	88.21
12/14	125.67	14	9	8.99	1.75	90.45
12/13	92.39	11	7	8.20	1.50	84.44
12/12	60.92	9	6	8.18	1.15	78.11
Annual Growth	**23.9%**	**—**	**—**	**3.0%**	**22.6%**	**5.1%**

Apache Corp

Apache Corporation an oil and gas exploration and production company has onshore and offshore operations in major oil patches around the world including in the US Egypt and the UK's North Sea oil fields. In the US it is active in the Gulf of Mexico the Gulf Coast of Texas and Louisiana the Permian Basin in West Texas the Anadarko Basin in Oklahoma. The company boasts worldwide estimated proved reserves of 1.3 billion barrels of oil equivalent.

HISTORY

Originally Raymond Plank wanted to start a magazine. Then it was an accounting and tax-assistance service. Plank and his co-founding partner Truman Anderson had no experience in any of these occupations but their accounting business succeeded. In the early 1950s Plank and Anderson branched out again founding APA a partnership to invest in new ventures including oil and gas exploration. The partnership founded Apache Oil in Minnesota in 1954. Investors put up the money and Apache managed the drilling spreading the risk over several projects.

As problems with government regulations in the oil industry mounted during the 1960s Apache diversified into real estate. The real estate operations were pivotal in driving a wedge between Plank and Anderson. In 1963 Anderson called a board meeting to ask the directors to fire Plank. Instead Anderson resigned and Plank took over.

Apache's holdings soon encompassed 24 firms including engineering electronics farming and water-supply subsidiaries. Understanding that its fortunes were tied to varying oil and gas prices the company reassessed its diversified structure in the 1970s. When the energy crisis rocketed oil prices skyward Apache sold its non-energy operations which would have been hurt by the price increases.

Apache formed Apache Petroleum in 1981 as an investment vehicle to take advantage of tax laws favoring limited partnerships. Initially the strategy was a success but it fell victim in the mid-1980s to a one-two punch: Oil prices sank like a rock and Congress put an end to the tax advantage. After suffering its first loss in 1986 Apache reorganized into a conventional exploration and production company.

Still under Plank's leadership the company began steadily buying oil and gas properties and companies in 1991. That year it purchased oil and gas sites with more than 100 million barrels of reserves from Amoco and put the wells back into production. By buying Hadson Energy Resources which operated fields in western Australia Apache gained entry into the relatively unexplored region in 1993.

In 1995 Apache merged with Calgary Canada-based DEKALB Energy (later renamed DEK Energy) and continued picking up properties. It bought $600 million worth of US reserves from Texaco (acquired by Chevron in 2001) that year. In 1996 it expanded its Chinese operations and bought Phoenix Resource Companies which operated solely in Egypt. A 1998 agreement with Texaco expanded its Chinese acreage thirtyfold. Apache also bought oil and gas properties and production facilities in waters off western Australia from a Mobil unit.

Apache joined with FX Energy and Polish Oil & Gas in 1998 to begin exploratory drilling in Poland. It also worked with XCL and China National Oil & Gas Exploration & Development in Bohai Bay though the project was slowed by a dispute between Apache and XCL over costs. In 1999 Apache bought Gulf of Mexico assets from a unit of Royal Dutch Shell and acquired oil and gas properties in western Canada from Shell Canada. That year Apache sold its Ivory Coast oil and gas holdings for $46 million.

Still shopping however Apache agreed in 2000 to buy assets in western Canada and Argentina with proved reserves of more than 700 billion cu. ft. of natural gas equivalent from New Zealand's Fletcher Challenge Energy. To help pay for the $600 million acquisition which closed in 2001 Apache sold $100 million in stock to Shell which acquired other Fletcher Challenge Energy assets. Apache bought the Canadian assets of Phillips Petroleum (later ConocoPhillips) for $490 million in

2000 and acquired the Egyptian assets of Repsol YPF for $410 million in 2001.

Late in 2002 in a move aimed at boosting its natural gas production by more than 10% Apache acquired 234000 net acres of land in southern Louisiana for $260 million. That year the company also announced three oil discoveries in the Carnarvon Basin offshore Western Australia.

Apache acquired UK and US oil and gas assets in 2003 from BP for $1.3 billion. The main prize was the Forties field one of the North Sea's oldest discoveries (dating back to the early 1970s) and its largest.

In 2004 it acquired more than two dozen mature US and Canadian fields from Exxon Mobil for $347 million and Gulf of Mexico properties from Anadarko Petroleum for $525 million. In 2005 Hurricane Katrina destroyed eight of its 241 Gulf rigs.

In 2009 Apache founder Raymond Plank retired as chairman of the company. He had been its chief executive from Apache's founding in 1954 until his retirement in 2002 when he remained as chairman. CEO Steven Farris took up the additional title of chairman when Plank stepped down completely.

The company bounced back from a sup-par 2009 when the global recession low commodities prices and a slump in demand suppressed its revenues.

In 2010 it bought Gulf of Mexico shelf assets from Devon Energy (which is shedding assets to raise cash) for $1 billion. The acquisition added some 41 million barrels of proved reserves and some 477200 acres to Apache's asset base.

It also acquired Mariner Energy for $2.7 billion (including Mariner Energy's debt of $1.6 billion) giving the company an entry into the deepwater Gulf of Mexico. Mariner's deepwater portfolio includes 125 blocks seven discoveries under development and more than 50 prospects. The deal is a natural extension of Apache's commitment to develop the Gulf of Mexico as a primary area of production and anticipates a rebounding economy and an increasing demand for oil.

With BP looking to raise cash to defray the cost of its rig disaster in the Gulf of Mexico in 2010 Apache took the opportunity to buy BP assets in Canada Egypt and the US (Permian Basin) for about $7 billion. The deal boosted Apache's estimated proved reserves by 385 million barrels of oil equivalent.

In Canada the company moved in 2010 to expand its supply base buying 51% of a proposed liquefied natural gas (LNG) export terminal in British Columbia operated by Kitimat LNG Inc.

The company grew its North Sea assets in 2012 buying Exxon Mobil's Beryl Field and related properties for about $1.75 billion.

Growing its unconventional assets in the US that year the company acquired Cordillera Energy Partners for $2.85 billion. The privately held company owned 254000 net acres of tight sand plays in Oklahoma and Texas. In 2012 Apache also bought 49% of Burrup Holdings an ammonia fertilizer plant in Western Australia for $439 million. The deal with one of the world's largest ammonia plants secures a long-term market for Apache's natural gas production in the region.

In 2012 Apache and Chevron agreed to build and operate the Kitimat LNG project and develop natural gas resources at the Liard and Horn River basins in British Columbia Canada. Chevron Canada will assume operatorship of the LNG plant and related pipeline.

On the exploration front in 2013 the company announced three new discovery wells in Egypt's Western Desert. Apache's discoveries made in three separate basins highlight the company's diverse potential for new oil and gas developments across its concessions. This exploration success extended Apache's production base to the northeast at the North Ras Qattara Concession and to the southwest in the Siwa Concession.

EXECUTIVES

Executive Vice President and Chief Operating Officer International, Thomas Voytovich
Senior Vice President Treasury and Administration, Matthew W Dundrea
Senior Vice President Global Communications and Corporate Affairs, Robert J Dye
Vice President Operations, Jon Sauer
Vice President, Lisa Stewart
EVP and General Counsel, P. Anthony Lannie, age 62, $675,000 total compensation
Senior Region Vice President Egypt Mid-Continent Gulf Coast Gulf of Mexico and International New Ventures, James L. (Jim) House, age 55, $600,000 total compensation
President and CEO, John J. Christmann, age 50, $1,100,000 total compensation
EVP Corporate Reservoir Engineering, W. Kregg Olson, age 63, $625,000 total compensation
Region VP North Sea Region and Managing Director Apache North Sea, Jon Graham, age 63
Senior Region VP Permian Region, Faron J. Thibodeaux, age 57
Senior Region VP North Sea and Canada, Grady L. Ables, age 56
Senior Region Vice President Delaware Basin Region, Steven J. Keenan, age 61
SVP North America Land Government Affairs and Real Estate, Timothy R. Custer, age 56
EVP and CFO, Stephen J. Riney, age 57, $675,000 total compensation
EVP Operations Support, Timothy J. Sullivan, age 61, $625,000 total compensation
Region Vice President Egypt Region and General Manager Apache Egypt, David Chi, age 43
SVP Midstream and Marketing, Brian W. Freed
Vice President, Sarah B Teslik
Vice President Information Technology, Phillip Vo
Vice President, Jeffrey Bender
Vice President Cao Contrl, Rebecca Hoyt
Executive Vice President and General Counsel, Anthony P Lannie
Vice President and Treasurer, Jim Kimble
VP Operations, Noe Casas
Vice President Engineering Technical Services, Lucian Wray
Executive Vice President, P Lannie
Vice President, T Sullivan
Executive Vice President Exploration And Production Technology, Michaels Bahorich
EXECUTIVE VICE PRESIDENT, Jon A Jeppesen
Chairman, John E. Lowe, age 59
Secretary to the Chief Financial Officer, Sandra Blundell
Board Member, John Kocur
Auditors: Ernst & Young LLP

LOCATIONS

HQ: Apache Corp
One Post Oak Central, 2000 Post Oak Boulevard, Suite 100, Houston, TX 77056-4400
Phone: 713 296-6000
Web: www.apachecorp.com

2016 sales

	% of total
US	37
Egypt	38
UK (North Sea)	19
Canada	6
Total	**100**

PRODUCTS/OPERATIONS

2016 sales

	% of total
Oil	78
Gas	18
Natural gas liquids	4
Other	
Total	**100**

COMPETITORS

Abraxas Petroleum	Hess Corporation
Adams Resources	Jones Energy
Anadarko Petroleum	Pioneer Natural
BP	Resources
Chesapeake Energy	Qatargas
Chevron	Range Resources
Devon Energy	Royal Dutch Shell
EOG	Santos Ltd
Exxon Mobil	XTO Energy
Helmerich & Payne	

HISTORICAL FINANCIALS

Company Type: Public

Income Statement

FYE: December 31

	REVENUE ($ mil.)	NET INCOME ($ mil.)	NET PROFIT MARGIN	EMPLOYEES
12/16	5,354	(1,405)	—	3,727
12/15	6,366	(23,119)	—	3,860
12/14	13,851	(5,403)	—	4,950
12/13	16,054	2,232	13.9%	5,342
12/12	17,078	2,001	11.7%	5,976
Annual Growth	**(25.2%)**	—	—	**(11.1%)**

2016 Year-End Financials

Debt ratio: 37.94%
Return on equity: (-31.83%)
Cash ($ mil.): 1,377
Current ratio: 1.76
Long-term debt ($ mil.): 8,544
No. of shares (mil.): 379
Dividends
Yield: 0.0%
Payout: —
Market value ($ mil.): 24,083

	STOCK PRICE ($) FY Close	P/E High/Low		PER SHARE ($) Earnings	Dividends	Book Value
12/16	63.47	—	—	(3.71)	1.00	16.44
12/15	44.47	—	—	(61.20)	1.00	6.79
12/14	62.67	—	—	(14.06)	0.95	68.89
12/13	85.94	17	12	5.50	0.77	84.38
12/12	78.50	23	15	4.92	0.66	80.00
Annual Growth	**(5.2%)**			—	**10.9%**	**(32.7%)**

APPLE HOSPITALITY REIT, INC.

LOCATIONS

HQ: APPLE HOSPITALITY REIT, INC.
333 WASHINGTON AVE, SAINT LOUIS, MO 631022116
Phone: 804 344-8121
Web: WWW.APPLEREIT.COM

HISTORICAL FINANCIALS

Company Type: Private

Income Statement

FYE: December 31

	ASSETS ($ mil.)	NET INCOME ($ mil.)	INCOME AS % OF ASSETS	EMPLOYEES
12/14	3,779	6	0.2%	102
12/13	1,491	115	7.7%	—
12/12	1,526	75	4.9%	—
12/11	1,700	69	4.1%	—
Annual Growth	**30.5%**	**(54.0%)**	—	—

Apple Inc

Ask Siri to name the most successful company in the world and it might respond: Apple. And it's not just out of familial pride. In terms of profit revenue market capitalization and consumer cachet it certainly ranks right up there. The iPhone in its 10th year and eighth and ninth generations has been the company's golden goose generating tens of billions in revenue and profit. In addition to the iPhone other familiar Apple products and services include Mac computers and iPad tablets as well as iTunes the App store and Apple Music. Primarily a consumer-oriented company Apple has inked several alliances with Accenture General Electric and IBM to deepen its penetration of the enterprise market. About 60% of revenue comes from outside the Americas.

HISTORY

College dropouts Steve Jobs (1955-2011) and Steve Wozniak founded Apple in 1976 in California's Santa Clara Valley. After Jobs' first sales call brought an order for 50 units the duo built the Apple I in his garage and sold it without a monitor keyboard or casing. Demand convinced Jobs there was a distinct market for small computers and the company's name (a reference to Jobs' stint on an Oregon farm) and the computer's user-friendly look and feel set it apart from others.

By 1977 Wozniak added a keyboard color monitor and eight peripheral device slots (which gave the machine considerable versatility and inspired numerous third-party add-on devices and software). Sales jumped from $7.8 million in 1978 to $117 million in 1980 the year Apple went public. In 1983 Wozniak left the firm and Jobs hired PepsiCo's John Sculley as president. Apple rebounded from failed product introductions that year by unveiling the Macintosh in 1984. After tumultuous struggles with Sculley Jobs left in 1985 and founded NeXT a designer of applications for developing software. That year Sculley ignored Microsoft founder Bill Gates' appeal for Apple to license its products and make the Microsoft platform an industry standard.

Apple blazed the desktop publishing trail in 1986 with its Mac Plus and LaserWriter printers. The following year it formed the software firm that later became Claris (and ultimately FileMaker). The late 1980s brought new competition from Microsoft whose Windows operating system (OS) featured a graphical interface akin to Apple's. Apple sued but lost its claim to copyright protection in 1992.

In 1993 Apple unveiled the Newton handheld computer but sales were slow. Earnings fell drastically so the company trimmed its workforce. (Sculley was among the departed.) In 1994 Apple cried "uncle" and began licensing clones of its OS hoping a flurry of cheaper Mac-alikes would encourage software developers. By 1996 struggling Apple realized Mac clones were stealing sales. That year it hired Gilbert Amelio formerly of National Semiconductor as CEO.

The company bought NeXT in 1997 but sales kept dropping and it subsequently cut about 30% of its workforce canceled projects and trimmed research costs. Meanwhile Apple's board ousted Amelio and Jobs took the position back on an interim basis. The CEO forged a surprising alliance with Microsoft which included releasing a Mac version of Microsoft's popular office software. To protect market share Jobs also stripped the cloning license from chief imitator Power Computing and put it out of business.

In 1998 Apple jumped back into the race with its colorful cocktail of iMacs and its first server software the Mac OS X. That year the company also revamped its profitable Claris unit (by cutting 300 employees shifting most operations to Apple and renaming it FileMaker) and stopped making its Newton handheld device and printer products.

Apple in 1999 opened a new chapter in portable computing with the introduction of its iBook laptop and (taking a cue from Dell) began selling built-to-order systems online. In 2000 after two and a half years as the semipermanent executive in charge Jobs took the "interim" out of his title and revamped the company's Web site around a suite of consumer Internet services. Jobs unveiled overhauled desktop lines later that year including an eight-inch cube-shaped G4. The company ended 2000 on a sour note as an industrywide slowdown and poor response to the G4 cube resulted in Apple's first unprofitable quarter in years.

Apple opened 2001 with another round of product upgrades including faster processors components such as CD and DVD burners and an ultra-slim version of its PowerBook called Titanium. The company also made a move to reclaim some of its slipping share in the education market purchasing software maker PowerSchool. Soon Apple confirmed a long-rumored plan to open a chain of retail stores in the US. The company then acquired DVD authoring software maker Spruce Technologies. In line with its strategy to market Macs as "digital hubs" for devices such as cameras and other peripherals Apple closed the year with the introduction of a digital music player called the iPod.

In 2002 Apple introduced a new look for its iMac line; featuring a half-dome base and a flat-panel display supported by a pivoting arm the redesign was the first departure from the original (and at the time radical) all-in-one design since iMac's debut in 1998. Looking to reclaim market share in the education sector Apple then introduced the eMac — a computer similar to the iMac to be sold only to students and educators (Apple later introduced a retail version). It continued its product push that year with the announcement that it would begin offering a rack-mount server called Xserve. In 2004 Apple debuted a streamlined iMac design powered by its G5 processor.

Apple announced it would begin incorporating Intel processors into its PC lines in 2005 ending more than a decade of using PowerPC microprocessors; the transition was completed the following year. Also that year Apple Motorola and Cingular Wireless (now AT&T Mobility) announced the debut of a mobile phone with iTunes functionality. Apple also unveiled the iPod nano an updated (and even smaller) version of its miniature iPod model as well as an iPod capable of playing video. In 2006 Apple reached a settlement in a dispute with Creative Technology over technology used in digital music players; Apple agreed to pay the company $100 million in exchange for a license to use Creative's patent related to navigation and organization.

The company also launched an online movie service in 2006 and previewed a device called iTV for watching downloaded content on televisions. (Apple announced availability of its television device redubbed Apple TV early the following year.)

Apple unveiled a mobile phone offering called the iPhone in 2007. To reflect the growing breadth of its product portfolio the company announced it would change its name from Apple Computer to simply Apple. The company kicked off 2008 with the release of an updated Apple TV device in conjunction with an iTunes movie rental service.

Looking toward the continued development of its mobile devices Apple purchased P.A. Semi a developer of low-power processors in 2008. In another move intended to bring more of its chip design in-house Apple bought Intrinsity a provider of chip design software in 2010.

After beginning 2011 with a leave of absence and then stepping down as CEO Steve Jobs died on October 5 2011. COO Tim Cook had been named CEO after Jobs' resignation though Jobs retained the chairman title until his death.

EXECUTIVES

CEO, Timothy D. (Tim) Cook, age 56, $2,000,000 total compensation

SVP Worldwide Marketing, Philip W. Schiller, age 57, $494,942 total compensation

SVP Software Engineering, Craig Federighi, age 48

SVP General Counsel and Secretary, D. Bruce Sewell, age 59, $1,000,000 total compensation

SVP Retail and Online Stores, Angela Ahrendts, age 56, $1,000,000 total compensation

VP Applications, Eduardo H. (Eddy) Cue, age 53, $1,000,000 total compensation

Chief Design Officer, Jonathan Ive

SVP and CFO, Luca Maestri, age 54, $1,000,000 total compensation

COO, Jeffrey E. (Jeff) Williams, age 53, $947,596 total compensation

SVP Hardware Engineering, Daniel (Dan) Riccio, age 55, $1,000,000 total compensation

SVP Hardware Technologies, Johny Srouji

VICE PRESIDENT TECHNOLOGY, KEVIN LYNCH

Vice President and Treasurer, Gary Wipfler

Vice President, Todd Teresi

Senior Vice President Corporate Communications, Deborah Wiley

VP IT, Juan Batista

Vice President Product Design, Dan Riccio

National Sales Manager, Todd Conneely

Senior Vice President, Dan Whisenhunt

Vice President Engineering, Lucy Chen

First Vice President Of Human Resources, Ann Bowers

Vice President Of Product Design, Doug Field

Vice President, Jasmine Mele

Vice President of Corporate Information Security, George Stathakopoulos

VP Operations, Deirdre O'Brien

Vice President Worldwide Talent and Human Resources, Denise Smith

VP OF MARKETING, BOB JONES

Vice President, Stefano Callera

Vice President of Marketing, Guerrino Luca

Vice President Customer Care, Gene Tyacke

VP, Barb Cook

Vice President, Marta Chudzinski

EXECUTIVE VICE PRESIDENT PARTNER, Dean Jackson

Vice President Sales Europe Middle East Africa, Michel Coulomb

Vice President Administrative Services, Tracy McHugh

Vice President Enterprise and Government, John Solomon

Vice President SCAD Hong Kong, Jenna McCusker

Vice President, Mike Fenger

Vice President VISI. Hardware Engineering, Bob Mansfield

Director of Nursing, Evelyn Colon

SVP, Thomas Wede

Vice President, Siobhan Murphy

Vice President CFO Apple Retail, Nicholas Severino

Vice President of Marketing, Peggy Ann

Chairman, Arthur D. (Art) Levinson, age 67

Board Member, Nancy Walker

Auditors: Ernst & Young LLP

LOCATIONS

HQ: Apple Inc
1 Infinite Loop, Cupertino, CA 95014
Phone: 408 996-1010   **Fax:** 408 974-2483
Web: www.apple.com

2017 Sales

	$ mil.	% of total
Americas	96,600	42
Europe	54,938	24
Asia/Pacific		
China	44,764	20
Japan	17,733	8
Rest of Asia Pacific	15,199	6
Total	**229,234**	**100**

PRODUCTS/OPERATIONS

2017 Sales

	% of total
iPhone	62
Services	14
Mac	11
iPad	8
Other products	5
Total	**100**

Selected Products

Hardware
  Desktop computers (iMac Mac mini Mac Pro)
  Displays (Cinema Thunderbolt)
  External hard drives (Airport Time Capsule)
  Keyboards
  Media devices (Apple TV)
  Mice (Magic Mouse)
  Mobile phones (iPhone)
  Portable computers (MacBook MacBook Air MacBook Pro)
  Portable digital music player (iPod touch)
  Tablet computers (iPad)
  Wearable technology (Apple Watch)
  Webcams (iSight)
  Wireless networking systems (AirPort)
Software
  MultimediaDVD Studio Pro FinalCut GarageBand iDVD iLife suite iMovie Photo iTunes Quicktime Soundtrack)
  Networking (Apple Remote Desktop AppleShare IP)
  Operating systems (macOS iOS watchOS tvOS)
  Personal productivity (AppleWorks FileMaker iWork Keynote Pages)
  Server (Mac OS X Server)
  Web browser (Safari)
Online Services
  Applications for iPad iPhone iPod touch (App Store)
  Applications for Mac (Mac App Store)
  Music Streaming (Apple Music)
  Cloud service (iCloud)
  E-books (iBooks)
  Electronic greeting cards (iCard)
  E-mail (Webmail)
  Online multimedia store (iTunes)
  Personal Web page creation (HomePage)
  Remote network storage (iDisk)
  Software (antivirus backup)
  Technical support (AppleCare)

COMPETITORS

AT&T	LG Electronics
Acer	Lenovo
Adobe Systems	MTV Networks
Alphabet Inc.	MediaNet Digital
Amazon.com	Microsoft
Best Buy	Motorola Mobility
BlackBerry	NEC
Bose	Netflix
CASIO COMPUTER	Nokia
Cisco Systems	Oracle
Comcast	Panasonic Corp
Creative Technology	PayPal
D-Link	Philips Electronics
Dell	RealNetworks
Ericsson	Red Hat
Facebook	Samsung Electronics
Fitbit	SanDisk
Fujitsu Technology Solutions	Seagate Technology
Garmin	Sharp Electronics
Google	Sony
HP	Sony Mobile
HTC Corporation	Target Corporation
IBM	Time Warner Cable
Intel	Toshiba
Iriver	Wal-Mart
Kyocera	Yahoo!
	eMusic.com

HISTORICAL FINANCIALS

Company Type: Public

Income Statement

FYE: September 30

	REVENUE ($ mil.)	NET INCOME ($ mil.)	NET PROFIT MARGIN	EMPLOYEES
09/17	229,234	48,351	21.1%	123,000
09/16	215,639	45,687	21.2%	116,000
09/15	233,715	53,394	22.8%	110,000
09/14	182,795	39,510	21.6%	97,000
09/13	170,910	37,037	21.7%	84,400
Annual Growth	**7.6%**	**6.9%**	**—**	**9.9%**

2017 Year-End Financials

Debt ratio: 30.82%—
Return on equity: 36.27%
Cash ($ mil.): 20,289
Current ratio: 1.28
Long-term debt ($ mil.): 97,207

Dividends
  Yield: 0.0%
  Payout: 26.0%
Market value ($ mil.): —

	STOCK PRICE ($) FY Close	P/E High/Low	PER SHARE ($) Earnings	Dividends	Book Value
09/17	154.12	18 11	9.21	2.40	26.15
09/16	112.71	15 11	8.31	2.18	24.03
09/15	114.71	14 10	9.22	1.98	21.39
09/14	100.75	100 14	6.45	1.81	19.02
09/13	482.75	117 68	5.68	1.63	19.63
Annual Growth	**(24.8%)**	**— —**	**12.9%**	**10.2%**	**7.4%**

Applied Materials, Inc.

Applied Materials makes the machines that make computer chips flat panel TVs and solar energy devices. The company's equipment vies for supremacy in many segments of the chip-making process including deposition (layering film on wafers) etching (removing portions of chip material to allow precise construction of circuits) and semiconductor metrology and inspection equipment. Its services business accounts for about a quarter of revenue. Applied's plan to acquire its rival Tokyo Electron the second biggest equipment maker died in 2015 due to antitrust concern from US regulators.

Operations

Applied operates in three segments: Semiconductor Systems Applied Global Services and Display.

Semiconductor Systems (65% of revenue) makes a wide range of manufacturing equipment used to fabricate integrated circuits.

Applied Global Services (25% of revenue) provides products that improve equipment and fab performance and productivity including spares upgrades services and factory automation software for semiconductor display and other products.

The Display segment (10% of revenue) engineers products for making liquid crystal displays (LCDs) organic light-emitting diodes (OLEDs) and other display technologies for TVs personal computers (PCs) tablets smart phones and other consumer-oriented devices as well as equipment for flexible substrates.

Geographic Reach

Applied has operations in the US Asia/Pacific and Europe. Customers in Taiwan accounts for about a quarter of revenue followed by China 21% South Korea 17% Japan 12% and the US 11%.

Sales and Marketing

Due to the highly technical nature of its products Applied's direct sales force does most of the company's marketing and selling worldwide. Leading customers for Applied's chip making equipment include Taiwan Semiconductor Manufacturing Company 16% of revenue and Samsung Electronics 13% of revenue and Intel and Micron 11% of revenue each.

Financial Performance

Applied posted significant increases in revenue net income and cash from operations in 2016 (ended October) from 2015. Revenue of $10.8 billion in 2016 eclipsed the company's previous high of $10.5 billion reached in 2011. While 2016's $1.7 billion of net income was 25% higher than the 2015 figure it didn't outpace the $1.9 billion hit in 2011.

In 2016 revenue from the semiconductor segment rose 12% on steady demand from manufacturers spurred by technology upgrades and capacity expansions. Foundry customers invested in new capacity to meet the demand for mobile chips while memory customers transitioned to 3D architectures. The global services revenue increased 6% from higher demand for spare parts and services. Display revenue jumped 28% as customers invested in mobile display manufacturing equipment. Sales to customers in China dropped 28% on slower investment in TV manufacturing equipment while sales to customers in Korea leaped more than 200% on purchases of mobile display manufacturing equipment.

The rise in net income came from higher revenue as well as even and reduced spending in research development and engineering sales and marketing and general and administration.

Cash flow from operations closed 2016 at about $2.5 billion compared to $1.2 billion in 2015 on increases in depreciation and amortization customers deposit and deferred revenue and decreases in inventories.

Strategy

Applied has asked where the semiconductor industry is going and aims its products at the destinations. And so far the company seems to have a pretty good map. It has developed equipment to address needs in logic 3D NAND patterning and advance displays. A look at two markets 3D NAND and display technology illustrates Applied's strategy.

The increasing market for mobile devices has driven the development and adoption of 3D NAND flash which is supplanting planar NAND. Applied's sales of equipment for making 3D NAND chips helped drive the 12% increase in fabrication equipment sales in 2016 (ended October). That includes sales to foundries such as Taiwan Semiconductor Manufacturing Corp. as chip firms continue to concentrate more on design and outsource production.

Display manufacturing is another focus for Applied. In 2016 China was second only to Taiwan in sales growth for the company. Sales of semiconductor and display equipment pushed China sales 23% higher in 2016. The company is producing the first generation of equipment for making bigger substrates for LCDs. The move toward larger screen TVs 60 inches and bigger drives the adoption of the new manufacturing technology. Applied estimates that its customers' capital spending on display technology will increase by about $2 billion in 2017.

To keep up with the chip industry's constant drive toward smaller circuits larger wafers and new technologies such as copper interconnects Applied relies heavily R&D efforts. The company spends more than 15% of sales on R&D each year.

Mergers and Acquisitions

Applied Materials and Tokyo Electron halted their proposed merger in April 2015 because they decided they couldn't clear antitrust concerns of regulators. The deal would have combined the two biggest companies in their industry but allowed them to cut costs and increase efficiencies. Now Applied will have to find other ways to deal with the rising costs of equipping a semiconductor fab with increasingly sophisticated instruments.

HISTORY

Applied Materials was founded in 1967 in Mountain View California as a maker of chemical vapor deposition systems for fabricating semiconductors. After years of rapid growth the company went public in 1972. Two years later it purchased wafer maker Galamar Industries.

In 1975 Applied Materials suffered a 45% drop in sales as the semiconductor industry (and the US economy) contracted. Financial and managerial problems plagued the company following the recession so in 1976 James Morgan a former division manager for conglomerate Textron was chosen to replace founder Michael McNeilly as CEO. Two years later Morgan also became chairman.

After selling Galamar (1977) and other non-core units and extending the company's line of credit Morgan announced a plan to move into Japan. The company's first joint venture Applied Materials Japan was set up in 1979.

Applied got into the ion implanter market in 1980 through its acquisition of the UK's Lintott Engineering.

EXECUTIVES

Vice President, William Mcclintock
SVP Engineering, Gino Addiego, age 57, $457,692 total compensation
Group VP; General Manager Transistor and Interconnect Group, Steve Ghanayem
SVP General Counsel and Secretary, Thomas F. Larkins, $489,231 total compensation
Group VP; General Manager Imaging and Process Control Group, Robert J. Perlmutter, age 60
SVP and CTO; President Applied Ventures, Omkaram (Om) Nalamasu, age 58, $468,846 total compensation
Group VP and CIO, Jay Kerley
SVP and CFO, Daniel (Dan) Durn, age 50
President and CEO, Gary E. Dickerson, age 59, $1,019,231 total compensation
SVP; General Manager New Markets and Service Group, Ali Salehpour, age 55, $560,577 total compensation
Group VP; General Manager Patterning and Packaging Group, Prabu G. Raja
Regional President, Russell Tham
Corporate Vice President Semi manufacturing and Co, Rick Gesing
Vice President Human Resources, Blake Wolfe
Vice President Of Engineering, John White
Vice President, Shelly Zeigler
Vice President, Robert Friess
Corporate Vice President and General Manager of Display Business Group, Brian Shieh
Vice President, Joe Nolan
Executive Vice President of Structured Finance, Sameer Deshpande
Vice President Marketing, Shayne Bennett
Vice President, Karin Basilio

Vice President and General Manager of Front End Products Division, Sundar Ramamurthy
Vice President and Executive Operations Lead, George Alajajian
Senior Vice President and Chief of Staff, Manfred Kerschbaum
Corporate Vice President, Kirk Hasserjian
Vice President, Mike Parcella
SVP Worldwide Operations and Supply Chain, Joseph G Flanagan
Vice President and General Manager Service and Spares Applied Global Services, Seehack Foo
Vice President, Brent Bloom
Vice president and General Manager, Mukund Srinivasan
Corporate Vice President, Hussein Fawaz
Chairman, Thomas J. (Tom) Iannotti, age 61
Assistant Treasurer, Randy Webb
Assistant Treasurer Customer, Brad Mccurrie
Assistant Treasurer, Avi Cohen-hillel
Auditors: KPMG LLP

LOCATIONS

HQ: Applied Materials, Inc.
3050 Bowers Avenue, P.O. Box 58039, Santa Clara, CA 95052-8039
Phone: 408 727-5555
Web: www.appliedmaterials.com

2016 Sales

	$ mil.	% of total
Asia/Pacific		
Taiwan	2,843	26
China	2,259	23
Korea	1,883	12
Japan	1,279	12
Southeast Asia	803	7
US	1,143	13
Europe	615	6
Total	**10,825**	**100**

PRODUCTS/OPERATIONS

2016 Sales

	$ mil.	% of total
Silicon Systems	6,873	64
Applied Global Services	2,589	24
Display	1,206	11
Corporate & Other	157	1
Total	**10,825**	**100**

Products and Technologies
Semiconductor
Display
Solar
Roll to Roll WEB Coating
Emerging Technologies and Products
Automation Software
Product Library

Selected Products

Chemical mechanical polishing/planarization systems (wafer polishing)
Deposition systems (deposit layers of conducting and insulating material on wafers)
Dielectric deposition (chemical vapor deposition or CVD)
Metal (CVD electroplating or physical vapor deposition)
Silicon and thermal deposition
Sputtering (physical vapor deposition) for solar cells
Thin-film silicon solar cells
Web coating for flexible solar cells
Etch systems (remove portions of a wafer surface for circuit construction)
Inspection systems (defect review for reticles — patterned plates which hold precise images of chip circuit patterns — and wafers)
Ion implant systems (implant ions into wafer surface to change conductive properties)
Manufacturing process optimization software
Metrology systems
CD-SEM (scanning electron microscope system)
Optical monitoring systems (for glass or web coating systems)
Rapid thermal processing systems (heat wafers to change electrical characteristics)

COMPETITORS

AIXTRON	Micronic Laser Systems
ASM International	Nanometrics
Axcelis Technologies	Nikon
EG Systems	Rennova Health
Ebara	Rudolph Technologies
FEI	SCREEN Holdings
GT Advanced Technologies	Spire Corp.
Hitachi	Sumitomo Heavy Industries
Hitachi Kokusai Electric	TEL FSI
Intevac	Tokyo Electron
KLA-Tencor	ULVAC
Lam Research	Veeco Instruments
Mattson Technology	Zygo

HISTORICAL FINANCIALS

Company Type: Public

Income Statement

FYE: October 29

	REVENUE ($ mil.)	NET INCOME ($ mil.)	NET PROFIT MARGIN	EMPLOYEES
10/17	14,537	3,434	23.6%	18,400
10/16	10,825	1,721	15.9%	16,700
10/15	9,659	1,377	14.3%	15,500
10/14	9,072	1,072	11.8%	14,950
10/13	7,509	256	3.4%	14,500
Annual Growth	**18.0%**	**91.4%**		**6.1%**

2017 Year-End Financials

Debt ratio: 27.31%
Return on equity: 41.57%
Cash ($ mil.): 5,010
Current ratio: 3.14
Long-term debt ($ mil.): 5,304
No. of shares (mil.): 1,060
Dividends
Yield: 0.0%
Payout: 12.6%
Market value ($ mil.): 60,091

	STOCK PRICE ($) FY Close	P/E High/Low		PER SHARE ($) Earnings	Dividends	Book Value
10/17	56.69	18	9	3.17	0.40	8.82
10/16	28.66	20	10	1.54	0.40	6.69
10/15	16.44	23	13	1.12	0.40	6.56
10/14	20.99	26	19	0.87	0.40	6.44
10/13	17.71	86	48	0.21	0.38	5.89
Annual Growth	**33.8%**	—	—	**97.1%**	**1.3%**	**10.6%**

Aramark

Keeping employees fed and clothed is one mark of this company. ARAMARK is the world's #3 contract foodservice provider (behind Compass Group and Sodexo) and the #2 uniform supplier (behind Cintas) in the US. It offers corporate dining services and operates concessions at many sports arenas and other entertainment venues while its ARAMARK Refreshment Services unit is a leading provider of vending and beverage services. The firm also provides facilities management services. Through ARAMARK Uniform and Career Apparel the company supplies uniforms for healthcare public safety and technology workers. Founded in 1959 ARAMARK became a public company again in 2013.

HISTORY

Davre Davidson began his career in foodservice by selling peanuts from the backseat of his car in the 1930s. He landed his first vending contract with Douglas Aircraft (later McDonnell Douglas now part of Boeing) in 1935. Through that relationship Davidson met William Fishman of Chicago who had vending operations in the Midwest. Davidson and Fishman merged their companies in 1959 to form Automatic Retailers of America (ARA). Davidson became chairman and CEO of the new company; Fishman served as president.

Focusing on candy beverage and cigarette machines ARA became the leading vending machine company in the US by 1961 with operations in 38 states. Despite slimmer profit margins ARA moved into food vending in the early 1960s. It acquired 150 foodservice businesses between 1959 and 1963 quickly becoming a leader in the operation of cafeterias at colleges hospitals and work sites. The company (which changed its name to ARA Services in 1966) grew so rapidly that the FTC stepped in; ARA agreed to restrict future food vending acquisitions.

ARA provided foodservices at the 1968 Summer Olympics in Mexico City beginning a long-term relationship with the amateur sports event. The company also diversified into publication distribution that year and in 1970 it expanded into janitorial and maintenance services. A foray into residential care for the elderly began in 1973 (and ended in 1993 with the sale of the subsidiary). ARA also entered into emergency room staffing services (sold 1997). The company expanded into child care (National Child Care Centers) in 1980.

CFO Joseph Neubauer became CEO in 1983 and was named chairman in 1984. To avoid a hostile takeover shortly thereafter he led a $1.2 billion leveraged buyout. After the buyout ARA began refining its core operations. It acquired Szabo (correctional foodservices) in 1986 Children's World Learning Centers in 1987 and Coordinated Health Services (medical billing services) in 1993.

ARA changed its name to ARAMARK in 1994 as part of an effort to raise its profile with its ultimate customers the public. The company's concession operations suffered from long work stoppages in baseball (1994) and hockey (1995). ARAMARK acquired Galls (North America's #1 supplier of public safety equipment) in 1996 and in 1997 announced plans to become 100% employee-owned.

The following year ARAMARK entered into a joint venture with privately held Anderson News Company exchanging its magazine distribution operations for a minority stake in the new business. In 2000 the company was on hand to supply foodservices to the Olympic Games in Sydney.

With the new millennium the company was focused on expansion buying the food and beverage concessions business of conglomerate Ogden Corp. for $236 million. The company penned a 10-year deal with Boeing in 2000 to supply foodservices to about 100 locations one of the biggest foodservice contracts ever. It also bought the Correctional Foodservice Management division of G4S Secure Solutions (USA) then named The Wackenhut Corporation.

ARAMARK continued its expansion with the purchase of ServiceMaster's management services division in 2001 for about $800 million — opening doors in nonfood management groundskeeping and custodial services. However the company lost a bid to cater the 2002 Olympic Games in Salt Lake City to rival Compass Group. In late 2001 ARAMARK went public.

The company bought Hilton's 14 Harrison Conference Centers and university lodgings for about $49 million in 2002. Also it paid $100 million for Premier Inc.'s Clinical Technology Services which maintains and repairs clinical equipment in about 170 hospitals and healthcare facilities in the US. ARAMARK also completed its acquisition of Fine Host Corporation which added approximately 900 client locations for about $100 million.

In 2003 ARAMARK exited the child care business when it sold its Educational Resources unit (operator of Children's World Learning Centers) to Michael Milken's Knowledge Learning Corporation for $225 million. ARAMARK later bought Restauraci n Colectiva and Rescot a foodservice company based in Zaragoza Spain. Longtime executive Bill Leonard was named president and CEO that year with Neubauer taking on the title of executive chairman.

Expanding its Canadian presence in cleanroom services in 2004 ARAMARK acquired Toronto-based Cleanroom Garments a supplier of apparel and accessories for Canadian manufacturers in pharmaceutical aerospace and automotive industries. The company's Healthcare Management Services group meanwhile signed a 10-year agreement with Evanston Northwestern Healthcare to provide managed services to three Chicago-area hospitals. That year ARAMARK made its first foray into China by acquiring a 90% stake in Bright China Service Industries a facilities services firm. After a brief reign Leonard resigned that year and Neubauer returned to being CEO of the company.

In 2007 Neubauer with the backing of such investment firms as CCMP Capital Thomas H. Lee Partners and Warburg Pincus took ARAMARK private for $8.3 billion including the assumption of $2 billion in debt.

The company provided catering and other foodservices for the 2008 Olympic Games in Beijing. That year ARAMARK also acquired The Patman Group expanding its reach into India.

In 2011 ARAMARK sold its ownership stake in SeamlessWeb to Spectrum Equity Investors for $50 million. SeamlessWeb provides online and mobile food ordering.

EXECUTIVES

Chairman President and CEO, Eric J. Foss, age 59, $1,622,625 total compensation
EVP Human Resources, Lynn B. McKee, age 61, $666,475 total compensation
SVP Controller and Chief Accounting Officer, Joseph M. (Joe) Munnelly, age 53, $384,503 total compensation
COO Uniform and Refreshment Services, Brad C. Drummond
COO International, Brent J. Franks
EVP and CFO, Stephen P. (Steve) Bramlage, age 46, $300,000 total compensation
COO Europe, Harrald F. Kroeker, age 59
COO Healthcare Education and Facilities, Victor L. Crawford, age 56
COO Sports Leisure Corrections and Business Dining, Marc Bruno
EVP General Counsel and Secretary, Stephen R. (Steve) Reynolds, age 59, $517,650 total compensation
COO Emerging Markets, Marty Welch
Senior Vice President Finance, Christina Morrison
Vice President Strategic Partnerships, Brian Drew
Vice President Finance, Barbara Ratliff
Associate Vice President of Marketing, Karen Parker
Vice President Of Operations, Chuck Reynolds
Vice President Strategic Partnerships, Ed Snowden
Vice President Operations, Thomas Shupe
Associate Vice President, Alan Leo
Associate Vice President, Terrance Ransfer
Associate Vice President Contact Center Global Business Services, Elizabeth Guthrie
Vice President Global Operatio, Autumn Bayles
Regional Vice President, Tracy Tomkiewicz
Vice President of Marketing, Mark S Mendes
Vice President Compliance, Julianne Duss
Associate Vice President Marketing Communications and Digital Strategy, Tom Carusona

Vice President compliance, Tara Hennessy
Region Vice President, Jim Hinds
Assistant Vice President, Ray Verlinghieri
Regional Vice President, Peter J Evola
VICE PRESIDENT BUSINESS DEVELOPMENT, Tim Grant
Vice President Of Sales, Betsy Kline
Vice President Supply Chain Fleet Manage, Art Wake
Vice President Of Global Business Servic, Brian Gabbard
Vice President finance, Sandra Demas
Operations Vice President, Dave Parsonage
Vice President Human Resources, Amna Shoro
Vice President Global Security, Edward Hanko
Regional Vice President, Winston Wright
Associate Vice President Marketing, Stephanie Provost
National Account Manager, David Romero
Assistant Vice President and Assistant General Counsel, Christopher D Stearns
Vice President Of Operations, Claude Bisang
Vice President, Steve Duffy
Senior Vice President, John Hanner
Assistant Vice President Financial Controls, Patrick Morgan
National Account Manager, Stephen J Dolph
Associate Vice President Commodities Global Supply Chain and Procurement, Mauricio Sirgo
Associate Vice President Channel Marketing (Healthcare), Vidya Plainfield
Associate Vice President Pricing, Vipin Kumar
Regional Vice President, Stewart McKinney
Regional Vice President, Victoria Pasquale
Associate Vice President Consumer Insights, Jill Marchick
Auditors: KPMG LLP

LOCATIONS

HQ: Aramark
Aramark Tower, 1101 Market Street, Philadelphia, PA 19107
Phone: 215 238-3000
Web: www.aramark.com

PRODUCTS/OPERATIONS

Brands
WearGuard
Crest
Aramark
Services
Food hospitality and facilities
Rental sale and maintenance of uniform apparel and other items

Selected Operations
Food and support services
  ARAMARK Colleges and Universities
  ARAMARK Conference Centers
  ARAMARK Convention Centers
  ARAMARK Correctional Services
  ARAMARK Cultural Attractions
  ARAMARK Facility Services
  ARAMARK Food Services
  ARAMARK Healthcare
  ARAMARK Higher Education
  ARAMARK Innovative Dining Solutions
  ARAMARK Parks and Resorts
  ARAMARK Refreshment Services (vending services)
  ARAMARK Senior Living
  ARAMARK Sports and Entertainment
Uniform and career apparel
  ARAMARK Cleanroom Services
  ARAMARK Uniform & Career Apparel
  Galls (tactical equipment and apparel)

COMPETITORS

ABM Industries	G&K Services
Autogrill	Healthcare Services
Centerplate	ISS A/S
Cintas	SSP

Compass Group   Serco
Delaware North   Sodexo
Elior   UniFirst

HISTORICAL FINANCIALS

Company Type: Public

Income Statement

FYE: September 29

	REVENUE ($ mil.)	NET INCOME ($ mil.)	NET PROFIT MARGIN	EMPLOYEES
09/17	14,604	373	2.6%	260,500
09/16*	14,415	287	2.0%	266,500
10/15	14,329	235	1.6%	265,500
10/14	14,832	148	1.0%	269,500
09/13	13,945	69	0.5%	272,000
Annual Growth	1.2%	52.4%	—	(1.1%)

*Fiscal year change

2017 Year-End Financials

Debt ratio: 47.87%
Return on equity: 16.23%
Cash ($ mil.): 238
Current ratio: 1.12
Long-term debt ($ mil.): 5,190

No. of shares (mil.): 245
Dividends
  Yield: 1.0%
  Payout: 29.8%
Market value ($ mil.): 9,974

	STOCK PRICE ($) FY Close	P/E High/Low		PER SHARE ($) Earnings	Dividends	Book Value
09/17	40.61	27	22	1.49	0.41	10.01
09/16*	38.03	32	25	1.16	0.38	8.83
10/15	30.83	34	26	0.96	0.35	7.85
10/14	26.44	45	34	0.63	0.23	7.34
Annual Growth	11.3%	—		24.0%	16.3%	8.1%

*Fiscal year change

Archer Daniels Midland Co.

Archer-Daniels-Midland (ADM) forges every link in the food chain from field to processing to store. One of the world's largest processors of agricultural commodities the company converts corn oilseeds and wheat into products for food animal feed industrial and energy uses at 280 processing plants worldwide. The company is also a leading manufacturer of protein meal vegetable oil corn sweeteners flour biodiesel ethanol and other value-added food and feed ingredients. ADM operates an extensive US grain elevator and global transportation network that buys stores transports and resells feed commodities for the agricultural processing industry connecting crops with markets on six continents.

Operations

Archer-Daniels-Midland (ADM) conducts its business through four operating segments: Agricultural Services Corn Processing Oilseeds Processing and Wild Flavors and Specialty Ingredients.

Agricultural Services accounts for nearly half of ADM's revenue and buys stores cleans and transports agricultural commodities such as oilseeds corn wheat milo oats rice and barley. It resells them as food and feed ingredients and as raw materials for the agriculture processing industry.

The Oilseeds segment generates nearly 45% of sales and processes soybeans and soft seeds (such as cottonseeds sunflower seeds canola rapeseed and flaxseed) into vegetable oils and protein meals.

Vegetable oils are either sold as raw oils or further refined into salad oils or hydrogenated into margarine and shortening. Partly refined oils are also turned into biodiesel or sold to other manufacturers for use in industrial applications such as paint and chemicals. The protein meals are typically used as a food for livestock particularly poultry. In Europe and South America the segment operates "grain elevators" (storage facilities) port facilities and transport assets.

The Corn Processing segment accounts for 15% of sales and carries out corn wet and dry milling to convert corn into sweeteners starches syrups glucose dextrose and bioproducts. The bulk of its operations are in the mid-US but it also has operations in China Bulgaria Morocco and Turkey. It also ferments dextrose to produce alcohol and amino acids.

Wild Flavors and Specialty Ingredients brings in most of the remaining revenue and produces natural flavor ingredients flavor systems natural colors proteins emulsifiers and soluble fiber among other specialty products. Additionally it buys processes and sells edible beans and soy proteins; it also sells gluten-free and high-protein pastas.

In total ADM has 271 owned or leased US or non-US processing plants and 514 owned or leased US or non-US procurement facilities.

A big part of ADM's business is getting products from one place to another. It has developed a comprehensive transportation network that moves commodities and processed products around the world. It owns or leases thousands of trucks trailers railroad tank and hopper cars river barges towboats and ocean-going vessels.

Geographic Reach

The US is Archer-Daniels-Midlands's largest market accounting for more than 45% of total sales. Switzerland accounts for more than 20% and Germany around 5%. More than 160 other countries contribute the rest. ADM currently owns or leases 270 processing plants and more than 510 procurement facilities 25% of which are located outside of the US.

The company also has 230 warehouses and terminals primarily used as bulk storage facilities and around 40 innovation centers.

ADM has Agricultural Services processing plants in North America and Europe; Agricultural Services procurement facilities in North America South America and Europe; Corn Processing plants in North America South America Europe and Asia. Oilseeds processing plants in North America South America Europe Asia and Africa; Oilseeds Processing procurement facilities in North America South America and Europe; and Wild Flavors and Specialty Ingredients operations in North America South America Europe and Asia.

Sales and Marketing

Archer-Daniels-Midland's products are distributed mainly in bulk from processing plants or storage facilities directly to customers' facilities. ADM has developed transportation capability to move both commodities and processed products virtually anywhere in the world.

Financial Performance

Archer-Daniels-Midland's revenue has declined steadily since 2013. In fiscal 2016 revenue fell a further 8% to $62.3 billion mostly because of lower average sales prices and the disposal of the sugar ethanol and cocoa businesses partially offset by contributions from acquisitions.

Net income fell 30% to $1.3 billion due to gains recorded in the previous year on the sale of the cocoa and chocolate business and lower earnings in fiscal 2016 due to their sale. The company also recorded lower global crushing and origination margins and lower international merchandising results.

Cash from operations fell by $1 billion to $1.5 billion due to changes in working capital.

Strategy

To stay abreast of changes in consumer tastes Archer-Daniels-Midland made a number of acquisitions in the gluten-free and high-protein space. Acquisitions include Harvest Innovations (minimally processed soy proteins and gluten-free ingredients) and Caterina Foods (gluten-free and high-protein pastas) integrated into the Wild Flavors segment.

The company's strategy involves expanding the volume and diversity of crops that it merchandises and processes expanding the global reach of its core model and expanding its value-added product portfolio. One of ADM's strategies is to expand the global reach of its core model may include expanding or developing its business in emerging market areas such as Asia Eastern Europe the Middle East and Africa. As the company adds new products to its portfolio it is keeps an eye on operations that fail to meet expectations. To that end in 2016 ADM sold its sugarcane ethanol operations in Limeira do Oeste in the Brazilian state of Minas Gerais and the year before that it sold its cocoa and chocolate business as well.

Mergers and Acquisitions

In early 2017 Archer-Daniels-Midland acquired Crosswind Industries a manufacturer of private label pet treats and foods as well as specialty ingredients.

The company made a number of acquisitions in 2016. In February it acquired Harvest Innovations an industry leader in minimally processed expeller-pressed soy proteins oils and gluten-free ingredients) for $84 million. In April it bought a 50% interest in Egyptian firm Medsofts Group that manages merchandising and supply chain operations; in September Caterina Foods a maker of gluten-free and high-protein pastas; and in May the remaining 60% interest in Amazon Flavors a Brazilian manufacturer of natural extracts emulsions and compounds. It also agreed to acquire from Tate & Lyle a Casablanca Morocco-based corn wet mill that produces glucose and native starch.

HISTORY

John Daniels began crushing flaxseed to make linseed oil in 1878 and in 1902 he formed Daniels Linseed Company in Minneapolis. George Archer another flaxseed crusher joined the company the following year. In 1923 the company bought Midland Linseed Products and became Archer Daniels Midland (ADM). ADM kept buying oil processing companies in the Midwest during the 1920s. It also started to research the chemical composition of linseed oil.

ADM entered the flour milling business in 1930 when it bought Commander-Larabee (then the #3 flour miller in the US). In the 1930s the company discovered a method for extracting lecithin (an emulsifier food additive used in candy and other products) from soybean oil significantly lowering its price.

The enterprise grew rapidly following WWII. By 1949 it was the leading processor of linseed oil and soybeans in the US and was fourth in flour milling. During the early 1950s ADM began foreign expansion in earnest.

In 1966 the company's leadership passed to Dwayne Andreas a former Cargill executive who had purchased a block of Archer family stock. Andreas focused ADM on soybeans including the production of textured vegetable protein a cheap soybean by-product used in foodstuffs.

EXECUTIVES

SVP Chief Risk Officer and President North America, Mark A. Bemis, age 56

SVP Agricultural Services Business Unit; President Europe, Joseph D. (Joe) Taets, age 51, $700,008 total compensation

EVP and CFO, Ray G. Young, age 56, $825,048 total compensation

SVP General Counsel and Secretary, D. Cameron Findlay, age 58, $700,000 total compensation

SVP Chief Strategy Officer and Chief Sustainability Officer, Ismael Roig, age 50

SVP and President Corn Processing, Christopher M. (Chris) Cuddy, age 43

Chairman and CEO, Juan R. Luciano, age 55, $1,283,340 total compensation

President ADM Europe Middle East and Africa (EMEA), Pierre-Christophe Duprat, age 49

SVP and CTO, Todd A. Werpy, age 54

SVP and President Oilseeds Processing Business Unit, Gregory A. (Greg) Morris, age 45, $650,004 total compensation

SVP and President Wild Flavors and Specialty Ingredients, Vince F. Macciocchi, age 51

President North Asia, Donald Chen, age 54

President Southeast Asia Australia and New Zealand and Global Destination Marketing, Ian Pinner, age 44

President Global Trade, Gary McGuigan

Vice President Of Research And Development, Leif Solheim

Executive Vice President and Chief Risk Officer, Roger Hoffman

Vice President Bio Products, John Hansen

Vice President Human Resources Canada And Cost Management, Crocifissa Mandraccia

Senior Vice President Human Resources, Michael D'Ambrose

Senior Vice President for the Research Division, Mark Matlock

Vice President Environmental, Mark E Calmes

Vice President and Chief Communications Officer, Victoria Podesta

Vice President And Director of Operations, Nicholas Lauer

Auditors: Ernst & Young LLP

LOCATIONS

HQ: Archer Daniels Midland Co.
77 West Wacker Drive, Suite 4600, Chicago, IL 60601
Phone: 312 634-8100
Web: www.adm.com

2015 Sales

	$ mil.	% of total
US	31,828	47
Switzerland	11,681	17
Germany	3,436	5
Other countries	20,757	31
Total	**67,702**	**100**

PRODUCTS/OPERATIONS

2015 Sales

	$ mil.	% of total
Agricultural services	33,658	44
Oilseeds processing	29,393	39
Corn processing	10,051	13
Wild Flavors and Specialty Ingredients	2,423	3
Other	634	1
Intersegment Elimination	(8457)	-
Total	**67,702**	**100**

Selected Commodities

Barley
Corn
Milo (sorghum)
Oats
Oilseeds
Rice
Rye
Wheat

Selected Brands

Consumer food
  Casa (canned refried beans)
  Commander (wheat flour)
  Five Roses (wheat flour)
  Gigantic (wheat flour)
  Midland Harvest (rice)
  Novasoy (soy supplement)
  Top King (wheat flour)
  VegeFull (cooked ground beans)
Industrial food
  Ambrosia (chocolate)
  CardioAid (plant sterol)
  EnviroStrip (dry-stripping)
  Evolution Chemicals (sustainable alternative chemical)
  NovaLipid (fats and oils)
  NovaSoy (isoflavones)
  VegeFull (dried bean-based food ingredient)

Selected Products

Agricultural
  Fertilizer
Feed ingredients
  Animal nutrition
  Corn co-products
  Milling products
  Oils/energy products
  Premixes
  Specialty feed ingredients
Food
  Acidulants
  Beverage alcohol
  Edible beans and bean ingredients
  Fiber
  Flour and whole grains
  Lecithin
  Natural-source vitamin E
  Oils
  Plant sterols
  Polyols and gums
  Proteins
  Rice
  Soy isoflavones
  Starches
  Sweeteners
Fuel
  Biodiesel
  Ethanol
Industrials
  Acidulants
  De-icers
  Dispersants
  Dust control products
  Emulsifiers and thickeners
  Fermentation nutrients
  Fertilizers
  Industrial oils
  Polyols
  Propylene glycol
  Solvents
  Starches
  Superabsorbents

Selected Services

Agriculture
  Grain merchandising
  Grain milling
  Grain processing
Information
  Billing and invoicing
  Inventory
  Logistics
  Payment
  Product search
Transportation
  Land
  Rail
  Truck
  Water
  Ocean
  River

Selected Subsidiaries Joint Ventures and Other Holdings

Almidones Mexicanos S.A. (50% wet corn milling plant Mexico)

Alfred C. Toepfer International (80% agricultural commodities trading and processed products Germany)

Compagnie Industrielle et Financiere des Produits Amylaces SA (Luxembourg) (42% joint venture investments in food feed ingredients and bioenergy)

Eaststarch C.V. (50% wet corn milling plants Netherlands)

Edible Oils Limited (50% procure package sell edible oils UK)

Golden Peanut LLC (100% peanut hulls oil meal and seed)

Gruma S.A.B. de C.V (23% corn flour and corn tortilla manufacturer Mexico)

Kalama Export Company (45% grain export elevator)

Red Star Yeast LLC (40% joint venture fresh and dry yeast manufacturer US and Canada)

Stratas Foods LLC (50% procure package sell edible oils North America)

Telles LLC (50% market sell corn-based bioplastic)

COMPETITORS

AGRI Industries	Liberty Vegetable Oil
Abengoa Bioenergy	LifeLine
Ag Processing Inc.	Little Sioux Corn
Ajinomoto	Processors
Andersons	Louis Dreyfus
Barry Callebaut	Commodities
Bartlett and Company	Louis Dreyfus Group
Bayer CropScience	MGP Ingredients
Brenntag North America	Malt Products
Bunge Limited	Corporation
CHS	Monsanto Company
CP Kelco	Nestlé©
Cargill	Nisshin Oillio
Cosun	Northern Growers
Danisco A/S	Omega Protein
Dow AgroSciences	Pacific Ethanol
DuPont Agriculture	Pioneer Hi-Bred
General Mills	Renewable Energy Group
Green Brick Partners	Riceland Foods
Green Plains	Scoular
Hain Celestial	Syngenta
Hershey	Südzucker
Ingredion	Tate & Lyle

HISTORICAL FINANCIALS

Company Type: Public

Income Statement

FYE: December 31

	REVENUE ($ mil.)	NET INCOME ($ mil.)	NET PROFIT MARGIN	EMPLOYEES
12/17	60,828	1,595	2.6%	31,300
12/16	62,346	1,279	2.1%	31,800
12/15	67,702	1,849	2.7%	32,300
12/14	81,201	2,248	2.8%	33,900
12/13	89,804	1,342	1.5%	31,100
Annual Growth	**(9.3%)**	**4.4%**	**—**	**0.2%**

2017 Year-End Financials

Debt ratio: 18.75%
Return on equity: 8.99%
Cash ($ mil.): 804
Current ratio: 1.59
Long-term debt ($ mil.): 6,623

No. of shares (mil.): 557
Dividends
  Yield: 0.0%
  Payout: 45.8%
Market value ($ mil.): 22,325

	STOCK PRICE ($) FY Close	P/E High/Low		PER SHARE ($) Earnings	Dividends	Book Value
12/17	40.08	17	14	2.79	1.28	32.88
12/16	45.65	22	14	2.16	1.20	29.97
12/15	36.68	18	11	2.98	1.12	30.08
12/14	52.00	16	11	3.43	0.96	30.73
12/13	43.40	22	13	2.02	0.76	30.59
Annual Growth	**(2.0%)**	**—**	**—**	**8.4%**	**13.9%**	**1.8%**

Arconic Inc

While many of its aluminum products may be lightweight Alcoa is anything but. It is one of the world's top producers of alumina (aluminum's principal ingredient from bauxite) and aluminum. Operations include bauxite mining alumina refining and aluminum smelting; products include alumina and alumina-based chemicals automotive components and sheet aluminum for beverage cans. Markets include the aerospace automotive and construction industries. Non-aluminum products include precision castings and aerospace and industrial fasteners. In 2015 the company announced plans to separate into two public companies — an upstream company (aluminum production) and a value-add company (aluminum products) — in 2016.

HISTORY

In 1886 two chemists one in France and one in the US simultaneously discovered an inexpensive process for aluminum production. The American Charles Hall pursued commercial applications. Two years later with an investor group led by Captain Alfred Hunt Hall formed the Pittsburgh Reduction Company. Its first salesman Arthur Davis secured an initial order for 2000 cooking pots.

In 1889 the Mellon Bank loaned the company $4000. In 1891 the firm recapitalized with the Mellon family holding 12% of the stock.

Davis led the business after Hunt died in 1899 and stayed on until 1957 (he died in 1962 at age 95). The company introduced aluminum foil (1910) and found applications for aluminum in new products such as airplanes and cars. It became the Aluminum Company of America in 1907.

By the end of WWI Alcoa had integrated backward into bauxite mining and forward into end-use production. By the 1920s the Mellons had raised their stake to 33%.

The government and Alcoa had debated antitrust issues in court for years since the smelting patent expired in 1912. Finally a 1946 federal ruling forced the company to sell many operations built during WWII as well as its Canadian subsidiary (Alcan).

In the competitive aluminum industry of the 1960s Alcoa's lower-cost production helped it seize market share especially in beverage cans. In the 1970s Alcoa began offering engineered products such as aerospace components and in the 1980s it invested in research acquisitions and plant modernization.

Paul O'Neill (former president of International Paper) arrived as CEO in 1987 and shifted the company's focus back to aluminum. Sales and earnings set records the next two years but plunged afterward reflecting a weak global economy and record-low aluminum prices. Then the fall of the Soviet Union in the early 1990s led to a worldwide glut as Russian exports soared.

In 1994 Alcoa cut its production as part of a two-year accord with Western and Russian producers. That year the company agreed to pool its alumina and chemical operations with Australia's Western Mining Corp.

Alcoa formed a joint venture with Shanghai Aluminum Fabrication Plant in China. The company expanded in Europe in 1996 acquiring Italy's state-run aluminum business followed by the purchase of Inespal Spain's state-run aluminum operations in 1998. Alcoa also bought #3 US aluminum producer Alumax for $3.8 billion in 1998 but only after divesting its cast-plate operations.

Known by the nickname "Alcoa" since the late 1920s the company adopted that as its official name in 1999. O'Neill retired as CEO in 1999; COO Alain Belda succeeded him. Later that year Alcoa bought the 50% of aluminum auto parts maker A-CMI that it did not already own from Hayes Lemmerz International .

In 2000 Alcoa bought aluminum extrusion maker Excel Extrusions from Noranda (now called Falconbridge) and paid $4.5 billion for Reynolds Metals after agreeing to divest some assets — including all of Reynolds' alumina refineries — to satisfy regulators. The same month Alcoa acquired Cordant Technologies. Alcoa also assumed Cordant's 85% ownership of Howmet International (castings) as a result of the transaction — and later acquired the remainder of Howmet. Late in 2000 President-elect George W. Bush named Alcoa's chairman Paul O'Neill to be treasury secretary. (O'Neill subsequently resigned the post in December 2002.)

Alcoa sold its majority stake in the Worsley alumina refinery (Australia) to BHP Billiton in 2001 for about $1.5 billion as part of its refinery divestments. Treasury Secretary O'Neill completed the sale of his more than $90 million worth of Alcoa stock and options in June. In late November Alcoa and BHP Billiton combined their North American metals distribution businesses to create Integris Metals — a joint venture with revenues of about $1.5 billion. (The two subsequently sold the JV to Ryerson in 2005.)

In 2013 Alcoa and Russia's VSMPO-AVISMA the world?s largest manufacturer of titanium ingots and forged products agreed to join forces to meet growing demand for high-end titanium and aluminum products for aircraft manufacturers worldwide. The joint venture combines Alcoa's expertise in manufacturing value-add products with VSMPO-AVISMA's leadership in titanium production to manufacture high-end aerospace goods such as landing gear and forged wing components at Alcoa's plant in Samara.

In 2013 Alcoa completed the expansion of aluminum lithium capacity at its Kitts Green facility in the UK to serve the growing demand for the company's 3rd generation aluminum lithium alloys. Alcoa projects its aluminum lithium revenues will quadruple by 2020 to nearly $200 million.

In 2013 the company also announced a second major North American expansion to meet the growing demand for light durable and recyclable aluminum sheet for automotive production.

EXECUTIVES

Vice President and General Manager Americas, Randall Scheps
EVP Corporate Development Strategy and New Ventures, Christoph Kollatz, age 56, $531,250 total compensation
CEO and Director, Charles P. (Chip) Blankenship, age 51
President International Project Development and Asset Management, Kenneth (Ken) Wisnoski, age 62
EVP; Group President Alcoa Engineered Products and Solutions, Karl Tragl, age 55, $453,125 total compensation
EVP and Group President Alcoa Transportation and Construction Solutions, Tim D. Myers, age 51
President Arconic Global Rolled Products and Arconic Defense, Eric V. Roegner, age 48
EVP and CTO, Raymond J. (Ray) Kilmer
EVP and CFO, Ken Giacobbe, $386,250 total compensation
EVP Human Resources and Environment Health Safety and Sustainability, Vas Nair, age 51
EVP Legal, Kate Ramundo
Vice President Finance, Jim Herring

Vice President Finance, Flavio Mizusaki
Vice President Global Media Relations, Shona Sabnis
Vice President Sales and Marketing, Anthony Ashe
Vice President, Margaret Cosentino
Chair, John C. Plant, age 64
Auditors: PricewaterhouseCoopers LLP

LOCATIONS

HQ: Arconic Inc
    390 Park Avenue, New York, NY 10022-4608
Phone: 212 836-2732
Web: www.arconic.com

2016 Sales

	$ mil.	% of total
United States	7,823	63
France	930	8
United Kingdom	711	6
Hungary	619	5
China	582	5
Russia	433	4
Germany	284	2
Canada	262	2
Brazil	250	2
Japan	145	1
Italy	127	1
Australia	53	—
Spain	4	—
Other	171	1
Total	**12,394**	**100**

PRODUCTS/OPERATIONS

2016 Sales

	$ mil.	% of total
Engineered Products and Solutions	5,728	46
Global Rolled Products	4,864	39
Transportation and construction Solutions	1,802	15
Total	**12,394**	**0**

2016 Sales

	$ mil.	% of total
Flat-rolled aluminum	4,864	39
Fastening systems	2,060	17
Investment castings	1,870	15
Other extruded and forged products	1,495	12
Architectural aluminum systems	1,010	8
Aluminum wheels	689	6
Other	406	3
Total	**12,394**	**100**

Selected Products

Engineering
Extruding
Finishing and electrostatic painting
Flat-rolled products
Rigid container sheet and foil (packaging market)
Sheet and plate mill products (transportation and construction markets)
Engineered products and solutions

COMPETITORS

Aleris Corp.	Novelis
BHP Billiton	Quanex Building
Chinalco	Products
Crown Holdings	RUSAL
Hydro Aluminium	Rio Tinto Alcan
National Aluminium	Superior Industries
Nippon Light Metal	

Income Statement

FYE: December 31

	REVENUE ($ mil.)	NET INCOME ($ mil.)	NET PROFIT MARGIN	EMPLOYEES
12/16	12,394	(941)	—	41,500
12/15	22,534	(322)	—	60,000
12/14	23,906	268	1.1%	59,000
12/13	23,032	(2,285)	—	60,000
12/12	23,700	191	0.8%	61,000
Annual Growth	(15.0%)	—	—	(9.2%)

2016 Year-End Financials

Debt ratio: 40.34%
Return on equity: (-10.94%)
Cash ($ mil.): 1,863
Current ratio: 2.14
Long-term debt ($ mil.): 8,044

No. of shares (mil.): 438
Dividends
Yield: 0.0%
Payout: —
Market value ($ mil.): 8,130

	STOCK PRICE ($) FY Close	P/E High/Low		PER SHARE ($) Earnings	Dividends	Book Value
12/16	18.54	—	—	(2.31)	0.09	11.66
12/15	9.87	—	—	(0.93)	0.00	27.58
12/14	15.79	28	16	0.63	0.00	30.34
12/13	10.63	—	—	(6.42)	0.36	29.67
12/12	8.68	20	15	0.54	0.36	37.10
Annual Growth (25.1%)	20.9%	—	—	—	—(29.3%)	

Arrow Electronics, Inc.

Arrow Electronics hits its target market with a quiver of thousands of electronic products. The company is a leading global distributor of electronic components and computer products alongside rival Avnet. It sells semiconductors passive components interconnect products and computer peripherals to more than 125000 equipment manufacturers and commercial customers. Arrow also provides value-added services such as materials planning design and engineering inventory management and contract manufacturing. It distributes products from manufacturers that include Hitachi Foxconn Microsoft Dell Technologies and Intel. The company operates from more than 460 locations across the globe; half of its sales comes from the Americas.

Operations

Arrow Electronics operates in two segments — global components and Enterprise Computing Solutions (ECS). Global components accounts for about two-thirds of sales. Its product offerings consist of semiconductors passive electro-mechanical interconnect products (capacitors resistors potentiometers power supplies relays switches and connectors) and computing and memory products. About two-thirds of the unit?s sales are from semiconductor products and related services.

Arrow's ECS business sells hardware software storage and security products to value-added resellers. ECS has added professional consulting cloud computing managed services and technical training to expand offerings for resellers and systems integrators. Software is the unit?s biggest seller accounting for more than 40% of revenue.

Geographic Reach

Arrow Electronics generates about 50% of sales from the Americas (mostly the US) with Europe the Middle East and Africa (EMEA) and the Asia-Pacific region contributing about 25% each.

The company has 300 sales offices and 40 distribution centers in 56 countries worldwide.

Sales and Marketing

Arrow Electronics serves more than 125000 OEMs and contract manufacturers through its components business segment and value-added resellers through its ECS business segment. Most of its sales are made on an order-by-order basis rather than through long-term sales contracts.

Industries the company sells to include aerospace and defense alternative energy automotive computers gaming industrial equipment instrumentation medical and scientific devices networking optoelectronics and telecommunications equipment.

Financial Performance

Arrow Electronics posted its third straight year of incremental revenue increases in 2016 with a 2% rise to $23.8 billion. The global components segment reported a 5% increase in 2016 from 2015 on increased demand in Asia and the impact of recent acquisitions. The increases were tempered by the costs of foreign currency exchange rates. For the ECS segment however sales dropped about 7% in from a decline in hardware sales and the impact of foreign currency exchange rates.

Net income rose 5% to about $523 million in 2016 from 2015. The profit increase stemmed from investment losses and pre-payment of debt in 2015 that weren't issues in 2016. The company did however have higher costs for restructuring and integration activities and amortization in 2016.

Cash flow from operations totaled about $356 million in 2016 a drop from $655 million the year before. The difference was an increase in working capital to support sales.

Strategy

Arrow Electronics has implemented what it calls a ?sensor to sunset? strategy which means supplying the hardware and software that companies need to use the full range of cloud computing and the Internet of Things. The strategy encompasses the components that gather data the computing power and software that analyze data and offerings that put it to use.

The company maintains its competitive edge by offering more value-added services to diversify its revenue stream. It also keeps a large supplier base so that customers can procure from a one-stop shop rather than purchase from several different vendors.

Along with rival Avnet Arrow has made acquisitions to corral competition increase its footprint and multiply product offerings.

Among its acquisitions have been several technology publications including EE Times. Tech Online and Datasheets.com. The company?s aim is to establish itself as a prime source of information on cloud Internet of Things and data center technologies as well as an authority and thought leader on those subjects.

Mergers and Acquisitions

Arrow Electronics continues to expand its service capabilities and global presence primarily through acquisitions. Most of the activity has been in the global components segment which made 14 deals in the past several years expanding products and services offerings extending its geographic reach in the Asia/Pacific region and to boost its digital capabilities.

In 2016 the company signed an agreement to acquire the global internet media portfolio focused on technology and electronic design from UBM including EE Times EDN ESM Embedded EBN TechONline and Datasheets.com. That followed the deal for the United Technical Publishing Division of Hearst Business Media in 2015.

In 2015 the company acquired immixGroup Inc. a provider supporting value-added resellers service providers and other public sector channel partners with specialized resources for $280 million to accelerate government sales located in North America.

The company bought another nine companies in 2015 for a total of about $263 million. Among the acquisition were ATM Electronic Corp. an electronic component distributor based in Taiwan; the; and RDC a technology returns and asset management company in Europe.

In 2014 Arrow bought five companies the largest of which was Data Mogul AG for about $105 million. The acquisition further extended Arrow's reach in Europe.

EXECUTIVES

Chairman President and CEO, Michael J. (Mike) Long, age 59, $1,150,000 total compensation
VP and CIO, Vincent P. (Vin) Melvin, age 53
President Global Components, Andrew D. (Andy) King, age 53, $500,000 total compensation
SVP and Chief Strategy Officer, M. Catherine (Cathy) Morris, age 58, $475,000 total compensation
President Global Enterprise Computing Solutions, Sean J. Kerins, age 54, $550,000 total compensation
SVP and CFO, Christopher D. (Chris) Stansbury, age 51, $452,308 total compensation
Vice President And Treasurer, Michael Taunton
Auditors: Ernst & Young LLP

LOCATIONS

HQ: Arrow Electronics, Inc.
9201 East Dry Creek Road, Centennial, CO 80112
Phone: 303 824-4000
Web: www.arrow.com

2016 Sales

	$ mil.	% of total
Americas	11,442	48
Europe Middle East & Africa	6,772	28
Asia/Pacific	5,609	24
Total	**23,825**	**100**

Selected Acquisitions

FY2015
immixGroup Inc.
FY2014
Data Mogul AG
FY 2013
ComputerLinks
FY 2012
ALTIMATE Group
Asset Recovery Corporation
Global Link Technology
Redemtech
Seed International
TechTurn

PRODUCTS/OPERATIONS

2016 Sales

	$ mil.	% of total
Global Components	15,408	65
Global Enterprise computing solutions (ECS)	8,416	35
Total	**23,825**	**100**

Selected Products and Services

Computer Products
  Communication control equipment
  Controllers
  Design systems
  Desktop computers
  Flat-panel displays
  Microcomputer boards and systems
  Monitors
  Printers
  Servers
  Software
  Storage products
  System chassis and enclosures
  Workstations
Electronic Components

Capacitors
Connectors
Potentiometers
Power supplies
Relays
Resistors
Switches

Services

Analysis implementation and support
Component design
Contract manufacturing
Forecast and order management
Inventory management

COMPETITORS

Avnet	Richardson Electronics
Digi-Key	SYNNEX
Future Electronics	TTI Inc.
Heilind Electronics	Tech Data
Ingram Micro	WPG Holdings
N.F. Smith	Yosun
Newark Corporation	ePlus

HISTORICAL FINANCIALS

Company Type: Public

Income Statement

FYE: December 31

	REVENUE ($ mil.)	NET INCOME ($ mil.)	NET PROFIT MARGIN	EMPLOYEES
12/17	26,812	401	1.5%	18,800
12/16	23,825	522	2.2%	18,700
12/15	23,282	497	2.1%	18,500
12/14	22,768	498	2.2%	17,000
12/13	21,357	399	1.9%	16,500
Annual Growth	5.9%	0.2%	—	3.3%

2017 Year-End Financials

Debt ratio: 19.98%
Return on equity: 8.58%
Cash ($ mil.): 730
Current ratio: 1.56
Long-term debt ($ mil.): 2,933

No. of shares (mil.): 87
Dividends
  Yield: —
  Payout: —
Market value ($ mil.): 7,051

	STOCK PRICE ($) FY Close	P/E High/Low	Earnings	Dividends	Book Value
12/17	80.41	19 15	4.48	0.00	56.47
12/16	71.30	13 8	5.68	0.00	49.64
12/15	54.18	12 10	5.20	0.00	45.56
12/14	57.89	12 9	4.98	0.00	43.32
12/13	54.25	14 9	3.85	0.00	41.83
Annual Growth	10.3%	— —	3.9%	—	7.8%

Arrow Financial Corp.

Arrow Financial has more than one shaft in its quiver. It's the holding company for two banks: $2 billion-asset Glens Falls National Bank operates 30 branches in eastern upstate New York while $400 million-asset Saratoga National Bank and Trust Company has around 10 branches in Saratoga County. Serving local individuals and businesses the banks offer standard deposit and loan products as well as retirement trust and estate planning services and employee benefit plan administration. Its subsidiaries include: McPhillips Insurance Agency and Upstate Agency which offer property and casualty insurance; Capital Financial Group which sells group health plans; and North Country Investment Advisors which provides financial planning services.

Operations

Arrow Financial's loan portfolio consisted of residential real estate mortgages and home equity loans (40% of loan assets) commercial and commercial real estate loans (31%) and indirect auto loans (29%) at the end of 2015.

The banking group makes more than 70% of its revenue from interest income. About 58% of Arrow Financial's total revenue came from loan interest (including fees) during 2015 while another 14% came from interest on taxable and tax-exempt investment securities. The rest of its revenue came from insurance commissions (9% of revenue) customer service fees (9%) fiduciary activity income (8%) and other miscellaneous income sources.

Geographic Reach

Glens Falls National Bank has 30 branches in eastern upstate New York (in Warren Washington Saratoga Essex and Clinton Counties). Saratoga Springs-based Saratoga National Bank operates nine branches in Saratoga Albany and Rensselaer Counties.

Financial Performance

Arrow Financial Corporation's revenues and profits have been slowly rising since 2013 mostly as steady — and more creditworthy — loan growth has spurred more interest income.

The group's revenue climbed 4% to $98.86 million during 2015 mostly as 7%-plus growth in loan and other interest-earning assets continued to spur additional interest income.

Revenue growth in 2015 pushed Arrow Financial's net income up 6% to $24.66 million. The banking group's operating cash levels dipped 6% to $28.93 million despite earnings growth mostly due to unfavorable working capital changes.

Strategy

Arrow Financial has been working its loan portfolio quality by implementing smarter lending strategies with stronger underwriting and collateral control procedures and credit review systems.

It's also slowly expanding its business and branch network in the Capital District of New York which has been a key market for the bnak's growth. In September 2015 its Saratoga National Bank subsidiary opened its ninth branch in Troy. In June 2014 it opened a new branch in Colonie after opening two new branches in Queensbury and Clifton Park in 2013.

EXECUTIVES

EVP Bank Card Business Development and Marketing Glen Falls National Bank and Trust, David S. (Dave) DeMarco, $178,500 total compensation
President Saratoga National Bank and Trust, Raymond F. (Ray) O'Conor, $178,500 total compensation
President and CEO, Thomas J. (Tom) Murphy, age 59, $300,000 total compensation
SVP and CFO Arrow Financial Corporation and EVP and CFO Glens Falls National Bank and Trust Company, Edward J. Campanella, age 49
Vice President, Jim Brown
Vice President, Paul Delzotto
Vice President Trust Officer, Laura Vamvalis
Vice President, Peter Capozzola
Chairman, Thomas L. Hoy, age 68
Auditors: KPMG LLP

LOCATIONS

HQ: Arrow Financial Corp.
250 Glen Street, Glens Falls, NY 12801
Phone: 518 745-1000
Web: www.arrowfinancial.com

PRODUCTS/OPERATIONS

2015 Sales

	$ mil.	% of total
Interest and dividend income		
Interest and Fees on Loans	56	58
Fully Taxable	8	8
Exempt from Federal Taxes	5	6
Non-interest income		
Fees for Other Services to Customers	9	9
Insurance Commissions	9	9
Income From Fiduciary Activities	7	8
Other	2	2
Total	**98**	**100**

Selected Subsidiaries

Glens Falls National Bank and Trust Company
  Arrow Properties Inc. (real estate investment trust)
  Capital Financial Group Inc.
  Glens Falls National Community Development Corporation
  Glens Falls National Insurance Agencies LLC (dba McPhillips Agency)
  Loomis & LaPann Inc.
  NC Financial Services Inc.
  North Country Investment Advisers Inc.
  Upstate Agency LLC
Saratoga National Bank and Trust Company

COMPETITORS

Ballston Spa Bancorp	Community Bank System
Bank of America	KeyCorp
Citizens Financial Group	NBT Bancorp
	TrustCo Bank Corp NY

HISTORICAL FINANCIALS

Company Type: Public

Income Statement

FYE: December 31

	ASSETS ($ mil.)	NET INCOME ($ mil.)	INCOME AS % OF ASSETS	EMPLOYEES
12/16	2,605	26	1.0%	524
12/15	2,446	24	1.0%	511
12/14	2,217	23	1.1%	513
12/13	2,163	21	1.0%	516
12/12	2,022	22	1.1%	518
Annual Growth	6.5%	4.6%	—	0.3%

2016 Year-End Financials

Debt ratio: 0.77%
Return on equity: 11.84%
Cash ($ mil.): 57
Current ratio: —
Long-term debt ($ mil.): —

No. of shares (mil.): 13
Dividends
  Yield: 0.0%
  Payout: 49.6%
Market value ($ mil.): 563

	STOCK PRICE ($) FY Close	P/E High/Low	Earnings	Dividends	Book Value
12/16	40.50	22 13	1.91	0.95	16.74
12/15	27.17	16 14	1.80	0.93	15.52
12/14	27.49	16 14	1.71	0.91	14.63
12/13	26.56	17 15	1.60	0.89	13.99
12/12	24.95	16 14	1.64	0.88	12.88
Annual Growth	12.9%	— —	3.9%	2.1%	6.8%

Asbury Automotive Group Inc

Car dealership giant Asbury Automotive Group oversees around 93 new vehicle franchises representing around 80 dealership locations in about a dozen states including the Carolinas Florida Texas and Virginia. The dealerships sell some 30 different brands of US and non-US new and used vehicles. Asbury also offer parts servicing and collision repair from about 25 repair centers and two stand-alone used vehicle stores as well as financing insurance and warranty and service contracts. The auto dealer has grown by acquiring large locally branded dealership groups as well as smaller groups and individually owned dealerships throughout the US. Customers include individual buyers and fleet operators.

Operations

Asbury sells in the region of 100000 new vehicles each year representing around 55% of its total revenues. Used car sales bring in 30%. The company also operates a parts and services division (10% of revenue) and a finance and insurance division (5%).

Some 80% of Asbury's sales come from import brands. Honda represents around 15% of new vehicle revenue while Nissan and Toyota each account for slightly more than 10%.

Geographic Reach

Duluth Georgia-based Asbury Automotive operates dealerships in more than 15 metropolitan markets throughout the US. Aside from the Carolinas Florida Texas and Virginia Asbury has dealerships in Indiana Georgia Mississippi and Missouri.

Sales and Marketing

Asbury advertises on TV radio and newspaper as well as through internet-based campaigns including search engine marketing website optimization and through third-party websites.

Financial Performance

Six consecutive years of revenue growthstalled in fiscal 2016 flattening out at $6.5 billion.

A slight fall in new and used vehicle sales was mostly offset by an increase in parts and service revenue to a net negative effect of $60.6 million or less than 1% of total sales.

Net income was also virtually unchanged falling $2.2 million to $167.2 million.

Cash from operations fell 8% to $142.3 million.

Strategy

With revenue growth flagging and net income not much better Asbury's management bought back shares to boost its share price. It spent around $162 million on share repurchases in the first four months of 2017.

Asbury has been selling off underperforming dealerships. It exited Arkansas entirely and sold four stores representing five franchises. On the other hand it acquired a Chevrolet franchise and an Isuzu truck franchise in Indianapolis Indiana in 2017.

To help drive sales in a more cost effective manner Asbury is decreasing its advertising spend per vehicle while increasing its focus on digital. It has improved its e-commerce offering and now sells vehicles online.

Mergers and Acquisitions

In 2017 Asbury bought Hare Chevrolet a Chevrolet dealership that also runs a collision center and Isuzu dealership and a truck center.

EXECUTIVES

Vice President Operations, John Stamm
SVP Corporate Development and Real Estate, George C. Karolis, age 42, $397,728 total compensation
President and CEO, David W. Hult, age 51, $745,182 total compensation
VP and CIO, Barry Cohen
SVP and CFO, Sean D. Goodman, age 52
Vice President, Matt Mees
Vice President, John Rooks

Vice President North Region, Daniel Clara
Vice President Manufacturer Relations, Matthew Mees
Vice President Finance Vice President Finance, Thomas Mccollum
Chairman, Thomas C. DeLoach, age 70
Vice Chairman, Craig T. Monaghan, age 60
Auditors: Ernst & Young LLP

LOCATIONS

HQ: Asbury Automotive Group Inc
2905 Premiere Parkway N.W., Suite 300, Duluth, GA 30097
Phone: 770 418-8200
Web: www.asburyauto.com

PRODUCTS/OPERATIONS

2016 Sales

	$ mil.	% of total
New vehicles	3,611	55
Used vehicles	1,876	29
Parts & service	778	12
Finance & insurance	261	4
Total	**6,527**	**100**

2016 New Vehicle Sales

	% of total
Imports	45
Luxury	34
Domestic	21
Total	**100**

Selected Brands

Coggin Automotive Group
Courtesy Autogroup
David McDavid Auto Group
Gray-Daniels Auto Family
Nalley Automotive Group
Plaza Motor Company

COMPETITORS

AutoNation	Penske Automotive Group
Buchanan Automotive	Ron Tonkin Family of Dealerships
CarMax	
Ferman Automotive	
Group 1 Automotive	Scott-McRae
Hendrick Automotive	Sonic Automotive
Island Lincoln-Mercury	

HISTORICAL FINANCIALS

Company Type: Public

Income Statement

FYE: December 31

	REVENUE ($ mil.)	NET INCOME ($ mil.)	NET PROFIT MARGIN	EMPLOYEES
12/16	6,527	167	2.6%	7,900
12/15	6,588	169	2.6%	8,600
12/14	5,867	111	1.9%	8,300
12/13	5,334	109	2.0%	7,600
12/12	4,640	82	1.8%	7,000
Annual Growth	**8.9%**	**19.4%**	**—**	**3.1%**

2016 Year-End Financials

Debt ratio: 73.13%
Return on equity: 56.12%
Cash ($ mil.): 3
Current ratio: 1.21
Long-term debt ($ mil.): 912
No. of shares (mil.): 21
Dividends
  Yield: —
  Payout: —
Market value ($ mil.): 1,311

	STOCK PRICE ($) FY Close	P/E High/Low		PER SHARE ($) Earnings	Dividends	Book Value
12/16	61.70	9	6	7.40	0.00	13.16
12/15	67.44	15	10	6.41	0.00	12.68
12/14	75.92	21	12	3.71	0.00	15.60
12/13	53.74	16	9	3.51	0.00	15.95
12/12	32.03	12	8	2.61	0.00	12.86
Annual Growth	**17.8%**	**—**	**—**	**29.8%**	**—**	**0.6%**

Ascena Retail Group Inc

Ascena Retail Group (formerly Dress Barn Inc.) has left the farm for greener retail pastures. The apparel and accessories retailer operates about 4900 specialty stores throughout the US Puerto Rico and Canada. Its 800-plus dressbarn stores court women ages 35 to 55. Maurices with some 990-plus locations targets 17-to-34-year-old females in towns with populations between 25000 and 100000. Its second-largest chain Justice and its Charming Shoppes subsidiary courts "tweens" at about 940 stores and online. In 2015 Ascena purchased upscale retailer ANN which became Ascena's largest segment and added Ann Taylor Lou & Grey and LOFT stores.

Operations

The company operates six business segments: ANN Justice Lane Bryant maurices dressbarn and Catherines.

ANN offers sells clothes for women under its Ann Taylor and LOFT brands and accounts for around a third of the company's revenue.

Justice makes clothes and related branded merchandise for girls age 6-12; Lane Bryant and maurices specialize in plus-sized fashion for women in suburban and small towns; the three chains each bring in around 16% of net revenue.

Catherines offers mid-range wear-to-work and casual clothing and accessories and brings in some 6% of revenue.

Dressbarn accounts for 14% of sales.

Geographic Reach

New Jersey-based Ascena Retail Group's +4900 specialty stores are located across the US states as well as in Puerto Rico and Canada. The Justice and maurices chains operate 42 stores and 35 stores in Canada respectively. While more are planned they contribute an insignificant amount of sales at present.

ANN has stores in 47 states the District of Columbia Canada and Puerto Rico as well as six international franchise stores. Justice has stores in 48 states and Canada as well as 68 international franchise stores while maurices has stores in 45 states and Canada. dressbarn Lane Bryant and Catherines have stores located in 48 47 and 44 states respectively.

ANN segment had 13 company-operated stores in Canada. ANN had the highest number of stores of about over 1020 in fiscal 2015.

Sales and Marketing

Ascena Retail employs a variety of advertising and marketing strategies across its six retail brands. The company engages in customer research promotional events window and in-store marketing materials as well as direct mail online and magazine advertising. In fiscal 2016 (ended July) the company spent $271 million on advertising and marketing compared with $177 million the previous year and $160 million in fiscal 2014.

Financial Performance

The acquisition of ANN in August 2015 bumped up revenue a healthy 46% in fiscal 2016 to $7.0 billion. Comparable sales fell by $214 million. The company reduced its net loss from $236.8 million to $11.9 million partly due to higher net revenue and partly due to the absence of impairment goodwill relating to the write-down in Lane Bryant value.

Cash from operations increased 3% to $445.4 million.

Strategy

Ascena Retail Group mines different retail niches including younger women (ages 17 to 34) tween (ages seven to 14) girls plus-size women (sizes 12 to 32) and "mature" women through its various retail brands. The recent acquisition of ANN and its Anne Taylor and LOFT brands taps into the working women market.

Acquisitions are key to the holding company's successful growth strategy. Concurrently the company is working to right-size its store network closing underperforming Dress Barn locations and adding Maurice's shops and Justice stores including locations in Canada. While the company's international presence is relatively light it's exploring other international opportunities for its brands. Licensing presents an opportunity for overseas growth.

Another focus for the company is its omnichannel strategy which includes traditional stores instore ordering capabilities and e-commerce operations. It made nearly $520 million from online sales in 2015 up 15%.

Mergers and Acquisitions

In 2015 the company doubled down on its plan to focus on older customers when it paid $2.2 billion for upscale retailer ANN parent of career-wear maker Ann Taylor and its more casual LOFT banner. The acquisition positioned Ascena as the third largest specialty apparel retailer and the single largest focused on women's apparel with a diverse brand portfolio that serves women of all ages sizes and demographics.

HISTORY

Roslyn Jaffe started The Dress Barn in 1962. Focusing on career women in need of reasonably priced wardrobes the store offered a 20%-50% discount from department store prices. By the mid-1970s Dress Barn had 18 stores and was expanding through acquisitions. It went public in 1983. The Dress Barn Woman division was introduced three years later. The company discontinued its casual apparel stores (SBX) in fiscal 1995.

The discount appeal of Dress Barn stores has been undermined in recent years by the increased use of moderately priced private-label brands by major department stores. Manufacturers such as Jones Apparel Group have also entered the retail market via factory outlets. In its rapid expansion during the 1990s Dress Barn countered this trend by focusing on combination stores offering both regular and larger-size merchandise. These larger stores (8000-9000 sq. ft.) provide the company a greater presence in shopping center locations and have lower operating costs.

Dress Barn added shoe departments and petite sizes in 1996 and 1997 and stepped up closures of poorly performing stores. It continued doing so in fiscal 1998 and 1999 while opening new combo stores and converting existing stores to the combo format. Dress Barn introduced a mail-order catalog in the fall of 1999 and launched a website the following year. The Jaffes' son David was named CEO in early 2002; Roslyn's husband Elliot remains chairman.

Dress Barn's longtime search for acquisition opportunities was consummated in January 2005 with the purchase of specialty chain Maurices which targets younger women (ages 17 to 34) in small to metro fringe markets with more fashion-forward merchandise.

In 2009 Dress Barn tapped into the teen market again with its purchase of Tween Brands and the retailer's Justice stores.

The company changed its name in January 2011 to Ascena Retail Group and adopted a holding company structure. In June 2012 the firm acquired plus-size retailer Charming Shoppes for about $900 million.

EXECUTIVES

Chairman and CEO, David R. Jaffe, age 58, $1,019,231 total compensation
President and CEO ascena Brands, Gary P. Muto, age 57
EVP and Chief Human Resources Officer, John Pershing, age 46, $557,812 total compensation
President and COO, Brian E. Lynch, age 60
EVP and CFO, Robb Giammatteo, age 45, $509,615 total compensation
EVP and General Counsel, Duane D. Holloway, $215,385 total compensation
Senior Vice President, Elise Jaffe
Vice President Real Estate Catherines, Mark Mueller
Assistant Vice President Procurement, Laura Rogers
Vice President Of Shared Services Accounting And Pay, Joan Maiers
Vice President of Operations, Dan Brunswick
Assistant Vice President Engineering and Facilities, Matthew Dippold
Vice President Treasurer, Heather Plutino
Auditors: DELOITTE & TOUCHE LLP

LOCATIONS

HQ: Ascena Retail Group Inc
933 MacArthur Boulevard, Mahwah, NJ 07430
Phone: 551 777-6700   **Fax:** 845 369-8001
Web: www.ascenaretail.com

PRODUCTS/OPERATIONS

Selected Brands
Ann Taylor
Ann Taylor Loft
Cacique
Catherines
Dressbarn
Justice
Lane Bryant
Lane Bryant Outlet
Loft
Lou & Grey
Maurices
Right Fit

2016 Stores

	No.
ANN	1,022
Maurices	993
Justice	937
DressBarn	809
Lane Bryant	772
Catherines	373
Total	**4,906**

2016 Sales

	$ mil.	% of total
ANN	2,330	33
Justice	1,106	16
Lane Bryant	1,130	16
Maurices	1,101	16
Dress Barn	993	14
Catherines	333	5
Total	**6,995**	**100**

COMPETITORS

American Eagle Outfitters	Kohl's
Avenue Stores	L Brands
Aéropostale	Macy's
Burlington Coat Factory	Old Navy
Christopher & Banks	Ross Stores
Deb Shops	Saks
Dillard's	Sears
J. C. Penney	Stage Stores
	Target Corporation
	Wal-Mart

HISTORICAL FINANCIALS

Company Type: Public

Income Statement

FYE: July 29

	REVENUE ($ mil.)	NET INCOME ($ mil.)	NET PROFIT MARGIN	EMPLOYEES
07/17	6,649	(1,067)	—	64,000
07/16	6,995	(11)	—	66,000
07/15	4,802	(236)	—	48,000
07/14	4,790	133	2.8%	48,000
07/13	4,714	151	3.2%	48,000
Annual Growth	**9.0%**	**—**		**7.5%**

2017 Year-End Financials

Debt ratio: 39.73%
Return on equity: (-79.74%)
Cash ($ mil.): 325
Current ratio: 1.20
Long-term debt ($ mil.): 1,494
No. of shares (mil.): 195
Dividends
  Yield: —
  Payout: —
Market value ($ mil.): 453

	STOCK PRICE ($) FY Close	P/E High/Low		PER SHARE ($) Earnings	Dividends	Book Value
07/17	2.32	—	—	(5.48)	0.00	4.21
07/16	8.13	—	—	(0.06)	0.00	9.59
07/15	12.56	—	—	(1.46)	0.00	9.30
07/14	16.12	27	19	0.81	0.00	10.74
07/13	18.60	23	17	0.93	0.00	9.76
Annual Growth	**(40.6%)**	**—**	**—**	**—**	**—**	**(19.0%)**

ASCENSION HEALTH ALLIANCE

Auditors: ERNST & YOUNG LLP

LOCATIONS

HQ: ASCENSION HEALTH ALLIANCE
4600 EDMUNDSON RD, SAINT LOUIS, MO 631343806
Phone: 314 733-8000
Web: WWW.ASCENSION.ORG

HISTORICAL FINANCIALS

Company Type: Private

Income Statement

FYE: June 30

	REVENUE ($ mil.)	NET INCOME ($ mil.)	NET PROFIT MARGIN	EMPLOYEES
06/16	21,898	(339)	—	111,489
06/15	20,538	(42)	—	
Annual Growth	**6.6%**	**—**	**—**	**—**

2016 Year-End Financials

Debt ratio: —
Return on equity: (-1.60%)
Cash ($ mil.): 696
Current ratio: 0.60
Long-term debt ($ mil.): —
Dividends
  Yield: —
  Payout: —
Market value ($ mil.): —

Associated Banc-Corp

A lot of Midwesterners are associated with Associated Banc-Corp the holding company for Associated Bank. One of the largest banks based in Wisconsin the bank operates about 200 branches in that state as well as in Illinois and Minnesota. Catering to consumers and local businesses it offers deposit accounts loans mortgage banking credit and debit cards and leasing. The bank's wealth management division offers investments trust services brokerage insurance and employee group benefits plans. Commercial loans including agricultural construction and real estate loans make up more than 60% of bank's loan portfolio. The bank also writes residential mortgages consumer loans and home equity loans.

Operations

Associated Banc-Corp boasts total assets of more than $27 billion making it one of the 50 largest publicly traded US bank holding companies. More than 70% of revenue comes from interest income mostly from loans. Roughly 60% of Associated Banc-Corp's $18 billion loan portfolio consists of commercial and industrial real estate construction commercial real estate loans and lease financing.

Nearly 30% of the company's income is from non-interest sources including: trust service fees service charges insurance commissions brokerage and annuity commissions and mortgage banking income among others. It also offers benefits consulting services through its Associated Financial Group subsidiary.

Geographic Reach

The company offers a full range of financial products and services in more than 200 banking locations serving more than 100 communities throughout Wisconsin Illinois and Minnesota and commercial financial services in Indiana Michigan Missouri Ohio and Texas.

Sales and Marketing

Associated Banc-Corp spent $26.1 million on business development and advertising in 2014 compared to $23.3 million in 2013 and $21.3 million in 2012.

Financial Performance

Associated Banc-Corp's revenue has remained flat for the past several years at just above $1 billion. Revenue in 2014 inched up by less than 1% to $1.03 billion mostly thanks to higher interest income as loan assets grew by 11% and as interest and dividends on investment securities also grew by double digits. Offsetting much of this growth the company's net mortgage banking income shrunk by $28 million (56%) driven by lower gains on sales and related income as secondary mortgage production declined.

Profit levels have been steadily rising over the past several years since losses in 2009 and 2010 with net income in 2014 rising by 1% to $190.51 million. Higher revenue combined with lower interest expenses on deposits and lower personnel costs all helped to boost the company's bottom line.

Despite higher earnings cash from operations fell 56% to $212.74 million primarily as the company made fewer net proceeds from the sale of its mortgage loans held for sale. The company's total loans grew by 11% to $17.6 billion in 2014 while total deposits rose by 9% to $18.77 billion.

Strategy

The company intends to continue pursuing a profitable growth strategy by carefully screening its prospective customers in light of the risks expenses and difficulties frequently encountered by companies in significant growth stages of development. Associated Banc-Corp hopes to keep its momentum going via organic growth including increasing its fee income and commercial deposits among other measures. It is also remodeling or relocating many of its branches.

Associated Banc-Corp also plans to continue strong loan business growth. For 2015 the company expects high single-digit annual average loan growth after posting loan double-digit loan growth across most categories in 2014.

Mergers and Acquisitions

In early 2015 subsidiary Associated Financial Group agreed to buy Minnesota-based Ahmann & Martin Co a risk and benefits consulting firm to gain new clients and expand its financial risk and insurance product and service lines.

Company Background

Hampered by one of the worst economic environments in recent history the bank saw an increase in nonperforming loans (particularly business- and housing-related loans) and more than tripled its provision for loan losses from 2008 to 2009. The company cut its losses in 2010 and nearly turned a profit as it concentrated on improving its credit quality. It moved away from construction lending and its nonperforming loans and its provisions for loan losses decreased. Even though 2011 revenues were down Associated Banc-Corp returned to profitability as credit quality continued to improve.

EXECUTIVES

EVP and Chief Risk Officer, Arthur G. (Art) Heise, age 59

President and CEO, Philip B. (Phil) Flynn, age 59, $1,250,000 total compensation

EVP General Counsel and Corporate Secretary, Randall J. Erickson, age 58, $406,667 total compensation

EVP and Head Retail Banking, David L. Stein, age 53, $545,849 total compensation

EVP and Chief Human Resources Officer, Judith M. Docter, age 56

EVP and Chief Credit Officer, Scott S. Hickey, age 61, $644,531 total compensation

EVP and Chief Strategy Officer, Oliver Buechse, age 48

EVP and Head Commercial Real Estate, Breck F. Hanson

EVP and Head Corporate Banking, Donna N. Smith

EVP and Head Specialized Industries and Commercial Financial Services, John A. Utz, $348,417 total compensation

EVP and Head Community Markets, Timothy J. Lau

EVP and CFO, Christopher J. Del Moral-Niles, $477,500 total compensation

EVP and Chief Audit Executive, Patrick J. Derpinghaus

EVP CIO and COO, James Yee, $458,333 total compensation

EVP and Head Private Client and Institutional Services, William M. Bohn

President Southern Illinois, Phillip Hickman

Senior Vice President Investment Officer, Sara Walker

Senior Vice President and Senior Relationship Manager, Edward Chidiac

Vice President Customer Care Program And Operations Manager, Wendy Kumm

Vice President Marketing Manager, Shawn Kesler

Vice President, Mark Vorel

Vice President and Trust Officer, Philip Gatien

Senior Vice President, Ron Murphy

Vice president, Tammy Kurey

Senior Vice President Commercial Banking Team Leader, David Winiecki

Vice President, Terry Zeske

Assistant Vice President Senior Bank Manager, Kim Klinkner

Vice President Commercial Loan Documentation Manager, David Sitter

Vice President Private Banking, Kristine Burke

Vice President, Angela O'neill

Senior Vice President Enterprise Project Management Office, Michael Gugluizza

Senior Vice President, Diane Gantner

Senior Vice President Experiential Marketing, Ryan Taylor

Assistant Vice President Corporate, Robert Brothers

Senior Vice President Community Markets, Sandra Earp

Executive Vice President and Director Human Resources, Judy Docter

Vice President, Jodi Sowinski

Vice President, Gina Frease

Vice President, Guy Ringle

Vice President, Charles Garcia

Vice President, Jenny Plebanski

Vice President Field Exams, Jeff Kohr

Assistant Vice President Branch Manager, Bret Kuether

Assistant Vice President Branch Systems and Integration Manager, Peg Yanke

Assistant Vice President Financial Crimes Investigator Lead, Eric Friedland

Vice President Commercial Banking Portfo, Bradley Anderson

Senior Vice President And Trust Manager, Robert Skowronski

Senior Vice President Commercial Real Estate, Lisa Cunningham

Vice President Senior Client Advisor, Chad Heath

Vice President Commercial Banking Relationship Manager, Scott Hoerth

Vice President Relationship Manager, Ty Earp

Vice President Commercial Relationship Manager, Wendy Carney

Assistant Vice President Residential Loa, Beverly Bourazak

Senior Vice President Marketing, Heidi Hahn

Vice President Commercial Real Estate Portfolio Manager, Christian Bryant

Vice President and Trust Officer, Andrew Dobzyn

Assistant Vice President Senior Loan Officer, Christine Howard

Assistant Vice President Branch Manager, Kenneth Alburg

Assistant Vice President of Retail Marketing, Shannon Krohn

Vice President and Trust Officer, John Kvamme

Vice President Private Banker, Chad Otte

Vice President, Daniel Zettinger

Vice President, Amy Kolb

Senior Vice President Process Excellence and Six Sigma, Don Vanpool

Vice President Senior Client Advisor, Mary Wettstein

Assistant Vice President Residential Loan Officer NMLS#762823, Jason Smith

Senior Vice President Private Banker, Mary Jarrett

Vice President, Jessica Brandom

Vice President Lead Network Engineer, Eric Sequin

Vice President Asset Based Lending, Mickey Moran

Senior Vice President Senior Manager Interactive Consumer Marketing, Jennifer Ott

Senior Vice President Market Manager, Kevin Jordan

Assistant Vice President, Kevin Greer

Senior Vice President Regional Sales Manager, Tim D'Amato

Senior Vice President, Farhan Iqbal

Vice President, Adam Demont

Senior Vice President Market Manager, Charles Cafazza

Vice President Commercial Banking, Dean Rosencrans

Vice President, Dave Bolwerk
Assistant Vice President Certified Appraiser
 Residential Loan Officer, Debbie Schlager
Assistant Vice President Certified Appraiser
 Residential Lending Officer Residential Lending,
 Joanette Cintron
Senior Vice President, Krista Casper
VICE PRESIDENT, David Brookfield
Assistant Vice President Certified Appraiser
 Residential Loan Officer, Gayle King
SENIOR VICE PRESIDENT, Anthony P Pecora
Vice President and Multicultural and Affordable
 Sales Integration Manager, LaDonna Reed
Senior Vice President, Mike Waltz
CTP Vice President, Melissa Fellows
Assistant Vice President Mortgage Lending, Mark
 Tripp
Senior Vice President, Shawn Bullock
Vice President Residential Lending Manager,
 Jerilynn Waller
Chairman, William R. Hutchinson, age 74
Treasurer, Tim Watson
Auditors: KPMG LLP

LOCATIONS

HQ: Associated Banc-Corp
 433 Main Street, Green Bay, WI 54301
Phone: 920 491-7500
Web: www.associatedbank.com

PRODUCTS/OPERATIONS

2016 Sales

	$ mil.	% of total
Interest		
Loans including fees	659	58
Investment securities including dividends and Interest	127	11
Other	4	0
Noninterest		
Insurance Commissions	80	7
Service charges on deposit accounts	66	6
Card-based & other nondeposit fees	50	4
Trust Service fees	46	4
Other	108	10
Total	1,144	100

2016 Sales

	% of total
Community Consumer and Business	59
Corporate and Commercial Specialty	36
Risk Management and Shared Services	5
Total	100

COMPETITORS

Bank Mutual	Northern Trust
Harris	TCF Financial
KeyCorp	U.S. Bancorp

HISTORICAL FINANCIALS

Company Type: Public

Income Statement

FYE: December 31

	ASSETS ($ mil.)	NET INCOME ($ mil.)	INCOME AS % OF ASSETS	EMPLOYEES
12/17	30,483	229	0.8%	4,388
12/16	29,139	200	0.7%	4,441
12/15	27,715	188	0.7%	4,383
12/14	26,821	190	0.7%	4,300
12/13	24,226	188	0.8%	4,600
Annual Growth	5.9%	5.0%	—	(1.2%)

2017 Year-End Financials

Debt ratio: 1.63%
Return on equity: 7.25%
Cash ($ mil.): 683
Current ratio: —
Long-term debt ($ mil.): —
No. of shares (mil.): 152
Dividends
 Yield: 0.0%
 Payout: 35.2%
Market value ($ mil.): 3,882

	STOCK PRICE ($) FY Close	P/E High/Low	PER SHARE ($) Earnings	Dividends	Book Value
12/17	25.40	18 15	1.42	0.50	21.18
12/16	24.70	20 12	1.26	0.45	20.32
12/15	18.75	17 14	1.19	0.41	19.42
12/14	18.63	17 13	1.16	0.37	18.48
12/13	17.40	16 12	1.10	0.33	17.61
Annual Growth	9.9%	—	6.6%	10.9%	4.7%

ASSOCIATED WHOLESALE GROCERS, INC.

Associated Wholesale Grocers (AWG) knows its customers can't live on bread and milk alone. The second-largest retailer-owned distribution cooperative in the US (behind Wakefern Food Corporation) AWG supplies more than 3800 grocery retail outlets in more than half of the US states from 10 distribution centers which collectively have some 7 million square feet of space. In addition to its wholesale grocery operation AWG offers a variety of business services to its members including marketing and merchandising programs retail accounting supermarket development and access to low-cost merchandise through its Value Merchandisers subsidiary. AWG was founded by a group of independent grocers in 1924.

Geographic Reach

Kansas City-headquartered Associated Wholesale Grocers began in Missouri and its operations are generally centered on that state. It operates ten wholesale divisions in Missouri Nebraska Kansas Oklahoma Louisiana Alabama Tennessee and Wisconsin. Its distribution activities extend into another 25 states.

AWG?s Valu Merchandisers subsidiary is gaining a foothold in non-US regions such as the Caribbean Central & South America and the Middle East.

Sales and Marketing

As a cooperative AWG serves the needs of its members who collectively determine how best to utilize the co-ops operations. Its board of directors is made up of nearly 20 people each a key executive at a grocer retail chain which receives products from AWG.

AWG serves up several private label brands to stores. They include Superior Selections Clearly Organic Best Choice Always Save and IGA.

Financial Performance

Associated Wholesale Grocers (AWG) has grown net sales in recent years from $7.8 billion in 2016 to more recent results exceeding $9.0 billion. Net income has trended positively over the same period from $175 million in 2012 to a spiked of more than $225 million in 2014 to a current result near $190 million.

For the year 2016 net sales grew 3% to $9.2 billion. Product price deflation pushed sales lower as did the loss of Albertsons? membership in the distribution co-op. AWG gained 800 new member stores in conjunction with its unification with Affiliated Foods Midwest which increased sales sufficiently to overcome the negative influencers.

Net income for the year was $190 million 4% lower than the prior year due to a corresponding increase in the co-op?s general and administrative expenses.

Strategy

As a supplier to primarily independent and non-national grocers the co-op must retain size in order to compete with larger corporate firms. Years 2016 and 2017 saw its size shrink in Texas particularly in the hotly contested Dallas-Fort Worth market. Associated Wholesale Grocers lost two key members Albertsons (owner of Tom Thumb?s and Safeway) and WinCo. It countered this by uniting with Affiliated Foods Midwest a distribution co-op with some 800 retail stores but the loss of such notable members is expected influence AWG?s posturing within the North Texas area.

AWG continues to build sales of its billion-dollar private-label products line which includes the Best Choice IGA and Always Save brands. In addition to marketing the products as lower-cost alternatives to brand-name products the co-op has been investing in efforts to make sure the quality of its private-label items matches competing national brands. The company also owns and operates the Value Merchandisers Company (VMC) which offers some 22000 nonfood items to its members including health and beauty care general merchandise and seasonal and promotional products.

Operating in a fragmented business AWG competes with a large number of local and regional suppliers as well as distributors of specialty items. The food wholesale business also has its share of national giants including C & S Wholesale Nash-Finch and wholesale grocery and retail company SUPERVALU.

EXECUTIVES

SVP and Division Manager Nashville, Mike Danes
EVP and Chief Marketing Officer, Steve Arnold
SVP and Division Manager Memphis, Gary Jennings
SVP Finance, David Carl
SVP Distribution, Richard Kearns
SVP and CIO, Jon Payne
SVP and Division Manager Fort Worth, Linda
 Lawson
SVP Springfield, Tim Bellanti
EVP Division Operations, David Smith
SVP and Division Manager Oklahoma City, Danny
 Lane
SVP Grocery Products, Dan Funk
SVP Perishables, Jerry Edney
SVP and Division Manager Gulf Coast, Bob Durand
President Valu Merchandisers Company (VMC),
 Dave Sutton
President Always Fresh, Michael Schumacher
SVP and Division Manager Kansas City, David
 Gates
Senior Vice President, Maurice Henry
Vice President Deli Bakery, Dan Koch
Vice President of Sales Great Lakes, Sonny Leon
Chairman, Bob Hufford
Vice Chairman, Don Woods

LOCATIONS

HQ: ASSOCIATED WHOLESALE GROCERS, INC.
 5000 KANSAS AVE, KANSAS CITY, KS 661061135
Phone: 913 288-1000
Web: WWW.AWGINC.COM

COMPETITORS

Affiliated Foods	GSC Enterprises
Affiliated Foods Midwest	H. T. Hackney
Albertsons	McLane
Alex Lee	SUPERVALU
C&S Wholesale	SpartanNash
Central Grocers	Wakefern Food
Dearborn Wholesale Grocers	Wal-Mart
	WinCo Foods

HISTORICAL FINANCIALS

Company Type: Private

Income Statement

FYE: December 26

	REVENUE ($ mil.)	NET INCOME ($ mil.)	NET PROFIT MARGIN	EMPLOYEES
12/15	8,935	198	2.2%	5,500
12/14	8,934	226	2.5%	—
12/13	8,380	192	2.3%	—
12/12	7,852	175	2.2%	—
Annual Growth	4.4%	4.2%	—	—

2015 Year-End Financials

Debt ratio: —
Return on equity: 2.20%
Cash ($ mil.): 166
Current ratio: 0.60
Long-term debt ($ mil.): —
Dividends
Yield: —
Payout: —
Market value ($ mil.): —

Assurant Inc

From appliance protection to trailer park coverage Assurant provides a diverse range of specialty insurance products. Through primary operating segments Assurant Solutions and Assurant Specialty Property the firm offers such products as manufactured home coverage creditor-placed homeowners insurance pre-need funeral policies and extended service contracts for electronics appliances and vehicles. Assurant's products are distributed through sales offices and independent agents across the US and in Latin America Europe and Asia.

Operations

Assurant operates through three primary segments: Global Lifestyle Global Housing and Global Preneed. The largest segment Global Lifestyle provides mobile device protection and extended service contracts for consumer electronics and appliances vehicle protection and credit and related insurance. That segment accounts for about half of the company's total revenues.

The Global Housing segment offers lender-placed insurance multi-family housing products (renters insurance and related offerings) and mortgage solutions (such as property inspection valuation and title services). Other products include homeowners flood and manufactured housing insurance. Global Housing brings in about 30% of Assurant's revenues.

The Global Preneed segment offers pre-funded funeral insurance and annuities in the US and Canada. It accounts for around 5% of total revenue.

Geographic Reach

More than 85% of Assurant's sales are in the US but the company also operates in Argentina Brazil Canada Chile China Colombia France Germany Italy Ireland Mexico Peru Puerto Rico South Korea Spain and the UK. The company has 45 offices worldwide including 34 offices in North America.

Sales and Marketing

Assurant sells its products through independent brokers agents financial institution representatives and third-party marketing organizations as well as through retail outlets including mortgage loan offices funeral homes and retailers. It markets multi-family housing products through property management companies and affinity marketing partners.

Financial Performance

After years of modest growth Assurant's revenue declined 27% to $7.5 billion in 2016. This was driven by a 40% decline in net earned premiums primarily in the housing segment. Improving economic conditions has lessened demand for lender-placed insurance for example. Net investment income also dropped that year.

Despite the lower revenue Assurant's net income rebounded (and then some) from the previous year. Having fallen 70% in 2015 net income rose nearly 300% to $565.4 million in 2016. This was largely due to a decline in losses and expenses related to the winding down of Assurant Health.

However cash flow from operations fell 40% to $134.5 million in 2016 due to changes in operating assets and liabilities such as premium stabilization program receivables and premiums and accounts receivables.

Strategy

Assurant typically expands by pursuing a conservative acquisition strategy investing in small purchases that neatly complement its existing offerings. In addition Assurant partners with other companies to expand its reach.

Assurant also works to develop innovative niche products. In 2016 the company launched Assurant Product Protection which allows e-commerce businesses to offer extended protection plans to their customers. Other new products include small business protection against losses from data breaches (offered in partnerships with cybersecurity firms My DigitalShield and SnoopWall) and protection from cyberattacks to small business website owners (offered in partnership with other cybersecurity firm GamaSec).

With its sights set on growth in the mortgage and multifamily markets Assurant sold its general agency business and carrier American Reliable Insurance Company (personal lines and agricultural property/casualty coverage) to a US subsidiary of Global Indemnity for $114 million in early 2015. The sale allowed the company to better organize its business structure and to have more funding towards market growth.

To focus on specialty housing and lifestyle protection products Assurant exited the health insurance and employee benefits markets in 2016. With a wary eye on US health care reform it divested the underperforming Assurant Health (which as an insurer focused on serving small employers and individuals struggled under the Affordable Care Act) that year. It sold certain Assurant Health assets to National General Holdings and shuttered the rest of the business.

Also that year the company sold Assurant Employee Benefits (another underperforming unit) to Sun Life Financial in a deal valued at some $975 million. That sale further allowed Assurant to focus on such products as property credit renters funeral and flood policies.

Mergers and Acquisitions

In 2016 Assurant acquired American Title (title and valuation services for home equity lenders) for $45 million. The following year Assurant bought Green Tree Insurance Agency from Walter Investment Management for $125 million plus additional performance-based payouts. Green Tree sells housing protection products such as homeowners' and manufacturing housing insurance.

Also in 2017 the company agreed to buy a controlling stake in The Warranty Group. The $2.5 billion deal will greatly expand the number of automobiles Assurant covers as well as boosting its financial service contract and extended service contract numbers and growing its international operations.

Company Background

Assurant traces its roots to the LaCrosse Mutual Aid Association which was founded in 1892 to provide disability insurance in Wisconsin. The company formerly known as Fortis Inc. was spun off by the Fortis group (now known as Ageas) in 2004 and became publicly traded.

EXECUTIVES

EVP Chief Legal Officer and Secretary, Bart R. Schwartz, age 64, $595,000 total compensation
President Global Home, Michael P. Campbell
EVP and Chief Communication and Marketing Officer, Francesca Luthi
President and CEO, Alan B. Colberg, age 55, $955,000 total compensation
EVP and Chief Risk Officer, Christopher J. Pagano, age 53, $639,583 total compensation
EVP CFO and Treasurer, Richard S. Dziadzio, age 54, $283,205 total compensation
EVP and COO, Gene E. Mergelmeyer, age 58, $657,500 total compensation
EVP and CTO, Ajay Waghray, age 55, $338,335 total compensation
EVP and Chief Human Resources Officer, Robyn Price Stonehill, age 45
President Global Lifestyle, Keith W. Demmings
EVP and Chief Strategy Officer, Robert A. Lonergan
Vice President Hazard Product Business Manager, Shawn Kelly
Senior Vice President, Lynn Gelsomin
Senior Vice President Global Sales And Business Development, Allen Tuthill
Executive Vice President Valuations, Jennifer Sells
Chair, Elaine D. Rosen, age 64
Auditors: PricewaterhouseCoopers LLP

LOCATIONS

HQ: Assurant Inc
28 Liberty Street, 41st Floor, New York, NY 10005
Phone: 212 859-7000
Web: www.assurant.com

2016 Sales

	$ mil.	% of total
US	6,239	83
Other countries	1,292	17
Total	**7,531**	**100**

PRODUCTS/OPERATIONS

2016 Sales

	$ mil.	% of total
Lifestyle	3,819	50
Housing	2,361	31
Preneed	431	6
Employee Benefits	199	3
Corporate & other	720	10
Total	**7,531**	**100**

Business Segments & Products
Assurant Solutions
   Credit insurance (domestic and international)
   Debt protection/deferment
   Preneed life insurance (pre-funded funeral insurance)
   Warranties and Extended Service Contracts (ESCs domestic and international)
Assurant Specialty Property
   Homeowners insurance (creditor-placed and voluntary)
   Manufactured housing insurance (creditor-placed and voluntary)
   Other specialty property personal lines (primarily flood and renters insurance)

COMPETITORS

Allstate	Home Buyers Warranty
AmTrust Financial	Homesteaders Life
American Home Shield	Maiden Holdings
Americo	Monumental Life
Asurion	Mutual of Omaha
Bankers Financial	NGL Insurance
Fidelity National	Nationwide
Financial	QBE First

First American
Great American
Insurance Company

State Farm
The Warranty Group
Warrantech

HISTORICAL FINANCIALS

Company Type: Public

Income Statement

FYE: December 31

	ASSETS ($ mil.)	NET INCOME ($ mil.)	INCOME AS % OF ASSETS	EMPLOYEES
12/17	31,843	519	1.6%	14,750
12/16	29,709	565	1.9%	14,700
12/15	30,043	141	0.5%	16,700
12/14	31,562	470	1.5%	17,600
12/13	29,714	488	1.6%	16,600
Annual Growth	1.7%	1.5%	—	(2.9%)

2017 Year-End Financials

Debt ratio: 3.35%
Return on equity: 12.42%
Cash ($ mil.): 996
Current ratio: —
Long-term debt ($ mil.): —

No. of shares (mil.): 52
Dividends
Yield: 0.0%
Payout: 22.9%
Market value ($ mil.): 5,286

	STOCK PRICE ($) FY Close	P/E High/Low		PER SHARE ($) Earnings	Dividends	Book Value
12/17	100.84	11	9	9.39	2.15	81.47
12/16	92.86	10	7	9.13	2.03	73.26
12/15	80.54	42	29	2.05	1.37	68.70
12/14	68.43	11	9	6.44	1.06	74.77
12/13	66.37	10	5	6.30	0.96	67.29
Annual Growth	11.0%	—	—	10.5%	22.3%	4.9%

AT&T Inc

If there's a way to communicate there's a good chance AT&T Inc. provides it. The company offers services via wireless wireline satellite WiFi IP network Virtual Private Network and fiber optic cable. The company is the biggest wireline voice provider and the second biggest wireless provider (behind Verizon Communications) in the US with more than 135 million subscribers. It offers digital TV (as well as voice and internet service) through its U-verse brand and satellite Pay TV through DIRECTV. AT&T in October 2016 agreed to buy Time Warner Inc. for $85 billion. The deal would unite AT&T's distribution capabilities with Time Warner's content which includes HBO.

Operations

AT&T's Business Solutions segment is its biggest unit generating about 45% of revenue. The unit provides services to business governmental and wholesale customers and individual subscribers who purchase wireless services through employers.

The Entertainment Group accounts for about 30% of revenue by providing video internet interactive and targeted advertising services and voice services to US residential customers. The group includes AT&T?s DIRECTV and U-verse operations. The Consumer Mobility business about 20% of revenue provides wireless services to consumers and wireless wholesale and resale services in the US. The international unit which consists mostly of operations in Brazil and Mexico accounts for the remaining revenue.

Geographic Reach

Dallas Texas-based AT&T has spectrum licenses in all 50 US states Puerto Rico and Washington

DC. About 95% of AT&T?s revenue is generated in the US. Its wireless services and mobile broadband services are available in about 200 countries but most of its international revenue comes from Mexico and Brazil.

Sales and Marketing

AT&T is a big advertiser to businesses and consumers with presence on TV print and online. The company operates its own retail stores. It offers smartphones from major manufacturers such as Apple and Samsung. The company spends more than $3.5 billion a year on advertising about $1 billion more than wireless rival Verizon Communications.

Financial Performance

AT&T posted $164 billion in revenue in 2016 a 12% gain from 2015 continuing a seven year string of increases. The company?s profit however was 3% lower in 2016 than 2015.

AT&T?s 2015 acquisition of the satellite DIRECTV service fueled the surge in revenue in 2016. The acquisition led to a 45% increase in sales for AT&T?s entertainment unit in 2016. The segment also had growth in consumer IP broadband offsetting reduced revenue from legacy voice and data products. In its business unit AT&T?s IP broadband (virtual private network and Ethernet-related) services brought in more revenue. Wireless revenue suffered as AT&T offered calling plans with lower monthly rates to counter offers from competitors. Revenue fell in the consumer mobility business as customers moved to the business solutions segment and Mobile Share plans. Plans that allow subscribers to buy wireless service through employer-sponsored plans for a reduced price are in the business solutions segment.

Average revenue per user (ARPU) a key measure for carriers has trended lower for AT&T. Postpaid phone ARPU was $59.45 in 2016 down from $60.45 in 2015 and $62.99 in 2014.

AT&T ended subsidizing phone purchases in early 2016. Now customers either buy phones from the company on installment or use phones bought elsewhere. At the end of 2016 more than 50% of postpaid smartphone customers were on an installment program compared to about 45% the year before. More than 90% of postpaid smartphone adds and upgrades during 2016 were either on installment plans or had their own phone compared to 77% in 2015. Customers who have their own phones don?t generate equipment revenue or expense for AT&T but the service revenue improves its margins.

Net income slipped 3% to about $13 billion in 2016 from 2015. Higher expenses in 2016 came from the acquisition of DIRECTV and the acquisition of content for entertainment purposes. The company also has greater noncash financing-related costs related to pension and post-retirement benefits.

Cash flow from operations rose to about $39 billion in 2016 from $36 billion in 2015. The increase was from the DIRECTV acquisition and the timing of working capital payments.

Strategy

As the US wireless phone market becomes saturated (AT&T and Verizon count more than 280 million subscribers between them) carriers are looking for ways to generate more traffic on their networks to generate revenue. AT&T Inc. bought a content carrier DIRECTV in 2015. Its acquisition of Time Warner and its properties such as HBO is pending. DIRECTV provided a revenue boost 2016. AT&T?s network is built to support video and the company has already launched a streaming service DIRECTV Now.

AT&T has spent billions in capital expenditures on its LTE network buying spectrum and extending fiber optic lines to more than 12 million locations. The company is implementing software-de-

fined networking technologies so changes to the network can be done through software not hardware. That lowers costs of maintaining and upgrading the network. To make sure it all works AT&T had undertaken a massive retraining program to move workers to new roles and out of ones that are going the way of copper landlines.

The company has outfitted nearly 5 million cars in deals with automakers. It bets that connected car agreements provide the opportunity to develop retail relationships. Beyond that AT&T?s connected cars strategy extends the networks that connect autonomous vehicles and other parts of the transportation infrastructure.

Wireless phone service is still the bulk of AT&T's business and the company intends to maintain its position as an industry leader. In 2016 the company introduced new plans such as Mobile Share and AT&T Next to keep customers and attract new ones. It gained about 8 million subscribers with a plan that allows for unlimited wireless data when combined with the company's video services. The has invested some $27 billion in spectrum over the past five years. It has 40 MHz of fallow spectrum.

AT&T continues to develop 5G network technology which is to offer faster speeds and more capacity than current 3G and 4G networks and will enable new applications. The company has set up test works in several US cities including Austin Texas and Indianapolis Indiana.

Mergers and Acquisitions

AT&T extended its efforts to use software to manage networks with its acquisition of the Vyatta network operating system from Brocade Communications. The deal reached in June 2017 includes the vRouter product line; AT&T intends to hire employees associated with the business. AT&T expects the Vyatta platform to help virtualize its network and control it with software. The deal was expected to close in summer 2017.

In April 2017 AT&T said it would spend $1.25 billion to buy Straight Path Communications which owns licenses to wireless spectrum. That is until rival Verizon Inc. swooped in with a $3.1 billion bid. Verizon gets Straight Path's large holdings of 28 GHz and 39 GHz millimeter wave spectrum used in mobile communications.

AT&T agreed to buy Time Warner for $85 billion in 2016 in a deal that would unite a creator of popular content with a distribution network that would reach screens of all sizes. Time Warner's holdings include HBO CNN TNT TBS and the Warner Bros. Studio which produces movies such as the Harry Potter franchise and TV shows (such as the Big Bang Theory). The blockbuster deal will face scrutiny from members of Congress and regulators concerning the concentration of end-to-end content creation and distribution.

The deal for Time Warner followed AT&T's acquisition of satellite pay-TV provider DIRECTV for $48.5 billion in mid-2015. The combination enables AT&T to offer new packaged services and deliver content on mobile devices TVs laptops cars and airplanes.

Two other significant acquisitions made AT&T one of the biggest mobile carriers in Mexico. The purchases of Iusacell and Nextel Mexico in 2015 brought AT&T nearly nationwide coverage of Mexico and about 100 million people.

In 2014 it purchased Leap Wireless (which operates under the Cricket brand) for some $1.2 billion in an effort to build its profile in the prepaid market and expand its LTE network.

The deal for Time Warner followed by about a year AT&T's acquisition of satellite pay-TV provider DIRECTV for $48.5 billion in mid-2015. The combination enables AT&T to offer new packaged services and deliver content on mobile devices TVs laptops cars and airplanes.

Two other significant acquisitions made AT&T one of the biggest mobile carriers in Mexico. The purchases of Iusacell and Nextel Mexico in 2015 brought AT&T nearly nationwide coverage of Mexico and a potential customer pool of 100 million.

In 2014 it purchased Leap Wireless (which operates under the Cricket brand) for some $1.2 billion in an effort to build its profile in the prepaid market and expand its LTE network.

EXECUTIVES

Senior Executive Vice President And Chief Financia, Richard Lindner
CEO Business Solutions and International, F. Thaddeus Arroyo, age 53
SEVP Human Resources, William A. (Bill) Blase, age 62
SEVP and CFO, John J. Stephens, age 58, $870,833 total compensation
Chairman and CEO, Randall L. Stephenson, age 57, $1,791,667 total compensation
CEO AT&T Entertainment and Internet Services AT&T Services Inc., John T. Stankey, age 55, $965,833 total compensation
SEVP and Global Marketing Officer, Lori M. Lee, age 51
President Public Sector and Wholesale Solutions, Xavier Williams
CEO AT&T Communications, John M. Donovan, age 56, $858,833 total compensation
SEVP External and Legislative Affairs AT&T Services Inc., Robert W. (Bob) Quinn, age 56
SEVP and General Counsel, David R. McAtee, age 48
SEVP and Chief Compliance Officer, David S. Huntley, age 58
CEO New Advertising & Analytics Company, Brian Lesser
President Business Operations AT&T Business, Sorabh Saxena
Senior Vice President Business Marketing Sbc Operations Inc, Mark Keiffer
Assistant Vice President Growth Platforms, Marcus Owenby
Vice President, Judy Phillips
Vice President Tax, Lawrence J Ruzicka
Senior Vice President Of Emerging Devices, Chris Penrose
Sales Vice President Premier Client Group, Sean Murphy
Area Vice President Government Solutions Group, Tim Walsh
Senior Vice President Finance, David Muro
Vice President Of Sales, Michael Eisenhardt
Assistant Vice President C And E Osp, James Keown
Vice President Of Workforce Development And Diversity, Belinda Grant-anderson
Regional Vice President, Craig Warbinton
Vice President Customer Service, Steve Schoonmaker
Vice President Wholesale Wireline Sales, Joan Jambor
Senior Vice President U Verse Field Oprations, Randy Tomlin
Area Vice President Mobility Solutions, Lee Wagner
Information Technology Vice President, Hulsey R David
Assistant Vice President Ran Engineering, Rajive Beri
Regional Vice President Business Integrated Solutions At At And T Mobility, Maurice Styles
Vice President Business Develo, Joseph Mosele
Sales Center Vice President, Craig Dieckhoner
Vice President Financial Planning, George Goeke
Senior Vice President Corporate Strategy, Steve McGaw
Vice President Of Acquisitions, James Bielar

Rvp, Meredith Caram
Associate Vice President, Tara Colon
Assistant Vice President Network Services, Raymond Perkins
Vice President Fleet Operations, Jerome Webber
Vice President Strategy and Capital Planning, Ebrahim Keshavarz
Vice President Communication S, Monte Cely
Assistant Vice President Network Contracting, Roland Tunez
Assistant Vice President Business Advertising, Kelly Thengvall
Vice President And General Manager, Gary Lackhouse
Assistant Vice President Product Management, Tony Driscoll
Sales Vice President, Steve Williams
Assistant Vice President Financial Analysis, Bonnie Gover
Senior Vice President and Assistant General Counsel, William Bill Drexel
Assistant Vice President Communications, Sarah Donohue
Regional Vice President Global Access Management, Bob Flappan
Vice President Att Com, Philip Bienert
Vice President, Michele Smith
Vice President International And Wholesale, Robert Rossi
Assistant Vice President Information Technology, Kristi Dryden
Vice President Investor Relations, John G Palmer
Assistant Vice President Information Technology Finance, Joe Parsons
Director Of Government Relations, Jane Sosebee
Vice President Supply Chain, Keith Connolly
Regional Vice President External Affairs, Brooke Thomson
Vice President Of Chemical Development, Damon Holzer
Vice President U Verse Product Managemetn, G W Shaw
Assistant Vice President Network Engineering, Phil Law
Assistant Vice President Financial Analysis, Matthew Davis
Att Ravpn Contact, Sam Tuffaha
Senior Vice President, Bruce Goemaat
Director Evpn, Gregory Feenstra
Assistant Vice President Enterprise Managed Services, Bill Kramer
Vice President Bus Solutions Digital Experience, Laura Merling
Area Vice President At And T Mobility Smb, Jeff Goldstein
Vice President, Michael Flanagan
Vice President Small Business Product Management, Tom Hughes
Regional Vice President, Stephen Vergine
Sales Center Vice President, Vicky Santangelo
Executive Vice President Wholesale And Gem Solutio, Sherry Morse
Assistant Vice President Global Media Relations, Fletcher Cook
Assistant Vice President Project Program Management, William Schutts
Assistant Vice President (Assistant Vice President) Accounting, Lonnie Shirey
Vice President Of Project Development, Jeff Lewis
Vice President, Polly Bessel
National Account Manager, Kevin Moore
National Account Manager, Dean Ramsey
Women of AT&T Vice President Communications, Vera Tveretinova
Sales Center Vice President, Steve D'Lugos
Assistant Vice President Financial Analysis, Shareron Willis
At And T Home Solutions Assistant Vice President, Valerie Scheder

Assistant Vice President and Chief Financial Officer Consumer IP Products, Jeff Fancher
Vice President, Dan Lafond
Vice President, Tim O'Brien
Vice President, Duff Armstrong
Assistant Vice President Accounting, James Lacy
Sales CENTER Vice President SCG, Robert Rothweiler
Assistant Vice President, Wendy Donoho
Sales Vice President, Dan Roche
National Sales Manager, Steve Mitchell
Mse And Vpn Engineering, Glenn Williman
Customer Network Operations Vice President, Marvonia Walker
Client Executive Vice President, Knute A Olson
Regional Sales Vice President and General Manager Americas Region, Joseph Ettore
Sales Vice President, Fred Monacelli
Vice President Audit Services, Gerry Chicoine
Senior Vice President External Affairs, Holly Reed
Vice President Broadband And Narrowband Operations, Diane Young
Vice President And Senior Counsel, Diana Fellure
Assistant Vice President, Andy Bouseman
Vice President Finance, Ed Claure
Vice President Marketing, John McEnaney
Regional Vice President Mobility Customer Care, Jenifer Robertson
Vice President Cpe Corporate Operations, John Wimmer
Area Vice President Industry Solutions Practice, Jim Huempfner
Vice President And Associate General Counsel, Michael Poddo
Vice President Business Development At And T Government Solutions, Robert Caffrey
Assistant Vice President Life Cycle Management Global Customer Service, Judy Miller
Senior Vice President Labor Relations Sbc Services, Michael Rodriguez
Assistant To Assistant Vice President Product Advertising, Pam Krueger
Vice President Antenna Solutions, Chad Townes
Executive Vice President Historian, Olga De La Vega
Senior Vice President Signature Global Client Groups, John Finnegan
Assistant Vice President Technical Project Management Antenna Solutions Group, Stephen McNamara
Vice President Supply Chain Operations, Jim McGuire
Vice President Corporate Strategy, Christopher Sambar
Vice President Finance, Philip Schmidt
Assistant Vice President Information Technology, Joanne Pate
Vice President Platforms And Enablers, Brad Mohs
Senior Vice President Advanced Solutions, Abhi Ingle
Architecture And Vendor Vice President, Ron Fowinkle
Assistant Vice President Billing Operations, Wesley Carpenter
Assistant Vice President Financial Analysis, Mike Kruger
Vice President Market Insights, Helen McGrath
Assistant Vice President Information Technology, Thomas E Hackemer
Vice President Service Platforms, Pari Bajpay
Vice President Consumer Marketing, Anthony Tuggle
Assistant Vice President Life Cycle Management, Armond Suraci
Vice President Premier Client Group, Trish Renz
Vice President Ip Platform, Maria Dillard
Vice President General Manager, Bob Holliday
Vice President Glbl Managed Services And Outsourcing, Constance Diehl-boyle
Vice President, Jack Duffy

Assistant Vice President Digital Care Strategy,
Kim Keating
Solution Implementation Manager At And T Vpn
Tunneling Services, Brian Congleton
Senior Vice President Managed Services, Robin
Young
Assistant Vice President National Security
Network Regulatory, Brooks Fitzsimmons
Vice President At&t University, Nate Edwards
First Vice President Membership, Barry Winkler
Senior Vice President Employee Communications
And Corporate Sponsorships, Gail Torreano
Assistant Vice President It At&t Inc, Judy Winkler
Rvp Sales, Jim Medenis
Vice President Sales, Kevin McKeand
Vice President Of U Verse Media Sales, Chris
Monteferrante
Auditors: Ernst & Young LLP

LOCATIONS

HQ: AT&T Inc
208 S. Akard St., Dallas, TX 75202
Phone: 210 821-4105
Web: www.att.com

2016 Sales

	$ mil.	% of total
United States	154,039	94
Latin America		
Brazil	2,797	2
Other	2,348	1
Mexico	2,472	2
Other	2,130	1
Total	**163,786**	**100**

PRODUCTS/OPERATIONS

2016 Sales

	% of total
Service	91
Equipment	9
Total	**100**

2016 Sales

	$ mil.	% of total
Business Solutions	70,988	43
Entertainment Group	51,295	31
Consumer Mobility	33,200	20
International	7,283	5
Corporate and Other	1,043	1
Certain Significant Items	(23)	–
Total	**163,786**	**100**

Selected Services

Voice
  Local
  Long-distance
  Wholesale
Data
  Application management
  Data equipment sales
  Data storage
  Database management
  Dedicated Internet service
  Digital television
  Directory and operator assistance
  Disaster recovery
  Enterprise networking
  Hardware and operating system management
  Internet access and network integration
  Managed Web hosting
  Network design
  Network implementation
  Network installation
  Network integration
  Network management
  Outsourcing
  Packet services
  Private lines
  Satellite video
  Switched and dedicated transport
  Voice-over-IP networks
  Wholesale networking
  WiFi

COMPETITORS

Altice USA	Level 3
CenturyLink	SAVVIS
Charter Communications	Sprint Communications
Comcast	T-Mobile USA
Consolidated	TDS Metrocom
Communications	Telephone & Data
Cox Communications	Systems
DISH Network	Time Warner Cable
EarthLink	U.S. Cellular
Equinix	Verizon
Frontier	XO Holdings
Communications	

HISTORICAL FINANCIALS

Company Type: Public

Income Statement

FYE: December 31

	REVENUE ($ mil.)	NET INCOME ($ mil.)	NET PROFIT MARGIN	EMPLOYEES
12/16	163,786	12,976	7.9%	268,000
12/15	146,801	13,345	9.1%	281,450
12/14	132,447	6,224	4.7%	253,000
12/13	128,752	18,249	14.2%	243,000
12/12	127,434	7,264	5.7%	242,000
Annual Growth	**6.5%**	**15.6%**	**—**	**2.6%**

2016 Year-End Financials

Debt ratio: 30.59%—
Return on equity: 10.53%
Cash ($ mil.): 5,788
Current ratio: 0.76
Long-term debt ($ mil.): 113,681

Dividends
  Yield: 0.0%
  Payout: 91.4%
Market value ($ mil.): —

	STOCK PRICE ($) FY Close	P/E High/Low	PER SHARE ($) Earnings	Dividends	Book Value
12/16	42.53	21 16	2.10	1.92	20.06
12/15	34.41	15 13	2.37	1.88	19.96
12/14	33.59	31 27	1.19	1.84	16.65
12/13	35.16	12 10	3.39	1.80	17.41
12/12	33.71	31 23	1.25	1.76	16.55
Annual Growth	**6.0%**	**— —**	**13.8%**	**2.2%**	**4.9%**

ATHENE ANNUITY & LIFE ASSURANCE COMPANY

LOCATIONS

HQ: ATHENE ANNUITY & LIFE ASSURANCE COMPANY
2000 WADE HAMPTON BLVD, GREENVILLE, SC
296151037
Phone: 864 609-1000
Web: WWW.ATHENEANNUITY.COM

HISTORICAL FINANCIALS

Company Type: Private

Income Statement

FYE: December 31

	ASSETS ($ mil.)	NET INCOME ($ mil.)	INCOME AS % OF ASSETS	EMPLOYEES
12/13	11,775	49	0.4%	120
12/12	10,481	11	0.1%	—
Annual Growth	**12.3%**	**330.4%**	**—**	**—**

Debt ratio: —
Return on equity: 22.80%
Cash ($ mil.): 331
Current ratio: —
Long-term debt ($ mil.): —

Dividends
  Yield: —
  Payout: —
Market value ($ mil.): —

Atlantic Capital Bancshares Inc

Auditors: Ernst & Young LLP

LOCATIONS

HQ: Atlantic Capital Bancshares Inc
3280 Peachtree Road NE, Suite 1600, Atlanta, GA
30305
Phone: 404 995-6050
Web: www.atlanticcapitalbank.com

HISTORICAL FINANCIALS

Company Type: Public

Income Statement

FYE: December 31

	ASSETS ($ mil.)	NET INCOME ($ mil.)	INCOME AS % OF ASSETS	EMPLOYEES
12/16	2,727	13	0.5%	347
12/15	2,638	(1)		361
12/14	1,314	7	0.6%	106
12/13	1,229	5	0.4%	
12/12	0	5	—	
Annual Growth	**—**	**22.6%**		

2016 Year-End Financials

Debt ratio: 1.81%
Return on equity: 4.52%
Cash ($ mil.): 165
Current ratio: —
Long-term debt ($ mil.): —

No. of shares (mil.): 25
Dividends
  Yield: —
  Payout: —
Market value ($ mil.): 477

	STOCK PRICE ($) FY Close	P/E High/Low	PER SHARE ($) Earnings	Dividends	Book Value
12/16	19.00	35 22	0.53	0.00	12.10
12/15	14.98	— —	(0.09)	0.00	11.79
Annual Growth	**6.1%**	**— —**	**—**	**—**	**0.7%**

Autoliv Inc.

The world's #1 manufacturer of car safety
equipment Autoliv aims to save lives by increasing
the survivability statistics of traffic accidents. It
makes components such as seat belts airbags anti-
whiplash systems and safety electronics. Other
products include rollover protection systems steering wheels (with airbags) night vision systems
radar systems and child seats. The company caters
to about every car maker in the industry and has
more than 100 locations around the globe. Car
making giant GM Renault/Nissan is one of its
largest customers. Autoliv was established in 1956.
  Operations
  Autoliv operates through two business segments: passive safety (75% of net sales; airbags

and seatbelts) and electronics (25%; passive safety electronics and active safety).

About 50% of its total revenue is generated from airbag products. The remainder of sales stem from seatbelt products (more than 25%) passive safety electronic products (10%) active safety products (more than 5%) and brake control systems (about 5%).

Geographic Reach

Autoliv has about 20 crash test tracks 20 technical centers and more than 80 production facilities in 27 countries. Its US operations are overseen by Autoliv ASP Inc. Its largest markets are the Americas (35% of total sales) Europe (31%) and Asia (34%).

Sales and Marketing

Renault/Nissan and Ford each contributed more than 10% of the company's total sales in 2016; Honda also represented 10%. In addition Hyundai/Kia (HKMC) is one of its fastest-growing customers also representing around 10% of sales. Other customers include BMW Mercedes Volvo Volkswagen Toyota FCA (Fiat Chrysler Automobiles) PSA Group and Great Wall Motors.

Financial Performance

Autoliv posted record-setting revenues of more than $10 billion in 2016. The historic total was fueled by 7% organic growth and additional sales from acquisitions.

Airbag products sales (including steering wheels) were favorably impacted by higher sales of inflatable curtains in Japan and Europe in addition to steering wheels especially in Europe. Sales of seatbelt products were also particularly strong in Europe and China during 2016. In addition the global trend towards more advanced and higher value-added seatbelt systems continued globally.

In North America Autoliv experienced a spike in sales of active safety products (automotive radars night vision systems cameras with driver assist systems and positioning systems). It also experienced growth for camera and radar products in Europe primarily as a result of Mercedes? increased demand for driving assistance. Sales of camera systems to BMW also contributed to the growth.

Autoliv's profits jumped 24% to reach $567 million in 2016 its highest total in about five years. This was due to the increased revenues coupled with the absence of restructuring charges it paid the previous year. Its operating cash flow increased from $751 million in 2015 to $868 million in 2016. Of the $868 million in cash for 2016 57% was used towards capital expenditures.

Strategy

The company is focused on growing by increasing its organic sales overseas. Over the years it has installed a propellant plant and a textile center in the surging region of China. A major advantage to expansion outside of its traditional market of North America is that cars built in developing economies have tended to lightly adopt safety features — so there is room for further penetration.

Mergers and Acquisitions

The company is focused on acquisitions in two key areas: active safety systems and growth markets.

In 2016 the company acquired a 51% interest in the entities that formed Autoliv-Nissin Brake Systems (ANBS) for approximately $263 million in cash. ANBS designs manufactures and sells products in the brake control and actuation systems business. Nissin Kogyo retained a 49% interest in ANBS.

Autoliv in 2015 also obtained the Automotive Solutions business of M/A-COM Technology Solutions Holdings (MACOM) for a total sum of $138.5 million. MACOM was combined with Autoliv's active safety product line and brought additional revenues of $30 million to its balance sheet.

HISTORY

Autoliv traces its origins back to 1956 when Autoliv AB a Swedish corporation pioneered automotive seat belt technology. By 1967 the company had invented the retractor belt. Granges Weda AB another maker of seat belt retractors acquired the company in 1975. Electrolux bought the Granges Group (later renamed SAPA) in 1989 and changed its name to Electrolux Autoliv. Throughout the 1980s and 1990s the company continued to grow through acquisitions buying seat belt manufacturing operations primarily in Europe but also in Australia and New Zealand. In 1994 the company changed its name to Autoliv AB and went public with Electrolux selling all its shares during the offering.

EXECUTIVES

Chairman President and CEO, Jan Carlson, age 57, $1,376,766 total compensation
CTO, Steven (Steve) Fredin, age 55, $578,240 total compensation
President Passive Safety, Mikael Bratt, age 50
Group VP Research and Development and CTO, Johan L ¶fvenholm, age 48
Group VP Finance and CFO, Mats Backman, age 49, $381,074 total compensation
China Vice President Quality, Jesse Crookston
Vice President Global Business Unit, Walter Guertler
Vice President, Erin Patrick
Vice President Corporate Communications, Thomas Jonsson
Vice President Engineering, Bernhard Pirkl
Treasurer, Thomas Williams
Auditors: Ernst & Young AB

LOCATIONS

HQ: Autoliv Inc.
Klarabergsviadukten 70, Section B,7th Floor, Box 70381, Stockholm SE-107 24
Phone: (46) 8 587 20 600
Web: www.autoliv.com

2016 Sales

	$ mil.	% of total
Asia		
China	1,766	18
Japan	949	9
Rest of Asia	901	9
Americas	3,380	34
Europe	3,075	30
Total	10,073	100

PRODUCTS/OPERATIONS

2016 Sales

	$ mil.	% of total
Passive Safety	7,918	78
Electronics	2,215	22
Corporate and other	5	
Inter-segment sales	(66.6)	-
Total	10,073	100

2016 Sales

	$ mil.	% of total
Airbags products	5,255	52
Seatbelts products	2,665	27
Passive Safety Electronics products	1,031	10
Active safety products	738	7
Brake control system	383	4
Total	10,073	100

Selected Products

Anti-whiplash seats
Child restraints
Electronics
Frontal airbags
Inflators
Leg airbags
Seat belts
Side-impact airbags
Steering wheels

Selected Subsidiaries and Affiliates

Airbags International Ltd (UK)
Autoflator AB
Autoliv AB
Autoliv Argentina SA
Autoliv ASP BV (The Netherlands)
Autoliv ASP Inc. (US)
Autoliv Australia Proprietary Ltd
Autoliv Autosicherheitstechnik GmbH (Germany)
Autoliv BKI SA (Spain)
Autoliv BV (The Netherlands)
Autoliv Canada Inc
Autoliv Cankor Otomotiv Emniyet Sistemleri Sanayi Ve (Turkey)
Autoliv China Electronics Co. Ltd
Autoliv do Brasil Ltda.
Autoliv East Europe AB
Autoliv Electronics AB
Autoliv Electronics SAS (France)
Autoliv France SNC
Autoliv Holding BV (The Netherlands)
Autoliv Holding Inc. (US)
Autoliv Holding Ltd. (UK)
Autoliv Italia S.P.A.
Autoliv Japan Ltd
Autoliv KFT (Hungary)
Autoliv KLE SAU (Spain)
Autoliv Ltd (UK)
Autoliv Nichiyo Co. (Japan)
Autoliv Overseas BV (The Netherlands)
Autoliv Poland Sp zoo
Autoliv Romania SA
Autoliv Safety Technology Inc. (US)
Autoliv Sicherheitstechnik GmbH (Germany)
Autoliv Southern Africa Pty Ltd
Autoliv Stakupress GmbH (Germany)
Autoliv Sverige AB
Autoliv Thailand Ltd
Autoliv UK Holding Ltd
Marling BV (The Netherlands)
Mei-An Autoliv Co. (59% Taiwan)
Nanjing Hongguang Autoliv Vehicle Safety Co. Ltd. (50% China)
NSK Safety Technology (Thailand) Co. Ltd.
OEA Inc. (US)
Svensk Airbag AB
Van Oerle Alberton BV (The Netherlands)
Van Oerle Alberton Holding BV (The Netherlands)
Van Oerle Webco Pty Ltd (Australia)

COMPETITORS

AISIN World Corp.	Key Safety Systems
ASHIMORI INDUSTRY CO. LTD.	Kongsberg Automotive
	Magna International
Autocam	Mitsubishi Electric
Bosch Corp.	NFA
CASCO Products	Neaton Auto Products
DENSO	Nihon Plast
Delphi Automotive Systems	Nippon Kayaku
	Sequa
Ensign-Bickford	Special Devices
Gentex	Takata
Hella	Toyoda Gosei
Honeywell International	Toyota Boshoku
International Textile Group	Valeo

HISTORICAL FINANCIALS

Company Type: Public

Income Statement

FYE: December 31

	REVENUE ($ mil.)	NET INCOME ($ mil.)	NET PROFIT MARGIN	EMPLOYEES
12/16	10,073	567	5.6%	70,300
12/15	9,169	456	5.0%	64,100
12/14	9,240	467	5.1%	60,000
12/13	8,803	485	5.5%	56,500
12/12	8,266	483	5.8%	50,900
Annual Growth	5.1%	4.1%	—	8.4%

2016 Year-End Financials

Debt ratio: 18.74%
Return on equity: 15.86%
Cash ($ mil.): 1,226
Current ratio: 1.59
Long-term debt ($ mil.): 1,323

No. of shares (mil.): 88
Dividends
Yield: 0.0%
Payout: 35.8%
Market value ($ mil.): 9,983

	STOCK PRICE ($) FY Close	P/E High/Low		PER SHARE ($) Earnings	Dividends	Book Value
12/16	113.15	20	15	6.42	2.30	41.68
12/15	124.77	25	19	5.17	2.22	39.22
12/14	106.12	21	17	5.06	2.12	38.63
12/13	91.80	19	13	5.07	2.00	42.18
12/12	67.39	13	10	5.08	1.89	39.36
Annual Growth	13.8%	—	—	6.0%	5.0%	1.4%

Automatic Data Processing Inc.

The original outsourcer Automatic Data Processing (ADP) has still got it. ADP is one of the largest payroll and tax filing processors in the world serving about 625000 clients. Employer services (payroll processing tax and benefits administration services) account for the majority of the company's sales and its PEO (professional employer organization) services are provided through ADP TotalSource. Other offerings include accounting auto collision estimates for insurers employment background checks desktop support and business development training services. The company in 2014 spun off its former dealer services segment.

Operations

In 2014 the company spun off its former dealer services segment (contributed 15% of 2014 revenue). It now operates across two segments.

The employer services segment (67%) offers a range of business outsourcing and HCM services throughout 35 countries. Its Professional Employer Organization (PEO) services segment (18%; aka ADP TotalSource) provides employment administration outsourcing services through a co-employment relationship in which employees who work at a client's location are co-employed by ADP and its client.

Geographic Reach

The company provides services in more than 100 countries spread across the Americas Europe the Middle East Africa and the Asia Pacific region.

Sales and Marketing

The company targets businesses of four types: Small Businesses with 1-49 employees; Midsized Business with 50-999 employees; Large Business with 1000+ employees; and Multinational Business with any number of employees.

Financial Performance

ADP has achieved unprecedented growth over the last several years with revenues climbing 8% from $11.3 billion in 2013 to peak at a record-setting $12.2 billion in 2014. Profits also jumped 8% from $1.4 billion to $1.5 billion over that same time period. Net cash inflow increased 16% in 2014 due to additional cash inflows.

The historic growth for ADP was fueled by increases in all its segments. Employer services sales spiked due to new business started during the year from new business bookings growth an increase in the number of employees on the company's clients' payrolls and the impact of price increases.

PEO services revenue increased due to a rise in the average number of worksite employees resulting in a surge in the number of new clients and growth in the company's existing clients.

The rise in profits for ADP in 2014 was driven by the increased revenues coupled with the absence of goodwill impairment losses it incurred the previous year.

Strategy

Over the years the data processing giant has been fortifying its core employer services and PEO operations while restructuring and working to cut costs in its dealer services division. Across all segments ADP has been expanding internationally and extending its services through acquisitions. It also continues to boost its Web-based software offerings and small-business services. In late 2014 it spun off its ADP Dealer Services operations to form CDK Global in order to focus on its core operations.

Mergers and Acquisitions

The company acquired two businesses during fiscal 2013 for approximately $40.4 million while it acquired seven businesses in fiscal 2012 for an aggregate purchase price of approximately $292.3 million.

HISTORY

In 1949 22-year-old Henry Taub started Automatic Payrolls a manual payroll preparation service in Paterson New Jersey. Taub's eight accounts created gross revenue of around $2000 that year. In 1952 his brother Joe joined the company and a childhood friend Frank Lautenberg took a pay cut to become its first salesman. Automatic Payrolls grew steadily during the 1950s. In 1961 the company went public and changed its name to Automatic Data Processing (ADP).

EXECUTIVES

President and CEO, Carlos A. Rodriguez, age 53, $1,000,000 total compensation
VP and CFO, Jan Siegmund, age 53, $650,000 total compensation
EVP Worldwide Sales and Marketing, Edward B. (Ed) Flynn, age 57, $525,000 total compensation
President Small Business Services Retirement Services and Insurance Services, John C. Ayala, age 49
President Added Value Services, Douglas W. (Doug) Politi, age 54
President Employer Services - TotalSource, Maria Black, age 42
VP Global Product and Technology, Stuart Sackman
President Major Account Services and ADP Canada, Tom Perrotti
Gvp Ivr Contact, Tong Lin
Vice President Global Procurement, Steve Verderano
Vice President of Sales Operations and Training, Art Baumann
Vice President Imp Operations, Chris Pollock
Vice President Operations, James Blake
Vice President Of Sales Minneapolis, Randy Nixon
Vice President, Randy Terbush
Vice President Technical Support Services, Jeffrey Abdool
Vice President Sales, Jeffrey Schilling
Vice President Product Managment, Linda Mougalian
Vice President of Sales Major Accounts, Trey Smith
Vice President Inside Sales, Mike Keim
Vice President And Assistant General Counsel, Barry Eisler
Vice President Of Sales, Jason Rayvis
Vice President Corporate, Michael Lindemann

Vice President of Information Technology, Bill Washkau
Division Vice President Sales, Peter Lynch
Vice President Offshore, Craig Spendiff
Vice President, Ram Janakiraman
Vice President Sales, Robert Sprague
Vice President Relationship Management, Chris Murphy
Vice President Telesales, Christina Badawy
Vice President and Head, Vipul Singh
Vice President Channel Sales, Gilbert Khreich
Vice President Sales, Nicholas Pirrung
Vice President, Mitch Kleiman
Vice President Enterprise Technology and Operations, Jim Cantwell
Staff Vice President Corporate Development, David Garfinkel
Vice President Sales Sbs, Anthony D Miskowiec
Vice President of National Accounts Marketing Programs, Amy Daniels
Vice President Information Technology Business Security, Josh Sowers
Vice President Sales, Ryan Anschuetz
Vice President Business Development, Jason Rusnak
Senior Vice President National Accounts, Christine Wood
Vice President of Sales Operations, Brant Biggers
Vice President Sales, Tim McGowan
Vice President, Joe Giampalmi
Vice President Business Operations and Portfolio Management, Bill O'Connell
Division Vice President Sales, Scott Halperin
Vice President Federal Taxes, David Curto
Vice President of Service ADP, Alexander Cruz
Vice President Technology, Jimmy Adams
VICE PRESIDENT OF SALES, Ted Huffman
Vice President and Chief Intellectual Property Counsel, Neal Feivelson
Vice President Financial, Johnathan Coleman
Vice President of Finance, Kristin Walle
Vice President of Sales, Jason Au
Vice President of Sales, Scott Tithof
Vice President Product Development, Vincent Vincent Civetta Civetta
Vice President Service Centers, Rob Longshore
Dvp Implementation, Troy Lamay
Vice President FP and A Sales Finance, Donna Lukasko
Vice President Marketing, John Antos
Dvp Rgm National Accounts, Jay Little
Vice President Sales, Venkatachalam Subramaniam
Vice President of Sales, Max Pearlstein
Vice President, Jaclyn Schweiger
Vice President Managing Counsel, Lisse Kravetz
Vice President of Strategic Alliances, Joe Brtalik
Senior Vice President, Joe DeSilva
Vice President Global Network Services O, Miriam Soza
Division Vice President Strategy and Business Development, Chris Rush
Division Vice President Business Engineering Solutions and Implementation, Greg Rowe
Vice President Fixed Income Portfolio Manager, Fran Migliocco
Senior Vice President of Corproate Procurement, Dee Dacosta
Area Vice President of Sales S Cal and Hawaii, Bob Grant
Vice President Administration, Kristine Fisher
Vice President Sales, Christine Talcott
Vice President of Strategic Advisory Services, Christopher Ryan
Vice President Storage Administration, Jim Sanandres
Vice President of Government Affairs, Tricia Russo
Vice President Benefits Outsrcng Cnsltnt, Linda Mott
Vice President Workforce Planning and Benefits Consulting, Sushma Tripathi

Vice President Inbound Service Specl Prod, Joseph Mullany

Regional Vice President of Sales, Javier Hernan

Vice President of Sales ADP TotalSource, Michael Sclafani

Vice President Client, Alisa Ross

Vice President Sales US and Canada, Tim Schmucker

Vice President, Sandy Angevine

National Sales Manager, Jerry Scholl

Vice President Sales, Anna Santolucito

Regional Vice President Of Sales, Sarah Pattermann

National Sales Manager, C J Donnelly

National Sales Manager, Gary Johnston

Vice President Of Sales, John Goglia

Div. Vice President Sales, Dave Piromalli

Vice President of Implementation, Courtney Orlowski

Vice President Broker Strategy, Courtney Simpkiss

Vice President Benefits Outsrcng Cnsltnt, Bernadette Nace

Vice President Client Services, Kathy Niswander

Senior Vice President, Jessica Mcilwain

Vice President Operations, Dan King

Vice President Sales, Matt Roberts

Vice President Sales, Vanessa Calderon

Vice President Sales Europe, Tim Johnson

Vice President of Sales, Jeff Phelps

Vice President Technical Services, Don Speer

Vice President, Ed Hurley-Wales

Vice President of Client Base Acquisitions, Wendy Hellman

Sbs Central Dvp, Michele Tomassetti

Vice President Assistant General Counsel, JONATHAN GLUCK

Vice President, Steve Nolan

Division Vice President, Jason Brower

Vice President Compensation, Val Stubbins

Vice President National Accounts of Canada, Stefan Sarazen

National Sales Manager, Scott Doherty

Vice President Marketing, Amy Selich

Division Vice President Sales, Craig Hamilton

Vice President Sales, John Piscioniere

Vice President of SBS Sales, April Jacob

Vice President Operations, Tim Seymour

Vice President of Process Management, Bill Snow

Senior Vice President Government Services, Deborah Sage

Workscape Vice President Consulting Services, Ellen Gonzalez

Vice President, Terri Sampson

Vice President, Nick Smith

Vice President Sales, Adrian Spires

Vice President And General Manager, Laurn Rice

Dvp Human Resources, Jill Altana

Vice President Human Resources Shared Services, Peggy Jude

Vice President Risk Management, Tom Duym

Vice President Comprehensive Bus Services, George Stanley

Adp Vice President Of Implementation, Greg Flach

Division Vice President General Manager Comprehensive Outsourcing Services, Glenn Pettigrew

Senior Vice President Human Resources Employer Services Group, Yvonne Surowiec

Vice President, Jeremy Dyer

Vice President Business Development and Strategy, Gautam Sukumar

National Sales Manager, Vince Scotto

Vice President and Director Internet Media, Grace Luongo

Vice President Executive Deferred Compensation, Rosemary Murphy-harris

Vice President Managing Counsel, Kevin Isom

Vice President Sales, Sean Burns

Associate Vice President, Manoj Jha

Vice President And General Manager Field Services Engineering, Doug Karlson

Vice President Sales, Gerald Nealon

Sales Director Vice President Major Accounts Bpo, Jeremy Samuelson

Vice President of Sales, Matthew Tuohy

Vice President, Michael Eberhard

Vice President and Assistant General Counsel, Lech Choroszucha

Auditors: Deloitte & Touche LLP

LOCATIONS

HQ: Automatic Data Processing Inc.
One ADP Boulevard, Roseland, NJ 07068
Phone: 973 974-5000   Fax: 973 974-5390
Web: www.adp.com

PRODUCTS/OPERATIONS

Selected Services

Dealer Services
  Business management
  Computer systems sales
  Employee productivity training
  Hardware maintenance
  Manufacturer and dealer data communications networks
  Software licensing and support
  Vehicle registration services
Employer Services
  401(k) record keeping and reporting
  Benefits administration and outsourcing
  Employment screening and background checks
  Human resource record keeping and reporting
  Payroll processing
  Tax filing
  Unemployment compensation management

COMPETITORS

Avatar Systems	Insperity
CBIZ	Intuit
Ceridian	Oasis Outsourcing
Computer Sciences Corp.	Paychex
	Reynolds and Reynolds
Enertia Software	Total System Services
Global Payments	TriNet Group
HP Enterprise Services	Ultimate Software

HISTORICAL FINANCIALS

Company Type: Public

Income Statement

FYE: June 30

	REVENUE ($ mil.)	NET INCOME ($ mil.)	NET PROFIT MARGIN	EMPLOYEES
06/17	12,379	1,733	14.0%	58,000
06/16	11,667	1,492	12.8%	57,000
06/15	10,938	1,452	13.3%	55,000
06/14	12,206	1,515	12.4%	61,000
06/13	11,310	1,405	12.4%	60,000
Annual Growth	2.3%	5.4%	—	(0.8%)

2017 Year-End Financials

Debt ratio: 5.39%
Return on equity: 40.99%
Cash ($ mil.): 2,780
Current ratio: 1.10
Long-term debt ($ mil.): 2,002

No. of shares (mil.): 445
Dividends
  Yield: 2.1%
  Payout: 57.8%
Market value ($ mil.): 45,595

	STOCK PRICE ($) FY Close	P/E High/Low		PER SHARE ($) Earnings	Dividends	Book Value
06/17	102.46	27	22	3.85	2.24	8.94
06/16	91.87	28	22	3.25	2.08	9.83
06/15	80.23	29	23	3.05	1.95	10.31
06/14	79.28	26	22	3.14	1.88	13.89
06/13	68.86	25	19	2.89	1.70	12.83
Annual Growth	10.4%	—	—	7.4%	7.1%	(8.6%)

AutoNation, Inc.

AutoNation wants to instill patriotic fervor in the fickle car-buying public. The brainchild of entrepreneur Wayne Huizenga (Waste Management Blockbuster) AutoNation is the #1 auto dealer in the US (ahead of Penske Automotive Group and Sonic Automotive). The firm owns more than 370 new-vehicle franchises in 15 states and it conducts online sales through AutoNation.com and individual dealer websites. It sells 35 new brands of new vehicles. AutoNation acquires local retail brands and transitions them to the AutoNation name. In addition to auto sales AutoNation provides maintenance and repair services sells auto parts and finances and insures vehicles which together account for the majority of profits.

Operations

AutoNation divides the vehicle market into three segments: Domestic Import and Premium Luxury all of which generate around a third of sales each. Imports accounts for more than 35% of sales while Domestic brands represent more than 30%. Its core brands of new vehicles include Toyota Ford Honda Nissan and General Motors.

The Premium Luxury Segment which sells new vehicles manufactured primarily by Mercedes-Benz BMW and Lexus contributes more than 30% of AutoNation's sales.

Geographic Reach

AutoNation has more than 370 new-vehicle franchises in +15 US states. Florida Texas and California are its largest markets accounting for 26% 21% and 17% respectively .

Sales and Marketing

AutoNation sells vehicles through its online website and its stores.

Financial Performance

The company has reported an upward trend in revenues since 2011.

In fiscal 2016 sales increased a further 4% to $21.6 billion on the back of growth in all product categories including $260.8 million growth in new vehicle sales and $226.6 million growth in used vehicle sales. Growth in new car sales primarily came from contributions from acquired businesses; same store sales declined 3% due to lower unit sales partially offset by a shift towards higher-value vehicles such as trucks and sports utility vehicles.

Net income fell 3% to $430.5 million due to disruptive manufacturer marketing and a more competitive automotive retail environment.

Cash from operations increased 2% to $516.0 million due to a decrease in working capital requirements partially offset by a decrease in earnings.

Strategy

The auto dealer is banking on the cach © of the AutoNation name to win sales and market share.

The company has invested and will continue to invest significantly in the AutoNation retail brand with the goals of enhancing its strong customer satisfaction and expanding its market share. It continues to make significant investments to build a seamless end-to-end customer experience in its stores and through its digital channels and to improve its ability to generate business through those channels.

A key element of the firm's business strategy is its diversified portfolio of 30-plus brands spanning imports premium luxury vehicles and domestic autos. Over the past decade AutoNation has increased the percentage of import and luxury cars it sells. It clusters dealerships within markets so that they can share inventory cross-sell to customers and reduce marketing costs — basically cutting and combining costs in an attempt to become the auto industry's Wal-Mart. As the economy improves AutoNation is looking for acquisition and new store opportunities.

In 2016 the company purchased 20 stores in Texas New York Colorado California and Maryland. It sold five Domestic stores and nine Import stores in the same year.

Hoping to capitalize on the possible takeover of self-driving cars in 2017 AutoNation signed a repair contract with Alphabet's self-drive unit Waymo. It will maintain and repair Waymo's Chrysler Pacific hybrid fleet as well as other brands that Waymo may develop in the future.

Mergers and Acquisitions

Historically AutoNation has been a driving force in the consolidation of the US car sales business. After an hiatus during the recession and credit crunch which put the brakes on acquisitions by mega dealers such as AutoNation the company is back in acquisition mode buying up around 20 stores and franchises each year.

In 2016 it acquired 20 stores in Texas New York Colorado California and Maryland. The acquisitions include Chrysler Dodge Jeep Ram Chevrolet Hyundai Mercedes-Benz Sprinter Jaguar Land Rover and BMW franchises.

HISTORY

AutoNation started in 1980 as Republic Resources which brokered petroleum leases did exploration and production and blended lubricants. In 1989 after oil prices crashed and a stockholder group tried to force Republic into liquidation Browning-Ferris Industries (BFI) founder Thomas Fatjo gained control of the company and refocused it on a field he knew well — solid waste. He renamed the firm Republic Waste.

Michael DeGroote founder of BFI rival Laidlaw bought into Republic in 1990. (Fatjo left the next year.) DeGroote's investment funded more acquisitions. Republic moved into hazardous waste in 1992 just before the industry nosedived due to stringent new environmental rules. In 1994 Republic spun off its hazardous-waste operations as Republic Environmental Systems and Republic's stock began rising immediately.

That attracted the attention of Wayne Huizenga who had founded Waste Management and Blockbuster Video. To him Republic was not merely a midsized solid-waste firm. No Huizenga saw Republic as a publicly traded vehicle that could allow him to tap into the stock market to fund his latest project: an integrated nationwide auto dealer — a first for the highly fragmented and localized industry.

In 1995 Republic bought Hudson Management a trash business owned by Huizenga's brother-in-law and Huizenga bought a large interest in Republic. As a result Huizenga took control of Republic's board. The firm became Republic Industries and DeGroote stepped back from active management.

Huizenga's investment helped Republic acquire more waste businesses and his name brought a flood of new investors. The firm diversified with electronic security acquisitions but growth in this field faltered with a failed bid to buy market leader ADT in 1996. (Republic sold its security division to Ameritech in 1997.)

By 1996 Huizenga's still-separate auto concept AutoNation was operational with 55 automobile franchises and seven used-car stores. Republic bought Alamo Rent A Car and National Car Rental System and in 1997 AutoNation was bought by Republic. The combined company continued buying dealerships and car rental firms at a sizzling rate.

Republic spun off its solid-waste operations to the public in 1998 as Republic Services. That year Republic bought or agreed to buy 181 new-car franchises opened nine AutoNation USA dealerships and opened 62 CarTemps USA insurance-replacement locations.

Republic became AutoNation in 1999.

Having survived a market downturn in the late 2000s in 2013 the company began marketing its domestic and import stores under the AutoNation retail brand in local markets. The re-branding of the stores which previously operated under various local market retail brands (including Mike Shad in Jacksonville Florida and GO in Colorado) was completed that year. (The exception is the company's luxury dealership business which will continue to operate under their existing retail brands.) Using its website store signage and media presence the car dealer is working to increase consumer awareness of the AutoNation brand.

In 2013 the company acquired 12 franchises.

EXECUTIVES

Executive Vice President Secretary and General Counsel, Jonathan Ferrando

Chairman and CEO, Michael J. (Mike) Jackson, age 69, $1,250,000 total compensation

EVP and Chief Marketing Officer, Marc Cannon, age 55

EVP and CFO, Cheryl Miller, age 44, $596,875 total compensation

EVP Franchise Operations Mergers & Acquisitions and Corporate Real Estate, Donna Parlapiano, age 52, $532,084 total compensation

EVP General Counsel and Corporate Secretary, Coleman Edmunds

President Eastern Region, Jim Bender

EVP and CTO, Thomas M. (Tom) Conophy, age 56

President Western Region, Lance Iserman

President Central Region, Ron Ardisonne

SVP, Scott Arnold

Vice President Assistant General Counsel, Jill Bilanchone

Auditors: KPMG LLP

LOCATIONS

HQ: AutoNation, Inc.
200 S.W. 1st Avenue, Fort Lauderdale, FL 33301
Phone: 954 769-6000
Web: www.autonation.com

2016 Stores

	No.
Florida	52
Texas	47
California	40
Georgia	23
Colorado	17
Washington	16
Arizona	15
Nevada	11
Tennessee	8
Maryland	8
Illinois	7
Alabama	5
Ohio	4
New York	4
Virginia	2
Minnesota	1
Total	**260**

PRODUCTS/OPERATIONS

2016 Sales

	$ mil.	% of total
Domestic	7,810	36
Import	6,886	32
Premium Luxury	6,665	31
Corporate and other	247	1
Total	**21,609**	**100**

2016 Sales

	$ mil.	% of total
New vehicle	12,255	57
Used vehicle	4,995	23
Parts and service	3,321	15
Finance and insurance net	894	4
Other	141	1
Total	**21,609**	**100**

COMPETITORS

Asbury Automotive	JM Family Enterprises
Brown Automotive	Lithia Motors
CarMax	Penske Automotive
Ed Morse Auto	Group
Group 1 Automotive	Potamkin Automotive
Hendrick Automotive	Sonic Automotive
Holman Enterprises	

HISTORICAL FINANCIALS

Company Type: Public

Income Statement

FYE: December 31

	REVENUE ($ mil.)	NET INCOME ($ mil.)	NET PROFIT MARGIN	EMPLOYEES
12/17	21,534	434	2.0%	26,000
12/16	21,609	430	2.0%	26,000
12/15	20,862	442	2.1%	26,000
12/14	19,108	418	2.2%	24,000
12/13	17,517	374	2.1%	22,000
Annual Growth	**5.3%**	**3.8%**	**—**	**4.3%**

2017 Year-End Financials

Debt ratio: 26.32%	No. of shares (mil.): 91
Return on equity: 18.57%	Dividends
Cash ($ mil.): 69	Yield: —
Current ratio: 0.85	Payout: —
Long-term debt ($ mil.): 1,959	Market value ($ mil.): 4,700

	STOCK PRICE ($) FY Close	P/E High/Low		PER SHARE ($) Earnings	Dividends	Book Value
12/17	51.33	13	9	4.43	0.00	25.88
12/16	48.65	14	10	4.15	0.00	22.95
12/15	59.66	17	14	3.89	0.00	21.20
12/14	60.41	17	13	3.52	0.00	18.29
12/13	49.69	18	13	3.04	0.00	17.05
Annual Growth	**0.8%**	**—**	**—**	**9.9%**	**—**	**11.0%**

AutoZone, Inc.

With about 5500 stores in the US and Puerto Rico AutoZone is one of the nation's leading auto parts chains. It also has more than 500 stores in Mexico and about a dozen in Brazil and operates some two dozen Interamerican Motor Corporation (parts distribution) branches in the US. AutoZone stores sell hard parts (alternators engines batteries) maintenance items (oil antifreeze) accessories (car stereos floor mats) and non-automotive merchandise under brand names and private labels. AutoZone's commercial sales program distributes parts and other products to garages dealerships and other businesses.

Operations

AutoZone operates through one primary segment Auto Parts Stores which accounts for more than 95% of total revenue. Leveraging a consistent store format each AutoZone store boasts between 85% and 90% of selling space — up to 40% to 45% of which is dedicated to hard parts inventory. Stores are outfitted with Z-net AutoZone's proprietary electronic catalog that gives employees advice and information for customers' vehicles down to the year make model and engine type.

Other revenue is generated by e-commerce operations (autozone.com and autoanything.com) and diagnostic and other software (provided through the company's ALLDATA business) used in automotive repair.

Geographic Reach

Based in Tennessee AutoZone operates about 5500 AutoZone stores in 50 US states the District of Columbia and Puerto Rico. Texas California Florida Ohio and Illinois represent the company's largest markets and together account for more than a third of locations. The company's fast-growing subsidiary in Mexico AutoZone de M ©xico operates more than 500 stores. AutoZone also has stores in Brazil.

AutoZone has distribution centers in the US (Arizona California Georgia Illinois Ohio Pennsylvania Tennessee Texas and Washington) and Mexico; store support centers are located in Tennessee as well as Mexico and Brazil.

Sales and Marketing

AutoZone sells to do-it-yourself (DIY) consumers as well as repair garages dealers service stations and other commercial customers.

The company relies on targeted advertising and promotions to build its brand offer advice about the overall importance of vehicle maintenance and position its business as a great value. To drive traffic to its stores the retailer advertises on broadcast and Internet media. It works to educate consumers about which products they need through use of in-store signage and circulars as well as creative product placement and promotions.

Advertising expense for the company was $93.1 million in fiscal 2017 (ended August) and $98.3 million in fiscal 2016.

Financial Performance

New locations drive revenue growth for AutoZone which has seen an average revenue increase of 5% per year since 2012 (similar to the 4% average location increase over the same period of time). Net income has also ticked up consistently since 2012 as the company is keeping its net profit margin between 11%-12%.

In fiscal 2017 (ended August) the company reported revenue of $10.9 billion up nearly 2.5% from the prior year. New AutoZone locations in the US powered the growth adding more than $170 million. Same-store sales increased by half a percent.

Net income that year rose 3% to a record $1.3 billion on the increase in revenue and tight controls over cost of sales and expenses.

Cash at the end of 2017 was $293 million an increase of more than $100 million from the prior year. Cash from operations contributed $1.6 billion to the coffers while investing activities used about $550 million with increases the result of new distribution centers and additional investment in existing locations. Financing activities subtracted about $915 million as AutoZone repaid about $400 million in debt and purchased more than $1 billion in treasury stock.

Strategy

AutoZone's core strategy includes expanding its store network and store inventory to meet customer needs. It added about 215 stores in fiscal 2017 (on top of 205 in 2016 and 202 in 2015) and is focusing on new-store development while also enhancing its existing stores and infrastructure. Nearly 50 of the new stores in 2017 were opened in Mexico and Brazil. The company also opened two new distribution centers that year and has one under construction for 2018.

With an eye on expanding inventory AutoZone is focused on hub and mega hub locations which offer inventory two to four times broader than typical stores. In 2017 it opened four hub stores for a total of nearly 190 and five mega hub locations bringing that total to about 15. The company plans to have a total of 40 mega hub stores in operation over the next few years.

HISTORY

Joseph "Pitt" Hyde took over the family grocery wholesale business Malone & Hyde (established 1907) in 1968. He expanded into specialty retailing opening drugstores sporting goods stores and supermarkets but his fortunes began to race on Independence Day 1979 when he opened his first Auto Shack auto parts store in Forrest City Arkansas.

Using retailing behemoth Wal-Mart as a model Hyde concentrated on smaller markets in the South and Southeast emphasizing everyday low prices and centralized distribution operations. He stressed customer service to provide his do-it-yourself customers with expert advice on choosing parts. While a number of retailers have tried to copy Wal-Mart's successful model Hyde had an inside track: Before starting Auto Shack he served on Wal-Mart's board for seven years.

Auto Shack had expanded into seven states by 1980 and by 1983 it had 129 stores in 10 states. The next year Malone & Hyde's senior management with investment firm Kohlberg Kravis Roberts (KKR) took the company private in an LBO. Auto Shack continued to expand reaching 192 stores in 1984. The company was spun off to Malone & Hyde's shareholders in 1987 and Malone & Hyde's other operations were sold. The company changed its name to AutoZone in 1987 in part to settle a lawsuit with RadioShack.

To build its online presence AutoZone in 2013 acquired AutoAnything an online retailer of specialized automotive products.

EXECUTIVES

EVP Finance Information Technology and ALLDATA and CFO, William T. (Bill) Giles, age 58, $560,539 total compensation
Chairman President and CEO, William C. (Bill) Rhodes, age 52, $1,000,000 total compensation
SVP Commercial, Larry M. Roesel, age 60, $425,308 total compensation
SVP Merchandising and Store Development, Mark A. Finestone, age 56, $430,154 total compensation
EVP Mexico Brazil IMC and Store Development, William W. Graves, age 57, $430,154 total compensation
EVP Store Operations Commercial and Loss Prevention, Thomas B. Newbern, age 55, $430,154 total compensation
SVP and CIO, Ronald B. (Ron) Griffin, age 64, $407,692 total compensation
SVP Marketing and E-Commerce, Albert (Al) Saltiel, age 54
Auditors: Ernst & Young LLP

LOCATIONS

HQ: AutoZone, Inc.
123 South Front Street, Memphis, TN 38103
Phone: 901 495-6500
Web: www.autozone.com

2017 Stores

	No.
US	5,465
Mexico	524
Brazil	14
IMC Branches	26
Total	**6,029**

PRODUCTS/OPERATIONS

2017 Sales

	$ mil.	% of total
Auto Parts Locations	10,523	97
Other	365	3
Total	**10,888**	**100**

Selected Merchandise

Accessories
  Car stereos
  Floor mats
  Lights
  Mirrors
Hard Parts
  Alternators
  Batteries
  Brake shoes and pads
  Carburetors
  Clutches
  Engines
  Spark plugs
  Starters
  Struts
  Water pumps
Maintenance Items
  Antifreeze
  Brake fluid
  Engine additives
  Oil
  Power steering fluid
  Transmission fluid
  Waxes
  Windshield wipers
Other
  Air fresheners
  Dent filler
  Hand cleaner
  Paint
  Repair manuals
  Tools

Selected Brands

ALLDATA
AutoZone
Duralast
Duralast Gold
ProElite
SureBilt
Valucraft

COMPETITORS

Advance Auto Parts	Goodyear Tire & Rubber
Amazon.com	O'Reilly Automotive
CARQUEST	Pep Boys
Costco Wholesale	Sears Holdings
Fisher Auto Parts	Target Corporation
Genuine Parts	Wal-Mart

HISTORICAL FINANCIALS

Company Type: Public

Income Statement

FYE: August 26

	REVENUE ($ mil.)	NET INCOME ($ mil.)	NET PROFIT MARGIN	EMPLOYEES
08/17	10,888	1,280	11.8%	87,000
08/16	10,635	1,241	11.7%	84,000
08/15	10,187	1,160	11.4%	81,000
08/14	9,475	1,069	11.3%	76,000
08/13	9,147	1,016	11.1%	71,000
Annual Growth	**4.5%**	**6.0%**	**—**	**5.2%**

2017 Year-End Financials

Debt ratio: 55.39%
Return on equity: ***,***.**%
Cash ($ mil.): 293
Current ratio: 0.97
Long-term debt ($ mil.): 5,081
No. of shares (mil.): 27
Dividends
  Yield: —
  Payout: —
Market value ($ mil.): 14,722

	STOCK PRICE ($)	P/E		PER SHARE ($)		
	FY Close	High/Low	Earnings	Dividends	Book Value
08/17	528.95	18 11	44.07	0.00	(51.32)
08/16	753.47	20 17	40.70	0.00	(61.39)
08/15	726.39	20 14	36.03	0.00	(55.49)
08/14	538.84	17 13	31.57	0.00	(50.21)
08/13	419.94	16 12	27.79	0.00	(49.20)
Annual Growth	5.9%	— —	12.2%	—	—

Avangrid Inc

Auditors: KPMG US, LLP

LOCATIONS

HQ: Avangrid Inc
180 Marsh Hill Road, Orange, CT 06477
Phone: 207 688-6000
Web: www.avangrid.com

HISTORICAL FINANCIALS

Company Type: Public

Income Statement

FYE: December 31

	REVENUE ($ mil.)	NET INCOME ($ mil.)	NET PROFIT MARGIN	EMPLOYEES
12/16	6,018	630	10.5%	6,801
12/15	4,367	267	6.1%	6,809
12/14	4,594	424	9.2%	4,977
12/13	4,313	(65)		—
12/12	4,055	243	6.0%	—
Annual Growth	10.4%	26.9%	—	—

2016 Year-End Financials

Debt ratio: 16.03%
Return on equity: 4.17%
Cash ($ mil.): 91
Current ratio: 0.83
Long-term debt ($ mil.): 4,510

No. of shares (mil.): 308
Dividends
  Yield: 0.0%
  Payout: 84.7%
Market value ($ mil.): 11,705

	STOCK PRICE ($)	P/E		PER SHARE ($)		
	FY Close	High/Low	Earnings	Dividends	Book Value
12/16	37.88	23 17	2.04	1.73	48.90
12/15	38.40	36 32	1.05	0.00	48.74
Annual Growth	(0.3%)	— —	18.1%	—	0.1%

Avery Dennison Corp

Avery Dennison has worked out how to make the most of a sticky situation. The company is a world-leader in sticky labels used by businesses to add their branding to products such as drinks food personal care and pharmaceuticals. Its adhesives also extend to vinyl wraps and reflective markings for cars. Under the Avery Dennison and Fasson brands it makes papers films and foils coated with adhesive and sold in rolls to printers. Its most widely used products are the self-adhesive stamps used by the US Postal Service. It also makes retail branding and security tags printer systems and fasteners as well as medical adhesive products.

HISTORY

Avery Dennison was created in 1990 by the merger of Avery International and Dennison Manufacturing. In 1935 Stanton Avery founded Kum-Kleen Products which would become Avery International. After a fire destroyed the plant's equipment in 1938 Avery who had renamed the company Avery Adhesives improved the machinery used in making the labels.

During and after WWII Avery Adhesives shifted toward the industrial market for self-adhesives. The company incorporated in 1946. At that time Avery Adhesives sold 80% of its production consisting of industrial labels to manufacturers that labeled their own products.

The company lost its patent rights for self-adhesive labels in 1952 transforming the firm and the entire industry. As a result a new division was created — the Avery Paper Company (later renamed Fasson) — to produce and market self-adhesive base materials.

Avery Adhesives went public in 1961. Three years later it had four divisions: label products base materials Rotex (hand-operated embossing machines) and Metal-Cal (anodized and etched aluminum foil for nameplates). Renamed Avery International in 1976 the company closed some manufacturing facilities and cut 8% of its workforce in the late 1980s.

In 1990 Avery International merged with Dennison Manufacturing. Dennison was started in 1844 by the father-and-son team of Andrew and Aaron Dennison to produce jewelry boxes. By 1849 Aaron's younger brother Eliphalet Whorf (E.W.) was running the business and expanding it into tags labels and tissue paper. Dennison was incorporated in 1878 with $150000 in capital.

By 1911 Dennison sold tags gummed labels paper boxes greeting cards sealing wax and tissue paper and it had stores in Boston Chicago New York City Philadelphia St. Louis and London. Henry Dennison E.W.'s grandson was president from 1917 to 1952.

From the 1960s to the 1980s Dennison spent heavily on research and development and helped to develop such products as electronic printers and pregnancy test supplies. In the mid-1980s the firm reorganized its operations selling seven businesses closing four others and focusing on stationery systems and packaging.

In addition to office products and product identification and control systems the 1990 merger combined Dennison's office products operations in France (Doret and Cheval Ordex) with Avery International's sizable self-adhesive base materials business.

Avery Dennison sold its 50% interest in a Japanese label converting company Toppan in 1996 clearing the way to develop its own businesses in Asia. In 1997 an alliance with Taiwanese rival Four Pillars turned sour when Avery Dennison accused the company of stealing trade secrets. (Two executives at Four Pillars were convicted of corporate espionage in 1999.)

President and COO Philip Neal was promoted to CEO in 1998. (He became chairman in 2000.) In 1999 adhering to its goal of global expansion Avery Dennison formed office products joint ventures in Germany with Zweckform Buro-Produkte and in Japan with Hitachi Maxell. Record 1998 sales and earnings were dampened by the news of slowing growth and in 1999 Avery Dennison closed five plants and began laying off workers. Later that year the company bought Stimsonite a maker of reflective highway safety products.

In early 2000 Avery Dennison began a $40 million expansion of its Chinese manufacturing operations while eliminating 1500 jobs worldwide. Later in the year the company agreed to jointly package instant imaging and labeling products with Polaroid. Several acquisitions in 2001 included CD Stomper (CD and DVD labels and software). Avery Dennison continued its acquisitive ways in 2002 acquiring Jackstadt (German maker of pressure-sensitive adhesive materials) RVL Packaging (maker of woven and printed labels and other tags for the apparel and retail industries) and L&E Packaging (key supplier and printer for RVL).

In 2003 the company sold its European package label converting business (including plants in Denmark and France) to label and packaging company CCL Industries. As part of the deal Avery Dennison began to supply pressure-sensitive base materials to CCL Industries. The divestiture was part of the company's strategy to concentrate its efforts in adhesive materials office products and retail information services.

Phillip Neal retired as chairman and CEO in 2005 and was replaced by director Kent Kresa as chairman and by Dean Scarborough as president and CEO.

The company completed a restructuring program in 2010 it began in 2008 that generated a total of $180 million in cost savings. It also paid down some $300 million in debt during that same period.

In 2011 Avery also decided to divest its Metalure pigments business which it sold to the Eckart Effect Pigments division of ALTANA. Eckart had been the distributor of the PVD-type aluminum pigments for more than 20 years.

In 2013 a subsidiary of Avery Dennison entered into a licensing agreement for RFID tags labels and readers with Round Rock Research LLC to facilitate further adoption of item-level RFID by US-based apparel retailers and brands.

In 2013 Avery Dennison sold its OCP and DES segments to CCL Industries for $500 million. The OCP segment makes school and office products (Avery Marks-A-Lot HI-LITER). It planned to use the proceeds from the deal to invest in its two core businesses and reduce debt and pension liability. (Avery had originally signed up 3M to buy OCP in 2011 but the deal fell through in 2012).

EXECUTIVES

SVP and Chief Human Resources Officer, Anne Hill, age 58, $512,787 total compensation
President Materials Group, Georges Gravanis, age 60, $523,775 total compensation
President and CEO, Mitchell R. Butier, age 46, $988,333 total compensation
SVP and CFO, Gregory S. (Greg) Lovins, age 44
Vice President Sales LGM, Gernot Ritzdorf
Chairman, Dean A. Scarborough, age 62
Auditors: PricewaterhouseCoopers LLP

LOCATIONS

HQ: Avery Dennison Corp
207 Goode Avenue, Glendale, CA 91203
Phone: 626 304-2000
Web: www.averydennison.com

2016 Sales

	$ mil.	% of total
Asia	1,996	33
Europe	1,838	30
US	1,525	25
Latin America	450	7
Other regions	275	5
Total	**6,086**	**100**

PRODUCTS/OPERATIONS

2016 Sales

	$ mil.	% of total
Label and Graphic Materials	4,187	69
Retail Branding and Information Solutions	1,445	24
Industrial and Healthcare Materials	453	7
Total	**6,086**	**100**

Selected Brands

Avery
Avery Dennison
Avery Graphics
Fasson

COMPETITORS

3M	Checkpoint Systems
ACCO Brands	Esselte
Beam Suntory	H.B. Fuller
Bemis	Newell Brands
Bostik	UPM-Kymmene
Brady Corporation	

HISTORICAL FINANCIALS

Company Type: Public

Income Statement

FYE: December 31

	REVENUE ($ mil.)	NET INCOME ($ mil.)	NET PROFIT MARGIN	EMPLOYEES
12/16*	6,086	320	5.3%	—
01/16	5,966	274	4.6%	—
01/15	6,330	248	3.9%	25,000
12/13	6,140	215	3.5%	26,000
12/12	6,035	215	3.6%	29,800
Annual Growth	**0.2%**	**10.5%**	**—**	**—**

*Fiscal year change

2016 Year-End Financials

Debt ratio: 29.40%
Return on equity: 34.01%
Cash ($ mil.): 195
Current ratio: 0.95
Long-term debt ($ mil.): 713

No. of shares (mil.): 88
Dividends
　Yield: 0.0%
　Payout: 45.2%
Market value ($ mil.): 6,201

	STOCK PRICE ($) FY Close	P/E High/Low	PER SHARE ($) Earnings	Dividends	Book Value
12/16*	70.22	22 16	3.54	1.60	10.48
01/16	62.66	22 17	2.95	1.46	10.73
01/15	51.79	20 16	2.60	1.34	11.79
12/13	50.48	23 16	2.16	1.14	15.51
12/12	34.40	17 13	2.08	1.08	15.82
Annual Growth	**19.5%**	**— —**	**14.2%**	**10.3%**	**(9.8%)**

*Fiscal year change

Avis Budget Group Inc

Avis Budget Group (ABG) has a car rental brand for you. The company's core brands include: Avis Rent A Car which targets corporate and leisure travelers at the high end of the market; Budget Rent A Car and Payless Car Rental both marketed to those on a budget; and Zipcar a car-sharing service. The rental car operator operates through 5500 Avis and 4050 Budget branches across 180 countries in North America Europe Australia and New Zealand and generates nearly 70% of its revenue from its on-airport locations. Avis's Budget Truck is one of the leading truck rental businesses in the US.

HISTORY

Cendant began life through the 1997 merger of CUC International and HFS. A giant in hospitality HFS was cobbled together as Hospitality Franchise Systems by LBO specialist Blackstone Group in 1992. With brands including Days Inn Ramada and Howard Johnson HFS went public that year. In 1995 HFS bought real estate firm Century 21. The next year it added Electronic Realty Associates (ERA) and Coldwell Banker. Also in 1996 HFS acquired the Super 8 Motels brand as well as car-rental firm Avis (founded by Warren Avis in 1946 it went through a succession of owners until acquired by HFS). The next year HFS sold 75% of Avis' #1 franchisee to the public and later bought relocation service firm PHH.

In an attempt to leverage the power of his brands HFS CEO Henry Silverman began looking at direct marketing giant CUC International. CUC was founded in 1973 as Comp-U-Card America by Walter Forbes and other investors envisioning a computer-based home shopping network. During the 1980s CUC developed as a discount direct marketer and catalog-based shopping club. It went public in 1983 with 100000 members. CUC saw explosive growth as it signed up 7.6 million members between 1989 and 1993. In 1996 CUC acquired Rent Net an online apartment rental service and later bought entertainment software publishers Davidson & Associates and Sierra On-Line. In 1997 CUC bought software maker Knowledge Adventure and launched online shopping site NetMarket.

CUC and HFS completed their $14.1 billion merger in December 1997 with Silverman as CEO and Forbes as chairman. While the name Cendant was derived from "ascendant" the marriage quickly headed in the opposite direction. Accounting irregularities from before the merger that had inflated CUC's revenue and pretax profit by about $500 million were revealed in 1998. Cendant's stock price tumbled taking a $14 billion hit in one day. Forbes resigned that summer. Silverman quickly took action and began to sell off operations. Cendant Software National Leisure Group (now World Travel Holdings) National Library of Poetry and Match.com all were sold that year for a total of about $1.4 billion. The company also acquired Jackson Hewitt the US's #2 tax-preparation firm and UK-based National Parking.

Through 1999 the company continued to sell assets. Cendant sold its fleet business — including PHH Vehicle Management Services — to Avis Rent A Car for $5 billion and sold its Entertainment Publications unit the world's largest coupon book marketer and publisher to The Carlyle Group. Cendant later paid $2.8 billion in one of the largest shareholder class action lawsuit settlements. (Accounting firm Ernst & Young also settled with Cendant shareholders for $335 million.)

In 2000 Cendant introduced Move.com a relocation and real estate Internet portal. Also that year the company launched Cendant Internet Group to help cement its presence on the Web and bought the brand name and franchising rights of AmeriHost Inns from AmeriHost Properties. Later in 2000 cable programming company Liberty Media (now Liberty Interactive) invested $400 million in Cendant. The next year the company began licensing and outsourcing its Incentives and Marketing Services business (practically all of the businesses that made up the former CUC International) to Trilegiant a new company formed by the units' management.

In 2001 after selling Move.com to Homestore (later called Move) for $761 million Cendant sought to expand its travel holdings with a slew of acquisitions. Its purchases included timeshare resort firm Fairfield Communities ($690 million);

travel services firm Galileo International ($2.4 billion); online travel reservation service Cheap Tickets ($425 million); and vacation timeshare marketer Equivest Finance ($100 million). In late 2001 Cendant cut some 6000 jobs to improve its bottom line and announced that during the next year or so it would cut an additional 10000 jobs and eliminate about 7% of its franchised hotels.

In 2002 the company sold its UK-based National Car Park unit which accounted for 3% of sales as part of its strategy to sell off noncore businesses. In June Cendant bought TRUST International from Bertelsmann and later that year purchased car-rental company Budget Rent A Car for about $110 million then slashed costs by closing facilities and laying off more than 450 employees. The company also purchased Novasol AS which rented out private vacation homes in Northern Europe.

Cendant terminated its licensing and services agreements with Trilegiant in January 2004 and in February Sotheby's Holdings sold its 15 Sotheby's International Realty offices (along with the brand's licensing rights) to the company for about $100 million. In March Cendant's Jackson Hewitt subsidiary filed for its IPO. In May the company purchased Dutch vacation rental company Landal Green Parks (LGP) for about $150 million. Also that month former chairman Walter Forbes and former vice chairman E. Kirk Shelton went on trial for federal fraud and conspiracy stemming from the pre-merger accounting irregularities. (Shelton was found guilty of multiple counts of fraud in early 2005.) In October CFO Ronald Nelson was named president taking over for Henry Silverman who remained chairman and CEO.

In 2004 Cendant acquired online travel firm Orbitz in a deal valued at about $1.25 billion. Quick on the heels of the Orbitz deal the company Cendant also purchased ebookers (a European online travel site now called Flightbookers) in a deal worth about $400 million and acquired two travel groups collectively known as Gullivers for about $1.1 billion.

As 2004 wound to a close Cendant completed the acquisition of the Ramada International Hotels & Resorts brand and franchising operations from Marriott International. Cendant already owned the rights to the brand and franchising operations in the US and Canada which included some 820 US properties and about 70 Canadian properties. In 2005 Cendant acquired the Wyndham hotel brand from Wyndham International Inc. for $101 million. The deal included the franchise agreements for 82 hotels and the management contracts for another 29 hotels but not the actual properties which were located in the US Mexico and the Caribbean. The next year Cendant acquired the Baymont Inn & Suites brand of limited-service midscale lodging from Blackstone's La Quinta Corporation (now LQ Management). The Baymont Inn & Suites brand covered 115 franchised properties; the properties themselves were not included in the deal.

Cendant in 2005 spun off its mortgage operations PHH Mortgage (formerly Cendant Mortgage) and fleet management (PHH Arval) businesses under the PHH Corporation umbrella. Also that year Cendant spun off Wright Express (payment processing and information services for fleet management) in an IPO and sold its marketing services division to Apollo Management for about $1.8 billion.

The divestitures that began in 2005 culminated in the unwinding of the Cendant conglomerate the next year. The company spun off its hotel and real estate operations and sold its travel services division in 2006 reconfiguring itself around its rental car businesses and renaming itself Avis Budget Group. Silverman became chairman and CEO of the company's real estate business Realogy and Nelson took over as chairman and CEO of the slimmed-down Avis Budget Group which took on its new name in September 2006.

Warren Avis the founder of Avis Rent A Car died in April 2007 at the age of 92. In October the company acquired a 48% stake in chauffeured transportation company Carey International for $60 million. (In 2009 due to losses at Carey it wrote down its investment in the company to zero.)

Avis Budget Group acquired Avis Europe plc in October 2011. The purchase followed ABG's withdrawal from its battle with rival Hertz to acquire Dollar Thrifty Automotive Group (DTG). Instead the company turned to Europe for growth by reuniting with Avis Europe which was legally separated from Avis in 1986. The deal created what ABG says is the largest publicly traded rental car business in the world.

In 2012 in continuing to bulk up its global operations after its purchase of Avis Europe ABG in 2012 acquired New Zealand's largest independently-owned car rental company Apex Car Rentals. The purchase added more than 4000 rental cars and strengthened Avis's position in New Zealand and Australia.

EXECUTIVES

President International, Mark J. Servodidio, age 52, $596,538 total compensation

Interim CFO, Martyn R. Smith, age 62

EVP and Chief Marketing Officer, W. Scott Deaver, age 66

CEO and COO, Larry D. De Shon, age 58, $1,000,000 total compensation

SVP and CIO, Gerard Insall

EVP General Counsel and Chief Compliance Officer, Michael K. Tucker, age 59

SVP North America Operations, Joseph A. (Joe) Ferraro, age 60, $623,269 total compensation

SVP and Chief Human Resources Officer, Edward P. (Ned) Linnen, age 47

EVP and Chief Innovation Officer, Arthur Orduna

Vice President IT, John Turato

Senior Vice President Cao, David T Calabria

Vice President International Controller, Gerard Monusky

Senior Vice President Strategic Customer Leadersh, Gina Bruzzichesi

Vice President Human Resources, April Scavone

Vice President Tax, Izzy Martins

Vice President Fleet Administration, Joseph Biondo

Vice President, Joe Biondo

Vice President Area, Jeff Eisenbarth

Executive Vice President Strategy and Pricing, Scott Deaver

Vice President Sales Southern Region, Malcolm McNett

Vice President Vehicle MandD, Jerry Bernacki

Vice President Sales And Marketing, John Barrows

Executive Vice President and Chief Human Resources Officer, Ned Linnen

Senior Vice President and Secretary, Jean Sera

Vice President of Engineering, Jennifer Rodean

Senior Vice President Information Technology, Jeff Edwards

Vice President Global Account Sales, Matthew Tolan

Senior Vice President Fleet Services, Michael Schmidt

Vice President Investor Relations, David Crowther

Vice President Information Technology, David Morgan

Vice President Sales, Joanne Cormier

Vice President Marketing, Jack Dailey

Vice President Cross Border Sales, Charles Crowder

Chairman, Ronald L. (Ron) Nelson, age 65

Board Member, John D Hardy

Auditors: Deloitte & Touche LLP

LOCATIONS

HQ: Avis Budget Group Inc
6 Sylvan Way, Parsippany, NJ 07054
Phone: 973 496-4700
Web: www.avisbudgetgroup.com

2016 Locations

	$ mil.	% of total
AvisBudget		
Americas		
Company-operated	1,550	1,400
Licensees	700	650
International		
Company-operated	1,200	650
Licensees	2,050	1,350
Total	**5,550**	**4,050**

2016 Sales

	$ mil.	% of total
United States	5,674	66
All other countries	2,985	34
Total	**8,659**	**100**

2016 Sales

	% of total
Americas	71
International	29
Total	**100**

2016 Car Rental Sales

	% of total
On-Airport	70
Off-airport	30
Total	**100**

PRODUCTS/OPERATIONS

2016 Sales

	$ mil.	% of total
Vehicle rental	6,081	70
Others	2,578	30
Total	**8,659**	**100**

COMPETITORS

AMERCO	Penske Truck Leasing
Enterprise Rent-A-Car	Ryder System
Europcar	Sixt
Herc Holdings	

HISTORICAL FINANCIALS

Company Type: Public

Income Statement

FYE: December 31

	REVENUE ($ mil.)	NET INCOME ($ mil.)	NET PROFIT MARGIN	EMPLOYEES
12/16	8,659	163	1.9%	30,000
12/15	8,502	313	3.7%	30,000
12/14	8,485	245	2.9%	30,000
12/13	7,937	16	0.2%	29,000
12/12	7,357	290	3.9%	28,000
Annual Growth	**4.2%**	**(13.4%)**	**—**	**1.7%**

2016 Year-End Financials

Debt ratio: 70.29%
Return on equity: 49.26%
Cash ($ mil.): 490
Current ratio: 1.03
Long-term debt ($ mil.): 12,122

No. of shares (mil.): 86
Dividends
  Yield: —
  Payout: —
Market value ($ mil.): 3,154

	STOCK PRICE ($) FY Close	P/E High/Low		PER SHARE ($) Earnings	Dividends	Book Value
12/16	36.68	23	12	1.75	0.00	2.57
12/15	36.29	22	11	2.98	0.00	4.48
12/14	66.33	30	15	2.22	0.00	6.29
12/13	40.42	263	132	0.15	0.00	7.24
12/12	19.82	7	4	2.42	0.00	7.07
Annual Growth	**16.6%**	**—**	**—**	**(7.8%)**		**(22.4%)**

Avnet Inc

If you need an electronic component Avnet probably has it. The company is one of the world's top distributor of electronic components (including connectors and semiconductors) enterprise computing and storage products and embedded subsystems with competitors Arrow Electronics and Ingram Micro. Avnet's suppliers include more than 800 component and systems makers; its largest supplier of parts for distribution is Texas Instruments. Avnet distributes these products to more than 100000 manufacturers and resellers worldwide. Avnet distributes products from about 400 locations in more than 125 countries. Most of its revenue comes from international customers.

Operations

Avnet is composed of two global operating groups each led by their own management teams and each with their own sales and marketing units geared at the Americas EMEA and Asia/Pacific markets.

Avnet Electronic Components generates 65% of revenue selling semiconductors embedded products and interconnect passive and electromechanical devices (IP&E) to the world's leading electronic component manufacturers. EC also offers design tools and engineering services to support product design as well as supply chain services to OEMs. Abacus Group or Avnet Abacus is a UK subsidiary that distributes electronic products in Europe.

After acquiring Premier Farnell Avnet made it an operating unit. Premier Farnell accounts for about 5% of revenue from distributing electronic components typically in small quantities primarily to support design engineers maintenance and test engineers and entrepreneurs as they develop technology products.

The Avnet Technology Solutions group sold to Tech Data in 2017 had generated about 35% of revenue as a global IT distributor that collaborates with customers and suppliers to create and deliver services hardware and software.

Additionally Avnet provides aftermarket services — from electronic product repair and refurbishment to asset recovery and reclamation — through a business unit called Avnet Integrated and it offers supply chain services including warehousing postponement and device programming through a unit called Avnet Logistics.

Geographic Reach

Avnet's products are sold around the world. The Asia/Pacific region accounts for about 36% of sales followed by Europe with about a third and the Americas with about 30%.

Headquartered in Phoenix Arizona the company has warehousing integration operations and offices in Arizona South Carolina and Ohio in the US and overseas in Belgium Germany and China.

Sales and Marketing

Avnet's customers include original equipment manufacturers electronic manufacturing services providers original design manufacturers systems integrators independent software vendors and value-added resellers.

The company sells and markets its products through its three primary regional divisions. EM Americas caters to small- to medium-sized customers global customers defense and aerospace customers and contract manufacturers. Its EMEA divisions are organized across the channels of semiconductors; interconnect passive and electromechanical (IP&E) products; and supply chain services and serve customers on both a pan-European and regional basis.

EM Asia has sales and marketing divisions within China South Asia Australia New Zealand

and Taiwan. EM Japan operates through sales and marketing divisions to serve Japanese OEMs in Japan Southeast Asia and China.

Products from Texas Instruments account for more than 10% of Avnet's sales.

Financial Performance

The sale of Avnet?s Technology Solutions group in 2016 unit showed up in the company?s sales for 2017 (ended July). It reported revenue of $17.4 billion in 2017 compared to $26 billion in 2016 which included the unit. In comparing revenue without Technology Solutions Avnet?s sales increased 4.2% to $17.4 billion in 2017 from $16.7 billion in 2016. The company reported growth in the EC business in Europe but a decline in Asia. Overall sales to Asia dropped about 7% in 2017 which followed an 8% drop in 2016.

Avnet posted a profit of $525 million in 2017 about a 4% rise from 2016 despite higher costs stemming from the Premier Farnell acquisition and restructuring moves begun in 2017.

Cash flow from operations rose to about $221 million in 2017 from a negative cash flow of $49 million in 2016.

Strategy

As Avnet exited the technical services business with the sale of its Technology Solutions unit the company built up its digital offerings through the acquisitions of Premier Farnell MakerSource and Hackster.io. The company maintains that its digital ecosystem is one of the biggest online communities focused on delivering information and components to hardware developers. Its digital units provide information design tools support and community for the world of engineers including startups with the Hackster.io element.

To better integrate sales leads from Premier Farnell and Avnet the company is investing in advanced analytics. The company mines analytics to move highly qualified leads from the digital side to the company?s marketing and sales teams so that they can offer tailored support to customers.

Operationally Avnet has reorganized its sales force in the Americas and established a program to improve HR programs compensation pricing and data analytics to increase the efficiency and effectiveness of its sales staff.

Mergers and Acquisitions

Avnet has a strong history of using acquisitions to grow its geographic footprint across the globe. That practice continues to be a key part of its strategy today with Avnet seeking to acquire primarily smaller businesses in markets where it is trying to expand its presence or increase its scale.

In 2016 Avnet agreed to buy Premier Farnell for about $900 million. Premier Farnell is a global distributor of electronic components and related products and should fortify Avnet's digital footprint.

In November 2016 the company acquired California based Hackster Inc an online community platform which helps users globally learn how to design create and program Internet-connected hardware. The acquisition will enable company users to accelerate their hardware knowledge and time-to-market.

In 2017 Avnet acquired Dragon Innovation which helps companies manage their manufacturing processes with a cloud-based platform. The deal complements Avnet?s digital strategy with the delivery of its services through software and access to subject matter experts matched to the customers? needs. It also adds to Avnet?s design and supply chain capabilities beyond electronic components to include the finished product.

EXECUTIVES

VP and President Avnet Technology Solutions EMEA, Graeme A. Watt, age 56
Vice President Senior Vice President Global Business Develo, Tom McCartney
Vice President Business Development Avnet Cilico, Alex Iuorio
CEO, William J. (Bill) Amelio, age 59
SVP Chief Human Resources Officer and Global Marketing and Communications, MaryAnn G. Miller, age 60, $540,000 total compensation
VP; SVP European Finance and Strategic Planning Electronics Marketing Europe Middle East and Africa, Patrick Zammit, age 50, $488,400 total compensation
VP and President Avnet Technology Solutions Americas, Jeff Bawol
President Avnet Electronics Marketing Americas, Chuck Delph
CIO, Kevin V. Summers
SVP and President Avnet Electronics Marketing Global, Gerald W. (Gerry) Fay, age 58, $600,000 total compensation
SVP and Chief Global Logistics and Operations Officer, Michael D. (Mike) Buseman, age 56
VP and President Avnet Technology Solutions Asia Pacific, William Chu
CFO, Thomas (Tom) Liguori, age 58
VP and President Avnet Electronics Marketing EMEA, Miguel Fernandez
President Avnet Asia Pacific, Frederick Fu
Vice President Of Engineering, Eileen Gibson
Vice President Business Development, Scott Delaney
VP Operations, Miriam Murphy
Vice President Finance, Steve Chlupsa
VP Human Resources, Jan Hermans
Vice President Marketing, Ian Basey
Vice President of Human Resources Ts Americas, Kaylene Moss
VP Operations, Jacob Kuryan
Vice President Sales, Brad Johnson
Vice President Sales, Bradley Fehling
SVP of Finance, Chuck Fries
Vice President Sales and Operations, Sandra Scott
Vice President Area Director, Rick Mackey
Vice President Finance, David Ward
Vice President Global Contracts, Steven Larson
Vice President Marketing, Brian Gosling
Vice President Materials Management, Annette Poleon
Vice President of Repair Sales, Robert Laughlin
Vice President and General Counsel, Cheree McAlpine
Area Vice President, Dan Oconnell
VICE PRESIDENT BUSINESS TRANSFORMATION, Sue Kotnik
Vice President and General Manager, Ray Ramey
Senior Vice President and General Manager, Sergio Farache
Vice President of Defense and Aerospace Americas, Bryan Brady
VP Operations, Doug Adams
Vice President of Global Operations Systems, Doug Halbert
Vice President, Glenn Bassett
Vice President Of Sales, Trisha Cooke
Vice President, Eric Berry
Senior Vice President, Dennis Losik
Vice President of Marketing, Ivan Ho
Vice President Human Resources, Aaron Dean
Vice President Global Transportation, Danny Stephens
Senior Vice President and Chief Human Resources Development Officer, Claudia Riley
Vice President Sales, Peter Rzonca
Vice President Global Operations, Derinda Ehrlich
National Account Manager, Will Plantillas
Vice President, Thomas McCartney
Vice President of Operations, Rich Fitzgerald
Vice President Sales and Marketing, Tal Segman
Senior Vice President Materials, Frank Hardin
Vice President, Fernando Lamus
Vice President and Assistant General Counsel, Viet Le
Vice President, Steve Gomez
Vice President Of Engineering, Lisa Friesenhahn
Senior Vice President Digital Transformation, Kevin Yapp
Vice President, Eric Williams
Vice President Cloud SBU North America, Brian Peterson
Vice President Director Of Investorrelations, Vince Keenan
Vice President Information Systems, Bob Laurie
Vice President Global Procurement and Administrative Services, James Azzinaro
Chairman, William H. (Bill) Schumann, age 66
Treasurer, Michael Mccoy
Treasurer, Joseph Burke
Board Member, Phillip Carabillas
Auditors: KPMG LLP

LOCATIONS

HQ: Avnet Inc
2211 South 47th Street, Phoenix, AZ 85034
Phone: 480 643-2000
Web: www.avnet.com

2016 Sales

	% of total
Americas	40
Europe Middle East & Africa	30
Asia/Pacific	30
Total	**100**

PRODUCTS/OPERATIONS

2017 Sales by Operating Group

	$ mil.	% of total
Electronic Components	16,474	95
Premier Farnell	965	5
Total	**17,440**	**100**

2016 Sales by Product Category

	$ mil.	% of total
Semiconductors	13,557	78
Interconnect passive & electromechanical	3,397	19
Other	504	3
Total	**17,440**	**100**

Selected Products

Amplifiers
Analog Switch Multiplexer
Batteries
Capacitor
Circuit Protection
Communication
Data Conversion
Discrete
Displays
DSP
Embedded Boards
Enclosures Racks & Cabinets
Filter
Inductor
Interconnect
Interface
Kits And Tools
Lighting
Logic And Timing
Memory
Microcontrollers
Miscellaneous
Motors
Optoelectronics
Peripherals
Power Management
Power Supplies
Processor
Programmable Logic
Resistor
RF And Microwave

Sensors And Transducers
Software
Storage
Switches And Relays
Systems
Test & Measurement
Thermal Management
Transformer

COMPETITORS

Allied Electronics	Plexus
Arrow Electronics	Premier Farnell
Digi-Key	SYNNEX
Future Electronics	TTI Inc.
Heilind Electronics	Tech Data
Ingram Micro	WPG Holdings
N.F. Smith	

HISTORICAL FINANCIALS
Company Type: Public

Income Statement
FYE: July 1

	REVENUE ($ mil.)	NET INCOME ($ mil.)	NET PROFIT MARGIN	EMPLOYEES
07/17	17,439	525	3.0%	15,700
07/16*	26,219	506	1.9%	17,700
06/15	27,924	571	2.0%	18,800
06/14	27,499	545	2.0%	19,000
06/13	25,458	450	1.8%	18,500
Annual Growth	(9.0%)	3.9%	—	(4.0%)

*Fiscal year change

2017 Year-End Financials
Debt ratio: 18.34%
Return on equity: 10.67%
Cash ($ mil.): 836
Current ratio: 3.07
Long-term debt ($ mil.): 1,729
No. of shares (mil.): 123
Dividends
  Yield: 0.0%
  Payout: 17.1%
Market value ($ mil.): 4,785

	STOCK PRICE ($) FY Close	P/E High	P/E Low	PER SHARE ($) Earnings	Dividends	Book Value
07/17	38.88	12	9	4.08	0.70	42.10
07/16*	40.27	12	10	3.80	0.68	36.84
06/15	42.09	11	9	4.12	0.64	34.58
06/14	43.71	12	9	3.89	0.60	35.37
06/13	33.60	11	8	3.21	0.00	31.29
Annual Growth	3.7%	—	—	6.2%	—	7.7%

*Fiscal year change

Avon Products, Inc.

EXECUTIVES

Chairman, Douglas R. (Doug) Conant, age 66
Senior Vice President Human Resources and Chief People Officer, Scott A. Crum, age 59
EVP Developing Market Group, Charles M. Herington, age 55, $627,322 total compensation
Chairman, Andrea Jung, age 56, $1,375,000 total compensation
Chairman, Fred Hassan
SVP Global Supply Chain, John F. Owen, age 58
SVP and Global Brand President, Jeri B. Finard, age 55
VP Corporate Communications, Victor Beaudet
SVP Human Resources and Corporate Responsibility, Lucien Alziari, age 55
SVP Global Communications, Nancy Glaser
EVP and CFO, Kimberly A. Ross, age 51
Senior Vice President & President Asia Pacific, Bob Briddon, age 62

SVP and President Europe Middle East and Africa, John P. Higson, age 57
SVP, Geralyn R. Breig, age 52
CEO and Director, Sherilyn S. (Sheri) McCoy, age 58
SVP CIO and eCommerce, Donagh Herlihy, age 52
SVP and President Western Europe Middle East & Africa, Anna Segatti, age 62
SVP and President Central and Eastern Europe, Srdjan Mijuskovic, age 59
General Manager Russia, Angela Cretu, age 40
Group VP and Corporate Controller, Stephen Ibbotson, age 55
SVP Global Insights and Marketing Intelligence, Michael (Mike) Schwartz
Group Vice President Global Corporate Relations and Chief Communications Officer, Cheryl Heinonen
SVP and President North America, Jorge Martinez-Quiroga, age 60
President Mark Brand, Vanessa Reggiardo
Senior Manager Corporate Communications, Jennifer Dwyer Vargas
Director Public Relations North America, Claudia Shaum
Senior Manager Public Relations and Promotions, Jennifer Iino-Harvey
Senior Manager Public Relations and Communications Avon Foundation for Women, Karyn Margolis
SVP and Chief Marketing Officer, Patricia Perez-Ayala
SVP and President Latin America, Fernando J. Acosta
SVP General Counsel and Chief Ethics and Compliance Officer, Jeff Benjamin
Director, Gary M. Rodkin, age 63
Director, V. Ann Hailey, age 63
Director, Paul S. Pressler, age 58
Director, Lawrence A. (Larry) Weinbach, age 75
Director, W. Don Cornwell, age 68
Director, Fred Hassan, age 69
Director, Paula Stern, age 70
Director, Ann S. Moore, age 65
Director, Maria Elena (Mel) Lagomasino, age 65
CEO and Director, Sherilyn S. (Sheri) McCoy, age 57
Auditors: PricewaterhouseCoopers LLP, United Kingdom

LOCATIONS

HQ: Avon Products, Inc.
  Building 6, Chiswick Park, London W4 5HR
Phone: (+44) 1604 232425
Web: www.avon.com

COMPETITORS

Alticor	Johnson Publishing
Amway China	Jostens
Bath & Body Works	Kracie
BeautiControl	L'Oreal
Beiersdorf	LJ International
Body Shop	LVMH
Carolee	Macy's
Chanel	Mary Kay
Clarins	Murad Inc.
Colgate-Palmolive	Nu Skin
Coty Inc.	Perrigo
Dana Classic Fragrances	Prestige Cosmetics
Dillard's	Procter & Gamble
Elizabeth Arden Inc	Revlon
Enesco	Sara Lee
Estee Lauder	Shaklee
Forever Living	Shiseido
Fossil Inc.	Target Corporation
Hanover Direct	Tiffany & Co.
J. C. Penney	Tupperware Brands
Jafra	Unilever
James Avery	Wal-Mart
Johnson & Johnson	Zale

HISTORICAL FINANCIALS
Company Type: Public

Income Statement
FYE: December 31

	REVENUE ($ mil.)	NET INCOME ($ mil.)	NET PROFIT MARGIN	EMPLOYEES
12/16	5,717	(107)	—	26,400
12/15	6,160	(1,148)	—	28,300
12/14	8,851	(388)	—	33,200
12/13	9,955	(56)	—	36,700
12/12	10,717	(42)	—	39,100
Annual Growth	(14.5%)	—	—	(9.4%)

2016 Year-End Financials
Debt ratio: 55.40%
Return on equity: ***,***.**%
Cash ($ mil.): 654
Current ratio: 1.34
Long-term debt ($ mil.): 1,875
No. of shares (mil.): 437
Dividends
  Yield: —
  Payout: —
Market value ($ mil.): 2,206

	STOCK PRICE ($) FY Close	P/E High	P/E Low	PER SHARE ($) Earnings	Dividends	Book Value
12/16	5.04	—	—	(0.29)	0.00	(0.92)
12/15	4.05	—	—	(2.60)	0.24	(2.46)
12/14	9.39	—	—	(0.88)	0.24	0.67
12/13	17.22	—	—	(0.13)	0.24	2.56
12/12	14.36	—	—	(0.10)	0.75	2.82
Annual Growth	(23.0%)					

Baker Hughes, A GE Company

LOCATIONS

HQ: Baker Hughes, A GE Company
  17021 Aldine Westfield Road, Houston, TX 77073
Phone: 713 439-8600
Web: www.bakerhughes.com

HISTORICAL FINANCIALS
Company Type: Public

Income Statement
FYE: December 31

	REVENUE ($ mil.)	NET INCOME ($ mil.)	NET PROFIT MARGIN	EMPLOYEES
12/16	13,269	403	3.0%	34,000
12/15	16,688	(606)	—	—
12/14	19,191	1,840	9.6%	—
Annual Growth	(16.8%)	(53.2%)	—	—

2016 Year-End Financials
Debt ratio: 1.28%—
Return on equity: 2.76%
Cash ($ mil.): 981
Current ratio: 1.50
Long-term debt ($ mil.): 38
Dividends
  Yield: —
  Payout: —
Market value ($ mil.): —

	STOCK PRICE ($) FY Close	P/E High	P/E Low	PER SHARE ($) Earnings	Dividends	Book Value
12/16	0.00	—	—	(2.08)	0.00	(0.00)
12/15	0.00	—	—	(0.00)	0.00	(0.00)
Annual Growth						

Ball Corp

When it comes to food beverage and household goods packaging Ball Corporation is on the ball. The company produces food and beverage packaging including metal cans containers and aluminum slugs. Ball's packaging revenue derives primarily from a relatively few beverage making customers owning brands spanning Asia Europe and the Americas. Additionally its Ball Aerospace & Technologies subsidiary manufactures an array of aerospace systems from satellites to tactical antennas as well as providing systems engineering services. Ball Corporation operates through 85 locations in 30 countries. It has recently grown by purchasing one of its rivals Rexam in mid-2016.

Operations

Ball divides its operations between five business segments. The largest is beverage packaging North and Central America and accounts for 40% of sales. This segment's operations are located in the US Canada and Mexico; it distributes containers mainly to companies that make carbonated soft drinks beer energy drinks and other beverages.

The beverage packaging Europe segment (almost 20% of sales) includes the manufacturing of metal beverage containers in the Czech Republic France Germany Poland Russia Serbia and the UK.

Food and aerosol packaging (15%) makes steel food aerosol paint and general line containers extruded aluminum aerosol containers and aluminum slugs in the US Canada Mexico Europe India and Argentina.

Beverage packaging South America (10%) includes the manufacturing of metal beverage containers across Brazil Argentina and Chile.

The company's smallest segment aerospace (almost 10%) makes and sells aerospace and related products for the defense civil space and commercial space markets.

Geographic Reach

Ball Corporation operates more than 85 locations and joint ventures spanning Asia Europe North America and South America. The US accounts for almost 55% of net sales.

Sales and Marketing

Ball's packaging revenue derives primarily from long-term contracts with a relatively few customers: Coca-Cola Molson Coors Anheuser-Busch and the US government each account for about 10% of net sales.

Financial Performance

Ball's revenues climbed by 13% from $8 billion in 2015 to almost $9.1 billion a historic milestone. The unprecedented growth for 2016 was fueled by increased sales of $1.5 billion related to its acquired Rexam business.

Profits however fell 6% from $281 million in 2015 to $263 million in 2016. This erosion of profits was attributed to increased costs associated with the Rexam acquisition and the absence of income from European operations it divested in 2016.

The company's operating cash flow nosedived from $1 billion in 2015 to $194 million in 2016. The massive drop in cash flow was due to payments related to the Rexam acquisition almost $300 million of additional pension funding and less cash inflows of $150 million from working capital due to the sale of the company?s legacy European business. Cash flow was also negatively affected by $90 million of payments to settle derivatives associated with the Rexam acquisition in addition to $50 million of additional interest payments associated with the financing of the transaction.

Mergers and Acquisitions

Ball's blueprint for growth has been pretty simple over the years: it acquires similar companies around the world to widen its customer base and extend its geographical reach.

In a sweeping move for the industry the company in mid-2016 acquired Rexam one of its biggest rivals for around $6.1 billion. The deal created the world's largest maker of food and beverage cans. The combined company posted more than $9 billion in revenue for 2016 the highest total in Ball's history. As part of the stipulations to complete the deal Ball sold a dozen plants in Europe and two in Brazil. The company also completed the required sale of eight aluminum-can plants and related assets in the US to Ardagh Group for $3.4 billion. Further it shut down Rexam's London headquarters in late 2016.

Ball in 2015 also completed its acquisition of Sonoco's metal end and closure facilities in Canton Ohio. The Canton plants which produce multiple-sized closures for the food can market will become part of Ball's global metal food and household products packaging division.

HISTORY

The Ball Corporation began in 1880 when Frank Ball and his four brothers started making wood-jacket tin cans to store and transport kerosene and other materials. In 1884 the company switched to tin-jacketed glass containers for kerosene lamps. The lamps however were soon displaced by Thomas Edison's electric light bulb.

The Ball brothers then learned that the patent to the original sealed-glass storage container (the Mason jar) had expired. By 1886 the brothers had entered the sealed-jar business and imprinted their jars with the Ball name. In their first year they made 12500 jars and sparked a patent war with the two reigning jar producers who asserted that they controlled the correct patents and threatened to sue. The Ball lawyers proved that the patents had expired and the jar remained Ball's mainstay for many years.

The company began diversifying but a 1947 antitrust ruling prohibited it from buying additional glass subsidiaries. Ball decided to take advantage of the space race by buying Control Cells (aerospace science research) in 1957; that operation became Ball Brothers Research Corporation (later Ball Aerospace Systems Division). The Soviets launched Sputnik that year igniting a massive US scientific effort in 1958 and Ball won federal contracts to make equipment for the US space program.

Ball established its metal beverage-container business in 1969 when it bought Jeffco Manufacturing of Colorado. The operation soon won contracts to supply two-piece cans to Budweiser Coca-Cola Dr Pepper Pepsi and Stroh's Beer.

EXECUTIVES

SVP and CFO, Scott C. Morrison, age 54, $666,728 total compensation

Chairman President and CEO, John A. Hayes, age 51, $1,238,615 total compensation

SVP Human Resources and Administration, Lisa A. Pauley, age 55, $464,443 total compensation

SVP and COO Global Beverage Packaging, Daniel W. Fisher, age 44

VP Technology, M. Andrew (Drew) Crouch

VP General Counsel and Corporate Secretary, Charles E. Baker, age 59, $492,871 total compensation

SVP; President Ball Aerospace and Technologies, Robert D. (Rob) Strain, age 60

SVP and COO Food and Aerosol Packaging, James N. Peterson, age 48

Vice President Information Technology and Services, Leroy Williams

Vice President Engineering, Joe Atwell

Director Progam Development Chief Sales Officer, Jim Good

Vice President Operational Planning and Administra, Jim Curtin

Vice President and General Manager Advanced Technologies, Andrew Crouch

Information Technology Vice President, Scott Chrisbacher

Vice President Global Sourcing, Robert Lauterbach

Vice President, Art Morrissey

Executive Vice President Administration and Corporate Secretary, David A Westerlund

Vice President and General Plant Manager, David Heller

VP Sales, Ruffalo Martin

Vice President of Human Resources, Randy Chastian

Purchasing Vice President, John Martin

Vice President and General Manager, Stan Platek

Vice President Ball Packaging Europe, James P Stevens

Vice President Manufacturing, Rick Garske

Vice President Of Marketing, Drew Couch

Vice President Of Marketing, Bill Braun

Vice President Financial Reporting and Tax, Douglas Bradford

Vice President Mission Assurance, Sherri Fike

Vice President Finance, Albert Schlesinger

Senior Vice President Chief Operating Officer, John Friedery

Senior Vice President of International Sales, David Fredericks

Sales Vice President, Don Brien

Vice President Human Resources, Caren Albarian

Vice President Of Engineering, Neil Anderson

Vice President Marketing and Corporate Affairs, Jim Peterson

Vice President and Controller, Nate Carey

Vice President And General Manager Of National Security Space, Fred Doyle

Vice President Of Information Technology, Fernando Diaz

Vice President Business Excellence and Supply Chain, Tom Schranz

Board Member, Chris Barkley

Board Member, Kristi Beshears

Auditors: PricewaterhouseCoopers LLP

LOCATIONS

HQ: Ball Corp
10 Longs Peak Drive, P.O. Box 5000, Broomfield, CO 80021-2510
Phone: 303 469-3131
Web: www.ball.com

2016 Sales

	$ mil.	% of total
US	4,929	54
Foreign	4,132	46
Total	**9,061**	**100**

PRODUCTS/OPERATIONS

2016 Sales

	$ mil.	% of total
Beverage packaging North and Central America	3,612	40
Beverage packaging Europe	1,915	21
Food and aerosol packaging	1,171	13
Beverage packaging South America	1,014	11
Aerospace	818	9
Others	531	6
Total	**9,061**	**100**

Selected Products

Aerospace and technologies
  Aerospace technology and components
  Antennas and microwave systems
  Satellites and spacecraft

Space-based instruments and sensors
Tactical instruments and sensors
Technical services
Packaging
Aerosol cans
Beverage cans
Food cans
Paint and general line cans

COMPETITORS

Amcor	Rio Tinto Alcan
Anchor Glass	Saint-Gobain
Arconic	Containers
Chinalco	Sequa
Consolidated Container	Silgan
Crown Holdings	Teledyne Technologies
Owens-Illinois	Tetra Laval

HISTORICAL FINANCIALS

Company Type: Public

Income Statement

FYE: December 31

	REVENUE ($ mil.)	NET INCOME ($ mil.)	NET PROFIT MARGIN	EMPLOYEES
12/16	9,061	263	2.9%	18,450
12/15	7,997	280	3.5%	15,200
12/14	8,570	470	5.5%	14,500
12/13	8,468	406	4.8%	14,600
12/12	8,735	403	4.6%	15,000
Annual Growth	0.9%	(10.1%)	—	5.3%

2016 Year-End Financials

Debt ratio: 46.57%	No. of shares (mil.): 349
Return on equity: 11.19%	Dividends
Cash ($ mil.): 597	Yield: 0.0%
Current ratio: 1.23	Payout: 31.9%
Long-term debt ($ mil.): 7,310	Market value ($ mil.): 26,254

	STOCK PRICE ($) FY Close	P/E High/Low	PER SHARE ($) Earnings	Dividends	Book Value
12/16	75.07	99 77	0.82	0.26	9.82
12/15	72.73	75 59	1.00	0.26	4.40
12/14	68.17	41 28	1.65	0.26	3.77
12/13	51.66	37 30	1.37	0.26	4.22
12/12	44.75	35 28	1.28	0.20	3.72
Annual Growth	13.8%	— —	(10.6%)	6.8%	27.5%

Banc Of California Inc

Banc of California offers deposit and loan services at 35 branches in Southern California's Los Angeles Orange County and San Diego. Customers enjoy checking savings and money market accounts as well as mobile online and card payment services telephone banking automated bill payment safe deposit boxes direct deposit and wire transfers. Customers can also access their accounts through a nationwide network of 55000 surcharge-free ATMs. In addition to its branches the $9 billion-asset Banc of California operates around 70 mortgage loan production offices in California Arizona Oregon Indiana Idaho Nevada and Virginia.

Operations

Banc of California operates three core segments: Commercial Banking which offers commercial consumer and real estate secured loans as well as deposit accounts; Mortgage Banking which originates conforming SFR loans and sells the loans in the secondary market; and the Financial Advisory segment which purchases sells and manages SFR mortgage loans.

Unlike most retail banks Banc of California's income streams are less dependent on interest rates. The bank made 50% of its revenue from loan interest (including fees) during 2015 and another 5% from interest on investments. But it also made 29% of its revenue from its mortgage banking business while the rest came from other non-interest income sources.

Geographic Reach

The Irvine California-based bank has 90-plus banking locations in California including 35 branches in San Diego Orange Santa Barbara and Los Angeles Counties (as of mid-2016). It has 68 loan production offices in California Arizona Oregon Virginia Indiana Maryland Colorado Idaho and Nevada.

Sales and Marketing

The bank spent $6.2 million on advertising during 2015 or 23% more than in the prior year due to higher overall marketing costs tied to the bank's continued expansion.

Financial Performance

Banc of California's revenue has risen sevenfold since 2011 as a slew of bank acquisitions and organic growth have driven its loan and deposit business as well as its mortgage banking business.

The bank's revenue jumped 46% to $486.5 million during 2015 thanks to a 34% spike in loan interest income on more loan origination and loan and lease purchase activity; and thanks to a 52% rise in mortgage banking income as the bank originated and sold nearly twice as many mortgage loans on the secondary market than in 2014.

Strong revenue growth in 2015 caused Banc of California's net income to double to $62 million despite an uptick in salary and benefits cost that stemmed from additional hiring and commercial banking and mortgage banking expansion. The bank's operations used $45.24 million during the year or less than one-tenth as much cash as in 2014 mostly after adjusting its earnings for non-cash items related to proceeds of mortgage banking loans held-for-sale and proceeds from other loans held-for-sale.

Strategy

With its eye on becoming "California's Bank" Banc of California sometimes acquires smaller banks or bank branch networks to boost its loan and deposit business while expanding its branch network (mostly around California).

From 2010 through 2015 the bank has made seven acquisitions including three bank acquisitions (Gateway Bancorp Beach Business Bank and The Private Bank of California) and three other specialty financial firm acquisitions (Palisades Group which it divested in 2016; CS Financial; and Renovation Ready.)

Mergers and Acquisitions

In November 2014 the bank bought 20 branches in Southern California from Banco Popular North America (BPNA) along with $1.07 billion in loans and $1.08 billion in deposits for a total price of $24 million.

In January 2014 Banc of California purchased service contracts and intellectual property of RenovationReady a specialized loan services provider that served financial institutions and mortgage bankers that originated agency-eligible residential renovation and construction loan products.

Company Background

In 2012 it paid $15.5 million for Gateway Business Bank and $37 million for Beach Business Bank. The next year it took over The Private Bank of California for $25 million and bought The Palisades Group a residential mortgage investment advisory firm and specialty finance company CS Financial. In 2014 it announced plans to buy 20

branches of Banco Popular North America to reach California's Hispanic community.

In 2013 it sold eight branches to AmericanWest Bank in order to reshape its retail branch network to focus on servicing small - to midsized businesses and high net worth families.

EXECUTIVES

EVP Division General Counsel Lending, John F. Madden, age 56
EVP Enterprise Risk Analytics, Gilda Youdeem
Managing Director Institutional Banking and Fiduciary Services, Steven C. (Steve) Canup
EVP and CFO Banc of California Inc. and Banc of California N.A., John A. Bogler
EVP and General Counsel Banking, Angelee J. Harris, age 47
Chief Investment Officer, Brian P. Kuelbs, age 54
Managing Director Community Banking, Gaylin D. Anderson
Vice Chairman and EVP, Jeffrey T. Seabold, age 50, $750,000 total compensation
President and CEO, Douglas H. (Doug) Bowers, age 59
Chief Risk Officer, Hugh F. Boyle, age 57, $599,679 total compensation
Managing Director Warehouse Lending, Zoila Price
EVP and Chief Compliance Officer, Diane M. Summers
EVP Community Development, Gary S. Dunn
EVP and CIO, Ken Plummer
EVP Division General Counsel Banking, Manisha K. Merchant
Managing Director Construction Lending, Jim Fraser
Managing Director CRE Lending, Thomas Senske
Managing Director SBA Lending, Heather Endresen
Managing Director Commercial Banking, David Park
Chief Credit Officer, Paul Simmons
Managing Director Portfolio Lending, Julie Duong
SVP Operations, Robert Villaneda
SVP Marketing, Samantha Haugh
Managing Director Payment Solutions, Ben Kessler
EVP General Counsel and Secretary, John C. Grosvenor, age 67, $501,378 total compensation
EVP Private Banking, Jay D. Sanders
Senior Vice President Secondary Marketing, James Shirreffs
Assistant Vice President Senior Project Analys, Marianna Helton
Assistant Vice President Quality Assurance Manager, Monique Bailon
Vice President Compliance Officer, Gladys Cantu
Vice President Relationship Manager, Kristin Koptyra
Vice President Director of Sales, Steve Preimesberger
Vice President Credit Administration, Edward Massey
Vice President, Karen Koepsell
Executive Vice President, Chang Liu
Vice President Loan Accounting, Barbara Curtis
Southern California Regional Vice President, Naz Mehdizadeh
Vice President, Sean Chaffins
Vice President, Joyce Jicka
Senior Vice President Residential Lending, Jon Irvine
Vice President, Cynthia Park
Assistant Vice President Credit Portfolio Manager, Aida Rodriguez
Senior Vice President Treasury Management Sales Director, Gary Tackoor
Vice President Treasury Manager Finance, Elaine Brodeur
Chairman, Robert D. Sznewajs, age 70
Auditors: KPMG LLP

LOCATIONS

HQ: Banc Of California Inc
3 MacArthur Place, Santa Ana, CA 92707
Phone: 855 361-2262
Web: www.bancofcal.com

PRODUCTS/OPERATIONS

2013 Sales

	% of total
Interest and dividend income	
Loans including fees	53
Securities and others	2
Noninterest income	
Net gain on mortgage banking activities	31
Gain on sale of branches	6
Net gain on sale of loans	4
Loan servicing income	1
Customer service fees	1
Others	2
Total	**100**

COMPETITORS

American Business Bank	East West Bancorp
Bank of America	JPMorgan Chase
Bank of the West	MUFG Americas Holdings
BofI	PacWest Bancorp
California Bank &	Pacific Mercantile
Trust	Pacific Premier
City National	Simplicity Bancorp
Comerica	U.S. Bancorp

HISTORICAL FINANCIALS

Company Type: Public

Income Statement

FYE: December 31

	ASSETS ($ mil.)	NET INCOME ($ mil.)	INCOME AS % OF ASSETS	EMPLOYEES
12/16	11,029	115	1.0%	1,797
12/15	8,235	62	0.8%	1,710
12/14	5,971	30	0.5%	1,470
12/13	3,628	0	0.0%	1,384
12/12	1,682	6	0.4%	614
Annual Growth	**60.0%**	**109.5%**	**—**	**30.8%**

2016 Year-End Financials

Debt ratio: 2.21%
Return on equity: 14.10%
Cash ($ mil.): 440
Current ratio: —
Long-term debt ($ mil.): —

No. of shares (mil.): 49
Dividends
Yield: 0.0%
Payout: 25.2%
Market value ($ mil.): 866

	STOCK PRICE ($) FY Close	P/E High/Low		PER SHARE ($) Earnings	Dividends	Book Value
12/16	17.35	12	6	1.94	0.49	19.65
12/15	14.62	11	8	1.34	0.48	17.15
12/14	11.47	15	11	0.91	0.48	14.47
12/13	13.41	—	—	(0.14)	0.48	16.13
12/12	12.27	33	26	0.40	0.48	15.87
Annual Growth	**9.0%**	**—**	**—**	**48.4%**	**0.5%**	**5.5%**

BancFirst Corp.
(Oklahoma City, Okla)

This Oklahoma bank wants to be more than OK. It wants to be super. BancFirst Corporation is the holding company for BancFirst a super-community bank that emphasizes decentralized man-

agement and centralized support. BancFirst operates more than 100 branches in more than 50 Oklahoma communities. It serves individuals and small to midsized businesses offering traditional deposit products such as checking and savings accounts CDs and IRAs. Commercial real estate lending (including farmland and multifamily residential loans) makes up more than a third of the bank's loan portfolio while one-to-four family residential mortgages represent about 20%. The bank also issues business construction and consumer loans.

Operations

The company operates three core units: metropolitan banks community banks and other financial service. Metropolitan and community banks offer traditional banking products such as commercial and retail lending and a full line of deposit accounts in the metropolitan Oklahoma City and Tulsa areas. Community banks consist of banking locations in communities throughout Oklahoma. Other financial services are specialty product business units including guaranteed small business lending residential mortgage lending trust services securities brokerage electronic banking and insurance.

The company's BancFirst Insurance Services arm sells property/casualty coverage while the bank's trust and investment management division oversees some $1.21 billion of assets on behalf of clients. Bank subsidiaries Council Oak Investment Corporation and Council Oak Real Estate focus on small business and property investments respectively.

Like other retail banks BancFirst makes the bulk of its money from interest income. More than 60% of its total revenue came from loan interest (including fees) during 2015 while another 2% came from interest on taxable securities. The rest of its revenue came from service charges on deposits (19% of revenue) insurance commissions (5%) trust revenue (3%) securities transactions (3%) and loan sales (1%).

Geographic Reach

BancFirst has 95 banking locations serving more than 52 communities across Oklahoma.

Sales and Marketing

The bank customers are generally small to medium-sized businesses engaged in light manufacturing local wholesale and retail trade commercial and residential real estate development and construction services agriculture and the energy industry.

BancFirst spent about $6.9 million for advertising and promotion during 2015 compared to $6.6 million in each of 2014 and 2013.

Financial Performance

BancFirst's annual revenues have risen 20% since 2011 thanks to continued loan asset and deposit growth (partly thanks to branch expansion). The company's annual profits have grown more than 40% over the same period as it's kept a lid on operating expenses and loan loss provisions.

BancFirst's revenue climbed 6% to $306.85 million during 2015 thanks to a combination of loan asset growth and gains on the sales of some of its securities.

Revenue growth in 2015 drove the company's net income up nearly 4% to $66.17 million. The bank's operating cash levels increased by almost 2% to $78.1 million with the rise in cash-based earnings.

Strategy

BancFirst's strategy focuses on providing a full range of commercial banking services to retail customers and small to medium-sized businesses in both the non-metropolitan trade centers and cities in the metropolitan statistical areas of Oklahoma. It operates as a 'super community bank' managing its community banking offices on a decentralized basis which permits it to be responsive to local

customer needs. Underwriting funding customer service and pricing decisions are made by presidents in each market within the company's strategic parameters.

Mergers and Acquisitions

In October 2015 BancFirst purchased $196 million-asset CSB Banchsares and its Bank of Commerce branches in Yukon Mustang and El Reno in Oklahoma. The deal also added $148 million in new loan business and $170 million in deposits.

Company Background

The company has been buying smaller banks to expand in Oklahoma. In 2011 it acquired FBC Financial Corporation and its subsidiary bank 1st Bank Oklahoma with about five branches throughout the state. In 2010 BancFirst acquired Union Bank of Chandler Okemah National Bank and Exchange National Bank of Moore adding about another five branches. It acquired First State Bank Jones in 2009 to expand in eastern Oklahoma.

President and CEO David Rainbolt owns some 40% of BancFirst .

EXECUTIVES

Senior Human Resources Vice President, Mike Rogers

EVP Investments BancFirst, Robert M. Neville, age 61

EVP Financial Services BancFirst, D. Jay Hannah, age 61

EVP Interim CFO and Chief Risk Officer, Randy P. Foraker, age 61, $174,423 total compensation

EVP Human Resources BancFirst, J. Michael Rogers, age 73

Executive Vice President of Sales and Marketing, William Bell

EVP and CIO BancFirst, Scott Copeland, age 52

SEVP and Chairman Executive Committee, Dennis L. Brand, age 69, $525,000 total compensation

Vice Chairman and CEO Council Oak Investment Corporation and Council Oak Real Estate Inc., William O. Johnstone, age 69, $200,000 total compensation

EVP and Chief Credit Officer BancFirst, Roy C. Ferguson, age 70

Regional Executive BancFirst, Karen James, age 61

President and CEO BancFirst, Darryl Schmidt, age 55, $350,000 total compensation

Regional Executive BancFirst, David M. Seat, age 66

EVP and CTO BancFirst, David Westman, age 61

Regional Executive BancFirst, David R. Harlow, age 54, $325,000 total compensation

Regional Executive BancFirst, Harvey G. Robinson, age 58

EVP CFO and Treasurer, Kevin Lawrence, age 38, $214,231 total compensation

President BancFirst Frederick, Jason McQueen

EVP and Chief Internal Auditor, Paul Fleming, age 66

Regional Executive BancFirst, John Anderson, age 61

Senior Vice President Technology, Ed Alexander

Senior Vice President, Jarrod Wise

Senior Vice President, Gail Norman

Senior Vice President, Patrick A Lippmann

Vice President, Linda Glass

Senior Vice President Business Development, Casey Bell

Assistant Vice President, Neisha Kelley

Senior Vice President, Rhonda Coffman

Senior Vice President Compliance, Kelly Foster

Vice President, Greg Piatt

Senior Vice President Stratford, Wes Westbrooks

Senior Vice President and TRUST Officer, Jon Bowers

Senior Vice President Controller, Jennifer Weast

Senior Vice President Treasury Sales Manager, Ashlea Briggs

Senior Vice President Commercial Lending, Tanner Eckler

Senior Vice President and Customer Service Officer, Brian Harris

Senior Vice President, Denise Duffle

Vice President Mortgage Production Manager, Billy Parsley

Senior Vice President, Brian Renz

Senior Vice President, Betsy Blue

Senior Vice President, Brian Stedman

Vice President, James Dickson

Vice President Lockbox Manager, Jennifer Seargent

Vice President and Trust Officer, Carolyn Pollock

Vice President Mortgage Lending, Shelly Matthews

Vice President, Connie Coker

Senior Vice President, Frances Petersen

Senior Vice President, Allen Scroggins

Assistant Vice President Financial Reporting, Chesney Whetstone

Senior Vice President, Blane Allen

Customer service Officer Senior Vice President, Alice Beine Alice Beine

Vice President, Kay Heath

Senior Vice President, Diane Sisemore

Vice President, Jana Blalock

Assistant Vice President Network Services, Dian Joysizemore

Senior Vice President, Cheryl Borelli

Senior Vice President and General Counsel, Brian Pierson

Senior Vice President, Terry Croll

Treasurer Executive Vice President Operations, Randy Forake

Vice President Marketing, Ben Harrington

Vice President Treasury Management CTP, Luis Castillo

Executive Vice President, Sean Shadid

Senior Vice President, Kevin Calabrese

Senior Vice President, David Vinall

EXECUTIVE VICE PRESIDENT, Janet W Gotwals

SENIOR VICE PRESIDENT, Kevin J Calabrese

Assistant Vice President and Consumer Loan Officer, Jenny Gifford

Assistant Vice President, Dauna Dines

Vice President, Deena Suddath

Vice President Trust Officer, Mike Reynolds

Vice Chairman, James R. Daniel, age 77

Vice Chairman, K. Gordon Greer, age 80

Chairman, David E. Rainbolt, age 61

Auditors: BKD, LLP

LOCATIONS

HQ: BancFirst Corp. (Oklahoma City, Okla)
101 N. Broadway, Oklahoma City, OK 73102
Phone: 405 270-1086 **Fax:** 405 270-1089
Web: www.bancfirst.com

PRODUCTS/OPERATIONS

2015 Sales

	$ mil.	% of total
Interest		
Loans including fees	190	63
Securities	6	2
Interest-bearing deposit	4	1
Noninterest		
Service charges on deposits	57	18
Insurance commissions	14	5
Security transactions	9	3
Trust revenue	9	3
Income from sale of loans	2	1
Cash management	7	2
Other	5	2
Total	**306**	**100**

Selected Subsidiaries

BancFirst
  BancFirst Agency Inc. (credit life insurance)
  BancFirst Community Development Corporation
  Council Oak Investment Corporation (small business investments)
  Council Oak Real Estate Inc. (real estate investments)
Council Oak Partners LLC
BancFirst Insurance Services Inc.

COMPETITORS

Arvest Bank	Midland Financial
BOK Financial	Southwest Bancorp
Bank of America	UMB Financial
International Bancshares	Wells Fargo

HISTORICAL FINANCIALS

Company Type: Public

Income Statement

FYE: December 31

	ASSETS ($ mil.)	NET INCOME ($ mil.)	INCOME AS % OF ASSETS	EMPLOYEES
12/16	7,018	70	1.0%	1,773
12/15	6,692	66	1.0%	1,744
12/14	6,574	63	1.0%	1,688
12/13	6,038	54	0.9%	1,653
12/12	6,022	51	0.9%	1,635
Annual Growth	**3.9%**	**8.0%**		**2.0%**

2016 Year-End Financials

Debt ratio: 0.46%
Return on equity: 10.31%
Cash ($ mil.): 1,850
Current ratio: —
Long-term debt ($ mil.): —

No. of shares (mil.): 31
Dividends
  Yield: 0.0%
  Payout: 33.3%
Market value ($ mil.): 2,942

	STOCK PRICE ($) FY Close	P/E High/Low	PER SHARE ($) Earnings	Dividends	Book Value
12/16	93.05	42 23	2.22	0.74	22.49
12/15	58.62	32 26	2.09	0.70	21.01
12/14	63.39	33 25	2.02	0.65	19.65
12/13	56.06	32 22	1.75	0.60	18.16
12/12	42.36	26 22	1.68	0.56	17.04
Annual Growth	**21.7%**	**— —**	**7.2%**	**7.2%**	**7.2%**

BancorpSouth Bank (Tupelo, MS)

Like Elvis Presley BancorpSouth has grown beyond its Tupelo roots. It's the holding company for BancorpSouth Bank which operates some 290 branches in nine southern and midwestern states. Catering to consumers and small and midszed businesses the bank offers checking and savings accounts loans credit cards and commercial banking services. BancorpSouth also sells insurance and provides brokerage investment advisory and asset management services throughout most of its market area. Real estate loans including consumer and commercial mortgages and home equity construction and agricultural loans comprise approximately three-quarters of its loan portfolio. BancorpSouth has assets of $13 billion.

Geographic Reach

Mississippi-based BancorpSouth Bank operates in Alabama Arkansas Florida Illinois Louisiana Mississippi Missouri Tennessee and Texas. BancorpSouth's insurance and financial advisory businesses also operate in Illinois and Florida respectively.

Financial Performance

BancorpSouth reported net income of $94.1 million in 2013 an increase of 12% versus 2012. The decreased provision for credit losses was the primary factor contributing to the rise. Net interest revenue — the bank's primary source of revenue — fell 4% year over year to $$398.9 million the fourth consecutive year of decline. Net interest revenue declined because the decrease in interest expense was more than offset by the decrease in interest revenue as the yield on earning assets declined by a greater amount than that of interest-bearing liabilities. Noninterest income also declined on lower mortgage origination revenue in 2013 versus 2012.

Strategy

The regional bank has grown via the acquisition of other banks and insurance agencies and by opening new branches most recently in Texas and Louisiana. To reduce its reliance on interest-related revenue BancorpSouth hopes to diversify its revenue stream by increasing the amount it generates from mortgage lending insurance brokerage and securities activities. To this end subsidiary BancorpSouth Insurance Services has acquired small insurance agencies in Arkansas Missouri and Texas.

Mergers and Acquisitions

In 2014 BancorpSouth agreed to acquire Central Community Corp. the holding company for First State Bank Central Texas headquartered in Austin Texas. First State Bank operates 31 branches in Austin Round Rock Killeen and several other Central Texas communities. BancorpSouth has also agreed to purchase Ouachita Bancshares Corp. with a dozen branches in Louisiana. Both deals were announced in January 2014 and were expected to close promptly. However they've been delayed because BancorpSouth needs more time to get regulatory approvals and to meet "closing conditions necessary to complete" the mergers.

EXECUTIVES

SEVP CFO and Treasurer, John G. Copeland, age 64

EVP and Corporate Secretary BancorpSouth and BancorpSouth Bank, Cathy S. Freeman, age 52

Chairman and CEO BancorpSouth Inc. and BancorpSouth Bank, James D. (Dan) Rollins, age 58, $840,000 total compensation

EVP BancorpSouth Inc. and Vice Chairman and Chief Lending Officer BancorpSouth Bank, James R. Hodges, $382,500 total compensation

President and COO, Chris A. Bagley, $495,000 total compensation

President Equipment Finance and Leasing, Kyle Gilliam

SEVP and General Counsel, Chuck Pignuolo, age 61

Executive Vice President, Clyde Guyse

Auditors: KPMG LLP

LOCATIONS

HQ: BancorpSouth Bank (Tupelo, MS)
One Mississippi Plaza, 201 South Spring Street, Tupelo, MS 38804
Phone: 662 680-2000
Web: www.bancorpsouth.com

PRODUCTS/OPERATIONS

2016 Sales

	$ mil.	% of total
Interest		
Loans & leases	440	58
Securities	41	5
Deposits with other banks	1	—
Noninterest		
Insurance commissions	115	15
Deposit service charges	43	6
Mortgage lending	41	5
Credit card debit card and merchant fees	37	5
Wealth management	21	3
Other	19	3
Total	**762**	**100**

Selected Subsidiaries

BancorpSouth Bank
  BancorpSouth Insurance Services Inc.
  BancorpSouth Investment Services Inc.
  BancorpSouth Municipal Development Corporation
  Century Credit Life Insurance Company
  Personal Finance Corporation

COMPETITORS

BBVA Compass	Hancock Holding
Bancshares	Regions Financial
Capital One	Renasant
First Horizon	SunTrust
Great Southern Bancorp	Trustmark

HISTORICAL FINANCIALS

Company Type: Public

Income Statement

FYE: December 31

	ASSETS ($ mil.)	NET INCOME ($ mil.)	INCOME AS % OF ASSETS	EMPLOYEES
12/16	14,724	132	0.9%	3,998
12/15	13,798	127	0.9%	4,002
12/14	13,326	116	0.9%	3,820
12/13	13,029	94	0.7%	4,005
12/12	13,397	84	0.6%	4,231
Annual Growth	2.4%	12.0%	—	(1.4%)

2016 Year-End Financials

Debt ratio: 3.69%
Return on equity: 7.83%
Cash ($ mil.): 222
Current ratio: —
Long-term debt ($ mil.): —

No. of shares (mil.): 93
Dividends
  Yield: 0.0%
  Payout: 31.9%
Market value ($ mil.): 2,909

	STOCK PRICE ($) FY Close	P/E High/Low	PER SHARE ($) Earnings	Dividends	Book Value
12/16	31.05	22 13	1.41	0.45	18.40
12/15	23.99	20 15	1.33	0.35	17.58
12/14	22.51	21 16	1.21	0.25	16.69
12/13	25.42	26 14	0.99	0.12	15.89
12/12	14.54	17 12	0.90	0.04	15.34
Annual Growth	20.9%	— —	11.9%	83.1%	4.6%

Bank of America Corp.

Among the United States' largest banks by assets (alongside JPMorgan Chase and Citigroup) ubiquitous Bank of America Corporation (BAC) operates one of the country's most extensive branch networks with some 4600 locations and 16000 ATMs. The bank's core services include consumer and small business banking corporate banking credit cards mortgage lending and asset management. Its online banking operation counts some 34 million active users and 22 million mobile users. BAC acquired Merrill Lynch in 2009 making it one of the world's leading wealth managers with more than $2 trillion assets under management and boasting a beefed up trading and international businesses.

HISTORY

Bank of America predecessor NationsBank was formed as the Commercial National Bank in 1874 by citizens of Charlotte North Carolina. In 1901 George Stephens and Word Wood formed what became American Trust Co. The banks merged in 1957 to become American Commercial Bank which in 1960 merged with Security National to form North Carolina National Bank.

In 1968 the bank formed holding company NCNB which by 1980 was the largest bank in North Carolina. Under the leadership of Hugh McColl who became chairman in 1983 NCNB became the first southern bank to span six states.

NCNB profited from the savings and loan crisis of the late 1980s by managing assets and buying defunct thrifts at fire-sale prices. The company nearly doubled its assets in 1988 when the FDIC chose it to manage the shuttered First Republicbank then Texas' largest bank. The company renamed itself NationsBank in 1991.

In 1993 the company bought Chicago Research & Trading a government securities dealer and provider of oil and gas financing. A 1993 joint venture with Dean Witter and Discover to open securities brokerages in banks led to complaints that customers were not fully informed of the risks of some investments and that brokers were paying rebates to banking personnel for customer referrals. Dean Witter withdrew from the arrangement in 1994 and SEC investigations and a class-action lawsuit ensued. NationsBank settled the lawsuit for about $30 million the next year. (The company agreed to pay nearly $7 million to settle similar charges in 1998.)

NationsBank scooped up St. Louis-based Boatmen's Bancshares and Montgomery Securities (now Banc of America Securities) in 1997. The next year it bought Barnett Banks Florida's #1 bank.

Enter BankAmerica. Founded in 1904 as Bank of Italy BankAmerica had once been the US's largest bank but had fallen behind as competitors consolidated. The company's board of directors was pondering ways to become more competitive and in 1998 decided a merger was the best way. With the ink barely dry on its Barnett Banks deal NationsBank obliged.

After the merger the combined firm announced it would write down a billion-dollar bad loan to D.E. Shaw & Co. which followed the same Russian-investment-paved path of descent as Long-Term Capital Management. David Coulter (head of the old BankAmerica which made the loan) took the fall for the loss resigning as president; the balance of power shifted to the NationsBank side in 1999 when Kenneth Lewis took the post.

The Russian debacle and merger hiccups led the firm in early 1999 to reorganize and reduce overseas operations; it sold its private banking operations in Europe and Asia to UBS. Also that year it bought the recreational-vehicle financing unit of Associates First Capital (now part of Citigroup) 50% of Denver-based mutual fund firm Marsico Capital Management (it bought the rest in 2001) and BA Merchant Services. The bank also changed its name to Bank of America and began offering online banking through America Online. To avoid a court battle the bank settled charges that it retained proceeds from unclaimed bonds in California.

In 1999 the company earned the ire of labor officials for a program in which employees were recruited to maintain ATMs without being paid or provided supplies. EVP Frank Gentry who crafted the NationsBank/BankAmerica deal retired in 2000 signaling an end to the company's buying spree. Its focus turned inward as it set about the difficult integration of the two firms.

McColl retired as chairman in 2001. Later that year the company announced it would cease its subprime lending and car leasing operations.

In 2003 Bank of America's mutual fund chief Robert Gordon was among several employees who left the firm amidst a New York attorney general's investigation into hedge fund client Canary Capital Partners which allegedly had access to Bank of America's trading platform to make illegal after-hours trades of the company's erstwhile Nations Funds. Bank of America also paid $10 million for failing to provide documents to the SEC during its investigation of the scandal the largest-ever fine levied by the regulatory body for such an infraction.

The company sold its securities clearing and broker/dealer services units to ADP in 2004. In early 2005 the company struck a deal with regulators to implement tighter controls cut fees charged to investors exit the mutual fund clearing business and pay more than $500 million in fines including $140 million to settle complaints against FleetBoston. Also that year Bank of America remitted about another $460 million to settle investor claims that it did not adequately conduct due diligence when underwriting bonds of doomed telecom firm WorldCom in 2001 and 2002. (The claim involved 17 other investment banks as well; Citigroup paid more than $2.2 billion to clear itself of similar charges in late 2004).

Bank of America previously fattened up by purchasing northeastern banking behemoth FleetBoston for some $50 billion in 2004 and credit card giant MBNA for approximately $35 billion in cash and stock in early 2006. The latter deal roughly doubled the bank's credit card customer base (as well as its income from credit card fees) and gave the bank access to some 5000 organizations and institutions with which MBNA had affinity marketing relationships.

In early 2007 the company shed its venture capital arm BA Venture Partners (now Scale Venture Partners) to focus on middle-market private equity investments carried out by its BA Capital Investors unit.

In 2007 Bank of America bought U.S. Trust from Charles Schwab for more than $3 billion and acquired Chicago-based LaSalle Bank from Netherlands-based ABN AMRO for some $21 billion. Following the acquisition of U.S. Trust Bank of America merged the asset manager with its private banking and wealth management business to form U.S. Trust Bank of America Private Wealth Management. Prior acquisitions include credit card giant MBNA in 2006 a deal that doubled the bank's credit card customer base and its income from credit card fees.

In an effort to boost the economy and stimulate lending the US government in 2008 bought some $250 billion worth of preferred shares in the country's top banks. Approximately $45 billion of that was slated for Bank of America ($20 billion more than the original investment total). As a result of the government intervention US Treasury official (and so-called "pay czar") ordered then-CEO Lewis to receive no salary in 2009 and slashed compensation for other highly paid employees. Bank of America finished paying back the debt in late 2009.

As the global economy reeled from a credit freeze and subsequent recession in 2008 Bank of America added to its coffers by buying up troubled mortgage lender Countrywide Financial and investment bank Merrill Lynch. Countrywide had fallen on hard times as one of the hardest-hit victims of the subprime mortgage crisis. The deal was initially for $4 billion in stock but was finalized at around $2.5 billion as the economic climate sunk.

The Countrywide purchase made Bank of America the largest residential mortgage lender and servicer in the US. The company also settled a lawsuit contending that Countrywide engaged in deceptive lending practices. Bank of America agreed to pay more than $8 billion toward reductions on interest rates and principals of some 400000 troubled mortgage accounts. To avoid the stigma of the subprime loan crisis Countrywide was renamed Bank of America Home Loans in 2009.

Bank of America paid some $50 billion in stock to buy Merrill Lynch which had been crippled by the global credit crisis. Hoping to increase its up-front account fee revenues Bank of America began making a concerted push to cross-promote Merrill Lynch's wealth management business to the bank's affluent clients.

However the Merrill Lynch deal also brought its fair share of headaches. With the approval of Bank of America leadership the failed investment bank gave early bonuses worth billions to its executives prompting angry Bank of America shareholders and lawmakers to cry foul. The Securities and Exchange Commission slapped Bank of America with a $33 million fine for misleading shareholders about the bonuses. That fine was rejected by a federal judge in 2009 and the matter was ordered to go to trial. Bank of America ultimately agreed to pay $150 million in a settlement. In another Merrill Lynch-related settlement Bank of America agreed to pay $315 million in 2011 for claims that Merrill Lynch made false and misleading statements about its mortgage-backed securities sold to investors.

Then-CEO Ken Lewis in particular came under fire for not disclosing how bleak Merrill Lynch's financial condition was prior to the purchase; Lewis in turn said he had been implicitly pressured by the government to keep the troubles under wraps to prevent the deal from collapsing. A push to oust Lewis at the company's annual meeting in 2009 didn't pass but shareholders split the chairman and CEO positions to provide more accountability to the public. Director Walter Massey was named chairman and Lewis stepped down at the end of the year. Brian Moynihan the head of consumer and small business banking succeeded Lewis as CEO. Longtime Dupont CEO Charles Holliday took over as chairman in 2010 replacing the retiring Massey.

EXECUTIVES

Senior Vice President Technology Delivery Executive, Michael Smith
Chairman and CEO, Brian T. Moynihan, age 57, $1,500,000 total compensation
Chief Operations and Technology Officer, Catherine P. (Cathy) Bessant, age 56
COO, Thomas K. (Tom) Montag, age 61, $1,000,000 total compensation
President Preferred and Small Business Banking and Co-head Consumer Banking, Dean C. Athanasia, age 50
President Retail Banking and Co-head Consumer Banking, Thong M. Nguyen, age 58
Vice Chairman and Head Global Wealth and Investment Management, Terence P. (Terry) Laughlin, age 62, $850,000 total compensation
Chief Risk Officer, Geoffrey S. Greener, age 52, $850,000 total compensation
CFO, Paul M. Donofrio, age 56, $850,000 total compensation
Head of Merrill Lynch Wealth Management, John Thiel
Head of Global Wealth and Retirement Solution, Andy Sieg
Senior Vice President Senior Client Manager Commercial Banking, Andrew Harris
Vice President, Michael Young
Senior Vice President Senior Technology Manager, Danny Mccoy
Senior Vice President; Senior Production Services Manager, Colleen Clark
Information Technology Team Manager Assistant Vice President, Leo Kaplin
Senior Vice President, Paul Mccormac
Senior Vice President;GWIM Credit Manager, John Sprajcar

Senior Vice President;GWIM Credit Manager, Teresa Lekich
Vice President Operations Project Consultant, Carol Rogers
Vice President Financial Governance, Rob Edwards
Vice President Senior Relationship Manager, Ani Jinian
Senior Vice President, Reagan Newcomer
Vice President Senior Technical Manager, John Syper
Vice President Human Resources Manager, Michelle John
Assistant Vice President, Carol Batson
Senior Vice President, Karina Glass
Vice President; Senior Marketing Advisor, Maggie Kennedy
Senior Vice President, Alok Joshi
Senior Vice President;consumer Market Executive, Ventura Perez
Vice President; Market Information Manager I, Richard Baker
Vice President, Kumar Mithipati
Vice President Business Enablement, Amanda Hite
Senior Vice President Reporting And Analysis, Dale Mcmahan
Vice President, Josie Jimenez
Vice President, William Gilley
Vice President, Amber Thorneburg
Vice President, Judith Krietsch
Vice President;GWIM Senior Credit Underwriter, Erin H Grow
Senior Vice President Enterprise Trans, Len Clamp
Assistant Vice President CRES Risk Reporting and Analytics Support, Heather Jones
Senior Vice President, Todd Tidwell
Senior Vice President, Michael Crawford
Senior Vice President Leadership Development Executive, Stephanie Asbury
Vice President; Systems Consultant Design Team Lead Infrastructure Architect, Toua Lee
Vice President, Sharon Waldbillig
Vice President, Sara Walsh
Vice President, Lisa Webber
Vice President, Myra Wardwell
Vice President, Timothy Webb
Vice President, Jennifer Whitemyer
Vice President Client Manager, Angela Meadows
Vice President, John Waccard
Vice President; Instructional Technical Designer, Douglas Eater
Vice President, Jason Willets
Senior Vice President, Steve Gaylord
Assistant Vice President Recruiter, Maria Melendez
Vice President and Senior Credit Products Officer Specialized Industries Southeast Region, Fred Chesson
Assistant Vice President, Tracy Newman
Vice President Brand Manager, Andrew L Fishkin
Senior Vice President Consumer Marketing Executive, Lisa Stec
Assistant Vice President;file Administrator II, Renee Beacham
SENIOR VICE PRESIDENT, Tammy Kennedy-nichols
Senior Vice President Technology Executive, Kelly Cornia
Vice President Banking Center Manager, Peter Ackermann
Assistant Vice President;GWIM Document Administrator, Kimberly Lewis
AVP Short Sale Closing Team, Michelle Holly
Assistant Vice President;gwim Loan Administrator, Lynne Reynolds
Vice President, Armida Warren
Senior Vice President Technical Project Solutions, Deborah Cormier
Vice President, Clay Walker
Vice President, Casey Whisenand
Vice President, Gene Werner

Vice President, Dipika Jain
Vice President; Platform Product Manager, Lara Lennaman
Senior Vice President; Market Planning Manager Southeast, Lori Mondor
Senior Vice President Global Marketing Heritage and Archives Management, Bill Dircks
Vice President Cnslt Systems Engineer, Mihir Gandhi
Assistant Vice President;gwim Loan Monitoring Specialist, Mildred Cuevas
Vice President;Senior Credit Products Underwriter, Jennifer Brown
Senior Vice President, Dianne Douglas
Vice President Supplier Diversity Development Manager, Ed Franklin
Executive Vice President, Brian Boudreau
Vice President;business Support Lead Iii, Terry Kennedy
Senior Vice President, Tim Gauvin
Vice President, Patty Spooner
Senior Vice President, Janet Lacasse
Vice President Finance Manager Corporate Workplace, Roberto Yon
Vice President Corporate Audit, Ruben Macias
Senior Vice President Operations Risk, William Kelly
Assistant Vice President;GWIM Loan Monitoring Specialist, Jacquelyn Capers
Assistant Vice President Treasury Quality Assurance, Monika Jayant
Senior Vice President, Robert Maloney
Assistant Vice President;gwim Document Administrator, Lorita Cagle
Vice President; Senior Change Consultant, Rhonda Hall
Assistant Vice President Operations Project Consultant, Shawna Taylor
Vice President, Kevin Kleinhomer
Vice President Interactive Design, Robert Pothier
Vice Presideni GT and O Innovation Innovation Lab Director, Alicia Jones
Assistant Vice President;gwim Document Administrator, Shelly Mccann
Senior Vice President, Thomas Gluckman
Senior Vice President, Darrell Minott
Senior Vice President, John McDuffie
Senior Vice President, Stacey Ware
Vice President of Information Technology, Peter Montano
Recruiter Vice President, Stacey Clark
Vice President Enterprise Data Services, Giovanni Simeone
Assistant Vice President; Senior Financial Analyst, Juan Franco
Senior Vice President Senior Credit Products Officer, Bill Franey
SENIOR VICE PRESIDENT, John Lenckos
Senior Vice President Credit Loss Forecasting Executive, Christian Ingerslev Christian Ingerslev
Vice President Technology Architecture and Operations, Jim Drake
Vice President Marketing, Michele Ekarius
Assistant Vice President Operations Project Consultant, Darci Lockhart
Vice President eCommerce Channel Consultant, Jennifer Deisinger
Senior Vice President, Anna Danilenko
Vice President, Susan Davis
Vice President;GWIM Credit Underwriter, Michael Boggess
Vice President Technology Manager, Eric Brueggmann
Senior Vice President, Jack Williams
Senior Vice President Small Business Banking Manager, Dean Bird
Vice President product Delivery Senior Officer Treasury, Brian Swanson
Vice President, Michael McKennon

**Assistant Vice President Consumer Banking
Architecture,** Sameer Leekha
**Senior Vice President; Human Resources
Business Control Executive,** Kristin Leavell
Assistant Vice President; Operations Manager, Ida
Howard
Senior Vice President, Rochelle Kelly Rochelle Kelly
Vice President, Jason Dyckes
Vice President of Process Design, Paul Sheehan
**Vice President Small Business Banking
Technology,** Gary Hammock
**Senior Vice President RISK Home Equity Loss
Forecasting,** Steven Lindsey
Vice President Whole Loan Portfolio Management,
Ivan Yeung
**Svp; Global Corporate Security; Intelligence and
Analysis Director,** Arian Avila
Vice President, James Gowen
**Assistant Vice President Credit Support
Associate,** Diane Baine
**Senior Vice President eCommerce Channel
Manager,** Randy Earley
Senior Vice President PORTFOLIO Manager,
Craig Murlless
Senior Vice President Information Architecture,
Michelle Boston
Vice President National Remarketing Manager,
Jeannie Chiaromonte
Assistant Vice President, Christopher Hopkins
Assistant Vice President; Executive Support, Joe
Louie
Vice President Card Services, Kelly Dinda
Senior Vice President; Manager, Adam Reisig
Vice President of Finance, Mahesh Bhashetty
**Vice President; Operations Project Consultant
Transportation Services Commercial Services,**
Dina Scott
Vice President, Dawn Weaver
**Assistant Vice President Quantitative Operations
Associate,** Ankit Tanwar
Senior Card Account Manager Vice President,
Janet Jernigan
**Assistant Vice President; Information Security
Engineer,** Sagun Shrestha
**Assistant Vice President; Banking Center
Manager,** Esteban Jimenez
Vice President Architect, Manjusha Pavuluri
Auditors: PricewaterhouseCoopers LLP

LOCATIONS

HQ: Bank of America Corp.
Bank of America Corporate Center, 100 N. Tryon
Street, Charlotte, NC 28255
Phone: 704 386-5681
Web: www.bankofamerica.com

PRODUCTS/OPERATIONS

2016 Sales

	$ mil.	% of total
Interest income	51,057	55
Non-interest income	42,605	45
Total	**93,662**	**100**

2016 sales

	% of total
Consumer Banking	38
Global Banking	22
Global Wealth & Investment Management	21
Global Markets	19
Total	**100**

Selected Products & Services

Capital raising and advisory
Card solutions
Equipment finance/leasing
Fraud prevention
Interest rate currency and commodity risk management
Investment solutions and management
Lending and financing
Liquidity management

Merchant services
Mergers and acquisitions
Payments/receivables management
Philanthropic management
Retirement and benefit plan services
Trade services

COMPETITORS

BB&T	JPMorgan Chase
Bank of New York	KeyCorp
Mellon	MUFG Americas Holdings
Capital One	Morgan Stanley
Citigroup	PNC Financial
Citizens Financial	RBC Financial Group
Group	State Street
Goldman Sachs	SunTrust
HSBC	U.S. Bancorp
HSBC USA	Wells Fargo

HISTORICAL FINANCIALS

Company Type: Public

Income Statement

FYE: December 31

	ASSETS ($ mil.)	NET INCOME ($ mil.)	INCOME AS % OF ASSETS	EMPLOYEES
12/16	2,187,702	17,906	0.8%	208,000
12/15	2,144,316	15,888	0.7%	213,000
12/14	2,104,534	4,833	0.2%	224,000
12/13	2,102,273	11,431	0.5%	242,000
12/12	2,209,974	4,188	0.2%	267,000
Annual Growth	(0.3%)	43.8%	—	(6.1%)

2016 Year-End Financials

Debt ratio: 9.90%—
Return on equity: 6.83%
Cash ($ mil.): 147,738
Current ratio: —
Long-term debt ($ mil.): —

Dividends
Yield: 0.0%
Payout: 16.6%
Market value ($ mil.): —

	STOCK PRICE ($) FY Close	P/E High/Low		Earnings	Dividends	Book Value
12/16	22.10	15	7	1.50	0.25	26.54
12/15	16.83	13	11	1.31	0.20	24.68
12/14	17.89	50	40	0.36	0.12	23.15
12/13	15.57	17	12	0.90	0.04	21.97
12/12	11.61	44	22	0.25	0.04	21.98
Annual Growth	17.5%	—	—	56.5%	58.1%	4.8%

Bank of Hawaii Corp

Bank of Hawaii knows there's no place like home. The firm is the holding company for Bank of Hawaii (familiarly known as Bankoh) which has about 75 branches and 460-plus ATMs in its home state plus an additional dozen in American Samoa Guam Palau and Saipan. Founded in 1897 the bank operates through four business segments: retail banking for consumers and small businesses in Hawaii; commercial banking including property/casualty insurance for middle-market and large corporations (this segment also includes the bank's activities beyond the state); investment services such as trust asset management and private banking; and treasury which performs corporate asset and liability management services.

Operations

Bank of Hawaii operates through several segments including retail banking commercial banking investment services and treasury. In fiscal 2013

consumer loans accounted for 59% of its total loan portfolio; commercial loans made up the rest.

Geographic Reach

Despite its name Bank of Hawaii provides a broad range of financial services and products to customers in not only Hawaii but in Guam and other Pacific islands.

Sales and Marketing

Bank of Hawaii spends about $5 million each year on advertising.

Financial Performance

The bank network in fiscal 2013 logged $584.7 million in revenue representing a $36 million drop from 2012's $620.7 million. Bank of Hawaii points to lower margins from reinvesting investment securities and the origination of new loans at lower yields for the declines. Additionally its mortgage banking income dropped by $16.5 million (or 46%) in 2013 vs. 2012 as rising interest rates slowed refinancing activity and its related loan sales margins. Net income dropped $15.6 million from 2012 to 2013's $150.5 million. Meanwhile cash flow from operations rose $241.9 million — by some $19.5 million — during the reporting period from $222.5 million.

Strategy

Banking in paradise isn't always easy: Hawaii is known for its high cost of living and its reliance on the tourism industry. As the second-largest bank on the archipelago Bank of Hawaii's performance often mirrors that of the state since loans secured by homes and new home construction represent the largest portion of the company's lending. Due to the recent economic environment in the state the bank has curtailed its lending activities which cut into its bottom line. Its 2011 results were also negatively impacted by a federal law that went into effect the previous year that puts caps on overdraft fees.

The company's growth — limited by geography — comes methodically. Bank of Hawaii continuously looks for ways to expand. It has installed some 60 ATMs inside McDonald's restaurants throughout Hawaii and it introduced ATMs inside McDonald's restaurants in Guam. In addition to growing its ATM network Bank of Hawaii has also introduced a special mobile banking fleet which includes shuttle-sized vehicles that offer ATMs and wireless technology inside.

EXECUTIVES

VICE PRESIDENT, James Lowson
Senior Vice President And Senior Lendi, Nancy Seawahl
SEVP and CFO, Dean Y. Shigemura
Chairman President and CEO, Peter S. Ho, age 53, $776,077 total compensation
Vice Chairman and Chief Risk Officer, Mary E. Sellers, age 61, $427,565 total compensation
Vice Chairman Client Solutions Group, Sharon M. Crofts
Vice Chairman and Chief Administrative Officer, Mark A. Rossi, age 68, $433,776 total compensation
Vice Chairman; Chief Commercial Officer, Wayne Y. Hamano, $355,170 total compensation
Vice Chairman; Residential and Consumer Lending Group Manager, Derek J. Norris, age 67, $224,615 total compensation
Executive Vice President and Division Manager, Todd Nohara
Vice President and Retail Credit Analytics and Reporting Manager for Retail Credit Department, Robyn Tanaka
Vice President of Operations, Andrew Boyles
Senior Vice President, Erlinda D Alegre
Assistant Vice President and Operations Manager, Chris Onzuka
Executive Vice President, Denis Isono
Senior Vice President, Kevin Baptist

Vice President, John Hulihee

Assistant Vice President Manager, Cassandra Yamamoto

Assistant Vice President, Gregory Biegen

Vice President and Manager Human Resources, Therese M Dickerson

Vice President Executive Loan Officer, Brenda Mitchell

Vice President of Lending, Cindy Okamura

Assistant Vice President Dealer Marketing Relationship Officer, Craig Ito

Vice President and Audit Consultant, Irene E B Kwan

Vice President and Wealth Advisor, Sean Rostron

Vice President, Rita C Jugo

Vice President, Tom Guinan

Assistant Vice President, Dora Rivera

Vice President, Cheryl Minaai

Senior Vice President, Terri Okada

Vice President and Dealer Commercial Services Manager, Robert Gardiner

Vice President and Service Manager, Susan Marciel

Vice President and Assistant Service Manager, Tina Nakahara

Senior Vice President Card Products, Anthony DeSanctis

Vice President, Toshiya Matsumoto

Asst. Vice President, Son Gina

Vice President, Maureen Coogan

Senior Vice President, Roberta Chu

Vice President, Dean Uyeda

Vice President and West Oahu Isb Area Manager Of Bank Of Hawaii, Charleen Deuprey

Vice President Risk Manager, Marc Adelberger

Vice President, Edison Kobayashi

Assistant Vice President, Lynette Sakamoto

Executive Vice President Human Resources, Lester Stiefel

Senior Vice President and Manager, Steven Nakahara

Vice President, Miki Ikeda

Senior Vice President and Manager, Dirk Yoshizawa

Executive Vice President, David Oyadomari

Vice President and Credit Compliance Officer Iii, Janis Okamoto

Assistant Vice President and Compensation Manager, Kaleo Kekoolani

Executive Vice President, Edward Kim

Senior Vice President, BO Wheeler

Vice President And Sales and Marketing And Client Development Manager, Dale Tanimoto

Vice President, Brian Watase

Vice President Financial Consultant, Christian Look

Vice President, Tim Chang

Vice President, Robert Trent

Vice President and Banking Center Manager, Reid Hinaga

Vice President, Malcom Lau

Vice President and Investment Services Group Compliance Manager, Catherine Fujisaki

Financial Consultant And Vice President, Christopher Otto

Vice President Mortgage, Shanae Souza

Senior Vice President and Manager of the Commercial Real Estate Lo, Tony Mizuno

Senior Vice President and Manager, Teri Young

Senior Vice President Director of Corporate Security, Brian Ishikawa

Executive Vice President and C, James P Garcia

Vice President, Rudy Alvior Rudy Alvior

Senior Vice President And Regional Manager East Oahu Region, Jon Murakami

Vice President, Derek Chang

Vice President, Arthur K Taniguchi

Senior Vice President, Leilani Williams

Vice President, Natalie Fogle

Assistant Vice President, Kathy Rodriguez

Executive Vice President, Cynthia Wyrick

Vice President and Senior Portfolio Manager, David Okamoto

Senior Vice President And Regional Manager East Oahu, Daniel Kim

Senior Vice President, Donovan Koki

Vice President, Janet Katakura

Assistant Vice President Corporate Risk Analyst, Arm Gregory Biegen

Vice President Administration, Pat Hulaton

Vice President and Wealth Advisor, Joan Martin

Vice President and Private Banking Officer Private Banking Division, Davin Nakasato

Vice President Product Manager Consumer Deposits, Lynette Louis

Vice President and Service Manager, Lisa Revilla

Assistant Vice President and Commercial Banking Officer, Chad Young

Vice President, Ryan Kitamura

Vice President and Engineering Manager, Joe Francher

Assistant Vice President and Branch Manager, Anne Banting

Vice President, Amy Honda

Vice President and International Private Banking Manager, Ken Niimura

Assistant Vice President Senior Consumer Loan Officer Dealer Indirect Lending Bank of Hawaii, Cheryl Kaohi

Vice President Commercial Banking, Vincent Perez

VP and Corporate Counsel, Val Ito

Vice President, Rosemarie Aquino

Assistant Vice President and Senior Auditor, Daniel Li

Executive Vice President and Manager, Dana Takushi

Senior Executive Vice President, Jim Polk

Assistant Vice President and Branch Manager, Rikki Ho

Vice President Manager, Mark Carkin

Assistant Vice President Service Manager, Kimberly Holani

Vice President Commercial Banking Officer, Christopher Frost

Vice President, Gunjan Doshi

Vice Chairman and Chief Strategy Officer, Kent T. Lucien, age 63

Vice Chairman, Donna A. Tanoue, age 63

Vice Chairman Consumer Banking Group, James C. (Jim) Polk

Secretary, Jill Rotolo

Secretary, SHERRY SERRANO

Auditors: Ernst & Young LLP

LOCATIONS

HQ: Bank of Hawaii Corp
130 Merchant Street, Honolulu, HI 96813
Phone: 888 643-3888
Web: www.boh.com

PRODUCTS/OPERATIONS

Selected Products/Services

Personal
Banking Products
Checking
Savings
Special Packages
Loans & Lines
Mortgages
Credit Cards
Debit Cards
Online & Mobile Banking
IRAs
Small Business
Banking Products
Checking
Savings
Special Packages
Credit Card
Debit Card
Loans & Leasing

Trade & International
Business Services
Online Banking
Corporate & Commercial
Checking
Savings
Cash Management
Loans & Leasing
International Trade Services
Business Needs

2015 Sales

	% of total
Interest Income	
Interest and Fees on Loans and Leases	48
Income on Investment Securities	21
Other	.
Non-interest Income	
Trust and Asset Management	8
Mortgage Banking	2
Service Charges on Deposit Accounts	6
Fees Exchange and Other Service Charges	9
Investment Securities Gains Net	2
Annuity and Insurance	1
Bank-Owned Life Insurance	1
Other	2
Total	**100**

Selected Subsidiaries

Bank of Hawaii
 Bank of Hawaii Leasing Inc.
 BNE Airfleets Corporation (Barbados)
 Pacific Century Leasing International Inc.
 Bank of Hawaii Insurance Services Inc.
 Bank of Hawaii International Inc.
 Bankoh Investment Partners LLC
 Bankoh Investment Services Inc.
 BOH Wholesale Insurance Agency Inc.
 Pacific Century Advisory Services Inc.
 Pacific Century Insurance Services Inc.
 Pacific Century Life Insurance Corporation

COMPETITORS

American Savings Bank
Australia and New Zealand Banking
Bank of America
Central Pacific Financial

HSBC
Territorial Bancorp
Westpac Banking

HISTORICAL FINANCIALS

Company Type: Public

Income Statement

	ASSETS ($ mil.)	NET INCOME ($ mil.)	INCOME AS % OF ASSETS	EMPLOYEES
12/16	16,492	181	1.1%	2,122
12/15	15,455	160	1.0%	2,200
12/14	14,787	163	1.1%	2,200
12/13	14,084	150	1.1%	2,200
12/12	13,728	166	1.2%	2,300
Annual Growth	4.7%	2.2%	—	(2.0%)

FYE: December 31

2016 Year-End Financials

Debt ratio: 0.11%	No. of shares (mil.): 42
Return on equity: 15.89%	Dividends
Cash ($ mil.): 172	Yield: 0.0%
Current ratio: —	Payout: 44.6%
Long-term debt ($ mil.): —	Market value ($ mil.): 3,781

	STOCK PRICE ($) FY Close	P/E High/Low	PER SHARE ($) Earnings	Dividends	Book Value
12/16	88.69	21 13	4.23	1.89	27.24
12/15	62.90	19 15	3.70	1.80	25.79
12/14	59.31	17 14	3.69	1.80	24.13
12/13	59.14	18 13	3.38	1.80	22.75
12/12	44.05	13 11	3.67	1.80	22.83
Annual Growth	19.1%	— —	3.6%	1.2%	4.5%

Bank of Marin Bancorp

Bank of Marin supports the wealthy enclave of Marin County north of San Francisco. The bank operates more than 20 branches in the posh California counties of Marin Sonoma and Napa as well as in San Francisco and Alameda counties. Targeting area residents and small to midsized businesses the bank offers standard retail products as checking and savings accounts CDs credit cards and loans. It also provides private banking and wealth management services to high net-worth clients. Commercial mortgages account for the largest portion of the company's loan portfolio followed by business construction and home equity loans.

Geographic Reach

Bank of Marin has branches in Alameda Corte Madera Emeryville Greenbrae Mill Valley Napa Novato Oakland Petaluma San Francisco San Rafael Santa Rosa Sausalito Sonoma and Tiburon.

Sales and Marketing

Its customer base is made up of individuals small to midsized businesses professionals and not-for-profit organizations.

Financial Performance

The bank makes its money through interest income and non-interest income such as service charges and fees. Interest income accounts for almost 90% of overall revenues. The bank has seen its revenue levels fluctuate over the years and in 2013 revenues fell 5% to $68 million due to lower yields on investments and new loans with lower interest rates.

Mergers and Acquisitions

In 2013 the bank gained a branch in Alameda with the purchase of NorCal Community Bancorp the holding company of the Bank of Alameda.

EXECUTIVES

President CEO and Director Bank of Marin Bancorp and Bank of Marin, Russell A. (Russ) Colombo, age 64, $400,355 total compensation
EVP Retail Banking Bank of Marin, Peter Pelham, age 60, $214,725 total compensation
EVP and CFO, Tani Girton, age 57, $239,500 total compensation
EVP and Chief Credit Officer Bank of Marin, Elizabeth Reizman, age 58, $221,250 total compensation
EVP Commercial Banking Bank of Marin, Timothy D. (Tim) Myers, age 46, $215,000 total compensation
EVP and CIO, James T. Burke, age 62
Vice President, Nancy Boatright
Assistant Vice President, Melanie Rempe
Executive Vice President And Chief Cre, Kevin Coonan
Assistant Vice President and Finance and Accounting Manager, Janice Freidig
FVP Business Banking Deposit Services Group Manager, Norma Saavedra
Vice President and Commercial Banking Officer, Jim Foot
Vice President Wealth Management Services, Deborah Smith
Vice President of Human Resources, Robert Gotelli
Vice President Compliance Manager, Barbara Collins
Assistant Vice President and Assistant Corporate Secretary, Megan Garner
Vice President, Allison Spitzer
Vice President, Fran Hoke
Vice President and Commercial Banking Officer, Maria DeBenedetti
Assistant Vice President and Assistant Branch Manager, Eddie Roslin

Assistant Vice President Branch Manager, Kathy Madsen
Vice President of Human Resources, Honey Garcia
Assistant Vice President Branch Manager, Greg Gener
First Vice President CRE Credit Administrator, Patrick McCarty
Chairman Bank of Marin Bancorp and Bank of Marin, Brian M. Sobel, age 62
Board Member, Jan Yanehiro
Board Director, Rafelina Maglio
Auditors: Moss Adams LLP

LOCATIONS

HQ: Bank of Marin Bancorp
504 Redwood Blvd., Suite 100, Novato, CA 94947
Phone: 415 763-4520
Web: www.bankofmarin.com

PRODUCTS/OPERATIONS

2015 Sales

	% of total
Interest and fees on loan	78
Interest on investment securities	10
Non-Interest income	
Wealth management & trust services	3
Service charges on deposit accounts	3
Debit card interchange fees	2
Others	4
Total	**100**

Selected Services

Business checking
Cash management
Credit cards
Floating home loans
Home equity lines
Lending
Online and mobile
Personal checking
Personal savings

COMPETITORS

Bank of America	MUFG Americas Holdings
Bank of the West	Patelco Credit Union
Citibank	SVB Financial
Community Bank of the Bay	U.S. Bancorp
FNB Bancorp (CA)	Wells Fargo
First Republic (CA)	Westamerica

HISTORICAL FINANCIALS

Company Type: Public

Income Statement

FYE: December 31

	ASSETS ($ mil.)	NET INCOME ($ mil.)	INCOME AS % OF ASSETS	EMPLOYEES
12/16	2,023	23	1.1%	262
12/15	2,031	18	0.9%	274
12/14	1,787	19	1.1%	278
12/13	1,805	14	0.8%	297
12/12	1,434	17	1.2%	253
Annual Growth	**9.0%**	**6.7%**	**—**	**0.9%**

2016 Year-End Financials

Debt ratio: 0.28%	No. of shares (mil.): 6
Return on equity: 10.37%	Dividends
Cash ($ mil.): 48	Yield: 0.0%
Current ratio: —	Payout: 26.9%
Long-term debt ($ mil.): —	Market value ($ mil.): 427

	STOCK PRICE ($) FY Close	P/E High/Low	PER SHARE ($) Earnings	Dividends	Book Value
12/16	69.75	20 12	3.78	1.02	37.63
12/15	53.40	18 15	3.04	0.90	35.34
12/14	52.59	16 13	3.29	0.80	33.68
12/13	43.39	18 14	2.57	0.73	30.78
12/12	37.46	13 10	3.28	0.70	28.17
Annual Growth	**16.8%**	**— —**	**3.6%**	**9.9%**	**7.5%**

Bank of New York Mellon Corp

The Bank of New York Mellon (BNY Mellon) is one of the world's largest global asset servicing companies and a leader in asset management and corporate trust and treasury services. The firm boasts $32 trillion in assets under custody and administration and some $1.8 trillion in assets under management. BNY Mellon's state-chartered bank subsidiary Bank of New York Mellon offers asset issuer treasury broker-dealer and advisor services while its other main subsidiary BNY Mellon N.A. offers wealth management services. Alexander Hamilton a founding father of the US and icon of the US $10 bill helped establish in 1784 The Bank of New York which merged in 2007 with Pittsburgh?s Mellon Financial to form BNY Mellon.

HISTORY

In 1784 Alexander Hamilton (at 27 already a Revolutionary War hero and economic theorist) and a group of New York merchants and lawyers founded New York City's first bank The Bank of New York (BNY). Hamilton saw a need for a credit system to finance the nation's growth and to establish credibility for the new nation's chaotic monetary system.

Hamilton became US secretary of the treasury in 1789 and soon negotiated the new US government's first loan — for $200000 — from BNY. The bank later helped finance the War of 1812 by raising $16 million and the Civil War by loaning the government $150 million. In 1878 BNY became a US Treasury depository for the sale of government bonds.

The bank's conservative fiscal policies and emphasis on commercial banking enabled it to weather economic turbulence in the 19th century. In 1922 it merged with New York Life Insurance and Trust (formed in 1830 by many of BNY's directors) to form Bank of New York and Trust. The bank survived the crash of 1929 and remained profitable paying dividends throughout the Depression. In 1938 it reclaimed its Bank of New York name.

During the mid-20th century BNY expanded its operations and its reach through acquisitions including Fifth Avenue Bank (trust services 1948) and Empire Trust (serving developing industries 1966). In 1968 the bank created holding company The Bank of New York Company to expand statewide with purchases such as Empire National Bank (1980).

BNY relaxed its lending policies in the 1980s and began to build its fee-for-service side boosting its American Depositary Receipts business by directly soliciting European companies and seeking government securities business. The bank bought

New York rival Irving Trust in a 1989 hostile takeover and in 1990 began buying other banks' credit card portfolios.

As the economy cooled in the early 1990s BNY's book of highly leveraged transactions and nonperforming loans suffered so the company sold many of those loans.

In the mid-1990s BNY bought processing and trust businesses and continued to build its retail business in the suburbs. It pared noncore operations selling its mortgage banking unit (and in 1998 moved its remaining mortgage operations into a joint venture with Alliance Mortgage); credit card business (1998); and factoring and asset-based lending operations (1999). In late 1997 and again in 1998 the bank tried to woo Mellon Bank (now Mellon Financial) into a merger but was rejected; it had better luck in 2006.

The growth of the firm's custody services accelerated in the late 1990s. In 1997 BNY bought operations from Wells Fargo Signet Bank (later part of First Union) and NationsBank (now Bank of America). By 1998 BNY had bought some two dozen corporate trust businesses. Two years later it acquired the trust operations of Royal Bank of Scotland and Barclays Bank.

During this period BNY also built its other operations largely through purchases. It bought the Bank of Montreal's UK-based fiscal agency business (1998) and Eastbrook Capital Management which manages assets for businesses and wealthy individuals (1999).

Scandal rocked the firm in 1999 when the US began investigating the possible flow of money related to Russian organized crime; the following year a former bank executive admitted to having laundered about $7 billion through BNY. The bank reached a non-prosecution agreement in the US in 2005 and four years later agreed to a $14 million settlement with Russia.

In 2000 BNY bought the corporate trust business of Dai-Ichi Kangyo Bank (now part of Mizuho Financial) and Harris Trust and Savings Bank. It also purchased a trio of securities clearing and processing firms in addition to hedge fund manager Ivy Asset Management. The next year BNY bought the corporate trust operations of U.S. Trust.

Purchases in 2002 included equity research firm Jaywalk institutional trader Francis P. Maglio & Co. and a pair of Boston-area asset managers for high-net-worth individuals Gannet Welsh & Kotler and Beacon Fiduciary Advisors. BNY bought Pershing from Credit Suisse First Boston in 2003.

Fallout from the money laundering scandal lingered. In 2006 the Federal Reserve accused the bank of not tightening its own controls to prevent a recurrence of illegal activity. But there were apparently no hard feelings between BNY and the federal government who tapped the company in 2008 to act as custodian for the US Treasury's $700 million Troubled Asset Relief Program (TARP) meant to provide liquidity to banks.

The Bank of New York jettisoned much of its traditional banking services for more lucrative fee-based securities and financial services swapping virtually all its retail branches in metropolitan New York for JPMorgan Chase's corporate trust business in 2006. Both units were valued at more than $2 billion each and JPMorgan Chase paid an additional $150 million in cash to make up the difference.

In 2007 Bank of New York merged with Mellon Financial to create BNY Mellon. It was the New York company's third attempt to acquire the Pittsburgh-based firm. The deal cemented the company's status as one of the largest securities servicing companies in the world and augmented its other other areas of focus including asset man-

agement and corporate trust and treasury services.

The company followed that transaction with the sale of Mellon 1st Business Bank to U.S. Bancorp in 2008.

In 2009 the company acquired Insight Investment Management which specializes in liability-driven investment services fixed income products and alternative investments from Lloyds Bank for some $387 million. Also that year BNY Mellon bought analytics firm Portsmouth Financial Systems. The acquisition offered customers more transparency in structured credit portfolios.

In 2010 BNY Mellon sold one of the last remnants of Mellon Financial's banking operations the Florida-based Mellon United National Bank to Banco de Sabadell. Mellon had previously sold most of its retail business to Royal Bank of Scotland's US banking arm Citizens Financial Group in 2001.

EXECUTIVES

Chairman and CEO, Gerald L. Hassell, age 65, $1,000,000 total compensation

CEO Clearing Markets and Client Management, Thomas P. (Todd) Gibbons, age 60, $650,000 total compensation

CEO Investment Management, Mitchell E. Harris, $625,000 total compensation

SEVP and General Counsel, J. Kevin McCarthy, age 53

CEO Pershing, Lisa Dolly

CEO Global Asset Servicing and Chairman Europe Middle East and Africa (EMEA), Hani Kablawi

SEVP and Chief Human Resources Officer, Monique R. Herena

SEVP and Head Client Service Delivery, Doug Shulman

SEVP and Chief Risk Officer, James S. (Jim) Wiener

CEO Exchange Traded Funds, Jeff McCarthy

Chairman Asia Pacific, J. David Cruikshank

CEO Issuer Services, Francis J. (Frank) La Salla

CEO Alternative Investment Services (AIS) and Structured Products, Chandresh Iyer

SEVP and CIO, Bridget E. Engle

CFO Investment Services, Michael P. Santomassimo

CEO BNY Mellon Markets, Michelle M. Neal

Senior Vice President, John Weisenhorn

Assistant Vice President Systems And Technology, Rebecca Stalker

Vice President Relationship Manager, Mary Snyder

Vice President, Deborah Guerra

Vice President Director of Sales, Donna Nemecek

Vice President, Erika Lunceford

Vice President, Peter Gesell

Vice President ETF Client Service Officer, Rocco Macri

Assistant Vice President Systems, Kenneth Kenneth Newman Newman

Vice President Information Technology, Joseph Aboulafia

Vice President, Andrew Zelter

Vice President, Jerry Chan

VICE PRESIDENT OF MARKETING, Lou Rodriguez

Vice President, Jeffrey McSteen

Vice President, Keith Koble

Senior Vice President and Director of Employee Benefits, Robert Perego

Vice President, Patricia Gallagher

Vice President Community Development Group, Jon Gamby

Assistant Vice President, Bryan Chan

Vice President Business Analysis Quality, Lynn Leshe

Vice President Global Trade Finance Servs Div, Andrea Ratay

Vice President, Thomas Powderly

Vice President, Randolph Medrano

Vice President, Cary Jones

Vice President Finance, Liya Wang

Vice President, Ellie Whalen

Vice President, Raymond Connery

Vice President And Regional Manager Latin America Division, Angelo Francica

Assistant Vice President, Jeffrey Roe

Vice President, Joseph Schnorr

Vice President, Victor Francis

Senior Vice President Legal Affairs, Bill Robinson

Vice President, Gopinath Tatachar

Vice President Investment Manager, Robert Mathisen

Assistant Vice President Investments, Remy Quito

Vice President Project Manager, Richard Fisher

Vice President, Edward Dougherty

Assistant Vice President, John Rushmore

Vice President, David Sunderwirth

Assistant Vice President, Ann Lynch

Vice President, Gordon Wong

Vice President, Mary Milner

Vice President Global Markets, Melanie Wong

Vice President Customer Technology Solutions Delivery, Carl Hagelin

Vice President, Charles Baker

Vice President, Justin Verdesca

Vice President, Brian Stern

Assistant Vice President Information Security, Sam Dekay

Assistant Vice President, Panagiota Bouboulis

Vice President And Relationship Manager, Mark Hochgesang

Vice President Global Trade Financial Services Division, Toula Tavlarides

Vice President, Brian Weddington

Vice President, Melinda Valentine

Vice President Information Technology, Joseph Hole

Vice President Alternative Investments Accounting, Ronald Caskran

Assistant Vice President Business Services Group, Danny Wong

Vice President, Paul Angotta

Vice President, Elizabeth Wagner

Vice President, Claudia Leslie

Vice President, Brenda Stone

Vice President North American Banks Division, Joseph Barnes

Vice President Business Solutions Group, Bradley Jones

Vice President, Reyne Macadaeg

Vice President Application Development, Brian Burton

Assistant Vice President, Glenn Obando

Vice President, Peter Helt

Vice President Mutual Funds Division, Linda Pizzuti

Assistant Vice President, Kerri Shenkin

Vice President, Paul Meskiewicz

Vice President, Rebecca Newman

Vice President, Derrick Cornelious

Vice President Relationship Manager Long Island Queens Brooklyn Regional Commercial Banking, Gail Rnian-bivona

Senior Vice President Customer Care, Bruce Falkin

Vice President Cash Management Division, Renee Leira

Vice President, Larisa Turetsky

Vice President, Peter Holland

Executive Vice President, John Moore

Vice President Information Risk Management, Michael Lam

Vice President Of Information Solutions, Peter Farrell

Vice President Marketing Communications, Geraldine Lutzel

Vice President, James Bingham

Vice President, David Cook

Vice President U S Corporate Banking, Mark O'Connor
Vice President, Lawrence Timmins
Assistant Vice President, Robert Kilborn
Vice President, Ron Giromonte
Vice President, Irene Kugel
Vice President, Carol Turi
Vice President, Joseph Sierra
Vice President Of Sales, Sarah Foster
Vice President Of Information Technology Learning, Michael Dermody
Assistant Vice President Internal Audit, Maria Dolinski
Vice President Benefits Disbursements, Steve Coates
Vice President It Procurement Bank Of New York Mellon, Rich Castman
Assistant Vice President; Critical System Engineer, Dan Gaffney
Senior Vice President, Douglas Owen
Vice President Global Corporate Trust, Mike Maio
Vice President, Timothy Fitzgerald
Vice President, Wayne Ross
Assistant Vice President, Clarence Burleigh
Assistant Vice President, Karen O'Donohoe
Assistant Vice President Technology Global Markets And Ecommerce, Vadim Kazakevich
Assistant Vice President, Neil Grill
Assistant Vice President, Jeff Charmatz
Senior Vice President Chief Information Officer, Kurt Wetzel
Senior Vice President, James McTiernan
Vice President, Carmela Ehret
Assistant Vice President Corporate General Services, Patrick Koziol
Executive Vice President The Bank Of New York, John R Mohr
Executive Vice President The Bank Of New York, Thomas V Ford
Assistant Vice President Enterprise BI Architect, Ron Van Der Laan
Assistant Vice President, Tanya Amaya
First Vice President Operations Strategy Group, Mary Hannon
Vice President, Cebert Boothe
Vice President and Project Manager Technology Project Officer, Anthony Del Busso
Vice President, Phyllis Cietek
Vice President US Structured Finance, Adam Metzinger
Vice President, Seth Crone
Executive Vice President The Bank Of New York, William Kerr
Vice President and Client Service Manager, Jason Stephens
Vice President FX Sales, Kirsten Martin
Vice President Officer Group Manager, Jeff Gross
Vice President CRA Community Development Officer, Mark Castle
Vice President CDO Client Services Client Service Manager, Keisha Gray
Vice President Securities Finance, Dennis Cahill
Vice President Private Banker, Bryan Monteverde
Vice President, Tanya Lincevski
Vice President, Robert Nelson
Vice President, Susan Kubar
Vice President, Jean McNicholas Earley
VP, Penni Herriott
Vice President Client Service Manager, Sandra Vincent
Vice President, Anthony Mastrocola
Middle Office Manager Vice President, Christopher Hart
Vice President, Jean Smarto
Auditors: KPMG LLP

LOCATIONS
HQ: Bank of New York Mellon Corp
225 Liberty Street, New York, NY 10286
Phone: 212 495-1784
Web: www.bnymellon.com

PRODUCTS/OPERATIONS

2016 Revenue

	$ mil.	% of total
Investment servicing fees		
Asset servicing	4,244	27
Clearing services	1,404	9
Issuer services	1,026	7
Treasury services	547	3
Interest net	3,138	22
Investment management & performance fees	3,350	23
Foreign exchange & other trading revenue	701	4
Investment & other income	341	2
Financing-related fees	219	1
Distribution & servicing	166	1
Net securities gains	75	1
Income from consolidated investment management funds	26	—
Total	15,237	100

Selected Subsidiaries and Business Lines
BNY Capital Funding LLC - State of Organization: Delaware
BNY Capital Markets Holdings Inc. - State of Incorporation: New York
BNY Capital Resources Corporation - State of Incorporation: New York
BNY International Financing Corporation - Incorporation: United States
BNY Mellon Capital Markets LLC - State of Organization: Delaware
BNY Mellon Fund Managers Limited - Incorporation: England
BNY Mellon Global Management Limited - Incorporation: Ireland
BNY Mellon International Asset Management Group Limited - Incorporation: England
BNY Mellon International Asset Management (Holdings) Limited - Incorporation: England and Wales
BNY Mellon International Asset Management (Holdings) No. 1 Limited - Incorporation: England and Wales
BNY Mellon Investment Management Cayman Ltd. - Incorporation: Cayman Islands
BNY Mellon Investment Management EMEA Limited - Incorporation: England
BNY Mellon Investment Management Europe Holdings Limited - Incorporation: England
BNY Mellon Investment Management (Europe) Limited - Incorporation: England
BNY Mellon Investment Management (Jersey) Limited - Incorporation: Jersey
BNY Mellon Investment Servicing (US) Inc. - State of Incorporation: Massachusetts
BNY Mellon National Association - Incorporation: United States
BNY Mellon Securities Services (Ireland) Limited - Incorporation: Ireland
BNY Mellon Trust Company (Ireland) Limited - Incorporation: Ireland
BNYM GIS Funding I LLC - State of Organization: Delaware
BNYM GIS Funding III LLC - State of Organization: Delaware
BNYM GIS (UK) Funding II LLC - State of Organization: Delaware
Insight Investment Funds Management Limited - Incorporation: England
Insight Investment Management (Global) Limited - Incorporation: England
Insight Investment Management Limited - Incorporation: England
MAM (MA) Holding Trust - State of Incorporation: Massachusetts
MBC Investments Corporation - State of Incorporation: Delaware
Mellon Canada Holding Company - Incorporation: Canada
Mellon Overseas Investment Corporation - Incorporation: United States
Pershing Group LLC - State of Organization: Delaware
Pershing Holdings (UK) Limited - Incorporation: England
Pershing Limited - Incorporation: England

Pershing LLC - State of Organization: Delaware
Pershing Securities Limited - Incorporation: England
Standish Mellon Asset Management Company LLC - State of Organization: Delaware
The Bank of New York Mellon - State of Organization: New York
The Bank of New York Mellon (International) Limited - Incorporation: England
The Bank of New York Mellon (Luxembourg) S.A. - Incorporation: Luxembourg
The Bank of New York Mellon SA/NV - Incorporation: Belgium
The Dreyfus Corporation - State of Incorporation: New York
Walter Scott & Partners Limited - Incorporation: Scotland

COMPETITORS

Bank of America	JPMorgan Chase
Barclays	Morgan Stanley
BlackRock	Northern Trust
Charles Schwab	PNC Financial
Citigroup	Prudential
Credit Suisse (USA)	State Street
Deutsche Bank	U.S. Bancorp
Franklin Templeton	Wells Fargo
HSBC	

HISTORICAL FINANCIALS
Company Type: Public

Income Statement
FYE: December 31

	ASSETS ($ mil.)	NET INCOME ($ mil.)	INCOME AS % OF ASSETS	EMPLOYEES
12/16	333,469	3,547	1.1%	52,000
12/15	393,780	3,158	0.8%	51,200
12/14	385,303	2,567	0.7%	50,300
12/13	374,310	2,111	0.6%	51,100
12/12	358,990	2,445	0.7%	49,500
Annual Growth	(1.8%)	9.7%	—	1.2%

2016 Year-End Financials
Debt ratio: 7.34%
Return on equity: 9.21%
Cash ($ mil.): 77,949
Current ratio: —
Long-term debt ($ mil.): —
No. of shares (mil.): 1,047
Dividends
  Yield: 0.0%
  Payout: 22.8%
Market value ($ mil.): 49,630

	STOCK PRICE ($) FY Close	P/E High/Low		Earnings	Dividends	Book Value
12/16	47.38	16	10	3.15	0.72	37.05
12/15	41.22	17	13	2.71	0.68	35.05
12/14	40.57	19	14	2.15	0.66	33.48
12/13	34.94	20	15	1.74	0.58	32.85
12/12	25.70	13	10	2.03	0.52	31.31
Annual Growth	16.5%	—	—	11.6%	8.5%	4.3%

Bank of the Ozarks Inc (New)

Bank of the Ozarks is the holding company for the bank of the same name which has about 260 branches in Alabama Arkansas California the Carolinas Florida Georgia New York and Texas. Focusing on individuals and small to midsized businesses the $12-billion bank offers traditional deposit and loan services in addition to personal and commercial trust services retirement and financial planning and investment management. Commercial real estate and construction and land development loans make up the largest portion of Bank of the Ozarks' loan portfolio followed by residential mortgage business and agricultural loans. Bank of the Ozarks grows its loan and deposit business by acquiring smaller banks and opening branches across the US.

Operations

The bank makes three-fourths of its total revenue from interest income while the rest comes from fee-based sources. About 43% of Bank of the Ozark's total revenue came from non-purchased loan interest in 2014 while another 26% came from interest on purchased loans and a further 8% came from interest on its investment securities. The rest of its revenue came from service charges on deposit accounts (8% of revenue) mortgage lending income (1%) trust income (1%) and other non-recurring sources.

Geographic Reach

Bank of the Ozarks had 174 branches in eight states at the end of 2014 with 81 of them in Alabama and another 75 branches split among Georgia North Carolina and Texas. It has two loan offices in Houston and Manhattan that serve as an extension of the bank's Dallas-based Real Estate Specialties Group.

Sales and Marketing

The bank spent $3.03 million on advertising and public relations expenses in 2014 compared to $2.2 million and $4.09 million in 2013 and 2012 respectively.

Financial Performance

Bank of the Ozarks' annual revenues and profits have doubled since 2010 mostly as its loan assets have doubled from recent bank acquisitions spawning higher interest income.

The bank's revenue jumped 31% to $376 million during 2014 mostly thanks to strong purchased and non-purchased loan asset growth during the year from recent bank acquisitions. Its non-interest income grew 12% thanks to a 20% increase in deposit account service charges stemming from newly acquired deposit customers.

Strong revenue growth in 2014 boosted Bank of the Ozarks' net income by 30% to $119 million for the year. Its operating cash levels jumped 22% to $61 million during the year mostly thanks to higher cash earnings.

Strategy

Bank of the Ozarks continues its strategy of loan and deposit volume growth by acquiring smaller banks in new and existing geographic markets. It has also opened new branches and loan offices sparingly. During 2014 for example the bank opened retail branches in Bradenton Florida; Cornelius North Carolina; and Hilton Head Island South Carolina along with a new loan production office in Asheville North Carolina.

Mergers and Acquisitions

In July 2016 Bank of the Ozarks acquired Georgia-based Community & Southern Holdings and its Community & Southern Bank subsidiary. Adding some 45 branch locations in Georgia plus another in Florida it was the company's largest acquisition to-date.

Also in July 2016 the bank purchased C1 Financial along with its 32 CI Bank branches on the west coast of Florida and in Miami-Dade and Orange Counties. The deal added $1.7 billion in total assets $1.4 billion in loans and $1.3 billion in deposits. This transaction was the bank's fifteenth acquisition in the past six years.

In August 2015 the bank purchased Bank of the Carolinas Corporation (BCAR) — and its eight Bank of the Carolinas branches in North Carolina $345 million in total assets $277 million in loans and $296 million in deposits — for a total price of $65.4 million.

In February 2015 Bank of the Ozarks bought Intervest Bancshares Corporation and its seven In-

tervest National Bank branches in (five in Clearwater Florida and two more in New York City and Pasadena Florida) for $238.5 million. The deal added $1.5 billion in assets including $1.1 billion in loans and $1.2 billion in deposits.

In May 2014 it bought Arkansas-based Summit Bancorp Inc. and its 23 Summit Bank branches across Arkansas for $42.5 million though it closed more than a handful of them later in the year.

In March 2014 the company acquired Houston-based Bancshares Inc. and its subsidiary Omnibank N.A. for $21.5 million adding three branches in Houston Texas and a branch each in Austin Cedar Park Lockhart and San Antonio.

Company Background

The expansion strategy of Bank of the Ozarks - which had a mere five branches in Arkansas 20 years ago — centered on opening new locations in smaller communities in Arkansas. But with the financial crash the bank was able to expand to more states through a series of FDIC-assisted transactions to take over failed banks. It bought Chestatee State Bank First Choice Community Bank Horizon Bank Oglethorpe Bank Park Avenue Bank Unity National and Woodlands Bank.

Chairman and CEO George Gleason initially bought the bank more than three decades ago at age 25.

EXECUTIVES

Chief Credit Officer Bank of the Ozarks, Darrel Russell, age 63, $252,308 total compensation

Chairman; Chief Executive Officer of the Company and the Bank, George G. Gleason, age 63, $1,730,769 total compensation

President Leasing Division Bank of the Ozarks, Scott Hastings, age 59, $181,925 total compensation

President Mortgage Division Bank of the Ozarks, Gene Holman, age 69, $150,042 total compensation

President Trust and Wealth Management Division Bank of the Ozarks, Rex Kyle, age 60, $241,674 total compensation

President Real Estate Specialties Group Bank of the Ozarks, Dan Thomas, age 54, $1,242,308 total compensation

CFO and Chief Accounting Officer Bank of the Ozarks Inc. and Bank of the Ozarks, Greg McKinney, age 49, $368,077 total compensation

EVP Retail Banking Bank of the Ozarks, Tyler Vance, age 42, $366,923 total compensation

President Western Division, Don Keesee

Senior Vice President Information Technology Security Officer, Chad Necessary

Vice President, Mike Atkins

Executive Vice President and Market Leader, Randy Whitaker

Vice President, Jeremy McAlister

Executive Vice President Customer Service, Shameka Hansberry

Vice President Training, Lorie Smith

Executive Vice President Human Resources Director, Tim Hodnett

Vice President Information Technology Webloyalty, Steve Due

Vice President Accounting, Tina Chandler

Senior Vice President, Wes Anderson

Vice President, Jeffery Martin

Executive Vice President, Stewart Griggs

Vice President, Janet Paulette

Vice President Branch Manager, Laura Wyne

Vice President, Kevin Gross

Vice President Of Leasing, Todd Parsley

Vice President Commercial Lending, Jason Wallis

Senior Vice President Human Resources, Cherylon Reid

Senior Vice President Market Leader, Russell Hewatt

Vice President, Dale E Crowe

Vice President and Branch Manager, Olivia Howard

Vice President Deposit Operations, Libby Buck

Senior Vice President Market Leader, Torrie Sunstrom

Vice President, Brad Webb

Assistant Vice President Special Assets Division, Nikki Kundrat

Executive Vice President Market Leader, Kenny Maguire

Vice President Originations, Carrie Nichols

South Central Vice President Mortgage Market Manager, Tammy Whitley

Vice President Marketing, Duane Bickings

Vice President Commercial Real Estate Originations, Matthew Mull

Executive Vice President Real Estate Specialties Group, Jason Choulochas

Senior Vice President of Information Systems, Malcolm Hicks

Vice President Payment Systems, Paula Shaw

Senior Vice President, Chris Bragg

Vice President Business Development, Diane Jester

Vice President Regional Manager, Lisa Amato

Assistant Vice President Community Development Officer, Kedrick Dobbins

Vice President Lending, Erik Larson

Assistant Vice President Community Development Officer, Kimberly L Marshall

Vice President Marketing, Mark Greenhaw

Senior Vice President Treasury Management, Steve Woodruff

Assistant Vice President Branch Operations Manager, Fabian Garantiva

Senior Vice President Commercial Lender, Jeni Chokron

Assistant Vice President, Donna Pilcher

Assistant Vice President Branch Manager, Derek Labrosse

Assistant Vice President Community Development Officer, Joann Smith

Executive Vice President, David Sarner

Executive Vice President, Martin Ball

Senior Vice President, Aram Zakian

Vice President Loan Officer, Dawn Speas

Vice President Treasury Management Wire Manager, Mona Kalchik

Auditors: PricewaterhouseCoopers LLP

LOCATIONS

HQ: Bank of the Ozarks Inc (New)
17901 Chenal Parkway, Little Rock, AR 72223
Phone: 501 978-2265   **Fax:** 501 978-2224
Web: www.bankozarks.com

PRODUCTS/OPERATIONS

2014 Sales

	$ mil.	% of total
Interest income		
Non-purchased loans and leases	162	43
Purchased loans	98	26
Investment securities	30	8
Non-interest income		
Service charges on deposit accounts	26	8
Other income from purchased loans net	14	4
Others	43	11
Total	**376**	**100**

Selected Services

Personal Banking
Apple PayChecking AccountsCredit CardsFree Bill PayFREE Debit CardsCustom Debit CardsEMV Chip CardsMobile BankingMortgage LoansMy Change KeeperOnline BankingOverdraft ProtectionPersonal LoansReloadable Spending CardsRetirement PlanningReorder ChecksSafe

Business Banking
Business ProductsApple Pay for BusinessDebit CardEMV Chip CardsBusiness Credit CardsChecking & Money MarketCommercial LoansExpress DepositMerchant ProcessingOnline BankingOverdraft ProtectionReorder ChecksTreasury Management Services

Online & Mobile Banking

Online BankingMobile BankingMobile DepositOnline
  Bill Pay
Wealth Management Services
Investment ProgramsFinancial PlanningCustomer
  Service

COMPETITORS

Arvest Bank	IBERIABANK
BOK Financial	JPMorgan Chase
BancorpSouth	Regions Financial
Bank of America	Simmons First
Bear State Financial	SunTrust
Cullen/Frost Bankers	Wells Fargo
Home BancShares	

HISTORICAL FINANCIALS

Company Type: Public

Income Statement

FYE: December 31

	ASSETS ($ mil.)	NET INCOME ($ mil.)	INCOME AS % OF ASSETS	EMPLOYEES
12/16	18,890	269	1.4%	2,315
12/15	9,879	182	1.8%	1,642
12/14	6,766	118	1.8%	1,479
12/13	4,787	87	1.8%	1,223
12/12	4,040	77	1.9%	1,120
Annual Growth	47.0%	36.8%	—	19.9%

2016 Year-End Financials

Debt ratio: 2.03%	No. of shares (mil.): 121
Return on equity: 12.65%	Dividends
Cash ($ mil.): 866	Yield: 0.0%
Current ratio: —	Payout: 24.4%
Long-term debt ($ mil.): —	Market value ($ mil.): 6,377

	STOCK PRICE ($) FY Close	P/E High/Low	Earnings	Dividends	Book Value
12/16	52.59	21 13	2.58	0.63	23.02
12/15	49.46	26 15	2.09	0.55	16.19
12/14	37.92	46 20	1.52	0.47	11.37
12/13	56.59	48 28	1.21	0.36	8.48
12/12	33.47	31 25	1.11	0.25	7.20
Annual Growth	12.0%	— —	23.6%	26.0%	33.7%

BankFinancial Corp

If you need a BankNow to handle your BankBusiness try BankFinancial. The bank serves individuals and businesses through about 20 branches in Cook DuPage Lake and Will counties in northeastern Illinois including parts of Chicago. It offers standard products such as checking and savings accounts credit cards and loans; services such as account management are available online. Multifamily residential mortgage loans make up 40% of its loan portfolio while another 40% is made up of commercial leases and non-residential mortgage loans. The bank also writes one-to-four family residential mortgages and home equity loans and lines of credit business loans and construction and land loans.

Operations

BankFinancial sells auto business disability homeowners and life insurance through subsidiary Financial Assurance Services while BF Asset Recovery Corporation sells foreclosed real estate. The bank also offers investment products and services such as annuities bonds mutual funds and financial and retirement planning through an a agreement

with third-party broker-dealer Cetera Financial Services.

Like other banks BankFinancial makes most of its revenue from interest from the loans it issues. About 85% of its revenue came from loan interest (including fees) during 2015 while another 3% came from interest income on securities. The rest of its revenue came from deposit service charges and fees (4% of revenue) other fee income (4%) insurance commissions and annuities income (1%) loan servicing fees (1%) and trust income (1%).

Sales and Marketing

The bank provides services to individuals families and businesses. It spent $991000 on advertising and public relations during 2015 compared to $1.1 million and $925000 in 2014 and 2013 respectively.

Financial Performance

The bank's annual revenues have fallen more than 25% since 2011 mostly due to shrinking interest margins from low market interest rates and yields and fierce competition for customers in the Chicago metropolitan area.

BankFinancial's revenue dipped 1% to $55.65 million during 2015 despite a three basis point uptick in net interest margins mostly as its average interest-earning asset balances fell slightly during the year. Its deposit service charges and fee income increased 14% thanks to higher deposit account fees while other fee income decreased 4% for the year on lower ATM surcharges and serve charges.

The company's net income plunged almost 80% to $8.7 million in 2015 mostly because in 2014 it had earned a non-recurring $35.1 million tax benefit related to a valuation allowance reversal. Excluding this item its earnings would have been 58% higher as the bank's loan provisions declined on a strengthened credit portfolio and as it spent less on non-interest expenses. BankFinancial's operating cash levels fell 17% to $14.9 million for the year mostly because of a decline in cash-based earnings.

Strategy

BankFinancial continued in 2016 to focus on boosting its core commercial loan and lease business by marketing its variety of services and growing its commercial banking officer talent in their respective markets. The bank regularly introduces new commercial loan and lease products as well as deposit products to better fit its customers' needs.

EXECUTIVES

Chairman President and CEO BankFinancial Corporation and BankFinancial F.S.B., F. Morgan Gasior, age 53, $405,804 total compensation
EVP Corporate Affairs Corporate Secretary and General Counsel BankFinancial Corporation and BankFinancial F.S.B., James J. Brennan, age 66, $325,468 total compensation
EVP and CFO, Paul A. Cloutier, age 53, $271,998 total compensation
Executive Vice President Marketing & Sales, Gregg T. Adams, age 58, $230,625 total compensation
President Commercial Real Estate Bankfinancial F.S.B., John G. Manos, age 56
President National Commercial Leasing Bankfinancial F.S.B., William J. Deutsch, age 49, $205,000 total compensation
Senior Vice President Finance, Elizabeth A Doolan
Executive Vice President of the Internal Audit Division, Thad F Stewart
Assistant Vice President Branch Manager, Yolanda Lott
Senior Vice President, Mary Tritsis
Vice President Research and Development, John Harrell
Vice President System Integration, Carol Johnson

Senior Vice President, Judith Witt
Vice President Portfolio Management, Richard Niemann
Assistant Vice President, Jodi Long
Vice President Internal Audit, Niki Pilotte
Executive Vice President Sales and Marketing, Amy Olson
Vice President, David Zalich
Vice President Apartment Lending, Rocky Rainbolt
Auditors: Crowe Horwath LLP

LOCATIONS

HQ: BankFinancial Corp
  15W060 North Frontage Road, Burr Ridge, IL 60527
Phone: 800 894-6900

PRODUCTS/OPERATIONS

2015 Sales

	$ mil.	% of total
Interest		
Loans including fees	47	85
Securities	1	2
Other	0	1
Noninterest		
Deposit service charges & fees	2	4
Other fee income	2	4
Other	2	4
Total	55	100

Selected Services

Checking
Savings & money market
Online banking & bill pay
CDs & IRAs services
Deposit accounts
Credit & loans
Merchant services
Retirement plans services

COMPETITORS

Banco Popular North America	Harris
	JPMorgan Chase
Bank of America	MB Financial
Citizens Financial Group	Northern Trust
	Old Second Bancorp
Fifth Third	U.S. Bancorp
First Midwest Bancorp	Wintrust Financial
HSBC North America	

HISTORICAL FINANCIALS

Company Type: Public

Income Statement

FYE: December 31

	ASSETS ($ mil.)	NET INCOME ($ mil.)	INCOME AS % OF ASSETS	EMPLOYEES
12/16	1,620	7	0.5%	264
12/15	1,512	8	0.6%	273
12/14	1,465	40	2.8%	290
12/13	1,453	3	0.2%	320
12/12	1,481	(27)	—	356
Annual Growth	2.3%	—	—	(7.2%)

2016 Year-End Financials

Debt ratio: —	No. of shares (mil.): 19
Return on equity: 3.59%	Dividends
Cash ($ mil.): 96	Yield: 0.0%
Current ratio: —	Payout: 53.8%
Long-term debt ($ mil.): —	Market value ($ mil.): 285

	STOCK PRICE ($) FY Close	P/E High/Low	Earnings	Dividends	Book Value
12/16	14.82	37 29	0.39	0.21	10.65
12/15	12.63	31 25	0.44	0.20	10.46
12/14	11.86	6 5	2.01	0.09	10.24
12/13	9.16	61 45	0.16	0.04	8.32
12/12	7.42	— —	(1.36)	0.04	8.20
Annual Growth	18.9%	— —	—	51.4%	6.7%

BankUnited Inc.

BankUnited is uniting the north and south again. It's the bank holding company for BankUnited N.A. which provides standard banking services to individuals and businesses through about 100 branches in 15 Florida counties and six banking centers in the New York metro area (following the purchase of the New York private bank Herald National). BankUnited was formed in 2009 following the demise of the former BankUnited FSB which collapsed under the weight of bad mortgages. A team of private investors bought BankUnited from the FDIC injected $900 million in fresh capital and in 2011 took the company public via an initial public offering (IPO); it was the first IPO of a rescued bank during the economic crisis.

IPO

BankUnited raised some $783 million in its IPO nearly 20% more than it sought in its pricing. The funds are helping the bank expand both in Florida (where it operates in about a dozen counties) and into select new markets (such as New York). CEO Kanasthe former head of North Fork Bank led a similar expansion for North Fork in the first half of the decade and will likely use his experience to repeat the strategy with BankUnited.

Financier Wilbur Ross who serves on BankUnited's board of directors owns 15% of the company through WL Ross & Co.

Financial Performance

BankUnited reported net income of $208.9 million in 2013 a decline of 1% versus 2012. Net interest income increased by $48.6 million over the same period to $646.2 million. Total deposits grew by $2 billion to $10.5 billion while demand deposits increased to 27% of total deposits.

Strategy

BankUnited has placed its bets on two large and growing markets: the Miami metro area; and the Tri-State area where its has four branches in Manhattan one in Long Island and another in Brooklyn. With Florida showing signs of economic recovery and growth potential in New York the bank hopes to use its capital strength and expertise to grow its loan portfolio both through originations and acquisitions with a primary focus on commercial and commercial real estate lending. (It also invests in residential real estate but does not acquire or write subprime residential loans.)

The company offers national equipment financing services through United Capital Business Lending and municipal leasing via Pinnacle Public Finance. BankUnited also provides wealth management through insurance agency BankUnited Investment Services.

Mergers and Acquisitions

In February 2012 BankUnited acquired Herald National Bank for $65 million in cash and stock. At the time of the purchase BankUnited converted to a bank holding company. It also converted the charter of subsidiary BankUnited from a thrift to a national commercial bank. Herald National was merged into BankUnited in mid-2012.

In 2010 BankUnited expanded its offerings and diversified its loan portfolio when it acquired a small business lending platform from Butler Capital Corporation. It also bought a municipal leasing business from Koch Financial Corp.

EXECUTIVES

President New York Region, Joseph (Joe) Roberto, age 60, $300,000 total compensation
Chief Risk Officer, Mark P. Bagnoli, age 65
President and CEO, Rajinder P. (Raj) Singh, age 46, $500,000 total compensation
CFO, Leslie N. Lunak, age 60, $400,000 total compensation
COO, Thomas M. Cornish, age 59, $500,000 total compensation
CIO, Julio Jogaib
Senior Vice President Investor Relations and Secre, Susan W Greenfield
Senior Vice President Commercial Real Estate, Robert Hummel
Vice President, Kenneth Lipke
Senior Vice President Treasury Management, Nicholas Schiralli
Senior Vice President Commercial Private Banking, Corey Prinz
Vice President Private Banker, Delphine Wharton
Vice President, Laura Lowy
Vice President Commercial Real Estate, Kitty Yen
Vice President, Bill Williams
Vice President Manager of Talent Management, Bill Boettcher
Vice President Credit Officer, Patrick Rigney
Senior Executive Vice Presiden, Vincent Post
Vice President and Branch Mana, Alden Bing
Assistant Vice President Design and Development, Sonya Moro
Vice President Portfolio Manager For Commercial Real Estate, Sabine SE Bouchereau
Svp Corp Banking Exec, Roger Harbeson
Senior Vice President Corporate Finance, Cristina Frias
Vice President, Dale Mather
Vice President, Frank Puccio
Vice President Private Banker, Rebecca Lozano
Vice President Electronic Banking, Juliana Tancrati
Vice President, Jaime Fimiani
Vice President Accounting Department, Dorrett Boothe
Vice President, Ellie Rodriguez
Senior Vice President Bsa Officer, Scott Nathan
Senior Vice President NYC Business Banking Team Leader, Gene Sullivan
Senior Vice President TM Product and Vendor Manager, Scott Abramson
Vice President Busines Banker, Nicholas Marrone
Assistant Vice President Default Call Ce, Thomas Rousseau
Senior Vice President Enterprise Stress Testing, Filippo Ghia
Vice President Financial Center Manager, John Hernandez
Senior Vice President Loan Operations and Loan Administration, Nancy Martel
Senior Vice President Corporate Banking, Joseph Disanti
Vice President Corporate Banking, Justin Allbright
Senior Vice President Relationship Manager Commercial Real Estate, Patricia Lubian
Vice President, Mireya Foster
Senior Vice President, Percy R Aguila
Vice President, Carlos X Ramos
Vice President Commercial Real Estate, Jeremy Romine
Loan Servicing Manager Assistant Vice President, Yvette Rosa
Senior Vice President, Michael Del Rocco
Vice President, Oleg Kochanov
Senior Vice President Senior Credit Officer Commercial Real Estate, John Kenyon
Senior Vice President Business Banking Sales Manager, Gregory Milford
Vice President Banking Center Manager, Pat Kelly
Vice President, Thomas McGregor
Vice President Commercial Real Estate, Chris Nielsen
Senior Vice President, Tyson Carballo
Executive Vice President, Gardner Semet
Vice President Corporate Portfolio Manager, Bradley Hendren
Senior Vice President, John Wamboldt
Vice President Corporate Banking, Jennifer Garcia-Barbon
Vice President Commercial Underwriter Bankunited, Gregory O'Brien
Vice President Commercial Real Estate, Chris Demeter
Executive Vice President Residential and Consumer Risk Manager, Eric Hibbert
Assistant Vice President, Shannie DeFreitas
Executive Vice President Mortgage Services, Ray Barbone
Assistant Vice President Private Client Services, Ian Cambria
Vice President Branch Sales Leader, Monica Ribeiro
Vice President Business Development Officer, Stephen Speer
Vice President, Sul Hemani
Senior Vice President, Steve Markowski
Vice President Senior Analyst Business Development Officer, Tom Francis
Vice President Branch Sales Leader Downtown Delray Branch, Glenn Milspaugh
Senior Vice President National Sales Manager Equipment Finance, Tom Goldsmith
AVP SBA Loan Closer, Muni Chum
Vice President Business Development Officer Capital Markets, Jim Pontier
Vice President Business Development Officer, Chris Theis
Vice President Business Banking Relationship Manager, Marshall Fulton
Vice President Business Development Officer Franchise Lending Specialist, Turner Gaw
AVP SBA Loan Closer, Leslie Giannantoni
Chairman, John A. Kanas, age 70
Auditors: KPMG LLP

LOCATIONS

HQ: BankUnited Inc.
  14817 Oak Lane, Miami Lakes, FL 33016
Phone: 305 569-2000
Web: www.bankunited.com

PRODUCTS/OPERATIONS

2016 Sales

	$ mil.	% of total
Interest income:		
Loans	896	75
Investment securities	150	13
Other	12	1
Non-interest income:		
Lease financing	36	4
Income from resolution of covered assets	19	3
Service charges and fees	14	2
Gain on investment securities available for sale	44	1
Other non-interest income	13	1
Adjustment -22.2 -		
Total	**1,165**	**100**

COMPETITORS

BB&T	Ocean Bankshares
BBX Capital	Regions Financial
Bank of America	Seacoast Banking
Capital One	Signature Bank
Citibank	SunTrust
Great Florida Bank	TD Bank USA
Interamerican Bank	Valley National
JPMorgan Chase	Bancorp
M&T Bank	Wells Fargo
New York Community	
Bancorp	

Company Type: Public

Income Statement

FYE: December 31

	ASSETS ($ mil.)	NET INCOME ($ mil.)	INCOME AS % OF ASSETS	EMPLOYEES
12/16	27,880	225	0.8%	1,706
12/15	23,883	251	1.1%	1,741
12/14	19,210	204	1.1%	1,647
12/13	15,046	208	1.4%	1,623
12/12	12,375	211	1.7%	1,429
Annual Growth	22.5%	1.7%	—	4.5%

2016 Year-End Financials

Debt ratio: 1.44%	No. of shares (mil.): 104
Return on equity: 9.66%	Dividends
Cash ($ mil.): 448	Yield: 0.0%
Current ratio: —	Payout: 40.1%
Long-term debt ($ mil.): —	Market value ($ mil.): 3,926

	STOCK PRICE ($) FY Close	P/E High/Low	PER SHARE ($) Earnings	Dividends	Book Value
12/16	37.69	18 13	2.09	0.84	23.22
12/15	36.06	17 11	2.35	0.84	21.65
12/14	28.97	18 14	1.95	0.84	20.19
12/13	32.92	16 12	2.01	0.84	19.09
12/12	24.44	13 11	2.05	0.72	19.02
Annual Growth	11.4%	— —	0.5%	3.9%	5.1%

Bankwell Financial Group Inc

Auditors: RSM US LLP

LOCATIONS

HQ: Bankwell Financial Group Inc
220 Elm Street, New Canaan, CT 06840
Phone: 203 652-0166
Web: www.mybankwell.com

HISTORICAL FINANCIALS

Company Type: Public

Income Statement

FYE: December 31

	ASSETS ($ mil.)	NET INCOME ($ mil.)	INCOME AS % OF ASSETS	EMPLOYEES
12/16	1,628	12	0.8%	127
12/15	1,330	9	0.7%	125
12/14	1,099	4	0.4%	130
12/13	779	5	0.7%	—
12/12	0	1	—	—
Annual Growth	—	78.6%		

2016 Year-End Financials

Debt ratio: 1.54%	No. of shares (mil.): 7
Return on equity: 8.87%	Dividends
Cash ($ mil.): 96	Yield: 0.0%
Current ratio: —	Payout: 13.5%
Long-term debt ($ mil.): —	Market value ($ mil.): 248

	STOCK PRICE ($) FY Close	P/E High/Low	PER SHARE ($) Earnings	Dividends	Book Value
12/16	32.50	21 12	1.62	0.22	19.14
12/15	19.85	17 14	1.21	0.05	17.53
12/14	21.00	28 21	0.78	0.00	17.98
12/13	20.90	16 9	1.44	0.00	17.93
12/12	13.50	38 32	0.38	0.00	(0.00)
Annual Growth	24.6%	— —	43.7%		

Banner Corp.

Flagging bank accounts? See Banner Corporation. Banner is the holding company for Banner Bank which serves the Pacific Northwest through about 100 branches and 10 loan production offices in Washington Oregon and Idaho. The company also owns Islanders Bank which operates three branches in Washington's San Juan Islands. The banks offer standard products such as deposit accounts credit cards and business and consumer loans. Commercial loans including business agriculture construction and multifamily mortgage loans account for about 90% of the company's portfolio. Bank subsidiary Community Financial writes residential mortgage and construction loans.

Geographic Reach

Washington-based Banner Bank is focused on five primary markets in the Northwest: the Puget Sound region of Washington; the greater Portland Oregon market; Boise Idaho; and Spokane Washington. The fifth is the bank's historical base in the agricultural communities in the Columbia Basin region of Washington and Oregon.

Sales and Marketing

Banner Corp. reported advertising and marketing expenses of $6.9 million in 2013 versus $7.2 million in 2012. Banner Bank launched a re-designed website and new ad campaign in Boise Seattle and Portland and on social media in fall 2014.

Financial Performance

The regional bank holding company reported revenue of $223 million in 2013 an increase of 4% versus 2012. The rise in revenue was due to increased operating income as a result of gains on the sale of securities and a fee received from the termination of the bank's proposed acquisition of Home Federal Bancorp. The bank's growing customer base led to increased income from deposit fees and other service charges of $1.3 billion (5%) in 2013 versus the prior year. Net income declined 28% in 2013 versus 2012 to $46.6 million primarily due to higher provision for income tax expenses. After three consecutive years of losses (2008 thru 2010) the bank returned to profitability in 2011 and has remained profitable.

Banner Corp. has total consolidated assets of about $4.5 billion.

Strategy

Historically Banner Corp. has grown by acquisition. Since going public (in 1995) Banner has acquired about 10 commercial banks. Islanders Bank was acquired in 2007 the same year Banner acquired F&M Bank and NCW Community Bank of Wenatchee both also based in Washington. After the spate of acquisitions the company focused on opening branches. The company continues to look for acquisition opportunities with an eye on banks shut down by regulators.

In 2013 however a plan to merge with Home Federal Bancorp was terminated when that bank received a better offer from Cascade Bancorp. Also the company abandoned plans to buy Idaho Banking Company out of bankruptcy after being out-bid.

Mergers and Acquisitions

In August 2014 Banner Bank acquired Siuslaw Financial Group the holding company for Siuslaw Bank the operator of 10 branches along the coast of Oregon. In June 2014 Banner Bank purchased six branches in Oregon from Sterling Savings Bank.

EXECUTIVES

EVP and CFO Banner Corporation, Lloyd W. Baker, age 68, $260,724 total compensation

EVP Retail Banking and Administration, Cynthia D. (Cindy) Purcell, age 59, $289,038 total compensation

EVP and Chief Lending Officer Banner Corporation and Banner Bank, Richard B. Barton, age 73, $264,895 total compensation

President and CEO, Mark J. Grescovich, age 52, $716,415 total compensation

EVP and Real Estate Lending Manager Banner Bank, Douglas M. Bennett, age 64, $236,174 total compensation

EVP and CIO, Steven W. (Steve) Rust, age 69

EVP Retail Products and Services, Gary W. Wagers, age 56

EVP and Commercial Executive East Region, M. Kirk Quillin, age 54

EVP and Commercial Executive West Region, James T. (Jim) Reed, age 54

EVP and CFO Banner Bank, Peter J. Conner, age 51

EVP Human Resources, Kayleen Kohler

EVP and Mortgage Banking Director, Kenneth A. (Ken) Larsen, age 47

EVP and General Counsel Banner Bank, Craig Miller

EVP and Chief Risk Officer Banner Bank, Judy Steiner

EVP and Commercial Executive (South Region), Keith A. Western, age 61

Vice President, Jamie Albertini

Assistant Vice President And Senior Underwriter, Nancy Piestrack

Assistant Vice President Training Manager, Terri Anderson

Vice Chairman Banner Corporation and Banner Bank, Jesse G. Foster, age 79

Chairman Banner Corporation and Banner Bank, Gary L. Sirmon, age 74

Auditors: Moss Adams LLP

LOCATIONS

HQ: Banner Corp.
10 South First Avenue, Walla Walla, WA 99362
Phone: 509 527-3636
Web: www.bannerbank.com

PRODUCTS/OPERATIONS

2016 Sales

	% of total
INTEREST INCOME:	
Loans receivable	75
Mortgage-backed securities	4
Securities and cash equivalents	3
NON-INTEREST INCOME:	
Deposit fees and other service charges	10
Mortgage banking operations	6
BOLI	1
Miscellaneous	1
Total	**100**

COMPETITORS

Bank of America	Sound Financial
Cascade Bancorp	U.S. Bancorp
Columbia Banking	Umpqua Holdings
FCA	Washington Federal
Glacier Bancorp	Wells Fargo
KeyCorp	

HISTORICAL FINANCIALS

Company Type: Public

Income Statement

FYE: December 31

	ASSETS ($ mil.)	NET INCOME ($ mil.)	INCOME AS % OF ASSETS	EMPLOYEES
12/16	9,793	85	0.9%	2,137
12/15	9,796	45	0.5%	2,143
12/14	4,723	54	1.1%	1,193
12/13	4,388	46	1.1%	1,131
12/12	4,265	64	1.5%	1,173
Annual Growth	23.1%	7.1%	—	16.2%

2016 Year-End Financials

Debt ratio: 2.05%
Return on equity: 6.54%
Cash ($ mil.): 247
Current ratio: —
Long-term debt ($ mil.): —

No. of shares (mil.): 33
Dividends
  Yield: 0.0%
  Payout: 25.7%
Market value ($ mil.): 1,853

	STOCK PRICE ($) FY Close	P/E High/Low		PER SHARE ($) Earnings	Dividends	Book Value
12/16	55.81	22	15	2.52	0.65	39.34
12/15	45.86	28	21	1.89	0.72	37.97
12/14	43.02	16	13	2.79	0.72	29.82
12/13	44.82	19	12	2.40	0.54	27.63
12/12	30.73	10	6	3.16	0.04	26.10
Annual Growth	16.1%	—	—	(5.5%)	100.8%	10.8%

BANNER HEALTH

Banner Health is one of the largest secular not-for-profit health systems in the US. The organization operates about 30 acute-care hospitals (with roughly 4000 beds). It also operates clinics nursing homes clinical laboratories ambulatory surgery centers home health agencies and other health care-related organizations including physician practices and a captive insurance company. Banner Health participates in medical research in areas such as Alzheimer's disease and spinal cord injuries through its Banner Sun Health Research division. The company which has more than 400000 members provides services in seven states in the western US; its largest concentration of facilities is in Arizona.

Operations

Banner Health is one of the first not-for-profit hospital operators to reinsure its employees through its captive insurance company Samaritan Insurance Funding. By offering this service Banner Health is able to diversify its risk improve cash flow and lower life insurance costs by about half a million dollars a year.

The multi-specialty system also operates a health plan in Arizona for Medicare-eligible patients. Its MediSunONE plan includes Medicare and Medicare Part D. The company has joined forces with Aetna in what is called an accountable care collaboration (ACO). An ACO uses technology and a team-based approach to care for the hospital's patients. Doctors and hospitals assume accounta-

bility for patient outcomes and are rewarded financially for achieving higher quality greater efficiency and overall better patient outcomes. The partnership also includes a new product called Aetna Whole Health that allows Banner's patients access to a line of Aetna services including their own electronic patient record.

The system's specialty centers include Banner Alzheimer's Institute Banner Concussion Center Banner Heart Hospital and the Western States Burn Center. In addition Banner Health trains 270 doctors per year at Banner Good Samaritan and Northern Colorado Medical Center.

Banner Health also partners with M.D. Anderson Cancer Center to operate a comprehensive cancer center in Phoenix. Services include medical oncology radiation oncology surgical oncology pathology laboratory diagnostic imaging as well as other supportive clinical services. M.D. Anderson has clinical oversight for all aspects of care delivery.

Education looms large on Banner Health's list of priorities — the hospital operates one of the country's largest simulation education centers at its Banner Corporate Center-Mesa. Simulation education is an expanding field in which medical students use computerized mannequins to improve their surgical and medical skills. The school's research has paid off and with Scottsdale Healthcare Osborn Medical Center Banner Health invented the Sapien Transcatheter Heart Valve an artificial heart valve that can replace a diseased aortic heart valve without the open heart surgery that previously was required.

Geographic Reach

Banner Health operates in Alaska Arizona California Colorado Nebraska Nevada and Wyoming.

The system's Banner Health Network is a group of health care providers located in Arizona's Maricopa and Pinal counties.

Financial Performance

Banner Health's income is generally derived through three channels: third-party payers such as commercial insurance managed care agreements Medicare and Medicaid and a small portion of self-pay patients as well as by borrowing funds and receiving philanthropic donations.

Its revenues grew by 29% in 2015 from $5.4 billion to $7 billion; higher net patient service medical insurance premium and other revenues drove that increase. However rising expenses and a $49.3 million loss for ACO Banner Health Network led to a drop in net income which fell 65% to $83.7 million.

Strategy

The health system has grown through construction. Banner Health is nearly always engaged in some sort of construction renovation or upgrading at its numerous facilities. The organization has more than $1 billion in construction projects in progress or completed in recent years. The system has expanded its facilities at Banner Baywood Medical Center Banner Del E. Webb Medical Center Banner Desert Medical Center Banner Thunderbird Medical Center Cardon Children's Medical Center and McKee Medical Center.

In 2015 Banner Health opened a Fort Collins facility on a 28-acre campus with a two-story hospital featuring an emergency department a 24-bed inpatient unit labor and delivery rooms medical imaging women's services surgical services and lab services.

Also that year the system merged with the University of Arizona Health Network (now named Banner - University Medicine) as well as establishing a 30-year affiliation with the University of Arizona. The moves align with its strategy of combining health care provision with medical schools and academic training as well as expanding operations into new markets (in this case the Tuscon region). Banner Health hopes to both improve access to

health care through a consumer-focused system and to provide opportunities for medical professionals to remain in Arizona. As part of the merger the company plans to build a new hospital and renovate an existing ambulatory campus.

In 2017 Banner Health restructured operations including cutting some 500 employees' positions. The move was part of its efforts to become more consumer-focused and included changes to its leadership lineup. Later that year after the restructuring was completed the company began recruiting to fill 1000 positions including spots for specialty nurses and physical and occupational therapists.

Mergers and Acquisitions

Banner Health does occasionally pick up a new hospital through acquisition. For instance in 2015 the company acquired The University of Arizona Health Network (now Banner - University Medicine). As a result University Medicine is the new academic medicine division of Banner Health which includes three academic medical centers: Banner - University Medical Center Tucson Banner - University Medical Center Phoenix and Banner - University Medical Center South.

In mid-2016 the company acquired more than 30 Arizona urgent-care centers from Urgent Care Extra. The centers to be rebranded under the Banner banner are among the expected 50 the company plans to have in Arizona by 2018.

In 2017 Banner Health acquired Medicare-certified home health agency SunLife Home Health which is based in Tucson Arizona. That deal allowed the system to expand its home care operations into southern Arizona.

Company Background

Banner Good Samaritan Medical Center first opened its doors as a 20-bed hospital in 1911. The medical center which is four months older than the state of Arizona marked its 100th anniversary in October 2011.

EXECUTIVES

EVP and Chief Administrative Officer, Ronald R. (Ron) Bunnell
President CEO and Director, Peter S. Fine, age 65
EVP and Chief Clinical Officer, John Hensing
CEO Banner Baywood Heart Hospital, Kathy Bollinger
COO, Rebecca (Becky) Kuhn
CEO Banner Estrella Medical Center, Tom Dickson
CFO, Dennis L. Laraway
President Western Region, Jim Ferando
CEO East Morgan County Hospital and Sterling Regional MedCenter, Linda Thorpe
President Arizona East Division, Todd S. Werner, age 49
CEO Banner Desert Medical Center and Interim CEO Cardon Children's Medical Center, Laura Robertson
CEO Platte County Memorial Hospital and Community Hospital, Shelby Nelson
CEO Banner Thunderbird Medical Center, Deb Krmpotic
CEO Banner Research, Eric (Bill) Reiman
President Banner Health Network, Chuck Lehn
CEO Banner Del E. Webb Medical Center and Banner Boswell Medical Center, Debbie Flores
CEO University Medical Center Phoenix, Steve Narang
CEO Banner Ironwood Medical Center and Banner Goldfield Medical Center, Sharon Lind
President and CEO Banner Health Foundation and Banner Alzheimer's Foundation, Andy Kramer Petersen
CIO, Ryan Smith
CEO Banner Casa Grande Medical Center, Rona Curphy

CEO Banner Estrella Medical Center, Courtney
Ophaug
CEO Banner Gateway Medical Center Banner MD
Anderson Cancer Center Banner Baywood
Medical Center and Banner Heart Hospital,
Lamont Yoder
VP Post Acute Services and CEO Banner Home
Care/Hospice, Lynn Rosenbach
CEO Banner Lassen Medical Center, Catherine
Harshbarger
CEO Banner Churchill Community Hospital, Hoyt
Skabelund
CEO Washakie Medical Center, Jay Stallings
CEO Ogallala Community Hospital, Drew Dostal
CEO Banner Behavioral Health Hospital, Brian
Beutin
CEO Page Hospital, Brian Kellar
Interim CEO Northern Colorado Service Area
including: Banner Fort Collins Medical Center
McKee Medical Center North Colorado Medical
Center, Scott Baker
Vice President of Materials Management, Doug
Bowen
Director of Infection Control, Marti Reich
Vice President Of Clinical Operations, Maggie Row
Director Of Pharmacy, Kurt Weibel
Director, Christopher H. (Chris) Volk
Chairman, Larry S. Lazarus
Secretary HP Statewide Customer Care, Josephine
Patino
Auditors: ERNST & YOUNG LLP

LOCATIONS

HQ: BANNER HEALTH
2901 N CENTRAL AVE # 160, PHOENIX, AZ
850122702
Phone: 602 747-4000
Web: WWW.BANNERHEALTH.COM

FEATURED SERVICES

Academic Medicine
Alzheimer's
Cancer
Heart
Insurance (Networks)
Maternity
Orthopedics
Pediatrics
Pharmacy
Physicians & Specialists
Research
Women's Health

COMPETITORS

Community Health
  Systems
Dignity Health
HCA
Inova
John C. Lincoln Health
  Network
Memorial Health System
  of East Texas
Northern Arizona
  Healthcare
Phoenix Children's
  Hospital

Poudre Valley Health
  System
Providence St. Joseph
  Health
Scottsdale Healthcare
Tenet Healthcare
Texas Health Resources
Wyoming Medical Center
Yuma Regional Medical
  Center

HISTORICAL FINANCIALS

Company Type: Private

Income Statement

FYE: December 31

	REVENUE ($ mil.)	NET INCOME ($ mil.)	NET PROFIT MARGIN	EMPLOYEES
12/15	6,971	119	1.7%	35,000
12/14	5,397	261	4.8%	—
12/13	5,085	854	16.8%	—
12/12	4,878	614	12.6%	—
Annual Growth	12.6%	(42.1%)	—	—

Debt ratio: ——
Return on equity: 1.70%
Cash ($ mil.): 91
Current ratio: 0.60
Long-term debt ($ mil.): —

Dividends
  Yield: —
  Payout: —
Market value ($ mil.): —

Bar Harbor Bankshares

Bar Harbor Bankshares which holds Bar Harbor
Bank & Trust is a Maine -stay. Boasting $1.6 bil-
lion in assets the bank offers traditional deposit
and retirement products trust services and a variety
of loans to individuals and businesses through 15
branches in the state's Hancock Knox and Washington counties. Commercial real estate and residential mortgages loans make up nearly 80% of
the bank's loan portfolio though it also originates
business construction agricultural home equity and
other consumer loans. About 10% of its loans are
to the tourist industry which is associated with
nearby Acadia National Park. Subsidiary Bar Harbor Trust Services offers trust and estate planning
services.

Operations
Around 80% of the bank's loan assets are tied
to real estate. About 41% of its loan portfolio was
made up of residential real estate mortgages at
the end of 2015 while another 37% was made up
of commercial real estate mortgages. The rest of
the portfolio was tied to commercial and industrial
loans (8% of loan assets) home equity loans (5%)
agricultural and farming loans (3%) commercial
construction (3%) and other consumer loans (1%).

More than 80% of Bar Harbor's revenue comes
from interest income. About 61% of its total revenue came from loan interest (including fees) during 2015 while another 25% came from interest
income on investment securities. The remainder
of its revenue came from trust and other financial
services (6% of revenue) debit card service charges
and fees (3%) deposit account service charges
(1%) and other miscellaneous income sources.

Geographic Reach
The Bar Harbor Maine-based group operates
15 branches across the downeast midcoast and
central regions of Maine more specifically in Bar
Harbor Northeast Harbor Southwest Harbor
Somesville Deer Isle Blue Hill Ellsworth Rockland
Topsham South China Augusta Winter Harbor
Milbridge Machias and Lubec.

Sales and Marketing
Bar Harbor serves individuals and retirees non-
profits municipalities as well as businesses that are
vital to Maine's coastal economy including retailers
restaurants seasonal lodging bio research laboratories.

Financial Performance
The group's annual revenues have risen more
than 10% since 2011 as its loan assets have
swelled over 35% to $990 million. Its profits have
grown more than 30% over the same period as
Bar Harbor has kept a lid on rising operating costs
and as it's enjoyed low interest rates.

Bar Harbor's revenue climbed 4% to $64.2 mil-
lion during 2015 mostly as its loan and other interest earning assets grew by more than 7%.

Revenue growth in 2015 drove the bank's net
income up 4% to $15.15 million. Bar Harbor's op-
erating cash levels spiked 31% to $20.33 million
for the year mainly thanks to favorable working
capital changes related to changes in other assets.

Strategy

Bar Harbor Bankshares looks to grow its loan
and deposit business organically and through
strategic bank acquisitions targeting the downeast
midcoast and central Maine markets. It also continued in 2016 to focus on managing its operating
expenses building upon its strong efficient ratio of
56.3% in 2015.

EXECUTIVES

EVP Business Banking Bar Harbor Bank & Trust,
  Gregory W. Dalton, age 57, $203,000 total
  compensation
EVP Retail Banking, Stephen M. Leackfeldt, age 60,
  $225,000 total compensation
EVP and Chief Risk Officer, Richard B. Maltz,
  $255,000 total compensation
EVP CFO and Treasurer, Josephine Iannelli, age 45
President and CEO Bar Harbor Bankshares and
  Bar Harbor Bank & Trust, Curtis C. Simard, age
  46, $438,000 total compensation
Assistant Vice President Branch Relationship
  Manager, Jody Warren
Assistant Vice President and Senior Risk
  Management Analyst, John Williams
Senior Vice President Finance, William Schaefer
Chairman, David B. Woodside, age 65
Auditors: KPMG LLP

LOCATIONS

HQ: Bar Harbor Bankshares
  P.O. Box 400, 82 Main Street, Bar Harbor, ME 04609-
  0400
Phone: 207 288-3314   Fax: 207 288-4560
Web: www.bhbt.com

PRODUCTS/OPERATIONS

2015 sales

	$ mil.	% of total
Interest and dividend income		
Interest and fees on loans	39	61
Interest on securities	15	24
Dividends on FHLB stock	0	1
Non-interest income		
Trust and other financial services	3	6
Debit card service charges and fees	1	3
Net securities gains	1	2
Other operating income	1	2
Service charges on deposit accounts	0	1
Total	64	100

Selected Services

Retail Products and Services
Retail Brokerage Services
Electronic Banking Services
Commercial Products and Services

COMPETITORS

Bangor Savings Bank
Bank of America
Camden National
People's United
  Financial

TD Bank USA
The First Bancorp

HISTORICAL FINANCIALS

Company Type: Public

Income Statement

FYE: December 31

	ASSETS ($ mil.)	NET INCOME ($ mil.)	INCOME AS % OF ASSETS	EMPLOYEES
12/16	1,755	14	0.9%	186
12/15	1,580	15	1.0%	221
12/14	1,459	14	1.0%	223
12/13	1,373	13	1.0%	185
12/12	1,302	12	1.0%	183
Annual Growth	7.7%	4.6%	—	0.4%

BATTELLE MEMORIAL INSTITUTE

Auditors: DELOITTE & TOUCHE LLP COLUMBU

LOCATIONS

HQ: BATTELLE MEMORIAL INSTITUTE
2555 INTERNATIONAL ST, COLUMBUS, OH
432284604
Phone: 800 201-2011
Web: WWW.BATTELLE.ORG

HISTORICAL FINANCIALS

Company Type: Private

Income Statement — FYE: September 30

	REVENUE ($ mil.)	NET INCOME ($ mil.)	NET PROFIT MARGIN	EMPLOYEES
09/14	4,775	(95)	—	20,000
09/13	4,795	(7)	—	—
09/12	5,228	(20)	—	—
Annual Growth	(4.4%)	—	—	—

BATTELLE MEMORIAL INSTITUTE INC

When you use a copier hit a golf ball or listen to a CD you're using technologies developed by Battelle Memorial Institute. The not-for-profit is one of the world's largest research enterprises with more than 22000 scientists engineers and staff serving corporate and government clients. Research areas include national security energy and health and life sciences. Battelle owns facilities in the US Asia and Europe and manages six Department of Energy-sponsored labs: Brookhaven National Laboratory Oak Ridge National Laboratory Idaho National Laboratory and Pacific Northwest National Laboratory. The institute was established by the family of steel industry pioneer Gordon Battelle in 1929.

Operations

Battelle's major subsidiaries include Battelle Arabia Battelle India Battelle Japan Battelle Ventures Bluefin Robotics and Winner Water Services.

Geographic Reach

Battelle's headquarters are located in Columbus Ohio. The company has about 130 locations globally.

Sales and Marketing

Battelle serves the national security health and life sciences and energy and environmental industries. Its major customer group includes government and commercial organizations in Laboratory Management National Security Health & Pharmaceutical Energy & Environment Consumer & Industrial and STEM Education.

Strategy

Battelle is in the process of building an advanced research-and-development facility that will expand its global footprint and capacity to provide advanced science and technology solutions for the agriculture food and health care industries. The new facility will augment Battelle's established global scientific expertise in formulation development toxicology and biotechnology programs that help agriculture and food customers accelerate product development and meet multi-national regulatory requirements.

HISTORY

Battelle Memorial Institute was founded with a $1.5 million trust willed by Gordon Battelle who died in 1923. Battelle was a champion of research for the advancement of humankind and before taking his father's place as president of several Ohio steel mills he had funded a former university professor's successful work to extract useful chemicals from mine waste. Battelle's mother upon her death in 1925 left the institute an additional $2.1 million. The institute opened in 1929.

The institute took on perhaps the most important project in its history in 1944 when it helped an electronics company's patent lawyer Chester Carlson find practical uses for his invention called xerography. Eventually Battelle developed the first photocopy machine and in 1955 it sold the patent rights for the machine to Haloid (now Xerox) in exchange for royalties.

During WWII Battelle worked on uranium refining for the Manhattan Project and in the early 1950s it established the world's first private nuclear research facility. The company also set up operations in Germany and Switzerland.

The tax man came knocking in 1961 questioning the tax-free status of some of Battelle's activities. The organization eventually had to pay $47 million. In 1965 Battelle developed a coin with a copper core and a copper-and-nickel-alloy cladding for the US Treasury.

As the result of a ruling that reinterpreted a clause in Gordon Battelle's will in 1975 the institute gave $80 million to philanthropic enterprises. This ruling coupled with the taxes that the organization was still unaccustomed to paying forced Battelle to re-examine its strategy.

Battelle co-developed the Universal Product Code (the bar code symbol found today on nearly all consumer goods packaging) in the 1970s. The institute also landed a lucrative contract from the US Department of Energy (DOE) to manage its commercial nuclear waste isolation program.

In 1987 Battelle chose Douglas Olesen — a 20-year veteran of the institute — to replace retiring CEO Ronald Paul. The company signed an extension with the DOE in 1992 to run its Pacific Northwest Laboratory (which it has operated since 1965).

An Ohio court in 1997 approved a seven-page agreement with the institute outlining the key principles that must be followed according to Gordon Battelle's will. This agreement replaced the 1975 decree and ended more than 20 years of scrutiny by the state attorney general's office.

In 1998 the DOE contracted Brookhaven Science Associates — a partnership between the State University of New York and Battelle — to operate Brookhaven National Laboratory. That year a Battelle contract to dispose of Vietnam War-era napalm drew national attention when subcontractor Pollution Control Industries backed out of the project citing safety concerns. Under Battelle's direction Houston-based GNI Group took the 3.4 million gallons of napalm off the US Navy's hands.

Battelle and the University of Tennessee in 1999 won a five-year contract to operate the US government's Oak Ridge National Laboratory. That year the institute made several breakthroughs in cancer research including FDA approval to test an inhalation delivery system for treating lung cancer.

In 2000 the company spun off OmniViz (data mining software) and Battelle Pulmonary Therapeutics (pulmonary and drug delivery technology) as wholly owned subsidiaries. In 2001 Battelle chose former Kodak EVP and CTO Carl Kohrt to replace Olesen. (Kohrt retired in January 2009 and was replaced by Jeffrey Wadsworth who has worked for the company since 2002.)

Battelle and several partners including BWX Technologies Washington Group International and Electric Power Research Institute won a 10-year contract in 2004 to operate Idaho National Laboratory a research facility established to focus on nuclear energy research and related technologies.

With offices in Japan and South Korea Battelle expanded its international reach to include India in 2008. The company formed a partnership in 2007 with oil and gas company PETRONAS to operate a renewable energy lab in Kuala Lumpur Malaysia.

Battelle underwent a leadership change in 2009 when Jeffrey Wadsworth took over as CEO replacing Carl Kohrt who retired.

EXECUTIVES

Vice President human Resources Battelle Columbus Operations, Robert Lincoln
Senior Vice President Chief Technology Officer, Richard Adams
President National Security, Stephen E. Kelly
President and CEO, Jeffrey (Jeff) Wadsworth, age 68
EVP Global Laboratory Operations, Ronald D. (Ron) Townsend
President Energy Health and Environmental business, Marty Toomajian
EVP and CFO, Dave Evans
President and CEO Winner Water Services, Carolyn Kotsol
Vice President, Victoria Loewengart
Vice President And Product Line Manager, Dennis Nelson
Vice President and Operations Manger, Daniel Taylor
Vice President, Sara F Kuczek
Senior Vice President Director Oak Ridge National Laboratory Global Laboratory Operations, Thomas Mason
Vice President for Systems Integration Services, Michael Janus
Executive Vice President, Martin Inglis
Vice President Application Development, Rod Barnaby

Vice President Business Development, Bradley Ashbrook

Senior Vice President Human Resources, Thomas Snowberger

Vice President navy and Special Operations Market Sector, Fred Byus

Vice President and Corporate Treasurer, Brian Smith

Vice President Client Insights, Jeanne Shaheen

Senior Vice President Human Resources, Malesa Litteral

Senior Vice President Business and Economic Development, Alexander Fischer

Executive Vice President and Chief Financial Officer, David Evans

Vice President Information Technology, Lavlesh Lamba

VICE PRESIDENT, Bob Dillon

Chairman, John K. Welch

Secretary, Tiffani Gollihue

Auditors: DELOITTE & TOUCHE LLP COLUMB

LOCATIONS

HQ: BATTELLE MEMORIAL INSTITUTE INC
505 KING AVE, COLUMBUS, OH 432012681
Phone: 614 424-6424
Web: WWW.BATTELLE-JAPAN.COM

PRODUCTS/OPERATIONS

Selected Laboratories and Research Facilities

Battelle Biomedical Research Center (West Jefferson OH)

Battelle Eastern Science and Technology Center (Aberdeen MD)

Battelle Frederick Operations (Maryland)

Battelle Geneva Operations (Switzerland)

Brookhaven National Laboratory (Upton NY)

Human Factors Transportation Center (Seattle)

Idaho National Laboratory (Idaho Falls)

Lawrence Livermore National Laboratory (Livermore CA)

Marine Science Laboratory (Sequim WA)

National Renewable Energy Laboratory (Golden CO)

Oak Ridge National Laboratory (Tennessee)

Battelle Duxbury Operations (Massachusetts)

Pacific Northwest National Laboratory (Richland WA)

Selected Inventions

Exploded-tip paintbrush (nylon brush for Wooster Brush Co. 1950)

Golf ball coatings (1965)

Heat Seat (microwaveable stadium cushion 1990s)

Holograms (work began in the 1970s)

Insulin injection pen (for Eli Lilly 1990s)

Oil spill outline monitor (1992)

PCB-cleaning chemical process (1992)

Photocopy machine (with Haloid 1940s)

Plastic breakdown process (1990s)

"Sandwich" coins (copper/copper-and-nickel-alloy cladding design for US Treasury 1965)

SenSonic toothbrush (with Teledyne/WaterPik 1990s)

Smart cards (cards embedded with tiny computer chips that store information 1980s)

Universal Product Code (co-creator; bar code 1970s)

COMPETITORS

Argonne National Laboratory	Institute for Defense Analyses
Berkeley Lab	SwRI
Charles Stark Draper Laboratory	

HISTORICAL FINANCIALS

Company Type: Private

Income Statement

FYE: September 30

	REVENUE ($ mil.)	NET INCOME ($ mil.)	NET PROFIT MARGIN	EMPLOYEES
09/16	4,810	(19)	—	7,457
09/15	4,783	(63)	—	
09/14	4,769	(111)	—	
09/13	4,795	(7)	—	
Annual Growth	0.1%	—	—	—

2016 Year-End Financials

Debt ratio: ——
Return on equity: (-0.40%)
Cash ($ mil.): 63
Current ratio: 1.40
Long-term debt ($ mil.): —

Dividends
Yield: —
Payout: —
Market value ($ mil.): —

Baxter International Inc

A medical products manufacturer Baxter International is a leading producer of intravenous (IV) fluids and systems. It also makes infusion pumps pre-filled syringes biological sealants and inhaled anesthetics as well as dialyzers and other products for the treatment of end-stage renal disease (ESRD). In 2015 Baxter split its operations into two companies — one focused on biopharmaceuticals (Baxalta) and the other on medical products (Baxter).The company traces its roots back to 1931 when it was founded as an intravenous products maker.

HISTORY

Idaho surgeon Ralph Falk his brother Harry and California physician Donald Baxter formed Don Baxter Intravenous Products in 1931 to distribute the IV solutions Baxter made in Los Angeles. Two years later the company opened its first plant located outside Chicago. Ralph Falk bought Baxter's interest in 1935 and began R&D efforts leading to the first sterilized vacuum-type blood collection device (1939) which could store blood for weeks instead of hours. Product demand during WWII spurred sales above $1.5 million by 1945.

In 1949 the company created Travenol Laboratories to make and sell drugs. Baxter went public in 1951 and began an acquisition program the next year. In 1953 failing health caused both Falks to give control to William Graham a manager since 1945. Under Graham's leadership Baxter absorbed Wallerstein (1957); Fenwal Labs (1959); Flint Eaton (1959); and Dayton Flexible Products (1967).

In 1975 Baxter's headquarters moved to Deerfield Illinois. In 1978 the company debuted the first portable dialysis machine and had $1 billion in sales. Vernon Loucks Jr. became CEO two years later. Baxter claimed the title of the world's leading hospital supplier in 1985 when it bought American Hospital Supply (a Baxter distributor from 1932 to 1962). Offering more than 120000 products and an electronic system that connected customers with some 1500 vendors Baxter captured nearly 25% of the US hospital supply market in 1988. That year it became Baxter International.

In 1992 Baxter spun off Caremark (home infusion therapy and mail-order drugs) but kept a division that controlled 75% of the world's dialysis machine market.

In 1993 Baxter pleaded guilty (and was temporarily suspended from selling to the Veterans Administration) to bribing Syria to remove Baxter from a blacklist for trading in Israel.

The company entered the US cardiovascular perfusion services market in 1995 with the purchases of PSICOR and SETA. Baxter along with two other silicone breast-implant makers agreed to settle thousands of claims (at an average of $26000 each) from women suffering side-effects from the implants. The next year Baxter spun off its cost management and hospital supply business as Allegiance (sold to Cardinal Health in 1999).

Buys in 1997 boosted Baxter's presence in Europe and its share of the open-heart-surgery devices market. That year it agreed to pay about 20% of a $670 million legal settlement in a suit relating to hemophiliacs infected with HIV from blood products.

In response to concerns posed by shareholders Baxter in 1999 said it would phase out the use of PVC (polyvinyl chloride) in some products by 2010. In 2000 the firm spun off its underperforming cardiovascular unit as Edwards Lifesciences. To strengthen core operations it lined up a number of purchases including North American Vaccine.

Purchases in 2001 included the cancer treatment unit of chemicals firm Degussa. Also that year Baxter withdrew dialysis equipment from Spain and Croatia after patients who used its products died. It also ended production of two types of dialyzers that were sold there. As the number of deaths mounted to more than 50 in seven countries Baxter began facing lawsuits; it later settled with the families of many of the patients. In September 2002 the FDA issued a warning when several patients died after using Baxter's Meridian dialysis machines. The same year Baxter bought Fusion Medical to expand its BioScience unit.

Robert L. Parkinson Jr. took over as chairman and CEO in April 2004. Parkinson succeeded Harry M. Jansen Kraemer Jr. William Graham who remained on the Baxter board of directors as honorary chairman emeritus after his official retirement in 1996 died in 2006.

In 2005 the FDA seized Baxter's existing inventories of previously recalled 6000 Colleague Volumetric Infusion Pumps and nearly 1000 Syndeo PCA Syringe Pumps; the federal agency resorted to these measures after the company did not fix production and design problems with the pumps in a suitable amount of time after batches of the product had been recalled earlier that year.

Baxter's product troubles didn't end there. In 2008 Baxter halted production of heparin after hundreds of bad reactions (including several deaths) occurred in patients using the drug. Subsequent investigations focused on raw heparin supplied to Baxter by a Chinese factory which apparently added a cheaper ingredient into the drug which contaminated it. Heparin-related litigation continued for Baxter in following years.

In 2009 the company acquired the hemofiltration (renal replacement therapy) product line of Edwards Lifesciences in a $65 million deal.

To meet increasing demand Baxter also expanded its infusion systems portfolio that year by entering an agreement to distribute medical device maker SIGMA's Spectrum large volume infusion pumps domestically and internationally. The deal also gave Baxter a 40% stake in the company (with the option to buy the rest) as well as access to future products under development. In 2012 Baxter exercised its right to buy and paid $90 million in cash for the remaining 60% of the company.

The addition of the Spectrum system was especially helpful when the FDA ordered the company to recall all of its Colleague infusion pumps in the US market in 2010. Patients were given the option of receiving Spectrum pumps to replace the Colleague systems.

As part of restructuring efforts in 2010 the company sold its noncore US generic injectables business to Hikma Pharmaceuticals for about $112 million. Baxter divested the business to focus on its proprietary injectable formulation and packaging operations. The sale also included Baxter's manufacturing facility in New Jersey and a warehouse and distribution center in Tennessee.

The company grew its BioScience operations in 2010 by acquiring all of the hemophilia-related assets from privately-held Archemix in a deal worth up to $315 million. Archemix has products under development including a synthetic hemophilia treatment to improve the body's blood clotting capabilities. Then to jump into the bone grafting market the company spent some $330 million to acquire UK-based ApaTech which sells bone grafting materials in the US and Europe; the deal gave Baxter manufacturing and research facilities in Germany the UK and the US.

EXECUTIVES

Corporate Vice President and Chief Inf, John Moon
Corporate Vice President and Treasurer, Robert J Hombach
Corporate VP and CIO, Paul E. Martin
Chairman and CEO, Jos © E. (Joe) Almeida, age 55, $1,300,000 total compensation
Corporate VP Human Resources, Jeanne K. Mason, age 61, $540,192 total compensation
Corporate VP and CFO, James K. Saccaro, age 44, $644,415 total compensation
Corporate VP and President Hospital Products, Brik V. Eyre, age 53, $618,533 total compensation
Corporate VP and Chief Scientific Officer, Marcus Schabacker, age 53
Corporate VP and President International, Paul Vibert, age 57
Corporate VP and President Renal, Giuseppe Accogli, age 46, $514,028 total compensation
Medical Director, Guenter Zuelow
Vice President of Marketing, Thomas Harrison
Vice President, Michael Baughman
Area Vice President, Eric Walker
Vice President Marketing, Shankar Kaul
Vice President Marketing, Chandra Sekhar
Vice President Finance Latin America, Maximino Caballero
Vice President Global Research And Development And Medical Affairs Bioscience, Hartmut Ehrlich
Vice President Clinical Development and Operations, Bander Halit
Vice President Compliance, Kris Rapp
Vice President Marketing and MEDICATION DELIVERY, Jeffery Nordquist
Corporate Vice President Investor Relations, Clare Trachtman
Vice President and General Manager, Peter Omalley
Vice President Information Technology, Tim Robi
Vice President Marketing, Paul Grozier
Vice President Strategy, Michael Bradley
Vice President Global Research And Development, Ken Fuetterer
Vice President Information Technology, Martin Donlon
Vice President Manufacturing Strategy, Kathleen Warren
Vice President Asia Pacific, Victoria Elegant
Vice President Marketing, Cindy Huey
Corporate Vice President Treasurer and Head of Investor Relations, Scott Bohaboy
Vice President Discovery And Scientific Support, Clifford Holmes
Vice President Employee Trust, Charles Thurman
Vice President Marketing, Timothy Davis
Corporate Vice President Global Manufacturing Operations, James Gatling

Vice President Strategy And Portfolio Planning, Bob Weiland
Vice President Information Technology Renal Divisi, Cathy Skala
Medical Director, Mahmoud Loghman-Adham
Associate Medical Director, Carol Schermer
Vice President Life Science and Operations, Halit Bander
Vice President Sales for National Accounts, Gregg Boyer
Vice President President Medication Del, Peter Arduini
Medical Director Medical Device Safety Operations, Daniel Jacob
Vice President Compensation and Benefits, Salvatore Dadouche
Vice President Human Resources, Mike Edicola
Vice President Talent Management, Irina Konstantinovsky
Vice President Talent Management, Steve King
Vice President Medical Sales, Chris Lykins
Area Vice President of Sales BioSurgery, Meg McKenna
Vice President Supply Chain Latin America and Canada, German Castaneda
Vice President Manufacturing And Supply, Timothy Lawrence
Vice President Sales, Joe Pudlo
Vice President assistant Controller, John Mccoy
Vice President Quality, Allen Harmon
Corporate Vice President And Cio, Karenann Terrell
Vice President Finance, Patrick Marschall
Human Resources Vice President Latin America, Paulo Bolgar
Vice President Clinical Affairs, Anita Stephens
Vice President Employee Services, Faye Katt
Vice President Biosurgery Research And Development, Russ Holscher
Vice President Manufacturing Strategy, Kathy Warren
Vice President Human Resources Latinamerica, Diana Pacheco
Vice President Operations of and Strategy, Donna Kopera
Vice President Sales and Marketing, Carlos Rodriguez
Corporate Vice President and Chief Scientific Officer, Norbert Riedel
Vice President Strategic Planning, Mike Martin
Vice President Information Technology, Kristie Zinselmeier
Senior Vice President, Alan Heller
Senior Vice President of Human Resources, Mike Tucker
Vice President Corporate Communications, Thomas Kline
Vice President Finance, Ken Robinson
Assistant Vice President and Business Development Officer, Nicholas Evans
Vice President Sales, Greg Neier
Corporate Vice President Human Resources, Jeannie K Mason
Vice President Marketing, Tom Progar
Executive Vice President Information Technology, Jeff Steward
Vice President Quality, Katherine Azuara
Medical Director, Farah Ali
Vice President and Head Baxter Ventures, Anne Sissel
Senior Vice President Qara, Joseph Tsiakals
Assistant Vice President Central Area, Craig Prather
Vice President Nutrition Global Marketing, James Fischer
Area Vice President Strategic Accounts, Alan Mavis
Vice President and Global Head of Clinical Research Hematology, Anne Prener
Vice President, Ann Carter

Global Vice President Information Technology and Chief Information Security Officer, Nicole Ford
VICE PRESIDENT OF FINANCE, Baxter Home
Area Vice President, Steve Czick
Board Member, Carole Shapazian
Assistant Treasurer, Jeff Schaible
Auditors: PricewaterhouseCoopers LLP

LOCATIONS

HQ: Baxter International Inc
One Baxter Parkway, Deerfield, IL 60015
Phone: 224 948-2000   **Fax:** 847 948-2964
Web: www.baxter.com

2016 Sales

	$ mil.	% of total
US	4,259	42
Europe	2,697	26
Asia/Pacific	2,029	20
Latin America & Canada	1,178	12
Total	**10,163**	**100**

PRODUCTS/OPERATIONS

2016 Sales

	$ mil.	% of total
Renal	3,855	38
Hospital Products		
Fluid systems	2,300	23
Integrated Pharmacy Solutions	2,245	22
Surgical care	1,321	13
Others	442	4
Total	**10,163**	**100**

Selected Acquisitions

COMPETITORS

Becton Dickinson	Genzyme
CSL	Grifols
CSL Behring	Hospira
CareFusion	Kimberly-Clark Health
Fresenius Medical Care	Terumo

HISTORICAL FINANCIALS
Company Type: Public

Income Statement
FYE: December 31

	REVENUE ($ mil.)	NET INCOME ($ mil.)	NET PROFIT MARGIN	EMPLOYEES
12/16	10,163	4,965	48.9%	48,000
12/15	9,968	968	9.7%	50,000
12/14	16,671	2,497	15.0%	66,000
12/13	15,259	2,012	13.2%	61,000
12/12	14,190	2,326	16.4%	51,000
Annual Growth	(8.0%)	20.9%	—	(1.5%)

2016 Year-End Financials

Debt ratio: 17.90%	No. of shares (mil.): 539
Return on equity: 57.79%	Dividends
Cash ($ mil.): 2,801	Yield: 0.0%
Current ratio: 2.40	Payout: 5.6%
Long-term debt ($ mil.): 2,779	Market value ($ mil.): 23,926

	STOCK PRICE ($) FY Close	P/E High/Low		PER SHARE ($) Earnings	Dividends	Book Value
12/16	44.34	5	4	9.01	0.51	15.36
12/15	38.15	41	18	1.76	1.27	16.15
12/14	73.29	17	14	4.56	2.05	14.97
12/13	69.55	20	17	3.66	1.92	15.58
12/12	66.66	16	12	4.18	1.57	12.70
Annual Growth	(9.7%)	—	—	21.2%	(24.7%)	4.9%

BB&T Corp.

BB&T Corporation provides traditional banking insurance investment banking and wealth management services through more than 2100 bank branches across the South and Southeastern US. The holding company's flagship subsidiary Branch Banking and Trust (BB&T) is one of North Carolina's oldest banks and a leading originator of residential mortgages in the Southeast. The company also operates investment bank Scott & Stringfellow. Boasting assets of around $220 billion BB&T is one of the largest financial services holding companies in the US.

Operations

In addition to standard services like deposits and loans BB&T also offers insurance mutual funds discount brokerage wealth management financial planning and business services such as leasing and venture capital.

As part of its business BB&T operates through six segments: Community Banking Residential Mortgage Banking Dealer Financial Services Specialized Lending Insurance Holdings and Financial Services.

More than 50% of the bank's total revenue comes from loan interest while just less than 10% comes from interest and dividend income on investments. Non-interest income accounts for the remaining and consists of insurance income (some 15% of total) service charges on deposits (over 5%) mortgage banking income (5%) investment banking and brokerage fees and commissions (5%) trust and investment advisory revenues (2%) and various other fee-related incomes.

Geographic Reach

North Carolina-based BB&T has US offices in Virginia Florida Georgia Maryland the Carolinas West Virginia Kentucky Alabama Tennessee Texas Pennsylvania New Jersey and Washington DC. Its largest markets are Virginia North Carolina and Florida each home to more than 300 bank branches.

Sales and Marketing

BB&T though its network of subsidiaries serves its target retail and commercial clients. BB&T's primary markets offer a diverse employment base and consist of manufacturing general services agriculture wholesale and retail trade technology government and financial services.

Financial Performance

In fiscal 2016 BB&T's revenue increased 12% to $11.5 billion amid strong increases in both interest and non-interest income. The acquisition of National Penn is the main factor behind the revenue increase.

Net income increased 17% to $2.3 billion due to higher revenue and higher yields on loans and an improved funding mix.

Cash from operations fell 40% to $1.2 billion as higher net income was offset by net changes in loans held for sale.

Strategy

BB&T has in recent years been following a long-term strategy of growing its branch network reach and diversifying its revenue streams through strategic bank acquisition. In 2016 the company acquired two banks: National Penn a Pennsylvanian retail and commercial bank with 126 offices; and CGSC America Holdings Corporation. It has also recently acquired more than 60 branches in Texas from Citibank at the time doubling BB&T's branch size in the state and adding more than $200 million worth new loan business and $6.3 billion in new deposits.

The company has been carrying out layoffs as its consolidates the acquired businesses. The for-

mer Susquehanna Bank (acquired in 2015) call center was shut down in 2017 for the loss of 82 jobs; the remaining staff have been relocated to other offices. It has made other branch closures too as the viability of branches is eroded by the rise of internet banking which is also the cheaper option for bank.

Mergers and Acquisitions

In 2016 BB&T acquired National Penn a PA-incorporated banking holding company. National Penn which operates mostly through subsidiary National Penn Bank provides a range of retail and commercial banking facilities and services. It has 126 offices. Also in 2016 the company acquired CGSC North America Holdings Corporation which was integrated into BB&T's wholesale property and casualty broker CRC Insurance Services.

HISTORY

In 1872 Alpheus Branch son of a wealthy planter founded Branch and Company a mercantile business in Wilson North Carolina. He and Thomas Jefferson Hadley who was organizing a public school system created the Branch and Hadley bank later that same year. The private bank helped rebuild farms and small businesses after the Civil War.

In 1887 Branch bought out Hadley and changed the bank's name to Branch and Company Bankers. Two years later Branch secured a state trust charter for the Wilson Banking and Trust Company. He never got the business running however and died in 1893. The trust charter was amended to change the name to Branch Banking and Company and Branch and Company Bankers was folded into it in 1900.

In 1907 the bank finally got its trust operations running and began calling itself Branch Banking and Trust Company. In 1922 it opened its first insurance department; the next year it started its mortgage loan activities.

BB&T survived the 1929 stock market crash with the help of the Post Office. Nervous customers withdrew their funds from BB&T and other banks and deposited them in postal savings accounts unaware that BB&T was the local Post Office's bank and the withdrawn funds went right back to the bank. BB&T opened six more branches between 1929 and 1933.

After WWII consumerism skyrocketed resulting in more car loans and mortgages. During the 1960s and 1970s the bank embarked on a series of mergers and acquisitions forming the thin end of a buying wedge that would widen significantly in the coming decades.

By 1994 BB&T was the fourth-largest bank in North Carolina. In 1995 it merged with North Carolina's fifth-largest bank Southern National Corp. founded in 1897.

With banking regulations loosening to allow different types of operations BB&T in 1997 made several acquisitions including banks thrifts and securities brokerage Craigie.

BB&T's 1998 activities included three bank acquisitions that pushed it into metro Washington DC. The company also increased holdings in fields such as insurance sales venture capital for Southern businesses and investment banking (through its acquisition of Scott & Stringfellow Financial the South's oldest NYSE member).

In 1999 Craigie was melded into Scott & Stringfellow. That year BB&T bought several insurance companies and small banks. The company continued its march through the South the following year buying several Georgia banks and Tennessee's BankFirst. In 2001 BB&T purchased South Carolina's FirstSpartan Financial multibank holding company Century South Banks Maryland-based FCNB Corporation and western Georgia's

Community First Banking Company. To bolster its presence in the Washington DC market it bought Virginia Capital Bancshares and F&M National.

BB&T purchased Alabama-based Cooney Rikard & Curtin a wholesale insurance broker active in 45 states in 2002. Also that year it added about 100 branches in Kentucky after buying MidAmerica Bancorp and AREA Bancshares and entered the coveted Florida market following its purchase of Regional Financial the privately held parent of First South Bank.

Acquisitions continued the following three years as the bank swallowed First Virginia Banks among other targets. It took a break in 2005 to assimilate its holdings before joining the acquisition hunt in 2006 with deals for banks in Georgia (Main Street Banks) and Tennessee (First Citizens Bancorp) and in South Carolina (Coastal Financial) in 2007.

EXECUTIVES

Chairman and CEO, Kelly S. King, age 68, $1,075,000 total compensation

President and COO BB&T Corporation and Branch Banking & Trust Company, Christopher L. (Chris) Henson, age 55, $700,000 total compensation

SEVP and CIO, Barbara F. Duck, age 50, $507,083 total compensation

SEVP and Deposit Services Manager, Donna C. Goodrich, age 54, $507,083 total compensation

SEVP and Chief Risk Officer, Clarke R. Starnes, age 58, $582,500 total compensation

SEVP and CFO, Daryl N. Bible, age 55, $590,000 total compensation

SEVP and President Community Banking, David H. Weaver, age 51

SEVP General Counsel Secretary and Chief Corporate Governance Officer, Robert J. Johnson, age 44

SEVP President and CEO BB&T Securities LLC and Capital Markets Manager, W. Rufus Yates, age 59

President West Florida Region, Jim Daly, age 56

SEVP and Chief Digital Officer, W. Bennett Bradley, age 55

SEVP and Lending Group Manager, Brant J. Standridge, age 41

SEVP and Chief Client Experience Officer, Dont L. Wilson, age 40

SEVP and Deputy Chief Risk Officer, Jim D. Godwin, age 48

Vice President, Cindy Powell

Senior Vice President, Martin Currin

Senior Vice President and Manager Credit Risk Review, Jimmy Godwin

Senior Vice President, Mieke Deboer

Senior Vice President Wealth Management Team Direc, Craig Frye

Assistant Vice President Small Business Specialist, Andrew Vinson

Vice President, Chris Furner

Vice President Business Deposits Officer, Laurie Zapletal

Senior Vice President, Cindy Mcgoldrick

Senior Vice President Simulation Manager, Tammy Jarrell

Senior Vice President, Ann Hardison

Vice President Information Technology Section, Greg Stone

Vice President Senior Team Leader Acquired Asset Group SFL, John Breitfelder

Vice President Family Risk Manager, Kimberly Smith

Vice President And Manager Is Section Bbandt Corporation, Bill Colon

Vice President, Debrah More

Commercial Banker Assistant Vice President, Bridget Nodianos

Vice President Asset Resolution Group, Jay Tucker

Assistant Vice President And Portfolio Manager, Melissa Hopp

Senior Vice President, Jim Sherrick

Senior Vice President, Samuel Scott

Senior Vice President, Michael Coleman

Senior Vice President Credit Operations, Lee S Patterson

Assistant Vice President at Market Risk, Jingnong Chen

Vice President, Stephen G Lewis

Regional Retail Banking Manager Senior Vice President a, Debbie Hance

Systems Support Team Leader Vice President at Branch Banking and Trust; Systems Analyst Team Leader, Matt Cox

Vice President and Commercial Account Officer, Randy O Spaw

Vice President And New Business Development Officer, Jeff Elliott

Assistant Vice President Payment Solutions Treasury Management, Chris Wells

Vice President and Financial Center Leader III, Jaime Dudleson

Assistant Vice President Commercial Real Estate Portfolio Manager, Seth Einstein

Vice President, Pam Goracke

Vice President Energy Group, James Giordano

Vice President, Sandra Abraham

Assistant Vice President, Sharna Pearson

Senior Vice President, Steve Sprecher

Vice President and Personal Trust Specialist, Sherry Ross

Vice President Sales Support Product Development, Connie Reeves

Executive Vice President, Howard Brooks

Assistant Vice President Mortgage Loan Officer, Chrissy Maddy

Private Advisor Vice President, Tommy Rhyne

Vice President, Jay Hall

Vice President, Nicole Irby

Vice President, Scott E Russell

Senior Vice President Payment Solutions Risk Manager, Joe Potuzak

Senior Internal Auditor Assistant Vice President, Ashley Farrell

Vice President Business Development, Aimee Creamer

Senior Vice President, Mark Desautels

Vice President Information Technology Enterprise Architecture, Fred Phillippi

Vice President Business Development, Claudy Gardner

Senior Vice President, Carletha Ward

Vice President, Karen Spong

Vice President Human Resources, Betty Putney

First Vice President Information Technology, Dave McMillan

Vice President Family Risk Management, Gina Jurch

Business Banker and T Wealth Vice President, Lindsey Leaverton

Senior Vice President Syndicated Finance, Mike Skorich

Certified Employment Consultant III Assistant Vice President, Lucinda Austin

Executive Vice President Marketing, Brenda Lean

Vice President Network Operations Manager, Ken Johnson

Area President, Ryan Kennedy

Vice President and Portfolio Risk Officer III, Diane Villaronga

Vice President Integrated Channel Management Strategist, David Barrick

Senior Vice President abl, Jennifer Cummins

Family Risk Manager Assistant Vice President, Kristin Walker

Vice President, Carl Dillon

Vice President, Vicky Hamblin

Vice President and Commercial Ins, Karen Y Witt

Vice President Enterprise Application and Integrat, Bala Kathiresan

Executive Vice President Marketing, Barbara Crane

Vice President, Derek Efird

Assistant Vice President Financial Center Leader Hablo Espaiiol, Gil Rolon

Information Technology Solutions Architect Vice President, Justin Blankenship

Vice President Institutional Sales, Angela Dreelin

Mortgage Loan Off And Assistant Vice President, Ann Adams

Vice President Sales And Service Leader, Kim Allen

Assistant Vice President, Marie Murrain

Financial Center Leader Assistant Vice President, John Killman

Vice President Private Advisor Wealth Management, Alan Majak

Vice President Portfolio Risk Officer, Matt Wagner

Vice President And Consultant, Andrew Zevola

Business Services Officer And Assistant Vice President, Paul Abell

Vice President, Duncan Moseley

Assistant Vice President, Cassie Pruitt

Vice President, Michael Walter

ML Underwriting Section Manager And Assistant Vice President, Ken Burnham

Assistant Vice President Healthcare Investment Banking, Michelle LE

Senior Vice President, Sam Fisher

Assistant Vice President Area Operations Officer II Hub Team Leader, Ann Hicks

Vice President Business Services Officer, Mark Spivey

Assistant Vice President, Patty Garcia

Assistant Vice President, Jason Matthews

Assistant Vice President, Scott Parks

Vice President, Lisa Allen

Assistant Vice President Operations Team Leader, Lucinda Beard

Vice President, Jane Phillips

Assistant Vice President Of Sports Marketing And Event Planning, Emily Brown

Vice President, Mark Holmes

Assistant Vice President Area Operations Officer, Kathleen Johnson

Vice President, Karen Starnes

Assistant Vice President, Dan Owens

Assistant Vice President, Travis O'quinn

Enterprise Management Systems Assistant Vice President, Ajit Khanna

Vice President Personal Trust Specialist, Kim Lamm

Client Sever Engineer IV Vice President BBandt, Dan Phelan

Vice President, Michael Trice

Assistant Vice President, Naomi Norris

Senior Vice President, Stanley Gunter

Vice President, Susan Holt

AIAM CPIA Vice President Personal Department Manager, Sarah Rodriguez

Vice President, Nanci Campbell

Assistant Vice President, Ted Flor

Mortgage Loan Officer Assistant Vice President, Emily Bennett

Assistant Vice President, William Boswell

Vice President And Relationship Manager, Barry Justus

Assistant Vice President And Production Support, Leigh Bradley

Senior Vice President, John Tulloss

Market Leader IV Vice President, Michael Benetto

Vice President Of District Operations, Wilborn Roberson

Vice President Credit Risk Review Officer, Kevin Yarbrough

Senior Vice President Corporate Bankin, Troy Weaver

Assistant Vice President Information Technology Business Planning and Reporting, Mala Kasthurirangan

Assistant Vice President Risk and Information Of, Chevol Davis

Senior Vice President Credit Risk Review Team Leader, Nancy Ortkiese

Senior Vice President, Siddharth Patel

Assistant Vice President Certified Mortgage Loan Officer, J Mel Williams

Senior Vice President Senior Credit Officer, Thomas Findlay

Vice President Information Technology, Jeff Anders

Assistant Vice President Marketing, Elizabeth Stepp

Information Technology Distinguished Technologist Vice President, Craig Gerber

Vice President and Credit Risk Controller, John Hood

Assistant Vice President Large Group Account Executive, Cathy Lyons

Senior Vice President Commercial Banking, Benjamin Sharpe

Assistant Vice President, Shante Myers

Vice President, Zane Brisson

Bb And T Vice President, Mark Stephens

Auditors: PricewaterhouseCoopers LLP

LOCATIONS

HQ: BB&T Corp.
200 West Second Street, Winston-Salem, NC 27101
Phone: 336 733-2000   Fax: 336 671-2399
Web: www.bbt.com

2016 sales

	No.
North Carolina	352
Virginia	344
Florida	318
Pennsylvania	262
Maryland	165
Georgia	155
Texas	124
South Carolina	111
Kentucky	110
Alabama	84
West Virginia	73
Tennessee	48
New Jersey	33
Washington D.C.	13
Total	**2,192**

PRODUCTS/OPERATIONS

2016 sales

	$ mil.	% of total
Interest income:		
Interest and fees on loans and leases	5,985	52
Interest and dividends on securities	1,029	9
Interest on other earning assets	52	-
Non-interest income:		
Insurance income	1,713	15
Service charges on deposits	664	6
Mortgage banking income	463	4
Investment banking and brokerage fees and commissions	408	3
Trust and investment advisory	266	2
Bankcard fees and merchant discounts	237	2
Checkcard fees	195	2
Operating lease income	137	1
Income from bank-owned life insurance	123	1
FDIC loss share income net	(142)	-
Other income	362	3
Securities gains (losses) net	46	-
Total	**11,538**	**100**

Selected Services

Commercial
    Asset management
    Association services
    Capital markets services
    Commercial deposit services
    Commercial finance
    Commercial middle market lending
    Commercial mortgage lending
    Institutional trust services
    Insurance
    Insurance premium finance
    International banking services
    Leasing

Merchant services
Payment solutions
Private equity investments
Real estate lending
Supply chain management
Retail
Asset management
Automobile lending
Bankcard lending
Consumer finance
Home equity lending
Insurance
Investment brokerage services
Mobile/online banking
Payment solutions
Retail deposit services
Sales finance
Small business lending
Wealth management/private banking

Selected Subsidiaries & Affiliates

American Coastal Insurance Company
BB&T Equipment Finance Corporation
BB&T Financial FSB
  Sheffield Financial
BB&T Insurance Services Inc.
BB&T Investment Services Inc.
BB&T Securities LLC
Branch Banking and Trust Company
Clearview Correspondent Services
CRC Insurance Services
Grandbridge Real Estate Capital LLC
Lendmark Financial Services Inc.
McGriff Seibels & Williams Inc.
MidAmerica Gift Certificate Company
Prime Rate Premium Finance Corporation Inc.
  AFCO Credit Corporation
Regional Acceptance Corporation
Stanley Hunt DuPree & Rhine Inc.
Sterling Capital Management LLC

COMPETITORS

Bank of America	PNC Financial
Capital One	Regions Financial
Fifth Third	SunTrust
First Citizens	Synovus
BancShares	United Bankshares
First Horizon	Wells Fargo
JPMorgan Chase	

HISTORICAL FINANCIALS

Company Type: Public

Income Statement

FYE: December 31

	ASSETS ($ mil.)	NET INCOME ($ mil.)	INCOME AS % OF ASSETS	EMPLOYEES
12/16	219,276	2,426	1.1%	37,500
12/15	209,947	2,084	1.0%	37,200
12/14	186,814	2,151	1.2%	33,400
12/13	183,010	1,679	0.9%	33,700
12/12	183,872	1,979	1.1%	34,000
Annual Growth	4.5%	5.2%	—	2.5%

2016 Year-End Financials

Debt ratio: 8.14%
Return on equity: 8.46%
Cash ($ mil.): 4,280
Current ratio: —
Long-term debt ($ mil.): —

No. of shares (mil.): 809
Dividends
  Yield: 0.0%
  Payout: 41.5%
Market value ($ mil.): 38,062

	STOCK PRICE ($) FY Close	P/E High/Low	PER SHARE ($) Earnings	Dividends	Book Value
12/16	47.02	17 11	2.77	1.15	36.91
12/15	37.81	16 13	2.56	1.05	34.99
12/14	38.89	15 13	2.75	0.95	33.77
12/13	37.32	17 13	2.19	1.12	32.21
12/12	29.11	12 9	2.70	0.76	30.24
Annual Growth	12.7%	— —	0.6%	10.9%	5.1%

BCB Bancorp Inc

EXECUTIVES

COO and Director; COO and CFO BCB Community Bank, Thomas M. Coughlin, age 56, $128,544 total compensation
Chairman, Mark D. Hogan, age 50
Director; Senior Lending Officer BCB Community Bank, James E. Collins, age 67, $131,222 total compensation
VP Commercial Lending BCB Community Bank, Amer Saleem, age 61, $94,500 total compensation
Independent Vice Chairman of the Board, Joseph Brogan, age 77
Chief Financial Officer of BCB Community Bank and BCB Bancorp, Kenneth Walter
COO and Director; COO and CFO BCB Community Bank, Thomas M. Coughlin, age 56
Director; Senior Lending Officer BCB Community Bank, James E. Collins, age 67
Independent Director, Robert Ballance, age 57
Independent Director, Judith Q. Bielan, age 51
Independent Director, Alexander Pasiechnik, age 54
Independent Director, Joseph Lyga, age 56
Independent Director, Gary Stetz
Independent Director, Robert Hughes
Independent Director, Spencer Robbins
Auditors: Baker Tilly Virchow Krause, LLP

LOCATIONS

HQ: BCB Bancorp Inc
  104-110 Avenue C, Bayonne, NJ 07002
Phone: 201 823-0700
Web: www.bcbcommunitybank.com

COMPETITORS

Bank of America	PNC Financial
City National	Provident Financial
Bancshares	Services
Hudson City Bancorp	Sterling Bank
Meridian Capital Group	Stewardship Financial
New York Community	
Bancorp	

HISTORICAL FINANCIALS

Company Type: Public

Income Statement

FYE: December 31

	ASSETS ($ mil.)	NET INCOME ($ mil.)	INCOME AS % OF ASSETS	EMPLOYEES
12/16	1,708	8	0.5%	353
12/15	1,618	7	0.4%	331
12/14	1,301	7	0.6%	327
12/13	1,207	9	0.8%	249
12/12	1,171	(2)	—	269
Annual Growth	9.9%	—	—	7.0%

2016 Year-End Financials

Debt ratio: 0.24%
Return on equity: 6.03%
Cash ($ mil.): 65
Current ratio: —
Long-term debt ($ mil.): —

No. of shares (mil.): 11
Dividends
  Yield: 0.0%
  Payout: 88.8%
Market value ($ mil.): 146

	STOCK PRICE ($) FY Close	P/E High/Low	PER SHARE ($) Earnings	Dividends	Book Value
12/16	13.00	21 16	0.63	0.56	11.63
12/15	10.40	18 14	0.69	0.56	11.91
12/14	11.73	17 14	0.81	0.54	12.18
12/13	13.45	14 8	1.06	0.48	12.01
12/12	9.45	— —	(0.23)	0.48	10.78
Annual Growth	8.3%	—	—	3.9%	1.9%

Bear State Financial Inc

Bear State Financial (formerly First Federal Bancshares of Arkansas) is the holding company for Bear State Bank and Metropolitan Bank which serve businesses and individuals through a total of 55 branches mostly in Arkansas but also in southeastern Oklahoma and southwestern Missouri. Founded in 1934 the thrift offers standard retail services such as checking and savings accounts money markets and CDs. More than 50% of the bank's loan portfolio is made up of one-to-four-family residential and commercial real estate mortgages while business loans make up another 15%. The bank changed its name in mid-2014 to match its holding company's brand.

Operations
The bank makes more than 80% of its revenue from interest income. About 77% of its total revenue came from loan interest during 2015 while another 5% came from interest on investment securities. The rest of its revenue came from deposit fee income (11%) loan sale gains (4%) earnings on life insurance policies (2%) and other miscellaneous income sources.

Bear State Financial had more than half of its loan portfolio split between one-to-four family residential mortgages and non-farm commercial real estate loans at the end of 2015. The remainder of its portfolio was tied to commercial loans (17% of loan assets) construction and land development mortgages (8%) farmland mortgages (6.5%) multifamily residential mortgages (5%) and consumer loans (3%).

Geographic Reach
The company operates more than 40 Bear State Bank branches across Arkansas and in Southeast Oklahoma; and a dozen Metropolitan National Bank branches in Southwest Missouri.

Sales and Marketing
Loans are originated through a variety of means such as walk-ins from its own banking branches or referrals from realtors and loan officers. Bear State uses radio online and newspaper advertisements to promote its services.

The bank spent $2.52 million on advertising and public relations during 2015 nearly twice as much as the $1.35 million it spent in 2014.

Financial Performance
Bear State Financials' revenues have more than tripled since 2011 as its loan assets have quadrupled to $1.44 billion. The bank's annual profits have soared back from losses in 2011 as it's managed to keep a lid on overhead cost growth.

The bank's revenue jumped 42% to $74.37 million during 2015 mostly thanks to its recent acquisitions of First National Security and Metropolitan Bank which drove higher interest income as its loan assets grew by 38% while boosting noninterest income by 35% on deposit fee and insurance policy growth.

Despite strong revenue growth in 2015 Bear State's net income fell by more than half to $10.57 million mostly on higher salary and compensation costs tied to added personnel from the two new bank acquisitions. The bank's operating cash levels more than doubled to $13.7 million after adjusting its cash for non-cash items related to net proceeds from loan sales.

Strategy
Bear State has been acquiring other banks to expand its branch network into new markets while boosting its loan and deposit business.

Mergers and Acquisitions

In October 2015 the group acquired $442 million-asset Metropolitan National Bank along with its $340 million in loans $375 million in deposits and 12 branches across Southwest Missouri.

In June 2014 Bear State expanded into central and southwest Arkansas and southeast Oklahoma after it acquired Hot Springs-based First National Security Corporation. The deal added 23 new branches (under the First National Bank and Heritage Bank brands) and boosted Bear State's total assets by over 160%.

EXECUTIVES

SEVP CFO and Chief Accounting Officer Bear State Financial Inc. and Bear State Bank, Sherri R. Billings, age 60, $202,975 total compensation
President and CEO Bear State Financial Inc. and CEO Bear State Bank, J. Matthew (Matt) Machen, age 36, $219,615 total compensation
SEVP and COO, R. Thomas (Tom) Fritsche, age 56, $320,097 total compensation
EVP and Chief Marketing Officer, Shelly Loftin, age 35
EVP and Human Resources Director, Donna Merriweather, age 57
EVP and Director Operations, Yurik Paroubek
Vice President loan Servicing Support, Amy Criner
Chairman, Richard N. Massey
Board Member, John P Hammerschmidt
Auditors: BKD, LLP

LOCATIONS

HQ: Bear State Financial Inc
9900 South Shackleford Rd, Suite 401, Little Rock, AR 72211
Phone: 501 975-6033
Web: www.ffbh.com

PRODUCTS/OPERATIONS

2015 sales

	% of total
Interest income	
Loans receivable	77
Investment securities	5
Other	0
Non Interest income	
Net gain on sales and calls of investment securities	0
Deposit fee income	11
Earnings on life insurance policies	2
Gain on sales of loans	4
Other	1
Total	**100**

COMPETITORS

Arvest Bank	IBERIABANK
BOK Financial	Regions Financial
Bank of America	Simmons First
Bank of the Ozarks	U.S. Bancorp
Home BancShares	

HISTORICAL FINANCIALS

Company Type: Public

Income Statement

FYE: December 31

	ASSETS ($ mil.)	NET INCOME ($ mil.)	INCOME AS % OF ASSETS	EMPLOYEES
12/16	2,053	17	0.9%	502
12/15	1,920	10	0.6%	586
12/14	1,514	24	1.6%	423
12/13	548	0	0.1%	190
12/12	530	0	0.1%	192
Annual Growth	**40.3%**	**119.3%**	**—**	**27.2%**

2016 Year-End Financials

Debt ratio: 1.07%
Return on equity: 7.63%
Cash ($ mil.): 78
Current ratio: —
Long-term debt ($ mil.): —
No. of shares (mil.): 37
Dividends
Yield: 0.0%
Payout: 16.3%
Market value ($ mil.): 382

	STOCK PRICE ($) FY Close	P/E High/Low		PER SHARE ($) Earnings	Dividends	Book Value
12/16	10.15	24	17	0.46	0.08	6.21
12/15	10.83	36	26	0.30	0.00	5.87
12/14	10.99	13	8	0.84	0.00	5.11
12/13	8.70	278	211	0.03	0.00	3.20
12/12	9.75	298	119	0.04	0.00	3.25
Annual Growth	**1.0%**	**—**	**—**	**89.1%**	**—**	**17.5%**

Becton, Dickinson & Co

Don't worry you'll only feel a slight prick if Becton Dickinson (BD) is at work. The company's BD Medical segment is one of the top global manufacturers of syringes and other injection and infusion devices. BD Medical also makes IV catheters and syringes pre-fillable drug delivery systems self-injection devices for diabetes patients and related supplies such as anesthesia trays and sharps disposal systems. The BD Life Sciences segment makes products for the safe collection and transportation of diagnostic specimens; it also makes instruments and reagent systems that detect cancers infectious diseases and health care associated infections (HAIs).The company is acquiring its US peer C. R. Bard in a $24 billion deal.

HISTORY

Maxwell Becton and Fairleigh Dickinson established a medical supply firm in New York in 1897. In 1907 the company moved to New Jersey and became one of the first US firms to make hypodermic needles.

During WWI Becton Dickinson (BD) made all-glass syringes and introduced the cotton elastic bandage. After the war its researchers designed an improved stethoscope and created specialized hypodermic needles. The company supplied medical equipment to the armed forces during WWII. Becton and Dickinson helped establish Fairleigh Dickinson Junior College (now Fairleigh Dickinson University) in 1942. The company continued to develop products such as the Vacutainer blood-collection apparatus its first medical laboratory aid.

After the deaths of Dickinson (1948) and Becton (1951) their respective sons Fairleigh Jr. and Henry took over. The company introduced disposable hypodermic syringes in 1961. BD went public in 1963 to raise money for new expansion. In the 1960s the company opened plants in Brazil Canada France and Ireland and climbed aboard the conglomeration bandwagon by diversifying into such businesses as industrial gloves (Edmont 1966) and computer systems (Spear 1968). BD also went on a major acquisition spree in its core fields during the 1960s and 1970s buying more than 25 medical supply testing and lab companies by 1980.

Wesley Howe successor to Fairleigh Dickinson Jr. expanded the company's foreign sales in the 1970s. Howe thwarted a takeover by the diversifying oil giant Sun Company (now Sunoco) in 1978 and began to sell BD's non-medical businesses in 1983 ending with the 1989 sale of Ed-

mont. Acquisitions including Deseret Medical (IV catheters surgical gloves and masks; 1986) sharpened BD's focus on medical and surgical supplies.

In the 1990s BD formed a number of alliances and ventures including a 1991 agreement to make and market Baxter International's InterLink needleless injection system which reduces the risk of accidental needle sticks and a 1993 joint venture with NeXagen (now part of Gilead Sciences) to make and market in vitro diagnostics. As tuberculosis reemerged in the US as a serious health threat the firm improved its TB-detection and drug-resistance test systems which cut testing time from as much as seven weeks to less than two.

In 1996 BD introduced GlucoWatch (a glucose monitoring device developed by Cygnus) and acquired the diagnostic business and brand name of MicroProbe (now Epoch Pharmaceuticals).

Previously known on Wall Street as a homely company that focused on cutting costs BD changed its image with a string of acquisitions beginning in 1997. The firm acquired PharMingen (biomedical research reagents) and Difco Laboratories (microbiology media) which broadened its product lines. BD also collaborated with Nanogen on diagnosis products for infectious disease.

EXECUTIVES

Chairman and CEO, Vincent A. (Vince) Forlenza, age 64, $1,105,000 total compensation
EVP and President Global Health, Gary M. Cohen, age 59, $605,700 total compensation
Sr V Pres Hr, Jerome V Hurwitz
EVP and General Counsel, Jeffrey S. Sherman, age 62, $560,333 total compensation
EVP Integrated Supply Chain Officer, Stephen (Steve) Sichak, age 59
EVP CFO and Chief Administrative Officer, Christopher R. (Chris) Reidy, age 60, $746,568 total compensation
EVP Strategic Planning and Chief Marketing Officer, Nabil Shabshab, age 51
EVP and Chief Human Resource Officer, Linda M. Tharby, age 49
President, Thomas E. Polen, age 44, $651,000 total compensation
EVP; President Greater Asia, James Lim, age 52
EVP; President Europe and the Americas, Alexandre Conroy, age 53, $530,334 total compensation
EVP and Chief Quality Officer, Pierre Boisier
EVP and President Life Sciences Segment, Alberto Mas, age 55
EVP Research and Development and Chief Medical Officer, Ellen R. Strahlman, age 59, $664,427 total compensation
EVP and Chief Regulatory Officer, Richard J. Naples
Vice President US Sales, Bob Ferrigno
Western Regional Vice President, Robert Blake
Vice President, J Natale
Strategic Customer Vice President, Maggie Hanson
Vice President, Daniel Schumann
Vice President of Sales, Laura Caswell
National Accounts Manager, Jane McCormick
Strategic Customer Vice President, Ted Woolschlager
Vice President of WW Marketing, Ajoy Mahtab
Vice President M and A Process, Tom Jaeger
Auditors: Ernst & Young LLP

LOCATIONS

HQ: Becton, Dickinson & Co
1 Becton Drive, Franklin Lakes, NJ 07417-1880
Phone: 201 847-6800
Web: www.bd.com

PRODUCTS/OPERATIONS

2017 Sales by Segment

	$ mil.	% of total
Medical	8,105	67
Life Sciences	3,988	33
Total	**12,093**	**100**

Selected Acquisitions

COMPETITORS

Abbott Labs	Kimberly-Clark Health
Affymetrix	Life Technologies
Agilent Technologies	Corporation
Alere	Meridian Bioscience
B. Braun Melsungen	Novo Nordisk
Bard	Retractable
Baxter International	Technologies
Beckman Coulter	Roche Diagnostics
Bio-Rad Labs	Safety Syringes
Boston Scientific	Sekisui Diagnostics
Dako	Terumo
Fresenius	Thermo Fisher
Gen-Probe	Scientific
Harvard Bioscience	Trinity Biotech
Hologic	Unilife
Hospira	bioM©rieux
Johnson & Johnson	

HISTORICAL FINANCIALS

Company Type: Public

Income Statement

FYE: September 30

	REVENUE ($ mil.)	NET INCOME ($ mil.)	NET PROFIT MARGIN	EMPLOYEES
09/17	12,093	1,100	9.1%	41,933
09/16	12,483	976	7.8%	50,928
09/15	10,282	695	6.8%	49,517
09/14	8,446	1,185	14.0%	30,619
09/13	8,054	1,293	16.1%	29,979
Annual Growth	**10.7%**	**(4.0%)**	**—**	**8.8%**

2017 Year-End Financials

Debt ratio: 50.00%
Return on equity: 10.69%
Cash ($ mil.): 14,179
Current ratio: 5.58
Long-term debt ($ mil.): 18,664

No. of shares (mil.): 227
Dividends
  Yield: 0.0%
  Payout: 63.4%
Market value ($ mil.): 44,665

	STOCK PRICE ($) FY Close	P/E High/Low	PER SHARE ($) Earnings	Dividends	Book Value
09/17	195.95	44 35	4.60	2.92	56.82
09/16	179.73	40 29	4.49	2.64	35.79
09/15	132.66	45 33	3.35	2.40	34.00
09/14	113.81	20 16	5.99	2.18	26.32
09/13	100.02	16 11	6.49	1.98	25.99
Annual Growth	**18.3%**	**— —**	**(8.2%)**	**10.2%**	**21.6%**

Bed, Bath & Beyond, Inc.

Bed Bath & Beyond (BBB) is the nation's #1 superstore domestics retailer with more than 1540 BBB stores throughout the US Puerto Rico and Canada. The stores' floor-to-ceiling shelves stock better-quality (brand-name and private-label) goods in two main categories: domestics (bed linens bathroom and kitchen items) and home furnishings (cookware and cutlery small household appliances picture frames and more). BBB also op- erates more than 275 Cost Plus and World Market stores and three smaller specialty chains: about 80 Christmas Tree Shops; 115 buybuy BABY stores; and more than 50 Harmon discount health and beauty shops.

Operations

Beyond its main BBB-branded chain of more than 1540 stores the retailer operates more than 275 stores under the names World Market Cost Plus World Market and World Market Stores ban- ners. It also operates 115 buybuy BABY shops al- most 80 Christmas Tree Shops and more than 50 stores under the names Harmon and Harmon Face Values. In Mexico BBB also has a joint venture with Mexican retailer Home & More where it cur- rently operates seven stores under the BBB ban- ner.

Sales of home furnishings generate more than 60% of the retailer's total revenue while domestic merchandise makes up almost 40% of total rev- enue each year.

Geographic Reach

Nearly all of the New Jersey-based retailer's more than 1540 stores are in the US though 55 of its stores are located across nine Canadian provinces while three are in Puerto Rico. About 40% of the company's stores are in five US states: California Texas Florida New York and New Jersey.

Sales and Marketing

BBB prefers to locate its stores in strip malls and power strip shopping centers in suburban areas of medium and large-sized cities. It also places its stores near major off-price and conven- tional malls.The chain relies exclusively on circu- lars mailings and word-of-mouth for advertising.

BBB purchases its merchandise from 10800 suppliers with the company's 10 largest suppliers accounting for almost 15% of such purchases. The company purchases substantially all of its mer- chandise in the US.

Financial Performance

BBB's sales have been steadily growing the last few years thanks to a strengthening US economy and increased business from acquisitions. In fiscal 2017 net sales increased by 1% to peak at a record-setting $12.2 billion due to higher sales driven by digital acquisitions and new store sales.

However BBB'snet income has steadily declined the last several years as it uses additional cash to improve its infrastructure and operations. Net in- come fell 9% from $842 million in 2016 to $685 million in 2017 due to additional expenditures for enhancements to its digital channels ongoing in- vestments in its data warehouse and data analytics and expenditures for the continued development and deployment of new systems and equipment in stores.

Strategy

BBB strategy is to expand its market reach ei- ther through strategic acquisitions or organically by adding stores in both new and existing markets. To this end in fiscal 2016 the company opened 29 new stores closed 12 stores and opened a new customer contact center in Layton Utah and a new distribution facility in Las Vegas.

BBB also wants to further enhance its om- nichannel capabilities through such initiatives as adding new functionality to its e-commerce and mobile sites and by opening new distribution cen- ters for both direct to consumer and store fulfill- ment. Additionally it plans to expand specialty de- partments in its stores in areas such as health and beauty care baby specialty food and specialty bev- erage sections.

The retailer's decentralized structure allows store managers to have more control than their peers at other retailers (and the company has less manager turnover). BBB cuts costs by locating its stores in strip shopping centers freestanding build- ings and off-price malls rather than in pricier re- gional malls. To cut costs further its vendors ship merchandise directly to the stores eliminating the expense of a central distribution center and reduc- ing warehousing costs.

Mergers and Acquisitions

BBB has used acquisitions as a means for quickly bolstering its online presence as it faces mounting competition from online retailers like Amazon.

In early 2017 it acquired Decorist an online in- terior design platform that provides personalized home design services. Decorist also offers photo- realistic 3-D renderings of how items will look in their actual homes and offers additional online services.

In 2016 the company acquired online home goods retailer One Kings Lane Inc. in an all-cash deal. The deal the value of which was undisclosed bolstered BBB's furniture and home d ©cor offer- ings in the online space. One Kings offers an ex- tensive collection of designer and vintage furniture rugs kitchenware lighting and other d ©cor for homes.

Also in 2016 the company acquired Personal- izationMall.com a online seller of personalized gifts for $190 in cash.

In 2015 BBB acquired Of a Kind an e-commerce website that features specially commissioned lim- ited edition items from emerging fashion and home designers.

HISTORY

Warren Eisenberg and Leonard Feinstein both employed by a discounter called Arlan's brain- stormed an idea in 1971 for a chain of stores of- fering only home goods. They were betting that customers were in Feinstein's words interested in a "designer approach to linens and housewares." The two men started two small linens stores (about 2000 sq. ft) named bed n bath one in New York and one in New Jersey.

Expansion came at a fairly slow pace as the company moved only into California and Connecti- cut by 1985. By then the time was right for such a specialty retailer: Department stores were cutting back on their houseware lines to focus on the more profitable apparel segment and baby boomers were spending more leisure time at their homes (and more money on spiffing them up). Eisenberg and Feinstein opened a 20000-sq.-ft. superstore in 1985 that offered a full line of home furnishings. The firm changed its name to Bed Bath & Beyond (BBB) two years later in order to reflect its new of- ferings.

With the successful superstore format the com- pany built all new stores in the larger design. BBB grew rapidly; square footage quadrupled between 1992 and 1996. The company went public in 1992. That year it eclipsed the size of its previous stores when it opened a 50000-sq.-ft. store in Man- hattan. (It later enlarged this store to 80000 sq. ft.; the company's stores now average 42000 sq. ft.)

BBB's management has attributed its success in part to the leeway it gives its store managers who monitor inventory and have the freedom to try new products and layouts. One example often cited by the company is the case of a manager who decided to sell glasses by the piece instead of in sets. Sales increased 30% and the whole chain incorporated the practice.

The retailer opened 28 new stores in 1996 33 in 1997 (its first-ever billion-dollar sales year) and 45 in 1998.

In 1999 the company dipped a toe into the wa- ters of e-commerce by agreeing to buy a stake in Internet Gift Registries which operates the Wed- dingNetwork website. The company later began offering online sales and bridal registry services. Keeping up its rapid expansion pace the company opened 70 stores in 1999 85 in 2000 and 95 in 2001.

In 2002 BBB acquired Harmon Stores a health and beauty aid retailer with 29 stores in three states. It acquired Christmas Tree Shops a giftware and household items retailer with 23 stores in six states for $200 million in 2003.

In March 2007 BBB acquired buybuy BABY which operates eight stores on the East Coast for $67 million. The retailer opened its first Canadian location in Ontario north of Toronto in December. In 2008 BBB added three more stores in Canada and its first locations in Mexico via a joint venture there under the Home & More banner.

In June 2012 the company bought Cost Plus which operates nearly 260 stores in 30 states under the World Market Cost Plus World Market and Cost Plus Imports banners for $495 million in cash.

EXECUTIVES

COO, Eugene A. (Gene) Castagna, age 51, $1,928,846 total compensation
Senior Vice President, Ronald Curwin
Vice President, William Plate
Vice President Real Estate, Seth Geldzahler
Vice President Supply Chain Logistics, Jeffrey Macak
President and Chief Merchandising Officer, Arthur (Art) Stark, age 62, $1,849,277 total compensation
VP Stores, Matthew Fiorilli, age 60, $1,730,468 total compensation
CEO, Steven H. (Steve) Temares, age 58, $3,967,500 total compensation
CFO and Treasurer, Susan E. Lattmann, age 49, $1,021,154 total compensation
VP and CIO, Robert Claybrook
Vice President Information Technology Finance, Tim Kirchner
Vice President Controller, Robyn D'Elia
Vice President Divisional Merchandise Manager, Pete Daleiden
Vice President Store Systems, John Mariani
Vice President of Design and Development, Robert Caruso
Vice President General Merchandise Manager, David Eckert
Senior Vice President of Sales, Josh Lighty
Vice President of Human Resources, Concetta Van Dyke
Vice President Sustainability, Kenneth Frankel
Vice President Customer Service And Bridal, Hank Reinhart
Vice President Finance, Jason Quint
Vice President Merchandise Planning and Allocation, Nika Markus
Vice President, Lisa Cavanagh
Vice President Divisional Merchandise Manager, Jack Solomon
Vice President Of Supply Chain, Jeff Macak
Vice President, Bill Plate
Vice President, George Elefther
Vice President, Sal Dimino
Vice President Digital Marketing, Jim Halliday
Vice President Loss Prevention and Safety, Jim OConnor
Department Head, Morgan Biggs
Vice President PMO, Andrea Arrowsmith
Co-Chairman, Leonard (Lenny) Feinstein, age 80
Co-Chairman, Warren Eisenberg, age 86
Auditors: KPMG LLP

LOCATIONS

HQ: Bed, Bath & Beyond, Inc.
650 Liberty Avenue, Union, NJ 07083
Phone: 908 688-0888   **Fax:** 908 810-8813
Web: www.bedbathandbeyond.com

2017 Stores

	No.
California	184
Texas	119
New York	101
Florida	96
New Jersey	91
Illinois	55
Ohio	49
Virginia	46
Massachusetts	44
Michigan	44
Pennsylvania	44
North Carolina	43
Arizona	42
Georgia	39
Washington	37
Colorado	35
Tennessee	29
Connecticut	25
Ontario Canada	25
Alabama	24
South Carolina	24
Indiana	23
Maryland	23
Missouri	23
Louisiana	20
Oregon	17
Utah	16
Wisconsin	16
Minnesota	15
Nevada	15
New Hampshire	14
Kansas	12
Alberta Canada	12
British Columbia Canada	12
Iowa	11
Kentucky	11
Idaho	10
New Mexico	10
Other	90
Total	**1,546**

PRODUCTS/OPERATIONS

2017 Stores

	No.
Bed Bath & Beyond	1,023
Cost Plus World Market	276
BABY Stores	113
Christmas Tree Shops	80
Harmon stores	54
Total	**1,546**

COMPETITORS

Amazon.com	Kmart
Art.com	Macy's
Babies "R" Us	Pier 1 Imports
Burlington Coat Factory	Ross Stores
Children's Place	Sears
Container Store	Sensational Beginnings
Dillard's	TJX Companies
Euromarket Designs	Target Corporation
Garden Ridge	Tuesday Morning Corporation
Gymboree	Wal-Mart
IKEA	Wayfair
J. C. Penney	Williams-Sonoma

HISTORICAL FINANCIALS

Company Type: Public

Income Statement

	REVENUE ($ mil.)	NET INCOME ($ mil.)	NET PROFIT MARGIN	EMPLOYEES
02/17	12,215	685	5.6%	65,000
02/16	12,103	841	7.0%	62,000
02/15*	11,881	957	8.1%	60,000
03/14	11,503	1,022	8.9%	58,000
03/13	10,914	1,037	9.5%	57,000
Annual Growth	**2.9%**	**(9.9%)**	**—**	**3.3%**

FYE: February 25
*Fiscal year change

2017 Year-End Financials

Debt ratio: 21.79%
Return on equity: 26.03%
Cash ($ mil.): 488
Current ratio: 1.87
Long-term debt ($ mil.): 1,491
No. of shares (mil.): 146
Dividends
  Yield: 0.0%
  Payout: 8.1%
Market value ($ mil.): 6,003

	STOCK PRICE ($) FY Close	P/E High/Low		PER SHARE ($) Earnings	Dividends	Book Value
02/17	41.04	11	8	4.58	0.38	18.59
02/16	48.99	15	8	5.10	0.00	16.34
02/15*	74.66	15	11	5.07	0.00	15.75
03/14	67.82	17	12	4.79	0.00	19.19
03/13	56.93	16	12	4.56	0.00	18.42
Annual Growth	**(7.9%)**	**—**	**—**	**0.1%**	**—**	**0.2%**

*Fiscal year change

Beneficial Bancorp Inc

Auditors: KPMG LLP

LOCATIONS

HQ: Beneficial Bancorp Inc
1818 Market Street, Philadelphia, PA 19103
Phone: 215 864-6000
Web: www.thebeneficial.com

HISTORICAL FINANCIALS

Company Type: Public

Income Statement

FYE: December 31

	ASSETS ($ mil.)	NET INCOME ($ mil.)	INCOME AS % OF ASSETS	EMPLOYEES
12/16	5,738	25	0.4%	798
12/15	4,826	22	0.5%	809
12/14	4,751	18	0.4%	830
12/13	4,583	12	0.3%	842
12/12	5,006	14	0.3%	—
Annual Growth	**3.5%**	**15.8%**	**—**	**—**

2016 Year-End Financials

Debt ratio: 8.55%
Return on equity: 2.39%
Cash ($ mil.): 287
Current ratio: —
Long-term debt ($ mil.): —
No. of shares (mil.): 75
Dividends
  Yield: 0.0%
  Payout: 35.2%
Market value ($ mil.): 1,392

	STOCK PRICE ($) FY Close	P/E High/Low		PER SHARE ($) Earnings	Dividends	Book Value
12/16	18.40	56	37	0.34	0.12	13.40
12/15	13.32	49	37	0.29	0.00	13.45
12/14	12.27	56	43	0.24	0.00	8.12
12/13	10.92	66	49	0.17	0.00	7.98
12/12	9.50	56	46	0.18	0.00	7.99
Annual Growth	**18.0%**	**—**	**—**	**17.2%**	**—**	**13.8%**

Berkley (WR) Corp

Holding company W. R. Berkley offers an assortment of niche commercial property/casualty insurance across two segments — Insurance and Reinsurance. The Insurance segment comprising more than 50 operating companies underwrites commercial insurance coverage including excess and surplus lines and admitted lines. It also develops self-insuring programs aimed at employers and employer groups. The Reinsurance segment allows insurance companies to pool their risks in order to reduce their liability. Berkley serves customers in 60 countries in the Americas Europe and the Asia/Pacific region.

Operations

Berkley's Insurance segment accounts for more than 80% of the company's total revenue while the Reinsurance segment accounts for about 10%. (The remainder is brought in by other operations.)

In addition to insurance products Berkley offers a variety of fee-based services such as claims administrative and consulting services.

Geographic Reach

Berkley offers insurance and reinsurance through more than 50 operating units in 60 nations in North America South America Europe Africa and the Asia/Pacific region.

Sales and Marketing

Berkley primarily serves small to midsized business customers. The insurer sells its high-risk coverage products directly and through retail and wholesale agents brokers and managing general agents to a wide variety of clients. The regional products business' offerings are sold through a network of non-exclusive commission-based independent agents.

Financial Performance

Continuing a multi-year trend of steady growth in 2016 Berkley reported a 6% increase in revenue from $7.2 billion to $7.7 billion. That increase was primarily due to higher investment gains and an increase in net premiums written but was partially offset by declines in underwriting income non-insurance income and service fee income.

Net income has fluctuated a bit for the past five years and in 2016 it rose 20% to $603 million. This was largely driven by the higher revenue and foreign currency gains. Cash flow from operations fell 4% to $848.4 million that year as the group established higher loss reserves on its balance sheet.

Strategy

Strategically Berkley's decentralized structure promotes the development of specialized expertise in a range of areas and enables the company to adapt to cyclical market conditions and insulate itself from great risk. While the company has made a handful of acquisitions through the years (for example it bought an aviation systems firm in 2015) it prefers to expand by forming new operating units after identifying needs in specific areas.For example in 2017 Berkley split its Specialty Underwriting Managers unit into two separate firms — Berkley Entertainment & Sports and Berkley Environmental — to better allow the businesses to grow within their respective niches. Other recent additions include firms specializing in cybersecurity and health care.

The company focuses on growing world markets including Scandinavia South America Australia and the Asia/Pacific region. Additionally Berkley exercises insightful discretion in exiting insurance lines as demand diminishes.

EXECUTIVES

EVP Investments, James G. Shiel, age 57, $650,000 total compensation
Senior Vice President Admitted Specialty Lines, Peter Kamford
Vice President Enterprise Development, Joan E Kapfer
Assistant Vice President and Actuarial, Thomas P Boyle
Vice President Internal Audit, Michele Fleckenstein
EVP, C. Fred Madsen

EVP and Secretary, Ira S. Lederman, age 64, $650,000 total compensation
EVP, Eugene G. Ballard, age 64, $650,000 total compensation
President and CEO, W. Robert (Rob) Berkley, age 44, $993,769 total compensation
EVP, Robert C. Hewitt, age 56
EVP, Philip S. Welt, age 58
EVP, Robert D. Stone, age 53
EVP, John K. Goldwater
EVP, William M. Rohde
EVP, Jeffrey M. (Jeff) Hafter
EVP, Lucille T. Sgaglione
SVP CFO and Treasurer, Richard M. Baio, $497,981 total compensation
EVP, Kathleen M. Tierney
VP and Chief Marketing Officer, Jonathan M. Levine
SVP and CIO, Richard M. Lowery
EVP, James P. Bronner
SVP and Chief Project Officer, Mir Mazhar
EVP, Kenneth P. Sroka
Vice President, Steven Samoskevich
Assistant Vice President Corporate Actuary, Laura Stevens
Senior Vice President Actuarial and Operations, James Gilbert
Assistant Vice President And Corporate Actuary, Gene Zhang
Senior Vice President, Julie Halper
Assistant Vice President of Application Development, Jim Leonardis
Assistant Vice President Information Technology, Kanchana Sarathy
Vice President, Marie Gwin
Assistant Vice President Catastrophe Risk Manager, Robert Sabio
Executive Vice President, Steven Walsh
Vice President, Andrea Trimble
Vice President Corporate Actuary, Jessica Somerfeld
Senior Vice President, C Madsen
Vice President External Financial Communications, Karen Horvath
Senior Vice President Underwriting, Joseph Walsh
Vice President, Carol La Punzina
Assistant Vice President and Actuary, Bryan V Spero
Senior Vice President International Operations, Steven W Taylor
Vice President, John Littzi
Assistant Vice President Corporate Actuary, David Atkinson
Assistant Vice President, Tatiana Connolly
Assistant Vice President Information Technology, Mark Gallo
Assistant Vice President Regulatory Compliance Manager, Kathleen Ferreira
Assistant Vice President Finance, Justin Woytowich
VICE PRESIDENT ACTUARY, Dustin J Turner
Chairman, William R. (Bill) Berkley, age 71
Vice Chairman, Javier Esteban
Assistant Treasurer, George Richardson
Auditors: KPMG LLP

LOCATIONS

HQ: Berkley (WR) Corp
475 Steamboat Road, Greenwich, CT 06830
Phone: 203 629-3000
Web: www.wrberkley.com

PRODUCTS/OPERATIONS

2016 Sales

	% of total
Insurance	81
Reinsurance	9
Other	10
Total	**100**

2016 Sales

	% of total
Net premiums earned	82
Net investment income	8
Revenues from non-insurance business	5
Net investment gains	3
Insurance service fees	2
Other income	—
Total	**100**

Selected Property/Casualty Segments

Specialty (includes excess and surplus lines and admitted specialty lines)
Regional (commercial lines property/casualty)
Alternative markets (includes excess workers' compensation monoline workers' compensation accident and health and insurance services)
Reinsurance (facultative or treaty basis; participates in business written through Lloyd's of London)
International business (global underwriting)

COMPETITORS

AIG	Munich Re America
Allied World Assurance	Munich Re Group
American Financial Group	Nationwide
	Ohio Casualty
Arch Capital	Old Republic
Berkshire Hathaway	PartnerRe
CNA Financial	Selective Insurance
Chubb Limited	Swiss Re
Everest Re	Transatlantic
Farmers Group	Reinsurance
General Re	Travelers Companies
HCC Insurance	White Mountains
Liberty Mutual	Insurance Group

HISTORICAL FINANCIALS

Company Type: Public

Income Statement

FYE: December 31

	ASSETS ($ mil.)	NET INCOME ($ mil.)	INCOME AS % OF ASSETS	EMPLOYEES
12/16	23,364	601	2.6%	7,683
12/15	21,730	503	2.3%	7,621
12/14	21,716	648	3.0%	7,521
12/13	20,551	499	2.4%	7,247
12/12	20,155	510	2.5%	7,412
Annual Growth	**3.8%**	**4.2%**	**—**	**0.9%**

2016 Year-End Financials

Debt ratio: 10.65%
Return on equity: 12.44%
Cash ($ mil.): 795
Current ratio: —
Long-term debt ($ mil.): —

No. of shares (mil.): 121
Dividends
  Yield: 0.0%
  Payout: 32.2%
Market value ($ mil.): 8,061

	STOCK PRICE ($) FY Close	P/E High/Low		PER SHARE ($) Earnings	Dividends	Book Value
12/16	66.51	14	10	4.68	1.51	41.65
12/15	54.75	14	12	3.87	0.47	37.31
12/14	51.26	11	7	4.86	1.43	36.21
12/13	43.39	12	10	3.55	0.39	32.79
12/12	37.74	11	9	3.56	1.35	31.66
Annual Growth	**15.2%**	**—**	**—**	**7.1%**	**2.8%**	**7.1%**

Berkshire Hathaway Inc

Berkshire Hathaway is the holding company where Warren Buffett one of the world's richest men makes his money and spreads his risk. The company invests in a variety of industries from insurance and utilities to apparel and food and from building materials and furniture retailers to jewelry shops. Its core insurance subsidiaries include GEICO National Indemnity and reinsurance giant General Re. The company's other large holdings include Marmon Group McLane Company MidAmerican Energy and Shaw Industries. Buffett holds a significant stake in Berkshire Hathaway which owns a majority of more than 50 firms in all and has equity stakes in about a dozen others.

Operations

Berkshire Hathaway operates as a holding company with a highly decentralized structure without integrated business functions (such as sales marketing purchasing legal and human resources). Practicing a minimal day-to-day management leadership style the firm owns a diverse group of companies from a variety of industries with its core subsidiaries being insurance reinsurance freight rail transportation utilities and energy generation companies.

The insurance businesses constitute about three quarters of total revenue and are composed of over a dozen large providers that insure for example automobiles boats commercial buildings businesses workers? compensation and medical practices. Its most recognizable holding is GEICO (auto insurance). Sales and service revenues make up almost 70% of the insurance business revenue while another 20% comes from insurance premiums.

Lesser known to most are the company?s investment in other industries. Berkshire Hathaway's holdings include a railroad transportation company (Burlington Northern Santa Fe) a real estate business (Berkshire Hathaway Property Advisors) a carpet manufacturer (Shaw Industries) a wholesale distributor of consumer goods (McLane) a manufacturer of clay bricks (Acme Brick) a battery company (Duracell) and a specialty chemicals producer (Lubrizol). Berkshire Hathaway provides capital and financial guidance ensures the companies are well managed and then takes a back seat to allow company leadership to run the entities.

More than 15% of Berkshire Hathaway revenue comes from its railroad utilities and energy subsidiaries and about 5% comes from its finance and financial product companies.

Additionally the company invests its treasure trove of excess cash (typically more than $60 billion) in shares of public companies or in commercial debt which it usually holds for a few years. Recent investments were in Wrigley Kraft Heinz Dow and Phillips 66.

Geographic Reach

Omaha Nebraska-headquartered Berkshire Hathaway operates primarily in the US although it does provide insurance (and reinsurance) to clients in the Asia Pacific and Western Europe geographies.

Financial Performance

Buffett's famed investment vehicle enjoyed upward trends in revenue and profit over recent years highlighting the legendary investors' knack for choosing financially successful companies over the long term. It grew revenue from $107 billion in 2008 to more than $223 billion in 2016. Net income expanded almost fivefold from $5 billion in 2008 to almost $25 billion in 2016.

In 2016 Berkshire's revenue climbed 6% to a record-setting $223 billion on increases in insurance and financial product revenue which more than overcame a slip in revenue from its railroad utilities and energy businesses. Its insurance business especially through higher demand for GEICO?s auto policies grew 7% year over year. The firm's Finance and Financial Products business revenue shot up 36% with higher home sales volumes and a significant jump in the segment?s investment gains.

Net income was flat in 2016 versus the prior year. A jump in insurance losses & adjustments coupled with higher costs for sales and services ate into the higher revenue leaving the firm with a still highly profitable $24 billion.

Cash on hand at the end of 2016 was $28 billion a decrease of $39 billion from 2015. While operating activities provided $32 billion and financing activities offered an additional $13 billion of cash investing activities (primarily the purchase of US Treasury Bills) used more than $84 billion.

Strategy

Berkshire Hathaway seeks out large companies with consistent earnings easy-to-understand business models and like-minded leadership. Most acquisitions are made with cash and most firms retain their management after the transaction. Buffett and longtime business partner Charlie Munger attempt to run Berkshire like a small business albeit on a much larger scale. It operates as a collection of individual enterprises; Buffett and Munger largely keep their hands off portfolio companies' day-to-day operations but allocate capital and control risk.

In a letter to shareholders Buffett once declared "Our elephant gun has been reloaded and my trigger finger is itchy." Hunting big game (i.e. acquiring big companies) has become somewhat of a necessity for Berkshire Hathaway to continue its growth trajectory but the company benefits from not being married to any industry as it seeks out its quarry. Following its ?big game? investment strategy Berkshire entered new markets with the 2017 purchase of 38% of Pilot Flying J truck stop company and the $32 billion 2016 acquisition of aerospace components giant Precision Castparts. It plans to purchase a further 41% of Pilot Flying J in 2023 as part of a long-term move to acquire majority ownership. Berkshire?s holds non-majority investment stakes in Apple ($19 billion) Bank of America ($16 billion) and many other household name companies.

Company Background

Chairman and CEO Warren Buffett along with associates slowly accumulated a majority of shares in the Berkshire Hathaway textile company in the early 1960s. To stabilize revenues and reduce financial risks Buffett diversified the company with a purchase of Indemnity and National Fire & Marine Insurance Company in 1967. Thus began the long prosperous road towards profitability and dozens of acquisitions. Buffett still owns about 20% of Berkshire Hathaway's shares.

HISTORY

Warren Buffett bought his first stock — three shares of Cities Service — at age 11. In the 1950s he studied at Columbia University under famed investor Benjamin Graham. Graham's axioms: Use quantitative analysis to discover companies whose intrinsic worth exceeds their stock prices; popularity is irrelevant; the market will vindicate the patient investor.

In 1956 Buffett then 25 founded Buffett Partnership. Its $105000 in initial assets multiplied as the company bought Berkshire Hathaway (textiles 1965) and National Indemnity (insurance 1967). When Buffett nixed the partnership in 1969 because he believed stocks were overvalued value per share had risen 30-fold.

In late 2012 the firm also acquired Omaha-based online party supplier Oriental Trading Company.

Berkshire Hathaway's $28-billion purchase of ketchup giant H.J. Heinz in 2013 is also a textbook example of the firm's investment strategy as the firm and its investment partner Brazil's 3G Capital took the ketchup maker private to speed its transformation into a global food business.

EXECUTIVES

Chairman BNSF Railway., Matthew K. (Matt) Rose, age 58
SVP and CFO, Marc D. Hamburg, age 67, $1,550,000 total compensation
Chairman and CEO, Warren E. Buffett, age 87, $100,000 total compensation
Head of Reinsurance, Ajit Jain, age 65
Head of Berkshire Hathaway Energy, Greg Abel
Vice President Human Resources and Administration, Jennifer Johnson
Vice Chairman, Charles T. (Charlie) Munger, age 93
Treasurer and Controller, Janet Saar
Auditors: Deloitte & Touche LLP

LOCATIONS

HQ: Berkshire Hathaway Inc
   3555 Farnam Street, Omaha, NE 68131
Phone: 402 346-1400
Web: www.berkshirehathaway.com

PRODUCTS/OPERATIONS

2016 sales

	% of total
Insurance and Other	
Sales and service revenues	53
Insurance premiums earned	21
Investment gains	2
Interest dividend and other investment income	2
Railroad Utilities and Energy	17
Finance and Financial Products	
Sales and service revenues	3
Investment gains	1
Interest dividend and other investment income	1
Derivative gains	0
Total	**100**

Subsidiaries and Selected Holdings

Acme Brick Company (bricks)
Applied Underwriters (workers' compensation)
Ben Bridge Jeweler (jewelry retailer)
Benjamin Moore (architectural and industrial paint)
Berkshire Hathaway Automotive
Berkshire Hathaway Energy Company
Berkshire Hathaway GUARD Insurance Companies
Berkshire Hathaway Homestate Companies
Berkshire Hathaway Life Insurance Company of Nebraska
BH Media Group (digital marketing publishing)
Boat U.S. (insurance)
Borsheim Jewelry Company (jewelry retailer)
Brooks (shoes)
The Buffalo News (newspaper)
Burlington Northern Santa Fe (railroad)
Business Wire Inc. (news service)
Central States Indemnity Co. of Omaha (credit and disability insurance)
Clayton Homes (manufactured housing and financing)
CORT Business Services Corp. (provider of rental furniture accessories and related services)
CTB International (manufacturer of equipment and systems for poultry hog and egg production)
The Fechheimer Brothers (uniforms and accessories)
FlightSafety International (high technology training to operators of aircraft and ships)
Forest River (recreational vehicles)
Fruit of the Loom (apparel)
Garan Inc. (apparel)
GEICO (property/casualty insurance)
General Re Corporation (property/casualty reinsurance)
H.H. Brown Shoe Company
Helzberg's Diamond Shops (jewelry retailer)
HomeServices of America (real estate services)
International Dairy Queen Inc. (licensing and servicing Dairy Queen Stores)
Johns Manville (building and equipment insulation)
Jordan's Furniture (retailing home furnishings)
Justin Brands (western footwear and apparel)
Kraft Heinz
Larson-Juhl
LiquidPower Speciality Products
Lubrizol (specialty chemicals)
Marmon Holdings (manufacturing and service)

McLane Company (wholesale distribution of groceries and non-food items)

MedPro Group (Med Pro; professional liability insurer)

MidAmerican Energy Holdings Company
HomeServices of America Inc. (residential real estate brokerage)
Kern River Gas Transmission Company
Northern Electric
Northern Natural Gas
Pacific Power
Rocky Mountain Power
Yorkshire Electricity

MiTek (building components)

National Indemnity Company (specialty insurance)

Nebraska Furniture Mart (retailing home furnishings)

NetJets Inc. (fractional ownership programs for general aviation aircraft)

Oriental Trading Company (party supplies)

Pampered Chef Ltd. (kitchenware and housewares)

Precision Castparts Corp (aerospace parts manufacturer)

Precision Steel Warehouse (steel service center)

R.C. Willey Home Furnishings (home furnishings retailer)

Richline Group (jewelry manufacturer)

Scott Fetzer Company (manufacture and distribution of diversified products)

See's Candies (boxed chocolates and other confectionery products)

Shaw Industries (carpets and rugs)

Star Furniture Co. (home furnishings retailer)

TTI Inc. (electronics distribution)

United States Liability Insurance Group

XTRA Corporation (transportation equipment)

COMPETITORS

AEA Investors	Lincoln Financial
Allstate	Group
Apollo Global	Progressive
Management	Corporation
Bain Capital	State Farm
BlackRock	TPG
Blackstone Group	The Carlyle Group
CNA Financial	The Hartford
KKR	

HISTORICAL FINANCIALS

Company Type: Public

Income Statement

FYE: December 31

	ASSETS ($ mil.)	NET INCOME ($ mil.)	INCOME AS % OF ASSETS	EMPLOYEES
12/16	620,854	24,074	3.9%	367,700
12/15	552,257	24,083	4.4%	331,000
12/14	526,186	19,872	3.8%	316,000
12/13	484,931	19,476	4.0%	32,000
12/12	427,452	14,824	3.5%	288,500
Annual Growth	9.8%	12.9%	—	6.3%

2016 Year-End Financials

Debt ratio: 16.37%
Return on equity: 8.92%
Cash ($ mil.): 86,370
Current ratio: —
Long-term debt ($ mil.): —

No. of shares (mil.): 1
Dividends
Yield: —
Payout: —
Market value ($ mil.): 401,413

	STOCK PRICE ($) FY Close	P/E High/Low		PER SHARE ($) Earnings	Dividends	Book Value
12/16	244,121	17	13	14,645	0.00	172,108
12/15	197,800.00	15	13	14,656.00	0.00	155,501
12/14	226,000.00	19	14	12,092.00	0.00	146,185
12/13	177,900.00	15	11	11,850.00	0.00	134,973
12/12	134,060.00	15	13	8,977.00	0.00	114,213
Annual Growth	16.2%	—	—	13.0%	—	10.8%

Berkshire Hills Bancorp Inc

Berkshire Hills Bancorp is the holding company for Berkshire Bank which serves individuals and small businesses through some 90 branches in Massachusetts New York Connecticut and Vermont. Established in 1846 the bank provides standard deposit products such as savings checking and money market accounts CDs and IRAs in addition to credit cards investments private banking wealth management and lending services. Real estate mortgages make up nearly three-quarters of Berkshire Hills Bancorp's loan portfolio which also includes business and consumer loans. In addition to its banking activities the company also owns insurance agency Berkshire Insurance Group.

Geographic Reach

Berkshire Hills Bancorp also is eyeing further expansion into Connecticut and other parts of New England and New York by opening new branches and through acquisitions.

Financial Performance

Berkshire Hills Bancorp's revenue increased in fiscal 2013 compared to the prior year. It reported $262 million in revenue for fiscal 2013 up from $230 million in fiscal 2012. Net income also went up to $58 million in fiscal 2013 compared to the $47 million Berkshire Hills Bancorp reported for net income in fiscal 2012.

The company's cash on hand increased by more than $100 million in fiscal 2013 compared to fiscal 2012 levels.

Strategy

Berkshire Hills Bancorp which was established in 1846 believes one of its competitive advantages is the regional niche it serves which has been relatively unscathed by the recession compared to other parts of the country.

The bank's performance has been boosted by an increase in business development in the company's market area in addition to growth in its asset-based lending and private banking businesses. The bank also has grown its loans and deposits and has plans to grow its insurance and wealth management operations as well.

In 2016 the company completed the $150 million acquisition of New Jersey-based First Choice Bank. That deal which add eight bank branches and introduce Berkshire Hills to the greater Philadelphia area will bring the bank's network to more than 100 branches.

EXECUTIVES

President and CEO, Michael P. Daly, age 55, $575,000 total compensation

EVP Human Resources, Linda A. Johnston

COO Berkshire Bank, Sean A. Gray, $350,000 total compensation

EVP Commercial Banking, George F. Bacigalupo, $229,554 total compensation

President Berkshire Bank, Richard M. Marotta, $350,000 total compensation

EVP, Glenn S. Welch, age 55

SEVP and CFO Berkshire Hills Bancorp Inc. and Berkshire Bank, James M. (Jamie) Moses

Vice President, Nancy Wurth

Senior Vice President, Mark Foster

Vice President Information Technology Infrastructure, John O White

Vice President, Theresa Wituszynski

Vice President Od, Lauren Harvey

Vice President Risk Credit Administration and Policy, Patricia Nebosky

Senior Vice President Business Banking Government Lending, Peter Rice

Vice President Regional Credit Officer and Underwriting Manager, Bruce Nichols

Vice President Commercial Workout, Steve Dunham

Vice President Relationship Manager, Justin Priddle

Senior Vice President and Treasurer, Richard Thevenet

Vice President Commercial Lending, Michael Grandfield

Assistant Vice President Relationship Manager, Levante Gregg

Vice President, John Mcnana

VICE PRESIDENT, Kevin Petzold

FIRST VICE PRESIDENT, Philip Martin

ASSISTANT VICE PRESIDENT, Gregory S Kay

Chairman, William J. (Bill) Ryan, age 74

Treasurer, Mike Macy

Auditors: Crowe Horwath LLP

LOCATIONS

HQ: Berkshire Hills Bancorp Inc
24 North Street, Pittsfield, MA 01201
Phone: 413 236-3149
Web: www.berkshirebank.com

PRODUCTS/OPERATIONS

2015 Sales

	% of total
Interest and dividend income	
Loans	70
Securities and other	12
Non-interest income	
Loan related income	3
Mortgage banking income	1
Deposit related fees	8
Insurance commissions and fees	3
Wealth management fees	3
Other	-
Gain on securities net	-
Total	**100**

COMPETITORS

Bank of America	KeyCorp
Citizens Financial	Pathfinder Bancorp
Group	Sovereign Bank
Hudson City Bancorp	TD Bank USA

HISTORICAL FINANCIALS

Company Type: Public

Income Statement

FYE: December 31

	ASSETS ($ mil.)	NET INCOME ($ mil.)	INCOME AS % OF ASSETS	EMPLOYEES
12/16	9,162	58	0.6%	1,731
12/15	7,831	49	0.6%	1,221
12/14	6,502	33	0.5%	1,091
12/13	5,672	41	0.7%	939
12/12	5,296	33	0.6%	1,012
Annual Growth	14.7%	15.3%	—	14.4%

2016 Year-End Financials

Debt ratio: 1.10%
Return on equity: 5.91%
Cash ($ mil.): 113
Current ratio: —
Long-term debt ($ mil.): —

No. of shares (mil.): 35
Dividends
Yield: 0.0%
Payout: 42.5%
Market value ($ mil.): 1,315

STOCK PRICE ($) FY Close	P/E High/Low	PER SHARE ($) Earnings	Dividends	Book Value
12/16	36.85	20 13	1.88	0.80	30.65
12/15	29.11	17 14	1.73	0.76	28.64
12/14	26.66	20 16	1.36	0.72	28.17
12/13	27.27	18 14	1.65	0.72	27.08
12/12	23.86	16 14	1.49	0.69	26.53
Annual Growth	11.5%	— —	6.0%	3.8%	3.7%

Berry Global Group Inc

With a portfolio that includes tapes tubes and trash bags Berry Global is a top maker of plastic products and engineered materials for customers across a broad range of industries. Among its 40-plus customizable products are shrink wrap and other packaging films cloth and foil tapes plastic cups and lids components for diapers and other personal care items and prescription bottles. Key markets include the healthcare personal care and food and beverage industries. Berry Global operates worldwide but North America is by far its largest market.

Operations

Berry Global reports three operating segments: Engineered Materials; Health Hygiene and Specialties; and Consumer Packaging each contributing roughly a third of total revenue.

Engineered Materials manufactures tapes and adhesives polyethylene-based film products can liners printed films and laminated products.

The Health Hygiene and Specialties segment primarily consists of nonwoven specialty materials and films used in hygiene infection prevention personal care industrial construction and filtration applications.

The Consumer Packaging segment primarily consists of containers foodservice items closures overcaps bottles prescription containers and tubes.

Geographic Reach

Berry Global has some 130 manufacturing facilities primarily in North America but also in Europe the Middle East Asia Australia and South America.

North America represents 95% of the company's sales.

Sales and Marketing

Berry Global sells its products to a very diverse customer base through a direct sales force and strategic distributors. Since many products are customized the sales team creates partnership with customers. The company?s top ten customers account for some 15% of total revenue.

Health and hygiene related products represent more than 40% of sales.

Financial Performance

Berry Global?s revenue has seen upward mobility increasing more than $2 billion in the last five years thanks to a string of acquisitions. In fiscal 2017 (ended September) the company reported net sales of $7.1 billion up 9% from the previous year primarily due to higher sales from its recent acquisition. All the growth came from its Engineered Materials segment while sales in both the Heath and Consumer Packaging segments declined slightly.

Berry has been profitable for five years straight but has enjoyed a sharp spike in the last couple of years. It posted $340 million in fiscal 2017 increasing some 45% from the year prior primarily due to higher revenue and tight control over its expenses. The company has increased profits by more than $280 million since 2013.

Cash from operations has also increased steadily for Berry Global rising by some 10% to $975 million in 2017.

Strategy

Enjoying half a decade of growing revenue and profits Berry Global is looking to turn competition up a notch. To that end the company is focusing on continuing strategic acquisitions on one hand and company restructuring to save money on the other.

In 2017 Berry acquired three companies — Clopay AEP Industries and Adchem?s tapes business — with an eye on market expansion for its complementary product lines especially in the technical film production sector. The company expects to save more than $50 million every year due to successful integrations of acquired companies.

In October 2016 the company also realigned the international operations of retail and industrial product lines to better leverage geographic management and cut administrative costs.

Mergers and Acquisitions

Berry announced plans to acquire Clopay for $475 million in November 2017. The acquisition is expected to bring $20 million in cost synergies while expanding Berry?s reach in the elastic films and laminates business.

Earlier that year Berry acquired Adchem Corp?s tapes business for $49 million. This gives the company access to high performance adhesive tape business used in the automotive construction electronics or even medical markets.

In January of the same year the Company completed the acquisition of AEP Industries for $791 million. AEP manufactures and markets flexible plastic packaging products with consumer industrial and agricultural applications.

EXECUTIVES

VP Global Purchasing, Scott Farmer
EVP Strategic Corporate Development, Brett C. Bauer
EVP Operations, Rodgers K. Greenwalt
CFO, Mark W. Miles, age 45, $453,380 total compensation
Chairman and CEO, Thomas E. (Tom) Salmon, age 54, $499,617 total compensation
EVP Supply Chain, Terri Pitcher
EVP Human Resources, Ed Stratton
EVP General Counsel and Secretary, Jason K. Greene, age 46
President Engineered Materials, Curt L. Begle, age 41, $420,288 total compensation
President Flexible Packaging, Lawrence A. (Larry) Goldstein, age 54
EVP International, Jeffrey D. (Jeff) Thompson, age 45
CIO, Mark Freeman
President Health Hygiene and Specialties, Scott Tracey, age 49
President Consumer Packaging, Jean-Marc Galvez
Auditors: Ernst & Young LLP

LOCATIONS

HQ: Berry Global Group Inc
101 Oakley Street, Evansville, IN 47710
Phone: 812 424-2904
Web: www.berryplastics.com

2017 Sales

	$ mil.	% of total
North America	5,850	82
Europe	646	9
South America	333	5
Asia	266	4
Total	**7,095**	**100**

PRODUCTS/OPERATIONS

Selected Brands
Versalite
Color Scents
Ruffies
Polyken
Nashua
Reemay
Stopaq
Qubic

2017 Sales

	$ mil.	% of total
Consumer Packaging	2,351	33
Health Hygiene & Specialties	2,369	33
Engineered Materials	2,375	34
Total	**7,095**	**100**

Selected Products
Rigid Plastics
  Bottles
  Containers
  Closures
  Foodservice items
  Housewares
  Overcaps
  Prescription vials
  Tubes
Engineered Materials
  Can liners
  Corrosion protection
  Polyethylene-based film products
  Specialty tapes and adhesives
Flexible packaging
  Custom films
  Flexible packaging products
  Printed bags
  Pouches

Selected Services
Berry Design Center
Creative services
Decorating services
Global services
Technical services

COMPETITORS

3M	Printpack
Amcor	Reynolds Food
AptarGroup	Packaging
Bemis	Sealed Air Corp.
Berlin Packaging	Shurtape Technologies
Dart Container	Sigma Plastics
Intertape Polymer	Silgan Plastics
Letica	Tredegar

HISTORICAL FINANCIALS

Company Type: Public

Income Statement

FYE: September 30

	REVENUE ($ mil.)	NET INCOME ($ mil.)	NET PROFIT MARGIN	EMPLOYEES
09/17*	7,095	340	4.8%	23,000
10/16	6,489	236	3.6%	21,000
09/15	4,881	86	1.8%	16,000
09/14	4,958	62	1.3%	16,000
09/13	4,647	57	1.2%	15,000
Annual Growth	**11.2%**	**56.3%**		**11.3%**

*Fiscal year change

2017 Year-End Financials

Debt ratio: 66.55%	No. of shares (mil.): 130
Return on equity: 55.44%	Dividends
Cash ($ mil.): 306	Yield: —
Current ratio: 1.77	Payout: —
Long-term debt ($ mil.): 5,608	Market value ($ mil.): 7,415

Best Buy Inc

Best Buy is one of the largest consumer electronics outlets in the US and beyond. The multinational retailer sells both products and services through roughly 1700 retail mobile stand-alone and smaller express stores under the Best Buy Best Buy Express Best Buy Mobile Five Star Future Shop Geek Squad Magnolia Audio Video and Pacific Kitchen and Home Sales banners. Its stores sell a variety of electronic gadgets and wearables tablets movies music computers mobile phones and appliances. On the services side it offers installation and maintenance technical support and subscriptions for mobile phone and Internet services.

HISTORY

Tired of working for a father who ignored his ideas on how to improve the business (electronics distribution) Dick Schulze quit. In 1966 with a partner he founded Sound of Music a Minnesota home/car stereo store. Schulze bought out his partner in 1971 and began to expand the chain. While chairing a school board Schulze saw declining enrollment and realized his target customer group 15- to 18-year-old males was shrinking. In the early 1980s he broadened his product line and targeted older more affluent customers by offering appliances and VCRs.

After a 1981 tornado destroyed his best store (but not its inventory) Schulze spent his entire marketing budget to advertise a huge parking-lot sale. The successful sale taught him the benefits of strong advertising and wide selection combined with low prices. In 1983 Schulze changed the company's name to Best Buy and began to open larger superstores. The firm went public two years later.

Buoyed by the format change and the fast-rising popularity of the VCR Best Buy grew rapidly. Between 1984 and 1987 it expanded from eight stores to 24 and sales jumped from $29 million to $240 million. In 1988 another 16 stores opened and sales jumped by 84%. But Best Buy began to butt heads with many expanding consumer electronics retailers and profits took a beating.

To set Best Buy apart from its competitors in 1989 Schulze introduced the Concept II warehouse-like store format. Thinking that customers could buy products without much help Schulze cut payroll by taking sales staff off commission and reducing the number of employees per store by about a third. The concept proved to be such a hit in the company's home territory Minneapolis/St. Paul that it drove major competitor Highland Appliance to bankruptcy. Customers were happy but many of Best Buy's suppliers believing sales help was needed to sell products pulled their products from Best Buy stores. The losses didn't seem to hurt Best Buy; it took on

Sears and Montgomery Ward in the Chicago market in 1989 and continued expanding.

In 1994 the company debuted Concept III an even larger store format. Best Buy opened 47 new stores in 1995 but found itself swimming in debt. Earnings plummeted in fiscal 1997 partly due to a huge PC inventory made obsolete by Intel's newer product. Best Buy started selling CDs on its website in 1997. That year it realized it had overextended itself with its expansion super-sized stores and financing promotions. Best Buy underwent a speedy massive makeover by scaling back expansion and doing away with its policy of "no money down no monthly payments no interest" (and next-to-no profits).

In 1999 Best Buy began to enter new markets (including New England) and introduced its Concept IV stores which highlighted digital products and featured stations for computer software and DVD demonstrations. Also in 1999 Best Buy formed a separate subsidiary for its online operations (BestBuy.com Inc.) and invested $10 million in consumer electronics information website etown.com (etown.com closed down in February 2001).

In 2000 Best Buy agreed to pay $88 million for Seattle-based Magnolia Hi-Fi a privately held chain of 13 high-end audio and video stores. In early 2001 Best Buy bought The Musicland Group (at the time operator of more than 1300 Sam Goody Suncoast On Cue and Media Play music stores) for about $425 million. The company began its international expansion in November 2002 with its $377 million acquisition of Future Shop Canada's leading consumer electronics retailer. Over the next year Best Buy opened eight of its own Best Buy stores in Ontario Canada.

In June 2002 Schulze turned over his responsibilities as CEO to vice chairman Brad Anderson; Schulze remained as chairman of the board. Best Buy acquired Geek Squad a computer support provider for $3 million the same year.

Best Buy shut down more than 100 Musicland stores (90 Sam Goody music stores and 20 Suncoast video stores) and laid off about 700 employees in January 2003; in June it sold the entire Musicland subsidiary (then about 1100 stores) to an affiliate of investment firm Sun Capital Partners. Three years later Best Buy purchased Pacific Sales Kitchen and Bath Centers which sells appliances and offers assistance on residential remodeling for $410 million.

Philip Schoonover a top executive in charge of customer segments defected to rival Circuit City in 2004. The company also dismissed Ernst & Young as its independent auditor after a former board member disclosed personal business dealings with the firm.

In 2006 the chain acquired home appliance and remodeling retailer Pacific Sales Kitchen and Bath Centers for about $410 million.

To facilitate its expansion in China Best Buy purchased a 75% stake in Jiangsu Five Star Appliance Co. in May 2006 and later opened the first Best Buy store in China in Shanghai.

To enhance its technology product offering for small businesses Best Buy in fiscal 2008 acquired Seattle-based Speakeasy a provider of broadband voice data and IT services. The deal valued at some $97 million made Speakeasy a wholly owned subsidiary that operates through the Best Buy for Business unit. Speakeasy CEO Bruce Chatterley as well as his management team was retained to run the Speakeasy operation once the deal closed. In a bid to add digital music downloads to its playlist Best Buy acquired a majority stake in Napster for about $127 million. The retailer's 2008 purchase of the music-swapping service included Napster's approximately 700000 digital entertainment subscribers.

In June 2008 Best Buy acquired a 50% stake in Carphone Warehouse's European and US retail interests for about $2.2 billion. In late October the company acquired digital music pioneer Napster for about $127 million via a tender offer for the firm's shares.

In early 2009 the retailer acquired the 25% of China's Jiangsu Five Star Appliance that it didn't already own. It also entered the Mexican market with its first store there.

CEO Brad Anderson retired in mid-2009 and COO and longtime employee Brian Dunn took over as CEO. Dunn's stint as chief executive lasted about three years. The 28-year company veteran stepped down in April 2012 handing his CEO title in the interim to board director Mike Mikan. In September 2012 the company named turnaround expert and Frenchman Hubert Joly to the position of CEO. Previously Joly served as head of T.G.I. Friday's and Radisson parent Carlson.

EXECUTIVES

Chairman and CEO, Hubert Joly, age 58, $1,175,000 total compensation
VP and General Manager Digital Imaging, R. Michael (Mike) Mohan, age 49, $833,654 total compensation
SEVP and President Multichannel Retail, Shari L. Ballard, age 50, $800,000 total compensation
President and COO Best Buy Canada, Ron Wilson
EVP General Counsel and Secretary, Keith J. Nelsen, age 53, $650,000 total compensation
President Services, Trish Walker, age 50
CFO, Corie S. Barry, age 42, $713,462 total compensation
Auditors: Deloitte & Touche LLP

LOCATIONS

HQ: Best Buy Inc
7601 Penn Avenue South, Richfield, MN 55423
Phone: 612 291-1000
Web: www.bestbuy.com

2017 Sales

	$ mil.	% of total
Domestic	36,248	92
International	3,155	8
Total	**39,403**	**100**

PRODUCTS/OPERATIONS

2017 US Stores by Brand

	No.
Best Buy	
US Best Buy	1,050
Mobile Stand-Alone Stores	367
Pacific Sales	29
Magnolia Audio Video	2
Total	**1,448**

2017 International Stores by Brand

	No.
Canada	
Future Shop	133
Best Buy	71
Best Buy Mobile	56
Mexico	
Best Buy	18
Express	5
Total	**283**

2017 Sales by Domestic Category

	% of total
Products	
Consumer Electronics	34
Computing and Mobile Phones	45
Entertainment	7
Appliances	9
Services	5
Other	
Total	**100**

2017 Sales by International Category

	% of total
Products	
Computing & mobile phones	48
Consumer electronics	31
Entertainment	7
Appliance	6
Services	7
Other	1
Total	**100**

Selected Brands

Domestic
Best Buy
Best Buy Mobile
Geek Squad
Magnolia Audio Video
Pacific Sales

International
Canada
  Best Buy
  Best Buy Mobile
  Cell Shop
  Connect Pro
  Future Shop
  Geek Squad
China
  Five Star
Europe
  The Carphone Warehouse
  The Phone House
  Geek Squad
Mexico
  Best Buy
  Geek Squad

Selected Products

Consumer Electronics
Audio
Car stereos
Home theater audio systems
MP3 players
Satellite radio systems
Video
Digital cameras and camcorders
DVD players
Televisions

Computing and mobile phones
Computers
Networking equipment
Office furniture
Printers
Scanners
Telephones

Entertainment
CDs
Computer software
DVDs
Subscription plans
Video game hardware and software

Appliances
Dishwashers
Microwave ovens
Refrigerators
Stoves and ranges
Vacuum cleaners
Washers and dryers

COMPETITORS

ARTISTdirect	METRO AG
Amazon.com	MSN
Apple Inc.	MediaNet Digital
Audible Inc.	Myspace
Barnes & Noble	Office Depot
Brilliant Digital	OfficeMax
Entertainment	RadioShack
Brookstone	RealNetworks
Buy.com	Sears Holdings
Buzz Media	Sony Music
Conn's	Staples
Costco Wholesale	Systemax
Dell	Target Corporation
Fry's Electronics	Trans World
Gateway Inc.	Entertainment
HMV Retail	Virgin Group
Hastings Entertainment	Wal-Mart
Home Depot	Yahoo!
Lowe's	eMusic.com

HISTORICAL FINANCIALS

Company Type: Public

Income Statement

FYE: January 28

	REVENUE ($ mil.)	NET INCOME ($ mil.)	NET PROFIT MARGIN	EMPLOYEES
01/17	39,403	1,228	3.1%	125,000
01/16	39,528	897	2.3%	125,000
01/15*	40,339	1,233	3.1%	125,000
02/14	42,410	532	1.3%	140,000
02/13	45,085	(441)	—	165,000
Annual Growth	**(3.3%)**	**—**		**(6.7%)**

*Fiscal year change

2017 Year-End Financials

Debt ratio: 9.85%
Return on equity: 27.10%
Cash ($ mil.): 2,240
Current ratio: 1.48
Long-term debt ($ mil.): 1,321

No. of shares (mil.): 311
Dividends
Yield: 0.0%
Payout: 41.2%
Market value ($ mil.): 13,524

	STOCK PRICE ($) FY Close	P/E High/Low		PER SHARE ($) Earnings	Dividends	Book Value
01/17	43.47	13	7	3.81	1.57	15.14
01/16	27.93	16	10	2.56	1.43	13.52
01/15*	35.20	11	6	3.49	0.72	14.21
02/14	23.54	28	10	1.53	0.68	11.50
02/13	16.11	—	—	(1.30)	0.66	9.05
Annual Growth	**28.2%**	—	—	**—**	**24.2%**	**13.7%**

*Fiscal year change

Big Lots, Inc.

Big Lots is North America's #1 broadline closeout retailer with more than 1400 Big Lots stores in 47 US states. It sells a variety of brand-name products including food and other consumables furniture housewares seasonal items and toys that have been overproduced returned discontinued or result from liquidations typically at 20%-40% below discounters' prices. Its wholesale division sells its discounted merchandise to a variety of retailers manufacturers distributors and other wholesalers.Big Lots' largest markets are California Texas Florida and Ohio.

Geographic Reach

The company's largest markets are California Texas Florida and Ohio home to about a third of its stores and representing 35% of fiscal 2017 (January year end) sales.

Big Lots boasts five regional distribution centers one each in Alabama California Oklahoma Ohio and Pennsylvania to receive process and distribute the majority of its merchandise to its retail locations across the US. (The retailer acquires a quarter of its merchandise from overseas vendors including about 20% from vendors in China.)

Sales and Marketing

Traditionally using television campaigns as its chief marketing channel Big Lots has shifted its marketing efforts to focus on capturing its customers' daily attention on mobile devices and digital media. It has significantly increased its presence in social and digital media outlets conducting entire campaigns on Facebook Instagram Pinterest Twitter and YouTube to drive increased brand awareness with its core customers and attract new potential customers.

In conjunction with those channels Big Lots still uses printed ad circulars in-store signage and television advertising to promote its brand and advertise special discounts in its stores.

Financial Performance

Big Lot's revenues have remained flat the last three fiscal years hovering around the $5.2 billion mark from 2015 to 2017.

The company experienced increases from several of its product categories in 2017 including Furniture (5%) Soft Home (5%) and Seasonal (2%). Furniture in 2017 experienced additional sales from its mattress case goods and upholstery departments which were positively impacted by an expansion of allocated square footage in approximately half of its stores. The other categories experienced improved product assortment and a favorable weather pattern that fueled strength in its lawn and garden and summer departments.

This growth in 2017 was offset by decreased sales from Hard Home (8%); Electronics Toys and Accessories (7%); Food (2%); and Consumables (1%). Hard Home sales were down due to an intentionally narrowed assortment mix and Electronics experienced a reduction in product offerings as Big Lots evaluated its portfolio within this category.

However Big Lots net income climbed 7% from $143 million in 2016 to $153 million in 2017 partially due to additional gains made from diesel fuel hedging contracts.

Strategy

The company's current strategic plan includes significantly ramping up its online retailing capabilities by improving its e-commerce platform which it launched in the spring of 2016. As the integrated e-commerce platform initially offered a narrowed grouping of its in-store offerings Big Lots is working to expand and refine its online options as it learns more about its customers' online shopping habits. It plans for its 2017 e-commerce platform to begin offering expanded fabric and color options on certain products in its Furniture category and certain outdoor furniture offerings from its Seasonal portfolio.

In addition to improving its digital expertise Big Lots in 2016 introduced its new Edit to Amplify operating strategy. Edit to Amplify applies to all aspects of Big Lots' business but particularly focuses on merchandising marketing and customers' shopping experience. The Edit focuses on continuously evaluating product mix and downsizing or potentially eliminating those departments within the company's merchandise categories and product offerings. The Amplify component enhances the assortment of those merchandise categories and product offerings. With the help of Edit to Amplify strategy the company has shifted its marketing efforts to focus on strengthening its connection with core customers through various forms of media.

HISTORY

As a kid growing up in Columbus Ohio Russian-born Sol Shenk (pronounced "Shank") couldn't stand to pay full price for anything. His frugality blossomed into a knack for buying low and wholesaling. After a failed effort to make auto parts Shenk began the precursor to Consolidated Stores in 1967 backed by brothers Alvin Saul and Jerome Schottenstein.

The company started by wholesaling closeout auto parts and buying retailers' closeout items to sell to other retailers. By 1971 Shenk had branched into retailing selling closeout auto parts through a small chain of Corvair Auto Stores.

One of Shenk's sons suggested they devote space in the Corvair stores to closeout merchandise other than car parts. Sales surged and Shenk decided to sell the Corvair outlets and focus on closeout stores. The first Odd Lots opened in 1982.

Consolidated grew more than 100% annually for the next three years. By 1986 the year after it went public the company was opening two stores a week in midsized markets around the Midwest.

Shenk found that people would buy anything as long as the price was right. Two years after the mania for Rubik's Cubes ended Odd Lots bought 6 million of the puzzles (once priced at $8) at 8 cents apiece marked them up 500% and sold them all.

By 1987 the company had nearly 300 Odd Lots/Big Lots stores. But runaway growth had created massive inventory shortages and losses as disappointed customers stopped browsing the company's sparsely stocked shelves. The woes coincided with a falling-out with the Schottensteins. Shenk retired in 1989.

Apparel and electronics retail executive William Kelley was named chairman and CEO the next year. Kelley returned Consolidated to its closeout roots and increased sales through acquisitions and creating new discount chains.

Consolidated doubled its size in 1996 with the $315 million purchase of more than 1000 struggling Kay-Bee Toys (now KB Toys) stores from Melville Corp. The expansion continued with the 1998 purchase of top closeout competitor Mac Frugal's Bargains - Closeouts. (Mac Frugal's had nearly bought Consolidated in 1989 before Consolidated board members vetoed the deal.) The $1 billion acquisition of Mac Frugal's gave Consolidated another 326 western stores under the Pic 'N' Save and Mac Frugal's names.

In 1999 Consolidated combined its online toy sales operations with those of BrainPlay.com to form KBkids.com. In mid-2000 Kelley was ousted as CEO handing the title over to CFO Michael Potter.

In December 2000 the company sold KB Toys (including KBkids.com) to a group led by KB management and global private equity firm Bain Capital for about $300 million. In mid-2001 the company changed its name to Big Lots and began converting all stores to that name to establish a national brand. Big Lots bought the inventory of bankrupt Internet home furnishings giant Living.com in June.

In 2002 the company completed converting 434 stores to the Big Lots banner including 380 stores previously operating under the names of Odd Lots Mac Frugal's and Pic 'N' Save. The name changes were part of a larger initiative to broaden the appeal of closeout retailing and to establish a unified national brand. During the year Big Lots opened 87 new stores and closed 42 others.

In 2003 Big Lots continued to remodel stores opened 86 new locations and closed 36 others. In 2004 the company opened about 100 new stores and continued to add furniture departments to its existing stores.

The company shuttered 174 stores in 2005 including 43 Big Lots Furniture stores and exited the frozen food business. Store closures continued in 2006 with a net loss of 25 locations.

In 2011 Big Lots acquired the Ontario Canada-based Liquidation World chain of 89 stores marking its entry into Canada. (It exited in 2014).

EXECUTIVES

EVP Chief Merchandising and Operating Officer, Lisa M. Bachmann, age 55, $738,277 total compensation

EVP Human Resources and Store Operations, Michael A. (Mike) Schlonsky, age 50, $481,931 total compensation

EVP Chief Administrative Officer and CFO, Timothy A. (Tim) Johnson, age 49, $578,317 total compensation

President CEO and Director, David J. (Dave) Campisi, age 61, $1,092,308 total compensation

VP Merchandise Support, Stewart Wenerstrom, age 50

Vice President Of Transportation, Carlos Rodriguez

Vice President Talent Management, Stella Keane

Regional Vice President, Mike Jasinowski

REGIONAL VICE PRESIDENT, William Boas

Vice President Dmm, Robert Lebrun

Vice President Asset Protection, Steve McClain

Vice President Information Technology, Kevin Kepp

Regional Vice President, Thomas R Myron

Regional Vice President, Gary E Huber

Vice President, Cathy Delucia

Vice President Home Texiles, Kevin Kuehl

Vice President, Joshua Nanberg

Vice President DMM, Bob LeBrun

Vice President Dmm, Deborah Kelley

Senior Vice President Merchandising, Michelle Christensen

RVP, Bill Coney

Chairman, Philip E. Mallott, age 59

Auditors: Deloitte & Touche LLP

LOCATIONS

HQ: Big Lots, Inc.
300 Phillipi Road, P.O. Box 28512, Columbus, OH 43228-5311
Phone: 614 278-6800   **Fax:** 614 278-6666
Web: www.biglots.com

PRODUCTS/OPERATIONS

2017 Sales

	$ mil.	% of total
Furniture	1,195	23
Food	830	16
Consumables	823	16
Soft Home	743	14
Seasonal	739	14
Hard Home	437	9
Electronics Toys & Accessories	431	8
Total	**5,200**	**100**

COMPETITORS

99 Cents Only	Michaels Companies
Amazon.com	Quality King
BJ's Wholesale Club	Ross Stores
Costco Wholesale	Salvation Army
Dollar General	Sears
Dollar Tree	Simply Amazing
Family Dollar Stores	TJX Companies
Fred's	Target Corporation
Goodwill Industries	Tuesday Morning
Gordon Brothers Group	Corporation
J. C. Penney	Variety Wholesalers
Jo-Ann Stores	Wal-Mart
Kmart	Walgreen

HISTORICAL FINANCIALS

Company Type: Public

Income Statement

FYE: January 28

	REVENUE ($ mil.)	NET INCOME ($ mil.)	NET PROFIT MARGIN	EMPLOYEES
01/17	5,200	152	2.9%	35,100
01/16	5,190	142	2.8%	35,900
01/15*	5,177	114	2.2%	36,100
02/14	5,301	125	2.4%	38,100
02/13	5,400	177	3.3%	37,300
Annual Growth	**(0.9%)**	**(3.6%)**	**—**	**(1.5%)**

*Fiscal year change

2017 Year-End Financials

Debt ratio: 6.62%
Return on equity: 22.35%
Cash ($ mil.): 51
Current ratio: 1.47
Long-term debt ($ mil.): 106

No. of shares (mil.): 44
Dividends
  Yield: 0.0%
  Payout: 25.3%
Market value ($ mil.): 2,154

	STOCK PRICE ($) FY Close	P/E High/Low		PER SHARE ($) Earnings	Dividends	Book Value
01/17	48.67	17	11	3.32	0.84	14.70
01/16	38.78	18	13	2.80	0.76	14.67
01/15*	45.91	24	12	2.06	0.51	14.92
02/14	26.79	18	12	2.16	0.00	15.66
02/13	32.34	16	9	2.93	0.00	13.24
Annual Growth	**10.8%**	**—**	**—**	**3.2%**	**—**	**2.7%**

*Fiscal year change

Biogen Inc

With its pipeline full of biotech drugs Biogen aims to meet the unmet needs of patients around the world. The biotech giant is focused on developing treatments in the areas of immunology and neurology. Its product roster includes best-selling drugs Tecfidera and Avonex (interferon) for the treatment of relapsing multiple sclerosis (MS); Tysabri a drug treatment for MS and Crohn's disease; and Fampyra which improves walking in adults with MS. Other products include Plegridy for MS. Founded in 1978 Biogen serves customers in more than 90 countries.

Operations

Biogen's top selling drug Tecfidera is sold in markets around the globe and accounts for around 35% of annual revenues. It is an oral therapy marketed in the US for the treatment of patients with relapsing forms of MS. It is sold in Europe for patients with relapsing-remitting MS (RRMS).

The firm's next-best seller Avonex (interferon) accounts for some 25% of revenues. A treatment to improve walking in adults with MS the Avonex pen is a single-use auto-injector version of the drug for once-weekly dosing.

Another top-selling global drug is Tysabri bringing in more than 15% of revenues. Despite the drug's troubled regulatory history — the drug can only be prescribed under a strict risk management plan due to the possible side effect of a rare brain condition — the company continues to pursue additional uses for the drug.

Rituxan sales conducted through a partnership with Genentech account for another 10% of sales and are classified as "unconsolidated joint business" revenues. In addition to non-Hodgkin's lymphoma and rheumatoid arthritis Rituxan is approved to treat leukemia follicular lymphoma and vasculitis.

Another drug MS treatment Fampyra (also known as Ampyra) is sold in partnership with Acorda Therapeutics. Biogen is also co-marketing Zinbryta another MS treatment in the US with AbbVie.

In addition to gaining revenue from the development and sales of its products (both directly and through partnerships) Biogen receives royalties on some patents it has licensed to other companies. For instance The Medicines Company pays royalties on sales of anticoagulant Angiomax.

Products in Biogen's pipeline include the anti-LINGO program for MS BAN2401 (in collaboration with Eisai) for Alzheimer's disease and STX-100 for idiopathic pulmonary fibrosis.

Geographic Reach

Biogen has offices in the US Australia Canada Japan the US and several European countries. It has direct sales operations in about 30 countries and operates through distribution partners in another 60 countries.

The US is Biogen's largest market bringing in more than 60% of total revenues. Europe follows with Germany alone representing more than 5% of revenues.

Sales and Marketing

Biogen primarily distributes its products in the US through wholesale pharmaceutical distributors mail-order specialty distributors and shipping service providers. Two wholesale distributors AmerisourceBergen and McKesson each bring in more than 10% of the firm's total revenues. Outside of the US distribution varies but includes wholesale pharmaceutical distributors and third-party distribution partners.

Avonex is marketed through Biogen's direct sales force to specialist physicians and hospitals in North America Europe and select other countries around the globe. The company also handles global marketing efforts for Tysabri. Genentech handles sales and marketing duties for Rituxan while marketing duties for Fampyra are split with Acorda (Biogen sells the drug in Europe and Canada).

In 2016 Biogen spent $106 million on advertising versus $108.6 million in 2015 and $92.9 million in 2014.

Financial Performance

Biogen's revenues and profits have steadily risen over the years as sales of its products have increased. In 2016 net revenue rose 6% to $11.4 billion largely due to higher sales of Tecfidera and Alprolix (which has since been spun off). Tecfidera sales rose 9% tto $4 billion that year as sales in existing markets increased; the drug also continues to be launched in new markets boosting sales even further. Alprolix sales rose 45% to $333.7 million that year.

In 2016 net income increased 4% to $3.7 billion due to the higher revenue and a relatively low increase in operating expenses. Cash flow from operations rose 22% to $4.5 billion that year primarily due to higher earnings and positive changes in current liabilities.

Strategy

Biogen is the industry leader in multiple sclerosis treatments and in Europe it has a strong business in biosimilars (Benepali a biosimilar version of Enbrel and Flixabi a biosimilar of Remicade). It launched four new therapies during 2016 and the approval of spinal muscular atrophy treatment Spinraza that year should provide the company with its next blockbuster.

Biogen's pipeline of drug candidates is focused on treatments for central nervous system ailments including Alzheimer's MS amyotrophic lateral sclerosis (ALS) neuropathic pain and lupus. In addition to proprietary candidates the company has collaborative development candidates with Genentech Portola Pharmaceuticals (lupus and rheumatoid arthritis) and other drugmakers and it continuously looks to expand its pipeline through acquisitions and partnerships.R&D expenses totaled $1.97 in 2016 down from $2.01 billion in 2015.

The company has had its share of setbacks though. In 2015 Tysabri failed in a late-stage clinical trial for secondary progressive MS. The company responded to the setback by initiating certain restructuring efforts including stopping tests for Tysabri's effectiveness against secondary progressive MS as well as stopping test for pipeline drug anti-TWEAK's effectiveness against lupus nephritis. Biogen also cut some 880 employees (about 11% of its workforce) that year. In 2016 the company's anti-LINGO MS drug failed in mid-stage tri-

als; Biogen is exploring additional studies for the treatment.

In early 2017 Biogen spun off its growing hemophilia operations into a separate publicly traded company named Bioverativ. That business' marketed products include Eloctate and Alprolix; the new firm continues its activities around the discovery and development of hemophilia therapies utilizing XTEN technology.

Mergers and Acquisitions

Biogen has expanded its operations through purchases of drug development firms as well as by purchasing commercialized and development-stage drugs. In 2015 the company acquired UK-based Convergence Pharmaceuticals a clinical-stage biopharmaceutical for $200.1 million. The deal added Convergence's CNV1014802 candidate (for the treatment of trigeminal neuralgia and sciatica) to Biogen's pipeline.

HISTORY

Biogen Idec was formed out of the 2003 merger of IDEC Pharmaceuticals and Biogen.

The company began experiencing troubles with its lead product — Tysabri developed with partner Elan— soon after its formation. Sales were temporarily halted in 2005 after several patients died from a rare neurological condition. The companies were allowed to reintroduce Tysabri in 2006 (when it was also launched in Europe) under a strict risk management plan that insures sufficient doctor and patient education about risks and proper usage.

Activist investor Carl Icahn held a minority stake in the company for several years and kept a watchful eye over his investment. In 2007 he bullied the company to put itself up for sale but no buyer came through. Then he began a series of proxy battles in an attempt to stack the board with his own nominees to gain further control. By 2010 he had secured three seats on the board filled with his own representatives and resumed talks of seeing Biogen Idec broken into parts and/or sold to a larger pharmaceutical company.

Ichan's persistence might have contributed to the retirement of Biogen Idec's long-time CEO James Mullen in mid-2010 with George Scangos (former CEO of Exelixis) stepping in as Mullen's replacement. Scangos implemented sharp changes in late 2010 launching a reorganization plan aimed at reducing operational costs and increasing efficiencies. The plan included a 13% workforce reduction and a streamlining of R&D programs to focus primarily on neurological disease. Biogen Idec halted or licensed out its oncology and cardiovascular development programs and consolidated a number of US sites. As a sign that he was pleased with Mullen's work in early 2011 Icahn reduced his ownership stake and did not seek to gain control of more board seats; he sold his remaining interests in the firm in mid-2011.

EXECUTIVES

EVP Chief Legal Officer and Corporate Secretary, Susan H. Alexander, age 60, $697,721 total compensation

EVP and CFO, Jeffrey D. (Jeff) Capello, age 52

EVP Human Resources, Kenneth A. (Ken) DiPietro, age 59, $648,023 total compensation

CEO and Director, Michel Vounatsos, $519,231 total compensation

EVP and Head of Research and Development, Michael D. (Mike) Ehlers, $491,827 total compensation

EVP Neurology Discovery and Development Center Neurodegeneration Therapeutic Area and Chief Medical Officer, Alfred W. Sandrock, age 59, $564,596 total compensation

EVP Pharmaceutical Operations and Technology, Paul McKenzie

VP and Chief Accounting Officer and Interim Principal Financial Officer, Greg Covino, age 51

EVP and Head of Global Marketing Market Access and Customer Innovation, Chirfi Guindo

Vice President Global Public Affairs, Katja Buller

Vice President Customer Support, Janis Meyer

Vice President, Adam Adamson

Medical Director, Martha Fournier

Senior Vice President Translational Medicine And Technology, Timothy Harris

Vice President Sales and Field Operations, Todd Nichols

Medical Director Clinical Development, Mark Beatty

Vice President Of Quality, Sid Senroy

Senior Vice President Program Management, Johnathan Palmer

Vice President Global Commercial Strategy, Adrian Gottschalk

Executive Vice President Human Resources, Scott Handren

Executive Vice President Of Human Resources, Kenneth Dipetrio

Vice President Of Global Medical Affairs Biogen Idec's Avonex, Thorsten Eickenhorst

Vice President Research And Development Technology, Andrew Allen

Vice President Executive Director Biogen Idec Innovation Incubator, Rainer Fuchs

Vice President Medical Research, Bradley Maroni

Senior Vice President, Anirvan Ghosh

Director, Stelios Papadopoulos, age 69

Abm, Karmon Warren

Abm, Don Benson

Vice President Treasurer, Michael Dambach

Auditors: PricewaterhouseCoopers LLP

LOCATIONS

HQ: Biogen Inc
225 Binney Street, Cambridge, MA 02142
Phone: 617 679-2000
Web: www.biogen.com

2016 Sales

	$ mil.	% of total
United States	7,050	62
Europe	1,533	13
Germany	703	6
Asia	217	2
Other regions	313	3
Unconsolidated joint business revenue	1,314	11
Other	316	3
Total	**11,448**	**100**

PRODUCTS/OPERATIONS

2016 Sales

	$ mil.	% of total
Products		
Tecfidera	3,968	35
Interferon	2,795	24
Tysabri	1,963	17
Eloctate	513	5
Alprolix	333	3
Benepali	100	1
Fampyra	84	1
Fumaderm	45	0
Zinbryta	7	0
Spinraza	4	0
Flixabi	0	0
Other products	316	11
Unconsolidated joint business	1,314	3
Total	**11,448**	**100**

Selected Products

Approved
Avonex (multiple sclerosis)
Fampyra (multiple sclerosis with Acorda Therapeutics)
Fumaderm (severe psoriasis in Germany only)

Rituxan (non-Hodgkin's lymphoma chronic lymphocytic leukemia follicular lymphoma rheumatoid arthritis vasculitis)
Tecfidera (multiple sclerosis)
Tysabri (multiple sclerosis Crohn's disease; with Elan Pharmaceuticals)
In development
BG-12 (relapsing multiple sclerosis)
Daclizumab (relapsing forms of multiple sclerosis)
GA101 (chronic lymphocytic leukemia non-Hodgkin's lymphoma)
Factor V111 Fc (hemophilia A)
Factor IX Fc (hemophilia B)
Plegridy (PEGylated interferon beta 1a relapsing forms of multipler sclerosis)
Tysabri (secondary-progressive MS)

COMPETITORS

AbbVie	Merck KGaA
Abbott Labs	Millennium: The Takeda
Amgen	Oncology Company
Bayer HealthCare	Novartis
Pharmaceuticals	Pfizer
Bristol-Myers Squibb	Roche Holding
Cephalon	Sanofi
Genmab	Teva
GlaxoSmithKline	UCB
Johnson & Johnson	

HISTORICAL FINANCIALS

Company Type: Public

Income Statement

FYE: December 31

	REVENUE ($ mil.)	NET INCOME ($ mil.)	NET PROFIT MARGIN	EMPLOYEES
12/17	12,273	2,539	20.7%	7,300
12/16	11,448	3,702	32.3%	7,400
12/15	10,763	3,547	33.0%	7,350
12/14	9,703	2,934	30.2%	7,550
12/13	6,932	1,862	26.9%	6,850
Annual Growth	15.4%	8.1%	—	1.6%

2017 Year-End Financials

Debt ratio: 25.11%
Return on equity: 20.52%
Cash ($ mil.): 1,573
Current ratio: 2.34
Long-term debt ($ mil.): 5,935

No. of shares (mil.): 211
Dividends
　Yield: —
　Payout: —
Market value ($ mil.): 67,378

	STOCK PRICE ($) FY Close	P/E High/Low		PER SHARE ($) Earnings	Dividends	Book Value
12/17	318.57	29	21	11.92	0.00	59.63
12/16	283.58	19	13	16.93	0.00	56.23
12/15	306.35	31	17	15.34	0.00	42.88
12/14	339.45	29	22	12.37	0.00	46.08
12/13	279.57	38	18	7.81	0.00	36.48
Annual Growth	3.3%	—	—	11.1%	—	13.1%

BIOURJA TRADING, LLC

Auditors: CARR RIGGS & INGRAM LLC HOUST

LOCATIONS

HQ: BIOURJA TRADING, LLC
　1080 ELDRIDGE PKWY # 1175, HOUSTON, TX
　770772582
Phone: 832 775-9000
Web: WWW.BIOURJA.COM

HISTORICAL FINANCIALS

Company Type: Private

Income Statement

FYE: December 31

	REVENUE ($ mil.)	NET INCOME ($ mil.)	NET PROFIT MARGIN	EMPLOYEES
12/13	4,622	26	0.6%	72
12/12	2,992	11	0.4%	—
12/11	299,106	16	—	—
Annual Growth	—	26.1%		

2013 Year-End Financials

Debt ratio: ——
Return on equity: 0.60%
Cash ($ mil.): 15
Current ratio: 0.90
Long-term debt ($ mil.): —

Dividends
　Yield: —
　Payout: —
Market value ($ mil.): —

BlackRock Inc

With some $5.1 trillion in assets under management BlackRock is the world's largest public investment management firm. It specializes in equity and fixed income products as well as alternative and multi-class instruments which it invests in on behalf of institutional and retail investors worldwide; it does not engage in proprietary trading. Clients include pension plans governments insurance companies mutual funds endowments foundations and charities. BlackRock also provides risk management services through BlackRock Solutions and is a leading provider of exchange-traded funds (ETFs) through iShares. The firm has offices in more than 30 countries.It has investments in some 90% of the Fortune 100.

Operations

BlackRock manages some $5.1 trillion in assets through 135 investment teams. The BlackRock Solutions division provides risk management advisory and enterprise investment system services. iShares one of BlackRock's brands is a leading provider of exchange-traded funds (ETFs). BlackRock's risk management technology platform Aladdin is used by around 25000 investment professionals around the world.

The company offers active and passive retail investment services. Mutual funds account for the majority of retail investment sums at around 80%. Retail has a US and an international arm.

BlackRock's iShares is the world's largest ETF in the world with $1.3 trillion in assets under management. iShares also operates in the US and internationally.

The company possesses $2.9 trillion in institutional assets of which $1.9 trillion are index funds and $1.0 trillion active. Its clients consist of pensions foundations and endowments; official institutions; and financial and other institutions.

Geographic Reach

New York-based BlackRock has more than 70 offices in more than 30 countries. The company makes 66% of its revenue in the Americas. Europe accounts for nearly 30% and the Asia-Pacific region 5%. BlackRock has clients and investments in more than 100 countries.

Sales and Marketing

BlackRock serves 21 out of the 25 largest endowments and foundation organizations in the US. It also serves around 90 of the Fortune 100 companies and more than 90% of the largest US retirement plans.

BlackRock focuses on establishing and maintaining its investment management relationships by marketing its services through financial professionals pension consultants third-party distribution relationships or directly to investors themselves.

Clients include tax-exempt institutions (defined benefit pension plans charities and foundations); official institutions (central banks sovereign wealth funds supranationals and other government entities); and taxable institutions (insurance companies financial institutions corporations and third-party fund sponsors and retail investors).

Financial Performance

Thanks to a rising stock market and a growing investor base BlackRock has more than tripled its assets under management since 2007 — from $1.3 trillion to $5.1 trillion at the end of 2016 — which has led strong fee and advisory income growth over the past few years.

Revenue declined slightly in fiscal 2016 (ended December) falling 2% to $11.2 billion due to lower investment advisory performance fees from equity and alternative products. Weakness was offset to an extent by stronger Aladdin revenue up $67 million.

Net income fell 3% to $3.2 billion on the back of lower revenue. A restructuring expense of $76 million also had a negative impact.

Cash from operating activities fell 28% to $2.2 billion due to changes in fair value of variable interest entities (VIEs).

Strategy

Even powerful fund managers' jobs are not immune to the threat of automation. In 2017 BlackRock sacked seven portfolio managers as part of a wider shift away from active stock pickers and towards a robot-led quantitative approach. Amid relative market stability active fund managers are less able to beat the market than passive trackers. Investors pulled some $40 billion from actively managed funds during 2016. The robo-funds can be offered at a lower price than the more expensive hand-picked investment funds.

Part of the shift to automation includes the transfer of $1 trillion in assets under custody of State Street to JP Morgan in 2017. BlackRock hopes the move will cut operating expenses; JP Morgan has been investing in automation technology enabling the cheaper provision of services.

Mergers and Acquisitions

In 2017 BlackRock acquired First Reserve's equity infrastructure franchise First Reserve Energy Infrastructure Funds. The acquisition will help connect BlackRock's clients with energy infrastructure projects.

In 2016 BlackRock Real Assets added to its wind generations holdings with the purchase of GE Energy Financial Services' 50% interest in the Grandview wind project in Texas. BlackRock's renewable energy assets have 2 GW of generating power.

BlackRock expanded its presence in Mexico with the 2015 purchase of Infraestructura Institucional the country's leading independently managed infrastructure investment firm. The acquisition opens infrastructure investments in Mexico to BlackRock's clients.

In November 2015 BlackRock agreed to buy Bank of America's $87 billion-money market fund business boosting its global cash-management business up 30% to $372 billion in assets under management. The deal comes as Bank of America and other large banks have faced regulatory pressure to simplify their businesses in the years following the global financial crisis.

Company Background

BlackRock is led by CEO Laurence Fink who has overseen a string of major acquisitions in recent years expanding into private equity real estate energy and hedge funds as investors look to diversify beyond stock and bond funds.

Fink engineered a blockbuster merger with Barclays Global Investors (BGI) in 2009. In the deal which was several years in the making BlackRock bought Barclays Global Investors from UK banking giant Barclays for some $15 billion. The deal resulted in a new company operating under the BlackRock name. Barclays Bank retained a 20% stake in the combined firm but Fink remained in charge of the enterprise. The merger nearly tripled BlackRock's assets under management and propelled the company to the top of the international money management industry by enhancing its investment and risk management capabilities. The deal also gave BlackRock a much larger footprint outside the US and added more than 3500 new employees.

EXECUTIVES

President and Director, Robert S. (Rob) Kapito, age 60, $750,000 total compensation
Chairman and CEO, Laurence D. (Larry) Fink, age 64, $900,000 total compensation
Senior Managing Director, Robert W. (Rob) Fairbairn, age 51, $350,000 total compensation
Senior Managing Director and Chief Risk Officer, Bennett W. Golub, age 59
Senior Managing Director and Global Head of Multi-Asset Strategies, J. Richard (Rich) Kushel, age 50, $500,000 total compensation
Senior Managing Director and Head of Trading Liquidity and Investments Platform, Richard L. (Richie) Prager
Chairman and Head of Asia/Pacific, Ryan D. Stork, age 45
Senior Managing Director Head of Global Active Equities and Chairman BlackRock Alternative Investors, Mark Wiseman
Senior Managing Director and Global Head of iShares and Index Investments, Mark K. Wiedman
Senior Managing Director and Head of Global Human Resources, Jeffrey A. Smith, age 46
Senior Managing Director Head of the Americas Region and Global Head of BlackRock Alternative Investors, Mark S. McCombe, age 51
Senior Managing Director and Head of Europe Middle East and Africa (EMEA), David J. Blumer, age 48
Senior Managing Director and CFO, Gary S. Shedlin, age 53, $500,000 total compensation
Senior Managing Director COO and Global Head BlackRock Solutions, Rob L. Goldstein, age 43, $500,000 total compensation
Senior Managing Director and Global Head Business Operations and Technology, Derek K. Stein
Vice President, ED Mallon
Regional Vice President, Robb Falaguerra
Vice President, Marie McCarthy
Vice President Institutional Sales Benelux, Norbert Van Veldhuizen
Vice President Value Add and Retirement Marketing, Courtney Golisano
Executive Vice President, Nick Hutton
Vice President Technology, Rob Smith
Vice President, Laura Tyrholm
Vice President, Derek Cook
Vice President of Information Systems, Saba Anvar
Vice President, Robert Chiolan
Vice President, Vineet Gupta
Vice President, John Kent
Vice President CRM Database Marketing Manager, Sorin Tudor
Vice President, Piyush Naik
Vice President, Paul Horowitz
Vice President, Adam Bobker
Vice President, Duane Liedl

Senior Compliance Manager Vice President, Beth Moore
Vice President Recruiting, Ken Daponte
Vice President, Brian Thackray
Vice President, Viola Dunne
Vice President, Jim Kim
Vice President, Sherrika Fuller
Vice President Investment Knowledge Strategist, Brooke Juniper
Advisory Vice President, Scott Jeffreys
Vice President, Gina Forziati
Vice President, Peter Falkowski
Vice President, Victor Glazer
Executive Vice President, Clinton Soose
Vice President, Nigel Benson
VICE PRESIDENT DESKTOP ENGINEERING, David Gagliardotto
Vice President Of Broker Dealer Services, Mark Persiani
Vice President, Betsy Mathews
Vice President, Lisa Sanner
Vice President Business Development, Joe Ernst
Vice President, Simone Gartmond
Vice President, Ada Aromando
Vice President, Richard Steel
Vice President, Bridget Dean-Hammel
Vice President program Management, Jennifer Galler
Vice President, Ryan Coulter
Vice President, Karen Goldman
Vice President, Uri Morris
Vice President Sourcing, Michael Schnalzer
Vice President, Peter Hirsh
Vice President, Amaurys Mercedes
Vice President, Andrew Chaiken
Vice President, Phil Green
Vice President, Brian Roberson
Vice President Fixed Income Portfolio Management Group, Sriram Reddy
Vice President, Richard Mejzak
Vice President Trader portfolio Manager Cash Managment, Gene Meshechek
Vice President User Experience And Design, Devjit Basu
Vice President, David Kurapka
Vice President, Jeff Puntney
Vice President, Jason Devlin
Vice President Compliance, John Longhurst
Vice President Event Management, Wendy Dooley
Vice President, Benjamin Cunningham
Vice President, Kelly Sanderson
Vice President Critical Infrastructure, Ed Cannon
Vice President, Prathima Nalluri
Vice President Information Technology and Legal Sourcing, Hillary Grand
Vice President, Lauren Giametta
Vice President, Kiran Vuppala
Vice President, Benjamin Friedlander
Vice President, Amanda Huckle
Vice President, Brian Fitzpatrick
Vice President Portfolio Manager, Edward Ingold
Vice President, Susan Lapczynski
Vice President, Loryn Sperber
Vice President, Ashish Sharma
Vice President, Sam Eisenberg
Vice President, Jeremy Jones
Vice President, Aaron Kipnis
Vice President, David Edson
Vice President, Miranda Harrison
Vice President, Ying Li
Vice President Product Management, Jeff Lambert
Vice President, Patricia Belcher
Vice President Securities, Jason Yanagihara
Vice President, Mufaddal Karachiwala
Vice President, David Curtin
Vice President, Ryan Shriber
Vice President, Blair Saunders
Vice President, Sukhbir Gill
Vice President of Human Resour, Toretha McGuire
Vice President, Kenny Ma

Vice President, Charles Harrington
Vice President, Amy Goldfarb
Vice President, Christine Brooks
Vicepresident, Rodrigo Castaneda
Vice President Access And Identity Management, Nikhil Mathur
Vice President, Jeff Brown
Vice President, Chen Ai
Vice President, Vidy Vairavamurthy
Vice President Aladdin And Technology, Paul Dearman
Vice President, Matthew Roberts
Vice President, Madhavi Chugh
Vice President Media Services, Lisa Sturdivant
Vice President US Board Governing services, Danielle Costantino
Vice President, Vincent Dellaglio
Vice President EMEA Retail Sales Strategy, Adam Riley
Vice President, Andrew Moyad
Vice President Risk and Quantitative Analysis, Ben Wu
Vice President Institutional Client Business Institutional Sales, Guido Bridelli
Vice President, Heinrich Schutze
Vice President, Joanne Mavra
Vice President, Davina Stickland
Vice President: Client Order Management, Suzanne Long
Vice President, Celia Chau
Vice President Internal Audit, Stella Yap
Vice President Director Account Management, Whitney Ehrlich
Vice President Service Center, Johnathan Keating
Vice President Governance Risk and Compliance, Bobby Singh
Vice President, Patricia Inlander
Vice President, Kirsten Filosa
Vice President, Nancy Dambrosio
Vice President Business Development, Luis Garcia
Vice President Telecommunications, Sharad Pandey
Product Development Vice President, Stephen Boustouler
Vice President Risk Analytics, Sangeeta Pandey
Vice President and Compensation Consultant, Michael Lebowitz
Vice President BlackRock, Brian Compton
Vice President BlackRock, Long Tran
Vice President BlackRock, Marc Chin
Vice President BlackRock, Raja Kurapati
Vice President, Sai Patnala
Vice President BlackRock, Scott Golub
Fixed Income Product Strategist Vice President, Terry Simpson
Vice President Legal, Michelle Galvez
Vice President, Richard Kovalchik
Vice President, Rupkumar Radhakrishnan
Vice President Implementations, Francia Fabian
Vice President Security Engineering, Rebecca Quinn
Auditors: Deloitte & Touche LLP

LOCATIONS

HQ: BlackRock Inc
55 East 52nd Street, New York, NY 10055
Phone: 212 810-5300
Web: www.blackrock.com

2016 Sales

	$ mil.	% of total
Americas	7,530	67
Europe	3,083	28
Asia/Pacific	542	5
Total	**11,155**	**100**

PRODUCTS/OPERATIONS

2016 Sales

	$ mil.	% of total
Investment advisory administration fees & securities lending		
Equity	5,018	45
Fixed income	2,664	24
Multi-asset class	1,157	10
Alternative investments	878	8
Cash management	458	4
Black Rock Solutions & advisory	714	6
Distribution fees	41	1
Other revenue	225	2
Total	**11,155**	**100**

COMPETITORS

Allianz Global Investors	Federated Investors
Bank of New York Mellon	Legg Mason
Charles Schwab	Morgan Stanley
Dimensional Fund Advisors	Principal Global
	State Street
	UBS
	Waddell & Reed

HISTORICAL FINANCIALS

Company Type: Public

Income Statement

FYE: December 31

	REVENUE ($ mil.)	NET INCOME ($ mil.)	NET PROFIT MARGIN	EMPLOYEES
12/16	11,155	3,172	28.4%	13,000
12/15	11,401	3,345	29.3%	13,000
12/14	11,081	3,294	29.7%	12,200
12/13	10,180	2,932	28.8%	11,400
12/12	9,337	2,458	26.3%	10,500
Annual Growth	4.5%	6.6%	—	5.5%

2016 Year-End Financials

Debt ratio: 2.23%
Return on equity: 10.98%
Cash ($ mil.): 6,091
Current ratio: 2.84
Long-term debt ($ mil.): 4,915

No. of shares (mil.): 161
Dividends
 Yield: 0.0%
 Payout: 48.1%
Market value ($ mil.): 61,470

	STOCK PRICE ($) FY Close	P/E High/Low	PER SHARE ($) Earnings	Dividends	Book Value
12/16	380.54	21 15	19.04	9.16	180.13
12/15	340.52	19 15	19.79	8.72	174.37
12/14	357.56	19 15	19.25	7.72	166.07
12/13	316.47	18 12	16.87	6.72	158.83
12/12	206.71	15 12	13.79	6.00	150.42
Annual Growth	16.5%	— —	8.4%	11.2%	4.6%

Blackstone Group LP (The)

Throw a rock and you're bound to hit a Blackstone investment. The Blackstone Group is one of the world's largest real estate private equity and alternative asset managers in the world with around $370 billion in assets under management and such notable past holdings as Michaels Stores and SeaWorld. The firm manages investment vehicles including private equity funds funds of hedge funds and real estate funds. Clients include public and corporate pensions financial institutions and individuals. The firm spun off its corporate advisory business as PJT Partners in late 2015.

Operations

The Blackstone Group is organized into four business segments: Private Equity Real Estate Credit and Hedge Fund Solutions.

The Private Equity segment produces about 25% of revenue and typically holds interests in more than 70 companies. It has some $100 billion in assets under management (about 75% of which are in the US) and has traditionally been involved in leveraged buyouts of developed companies investments in growth-oriented companies development projects and funding for smaller companies needing money and leadership to scale in fragmented industries.

The Real Estate segment is one of the largest real estate investment management operations in the world with $100 billion in assets under management. The operations focus on acquiring high quality well-located real estate that is undermanaged and for sale at attractive prices. It then addresses property or business issues through active management and once the property reaches potential it sells the real estate. Its portfolio includes retail residential industrial office and hotel properties. It generated a bit more than 40% of Blackstone revenue.

The company's Credit business GSO Capital Partners accounts for 20% of revenue. It focuses on credit-oriented financial arrangements in alternative assets using senior and subordinated debt preferred stock and even common stock as vehicles for its investment. GSO has about $95 billion in assets under management.

Blackstone's Hedge Fund Solutions business primarily made up of Blackstone Alternative Asset Management (BAAM) has more than $70 billion in assets under management and has among its clients public and corporate pension funds and high net worth individuals.

Geographic Reach

New York-based Blackstone Group has 18 offices worldwide in the Americas the Asia Pacific region and in Europe. In the US the firm has branches in Houston Los Angeles and Santa Barbara. Its overseas offices are in Beijing Dubai Dublin Dusseldorf Hong Kong London Madrid Mexico City Montecito Mumbai Paris San Paulo Seoul Shanghai Singapore Sydney Tokyo and Toronto.

The firms clients and its many holdings of companies real estate etc. are located throughout the world.

Financial Performance

In recent years Blackstone?s revenue and income trends moved in unison both peaked dipped and pushed back upwards. It has been a highly profitable company over the years.

In 2016 Blackstone revenue topped $5.1 billion up 10% year over year but well below the 2014 peak of $7.5 billion. The increase was the result of a 20% boost in performance fees from the Credit and Real Estate segments (against a drop in Private Equity) and a 75% increase in investment income mostly from the Real Estate segment.

Net income soared 46% to $1.0 billion in 2016 compared to the prior year but still down 55% from 2014?s peak of $1.6 billion. The company managed expenses well in 2016 pushing them lower versus 2015 despite the $500 million rise in revenue.

Cash at year end was $1.8 billion essentially unchanged from the prior year. During 2016 Blackstone used about $540 million of cash for operating activities mainly driven by a large amount of purchased investments. Cash used by investing activities was negligible and financing activities contributed $570 million primarily from debt issuance.

Strategy

Blackstone?s four segments each follow a set of investment policies to achieve their respective financial objectives. Depending on market conditions and anticipated economic activity one segment might be more active than others. In 2016 Blackstone?s Real Estate segment participated in a slew of transactions continuing a multi-year upward trend.

Real Estate has been growing at an even faster clip (and is now larger) than its Private Equity business over the past few years thanks to prudent property investments that have seen healthy valuation gains in the hot real estate market. In 2017 it committed a $500 million investment to refurbish and redevelop its Chicago-located 110 story Willis Tower. In that same year it purchased Hotel Investment Partners a Spanish owner of 14 tourist focused hotels on Spain?s southern coast.

Not to be forgotten Blackstone's legacy Private Equity division is known as a hands-on investor that builds up its portfolio companies' values before selling them off for large profits. Some of its pending and completed acquisitions in 2016 included: Aon (a human resources services operation) EagleClaw Midstream Ventures (an oil & gas company) and a majority stake in Cloudreach (a technology company providing cloud services).

Mergers and Acquisitions

In 2017 Anadarko Petroleum agreed to sell its South Texas oil and gas assets to Sanchez Energy and The Blackstone Group for $2.3 billion. In that same year Spanish company Banco Popular agreed to sell a majority stake in its ?30 billion ($33 billion) real estate asset portfolio to Blackstone.

Also in 2017 Blackstone acquired Aon's human resources outsourcing business for $4.8 billion. The business supplies some 15% of the United States' entire working population and conducts health retirement and HR services.

Company Background

In 2013 the firm purchased the Hughes Center complex in Las Vegas for $347 million to eventually benefit from the region's rebound. Blackstone was also part of an investor group that bought Extended Stay Hotels owner HVM which was in bankruptcy. All of the hospitality investment activity helped bring in a dramatic rise in revenues in 2013.

In China following its strategy to invest in high-growth Chinese companies through its partnership with the Shanghai-Pudong district government a consortium led by Blackstone agreed in late 2013 to acquire China-based global consulting and technology services company Pactera Technology International Ltd. for about $600 million. The move marked Blackstone's foray into China's technology outsourcing industry a sector traditionally dominated by Indian firms.

In 2012 in capitalizing on the boom in energy markets Blackstone completed fundraising for its first energy-focused private equity fund Blackstone Energy Partners L.P. with total fund commitments of $2.4 billion. The firm also raised $13.3 billion for its seventh global real estate fund BREP VII making it the biggest real estate fund in the world. In 2013 Blackstone acquired secondary private fund of funds unit Strategic Partners Fund Solutions in a deal that added some $9.4 billion in assets under management.

Founded in 1985 by industry veterans Peter Peterson and CEO Stephen Schwarzman the once-reclusive Blackstone went public in June 2007. The public offering which was a first among major US private equity firms valued Blackstone at upwards of $4 billion.

HISTORY

In 2013 the firm purchased the Hughes Center complex in Las Vegas for $347 million to eventually benefit from the region's rebound. Blackstone was also part of an investor group that bought Extended Stay Hotels owner HVM which was in bankruptcy. All of the hospitality investment activity helped bring in a dramatic rise in revenues in 2013.

In China following its strategy to invest in high-growth Chinese companies through its partnership with the Shanghai-Pudong district government a consortium led by Blackstone agreed in late 2013 to acquire China-based global consulting and technology services company Pactera Technology International Ltd. for about $600 million. The move marked Blackstone's foray into China's technology outsourcing industry a sector traditionally dominated by Indian firms.

In 2012 in capitalizing on the boom in energy markets Blackstone completed fundraising for its first energy-focused private equity fund Blackstone Energy Partners L.P. with total commitments of $2.4 billion. The firm also raised $13.3 billion for its seventh global real estate fund BREP VII making it the biggest real estate fund in the world. In 2013 Blackstone acquired secondary private fund of funds unit Strategic Partners Fund Solutions in a deal that added some $9.4 billion in assets under management.

Founded in 1985 by industry veterans Peter Peterson and CEO Stephen Schwarzman the once-reclusive Blackstone went public in June 2007. The public offering which was a first among major US private equity firms valued Blackstone at upwards of $4 billion.

EXECUTIVES

President and COO, Hamilton E. (Tony) James, age 66, $350,000 total compensation
President and CEO, Stephen A. Schwarzman, age 70, $350,000 total compensation
Senior Managing Director and Head of Private Equity Portfolio Operations, David L. (Dave) Calhoun, age 60
Senior Managing Director and CFO, Michael S. Chae, age 48, $350,000 total compensation
Senior Managing Director GSO Capital Partners, Bennett J. Goodman, age 59
Senior Managing Director and Head of Tactical Opportunities, David S. Blitzer, age 47
Senior Managing Director and Global Head of Real Estate, Jonathan D. Gray, age 47
Senior Managing Director and Head of Multi-Asset Investing and External Relations, Joan Solotar, age 52, $350,000 total compensation
Vice Chairman and President and CEO Blackstone Alternative Asset Management, J. Tomilson Hill, age 68, $350,000 total compensation
Senior Managing Director Private Equity London, Joseph P. Baratta, age 46
Senior Managing Director and Chief Legal Officer, John G. Finley, age 60, $350,000 total compensation
Senior Managing Director and CTO, William Murphy
Chairman Asia-Pacific, Christopher (Chris) Heady
Senior Managing Director and Head of Energy Practice GSO Capital Partners, Dwight Scott, age 53
Senior Managing Director and CEO Blackstone Insurance Solutions, Chris Blunt
Vice President, Melanie Endo
Vice President Credit Business, Juliann O'Sullivan
Vice President, Rita Mangalick
Vice President, John Wander
Vice President Finance, Masako Sunada
Vice President, Ronald Lintag

Divisional Vice President, Byung U Choi
Vice President, Brij Kalaria
Vice President of Middle Atlantic Region, Mario Fasano
Vice President, Nentcho Nentchev
Vice President Credit Businesses, Justin Hall
Vice President, Raphael Kiam
Vice President, Michael Schlappig
Vice President, Justin Smith
Vice President, John Miller
Vice President, Thomas Kali
Vice President, Stephen O'Connor
Vice President, Michael Distefano
Vice President, Bryan Shelby
Vice President, Taylor Carvajal
Vice President, Brett Crandall
Vice President, Christian Vardeleon
Vice President, Jack Pitts
Vice President, Katherine Daco
Vice President, Sebastian Grasso
Vice President, Gregory Bilse
Senior Vice President, Bryan Sullivan
Vice President, Kevin Gee
Vice President, Paul Sheaffer
Vice President, Daniel Aron
Vice President, Matthew Pedley
Vice President, Mark Tornga
Vice President, Michelle Harika
Vice President, Roberta Osborne
Vice President Finance, Walter Dinsmore
Vice President, Adam Hermida
Vice President, Matthew Howell
Vice President, Sal Aloia
Vice President, Daniel Chang
Vice President, Sobin Mathew
Vice President, Thomas Procida
Vice President, Gordon McKemie
Vice President, Cooper Wright
Vice President, Michael Pierog
Vice President, Jared Becker
Vice President, Milca Beltre
Vice President Real Estate Debt Strategies, Damiano Buffa
Vice President, Marni Blivice
Vice President Credit Businesses New Yor, John Beberus
Senior Vice President Data Governance And Portfolio Reporting, Jana Douglas
Vice President, Bill Sheehan
Vice President, Ryan Chapman
Vice President, Simon Mahler
Vice President, Mollie Frail
Senior Vice President, Cathleen Becker
Vice President, Davitt Kelly
Auditors: Deloitte & Touche LLP

LOCATIONS

HQ: Blackstone Group LP (The)
345 Park Avenue, New York, NY 10154
Phone: 212 583-5000
Web: www.blackstone.com

PRODUCTS/OPERATIONS

2016 Sales

	% of total
Real Estate	43
Private Equity	27
Credit	18
Hedge fund solutions	12
Total	**100**

2016 Sales

	$ mil.	% of total
Management and advisory fees	2,443	48
Performance fees	2,176	42
Investment income	356	7
Interest & dividends &Other	150	3
Total	**5,125**	**100**

Selected Investments

Allcargo
Alliant Insurance Services
AlliedBarton Security Services
Antares Restaurant Group
Apria Healthcare
Axis Capital
BankUnited
Bayview Asset Management
Biomet
Caesars Entertainment (formerly Harrah's Entertainment)
Catalent Pharma Solutions
Celanese
Center Parcs
Charter Communications
China Animal Healthcare Ltd.
China National Bluestar Group
CMS Computers Ltd.
Crestwood Midstream Partners
CTI Holdings
Cumulus Media Partners
DJO
Dili Group
eAccess
Emcure
Equity Office Properties
Extended Stay America
Freescale Semiconductor Group
Gates Corporation
Gateway Rail Freight Ltd.
Gerresheimer Group
Gokaldas Exports Limited
Gold Toe-Moretz
Houghton Mifflin
Imperial Home Dé;cor
Independent Clinical Services
Intelenet Global Services
Intertrust
Klöckner Pentaplast
Leica Camera
Maldivian Air
Michaels Stores
Mivisa Envases S.A.U.
Monnet
Montecito
Moser Baer Energy
MTAR Technologies Private
Nuziveedu Seeds
Osum Oil Sands Corp.
PBF Energy
People's Choice TV
Performance Food Group
Pinnacle Foods Corporation
Polymer Group Inc.
RGIS Inventory Specialists
Sonalike International Tractors
SeaWorld Parks & Entertainment
Summit Materials
Stiefel Laboratories
SunGard
Team Health
Texas Genco
Tragus
TRW Automotive
UCAR
United Biscuits
Vivint Inc.
The Weather Channel
Western Integrated Networks

COMPETITORS

AEA Investors	Haas Wheat
American Financial Group	Heico Companies
	Investcorp
Apollo Global Management	Jordan Company
	KKR
Bain Capital	Leonard Green
Berkshire Hathaway	MacAndrews & Forbes
BlackRock	Silver Lake
Clayton Dubilier & Rice	TPG
	The Carlyle Group
Goldman Sachs	Thomas H. Lee Partners

HISTORICAL FINANCIALS

Company Type: Public

Income Statement

FYE: December 31

	REVENUE ($ mil.)	NET INCOME ($ mil.)	NET PROFIT MARGIN	EMPLOYEES
12/16	5,125	1,039	20.3%	2,120
12/15	4,646	709	15.3%	2,060
12/14	7,484	1,584	21.2%	2,190
12/13	6,613	1,171	17.7%	2,010
12/12	4,019	218	5.4%	1,780
Annual Growth	6.3%	47.7%	—	4.5%

2016 Year-End Financials

Debt ratio: 33.58%
Return on equity: —
Cash ($ mil.): 2,842
Current ratio: 1.05
Long-term debt ($ mil.): 8,866

No. of shares (mil.): 643
Dividends
Yield: 0.0%
Payout: 106.4%
Market value ($ mil.): 17,393

	STOCK PRICE ($) FY Close	P/E High/Low	PER SHARE ($) Earnings	Dividends	Book Value
12/16	27.03	19 14	1.56	1.66	10.04
12/15	29.24	39 25	1.04	2.90	10.04
12/14	33.83	14 11	2.58	1.92	11.85
12/13	31.50	16 8	1.98	1.18	11.01
12/12	15.59	41 28	0.41	0.52	9.83
Annual Growth	14.7%	— —	39.7%	33.7%	0.5%

Blue Hills Bancorp Inc

Auditors: Wolf & Company, P.C.

LOCATIONS

HQ: Blue Hills Bancorp Inc
500 River Ridge Drive, Norwood, MA 02062
Phone: 617 360-6520
Web: www.bluehillsbancorp.com

HISTORICAL FINANCIALS

Company Type: Public

Income Statement

FYE: December 31

	ASSETS ($ mil.)	NET INCOME ($ mil.)	INCOME AS % OF ASSETS	EMPLOYEES
12/16	2,469	8	0.4%	228
12/15	2,114	7	0.3%	209
12/14	1,728	(0)	—	202
12/13	1,314	2	0.2%	147
12/12	1,228	7	0.6%	—
Annual Growth	19.1%	2.5%	—	—

2016 Year-End Financials

Debt ratio: 4.25%
Return on equity: 2.20%
Cash ($ mil.): 30
Current ratio: —
Long-term debt ($ mil.): —

No. of shares (mil.): 26
Dividends
Yield: 0.0%
Payout: 31.4%
Market value ($ mil.): 502

	STOCK PRICE ($) FY Close	P/E High/Low	PER SHARE ($) Earnings	Dividends	Book Value
12/16	18.75	54 38	0.35	0.11	14.46
12/15	15.31	59 46	0.28	0.04	14.00
12/14	13.58	— —	(0.00)	0.00	14.46
Annual Growth	8.4%	— —	—	—	(0.0%)

BOARD OF EDUCATION OF CITY OF CHICAGO

Auditors: MCGLADREY LLP CHICAGO ILLINO

LOCATIONS

HQ: BOARD OF EDUCATION OF CITY OF CHICAGO
42 W MADISON ST FL 2, CHICAGO, IL 606024309
Phone: 773 553-1000

HISTORICAL FINANCIALS

Company Type: Private

Income Statement

FYE: June 30

	REVENUE ($ mil.)	NET INCOME ($ mil.)	NET PROFIT MARGIN	EMPLOYEES
06/12	5,760	324	5.6%	43,000
06/11	5,660	238	4.2%	—
Annual Growth	1.8%	36.0%	—	—

Boeing Co. (The)

Boeing has built a big name for itself as one of the world's largest aerospace companies. Its commercial jet aircraft models include the 737 narrow body; the fuel efficient 737 MAX; the 747 767 and 777 wide bodies; and the 787 Dreamliner. Serving the military science and space and sea exploration sectors the company also produces KC-46 aerial refueling aircraft the AH-64 Apache helicopter the 702 family of satellites CST-100 Starliner spacecraft and the Echo Voyager unmanned undersea vehicle. Major customers include the US Department of Defense and NASA. Additionally Boeing provides airplane financing and leasing services to both commercial and military customers.

Operations

Boeing's operations are divided into three business units: Commercial Airplanes; Defense Space & Security (DSS); and Boeing Global Services (BGS) which began operations in mid-2017. Supporting these segments is Boeing Capital its global financing operations.

Boeing Commercial Airplanes designs manufactures and services commercial jet aircraft for both passengers and cargo. Models include the 737 narrow body the fuel efficient 737 MAX and the 747 767 777 and 787 families. New product development initiatives include the Boeing 787-10 Dreamliner the 737 MAX and the 777X.

DSS provides design modification and support services for large-scale systems including missiles munitions aerial refuelers transporters and spacecraft. It acts as a systems integrator on several programs including NASA's International Space Station and Missile Defense Agency's Ground-based Midcourse Defense.

The newly formed BGS division caters to aerospace and defense needs across the following four areas: supply chain management engineering aircraft modification digital analytics and training and professional services. The division is also tasked with expanding Boeing's data analytics and information-based services capabilities.

Geographic Reach

Boeing's principal operations are in the US Canada and Australia with some key suppliers and subcontractors located in Europe and Japan. Boeing makes about 40% of its total revenues in the US and about 60% from international markets (primarily Europe Asia/Pacific and the Middle East).

Sales and Marketing

Boeing's main customer is the Department of Defense with approximately 65% of revenues (excluding foreign military sales through the US government). Other significant revenues are derived from international defense markets civil markets and the commercial satellite market.

Financial Performance

After posting record-setting revenues of $96 billion in 2015 Boeing saw its revenues slip 2% to $95 billion in 2016. This was attributed to declines across the majority of its segments.

Commercial Airplanes revenues decreased 1% in 2016 primarily due to lower deliveries. The DSS segment also experienced decreased revenues related to its Commercial Crew program lower milestone revenue related to fewer C-17 aircraft deliveries and lower volume on proprietary programs. In addition Boeing Capital's revenues plummeted due to lower lease income and lower end of lease settlement payments during 2016.

Boeing's profits fell 5% from $5.2 billion in 2015 to $4.9 billion in 2016 due to higher research and development costs related to 787 aircraft flight tests. Despite the revenue and profit declines Being's operating cash flow climbed from nearly $9.4 billion in 2015 to $10.5 billion in 2016. The rise in cash flow was largely due to lower expenditures on commercial airplane program inventory primarily for its 787.

Strategy

Boeing's growth strategy is centered around its new product development initiatives. Flight testing of the 787-9 Dreamliner variant occurred in 2014 and its first delivery was in mid-2014. The 787-10 is on plan for first delivery in 2018 and will incorporate a high degree of shared design elements and parts commonality with the 787-9 to likewise minimize risk and lower development and fleet maintenance costs. The 777X (Boeing's newest twin-engine jet with 12% lower fuel consumption and 10% lower operating costs than its competitors) is slated for its first delivery in 2019.

In a significant move to make it less reliant on suppliers Boeing in 2017 created a new avionics and aircraft computer system manufacturing division that will produce aircraft electronics systems such as navigation flight controls communications sensors and displays. The move is part of Boeing?s strategy of growing its aftermarket services segment from $14 billion to $50 billion within five to 10 years. By creating its avionics components and systems itself Boeing can continue to reap sales from maintenance and upgrade contracts of its planes for years after they?re sold.

Mergers and Acquisitions

Boeing achieves growth by acquiring businesses that focus on specific technology products and target the needs of emerging markets.

In late 2016 Boeing acquired Liquid Robotics a manufacturer of Wave Glider the first wave and solar-powered autonomous ocean drone. Boeing made the deal to enhance its seabed-to-space autonomous capabilities. It also plans to meet the challenges facing defense commercial and science customers by making ocean data collection and communications easier and safer.

Boeing in late 2015 also acquired Germany-based Peters Software a provider of European Aviation Safety Agency (EASA)-based training software for early stage pilot training. The deal enhanced Boeing's customized pilot training content as it strives to meet the growing global demand for qualified aviation personnel.

HISTORY

Bill Boeing who had already made his fortune in Washington real estate built his first airplane in 1916 with naval officer Conrad Westervelt. His Seattle company Pacific Aero Products changed its name to Boeing Airplane Company the next year. During WWI Boeing built training planes for the US Navy and began the first international air-mail service (between Seattle and Victoria British Columbia). The company added a Chicago-San Francisco route in 1927 and established an airline subsidiary Boeing Air Transport. The airline's success was aided by Boeing's Model 40A the first plane to use Frederick Rentschler's new air-cooled engine.

Rentschler and Boeing combined their companies as United Aircraft and Transport in 1929 and introduced the all-metal airliner in 1933. The next year new antitrust rules forced United Aircraft and Transportation to sell portions of its operations as United Air Lines and United Aircraft (later United Technologies). This left Boeing Airplane (as it was known until 1961) with the manufacturing concerns.

EXECUTIVES

Vice President of Business Development, Jeff Trauberman

EVP and CEO Boeing Global Services, Stanley A. (Stan) Deal, age 53

EVP and General Counsel, J. Michael (Mike) Luttig, age 62, $903,673 total compensation

SVP Supply Chain and Operations, Patrick M. (Pat) Shanahan, age 55

Chairman President and CEO, Dennis A. Muilenburg, age 53, $1,640,962 total compensation

President Phantom Works Boeing Defense Space and Security, Darryl W. Davis

EVP and President and CEO Boeing Commercial Airplanes, Kevin G. McAllister, age 54, $92,308 total compensation

SVP Sales Asia Pacific and President Boeing India, Dinesh A. Keskar, age 63

EVP Business Development and Strategy and CFO, Gregory D. (Greg) Smith, age 50, $911,442 total compensation

President Boeing Military Aircraft Boeing Defense Space and Security, Shelley K. Lavender, age 53

SVP and President Boeing International, Bertrand-Marc (Marc) Allen, age 43

SVP Information and Analytics and CIO, Theodore (Ted) Colbert, age 43

VP and General Manager Boeing Research and Technology, Gregory L. (Greg) Hyslop, age 58

President Boeing Capital Corporation, Timothy Myers

EVP and President and CEO Defense Space and Security (BDS), Leanne G. Caret, age 50

President Network and Space Systems, Jim Chilton

President Boeing Defense Space and Security Development (BDS), Patrick (Pat) Goggin

Vice President Supplier Management 787, Robert Noble

Vice President Global Trade Services, Haynes Arnett

Vice President of Product Management and Marketing, Shawn Hill

Boeing Vice President of Leasing Sales, Bill Collins

Vice President, Mark Harris

Vice President, Bernard Hensey

Vice President and Communications Architect, Dave Blue

Vice President, Bill McSherry

Vice President Legislative Affairs, Steve Bachmann

Regional Vice President, David Cazer

Vice President Human Resources, Grace Miller

Executive Vice President, Pete Desalvo

Vice President, Darcel Wesen

Vice President Australia and Pacific Sales, Rick Westmoreland

Vice President Corporate Strategy, Rik Geiersbach

Vice President Sales, Mitzy Gough

Senior Vice President and Senior Lending Officer, Eric S Cohen

Vice President, Paula Nosca-lay

Vice President Finance, Rick Gross

Vice President, James W Hoskinson

Vice President of Sales for Digital Division, Keith P White

Vice President Procurement Contracting and Risk Management, Karl Jeppesen

Vice President and P 8 Program Manager, Chuck Dabundo

Vice President Integrated Defense System, Gregory Laxton

Vice President Customer Support Americas, Larry Slate

Vice President F A 18 Programs, Mike Gibbons

Vice President Business Systems and Administration, Renee L Stober

Vice President Airplane Development Engineering, Ed Petkus

Vice President, Sherry Carbary

Vice President, Brad McMullen

National Account Manager, Jacqueli Stephenson

Vice President Develop, John Roundhill

VP Engineering, William Carrier

Vice President, Jay Byunn

Vice President Business Development, Christopher Raymond

VICE PRESIDENT, Peter Hoffman

Vice President Of Marketing And Sales, Lynn Johnson

Vice President And Program Manager, Joy Bryant

Boeing Vice President Of The Aew And C Program, Maureen Dougherty

Vice President, Tim Sele

Vice President Accounting And Financial Reporting, Michael Cleary

Vice President, Randy Woolard

Vice President, Bruce Dennis

Vice President, Thomas Brennan

Vice President, Tobias Bright

Executive Vice President Global Franchise Development, Rich Hoffman

Oa To Vice President Process Tools And Affordabil, Julia Butler

Vice President And General Manager For Supplier Management, Steve Schaffer

Vice President Supply Chain, Ken Shaw

Vice President, Paul Pasquier

Vice President of Sales and Marketing, Harry W Gray

Israel Vice President Mds, Avi Barber

Capital Vice President For Asia And, Foster Arata

Vice President Navigation and Communication Systems Military Satellite Communica, Ken Torok

Vice president, Maureen Cragin

Executive Vice President, James Bell

Senior Vice President Public Policy, Tim Keating

Vice President Air Force Precision En, Jack Catton

Senior Vice President Operations, Ed Dolanski

VICE PRESIDENT AND PROGRAM DIRECTOR MISSILE DEFENSE NATIONAL TEAMS, Gregory Brown

Vice President, Catherine J Pruss-Jones

Vice President Engineering, Russell E Shue

Vice President and General Manager 717 Program, Jim Phillips

Vice President of Commercial Airplane Contracts, Thomas J Hyland

Vice President and Program Manager C 130 Avionics Modernization Program, Michael Harris

Office of the Vice President of Engineering, Patricia Sandoval

Vice President, STEVE WALLACE

Vice President, Kim Hammonds

Vice President Edelman Employee Engagement Practice, Nicole Silva

Vice President of Decision Support, Rebecca Fasano

Vice President of International Relations, Troy Thomason

Vice President, Michael Zavada

Vice President, Anbessie Yitbarek

Executive Vice President, Jordan Muller

Vice President and Deputy General Manager Government Information and Communications Systems, Art Cohen

Vice President Director of Marketing, Paul Mittmann

Vice President Investor Relations, Troy Lahr

Senior Vice President Supplier Management, Jim Morris

Vice President Legislative Affairs Authorizations, Michael Waclawski

Vice Chairman, Raymond L. (Ray) Conner, age 61

Board Member, Jack Commerford

Board Member, Bill Crawford

Secretary, Mark Little

Assistant Treasurer, Ruud Roggekamp

Secretary, Kandice Taylor

Secretary, Bruce J Cadiz

Board Member, James W Powers

Board Member, Daniel Anderson

Assistant Treasurer, Verett Mims

Board Member, Nancy J Kaatman

Treasurer, Roger Pullman

Board Member, Scott Bolton

Board Member, George Durham

Chapter Treasurer, Daniel Hill

Secretary, Chris Tavares

Treasurer, Laura LU

Secretary, Dale Armstrong

Board Member, Ed Dreyer

Office of the Treasurer, Kim Rainey

Board Member, Charles Lee

TREASURER, Melinda Donaldson

Auditors: DELOITTE & TOUCHE LLP

LOCATIONS

HQ: Boeing Co. (The)
100 North Riverside Plaza, Chicago, IL 60606-1596
Phone: 312 544-2000
Web: www.boeing.com

2016 Sales

	$ mil.	% of total
US	38,765	41
Asia		
China	10,312	11
Other Asia	10,553	11
Europe	13,790	15
Middle East	13,297	14
Oceania	1,843	2
Canada	2,076	2
Africa	1,999	2
Latin American Caribbean & other	1,936	2
Total	**94,571**	**100**

PRODUCTS/OPERATIONS

2016 Sales

	$ mil.	% of total
Sales of products	84,399	89
Sales of services	10,172	11
Total	**94,571**	**100**

2016 Sales

	$ mil.	% of total
Commercial Airplanes	65,069	69
Defense Space & Security		
Military Aircraft	12,515	13
Global Services & Support	9,937	11
Network & Space Systems	7,046	7
Boeing Capital	298	-
Adjustments	(294)	-
Total	**94,571**	**100**

Selected Products and Services

Commercial Airplanes
Products
  737 Next Generation (short-to-medium-range two-engine jet)
  747 (long-range four-engine jet)
  767 (medium-to-long-range two-engine jet)
  777 (long-range two-engine jet)
  Boeing Business Jet
  787 Dreamliner (in development; long-range super-efficient 200-250 passenger capacity)
  747-8 (in development;
Services
  Engineering modification and logistics
  Maintenance repair and overhaul
  Boeing Training & Flight Services
Defense Space & Security
  Military Aircraft
  AH-64 Apache
  B-1B Lancer
  B-2 Spirit
  F/A-18 Hornet
  F-15E Strike Eagle
  F-22 Raptor
  T-45 Flight Training System
  A160 Hummingbird
  Harpoon
  Insitu
  C-17 Globemaster III
  CH-47D/F Chinook
  V-22 Osprey
  Global Services & Support
  Integrated logistics
  Maintenance modifications and upgrades
  Training systems
  Government services
  Network & Space Systems
  Electronic and mission
  Cyber security
  Infrastructure
  Intelligence
  Logistics command and control
  Satellite and ground operations
  Space exploration

COMPETITORS

AgustaWestland	Lockheed Martin
Airbus	Northrop Grumman
Airbus Group	Raytheon
BAE SYSTEMS	Rockwell Collins
Dassault Aviation	Space Exploration
Embraer	Technologies
General Dynamics	Thales
Kaman	United Technologies
Leonardo	

HISTORICAL FINANCIALS

Company Type: Public

Income Statement

FYE: December 31

	REVENUE ($ mil.)	NET INCOME ($ mil.)	NET PROFIT MARGIN	EMPLOYEES
12/17	93,392	8,197	8.8%	140,800
12/16	94,571	4,895	5.2%	150,500
12/15	96,114	5,176	5.4%	161,400
12/14	90,762	5,446	6.0%	165,500
12/13	86,623	4,585	5.3%	168,400
Annual Growth	1.9%	15.6%	—	(4.4%)

2017 Year-End Financials

Debt ratio: 12.04%	No. of shares (mil.): 591
Return on equity: 1,398.81%	Dividends
Cash ($ mil.): 8,813	Yield: 0.0%
Current ratio: 1.16	Payout: 42.2%
Long-term debt ($ mil.): 9,782	Market value ($ mil.): 174,303

	STOCK PRICE ($) FY Close	P/E High/Low	PER SHARE ($) Earnings	Dividends	Book Value
12/17	294.91	22 12	13.43	5.68	0.60
12/16	155.68	20 14	7.61	4.36	1.32
12/15	144.59	21 17	7.44	3.64	9.50
12/14	129.98	19 16	7.38	2.92	12.26
12/13	136.49	23 12	5.96	1.94	19.90
Annual Growth	21.2%	— —	22.5%	30.8%	(58.3%)

BofI Holding, Inc.

Skip the teller lines by banking with a branchless online-only bank BofI Holding Inc. It is the holding company for BofI Federal Bank which provides consumers and businesses a variety of banking choices for both deposits and loans. It conducts its business without any physical bank branches preferring to support its customers through a comprehensive online banking platform supported occasionally by physical retail locations of its partners. The majority of its business originates in its headquarter state of California though its online operations attract customers from every US state.

Operations

BofI operates a single financial reporting segment. Its operations are generally divided into attracting money (deposits) and then lending it out (loans).

The lending business originates purchases and sometimes sells loans. The bank issues loans for single family homes commercial real estate (for example multi-family units) commercial & industrial needs small business operations and consumer purchases (such as for automobiles). Single family residential and multi-family mortgages make up more than 70% of its loan portfolio. About 85% of its loan and lease holdings are adjustable rate loans.

The bank?s deposit operations attract money from consumers and businesses with about 50% held in checking and other demand deposit accounts roughly 35% in savings accounts and the rest in time deposits (CDs) and IRA accounts. The bank?s deposits have grown dramatically between 2013 and 2017 from $2.1 billion to $6.8 billion because of significant growth in business deposits (10X increase over the same time).

Behind the scenes BofI operates a robust software platform that enables secure responsive banking interactions with nationwide customers who use smartphones and computers to access their accounts.

Geographic Reach

San Diego-based BofI holds deposits from customers in every US state with large sources of balances in Florida the Mid-Atlantic states and the California coast. Nearly 70% of its loans are secured by real estate in California.

Sales and Marketing

Because the bank is branchless the traditional means of attracting customers ? such as local advertising a physical bank presence community charity sponsorship ? are not used. Rather the bank creates brand awareness through digital marketing ensures a productive and intuitive user experience and gathers analytical data about their customers to help cross-sell other products and generate ideas for product/service enhancements.

Financial Performance

In recent years BofI experienced strong annual increases in revenue composed mainly of interest and non-interest income and in net income. Interest income jumped from $63 million in FY2009 (ending June 30) to more than $380 million in FY2017. Non-interest income typically fees and gains from loan sales rose from $1.4 million to more than $68 million in the same time. Net income experienced a similar rise swelling from $3.9 million in 2009 to almost $135 million in 2017.

For the fiscal year 2017 BofI generated $387 million of interest income a 22% increase from FY2016. An increase in the bank?s net interest margin to 3.95% in FY2017 (versus 3.91% in the prior year) as well as a larger loan portfolio ($7.4 billion vs $6.4 billion) produced most of the increase. The bank also saw its non-interest income rise 3% to $68 million.

Net income rose 13% in FY2017 to $134 million compared to the prior year. The rise in interest income as the result of a larger loan portfolio was the primary reason for increased net income.

Cash and cash equivalents rose $156 million in FY2017 to $644 million. The cash buildup was the result of $753 million from financing activities (mainly from an increase in bank deposits) and $224 million from operations both offset by an $821 million use by investing activities (due to loan origination amounts higher than repayment amounts).

Strategy

BofI?s strategy is simply to grow its loan portfolio ? and therefore its interest income ? through new products expanded distribution channels leveraged data mining and occasional acquisitions.

In FY2017 the bank introduced two new products: retail auto loans and unsecured lending offerings. It also established a US tax refund advance through H&R Block. It?s partnership with H&R Block began in 2015 when it acquired $419 million in deposits from tax preparer?s owned bank. From there the H&R Block distribution channel has blossomed to include several BofI services made available to the tax preparer?s nearly 20 million customers including coordinating the US government?s electronically delivered tax refund and an offer made by H&R Block tax preparers to open a BofI-originated IRA account.

The amount of customer data gathered by BofI through its own customer base and through the H&R Block customers that choose to use BofI?s tax refund services is a significant data mining asset. The bank analyzes this information to help cross-sell other products & services and even anticipates deploying artificial intelligence to assist with the effort.

From time to time the bank purchases loans and leases from other entities. It did so in early 2016 with the acquisition of $140 million of equipment leases from Pacific Western Equipment Finance and with the 2015 acquisition of H&R Block Bank deposits.

EXECUTIVES

EVP and CFO BofI Holding Inc. and BofI Federal Bank, Andrew J. Micheletti, age 60, $231,000 total compensation
President and CEO BofI Holding Inc. and BofI Federal Bank, Gregory Garrabrants, age 46, $375,000 total compensation
EVP Specialty Finance and Chief Legal Officer BofI Federal Bank, Eshel Bar-Adon, age 62, $250,000 total compensation
EVP and Chief Credit Officer BofI Federal Bank, Thomas Constantine, age 55, $235,000 total compensation
EVP and Chief Lending Officer BofI Federal Bank, Brian Swanson, age 37, $235,000 total compensation
EVP Chief of Staff and Chief Performance Officer BofI Federal Bank, Jan Durrans

EVP Chief Deposit Officer and Chief Marketing Officer BofI Federal Bank, Eduardo Urdapilleta
Senior Vice President Chief Accounting Officer, Derrick Walsh
Chairman, Paul J. Grinberg, age 56
Vice Chairman, Nicholas A. Mosich
Auditors: BDO USA, LLP

LOCATIONS

HQ: BofI Holding, Inc.
4350 La Jolla Village Drive, Suite 140, San Diego, CA 92122
Phone: 858 350-6200
Web: www.bofiholding.com

PRODUCTS/OPERATIONS

2016 Sales

	$ mil.	% of total
Interest and dividend income:		
Loans and leases including fees	358	79
Investments	28	6
Non-interest income	68	14
Total	**455**	**100**

COMPETITORS

Ally Bank	ISN Bank
California Bank & Trust	MUFG Americas Holdings
Discover	PacWest Bancorp
E*TRADE Bank	San Diego County Credit Union
First IB	Scottrade
HSBC USA	

HISTORICAL FINANCIALS

Company Type: Public

Income Statement   FYE: June 30

	ASSETS ($ mil.)	NET INCOME ($ mil.)	INCOME AS % OF ASSETS	EMPLOYEES
06/17	8,501	134	1.6%	681
06/16	7,601	119	1.6%	647
06/15	5,823	82	1.4%	467
06/14	4,403	55	1.3%	366
06/13	3,090	40	1.3%	312
Annual Growth	**28.8%**	**35.2%**	**—**	**21.5%**

2017 Year-End Financials

Debt ratio: 0.64%
Return on equity: 17.75%
Cash ($ mil.): 628
Current ratio: —
Long-term debt ($ mil.): —
No. of shares (mil.): 63
Dividends
Yield: —
Payout: —
Market value ($ mil.): 1,507

	STOCK PRICE ($) FY Close	P/E High/Low		PER SHARE ($) Earnings	Dividends	Book Value
06/17	23.72	16	7	2.07	0.00	13.13
06/16	17.71	77	7	1.85	0.00	10.81
06/15	105.71	79	49	1.34	0.00	8.59
06/14	73.47	109	48	0.96	0.00	6.41
06/13	45.82	65	26	0.72	0.00	4.88
Annual Growth	**(15.2%)**	**—**		**30.1%**	**—**	**28.1%**

BOK Financial Corp

Will your money BOK? Multibank holding company BOK Financial tries to make sure it is. With seven principal banking divisions in eight midwestern and southwestern states BOK offers a range of financial services to consumers and regional businesses. In addition to traditional deposit lending and trust services the banks provide investment management wealth advisory and mineral and real estate management services through a network of about 200 branches in Arizona Arkansas Colorado Kansas Missouri New Mexico Oklahoma and Texas. Brokerage subsidiary BOSC underwrites public private and municipal securities. BOK also owns electronic funds network TransFund and institutional asset manager Cavanal Hill.

Geographic Reach

Tulsa-based BOK Financial offers full service banking in Arizona northwest Arkansas Colorado Kansas Missouri New Mexico Oklahoma and Texas. Oklahoma is the company's largest market. Indeed BOK is the largest financial institution in Oklahoma with 14% of the state's total deposits. Bank of Oklahoma has 31% and 11% of the market share in the Tulsa and Oklahoma City areas respectively.

Financial Performance

BOK's revenue declined by nearly 7% in 2013 versus 2012 to $1.36 billion on a continuing slide in interest revenue and lower fees and commissions on mortgages. Trust fees and commissions were up $16 million (20%) and transaction card revenue was up $8.8 million over the prior year. Net income declined by 10% over the same period to $316.6 million on higher operating expenses for personnel and data processing and communications. Loan volume increased for the third consecutive year while nonperforming assets continued their steady decline.

Strategy

BOK emphasizes local decision-making at its flagship subsidiary Bank of Oklahoma and its operating divisions Bank of Texas Bank of Albuquerque Bank of Arkansas Colorado State Bank Bank of Kansas City and Bank of Arizona. Commercial loans primarily to the energy services health care and wholesale and retail industries make up the majority of the company's loan portfolio. Commercial real estate residential mortgage car and consumer loans round out its lending activities.

With nearly half of its business in its home state of Oklahoma BOK is looking to metropolitans areas such as Dallas/Fort Worth Houston Denver Kansas City and Phoenix for expansion either through acquisitions or by opening new branches. In 2013 Bank of Kansas City continued to grow in the Kansas City market with a new full-service banking center there as well as a wealth management and mortgage office.

The company is also focused on diversifying its revenue stream by growing its mortgage banking brokerage and wealth management operations. (In 2012 it acquired Denver-based The Milestone Group which oversees some $1.3 billion for wealthy investors.)

Mergers and Acquisitions

In March 2014 BOK acquired GTRUST Financial Corp. an independent trust and asset management company in Topeka Kansas. The acquisition added $600 million in assets to BOK's wealth management business and extended its product offering and client base in the Kansas market. In April 2014 the firm bought MBM Advisors a Houston-based independent full service retirement and pension plan investment firm and SEC registered investment adviser. The purchase increased BOK's retirement and assets under management by $1.25 billion while expanding its wealth management capabilities and presence in Houston.

EXECUTIVES

President and CEO, Steven G. (Steve) Bradshaw, age 57, $484,275 total compensation
EVP and CFO, Steven E. Nell, age 55, $439,354 total compensation
EVP Corporate Banking, Stacy C. Kymes, age 46
Chief Credit Officer, Marc C. Maun, age 59
Chairman and CEO Bank of Texas, Norman P. Bagwell, age 54, $403,054 total compensation
EVP and Chief Human Resources Officer, Stephen D. Grossi
EVP and CIO, Donald T. Parker
EVP Consumer Banking, Patrick E. Piper
EVP Wealth Management and CEO BOSC. Inc., Scott B. Grauer
President Oklahoma City Market, John Higginbotham
Senior Vice President, Charlie D Anderson
Vice President Senior Petroleum Engineer, Sterling Kirk Condry
Assistant Vice President Project Manager II Operations, Michael Vegher
Senior Vice President, Pam Schloeder
Vice President and Manager Product Integration, Kristy Hursh
Vice President Production, Kathy Davis
Vice President of Community Development Group, Paula Bryant-Ellis
Senior Vice President, Michael Bickel
Senior Vice President Of Information Security, Brian Foster
Vice President, Alice Worthington
Senior Vice President Credit Administration, Carol Cable
Senior Vice President, Lee Allen
Senior Vice President Institutional Investments BOSC, Michael Brown
Vice President, Debi Briscoe
Vice President Consumer Compliance, Dean Miller
Vice President of Corporate Recruiting Banking and Finance, Roxanna Maciel
Vice President, Lisa Albers
Assistant Vice President of Benefits, Terry Stanford
Senior Vice President, Jill Hall
Vice President, Brent Varzaly
Vice President, Mary Campbell
Vice President, Tom Williams
Vice President, Scott Smith
Vice President BSA AML Compliance Officer, Renee Huffaker
Chairman, George B. Kaiser, age 74
Auditors: Ernst & Young LLP

LOCATIONS

HQ: BOK Financial Corp
Bank of Oklahoma Tower, Boston Avenue at Second Street, Tulsa, OK 74172
Phone: 918 588-6000
Web: www.bokf.com

PRODUCTS/OPERATIONS

2016 Sales

	$ mil.	% of total
Interest		
Loans	581	38
Available-for-sale securities	175	12
Other	72	5
Non-interest		
Brokerage & trading	138	9
Transaction card revenue	135	9
Mortgage banking	133	9
Fiduciary and asset management	135	9
Deposit service charges and fees	92	6
Other	51	3
Adjustment	(12.7)	-
Total	**1,503**	**100**

Selected Banking Subsidiaries

Bank of Albuquerque National Association
Bank of Arizona National Association
Bank of Arkansas National Association
Bank of Kansas City National Association
Bank of Oklahoma National Association
Bank of Texas National Association
Colorado State Bank & Trust

COMPETITORS

BBVA Compass Bancshares	First National of Nebraska
Bank of America	JPMorgan Chase
Bank of the West	Regions Financial
CoBiz Financial	UMB Financial
Comerica	Wells Fargo
Commerce Bancshares	Zions Bancorporation

HISTORICAL FINANCIALS

Company Type: Public

Income Statement

FYE: December 31

	ASSETS ($ mil.)	NET INCOME ($ mil.)	INCOME AS % OF ASSETS	EMPLOYEES
12/16	32,772	232	0.7%	4,884
12/15	31,476	288	0.9%	4,789
12/14	29,089	292	1.0%	4,743
12/13	27,015	316	1.2%	4,632
12/12	28,148	351	1.2%	4,704
Annual Growth	3.9%	(9.8%)	—	0.9%

2016 Year-End Financials

Debt ratio: 15.23%	No. of shares (mil.): 65
Return on equity: 7.13%	Dividends
Cash ($ mil.): 2,537	Yield: 0.0%
Current ratio: —	Payout: 49.0%
Long-term debt ($ mil.): —	Market value ($ mil.): 5,426

	STOCK PRICE ($) FY Close	P/E High/Low		PER SHARE ($) Earnings	Dividends	Book Value
12/16	83.04	24	13	3.53	1.73	50.12
12/15	59.79	17	13	4.21	1.69	49.03
12/14	60.04	17	14	4.22	1.62	47.78
12/13	66.32	15	12	4.59	1.54	43.86
12/12	54.46	12	10	5.13	2.47	43.29
Annual Growth	11.1%	—	—	(8.9%)	(8.5%)	3.7%

Booz Allen Hamilton Holding Corp.

For almost a century consultants at Booz Allen Hamilton have been helping US government agencies operate more efficiently at home and abroad. The firm provides a wide range of management consulting and technology integration services; its specialties include information technology operations organization and change program management strategy training programs cybersecurity and systems engineering. Booz Allen has long-established relationships with such agencies as the Department of Defense the Federal Aviation Administration and the Internal Revenue Service. Investment firm The Carlyle Group owns a majority interest in the consulting firm which was founded in 1914.

Geographic Reach

Booz Allen's headquarters are located in McLean Virginia. The firm also has offices in An-

napolis Junction Maryland; Rockville Maryland; San Diego California; Herndon Virginia; and Washington D.C. It opened an office in Singapore during 2015 that will serve as the firm's base for operations in Southeast Asia.

Sales and Marketing

Besides the US defense industry and its other major government clients (which accounted for nearly 50% of the total revenue in fiscal 2016) the firm serves customers in the financial services healthcare energy retail and automotive markets.

Financial Performance

Booz Allen reported revenue of $5.41 billion for fiscal 2016. That was an increase of 2% compared to its fiscal 2015 revenue. The slight increase was due to a spike in client demand.

The firm claimed a net income of $294.09 million in fiscal 2016. That was an increase of $61.52 million (or 26%) compared to its net income in fiscal 2015. The increase was the result of increased net sales combined with a decrease in expenses.

Booz Allen ended fiscal 2016 with $249.23 million in cash on hand from operations. That was a drop of 20% compared to its cash levels at the end of the prior fiscal period.

Strategy

The consulting firm plans to continue to grow its client base across a wide spectrum of government agencies and departments. Though almost entirely focused on US government clients (98% of revenue) Booz Allen undertakes a variety of engagements. Key markets include civil government agencies responsible for energy finance health and transportation.

Booz Allen is also focused on enhancing its cyber-security products and services in the commercial market. The firm has invested heavily in advanced technical capabilities including engineering systems delivery cyber and analytics.

Mergers and Acquisitions

During fiscal 2015 Booz Allen acquired the software services unit of the Charleston South Carolina technology firm SPARC. The deal further strengthened and complemented the firm's growing capabilities in Agile software development a key component in its approach to solving complex technology and mission-critical systems challenges. The acquisition expanded and enhanced the firm's ability to integrate technical and mission-related requirements to deliver technologies like cloud mobile and modular services using contemporary methodologies such as Agile DevOps and open source.

During fiscal 2014 the firm acquired Boston-based Epidemico. Epidemico is an informatics company providing early insights continuous monitoring and consumer engagement for varied aspects of population health. Also that year Booz Allen Hamilton acquired a Baltimore-based healthcare unit of Genova Technologies.

HISTORY

Edwin Booz graduated from Northwestern University in 1914 with degrees in economics and psychology and started a statistical analysis firm in Chicago. After serving in the army during WWI he returned to his firm renamed Edwin Booz Surveys. In 1925 Booz hired his first full-time assistant George Fry and in 1929 he hired a second James Allen. By then the company had a long list of clients including U.S. Gypsum the Chicago Tribune and Montgomery Ward which was losing a retail battle with Sears Roebuck and Co.

In 1935 Carl Hamilton joined the partnership and a year later it was renamed Booz Fry Allen & Hamilton. The firm prospered well into the next decade by providing advice based on "independence that enables us to say plainly from the out-

side what cannot always be said safely from within" according to a company brochure.

During WWII the firm worked increasingly on government and military contracts. Fry opposed the pursuit of such work for consultants and left in 1942. The firm was renamed Booz Allen & Hamilton. Hamilton died in 1946 and the following year Booz retired (he died in 1951) leaving Allen as chairman. He successfully steered the firm into lucrative postwar work for clients such as Johnson Wax RCA and the US Air Force.

A separate company Booz Allen Applied Research Inc. (BAARINC) was formed in 1955 for technical and government consulting including missile and weaponry work as well as consulting with NASA. By the end of the decade Timehad dubbed Booz Allen "the world's largest most prestigious management consultant firm." The partnership was incorporated as a private company in 1962 and in 1967 commissioner Pete Rozelle requested its services for the merger of the National Football League and American Football League.

When Allen retired in 1970 Charlie Bowen became the new chairman and the company went public. However as the economy stalled during the energy crisis spending for consultants plunged. Jim Farley replaced Bowen in 1975 and the company was taken private again in 1976. A turnaround was engineered and the firm was soon helping Chrysler through its 1979 bailout and developing strategies for the breakup of AT&T in 1984.

Booz Allen again experienced trouble in the 1980s after Farley instituted a competition to select his successor. Michael McCullough was eventually chosen in 1984 but the 10-month election process turned into a dogfight that pitted partner against partner taking an enormous toll on morale. McCullough began restructuring the firm along industry lines creating a department store of services in an industry characterized by boutique houses. The turmoil was too much and by 1988 nearly a third of the partners had quit.

William Stasior became chairman in 1991 and reorganized Booz Allen yet again splitting it down public and private sector lines. Allen died in 1992 the same year the firm moved to McLean Virginia. The company began privatization work in the former Soviet Union and in Eastern Europe in 1992 and continued to emphasize government business including contracts with the IRS (1995) for technology modernization and with the General Services Administration (1996) to provide technical and management support for all federal telecommunications users.

In 1998 the company won a 10-year $200 million contract with the US Defense Department to establish a scientific and technical data warehouse. Ralph Shrader was appointed CEO in early 1999; Stasior retired as chairman later that year. Booz Allen acquired Scandinavian consulting firm Carta in 1999 and formed a venture capital firm for startups with Lehman Brothers in 2000. The company announced in late 2000 that it would spin off Aestix its e-commerce business but reconsidered amid a general economic slowdown and hostile IPO market. (The unit was integrated back into Booz Allen in 2002.)

Booz Allen saw an increase in work related to defense and national security after the terrorist attacks of September 11 2001. Engagements included work related to the reconstruction of Iraq (as a subcontractor on telecommunications projects managed by Lucent) and in 2003 Booz Allen was awarded a contract from the US Health Resources and Services Administration to help establish and operate a bioterrorism technical support center.

In 2008 Booz Allen spun off its commercial consulting business as an independent firm Booz &

Company. The spinoff was part of a transaction in which investment firm The Carlyle Group acquired a controlling interest in the Booz Allen's government-related consulting business which retained the Booz Allen name.

Striving to alleviate debt Booz Allen launched an initial public offering on the New York Stock Exchange in November 2010.

EXECUTIVES

Vice President and Member of the Firm's Global Information Technology Business U, Ronald Hodge
EVP Middle East and North Africa (MENA), Nabih Maroun
EVP Digital Solutions, Gary D. Labovich
President and CEO, Horacio D. Rozanski, age 49, $1,437,500 total compensation
EVP Justice and Homeland Security Business, Thad W. Allen
EVP Directed Energy Innovation, Henry A. (Trey) Obering
EVP CFO and Treasurer, Lloyd W. Howell, age 55, $1,000,000 total compensation
EVP Chief Administrative Officer (CAO) and Chief Information Security Officer (CISO), Joseph W. (Joe) Mahaffee, age 59, $765,000 total compensation
EVP Strategic Transformation, Michael M. (Mike) Thomas
EVP Homeland Security and Transportation, Patrick F. Peck, age 59
VP, Fred K. Blackburn
EVP Digital Solutions, Gary C. Cubbage
EVP Civil Commercial Group (CCG), Karen M. Dahut, age 53, $1,000,000 total compensation
EVP, Maria Darby
EVP Joint Combatant Command, Judith H. (Judi) Dotson
EVP Infrastructure and Military Health, Laurene (Laurie) Gallo
EVP Engineering and Science and C4ISR Crosscut, Patricia Goforth
EVP Defense Business, Tom Greenspon
VP, Gregory Harrison
VP, David Kletter
EVP International Business, Christopher Ling
EVP Defense and Intelligence Group, Joseph (Joe) Logue, age 52, $1,250,000 total compensation
EVP Innovation Service Officer (ISO) and Cyber Functional Service Officer (FSO), Angela M. (Angie) Messer
EVP and Deputy Lead Defense and Intelligence, Anthony (Tony) Mitchell
EVP and Chief Innovation Officer, Susan L. Penfield
VP, Gary Rahl
EVP and Lead U.S. Defense and Military Intelligence and Operations, Joseph F. (Joe) Sifer
EVP Defense and Intelligence, Ted Sniffin
EVP Commercial Cyber Business, William (Bill) Stewart
EVP and Chief Personnel Officer, Elizabeth M. (Betty) Thompson, age 62
EVP Strategic Innovation Group (SIG), Gregory G. (Greg) Wenzel
EVP Cyber Business, Christopher Pierce
EVP and Deputy Director Defense and Intelligence, Joan A. Dempsey
EVP Civil Health Business, Kristine Martin Anderson
EVP Chief Legal Officer and Secretary, Nancy J. Laben, age 55
VP and CIO, Kevin Winter
EVP Energy Chemicals and Utilities, Walid Fayad
EVP Middle East and North Africa, Ramez Shehadi
EVP Command Control Communications Computers Intelligence Surveillance and Reconnaissance (C4ISR), Steve Soules

EVP Army Market, Brian M. McKeon
EVP Digital Practice Middle East and North Africa (MENA), Raymond Khoury
Vice President, Jeff Fossum
Vice President, Kevin Vigilante
EXECUTIVE VICE PRESIDENT, Michael Farber
Vice President, Theodore Kraemer
Vice President, Julie Mcpherson
Vice President, Larry Scheuble
Vice President, Tom Moorman
Vice President, Ralph Lawrence
Vice President, Souheil Moukaddem
Vice President, Lucy Stribley
Vice President, Lutfi Zakhour
Vice President, Danny Karam
Vice President, Adham Sleiman
Vice President, Donald Busson
Vice President, Fady Kassatly
Vice President, Chris Pierce
Vice President Sales And Marketing, Scott Barr
Vice President, Stephen Moore
Executive Vice President and the Chief Information Security Officer, Joe Mahaffee
Vice President, Jason Escaravage
Vice President, Terry Thompson
Senior Vice President and Chief Administrative Officer, Samuel R Strickland
Vice President of Information Technology, Joe Sifer
Vice President, Scott Welles
Vice President Human Capital Management, Abe Zwany
Senior Vice President, Andrea Inserra
Vice President, Ralph Wade
Senior Vice President, Robert Smith
VICE PRESIDENT, Tim Lawrence
Vice President, Deane Edelman
Vice President, Paul Tartaglione
Executive Vice President, Judy Dotson
VICE PRESIDENT, Chris Ellis
Chairman, Ralph W. Shrader, age 73
Auditors: Ernst & Young LLP

LOCATIONS

HQ: Booz Allen Hamilton Holding Corp.
8283 Greensboro Drive, McLean, VA 22102
Phone: 703 902-5000
Web: www.boozallen.com

PRODUCTS/OPERATIONS

Selected Markets Served
Civil government
 Benefits and entitlements
 Federal finance
 International development and diplomacy
Defense
 Air Force
 Army
 Joint staff and combatant commands
 Navy and Marine Corps
 Office of the Secretary of Defense and defense agencies
 Space
Energy
Environment
Health
 Health informatics
 Health not-for-profit/nongovernmental organizations
 International public health
 US public health
Homeland security
Intelligence
Law enforcement
Not-for-profit/nongovernmental organizations
Transportation
 Aviation infrastructure
 Highways and automotive technology
 Passenger rail and mass transit

Selected Practice Areas
Assurance and resilience
Economic and business analysis
Information technology

Modeling and simulation
Organization and strategy
Supply chain and logistics
Systems engineering and integration

COMPETITORS

A.T. Kearney	IBM
Accenture	L3 Technologies
BAE SYSTEMS	Leidos
Bain & Company	Lockheed Martin
Boeing	MAXIMUS
Boston Consulting	ManTech
CACI International	McKinsey & Company
Capgemini	Northrop Grumman
Computer Sciences Corp.	PA Consulting
Deloitte Consulting	PRTM Management
General Dynamics	Raytheon
HP Enterprise Services	Unisys

HISTORICAL FINANCIALS
Company Type: Public

Income Statement
FYE: March 31

	REVENUE ($ mil.)	NET INCOME ($ mil.)	NET PROFIT MARGIN	EMPLOYEES
03/17	5,804	252	4.4%	23,300
03/16	5,405	294	5.4%	22,600
03/15	5,274	232	4.4%	22,500
03/14	5,478	232	4.2%	22,700
03/13	5,758	219	3.8%	24,500
Annual Growth	0.2%	3.6%	—	(1.2%)

2017 Year-End Financials

Debt ratio: 49.31%	No. of shares (mil.): 148
Return on equity: 51.42%	Dividends
Cash ($ mil.): 217	Yield: 1.7%
Current ratio: 1.18	Payout: 37.1%
Long-term debt ($ mil.): 1,470	Market value ($ mil.): 5,269

	STOCK PRICE ($) FY Close	P/E High/Low	PER SHARE ($) Earnings	Dividends	Book Value
03/17	35.39	23 16	1.67	0.62	3.85
03/16	30.28	16 12	1.94	0.54	2.76
03/15	28.94	19 13	1.52	1.46	1.25
03/14	22.00	14 8	1.54	2.40	1.15
03/13	13.44	12 8	1.45	8.36	1.55
Annual Growth	27.4%	— —	3.6%	(47.8%)	25.5%

BorgWarner Inc

If suburbanites need four-wheel-drive vehicles to turbocharge their urban drive that's OK with BorgWarner. The company is a leading maker of engine and drivetrain products for the world's major automotive manufacturers. Products include turbochargers air pumps timing chain systems four-wheel-drive and all-wheel-drive transfer cases (primarily for light trucks and SUVs) and transmission components. Its largest customers include Volkswagen Ford and Daimler. The company nets around 75% of its sales from outside the US.

Operations

BorgWarner divides its operations into the two segments of engine products (about 60% of total sales) and drivetrain products (40%). The engine group optimizes engines for fuel efficiency reduced emissions and enhanced performance and includes engine timing systems boosting systems ignition systems air and noise management and cooling and controls. The drivetrain group provides automotive transmission components. Turbochargers for light vehicles is the company's largest product line representing 30% of sales.

Key divisions and units include BorgWarner TorqTransfer Systems BorgWarner Transmission Systems BorgWarner Morse TEC and BorgWarner BERU Systems. BorgWarner also operates nine joint ventures located in China India and South Korea.

Geographic Reach

BorgWarner operates nearly 60 manufacturing and technical facilities in some 20 countries (including more than a dozen in the US and about half a dozen each in Germany China and South Korea). Europe is by far BorgWarner's largest market; Germany accounts for roughly 20% of total sales and Hungary and France collectively account for nearly 10%. The US generates around 25% of its sales with South Korea and China combined representing almost 25%.

Sales and Marketing

The company markets its products to OEMs of light vehicles (passenger cars sport-utility vehicles vans and light trucks) through separate sales teams for its two product divisions. In 2016 Volkswagen and Ford each generated 15% and 15% of the company's overall sales respectively. Other key customers include Chrysler Nissan and General Motors.

Financial Performance

BorgWarner in 2016 enjoyed unprecedented growth with revenues peaking at a record-setting $9.1 billion. The growth was fueled by a 38% rise in drivetrain products due to higher sales of all-wheel drive systems. The company also experienced increased growth within the countries of Mexico (158%) South Korea (28%) and China (21%).

However BorgWarner's profits nosedived by more than 80% from $610 million in 2015 to $119 million in 2016. This was primarily due to a $127 million recorded loss on a divestiture associated with Remy's light vehicle aftermarket business. In addition BorgWarner paid $27 million in restructuring expenses and $24 million in realignment fees in 2016 which ate into its bottom line.

Strategy

The engine maker's strategy is to follow market share as it shifts away from Detroit and toward Asia and Europe. Manufacturing operations are situated close to demand enabling the company to ship products directly from its plant to the customer. Western automotive companies are scrambling to grab a piece of the market in Asia particularly in China which is signaling to overtake the US as the largest automotive market in the world.

Mergers and Acquisitions

BorgWarner has been generating additional revenue over the years through the use of acquisitions. In a milestone transaction in late 2015 the company acquired Remy International for $1.2 billion. Remy is a global producer of rotating electrical components with key technologies and operations spanning 10 countries. The deal enhanced BorgWarner's rapidly developing powertrain electrification technology line.

HISTORY

BorgWarner traces its roots to the 1928 merger of major Chicago auto parts companies Borg & Beck (clutches) Warner Gear (transmissions) Mechanics Universal Joint and Marvel Carburetor. The newly named Borg-Warner Corporation quickly began buying other companies including Ingersoll Steel & Disc (agricultural blades and discs) and Norge (refrigerators).

EXECUTIVES

Vice President, Pete Kohler

VP General Counsel and Secretary, John J. Gasparovic, age 59, $477,250 total compensation

VP; President and General Manager BorgWarner Transmissions Systems, Robin Kendrick, age 52, $406,250 total compensation

VP Marketing Public Relations Communications and Government Affairs, Scott D. Gallett, age 51

EVP and CFO, Ronald T. (Ron) Hundzinski, age 58, $665,750 total compensation

President and CEO, James R. Verrier, age 54, $1,245,000 total compensation

VP and President and General Manager BorgWarner Emissions Systems, Brady D. Ericson, age 45, $415,000 total compensation

VP and President and General Manager BorgWarner Morse Systems, Joseph F. Fadool, age 50, $416,250 total compensation

VP; President and General Manager BorgWarner Turbo Systems, Frédéric B. Lissalde, age 49, $606,630 total compensation

VP and President and General Manager BorgWarner PowerDrive Systems, Stefan Demmerle, age 52, $442,750 total compensation

Vice President And Treasurer, Jan Bertsch

Vice President of Finance, Jim Hohenadel

Vice President Information Technology, Andre Rothfuss

Vice President and General Manager II, Joel Wiegert

Vice President Global Supply Chain Management, Thomas Babineau

Vice President Sales and Business Development, Brad Lafaive

Vice President Sales and Marketing Turbo, Ulli Froehn

Vice President Human Resources, Monica Rottman

Vice President Director Finance, Karsten Edel

Vice President Global Supply Chain Turbo Systems, Radhika Batra

Vice President Manufacturing Strategi, Steve Snyder

Vice President Global Supply Chain Management, Marco Caputo

VP Human Resources, Shelley Bridarolli

Vice President Global Engineering and Sales Commercial Vehicle, Wouter Nijenhuis

Vice President and Treasurer, Tom McGill

Chairman, Alexis P. Michas, age 59

Auditors: PricewaterhouseCoopers LLP

LOCATIONS

HQ: BorgWarner Inc
3850 Hamlin Road, Auburn Hills, MI 48326
Phone: 248 754-9200
Web: www.borgwarner.com

2016 Sales

	$ mil.	% of total
United States	2,236	25
Europe		
Germany	1,735	19
Hungary	541	6
France	305	3
Other countries	888	10
China	1,218	13
South Korea	948	11
Mexico	805	9
Other regions	393	4
Total	**9,071**	**100**

PRODUCTS/OPERATIONS

2016 Sales

	$ mil.	% of total
Engine	5,590	61
Drivetrain	3,523	39
Elimination	(42.8)	-
Total	**9,071**	**100**

Selected Products

Engine Group

Air-control valves
Chain tensioners and snubbers
Complete engine induction systems
Complex solenoids and multi-function modules
Crankshaft and camshaft sprockets
Diesel cabin heaters
Diesel cold starting systems (glow plugs and instant starting systems)
Electric air pumps
Engine hydraulic pumps
Exhaust gas-recirculation (EGR) coolers modules tubes and valves
Fan clutches
Fans and fan drives
Front-wheel and four-wheel-drive chain and timing-chain systems
High-temperature sensors (for exhaust gas aftertreatment systems)
Ignition coils
Intake manifolds
On-off fan drives
Single-function solenoids
Throttle bodies
Throttle position sensors
Tire pressure sensors
Transfer cases
Turbochargers
Drivetrain Group
Four-wheel-drive and all-wheel-drive transfer cases
Friction plates
One-way clutches
Torque converter lock-up clutches
Transmission bands

Selected Joint Ventures

BERU Korea Co. Ltd. (51% South Korea ignition coils and pumps)
Borg-Warner Shenglong (Ningbo) Co. Ltd. (70% China fans and fan drives)
BorgWarner TorqTransfer Systems Beijing Co. Ltd. (80% China transfer cases)
BorgWarner Transmission Systems Korea Inc. (60% South Korea transmission components)
BorgWarner United Transmission Systems Co. Ltd. (66% China transmission components)
BorgWarner-Vikas Emissions Systems India Private Limited (60% India EGR coolers)
Divgi-Warner Limited (60% India transfer cases and automatic locking hubs)
SeohanWarner Turbo Systems Ltd. (71% South Korea turbochargers)

COMPETITORS

American Axle & Manufacturing	Magna Powertrain
	Meritor
DENSO	Mitsubishi Heavy
Dana	Industries
Delphi Automotive Systems	Modine Manufacturing
	NGK SPARK PLUG
GKN	Renold
Honeywell International	Robert Bosch
	Schaeffler
IHI Corp.	Tsubaki Nakashima
JTEKT	Valeo
Kolbenschmidt Pierburg	Visteon

HISTORICAL FINANCIALS

Company Type: Public

Income Statement

FYE: December 31

	REVENUE ($ mil.)	NET INCOME ($ mil.)	NET PROFIT MARGIN	EMPLOYEES
12/17	9,799	439	4.5%	29,000
12/16	9,071	118	1.3%	27,000
12/15	8,023	609	7.6%	30,000
12/14	8,305	655	7.9%	22,000
12/13	7,436	624	8.4%	19,700
Annual Growth	**7.1%**	**(8.4%)**	**—**	**10.1%**

2017 Year-End Financials

Debt ratio: 22.36%
Return on equity: 12.69%
Cash ($ mil.): 545
Current ratio: 1.46
Long-term debt ($ mil.): 2,103

No. of shares (mil.): 210
Dividends
Yield: 0.0%
Payout: 28.3%
Market value ($ mil.): 10,770

STOCK PRICE ($)		P/E		PER SHARE ($)		
	FY Close	High/Low		Earnings	Dividends	Book Value
12/17	51.09	27	18	2.08	0.59	17.63
12/16	39.44	79	50	0.55	0.53	15.16
12/15	43.23	23	14	2.70	0.52	16.20
12/14	54.95	23	17	2.86	0.51	15.97
12/13	55.91	40	20	2.70	0.25	15.62
Annual Growth	(2.2%)	—	—	(6.3%)	23.9%	3.1%

Boston Private Financial Holdings, Inc.

Boston Private Financial Holdings (BPFH) is a holding company for firms engaged in wealth management and private banking including Boston Private Bank & Trust which operates branches in New England New York Los Angeles and the San Francisco Bay Area. (The bank sold its branches in the Pacific Northwest in 2013.) BPFH also owns four other wealth advisory and investment management firms. The company offers private banking wealth advisory investment management deposits and lending and trust services to wealthy individuals corporations and institutional clients. All told BPFH and its affiliates have more than $30 billion in managed or advised assets.

Operations

In addition to Boston Private Bank & Trust Co. BPFH's other affiliates include: investment advisory firms Anchor Capital Advisors and Dalton Greiner Hartman Maher & Co.; wealth managers Bingham Osborn & Scarborough and KLS Professional Advisors Group; as well as newly-acquired Banyan Partners a registered investment advisor. BPFH sold its majority-owned affiliate Davidson Trust Co. (DTC) in 2012. DTC was part of the holding company's wealth advisory business.

Financial Performance

Boston Private Financial Holdings (BPFH) reported revenue of $339.5 million in 2013 an increase of less than 1% versus 2012. The modest uptick was due to increased recurring fees from its investment management wealth advisory and private banking wealth management and trust businesses as well as other income and a gain on the sale of loans. Assets under management and advisory (AUM) increased 19% during 2013 due to $3.7 billion of market appreciation and $0.2 billion of net flows. All three of the BPFH's segments experienced gains in AUM.

Net income grew 32% in 2013 compared with 2012 to $70.5 million on a decline in interest expense on deposits partially offset by a 2% increase in average balance. The lower interest rate environment in the US has allowed the company's banking arm to lower interest rates on money markets accounts and certificates of deposit.

Strategy

Since its founding in 1987 Boston Private has had a voracious appetite for acquiring smaller trust companies private banks and wealth managers. While the firm put the brakes on its expansion and shifted strategies amid the economic recession. Indeed it divested about a half-dozen money management subsidiaries as way to raise capital and reduce risk. Also in 2011 the company consolidated its four banking charters into Boston Private Bank & Trust to simplify its structure and cut costs.

However with the economy and financial markets on the mend the company has resumed making acquisitions most recently to build its wealth management business.

Mergers and Acquisitions

In October 2014 Boston Private Bank & Trust Co. acquired Banyan Partners LLC an independent registered investment advisory firm based in Palm Beach Florida. With more than $4.5 billion in client assets Banyan has offices in Boston Miami Naples Atlanta Wisconsin Texas and California. The purchase furthered the bank's aim of expanding the reach and accelerating the development of its wealth management business.

In May 2013 Boston Private Bank & Trust sold three offices in the Pacific Northwest to focus on its banking business in California and New England. The bank recorded a $10.6 million pretax gain on the sale.

EXECUTIVES

EVP General Counsel Secretary and Chief Legal Officer, Margaret W. (Megan) Chambers, age 58, $360,000 total compensation
EVP CFO and Chief Administrative Officer Boston Private Bank & Trust, Anne L. Randall
CEO Private Banking Group; President Boston Private Bank & Trust Company, George G. Schwartz
SVP and Chief Lending Officer Boston Private Bank & Trust, James C. Brown
EVP CFO and Chief Administrative Officer, David J. Kaye, age 53, $425,000 total compensation
CEO; CEO Boston Private Bank and Trust, Clayton G. (Clay) Deutsch, $675,000 total compensation
EVP and Chief Risk Officer, W. Timothy MacDonald, $350,000 total compensation
CEO Boston Private Wealth LLC, Corey A. Griffin, $400,000 total compensation
EVP and Chief Human Resource Officer, Martha T. Higgins
President Boston Private Wealth LLC, Peter J. Raimondi
Co-President Private Banking Group, Torrance Childs
EVP Commercial Banking Group, Robert J. Nentwig
EVP and Client Development Officer, Jacqueline S. Shoback
SVP and Chief Fiduciary Officer, Lynn Swenson
Assistant Vice President, Joe Lavigne
Assistant Vice President Senio, Jill Amato
Assistant Vice President Commercial Lending, Jonathan Willis
Vice President Manager of Credit Administration, Susan Tackitt
Senior Vice President, Mary Rohan
Vice President Office Manager II, Meline Kalendjian
Senior Vice President Residential Lending, Rob Kinasewich
Vice President Commercial Real Estate, Andrew Garfinkle
Senior Vice President Market Leader Residential Lending, Patrick Skovran
Vice President Certified Appraiser Residential Loan Officer, Rosa Amaya
Assistant Vice President Private Banking Relationship Officer, Ida Solari
Senior Vice President Venture and Private Equity Group West Coast Leader, Mark Shang
Vice President Commercial Banking, Sean Burke
Chairman, Stephen M. Waters, age 70
Auditors: KPMG LLP

LOCATIONS

HQ: Boston Private Financial Holdings, Inc.
Ten Post Office Square, Boston, MA 02109
Phone: 617 912-1900
Web: www.bostonprivate.com

PRODUCTS/OPERATIONS

2015 Sales

	$ mil.	% of total
Interest and dividend income		
Loans	192	51
Mortgage-backed securities	10	3
Investment securities	9	2
Federal funds sold and other	1	1
Fees and other income		
Investment management & trust fees	45	12
Wealth advisory fees	50	14
Wealth management and trust fees	51	14
Other	13	3
Total	**374**	**100**

Selected Subsidiaries & Affiliates

Anchor Capital Advisors LLC
Bingham Osborn & Scarborough LLC
Boston Private Bank & Trust Company
Dalton Greiner Hartman Maher & Co. LLC
KLS Professional Advisors Group LLC

COMPETITORS

Bank of America	FMR
Brown Brothers	JPMorgan Chase
Harriman	Morgan Stanley
Central Bancorp	Sovereign Bank
Century Bancorp (MA)	TD Bank USA
Citigroup	TriState Capital
Citizens Financial Group	Wells Fargo

HISTORICAL FINANCIALS

Company Type: Public

Income Statement

FYE: December 31

	ASSETS ($ mil.)	NET INCOME ($ mil.)	INCOME AS % OF ASSETS	EMPLOYEES
12/16	7,970	71	0.9%	888
12/15	7,542	64	0.9%	890
12/14	6,797	68	1.0%	875
12/13	6,437	70	1.1%	781
12/12	6,465	53	0.8%	827
Annual Growth	5.4%	7.7%	—	1.8%

2016 Year-End Financials

Debt ratio: 1.33%	No. of shares (mil.): 83
Return on equity: 9.48%	Dividends
Cash ($ mil.): 106	Yield: 0.0%
Current ratio: —	Payout: 49.3%
Long-term debt ($ mil.): —	Market value ($ mil.): 1,386

	STOCK PRICE ($)	P/E		PER SHARE ($)		
	FY Close	High/Low		Earnings	Dividends	Book Value
12/16	16.55	20	11	0.81	0.40	9.13
12/15	11.34	18	14	0.74	0.36	8.91
12/14	13.47	18	14	0.79	0.32	8.48
12/13	12.62	18	13	0.68	0.24	7.94
12/12	9.01	17	13	0.61	0.04	7.66
Annual Growth	16.4%	—	—	7.3%	77.8%	4.5%

Boston Scientific Corp.

Boston Scientific makes medical supplies and devices used to diagnose and treat medical conditions with an emphasis on cardiovascular products and cardiac rhythm management (CRM). It also makes devices used for electrophysiology endoscopy pain management (neuromodulation) urology and women's health. Its roughly 13000 products — made in more than a dozen factories worldwide — include biopsy forceps catheters coronary and urethral stents defibrillators needles and pacemakers. Boston Scientific markets its products in around 120 countries.

HISTORY

Many medical companies start near a hospital but Boston Scientific's roots sprouted at a children's soccer game where two dads found common ground. John Abele and Peter Nicholas had complementary interests: Wharton MBA Nichols wanted to run his own company; philosophy and physics graduate Abele wanted a job that would help people.

In 1979 the two men founded Boston Scientific to buy medical device maker Medi-Tech. Abele and Nicholas had to borrow half a million dollars from a bank and raise an additional $300000. Medi-Tech's primary product was a steerable catheter a soft-tipped device that could be maneuvered within the body. The catheter revolutionized gallstone operations in the early 1970s and Boston Scientific expanded on the success of the product. The company adapted it for a slew of new procedures for the heart lungs intestines and other organs.

Boston Scientific's sales were healthy in 1983 but the firm still lacked funds. It eagerly accepted $21 million from Abbott Laboratories in exchange for a 20% stake. New FDA regulations slowed product introduction and put a crimp in the company's growth. Boston Scientific found a legal loophole in the late 1980s to avoid lengthy delays: The company described its products in the vaguest possible terms so upgraded devices were considered similar enough to predecessors to escape the in-depth scrutiny of the new approval process. Still Abele and Nicholas had to mortgage their personal properties to stay afloat before this linguistic legerdemain helped to clear government red tape. Boston Scientific returned to profitability in 1991 and went public the next year buying back Abbott Laboratories' interest in the company as well.

Boston Scientific acquired a bevy of medical device companies throughout the late 1990's which expanded its range of cardiology products and doubled sales. Among them were SCIMED Life Systems Heart Technology Meadox Medicals EP Technologies and Symbiosis Target Therapeutics and Pfizer's catheter stent and angioplasty equipment business.

EXECUTIVES

Chairman President and CEO, Michael F. (Mike) Mahoney, age 52, $1,042,191 total compensation
EVP and President Rhythm Management, Joseph M. (Joe) Fitzgerald, age 53, $499,241 total compensation
EVP and CFO, Daniel J. (Dan) Brennan, age 51, $544,421 total compensation
SVP and President Neuromodulation, Maulik Nanavaty, age 55
EVP and President Medical Surgery (MedSurg), Michael P. (Mike) Phalen, age 58
EVP Chief Administrative Officer General Counseland Secretary, Timothy A. (Tim) Pratt, age 67, $640,017 total compensation
EVP and President Asia-Pacific Middle East and Africa, Supratim Bose, age 64, $537,326 total compensation
SVP and President Endoscopy, David A. (Dave) Pierce, age 53
SVP and President Interventional Cardiology, Kevin J. Ballinger, age 44, $476,647 total compensation
EVP Operations, Edward F. Mackey, age 54, $410,548 total compensation
SVP Manufacturing and Supply Chain, John B. (Brad) Sorenson, age 49
SVP and President Europe, Eric Th ©paut, age 55
SVP and President Endoscopy, Art Butcher
EVP and Global Chief Medical Officer, Ian Meredith
SVP and President Peripheral Interventions, Jeff Mirviss
Vice President Mg And Galway Operations, Aaron Milton
Vice President Marketing Peripheral Interventions, John Crowley
Vice President Corporate Tax, Douglas J Cronin
Vice President Global Distribution and International Quality, Rosaleen Burke
Vice President of Call Center, Ashley Condon
National Account Manager, Benjamin Bottcher
Vice President Corporate Accounting, Jon Monson
Vice President Manager Director, Ru Zheng
Vice President Of Operations, Sean Aherne
Vice President Finance And Japan, David Morris
Area Vice President, Matthew Hinton
Vice President Global Marketing Endoscopy, Meghan Scanlon
Vice President Of Information Technology And General Superintendent, Neha Khera
National Sales Manager, Rahul Garg
Vice President Operations and General Manager, Luis Javier Serrano
Executive Vice President Operations, Edward Macky
Vice President Global Supply Chain, Tony Stallings
Board Member, Charles Dockendorff
Assistant Treasurer, Graeme Williamson
Auditors: Ernst & Young LLP

LOCATIONS

HQ: Boston Scientific Corp.
300 Boston Scientific Way, Marlborough, MA 01752-1234
Phone: 508 683-4000
Web: www.bostonscientific.com

2016 Sales

	$ mil.	% of total
US	4,759	57
Japan	750	9
Other countries	2,877	34
Total	**8,386**	**100**

PRODUCTS/OPERATIONS

2016 Sales

	$ mil.	% of total
Interventional cardiology	2,281	27
Cardiac rhythm management	1,850	22
Endoscopy	1,440	17
Peripheral interventions	1,011	12
Urology/Pelvic health	1,005	12
Neuromodulation	556	7
Electrophysiology	243	3
Total	**8,386**	**100**

2016 Sales

	$ mil.	% of total
Cardiovascular	3,292	39
Rhythm Management	2,093	25
Medsurg	3,001	36
Total	**8,386**	**100**

Selected Products

Cardiovascular
  Interventional Cardiology
  PolarCath peripheral dilation system
  PROMUS drug-eluting stents
  TAXUS drug-eluting stents
  VeriFLEX bare-metal stents
  WALLSTENT carotid artery stents
  Cardiac Rhythm Management (CRM)
  ACUITY steerable ventricular leads
  COGNIS cardiac resynchronization defibrillator
  LATITUDE remote patient monitoring system
  TELIGEN implantable cardiac defbrillator
  Other cardiovascular
  Cutting Balloon dilation device
  FilterWire EZ embolic protection system
  iLab ultrasound imaging catheter system
  Maverick balloon catheters
Endoscopy
  Radial Jaw 4 single-use biopsy forceps (gastrointestinal)
  RX Biliary System (bile duct surgeries)
  SpyGlass direct visualization system (pancreatic system)
Urology/Pelvic health
  Genesys Hydro ThermAblator (endometrial ablation system)
Neuromodulation
  Precision Spinal Cord Stimulation system (chronic pain)
Electrophysiology
  Blazer Prime temperature ablation catheters

Selected Acquisitions

COMPETITORS

Abbott Labs	Hologic
American Medical Systems	Johnson & Johnson
Bard	LeMaitre Vascular
Cook Group	Medtronic
Edwards Lifesciences	St. Jude Medical
	ZOLL

HISTORICAL FINANCIALS

Company Type: Public

Income Statement

FYE: December 31

	REVENUE ($ mil.)	NET INCOME ($ mil.)	NET PROFIT MARGIN	EMPLOYEES
12/17	9,048	104	1.1%	29,000
12/16	8,386	347	4.1%	27,000
12/15	7,477	(239)	—	25,000
12/14	7,380	(119)	—	24,000
12/13	7,143	(121)	—	23,000
Annual Growth	**6.1%**	**—**	**—**	**6.0%**

2017 Year-End Financials

Debt ratio: 29.49%	No. of shares (mil.): 1,373
Return on equity: 1.51%	Dividends
Cash ($ mil.): 188	Yield: —
Current ratio: 0.68	Payout: —
Long-term debt ($ mil.): 3,815	Market value ($ mil.): 34,049

	STOCK PRICE ($) FY Close	P/E High/Low	PER SHARE ($) Earnings	Dividends	Book Value
12/17	24.79	373 274	0.08	0.00	5.11
12/16	21.63	94 62	0.25	0.00	4.94
12/15	18.44	— —	(0.18)	0.00	4.69
12/14	13.25	— —	(0.09)	0.00	4.86
12/13	12.02	— —	(0.09)	0.00	4.95
Annual Growth	**19.8%**	**—**	**—**	**—**	**0.8%**

Bridge Bancorp, Inc. (Bridgehampton, NY)

Bridge Bancorp wants you to cross over to its subsidiary The Bridgehampton National Bank which operates about 25 branches on eastern Long Island New York. Founded in 1910 the bank offers traditional deposit services to area individuals small businesses and municipalities including checking savings and money market accounts and CDs. Deposits are invested primarily in mortgages which account for some 80% of the bank's loan portfolio. Title insurance services are available through bank subsidiary Bridge Abstract; wealth management services include financial planning estate administration and trustee services. Bridge Bancorp bought Hamptons State Bank in 2011 to fortify its presence on Long Island.

Geographic Reach

Bridgehampton New York-based Bridge Bancorp's market area is Suffolk County in eastern Long Island. The bank serves customers in the towns of East Hampton Southampton Southold and Riverhead. It also has branches in Brookhaven Babylon and Islip.

Financial Performance

The bank reported net income of $13.1 million in 2013 versus $12.8 million in 2012. Revenue increased 3% to $67.3 million on rising net interest income. Bridge Bancorp had total assets of $1.9 billion in 2013 an increase of 17% versus the prior year. Total deposits rose 9% in 2013 versus 2012 to $1.5 billion.

Mergers and Acquisitions

In February 2014 Bridge Bancorp acquired FNBNY Bancorp and its wholly-owned subsidiary the First National Bank of New York and converted its three branches to Bridgehampton National Bank (BNB) branches. The purchase expanded BNB's reach into Nassau County. Following the acquisition Bridge Bancorp's assets totaled approximately $2.1 billion with loans of approximately $1.1 billion and deposits of $1.7 billion with 26 branches throughout Long Island and one loan production office in Manhattan.

EXECUTIVES

President and CEO, Kevin M. O'Connor, age 54, $300,000 total compensation
SVP and Chief Lending Officer Bridgehampton National Bank, Kevin L. Santacroce, $180,000 total compensation
SVP and CIO Bridgehampton National Bank, Thomas H. Simson, $175,000 total compensation
President CEO and Director, Kevin OConnor
Chief Financial Officer, Adam Hall
EVP and Chief Retail Banking Officer, James J. Manseau, $235,000 total compensation
Vice Chairman, Dennis A. Suskind, age 74
Chairman, Marcia Z. Hefter, age 73
Auditors: Crowe Horwath LLP

LOCATIONS

HQ: Bridge Bancorp, Inc. (Bridgehampton, NY)
2200 Montauk Highway, Bridgehampton, NY 11932
Phone: 631 537-1000
Web: www.bridgenb.com

COMPETITORS

Bank of America	JPMorgan Chase
Bank of New York Mellon	Suffolk Bancorp

HISTORICAL FINANCIALS

Company Type: Public

Income Statement
FYE: December 31

	ASSETS ($ mil.)	NET INCOME ($ mil.)	INCOME AS % OF ASSETS	EMPLOYEES
12/16	4,054	35	0.9%	477
12/15	3,781	21	0.6%	433
12/14	2,288	13	0.6%	348
12/13	1,896	13	0.7%	271
12/12	1,624	12	0.8%	257
Annual Growth	25.7%	29.1%	—	16.7%

2016 Year-End Financials

Debt ratio: 2.31%
Return on equity: 9.45%
Cash ($ mil.): 113
Current ratio: —
Long-term debt ($ mil.): —
No. of shares (mil.): 19
Dividends
Yield: 0.0%
Payout: 46.0%
Market value ($ mil.): 724

	STOCK PRICE ($) FY Close	P/E High/Low		PER SHARE ($) Earnings	Dividends	Book Value
12/16	37.90	19	13	2.00	0.92	21.36
12/15	30.43	22	17	1.43	0.92	19.62
12/14	26.75	23	20	1.18	0.92	15.03
12/13	26.00	19	14	1.36	0.92	14.10
12/12	20.34	17	13	1.48	1.15	13.32
Annual Growth	16.8%	—	—	7.8%	(5.4%)	12.5%

Brighthouse Financial Inc

LOCATIONS

HQ: Brighthouse Financial Inc
Gragg Building, 11225 North Community House Road, Charlotte, NC 28277
Phone: 980 365-7100
Web: www.brighthousefinancial.com

HISTORICAL FINANCIALS

Company Type: Public

Income Statement
FYE: December 31

	ASSETS ($ mil.)	NET INCOME ($ mil.)	INCOME AS % OF ASSETS	EMPLOYEES
12/16	221,930	(2,939)	—	1,100
12/15	226,725	1,119	0.5%	—
12/14	0	1,159	—	—
Annual Growth	—	—	—	—

2016 Year-End Financials

Debt ratio: 2.12%—
Return on equity: (-18.49%)
Cash ($ mil.): 5,228
Current ratio: —
Long-term debt ($ mil.): —
Dividends
Yield: —
Payout: —
Market value ($ mil.): —

	STOCK PRICE ($) FY Close	P/E High/Low		PER SHARE ($) Earnings	Dividends	Book Value
12/16	0.00	—	—	(24.62)	0.00	(0.00)
12/15	0.00	—	—	(0.00)	0.00	(0.00)
Annual Growth	—	—	—	—	—	—

Brighthouse Life Insurance Co - Insurance Products

Auditors: Deloitte & Touche LLP

LOCATIONS

HQ: Brighthouse Life Insurance Co - Insurance Products
11225 North Community House Road, Charlotte, NC 28277
Phone: 980 365-7100
Web: www.metlife.com

HISTORICAL FINANCIALS

Company Type: Public

Income Statement
FYE: December 31

	ASSETS ($ mil.)	NET INCOME ($ mil.)	INCOME AS % OF ASSETS	EMPLOYEES
12/16	199,273	(2,937)	—	—
12/15	202,362	839	0.4%	—
12/14	205,863	295	0.1%	—
12/13	188,039	720	0.4%	—
12/12	184,796	1,223	0.7%	—
Annual Growth	1.9%			

2016 Year-End Financials

Debt ratio: 0.40%
Return on equity: (-27.53%)
Cash ($ mil.): 1,888
Current ratio: —
Long-term debt ($ mil.): —
No. of shares (mil.): 0
Dividends
Yield: —
Payout: —
Market value ($ mil.): —

Bristol-Myers Squibb Co.

Pharmaceutical giant Bristol-Myers Squibb (BMS) treats an array of maladies through its vast lineup of therapies. The biopharmaceutical's blockbuster drugs include rhemuatoid arthritis treatment Orencia and ELIQUIS for stroke prevention. BMS also makes antipsychotic medication Abilify and HIV treatments Reyataz and Sustiva. Most of its sales come from products in the therapeutic areas of cardiovascular care hepatitis immunology metabolics neuroscience oncology and virology. BMS has global research facilities and manufacturing plants mainly in the US and Europe and its products are marketed to health care practitioners hospitals and managed care providers in 100 countries.

HISTORY

Bristol-Myers Squibb is the product of a merger of rivals.

Squibb was founded by Dr. Edward Squibb in New York City in 1858. He developed techniques for making pure ether and chloroform; he turned the business over to his sons in 1891.

Sales of $414000 in 1904 grew to $13 million by 1928. The company supplied penicillin and morphine during WWII. In 1952 it was bought by Mathieson Chemical which in turn was bought by Olin Industries in 1953 forming Olin Mathieson Chemical. Squibb maintained its separate identity.

From 1968 to 1971 Olin Mathieson went through repeated reorganizations and adopted the Squibb name. Capoten and Corgard two major cardiovascular drugs were introduced in the late 1970s. Capoten was the first drug engineered to attack a specific disease-causing mechanism. Squibb formed a joint venture with Denmark's Novo (now Novo Nordisk) in 1982 to sell insulin.

William Bristol and John Myers founded Clinton Pharmaceutical in Clinton New York in 1887 (renamed Bristol-Myers in 1900) to sell bulk pharmaceuticals. The firm made antibiotics after the 1943 purchase of Cheplin Biological Labs. It began expanding overseas in the 1950s and eventually bought Clairol (1959); Mead Johnson (drugs infant and nutritional formula; 1967); and Zimmer (orthopedic implants 1972). Bristol-Myers launched new drugs to treat cancer (Platinol 1978) and anxiety (BuSpar 1986). That year it acquired biotech companies Oncogen and Genetic Systems.

The firm bought Squibb in 1989. In 1990 the new company bought arthroscopy products and implant business lines and joined Eastman Kodak and Elf Aquitaine to develop new heart drugs in 1993. Despite these initiatives earnings slipped. In 1994 company veteran Charles Heimbold became CEO and moved to increase profits. BMS in 1995 bought wound and skin care products firm Calgon Vestal Laboratories. Also that year the company along with fellow silicone breast implant makers 3M and Baxter International agreed to settle thousands of personal injury claims at an average of $26000 per claim.

Facing an antitrust suit filed by independent drugstores BMS and other major drugmakers agreed in 1996 to charge pharmacies the same prices as managed care groups for medications. That year the company formed a generic drug unit and launched Pravachol.

Over the next two years BMS tweaked its product line buying drug cosmetics and consumer products companies and brands. Having refined its product line the firm began a series of officer reassignments that were widely interpreted as an effort to find a successor for Heimbold who retired in 2001.

In 1999 the firm pulled its backing for EntreMed after the biotech had problems duplicating results for a cancer drug candidate. BMS helped market promising diabetes drug Avandia (from GlaxoSmithKline which ended the deal in 2002) and teamed with Millennium Pharmaceuticals to study the genetic makeup of tumors.

As the company entered the 21st century it began streamlining. It sold its Sea Breeze skin care brand (1999); Matrix Essentials hair care products unit (2000); and Clairol hair and personal care products business (2001). BMS also spun off its Zimmer orthopedic implant unit in 2001. More changes came in 2004: The firm sold its Mead Johnson Adult Nutritional business.

In 2002 BMS was dealt a blow when a judge ruled that the company had illegally blocked Mylan Labs and Watson Pharmaceuticals from selling generic versions of BuSpar.

The firm bought a 20% stake in ImClone to collaborate on the development of cancer drug Erbitux and to stay on top of the cancer drug market. Instead BMS found itself embroiled in the controversy over insider information and stock deals surrounding the biotech. Persistence paid off however; Erbitux was approved by the FDA in 2004.

During 2005 the company cleaned out parts of its medicine cabinet. Analgesics Excedrin and Bufferin had made the company a household name but in 2005 the company sold its US and Canadian

consumer products operations to Novartis. The deal also meant saying goodbye to such brands as Comtrex (cold medications) Choice (blood sugar monitoring supplies) and Keri (lotions skin care). Sales for the its US and Canadian consumer products operations reached about $270 million in 2004.

That same year BMS sold Oncology Therapeutics Network which distributes cancer drugs to oncology doctors to private equity firm One Equity Partners. The unit had accounted for about 13% of sales in 2004.

As part of an agreement with the New Jersey US Attorney's office in 2005 to settle an investigation into inventory control and accounting practices the company split the role of chairman and CEO into two separate offices. Long-time BMS director James Robinson III was elected the company's new chairman with Peter Dolan in the CEO role. James Cornelius took over as CEO in 2006 and became chairman in 2008 bring the two roles back together.

While the patent expiration on blockbuster Plavix was still five years off in mid-2006 Canadian generics maker Apotex managed to flood the market with a generic version of Plavix for several weeks. The release of the drug followed bungled attempts by BMS to negotiate a deal with Apotex that would have kept it off the market. The debacle led to federal investigations into whether that deal violated anti-trust laws (among other things) and also resulted in the ouster of CEO Peter Dolan (replaced by James Cornelius). Though a judge put a halt to the manufacturing of the generic until the courts could straighten the whole thing out the short-term generic competition hurt Plavix sales to the tune of more than $1 billion. BMS ultimately wound up paying more than $150 million to settle lawsuits and agreed that it would report any future deals struck with generics makers.

The company announced a reorganizational plan in 2007 named the string-of-pearls strategy. As part of its efforts to remake itself into a purely biopharmaceutical player BMS began jettisoning its non-pharmaceutical businesses. During 2008 the company sold its Medical Imaging unit to private equity firm Avista Capital Partners for $525 million and Avista Capital Partners and Nordic Capital paid $4.1 billion to acquire BMS' ConvaTec ostomy and wound-care subsidiary. Then in 2009 the company divested its Mead Johnson subsidiary which sold Enfamil infant formula and other nutritional products for children.

EXECUTIVES

EVP and General Counsel, Sandra Leung, age 56, $919,945 total compensation
Chairman and CEO, Giovanni Caforio, age 53, $1,513,077 total compensation
EVP CFO and Global Business Operations, Charles A. Bancroft, age 58, $966,115 total compensation
SVP and CIO, Paul von Autenried, age 55
President Global Manufacturing and Supply, Louis S. (Lou) Schmukler, age 61
EVP and Chief Commercial Officer, Murdo Gordon, age 50, $737,225 total compensation
EVP and Chief Scientific Officer R&D, Thomas J. Lynch
Vice President, John Pinter
Medical Director Sprycel, Robyn Bilmes
Vice President and Deputy General Counsel, Henry Hadad
Medical Director, William Petkun
Senior Vice President and CHRO, Ann Judge
Medical Director, Xuemei Li
VP Research and Development, Saurabh Saha
Vice President: Head of Strategic Payer Marketing, Laurent Carter

Vice President and Head of Strategic Corporate Development, Matthew Roden
Medical Director, Fraz Ismat
Vice President and General Manager, Anibal Carlo
Associate Medical Director, Yanfang Liu
Senior Vice President Global Supply Chain, Ricardo Zayas
Medical Director, Roland Meier
Associate Medical Director Immuno Oncology Exploratory Clinical and Translational Research, Praveen Aanur
Assistant Treasurer, Scott R Massengill
Auditors: DELOITTE & TOUCHE LLP

LOCATIONS

HQ: Bristol-Myers Squibb Co.
345 Park Avenue, New York, NY 10154
Phone: 212 546-4000   **Fax:** 212 546-4020
Web: www.bms.com

2016 Sales

	$ mil.	% of total
US	10,720	55
Europe	4,215	22
Other countries & regions	3,964	20
Other	528	3
Total	**19,427**	**100**

PRODUCTS/OPERATIONS

Sales 2016

	% of total
Opdivo	19
Eliquis	17
Orencia	12
Sprycel	9
Hepatitis C Franchise	8
Baraclude	6
Sustiva	6
Reyataz	5
Yervoy	5
Abilify	1
Empliciti	1
Erbitux	—
Mature products & other	11
Total	**100**

Selected Pharmaceuticals

Cardiovascular
   Eliquis (atrial fibrillation with Pfizer)
Immunology
   Nulojix (kidney rejection)
   Orencia (rheumatoid arthritis)
Metabolism
   Bydureon (type 2 diabetes)
   Byetta (type 2 diabetes)
Neuroscience
   Abilify (schizophrenia bipolar disorder major depressive disorder; with Otsuka)
   Emsam (major depressive disorder)
Oncology
   Erbitux (colorectal head and neck cancer with Lilly)
   Sprycel (chronic myeloid leukemia with Otsuka)
   Yervoy (metastatic melanoma)
Virology
   Baraclude (chronic hepatitis B)
   Reyataz (HIV)
   Sustiva Franchise (includes Atripla and Sustiva for HIV with Gilead)

COMPETITORS

AbbVie	Johnson & Johnson
Abbott Labs	Merck
Allergan plc	Mylan
Amgen	Novartis
Apotex	Pfizer
AstraZeneca	Roche Holding
Biogen	Sandoz International
Boehringer Ingelheim	GmbH
Eli Lilly	Sanofi
Genentech	Teva
GlaxoSmithKline	

HISTORICAL FINANCIALS

Company Type: Public

Income Statement

FYE: December 31

	REVENUE ($ mil.)	NET INCOME ($ mil.)	NET PROFIT MARGIN	EMPLOYEES
12/17	20,776	1,007	4.8%	23,700
12/16	19,427	4,457	22.9%	25,000
12/15	16,560	1,565	9.5%	25,000
12/14	15,879	2,004	12.6%	25,000
12/13	16,385	2,563	15.6%	28,000
Annual Growth	6.1%	(20.8%)	—	(4.1%)

2017 Year-End Financials

Debt ratio: 23.73%	No. of shares (mil.): 1,625
Return on equity: 7.21%	Dividends
Cash ($ mil.): 5,421	Yield: 0.0%
Current ratio: 1.55	Payout: 255.7%
Long-term debt ($ mil.): 6,975	Market value ($ mil.): 99,580

	STOCK PRICE ($) FY Close	P/E High/Low		PER SHARE ($) Earnings	Dividends	Book Value
12/17	61.28	107	77	0.61	1.56	7.23
12/16	58.44	29	18	2.65	1.14	9.72
12/15	68.79	75	61	0.93	1.49	8.55
12/14	59.03	51	39	1.20	1.45	8.94
12/13	53.15	35	21	1.54	1.41	9.19
Annual Growth	3.6%	—	—	(20.7%)	2.6%	(5.8%)

BRIXMOR LLC

Auditors: ERNST & YOUNG LLP

LOCATIONS

HQ: BRIXMOR LLC
450 LEXINGTON AVE FL 13, NEW YORK, NY
100173956
Phone: 212 869-3000
Web: WWW.CENTROPROP.COM

HISTORICAL FINANCIALS

Company Type: Private

Income Statement

FYE: December 31

	ASSETS ($ mil.)	NET INCOME ($ mil.)	INCOME AS % OF ASSETS	EMPLOYEES
12/08	4,157	(550)	—	456
12/07	5,702	(486)	—	—
Annual Growth	(27.1%)	—	—	—

2008 Year-End Financials

Debt ratio: ——	
Return on equity: (-131.60%)	Dividends
Cash ($ mil.): 51	Yield: —
Current ratio: —	Payout: —
Long-term debt ($ mil.): —	Market value ($ mil.): —

Brookdale Senior Living Inc

Over the brook and through the dale to grandmother's house we go! Brookdale Senior Living operates assisted and independent living centers and retirement communities for middle- and upper-income elderly clients. The US' largest senior living provider Brookdale has more than 1000 facilities offering approximately 308600 studio one-bedroom and two-bedroom units in 47 states. Services for its residents include meals 24-hour emergency response housekeeping concierge services transportation and recreational activities. Brookdale's continuing care retirement centers include skilled nursing units that serve Alzheimer's patients and others who require ongoing care.

Operations

Brookdale operates in five segments: assisted living retirement centers continuing care retirement communities (CCRC) - rental ancillary services and management services. Its largest operating segment is its assisted living division which provides daily living services to residents and accounts for about half of all revenues. The retirement centers segment operates upscale independent living facilities for middle and upper-income seniors and accounts for some 15% of sales. The CCRC rental segment provides a mix of independent assisted and nursing care services within one location. It accounts for more than 10% of revenue.

The remainder of Brookdale's sales comes from its management services and ancillary services segments. The management services segment (more than 15% of revenue) receives fees for facilities that Brookdale operates on behalf of third parties. The ancillary services division (nearly 10% of revenue) provides outpatient therapy home health and hospice services to residents of Brookdale and non-Brookdale facilities as well as to seniors living in their own homes.

The company owns or leases more than 900 communities with about 77300 units; it manages approximately 155 third-party-owned or partially owned communities with more than 26000 units.

While some of Brookdale's facilities provide intensive nursing services that are reimbursed by third-parties including Medicare and Medicaid most of the company's facilities are independent or assisted-living centers that target higher-end clients with minimal medical needs.

Geographic Reach

Brookdale has approximately 1050 communities in 47 states. Its largest markets Florida and Texas are home to almost 25% of its communities. Other key states include North Carolina California Ohio and Washington. About half of the company's sales come from its leased communities and some 40% are generated from owned communities.

Sales and Marketing

For its retirement centers Brookdale targets residents of age 75 and older who are seeking a more supportive living situation. Its assisted living residents are primarily aged 80 and higher requiring daily assistance with two or more activities of daily living.

Due to Brookdale's focus on high-income customers more than 80% of its revenues come from private pay customers. By keeping its exposure to federal programs (Medicare and Medicaid) to a minimum the company is less vulnerable (though not immune) to changes in reimbursement levels.

Brookdale uses direct marketing teams to target potential residents and family members as well as referral sources including hospital discharge agents social workers physicians local agencies home health agents and clergy members. It also seeks to promote its brand through event sponsorships and online print signage and direct mail advertising programs.

Financial Performance

Generally Brookdale has seen strong growth especially after the 2015 acquisition of Emeritus Corporation. However revenue remained relatively flat in 2016 rising less than 1% to $5 billion. The company's assisted living and continuing care retirement centers segments declined but the retirement centers and ancillary services segments showed growth. An overall drop in resident fees that year was offset by an increase in management fees.

Despite the growth in revenue the company has reported losses over a period of several years. Its net loss in 2016 totaled $404.6 million an improvement over its $458 million loss in 2015. Reductions in general and administrative expenses transaction costs and losses on lease terminations plus increases in interest asset sale and joint venture earnings all helped Brookdale's bottom line that year.

Cash flow from operations has been rising since its decline in 2014; in 2016 it rose 25% to $365.7 million. This was largely due to the lower net loss as well as other factors such as changes in operating assets and liabilities.

Strategy

In 2016 Brookdale after completing the integration of its recently acquired Emeritus Corporation operations outlined a new strategy for growth in its core business. That strategy includes five priorities outlined below.

One priority is improving the experiences of its customers and employees which the company is doing by simplifying the roles of its communities' executive directors implementing new training and development programs and expanding its quality tracking initiatives.

Secondly Brookdale is implementing new network sales and lead management systems. It intends to utilize customized marketing campaigns in markets with strong growth potential and it is segmenting its communities to offer the right services amenities programs and price levels based on market needs. In terms of sales the company is working to improve coordination between different teams within their markets.

Brookdale is also streamlining its operations to cut costs. It has removed certain layers of its organization and has been establishing corporate shared service centers of excellence to improve business effectiveness.

To optimize its portfolio the company is examining opportunities to sell (and lease) certain communities restructure existing leases or buy leased communities where it has favorable purchase options. Additionally it intends to take advantage of its sheer size in deals with partners and carefully invest in community expansions renovations and repositionings. In 2016 the company invested $23.9 million in expansion and conversion projects adding 237 units; it plans to continue with these projects ultimately adding another 129 net new units.

Brookdale's fifth priority is to evaluate innovative ideas and working models that could improve the way it serves its residents.

Although the company has a refined strategy its modus operandi remains the same: keeping an eagle eye on its holdings and seeking opportunities to buy existing communities or to sell and lease communities already in its portfolio. During 2016 it sold 51 owned communities cutting its mortgage debt levels by $94.5 million; it also restructured the leases of nearly 100 communities. The company began 2017 with 16 communities held for sale.

The company hopes to increase occupancy rates which have fallen below expectations of 90% or higher. Increased competition in some markets has put some pressure on Brookdale which has in turn responded by offering discounts and other incentives to residents and increasing employees' salaries to prevent poaching. The company should benefit from an uptick in demand as the US population of seniors steadily increases.

The company is also increasing its ancillary services revenues by extending those programs to new facilities as well as by introducing new services such as wellness and physical fitness programs.

Brookdale is in talks to be acquired by Chinese real estate firm Zhonghong Zhuoye Group which has bid $3 billion for the company. Other investors have also made moves to buy Brookdale.

Mergers and Acquisitions

In 2015 HCP and Brookdale acquired 35 private pay senior housing communities from Chartwell Retirement Residences for $847 million. The portfolio which Brookdale manages is 90% owned by HCP and 10% owned by Brookdale.

HISTORY

Brookdale Senior Living was formed through the 2005 merger of Brookdale Living Communities and Alterra Healthcare. The combined organization expanded through additional acquisitions in the following years.

Difficult economic conditions caused Brookdale to cut back on its spending during 2009 and 2010. During that time it turned its attention inward and worked to improve occupancy rates at existing facilities. The senior housing industry as a whole was affected by the downturn in the housing market causing a precipitous drop in occupancy rates industry-wide.

Sensing improved economic conditions in 2011 Brookdale acquired private facility operator Horizon Bay adding 90 residential facilities in the southern and midwestern US. Horizon Bay's independent and assisted living facilities complement Brookdale's existing properties as they cater to high-end customers. The acquisition also reinforced the company's existing presence in several markets and opened a few new markets. As part of the deal Brookdale entered restructured lease arrangements on certain facilities with Horizon Bay's former shareholders Chartwell Seniors Housing REIT and HCP.

In 2012 it partnered with online services firm Connected Living to increase Internet training and social networking capabilities at several Brookdale communities in California. In early 2012 the company paid $121 million for nine communities it had formerly operated through lease agreements. The facilities included a total of some 1300 living units.

In 2014 Brookdale purchased fellow senior living firm Emeritus for nearly $3 billion. The move gave Brookdale a nationwide network of senior care facilities adding 10 states and bringing its total number of communities to 1100.

EXECUTIVES

EVP Corporate Development, H. Todd Kaestner, age 62

EVP Finance and Treasurer, George T. Hicks, age 60

EVP and Chief Administrative Officer, Bryan D. Richardson, age 59, $432,115 total compensation

CFO, Lucinda M. (Cindy) Baier, age 52, $552,115 total compensation

President and CEO, T. Andrew (Andy) Smith, age 56, $953,654 total compensation

EVP and Chief People Officer, Cedric T. Coco, age 49

EVP Community and Field Operations, Mary Sue Patchett, age 54, $426,635 total compensation

Executive Vice President And Chief People Officer, Glenn Maul

Vice President Of Business Legal Affairs, Eric Hoaglund

Vice President Corporate Development, Teddy Hillard

Vice President, James Alspaugh

Vice President, Sara Terry

RVP Operations, Debra Dunigan

Executive Vice President, H Todd Kaestner

Vice President Legal Employment Affairs, Jack Leebron

Senior Vice President, Don Ross

Vice President, Jack Carney

Vice President, Marla Sovereign

Vice President Sales and Business Development, Christian Lanham

Physical Therapy Director, Becky Lemery

Senior Vice President of Acquisitions, Christian Maingot

Vice President of Benefits and Compensation, Pam Engle

Director of Nursing Services, Christine Pepito

RVP, Susannah Dwyer

Director of Clinical Services, Claudia Crawford

Divisional Vice President Of Operations, Cindy Chastulik

Physical Therapy, Debbie Dobias

Regional Vice President, Frankie Knighton

Regional Vice President Of Operations, Karen Doering

Senior Vice President Of Clinical Services, Kim Estes

Vice President Total Rewards, Pamela Engle

Vice President of Clinical Services, Wendy McKenna

Vice President Of Development And Acqusition Analysis, Ming-Fang Jiang

Vice President of Quality Service Programs, Sara Padilla

Rvp, Sheri Garrett

Regional Vice President of Operations, Susan Hess

Division President, Anthony Mollica

Regional Vice President of Operations Southeast Division, Steve Martin

Director of Admissions, Erica Davis

Head Nurse, Amy Lubinskas

Chairman, Daniel A. Decker, age 64

Auditors: Ernst & Young LLP

LOCATIONS

HQ: Brookdale Senior Living Inc
111 Westwood Place, Suite 400, Brentwood, TN 37027
Phone: 615 221-2250
Web: www.brookdale.com

2016 Community Locations

	No.
Texas	128
Florida	124
California	91
North Carolina	60
Washington	51
Ohio	51
Oregon	43
Colorado	39
New York	35
Arizona	34
Michigan	33
Tennessee	31
Oklahoma	27
South Carolina	24
Kansas	22
Georgia	21
Wisconsin	20
Other states	221
Total	**1,055**

PRODUCTS/OPERATIONS

2016 Revenues

	$ mil.	% of total
Resident fees		
Assisted living	2,419	49
Retirement centers	679	14
Continuing care retirement communities (CCRCs) - rental	592	12
Brookdale Ancillary Services	476	9
Management services	808	16
Total	**4,977**	**100**

2016 Units

	No.
% of total	
Managed communities	25
Home health service	21
Assisted living	19
Retirement centers	8
Third parties	8
CCRCS	7
Hospice Services	6
Therapy services	6
Total	**100**

COMPETITORS

ACTS Retirement-Life Communities
Amedisys
American Baptist Homes of the West
Apria Healthcare
Atria Senior Living
BPM Senior Living
Capital Senior Living
Colson & Colson
Consulate Health Care
Enlivant
Evangelical Lutheran Good Samaritan Society
Five Star Senior Living
Golden Horizons
HCP
Horizon Bay
Life Care Centers
Life Care Services
SavaSeniorCare
Sunrise Senior Living
Ventas
Welltower

HISTORICAL FINANCIALS

Company Type: Public

Income Statement

FYE: December 31

	REVENUE ($ mil.)	NET INCOME ($ mil.)	NET PROFIT MARGIN	EMPLOYEES
12/16	4,976	(404)	—	77,600
12/15	4,960	(457)	—	81,300
12/14	3,831	(148)	—	82,000
12/13	2,891	(3)	—	49,000
12/12	2,770	(65)	—	47,900
Annual Growth	15.8%	—	—	12.8%

2016 Year-End Financials

Debt ratio: 65.58%
Return on equity: (-17.78%)
Cash ($ mil.): 216
Current ratio: 0.85
Long-term debt ($ mil.): 5,829

No. of shares (mil.): 190
Dividends
  Yield: —
  Payout: —
Market value ($ mil.): 2,360

	STOCK PRICE ($) FY Close	P/E High/Low	PER SHARE ($) Earnings	PER SHARE ($) Dividends	PER SHARE ($) Book Value
12/16	12.42	— —	(2.18)	0.00	10.93
12/15	18.46	— —	(2.48)	0.00	13.06
12/14	36.67	— —	(1.01)	0.00	15.41
12/13	27.18	— —	(0.03)	0.00	7.99
12/12	25.32	— —	(0.54)	0.00	7.91
Annual Growth	(16.3%)	— —	—	—	8.4%

Brookline Bancorp Inc (DE)

Brookline Bancorp is the holding company for Brookline Bank Bank Rhode Island (BankRI) and First Ipswich Bank (formerly The First National Bank of Ipswich) which together operate more than 45 full-service branches in eastern Massachusetts and Rhode Island. Commercial and multifamily mortgages backed by real estate such as apartments condominiums and office buildings account for the largest portion of the company's loan portfolio followed by indirect auto loans commercial loans and consumer loans. Established in 1997 as Brookline Savings Bank the bank went public five years later and changed its name to Brookline Bank in 2003. Brookline Bancorp. has expanded by acquiring other regional banks.

Operations

The holding company also provides indirect automobile loans through Brookline Bank and equipment financing through its Eastern Funding and Macrolease Corp. subsidiaries. Eastern Funding LLC a majority-owned firm with more than $1 billion in in direct loans that specializes in financing coin-operated laundry dry cleaning and convenience store equipment in the New York City metropolitan area.

Geographic Reach

Boston-based Brookline Bancorp operates 47 full-service branches in greater Boston and greater Providence Rhode Island.

Financial Performance

The multi-bank holding company has $5.3 billion in assets. In 2013 Brookline Bancorp reported net income of $35.4 million compared with $37.1 million in 2012. Net earnings from operations were $36 million in 2013 compared to $41.1 million for 2012.

Strategy

Brookline has grown from a sleepy suburban community savings bank to a publicly-traded commercial lender with loan volumes that put it among Massachusetts' top banks. As it transitions to a commercial bank Brookline has also been growing geographically through acquisitions.

Mergers and Acquisitions

In January 2012 Brookline acquired Providence-headquartered Bancorp Rhode Island for $234 million in cash and stock adding 18 BankRI branches in that state. BankRI retained its brand and operates as a subsidiary of Brookline Bancorp.

In February 2011 it acquired The First National Bank of Ipswich a six-branch bank serving Massachusetts' North Shore. The $19.7 million transaction gave First National Bank of Ipswich a much-needed boost as that bank had been struggling with loan losses during the recession. It also expanded Brookline Bancorp's market area as there was no overlap between the two banks.

Brookline Bancorp's board rejected a takeover offer by an unnamed suitor in early 2010. Two directors had voted to accept the bid however including former longtime chairman Richard Chapman. Both resigned in the aftermath of the vote.

EXECUTIVES

President and CEO, Paul A. Perrault, age 66, $715,000 total compensation

COO, James M. Cosman, age 66, $265,000 total compensation

President and CEO Bank Rhode Island, Mark J. Meiklejohn, age 53, $330,000 total compensation

Chief Risk Officer General Counsel and Secretary, Michael W. McCurdy, age 48

Chief Credit Officer, M. Robert Rose, age 65, $288,000 total compensation

President and CEO The First National Bank of Ipswich, Russell G. Cole, age 59

CFO, Carl M. Carlson, age 53, $335,000 total compensation

Senior Vice President, Bill Mackenzie

Vice President Regional Manager, Cathy Pierce

Vice President, Tony Glazier

Vice President Of Commercial Lending, Tim Steiner

Vice President Underwriting And Operations, Gretchen Annese

Chairman, Joseph J. Slotnik, age 81

Treasurer, Reed H Whitman

Auditors: KPMG LLP

LOCATIONS

HQ: Brookline Bancorp Inc (DE)
131 Clarendon Street, Boston, MA 02116
Phone: 617 425-4600
Web: www.brooklinebancorp.com

PRODUCTS/OPERATIONS

2015 sales

	$ mil.	% of total
Interest and dividend income:		
Loans and leases	212	86
Debt securities	11	5
Marketable and restricted equity securities	2	1
Short-term investments	0	-
Non-interest income:		
Deposit fees	8	4
Loan level derivative income net	3	1
Gain on sales of loans and leases held-for-sale	2	1
Other	5	2
Total	**247**	**100**

Selected Services

Personal
Checking
Savings
Borrowing
Investment Services
Business
Signature Business Banking
Business Checking Accounts
Business Savings
Business Lending
Business Online Banking
Cash Management
Service Center
Branch Locations
ATM Locations
Online Banking
Mobile Banking
Telephone Services
Mail Services
Order Checks
Order Foreign Currency
Overdraft Privilege Service

COMPETITORS

Bank of America	Eastern Bank
Boston Private	Sovereign Bank
Central Bancorp	TD Bank USA
Century Bancorp (MA)	
Citizens Financial	
Group	

HISTORICAL FINANCIALS

Company Type: Public

Income Statement

FYE: December 31

	ASSETS ($ mil.)	NET INCOME ($ mil.)	INCOME AS % OF ASSETS	EMPLOYEES
12/16	6,438	52	0.8%	743
12/15	6,042	49	0.8%	718
12/14	5,799	42	0.7%	725
12/13	5,325	35	0.7%	720
12/12	5,147	37	0.7%	662
Annual Growth	**5.8%**	**9.0%**	**—**	**2.9%**

2016 Year-End Financials

Debt ratio: 1.29%	No. of shares (mil.): 70
Return on equity: 7.66%	Dividends
Cash ($ mil.): 67	Yield: 0.0%
Current ratio: —	Payout: 48.6%
Long-term debt ($ mil.): —	Market value ($ mil.): 1,162

	STOCK PRICE ($) FY Close	P/E High/Low		Earnings	PER SHARE ($) Dividends	Book Value
12/16	16.40	22	14	0.74	0.36	9.82
12/15	11.50	17	13	0.71	0.36	9.45
12/14	10.03	17	14	0.61	0.34	9.09
12/13	9.55	20	16	0.51	0.34	8.73
12/12	8.50	18	14	0.53	0.34	8.74
Annual Growth	**17.9%**	**—**	**—**	**8.7%**	**1.4%**	**2.9%**

Bryn Mawr Bank Corp

Bryn Mawr Bank Corporation stands atop a "big hill" in Pennsylvania. Bryn Mawr (which in Welsh translates as "big hill") is the bank holding company for Bryn Mawr Trust operates some 20 offices in Pennsylvania and Delaware. The bank offers traditional services as checking and savings accounts CDs mortgages and business and consumer loans in addition to insurance products equipment leasing investment management retirement planning tax planning and preparation and trust services. Founded in 1889 Bryn Mawr boasts more than $5 billion of assets under administration and management.

Operations

Bryn Mawr operates two business segments. Its Banking segment which makes up two-thirds of overall business provides commercial and retail banking services. The Wealth Management division which includes the Bryn Mawr Trust of Delaware and Lau Associates businesses makes up about one-third of the bank's overall revenue and provides a variety of custody investment management tax and brokerage services.

Broadly speaking the company generated 60% of its total revenue from interest and fees on loans and leases in 2014 while another 30% of its total revenue came from fees for wealth management services.

Bryn Mawr operated 19 full-service branches seven Life Care Community Offices five wealth offices and a full-service insurance agency in 2014.

Geographic Reach

The bank corporation has branches and offices across Montgomery Delaware Chester and Dauphin counties in Pennsylvania and New Castle county in Delaware.

Financial Performance

Bryn Mawr has enjoyed rising revenues and profits over the past several years reflecting strong growth in its loan business and wealth management business.

The bank's revenue rose by 4% to a record $131.23 million in 2014 mostly thanks to higher interest income from loans as it grew its loan assets by $153.9 million during the year. The company's Wealth Management services fees also grew by 5% thanks to new business acquisitions and solid market appreciation during the year which resulted in higher assets under management.

Higher revenue and a strong grip on costs in 2014 also boosted Bryn Mawr's net income by 14% to a record $27.84 million. Despite higher earnings the bank's operating cash declined by 6% to $37.68 million for the year as it made less in net proceeds from the sales of its loans held for resale.

Strategy

Bryn Mawr Bank Corporation continued to push its acquisition strategy in 2015 designed to broaden its service offerings boost its loan and deposit business and expand its branch network. The bank looks to strategically acquire smaller insurance businesses small to mid-sized banks and community banks wealth management companies and advisory and planning services firm that complement its existing businesses.

Besides acquisitions the company has been growing its wealth management business through marketing campaigns to raise brand awareness.

Mergers and Acquisitions

In April 2015 to grow its wealth management business the bank purchased Robert J. McAllister Agency which provides insurance and risk management solutions to individuals and businesses in the Philadelphia region.

In January 2015 Bryn Mawr acquired the Continental Bank Holdings and its Plymouth Meeting-based flagship Continental Bank adding some $433 million in loans and $480 million in deposits along with 10 full-service branches located in key markets in Montgomery Chester and Philadelphia counties.

In October 2014 Bryn Mawr bought the Rosemont Pennsylvania-based insurance agency Powers Craft Parker & Beard Inc. (PCPB) for $7 million to enhance its own insurance business among individuals and commercial clients.

In 2012 as part of a strategy to build its wealth management division the company acquired Davidson Trust adding some $1 billion in assets under management.

Company Background

In 2011 the company bought the private wealth management business of Hershey Trust Company for more than $14.5 million; that deal brought in approximately $1 billion of assets under management. In 2010 the company purchased First Keystone Financial adding about 10 bank branches in Pennsylvania and some $2.7 billion in trust and investment assets.

EXECUTIVES

Executive Vice President Wealth Management Division, Matthew Waschull

EVP and COO, Alison E. Gers, age 59, $250,000 total compensation

EVP and Chief Lending Officer Bryn Mawr Trust, Joseph G. (Joe) Keefer, age 58, $238,500 total compensation

President and CEO, Francis J. Leto, age 57, $310,000 total compensation

EVP Secretary and Chief Risk Officer, Geoffrey L. Halberstadt

CFO and Treasurer Bryn Mawr Bank Corporation; EVP CFO and Treasurer Bryn Mawr Bank, Michael W. (Mike) Harrington, age 54

EVP Wealth Management Division, Harry R. Madeira

Senior Vice President and Senior Trust Officer, Lisa L Piergallini

Vice President, John Metz

Senior Vice President, Richard Gentile

Vice President Construction Real Estate, Michelle Wilson

Vice President, Robert Ricciardi

Senior Vice President, Susan O'Donnell

Vice President Real Estate Lending, Kristin Reese

Vice President Wealth Management Division, J Keefer-Hugill

Vice President, Cheryl Howard

Vice President Small Business Account Lending Division, Douglas Whalen

Vice President, Sally Worrell

Vice President, Drew Smith

Vice President Relationship Manager, Shawn Williams

Vice President Director of Investment Services, Bryan Andersen

Vice President Mortgage Division, Patrick McGowan

Senior Vice President Managing Partner, Robert McLaughlin

Senior Vice President, Ron Dankanich

Chairman, Britton H. Murdoch

Assistant Treasurer, Linda McLaughlin

Auditors: KPMG LLP

LOCATIONS

HQ: Bryn Mawr Bank Corp
801 Lancaster Avenue, Bryn Mawr, PA 19010
Phone: 610 525-1700
Web: www.bmtc.com

PRODUCTS/OPERATIONS

2014 Sales

	$ mil.	% of total
Interest		
Interest & fees on loans & leases	78	60
Investment securities	4	3
Cash & cash equivalents	0	-
Noninterest		
Fees for wealth management services	36	30
Service charges on deposits	2	2
Net gain on sale of residential mortgages	1	1
Loan Servicing and other fees	1	1
Other	5	3
Total	**131**	**100**

Selected Subsidiaries

Bryn Mawr Advisors Inc.
Bryn Mawr Asset Management Inc.
Bryn Mawr Brokerage Co. Inc.
Bryn Mawr Financial Services Inc.
Bryn Mawr Trust Company of Delaware
Joseph W. Roskos Co. Inc.
Lau Associates LLC
The Bryn Mawr Trust Company
    BMT Leasing Inc.
    BMT Mortgage Services Inc.
    BMT Settlement Services Inc.
    Insurance Counsellors of Bryn Mawr Inc.

COMPETITORS

Alliance Bancorp of Pennsylvania	Royal Bancshares
	Sovereign Bank
Firstrust Savings Bank	Wells Fargo
PNC Financial	

HISTORICAL FINANCIALS

Company Type: Public

Income Statement

FYE: December 31

	ASSETS ($ mil.)	NET INCOME ($ mil.)	INCOME AS % OF ASSETS	EMPLOYEES
12/16	3,421	36	1.1%	544
12/15	3,031	16	0.6%	530
12/14	2,246	27	1.2%	444
12/13	2,061	24	1.2%	432
12/12	2,035	21	1.0%	432
Annual Growth	**13.9%**	**14.3%**	**—**	**5.9%**

2016 Year-End Financials

Debt ratio: 0.86%	No. of shares (mil.): 16
Return on equity: 9.62%	Dividends
Cash ($ mil.): 50	Yield: 0.0%
Current ratio: —	Payout: 38.6%
Long-term debt ($ mil.): —	Market value ($ mil.): 714

	STOCK PRICE ($) FY Close	P/E High/Low	PER SHARE ($) Earnings	Dividends	Book Value
12/16	42.15	20 11	2.12	0.82	22.50
12/15	28.72	33 29	0.94	0.78	21.42
12/14	31.30	15 13	2.01	0.74	17.83
12/13	30.18	17 12	1.80	0.69	16.84
12/12	22.27	14 12	1.60	0.64	15.18
Annual Growth	**17.3%**	**— —**	**7.3%**	**6.4%**	**10.3%**

BSB Bancorp Inc. (MD)

BSB Bancorp is the holding company for Belmont Savings Bank a community back with about half a dozen branches in southeastern Middlesex County in the suburbs of Boston. Serving local businesses and individuals the $2 billion-asset bank offers checking savings money market retirement accounts and a variety of lending products. Almost 50% of its loan portfolio is made up of one-to-four family residential mortgages while commercial real estate loans make up another 30%. While Belmont Savings Bank traces its roots back to 1885 BSB Bancorp was formed in 2011 to take the company public.

Operations

BSB Bancorp mostly originates one-to-four family residential mortgages and commercial real estate loans for office buildings owner-occupied commercial buildings industrial buildings and strip mall centers. About 46% of its loan portfolio was made up of one-to-four family residential mortgages at the end of 2015 while another 29% was made up of commercial real estate loans. The rest of the portfolio was made up of home equity loans (10% of loan assets) construction (4%) business loans (3.5%) auto loans (6%) and other consumer loans (less than 1%).

The bank also makes more than 90% of its revenue from interest income. About 87% of its total revenue came from loan interest (including fees) during 2015 while another 7% came from interest on investment securities. The remainder of its revenue came from non-interest income sources including customer service fees.

Geographic Reach

While its primary market area is in the greater Boston area the company serves southeastern Massachusetts in the Essex Middlesex Norfolk and Suffolk Counties from branches in Belmont Watertown Waltham Newton and Cambridge.

Sales and Marketing

BSB Bancorp has been cutting back on its marketing in recent years. It spent $926000 on marketing in 2015 down from $975000 and $999000 in 2014 and 2013 respectively.

Financial Performance

BSB Bancorp's annual revenues have doubled since 2011 as its loan assets have more than tripled to $1.53 billion as a result new branch openings and organic growth with the strengthening economy around Boston. The bank's net income has skyrocketed more than five-fold over the time period as it's kept a lid on rising operating costs and benefited from the low-interest environment.

The bank's revenue jumped 23% to $51.57 million during 2015 mostly as a 30% increase in loan assets spurred higher interest income.

Strong revenue growth in 2015 drove BSB Bancorp's net income higher by 61% to $6.91 million. The bank's operating cash levels fell 14% to $18.1 million for the year mostly after adjusting its earnings for non-cash items related to its net proceeds from loan sales.

Strategy

BSB Bancorp reiterated in 2016 that it planned to continue focusing on growing its one-to-four family residential mortgage commercial real estate and home equity lending business which made up more than 85% of its loan assets in 2015. With its eye on being the "Bank of Choice" for small businesses and municipalities in its core Boston market area it plans to organically grow its deposit and lending business in the parts of Eastern Massachusetts that weren't as affected by the most recent recession.

In 2013 BSB Bancorp expanded its reach by 50% after opening two branches inside Shaw's Supermarkets in Cambridge and Newton (its first supermarket branch was opened in Waltham in 2012).

EXECUTIVES

President and CEO, Robert M. (Bob) Mahoney, age 68

EVP COO and Director BSB Bancorp Inc.; EV and COO Belmont Savings Bank, Hal R. Tovin, age 61

EVP Consumer Lending and Auto Finance Belmont Savings Bank, Christopher Y. (Chris) Downs, age 66

SVP CFO and Secretary BSB Bancorp Inc. and Belmont Savings Bank, John A. Citrano, age 53

President Bob Mahoney, Belmont Bank

Senior Vice President, Morgan Cambern

Board Member, Warren Farrell

Board Member, John Whittemore

Board Member, Richard Fougere

Board Member, Paul Petry

Auditors: Baker Newman & Noyes LLC

LOCATIONS

HQ: BSB Bancorp Inc. (MD)
2 Leonard Street, Belmont, MA 02478
Phone: 617 484-6700
Web: www.belmontsavings.com

COMPETITORS

Bank of America	Hingham Institution
Boston Private	for Savings
Brookline Bancorp	Independent Bank (MA)
Century Bancorp (MA)	Meridian Bancorp
Citizens Financial	Middlesex Savings
Group	Peoples Federal
DCU	Bancshares Inc.
Eastern Bank	Sovereign Bank
Enterprise Bancorp	TD Bank USA

HISTORICAL FINANCIALS

Company Type: Public

Income Statement

FYE: December 31

	ASSETS ($ mil.)	NET INCOME ($ mil.)	INCOME AS % OF ASSETS	EMPLOYEES
12/16	2,158	11	0.6%	125
12/15	1,812	6	0.4%	132
12/14	1,425	4	0.3%	128
12/13	1,054	1	0.2%	127
12/12	838	1	0.2%	119
Annual Growth	26.7%	71.0%	—	1.2%

2016 Year-End Financials

Debt ratio: —	No. of shares (mil.): 9
Return on equity: 7.78%	Dividends
Cash ($ mil.): 59	Yield: —
Current ratio: —	Payout: —
Long-term debt ($ mil.): —	Market value ($ mil.): 264

	STOCK PRICE ($) FY Close	P/E High/Low		PER SHARE ($) Earnings	Dividends	Book Value
12/16	28.95	21	15	1.33	0.00	17.66
12/15	23.39	30	23	0.78	0.00	16.09
12/14	18.63	38	30	0.49	0.00	15.11
12/13	15.09	69	56	0.22	0.00	14.40
12/12	12.23	84	66	0.16	0.00	13.98
Annual Growth	24.0%	—	—	69.8%	—	6.0%

Builders FirstSource Inc.

Builders FirstSource makes and sells building materials and manufactured components for homebuilders contractors remodelers and DIY consumers. It also offers construction-related services. The company's products and services — which include lumber windows and doors and millwork as well as installation and shell construction — are offered through some 400 locations across the US. Homebuilders such as Pulte Homes and Lennar are among its largest customers. Builders FirstSource was founded in 1998 as BSL Holdings.

Operations

Builders FirstSource operates through half a dozen product categories. Its largest lumber & lumber sheet goods accounts for about 35% of revenue and includes plywood and oriented strand board among other items. Windows doors & millwork (windows interior and exterior doors trim) and manufactured products (roof trusses wall panels stairs) together contribute another 35% of revenue.

The company's other product categories include gypsum roofing & insulation; siding metal & concrete; and other products & services.

Geographic Reach

Builders FirstSource operates only in the US with sales reported by region. The western US is its largest region accounting for some 30% of sales; the South and the Southeast contribute more than 25% and about 20% respectively.

The company has facilities in about 40 US states and serves 75 of the top 100 Metropolitan Statistical Areas.

Sales and Marketing

Builders FirstSource serves a range of customers from individual consumers to repair and remodel contractors to large homebuilders. Its top 10 customers mostly large homebuilders such as D.R. Horton CalAtlantic and Hovnanian Enterprises account for more than 15% of sales.

The company markets its products and services through a locally focused sales force of some 1700.

Financial Performance

After five years of steady revenue growth Builders FirstSource has doubled or nearly doubled its sales the past two years. It reported revenue of $6.4 billion in 2016 up about 80% from the prior year due to the impact of the mid-2015 purchase of building materials supplier ProBuild. Sales increased across all product lines and all geographic regions.

Following revenue net income was also up in 2016 jumping to $144 million from a loss of $23 million the prior year. The company was helped by reduced selling general and administrative expenses as well as an income tax benefit of $123 million. Cash from operations fell about 10% to $158 million as working capital increased in 2016 (primarily related to the ProBuild acquisition) compared to a decrease the prior year.

Strategy

An aggressive acquisition strategy — some three dozen companies since 1998 — enabled Builders FirstSource to become a construction powerhouse. It is relying on its standing in the industry (particularly within the professional segment of the US residential building products market) to propel growth.

Amid continued improvement in the US housing market the company believes its "one-stop-shop" offering will be a draw for homebuilders focused on competitive pricing on-site services and an expansive product portfolio.This is especially important as customers reduce supplier relationships in search of efficiencies. In addition Builders FirstSource continues to emphasize and invest in its value-added manufactured products category which again helps drive efficiencies for its customer base.

In 2017 the company has also made the expansion of its sales force a focus. Through mid-year it had added more than 100 new sales associates with additional hires planned.

Mergers and Acquisitions

Historically an acquisitive company Builders FirstSource made its last big purchase in mid-2015 when it paid some $1.6 billion for competitor ProBuild Holdings. The deal created a giant professional building materials company with more than $6 billion in combined sales and more than 400 locations across the US.

EXECUTIVES

Senior Vice President Oprs, Morris Tolly

SVP and General Counsel, Donald F. McAleenan, age 62, $415,481 total compensation

President and CEO, M. Chad Crow, age 49, $625,000 total compensation

SVP and CFO, Peter Jackson

Vice President Treasury, Mark Cooper

Area Vice President, Dave Rush

Vice President, Gary Raven

Vice President and Associate General Counsel, Jeff A Wier

Vice President Sales, Matt Liska

Senior Vice President and General Counsel, Don McAleenan

Vice President Sales, Chris Lemly

Senior Vice President Investor Relations, Jennifer Pasquino

Vice President Purchasing, Jeff Rettig

Vice President Forest Products and Transportation, Steve LaValley

Senior Vice President of Operations Region 1, Tom Adams

VICE PRESIDENT DEVELOPMENT SEATTLE,
Steve Yoon
Area Vice President, Dave Challenger
Vice President National Accounts, Mike McCrobie
Chairman, Paul S. Levy, age 69
Auditors: PricewaterhouseCoopers LLP

LOCATIONS

HQ: Builders FirstSource Inc.
 2001 Bryan Street, Suite 1600, Dallas, TX 75201
Phone: 214 880-3500   **Fax:** 214 880-3599
Web: www.bldr.com

2016 Sales

	$ mil.	% of total
US		
West	1,939	30
South	1,704	27
Southeast	1,367	22
Northeast	1,204	19
Other	151	2
Total	**6,367**	**100**

PRODUCTS/OPERATIONS

2016 Sales

	$ mil.	% of total
Lumber & lumber sheet goods	2,131	34
Windows doors & millwork	1,286	20
Manufactured products	1,097	17
Siding metal & concrete products	622	10
Gypsum roofing & insulation	520	8
Other building products & services	709	11
Total	**6,367**	**100**

Selected Products

Building Materials
 Concrete
 Concrete block
 Decking
 Gypsum
 Paint
 Roofing
 Sheathing
Interior Items
 Builder hardware
 Cabinets
 Cabinet hardware
 Countertops
 Fireplaces
Lumber and Related Products
 Dimensional lumber
 Engineered wood
 Oriented strand board
 Plywood
 Pressure-treated lumber
Manufactured Components
 Floor trusses
 I-Joist floor systems
 Interior and exterior doors
 Open wall panels
 Roof trusses
 Stairs
Millwork
 Columns
 Custom millwork
 Interior and exterior doors
 Moldings
 Special-order millwork
 Windows
Tools
 Pneumatic tools
 Power tools

COMPETITORS

84 Lumber	HD Supply
Ace Hardware	Lowe's
BMC Stock	McCoy Corp.
BlueLinx	Menard
Boise Cascade Company	True Value
Carter Lumber	Universal Forest
CertainTeed	Products

HISTORICAL FINANCIALS

Company Type: Public

Income Statement

FYE: December 31

	REVENUE ($ mil.)	NET INCOME ($ mil.)	NET PROFIT MARGIN	EMPLOYEES
12/16	6,367	144	2.3%	14,000
12/15	3,564	(22)	—	14,000
12/14	1,604	18	1.1%	3,800
12/13	1,489	(42)	—	3,300
12/12	1,070	(56)	—	2,750
Annual Growth	**56.2%**	**—**	**—**	**50.2%**

2016 Year-End Financials

Debt ratio: 63.25%
Return on equity: 62.75%
Cash ($ mil.): 14
Current ratio: 1.61
Long-term debt ($ mil.): 1,785

No. of shares (mil.): 111
Dividends
 Yield: —
 Payout: —
Market value ($ mil.): 1,224

	STOCK PRICE ($) FY Close	P/E High/Low		PER SHARE ($) Earnings	Dividends	Book Value
12/16	10.97	11	5	1.27	0.00	2.78
12/15	11.08	—	—	(0.22)	0.00	1.36
12/14	6.87	48	26	0.18	0.00	0.41
12/13	7.13	—	—	(0.44)	0.00	0.16
12/12	5.58	—	—	(0.60)	0.00	0.50
Annual Growth	**18.4%**	**—**	**—**	**—**	**—**	**53.8%**

Burlington Northern & Santa Fe Railway Co. (The)

BNSF Railway operates one of the largest railroad networks in North America. A wholly-owned subsidiary of Burlington Northern Santa Fe itself a unit of Berkshire Hathaway the company provides freight transportation over a network of about 32500 route miles of track across two-thirds of the western US and two provinces in Canada. BNSF Railway owns or leases a fleet of about 8000 locomotives. It also has some 30 intermodal facilities that help to transport agricultural consumer and industrial products as well as coal. In addition to major cities and ports BNSF Railway serves smaller markets in alliance with short-line partners.

Operations

BNSF Railway serves more than 40 ports and 30 intermodal facilities and operates 1600 trains per day.

In 2014 it hauled nearly 1 million carloads of agricultural commodities; more than 5 million intermodal shipments (truck trailers or containers); nearly 2 million carloads of industrial products; and almost 2.3 million coal shipments. All told the company hauled more than 10 million carloads in 2014.

Geographic Reach

The company's network is spread across 28 US states and three Canadian provinces.

Sales and Marketing

BNSF Railway serves smaller markets by working closely with 200 shortline partners. It has also forms marketing agreements with other rail carriers expanding the marketing reach for each railroad and their customers.

Financial Performance

In 2014 the company's revenues rose by 5.6% due to increased capacity offset by the negative effects of severe winter weather conditions early in the year which dampened transportation activities.

BNSF Railway generated 31% of its revenues in 2014 from consumer products; 28% from industrial products; 22% from coal; and 19% from agricultural products.

It also reported a 1.8% increase in cars/units handled and a 3.5% increase in average revenue per car/unit for the year.

The company accounted for more than 56% of Burlington Northern Santa Fe's net revenues for 2014.

Strategy

As part of its capital plan of $6 billion for 2015 the company has planned some major capital projects to maintain and grow its rail network.

In its northern region the company has plans to invest $1.5 billion across eight states for engineering maintenance and line expansion projects of which $700 million is planned for projects to expand the rail lines and Positive Train Control (PTC advanced technologies designed to automatically stop or slow a train before accidents occur) in that region. In the southern region it plans to spend $800 million in nine states for engineering maintenance and line expansion projects of which $175 million is planned for line expansion initiatives and continued implementation of PTC.

The overall $6 billion investment for 2015 includes $2.9 billion to replace and maintain core network and related assets nearly $1.5 billion on expansion and efficiency projects $200 million for continued implementation of PTC and $1.4 billion for locomotives freight cars and other equipment acquisitions.

In 2014 the company made capital investments for line expansion system improvement projects additional equipment and new employee hires. BNSF Railway had a 2013 capital program (to strengthen its infrastructure) valued at $4.1 billion.

EXECUTIVES

President and CEO, Carl R. Ice, age 60
EVP Law and Corporate Affairs, Roger Nober, age 52
EVP and CFO, Julie A. Piggott
EVP and Chief Marketing Officer, Stevan B. Bobb
EVP Operations, Gregory C. Fox
Executive Chairman, Matthew K. (Matt) Rose, age 58
Auditors: Deloitte & Touche LLP

LOCATIONS

HQ: Burlington Northern & Santa Fe Railway Co. (The)
 2650 Lou Menk Drive, Fort Worth, TX 76131-2830
Phone: 800 795-2673
Web: www.bnsf.com

COMPETITORS

American Commercial Lines	Kansas City Southern Railway
Canadian National Railway	Kirby Corporation
Canadian Pacific Railway	Landstar System
Ingram Industries	Norfolk Southern
J.B. Hunt	Schneider National
	Union Pacific Railroad
	Werner Enterprises

HISTORICAL FINANCIALS

Company Type: Public

Income Statement

FYE: December 31

	REVENUE ($ mil.)	NET INCOME ($ mil.)	NET PROFIT MARGIN	EMPLOYEES
12/16	19,278	4,260	22.1%	41,000
12/15	21,401	4,915	23.0%	44,000
12/14	22,714	4,397	19.4%	48,000
12/13	21,552	4,271	19.8%	43,000
12/12	20,478	3,720	18.2%	41,000
Annual Growth	(1.5%)	3.4%	—	0.0%

2016 Year-End Financials

Debt ratio: 1.90%
Return on equity: 7.91%
Cash ($ mil.): 570
Current ratio: 0.89
Long-term debt ($ mil.): 1,467

No. of shares (mil.): 0
Dividends
Yield: —
Payout: —
Market value ($ mil.): —

Burlington Stores Inc

Burlington Stores (dba Burlington Coat Factory) takes the "Brrr!" out of your life. The clothing retailer which made its name selling coats operates more than 590 no-frills retail stores (averaging 76000 square feet) offering off-price current brand-name clothing in about 45 states plus Puerto Rico. Although it is one of the nation's largest coat sellers the stores also sells a full wardrobe of products including children's apparel bath items furniture gifts jewelry linens and shoes. Sister chains include a pair of higher-priced Cohoes Fashions shops and about a dozen MJM Designer Shoe stores. Burlington Stores was founded in 1972.

Operations

About 98% of the company's sales are rung up at its Burlington Coat Factory Warehouse stores. Women's ready-to-wear apparel is its biggest earner at 24% of sales followed by accessories and shoes (22%) menswear (20%) youth and baby apparel (16%) home (12%) and coats (6%).

Its three other smaller businesses — Cohoes Fashions (off-price designer apparel) MJM Designer Shoe and Super Baby Depot — account for the rest. As its name suggests Super Baby Depot's two stores sell baby clothing accessories furniture and everything else a baby might need in the middle to higher price range. The company's MJM Designer Shoe chain has stores in New Jersey and New York and several other states. Like its larger sister chain MJM Designer Shoes sells brand names at significant discounts. The company also sells merchandise online at burlingtoncoatfactory.com and babydepot.com.

Geographic Reach

The New Jersey-based off-price retail chain has stores in 45 states and Puerto Rico. Its two primarily distribution centers which ship about 95% of its merchandise are located in Edgewater Park New Jersey and San Bernardino California.

Sales and Marketing

The chain is known for its year-round selection of about 10000 to 20000 discounted coats (compared to about 1500 to 2000 coats at department stores). Burlington Coat Factory takes less of a markup than its department store competition and has lower profit margins than other clothing retailers. It buys the coats early in the season (up to five months before department stores) to lock in lower prices.

Financial Performance

The company has recorded increasing revenue in the last six years.

In fiscal 2017 (ending January) revenue climbed 9% to $5.6 billion with gains spread evenly between comparable and non-comparable store sales. The company attributes the increase in its comparable store sales to an improved execution of its business model and the transition of its fragrance business from leased department rental income to an owned business.

Net income ticked up 43% to $215.9 million due to higher revenue and a reduction in selling general and administrative expenses as a proportion of total sales.

Cash from operating activities leaped 84% to $602.4 million on the back of higher net income and lower income tax and compensation payments.

Strategy

Burlington's primary growth driver is store expansions. In 2016 the company added a further 25 stores taking its store base to nearly 600. Burlington's goal is to have 1000 stores in operation.

Burlington Coat Factory's off-price niche has resonated with consumers looking for bargains both during the recession and continuing during the recovery. To grow the company is focusing on its core customers: 25-49 year-old women.

HISTORY

Russian-Jewish immigrant Abe Milstein and a partner started coat wholesaler and manufacturer Milstein and Feigelson in 1924. Abe's son Monroe was a quick study. He graduated from New York University with a business degree in 1946 at age 19 and started his own coat and suit wholesaling business called Monroe G. Milstein Inc. His mother provided free labor at her son's company six days a week to keep the business alive. Abe ended his partnership in 1953 and joined his son's business.

Family relations were strained temporarily in 1972 when Monroe disregarded his father's advice not to buy a faltering coat factory outlet store in Burlington New Jersey. (Abe believed that his son did not have enough retailing experience.) Monroe however thought owning a retail store would provide a guaranteed sales outlet for their merchandise and he bought Burlington Coat Factory for $675000 (using $60000 of his wife Henrietta's savings). His company also adopted the Burlington Coat Factory Warehouse moniker as its own.

To become less dependent on the season-specific coat business the company soon expanded its merchandise mix by adding a children's division (started by Henrietta deceased in 2001) and subleased departments. It opened a second store in Long Island New York in 1975.

Settling a trademark dispute with fabric maker Burlington Industries in 1981 Burlington Coat Factory agreed to say in advertising — as it does to this day — that the two companies are not affiliated. The 31-store company went public two years later using the money it raised to open almost 30 stores that year. As part of its expansion in the 1980s Burlington Coat Factory opened stores in warmer climates such as Texas and Florida.

The firm tried to grow through acquisitions that decade but failed in its attempts to buy a number of department store retailers. It made a successful bid in 1989 for New York discount retailer Cohoes.

Burlington Coat Factory's sales topped the $1 billion mark for the first time in fiscal 1993. Also that year the company bought Boston-based off-price family apparel chain Decelle. It then opened its first store outside the US (in Mexico) and tried new stand-alone store concepts based on successful in-store departments such as Luxury Linens and Baby Depot. A warm winter in 1994 hurt the company: Profits fell by two-thirds and it sold off inventory for two years afterward.

The company pulled a line of men's parkas in late 1998 after a Humane Society investigation revealed that the coats were trimmed with hair from dogs killed inhumanely in China. Burlington Coat Factory launched a baby gift registry in 2000 and later that year opened a silk floral division in selected stores. In 2001 the company acquired 16 stores formerly occupied by bankrupt Montgomery Ward. Burlington Coat Factory began operating MJM Designer Shoes in fiscal 2002 opening nine of the stand-alone specialty shoe stores. The company closed its Decelle stores in 2003 but converted most of them to the Burlington Coat Factory and Cohoes names while launching 25 new stores in 2004 (most under the Burlington Coat Factory moniker).

In 2005 the company opened two Super Baby Depot stores. Burlington Coat Factory was acquired by the Boston-based private equity firm Bain Capital Partners in April 2006 for about $2.1 billion.

In fiscal year 2006 the company opened three MJM Designer Shoes stores. The company's two stand-alone Luxury Linens stores were shut down and instead operate as departments within Burlington Coat Factory stores.

In December 2008 Thomas Kingsbury was named president and CEO of Burlington Coat Factory Warehouse succeeding Mark Nesci who retired after 37 years with the retailer. Prior to joining the company Kingsbury was a SEVP at Kohl's.

In February 2010 the company changed its fiscal year end from May to January to better comply with its peers in the retail industry. In October Burlington Coat Factory agreed to pay $10 million to settle a long-running legal fight with Italian luxury goods maker Fendi over the sale of counterfeit handbags and other leather goods.

Burlington went public in 2013.

EXECUTIVES

Vp And Senior Divisional Merchandise Manager, Steven Koster, age 69

Chairman President and CEO, Thomas A. (Tom) Kingsbury, age 64, $1,164,257 total compensation

EVP Human Resources, Joyce Manning Magrini, age 62, $386,539 total compensation

CFO and Principal, Marc D. Katz, age 52, $654,400 total compensation

EVP General Counsel and Corporate Secretary, Janet L. Dhillon, age 54

Chief Merchandising Officer and Principal, Jennifer Vecchio, age 51, $677,195 total compensation

Chief Customer Officer and Principal, Fred Hand, age 53, $654,400 total compensation

EVP and Chief Marketing Officer, Hobart (Bart) Sichel, age 52, $326,923 total compensation

EVP Supply Chain Corporate Services and Asset Protection, Mike Metheny, age 50

EVP Merchandising, Rick Seeger, age 55, $629,826 total compensation

EVP Stores, Forrest David Coder

EVP Planning & Allocation and Merchandise Information Operations (MIO), Eliot M. Rosenfield

Vice President Supply Chain Support, Steven Bienstock

Regional Vice President, Marty Frent

Senior Vice President Visual Merchandising, Jean M Hill

Vice President Store Administration, Steve Riley

Vice President Accounting Operations, Tony Hughes

Vice President Tax, Shobna Daga

Vice President, Jeff Armenti
Auditors: Deloitte & Touche LLP

LOCATIONS

HQ: Burlington Stores Inc
2006 Route 130 North, Burlington, NJ 08016
Phone: 609 387-7800
Web: www.burlingtonstores.com

PRODUCTS/OPERATIONS

2017 Sales

	% of total
Women's ready-to-wear apparel	24
Accessories and Footwear	22
Menswear	21
Youth Apparel/Baby	16
Home	11
Coats	6
Total	**100**

2017 stores

	No.
Burlington Coat Factory	576
MJM Designer Shoes	10
Cohoes Fashions	2
Super Baby Depot	2
Burlington shoes	1
Online store	1
Total	**592**

Selected Store Banners

Burlington Coat Factory Warehouse (value-priced
  apparel accessories linens bath items gifts)
Cohoes Fashions (higher-priced apparel and accessories)
MJM Designer Shoes (designer and fashion shoes)
Super Baby Depot (baby clothing accessories furniture)

COMPETITORS

Ascena Retail	Nordstrom
Babies "R" Us	Payless ShoeSource
Bed Bath & Beyond	Ross Stores
Belk	Saks
Bon-Ton Stores	Sears
DSW	Stein Mart
Dillard's	TJX Companies
J. C. Penney	Target Corporation
Kohl's	Wal-Mart
Macy's	

HISTORICAL FINANCIALS

Company Type: Public

Income Statement

FYE: January 28

	REVENUE ($ mil.)	NET INCOME ($ mil.)	NET PROFIT MARGIN	EMPLOYEES
01/17	5,590	215	3.9%	40,000
01/16	5,129	150	2.9%	37,500
01/15*	4,849	65	1.4%	34,000
02/14	4,461	16	0.4%	30,095
02/13	4,165	25	0.6%	29,556
Annual Growth	**7.6%**	**70.9%**	**—**	**7.9%**

*Fiscal year change

2017 Year-End Financials

Debt ratio: 43.91%
Return on equity: ***.***.**%
Cash ($ mil.): 81
Current ratio: 0.93
Long-term debt ($ mil.): 1,128

No. of shares (mil.): 70
Dividends
  Yield: —
  Payout: —
Market value ($ mil.): 5,678

	STOCK PRICE ($) FY Close	P/E High/Low	Earnings	PER SHARE ($) Dividends	Book Value
01/17	80.91	29 16	3.01	0.00	(0.71)
01/16	53.73	30 20	1.99	0.00	(1.37)
01/15*	49.89	58 27	0.87	0.00	(0.88)
02/14	25.58	— —	(0.39)	0.00	(2.04)
Annual Growth	**33.4%**				

*Fiscal year change

Byline Bancorp Inc

LOCATIONS

HQ: Byline Bancorp Inc
180 North LaSalle Street, Suite 300, Chicago, IL
60601
Phone: 773 244-7000
Web: www.bylinebank.com

HISTORICAL FINANCIALS

Company Type: Public

Income Statement

FYE: December 31

	ASSETS ($ mil.)	NET INCOME ($ mil.)	INCOME AS % OF ASSETS	EMPLOYEES
12/16	3,295	66	2.0%	791
12/15	2,479	(14)	—	—
Annual Growth	**32.9%**	**—**	**—**	**—**

2016 Year-End Financials

Debt ratio: 1.44%
Return on equity: 23.31%
Cash ($ mil.): 46
Current ratio: —
Long-term debt ($ mil.): —

No. of shares (mil.): 24
Dividends
  Yield: —
  Payout: —
Market value ($ mil.): —

	STOCK PRICE ($) FY Close	P/E High/Low	Earnings	PER SHARE ($) Dividends	Book Value
12/16	0.00	— —	3.27	0.00	15.54
12/15	0.00	— —	(0.86)	0.00	10.86
/0.00		—	(0.00) 0.00	(0.00)	
Annual Growth	**—**	**—**	**—**	**—**	**—**

Cadence Bancorporation

LOCATIONS

HQ: Cadence Bancorporation
2800 Post Oak Boulevard, Suite 3800, Houston, TX
77056
Phone: 713 871-4000
Web: www.cadencebank.com

HISTORICAL FINANCIALS

Company Type: Public

Income Statement

FYE: December 31

	ASSETS ($ mil.)	NET INCOME ($ mil.)	INCOME AS % OF ASSETS	EMPLOYEES
12/16	9,530	65	0.7%	1,193
12/15	8,811	39	0.4%	—
12/14	0	44	—	—
Annual Growth	**—**	**21.1%**	**—**	**—**

2016 Year-End Financials

Debt ratio: 3.44%
Return on equity: 6.15%
Cash ($ mil.): 247
Current ratio: —
Long-term debt ($ mil.): —

No. of shares (mil.): 75
Dividends
  Yield: —
  Payout: —
Market value ($ mil.): —

	STOCK PRICE ($) FY Close	P/E High/Low	Earnings	PER SHARE ($) Dividends	Book Value
12/16	0.00	— —	0.87	0.00	14.41
12/15	0.00	— —	0.52	0.00	14.06
Annual Growth	**—**		**29.3%**	**—**	**1.2%**

Calpine Corp

Independent power producer and marketer Calpine controls nearly 26000 MW of generating capacity and some 830 MW under construction through interests in about 80 primarily natural gas-fired power plants in 25 US states Canada and Mexico. This fleet also includes more than 10 geothermal power plants in California. Calpine the leading geothermal power producer in North America owns 760 MW of capacity at the largest geothermal facility in the US (the Geysers in northern California) which accounts for 40% of the country's geothermal energy. The company has major presence in the wholesale power markets in California the Mid-Atlantic and Texas. In 2017 the company agreed to sell itself to a consortium led by private equity firm Energy Capital Partners for $5.6 billion.

Change in Company Type

In August 2017 Calpine agreed to be bought for about $5.6 billion by Energy Capital Partners and a consortium of investors led by Access Industries and the Canada Pension Plan Investment Board. The deal removes Calpine from the ranks of publicly traded energy generation companies which have not been treated well by capital markets. The change in ownership due to become effective in early 2018 was not expected to bring about major operational changes at Calpine.

Operations

Calpine?s segments are West (including geothermal) Texas and East (including Canada). Texas accounts for more than 40% of Calpine's revenues in 2015; the East about a third; and the West about a quarter.

Other Calpine operations include construction consulting and management services; turbine component manufacturing; and critical power provision for high-tech companies.

Its indirect subsidiaries include Calpine Construction Finance Company L.P. (and its units Hermiston Power LLC and Brazos Valley Energy LLC) and Calpine Development Holdings Inc.

Its subsidiaries include Calpine Newark LLC; Calpine Northbrook Holdings Corp.; Calpine Northbrook Investors LLC; Calpine Northbrook Project Holdings LLC; and Calpine Operating Services Company Inc.

Geographic Reach

Serving customers in 25 US states Canada and Mexico Calpine's operating segments are West (including geothermal) Texas and East (including Canada). The company has regional offices in Dublin (California) Wilmington (Delaware) Pasadena (Texas) Washington DC Sacramento and Austin (Texas).

California Texas and the Northeast region are the largest wholesale power markets in the US.

Sales and Marketing

Calpine sells wholesale power steam capacity renewable energy credits and ancillary services to utilities independent electric system operators industrial and agricultural companies retail power providers municipalities power marketers and others.

Calpine's utility electricity is distributed via its distribution network underground lines and transmission system.

The company sells electricity to wholesalers and end-users primarily through long-term contracts; the firm also trades power on the wholesale market.

Financial Performance

In 2016 Calpine?s revenue increased 4% to $6.7 billion from 2015 driven by the performance of the East up 15% and Texas up 19% segments.

Revenue from the West segment however slipped 25% in 2016 from the year before on lower contribution from hedges because of lower power prices at the company?s Geysers Assets from lower forward natural gas prices.

The commodity margin in the Texas segment dropped 11% in 2016 because of lower realized Spark Spreads resulting from a decrease in hedge value and lower market liquidations. The commodity margin in the East segment increased by $14 million in 2016 from 2015 from the net year-over-year effect of the company?s portfolio management activities which includded the acquisition of the 695 MW Granite Ridge Energy Center in 2016 and the start of commercial operations at the 309 MW Garrison Energy Center in 2015.

Calpine?s profit slid about 60% to $92 million in 2016 from 2015 on higher energy prices.

Cash from operating activities increased to about $1 billion in 2016 from $863 million in 2015 due in part to lower interest payments.

Strategy

Calpine?s goal is to continue to grow its generation presence in core markets with an emphasis on acquisitions expansions or modernization of existing power plants. Calpine is also actively seeking divestiture opportunities of non-core assets to pay down debt.

In 2016 the company sold the assets comprising South Point Energy Center to Nevada Power Company as well as the Mankato Power Plant in Minnesota. The transactions were part of the company?s effort to divest non-core assets.

Calpine has established a retail energy portfolio to provide an additional source of liquidity for its generation fleet. In 2015 2016 and 2017 the company acquired Champion Energy Calpine Solutions and North American Power to bulk up its retail operations.

The company also initiated a $2.8 billion debt reduction program to give it more room to make investments.

Mergers and Acquisitions

In 2017 Calpine acquired North American Power for about $105 million to add to its retail portfolio. North American Power is concentrated in the Northeast US where Calpine has a substantial power generation presence and where Champion Energy (a 2016 Calpine acquisition) has a substantial retail sales footprint. North American Power will be integrated into the Champion Energy retail platform.

In 2016 the company bought Noble Group' s North American energy business for about $800 million.

That year Calpine acquired the Granite Ridge Energy Center from Granite Ridge Holdings LLC a natural gas-fired combined-cycle power plant located in Londonderry New Hampshire the cost of deal was $500 million. The addition of Granite Ridge strategically enhances its footprint in New England.

In 2015 Calpine acquired retail electric provider Champion Energy Marketing for $240 million plus working capital adjustments. Champion's presence in Texas and the Northeast made it the ideal retail complement to the company's wholesale generation portfolio.

Company Background

In 2013 to raise cash Calpine sold its Riverside Energy Center (a 600 MW natural gas plant in Beloit Wisconsin to Wisconsin Power and Light for $400 million.

In 2012 the company acquired an 800-MW natural gas-fired combined-cycle power plant in Central Texas from Bosque Power Co. for $432 million. That year it sold the Broad River Energy Center to Broad River Power LLC an affiliate of Energy Capital Partners LLC for $427 million.

In 2010 Calpine purchased 4490 MW of power plants from Pepco Holdings for about $1.7 billion. The acquisition added Conectiv Energy's power plants (18 operating and one under construction) to Calpine's fleet helping to strengthen its market position in the Eastern US.

EXECUTIVES

EVP Chief Legal Officer and Secretary, W. Thaddeus (Thad) Miller, age 66, $870,228 total compensation

President Calpine Energy Solutions, James M. (Jim) Wood

President and CEO, John B. (Thad) Hill, age 50, $1,129,410 total compensation

EVP and CFO, Zamir Rauf, age 57, $630,173 total compensation

EVP; President Calpine Retail, W. G. (Trey) Griggs, age 46, $513,976 total compensation

President and CEO Champion Energy, Michael Sullivan

EVP Power Operations, Charles M. (Charlie) Gates, age 66, $356,713 total compensation

SVP Finance and Chief Risk Officer, Mauricio Del Valle

Vice President Internal Audit and SOX, David M Neary

Vice President NE Power Trading, Will Stokes

Vice President. Financial Planning and Analysis, Mauricio Delvalle

Vice President Commercial Information Systems, Joel McKnight

Vice President Engineering And Constr, Darron Granger

Vice President Physical Trading And Operations, Bob Hayes

Vice President Government and Regulatory Affairs, Randy Jones

Senior Vice President, Tom Long

Vice President of Tax, James Sandt

Vice President and Information Technology Information Officer, Jp Arcuri

Vice President Technical Services, Greg McAuley

Executive Vice President Power, Charlie Gates

Executive Vice President Chief Legal Off, W Miller

Vice President Natural Gas Trading, James Tinsley

VICE PRESIDENT REGIONAL OPERATIONS, Robert Parker

VICE PRESIDENT AND MANAGING COUNSEL, Kaiser Malik

Chairman, Frank Cassidy, age 70

Vice Chairman, Keith Young

Auditors: PricewaterhouseCoopers LLP

LOCATIONS

HQ: Calpine Corp
717 Texas Avenue, Suite 1000, Houston, TX 77002
Phone: 713 830-2000
Web: www.calpine.com

2016 sales

	$ mil.	% of total
Texas	2,815	42
East	2,364	35
West	1,569	23
Elimination	(32)	-
Total	**6,716**	**100**

COMPETITORS

AEP	Duke Energy
AES	Edison International
Berkshire Hathaway Energy	Enel North America
	PG&E Corporation
CMS Energy	PSEG Power
Covanta	Sempra Energy

HISTORICAL FINANCIALS

Company Type: Public

Income Statement

FYE: December 31

	REVENUE ($ mil.)	NET INCOME ($ mil.)	NET PROFIT MARGIN	EMPLOYEES
12/16	6,716	92	1.4%	2,372
12/15	6,472	235	3.6%	2,209
12/14	8,030	946	11.8%	2,052
12/13	6,301	14	0.2%	2,157
12/12	5,478	199	3.6%	2,151
Annual Growth	5.2%	(17.5%)	—	2.5%

2016 Year-End Financials

Debt ratio: 63.05%
Return on equity: 2.88%
Cash ($ mil.): 418
Current ratio: 1.20
Long-term debt ($ mil.): 11,431

No. of shares (mil.): 359
Dividends
　Yield: —
　Payout: —
Market value ($ mil.): 4,104

	STOCK PRICE ($) FY Close	P/E High/Low		Earnings	PER SHARE ($) Dividends	Book Value
12/16	11.43	62	40	0.26	0.00	9.10
12/15	14.47	36	18	0.64	0.00	8.72
12/14	22.13	10	8	2.31	0.00	8.84
12/13	19.51	734602		0.03	0.00	8.19
12/12	18.13	44	34	0.42	0.00	8.74
Annual Growth	(10.9%)	—	—	(11.3%)	—	1.0%

Cambridge Bancorp

Cambridge Bancorp is the nearly $2 billion-asset holding company for Cambridge Trust Company a community bank serving Cambridge and the Greater Boston area through about a dozen branch locations in Massachusetts. It offers standard retail products and services including checking and savings accounts CDs IRAs and credit cards. Residential mortgages including home equity loans account for about 50% of the company's loan portfolio while commercial real estate loans make up more than 40%. The company also offers commercial industrial and consumer loans. Established in 1892 the bank also offers trust and investment management services.

Operations

The commercial bank operates a traditional retail banking line focused on lending as well as its Wealth Management Group which investment management and trust business. The bank had $1.8 billion in total assets and $2.4 billion in client assets under management at the end of 2015.

As with other retail banks Cambridge Bancorp makes the bulk of its revenue from interest income. About 58% of its total revenue came from loan interest during 2015 while another 10% came from interest on taxable and tax-exempt investment securities. The rest of its revenue came from wealth management income (24% of revenue) deposit account fees (3%) ATM/Debit card income (1%) and other non-interest income sources.

Geographic Reach

Cambridge Bancorp has 12 branches in Massachusetts in Cambridge Boston Belmont Concord Lexington Lincoln and Weston. It also has wealth management offices in Boston as well as in New Hampshire in Concord Manchester and Portsmouth.

Sales and Marketing

The company spent $2.38 million on marketing during 2015 up from $2.12 million in 2014.

Financial Performance

Cambridge's annual revenues and profits have been steadily rising over the past several years thanks to continued commercial real estate mortgage growth and as its Wealth Management business has nearly doubled its managed assets since 2011 spurring higher fee revenue.

The bank's revenue climbed 7% to $80.2 million during 2015 on 10% loan growth mostly driven by commercial real estate loans which spurred higher interest income. The company's wealth management business income grew 7% as its client assets continued to grow with new investor inflows.

Revenue growth in 2015 drove Cambridge Bancorp's net income up 5% to $15.7 million. The bank's operating cash levels rose 24% to $20 million for the year with an increase in cash-based earnings and favorable changes in working capital mostly related to a change in accrued interest receivable deferred taxes and other assets and liabilities.

Strategy

Cambridge Bancorp continued in 2016 to lean on the success of its commercial mortgage business though it plans to pivot more to commercial and industrial lending to diversify its commercial lending portfolio.

To better prepare for rising interest rates Cambridge Bancorp in 2015 and 2016 modified its commercial loan strategy from long-term fixed-rate loans (which are vulnerable to interest rate risk) to a new interest rate derivative product to offer an alternative long-term financing for its customers while helping the bank earn a variable rate of interest on its loans. For its consumer banking unit the bank in 2015 began a plan to sell the majority of its long-term residential mortgage production including secondary loans to the secondary market.

EXECUTIVES

Chairman President and CEO, Denis K. Sheahan, age 51
SVP and Chief Investment Officer, James F. Spencer
EVP and Chief Lending Officer, Martin B. Millane
EVP and CIO Cambridge Trust, Lynne M. Burrow
EVP and Head of Wealth Management Cambridge Trust, Michael A. Duca
EVP and Consumer Banking Director Cambridge Trust, Thomas A. Johnson
CFO, Michael Carotenuto
SVP and President Cambridge Trust Company of New Hampshire, Susan Martore-Baker
SVP and Marketing Director, Robert N. Siegrist
Auditors: KPMG LLP

LOCATIONS

HQ: Cambridge Bancorp
1336 Massachusetts Avenue, Cambridge, MA 02138
Phone: 617 876-5500
Web: www.cambridgetrust.com

PRODUCTS/OPERATIONS

2015 Sales

	% of total
Interest Income	
Interest on loans	58
Interest on taxable investment securities	7
Interest on tax exempt investment securities	3
Non-Interest Income	
Wealth Management Income	24
Deposits accounts fee	3
ATM/Debit card income	1
Bank Owned life insurance income	1

Gain on disposition on investment securities	1
Gain on loans held of sale	1
Other income	1
Loan related derivative income	
Total	**100**

PRODUCTS/SERVICES

Personal Banking
Checking
Savings CDs & IRAs
Online Banking
Mobile Banking
Mortgages
Home Equity
Credit Cards
Personal Loans
More Services
Business Banking
Checking & Savings
Commercial Lending
Commercial Real Estate
Cash Management
Remote Deposit Capture
Online Banking
Mobile Banking
Professional Services Program
More Services
Wealth Management
Investment Process
Investment Management
Fiduciary & Planning Services
Estate Settlement
Wealth Management Personnel
Forums
Online Access

COMPETITORS

Bank of America	Eastern Bank
Cambridge Financial	Middlesex Savings
Central Bancorp	Peoples Federal
Century Bancorp (MA)	Bancshares Inc.
Citizens Financial Group	

HISTORICAL FINANCIALS

Company Type: Public

Income Statement

FYE: December 31

	ASSETS ($ mil.)	NET INCOME ($ mil.)	INCOME AS % OF ASSETS	EMPLOYEES
12/16	1,849	16	0.9%	—
12/15	1,706	15	0.9%	—
12/14	1,573	14	0.9%	—
12/13	1,533	14	0.9%	123
12/12	1,417	13	0.9%	123
Annual Growth	**6.9%**	**6.0%**	**—**	**—**

2016 Year-End Financials

Debt ratio: 0.20%	No. of shares (mil.): 4
Return on equity: 12.97%	Dividends
Cash ($ mil.): 54	Yield: 0.0%
Current ratio: —	Payout: 44.3%
Long-term debt ($ mil.): —	Market value ($ mil.): 251

	STOCK PRICE ($) FY Close	P/E High/Low	Earnings	PER SHARE ($) Dividends	Book Value
12/16	62.29	15 11	4.15	1.84	33.36
12/15	47.40	13 11	3.93	1.80	31.26
12/14	46.50	13 10	3.78	1.68	29.50
12/13	40.01	12 10	3.62	1.59	28.13
12/12	36.60	11 9	3.45	1.50	27.21
Annual Growth	**14.2%**	**— —**	**4.7%**	**5.2%**	**5.2%**

Camden National Corp. (ME)

Camden National Corporation is the holding company for Camden National Bank which boasts nearly 45 branches in about a dozen Maine counties and provides standard deposit products such as checking and savings accounts CDs and IRAs. Commercial mortgages and loans make up 50% of its loan portfolio while residential mortgages make up another 40% and consumer loans constitute the remainder. Subsidiary Acadia Trust provides trust fiduciary investment management and retirement plan administration services while Camden Financial Consultants offers brokerage and insurance services. The largest bank headquartered in Maine Camden National Bank was founded in 1875 and once issued its own US currency.

Operations

About 63% of Camden National's total revenue came from loan interest (including fees) in 2014 while another 15% came from interest on its US government and sponsored enterprise obligations (investment securities). The rest of its revenue came from deposit account service charges (5%) other service charges and fees (5%) income from fiduciary services (4%) brokerage and insurance commissions (2%) and other miscellaneous income sources. The bank had a staff of 471 employees at the end of 2014.

Geographic Reach

Camden National has around 45 branches in 12 counties throughout Maine with one commercial loan office in Manchester New Hampshire. Its primary markets are in the counties of Androscoggin Cumberland Hancock Kennebec Knox Lincoln Penobscot Piscataquis Somerset Waldo Washington and York.

Sales and Marketing

The company offers deposit and loan services to consumers institutions municipalities non-profits and commercial customers.

Financial Performance

The company has struggled to consistently grow its revenues and profits in recent years mostly due to shrinking interest margins on loans amidst the low-interest environment.

Camden National's revenue dipped by 3% to $112.8 million in 2014 mostly because the bank in 2013 had collected a non-recurring $2.7 million gain from the sale of its five Franklin County branches and because its mortgage banking income fell by $1.1 million as it decided to retain most of its 30-year fixed rate residential mortgage production in 2014.

Despite revenue declines in 2014 the bank's net income jumped by 8% to $24.6 million mostly because in 2013 it had recorded a non-recurring $2.8 million goodwill impairment charge related to its financial services reporting unit. Camden's operating cash levels rose by 1% to $29.9 million for the year on higher cash earnings.

Strategy

The bank competes with larger financial institutions by emphasizing customer service to build customer loyalty and long-term relationships. It also sometimes pursues acquisitions of banks and branches in its target markets in Maine to grow its loan and deposit business.

Camden may also be expanding its franchise beyond Maine in future years. In 2014 it opened a commercial loan office in Manchester New Hampshire enabling it to serve more customers across northern New England.

Mergers and Acquisitions

In March 2015 Camden National Corporation agreed to purchase SBM Financial along with its subsidiary The Bank of Maine subsidiary. The deal expected to be completed in late 2015 would add $813 million in assets and make Camden National Bank Maine's largest community bank.

In late 2012 the bank acquired 15 full-service branches from Bank of America for $12 million.

EXECUTIVES

EVP COO and CFO, Deborah A. Jordan, age 51, $223,327 total compensation
EVP Retail Banking, June B. Parent, age 53, $189,248 total compensation
EVP Risk Management, Joanne T. Campbell, age 54, $124,585 total compensation
President and CEO, Gregory A. (Greg) Dufour, age 56, $398,077 total compensation
SVP Information Technology, Scott Buckheit
EVP Commercial Lending, Timothy P. Nightingale, age 59, $213,846 total compensation
Vice President Commercial Portfolio Manager Commercial Loan Administrator Team Leader, Libby Arrico
Vice President, Richard Nickerson
Vice President, Craig Day
Assistant Vice President, Jody Landrith
Senior Vice President, Vera Rand Roberts
Vice President Commercial Loan Officer, Brent Folster
Vice President Human Resources, Carolyn Crosby
Vice President Information Security Manager, Anthony Mazzeo
Senior Vice President and Managing Director, Stephen M Sessler
Vice President Credit Risk Officer, Susan Weber
Vice President Commercial Lending, Jennifer Morin
Senior Vice President, AL Butler
Vice President of Mortgage Operations, Betsy Hauser
Assistant Vice President Banking Center Manager, Nancy Smith
Vice President of Mortgage Operations, Paul Palmer
Vice President Collections, Tim Crowe
Senior Vice President Retail Regional Manager, Maureen St John
Assistant Vice President Senior Client Services Specialist, Amanda Neuts
Vice President Senior Retail Loan Officer, Pam Fowler
Chairman Camden National Corporation and Camden National Bank, Karen W. Stanley, age 71
Secretary, Diane Marion
Auditors: Berry Dunn McNeil & Parker, LLC

LOCATIONS

HQ: Camden National Corp. (ME)
2 Elm Street, Camden, ME 04843
Phone: 207 236-8821   **Fax:** 207 236-6256
Web: www.camdennational.com

PRODUCTS/OPERATIONS

2014 Sales

	$ mil.	% of total
Interest		
Loans including fees	70	63
US government & agency securities	17	14
Other investments	0	1
Noninterest		
Service charges on deposit accounts & others	12	11
Income from fiduciary services	5	4
Brokerage and insurance commission	1	2
Other	5	5
Total	**112**	**100**

COMPETITORS

Bangor Savings Bank
Bar Harbor Bankshares
KeyCorp
Northeast Bancorp
Norway Bancorp
People's United Financial
TD Bank USA
The First Bancorp

HISTORICAL FINANCIALS

Company Type: Public

Income Statement

FYE: December 31

	ASSETS ($ mil.)	NET INCOME ($ mil.)	INCOME AS % OF ASSETS	EMPLOYEES
12/16	3,864	40	1.0%	631
12/15	3,709	20	0.6%	652
12/14	2,789	24	0.9%	471
12/13	2,603	22	0.9%	481
12/12	2,564	23	0.9%	550
Annual Growth	10.8%	14.4%		3.5%

2016 Year-End Financials

Debt ratio: 1.54%
Return on equity: 10.59%
Cash ($ mil.): 87
Current ratio: —
Long-term debt ($ mil.): —

No. of shares (mil.): 15
Dividends
Yield: 0.0%
Payout: 31.1%
Market value ($ mil.): 688

	STOCK PRICE ($) FY Close	P/E High/Low	Earnings	Dividends	Book Value
12/16	44.45	19 11	2.57	0.80	25.30
12/15	44.09	26 21	1.73	0.80	23.69
12/14	39.84	19 16	2.19	0.72	22.00
12/13	41.84	22 16	1.98	0.71	20.33
12/12	33.97	19 15	2.03	1.00	20.45
Annual Growth	7.0%	— —	6.0%	(5.4%)	5.5%

Campbell Soup Co.

Soup boils down to M'm! M'm! Money! at the world's #1 soup maker Campbell Soup. The company's most popular selections among its extensive soup portfolio in the US include chicken noodle tomato and cream of mushroom. Campbell also makes many other simple foods snacks and beverages including SpaghettiOs canned pasta Pace picante sauce V8 beverages Aussie favorite Arnott's biscuits and Pepperidge Farm baked goods (including those popular tiny Goldfish crackers). Newer products for the soup company include Garden Fresh Gourmet salsas and dips and Bolthouse Farms carrots and organic baby foods. Campbell sells its products worldwide.

HISTORY

Campbell Soup Company began in Camden New Jersey in 1869 as a canning and preserving business founded by icebox maker Abram Anderson and fruit merchant Joseph Campbell. Anderson left in 1876 and Arthur Dorrance took his place. The Dorrance family assumed control after Campbell retired in 1894.

Arthur's nephew John Dorrance joined Campbell in 1897. The young chemist soon found a way to condense soup by eliminating most of its water. Without the heavy bulk of water-filled cans distribution was cheaper; Campbell products quickly spread.

In 1904 the firm introduced the Campbell Kids characters. Entering the California market in 1911

Campbell became one of the first US companies to achieve national distribution of a food brand. It bought Franco-American the first American soup maker in 1915.

The company's ubiquity in American kitchens made its soup can an American icon (consider Andy Warhol's celebrated 1960 print) and brought great wealth to the Dorrance family.

With a reputation for conservative management Campbell began to diversify acquiring V8 juice (1948) Swanson (1955) Pepperidge Farm (1961) Godiva Chocolatier (33% in 1966 full ownership in 1974) Vlasic pickles (1978) and Mrs. Paul's seafood (1982). It introduced Prego spaghetti sauce and LeMenu frozen dinners in the early 1980s.

Much of Campbell's sales growth in the 1990s came not from unit sales but from increasing its prices. In 1993 it took a $300 million restructuring charge and over the next two years it sold poor performers at home and abroad. John Sr.'s grandson Bennett Dorrance took up the role of vice chairman in 1993 becoming the first family member to take a senior executive position in 10 years.

Two years later Campbell paid $1.1 billion for Pace Foods (picante sauce) and acquired Fresh Start Bakeries (buns and muffins for McDonald's) and Homepride (popular cooking sauce in the UK).

As part of its international expansion in 1996 the firm acquired Erasco a top German soup maker and Cheong Chan a food manufacturer in Malaysia. However back at home it sold Mrs. Paul's. In 1997 Campbell sold its Marie's salad dressing operations and bought Groupe Danone's Liebig (France's leading wet-soup brand). Also that year Dale Morrison a relative newcomer to the firm succeeded David Johnson as president and CEO. To reduce costs and focus on other core segments in 1998 Campbell spun off Swanson frozen foods and Vlasic pickles into Vlasic Foods International. (Vlasic later filed bankruptcy and was snapped up in a leveraged buyout.) In 1999 Campbell redesigned its soup can labels altering an American icon.

Morrison resigned abruptly as president and CEO in 2000; Johnson returned to the helm during the search for a permanent chief. In early 2001 Douglas Conant previously of Nabisco Foods joined Campbell as president and CEO. A fresh plan was introduced to spend up to $600 million on marketing product development and quality upgrades (at the expense of shareholder dividends). In 2001 Campbell also bought the Batchelors Royco and Heisse Tasse brands of soup as well as the OXO brand of stock cubes from Unilever for about $900 million. The deal made Campbell the leading soup maker in Europe. In 2003 Campbell bought Snack Foods Limited a leading snack food maker in Australia and Irish dry soup maker Erin Foods from Greencore.

Campbell reorganized its North American business in 2004 into the following units: US Soup Sauces and Beverages; Campbell Away From Home and Canada Mexico and Latin America; Pepperidge Farm; and Godiva Worldwide. (In response to dietary trends the company announced that year that it was removing all trans-fatty acids from its Pepperidge Farm breads.) The company retired the Franco-American brand in 2004; products that carried the brand (most notably SpaghettiOs) now bear the Campbell brand. Also that year company chairman George M. Sherman retired and was replaced by Harvey Golub.

In 2006 Campbell sold its UK and Irish businesses to Premier Foods for about $870 million. Brands involved in the sale included Homepride sauces OXO stock cubes and Batchelors McDonnells and Erin soups.

In 2012 the company purchased Bolthouse Farms for about $1.55 billion from Madison Dearborn Partners. Bolthouse known for selling fresh carrots beverages and salad dressings was expected to further fuel Campbell's US beverage division which had benefited from the rising popularity of the V8 juice brand.

In fiscal 2013 Campbell expanded its access to manufacturing and distribution capabilities in Mexico for its beverages soups broths and sauces after it signed a deal with Grupo Jumex and Conservas La Coste ±ato. That year it also sold its European simple meals business closing facilities in Belgium France Germany and Sweden.

In August 2013 the soup giant acquired the Denmark-based baked snack maker Kelsen Group for $325 million.

In June 2013 it bought Plum Organics one of the top brands of organic baby food in the US. The company makes organic foods and snacks for babies toddlers and children a fast-growing premium food category. It hoped the purchase would bring a new generation of consumers to Campbell.

EXECUTIVES

President and CEO, Denise M. Morrison, age 63, $1,100,000 total compensation
VP and Controller, Anthony P. DiSilvestro, age 58, $642,500 total compensation
President Americas Simple Meals and Beverages, Mark R. Alexander, age 53, $696,667 total compensation
SVP and General Counsel, Adam G. Ciongoli, age 49, $700,000 total compensation
President Campbell Fresh, Edward L. (Ed) Carolan, age 48
President Global Biscuits and Snacks, Luca Mignini, age 54, $674,042 total compensation
SVP Global Research and Development and Quality, Carlos J. Barroso, age 58, $470,000 total compensation
President Campbell Soup Foundation, Kim Fremont Fortunato
VP and Chief Technology and Information Officer, Francisco Fraga
SVP Integrated Global Services, Bethmara Kessler
Vice President Research and Development Beverage and Breakthrough Innovation, Patricia Principato
Vice President of Logistics, Skip Tappan
Senior Vice President And Chief Legal And Public Affairs Officer, Ellen O Kaden
Vice President, Chris Calabretta
Chairman, Les C. Vinney, age 68
Auditors: PricewaterhouseCoopers LLP

LOCATIONS

HQ: Campbell Soup Co.
1 Campbell Place, Camden, NJ 08103-1799
Phone: 856 342-4800 **Fax:** 856 342-3878
Web: www.campbellsoupcompany.com

2016 Sales

	$ mil.	% of total
US	6,437	81
Australia	590	7
Other	934	12
Total	**7,961**	**100**

PRODUCTS/OPERATIONS

2016 Sales

	$ mil.	% of total
Americas Simple Meals and Beverages	4,380	55
Global Biscuits and Snacks	2,564	32
Campbell Fresh	1,017	13
Total	**7,961**	**100**

2016 Sales

	$ mil.	% of total
Soup	2,690	34
Baked snacks	2,479	31
Other simple meals	1,702	21
Beverages	1,090	14
Total	**7,961**	**100**

Selected Brand Names

Domestic
  Away From Home
  Bolthouse Farms
  Campbell
  Ecce Panis
  Pace
  Pepperidge Farm
  Plum Organics
  Prego
  Select Harvest
  StockPot
  Swanson
  V8 and V8 Splash
  Wolfgang Puck
International
  Arnott's (Australia)

Selected Subsidiaries

Arnott's Biscuits Limited (Australia)
Bolthouse Holding Corp. (US)
Ecce Panis Inc.
Pepperidge Farm Incorporated
Players Group Limited (Australia)
Sinalopasta S.A. de C.V. (Mexico)
Stockpot Inc.

COMPETITORS

Associated British Foods	Hanover Foods
B&G Foods	Harry's Fresh Foods
Barbara's Bakery	Heinz
Baxters	Hormel
Beech-Nut	Kellogg U.S. Snacks
Big Heart Pet Brands	Mondelez International
Bush Brothers	Morgan Foods
Canyon Creek Food	NORPAC
ConAgra	Nestle
Dole Food	Odwalla
Frito-Lay	Pacific Coast Producers
General Mills	Peter Rabbit Farms
Gerber Products	Red Gold
Golden Enterprises	Reily Foods
Grimmway Enterprises	Rene's Gourmet Foods
H. J. Heinz Limited	Snyder's-Lance
Hain Celestial	Walkers Snack Foods

HISTORICAL FINANCIALS

Company Type: Public

Income Statement

FYE: July 31

	REVENUE ($ mil.)	NET INCOME ($ mil.)	NET PROFIT MARGIN	EMPLOYEES
07/17	7,890	887	11.2%	18,000
07/16*	7,961	563	7.1%	16,500
08/15	8,082	691	8.5%	18,600
08/14	8,268	818	9.9%	19,400
07/13	8,052	458	5.7%	20,000
Annual Growth	**(0.5%)**	**18.0%**	**—**	**(2.6%)**

*Fiscal year change

2017 Year-End Financials

Debt ratio: 45.77%
Return on equity: 56.10%
Cash ($ mil.): 319
Current ratio: 0.79
Long-term debt ($ mil.): 2,499

No. of shares (mil.): 301
Dividends
  Yield: 2.6%
  Payout: 48.4%
Market value ($ mil.): 15,902

	STOCK PRICE ($) FY Close	P/E High/Low		PER SHARE ($) Earnings	Dividends	Book Value
07/17	52.83	22	18	2.89	1.40	5.44
07/16*	62.27	37	25	1.81	1.25	4.95
08/15	49.31	22	19	2.21	1.25	4.45
08/14	41.96	18	15	2.59	1.25	5.16
07/13	47.07	33	22	1.44	1.16	3.90
Annual Growth	**2.9%**	**—**	**—**	**19.0%**	**4.8%**	**8.7%**

*Fiscal year change

CANDID COLOR SYSTEMS, INC.

LOCATIONS

HQ: CANDID COLOR SYSTEMS, INC.
1300 METROPOLITAN AVE, OKLAHOMA CITY, OK 731082042
Phone: 405 947-8747
Web: WWW.OKLAHOMAPARTYPICS.COM

HISTORICAL FINANCIALS

Company Type: Private

Income Statement

FYE: July 31

	REVENUE ($ mil.)	NET INCOME ($ mil.)	NET PROFIT MARGIN	EMPLOYEES
07/07	21,742	2,534	11.7%	300
07/05	22	1	8.3%	—
07/04	21	2	10.9%	—
07/03	21	1	9.4%	—
Annual Growth	**467.2%**	**498.3%**		

2007 Year-End Financials

Debt ratio: —
Return on equity: 11.70%
Cash ($ mil.): 2
Current ratio: 1.70
Long-term debt ($ mil.): —

Dividends
  Yield: —
  Payout: —
Market value ($ mil.): —

Capital City Bank Group, Inc.

Capital City Bank Group is the holding company for Capital City Bank (CCB) which serves individuals businesses and institutions from some 70 branches in Florida Georgia and Alabama. CCB offers checking savings and money market accounts; CDs; IRAs; Internet banking; and debit and credit cards. Commercial real estate mortgages account for about 40% of its loan portfolio; residential real estate loans also hover near 40%. The bank also originates business loans and consumer loans including credit cards. Capital City also performs data processing services for other financial institutions in its market area.

Operations

In addition to its CCB bank subsidiary which accounts for about 94% of Capital City Bank Group's total revenue the holding company operates three other subsidiaries: Capital City Trust a provider of trust and asset management services; Capital City Banc Investments which offers investments retirement plans and life and long-term care insurance through an agreement with third-party provider INVEST Financial Corporation a subsidiary of Jackson National Life Insurance Company; and data processor Capital City Services Co.

Geographic Reach

Florida is CCB's largest market accounting for about 78% of its revenue. Georgia and Alabama account for 21% and 1% respectively.

Financial Performance

Capital City Bank Group's revenue has slid since the onset of the recession and housing crisis which battered the Florida market and during the uneven recovery. Revenue fell 5% in 2011 vs. 2010 marking the fourth consecutive year of decline. Indeed revenue plunged 74% between 2007 and 2011. However in 2011 the group returned to profitability with net income of $4.9 million following losses in 2010 and 2009.

Interest income decreased by 10% while noninterest income increased 4% in 2011 vs. 2010. Lower interest and fees on loans contributed to the decline in interest income. Growth in bank card and retail brokerage fees contributed to the rise in non-interest income.

Strategy

Capital City Bank Group was founded in 1982 to acquire six banks and has never looked back. While its growth has slowed the company has continued its acquisition strategy buying 15 banks since 1984; it has also expanded by opening new offices. However its home state of Florida was one of the hardest hit during the recession. High unemployment levels contributed to an increase in nonperforming loans in the bank's portfolio which in turn translated to net losses in 2009 and 2010. (Nonperforming loans totaled $75 million or 4.6% of the company's total loan portfolio at the end of 2011.) Capital City is focusing on diversifying its portfolio and reducing problem assets.

EXECUTIVES

EVP and CFO, J. Kimbrough (Kim) Davis, age 63, $260,000 total compensation
Chairman President and CEO, William G. (Bill) Smith, age 63, $350,000 total compensation
Credit Administration, Dale A. Thompson
Chief People Officer and President Capital Services Company, Bethany H. (Beth) Corum
President Capital City Banc Investments; President Capital City Trust Company, Bill Moor
President Leon County, Ed West
Residential Mortgage, Tom Allen
Commercial Banking, Ed Canup
Community Banking, Mitch Englert
Vice President And Trust Officer, Janice White
Assistant Vice President Community Banker, Brian Timmons
Senior Vice President, David Caldwell
VICE PRESIDENT, Skip Smith
Vice President, Joel Ginaldi
Assistant Vice President, Cindy Richardson
Vice President Lender, Todd Troyer
Assistant Vice President Human Resources, Sharon Martin
Assistant Vice President, Janette Wagner
Vice President of Digital Engagement, Craig Ellard
Vice President, Francis Rolfes
Vice President Marketing, Walter Hoskins
Capital City Trust Company Assistant Vice President and Controller, Erica Hunter
Assistant Vice President, Sylvia White
Assistant Vice President, Edie Frasier
Vice President, Karen C Meadows
Assistant Vice President And Community Banker, Janie Stewart

Assistant Vice President and Manager, Alicia Ronan
Vice President Information Security, Leanne Staalenburg
Vice President and Trust Officer, Angela Williamson
Senior Vice President Capital City Bank, Mark Strickland
Assistant Vice President Business Banker, Terry Huiskens
Assistant Vice President, Anthony Freeman
Vice President, Catherine Sherman
Vice President, Sterling Bryant
Vice President andamp; Deposit Operations Manager, Sue Joiner
VICE PRESIDENT AND COMPLIANCE MANAGER, Sheila Reddick
ASSISTANT VICE PRESIDENT, Francis M Rolfes
Senior Vice President, Lee Nichols
Auditors: Ernst & Young LLP

LOCATIONS

HQ: Capital City Bank Group, Inc.
217 North Monroe Street, Tallahassee, FL 32301
Phone: 850 402-7821
Web: www.ccbg.com

PRODUCTS/OPERATIONS

2015 Sales

	$ mil.	% of total
Interest		
Loans including fees	73	55
Investment securities	5	5
Funds sold	0	-
Noninterest income		
Deposit fee	22	17
Bank card fees	11	8
Wealth management fees	7	6
Mortgage Banking fees	4	3
Data processing fees	1	1
Other	6	5
Total	**133**	**100**

COMPETITORS

Ameris	Regions Financial
BBX Capital	SunTrust
Bank of America	Thomasville Bancshares
Delta Community Credit Union	

HISTORICAL FINANCIALS

Company Type: Public

Income Statement

FYE: December 31

	ASSETS ($ mil.)	NET INCOME ($ mil.)	INCOME AS % OF ASSETS	EMPLOYEES
12/16	2,845	11	0.4%	853
12/15	2,797	9	0.3%	894
12/14	2,627	9	0.4%	937
12/13	2,611	6	0.2%	927
12/12	2,633	0	0.0%	913
Annual Growth	**1.9%**	**222.9%**	**—**	**(1.7%)**

2016 Year-End Financials

Debt ratio: 2.38%	No. of shares (mil.): 16
Return on equity: 4.26%	Dividends
Cash ($ mil.): 296	Yield: 0.0%
Current ratio: —	Payout: 24.6%
Long-term debt ($ mil.): —	Market value ($ mil.): 345

	STOCK PRICE ($) FY Close	P/E High/Low		PER SHARE ($) Earnings	Dividends	Book Value
12/16	20.48	32	19	0.69	0.17	16.34
12/15	15.35	31	26	0.53	0.13	15.99
12/14	15.54	30	22	0.53	0.09	15.62
12/13	11.77	37	30	0.35	0.00	15.92
12/12	11.37	1169651		0.01	0.00	14.33
Annual Growth	**15.8%**	**— —**		**188.2%**	**—**	**3.3%**

Capital One Financial Corp

Thanks to its ?What?s in Your Wallet? branding campaign Capital One Financial Corporation is one of the most recognizable issuers of Visa and MasterCard credit cards in the US. It also provides typical banking products such as mortgage loans and checking accounts and has a unit focused on auto financing. It also sells insurance and manages assets for institution and high-net-worth individuals. Capital One holds more than 65 million customer accounts in the US Canada and the UK and maintains a deposit portfolio worth over $200 billion. It boasts a banking network of hundreds of branches in about half a dozen US states and maintains a strong online presence with its internet and mobile banking applications.

HISTORY

Capital One Financial is a descendant of the Bank of Virginia which was formed in 1945. The company began issuing products similar to credit cards in 1953 and was MasterCard issuer #001. Acquisitions and mergers brought some 30 banks and several finance and mortgage companies under the bank's umbrella between 1962 and 1986 when Bank of Virginia became Signet Banking.

Signet's credit card operations had reached a million customers in 1988 when the bank hired consultants Richard Fairbank and Nigel Morris (Fairbank is now chairman and CEO) to implement their "Information-Based Strategy." Under the duo's leadership the bank began using sophisticated data-collection methods to gather massive amounts of information on existing or prospective customers; it then used the information to design and mass-market customized products to the customer.

In 1991 — after creating an enormous database and developing sophisticated screening processes and direct-mail marketing tactics — Signet escalated the credit card wars luring customers from its rivals with its innovative balance-transfer credit card. The card let customers of other companies transfer what they owed on higher-interest cards to a Signet card with a lower introductory rate.

The new card immediately drew imitators (by 1997 balance-transfer cards accounted for 85% of credit card solicitations). After skimming off the least risky customers Fairbank and Morris began going after less desirable credit customers who could be charged higher rates. The result was what they call second-generation products — secured and unsecured cards with lower credit lines and higher annual percentage rates and fees for higher-risk customers.

The credit card business had grown to 5 million customers by 1994 but at a high cost to Signet which had devoted most of its resources to finding and servicing credit card holders. That year Signet spun off its credit card business as Capital One to focus on banking. (Signet was later acquired by First Union.)

The company moved into Florida and Texas in 1995 and into Canada and the UK in 1996; that year it established its savings bank mainly to offer products and services to its cardholders. In 1997 the company used this unit to move into deposit accounts buying a deposit portfolio from J. C. Penney. In 1998 the company began marketing its products to such clients as immigrants and high school students (whose parents must co-sign for the card). The company also expanded in terms of products and geography acquiring auto lender Summit Acceptance and opening a new office in Nottingham England.

In 1999 the firm's growth continued. The company stepped up its marketing efforts and was rewarded with significant boosts to its non-interest income and customer base. The next year the company launched The Capital One Place an Internet shopping site. In 2001 the company acquired AmeriFee which provides loans for elective medical and dental surgery; and PeopleFirst Inc. the nation's largest online provider of direct motor vehicle loans.

In response to industry-wide concern over subprime lending Capital One agreed in 2002 to beef up reserves on its subprime portfolio. Also in 2002 the company's UK operations proved profitable for the first time.

The company expanded into banking in 2005 and 2006 with the acquisitions of Hibernia and North Fork Bancorporation respectively. The deals gave it a boost in the banking sector expanding its presence both geographically in the Northeast and in the South and turning the company into one of the top bank holding companies in the US. The $13.2 billion stock-and-cash North Fork deal gave the company more than 300 bank branches in New York New Jersey and Connecticut.

The 2005 purchase of New Orleans-based Hibernia was a stock-and-cash transaction valued at some $5 billion nearly 10% less than the originally agreed-upon price. The transaction was delayed then renegotiated after Hurricane Katrina devastated Hibernia's home city. Hibernia which relocated to Houston adopted the Capital One moniker.

Capital One closed wholesale lender GreenPoint Mortgage Funding acquired as part of its acquisition of North Fork in 2007. The unit suffered from the credit woes that have plagued the subprime mortgage industry.

The company expanded its franchise into the Washington DC market in 2009 by buying Chevy Chase Bank for some $475 million in cash and stock.

In 2011 the company boosted its credit card business with the acquisition of GE Capital's $1.3 billion Hudson's Bay credit card portfolio tripling the number of Canadian customer accounts Capital One services. That year Capital One also acquired Kohl's existing $3.7 billion private-label credit card portfolio.

Capital One grew its US credit card business once again with the 2012 acquisition of HSBC's US card portfolio for some $2.6 billion.

In 2013 Capital One introduced its Capital One Quicksilver credit card offering cardholders a simple way to earn and redeem higher-than-average cash back rewards.

EXECUTIVES

General Counsel and Corporate Secretary, John G. Finneran, age 67, $1,016,538 total compensation

Chairman and CEO, Richard D. (Rich) Fairbank, age 66

VICE PRESIDENT, Salvatore Chierico

Senior Vice President manager, Gerald Shepard

Head of Finance and Corporate Development, Stephen S. (Steve) Crawford, age 52, $1,592,692 total compensation

CFO, R. Scott Blackley, age 49, $617,769 total compensation

CIO, Robert M. Alexander, age 52

President Commercial Banking, Michael C. Slocum, age 60

President Financial Services, Sanjiv Yajnik, age 60, $962,654 total compensation

President Retail and Direct Banking, Jonathan W. Witter, age 47, $870,769 total compensation

Chief Enterprise Services Officer and Chief of Staff to the CEO, Frank G. LaPrade, age 50, $974,577 total compensation

Chief Risk Officer, Kevin S. Borgmann, age 45

President U.S. Card, Michael J. Wassmer, age 47

President International and Small Business Card, Christopher T. Newkirk, age 46

MVP, Suzette Prechter

Senior Vice President, Jeff Lee

Vice President, Carol Anderson

Vice President, Ashish Tandon

Vice President Corporate Accounting and Reporting, Pam Koch

Assistant Vice President Information S, Carl Pomplon

Assistant Vice President, Disnalda Cuevas

Vice President, Anthony Fermo

Vice President, Brad Dolbec

Assistant Vice President, Karla Lastrap

Senior Vice President, Robert Harvey

Vice President Risk and Finance Technology, Mark Mathewson

Executive Vice President, Murray Abrams

Senior Vice President, Roy Aksdal

Treasurer Senior Vice President, Thomas A Feil

Vice President Human Resources, Guenet Beshah

Senior Vice President, Karen Bauer

Vice President, Theodore McField

Vice President, Ehab Awadallah

Vice President In US Card Recoveries Division, Amanda N Aghdami

Vice President and CRA Business Development Officer, Lydia Jackson

Vice President Corporate Audit Services, Erika Ray

Vice President, Michael Lockery

Vice President Sales and Service Strategy, Shail Moorjani

Senior Vice President, Jon Oldham

Managing Vice President Treasury Balance, Jeffrey Kuzbel

Managing Vice President, Johan Gericke

Senior Vice President, Stephen Block

Vice President, Shahram Elghanayan

Vice President Of Sales And Service, Rob Younger

Vice President Private Banking, Bob Sferrazza

Vice President and Senior Business Relationship Banker, Franklin Carrero

Vice President, Theresa Bedeau

Senior Vice President, Gregory Horstman

Vice President And Manager Of Treasury Management Client Service, Marty Paris

Vice President Underwriter, Lawrence Cannariato

Senior Vice President, Elisa Depalma

Vice President Business Banking, Nate Hoffman

Senior Vice President Capital One Equipment Finance Corp, Ellen Barry

Assistant Vice President, Alexander Thezan

Vice President, Erin Coveny

Managing Vice President, John Walker

Senior Vice President Senior Director Mid Corporate and Healthcare Banking, Philip Davi

Vice President Business Banking, Maria Brosnahan

Vice President Bank Project Management Office, Jonathan Topp

Vice President, Kim Dean

Assistant Vice President, Carter King

Senior Vice President, Spencer Gagnet

Vice President, David P Blasini

Vice President Strategy, Sarah Strauss

Vice President Us Card, Emilia Lopez

Assistant Vice President Quality Assurance Manager, Gloria Stafford

Vice President, Kader Ma

Managing Vice President Chief Compliance Officer retail Bank, Celie Niehaus

Senior Vice President, Ric Kearny

Senior Vice President Bank External Fraud Risk Management, Yu Huang

Vice President and Trust Officer, Jean Moncla

Senior Vice President and Senior Market Sales Executive, Brian Oatsvall

Vice President Of Human Resources, Joel Martinez

Senior Vice President, Chad Marshall

Vice President Senior Audit Manager, Sandra Dato

Senior Vice President, Katharine Kay

Vice President Investor Real Estate, Kevin Lemoine

Assistant Vice President, Lawren Allen

Assistant Vice President, Karen Eleser

Vice President Human Resources, Meghan Welch

Senior Vice President Commercial Real Estate, Jeff Wallace

Vice President Internal Audit and Information Technology, David Dunn

Executive Vice President Marketing, Ashley Taylor

Vice President Internet Services, Marie Kraus

Vice President Senior Business Banker, Richard Ziegler

Assistant Vice President, Hosai Akbarzadeh

Assistant Vice President, Jason Allalouf

Vice President, Sheikh Quddus

Vice President Corporate Security, Timothy Rigg

Assistant Vice President, Stephen Marshall

Vice President Regional Operations Manager, Farina Hanif

Assistant Vice President, Julie Billelo

Vice President Branch Manager III, Amos Brunson

Vice President, Nathan Burlingame

Vice President, Becky White

Vice President Credit, Haig Kilicyan

Assistant Vice President, Todd Gaspar

Assistant Vice President, Cristina Brum

Senior Vice President, Fran Nuchims

Vice President, Diana Macculley

Vice President Credit Platform Product Manager, Nathan Rocklein

Vice President, Henriette Henriette Harris

Assistant Vice President, Marroy Michael

Senior Vice President, Patti Hansen

Senior Vice President, Louis Rosado

Vice President Portfolio Manager, Nosser Crc Julie

Assistant Vice President Treasury Management, Michele Reilly

Vice President, Billy McArdle

Vice President, Ken Shah

Assistant Vice President Branch Manager, Jessica Kitzmann

Assistant Vice President, David Mialaret

Vice President Private Underwriter, Curtis Vincent

Senior Vice President, Enrico Panno

Assistant Vice President Manager, James Rocco

Vice President Business Banking, Fabian Martin

Senior Vice President, Joshua Howes

Unit Manager Assistant Vice President, Michelle Jordan

Vice President, Bonnie Lowrimore

Senior Vice President Relationship Manager, Don Potts

District Operations Consultant Assistant Vice President, Victor Padilla

Assistant Vice President Branch Manager, Kristi Whaley

Assistant Vice President Senior Underwriter, Quynh Nguyen

Assistant Vice President Branch Manager, Jana Akintola

Vice President and Senior Trust Officer, Lorraine Gallagher

Assistant Vice President: Financial Advisors, Rupal Jhaveri

Executive Vice President Card Operations, Noelle Eder

Vice President And Trust Officer, Sharda Setia

Assistant Vice President Merchant Services Sales Advisor, Diane Slatkin

Front Line Manager Assistant Vice President, Patricia Milton

Vice President, Scott Soignier

Assistant Vice President, Cindy Lau

Vice President, Julianne Low

Assistant Vice President, Stanley Liu

Vice President Business Banker, Joshua Prejean

Assistant Vice President Capital One Bank, Michael Knight

Vice President, Haley Douds

Vice President Branch Manager Iii, Yenisel Gamez

Vice President Managing Underwriter, Albert Lopez

Assistant Vice President, Milos Milosevic

Vice President, Michael Tomek

Vice President District Manager, Lynda Reissman

Vice President, Dana Thompson

Assistant Vice President Proposal Manager, Paula Wiesner

Senior Vice President, Robert Fanelli

Assistant Vice President CSS, Almedilia Cruz

Vice President, Lawrence Montz

Vice President, Daniel Mouadeb

Vice President Commercial Real Estate, Michael Monroe

Assistant Vice President, Talisha Fellows

Vice President, Michael Tsentas

Auditors: Ernst & Young LLP

LOCATIONS

HQ: Capital One Financial Corp
1680 Capital One Drive, McLean, VA 22102
Phone: 703 720-1000
Web: www.capitalone.com

PRODUCTS/OPERATIONS

2016 Sales

	$ mil.	% of total
Interest		
Loans held for investment	21,203	77
Investment securities	1,599	6
Other	89	-
Non interest		
Interchange fees	2,452	9
Service charges & other customer fees	1,646	6
Other	541	2
Adjustments	(11)	-
Total	**27,519**	**100**

2016 Segment sales

	% of total
Credit card	62
Consumer banking	26
Commercial banking	11
Others	1
Total	**100**

Selected Products

Auto Loans
Business Credit Cards
Commercial Banking
Home Equity Lines
Home Loans
Investing
Personal Banking
Personal Credit Cards
Small Business Banking

COMPETITORS

Alliance Data Systems	GM Financial
American Express	HSBC USA
Bank of America	JPMorgan Chase
Citigroup	PNC Financial
Credit Acceptance	Regions Financial
Discover	Wells Fargo

HISTORICAL FINANCIALS
Company Type: Public

Income Statement
FYE: December 31

	ASSETS ($ mil.)	NET INCOME ($ mil.)	INCOME AS % OF ASSETS	EMPLOYEES
12/16	357,033	3,751	1.1%	47,300
12/15	334,048	4,050	1.2%	45,400
12/14	308,854	4,428	1.4%	46,000
12/13	297,048	4,159	1.4%	41,951
12/12	312,918	3,517	1.1%	39,593
Annual Growth	**3.4%**	**1.6%**	**—**	**4.5%**

2016 Year-End Financials

Debt ratio: 16.93%
Return on equity: 7.89%
Cash ($ mil.): 9,976
Current ratio: —
Long-term debt ($ mil.): —

No. of shares (mil.): 480
Dividends
Yield: 0.0%
Payout: 23.2%
Market value ($ mil.): 41,894

	STOCK PRICE ($) FY Close	P/E High/Low		PER SHARE ($) Earnings	Dividends	Book Value
12/16	87.24	13	8	6.89	1.60	98.94
12/15	72.18	13	10	7.07	1.50	89.68
12/14	82.55	11	9	7.59	1.20	81.41
12/13	76.61	11	7	6.96	0.95	72.89
12/12	57.93	10	7	6.16	0.20	69.56
Annual Growth	**10.8%**	**—**	**—**	**2.8%**	**68.2%**	**9.2%**

Capitol Federal Financial Inc

Dorothy and Toto may not be in Kansas anymore but Capitol Federal Financial is. The holding company owns Capitol Federal Savings Bank the largest bank headquarted there. The savings bankÂ serves metropolitan areasÂ of the Sunflower StateÂ as well asÂ Kansas City Missouri throughÂ aboutÂ 45 branches includingÂ nearly aÂ dozen inside retail stores such as Target Price Chopper and Dillons. Serving consumers and commercial customers theÂ thrift offers standard servicesÂ such as mortgages and loans depositsÂ and retail investments. Its Capitol Agency affiliate sells life liability homeowners renters and vehicle insurance.

EXECUTIVES

Chairman President and CEO, John B. Dicus, age 56, $581,484 total compensation

EVP CFO and Treasurer, Kent G. Townsend, age 55, $303,991 total compensation

EVP and Chief Lending Officer, Rick C. Jackson, $163,690 total compensation

EVP Corporate Services, Carlton A Ricketts

EVP General Counsel, Natalie Haag

EVP Retail Operations, Frank H. Wright, $202,362 total compensation

Vice President Information Technology Delivery Systems, Tamara Vande Velde

Vice President Consumer Lending, Kevin Morgison

First Vice President, Rhonda Dennis

First Vice President, Rodney Martin

First Vice President Lending, Jacque Taylor

Senior Vice President, Deb Campos

First Vice President Principal Accounting Officer and Reporting Director Capitol Federal Financia, Tara Van Houweling

Assistant Vice President Network and Telecom Supervisor, Kevin Nelson

Vice President Chief Information Secur, Mark Hernandez

Vice President Deposit Services, Clint Devoe

First Vice President, Sarah Sanders

Assistant Vice President, Jared Ringels

Executive Vice President Corporate Services, Carl Ricketts

Auditors: DELOITTE & TOUCHE LLP

LOCATIONS

HQ: Capitol Federal Financial Inc
700 South Kansas Avenue, Topeka, KS 66603
Phone: 785 235-1341
Web: www.capfed.com

PRODUCTS/OPERATIONS

2016 Sales

	% of total
Interest Income	
Loans receivable	75
Mortgage backed securities	9
FHLB stock	4
Cash and cash equivalents	3
Investment securities	2
Non-Interest Income	
Retail fees and charges	4
Income from bank-owned life insurance	1
Other non-interest income	2
Total	**100**

COMPETITORS

Bank of America	Landmark Bancorp
Commerce Bancshares	U.S. Bancorp
First Federal of Olathe	UMB Financial

HISTORICAL FINANCIALS
Company Type: Public

Income Statement
FYE: September 30

	ASSETS ($ mil.)	NET INCOME ($ mil.)	INCOME AS % OF ASSETS	EMPLOYEES
09/17	9,192	84	0.9%	708
09/16	9,267	83	0.9%	676
09/15	9,844	78	0.8%	691
09/14	9,865	77	0.8%	716
09/13	9,186	69	0.8%	724
Annual Growth	**0.0%**	**5.0%**	**—**	**(0.6%)**

2017 Year-End Financials

Debt ratio: —
Return on equity: 6.09%
Cash ($ mil.): 351
Current ratio: —
Long-term debt ($ mil.): —

No. of shares (mil.): 138
Dividends
Yield: 0.0%
Payout: 139.6%
Market value ($ mil.): 2,032

	STOCK PRICE ($) FY Close	P/E High/Low		PER SHARE ($) Earnings	Dividends	Book Value
09/17	14.70	27	21	0.63	0.88	9.90
09/16	14.07	23	19	0.63	0.84	10.13
09/15	12.12	22	20	0.58	0.84	10.33
09/14	11.82	24	21	0.56	0.98	10.59
09/13	12.43	27	24	0.48	1.00	11.04
Annual Growth	**4.3%**	**—**	**—**	**7.0%**	**(3.1%)**	**(2.7%)**

Cardinal Health, Inc.

When your local pharmacy runs low on drugs or supplies it might just call Cardinal Health. The company is a top distributor of pharmaceuticals and other medical supplies and equipment in the US. Its pharmaceutical division provides supply chain services including branded generic and specialty pharmaceutical and OTC drug distribution. It also franchises Medicine Shoppe retail pharmacies. Cardinal's medical division parcels out medical laboratory and surgical supplies and provides logistics consulting and data management. Customers include retail pharmacies hospitals nursing homes doctor's offices and other health care businesses.

Operations

Cardinal Health operates through two primary segments — Pharmaceutical and Medical.

Pharmaceutical distribution primarily to pharmacy customers across the US accounts for around 90% of Cardinal Health's sales. It operates more than 20 distribution warehouses six specialty distribution facilities and more than 140 nuclear pharmacy labs (for the preparation and distribution of medical imaging agents) throughout the US and in Puerto Rico. The division also includes the Medicine Shoppe retail pharmacy subsidiary; the Specialty Solutions unit distributes specialty pharmaceuticals such as cancer injectables plasma products and intensive care therapies that require special handling.

The smaller Medical segment offers branded and private-label supplies including scientific laboratory equipment and general hospital and physician practice supplies primarily from its more than 70 warehouses manufacturing facilities and other locations in the US. It also operates 20 manufacturing research or distribution facilities in Canada the Dominican Republic Malaysia Malta Mexico and Thailand. The segment's private-label offerings which include surgical gowns exam gloves and fluid collection equipment are distributed directly and through third parties in the US Canada Europe and Asia. Cardinal Health Medical also assembles medical procedure kits and provides consulting and logistics services.

Cardinal Health and CVS Health operate a 50:50 joint venture Red Oak Sourcing (ROS) that sources and negotiates generic supply contracts for both companies. ROS is the largest generic sourcing entity in the US.

Geographic Reach

Cardinal Health's Pharmaceutical segment operates 24 primary distribution facilities six specialty distribution facilities more than 140 nuclear pharmacies and radiopharmaceutical manufacturing facilities and a national logistics center; these facilities are all located in 45 US states and Puerto Rico.

The Medical segment has more than 70 manufacturing assembly and distribution locations in the US and Puerto Rico. It operates 20 international locations in Canada the Dominican Republic Malaysia Malta Mexico and Thailand.

Altogether the group owns more than 70 operating facilities and leases more than 230 facilities around the world.

Sales and Marketing

Cardinal Health sells to thousands of pharmacies and provides support to hospitals throughout the US. Its largest customers are CVS Health and OptumRx; its five largest customers combined account for about half of its total revenues. Group purchasing organizations are also key to the company's business with Vizient and Premier together accounting for some 20% of total revenues. Other customers include surgery centers clinics physician practices and clinical laboratories.

Though the bulk of the company's operations consist of direct promotion sales and distribution of drugs and medical supplies Cardinal Health does use some third-party distributors for the manufactured products from its Medical segment.

Financial Performance

Cardinal Health's net revenues have been trending upward for the last five years. In fiscal 2017 (ended June) growth slowed somewhat as revenue increased 7% to $130 billion (versus a 19% increase in fiscal 2016). Both the Pharmaceutical and Medical segments had higher sales in 2017 but the impact of generic pricing changes ultimately impacted overall income.

Net income fell that year dropping 10% to $1.3 billion. That decline was driven by an increase in operating expenses including distribution selling general and administrative expenses; amortization and other acquisition-related costs and restructuring and employee severance expenses.

Operating cash flow fell from $3 billion in fiscal 2016 to $1.2 billion in fiscal 2017. Factors contributing to that fall included a decrease in accounts payable and an increase in net accrued liabilities and operating items.

Strategy

Cardinal has grown through acquisitions of companies and products within all of its operating segments. Recent purchases have focused on medical supplies and devices. In 2017 the company acquired several medical supplies units from Medtronic for about $6.1 billion. That followed the 2015 purchase of cardiology and endovascular device maker Cordis from Johnson & Johnson in a $1.94 billion transaction. In fiscal 2016 (ended June) the company spent $3.6 billion on acquisitions including $1.1 billion to acquire Harvard Drug.

In addition to acquisitions the company aims to grow through new customer contracts facility expansion efforts and collaborations with other medical and drug firms. Growth efforts aim to expand operations in core pharma and medical distribution fields as well as niche service areas such as the provision of data management and procurement services for specialty health providers.

Cardinal Health also aims to keep revenues and profits on the rise by keeping its operations lean and nimble an important factor in thin-margin distribution industries. To that end Cardinal Health has conducted some cost-cutting programs such as asset divestitures in recent years. For example it sold its physician office business to Henry Schein in 2015. As part of that strategic agreement Henry Schein has committed to buying Cardinal Health-brand and other medical products. In response to upcoming drug distribution reforms in China the company sold its Chinese pharmaceutical and medical distribution operations to Shanghai Pharmaceuticals for $1.2 billion in 2018 (although it retains certain businesses in the country such as Cordis its patient recovery business).

Mergers and Acquisitions

Cardinal Health in 2017 bought the medical supplies businesses of Medtronic for about $6.1 billion. The units acquired sell products for patient care deep vein thrombosis and nutritional insufficiency. They cover more than 20 product categories and include brands such as Curity Kendall Dover Argyle and Kangaroo. The units are complementary to Cardinal's medical supply offerings.

In 2015 Cardinal Health acquired Harvard Drug Group for $1.12 billion; that transaction increased its generic drugs distribution. In another deal it bought Johnson & Johnson's Cordis' heart-product business (which includes such products as stents and catheters) for $1.94 billion. It was interested in Cordis' products in light of an aging population and a growing demand for less invasive medical treatments.

HISTORY

Cardinal Health harks back to Cardinal Foods a food wholesaler named for Ohio's state bird. In 1971 Robert Walter then 26 and with the ink still fresh on his Harvard MBA acquired Cardinal in a leveraged buyout. He hoped to grow Cardinal by acquisitions but was frustrated when he found that the food distribution industry was already highly consolidated.

In 1980 Cardinal moved into pharmaceuticals distribution with the acquisition of Zanesville. It went public in 1983 as Cardinal Distribution and Walter began looking for more acquisitions. Cardinal soon expanded nationwide by swallowing other distributors. During the 1980s these purchases included two pharmaceuticals distributors headquartered in New York and a Massachusetts-based pharmaceuticals and food distributor.

In 1988 Cardinal sold its food group including Midland Grocery and Mr. Moneysworth to Roundy's and narrowed its focus to pharmaceuticals.

Drug distributors joined the rest of the pharmaceutical industry in its rush toward consolidation during the 1990s. Cardinal's acquisitions in those years included Ohio Valley-Clarksburg (1990 the Mid-Atlantic) Chapman Drug Co. (1991 Tennessee) PRN Services (1993 Michigan) Solomons Co. (1993 Georgia) Humiston-Keeling (1994 Illinois) and Behrens (1994 Texas).

One of Cardinal's most important acquisitions during this period was its cash purchase of Whitmire Distribution in 1994. Formerly Amfac Health Care Whitmire had been a subsidiary of Amfac one of Hawaii's "Big Five" landholders. When Amfac Health Care was spun off in 1988 its president Melburn Whitmire led a management group that acquired a majority interest. When Cardinal bought it Whitmire was the US's #6 drug wholesaler; the purchase bumped Cardinal up to #3. At that time the company changed its name to Cardinal Health and Melburn Whitmire became Cardinal's vice chairman.

In 1995 Cardinal made its biggest acquisition yet when it purchased St. Louis-based Medicine Shoppe International the US's largest franchisor of independent retail pharmacies. Founded by two St. Louis obstetricians in 1970 the Medicine Shoppe had 987 US outlets and 107 abroad at the time of its purchase by Cardinal (for $348 million in stock).

Over the next few years Cardinal continued to grow through acquisitions including automatic drug-dispensing system maker Pyxis pharmaceutical packaging company PCI Services and pharmacy management services company Owen Healthcare (which became Cardinal Health Pharmacy Management).

EXECUTIVES

EVP Customer Support Services and CIO, Patricia B. (Patty) Morrison, age 58
Chief Human Resources Officer, Pamela O. (Pam) Kimmet, age 58
President Nuclear Pharmacy Services, Tiffany P. Olson, age 58
CEO and Director, Michael C. (Mike) Kaufmann, age 54, $721,311 total compensation
CEO Medical Segment, Donald M. (Don) Casey, age 58, $671,311 total compensation
Chief Legal and Compliance Officer, Craig S. Morford, age 58, $531,311 total compensation
President Cardinal Health Specialty Solutions, Joseph I. DePinto, age 50

President U.S. Pharmaceutical Distribution, Jon Giacomin, age 52, $542,623 total compensation
EVP Global Sourcing, Craig Cowman
President Cordis, David J. Wilson
President Cardinal Health at Home, Steve Mason
President Global Commercial Solutions, Steve Blazejewski
EVP Strategy and Corporate Development, Michele Holcomb
EVP Deputy General Counsel and Corporate Secretary, Jessica L. Mayer
President US Pharmaceutical Distribution, Debbie Weitzman
SVP and CFO Cardinal Health Midecal Division, Jorge M. Gomez
Vice President and Agc, Ryan McGraw
Vice President Alternate Care Sales, Jim Scott
Corp Vice President, Victor Ruiz
Senior Vice President Global Sourcing, Stefan Grunwald
Pharmacy Manager, John Miller
Vice President Business Development, Jody Rogers
Vice President of Sales and Marketing, Dan Farrell
Vice President, Shaden Marzouk
Vice President Sales, Douglas Katz
Vice President Operations, Micheal Brown
Vice President and Associate General Counsel Finance, Rylan Rawlins
Vice President Marketing And Product Management, David Allen
Vice President Regulatory Affairs, Gary Cacciatore
Vice President Strategic Planning and Execution, Pat Brock
Vice President, Warren Hastings
Vice President MW Region Operations, Brian Bejarano
Senior Vice President Finance Medical, Dennis Braun
Vice President of Operations, Sean McCaffrey
Director of Pharmacy, Laurie Sobas
Pharmacy Manager Radiation Safety Officer, Mirta Vargas
Vice President Marketing and P, David Mitchell
Director of Pharmacy, Sharon Greasheimer
Vice President Finance Yong Yu, Allen Lueth
Executive Vice President, Gilberto Quintero
Vice President, Alanna Krutsch
Vice President Strategic Intelligence and Analytics, Troy Zimpfer
Vice President Compensation, Melanie Filas
Senior Vice President And Chief Scientific Officer, Robert Berus
Manager Government Relations, Laura Padgitt
Vice President Sales, Bill Hayden
Senior Vice President and Chief Security Officer, Greg Halvacs
Vice President, Bob Glover
Vice President of Sales Scientific Products, Ryan Cox
Vice President Warehouse Operations, Kevin Kannally
Vice President of Operational Excellence, Alan Deutschendorf
Vice President Operations, Peter Brennan
Vice President of Government Accounts, Kate Spirko
Vice President Ethics and Compliance, Ed Daniels
Vice President Government Relations, Cassi Baker
Senior Vice President Cardinal Health, Ramon Gregory
Senior Vice President Cardinal Health and General Manager, Daniel Movens
Vice President, Mike Scholze
Vice President Regulatory Affairs and Associate General Counsel, Leah Kendall
Pharmacy Manager, Michael Wyant
Vice President and Associate General Counsel, Patricio Garavito
Vice President Inventory Management, Andy Keller
Medical Director, Kevin J Soden

Vice President Sales and Marketing, Michele Montalvo
Pharmacy Manager, Tally Townsend
Vice President, Lisa Patterson
Senior Vice President and General Manager for the Midwest Region, Brian Ellis
Vice President Marketing, Don Cere
Director of Pharmacy, Robert Shuminski
Senior Vice President eCommerce Enterprise Architecture and Chief Information Security Officer, Talvis Love
Pharmacy Manager, Sam Ling
VICE PRESIDENT, Ken Robinette
Director of Pharmacy, Michelle Dalton
Vice President, Colleen McGuffin
Vice President Market and Product Management, Todd Treon
Group Vice President, Gregg Brewster
Vice President, Nicholas Rausch
Director of Pharmacy Operations and Account Manager, Sue Raymoure
Vice President, Constance Mantel
Vice President Medical Business Transformation, Cathy King
Vice President and Associate General Counsel, Charles Aragon
Vice President, Brian Waeltz
Vice President EIT Client Services, Michael Scrase
Senior Vice President Information Technology, Annlea Rumfola
Vice President of Human Resour, Ola Snow
Group Vice President Health Systems, Therese Grossi
Executive Vice President Packaging Service Group, Renard Pawlak
Vice President Telecommunications, Debbie Partyka
Pharmacy Manager, Sherry Miller
Pharmacy Manager, Jay Dyer
Vice President, Kent Oakley
Pharmacy Manager, Todd Lamb
Pharmacy Manager, Bevan Callicott
Director Of Pharmacy, Lynn Staggs
National Account Manager, Alan Pinyerd
Pharmacy Manager, Mary Johnson
Pharmacy Manager, Raymond Moy
Pharmacy Manager, John Miano
Vice President And Executive Director of Training, Lori Rivers
Pharmacy Manager, Arthur Bowman
Director of Pharmacy, Jessica Hoover
Vice President Business Development, Luke Augustine
Pharmacy Manager, Jeff Parrish
Vice President, Kendell Sherrer
Director Of Pharmacy, Rande Hempen
Vice President, Pete Beckwith
Vice President Enterprise Information Technology, Cyndi Carter
Vice President, Paul Gotti
Vice President Marketing, Melody Young
Vice President Business Development, Michelle Zaluzney
Pharmacy Manager, Chad Walker
Pharmacy Manager, Rachel Schwartz
Vice President Operations, Ron Wadsworth
Vice President General Manager OptiFreight, Tony Vahedian
Vice President Health Systems, Craig Rothman
Pharmacy Manager, Abdul Kamara
Vice President, James Barker
Vice President Associate General Counsel, Cheryl Kahn
Senior Vice President, Gale Howard
Vice President Health Systems, Jim Bonanni
Director of Pharmacy Charles Cole Memorial Hospital, John Coggins
Vice President human Resources Business Partner, Bill Rozich
Pharmacy Manager, Anna Keller

Vice President Information Technology Management, Dale Swoffer
Vice President and General Manager, Guru Shankar
Pharmacy Manager, Kelli Love
Senior Vice President Supply Chain, Scott Nelson
Vice President, David Emison
Director of Pharmacy, Anita Ward
Senior Vice President Government Relations, Sean Callinicos
Vice President and CMO, Chadi Nabhan
Director of Pharmacy, Anna Kim
Vice President Consumer Health, Steve Light
World Wide Vice President Human Resources Medical Segment, Lori Gordon
Chairman, George S. Barrett, age 62
Board Member, Shannon Kelly
Secretary, Shelley Lebeck
Board Member, Janet Nichols
Board Member, Lesbia Martinez
Auditors: Ernst & Young LLP

LOCATIONS

HQ: Cardinal Health, Inc.
  7000 Cardinal Place, Dublin, OH 43017
Phone: 614 757-5000
Web: www.cardinalhealth.com

2016 Sales

	$ mil.	% of total
US	116,864	96
Other countries	4,682	4
Total	**121,546**	**100**

PRODUCTS/OPERATIONS

2017 Sales

	$ mil.	% of total
Pharmaceutical	116,463	90
Medical	13,524	10
Corporate	(11)	-
Total	**129,976**	**100**

Selected Acquisitions

COMPETITORS

AmerisourceBergen	Medline Industries
Ansell	Molnlycke
CVS	Moore Medical
Deroyal Industries	Omnicare
Franz Haniel	Owens & Minor
H. D. Smith Wholesale	PSS World Medical
Drug	PharMerica
Henry Schein	Quality King
Kimberly-Clark	Rite Aid
McKesson	Thermo Fisher
Medical Action	Scientific
Industries	Walgreen

HISTORICAL FINANCIALS

Company Type: Public

Income Statement

FYE: June 30

	REVENUE ($ mil.)	NET INCOME ($ mil.)	NET PROFIT MARGIN	EMPLOYEES
06/17	129,976	1,288	1.0%	40,400
06/16	121,546	1,427	1.2%	37,300
06/15	102,531	1,215	1.2%	34,500
06/14	91,084	1,166	1.3%	34,000
06/13	101,093	334	0.3%	33,600
Annual Growth	**6.5%**	**40.1%**	**—**	**4.7%**

2017 Year-End Financials

Debt ratio: 25.91%	No. of shares (mil.): 316
Return on equity: 19.28%	Dividends
Cash ($ mil.): 6,879	Yield: 2.3%
Current ratio: 1.34	Payout: 44.8%
Long-term debt ($ mil.): 9,068	Market value ($ mil.): 24,623

STOCK PRICE ($) FY Close	P/E High/Low	PER SHARE ($) Earnings	Dividends	Book Value
06/17	77.92	21 16	4.03	1.81	21.54
06/16	78.01	21 17	4.32	1.61	20.35
06/15	83.65	25 19	3.62	1.41	19.07
06/14	68.56	22 14	3.38	1.25	18.99
06/13	47.20	50 39	0.97	1.09	17.63
Annual Growth	13.4%	— —	42.8%	13.5%	5.1%

Carmax Inc.

CarMax helps drivers find late-model used autos. Typically selling vehicles that are less than ten years old with less than 100000 miles the US's largest specialty used-car retailer buys reconditions and sells cars and light trucks through more than 170 superstores in 85-plus television markets (markets in which CarMax has a television advertising presence) mainly in the Southeast and Midwest. CarMax also operates two new-car franchises and sells older vehicles through more than 390000 in-store auctions each year at over 70 stores. Additionally it sells older cars and trucks with higher mileage and offers vehicle financing through its CarMax Auto Finance unit.

Operations

CarMax operates through two business segments: CarMax Sales Operations and CarMax Auto Finance (CAF).

CarMax Sales Operations which sells more than 670000 used cars per year represents the nation's largest used-car retailer. The company's finance arm CarMax Auto Financing (CAF) offers financing solely to CarMax customers and finances more around 45% of the company's retail vehicle unit sales. CAF also serviced over 800000 customer accounts in its $9.6 billion portfolio of managed receivables.

The company's used vehicle sales generate over 80% of total revenue wholesale vehicle sales nearly 15% and new vehicle sales less than 5%.

Geographic Reach

While Richmond-based CarMax sells cars in 39 US states it sells most of its vehicles in Florida Texas Southern California Virginia and the Washington DC/Baltimore area.

Sales and Marketing

CarMax focuses on developing brand awareness and detailing the advantages of shopping at its stores. It reaches customers through TV and radio broadcasts carmax.com search engine optimisation and online classified listings such as Pandora and Hulu. Additionally it looks to connect with consumers through Facebook Twitter and mobile apps.

CarMax's customers often take advantage of its transfer option which allows a customer to get a vehicle of their choice relocated to a more local CarMax store. About 30% of vehicles sold are transferred via customer request.

Financial Performance

CarMax has recorded a fairly sharply increasing net revenue trend for more than five years.

In fiscal 2017 (ended February) revenue increased 5% to $15.9 billion. The growth was concentrated in used car sales which grew $831 million; wholesale vehicle sales recorded a $106 million contraction. Used vehicle revenue was pushed up by an 8% increase in total unit sales partly due to acquisitions and partly due to higher same-store sales. The higher volume more than compensated for 2% lower average selling prices. Wholesale revenue was impacted by lower appraisal traffic and a reduction in cars aged 7-9 years old a long-term lag relating to lower car purchases during and after the 2008 global financial crisis.

Net income crept up less than 1% to $627 million as an increase in selling general and administrative expenses offset higher revenue.

Cash from operations fell 18% to $746.6 million due to changes in inventory.

Strategy

CarMax's main strategy is to "revolutionize the used auto retail market" by resolving the major sources of complaint that customers face at traditional used car retailers with superior customer service offerings. Some of these offerings include the 5-day money-back guarantee and the vehicle transfer service which allows a customer to get a vehicle of their choice relocated from a distant CarMax store to a more local one. CarMax is taking steps to distance itself from the much-maligned used car dealership image by shaping its selling around transparency and honesty so that customers don't go in expecting a battle with a salesperson. It wants to be a low risk place to buy a car.

Leveraging its successful "no-haggle" pricing business model CarMax has been aggressively expanding its geographic footprint over the past several years. The auto dealer has already tripled its store count from 58 locations in 2005 to 173 stores in 2017. As a rule CarMax aims to average around 15 store openings each year.

HISTORY

Looking for new retailing channels to conquer in 1993 Circuit City Stores began test-driving the used-car concept when it opened its first CarMax outlet in Richmond Virginia. Richard Sharp who was named Circuit City's CEO in 1986 became the chairman and CEO for CarMax Group as well.

A pioneer in the car industry CarMax offered computerized shopping play areas for children and no-haggle pricing. Competing car dealers criticized CarMax's TV ads which tarred rivals with a stereotype of sleaze and greed. Some dealers disputed CarMax's low-price claims.

The company extended its geographical reach into North Carolina Georgia and Florida in 1995 and 1996. In 1996 CarMax began selling new cars at an Atlanta store.

No longer riding it as a test-drive Circuit City spun off about 25% of CarMax to the public in 1997. The following year it moved into Illinois.

Also in 1998 CarMax bought a new-car Toyota dealership in Maryland and the multi-make Mauro Auto Mall of Wisconsin. It entered South Carolina that year and added a Georgia Mitsubishi dealership in early 1999. The company acquired two new-car franchises in the competitive Los Angeles market in mid-1999.

In mid-2001 Circuit City reduced its share in CarMax from 75% to about 65% having sold some stock to help remodel the company's electronics stores. Circuit City then spun off CarMax as an independent company in October 2002. President Austin Ligon took the CEO title at that time (Sharp remained chairman).

CarMax opened five superstores but sold four new-car dealerships in 2003.

EXECUTIVES

VP IT, Dave Banks
Vice President Marketing CarMax, Rob Sorenson
Vice President Sales, Daniel Johnston
Regional Vice President, Rodney Baker
Vice President, Jon Geske

Region Vice President Service Operations Southwest Region, Brian Dunne
Vice President Marketing Services, Laura Donahue
Vice President Investor Relations, Katharine Kenny
Vice President Controller, Natalie Wyatt
EVP Strategy and Business Transformation, Edwin J. (Ed) Hill, age 57, $597,209 total compensation
EVP General Counsel and Secretary, Eric M. Margolin, age 64, $572,801 total compensation
EVP and CFO, Thomas W. (Tom) Reedy, age 53, $699,039 total compensation
President CEO and Director, William D. (Bill) Nash, age 48, $902,308 total compensation
EVP and COO, William C. (Cliff) Wood, age 50, $699,039 total compensation
SVP and Chief Marketing Officer, James (Jim) Lyski, age 54
SVP and CIO, Shamim Mohammad, age 48
SVP CarMax Auto Finance, Jon G. Daniels, age 45
Vice President Human Resources, Peggy Philips
Vice President Of Information Technology, Michelle Ellwood
Assistant Vice President Management Information Systems, Troy Downs
Senior Vice President, Fred Hayton
Assistant Vice President Process Engineering, Gary Sheehan
Vice President Finance, Enrique Mayor-Mora
Assistant Vice President Treasurer, Andrew McMonigle
Assistant Vice President Construction And Design, Scott Sawyer
Legal Secretary, Kim Wickens
Vice President Assistant Controller, Veronica Hinckle
Assistant Vice President Account Services, Jeff Austin
Assistant Vice President Sale, Greg Tigani
Vice President of Business Strategy, Anu Agarwal
Vice President Treasurer, Tom Reedy
Regional Vice President, Chris Bartee
Assistant Vice President, Robert W Mitchell
Vice President Merchandising, Bill Nash
Senior Vice President Service Operations, ED Hill
Assistant Vice President Public Affairs and Communications, Trina Hoppin Lee
Vice President Auction Services and Merchandising Development, Joseph Wilson
VICE PRESIDENT MARKETING, Rob Sorensen
Regional Vice President General Manager XF Nashville Region, Dave Cantu
Chairman, Thomas J. (Tom) Folliard
Vice President Treasurer, Andy McMonigle
Auditors: KPMG LLP

LOCATIONS

HQ: Carmax Inc.
12800 Tuckahoe Creek Parkway, Richmond, VA 23238
Phone: 804 747-0422
Web: www.carmax.com

2017 Stores

	No.
California	23
Florida	16
Texas	16
Virginia	10
Georgia	9
Illinois	9
North Carolina	9
Tennessee	8
Maryland	6
Colorado	5
Ohio	5
Alabama	4
Massachusetts	4
Wisconsin	4
Arizona	3
Missouri	3
Nevada	3
Pennsylvania	3
South Carolina	3

Connecticut	2
Indiana	2
Kansas	2
Kentucky	2
Minnesota	2
Mississippi	2
New Jersey	2
New York	2
Oklahoma	2
Oregon	2
Delaware	1
Idaho	1
Iowa	1
Louisiana	1
Michigan	1
Nebraska	1
New Mexico	1
Rhode Island	1
Utah	1
Washington	1
Total	**173**

PRODUCTS/OPERATIONS

2017 Sales

	$ mil.	% of total
Used vehicles	13,270	84
Wholesale vehicles	2,082	13
Other sales & revenue	522	3
Total	**15,875**	**100**

COMPETITORS

Asbury Automotive	Holman Enterprises
AutoNation	Internet Brands
AutoTrader	JM Family Enterprises
Brown Automotive	KAR Auction Services
Cox Automotive	McCombs Enterprises
Danner Company	Penske Automotive
DriveTime Automotive	Group
Ed Morse Auto	Serra Automotive
Group 1 Automotive	Sonic Automotive
Hendrick Automotive	

HISTORICAL FINANCIALS

Company Type: Public

Income Statement

FYE: February 28

	REVENUE ($ mil.)	NET INCOME ($ mil.)	NET PROFIT MARGIN	EMPLOYEES
02/17	15,875	626	3.9%	24,344
02/16	15,149	623	4.1%	22,429
02/15	14,268	597	4.2%	22,064
02/14	12,574	492	3.9%	20,171
02/13	10,962	434	4.0%	18,111
Annual Growth	**9.7%**	**9.6%**	**—**	**7.7%**

2017 Year-End Financials

Debt ratio: 74.76%
Return on equity: 20.85%
Cash ($ mil.): 38
Current ratio: 2.60
Long-term debt ($ mil.): 11,826

No. of shares (mil.): 186
Dividends
  Yield: —
  Payout: —
Market value ($ mil.): 12,040

	STOCK PRICE ($) FY Close	P/E High/Low		PER SHARE ($) Earnings	Dividends	Book Value
02/17	64.54	21	14	3.26	0.00	16.66
02/16	46.26	24	14	3.03	0.00	14.92
02/15	67.11	25	15	2.73	0.00	15.11
02/14	48.43	24	17	2.16	0.00	14.96
02/13	38.41	21	13	1.87	0.00	13.36
Annual Growth	**13.9%**	**—**	**—**	**14.9%**	**—**	**5.7%**

Carolina Financial Corp (New)

Auditors: Elliott Davis Decosimo, LLC

LOCATIONS

HQ: Carolina Financial Corp (New)
288 Meeting Street, Charleston, SC 29401
Phone: 843 723-7700

HISTORICAL FINANCIALS

Company Type: Public

Income Statement

FYE: December 31

	ASSETS ($ mil.)	NET INCOME ($ mil.)	INCOME AS % OF ASSETS	EMPLOYEES
12/16	1,683	17	1.0%	441
12/15	1,409	14	1.0%	421
12/14	1,199	8	0.7%	394
12/13	881	16	1.9%	—
Annual Growth	**24.1%**	**1.5%**	**—**	**—**

2016 Year-End Financials

Debt ratio: 0.92%
Return on equity: 11.56%
Cash ($ mil.): 24
Current ratio: —
Long-term debt ($ mil.): —

No. of shares (mil.): 12
Dividends
  Yield: 0.0%
  Payout: 9.1%
Market value ($ mil.): 386

	STOCK PRICE ($) FY Close	P/E High/Low		PER SHARE ($) Earnings	Dividends	Book Value
12/16	30.79	21	11	1.42	0.13	13.00
12/15	18.00	12	9	1.48	0.11	11.63
12/14	13.99	48	15	0.88	0.09	9.64
12/13	31.51	22	17	1.77	0.02	8.53
/0.00	—	—	(0.00)	0.00	(0.00)	
Annual Growth	**—**	**—**	**—**	**—**	**—**	**—**

Carter Bank & Trust (Martinsville, VA)

LOCATIONS

HQ: Carter Bank & Trust (Martinsville, VA)
1300 Kings Mountain Road, Martinsville, VA 24112
Phone: 276 656-1776

HISTORICAL FINANCIALS

Company Type: Public

Income Statement

FYE: December 31

	ASSETS ($ mil.)	NET INCOME ($ mil.)	INCOME AS % OF ASSETS	EMPLOYEES
12/16	4,505	15	0.4%	—
12/15	4,893	39	0.8%	—
12/14	0	33	—	—
Annual Growth	**—**	**(30.9%)**	**—**	**—**

2016 Year-End Financials

Debt ratio: —
Return on equity: 3.70%
Cash ($ mil.): 87
Current ratio: —
Long-term debt ($ mil.): —

No. of shares (mil.): 26
Dividends
  Yield: 0.0%
  Payout: 49.1%
Market value ($ mil.): 349

	STOCK PRICE ($) FY Close	P/E High/Low		PER SHARE ($) Earnings	Dividends	Book Value
12/16	13.29	23	20	0.61	0.30	16.55
12/15	13.50	9	8	1.49	0.40	16.24
12/14	12.70	10	9	1.27	0.40	(0.00)
/0.00	—	—	(0.00)	0.00	(0.00)	
/0.00	—	—	(0.00)	0.00	(0.00)	
Annual Growth	**—**	**—**	**—**	**—**	**—**	

Casey's General Stores, Inc.

Casey's General Stores makes sure that small towns in the US Midwest get their fill of convenient shopping. It operates some 2000 company-owned convenience stores in 15 states primarily in the Midwest and all within about 500 miles of its Iowa headquarters and distribution center. Towns with 5000 people or fewer where rent is low are home to about 60% of the chain's stores. Casey's sells lots of gasoline (some 60% of total sales) as well as beverages groceries and fresh prepared foods including from-scratch pizza donuts and hot sandwiches. It also sells tobacco products automotive goods and other nonfood items.

Operations

Casey's is engaged in offering a broad selection of merchandise fuel and other products and services. Its stores typically stock over 3000 food and non-food items mostly nationally advertised brands but also an assortment of owned brand goods. It puts higher margin snack items in its "snack centers" located in the majority of its stores that also include things like donuts made on site as well as cookies brownies and other bakery items. Its made from scratch pizza is available in 99% of stores.

Casey's generates 60% of its revenue from fuel 30% from grocery and other merchandise and more than 10% from prepared food and fountain sales.

Geographic Reach

Casey's operates stores in 15 states including its largest markets — Iowa Illinois and Missouri — as well as Kansas Minnesota Nebraska Wisconsin Indiana Oklahoma Arkansas Tennessee and North and South Dakota. New markets for the chain include Kentucky and Tennessee.

Sales and Marketing

Casey's supplies all stores with groceries food health and beauty aids and general merchandise from their distribution centers. The company transports a significant portion of their motor fuel in their own trucks instead of by third-party carriers.

Sales of tobacco products have average approximately 10% of total sales each year and account for around approximately 10% of total gross profit.

Financial Performance

After low oil prices put a dent in Casey's 2016 revenue in fiscal 2017 (ended April) sales bounced back climbing 5% to $7.5 billion. A 6% increase in fuel volume sold more than compensated for a further 1% decline in average fuel prices across the year. New store openings also had a significant impact.

Net income fell 21% to $177.5 million as the company's store-expansion program required an uptick in capital expenditure and operating expenses.

Cash from operations fell 3% to $459.3 million due to lower net income.

Strategy

Casey's seeks to meet the needs of its small town clientele by combining the features of a general store and convenience store. The stores which offer more than 3000 food and nonfood products carry a broader selection than a typical convenience store. The company is finding ways to increase the same of higher margin products led by the installation of snack centers in store. Snack centers sell sandwiches fountain drinks and other items with profit margins that exceed general goods such as bakery items donuts and pizza. Indeed Casey's is the fifth largest pizza chain in the US. Grocery items account for less than half of Casey's total sales (oil brings in the majority) but generate around 80% of gross profits.

To make more room for food the convenience store operator has been opening larger (about 3800 sq. ft.) "O-shaped" stores. The format (launched in 2008) devotes additional space to food and beverages allowing for a wider selection of beer energy drinks and other high-margin items.

The company's annual goal is to increase its store count by 4% to 6%. To that end Casey's has been building and acquiring new stores; in fiscal 2017 it built 48 new stores and acquired 22 others (while closing 20 more).

Mergers and Acquisitions

Casey's grows its store base organically and through acquisitions. In 2017 it acquired 22 stores of which it opened 18. It will continue to add to its store base each year.

Company Background

Donald Lamberti who had run his family's grocery store founded Casey's General Stores with Kurvin C. "K. C." Fish. The men converted a gas station into the first Casey's convenience store in 1968. To expand and build brand recognition the company began franchising outlets two years later. By focusing on small towns the company avoided competition and expensive building and property costs. A significant growth spurt in 1979 took Casey's from 119 stores to 226. Fish retired the following year and the company went public in 1983.

EXECUTIVES

SVP and CFO, William J. (Bill) Walljasper, age 56, $550,000 total compensation

VP Advertising, Michael R. (Mike) Richardson, $195,000 total compensation

President and CEO, Terry W. Handley, age 58, $770,000 total compensation

SVP General Counsel and Secretary, Julia L. (Julie) Jackowski, age 52, $530,000 total compensation

VP Information Technology, Rich Schappert

SVP Operations, John C. (Jay) Soupene, age 49

Chairman, Robert J. (Bob) Myers, age 71

Auditors: KPMG LLP

LOCATIONS

HQ: Casey's General Stores, Inc.
One SE Convenience Boulevard, Ankeny, IA 50021
Phone: 515 965-6100
Web: www.caseys.com

PRODUCTS/OPERATIONS

2016 Sales

	$ mil.	% of total
Fuel	4,214	59
Grocery & other merchandise	1,974	28
Prepared food & fountain	880	12
Other	52	1
Total	7,122	100

Selected Merchandise

Ammunition
Automotive products
Beverages
Food including fresh foods
Gasoline (self-service)
Health and beauty aids
Housewares
Pet products
Photo supplies
School supplies
Tobacco products

COMPETITORS

7-Eleven	Kroger
CVS	Kwik Trip
Chevron	Martin & Bayley
Couche-Tard	McDonald's
Exxon Mobil	Pizza Hut
Holiday Companies	QuikTrip
Hy-Vee	Royal Dutch Shell
IGA	Walgreen
Krause Gentle	

HISTORICAL FINANCIALS

Company Type: Public

Income Statement

FYE: April 30

	REVENUE ($ mil.)	NET INCOME ($ mil.)	NET PROFIT MARGIN	EMPLOYEES
04/17	7,506	177	2.4%	35,014
04/16	7,122	225	3.2%	34,997
04/15	7,767	180	2.3%	31,766
04/14	7,840	134	1.7%	29,749
04/13	7,250	110	1.5%	27,079
Annual Growth	0.9%	12.5%	—	6.6%

2017 Year-End Financials

Debt ratio: 30.58%
Return on equity: 15.61%
Cash ($ mil.): 76
Current ratio: 0.79
Long-term debt ($ mil.): 907

No. of shares (mil.): 38
Dividends
Yield: 0.0%
Payout: 21.4%
Market value ($ mil.): 4,344

	STOCK PRICE ($) FY Close	P/E High/Low	PER SHARE ($) Earnings	Dividends	Book Value
04/17	112.07	30 24	4.48	0.96	30.71
04/16	112.00	22 14	5.73	0.88	27.74
04/15	82.18	20 14	4.62	0.80	22.51
04/14	68.66	22 16	3.46	0.72	18.69
04/13	57.91	22 16	2.86	0.66	15.70
Annual Growth	17.9%	— —	11.9%	9.8%	18.3%

Cass Information Systems Inc.

Cass Information Systems wants to pay your company's bills. The information services firm provides freight payment and information processing services to large manufacturing distribution and retail companies across the US. Its offerings include freight bill payment audit and rating services as well as outsourcing of utility bill processing and payments. Its telecommunications division manages telecom expenses for large companies. Cass grew out of Cass Commercial Bank (now a subsidiary) which provides banking services to private companies and churches as well as to consumers in the St. Louis area and Orange County California. Other major customer bases include Massachusetts Ohio and South Carolina.

Geographic Reach

Cass has locations in St. Louis Missouri; Columbus Ohio; Boston Massachusetts; Greenville South Carolina; Wellington Kansas; and Jacksonville Florida. It opened an office in Breda Netherlands — its first outside the US — in 2011 to support its multinational information processing clients.

Sales and Marketing

Cass lists some of the nation's largest companies including Macy's Dole and PepsiCo among its clients.

Financial Performance

Cass achieved record results in 2012 surpassing $115 million in revenues and earning $23 million in net profits. The firm's revenue increased 4% in 2012 vs. 2011 while net income rose by 1% over the same period. It was the third consecutive year of rising sales and profits for the company following a couple of lean years during the recession when businesses were either failing or more likely cutting back on outsourcing. The recent rise in revenue resulted from higher fees and other income including interest.

Strategy

Geographic expansion and technology improvements are on the list of goals for Cass as it looks to the future. The expense management firm is seeking new markets to enter in order to grow its customer base. Indeed Cass began 2012 with the acquisition of Jacksonville Florida-based Waste Reduction Consultants a provider of environmental expense management services. The deal expanded Cass' portfolio of services for controlling facility-related expenses. Previously Cass acquired telecom procurement technology from TelAdvisor Group in 2010. The technology allowed Cass to offer consulting services directly to clients.

EXECUTIVES

Chairman President and CEO, Eric H. Brunngraber, age 60, $557,874 total compensation

President Expense Management Services, Gary B. Langfitt, age 61, $236,862 total compensation

President Transportation Information Services, Mark A. Campbell, age 55, $206,157 total compensation

EVP CFO and Secretary, P. Stephen (Steve) Appelbaum, age 59, $264,337 total compensation

President and COO Cass Commercial Bank, Robert J. Mathias, age 64, $276,100 total compensation

Senior Vice President, Tony Urban

Vice President Sales and Marketing, Gary Nutter

VICE PRESIDENT, Terrence Cowee

Auditors: KPMG LLP

LOCATIONS

HQ: Cass Information Systems Inc.
12444 Powerscourt Drive, Suite 550, St. Louis, MO 63131
Phone: 314 506-5500
Web: www.cassinfo.com

2016 Sales

	$ mil.	% of total
Fee Revenue and Other Income:		
Information services payment & processing revenue	83	66
Bank service fees	1	1
Gains on sales of securities	0	0
Other	0	1
Interest Income:		
Interest and fees on loans	29	23
Interest and dividends on securities:		
Taxable	0	
Exempt from federal income taxes	9	8
Interest on federal funds sold and other short-term investments	1	1
Total	**126**	**100**

PRODUCTS/SERVICES

Transportation
Business Process
Freight Accounting
Freight Audit & Payment
Supply Chain Analysis
Utility
Energy Savings
Facility Cost Reporting
Utility Bill Payment
Telecom
Business Analytics
Procure To Pay
Telecom Consulting
Telecom Expense Management
Waste
Corporate Recycling
Industry Solutions
Waste Management
Waste Plans

COMPETITORS

ACCUSHIP
Alliance Data Systems
C.H. Robinson
 Worldwide
CTSI
Data2Logistics

First Banks
MER Telemanagement
 Solutions
Pulaski Financial
U.S. Bancorp

HISTORICAL FINANCIALS

Company Type: Public

Income Statement

FYE: December 31

	ASSETS ($ mil.)	NET INCOME ($ mil.)	INCOME AS % OF ASSETS	EMPLOYEES
12/16	1,504	24	1.6%	1,075
12/15	1,455	23	1.6%	989
12/14	1,500	24	1.6%	1,077
12/13	1,326	23	1.8%	1,087
12/12	1,287	23	1.8%	1,047
Annual Growth	4.0%	1.1%	—	0.7%

2016 Year-End Financials

Debt ratio: —
Return on equity: 11.69%
Cash ($ mil.): 266
Current ratio: —
Long-term debt ($ mil.): —

No. of shares (mil.): 12
Dividends
 Yield: 0.0%
 Payout: 41.4%
Market value ($ mil.): 905

	STOCK PRICE ($) FY Close	P/E High/Low	PER SHARE ($) Earnings	Dividends	Book Value
12/16	73.57	38 23	1.95	0.81	16.90
12/15	51.46	32 24	1.82	0.77	16.64
12/14	53.25	35 21	1.87	0.74	15.84
12/13	67.35	36 20	1.84	0.67	15.03
12/12	42.20	25 19	1.84	0.59	13.80
Annual Growth	14.9%	— —	1.6%	8.4%	5.2%

Caterpillar Inc.

Whether digging loading paving or moving Caterpillar does it all. The company is the world's #1 manufacturer of construction and mining equipment which includes excavators loaders and tractors as well as forestry paving and tunneling machinery. It also manufactures diesel and natural gas engines industrial gas turbines and diesel-electric locomotives. Subsidiary Caterpillar Financial Services offers a slew of financing leasing insurance and warranty products and services for dealers and customers. Caterpillar also offers remanufacturing services in addition to rail-related upgrade repair and maintenance services through Progress Rail Services.

Operations

Caterpillar is organized into four main operating segments.

Construction Industries (40% of net sales) caters to customers using machinery in infrastructure forestry and building construction applications.

Energy and Transportation (almost 40%) makes and sells reciprocating engines turbines diesel-electric locomotives and related parts across sectors serving power generation industrial oil and gas and transportation applications.

Resource Industries (15%) makes and sells machinery with mining quarry waste and material handling applications.

Financial Products accounts for the remainder of revenues and consists of subsidiaries Caterpillar Financial Services Corporation (Cat Financial) Caterpillar Insurance Holdings Inc. (Cat Insurance) and their respective subsidiaries.

Geographic Reach

Caterpillar's construction mining and power equipment manufacturing operations are conducted in facilities scattered across the US. It also operates a technical center in Mossville Illinois. Additionally the company has marketing and operating locations in the US Switzerland Japan China Singapore and Brazil. Parts distribution centers are located in the US Mexico Belgium Russia China Singapore Australia South Africa United Arab Emirates and Brazil.

Caterpillar sells its products and services in North America Asia/Pacific Europe Africa & Middle East (EAME) and Latin America.

Sales and Marketing

Caterpillar machinery is distributed primarily through a worldwide network of dealers many of which provide sales rental service and aftermarket support. Most are independently owned and operated though Caterpillar owns and operates its own dealerships in Japan. Within its global dealer network about 50 are located in the US and about 125 are located outside of the US. This network serves more than 190 countries. Caterpillar engines are sold through the dealer network and to other manufacturers for use in their products.

Caterpillar serves several different customer segments including those using machinery in mine and quarry applications (Resource Industries); those using machinery in building construction and infrastructure applications (Construction Industries); those using reciprocating engines and turbines in industries serving electric power industrial marine and petroleum applications as well as those needing the provision of rail services (Energy and Transportation); and retail and dealer customers needing financing leasing and insurance for their equipment (Financial Products). At the front end of a purchase Caterpillar provides financing to its customers; at the back end it offers support for the purchase and lease of its equipment.

Financial Performance

Caterpillar's revenues have declined the last three years dipping 18% from $47 billion in 2015 to $38.5 billion in 2016. This was the result of declines across all its segments and geographical regions. The company in 2016 experienced weak end-user demand across most of the industries it serves especially construction oil and gas mining and rail.

Resource Industries experienced a 26% sales decline in 2016 as mining customers continued to focus on improving productivity and reducing their total capital expenditures. Lower oil prices had a substantial negative impact on its Energy and Transportation operations (22% decline) which supports oil drilling and well servicing.In addition Construction Industries (12% decline) experienced unfavorable changes in dealer inventories as dealers overall lowered their inventories more significantly in 2016 than in 2015.

Caterpillar also posted its first net loss ($67 million) in at least 10 years in 2016. This was attributed to a goodwill impairment charge of $595 million related to its Resource Industries segment and about $985 million in losses related to a re-measurement of its pension and retirement plans.

Like its revenues Caterpillar's operating cash flow has declined the last three years falling from $6.68 billion in 2015 to $5.61 billion in 2016. This was mostly due to the revenue decreases across all its segments coupled with higher payments associated with layoffs.

Strategy

Caterpillar sets forth multiple goals that it is striving to achieve over the course of the next few years. Its immediate goal is to simplify its cost structure as it suffered a rare net loss during 2016. Through the end of 2015 Caterpillar reduced about 4% of its manufacturing square footage and is planning further closures and consolidation initiatives. By the end of 2016 Caterpillar consolidated or closed more than 30 facilities reducing manufacturing floor space by about 14%. It also reduced variable manufacturing costs and period costs by $2.3 billion in 2016 which helped to offset lower sales.

In conjunction with these cost-control efforts Caterpillar is open to investments in digital technologies data analytics and automation equipment which will optimize the efficiency of its machines and engines. It currently boasts about 470000 connected assets.

Mergers and Acquisitions

In line with its goal of expanding its role as an equipment and services provider Caterpillar in late 2016 purchased Illinois-based Kemper Valve & Fittings Corp. a manufacturer of high and low pressure flow iron products serving the oil and gas industry. Caterpillar paid about $95 million for Kemper and the transaction gave it a new product offering within its well service product portfolio. Specifically it obtained the ability to offer low and high pressure flow iron fluid control products to its oil and gas customers.

In late 2015 Caterpillar acquired RDS Manufacturing an Oklahoma-based manufacturer of highly engineered turbomachinery parts primarily for the turbine engine and aerospace markets. The acquisition of RDS is expected to help grow its turbine business and deepen its manufacturing expertise. The purchase price was approximately $95 million.

Months earlier Caterpillar picked up Rail Product Solutions (RPS) from Amsted Rail Company for $165 million. RPS is a leading North American provider of mission critical track fastening products and integrated fastening systems and the deal expanded Caterpillar's portfolio of track-related products.

HISTORY

In 1904 in Stockton California combine maker Benjamin Holt modified the farming tractor by substituting a gas engine for steam and replacing iron wheels with crawler tracks. This improved the tractor's mobility over dirt.

The British adapted the "caterpillar" (Holt's nickname for the tractor) design to the armored tank in 1915. Following WWI the US Army donated tanks to local governments for construction work. The caterpillar's efficiency spurred the development of earthmoving and construction equipment.

Holt merged with Best Tractor in 1925. The company renamed Caterpillar moved to Peoria Illinois in 1928. Cat expanded into foreign markets in the 1930s and phased out combine production to focus on construction and road-building equipment.

EXECUTIVES

VP and Chief Procurement Officer, Frank J. Crespo

SVP and President and CEO Progress Rail Services, William P. (Billy) Ainsworth, age 61

VP Large Power Systems Division, Tana L. Utley, age 53

VP Innovation & Technology Development Division (ITDD) and CTO, Thomas J. (Tom) Bluth

Group President and CFO, Bradley M. (Brad) Halverson, age 56, $786,312 total compensation

Group President Customer and Dealer Support, Robert B. (Rob) Charter, age 54, $729,768 total compensation

VP Industrial Power Systems, Ramin Younessi

Group President Resources Industries, Denise C. Johnson, age 51

CEO, D. James (Jim) Umpleby, age 58, $825,636 total compensation

VP China Operations, Qihua Chen

Group President Energy and Transportation Group, Thomas (Tom) Pellette, age 54

VP and President Solar Turbines, Pablo M. Koziner

VP Global Information Services (GIS) and CIO, Julie A. Lagacy

VP Surface Mining & Technology Division (SM&T), Jean Savage

Interim EVP Law and Public Policy, Suzette M. Long

Group President Construction Industries, Bob De Lange

VP Asia Pacific CIS Africa & Middle East Distribution Division (APDS), Wai Man (Raymond) Chan

VP Global Power Solutions, Thomas G. (Tom) Frake

VP Building Construction Products (BCP), Kenneth J. (Ken) Hoefling

VP Material Handling and Underground Division, Karl E. Weiss

VP and President Caterpillar Financial Services Corporation, David T. (Dave) Walton

VP Product Support & Logistics Division (PSLD), Chris Snodgrass

VP Global Construction & Infrastructure (GCI), Damien Giraud

VP Earthmoving Division, Frederic Istas

Chairman, David L. (Dave) Calhoun, age 60

Auditors: PricewaterhouseCoopers LLP

LOCATIONS

HQ: Caterpillar Inc.
510 Lake Cook Road, Suite 100, Deerfield, IL 60015
Phone: 224 551-4000
Web: www.caterpillar.com

2016 Sales

	$ mil.	% of total
Inside United States	15,956	41
Outside United States	22,581	59
Total	**38,537**	**100**

2016 Sales

	$ mil.	% of total
North America	17,962	47
EAME	9,053	23
Asia/Pacific	8,067	21
Latin America	3,455	9
Total	**38,537**	**100**

PRODUCTS/OPERATIONS

2016 Sales

	$ mil.	% of total
Machinery Energy & Transportation		
Construction Industries	15,612	40
Energy & Transportation	14,411	37
Resource Industries	5,726	15
All Other Segments	139	-
Corporate Items and Eliminations	(115)	-
Financial Products		
Financial Products Segment	2,993	8
Corporate Items and Eliminations	(229)	-
Total	**38,537**	**100**

Selected Brands

CAT
Caterpillar
Electro-Motive
FG Wilson
MaK
MWM
Olympian
Perkins
Progress Rail
SEM
Solar Turbines

COMPETITORS

ALSTOM	Mitsubishi Heavy
Atlas Copco	Industries
Bombardier	Navistar International
Charles Machine Works	Nortrak
Cummins	Rolls-Royce
DEUTZ	Rolls-Royce Power
Deere	Systems
Detroit Diesel	Sandvik
Doosan Infracore	Sany Heavy Industry
GE	Siemens Energy
Generac Holdings	Sumitomo Heavy
Hitachi Construction	Industries
Machinery	Terex
Hyundai Heavy	Volvo
Industries	Vossloh
J C Bamford Excavators	Weichai Power
Kohler	Wells Fargo Equipment
Komatsu	Finance
Kubota	Wärtsilä
MAN	

HISTORICAL FINANCIALS

Company Type: Public

Income Statement

FYE: December 31

	REVENUE ($ mil.)	NET INCOME ($ mil.)	NET PROFIT MARGIN	EMPLOYEES
12/17	45,462	754	1.7%	98,400
12/16	38,537	(67)	—	98,400
12/15	47,011	2,102	4.5%	105,700
12/14	55,184	3,695	6.7%	114,233
12/13	55,656	3,789	6.8%	118,501
Annual Growth	**(4.9%)**	**(33.2%)**		**(4.5%)**

2017 Year-End Financials

Debt ratio: 45.32%
Return on equity: 5.62%
Cash ($ mil.): 8,261
Current ratio: 1.35
Long-term debt ($ mil.): 23,847
No. of shares (mil.): 597
Dividends
  Yield: 0.0%
  Payout: 246.0%
Market value ($ mil.): 94,174

	STOCK PRICE ($) FY Close	P/E High/Low	PER SHARE ($) Earnings	Dividends	Book Value
12/17	157.58	125 72	1.26	3.10	22.92
12/16	92.74	— —	(0.11)	3.08	22.40
12/15	67.96	26 18	3.50	2.94	25.43
12/14	91.53	19 14	5.88	2.60	27.63
12/13	90.81	17 14	5.75	2.24	32.63
Annual Growth	**14.8%**	**— —**	**(31.6%)**	**8.5%**	**(8.5%)**

Cathay General Bancorp

Cathay General Bancorp is the holding company for Cathay Bank which mainly serves Chinese and Vietnamese communities from some 30 branches in California and about 20 more in Illinois New Jersey New York Massachusetts Washington and Texas. It also has a branch in Hong Kong and offices in Shanghai and Taipei. Catering to small to medium-sized businesses and individual consumers the bank offers standard deposit services and loans. Commercial mortgage loans account for more than half of the bank's portfolio; business loans comprise nearly 25%. The bank's Cathay Wealth Management unit offers online stock trading mutual funds and other investment products and services through an agreement with PrimeVest.

Geographic Reach

California state-chartered Cathay Bank has branches in California Illinois Massachusetts New Jersey New York Texas and Washington. Overseas it has a branch in Hong Kong and offices in Shanghai and Taipei.

Financial Performance

The bank's revenue is on a downward trend. In 2012 revenue declined more than 5% vs. 2011 after posting a 3% decline in the previous annual comparison. Indeed between 2008 and 2012 revenue dipped by about 17% on lower interest income and dividend income. However the bank's profit picture is improving with net income up in 2012 for the third consecutive year.

Strategy

With 60% of its branches in California — a state hard hit by the downturn in the housing market — Cathay Bank's real estate secured loan portfolio has suffered as the value of the underlying collateral plummeted. In 2010 the company entered into a memorandum of understanding with the FDIC to reduce its concentration of commercial real estate loans improve its capital ratios reduce overall risk and strengthen asset quality. The moves have helped the company to cut its losses. The bank has also been successful growing deposits.

Mergers and Acquisitions

In 2016 Cathay Bank agreed to buy SinoPac Bancorp from Taiwan's Bank SinoPac for $340 million. SinoPac's Far East National Bank operates nine branches including five in Los Angeles. After the deal closes Cathay plans to close a number of branches. The transaction will help boost the company's balance sheet.

EXECUTIVES

SEVP and COO, Irwin Wong, age 68, $339,777 total compensation

EVP and Chief Credit Officer Cathay Bank, Donald S. Chow, age 66, $312,615 total compensation
EVP CFO and Treasurer, Heng W. Chen, age 65, $416,542 total compensation
Chairman President and CEO Cathay General Bancorp and Chairman and CEO Cathay Bank, Pin Tai, $424,900 total compensation
EVP and Chief Risk Officer Cathy Bank, Kim R. Bingham, age 60
Assistant Vice President Marketing, Chris Lu
Auditors: KPMG LLP

LOCATIONS

HQ: Cathay General Bancorp
777 North Broadway, Los Angeles, CA 90012
Phone: 213 625-4700
Web: www.cathaybank.com

2015 Branch offices

	No.
Southern California Branches	21
Northern California Branches	12
New York Branches	12
Illinois Branches	4
Washington Branches	3
Texas Branches	2
Massachusetts Branch	1
Nevada Branch	1
New Jersey Branch	1
Maryland Branch	1
Overseas Branch	1
Total	**59**

PRODUCTS/OPERATIONS

2015 sales

	$ mil.	% of total
Interest and Dividend income		
Loan receivable	427	88
Investment securities- taxable	21	4
Federal Home Loan Bank stock	3	1
Deposits with banks	1	-
Non-Interest income		
Securities losses net	(3.3)	-
Letters of credit commissions	5	1
Depository service fees	5	1
Other operating income	25	5
Total	**486**	**100**

Products/Services
Personal
Accounts
Checking Accounts
Savings Accounts
CDs
IRA CD
Debit Cards
Loans
Mortgage Loan
Home Equity Financing
Auto Loan
Credit Cards
Cathay Online Banking
Mobile Banking
Business/Commercial
Business Accounts
Business Checking Account
Business Savings Account
CDs
Cash Management Services
Merchant Deposit Capture
Zero Balance Account
Lockbox Service
Merchant Bankcard Services
Courier Deposit Service
Armored Transport Services
Cash Vault Services
Business Online Banking
Loans
Commercial Financing
Real Estate & Construction Financing
International Banking & Financing
Smart Capital Line
SBA Guaranteed Loan Program
Credit Cards

COMPETITORS

Bank of America	Grandpoint
Citibank	Hanmi Financial
East West Bancorp	Hope Bancorp
Far East National Bank	U.S. Bancorp

HISTORICAL FINANCIALS

Company Type: Public

Income Statement

FYE: December 31

	ASSETS ($ mil.)	NET INCOME ($ mil.)	INCOME AS % OF ASSETS	EMPLOYEES
12/16	14,520	175	1.2%	1,129
12/15	13,254	161	1.2%	1,122
12/14	11,516	137	1.2%	1,074
12/13	10,989	123	1.1%	1,132
12/12	10,694	117	1.1%	1,092
Annual Growth	**7.9%**	**10.5%**		**0.8%**

2016 Year-End Financials

Debt ratio: 0.94%	No. of shares (mil.): 79
Return on equity: 9.77%	Dividends
Cash ($ mil.): 1,185	Yield: 0.0%
Current ratio: —	Payout: 34.2%
Long-term debt ($ mil.): —	Market value ($ mil.): 3,028

	STOCK PRICE ($) FY Close	P/E High/Low	PER SHARE ($) Earnings	Dividends	Book Value
12/16	38.03	17 12	2.19	0.75	22.97
12/15	31.33	17 12	1.98	0.56	21.63
12/14	25.59	16 13	1.72	0.29	20.08
12/13	26.73	19 13	1.43	0.08	18.33
12/12	19.53	15 12	1.28	0.04	20.58
Annual Growth	**18.1%**	**— —**	**14.4%**	**108.1%**	**2.8%**

CATHOLIC HEALTH INITIATIVES

For Catholic Health Initiatives (CHI) returning sick people to good health is more than a business — it's a mission. Formed in 1996 through the merger of three Catholic hospital systems the giant not-for-profit organization is one of the largest Catholic hospital operators in the US. It covers more than 90 sites including hospitals and clinics as well as long-term care assisted-living and senior residential facilities in about 20 states from Washington to Maryland. Its hospitals range from large urban medical centers (many with educational and research programs) to small hospitals in rural areas. All told CHI has more than 14000 acute-care beds. It is sponsored by a dozen different congregations of nuns.CHI plans to merge with San Francisco-based hospital system Dignity Health.

Operations

CHI's network includes 105 hospitals four of which are academic and teaching facilities and 30 rural facilities with critical-care access as well as nursing colleges home-health agencies community health services organizations long-term care facilities assisted-care and residential senior homes research and development programs and labs.

Geographic Reach

CHI operates in Arkansas Colorado Indiana Iowa Kansas Kentucky Minnesota Nebraska New Jersey New Mexico North Dakota Ohio Oregon Pennsylvania South Dakota Tennessee Texas Washington and Wisconsin — 19 states in all.

Sales and Marketing

For CHI in 2014 managed care accounted for 40% of patient revenue and Medicare accounted for 32%.

Financial Performance

In 2014 revenue increased 30% to $13.9 billion on an increase in net patient services revenues and non-patient revenues (investments gains on business combinations insurance premiums). Net income decreased 7% to $871 million though due to an increase in restructuring impairment and other losses. Cash flow from operations also fell dropping 13% to $1.1 billion.

Strategy

CHI whose mission covers "expressing Christ's love by caring for those in need" is issuing nearly $2 billion in taxable and tax-exempt bonds to fund several initiatives including a system-wide IT infrastructure upgrade (in part to facilitate its federally mandated conversion to universal electronic health records) virtual health programs (telemedicine) insurance products and clinic networks. In 2013 it added physician practice management services and clinical engineering consultation.

In the years since its founding the organization has grown through a number of affiliations and acquisitions. In 2013 CHI purchased or formed partnerships with St. Luke's Health System (Texas) Centura Health (Colorado) TriHealth (Ohio) and Mercy (Iowa). It also partnered with Ascension Health to create an internal audit and financial advisory consulting group for health care organizations.

In 2016 the company announced plans to exit the health insurance business by selling its Qual-Choice Health insurance subsidiary acquired in 2014. The unit lost nearly $97 million in the first three quarters of fiscal 2016 (ended March) and CHI posted an operating loss of some $19 million.

Mergers and Acquisitions

After years of discussions CHI and Dignity Health announced plans to merge in late 2017. The combined health system with 139 hospitals in 28 states will be the largest not-for-profit hospital system in the US. The size of the system will allow for it to provide expanded care to patients through such methods as virtual appointments a broader range of clinical programs and advanced technologies. The new organization will be headquartered in Chicago but hospitals will continue to operate under their current names.

In 2014 CHI bought St. Alexius Health in North Dakota adding St. Alexius Medical Center and two critical access hospitals to the system. The company also acquired Sylvania Franciscan Health adding hospitals and residential communities in Texas Kentucky and Ohio.

CHI bought insurance provider QualChoice Holdings of Arkansas for an undisclosed amount also in 2014.

HISTORY

In 1860 the Sisters of St. Francis established a hospital in Philadelphia laying the foundation for a larger health care organization. In 1981 Franciscan Health System was formally established to be a national holding company for Catholic hospitals and related organizations. By the mid-1990s the system consisted of 12 member and two affiliate hospitals and 11 long-term-care facilities located in the mid-Atlantic states and the Pacific Northwest.

Sisters of Charity of Cincinnati and the Sisters of St. Francis Perpetual Adoration of Colorado Springs co-sponsored The Sisters of Charity Health Care Systems incorporated in 1979 as a multi-institutional health care network. By the mid-1990s the system included 20 hospitals in Colorado Kentucky Nebraska New Mexico and Ohio.

Three congregations collaborated to form Catholic Health Corporation in 1980 one of the first such health care partnerships between religious communities within the Roman Catholic Church in the US. By 1996 this coalition operated 100 health care facilities in 12 states.

The development of modern managed care health care systems put pressure on the smaller Catholic hospital operations so the three systems established Catholic Health Initiatives (CHI) in 1996 as a national entity serving five geographic regions. Patricia Cahill a lay health care veteran who previously served the Archdiocese of New York was appointed president and CEO of CHI. The following year CHI absorbed the 10-hospital Sisters of Charity of Nazareth Health Care System based in Bardstown Kentucky (founded in a log cabin in 1812).

That year CHI continued to seek new partnerships to improve efficiency. With Alegent Health it formed provider network Midwest Select with nearly 200 hospitals marketing discounted rates to businesses. CHI allied with the Daughters of Charity to form for-profit joint venture Catholic Healthcare Audit Network to provide operational financial compliance and information systems audits as well as due diligence reviews. CHI also joined insurance joint venture NewCap Insurance with the Daughters of Charity and Catholic Health East; the firm allowed CHI to operate independently of commercial insurers.

CHI made a secular tie-in with the University of Pennsylvania Health System in 1998 whereby the university's system would offer care through five Catholic hospitals (CHI made plans to transfer these hospitals to Catholic Health East in 2001). The next year CHI announced its first loss due to lackluster performance in the Midwest. During 2000 the company responded by streamlining operations and changing management resulting in a positive bottom line. In 2001 it sold three hospitals in Pennsylvania one in Delaware and one in New Jersey to Catholic Health East.

EXECUTIVES

President and Chief Executive Officer, Kevin E. Lofton, age 62
President Enterprise Business Lines and CFO, J. Dean Swindle
SVP Divisional Operations (Texas), Michael H. Covert
SVP Marketing and Communications, Joyce M. Ross
Executive Vice President Mission, Thomas R. Kopfensteiner
SVP Divisional Operations and CEO CHI Memorial (Tennessee), Larry Schumacher, age 59
EVP Corporate Affairs and Chief Legal Officer, Mitch H. Melfi
EVP Growth and Business Acquisitions, Paul W. Edgett
EVP Chief Administrative Officer and Chief Human Resources Officer, Patricia G. (Pat) Webb
SVP Divisional Operations and CEO CHI Health (Nebraska and Southwest Iowa), Cliff A. Robertson
Senior Vice President and Division Executive Officer, Jeffrey S. Drop
SVP and Chief Nursing Officer, Kathleen D. Sanford
SVP Divisional Operations and CEO Mercy Health Network (Iowa), David H. Vellinga
SVP Divisional Operations and CEO CHI Franciscan Health (Tacoma), Ketul J. Patel
SVP and President and CEO KentuckyOne Health, Ruth W. Brinkley
CEO CHI St. Alexius Health, Matt Grimshaw, age 42
Interim EVP Operations, Anthony Jones
SVP and Chief Medical Officer, Robert J. Weil

Senior Vice President and Chief Medical Officer, Stephen L Moore
Senior Vice President Divisional OperationsCEO, Robert Ratzi
Vice President Strategy And Operations, Clarence Hauer
Vice President Clinical Leadership Development, Pat Patton
Vice President Human Resource Business Practices, Thomas Sams
Vice President Supply Chain Data Analytics, Kevin Kakuda
Vice President Public Policy, Marcia Desmond
Vice Presrent Mission, Susanne Decrane
Vice President Mission And Ministry, Janet Henry
Vice President Finance, Steve Schramm
Vice President Mission Integration, Luke Larson
Vice President and Chief Nursing Informatics and Telehealth Officer, Ann Shepard
Vice President Chi Foundation National Support Services, Jim Bocian
Vice President National Cardiovascular Service Line, Jennifer Bringardner
Vice President Ministry Formation, Patrick Gaughan
Senior Vice President And Chief Revenu, Phil Foster
Vice President Corporate Responsibility, Leigh Bertholf
Health Care Director, Ruth Heitke
Vice President Finance, Brad Ludford
Vice President Business Intelligence, Evon Holladay
Regional Vice President Payer Strategy, Jamie Reynoso
Vice President Legal Transactions and Tax, Cynthia Leon
Vice President Corporate Responsibility, Susan Shiflett
Vice President Clinical Operations and Physician Leadership Development, Manoj Pawar
Vice President of Patient Care, Deb Haagenson
Vice President Outreach, Ellen Lee
VICE PRESIDENT, BEV LIVEZEY
Director of Pharmacy, Nicki Bohl
Senior Vice President, Robert G Strickland
Vice President Materials, Sandra French
Vice President of nursing, Heike Duban
Vice President Corporate Responsibility, Betsy Wade
Vice President Real Estate, Dave Glasscock
Senior Vice President System Chief Nursing Officer, Velinda J Block
Vice President of Finance, Christy Spitser
Vice President, Deeanna Opstedahl
Senior Vice President Mission Integration, Bonnie Burnett
Vice President Clinic and Outpatient Setvices, Trina Bressler
Administrative VP National Oncology Service Line, Cory Jones
Auditors: ERNST & YOUNG LLP DENVER CO

LOCATIONS

HQ: CATHOLIC HEALTH INITIATIVES
198 INVERNESS DR W, ENGLEWOOD, CO 801123637
Phone: 303 298-9100

Selected Facilities and Operations

Arkansas
St. Vincent Health System
St. Vincent Doctors Hospital (Little Rock)
St. Vincent Infirmary Medical Center (Little Rock)
St. Vincent Medical Center North (Sherwood)
St. Vincent Morrilton (formerly St. Anthony's Medical Center Morrilton)
St. Vincent Rehabilitation Hospital (Sherwood)
Colorado
Centura Health
Centura Senior Services
The Gardens at St. Elizabeth (Denver)

Medalion Retirement Center (Colorado Springs)
Namaste Alzheimer Center (Colorado Springs)
Progressive Care Center (Canon City)
Villa Pueblo (Pueblo)
The Villas at Sunny Acres (Thornton)
Mercy Regional Medical Center (Durango)
Penrose-St. Francis Health Services
Penrose Hospital (Colorado Springs)
St. Francis Health Center (Colorado Springs)
St. Francis Medical Center (Colorado Springs)
St. Anthony Hospitals
St. Anthony Central Hospital (Denver)
St. Anthony North Hospital (Westminster)
St. Anthony Summit Medical Center (Frisco)
St. Mary-Corwin Medical Center (Pueblo)
St. Thomas More Hospital (Canon City)
Iowa
Alegent Health
Alegent Health-Mercy Hospital (Corning)
Alegent Health-Mercy Hospital (Council Bluffs)
Mercy Health Network
Bishop Drumm Retirement Center (Johnston)
Mercy Clinics (Des Moines)
Mercy College of Health Sciences (Des Moines)
Mercy Court (Des Moines)
Mercy Franklin Center (Des Moines)
Mercy Medical Center - Centerville (Centerville)
Mercy Medical Center - West Lakes (Des Moines)
Mercy Park Apartments (Des Moines)
Kansas
St. Rose Ambulatory and Surgery Center (formerly Central Kansas Medical Center Great Bend)
St. Catherine Hospital (Garden City)
Kentucky
KentuckyOne Health
Jewish Hospital and St. Mary's HealthCare (with Jewish Hospital HealthCare Services)
Our Lady of Peace (Louisville)
Sts. Mary & Elizabeth Hospital (Louisville)
Saint Joseph Health System
Continuing Care Hospital Inc. (Lexington)
Flaget Memorial Hospital (Bardstown)
Saint Joseph Berea Hospital (Berea)
Saint Joseph Hospital (Lexington)
Saint Joseph Hospital East (Lexington)
Saint Joseph Hospital Mount Sterling (Mt. Sterling)
Marymount Medical Center (London)
Our Lady of the Way Hospital (Martin)
Maryland
St. Joseph Medical Center (Towson)
Minnesota
LakeWood Health Center (Baudette)
St. Francis Healthcare Campus (Breckenridge)
St. Francis Home (Breckenridge)
St. Joseph's Area Health Services (Park Rapids)
Unity Family Healthcare (dba St. Gabriel's Healthcare)
Albany Area Hospital and Medical Center
Alverna Apartments (Little Falls)
St. Camillus Place (Little Falls)
St. Gabriel's Hospital (Little Falls)
Nebraska
Alegent Health (joint venture with Immanuel Healthcare System)
Alegent Health-Bergan Mercy Medical Center (Omaha)
Alegent Health-Mercy Hospital (Council Bluffs)
Good Samaritan Hospital (Kearney)
Richard H. Young Hospital (Kearney)
Saint Elizabeth Regional Medical Center (Lincoln)
Saint Francis Medical Center (Grand Island)
St. Mary's Community Hospital (Nebraska City)
New Jersey
Saint Clare's Health System (Denville)
Saint Clare's Hospital (Boonton)
Saint Clare's Hospital (Denville)
Saint Clare's Hospital (Dover)
Saint Clare's Hospital (Sussex)
New Mexico
St. Joseph Community Health (Albuquerque)
North Dakota
CHI North Dakota
Carrington Health Center (Carrington)
Lisbon Area Health Services
Mercy Hospital (Valley City)
Oakes Community Hospital
Mercy Hospital (Devils Lake)
Mercy Medical Center (Williston)
St. Joseph's Hospital and Health Center (Dickinson)
Villa Nazareth Corporation
Friendship (Fargo)
Riverview Place (Fargo)
Ohio

Premier Health Partners
Good Samaritan Hospital (Dayton)
The Maria-Joseph Center (Dayton)
TriHealth
Good Samaritan Hospital (Cincinnati)

Oregon
Mercy Medical Center
Linus Oakes Inc. (Roseburg)
St. Anthony Hospital (Pendleton)

Pennsylvania
St. Joseph Health Ministries (Lancaster)
St. Joseph Regional Health Network
St. Joseph Medical Center (Reading)

South Dakota
St. Mary's Healthcare Center
Gettysburg Medical Center
Maryhouse Long-term Care Facility (Pierre)
ParkWood Retirement Apartments (Pierre)
Oahe Manor (Gettysburg)
Oahe Villa (Gettysburg)
St. Mary's Hospital (Pierre)

Tennessee
Memorial Health Care System
Memorial Hospital (Chattanooga)
Memorial North Park Hospital (Hixson)

Washington
Franciscan Health System
Enumclaw Regional Hospital (Enumclaw)
St. Anthony Hospital (Gig Harbor)
St. Clare Hospital (Lakewood)
St. Francis Hospital (Federal Way)
St. Joseph Medical Center (Tacoma)

Wisconsin
Franciscan Villa (South Milwaukee)

PRODUCTS/OPERATIONS

2014 Sales

	% of total
Net patient service revenues	96
Gain on business combinations	3
Other	1
Total	**100**

COMPETITORS

Adventist Health System Sunbelt Healthcare
Allina Hospitals
Ascension Health
Baptist Health
Baptist Health (Arkansas)
BryanLGH Medical Center
Denver Health and Hospital Authority
Exempla Healthcare
Golden Horizons
HCA
Kettering Health Network
Life Care Centers
Memorial Health System (Colorado)
Mercy Health (OH)
Methodist Health System
MultiCare Health System
OhioHealth
Tenet Healthcare
UC Health
Universal Health Services
University of Colorado Hospital

HISTORICAL FINANCIALS

Company Type: Private

Income Statement

FYE: June 30

	REVENUE ($ mil.)	NET INCOME ($ mil.)	NET PROFIT MARGIN	EMPLOYEES
06/07	7,731	902	11.7%	72,500
06/06	7,636	693	9.1%	—
Annual Growth	1.2%	30.0%	—	—

2007 Year-End Financials

Debt ratio: ——
Return on equity: 11.70%
Cash ($ mil.): 386
Current ratio: 0.90
Long-term debt ($ mil.): —

Dividends
Yield: —
Payout: —
Market value ($ mil.): —

CBRE Group Inc

CBRE is all about location location location — not to mention ubicaci n l'emplacement posizione and Standort. As the world's largest commercial real estate services company by revenue CBRE provides property and facilities management leasing brokerage appraisal and valuation asset management financing and market research services from more than 450 offices worldwide and manages 1.6 billion sq. ft. of commercial space for third-party owners and occupants. Subsidiary Trammell Crow provides property development services for corporate and institutional clients primarily in the US. CBRE Global Investors manages real estate investments for institutional clients.

HISTORY

Colbert Coldwell and Albert Tucker started real estate brokerage Tucker Lynch & Coldwell in 1906 in San Francisco. In 1922 the company expanded to Los Angeles where it began developing real estate in 1933 with a 60-acre subdivision in the burgeoning city.

Having profited from California's rapid growth in the 1950s and 1960s the firm expanded out of state. The partnership incorporated in 1962 as Coldwell Banker which went public in 1968. Sears Roebuck & Co. bought the company in 1981 for 80% above its market price. But by 1991 Sears had abandoned aims to become a financial services giant and sold Coldwell Banker's commercial operations to The Carlyle Group as CB Commercial Real Estate Services Group.

Free of Sears but $56 million in the red the company didn't return to profitability until 1993. Two years later it embarked on a shopping spree in real estate services buying tenant representatives Langon Rieder and Westmark Realty. In 1996 the company went public and bought mortgage banker L. J. Melody & Company (which was renamed CBRE | Melody); it purchased Koll Real Estate Services in 1997.

In 1998 the company widened its global scope with the acquisition of REI Limited the non-UK operations of Richard Ellis; it was renamed CB Richard Ellis Services. CB Richard Ellis also bought Hillier Parker May & Rowden (now operating in the UK as CB Hillier) a London-based provider of commercial property services.

CB Richard Ellis experienced a revenue crunch in 1999 and responded by restructuring its North American operations into three divisions (transaction financial and management services) and cutting management ranks by 30%. Growth continued in 1999 with the purchase of Pittsburgh-based Gold & Co. the addition of an office in Venezuela and a fat contract to manage more than 1100 locations for Prudential.

In 2000 the company committed significant resources to the Internet inking a deal to offer the lease management services of MyContracts.com and investing in Canadian real estate transaction tracker RealNet Canada.

A group of investors including then-CEO Ray Wirta chairman Richard Blum (and his BLUM Capital Partners) and Freeman Spogli took the company private in 2001. Blum Capital Partners bought the 60% of publicly traded CBRE that it did not already own forming CBRE Holding. Three years later the company went public once again.

In 2003 CBRE merged with top commercial real estate broker and property manager Insignia Financial. The next year the company changed its name to CB Richard Ellis Group and went public. It bought rival Trammell Crow in 2006 as well as a dozen or so other companies as it sought to fill in its holdings. The acquisitions deepened CBRE's outsourcing services especially project and facilities management for corporate and institutional clients in the US.

CBRE spun off former subsidiary Realty Finance Corporation in 2008 after the real estate investment trust continued to post losses in a troubled credit market.

Also in 2008 it opened its first offices in Bahrain and joined forces with Vanke to provide residential property management services in China. The following year CBRE expanded its existing UK-based investment banking business (advisory and restructuring services for real estate hospitality and gaming companies) to the Americas.

CBRE in 2011 made one of its largest deals in several years. The company bolstered its global real estate investment management business with the acquisition of ING Groep's real estate investment management operations for some $940 million. The Dutch firm's real estate investment management business in Asia and Europe was merged into CBRE Global Investors and more than doubled the size of the unit. The transaction also included US-based Clarion Real Estate Securities and interests in commercial real estate co-investments. (The ING deal helped boost CBRE's investment management revenue by more than 60% in 2012.)

In November 2012 CBRE acquired EA Shaw. a independent commercial and residential property partnership specializing in central London. The purchase significantly enhanced the firm's business in central London.

In 2013 CBRE acquired technical engineering services firm Norland Managed Services Ltd. which specialized in commercial buildings in the UK and Ireland and had a growing customer base in the US and Singapore.

The firm also in 2013 purchased The CAC Group a top commercial real estate services firm based in San Francisco. The move made CBRE the #1 provider of commercial property management and leasing in the market. CBRE also bought property and asset management specialist SOGES-MAINT-CBRE to build on its previous acquisitions in the Netherlands the Czech Republic Slovakia Poland Latvia and Lithuania. Additionally in 2013 CBRE acquired commercial real estate services business Resource Estate Partners and TPA Realty Services both based in Atlanta where it's working to boost its market share.

EXECUTIVES

President CEO and Director, Robert E. (Bob) Sulentic, age 61, $990,000 total compensation
President Global Corporate Services, William F. (Bill) Concannon, age 61, $675,000 total compensation
Global President Capital Markets, Christopher R. Ludeman
CFO and Global Director of Corporate Development, James R. (Jim) Groch, age 55, $770,000 total compensation
Global Group President Geographies, Calvin W. (Cal) Frese, age 61, $680,000 total compensation
Executive Managing Director and COO L. J. Melody & Company, Brian F. Stoffers
CEO Asia Pacific, Steven A. (Steve) Swerdlow
Global Group President Lines of Business & Client Care, Michael J. (Mike) Lafitte, age 56, $700,000 total compensation
Global Chief Investment Officer and CEO CBRE Global Investors and CBRE Clarion Securities, T. Ritson Ferguson, age 57, $800,000 total compensation
Chairman Asia Pacific, Robert (Rob) Blain, age 62, $560,000 total compensation

EVP and General Counsel, Laurence H. Midler, age 52, $325,000 total compensation
Global Director Client Care, Tony Long
CEO Trammell Crow Company., Matt Khourie
President CBRE Global Investors, Daniel (Danny) Queenan
EVP Global Brokerage and Sales Management, Laura OBrien
CEO Americas, Jack Durburg
CEO CBRE Europe Middle East and Africa (EMEA), Martin Samworth
Global President Occupier Advisory and Transaction Services, Whitley Collins
Global President Asset Services and Valuation and Advisory Services (VAS), Mary Jo Eaton
President CBRE Southern California - Hawaii, Lewis Horne
Vice Chairman Capital Markets and Institutional Properties, Michael Hines
Chief Digital and Technology Officer, Chandra Dhandapani
Vice Chairman CBRE Capital Markets Debt and Structured Finance, Rocco Mandala
Vice President, Connor Kerr
Vice President, Mary Dunn
Senior Vice President, Tom Bohman
Senior Vice President, Nate Sahn
Associate Vice President Investment Properties, Stirling Richmond
First Vice President, Christopher Bates
Vice President, Kelly Kayl
Vice President, Miles Kettner
First Vice President, Carol Trapani
VAS Vice President, Bob Holman
Executive Vice President, Kevin Calihan
Senior Vice President, Stephen Heffner
Senior Vice President, Michael Roden
Vice President, Dick Keller
Senior Vice President, Paul Runkle
Vice President, James Angelotti
Senior Vice President And Partner, Robert Daglio
Senior Vice President, Gregg Haly
Senior Vice President, Jeffrey Bell
Senior Vice President, Peery Wood
Spqrea First Vice President, Geoff Pendergast
Vice President, Nick Spatafore
Associate Vice President, David Ho
Vice President, Grant Larmour
First Vice President, Sior P Kluck
Senior Vice President, Steven Brabant
Executive Vice President, Richard Ratner
Vice President, James Lee
Senior Vice President Investment Properties Net Lease Property Group, Maurice Nieman
Executive Vice President, Jeffrey C Babikian
First Vice President, Laurence Schuler
First Vice President, Ron McWherter
First Vice President, Don Weis
Senior Vice President, Mark Darrington
MAI Vice President, Chris Karlen
Vice President, Robert Morton
Vice President, John Slivka
Senior Vice President, Cynthia Kamin
Executive Vice President, Rob Faktorow
First Vice President, Thomas Boyd
Senior Vice President, Troy Holme
Senior Vice President Advisory and Transaction Services, Peggy McTigue
Vice President, Chad Lesley
SP Senior Vice President, Terry Kittleson
Executive Vice President, Richard Hodos
Vice President, Michael Thompson
Senior Vice President, John Brewer
First Vice President, Phillip Linton
Vice President, Chris van Keulen
Senior Vice President, Chris Henderson
Vice President, Craig Hall
First Vice President, Xan Saks
First Vice President, Joshua Kleinberg

Executive Vice President Infrastructure Group, John Porter
Legal Secretary, Carol Evans
Vice President Cost Segregation, Gregory Hartigan
First Vice President, Robert Dubbins
Associate Vice President, Rob Coleman
MAI First Vice President, Michael Eschmann
Senior Vice President, Jim Koenig
Vice President, Nancy Johnson
MAI Vice President, Michael Lloyd
First Vice President Partner, Michael Svoboda
Senior Vice President, Mark Teitelbaum
Vice President Facility Management, Kenneth Lawson
Vice President, Vince Femiano
Senior Vice President, Brant Bernet
Senior Vice President Institutional Properties Multifamily, Jeremy Faltys
Vice President, Steve Yi
Vice President, Loralie Ogden
Vice Presidenl, Julius Tabert
Vice President, Michael Shipley
Senior Vice President, Trey Pennington
Vice President, Tom Low
Vice President, Nick Pappas
Vice President Information Technology, Mike Washington
Senior Vice President, Ned Burns
Vice President, Xavier Ramos
Vice President, Karen Walsh
Senior Vice President Of Brokerage Services, Jeffrey Counsell
First Vice President Investment Properties, Marcello Campanini
MAI Vice President, Haydon Burns
Senior Vice President, Warren Savery
Senior Vice President Global Compliance, Tyson Avery
Senior Vice President, Bradley Gingerich
Senior Vice President, Pat O'Keefe
Vice President Senior, Mary O'Connor
Vice President, Brian Beaty
Senior Vice President, Joel Wechsler
Senior Vice President, Patrick Scruggs
Executive Vice President, William Waxman
VAS Vice President, Ian Parker
Vice President, Mitchell Stravitz
Senior Vice President, Jack Hoskins
Senior Vice President, Jesse Weber
Firsl Vice President, Todd Folger
Vice President, Neil Kolatkar
Executive Vice President, Thomas Bohlinger
First Vice President, Michael Kaider
Vice President, Andy Nott
Spqrea Senior Vice President, Dave Terzolo
MAI Vice President, Daniel Lincoln
Vice President, Greg Steinhilber
Vice President Corporate Capital Markets, Anne Rahm
Senior Vice President, Jesse Grant
Vice President, Don Hirose
Senior Vice President, Lon Rubackin
Senior Vice President, Kevin Bender
Senior Vice President, Greg Geraci
Senior Vice President Investment Properties Multifamily, Spencer Ballif
Vice President, Sean Weidlein
Senior Vice President, Jerome Kranzel
Vice President, Kevin Mulhern
Senior Vice President, Phillip Sample
First Vice President, Joseph Mangiacotti
Executive Vice President, Bethany Grace
First Vice President, Jeffrey Calentino
Vice President, Matt Burnett
Senior Vice President, Dean Chandler
Vice President, Clay Gilbert
Senior Vice President, Chris Komanowski
Senior Vice President, Christian Charre
Senior Vice President, Rod Apodaca
Senior Vice President, Gene Pride

Executive Vice President, David Anderson
Senior Vice President Investment Properties, Alex Kozakov
Senior Vice President, Mark Emerick
Vice President, John Zanetos
Auditors: KPMG LLP

LOCATIONS

HQ: CBRE Group Inc
400 South Hope Street, 25th Floor, Los Angeles, CA 90071
Phone: 213 613-3333
Web: www.cbre.com

2016 Sales

	$ mil.	% of total
Americas	7,226	55
Europe Middle East & Africa	3,917	30
Asia/Pacific	1,485	11
Global investment management	369	3
Development services	71	1
Total	**13,071**	**100**

2016 Sales

	% of total
US	55
UK	18
Other countries	27
Total	**100**

PRODUCTS/OPERATIONS

Selected Industries

CBRE Hotels
Data Centers
Energy & Sustainability
Golf & Resort Properties
Healthcare
Industrial & Logistics
Labor Analytics
Multifamily
Office
Public Institutions & Education
Residential
Retail
Alternative Investments Practice
Labor Analytics
Life Sciences

Selected Subsidiaries

CBRE Inc.
CBRE Capital Markets Inc.
CB/TCC LLC
CBRE Global Holdings SARL
CBRE Finance Europe LLP
CBRE Limited
CBRE Services Inc.
Norland Managed Services Ltd.
Trammell Crow Company LLC
CBRE Luxembourg Holdings SARL
CBRE Global Acquisition Company SARL
Relam Amsterdam Holdings
CBRE Limited Partnership

Selected service Investors

Financing
Investment Administration
Investment Banking
Leasing & Advisory
Loan Servicing
Property Management
Property Sales
Valuation & Advisory

Selected services for occupiers

Facilities Management
Leasing & Advisory
Management Consulting
Project Management
Valuation & Advisory
Workplace

Selected Business Lines

Advisory & Transaction Services
Asset Services
Capital Markets
Global Workplace Solutions

Valuation & Advisory Services
Investment Management (CBRE Global Investors)
Development Services (Trammell Crow Company)
CB/TCC LLC
CBRE Finance Europe LLPCBRE Luxembourg Holdings
 SARLCBRE Global Acquisition Company SARLRelam
 Amsterdam HoldingsCBRE Limited Partnership

COMPETITORS

BGC Partners	Inland Group
Cassidy Turley	Jones Lang LaSalle
Colliers International	Lincoln Property
Colliers International	Marcus & Millichap
Group	Mitsui Fudosan
Cushman & Wakefield	Realogy Holdings
Eastdil Secured	Savills Studley
HFF	

HISTORICAL FINANCIALS

Company Type: Public

Income Statement

FYE: December 31

	REVENUE ($ mil.)	NET INCOME ($ mil.)	NET PROFIT MARGIN	EMPLOYEES
12/16	13,071	571	4.4%	75,000
12/15	10,855	547	5.0%	70,000
12/14	9,049	484	5.4%	52,000
12/13	7,184	316	4.4%	44,000
12/12	6,514	315	4.8%	37,000
Annual Growth	19.0%	16.0%	—	19.3%

2016 Year-End Financials

Debt ratio: 35.28%	No. of shares (mil.): 337
Return on equity: 19.92%	Dividends
Cash ($ mil.): 762	Yield: —
Current ratio: 1.13	Payout: —
Long-term debt ($ mil.): 2,548	Market value ($ mil.): 10,621

	STOCK PRICE ($) FY Close	P/E High/Low	PER SHARE ($) Earnings	Dividends	Book Value
12/16	31.49	20 14	1.69	0.00	8.94
12/15	34.58	24 19	1.63	0.00	8.12
12/14	34.25	24 17	1.45	0.00	6.79
12/13	26.30	27 21	0.95	0.00	5.71
12/12	19.90	21 15	0.97	0.00	4.66
Annual Growth	12.2%	— —	14.9%	—	17.7%

CBS Corp

You might say this company has a real eye for broadcasting. CBS Corporation is a leading mass media conglomerate with television radio online content and publishing operations. Its portfolio is anchored by CBS Broadcasting which operates the #1 rated CBS television network along with a group of local TV stations. CBS also owns cable network Showtime and produces and distributes TV programming through CBS Television Studios and CBS Television Distribution. Other operations include CBS Radio CBS Interactive and book publisher Simon & Schuster. Chairman Emeritus Sumner Redstone controls CBS Corporation through National Amusements.

HISTORY

The company that would eventually become CBS Corporation began as Viacom in 1970. It was the result of numerous mergers and acquisitions dating back nearly 90 years combining everything from a movie studio to a company that made car bumpers. CBS launched Viacom after the FCC ruled that TV networks could not own cable systems and TV stations in the same market. Viacom took over CBS's program syndication division and bought TV and radio stations in the late 1970s and early 1980s. In 1978 it co-founded pay-TV network Showtime. Viacom became full owner in 1982 and combined Showtime with The Movie Channel the following year to form Showtime Networks. Viacom also began producing TV series and bought MTV Networks in 1986.

After a bidding war with renowned financier Carl Icahn and a Viacom management group Sumner Redstone's National Amusements bought 83% of Viacom in 1987. Viacom bought King's Entertainment (theme parks) shortly thereafter and followed that with two mega-deals in 1994: it bought Paramount Communications for about $10 billion (which included Simon & Schuster) and Blockbuster for $8.4 billion (which included Spelling Entertainment). The next year along with Chris-Craft Viacom launched UPN (United Paramount Network) the fifth commercial-broadcast TV network in the US.

Chiseling away at a mountain of debt Viacom dumped its radio stations and sold its share in USA Networks (now named IAC/InterActiveCorp) to Universal for $1.7 billion in 1997. In 1998 it sold the reference and education publishing divisions of Simon & Schuster to Pearson for $4.6 billion and unloaded the unprofitable Blockbuster Music chain to Wherehouse Entertainment for $115 million.

Viacom created an Internet division (MTV Networks Online) in 1999 to house its MTV VH1 and Nickelodeon Web sites (later decentralized into The MTVi Group and Nickelodeon Online). Later that year it sold 18% of Blockbuster in an IPO and sold 10% of MTVi to TCI Music (later Liberty Digital) in exchange for the SonicNet websites.

Viacom bought Chris-Craft's 50%-stake in the struggling UPN Network for a paltry $5 million in 2000 by exercising a buy-sell clause in the contract. BHC Communications (Chris-Craft's 80%-owned subsidiary that actually owned the stake in UPN) filed suit to block Viacom's merger with CBS claiming that it violated a non-compete clause in the contract but the New York Supreme Court ruled in Viacom's favor. Its $45 billion merger with CBS went through (reuniting two companies split apart by the government 30 years ago) and Viacom was given one year to sell UPN. However a federal law prohibiting ownership of more than one TV network was overturned in 2001 allowing Viacom to keep the network.

Later that year Viacom's victory over Chris-Craft turned to sour grapes when News Corp. agreed to buy Chris-Craft. The deal could have forced UPN to fold if News Corp. had turned Chris-Craft's large-market UPN stations into FOX affiliates (a new pact later signed with Chris-Craft keeps UPN as the stations' network).

In 2001 Viacom bought the rest of Infinity Broadcasting that it didn't already own as well as Black Entertainment Television (the media company targeting African-Americans) for $3 billion. It also folded MTVi back into parent MTV Networks. Other cost cutting measures in 2002 included combining the business operations of UPN and CBS and placing Simon & Schuster under the same division as its film and TV production holdings.

Two years later Viacom finally sold its majority stake in Blockbuster which never really fit in with Viacom's other media properties. The media firm also didn't want to deal with the new challenges facing Blockbuster such as stiff competition from video on demand services the cheap DVD market and mail order video rental company Netflix.

In a move designed to simplify the firm's operations and re-focus the company on its core assets in late 2005 Viacom split into two separately traded firms — one called CBS Corporation consisting of traditional television and radio broadcasting operations and headed by former co-COO Les Moonves; and the other called the "new" Viacom made up of cable television and film operations and headed by former co-COO Tom Freston. (Freston resigned in 2006.) Redstone retained his title as chairman of both firms as well as his majority control.

Shortly after the split CBS Corp. sold Paramount Parks to Cedar Fair for $1.2 billion. A newly formed network called The CW a combination of UPN and The WB debuted in 2006. The following TV season the CBS network fell from first place in the ratings for the first time in six years. CBS Corp. expanded its online publishing operations in 2008 with the $1.8 billion acquisition of CNET Networks.

In 2011 production on the eighth season of its hit comedy Two and a Half Men ceased as a result of the erratic behavior of actor Charlie Sheen. CBS fired Sheen and has put the show on hiatus for an undetermined period of time.

In 2014 the company spun off its CBS Outdoor Americas advertising business.

EXECUTIVES

Chairman President and CEO, Leslie (Les) Moonves, age 67, $3,500,000 total compensation
SEVP and Chief Communications Officer, Gil Schwartz, age 66, $896,923 total compensation
SEVP Chief Administrative Officer and Chief Human Resources Officer, Anthony G. Ambrosio, age 57, $964,423 total compensation
SEVP and Chief Legal Officer, Lawrence P. (Larry) Tu, age 62, $1,200,000 total compensation
EVP Government Affairs, John Orlando
EVP Investor Relations, Adam Townsend
EVP Deputy General Counsel and Secretary, Jonathan H. Anschell
COO, Joseph R. Ianniello, age 50, $2,500,000 total compensation
EVP General Tax Counsel and Chief Veteran Officer, Richard M. Jones, age 52
EVP Controller and Chief Accounting Officer, Lawrence (Larry) Liding, age 48
Vice President and Assistant Counsel Intellectual Property, Mallory Levitt
Vice President Content, Adam Bloom
Vice President Production, Al Kennedy
Vice President Advertising and Promotion, Michael Pollack
Assistant Vice President and Controller, Kenneth Silver
Vice President, Robert Noethiger
Vice President And Assistant General Counsel, Michael Rona
Vice President, Wendy Hogan
Senior Vice President Corporate Security, Thomas Cruthers
Vice President And Assistant Treasurer, Jim Morrison
Vice President and General Manager, Tom Herschel
Vice President And Assistant General Counsel, Joseph Richburg
Vice President of Information Technology, Michael Grant
Vice President Senior Tax Counsel, Kenneth Koen
Vice President and Director of Information Technology, Mariel Brady
Vice President Programming, Emilie Deutsch
Vice President National Sports Sales, Bob Malmgren
Seniorvice President, Sue Lamphear
Senior Vice President Workforce Development, Jennifer Suarez

Executive Vice President and General Counsel CBS Films, Rik Toulon
Vice President Finance, Steve Grosso
Senior Vice President Sales CBS Paramount Internat, Barry Chamberlain
Vice President Diversity and Communications, Fern Orenstein
Vice President Comedy Development, Edy Mendoza
Senior Vice President And Director Of Sales Analysis Operations, Bob Kaplan
Vice President Information Technology, Wendy Hancock
Vice President And Assistant General Counsel, Mary Tischler
Vice President And Assistant General Counsel, Mary Moy
Vice President Of Sales, Kevin Barth
Vice President And News Director, Jeff Kiernan
Vice President Distribution, Ken Hinshaw
Vice President And General Sales Manager, Doug Smith
Senior Vice President Sales, Marty Daly
Vice President Human Resources, Michael Niceberg
Vice President Ad Operations, Mark Halstead
Senior Vice President Human Resources, Charles Becker
Vice President Marketing, Belinda Jones
Vice President Executive Creative Director, James Shefcik
Senior Vice President Alt Series Development, Ghen Maynard
Vice President Business Development at CBS Interactive, Adam London
Executive Vice President Marketing Publicity and Promotions, Christine Batista
Vice President Enterprise Solution Delivery, Mark Groner
Vice President West Coast, Josh Comay
National Sales Manager, Vince Mccarthy
Vice President Of Finance, David Larson
Vice President Product Management and Marketing, Patrick Herde
Executive Vice President, Kurt Davis
National Sales Manager and Digital Sales Manager, Ron Bartholomew
Executive Vice President Post Production, Jack Schuster
Vice President Creative Services, Betsy Siciliano
Vice President and General Manager, Scott Schuman
Senior Vice President Sports Sales, Tony Taranto
Vice President Finance, Steven Haft
Vice President, Carter Skeath
Senior Vice President and Deputy General Counsel, Andrea Simon
Vice President and Counsel, Mark Maher
Senior Vice President Digital Sales, Andi Poch
Vice President and General Manager, Adam Levy
Senior Vice President, Roni Mueller
Vice President, Cristina McCarthy
Vice President, Kate Adler
Senior Vice President Business Development, Jeff Shultz
Senior Vice President Market Manager, Dan Kearney
Senior Vice President, Kim Metcalf
Vice President Current Programs, Marci Cooperstein
Senior Vice President Specials, Courtney Conroy
Senior Vice President and Associate General Counsel, Naomi Waltman
Senior Vice President Supplier Category Management, Mike Smyklo
Executive Vice President Digital, JD Crowley
Vice President, Gene Mellevold
Senior Vice President, Jonathan Bingaman
Vice President Post Production, Jeff Henry
Vice Chair, Shari E. Redstone, age 63
Board Member, Patrick Corr
Treasurer, Georgette Morrow

Treasurer, Jacqueline Miller
Auditors: PricewaterhouseCoopers LLP

LOCATIONS

HQ: CBS Corp
51 W. 52nd Street, New York, NY 10019
Phone: 212 975-4321
Web: www.cbscorporation.com

2016 Sales

	$ mil.	% of total
United States	11,317	86
International	1,849	14
Total	**13,166**	**100**

PRODUCTS/OPERATIONS

2016 Sales

	$ mil.	% of total
Entertainment	8,877	65
Cable Networks	2,160	16
Local Media	1,779	13
Publishing	767	6
Corporate/Eliminations	(417)	-
Total	**13,166**	**100**

2016 Sales

	$ mil.	% of total
Advertising	6,288	48
Content licensing and distribution	3,673	28
Affiliate and subscription fees	2,978	22
Other	227	2
Total	**13,166**	**100**

Selected Operations

Entertainment
   CBS Films (motion picture production)
   CBS Interactive (online content)
   BNET
   CBS.com
   CBSSports.com
   CNET
   GameSpot
   TV.com
   CBS Studios International (international program syndication)
   CBS Television Distribution (domestic programming syndication)
   CBS Television Network (broadcast television network)
   CBS Entertainment
   CBS News
   CBS Sports
   CBS Television Studios (television production)
   The CW Network (50% broadcast television network)
Local broadcasting
   CBS Television Stations
Outdoor advertising
   CBS Outdoor
Cable networks
   CBS College Sports Network
   Showtime (pay-TV service)
Publishing
   Simon & Schuster

COMPETITORS

21st Century Fox	Penguin Random House
AOL	SIRIUS XM
Cumulus Media	Sony Pictures
Disney	Entertainment
JCDecaux	Time Warner
Lamar Advertising	Yahoo!
NBCUniversal	iHeartCommunications

HISTORICAL FINANCIALS

Company Type: Public

Income Statement

FYE: December 31

	REVENUE ($ mil.)	NET INCOME ($ mil.)	NET PROFIT MARGIN	EMPLOYEES
12/16	13,166	1,261	9.6%	21,270
12/15	13,886	1,413	10.2%	16,260
12/14	13,806	2,959	21.4%	17,310
12/13	15,284	1,879	12.3%	19,490
12/12	14,089	1,574	11.2%	20,930
Annual Growth	(1.7%)	(5.4%)	—	0.4%

2016 Year-End Financials

Debt ratio: 38.68%
Return on equity: 27.18%
Cash ($ mil.): 598
Current ratio: 1.64
Long-term debt ($ mil.): 8,902

No. of shares (mil.): 412
Dividends
   Yield: 0.0%
   Payout: 23.4%
Market value ($ mil.): 26,211

	STOCK PRICE ($) FY Close	P/E High/Low	PER SHARE ($) Earnings	Dividends	Book Value
12/16	63.62	23 15	2.81	0.66	8.95
12/15	47.13	22 13	2.89	0.60	12.02
12/14	55.34	13 9	5.27	0.54	13.75
12/13	63.74	21 12	3.01	0.48	16.72
12/12	38.05	15 11	2.39	0.44	16.21
Annual Growth	13.7%	— —	4.1%	10.7%	(13.8%)

CBTX Inc

LOCATIONS

HQ: CBTX Inc
5999 Delaware Street, Beaumont, TX 77706
Phone: 409 861-7200
Web: www.communitybankoftx.com

HISTORICAL FINANCIALS

Company Type: Public

Income Statement

FYE: December 31

	ASSETS ($ mil.)	NET INCOME ($ mil.)	INCOME AS % OF ASSETS	EMPLOYEES
12/16	2,951	27	0.9%	472
12/15	2,882	24	0.8%	—
Annual Growth	2.4%	12.7%	—	—

2016 Year-End Financials

Debt ratio: 1.17%
Return on equity: 7.73%
Cash ($ mil.): 382
Current ratio: —
Long-term debt ($ mil.): —

No. of shares (mil.): 22
Dividends
   Yield: 0.0%
   Payout: 16.3%
Market value ($ mil.): —

	STOCK PRICE ($) FY Close	P/E High/Low	PER SHARE ($) Earnings	Dividends	Book Value
12/16	0.00	— —	1.22	0.20	16.21
12/15	0.00	— —	1.06	0.20	15.44
/0.00	—	—(0.00)	0.00	(0.00)	
Annual Growth		— —	—	—	—

CDW Corp

Auditors: Ernst & Young LLP

LOCATIONS

HQ: CDW Corp
75 Tri-State International, Lincolnshire, IL 60069
Phone: 847 465-6000
Web: www.cdw.com

HISTORICAL FINANCIALS

Company Type: Public

Income Statement

FYE: December 31

	REVENUE ($ mil.)	NET INCOME ($ mil.)	NET PROFIT MARGIN	EMPLOYEES
12/16	13,981	424	3.0%	8,516
12/15	12,988	403	3.1%	8,465
12/14	12,074	244	2.0%	7,211
12/13	10,768	132	1.2%	7,000
12/12	10,128	119	1.2%	6,800
Annual Growth	8.4%	37.4%	—	5.8%

2016 Year-End Financials

Debt ratio: 46.55%
Return on equity: 39.53%
Cash ($ mil.): 263
Current ratio: 1.42
Long-term debt ($ mil.): 3,215

No. of shares (mil.): 160
Dividends
Yield: 0.0%
Payout: 18.8%
Market value ($ mil.): 8,350

	STOCK PRICE ($) FY Close	P/E High/Low	PER SHARE ($) Earnings	PER SHARE ($) Dividends	PER SHARE ($) Book Value
12/16	52.09	21 13	2.56	0.48	6.52
12/15	42.04	20 14	2.35	0.31	6.52
12/14	35.17	25 16	1.42	0.20	5.44
12/13	23.36	29 22	0.84	0.04	4.14
Annual Growth	22.2%	— —	32.1%	83.6%	12.0%

Celanese Corp (DE)

Celanese Corporation gets a lot of good ink about its acetates. The global technology and specialty materials company manufactures of building block chemicals like acetic acid and vinyl acetate monomers used in everything from inks and paints to agricultural products and chewing gum. Texas-based Celanese also makes advanced plastics products such as precision molds for injection molding flame- and heat-resistance plastics and acetate film. Other products include acetate tow (in cigarette filters) and industrial specialties like ethylene vinyl acetate.Celanese was established in the US in 1918 by famed chemists Henry and Camille Dreyfus.

Operations

The company is one of the world's largest producers of acetyl products as well as a top global producer of engineered polymers.

Celanese operates through four business segments: Acetyl Intermediates Advanced Engineered Materials Consumer Specialties and Industrial Specialties.

Acetyl Intermediates is the largest at around 45% of total company revenue and produces acetic acid vinyl acetate monomer acetic anhydride and acetate esters. The segment's products are commonly used in colorants paints adhesives coatings and pharmaceuticals. It also produces organic sol-

vents and intermediates for pharmaceutical agricultural and chemical products.

Advanced Engineered Materials worth nearly 30% of sales makes high performance plastics mostly for automotive and medical applications.

The Consumer Specialties segment brings in over 15% of sales and mostly makes acetate tow for use in cigarette filters. It also makes preservatives for the food and drink industries such as sorbic acid and potassium sorbate. It also makes Qorus and Sunett sweeteners.

Industrial Specialties accounts for over 15% of sales and includes the emulsion polymers and EVA polymers businesses. The former's products find use in paints and coatings adhesives construction glass fiber textiles and paper. EVA polymers makes specialty ethylene vinyl acetate resins and compounds and low-density polyethylene for use in packaging lamination film hot melt adhesives auto parts and carpeting.

Geographic Reach

Irving Texas-based Celanese has 30 production facilities scattered across the globe as well as an additional eight affiliate production sites.

Besides the US Celanese has properties plants or other operations in Belgium Brazil Canada China Germany Hungary Malaysia Mexico the Netherlands South Korea Sweden Singapore and the UK.

Germany and the US each account for around 30% of the company's sales.

Sales and Marketing

Celanese markets its products both directly to customers and through distributors. Sales to major global customers in a wide range of industries are usually made under multi-year contracts. The company serves a broad range of industries including consumer and industrial adhesives paints and coatings textiles food and beverage automotive applications consumer and medical applications performance industrial applications filter media paper and packaging chemical additives and construction applications.

Acetate tow is sold principally to the major tobacco companies that account for a majority of worldwide cigarette production. Customers of Clarifoil film include printers carton manufacturers retailers packaging buyers publishers designers and freezer door manufacturers. Food protection ingredients are primarily sold through regional distributors to small and medium sized customers and directly to large multinational customers in the food industry.

Financial Performance

Celanese's net sales fell 5% in fiscal 2016 the second consecutive year of revenue falls.

Most significant was a $303 million fall in the Acetyl Intermediates segment as lower industry utilization impacted on prices. VAM (vinyl acetate monomers) sales volume also decreased. The Industry and Consumer Sepcialties segments also saw revenue fall.

The main bright point for the year was the Advanced Engineered Materials business which grew 9% or $118 million. It recorded higher sales volumes in Europe and Asia driven by project launches and organic growth.

Net income increased 196% to $900 million due to lower incentive compensation costs productivity initiatives lower raw material costs and a $340 million gain relating to the termination of an agreement with a Singaporean supplier.

Cash from operations increased 4% or $31 million to $893 million due to an increase in net income partially offset by an increase in pension plan contributions and unfavorable changes to working capital.

Strategy

Celanese is pumping up its value-add Advanced Engineered Materials businessdue to its higher

margins and lower exposure to price fluctuations. The company made two acquisitions in the space in 2015-17 — SO.F.TER and Nilit — adding thermoplastics and thermoplastic elastomers to its product lines.

Mergers and Acquisitions

In 2017 Celanese acquired Nilit Plastics the nylon compounding division of Nilit an Israeli nylon manufacturer.

In 2015 Celanese bought Italy-based SO.F.TER. Group one of the world's largest independent thermoplastic compounders.

Company Background

Celanese Corporation was created in 2004 by the Blackstone Group which had acquired a majority share in Celanese AG turned it private and then flipped it in a 2005 public offering. Blackstone finally divested its remaining holdings in Celanese in 2007.

EXECUTIVES

Senior Vice President Asia, Mark Oberle
Svp Business Strategy Development Procurement And Advanced Fuels Technology, Jay Townsend
Chairman and CEO, Mark C. Rohr, age 65, $1,142,308 total compensation
EVP and Chief Administrative Officer, Lori A. Johnston, age 52, $475,000 total compensation
EVP and General Counsel, Peter G. Edwards, age 55
EVP and President Acetyl Chain and Integrated Supply Chain, Patrick D. (Pat) Quarles, age 49, $627,692 total compensation
EVP COO and President Materials Solutions, Scott M. Sutton, age 52, $581,538 total compensation
SVP Finance and CFO, Christopher W. (Chris) Jensen, age 50, $546,154 total compensation
CIO, Rajesh Nagarajan
Vice President Europe Region, Amy Hebert
Vice President Human Resources and Employment Law, Joe Fox
Vice President and Treasurer, Jamie Beggs
Vice President Strategic Resources, Bruce Bennett
Vice President Global Sales Americas Region, John Caamano
Vice President And Deputy General Counsel, Jay Felkins
Senior Vice President Supply Management, William Antonace
Senior Vice President Chief Financial Officer, Steven Sterin
Executive Vice President, Sandy Lin
Vice President Global HSE, Christo Zemering
Vice President and Deputy General Counsel, Michael Silberman
Vice President Human Resources and Employment Law, Joseph Fox
Treasurer, Divya Kottayil
Auditors: KPMG LLP

LOCATIONS

HQ: Celanese Corp (DE)
222 West Las Colinas Blvd., Suite 900N, Irving, TX 75039-5421
Phone: 972 443-4000
Web: www.celanese.com

2016 sales

	$ mil.	% of total
Germany	1,540	29
US	1,451	27
China	758	14
Singapore	745	14
Belgium	408	8
Canada	214	4
Mexico	150	2
Others	123	2
Total	5,389	100

PRODUCTS/OPERATIONS

2016 sales

	$ mil.	% of total
Advanced Engineered Materials	1,444	27
Acetyl Intermediates	2,441	45
Industrial Specialties	979	18
Consumer Specialties	929	17
Adjustments	(404)	-7
Total	**5,389**	**100**

Selected Products

Acetyl Intermediates
  Acetate esters
  Acetic acid
  Acetic anhydride
  Carboxylic acids
  Methanol
  Vinyl acetate monomer (VAM)
Industrial Specialties
  Emulsions
Consumer Specialties
  Acetate tow
  Sunett sweetener
Advanced Engineered Materials
  Polyacetal products (POM)
  Polyphenylene sulfide (Forton)
  UHMW-PE (GUR)

Selected Brand Names

AOPlus
BuyTiconaDirect
Celanex
Celcon
Celstran
Celvolit
Clarifoil
Compel
Erkol
GUR
Hostaform
Impet
Mowilith
Nutrinova
Riteflex
Sunett
Thermx
Vandar
Vectra
Vinamul

COMPETITORS

Asahi Kasei	LANXESS
BASF SE	Methanex
DSM	NutraSweet
Daicel Chemical	Rhodia
Dow Chemical	SABIC Innovative
DuPont	Plastics
Eastman Chemical	Solvay
Hexion	

HISTORICAL FINANCIALS

Company Type: Public

Income Statement

FYE: December 31

	REVENUE ($ mil.)	NET INCOME ($ mil.)	NET PROFIT MARGIN	EMPLOYEES
12/17	6,140	843	13.7%	7,592
12/16	5,389	900	16.7%	7,293
12/15	5,674	304	5.4%	7,081
12/14	6,802	624	9.2%	7,468
12/13	6,510	1,101	16.9%	7,430
Annual Growth	**(1.5%)**	**(6.5%)**	**—**	**0.5%**

2017 Year-End Financials

Debt ratio: 38.17%
Return on equity: 30.79%
Cash ($ mil.): 576
Current ratio: 1.79
Long-term debt ($ mil.): 3,315

No. of shares (mil.): 135
Dividends
  Yield: 0.0%
  Payout: 28.5%
Market value ($ mil.): 14,538

	STOCK PRICE ($) FY Close	P/E High/Low		PER SHARE ($) Earnings	Dividends	Book Value
12/17	107.08	18	13	6.09	1.74	21.26
12/16	78.74	13	9	6.18	1.38	18.40
12/15	67.33	36	26	2.00	1.15	16.20
12/14	59.96	16	12	4.00	0.93	18.43
12/13	55.31	8	6	6.91	0.53	17.20
Annual Growth	**18.0%**	**—**	**—**	**(3.1%)**	**34.9%**	**5.4%**

Celgene Corp

Celgene lines up cells and genes to create good health. The biopharmaceutical company's lead product is Revlimid which is approved in the US Europe and other select markets as a treatment for multiple myeloma (bone marrow cancer). Revlimid also is used to treat a blood disorder called myelodysplastic syndrome (MDS). The company's second-biggest seller is Pomalyst/Imnovid which is approved in various markets for the treatment of multiple myeloma. Other products include Otezla for the treatment of psoriatic arthritis and chemotherapy agent Abraxane. The firm has other drugs in development that combat inflammatory diseases and cancer.

Operations

Revlimid is by far Celgene's biggest seller making up nearly two-thirds of its annual sales. Its other top selling products — Pomalyst Otezla Abraxane and Vidaza — make up most of its remaining revenues.

Outside of blood cancers and diseases Celgene receives royalties on sales of ADHD drugs Focalin Focalin XR and Ritalin which are licensed to and sold by global drug maker Novartis. (Those drugs have lost sales due to competition from generics.)

Other therapies in the works include CC-122 and CC-220 which are being tested for hematological and solid tumor cancers MS and for neuro-inflammation.

Geographic Reach

The US is Celgene's largest market accounting for about 60% of revenues with Europe accounting for most of the rest of sales. However Celgene is working to expand its global presence. Its products reach customers in more than 50 countries.

In addition to global sales and service locations Celgene operates manufacturing plants in the US (Phoenix) and Switzerland (Boudry and Zofingen) that meet a majority of its needs though some of the firm's products are made by third-party manufacturers. The company also has sales and research offices in California Florida Kansas Massachusetts New Jersey North Carolina Texas and Washington DC.

Sales and Marketing

Celgene sells its products through a global direct sales force as well as via independent representatives in select markets (primarily in Latin America). In the US products are distributed primarily to wholesalers and in the case of Revlimid Pomalyst and Thalomid specialty pharmacies (the drugs must be handled under special risk-management programs due to blood clot risks associated with the drugs). Otezla is marketed directly to consumers through print and television advertising.

CVS and McKesson are the company's two largest customers representing more than 10% of sales each.

Financial Performance

Celgene's strategies of making select acquisitions finding new uses for existing drugs and conducting proprietary R&D to keep its pipeline well-stocked seem to be paying off. Celgene has achieved rapidly climbing revenues in recent years as its product offerings have grown including a 21% revenue increase to $11.2 billion in 2016. Higher sales of Revlimid Otezla and Pomalyst both in the US and abroad have helped strengthen the company's earning power. These gains were partially offset however by declines in sales of Vidaza generic formula azacitidine and Thalomid.

Net income which dipped 20% in 2015 bounced back 25% to $2 billion in 2016. This was largely due to a decrease in net acquisition-related charges but was partially offset by an increase in research and development expenses.

The higher net income plus positive adjustments to reconcile net cash provided by operating activities (related to impairment charges and derivative instruments) led to an increase in operating cash flow which rose 60% to $4 billion that year.

Strategy

Key focus areas for Celgene include protein homeostasis immuno-oncology epigenetics and inflammation and immunology. Though Celgene has a little breathing room before it loses market exclusivity on most of its products the firm is working avidly to stay ahead of patent losses by adding or developing new drugs and pipeline candidates. The company has expanded its portfolio through internal development collaborations and acquisitions. It expects to move about 10 novel agents into testing within the next couple of years; Celgene also plans to release data from about 20 phase III trials within that time period.

In the largest up-front payment for a biotechnology licensing agreement to date Celgene in 2015 paid $1 billion to gain access to innovative cancer treatments being developed by Juno Therapeutics. As part of the collaboration deal Celgene began partnering with Juno on the commercialization of its cancer drugs and cell therapies for the treatment of autoimmune diseases; Juno retained responsibilities for R&D and commercialization in North America while Celgene took on the development and commercialization duties in the rest of the world. The deal also gave Celgene a 10% stake in Juno.

Also in 2015 Celgene entered into a global development deal with Agios. The partners are testing AG-881 for the treatment of brain cancer. In another collaboration with AstraZeneca subsidiary MedImmune Celgene is exploring the treatment of blood cancer through the antibody CC-900011.

The company also has collaboration agreements with Lycera and Nurix.

Mergers and Acquisitions

In 2015 Celgene moved to expand its position in the field of innovative cancer therapies when it bought privately held Quanticel Pharmaceuticals for some $100 million. Through the deal Celgene gained access to Quanticel's platform for the single-cell genomic analysis of cancer and its lead programs targeting epigenetic modifiers. Also that year Celgene bought Receptos gaining that firm's ozanimod candidate for the treatment of multiple ailments including relapsing multiple sclerosis. That deal was valued at $7.2 billion.

In early 2017 Celgene bought Delinia a private biotech with a focus on developing novel therapeutics for autoimmune diseases for an initial payment of $300 million plus a potential $475 million in milestone payments.

The following year Celgene agreed to buy the privately held Impact Biomedicines in a deal that with milestone payments could be worth as much as $7 billion. The company will pay $1.1 billion upfront to gain access to fedratinib Impact's experimental blood cancer treatment.

Also in 2018 the company agreed to buy Juno Therapeutics for $9 billion. Juno specializes in CAR-T therapies for cancer; Celgene has partnered with firms including Juno toward the development of CAR-T treatments. The acquisition will give Celgene access to Juno's lead asset JCAR017 which is expected to gain approval for the treatment of lymphoma in 2019.

Company Background

Celgene was founded in 1986 as a spinoff entity; it was formerly part of Celanese Corporation.

EXECUTIVES

EVP and CFO, Peter N. Kellogg, age 61, $845,667 total compensation

EVP General Counsel and Corporate Secretary, Gerald F. Masoudi, age 49

President and COO, Scott A. Smith, age 55, $691,667 total compensation

EVP and President Research and Early Development, S.J. Rupert Vessey, $673,141 total compensation

CEO and Director, Mark J. Alles, age 58, $1,062,583 total compensation

President Global Inflammation and Immunology (I&I) Franchise, Terrie Curran

President Hematology & Oncology, Nadim Ahmed

Corporate Vice President of International Finance, Jurg Oehen

Vice President Global Marketing Oncology, Mark Miocevich

Senior Vice President Of Research And Development, Garth McGrath

Vice President, Niall McConnell

Vice President Chief Compliance Officer, Gabriel Flores

Executive Vice President, George Golumbeski

Vice President, Rick Couch

Senior Vice President and CIO, Richard Williams

NATIONAL ACCOUNT MANAGER, Jeff Presson

Executive Vice President, Beatriz C Mateos

Senior Vice President, Joe Camardo

Executive Vice President and General Counsel, Paul Sherrington

Vice President and Business Manager, Julie Mathew

Vice President, Oliver Kong

Vice President and Chief Legal Counsel, Maria E Pasquale

Medical Director, Ahmet Hasaligil

Vice President Human Resources, Dorothea Klein

Vice President Asia Pacific, George Varkanis

Vice President Corporate Communications, William Westlin

Vice President of Clinical Trial Operations, Patricia Moenaert

Vice President, Deborah Tady

Chief Sales Officer, James Carmichael

Vice President Regulatory Affairs Emea, Patricia Pallier

Vice President Clinical Research And Development, Patricia Rohane

Senior Vice President, Richard Bagger

National Account Manager, Dave Orlando

Medical Director, Giovanni De Crescenzo

Medical Director, Christina Ornauer

Vice President Inflammation and Immunology EMEA, Lee Heeson

Senior Vice President And Chief Commercial Officer, Emily Severe

Pharm.D, Montserrat Valles

Corporate Vice President, Kimberly Foster

CORPORATE VICE PRESISDENT, Peter Callegari

Vice President, Myron Czuczman

National Account Manager Payer, Daniel Van Horn

Vice President Biotherapeutics, Ho Cho

Chairman, Robert J. (Bob) Hugin, age 62

Board Member, Stacy Deserio

Assistant Treasurer, Sandra Alves

Board Member, Simona Bortolazzi

Assistant Treasurer, Michael Bradley

Assistant Treasurer, Doug Bressette

Auditors: KPMG LLP

LOCATIONS

HQ: Celgene Corp
86 Morris Avenue, Summit, NJ 07901
Phone: 908 673-9000
Web: www.celgene.com

2016 Sales

	$ mil.	% of total
US	7,009	62
Europe	3,046	27
Other regions	1,173	11
Total	**11,229**	**100**

PRODUCTS/OPERATIONS

2016 Sales

	$ mil.	% of total
Products		
Revlimid	6,973	62
Pomalyst/Imnovid	1,310	12
Otezla	1,017	9
Abraxane	973	9
Vidaza	608	5
Thalomid	152	1
Istodax	79	1
Azacitidine for injection	66	1
Other	4	-
Other	44	-
Total	**11,229**	**100**

Selected Products

Approved
Abraxane (breast cancer treatment)
Istodax (cancer treatment gained through Gloucester buy)
Revlimid (multiple myeloma myelodysplastic syndromes)
Pomalyst (multiple myeloma)
Thalomid (complications from leprosy multiple myeloma)
Vidaza (myelodysplastic syndromes)

COMPETITORS

Abbott Labs	Merck
Amgen	Millennium: The Takeda
Astex Pharmaceuticals	Oncology Company
AstraZeneca	Novartis
Biogen	Onyx Pharmaceuticals
Bristol-Myers Squibb	Pfizer
CTI BioPharma	Roche Holding
Eisai	Sanofi
Eli Lilly	Shire
Gilead Sciences	Takeda Pharmaceutical
Johnson & Johnson	

HISTORICAL FINANCIALS

Company Type: Public

Income Statement

FYE: December 31

	REVENUE ($ mil.)	NET INCOME ($ mil.)	NET PROFIT MARGIN	EMPLOYEES
12/17	13,003	2,940	22.6%	7,467
12/16	11,229	1,999	17.8%	7,132
12/15	9,256	1,602	17.3%	6,971
12/14	7,670	1,999	26.1%	6,012
12/13	6,493	1,449	22.3%	5,100
Annual Growth	**19.0%**	**19.3%**	**—**	**10.0%**

2017 Year-End Financials

Debt ratio: 52.55%	No. of shares (mil.): 759
Return on equity: 43.49%	Dividends
Cash ($ mil.): 7,013	Yield: —
Current ratio: 4.99	Payout: —
Long-term debt ($ mil.): 15,838	Market value ($ mil.): 79,241

	STOCK PRICE ($) FY Close	P/E High/Low	PER SHARE ($) Earnings	Dividends	Book Value
12/17	104.36	39 26	3.64	0.00	9.11
12/16	115.75	48 37	2.49	0.00	8.48
12/15	119.76	69 52	1.94	0.00	7.52
12/14	111.86	69 33	2.39	0.00	8.15
12/13	168.97	98 45	1.69	0.00	6.82
Annual Growth	**(11.3%)**	**— —**	**21.2%**	**—**	**7.5%**

Centene Corp

Centene provides managed care and related services in more than a dozen states under names such as Managed Health Services (Wisconsin and Indiana) Superior HealthPlan (Texas) and Buckeye Community Health Plan (Ohio). Centene provides services to some 10.4 million low-income elderly and disabled people receiving benefits from programs including Medicaid Supplemental Security Income (SSI) and state Children's Health Insurance Program (CHIP). Centene also offers specialty services in areas such as behavioral health (through Cenpatico) vision benefits (OptiCare) and pharmacy benefits management (US Script).

Operations

Centene operates in two primary segments: Managed Care and Specialty Services.

The Managed Care segment provides services through Medicaid CHIP SSI LTC (long-term care) foster care and ABD (aged blind and disabled) programs.Centene's Medicaid contracts account for about three-fourths of total revenues. Its largest contracts are with the state of California accounting for about a fifth of revenues.

The Specialty Services segment is composed of companies offering a range of health care services and products to state programs health care organizations correctional facilities employer groups and other organizations. Services include telehealth advisory (NurseWise) case management (CaseNet) and disease and wellness management (Nurtur). Centene's Celtic Insurance subsidiary specializes in providing low-cost consumer-directed insurance policies to uninsured customers nationwide and its Bridgeway Health Solutions provides long-term care policies in select territories.

Geographic Reach

Centene serves more than 1400 hospitals and care facilities in 24 states: Arizona Arkansas California Florida Georgia Illinois Indiana Kansas Louisiana Massachusetts Michigan Minnesota Mississippi Missouri New Hampshire New Mexico Ohio Oregon South Carolina Texas Tennessee Vermont Washington and Wisconsin.

Sales and Marketing

Most of Centene's revenue comes under contract or subcontract with state Medicaid managed care programs. Its largest markets are California and Texas.

The company serves clients including Fortune 100 companies government agencies multi-employer funds and affiliates gained through the recently acquired insurer Health Net.

Financial Performance

Centene's revenue and net income have been rising steadily for the past five years. In 2016 revenue rose 78% to $40.6 billion. Premiums jumped 83% that year primarily due to that year's acquisition of Health Net as well as organic growth which saw new programs introduced in several states.

Thanks to the higher revenue (and despite increased operating expenses across the board) net income rose 58% to $562 million in 2016. After falling 46% in 2015 cash flow from operations more than doubled to $1.9 billion. This was due to positive adjustments to net cash provided by operating activities including depreciation and amortization and deferred income taxes.

Strategy

Centene's primary growth strategies are to enter new markets and expand in existing markets via acquisitions and by gaining new contracts with state Medicaid agencies. The company is benefiting from the growing number of mandated managed care plans in states that are looking to control Medicaid spending.

In addition to geographic expansion the company looks to grow its membership by adding new services in its existing state markets such as small business health plans and low-income individual plans. It also evaluates opportunities to grow in new fields such as health-related information technology and non-Medicaid health plans. It has a joint venture with MHM Services named Centurion which operates in the correctional facility managed care market. In 2016 it partnered with researchers at Washington University in St. Louis and Duke University to launch the Envolve Center for Health Behavior Change; the center is designed to study effective behavioral health care methods.

Centene also occasionally divests or exits operations in smaller service areas to focus on its core growth regions.

Mergers and Acquisitions

Centene agreed to buy not-for-profit insurer Fidelis Care for $3.75 billion in mid-2017. Fidelis offers Medicaid CHIP and other affordable coverage to some 1.6 million individuals. Through that deal the company will enter the New York market.

In a similar move Centene acquired insurer Health Net in a $6.3 billion deal in 2016. That acquisition also broadened its presence in the Medicare Advantage and Medicaid programs. After that deal Centene became the nation's largest Medicaid Managed Care organization.

In 2015 the company purchased Oregon-based Agate Resources. It also bought the rest of LiveHealthier (health management solutions) it didn't already own.

EXECUTIVES

Senior Vice President, Donald G Imholz
Regional VP Markets, Kevin J. Counihan
President and COO, Cynthia J. (Cindy) Brinkley, age 57, $650,000 total compensation
Chairman and CEO, Michael F. Neidorff, age 74, $1,500,000 total compensation
EVP Mergers & Acquisitions and Chief Strategy Officer, Jesse N. Hunter, age 41, $650,000 total compensation
EVP Markets, Christopher D. Bowers, age 61
EVP General Counsel and Secretary, Keith H. Williamson, age 64, $600,000 total compensation
EVP CFO and Treasurer, Jeffrey A Schwaneke, age 42, $632,671 total compensation
EVP and CIO, Mark J. Brooks, age 47
Senior Vice President and Chief Medical Officer, Mary V Mason
Svp Operations, Patricia Darnley
Vice President of Finance, Trip Peeples
Senior Vice President Patient Services, Susan Ekvall
Vice President and Director, Linda Taylor
Vice President And Director, Marian Williams
Senior Vice President Claims and System Integrity, Irene Armendariz
Vice President And Director, Tiffany Smith
Vice President Of Medical Affairs, David Harmon
Vice President And Director, Deborah Robbins

Vice President, Nathan Moore
Vice President And Director, Michelle Whitener
Vice President And Director, Sharon Casey
Executive Vice President, Brandy Burkhalter
Executive Vice President Of Finance, Theresa Erickson
Vice President and Director, Thomas Welch
Vice President For Medicare and Duals, Gale Arden
Medical Director, David Gilchrist
Senior Vice President of Medical Management, Angie Kurosaka
Executive Vice President Vice President sales, Bob Tomek
Vice President And Director, Janie Fauconneau
Vice President Member and Provider Solutions, Jennifer Weigand
Senior Vice President Business Development, Debra Cooper
Vice President And Director, Jennifer Clark
Senior Vice President, Michael McKinney
Regional Vice President, Alida Dodd
Vice President Clinical Programs, Amy Poole-Yaeger
Vice President of Medical Management, Wendy Faust
Senior Vice President of Clinical Operations, Patricia Murray
Vice President of Human Resources, Stephanie Hall
Vice President Of Payment Innovation, Ananth Lalithakumar
Vice President And Director, Karen Dockerty
Vice President of Compliance and Regulatory Affairs, Cheyenne Ross
Vice President and Director, Carolyn Thomas
Vice President And Director, Helen Bryson
Senior Vice President And Chief Communications Officer, Marcela Manjarrez-Williams
Vice President Pharmacy Operations, Justin Weiss
Vice President Of Medicare Operations and Business Strategy, Ela Alarcon-Cabrera
Vice President Facility Management And Construction, Andrea Cruce
Vice President of Enrollment Operations, Michael Boone
Vice President of Medical Affairs, Ronald Charles
Executive Vice President Specialty Company Business Unit, Jason M Harrold
Area Vice President, Kelly Stilts
Senior Vice President General Counsel And Secretary, Yolanda Marsh
Vice President Health Plan Operations, Kevin OToole
Executive Vice President, Mark Eggert
Director of Pharmacy, James Frank Reynolds
Vice President Customer Service, Rodney Long
Vice President Marketing, John Howell
Director of Pharmacy Operations, Martha Exton
Vice President of Medical Management New Business, Judy Bauer
Vice President of Finance, Nitin Jain
Vice President Medical Management Clinical Systems, Alice Stewart
Senior Vice President and Chief Security Risk Officer, Louis Desorbo
Vice President Business Intelligence Strategy Cenpatico Behavioral Health, Ryan Gregory
National Sales Manager, Greg Siegel
Senior Vice President, Lisa Brubaker
SENIOR VICE PRESIDENT, William J Hurwick
SENIOR VICE PRESIDENT, Cassidy Turley
ASSOCIATE VICE PRESIDENT, Daniel Wessel
Senior Vice President and Chief Communications Officer, Marcela Manjarrez Hawn
Auditors: KPMG LLP

LOCATIONS

HQ: Centene Corp
7700 Forsyth Boulevard, St. Louis, MO 63105
Phone: 314 725-4477   **Fax:** 314 725-5180
Web: www.centene.com

PRODUCTS/OPERATIONS

2016 Sales

	$ mil.	% of total
Managed Care	37,722	81
Specialty Services	9,037	19
Eliminations	(6152)	-
Total	**40,607**	**100**

2016 Sales

	$ mil.	% of total
Premium	35,399	87
Service	2,180	5
Premium tax and health insurer fee	3,028	8
Total	**40,607**	**100**

COMPETITORS

AMERIGROUP
Aetna
Anthem
Blue Cross and Blue Shield of South Carolina
Blue Cross and Blue Shield of Texas
CIGNA
Coventry Health Care
Humana
Kaiser Foundation Health Plan
Molina Healthcare
Schaller Anderson Inc
Scott & White Health Plan
Security Health Plan of Wisconsin
UCare Minnesota
UnitedHealth Group
WellCare Health Plans

HISTORICAL FINANCIALS

Company Type: Public

Income Statement

FYE: December 31

	REVENUE ($ mil.)	NET INCOME ($ mil.)	NET PROFIT MARGIN	EMPLOYEES
12/16	40,607	562	1.4%	30,500
12/15	22,760	355	1.6%	18,200
12/14	16,560	271	1.6%	13,400
12/13	10,863	165	1.5%	8,800
12/12	8,667	1	0.0%	6,800
Annual Growth	**47.1%**	**317.0%**	**—**	**45.5%**

2016 Year-End Financials

Debt ratio: 23.05%	No. of shares (mil.): 171
Return on equity: 13.92%	Dividends
Cash ($ mil.): 3,930	Yield: —
Current ratio: 0.97	Payout: —
Long-term debt ($ mil.): 4,651	Market value ($ mil.): 9,715

	STOCK PRICE ($) FY Close	P/E High/Low	PER SHARE ($) Earnings	Dividends	Book Value
12/16	56.51	21 14	3.43	0.00	34.29
12/15	65.81	40 18	2.88	0.00	17.92
12/14	103.85	46 24	2.25	0.00	14.73
12/13	58.95	44 27	1.47	0.00	11.15
12/12	41.00	2540 1342	0.02	0.00	9.11
Annual Growth	**8.4%**	**—**	**—288.9%**	**—**	**39.3%**

CenterPoint Energy, Inc

CenterPoint Energy makes a point of selling energy through power and gas distribution utilities and natural gas pipeline gathering and marketing operations. CenterPoint Energy's regulated utilities distribute natural gas to 3.4 million customers in six US states and electricity to more than 2.4 million customers on the Texas Gulf Coast. The company's main stomping ground is Texas where it has regulated power distribution operations through subsidiary CenterPoint Energy Houston Electric. CenterPoint Energy operates more than 56300 miles of power distribution lines 74000 miles of gas distribution mains It also provides natural gas field services.

Operations

CenterPoint Energy's business segments include Electric Transmission & Distribution Natural Gas Distribution Energy Services Midstream Investments and Other Operations.

Electric Transmission & Distribution accounts for around 40% of total sales and operates CenterPoint Houston a transmission and distribution electric utility in Texas.

The Natural Gas Distribution segment brings in more than 30% of sales and sells transports and distributes natural gas to residential commercial industrial and transport customers. It serves 3.4 million customers in six states.

Energy Services more than 25% of sales represents CenterPoint Energy's non-rate regulated gas sales and services operations.

Midstream Investments consists of CenterPoint Energy's 55.4% limited partner interest in Enable Midstream Partners a partnership it jointly controls with OGE Energy Corp which owns operates and develops natural gas and crude oil infrastructure assets.

Other Operations consist of other corporate operations which support all of CenterPoint Energy's businesses.

Geographic Reach

CenterPoint's natural gas distribution subsidiaries serve customers in Arkansas Louisiana Minnesota Mississippi Oklahoma and Texas. The company's electric distribution assets are all in Texas.

Sales and Marketing

CenterPoint Energy distributes electricity via substations and delivers electricity to end users through distribution feeders and sells natural gas directly to commercial and industrial customers and metered sales.

The company's customers including biofuel companies government entities manufacturers small businesses refineries and utilities. NRG Energy accounts for around 35% of CenterPoint Energy's revenues; Energy Future Holdings represents 10% of sales.

About 35% of CenterPoint Energy's natural gas distribution total throughput was to residential customers; and the rest to commercial and industrial and transportation customers.

Financial Performance

After lower natural gas prices put a heavy dent in CenterPoint's revenue in 2015 revenue recovered somewhat in 2016. Sales increased 2% to $7.5 billion as the Continuum acquisition contributed some $466 million in revenue to the electric transmission and distribution and energy services business. Natural gas distribution sales fell.

Net income increased by $1.1 billion to $432 million. The significant increase was mostly down to $1.8 billion in impairment charges on its Enable investment in 2015. Other factors included a $419 million gain on marketable securities offset by a

$692 increase in income taxes and a $487 million increase in loss on indexed debt securities.

Cash from operations increased 3% to $1.9 billion due to higher net income partially offset by changes in working capital.

Strategy

CenterPoint Energy's strategy is focused on enhancing and expanding its existing core electricity and gas operations while acquiring complementary and synergistic businesses and teaming up with other major entities to enhance its operations.It acquired the retail energy businesses of Continuum and Atmos in 2016-17 to position it to access new markets and customer segments. Additionally the Continuum acquisition included its wholesale gas business.

Mergers and Acquisitions

In 2017 CenterPoint acquired Atmos Energy's retail energy business Atmos Energy Marketing. The acquisition will bring increased scale geographic reach expanded capabilities. And in 2016 it acquired Continuum's retail energy services and its wholesale gas business. The two acquisitions grew CenterPoint's customer base to over 100000 two thirds being retail customers and one third commercial and industrial.

HISTORY

CenterPoint Energy's earliest predecessor Houston Electric Lighting and Power was formed in 1882 by a group including Emanuel Raphael cashier at Houston Savings Bank and Mayor William Baker. In 1901 General Electric's financial arm United Electric Securities Company took control of the utility which became Houston Lighting & Power (HL&P). United Electric sold HL&P five years later; by 1922 HL&P ended up in the arms of National Power & Light Company (NP&L) a subsidiary of Electric Bond & Share (a public utility holding company that had been spun off by General Electric).

In 1942 NP&L was forced to sell HL&P in order to comply with the 1935 Public Utility Holding Company Act. As the oil industry boomed in Houston after WWII so did HL&P.

HL&P became the managing partner in a venture to build a nuclear plant on the Texas Gulf Coast in 1973. Construction on the South Texas Project with partners Central Power and Light and the cities of Austin and San Antonio began in 1975. In 1976 Houston Industries (HI) was formed as the holding company for HL&P.

By 1980 the nuke was four years behind schedule and over budget. HL&P and its partners sued construction firm Brown & Root in 1982 and received a $700 million settlement in 1985. (The City of Austin also sued HL&P for damages but lost.) The nuke was finally brought online in 1988 with the final cost estimated at $5.8 billion.

Meanwhile HI diversified into cable TV in 1986 by creating Enrcom (later Paragon Communications) through a venture with Time Inc. Two years later it bought the US cable interests of Canada's Rogers Communications. HI left the cable business in 1995 selling out to Time Warner.

Developing Latin fever HI joined a consortium that bought 51% of Argentinean electric company EDELAP in 1992. (However in 1998 HI sold its stake to AES.) On a roll HI acquired 90% of Argentina's electric utility EDESE (1995); joined a consortium that won a controlling stake in Light a Brazilian electric utility (1996); bought a stake in Colombian electric utility EPSA (1997); and bought interests in three electric utilities in El Salvador (1998). It also won a permit to develop and operate a natural gas system in Mexico (1998).

Back in the US HI acquired gas dealer NorAm for $2.5 billion in 1997. The next year it bought five generating plants in California from

Edison International and laid plans to build merchant plants in Arizona (near Phoenix) Illinois Nevada (near Las Vegas in partnership with Sempra Energy) and Rhode Island. Overseas HI finished a power plant in India in 1998. It also bought a 65% interest in Colombian electric utilities Electricaribe and Electrocosta; EPSA bought about 55% of CET in Colombia and Light bought about 75% of Metropolitana (S o Paulo Brazil).

In 1999 HI became Reliant Energy and HL&P became Reliant Energy HL&P. That year the company bought a 52% stake in Dutch power generation firm UNA; it bought the remaining 48% the next year. Also in 2000 Reliant Energy paid Sithe Energies (now a part of Dynegy) $2.1 billion for 21 power plants in the mid-Atlantic states. It sold its operations in Brazil Colombia and El Salvador that year and transferred all of its nonregulated operations to subsidiary Reliant Resources. Reliant Energy also announced plans to spin off Reliant Resources that year.

Reliant Energy netted about $1.7 billion in 2001 from the sale to the public of nearly 20% of Reliant Resources. Later that year Reliant Resources announced that it would acquire US independent power producer Orion Power Holdings in a $4.7 billion deal; the deal was completed in 2002. Deregulation took effect in Texas that year and Reliant Energy transferred its retail power supply business to Reliant Resources.

As the finances of wholesale energy companies came under scrutiny in 2002 the SEC issued a formal investigation into "round-trip" energy trades completed by Reliant Resources. These activities artificially inflated the company's trading volumes and led it to restate its 1999 2000 and 2001 financial results; it also reduced its energy marketing and trading workforce by about 35%.

Reliant Energy announced plans in 2001 to form a new holding company (CenterPoint Energy) for itself and Reliant Resources; it completed the name change in 2002.

CenterPoint Energy changed its name in 2002 in preparation for the spin-off of its 83% stake in Reliant Resources (now GenOn Energy) a global independent power producer and energy marketer; the spinoff was completed later that year. (Reliant Resources changed its name to Reliant Energy in 2004.) CenterPoint Energy transferred its nonregulated Texas retail power supply business to Reliant Resources before spinning off the unit.

EXECUTIVES

EVP and President Electric Division, Tracy B. Bridge, age 58, $481,250 total compensation
President CEO and Director, Scott M. Prochazka, age 50, $996,525 total compensation
SVP Electric Utility Business, Kenneth M. Mercado
SVP Gas Operations, Richard A. (Rick) Zapalac
EVP and CFO, William D. (Bill) Rogers, age 56, $485,000 total compensation
SVP Natural Gas Distribution, Scott E. Doyle
SVP Energy Services, Joseph J. (Joe) Vortherms
Vice President Marketing, Carol Burchfield
Division Vice President of Reginal, David Baker
Board Member, Walter Ferguson
Chairman, Milton Carroll, age 66
Auditors: Deloitte & Touche LLP

LOCATIONS

HQ: CenterPoint Energy, Inc
1111 Louisiana, Houston, TX 77002
Phone: 713 207-1111
Web: www.centerpointenergy.com

PRODUCTS/OPERATIONS

2016 Sales

	$ mil.	% of total
Retail gas	3,329	44
Electric delivery	3,060	41
Wholesale gas	977	13
Energy products & services	139	2
Gas transportation and processing	23	-
Total	**7,528**	**100**

2016 Sales

	$ mil.	% of total
Electric Transmission & Distribution	3,060	41
Natural Gas Distribution	2,380	32
Energy Services	2,073	27
Midstream Investments	0	0
Other	15	0
Total	**7,528**	**100**

COMPETITORS

AEP	Exelon
AEP Texas Central	Koch Industries Inc.
AEP Texas North	Mississippi Power
Ameren	OGE Energy
Avista	ONEOK
CMS Energy	Progress Energy
Cleco	Southern Company
Constellation Energy Group	Southwestern Electric Power
Dominion Energy	Southwestern Energy
Duke Energy	Williams Companies
Energy Future	Xcel Energy
Entergy	

HISTORICAL FINANCIALS

Company Type: Public

Income Statement

FYE: December 31

	REVENUE ($ mil.)	NET INCOME ($ mil.)	NET PROFIT MARGIN	EMPLOYEES
12/16	7,528	432	5.7%	7,727
12/15	7,386	(692)	—	7,505
12/14	9,226	611	6.6%	8,540
12/13	8,106	311	3.8%	8,591
12/12	7,452	417	5.6%	8,720
Annual Growth	0.3%	0.9%	—	(3.0%)

2016 Year-End Financials

Debt ratio: 39.36%
Return on equity: 12.45%
Cash ($ mil.): 341
Current ratio: 0.95
Long-term debt ($ mil.): 7,532

No. of shares (mil.): 430
Dividends
Yield: 0.0%
Payout: 103.0%
Market value ($ mil.): 10,612

	STOCK PRICE ($) FY Close	P/E High/Low	PER SHARE ($) Earnings	Dividends	Book Value
12/16	24.64	25 17	1.00	1.03	8.03
12/15	18.36	— —	(1.61)	0.99	8.05
12/14	23.43	18 15	1.42	0.95	10.58
12/13	23.18	34 26	0.72	0.83	10.09
12/12	19.25	22 19	0.97	0.81	10.05
Annual Growth	6.4%	— —	0.8%	6.2%	(5.4%)

CenterState Bank Corp

CenterState Banks is the holding company for CenterState Bank of Florida which serves the Sunshine State through about 60 branches. The bank offers standard deposit products such as checking and savings accounts money market accounts and CDs. Real estate loans primarily residential and commercial mortgages make up 85% of the company's loan portfolio while the rest is made up of business loans and consumer loans. The bank's correspondent division provides bond securities accounting and loans to small and mid-sized banks across the Southeast and Texas. It also sells mutual funds annuities and other investment products.

Operations

About 65% of CenterState Banks' total revenue came from loan interest in 2014 while another 10% came from interest on its investment securities. The rest of the bank's revenue came form correspondent banking capital markets revenue and related revenue (11%) deposit account service charges (5%) debit/ATM and merchant card fees (3%) wealth management fees (2%) and other miscellaneous income sources. The company had a staff of 785 employees by the end of 2014.

Geographic Reach

CenterState has nearly 60 branches across 20 counties in central southeast and northeast Florida. Its loan production offices are in Tampa Gainesville Crystal River and Ft. Meyers.

Sales and Marketing

CenterState offers consumer and commercial banking services to individuals businesses and industries across Florida.

Financial Performance

The company has struggled to consistently grow its revenues in recent years due to shrinking interest margins on loans amidst the low-interest environment. Its profits however have been rising thanks to declining loan loss provisions as its loan portfolio's credit quality has improved with higher property valuations in the strengthened economy.

CenterState had a breakout year in 2014 however with its revenue jumping 22% to $164.5 million thanks to higher interest income stemming from new loan business from its acquisitions of First Southern Bancorp and Gulfstream Bancshares during the year.

Higher revenue and stable costs in 2014 also drove the bank's net income higher by 6% to a record $12.96 million. CenterState's operating cash levels plummeted by 90% to $1.4 million after adjusting its earnings for non-cash items mostly related to the net proceeds from its trading securities sales.

Strategy

CenterState Banks continues to seek out additional acquisition opportunities to boost its loan and deposit business and expand into more markets across Florida. To this end the bank's 2014 acquisitions extended its reach into Broward Palm Beach and Martin counties for the first time while adding more than $1.3 billion in new deposits and over $600 million in new loan business to its books.

Struggling to grow its revenues the bank has also worked to become more efficient and profitable through selective branch closures. During 2014 the company closed seven smaller branches and a standalone drive-thru facility to free up resources for more profitable bank acquisitions.

Mergers and Acquisitions

CenterState is buying Platinum Bank Holding Company parent company of Platinum Bank for approximately $83.9 million. The acquisition will add seven banking branches in the Tampa-St. Petersburg-Clearwater and Lakeland-Winter Haven areas. It will also add some $584 million in assets.

In June 2014 CenterState purchased First Southern Bancorp which expanded its market reach into Broward County after adding a net of seven new branches. The deal also added some $600 million in new loan assets and $853 million in deposits.

In January 2014 the company expanded into Palm Beach and Martin counties after buying Gulfstream Bancshares and its four branches with $479 million in deposits.

EXECUTIVES

SVP and CFO, James J. Antal, age 66, $312,750 total compensation
Senior Vice President, Rick Alspaugh
President CEO and Director CenterState Banks Inc. and Centerstate Bank of Florida, John Corbett, age 48, $420,250 total compensation
Corporate Chief Risk Officer, Daniel E. Bockhorst, $217,500 total compensation
Treasurer, Stephen Young, $278,333 total compensation
Senior Vice President, Tammy Roncaglione
First Vice President Business Development, Chris Wright
Assistant Vice President Residential Loan Operations Manager, Becky Chiasson
Vice President Division Controller, John Rust
Senior Vice President, Brett Rawls
Vice President Retail Service Leader, Annette Fortunato-diaz
Vice President And Treasury Management Officer, Jarrod Hurd
Senior Vice President And Commercial Lending Officer, Bill Daniels
Senior Vice President Capital Markets, Jim Bigger
Assistant Vice President Merchant Services Divison, Deborah Joyce
Assistant Vice President Business Analyst Ii, Chante Carlson
Assistant Vice President Commercial Banker, Angel K Gonzalez
First Vice President, Stacey A Dunn
Senior Vice President and Chief Operations Officer, Stacy Byrd
Vice President Compliance, Don Stoltz
Senior Vice President Credit Administration, Matthew Utter
Vice President Commercial Lending, Randy Pennington
Retail Market Manager Senior Vice President, Kendra Salerno
Assistant Vice President, Mary Young
Assistant Vice President Office Manager, Antonella Mintz
Vice President, Tanya Isaman
Vice President BSA Manager, Julie Sbrocco
Vice President Retail Market Manager, Bretta Christakos
Assistant Vice President Human Resources Employee Relations Officer, Raquel Morales
Assistant Vice President Treasury Management Sales Officer, Amanda Watson
Assistant Vice President Project Manager, Lexie Williams
Vice President, Gail Copa
I Senior Vice President, James Garner
First Vice President, Richard Skopick
Vice President, Tanesha Samuels
I Vice President, Sandy Bryan
I Senior Vice President, Willie Carpenter
Vice President And Asset Liability Manager, William Fielding
Senior Vice President, Bette Brown
I Assistant Vice President, Grace Martin
Senior Vice President, Lisa Rabinsky
I Vice President, William Doxey
I Vice President Market Manager I, Adriana Cuomo
Senior Vice President And Fixed Income Sales, Patty Gorman
Assistant Vice President And Commercial Lending Assistant, Patti Wilcher
Senior Vice President Community President, Mark Stevens

Vice President Commercial And Agribusiness
  Banking, Ted Hicks
Assistant Vice President And Fixed Income Sales
  Assistant, Pam Todd
Vice President, Elfa Mora
First Vice President Prepaid Cards Division, Bruce
  Davidson
Vice President Commercial Lender, Mike Clanton
Assistant Vice President And Fed Funds Trader,
  Rebecca Henderson
Vice President And Commercial Relationship
  Manager III, Bill Mang
Chairman, Ernest S. (Ernie) Pinner, age 69
Auditors: Crowe Horwath LLP

LOCATIONS

HQ: CenterState Bank Corp
  1101 First Street South, Suite 202, Winter Haven, FL
  33880
Phone: 863 293-4710
Web: www.centerstatebanks.com

PRODUCTS/OPERATIONS

2011 Sales

	$ mil.	% of total
Interest		
Loans	65	36
Investment securities available for sale	15	9
Other	0	-
Noninterest		
Bargain purchase gain	57	31
Correspondent banking & bond sales	24	13
Service charges on deposit accounts	6	3
Net gain on sale of securities	3	2
Other	10	6
Total	**184**	**100**

COMPETITORS

BB&T	Regions Financial
BBX Capital	Seacoast Banking
Bank of America	SunTrust
Fifth Third	Wells Fargo
JPMorgan Chase	

HISTORICAL FINANCIALS

Company Type: Public

Income Statement

FYE: December 31

	ASSETS ($ mil.)	NET INCOME ($ mil.)	INCOME AS % OF ASSETS	EMPLOYEES
12/16	5,078	42	0.8%	952
12/15	4,022	39	1.0%	784
12/14	3,776	12	0.3%	785
12/13	2,415	12	0.5%	693
12/12	2,363	9	0.4%	689
Annual Growth	**21.1%**	**43.8%**	**—**	**8.4%**

2016 Year-End Financials

Debt ratio: 0.51%	No. of shares (mil.): 48
Return on equity: 8.10%	Dividends
Cash ($ mil.): 175	Yield: 0.0%
Current ratio: —	Payout: 18.1%
Long-term debt ($ mil.): —	Market value ($ mil.): 1,212

	STOCK PRICE ($) FY Close	P/E High/Low	PER SHARE ($) Earnings	Dividends	Book Value
12/16	25.17	29 15	0.88	0.16	11.47
12/15	15.65	19 13	0.85	0.07	10.79
12/14	11.91	37 31	0.31	0.04	9.98
12/13	10.15	26 18	0.41	0.04	9.08
12/12	8.53	27 20	0.33	0.04	9.09
Annual Growth	**31.1%**	**— —**	**27.8%**	**41.4%**	**6.0%**

Central Pacific Financial Corp

When in the Central Pacific do as the islanders do. This may include doing business with Central Pacific Financial the holding company for Central Pacific Bank which operates more than 35 branch locations and 110 ATMs across the Hawaiian Islands. Targeting individuals and local businesses the $5 billion bank provides such standard retail banking products as checking and savings accounts money market accounts and CDs. About 70% of the bank's loan portfolio is made up of commercial real estate loans residential mortgages and construction loans though it also provides business and consumer loans.

Operations

Central Pacific Financial operates through two core segments. The Banking Operations segment provides construction and real estate development loans commercial loans residential mortgage loans consumer loans trust services retail brokerage services and traditional banking products and services. The Treasury segment manages the company's investment securities portfolio and wholesale funding activities.

Boasting total assets of $5 billion Central Pacific Bank ranked as the fourth-largest bank by deposits in the state of Hawaii in 2014. The bank makes nearly 60% of its total revenue from interest and fees on loans and leases and nearly 20% from interest and dividends on its investment securities. It makes about 10% on service charges on deposit accounts and other charges and fees while the small remainder of its revenue comes from a mix of loan servicing fees gains on sales of residential loans and foreclosed assets income from fiduciary activities and income from bank-owned life insurance.

Central Pacific Financial's other wholly-owned subsidiaries include CPB Capital Trust II; CPB Statutory Trust III; CPB Capital Trust IV; and CPB Statutory Trust V. Central Pacific Bank holds 50% stakes in Pacific Access Mortgage Gentry HomeLoans and Island Pacific HomeLoans.

Geographic Reach

Honolulu-based Central Pacific boasts more than 35 branches and 110 ATMs across Hawaii. The island of Oahu holds 28 branches while the Maui Hawaii and Kauai islands host the remaining branches.

Sales and Marketing

Central Pacific Financial spent $2.34 million on advertising in 2014 compared to $2.67 million and $3.52 million in 2013 and 2012 respectively.

Financial Performance

Central Pacific Financial's revenue performance has been mixed in recent years. Its mortgage banking business has suffered from lower residential mortgage origination volumes while its loan business has been growing at a healthy clip thanks to higher loan balances from added assets.

Following two years of modest top-line growth driven by growing loan business Central Pacific's revenue dipped by 1% to $193.63 million in 2014 as it collected lower net gains on sales of foreclosed assets and lower net gains on sales of residential mortgage loans. The bank's interest income from loans continued to grow however as the bank added more than $403 million in new loan assets.

Central Pacific's net income declined by 76% to $40.45 million in 2014 mostly because in 2013 the bank received a $112.25 million income tax benefit as it reversed a significant portion of its valuation allowance for its doubtful accounts from

2009. Beyond this non-recurring event the bank managed to cut its salaries and employee benefit expenses by 22% saving about $8 million for the year.

The bank's operating cash also fell by 15% during the year to $71.43 million primarily due to lower cash earnings.

Strategy

Central Pacific reiterated in 2015 that its strategy is to continue growing its loan business particularly focusing on providing more commercial loans and mortgages as well as construction loans and leases to small and mid-sized companies business professionals and real estate developers. Though its residential mortgage and consumer loans made up just 25% of its loan portfolio that year the bank will also continue its focus on extended those loans to more local homebuyers and individuals.

The bank's key to drumming up its commercial loan business has traditionally come from its community-oriented commercial real estate team and banking officers which are able to develop deep relationships with local communities and industries that they serve.

EXECUTIVES

President and CEO, A. Catherine Ngo, age 57,
  $345,833 total compensation
Chairman, John C. Dean, age 70, $265,625 total
  compensation
SVP and Chief Marketing Officer Central Pacific
  Financial Corp. and Central Pacific Bank, Wayne
  H. Kirihara
Interim Vice Chairman and COO, Denis K. Isono,
  age 66, $244,792 total compensation
EVP and CIO Central Pacific Financial Corp. and
  Central Pacific Bank, Lee Y. Moriwaki, age 58,
  $205,625 total compensation
EVP CFO and Treasurer, David S. Morimoto, age 49,
  $201,208 total compensation
EVP Chief Legal Officer and Risk Management
  Division Manager Central Pacific Financial Corp.
  and Central Pacific Bank, K.C. (Glenn) Ching, age
  58
EVP Community Banking Division Manager
  Central Pacific Financial Corp. and Central
  Pacific Bank, David W. Hudson, age 58, $220,000
  total compensation
SVP and Commercial Real Estate Lending
  Division Manager Central Pacific Financial Corp.
  and Central Pacific Bank, Arnold D. Martines, age
  52
Vice President and Controller, Dayna Matsumoto
Vice President and Manager Information Security,
  Ken Newman
Assistant Vice President And Commercial Branch
  Manager, Jolene Kiyono
Vice President, Joseph Miller
Vice President and Senior Commercial Banking
  Officer, Patrick Matsumoto
Vice President and Commercial Banking Officer,
  Chong Pak
Assistant Vice President And Branch Manager,
  Sharlene Chae
Vice President And Senior Commercial Banking
  Officer, Ben Pulmano
Assistant Vice President And Senior Commercial
  Loan Specialist, Stephanie Belaski
Vice President And Commercial Branch Manager,
  Lance Takahashi
Senior Vice President, John Taira
Vice President And Private Banking Officer, Shaun
  Mitsui
Vice President, Peter Sheehan
Vice President And Commercial Real Estate
  Officer, Keith Wakamura
Vice President, Michael Waring

Vice President And Manager Call Center, Norman Nakasone
Vice President and Branch Manager, Miyuki Almario
Assistant Vice President and Senior Customer Service Manager, Sharon Sato
Vice President and Manager Information Security Department, Emanuel Edmondson
Vice President and Neighbor Island Region Manager, Russell Rodriguez
Auditors: KPMG LLP

LOCATIONS

HQ: Central Pacific Financial Corp
220 South King Street, Honolulu, HI 96813
Phone: 808 544-0500   **Fax:** 808 531-2875
Web: www.centralpacificbank.com

PRODUCTS/OPERATIONS

2014 Sales

	$ mil.	% of total
Interest income		
Loans and leases	112	58
Securities	37	19
Non-interest income		
Other service charges and fees	11	6
Service Charges on deposit accounts	8	4
Loan Servicing fees	5	3
Others	18	10
Total	**193**	**100**

COMPETITORS

American Savings Bank	Mitsubishi UFJ
Bank of Hawaii	Financial Group
First Hawaiian	Territorial Bancorp

HISTORICAL FINANCIALS

Company Type: Public

Income Statement

FYE: December 31

	ASSETS ($ mil.)	NET INCOME ($ mil.)	INCOME AS % OF ASSETS	EMPLOYEES
12/16	5,384	46	0.9%	837
12/15	5,131	45	0.9%	876
12/14	4,852	40	0.8%	841
12/13	4,741	172	3.6%	903
12/12	4,370	47	1.1%	948
Annual Growth	**5.4%**	**(0.2%)**	**—**	**(3.1%)**

2016 Year-End Financials

Debt ratio: 1.72%	No. of shares (mil.): 30
Return on equity: 9.38%	Dividends
Cash ($ mil.): 84	Yield: 0.0%
Current ratio: —	Payout: 40.0%
Long-term debt ($ mil.): —	Market value ($ mil.): 968

	STOCK PRICE ($) FY Close	P/E High/Low		PER SHARE ($) Earnings	Dividends	Book Value
12/16	31.42	21	12	1.50	0.60	16.39
12/15	22.02	18	13	1.40	0.82	15.77
12/14	21.50	20	16	1.07	0.36	16.12
12/13	20.08	5	4	4.07	0.16	15.68
12/12	15.59	14	11	1.13	0.00	12.06
Annual Growth	**19.1%**	**—**	**—**	**7.3%**	**—**	**8.0%**

Century Bancorp, Inc.

Century Bancorp is the holding company for Century Bank and Trust which serves Boston and surrounding parts of northeastern Massachusetts from more than 25 branches. Boasting some $3.6 billion in total assets the bank offers standard deposit products including checking savings and money market accounts; CDs; and IRAs. Nearly two-thirds of its loan portfolio is comprised of commercial and commercial real estate loans. while residential mortgages and home equity loans make up around 30%. The bank also writes construction and land development loans business loans and personal loans. It offers brokerage services through an agreement with third-party provider LPL Financial.

Operations
Century Bank also provides cash management short-term financing and transaction processing services to municipalities in Massachusetts and Rhode Island. It offers automated lockbox collection services to its municipal customers as well as commercial clients. The bank also continues to open new branches in its traditional market area in metropolitan Boston.

The bank gets more than 80% of its revenue in the form of interest income (mostly from loans). It generated 32% of its total revenue from taxable loans in 2014 while another 18% came from non-taxable loans and 35% came from interest income on the bank's investment securities. On the non-interest side the bank made 8% of its overall revenue from service charges on deposit accounts 3% from lockbox fees and a negligible amount on brokerage commissions and gains on sales of securities or mortgage loans.

Geographic Reach
The bank operates more than 25 branches in 20 cities and towns across Massachusetts ranging from Braintree in the South to Andover in the northern part of the state.

Sales and Marketing
Most of Century Bank's business comes from small and medium-sized businesses needing commercial loans though the bank also serves retail customers as well as local governments and other institutions throughout Massachusetts.

The bank spent $1.79 million on advertising in 2014 compared to $1.75 million and $1.85 million in 2013 and 2012 respectively.

Financial Performance
Century Bancorp's revenues and profits have been steadily rising over the past few years thanks to increased loan business and declining loan loss provisions as its loan portfolio's credit quality has been improving in the strengthening economy.

The bank's revenue rose by more than 2% to a record $100.64 million in 2014 mostly as it collected more interest income from long-term securities and non-taxable loans during the year. The bank's earning securities assets grew by 8.5% during the year while the size of its loan business swelled by double-digits with increased tax-exempt lending and residential second mortgage lending; all of which boosted interest income during the year.

Higher revenue lower interest expenses on deposits and a continued dip in loan loss provisions in 2014 pushed Century's net income higher by 9% to a record $21.86 million. The bank's operating cash also grew by 7% to $22.39 million thanks to higher cash earnings.

Strategy
Century Bancorp has been growing organically through new branch openings and digital bank product launches in recent years. In 2014 for ex-

ample the bank opened its new branch in Woburn Massachusetts and launched its all-new Century Bank Mobile App which boosted customer convenience and allowed the bank to better compete with larger banks with more expansive branch networks.

Showcasing its strong financial capitalization the bank received an "A" rating from the Standard and Poor's credit ratings agency in 2015 making Century Bank the only regional bank in the state to receive such a rating.

EXECUTIVES

EVP Century Bank and Trust Company, Paul A. Evangelista, age 53, $337,614 total compensation
EVP Century Bank and Trust Company, David B. Woonton, age 61, $337,614 total compensation
President CEO and Director, Barry R. Sloane, age 62, $569,207 total compensation
CFO and Treasurer, William P. Hornby, age 50, $294,708 total compensation
EVP Century Bank and Trust Company, Linda Sloane Kay, age 55, $294,708 total compensation
EVP Century Bank and Trust, Brian J. Feeney, age 56, $294,708 total compensation
Assistant Vice President Electronic Services, Toni Chardo
Vice President, Jim Smith
VICE PRESIDENT, Anna Gorska
Chairman, Marshall M. Sloane, age 90
Auditors: KPMG LLP

LOCATIONS

HQ: Century Bancorp, Inc.
400 Mystic Avenue, Medford, MA 02155
Phone: 781 391-4000
Web: www.centurybank.com

PRODUCTS/OPERATIONS

2014 Sales

	$ mil.	% of total
Interest		
Loans	50	50
Securities	2	3
Other	32	32
Noninterest		
Service charges on deposit accounts	8	8
Lockbox fees	3	3
Gains on sales of Mortgage loans	2	3
Other	1	1
Total	**100**	**100**

COMPETITORS

Boston Private	Eastern Bank
Brookline Bancorp	Middlesex Savings
Cambridge Financial	Peoples Federal
Capital Crossing	Bancshares Inc.
Central Bancorp	Sovereign Bank
Citizens Financial Group	

HISTORICAL FINANCIALS

Company Type: Public

Income Statement

FYE: December 31

	ASSETS ($ mil.)	NET INCOME ($ mil.)	INCOME AS % OF ASSETS	EMPLOYEES
12/16	4,462	24	0.5%	438
12/15	3,947	23	0.6%	438
12/14	3,624	21	0.6%	440
12/13	3,431	20	0.6%	428
12/12	3,086	19	0.6%	418
Annual Growth	**9.7%**	**6.5%**	**—**	**1.2%**

2016 Year-End Financials

Debt ratio: 7.37%
No. of shares (mil.): 5
Return on equity: 10.76%
Dividends
Cash ($ mil.): 236
Yield: 0.0%
Current ratio: —
Payout: 10.8%
Long-term debt ($ mil.): —
Market value ($ mil.): 334

	STOCK PRICE ($) FY Close	P/E High/Low		PER SHARE ($) Earnings	Dividends	Book Value
12/16	60.00	12	7	4.41	0.48	43.11
12/15	43.46	9	8	4.13	0.48	38.53
12/14	40.06	8	7	3.93	0.48	34.57
12/13	33.25	9	7	3.61	0.48	31.76
12/12	32.95	8	6	3.43	0.48	32.40
Annual Growth	16.2%	—	—	6.5%	(0.0%)	7.4%

CenturyLink Inc

CenturyLink provides cyber links throughout the country on one of the longest fiber networks in the US. Historically a regional wireline local and long-distance telephone provider it's connecting with the times by transforming into a broadband and network services provider for business residential and government clients. It spends around $3 billion a year on capital costs to further develop its network. The company is the one of the largest US wireline telecom companies by total access lines (it has about 11 million of them) and is the incumbent local carrier in nearly 40 states though three-quarters of its lines are in just a dozen. In 2017 CenturyLink and Level 3 Communications merged in a $34 billion deal.

Operations

CenturyLink operates in two main segments with the Business segment accounting for 60% of sales. It provides private line broadband Ethernet Multiprotocol Label Switching (MPLS) Voice over Internet Protocol (VoIP) network management services colocation and managed hosting and cloud hosting services for enterprise wholesale and governmental customers including other communication providers.

The Consumer segment about a third of sales offers broadband wireless and video services including Prism TV service and an over-the-top streaming service. It also offers local and long-distance phone service as well as satellite TV through DirecTV and wireless service through Verizon.

The company?s ?other? segment which includes federal payments for serving rural areas accounts for the rest of revenue.

CenturyLink operates a 265000-route-mile US fiber network in the US and a 360000-route-mile international transport network.

Geographic Reach

CenturyLink operates about 75% of its total access lines in portions of Arizona Colorado Florida Iowa Minnesota Missouri New Mexico Nevada North Carolina Oregon Utah and Washington (the company has paid a reported $75 million to put its name on the Seattle Seahawks stadium on the city's waterfront for 15 years).

It also provides local service in parts of Alabama Arkansas California Georgia Idaho Illinois Indiana Kansas Louisiana Ohio Michigan Mississippi Montana Nebraska New Jersey North Dakota Oklahoma Pennsylvania South Carolina South Dakota Tennessee Texas Virginia Wisconsin and Wyoming.

Financial Performance

CenturyLink?s revenue dropped about 2% in 2016 to $17.5 billion from 2015 continuing a string of incremental declines over the past five years. Business segment sales fell 3% in 2016 from 2015 mainly on declines in legacy services revenues from fewer in local service access lines and lower volumes of long-distance and access services. The continued erosion of legacy services (traditional phone service) also drove the consumer segment?s revenue 2% lower in 2016 from 2015. Revenue from strategic services rose in the business and consumer segments from increased MPLS Ethernet and VoIP services in business and rate increases and pricing initiatives for broadband and Prism TV in consumer.

The company reported net income of $626 million in 2016 a 29% drop from 2015. Although the company had lower expenses for the most part in 2016 they didn?t outweigh the drop in revenue.

Cash flow from operations slipped to $4.6 billion in 2016 from $5.1 billion in 2015 on lower net income.

Strategy

The network is at the heart of CenturyLink?s business and its strategy. Already big with 265000-route miles of fiber in the US the network is poised to get even bigger with CenturyLink?s pending acquisition of Level 3 and its 200000 route miles of fiber. The company delivers video streaming applications and services related to the Internet of Things (IoT) and emerging technologies like virtual and augmented reality and still-to-come 5G wireless technology over the network.

Besides extending its network the Level 3 deal would add to the revenue CenturyLink gets from business customers. CenturyLink?s business revenue which is more stable and carries higher margins would rise to 75% of sales from 60%. Recently introduced products and services geared to businesses include cloud data analytics and security offerings.

The consumer remains an integral part of CenturyLink?s plans. The company is working to improve network speeds and the customer experience. It has invested in broadband to supply speeds of 100 Mbps to 1 Gbps to more service areas. The company also has simplified its pricing plans and offers an over-the-top (OTT) video service for cord-cutters.

On the operations side CenturyLink implemented cost-containment moves in 2016 that included reducing employee-related expenses up to 8%.

CenturyLink sold its data centers and colocation business in 2017 for about $1.8 billion to a consortium of investors who formed Cyxtera Technologies. CenturyLink maintained an ownership stake in the new business and can sell services to its customers.

Mergers and Acquisitions

The $34 billion-dollar merger of CenturyLink and Level 3 Communications which closed in November 2017 created one of the largest telecommunications service providers in the US. The combined company's network connects more than 350 metro areas in the US and it has a presence in more than 60 countries. While each company has a nationwide network they say their combination brings together complementary assets and not result in less competition. With Level 3 carrying some $10 billion in net operating losses the combined company's tax bill should be lower freeing up cash flow for developing more infrastructure.

CenturyLink expanded its capabilities in IT services with the acquisition of SEAL Consulting a provider of SAP tools for enterprise business and technology needs.

In 2016 CenturyLink added a security element to its networking business with the acquisition in 2016 of netAura. The company specializes in engineering developing and consulting on managed security technologies.

EXECUTIVES

EVP Controller and Assistant Secretary, David D. Cole, age 59, $482,687 total compensation

President and CEO, Glen F. Post, age 64, $1,250,000 total compensation

Senior Vice President Business Service Delivery And Operations, Todd Schafer

President Small and Mid-Size Business (SMB) and GES/SLED, Vernon L. Irvin, age 55

EVP and CFO, Sunit S. Patel, age 55

EVP Chief Administrative Officer General Counsel and Secretary, Stacey W. Goff, age 51, $540,758 total compensation

EVP and CTO, Aamir Hussain, $496,049 total compensation

President Consumer Markets, Maxine L. Moreau, age 55

EVP Human Resources, Scott A. Trezise, age 48

President Global Accounts Management and International, Laurinda Y. Pang, age 47

SVP Cyber Engineering and Technology Services, William E. (Bill) Bradley

President Advanced Solutions Group and Chief Enterprise Relationship Officer, Gary Gauba

President and COO, Jeffrey K. (Jeff) Storey

President Wholesale Indirect Channels and Alliances, Lisa Miller

President Strategic Enterprise Federal Government and GES/SLED, Ed Morche

Vice President External Relations, Jeff Glover

Vice President Of Sales, Harman Steve

Vice President Financial Planning and Analysis, Wes Gibson

Secretary To The Senior Vice President Operations, Mitzi Reed

Vice President and General Counsel, Laurie Korneffel

Vice President, Bruce Kipperman

Vice President And Assistant Controller, Lyle Hippen

Regional Vice President Project Management, Monte Johnson

Vice President of Engineering and Construction Midwest, Trent Clausen

National Account Manager, Frank Palazzo

Area Vice President Strategic Initiatives, Dana Albright

Vice President of External Relations Middle Atlantic Region, William Hanchey

Vice President Of Information Technology Security, Tim Kelleher

Vice President Of Corporate Development And Strategy, Kenneth Dunn

Area Vice President Global Data Center Sales, David Schiffman

Vice President Compensation and Analytics, Jill Turner

Senior Vice President, Clay Bailey

Vice President and Treasurer, Glynn Williams

Vice President of CLEC, Jeff Mitchell

Area Vice president Post sales Engineering and Operations, Beth Mitchell

Vice President Global Sales and Marketing, Avinash Gupta

Area Vice President, Jackie Slate

Vice President Federal Sales and Marketing, Lisa Bruch

Area Vice President, Leann Coe

Vice President Operational Transformation, Bob Reedy

Senior Vice President and General Management, Erich Sanchack

Vice President of Network, Matt Rotter

Vice President and Country Manager, Ash Mathur

Vice President Operations Integration Fed Solutions, Jason Seibel

Vice President Investor Relations Comm and Brand, Tony Davis
Vice President Marketing, Patrick Glavin
Vice President Channel Alliances, John Delozier
Vice President West Region, Marty Leavengood
Vice President Project Management, Bill Bickham
Vice President Operations, Karen Currington
Vice President Customer Care, Jeff Johnstone
Vice President Regional Reg and Legislative Affairs, Jeff Lindsey
Segment Vice President, Lynn Smullen-Volz
Vice President Federal Contracts, Martha Palus
Vice President Cloud Products, Partha Teerdhala
Regional Vice President Advanced Services, Dan King
Region Vice President, Gregory Trenski
Vice President Real Estate and Fleet, LaRae Dodson
Area Vice President, Chris Rommeney
NW Region Vice President, Mark Reynolds
Vice President Decision Science, Mic Farris
Vice President Process Excellence, Bruce Fullerton
Vice President Public Markets, Shane Matson
Vice President Global Infrastructure Operations, Todd Miller
Vice President, Vish Vishwanathan
Vice President Global Assistant Special Delivery, Jinesh Jain
Vice President Global Business Process Innovation, Beth Hannan
Chairman, Harvey P. Perry, age 72
Vice Chairman, W. Bruce Hanks, age 62
Treasurer, Carol Ott
Secretary, Melissa Brocato
Board Member, Andy Olson
Auditors: KPMG LLP

LOCATIONS

HQ: CenturyLink Inc
100 CenturyLink Drive, Monroe, LA 71203
Phone: 318 388-9000   **Fax:** 318 789-8656
Web: www.centurylink.com

PRODUCTS/OPERATIONS

2016 Sales by Category

	$ mil.	% of total
Strategic services	8,050	46
Legacy services	7,672	44
Data integration	533	3
Other	1,215	7
Total	**17,470**	**100**

2016 Sales

	% of total
Business segment	59
Consumer segment	34
Other	7
Total	**100**

Selected Products & Services

Local and long-distance voice
High-speed Internet
MPLS
Private line (including special access)
Data integration
Ethernet
Colocation
Managed hosting (including cloud hosting)
Network
Public access
Video
Wireless
Other ancillary services

COMPETITORS

AT&T	Frontier
Cavalier Telephone	Communications
Comcast	Level 3
Cox Communications	Nsight
DISH Network	Sprint Communications

Equinix	Telephone & Data
FairPoint	Systems
Communications Inc.	Time Warner Cable
Farmers	Verizon
Telecommunications	XO Holdings

HISTORICAL FINANCIALS

Company Type: Public

Income Statement
FYE: December 31

	REVENUE ($ mil.)	NET INCOME ($ mil.)	NET PROFIT MARGIN	EMPLOYEES
12/16	17,470	626	3.6%	40,000
12/15	17,900	878	4.9%	43,000
12/14	18,031	772	4.3%	45,000
12/13	18,095	(239)	—	47,000
12/12	18,376	777	4.2%	47,000
Annual Growth	**(1.3%)**	**(5.3%)**	**—**	**(4.0%)**

2016 Year-End Financials

Debt ratio: 41.87%	No. of shares (mil.): 546
Return on equity: 4.55%	Dividends
Cash ($ mil.): 222	Yield: 0.0%
Current ratio: 0.97	Payout: 186.2%
Long-term debt ($ mil.): 18,185	Market value ($ mil.): 12,997

	STOCK PRICE ($) FY Close	P/E High/Low		PER SHARE ($) Earnings	Dividends	Book Value
12/16	23.78	28	19	1.16	2.16	24.52
12/15	25.16	26	15	1.58	2.16	25.86
12/14	39.58	31	21	1.36	2.16	26.42
12/13	31.85	—	—	(0.40)	2.16	29.45
12/12	39.12	34	29	1.25	2.90	30.83
Annual Growth	**(11.7%)**	**—**	**—**	**(1.9%)**	**(7.1%)**	**(5.6%)**

Cerner Corp.

Cerner Corp. provides health care organizations with health care IT (HCIT). The company develops and sells software systems designed to help improve processes and eliminate errors and waste for organizations ranging from single-doctor practices to the pharmaceutical and medical device industries. Its software combines clinical financial and administrative information management applications including tools for managing electronic health records (EHRs). Complementary services include support and maintenance implementation and training remote hosting data analytics and transaction processing. The company's products are licensed by some 25000 facilities around the globe although the US is by far its largest market.

Operations

About 50% of Cerner Corp.?s revenue comes from services which includes professional and managed services with system sales accounting for about 25% of revenue and support and maintenance bringing in about 20% of revenue.

The company offers its technologies on two main software platforms. The Cerner Millennium architecture includes integrated clinical financial and management information systems. It organizes and delivers information for physicians nurses laboratory technicians pharmacists front- and back-office professionals and consumers.

The HealtheIntent cloud-based platform is designed to grow with an institution?s patient population while facilitating care for patient and provider. The HealtheIntent platform offers applications that can run on any EHR system (including

those that aren?t Cerner?s) for gathering and processing data across the continuum of care.

Cerner?s strong services segment is anchored by its CernerWorks managed services business which is designed to help customer spend more effectively. Other service products are Cerner IT-Works which helps customers manage IT functions and Cerner RevWorks which helps with customer revenue cycle functions.

Geographic Reach

Cerner has operations in about two dozen countries in Asia Australia Europe and North and South America. The company?s sales are split about 90% to customers in the US and about 10% to international customers.

Sales and Marketing

Although hospitals and health systems account for most of sales Cerner's clients include physician groups and networks blood banks home health agencies laboratories managed care organizations pharmacies pharmaceutical manufacturers and public health organizations. The company markets its offerings directly via industry seminars and trade shows as well as by leveraging current customers for new leads in addition to upsell and cross-sell opportunities.

Financial Performance

Cerner Corp. added to several years of revenue and net income growth in 2016. Sales increased 4% to $4.8 billion in 2016 from 2015 while profit shot 18% higher to $636 million in 2016 from $540 million the year before.

Services which includes professional and managed services rose 16% over 2015 driven by growth in professional services from implementation and consulting activities and demand for hosting services. Support and maintenance became a $1 billion business with a 4% increase in 2016 fueled by sales of Cerner Millennium applications. Revenue from the systems business fell 4% in 2016 from lower sales in the technology resale segment. The company blamed the drop in part on uncertainty in the overall health care market.

Cerner?s net income increase came from higher revenue and a decline in costs associated with the acquisition of the Siemens Health Services business.

Cash flow from operations increased $208 million to $1.2 billion in 2016 from 2015 because of a reduction in cash to fund working capital requirements and the higher earnings.

Strategy

Cerner's fundamental strategy is to create organic growth by continuing to make large investments in R&D. This strategy has proven itself over time as Cerner reports 10-year compound annual growth rates of 10% or more in revenue and 20% or more in earnings. With a strong foothold in many of its client markets part of the company's strategy is to sell additional products and services to its customers.

The company has introduced new health care IT (HCIT) services as clients increase their IT spending. Cerner ITWorks is a service that helps hospitals meet their technology needs while Cerner RevWorks helps health care organizations improve their revenue cycle functions. Additionally the company has introduced applications used to automate information collection from medical devices as part of its integrated Smart Room software.

Another path to growth is outside the Cerner?s core HCIT market. Using its own experience the company has developed products for clinic pharmacy wellness and third-party administrator services that the company offers directly to employers.

Cerner also is targeting population health which involves the collection of large amounts of data from people who interact with health care systems. The collected data can be analyzed to provide new health care products and services. The company?s

HealtheIntent cloud platform is its population health engine. About 100 customers use the platform building up more 6 petabytes of data.

Cerner has won multi-billion dollar contracts to modernize EHR records for the US Department of Defense and the Veterans Administration. The high-profile projects present a big opportunity for Cerner to showcase its technologies if it can provide a seamless system for keeping track of the millions of records in each organization?s system. Should it and its partners Accenture Federal and Leidos falter in implementing the technology it could damage the company?s reputation and financials.

Mergers and Acquisitions

In a major move Cerner bought the hospital information system business of Siemens for $1.3 billion in early 2015. The business is focused on administrative hospital IT and electronic patient records for around 5000 client facilities in 40 countries. The acquisition added 6000 employees in the US Europe (particularly Germany) and Asia. At the same time Siemens and Cerner agreed to each put up $50 million to jointly invest in projects integrating health IT with medical technologies.

EXECUTIVES

EVP and Chief of Staff, Jeffrey A. (Jeff) Townsend, age 53, $657,596 total compensation

Chairman and Interim CEO, Clifford W. (Cliff) Illig, age 66

EVP and CFO, Marc G. Naughton, age 61, $524,712 total compensation

President, Zane M. Burke, age 50, $657,596 total compensation

EVP and COO, Michael R. (Mike) Nill, age 52, $657,596 total compensation

VP and General Manager United Kingdom, Donald D. Trigg

EVP and Chief People Officer, Julia M. (Julie) Wilson, age 54

Vp And General Manager Academic/children's Northeast, Debbie Yantis

Vice President, John Gresham

Vice President Ambulatory Sales, Julie Kay

Auditors: KPMG LLP

LOCATIONS

HQ: Cerner Corp.
2800 Rockcreek Parkway, North Kansas City, MO 64117
Phone: 816 221-1024
Web: www.cerner.com

2016 Sales

	$ mil.	% of total
Domestic	4,245	89
Global	551	11
Total	**4,796**	**100**

PRODUCTS/OPERATIONS

2016 Sales

	$ mil.	% of total
Services	2,426	51
System sales	1,266	26
Support & maintenance	1,015	21
Reimbursed travel	88	2
Total	**4,796**	**100**

Selected Services

Population Health Management
Clinical Solutions
Open & Interoperable
Revenue Cycle Management

COMPETITORS

Accenture	Healthland
Accretive Health	IBM Global Services
Allscripts	MEDHOST
CPSI	MEDITECH
Capgemini North	McKesson
America	MedAssets
CareFusion	NTT Data
Conceptual MindWorks	Omnicell
Dell	QuadraMed
Deloitte LLP	Quality Systems
Epic Systems	SSI Group
GE Healthcare	Sage Software
Greenway Medical	athenahealth
Technologies	e-MDs
HP	eClinicalWorks
Healthcare Holdings	

HISTORICAL FINANCIALS

Company Type: Public

Income Statement

FYE: December 30

	REVENUE ($ mil.)	NET INCOME ($ mil.)	NET PROFIT MARGIN	EMPLOYEES
12/17	5,142	866	16.9%	26,000
12/16*	4,796	636	13.3%	24,400
01/16	4,425	539	12.2%	22,200
01/15	3,402	525	15.4%	15,800
12/13	2,910	398	13.7%	14,200
Annual Growth	**15.3%**	**21.5%**	**—**	**16.3%**

*Fiscal year change

2017 Year-End Financials

Debt ratio: 8.14%
Return on equity: 19.95%
Cash ($ mil.): 370
Current ratio: 3.01
Long-term debt ($ mil.): 515
No. of shares (mil.): 332
Dividends
Yield: —
Payout: —
Market value ($ mil.): 22,405

	STOCK PRICE ($) FY Close	P/E High/Low		PER SHARE ($) Earnings	Dividends	Book Value
12/17	67.39	28	18	2.57	0.00	14.39
12/16*	47.37	36	25	1.85	0.00	11.92
01/16	60.17	48	36	1.54	0.00	11.38
01/15	65.03	43	32	1.50	0.00	10.42
12/13	55.58	86	40	1.13	0.00	9.21
Annual Growth	**4.9%**	**—**	**—**	**22.8%**	**—**	**11.8%**

*Fiscal year change

CFJ PROPERTIES LLC

Auditors: KPMG LLP SALT LAKE CITY UTAH

LOCATIONS

HQ: CFJ PROPERTIES LLC
5508 LONAS DR, KNOXVILLE, TN 379093221
Phone: 801 624-1000
Web: WWW.PEPPERONIGRILLNC.COM

HISTORICAL FINANCIALS

Company Type: Private

Income Statement

FYE: January 31

	REVENUE ($ mil.)	NET INCOME ($ mil.)	NET PROFIT MARGIN	EMPLOYEES
01/09	7,672	157	2.1%	6,250
01/07	6,769	50	0.7%	—
Annual Growth	**6.5%**	**77.6%**		

2009 Year-End Financials

Debt ratio: ——
Return on equity: 2.10%
Cash ($ mil.): 37
Current ratio: 0.40
Long-term debt ($ mil.): —
Dividends
Yield: —
Payout: —
Market value ($ mil.): —

CGB ENTERPRISES, INC.

The farmer in the delta relies on CGB Enterprises. Located in Louisiana on the shores of Lake Pontchartrain and the mouth of the Mississippi River the agricultural company provides US farmers with a range of services including grain handling storage and merchandising. It offers inland grain transportation by barge rail and truck and also markets and sells seeds agricultural chemicals and insurance. CGB's Consolidated Terminals and Logistics Co. (CTLC) subsidiary provides transportation logistics and bulk commodity services for both agricultural and non-agricultural customers. The company operates more than 95 locations across the US. Japanese trading conglomerates ITOCHU and ZEN-NOH own CGB.

Geographic Reach

From its headquarters in the city of Mandeville Louisiana CGB operates its business through more than 95 locations nationwide including 74 grain elevators across the Midwest. It boasts grain facilities in nearly 10 states including Nebraska Oklahoma Arkansas Iowa Illinois Indiana Ohio Kentucky and Missouri. The company's fertilizer operations span Ohio Illinois Arkansas and Michigan.

Sales and Marketing

Besides its core services of inland grain transportation via barge rail and truck CGB markets and sells seeds agricultural chemicals and insurance as part of its operations.

Strategy

CGB has expanded its CTLC business in recent years. To give the unit an extended reach CTLC now serves the transportation bulk commodity and logistics needs of a global base of customers rather than just CGB's core businesses.

CGB also regularly invests in its own holdings. The company is constructing a rail shipment facility in Defiance Ohio to boost its production capacity and existing transportation system. In 2014 CGB began building a new facility on the Ohio River near Brandenburg Kentucky.

Mergers and Acquisitions

In mid-2014 CGB Enterprises acquired a grain storage facility in Savage Minnesota from Ceres Global Ag Corp. Under the terms of the deal Ceres will lease back 3.5 million bushels of storage capacity from CGB for a six-year term. The purchase of the grain storage facility in Savage brings new customers to CGB which also plans to expand its fertilizer diversified services and other divisions in the Minnesota market. Also CGB acquired Oklahoma's W.B. Johnston Grain (WBJ) in April 2014.

WBJ operates 19 grain elevators in Oklahoma and Texas including two grain terminals.

Strengthening its foothold on the Mississippi River CGB acquired the grain and fertilizer assets of Twomey based in Smithshire Illinois. The deal consummated in 2011 added valuable loading capacity on the river and offered CGB with a solid customer base in northwestern Illinois.

EXECUTIVES

President CEO, Kevin D. Adams
VP Grain Group, Gregory Beck
VP Diversified Services, Rodney L. Clark
General Manager Agri Financial Services, Alan Singleton
Manager CGB Fertilizer, George Porvaznik
VP CTLC and Marine, Scott Leininger
General Manager Feed Ingredients, Mark Cruse
Vice President, Koji Miura
VICE PRESIDENT, James Mcclelland
Vice President, Osamu Yako
Vice President Human Resources, Mark Berry
Executive Vice President, Koji Shinohara
Auditors: KPMG LLP NEW ORLEANS LA

LOCATIONS

HQ: CGB ENTERPRISES, INC.
1127 HWY 190 E SERVICE RD, COVINGTON, LA
704334929
Phone: 985 867-3500
Web: WWW.CGBGRAIN.COM

PRODUCTS/OPERATIONS

Selected Business Units
Feed Ingredients
Fertilizer
Financial Services
Grain
Marine
Premium Grains
Risk Management
Soybean Processing
Terminals & Logistics

COMPETITORS

ADM	Crosby Tugs
Ag Processing Inc.	Jimmy Sanders
Alabama Farmers	Kirby Corporation
Cooperative	Southern States
Canal Barge Company	Tennessee Farmers
Cargill	Co-op

HISTORICAL FINANCIALS

Company Type: Private

Income Statement

FYE: May 31

	REVENUE ($ mil.)	NET INCOME ($ mil.)	NET PROFIT MARGIN	EMPLOYEES
05/16	5,934	33	0.6%	1,250
05/15	6,656	62	0.9%	—
05/14	7,227	53	0.7%	—
05/13	6,212	30	0.5%	—
Annual Growth	(1.5%)	3.7%		

2016 Year-End Financials

Debt ratio: —	
Return on equity: 0.60%	Dividends
Cash ($ mil.): 13	Yield: —
Current ratio: 0.20	Payout: —
Long-term debt ($ mil.): —	Market value ($ mil.): —

CH2M Hill Companies Ltd

Auditors: KPMG LLP

LOCATIONS

HQ: CH2M Hill Companies Ltd
9191 South Jamaica Street, Englewood, CO 80112-5946
Phone: 303 771-0900

HISTORICAL FINANCIALS

Company Type: Public

Income Statement

FYE: December 30

	REVENUE ($ mil.)	NET INCOME ($ mil.)	NET PROFIT MARGIN	EMPLOYEES
12/16	5,287	15	0.3%	20,000
12/15	5,408	80	1.5%	22,000
12/14	5,468	(181)	—	25,000
12/13	5,931	118	2.0%	—
12/12	6,224	92	1.5%	—
Annual Growth	(4.0%)	(36.6%)		

2016 Year-End Financials

Debt ratio: 18.64%	No. of shares (mil.): 25
Return on equity: 3.09%	Dividends
Cash ($ mil.): 131	Yield: —
Current ratio: 1.06	Payout: —
Long-term debt ($ mil.): 495	Market value ($ mil.): —

CH2M HILL COMPANIES, LTD.

Engineering and construction firm CH2M HILL (named for its founders Cornell Howland Hayes and Merryfield; dba CH2M) operates five divisions that offer up consulting design build operations and maintenance services. It is active across five markets: energy and industrial; environment and nuclear transportation water and power. CH2M's top client is the US Government and public sector clients include the US Department of Energy and the Department of Defense. CH2M also works for state and local governments building water and wastewater systems airports highways and other transportation projects. Founded in 1946 the privately held company is owned by private equity firm Apollo Global Management.

Operations

CH2M operates five business segments reflecting the markets they serve: Energy and Industrial Environment and Nuclear Transportation Water and Power EPC (engineering procurement construction).

The Environment and Nuclear segment which makes up over 40% of company revenue provides consulting design build engineering operations and maintenance construction management and program management services. The segment is broken down into three further units: environmental; government facilities and infrastructure; and nuclear.

The Water segment (around 25% of revenue) works on various water-related projects for the

wastewater drinking water industrial water conveyance and storage water resources and ecosystem management and intelligent water services markets.

CH2M's Transportation segment (nearly 20% of revenue) provides horizontal and vertical infrastructure development services for the Aviation Highway and Bridge Ports and Maritime and Transit and Rail market sectors.

Energy and Industrial (15% of revenue) comprises CH2M's oil and gas chemicals and industrial and advanced technology businesses. It provides consulting planning design engineering ops and maintenance and construction.

The Power EPC (engineering procurement construction) segment (15% of revenue) builds power plants of various types including natural gas coal solar wind biomass and geothermal.

Geographic Reach

Colorado-based CH2M generates about 65% of its revenue from the US. The remainder comes from Asia Australia New Zealand Canada Europe Latin America the Middle East and Africa.

Sales and Marketing

The company's clients include US federal and foreign government agencies state and local governments private sector companies and utilities. The US government (and federally-regulated agencies) is the company's largest client accounting for around 20% of total sales.

Financial Performance

CH2M's annual revenues and profits have been slowly declining since 2012 as oil and gas projects have been stifled amid low fuel prices in recent years and as government budgets have been squeezed.

In fiscal 2016 (ended December) revenue fell 2% to $5.2 billion. On a segment basis the company saw some sharp falls: Energy and Industrial fell 25% as the lower oil price impacted on volume and client concessionson direct hire construction operations and maintenance program management and professional services. Water segment revenue fell 13% due to decreased activities on two design-build-operate contracts for water treatment facilities in the US.

However strong growth was found in the Environment and Nuclear segment which grew 33% as a result of a large nuclear joint-venture project in Canada.

Net income fell from $80 million in 2015 to $15 million in 2016. The fall was due to project losses and restructuring activities offset by the release of a tax valuation allowance.

CH2M incurred a cash outflow from operating activities of $245.5 million a decrease of $348.7 million. The cash outflow was a result of a decrease in earnings and a hefty contribution to the company's defined benefit plans.

Strategy

CH2M began a refocusing strategy in 2016 to follow a client-centric approach with a lower-cost deliver model. It simplified its structure and delivery model including layoffs and facilities consolidations. The company expected the process to complete in 2017 and generate cost savings of $100 million. Its segment reporting will likely be revised as well.

In 2017 CH2M landed a major nuclear deal worth $1.5 billion. The company was awarded a deactivation and remediation contract for a uranium enrichment plant in Kentucky. Works will be carried out over five years followed by an optional 2-3 years.

Mergers and Acquisitions

CH2M occasionally acquires similar businesses to bolster its own service lines. However the acquisition front has been quiet for several years. In 2016 it acquired a controlling stake in a joint venture for $6.3 million.

Company Background

In November 2011 the company acquired Halcrow Group a London-based specialist in environmental infrastructure and transport projects for an estimated $192 million. The deal helped boost CH2M's facilities and infrastructure revenues and expanded the company's global reach adding Halcrow's extensive client list and about 100 offices worldwide.

In 2011 CH2M expanded its public transit business when it acquired the state and local government transit consulting business of Booz Allen Hamilton.

The company which is owned by its employees was founded in 1946.

EXECUTIVES

EVP Growth and Sales, Lisa Glatch, age 54, $328,852 total compensation

EVP and CFO, Gary L. McArthur, age 57, $599,248 total compensation

President State and Local Governments Client Sector, Gregory T. (Greg) McIntyre, age 58, $477,117 total compensation

SVP and Regional Managing Director Middle East North Africa and India, Neil Reynolds

President Water Business Group, Peter G. Nicol

Chairman and CEO, Jacqueline C. (Jacque) Hinman, age 55, $996,156 total compensation

President National Governments Client Sector, Terry A. Ruhl

SVP and Managing Director Operations Management Services, Steve Meininger

EVP Legal, Thomas M. (Tom) McCoy, age 66, $519,231 total compensation

President Industrial and Urban Environments, Thomas L. Pennella

EVP Project Services, Carlo Orsenigo

President Private Client Sector, Matthew Sutton, $346,160 total compensation

Vice President Area Manager, Didier Menard

Vice President And Director Corporate Real Estate, John Spencer

Vice President Of Information Systems, Rick Robertson

Senior Vice President Corporate Affairs, Patrick O'Keefe

Executive Vice President Marketing, Gail Chamberlain

Senior Vice President, Ken Miller

Vice President for National Security Programs, Rob Hood

Vice President for Engineering Project and Construction, Kent Dorr

Executive Vice President Marketing, Henry Abiera

Vice President, Maria Sheridan

Vice President, Dale Gabel

Assistant Vice President, Scott Barber

Executive Vice President Marketing, Grace Wachira

Senior Vice President, Stephen Browning

Vice President and Senior Project Manager, Lidia Pilecky

Vice President of Sales, Julie Thomas

Executive Vice President Marketing, Gary Colgan

Vice President Of Information Systems, Donna Riley

Vice President of Information Technology, Kristina Nygaard

Vice President Creative, Rosemarie Gumba

Vice President Bd Energy And Chemicals, Sun Pao

Senior Vice President Operations Energy And Chemicals, Pete Wiggin

Vice President, Mike Tilchin

Vice President, Jay Witherspoon

Vice President of Technology, Cathy Zou

Vice President, Christopher Thomas

Vice President, Vijay Kumar

Senior Vice President; Managing Director Strategic Consulting, Scott Haskins

Vice President, Russell Bowen

Vice President of Transportation, Les Melhorn

Vice President of Information Technology, Rick Riker

Vice President, Pete Butler

Vice President And Senior Program Manager, Don Holmes

Executive Vice President Marketing, James Gorham

Vice President Sales, Andrew Barash

Executive Vice President Marketing, James Maughan

Senior Vice President, Don Olson

Vice President, Alan Ispass

Vice President Sales, Anja Schoenberger

Executive Vice President Marketing, Gregg Thompson

Executive Vice President Marketing, Gregg Hughes

Vice President Of Information Technology, Louise Lella

Vice President Of Information Technology, Tim Constantine

Executive Vice President Marketing, Emilio Candanoza

Vice President Sales, Alan Teare

Vice President Of Information Technology, Thomas Higgins

Vice President Sales, Anne Vealey

Regional Business Group Manager Vice President, Rod Brauer

Executive Vice President Marke, Gerald Simpson

Vice President Engineering, Tom Heinemann

Vice President And Area Manager, Deron Huck

Vice President Business Development and Strategy, William Badger

Executive Vice President Marketing, Fair Yeager

Executive Vice President Marketing, Janie Iseri

Vice President International Government Affairs, Theresa Loar

Technology Vice President, Korkud Egrican

Executive Vice President Marketing, Imad Feghali

Executive Vice President Marketing, Gretchen Engel

Vice President, Pam Riddle

Vice President Site Management, Saeed Khan

VP Of Finance, Todd Heskett

Executive Vice President Marketing, Elizabeth Bryant

Vice President and Director, Vinod Singh

Executive Vice President Marketing, Howard Thomas

Executive Vice President Marketing, Greg Eldridge

Executive Vice President Marketing, Iosefa Matagi

Vice President, Tom Price

Vice President Tunnels, Mark Johnson

Vice President North West Regional Business Manager, Vicki Bogenberger

Senior Vice President Latin America Region Energy And Chemicals, Jose Montalvo

Vice President ??? International, Dan Baublis

Vice President Of Information Technology, Stuart Jeffcoat

Vice President and Business Manager, Brent Diemer

Vice President of Community Investment and Director of CH2M HILL Foundation, Ellen Y Sandberg

Vice President, Jerry J Notte

Vice President, Beth French

Global Vice President And Director Of Wastewater Market Segment, Liliana Maldonado

Vice President Senior Program Manager, Daniel Wetstein

Vice President, Phil Yerby

Vice President (Business Development), Chris Coggans

Vice President International Operations Director, Matthew Radek

Executive Vice President Marketing, Emilee Edginton

Vice President, Jed Campbell

Vice President Sales, Anne Lynch

Vice President, Paul Wobma

Vice President, Tom Waters

Vice President Marketing, Morgan Hanscom

Vice President of Information Technology, Jonathan James

Vice President, Chuck Smith

Executive Vice President and General Counsel, Shane Burley

Vice President Waste Management Market Segment Director, John J Wood

Vice President, Mel Hatcher

Vice President, Gwo J Ching Hwang

Vice President and Regional Manager, John Richardson

Vice President Of Construction, Sonny Webb

Vice President, Jaason Englesmith

Vice President Chief Investment Officer, Michael Brown

Vice President Chief Engineer For Highwa, Michael Falini

Vice President Maryland Transportation L, Bruce Gartner

Senior Vice President and Regional Manager Southeastern Us, Robert Bailey

Vice President, Bill Beddow

Vice President, Joseph Sandrin

Vice President, Jonathan Harris

Vice President and Senior Program Manager, Seema Alim

Vice President Strategic Planning, Allen Schubert

Vice President and Global Oil and Gas Market Sector Leader for Ports and Maritime Group, Colin Skipper

VICE PRESIDENT, JD SOLOMON

Vice President, Jerry O'Leary

Treas, Steven Mathews

Board Member, Bill Farmer

Board Member, Hank Postrozny

Treasurer, Rene Loya

Auditors: KPMG LLP DENVER COLORADO

LOCATIONS

HQ: CH2M HILL COMPANIES, LTD.
9191 S JAMAICA ST, ENGLEWOOD, CO 801125946
Phone: 303 771-0900
Web: WWW.CH2M.COM

2016 sales

	$ mil.	% of total
US	3,304	63
International	1,931	37
Total	**5,235**	**100**

PRODUCTS/OPERATIONS

2016 sales

	$ mil.	% of total
Environmental and Nuclear	2,213	42
Water	1,190	23
Transportation	930	18
Energy and Industrial	860	16
Power EPC	40	1
Total	**5,235**	**100**

Selected Subsidiaries

CH2M HILL Alaska Inc.
CH2M HILL Canada Inc.
CH2M HILL Constructors Inc.
CH2M Hill Energy Ltd.
CH2M HILL Engineers Inc.
CH2M HILL Hanford Inc.
CH2M HILL Inc.
CH2M HILL International Ltd.
Halcrow Group Ltd.
HEBL Inc.

COMPETITORS

AECOM	Jacobs Engineering
Amec Foster Wheeler	KBR
Balfour Beatty	MWH Global
Bechtel	Parsons Brinckerhoff
Black & Veatch	Parsons Corporation
ERM	Tetra Tech
Fluor	Tutor Perini

HISTORICAL FINANCIALS
Company Type: Private

Income Statement
FYE: December 30

	REVENUE ($ mil.)	NET INCOME ($ mil.)	NET PROFIT MARGIN	EMPLOYEES
12/16	5,287	(124)	—	22,000
12/15	5,408	92	1.7%	—
12/14	5,468	(318)	—	—
12/13	5,931	131	2.2%	—
Annual Growth	(3.8%)	—	—	—

2016 Year-End Financials

Debt ratio: —
Return on equity: (-2.30%)
Cash ($ mil.): 131
Current ratio: 0.60
Long-term debt ($ mil.): —
Dividends
Yield: —
Payout: —
Market value ($ mil.): —

CHALMETTE REFINING, L.L.C.

LOCATIONS

HQ: CHALMETTE REFINING, L.L.C.
500 W SAINT BERNARD HWY, CHALMETTE, LA 700434821
Phone: 504 281-1212
Web: WWW.CHALMETTEREFINING.COM

HISTORICAL FINANCIALS
Company Type: Private

Income Statement
FYE: December 31

	REVENUE ($ mil.)	NET INCOME ($ mil.)	NET PROFIT MARGIN	EMPLOYEES
12/07	5,647	364	6.4%	600
12/06	5,020	423	8.4%	—
12/05	3,462	264	7.6%	—
12/04	3,130	221	7.1%	—
Annual Growth	21.7%	18.1%	—	—

2007 Year-End Financials

Debt ratio: —
Return on equity: 6.40%
Cash ($ mil.): 302
Current ratio: 0.50
Long-term debt ($ mil.): —
Dividends
Yield: —
Payout: —
Market value ($ mil.): —

CHARLES AND LYNN SCHUSTERMAN FAMILY FOUNDATION

LOCATIONS

HQ: CHARLES AND LYNN SCHUSTERMAN FAMILY FOUNDATION
110 W 7TH ST, TULSA, OK 741191031
Phone: 918 591-1090

HISTORICAL FINANCIALS
Company Type: Private

Income Statement
FYE: December 31

	ASSETS ($ mil.)	NET INCOME ($ mil.)	INCOME AS % OF ASSETS	EMPLOYEES
12/15	2,231	(6)	—	2
12/14	2,244	(10)	—	—
12/13	2,290	50	2.2%	—
12/09	61	(21)	—	—
Annual Growth	82.0%	—	—	—

2015 Year-End Financials

Debt ratio: —
Return on equity: (-7.10%)
Cash ($ mil.): 45
Current ratio: —
Long-term debt ($ mil.): —
Dividends
Yield: —
Payout: —
Market value ($ mil.): —

Charter Communications Inc (New)

EXECUTIVES

COO, John R. Bickham, age 64
President CEO and Director, Thomas M. (Tom) Rutledge, age 62
Chairman, Eric L. Zinterhofer, age 44
EVP; President Commercial Services, Donald F. (Don) Detampel Jr., age 60
President Charter Media, James M. (Jim) Heneghan, age 57
Executive Vice President Customer Operations, Kathleen Mayo
Executive Vice President General Counsel and Corporate Secretary, Richard R. Dykhouse, age 52
EVP Government Affairs, Catherine Bohigian
SVP Controller and Chief Accounting Officer, Kevin D. Howard, age 46
SVP Customer Experience, John A. Birrer
Executive Vice President and Chief Financial Officer, Christopher L. (Chris) Winfrey, age 40
SVP Product and Strategy, Rich DiGeronimo
EVP Engineering and Information Technology, James A. (Jim) Blackley
Communications and Media Relations, John R. Miller
EVP and Chief Marketing Officer, Jonathan Hargis
Executive Vice President and Chief Administrative Officer, Robert E. Quicksilver, age 61
President Chief Executive Officer, Jim Fogarty

EVP Field Operations, Tom Adams
Executive Vice President Engineering and Information Technology, Jim Blackley
Executive Vice President Network Operations, Scott Weber
EVP Field Operations, Thomas E. Adams
Senior Vice President of Inbound Sales & Retention, Richard Schultz
Director, Jeffrey A. (Jeff) Marcus, age 68
Director, Bruce A. Karsh, age 60
Director, Robert Cohn, age 65
President CEO and Director, Thomas M. (Tom) Rutledge, age 62
Director, W. Lance Conn, age 47
Director, David C. Merritt, age 61
Director, Stan Parker, age 40
Director, Craig A. Jacobson, age 63
Director, Edgar Lee, age 39
Director, Darren Glatt, age 39
Director, John D. Markley Jr., age 51
Auditors: KPMG LLP

LOCATIONS

HQ: Charter Communications Inc (New)
400 Atlantic Street, Stamford, CT 06901
Phone: 203 905-7800
Web: www.charter.com

COMPETITORS

AT&T	Mediacom
Apple Inc.	Communications
Bright House Networks	Netflix
Cablevision Systems	RCN Corporation
Clearwire	Skype
Comcast	Sprint Communications
Cox Communications	Suddenlink
DIRECTV	Communications
DISH Network	T-Mobile USA
EarthLink	Time Warner Cable
Frontier	United Online
Communications	Verizon
Hulu	Vonage
Insight Communications	YouTube
LodgeNet	

HISTORICAL FINANCIALS
Company Type: Public

Income Statement
FYE: December 31

	REVENUE ($ mil.)	NET INCOME ($ mil.)	NET PROFIT MARGIN	EMPLOYEES
12/17	41,581	9,895	23.8%	94,800
12/16	29,003	3,522	12.1%	91,500
12/15	9,754	(271)	—	23,800
12/14	9,108	(183)	—	23,200
12/13	8,155	(169)	—	21,600
Annual Growth	50.3%	—	—	44.7%

2017 Year-End Financials

Debt ratio: 47.90%
Return on equity: 24.98%
Cash ($ mil.): 621
Current ratio: 0.23
Long-term debt ($ mil.): 68,186
No. of shares (mil.): 238
Dividends
Yield: —
Payout: —
Market value ($ mil.): 80,128

	STOCK PRICE ($) FY Close	P/E High/Low		PER SHARE ($) Earnings	Dividends	Book Value
12/17	335.96	10	7	34.09	0.00	163.87
12/16	287.92	17	9	15.94	0.00	149.27
12/15	183.10	—	—	(2.43)	0.00	(0.41)
12/14	166.62	—	—	(1.70)	0.00	1.30
12/13	136.76	—	—	(1.65)	0.00	1.42
Annual Growth	25.2%	—	—	—	—	-227.6%

Charter Financial Corp (MD)

Auditors: Dixon Hughes Goodman LLP

LOCATIONS

HQ: Charter Financial Corp (MD)
1233 O.G. Skinner Drive, West Point, GA 31833
Phone: 706 645-1391
Web: www.charterbank.net

HISTORICAL FINANCIALS

Company Type: Public

Income Statement

FYE: September 30

	ASSETS ($ mil.)	NET INCOME ($ mil.)	INCOME AS % OF ASSETS	EMPLOYEES
09/17	1,640	14	0.9%	360
09/16	1,438	11	0.8%	331
09/15	1,027	5	0.5%	278
09/14	1,010	5	0.6%	288
09/13	1,089	6	0.6%	294
Annual Growth	10.8%	23.2%	—	5.2%

2017 Year-End Financials

Debt ratio: 4.07%
Return on equity: 6.92%
Cash ($ mil.): 152
Current ratio: —
Long-term debt ($ mil.): —
No. of shares (mil.): 15
Dividends
  Yield: 0.0%
  Payout: 26.3%
Market value ($ mil.): 280

	STOCK PRICE ($) FY Close	P/E High/Low	PER SHARE ($) Earnings	Dividends	Book Value
09/17	18.53	20 12	0.95	0.25	14.17
09/16	12.88	17 15	0.79	0.20	13.52
09/15	12.68	36 31	0.34	0.20	12.79
09/14	10.70	39 36	0.28	0.20	12.32
09/13	10.80	37 33	0.30	0.35	12.03
Annual Growth	14.4%	— —	33.4%	(8.1%)	4.2%

Chemical Financial Corp

Chemical Financial has banking down to a science. It's the holding company for Chemical Bank which provides standard services such as checking and savings accounts CDs and IRAs credit and debit cards and loans and mortgages to individuals and businesses through nearly 190 branches in the lower peninsula of Michigan. The majority of the bank's loan portfolio is made up of commercial loans while consumer loans make up the remainder. Boasting assets of $9 billion Chemical is the second largest bank in Michigan. The company also offers trust investment management brokerage and title insurance services through subsidiaries.

Operations

Its Wealth Management division which has some $4 billion in assets under custody offers trust services estate planning investment management and employee benefit programs. Chemical Financial

Advisors offers mutual funds and marketable securities while CFC Title Services issues title insurance for mortgage properties. CFC Capital manages the company's municipal investment securities portfolio.

About 72% of Chemical Financial's total revenue came from loan interest (including fees) in 2014 while another 6% came from interest on its investment securities. The rest of its revenue came from deposit account service charges and fees (8%) wealth management revenue (6%) mortgage banking income (2%) and other miscellaneous sources of income.

Sales and Marketing

Chemical Financial spent $3.45 million on advertising in 2014 up from $2.97 million and $3.11 million in 2013 and 2012 respectively.

Financial Performance

Chemical Financial's revenues and profits have been rising over the past few years thanks growing loan and deposit business from acquisitions lower interest expenses on deposits and declining loan loss provisions as its loan portfolio's credit quality has improved with higher property valuations in the strengthened economy.

The bank's revenue rose by 6% to $290.4 million in 2014 as the bank as its acquisition of Northwestern Bancorp boosted its loan business during the year. Higher revenue lower interest expenses and a continued decline in loan loss provisions drove the bank's net income up by 9% to a record $62.1 million. The bank's operating cash levels inched higher to $89.9 million on higher cash earnings.

Strategy

The bank follows an aggressive acquisition strategy to boost its loan and deposit business while expanding its branch network into key parts of Michigan. Indeed its acquisitions in 2015 and 2014 boosted the bank's presence in northwestern Michigan and along the Michigan-Indiana border. By the end of 2014 the bank had acquired some 21 community banks and 36 branch bank offices.

Mergers and Acquisitions

In June 2015 it acquired Lake Michigan Financial Corporation along with its The Bank of Holland and The Bank of Northern Michigan subsidiaries and branches for some $187.4 million. The acquisition added $1.2 billion in assets $959 million in loans and $956 million in deposits to Chemical's books.

In April 2015 Chemical Financial purchased Monarch Community Bancorp and its Monarch Community Bank subsidiary for $27.2 million which grew the company's presence and market share along the Michigan-Indiana border. The deal also added $174 million in assets $130 million in new loan assets and $142 million in new deposits.

In October 2014 Chemical Financial bought Northwestern Bancorp and its Northwestern Bank subsidiary for $121 million representing its largest expansion into northwestern Michigan to date.

The company now plans to buy Talmer Bancorp holding company of Talmer Bank and Trust in a $1.4 billion transaction.

Company Background

In late 2012 the company acquired 21 branches in northeastern Michigan and Battle Creek from Independent Bank. That more than $8-million transaction further expands Chemical Bank's presence geographically. Additional acquisitions including FDIC-assisted takeovers of failed banks are possible.

EXECUTIVES

First Vice President Corporate Human Resources, Joseph Torrence

EVP Special Projects Chemical Bank, Lori A. Gwizdala, age 59, $344,720 total compensation

Vice Chairman and President Chemical Bank, Thomas C. (Tom) Shafer, age 58

SEVP Private Banking Trust and Investments Division Chemical Bank Shoreline, James E. Tomczyk, age 65, $225,504 total compensation

Vice Chairman Chemical Bank and CEO InSite Capital LLC, Thomas W. Kohn, age 63, $329,174 total compensation

EVP Commercial Lending Chemical Bank, Daniel W. Terpsma, age 63

EVP and CFO Chemical Financial and Chemical Bank, Dennis L. Klaeser, age 59, $183,483 total compensation

President and CEO, David T. Provost

Director Chemical Financial and Chairman Chemical Bank, Franklin C. Wheatlake, age 69

EVP and COO Business Operations Chemical Bank, Leonardo Amat, age 48, $309,477 total compensation

EVP and Chief Risk Officer Chemical Bank, Lynn M. Kerber, age 48

EVP General Counsel and Secretary, William C. Collins, age 64

EVP and COO Customer Experience Chemical Bank, Robert S. Rathbun, age 53, $309,477 total compensation

SVP and CIO, Greg Meidt

Assistant Vice President Product Development, Jim Hubinger

Vice President Commercial Loan Officer, Jeff Hyde

Executive Vice President Chief Operating Officer, James Milroy

Vice President And Trust Officer, David Farkas

Vice President Information Systems, Laurie Soren

Senior Vice President and Trust Officer, Jude Patnaude

Vice President Commercial Lending, Kip Miller

Vice President Data Services, Brian Beall

Vice President and Trust Investment Officer, Glen Matz

Mortgage Officer Assistant Vice President, Sue Moody

Vice President and Community Reinvestment Act Officer, Robert BurgessJr

Assistant Vice President, Jane Pontious

Assistant Vice President Mortgage Loan Officer, Mara Hill

Vice President Commercial Loan Officer, Catherine Yates

Vice President Retail Sales Manager, Jeff Sharpe

Chairman, Gary H. Torgow, age 59

Auditors: KPMG LLP

LOCATIONS

HQ: Chemical Financial Corp
235 E. Main Street, Midland, MI 48640
Phone: 989 839-5350
Web: www.chemicalbankmi.com

PRODUCTS/OPERATIONS

2014 Sales

	$ mil.	% of total
Interest		
Loans including fees	209	72
Investment securities	17	6
Other	0	-
Non-interest		
Service charges on deposit accounts	22	8
Wealth management revenue	16	6
Other customer service charges & fees	18	6
Other	6	2
Total	**290**	**100**

COMPETITORS

1st Source Corporation	Flagstar Bancorp
Bank of America	Huntington Bancshares
Comerica	Independent Bank (MI)
Fifth Third	Mercantile Bank
Firstbank	

HISTORICAL FINANCIALS
Company Type: Public

Income Statement
FYE: December 31

	ASSETS ($ mil.)	NET INCOME ($ mil.)	INCOME AS % OF ASSETS	EMPLOYEES
12/16	17,355	108	0.6%	3,300
12/15	9,188	86	0.9%	2,100
12/14	7,322	62	0.8%	2,000
12/13	6,184	56	0.9%	1,700
12/12	5,917	51	0.9%	1,859
Annual Growth	30.9%	20.6%	—	15.4%

2016 Year-End Financials

Debt ratio: 0.92%	No. of shares (mil.): 70
Return on equity: 5.99%	Dividends
Cash ($ mil.): 474	Yield: 0.0%
Current ratio: —	Payout: 48.8%
Long-term debt ($ mil.): —	Market value ($ mil.): 3,824

	STOCK PRICE ($) FY Close	P/E High/Low	Earnings	PER SHARE ($) Dividends	Book Value
12/16	54.17	25 13	2.17	1.06	36.57
12/15	34.27	15 12	2.39	1.00	26.62
12/14	30.64	17 13	1.97	0.94	24.32
12/13	31.67	16 12	2.00	0.87	23.38
12/12	23.76	13 10	1.85	0.82	21.69
Annual Growth	22.9%	— —	4.1%	6.6%	14.0%

Chemours Co (The)

Auditors: PricewaterhouseCoopers LLP

LOCATIONS
HQ: Chemours Co (The)
1007 Market Street, Wilmington, DE 19899
Phone: 302 773-1000
Web: www.chemours.com

HISTORICAL FINANCIALS
Company Type: Public

Income Statement
FYE: December 31

	REVENUE ($ mil.)	NET INCOME ($ mil.)	NET PROFIT MARGIN	EMPLOYEES
12/16	5,400	7	0.1%	7,000
12/15	5,717	(90)	—	8,100
12/14	6,432	400	6.2%	9,000
12/13	6,859	423	6.2%	—
12/12	7,365	1,057	14.4%	—
Annual Growth	(7.5%)	(71.5%)	—	—

2016 Year-End Financials

Debt ratio: 58.48%	No. of shares (mil.): 182
Return on equity: 6.18%	Dividends
Cash ($ mil.): 902	Yield: 0.0%
Current ratio: 1.44	Payout: 300.0%
Long-term debt ($ mil.): 3,529	Market value ($ mil.): 4,034

	STOCK PRICE ($) FY Close	P/E High/Low	Earnings	Dividends	Book Value
12/16	22.09	674 78	0.04	0.12	0.55
12/15	5.36		(0.50)	0.58	0.70
Annual Growth	42.5%	— —	—	(32.6%)	(5.8%)

Chemung Financial Corp.

EXECUTIVES

Vice President Private Banker, ED Morton
Assistant Vice President Bus Client Services, Mary Narosky
Vice President and Compliance Officer, Lucimar Escudero
Vice President, Catherine B Crandall
Auditors: Crowe Horwath LLP

LOCATIONS
HQ: Chemung Financial Corp.
One Chemung Canal Plaza, Elmira, NY 14901
Phone: 607 737-3711
Web: www.chemungcanal.com

COMPETITORS

Astoria Financial	Financial Institutions
Citizens Financial Group	HSBC USA
	M&T Bank
Community Bank System	Tompkins Financial
Elmira Savings Bank	

HISTORICAL FINANCIALS
Company Type: Public

Income Statement
FYE: December 31

	ASSETS ($ mil.)	NET INCOME ($ mil.)	INCOME AS % OF ASSETS	EMPLOYEES
12/16	1,657	10	0.6%	368
12/15	1,619	9	0.6%	377
12/14	1,524	8	0.5%	393
12/13	1,476	8	0.6%	390
12/12	1,248	11	0.9%	356
Annual Growth	7.3%	(2.3%)	—	0.8%

2016 Year-End Financials

Debt ratio: 0.28%	No. of shares (mil.): 4
Return on equity: 7.12%	Dividends
Cash ($ mil.): 74	Yield: 0.0%
Current ratio: —	Payout: 49.2%
Long-term debt ($ mil.): —	Market value ($ mil.): 171

	STOCK PRICE ($) FY Close	P/E High/Low	Earnings	PER SHARE ($) Dividends	Book Value
12/16	36.35	17 12	2.11	1.04	30.51
12/15	27.50	14 13	2.00	1.04	29.40
12/14	27.66	20 15	1.74	1.04	28.87
12/13	34.17	19 15	1.87	1.04	30.11
12/12	29.89	13 10	2.38	1.00	28.62
Annual Growth	5.0%	— —	(3.0%)	1.0%	1.6%

Chesapeake Energy Corp.

Chesapeake Energy builds hydrocarbon reserves through the acquisition and development of oil and gas assets across the US. The company one of the biggest natural gas producers in the US and the world has estimated proved reserves of some 6.5 trillion cu. ft. of natural gas equivalent. Chesapeake has exploration and production assets in Appalachia the Mid-Continent the Barnett Bossier and Haynesville shale plays the Permian Basin and the Rockies. The company boasts 22700 producing oil and natural gas wells that turn out 575000 barrels of oil equivalent per day. The company was founded in 1989 by fracking pioneer Aubrey McClendon who died in a car crash in 2016 shortly after being indicted for bid rigging.

Operations

The company has two reportable operating segments: marketing gathering and compression (MGC); and production and exploration.

MGC through Chesapeake Energy Marketing provides oil natural gas and NGL marketing services including commodity price structuring; securing and negotiating gathering hauling processing and transportation services; and marketing services for third party producers in wells in which it does not have an interest. It also conducts gas compression through subsidiary Compass Manufacturing and MidCon Compression. The segment accounts for some 60% of sales.

Production and exploration conducts natural gas oil and NGLs (natural gas liquids) mining. Natural gas accounts for about 65% of segment sales; oil 35%; and NGLs 5%.

Geographic Reach

Chesapeake Energy has natural gas resources in the Haynesville and Bossier Shales in northwestern Louisiana and East Texas; the Marcellus Shale in the northern Appalachian Basin of West Virginia and Pennsylvania; and the Barnett Shale in the Fort Worth Basin of north-central Texas. In addition it has built leading positions in the liquids-rich resource plays of the Eagle Ford Shale in South Texas; the Utica Shale in Ohio and Pennsylvania; the Granite Wash Cleveland Tonkawa and Mississippi Lime plays in the Anadarko Basin in western Oklahoma and the Texas Panhandle; and Utica Shale in the Powder River Basin in Wyoming.

Sales and Marketing

Chesapeake Energy Marketing provides natural gas oil and NGL marketing services including commodity price structuring contract administration and nomination services for Chesapeake its partners and other producers. By aggregating volumes it seeks to increase the value of products to be sold to in various intermediary markets end markets and pipelines. Chesapeake's oil and NGL production is sold under market sensitive short-term or spot price contracts while its natural gas production is sold to purchasers under spot price contracts or percentage-of-proceeds and percentage-of-index contracts.

Sales to BP and Exxon Mobil account for more than 10% each.

Financial Performance

The oversupply-related fall in natural gas prices in recent years put a hefty dent in Chesapeake's revenue.

In fiscal 2016 revenue fell a further 38% to $7.9 billion due to lower prices and a 6% fall in total hydrocarbon output relating to asset sales; oil sales fell 20% on prior year.

Chesapeake lost $4.9 billion in 2016 down from the $14.9 billion loss the previous year. The relative improvement was down to a reduction in impairments although derivative losses of $578 billion (versus gains of $624 million and $1.0 billion the previous two years) weighed heavily on the bottom line.

Cash from operations in 2016 constituted an outflow of $204 million compared to cash provided by operations of $1.2 billion the previous year. The fall was down to lower realized oil prices and lower volumes.

Strategy

Chesapeake is focused on maximizing liquidity by reducing its capital budget; optimizing its portfolio through divestitures of assets; continuing to improve its gathering and transportation agreements and reducing its production and G&A expenses; and continuing to reduce its debt focusing primarily on its 2017 and 2018 maturities.It downscaled drilling activities in 2016 from 18 to 10 operating rigs on average. But with the price of natural gas showing shoots of recovery (in tandem with cash from asset sales) Chesapeake has sufficient liquidity to ramp up capital expenditure once more — it plans to invest $1.9-2.5 billion in 2017.

To further improve its near-term liquidity the company closed or signed asset sales totaling $2.5 billion in 2016 with further sales planned. As well as new drilling the cash raised will help pay down debt.

HISTORY

Aubrey McClendon (who grew up near Maryland's Chesapeake Bay) and Tom Ward had been non-operating partners in about 600 wells in Oklahoma before forming their own company in 1989 to develop new fields in Texas and Oklahoma during the 1990s. The firm went public in 1993. In 1995 the company acquired oil and gas acreage in Louisiana as well as Princeton Natural Gas an Oklahoma City-based gas marketing firm.

Oil finds in Louisiana and strong production from its Texas and Oklahoma wells helped lift Chesapeake's sales in 1996. That year it acquired Amerada Hess' (later renamed Hess) half of their joint operations in two Oklahoma fields. In 1997 chairman McClendon and president Ward acquired control of Chesapeake.

The company's success was based on its "growth through the drillbit" strategy — developing new wells. But after a 1997 loss Chesapeake modified its strategy and sought to grow by acquiring other companies. That year it bought energy company AnSon Production. Chesapeake subsequently bought oil and gas explorer-producer Hugoton Energy and energy company DLB Oil & Gas.

In 1998 the company acquired a 40% stake in Canadian oil producer Ranger Oil and paid Occidental Petroleum$105 million for natural gas reserves in the Texas Panhandle. Chesapeake then began to transform itself from a hotshot driller to an acquirer of natural gas properties almost tripling its proved reserves. The company suffered a huge loss that year in part from the acquisitions and continuing lower gas prices.

With gas prices soaring again the company continued its buying spree into 2000 when it agreed to buy midcontinent natural gas producer Gothic Energy for $345 million in stock and assumed debt. The deal closed in 2001. The company also sold its Canadian assets that year in order to focus on its core US properties.

In 2002 Chesapeake acquired oil and gas producer Canaan Energy for about $118 million. Later that year the company announced plans to sell or trade its Permian Basin assets.

Chesapeake acquired in 2003 a 25% stake in Pioneer Drilling (which it subsequently sold). In

2004 the company acquired Barnett Shale assets from Hallwood Energy for $292 million. That year it also bought privately owned Concho Resources for $420 million. The next year the company acquired privately held BRG Petroleum which held assets of more than 450 wells with proved reserves of more than 275 billion cu. ft. of natural gas for $325 million.

In 2005 Chesapeake acquired 20% of Gastar Exploration (reduced to 15% by 2007). That year in a major move the company acquired Columbia Natural Resources for $2.2 billion.

To get better financial returns the company is selling assets to secure capital. Hurt by continuing low natural gas prices the company sold its midstream assets in 2012 and 2013 for $4.9 billion in three separate deals. As part of this move in 2012 the company sold its limited partner units and its general partner interests in Chesapeake Midstream Partners to Global Infrastructure Partners for $2 billion. That year the company also sold about $6.9 billion of its Permian basin properties in order to pay down debt.

To simplify its operations in 2012 Chesapeake spun off its oilfield service affiliate Chesapeake Oilfield Services.

In 2013 it also sold assets in the Northern Eagle Ford Shale and Haynesville Shale to an EXCO Resources subsidiary for $1 billion.

In 2013 the company sold its 50% undivided interest in 850000 acres in northern Oklahoma (its Mississippi Lime joint venture with Sinopec International Petroleum Exploration and Production) for $1.02 billion.

Other asset sales in 2013 included Granite Wash Midstream Gas Services (to a subsidiary of Mark-West Energy Partners for $252 million) and its interests in certain gathering system assets in Pennsylvania to Western Gas Partners for $134 million.

EXECUTIVES

SVP Information Technology and CIO, Cathlyn L. (Cathy) Tompkins, age 56
EVP and CFO, Domenic J. (Nick) Dell'Osso, age 41, $725,001 total compensation
EVP Exploration and Production, Frank J. Patterson, age 58, $600,000 total compensation
EVP General Counsel and Corporate Secretary, James R. Webb, age 49, $625,000 total compensation
President and CEO, Robert D. (Doug) Lawler, age 50, $1,300,000 total compensation
EVP Operations and Technical Services, M. Jason Pigott, age 43, $574,999 total compensation
Vice President Operations, Randy Goben
Vice President Gas Marketing, Richard Easterly
Vice President Marketing and Corporate Business Development, Bryan Lemmerman
Vice President Drilling, Dave Bert
Vice President Marine Information Technology, Steve A Melton
Vice President Human Resources, James jay Hawkins
Second Vice President, Mandy Duane
Vice president, H Dewitt
Vice President Investor Relations Communications, Brad Sylvester
Senior Vice President Information Technology and CIO, Cathy Tompkins
Vice President of Human Resour, Jay james Hawkins
Senior Vice President Operations, Jason Pigott
Vice President, Michael Harris
Treasurer, Martha Burger
Chairman, R. Brad Martin, age 65
Auditors: PricewaterhouseCoopers LLP

LOCATIONS

HQ: Chesapeake Energy Corp.
6100 North Western Avenue, Oklahoma City, OK 73118
Phone: 405 848-8000
Web: www.chk.com

PRODUCTS/OPERATIONS

2016 Sales

	$ mil.	% of total
Marketing gathering & compression	4,584	58
Natural gas Oil and NGL	3,288	42
Total	**7,872**	**100**

COMPETITORS

Adams Resources	Koch Industries Inc.
Anadarko Petroleum	Noble Energy
Apache	OGE Energy
Ashland	Occidental Petroleum
BP	Par Pacific
Bonanza Creek	Patterson-UTI Energy
Chevron	Pioneer Natural
ConocoPhillips	Resources
Exxon Mobil	SandRidge Energy
Freeport-McMoRan Oil &	Southwestern Energy
Gas LLC	Unit Corporation

HISTORICAL FINANCIALS

Company Type: Public

Income Statement

FYE: December 31

	REVENUE ($ mil.)	NET INCOME ($ mil.)	NET PROFIT MARGIN	EMPLOYEES
12/16	7,872	(4,401)	—	3,300
12/15	12,764	(14,685)	—	4,400
12/14	20,951	1,917	9.1%	5,500
12/13	17,506	724	4.1%	10,800
12/12	12,316	(769)	—	12,000
Annual Growth	(10.6%)	—	—	(27.6%)

2016 Year-End Financials

Debt ratio: 80.14%	No. of shares (mil.): 895
Return on equity: (-1,294.68%)	Dividends
Cash ($ mil.): 882	Yield: —
Current ratio: 0.59	Payout: —
Long-term debt ($ mil.): 9,938	Market value ($ mil.): 6,283

	STOCK PRICE ($) FY Close	P/E High/Low		PER SHARE ($) Earnings	Dividends	Book Value
12/16	7.02	—	—	(6.45)	0.00	(1.63)
12/15	4.50	—	—	(22.43)	0.26	3.22
12/14	19.57	16	9	1.87	0.35	25.48
12/13	27.14	40	23	0.73	0.35	24.08
12/12	16.62	—	—	(1.46)	0.35	23.44
Annual Growth	(19.4%)			—	—	—

Chevron Corporation

Chevron has earned its stripes as the #2 integrated oil company in the US behind Exxon Mobil. Its global operations explore for and produce oil and oil equivalents refines them into various fuels and other end products and sells them through gas stations airport fuel depots and industrial channels. Chevron boasts more than 11 billion barrels of proved reserves produces about 2.5 million barrels of oil per day and has refining capacity for nearly 1.7 million barrels per day. The company sells refined products branded under the Chevron Texaco and Caltex names through nearly 8000 gas stations in the US and 6000 outside the US.

HISTORY

Thirty years after the California gold rush a small firm began digging for a new product — oil. The crude came from wildcatter Frederick Taylor's well located north of Los Angeles. In 1879 Taylor and other oilmen formed Pacific Coast Oil attracting the attention of John D. Rockefeller's Standard Oil. The two competed fiercely until Standard took over Pacific Coast in 1900.

When Standard Oil was broken up in 1911 its West Coast operations became the stand-alone Standard Oil Company (California) which was nicknamed Socal and sold Chevron-brand products. After winning drilling concessions in Bahrain and Saudi Arabia in the 1930s Socal summoned Texaco to help and they formed Caltex (California-Texas Oil Company) as equal partners. In 1948 Socony (later Mobil) and Jersey Standard (later Exxon) bought 40% of Caltex's Saudi operations and the Saudi arm became Aramco(Arabian American Oil Company).

Socal exploration pushed into Louisiana and the Gulf of Mexico in the 1940s. In 1961 it bought Standard Oil Company of Kentucky (Kyso). The 1970s brought setbacks: Caltex holdings were nationalized during the OPEC-spawned upheaval and the Saudi Arabian government claimed Aramco in 1980.

In 1984 Socal was renamed Chevron and doubled its reserves with its $13 billion purchase of Gulf Corp. which had origins in the 1901 Spindletop gusher in Texas. Gulf became an oil power by developing Kuwaiti concessions but was hobbled when those assets were nationalized in 1975. After Gulf was rocked by disclosures that it had an illegal political slush fund Socal stepped in. The deal loaded the new company with debt and it cut 20000 jobs and sold billions in assets.

Chevron bought Tenneco's Gulf of Mexico properties in 1988 and in 1992 swapped fields valued at $1.1 billion for 15.7 million shares of Chevron stock owned by Pennzoil. It also moved into the North Sea in 1994.

In the 1990s Chevron gave its retailing units a tune-up. It allied with McDonald's (1995) to combine burger stands and gas stations in 12 western states. In addition the company sold 450 UK gas stations and a refinery to Shell (1997). Meanwhile Chevron sold its natural gas operation in 1996 for a stake in Houston-based NGC (later Dynegy ; sold in 2007) and it signed an onshore exploration contract in China the next year.

Poor economic conditions in Asia and slumping oil prices in 1998 forced Chevron to shed some US holdings including California properties. Looking for growth overseas in 1999 it bought Rutherford-Moran Oil increasing its interests in Thailand and Petrolera Argentina San Jorge Argentina's #3 oil company.

Chevron trimmed about 10% of its workforce in 1999 and 2000 in an effort to cut costs. As the rest of the industry consolidated Chevron discussed merging with Texaco but the talks collapsed in 1999. Later that year CEO Ken Derr retired and vice chairman Dave O'Reilly replaced him.

In 2000 Chevron formed a joint venture with Phillips Petroleum (later ConocoPhillips) that combined the companies' chemicals businesses as Chevron Phillips Chemical. That year talks with Texaco were revived and Chevron agreed to acquire its Caltex partner for about $35 billion in stock and about $8 billion in assumed debt. The deal completed in 2001 formed ChevronTexaco.

Part of the 2001 deal to acquire Texaco required Chevron to sell exclusive rights to the Texaco brand for a period of three years. A division of Royal Dutch Shell owned rights to the Texaco brand until 2004 and changed the name of the service stations to Shell. Once Chevron regained the rights to the Texaco name it revitalized the brand name by adding about 400 Texaco stations in the western US.

In 2002 ChevronTexaco divested its stakes in US downstream joint ventures Equilon (to Shell) and Motiva (to Shell and Saudi Aramco). It also sold part of a Gulf of Mexico pipeline and two natural gas plants in Louisiana to Duke Energy and its 12.5% stake in a natural gas liquids fractionator to Enterprise Products Partners. In 2004 ChevronTexaco sold 150 US natural gas and oil properties to XTO Energy for $912 million. The company changed its name to Chevron Corporation in 2005.

Chevron acquired Unocal in 2005 for more than $16 billion boosting its proved reserves by about 15%. Equally attractive to Chevron was the strategic position of Unocal's operations; at a time when industries are trying to get a foothold in China the reserves in Southeast Asia could easily be transported not only there but also to a surging India as well. Unocal's other operations easily supplied the US (from the Gulf of Mexico) and Europe (Caspian Sea) with gas and oil. Chevron bought a 5% stake in Indian refiner Reliance Petroleum for about $300 million in 2006. That year a company-led group of exploration firms announced a new successful oil strike in the Gulf of Mexico.

The company has also been growing its natural gas assets. In 2008 it announced plans to construct a $3.1 billion natural gas project in the Gulf of Thailand. The project will have the capacity to meet 14% of Thailand's natural gas needs.

Ultrapar acquired Chevron's Texaco-branded fuel distribution business in Brazil for $720 million in 2008 and the next year Chevron sold its Nigerian fuel marketing business.

A leading producer of viscous heavy oil in 2010 a Chevron-led consortium was awarded the rights to 40% of a heavy oil project in Venezuela's Orinoco Oil Belt.

In 2010 in the wake of the BP oil rig disaster in the Gulf of Mexico Chevron announced it was forming a $1 billion joint venture with Exxon Mobil Royal Dutch Shell and ConocoPhillips to create a rapid-response system capable of capturing and containing up to 100000 barrels of oil from an oil spill in water depths of 10000 feet.

Looking to develop a deepwater area unaffected by US regulations in 2010 the company acquired a 70% stake in three concessions in Liberia in West Africa. Other deepwater exploration asset acquisitions that year included purchases in China and the Turkish Black Sea.

In 2010 the company began to cut its US refining and marketing business staff by 20% and as part of this realignment it sold its 23% stake in Colonial Pipeline to a KKR affiliate.

In 2013 company acquired exploration interests in offshore Blocks EPP44 and EPP45 (more than 8 million acres in the Bight Basin off the South Australian coast).

Growing its LNG supply and export capacity in 2013 Chevron acquired a 50% operating interest in the Kitimat liquefied natural gas project and proposed Pacific Trail Pipeline and a 50% stake in 644000 acres of petroleum and natural gas rights in the Horn River and Liard Basins in British Columbia Canada. The company bought the assets from Apache for $405 million.

In a major move in 2011 Chevron acquired Atlas Energy in a $4.3 billion deal. The acquisition is part of the company's strategy of finding new reserves to replace reserves lost from declining fields. It also marked Chevron's move to become a major

player in the prolific Marcellus Shale play in Pennsylvania where a number of majors are seeking to cash in on the improved drilling technology that has made the exploitation of unconventional gas finds more commercially viable. The purchase gave Chevron Atlas Energy's 850 billion cu. ft. of proved natural gas reserves and 80 million cu. ft. of daily natural gas production. It also complements Chevron's earlier acquisitions of shale gas assets in Canada Poland and Romania as well as its purchase of an additional 228000 acres in the Marcellus Shale from Chief Oil & Gas LLC and Tug Hill Inc. (The acquisitions added up to 5 trillion cubic feet of natural gas resources to Chevron's existing Marcellus Shale operations.)

An earlier chapter of Chevron's history reemerged in 2011 when the company was slapped with a bill for $18 billion in fines and charges by a court in Ecuador regarding environmental damages allegedly caused by Texaco (acquired in 2001) in the 1970s and 1980s. Chevron challenged the findings as illegitimate and unenforceable.

Restructuring its refinery and retail businesses to cut costs in 2011 Chevron sold its Chevron Ltd. UK unit which operated the Pembroke refinery to Valero for $730 million. In addition Valero agreed to pay more that $1 billion for other Chevron Ltd. assets including 1000 gas stations. That year Chevron also sold its fuels marketing and aviation businesses in 16 countries in the Caribbean and Latin America and some marketing businesses in five African countries.

In 2012 the company signed a 20-year deal with Tohoku Electric Power for the delivery of liquefied natural gas (LNG) from the Chevron-operated Wheatstone natural gas project in Australia.

Growing its shale assets in 2013 Chevron agreed to a $1.24 billion investment in YPF to help YPF develop the world's second-largest shale gas deposit and fourth-largest shale oil reservoir located in Argentina's Vaca Muerta region. In 2013 and 2012 the company also announced new exploration and production deals to expand its assets in China Kurdistan the Republic of Congo Surinam and the US.

In 2013 50%-owned affiliate GS Caltex opened a 53000-barrel-per-day gas oil fluid catalytic cracking unit at the Yeosu Refinery in South Korea.

The company consolidated the supply and trading functions in 2013 into a single supply and trading group within Chevron's Gas and Midstream organization.

EXECUTIVES

Senior Vice President, Jay Pryor
VP and CFO, Patricia E. (Pat) Yarrington, age 60, $1,073,242 total compensation
Chairman and CEO, Michael K. (Mike) Wirth, age 57, $1,094,492 total compensation
EVP Downstream and Chemicals, Pierre R. Breber, age 52
VP and General Counsel, R. Hewitt (Hew) Pate, age 55, $867,000 total compensation
EVP Technology Projects and Services, Joseph C. (Joe) Geagea, age 57, $906,367 total compensation
EVP Upstream, James W. (Jay) Johnson, age 58, $1,012,417 total compensation
Managing Director Chevron Nigeria Mid-Africa, Clay Neff, age 55
Senior Vice President Marketing, Bradley Smith
Vice President Deepwater Exploration, Stephen Thurston
Vice President, Robert Kimmel
Vice President, Hendro Santoso
Vice President Chevron Natural Gas Trading, Brent Faulk
Vice President Security, Patrick Donovan

Senior Vice President of Asset Management for Cpl, William Lacobie
National Sales Manager Consumer Products, Paul Dudley
Vice President, Mark Skalinski
Vice President Marketing, Jose Parra
Vice President, Roger Griffith
Vice President and General Counsel, Charles James
Vice President, Stephen Decker
Vice President, Jay Byers
Vice President, Gerard Flaherty
Vice President of Finance, Uriel Ose
Vice President, Petros Papazis
VP Safety, Wes Lohec
Vice President, Andy Walz
Vice President Marketing, Jeff Petro
Vice President and General Counsel, Dotson John
Senior Vice President Asset Management, Charles Hall
Vice President, Alan Levine
VICE PRESIDENT HUMAN RESOURCES, Juan Garcia
Vice President, Mark Macleod
Vice President and General Cou, Wendy Daboval
Vice President of Montgomery Operations, Julia Martin
Senior Vice President, Jennifer M Papier
Vice President, Dorcus Chu
Senior Vice President Operations, Ted Etchison
Vice President, Michael Kisucky
Vice President Retail Distribution Network, Desmond Cecil
Vice President of Global Exploration, Robert Ryan
Chief Sales Officer, Neil Holmes
National Account Manager, Steve Faggard
Vice President, Peter Martin
Vice President Americas East and Latin America, George Wall
Assistant Vice President Information Technology Operations, Antonio Calombo
Vice President Of Membership, Yolanda Peria
Vice President Global Manufacturing, Brant Fish
Vice President Operations, Jill Lambert Seal
Vice President, Maud Faulmann
Canadian Area Vice President, Bob Bradbury
Vice President Business Development Portfolio Management, Martin Donohue
Executive Vice President, Sandy Cab
Vice President, Stephen Switzer
Vice President, Min Chen
Vice President Finance, Brenda Young
National Account Manager, Marcella Love
Executive Vice President, George L Kirkland
Vice President, Shariq Yosufzai
Senior Vice President of South Florida Operations, Diane Mayo
Vice President Planning and Technology, Rachmat Abdoellah
Vice President and Comtroller, Matthew Foehr
Vice President Of Global Exploration, Rishma Tidwell
Vice President and General Manager, Estrella Rogel
Legal Secretary, Robert Dechristofaro
National Sales Manager, Patricia Looney
Vice President, Frank Semancik
Vice President, Bruce Niemeyer
Fusta Vice President Chairman US Competition Committee, Fred DeMarse
Vice Chairman Of The Board, Glenn F Tilton
Board Member, Eric Upchurch
Secretary, H Xun
Board Member, Bruce Thompson
Board Member, Thomas Hebert
Treasurer Chevron Stations, Ravinder Bhumbla
Board Of Directors, Mark Barambani
Pac Treasurer, Lydia Wylie
Board Member, Kelley Mobley
Auditors: PricewaterhouseCoopers LLP

LOCATIONS

HQ: Chevron Corporation
6001 Bollinger Canyon Road, San Ramon, CA 94583-2324
Phone: 925 842-1000   Fax: 925 894-6017
Web: www.chevron.com

2016 sales

	$ mil.	% of total
US	56,187	42
International	72,843	55
Equity income and others	4,257	3
Adjustments	(18815)	-
Total	**144,472**	**100**

PRODUCTS/OPERATIONS

2016 Sales

	$ mil.	% of total
Downstream	94,743	71
Upstream	33,145	25
Equity income and others	4,257	3
Other	1,142	1
Adjustments	(18815)	-
Total	**114,472**	**100**

COMPETITORS

Anadarko Petroleum	Marathon Petroleum
BP	PEMEX
ConocoPhillips	PETROBRAS
Devon Energy	Petr□□leos de
Eni	Venezuela
Exxon Mobil	Repsol
Hess Corporation	Royal Dutch Shell
Imperial Oil	Sinopec Corp.
Koch Industries Inc.	TOTAL

HISTORICAL FINANCIALS

Company Type: Public

Income Statement

FYE: December 31

	REVENUE ($ mil.)	NET INCOME ($ mil.)	NET PROFIT MARGIN	EMPLOYEES
12/16	114,472	(497)	—	55,200
12/15	138,477	4,587	3.3%	61,500
12/14	211,970	19,241	9.1%	64,700
12/13	228,848	21,423	9.4%	64,600
12/12	241,909	26,179	10.8%	62,000
Annual Growth	(17.1%)	—	—	(2.9%)

2016 Year-End Financials

Debt ratio: 17.74%
Return on equity: (-0.33%)
Cash ($ mil.): 6,988
Current ratio: 0.93
Long-term debt ($ mil.): 35,286

No. of shares (mil.): 1,891
Dividends
Yield: 0.0%
Payout: —
Market value ($ mil.): 222,630

	STOCK PRICE ($) FY Close	P/E High/Low	PER SHARE ($) Earnings	Dividends	Book Value
12/16	117.70	— —	(0.27)	4.29	76.95
12/15	89.96	46 28	2.45	4.28	81.11
12/14	112.18	13 10	10.14	4.21	82.48
12/13	124.91	11 10	11.09	3.90	77.92
12/12	108.14	9 7	13.32	3.51	70.13
Annual Growth	2.1%	— —	—	5.1%	2.3%

CHEVRON PHILLIPS CHEMICAL COMPANY LLC

Among the world's largest petrochemical firms Chevron Phillips Chemical (CPChem) produces ethylene propylene polyethylene and polypropylene — sometimes used as building blocks for the company's other products such as pipe. Chevron Phillips Chemical also produces aromatics such as benzene and styrene specialty chemicals such as acetylene black (a form of carbon black) and mining chemicals. Chevron Phillips Chemical Company LP is CPChem's wholly-owned primary US operating subsidiary. CPChem is 50% owned by Chevron U.S.A. Inc. an indirect wholly-owned subsidiary of Chevron Corporation and 50% by wholly-owned subsidiaries of Phillips 66.

Operations

CPChem is a leading global producer of olefins and polyolefins (more than 80% of total sales) and a major supplier of aromatics alpha olefins styrenics specialty chemicals as well as piping material and other proprietary plastics. It is the Western Hemisphere's largest producer of high-density polyethylene — used in blow/injection molding plastic bags and pipes and films. CPChem also is near the top in styrene ethylene and aromatics production.

CPChem has several petrochemical joint ventures in the Middle East including Saudi Chevron Phillips Company (50%) and Qatar Chemical Company (not quite 50%). Subsidiary Chevron Oronite produces fuel additives.

The company's chemical products are used in more than 70000 consumer and industrial products. Its brands include Marlex Aromax Scentinel Soltex and K-Resin.

Geographic Reach

CPChem operates 35 manufacturing facilities and two research and development centers in Belgium China Colombia Qatar Saudi Arabia Singapore South Korea and the US.

Sales and Marketing

The company serves a range of markets including Adhesives and Sealants Agricultural Appliances Automotive Building and Construction Chemical Manufacturing Drycleaning Textiles Pharmaceuticals Paint and Coatings Imaging and Photography Packaging and Electronics.

Strategy

CPChem is growing its complex of chemical plants taking advantage of the deep pockets of its multinational parents increased demand for chemical products (especially in Asia) and the abundance of chemical raw materials generated by natural gas production in North American shale basins.

In 2015 the company completed an expansion of its normal alpha olefins capacity at its Cedar Bayou plant in Baytown. Alpha olefins are used in synthetic motor oils lubricants surfactants and other specialty applications.

Growing its infrastructure during 2014 CPChem completed the construction of a 1-hexene plant (the world's largest) at the company's Cedar Bayou complex in Baytown Texas with a design capacity of 250000 metric tons per year. The product 1-hexene is a component used in the manufacture of polyethylene a plastic resin commonly converted into film plastic pipe milk jugs detergent bottles and food and beverage containers.

In 2014 CPChem completed an ethylene expansion at its Sweeny complex in Old Ocean Texas.

That year to take advantage of chemical supply from nearby oil and gas basins the company committed $6 billion to build a 1.5-million-metric-tons/year (3.3 billion pounds/year) ethane cracker and two ethylene derivatives facilities on the US Gulf Coast. The two new polyethylene facilities will each have an annual capacity of 500000 metric tons (1.1 billion pounds). The projects are due to be completed in 2017.

To raise cash in 2015 the company sold its its Ryton polyphenylene sulfide business to Solvay for $220 million.

Company Background

In 2011 to expand its portfolio in Europe the company acquired a polyalphaolefin plant in Beringen Belgium from Neste Oil. The acquisition also added to the company's existing production of polyalphaolefins (PAOs) which are used in high-performance lubricants.

A coin toss determined whose name would go first when Chevron and Phillips Petroleum (now Phillips 66) formed 50-50 joint venture Chevron Phillips Chemical Company in 2000.

EXECUTIVES

SVP Petrochemicals, D. S. (Dave) Smith
President and CEO, Mark E. Lashier
VP and CIO, Peggy Colsman
SVP CFO and Controller, Tim D. Leveille
SVP Projects and Supply Chain, R. E. (Ron) Corn
SVP Manufacturing, M. S. (Scott) Sharp
SVP Polymers, David Morgan
Vice President of Human Resources, Greg Wagner
Vice President, Ken Hope
Vice President human Resources, Donald Kremer
Auditors: ERNST & YOUNG LLP HOUSTON TE

LOCATIONS

HQ: CHEVRON PHILLIPS CHEMICAL COMPANY LLC
10001 SIX PINES DR, THE WOODLANDS, TX
773801498
Phone: 832 813-4100
Web: WWW.CPCHEM.COM

PRODUCTS/OPERATIONS

Selected Products

Olefins and polyolefins
  Ethylene
  Polyethylene
  Polyethylene pipe
  Polypropylene
  Propylene
Aromatics and styrenics
  Benzene
  Cumene
  Cyclohexane
  Paraxylene
  Styrene
Specialty products
  Acetylene black
  Alpha olefins
  Dimethyl sulfide
  Drilling specialty chemicals
  High-purity hydrocarbons and solvents
  Mining chemicals
  Neohexene
  Performance and reference fuels
  Polyalpha olefins
  Polystyrene

Selected Joint Ventures

Americas Styrenics (50%)
Chevron Phillips Singapore Chemicals (Private) Limited (50%)
KR Copolymer Co. Ltd. (60% South Korea)
Qatar Chemical Company Ltd. (Q-Chem 49%)
Saudi Chevron Phillips Company (50%)
Shanghai Golden Phillips Petrochemical Co. Ltd. (40%)

COMPETITORS

Dow Chemical	NOVA Chemicals
DuPont	SABIC
ExxonMobil Chemical	Sasol
Kraton	Total Petrochemicals
LyondellBasell	Westlake Chemical

HISTORICAL FINANCIALS

Company Type: Private

Income Statement

FYE: December 31

	REVENUE ($ mil.)	NET INCOME ($ mil.)	NET PROFIT MARGIN	EMPLOYEES
12/15	9,859	2,651	26.9%	5,000
12/14	14,148	3,288	23.2%	—
12/13	13,790	2,743	19.9%	—
12/08	12,828	276	2.2%	—
Annual Growth	(3.7%)	38.2%	—	—

2015 Year-End Financials

Debt ratio: ——
Return on equity: 26.90%
Cash ($ mil.): 350
Current ratio: 1.00
Long-term debt ($ mil.): —

Dividends
  Yield: —
  Payout: —
Market value ($ mil.): —

CHEVRON PHILLIPS CHEMICAL COMPANY LP

Auditors: ERNST & YOUNG LLP HOUSTON T

LOCATIONS

HQ: CHEVRON PHILLIPS CHEMICAL COMPANY LP
10001 SIX PINES DR, THE WOODLANDS, TX
773801498
Phone: 832 813-4100

HISTORICAL FINANCIALS

Company Type: Private

Income Statement

FYE: December 31

	REVENUE ($ mil.)	NET INCOME ($ mil.)	NET PROFIT MARGIN	EMPLOYEES
12/15	7,990	2,020	25.3%	5,000
12/14	11,758	2,444	20.8%	—
12/13	11,439	1,950	17.0%	—
Annual Growth	(16.4%)	1.8%	—	—

2015 Year-End Financials

Debt ratio: ——
Return on equity: 25.30%
Cash ($ mil.): 113
Current ratio: 1.20
Long-term debt ($ mil.): —

Dividends
  Yield: —
  Payout: —
Market value ($ mil.): —

CHRISTIAN BROTHERS INVESTMENT SERVICES, INC.

LOCATIONS

HQ: CHRISTIAN BROTHERS INVESTMENT SERVICES, INC.
20 N WACKER DR STE 2000, CHICAGO, IL
606063002
Phone: 312 526-3343
Web: WWW.CBISONLINE.COM

HISTORICAL FINANCIALS

Company Type: Private

Income Statement

FYE: December 30

	ASSETS ($ mil.)	NET INCOME ($ mil.)	INCOME AS % OF ASSETS	EMPLOYEES
12/11	2,079	100	4.8%	45
12/10	2,167	68	3.1%	—
12/09	1,863	0	—	—
12/05	2,191	0	—	—
Annual Growth	(0.9%)	—	—	—

2011 Year-End Financials

Debt ratio: ——
Return on equity: 87.10%
Cash ($ mil.): 0
Current ratio: —
Long-term debt ($ mil.): —

Dividends
  Yield: —
  Payout: —
Market value ($ mil.): —

CHS Inc

CHS goes with the grain. The company is a leading publicly traded cooperative marketer of grain oilseed and energy resources in the US. It represents farmers ranchers and co-ops from the Great Lakes to Texas. CHS trades grain and sells farm supplies through its stores to members. The group processes soybeans for use in food and animal feeds and grinds wheat into flour. Through joint ventures and a variety of business segments it sells soybean oil and crop nutrient products and markets grain. CHS also provides insurance financial and risk-management services and operates petroleum refineries to sell Cenex-brand fuels lubricants and other energy products.

HISTORY

To help farmers through the Great Depression the Farmers Union Terminal Association (a grain marketing association formed in 1926) created the Farmers Union Grain Terminal Association (GTA) in 1938. With loans from the Farmers Union Central Exchange (later known as CENEX) and the Farm Credit Association the organization operated a grain elevator in St. Paul Minnesota. By 1939 GTA had 250 grain-producing associations as members.

GTA leased terminals in Minneapolis and Washington and built others in Wisconsin and Montana in the early 1940s. It then took over a Minnesota flour mill and created Amber Milling. GTA also began managing farming insurance provider Terminal Agency. In 1958 the association bought 57 elevators and feed plants from the McCabe Company.

Adding to its operations in 1960 GTA bought the Honeymead soybean plant. The next year the co-op acquired Minnesota Linseed Oil. In 1977 it acquired Jewett & Sherman (later Holsum Foods) which helped transform the company into a provider of jams jellies salad dressings and syrups.

In 1983 GTA combined with North Pacific Grain Growers a Pacific Northwest co-op incorporated in 1929 to form Harvest States Cooperatives. Harvest States grew in the early and mid-1990s by acquiring salad dressing makers Albert's Foods Great American Foods and Saffola Quality Foods; soup stock producer Private Brands; and margarine and dressings manufacturer and distributor Gregg Foods.

The company started a joint venture to operate the Ag States Agency agricultural insurance company in 1995. The next year the co-op's Holsum Foods division and Mitsui & Co.'s edible oils unit Wilsey Foods merged to form Ventura Foods a distributor of margarines oils spreads and other food products.

Harvest States merged in 1998 with Minnesota-based CENEX a 16-state agricultural supply co-op that had been founded in 1931 as Farmers Union Central Exchange. (Among CENEX's major operations was a farm inputs services marketing and processing joint venture with dairy cooperative Land O'Lakes formed in 1987.) CENEX CEO Noel Estenson took the helm of the resulting co-op Cenex Harvest States Cooperatives which soon formed a petroleum joint venture called Country Energy with Farmland Industries.

CHS members rejected a proposed merger with Farmland Industries in 1999. Also that year Cenex/Land O'Lakes Agronomy (it became Agriliance in 2000 when Farmland Industries joined the joint venture) bought Terra Industries' $1.7 billion distribution business (400 farm supply stores seed and chemical distribution operations partial ownership of two chemical plants).

CHS bought the wholesale propane marketing operations of Williams Companies in 2000 and the co-op paid $14 million for tortilla and tortilla chip maker Sparta Foods. Additionally Estenson retired that year and company president John Johnson took over as CEO. CHS launched an agricultural e-commerce site (Rooster.com) in conjunction with Cargill and DuPont in 2000. The site was shut down the next year however because of a lack of funds. Also in 2001 the cooperative became the full owner of Country Energy by purchasing Farmland Industries' share.

In 2002 CHS acquired Agway's Grandin North Dakota-based sunflower business and formed a wheat-milling joint venture (Horizon Milling) with Cargill. In 2003 the company changed its name from Cenex Harvest States Cooperatives to CHS Inc. and began trading on the NASDAQ. It used the proceeds from the stock offering to repay its short-term debts.

In 2004 CHS purchased all of bankrupt Farmland Industries' ownership of Agriliance thus giving CHS a 50% ownership of Agriliance (with Land O'Lakes owning the other 50%). With an eye to this growing energy sector CHS acquired a 28% ownership of ethanol producer and marketer US BioEnergy Corporation in 2005. Also that year it sold off its Mexican foods business and sold 81% of its 20% ownership of crop-nutrient manufacturer CF Industries in an initial public offering.

CHS and Land O'Lakes realigned the businesses of their 50-50 joint venture Agriliance in 2007 with CHS acquiring its crop-nutrients wholesale-products business and Land O'Lakes acquiring the crop-protection products business. Canadian ag cooperative La Coop f©d©r©e purchased Agriliance's retail agronomy operation the follow-

ing year. Adding to its lubricants offerings in 2007 the company acquired two Minnesota companies: Nor-Lakes Services Midwest and The Farm-Oyl Company. In 2008 it sold off all its remaining shares of CF.

Recognizing the growing demand for soy-based food products and in turn to increase shareholder value the company in 2008 acquired Legacy Foods maker of Ultra Soy and TSP brands of textured soybean products for use by both human food and pet food manufacturers. Legacy's operations are overseen by CHS's oilseed processing division.

On the energy front CHS became the sole owner of Provista Renewable Fuels Marketing in 2008 by purchasing US BioEnergy's 50% interest in the biofuels maker. (VeraSun Energy bought out US BioEnergy later that year.

In 2009 CHS acquired Winona River & Rail including 90000 tons of dry-fertilizer storage capacity a dedicated river dock and a 65-car railroad track capacity. The acquisition of the Minnesota operations bolstered the company's storage capacity and rail access in the midwestern and upper Mississippi River regions. Later that year it formed a joint venture with Russia's farm operation Agrico Group (called ACG) in order to manage the export and worldwide marketing of its wheat and feed grains. In turn it gave CHS access to the Russian grain market and improved its ability to serve its global customers.

Also in 2009 CHS formed another of its joint ventures this time at home. It joined with Nebraska's Central Valley Ag Cooperative (CVA) to form Advanced Energy Fuels to provide customers with an industry-leading fuel delivery system.

Beyond the US the company was part of a grain marketing joint venture (Multigrain A.G.) with Brazilian commodities-company PMG Trading and Mitsui. In 2011 CHS sold a nearly 45% stake in Multigrain to the Japanese firm for Å 47 billion yen (roughly $510 million). Mitsui which already owned about a 45% stake also bought PMG's interest. The deal marked one of the largest overseas farming investments made by a Japanese trading house.

Building on the success of its joint ventures in 2013 CHS formed a flouring-milling partnership with agri-giants Cargill and ConAgra called Ardent Mills. The newly-formed partnership was North America's largest flour miller with annual sales of more than $4 billion. CHS held 12% of Ardent Mills while ConAgra and Cargill each owned 44%.

EXECUTIVES

President and CEO, Jay D. Debertin, age 57, $667,242 total compensation

EVP Business Solutions, Lisa Zell, age 48, $438,600 total compensation

EVP and COO Country Operations, Lynden E. Johnson, age 56

EVP and COO Ag Business and Enterprise Strategy, Shirley Cunningham, age 56, $593,983 total compensation

EVP and CFO, Timothy Skidmore, age 55, $487,135 total compensation

EVP and Chief Human Resources Officer, Adam Holton

EVP and General Counsel, James (Jim) Zappa, age 52, $423,667 total compensation

Vice President And General Manager, Roger Baker

Chairman, Daniel (Dan) Schurr, age 51

Second Vice Chairman, Jon Erickson

First Vice Chairman, Clinton J. (C.J.) Blew

Auditors: PricewaterhouseCoopers LLP

LOCATIONS

HQ: CHS Inc
5500 Cenex Drive, Inver Grove Heights, MN 55077
Phone: 651 355-6000
Web: www.chsinc.com

2016 Sales

	$ mil.	% of total
North America	23,276	77
EMEA	4,166	14
South America	1,847	6
APAC	1,058	3
Total	**30,347**	**100**

PRODUCTS/OPERATIONS

2016 Sales

	$ mil.	% of total
Ag	24,849	81
Energy	5,789	19
Others	92	-
Adjustments	(384.4)	-
Total	**30,347**	**100**

Selected Operations

Ag business
  Grain exporter
  Grain merchandising in Argentina
  Grain merchandising in Europe
  Grain merchandising in Spain
  Grain procurement and merchandising in Russia
  Grain procurement and merchandising in Ukraine
  Retail distribution of agronomy products
  Soybean procurement in Brazil
Corporate and Other
  Finance company
  Insurance agency
  Insurance brokerage
  Risk management products broker
Energy
  Crude oil transportation
  Finished product transportation
  Petroleum refining
Processing
  Food manufacturing and distribution
  Wheat milling in Canada
  Wheat milling in US

COMPETITORS

ACH Food Companies	JR Simplot
ADM	Koch Industries Inc.
Ag Processing Inc.	Land O'Lakes Purina
AmeriGas Partners	Feed
Andersons	Louis Dreyfus Group
BP	Marathon Petroleum
Bartlett and Company	Marzetti
Bunge Limited	Mondelez International
C.F. Sauer	Mosaic Company
CF Industries	Nestl©
CGC	Riceland Foods
CITGO	Ridley Inc.
Cargill	Scoular
Columbia Grain	Shell Oil Products
ConAgra	Smucker
ConocoPhillips	U.S. Venture
Dakota Growers	US Soy
ExxonMobil Chemical	Unilever NV
Ferrellgas Partners	Valero Energy
Flint Hills	Western Petroleum
GROWMARK	Whole Harvest Foods
Gavilon Group	Wilbur-Ellis
Helena Chemical	

HISTORICAL FINANCIALS

Company Type: Public

Income Statement

FYE: August 31

	REVENUE ($ mil.)	NET INCOME ($ mil.)	NET PROFIT MARGIN	EMPLOYEES
08/17	31,934	127	0.4%	11,626
08/16	30,347	424	1.4%	12,157
08/15	34,582	781	2.3%	12,511
08/14	42,664	1,081	2.5%	11,824
08/13	44,479	992	2.2%	10,716
Annual Growth	(7.9%)	(40.1%)	—	2.1%

2017 Year-End Financials

Debt ratio: 26.09%—
Return on equity: 1.62%
Cash ($ mil.): 387
Current ratio: 1.03
Long-term debt ($ mil.): 2,023

Dividends
Yield: 5.8%
Payout: —
Market value ($ mil.): —

	STOCK PRICE ($) FY Close	P/E High/Low	PER SHARE ($) Earnings	Dividends	Book Value
08/17	29.51	— —	(0.00)	1.69	(0.00)
08/16	31.22	— —	(0.00)	1.69	(0.00)
08/15	27.28	— —	(0.00)	1.34	(0.00)
Annual Growth	2.0%	— —	—	5.9%	—

CHUGACH GOVERNMENT SOLUTIONS, LLC

LOCATIONS

HQ: CHUGACH GOVERNMENT SOLUTIONS, LLC
3800 CNTRPINT DR STE 1200, ANCHORAGE, AK 99503
Phone: 907 563-8866
Web: WWW.CHUGACH.COM

HISTORICAL FINANCIALS

Company Type: Private

Income Statement

FYE: December 31

	ASSETS ($ mil.)	NET INCOME ($ mil.)	INCOME AS % OF ASSETS	EMPLOYEES
12/15	4,720	42	0.9%	4,300
12/14	4,136	28	0.7%	—
Annual Growth	14.1%	48.8%	—	—

Cigna Corp

With a significant position in the US health insurance market CIGNA covers some 15 million Americans with its various medical plans. The firm's offerings include PPO HMO point-of-service (POS) indemnity and consumer-directed products as well as specialty coverage in the form of dental vision pharmacy and behavioral health plans. It also sells group accident life and disability insurance. Customers include employers government entities unions Medicare recipients and other groups and individuals in North America. Internationally CIGNA sells life accident and health insurance in parts of Europe and Asia and provides health coverage to expatriate employees of multinational companies. In 2017 Cigna's planned merger with rival Anthem was terminated.

HISTORY

The Insurance Company of North America (INA) was founded in 1792 by Philadelphia businessmen. INA was the US's first stock insurance company and its first marine insurer. It later issued life insurance fire insurance and coverage for the contents of buildings. In 1808 it began using agents outside Pennsylvania. INA grew internationally in the late 1800s appointing agents in Canada as well as in London and Vienna in Europe. It was the first US company to write insurance in China beginning in Shanghai in 1897.

In 1942 INA provided both accident and health insurance for men working on the Manhattan Project which developed the atomic bomb. It introduced the first widely available homeowner coverage in 1950. In 1978 INA bought HMO International which was then the largest publicly owned health maintenance organization in the US. INA merged with Connecticut General in 1982 to form CIGNA.

Connecticut General began selling life insurance in 1865 and health insurance in 1912. It wrote its first group insurance (for the Hartford Courant newspaper) in 1913 and the first individual accident coverage for airline passengers in 1926. In the late 1930s Connecticut General was a leader in developing group medical coverage. The company offered the first group medical coverage for general use in 1952 and in 1964 added group dental insurance.

After the merger CIGNA bought Crusader Insurance (UK 1983; sold 1991) and AFIA (1984). To begin positioning itself as a provider of managed health care the company sold its individual insurance products division to InterContinental Life in 1988 and its Horace Mann Cos. (individual financial services) to an investor group in 1989. To further its goal in 1990 CIGNA bought EQUICOR an HMO started by Hospital Corporation of America (now part of HCA Inc.) and what is now AXA Equitable Life Insurance.

In the early 1990s it began to withdraw from the personal property/casualty business to focus on small and midsized commercial clients in the US cutting sales overseas and combining them with life and health operations. It also exited such areas as airline insurance and surety bonds.

CIGNA expanded internationally in the mid-1990s opening a Beijing office in 1993 43 years after its departure from China. The next year the company bought 60% of an Indonesian insurance company. It also acquired 45% of Mediplan a managed health care organization in Mexico.

Reeling from unforeseen environmental liabilities (chiefly related to asbestos) CIGNA in 1995 split its remaining property/casualty business between a healthy segment that continued to write new policies and one for run-off business. Four years later it finally sold these operations (including Cigna Insurance Co. of Europe) to ACE Limited (later renamed Chubb Limited) in order to fund internal growth and acquisitions.

In the late 1990s the company continued to cultivate its health care segment acquiring managed care provider Healthsource in 1997. The company expanded its group benefits operations to India Brazil and Poland; at home it cut its payroll by 1300 in the US to counter rising costs. The company sold its domestic individual life insurance and annuity business in 1998 but began offering investment and pension products in Japan in 1999.

In 2000 CIGNA settled a federal lawsuit over Medicare billing fraud. It also sold its reinsurance businesses that year to a subsidiary of Swiss Reinsurance Company while continuing to maintain some previous reinsurance policies on a runoff basis.

EXECUTIVES

Chief Medical Officer and Total Health & Network Lead, Alan M. Muney, age 64
EVP Human Resources and Services, John M. Murabito, age 59, $592,250 total compensation
EVP and Global CIO, Mark L. Boxer, age 58
President and CEO, David M. Cordani, age 51, $1,200,000 total compensation
EVP and General Counsel, Nicole S. Jones, age 46, $581,137 total compensation
President U.S. Markets, Michael W. Triplett
President International Markets, Jason D. Sadler, age 48, $589,463 total compensation
EVP Chief Marketing and Customer Officer, Lisa R. Bacus, age 52
President Select Segment and Pharmacy Benefits Management, Christopher Hocevar
CFO Cigna-HealthSpring, Eric P. Palmer, age 41
President Mountain States (Colorado New Mexico Utah and Wyoming), John Roble
Vice President Sucurity, James Husovsky
Vice President Corporate Communications At Cigna, Jon Sandberg
Vice President National Account Executive, Jean Chadbourne
Vice President, Colin M Hill
Vice President Sales, Sean Hughes
Vice President Middle Market Account Services, Paul Fruhwirth
Assistant Vice President Pharmaceutical Contracting, Rich Hoeckh
Senior Vice President, Jack Wright
Vice President Information Technology, Gerald Sweeney
Regional Assistant Vice President of Healthplan Operations, Lora McPhail
Regional Vice President, Tobin Hawkins
National Accounts Manager, Jonathan Espinosa
Vice President, Marc Wiersma
National Account Manager, Steve Black
Vice President Talent Optimization, Charlene Parsons
Senior Vice President of Sales, Mark Butler
Vice President Supplier Account Management, Rob Johnson
Vice President National Accounts Dental, Karen Wever
Vice President Sales and Client Management, Brian Cuddeback
Vice President, James Guemple
Assistant Vice President Provider Contracting, Mark Still
Vice President, Joan Mastropaolo
Senior Vice President Sales and Marketing, Robert Picinich
Assistant Vice President Compensation, Edward G Miller
Regional Vice President, Tom Golias
Vice President Regional Sales, Lynn Withrow
Vice President, Lynn Rossitto
Senior Vice President of Sales, Jim Holder
Vice President, Phyllis Petro
Vice President, John Palmieri
Vice President, Bob McNamara
Vice President Underwriting; CGHB, Frank Weltz
Vice President Global Digital Internet Strategy, William Gagnon
Vice President and National Medical Officer, Scott Josephs
Vice President, Linda Toolen
Vice President, David Harman
Medical Director, Hundt John

Vice President Global Marketing Customer Relationship Management, Michele Paige
Vice President, Ed Eberhard
Vice President Middle Market Sales, Gary Edwards
Vice President Information Technology, Rahul Singh
Vice President of Client Management, Gene Dours
Assistant Vice President Global Storage And Backup Engineer, Anthony Szwankowski
Vice President, Alan Carkner
Senior Vice President And Chief Actuary Cigna Supplemental Benefits, Tracy Maples
Senior Vice President And Associate Chief Counsel, Teresa Jordan
Vice President, Sanjiv Awasthi
Assistant Vice President Product Management, Craig Iredell
Vice President Network Management San Antonio Tx Markets, David Dupree
Domain Architect Avice President, Michelle Zaremskas
Vice President, Susan Quish
Assistant Vice President Operational Effectivness, Kevin Hutt
Vice President Clinical Operations, Jennifer Joy
Vice President Information Technology, Christine Snyder
Assistant Vice President Operational Effectiveness And Bpo Strategy; Service Operations, Leeanne Engels
Vice President, Matt Kenyon
Vice President of Sales, Christine Castellvi
Vice President, Brian Smith
Vice President Sales and Accou, Matt Alberico
Vice President Strategy and Marketing, Thor Kayeum
Assistant Vice President National Contracting, Chester Tom
Assistant Vice President Network Operations, Maryanne Bourdier
Vice President, Andrew Sullivan
Vice President Sales and Account Services, Kevin Ritchie
Vice President, William O'Donnell
Assistant Vice President Financial Systems, Richard Natale
Vice President National Account Executive, Barnett Michele
Medical Director, Andrea Houfek
Vice President Information Management, J Oates
Assistant Vice President Clinical Pharmacy Strategy, Michael Arvesen
Vice President, Kristen Gorodetzer
Medical Director, Lee Campbell
Regional Vice President Broker Sales CSB, Melissa Duong
Vice President and Chief Information Security Officer, James Beeson
National Account Manager, Patricia Lynn
Chairman, Isaiah (Ike) Harris, age 64
Auditors: PricewaterhouseCoopers LLP

LOCATIONS

HQ: Cigna Corp
900 Cottage Grove Road, Bloomfield, CT 06002
Phone: 860 226-6000   Fax: 860 226-6741
Web: www.cigna.com

PRODUCTS/OPERATIONS

2016 Sales

	$ mil.	% of total
Global health care	31,199	79
Global disability & life	4,443	11
Global supplemental benefits	3,385	9
Other operations	472	1
Net realized investment gains	169	-
Total	**39,668**	**100**

Selected Products and Services

Health care
  Behavioral health care benefits
  CareAllies (disease management and health advocacy)
  CIGNA Choice Fund (consumer-directed products)
  CIGNA Tel-Drug (mail order pharmacy)
  Dental insurance
  Managed care health plans (HMO PPO POS)
  Medicare Part D (prescription drug coverage)
  Prescription drug coverage
  Stop-loss coverage
  Voluntary plans
Disability and life
  Group disability insurance
  Group term life insurance
  Leave management services
  Workers' compensation case management
International
  Expatriate insurance
  Life accident and supplemental health insurance

COMPETITORS

AEGON	Humana
AIG	ING
AMERIGROUP	John Hancock Financial
AXA	Services
Aetna	Kaiser Foundation
Allianz	Health Plan
Allstate	MassMutual
Anthem	MetLife
Aon	Molina Healthcare
BUPA	New York Life
Blue Cross	Northwestern Mutual
CNA Financial	Principal Financial
CVS	Prudential
Centene	The Hartford
Coventry Health Care	UnitedHealth Group
Express Scripts	Unum Group
Health Net	WellCare Health Plans
Highmark	

HISTORICAL FINANCIALS

Company Type: Public

Income Statement
FYE: December 31

	ASSETS ($ mil.)	NET INCOME ($ mil.)	INCOME AS % OF ASSETS	EMPLOYEES
12/16	59,360	1,867	3.1%	41,000
12/15	57,088	2,094	3.7%	39,300
12/14	55,896	2,102	3.8%	37,200
12/13	54,336	1,476	2.7%	36,500
12/12	53,734	1,623	3.0%	35,800
Annual Growth	2.5%	3.6%	—	3.4%

2016 Year-End Financials

Debt ratio: 8.43%
Return on equity: 14.46%
Cash ($ mil.): 3,185
Current ratio: —
Long-term debt ($ mil.): —
No. of shares (mil.): 256
Dividends
  Yield: 0.0%
  Payout: 0.5%
Market value ($ mil.): 34,264

	STOCK PRICE ($) FY Close	P/E High/Low		PER SHARE ($) Earnings	Dividends	Book Value
12/16	133.39	20	16	7.19	0.04	53.42
12/15	146.33	21	12	8.04	0.04	46.91
12/14	102.91	13	9	7.83	0.04	41.55
12/13	87.48	17	10	5.18	0.04	38.35
12/12	53.46	10	7	5.61	0.04	34.18
Annual Growth	25.7%	—	—	6.4%	(0.0%)	11.8%

CIM Commercial Trust Corp

EXECUTIVES

EVP COO Chief Investment Officer and Treasurer, Jan F. Salit, age 62, $282,329 total compensation
EVP and CFO, Barry N. Berlin, age 52, $282,329 total compensation
President CEO and Secretary, Lance B. Rosemore, age 64, $418,903 total compensation
Independent Trustee, Nathan G. Cohen, age 70
Independent Trustee, Irving Munn, age 67
Independent Trustee, Barry A. Imber, age 69
Trustee, Martha Morrow
Auditors: BDO USA, LLP

LOCATIONS

HQ: CIM Commercial Trust Corp
17950 Preston Road, Suite 600, Dallas, TX 75252
Phone: 972 349-3200
Web: www.cimcommercial.com

COMPETITORS

Amerisource Funding	JER Investors Trust
Archon Group	Jameson Inns
Ashford Hospitality	Janus Hotels
Trust	Texas Capital
Capital Trust	Bancshares
Cullen/Frost Bankers	Vestin
FirstCity Financial	

HISTORICAL FINANCIALS

Company Type: Public

Income Statement
FYE: December 31

	ASSETS ($ mil.)	NET INCOME ($ mil.)	INCOME AS % OF ASSETS	EMPLOYEES
12/16	2,022	34	1.7%	10
12/15	2,098	24	1.2%	10
12/14	2,094	24	1.2%	33
12/13	253	2	0.8%	32
12/12	247	(2)	—	32
Annual Growth	69.0%	—	—	(25.2%)

2016 Year-End Financials

Debt ratio: 47.85%
Return on equity: 3.04%
Cash ($ mil.): 144
Current ratio: —
Long-term debt ($ mil.): —
No. of shares (mil.): 84
Dividends
  Yield: 0.0%
  Payout: 257.3%
Market value ($ mil.): 1,299

	STOCK PRICE ($) FY Close	P/E High/Low		PER SHARE ($) Earnings	Dividends	Book Value
12/16	15.45	59	44	0.34	0.88	11.51
12/15	15.54	84	58	0.25	0.88	13.28
12/14	15.01	93	18	0.25	0.66	13.93
12/13	8.60	10	7	1.00	2.50	63.77
12/12	7.10	—	—	(1.05)	3.00	65.31
Annual Growth	21.5% (35.2%)	—	—	—	(26.5%)	

Cincinnati Financial Corp.

Cincinnati Financial Corporation (CFC) provides a wide range of financial security products and services primarily in the Midwest and Southeast United States. Its flagship firm Cincinnati Insurance (operating through four property/casualty subsidiaries) sells commercial property liability excess and surplus auto bond and fire insurance. The companies' personal lines include homeowners auto and liability products. Another CFC subsidiary Cincinnati Life sells life disability income and annuities. The company's CFC Investment unit provides commercial financing leasing and real estate services to its independent insurance agents. Its CSU Producers Resources offers insurance brokerage services to independent agencies. The Schiff family formed CFC in 1968.

Operations

CFC operates through five segments: Commercial Lines Insurance Personal Lines Insurance Excess and Surplus Lines Insurance Life Insurance and Investments. The Commercial Lines Insurance segment which accounts for about 60% of total sales provides coverage including commercial property/casualty workers' compensation and management liability. Personal Lines Insurance accounting for more than 20% of sales writes personal automobile and homeowner products.

Investment earnings represent nearly 15% of revenue while excess and surplus lines and life insurance make up the remainder.

Subsidiaries include standard property/casualty insurers Cincinnati Casualty Company Cincinnati Indemnity Company Cincinnati Life Insurance Company and Cincinnati Specialty Underwriters Insurance Company.

Geographic Reach

CFC markets its policies in 41 states but does most of its business in the Midwest and Southeast US. The company writes some 20% of its business in Ohio and is strong in Illinois Indiana Georgia and Pennsylvania. It is licensed in 49 states the District of Columbia and Puerto Rico.

Sales and Marketing

CFC maintains a force of more than 1550 field associates who provide local service to some 1530 distributing independent agencies and policy holders.

Its commercial lines segment targets primarily small to mid-sized businesses. CFC has tied its growth to expanding the territories in which it markets and increasing the number of new agencies with which it strikes new relationships.

Cincinnati Insurance launched its first-ever national television ad in 2015.

Financial Performance

CFC revenue which has been on the rise for the past five years rose 6% to $6 billion in 2016. That gain was largely due to higher earned premiums but the company also saw higher net investment income net realized investment gains and fee revenues that year. The Commercial Lines Insurance Personal Lines Insurance and Excess and Surplus Lines Insurance all had increases in renewal written premiums that included higher prices while earned life insurance premiums rose nearly 10%.

Due to the company's growing revenues net income has generally been on the rise but it fell 7% to $591 million in 2016. Higher operating expenses including insurance losses contract holders' benefits and underwriting acquisition and insurance expenses took their toll on CFC's bottom line. A decrease in property/casualty underwriting in-

come included $114 million from higher catastrophe losses.

Cash flow from operations increased 4% to $1.1 billion in 2016 primarily due to changes in losses and loss expense reserves.

Strategy

Going forward CFC plans to wring more profit out of policies by raising deductibles and conducting more site inspections of properties it insures. CFC also works on developing new products and helping its independent and captive agents better market existing policies. To further broaden its operations the company works toward deepening its penetration into each market it serves. For example it has been introducing workers' compensation coverage in more states and new types of coverage include cyber protection and management liability.To counteract the negative impact that can occur in years with numerous catastrophes CFC plans to continue its geographic expansion and improved underwriting activities. And to decrease the frequency and severity of auto losses — which have been rising across the industry — the company has partnered with software firm LifeSaver to help employers enforce safety policies and prevent fleet drivers from phone-related distracted driving practices.

The group is also expanding its products and services for wealthy individuals. Since 2015 it has introduced the Executive Capstone program in New York California Colorado Texas and New Jersey; it plans to launch these offerings in additional markets including the District of Columbia Washington and Massachusetts.

HISTORY

Jack Schiff spent three years with the Travelers Company before he joined the Navy in WWII. He returned to Cincinnati to start his own independent insurance agency in 1946 and was joined by his younger brother Robert; both were Ohio State graduates whose affection for the Buckeyes led them in later years to close company banquets with the school fight song. The brothers incorporated Cincinnati Insurance with $200000 from investors.

Under Harry Turner the company's first president the company offered property/casualty insurance to small businesses and homeowners through its network of agents. By 1956 the company had spread into neighboring Kentucky and Indiana. During the next decade Cincinnati Insurance expanded its products and network adding auto burglary and commercial all-risk lines and enlisting agents throughout the Midwest.

In 1963 Turner took the chairman's seat and Jack Schiff became president introducing a more aggressive leadership style. In 1969 the company reorganized and went public forming Cincinnati Financial Corporation as a holding company for the insurance operation. CFC used the money to pay off debts and buy new businesses forming two subsidiaries: CFC Investment Company in 1970 to deal in commercial real estate and financing; and Queen City Indemnity (later named The Cincinnati Casualty Company) in 1972 to offer direct-bill personal policies.

By 1973 operations included The Life Insurance Company of Cincinnati Queen City Indemnity and fellow Cincinnati giant Inter-Ocean Insurance Company. That year Jack Schiff added CEO to his title.

CFC continued to grow throughout the 1970s with a new emphasis on independent investments. In 1982 Cincinnati Financial veteran Robert Morgan became president and CEO. The company's conservative roots and investment base helped it shake off the early-1980s recession and a string

of natural disasters that left many other insurers dangling in the wind.

Also during the 1980s the company started to shift its focus from personal to commercial lines. In 1988 it reorganized its life insurance subsidiaries under the Cincinnati Life banner and formed The Cincinnati Indemnity Company to offer workers' compensation and personal insurance. In 1998 a string of storms (reminiscent of others earlier in the decade) dampened the company's earnings.

EXECUTIVES

Senior Vice President Sales And Marketing Property Casualty Insuranc, Jacob Scherer

Senior Vice President of Operations, Timothy Timmel

Senior Vice President Strategic Planning Cincinnati Insurance, Donald Doyle

Senior Vice President Commercial Lines, Charles Stoneburner

President CEO and Director, Steven J. Johnston, age 57, $960,814 total compensation

Vice President Commercial, Anthony Henn

SVP CFO and Treasurer, Michael J. (Mike) Sewell, age 53, $784,665 total compensation

SVP Chief Investment Officer Assistant Secretary and Assistant Treasurer, Martin F. Hollenbeck, age 57, $646,808 total compensation

Assistant Vice President Fiel, Jack Douglas Kelley

Vice President, Matt Laws

Vice President, Craig Forrester

Assistant Vice President of Information Security, Michael Barron

Assistant Vice President Government Relations Of, Scott Gilliam

Vice President, Gary J Kline

Senior Vice President and Senior Marketing Officer, Glenn Nicholson

Vice President Commercial Lines, Mark Wietmarschen

Vice President Information Technology, Rich Mathews

Vice President Information Technology, Rich Williamson

Vice President of Personal Lines, Stephen Leibel

Vice President, Tom Scheid

Assistant Vice President, Carol Oler

Vice President and Manager Target Markets, Ronald Klimkowski

Vice President Marketing, Mike Terrell

Assistant Vice President, David Hartkemeier

Vice President and Corporate Counsel, Thomas Hogan

Legal Secretary, Rebecca Alexander

Vice President Sales And Marketing, Duane Swanson

Assistant Vice President, Frank Obermeyer

Assistant Vice President Information Technolog, Ryan Osborn

Vice President of Business Development, Phil Howard

Vice President Corporate Accounting The Cincinnati Insurance C, Todd Pendery

Vice President Assistant, Brett Starr

Senior Vice President Chief Underwriter The Cincinnati Life Insurance Company, Brad Behringer

Assistant Vice President Director of Worksite Marketing, Eric Taylor

Executive Vice President, Blake Slater

Assistant Vice President Commercial Lines Proper, David E McKinney

Assistant Vice President and Director Information Technology, Sean Sweeney

Vice President, Richard Matson

Vice President nformation Technology, Bill Geir

Vice President Finance Executive, Michael Abrams

Assistant Vice President Manager Learning and Development, Brad DeLaney
Assistant Vice President, Tony Henn
Legal Secretary, Amanda Turner
Assistant Vice President Commercial Lines, Carolyn MacDonald
Vice President, David Helmers
Vice President Target Markets, Klimkowski Ron
Executive Vice President, Jf Scherer
Vice President Field Claims, Charles Robinson
Vice President Target Markets, Stephen Spray
Vice President Administration Services, Dawn Alcorn
Vice President Director of Risk Management, Vicki Walno
Legal Secretary, Megan VanLeuven
Region Vice President, Pat Luchtel
Chairman, Kenneth W. (Ken) Stecher, age 70
Assistant Secretary Manager Life And Health Claims, Ann Binzer
Assistant Secretary Information Technology, Michael Hingsbergen
Assistant Secretary Excess And Surplus, Scott Hintze
Secretary, William Gregory
Assistant Sec Sales Field, Russell A Blessing
Assistant Secretary, Sean Givler
Secretary Planning and Risk Management, Dennis E Mcdaniel
Treasurer, Theresa Hoffer
Auditors: Deloitte & Touche LLP

LOCATIONS

HQ: Cincinnati Financial Corp.
  6200 S. Gilmore Road, Fairfield, OH 45014-5141
Phone: 513 870-2000
Web: www.cinfin.com

PRODUCTS/OPERATIONS

2016 Sales

	$ mil.	% of total
Earned premiums	4,710	87
Investment incomenet of expenses	595	11
Realized investment gains	124	2
Fee revenues	15	—
Other	5	—
Total	**5,449**	**100**

2016 Sales

	$ mil.	% of total
Commercial lines insurance	3,094	57
Personal lines insurance	1,165	22
Investment income	719	13
Life Insurance	233	4
Excess & surplus insurance	184	3
Other	54	1
Total	**5,449**	**100**

Selected Subsidiaries

CFC Investment Company
CSU Producer Resources Inc.
The Cincinnati Insurance Company
  The Cincinnati Casualty Company
  The Cincinnati Indemnity Company
  The Cincinnati Life Insurance Company
  The Cincinnati Specialty Underwriters Insurance Company

COMPETITORS

American Financial Group	OneBeacon
CNA Financial	Progressive Corporation
Erie Indemnity	Selective Insurance
Farmers Group	The Hartford
Great American Insurance Company	Travelers Companies
Indiana Insurance	Westfield Insurance
Ohio Casualty	Zurich American

HISTORICAL FINANCIALS

Company Type: Public

Income Statement

FYE: December 31

	ASSETS ($ mil.)	NET INCOME ($ mil.)	INCOME AS % OF ASSETS	EMPLOYEES
12/16	20,386	591	2.9%	4,754
12/15	18,888	634	3.4%	4,493
12/14	18,753	525	2.8%	4,305
12/13	17,662	517	2.9%	4,163
12/12	16,548	421	2.5%	4,057
Annual Growth	**5.4%**	**8.8%**	**—**	**4.0%**

2016 Year-End Financials

Debt ratio: 4.15%
Return on equity: 8.74%
Cash ($ mil.): 777
Current ratio: —
Long-term debt ($ mil.): —

No. of shares (mil.): 164
Dividends
Yield: 0.0%
Payout: 54.0%
Market value ($ mil.): 12,453

	STOCK PRICE ($) FY Close	P/E High/Low	PER SHARE ($) Earnings	Dividends	Book Value
12/16	75.75	22 15	3.55	1.92	42.94
12/15	59.17	16 13	3.83	2.30	39.21
12/14	51.83	16 14	3.18	1.76	40.15
12/13	52.37	17 12	3.12	1.66	37.24
12/12	39.16	16 12	2.57	1.62	33.45
Annual Growth	**17.9%**	**— —**	**8.4%**	**4.3%**	**6.4%**

Cintas Corporation

Cintas has a uniform approach to business. The #1 uniform supplier in the US boasts more than 1 million clients (McDonald's MGM Resorts) and some 5 million people wear its garb each day. Cintas — which sells leases and rents uniforms — operates 385 facilities in 288 cities across the US and Canada; it leases about half of them. Besides offering shirts jackets slacks and footwear the company provides clean-room apparel and flame-resistant clothing. Other products offered by Cintas include uniform cleaning first-aid and safety products and clean-room supplies. Richard Farmer founded the company in 1968. Cintas is run by his son CEO Scott Farmer.

Operations

In 2015 Cintas realigned its organizational structure and updated its reportable operating segments in light of certain changes in its business including the acquisition of ZEE Medical. It now has two segments - Uniform Rental and Facility Services and First Aid and Safety Services.

Uniform Rental and Facility Services (77% of total revenues in 2016) consists of the rental and servicing of uniforms and other garments including flame resistant clothing mats mops and shop towels and other ancillary items. In addition to these rental items it provides restroom cleaning services and supplies and carpet and tile cleaning services.

First Aid and Safety Services (9%) consists of first aid and safety products and services.

The remainder of Cintas' businesses (14%) consist primarily of Fire Protection Services and its Direct Sale business.

Geographic Reach

Cincinnati-based Cintas operates about 377 facilities including five manufacturing plants and eight distribution centers in some 286 cities across the US and Canada. It also serves businesses in Asia Europe and Latin America. The company has approximately 9000 local delivery routes.

Sales and Marketing

Cintas provides its products and services to more than 1 million businesses of all sizes. Cintas uses its corporate website www.cintas.com as a channel for routine distribution of important information including news releases analyst presentations and financial information.

Financial Performance

The company has seen an upward trend in its revenues since 2011.

In fiscal 2016 Cintas' net revenues increased by 10%.

Revenues from the Uniform Rental and Facility Services grew by 6.7% including an organic revenue increase of 6.4%. The amount of new business grew resulting from an increase in the number and productivity of sales representatives due to increased tenure and improved training which resulted in a higher number of products and services sold. Revenues also rose via acquisitions and increased working days in fiscal 2016.

First Aid and Safety Services and All Other revenues increased 20.3%. Some 8% was due to improved sales representative productivity. Acquisitions positively impacted the growth rate by 11.8% and two more workdays positively impacted growth.

Cintas has recorded an increasing trend net income over the last five years.

In fiscal 2016 net income increased by 61% due to income from discontinued operations (Shred-it).

Cash from operating activities decreased by 20% due to the $229.5 million payment of taxes due on the gain on the sale of Shred-it. Excluding the impact of this tax payment net cash provided by operations increased $115 million as a result of increased net income partially offset by changes in working capital.

Strategy

Cintas' strategy for adding to its customer base includes investing in its sales force across all business segments as well expanding geographically. Beyond its dominant position in uniform rental and sales Cintas is looking to emerging businesses such as First Aid Safety and Fire Protection Services for growth. While still relatively small representing 9% of sales the business is growing through acquisitions and the introduction of new services. It is looking to increase its penetration with existing customers and by broadening its customer base to include business segments to which it has not historically served. It will also continue to identify additional product and service opportunities for its current and future customers.

The company pursues the strategy of broadening its customer base in several ways. Cintas has a national sales organization introducing all of its products and services to prospects in all business segments. Its broad range of products and services allows its sales organization to consider any type of business a prospect. It also broadens its customer base through geographic expansion especially in its first aid and safety and fire protection businesses.

To raise cash to pay down debt and reinvest in its core businesses in 2015 Cintas sold its 42% stake in Shred-it International to JV partner Stericycle for about $600 million. In 2014 the company exited another line of business when it sold a portion of its document management operations for $180 million.

Mergers and Acquisitions

As part of the strategy in 2016 Cintas acquired two businesses included in the Uniform Rental and Facility Services segment two businesses included in the First Aid and Safety Services segment and six businesses included in All Other. The company also acquired Zee Medical for $130 million which expanded its footprint in van-delivered first aid safety training and emergency products.

In 2017 Cintas acquired rival G&K Services a top-five uniform rental company for $2.2 billion. The acquisition will bolster Cintas' business customer base broaden its service areas and strengthen its route operations. G&K Services now operates as a subsidiary of the company.

HISTORY

In 1929 onetime animal trainer boxer and blacksmith Richard "Doc" Farmer started a business of salvaging old rags cleaning them and then selling them to factories. Farmer later began renting the rags to his customers. He would pick up the dirty rags clean them and return them to the factory. By 1936 the Acme Overall & Rag Laundry had established itself in Cincinnati with plans to convert an old bathhouse into a laundry. Farmer along with his adopted son Herschell suffered a setback from flood damage in 1937 but the family rebuilt and continued to grow the business.

Doc Farmer died in 1952 and Herschell assumed command of the company. Five years later Herschell turned the reins over to his 23-year-old son Richard who immediately moved Acme into the uniform rental market and the company blossomed. Throughout the 1960s the company grew enormously aided by Richard's innovative leadership. (Acme was the first to use a polyester-cotton blend that lasted twice as long as normal cotton work uniforms.) Through a holding company Richard established a string of uniform plants in the Midwest starting with a factory in Cleveland in 1968. Four years later the company changed its name to Cintas.

At this time the company began tapping into the new corporate identity market pushing the idea that uniforms convey a sense of professionalism and present a cleaner safer image. The company began to custom-design the uniforms adding logos and distinctive colors. This aspect of the business compelled Cintas to expand to help accommodate its national clients; by 1972 the company had offices throughout Ohio and in Chicago Detroit and Washington DC. By 1975 Cintas was operating in 13 states.

The company went public in 1983. For the rest of the 1980s Cintas rode the wave of consolidation in the uniform rental industry making a slew of acquisitions. The company also expanded from its blue-collar base into the service industry and began to supply uniforms to hotels restaurants and banks. By the early 1990s Cintas was a presence in most major US cities and its share of the US market had climbed to about 10%. Farmer turned over the title of CEO to president Robert Kohlhepp in 1995. That year the company acquired Cadet Uniform Services a Toronto uniform rental business for $41 million.

Scott Farmer Richard's 38-year-old son was named president and COO in 1997. That year Cintas made a number of acquisitions including Micron-Clean Uniform Service and Canadian firms Act One Uniform Rentals and DW King Services. The company also moved into the first aid supplies industry with its purchase of American First Aid and added clean-room garments to its expanding list of uniform rentals. In 1998 Cintas acquired uniform rental company Apparelmaster as well as Chicago-based Uniforms To You a $150 million design and manufacturing company. In an effort to expand its corporate uniform business the company acquired rival Unitog in 1999 for about $460 million.

As part of the integration of Unitog in 2000 Cintas closed several of Unitog's uniform rental operations distribution centers and manufacturing plants. The company also established first aid supplies and safety equipment unit Xpect. In 2002 Cintas purchased Omni Services marking its largest acquisition to date.

Cintas purchased more than 10 document management businesses and three first-aid and fire protection businesses in fiscal 2009.

In fiscal 2013 it launched its AR Red Suiting Collection (made with renewable-sourced fiber) as well as its Signature Series line of designer soap and toilet paper dispensers and related products.

EXECUTIVES

VP Research and Development, J. Phillip Holloman, age 62, $643,966 total compensation
Chairman and CEO, Scott D. Farmer, age 58, $1,000,000 total compensation
SVP Secretary and General Counsel, Thomas E. Frooman, age 50, $499,550 total compensation
VP Finance and CFO, J. Michael (Mike) Hansen, age 49, $360,000 total compensation
VP and Treasurer, Paul F. Adler, age 46, $250,000 total compensation
Regional Vice President, Greg Eling
Vice President of Application Services Finance SupplyChain Human Resources, Mark Greiner
VICE PRESIDENT OF ADMINISTRATION, Keith Fleming
VICE PRESIDENT AND MARRIOTT LODGING UNIFORMS AND SERVICES, Donna L Williams
Board Member, Lynn Burton
Treasurer, Mike Thompson
Auditors: Ernst & Young LLP

LOCATIONS

HQ: Cintas Corporation
6800 Cintas Boulevard, P.O. Box 625737, Cincinnati, OH 45262-5737
Phone: 513 459-1200 **Fax:** 513 573-4030
Web: www.cintas.com

PRODUCTS/OPERATIONS

2016 sales

	$ mil.	% of total
Uniforms Rental & Facility Services	3,777	77
First aid and safety services	461	9
All others	665	14
Total	**4,905**	**100**

Selected Products and Services

Clean-room supplies
Entrance mats
Fender covers
Fire protection
First aid and safety products and services
Linen products
Mops
Restroom supplies
Towels
Uniform cleaning
Uniform rental and sales

COMPETITORS

ARAMARK	NCH
Alsco	Superior Uniform Group
Angelica Corporation	UniFirst
Iron Mountain Inc	

HISTORICAL FINANCIALS

Company Type: Public

Income Statement

FYE: May 31

	REVENUE ($ mil.)	NET INCOME ($ mil.)	NET PROFIT MARGIN	EMPLOYEES
05/17	5,323	480	9.0%	42,000
05/16	4,905	693	14.1%	35,000
05/15	4,476	430	9.6%	32,000
05/14	4,551	374	8.2%	33,000
05/13	4,316	315	7.3%	32,000
Annual Growth	**5.4%**	**11.1%**	**—**	**7.0%**

2017 Year-End Financials

Debt ratio: 45.78%	No. of shares (mil.): 105
Return on equity: 23.19%	Dividends
Cash ($ mil.): 169	Yield: 1.0%
Current ratio: 1.73	Payout: 27.5%
Long-term debt ($ mil.): 2,770	Market value ($ mil.): 13,268

	STOCK PRICE ($) FY Close	P/E High/Low		PER SHARE ($) Earnings	Dividends	Book Value
05/17	125.88	28	20	4.38	1.33	21.85
05/16	94.80	15	13	6.21	1.05	17.68
05/15	86.09	23	17	3.63	1.70	17.30
05/14	62.12	20	15	3.05	0.77	18.74
05/13	45.66	18	14	2.52	0.64	18.00
Annual Growth	**28.9%**	**—**	**—**	**14.8%**	**20.1%**	**5.0%**

Cisco Systems Inc

Cisco Systems makes the network gear — routers switches and servers as well as software — that move information around the internet and corporate networks. The company which has dominated the market for internet protocol-based networking equipment also makes security devices internet conferencing systems set-top boxes and other networking equipment to businesses and government agencies. Software that controls networks has become an increasing focus for Cisco which also provides consulting services. Most sales come from customers in the Americas. Cisco's primary customers are large enterprises and telecommunications service providers but it also sells products designed for small businesses.

Operations

The meat-and-potatoes of Cisco has been its switching equipment which generates 30% of its revenue while its next-generation networking routing gear accounts for 15% of revenue. Services provide about a quarter of the company's. The rest of the company?s product lines are collaboration products (about 10% of revenue) data center (less than 10%) and wireless and security (about 5% each).

Cisco engages independent third-party contractors to make printed-circuit boards conduct in-circuit testing make product repairs and assemble products.

Geographic Reach

While the Americas is Cisco's largest market accounting for some 60% of its sales about half its employees reside outside of the US. European customers generate 25% of revenue and the Asia/Pacific region supplies about 15%.

Cisco's headquarters is in San Jose California. It also has regional headquarters in Amsterdam and Singapore. Cisco has a Globalization Center East campus in Bangalore India. The company has other significant operations in Belgium China France Germany India Israel Italy Japan Norway and the UK.

Financial Performance

Cisco Systems? revenue slipped 3% to $48 billion in 2017 (ended July) from 2016. Product revenue fell 4% while service revenue rose 3% year-to-year. Revenues from Switching and NGN Routing were off 5% and 4% respectively in 2017. Switching sales were hurt by lower sales of switches used in campus environments due to general economic uncertainty and competition. Sales in Security and Wireless grew by 9% and 5% respectively.

Net income dropped 11% to $9.6 billion in 2017 from 2016. While the company reduced costs in 2017 it had a higher effective tax rate for the year.

Cash flow from operations closed out 2017 at $13.8 billion compared to about $13.6 billion in 2016.

Strategy

Cisco has been a hardware company making the switches and routers and other devices that transfer information. But it is building up its software offerings for cloud computing and software-defined networks (SDN). Telecom service providers in particular are moving toward SDN to program their networks. In response Cisco is shifting its business to a more subscription and software-based model. To address the emergence of SDN the company offers its Application Centric Infrastructure (ACI) which delivers centralized application-driven policy automation management and visibility of both physical and virtual environments as a single system. The system is composed of Cisco's Nexus 9000 portfolio of switches improved versions of its NX-OS operating system and the Application Policy Infrastructure Controller (APIC).

In another software-centric strategy the company?s Cisco DNA Center a centralized management dashboard for its intuitive network and ETA are available through subscriptions on the Cisco Catalyst 9000 Series Switches. Such moves get Cisco closer to cloud-managed products and services across our its networking portfolio. In 2017 (ended July) the company?s deferred product revenue related to software and subscriptions grew to $5 billion a 50% year-to-year increase and a doubling over two years.

The company is also addressing its software capabilities through acquisitions. In 2017 the company was to spend nearly $6 billion to shore up its software side in networking file systems and telecommunications.

In 2015 Cisco partnered with Ericsson to develop products and services in areas such as 5G cloud computing internet protocol and the Internet of Things. Their goal is to add $1 billion in revenue for each company by 2018. The deal helps Cisco and Ericsson counter the merger of Alcatel-Lucent and Nokia which created the second biggest provider of telecom equipment (Huawei is #1).

In 2017 Cisco teamed up with Google to build more efficient hybrid cloud offerings. They are to work on the security configuration and policy requirements of enterprises as well as capabilities for delivering real-time networking and performance data.

Mergers and Acquisitions

Cisco actively acquires companies to expand technologies and fill gaps.

Cisco started 2017 with the $3.7 billion acquisition of AppDynamics which develops software that monitors performance of applications. The acquisition further fills out Cisco's networking software lineup. Cisco's acquisition offer came just before AppDynamics sold stock to the public in an initial public offering. The deal concluded in March 2017 reinforced Cisco's software-centric strategy.

In mid-2017 Cisco agreed to acquire Springpath Inc. a developer of a distributed file system built for hyperconvergence that enables server-based storage systems for about $320 million in cash. The companies have had a relationship that includes development of HyperFlex an integrated hyperconvergence infrastructure. Cisco also was an investor in Springpath. Hyperconvergence integrates computing storage networking and virtualization resources in hardware. The deal further builds out Cisco's data center capabilities.

Cisco continued its software shopping spree later in 2017 with its agreement to buy BroadSoft a developer of telecommunications software for $1.9 billion. The deal would provide Cisco with a range of software and services that allow mobile fixed-line and cable service providers to offer unified communications over their internet protocol networks. The transaction was approved by the boards of both companies and was expected to close in early 2018.

In another 2017 deal Cisco acquired MindMeld Inc. an artificial intelligence company that develops conversational interfaces for applications and devices for about $125 million. The acquisition would help Cisco build voice and text capabilities into its collaboration products.

In 2016 Cisco completed the acquisition of Jasper which develops a cloud-based Internet of Things (IoT) service platform for $1.4 billion. With the deal Cisco can provide more comprehensive range of IoT products and services.

In 2016 Cisco completed the acquisition of Jasper which develops a cloud-based Internet of Things (IoT) service platform for $1.4 billion. With the deal Cisco can provide more comprehensive range of IoT products and services.

EXECUTIVES

Vice President Information Technology, Joel Bion
Vp Application Delivery Business Unit, George Kurian
Vice President, Ross Fowler
VP; General Manager Broadband Edge and Midrange Routing Business Unit, Pankaj S. Patel, $749,135 total compensation
EVP Worldwide Sales and Field Operations, Chris Dedicoat, $691,490 total compensation
SVP Cloud Services and Platforms; CTO, Zorawar Biri Singh
Chairman and CEO, Charles H. (Chuck) Robbins, age 51, $1,172,115 total compensation
Chairman and CEO Cisco Greater China, Owen Chan
SVP and Chief Operations, Rebecca J. Jacoby
SVP and General Manager Collaboration Technology Group, Rowan M. Trollope
President Cisco Capital, Kristine A. (Kris) Snow, age 57
President Latin America Theater, Jordi Botifoll
President Smart+Connected Communities and Deputy Chief Globalization Officer, Anil Menon
SVP and General Manager Cisco Security Solutions, Bryan Palma
EVP and CFO, Kelly A. Kramer, $749,135 total compensation
SVP IT, Guillermo Diaz
SVP and Chief Marketing Officer, Karen Walker
President Cisco India and Saarc, Sameer Garde
Svp And General Manager Service Provider Video Technology Group, Jesper Andersen
Vice President, Mark Gorman
Senior Vice President Enterprise Products and Solutions, Robert Soderbery
Vice President, Ole Troan
Vice President Operations, Ana Corrales
Vice President Of Business Development, Mario Mastromattei

Vice President Of Service Provider Marketing, Suraj Shetty
Senior Vice President Corporate Controller and Chief Accounting Officer, Prat Bhatt
Corporate Vice President, Jack Xu
Vice President and CISO, Steve Martino
Vice President Marketing Deutsche Telekom Ag, Hanswerner Neubert
Vice President US Partner Organization, Todd Meister
Vice President, Arcangelo Fanelli
Senior Vice President Worldwide Sales Strategy and Operations, Mark Patterson
Head Of Research Director Vice President, John Shaw
Vice President, Bruce Laird
Vice President Canadian Services Operations, Derek Mak
Vice President Strategic Accounts, Peter Lynskey
Senior Vice President Planning Information Technology, Ana Cardamon
Vice President Market Development, Paul Bosco
Vice Presidentglobal Manufacturing Operations Supply Chain Operations, Jeff Gallinat
Vp sales, Pankaj Lulla
Vice President Plant, Don McClaughlin
Area Vice President, Jesper Knutsson
Senior Vice President, David Chai
Vice President And Deputy General Counsel, Lynn Easterling
Inside Sales Select Vpam, Harold Ellis
Vice President Global Video and Connected Life Solutions, Stephen Silva
Vice President Enterprise and Mid Market Solutions Marketing, Paul McNab
Vice President and CTO, Bret Hartman
Senior Vice President Software, John Brigden
Vice President Corporate Strategy, Rama Naageswaran
Regional Vice President Cisco Systems Administrator, Mark Guerrazzi
Vice President Manufacturing, Chee Wai Foong
Vice President Advanced Services, Flint Brenton
Senior Vice President and General Manager: Server Access Virtualization Group, David Yen
Vice President Marketing, Sharad Rastogi
Vice President Global Government Solutions, Robert Jones
VP Supply Chain, Gary Cooper
Vice President of Worldwide Channel Account Managers, Mary Iverson
Vice President E Commerce, Karthik Krishnamurthy
Vice Presidentproduct Management, Steve Chazin
Area Vice President Us Sales, Georges Antoun
Vpam Small Business Fl South North Carolina South Carolina, Richard Hinkley
Vpss Flexpod, Cesar Hurtado
Vice President of Customer Service and Energy Delivery, Ania Nachajska
Vice President Systems Engineering, Michael Koons
Vice President Banking and Financial Services At Cisco Systems, Arindam Mukherjee
Vice President Federal Operations, Ed McCrossen
Vice President, Randy Harrell
Vice President Customer Value Chain Management, Jeff Devine
Vice President New Business Ventures, Sanjay Pol
Vice President Finance Operations, Debbie Normington
Area Vice President Us Sales, Roxann Swanson
Vice Presidentibsg, Richard Cantwell
Vice President Finance, Phil Roush
VICE PRESIDENT, Kathleen Weslock
Vice President Of Corporate Portfolio Management A, Inder Singh
Senior Vice President of Engineering, Sumeet Arora
Vice President Information Technology Customer Strategy and Success, Lance Perry

Consulting Systems Engineer Northeast Security VPN Cisco Representative, Ken Kaminski
Vice President and General Manager, Bill Gartner
Vice President Engineering Network Software and Systems, Amit S Phadnis
Vice President Of Marketing, Andy Blackburn
Vice President of Software Engineering, Ramesh Bodapati
Vice President Sales and Purchasing, Peter Buchmeier
Vice President, Parvesh Sethi
Vice President Sales and Marketing, Leon Baranovsky
Area Vice President Commercial Sales S, David Ruggiero
Major Vice President Marketing Cisco Systems, Mitch Connor
Vice President World Wide Supply Chain Management, Steve Darendinger
Vice President Systems Engineering, Maria Cannon
Vice President Sales, David Copley
Vice President Ethernet Switching Technology Group, Jeff Reed
Vice President Marketing Smb, Joseph Puthussery
Vice President of Sales, Kamil Budny
Vice President Technology Marketing, John John Bruno
SA VP Human Resources, Cindy Cato
Area Vice President, Tim Coogan
Vice President United Kingdom and Ireland, Duncan Mitchell
Senior Vice President And General Counsel, Mark Chandler
Vice President of Sales and Marketing, Debbie Bernard
Vice President Finance, Anthony Gould
Senior Vice President Asia Pacific and Japan, Irving Tan
Vice President Marketing, Jermey Bevan
Senior Vice President, Michael Ganser
Area Vice President for State and Local Government and Education, Tony Morelli
Vice President Global Sales and Human Resources, Charlie Johnston
Vice President of Operations for North America and Japan, Gaurav Saple
Vice President North American Center of Excellence, Conrad Clemson
Regional Vice President Sales, Doug Chamberlain
Vice President and Chief Privacy Officer, Michelle Dennedy
Sales Vice President, Marcy Blair
Vice President, Eli Neumann
National Account Manager, Daniel Lungu
VPN, Gowthami Rao
Vice President.europe, Santiago Solanas
Virtual Sales vPAM, Mohamed Sharkawi
Vice President For Student Services, Jerry Dodson
Vice President Strategy, Macario Namie
Vice President EMEA Marketing, Jeremy Bevan
Corporate Senior Vice President and President of Subscriber Networks, Michael Harney
Vice President Services Marketing, Mike Riegel
Vice President Engineering, Ranganathan Sudhakar
Deputy City Clerk Treasurer, Hal Ogata
Board Member, Kevin Hughes
Board Member, Richard Kovacevich
Board Member, Mary Cirillo
Board Member, David Draper
Auditors: PricewaterhouseCoopers LLP

LOCATIONS

HQ: Cisco Systems Inc
 170 West Tasman Drive, San Jose, CA 95134
Phone: 408 526-4000
Web: www.cisco.com

2017 sales

	$ mil.	% of total
Americas	28,341	60
Europe the Middle East& Africa	12,004	25
Asia-Pacific regionJapan & China	7,650	15
Total	**48,005**	**100**

PRODUCTS/OPERATIONS

2017 sales

	$ mil.	% of total
Product		
Switching	13,949	29
NGN Routing	7,831	16
Service provider video	946	2
Collaboration	4,352	9
Data Center	4,278	9
Wireless	2,766	6
Security	2,153	4
Other	554	-
Service	12,300	25
Total	**48,005**	**100**

Selected Products

Access servers
Blade servers
Cable modems
Cables and cords
Content delivery devices
Customer contact software
Digital video recorders
Ethernet concentrators hubs and transceivers
Interfaces and adapters
Network management software
Networked applications software
Optical platforms
Power supplies
Routers
Security components
Switches
Telephony access systems
Television set-top boxes
Video networking
Virtual private network (VPN) systems
Voice integration applications
Wireless networking

Selected Acquisitions

COMPETITORS

ARRIS	Huawei Technologies
Amazon.com	IBM
Aruba Networks	Juniper Networks
Avaya	LogMeIn
Belden	MRV Communications
Brocade Communications	Meru Networks
CA Inc.	Microsoft
Check Point Software	Motorola Mobility
Ciena	NETGEAR
Citrix Systems	NSN
D-Link	Nutanix
Dell	Pace
ECI Telecom	Palo Alto Networks
Ericsson	Polycom
Extreme Networks	Symantec
F5 Networks	Technicolor
Fortinet	Tellabs
Harris Corp.	VMware
Hewlett Packard Enterprise	ZTE

HISTORICAL FINANCIALS
Company Type: Public

Income Statement
FYE: July 29

	REVENUE ($ mil.)	NET INCOME ($ mil.)	NET PROFIT MARGIN	EMPLOYEES
07/17	48,005	9,609	20.0%	72,900
07/16	49,247	10,739	21.8%	73,700
07/15	49,161	8,981	18.3%	71,833
07/14	47,142	7,853	16.7%	74,042
07/13	48,607	9,983	20.5%	75,049
Annual Growth	(0.3%)	(1.0%)	—	(0.7%)

2017 Year-End Financials
Debt ratio: 25.97%—
Return on equity: 14.86%
Cash ($ mil.): 11,708
Current ratio: 3.03
Long-term debt ($ mil.): 25,725
Dividends
 Yield: 0.0%
 Payout: 57.8%
Market value ($ mil.): —

	STOCK PRICE ($) FY Close	P/E High/Low		PER SHARE ($) Earnings	Dividends	Book Value
07/17	31.52	18	15	1.90	1.10	13.27
07/16	30.53	14	11	2.11	0.94	12.64
07/15	28.40	17	13	1.75	0.80	11.74
07/14	25.97	18	13	1.49	0.72	11.09
07/13	25.50	14	8	1.86	0.62	10.97
Annual Growth	5.4%	—	—	0.5%	15.4%	4.9%

CIT Group Inc

On the big-business landscape for about a century CIT Group is a financial holding company that offers lending leasing debt restructuring equipment financing and advisory services to small- and mid-sized businesses in such industries as energy health care retail communications manufacturing IT services and sports. The company also operates $40 billion-asset CIT Bank in Utah which offers commercial financing and leasing as well as online deposit products such as CDs. Founded in 1908 CIT serves clients worldwide.

HISTORY

Henry Ittleson founded CIT Group as Commercial Credit and Investment Trust in St. Louis in 1908. Initially financing horse-drawn carriages it moved to New York in 1915 as Commercial Investment Trust (CIT) to participate in one of the milestones of modern consumer debt: Its auto financing program launched in collaboration with Studebaker was the first of its kind.

CIT diversified into industrial financing during the 1920s and went public in 1924 on the NYSE. Cars remained a strong focus though: When Ford Motor Co. ran into difficulties in 1933 it sold financing division Universal Credit Corp. to CIT. CIT continued to expand into industrial financing incorporating its industrial business as CIT Financial Corp. in 1942.

During the post-WWII boom CIT began financing manufactured home sales and offering small loans. In 1964 it consolidated factoring operations into Meinhard-Commercial Corp. By the end of the 1960s the firm started to retreat from auto financing focusing instead on industrial leasing factoring and equipment financing.

In 1980 RCA bought CIT seeking to buy financing to develop its other businesses. RCA found the debt from the purchase unwieldy however and sold

CIT to Manufacturers Hanover Bank (Manny Hanny) in 1984. The bank bought CIT to expand outside its home state of New York: Though it could not open banks out of state Manny Hanny could still offer financial services through CIT which became The CIT Group in 1986.

Manny Hanny executives tried to bring aggressive management to staid top-heavy CIT. The company sold its Inventory Finance division in 1987 divested the consumer loan business in 1988 and consolidated the Meinhard-Commercial and Manufacturers Hanover factoring units in 1989. By then Manny Hanny was cash-strapped over losses incurred from foreign loans so it sold a 60% stake in CIT to The Dai-Ichi Kangyo Bank of Japan.

CIT gave Dai-Ichi entr©e into US financial services and it began expanding CIT's range of services again including equity investment (1990) credit finance (from its purchase of Fidelcor Business Credit in 1991) and venture capital (1992). CIT also reentered the consumer loan market (including home equity lending) with a new Consumer Finance group (1992).

In 1995 Chemical Bank (Manny Hanny's successor; now part of JPMorgan Chase) sold an additional 20% share to Dai-Ichi bumping the Japanese bank's holdings to 80% and arranging to sell its remaining shares to Dai-Ichi. In 1997 instead of Dai-Ichi buying the rest of Chase's shares CIT bought them and spun them off to the public. In 1998 Dai-Ichi reduced its stake.

In 1999 CIT bought Newcourt Credit Group North America's #2 equipment finance and leasing firm; it also bought Heller Financial's commercial services unit. In 2000 the firm worked on integrating Newcourt and sold its Hong Kong consumer finance unit.

Tyco International bought CIT in 2001 renaming the new subsidiary Tyco Capital. Under Tyco's umbrella it sold its manufactured home loan portfolio to Lehman Brothers and recreational vehicle portfolio to Salomon Smith Barney in an effort to exit noncore businesses. Tyco however expanded too far too fast and the next year announced an about-face on its financial services subsidiary deciding to spin off the division and return it to its CIT identity.

Jeff Peek took the reins of the company from longtime chairman and CEO Al Gamper in 2004.

CIT Group's Student Loan Xpress unit was one of several companies in the student-lending industry that came under investigation for business practices in 2007. It discontinued its private student loans that year and in 2008 it stopped originating government-guaranteed student loans.

Amid losses the company also exited the consumer finance business to focus on commercial lending. In 2008 it sold its home loan unit to Lone Star Funds and its manufactured housing portfolio to Vanderbilt Mortgage and Finance. The previous year it sold its construction lending unit to Wells Fargo and its 30% stake in Dell Financial Services to Dell.

CIT was hit hard in the economic recession which nearly shut down the credit markets. The company struggled to stay afloat as liquidity levels sank (a situation exacerbated as nervous customers drew on their credit lines). It exited money-losing businesses sold units and secured $3 billion from company bondholders including PIMCO and Oaktree Capital. The company also converted to a bank holding company enabling it to access government bailout funds. Still struggling CIT filed for Chapter 11 in November 2009. The restructuring lasted six weeks and helped the company eliminate more than $10 billion in debt. None of CIT's operating subsidiaries were included in the bankruptcy.

Jeffrey Peek who oversaw CIT's untimely expansion activities stepped down as CEO in early 2010. He was succeeded by John Thain who has also led Merrill Lynch and New York Stock Exchange. No stranger to turning ailing companies around Thain is credited with bringing the NYSE into the modern era with electronic trading. He also merged NYSE with Euronext establishing the first trans-Atlantic exchange.

EXECUTIVES

President CIT Rail, George D. Cashman, age 63

EVP and CFO, John J. Fawcett

EVP and Head of Technology and Operations, Denise M. Menelly, age 55, $253,846 total compensation

EVP and Chief Marketing and Communications Officer, Gina M. Proia, age 45

President CIT Commercial Finance, James L. (Jim) Hudak, age 53, $503,526 total compensation

EVP and Chief Risk Officer, Robert C. Rowe, age 56

EVP General Counsel and Corporate Secretary, Stuart Alderoty, age 58

President CIT Real Estate Finance, Matthew E. (Matt) Galligan, age 63

Chairman and CEO; President and CEO CIT Bank, Ellen R. Alemany, age 61, $883,333 total compensation

EVP and Chief Strategy Officer, Kelley Morrell, age 37

President Consumer Banking CIT Business Capital and California, Steven (Steve) Solk, age 62

EVP and Chief Human Resources Officer, James J. (Jim) Duffy, age 62

President Aviation Lending, Jennifer Villa Tennity

Managing Director Aerospace Defense and Government Services, John Heskin

Senior Vice President and Corporate Controller, Carol Hayles

Executive Vice President and Chief Auditor, Robert Hart

Executive Vice President and Treasurer, Israel Kaufman

Senior Vice President, Monahan Mike

Vice President Sarbanes Oxley Compliance, Sharon Stevens

Vice President, Yak Tan

Assistant Vice President Senior Business Analyst BI, Jennifer Repik

Assistant Vice President Fleet Engineering, Barry Parmenter

Credit Officer Special Handling Assistant Vice President, Amy Pratt

Senior Vice President, John Edel

Assistant Vice President Risk Management Reporting and Analytics, Maria ReCasino

Vice President, Julianne Allen

Vice President Strategy and Business Development, Ritche Redondo

Vice President Strategic Marketing, Ann Crater

Assistant Vice President Fleet Operations, Charles Burdic

Assistant Vice President Credit Scoring, Xiaoman Wang

Vice President Dealer Service, Rob Sureda

Vice President, Jeff Rushnak

Audit Vice President, Janet Simms

Assistant Vice President Information Technology, Terrell Woods

Vice President New Aircraft, Craig McIntyre

Senior Vice President Bsa Aml And Ofac Sanctions Compliance Head, Michelle Goodsir

Vice President Data Governance, Mark Burge

Vice President, George Fikaris

Vice President Threat and Vulnerability Management Information, Roman Brozyna

Vice President Finance, Lucas Develder

Senior Vice President National Manager, Kenneth Wendler

Senior Vice President And Chief M And A Counsel, Christopher Paul

Vice President, Joel Wolitzer

Senior Vice President and Chief Counsel Transportation Finance, Randy Feuerstein

Vice President Collections, Denise Byrd

Assistant Vice President Financial Analyst, Darby Marasigan

Vice President Sponsor Finance, Ian Walsh

Vice President, Kristin Appelbaum

Vice President, Ronald Gibney

Executive Vice President Chief Credit And Risk Officer Corporate Credit Risk Management, Nancy Foster

Assistant Vice President, Randy Lane

Vice President Aml Compliance, Rachel Benjamin

Assistant Vice President Portfolio Manager, Carolle Sorel

Assistant Vice President, Joshua Hare

Assistant Vice President, Rosalyn Jones

Compensation and Benefits Vice President, Catherine Cloake

Vice President, Sohail Khan

Vice President Sox, Doreen Chambers

Assistant Vice President, Soheir Krauss

Vice President, Debra Brown

Assistant Vice President Sales Support, Haley Werle

Vice President, Patricia Matos

Vice President Enterprise Architecture, Woodie Westbrook

Vice President Enterprise Portfolio Manager, Katherine Mahoney

Vice President, Kai Liang

Vice President Corporate Compliance, Khyati Desai

Vice President, William Riggin

Vice President, Jim Condina

Assistant Vice President Events, James Spencer

Senior Vice President, Eugene Schwartz

Sales Support Manager Assistant Vice President, James Bailey

Vice President Consumer Finance Operations, Krista Neal

Vice President Employment Human, Tammy Haynie

Vice President Sales, Thomas Gonnella

Executive Vice President, Kenneth Brown

Vice President Finance, Frederick Rick

Senior Vice President, Munish Gupta

Vice President Finance (Vendor LATAM Reg Reporting Data quality), Raul Santoyo

Assistant Vice President, Adam Schacter

Assistant Vice President Of New Aircraft Programs, Howard Mitchell

Assistant Vice President Of Fleet Planning And Tec, Joy Kelly

Vice President Cit Healthcare, Kirk Strittmatter

Executive Vice President and Treasurer, Glenn Alan Votek

Vice President Finance, Henry Trautfetter

Executive Vice President, Ken Brause

Vice President Sales, Ken Brown

Assistant Vice President Corporate Finance, Nicole C Rapport

Vice President, Diane Harris

Vice President Compliance, Alison Anderson

Vice President Finance, Patricia Meyerhoefer

Vice President Project and Service Management, Russell Hansen

Vice President Operational Risk, Dan Beck

Senior Vice President, Mike Cleary

Vice President, Daniel Bernstein

Assistant Vice President Human Resources, Craig Harada

Vice President Business Continuity Readiness, Walter Hall

Vice President Information Technology, Arun Mathur

Vice President Of Information Technology, Kevin Bradley

Assistant Vice President, Neil Perry

Senior Vice President, Michael Aliberto

Assistant Vice President, Munindra Nath
Vice President, Rick Dusek
Executive Vice President Residential Servicing Operations, Jay Jones
Vice President Global Accounting Operations, Stacy Klein
Assistant Vice President Project Manager of Accounting Operations, John Schatz
Assistant Vice President Accounting Manager, Amey Kelley
Internal Audit Vice President, Sandra Guzman
Vice President Sales and Leasing, Craig Newlun
Vice President Finance, Nina Boynton
Vice President New Business Development, Ying Yang
Vice President Account Executive Client Service Officer, Gary Timchak
Vice President Business Development, Brian Mobley
Vice President Finance and Accounting, Steve Sanislo
Vice President Financial Systems, Thomas Angus
Vice President Information Technology .NET Enterprise Architecture, Harvey Orloff
Assistant Vice President Human Resources Project Management Office Project Manager, Janine Santangelo
Vice President Corporate Treasury Services, Jay D'Auria
Vice President Of Factoring Operations For Ny Region, Sam Macrillo
Vice President Information Technology for Equipment Finance Risk Management Systems, Khundnir Mohammed
Vice President Capital Markets, Elias Uribe
VP, Jason Ahl
AVP, Rebecca Wong
AVP SOX, Liana Balseiro
AVP Perimeter Security Engineer, Benjamin Madison
AVP Compliance AML EDD, Cynthia Hernandez
Assistant Vice President, Oscar Menendez
AVP Treasury Controllers, Robert Bickerstaff
Assistant Vice President Third Party Management, Jennifer Terribile
Vice President, William Sheridan
Assistant Vice President Accounting Manager, Irene Yang
Auditors: PricewaterhouseCoopers LLP

LOCATIONS

HQ: CIT Group Inc
  11 West 42nd Street, New York, NY 10036
Phone: 212 461-5200
Web: www.cit.com

2016 Sales

	$ mil.	% of total
US	2,755	89
Europe	139	5
Rest of the world	198	6
Total	**3,093**	**100**

PRODUCTS/OPERATIONS

Products and Services

Account receivables collection
Acquisition and expansion financing
Advisory services investment and trust
Asset management and servicing
Asset-based loans
Cash management and payment services
Credit protection
Debt restructuring
Debt underwriting and syndication
Deposits
Enterprise value and cash flow loans
Equipment leases
Factoring services
Financial risk management
Import and export financing

Insurance services
Letters of credit / trade acceptances
Merger and acquisition advisory services
Private banking
Residential mortgage loans
Secured lines of credit
Small Business Administration loans

Sales 2016

	$ mil.	% of total
Commercial Banking	2,601	81
Consumer Banking	460	14
Non-Strategic Portfolios	144	5
Corporate & Other	(113.3)	-
Total	**3,093**	**100**

2016 Sales

	$ mil.	% of total
Interest income		
Interest & fees on loans	1,779	58
Other interest and dividends	131	4
Non-interest income		
Rental income on operating leases	1,031	33
Other income	150	5
Total	**3,093**	**100**

Selected Subsidiaries

Aireal Technologies of Harrisburg LLC
ATMOR Properties Inc.
Capita Colombia Holdings Corp.
Education Lending Services Inc.
Education Loan Servicing Corporation
The Equipment Insurance Company
Flex Holdings LLC
Flugzeug Limited (Ireland)
Imaginarium LLC
North Romeo Storage Corporation
Waste to Energy II LLC
Wellington Capital Corporation (Barbados)

COMPETITORS

Ally Financial	ILFC
Citigroup	JPMorgan Chase
Deutsche Bank	ORIX

HISTORICAL FINANCIALS

Company Type: Public

Income Statement

FYE: December 31

	ASSETS ($ mil.)	NET INCOME ($ mil.)	INCOME AS % OF ASSETS	EMPLOYEES
12/16	64,170	(848)	—	4,410
12/15	67,498	1,056	1.6%	4,900
12/14	47,880	1,130	2.4%	3,360
12/13	47,139	675	1.4%	3,240
12/12	44,012	(592)	—	3,560
Annual Growth	**9.9%**	**—**	**—**	**5.5%**

2016 Year-End Financials

Debt ratio: 19.52%
Return on equity: (-8.06%)
Cash ($ mil.): 6,430
Current ratio: —
Long-term debt ($ mil.): —
No. of shares (mil.): 202
Dividends
Yield: 0.0%
Payout: —
Market value ($ mil.): 8,625

	STOCK PRICE ($) FY Close	P/E High/Low		PER SHARE ($) Earnings	Dividends	Book Value
12/16	42.68	—	—	(4.20)	0.60	49.50
12/15	39.70	9	7	5.67	0.60	54.61
12/14	47.83	9	7	5.96	0.50	50.13
12/13	52.13	15	11	3.35	0.10	44.78
12/12	38.64	—	—	(2.95)	0.00	41.49
Annual Growth	**2.5%**	**—**	**—**	**—**	**—**	**4.5%**

Citigroup Inc

This is the Citi that never sleeps. One of the largest financial services firms known to man Citigroup (also known as Citi) has some 200 million customer accounts and serves clients around the globe. It offers deposits and loans (mainly through Citibank) investment banking brokerage wealth management and other financial services. Few other banks can equal Citigroup's global reach: In addition to Citibank it owns stakes in several international regional banks and has more than 130 million Citi-branded credit cards in circulation. Hit hard by the 2008 financial crisis Citi has been refocusing on its original mission — traditional banking.Citi has some $1.7 trillion in assets and some $930 billion in deposits.

HISTORY

Empire builder Sanford "Sandy" Weill who helped build brokerage firm Shearson Loeb Rhoades sold the company to American Express (AmEx) in 1981. Forced out of AmEx in 1985 Weill bounced back in 1986 buying Control Data's Commercial Credit unit.

Primerica caught Weill's eye next. Its predecessor American Can was founded in 1901 as a New Jersey canning company; it eventually expanded into the paper and retail industries before turning to financial services in 1986. The firm was renamed Primerica in 1987 and bought brokerage Smith Barney Harris Upham & Co.

Weill's Commercial Credit bought Primerica in 1988. In 1993 Primerica bought Shearson from AmEx as well as Travelers taking its name and logo.

Weill set about trimming Travelers. He sold life subsidiaries and bought Aetna's property/casualty business in 1995. In 1996 he consolidated all property/casualty operations to form Travelers Property Casualty and took it public. The next year Travelers bought investment bank Salomon Brothers and formed Salomon Smith Barney Holdings (now Citigroup Global Markets).

Weill sold Citicorp chairman and CEO John Reed on the idea of a merger in 1998 in advance of the Gramm-Leach-Bliley act which deregulated the financial services industry in the US. By the time the merger went through a slowed US economy and foreign-market turmoil brought significant losses to both sides. The renamed Citigroup consolidated in 1998 and 1999 laying off more than 10000 employees. So many executives (including co-chairmen and co-CEOs Weill and Reed) were paired through "co" titling that the company was dubbed "the ark."

In 1999 Citigroup moved deeper into subprime lending. Also that year former Treasury Secretary Robert Rubin joined Citigroup as a co-chairman.

In 2000 Reed retired and the company bought the investment banking business of British firm Schroders. Citigroup also bought subprime lender Associates First Capital (now part of CitiFinancial) for approximately $27 billion to expand its consumer product lines and its international presence. The deal however also brought Citigroup federal scrutiny regarding perceived predatory lending tactics. In 2001 the company bought New York-based European American Bank from ABN AMRO and purchased Grupo Financiero Banamex one of Mexico's biggest banks.

The company parlayed the $4 billion it netted from the 2002 spinoff of 20% of Travelers Property Casualty (it distributed most of the remaining stock to Citigroup shareholders) into a $5.8 billion purchase of California-based Golden State Bancorp the parent of the then-third-largest thrift in the US Cal Fed.

Also that year Citigroup paid some $215 million to settle federal allegations that Associates First Capital made customers unwittingly purchase credit insurance by automatically billing for the service. The agreement was one of the largest consumer-protection settlements ever.

The company also became embroiled in the Enron mess as regulators scrutinized short-term loans that Citigroup floated to the energy trader and were possibly used by Enron in transactions with offshore entities to mask debt and inflate cash flow figures. Citigroup neither confirmed nor denied allegations that it helped fudge Enron's books but in 2003 remitted more than $100 million earmarked to pay victims who lost money because of Enron's malfeasance.

A landmark ruling by the SEC in 2003 implied that Citigroup issued favorable stock ratings to companies in exchange for investment banking contracts (predictably the company neither confirmed nor denied the allegations). Also as part of the ruling erstwhile star analyst Jack Grubman agreed to pay some $15 million in fines for his overly rosy stock reports and accepted a lifetime ban from working in the securities industry. Citigroup forked over $400 million in fines the largest portion of a total of some $1.4 billion levied against 10 brokerage firms regarding conflicts of interest between analysts and investment bankers.

Amid the investigations Citigroup separated its stock-picking and corporate advisory businesses creating a retail brokerage and equity research unit called Smith Barney. In the SEC's 2003 ruling such a "Chinese Wall" between bankers and analysts was later made mandatory at all firms. Still Citigroup raked in net profits of nearly $18 billion (on revenues in excess of $94 billion) in 2003 one of the largest-ever yearly takes in US corporate history.

In 2004 the company — while admitting no wrongdoing — paid $2.65 billion to investors who were burned when WorldCom went bankrupt amid an accounting scandal. (Citigroup was one of the lead underwriters of WorldCom stocks and bonds.) The settlement was one of the largest ever for alleged securities fraud and compelled Citigroup to set aside an additional $5 billion to cover legal fees for this case and others involving Enron and spinning. The company eventually paid $2 billion in mid-2005 to investors who lost money on publicly traded Enron stocks and bonds again settling the matter while denying it broke any laws. Enron shareholders had argued that Citigroup helped Enron to set up offshore companies and shady partnerships to exaggerate the energy trader's cash flow.

In Japan where Citigroup is one of the leading foreign banks regulators pulled the plug on the company's private banking operations in 2004 after determining that Citigroup misled customers regarding the sale of certain structured bonds. The closures led to the forced resignation of three top executives in the company's asset management and private banking units about a month later.

Citigroup sold The Travelers Life and Annuity Company (now MetLife Life and Annuity Company of Connecticut) plus most of its international insurance business to MetLife in 2005. Later that year a convoluted deal with Legg Mason netted Citigroup that company's retail brokerage and capital markets business (and $1.5 billion of Legg Mason stock) in exchange for most of Citigroup's asset management and mutual fund division; Citigroup concurrently sold Legg Mason's capital markets operations to Stifel Financial.

Seeking growth internationally Citigroup was part of a consortium that acquired a controlling stake in Guangdong Development Bank in 2006.

Also that year the company opened more than 800 bank branches and consumer finance offices outside the US.

Weill ended years of speculation in 2003 by anointing corporate and investment bank head Chuck Prince as his successor. Weill retired as chairman in 2006 and Prince assumed that title as well. Prince resigned in 2007 as Citigroup dealt with losses on mortgage-related securities and other investments.

Prince was succeeded by Vikram Pandit a Morgan Stanley veteran who came to Citigroup when it acquired hedge fund and private equity manager Old Lane Partners in 2007. Pandit was at Citigroup only a few months before he was named CEO but during that time he oversaw the company's alternative investments and led its institutional clients group. The following year Citigroup disbanded Old Lane and wound up its flagship fund.

Citigroup further expanded its fund services operations via its 2007 acquisition of BISYS. As part of the deal the company sold BISYS' insurance services division to investment firm J.C. Flowers & Co.

Also that year it picked up remnants of the subprime mortgage collapse when it acquired ACC Capital Holding's wholesale mortgage origination operations as well as the servicing rights to some $5 billion in home loans. It also bought ABN AMRO Mortgage Group and shelled out more than $1 billion to buy Egg one of the largest online-only banks in the world from Prudential plc. The deal boosted its UK consumer operations by adding some 3 million customers.

The company sold its trademark red umbrella logo back to insurance firm Travelers which began using the symbol nearly 150 years before. Citigroup acquired the iconic logo when it bought the insurance company in 1993 and held onto it after it spun off Travelers in 2002. But the company ultimately decided that customers associated the umbrella with insurance and sold it in 2007.

In order to shore up its balance sheet Citigroup sold some 5% of itself to the Abu Dhabi Investment Authority a Middle Eastern sovereign fund for $7.5 billion in 2007. It later raised more than $12 billion by selling preferred shares to investors including a Singapore government-owned investment fund former CEO Sandy Weill and Saudi investor Prince Al-Walid bin Talal who owns roughly 5% stake of Citigroup.

Citigroup bought a majority stake in one of Japan's largest brokerages Nikko Cordial in 2007. It acquired the remaining shares of Nikko Cordial in early 2008 and merged it with Citigroup Japan Holdings to form Nikko Citi Holdings.

In 2008 Citigroup sold several of its commercial finance lines to GE Capital. It sold its German consumer banking business to French bank Groupe Cr©dit Mutuel.

As the global credit crisis mounted in 2008 the US government injected some $700 billion into the nation's banking industry including $45 billion investment in Citigroup. It further stepped in to aid the faltering bank by backing more than $300 in loans and securities to boost confidence in the bank and protect its investments. In exchange the government took a 34% stake in Citigroup. The company received approval to pay the funds back in 2009 and the government began reducing its ownership.

Citigroup shed numerous noncore operations (grouped into its new Citi Holdings division) to raise money to repay the government bailout funds. In 2009 it sold Japanese brokerage Nikko Cordial (now SMBC Nikko) and other parts of Nikko Citi Holdings for $8.7 billion to Sumitomo Mitsui Financial Group. Also in 2009 Citigroup combined its Smith Barney and Quilter wealth management units with those of Morgan Stanley

to create Morgan Stanley Smith Barney taking a 49% of the combined firm.

Sales in 2010 include its $1.93 billion Canadian MasterCard portfolio (to CIBC) a $3.5 billion real estate loan portfolio (to JPMorgan Chase) a $3.2 billion auto loan portfolio (to Santander) and a $1.6 billion portfolio of retail credit card assets (to GE). In 2011 it sold a $1.7 billion private equity portfolio to AXA. Also in 2010 the company spun off Primerica in an IPO selling remaining shares by 2011.

Furthermore Citigroup exited the student loan business in the wake of federal legislation eliminating subsidies for private lenders: It sold its 80% stake in Student Loan Corporation and much of its private student loans portfolio to Discover Financial Services and Sallie Mae. The company also sold three hedge fund businesses with a combined $4.2 billion in assets under management to New York-based SkyBridge Capital.

The firm began withdrawing from the consumer lending business in Europe by selling its Egg UK credit card business to Barclays in 2011 and its UK/Ireland Diners Club business to Affiniture Cards in 2012.

EXECUTIVES

CEO Citibank N.A., Barbara J. Desoer, age 64
CEO North America, William J. (Bill) Mills, age 61
President Citigroup Inc. and CEO Institutional Clients Group, James A. (Jim) Forese, age 54, $500,000 total compensation
CEO, Michael L. Corbat, age 56, $1,500,000 total compensation
Global Head Markets and Securities Services, Paco Ybarra
CFO, John C. Gerspach, age 64, $500,000 total compensation
CEO North Asia; Head Consumer Banking and Global Cards Asia Pacific, Stephen Bird, age 50, $499,623 total compensation
CEO Citi Holdings, Francesco Vanni d'Archirafi
Head Operations and Technology, Don Callahan, age 60, $500,000 total compensation
EVP Global Public Affairs, Edward Skyler, age 43
CEO Latin America, Jane Fraser, age 49, $500,000 total compensation
Head EMEA Markets Institutional Clients Group, James C. Cowles, age 61
CEO Citi Cards, Jud Linville
CEO Asia Pacific, Francisco A. Aristeguieta Silva, age 51
Chief Risk Officer, Bradford Hu, age 53
CEO Citi Mexico and Banco Nacional de M©xico (Banamex), Ernesto Torres Cantu
Senior Vice President, Brad Sandstrom
Vice President Information Technology, Hristo Mirkov
Assistant Vice President Systems Engineer, Jeffrey Serzon
Assistant Vice President And Business Information Security Officer, Veena Srinivasan
Senior Vice President Asset Management, Gustav Gollisz
Senior Vice President, Jason Root
Private Banker Senior Vice President Citi Private Bank, Cesar Gomez
Senior Vice President, Sean Rogers
Vice President Information Technology, Omer Oztan
Vice President, Charles Kim
Vice President, Jim Gallo
Vice President ICG Global Information Security, Domenic Colella
Senior Vice President, Carol Williams
Senior Vice President, Judy Bassanello
Senior Vice President, Ryan McCaughey
Vice President, Ashwin Shirvaikar
Vice President Creative Director, David Lockhart

Vice President, Kevin Byrne
Vice President Information Technology, Anantha Vilandai
Vice President: Price Management Execution, Jason Humphrey
Senior Vice President, Andres Rodriguez
Senior Vice President, Jack Crowley
Senior Vice President, Peter Sullivan
Vice President Operations and Technology, Julie Turner
Vice President, Michelle Murray
Senior Vice President, Linda Basher
ASSISTANT VICE PRESIDENT, Savio Fernandes
Vice President Global Technology Sourcing Services, Charlotte Lawrence
Senior Vice President, Meg Confrey
Vice President Global Investment Banking, Arun Mathew
Assistant Vice President, Eliza Eubank
Vice President Trade Finance, Manohar Bindi Sood
Vice President, Faiz Hashim
Vice President Business Initiatives, Raj Mohan
Vice President Associate Program Manager, Delfina Wood
Vice President, Kumar Gandhi
Vice President, Michael Herzfeld
Vice President Repurchase Reporting and Analytics Manager, Eric Hulseberg
VICE PRESIDENT, Cynthia Maclean
Vice President Prime Finance Citi Military Veterans Network, Sam Lanasa
Vice President Financial Institutions Gl, Marcos Diaz
Vice President, Alex Juricev
Senior Vice President Digital Innovation, Roshanie Ross
Vice President RMBS Trading and Securitization, Thomas Rollauer
Vice President, Alex Ng
Assistant Vice President, Nabin Banskota
Vice President Treasury Sales Consultant, Teri Estes
Assistant Vice President, Amit Verma
Senior Vice President Strategic Projectsmanda, Jesse Reeves
Vice President Citi Technology Infrastructure, Andre Pershad
Senior Vice President, Nareg Dermanuelian
Vice President, Patricia McGuire
Senior Vice President, Adam Gillam
Assistant Vice President, Stephen Szczesniak
Assistant Vice President, Nathan Stone
Senior Vice President Recovery Group Manager, Terri Bergman
First Vice President Wealth Management, Drew Newman
Assistant Vice President Senior Technical Analyst, Dennis Lugo
Vice President Mortgage Specialist, Choylin Chan
Vice President of Containers and Packaging, Timothy Thein
Senior Vice President Relationship Manager, Betty Silfa
Vice President Information Technology Security, Normajo Piggery
Vice President, Oscar Sanz
Assistant Vice President, Steve Chang
Senior Vice President, Lesley Glazer
Senior Vice President, Clinton Taylor
Vice President Client Executive, Keri Reed
Senior Vice President, Ali Hirji
Vice President Global Consumer Group Global Banking, Barbara Chrzan
Vice President Sales, Morgan Sall
Senior Vice President Engineered Systems, Don Molaro
Assistant Vice President Equity Derivatives Trading, Peter Plevritis
Assistant Vice President, Donna Chan

Vice President Senior Associate Banker UHNW Metro New York Region, Jason Wang
Senior Vice President, Robert Hidalgo
Vice President, James DeLuise
Assistant Vice President, David Baker
Senior Vice President Relationship Manager, Ryan Watson
Vice President Finance Sales, Jonathan Villaman
Senior Vice President Wealth Management, Chris Cralle
Senior Vice President, Irvinder Singh
Vice President Global Transaction Services Structured Finance Agency and Trust, Thomas Varcados
Assistant Vice President Financial Business Analyst, Veronica Chavez
Assistan Vice President Electronic Execution Services, Brian Raiti
Senior Vice President Technology, Leandro Martino
Senior Vice President Compliance, Joseph Morgo
Assistant Vice President Global Strategic Operations, Michael Sanders
Vice President, Brad Randlett
Vice President Interest Rate Sales, Bryant Schlichting
Senior Vice President Manager Of Regulatory Reporting Department For Derivatives (Otc And Et), Yanina Kulchitskaya
Vice President, Gam Lee
Assistant Vice President, Anthony Thomas
Senior Vice President, Frank Zhang
Vice President, Jim Akasala
Vice President Crm Process Manager, Brian Lilly
Assistant Vice President, David Garcia
Assistant Vice President, Martha Fernandez
Assistant Vice President Client Relationship Officer, Craig McKenzie
Vice President, Harim Shon
Assistant Vice President Recovery Senior Supervisor Litigation, John Linnenbrink
Senior Vice President, Tim Walter
Vice President Senior Business Analyst Project Manager, Ratnesh Shah
Assistant Vice President At Citi Loan Syndications Group, Christopher Romanelli
Vice President Global Portfolio Trading, Eric Shattenkirk
Assistant Vice President, Timothy Seaton
Vice President, Diego Szuldman
Assistant Vice President, Kyle Moeller
Vice President, Donna McCafferty
Vice President, Evan Elisseou
Vice President, Nancy R Lex
Assistant Vice President, Magaly Sanabria
Vice President Program Management Analyst, Elizabeth Donovan
Vice President Customer Engagement Risk, Pankaj Agarwal
Senior Vice President, Diana Alfonso
Vice President Sales Development Counsultant Cit, Leta Bajraktari
Assistant Vice President, Lucia P Ferreira
Senior Vice President, Norene Chin
Assistant Vice President, Sharon Eng
Senior Vice President, Mark Jackson
Assistant Vice President, Cherry Tam
Vice President And Senior Quality Assurance, Stella Zhang
Vice President, Catherine Hughes
Vice President At Citibank, Ramon Cabrera
Vice President, Christa Coughlin
Senior Vice President Mobile Technology, Nick Leitch
Vice President Executive Recruiter, Carlos Fernandez
Vice President And Compliance Officer, Yolette Mazile
Vice President, Kevin Moore
Vice President Call Centers, Karen Young
Senior Vice President, Patrick DeFeciani

Senior Vice President, Stuart Berman
Executive Vice President, Mark Morgenlender
Vice President Project Manager, Robert Lax
Vice President Marketing and Revenue Services, Ben Bartscht
Vice President of Commercial Real Estate Group, Beth Raba
Auditors: KPMG LLP

LOCATIONS

HQ: Citigroup Inc
388 Greenwich Street, New York, NY 10013
Phone: 212 559-1000
Web: www.citigroup.com

PRODUCTS/OPERATIONS

2016 Sales

	$ mil.	% of total
Interest	57,615	69
Non-interest		
Commissions & fees	10,521	13
Principal transactions	7,585	9
Administration & other fiduciary fees	3,364	4
Realized gains on sales of investments	948	1
Insurance premiums	836	1
Other	2,137	3
Adjustments	(620)	-
Total	82,386	100

2016 Sales

	% of total
Institutional Clients Group	48
Global Consumer Banking	45
Corporate/Other	1
Citi Holdings	6
Total	100

2016 Sales

	% of total
North America	47
Asia	20
Latin America	13
EMEA	13
Corporate/Other	1
Citi Holdings	6
Total	100

Selected Products

Banamex
Bill Consolidation
Checking
Citi Cards
Citi Private Bank
CitiMortgage
Commercial Real Estate Loans
Home Equity
Mortgages
Online Banking
Personal Loans
Savings
Student Loans

COMPETITORS

American Express	Goldman Sachs
Bank of America	HSBC
Bank of New York Mellon	JPMorgan Chase
Barclays	Mizuho Financial
Capital One	U.S. Bancorp
Deutsche Bank	UBS
FMR	USAA
GE	Wells Fargo

Company Type: Public

Income Statement

FYE: December 31

	ASSETS ($ mil.)	NET INCOME ($ mil.)	INCOME AS % OF ASSETS	EMPLOYEES
12/16	1,792,077	14,912	0.8%	219,000
12/15	1,731,210	17,242	1.0%	231,000
12/14	1,842,530	7,313	0.4%	241,000
12/13	1,880,382	13,673	0.7%	251,000
12/12	1,864,660	7,541	0.4%	259,000
Annual Growth	(1.0%)	18.6%	—	(4.1%)

2016 Year-End Financials

Debt ratio: 11.50%—
Return on equity: 6.65%
Cash ($ mil.): 160,494
Current ratio: —
Long-term debt ($ mil.): —

Dividends
Yield: 0.0%
Payout: 8.9%
Market value ($ mil.): —

	STOCK PRICE ($) FY Close	P/E High/Low		PER SHARE ($) Earnings	Dividends	Book Value
12/16	59.43	13	7	4.72	0.42	81.20
12/15	51.75	11	9	5.40	0.16	75.12
12/14	54.11	26	21	2.20	0.04	69.62
12/13	52.11	12	9	4.35	0.04	67.46
12/12	39.56	16	10	2.44	0.04	62.42
Annual Growth	10.7%	—	—	17.9%	80.0%	6.8%

Citizens Financial Group Inc (New)

Paper plastic or coin? No matter — Citizens Financial Group can handle it all. The company's main operating subsidiary is Citizens Bank which boasts $150 billion in assets and some 1200 branches across eleven US states in the Northeast and the Midwest. The bank's branches are often found in supermarkets and offer standard retail and commercial services as well as investment services insurance and employer-sponsored retirement plans. The bank also offers student loans and vehicle lending. Citizens Financial also operates a network of non-branch banking offices. Formerly owned by debt-strapped Royal Bank of Scotland RBS sold its remaining stake in Citizens Financial in late 2015.

Operations

Citizens Financial offers customers mortgage lending auto lending student lending and commercial banking services. Altogether its portfolio includes 1200 branches 100 non-branch offices and 3200 ATMs.

The bank operates two segments: Consumer Banking which serves individuals and counts for nearly 65% of the bank's total revenue; and Commercial Banking which serves businesses and accounts for 33% of revenue.

Geographic Reach

Rhode Island-based Citizens Financial operates branches in New England and in the Mid-Atlantic and the Midwest. Its largest markets are Boston Philadelphia Providence and Pittsburgh.

Sales and Marketing

Citizens Financial which boasts more than 5 million customers including individuals small businesses middle-market companies large corporations and institutions. Its business clients typically operate out of the healthcare technology franchise and energy sectors.

Financial Performance

Citizens Financial has struggled to consistently grow its revenues in recent years due to shrinking interest margins on loans amidst the low-interest environment. Its profits however have been rising thanks to declining loan loss provisions as its loan portfolio's credit quality has improved with higher property valuations in the strengthened economy.

In fiscal 2016 the company turned in a stronger performance than in years previously. Revenue ticked up 9% on the back of higher interest income which benefited from a better balance sheet and higher rates on loans and leases. Noninterest income grew a modest $75 million mostly due to a notable pre-tax benefit although higher capital market fees and service charges. Reclassification of card rewards and lower securities gains partially offset gains.

Net income rose 23% to $1.0 billion partly due to the aforementioned pre-tax gain but mostly due to higher revenue.

Cash from operating activities grew 21% to $1.5 billion mostly as a result of higher net income.

Strategy

Citizen Financial's growth strategy is based outperforming its rivals in terms of customer relationships. The company is leveraging analytics to target customers with customized products and offers with the goal of winning expanding and retaining customer relationships. It is working to increase convenience by investing in its digital channels (online mobile ATM) while implementing a more personal in-branch experience with "Citizens Checkup" consultations.

Citizens Financial is also tightening its focus on the Mass Affluent and Affluent customer segments which have higher growth potential. To do so the company is working on its Wealth Management business which includes improving its advice services (including digital advice) and product suite and services.

The company has been leaning on student lending and installment loans in recent years to drive growth. The group has launched several new products including student loan refinancing partnered with Apple on iPhone upgrade financing and launched a new credit card.

Company Background

In September 2014 Royal Bank of Scotland (RBS) sold a 25% ownership interest or 140 million shares of the regional US bank for $21.50 each (below the company's expected range of $23 to $25 per share). The deal which valued Citizens Financial Group (CFG) at $3 billion was one of the largest bank IPOs on record. In October 2015 RBS sold its remaining stake (the last 20.9% of Citizens common stock) for $23.38 per share raising some $2.6 billion.

After being bought by RBS in 1988 Citizens Financial went on an acquisition spree making more than two dozen deals. In 2000 and through later years the company gobbled up Mellon's retail banking network Medford Bancorp and Port Financial in Massachusetts and Pennsylvania's Commonwealth Bancorp and Thistle Group Holdings among others. The company expanded into the Midwest by buying superregional bank Charter One in 2004. Following its acquisition of Charter One its largest deal yet Citizens Financial retained the Charter One Bank name in Midwestern markets but converted the bank's branches to Citizens Bank in New York and Pennsylvania. That was the company's last major acquisition however.

Like many banks the company was hamstrung by the mortgage crisis. It posted a nearly $1 billion loss in 2008 as its nonperforming loans roughly doubled. The developments compelled the company to re-evaluate its acquisition strategy and it has reversed its field: Citizens Financial sold 18 of its branches in northern New York to Community Bank System in 2008 and all 65 Charter One branches in Indiana to Old National Bancorp the following year. The company also pegged certain operations as noncore including its dealer finance program and portions of its auto lending business. In 2012 Citizens Financial unloaded more branches selling nearly 60 supermarket locations to People's United Financial. In 2013 it opted to unload its Chicago branches.

In 2015 RBS sold its remaining stake in Citizens Financial.

EXECUTIVES

EVP and CFO, John F. Woods, age 52
EVP and Chief Risk Officer, Malcolm D. Griggs, age 56
Vice Chairman Commercial Banking, Donald H. (Don) McCree, age 55, $700,000 total compensation
EVP General Counsel and Chief Legal Officer, Stephen T. (Steve) Gannon, age 64, $600,000 total compensation
Vice Chairman Consumer Banking, Brad L. Conner, age 55, $700,000 total compensation
Chairman and CEO, Bruce Van Saun, age 59, $1,487,000 total compensation
Chief Marketing Officer and Head of Consumer Strategy, Beth Johnson
Head of Technology Services, Brian OÂ'Connell
President Citizens Bank Rhode Island, Keith Kelly
EVP and Head of Business Services, Mary Ellen Baker, age 58
Assistant Vice President Multi Site Manager, Andrew Charlton
Vice President Senior Risk Manager, Pat Coutu
Vice President and REGULATORY LIAISON LAW Department, Pam Brown
Assistant Vice President Portfolio Manager, Laurie Charest
Vice President Commerical Operations Citizens Bank, Stephanie Preston
Senior Vice President Strategy and Analytics, Jeff Lehman
Assistant Vice President Windows Server Infrastructure and Principal Architect, Dean Grammas
Senior Vice President, Louis Noppenberger
Assistant Vice President Relationship Manager, Jovita Coelho
Relationship Manager Assistant Vice President, Dennis Piccone
Assistant Vice President, Jacquelyn Heffner
Assistant Vice President, Kimberly Barley
Business Banking Relationship Manager Vice President, Gosia Goddard
Treasurer Linden Square Townhomes Condominium Association, Tom Cooney
Auditors: Deloitte & Touche LLP

LOCATIONS

HQ: Citizens Financial Group Inc (New)
One Citizens Plaza, Providence, RI 02903
Phone: 401 456-7000   **Fax:** 401 455-5927
Web: www.citizensbank.com

2016 Branches

	Nos
Pennsylvania	357
Massachusetts	246
New York	142
Ohio	110
Michigan	97
Rhode Island	81
New Hampshire	72
Connecticut	43
Delaware	23
Vermont	20
New Jersey	11
Total	**1,202**

PRODUCTS/OPERATIONS

2016 Sales

	$ mil.	% of total
Interest income		
Interest on loans & fees	3,653	63
Investment securities	584	10
others	29	-
Non-interset income		
Service charges and fees	599	10
Card fees	203	4
Trust & investment services fees	146	3
Capital markets fees	125	2
Mortgage banking fees	112	2
Others	324	6
Net security impairment loss	(12)	-
Total	**5,763**	**100**

Sales 2016

	% of total
Consumer Banking	63
Commercial Banking	34
others	3
Total	**100**

COMPETITORS

Bank of America	M&T Bank
Bank of New York	PNC Financial
Mellon	People's United
Citigroup	Financial
Fifth Third	Sovereign Bank
HSBC USA	TD Bank USA
Huntington Bancshares	U.S. Bancorp
JPMorgan Chase	Wintrust Financial
KeyCorp	

HISTORICAL FINANCIALS

Company Type: Public

Income Statement

FYE: December 31

	ASSETS ($ mil.)	NET INCOME ($ mil.)	INCOME AS % OF ASSETS	EMPLOYEES
12/16	149,520	1,045	0.7%	18,000
12/15	138,208	840	0.6%	17,700
12/14	132,857	865	0.7%	18,310
12/13	122,154	(3,426)	—	18,160
12/12	127,053	643	0.5%	
Annual Growth	**4.2%**	**12.9%**	**—**	**—**

2016 Year-End Financials

Debt ratio: 3.70%	No. of shares (mil.): 511
Return on equity: 5.29%	Dividends
Cash ($ mil.): 4,143	Yield: 0.0%
Current ratio: —	Payout: 23.3%
Long-term debt ($ mil.): —	Market value ($ mil.): 18,241

	STOCK PRICE ($) FY Close	P/E High/Low	PER SHARE ($) Earnings	Dividends	Book Value
12/16	35.63	19 9	1.97	0.46	38.57
12/15	26.19	18 15	1.55	0.40	37.22
12/14	24.86	16 14	1.55	0.10	35.30
Annual Growth	**9.4%**	**— —**	**6.2%**	**46.5%**	**2.2%**

Citizens, Inc. (Austin, TX)

Citizens aims to prepare its customers for two of life's certainties: living and dying. A holding company Citizens provides ordinary life insurance in niche markets through its various operating subsidiaries. Through its CICA Life Insurance Company it issues life insurance in US dollars to wealthy individuals in Latin America and Taiwan. On the other end of the economic and life spectrum its Home Service segment sells life insurance to lower-income individuals in the a few Midwest and southern states primarily to cover final expenses and burial costs. The company has $1.4 billion of assets and $4.7 billion of insurance in force.

Operations

Citizens operates two primary business segments: Life Insurance (73% of sales) and Home Service which accounts for most of the rest. The Home Service segment operates through subsidiaries Security Plan Life Insurance (SPLIC) and Security Plan Fire Insurance Co. (SPFIC). Both focus on the needs of middle and lower income earners primarily in Louisiana Mississippi and Arkansas.

Geographic Reach

The US accounts for about 30% of the firm's insurance sales. Colombia and Venezuela each account for around 15% of sales. Other foreign markets include Taiwan Ecuador and Argentina. In total the firm sells insurance in about 30 Latin American and the Pacific Rim countries.

Sales and Marketing

The policies are sold through some 300 field agents who make home visits and more than 200 funeral homes and independent agents. SPFIC writes a small amount of modest property/casualty insurance and is distributed through the same field agents that represent its life insurance products.

Its distribution strategy is conducted through marketing consultants comprised primarily of part-time second-career sales associates (such as teachers coaches community leaders and others) in rural and urban areas.

Financial Performance

The company has seen slow revenue growth in last five years. In 2014 revenues increased by 8% thanks to higher premium income from renewals and new sales in life insurance. Home Service Insurance premium growth was related to the acquisition of Magnolia Guaranty Life Insurance Company which offers industrial life policies.

Citizens' net investment income increased due to higher yields from new investments primarily in municipal and corporate issues and as the company experienced higher average invested assets as a result of the investment of new premium revenues.

In 2014 the company's net loss ($6.5 million compared to a net gain of $4.8 million in 2013) was due to higher insurance benefits paid or provided (including claims and surrenders and an increase in future policy benefit reserves commissions and other general expenses.

Operating cash flow has followed the revenue trend over the last five years. Operating cash flow increased by 20% in 2014 due to a rise in cash provided by future policy benefit reserves and federal income tax receivable.

Strategy

Citizens has been building its life insurance business in the US for several years having acquired about 17 life insurance companies since 1987. Despite its efforts revenue earned from its US life insurance business has been relatively flat in recent years.

Its strategy both international and domestic has kept the company operating in the black. As many insurance companies crumbled around it during the economic crisis Citizens has logged steady growth in insurance premium sales for the past four years.

The company's acquisition transition strategy focuses on the introduction of its cash accumulation ordinary whole life products to independent marketing consultants associated with companies it has acquired while continuing to service the needs of acquired policyholders.

Mergers and Acquisitions

In 2014 Citizens acquired Mississippi-based Magnolia Guaranty Life Insurance Company for $5.2 million. This company began writing business in 1992 and issues primarily industrial life policies through independent funeral homes in the state of Mississippi.

Company Background

The family of Harold E. Riley who founded Citizens in 1969 hold a controlling share of the company.

EXECUTIVES

COO, Terry Festervand
President and Chief Corporate Officer, Kay E. Osbourn, age 50, $379,173 total compensation
CEO, Geoffrey M. Kolander, age 41, $379,173 total compensation
VP CFO and Treasurer, David S. Jorgensen, age 53, $43,751 total compensation
Chairman, Rick D. Riley, age 63
Vice Chairman, E. Dean Gage, age 74
Auditors: Deloitte & Touche LLP

LOCATIONS

HQ: Citizens, Inc. (Austin, TX)
2900 Esperanza Crossing, 2nd Floor, Austin, TX 78758
Phone: 512 837-7100
Web: www.citizensinc.com

2014 Premium Earned

	% of total
US	28
Venezuela	16
Colombia	14
Taiwan	9
Ecuador	8
Other	25
Total	**100**

PRODUCTS/OPERATIONS

2014 Sales

	$ mil.	% of total
Life insurance	169	73
Home service	59	26
Other non-insurance enterprises	1	1
Total	**230**	**100**

Selected Subsidiaries

CICA Life Insurance Company of America (CICA)
Citizens National Life Insurance Company (CNLIC)
Computing Technology Inc.
Insurance Investors Inc.
Security Plan Fire Insurance Company (SPFIC)
Security Plan Life Insurance Company (SPLIC)

COMPETITORS

AIG	Monumental Life
BMI Financial Group	National Western
Guardian Holdings	Nationwide
Kemper Corp	Pan-American Life
MetLife	

Company Type: Public

Income Statement

FYE: December 31

	ASSETS ($ mil.)	NET INCOME ($ mil.)	INCOME AS % OF ASSETS	EMPLOYEES
12/16	1,583	1	0.1%	730
12/15	1,484	(3)	—	620
12/14	1,417	(6)	—	306
12/13	1,216	4	0.4%	350
12/12	1,174	4	0.4%	550
Annual Growth	7.7%	(18.8%)	—	7.3%

2016 Year-End Financials

Debt ratio: —
Return on equity: 0.80%
Cash ($ mil.): 35
Current ratio: —
Long-term debt ($ mil.): —

No. of shares (mil.): 50
Dividends
Yield: —
Payout: —
Market value ($ mil.): 492

	STOCK PRICE ($) FY Close	P/E High/Low	PER SHARE ($) Earnings	Dividends	Book Value
12/16	9.82	292 154	0.04	0.00	4.97
12/15	7.43	— —	(0.07)	0.00	4.84
12/14	7.60	— —	(0.13)	0.00	5.16
12/13	8.75	115 60	0.10	0.00	4.91
12/12	11.05	126 87	0.09	0.00	5.25
Annual Growth	(2.9%)	— —	(18.4%)	—	(1.4%)

City Holding Co.

"Take Me Home Country Roads" may be the (unofficial) state song of West Virginia but City Holding hopes all roads lead to its City National Bank of West Virginia subsidiary which operates more than 80 branches in the Mountaineer State and in neighboring areas of southern Ohio eastern Kentucky and northern Virginia. Serving consumers and regional businesses the nearly $4 billion bank offers standard deposit products loans credit cards insurance trust and investment services. Residential mortgages and home equity loans constitute more than half of City Holding's $2.5 billion loan portfolio though the bank also writes commercial industrial commercial mortgage and installment consumer loans.

Operations

City National Bank (CNB) operates four main business divisions: Commercial banking Consumer Banking Mortgage Banking and Wealth Management and Trust Services.

Commercial Banking provides traditional banking products commercial and industrial loans and different kinds of real estate loans to corporations and other business customers. Consumer Banking provides deposit products installment loans and real estate loans and lines of credit. The bank's Mortgage Banking division offers fixed and adjustable-rate mortgages construction financing production of conventional and government-backed mortgages secondary marketing and mortgage servicing.

Wealth Management and Trust Services offers personal trust and estate administration investment management and investment and custodial services for commercial and individual customers. This includes management of investment accounts for individuals employee benefit plans and charitable foundations.

Altogether the company earned 62% of its total revenue from interest and fees on loans in 2014 plus another 7% from interest on its investment securities. About 14% of revenue came from service charges 8% came from bankcard revenue and 2% came from trust and investment management fee income.

Geographic Reach

City boasts around 80 branches in four US states including more than 55 branches in West Virginia nearly 15 in Virginia around 10 in Kentucky and less than a handful of branches in Ohio.

Sales and Marketing

The bank spent $3.27 million on advertising in 2014 compared to $2.67 million and $2.59 million in 2013 and 2012 respectively.

Financial Performance

City Holding's revenues and profits have mostly been on the uptrend in recent years as the bank has grown its loan business through acquisitions.

The bank's revenue dipped by 4% to $188.29 million in 2014 mostly because it generated less in loan interest due to an expected drop in accretion from fair value adjustments related to its recent Virginia Savings Bank and Community Bank acquisitions. Interest margins also shrank amidst the low interest environment which caused further headwinds to interest income. The bank did have some bright spots with 16% growth in trust and investment fee income and 11% growth in bankcard revenue as it continued to push those services.

Despite lower revenue in 2014 City Holdings net income jumped by 10% to $52.96 million — the highest its profit has been since 2007. The rise was mostly thanks to a combination of a non-income based tax rebate (non-recurring) decreased legal and professional fees from lower legal settlements a $2.7 million decline in loan loss provisions as the credit quality of the bank's loan portfolio improved and a $1.3 million reduction in interest expense on deposits.

City's operating cash fell to $53.35 million despite higher earnings during the year primarily because the bank used more of its cash toward purchasing assets and generated less net cash proceeds from its loans held for sale.

Strategy

City Holding's flagship subsidiary City National Bank has been growing its loan business and branch network in target markets through acquisitions in recent years. In mid-2015 for example the bank agreed to acquire three bank branches in Lexington Kentucky from American Founders Bank boosting CNB's presence in the state to 11 branches while adding $164.2 million in new deposits and $125 billion in performing loans to its books.

Beyond buying just select branches the bank has also been known to buy smaller community banks outright in its target markets.

To free up resources for more investment in its core business City National sold its insurance operations to The Hilb Group in early 2015 netting an after-tax gain of $5.80 million.

Mergers and Acquisitions

In January 2013 City Holding acquired Community Financial Corporation holding company of the 11-branch Community Bank in Virginia.

In 2012 the company entered a new market in Virginia through its acquisition of Virginia Savings Bank which had five branches in the northern part of the state.

EXECUTIVES

EVP Marketing Human Resources and Retail Banking, Craig G. Stilwell, age 61, $330,000 total compensation

Senior Vice President and Chief Legal Counsel, John Alderman

President and CEO, Charles R. (Skip) Hageboeck, age 54, $500,000 total compensation

EVP Commercial Banking, John A. DeRito, age 67, $250,000 total compensation

CFO, David L. Bumgarner, age 52, $207,000 total compensation

CIO, Jeffrey D. (Jeff) Legge, $175,000 total compensation

Vice President And Trust Investment Of, Jason Rogers

Senior Vice President, Michael Quinlan

Assistant Vice President and Trust Officer, John Chandler

Vice President Information Technology, Tim Quinlan

Vice President and Trust Officer, Larry Thornton

Executive Vice President Customer Service, Jack Cavender

Executive Vice President Marketing, Carolyn Hays

Vice President of Customer Service, John Kelly

Assistant Vice President, Patricia Davis

Vice President Information Technology, Vince Workman

Senior Vice President and Branch Manager, Ron McCloud

Vice President and Senior Trust Officer, P K Ellison

Senior Vice President Director of Security, Joe Flueckiger

Vice President Business Develo, Sharon Hughes

Vice President and Trust Officer, Charles Wilkinson

Senior Vice President of Information Technology, Abigail Scott

Vice President Treasury Management, Dewey Kuhns

Vice President Information Technology, David Payne

Vice President, Jeff Lilly

Senior Vice President Information Technology, Abigal Scott

Vice President Of Information Technologist, Jeff Legge

Senior Vice President Retail Administration, Terry Childers

Assistent Vice President, Christina Pocrnich

Vice President Financial Reporting Manager, Vivian Qiang

Senior Vice President, David Irvin

Chairman, C. Dallas Kayser, age 65

Board Member, Tracy Hylton

Auditors: Ernst & Young LLP

LOCATIONS

HQ: City Holding Co.
25 Gatewater Road, Charleston, WV 25313
Phone: 304 769-1100
Web: www.bankatcity.com

PRODUCTS/OPERATIONS

2014 Sales

	$ mil.	% of total
Interest		
Loans including fees	116	62
Investment securities & other	13	7
Noninterest		
Service charges	265	14
Bankcard revenue	15	8
Other	171	9
Total	188	100

COMPETITORS

1st West Virginia Bancorp	Huntington Bancshares
BB&T	Ohio Valley Banc
Fifth Third	Premier Financial Bancorp
First Community Bancshares	United Bankshares
	WesBanco

HISTORICAL FINANCIALS

Company Type: Public

Income Statement

FYE: December 31

	ASSETS ($ mil.)	NET INCOME ($ mil.)	INCOME AS % OF ASSETS	EMPLOYEES
12/16	3,984	52	1.3%	847
12/15	3,714	54	1.5%	853
12/14	3,461	52	1.5%	889
12/13	3,368	48	1.4%	923
12/12	2,917	38	1.3%	843
Annual Growth	8.1%	7.6%	—	0.1%

2016 Year-End Financials

Debt ratio: 0.41%
Return on equity: 12.07%
Cash ($ mil.): 88
Current ratio: —
Long-term debt ($ mil.): —

No. of shares (mil.): 15
Dividends
Yield: 0.0%
Payout: 49.5%
Market value ($ mil.): 1,023

	STOCK PRICE ($) FY Close	P/E High/Low		PER SHARE ($) Earnings	Dividends	Book Value
12/16	67.60	20	12	3.45	1.71	29.25
12/15	45.64	15	12	3.53	1.66	27.62
12/14	46.53	14	12	3.38	1.57	25.79
12/13	46.33	16	11	3.04	1.46	24.61
12/12	34.85	14	12	2.61	1.40	22.47
Annual Growth	18.0%	—		7.2%	5.1%	6.8%

Clorox Co (The)

Bleach is the cornerstone of Clorox. The company's namesake household cleaning products are world leaders but the Clorox business reaches far beyond bleach. While it makes laundry and cleaning items (Formula 409 Pine-Sol Green Works) its vast products portfolio extends into dressings/sauces (Hidden Valley KC Masterpiece) plastic wrap and containers (Glad) cat litters (Fresh Step Scoop Away) and infection control items (HealthLink Aplicare Soy Vay). Other items include filtration systems (Brita in the Americas) charcoal briquettes (Kingsford Match Light) and natural personal care items (Burt's Bees). Clorox makes and sells its products worldwide.

HISTORY

Known first as the Electro-Alkaline Company The Clorox Company was founded in 1913 by five Oakland California investors who put up $100 apiece to make bleach using water from salt ponds around San Francisco Bay. The next year the company registered the brand name Clorox (the name combines the bleach's two main ingredients chlorine and sodium hydroxide). At first the company sold only industrial-strength bleach but in 1916 it formulated a household solution.

With the establishment of a Philadelphia distributor in 1921 Clorox began national expansion. The company went public in 1928 and built plants in Illinois and New Jersey in the 1930s; it opened nine more US plants in the 1940s and 1950s. In 1957 Procter & Gamble (P&G) bought Clorox. The Federal Trade Commission raised antitrust questions and litigation ensued over the next decade. P&G was ordered to divest Clorox and in 1969 Clorox again became an independent company.

Following its split with P&G the firm added household consumer goods and foods acquiring the brands Liquid-Plumr (drain opener 1969) Formula 409 (spray cleaner 1970) Litter Green (cat litter 1971) and Hidden Valley (salad dressings 1972). Clorox entered the specialty food products business by purchasing Grocery Store Products (Kitchen Bouquet 1971) and Kingsford (charcoal briquettes 1973).

Henkel a large West German maker of cleansers and detergents purchased 15% of Clorox's stock in 1974 as part of an agreement to share research. Beginning in 1977 Clorox sold off subsidiaries and brands such as Country Kitchen Foods (1979) to focus on household goods.

During the 1980s Clorox launched a variety of new products including Match Light (instant-lighting charcoal 1980) Tilex (mildew remover 1981) and Fresh Step (cat litter 1984). Clorox began marketing Brita water filtration systems in the US in 1988 (adding Canada in 1995). In 1990 it paid $465 million for American Cyanamid's household products group including Pine-Sol cleaner and Combat insecticide. (It sold Combat and Soft Scrub to Henkel in 2004.)

Clorox left the laundry detergent business in 1991 (begun in 1988) after it was battered by heavyweights P&G and Unilever. Household products VP Craig Sullivan became CEO the next year (stepping down in December 2003). In 1993 Clorox dumped its frozen food and bottled water operations. It began marketing its liquid bleach in Hungary through a Henkel subsidiary in 1994 and also bought S.O.S soap pads from Miles Inc.

A string of acquisitions brought the company into new markets as it built on existing brands. Clorox bought Black Flag and Lestoil in 1996 and car care product manufacturer Armor All in 1997. With its 1999 purchase of First Brands — for about $2 billion in stock and debt — Clorox added four more brands of cat litter and diversified into plastic products (Glad).

Despite adding 115 new products in 2000 the company said it would put more emphasis on core brands going forward; it pushed its struggling Glad brand with more trade promotions and coupons.

Clorox in January 2001 announced a joint venture with Bombril Brazil's leading name in steel wool to form Detergentes Bombril; however Clorox canceled the agreement in April 2001 claiming that various conditions of the deal had not been met. A year later Clorox further distanced itself from the Brazilian market selling its SBP insecticides business to Reckitt Benckiser. In 2002 Clorox announced that due to the difficult economic environment in the region it was selling its Brazil business.

In 2003 it jumpstarted a joint venture with Procter & Gamble to take advantage of P&G's manufacturing acumen to improve its Glad products. P&G received a 10% stake in Glad. Clorox also sold its Jonny Cat Litter business to Oil-Dri Corporation of America and Black Flag operations in 2003.

In January 2004 Robert Matschullat the company's nonexecutive chairman replaced Sullivan upon his retirement. Matschullat stepped down as chairman and became a director in January 2005; he passed the title to Jerry Johnston. Matschullat reclaimed the titles of chairman and CEO on an interim basis when Johnston suffered a heart attack and retired in 2006. Former Coca-Cola executive Donald Knauss was named chairman and CEO in late 2006; Matschullat remained a director.

Chemical giant Henkel once owned nearly 30% of Clorox but Clorox bought it back in 2004 through an asset swap valued at $2.8 billion. The transaction involved Henkel's purchase of Clorox's 20% stake in Henkel Iberica a joint venture between the two firms operating in Portugal and Spain. Henkel also bought Clorox's stake in a pesticide company.

In late 2004 though P&G boosted its share in the joint venture (with $133 million) from 10% to 20% which is the maximum it can invest according to the agreement.

In 2010 Clorox began to explore strategic alternatives for its $300-million-in-sales car-care brands (Armor All STP) culminating in their sale to private equity firm Avista Capital Partners for $780 million.

EXECUTIVES

EVP General Counsel and Corporate Affairs, Laura Stein, age 56, $582,050 total compensation
Chairman and CEO, Benno Dorer, age 53, $976,154 total compensation
EVP and CFO, Stephen M. (Steve) Robb, age 52, $576,846 total compensation
EVP Product Supply Enterprise Performance and IT, James Foster, age 54
SVP and Chief Innovation Officer, Denise Garner, age 53
SVP and CIO, Manjit Singh, age 47
SVP International Division, Michael Costello, age 50
SVP; General Manager Specialty Division, Jon Balousek, age 48
EVP and COO, Dawn Willoughby, age 48, $515,154 total compensation
SVP and Chief Marketing Officer, Eric Reynolds, age 46
Senior Vice President and Chief Product Supply Officer, Andy Mowery
Auditors: Ernst & Young LLP

LOCATIONS

HQ: Clorox Co (The)
1221 Broadway, Oakland, CA 94612-1888
Phone: 510 271-7000
Web: www.thecloroxcompany.com

2016 sales

	% of total
United States	83
International	17
Total	**100**

PRODUCTS/OPERATIONS

2016 sales

	$ mil.	% of total
Cleaning	1,912	33
Household	1,862	33
International	997	17
Lifestyle	990	17
Total	**5,761**	**100**

Selected Mergers & Acquisitions

FY 2007
Latin American and Canadian bleach brands (Javex Agua Jane Nevex) from Colgate-Palmolive Company ($126 million plus inventory)
Burt's Bees line of natural skin and hair-care products ($925 million)
FY 2006
Tom's of Maine natural oral care products

Selected Food-Related Products

Brita
Glad
Glad Press 'n Seal
GladWare
Hidden Valley
K.C. Masterpiece

Selected Household & Professional Cleaning Products

Aplicare
Clorox
Clorox 2
Clorox Clean-Up

Clorox Disinfecting Wipes
Clorox Dispatch
Clorox FreshCare
Clorox Healthcare
Clorox Oxi Magic
Clorox ReadyMop
Clorox Toilet Bowl Cleaner
Formula 409
Formula 409 Carpet Cleaner
Green Works
Handi-Wipes
HealthLink
Lestoil
Liquid-Plumr
Pine-Sol
S.O.S
Stain Out
Tilex
ToiletWand
Tuffy
Ultra Clorox Bleach

Selected International Products

Agua Jane (bleach Uruguay)
Ant Rid (insecticides)
Arela (waxes)
Astra (disposable gloves)
Bluebell (cleaners)
Chux (cleaning tools)
Clorisol (bleach)
Clorox Gentle (color-safe bleach)
Glad (containers)
Glad-Lock (resealable bags)
Guard (shoe polish)
Gumption (cleaners)
Home Mat (insecticides)
Home Keeper (insecticides)
Javex (bleach Canada)
Mono (aluminum foil)
Nevex (bleach Venezuela)
OSO (aluminum foil)
Prestone (coolant)
Selton (insecticides)
S.O.S (cleaners)
Super Globo (bleach)
XLO (sponges)
Yuhanrox (bleach)

Selected Specialty Products

BBQ Bag
Burt's Bees
EverClean
EverFresh
Fresh Step
Fresh Step Scoop
Kingsford
Match Light
Rain Dance
Scoop Away
Son of a Gun!
Tuff Stuff

COMPETITORS

Alticor	Kiehl's
Big Heart Pet Brands	Kiss My Face
Blistex	McBride plc
Bonne Bell	Mondelez International
CalCedar	Natural Health Trends
Campbell Soup	Nature's Sunshine
Church & Dwight	Newman's Own
Colgate-Palmolive	Oil-Dri
ConAgra	Pactiv
Diversey	Procter & Gamble
Dow Chemical	Reckitt Benckiser
Dr. Bronner's	S.C. Johnson
Est ©e Lauder	Seventh Generation
Forever Living	The Dial Corporation

HISTORICAL FINANCIALS

Company Type: Public

Income Statement

FYE: June 30

	REVENUE ($ mil.)	NET INCOME ($ mil.)	NET PROFIT MARGIN	EMPLOYEES
06/17	5,973	701	11.7%	8,100
06/16	5,761	648	11.2%	8,000
06/15	5,655	580	10.3%	7,700
06/14	5,591	558	10.0%	8,200
06/13	5,623	572	10.2%	8,400
Annual Growth	1.5%	5.2%	—	(0.9%)

2017 Year-End Financials

Debt ratio: 48.00%
Return on equity: 167.10%
Cash ($ mil.): 418
Current ratio: 0.84
Long-term debt ($ mil.): 1,391
No. of shares (mil.): 129
Dividends
  Yield: 2.4%
  Payout: 60.0%
Market value ($ mil.): 17,190

	STOCK PRICE ($) FY Close	P/E High/Low	PER SHARE ($) Earnings	Dividends	Book Value
06/17	133.24	26 21	5.33	3.20	4.20
06/16	138.39	27 21	4.92	3.08	2.30
06/15	104.02	25 19	4.37	2.96	0.92
06/14	91.40	22 19	4.23	2.84	1.20
06/13	83.14	20 16	4.30	2.56	1.12
Annual Growth	12.5%	— —	5.5%	5.7%	39.2%

CMS Energy Corp

Michigan relies on CMS Energy. The energy holding company's regulated utility subsidiary Consumers Energy serves 1.8 million electricity and 1.8 million natural gas customers. It has electric generating capacity of 5600 MW and purchases an additional 2700 MW from third party electricity providers. Another subsidiary CMS Enterprises operates the non-regulated businesses of CMS Energy and is an operator of independent power generating plants. CMS Enterprises? independent power plants (coal- gas- and biomass-fired) have a capacity of 1200 MW and are located in Michigan and North Carolina.

HISTORY

In the late 1880s W. A. Foote and Samuel Jarvis formed hydroelectric company Jackson Electrical Light Works in Jackson Michigan. After building plants in other Michigan towns Foote formed utility holding company Consumers Power. In 1910 the firm merged with Michigan Light to create Commonwealth Power Railway and Light (CPR&L) and began building a statewide transmission system.

Foote died in 1915 and after nine years of acquisitions successor Bernard Cobb sold the rail systems and split CPR&L into Commonwealth Power (CP) and Electric Railway Securities. In 1928 Cobb bought Southeastern Power & Light (SP&L) and merged CP with Penn-Ohio Edison to form Allied Power & Light. Commonwealth and Southern (C&S) was then created as the parent of Allied and SP&L.

In 1932 future GOP presidential nominee Wendell Willkie took the helm and became a national political figure by opposing the Public Utility Holding Company Act of 1935 which began 60 years of regulated monopolies. Consumers Power was divested from C&S after WWII.

Consumers brought a nuclear plant on line in 1962 and the next year began buying Michigan oil and gas fields. In 1967 it formed NOMECO (now CMS Oil and Gas) to guide its oil and gas efforts.

The completion of the Palisades nuke in 1971 began a 13-year run of chronic problems and lengthy shutdowns. Cost overruns and an environmental lawsuit killed the firm's third nuke (Midland) in 1984 — after $4.1 billion was spent.

A rate hike and new CEO William McCormick set the firm on a new path in 1985. McCormick formed a subsidiary to develop and invest in independent power projects in 1986 and created holding company CMS (short for "Consumers") Energy the next year. CMS Gas Transmission was formed in 1989.

Midland Cogeneration Venture (CMS Energy and six partners) completed converting Midland to a natural gas-fueled cogeneration plant in 1990 and CMS Energy wrote off $657 million from its losses at the former nuke. It regained profitability in 1993.

McCormick split the utilities into electric and gas divisions in 1995 and also issued stock for its gas utility and transmission businesses Consumers Gas Group. The next year CMS Energy formed an energy marketing arm.

In 1996 and 1997 CMS Energy invested in power plants in Morocco and Australia and bought a stake in a Brazilian electric utility. The next year it began developing a gas-fired plant in Ghana and won a bid to build a plant in India. CMS Energy also bought gas gathering and processing firms Continental Natural Gas and Heritage Gas Services in 1998.

Michigan's public service commission (PSC) issued utility restructuring orders in 1997 and 1998 but in 1999 the state Supreme Court ruled that the PSC lacked restructuring authority. Facing less-favorable proposed legislation CMS Energy and DTE Energy moved to implement competition per the PSC's guidelines.

CMS Energy bought Panhandle Eastern Pipe Line from Duke Energy for $2.2 billion in 1999. It also grabbed a 77% stake in another Brazilian utility and began building its Powder River Basin gas pipeline. In 2000 the company partnered with Marathon Ashland Petroleum (now Marathon Petroleum) and TEPPCO to operate a pipeline transporting refined petroleum from the US Gulf Coast to Illinois. Later that year CMS Energy announced plans for an IPO for its CMS Oil and Gas unit; however the IPO was withdrawn in 2001.

CMS Energy agreed in 2001 to sell Consumers' high-voltage electric transmission assets to independent transmission operator Trans-Elect for about $290 million; the deal which was the first of its kind in the US was completed in 2002. That year the company sold its Equatorial Guinea (West Africa) oil and gas assets to Marathon Oil for about $1 billion. Also that year McCormick stepped down amid controversy over "round trip" power trades that artificially inflated the company's sales and trading volume; CMS Energy later announced that it would restate its 2000 and 2001 financial results to eliminate the effects of the trades.

Later in 2002 the company exited the exploration and production business. It sold CMS Oil and Gas' North American and African assets to private French energy firm Perenco for $167 million and it sold the unit's Colombian properties to Spanish energy firm Compa ±ia Espa ±ola de Petr leos (Cepsa) for $65 million. CMS Energy sold its CMS Panhandle companies which together operated an 11000-mile pipeline system to Southern Union for $1.8 billion in 2003.

CMS Energy's nonregulated operations grew to account for more than half of sales in 2001 and 2002; however as the wholesale power marketing industry has experienced a downturn the company has refocused on its regulated energy distribution operations. The company has exited the speculative wholesale energy-trading business which was conducted through its CMS Energy Resource Management (formerly CMS Marketing Services and Trading) unit; it has sold its wholesale natural gas trading book to Sempra Energy and has sold its electricity trading book to Constellation Energy Commodities Group (formerly Constellation Power Source).

In 2013 The Utility Workers Union of America signed a new five-year labor agreement with Consumers Energy under which the union will assume a leading role in training employees at Michigan's largest electric and gas utility.

That year Consumers Energy teamed up with global IT services provider HCL Technologies to open the Michigan Technology Development Center in Jackson Michigan. HCL provides IT services for Consumers Energy at the center.

EXECUTIVES

Vice Chairman CMS Energy and Consumers Energy, Thomas J. (Tom) Webb, age 65, $705,000 total compensation

SVP Governmental Regulatory and Public Affairs, David G. Mengebier, age 60, $375,000 total compensation

SVP Energy Resources, Daniel J. (Dan) Malone, age 56, $490,000 total compensation

SVP and General Counsel, Catherine M. Reynolds, age 59, $516,667 total compensation

EVP and CFO CMS Energy and Consumers Energy, Rejji P. Hayes, age 42

SVP Customer Experience and CIO, Brian F. Rich, age 42

President and CEO, Patricia K. (Patti) Poppe, age 49, $775,000 total compensation

Director of Health and Safety, Shajahan Kamalbatcha

Senior Vice President, John Butler

Senior Vice President, Jackson Hanson

Senior Vice President Finance, Tim Kowaleski

Senior Vice President Transformation and Shared Services (Senior Vice President Engineering SOM November 2017), Jean-Francois Brossoit

Chairman, John G. Russell, age 60

Auditors: PricewaterhouseCoopers LLP

LOCATIONS

HQ: CMS Energy Corp
One Energy Plaza, Jackson, MI 49201
Phone: 517 788-0550
Web: www.cmsenergy.com

PRODUCTS/OPERATIONS

2016 Sales

	$ mil.	% of total
Electric utility	4,379	68
Gas utility	1,685	26
Enterprises	215	4
Other reconciling items	120	2
Total	**6,399**	**100**

Selected Subsidiaries

Consumers Energy Company (electric and gas utility)
CMS Capital
  EnerBank USA (banking services)
CMS Enterprises Company (nonutility holding company)
EnerBank USA

COMPETITORS

AEP	NiSource
Alliant Energy	Progress Energy
Calpine	Resources Corp.
Con Edison	SCANA
DTE	SEMCO ENERGY

Dynegy	TECO Energy
Edison International	WEC Energy
NextEra Energy	Xcel Energy

HISTORICAL FINANCIALS

Company Type: Public

Income Statement

FYE: December 31

	REVENUE ($ mil.)	NET INCOME ($ mil.)	NET PROFIT MARGIN	EMPLOYEES
12/17	6,583	460	7.0%	7,952
12/16	6,399	551	8.6%	7,366
12/15	6,456	523	8.1%	7,804
12/14	7,179	477	6.6%	7,388
12/13	6,566	452	6.9%	7,781
Annual Growth	**0.1%**	**0.4%**	**—**	**0.5%**

2017 Year-End Financials

Debt ratio: 44.76%	No. of shares (mil.): 281
Return on equity: 10.58%	Dividends
Cash ($ mil.): 182	Yield: 0.0%
Current ratio: 0.89	Payout: 81.1%
Long-term debt ($ mil.): 9,214	Market value ($ mil.): 13,320

	STOCK PRICE ($) FY Close	P/E High/Low	PER SHARE ($) Earnings	Dividends	Book Value
12/17	47.30	31 25	1.64	1.33	15.77
12/16	41.62	23 18	1.98	1.24	15.23
12/15	36.08	20 17	1.89	1.16	14.21
12/14	34.75	21 15	1.74	1.08	13.34
12/13	26.77	18 14	1.66	1.02	12.98
Annual Growth	**15.3%**	**— —**	**(0.3%)**	**6.9%**	**5.0%**

CNA Financial Corp

CNA Financial is an umbrella organization for a wide range of insurance providers including Continental Casualty and Continental Insurance. It primarily provides commercial policies such as workers' compensation auto and general liability. CNA also sells specialty insurance including professional liability (doctors lawyers and architects) and vehicle warranty service contracts. The firm offers commercial surety bonds (through CNA Surety) risk management claims administration and information services. Its products are sold by independent agents and brokers in the US and through partners abroad. Holding company Loews owns 90% of CNA which was formed in 1897.

Operations
In late 2014 the company realigned its core property/casualty segments to Specialty (40% of sales) Commercial (40% of sales) and International. Its non-core business segments are Life & Group Non-Core and Corporate & Other Non-Core.

The Specialty segment provides professional financial and specialty products and services through independent agents brokers and managing general underwriters. The Commercial segment includes products sold to small and mid-market organizations primarily through an independent agency distribution system; it also sells commercial insurance and risk management products to large corporations primarily through insurance brokers. Meanwhile the International segment offers management and professional liability products and services outside of the US; distribution is via a network of brokers independent

agencies and managing general underwriters. It also sells on the Lloyd's marketplace.

Most of CNA Financial's non-core insurance products are in run-off including a few remaining life annuity and pension products as well as accident and health insurance.

Geographic Reach
CNA is headquartered in Chicago and has offices throughout the US and Canada; it also has locations in Europe and Asia.

Sales and Marketing
In the US independent agents and brokers market CNA products while partners handle the coverage abroad. It primarily targets companies in the health care manufacturing education financial services and construction industries.

Financial Performance
CNA's revenue has seen slow growth over the past few years. In 2014 revenue decreased 2% to $9.6 billion on decreases in the Commercial segment which saw net written premiums decline $143 million. That slowdown was indicative of a lower level of new business in an increasingly competitive market although offset by rate increases. The decline in Commercial was partially offset by a $43 million increase in the Specialty segment. Net written premiums in the International segment fell $79 million largely due to changes in the recently acquired London-based Hardy subsidiary and the termination of a specialty product managing general underwriter relationship in Canada.

The lower revenue as well as a $211 million loss from discontinued operations from the 2014 sale of Continental Assurance Company led to a 26% decline in net revenue (to $691 million).

Cash flow from operations rose 20% to $1.4 billion in 2014 on lower net claim payments and other factors.

Strategy
CNA is focused on strengthening its core commercial operations through both enhanced customer retention efforts and new customer additions. In 2015 it expanded its Allied Vendor Program for law firms by adding three companies offering services to strengthen customers' risk control programs. Also that year the company expanded its specialty lines business into Canada.

CNA partnered with equipment maintenance and asset management service provider Remi in 2014. The company intends to offer a program to manage the risk of equipment maintenance and repair.

In 2014 the company began efforts to sell its run-off and pension deposit business. It also sold Continental Assurance Company a structured settlement and group annuity subsidiary.

EXECUTIVES

EVP General Counsel and Secretary, Jonathan D. (Jon) Kantor, age 61, $800,000 total compensation

Evp And Chief Administration Officer, Thomas Pontarelli

President and COO CNA Specialty, Mark I. Herman, age 58, $675,000 total compensation

EVP and CFO, D. Craig Mense, age 65, $825,000 total compensation

President and CEO CNA Canada, Nick Creatura

CEO CNA Europe and Hardy Underwriting, David J. (Dave) Brosnan, age 54

EVP and Chief Underwriting Officer, Douglas M. (Doug) Worman

EVP Worldwide Property and Casualty Claim, Andrew J. Pinkes, age 54

Chairman and CEO, Dino E. Robusto, age 58, $114,103 total compensation

EVP and Chief Actuary, Larry A. Haefner, age 60, $367,628 total compensation

President Worldwide Field Operations, Timothy J. (Tim) Szerlong, age 64, $700,000 total compensation

President Long Term Care, Albert J. (Al) Miralles, age 47

President and COO CNA Commercial, Kevin Leidwinger, age 53

EVP Technology and Operations, Joseph (J.) Merten

Auditors: Deloitte & Touche LLP

LOCATIONS

HQ: CNA Financial Corp.
333 S. Wabash, Chicago, IL 60604
Phone: 312 822-5000   Fax: 312 822-6419
Web: www.cna.com

PRODUCTS/OPERATIONS

2014 Sales

	$ mil.	% of total
Commercial		
Middle market	1,631	17
Small business insurance	709	7
Other commercial insurance	1,343	14
Specialty		
Management & professional	2,818	29
Surety	509	5
Warranty & alternative risks	381	4
International		
Hardy	365	4
CNA Europe	335	3
Canada	273	3
Life & Group	1,279	13
Corporate & other	56	1
Adjustments	(7)	-
Total	**9,692**	**100**

Selected Solutions

Business interruption
Cargo (ocean marine)
CNA connect
CNA paramount
Commercial auto
Commercial general liability
Cyber liability
Directors & officers (d&o)
Employment practices liability (epl)
Epack extra
Equipment breakdown
Fidelity and crime insurance
Inland marine
International
Kidnap ransom and extortion
Professional liability (errors & omissions)
Property
Surety
Umbrella liability
Warranty
Workers' compensation

COMPETITORS

ACMAT	Nationwide
AIG	Old Republic
American Financial	State Farm
Group	The Hartford
Aspen Insurance	Travelers Companies
Assurant	United Fire
Berkshire Hathaway	W. R. Berkley
Cincinnati Financial	White Mountains
Everest Re	Insurance Group
Liberty Mutual	Zurich Insurance Group

HISTORICAL FINANCIALS

Company Type: Public

Income Statement

FYE: December 31

	ASSETS ($ mil.)	NET INCOME ($ mil.)	INCOME AS % OF ASSETS	EMPLOYEES
12/16	55,233	859	1.6%	6,700
12/15	55,047	479	0.9%	6,900
12/14	55,566	691	1.2%	6,900
12/13	57,194	937	1.6%	7,035
12/12	58,522	628	1.1%	7,500
Annual Growth	(1.4%)	8.1%	—	(2.8%)

2016 Year-End Financials

Debt ratio: 4.91%	No. of shares (mil.): 270
Return on equity: 7.22%	Dividends
Cash ($ mil.): 271	Yield: 0.0%
Current ratio: —	Payout: 94.6%
Long-term debt ($ mil.): —	Market value ($ mil.): 11,226

	STOCK PRICE ($) FY Close	P/E High/Low		PER SHARE ($) Earnings	Dividends	Book Value
12/16	41.50	13	9	3.17	3.00	44.25
12/15	35.15	25	19	1.77	3.00	43.50
12/14	38.71	17	14	2.55	2.00	47.39
12/13	42.89	12	8	3.47	0.80	46.90
12/12	28.01	13	11	2.33	0.60	45.71
Annual Growth	10.3%	—		8.0%	49.5%	(0.8%)

CNB Financial Corp. (Clearfield, PA)

CNB Financial is the holding company for CNB Bank ERIEBANK and FCBank. The banks and subsidiaries provide traditional deposit and loan services as well as wealth management merchant credit card processing and life insurance through nearly 30 CNB Bank- and ERIEBANK-branded branches in Pennsylvania and nine FCBank branches in central Ohio. Commercial industrial and agricultural loans make up more than one-third of the bank's loan portfolio while commercial mortgages make up another one-third. It also makes residential mortgages consumer and credit card loans. The company's non-bank subsidiaries include CNB Securities Corporation Holiday Financial Services Corporation and CNB Insurance Agency.

Operations

Commercial industrial and agricultural loans made up 36% of the bank's $16.74 billion loan portfolio at the end of 2015 while commercial mortgages made up another 33%. The rest of the portfolio was made up of residential mortgages (15% of loan assets) consumer (14%) overdrafts (less than 1%) and credit card loans (less than 1%).

The group makes more than 80% of its revenue from interest income. About 70% of its revenue came from loan interest during 2015 while another 15% came from interest income from taxable and tax-exempt securities. The remainder of its revenue came from deposit account service charges (4% of revenue) wealth and asset management fees (3%) and other miscellaneous income sources.

Geographic Reach

Clearfield Pennsylvania-based CNB Financial serves clients in its home state as well as in Ohio. CNB Financial serves a specific market area such as the Pennsylvania counties of Cambria Cameron Centre Clearfield Crawford Elk Erie Indiana Jefferson McKean and Warren.

Sales and Marketing

The group serves individuals businesses government and institutional customers.

CNB Financial has been increasing its advertising spend in recent years. It spent $1.6 million during 2015 up from $1.5 million and $1 million in 2014 and 2013 respectively.

Financial Performance

CNB Financial's revenues have risen more than 30% since 2011 as its loan assets have nearly doubled to $1.58 billion. The firm's profits have grown

nearly 50% over the same period as low-interest rates and declining loan loss provisions have lowered operating costs.

The group's revenue climbed 1% to $102 million during 2015 thanks to a modest rise in interest income stemming mostly from 16% loan asset growth.

Despite revenue growth in 2015 CNB Financial's net income dipped 4% to $22.2 million mostly due to nearly 10% rise in salary and employee benefit costs from new hires and more expensive benefits. The group's operating cash levels jumped 16% to $34 million for the year thanks to favorable working capital changes related to accrued interest payables and other liabilities.

Strategy

CNB Financial has been acquiring other banks and opening branches in new geographic markets in recent years to boost its loan and deposit business. As a sign of success the bank noted that its assets have nearly doubled in size since 2009 from $1.16 billion to $2.29 billion at the end of 2015.

Toward its branch expansion plans the group's ERIEBANK brand entered Ohio by opening a loan production office there in 2014 with plans to open another by the end of 2016. After opening an FCBank branch in Dublin Ohio in 2014 the group in 2016 also continued to push its FCBank brand which has been enjoying double-digit loan and deposit business growth in the Columbus and Lancaster regions in Ohio. It plans to open a new FCBank branch in Worthington Ohio by the end of 2016.

Mergers and Acquisitions

In 2016 CNB looked expanded into Northeast Ohio after buying Mentor Ohio-based Lake National Bank — and its $152 million in assets — for nearly $25 million. Lake National Bank's operations were folded into ERIEBANK's operations when the transaction closed.

In 2013 extending its reach in Ohio CNB Financial acquired FC Banc Corp. for $41.6 million. The deal gave CNB Financial Farmers Citizens Bank which serves the northern Ohio communities of Bucyrus Cardington Fredericktown Mount Hope and Shiloh as well as the greater Columbus Ohio area.

Company Background

In 2012 CNB Financial acquired an Ebensburg Pennsylvania-based consumer discount company which brought with it a loan portfolio valued at about $1 million.

EXECUTIVES

EVP Human Resources, Mary Ann Conaway

SEVP and Chief Credit Officer CNB Bank, Mark D. Breakey, age 58, $211,000 total compensation

President and CEO, Joseph B. Bower, age 53, $458,000 total compensation

SEVP and COO CNB Bank, Richard L Greslick, age 41, $221,000 total compensation

EVP CFO and Treasurer CNB Bank and Treasurer Principal Financial Officer and Principal Accounting Officer CNB Financial Corporation, Brian W. Wingard, age 43, $210,000 total compensation

EVP and Chief Commercial Banking Officer CNB Bank, Joseph E. Dell, age 61, $211,000 total compensation

EVP Customer Experience, Leanne D. Kassab

Assistant Vice President of Credit Administration, Gregory Dixon

Assistant Vice President of Regional Branch Administration, Vickie Baker

Vice Presidents Commercial Banking, Joseph Yaros

Chairman, Peter F. Smith, age 62

Auditors: Crowe Horwath LLP

HQ: CNB Financial Corp. (Clearfield, PA)
1 South Second Street, P.O. Box 42, Clearfield, PA 16830
Phone: 814 765-9621   **Fax:** 814 765-8294
Web: www.bankcnb.com

PRODUCTS/OPERATIONS

2015 Sales

	% of total
Interest and Dividend Income	
Loans including fees	70
Securities	
Taxable	10
Tax-exempt	4
Dividends	1
Non-Interest Income	
Wealth and asset management fees	3
Service charges on deposit accounts	4
Other service charges and fees	3
Other revenues	5
Total	**100**

Selected Services

Checking
Credit cards
Loans
Savings

COMPETITORS

AmeriServ Financial	M&T Bank
CBT Financial	Northwest Bancshares
Citizens Financial	PNC Financial
Group	S&T Bancorp
First Commonwealth	
Financial	

HISTORICAL FINANCIALS

Company Type: Public

Income Statement
FYE: December 31

	ASSETS ($ mil.)	NET INCOME ($ mil.)	INCOME AS % OF ASSETS	EMPLOYEES
12/16	2,573	20	0.8%	507
12/15	2,285	22	1.0%	454
12/14	2,189	23	1.1%	426
12/13	2,131	16	0.8%	395
12/12	1,773	17	1.0%	337
Annual Growth	**9.8%**	**4.6%**	**—**	**10.8%**

2016 Year-End Financials

Debt ratio: 6.74%
Return on equity: 9.90%
Cash ($ mil.): 29
Current ratio: —
Long-term debt ($ mil.): —
No. of shares (mil.): 14
Dividends
  Yield: 0.0%
  Payout: 46.4%
Market value ($ mil.): 387

	STOCK PRICE ($) FY Close	P/E High/Low	PER SHARE ($) Earnings	Dividends	Book Value
12/16	26.74	20 12	1.42	0.66	14.64
12/15	18.03	12 11	1.54	0.66	14.01
12/14	18.50	12 10	1.60	0.66	13.09
12/13	19.00	16 12	1.29	0.66	11.43
12/12	16.38	13 10	1.38	0.66	11.65
Annual Growth	**13.0%**	**— —**	**0.7%**	**(0.0%)**	**5.9%**

CNO Financial Group Inc

Have a modest but stable income? Graying at the temples? CNO Financial Group finds that especially attractive and has life insurance and related products targeted at you and millions of others. With a focus on middle-income working families and seniors the holding company's primary units include Bankers Life and Casualty which provides Medicare supplement life annuities and long-term care insurance; Washington National which offers specified disease insurance accident insurance life insurance and annuities; and Colonial Penn which offers life insurance to consumers. The company also offers reinsurance. CNO Financial operates nationwide.

Operations

CNO operates through four segments: Bankers Life Washington National Colonial Penn and Long-term care in run-off. The Bankers Life segment accounts for about 70% of CNO's annual revenues and the Washington National segment accounts for more than 20% of sales. Colonial Penn (nearly 10%) and Long-term care in run-off (1%) round out the group's revenues.

CNO has some 3.5 million policies in force including third-party policies sold by its Bankers Life agents.

Geographic Reach

With operations throughout the US (including the District of Columbia and certain protectorates) CNO counts Florida Pennsylvania California and Texas among its largest markets. Together the four states account for more than a quarter of CNO's total premiums.

Sales and Marketing

CNO's largest segment Bankers Life sells products through its own team of more than 4200 career agents; it also markets Medicare Advantage plans through distribution arrangements with Humana and United HealthCare. The Washington National segment uses a combination of brokers independent agents and worksite marketing programs. The smaller Colonial Penn segment sells policies through direct sales efforts including television advertising direct mail telemarketing and online sales campaigns.

The group's career agent distribution channel brings in the bulk of its business representing some three-fourths of premiums collected.Independent producers account for more than 15% of collected premiums and direct marketing accounts for some 10%.

CNO leases more than 300 sales offices.

Financial Performance

CNO had steady single-digit revenue growth until the 2014 sale of Conseco Life Insurance brought revenues down for a couple of years. Revenue recovered 5% to $4 billion in 2016. Insurance policy income rose 2% that year and net investment income and total realized gains increased.

Net income which plummeted in 2014 has been rising since. In 2016 it increased 32% to $358.2 million thanks to the higher revenue that year. Cash flow from operations has followed net income's trajectory for the past few years. It increased 2% to $759.5 million in 2016.

Strategy

CNO believes its target markets of seniors and middle-income families are often overlooked and underserved giving the company opportunity in the senior market which is expected to double over the next decade. The company is interested in both organic growth and strategic acquisitions.

A major priority is growth across a number of areas including broadening its product portfolio revamping its distribution channels to increase efficiency and reach and deepening its reach within certain of its target demographics. For example in 2016 the company launched its own broker-dealer (Bankers Life Securities) and registered investment advisor (Bankers Life Advisory Services) subsidiaries. Those financial services units are a direct response to Middle America 's increasing concern with financial security in retirement when health care costs typically increase.

To increase profits CNO is working to reduce unnecessary costs across the entire organization while expanding its number of locations. It also works to attract and retain talented employees in part by offering professional development opportunities.

In 2015 the company struck up a partnership with Cognizant to improve its information technology processes and enable more rapid innovation.

Company Background

In 2010 the company changed its name from Conseco to CNO Financial Group to reflect a broader identity. (The firm also sought to distance itself from historical financial instabilities associated with the Conseco brand.) The name change came after several years' worth of management efforts to conserve capital reduce complexity and debt and sequester or divest less profitable operations.

HISTORY

The company evolved from Security National an Indiana insurance company formed in 1979 by Stephen Hilbert. The former encyclopedia salesman and Aetna executive believed most insurance companies were bloated and the industry itself overcrowded as well as ripe for consolidation by a smart lean organization.

In 1982 it began a growth-by-acquisition strategy with the purchase of Executive Income Life Insurance (renamed Security National Life Insurance). The next year it bought Consolidated National Life Insurance and renamed the expanded company Conseco.

The firm went public in 1985 using the proceeds to fund an acquisitions spree that included Lincoln American Life Insurance Lincoln Income Life (sold 1990) Bankers National Life Insurance Western National Life Insurance (sold 1994) and National Fidelity Life Insurance.

In 1990 the company formed Conseco Capital Partners (with General Electric and Bankers Trust) to finance acquisitions without seeming to burden the parent company with debt. This device financed the purchase of Great American Reserve and the 1991 acquisition of Beneficial Standard Life. The former Conseco bought Bankers Life Insurance in 1992 then sold 67% of it the next year. Also in 1993 the company formed the Private Capital Group to invest in noninsurance companies.

In 1994 the company tried to acquire the much larger Kemper Corp. but shied away from the debt load that the $2.6 billion deal would have entailed. The aborted deal cost $36 million in bank and accounting fees and spelled the end of the company's relationship with Merrill Lynch which had underwritten the company's IPO when a Merrill Lynch analyst downgraded its stock after the fiasco.

Meanwhile Private Capital's success led the company to form Conseco Global Investments. Other investments included stakes in racetrack and riverboat gambling operations in Indiana.

In 1996 and 1997 the firm absorbed eight life health property/casualty and specialty insurance companies and raised its interest in American Life Holdings to 100%.

Itching to move beyond insurance in 1998 the company bought Green Tree Financial the US's #1 mobile home financier. Charges of Green Tree's own fuzzy accounting practices helped torpedo the company's quest for a federal thrift charter. But the troubles had just begun. The mobile home finance industry took a dive as customers refinanced at lower rates and prepayments slammed Green Tree Financial reducing Conseco's earnings.

The company tried to recoup in 1999 by launching an ad campaign portraying the company as the "Wal-Mart of financial services." It also continued the acquisition spree. But Green Tree Financial (renamed Conseco Finance that year) couldn't stanch the flow of red ink: Buyers grew wary of the quality of the finance unit's loan securities and changes in accounting methods cost the parent company a $350 million charge against earnings for 1999.

In 2002 due to its financial woes Gary Wendt stepped down as CEO the NYSE suspended trading in the company and its stock was moved to the OTC. The company also filed for Chapter 11 protection in 2002. As part of the reorganization agreement it agreed to sell Conseco Finance. The company's insurance operations were not subject to the Chapter 11 agreement.

In 2003 it finally unloaded the Conseco Finance unit to CFN Investment Holdings LLC an investor group and General Electric Co.'s consumer finance unit for $1 billion. The company emerged from bankruptcy in September 2003.

The company agreed to pay a fine of $6.3 million in 2008 after an investigation determined that its long-term care insurance business Conseco Senior Health had wrongly denied claims and mishandled complaints and that some sales and marketing practices at Banker's Life did not comply with industry standards. To put what it could in the past in late 2008 the firm spun off its closed block of long-term care insurance. The new entity was named Senior Health Insurance Company of Pennsylvania and consisted entirely of policies in run-off.

EXECUTIVES

CEO and Director, Gary C. Bhojwani, age 49, $517,307 total compensation
EVP COO and CTO, Bruce K. Baude, age 53, $559,487 total compensation
Chief Investment Officer and President 40|86 Advisors, Eric R. Johnson, age 57, $500,000 total compensation
EVP Human Resources, Susan L. (Sue) Menzel, age 51
President Bankers Life and Casualty Company, Scott L. Goldberg, age 46
EVP and Chief Actuary, Christopher J. (Chris) Nickele, age 61, $416,667 total compensation
EVP and General Counsel, Matthew J. (Matt) Zimpfer, age 50
EVP and CFO, Erik M. Helding, age 44, $357,813 total compensation
President Washington National, Mike Heard
President Colonial Penn, Joel Schwartz
Senior Vice President Underwriting And New Business, David Vega
Vice President Application Development, Sean Fallon
Vice President Finance, John Rizzo
Vice President, Gregory Turner
Vice President Compensation and Benefits, Grace Brothers
Vice President, Kent Dinius
Second Vice President Sox, Natalie Schneider
Vice President Communications, Barbara Ciesemier
Vice President, Brian Millsap
Vice President, Jeremy Williams
Vice President Operations, Ken Kueber

Assistant Vice President Internet T Senior Director Customer Service, Ming Tong
Senior Vice President Operations, Chris McKee
Senior Vice President and Secretary, Karl Kindig
Senior Vice President and Valuation Actuary, Mark Billingsley
Assistant Vice President, David Sadler
Assistant Vice President Director Field Support Services, Shawn Ardizone
Assistant Vice President, Shawn Dillon-Falk
Executive Vice President Chief Actuary, Chris Nickele
Vice President, Mark Cecil
Executive Vice President and General Counsel, Matt Zimpfer
Vice President Human Resources Services, Mitch Schulz
Chairman, Neal C. Schneider, age 73
Auditors: PRICEWATERHOUSECOOPERS LLP

LOCATIONS

HQ: CNO Financial Group Inc
11825 N. Pennsylvania Street, Carmel, IN 46032
Phone: 317 817-6100
Web: www.cnoinc.com

PRODUCTS/OPERATIONS

2016 Sales

	$ mil.	% of total
Insurance policy income	2,601	65
General account assets	1,204	30
Policyholder and reinsurer accounts and other special-purpose portfolios	121	3
Fee revenue and other income	50	1
Net realized investment gains (losses) excluding impairment losses	47	1
Net impairment losses recognized	(32.3)	-
Gain (loss) on dissolution of variable interest entities	(7.3)	-
Total	**3,985**	**100**

2016 sales

	% of total
Bankers Life	67
Washington National	23
Colonial Penn	8
Long-term care in run-off	1
corporate	1
Total	**100**

COMPETITORS

Aetna	Mutual of Omaha
Aflac	Northwestern Mutual
American General	Protective Life
Lincoln Financial Group	Prudential
MassMutual	Securian Financial
MetLife	Torchmark
Monumental Life	Unum Group

HISTORICAL FINANCIALS

Company Type: Public

Income Statement
FYE: December 31

	ASSETS ($ mil.)	NET INCOME ($ mil.)	INCOME AS % OF ASSETS	EMPLOYEES
12/16	31,975	358	1.1%	3,400
12/15	31,125	270	0.9%	3,500
12/14	31,184	51	0.2%	4,200
12/13	34,780	478	1.4%	4,250
12/12	34,131	221	0.6%	4,200
Annual Growth	**(1.6%)**	**12.8%**	**—**	**(5.1%)**

2016 Year-End Financials

Debt ratio: 13.21%	No. of shares (mil.): 173
Return on equity: 8.28%	Dividends
Cash ($ mil.): 668	Yield: 0.0%
Current ratio: —	Payout: 15.4%
Long-term debt ($ mil.): —	Market value ($ mil.): 3,327

	STOCK PRICE ($) FY Close	P/E High/Low		PER SHARE ($) Earnings	Dividends	Book Value
12/16	19.15	10	7	2.01	0.31	25.82
12/15	19.09	15	11	1.39	0.27	22.49
12/14	17.22	80	65	0.24	0.24	23.06
12/13	17.69	8	4	2.06	0.11	22.49
12/12	9.33	11	6	0.83	0.06	22.80
Annual Growth	**19.7%**			**24.7%**	**50.8%**	**3.2%**

COASTAL FEDERAL CREDIT UNION

LOCATIONS

HQ: COASTAL FEDERAL CREDIT UNION
1000 SAINT ALBANS DR, RALEIGH, NC 276097347
Phone: 919 420-8000
Web: WWW.COASTAL24.COM

HISTORICAL FINANCIALS

Company Type: Private

Income Statement
FYE: December 31

	ASSETS ($ mil.)	NET INCOME ($ mil.)	INCOME AS % OF ASSETS	EMPLOYEES
12/08	2,087	2	0.1%	400
12/07	1,881	13	0.7%	—
12/06	46	16	34.9%	—
Annual Growth	**566.5%**	**(63.2%)**	**—**	**—**

2008 Year-End Financials

Debt ratio: —	
Return on equity: 1.60%	Dividends
Cash ($ mil.): 19	Yield: —
Current ratio: —	Payout: —
Long-term debt ($ mil.): —	Market value ($ mil.): —

COBANK ACB

You could say CoBank is dependent on its rural customers and vice versa. A member of the Farm Credit System (which is regulated by the FCA) the $110 billion cooperative bank provides seasonal and wholesale loans to agribusinesses as well as to rural power water and communications cooperatives across the US. The bank also leases vehicles farming equipment and agricultural facilities through various Farm Credit System affiliates. Its core agribusiness customers range from local and regional farmers' cooperatives to multinational food companies. It has counted Land O' Lakes Blue Diamond Almonds and National Beef as among its larger customers. Formed in 1989 CoBank merged with US AgBank in early 2012.

Operations

CoBank operates three main business segments: Strategic Relationships Agribusiness and Rural Infrastructure. Its Strategic Relationships loans made up 50% of its $80 billion loan portfolio at the end of 2014 while Agribusiness and Rural Infrastructure made up another 30% and 20% respectively.

About 76% of CoBank's total revenue came from loan interest in 2014 while another 16% came from interest income on investment securities. The rest of its revenue came from fee income (5% of revenue) prepayment income (1%) and other miscellaneous sources.

Geographic Reach

Based in Colorado the bank operates 15 regional offices throughout the US including locations in Iowa Georgia Texas Connecticut Kansas Missouri and Kentucky. It also has an international office in Singapore.

Sales and Marketing

CoBank mainly serves clients in rural America in the agribusiness water communications and power sectors.

Financial Performance

CoBank's annual revenues and profits have been rising over the past several years thanks to steady loan asset growth across all three of its target loan types (Strategic Relationships Agribusiness and Rural Infrastructure).

The bank's revenue jumped 5% to $2.2 million during 2014 mostly thanks to higher average loan volume and increased earnings from a strengthened balance sheet. CoBank's lending business grew with food and agribusiness customers Farm Credit Association customers and rural energy and communications customers which all in turn contributed to its top-line growth.

Revenue growth in 2014 drove CoBank's net income up 6% to $904.3 million for the year. The bank's operating cash levels dipped 2% to $883.1 million during the year due to unfavorable working capital changes related to accrued interest balance changes.

EXECUTIVES

CFO, David P. Burlage
Chief Risk Officer, Lori L. O'Flaherty
COO, Ann Trakimas
EVP Banking Services Group, Antony M. Bahr
SVP and CIO, James R. Bernsten
EVP Regional Agribusiness Banking Group, Amy H. Gales
Central Region President Regional Agribusiness Banking Group, Mike Hechtner
Chief Credit Officer, Daniel Key
EVP Corporate Agribusiness Banking Group, Jonathan B. Logan
Southern Region President Regional Agribusiness Banking Group, Lynn Scherler
SVP and Manager Communications Division, Robert F. (Rob) West
Eastern Region President Regional Agribusiness Banking Group, David Sparks
Western Region President Regional Agribusiness Banking Group, Leili Ghazi
CEO, Robert B. Engel, $880,000 total compensation
President, Mary E. McBride
Chief Banking Officer; Member Management Executive Committee, Thomas Halverson
VP and Managing Counsel Legal and Loan Processing Division, Chris Clayton
President Farm Credit Leasing, Mike Romanowski
SVP Power Energy and Utilities Banking Division, Todd E. Telesz
SVP Electric Distribution Water and Community Facilities, Nivin Elgohary
Executive Vice President Regional Agribusiness Banking Group, Paul Narduzzo
Regional Vice President, Todd Sogge
Senior Vice President, Karen Lowe
Vice President, Marshall Essig
Vice President, Kent Erhardt
Vice President, Andrew Haberern
Vice President and Director of Internal Audit, Steven Wittbecke
Vice President Infrastructure, Shawn Dombowsky

Vice Presidnet, Bert Johnson
Regional Vice President Electric Distribution Division ACB, Tamra Reynolds
Vice President, Kenneth Allen
Vice President Information TEC, Arthur Hodges
Associate Vice President, Chris Schneider
Vice President, Brock Taylor
Vice President, Andy Glover
Vice President Energy Banking, Allison Dunn
Vice President and Managing Counsel, Amy J Diaz
Vice President, Rachel Hanson
Vice President and Manager Power Supply Division, Jill Martinez
Vice President, John Cole
Vice President, Weldon Schiller
Sector Vice President, Dave Dornbirer
Vice President, James Matzat
Vice President Government Affairs, Sarah Tyree
Senior Vice President of Operations, Horst Kisch
Vice President Project Finance, Jennifer Daurio
Vice President Digital Business Solutions Sales, Noelle Daghe
Sector Vice President, Christopher Shaffner
Second Vice Chair, Kevin A. Still
First Vice Chair, Daniel T. (Dan) Kelley
Chairman, Everett M. Dobrinski

LOCATIONS

HQ: COBANK ACB
6340 S FIDDLERS GREEN CIR, GREENWOOD VILLAGE, CO 801114951
Phone: 303 740-6527
Web: WWW.COBANK.COM

Selected Regional Offices
Ames IA
Atlanta GA
Austin TX
Enfield CT
Fargo ND
Louisville KY
Lubbock TX
Minneapolis MN
Omaha NE
Roseville CA
Spokane WA
St. Louis MO
Washington D.C.
Wichita KS

COMPETITORS

AgFirst	Northwest Farm Credit
AgStar	Rabo AgriFinance
AgriBank	Wells Fargo
Bank of America	
Farm Credit Services of Mid-America	

HISTORICAL FINANCIALS

Company Type: Private

Income Statement

FYE: December 31

	ASSETS ($ mil.)	NET INCOME ($ mil.)	INCOME AS % OF ASSETS	EMPLOYEES
12/15	117,470	936	0.8%	500
12/14	107,428	904	0.8%	—
12/10	67,700	818	1.2%	—
12/09	58,160	565	1.0%	—
Annual Growth	12.4%	8.8%		

2015 Year-End Financials

Debt ratio: ——
Return on equity: 39.40%
Cash ($ mil.): 3,113
Current ratio: ——
Long-term debt ($ mil.): ——

Dividends
Yield: ——
Payout: ——
Market value ($ mil.): ——

CoBiz Financial Inc

CoBiz Financial is reaching new heights in the Rockies and in the Valley of the Sun. The $3.5 billion-asset holding company for CoBiz Bank operates Colorado Business Bank and Arizona Business Bank. The former operates more than 10 branches in the Denver Boulder and Vail areas while the latter has about a half-dozen branches in and around Phoenix. CoBiz mostly originates business loans and commercial and residential real estate mortgages. The company also offers insurance through CoBiz Insurance and wealth management services through CoBiz Investment Management CoBiz Trust and Financial Designs.

Operations

CoBiz Financial operates two core business segments. Commercial Banking provides commercial real estate and private banking as well as treasury management interest-rate hedging and deposit services. The Fee-Based Lines segment includes its CoBiz Wealth investment advisory services for affluent individuals families and businesses and insurance brokerage business while its CoBiz Insurance subsidiary offers property and casualty and employee benefit group insurance services for small to mid-sized employers commercial enterprises and and business owners. The company exited the investment banking business (which operated through subsidiary Green Manning & Bunch) in early 2015.

Business loans made up nearly 45% of CoBiz's loan portfolio at the end of 2015 while residential and commercial real estate mortgages made up 40%. The rest of its portfolio consisted of consumer loans (9% of loan assets) construction and land loans (8%) and other loans.

Like other retail banks CoBiz Financial makes the bulk of its revenue from interest income. About 71% of its revenue came from loan interest (including fees) during 2015 while interest on taxable securities made up another 8%. The remaining sources of revenue came from insurance income (8% of revenue) service charges (4%) investment advisory income (4%) and other non-interest sources.

Geographic Reach

The bank had 13 branches in Colorado (Denver Boulder and Vail) and five branches in and around Phoenix Arizona at the end of 2015.

Sales and Marketing

CoBiz courts professionals high-net-worth individuals and families small and midsized business clients.

Financial Performance

The bank's annual revenues have risen more than 10% since 2012 mainly thanks to higher interest income as its loan assets have swelled more than 25%. Its profits have grown a bit more slowly however as its operating expenses have outpaced its top-line growth.

CoBiz Financial's revenue climbed 4% to $151.93 million during 2015 mostly as its loan asset balances grew by double-digits spurring an increase in interest income. The bank's insurance income grew by 8% for the year while its investment advisory income increased 2% as its assets under management ticked up 4% to $876 million.

Despite revenue growth in 2015 the bank's net income tumbled 10% to $26.07 million mostly because in 2014 it had benefited from a loan loss provision reversal of $4.2 million whereas in 2015 it incurred loan loss provisions of $6.4 million that came with normal loan portfolio growth. CoBiz's operating cash levels jumped 25% to $34.12 million for the year after adjusting its earnings for non-cash loan loss provisions.

Strategy

CoBiz Financial continued in 2016 to focus on diversifying and growing its loan portfolio pushing jumbo mortgage lending public financing SBA loans structured-finance lending and niche-focused healthcare lending to remain competitive in a challenging environment. It hopes its positioning in the fast-growing markets of Denver and Phoenix will keep its risk minimal in the event of an industry downturn.

The bank believes that it is able to provide more personalized services than its larger competitors while offering more sophisticated products than smaller banks. It looks to extend its relationships with customers often requiring borrowers to procure other products and services from the bank such as deposit accounts or treasury management.

EXECUTIVES

EVP and CFO, Lyne B. Andrich, age 50, $300,000 total compensation

EVP and COO, Richard J. Dalton, age 60, $275,000 total compensation

Vice Chairman and President; Vice Chairman and CEO Colorado Business Bank and Director, Jonathan C. Lorenz, age 65, $380,000 total compensation

Chairman and CEO, Steven Bangert, age 60, $522,500 total compensation

CEO Colorado Business Bank and Arizona Business Bank, Scott E. Page, $297,500 total compensation

Senior Vice President Commical of Loan Production, Stacia Freimuth

Assistant Vice President Client Services Manager, Rhiannon Davis

Assistant Vice President, Eric Curry

Executive Vice President, Margaret Battiste

Assistant Vice President Portfolio Manager, Michael Godo

Vice President Deposit and Treasury Management Services, Jennifer Smyth

Assistant Vice President Portfolio Manager, Greg Hottman

Auditors: Crowe Horwath LLP

LOCATIONS

HQ: CoBiz Financial Inc
1401 Lawrence St., Ste. 1200, Denver, CO 80202
Phone: 303 312-3400
Web: www.cobizbank.com

COMPETITORS

BBVA Compass Bancshares	KeyCorp
Bank of America	U.S. Bancorp
FirstBank Holding Company	Vectra Bank
	Wells Fargo

HISTORICAL FINANCIALS

Company Type: Public

Income Statement

FYE: December 31

	ASSETS ($ mil.)	NET INCOME ($ mil.)	INCOME AS % OF ASSETS	EMPLOYEES
12/16	3,630	34	1.0%	533
12/15	3,351	26	0.8%	532
12/14	3,062	29	0.9%	534
12/13	2,800	27	1.0%	513
12/12	2,653	24	0.9%	512
Annual Growth	8.1%	9.2%	—	1.0%

2016 Year-End Financials

Debt ratio: 3.62%	No. of shares (mil.): 41
Return on equity: 12.09%	Dividends
Cash ($ mil.): 96	Yield: 0.0%
Current ratio: —	Payout: 22.6%
Long-term debt ($ mil.): —	Market value ($ mil.): 702

	STOCK PRICE ($) FY Close	P/E High/Low	PER SHARE ($) Earnings	PER SHARE ($) Dividends	PER SHARE ($) Book Value
12/16	16.89	20 12	0.84	0.19	7.27
12/15	13.42	22 17	0.62	0.17	6.65
12/14	13.13	19 14	0.70	0.15	7.57
12/13	11.96	18 11	0.66	0.12	6.96
12/12	7.47	13 10	0.55	0.07	6.46
Annual Growth	22.6%	— —	11.2%	28.4%	3.0%

Coca-Cola Co (The)

Coke is it — it being the #1 nonalcoholic beverage company as well as one of the world's most recognizable brands. The Coca-Cola Company is home to 21 billion-dollar-brands including four of the top five soft drinks: Coca-Cola Diet Coke Fanta and Sprite. Other top brands include Minute Maid Powerade and vitaminwater. All told the company owns or licenses and markets more than 500 beverage brands mainly sparkling drinks but also waters juice drinks energy and sports drinks and ready-to-drink teas and coffees. With the world's largest beverage distribution system The Coca-Cola Company reaches thirsty consumers in more than 200 countries.

HISTORY

Atlanta pharmacist John Pemberton invented Coke in 1886. His bookkeeper Frank Robinson named the product after two ingredients coca leaves (later cleaned of narcotics) and kola nuts. By 1891 druggist Asa Candler had bought The Coca-Cola Company and within four years the soda-fountain drink was available in all states; it was in Canada and Mexico by 1898.

Candler sold most US bottling rights in 1899 to Benjamin Thomas and John Whitehead of Chattanooga Tennessee for $1. The two designed a regional franchise bottling system that created more than 1000 bottlers within 20 years. In 1916 Candler retired to become Atlanta's mayor; his family sold the company to Atlanta banker Ernest Woodruff for $25 million in 1919. Coca-Cola went public that year.

The firm expanded overseas and introduced the slogans "The Pause that Refreshes" (1929) and "It's the Real Thing" (1941). To keep WWII soldiers in Cokes at a nickel a pop the government built 64 overseas bottling plants. Coca-Cola bought Minute Maid in 1960 and began launching new drinks — Fanta (1960) Sprite (1960) TAB (1963) and Diet Coke (1982).

In 1981 Roberto Goizueta became chairman. Four years later with Coke slipping in market share the firm changed its formula and introduced New Coke which consumers soundly rejected (thus Coca-Cola Classic was born). In 1986 it consolidated the US bottling operations it owned into Coca-Cola Enterprises and sold 51% of the new company to the public. Goizueta also engineered the company's purchase of Columbia Pictures in 1982. (Columbia earned Coke a $1 billion profit when it sold the studio to Sony in 1989.)

In 1995 it bought Barq's root beer. Goizueta died of lung cancer in 1997; while he was at the helm the firm's value rose from $4 billion to $145 billion. Douglas Ivester the architect of Coca-Cola's restructured bottling operations succeeded him. An agreement to buy about 30 Cadbury Schweppes beverage brands — including Canada Dry Dr Pepper and Schweppes — outside the US and France was scaled down because of antitrust concerns. Completed in 1999 the deal also excluded Canada much of continental Europe and Mexico. (Cadbury in 2008 spun off its beverage division which became Dr Pepper Snapple Group.)

A battered Ivester resigned in 2000; president and COO Douglas Daft was named chairman and CEO. Coca-Cola began its largest cutbacks ever slashing nearly 5000 jobs and later agreed to pay nearly $193 million to settle a race-discrimination suit filed by African-American workers.

To fortify its portfolio in the fast-growing noncarbonated drinks segment Coca-Cola acquired Mad River Traders (teas juices sodas) and Odwalla (juices and smoothies) in 2001. The company also bought a 35% interest (San Miguel Corporation owned the rest) in bottler Coca-Cola Philippines from Coca-Cola Amatil. (In 2005 Coke bought the remaining percentage of the Philippine bottler.) The company announced the creation of a huge beverage and snack distribution joint venture with Procter & Gamble but the multibillion-dollar operation fell apart before it could begin. Coca-Cola also announced that it would invest $150 million to build bottling facilities in China.

In 2002 Coca-Cola introduced Vanilla Coke its biggest new product launch since the disastrous New Coke debacle. The company also secured distribution rights to Danone's Evian brand in North America and paid about $128 million when it formed a joint venture (CCDA Waters LLC) with Danone to produce market and distribute Danone's bottled water in the North America (including Dannon and Sparkletts brands under license). Also in 2002 Steven Heyer president and COO of Coca-Cola Ventures and Coca-Cola Latin America was named Coca-Cola's new president and COO. (The company's former president Jack Stahl had left after a reorganization in 2001.)

As part of the restructuring initiated by Daft in 2000 another 1000 employees (half in Atlanta) were laid off in 2003 after the company decided to combine several business units under the Coca-Cola North America umbrella. The company laid off 2800 employees worldwide in 2003.

Those layoffs led one former employee to sue claiming the soft drink maker improperly accounted for funds discriminated against minorities and in 2000 rigged test marketing of frozen Coca-Cola at a Virginia Burger King. Coca-Cola said it does not violate general accounting principles and does not discriminate. However the company said it had already disciplined employees involved in the Burger King tests and Coke executive Thomas Moore who led the fountain drinks division responsible for the questionable tests resigned. Coke also agreed to pay Burger King as much as $21 million to settle the matter. Coke said in 2003 it would reduce its revenue by $9 million to make up for accounting errors from the fountain drinks division that managed the troubled tests. Coke later settled its dispute with the former employee who first raised concerns about Coke's conduct agreeing to pay $500000 in severance and legal costs.

Later in 2003 trouble broke out for the company overseas. Claims surfaced in India that both Coke and Pepsi bottled in that country contain traces of DDT malathion and other pesticides that exceed government limits. Both Coke and Pepsi denied the reports in a joint press conference. Government labs cleared the colas saying the drinks were safe but not before both soft drink companies saw sales dip by as much as 50% in a two-week period.

Trying to boost the younger consumer's interest in its flagship cola Coca-Cola launched new marketing and ad campaigns in 2003. Efforts included changing graphics on Coke bottles and cans back to a more traditional look. However Coca-Cola took the opposite tactic to spur interest in Sprite unveiling Sprite Remix a tropical-flavored version of the soft drink. Minute Maid unveiled Minute Maid Premium Heart Wise which claims to lower cholesterol as long as people consistently drink two glasses a day.

Coca-Cola rolled out a lime version of its Diet Coke in 2004. (The non-diet version came out in 2005.) The flavor joined diet cherry lemon and vanilla. In making the announcement Coca-Cola said it also had reformulated its lemon flavor so that it tastes "lighter." Also in 2004 Coke opened an online music store in the UK called MyCokemusic.com. A month later Coke began selling its Dasani bottled water in the UK and 19 other countries. Later in 2004 the company recalled Dasani water in Europe because of elevated levels of bromate. In addition Daft retired as Coca-Cola's chairman and CEO in 2004 and former Coca-Cola HBC CEO E. Neville Isdell replaced him.

Responding to the growing awareness by consumers of health problems associated with obesity and inactive lifestyles in 2004 Coca-Cola created The Beverage Institute for Health & Wellness a beverage research and educational operation which the company hopes will lead to the creation of more healthful beverage products.

Having introduced Minute Maid products in Russia in 2004 Coke furthered its juice presence in the country with the 2005 purchase of Russian juice maker Multon. Coke bought the company in conjunction with Coca-Cola Hellenic Bottling Co. Later that year Coke began test marketing a Mountain Dew-like drink named Vault in Alabama North Carolina and Tennessee. (Surge a previous Mountain Dew competitor tried by Coke failed in testing.) In 2005 the company announced the phasing out of Vanilla Coke and introduction of Black Cherry Coke.

In 2005 Coke bought Danone's 49% stake in their North American bottled-water venture for about $100 million. The joint venture never turned a profit during its three-year run but Coke hopes full ownership of the Dannon and Sparkletts brands will prove profitable. Coke still shares North American import and marketing rights of Danone's premier water brand Evian which although the world's top-selling bottled water has seen declining in US sales.

The company's rivalry with PepsiCo goes beyond soda to juice products (Coca-Cola's Minute Maid vs. PepsiCo's Tropicana) bottled water (Dasani vs. Aquafina) and other noncarbonated products. Feeling pressure to stay competitive with these faster selling beverages Coca-Cola introduced an energy drink Full Throttle in 2005.

Also in 2005 Coke also announced a revamping of its global marketing team announcing the retirement of Sandy Allen president of its European division. In an effort to expand its international product offerings later that same year it acquired Brazilian juice maker Sucos Mais for some $48 million.

New drinks introduced in 2006 included Vault (a Mountain Dew knock-off). That year Blak a coffee-flavored Coke (with half the calories and twice the caffeine of a regular Coke that was in development for two years) was first test-marketed in France and subsequently introduced in the US. (The pricey soda — $1.99 for an 8-ounce bottle — was discontinued in the US in 2007 due to poor sales.)

Boosting its drinks in the reduced-calorie category in 2006 the company introduced a so-called "calorie-burning" drink called Enviga a green-tea-based drink. It is marketed through a joint venture with Nestl ©. (The joint venture called Beverage Partners Worldwide primarily focuses on black tea drinks.)

The company also launched a new line of premium coffee and tea beverages called Far Coast in 2006. The drinks were launched in Canada along with Far Coast concept stores where consumers can taste test the flavors. The company expanded its reach into coffee further with a deal with coffeehouse chain Caribou Coffee. Coca-Cola and Caribou created a new line of ready-to-drink iced coffee beverages.

In 2013 Coca-Cola opened a new bottling plant in Myanmar as part of a planned $200 million investment during the next five years there which also includes adding more than 22000 jobs during that time period.

In 2013 it bought ZICO Beverages a maker of ZICO Pure Premium Coconut Water.

Growing its distribution network in 2013 The Coca-Cola Company bought Sacramento Coca-Cola Bottling Company the sixth-largest independent Coca-Cola bottler in the nation that serves nine northern California counties.

EXECUTIVES

EVP and President Bottling Investments and Supply Chain, Irial Finan, age 60, $908,108 total compensation
EVP and President Coca-Cola North America, J. Alexander M. (Sandy) Douglas, age 56, $698,091 total compensation
EVP and Chief Marketing Officer, Marcos de Quinto, age 58, $778,379 total compensation
President Europe Middle East and Africa (EMEA), Brian J. Smith, age 61
SVP and CIO, Barry N. Simpson, age 56
President and CEO, James R. Quincey, age 53, $923,625 total compensation
EVP and CFO, Kathy N. Waller, age 59, $749,365 total compensation
President Coca-Cola Refreshments North America, Paul Mulligan
SVP and CTO, Ed Hays, age 58
SVP and Chief Customer and Commercial Leadership Officer, Julie Hamilton, age 51
President Asia Pacific Group, John Murphy, age 55
President West Africa, Peter Njonjo
President South and East Africa, Kelvin Balogun
SVP and President The McDonald's Division, Craig Williams
President Latin America Group, Alfredo Rivera, age 55
President Coca-Cola Ltd., Shane Grant
President Coca-Cola South Pacific, Vamsi Mohan
Vice President Government Relations, Connell Stafford
Vice President Of Tamacc, Ish Arebalos
Vice President Sprite Flavors, Kim Venkatesh
Vice President Environment, Jefferson Seabright
Vice President Purchasing And Information Technologist, Janine Shearer
Vice President Supply Chain Technical Services, Scott Figura
Chairman, Muhtar Kent, age 64
Auditors: Ernst & Young LLP

LOCATIONS

HQ: Coca-Cola Co (The)
One Coca-Cola Plaza, Atlanta, GA 30313
Phone: 404 676-2121   **Fax:** 404 676-6792
Web: www.coca-colacompany.com

2016 Sales

	$ mil.	% of total
US	19,899	48
Other countries	21,964	52
Total	**41,863**	**100**

2016 Unit Sales

	% of total
Bottling Investments	43
North America	22
Europe Middle East & Africa	16
Asia Pacific	11
Latin America	8
Corporate	-
Total	**100**

PRODUCTS/OPERATIONS

2016 Sales

	% of total
Finished product operations	60
Concentrate operations	40
Total	**100**

Selected Brands

Sparkling Beverages
  Core sparkling
  Barq's
  Coca-Cola
  Coca-Cola Zero/Coke Zero
  Diet Coke/Coca-Cola Light
  Fanta
  Fresca
  Inca Kola
  Lift
  Schweppes
  Sprite
  Thums Up
  Energy drinks
  Burn
  Nos
  Real Gold
Still Beverages
  Coffee & teas
  Ayataka teas
  Dogadan teas
  Georgia coffees
  Leão/Matte Leão teas
  Nestea teas
  Sokenbicha teas
  Juices and juice drinks
  Cappy
  Del Valle
  Dobriy
  Hi-C
  Minute Maid
  Minute Maid Pulpy
  Simply
  Other still beverages
  glaceau vitaminwater
  Fuze
  Sports drinks
  Aquarius
  Powerade
  Waters
  Bonaqua/Bonaqa
  Ciel
  Dasani
  Ice Dew
  Kinley
  ZICO Pure Premium Coconut Water

Selected Anchor Bottlers

Coca-Cola Amatil Limited (29%; Australia Fiji Indonesia New Zealand and Papua New Guinea)
Coca-Cola FEMSA S.A.B. de C.V. (29%; parts of Argentina Brazil Colombia Costa Rica Guatemala Mexico Nicaragua Panama and Venezuela)
Coca-Cola Hellenic Bottling Company S.A. (23%; Armenia Austria Belarus Bosnia-Herzegovina Bulgaria Croatia Cyprus the Czech Republic Estonia Greece Hungary Italy Latvia Lithuania Macedonia Moldova Montenegro Nigeria Northern Ireland Poland Republic of Ir

Selected Subsidiaries

Atlantic Manufacturing
Caribbean Refrescos Inc.

Caribbean Refrescos Inc.
Coca-Cola China Industries Ltd.
Coca-Cola Refreshments USA Inc.
Energy Brands Inc.
Hindustan Coca-Cola Beverages Private Limited
Coca-Cola India Private Limited

COMPETITORS

American Beverage	Lassonde
Aquaterra Corporation	Leading Brands
Big Heart Pet Brands	Monarch Beverage (GA)
Britvic	Mondelez International
Chiquita Brands	Mountain Valley
Citrus World	Naked Juice
Clearly Canadian	National Beverage
Clement Pappas	Naumes
Cott	Nestlé
Cranberries Limited	Ocean Spray
Danone	Old Orchard
Dole Food	PepsiCo
Dr Pepper Snapple	Pernod Ricard
Group	Red Bull
Faygo	Silver Springs
Fiji Water	South Beach Beverage
Fresh Del Monte	Southern Gardens
Produce	Citrus
Great Western Juice	Sun-Rype
Hawaiian Springs	Sunny Delight
Hornell Brewing	Suntory Holdings
IZZE	Tree Top
Impulse Energy USA	True Drinks
Jamba	Welch's
Jones Soda	Wet Planet Beverages
Kirin Holdings Company	

HISTORICAL FINANCIALS

Company Type: Public

Income Statement

FYE: December 31

	REVENUE ($ mil.)	NET INCOME ($ mil.)	NET PROFIT MARGIN	EMPLOYEES
12/16	41,863	6,527	15.6%	100,300
12/15	44,294	7,351	16.6%	123,200
12/14	45,998	7,098	15.4%	129,200
12/13	46,854	8,584	18.3%	130,600
12/12	48,017	9,019	18.8%	150,900
Annual Growth	(3.4%)	(7.8%)	—	(9.7%)

2016 Year-End Financials

Debt ratio: 52.38%—
Return on equity: 26.78%
Cash ($ mil.): 8,555
Current ratio: 1.28
Long-term debt ($ mil.): 29,684

Dividends
　Yield: 0.0%
　Payout: 93.9%
Market value ($ mil.): —

	STOCK PRICE ($) FY Close	P/E High/Low	PER SHARE ($) Earnings	Dividends	Book Value
12/16	41.46	31 27	1.49	1.40	5.38
12/15	42.96	26 22	1.67	1.32	5.91
12/14	42.22	28 23	1.60	1.22	6.94
12/13	41.31	22 19	1.90	1.12	7.54
12/12	36.25	41 18	1.97	1.02	7.34
Annual Growth	3.4%	— —	(6.7%)	8.2%	(7.5%)

Codorus Valley Bancorp, Inc.

EXECUTIVES

Senior Vice President Enterprise Risk Mana, Diane E Baker
Senior Vice President Director of Commercial Lending, Eric Warfel
Senior Vice President, Neil Brownawell
Vice President Human Resources Manager Human Resources, Jennifer Grove
Senior Vice President, Thomas Hodgins
Vice President Commercial Relationship Officer, Emily Doxzon
Auditors: BDO USA, LLP

LOCATIONS

HQ: Codorus Valley Bancorp, Inc.
　105 Leader Heights Road, P.O. Box 2887, York, PA 17405
Phone: 717 747-1519
Web: www.peoplesbanknet.com

COMPETITORS

Citizens Financial Group	M&T Bank
Fulton Financial	Northwest Bancshares

HISTORICAL FINANCIALS

Company Type: Public

Income Statement

FYE: December 31

	ASSETS ($ mil.)	NET INCOME ($ mil.)	INCOME AS % OF ASSETS	EMPLOYEES
12/16	1,611	13	0.8%	304
12/15	1,456	11	0.8%	292
12/14	1,213	11	1.0%	258
12/13	1,150	10	0.9%	248
12/12	1,059	9	0.9%	236
Annual Growth	11.0%	8.7%	—	6.5%

2016 Year-End Financials

Debt ratio: 0.64%
Return on equity: 8.32%
Cash ($ mil.): 74
Current ratio: —
Long-term debt ($ mil.): —

No. of shares (mil.): 8
Dividends
　Yield: 0.0%
　Payout: 31.9%
Market value ($ mil.): 253

	STOCK PRICE ($) FY Close	P/E High/Low	PER SHARE ($) Earnings	Dividends	Book Value
12/16	28.60	20 13	1.48	0.47	17.51
12/15	20.34	14 12	1.59	0.44	18.14
12/14	19.68	13 11	1.75	0.40	17.55
12/13	19.53	12 8	1.75	0.36	18.45
12/12	15.05	10 5	1.57	0.30	17.71
Annual Growth	17.4%	— —	(1.5%)	12.1%	(0.3%)

Cognizant Technology Solutions Corp.

Cognizant Technology Solutions is aware of the desire to shift business processes to digital technologies and it very much wants to help. The information technology outsourcing company works with its customers to digitize operations. It provides application maintenance services business intelligence data warehousing software and systems development and integration and re-engineering services for legacy systems. Its customers are primarily corporations from the Forbes Global 2000 and it targets companies in financial services health care manufacturing retail and logistics. Most of Cognizant's software development centers and employees are in India although it has development and delivery facilities around the world.

Operations

Cognizant offers a mix of on-site and near-shore and offshore service. Unlike competitors that provide no on-site assistance Cognizant typically locates technical and account management teams at its customers' locations with development work handled at dedicated development centers offshore. This boosts Cognizant's bottom line by taking advantage of cheaper labor costs while maintaining a close connection with its customers.

The company?s financial services business brings in about 40% of revenue; followed by healthcare 30%; manufacturing retail and logistics about 20%; and its Other segment (services for information media entertainment and communications customers) some 10% of revenue.

Geographic Reach

Cognizant has more than 150 delivery centers in more than 30 countries along with business development offices in more than 70 cities and about 40 countries. The company generates about 80% of its revenue in North America. Combined Europe and the UK constitute the next biggest market accounting for about 15% of sales.

Sales and Marketing

Cognizant markets and sells through its direct sales force which operates from 32 offices in the US and around the world. The sales process can last between two months to a year depending on the products or services under negotiation.

Cognizant's Top 10 customers account for about 15% of its revenue.

Financial Performance

Cognizant has posted steady revenue gains and profits for the past decade.

Sales increased about 9% in 2016 to about $13.5 billion from $12.4 billion in 2015. Financial services its biggest business added $366 million of revenue (a 7% increase) while sales for the smaller manufacturing/retail/logistics business grew by about $320 million (a 13% jump).

Sales to financial services customers were driven by the adoption and integration of digital technologies that affect cost optimization regulatory and compliance initiatives cyber security and vendor consolidation. Demand from manufacturing/retail/logistics customers came from adoption of digital technologies as well as for analytics supply chain consulting internet of things omni-channel commerce and integration services. In the healthcare segment life sciences drove most of the 5% revenue increase for 2016 as customers bought business process services and advanced data analytics as well as cloud technologies and platforms.

Geographically business from the North American market rose 8% while revenue from Europe and other international markets increased about 20%. In the UK however sales were 1% lower. Overseas sales were reduced by the impact of the strong US dollar.

Cognizant?s net income slumped 4% to $1.5 billion in 2016 from $1.6 billion in 2015. The company maintained most spending at the same levels (as a percentage of revenue) in 2016 as in 2015. It did however pay more in taxes due to changes in Indian tax laws which cut into profit.

The lower net income helped reduce cash flow from operations to $1.6 billion in 2016 from $2.1 billion in 2015. Higher incentive-based compensation also played a role in the reduced cash flow.

Strategy

With a nudge from private equity firm Elliott & Associates Cognizant has accelerated the shift of its business to digital technologies and services. Helping its customers digitize their operations should provide higher profit margins for Cognizant. The plan is to return operating profits that exceed 20% to shareholders. Elliott which bought about 5% of Cognizant shares gained three positions on the company?s board of directors.

Cognizant has aligned its operations to pursue its new strategy which was unveiled in early 2017. The company?s Digital Business area is to help customers designed and implement new digitally-enabled business models. In the Digital Operations area Cognizant is to help customers change and manage customers? business processes with digital technology. And the Cognizant Digital Systems and Technology area is to help customers simplify modernize and protect applications platforms and infrastructure. The company will continue focus its strongest customer groups in financial and health technology and smart products.

In another element of the plan Cognizant will devote attention to make operations more efficient leveraging its growing size to shave costs. The company will employ automation to optimize its more traditional application infrastructure and process services.

The company will sift through opportunities to avoid less profitable areas in favor of those with higher profit potential. It acknowledged that such a focus could reduce revenue as it seeks heftier margins.

While it looks to increase efficiency to streamline costs Cognizant will significantly increase the number of employees in its operations in the US which generates about 80% of revenue in 2017. The company recruits from the undergraduate up to MBA level. It also invests in training and retraining programs to arm US workers with in-demand skills.

Mergers and Acquisitions

With recent acquisitions Cognizant has expanded its reach in international markets particularly the Asia/Pacific region while adding to its digital capabilities.

In March 2017 the company acquired Brilliant Service a Japan-based company that develops intelligent products. The acquisition adds to Cognizant?s digital service offerings in Japan and expands its presence in Osaka and Tokyo.

Cognizant bought Adaptra a consulting business transformation and IT services provider in Australia. The deal bolsters the company?s digital business operations and systems capabilities for insurance. Over in Europe Cognizant picked up Mirabeau BV a digital marketing and customer experience agency in the Netherlands. Also in 2016 Cognizant acquired KBACE Technologies Inc. US-based consulting and technology services company specializing in cloud strategy implementation and integration.

Company Background

Cognizant Technology Solutions began as an in-house technology center for Dun & Bradstreet in 1994 and was spun off from D&B in 1996. Two years later Cognizant reorganized and spun off its market research operations into two public companies IMS Health and Nielsen Media Research in order to focus on IT services.

EXECUTIVES

President, Rajeev (Raj) Mehta, age 50, $574,100 total compensation
SVP Marketing and Strategy, Malcolm Frank, age 51, $417,000 total compensation
Executive Vice Chairman Cognizant India, Ramakrishnan Chandrasekaran, age 59, $152,925 total compensation
CFO, Karen McLoughlin, age 52, $426,500 total compensation
CEO and Director, Francisco D'Souza, age 48, $664,300 total compensation
COO, Srinivasan Veeraghavachary
EVP and President Global Industries and Consulting, Ramakrishna Prasad Chintamaneni, age 47, $417,250 total compensation
EVP and President Global Client Services, Dharmendra Kumar Sinha, age 54, $356,504 total compensation
Assistant Vice President Projects, Ronald Trella
Vice President Projects, Robert Fritz
Assistant Vice President Consulting, Karl Swensen
Senior Vice President and Head of Life Sciences North America, Nagaraja Srivatsan
Vice President and Corporate C, Robert Telesmanic
Associate Vice President Product Management and Design, Norah Brennan
Vice President Projects, Ingo Piroth
Vice President Product Mgt, Marilyn Daly
AVP Projects, Lee Dobrec
Vice Chairman, Lakshmi Narayanan, age 64
Chairman, John E. Klein, age 75
Auditors: PricewaterhouseCoopers LLP

LOCATIONS

HQ: Cognizant Technology Solutions Corp.
Glenpointe Centre West, 500 Frank W. Burr Blvd.,
Teaneck, NJ 07666
Phone: 201 801-0233   **Fax:** 201 801-0243
Web: www.cognizant.com

2016 Sales

	$ mil.	% of total
North America	10,546	78
Europe		
United Kingdom	1,176	9
Rest of Europe	969	7
Other	796	6
Total	**13,487**	**100**

PRODUCTS/OPERATIONS

Selected Services

Application design development integration and re-engineering
    Complex custom systems development
    Customer relationship management (CRM)
    Data warehousing/Business intelligence (BI)
    Enterprise resource planning (ERP)
    Software testing services
IT consulting and technology services
    Business and knowledge process consulting
    IT strategy consulting
    Program management consulting
    Technology consulting
Outsourcing services
    Application maintenance
    Business and knowledge process outsourcing
    Cloud
    CRM and ERP maintenance
    Custom application maintenance
    IT infrastructure outsourcing
    Mobility

Selected Mergers and Acquisitions

FY2017
Brilliant Service (Intelligent Products and Solutions
    Company)
FY2016
KBACE Technologies Inc (global consulting and
    technology services company)
FY2014
TriZetto (Healthcare information processing services)

FY2011
CoreLogic Global Services (business processing services)
FY2010
Galileo Performance (IT testing)
The PIPC Group (management consulting)
FY2009
UBS India Service Centre (financial-services
    outsourcing)
Pepperweed Advisors (IT consulting)
Active Intelligence (systems integration)

2016 Sales

	$ mil.	% of total	
Financial services	5366	40	
Health care	3871	28	
Manufacturing retail & logistics	2660		20
Other	1590	12	
Total	13487	100	

Industries
Banking & Financial Services
Communications
Consumer Goods
Education
Energy & Utilities
Healthcare
Information Services
Insurance
Life Sciences
Manufacturing
Media & Entertainment
Retail
Technology
Transportation & Logistics
Travel & Hospitality

COMPETITORS

3i Infotech	Infosys
Accenture	Mastek
Capgemini	MindTree
Computer Sciences	MphasiS
Corp.	Ness Technologies
HCL Technologies	Tata Consultancy
HP Enterprise Services	Wipro
IBM Global Services	Zensar Technologies
ITC Infotech India	

HISTORICAL FINANCIALS

Company Type: Public

Income Statement

FYE: December 31

	REVENUE ($ mil.)	NET INCOME ($ mil.)	NET PROFIT MARGIN	EMPLOYEES
12/16	13,487	1,553	11.5%	260,200
12/15	12,416	1,623	13.1%	221,700
12/14	10,262	1,439	14.0%	211,500
12/13	8,843	1,228	13.9%	171,400
12/12	7,346	1,051	14.3%	156,700
Annual Growth	16.4%	10.2%	—	13.5%

2016 Year-End Financials

Debt ratio: 6.16%
Return on equity: 15.48%
Cash ($ mil.): 2,034
Current ratio: 3.56
Long-term debt ($ mil.): 797

No. of shares (mil.): 608
Dividends
    Yield: —
    Payout: —
Market value ($ mil.): 34,066

	STOCK PRICE ($) FY Close	P/E High/Low	PER SHARE ($) Earnings	Dividends	Book Value
12/16	56.03	25 19	2.55	0.00	17.64
12/15	60.02	26 19	2.65	0.00	15.23
12/14	52.66	45 18	2.35	0.00	12.70
12/13	100.98	49 30	2.02	0.00	10.10
12/12	73.88	45 32	1.72	0.00	8.05
Annual Growth	(6.7%)	— —	10.3%	—	21.7%

Colgate-Palmolive Co.

Colgate-Palmolive takes a bite out of grime. The company is a top global maker and marketer of toothpaste and soap and cleaning products. Colgate-Palmolive also offers pet nutrition products through subsidiary Hill's Pet Nutrition which makes Science Diet and Prescription Diet pet foods. Many of its oral care products fall under the Colgate brand and include toothbrushes mouthwash and dental floss. Its Tom's of Maine unit covers the natural toothpaste niche. Personal and home care items include Ajax brand household cleaner Palmolive dishwashing liquid Softsoap shower gel and Sanex and Speed Stick deodorants. The company has operations in 80-plus countries and sells its products in more than 200 countries.

HISTORY

William Colgate founded The Colgate Company in Manhattan in 1806 to produce soap candles and starch. Colgate died in 1857 and the company was passed to his son Samuel who renamed it Colgate and Company. In 1873 the company introduced toothpaste in jars and in 1896 it began selling Colgate Dental Cream in tubes. By 1906 Colgate was making 160 kinds of soap 625 perfumes and 2000 other products. The company went public in 1908.

In 1898 Milwaukee's B. J. Johnson Soap Company (founded 1864) introduced Palmolive a soap made of palm and olive oils rather than smelly animal fats. It became so popular that the firm changed its name to The Palmolive Company in 1916. Ten years later Palmolive merged with Peet Brothers a Kansas City-based soap maker founded in 1872. Palmolive-Peet merged with Colgate in 1928 forming Colgate-Palmolive-Peet (shortened to Colgate-Palmolive in 1953). The stock market crash of 1929 prevented a planned merger of the company with Hershey and Kraft.

During the 1930s the firm purchased French and German soap makers and opened branches in Europe. Colgate-Palmolive-Peet introduced Fab detergent and Ajax cleanser in 1947 and the brands soon became top sellers in Europe. The company expanded to Asia in the 1950s and by 1961 foreign sales were 52% of the total.

Colgate-Palmolive introduced a host of products in the 1960s and 1970s including Palmolive dishwashing liquid (1966) Ultra Brite toothpaste (1968) and Irish Spring soap (1972). During the same time the company diversified by buying approximately 70 other businesses including Kendall hospital and industrial supplies (1972) Helena Rubinstein cosmetics (1973) Ram Golf (1974) and Riviana Foods and Hill's Pet Products (1976). The strategy had mixed results and most of these acquisitions were sold in the 1980s.

Reuben Mark became CEO of Colgate-Palmolive in 1984. The company bought 50% of Southeast Asia's leading toothpaste Darkie in 1985; it changed its name to Darlie in 1989 following protests of its minstrel-in-blackface trademark. Both Palmolive automatic dishwasher detergent and Colgate Tartar Control toothpaste were introduced in 1986. That year Colgate-Palmolive purchased the liquid soap lines of Minnetonka the most popular of which is Softsoap. In 1992 the company bought Mennen maker of Speed Stick (the leading US deodorant).

Increasing its share of the oral care market in Latin America to 79% in 1995 Colgate-Palmolive acquired Brazilian company Kolynos (from Wyeth for $1 billion) and 94% of Argentina's Odol Saic. The company also bought Ciba-Geigy's oral hygiene business in India increasing its share of that toothpaste market. At home however sales and earnings in key segments were dismal so in 1995 Colgate-Palmolive began a restructuring that included cutting more than 8% of its employees and closing or reconfiguring 24 factories in two years.

The company introduced a record 602 products in 1996 and continued to expand its operations in countries with emerging economies. In 1997 Colgate-Palmolive took the lead in the US toothpaste market for the first time in 35 years (displacing P&G).

In 1999 the company sold the rights to Baby Magic (shampoos lotions oils) in the US Canada and Puerto Rico to Playtex Products retaining the rights in all other countries. Two years later the company sold its heavy-duty laundry detergent business in Mexico (primarily the Viva brand) to Henkel one of Europe's leading detergent producers.

In 2002 Colgate-Palmolive introduced a teeth-whitening gel Simply White to compete with rival P&G's Crest Whitestrips. The company saw success that year when its Hill's Pet Nutrition subsidiary launched new specialty foods for cats and dogs; one of its dog foods reportedly slows brain aging in canines.

In late 2004 Colgate-Palmolive implemented a four-year restructuring plan. Its three primary objectives were to increase profit reallocate resources to promising growth areas and leverage global market efficiencies. It implemented the plan by reducing its global workforce by some 12% closing about 25 of its 78 factories and focusing on core units. Colgate-Palmolive also built new state-of-the-art plants to produce toothpaste in the US and Poland. The company believed that its savings estimated at $500 million altogether would allow it to fund investments in its key businesses as well as provide for new product development.

By selling its North American laundry detergent brands in 2005 Colgate-Palmolive began focusing on the high-margin pearly whites (with bite) of its portfolio — oral care and pet care. The company's purchase of natural oral-care products maker Tom's of Maine in 2006 marked its effort to target the natural niche. It bought some 84% of the firm for about $100 million.

Chairman and CEO Reuben Mark handed over the title of CEO to then-president and COO Ian Cook in July 2007 and the title of chairman to Cook in January 2009; Mark retired at the end of 2008.

Colgate-Palmolive in early 2010 sold its Code 10 brand which boasted about a 10% market share. Indian consumer goods maker Marico acquired the Malaysian hair-styling name; the move was intended to allow Colgate-Palmolive to focus on its oral personal and pet care businesses.

EXECUTIVES

VP and Controller, Dennis J. Hickey, age 68, $910,000 total compensation
Chairman President and CEO, Ian M. Cook, age 65, $1,309,000 total compensation
Vice President of Global Human Resources, Martin Collins
Vice President of Global Information Technology, Tom Greene
Vice President, Laura Flavin
Vice President, Malcolm Williams
VP Global Customer Development, Antonio Caro
President Global Oral Care, Suzan F. Harrison
VP and General Manager Colgate South Pacific, Chris E. Pedersen
VP and General Manager Colgate Brazil, Ricardo (Ricky) Ramos
Chief Supply Chain Officer, Michael A. (Mike) Corbo

President Colgate-Europe and South Pacific, Panagiotis Tsourapas
COO Global Innovation and Growth and Hill's Pet Nutrition, Noel R. Wallace
President and CEO Hill's Pet Nutrition, Peter Brons-Poulsen
COO North America Europe Africa/Eurasia and Global Sustainability, P. Justin Skala, age 58, $734,333 total compensation
VP and General Manager Colgate Canada, Derek A. Gordon
VP and General Manager Colgate Caribbean, Bernal Saborio
VP and General Manager Colgate Nordic, Henning Jakobsen, age 57
Chief Dental Officer, William (Bill) DeVizio
President Colgate-Africa/Eurasia, Jean-Luc Fischer
VP and General Manager Colgate Central Europe East, Wojciech Krol
VP and General Manager Colgate Brazil, Andrea Lagioia
VP and General Manager Colgate Venezuela, Francisco Munoz Ramirez
VP Global Research and Development, Patricia Verduin, age 57
VP and General Manager Colgate-China, Juan Pablo Zamorano
President Hill's Pet Nutrition North America, Kostas Kontopanos
VP and General Manager Colgate UK and Ireland, Massimo Poli
VP and General Manager Colgate Greater Indo-China, Ruben Young
VP; General Manager Colgate-Italy, Vinod Nambiar
VP and General Manager Colgate Russia and Central Asia, Burc Cankat
VP and General Manager Colgate UK and Ireland, Philip Durocher
CIO, Mike Crowe
VP and General Manager Colgate India and South Asia, Issam Bachaalani
President Colgate Europe, Prabha Parameswaran
VP and General Manager Colgate Global Export and Egypt, Arvind Sachdev
VP and General Manager Colgate Central America, David Scharf
VP and General Manager Colgate Central Europe West, Dany Schmidt
VP and General Manager Colgate Southern Europe, Natasha Chen
VP and General Manager Greater China, Stephen Lau
VP and General Manager Colgate North America, Bill Van de Graaf
VP and General Manager Global Home Care, Lucie Claire Vincent
VP and General Manager Colgate North Africa and Middle East, Scott Geldart
VP and GM Colgate Andina Region, Hector Pedraza
VP and General Manager Hill's Pet Nutrition Japan, Gordon Dumesich
Chief Information and Business Services Officer, Thomas (Tom) Greene
VP and General Manager Global Toothbrush Division, Christopher Rector
VP and General Manager Colgate-North America, Anne-Marie Motte
VP and General Manager Colgate-North America, Julie Dillon
VP and General Manager Tom's of Maine, Nancy Pak
VP and General Manager Colgate Western Europe, Andrew Shepard
VP and General Manager Colgate South Africa, Orlando Tenorio
VP and General Manager Global Personal Care, John Hazlin
VP and General Manager Colgate Southern Cone, Adriana Leite

VP and General Manager Hawley & Hazel, Eddie Niem
Vice President Sourcing, Katherine Freeley
National Account Manager, Crystal Harris
Vice President Deputy General Counsel Operations, Rosemary Nelson
Vice President General Manager Oral Care US, Spencer Pingel
Vice President of Hills Pet Nutrition, Neil Stout
Vice President Global Finance, Scott Cain
Vice President, Vicky Chaparro
National Account Manager, Jenny Squier
Vice President, Steve Renard
Vice President, Ebba Bartz
Vice President Customer Service, Mari Bishop
Vice President Worldwide Shopper Marketing, Steve Fogarty
Vice President, Marty Stern
Vice President Supply Chain, Rick Spann
Vice President IT Finance, Gary Palmietto
Vice President Colgate Africa Middle East, Robert Tatera
Vice President, Ralph Hadley
Vice President, Jack Haber
Vice President Global Legal, Andrea Bernard
Vice President, Lindsey Skerker
Vice President Europe And South Pacific, Tina Stoian
Vice President, Debbie Peru
Vice President, Rich Cuprys
Vice President, Joe Vazquez
Vice President, Ps Venkatachalam
Vice President Colgateafricaeurasia, Rosario Carlino
Vice President, Jose Fernando Serrano
Vice President Global Information Technology, Javier Llinas
Senior Vice President General Counsel, Andrew Hendry
National Account Manager, Arthur Lujan
VP Manufacturing, Liz Sorota Orbuch
Vice President, Thomas Quinlan
Vice President, Danielle Koffer
Vice Chairman, Franck J. Moison, age 64
Assistant Treasurer, Elaine Paik
Auditors: PricewaterhouseCoopers LLP

LOCATIONS

HQ: Colgate-Palmolive Co.
300 Park Avenue, New York, NY 10022
Phone: 212 310-2000   Fax: 212 310-3284
Web: www.colgatepalmolive.com

2016 Sales

	$ mil.	% of total
Oral personal & home care		
Latin America	3,650	24
North America	3,183	21
Asia Pacific	2,796	19
Europe	2,342	15
Africa/Eurasia	960	6
Pet nutrition	2,264	15
Total	**15,195**	**100**

PRODUCTS/OPERATIONS

2016 Sales

	$ mil.	% of total
Oral personal & home care	12,931	85
Pet nutrition	2,264	15
Total	**15,195**	**100**

Selected Brands

Home Care
  Ajax
  Fabuloso
  Murphy Oil Soap
  Palmolive
  Suavitel
Oral Care
  Colgate
Personal Care

Afta
Irish Spring
Sanex
Skin Bracer
Softsoap
Speed Stick
Pet Nutrition
  Prescription Diet
  Science Diet

COMPETITORS

Amden	Johnson & Johnson
Avon	Kellogg
Campbell Soup	Kimberly-Clark
Church & Dwight	Kraft Heinz
Clorox	Mondelez International
Coca-Cola	Nestl©
ConAgra	Nu Skin
Dr. Fresh	PepsiCo
Est©e Lauder	Philips Oral
General Mills	Procter & Gamble
GlaxoSmithKline	Reckitt Benckiser
Hain Celestial	Sun Products
Henkel	Unilever NV

HISTORICAL FINANCIALS

Company Type: Public

Income Statement   FYE: December 31

	REVENUE ($ mil.)	NET INCOME ($ mil.)	NET PROFIT MARGIN	EMPLOYEES
12/17	15,454	2,024	13.1%	35,900
12/16	15,195	2,441	16.1%	36,700
12/15	16,034	1,384	8.6%	37,900
12/14	17,277	2,180	12.6%	37,700
12/13	17,420	2,241	12.9%	37,400
Annual Growth	**(2.9%)**	**(2.5%)**	**—**	**(1.0%)**

2017 Year-End Financials

Debt ratio: 51.89%
Return on equity:
Cash ($ mil.): 1,535
Current ratio: 1.36
Long-term debt ($ mil.): 6,566

No. of shares (mil.): 874
Dividends
  Yield: 0.0%
  Payout: 69.7%
Market value ($ mil.): 65,996

	STOCK PRICE ($) FY Close	P/E High/Low	PER SHARE ($) Earnings	Dividends	Book Value
12/17	75.45	34 28	2.28	1.59	(0.07)
12/16	65.44	27 23	2.72	1.55	(0.28)
12/15	66.62	47 39	1.52	1.50	(0.33)
12/14	69.19	30 25	2.36	1.42	1.26
12/13	65.21	52 23	2.38	1.33	2.51
Annual Growth	**3.7%**	**— —**	**(1.1%)**	**4.6%**	**—**

COLORADO HOUSING AND FINANCE AUTHORITY

Auditors: CLIFTON & GUNDERSON LLP GREEN

LOCATIONS

HQ: COLORADO HOUSING AND FINANCE AUTHORITY
1981 BLAKE ST, DENVER, CO 802021229
Phone: 303 297-2432
Web: WWW.CHFAINFO.COM

HISTORICAL FINANCIALS

Company Type: Private

Income Statement   FYE: December 31

	ASSETS ($ mil.)	NET INCOME ($ mil.)	INCOME AS % OF ASSETS	EMPLOYEES
12/09	3,671	(15)	—	150
12/08	4,059	13	0.3%	—
12/07	3,596	21	0.6%	—
12/06	3,293	18	0.6%	—
Annual Growth	**3.7%**	**—**	**—**	**—**

2009 Year-End Financials

Debt ratio: ——
Return on equity: (-6.90%)
Cash ($ mil.): 35
Current ratio: 0.20
Long-term debt ($ mil.): —

Dividends
  Yield: —
  Payout: —
Market value ($ mil.): —

Columbia Banking System Inc

Columbia Banking System (CBS) is the $8.5 billion-asset holding company for Columbia State Bank (also known as Columbia Bank). The regional community bank has about 150 branches in Washington from Puget Sound to the timber country in the southwestern part of the state as well as in northern Oregon and Idaho. Targeting retail and small and medium-sized business customers the bank offers standard retail services such as checking and savings accounts CDs IRAs credit cards loans and mortgages. Commercial and multifamily real estate loans make up more than 40% of the company's loan portfolio while business loans make up another 40%. CBS is expanding in the Pacific Northwest through acquisitions of other community banks.

Operations

The bank's Columbia Private Banking division offers customized financial services for businesses and affluent families. Subsidiary CB Financial Services provides investment products through a pact with third-party provider PrimeVest.

Like other retail banks Columbia makes most of its money from interest income. About 68% of its total revenue came from loan interest during 2015 while another 10% came from interest on taxable and tax-exempt securities. The rest of its revenue came from service charges and other fees (15% of revenue) merchant service fees (2%) and other non-interest income sources.

Geographic Reach

Tacoma-based Columbia Banking System has 149 bank branches (as of mid-2016) with about half in the state of Washington 60 across Oregon and 16 in Idaho.

Sales and Marketing

The bank spent $4.7 million on advertising and promotion in 2015 up from $3.9 million and $4.1 million in 2014 and 2013 respectively.

Financial Performance

Columbia Bank's annual revenues have nearly doubled since 2011 as its loan assets have more than doubled to $5.8 billion (at the end of 2015). Its profits have also doubled over the time period as it's kept a handle on costs.

The bank's revenue jumped 14% to $420.36 million during 2015 on higher interest income as it increased its loan business and interest-earning security assets. The company also earned more in service charges and other non-interest income thanks to its organically growing customer base and its Intermountain acquisition.

Revenue growth in 2015 drove the bank's net income up 21% to $98.83 million. Columbia Bank's operating cash levels dipped 2% to $134.76 million for the year mostly due to unfavorable working capital changes related to other liabilities.

Strategy

Columbia reiterated in 2016 that it would focus on expanding its branches into new markets (either on its own or through acquisitions) while focusing on high-quality loan growth. One of its most recent acquisitions — the purchase of Intermountain Community Bancorp — expanded its presence in Idaho for the first time.

Mergers and Acquisitions

In November 2014 the bank expanded its presence into Idaho after purchasing $960 million-asset Intermountain Community Bancorp and its Panhandle State Bank branches in the state.

In April 2013 Columbia acquired West Coast Bancorp— the parent company of West Coast Bank which operated nearly 60 bank branches in Oregon and Washington. The purchase boosted Columbia's total assets to more than $7 billion and furthered Columbia's goal of becoming the leading regional community bank in the Pacific Northwest.

Company Background

Columbia Banking System took advantage of the rash of bank failures in past years to increase its presence in the Pacific Northwest region. It added more than 30 branches in 2010 when it acquired most of the deposits and assets of failed banks Columbia River Bank and American Marine Bank a week apart. In similar transactions in 2011 it acquired most of the operations of the failed institutions Summit Bank First Heritage Bank and Bank of Whitman. Those deals added more than a dozen branches in Washington.

EXECUTIVES

EVP and Chief Credit Officer, Andrew L. (Andy) McDonald, age 58, $298,000 total compensation

EVP and CFO, Clint E. Stein, age 46, $345,000 total compensation

CEO, Hadley S. Robbins, age 60, $369,827 total compensation

EVP and General Counsel, Kumi Yamamoto Baruffi, age 47

EVP and Chief Human Resources Officer, David C. (Dave) Lawson, age 59, $247,500 total compensation

Senior Vice President Senior Financial Advisor, Rhonda Arnett

Vice President, Thomas Poole

Vice President, Jennifer Kinkade

Vice President, Harold Boucher

Vice President, Saira Russell

Vice President, Rhonda Seagraves

Chairman and Interim CEO Columbia Banking System; Chairman Columbia Bank, William T. Weyerhaeuser, age 74

Auditors: Deloitte & Touche LLP

LOCATIONS

HQ: Columbia Banking System Inc
1301 "A" Street, Tacoma, WA 98402-2156
Phone: 253 305-1900
Web: www.columbiabank.com

2015 Branches

	No.
Washington	74
Oregon	59
Idaho	16
Total	**149**

PRODUCTS/OPERATIONS

2015 Sales

	$ mil.	% of total
Interest Income:		
Loans	286	68
Taxable securities	30	7
Tax-exempt securities	11	3
Deposits in banks	0	-
Non-interest Income:		
Service charges and other fees	61	15
Merchant services fees	9	2
Other	24	5
FDIC loss-sharing asset	(4.0)	-
Total	**420**	**100**

COMPETITORS

BECU	JPMorgan Chase
Bank of America	KeyCorp
Banner Corp	U.S. Bancorp
Heritage Financial	Washington Federal
HomeStreet	Wells Fargo

HISTORICAL FINANCIALS

Company Type: Public

Income Statement

FYE: December 31

	ASSETS ($ mil.)	NET INCOME ($ mil.)	INCOME AS % OF ASSETS	EMPLOYEES
12/16	9,509	104	1.1%	1,819
12/15	8,951	98	1.1%	1,868
12/14	8,578	81	1.0%	1,844
12/13	7,161	60	0.8%	1,695
12/12	4,906	46	0.9%	1,198
Annual Growth	**18.0%**	**22.8%**	**—**	**11.0%**

2016 Year-End Financials

Debt ratio: —
Return on equity: 8.39%
Cash ($ mil.): 224
Current ratio: —
Long-term debt ($ mil.): —
No. of shares (mil.): 58
Dividends
  Yield: 0.0%
  Payout: 84.5%
Market value ($ mil.): 2,593

	STOCK PRICE ($) FY Close	P/E High/Low	PER SHARE ($) Earnings	PER SHARE ($) Dividends	PER SHARE ($) Book Value
12/16	44.68	25 15	1.81	1.53	21.55
12/15	32.51	21 15	1.71	1.34	21.52
12/14	27.61	19 16	1.52	0.94	21.38
12/13	27.49	23 14	1.21	0.41	20.55
12/12	17.94	20 14	1.16	0.98	19.25
Annual Growth	**25.6%**	**— —**	**11.8%**	**11.8%**	**2.9%**

Comcast Corp

Comcast has its content and broadcasts it too. On the content side the company owns NBCUniversal including the NBC TV network and movie studios Universal Pictures and DreamWorks Animation. Cable channels CNBC MSNBC and the USA Network are also under the Comcast tent. As for distribution the company is one of the biggest pay-TV providers in the US with more than 28 million subscribers to one or more of its cable services. Its broadband internet service has nearly 25 million subscribers and its voice service has more than 11.5 million customers. Other Comcast properties include the Universal Studios theme parks and Telemundo a leading Spanish-language TV network in the US.

Operations

Comcast generates revenue in five business segments led by the cable communications service that accounts for about 60% of revenue. Then come the cable networks about 15% of revenue broadcast TV more than 10% of revenue and filmed entertainment and theme parks a bit more than 5% each.

Comcast hasn't forgotten its hometown roots in Philadelphia. Through its majority-owned subsidiary Comcast Spectacor the company owns Philadelphia's NHL franchise the Flyers as well as the team?s arena the Wells Fargo Center. The subsidiary also manages other venues used for sporting events and music concerts in Philadelphia as well as related service businesses including Ovations Food Services and facilities management provider Global Spectrum.

Geographic Reach

Comcast has operations of one kind or another in all 50 states. Its cable communications operations are along the East Coast in the South the Midwest the West Coast and Pacific Northwest. The company owns and operates NBC-affiliate TV stations in the seven top markets in the country as well as three others in the Top 30.

Sales and Marketing

Comcast offers its services directly to residential and business customers through call centers door-to-door selling direct mail advertising television advertising internet advertising local media advertising telemarketing and retail outlets. The company spends about $6 billion a year on advertising marketing and promotion.

Financial Performance

Comcast posted higher top and bottom lines in 2016 continuing a decade-long rise in revenue and a six-year increase in net income.

Revenue increased 9% to almost about $80 billion in 2016 from 2015. Cable communications revenue rose about 8% from more subscribers overall and more signing up for additional services. The average revenue per cable customer relationship increased to more than $148 a month in 2016 from about $143 a month in 2015. Revenue jumped about 20% at NBC and about 10% at the cable channels boosted by the 2016 Rio Olympics. Revenue from the company?s movie unit fell in 2016 due to a smaller less lucrative slate of releases. High performers for the year were The Secret Lives of Pets and Sing. Theme park revenue rose with help from the acquisition of 51% of Universal Studios Japan in late 2015.

Comcast reported that net income rose about 7% to some $8.7 billion in 2016 from 2015 as revenue kept pace with costs.

Cash flow from operations in 2016 rose to about $19.25 billion from about to $18.8 billion in 2015 due to higher net income and a change in working capital.

Strategy

To stanch the flow of video cable customers from its services Comcast has bundled multiple services and offered slimmed-down cable deals (fewer more selective channels) to attract and retain customers. The company also has improved its customer service reducing wait times increased on-time arrivals and added representatives to its customer call centers. The changes might be paying off: Comcast added more than 160000 cable subscribers in 2016 after losing some 230000 cable customers in 2014 and 2015. The company and other cable providers have lost customers — called cord cutters — who prefer to get their entertainment from streaming services such as Netflix YouTube Hulu and other over-the-top services.

Another factor has been Comcast's X1 platform a cloud-based set-top box that offers live video on-demand video and digital video recording. It stores customers' recordings in the cloud which add to the amount they can record. The service is available to Comcast customers across the country. Besides added revenue from the X1 services Comcast looks for additional advertising revenue by using data gained from viewer habits to customize ad targeting.

Adding to its array of services Comcast in 2017 rolled out wireless phone service to its internet customers. Called Xfinity Mobile the service offers several calling plans. Comcast rents space on Verizon?s network but the service is available over Comcast Wi-Fi.

Mergers and Acquisitions

In 2016 NBCUniversal acquired DreamWorks Animation SKG Inc. a maker of animated movies and TV shows for about $3.8 billion. This acquisition of the maker of films such as Shrek and Kung Fu Panda series was made to bolster Comcast?s offerings for children?s pictures for theatrical release.

Comcast acquired 51% of Universal Studios Japan for $1.5 billion in 2015. The deal gives Comcast control of the Universal theme park in Osaka Japan.

EXECUTIVES

SEVP and CEO NBCUniversal, Stephen B. (Steve) Burke, age 58, $2,797,499 total compensation

Chairman and CEO, Brian L. Roberts, age 58, $3,013,510 total compensation

Chairman NBC News and MSNBC, Andrew R. (Andy) Lack, age 70

Chairman and CEO Universal Parks & Resorts (UPR), Thomas L. (Tom) Williams, age 69

Chairman NBC Broadcasting and Sports, Mark H. Lazarus, age 54

SEVP; President and CEO Comcast Cable, David N. (Dave) Watson

Chairman NBCUniversal Cable Entertainment Group, Bonnie Hammer, age 66

President Comcast Spotlight, Charlie Thurston

SEVP, David L. Cohen, age 61, $1,475,621 total compensation

EVP General Counsel and Secretary, Arthur R. Block, age 62, $900,000 total compensation

SVP and Managing Director and Head of Funds Comcast Ventures, Amy L. Banse

Chairman NBC Entertainment, Robert (Bob) Greenblatt

EVP and Chief Communications Officer, D'Arcy F. Rudnay

Head of Comcast Mobile, Greg R. Butz

President and CEO Comcast-Spectator, David A. (Dave) Scott

SEVP and CFO, Michael J. (Mike) Cavanagh, age 51, $1,843,408 total compensation

President and CEO CNBC, Mark Hoffman

President Comcast Business Services, William R. (Bill) Stemper

Chairman NBCUniversal International, Kevin MacLellan

Chairman NBCUniversal International Group and NBCUniversal Telemundo Enterprises, Cesar Conde, age 42

Chairman NBC Universal Content Distribution, Matt Bond

EVP Consumer Services Comcast Cable Communications, Marcien Jenckes

Chairman Universal Filmed Entertainment Group, Jeff Shell

SVP Global Chief Information Security Officer (GCISO), Myrna Soto

EVP Global Corporate Development and Strategy, Bob Eatroff

President Comcast Foundation, Dalila Wilson-Scott

President Technology and Product Comcast Cable, Tony G. Werner

President Comcast Cable West Division, Steve White

President Comcast Cable Central Division, Bill Connors

Senior Vice President Marketing, Peter Intermaggio

Vice President Platform Quality, Jacques Louvet

Vice President, David Lorenzi

Vice President Business Development, Scott McGill

Vice President, Brandon Thompson

Vice President Backbone Architecture, Matt Scully

Vp- Regulatory Policy, David Don

Vice President, Steve Thomas

Vice President Customer Service Strategy and Operati, Julia Bross

Senior Vice President, Mark Muehl

Vice President Business Services, Shawn Adamson

National Account Manager, Joann Renner

Division Vice President, Dave Kowolenko

Vice President Finance and Accounting, Chris Lawler

Vice President Brand Development and Comm, Todd Arata

Corporate Vice President Xfinity Stores, Chris Frank

Vice President, Jack Birnbaum

Senior Vice President Finance and Accounting, John Iadanza

Vice President Information Technology Comcast Business Services, Christer Peltomaa

Vice President of Human Resour, Michael Cindric

National Sales Manager, David Klein

Regional Vice President Human Resources, Suzy Persutti

Region Vice President Engineering, Scott Melter

Vice President, Jonathan Palmatier

Vice President Finance and ADM, Bill Haase

Vice President Product Planning, John Vonk

Vice President Affiliate Finance, Victor Viola

Vice President Technology Assessment and Strategy, Dan Wang

Executive Vice President and Chief Product Officer, Chris Satchell

Vice President Outsourcing Strategy and Operations, Brian Duffy

Vice President Of Information Services And Information Technology, Bob Rittler

Vice President, Joseph McGinley

Vice President of Human Resources, Samantha Callahan

Senior Vice President Sales and Operations, Terry Connell

Vice President Public Policy, Rebecca Arbogast

Vice President Strategic Development, Marc Siry

Executive Vice President, Chip Sullivan

Vice President of Communications, Brian Farley

Vice President of Communications, Jack Segal

Executive Vice President Global Communications Universal Pictures, Teri Everett

Vice President, Michael Ruger

Vice President Product Sales, Rich Rollins

Senior Vice President Total Rewards NBCUniversal, Shawn Leavitt

Senior Vice President Interim President Services, Franklyn Athias

Senior Vice President Beltway Region, Mary McLaughlin

Senior Vice President and General Manager, Eric Schaefer

Vice President Xfinity Wifi, Cole Reinwand

Vp Hr, Michael Eagles

Regional Vice President Customer Care, Troy Griffin

Vice President Sales and Marketing, Carolyne Hannan

Vice President Field Operations, Bryan Mark

Executive Vice President Regulatory and State Legislative Affairs Comcast Corp., Kathy Zachem

National Sales Manager, Richard Baudo

Vice President Project Management, Alicia Daugherty

National Sales Manager, Michelle Muniz

Vice President Sales and Marketing, Stephen Krom

National Sales Manager, Kristin Del Balzo

Regional Vice President Government Affairs, Marc Farrar

Evp Hr, William Strahan

Vice President Engineering and XOC Comcast Central Division, Aaron Weimer

Vice Presidentleeneral Manager, Glenn Katz

Vice President Product Management and Customer Experience, Rui Costa

Senior Vice President of Government Affairs, Klayton Fennell

National Account Manager, Michelle Asher

Vice Chairman, Neil Smit, age 58

Board Member, Robert Peronto

Auditors: DELOITTE & TOUCHE LLP

LOCATIONS

HQ: Comcast Corp
One Comcast Center, Philadelphia, PA 19103-2838
Phone: 215 286-1700
Web: www.comcastcorporation.com

PRODUCTS/OPERATIONS

2016 Sales

	$ mil.	% of total
Cable Communications	50,048	61
NBC Universal		
Cable Networks	10,464	13
Broadcast Television	10,147	12
Filmed Entertainment	6,360	8
Theme parks	4,946	6
Headquarters & others	20	0
Eliminations	(334)	0
Corporate and others	750	0
Eliminations	(1988)	0
Total	**80,403**	**100**

Cable Networks

Cable Networks
Bravo
Chiller
Cloo (formerly Sleuth)
CNBC
CNBC World
E!
Esquire Network
Golf Channel
MSNBC
NBC Sports Network (formerly VERSUS)
Oxygen
Style
Syfy
Universal HD
USA Network

COMPETITORS

21st Century Fox	EVINE Live
AT&T	EarthLink
Altice USA	Google
CenturyLink	Liberty Interactive
Charter Communications	Netflix
Cox Communications	RCN Corporation
DISH Network	Verizon
Disney	Viacom

HISTORICAL FINANCIALS

Company Type: Public

Income Statement
FYE: December 31

	REVENUE ($ mil.)	NET INCOME ($ mil.)	NET PROFIT MARGIN	EMPLOYEES
12/17	84,526	22,714	26.9%	164,000
12/16	80,403	8,695	10.8%	159,000
12/15	74,510	8,163	11.0%	141,000
12/14	68,775	8,380	12.2%	139,000
12/13	64,657	6,816	10.5%	136,000
Annual Growth	**6.9%**	**35.1%**	—	**4.8%**

2017 Year-End Financials

Debt ratio: 34.53%—
Return on equity: 37.07%
Cash ($ mil.): 3,428
Current ratio: 0.74
Long-term debt ($ mil.): 59,422

Dividends
Yield: 0.0%
Payout: 9.9%
Market value ($ mil.): —

	STOCK PRICE ($) FY Close	P/E High/Low		PER SHARE ($) Earnings	Dividends	Book Value
12/17	40.05	16	7	4.75	0.47	14.77
12/16	69.05	39	30	1.79	0.68	11.35
12/15	56.43	39	32	1.62	0.49	10.70
12/14	58.01	36	30	1.60	0.44	10.37
12/13	51.97	40	29	1.28	0.39	9.72
Annual Growth	(6.3%)	—	—	38.8%	4.9%	11.0%

COMENITY BANK

LOCATIONS

HQ: COMENITY BANK
1 RIGHTER PKWY STE 100, WILMINGTON, DE
198031533
Phone: 614 729-4000

COMPETITORS

American Express
Bank of America
Barclays Bank Delaware
Citigroup
Target Receivables

HISTORICAL FINANCIALS

Company Type: Private

Income Statement

FYE: December 31

	ASSETS ($ mil.)	NET INCOME ($ mil.)	INCOME AS % OF ASSETS	EMPLOYEES
12/14	9,149	389	4.3%	200
12/13	7,453	350	4.7%	—
12/05	332	10	3.2%	—
12/03	672	88	13.2%	—
Annual Growth	26.8%	14.4%	—	—

2014 Year-End Financials

Debt ratio: ——
Return on equity: 19.70%
Cash ($ mil.): 392
Current ratio: —
Long-term debt ($ mil.): —

Dividends
Yield: —
Payout: —
Market value ($ mil.): —

Comerica, Inc.

Comerica is the holding company for Comerica Bank which has around 460 branches primarily in five US states and Canada. The company is organized into three main segments. The Business Bank division is the largest offering loans deposits and capital markets products to middle-market large corporate and government clients. The Retail Bank serves small businesses and consumers while the Wealth Management arm provides private banking investment management financial advisory investment banking brokerage insurance and retirement services. Comerica boasts total assets of around $75 billion and total deposits of some $60 billion.

Operations

Broadly speaking Comerica generates nearly 55% of its revenue from loan interest and almost 10% from interest on investment securities and short-term investments. The remainder of the bank's revenue is fee-based coming mostly from card fees (10% of revenue) service charges on deposit accounts (more than 5%) fiduciary income (more than 5%) and commercial lending fees (less than 5%).

The bank divides its operations into several segments: The Business Bank (commercial loans and lines of credit to middle market businesses multinational corporations and government agencies) The Retail Bank (small business banking and personal financial services) and Wealth Management (fiduciary services private banking and retirement and investment management services). In addition to these segments Comerica manages a securities portfolio and offers asset and liability management services.

Geographic Reach

Comerica operates out of some 590 locations include 460 branches as well as banking centers trust services locations loan production or other financial services offices. It's biggest markets are Michigan Texas California Arizona and Florida but it also operates and Canada and has 25 other businesses in various other states.

Sales and Marketing

Beyond retail customers Comerica caters to businesses and others operating in the energy automotive production and real estate industries.

Financial Performance

After enduring several years of flat sales Comerica has recorded two years of strong growth.

In fiscal 2016 revenue grew 5% to $2.9 billion following on from an 8% jump the previous year. The increase in 2016 was down to higher interest rates loan growth and a larger securities portfolio. Noninterest income crept up $16 million due to an increase in customer-driven fees partially offset by a fall in non-fee items.

Net income fell 8% to $447 million due to restructuring charges and the release in 2015 of litigation reserves. Excluding these two significant one-off items noninterest expense decreased by $23 million due to lower salary and benefit expenses as a result of the restructuring.

Cash from operations fell 42% to $493 million due to net changes in other items.

Strategy

Comerica's management is grappling with the issue of a sharp deterioration in the performance of loans to the beleaguered oil industry. While a number of US banks are under pressure from oil weakness Comerica has the largest exposure of an US bank to the industry at about 6% of its total loans.

To deal with the issue the company is cutting costs to free up cash in preparation for heavy losses. Its GEARup program has consisted of layoffs renegotiated vendor contracts a reduction in real estate and lower executive bonuses. It has also reduced lending to oil drillers.

HISTORY

Comerica traces its history to 1849 when Michigan governor Epaphroditus Ransom tapped Elon Farnsworth to found the Detroit Savings Fund Institute. At that time Detroit was a major transit point for shipping between Lakes Huron and Erie as well as between the US and Canada. The bank grew with the town and in 1871 became Detroit Savings Bank.

By 1899 Detroit was one of the top 10 US manufacturing centers and thanks to a group of local tinkerers and mechanics that included Henry Ford was on the brink of even greater growth. Detroit

Savings grew also fueled by the deposits of workers whom Ford paid up to $5 a day. Detroit Savings was not however the beneficiary of significant business with the auto makers; for corporate banking they turned first to eastern banks and then to large local banks in which they had an interest.

Detroit boomed during the 1920s as America went car-crazy but after the 1929 crash Detroiters defaulted on mortgages by the thousands. By 1933 Michigan's banks were in such disarray that the governor shut them down three weeks prior to the federal bank holiday. Detroit Savings was one of only four Detroit banks to reopen. None of the major banks associated with auto companies survived.

A few months later Manufacturers National Bank backed by a group of investors that included Edsel Ford (Henry's son) was founded. Although its start was rocky Manufacturers National was on firm footing by 1936; around the same time Detroit Savings Bank renamed itself the Detroit Bank to appeal to a more commercial clientele.

WWII and the postwar boom put Detroit back in gear. In the 1950s and 1960s both banks thrived. In the 1970s statewide branching was permitted and both banks formed holding companies (DETROITBANK Corp. and Manufacturers National Corp.) and expanded throughout Michigan. As they grew they added services; when Detroit's economy was hit by the oil shocks of the 1970s these diversifications helped them through the lean years.

DETROITBANK opened a trust operation in Florida in 1982 to maintain its relationship with retired customers and renamed itself Comerica to be less area-specific. Manufacturers National also began operating in Florida (1983) and made acquisitions in the Chicago area (1987). Comerica went farther afield buying banks in Texas (1988) and California (1991).

Following the national consolidation trend in 1992 Comerica and Manufacturers National merged (retaining the Comerica name) but did not fully integrate until 1994 when the new entity began making more acquisitions. To increase sales and develop its consumer business the company reorganized in 1996. It sold its Illinois bank and its Michigan customs brokerage business and acquired Fairlane Associates to expand its property/casualty insurance line.

As part of its strategy to have operations in all three NAFTA countries Comerica opened a bank in Mexico in 1997 and one in Canada in 1998. That year it dropped $66 million for the naming rights to the Detroit Tigers' baseball stadium which opened as Comerica Park in 2000. It also started a Web-based payment system for its international trade business.

To fortify its business lending operations in California Comerica bought Imperial Bancorp in 2001. At the beginning of 2002 chairman Eugene Miller handed the CEO reins to Ralph Babb who had been CFO. Later that year Babb became chairman as well.

EXECUTIVES

Chairman President and CEO Comerica Incorporated and Comerica Bank, Ralph W. Babb, age 68, $1,265,000 total compensation
EVP and President Comerica Bank (California Market), Judith S. Love, age 60
EVP and Chief Risk Officer Comerica Incorporated and Comerica Bank, Michael H. Michalak, age 59
EVP and Director of Operations Services, Paul R. Obermeyer, age 59
EVP, David E. Duprey, age 59, $573,731 total compensation

EVP Governance Regulatory Relations and Legal Affairs Comerica Incorporated and Comerica Bank, John D. Buchanan, age 53, $573,846 total compensation

President Comerica Incorporated and Comerica Bank, Curtis C. Farmer, age 54, $700,000 total compensation

EVP and CFO, Muneera S. Carr, age 49

EVP and President Comerica Bank Michigan Market, Michael T. Ritchie, age 48

EVP and Chief Human Resources Officer Comerica Incorporated and Comerica Bank, Megan D. Burkhart, age 45

EVP and Chief Credit Officer, Peter W. Guilfoile, age 56

EVP and President Comerica Bank Texas Market, Peter L. Sefzik, age 41

EVP and General Auditor, Christine Moore

Assistant Vice President Senior Systems Engineer, David Walker

Vice President Texas Market, Greg Wilcox

Vice President, Cindy Morgan

First Vice President Corporate Information Security Services, Kenneth Schaeffler

Vice President, Lake McGuire

Vice President Western Market, Peter Fitzpatrick

Vice President Loan Officer, Melanie Rice

First Vice President Regional Sales Manager, Darla Mick Darla Mick

Senior Vice President, William Purcell

Assistant Vice President, Catherine Cornell

Senior Vice President Energy Finance, Jeff Treadway

Vice President Technology and Life Sciences, Jeff Hasselman

Assistant Vice President Information Systems, Ken Lootens

Vice President CBO, Angela Knight

Vice President Human Resources Staffing, Dan Dunn

Vice President, Daniel Roesner

Senior Vice President Western Market, Michael Silva

Vice President, Jon E Haffner

Vice President Relationship Manager, Colleen Machado

Senior Vice President and Houston Market Manager Business Banking, Mark A Simmons

Vice President, Kelly McConnell

Senior Vice President, Cynthia Jordan

Vice President End User Technology Ser, Kim Martin

Vice President, Douglas Muniga

Vice President Treasury Management Sales Texas, Marcia F Graves

Vice President, Jake Friemel

Vice President Buseness Development Healthcar, Christopher Healy

Assistant Vice President, Steve Hattey

Vice President and Treasurer, Brad Bell

Vice President Western Market, Peter Wentworth

Vice President, Thomas Jones

Assistant Vice President, Padmanabhan Karatha

SENIOR VICE PRESIDENT OF IT, Andrew Straube

Vice President, Ian Mearns

Executive Vice President Lending and Trade Services, Helen Arsenault

Senior Vice President, David P Cagle

Vice President Credit Administration, Lori Yu

Vice President, Brett Jackson

Senior Vice President And North Texas Director Of Business Banking, David Milton

Vice President Bank Properties, Donald J Truschke

Banking Center Manager Vice President, Ruth Bonilla

Private Banking Vice President, Jennifer J Zuniga

Vice President, Josie Fenech

Vice President, Lynn M Hough

Vice President Private Banking, Gary J Beyer

Assistant Vice President, Dave Samra

Treasury Management Vice President, Danette R Hames

Vice President Middle Market Banking, Bryan L Johnston

Vice President, Marc P Abello

Senior Vice President, William Osbach

Assistant Vice President Cash Services, Larry Kwiatkowski

Vice President, Yvonne Auyang

Vice President, Lesley B Higginbotham

Senior Vice President Equity Fund Services, Steve Kattner

Vice President Alternate Group Manager Commercial Real Estate, Cynthia Porter

Banking Center Manager And Assistant Vice President, Alfonso J Ugarte

Vice President, Debbie Tuftee

Vice President, Doreen Boelstler

Vice President Enterprise Program Management Office, Bill Emmons

First Vice President Group Manager, James Robinson

Assistant Vice President Asset Based Auditing, Christopher Anthony

Global Corporate Product Management Assistant Vice President, Angie Roche

Vice President, Frank Gormley

Assistant Vice President, Heath Hawkins

Vice President International Finance, Jorge L Vargas

Vice President And Banking Center Manager, Jeremy Farr

Vice President Treasury Management Global Sales Consultant, Sheila Ausberry

Assistant Vice President Treasury Management, Pamela G Porter

Vice President, Nancy Blake

Senior Vice President And Alternate Credit Administration Officer, Mike Hammond

Vice President, Kristy Denby

Vice President Middle Market Banking, Kelly L Mione

Vice President Estate Administration, Angela W Aycock

Vice President Lakeshore District, Christopher Scott

Vice President, Tien G Huynh

Vice President And Alternate Group Manager, Stephen G Wells

Senior Vice President and Managing Director, Alan Jepsen

Vice President Western Market, Julie Foreman

Vice President Market Planning, Kevin Cornell

Vice President western Market Treasury Management Officer, Sharon Slofkosky

Banking Center Manager Assistant Vice President, Teresa Nolasco

Vice President U S. Banking Midwest, Mark Leveille

Senior Vice President and Chief Accounting Officer, Mauricio Ortiz

Banking Center Manager Vice President, Gordon McKinley

Senior Vice President middle Market Banking Iv, Steven Swiftney

Vice President and Alt. Credit Admin. Officer, John Ryan

Banking Center Manager Assistant Vice President, Lisa Thompson

Senior Vice President Director Product Management and Investment Advisory Services, Joshua Rockwell

Senior Vice President Texas Market Small Business Banking, Paul Orsborn

Vice President, Laura Wrocklage

Vice President Business Banking Coastal Counties, Angela Reed

Vice President, Cynthia Walters

Vice President agm, Matthew Breight

Vice President National Real Estate Services, Matt Maberry

Vice President Business Banking, Patricia Alexander

First Vice President and General Counsel, Nicole Gersch

Vice President, Ann Day-Salo

Assistant Vice President Senior Examiner, Diane Chang

Vice President National Developers, Casey Stevenson

Vice President, Raffi Khelghatian

Senior Vice President Energy Finance Group, John Lesikar

Vice President, Gary P Mach

Vice President Commercial Banking, Jason Syrinek

Banking Center Manager Assistant Vice President, Brandy DeWilde

Vice President and Commercial Loan Officer, Katherine Happy

Banking Center Manager Assistant Vice President, Ryan McCullough

Vice President Business Bank, Garrett Hill

Assistant Vice President Healthcare An, Kyle Weiss

Vice President, Sharon Feigelson

Assistant Vice President, Cedric Jordan

Assistant Vice President Institutional Trust, Scott Canup

Banking Center Manager Assistant Vice President, Servando Andrade

Senior Vice President and Director Compensation, Sarah Stratton

Vice President Assistant General Manager, Jim Schoettley

First Vice President Security Director, Robert Rayner

Vice President Treasury Management, Kathleen Sidor

First Vice President Western Market, Philip Diorio

Vice President Treasury Management Services Corporate Product Management, Richard Moore

Banking Center Manager Assistant Vice President, Henry Tran

Vice President Retail Prod Management, John MacMillan

Senior Vice President and Assistant General Counsel, Terrance Henderson

Assistant Vice President texas Market, August Knight

Senior Vice President Texas Market North Texas Region Manager, Barry Brundage

Senior Vice President Midwest Region Commercial Real Estate Finance, James Preston

Vice President Business Banking, Karen Gladney

Vice President, Kathy Pitton

Vice President Product Development, William Anderson

Senior Vice President, Dan Evans

Vice President, Tom O'connell

Vice President, Peter Kennedy

Senior Vice President, Vern Hawkins

Assistant Vice President, Bryndon Skelton

First Vice President Marketing Support, Mary Weiss

Vice President Commercial Card Sales, Keith Kim

Vice President Banking Center Manager, Milanka Miskovic

Vice President and Manager Infrastructure Project Services, Bob Olech

Vice President U S Banking Midwest, Brandon Welling

Vice President Regional Banking Officer Financial Services Division, Laura Reyes

Auditors: Ernst & Young LLP

LOCATIONS

HQ: Comerica, Inc.
  Comerica Bank Tower, 1717 Main Street, MC 6404,
  Dallas, TX 75201
Phone: 214 462-6831
Web: www.comerica.com

2016 Banking Centers

	No.
Michigan	209
Texas	127
California	97
Other Markets	
Arizona	17
Florida	7
Canada	1
Total	**458**

Selected Markets

Arizona
California
Colorado
Florida
Illinois
Michigan
Nevada
Ohio
Texas
Washington

PRODUCTS/OPERATIONS

2016 Sales

	$ mil.	% of total
Interest		
Fees on Loans	1,635	55
Investment securities	247	8
Short-term investments	27	1
Noninterest		
Card fees	303	10
Service charges on deposit accounts	219	7
Fiduciary income	190	6
Commercial lending fees	89	3
Letter of credit fees	50	2
Foreign exchange	42	2
Bank-owned life insurance	42	2
Brokerage fee	19	1
Others	102	3
Net Securities(losses) gaints	(5)	0
Total	**2,960**	**100**

2016 Sales

	% of total
Business Bank	88
Wealth Management	11
Retail Bank	1
Total	**100**

Selected Subsidiaries

Comerica Bank
Comerica Bank & Trust National Association
Comerica Capital Advisors Incorporated
Comerica Financial Incorporated
Comerica Holdings Incorporated
Comerica Insurance Group Inc.
Comerica Insurance Services Inc.
Comerica Investment Services Inc.
Comerica Investments LLC
Comerica Leasing Corporation
Comerica Merchant Services Inc.
Comerica Securities Inc.
Wilson Kemp & Associates Inc.
World Asset Management Inc.

COMPETITORS

Bank of America	Regions Financial
Citigroup	SVB Financial
Cullen/Frost Bankers	SunTrust
Fifth Third	TCF Financial
Huntington Bancshares	U.S. Bancorp
JPMorgan Chase	Wells Fargo
MUFG Americas Holdings	

HISTORICAL FINANCIALS

Company Type: Public

Income Statement

FYE: December 31

	ASSETS ($ mil.)	NET INCOME ($ mil.)	INCOME AS % OF ASSETS	EMPLOYEES
12/17	71,567	743	1.0%	8,190
12/16	72,978	477	0.7%	8,149
12/15	71,877	521	0.7%	9,103
12/14	69,190	593	0.9%	9,115
12/13	65,227	541	0.8%	9,207
Annual Growth	**2.3%**	**8.3%**	**—**	**(2.9%)**

2017 Year-End Financials

Debt ratio: 2.55%
Return on equity: 9.43%
Cash ($ mil.): 5,845
Current ratio: —
Long-term debt ($ mil.): —

No. of shares (mil.): 174
Dividends
Yield: 0.0%
Payout: 26.3%
Market value ($ mil.): 15,179

	STOCK PRICE ($) FY Close	P/E High/Low	PER SHARE ($) Earnings	Dividends	Book Value
12/17	86.81	21 15	4.14	1.09	45.54
12/16	68.11	26 11	2.68	0.89	44.47
12/15	41.83	18 14	2.84	0.83	43.03
12/14	46.84	16 13	3.16	0.79	41.35
12/13	47.54	16 10	2.85	0.68	39.24
Annual Growth	**16.2%**	**— —**	**9.8%**	**12.5%**	**3.8%**

Commerce Bancshares Inc

Commerce Bancshares owns bank branch operator Commerce Bank. The financial institution boasts a network of more than 360 locations across several US states including Missouri Kansas Illinois Oklahoma and Colorado. The bank focuses on retail and commercial banking services such as deposit accounts mortgages loans and credit cards. Commerce Bank also runs a wealth management division that offers asset management trust private banking brokerage and estate planning services and also manages proprietary mutual funds. As part of its operations Commerce Bank has subsidiaries devoted to insurance leasing and private equity investments.

Operations

The company operates three main segments: Consumer Commercial and Wealth.

The Commercial segment which collects roughly 65% of the bank's total revenue provides corporate lending merchant and commercial bank card products leasing and international services as well as business and government deposit and cash management services. Fixed income investments are sold to individuals and institutional investors through the segment's Capital Markets Group.

Another 20% of bank revenue is generated through the Consumer segment which includes the retail branch network consumer installment lending personal mortgage banking and consumer debit and credit bank card activities. It provides services through a network of more than 200 full-service branches a 400-machine ATM network and alternative delivery channels such as extensive online banking and telephone banking services.

The remaining bank revenue (around 15%) comes from the Wealth segment which manages

investments with a market value of $20.4 billion and administers an additional $14.8 billion in non-managed assets provides traditional trust and estate tax-planning services brokerage services and advisory and discretionary investment portfolio management services targeted to personal and institutional corporate customers. The Wealth segment also manages Commerce Bank's proprietary mutual funds.

Broadly speaking interest income from the bank's portfolio of loans make up more than 40% of total revenue. Roughly 60% of the portfolio is comprised of commercial loans (mostly business real estate loans but also construction and land loans and other business-related loans). Personal banking loans make up the remaining 40% of the portfolio and mostly include real estate loans and consumer lines of credit but also consumer credit cards revolving home equity loans and some overdraft lines of credit.

Geographic Reach

Commerce Bancshares through its Commerce Bank business operates more than 360 branch banks in five central US states with major focus in Peoria and Bloomington Illinois; St. Louis; Kansas City and Wichita Kansas; Denver; Tulsa Oklahoma; Nashville; Cincinnati; and Dallas. The bank also has commercial offices in Cincinnati Nashville and Dallas. The company's two largest markets include St. Louis and Kansas City. To this end the cities serve as the central hubs for its operation.

Sales and Marketing

The bank spent $14.2 million on marketing in fiscal 2013 down 6% from $15.1 million in 2012 and down 15% from the $16.8 million it spent on marketing in 2011.

Financial Performance

In the recent low interest environment Commerce Bancshares has seen its revenue slowly decline over the past few years from declining interest income from its loans and investment securities. In fiscal 2013 revenue fell by $8.9 million to $1.08 billion as the bank earned lower rates on investment securities and loans (from smaller interest margins) despite higher loan balances and lower rates paid on deposits. The bank was able to offset some of its revenue losses by earning $18.8 million more from bank card transaction trust and brokerage fees.

The bank's net income also dipped by $8.4 million (or 3%) to $261 million in 2013. This is mostly from the drop in revenue but also because the bank paid $6 million more toward employee salaries and benefits (from higher salaries) and $4.4 million more toward data processing and software expenses as bank card processing costs went up. Profits are still up significantly from the bank's recovery period in 2009 and 2010 when it earned $169.1 million and $221.7 million respectively.

The amount of cash provided from operations fell for the third straight year to $360.9 million in 2013 down 6% from the $383.1 million provided in 2012. This was primarily because of lower net income but also because it paid $11.7 million more toward its income tax obligations than in the prior year.

Unlike its revenue and earnings Commerce's assets have been growing. Total loans were $10.96 billion in 2013 representing an increase of $1.13 billion or 11% over balances in 2012. While loan assets have increased across the board business loan assets contributed the most growing by $580.5 million in 2013 to a total of $3.7 billion. Deposit assets also rose by 4% to $19.05 billion in 2013.

Strategy

Commerce Bancshares serves its local retail markets through relationship banking and high touch service. It works to grow its core revenue by expanding new and existing customer relationships leveraging improved technology and enhancing customer satisfaction. To respond to changes in consumer banking preferences the bank will work to improve its distribution strategy by de-emphasizing the central role of traditional branch banking and providing more customers access to its services through ATMs call centers mobile and house lines internet. It will also work to develop new products and focus on expense reductions wherever possible to improve the company's bottom line.

To grow its commercial business segment which already provides two-thirds of all bank revenue Commerce plans to invest in distinctive lower-risk/higher return businesses to increase its loan business. In addition it intends to deepen its relationships with existing commercial customers and provide more products to them to increase profitability while taking on little additional risk or cost.

Thanks to higher brokerage and trust fees Commerce Bancshares' Wealth division saw the largest segment revenue growth in 2013. The bank is optimistic that its new hires in the division will contribute to higher sales productivity over the next few years particularly in the institutional and St. Louis Family Office. In addition management believes that the improving US economy and booming stock market will improve investor confidence and M&A activity which should help grow the segment in the years ahead.

Mergers and Acquisitions

Commerce Bancshares in May 2013 inked a merger agreement with Summit Bancshares whereby Summit merged into a wholly-owned subsidiary of Commerce Bancshares. The transaction valued at approximately $40.6 million consisted entirely of Commerce Bancshares' stock and added more than $200 million in new loans to the bank's portfolio. The deal significantly boosted Commerce Bank's foothold in the Tulsa Oklahoma market and allowed it to enter the Oklahoma City market.

EXECUTIVES

SVP; Director Operations and Information Services, Robert J. Rauscher, age 59

CFO, Charles G. (Chuck) Kim, age 57, $415,080 total compensation

EVP Commercial Line of Business; President and COO Commerce Bank Kansas City Region, Kevin G. Barth, age 57, $408,705 total compensation

EVP; Chief Human Resources Officer and Director Internal Support Services, Sara E. Foster, age 57

Chairman and CEO, David W. Kemper, age 66, $896,073 total compensation

EVP Trust Line of Business; President The Commerce Trust Company a division of Commerce Bank, V. Raymond (Ray) Stranghoener, age 66, $235,900 total compensation

EVP; Chief Credit Officer and Chief Risk Officer, Daniel D. Callahan

SVP; Director Commercial Card and Merchant Services, Jeff Burik

SVP; Director Community Bank Administration, Michael J. Petrie

President and COO, John W. Kemper, $462,287 total compensation

Senior Vice President Financial Advisor, Pat Huelskoetter

Vice President, Jason Boyer

Assistant Vice President Information Technology Manager, Joel Verwers

Senior Vice President, Richard Shulusky

Assistant Vice President Commerce Bank Kansas City Mo, Kent Galbraith

Vice President Private Client Group, Joe Morris

Vice President Of Human Resources, Betty Maes

Senior Vice President Retail Group and Manager Operations, Darryl Collins

Vice President of Commercial Lending, Jeffrey Hotop

Assistant Vice President Regional Marketing, Jenny Stanley

Vice President, Jeffrey Turner

Senior Vice President, Mary McClain

Vice President, Joe Mccaddon

Vice President, James Roman

Senior Vice President Retail and Small Business Group Manager, Robin Wandschneider

Assistant Vice President Information Technology MA, Kaz Verwers

Senior Vice President and Director Operations, Eric Rauscher

Vice President Information Technology, Dino Spatoulis

Vice President Financial Advisor, Aaron Alexander

Vice President Treasury Sales, Chuck Peterson

Senior Vice President, Dee Joyner

Vice President Server Operations Manager Information Technology, Wanda Edgmond

Senior Vice President, Mark Tankesley

Assistant Vice President Information Technology Manager, Chad Boline

Vice President and Contact Center Director, Mossie Schallon

Assistant Vice President Product Development and New Business, Susan Wilborn

Executive Vice President Trust Line of Business; President The Commerce Trust Company a division o, V Stranghoener

Vice President Human Resources, Robert Heflin

Vice President of Information Technology, Allan Smith

Vice President, Pam Hill

Senior Vice President, William Gamewell

Vice President and Director of Finance, Duane Locher

Executive Vice President, Gaylyn McGregor

Vice President, Ron Koenig

Vice President, Craig Duerksen

Vice President, James Fallon

Assistant Vice President Business Line Systems Manager, Kevin Belloma

Vice President, Frank Hill

Vice President, Steven Sebade

Vice President, JO Hicks

Vice President, Barbara Mccaslin

Vice President, Lance Wright

Vice President, Dave Young

Senior Vice President, Gordon Roewe

Vice President Interest Rate Swaps Marketing, Jessie Kelley

Vice President Product Development, Bruce Bienhoff

Senior Vice President, Nick Fafoglia

Senior Vice President, Steve Sebade

Vice President, Wayne Lewis

Vice President Finance, Lynn McLaughlin

Vice President Market Research, Mindy Hauptman

Vice President, Judy Shilling

Vice President, Ryan Fleming

Vice President, Garth Kilburn

Vice President, Paul Manuel

Vice President of Commercial Banking, Sam Jarvis

Assistant Vice President, Jim Hanson

Vice President, Lyons Lon

Assistant Vice President Small Business Banking Specialist, Darin Crump

Assistant Vice President Information Technology MA, George Verwers

Vice President Mortgage Technology Manager, Sarah Vande

Vice President Commercial Banking, Richard Ringwald

Assistant Vice President, Andrew Fogt

Vice President Team Leader, Matt Dority

Vice President Business Development, Brent Miller

Senior Vice President, Richard Jankovich

Vice President Human Resources, Charles Hunter

Senior Vice President, John Meyer

Vice President, Ben Wanless

Vice President, Parker Heikes

Vice President, Robert Whitney

Assistant Vice President, Melissa Caputo

Vice President, Jack Stapleton

Vice President National Accounts, Venus Vega

Assistant Vice President, Crystal Sharp

Assistant Vice President, Cole Higginbotham

Vice President Retail Banking Manager, Kathy Wilkes

Assistant Vice President Small Business Banking, Sonya Tandy

Assistant Vice President Small Business Banking, Donald Reynolds

Assistant Vice President, Angela Wright-Jones

Assistant Vice President, Amy Winter

Corporate Banking Senior Vice President, Steven Bloemer

Vice President C and I Relationship Manager, Chris Steuterman

Vice President of Information Technology, Ken Isbell

Assistant Vice President, Isaac Mishler

Assistant Vice President Fixed Income Trading, Matt Koch

Senior Vice President Commercial Loan Servicing, Jeremy Allen

Vice Chairman, Seth M. Leadbeater, age 66

Vice Chairman, Jonathan M. Kemper, age 64

Auditors: KPMG LLP

LOCATIONS

HQ: Commerce Bancshares Inc
1000 Walnut, Kansas City, MO 64106
Phone: 816 234-2000   **Fax:** 816 234-2369
Web: www.commercebank.com

2016 Sales by Market

	% of total
Kansas City	32
St. Louis	28
Other regions	40
Total	**100**

PRODUCTS/OPERATIONS

2016 Sales

	$ mil.	% of total
Interest Income		
Interest and fees on loans	490	42
Interest on investment securities	207	18
Interest on long-term securities purchased under agreements to resell	13	1
Interest on loans held for sale	1	0
Interest on federal funds sold and short-term securities purchased under agreements to resell	0	0
Interest on deposits with banks	1	0
Non-Interest Income		
Bank card transaction fees	181	15
Trust fees	121	10
Deposit account charges and other fees	86	7
Consumer brokerage services	13	1
Loan fees and sales	11	1
Capital market fees	10	1
Other	48	4
Total	**1,187**	**100**

Selected Services

Commercial Banking
  Financing
  Treasury Services
  Commercial Card Products
  Merchant Services
  International Services
  Capital Markets
  Investment Management
  Corporate Trust
Personal Banking
  Checking Accounts
  Savings Accounts
  Money Market Accounts & CDs
  Borrowing Solutions & Loans
  Mortgages

Credit Cards
Check Cards & Prepaid Cards
Online Banking Services & Mobile Banking
Small Business Banking
Small Business Checking Accounts
Small Business Online Services
Small Business Loans
Business Credit Cards & Check Cards
Business Resource Center
Merchant Services
Wealth Management
The Commerce Trust Company
Investment Management
Private Banking Services
Financial Advisory Services
Trust Services
Institutional Trust Services
Corporate Trust
Brokerage Services
Insurance Services

Selected Subsidiaries

Capital for Business Inc.
CBI-Kansas Inc.
CFB Partners LLC
CFB Venture Fund L.P.
Clayton Financial Corp.
Clayton Holdings LLC
Clayton Realty Corp.
Commerce Bank National Association
Commerce Brokerage Services Inc.
Commerce Insurance Services Inc.
Commerce Investment Advisors Inc.
Commerce Mortgage Corp.
Illinois Financial LLC
Illinois Realty LLC
Tower Redevelopment Corporation

COMPETITORS

BOK Financial	First National of
Bank of America	Nebraska
Bank of the West	Great Western Bancorp
Capitol Federal	INTRUST
Financial	U.S. Bancorp
Dickinson Financial	UMB Financial
First Banks	Wells Fargo

HISTORICAL FINANCIALS

Company Type: Public

Income Statement

FYE: December 31

	ASSETS ($ mil.)	NET INCOME ($ mil.)	INCOME AS % OF ASSETS	EMPLOYEES
12/16	25,641	275	1.1%	4,877
12/15	24,604	263	1.1%	4,859
12/14	23,994	261	1.1%	4,866
12/13	23,072	260	1.1%	4,889
12/12	22,159	269	1.2%	4,878
Annual Growth	3.7%	0.6%	—	(0.0%)

2016 Year-End Financials

Debt ratio: 0.40%
Return on equity: 11.31%
Cash ($ mil.): 789
Current ratio: —
Long-term debt ($ mil.): —

No. of shares (mil.): 106
Dividends
  Yield: 0.0%
  Payout: 32.8%
Market value ($ mil.): 6,169

	STOCK PRICE ($) FY Close	P/E High/Low	PER SHARE ($) Earnings	Dividends	Book Value
12/16	57.81	24 15	2.49	0.82	23.39
12/15	42.54	21 17	2.32	0.78	22.00
12/14	43.49	21 18	2.25	0.74	20.87
12/13	44.91	21 16	2.24	0.71	18.94
12/12	35.06	19 15	2.27	1.81	18.55
Annual Growth	13.3%	— —	2.3%	(18.0%)	6.0%

Commercial Metals Co.

EXECUTIVES

President CMC Cometals, Eliezer Skornicki
Chairman and CEO, Murray R. McClean, age 66, $654,231 total compensation
VP and Treasurer, Louis A. Federle, age 66
SVP and CFO, Barbara R. Smith, age 56
Director Public Relations, Debbie L. Okle
EVP and Division Manager Howell Metal, James K. Forkovitch
Director Marketing Strategy CMC Recycling, Robert J. Melendi
VP and Director Internal Audit, Manny Rosenfeld
Chairman President and CEO, Joseph (Joe) Alvarado, age 64
EVP; President CMC International, Hanns Zoellner, age 66, $443,302 total compensation
VP CMC Recycling, Brian Halloran
VP and Director Internal Audit, Leon K. Rusch, age 64
VP and Treasurer, Carey J. Dubois, age 56
President CMC Europe, Ludovit Gajdos
SVP Business Development and Business Processes, Devesh Sharma
SVP Human Resources and Organizational Development, James (Jim) Alleman
SVP Law Government Affairs and Global Compliance; General Counsel and Corporate Secretary, Ann J. Bruder
SVP; President CMC Americas, Tracy L. Porter
VP and CIO, Tracy Nolan
SVP and President CMC International, John C. Elmore
VP and Controller, Adam Hickey
Director, Richard B. (Rick) Kelson, age 68
Director, Robert R. Womack, age 78
Director, Rhys J. Best, age 68
Director, Anthony A. (Tony) Massaro, age 71
Director, Sarah E. Raiss, age 58
Director, Robert D. Neary, age 82
Director, Harold L. Adams, age 75
Director, J. David Smith, age 66
Director, Robert L. Guido, age 69
Auditors: Deloitte & Touche LLP

LOCATIONS

HQ: Commercial Metals Co.
  6565 North MacArthur Blvd., Irving, TX 75039
Phone: 214 689-4300   **Fax:** 214 689-5886
Web: www.cmc.com

COMPETITORS

AK Steel Holding	Roanoke Bar Division
Corporation	Ryerson
BHP Billiton	Schnitzer Steel
Blue Tee	Severstal North
Connell LP	America
David J. Joseph	Simec
Gerdau Ameristeel	Steel Dynamics
Indel	Tube City IMS
Keywell	United States Steel
Metals USA	Universal Forest
Mueller Industries	Products
Nucor	Worthington Industries
OmniSource	
Quanex Building	
Products	

HISTORICAL FINANCIALS

Company Type: Public

Income Statement

FYE: August 31

	REVENUE ($ mil.)	NET INCOME ($ mil.)	NET PROFIT MARGIN	EMPLOYEES
08/17	4,569	46	1.0%	8,797
08/16	4,610	54	1.2%	8,388
08/15	5,988	141	2.4%	9,126
08/14	7,039	115	1.6%	9,293
08/13	6,889	77	1.1%	9,411
Annual Growth	(9.8%)	(12.0%)	—	(1.7%)

2017 Year-End Financials

Debt ratio: 27.72%
Return on equity: 3.35%
Cash ($ mil.): 252
Current ratio: 2.82
Long-term debt ($ mil.): 805

No. of shares (mil.): 115
Dividends
  Yield: 2.5%
  Payout: 73.8%
Market value ($ mil.): 2,187

	STOCK PRICE ($) FY Close	P/E High/Low	PER SHARE ($) Earnings	Dividends	Book Value
08/17	18.89	61 37	0.39	0.48	12.10
08/16	15.52	38 27	0.47	0.48	11.93
08/15	15.70	15 11	1.20	0.48	11.41
08/14	17.28	21 15	0.97	0.48	11.44
08/13	14.88	26 19	0.66	0.48	10.85
Annual Growth	6.1%	— —	(12.3%)	(0.0%)	2.7%

CommScope Holding Co., Inc.

Auditors: Ernst & Young LLP

LOCATIONS

HQ: CommScope Holding Co., Inc.
  1100 CommScope Place, S.E., Hickory, NC 28602
Phone: 828 324-2200
Web: www.commscope.com

HISTORICAL FINANCIALS

Company Type: Public

Income Statement

FYE: December 31

	REVENUE ($ mil.)	NET INCOME ($ mil.)	NET PROFIT MARGIN	EMPLOYEES
12/16	4,923	222	4.5%	25,000
12/15	3,807	(70)	—	23,000
12/14	3,829	236	6.2%	13,000
12/13	3,480	19	0.6%	13,000
12/12	3,321	5	0.2%	12,500
Annual Growth	10.3%	154.0%	—	18.9%

2016 Year-End Financials

Debt ratio: 63.88%
Return on equity: 16.98%
Cash ($ mil.): 428
Current ratio: 2.32
Long-term debt ($ mil.): 4,549

No. of shares (mil.): 193
Dividends
  Yield: —
  Payout: —
Market value ($ mil.): 7,211

Community Bank System Inc

Community Bank System is right up front about what it is. The holding company owns Community Bank which operates about 195 branches across upstate New York and northeastern Pennsylvania where it operates as First Liberty Bank and Trust. Focusing on small underserved towns and non-urban markets the bank offers standard products and services such as checking and savings accounts certificates of deposit and loans and mortgages to consumer business and government clients. Boasting over $11.0 billion in assets the bank's loan portfolio consists of mostly business loans residential mortgages and consumer loans. Community Bank System's subsidiaries offer employee benefit services wealth management and insurance products and services.

Operations

Community Bank System operates three business segments. The Banking segment which made up 83% of the company's total revenue during 2015 provides lending and deposit services to individuals businesses and municipalities. Employee Benefit Services (12% of revenue) offers trust investment fund retirement plan actuarial healthcare consulting and other administrative services through Benefit Plan Administrative Services (BPAS). The All Other segment (5% of revenue) includes its Wealth Management (operating through Community Investment Services) and Insurance businesses (operating through CBNA Insurance Agency).

Nearly 70% of the company's revenue comes from interest income. About 49% of its revenue came from loan interest during 2015 while another 19% came from interest on taxable and nontaxable investments. The rest of its revenue came from deposit service fees (14% of revenue) employee benefit services (12%) wealth management and insurance services (5%) and other banking revenues (1%).

Geographic Reach

Community Bank System operated 194 branches and six back-office operating facilities in 36 counties in upstate New York and six counties in northeastern Pennsylvania at the end of 2015.

Sales and Marketing

The bank has been ramping up its advertising spend in recent years. It spent $3.6 million on advertising during 2015 up from $3.2 million and $3.0 million in 2014 and 2013 respectively.

Financial Performance

Community Bank System's annual revenues have been slowly trending higher since 2013 despite a decline in loan interest mostly as it's been building its non-interest related business lines. Meanwhile its net income has risen more than 15% as it's had to pay less in interest expenses on deposits amidst the low interest environment.

The bank's revenue grew 2% to $382.92 million during 2015 thanks to a combination of employee benefit services business growth from new customers and expanding business relationships with existing customers as well as from new service offerings; higher interest income from loans and taxable investments as such interest-earning asset balances grew modestly; and a 13% jump in wealth management and insurance services revenue stemming from the acquisition of OneGroup from the Oneida Financial Group acquisition.

Despite revenue growth in 2015 Community's net income dipped less than 1% to $91.23 million for the year due to costs related to the Oneida acquisition. The company's operating cash levels shrank 5% to $116.46 million mostly due to unfavorable working capital changes related to deferred income tax provisions and changes in other assets and liabilities.

Strategy

Community Bank System looks to continue building its loan and deposit business as well as its non-interest service lines organically and through strategic acquisitions of other banks and financial companies. The financial company in 2015 began exploring expansion opportunities into neighboring markets in eastern Ohio upper New England and New Jersey and in 2017 acquired Northeast Retirement Services (NRS) for around $146 million. NRS provides institutional transfer agency master recordkeeping services custom target date fund administration trust product administration and customized reporting services to institutional clients.

Mergers and Acquisitions

In spring 2017 Community Bank System acquired Vermont-based Merchants Bancshares. Merchants operates nearly 35 branches and has assets in excess of $1.8 billion; the acquisition will expand Community Bank's operations into Vermont and western Massachusetts.

In December 2015 the company and subsidiary Community Bank NA expanded its presence in the Mohawk Valley and Central New York after it purchased Oneida Financial Corp and its subsidiaries The Oneida Savings Bank and State Bank of Chittenango. The deal added a dozen branch locations in the Oneida and Madison counties as well as its OneGroup and OWM non-banking subsidiaries $769 million in assets $399 million in loans $699 million in deposits and $226 million in investment securities.

In January 2015 subsidiary BPAS-APS purchased the professional services practice of EBS-RMSCO Inc. (a subsidiary of The Lifetime Healthcare Companies) expanding its non-banking actuarial valuation and consulting services to clients who sponsor pension and post-retirement related medical and welfare plans.

Company Background

In mid-2012 the bank purchased about 20 branches in upstate New York from HSBC. The deal which was made to satisfy antitrust concerns regarding First Niagara's purchase of 195 branches in New York from HSBC strengthened Community Bank Systems' geographic footprint.

In 2011 the company bought bank holding company The Wilber Corporation adding about 20 locations in the Catskills Mountains region of central New York.

In 2011 expanding its trust and benefits administration business it bought retirement plan administrator CAI Benefits which has offices in New York and Northern New Jersey.

EXECUTIVES

EVP and CFO, Scott A. Kingsley, age 52, $422,500 total compensation

President CEO and Director, Mark E. Tryniski, age 56, $725,000 total compensation

EVP and Chief Banking Officer, Brian D. Donahue, age 61, $350,000 total compensation

CTO, J. Michael Wilson, age 46

SVP Retail Banking Sales and Marketing, Harold M. (Harry) Wentworth, age 52

SVP and Chief Investment Officer, Joseph J. Lemchak, age 55

President Pennsylvania Banking, Robert P. Matley, age 65

SVP Municipal Banking Director, Joseph E. Sutaris, age 49

SVP and Senior Commercial Lending Officer Northern New York, Nicholas S. (Nick) Russell, age 49

SVP and Chief Credit Administrator, Stephen G. Hardy, age 62

EVP and General Counsel, George J. Getman, age 60, $375,000 total compensation

SVP and Chief Risk Officer, Paul J. Ward

SVP and Chief Credit Officer, Joseph Serbun, $248,107 total compensation

Assistant Vice President Marketing an, Mary K Barnette

Senior Vice President and Special Projects Director, Timothy Baker

Vice President, David Blackburn

Executive Vice President Marketing, Deborah Fitch

Executive Vice President Marketing, Caryn Wake

Vice President Finance, Michael Ervin

Vice President Marketing, Art Gentry

Executive Vice President, Barbara Call

Senior Vice President Director Of Sales And Marketing, Hal Wentworth

Vice President and Manager Financial Analysis, Robert Frost

Vice President Director Mortgage Lending, George J Burke

Vice President and Information Technology Manager, James Wilson

Senior Vice President and Chief Investment Officer, Joe Lemchak

Vice President Cash Management Product and Sales Manager, Cindy Lefko

Vice President Loan Operations Manager, Barbara Snyder

Finance Senior Vice President, Richard Heidrick

Vice President Commercial Banker, Allison Mosher

Assistant Vice President Commercial Banking Officer, Stacia Arnaud

Chair, Sally A. Steele, age 61

Auditors: PricewaterhouseCoopers LLP

LOCATIONS

HQ: Community Bank System Inc
5790 Widewaters Parkway, DeWitt, NY 13214-1883
Phone: 315 445-2282
Web: www.communitybankna.com

PRODUCTS/OPERATIONS

2015 Sales

	$ mil.	% of total
Interest Income:		
Interest and fees on loans	187	49
Taxable investments	52	14
Nontaxable investments	19	5
Noninterest		
Deposit service fees	52	14
Employee benefit services	45	12
Wealth management	20	5
Other	5	1
Total	382	100

Selected Subsidiaries & Affiliates

Benefit Plans Administrative Services Inc.
Benefit Plans Administrative Services LLC
Brilie Corporation
CBNA Insurance Agency Inc.
CBNA Preferred Funding Corp.

CBNA Treasury Management Corporation
Community Bank N.A. (also dba First Liberty Bank & Trust)
Community Investment Services Inc.
First of Jermyn Realty Company
First Liberty Service Corporation
Flex Corporation
Hand Benefit & Trust Company
Hand Securities Inc.
Harbridge Consulting Group LLP
Nottingham Advisors Inc.
Town & Country Agency LLC
Western Catskill Realty Inc.

COMPETITORS

Arrow Financial	Financial Institutions
Bank of America	HSBC USA
Canandaigua National	JPMorgan Chase
Chemung Financial	KeyCorp
Citizens Financial	M&T Bank
Group	NBT Bancorp
Elmira Savings Bank	

HISTORICAL FINANCIALS
Company Type: Public

Income Statement
FYE: December 31

	ASSETS ($ mil.)	NET INCOME ($ mil.)	INCOME AS % OF ASSETS	EMPLOYEES
12/16	8,666	103	1.2%	2,499
12/15	8,552	91	1.1%	2,490
12/14	7,489	91	1.2%	2,182
12/13	7,095	78	1.1%	2,215
12/12	7,496	77	1.0%	2,188
Annual Growth	3.7%	7.7%	—	3.4%

2016 Year-End Financials

Debt ratio: 2.87%	No. of shares (mil.): 44
Return on equity: 8.85%	Dividends
Cash ($ mil.): 173	Yield: 0.0%
Current ratio: —	Payout: 54.3%
Long-term debt ($ mil.): —	Market value ($ mil.): 2,746

	STOCK PRICE ($) FY Close	P/E High/Low		PER SHARE ($) Earnings	Dividends	Book Value
12/16	61.79	27	15	2.32	1.26	26.96
12/15	39.94	20	15	2.19	1.22	26.06
12/14	38.13	18	15	2.22	1.16	24.24
12/13	39.68	21	14	1.94	1.10	21.66
12/12	27.36	15	13	1.93	1.06	22.78
Annual Growth	22.6%	—	—	4.7%	4.4%	4.3%

Community Health Systems, Inc.

Community Health Systems (CHS) isn't much of a city dweller. The hospital operator prefers small-town America owning or leasing more than 145 hospitals — mostly in rural areas or small cities — in 21 states. Its hospitals (which house roughly 24000 beds) typically act as the sole or primary acute health care provider in a service area and offer a variety of medical surgical and emergency services (though a handful are specialty centers). The hospitals generally have ancillary facilities including doctors' offices surgery centers and diagnostic imaging facilities as well as home health and hospice agencies.

Operations

CHS operates two segments: hospital operations (the bulk of the company's business) and home care agency operations. The hospital operations segment includes inpatient centers and their related outpatient care facilities and accounts for some 99% of annual revenues. The home care agency segment provides in-home outpatient care; it operates some 75 home care agencies and 15 hospice agencies primarily in markets where the firm also runs a medical center.

Altogether CHS employs some 20000 physicians and their medical staffs.

Geographic Reach

CHS has hospitals in more than 20 states with its largest market concentrations in Florida Indiana Texas and Pennsylvania.

Sales and Marketing

CHS receives more than half of its revenues from commercial insurance companies through managed care contracts. Approximately 35% of revenues come from Medicare and Medicaid reimbursements for patient services and the rest of revenue comes from self-pay patients.

Financial Performance

CHS revenue rose significantly in 2014 when the company acquired rival Health Management Associates and expanded its network of facilities. Revenues have since struggled growing a modest 4% in 2015 and then slipping 5% to $18.4 billion in 2016. Hospital operations income the primary source of revenue fell 5% that year largely due to the spin-off of Quorum Health Resources.

Net income hovered at around $150 million until 2016 when CHS posted a net loss of $1.7 billion. This was driven by a $1.7 billion loss from continuing operations before income taxes which included such expenses as an after-tax charge of $1.5 billion related to the impairment of goodwill and assets and an after-tax charge or $320 million for the impairment of goodwill and assets of for-sale hospitals.

Cash flow from operations which has been fairly turbulent rose 24% to $1.1 billion in 2016. Positive adjustments to reconcile net income such as to net impairment and loss on sale of businesses and to patient accounts receivable offset the net loss that year.

Strategy

CHS has been shedding non-core assets in light of financial struggles — it reported a net loss of $1.7 billion in fiscal 2016. In 2015 the company sold interests in several hospitals including two which were required by the FTC as a condition of it $7.6 billion acquisition of rival health system Health Management Associates. The following year CHS spun off nearly 40 of its hospitals along with its Quorum Health Resources unit (which provides management services to around 150 non-affiliated hospitals) forming a new public company named Quorum Health Corporation. That split created two distinct companies with their own strategies and opportunities for growth. Also in 2016 it sold two Florida hospitals (Bartow Regional Medical and Lehigh Regional Medical) for a combined $71 million.

The company sold an 80% stake in its home health and hospice operations to Almost Family for $128 million in early 2017. Later that year it sold eight more hospitals to Massachusetts-based Steward Health Care System. CHS then announced plans to divest up to 30 hospitals over the next 18 months.

Historically CHS has expanded by acquiring hospitals especially in growing non-urban markets. It expects to ultimately return to that strategy once its portfolio of holdings is streamlined through divestitures. The company now believes it is better positioned to focus on some of the larger markets it serves a bit of a turnaround from its previous trajectory.

To promote future growth the company has a number of strategies in place. It plans to grow and strengthen its care networks in certain markets aligning its expanding suite of services with larger hospitals to establish a broad continuum of care. Within those networks it is working to increase revenues at its facilities through such efforts as hiring additional physicians expanding services such as its orthopedic program and free-standing emergency departments and evaluating opportunities to participate in managed care contracts.

Additionally CHS is standardizing and centralizing operations across its facilities to improve efficiency and contain costs. (For instance it trims supply costs through its membership in group purchasing organization HealthTrust.) All the while the company emphasizes patient safety and quality care through systematic improvements that improve physician and employee satisfaction.

However due to the drop in earnings CHS has been weighing various options it has going forward. In September 2016 it revealed that it was exploring a possible sale of itself; shortly thereafter it threw up a temporary block (a "poison pill") to prevent any buyer from taking a controlling stake in CHS. The company is still open to the idea of a full buyout though.

Mergers and Acquisitions

You don't become one of the largest for-profit hospital operators in the nation without a pretty aggressive acquisition strategy and CHS certainly has that. CHS target hospitals in non-urban locations poised for growth. Because such areas have fewer people they generally have fewer hospitals (meaning less competition for patients and for managed care contracts). CHS typically purchases a number of small community hospitals each year though it also sometimes conducts larger acquisitions of hospital operating groups.

In 2016 the company acquired majority stakes in the 20-bed Arkansas-based Physicians' Specialty Hospital and in a joint venture with Indiana University Health that operates outpatient centers and physician practices in Indiana.

HISTORY

Community Health Systems (CHS) was founded in 1985.

In 1996 it was acquired by investment firm Forstmann Little & Co. in a leveraged buyout transaction worth some $1.1 billion. It also moved its headquarters from Houston to Nashville Tennessee that year.

CHS once again became a public entity through an IPO in 2000. It engaged is engaged in a flurry of acquisition activity of small regional hospitals each year following its IPO.

However CHS limited its purchases somewhat after plunking down $7 billion in 2007 to acquire Triad Hospitals (and its more than 50 hospitals). After conducting integration efforts at the former Triad hospitals CHS fully resumed its acquisition activity when it purchased five hospitals during 2010 including the Marion Regional Hospital in South Carolina the Forum Health (later Valley-Care) hospitals in Ohio and the Bluefield Hospital in West Virginia.

Buoyed by those purchases CHS launched a campaign to acquire fellow hospital operator and rival Tenet in late 2010 in a deal worth some $7.3 billion in cash stock and debt. However after much back and forth between the firms — including lawsuits and hostile tender offers — CHS halted its acquisition attempts the following year due to a lack of response from Tenet's shareholders and board members.

CHS instead completed several smaller purchases that year including the acquisition of the Mercy Health Partners Scranton operations in

Pennsylvania from Catholic Health Partners. The company also purchased Tomball Regional Medical Center (TRMC) located near Houston.

As part of its periodic practice of divesting non-core centers in 2011 it sold two Oklahoma facilities SouthCrest Hospital and Claremore Regional Hospital to Ardent Health Services' Hillcrest Health-Care System unit for an undisclosed price. It also sold a Texas hospital Cleveland Regional Medical Center that year to New Directions Health Systems.

EXECUTIVES

EVP and CFO, W. Larry Cash, age 69, $850,000 total compensation
Chairman and CEO, Wayne T. Smith, age 71, $1,600,000 total compensation
President Division II Operations, Michael T. Portacci, age 59, $663,341 total compensation
EVP Administration, Martin G. (Marty) Schweinhart, age 62
SVP Corporate Communications Marketing and Public Affairs, Tomi Galin
President and COO, Tim L. Hingtgen, age 50, $655,007 total compensation
VP and Chief Purchasing Officer, Tim G. Marlette
President Division III Operations, P. Paul Smith, age 54
SVP and CIO, Manish Shah
President Division IV Operations, John W. McClellan
Chief Quality Officer; President Clinical Services, Lynn T. Simon, age 54
President Division I Operations, Martin J. Bonick, age 44
SVP and Chief Nursing Officer, Pamela T. Rudisill
CFO, Thomas J. (Tom) Aaron
Vice President Division Operations, Christopher Costello
Medical Director, Scott Wagner
Clinic Manager, Amanda Anderton
Vice President, Laurence Bludau
Auditors: Deloitte & Touche LLP

LOCATIONS

HQ: Community Health Systems, Inc.
4000 Meridian Boulevard, Franklin, TN 37067
Phone: 615 465-7000
Web: www.chs.net

PRODUCTS/OPERATIONS

2016 Sales

	$ mil.	% of total
Hospital operations	18,210	99
Corporate and all other	228	1
Total	**18,438**	**100**

2016 Sales

	% of total
Managed Care and other third-party payors	53
Medicare	24
Self-pay	12
Medicaid	11
Total	**100**

COMPETITORS

Adventist Health System Sunbelt Healthcare
Adventist Health System West
Ascension Health
Banner Health
CHRISTUS Health
Carolinas HealthCare System
Catholic Health Initiatives
Dignity Health
HCA
HealthSouth
LifePoint Health

Mercy Health
Mercy Health (OH)
SSM Health Care
SunLink Health Systems
Sutter Health
Tenet Healthcare
Texas Health Resources
Trinity Health (Novi)
Universal Health Services
University Health Services
WellStar Health System

HISTORICAL FINANCIALS

Company Type: Public

Income Statement
FYE: December 31

	REVENUE ($ mil.)	NET INCOME ($ mil.)	NET PROFIT MARGIN	EMPLOYEES
12/16	18,438	(1,721)	—	120,000
12/15	19,437	158	0.8%	137,000
12/14	18,639	92	0.5%	167,000
12/13	12,997	141	1.1%	87,000
12/12	13,028	265	2.0%	96,000
Annual Growth	**9.1%**	**—**	**—**	**5.7%**

2016 Year-End Financials

Debt ratio: 69.47%
Return on equity: (-60.93%)
Cash ($ mil.): 238
Current ratio: 1.62
Long-term debt ($ mil.): 14,789
No. of shares (mil.): 113
Dividends
Yield: —
Payout: —
Market value ($ mil.): 637

	STOCK PRICE ($) FY Close	P/E High/Low		PER SHARE ($) Earnings	Dividends	Book Value
12/16	5.59	—	—	(15.54)	0.00	14.18
12/15	26.53	46	18	1.37	0.00	35.64
12/14	53.92	70	43	0.82	0.00	34.29
12/13	39.27	34	20	1.51	0.00	32.29
12/12	30.74	11	6	2.96	0.25	29.70
Annual Growth	**(34.7%)**	**—**	**—**	**—**	**—**	**(16.9%)**

Community Trust Bancorp, Inc.

Community Trust Bancorp is the holding company for Community Trust Bank one of the largest Kentucky-based banks. It operates 70-plus branches throughout the state as well as in northeastern Tennessee and southern West Virginia. The bank offers standard services to area businesses and individuals including checking and savings accounts credit cards and CDs. Loans secured by commercial properties and other real estate account for nearly 70% of the bank's portfolio which also includes business consumer and construction loans. Subsidiary Community Trust and Investment Company provides trust estate retirement brokerage and insurance services through a handful of offices in Kentucky and Tennessee.

Operations

Community Trust Bancorp's lending activities include making commercial construction mortgage and personal loans. It also offers lease-financing lines of credit revolving lines of credit term loans and other specialized loans including asset-backed financing.

Some 69% of Community Trust Bancorp's portfolio of loans is secured real estate (36% of which consists of commercial real estate).

Geographic Reach

Kentucky-based Community Trust Bancorp operates more than 70 banking locations across Kentucky West Virginia and Tennessee. Its trust offices are located in Kentucky and Tennessee.

Sales and Marketing

Community Trust Bancorp specializes in serving both small and medium-sized businesses.

Financial Performance

Despite weak loan demand Community Trust Bancorp has grown its revenue from 2009 to 2011 followed by a marginal decline in 2012. Thanks to a decline in both interest expenses and provisions for loan losses Community Trust Bancorp has seen its net income rise during the past five years.

While Community Trust Bancorp logged marginal decreases (1%) in revenue in fiscal 2012 vs. 2011 the financial institution posted net income increases of 16% to $45 million during the reporting period.

Mergers and Acquisitions

Community Trust Bancorp bought LaFollette First National Corporation the holding company for First National Bank of LaFollette for some $16 million. The 2010 acquisition gave the company its first four bank branches and first trust office in Tennessee.

Community Trust is considering additional acquisitions of smaller competitors. It also grows by opening new branches.

EXECUTIVES

Senior Vice President Human Resources, Howard W Blackburn
Chairman President and CEO and Chairman Community Trust Bank, Jean R. Hale, age 71, $548,077 total compensation
EVP and CFO Community Trust Bancorp and EVP and Treasurer Community Trust Bank, Kevin J. Stumbo, age 57, $231,539 total compensation
EVP and Secretary Community Trust Bancorp President and CEO Community Trust Bank and VP Community Trust and Investment Company, Mark A. Gooch, age 59, $397,000 total compensation
EVP Community Trust Bancorp and EVP and Chief Credit Officer Community Trust Bank, James J. (Jim) Gartner, age 76
EVP Community Trust Bancorp and EVP Operations Community Trust Bank, James B. (Jim) Draughn, age 58, $241,231 total compensation
EVP Community Trust Bancorp and EVP and South Central Region President Community Trust Bank, Ricky D. Sparkman, age 54
EVP Community Trust Bancor and EVP and Eastern Region President Community Trust Bank, Richard W. (Rick) Newsom, age 62
EVP Community Trust Bancorp and EVP and President Central Kentucky Region Community Trust Bank Inc., Larry W. Jones, age 70, $249,231 total compensation
EVP Community Trust Bancorp and EVP and Chief Internal Audit and Risk Officer Community Trust Bank, Steven E. (Steve) Jameson, age 60
EVP Community Trust Bancorp and EVP and President North East Region Community Trust Bank Inc., D. Andrew Jones, age 54
EVP Community Trust Bancorp and President and CEO Community Trust and Investment Co., Andy D. Waters, age 51
EVP Community Trust Bancorp Inc. and EVP and Senior Staff Attorney Community Trust Bank Inc., C. Wayne Hancock, age 42
Assistant Vice President Technology, Brian Hatmaker
Auditors: BKD, LLP

LOCATIONS

HQ: Community Trust Bancorp, Inc.
346 North Mayo Trail, Pikeville, KY 41501
Phone: 606 432-1414
Web: www.ctbi.com

PRODUCTS/OPERATIONS

2016 Sales

	% of total
Interest income	
Interest and fees on loans	69
Interest and dividends on securities	6
Noninterest income	
Service charges on deposit accounts	13
Gains on sales of loans	1
Trust and wealth management income	5
Loan related fees	2
Bank owned life insurance	1
Brokerage revenue	1
Securities gains (losses)	
Other noninterest income	2
Total	**100**

Selected Products & Services

Business Banking
  Business CDs
  Business Checking
  Corporate Services
  Lending
  Merchant Services
  Online Services
  Savings & Money Market
Financial Services
Personal Banking
  Card Services
  CDs & IRAs
  Consumer Loans
  Home Equity
  Interest Checking
  Mobile Banking
  Mortgages
  Personal Checking
  Savings & Money Market
Wealth & Trust Management

COMPETITORS

BB&T	Premier Financial
Farmers Capital Bank	Bancorp
Fifth Third	Republic Bancorp
Home Federal	U.S. Bancorp

HISTORICAL FINANCIALS

Company Type: Public

Income Statement
FYE: December 31

	ASSETS ($ mil.)	NET INCOME ($ mil.)	INCOME AS % OF ASSETS	EMPLOYEES
12/16	3,932	47	1.2%	996
12/15	3,903	46	1.2%	984
12/14	3,723	43	1.2%	1,012
12/13	3,581	45	1.3%	1,022
12/12	3,635	44	1.2%	1,035
Annual Growth	**2.0%**	**1.4%**	**—**	**(1.0%)**

2016 Year-End Financials

Debt ratio: 1.56%
Return on equity: 9.67%
Cash ($ mil.): 145
Current ratio: —
Long-term debt ($ mil.): —

No. of shares (mil.): 17
Dividends
  Yield: 0.0%
  Payout: 46.6%
Market value ($ mil.): 874

	STOCK PRICE ($) FY Close	P/E High/Low	PER SHARE ($) Earnings	Dividends	Book Value
12/16	49.60	18 12	2.70	1.26	28.40
12/15	34.96	14 12	2.66	1.22	27.12
12/14	36.61	18 13	2.49	1.18	25.64
12/13	45.16	17 12	2.62	1.27	23.70
12/12	32.78	14 11	2.63	1.25	23.31
Annual Growth	**10.9%**	**— —**	**0.7%**	**0.2%**	**5.1%**

COMMUNITYBANK OF TEXAS NATIONAL ASSOCIATION

LOCATIONS

HQ: COMMUNITYBANK OF TEXAS NATIONAL
ASSOCIATION
5999 DELAWARE ST, BEAUMONT, TX 777067607
Phone: 409 861-7200
Web: WWW.COMMUNITYBANKOFTX.COM

HISTORICAL FINANCIALS

Company Type: Private

Income Statement
FYE: December 31

	ASSETS ($ mil.)	NET INCOME ($ mil.)	INCOME AS % OF ASSETS	EMPLOYEES
12/15	2,881	25	0.9%	60
12/14	2,629	23	0.9%	—
12/13	2,454	16	0.7%	—
Annual Growth	**8.3%**	**24.7%**	**—**	**—**

2015 Year-End Financials

Debt ratio: ——
Return on equity: 20.90%
Cash ($ mil.): 435
Current ratio: —
Long-term debt ($ mil.): —

Dividends
  Yield: —
  Payout: —
Market value ($ mil.): —

Conagra Brands Inc

ConAgra Foods fills the refrigerators freezers and pantries of most households. The company makes and markets name-brand packaged and frozen foods that are sold in most retail outlets. ConAgra's cornucopia of America's best-known brands includes Banquet Chef Boyardee Egg Beaters Healthy Choice and Marie Callender. It is also one of the biggest producers of seasoning and grain ingredients for the US food service food manufacturing and industrial markets. ConAgra Foods sold its private-label food business to TreeHouse Foods for $2.7 billion in early 2016. In July 2016 the company filed with the SEC to split into two public companies: Lamb Weston Holdings and Conagra Brands.

HISTORY

Alva Kinney founded Nebraska Consolidated Mills in 1919 by combining the operations of four Nebraska grain mills. It did not expand outside Nebraska until it opened a mill and feed processing plant in Alabama in 1942.

Consolidated Mills developed Duncan Hines cake mix in the 1950s. But Duncan Hines failed to raise a large enough market share and the company sold it to Procter & Gamble in 1956. Consolidated Mills used the proceeds to expand opening a flour and feed mill in Puerto Rico the next year. In the 1960s while competitors were moving into prepared foods the firm expanded into animal feeds and poultry processing. By 1970 it had poultry processing plants in Alabama Georgia and Louisiana. In 1971 the company changed its name

to ConAgra (Latin for "in partnership with the land"). During the 1970s it expanded into the fertilizer catfish and pet accessory businesses.

Poorly performing subsidiaries and commodity speculation caused ConAgra severe financial problems until 1974 when Mike Harper a former Pillsbury executive took over. Harper trimmed properties to reduce debt and had the company back on its feet by 1976. ConAgra stayed focused on the commodities side of the business but was thus tied to volatile price cycles. In 1978 it bought United Agri Products (agricultural chemicals).

ConAgra moved into consumer food products in the 1980s. It bought Banquet (frozen food 1980) and within six years had introduced almost 90 new products under that label. Other purchases included Singleton Seafood (1981) Armour Food Company (meats dairy products frozen food; 1983) and RJR Nabisco's frozen food business (1986). ConAgra became a major player in the red meat market with the 1987 purchases of E.A. Miller (boxed beef) Monfort (beef and lamb) and Swift Independent Packing.

Confident it had found the right path ConAgra continued with acquisitions of consumer food makers including Beatrice Foods (Orville Redenbacher's popcorn Hunt's tomato products) in 1991. In 1997 the company agreed to pay $8.3 million to settle federal charges of wire fraud and watering down grain. That year ConAgra named vice chairman and president Bruce Rohde as CEO; he became chairman in 1998. Also in 1998 the company bought GoodMark Foods maker of Slim Jim and Nabisco's Egg Beaters and table spread unit(Parkay). ConAgra bought Holly Ridge Foods (pastries) in 1999 and announced a major restructuring.

ConAgra bought Emerge an agricultural and land-use information software provider from Litton Industries in 2000. It also acquired Seaboard's poultry division and refrigerated meat alternatives maker Lightlife (Tofu pups Smart Dogs) before buying major brand holder International Home Foods from HM Capital Partners (known as Hicks Muse Tate & Furst at the time) for about $2.9 billion. The company then became ConAgra Foods.

During 2001 the company drew SEC attention and was forced to restate earnings for the previous three years due to accounting no-no's in its United Agri Products division.

In 2002 the USDA forced ConAgra to recall 19 million pounds of ground beef because of possible E. coli contamination making it the second-largest food recall in US history. (The largest recall occurred in 1997 when Hudson Foods later purchased by Tyson Foods withdrew 35 million pounds of beef.) Later in 2002 ConAgra sold its fresh beef and pork processing business — one of the largest in the US — to Booth Creek Management and HM Capital Partners and it was renamed Swift & Company Swift & Company . (Swift was acquired by Brazilian beef giant JBS in 2007.)

In 2003 the company began supplying packaged meat products for grilling to George Foreman Foods which sells them via its Web site. That year it sold its Bumble Bee canned seafood business to members of Bumble Bee management and private investment firm Centre Partners Management and its blue cheese brands (Treasure Cave Nauvoo) to Canada's Saputo Inc. for undisclosed prices. It also sold its chicken processing business to Pilgrim's Pride for a stock and cash deal worth about $550 million in 2003.

Also in 2003 ConAgra agreed to pay $1.5 million in cash and job offers to settle an EEOC lawsuit charging bias against disabled workers at the company's California-based Gilroy Foods plant. The agreement involves the largest disability settlement in the agriculture industry. The dispute dated back to 1999 when Gilroy Foods then owned by Basic Vegetable Products (ConAgra bought the facility in 2000) after a strike failed to recall disabled workers who were on leaves of absence due to illness or pregnancy or who had a history of illness or injury.

In keeping with its strategy to focus on its branded and value-added food business in 2003 ConAgra sold United Agri Products to Apollo Management for stock and securities. The deal was worth about $600 million. In 2004 it sold its minority interest in the beef and pork processing operations of Swift Foods to HM Capital Partners. The deal was worth $194 million. ConAgra also sold Swift's feedlot operations to Smithfield Foods for an undisclosed amount.

ConAgra sold its turkey hatchery and breeding business to Ag Forte in 2004. It sold its Canadian and US crop inputs businesses and its Spanish feed and Portuguese poultry businesses that year as well. In addition it sold Casa de Oro Foods (the US's third-largest tortilla maker) to the Plaza Belmont Fund II. Also that year ConAgra introduced Golden Cuisine a line of frozen meals designed for seniors. The company began manufacturing and supplying Golden Cuisine to Meals On Wheels which distributes the meals which are formulated for seniors to the homebound elderly. That year ConAgra also introduced a high-fiber flour called Ultragrain that has the taste and texture of refined flour but the nutrition of whole grain.

In 2005 ConAgra sold its remaining 15 million shares of Pilgrim's Pride to that company for about $480 million. That year CEO Bruce Rhode retired. His replacement was former chairman and CEO of PepsiCo Beverages and Foods North America Gary Rodkin who began a company-wide restructuring. The company reorganized its business structure from three channels to two: Foodservice was merged with Food Ingredients and became ConAgra Foods Commercial ; the ConAgra Retail channel remained the same.

ConAgra agreed to pay a $14 million shareholder settlement in 2005 regarding a lawsuit claiming fictitious sales and mis-reported earnings at its former subsidiary United Agri Products.

In a move to demonstrate its commitment to the humane treatment of animals in 2006 ConAgra urged its poultry suppliers to consider slaughtering chickens in a more humane manner called controlled-atmosphere killing. The process which ConAgra has only suggested to its suppliers is approved by the People for the Ethical Treatment of Animals.

Rodkin continued the company redo focusing on portfolio trimming when in early 2006 he announced plans to sell a large part of ConAgra's refrigerated-meats business. The brands involved in the sale include some of the company's best-known: Armour Butterball and Eckrich. (The Brown 'N Serve Healthy Choice Hebrew National Pemmican and Slim Jim brands were not included in the portfolio reduction.) It sold its Cook's ham business to Smithfield Foods for $260 million that year.

Not long after that it agreed to sell off the rest of its refrigerated meats business that it had for sale to Smithfield as well. The deal which became final in October 2006 cost Smithfield $571 million in cash. That same month it sold its Butterball Turkey unit to Carolina Turkeys for $325 million. (Carolina subsequently changed its company name to Butterball LLC .)

Divesting almost faster than one can keep track of one day after the Butterball deal was completed ConAgra sold its MaMa Rosa's Pizza operations to investment firm the Plaza Belmont Management Group. (MaMa Rosa's is refrigerated — not frozen pizza — and competes in a different market than other pizzas albeit frozen powerhouses such as Di Giorno Tombstone or Tony's .)

In another move to improve long-term operating performance ConAgra announced its intention to sell off its seafood and domestic and imported cheese businesses. To that end the company sold its surimi business including the Louis Kemp brand to Trident Seafoods and its Singleton Seafood and Meridian Seafood to Singleton Fisheries. It sold its specialty and imported cheese operation Swissrose International to investment company Fairmount Food Group. Late in 2006 the company sold its oat-milling business to investment companies Sequel Holdings and Falcon Investment Advisors.

The company added to its Lamb Weston branded potato products with the 2008 acquisition of Watts Brothers. With operations in Washington and Oregon Watts is a vegetable-processing company that has annual sales of some $100 million. It has retail foodservice and industrial customers throughout the US as well as in Mexico Japan China and other Far East countries. The deal also included Watts' organic dairy fertilizer cold storage packaging and agricultural farming businesses.

In early 2007 salmonella was found in some of the company's Peter Pan and Great Value (a Wal-Mart product) brands of peanut butter forcing a nationwide recall of the peanut butter bearing the product code involved. Salmonella food poisoning was linked to some 600 people in 47 states. No deaths related to the peanut better were confirmed. The recall eventually included products made as far back as October 2004. ConAgra shut down the Sylvester Georgia plant that was involved in the outbreak and reopened it in Augusts 2007 having spent $15 million on renovation which included repairing the roof installing new equipment and creating a manufacturing process that better separated raw materials from the finished peanut butter.

Just two months later the company voluntarily stopped production at the Missouri plant that makes its Banquet and generic brands of frozen turkey and chicken pot pies after learning that the were linked to some 140 cases of salmonella in 30 states. ConAgra did not recall the pies but offered mail-in refunds and store returns. The USDA began an investigation and advised consumers not to eat the pies.

As part of its strategy to add to its brand-name offerings in 2007 ConAgra acquired Alexia Foods a maker of natural frozen potatoes appetizers and artisan breads for about $50 million in cash. Later that year the company paid a penalty of $45 million in the wake of SEC charges that alleged the company had misreported its profits for the fiscal years 1999 2000 and 2001.

The company acquired Lincoln Snacks Company in 2007. Lincoln's well-known brands such as Fiddle Faddle and Poppycock extended ConAgra's name-brand lineup which is in line with company strategy. That year it also announced the removal of the chemicals from its microwave popcorn products that are suspected of causing lung ailments in popcorn-plant workers.

ConAgra sold its trading and merchandising operations (ConAgra Trade Group) in 2008 to a group of investors that included the Ospraie Special Opportunities Fund for $2.8 billion. The sale was part of the company's long-term strategy to exit the commodities business and concentrate on its consumer food products. Saying it couldn't give the brand the attention it needs in 2008 the company sold its Knott's Berry Farm jam and jelly business to J. M. Smucker .

In a tragedy that made the evening news three ConAgra workers were killed and some 40 were injured in an explosion and fire at a company Slim Jim manufacturing plant in Garner North Carolina in June 2009. It was later determined that the blast was caused by a natural-gas leak. ConAgra part-

nered with the United Way forming the Garner Plant Fund that raised money to assist the victims and their families. The company also continued to pay workers salaries while the plant remained closed for investigation. ConAgra was fined $106000 by the government in 2010 and the plant was eventually closed.

During 2010 ConAgra unloaded its Gilroy Foods & Flavors business-to-business unit to Olam International for $250 million. The sale excluded Gilroy's seasonings and flavors businesses.

In 2011 ConAgra Foods made an unsolicited takeover bid to buy Ralcorp Holdings a leading maker of private-label snack foods cereals and condiments. After proffering an initial bid of $82 per share ConAgra ultimately offered $94 (valuing Ralcorp at more than $5 billion). However Ralcorp spurned all bids saying they were not in the best interests of shareholders.

In May 2012 the company completed the acquisition of Odom's Tennessee Pride the #2 producer of frozen breakfast sandwiches in the US.

In January 2013 ConAgra completed its $6.8 billion purchase of Ralcorp Holdings.

In September 2013 it purchased the frozen dessert producer business of Harlan Bakeries which made frozen fruit pies cream pies pastry shells and loaf cakes.

In early 2013 ConAgra acquired Ralcorp the nation's #1 maker of private-label food in a deal valued at about $6.8 billion (including debt). The combined company was expected to generate $18 billion in sales and made ConAgra the largest private-brand packaged foods business in North America with annual private brand sales of about $4.5 billion a year. The private brands segment makes private-label ready-to-eat cereals cereal bars snack mixes cookies crackers and other products for retailers under their own brand names.

EXECUTIVES

Senior Vice President and Chief Litigation Counsel, Leo Knowles

EVP General Counsel and Corporate Secretary, Colleen Batcheler, age 43, $521,635 total compensation

EVP and CFO, John F. Gehring, age 56, $643,269 total compensation

CEO, Sean M. Connolly, $1,100,000 total compensation

President Consumer Foods, Thomas M. (Tom) McGough, age 52, $636,538 total compensation

EVP and President Sales, Derek De La Mater

President Commercial Foods, Tom Werner, $438,654 total compensation

EVP and Chief Supply Chain Officer, Dave Biegger

EVP and Chief Human Resources Officer, Charisse Brock

CIO, Mindy Simon

Vice President Human Resources, Kelly Schaefer

Vice President General Manager, Taylor Strubell

Vice President Organization Development, Lucy Dinwiddie

Vice President Of Marketing, Andy Johnston

National Account Manager, Chad Yuza

Vice President Research Quality And Innovation, Christian Rhynalds

Vice President General Manager Spicetec, Mark Duffy

Senior Vice President Marketing, Karen E Carey

Chairman, Steven F. (Steve) Goldstone, age 72

Board Member, Jennifer Hudson

Auditors: KPMG LLP

LOCATIONS

HQ: Conagra Brands Inc
222 Merchandise Mart Plaza, Suite 1300, Chicago, IL
60654
Phone: 312 549-5000
Web: www.conagrafoods.com

PRODUCTS/OPERATIONS

2016 Sales

	% of total
Consumer foods	62
Commercial foods	38
Total	**100**

2016 Sales

	% of total
Consumer Foods	
Grocery	29
Frozen	25
International	7
Other Brands	1
Commercial Foods	
Specialty potatoes	25
Food services	13
Total	**100**

Selected Brands

Commercial foods
ConAgra Mills
Lamb Weston
Spicetec Flavors & Seasonings
Consumer foods
Act II
Alexia
Banquet
Bertolli
Blue Bonnet
Chef Boyardee
DAVID Seeds
Egg Beaters
Healthy Choice
Hebrew National
Hunt's
Marie Callender's
Odom's Tennessee Pride
Orville Redenbacher's
PAM
Peter Pan
P.F. Chang's
Reddi-wip
Slim Jim
Snack Pack
Swiss Miss
Van Camp's
Wesson

COMPETITORS

American Pop Corn	Jenny Craig
B&G Foods	Kellogg
Big Heart Pet Brands	Link Snacks
Boulder Brands	MOM Brands
Bush Brothers	Manischewitz Company
Campbell Soup	McCain Foods
Clorox	McIlhenny
Eden Foods	Monterey Gourmet Foods
Frito-Lay	Mott's
General Mills	Nestl©©©
Gilster-Mary Lee	Newman's Own
Goya	Nutrisystem
H. J. Heinz Limited	Pinnacle Foods
Hain Celestial	Schwan's
Hanover Foods	Seneca Foods
Heinz	Slim-Fast
Hormel	Smucker
Inventure foods	Snappy Popcorn
J-OIL MILLS	Weaver Popcorn Company
JR Simplot	

HISTORICAL FINANCIALS

Company Type: Public

Income Statement

FYE: May 28

	REVENUE ($ mil.)	NET INCOME ($ mil.)	NET PROFIT MARGIN	EMPLOYEES
05/17	7,826	639	8.2%	12,600
05/16	11,642	(677)	—	20,900
05/15	15,832	(252)	—	32,900
05/14	17,702	303	1.7%	32,800
05/13	15,491	773	5.0%	34,840
Annual Growth	**(15.7%)**	**(4.7%)**		**(22.5%)**

2017 Year-End Financials

Debt ratio: 29.68%
Return on equity: 16.64%
Cash ($ mil.): 251
Current ratio: 1.17
Long-term debt ($ mil.): 2,769

No. of shares (mil.): 416
Dividends
Yield: 0.0%
Payout: 61.6%
Market value ($ mil.): 16,257

	STOCK PRICE ($) FY Close	P/E High/Low		PER SHARE ($) Earnings	Dividends	Book Value
05/17	39.03	33	23	1.46	0.90	9.58
05/16	45.29	—	—	(1.56)	1.00	8.48
05/15	38.61	—	—	(0.60)	1.00	10.57
05/14	31.61	52	39	0.70	1.00	12.46
05/13	34.77	19	13	1.85	0.99	12.55
Annual Growth	**2.9%**			**(5.7%)**	**(2.4%)**	**(6.5%)**

Conduent Inc

LOCATIONS

HQ: Conduent Inc
100 Campus Drive, Suite 200E, Florham Park, NJ
07932
Phone: 844 663-2638
Web: www.conduent.com

HISTORICAL FINANCIALS

Company Type: Public

Income Statement

FYE: December 31

	REVENUE ($ mil.)	NET INCOME ($ mil.)	NET PROFIT MARGIN	EMPLOYEES
12/16	6,408	(983)	—	96,000
12/15	6,662	(414)	—	93,700
12/14	6,938	(81)	—	—
12/13	6,879	182	2.6%	—
Annual Growth	**(2.3%)**	**—**		**—**

2016 Year-End Financials

Debt ratio: 25.18%
Return on equity: (-22.82%)
Cash ($ mil.): 390
Current ratio: 1.37
Long-term debt ($ mil.): 1,913

No. of shares (mil.): 202
Dividends
Yield: —
Payout: —
Market value ($ mil.): —

	STOCK PRICE ($) FY Close	P/E High/Low		PER SHARE ($) Earnings	Dividends	Book Value
12/16	0.00	—	—	(4.85)	0.00	16.91
Annual Growth	**—**			**—**	**—**	**—**

ConnectOne Bancorp Inc (New)

ConnectOne Bancorp (formerly Center Bancorp) is the holding company for ConnectOne Bank which operates some two dozen branches across New Jersey. Serving individuals and local businesses the bank offers such deposit products as checking savings and money market accounts; CDs; and IRAs. It also performs trust services. Commercial loans account for about 60% of the bank's loan portfolio; residential mortgages account for most of the remainder. It also has a subsidiary that sells annuities and property/casualty life and health coverage. The former Center Bancorp acquired rival community bank ConnectOne Bancorp in 2014 and took that name.

Geographic Reach

ConnectOne has 24 branches in Bergen Essex Hudson Manhattan Mercer Monmouth Morris and Union Counties in New Jersey.

Mergers and Acquisitions

In 2014 Center Bancorp acquired ConnectOne Bancorp in an all-stock deal valued at approximately $243 million. The merged bank with nearly $4 billion in assets now does business under the ConnectOne brand name.

EXECUTIVES

President; Chief Executive Officer; Director, Anthony C. (Tony) Weagley, age 55, $225,000 total compensation
VP; SVP Union Center National Bank, Lori A. Wunder, age 51, $128,750 total compensation
Chairman Center Bancorp and Union Center National Bank, Alexander A. Bol, age 68
VP; SVP and Branch Administrator Union Center National Bank, Mark S. Cardone, age 53, $119,525 total compensation
VP and Credit Administrator Union Center National Bank, John J. Lukens
VP; SVP Union Center National Bank, William J. Boylan, age 51, $125,000 total compensation
VP and Senior Lending Officer; SVP and Senior Lending Officer Union Center National Bank, Ronald M. Shapiro, age 64, $132,500 total compensation
Executive Assistant Investor Relations Officer and Secretary Center Bancorp and Union Center National Bank, Joseph D. Gangemi
VP and Senior Auditor Union Center National Bank, George J. Theiller
Vice President and Director - Communications & Public Relations, France Donne
Vice President; Compliance Officer, James Sorge
Senior Vice President; Loan Officer, Nicholas Anthony
Vice President; Chief Loan Officer, Vincent Bagarozza
Chief Financial Officer; Vice President; Treasurer, Vincent Tozzi
President CEO and Director Center Bancorp and Union Center National Bank, Anthony C. (Tony) Weagley, age 55
Director, Lawrence B. Seidman, age 68
Director, William A. Thompson, age 58
Director, James J. Kennedy, age 60
Director, Harold A. Schechter, age 70
Director, Raymond Vanaria, age 57
Director, Howard Kent, age 68
Director, Nicholas Minoia, age 61
Director, Phyllis S. Klein, age 53
Director, Allan H. Strauss
Independent Director, Frederick Fish
Auditors: Crowe Horwath LLP

LOCATIONS

HQ: ConnectOne Bancorp Inc (New)
301 Sylvan Avenue, Englewood Cliffs, NJ 07632
Phone: 201 816-8900
Web: www.centerbancorp.com

COMPETITORS

BCB Bancorp	New York Community
Bank of America	Bancorp
Citizens Financial	Oritani Financial
Corp.	PNC Financial
Fulton Financial	Provident Financial
Hudson City Bancorp	Services
Investors Bancorp	Sovereign Bank
JPMorgan Chase	Valley National
Kearny Financial	Bancorp
Lakeland Bancorp	Westamerica

HISTORICAL FINANCIALS

Company Type: Public

Income Statement

FYE: December 31

	ASSETS ($ mil.)	NET INCOME ($ mil.)	INCOME AS % OF ASSETS	EMPLOYEES
12/16	4,426	31	0.7%	—
12/15	4,016	41	1.0%	—
12/14	3,448	18	0.5%	—
12/13	1,673	19	1.2%	166
12/12	1,629	17	1.1%	178
Annual Growth	28.4%	15.4%	—	—

2016 Year-End Financials

Debt ratio: 11.99%
Return on equity: 6.15%
Cash ($ mil.): 200
Current ratio: —
Long-term debt ($ mil.): —

No. of shares (mil.): 31
Dividends
  Yield: 0.0%
  Payout: 29.7%
Market value ($ mil.): 829

	STOCK PRICE ($) FY Close	P/E High/Low		PER SHARE ($) Earnings	Dividends	Book Value
12/16	25.95	26	15	1.01	0.30	16.62
12/15	18.69	16	13	1.36	0.30	15.87
12/14	19.00	25	21	0.79	0.30	15.03
12/13	18.76	16	10	1.21	0.26	10.30
12/12	11.58	11	9	1.05	0.17	9.83
Annual Growth	22.4%	—	—	(1.0%)	15.3%	14.0%

ConocoPhillips

Auditors: El Sayed El Ayouty & Co.

LOCATIONS

HQ: ConocoPhillips
600 North Dairy Ashford, Houston, TX 77079
Phone: 281 293-1000   **Fax:** 281 661-7636
Web: www.conocophillips.com

HISTORICAL FINANCIALS

Company Type: Public

Income Statement

FYE: December 31

	REVENUE ($ mil.)	NET INCOME ($ mil.)	NET PROFIT MARGIN	EMPLOYEES
12/16	24,360	(3,615)	—	13,300
12/15	30,935	(4,428)	—	15,900
12/14	55,517	6,869	12.4%	19,100
12/13	58,248	9,156	15.7%	18,400
12/12	62,004	8,428	13.6%	16,900
Annual Growth	(20.8%)	—	—	(5.8%)

2016 Year-End Financials

Debt ratio: 30.38%
Return on equity: (-9.65%)
Cash ($ mil.): 3,610
Current ratio: 1.25
Long-term debt ($ mil.): 26,186

No. of shares (mil.): 1,237
Dividends
  Yield: 0.0%
  Payout: —
Market value ($ mil.): 62,037

	STOCK PRICE ($) FY Close	P/E High/Low		PER SHARE ($) Earnings	Dividends	Book Value
12/16	50.14	—	—	(2.91)	1.00	28.27
12/15	46.69	—	—	(3.58)	2.94	32.17
12/14	69.06	16	11	5.51	2.84	42.16
12/13	70.65	10	8	7.38	2.70	42.49
12/12	57.99	12	8	6.72	2.64	39.33
Annual Growth	(3.6%)	—	—	—	(21.5%)	(7.9%)

Consolidated Edison Co. of New York, Inc.

Consolidated Edison Company of New York (Con Edison of New York) keeps the nightlife pulsing in The Big Apple. The utility a subsidiary of Consolidated Edison distributes electricity throughout most of New York City and Westchester County. The company distributes electricity to 3.4 million residential and business customers in New York City; it also delivers natural gas to about 1.1 million customers. The utility also provides steam services to 1703 customers in portions of the New York metropolitan area. Con Edison of New York owns and operates more than 133900 miles of overhead and underground power distribution lines.

Operations

The company has three segments: electric gas and steam — which contributed 79% 15% and 6% of total revenues in 2015.

Its assets include more than 4300 miles of gas distribution mains a gas liquefaction and storage facility and electric and steam generating stations. It also owns a range of power transmission assets which are operated by the New York Independent System Operator. Con Edison of New York's electric generating facilities consist of plants located in New York City with an aggregate capacity of 724 MW.

The company's distribution system had a transformer capacity of 29762 MVA with 36929 miles of overhead distribution lines and 97286 miles of underground distribution lines. The underground distribution lines represent the single longest underground electric delivery system in the United States.

Geographic Reach

Con Edison of New York has distribution facilities throughout New York City and Westchester County and operates manufactured gas plants at 51 sites.

Sales and Marketing

Con Edison of New York delivers electricity to state and municipal customers of NYPA and economic development customers of municipal electric agencies. Its customers include residential commercial industrial public authorities retail choice customers.

Financial Performance

In fiscal 2015 its net revenues decreased by 4% due to the lower gas steam and electric sales.

Revenues from electric decreased due to lower purchased power expenses and lower fuel expenses offset in part by higher revenues from the electric rate plan.

Con Edison of New York's gas revenues declined due to a decrease in gas purchased for resale expenses offset in part by higher revenues from the gas rate plan (reflecting higher delivery volumes attributable to oil-to-gas conversions). However revenues from steam increased due primarily to higher fuel expenses and higher revenues from the steam rate plan offset by the weather impact on revenues and lower purchased power costs.

In fiscal 2015 net income increased by 2% due to lower gas purchased for resale and purchased power.

Cash from operating activities increased by 16% due to lower income taxes paid net of refunds received offset in part by increased pension contributions.

Strategy

In 2016 Con Edison of New York filed a request with the New York State Public Service Commission for an electric rate increase of $482 million. It also entered into an agreement to sell certain electric transmission projects to NY Transco.

The company (in 2015) partnered with Drive Electric Vehicle Research Forward to help promote electric vehicles.

In 2014 Con Edison of New York was in the middle of a four-year $1 billion storm hardening program in the wake of 2012's Superstorm Sandy. Investments include the installation of 3000 devices that isolate and clear temporary faults on overhead electric systems and more than 150 smart switches that minimize outages caused by fallen trees. More than a mile of flood walls and 260 pieces of submersible equipment also have been installed. For its efforts the utility was named as the winner of the 2014 Outstanding System Reliability Award by the PA Consulting Group. The award recognizes the PA Consulting Group ReliabilityOne regional award recipient that demonstrated superior annual system-wide reliability performance for its customers. Con Edison of New York was also named best in the Northeast Region.

Company Background

Citing a 20% growth rate during the 2000s Con Edison of New York in 2011 spent almost $1.8 billion ($2 billion in 2010) to upgrade the company's aging electrical delivery systems (new high-voltage transmission cables) in New York City and surrounding areas. In 2010 Con Edison of New York and sister company Orange and Rockland also received $200 million in federal grants to install smart grid technology (automated more efficient meters and other systems) across their service area. By mid-2011 the company had also supported the installation of 8.5 MW of solar power units across its service region.

EXECUTIVES

Svp Gas Operations, Claude Trahan, age 65
Chairman and CEO, Kevin Burke, age 67,
  $1,107,200 total compensation
SVP and CRO, Robert N. Hoglund, age 56, $584,200
  total compensation
**President of Consolidated Edison Company of
  New York; Inc.,** Craig S. Ivey, age 54
**President and CEO Orange and Rockland Utilities
  Inc.,** John T. McAvoy, age 56
Owner, Linda Goldberg
Auditors: PricewaterhouseCoopers LLP

LOCATIONS

HQ: Consolidated Edison Co. of New York, Inc.
4 Irving Place, New York, NY 10003
Phone: 212 460-4600
Web: www.coned.com

COMPETITORS

Commerce Energy Group	New York Power
Delmarva Power	Authority
Green Mountain Energy	Public Service
Integrys Energy	Enterprise Group
Services	Rochester Gas and
NYSEG	Electric
National Grid USA	

HISTORICAL FINANCIALS

Company Type: Public

Income Statement

FYE: December 31

	REVENUE ($ mil.)	NET INCOME ($ mil.)	NET PROFIT MARGIN	EMPLOYEES
12/16	10,165	1,056	10.4%	13,531
12/15	10,328	1,084	10.5%	13,393
12/14	10,786	1,058	9.8%	13,200
12/13	10,430	1,020	9.8%	13,235
12/12	10,187	1,017	10.0%	13,130
Annual Growth	(0.1%)	0.9%	—	0.8%

2016 Year-End Financials

Debt ratio: 29.55%	No. of shares (mil.): 235
Return on equity: 9.06%	Dividends
Cash ($ mil.): 702	Yield: —
Current ratio: 0.96	Payout: 70.4%
Long-term debt ($ mil.): 12,073	Market value ($ mil.): —

Consolidated Edison Inc

Utility holding company Consolidated Edison (Con Edison) is the night light for the city that never sleeps. Con Edison's main subsidiary Consolidated Edison Company of New York distributes electricity to 3.4 million residential and business customers in a 604-mile service territory centered on New York City. It delivers natural gas to about 1.1 million customers and operates the country?s largest steam distribution service to deliver energy to parts of Manhattan. Subsidiary Orange and Rockland Utilities serves more than 300000 electric and gas customers in New York and New Jersey. Con Edison also owns or operates renewable energy facilities and advises large clients on energy efficiency programs.

HISTORY

Several professionals led by Timothy Dewey formed The New York Gas Light Company in 1823 to illuminate part of Manhattan. In 1884 five other gas companies joined New York Gas Light to form the Consolidated Gas Company of New York.

Thomas Edison's incandescent lamp came on the scene in 1879 and The Edison Electric Illuminating Company of New York was formed in 1880 to build the world's first commercial electric power station (Pearl Street) financed by a group led by J.P. Morgan. Edison supervised the project and in 1882 New York became the first major city with electric lighting.

Realizing electricity would replace gas Consolidated Gas acquired electric companies including Anthony Brady's New York Gas and Electric Light Heat and Power Company (1900) which joined Edison's Illuminating Company in 1901 to form the New York Edison Company. More than 170 purchases followed including that of the New York

Steam Company (1930) a cheap source of steam for electric turbines.

The Public Utility Holding Company Act of 1935 ushered in the era of regulated regional monopolies. The next year New York Edison combined its holdings to form the Consolidated Edison Company of New York (Con Ed).

Con Ed opened its first nuclear station in 1962. By then Con Ed had a reputation for inefficiency and poor service and shareholders were angry about its slow growth and low earnings. Environmentalists joined the grousers in 1963 when Con Ed began constructing a pumped-storage plant in Cornwall near the Hudson River. Charles Luce a former undersecretary with the Department of Interior was recruited to rescue Con Ed in 1967. He added power plants and beefed up customer service.

In the 1970s inflation and the energy crisis drove up oil prices (Con Ed's main fuel source) and in 1974 Luce withheld dividends for the first time since 1885. He persuaded the New York State Power Authority to buy two unfinished power plants saving Con Ed $200 million. In 1980 Luce ended the Cornwall controversy and donated the land for park use. He retired in 1982.

The utility started buying power from various suppliers and in 1984 began a two-year price freeze a boon to rate-hike-weary New Yorkers. The New York State Public Service Commission didn't approve another rate increase until 1992.

In 1997 Con Ed government officials consumer groups and other energy firms outlined the company's deregulation plan which included the formation of the Consolidated Edison Inc. holding company (known as Con Edison) and a power marketing unit in 1998. The next year Con Edison sold New York City generating facilities to KeySpan Northern States Power and Orion Power for a total of $1.65 billion.

Also in 1999 Con Edison bought Orange and Rockland Utilities for $790 million to increase its New York base and expand into New Jersey and Pennsylvania. In an effort to push into New England the company that year agreed to buy Northeast Utilities (NU since renamed Eversource Energy) for $3.3 billion in cash and stock and $3.9 billion in assumed debt. But the deal broke down in 2001. NU accused Con Edison of improperly trying to renegotiate terms while Con Edison accused NU of concealing information about unfavorable power supply contracts.

Con Edison's Indian Point Unit 2 nuclear plant was shut down temporarily in 2000 after a radioactive steam leak; later that year it agreed to sell Indian Point Units 1 and 2 to Entergy for $502 million. The sale was completed in 2001. That year Con Edison also incurred an estimated $400 million in costs related to emergency response and asset damage from the September 11 terrorist attacks on New York City.

In 2013 Con Edison announced plans to make it easier and less expensive for customers to convert from heating oil to lower cost natural gas in Manhattan and the Bronx. Its gas infrastructure expansion program includes investing a $100 million on new mains regulators and other upgrades in several neighborhoods.

It also plans to develop 25 MW of solar energy resources in New York City by the end of 2015. The solar power generated in the New York project would annually offset about 16000 tons of carbon dioxide.

EXECUTIVES

Vice President Human Resources, Claude Trahan, age 65
President and CEO Con Edison Transmission Inc., Joseph P. Oates, age 56

SVP and CFO Con Edison and CECONY, Robert N. Hoglund, age 56, $721,242 total compensation
Chairman and CEO ConEd and CECONY, John T. McAvoy, age 56, $1,220,767 total compensation
President Consolidated Edison Company of New York Inc. (CECONY), Timothy P. Cawley, age 52, $409,033 total compensation
SVP and General Counsel Consolidated Edison and CECONY, Elizabeth D. Moore, age 62, $608,017 total compensation
President and CEO Con Edison Clean Energy Businesses Inc., Mark Noyes, age 52
Office Of The Vice President Central Engineering, Laurens Irizarry
Auditors: PricewaterhouseCoopers LLP

LOCATIONS

HQ: Consolidated Edison Inc
4 Irving Place, New York, NY 10003
Phone: 212 460-4600
Web: www.conedison.com

PRODUCTS/OPERATIONS

2016 Sales

	$ mil.	% of total
Electric	8,741	72
Gas	1,692	14
Non-utility	1,091	9
Steam	551	5
Total	**12,075**	**100**

2016 sales

	% of total
CECONY	84
Clean Energy Business	9
O&R (Orange and Rockland)	7
Other	0
Total	**100**

Selected Subsidiaries

Consolidated Edison Inc. (Con Edison)
Consolidated Edison Company of New York Inc. (CECONY)
Con Edison Clean Energy Businesses Inc.
  Consolidated Edison Development Inc.
  Consolidated Edison Energy Inc.
  Consolidated Edison Solutions Inc.
Con Edison Transmission Inc.
  Consolidated Edison Transmission LLC (CET Electric)
  Consolidated Edison Gas Pipeline and Storage LLC (CET Gas)
Orange and Rockland Utilities Inc. (O&R)
Pike County Light & Power Company
Rockland Electric Company (RECO)

COMPETITORS

AEP	PPL Corporation
Avangrid	Public Service
CH Energy	Enterprise Group
Green Mountain Energy	South Jersey
NSTAR	Industries
National Fuel Gas	USPowerGen
National Grid USA	

HISTORICAL FINANCIALS

Company Type: Public

Income Statement

FYE: December 31

	REVENUE ($ mil.)	NET INCOME ($ mil.)	NET PROFIT MARGIN	EMPLOYEES
12/16	12,075	1,245	10.3%	14,960
12/15	12,554	1,193	9.5%	14,806
12/14	12,919	1,092	8.5%	14,601
12/13	12,354	1,062	8.6%	14,648
12/12	12,188	1,141	9.4%	14,529
Annual Growth	(0.2%)	2.2%	—	0.7%

2016 Year-End Financials

Debt ratio: 30.62%	No. of shares (mil.): 305
Return on equity: 9.08%	Dividends
Cash ($ mil.): 776	Yield: 0.0%
Current ratio: 0.89	Payout: 65.0%
Long-term debt ($ mil.): 14,735	Market value ($ mil.): 22,472

	STOCK PRICE ($) FY Close	P/E High/Low	PER SHARE ($) Earnings	Dividends	Book Value
12/16	73.68	20 15	4.12	2.68	46.88
12/15	64.27	18 14	4.05	2.60	44.55
12/14	66.01	18 14	3.71	2.52	42.94
12/13	55.28	18 15	3.61	2.46	41.81
12/12	55.54	17 14	3.86	2.42	40.53
Annual Growth	7.3%	— —	1.6%	2.6%	3.7%

CONSOLIDATED GRAIN & BARGE COMPANY

Auditors: KPMG LLP NEW ORLEANS LOUISIA

LOCATIONS

HQ: CONSOLIDATED GRAIN & BARGE COMPANY
127 HWY 190 E SERVICE RD, COVINGTON, LA 70433
Phone: 985 867-3500
Web: WWW.CGB.COM

HISTORICAL FINANCIALS

Company Type: Private

Income Statement

FYE: May 31

	REVENUE ($ mil.)	NET INCOME ($ mil.)	NET PROFIT MARGIN	EMPLOYEES
05/16	5,759	21	0.4%	650
05/14	7,093	44	0.6%	—
05/12	5,996	50	0.8%	—
05/08	4,386	31	0.7%	—
Annual Growth	3.5%	(4.8%)	—	—

2016 Year-End Financials

Debt ratio: ——	
Return on equity: 0.40%	Dividends
Cash ($ mil.): 0	Yield: —
Current ratio: 0.10	Payout: —
Long-term debt ($ mil.): —	Market value ($ mil.): —

Constellation Brands Inc

Constellation Brands is the world's largest premium wine producer. It offers more than 100 brands including Robert Mondavi Clos du Bois and Meiomi. The company is also the US's third-largest beer distributor and the sole US distributor for Mexican beer giant Grupo Modelo the brewer of Corona Modelo Especial Negra Modelo and other beers. Constellation Brands also markets premium spirits including Black Velvet whiskey and SVEDKA vodka. Constellation Brands' wine beer and spirits are sold in countries throughout the world. Brothers Richard and Robert Sands control the company which was founded by the late Marvin Sands.

Operations

Constellation Brands reports its business in two main segments: Beer and Wine & Spirits. The beer segment accounting for nearly 60% of group revenue has an exclusive license to import and sell Grupo Modelo's Corona Modelo and other brands. Wine & Spirits accounting for the remaining revenue covers a wide range of wine types brands and price points. Wine brands include Charles Smith Wines Meiomi and Ruffino while spirits brands include SVEDKA a Swedish import and the largest imported vodka brand in the US.

It has operations in the US New Zealand Italy and Canada.

Geographic Reach

New York-based Constellation Brands sells its products in roughly 100 countries. That being said the company gets virtually all its revenue from two countries: its generates over 90% of its sales in the US and most of the rest comes from Canada. The company is also a leading wine company in New Zealand.

Sales and Marketing

Constellation Brands staffs in-house marketing sales and customer service teams to increase its sales. These teams deploy a variety of marketing strategies conducting market research consumer and trade advertising price promotions point-of-sale materials event sponsorship on-premise promotions and public relations activities.

Financial Performance

Constellation set record revenue figures in fiscal 2017. At $8.1 billion revenue was 11% higher than the previous year. Sales growth was largely as a result of a series of acquisitions including Ballast Point Prisoner and Meiomi. Sales were also boosted by strong consumer demand across wine spirits and beer. The sale of the Canadian wine business weighed on growth.

Net income increased a strong 46% to $1.5 billion due to the favorable impact of pricing and lower cost of sales in the Mexican beer portfolio and gross profits from the acquired Ballast Point brand of $53.4 million.

Cash from operating activities increased 20% or $283 million to $1.7 billion due to strong cash generation in both the Beer and Wine and Spirits segments. Beer was aided by volume growth and favorable pricing and wine by a favorable timing of payments from accounts payable.

Strategy

Constellation's long-term growth strategy is to increase its mix of premium brands improve profit margins expand distribution of key brands and create operating efficiencies. The company sold its Canadian wine business in 2016 due to inadequate profitability. The business which holds the largest share of the wine market in Canada was sold to Ontario Teachers' Pension Plan for C$1 billion. The sale included brands like Jackson-Triggs and Inniskillin.

To increase its number of premium brands the company made a raft of acquisitions in 2016. It bought no less than six beer or wine and spirits brands in 2015-16: Charles Smith (ultra-premium wine) and High West (high-end whiskeys) in October 2016 Prisoner (high margin wines) in April 2016 Ballast Point (craft beer) in December 2015 and Meiomi (red wine) in August 2015.

It also acquired Obregon Brewery in December 2016 to expand its brewing capacity.

Mergers and Acquisitions

Constellation has been through a heavy-acquisition period.

In December 2016 it acquired Obregon Brewery for $568.7 million to provide immediate brewing capacity to support its fast-growing Mexican beer portfolio.

In October 2016 it acquired Charles Smith and its collection of five super and ultra-premium wines (including Kung Fu Girl Riesling and Velvet Devil Merlot) $120 million. In the same month it bought fast-growing high-end craft whiskey maker High West for $160 million.

In August 2016 it acquired Prisoner which owns five super-luxury wine brands for $285 million.

In late 2017 in a move outside the realm of alcoholic beverages but in line with the company's strategy of staying on top of consumer trends Constellation agreed to pay C$245 million for a nearly 10% stake in medicinal cannabis provider Canopy Growth Corporation.

HISTORY

Marvin Sands the son of winemaker Mordecai (Mack) Sands exited the Navy in 1945 and entered distilling by purchasing an old sauerkraut factory in Canandaigua New York. His business Canandaigua Industries struggled while making fruit wines in bulk for local bottlers in the East. Aiming at regional markets the company began producing its own brands two years later. Marvin opened the Richards Wine Cellar in Petersburg Virginia in 1951 and put his father in charge of the unit. In 1954 Marvin developed his own brand of "fortified" wine — boosted by 190-proof brandy — and named it Richards Wild Irish Rose after his son Richard.

The company slowly expanded buying a number of small wineries in the 1960s and 1970s. It went public in 1973 changing its name to Canandaigua Wine. A year later the company expanded to the West Coast thus gaining access to the growing varietal market.

Canandaigua continued to grow through acquisitions and new product introductions in the early 1980s. In 1984 when wine coolers became popular the company introduced Sun Country Coolers doubling sales to $173 million by 1986.

The short-lived wine cooler fad made Canandaigua realize that its distribution network could handle more volume so it began looking for additional brands. After a flurry of acquisitions in the late 80s and 90s the company changed its name in 1997 to Canandaigua Brands.

Founder Marvin Sands died in 1999. His son Richard who had been CEO since 1993 succeeded his father as chairman. In 2000 the firm changed its name to Constellation Brands.

In June 2013 Constellation Brands completed its acquisition of Grupo Modelo's US beer business from Anheuser-Busch InBev for approximately $5.23 billion. The transaction included full ownership of Crown Imports LLC which provided Constellation with complete independent control of all aspects of the US commercial business; a state-of-the-art brewery in Nava (Piedras Negras) Mexico; and an exclusive perpetual brand license in the US to import market and sell Corona and the Modelo brands. The deal gave Constellation ownership of six of the top 20 imported beer brands in the US.

EXECUTIVES

President and CEO, Robert S. (Rob) Sands, age 58, $1,310,383 total compensation
EVP and COO, William A. (Bill) Newlands, age 58
EVP and General Counsel, Thomas J. (Tom) Mullin, age 66, $497,663 total compensation
EVP and President Beer, F. Paul Hetterich, age 54, $600,000 total compensation

EVP and President Wine and Spirits Division,
Christopher (Chris) Stenzel, age 49
EVP and Chairman Beer, William F. (Bill) Hackett,
age 65, $607,046 total compensation
SVP and CIO, Joseph D. (Joe) Bruhin
EVP and Chief Human Resources Officer, Thomas
M. (Tom) Kane, age 56
EVP and CFO, David Klein, age 53, $600,000 total
compensation
Vice President Information Technology, George
Heltz
**Vice President and Legal Counsel Beer Division
Mexico,** Abdon Hernandez
National Account Manager, Jorey Newcomb
Vice President And Controller, Deb Price
Vice President Strategic Accounts, Phil Parker
Vice President Financial Services, Paula Fitzgerald
National Account Manager, Stephen Civello
Vice President Assistant Treasurer, Sandy
Dominach
Senior Vice President General Manager, John
Clemens
Vice President Engineering, Michael Drewel
Vice President Sales, Marty McCafferty
Senior Vice President Operations, Martin Van Der
Merwe
National Account Manager, Chris Beletti
National Account Manager, Eric Ramey
National Account Manager, Paul Hays
National Account Manager, Tom Becks
Vice President Of Financial, Elizabeth Choate
Senior Vice President Corporate Affairs, Jim Ryan
Vice President National Accounts, Shawn Keller
National Account Manager, Lori Welsh
Vice President Of Sales, William Renspie
Vice President and Associate General Counsel, K
Kristann Carey
Vice President, Bryon Boughton
Vice President Europe, Tim Fogarty
Senior Vice President Sales, Matt Deegan
Executive Vice President and General Counsel,
Tom Mullin
National Account Manager, Matt Pinchera
Vice President Associate General Counsel, Tiffanie
De Liberty
Chairman, Richard Sands, age 66
Auditors: KPMG LLP

LOCATIONS

HQ: Constellation Brands Inc
207 High Point Drive, Building 100, Victor, NY 14564
Phone: 585 678-7100
Web: www.cbrands.com

2017 Sales

	$ mil.	% of total
US	6,807	93
International	523	7
Total	**7,331**	**100**

PRODUCTS/OPERATIONS

2017 Sales

	$ mil.	% of total
Beer	4,229	58
Wine	2,739	37
Spirit	362	5
Total	**7,331**	**100**

Selected Subsidiaries and Operations

Constellation Spirits Inc.
Constellation Wines U.S.
Crown Imports LLC (beer)
Vincor International Inc. (wine Canada)

Selected Brands

Wine
　Black Box
　Clos du Bois
　Estancia
　Franciscan Estate
　Inniskillin
　Kim Crawford
　Mark West
　Mount Veeder
　Nobil
　Robert Mondavi
　Ruffino
　SIMI
　Wild Horse
Beer
　Corona Extra
　Corona Light
　Modelo Especial
　Negra Modelo
　Pacifico
Spirits
　SVEDKA Vodka

COMPETITORS

Andrew Peller	Lion
Anheuser-Busch InBev	MillerCoors
Bacardi	Patrᴄn Spirits
Beam Suntory	Pernod Ricard
Boston Beer	SABMiller
Bronco Wine Co.	Scheid Vineyards
Brown-Forman	Sebastiani Vineyards
Carlsberg	Taittinger
Diageo	Terlato Wine
E. & J. Gallo	Treasury Wine Estates
GIV	Trinchero Family
Halewood	Estates
Heineken	W.J. Deutsch
Jackson Family Wines	Willamette Valley
Korbel	Vineyards
LVMH	Wine Group

HISTORICAL FINANCIALS

Company Type: Public

Income Statement

FYE: February 28

	REVENUE ($ mil.)	NET INCOME ($ mil.)	NET PROFIT MARGIN	EMPLOYEES
02/17	7,331	1,535	20.9%	8,700
02/16	6,548	1,054	16.1%	9,000
02/15	6,028	839	13.9%	7,200
02/14	4,867	1,943	39.9%	6,300
02/13	2,796	387	13.9%	4,500
Annual Growth	**27.3%**	**41.1%**	—	**17.9%**

2017 Year-End Financials

Debt ratio: 49.66%
Return on equity: 22.83%
Cash ($ mil.): 177
Current ratio: 1.20
Long-term debt ($ mil.): 7,720
No. of shares (mil.): 194
Dividends
Yield: 1.0%
Payout: 21.2%
Market value ($ mil.): 30,904

	STOCK PRICE ($) FY Close	P/E High/Low		PER SHARE ($) Earnings	Dividends	Book Value
02/17	158.81	22	18	7.52	1.60	35.41
02/16	141.43	28	20	5.18	1.24	32.89
02/15	114.72	26	18	4.17	0.00	29.66
02/14	81.03	8	4	9.83	0.00	26.02
02/13	44.24	21	9	2.04	0.00	15.48
Annual Growth	**37.6%**	—	—	**38.6%**	—	**23.0%**

Consumers Energy Co.

Consumers Energy Company makes sure that energy consumers in Michigan have the power to crank up their heaters and the gas to fire up their stoves. The company's operating area includes all 68 counties of Michigan's lower peninsula. All told

Consumers Energy (the primary operating unit of CMS Energy) has a generating capacity of more than 5600 MW (primarily fossil-fueled) and distributes electricity to 1.8 million customers and natural gas to 1.8 million customers. Included in the utility's arsenal of power production is electricity generated from coal natural gas wind and hydroelectric power plants. Utility customers are a mix of residential commercial and diversified industrial clients.

Operations

Consumers Energy is the regulated utility subsidiary of CMS Energy.

Electric utility operations (70% of revenue) include the generation purchase distribution and sale of electricity. It owns some dozen power generation facilities and purchased some 2700 MW from third parties. It shuttered seven of its smaller coal-fired plants in 2016 and is replacing some of the lost capacity with gas-fired facilities. The company's electric distribution system has more than 60000 miles of electric lines.

Its gas utility operations (30%) include the purchase transmission storage distribution and sale of natural gas. The gas distribution system delivers roughly 350 billion cubic feet of natural gas per year

Geographic Reach

Consumers provides electric service to 275 cities and villages in 61 counties in Michigan. Principal cities served are Battle Creek Bay City Cadillac Flint Grand Rapids Jackson Kalamazoo Midland Muskegon and Saginaw.

Consumers gas business purchases about 5% of its gas from Canadian sources and the rest from US suppliers including several along the US Gulf Coast. It serves a 13000-square mile area that includes more than 200 cities and villages. More than one half of its customers are in metro Detroit.

Sales and Marketing

The company serves 1.8 million electric customers and 1.8 million gas customers in Michigan's Lower Peninsula.

The company serves residential commercial industrial and other customers. Though it is a regulated utility Consumers Energy is open to electricity competition in its service area at a rate of up to 10% of its previous year?s retail sales. Gas competition also exists from Gulf Coast companies as well as alternative fuels such as propane oil and electricity.

Financial Performance

Consumers Energy's overall revenue decreased by almost 2% (reflecting lower gas prices and sales volumes) in 2016 to $6.1 billion and its net income increased by about 4% to $616 million.

From a net income perspective electric operating revenues increased by $122 million reflecting $91 million from rate increases and a $62 million increase in sales due to favorable weather. These increases were partially offset by a $25 million net decrease in securitization revenue and a $6 million drop in other revenue.

Gas operating revenue increased by $15 million reflecting $33 million from a 2016 rate increase offset partially by an $18 million decrease in sales due to milder winter weather.

Net cash provided by operating activities dropped from $1.8 million to $1.7 million. This decline was due to lower customer collections offset partially by higher income tax payments to CMS Energy lower post-retirement benefits contributions and higher net income.

Strategy

Addressing new regulatory mandates Consumers is making big changes its energy generation mix mostly from coal to natural gas. In 2016 after retiring seven of its smaller coal-fired plants (representing 950 MW of capacity) the percent of power coming from the black commodity dropped from 79% to 58%. That same year Consumers adjusted a Power Purchase Agreement (PPA) with an Entergy nuclear plant to terminate the agreement in May 2018 four years ahead of schedule. The lost capacity will be replaced with the output of Consumers? 2015-acquired 540 MW gas-fueled plant in Jackson MI along with a reduction in consumer demand updated PPA agreements and power from renewable energy sources.

Consumers informed state regulators in 2017 that it is interested in acquiring an additional gas-fired electricity plant in Michigan. As well the utility broke ground on its third wind energy project Cross Winds Energy Park II in Tuscola County. Phase I is expected to have 19 turbines capable of generating 44 MW of electricity and will commence service in early 2018. When completed it will have more than 80 wind turbines and 155 MW of energy production (enough to serve 60000 residents).

Consumers gas business is working on a $610 million 5-year project to replace 78 miles of gas pipe dating to the 1940s and located in Saginaw Genesee and Oakland counties. Construction began in mid-2017 and will continue until the end of 2022. Additional capital is being deployed to address anticipated growth installing new pipes to serve an increase of nearly 8000 new business customers and 2500 residential customers in its service area.

To improve its bottom line and the efficiency of its operations and in an effort to stem the tide of commercial and residential customers jumping ship for other electricity providers Consumers Energy is looking at options to reform its rate structures.

The company is being guided by its "Balanced Energy Initiative" a comprehensive 20 year plan (introduced in 2007). The plan calls for the utility to develop new power plants increase the efficiency of its operations and expand its renewable energy projects.

Consumers anticipates a continued rise in industrial production in its service territory will drive its total electric deliveries to increase annually by 0.5% through 2021. Excluding the impacts of energy efficiency programs the company expects its total electric deliveries to increase by 1% a year over the same time period. It also expects that its gas deliveries will remain stable through 2021 reflecting growth in gas demand being offset by energy efficiency and conservation activities.

The company's planned base capital investments of $4.6 billion in 2017 include $2.6 billion to preserve electric utility reliability and capacity and $2 billion at the gas utility to sustain the delivery system and enhance pipeline integrity.

Between 2012 and 2017 the company installed smart meters (advanced meters that allow customers to have better control over their energy use) across its electric power distribution system.

EXECUTIVES

EVP and CFO, Thomas J. (Tom) Webb, age 65, $695,000 total compensation
SVP Energy Resources, Daniel J. (Dan) Malone, age 56, $465,000 total compensation
SVP, John M. Butler, age 53, $470,000 total compensation
SVP Customer Experience and CIO, Brian F. Rich, age 42
President and CEO, Patricia K. (Patti) Poppe, age 49, $430,000 total compensation
Vice President Gas Operations, Charles C Crews
Chairman, John G. Russell, age 60
Auditors: PRICEWATERHOUSECOOPERS LLP

LOCATIONS

HQ: Consumers Energy Co.
One Energy Plaza, Jackson, MI 49201
Phone: 517 788-0550
Web: www.consumersenergy.com

PRODUCTS/OPERATIONS

2016 Sales

	$ mil.	% of total
Electric	4,379	72
Gas	1,685	28
Total	**6,064**	**100**

COMPETITORS

DTE Electric	SEMCO ENERGY
DTE Gas Company	We Energies
Indiana Michigan Power	Xcel Energy

HISTORICAL FINANCIALS

Company Type: Public

Income Statement

FYE: December 31

	REVENUE ($ mil.)	NET INCOME ($ mil.)	NET PROFIT MARGIN	EMPLOYEES
12/16	6,064	616	10.2%	7,366
12/15	6,165	594	9.6%	7,394
12/14	6,800	567	8.3%	7,388
12/13	6,321	534	8.4%	7,435
12/12	6,013	439	7.3%	7,205
Annual Growth	**0.2%**	**8.8%**	**—**	**0.6%**

2016 Year-End Financials

Debt ratio: 30.87%	No. of shares (mil.): 84
Return on equity: 10.70%	Dividends
Cash ($ mil.): 131	Yield: 0.0%
Current ratio: 0.93	Payout: 81.2%
Long-term debt ($ mil.): 5,363	Market value ($ mil.): 8,654

	STOCK PRICE ($) FY Close	P/E High/Low		Earnings	PER SHARE ($) Dividends	Book Value
12/16	102.90	—	—	(0.00)	4.50	70.62
12/15	97.00	—	—	(0.00)	4.50	65.95
12/14	104.51	—	—	(0.00)	4.50	62.75
12/13	96.32	—	—	(0.00)	4.50	57.75
12/12	93.74	—	—	(0.00)	4.50	54.48
Annual Growth	**2.4%**	—	—	**—**	**(0.0%)**	**6.7%**

Core Mark Holding Co Inc

Smokes and snacks are at the center of Core-Mark Holding's cosmos. The company distributes packaged consumables (including cigarettes and other tobacco products candy snacks grocery items perishables nonalcoholic beverages and health and beauty aids) to about 43000 convenience stores; mass merchandisers; supermarkets; and drug liquor and specialty retailers. Cigarettes and other tobacco products are its top sellers generating about 80% of net sales. Core-Mark serves customers in all 50 US states as well as five Canadian provinces. Its 10 biggest clients (which include Murphy U.S.A Couche-Tard and CST Brands) contribute about 45% of sales.

Operations

Core-Mark supplies its customers with consumable items from a network of nearly 30 distribution centers in the US and Canada. It also operates dedicated facilities for its largest customers Couche-Tard and CST Brands in Phoenix and San Antonio respectively.

The company also conducts marketing research to provide its convenience store customer base with consumer and market insight it might otherwise be unable to obtain.

Geographic Reach

South San Francisco California -based Core-Mark operates in the US where it generates more than 90% of its revenue. The company's remaining revenue of about 10% comes from Canada.

The company operates a network of about 28 distribution centers in the US and Canada (excluding two distribution facilities it operates as a third party logistics provider). Of its distribution centers around 25 are located in the US and the rest are located in Canada.

Sales and Marketing

Canadian convenience store operator Murphy U.S.A is Core-Mark's largest customer representing around 12% of sales while Alimentation Couche-Tard Inc accounted around 11%.

The company's primary customer base consists of traditional convenience stores as well as alternative outlets selling consumer packaged goods. Its traditional convenience store customers include many of the major national and super-regional convenience store operators as well as independently owned convenience stores. Its alternative outlet customers comprise a variety of store formats including grocery stores drug stores liquor stores cigarette and tobacco shops hotel gift shops military exchanges college and corporate campuses casinos hardware stores airport concessions and other specialty and small format stores that carry convenience products.

Its trucking fleet consists of around 2000 tractors trailers trucks and vans. More than 95% of its trailers were tri-temp with the remainder capable of delivering refrigerated and non-refrigerated foods.

Financial Performance

Core-Mark's net sales increased 31.3% in fiscal 2016 or $34 billion to $14.5 billion compared to $11 billion for 2015. The increase in net sales was driven primarily by market share gains including the addition of Murphy U.S.A. the acquisition of Pine State Convenience (Pine State) in June 2016 and the continued success of Core-Mark's core strategies.

Core-Mark's gross profit increased $99.0 million in fiscal 2016 or 15.5% to $736.9 million from $637.9 million in 2015 driven primarily by the increase in sales. Gross profit margin was 5.1% of total net sales in fiscal 2016 compared to 5.8% in 2015. The decrease in gross profit margin was due primarily to market share gains including the addition of Murphy U.S.A.

The company's operating expenses in fiscal 2016 increased 17.3% or $95.6 million to $646.8 million from $551.2 million in 2015. Increases in the amount of cubic feet of product handled incremental customer deliveries the acquisition of Pine State and costs related to the on-boarding of significant new customers contributed to higher operating expenses in 2016.

Core-Mark's net income in fiscal 2016 was $54.2 million compared to $51.5 million in 2015. Despite the strong revenue and net income in fiscal 2016 the company ended the year with negative cash from operations.

Strategy

During fiscal 2016 Core-Mark's continued to grow its market share and increase its food/non-food sales and gross profit through its core strategies including its Vendor Consolidation Initiative

(VCI) leveraging its ?Fresh? product solutions and providing category management expertise in order to make our customers more relevant and profitable.

Core-Mark's business model is to increase supply chain efficiency for convenience stores. It does this by consolidating the numerous daily deliveries from disparate product segments received by convenience stores into multiple unified weekly deliveries of the bulk of their products.

The company is leaning more towards fresh produce which has a higher margin and strong growth potential as consumers buy more fresh food and dairy products from convenience stores. To keep perishables fresh on the way to market the company has an upgraded refrigerated capacity chilling docks and other systems designed to deliver fresh goods quickly.

The company's Focused Marketing Initiative conducts marketing research to provide its customers with consumer insight. It is Core-Mark's interest for its customers to generate sales growth.

Mergers and Acquisitions

To grow market share and extend its geographic reach Core-Mark has been active on the acquisition front. In June 2016 Core-Mark acquired Convenience Division of Pine State Trading Company for $88 million. Based in Gardiner Maine Pine State markets and distributes convenience and beverage products. The acquisition widened Core-Mark's geographic footprint in an area where it has a limited presence and offered Pine State customers a new spectrum of products and marketing programs.

In 2015 Core-Mark paid $8 million for the assets of Karrys Bros a regional distributor in Ontario and surrounding provinces.

Company Background

The company's roots reach back to 1888 when it was known as Glaser Bros. a family-run candy and tobacco distribution business in San Francisco.

EXECUTIVES

VP and Chief Accounting Officer, Christopher M. (Chris) Miller, age 56, $312,885 total compensation
President and COO, Scott E. McPherson, age 47, $296,640 total compensation
CEO and Director, Thomas B. Perkins, age 58, $515,412 total compensation
President Core-Mark Canada, Eric J. Rolheiser, age 46
SVP US Distribution-West, Christopher K. (Chris) Hobson, age 48, $270,375 total compensation
SVP US Distribution East, William G. Stein, age 47, $263,718 total compensation
Chairman, Randolph I. Thornton, age 71
Auditors: Deloitte & Touche LLP

LOCATIONS

HQ: Core Mark Holding Co Inc
395 Oyster Point Boulevard, Suite 415, South San Francisco, CA 94080
Phone: 650 589-9445
Web: www.core-mark.com

2016 Sales

	$ mil.	% of total
United States	13,133	91
Canada	1,356	9
Corporate	40	—
Total	14,529	100

PRODUCTS/OPERATIONS

2016 Sales

	$ mil.	% of total
Cigarettes	10,335	71
Food	1,422	10
Candy	620	3
Fresh	389	4
Other tobacco products	1,133	8
Health beauty & general	446	3
Beverages	176	1
Equipment/other	4	—
Total	14,529	100

COMPETITORS

800-JR Cigar	H. T. Hackney
AMCON Distributing	McLane
Associated Food	Roundy's
BJ's Wholesale Club	SUPERVALU
C&S Wholesale	Sam's Club
Coca-Cola	Southern Glazer's Wine
Costco Wholesale	and Spirits
Eby-Brown	Stephenson Wholesale
Frito-Lay	Company
GSC Enterprises	Wal-Mart

HISTORICAL FINANCIALS

Company Type: Public

Income Statement

FYE: December 31

	REVENUE ($ mil.)	NET INCOME ($ mil.)	NET PROFIT MARGIN	EMPLOYEES
12/16	14,529	54	0.4%	7,688
12/15	11,069	51	0.5%	6,655
12/14	10,280	42	0.4%	5,933
12/13	9,767	41	0.4%	5,617
12/12	8,892	33	0.4%	5,225
Annual Growth	13.1%	12.4%	—	10.1%

2016 Year-End Financials

Debt ratio: 23.23%	No. of shares (mil.): 46
Return on equity: 10.56%	Dividends
Cash ($ mil.): 26	Yield: 0.0%
Current ratio: 2.18	Payout: 28.2%
Long-term debt ($ mil.): 347	Market value ($ mil.): 1,988

	STOCK PRICE ($) FY Close	P/E High/Low		PER SHARE ($) Earnings	Dividends	Book Value
12/16	43.07	79	28	1.17	0.33	11.48
12/15	81.94	81	47	1.11	0.28	10.71
12/14	61.93	101	47	0.92	0.23	9.99
12/13	75.93	84	51	0.90	0.20	9.42
12/12	47.35	67	51	0.73	0.22	8.74
Annual Growth	(2.3%)	—	—	12.6%	10.4%	7.1%

Corning Inc

The source of Corning Inc.'s revenue is transparently obvious: it's glass. Once known for kitchenware and lab products the company makes glass ceramic and other components for the consumer electronics telecommunications automotive and life sciences industries. Its products include substrates for flat-panel displays and computer monitors optical fiber and cable substrates and filters for automotive emissions control products labware and scientific equipment and glass and optical materials for a wide range of industries. Corning operates about100 manufacturing and processing facilities in nearly 20 countries. More than half of its sales come from the Asia/Pacific region.

Operations

Corning operates in five segments. Its largest Display Technologies accounts for about a third of sales and includes glass substrates for flat-panel liquid crystal displays. Optical Communications which includes fiber and cable and other components for the telecom industry also brings in about a third of sales. The Specialty Materials business about an eighth of sales is powered by superstar product Gorilla Glass which is used in consumer electronics devices such as notebook computers mobile phones and TVs.

Other Corning segments are Environmental Technologies (substrates and filters for automotive and diesel products) and Life Sciences (glass and plastic equipment for labs and other scientific applications) which each account for about 10% of sales.

Geographic Reach

Corning?s customers based in the US generate 30% of its revenue followed by China and South Korea which account for more than 20% and about 15% of sales respectively. The Asia-Pacific region accounts more than half of revenue.

The company operates manufacturing facilities in three US states and in Europe Brazil China India Australia and Israel.

Sales and Marketing

Corning has a concentrated set of customers with two or three accounting for about half or more of revenue in four of the company?s five segments. Among its biggest customers are Korean LCD panel makers including Samsung Display Co. (11% of revenue) and LG Display Co.

Financial Performance

Corning Inc. displayed a 3% revenue increase to about $9.4 billion in 2016 with growth in each segment but Environmental Technologies. The biggest increase 5% was in Display Technologies boosted by a volume increase and a stronger Japanese yen. The Optical Segment?s sales were slowed in the first half of the year by problems with new manufacturing software. The company also reported higher sales of Gorilla Glass 5 and advanced optics products. Slower sales of diesel products in the US automotive market helped reduce sales for Environmental Technologies.

The company?s profit for 2016 was $3.7 billion a 175% increase from 2015. Corning realized a $2.7 billion gain from a tax adjustment on the strategic realignment of its ownership in Dow Corning in 2016. On the operations side net income from the Display Technologies segment dropped 15% because of lower LCD glass prices.

Cash generated by operations fell to $2.5 billion in 2016 from $2.8 billion in 2015 on an increase in accounts receivable in the Optical Communications and Specialty Materials segments. That was somewhat offset by an increase in accounts payable and other current liabilities.

Strategy

Corning Inc. thinks that the Glass Age is at hand — on the desk and on the wall and in the car. It's got a point: People interact with technology through a glass screen whether to view or touch or both. The company's R&D process came up with Gorilla Glass its protective cover glass used in thousands of consumer products such as cell phones computers and TVs. The company will keep up the R&D tradition by pumping $10 billion into the search for and development of new products. It will look for advances in products for optical communications mobile consumer electronics displays automotive and life sciences vessels.

Corning continues its drive into the automotive market beginning production of its first windshield sunroof and backlite windows in 2016. Beyond customer contact areas Corning makes gas particulate filters for automotive engines.

Getting into the automotive market could blunt Corning?s biggest weakness: Concentration of customers. Three customers for its Display Technologies segment generated about two-thirds of the unit?s while three customers account for more than 50% of sales for Specialty Materials. To find even more room in vehicles the company has formed a joint venture with Saint-Gobain Sekurit normally one of its many competitors to produce lightweight auto glazing that could be use throughout a vehicle.

In automotive as well as other markets Corning faces stiff competition. Asahi Glass Company one of Corning's key competitors has entered the automotive market even building a plant for automotive glass in Mexico.

Mergers and Acquisitions

Corning Inc.?s recent acquisitions have been made to strengthen its Optical Communications business. In late 2017 the company agreed to acquire 3M's Communications Markets Division which consists of optical fiber and copper passive connectivity tools for about $900 million. The 3M operations will be part of Corning's Optical Communications unit. The 3M assets expand Corning's reach in global markets and its high-bandwidth portfolio. The deal is expected to close in 2018.

Also in 2017 the company acquired SpiderCloud Wireless Inc. a provider of in-building wireless technologies. SpiderCloud?s products would help extend the Corning?s fiber optic cables in building networks.

In 2016 Corning acquired Stran Technologies which makes interconnect products for use in harsh environments. Besides adding to its product line the deal gives Corning greater exposure to military and aerospace and oil and gas customers.

In another 2016 deal Corning acquired Alliance Fiber Optic Products which makes high-performance passive optical components for cloud data center operators and data communications and telecommunications OEMs.

EXECUTIVES

Chairman and CEO, Wendell P. Weeks, age 58, $1,337,740 total compensation
Vice Chairman and Corporate Development Officer, Lawrence D. (Larry) McRae, age 59, $731,971 total compensation
SVP and CFO, R. Tony Tripeny, age 58, $504,808 total compensation
EVP and Corning Innovation Officer, Martin J. (Marty) Curran, age 58
EVP Corning Optical Telecommunications, Clark S. Kinlin, age 57
President Corning Glass Technologies (CGT), James P. Clappin, age 60, $686,538 total compensation
EVP Corning Technologies and International, Eric S. Musser, age 58
EVP and CTO, David L. Morse, age 65, $631,010 total compensation
Vice President Flat Glass Photovoltaics Program, Marc Giroux
Vice President New Opportunity Development New Business Development, Robert Ritchie
Vice President of Sales, Allen Smith
Vice President Of Sales, Eric Marinakis
Vice President of Product Management, Jeff Kunst
Vice President, William Cash
Division Vice President, John Sharkey
Vice President Marketing, Dan Krawiec
Vice President Of Chemical Engineering, Thomas Capek
Vice President Sales, Peter King
Senior Vice President, Alan Eusden
Vice President, Adriane Brown
Vice President Of Communications, Joe Dunning
Vice President, Daniela Lavric
Senior Vice President Global Benefits and Compensation, John P MacMahon
NATIONAL SALES MANAGER, Gareth Ireland
Senior Vice President and Treasurer, Mark Rogus
Vice President Corporate Communications, Daniel Collins
Senior Vice President of Sales, Rodney Lewis

Vice President and Chief Technologist, Waguih Ishak
Vice President Commercial Technology, Bill Cune
Vice President and General Manager, Richard Eglen
Vice President, David Watson
Treasurer, Lee Starnes
Board Member, Lisa Emel
Assistant Treasurer, Rob Vanni
Secretary, Kathy McClure
Auditors: PricewaterhouseCoopers LLP

LOCATIONS

HQ: Corning Inc
One Riverfront Plaza, Corning, NY 14831
Phone: 607 974-9000
Web: www.corning.com

2016 Sales

	$ mil.	% of total
North America		
United States	2,625	28
Canada	282	3
Mexico	50	-
Asia Pacific		
China	2,083	22
Korea	1,444	15
Taiwan	840	9
Japan	450	5
Other	363	4
Europe		
Germany	363	4
United Kingdom	182	2
France	83	1
Other	352	4
All Other	273	3
Total	**9,390**	**100**

PRODUCTS/OPERATIONS

2016 Sales

	$ mil.	% of total
Display Technologies	3,238	34
Optical Communications	3,005	32
Specialty Materials	1,124	12
Environmental Technologies	1,032	11
Life Sciences	839	9
All Other	152	2
Total	**9,390**	**100**

Selected Products

Display technologies
  Liquid crystal displays (LCD)
  Organic light-emitting diode (OLED) displays
Telecommunications
  Optical fiber and cable
  Optical networking components
Environmental technologies
  Industrial and stationary emissions products
  Mobile emissions and automotive catalytic converter products
Life sciences
  Genomics and laboratory equipment
Specialty Materials
  Gorilla Glass
Other
  Polarized glass
  Semiconductor materials

COMPETITORS

3M	Nippon Electric Glass
Alcatel-Lucent	Nippon Sheet Glass
Amphenol	Nortel Networks
Asahi Glass	Oerlikon
Becton Dickinson	Prysmian
Belden	SCHOTT
Carl-Zeiss-Stiftung	SWCC SHOWA
CommScope	Saint-Gobain
DENSO	Shin-Etsu Chemical
Dai Nippon Printing	Sumitomo Electric
Fujikura Ltd.	Superior Essex
Furukawa Electric	TE Connectivity
General Cable	Thermo Fisher
Heraeus Holding	Scientific
Hoya Corp.	Thomas & Betts

IBIDEN	Toppan Printing
NGK INSULATORS	Viavi Solutions
Nikon	

HISTORICAL FINANCIALS

Company Type: Public

Income Statement
FYE: December 31

	REVENUE ($ mil.)	NET INCOME ($ mil.)	NET PROFIT MARGIN	EMPLOYEES
12/16	9,390	3,695	39.4%	40,700
12/15	9,111	1,339	14.7%	35,700
12/14	9,715	2,472	25.4%	34,600
12/13	7,819	1,961	25.1%	30,400
12/12	8,012	1,728	21.6%	28,700
Annual Growth	**4.0%**	**20.9%**	**—**	**9.1%**

2016 Year-End Financials

Debt ratio: 13.99%
Return on equity: 20.09%
Cash ($ mil.): 5,291
Current ratio: 3.29
Long-term debt ($ mil.): 3,646

No. of shares (mil.): 926
Dividends
  Yield: 0.0%
  Payout: 16.7%
Market value ($ mil.): 22,474

	STOCK PRICE ($) FY Close	P/E High/Low		PER SHARE ($) Earnings	Dividends	Book Value
12/16	24.27	7	5	3.23	0.54	19.32
12/15	18.28	25	16	1.00	0.48	16.63
12/14	22.93	13	9	1.73	0.40	16.94
12/13	17.82	13	9	1.34	0.39	15.13
12/12	12.62	13	9	1.15	0.32	14.62
Annual Growth	**17.8%**	**—**		**—**	**29.5% 14.4%**	**7.2%**

Costco Wholesale Corp

Operating more than 740 membership warehouse stores Costco is the nation's largest wholesale club operator (ahead of Wal-Mart's SAM'S CLUB). Primarily under the Costco Wholesale banner it serves more than 90 million cardholders in 44 US states Washington DC and Puerto Rico as well as in Australia Canada Mexico the UK Japan South Korea Taiwan and Spain. Stores offer discount prices on an average of about 3700 products (many in bulk packaging) ranging from alcoholic beverages and appliances to fresh food pharmaceuticals and tires. Certain club memberships also offer products and services such as car and home insurance mortgage and real estate services and travel packages.

HISTORY

From 1954 to 1974 retailer Sol Price built his Fed-Mart discount chain into a $300 million behemoth selling general merchandise to government employees. Price sold the company to Hugo Mann in 1975 and the next year with son Robert Rick Libenson and Giles Bateman opened the first Price Club warehouse in San Diego to sell in volume to small businesses at steep discounts.

Posting a large loss its first year prompted Price Club's decision to expand membership to include government utility and hospital employees as well as credit union members. In 1978 it opened a second store in Phoenix. With the help of his father Sol's other son Laurence began a chain of tire-mounting stores (located adjacent to Price Club outlets on land leased from the company and using tires sold by the Price Clubs).

The company went public in 1980 with four stores in California and Arizona. Price Club moved into the eastern US with its 1984 opening of a store in Virginia and continued to expand including a joint venture with Canadian retailer Steinberg in 1986 to operate stores in Canada; the first Canadian warehouse opened that year in Montreal.

Two years later Price Club acquired A. M. Lewis (grocery distributor Southern California and Arizona) and the next year it opened two Price Club Furnishings offering discounted home and office furniture.

Price Club bought out Steinberg's interest in the Canadian locations in 1990 and added stores on the East Coast and in California Colorado and British Columbia. However competition in the East from ensconced rivals such as SAM'S CLUB and PACE forced the closure of two stores two years later. A 50-50 joint venture with retailer Controladora Comercial Mexicana led to the opening of two Price Clubs in Mexico City one each in 1992 and 1993.

Price Club merged with Costco Wholesale in 1993. Founded in 1983 by Jeffrey Brotman and James Sinegal (a former EVP of Price Company) Costco Wholesale went public in 1985 and expanded into Canada.

In 1993 Price/Costco opened its first warehouse outside the Americas in a London suburb. Merger costs led to a loss the following year and Price/Costco spun off its commercial real estate operations as well as certain international operations as Price Enterprises (now Price Legacy). In 1995 the company launched its Kirkland Signature brand of private-label merchandise. Two years later the company changed its corporate name to Costco Companies.

Costco began online sales and struck a deal to buy two stores in South Korea in 1998 and opened its first store in Japan in 1999. Under industrywide pressure over the way members-only chains record fees Costco took a $118 million charge for fiscal 1999 to change accounting practices. That year the company made yet another name change to Costco Wholesale (emphasizing its core warehouse operations).

In 2000 the company purchased private retailer Littlewoods' 20% stake in Costco UK increasing Costco's ownership to 80%. Costco began expanding into the Midwest in 2001 as part of plans to open 40 new clubs a year including ones in China.

During fiscal 2002 Costco opened 29 new warehouse clubs. In December 2002 the retailer opened its first home store — called Costco Home — in Kirkland Washington stocked with mostly high-end furniture. A second Costco Home store opened in Tempe Arizona in December 2004.

Costco increased its equity interest in Costco Wholesale UK in October 2003 to 100% when it purchased Carrefour Nederland's 20% stake.

In 2006 Costco began offering more than 200 generic prescription medicines (100 count) for $10 or less. The following year Costco.com logged sales in excess of $1 billion.

In July 2009 Costco shuttered its two Costco Home stores which were located in Washington and Arizona. The retailer cited the weak economy and market for home furnishings and the fact that the concept didn't fit with its expansion plans for their closure. In August the company opened its first warehouse club in Australia.

CEO Jim Sinegal stepped down in 2012 after more than 20 years at the helm. Sinegal who together with chairman Jeffrey Brotman founded Costco in 1983 handed the reins to Craig Jelinek a 28-year veteran and former president and COO of the company.

In 2012 Costco bought the remaining 50% stake in Costco Mexico for $789 million from its joint venture partner Controladora Comercial Mexicana.

EXECUTIVES

SVP Operations, Roger A. Campbell

EVP Costco Wholesale Industries, Timothy L. Rose, age 64

EVP Information Systems, Paul G. Moulton, age 66, $602,519 total compensation

Senior Vice President Human RE, John Matthews

EVP Administration and Human Resources, Franz E. Lazarus, age 70

EVP and COO Eastern and Canadian Divisions, Joseph P. (Joe) Portera, age 65, $645,297 total compensation

President and CEO, W. Craig Jelinek, age 65, $699,810 total compensation

EVP and COO Southwest and Mexico Divisions, Dennis R. Zook, age 68, $642,618 total compensation

EVP and CFO, Richard A. Galanti, age 61, $712,888 total compensation

EVP International, James P. (Jim) Murphy, age 64

EVP and COO Northern Division and Midwest Region, John D. McKay, age 60

SVP and General Manager Northeast Region, Jeffrey R. Long

SVP and General Manager Midwest Region, John B. Gaherty

SVP and General Manager Mexico, Jaime Gonzalez

EVP and COO Merchandising, Douglas W. (Doug) Schutt, age 58

SVP and General Manager Bay Area Region, Jeffrey Abadir

SVP and General Manager Northwest Region, Mario Omoss

SVP and General Manager San Diego Region, Yoram Rubanenko

SVP and General Manager Eastern Canada Region, Pierre Riel

SVP and General Manager Los Angeles Region, Caton Frates

SVP and General Manager Western Canada Region, Russ Miller

Pharmacy Manager, Hassan Awada

Vice President Real Estate, Larry Farren

Senior Vice President Depot Operations, John Thelan

Vice President, Darby Greek

Pharmacy Manager, Jeff Mrowczynski

Senior Executive Vice President, Richard Dicerchio

Vice President Finance Loan Accounting, Joseph Cawley

Vice President, Erin Haag

Assistant Vice President, Todd Thull

Vice President and Government, Nick Strode

Costco Southeast Vice President, Jerry Dempsey

VP Operations, Gino Dorico

Pharmacy Manager, Hammad Syed

Regional Vice President, Stevie Nemec

Assistant Vice President, Tim Flowers

ASSISTANT VICE PRESIDENT, Dan Mcmurray

PHARMACY MANAGER, Bill Jones

ASSISTANT VICE PRESIDENT, Scott Jacobs

ASSISTANT VICE PRESIDENT AGMM FOODS NORTHEAST REGION, Nick Dagostino

ASSISTANT VICE PRESIDENT GMM, Scott Stearns

Vice President Gmm, Debbie Ells

Senior Vice President, Bob Hicok

Auditors: KPMG LLP

LOCATIONS

HQ: Costco Wholesale Corp
999 Lake Drive, Issaquah, WA 98027
Phone: 425 313-8100
Web: www.costco.com

2017 Sales

	$ mil.	% of total
US	93	73
Canada	18	14
Other international	16	13
Total	**129**	**100**

PRODUCTS/OPERATIONS

2017 Sales (Merchandise)

	% of total
Food (dry & institutionally packaged)	21
Sundries (including candy snacks beverages cleaning products & tobacco)	20
Hardlines (including major appliances electronics & office & auto supplies)	16
Fresh food (meat bakery deli & produce)	14
Softlines (including apparel housewares media home furnishings & jewelry)	12
Other (including pharmacy optical photo & gas stations)	17
Total	**100**

2017 Sales

	$ mil.	% of total
Sales	126	98
Membership fees	2	2
Total	**129**	**100**

COMPETITORS

1-800 CONTACTS	Kohl's
ALDI	Kroger
Amazon.com	Office Depot
Army and Air Force Exchange	PETCO
Aurora Wholesalers	PetSmart
AutoZone	Safeway
BJ's Wholesale Club	Sam's Club
Best Buy	Staples
Big Lots	Target Corporation
Dollar General	Toys "R" Us
Family Dollar Stores	Trader Joe's
Home Depot	Wal-Mart
Kmart	Whole Foods

HISTORICAL FINANCIALS

Company Type: Public

Income Statement

FYE: September 3

	REVENUE ($ mil.)	NET INCOME ($ mil.)	NET PROFIT MARGIN	EMPLOYEES
09/17*	129,025	2,679	2.1%	231,000
08/16	118,719	2,350	2.0%	218,000
08/15	116,199	2,377	2.0%	205,000
08/14	112,640	2,058	1.8%	195,000
09/13	105,156	2,039	1.9%	184,000
Annual Growth	**5.2%**	**7.1%**	**—**	**5.9%**

*Fiscal year change

2017 Year-End Financials

Debt ratio: 18.32%	No. of shares (mil.): 437
Return on equity: 23.06%	Dividends
Cash ($ mil.): 4,546	Yield: 0.0%
Current ratio: 0.99	Payout: 146.3%
Long-term debt ($ mil.): 6,573	Market value ($ mil.): 69,183

	STOCK PRICE ($) FY Close	P/E High/Low		PER SHARE ($) Earnings	Dividends	Book Value
09/17*	158.24	30	23	6.08	8.90	24.65
08/16	163.93	32	26	5.33	1.70	27.61
08/15	139.95	29	22	5.37	6.51	24.24
08/14	121.08	27	23	4.65	1.33	28.11
09/13	111.87	26	20	4.63	8.17	24.80
Annual Growth	**9.1%**	**—**	**—**	**7.0%**	**2.2%**	**(0.1%)**

*Fiscal year change

Coty, Inc.

Sarah Jessica Parker Beyonc © and Lady Gaga are just a few of the celebs to promote Coty the third-largest maker of fragrances and beauty products for men and women (behind LOr ©al and

Unilever). Coty has turned heads since Fran§ois Coty created his first perfume La Rose Jacqueminot in 1904. Its lineup ranges from moderately priced scents sold globally by mass retailers to prestige fragrances and nail polishes found in department stores. Coty's brands include COVERGIRL adidas philosophy Rimmel and Sally Hansen. Its prestige perfume labels are led by Calvin Klein and Gucci. In 2016 the company acquired Procter & Gamble's Specialty Beauty Business for $11.4 billion to boost its image in the beauty products industry.

Operations

Coty divides its activities among four product segments: Fragrances; Brazil acquisition; Color Cosmetics; and Skin and Body Care. Fragrances are its main revenue engine and traditionally deliver 46% of all sales. Across the segments Coty identifies "power brands;" its top 10 brands are leading sellers and have the strongest potential for further growth thanks to their presence in all major distribution channels in both prestige and mass markets. The vast remaining portfolio is recognized as "beauty brands" or mass-market products positioned to retain a mainstream following.

Coty manufactures about two-thirds of its scents and other beauty products at eight facilities dotting China France Monaco Spain the UK and the US (Sanford North Carolina). About 30% of Coty's products are made to specification by third parties.

The Brazil Acquisition segment represents revenues and expenses generated from multiple product groupings such as skin care nail care deodorants and hair care products which are principally sold within Brazil.

Geographic Reach

The US accounts for 29% of Coty's sales. Europe the Middle East and Africa accounts for 50% of sales while the Asia-Pacific Region contributes about 12%. The New York-based company has five R&D facilities in the US (California New Jersey) Europe (Switzerland Monaco) and China. It also has eight manufacturing plants in the US UK China France and Spain.

The company has offices in more than 35 countries and markets sells and distributes products in more than 130 countries and territories.

Sales and Marketing

Coty's products are sold in retail stores and through travel retail sales channels including duty-free shops airlines cruise ships and other tax-free zones. It also sells products online door-to-door in some markets and via TV shopping channels such as QVC. The company's advertising and promotional costs for fiscal 2016 2015 and 2014 was $1.3 billion $1.4 billion and $1.5 billion respectively.

Recent ad campaigns have included Kate Moss Georgia May Jagger and Rita Ora for Rimmel Gwen Stefani for OPI Christy Turlington and Ed Burns for Calvin Klein Eternity and a TV spot for Marc Jacobs Daisy Dream directed by long-time Marc Jacobs muse Sofia Coppola.

Financial Performance

Coty has seen its net sales decline since 2014. In fiscal 2016 (ended June) net sales decreased by $46 million compared to 2015. The primary reason was due to decreased sales from its Fragrances segment. The Skin and Body care segment also contributed to the decrease.

The decline in Fragrance segment net revenues reflected negative foreign currency exchange translations and a decrease in unit volume. It also reflected lower net revenues from celebrity and lifestyle brands in the mass retail channel in part due to brands that are later in their lifecycles and Coty's continued efforts to execute portfolio rationalization on lower-volume product lines in non-strategic distribution channels.

The Skin and Body care segment's net revenues decrease was the result of a negative foreign currency exchange translations a decrease in unit volume and a negative price and mix impact. The discontinuation of TJoy and China Optimization also had a negative impact on net revenues as the result of unit decline.

In fiscal 2016 Coty's net income decreased by $80 million due to increased acquisition-related costs and lower sales. That year the company incurred $197.5 million of costs related to acquisition activities including $174 million primarily in connection with the acquisition of P&G Beauty Brands and $20.3 million of costs related to the Brazil and Bourjois acquisitions.

Net cash provided by the operating activities decreased by $25 million compared to 2015.

Strategy

The Coty 2020 strategic plan includes developing its power brands with a strong focus on superior innovation and increased investment in brand support; strengthening the company's global positions in fragrances and color cosmetics and expanding its presence in skin and body care through organic growth and acquisitions; expanding in emerging markets; leveraging its multichannel distribution capabilities; and gaining organizational efficiency and simplification through a global efficiency plan.

With soft sales in the developed world Coty is looking to expand distribution in developing markets including Brazil China India and Thailand. In 2014 the company entered into an agreement in which Li & Fung will distribute some of Coty's power brands in China including adidas Rimmel and Playboy. Coty and Avon Products also signed a deal that year by which select Coty fragrances will be marketed and sold through Avon Brazil's network of 1.5 million independent sales Representatives.

It is looks to joint ventures including those with Piaggio Group in 2014 Frajo Internacional in 2013 and LG Household & Health Care in 2012.

Strategically Coty has made the most of a number of licensing agreements. It holds a pact with the Italian design house Bottega Veneta owned by Kering. Other high-profile agreements include fragrance partnerships with Beyonc © Jennifer Lopez and Lady Gaga. Brand names in Coty's prestige portfolio include Chopard Davidoff Jil Sander and Vera Wang to name just a few.

The company is known for back-to-back revisions to its growth strategy while rallying as "the new emerging leader in beauty." Coty is focused on making over its global power brand lineup through product innovation and diversification acquisitions and licensing agreements with high-dollar names.

Mergers and Acquisitions

In early 2017 Coty agreed to acquire 60% of privately held Younique LLC for $600 million in order to reduce dependence on Coty's ailing fragrance business.

In 2016 the company acquired Procter & Gamble Company's Specialty Beauty Business including the COVERGIRL and Max Factor cosmetics brands and the Hugo Boss and Gucci fragrance brands. The deal valued at a hefty $11.4 billion bolstered Coty's market presence as a beauty products company ranking it third behind LOr ©al and Unilever. Coty also closed the acquisition ranked #1 in the market in fragrance products and #2 in salon hair products. Coty's geographic presence was also significantly expanded following the deal which boosted its presence in its existing North America Europe Middle East and Asia territories. It also gained greater access to key markets in Japan and Brazil.

That year Coty acquired the personal care and beauty business (The Beauty Business) of Hyper-marcas S.A. for R$3599.5 million providing Coty with a critical mass platform in the Brazilian beauty market. The Beauty Business's leading brands include Monange Risqu © Bozzano Paix o and Bio-color.

In 2015 Coty bought the Bourjois cosmetics brand from Chanel S.A. to strengthen its global position in color cosmetics. Based in France Bourjois operates in more than 50 countries.

That year the company acquired UK based Lena White Ltd. an international distributor of nail care brand OPI Coty's power brands. Lena White Ltd has served as OPI's distributor in the UK for the professional and retail beauty channels. Following the acquisition Coty directly distributes its branded products.

Company Background

The German investment firm Joh. A. Benckiser SE bought Coty from Pfizer in 1992 to steer its fragrance and cosmetics business. In 2013 the company went public. Coty sold 57.1 million shares at $17.50 each to raise about $1 billion in its June 2013 initial public offering. By opening its doors to public ownership the beauty products maker gave its owners which included the billionaire Reimann family through Joh. A. Benckiser (JAB) an opportunity to cash out. Following the IPO JAB and two other Coty owners Berkshire Partners and Rhone Capital control nearly 98% of the company's voting rights. Coty did not receive any proceeds from the offering.

Coty was founded in Paris in 1904 after Fran§ois Coty created his first perfume La Rose Jacqueminot.

EXECUTIVES

President Global Markets, Edgar O. Huber

SVP General Counsel and Secretary, Jules P. Kaufman, age 59, $525,000 total compensation

SVP Global Research and Development and Chief Scientific Officer, Ralph Macchio, age 60

Chairman and Interim CEO, Lambertus J. H. (Bart) Becht, age 60

EVP and CFO, Patrice de Talhouet, age 51, $784,100 total compensation

EVP Supply Chain, Mario Reis, age 57, $609,560 total compensation

EVP Category Development, Camillo Pane, age 47, $592,320 total compensation

Senior Vice President And Corporate Controller, James Shiah

Vice President Public Relations, Anne Nugent

Vice President Customer Information technology And, Robert Kelly

Vice President, Gary Gallant

Vice President of Advertising, Cat Eckart

Vice President Marketing, Lori Singer

Vice President Information Services, Erik Dewit

Vice President Finance, Joseph Tomasso

Global Vice President Information Management, Joan Luzzi

Vice President Global Public Relations, Patricia White

Vice President Research, William Wohland

Vice President External Operations Purchasing Manufacturing, Paul Buchbauer

National Account Manager, Sarah Rack

Vice President Corporate Finance, Leah Zaslavsky

Senior Vice President and Global CIO, Jerry Flasz

Senior Vice President American Fragrances Coty Prestige, Catherine Walsh

Vice President Marketing, Trent Hurst

Vice President Global Marketing (Coty Presitige Skincare), Rachel Shelowitz

Vice President Field Sales, Bob Ford

Vice President Corporate Finance, Jerome Estampes

Vice President packaging concept Development, Bernard Quennessen

Vice President Marketing, Laura Weinstein

Vice President Sales, David Russell
Vice President Sales National Accounts, Mary Van-
praag
Senior Vice President Human Resources,
Gtraudmarie Lacassagne
Vice President Marketing, Barry Miller
Vice President Infrastructure Services, Glen
Dalgleish
Senior Vice President Global Supply Chain, Franco
Valenti
Vice President Global Information Technology,
Natalie Stone
Vice President Global Information Technology,
Natalie Elgart
VP Supply Chain, German Alonso
Vice President Sales, Judi Bene
Senior Vice President of Business Development,
Bryan Falcone
Vice President and General Manager, Pat Bourque
Global Vice President Influencer Marketing
(Consumer Beauty), Laura Brinker
ADMIN TO SENIOR VICE PRESIDENT CHIEF
INFORMATION OFFICER, Nadia Pinyate
Vice President Creative and Design Excellence,
Joseph Salah
Advisory Board Member, Kert Layton
Auditors: Deloitte & Touche LLP

LOCATIONS

HQ: Coty, Inc.
350 Fifth Avenue, New York, NY 10118
Phone: 212 389-7300
Web: www.coty.com

2016 Sales

	% of total
Europe the Middle East & Africa	50
Americas	38
Asia Pacific	12
Total	**100**

PRODUCTS/OPERATIONS

2016 Sales

	% of total
Fragrances	46
Color Cosmetics	36
Skin & Body Care	16
Brazil Acquisition	2
Total	**100**

Selected Brands by Segment

Color Cosmetics
 Astor
 CK One Color
 Manhattan
 Miss Sporty
 N.Y.C. New York Color
 Nicole by OPI
 OPI
 Rimmel
 Sally Hanson
Fragrances
 adidas
 Balenciaga
 Beyoncé;
 Bottega Veneta
 Calvin Klein
 Cerruti
 Chloé;
 Chopard
 David and Victoria Beckham
 Davidoff (Cool Water)
 Elite Models
 Esprit
 Faith Hill
 Guess?
 Halle Berry
 Heidi Klum
 Jennifer Lopez
 Jil Sander
 JOOP!
 Jovan
 Kate Moss

 Kylie Minogue
 Lady Gaga Fame
 Lancaster
 Madonna
 Marc Jacobs
 Nautica
 Nikos
 philosophy
 Pierre Cardin
 Playboy
 Roberto Cavalli
 Sarah Jessica Parker
 Stetson
 Tim McGraw
 Tonino Lamborghini
 Vera Wang
 Vivienne Westwood
Power brands (cosmetics fragrances and skin and
 bodycare)
 adidas
 Calvin Klein
 Chloé;
 Davidoff (Cool Water)
 Marc Jacobs
 OPI
 philosophy
 Playboy
 Rimmel
 Sally Hansen
Skin and Body Care
 adidas
 Lancaster
 philosopy
 TJoy

COMPETITORS

Avon	L Brands
Body Shop	L'Oreal
Bonne Bell	LVMH
CCA Industries	Markwins International
Chanel	Mary Kay
Creative Nail Design	Nu Skin
Dana Classic	Orly International
Fragrances	Parlux Fragrances
Elizabeth Arden Inc	Procter & Gamble
Este Lauder	Revlon
Forsythe Cosmetic	Star Nail
Group Ltd.	The Dial Corporation
Inter Parfums	The Gap

HISTORICAL FINANCIALS

Company Type: Public

Income Statement

FYE: June 30

	REVENUE ($ mil.)	NET INCOME ($ mil.)	NET PROFIT MARGIN	EMPLOYEES
06/17	7,650	(422)	—	22,000
06/16	4,349	156	3.6%	10,060
06/15	4,395	232	5.3%	8,100
06/14	4,551	(97)	—	9,000
06/13	4,649	168	3.6%	10,000
Annual Growth	13.3%	—	—	21.8%

2017 Year-End Financials

Debt ratio: 31.65%
Return on equity: (-8.73%)
Cash ($ mil.): 535
Current ratio: 0.94
Long-term debt ($ mil.): 6,928
No. of shares (mil.): 747
Dividends
 Yield: 3.4%
 Payout: —
Market value ($ mil.): 14,031

	STOCK PRICE ($) FY Close	P/E High/Low		PER SHARE ($) Earnings	Dividends	Book Value
06/17	18.76	—	—	(0.66)	0.65	12.45
06/16	25.99	73	48	0.44	0.25	1.07
06/15	31.97	49	24	0.64	0.20	2.69
06/14	17.13	—	—	(0.26)	0.20	2.38
06/13	17.18	40	38	0.42	0.15	3.89
Annual Growth	2.2%	—	—	—	44.3%	33.7%

Crown Holdings Inc

Crown Holdings is a leading global manufacturer of consumer packaging products including
steel and aluminum food and beverage cans. Its
portfolio includes aerosol cans and various metal
vacuum closures marketed under brands Liftoff
SuperEnd and Easylift as well as specialty packaging products such as novelty containers and industrial cans. Crown also supplies can-making
equipment and parts. Its roster of customers has
included Coca-Cola SC Johnson Unilever and Procter & Gamble which owns Gillette another cus-
tomer.Crown traces its historical roots all the way
back to 1892.
 Operations
 Crown is focused on growing on a global scale
and has divided its business along geographic
lines. The company?s reportable segments are
Americas Beverage North America Food European
Beverage European Food and Asia Pacific. Its segments make steel and aluminum food/ beverage
cans and ends glass bottles steel crowns and metal
vacuum closures.
 Geographic Reach
 Crown operates roughly 150 plants in 35 countries with about 75% of net sales coming from
outside the US.
 Crown's US headquarters is stationed in
Philadelphia while its European headquarters is in
Baar Switzerland. In addition its Asia/Pacific headquarters resides in Singapore and it has additional
research facilities in Alsip Illinois; and Wantage
England.
 Sales and Marketing
 Crown markets and sells products to customers
through its own sales and marketing staffs. In
some instances contracts with customers are centrally negotiated but products are ordered through
and distributed directly by its local facilities. Its top
10 global customers collectively represent more
than 30% of its overall revenue.
 Financial Performance
 Crown's revenues have decreased the last two
years dipping 4% from $8.8 billion in 2015 to $8.3
billion in 2016. The decline was attributed to unfavorable foreign currency translations and the
pass-through of lower material costs. This was partially offset by a 6% increase in sales unit volumes
from its Americas Beverage segment.
 From 2015 to 2016 Crown's net income increased 26% from $393 million to $496 million
mainly due to a reduction in restructuring expenses and a decrease in the cost of products sold.
In addition cash provided by operating activities
decreased from $956 million in 2015 to $930 million in 2016 primarily due to a spike in pension
contributions premiums paid to retire debt and
lower contributions from working capital changes.
 Strategy
 Crown grows its businesses in specific international growth markets while improving its operations and results in more mature markets through
disciplined pricing and improvements in manufacturing and productivity. However with international
expansion Crown like its rivals risks exposure to
unfavorable foreign-currency exchange rates of
the euro pound sterling and Canadian dollar as
well as cyclical consumer spending on food and
beverages. Its net sales are also impacted by the
rise or decrease in the cost of aluminum and steel
which is passed on to customers.
 However the company believes that technological innovation will help mitigate for usual risks
and cycles. Not content with making containers
the same old way Crown Holdings operates research development and engineering centers in

the US and the UK. Its mission is to design cost-efficient manufacturing processes reduce material content while maintaining freshness and develop new products with the application of new technologies.

Crown is specifically targeting Asia/Pacific as a region ripe with growth opportunities. In 2016 Crown opened a third new plant in Cambodia. It also plans to open two new can facilities in Indonesia and Vietnam in 2017 and a new beverage can plant in Myanmar in 2018 to support further growth in the region.

Mergers and Acquisitions

Crown has been earning additional revenue in key markets through the use of acquisitions. In early 2015 Crown acquired EMPAQUE a leading Mexican manufacturer of aluminum cans and ends bottle caps and glass bottles for the beverage industry. Crown purchased EMPAQUE from Heineken N.V. in a cash transaction valued at $1.23 billion. The acquisition enhanced Crown's strategic position in beverage cans both regionally and globally. As a result of the deal Crown is now one of the largest beverage can producers in North America supplying over 24 billion units annually to a balanced portfolio of beer and soft drink customers.

HISTORY

Formed as Crown Cork & Seal Co. (CC&S) of Baltimore in 1892 the company was consolidated into its present form in 1927 when it merged with New Process Cork and New York Patents. The next year CC&S expanded overseas and formed Crown Cork International. In 1936 CC&S acquired Acme Can and benefited from the movement at the time from home canning to processed canning. A decade later the company launched its new product in 1946 — the first aerosol can.

EXECUTIVES

President CEO and Director, Timothy J. Donahue, age 55, $915,000 total compensation
SVP and CFO, Thomas A. Kelly, age 58, $575,000 total compensation
EVP Corporate Technology and Regulatory Affairs and President Crown Packaging Technology, Daniel A. Abramowicz
EVP and COO, Gerard H (Jerry) Gifford, age 62, $600,000 total compensation
President Crown Aerosol Packaging North America, C. Anderson (Andy) Bolton
President Crown Food Packaging North America Crown Closures and Specialty Packaging, James D. (Jim) Wilson
President Americas Division, Djalma Novaes, age 56, $510,000 total compensation
President CROWN Beverage Packaging South America, Wilmar Arinelli
President CROWN Beverage Packaging Mexico, Abel Coello Quintanilla
President CROWN Beverage Packaging North America, Timothy J. (Tim) Lorge
SVP Crown Beverage Packaging China and Hong Kong, Robert H. Bourque, age 47, $302,413 total compensation
SVP Food Europe, Didier Sourisseau, age 51
Vice President Sales, Tom Gordon
Vice President, Randall Chaffins
Vice President, Kevin Clothier
Senior Vice President Finance, Edward Bisno
Vice President Steel Sourcing, Daniel Shackell
Vice President Sourcing, Richard Nunn
Vice President, David A Beaver
Vice President Corporate Risk Management, Christopher A Blaine
Regional Vice President Sales, Michelle Hinton
Vice President Corporate Tax, Joseph Pearce

Vice President Sales, Ralph Menichini
Vice President Logistics, Johnathan Gahan
Executive Vice President, Ronald Thoma
Vice President Of Environment Health and Safety
Vice President, Robert Vatistas
Senior Vice President and General Counsel, William Gallagher
Vice President Sales and Marketing, Dahlgren Brad
Vice President Corporate Affairs and Public Relations, Michael F Dunleavy
Vice President Sales North America Aerosol Division, Bradley Dahlgren
Vice President Finance, Tom Bryant
Vice President Supply Chain Management, Debbie Fortnum
Vice President Interactive Marketing, Tom Fisher
Vice President Business Process Improvement, Andy Navarro
Chairman, John W. Conway, age 71
Auditors: PricewaterhouseCoopers LLP

LOCATIONS

HQ: Crown Holdings Inc
One Crown Way, Philadelphia, PA 19154-4599
Phone: 215 698-5100
Web: www.crowncork.com

2016 Sales

	$ mil.	% of total
US	1,918	23
Mexico	688	8
Spain	645	8
UK	559	7
Other regions	4,474	54
Total	**8,284**	**100**

PRODUCTS/OPERATIONS

2016 Sales

	$ mil.	% of total
Metal beverage cans & ends	4,834	58
Metal food cans & ends	2,213	27
Other metal packaging	877	11
Other products	360	4
Total	**8,284**	**100**

2016 Sales by Segment

	$ mil.	% of total
Americas beverage	2,757	33
European food	1,855	23
European beverage	1,420	17
Asia Pacific	1,116	13
North America food	652	8
Non-reportable segments	484	6
Total	**8,284**	**100**

Selected Products

Metal packaging
  Aerosol cans
  Beverage cans
  Closures and caps
  Crowns
  Ends
  Food cans
Plastics packaging
Other products
  Can making equipment and spares

Selected Markets

Food and beverage
Health and beauty
Household / Industrial
Luxury Goods
Promotional

COMPETITORS

Amcor	Metal Container
AptarGroup	Corporation
Arconic	Owens-Illinois
Ardagh Group	Silgan
BWAY	Sonoco Products
Ball Corp.	Tetra Laval
Berry Global	

HISTORICAL FINANCIALS

Company Type: Public

Income Statement

FYE: December 31

	REVENUE ($ mil.)	NET INCOME ($ mil.)	NET PROFIT MARGIN	EMPLOYEES
12/16	8,284	496	6.0%	24,000
12/15	8,762	393	4.5%	24,000
12/14	9,097	387	4.3%	23,000
12/13	8,656	324	3.7%	21,300
12/12	8,470	557	6.6%	21,900
Annual Growth	**(0.6%)**	**(2.9%)**	**—**	**2.3%**

2016 Year-End Financials

Debt ratio: 51.16%
Return on equity: 193.98%
Cash ($ mil.): 559
Current ratio: 0.98
Long-term debt ($ mil.): 4,717

No. of shares (mil.): 139
Dividends
  Yield: —
  Payout: —
Market value ($ mil.): 7,351

	STOCK PRICE ($) FY Close	P/E High/Low		PER SHARE ($) Earnings	Dividends	Book Value
12/16	52.57	16	12	3.56	0.00	2.62
12/15	50.70	20	16	2.82	0.00	1.03
12/14	50.90	19	14	2.79	0.00	0.86
12/13	44.57	19	16	2.30	0.00	0.03
12/12	36.81	10	9	3.75	0.00	(1.13)
Annual Growth	**9.3%**	—	—	**(1.3%)**	—	—

CSRA Inc

Auditors: Deloitte & Touche LLP

LOCATIONS

HQ: CSRA Inc
3170 Fairview Park Drive, Falls Church, VA 22042
Phone: 703 641 2000
Web: www.csra.com

HISTORICAL FINANCIALS

Company Type: Public

Income Statement

FYE: March 31

	REVENUE ($ mil.)	NET INCOME ($ mil.)	NET PROFIT MARGIN	EMPLOYEES
03/17*	4,993	304	6.1%	18,500
04/16	4,250	87	2.1%	18,000
04/15	4,069	251	6.2%	14,000
03/14	4,102	296	7.2%	—
03/13	4,675	280	6.0%	—
Annual Growth	**1.7%**	**2.0%**	**—**	**—**

*Fiscal year change

2017 Year-End Financials

Debt ratio: 57.26%
Return on equity: 154.52%
Cash ($ mil.): 126
Current ratio: 1.01
Long-term debt ($ mil.): 2,683

No. of shares (mil.): 163
Dividends
  Yield: 1.3%
  Payout: 21.7%
Market value ($ mil.): 4,781

	STOCK PRICE ($) FY Close	P/E High/Low		PER SHARE ($) Earnings	Dividends	Book Value
03/17*	29.29	18	12	1.84	0.40	2.02
04/16	27.27	61	41	0.53	0.20	0.40
Annual Growth	**1.8%**	—	—	**36.5%**	**18.9%**	**50.3%**

*Fiscal year change

CSX Corp

Through its main subsidiary CSX Transportation (CSXT) CSX Corporation operates a major rail system of some 21000 route miles in the eastern US. The freight carrier links 23 states 70 ports 240 short-line railroads the District of Columbia and two Canadian provinces (Ontario and Quebec). Freight hauled by the company includes a wide variety of merchandise (food chemicals and consumer goods) coal and automotive products. CSX also transports via intermodal containers and trailers (Intermodal freight hauling uses multiple modes of transportation). CSX's rail segment also includes units that operate motor vehicle distribution centers and bulk cargo terminals.

Operations

CSX's transportation services operate through three lines of businesses: merchandise (its largest segment by revenue) coal and intermodal. The company's subsidiary CSX Real Property handles real estate sales leasing acquisition and management and development activities. CSX Intermodal Terminals provides intermodal terminal and trucking services though more than 50 terminals across the eastern US.

CSXT operates with a fleet of more than 4400 locomotives (98% are owned by CSXT) and around 83300 railcars (gondolas hoppers and box/flat cars). Other CSX holdings include Total Distribution Services a storage and distribution company for the automotive industry; Transflo Terminal Services a logistics company for transferring shipments from rail to truck; and CSX Technology which provides IT services to its parent company.

Geographic Reach

CSX operates in two dozen states primarily in the Eastern US and along the Eastern Seaboard. It also operates in Washington DC and the two Canadian provinces of Ontario and Quebec. The company has representative offices in strategic parts of the world including Mexico City Monterrey Buenos Aires Sao Paolo Rio de Janeiro and Munich.

Sales and Marketing

CSX operates sales representative offices in strategic parts of the world including Mexico City Monterrey Buenos Aires Sao Paolo Rio de Janeiro and Munich. Noteworthy customers include Ascend Performance Materials Aux Sable Liquid Products Cargill Dow Corning MarkWest Hydrocarbon SABIC Americas and United Refining.

Financial Performance

CSX has posted revenue declines the last two years with revenues falling 6% to $11.1 billion in 2016. Profits also fell 15% to $1.71 billion in 2016. In addition its operating cash flow decreased from $3.37 billion in 2015 to $3.04 billion in 2016 mainly due to contributions it made to pension plans for the year.

The revenue decline for 2016 was primarily due to slumping fuel surcharges as a result of the ongoing steep decline in oil prices. For several years in a row CSX experienced a decline in coal business revenue as a result of mild weather high stockpiles and low natural gas prices favoring natural gas power generation. In addition its merchandise revenue in 2016 dipped due to lower volumes of agricultural industrial and forest products shipped.

Strategy

Citing fuel prices and environmental efficiency CSX hopes to persuade more shippers to shift freight from trucks to trains especially for cross-country journeys. It has invested almost $400 million and is working with several states and the federal government to outfit tunnels bridges and overpasses to accommodate the taller railcars.

To combat years of sagging coal volumes negatively affecting its balance sheet CSX in 2016 introduced a new operating plan that will restructure how the railroad manages its trains and resources. Its "CSX of Tomorrow? plan will realign its network to de-emphasize coal traffic and optimize the volume-growth potential of the more promising intermodal sector and solid merchandise segment. It will also deploy more high tech equipment and information systems to establish a highly automated and more modernized railroad.

HISTORY

CSX Corporation was formed in 1980 when Chessie System and Seaboard Coast Line (SCL) merged in an effort to improve the efficiency of their railroads. Chessie's oldest railroad the Baltimore & Ohio (B&O) was chartered in 1827 to help Baltimore compete against New York and Philadelphia for freight traffic. By the late 1800s the railroad served Chicago Cincinnati New York City St. Louis and Washington DC. Chesapeake & Ohio (C&O) acquired it in 1962.

C&O originated in Virginia with the Louisa Railroad in 1836. It gained access to Chicago Cincinnati and Washington DC and by the mid-1900s was a major coal carrier. After B&O and C&O acquired joint control of Baltimore-based Western Maryland Railway (1967) the three railroads became subsidiaries of newly formed Chessie System (1973).

One of SCL's two predecessors Seaboard Air Line Railroad (SAL) grew out of Virginia's Portsmouth & Roanoke Rail Road of 1832. SCL's other predecessor Atlantic Coast Line Railroad (ACL) took shape between 1869 and 1893 as William Walters acquired several southern railroads. In 1902 ACL bought the Plant System (railroads in Georgia Florida and other southern states) and the Louisville & Nashville (a north-south line connecting New Orleans and Chicago) giving ACL the basic form it was to retain until 1967 when it merged with SAL to form SCL.

EXECUTIVES

President CEO and Director, James M. Foote
EVP and CFO, Frank A. Lonegro, age 48, $500,000 total compensation
SVP and CIO, Kathleen Brandt
VP and Chief Transportation Officer, Mike Pendergrass
President CSX Real Property Inc., Shantel Davis
EVP Chief Legal Officer and Corporate Secretary, Nathan D. Goldman
EVP Corporate Affairs and Chief of Staff, Mark K. Wallace
Vice President Network Operations, Steve Potter
Vice President Sales and Marketing, Derrick Smith
Resident Vice President, Brian Hammock
Assistant Vice President Network, Mark Hinsdale
Assistant Vice President, Sean Craig
Assistant Vice President Load Engineering, Mitch Hobbs
Assistant Vice President Procurement and Supply Chain, Tom Holmes
Vice President Legal Affairs, Peter Shudtz
Assistant Vice President Finance, Erik Palm
Regional Vice President, Bryan Rhode
Executive Vice President Information Services, Wendy Hausler
Assistant Vice President Talent Management, Terri Baumgardner
Assistant Vice President Advanced Engineering, Timothy Male
Vice President And Chief Transportation Officer Csx Transportation, Cindy Sandborn
Vice President Network Operations, Cary Helton
Assistant Vice President Passenger Operations, Dave Dech
Assistant Vice President Network Operations Locomotive Management, Peter Burrus
Vice PresidentHuman Resources, Alison Brown
Assistant Vice President, Mark Holder
Assistant Vice President Corporate Real Estate, Emerson Lotzia
Assistant Vice President Intermodal Marketing, Ryan D Houfek
Chairman, Edward J. (Ned) Kelly, age 64
Auditors: Ernst & Young LLP

LOCATIONS

HQ: CSX Corp
500 Water Street, 15th Floor, Jacksonville, FL 32202
Phone: 904 359-3200
Web: www.csx.com

PRODUCTS/OPERATIONS

2016 Sales

	% of total
Merchandise	64
Coal	17
Intermodal	16
Other	3
Total	**100**

Selected Services

Commodities
Industrial Development
Intermodal
International
Load Engineering and Design Services
Product Transloading and Distribution
Property Services
Property/Real Estate
Specialized Rail Training

COMPETITORS

APL Logistics	Hub Group
Burlington Northern Santa Fe	J.B. Hunt
	Norfolk Southern
Canadian National Railway	Schneider National
Canadian Pacific Railway	Union Pacific
	Washington Companies

HISTORICAL FINANCIALS

Company Type: Public

Income Statement

FYE: December 31

	REVENUE ($ mil.)	NET INCOME ($ mil.)	NET PROFIT MARGIN	EMPLOYEES
12/17	11,408	5,471	48.0%	24,000
12/16	11,069	1,714	15.5%	27,000
12/15	11,811	1,968	16.7%	29,000
12/14	12,669	1,927	15.2%	31,511
12/13	12,026	1,864	15.5%	31,254
Annual Growth	(1.3%)	30.9%	—	(6.4%)

2017 Year-End Financials

Debt ratio: 33.04%	No. of shares (mil.): 889
Return on equity: 41.36%	Dividends
Cash ($ mil.): 401	Yield: 0.0%
Current ratio: 1.01	Payout: 13.0%
Long-term debt ($ mil.): 11,790	Market value ($ mil.): 48,951

	STOCK PRICE ($) FY Close	P/E High/Low	PER SHARE ($) Earnings	Dividends	Book Value
12/17	55.01	10 6	5.99	0.78	16.53
12/16	35.93	21 12	1.81	0.72	12.58
12/15	26.13	19 12	2.00	0.70	12.07
12/14	36.68	20 13	1.92	0.63	11.25
12/13	28.29	16 11	1.83	0.59	10.39
Annual Growth	18.1%	— —	34.5%	7.2%	12.3%

Cullen/Frost Bankers, Inc.

One of the largest independent bank holding companies in Texas Cullen/Frost Bankers owns Frost Bank and other financial subsidiaries through a second-tier holding company The New Galveston Company. The community-oriented bank serves individuals and local businesses as well as clients in neighboring parts of Mexico through 120-plus branches in Texas metropolitan areas. It offers commercial and consumer deposit products and loans trust and investment management services mutual funds insurance brokerage and leasing. Subsidiaries include Frost Insurance Agency Frost Brokerage Services Frost Investment Advisors and investment banking arm Frost Securities. Cullen/Frost has total assets of $26.5 billion.

Geographic Reach

San Antonio-based Cullen/Frost Bankers has branches throughout Texas including the Austin Corpus Christi Dallas Fort Worth Houston Permian Basin the Rio Grande Valley and San Antonio regions.

Financial Performance

Cullen/Frost reported revenue of $945.3 million in 2013 an increase of 3% versus 2012 on increased interest income on loans and deposits and an increase in trust and investment management fees. Net income was $237.9 a flat comparison with the prior year. 2013 marked the third consecutive year of rising revenue following a dip in 2010. The bank's fortunes are rising along with the thriving energy and technology sectors in Texas.

Strategy

Cullen/Frost has built its insurance business through acquisitions in recent years; since 2009 it has bought agencies in Dallas Houston San Antonio and San Marcos that provide group employee benefit plans. The company continues to seek out acquisition opportunities while it also looks for ways to expand and diversify within its existing markets. To reduce its reliance on interest rate spreads Cullen/Frost wants to grow its income from fees such as insurance commissions trust investment fees and service charges on deposit accounts.

Mergers and Acquisitions

In June 2014 Frost Bank acquired Odessa Texas-based Western National Bank (WNB) increasing its presence in the oil-rich Permian Basin Midland and Odessa markets in West Texas. Seven of WNB's eight branches were converted to the Frost name (an office in San Antonio was closed) increasing the number of Frost branches statewide to more than 120. The acquisition of WNB added $1.8 billion in assets $1.6 billion in deposits and $668 million in total loans to Cullen/Frost. The purchase of WNB was the first time in nearly seven years that Frost acquired another bank.

EXECUTIVES

Group Vice President, Robert Berman
Chairman and CEO, Phillip D. Green, age 62, $565,000 total compensation
President Frost Bank; EVP Frost Wealth Advisors, Patrick B. (Pat) Frost, age 57, $485,000 total compensation
President, Paul H. Bracher, age 60, $500,000 total compensation
EVP and CFO, Jerry Salinas, $400,000 total compensation
Vice President of Marketing, Bobby Jacob
Executive Vice President Information Technology Division, Carl Bush
Executive Vice President, Cindy Ramirez
Senior Vice President It, Harvey Gutierrez
Executive Vice President Marketing Research, Mary Beach
Senior Vice President Director Of Investor Relatio, Greg Parker
Vice President of Finance, Vicki Ball
Vice President Community Development, Betty Davis
Assistan Vice President, Maralessa Gonzales
Vice President Sales, Jeffrey Tarr
Senior Vice President Treasury Management, Darlene Selsor
Executive Vice President, John Robb
Executive Vice President, David Perdue
Vice President of Operation, Cliff McCauley
Vice President, Gregory Dreier
Senior Vice President, Dan Taaffe
Vice President, Oscar Molina
Senior Vice President, Cliff Perez
Vice President, Cathy Garison
Vice President, Jonathan Pursch
Senior Vice President, Casey Maxfield
Vice President Corporate Communications, Sheri Rosen
Vice President Of Finance, Mike Benson
Senior Vice President, Charles Plummer
Vice President, Matt Bryant
Senior Vice President, Jill Stacy
Vice President Sales, Talal Tay
Vice President of Marketing, Wendy Erickson
Vice President of Finance, Wayne Baker
Vice President Marketing, Ericka Pullin
Senior Executive Vice President, Michael S Cain
Vice President, James Valdez
Vice President, Scott Tellkamp
Senior Vice President, John Harris
Senior Vice President, David Seitze
Senior Vice President Capital Markets, Mark Brell
Senior Vice President, Roger Lind
Senior Vice President, Gene Witter
Vice President, Clay Jones
Vice President Private Banking Officer, Beverly Hankinson
Senior Vice President, Diane Madalin
Senior Vice President Project Manager, Terrie Ramirez
Senior Vice President, Leigh Olejer
Senior Vice President, Michael Nutter
Senior Vice President, Ronnie Miksch
Vice President, Todd Weber
Senior Vice President, Mike Davis
Senior Vice President and Senior Cra O, Donna Normandin
Senior Vice President, Carl A Mclaughlin
Vice President, Maro Rodriguez
Vice President, Susan Carruthers
Vice President Internal Audit, Natalie McCabe
Regional Vice President, Lorraine Neff
Vice President, Olga Harrison
Senior Executive Vice President Operations And Processing, Gary Mcknight

Assistant Vice President, Austin Burns
Assistant Vice President, Hope S Molina
Vice President, Larry Inman
Vice President, Matt Badders
Senior Vice President Institutional Trust Administration, Steven A Klein
Assistant Vice President, Sarah Agnich
Senior Vice President, Letty Dominguez
Senior Vice President Community Leader, Jeff Fuller
Vice President, Yolanda Maness
Vice President Technology Infrastructure, Robert Jacobs
Senior Vice President Wealth Advisor Private Trust, John Sands
Vice President Mineral Asset Management Frost Banking Investments, Robert Turnbull
Vice President of Marketing, Daryl Hoffmann
Senior Vice President Business Development, Linda Baker
Executive Vice President, Sue Turnage
Senior Vice President Workout Officer, Jennifer Crabtree
Community Leader And Assistant Vice President, Travis Buchanan
Senior Vice President of Investment Division, Jeanne Glorioso
Assistant Vice President of Network Engineering, Danny Leal
Senior Vice President, Michael Williams
Senior Vice President Application Support, Jeff Sanders
Assistant Vice President, Elsie Boone
Senior Vice President Investme, Linnie Phebus
Executive Vice President Marketing, Debbie Danmeter
Vice President, Ben Kavanagh
Senior Vice President Deposit Service, Gloria Navarro
Vice President, Omar Quintanilla
Vice President Sales, Anthony Vallejo
Senior Vice President, Carol Lampier
Assistant Vice President, Beth Pence
Senior Vice President, Gina Prill
Vice President Private Banking, Brannon Kroll
Assistant Vice President, Rene Ramirez
Senior Vice President, Melissa Adams
Executive Vice President Information Technology Division, Carl Pachalska
Vice President And Relationship Manager, Paul R Haney
Vice President Energy Finance, Alex Zemkoski
Vice President Public Finance, Duncan Morrow
Senior Vice President Special Assets, Betsy Gleiser
Regional President, Paul C Koch
Vice President, Zada Cisneros
Executive Vice President, Roderick Washington
Vice President Finance, Charles Stockton
Senior Vice President Compliance, Verna Fletcher
Vice President, Stephen Spears
Senior Vice President Of Private Trust Services, Debbie Eippert
Vice President Commercial Middle Market Banking, Colin Jones
Senior Vice President, Mark Ritter
Vice President, Chris Brower
Assistant Vice President, J Rosow Jaroszewski
Executive Vice President Retail Loans, Genny Rakowitz
Vice President, Ben Brandenburg
Assistant Vice President, Patricio Perez
Assistant Vice President Commercial Banking, Jennifer Grimes
Assistant Vice President, Yolanda Gonzales
Senior Vice President, Daniel O'Connor
Vice President of Finance, Michael Aubuchon
Assistant Vice President Financial Center Manager, David Newman

246

Senior Vice President Professional and Executive Banking Frost Banking Investments, David Landry
Vice President, Van C Carter
Senior Vice President, Jon Daubert
Vice President, Anna Sanchez
Senior Vice President, Brent Bike
Senior Vice President, Tom McDonnell
Vice President Corporate Banking Frost Banking Investments, Luke Healy
Vice President Equipment Leasing And Finance, Laura Eckhardt
Vice President, Sallie Newman
Vice President Mutual Fund Marketing Liaison, Margaret Velasquez
Assistant Vice President, Justin Steinbach
Assistant Vice President, Samuel Lopez
Senior Vice President, Eduardo Berain
Senior Vice President, Carole Kilpatrick
Assistant Vice President, Karla Riley
Vice President Intl Private Banking, Elvia Daley
Assistant Vice President, Trey McCord
Senior Vice President, Anthony White
Senior Vice President Trust Internal Audit, Deanna Rankin
Vice President, Lou Kissling
Executive Vice President, Tom Stringfellow
Vice President In Human Resources Department, Janet Lane
Vice President, Albert Shannon
Senior Vice President Technology, Ray Zapata
Vice President, Susie Smith
Executive Vice President And General Counsel, Stanley McCormick
Executive Vice President, Chas Mella
Senior Vice President, Sue Frye
Executive Vice President, Jerry Yost
Vice President, John Lack
Senior Vice President, Kaye Carpenter
Vice President, Denise Stroud
Vice President, Gloria Kopycinski
Auditors: Ernst & Young LLP

LOCATIONS

HQ: Cullen/Frost Bankers, Inc.
100 W. Houston Street, San Antonio, TX 78205
Phone: 210 220-4011   Fax: 210 220-5578
Web: www.frostbank.com

PRODUCTS/OPERATIONS

2016 Sales

	% of total
Interest	
Loans including fees	40
Securities	28
Interest-bearing deposits	1
Federal funds sold and resell agreements	-
Non-interest	
Trust and investment management fees	9
Service charges on deposit accounts	7
Insurance commissions & fees	4
Interchange and debit card transaction fees	2
Other charges commissions and fees	4
Net gain (loss) on securities transactions	1
Other	4
Total	100

2016 Sales

	% of total
Banking	88
Frost Wealth Advisors	12
Total	100

Selected Subsidiaries

Carton Service Corporation
Cullen BLP Inc.
Cullen/Frost Capital Trust II
Frost Bank
Frost Brokerage Services Inc.
Frost Insurance Agency Inc.
Frost Investment Advisors Inc.
Main Plaza Corporation
Tri-Frost Corporation

COMPETITORS

BBVA Compass Bancshares	JPMorgan Chase
Bank of America	Lone Star Bank
Broadway Bancshares	PlainsCapital
Capital One	Prosperity Bancshares
Comerica	Texas Capital Bancshares
Extraco	Wells Fargo
First Financial Bankshares	Woodforest Financial
International Bancshares	

HISTORICAL FINANCIALS

Company Type: Public

Income Statement

FYE: December 31

	ASSETS ($ mil.)	NET INCOME ($ mil.)	INCOME AS % OF ASSETS	EMPLOYEES
12/17	31,747	364	1.1%	4,270
12/16	30,196	304	1.0%	4,217
12/15	28,567	279	1.0%	4,211
12/14	28,277	277	1.0%	4,154
12/13	24,312	237	1.0%	3,979
Annual Growth	6.9%	11.2%	—	1.8%

2017 Year-End Financials

Debt ratio: 0.74%
Return on equity: 11.56%
Cash ($ mil.): 4,893
Current ratio: —
Long-term debt ($ mil.): —

No. of shares (mil.): 63
Dividends
  Yield: 0.0%
  Payout: 40.8%
Market value ($ mil.): 6,008

	STOCK PRICE ($) FY Close	P/E High/Low	PER SHARE ($) Earnings	Dividends	Book Value
12/17	94.65	18 15	5.51	2.25	51.95
12/16	88.23	19 9	4.70	2.15	47.30
12/15	60.00	19 14	4.28	2.10	46.63
12/14	70.64	19 16	4.29	2.03	45.15
12/13	74.43	20 14	3.80	1.98	41.51
Annual Growth	6.2%	— —	9.7%	3.2%	5.8%

Cummins, Inc.

Cummins makes diesel and natural gas powered engines for the heavy and mid-duty truck RV automotive and industrial markets along with marine rail mining and construction. In addition to its flagship Engine segment other business segments include Components (filtration products and fuel systems) Power Systems (vehicle and residential generators) and Distribution (product distributors and servicing). Major customers include OEMs Chrysler Daimler Ford Komatsu PACCAR Navistar and Volvo. The company traces its historical roots back to 1919 when it was founded by Clessie Cummins.

Operations

The company's 49 to 5500 horsepower engines are made under the Cummins brand name. The Components segment manufactures products that are complementary to commercial diesel applications; more than 8300 filtration products are offered some branded as Fleetguard. Other products within this segment include turbo technologies for air handling in engines and exhaust after-treatment technology as well as new used and remanufactured fuel systems.

Power Systems' standby power products (alternators transfer switches and controls) serve commercial and consumer needs as well as those of the military. Brands include Onan (generator sets) and Stamford (alternators).

Cummins' Distribution segment comprises a network of more than 600 company owned and independent distributors that serve 190 countries worldwide.

Geographic Reach

Cummins has main domestic operating facilities in Columbus Indiana; Nashville Tennessee; and Washington DC. Key international locations reside in Beijing; Shanghai; Pune India; and Staines and Stanton UK. The US generates about 55% of its total sales.

Sales and Marketing

Cummins serves customers through a network of 600 wholly owned and independent distributor locations and more than 7400 dealer locations spanning more than 190 countries and territories. Major customer PACCAR accounts for almost 15% of the company's net sales.

Financial Performance

Cummins' revenues have declined the last two years dipping 8% from $19.1 billion in 2015 to $17.5 billion in 2016.

Engine segment sales declined 10% due to lower demand within the North American heavy-duty and medium-duty on-highway markets and lower demand in most North American off-highway markets partially offset by a spike in sales in the light-duty automotive market.

Power Systems segment sales also decreased 14% primarily due to lower demand across all product lines and decreased sales in most regions including North America Asia China Latin America the Middle East Africa and Western Europe.

Cummins' profits remained static from 2015 to 2016 hovering around the $1.5 billion mark for both years. This was attributed to lower sales volumes and unfavorable foreign currency fluctuations (primarily from the Brazilian real South African rand and Canadian dollar).

Strategy

The company's fortunes are shaped in large part by the cyclical booms and busts of the on-highway construction and industrial markets. Its customers are particularly sensitive to the general economic climate interest rates and access to credit as well as regulatory issues (environmental and emissions standards) and political shifts.

In an effort to mitigate a slump in demand in any one market or region Cummins is continuing to transform itself from a company concentrated in North America to one whose business is seizing up opportunities in developing countries. Following the US China Brazil Russia and India are Cummins' largest markets.

To increase its market penetration the company also relies on joint ventures that allow it to reduce capital spending streamline its supply chain management and boost its technology development. Some of the partnering companies include Dongfeng Automotive and Beijing Foton Motor in China Tata Motors in India and Japan's Komatsu.

On the technological front Cummins in mid-2017 announced its entrance into the burgeoning electrical vehicle market. It unveiled a Class 7 heavy-duty truck cab that features an advanced 140 kWh battery pack that it will sell to bus operators and commercial truck fleets starting in 2019. Cummins is not building the trucks however but will instead supply the fully integrated battery electronics system and will buy the cells from an unnamed provider. The move signals that Cummins intends to remain a key player in the commercial truck sector even if that business shifts away from its core diesel engine business. It aims to be well-positioned against competition from new players like Tesla Proterra and Nikola Motor Company.

HISTORY

Chauffeur Clessie Cummins believed that Rudolph Diesel's cumbersome and smoky engine could be improved for use in transportation. Borrowing money and work space from his employer — Columbus Indiana banker W. G. Irwin — Cummins founded Cummins Engine in 1919. Irwin invested more than $2.5 million and in the mid-1920s Cummins produced a mobile diesel engine. Truck manufacturers were reluctant to switch from gas to diesel so Cummins used publicity stunts (such as racing in the Indianapolis 500) to advertise his engine.

The company was profitable by 1937 the year Irwin's grandnephew Irwin Miller took over. During WWII the Cummins engine was used in cargo trucks. Sales jumped from $20 million in 1946 to more than $100 million by 1956. That year Cummins started its first overseas plant in Scotland and bought Atlas Crankshafts in 1958. By 1967 it had 50% of the diesel-engine market.

EXECUTIVES

Vice President Global Supply Chain and Manufacturing, Lisa M Yoder
Vice President, Tony Satterthwaite
Vice President High Horsepower Engine Bu, Ed Pence
Vice President PowerCare, Robert Hutchinson
Chairman and CEO, N. Thomas (Tom) Linebarger, age 54, $1,375,000 total compensation
VP and Chief Administrative Officer, Marya M. Rose, age 55, $634,000 total compensation
President and COO, Richard J. (Rich) Freeland, age 60, $848,000 total compensation
VP and President Distribution Business, Livingston L. (Tony) Satterthwaite, age 56, $570,000 total compensation
Group VP China and Russia, Steven M. (Steve) Chapman, age 62
VP and CIO, Sherry A. Aaholm, age 54
Managing Director International India, Anant Talaulicar, age 56, $537,500 total compensation
VP and President Engine Business, Srikanth Padmanabhan, age 53
VP and CFO, Patrick J. (Pat) Ward, age 53, $726,000 total compensation
VP and President Components Group and Business Development, Tracy A. Embree, age 43
VP and President Power Systems, Norbert Nusterer, age 48
VP and CTO, Jennifer Rumsey, age 43
Vice President Chief Manufacturing and Procurement Officer, Ignacio Garcia
Vice President, James Kelly
Quality VPI Analyst Intern, John Wheeler
HHP Vice President Rebuild, Terry Wham
Vice President, Thaddeus Ewald
Vice President And Chief Investment Officer, Richard Harris
Lead Vpi Sqie, Larry Frasier
Vice President Research and Technology, Wayne Eckerle
Vice President Information Technology, Joe D Mills
Vice President Engine Business, Seth Erdman
Vpi Sourcing Manager Engine Business Glo, Kurt Metzloff
Vice President Sales, Barry Kreuzer
Vice President mining Market, Kevin Spiller
VPI Sourcing Director, Michelle Stall
Advanced Sourcing Vpi Team, Greg Thomas
Vpi Manufacturing Program Manager, Hamilton Harper
Vpi Sourcing Manager, Susie Baker-Coy
Vice President and Treasurer, Donald Jackson
Vice President Engine Business Quality, Robert Weimer
Vice President, Bruce Carver

Vice President Government Relations, Stephen May
Asq Cqe Vpi Sqe, Tao Gan
Vice President and Controller Engine Business, Glyn Price
Vice President, Scot Lenger
Vice President General Manager, Merritt Becker
National Account Manager, Jeff Poferl
Vice President Oem S Human Resources Manager, Robert Shockman
Vice President Nebraska and South Dakota Operations, Rick Gomel
PPT and VPI Sourcing Manager, Tom Rager
Vice President Research and Development, Abhay Bhagwat
Executive Vice President President Power Generation Business, Thomas Linebarge
VICE PRESIDENT OEM BUSINESS, Ed Pense
Vice President Truck and Business OEM Business, Lori Thompson
VICE PRESIDENT, Mark Gestle
Vice President Advanced Product Development, Julius Perr
Executive Vice President, J T White
Vice President, Victor Meek
VPI Manufacturing Engineer, Brent Nelson
VPI Sourcing Specialist, GE Li
VPI Sourcing Manager, Brad Covert
Vice President of Finance, Michael Doherty
Vice President Financial Operations, Marc Smith
Materials VPI and Continuous Improvement Leader, Chandrashekar Chandramowleeswaran
Board Member, Ian Kohen
Secretary, Pedro Silva
Secretary, Maria Ward
Secretary Vice President Finance Vice President, Joseph JR
Board Member, JULIE DELGENIO
Auditors: PricewaterhouseCoopers LLP

LOCATIONS

HQ: Cummins, Inc.
500 Jackson Street, P.O. Box 3005, Columbus, IN 47202-3005
Phone: 812 377-5000   **Fax:** 812 377-4937
Web: www.cummins.com

2016 Sales

	$ mil.	% of total
United States	9,476	54
International	8,033	46
Total	**17,509**	**100**

PRODUCTS/OPERATIONS

2016 Sales

	$ mil.	% of total
Engine	7,804	35
Distribution	6,181	28
Components	4,836	21
Power Generation	3,517	16
Intersegment eliminations	(4829)	-
Total	**17,509**	**100**

Selected Products

Components business
Emission solutions
Filtration (heavy-duty air fuel hydraulic and lube filtration and chemicals)
Fuel systems (new fuel systems remanufactured electronic control modules)
Turbo technologies (turbochargers)
Emissions solutions
Engine business
Bus engines
Heavy- and medium-duty truck engines
Industrial engines for construction mining agricultural rail and marine equipment
Light commercial vehicle engines
Marine diesels (recreational and commercial)
Filtration business
Air system
Cooling system (crankcase ventilation)

Diesel emission additives
Fuel system (hydraulic)
Lube system (transmission)
Fuel systems
CELECT electronically controlled unit injection system
Common rail pump
Extreme pressure injection system
High Pressure Injection (HPI) system
Remanufactured products
Power generation business
Diesel and alternative-fuel electrical generator sets (PowerCommand Onan Newage AVK SEG G-Drive)
Turbo technologies Holset (medium and heavy-duty diesel engines)

COMPETITORS

BorgWarner
Briggs & Stratton
 Power Products
CLARCOR
Caterpillar
China Yuchai
DENSO
DEUTZ
Danaher
Donaldson Company
Eaton
Emerson Electric
Fiat Chrysler
MAN

Mack Trucks
Mitsubishi Heavy
 Industries
Navistar International
PACCAR
Parker-Hannifin
Regal Beloit
Robert Bosch
Rolls-Royce Power
 Systems
Tenneco
Textron
Volvo

HISTORICAL FINANCIALS

Company Type: Public

Income Statement

FYE: December 31

	REVENUE ($ mil.)	NET INCOME ($ mil.)	NET PROFIT MARGIN	EMPLOYEES
12/17	20,428	999	4.9%	58,600
12/16	17,509	1,394	8.0%	55,400
12/15	19,110	1,399	7.3%	55,200
12/14	19,221	1,651	8.6%	54,600
12/13	17,301	1,483	8.6%	47,900
Annual Growth	**4.2%**	**(9.4%)**	**—**	**5.2%**

2017 Year-End Financials

Debt ratio: 11.10%
Return on equity: 14.14%
Cash ($ mil.): 1,369
Current ratio: 1.57
Long-term debt ($ mil.): 1,588

No. of shares (mil.): 165
Dividends
 Yield: 0.0%
 Payout: 70.5%
Market value ($ mil.): 29,269

	STOCK PRICE ($) FY Close	P/E High/Low	PER SHARE ($) Earnings	Dividends	Book Value
12/17	176.64	30 23	5.97	4.21	43.81
12/16	136.67	18 10	8.23	4.00	40.87
12/15	88.01	19 11	7.84	3.51	42.27
12/14	144.17	18 14	9.02	2.81	42.53
12/13	140.97	18 13	7.91	2.25	40.22
Annual Growth	**5.8%**	**— —**	**(6.8%)**	**17.0%**	**2.2%**

Customers Bancorp Inc

Customers Bancorp makes it pretty clear who they want to serve. Boasting some $8.5 billion in assets the bank holding company operates about 15 branches mostly in southeastern Pennsylvania but also in New York and New Jersey. It offers personal and business checking savings and money market accounts as well as loans certificates of deposit credit cards and concierge or appointment banking (they come to you seven days a week). Around 95% of the bank's loan portfolio is made up of commercial loans while the rest consists of consumer loans. It was formed in 2010 as a holding company for Customers Bank which was created in 1994 as New Century Bank.

Operations

Customers Bancorp operates two main business lines: Commercial Lending and Consumer Lending. Its Commercial Lending business provides commercial and industrial loans small and middle-market business banking and small business administration (SBA) loans multi-family and commercial real estate loans and commercial loans to mortgage originators. Its Consumer Lending division mostly makes local market mortgage loans and home equity loans. More than 95% of the bank's loan portfolio was made up of commercial loans at the end of 2015 while the rest consisted of consumer loans.

Broadly speaking the bank makes roughly 90% of its revenue from interest income. About 66% of its revenue came from loan interest during 2015 while another 19% came from interest loans held for sale and 4% came from interest on investment securities. The remainder of its revenue came from mortgage warehouse transactional fees (4%) and other miscellaneous and non-recurring sources.

Geographic Reach

The bank had 14 branches at the end of 2015 including nine in Philadelphia and Southeastern Pennsylvania; four in Berks County Pennsylvania; one in Westchester County New York; and one in Mercer County New Jersey. It also had a handful of additional offices in Boston; New York City; Portsmouth New Hampshire; Providence Rhode Island; and Suffolk County New York.

Sales and Marketing

Customers Bancorp's customers include private businesses business customers non-profits and consumers. Its commercial lending division typically makes loans to companies with revenues between $1 million to $50 million needing between $0.5 million to $10 million in credit.

The bank has been ramping up its advertising spend in recent years. It spent $1.48 million in advertising in 2015 up from $1.33 million and $1.27 million in 2014 and 2013 respectively.

Financial Performance

The bank's annual revenues have nearly quadrupled since 2011 as its loan assets have more than tripled (its loan assets reached $5.45 billion by of the end of 2015). Meanwhile growing revenues strong cost controls and low interest rates have pushed the bank's annual profits up almost 15-fold over the same period.

Customers Bancorp's revenue jumped 29% to $277.5 million during 2015 mostly as its average balance of interest-earning loan and securities assets rose by 31% to $6.7 billion for the year.

Revenue growth in 2015 drove the bank's net income up 36% to $58.5 million. Customer Bancorp's operating cash levels declined sharply to $356.6 million for the year as the bank originated more loans held for sale than it actually sold.

Strategy

With its eye on becoming the leading regional bank holding company Customers Bancorp continued in 2016 to focus on expanding its market share with its high-touch personalized Concierge Banking services and its "high-tech" BankMobile offerings which include remote account opening remote deposit capture and mobile banking. The BankMobile and online banking channels allow Customers Bancorp to slow expensive branch-expansion plans and cut operating costs significantly while giving customers faster access to banking services.

But even with digital banking the bank occasionally opens new branches (and selectively acquire others) to grow its loan and deposit business.

In January 2016 it opened and replaced an existing branch in Hamilton New Jersey onto Route 33 in the same city. In June 2015 Customers opened a new Long Island location in Mellville New York to expand its private and commercial banking services to local clients there.

Mergers and Acquisitions

In December 2015 Customers Bank expanded its deposit business and added 2 million new student customers after buying the One Account Student Checking and Refund Management Disbursement Services business from higher education refund disbursement provider Higher One Inc for $42 million.

Company Background

In late 2011 Customers purchased Berkshire Bancorp and picked up five branches in Berks County Pennsylvania for about $11.3 million.

EXECUTIVES

Chairman and CEO, Jay S. Sidhu, age 65, $300,000 total compensation
President and COO, Richard A. Ehst, age 71, $225,000 total compensation
Executive Vice President President of Community Banking, Warren Taylor, age 59, $190,000 total compensation
EVP and Chief Credit Officer, Thomas Jastrem
EVP and Chief Administrative Officer, Jim Collins
EVP and Chief Lending Officer, Timothy D. Romig
EVP and President Special Assets Group, Robert A. White
EVP and CFO, James D. Hogan
EVP and Director Multi-Family and Investment CRE Lending, Kenneth A. Keiser
Executive Vice President Market Chief Lending Officer, George Maroulis
Vice President of Operations, Richard Kirk
Vice President Government Guaranteed Lending, Michele Vervlied
VICE PRESIDENT COMMERCIAL CREDIT MANAGER, Jason Rauenzahn
Senior Vice President, Kevin Cornwall
ASSISTANT VICE PRESIDENT AND PORTFOLIO MANAGER, Christopher Haley
Vice President Business Resiliency, Rob McHugh
Vice President And Government Guaranteed Lender, Stephanie Schwandt
Vice President Government Guaranteed Lending New England, Jennifer McKay
Vice President SBA Loan Specialist, Stacey Kuzniasz
Vice President, Laura Simon
Senior Vice President Commercial Real Estate Lending, Stephen King
Vice President Senior Business Analyst Portfolio Manager, Brian Desmarais
Vice President Small Business Lending, Martin Hernandez
Assistant Vice President Collateral Manager, Donna Abel
Vice President Commercial Lending Philadelphia Market, Edwin Roman
Business Development Officer Vice President, Sunita Raina
Senior Vice President, Doreen Goch
Auditors: BDO USA, LLP

LOCATIONS

HQ: Customers Bancorp Inc
1015 Penn Avenue, Suite 103, Wyomissing, PA 19610
Phone: 484 359-7113
Web: www.customersbank.com

PRODUCTS/OPERATIONS

2015

	% of total
Interest income	
Loans receivable including fees	66
Loans held for sale	19
Investment securities	4
Other	2
Non interest income	
Mortgage warehouse transnational fees	4
Bank-owned life insurance	3
Gains on sales of loans	1
Deposit fees	0
Mortgage loan and banking income	0
Gain (loss) on sale of investment securities)	0
Other	1
Total	**100**

Products include
Equipment Loans
Mortgage Warehouse Loans
Multi-Family And Commercial Real Estate Loans
Residential Mortgage Loans
Small Business Loans

COMPETITORS

Bank of America	Huntington Bancshares
Capital One	JPMorgan Chase
Citigroup	KeyCorp
Comerica	PNC Financial
Fifth Third	U.S. Bancorp
HSBC	Wells Fargo

HISTORICAL FINANCIALS

Company Type: Public

Income Statement

FYE: December 31

	ASSETS ($ mil.)	NET INCOME ($ mil.)	INCOME AS % OF ASSETS	EMPLOYEES
12/16	9,382	78	0.8%	739
12/15	8,401	58	0.7%	517
12/14	6,825	43	0.6%	426
12/13	4,153	32	0.8%	388
12/12	3,201	23	0.7%	255
Annual Growth	**30.8%**	**34.8%**	**—**	**30.5%**

2016 Year-End Financials

Debt ratio: 2.09%	No. of shares (mil.): 30
Return on equity: 11.13%	Dividends
Cash ($ mil.): 244	Yield: —
Current ratio: —	Payout: —
Long-term debt ($ mil.): —	Market value ($ mil.): 1,085

	STOCK PRICE ($) FY Close	P/E High/Low		PER SHARE ($) Earnings	Dividends	Book Value
12/16	35.82	15	9	2.31	0.00	28.26
12/15	27.22	15	9	1.96	0.00	20.59
12/14	19.46	14	11	1.55	0.00	16.57
12/13	20.46	15	11	1.30	0.00	14.51
12/12	14.50	11	6	1.57	0.00	13.27
Annual Growth	**25.4%**	**—**	**—**	**10.1%**	**—**	**20.8%**

CVB Financial Corp.

CVB Financial is into the California Vibe Baby. The holding company's Citizens Business Bank offers community banking services to primarily small and midsized businesses but also to consumers through nearly 50 branch and office locations across central and southern California. Boasting more than $7 billion in assets the bank offers checking money market CDs and savings accounts trust and investment services and a variety of loans. Commercial real estate loans account for about two-thirds of the bank's loan portfolio which is rounded out by business consumer and construction loans; residential mortgages; dairy and livestock loans; and municipal lease financing.

Operations

In addition to its 40 business financial centers CVB operates seven Commercial Banking Centers (CBCs). The CBCs operate primarily as sales offices and focus on business clients professionals and high-net-worth individuals. The bank also has three trust offices.

Citizens Business Bank provides auto and equipment leasing and brokers mortgage loans through its Citizens Financial Services Division; CitizensTrust offers trust and investment services.

Overall the bank made 63% of its total revenue from interest income on loans and leases in 2014 with another 24% of total revenue coming from interest income on the bank's investment securities. About 5% of total revenue came from service charges on deposit accounts and 3% came from trust and investment services income.

Geographic Reach

CVB Financial has 40 Business Financial Centers located in the Inland Empire Los Angeles County Orange County San Diego County and the Central Valley regions in California.

Sales and Marketing

CVB Financial provides services to companies from a variety of industries including: industrial and manufacturing dairy and livestock agriculture education nonprofit entertainment medical professional services title and escrow government and property management.

Financial Performance

CVB's revenue has been in decline in recent years due to shrinking interest margins on loans amidst the low-interest environment. The firm's profits however have been rising thanks to declining loan loss provisions as its loan portfolio's credit quality has been improving in the strengthening economy.

CVB enjoyed a breakout year in 2014 with revenue rebounding by 12% to $289.32 million mostly thanks to higher interest income as the bank grew its loan and lease assets by 7% during the year and grew its investment security assets by 18%. Most of its loan growth came from commercial real estate loans while SFR mortgage loans consumer loans and construction loans also helped boost the company's top line. The bank's non-interest income also jumped by 44% during the year thanks to a $6 million gain on loans held-for-sale and a net $3.6 million decrease in its FDIC loss sharing asset.

Higher revenue and a $16.1 million loan loss provision recapture in 2014 also drove the bank's net income higher by 9% to $104.02 million.

Despite higher earnings for the year CVB's operating cash levels shrank by 22% to $87.70 million as the bank used more cash toward employee payments and income taxes.

Strategy

CVB Financial continues to seek out acquisitions of smaller banking trust and investment companies to grow its loan and deposit business as well as its geographic reach in key markets in (mostly Southern) California. With its 2014 acquisition of American Security Bank for example CVB boosted its assets by 6% to over $7 billion while adding branches in more than a handful of key markets in Southern California.

Remaining profitable throughout the economic downturn CVB Financial credits its success in part to its strict loan underwriting standards. The bank targets family-owned or other privately held businesses with annual revenues of up to $200 million

with the goal of maintaining its client relationships for decades.

Mergers and Acquisitions

In March 2014 CVB Financial through its Citizens Business Bank (CBB) subsidiary purchased Southern California-based American Security Bank (the flagship subsidiary of American Bancshares) for a total of $57 million. The deal would add American Security Bank's $431 million in assets and boost CBB's branch presence across key markets in Newport Beach Corona Laguna Niguel Lancastar Victorville and Apple Valley.

In 2016 CVB Financial agreed to buy the $416 million-asset Valley Commerce Bancorp the holding company for Valley Business Bank. Valley Business has four banking locations in California's Visalia Tulare Fresno and Woodlake.

Company Background

In 2009 CVB Financial healthier than most California banks acquired the failed San Joaquin Bank after the FDIC took it over. The deal added five branches banking centers in the Bakersfield area.

EXECUTIVES

Senior Vice President and Regional Manager, Vince Gottuso
EVP and General Counsel CVB Financial Corporation and Citizens Business Bank, Richard H. Wohl, age 58
President and CEO CVB Financial and Citizens Business Bank, Christopher D. (Chris) Myers, age 54, $800,000 total compensation
EVP and CFO, E. Allen Nicholson, age 50
EVP and CIO, Elsa I. Zavala
EVP and Dairy and Livestock Industries Group Manager Citizens Business Bank, G. Larry Zivelonghi
EVP and Senior Lender, Ted J. Dondanville
EVP Sales Citizens Business Bank, David A. Brager, $300,000 total compensation
EVP and COO Citizens Business Bank, David C. Harvey, $300,000 total compensation
EVP; Head CitizensTrust, R. Daniel Banis
EVP and Chief Risk Officer Citizens Business Bank, Yamynn De Angelis
EVP Ventura/Santa Barbara, Donald R. Toussaint
Senior Vice President And Deputy Chief C, Hector Gutierrez
Vice President Relationship Manager, Nadine Ortega
Executive Vice President and Chief Credit Officer Citizens Business Bank, James Dowd
Vice President Relationship Manager, Jason Gould
Vice President Senior Product Manager, John Outwater
EXECUTIVE VICE PRESIDENT, Angelis Yamynn
Vice Chairman, George A. Borba, age 84
Chairman, Raymond V. OA'Brien
Auditors: KPMG LLP

LOCATIONS

HQ: CVB Financial Corp.
701 North Haven Ave., Suite 350, Ontario, CA 91764
Phone: 909 980-4030
Web: www.cbbank.com

Selected Branch Locations
Fresno County
Kern County
Los Angeles County
Madera County
Orange County
Riverside County
San Bernardino County
Tulare County

PRODUCTS/OPERATIONS

2014 Sales

	$ mil.	% of total
Interest		
Loans including fees	181	62
Investment securities	68	24
Other	2	1
Noninterest		
Service charges on deposit accounts	15	5
Trust & investment services	8	3
Bankcard services	3	1
BOLI income	2	1
Other	10	3
Adjustments	(3.6)	-
Total	**289**	**100**

COMPETITORS

Bank of America	Popular Inc.
Bank of the West	Provident Financial
City National	Holdings
Comerica	U.S. Bancorp
JPMorgan Chase	Wells Fargo
MUFG Americas Holdings	

HISTORICAL FINANCIALS

Company Type: Public

Income Statement FYE: December 31

	ASSETS ($ mil.)	NET INCOME ($ mil.)	INCOME AS % OF ASSETS	EMPLOYEES
12/16	8,073	101	1.3%	—
12/15	7,671	99	1.3%	—
12/14	7,377	104	1.4%	—
12/13	6,664	95	1.4%	784
12/12	6,363	77	1.2%	810
Annual Growth	6.1%	7.0%	—	—

2016 Year-End Financials

Debt ratio: 0.32%	No. of shares (mil.): 108
Return on equity: 10.57%	Dividends
Cash ($ mil.): 169	Yield: 0.0%
Current ratio: —	Payout: 38.3%
Long-term debt ($ mil.): —	Market value ($ mil.): 2,482

	STOCK PRICE ($) FY Close	P/E High/Low		PER SHARE ($) Earnings	Dividends	Book Value
12/16	22.93	25	15	0.94	0.36	9.15
12/15	16.92	20	16	0.93	0.48	8.68
12/14	16.02	17	14	0.98	0.40	8.29
12/13	17.07	19	11	0.91	0.39	7.33
12/12	10.40	17	13	0.74	0.43	7.27
Annual Growth	21.9%	—	—	6.2%	(4.1%)	5.9%

CVR Energy Inc

CVR Energy's CV says that it puts its energy into oil refining and ammonia production. It operates a 115000 barrels-per-day-throughput-capacity oil refinery in Coffeyville Kansas and a 70000 barrels-per day refinery in Oklahoma and a crude oil gathering system in Kansas and Oklahoma. CVR Energy's Coffeyville refinery has 1.4 million barrels of storage tanks and it also has 2.8 million barrels of leased storage capacity in Cushing Oklahoma. It has asphalt and refined fuels storage and terminalling plants in Phillipsburg Kansas. The company controls public traded CVR Refining (refining assets) and CVR Partners LP (a producer of ammonia and urea ammonium nitrate fertilizers).

Operations

The company has two businesses: Petroleum (the petroleum and related businesses operated by CVR Refining); and Nitrogen Fertilizer (the nitrogen fertilizer business operated by the CVR Partners). Most nitrogen fertilizer producers use more expensive natural gas. CVR Partners operates the only nitrogen fertilizer plant in North America that uses coke gasification (superheating using low cost petroleum coke to generate the hydrogen used in fertilizer production). About 85% of the company's nitrogen products are for agricultural use. e petroleum business accounted for 97% of total net sales in fiscal 2014 and the remaining was accounted for by its nitrogen business.

Geographic Reach

The petroleum business focuses its Coffeyville petroleum product marketing efforts in the central Mid-continent and Rockies because of its proximity to the refinery and pipeline access also has access to the Rocky Mountain area. The company also directly supplies customers in close geographic proximity to the refinery through tanker trucks and customers at throughput terminals on the refined products distribution systems of Magellan and NuStar. The company has its headquarters in Texas and a presence in Kansas and Oklahoma.

Sales and Marketing

Customers include other refiners convenience store chains railroads and farm cooperatives.

CVR Energy's major customers include CHS Dyno Nobel MFA National Cooperative Refinery Association and Transammonia.

In 2014 the company's top five ammonia customers accounted for 41% of the nitrogen fertilizer business' ammonia sales. The nitrogen fertilizer business' top two customers (Gavilon Fertilizer and United Suppliers) accounted for 17% and 10% respectively of the CVR Energy's nitrogen fertilizer business revenues.

Financial Performance

CVR Energy's net sales have been on an upward trend since 2010.

In 2014 net sales increased by 1% due to higher sales from the petroleum business partially offset by lower nitrogen fertilizer sales.

Petroleum sales grew due to higher overall sales volumes largely offset by lower sales prices for gasoline and distillates.

Nitrogen fertilizer sales decreased by $25 million due to lower UAN sales prices a drop in ammonia sales volumes and lower ammonia sales prices partially offset by higher UAN sales volumes.

In 2014 CVR Energy's net income decreased by $196.8 million due to higher products costs partially offset by increased sales.

Consolidated cost of products sold increase of $502.8 million primarily resulting from an increase of $486.7 million in cost of petroleum products sold due to higher costs of consumed crude oil and higher refined fuels purchased for resale. The increase in consumed crude costs was due to higher consumed volumes.

The nitrogen fertilizer segment cost of products sold increased by $13.9 million as a result of higher distribution costs due to increased railcar regulatory inspections and repairs and a growth in ammonia purchases.

Net cash provided by the operating activities increased by 45% due to change in accounts receivable and inventories.

Strategy

Both the petroleum business and the nitrogen fertilizer business are considering pursuing acquisitions and expansion projects in order to continue to grow and increase profitability.

Company Background

To improve shareholder return and raise cash to pay down debt in 2013 CVR Energy spun off its refining assets as CVR Refining for about $600 million.

The Nitrogen Fertilizer Partnership will continue to expand the nitrogen fertilizer business' existing asset base to execute its growth strategy. The growth strategy includes expanding production of UAN and acquiring additional infrastructure and production assets. The Nitrogen Fertilizer Partnership completed a significant two-year plant expansion in 2013 which increased its UAN production capacity by 400000 tons or approximately 50% per year.

The UAN expansion provides the nitrogen fertilizer business with the ability to upgrade substantially all of its ammonia production to UAN. If the premium that UAN currently earns over ammonia decreases this expansion project may not yield the economic benefits and accretive effects that the nitrogen fertilizer business currently anticipates.

In 2012 investor Carl Icahn (and 82% owner) made a $2.6 billion bid to acquire CVR Energy claiming that it could be sold to a larger oil company for up to $7 billion. The board of directors and stockholders rejected the offer. (Icahn subsequently succeed in spinning off the refining unit).

In 2011 the company spun off its CVR Partners unit (formed in 2007 to operate its nitrogen fertilizer business) for $307 million.

Seeking to expand its refining base in 2011 the company acquired Denver-based independent Gary-Williams Energy and its Wynnewood Oklahoma refinery for $593 million. The refinery has the capacity to produce 70000 barrels per day of crude oil. With the acquisition CVR Energy bumped up its processing capacity to 185000 barrels per day.

The company traces its roots to the National Refining Company which in 1906 built a refinery in Coffeyville. The completed refinery was the second largest in the US at the time.

EXECUTIVES

President and CEO, John J. (Jack) Lipinski, age 66, $950,000 total compensation
EVP Refining Operations, Robert W. Haugen, age 59, $315,000 total compensation
CFO and Treasurer, Susan M. Ball, age 54, $360,000 total compensation
Vice President Environmental Health Safety, Janice Develasco
Executive Vice President Crude Oil Acquisition And, Wyatt Jernigan
Vice President Government Relations, Gina Bowman
Vice President Human Resources, Alicia Skalnik
Vice President Logistics, Reed Copeland
Executive Vice President, Bill White
Vice President Business Development, Angie Dasbach
Vice President, David Andreth
Vice President Refined Products, Mike Puddy
VP Operations, Robert Haugeh
Chairman, Carl C. Icahn
Auditors: GRANT THORNTON LLP

LOCATIONS

HQ: CVR Energy Inc
2277 Plaza Drive, Suite 500, Sugar Land, TX 77479
Phone: 281 207-3200
Web: www.cvrenergy.com

PRODUCTS/OPERATIONS

2016 Sales

	$ mil.	% of total
Petroleum	4,431	93
Nitrogen Fertilizer	356	7
Intersegment elimination	(5.2)	-
Total	**4,782**	**100**

COMPETITORS

CF Industries	Phillips 66
ConocoPhillips	Potash Corp
Flint Hills	Sinclair Oil
HollyFrontier	Valero Energy
Koch Industries Inc.	
National Cooperative	
Refinery Association	

HISTORICAL FINANCIALS

Company Type: Public

Income Statement

FYE: December 31

	REVENUE ($ mil.)	NET INCOME ($ mil.)	NET PROFIT MARGIN	EMPLOYEES
12/16	4,782	24	0.5%	1,487
12/15	5,432	169	3.1%	1,332
12/14	9,109	173	1.9%	1,298
12/13	8,985	370	4.1%	1,192
12/12	8,567	378	4.4%	1,091
Annual Growth	(13.6%)	(49.5%)	—	8.0%

2016 Year-End Financials

Debt ratio: 28.75%
Return on equity: 2.67%
Cash ($ mil.): 735
Current ratio: 2.32
Long-term debt ($ mil.): 1,162

No. of shares (mil.): 86
Dividends
Yield: 0.1%
Payout: 714.2%
Market value ($ mil.): 2,205

	STOCK PRICE ($) FY Close	P/E High/Low	PER SHARE ($) Earnings	Dividends	Book Value
12/16	25.39	141 45	0.28	2.00	9.88
12/15	39.35	25 17	1.95	2.00	11.33
12/14	38.71	25 18	2.00	5.00	11.38
12/13	43.43	16 8	4.27	14.25	13.69
12/12	48.79	11 5	4.33	0.00	17.56
Annual Growth	(15.1%)	— —	(49.6%)	—	(13.4%)

CVS Health Corporation

CVS Health Corp. is a leading pharmacy benefits manager with nearly 90 million plan members as well as the nation's largest drugstore chain (pipping Walgreens). It runs more than 9700 retail and specialty drugstores under the CVS Navarro and Longs Drug banners. In addition to its stand alone pharmacy operations the company operates CVS locations inside Target stores and runs a prescription management company Caremark Pharmacy Services. The company also offers specialty pharmainfusion services business as well as walk-in health services through its retail network of MinuteClinics that are located in around 1000 CVS stores. In late 2017 CVS agreed to acquire health insurer Aetna in a $70 billion megadeal..

HISTORY

Brothers Stanley and Sid Goldstein who ran health and beauty products distributor Mark Steven branched out into retail in 1963 when they opened up their first Consumer Value Store in Lowell Massachusetts with partner Ralph Hoagland.

The chain grew rapidly amassing 17 stores by the end of 1964 (the year the CVS name was first used) and 40 by 1969. That year the Goldsteins sold the chain to Melville Shoe to finance further expansion.

Melville had been founded in 1892 by shoe supplier Frank Melville. Melville's son Ward grew the company creating the Thom McAn shoe store chain and later buying its supplier. By 1969 Melville had opened shoe shops in Kmart stores (through its Meldisco unit) launched one apparel chain (Chess King sold in 1993) and purchased another (Foxwood Stores renamed Foxmoor and sold in 1985).

In 1972 CVS bought the 84-store Clinton Drug and Discount a Rochester New York-based chain. Two years later when sales hit $100 million CVS had 232 stores — only 45 of which had pharmacies. The company bought New Jersey-based Mack Drug (36 stores) in 1977. By 1981 CVS had more than 400 stores.

CVS's sales hit $1 billion in 1985 as it continued to add pharmacies to many of its older stores. In 1987 Stanley's success was recognized company-wide when he was named chairman and CEO of CVS's parent company which by then had been renamed Melville.

CVS bought the 490-store Peoples Drug Stores chain from Imasco in 1990 giving it locations in Maryland Pennsylvania Virginia West Virginia and Washington DC. CVS created PharmaCare Management Services in 1994 to take advantage of the growing market for pharmacy services and managed-care drug programs. Pharmacist Tom Ryan was named CEO that year.

With CVS outperforming Melville's other operations in 1995 Melville decided to concentrate on the drugstore chain. By that time Melville's holdings had grown to include discount department store chain Marshalls and furniture chain This End Up both sold in 1995; footwear chain Footaction spun off as part of Footstar in 1996 along with Meldisco; the Linens 'n Things chain spun off in 1996; the Kay-Bee Toys chain sold in 1996; and Bob's Stores (apparel and footwear) sold in 1997.

Melville was renamed CVS in late 1996. Amid major consolidation in the drugstore industry in 1997 CVS — then with about 1425 stores — paid $3.7 billion for Revco D.S. which had nearly 2600 stores in 17 states mainly in the Midwest and Southeast. The next year the company bought Arbor Drugs (200 stores in Michigan later converted to the CVS banner) for nearly $1.5 billion.

CVS opened about 180 new stores and relocated nearly 200 in 1998 as it shifted from strip malls to freestanding stores. (It also closed nearly 160 stores.) Stanley retired as chairman in 1999 and was succeeded by Ryan.

In 1999 the company bought online drugstore pioneer Soma.com renamed CVS.com. It also launched the CVS ProCare pharmacy to serve customers in need of complex drug therapies. A year later CVS bought Stadtlander Pharmacy of Pittsburgh from Bergen Brunswig (now Amerisource-Bergen) for $124 million.

In early 2001 Wolverine Equities paid $288 million for 96 stores which CVS said it would continue to operate. In 2001 CVS opened 43 stores in new markets including Miami and Fort Lauderdale Florida; Las Vegas; and Dallas Houston and Fort Worth Texas. As part of a strategic restructuring begun in 2001 CVS closed more than 200 stores and moved others from strip malls to freestanding locations.

In July 2002 CVS was among the winning bidders for the remaining assets of bankrupt rival Phar-Mor. CVS acquired the majority of Phar-Mor's prescription lists. In October CVS named KB Toys as the exclusive toy supplier to its drugstores. CVS opened 266 new stores in 2002 and another 150 new stores in 2003.

In April 2003 specialty pharmacy division CVS ProCare changed its name to PharmaCare Specialty Pharmacy.

With those store closings behind it the drugstore chain began opening stores in Minneapolis the 10th-largest drugstore market in the US in 2004. CVS opened about 10 stores in the Los Angeles area in 2004 marking the drugstore chain's return to Southern California after a 12-year absence. CVS is also targeting other high-traffic markets including Chicago Florida Las Vegas Phoenix and Texas for expansion.

In July 2004 CVS completed the acquisition of 1260 Eckerd stores Eckerd Health Services (which included Eckerd's $1 billion mail order and pharmacy benefits management businesses) and three distribution centers from J. C. Penney Company for $2.15 billion. The acquisition of the Eckerd stores (622 in Florida) gave CVS more stores than archrival Walgreen. CVS completed the conversion of Eckerd stores in Alabama Arizona Colorado Florida Kansas Louisiana Mississippi Missouri New Mexico Oklahoma and Texas to its own banner within about a year.

In June 2005 CVS agreed to pay $110 million to settle a shareholders' lawsuit filed in 2001 that alleged the company had made misleading statements to artificially raise its stock price and violated accounting practices. CVS denied the charges and said the settlement was "purely a business decision."

In June 2006 CVS completed the acquisition of some 700 stand-alone Sav-On and Osco drugstores from Albertson's. CVS was part of a consortium that bought the nation's #2 supermarket chain and split it up amongst themselves. The transaction gave CVS access to Southern California and key Midwest markets. In September the company purchased the retail-based health clinic operator MinuteClinic for an undisclosed amount. The acquisition allowed CVS to provide in-store care to its customers for minor ailments.

In March 2007 CVS changed its name to CVS Caremark Corporation following its acquisition of the pharmacy benefits manager Caremark RX after months of bidding between CVS and Express Scripts. Ultimately CVS paid about $26.5 billion for Caremark. In November CEO Ryan added the chairman's title to his job description following the retirement of Mac Crawford.

In October 2008 CVS Caremark acquired Longs Drug Stores for about $2.9 billion. Longs Drug operates 521 pharmacies in California Hawaii Nevada and Arizona. The purchase included Long's Rx America subsidiary a pharmacy benefits management service to more than 8 million members. Also in 2008 the company opened about 190 new retail pharmacies.

In 2008 CVS settled a lawsuit regarding drug-switching allegations for $36.7 million. The company had been accused of switching Medicaid customers to a more expensive capsule form of Zantac from a tablet form; CVS denied the allegations.

In June 2009 CVS agreed to pay almost $1 million to settle allegations stemming from the sale of expired OTC medications infant formula and dairy products.

CVS Caremark in early 2011 won a contract to administer Aetna's retail pharmacy network. CVS Caremark is managing both purchasing and prescription filling for Aetna's mail-order and specialty pharmacy operations. Prior to his retirement in May 2011 Ryan assumed the title of non-executive chairman in March when Larry Merlo took over as president and CEO of CVS.

In 2012 CVS opened drugstores in four new states: Arkansas Colorado Oregon and Washington.

In September 2014 the company changed its name to CVS Health Corporation to reflect its broader commitment to health care. The corporate name change coincided with the cessation of tobacco sales at its retail stores in September.

EXECUTIVES

EVP Health Plans, Tracy L. Bahl, age 54

President and CEO, Larry J. Merlo, age 61, $1,630,000 total compensation

EVP; President CVS/pharmacy, Helena B. Foulkes, age 52, $950,000 total compensation

EVP and CIO, Stephen J. Gold, age 58

EVP and Chief Human Resources Officer, Lisa Bisaccia, age 61

SVP and Chief Marketing Officer, Norman de Greve

EVP Specialty Pharmacy CVS/Caremark, Alan M. Lotvin, age 55

EVP and Chief Medical Officer, Troyen A. Brennan, age 63, $637,500 total compensation

EVP and Head of Retail Operations, Scott Baker

EVP and COO, Jonathan C. Roberts, age 61, $950,000 total compensation

EVP and CFO, David M. (Dave) Denton, age 52, $850,000 total compensation

EVP and Associate Chief Medical Officer; President CVS/minuteclinic, Andrew J. (Andy) Sussman, age 51

EVP Sales and Marketing CVS/caremark, J. David Joyner, age 52

EVP Chief Health Strategy Officer and General Counsel, Thomas M. Moriarty, age 54, $750,000 total compensation

EVP Enterprise Strategy and Corporate Development, Joshua (Josh) Flum

EVP and President Omnicare, Robert O. (Rocky) Kraft, age 47

Senior Vice President Retail Field Operations CVS Pharmacy, Hanley Wheeler

Vice President Sales and Marketing, Harry Boysen

Vice President and Senior Legal Counsel, Brenna Jordan

Vice President Corporate Logistics, June Youngs

Senior Vice President and Chief Technology Officer, Gregg McNulty

Medical Director, Dick Creager

Vice President Human Resources, Bob Botsford

Senior Vice President Investor Relations, Michael McGuire

Area Vice President, Jeff Raman

Pharmacy Manager, Thuy Nguyen

Senior Vice President Tax, John Kennedy

Pharmacy Manager, Jamie Hartman

Senior Vice President Trade Relations, Gary Loeber

Vice President Government Accounts, Diane Galo

Pharmacy Manager, Michael Brito

Pharmacy Manager, Avery Hagedorn

Area Vice President, Roger Francis

Vice President and Chief Information Technology Operations Officer, Jay Johnson

Pharmacy Manager, Neil Foglio

Pharmacy Manager, Carmen Rodriguez

Senior Vice President, Mario Ramos

Pharmacy Manager, Jenny Gardner

Pharmacy Manager, Harsh Patel

Senior Vice President Controller and Chief Accounting Officer, Eva Boratto

Vice President Customer Insights and Market Research, Seth Kamen

Vice President Information Technology, Dawn Pagano

Vice President of Operations, Everett Moore

Director of Pharmacy Information Technology, Lisa Newton

Vice President Finance, Jeffrey Knudson

Vice President of Real Estate, Clay Wilson

Vice President Information Technology Infrastructure, John Criddle

Vice President Health System Affiliations, Willis Chandler

Vice President of Operations, Dan May

Pharm.D, Lisa Marsh

Vice President, Shannon Penberthy

Vice President, Joan O'Rourke

Vice President, Stephen Holodak
Pharmacy Manager, Jesse Tang
Pharmacy Manager, Ashlie Miller
Chairman, David W. (Dave) Dorman, age 63
Auditors: Ernst & Young LLP

LOCATIONS

HQ: CVS Health Corporation
One CVS Drive, Woonsocket, RI 02895
Phone: 401 765-1500   **Fax:** 401 762-2137
Web: www.cvshealth.com

PRODUCTS/OPERATIONS

2016 Retail Sales

	% of total
Prescription drugs	75
Over-the-counter & personal care	10
Beauty/cosmetics	4
General merchandise & other	11
Total	**100**

2016 Sales

	$ bil.
% of total	
Pharmacy services	60
Retail/LTC Segment	40
Adjustments	-
Total	**100**

COMPETITORS

A&P	MedImpact
Aetna	Medicine Shoppe
Anthem	OptumRx
BioScrip	PharMerica
CIGNA	Prime Therapeutics
Costco Wholesale	Rite Aid
Express Scripts	Target Corporation
H-E-B	UnitedHealth Group
Humana	Wal-Mart
Kmart	Walgreen
Kroger	

HISTORICAL FINANCIALS

Company Type: Public

Income Statement

FYE: December 31

	REVENUE ($ mil.)	NET INCOME ($ mil.)	NET PROFIT MARGIN	EMPLOYEES
12/17	184,765	6,622	3.6%	246,000
12/16	177,526	5,317	3.0%	250,000
12/15	153,290	5,237	3.4%	243,000
12/14	139,367	4,644	3.3%	297,800
12/13	126,761	4,592	3.6%	286,000
Annual Growth	9.9%	9.6%	—	(3.7%)

2017 Year-End Financials

Debt ratio: 28.38%	No. of shares (mil.): 1,014
Return on equity: 17.77%	Dividends
Cash ($ mil.): 1,696	Yield: 0.0%
Current ratio: 1.02	Payout: 31.0%
Long-term debt ($ mil.): 22,181	Market value ($ mil.): 73,515

	STOCK PRICE ($) FY Close	P/E High/Low	PER SHARE ($) Earnings	Dividends	Book Value
12/17	72.50	13 10	6.44	2.00	37.17
12/16	78.91	22 15	4.90	1.70	34.71
12/15	97.77	24 20	4.63	1.40	33.78
12/14	96.31	25 16	3.96	1.10	33.30
12/13	71.57	19 13	3.74	0.90	32.15
Annual Growth	0.3%	— —	14.6%	22.1%	3.7%

DAIRY FARMERS OF AMERICA, INC.

The members of Dairy Farmers of America (DFA) are partners in cream. DFA is one of the world's largest dairy cooperatives with nearly 15000 member/farmers in 48 states. About 3 million cows belonging to member/farmers produce 64 billion pounds of milk a year (roughly 30% of milk production in the US) which DFA markets. Along with fresh and shelf-stable fluid milk the co-op produces cheese butter dried milk powder and other dairy products for industrial wholesale and retail customers. It also offers contract manufacturing services. The co-op owns more than 30 manufacturing plants nationwide. DFA whose profits are shared based on member contribution is a major supplier to dairy giant Dean Foods.

Operations

DFA owns 33 manufacturing plants nationwide. The facilities are focused on several functions and product categories including consumer cheese and butter consumer fluid ingredient cheese and protein and contract manufacturing.

Geographic Reach

The national milk cooperative is based in Kansas City Missouri and divides the US into seven areas (Central Mideast Mountain Northeast Southeast Southwest and Western) to ensure grassroots representation.

Sales and Marketing

DFA's customers include big names in the dairy food and retail businesses including Hiland Dairy Borden supermarket giant Kroger Dean Foods Kraft Foods J.M. Smucker and many others.

Financial Performance

DFA reported net sales of $17.9 billion in 2014 a 28% increase compared with 2013's $12.8 billion in sales. The uptick in sales primarily resulted from higher milk prices in the US. The cooperative's adjusted net income was $61.3 million and it returned a total of $43.1 million to members in 2014.

Strategy

Although DFA's primary business is to market its members' milk the cooperative has invested heavily in facilities and joint ventures to process its fluid milk into value-added products and high-end dairy-based ingredients to expand its product portfolio and protect members from price swings for fluid milk. To that end it makes and markets cheese butter nonfat milk powders and other dairy ingredients under household name brands including Borden Breakstone's and Keller's as well as private label products through contract manufacture.

In 2015 the co-op opened a 33000-square-foot ingredient processing plant in Cass City Michigan. The $40 million plant will serve a region where milk production is outpacing local plant capacity.

In 2014 DFA opened a new cold process milk separation plant in Linwood New York to produce cream and skim milk for regional customers. It also opened a plant in Fallon Nevada that produces powdered milk for global customers.

The co-op expects to continue to benefit from its diverse activities coupled with higher average commodity prices for dairy products. The marketing of raw milk accounted for approximately 74% of sales. Sales have been bolstered by the acquisition of Berkshire Dairy and Food Products a producer of dairy ingredients and DFA's investment in Castro Cheese Company which makes and markets queso fresco panea and queso quesadilla under the La Vaquita brand. Control of the brand launched DFA into the increasingly popular His-

panic cheese market. DFA's efforts to shore up earnings and mitigate a volatile commodity market have included trimming certain investments.

Mergers and Acquisitions

In January 2014 DFA acquired family-owned Oakhurst Dairy which sources milk from 70 farmers in Maine and has processing and bottling facilities in Portland Maine. Oakhurst which became a wholly-owned subsidiary of DFA and continues to operate independently distributes milk throughout northern New England and eastern Massachusetts. Oakhurst's annual sales are estimated to be $110 million. In April 2014 DFA purchased Dairylea Cooperative based in East Syracuse New York with some 1200 members. The two cooperatives have worked together since DFA was formed in 1998 coordinating milk assembly transportation and marketing as well as joint management of Farm Services and membership operations in the Northeast.

DFA acquired Frederick Maryland-based Dairy Maid Dairy a family-owned processor of milk juice and fruit drinks in September 2013. The purchase was consistent with DFA's strategy to increase its commercial footprint and expand ownership in the fluid and fresh dairy category. Dairy Maid's customers include major grocery chains schools prisons and military bases.

HISTORY

Mid-America Dairymen (Mid-Am) the largest of the cooperatives that merged to form Dairy Farmers of America (DFA) was born in 1968. At that time several Midwestern dairy co-ops banded together to attack common economic problems such as reduced government subsidies price drops resulting from a rising milk surplus dealer consolidation and improvements in production processing and packaging. The merging organizations — representing 15000 dairy farmers — were Producers Creamery Company (Springfield Missouri) Sanitary Milk Producers (St. Louis) Square Deal Milk Producers (Highland Illinois) Mid-Am (Kansas City Missouri) and Producers Creamery Company of Chillicothe (north central Missouri).

During the early 1970s Mid-Am struggled with internal restructuring. Most dairy farmers and co-ops were hit hard by the energy crisis and the government's decision to allow increased dairy imports in 1973 the same year the US Justice Department filed an antitrust suit against Mid-Am. (A judge cleared the co-op 12 years later.)

In 1974 Mid-Am lost almost $8 million on revenues of $625 million chalked up to record-high feed prices a weakened economy a milk surplus and a massive inventory loss. Co-op veteran Gary Hanman was named CEO that year. Over the next two years Mid-Am cut costs sold corporate frills downsized management and began marketing more of its own products under the Mid-America Farms label thus reducing dependency on commodity sales.

Mid-Am expanded its research and development efforts throughout the 1980s. The co-op opened its services to farmers in California and New Mexico in 1993 and a series of mergers in 1994 and 1995 nearly doubled its size. In 1997 it purchased some of Borden's dairy operations including rights to the valuable Elsie the Cow and Borden's trademarks.

Wary of falling milk prices Mid-Am merged with Western Dairymen Cooperative Milk Marketing and the Southern Region of Associated Milk Producers at the end of 1997 to form DFA. Hanman moved into the seat of CEO at the new co-op. DFA began a series of joint ventures with the #1 US dairy processor Suiza Foods (now Dean Foods).

DFA added California Gold (more than 330 farmers 1998) and Independent Cooperative Milk

Producers Association (730 dairy farmer members in Michigan and parts of Ohio and Indiana 1999). In another joint venture with Suiza in early 2000 DFA sold its 50% stake in the US's #3 fluid milk processor Southern Foods in exchange for 34% of a new company named Suiza Dairy Group.

After mollifying the government's antitrust fears DFA acquired the butter operations of Sodiaal North America in 2000. It then molded all its butter businesses into a new entity Keller's Creamery. However another acquisition did not fare as well. The same year DFA acquired controlling interest in Southern Belle Dairy only to have the merger challenged three years later by the Department of Justice. Arguing that the merger formed a monopoly in school milk sales in several states the Department of Justice filed suit which a federal judge later dismissed.

During 2001 the cooperative went in with Land O'Lakes 50/50 to purchase a cheese plant from Kraft. Later in the year as Suiza Foods acquired Dean Foods (and took on its name) DFA sold back its stake in Suiza Dairy Group to the new Dean Foods. DFA then teamed up with a group of dairy investors to form a new 50/50 joint venture National Dairy Holdings which received 11 processing plants from Dean Foods as part of the exchange for Suiza Dairy.

EXECUTIVES

Senior Adviser; President Affiliate Division, Alan J. Bernon, age 62
COO Northeast Area, Gregory I. (Greg) Wickham
President CEO and Director, Richard P. (Rick) Smith
EVP; President Global Dairy Products Group, Mark Korsmeyer
SVP Finance, David Meyer
Executive Vice President of Commercial Operations, Doug Glade
Vice Chairman, Bill Siebenborn
First Vice Chairman, Randy Mooney
Vice Chairman, Wayne Palla
Vice Chairman, George Mertens
Auditors: KPMG LLP KANSAS CITY MISSOUR

LOCATIONS

HQ: DAIRY FARMERS OF AMERICA, INC.
1405 N 98TH ST, KANSAS CITY, KS 661111865
Phone: 816 801-6455
Web: WWW.DFAMILK.COM

PRODUCTS/OPERATIONS

Selected Products and Brands
Consumer brands
  Borden cheese
  Breakstone's butter
  Cache Valley cheese
  Keller's Creamery butter
  Plugrá; butter
  Sport Shake energy milk shake
Contract manufacturing
  Cheese dips
  Cheese powders & flavors
  Coffee-based flavored drinks
  Instant formula
  Sour cream
  Sports drinks
Dairy ingredients
  Cheeses (American & Italian)
  Nonfat dry milk powder
  Skim milk powder
  Sweetened condensed milk

Selected Joint Venture Partners
Dean Foods
Hiland Dairy Foods
Roberts Dairy

COMPETITORS

Arla Foods	Glanbia plc
Associated Milk Producers	Great Lakes Cheese
	HP Hood
Berkeley Farms	Humboldt Creamery
California Dairies Inc.	Lactalis
	Land O'Lakes
ConAgra	Marathon Cheese
Darigold Inc.	Mayfield Dairy Farms
Dean Foods	Northwest Dairy
Farmland Dairies	Prairie Farms Dairy
Foremost Farms	Quality Chekd
Friendship Dairies	Sargento
Garelick Farms	

HISTORICAL FINANCIALS
Company Type: Private

Income Statement
FYE: December 31

	REVENUE ($ mil.)	NET INCOME ($ mil.)	NET PROFIT MARGIN	EMPLOYEES
12/15	13,803	98	0.7%	7,000
12/14	17,856	48	0.3%	—
12/13	12,826	58	0.5%	—
12/12	12,082	(126)	—	—
Annual Growth	4.5%	—	—	—

2015 Year-End Financials

Debt ratio: —
Return on equity: 0.70%
Cash ($ mil.): 228
Current ratio: 0.70
Long-term debt ($ mil.): —

Dividends
Yield: —
Payout: —
Market value ($ mil.): —

Dana Inc

Dana is a global maker of car parts. In addition to its core offerings which include driveline products (rear and front axles driveshafts transmissions) it provides power technologies (sealing thermal-management products) and service parts. It makes products for vehicles in the light medium/heavy (commercial) and off-highway markets. The company's products carry brand names that include Spicer Victor Reinz and Long. Dana operates through some 90 facilities across the globe. It traces its historical roots back to 1904 when it introduced the automotive universal joint.

Operations
Dana divides its operations across four business segments: Light vehicle driveline (45% of total sales) commercial vehicle (roughly 20%) off-highway (15%) and power technologies (roughly 20%).

Geographic Reach
Dana manufactures its products in about 90 facilities in 25 countries in North America Europe South America and Asia/Pacific. The company also has engineering centers located throughout the world.

North America accounts for about 50% of its revenue while Europe contributes roughly 30%. The Asia/Pacific region generates almost 15% while South America accounts for the remaining amount.

Sales and Marketing
Ford accounts for 20% of Dana's total revenue while Fiat Chrysler Automobile represents almost 10%. Other large customers have included OEMs such as Tata Motors Volkswagen AG Nissan Alliance PACCAR and General Motors.

Financial Performance

Dana's revenues have gradually declined the last several years dipping 4% from $6.1 billion in 2015 to $5.8 billion in 2016. Weaker international currencies decreased sales by $173 million in 2016. Organic sales also decreased due to weaker global off-highway demand lower commercial vehicle production in North America and Brazil and decreased sales from a major North America commercial vehicle customer.

Profits skyrocketed by more than 300% from $159 million in 2015 to $640 million in 2016 mainly due to a tax valuation adjustment that resulted in around $424 million earned on income tax benefits.

In addition to its revenues Dana's operating cash flow has decreased the last several years declining from $406 million in 2015 to $384 million in 2016. This decrease was attributed to a year-over-year increase in cash paid for interest of $15 million and cash paid on the settlement of foreign currency forward contracts during 2016.

Strategy
Desiring to reduce its dependence on any one geographic market the company is expanding into growth regions with a particular emphasis on China Hungary and India. In 2017 Dana began construction of a new 140000 sq. ft. facility in Hungary to provide new gear-manufacturing services to support new business growth across Europe. The facility will be Dana's fourth in Hungary.

Dana also seeks opportunities via acquisitions that have a strategic fit with its existing core businesses. In 2016 the company acquired Magnum Gaskets a US-based supplier of aftermarket gaskets and sealing products for automotive and commercial-vehicle applications.

In 2017 Dana acquired the axle housing and driveline shaft manufacturing operations belonging to U.S. Manufacturing Corporation. The company plans for the deal to generate additional revenue from passenger and commercial vehicle manufacturers and provide it with new product and process technologies for lightweighting.

EXECUTIVES

President Light Vehicle Driveline Technologies, Robert (Bob) Pyle, age 50, $477,000 total compensation
EVP and Group President Commercial Vehicle Driveline Technologies, Mark E. Wallace, age 50, $580,000 total compensation
President and CEO, James K. (Jim) Kamsickas, age 50, $1,100,000 total compensation
President Off-Highway Drive and Motion Technologies, Aziz S. Aghili, age 58, $515,000 total compensation
President Power Technologies, Dwayne E. Matthews, age 57
EVP and CFO, Jonathan M. Collins, age 37, $381,944 total compensation
SVP Dana China, Antonio Valencia
SVP and CTO, Christophe Dominiak
Vice President of Finance, Jorge Delgado
Chairman, Keith E. Wandell, age 67
Auditors: PricewaterhouseCoopers LLP

LOCATIONS

HQ: Dana Inc
3939 Technology Drive, Maumee, OH 43537
Phone: 419 887-3000   **Fax:** 419 887-5200
Web: www.dana.com

2016 Sales

	$ mil.	% of total
North America	3,128	53
Europe	1,616	28
Asia/Pacific	744	13
South America	338	6
Total	**5,826**	**100**

PRODUCTS/OPERATIONS

2016 Sales

	$ mil.	% of total
Light vehicle driveline	2,607	45
Commercial vehicle	1,254	21
Power technologies	1,056	18
Off-highway	909	16
Total	**5,826**	**100**

Selected Products

Automotive (light vehicle driveline)
  Axles (front and rear)
  Differentials
  Driveshafts
  Modular assemblies
  Side rails
  Torque couplings
Commercial vehicle (medium-heavy)
  Axles
  Driveshafts
  Steering shafts
  Suspension and tire management systems
Off-highway
  Axles
  Driveshafts
  Electronic controls
  Torque converters
  Transaxles
  Transmissions
Power technologies
  Cooling and heat transfer
  Cover modules
  Engine sealing systems
  Heat shields
  Gaskets
Structures (for light and medium/heavy)
  Cradles
  Frames
  Side rails

COMPETITORS

AISIN World Corp.	Hitachi Automotive
American Axle &	Systems Americas
Manufacturing	Magna International
AxleTech International	Mahle International
Boler	Martinrea
BorgWarner	International
Carraro	Meritor
DENSO	Modine Manufacturing
Dayco Products	Neapco
ElringKlinger	Tower International
FCA US	Valeo
Federal-Mogul	Visteon
Freudenberg-NOK	Wanxiang
GKN	ZF Friedrichshafen

HISTORICAL FINANCIALS

Company Type: Public

Income Statement

FYE: December 31

	REVENUE ($ mil.)	NET INCOME ($ mil.)	NET PROFIT MARGIN	EMPLOYEES
12/17	7,209	111	1.5%	30,100
12/16	5,826	640	11.0%	24,900
12/15	6,060	159	2.6%	23,100
12/14	6,617	319	4.8%	22,600
12/13	6,769	244	3.6%	23,000
Annual Growth	**1.6%**	**(17.9%)**		**7.0%**

2017 Year-End Financials

Debt ratio: 31.87%	No. of shares (mil.): 144
Return on equity: 10.23%	Dividends
Cash ($ mil.): 603	Yield: 0.0%
Current ratio: 1.69	Payout: 33.8%
Long-term debt ($ mil.): 1,759	Market value ($ mil.): 4,641

	STOCK PRICE ($) FY Close	P/E High/Low		PER SHARE ($) Earnings	Dividends	Book Value
12/17	32.01	46	24	0.71	0.24	6.99
12/16	18.98	5	2	4.36	0.24	8.04
12/15	13.80	23	13	0.99	0.23	4.85
12/14	21.74	12	9	1.84	0.20	6.50
12/13	19.62	—	—	(0.09)	0.20	9.01
Annual Growth	**13.0%**	—	—	—	**4.7%**	**(6.2%)**

Danaher Corp

Danaher is a well-diversified industrial and medical conglomerate whose products test analyze and diagnose. Its subsidiaries design manufacture and market products and offer services geared at worldwide professional medical industrial and commercial markets. Danaher operates through five segments: Life Sciences & Diagnostics (research and clinical tools) Test & Measurement (electronic measurement instruments) Industrial Technologies (product identification motion control equipment and sensors) Environmental (turbine pumps and air/water analysis and treatment equipment) and Dental (orthodontic bracket systems and lab products). In a milestone transaction Danaher acquired Pall Corp. for $13.6 billion in 2015.

Change in Company Type

Danaher acquired Pall Corporation a major supplier of filtration separation and purification technologies for $13.6 billion in mid-2015. Danaher plans to separate the combined company into two independent publicly traded companies: a science and technology company which will retain the Danaher name (and will include Pall); and a diversified industrial company which will comprise Danaher's test and measurement instruments operations. The spin-off is scheduled to be completed in the third quarter of 2016.

Operations

Built largely through acquisitions Danaher's five business segments reflect a well balanced portfolio. Top segments Life Sciences & Diagnostics and Environmental accounted for 40% and 18% of revenues in fiscal 2015 respectively. Life Sciences products include imaging systems acute care equipment (blood gas measurement devices) pathology diagnostics (tissue embedding and chemical reagents) and instrumentation (microscopes).

Key Danaher subsidiaries include Beckman Coulter Matco Tools Corporation Jacobs Vehicle Systems Tektronix X-Rite EskoArtwork Linx Printing Technologies Fluke Corporation Keithley Instruments Sybron Dental Specialties Trojan Technologies Gems Sensors Gilbarco and Sea-Bird Electronics.

Geographic Reach

Danaher has around 335 manufacturing and distribution facilities worldwide. Almost 160 of these facilities are located in the US in more than 25 states; roughly 175 locations reside outside the US in over 50 other countries throughout Asia Europe North America South America and Australia. The company generates almost half of its revenue from North America primarily the US (44% of sales).

Financial Performance

Danaher has enjoyed five straight years of unprecedented growth. Its revenues rose by 3% from $19.9 billion in 2014 to peak at a record-setting $20.1 billion in 2015. Profits also surged 29% from $2.6 billion in 2014 to reach $3.4 billion in 2015 another company milestone.

The company's historic growth for 2015 was led by a 14% bump in Life Sciences & Diagnostics sales due to higher demand of its existing businesses across China and other high-growth markets along with additional revenue from the Pall Corporation acquisition. Dental sales spiked by 25% resulting from demand for dental treatment units and consumable products including orthodontic products.

In addition Environmental segment sales increased by 2% in 2015 resulting from growth in its analytical instrumentation product lines within North America China and Europe and growth within its business' chemical treatment solutions product line in Latin America.

Strategy

Already its top segment Danaher is working to get an even larger foothold in the life sciences sector whose growth is being driven by such factors as aging populations increased preventive health care and US health care reforms. It is also seeking opportunities to beef up its industrial business. To this end Danaher uses a combination of divestitures and acquisitions.

In 2016 Danaher bought molecular diagnostics firm Cepheid for some $4 billion. Cepheid's GeneXpert and SmartCycler platforms perform molecular testing for a variety of issues.

In its largest acquisition to date Danaher acquired Pall Corporation a major supplier of filtration separation and purification technologies for $13.8 billion in mid-2015. Pall now operates as a subsidiary in Danaher's portfolio and maintained its brand. During the third quarter of 2016 Danaher will also separate the combined company into two independent publicly traded companies: a science and technology company which will retain the Danaher name (and will include Pall); and a diversified industrial company which will comprise Danaher's test and measurement instruments operations.

In 2014 Danaher purchased Nobel Biocare Holding for $2.2 billion. The deal is expected to significantly widen Danaher's market presence in the global dental industry. Headquartered in Zurich Switzerland Nobel Biocare serves customers in 80 markets globally supplying dental implant systems high-precision individualized prosthetics and biomaterials and digital diagnostics products.

HISTORY

Danaher (from the Celtic word dana meaning "swift flowing") is named for a fishing stream off the Flathead River in Montana. The term is also an appropriate description of the spotlight-averse Rales brothers. The two have proven to be fishers not only of trout but also of companies buying underperforming companies with strong market shares and recognizable brand names.

Once dubbed "raiders in short pants" by Forbes Steven and Mitchell Rales began making acquisitions in their 20s. In 1981 they bought their father's 50% stake in Master Shield a maker of vinyl building products. The brothers bought tire manufacturer Mohawk Rubber the following year. In 1983 they acquired control of publicly traded DMG a distressed Florida real-estate firm; the next year they sold DMG's real estate holdings and folded Mohawk and Master Shield into the company which they renamed Danaher.

EXECUTIVES

Senior Vice President and Chief Accounting Officer, Robert S Lutz

Senior Vice President, Henk Van Duijnhoven

EVP and CFO, Daniel L. Comas, age 53, $862,357 total compensation

President and CEO, Thomas P. Joyce, age 56, $1,100,000 total compensation

EVP Diagnostics and Dental, William K. (Dan) Daniel, age 52, $730,144 total compensation

SVP Human Resources, Angela S. Lalor, age 51, $603,986 total compensation

EVP Life Sciences, Rainer M. Blair, age 52

Vice President Marketing, Cathy Clausen

Vice President Talent Acquisition and Corporate Human Resources, Mark Hamberlin

Vice President, Larry Byrnes

Vice President Leadership Development, Patrick Donahue

Corporate Vice President and Chief Financial Officer Asia, Samuel Liao

Vice President Finance, Emily Weaver

Vice President Internal Audit, Christopher Sandberg

Vice President and BU Manager, Raj Karanam

Senior Vice President of Human Resources, Angie Lalor

Vice President Corporate Development, Jonathan Schwarz

Vice President, Jonathan Graham

National Sales Manager, Jim White

Vice President, Rick Hoffman

Group Vice President Finance, Dave Bergmann

Senior Vice President and General Counsel, Brian Ellis

Vice President and General Counsel, Vibeke Holst-Andersen

Vice President, Brain Ellis

Vice President, Daniel Rakas

Chairman, Steven M. Rales, age 65

Auditors: Ernst & Young LLP

LOCATIONS

HQ: Danaher Corp
2200 Pennsylvania Avenue, N.W., Suite 800W, Washington, DC 20037-1701
Phone: 202 828-0850   **Fax:** 202 828-0860
Web: www.danaher.com

2016 Sales

	$ mil.	% of total
United States	6,377	38
China	1,799	11
Germany	1,084	6
Japan	864	5
All other	6,756	40
Total	**16,882**	**100**

PRODUCTS/OPERATIONS

2016 Sales

	$ mil.	% of total
Life Sciences	5,365	32
Diagnostics	5,038	30
Environmental & Applied Solutions	3,692	22
Dental	2,785	16
Total	**16,882**	**100**

2016 Sales

	$ mil.	% of total
Research and medical products	10,366	61
Dental products	2,785	17
Analytical and physical instrumentation	2,088	12
Product identification	1,641	10
Total	**16,882**	**100**

COMPETITORS

ABB	PerkinElmer
Bosch Rexroth Corp.	Rockwell Automation
Datamax-O'Neil	SPX
Emerson Electric	Schneider Electric
GE	Siemens Water
Greenlee Textron	Technologies
Hitachi	Snap-on

Johnson & Johnson Medical	Stanley Black and Decker
Labfacility	Thermo Fisher
Makita	Scientific
Mettler-Toledo	Wayne
Parker-Hannifin	

HISTORICAL FINANCIALS

Company Type: Public

Income Statement

FYE: December 31

	REVENUE ($ mil.)	NET INCOME ($ mil.)	NET PROFIT MARGIN	EMPLOYEES
12/16	16,882	2,553	15.1%	62,000
12/15	20,563	3,357	16.3%	81,000
12/14	19,913	2,598	13.0%	71,000
12/13	19,118	2,695	14.1%	66,000
12/12	18,260	2,392	13.1%	63,000
Annual Growth	**(1.9%)**	**1.6%**	**—**	**(0.4%)**

2016 Year-End Financials

Debt ratio: 27.09%
Return on equity: 10.91%
Cash ($ mil.): 963
Current ratio: 0.97
Long-term debt ($ mil.): 9,674

No. of shares (mil.): 692
Dividends
  Yield: 0.0%
  Payout: 15.6%
Market value ($ mil.): 53,881

	STOCK PRICE ($) FY Close	P/E High/Low	PER SHARE ($) Earnings	Dividends	Book Value
12/16	77.84	28 21	3.65	0.57	33.23
12/15	92.88	20 17	4.74	0.54	34.49
12/14	85.71	24 19	3.63	0.40	33.19
12/13	77.20	20 14	3.80	0.10	32.07
12/12	55.90	16 14	3.36	0.10	27.66
Annual Growth	**8.6%**	**— —**	**2.1%**	**54.5%**	**4.7%**

Darden Restaurants, Inc.

Darden Restaurants is the #1 casual-dining operator in the US and Canada. The company operates more than 1500 restaurants. Its flagship chain is Italian-themed concept Olive Garden. Olive Garden caters to families by offering mid-priced menu items themed interiors and primarily suburban locations. Darden also operates the LongHorn Steakhouse chain. Other Darden dining concepts include The Capital Grille (upscale steakhouse) Bahama Breeze (Caribbean food and drinks) Eddie V's and Seasons 52 (casual grill and wine bar). The company 2015 it spun off a chunk of its real estate portfolio as Four Corners Property Trust; the portfolio includes about 425 US restaurants that are all leased to Darden subsidiaries.

Operations

Darden's Olive Garden restaurants accounted about 55% the company's revenue during fiscal 2016 while LongHorn Steakhouse locations accounted for almost 25%.

Geographic Reach

The company operates 1536 restaurants in the US and Canada (consisting of 843 Olive Garden 481 LongHorn Steakhouses 54 The Capital Grille 65 Yard House 40 Seasons 52 37 Bahama Breeze and 16 Eddie V's).

Darden is looking outside of the US for growth including plans to develop Olive Garden and Long-Horn Steakhouse locations in Brazil Colombia the Dominican Republic Panama and Puerto Rico. Most of the company's international growth emphasis has been on its Olive Garden and LongHorn Steakhouse chains. Darden has been remodeling many of its domestic Olive Garden and LongHorn Steakhouse units in lieu of adding new locations.

Sales and Marketing

Olive Garden has come to epitomize the chain restaurant experience. Olive Garden offer a version Italian cuisine designed for mass appeal and affordability.

Darden spends heavily on research and development in order to roll out a succession of new menu items that are heavily promoted through television advertising. The chains also utilize discount pricing and special offers to win business against the competition including Applebee's Chili's (operated by Brinker International) and Outback Steakhouse (OSI Restaurant Partners).

Financial Performance

Darden reported $6.93 billion in revenue for fiscal 2016. That was an increase of $170 million (or 3%) compared to the company's revenue during the prior fiscal period. The increase was driven by a combined same-restaurant sales increase and the addition of two new company-owned restaurants.

Darden's net income was $375 million in fiscal 2016. That was a decrease of $335 million compared to its net income in fiscal 2015. The primary causes of the drop in net income were decreased earnings from discontinued operations and incurred income tax expenses.

Despite the drop in net income Darden finished fiscal 2016 with $820.4 million in cash on hand from operations. That was a decrease of $54 million (or 6%) compared to the company's cash levels at the end of fiscal 2015.

Strategy

Darden has built its dining empire without the aid of franchising a strategy that allows the company the highest degree of control for maintaining food and service quality. The major downside is the cost of operating and maintaining all those restaurants. The company is constantly focused on improving margins by negotiating lower prices for food and other ingredients and by adjusting its workforce to reduce labor costs.

The recession of recent years has posed serious challenges for most casual dining operators but Darden's chains fared better than some of the company's competitors thanks to intense customer loyalty. The company did sell off the struggling Red Lobster chain to focus more on getting Olive Garden back to growth and profitability.

Darden has also been working to consolidate its various restaurant brands onto a single digital technology platform.

Mergers and Acquisitions

In early 2017 Darden announced plans to acquire the Cheddar's casual dining chain from private equity firms L Catterton and Oak Investment Partners among other owners. The $780 million deal brings some 165 locations across more than two dozen states.

EXECUTIVES

Senior Vice President Finance, Dave Lothrop

CEO and Director, Eugene I. (Gene) Lee, age 56, $953,750 total compensation

SVP and Chief Human Resources Officer, Danielle Kirgan, age 53, $378,462 total compensation

EVP and President Olive Garden, David C. (Dave) George, age 61, $576,539 total compensation

SVP and CFO, Ricardo (Rick) Cardenas, age 49, $474,539 total compensation

President Yard House, Michael (Mike) Kneidinger

VP Operations The Capital Grille, Brian Foye

President **LongHorn Steakhouse**, Todd Burrowes, $442,211 total compensation
SVP and CIO, Chris Chang
President The Capital Grille and Eddie V's, John Martin
Vice President Information Technology, Norma Sica
Senior Vice President Division, Sam Pereira
Vice President General Counsel and Secretary, Barbara Posada
Vice President Brand Management, Jaime Allen
Vice President, Kathy Janiga
Senior Vice President Division, Paula Britton
Vice President Quality Assurance, Ana Hooper
SENIOR VICE PRESIDENT SUPPLY, Barry Moullet
Senior Vice President Group Human Resources, Ronald Bojalad
Senior Vice President Operations, Kathy Nahlovsky
Senior Vice President Human Resources, Ron Bojalad
Vice President Culinary Operations and Operations Excellence, Tim Blaise
Executive Vice President Operations, Valerie Insignares
Vice President Information Technology Service Delivery and Infrastructure, Jeff Cooper
Senior Vice President Franchising President International Operations, Michael Beacham
Senior Vice President, Bill Holmes
Senior Vice President Operations, Bryan Clements
Chairman, Charles M. (Chuck) Sonsteby
Auditors: KPMG LLP

LOCATIONS

HQ: Darden Restaurants, Inc.
1000 Darden Center Drive, Orlando, FL 32837
Phone: 407 245-4000
Web: www.darden.com

PRODUCTS/OPERATIONS

Restaurant Brands
Bahama Breeze
Eddie V's
LongHorn Steakhouse
Olive Garden
The Capital Grille
Yard House

2016 Sales

	$ mil.	% of total
Olive Garden	3,838	56
LongHorn Steakhouse	1,587	23
Fine Dining	514	7
Other Business	993	14
Total	**6,933**	**100**

COMPETITORS

Bob Evans	DineEquity
Brinker	Hooters
Carlson Restaurants	OSI Restaurant
Cheesecake Factory	Partners
Cracker Barrel	Perkins & Marie
Denny's	Callender's

HISTORICAL FINANCIALS

Company Type: Public

Income Statement

FYE: May 28

	REVENUE ($ mil.)	NET INCOME ($ mil.)	NET PROFIT MARGIN	EMPLOYEES
05/17	7,170	479	6.7%	178,729
05/16	6,933	375	5.4%	150,000
05/15	6,764	709	10.5%	150,000
05/14	6,285	286	4.6%	206,489
05/13	8,551	411	4.8%	206,000
Annual Growth	(4.3%)	3.9%	—	(3.5%)

2017 Year-End Financials

Debt ratio: 17.02%
Return on equity: 23.70%
Cash ($ mil.): 233
Current ratio: 0.62
Long-term debt ($ mil.): 936
No. of shares (mil.): 125
Dividends
Yield: 0.0%
Payout: 58.9%
Market value ($ mil.): 11,029

	STOCK PRICE ($) FY Close	P/E High/Low		PER SHARE ($) Earnings	Dividends	Book Value
05/17	87.95	23	16	3.80	2.24	16.76
05/16	67.48	25	18	2.90	2.10	15.47
05/15	65.54	13	8	5.47	2.20	18.42
05/14	49.55	25	21	2.15	2.20	16.30
05/13	52.83	18	14	3.13	2.00	15.81
Annual Growth	13.6%	—	—	5.0%	2.9%	1.5%

DaVita Inc

DaVita gives life in the form of dialysis treatments to patients suffering from end-stage renal disease (ESRD chronic kidney failure). Through its Kidney Care division the firm is one of the US' largest providers of dialysis providing administrative services to more than 2380 outpatient centers across the US; it serves some 189000 patients. The company also offers home-based dialysis services as well as inpatient dialysis in about 900 hospitals. It operates two clinical laboratories that specialize in routine testing of dialysis patients and serve the company's network of clinics.

Operations
DaVita operates through two divisions — Kidney Care (dialysis and related lab and support services) and DaVita Medical Group (DMG formerly known as HealthCare Partners or HCP).

Dialysis and lab services account for around 60% of the company's revenues. DaVita and its main competitor Fresenius Medical Care together control nearly three-fourths of the US dialysis clinic market. (DaVita controls about 35% of the market while Fresenius controls another 45%. Fresenius actually manufactures dialysis supplies and DaVita is a customer.)

A portion of DaVita's dialysis and lab-related revenues comes from administering specialty pharmaceuticals to patients receiving dialysis. The pharmaceuticals include vitamin D iron supplements and EPO — a genetically engineered protein that stimulates the production of red blood cells. EPO is used during dialysis to treat anemia (a common complication). Amgen is the only company manufacturing EPO and to buffer against price fluctuations or shortages DaVita has a multi-year agreement with Amgen to secure its supply of EPO at discounted pricing.

DMG is a patient- and physician-focused integrated health care delivery and management company. DMG has roughly 750000 members under its care in Southern California Central and South Florida southern Nevada central New Mexico and central Arizona through capitation contracts. Sales from the DMG business accounts for about 30% of revenues. In late 2017 the company announced plans to sell DMG to health insurer UnitedHealth for $4.9 billion.

Geographic Reach
California Florida and Texas are home to about 30% of all DaVita dialysis centers though the firm has locations in more than 45 US states and Washington DC. The DMG unit operates and manages medical groups and physician practice networks in California Colorado Florida Georgia Nevada New Mexico and Washington.

While its international operations (150 outpatient dialysis centers in more than 10 countries) are still a tiny fraction of its total business the company is involved in a long-term strategy to expand into overseas markets for growth through acquisitions and partnerships. The company has established a presence in select international markets including Europe Latin America the Middle East and the Asia/Pacific region. Colombia Germany India and Malaysia together account for more than 70% of DaVita's outpatient dialysis centers outside of the US.

Sales and Marketing
Almost 90% of DaVita's dialysis patients are covered by government-based health plans including Medicare and Medicaid agencies and the VA making DaVita particularly vulnerable to changes in government reimbursement rates (which are regularly under threat of being lowered by state and federal governments facing budget pressures). Government plan reimbursements account for about 65% of the company's annual revenues; the balance of the income comes from commercial insurance payers (including hospital dialysis services) as their primary payor.

DMG provides medical services through a network of about 700 primary care physicians as well as several thousand specialists in some 200 hospitals. Its teammates employed clinicians and affiliated clinicians provided care for some 1.7 million patients.

One commercial payor Humana accounts for roughly 10% of DaVita's total consolidated net revenues each year.

Financial Performance
DaVita has achieved unprecedented growth the last few years with revenues peaking at a record-setting $14.8 billion in 2016. The most recent growth was fueled by increased treatment volume primarily from non-acquired growth at existing and new dialysis centers cost control initiatives and payor mix improvements within its dialysis business.

In addition to the historic revenue growth DaVita's profits more than tripled from $270 million in 2015 to $880 million in 2016 another company milestone. This was attributed to the increase in revenues and the absence of debt refinancing and redemption charges it incurred the previous year.

Strategy
While DaVita has primarily grown through acquisitions over the years it also expands its operations through joint ventures and partnerships. In 2015 it formed a joint venture to operate kidney care specialty hospitals in Shadong Province China. Also that year it entered the Brazilian market and it opened an outpatient vascular access center in Saudi Arabia.

In late 2017 DaVita announced plans to sell its DMG segment to UnitedHealth for $4.9 billion. The company will focus on its core kidney care business but is also exploring options to enter other areas of health care.

Mergers and Acquisitions
Historically DaVita has grown its network of facilities through acquisition of outpatient dialysis centers.

In 2017 it bought Colorado-based Renal Ventures for $415 million. Renal Ventures operates 36 dialysis clinics in six states; it also has units that operate infusion and vascular centers. Also that year the company acquired Nevada-based WellHealth Quality Care operator of about a dozen centers specializing in such areas as anesthesiology and obstetrics/gynecology.

During 2016 DaVita achieved a net increase of 99 US dialysis centers and 36 international dialysis centers.

HISTORY

Hospital chain National Medical Enterprises (NME now Tenet) formed Medical Ambulatory Care in 1979 to run its in-hospital dialysis centers. The unit bought other centers in NME's markets. In 1994 the subsidiary's management backed by a Donaldson Lufkin & Jenrette — now Credit Suisse First Boston (USA) — investment fund bought the dialysis business and renamed it Total Renal Care (TRC).

To become a leader in its consolidating field TRC began buying other centers and soon added clinical laboratory and dialysis-related pharmacy services and home dialysis programs. It went public in 1995.

The next year the firm added 66 facilities 32 from its acquisition of Caremark International's dialysis business. In 1997 TRC expanded abroad buying UK-based Open Access Sonography (vein care) and partnering with UK-based Priory Hospitals Group.

In 1998 TRC bought Renal Treatment Centers nearly doubling its size. But the acquisition costs caused a loss that year and sparked shareholder lawsuits (settled in 2000) over alleged misleading statements. The firm also became embroiled in a reimbursement dispute with Florida's Medicare program. Problems continued into 1999 as the company struggled to meld operations. The company took a charge to cover a billing shortfall and chairman and CEO Victor Chaltiel and COO/CFO John King resigned. New management began improving billing procedures and took other cost-cutting measures.

The company changed its name in 2000 to DaVita an Italian phrase loosely translated as "he/she gives life." It also sold its international operations to competitor Fresenius.

In 2005 the company acquired Gambro's US dialysis operations for about $3 billion adding some 565 dialysis clinics to its operations. To meet FTC requirements for the deal DaVita sold about 70 clinics to RenalAmerica a company founded by former Gambro Healthcare executive Michael Klein.

In 2007 DaVita expanded its health care offerings by acquiring a majority stake in HomeChoice Partners a provider of home infusion services. The company added about 80 new centers through acquisitions in 2009.

DaVita significantly widened its domestic network of dialysis centers when it acquired regional dialysis chain DSI Renal for $690 million in 2011. To secure approval for the deal from the FTC DaVita agreed to divest 30 clinics but overall the acquisition added more than 100 dialysis centers to its holdings.

Elsewhere around the world DaVita entered Germany with the 2011 purchase of DV Care. It also expanded into the Middle East through the acquisition of a majority stake in Lehbi Care a leading Riyadh-based kidney care company with three clinics.

The company has also been looking to branch out into new areas of health care including medical practice management a mission it accomplished through the 2012 purchase of private medical group management firm HealthCare Partners through a merger transaction worth some $4.4 billion.

Following the deal the company changed its legal name from DaVita to DaVita HealthCare Partners to reflect its broadened operations; the dialysis division continues to operate under the DaVita name while HealthCare Partners operates as an independent subsidiary of DaVita HealthCare Partners. The two companies both count California and Florida as key markets and DaVita HealthCare Partners has used HealthCare Partners' integrated care model to help it offer a wider range of health care services.

Internationally the company entered China in 2012 through a joint venture to provide dialysis services with Chinese biotech company 3SBio.

EXECUTIVES

Executive Chair DaVita Medical Group, Charles G. (Chuck) Berg, age 60
Chairman and CEO, Kent J. Thiry, age 61, $1,273,077 total compensation
CFO, Joel Ackerman, age 52
Group VP Purchasing and Public Affairs, LeAnne M. Zumwalt, age 58, $400,000 total compensation
Chief Compliance Officer, Jeanine M. Jiganti, age 58
Chief Accounting Officer, James K. (Jim) Hilger, age 55, $375,000 total compensation
CEO DaVita Kidney Care, Javier J. Rodriguez, age 46, $865,385 total compensation
Chief Medical Officer DaVita Kidney Care, Allen R. Nissenson, age 70
President Colorado Springs Health Partners, Oraida Roman
CEO DaVita International, Robert Lang
Division Vice President, Thomas Dudley
Senior Vice President Clinical Informatics, Douglas Allen
Vice President and Associate General Counsel, David Witek
Vice President revenue Management, David Corlett
Senior Vice President Strategy, James Rechtin
Vice President Corporate Devel, Scott Lloyd
Vice President Finance, Chitra Goswami
Vice President, Martha Wofford
Vice President and General Counsel, Cecilia Lim
Division Vice President Crossroads Division, Roxanne Ramoutar
Auditors: KPMG LLP

LOCATIONS

HQ: DaVita Inc
2000 16th Street, Denver, CO 80202
Phone: 303 405-2100
Web: www.davita.com

PRODUCTS/OPERATIONS

2016 Revenues by Payer

	% of total
Government-based programs	
Medicare & Medicare-assigned plans	55
Medicaid	5
Other government-based programs	4
Commercial	36
Total	**100**

2016 Dialysis Revenues

	% of total
Outpatient hemodialysis centers	79
Peritoneal dialysis & home-based hemodialysis	16
Hospital inpatient hemodialysis	5
Total	**100**

2016 Sales

	$ mil.	% of total
US dialysis & related lab services	9,138	61
DaVita Medical Group (DMG)	4,113	28
Ancillary services	1,621	11
Adjustments	(127.9)	-
Total	**14,745**	**100**

Selected Operations
Astro Hobby West Mt. Renal Care Limited Partnership
Austin Dialysis Centers L.P.
Beverly Hills Dialysis Partnership
Brighton Dialysis Center LLC
Capital Dialysis Partnership
Carroll County Dialysis Facility L.P.
Central Carolina Dialysis Centers LLC
Chicago Heights Dialysis LLC
Continental Dialysis Center Inc.
Dallas-Fort Worth Nephrology L.P.
Dialysis of Des Moines LLC
Dialysis Specialists of Dallas Inc.
Downriver Centers Inc.
Downtown Houston Dialysis Center L.P.
Durango Dialysis Center LLC
DVA Healthcare of Maryland Inc.
East End Dialysis Center Inc.
Elberton Dialysis Facility Inc.
Empire State DC Inc.
Greenwood Dialysis LLC
Hawaiian Gardens Dialysis LLC
HealthCare Partners LLC
HuntingtonPark Dialysis LLC
Indian River Dialysis Center LLC
Jedburg Dialysis LLC
Kidney Centers of Michigan L.L.C.
Lincoln Park Dialysis Services Inc.
Mason-Dixon Dialysis Facilities Inc.
Middlesex Dialysis Center LLC
Natomas Dialysis
Nephrolife Care (India) Pte. Ltd.
North Colorado Springs Dialysis LLC
Open Access Lifeline LLC
Palomar Dialysis LLC
Physicians Choice Dialysis of Alabama LLC
Physicians Dialysis of Houstin LLP
Renal Life Link Inc.
Renal Treatment Centers Inc.
RMS Lifeline Inc.
Rocky Mountain Dialysis Services LLC
Shining Star Dialysis Inc.
Soledad Dialysis Center LLC
Summit Dialysis Center L.P.
Tortugas Dialysis LLC
Total Renal Care Inc.
Total Renal Laboratories Inc.
Total Renal Research Inc.
TRC West Inc.
Tulsa Dialysis Center LLC
Upper Valley Dialysis L.P.

COMPETITORS

Apria Healthcare	Lincare Holdings
Critical Care Systems	Molina Healthcare
International	Permanente Medical
Dialysis Clinic Inc	Groups
FMCNA	Quest Diagnostics
Gentiva	U.S. Renal Care
LabCorp	UnitedHealth Group

HISTORICAL FINANCIALS
Company Type: Public

Income Statement   FYE: December 31

	REVENUE ($ mil.)	NET INCOME ($ mil.)	NET PROFIT MARGIN	EMPLOYEES
12/16	14,745	879	6.0%	70,300
12/15	13,781	269	2.0%	60,400
12/14	12,795	723	5.7%	57,900
12/13	11,764	633	5.4%	57,400
12/12	8,186	536	6.5%	53,400
Annual Growth	**15.8%**	**13.2%**	**—**	**7.1%**

2016 Year-End Financials

Debt ratio: 48.62%	No. of shares (mil.): 194
Return on equity: 18.44%	Dividends
Cash ($ mil.): 913	Yield: —
Current ratio: 1.48	Payout: —
Long-term debt ($ mil.): 8,947	Market value ($ mil.): 12,490

STOCK PRICE ($)	P/E		PER SHARE ($)		
FY Close	High/Low	Earnings	Dividends	Book Value
12/16	64.20	18 13	4.29	0.00	23.89
12/15	69.71	66 53	1.25	0.00	23.22
12/14	75.74	23 18	3.33	0.00	23.98
12/13	63.37	43 18	2.95	0.00	20.79
12/12	110.53	41 28	2.74	0.00	17.84
Annual Growth	(12.7%)	— —	11.9%	—	7.6%

Dean Foods Co.

Dean Foods is the nation's largest milk bottler. The company markets fluid milk ice cream cultured dairy products and beverages (juices teas and bottled water) under more than 50 local regional and private-label brands including Dairy Pure Borden Pet Country Fresh Meadow Gold and TruMoo a leading national flavored milk brand. Dean Foods owns and operates a number of smaller regional dairy companies including Friendly?s Berkeley Farms and Garelick Farms. The company distributes dairy products across the US from regional manufacturing facilities.

HISTORY

Investment banker Gregg Engles formed a holding company in 1988 with other investors including dairy industry veteran Cletes Beshears to buy the Reddy Ice unit of Dallas-based Southland (operator of the 7-Eleven chain). The company also bought Circle K's Sparkle Ice and combined it with Reddy Ice. By 1990 it had acquired about 15 ice plants.

The company changed its name to Suiza Foods when it bought Suiza Dairy in 1993 for $99 million. The Puerto Rican dairy was formed in 1942 by Hector Nevares Sr. and named for the Spanish word for "Switzerland." By 1993 it was Puerto Rico's largest dairy controlling about 60% of the island's milk market.

Suiza Foods bought Florida's Velda Farms manufacturer and distributor of milk and dairy products in 1994. The company went public in 1996 the same year it bought Swiss Dairy (dairy products California and Nevada) and Garrido y Compa ± a (coffee products Puerto Rico).

The company became one of the largest players in the North American dairy industry through its acquisitions in 1997. It paid $960 million for Morningstar (Lactaid brand lactose-free milk Second Nature brand egg substitute) which — like Suiza Foods itself — was a Dallas-based company formed in 1988 through a Southland divestiture. The company entered the Midwest with its $98 million purchase of Country Fresh and the Northeast with the Bernon family's Massachusetts-based group of dairy and packaging companies including Garelick Farms and Franklin Plastics (packaging).

Suiza Foods strengthened its presence in the southeastern US in 1998 with its $287 million acquisition of Land-O-Sun Dairies operator of 13 fluid-dairy and ice-cream processing facilities. Also that year Suiza Foods purchased Continental Can (plastic packaging) for about $345 million and sold Reddy Ice to Packaged Ice for $172 million.

After settling an antitrust lawsuit brought by the US Department of Justice in 1999 Suiza Foods bought dairy processors in Colorado Ohio and Virginia. That year Suiza Foods combined its US packaging operations with Reid Plastics to form Consolidated Containers retaining about 40% of the new company.

In 2001 Suiza Foods announced it had agreed to purchase rival Dean Foods for $1.5 billion and the assumption of $1 billion worth of debt. Dean Foods had begun as Dean Evaporated Milk founded in 1925 by Sam Dean a Chicago evaporated-milk broker. By the mid-1930s it had moved into the fresh milk industry. The company went public in 1961 and was renamed Dean Foods in 1963.

Suiza Foods completed the acquisition and took on the Dean Foods name later in 2001. The new Dean Foods bought out Dairy Farmers of America's interest in Suiza Dairy and merged it with the "old" Dean's fluid-dairy operations to create its internal division Dean Dairy Group.

Along with the purchase of "old" Dean came a 36% ownership of soy milk maker WhiteWave and in 2002 Dean Foods purchased the remaining 64% for approximately $189 million. By the end of the year Dean had sold off some smaller businesses (boiled peanuts and contract hauling) and its Puerto Rico operations for $119 million in cash.

EXECUTIVES

CEO, Ralph P. Scozzafava, age 58, $850,000 total compensation
EVP General Counsel Corporate Secretary and Government Affairs, Russell F. Coleman
EVP and Chief Human Resources Officer, Kimberly (Kim) Warmbier, age 55, $432,000 total compensation
SVP Logistics, S. Craig McCutcheon, age 56
EVP Supply Chain, Brad Cashaw, age 53, $343,674 total compensation
Interim CFO, Scott K. Vopni, age 49
Vice President Legal, Mark Niermann
VP Human Resources, Jose Motta
Vice President of Labor Relations, Shane Keith
Vice President Business Development Group, Christopher Anderson
Vice President Sales, Terry Dana
Vice President Finance, Kim Lechner
VP Safety, Michael Miller
Vice President Commercial Finance, Manoj Bhatnagar
Vice President Research And Development Fresh Dairy Direct, Kathleen Dacunha
Vice President Finance, Eddie Tollison
Vice President, Scott Toth
Vice President and Corporate Treasurer, James Kenwood
Senior Vice President Industry Relations, Marty Devine
Vice President Sales South Region, Marvin Monroe
Vice President Prc, Gary Tritt
Vice President Corporate Development, Steve Schultz
Vice President Tax Planning, Shan Luton
Vice Presidentof Facilities, Keith Davidson
Executive Vice President General Counsel Corporate Secretary Government Affairs, Marc Kesselman
Vice President Of Finance, Tim Jones
Vice President, David Hurst
Vice President of Sales National Accounts, Tim Heil
Vice President Sales North Region, David Stis
Vice President National Warehouse Sales, John White
Chairman, Jim L. Turner, age 71
Auditors: Deloitte & Touche LLP

LOCATIONS

HQ: Dean Foods Co.
2711 North Haskell Avenue, Suite 3400, Dallas, TX 75204
Phone: 214 303-3400
Web: www.deanfoods.com

2015 Sales

	% of total
Domestic	99
Foreign	1
Total	**100**

2016 Sales

	% of total
Domestic	99
Foreign	1
Total	**100**

PRODUCTS/OPERATIONS

2016 Sales

	$ mil.	% of total
Fluid milk	5,339	69
Ice cream	1,041	13
Fresh cream	359	5
Cultured	299	4
Other beverages	308	4
Extended shelf life and other dairy products	231	3
Other	133	2
Total	**7,710**	**100**

2016 Fresh Dairy Direct Sales

	% of total
Private-label brands	51
Company brands	49
Total	**100**

Selected Brands

Alpro (Europe)
Alta Dena
Berkeley Farms
Borden (licensed)
Brown Cow
Brown's Dairy
Dean's
Friendly's
Garelick Farms
Gandy's
Hershey's (licensed)
Horizon Organic
Knudsen (licensed)
LAND O'LAKES (licensed)
Mayfield Creamery
Oak Farms
Over the Moon
Pet (licensed)
Provamel (Europe)
Robinson Dairy
Silk
Swiss Premium
Tru Moo
Tuscan
WhiteWave

Selected Products

Bottled waters
Eggnog
Eggs
Cottage cheese
Half-and-half
Ice cream
Juice
Milk
Pudding
Sour cream
Soymilk
Whipping cream

COMPETITORS

Associated Milk Producers
Aurora Organic Dairy
Ben & Jerry's
Blue Bell
Brewster Dairy
California Dairies Inc.

ConAgra
Crystal Farms Refrigerated Distribution Company
Dairy Farmers of America
Danone
Darigold Inc.
Dreyer's
Foster Dairy Farms
Galaxy Nutritional Foods
Grupo LALA
HP Hood
Hain Celestial
Hiland Dairy
Lactalis
Lifeway Foods
Maryland & Virginia Milk Producers
Mondelez International
National Dairy
Nestl © USA
Northwest Dairy
Organic Valley
Prairie Farms Dairy
Quality Chekd
Rockview Dairies
Stonyfield Farm
Tillamook County Creamery Association
Vitasoy International

HISTORICAL FINANCIALS

Company Type: Public

Income Statement

FYE: December 31

	REVENUE ($ mil.)	NET INCOME ($ mil.)	NET PROFIT MARGIN	EMPLOYEES
12/16	7,710	119	1.6%	17,000
12/15	8,121	(8)	—	16,960
12/14	9,503	(20)	—	17,246
12/13	9,016	813	9.0%	18,040
12/12	11,462	158	1.4%	21,915
Annual Growth	(9.4%)	(6.8%)	—	(6.2%)

2016 Year-End Financials

Debt ratio: 34.00%	No. of shares (mil.): 90
Return on equity: 20.69%	Dividends
Cash ($ mil.): 17	Yield: 0.0%
Current ratio: 1.25	Payout: 27.4%
Long-term debt ($ mil.): 745	Market value ($ mil.): 1,973

	STOCK PRICE ($) FY Close	P/E High/Low		PER SHARE ($) Earnings	Dividends	Book Value
12/16	21.78	17	12	1.31	0.36	6.74
12/15	17.15	—	—	(0.09)	0.28	5.97
12/14	19.38	—	—	(0.22)	0.28	6.67
12/13	17.19	2	1	8.58	0.00	7.53
12/12	16.51	11	6	1.70	0.00	3.85
Annual Growth	7.2%	—	—	(6.3%)	—	15.0%

Deere & Co.

Deere & Co. is interested in seeing its customers go to seed and grow. The company one of the world's largest makers of farm equipment is also a major producer of construction forestry and commercial and residential lawn care equipment. Deere operates through three business segments: the agriculture and turf and construction and forestry segments make up its equipment operations; a credit segment provides financial services. Deere famous for its "Nothing Runs Like A Deere" marketing sells John Deere and other brands through retail dealer networks and also makes products for outlets Home Depot and Lowes.

Operations

Deere's largest operating segment is agriculture and turf which accounts for 70% of revenue. Consolidated into five product platforms — crop harvesting turf and utility hay and forage crop care and tractors — the segment makes such products as loaders combines corn pickers cotton and sugarcane pickers and even golf course equipment and outdoor power products. Besides John Deere brands include Frontier Green Systems as well as SABO in Europe and Benye in China.

The company's construction and forestry segment represents 20% of its total revenue. Making 90% of the types of equipment used in North America this segment distributes backhoe loaders crawler dozers motor graders log skidders and skid-steer loaders.

Besides equipment the company's other main operational division financial services provides credit services for Deere dealers and wholesalers.

Geographic Reach

North America accounts for around 65% of Deere's revenue each year. The company owns nine facilities housing one centralized parts distribution center and eight regional parts depots and distribution centers throughout North America. The company also owns centralized parts distribution centers in Brazil Germany India and Russia and regional parts depots and distribution centers located in Argentina Australia China Mexico South Africa Sweden and the UK.

Sales and Marketing

Deere operates through roughly 25 sales and marketing locations and nearly 20 warehousing locations spanning 15 countries including Argentina Australia Brazil Chile China Ecuador France India Israel Italy Mexico Russia Spain Turkey and the US.

Through US and Canadian facilities Deere markets products to approximately 2365 dealer locations most of which are independently owned and operated. Of these about 1520 sell agricultural equipment while approximately 425 sell construction earthmoving material handling and/or forestry equipment. Nortrax owns some of the dealer locations. Outside the US and Canada Deere agriculture and turf equipment is also sold to distributors and dealers for resale.

Financial Performance

Deere has seen its revenues drop the last three years. From 2015 to 2016 revenues declined 8% from $29 billion to $27 billion and profits plunged 21% from $1.9 billion to $1.5 billion. Its cash flow from operations however has remained consistent the last three years hovering around the $3.7 billion mark for each of those years.

Throughout 2016 Deere experienced lower equipment sales resulting from difficult conditions in the farm and construction equipment markets. This and other factors led to sales drops across its construction and forestry (13%) and agriculture and turf (7%) segment sales.

The erosion of profits in 2016 was fueled by higher production costs primarily related to the impact of engine emission programs in the company's equipment operations and a higher effective tax rate.

Strategy

Deere is focused on enhancing its operations as strong demand for agricultural commodities (mainly grain and oilseeds) continues. To keep manufacturing in sync with demand Deere increases production during the second and third quarters when customers are buying more.

The company is specifically focused on the precision agriculture market as a means for growth. This involves equipment and machinery used to monitor and measure crop yield moisture content or seeding population in real time. Other products generate prescriptions for planting seeds and applying fertilizer or pesticide with better accuracy.

All of this helps farmers manage costs and increase revenue through improved productivity and higher yields. One of these products was Deere's StarFire 6000 receiver introduced in 2016.

Mergers and Acquisitions

In 2016 the company acquired Hagie Manufacturing Company a manufacturer of high-clearance sprayers located in Clarion Iowa for $53 million. The deal accelerated John Deere's market reach in precision planting equipment and added engineering expertise to further develop planting technology.

Looking to grow internationally Deere in 2016 also picked up Monosem a European market leader in precision planters. The purchase included four facilities in France and two in the US.

HISTORY

Vermont-born John Deere moved to Grand Detour Illinois in 1836 and set up a blacksmith shop. Deere and other pioneers had trouble with the rich black soil of the Midwest sticking to iron plows designed for sandy eastern soils so in 1837 Deere used a circular steel saw blade to create a self-scouring plow that moved so quickly it was nicknamed the "whistling plow." He sold only three in 1838 but by 1842 he was making 25 a week.

Deere moved his enterprise to Moline in 1847. His son Charles joined the company in 1853 beginning a long tradition of family management. (All five Deere presidents before 1982 were related by blood or marriage.) Charles eventually set up an independent dealership distribution system and added wagons buggies and corn planters to the product line.

EXECUTIVES

Vice President IT, Martin L Wilkinson
Vice President Corporate Business Development, Ganesh Jayaram
Senior Vice President Engineering and, Randal Sergesketter
Senior Vice President of Sales and Marketing, Domenic Ruccolo
Chairman President and CEO, Samuel R. (Sam) Allen, age 64, $1,500,000 total compensation
President Agriculture and Turf Americas Australia and Global Harvesting and Turf Platforms, James M. Field, age 54, $686,266 total compensation
VP Engineering and Manufacturing (Worldwide Construction & Forestry Division & Deere Power Systems Group), Max A. Guinn, age 59
President Agriculture and Turf Division Europe Asia Africa and Global Tractor Platform, Mark von Pentz, age 54
SVP and CFO, Rajesh (Raj) Kalathur, age 49, $615,312 total compensation
President Agricultural Solutions and CIO, John C. May, age 48, $599,840 total compensation
VP Global Supply Management and Logistics, Pierre Guyot
SVP John Deere Power Systems Worldwide Parts Services Advanced Technology and Engineering and Global Supply Management and Logistics, Jean H. Gilles, age 60, $614,823 total compensation
SVP and Chief Administrative Officer, Marc A. Howze, age 54
President John Deere Financial, Cory J. Reed, age 46
Vice President Information Technology, James Jabanoski
Vice President, Dan Hastings
Senior Vice President Manufacturing An, Daniel J Reilly
Vice President of Sales and Marketing, Michael Triplett
Executive Vice President, Adel Zkri

Vice President Marketing, Jim Anderson
Vice President Information Systems, Ronald McDermott
Vice President Sales and Marketing, Wigger Chris
Vice President Information Services, Daniel Weber
Vice President, Bernard Haas
Vice President Worldwide Supply Management, David Nelson
Vice President strategic Partnerships And Worldwide Construction, Douglas Gage
Vice President and Comptroller, Ryan Campbell
Vice President Information Technology, Dave Garrison
Vice President Manager Director, James Ryan
Senior Vice President Information Technology, Randy Sergesketter
Vice President Information Technology, Martin Wikinson
Vice President Sales, Vanessa Stiffler-claus
Vice President Corporate Textile Accounts, Paul Bauer
Vice President Of Financial, Mark Halupnik
Vice President Worldwide Supply Management, William Bill Norton
Vice President Of Finance, Paul J Nagel
Senior Vice President Finance and Accounting and Chief Financial Officer, Todd Davies
Vice President, Craig Purvis
Vice President Information Systems, Ray Lybarger
Finance Vice President, Mark Theuerkauf
Vice President and Chief Compliance Officer, Linda Newborn
Vice President Purchasing, Chuck Dupree
Vice President Engineering, Brian Buchholz
Senior Vice President Agricultural Marketing North Ame, Douglas Devries
Vice PresidentHuman Resources, Mertroe Hornbuckle
Executive Vice President Operations And Technology Whitney Holding And Whitney National Bank, Karrie Fuhr
Vice President, Ted Norton
Vice President, James Cousins
Vice President Human Resources, Jeffrey Peterson
Vice President Of Planning and Corporate Development, Dan Reilly
Vice President Finance, Roxanne Paper
Senior Vice President Technology and Human Resources, Johnathan Lawson
Vice President Information Services, Pat Weber
Vice President mkt, Randy Rulin
Senior Vice President, Doug Devries
Vice President, Luann K Rickert
Vice President Information Technology, Laura Sivertsen
Senior Vice President Corporate Communications, Frances Emerson
Vice President, Mertroe Hornuckle
Vice President Information Technology, Martin Henry
Vice President Of Information Technology, Daniel Heintzelman
Vice President of Management Informati, Richard Townsend
National Account Manager, Leanne Meyers
Sr.Vice President, Sidwell Lawrence
Vice President Training, Scott Clarke
Vice President of Marketing, Randy Sergesketer
Director of Health and Safety, Jack Kearns
Vice President Vendor Relations Information Technology, Catherine Porter
Vice President, Kimberly Beardsley
Board Member, Crandall Bowles
Secretary, Victoria Graves
Assistant Treasurer, Jeff Trahan
Board Member, Brandt Boland
Board Member, Sherry Smith
Vice President Treasurer, Thomas Spitzfaden
Board Member, Shukla Abhishek
Treasurer Chief Financial Officer, Rob Hovde

Vice Chair Career Development, Shufeng Han
Assistant Treasurer, Richard Lynn
Treasurer, Michael Despain
Treasurer, Candace Schnoor
Auditors: DELOITTE & TOUCHE LLP

LOCATIONS

HQ: Deere & Co.
One John Deere Place, Moline, IL 61265
Phone: 309 765-8000   Fax: 309 765-9929
Web: www.johndeere.com

2016 Sales

	$ mil.	% of total
US & Canada	16,742	63
Outside U.S. and Canada	9,339	35
Other	563	2
Total	**26,644**	**100**

PRODUCTS/OPERATIONS

2016 Sales

	$ mil.	% of total
Agriculture & turf	18,487	70
Construction & forestry	4,900	18
Financial services	2,694	10
Other	563	2
Total	**26,644**	**100**

Selected Products and Services

Agricultural and turf equipment
  Balers
  Combines
  Cotton harvesting equipment
  Golf course equipment
  Harvesters
  Hay and forage equipment
  Irrigation
  Landscape and nursery
  Loaders
  Mowers (commercial riding lawn equipment and walk-behind mowers)
  Planting and seeding equipment
  Power products (outdoor)
  Sprayers
  Tillage
  Tractors (large medium and utility)
  Utility vehicles
Construction and forestry equipment
  Articulated dump trucks
  Backhoe loaders
  Crawler dozers
  Crawler loaders
  Excavators
  Landscape loaders
  Log skidders and loaders
  Material handling equipment
  Motor graders
  Skid-steer loaders
Credit
  Leasing
  Retail and wholesale financing
Power systems
  Diesel and natural gas engines (marine industrial mining)
  Powertrain components
  Transmissions

COMPETITORS

AGCO	Kubota
Buhler Industries	Mahindra
Caterpillar	Navistar International
Great Plains	Terex
Manufacturing	Toro Company
Honda	Valmont Industries
Komatsu	Volvo

HISTORICAL FINANCIALS
Company Type: Public

Income Statement
FYE: October 29

	REVENUE ($ mil.)	NET INCOME ($ mil.)	NET PROFIT MARGIN	EMPLOYEES
10/17	29,737	2,159	7.3%	60,476
10/16	26,644	1,523	5.7%	56,800
10/15	28,862	1,940	6.7%	57,200
10/14	36,066	3,161	8.8%	59,623
10/13	37,795	3,537	9.4%	67,044
Annual Growth	(5.8%)	(11.6%)	—	(2.5%)

2017 Year-End Financials

Debt ratio: 60.87%   No. of shares (mil.): 321
Return on equity: 27.01%   Dividends
Cash ($ mil.): 9,334   Yield: 0.0%
Current ratio: 0.83   Payout: 35.9%
Long-term debt ($ mil.): 25,891   Market value ($ mil.): 42,885

	STOCK PRICE ($) FY Close	P/E High/Low		PER SHARE ($) Earnings	Dividends	Book Value
10/17	133.25	20	13	6.68	2.40	29.70
10/16	88.30	18	15	4.81	2.40	20.71
10/15	78.00	17	13	5.77	2.40	21.29
10/14	85.54	11	9	8.63	2.22	26.23
10/13	81.84	10	9	9.09	1.99	27.46
Annual Growth	13.0%	—	—	(7.4%)	4.8%	2.0%

Dell Technologies Inc

LOCATIONS

HQ: Dell Technologies Inc
One Dell Way, Round Rock, TX 78682
Phone: 800 289-3355
Web: www.delltechnologies.com

HISTORICAL FINANCIALS
Company Type: Public

Income Statement
FYE: February 3

	REVENUE ($ mil.)	NET INCOME ($ mil.)	NET PROFIT MARGIN	EMPLOYEES
02/17*	61,642	(1,672)	—	138,000
01/16	50,911	(1,104)	—	—
01/15	54,142	(1,221)	—	—
Annual Growth	6.7%	—	—	—

*Fiscal year change

2017 Year-End Financials

Debt ratio: 41.78%   No. of shares (mil.): 778
Return on equity: (-21.87%)   Dividends
Cash ($ mil.): 9,474   Yield: —
Current ratio: 0.81   Payout: —
Long-term debt ($ mil.): 43,061   Market value ($ mil.): 50,064

	STOCK PRICE ($) FY Close	P/E High/Low		PER SHARE ($) Earnings	Dividends	Book Value
02/17*	64.35	44	30	1.43	0.00	17.32
01/16	0.00	—	—	(2.72)	0.00	3.88
01/15	0.00	—	—	(3.02)	0.00	(0.00)
Annual Growth	—	—	—	—	—	—

*Fiscal year change

Delta Air Lines Inc (DE)

Delta Air Lines is one of the world's largest airlines by traffic. Through its regional carriers (including subsidiary Comair) the company serves about 320 destinations in about 60 countries and it operates a mainline fleet of 800-plus aircraft as well as maintenance repair and overhaul (MRO) and cargo operations. The airline serves nearly 180 million customers each year and offers more than 15000 daily flights. Delta is a founding member of the SkyTeam marketing and code-sharing alliance (airlines extend their networks by selling tickets on flights) which includes carriers Air France KLM and Alitalia.

Operations

Delta divides its operations into two chief segments: airline and refinery. The airline segment provides scheduled air transportation for passengers and cargo throughout the US and around the world and other ancillary airline services including maintenance and repair services for third parties.

The refinery segment provides jet fuel to the airline segment from its own production and through jet fuel obtained through agreements through third parties. The costs included in the refinery segment are primarily for the benefit of the airline segment.

Geographic Reach

Delta operates from domestic hubs in Atlanta Boston Detroit London Los Angeles Minneapolis/St. Paul New York Seattle and Salt Lake City. Delta has international hubs in Amsterdam Paris and Tokyo. The US market is its largest representing about 70% of net sales.

Sales and Marketing

Delta's tickets are sold through various distribution channels including telephone reservations Delta.com and traditional brick and mortar and online travel agencies. It spent about $277 million on advertising in 2016.

Financial Performance

After peaking at a record-setting $40.7 billion in 2015 Delta's revenues dipped 3% to $39.6 billion in 2016. This was attributed to a 5% decline in passenger revenue per available seat mile (PRASM) on 2% higher capacity compared to 2015. The decrease in PRASM was largely driven by competitive pressure within the low fuel price environment and the impact of US dollar strength on tickets sold in international markets which are largely priced in local currency.

In addition to the revenue decline profits fell 3% from $4.5 billion in 2015 to $4.4 billion in 2016 as lower passenger revenue and higher salaries and related costs offset the benefits of lower fuel prices. Cash flow from operations also fell from $7.9 billion in 2015 to $7.2 billion in 2016 mainly due to unfavorable changes in accounts receivable and fuel inventories.

Strategy

The airline industry is fueled by strategic alliances that allow individual carriers to extend their service without physically flying into new territory. Delta's alliance with SkyTeam allows the airline's reach to extend to more than 900 destinations in 170-plus countries around the globe. The company gets a boost in global coverage with airlines around the world coming aboard the SkyTeam alliance.

To boost its position in the important region of China Delta in 2015 expanded its global network with China Eastern one of the leading airlines in China. The agreement included a $450 million investment by Delta to acquire an almost 4% stake in China Eastern. The move allowed Delta and China Eastern to compete more effectively on routes between the US and China and provided more travel options for customers in both countries.

Looking to Europe Delta plans to build its presence in its strategically advantaged hubs in London Paris and Amsterdam while de-emphasizing higher Europe point-of-sale markets. Its 49% equity investment in Virgin Atlantic has improved its presence in London one of the largest revenue markets from the US while also enhancing its transatlantic network including its existing joint venture relationship with Air France-KLM and Alitalia.

Targeting the Asia/Pacific region for growth in mid-2017 Delta and Korean Air announced a joint venture that will create a combined network serving more than 290 destinations in the Americas and more than 80 in Asia. The increase in scale between the carriers includes expanded codesharing in the trans-Pacific market joint sales and marketing initiatives in Asia and the US and co-location at key hubs.

Another important key growth component for airlines that has made headlines recently is customer satisfaction. Delta has significantly invested in its business since 2010 to improve its operational performance which it states consistently ranks first among the major US carriers. During 2016 the carrier operated 241 days with zero mainline canceled flights a nearly 50% improvement over its 2015 performance.

HISTORY

Delta Air Lines was founded in Macon Georgia in 1924 as the world's first crop-dusting service Huff-Daland Dusters to combat boll weevil infestation of cotton fields. It moved to Monroe Louisiana in 1925. In 1928 field manager C. E. Woolman and two partners bought the service and renamed it Delta Air Service after the Mississippi Delta region it served. About 80 years later Delta became one of the world's largest airlines by traffic after its $2.8 billion acquisition of Northwest Airlines in 2008.

EXECUTIVES

Executive Vice President Human Resources and Labor Relations, Michael Campbell
Vice President In Flight Service Operations and Training, Sandy Gordon
CEO, Edward H. (Ed) Bastian, age 59, $741,669 total compensation
President, Glen W. Hauenstein, age 56, $604,997 total compensation
EVP and CFO, Paul A. Jacobson, age 45, $525,000 total compensation
SEVP and COO, Wayne G. (Gil) West, $617,977 total compensation
EVP and Chief Human Resources Officer, Joanne Smith
SVP and CIO, Rahul Samant
EVP Global Sales; President International, Steve Sear
EVP and Chief Legal Officer, Peter W. Carter, $500,000 total compensation
Vice President Finance and Chief Risk Officer, Christopher Duncan
Vice President Learning, Sharon Mickelson
Vp Sales, Ranjan Goswami
REGIONAL VICE PRESIDENT, Randy Mckinney
Vice President, Erik Snell
Vice President and Chief Accounting Officer, Craig Meynard
General Manager Executive Vice President Safety, Joseph Seguin
Vice President Facilities And Maintenanc, Robert Anderson
Vice President and Treasurer, Kenneth Morge
Senior Vice President and General Counsel, Ben Hirst
Vice President, Jerry Allen
Vice President, Patrick Redahan
SENIOR VICE PRESIDENT EUROPE, Perry Cantarutti
Vice President Technical Services, Mark Benson
Assistant Vice President Retail Information Technology, Timothy W Harms
Vice President Corporate Strategic Planning, Wayne Aaron
Vice President Compensation Benefits and Services, Rob Kight
Vice President Information Systems, Robert Olson
Senior Vice President Delta Connection, Don Bornhurst
Senior Vice President Delta Connection, Donald Bornhorst
Senior Vice President Fuels Optimization, Graeme Burnett
Vice President, Shreve Lee
Vice President Finance, Michael Corbridge
Vice President eCommerce, Rhonda Crawford
AA TO VICE PRESIDENT, Keila Workley
Vice President of Business Operations, Thomas E Schull
Regional Vice President, Richard R Marr
Vice President, Sandeep Dube
Senior Vice President and Deputy General Counsel, Matthew Knopf
Senior Vice President Worldport Operations, Greg Kennedy
Senior Vice President, Don Mitacek
Vice President, Mark Pearson
VICE PRESIDENT OF OPERATIONS, Lora Sarah
Senior Vice President, Tonia Palmieri
SENIOR VICE PRESIDENT CENTRAL REGION, Trevor O Pickle
NATIONAL ACCOUNT MANAGER, Amy Shaw
SENIOR VICE PRESIDENT GOVERNMENT AFFAIRS, Andrea F Newman
ATG VICE PRESIDENT FLD STNS XY, Kristin K Rice
ASSISTANT VICE PRESIDENT PAX SERVICE AGENT DL, Patrice Boystak
ATG VICE PRESIDENT HUMAN RESOURCES XY, Jannie Richardson
VPCORP AUDIT, Brandi Thomas
ASSISTANT VICE PRESIDENT PAX SERVICE SUPERVISOR DL, Brenda Mucciolo
ASSISTANT VICE PRESIDENT PAX SERVICE SUPERVISOR DL, Eileen Griffis
Chairman, Francis S. (Frank) Blake, age 67
Secretary, Wendy Tistinic
Board Member, TONY CARR
SECRETARY, Smith Wilbert
Auditors: Ernst & Young LLP

LOCATIONS

HQ: Delta Air Lines Inc (DE)
Post Office Box 20706, Atlanta, GA 30320-6001
Phone: 404 715-2600
Web: www.delta.com

2016 Sales

	$ mil.	% of total
Domestic	28,108	71
Atlantic	5,919	15
Pacific	2,939	7
Latin America	2,673	7
Total	**39,639**	**100**

PRODUCTS/OPERATIONS

2016 Sales

	$ mil.	% of total
Passenger		
Mainline	28,105	71
Regional carriers	5,672	14
Cargo	668	2
Other	5,194	13
Total	**39,639**	**100**

2016 Sales

	$ mil.	% of total
Airline	39,406	91
Refinery	3,843	9
Intersegment Sales/Other	(3610)	-
Total	**39,639**	**100**

Selected Aircraft

Type
B-717-200
B-737-700
B-737-800
B-737-900
ERB-747-400
B-757-200
B-767-300
B-777-200
ERE190-100
MD-88

COMPETITORS

Air Canada	Lufthansa
AirTran Airways	Qantas
American Airlines	SAS
Group	Singapore Airlines
British Airways	Southwest Airlines
Cathay Pacific	United Continental
Japan Airlines	Virgin Atlantic
JetBlue	Airways

HISTORICAL FINANCIALS

Company Type: Public

Income Statement

FYE: December 31

	REVENUE ($ mil.)	NET INCOME ($ mil.)	NET PROFIT MARGIN	EMPLOYEES
12/16	39,639	4,373	11.0%	84,000
12/15	40,704	4,526	11.1%	83,000
12/14	40,362	659	1.6%	80,000
12/13	37,773	10,540	27.9%	78,000
12/12	36,670	1,009	2.8%	74,000
Annual Growth	**2.0%**	**44.3%**	—	**3.2%**

2016 Year-End Financials

Debt ratio: 14.30%
Return on equity: 37.70%
Cash ($ mil.): 2,762
Current ratio: 0.49
Long-term debt ($ mil.): 6,201

No. of shares (mil.): 730
Dividends
Yield: 0.0%
Payout: 11.6%
Market value ($ mil.): 35,945

	STOCK PRICE ($) FY Close	P/E High/Low		PER SHARE ($) Earnings	Dividends	Book Value
12/16	49.19	9	6	5.79	0.68	16.81
12/15	50.69	9	7	5.63	0.45	13.93
12/14	49.19	62	35	0.78	0.30	10.68
12/13	27.47	2	1	12.29	0.12	13.67
12/12	11.87	10	7	1.19	0.00	(2.50)
Annual Growth	**42.7%**	—	—	**48.5%**	—	—

Devon Energy Corp.

Independent oil and gas producer Devon Energy gets its energy from oil and gas fields primarily in Western North America. It focuses on exploration and production assets in Oklahoma Texas Wyoming and Western Canada. The company boasts proved reserves of about 1.9 billion barrels of oil equivalent. Devon Energy produces about 2.4 billion cu. ft. of of gas equivalent a day (3% of all the gas consumed in North America). It also has midstream and marketing assets. It is the largest producer and lease holder in the Barnett Shale (Texas).

HISTORY

Larry Nichols (a lawyer who clerked for US Supreme Court Chief Justice Earl Warren) and his father John founded Devon Energy in 1969. John Nichols was a partner in predecessor company Blackwood and Nichols an oil partnership formed in 1946.

In 1981 the company bought a small stake in the Northeast Blanco Unit of New Mexico's San Juan Basin. To raise capital Devon formed the limited partnership Devon Resource Investors and took it public in 1985. In 1988 Devon consolidated all of its units into a single publicly traded company.

The firm increased its stake in Northeast Blanco in 1988 and again in 1989 ending up with about 25%. By 1990 Devon had drilled more than 100 wells in the area and had proved reserves of 58 billion cu. ft. of natural gas.

During the 1990s the company launched a major expansion program using a two-pronged strategy: acquiring producing properties and drilling wells in proven fields. In 1990 it bought an 88% interest in six Texas wells; two years later Devon snapped up the US properties of Hondo Oil & Gas. After its 1994 purchase of Alta Energy which operated in New Mexico Oklahoma Texas and Wyoming Devon had proved reserves of more than 500 billion cu. ft. of gas.

Between 1992 and 1997 the company also drilled some 840 successful wells. Buoyed by new seismic techniques that raise the odds of finding oil Devon devoted more resources to pioneering fields in regions where it already had expertise.

Continuing its buying spree Devon bought Kerr-McGee's onshore assets in 1997. Two years later it bought Alberta Canada-based Northstar for $775 million creating a company with holdings divided almost evenly between oil and gas.

Also in 1999 Devon grabbed its biggest prize when it purchased PennzEnergy of Houston in a $2.3 billion stock-and-debt deal that analysts called a bargain. PennzEnergy spun off from Pennzoil in 1998 dates back to the Texas oil boom after WWII. In addition to new US holdings the deal gave Devon a number of international oil and gas assets in such places as Azerbaijan Brazil Egypt Qatar and Venezuela.

On a roll Devon in 2000 bought Santa Fe Snyder for $2.35 billion in stock and $1 billion in assumed debt. The deal increased Devon's proved reserves by nearly 400 million barrels of oil equivalent.

In 2001 the company agreed to a major deal to supply Indonesian natural gas to Singapore. It also made an unsuccessful bid for rival Barrett Resources that was trumped by a bid from Williams Companies. Undaunted that year Devon acquired Anderson Exploration for $3.4 billion in cash and $1.2 billion in assumed debt. It also purchased Mitchell Energy & Development for $3.1 billion in cash and stock and $400 million in assumed debt.

As part of its strategy to refocus on core operations in 2002 the company sold its Indonesian assets to PetroChina for $262 million. By mid-year the company had raised about $1.2 billion through the disposition of oil properties worldwide.

Over this decade Devon Energy bought its way into the big leagues as a North American producer through a series of multibillion-dollar acquisitions of oil and gas producers including Ocean Energy in 2003 for $3.5 billion and US-based Chief Holdings LLC in 2006 for $2.2 billion.

In 2007 Devon began to divest all of its assets in West Africa. It sold its oil and gas business in Egypt to Dana Petroleum for $375 million and its Gabon assets for $206 million. In 2008 it sold its oil and gas business in C´te d'Ivoire to Afren plc for $205 million and in Equatorial Guinea (to that country's national oil company GE Petrol) for $2.2 billion.

In 2010 it sold most of its remaining international assets to BP for $7 billion. As part of this deal BP sold undeveloped oil sand leases in Canada to Devon Energy for $500 million and formed a joint venture with the company to exploit them. The company also sold its Panyu field offshore China to China National Offshore Oil for $515 million.

Consolidating its North American assets to just its onshore properties In 2010 Devon Energy sold its stakes in the Cascade Jack and St. Malo fields in the Gulf of Mexico (about 200 million barrels of estimated recoverable reserves) to AP Moller-Maersk's oil unit for $1.3 billion. It also sold its remaining Gulf of Mexico shelf assets to Apache for $1 billion.

In 2012 it sold its last international offshore asset in Angola for about $71 million.

Boosting its financial resources in 2012 Devon Energy secured a commitment from Sinopec International Petroleum Exploration & Production for the Chinese company to invest $2.2 billion in exchange for one-third of Devon's interest in five new joint venture plays in the Tuscaloosa Marine Shale Niobrara Mississippian Ohio Utica Shale and the Michigan Basin.

That year it also closed a similar $1.4 billion joint venture deal with Sumitomo Corp. to develop 650000 net acres in the Cline Shale and the Midland-Wolfcamp Shale in West Texas.

In 2013 it combined all of its midstream assets with the assets of the former Crosstex Energy Inc. and Crosstex Energy L.P. to form EnLink Midstream LLC and EnLink Midstream Partners LP. The creation of EnLink improves the diversification and growth of midstream holdings while preserving Devon's capital for its core business.

In a cost savings move in 2013 the company closed its office in Houston and consolidated its US personnel into a single operations group at its corporate headquarters in Oklahoma City.

EXECUTIVES

EVP Administration, R. Alan Marcum, age 50, $550,000 total compensation
President and CEO, David A. (Dave) Hager, age 61, $1,275,000 total compensation
EVP and General Counsel, Lyndon C. Taylor, age 59, $625,000 total compensation
VP and CIO, Ben Williams, age 45
COO, Tony D. Vaughn, age 60, $735,192 total compensation
SVP Canadian Operations and President Devon Canada, Rob Dutton, age 47
VP Southern Business Unit, Gregg Jacob, age 56
VP Anadarko Basin Business Unit, Todd Moehlenbrock, age 52
VP Delaware Basin Business Unit, Frank Schroeder, age 46
SVP Exploration and Production, Richard A. (Rick) Gideon, age 41
SVP Exploration and Production, Kevin Lafferty, age 42
VP Rockies Business Unit, John Raines, age 34
EVP and CFO, Jeff L. Ritenour, age 43
SVP Exploration and Production, David G. Harris, age 43
Vice President, Mike Dionisio
Vice President Project Development, Jimmy Turnini
Senior Vice President Marketing, Sue Alberti
Senior Vice President US Operations, Rick Gideon
First Vice President, Gilbert Horton
Assistant To Rick Gideon Senior Vice President of US Operations, Heather Powell
Vice President and CIO, Benjamin Williams
Chairman, John Richels, age 66
Auditors: KPMG LLP

LOCATIONS

HQ: Devon Energy Corp.
333 West Sheridan Avenue, Oklahoma City, OK 73102-5015
Phone: 405 235-3611
Web: www.devonenergy.com

2016 Sales

	% of total
US	56
EnLink	34
Canada	10
Total	**100**

PRODUCTS/OPERATIONS

2016 Sales

	$ mil.	% of total
Marketing & midstream	6,323	51
Oil gas & natural gas liquids	4,182	34
Asset dispositions and other	1,893	15
Oil gas & natural gas liquids derivatives	(201)	0
Total	**12,197**	**100**

COMPETITORS

Abraxas Petroleum	Exxon Mobil
Apache	Hess Corporation
BP	JKX
Bonanza Creek	Jones Energy
Cabot Oil & Gas	Marathon Oil
Chesapeake Energy	Occidental Petroleum
Chevron	Royal Dutch Shell
ConocoPhillips	Williams Companies
EOG	XTO Energy
Encana	

HISTORICAL FINANCIALS

Company Type: Public

Income Statement

FYE: December 31

	REVENUE ($ mil.)	NET INCOME ($ mil.)	NET PROFIT MARGIN	EMPLOYEES
12/16	12,197	(3,302)	—	5,000
12/15	13,145	(14,454)	—	6,600
12/14	19,566	1,607	8.2%	6,600
12/13	10,397	(20)	—	5,900
12/12	9,502	(206)	—	5,700
Annual Growth	**6.4%**	**—**		**(3.2%)**

2016 Year-End Financials

Debt ratio: 39.18%
Return on equity: (-50.75%)
Cash ($ mil.): 1,959
Current ratio: 1.44
Long-term debt ($ mil.): 10,154
No. of shares (mil.): 523
Dividends
 Yield: 0.0%
 Payout: —
Market value ($ mil.): 23,885

	STOCK PRICE ($) FY Close	P/E High/Low	PER SHARE ($) Earnings	Dividends	Book Value
12/16	45.67	— —	(6.52)	0.42	11.33
12/15	32.00	— —	(35.55)	0.96	16.86
12/14	61.21	20 13	3.91	0.94	52.66
12/13	61.87	— —	(0.06)	0.86	50.49
12/12	52.04	— —	(0.52)	0.80	52.41
Annual Growth (31.8%)	**(3.2%)**	**— —**			**—(14.9%)**

Dick's Sporting Goods, Inc

Dick's Sporting Goods operates almost 800 stores in 45-plus US states. Its stores usually contain five smaller shops ("stores within a store") that feature sporting goods apparel and footwear for leisure pursuits ranging from football golf and cycling to hunting and camping. In addition to brands including NIKE and adidas Dick's carries Ativa Walter Hagen Top-Flite and others exclusive to the firm. The company also operates more than 90 Golf Galaxy stores in about 30 states as well as 25 Field & Stream stores in 10 states. Dick's owns the True Runner and Chelsea Collective chains of specialty stores as well.

Operations

Dick's operates 797 stores which include some 675 Dick's Sporting Goods and 91 Specialty Stores. Its products include hard lines — 45% (which includes sporting goods equipment fitness equipment golf equipment and hunting and fishing gear) apparel 35%; footwear 20%; and other 1% (which includes non-merchandise sales categories including in-store services and shipping revenues).

Geographic Reach

Dick's has a presence in more than 45 US states and maintains distribution centers in Georgia Indiana Arizona and Pennsylvania.

The company's top five states in terms of stores are California New York North Carolina Ohio and Pennsylvania which together account for about 30% of total stores.

Sales and Marketing

Dick's sells its products through retail stores — its primary sales channel — and e-commerce sites.

The company markets its products through traditional channels such as newspaper and direct mail pieces. It has developed brand-building marketing campaigns focused on building customer relationship to the Dick's Sporting Goods brand and shifted its advertising mix to include more digital marketing. It continues to optimize its media mix by shifting to marketing channels and by leveraging its expanding customer relationship marketing database from its ScoreCard loyalty program.

Dick's spent $304.9 million on advertising in fiscal 2017. Nike and Under Armour its largest vendors account for about 20% and 10% of merchandise sales respectively.

Financial Performance

The company's has seen strong revenue growth over the last several fiscal years. In fiscal 2017 (ended January) revenues increased to $7.92 billion from $7.27 billion the prior fiscal year. The spike was the result of a rise in non-comparable sales as a result of new stores sales partially offset by a decrease in consolidated same store sales. An increase in eCommerce sales also contributed to the growth.

Dick's' net income decreased from $330 million in fiscal 2016 to $287 million in fiscal 2017. The drop was caused by increased selling general and administrative expense and pre-opening expenses.

Operating cash flows increased due to higher cash provided by deferred construction allowances primarily as a result of the timing and increase in the number of self-developed stores where tenant allowances are provided by landlords.

Strategy

Believing that the sporting goods retailing market can bear at least 1100 Dick's locations nationwide the company has been focused on expanding its retail footprint east of the Mississippi River in Atlanta Chicago and the corridor between New York and Washington DC.

The company is focusing on increasing its omni-channel service so that its customers are able to shop online or in-store easily. Its omni-channel strategy includes the transition to an internal eCommerce platform for www.DICKS.com.

Opening stores in new and existing markets is a part of its business strategy. Dick's opened nine Field & Stream stores during 2016 and the company plans to open eight additional Field & Stream stores by the end of 2017.

The company also grows its exclusive private brand offerings through a combination of brands that it owns and brands that it licenses from third parties. The company invests in its development and procurement resources and marketing efforts relating to these private brand offerings and new retail concepts.

Mergers and Acquisitions

During 2016 Dick's acquired San Diego-based Affinity Sports a sports management technology company. The deal will help Dick's grow its footprint in youth sports technology space.

Also during 2016 Dick's acquired New York ?based GameChanger Media company. GameChanger develops a software platform for amateur teams to collect manage and share information. The acquisition will help Dick?s provide unparalleled technological capabilities to youth teams and leagues across the country.

Company Background

Dick's was founded in 1948 when Dick Stack father of company chairman and CEO Edward Stack opened a bait and tackle shop.

EXECUTIVES

Chairman and CEO, Edward W. (Ed) Stack, age 62, $1,000,000 total compensation
CTO, Paul J. Gaffney, age 46
EVP and CFO, Lee J. Belitsky, age 56, $541,983 total compensation
President, Lauren R. Hobart, age 48, $520,000 total compensation
EVP and Chief Merchant, Keri Jones
SVP Information Technology and CIO, Kurt J. Schnieders
EVP and Chief Strategy Officer, Michele B. Willoughby, age 51, $538,024 total compensation
SVP Operations, Don Germano
Vice President GMM, Alan Epler
Vice President of Marketing, Tom Hassett
Vice Chairman, William J. (Bill) Colombo, age 61
Auditors: Deloitte & Touche LLP

LOCATIONS

HQ: Dick's Sporting Goods, Inc
345 Court Street, Coraopolis, PA 15108
Phone: 724 273-3400
Web: www.DICKS.com

PRODUCTS/OPERATIONS

2016 Sales

	% of total
Hardlines	45
Apparel	35
Footwear	19
Other	1
Total	**100**

Selected Categories

Archery
Backpacking
Baseball
Basketball
Boating
Bowling
Camping

Cycling
Exercise
Fishing
Football
Golf
Hockey (ice and roller)
Hunting
In-line skating
Lacrosse
Optics/telescopes
Paintball
Racquetball/squash
Running
Skateboarding
Snow sports
Soccer
Tennis
Volleyball
Water sports

COMPETITORS

Academy Sports	Hibbett Sports
Big 5	J. C. Penney
Cabela's	Kmart
Callaway Golf	L.L. Bean
Costco Wholesale	Modell's
Dunham's	Olympia Sports
Eastern Mountain	REI
Sports	Sears
Finish Line	Sports Authority
Foot Locker	Target Corporation
Gander Mountain	Wal-Mart
Golfsmith	Winmark

HISTORICAL FINANCIALS

Company Type: Public

Income Statement

FYE: January 28

	REVENUE ($ mil.)	NET INCOME ($ mil.)	NET PROFIT MARGIN	EMPLOYEES
01/17	7,921	287	3.6%	40,500
01/16	7,270	330	4.5%	37,200
01/15*	6,814	344	5.1%	37,600
02/14	6,213	337	5.4%	34,300
02/13	5,836	290	5.0%	29,800
Annual Growth	7.9%	(0.3%)	—	8.0%

*Fiscal year change

2017 Year-End Financials

Debt ratio: 0.13%
Return on equity: 15.50%
Cash ($ mil.): 164
Current ratio: 1.43
Long-term debt ($ mil.): 4

No. of shares (mil.): 110
Dividends
Yield: 0.0%
Payout: 23.6%
Market value ($ mil.): 5,661

	STOCK PRICE ($) FY Close	P/E High/Low	PER SHARE ($) Earnings	Dividends	Book Value
01/17	51.31	24 14	2.56	0.61	17.49
01/16	39.08	21 12	2.83	0.55	16.01
01/15*	51.65	20 14	2.84	0.50	15.51
02/14	52.50	21 16	2.69	0.50	13.99
02/13	47.90	23 17	2.31	2.50	12.90
Annual Growth	1.7%	— —	2.6%	(29.9%)	7.9%

*Fiscal year change

DIGNITY HEALTH

Dignity Health has steadily grown to become the largest private not-for-profit health care provider in the state of California. Dignity Health operates a network of 40 acute-care facilities located in the Golden State and to a lesser extent in Arizona and Nevada. Those facilities house 8500 acute care beds as well as 700 skilled nursing beds. Dignity Health provides home health and hospice services through agencies in California and Nevada. It also operates more than 300 emergency and specialty clinics imaging centers and medical labs as well as managed care and wellness programs. Dignity Health is the official health care provider of the San Francisco Giants. The system plans to merge with Denver-based hospital group Catholic Health Initiatives.

Operations

Dignity Health employs more than 60000 caregivers and staff in communities across Arizona California and Nevada. Founded in 1986 and headquartered in San Francisco Dignity Health is the fifth-largest hospital provider in the nation and the largest hospital system in California. Offering include inpatient outpatient sub-acute and home health care services as well as physician services through affiliates including Dignity Health Medical Foundation. Through another affiliate U.S. Health-Works Dignity Health provides occupational health and urgent care services in more than 20 additional states.

Geographic Reach

Dignity Health offers health care services in more than 20 states primarily in California Nevada and Arizona.

Sales and Marketing

Government payments (Medicare and Medicaid) accounted for 46% of Dignity Health's patient revenue in fiscal 2014; contracted payments (including contracted rate and commercial capitated patient accounts) represented 41% and self-pay accounted for 13% of total payments.

Financial Performance

Dignity Health's revenue increased 3% to $10.7 billion in 2014 due to increases in premiums health-related activities and other operating earnings (including a gain on sale of certain assets related to outreach lab services). Net income fell 21% to $281 million as a result of higher salaries and benefits as well as income tax expenses.

Cash flow from operations grew 33% in 2014 to $422 million mostly due to cash generated from accounts payable and a decline in cash used in estimated receivables and payables.

Strategy

Dignity Health has stated that it wants to become a national integrated care provider by 2020. The company intends to expand its network of owned and affiliated medical centers in both the Catholic and non-Catholic categories. It also aims to coordinate care and reduce expenses across its broad network of facilities through measures such as its $1.8 billion electronic health record (EHR) initiative which will improve patient record and physician communication systems over a five-year period.

In 2017 Dignity Health agreed to join forces with Concentra to operate urgent care centers. Concentra will buy Dignity subsidiary U.S. Health-Works which operates about 250 urgent care centers and onsite clinics in 21 states. The combined urgent care operator which will operate more than 550 urgent care centers will be majority owned by Concentra; Dignity will own a 20% stake. The deal will allow the companies to standardize best practices while reaching more patients as rising demand for urgent care centers brings more business to their operators.

Mergers and Acquisitions

After years of discussions Dignity Health and Catholic Health Initiatives announced plans to merge in late 2017. The combined health system with 139 hospitals in 28 states will be the largest not-for-profit hospital system in the US. The size of the system will allow for it to provide expanded care to patients through such methods as virtual appointments a broader range of clinical programs and advanced technologies. The new organization will be headquartered in Chicago but hospitals will continue to operate under their current names.

HISTORY

Dignity Health formerly Catholic Healthcare West (CHW) traces its roots to 1857 when the Sisters of Mercy founded St. Mary's Hospital in San Francisco. The order expanded in that area and in 1986 two different communities of the Sisters of Mercy merged their hospitals into an organization with one retirement home and 10 hospitals from the Bay Area to San Diego. Declining membership in Roman Catholic religious orders combined with consolidation in the field led the orders to see merger as their only route to survival.

CHW continued to add facilities including AMI Community Hospital in Santa Cruz California in 1990. Since CHW already owned the area's only other acute care hospital Dominican Santa Cruz Hospital CHW in 1993 was ordered not to acquire any more acute care hospitals in Santa Cruz County without FTC approval.

As the trend to managed care became a stampede in the 1990s CHW moved more into preventive care and began reigning in costs through productivity improvement plans. It continued to add hospitals including tax-supported institutions trying to compete with national for-profit systems.

The network increased its medical clout in 1994 by allying with San Diego-based Scripps one of the state's largest HMO systems. In 1995 the Daughters of Charity Province of the West realigned its six-hospital operation with CHW. The next year the Dominican Sisters (California) the Dominican Sisters of St. Catherine of Siena (Wisconsin) and the Sisters of Charity of the Incarnate Word allied their California hospitals with CHW. New community hospitals included Bakersfield Memorial Sierra Nevada Memorial (Grass Valley) Sequoia Hospital (Redwood City) and Woodland Healthcare.

Charity and cost-consciousness clashed in 1996 when union members staged a walkout to protest nonunion outsourcing of vocational nursing housekeeping and kitchen jobs. This dispute was settled but CHW continued to be a target for union organizers with a bitter battle against the Service Employees International Union (SEIU) starting in 1998.

The year 2000 brought CHW more problems with labor relations: SEIU argued that the organization was resistant to unionization. Continued losses led the organization to implement major restructuring the following year as its 10 regional divisions were consolidated into four.

The company parted ways with one of its sponsoring organizations the Franciscan Sisters of the Sacred Heart of Frankfort Illinois in 2003. The sponsorship ended when CHW closed St. Francis Medical Center of Santa Barbara. However the hospital operator that fiscal year posted its first operating profit in seven years.

The company changed its name from Catholic Healthcare West (CHW) to Dignity Health in early 2012 as part of a governance restructuring program. While the firm remained a not-for-profit organization with Catholic roots and its Catholic hospitals continued to be sponsored by their founding congregations (and governed by the Catholic health care directives) the parent organization itself was no longer an official ministry of the Catholic church.

The company's rebranding and restructuring aimed to give it more flexibility to pursue its growth strategy of widening its presence into additional regions of the US while lowering the overall cost of care (a desire of most large hospital operators as the US government works to reform its ailing health system). At the time of the governance shift Dignity Health operated 25 Catholic hospitals and 15 non-Catholic hospitals.

EXECUTIVES

EVP Sponsorship Mission Integration and Philanthropy, Bernita McTernan
President and CEO, Lloyd H. Dean, age 67
EVP and Chief Human Resources Officer, Darryl L. Robinson
EVP and Chief Administrative Officer, Elizabeth Shih
SEVP and COO, Marvin O'Quinn
SEVP and CFO, Daniel J. Morissette
SEVP and Chief Strategy Officer, Charles P. Francis
EVP and CIO, Deanna L. Wise, age 48
EVP and Chief Medical Officer, Robert L. Wiebe
EVP and General Counsel, Rick Grossman
EVP Sponsorship and Mission Integration, Elizabeth Keith
Vice President and Associate General Counsel, Judy Coffin
Senior Vice President Treasury and Strategic Investments, Lisa Zuckerman
Vice President of Corporate Communications and Marketing, Mark Klein
Vice President Hris, Barbara Estes
Vice President, Jeff Land
Medical Director Health Informatics, David Camitta
Vice President and Chief Physician Executive For Physician Integration, Gary Greensweig
Director Of Him, Swaran Dwarka
Director Of Pharmacy, Inaya Hazime
Vice President of External Affairs, Shirley Gunther
Vice President And Associate General Counsel, Matthew Stockslager
Vice President of Real Estate, Jeffrey Land
Vice President EPMO and Performance Excellence, Joan Beach
Vice President Population Health, Julie Bietsch
Senior Vice President Of Operations Nevada, Rod Davis
Clinical Director, Autumn Hilger
Medical Director For Clinical Informatics, Francisco Rhein
Vice President Ambulatory Services, Margie Roper
Vice President Of Human Resources, Sherri Comaianni
Vice President Of Care Management, Jackie Aragon
Vice President Medical Affairs, John Morelli
Vice President Network Develop, Scott Carswell
Vice President And Executive Director, Paula Lamar
Senior Vice President of Philanthropy, Fred Najjar
Director Of Radiology, Richard Siegel
Vice President of Finance, John Petersdorf
Operating Room Director, Larry Hand
Vice President of Home Care Services, Kathleen Sullivan
Vice President Chief Nurse Executive, Josh Freilich
Supervisor Physical Therapy, Abe Rodriguez
Medical Director, Christina Kwasnica
Vice President Medical Affairs, Yagnesh Patel
Vice President of Philanthropy, Wayne Herron
Co medical Director, Patricia Glick
Senior Vice President Financial Operations, Karl Silberstein
Chief Sales Officer Strategy and Business Development Southern California, Beth Purcell
Medical Director Sfo Medical Clinic, Arnold Traynis
Vice President Medical Affairs, Anita Chandrasena
Director of Pharmacy, Anthony Lucchi
Pharmacy Manager, Neal Cardosa
Medical Director, David Oates
Director of Pharmacy, Jacquelyn Cituk
Vice President, Debbie Plass
Pharmacy Manager, Kyle Towne

Vice President Chief Strategy Office, Jordan Wright
ADMISSIONS Director, Heather Driml
Vice President, Victoria Selby
Director of Pharmacy and Retail Services, Mark Leach
Medical Director, Javier Cardenas
Director of Pharmacy and Medication Safety, Candace Fong
Vice President Foundation, Beverly Grova
Vice President Medical Affairs, Sahin Yanik
Director Managed Care, Creg Parks
Director Managed Care, Warren Wolf
Vice President Physician Integration, Julie Sprengel
Chairman, Caretha Coleman
Vice Chair, Judy Carle
Secretary, Erin Didion
Auditors: DELOITTE & TOUCHE LLP SAN FRA

LOCATIONS

HQ: DIGNITY HEALTH
185 BERRY ST STE 300, SAN FRANCISCO, CA 941071773
Phone: 415 438-5500
Web: WWW.DIGNITYHEALTH.ORG

Selected Facilities
Arizona
Barrow Neurological Institute (Phoenix)
Chandler Regional Medical Center
Mercy Gilbert Medical Center
St. Joseph's Hospital and Medical Center (Phoenix)
California
Arroyo Grande Community Hospital
Bakersfield Memorial Hospital
California Hospital Medical Center (Los Angeles)
Community Hospital of San Bernardino
Dominican Hospital (Santa Cruz)
French Hospital Medical Center (San Luis Obispo)
Glendale Memorial Hospital and Health Center
Marian Medical Center (Santa Maria)
Mark Twain St. Joseph's Hospital (San Andreas)
Mercy General Hospital (Sacramento)
Mercy Hospital of Bakersfield
Mercy Hospital of Folsom
Mercy Medical Center Merced Community Campus
Mercy Medical Center Merced Dominican Campus
Mercy Medical Center Mt. Shasta
Mercy Medical Center Redding
Mercy San Juan Medical Center (Carmichael)
Mercy Southwest Hospital (Bakersfield)
Methodist Hospital of Sacramento
Northridge Hospital Medical Center
Oak Valley Hospital (Oakdale)
Saint Francis Memorial Hospital (San Francisco)
Sequoia Hospital (Redwood City)
Sierra Nevada Memorial Hospital (Grass Valley)
St. Bernardine Medical Center (San Bernardino)
St. Elizabeth Community Hospital (Red Bluff)
St. John's Pleasant Valley Hospital (Camarillo)
St. John's Regional Medical Center (Oxnard)
St. Joseph's Behavioral Health Center (Stockton)
St. Joseph's Medical Center (Stockton)
St. Mary Medical Center (Long Beach)
St. Mary's Medical Center (San Francisco)
Woodland Healthcare
Nevada
St. Rose Dominican Hospital Rose de Lima Campus (Henderson)
St. Rose Dominican Hospital San Martín Campus (Las Vegas)
St. Rose Dominican Hospital Siena Campus (Henderson)

PRODUCTS/OPERATIONS

2014 Sales

	$ mil.	% of total
Net patient revenue	9,458	89
Premiums	497	5
Net health-related activities	152	1
Contributions & other	568	5
Total	**10,677**	**100**

Sponsoring Organizations
Sponsoring Organizations
Congregation of the Dominican Sisters of St. Catherine of Siena of Kenosha (Kenosha Wisconsin)
Congregation of the Sisters of Charity of the Incarnate Word (Houston Texas)
Sisters of Mercy of the Americas West Midwest Community (Omaha Nebraska; formerly Auburn Regional Community of the Sisters of Mercy and Burlingame Regional Community of the Sisters of Mercy in California)
Sisters of St. Dominic Congregation of the Most Holy Rosary (Adrian Michigan)
Sisters of St. Francis of Penance and Christian Charity St. Francis Province (Redwood City California)
Sisters of the Third Order of St. Dominic Congregation of the Most Holy Name (San Rafael California)

COMPETITORS
Adventist Health System West
Alta Bates Summit Medical Center
Banner Health
Community Health Systems
Community Hospital of the Monterey Peninsula
Ensign Group
HCA
John C. Lincoln Health Network
John Muir Health
Loma Linda University Medical Center
Memorial Health Services
Prospect Medical
Providence St. Joseph Health
Salinas Valley Memorial
Shasta Regional Medical Center
Stanford Health Care
Sutter Health
Tenet Healthcare
UCSF Medical
Universal Health Services
VITAS Healthcare

HISTORICAL FINANCIALS
Company Type: Private

Income Statement

	REVENUE ($ mil.)	NET INCOME ($ mil.)	NET PROFIT MARGIN	EMPLOYEES
06/09	8,957	(799)	—	49,363
06/08	8,401	169	2.0%	—
Annual Growth	6.6%	—	—	—

2009 Year-End Financials
Debt ratio: ——
Return on equity: (-8.90%)
Cash ($ mil.): 868
Current ratio: 0.70
Long-term debt ($ mil.): —
Dividends
Yield: —
Payout: —
Market value ($ mil.): —

Dillard's Inc.

Tradition is trying to catch up with the times at Dillard's. Sandwiched between retail giant Macy's and discount chains such as Kohl's Dillard's is rethinking its strategy and trimming its store count. The department store chain operates about 290 locations (down from 330 in 2005) in some 30 US states covering the Sunbelt and the central US. Its stores cater to middle- and upper-middle-income women selling name-brand and private-label merchandise with a focus on apparel and home furnishings. Founded in 1938 by William Dillard family members through the W. D. Company control the company.
Operations

Dillard's' largest product category is ladies' apparel at over 20% of sales followed by men's apparel and accessories (17%) ladies' accessories and lingerie (16%) shoes (16%) and cosmetics (14%). Children's apparel home and furniture and construction bring in the remainder.

Dillard's exclusive brand lines include Antonio Melani Gianni Bini GB Roundtree & York and Daniel Cremieux.

Beyond department stores Dillard's owns CDI Contractors a Little Rock Arkansas-based construction firm that was started to build and remodel Dillard's' stores.

Geographic Reach

Texas and Florida are the Arkansas-based department store chain's two largest markets accounting for about a third of total stores. The company operates 293 Dillard's stores and 25 clearing centers — representing more than 50 million sq. ft. of space — in 29 states.

Sales and Marketing

Dillard's sells its products in shopping malls open-air centers and online.

Financial Performance

Dillard's sales and profits have remained mostly flat over the past few years with its rising comparable store sales offset by its shrinking net store count.However in fiscal 2017 (ended January) sales fell 5% to $6.4 billion due to persistent mall traffic declines.

Net income fell $100 million to $169.2 million as the retailer scrambled to cut prices in an effort to prop up store traffic.

Cash flow from operations increased 15% to $517 million due to a sharp increase in trade accounts payable.

Strategy

To try and reverse falling sales the department store chain has moved "up market" positioning itself above Macy's and Belk and below high-end chains such as Nordstrom and Bloomingdale's. To attract more customers Dillard's is focusing on adding more fashion much like J. C. Penney has done in recent years. The firm's new direction is inspired on the success of specialty stores with their edited displays or merchandise in boutique-like settings rather than an endless sea of apparel racks. New stores are smaller (averaging 170000 sq. ft.) and located in open-air lifestyle centers rather than enclosed malls. Dillard's which has been averse to marking down merchandise but has been forced to discount by its lower-end competitors hopes its move up market will stop the markdowns.The shift in product alignment might help stave off the onslaught on the internet as when buying high-value items customers are less willing to "get it wrong" — much more likely when shopping online.

HISTORY

At age 12 William Dillard began working in his father's general store in Mineral Springs Arkansas. After he graduated from Columbia University in 1937 the third-generation retailer spent seven months in the Sears Roebuck manager training program in Tulsa Oklahoma.

With $8000 borrowed from his father William opened his first department store in Nashville Arkansas in 1938. Service was one of the most important things he had to offer he said and he insisted on quality — he personally inspected every item and would settle for nothing but the best. William sold the store in 1948 to finance a partnership in Wooten's Department Store in Texarkana Arkansas; he bought out Wooten and established Dillard's the next year.

Throughout the 1950s and 1960s the company became a strong regional retailer developing its strategy of buying well-established downtown stores in small cities; acquisitions in those years included Mayer & Schmidt (Tyler Texas; 1956) and Joseph Pfeifer (Little Rock Arkansas; 1963). Dillard's moved its headquarters to Little Rock after buying Pfeifer. When it went public in 1969 it had 15 stores in three states.

During the early 1960s the company began computerizing operations to streamline inventory and information management. In 1970 Dillard's added computerized cash registers which gave management hourly sales figures.

The chain continued acquiring outlets (more than 130 over the next three decades including stores owned by Stix Baer & Fuller Macy's Joske's and Maison Blanche). In a 1988 joint venture with Edward J. DeBartolo Dillard's bought a 50% interest in the 12 Higbee's stores in Ohio (buying the other 50% in 1992 shortly after Higbee's bought five former Horne's stores in Ohio).

In 1991 Vendamerica (subsidiary of Vendex International and the only major nonfamily holder of the company's stock) sold its 8.9 million shares of Class A stock (25% of the class) in an underwritten public offering.

Dillard's purchase of 12 Diamond stores from Dayton Hudson in 1994 gave it a small-event ticket-sales chain in the Southwest which it renamed Dillard's Box Office. A lawsuit filed by the FTC against Dillard's that year claiming the company made it unreasonably difficult for its credit card holders to remove unauthorized charges from their bills was dismissed the following year.

Dillard's continued to grow; it opened 11 new stores in 1995 and 16 more in 1996 (entering Georgia and Colorado). The next year it opened 12 new stores and acquired 20 making its way into Virginia California and Wyoming.

William retired in 1998 and William Dillard II took over the CEO position while brother Alex became president. The company then paid $3.1 billion for Mercantile Stores which operated 106 apparel and home design stores in the South and Midwest. To avoid redundancy in certain regions Dillard's sold 26 of those stores and exchanged seven others for new Dillard's stores. The assimilation of Mercantile brought distribution problems that cut into earnings for fiscal 1999. In late 2000 with a slumping stock price and declining sales Dillard's said it would de-emphasize its concentration on name-brand merchandise and offer deep discounts on branded items already in stock. Despite these efforts sales and earnings continued to slide in 2001.

Founder and patriarch William Dillard (the company's guiding force) died in February 2002. Son William II became chairman of the company which has been family-controlled for half a century. Dillard's opened four new stores and closed nine in 2002. Sales declined 3% versus the previous year.

In 2003 Dillard's shuttered 10 stores and opened five new store locations.

In November 2004 Dillard's completed the sale of Dillard National Bank the retailer's credit card portfolio to GE Consumer Finance for about $1.1 billion (plus debt). Dillard's had said it would use the proceeds to reduce debt repurchase stock and to achieve general corporate purposes.

In the spring of 2005 Dillard's shuttered the last of 16 home and furniture stores acquired when the department store chain acquired Mercantile Stores Co. in 1998. Hurricanes Katrina Rita and Wilma took a toll on Dillard's in 2005 interrupting business in about 60 of the company's stores at various times.

In August 2008 Dillard's purchased the 50% stake in the Arkansas-based construction firm CDI Contractors that it didn't already own for about $9.8 million. CDI is a general contactor that also builds stores for Dillard's. In November Dillard's announced 500 job cuts including about 60 at headquarters.

Amid falling sales and rising investor discontent Dillard's bowed to pressure from hedge funds Barington Capital Group and Clinton Group and appointed four new directors in April 2008 to avoid a proxy fight.

In February 2012 Dillard's acquired Acumen Brands an e-commerce company located in Fayetteville Arkansas.

EXECUTIVES

EVP, Drue Matheny, age 70, $735,000 total compensation

EVP, Mike Dillard, age 65, $735,000 total compensation

President, Alex Dillard, age 67, $1,000,000 total compensation

Chairman and CEO, William (Bill) Dillard, age 72, $1,000,000 total compensation

SVP Co-Principal Financial Officer and Principal Accounting Officer, Phillip R. Watts, age 54, $500,000 total compensation

SVP and Co-Principal Financial Officer, Chris B. Johnson, age 45, $500,000 total compensation

Vice President and Treasurer, Sherrill Wise

Vice President, Mike McNiff

Vice President of Mens, Jim Northup

Vice President, James Stockman

Vice President Accounting, Steve Gelwix

Vice President, Mike Litchford

Vice President Merchandising ST Louis Division, Mark Killingsworth

Executive Vice President and Director, Drue Corbusier

Vice President of Corporate Governance, Aurora Huston

Vice President Mens, Gianni Duarte

Vice President of Corporate Advertising and Product, Denise Mahaffy

Vice President and General Merchandise Manager, Alexandra Lucie

Auditors: KPMG LLP

LOCATIONS

HQ: Dillard's Inc.
1600 Cantrell Road, Little Rock, AR 72201
Phone: 501 376-5200
Web: www.dillards.com

2017 Stores

	No.
Texas	58
Florida	42
Arizona	17
Louisiana	15
North Carolina	14
Ohio	14
Georgia	12
Oklahoma	10
Tennessee	10
Alabama	9
Missouri	9
Arkansas	8
Colorado	7
South Carolina	7
Kansas	6
Kentucky	6
Mississippi	6
New Mexico	6
Virginia	6
Iowa	5
Nevada	5
Utah	4
California	3
Illinois	3
Indiana	3
Nebraska	3
Idaho	2
Montana	2
Wyoming	1
Total	**293**

PRODUCTS/OPERATIONS

2017 Sales

	% of total
Ladies' apparel	22
Men's apparel & accessories	17
Shoes	16
Ladies' accessories & lingerie	16
Cosmetics	14
Juniors' & children's apparel	8
Home & furniture	4
Construction segment	3
Total	**100**

COMPETITORS

Abercrombie & Fitch	Macy's
American Eagle	Mattress Firm
Outfitters	Neiman Marcus
Ann Taylor	Nordstrom
Bed Bath & Beyond	Sears
Belk	Stein Mart
Bon-Ton Stores	TJX Companies
Burlington Coat	Tailored Brands
Factory	Talbots
Caleres	Target Corporation
Eddie Bauer LLC	The Gap
Foot Locker	Tuesday Morning
J. C. Penney	Corporation
J. Crew	Von Maur
Kohl's	Walgreen
Lands' End	

HISTORICAL FINANCIALS

Company Type: Public

Income Statement

FYE: January 28

	REVENUE ($ mil.)	NET INCOME ($ mil.)	NET PROFIT MARGIN	EMPLOYEES
01/17	6,418	169	2.6%	40,000
01/16	6,754	269	4.0%	40,000
01/15*	6,780	331	4.9%	40,000
02/14	6,691	323	4.8%	40,000
02/13	6,751	335	5.0%	38,000
Annual Growth	**(1.3%)**	**(15.8%)**	**—**	**1.3%**

*Fiscal year change

2017 Year-End Financials

Debt ratio: 21.10%
Return on equity: 9.66%
Cash ($ mil.): 346
Current ratio: 1.88
Long-term debt ($ mil.): 730

No. of shares (mil.): 32
Dividends
Yield: 0.0%
Payout: 5.6%
Market value ($ mil.): 1,757

	STOCK PRICE ($) FY Close	P/E High/Low		PER SHARE ($) Earnings	Dividends	Book Value
01/17	54.65	18	11	4.93	0.28	53.41
01/16	70.41	21	9	6.91	0.26	49.98
01/15*	113.60	16	11	7.79	0.24	49.02
02/14	87.30	14	11	7.10	0.22	45.33
02/13	85.41	13	6	6.87	5.20	41.24
Annual Growth	**(10.6%)**			**(8.0%)**	**(51.8%)**	**6.7%**

*Fiscal year change

Dime Community Bancshares, Inc

Dime Community Bancshares is in a New York state of mind. It is the holding company for Dime Community Bank (formerly The Dime Savings Bank of Williamsburgh) which boasts $4.5 billion in assets and operates more than 25 branches in Brooklyn Queens and the Bronx as well as Nassau County on Long Island. Founded in 1864 the bank provides standard products and services including checking savings retirement money market and club accounts accounts. Multifamily residential and commercial real estate loans comprise the vast majority of the bank's loan portfolio. Subsidiary Dime Insurance Agency (formerly Havemeyer Investments) offers life policies fixed annuities and wealth management services.

Operations

Multifamily residential real estate loans accounted for 80% of Dime Savings' $4 billion loan portfolio in 2014; most of these were secured by properties in Brooklyn Queens and Manhattan. Another 18% of the portfolio was made up of commercial real estate loans. The community-oriented bank believes that multifamily residential and mixed-use loans in the New York City area produce higher yields than securities with similar maturities.

The bank generated 93% of its total revenue from interest income on loans secured by real estate in 2014 while interest on mortgage-backed securities service charge fees mortgage banking income and other miscellaneous fees made up the rest of revenues.

Geographic Reach

The Brooklyn-based bank operates 25 branches in New York City in the boroughs of Brooklyn Queens and the Bronx as well as in Nassau County in New York.

Sales and Marketing

Dime Community's primary lending area is in the New York Metro area though its total lending area spans 50 miles from its headquarters' radius.

Financial Performance

Dime Community's revenue has been in decline in recent years due to shrinking interest margins on loans amidst the low-interest environment. The firm's profits however have been rising since 2012 thanks to declining loan loss provisions as its loan portfolio's credit quality has improved with the strengthened economy.

Dime's revenue dipped by less than 1% to $182 million in 2014 as the bank's interest income continued to decline on shrinking interest margins on both real estate loans and mortgage-backed securities. The bank blamed fierce mortgage refinancing competition for much of the 49 basis point-reduction of interest yields on its loan portfolio which led to lower interest income.

Despite lower revenue in 2014 the company's net income rose by nearly 2% to $44.25 million thanks to a continued decline in the provision for loan losses. Dime Community's operating cash fell by 23% to $47.26 million during the year due to lower cash earnings.

Strategy

Dime Community Bancshares has been moving toward digital banking channels that are quickly taking the industry by storm allowing the bank to slow expensive branch-expansion plans and cut operating costs significantly while giving customers faster access to banking services. In 2014 as part of its eBanking platform initiative to expand into online banking mobile banking bill pay and remote deposit the bank launched its Dime Mobile Banking platform which allowed customer to deposit checks pay bills transfer funds and check account balances and status from their smartphones.

EXECUTIVES

EVP and Chief Risk Officer, Timothy B. King, age 58, $342,000 total compensation
President and CEO, Kenneth J. Mahon, age 66, $550,000 total compensation
Secretary, Lance J. Bennett, age 65
SEVP Business Banking, Stuart H. Lubow, age 59
SEVP and COO, Robert S. Volino, age 45
EVP and CTO, Timothy K. Lenhoff, age 59
EVP and Chief Retail Officer, William E. Brown, age 50
EVP and Chief Administrative Officer, Anthony J. Rose, age 46
EVP Business Banking, Conrad J. Gunther, age 70
Principal Financial Officer Dime Community Bancshares Inc. and Dime Community Bank, James L. Rizzo
Vice President, Tom Dippolito
Vice Chairman, Michael P. Devine, age 70
Chairman, Vincent F. Palagiano, age 76
Auditors: Crowe Horwath LLP

LOCATIONS

HQ: Dime Community Bancshares, Inc
300 Cadman Plaza West, 8th Floor, Brooklyn, NY 11201
Phone: 718 782-6200
Web: www.dime.com

PRODUCTS/OPERATIONS

2014 Sales

	$ mil.	% of total
Interest		
Loans secured by real estate	169	93
Mortgage-backed securities	0	1
Other	2	1
Noninterest		
Service charges & other fees	3	2
Bank-owned life insurance	1	1
Other	4	2
Total	**182**	**100**

COMPETITORS

Astoria Financial	HSBC
Carver Bancorp	JPMorgan Chase
Citigroup	Valley National
First of Long Island	Bancorp
Flushing Financial	

HISTORICAL FINANCIALS

Company Type: Public

Income Statement

FYE: December 31

	ASSETS ($ mil.)	NET INCOME ($ mil.)	INCOME AS % OF ASSETS	EMPLOYEES
12/16	6,005	72	1.2%	386
12/15	5,032	44	0.9%	388
12/14	4,497	44	1.0%	409
12/13	4,028	43	1.1%	413
12/12	3,905	40	1.0%	421
Annual Growth	**11.4%**	**15.8%**	**—**	**(2.1%)**

2016 Year-End Financials

Debt ratio: 1.18%
Return on equity: 13.65%
Cash ($ mil.): 113
Current ratio: —
Long-term debt ($ mil.): —

No. of shares (mil.): 37
Dividends
Yield: 0.0%
Payout: 28.4%
Market value ($ mil.): 753

	STOCK PRICE ($) FY Close	P/E High/Low		PER SHARE ($) Earnings	Dividends	Book Value
12/16	20.10	10	8	1.97	0.56	15.11
12/15	17.49	15	12	1.23	0.56	13.22
12/14	16.28	14	11	1.23	0.56	12.47
12/13	16.92	14	11	1.23	0.56	11.86
12/12	13.89	13	11	1.17	0.56	10.96
Annual Growth	**9.7%**			**13.9%**	**(0.0%)**	**8.4%**

Discover Financial Services

Discover Financial Services is best known for issuing Discover-brand credit cards which are used by more than 25 million members. The company's cards which include several levels of business and consumer accounts repay cardholders a percentage of the purchase price each time they use their cards. Discover also licenses Diners Club credit cards which are accepted in more than 185 countries. But there's more to this business than just plastic. The company also offers direct banking services makes student and personal loans and runs the PULSE Network ATM system. Morgan Stanley spun off Discover Financial Services in 2007.

Operations

DFS has two operating segments. Direct Banking is the largest accounting for 97% of its revenue. It includes Discover-branded credit cards issued to individuals and small businesses as well as other consumer products and services such as private student loans personal loans home loans prepaid cards and other consumer lending and deposit products. The company's smaller Payment Services segment includes PULSE the automated teller machine debit and electronic funds transfer network; and Diners Club.

The PULSE network of ATMs and POS terminals operates from some 4600 financial institutions across the US and has a direct relationship with over 70% of them. PULSE also provides cash from more than 1.9 million ATMs in 125 countries.

Discover Financial Services makes the bulk of its money from credit card loan interest. About 70% of its total revenue came from interest income from credit card loans while interest income from other loans made up another 13%. The rest of its revenue came from discount and interchange revenue (10% of revenue) protection products revenue (2%) and loan fee income (3%) as well as non-recurring income sources.

Geographic Reach

The Illinois-based company offers services in 185-plus countries. Over 30% of its credit card loans are tied to customers across California Texas Florida and New York.

Sales and Marketing

The direct banking and payment services company markets its credit cards and other loans products via direct mail media advertising and merchant or partner relationships.

Financial Performance

Like many in its industry Discover has enjoyed several years of revenue and profit growth thanks to the increased spending on credit and debit cards and higher credit card balances.

In fiscal 2016 (ended December) revenue climbed 5% to $10.5 billion with most of the growth coming from credit card-related interest income amid higher yields. Interest growth was partially offset by an increase in interest expense due to higher market rates. Discover?s ?other? income streams declined in the year due to the ending of its mortgage banking activities in 2015 as well as a decrease in discount and interchange revenue.

Net income squeaked up from $2.3 billion to $2.4 billion due to higher revenue net of interest expense. Cash provided by operating activities increased 44% to $234 million due to higher provision for loan losses.

Strategy

DFS continues to introduce new credit card products to entice new customers and persuade existing members to spend more on their cards. In 2016 the company launched its Discover it Secured Credit Card to appeal to consumers with bad or no credit. In 2015 it launched its Freeze It program allowing its credit card users to switch on/off their Discover accounts if they had misplaced their card.

Meanwhile the company has been busy building its international business to increase the acceptance of its cards worldwide. The company has reciprocity alliances with card issuers in countries such as Canada China France Germany Japan South Korea and the UK to increase its cards' acceptance in those markets and allow cardholders access to Discover's network anywhere in the world.

In past years the card issuer has also sought growth in its credit card and student and personal loan operations by acquiring new accounts and by purchasing other companies. It exited the mortgage origination business in 2015 just three year entering the market by acquiring Tree.com.

Company Background

To gain access to federal funds made available through the Troubled Asset Relief Program (TARP) Discover Financial converted to a bank holding company in 2009. It received $1.2 billion from the program which it repaid the following year.

HISTORY

Morgan Stanley spun off Discover Financial Services in 2007.

To gain access to federal funds made available through the Troubled Asset Relief Program (TARP) Discover Financial converted to a bank holding company in 2009. It received $1.2 billion from the program which it repaid the following year.

Discover boosted its lending operations in 2010 with its $600 million purchase of Citibank's 80% stake in Student Loan Corporation. It also acquired a $4.2 billion portfolio of private student loans from Citibank. The company later divested its portfolio of federal student loans after the government overhauled its lending program and became the sole provider of government-backed student loans in 2010. The following year Discover bought another $2.5 billion in student loans from Citibank.

In 2012 DFS bought Home Loan Center the mortgage origination operations of Tree.com for nearly $56 million.

In 2013 Discover inked a deal with Network International a top payment solutions provider in the Middle East that promotes the newly launched Mercury domestic card network. As part of their alliance Mercury network cards will be accepted on Discover Diners Club and PULSE networks for international purchases and cash access outside the United Arab Emirates. In 2012 Discover issued its first cards outside the US (in Ecuador) and entered into an alliance with National Payments Corporation to increase network acceptance in India.

EXECUTIVES

Chairman and CEO, David W. Nelms, age 56, $1,000,000 total compensation
President and COO, Roger C. Hochschild, age 53, $800,000 total compensation
EVP and CFO, R. Mark Graf, age 52, $650,000 total compensation
EVP and President Payment Services, Diane E. Offereins, age 60, $650,000 total compensation

EVP and President Consumer Banking, Carlos M. Minetti, age 55, $650,000 total compensation
EVP General Counsel and Secretary, Kelly McNamara Corley, age 57
EVP and President Credit and Card Operations, James V. Panzarino, age 65
EVP and CIO, Glenn P. Schneider, age 55
EVP and Chief Risk Officer, Brian D. Hughes, age 50
EVP and Chief Marketing Officer, Julie A. Loeger, age 53
VICE PRESIDENT, Dana Traci
Vice President Technology Products, Joseph Bonefas
Vice President Internet Solutions, Joel Suchomel
Vice President Legal, James Swift
Vice President Of Marketing, Mark Scarborough
Vice President Business Unit Risk, Steve Carmichael
Vice President and Assistant General Counsel, Simon Halfin
Vice President and Assistant General Counsel, David Oppenheim
Vice President Compliance, Layne Bussell
Vice President, Kevin Odonnell
Vice President and Assistant General Counsel, Carol Sulkes
Vice President Of Purchasing, Gerry Fitzmaurice
Vice President, Shilpa Wadhera
Vice President, Cathy Davis
Vice President, Alisa Ellis
Vice President Human Resources, Kerry Piercy
Vice President National Recovery Center, Mike Daverio
Auditors: DELOITTE & TOUCHE LLP

LOCATIONS

HQ: Discover Financial Services
2500 Lake Cook Road, Riverwoods, IL 60015
Phone: 224 405-0900
Web: www.discover.com

PRODUCTS/OPERATIONS

2016 Sales

	$ mil.	% of total
Direct banking	10,227	97
Payment services	270	3
Total	**10,497**	**100**

2016 Sales

	$ mil.	% of total
Interest		
Credit card loans	7,155	68
Other loans	1,361	13
Investment securities	38	0
Other	62	1
Non-interest		
Net discount & interchange revenue	1,055	10
Loan fees	343	3
Protection products	239	2
Transaction processing	155	2
Other	89	1
Total	**10,497**	**100**

COMPETITORS

Ally Financial	JPMorgan Chase
American Express	MasterCard
Bank of America	PNC Financial
Barclays Bank Delaware	Sallie Mae
Capital One	USAA
Citigroup	Visa Inc
First Data	Wells Fargo

HISTORICAL FINANCIALS

Company Type: Public

Income Statement

FYE: December 31

	ASSETS ($ mil.)	NET INCOME ($ mil.)	INCOME AS % OF ASSETS	EMPLOYEES
12/16	92,308	2,393	2.6%	15,549
12/15	86,936	2,297	2.6%	15,036
12/14	83,126	2,323	2.8%	14,676
12/13*	79,340	2,470	3.1%	14,128
11/12	75,283	2,345	3.1%	13,009
Annual Growth	5.2%	0.5%	—	4.6%

*Fiscal year change

2016 Year-End Financials

Debt ratio: 27.56%
Return on equity: 21.12%
Cash ($ mil.): 11,914
Current ratio: —
Long-term debt ($ mil.): —

No. of shares (mil.): 388
Dividends
Yield: 0.0%
Payout: 20.1%
Market value ($ mil.): 28,026

	STOCK PRICE ($) FY Close	P/E High/Low		PER SHARE ($) Earnings	Dividends	Book Value
12/16	72.09	13	7	5.77	1.16	29.13
12/15	53.62	13	10	5.13	1.08	26.74
12/14	65.49	14	11	4.90	0.92	24.79
12/13*	55.95	11	8	4.96	0.74	22.89
11/12	41.61	9	5	4.46	0.40	19.64
Annual Growth	14.7%	—	—	6.6%	30.5%	10.4%

*Fiscal year change

Discovery Communications Inc

Discovery Communications allows viewers to go on safari without ever having to leave their couch. The company is the world's #1 non-fiction media company with more than 150 worldwide cable TV networks including Discovery Channel Animal Planet Oprah Winfrey Network (OWN) and The Learning Channel (TLC). Discovery's various networks reach 3 billion subscribers in more than 220 countries. In addition the company offers educational products and services to school; a diverse set of digital media services; and online content through Discovery.com and AnimalPlanet.com.

HISTORY

John Hendricks a history graduate who wanted to expand the presence of educational programming on TV founded Cable Educational Network in 1982. Three years later he introduced the Discovery Channel. Devoted entirely to documentaries and nature shows the channel premiered in 156000 US homes. After dodging bankruptcy (it had $5000 cash and $1 million in debt to the BBC) within a year the Discovery Channel had 7 million subscribers and a host of new investors including Cox Communications and TCI (later AT&T Broadband). It expanded its programming from 12 hours to 18 hours a day in 1987.

Discovery continued to attract subscribers reaching more than 32 million by 1988. The next year it launched Discovery Channel Europe to more than 200000 homes in the UK and Scandinavia. The company began selling home videos in 1990 and entered the Israeli market. The following year Discovery Communications Inc. (DCI) was formed to house the company's operations and it bought The Learning Channel (TLC founded 1980). The company revamped TLC's programming and in 1992 introduced a daily six-hour commercial-free block of children's programs. The next year it introduced its first CD-ROM title In the Company of Whales based on the Discovery Channel documentary.

DCI increased its focus on international expansion in 1994 moving into Asia Latin America the Middle East North Africa Portugal and Spain. The next year the company introduced its website and began selling company merchandise such as CD-ROMs and videos. DCI solidified its move into the retail sector in 1996 with the acquisition of The Nature Company and Scientific Revolution chains (renamed Discovery Channel Store). Also that year it launched its third major cable channel Animal Planet.

The company continued expanding internationally throughout the mid-1990s establishing operations in Australia Canada India New Zealand and South Korea (1995); Africa Brazil Germany and Italy (1996); and Japan and Turkey (1997). DCI also added to its stable of cable channels with the purchase of 70% of the Travel Channel from Paxson Communications (later ION Media Networks) in 1997. (It acquired the remaining 30% interest in 1999.) The company's 1997 original production "Titanic: Anatomy of a Disaster" attracted 3.2 million US households setting a network ratings record.

The following year DCI and the BBC launched Animal Planet in Asia through a joint venture and agreed to market and distribute new cable channel BBC America. It also bought CBS's Eye on People renaming the channel Discovery People (DCI shut the channel down in 2000). DCI spent $330 million launching its new health and fitness channel Discovery Health in 1999 and formed partnerships with high-speed online service Road Runner (to provide interactive information and services to Road Runner customers) and Rosenbluth Travel (to provide vacation packages based on DCI programming).

DCI reorganized its Internet activities into one unit called Discovery.com in 2000 with plans to eventually take it public. Later that year the Discovery Channel set back-to-back records with the two highest-rated documentaries ever on cable "Raising the Mammoth" (10.1 million people) and "Walking With Dinosaurs" (10.7 million people). In 2001 the company cut about 50 jobs as part of a restructuring. Later that year Discovery Communications struck a three-year deal to lease time from NBC on Saturday mornings (paying $6 million per season) to show its Discovery Kids programs.

In 2002 the company launched a 24-hour high-definition television network called Discovery HD Theater. Two years later founder John Hendricks relinquished his CEO duties (he remained chairman). President Judy McHale replaced him.

DCI started off 2005 by rebranding its aviation-themed Discovery Wings channel as the Military Channel. Later that year former majority owner Liberty Media placed its stake in DCI into a new company called Discovery Holding which it then spun off to Liberty shareholders.

Early in 2007 former NBC Universal Cable executive David Zaslav was named CEO replacing McHale. DCI later bought out 25%-partner Cox Communications in exchange for $1.3 billion in cash along with such assets as the Travel Channel and Antenna Audio. It also began shuttering its chain of Discovery Channel Stores as part of a cost-cutting effort.

Joint venture partners Discovery Holding and Advance/Newhouse (an affiliate of Advance Publications) combined their stakes in Discovery Communications in 2008 spinning off DCI as a public company.

Over the next few years DCI worked diligently to launch new networks targeting a diverse selection of audience segments. In 2010 it rolled out The Hub a channel targeting kids ages 2-11. Another 50/50 joint venture with toy maker Hasbro The Hub offers programming based on many of Hasbro's popular brands including G.I. Joe Scrabble Tonka and Transformers.

In early 2011 the company helped launch OWN talk show host Oprah Winfrey's new network and 3net one of the first networks dedicated to providing 3D programming 24 hours a day.

EXECUTIVES

President CEO and Director, David M. Zaslav, age 58, $3,000,000 total compensation
Group President Discovery Channel Animal Planet and Science Channel, Rich Ross, age 56
President OWN: Oprah Winfrey Network and Harpo Studios, Erik Logan
Chief Commercial Officer, Paul (Guyardo) Guagliardo, age 53, $1,400,000 total compensation
Group President Investigation Discovery American Heroes Channel and Destination America, Henry S. Schleiff, age 68
EVP and Head International Business Operations Discovery Networks International, John Honeycutt
President Discovery Networks International, Jean-Briac (JB) Perrette, $1,381,557 total compensation
President and Managing Director Discovery Networks Asia-Pacific, Arthur Bastings
President and CEO Discovery Education, Bill Goodwyn
President International Development Digital and Discovery Nordics, Michael (Mike) Lang, age 52
Chief Corporate Operations and Communications Officer, David C. Leavy
Chief Development Distribution and Legal Officer, Bruce L. Campbell, age 50, $1,544,423 total compensation
VP Development and Production Discovery Studios, Nancy Daniels
President and Managing Director Discovery Networks Latin America/U.S. Hispanic and Canada, Enrique R. (Henry) Mart nez
Chief Human Resources and Global Diversity Officer, Adria Alpert-Romm, age 62, $801,058 total compensation
President and Managing Director Discovery Networks Central & Eastern Europe Middle East and Africa, Kasia Kieli
CFO, Gunnar Wiedenfels
CEO Eurosport, Peter Hutton
President Domestic Distribution, Eric Phillips
President and Managing Director Discovery Networks Southern Europe, Marinella Soldi
President International Content Group, Susanna Dinnage
Vice President Operations And Prod Development Partnerships, Kevin Malone
Vice President Operations, Toni Herbert
Vice President Financial Planning And Analysis, Matthew Deprey
Executive Vice President Advertising Sales Mtv Networks Kids And Family Group, Jim Perry
Vice President Technology, Jim Boyle
Carrie D Storer Senior Vice President Human Resources And Compliance Legal, Carrie Storer
Senior Vice President Of Operations, Veronica Cajigas
Vice President, John Saag
Vice President, Michela Giorelli
Senior Vice President Investor Relations, Craig Felenstein
Senior Vice President Distribution, Meg Lowe

Senior Vice President Us Media Operations, Don Johnson
Vice President Strategy And Account Management, Todd Richards
Chairman, Robert J. (Bob) Miron, age 80
Auditors: PricewaterhouseCoopers LLP

LOCATIONS

HQ: Discovery Communications Inc
One Discovery Place, Silver Spring, MD 20910
Phone: 240 662-2000
Web: www.discoverycommunications.com

PRODUCTS/OPERATIONS

2016 Sales

	$ mil.	% of total
Distribution	3,213	49
Advertising	2,970	46
Other	314	5
Total	**6,497**	**100**

2016 Sales

	$ mil.	% of total
US networks	3,285	50
International networks	3,040	47
Education & other	174	3
Corporate & adjustments	(2)	-
Total	**6,497**	**100**

Selected Mergers and Acquisitions

FY2012
Revision3 ($30 million; San Francisco CA; digital video provider)

Selected Operations

Cable channels
  Animal Planet
  Discovery Channel
  Discovery Kids
  Investigation Discovery
  Planet Green
  Science Channel
  TLC (The Learning Channel)
Commerce and education
  Discovery Education
  DiscoveryStore.com
Business and Brands
U.S. Networks
Discovery Networks International
Discovery Education
Discovery Commerce
Discovery Digital Media
Revision3
Discovery Enterprises International
Discovery Studios

COMPETITORS

A&E Networks	NBCUniversal
AMC Networks	PBS
CBS Corp	Scripps Networks
Disney	Turner Broadcasting
E! Entertainment Television	Viacom

HISTORICAL FINANCIALS

Company Type: Public

Income Statement

FYE: December 31

	REVENUE ($ mil.)	NET INCOME ($ mil.)	NET PROFIT MARGIN	EMPLOYEES
12/16	6,497	1,194	18.4%	7,000
12/15	6,394	1,034	16.2%	7,000
12/14	6,265	1,139	18.2%	6,800
12/13	5,535	1,075	19.4%	5,700
12/12	4,487	943	21.0%	4,500
Annual Growth	**9.7%**	**6.1%**	**—**	**11.7%**

2016 Year-End Financials

Debt ratio: 50.28%	No. of shares (mil.): 388
Return on equity: 22.43%	Dividends
Cash ($ mil.): 300	Yield: —
Current ratio: 1.66	Payout: —
Long-term debt ($ mil.): 7,841	Market value ($ mil.): 10,653

	STOCK PRICE ($) FY Close	P/E High/Low		PER SHARE ($) Earnings	Dividends	Book Value
12/16	27.41	15	12	1.96	0.00	13.29
12/15	26.68	22	16	1.58	0.00	13.30
12/14	34.45	54	19	1.66	0.00	12.75
12/13	90.42	60	42	1.49	0.00	13.23
12/12	63.48	51	33	1.24	0.00	12.83
Annual Growth	**(18.9%)**	**—**	**—**	**12.1%**	**—**	**0.9%**

Dish Network Corp

DISH Network believes entertainment (and news and sports) is a dish best served from the sky and over the internet. The company is the #2 provider of satellite-based pay-TV in the US (behind AT&T-owned DIRECTV) serving nearly 14 million household subscribers as well as hospitality restaurants retail and other commercial accounts. Programming includes premium movies on-demand video service regional and specialty sports local and international channels and pay-per-view in addition to basic video programming. Its Sling TV offering provides streaming video over the internet. DISH also offers bundled voice and internet services through partnerships with voice and data communications providers. DISH generates all sales in the US.

Operations

DISH Network?s revenue comes from its satellite and streaming pay-TV subscriptions. The satellite service relies on satellite dishes that are set up on customers? structures (homes and commercial buildings) to receive signals. The Sling streaming service is transmitted over the internet and is geared to consumers who don?t subscribe to cable or satellite services. Sling branded pay-TV services consist of live streaming in versions for the domestic US international markets. The company counts about 14 million pay-TV subscribers but doesn?t break them down between satellite and streaming. Besides TV DISH Network?s pay-TV services include broadband internet and telephone service. It has about 580000 subscribers to those services.

The company also owns spectrum licenses for wireless telephone service but it has yet to offer anything. It has accumulated spectrum licenses since 2008 and intends to seek more.

Geographic Reach

While the satellite TV service is offered nationally (all revenue is generated in the US) DISH Network's voice and internet services are confined to a swath of the western US that includes Arizona Colorado New Mexico the Dakotas Oregon and Washington. The company operates about a dozen call centers in the US.

Sales and Marketing

DISH Network gains new subscribers through third parties including national retailers and telecommunications firms local and regional electronics stores and small satellite retailers among other channels. Customer acquisition costs have continued to fall in recent years while average revenue per user has risen as has the company?s

churn rate (which measures customers adding and dropping service).

Financial Performance

DISH Network has produced steady if unspectacular revenue growth in the past few years and that continued in 2016 although with a barely registered gain. The company's revenue came in at just more than $15 billion an increase of about $25 million from 2015. It continued to lose subscribers during the year but had higher prices and higher average revenue per customer.

The company?s net income soared 94% to $1.4 billion in 2016 from 2015. The company didn't spend to buy spectrum licenses in 2016 after spending more than $500 million for spectrum rights in 2015. It also had lower satellite and transmission costs and depreciation and amortization costs in 2016 compared to 2015.

Cash flow from operations rose to $2.8 billion in 2016 from $2.4 billion in 2015 from an increase in income adjusted to exclude non-cash charges for gain and losses on investments depreciation and amortization expense and impairment of long-lived assets.

Strategy

DISH Network has focused much of its attention on its Sling TV packages aimed at customers who have cut their subscription to cable and satellite TV services. The company expanded its Sling packages to offer consumers more choices: The Sling TV Blue service offers streaming over multiple devices while the original service now Sling TV Orange streams to one device. It is working on a cloud-based DVR system that enable Sling subscribers to record programs. First aimed at millennials the company has expanded Sling's scope to target other groups of consumers interested in cutting the pay TV cord as well as other populations becoming more comfortable with technology.

For satellite subscribers DISH Network introduced Flex Pack a group of channels consumers bundle selectively for more choice at lower prices. The company also has worked to improve customer service with apps that allow customers to manage and track a DISH technician headed to their homes.

In early 2017 DISH Network swapped some assets with EchoStar that gave DISH greater control over Sling and satellite hardware and software development. The move allows DISH to integrate DISH and Sling customer experiences which should include operating efficiencies.

DISH Network has been stockpiling wireless spectrum licenses but has yet to deploy services such as phone service. The company has indicated it might roll out service at the 5G level the next generation of wireless service that should enable faster and more powerful connections than the previous 3G and 4G levels now dominating the market. Another purpose for the spectrum stockpile could be to make DISH more attractive for acquisition by merger by another industry player in need of spectrum.

EXECUTIVES

EVP Strategic Planning, Bernard L. (Bernie) Han, age 52, $500,000 total compensation
Executive Vice President Human Resources, Stephen Wood
EVP Sales and Distribution and Director, James (Jim) DeFranco, age 65, $374,640 total compensation
Chairman and CEO, Charles W. (Charlie) Ergen, age 63, $1,000,000 total compensation
EVP Corporate Development, Thomas A. (Tom) Cullen, age 57, $450,000 total compensation
President and COO, W. Erik Carlson, age 47, $515,000 total compensation

EVP General Counsel and Secretary, R. Stanton Dodge, age 49, $296,155 total compensation
EVP and CTO, Vivek Khemka, age 44
EVP Operations, John W. Swieringa, age 39
EVP Customer Acquisition and Retention, Brian V. Neylon, age 51
SVP and CFO, Steven E. (Steve) Swain, age 49, $357,539 total compensation
EVP Marketing Programming and Media Sales, Warren W. Schlichting, age 55, $372,885 total compensation
SVP and CIO, Rob Dravenstott
SVP and Chief Marketing Officer, Jay Roth
Vice President and Corporate Controller, Paul W Orban
Senior Vice President Programming, David Shull
Vice President Of Programming, Andrew Lecuyer
Vice President Wireless Development, David Zufall
Vice President Customer Care, Melissa Gonzalez
Vice President of Sales, Dennis Newman
Vice President Of Finance, Kevin Gelston
National Sales Manager, Glen Smith
National Account Manager, Brian Cox
National Accounts Manager, Christopher Guthery
Vice President of Business Development, Robert Grosz
National Sales Manager, Milena Bontcheva
Vice President Financial Planning and Analysis, Kathy Schneider
Marketing Vice President, Alfredo Rodriguez
Vice President Corporate Taxes, Matthew Sheers
Senior Vice President, Amir Ahmed
National Sales Manager, Andrew Hirko
National Accounts Manager, Stephen Butters
Vice President Of Marketing, Melanie Polvoriza
Vice President of Corporate Initiatives, Rex Povenmire
Vice President Sales, Carolyn Crawford
Vice President Of Marketing, Stephanie Pence
Vice President of Tax, Nicholas Mast
National Accounts Manager Strategic Sales Partners, Richard Brilli
Vice President, Karen Frank
Vice President Information Technology Operations, Paul Mino
National Account Manager, Laura Haessler
Vice President and Associate General Counsel, Nick Sayeedi
Vice President, Nick Rossetti
Vice President, Andy Cipra
Executive Vice President and Special Advisor to the Chief Executive Officer, Jim DeFranco
Senior Vice President of Sales, Carlos Barberi
Vice President Marketing, Michael Kinner
Vice President Wireless Development, Kathy Buff
Vice President of Customer Service, Alexander Greengold
Vice President of Marketing, Shathabi Ravindra
Auditors: KPMG LLP

LOCATIONS

HQ: Dish Network Corp
9601 South Meridian Boulevard, Englewood, CO 80112
Phone: 303 723-1000   **Fax:** 303 723-1499
Web: www.dishnetwork.com

PRODUCTS/OPERATIONS

2016 Sales

	$ mil.	% of total
Subscriber-related revenue	15,033	100
Equipment sales and other revenue	0	-
Total	**15,094**	**100**

COMPETITORS

AMC Networks	Grande Communications
AT&T	Hulu
Altice USA	Netflix
Charter Communications	RCN Corporation
Comcast	Roku
Cox Communications	Time Warner Cable
DIRECTV	Verizon

HISTORICAL FINANCIALS

Company Type: Public

Income Statement

FYE: December 31

	REVENUE ($ mil.)	NET INCOME ($ mil.)	NET PROFIT MARGIN	EMPLOYEES
12/16	15,094	1,449	9.6%	16,000
12/15	15,068	747	5.0%	18,000
12/14	14,643	944	6.5%	19,000
12/13	13,904	807	5.8%	25,000
12/12	14,266	636	4.5%	35,000
Annual Growth	1.4%	22.8%	—	(17.8%)

2016 Year-End Financials

Debt ratio: 58.66%	No. of shares (mil.): 465
Return on equity: 39.15%	Dividends
Cash ($ mil.): 5,323	Yield: —
Current ratio: 1.83	Payout: —
Long-term debt ($ mil.): 15,541	Market value ($ mil.): 26,952

	STOCK PRICE ($) FY Close	P/E High/Low		PER SHARE ($) Earnings	Dividends	Book Value
12/16	57.93	19	13	3.05	0.00	9.97
12/15	57.18	49	35	1.61	0.00	5.92
12/14	72.89	39	26	2.04	0.00	4.36
12/13	57.92	33	19	1.76	0.00	2.13
12/12	36.40	27	19	1.41	1.00	0.08
Annual Growth	12.3%	—	—	21.3%	—	232.7%

Disney (Walt) Co. (The)

The monarch of this magic kingdom is no man but a mouse: Mickey Mouse. The Walt Disney Company is the world's largest media conglomerate with assets encompassing movies television publishing and theme parks. Its Disney/ABC Television Group includes the ABC television network and 10 broadcast stations as well as a portfolio of cable networks including ABC Family Disney Channel and ESPN (80%-owned). Walt Disney Studios produces films through imprints Walt Disney Pictures Disney Animation and Pixar. It also owns Marvel Entertainment and Lucasfilm two extremely successful film producers. In addition Walt Disney Parks and Resorts runs its popular theme parks including Walt Disney World and Disneyland.

HISTORY

After getting started as an illustrator in Kansas City Walt Disney and his brother Roy started Disney Brothers Studio in Hollywood California in 1923. Walt directed the first Mickey Mouse cartoon Plane Crazy in 1928 (the third Steamboat Willie was the first cartoon with a soundtrack). The studio produced its first animated feature film Snow White and the Seven Dwarfs in 1937. Walt Disney Productions went public in 1940 and later produced classics such as Fantasia and Pinocchio. The Disneyland theme park opened in 1955.

Roy Disney became chairman after Walt died of lung cancer in 1966. Disney World opened in Florida in 1971 the year Roy died. His son Roy E. became the company's principal individual shareholder. Walt's son-in-law Ron Miller became president in 1980. Two years later Epcot Center opened in Florida. In 1984 the Bass family of Texas in alliance with Roy E. bought a controlling interest in the company. New CEO Michael Eisner (from Paramount) and president Frank Wells (from Warner Bros.) ushered in an era of innovation prosperity and high executive salaries.

The company later launched The Disney Channel and opened new theme parks including Tokyo Disneyland (1984) and Disney-MGM Studios (1989; eventually renamed Hollywood Studios). In 1986 the company changed its name to The Walt Disney Company. The Disney Store retail chain debuted in 1987. Disneyland Paris (originally Euro Disney) opened in 1992. The following year Disney expanded its movie studio with the purchase of independent film company Miramax the brainchild of producers Bob and Harvey Weinstein.

Following Wells' death in a helicopter crash in 1994 boardroom infighting led to the acrimonious departure of studio head Jeffrey Katzenberg. (He was awarded $250 million in compensation in 1999.) The next year Eisner appointed Hollywood agent Michael Ovitz as president. (Ovitz left after 16 months with a severance package of more than $100 million.) Disney bought Capital Cities/ABC (now ABC Inc.) for $19 billion in 1996 and two years later it bought Web services firm Starwave from Microsoft co-founder Paul Allen. It later acquired 43% of Internet search engine Infoseek for $70 million and together they launched the GO Network in 1999. Disney bought the remaining 57% of Infoseek later that year and formed GO.com (later Disney Online) which began trading as a separate tracking stock.

In early 2000 ABC chairman Robert Iger was named Disney's president and COO. Later that year Time Warner Cable briefly suspended ABC broadcasts during a dispute over re-broadcasting rights drawing the ire of some 3.5 million cable customers. (The FCC later ruled that Time Warner violated rules against dropping a station from cable systems during sweeps periods.)

The company expanded its theme parks in Anaheim in 2001 opening Downtown Disney and Disney's California Adventure. It also announced a further restructuring of its Internet business including closing the GO.com search site and converting its Internet tracking stock back into Disney common stock. That year Disney formed a joint venture with Wenner Media (US Weekly LLC) and took a 50% stake in entertainment magazine US Weekly (sold in 2006) . Later Disney bought Fox Family Channel which it renamed ABC Family from News Corporation and Haim Saban for $2.9 billion in cash and assumption of $2.3 billion in debt.

In 2003 Disney began its exit from the sports world by selling the Anaheim Angels. (The company had acquired a 25% stake in the baseball team in 1995 and purchased the remaining interest four years later.)   At Disney's annual shareholder meeting in 2004 about 45% of stock owners voted to not re-elect the embattled Eisner to the board. In response Disney directors stripped Eisner of the chairman title and named director and former US senator George Mitchell to that position.

Disney sold its under-performing chain of Disney Store retail outlets to The Children's Place in 2004. Amid all the strife the company boosted its children's entertainment properties by purchasing the Muppet and Bear in the Big Blue House characters along with their film and television libraries from The Jim Henson Company.

Several big executive shakeups occurred at Walt Disney in late 2005. Eisner finally passed the CEO torch after more than 20 years to former COO Iger. That same year Disney Parks opened Hong Kong Disneyland the company's biggest foray into the world's most populated country. In addition the Weinstein brothers left Miramax to form The Weinstein Company ending two of the most successful tenures of the independent film movement. (Disney ceased the operations of Miramax in a cost-cutting move in 2010 and announced plans to sell the Miramax label later that year.)

In mid-2006 Walt Disney completed a crucial acquisition — the $7.4 billion purchase of Pixar Animation. Disney almost lost Pixar as a production partner in the animation house's blockbuster films but Iger successfully dodged the bullet. Disney Studios' release of Pirates of the Caribbean: Dead Man's Chest that year topped box office records when it brought in $132 million during its opening weekend. The mark was broken by the third installment of the series Pirates of the Caribbean: At World's End which took in $156 million when it was released the next year. Also in 2007 Disney spun off ABC's radio broadcasting operations to Citadel Broadcasting for $2.7 billion in cash and stock.

Disney re-acquired the Disney Store chain in 2008 from Hoop Holdings a subsidiary of retailer The Children's Place in an effort to save the stores from closing. Hoop Holdings had filed bankruptcy that year citing continued losses and rising debt. (The Children's Place was not involved in the bankruptcy filing.) Also in 2008 the company reorganized its digital holdings with the formation of Disney Interactive Media Group. The following year the company purchased a 30% stake in video streaming website Hulu.

Roy E. died in late 2009 at age 79. Also that year Disney acquired Marvel Entertainment bringing Spider-Man Iron Man and other comic book characters into the Magic Kingdom. The deal was worth a whopping $4 billion and changed the course of its movie-making strategy reducing the number of films the studio releases each year while significantly ramping up production of costly big-budget franchises.

In attempts to cut costs Disney Studios in 2010 sold its venerable Miramax production unit (producer of films as Pulp Fiction and Shakespeare in Love) in 2010 to a group of investors (including Ron Tutor private equity firm Colony Capital and Qatar Holdings) for some $663 million. Also that year the company spent $563.2 million to acquire Playdom a popular social game company on Facebook in order to boost its DIMG holdings. Meanwhile Pixar's Toy Story 3 was the top grossing summer release in 2010.

Jobs who stepped down as CEO of Apple in 2011 for medical reasons and died of pancreatic cancer later that year had been Disney's largest individual stockholder with a 7% stake he acquired when the company purchased Pixar. (Jobs had bought Pixar from Lucasfilm in 1986.) Upon his death his Disney shares were converted to the Steven P. Jobs Trust led by his widow Laurene Powell Jobs.

Disney's 2012 box office bomb John Carter lost some $200 million and is reported to be one of the biggest money-losing films of all time.

EXECUTIVES

EVP Corporate Communications, Zenia Mucha
SEVP General Counsel and Secretary, Alan N. Braverman, age 68, $1,549,000 total compensation
Senior Vice President, Steven Bardwil
Chairman and CEO, Robert A. (Bob) Iger, age 64, $2,500,000 total compensation

President ESPN and Co-Chairman Disney Media Networks, John Skipper
SEVP and CFO, Christine M. McCarthy, age 61, $1,287,692 total compensation
EVP Controllership Financial Planning and Tax, Brent A. Woodford
Chairman The Walt Disney Studios, Alan F. Horn
Chairman Walt Disney Parks and Resorts, Robert (Bob) Chapek
Chairman Walt Disney International, Andy Bird, age 54
SEVP Chief Strategy Officer, Kevin A. Mayer, age 54, $1,287,692 total compensation
Chairman Disney Consumer Products and Interactive Media, James A. (Jimmy) Pitaro
EVP and Chief Human Resources Officer, Mary Jayne Parker, age 55, $826,385 total compensation
President The Walt Disney Company Europe Middle East and Africa (EMEA), Rebecca Campbell
Co-Chair Disney Media Networks and President Disney/ABC Television Group, Ben Sherwood
President Disney Cruise Line and New Vacation Operations, Anthony Connelly
Senior Vice President Human Resources, Steven Milovich
Senior Vice President Chief Financial Officer Disney Consumer Products, Robert Langer
Vice President World Wide Marketing and Franchise Management, Gregory Coleman
Vice President Mrktg and Sales Strategy AbD and DCL and Aulani, Tiffany Rende
Senior Vice President Of Marketing, David Sameth
Vice President Operations and Sales Development, Helen Faust
Vice President Operations Asia Pacific, Dennis Chau
VP Human Resources, Rochelle Holden
Vice President Strategic Business Innovation, David Min
VICE PRESIDENT, Trevor Kelley
Vice President Global Security Operations, Grant Crabtree
Vice President, Kris Theiler
Vice President Marketing Walt Disney Studios UK EMEA Disney Branded Movies and Lucasfilm, Charlotte Tudor
Vice President WorldWide Post Production, Stephen Swofford
Vice President Porfolio Development, Cynthia Derick
Senior Vice President International, Ron Kollen
Senior Vice President Human RE, Marjorie Randolph
Senior Vice President Advertising Sales, Irv Schulman
Senior Vice President Advertising Sales Disney Online, Spencer Moseska
Senior Vice President of Enterprise Infrastructure Services, Charles Weiner
Vice President, Jack Eldon
Senior Vice President Finance, Tracy Wilson
Vice President, Eric Coleman
Vice President human Resources Business Partner, Josefina Leon
Vice President Business Affairs, Lisa Mucci
Vice President Business Management, Robert Vanderhyde
Senior Vice President, Jerry Ketcham
Vice President Employee and Organization Development, Carolyn Wilson
Vice President Walt Disney Co. The, Vincent Vedrenne
Vice President of Marketing Creative Film Services, Ticole Richards
Vice President Operations Dcvi, Andrew Aherne
Vice President Corporate Brand Management, Charlie Cain
Vice President Finance, Graham Burridge
VICE PRESIDENT, Douglas Ligons

Senior Vice President Planning and Sales Strategy, Laura Nelson
Vice President of Finance, Clark Jones
Senior Vice President, Ken Caldwell
Vice President Online and On Demand Marketing, David Kite
Vice President Applications Development, Michelle Kong
Office Of Vlad Rak Vice President, Isabel Macdonald
Vice President Magic Kingdom Park Walt Disney World Resort, Phil Holmes
Vice President, Ellen Blackler
Vice President Rsm Finance, Adriana Jaramillo
Vice President Sales, Jeremiah Tachna
Executive Vice President and General Sales Manager, Jed Cohen
Government Relations, Jessica Moore
Vice President Finance, Tim Adam
Senior Vice President Online, Vivek Sharma
Vice President Counsel, Steve Plotkin
Vice President, Kristi Breen
Vice President, Gilberto Kladt
Senior Vice President Deputy General Counsel, Suzanne V Wilson
Vice President Management Audit, Gary D Hansen
Senior Vice President Production, Susette Hsiung
Vice President and Lead Tax Counsel, Michael Salama
Vice President Estimating, Jeffrey Webb
Senior Vice President Innovation, Michael Abrams
Vice President Of Promotions And Marketing, Laura Kuhn
Vice President Creative Film Services, Barbara Lange
Vice President Pay Television And Digital, Lindsey Green
Vice President Human Resources and DI DCL and New Vacation Operations, Yvonne Sweeney
Senior Vice President Sales and Marketing, Patrick Scanlan
Vice President Manager Director, Chris Gray
Vice President Of Forecasting, Mark Haskell
Vice President, Hugh Wood
Vice President Creative Music and Soundtracks, Kaylin Frank
Vice President Sales and Marketing, Jeff James
Vice President, Tod Devine
Executive Vice President Marketing, Jason Taback
Vice President Marketing, Sandra Gomes
Senior Vice President Creative, Joe Rohde
Vice President Creative Development, Michael Karafilis
Vice President Finance, Michelle Long-Knize
Senior Vice President Corporate Strategy, Nick Van Dyk
Vice President of Blu ray and DVD Creative Production, David Jessen
Executive Vice President Finance and Acctng, Paul Gregg
Vice President Media Operations, Nina Anderson
Vice President Internal Communications, Cathi Killian
Executive Vice President, Lane Merrifield
Vice President Revenue and Profit Management, Mark Shafer
Vice President Finance and Business Development, Mario Iannetta
Vice President Of Human Resources, Jayne Parker
Senior Vice President International Publicity WDSMP International, Michelle Sewell
VICE PRESIDENT, NANCY KANTER
Vice President, Greg Head
Vice President Dcom Kids Entertainment, Kyle Laughlin
Senior Vice President Unscripted Programming and Development Freeform the New Name For ABC Family, Kary McHoul
Vice President Compensation, Shawn Bacon
Senior Vice President Tax, John A Stowell

Executive Vice President Programming, Karey Burke
Vice President Contract Management And A, Adam Wolff
Vice President Emea Central Planning, Katrina Strauss
Vice President of Business Development, Maribeth Bisienere
Senior Vice President Sales, Heidi Lobel
Vice President Of Retail Sales, Chip Lister
Vice President WDPandR Design and Engineer and IFP Strategy, Dennis Lind
Vice President Counsel, Suet Lai
Vice President Finance, Richard Leon
Vice President Finance And Business Development, Sherri Lombra
VICE PRESIDENT MUSIC CLEARANCE, Lesley Allery
SENIOR VICE PRESIDENT HUMAN RESOURCES AND DIVERSITY AND INCLUSION, Julie Hodges
Vice President Resort Sales And Services, Anne Hamilton
Vice President Sales Latin America Buena Vista International, Fernando Barbosa
Vice President Finance and Planning Disney ABC Cable Networks Group, Naomi Gagliano
Vice President Litigation, Gordon Goldsmith
Vice President DCL Shoreside Travel Operations, Joann Arndt
Vice President International Sales Disne, Peter Fitton
Vice President, Frank Ritti
Help Desk Vice President, Chris Healy
Executive Vice President Production, Sam Dickerman
Vice President Information Technology, Howard Davine
Vice President Of Sales, Craig Relyea
Senior Vice President Corporate Taxes, Anne Buettner
Vice President, Tom Stauffer
Vice President, Karen Holm
Vice President of Business Strategy and Operations, Jeri Anderson
Vice President European Operations, Edwin van der Meerendonk
Vice President Business Affairs, David Garcia
Vice President Of Sales, Angela Emery
Vice President Casting Original Movies, Judy Taylor
SVP Global Human ResourcesTalent and Workforce Diversity Disney ABC Television Group, Steve Milovich
Vice President Sales, Anthony Macina
Senior Vice President, Barrie Godwin
SVP Strategy and Business Development Disney Consumer Products and Interactive Media, Kareem Daniel
Vice President Information Technology, Mark Canavan
Vice President Marketing and Creative, Kristin Moss
VICE PRESIDENT, RUTH BOND
Vice President Project Management, James M Kearns
Manager Government Relations, Valerie Carney
Vice President of Sales and Marketing, Annabelle Marlow
Senior Vice President, Meredith Roberts
Senior Vice President, Chris Oldre
Auditors: PricewaterhouseCoopers LLP

LOCATIONS

HQ: Disney (Walt) Co. (The)
500 South Buena Vista Street, Burbank, CA 91521
Phone: 818 560-1000
Web: www.disney.com

2016 Sales

	$ mil.	% of total
US & Canada	42,616	77
Europe	6,714	12
Asia/Pacific	4,582	8
Latin America & other regions	1,720	3
Total	**55,632**	**100**

PRODUCTS/OPERATIONS

2016 Sales

	$ mil.	% of total
Media networks	23,689	43
Parks & resorts	16,974	30
Studio entertainment	9,441	17
Consumer products & Interactive media	5,528	10
Total	**55,632**	**100**

2016 Sales

	$ mil.	% of total
Service	47,130	85
Product	8,502	15
Total	**55,632**	**100**

Selected Operations

Consumer products
  Disney Publishing Worldwide
  Disney Stores (retail outlets)
Interactive media
  Disney Interactive Studios (video games)
  Club Penguin (social networking for children)
  Disney Online
  Disney.com
  DisneyFamily.com
Media networks
  A&E Television Networks (42%)
  A&E
  Bio (The Biography Channel)
  The History Channel
  History International
  Lifetime
  Lifetime Movie Network
  Lifetime Real Women
  The Military History Channel
  ABC Family Channel
  ABC Television Network
  Disney Channel
  ESPN (80%)
  ESPN2
  ESPN Classic
  ESPNEWS
  JETIX Europe
  SOAPnet
  Television broadcast stations
  KABC (Los Angeles)
  KFSN (Fresno CA)
  KGO (San Francisco)
  KTRK (Houston)
  WABC (New York City)
  WJRT (Flint MI)
  WLS (Chicago)
  WPVI (Philadelphia)
  WTVD (Raleigh-Durham NC)
  WTVG (Toledo OH)
  Toon Disney
Studio entertainment
  Dimension
  Disney Music Group (music production and distribution)
  Disney Theatrical Group (live entertainment events)
  Lucasfilm
  Marvel Entertainment
  Pixar
  Touchstone Pictures
  Walt Disney Pictures
Theme parks and resorts
  Adventures by Disney (vacation packages)
  Disney Cruise Line
  Euro Disney (40%)
  Disney Village
  Disneyland Paris
  The Walt Disney Studios Park (Marne-La-Vallee France)
  Disneyland Resort (Anaheim CA)
  Disneyland
  Disney's California Adventure
  Hong Kong Disneyland (47%)

Tokyo Disney Resort (owned and operated by Oriental Land Co.; Disney earns royalties)
Tokyo Disneyland
Tokyo DisneySea
Walt Disney Imagineering (planning and development)
Walt Disney World Resort (Orlando FL)
Disney Vacation Club
Disney's Animal Kingdom
Disney's Hollywood Studios
Disney's Wide World of Sports
Downtown Disney
Epcot
Magic Kingdom

COMPETITORS

21st Century Fox	MGM
AOL	SeaWorld
CBS Corp	Six Flags
Comcast	Sony Pictures
Discovery	Entertainment
Communications	Time Warner
DreamWorks Animation	Viacom
Liberty Interactive	Yahoo!

HISTORICAL FINANCIALS

Company Type: Public

Income Statement
FYE: September 30

	REVENUE ($ mil.)	NET INCOME ($ mil.)	NET PROFIT MARGIN	EMPLOYEES
09/17*	55,137	8,980	16.3%	199,000
10/16	55,632	9,391	16.9%	195,000
10/15	52,465	8,382	16.0%	185,000
09/14	48,813	7,501	15.4%	180,000
09/13	45,041	6,136	13.6%	175,000
Annual Growth	5.2%	10.0%	—	3.3%

*Fiscal year change

2017 Year-End Financials

Debt ratio: 26.40%
Return on equity: 21.29%
Cash ($ mil.): 4,017
Current ratio: 0.81
Long-term debt ($ mil.): 19,119
No. of shares (mil.): 1,500
Dividends
  Yield: 0.0%
  Payout: 27.4%
Market value ($ mil.): 147,855

	STOCK PRICE ($) FY Close	P/E High/Low		Earnings	Dividends	Book Value
09/17*	98.57	20	16	5.69	1.56	27.54
10/16	92.86	21	15	5.73	1.42	27.04
10/15	103.00	25	17	4.90	1.81	27.83
09/14	88.74	21	15	4.26	0.86	26.34
09/13	65.19	20	14	3.38	0.75	25.24
Annual Growth	10.9%	—	—	13.9%	20.1%	2.2%

*Fiscal year change

DIVIDEND CAPITAL DIVERSIFIED PROPERTY FUND INC.

Auditors: KPMG LLP DENVER COLORADO

LOCATIONS

HQ: DIVIDEND CAPITAL DIVERSIFIED PROPERTY FUND INC.
518 17TH ST STE 1200, DENVER, CO 802024108
Phone: 303 228-2200

Company Type: Private

Income Statement
FYE: December 31

	ASSETS ($ mil.)	NET INCOME ($ mil.)	INCOME AS % OF ASSETS	EMPLOYEES
12/16	1,783	55	3.1%	15
12/15	1,967	131	6.7%	—
12/14	2,148	33	1.6%	—
12/13	2,305	56	2.4%	—
Annual Growth	(8.2%)	(0.8%)	—	—

2016 Year-End Financials

Debt ratio: ——	
Return on equity: 25.50%	Dividends
Cash ($ mil.): 13	Yield: —
Current ratio: —	Payout: —
Long-term debt ($ mil.): —	Market value ($ mil.): —

Dollar General Corp

Dollar General commands the field of discount general merchandise. The fast-growing retailer boasts more than 14300 discount stores in some 45 US states mostly in the South East the Midwest and the Southwest. It generates more than 75% of its sales from consumables (including refrigerated shelf-stable and perishable foods) and another 12% from seasonal items. The stores also offer household products (cleaning supplies and health and beauty aids) and apparel. Dollar General targets low- middle- and fixed-income shoppers pricing items at $10 or less. The no-frills stores typically measure about 7400 sq. ft. and are located in small towns that are off the radar of giant discounters.

Operations

Dollar General's massive stores network is supported by nearly 15 distribution centers that are strategically located throughout its geographic footprint. Dollar General owns several trademarks including Dollar General Dollar General Market Clover Valley DG DG Deals Smart & Simple trueliving Forever Pals I*Magine OT Sport and Sweet Smiles. It also boasts a few licenses such as Bobbie Brooks for clothing and Rexall for health and beauty aids.

Geographic Reach

Dollar General operates nearly 13430 stores in 45 US states. Texas has the most number of stores at around 1350.

Sales and Marketing

The retailer devotes its marketing dollars to promotional circulars targeted circulars that support new stores television and radio advertising in-store signage and costs associated with the sponsorship of certain auto racing activities.

Because Dollar General's customers typically live in small towns (with fewer than 20000 people) the company doesn't allocate large amounts of money to advertising. It has spent more on advertising in recent years however as the company expands.

Dollar General sells brand-name products from manufacturers such as Procter & Gamble Kimberly-Clark Unilever Kellogg's General Mills Nabisco Hanes PepsiCo and Coca-Cola.

Financial Performance

Dollar General's sales and profits have been rising the past several years thanks to aggressive store expansion and increased same-store sales as its consumable item selection have become increasingly popular.

The retailer's revenues rose 8% to a record $22 billion in 2017 (ended February 3) driven by 1% growth in same-store sales and a 9% rise in Consumables product sales. Seasonal product and Home products sales grew by 6% and 7% respectively while Apparel product sales increased 4%.

Higher revenue drove Dollar General's net income up 7% to a record $1.3 billion. The retailer's operating cash levels climbed to $1.6 billion in 2017 from $1.4 billion in 2016 as its cash earnings rose.

Strategy

With its small-box stores typically measuring some 7400 sq. ft Dollar General targets cost-conscious consumers that prefer easier and quicker access to items than at super-sized competitors such as Wal-Mart and Costco (which are also often much farther away). Indeed Dollar General's strategy of catering to the value conscious has paid off big both during and after the recession. The discount retailer boasted its 27th consecutive year of same-store sales growth in 2017 (ended February 3) attributable to its value and convenience proposition.

Dollar General continues to aggressively open new stores in existing and new states to boost sales. It also continues to evaluate its long-term opportunities to best serve the needs of customers in new markets and more densely populated metropolitan areas. Throughout 2017 the company intends to open about 1300 stores and relocate or remodel approximately 750 stores. Dollar General's 2018 roadmap includes another 900 new stores and about 1000 remodels.

Banking on its lucrative and growing consumables sales the retailer has initiatives underway to increase its margins on many items within its consumables category. To this end Dollar General anticipates adding more private-brand consumables each year and offer tobacco products in most of its locations. It's also been expanding its refrigerated food offerings in more than 1500 of its stores.

HISTORY

J. L. Turner was 11 when his father was killed during the 1890s in a Saturday night wrestling match. This forced J. L. to drop out of school and work on the family farm which was weighted by a mortgage. By his 20s J. L. who never learned to read well was running an area general store. Experiencing some success he branched out and purchased two stores of his own. They failed but J. L. rebounded going to work for a wholesaler. With the onset of the Depression J. L. found he could buy out the inventories of failing merchants for next to nothing using short-term bank loans that were quickly repaid.

In 1939 J. L. was joined by his son Cal. The two each put up $5000 to start a new Scottsville Kentucky-based dry goods wholesaling operation called not surprisingly J.L. Turner & Son. It was not until 1945 when the company experienced a glut of women's underwear that it expanded into retail. J.L. Turner & Son sold off the dainties in their first store located in Albany Kentucky. Within a decade the company was operating 35 stores. In 1956 J.L. Turner & Son introduced its first experimental Dollar General Store — all items priced less than a dollar — in Springfield Kentucky. Like the company's first stores the dollar store concept would grow: Dollar General Stores numbered 255 a decade later.

Cal Jr. J. L.'s 25-year-old grandson joined the family business in 1965 and became a director in 1966. The company changed its name to Dollar General and went public two years later. In 1977 Cal Jr. was named president and CEO. That year Dollar General acquired Arkansas-based United Dollar Stores.

The early 1980s saw Dollar General continue its acquisition-powered growth. The company bought INTERCO's 280-store P.N. Hirsch chain and the 203-store Eagle Family Discount chain in 1983 and 1985 respectively. To cope with expanded distribution demands Dollar General opened an additional distribution center in Homerville Georgia in 1986 to help out the original Scottsville facility. The acquisitions led by Cal Jr.'s brother Steve ended up costing the company dearly; Dollar General's 1987 stock price dropped nearly 85%. The next year they also cost Steve his job: He was forced out by the company's new chairman Cal Jr. In addition to ousting Steve Cal Jr. replaced more than half of Dollar General's executives in 1988. The retailer began moving toward everyday low pricing (la Wal-Mart) in the late 1980s.

Growth from then on was powered by internal expansion. In 1990 the company operated nearly 1400 stores; by 1995 it had more than 2000. To accommodate the growth Dollar General built a third distribution center in Ardmore Oklahoma in 1995 and another in South Boston Virginia in 1997.

While continuing to focus on small towns and neighborhoods Dollar General has expanded beyond the Southeast and Midwest opening its first stores in New York and New Jersey in 2001. In 2004 the company opened more than 700 locations and expanded into Arizona New Mexico and Wisconsin.

In April 2005 the company settled a Securities and Exchange Commission investigation into the circumstances that resulted in a $100 million earnings restatement for the years 1998 through 2000 with payment of a $10 million civil penalty.

To support its growth Dollar General opened a new distribution center in South Boston (its ninth) in 2006 and one in Union County South Carolina in mid-2005. Also in 2006 the retailer expanded its warehouse in Ardmore Oklahoma.

In July 2007 Dollar General was taken private by Kohlberg Kravis & Roberts GS Capital Partners (an affiliate of Goldman Sachs) and Citi Private Equity an investment arm of Citigroup in a deal valued at $7.3 billion.

In November 2009 the company went public with an offering valued at $716 million. The fast-growing chain opened its 9000th store in late July 2010.

Dollar General in August 2014 bid $78.50 per share for its smaller rival Family Dollar Stores. The all-cash offer which valued Family Dollar at about $9.7 billion topped a standing offer for Family Dollar from Dollar Tree of $74.50 in cash and stock. The addition of Family Dollar's 8200 stores would solidify Dollar General's standing as the largest in its industry. By July 2015 however Dollar Tree had prevailed in the bid and completed its acquisition that month. Before Dollar Tree's triumph Dollar General revealed that it may have had to sell between 1500 and 4000 stores prior to the deal closing in order to comply with regulators.

EXECUTIVES

Vice President, Susan Lanigan
Senior Vice President And Chief Information Officer, Bruce Ash
CEO, Todd J. Vasos, age 55, $1,083,375 total compensation
EVP and Chief People Officer, Robert D. (Bob) Ravener, age 58, $521,999 total compensation
EVP and General Counsel, Rhonda M. Taylor, age 49, $539,371 total compensation
EVP and Chief Merchandising Officer, Jason S. Reiser, age 49

EVP and CFO, John W. Garratt, age 48, $511,603 total compensation

EVP Store Operations, Jeffrey C. (Jeff) Owen, age 47, $613,924 total compensation

EVP and CIO, Carman Wenkoff

Vice President Inventory And Demand Management, Tony Zuazo

Divisional Vice President, Tom Balchak

Vice President Assistant Controller, Lee Carlisle

Vice President Dmm Household, Brian Hartshorn

Vice President Dmm, Steve Jacobson

Marketing Vice President, Ginny Evans

Vice President Merchandising Operations, Scott Northcutt

Vice President, Steven Deckard

Vice President and Credit Administrator, John Flanigan

Vice President Talent Management, Cris Debord

Vice President Operations, Bill Bass

Senior Vice President, Thomas Mitchell

Vice President, Debbie Combest

Vice President of Basketball Operations and Director of Basketball Operations, Anthony Zuazo

Vice President of Distribution, Adam Janastch

Vice President Merchandise Operations, Emily Taylor

Vice President Dmm, Jerry Reinhardt

Vice President of Construction and Store Development, Daniel Nieser

Seasonal Vice President, Jeff Elliott

VICE PRESIDENT DISTRIBUTION, Adam Janatsch

Division Vice President, Connie Droge

Vice President of Risk Management, Tina Schaell

Vice President of Information Technology, Scott Retail

Division Vice President, John Culbreth

Chairman, Michael M. Calbert, age 54

Assistant Treasurer, Matthew Hancock

Auditors: Ernst & Young LLP

LOCATIONS

HQ: Dollar General Corp
100 Mission Ridge, Goodlettsville, TN 37072
Phone: 615 855-4000 **Fax:** 615 855-5527
Web: www.dollargeneral.com

No. of stores in 2017

	No.
Texas	1,353
Florida	781
Georgia	758
North Carolina	730
Ohio	705
Tennessee	700
Alabama	688
Other states	7,714
Total	**13,429**

PRODUCTS/OPERATIONS

2017 Sales

	$ mil.	% of total
Consumables	16,798	77
Seasonal	2,674	12
Home Products	1,373	6
Apparel	1,140	5
Total	**21,986**	**100**

Selected Merchandise

Basic apparel
Cleaning supplies
Dairy products
Frozen foods
Health and beauty aids
Housewares
Packaged foods
Seasonal goods
Stationery

COMPETITORS

99 Cents Only	Kroger
Big Lots	Rite Aid
CVS	TJX Companies
Costco Wholesale	Target Corporation
Dollar Tree	Variety Wholesalers
Family Dollar Stores	Wal-Mart
Fred's	Walgreen
Kmart	

HISTORICAL FINANCIALS

Company Type: Public

Income Statement

FYE: February 3

	REVENUE ($ mil.)	NET INCOME ($ mil.)	NET PROFIT MARGIN	EMPLOYEES
02/17*	21,986	1,251	5.7%	121,000
01/16	20,368	1,165	5.7%	113,400
01/15	18,909	1,065	5.6%	105,500
01/14	17,504	1,025	5.9%	100,600
02/13	16,022	952	5.9%	90,500
Annual Growth	8.2%	7.1%	—	7.5%

*Fiscal year change

2017 Year-End Financials

Debt ratio: 27.51%	No. of shares (mil.): 275
Return on equity: 22.83%	Dividends
Cash ($ mil.): 187	Yield: 1.3%
Current ratio: 1.40	Payout: 22.5%
Long-term debt ($ mil.): 2,710	Market value ($ mil.): 20,129

	STOCK PRICE ($) FY Close	P/E High/Low		PER SHARE ($) Earnings	Dividends	Book Value
02/17*	73.14	22	15	4.43	1.00	19.64
01/16	75.06	21	15	3.95	0.88	18.76
01/15	67.06	20	15	3.49	0.00	18.82
01/14	56.32	20	14	3.17	0.00	17.04
02/13	46.28	19	15	2.85	0.00	15.24
Annual Growth	12.1%	—	—	11.7%	—	6.5%

*Fiscal year change

Dollar Tree Inc

Dollars may not grow on trees but Dollar Tree brings in the green. The company operates more than 14300 Dollar Tree Deal$ Dollar Bills and Family Dollar discount stores in 48 US states and the District of Columbia and in five provinces in Canada. Stores carry a mix of housewares toys seasonal items food health and beauty aids gifts and books. At Dollar Tree shops most goods are priced at $1 or less while Family Dollar merchandise is usually less than $10. The stores are located in high-traffic strip centers and malls often in small towns. It purchased fellow discounter Family Dollar in 2015 bolstering its competitive position against Dollar General.

Operations

With the acquisition of Family Dollar Dollar Tree divides its operations into Dollar Tree and Family Dollar units.

The Dollar Tree division runs about 6360 stores each with about 8000 - 10000 sq. ft. of sales space. Family Dollar operates through almost 8000 stores which are a bit smaller at 6000-8000 sq.ft. of sales space. Each unit generates about half of the company's overall revenue.

Geographic Reach

The Dollar Tree segment has 11 distribution centers in the US two distribution centers in Canada and a store support center in Chesapeake Virginia. The Family Dollar segment has over 10 distribution centers and a store support center in Matthews North Carolina. The company also has distribution services in Canada (facilities in British Columbia and Ontario).

Sales and Marketing

With the addition of Family Tree the company's advertising costs jumped to about $60 million in 2017 (ended January) from about $32 million in 2016 and about $18 million in 2015. The company processed $2.2 billion customer transactions in 2017.

Financial Performance

Thanks mainly to its 2015 acquisition of former rival Family Dollar Dollar Tree has achieved explosive revenue growth the last few years. Revenues jumped 34% from $15.5 billion in 2016 to a record-shattering $20.7 billion in 2017 mainly due to an additional $4.4 billion in revenue from Family Dollar. Dollar Tree also showed gains in same-store sales for the year.

With acquisition expenses related to its Family Dollar purchase behind it Dollar Tree saw its profits skyrocket by more than 200% from $282 million in 2016 to $896 million in 2017.

Cash flow from operations surged from $781 million in 2016 to $1.67 billion in 2017 mainly due to the increased profits coupled with favorable changes in liabilities and decreases in other assets and inventories.

Strategy

The fast-growing chain opens hundreds of new locations each year. It added more than 580 new stores (360 Dollar Tree 225 Family Dollar) to its network during 2017. It also plans to remodel relocate or expand approximately 100 of its stores and it especially plans to renovate many of its older Family Dollar stores. Overall selling square footage is expected to expand by 4% for 2017.

Dollar Tree and its rivals have transformed and expanded their businesses over the past decade or so by offering more consumables including frozen and refrigerated foods thereby stealing sales from convenience and grocery stores. Indeed consumables account for 50% of Dollar Tree's annual sales.

Mergers and Acquisitions

After nearly a year of wrangling in mid-2015 Dollar Tree beat out rival Dollar General and gained approval from the FTC to close its purchase of Family Dollar. The deal created a 14000 location discount behemoth with the size and scope to do battle with Wal-Mart and Dollar General.

Company Background

Founded in 1986 as Dollar Tree Stores the company later changed its name to Dollar Tree Inc.

EXECUTIVES

Chief Supply Chain Officer, Gary A. Maxwell, age 55

CFO, Kevin S. Wampler, age 54, $690,385 total compensation

President CEO and Director, Gary M. Philbin, age 60, $1,121,154 total compensation

CIO, Joshua R. (Josh) Jewett, age 47

President and COO Family Dollar Stores, Duncan C. Mac Naughton, age 55, $61,538 total compensation

Chief Administrative Officer, Michael (Mike) Matacunas, age 50, $537,500 total compensation

Chief Merchandising Officer, Robert H. (Bob) Rudman, age 66, $740,385 total compensation

President and COO Dollar Tree, Michael Witynski, age 54

Chairman, Bob Sasser, age 65

Auditors: KPMG LLP

LOCATIONS

HQ: Dollar Tree Inc
500 Volvo Parkway, Chesapeake, VA 23320
Phone: 757 321-5000
Web: www.dollartree.com

2017 Canadian Stores

	No.
Ontario	109
British Columbia	53
Alberta	38
Saskatchewan	14
Manitoba	12
Total	**225**

2017 US Stores

	No.
Texas	1,492
Florida	1,054
Ohio	712
North Carolina	685
California	679
Georgia	620
Michigan	609
New York	606
Pennsylvania	589
Illinois	462
Virginia	415
Louisiana	420
Tennessee	394
South Carolina	348
Indiana	334
Kentucky	309
Alabama	296
Arizona	273
Wisconsin	258
New Jersey	257
Mississippi	231
Missouri	239
Colorado	216
Massachusetts	208
Maryland	209
Oklahoma	204
Minnesota	184
Arkansas	187
New Mexico	174
West Virginia	159
Connecticut	113
Utah	116
Washington	117
Maine	99
Oregon	91
Kansas	93
Nevada	97
Idaho	77
Iowa	81
New Hampshire	66
Nebraska	58
Delaware	57
Rhode Island	52
Wyoming	44
South Dakota	39
North Dakota	30
Montana	27
Vermont	22
District of Columbia	6
Total	**0**	**14,108**

PRODUCTS/OPERATIONS

2017 Sales

	% of total
Consumables	49
Variety categories	46
Seasonal	5
Total	**100**

2017 Sales

% of total	
Dollar Tree	49
Family Dollar	51
Total	**100**

Store Names

Store Names
Deal$
Dollar Bills
Dollar Giant
Dollar Tree
Dollar Tree Deal$
Family Dollar

Selected Products

Books
Candy
Cards
Food
Gifts
Health and beauty care products
Housewares
Party goods
Personal accessories
Seasonal goods
Stationery
Toys

COMPETITORS

99 Cents Only	Party City
ALDI	Rite Aid
Big Lots	Salvation Army
CVS	Save-A-Lot Food Stores
Dollar General	Savers Inc.
Fred's	Target Corporation
Goodwill Industries	Wal-Mart
Grocery Outlet	Walgreen
Kmart	Winn-Dixie

HISTORICAL FINANCIALS

Company Type: Public

Income Statement

FYE: January 28

	REVENUE ($ mil.)	NET INCOME ($ mil.)	NET PROFIT MARGIN	EMPLOYEES
01/17	20,719	896	4.3%	176,800
01/16	15,498	282	1.8%	167,800
01/15*	8,602	599	7.0%	90,000
02/14	7,840	596	7.6%	87,400
02/13	7,394	619	8.4%	81,920
Annual Growth	**29.4%**	**9.7%**	**—**	**21.2%**

*Fiscal year change

2017 Year-End Financials

Debt ratio: 40.26%	No. of shares (mil.): 236
Return on equity: 18.35%	Dividends
Cash ($ mil.): 866	Yield: —
Current ratio: 1.87	Payout: —
Long-term debt ($ mil.): 6,169	Market value ($ mil.): 17,486

	STOCK PRICE ($) FY Close	P/E High/Low		PER SHARE ($) Earnings	Dividends	Book Value
01/17	74.05	26	19	3.78	0.00	22.82
01/16	81.32	66	48	1.26	0.00	18.76
01/15*	71.10	25	17	2.90	0.00	8.68
02/14	50.52	22	14	2.72	0.00	5.62
02/13	40.12	42	14	2.68	0.00	7.42
Annual Growth	**16.6%**	**—**	**—**	**9.0%**	**—**	**32.4%**

*Fiscal year change

Dominion Energy Inc (New)

Dominion Energy (formerly Dominion Resources) is one of the top energy players in the US. Dominion Generation manages regulated and non-regulated power plants. Through its Dominion Virginia Power unit the company transmits and distributes electricity across 57300 miles of electric distribution lines to 2.5 million customers and natural gas to 1.3 million customers. Another division trades and markets energy oversees natural gas transmission pipelines and operates underground gas storage facilities (933 billion cu. ft. of capacity.) The former Dominion Resources changed its name to Dominion Energy in 2017.

HISTORY

In 1781 the Virginia General Assembly established a group of trustees including George Washington and James Madison to promote navigation on the Appomattox River. The group (named the Appomattox Trustees) formed the Upper Appomattox Company in 1795 to secure its water rights. The company eventually began operating hydroelectric plants on the river and by 1888 it had added a steam-powered plant to its portfolio.

The Virginia Railway and Power Company (VR&P) led by Frank Jay Gould purchased the Upper Appomattox Company (which had changed its name) in 1909. The next year the firm acquired several electric and gas utilities as well as some electric streetcar lines.

In 1925 New York engineering company Stone & Webster acquired VR&P. The company became known as Virginia Electric and Power Company (Virginia Power) and was placed under Engineers Public Service (EPS) a new holding company. Virginia Power purchased several North Carolina utilities following its acquisition.

During the 1930s the Depression (and the popularity of the automobile) led the company to exit the trolley business. The Public Utility Holding Company Act of 1935 (repealed 2005) which ushered in an era of regulated utility monopolies forced EPS to divest all of its operations except Virginia Power. However the utility soon merged with the Virginia Public Service Company thus doubling its service territory.

The company added new power plants to keep up with growing customer demand in the 1950s. Always an innovator it also built an extra-high-voltage transmission system the first in the world.

In the 1970s Virginia Power's first nuclear plants became operational. By 1980 however the firm was near bankruptcy. That year William Berry who had completed a 23-year rise through the ranks to become president canceled two other nuclear units. He also became an early supporter of competition in the electric utility industry. In 1983 he formed Dominion Resources as a parent company for Virginia Power and halted nearly all plant construction. Two additional subsidiaries were soon formed: Dominion Capital in 1985 and Dominion Energy in 1987.

In 1990 the year Thomas Capps took over as CEO Dominion sold its natural gas distribution business and in 1995 Dominion Energy began developing natural gas reserves through joint ventures and by purchasing three natural gas exploration and production companies.

The company acquired UK utility East Midlands Electricity in 1997. However after it was hit by a hefty windfall tax by the newly elected Labour Party and its hopes for mergers with other UK utilities were dashed it sold East Midlands to PowerGen just 18 months after acquiring it.

In 1999 Dominion prepared for energy deregulation through reorganization. It separated its electricity generation activities from its transmission and distribution operations. In 2000 Dominion bought Consolidated Natural Gas (CNG) for $9 billion making it one of the largest fully integrated gas and electric power companies in the US; it then sold CNG's Virginia Natural Gas to AGL Resources and the two firms' combined Latin American assets to Duke Energy.

Virginia Power moved to head off state and federal lawsuits in 2000 by agreeing to spend $1.2 billion over 12 years to reduce pollution from coal-fired plants. The company also agreed to pay $1.3 billion for Eversource Energy's Millstone nuclear power complex that year (the deal closed in 2001). Also in 2000 Dominion changed its brand name from Dominion Resources to just Dominion and rebranded several of its subsidiaries as well.

In 2001 Dominion bought exploration and production company Louis Dreyfus Natural Gas for about $1.8 billion in cash and stock and $500 million in assumed debt; the acquisition added 1.8 trillion cu. ft. of natural gas equivalent to Dominion's proved reserves. The company also sold the assets of its financial services unit Dominion Capital that year.

The following year Dominion purchased a 500-MW Chicago power plant from US power producer Mirant (now GenOn Energy)for $182 million and it purchased the Cove Point LNG (liquefied natural gas) import facility from The Williams Companies for $217 million.

Dominion began to prepare for power deregulation implemented in most of its service territories by expanding its nonregulated electric operations. The company also divested its non-US operations to focus on its businesses in the Northeast Mid-Atlantic and Midwest. In 2004 it sold its telecom business to private firm Elantic Networks. The firm completed the acquisition of three fossil-fueled plants (2800 MW) from USGen New England a subsidiary of National Energy & Gas Transmission for $656 million in 2005. That was the same year Dominion purchased the 550-MW Kewaunee nuclear plant from WPS Resources subsidiary Wisconsin Public Service and Alliant Energy subsidiary Wisconsin Power & Light for $220 million.

At the end of 2006 Dominion Exploration & Production had proved reserves of 6.5 trillion cu. ft. of natural gas equivalent. The next year Dominion began to dismantle the unit selling its offshore operations in the Gulf of Mexico to Eni; its assets in Alabama Michigan and Texas to Loews Corp.; its Mid-Continent operations to Linn Energy; and operations in the Rocky Mountain and Gulf Coast regions to XTO Energy. Dominion Resources pocketed almost $14 billion from the sales.

To free up cash and hone its business focus the company has sold most of its exploration and production operations in recent years. In 2010 the company sold its remaining Appalachian exploration and production assets to CONSOL Energy for about $3.5 billion. The acquisition doubled CONSOL's natural gas reserves to 3 million cu. ft. (In 2007 Dominion sold the bulk of its oil and gas exploration and production assets — excluding its Appalachian operations because at the time they offered less risk — for nearly $14 billion.)

In a related move Dominion agreed to sell its Appalachian gas distribution companies The Peoples Natural Gas Company and Hope Gas located in Pennsylvania and West Virginia to investment firm SteelRiver Infrastructure Partners for $910 million. After receiving approval from Pennsylvania the deal was rejected in late 2009 by West Virginia saying the terms of the agreement were not in the public interest. The company then sold just Peoples Natural Gas to SteelRiver in 2010 for $780 million.

Dominion's divestments allow it to concentrate its efforts on its core power generation and gas and electricity distribution businesses along with its trading and marketing activities.

In 2012 Dominion announced plans to sell three fossil fuel-fired merchant power stations (one in Massachusetts and two in Illinois) as part of its transition to cleaner burning and renewable power plants.

On the gas side of the business in 2012 Dominion and Caiman Energy II LLC formed a $1.5 billion joint venture (Blue Racer Midstream LLC) to provide midstream services to natural gas produc-

ers operating in the Utica shale in Ohio and portions of Pennsylvania.

In 2013 Dominion Virginia Power put the Altavista Power Station into commercial operation with renewable biomass as its fuel the first of three such stations to be converted from coal to biomass.

EXECUTIVES

CEO Dominion Generation Group, Paul D. Koonce, age 57, $680,138 total compensation
Chairman President and CEO, Thomas F. Farrell, age 62, $1,502,372 total compensation
EVP and CFO, Mark F. McGettrick, age 59, $850,055 total compensation
CEO Energy Infrastructure Group; CEO Dominion Virginia Power, David A. Christian, age 62, $680,138 total compensation
President and Chief Nuclear Officer Dominion Nuclear, David A. Heacock, age 59, $528,098 total compensation
President and CEO Dominion Virginia Power, Robert M. (Bob) Blue, age 49
SVP and CIO, P. Rodney Blevins
SVP Dominion Transmission, Diane G. Leopold, age 50
President Dominion Questar, Craig C. Wagstaff
SVP Operations Engineering and Construction, Scot C. Hathaway
SVP Corporate Affairs and Chief Legal Officer, Mark O. Webb, age 52
President Dominion Midstream Operations, Paul F. Ruppert
Vice President Distribution Operations, Rodney Blevins
Auditors: Deloitte & Touche LLP

LOCATIONS

HQ: Dominion Energy Inc (New)
120 Tredegar Street, Richmond, VA 23219
Phone: 804 819-2000   **Fax:** 804 775-5819
Web: www.dom.com

PRODUCTS/OPERATIONS

2016 Sales

	$ mil.	% of total
Dominion Generation	6,757	55
Dominion Energy	2,766	22
DVP	2,233	18
Corporate and Other	602	5
Adjustments & Eliminations	(621)	-
Total	**11,737**	**100**

2016 Sales

	$ mil.	% of total
Electric Sales	8,867	76
Gas transportation and Storage	1,636	14
Gas Sales	854	7
Other	380	3
Total	**11,737**	**100**

Selected Subsidiaries and Business Units

Dominion Generation Corporation (power plant management)
Dominion Energy (energy marketing gas and power transmission)
  Dominion Transmission Inc. (natural gas pipelines)
Dominion Virginia Power
  Consolidated Natural Gas
  Dominion East Ohio (or The East Ohio Gas Company gas distribution)
  Dominion Hope (or Hope Gas Inc. West Virginia gas distribution)
  Dominion North Carolina Power (or Virginia Electric and Power Company electricity distribution)
  Dominion Retail Inc. (retail energy marketing)
  Virginia Electric and Power Company (electricity distribution)

COMPETITORS

AEP	Exelon
CenterPoint Energy	Koch Industries Inc.
Duke Energy	NiSource
Entergy	Piedmont Natural Gas

HISTORICAL FINANCIALS

Company Type: Public

Income Statement

FYE: December 31

	REVENUE ($ mil.)	NET INCOME ($ mil.)	NET PROFIT MARGIN	EMPLOYEES
12/16	11,737	2,123	18.1%	16,200
12/15	11,683	1,899	16.3%	14,700
12/14	12,436	1,310	10.5%	14,400
12/13	13,120	1,697	12.9%	14,500
12/12	13,093	302	2.3%	15,500
Annual Growth	**(2.7%)**	**62.8%**	**—**	**1.1%**

2016 Year-End Financials

Debt ratio: 46.62%
Return on equity: 15.53%
Cash ($ mil.): 261
Current ratio: 0.52
Long-term debt ($ mil.): 30,231

No. of shares (mil.): 628
Dividends
  Yield: 0.0%
  Payout: 81.4%
Market value ($ mil.): 48,099

	STOCK PRICE ($) FY Close	P/E High/Low		Earnings	PER SHARE ($) Dividends	Book Value
12/16	76.59	23	20	3.44	2.80	23.26
12/15	67.64	25	20	3.20	2.59	21.25
12/14	76.90	36	28	2.24	2.40	19.75
12/13	64.69	23	18	2.93	2.25	20.48
12/12	51.80	104	93	0.53	2.11	18.79
Annual Growth	**10.3%**	**—**	**—**	**59.6%**	**7.3%**	**5.5%**

Domtar Corp

Auditors: PricewaterhouseCoopers LLP

LOCATIONS

HQ: Domtar Corp
234 Kingsley Park Drive, Fort Mill, SC 29715
Phone: 803 802-7500
Web: www.domtar.com

HISTORICAL FINANCIALS

Company Type: Public

Income Statement

FYE: December 31

	REVENUE ($ mil.)	NET INCOME ($ mil.)	NET PROFIT MARGIN	EMPLOYEES
12/16	5,098	128	2.5%	10,000
12/15	5,264	142	2.7%	9,850
12/14	5,563	431	7.7%	9,800
12/13	5,391	91	1.7%	9,400
12/12	5,482	172	3.1%	9,300
Annual Growth	**(1.8%)**	**(7.1%)**		**1.8%**

2016 Year-End Financials

Debt ratio: 22.76%
Return on equity: 4.79%
Cash ($ mil.): 125
Current ratio: 2.08
Long-term debt ($ mil.): 1,218

No. of shares (mil.): 62
Dividends
  Yield: 0.0%
  Payout: 80.6%
Market value ($ mil.): 2,443

STOCK PRICE ($)		P/E		PER SHARE ($)		
	FY Close	High/Low		Earnings	Dividends	Book Value
12/16	39.03	21	15	2.04	1.65	42.76
12/15	36.95	21	16	2.24	1.60	42.20
12/14	40.22	17	5	6.64	1.40	45.15
12/13	94.34	70	48	1.36	1.05	42.91
12/12	83.52	42	29	2.38	0.85	41.28
Annual Growth	(17.3%)	—	—	(3.8%)	17.9%	0.9%

Donegal Group Inc.

"Risk" is Donegal Group's middle name. Through its subsidiaries including Atlantic States Insurance and Southern Insurance Company of Virginia Donegal Group provides clients in 22 mid-Atlantic Midwestern and Southeastern states with personal farm and commercial property/casualty insurance products. The group's personal insurance offerings range from auto and boat policies to homeowners and fire coverage; its commercial insurance products include business owners multiperil and workers' compensation. Donegal's financial services arm owns Union Community Bank with 13 branches in Pennsylvania. Donegal Mutual Insurance controls two-thirds of the company's voting stock.

Operations

Donegal Group's subsidiaries provide insurance cooperatively with Donegal Mutual.

Sales and Marketing

The collective insurance businesses target customers in small to midsized regional communities to allow for local market knowledge and more personal services. Pennsylvania is the company's largest market accounting for more than a third of revenues; personal auto policies are account for 40% of its written net premiums. It distributes it products through some 2500 independent agencies.

Financial Performance

The company's revenue has been increasing year-over-year. Its net income and cash flow also increased in fiscal 2013 compared to fiscal 2012 levels.

Strategy

Donegal Group's growth strategy is to acquire property/casualty insurance companies to augment its organic growth in existing markets and to expand into new markets.

EXECUTIVES

Senior Vice President and Chief Actuary, Chet Szczepanski
Vice President, Francis J Haefner
SVP Claims, Robert G. Shenk, age 63, $292,000 total compensation
President and CEO, Kevin G. Burke, age 51, $305,000 total compensation
SVP and CFO, Jeffrey D. Miller, age 52, $310,000 total compensation
SVP and Chief Underwriting Officer, Cyril J. Greenya, age 72, $280,000 total compensation
VP Marketing and Advertising, David S. Krenkel
SVP and Chief Actuary, Chester J. Szczepanski
SVP and CIO, Sanjay Pandey, age 50, $280,000 total compensation
SVP and Chief Investment Officer, V. Anthony Viozzi
President and Treasurer Sheboygan Falls Insurance Company, Lee F. Wilcox
President Peninsula Insurance Group, G. Eric Crouchley
President Michigan Insurance Company, Ermil L. Adamson
President and Treasurer Southern Mutual Insurance Company, Allen R. Green
Assistant Vice President Personal Lines Underwriting, Karen Colwill
Senior Vice President Chief Investment Officer, Tony Viozzi
Vice President of Commercial Lines Underwriting, Kevin Cawley
Vice President Vice President Engineering r Vice President Engineering r Research, Ken Dull
Vice President, Teresa Shertzer
Vice President Regional, James Stiegler
Senior Vice President Sales and Business Development, Richard Kelley
Regional Vice President, Wayne Smith
Assistant Vice President Research and Development, Jason McAfee
Assistant Vice President and Programming Manager Information Services, Michael Simms
Vice President of Claims, William Folmar
Assistant Vice President Regional Sales Manager, Keith Captain
Chairman, Donald H. Nikolaus, age 74
Assistant Treasurer, Jerry Demastus
Secretary, Rebecca Simowitz
Auditors: KPMG LLP

LOCATIONS

HQ: Donegal Group Inc.
1195 River Road, P.O. Box 302, Marietta, PA 17547
Phone: 717 426-1931
Web: www.donegalgroup.com

PRODUCTS/OPERATIONS

2016 Sales

	$ mil.	% of total
Premiums earned:		
Personal lines	361	53
Commercial lines	295	43
Net investment income	22	3
Realized investment gains	2	0
Equity in earnings of DFSC	1	0
Other	6	1
Total	688	100

Selected Subsidiaries

Atlantic States Insurance Company
Donegal Financial Services Corporation (48%)
  Union National Financial
  Union Community Bank
Le Mars Insurance Company
Michigan Insurance Company
The Peninsula Insurance Company
  Peninsula Indemnity Company
Sheboygan Falls Insurance Company
Southern Insurance Company of Virginia

COMPETITORS

AIG	GEICO
Allstate	Liberty Mutual
American National Insurance	Penn National Mutual Casualty
Berkley Mid-Atlantic Group	Penn-America
COUNTRY Financial	Progressive Corporation
Erie Indemnity	State Farm

HISTORICAL FINANCIALS

Company Type: Public

Income Statement

FYE: December 31

	ASSETS ($ mil.)	NET INCOME ($ mil.)	INCOME AS % OF ASSETS	EMPLOYEES
12/16	1,623	30	1.9%	—
12/15	1,537	20	1.4%	—
12/14	1,458	14	1.0%	—
12/13	1,385	26	1.9%	—
12/12	1,336	23	1.7%	—
Annual Growth	5.0%	7.5%	—	—

2016 Year-End Financials

Debt ratio: 0.31%
Return on equity: 7.25%
Cash ($ mil.): 24
Current ratio: —
Long-term debt ($ mil.): —
No. of shares (mil.): 27
Dividends
  Yield: 0.0%
  Payout: 47.2%
Market value ($ mil.): 473

STOCK PRICE ($)		P/E		PER SHARE ($)		
	FY Close	High/Low		Earnings	Dividends	Book Value
12/16	17.48	15	11	1.16	0.55	16.21
12/15	14.08	21	17	0.77	0.54	15.66
12/14	15.98	29	25	0.55	0.52	15.40
12/13	15.90	16	13	1.02	0.51	15.02
12/12	14.04	17	13	0.91	0.49	15.63
Annual Growth	5.6%	—	—	6.3%	2.9%	0.9%

Donnelley (RR) & Sons Company

If you can read it R.R. Donnelley & Sons can print it. The formerly huge printing firm split itself up into three smaller companies with separate management teams in 2016. Donnelley formed LSC Communications to serve its retail and merchandise clients. In addition to LSC and the R.R. Donnelley core printing business the split created Donnelley Financial Solutions to focus on printing work for the financial investment and legal industries. R.R. Donnelley & Sons remains the biggest of the three companies with about $7 billion in revenue and 42000 employees. R.R. Donnelley & Sons will provide legacy printing services for direct mail labels forms and other commercial and digital printing jobs.

Sales and Marketing

As the demand for printed catalogs magazines brochures and other documents continues to shrink printing companies are lowering prices in a effort to retain customers.

Financial Performance

Prior to its splitting up Donnelley's revenue had been steady over the past several fiscal years. However its profit margins had been shrinking.

Strategy

Before its breakup Donnelley was twice as large as the printing industry's next biggest company Quad/Graphics. It hopes that by serving niches customer groups the three different companies can maximizes profit margins and shareholder value.

EXECUTIVES

EVP and CFO, Terry D. Peterson, age 52, $168,750 total compensation

CEO, Daniel L. (Dan) Knotts, age 53, $781,250 total compensation
EVP and Chief Administrative Officer, Thomas M. Carroll, age 51, $450,000 total compensation
CIO, Ken O'Brien
EVP Global Markets, John P. Pecaric, age 51, $396,250 total compensation
EVP Domestic Operations, Glynn Perry
President DLS, Charles Fattore
Chairman, John C. (Jack) Pope, age 67
Auditors: Deloitte & Touche LLP

LOCATIONS

HQ: Donnelley (RR) & Sons Company
35 West Wacker Drive, Chicago, IL 60601
Phone: 312 326-8000
Web: www.rrdonnelley.com

2016 sales

	$ mil.	% of total
U.S	5,278	77
Asia	766	11
Other	851	12
Total	**6,895**	**100**

PRODUCTS/OPERATIONS

2016 Sales

	$ mil.	% of total
Variable Print	3,145	46
Strategic Services	1,726	25
International	2,023	29
Total	**6,895**	**100**

2016 Sales

	$ mil.	% of total
Product	5,288	77
Services	1,607	23
Total	**6,895**	**100**

Selected Operations

US print and related services
  Book (consumer religious educational and specialty and telecommunications)
  Direct mail (content creation database management printing personalization finishing and distribution in North America)
  Directories (yellow and white pages)
  Logistics (consolidation and delivery of printed products; expedited distribution of time-sensitive and secure material; print-on-demand warehousing and fulfillment services)
  Magazine catalog and retail inserts
  Short-run commercial print (annual reports marketing brochures catalog and marketing inserts pharmaceutical inserts and other marketing retail point-of-sale and promotional materials and technical publications)
International
  Business process outsourcing
  Global Turnkey Solutions (product configuration customized kitting and order fulfillment)
  Selected Capabilities:
  Digital
  Print
  Consulting & Execution
  Logistics & supply chain
  Industry solutions

COMPETITORS

Accenture	Merrill
Arandell	Penn Lithographics
Capgemini	Quad/Graphics
Cenveo	St Ives
Dai Nippon Printing	St. Joseph
Deluxe Corporation	Communications
EBSCO	Taylor Corporation
Harte-Hanks	Toppan Printing
IBM Global Services	Transcontinental Inc.
Infosys	Valassis
M & F Worldwide	

HISTORICAL FINANCIALS

Company Type: Public

Income Statement

FYE: December 31

	REVENUE ($ mil.)	NET INCOME ($ mil.)	NET PROFIT MARGIN	EMPLOYEES
12/16	6,895	(495)	—	44,360
12/15	11,256	151	1.3%	68,400
12/14	11,603	117	1.0%	68,000
12/13	10,480	211	2.0%	57,000
12/12	10,221	(651)	—	57,000
Annual Growth	**(9.4%)**	**—**	**—**	**(6.1%)**

2016 Year-End Financials

Debt ratio: 55.72%
Return on equity: (-171.42%)
Cash ($ mil.): 317
Current ratio: 1.62
Long-term debt ($ mil.): 2,379
No. of shares (mil.): 69
Dividends
  Yield: 0.0%
  Payout: —
Market value ($ mil.): 1,141

	STOCK PRICE ($) FY Close	P/E High/Low		PER SHARE ($) Earnings	Dividends	Book Value
12/16	16.32	—	—	(7.09)	0.14	(1.51)
12/15	14.72	9	7	2.19	3.12	9.81
12/14	16.81	12	8	1.77	3.12	8.92
12/13	20.28	6	3	3.45	3.12	10.43
12/12	8.99	—	—	(10.83)	3.12	0.88
Annual Growth	**16.1%**	—	—	—	**(54.0%)**	—

Dover Corp

The "D" in Dover could stand for diversity. Dover manages 35 companies that make equipment ranging from car wash systems to aerospace components. Dover operates in four segments: engineered systems (products for printing and identification transportation waste handling and industrial markets) energy (extraction and handling of oil and gas); fluids (fluid handling products for retail fueling oil and gas chemical and hygienic markets); and refrigeration and food equipment (systems and products serving the commercial refrigeration and food service industries). Dover traces its historical roots back to 1955.

Operations

Dover operates through the segments of engineered systems (products for printing and identification transportation waste handling and industrial markets); energy (extraction and handling of oil and gas); fluids (fluid handling products for oil and gas chemical and hygienic markets); and refrigeration and food equipment (systems and products serving the commercial refrigeration and food service industries).

Geographic Reach

Dover has a significant worldwide presence and operates in Australia Brazil Canada China Eastern Europe France Germany India Malaysia Mexico the Middle East the Netherlands Switzerland Sweden the UK and the US.

The US generates about 60% of its revenue while Europe accounts for nearly 10%. Other countries in the Americas generate 9% while Asia contributes 10%.

Sales and Marketing

Dover sells directly to customers as well as through a network of distributors. It caters to the supermarket industry including big-box retail and convenience stores the commercial/industrial refrigeration industry institutional and commercial food service and food production markets and beverage can-making industries.

Its products are sold to national dealership networks original equipment manufacturers national multi-shop operations groups independent repair and service shops large national accounts and government/transit customers through a network of distributors and channel partners.

Financial Performance

Dover's revenues have declined the last three years falling 2% from $6.96 billion in 2015 to $6.79 billion in 2016. Profits declined 42% from $870 million to $509 million over that same time period primarily due to a 15% decline in earnings from continuing operations. In addition Dover's operating cash flow has trended downwards for five straight years dropping from $949 million in 2015 to $862 million in 2016.

The dip in revenue for 2016 was driven by a 25% decline in energy sales and a 6% dip in refrigeration and food equipment sales. Both segments were unfavorably affected by foreign currency translations; the energy segment was hurt by a 24% drop in organic revenue that was largely attributable to lower demand from customers as a result of the dramatic decrease in the price of oil in 2016 and a decline in the year-over-year average number of active drilling rigs in the US.

Strategy

Dover relies on a steady stream of divestitures and acquisitions as its principal means for growth. In 2016 it completed the divestitures of its Texas Hydraulics (for $47 million) and Tipper Tie ($159 million) businesses. In 2015 Dover sold its Sargent Aerospace & Defense unit headquartered in Tucson Arizona to RBC Bearings for $500 million. It also divested its Datamax O'Neil unit headquartered in Orlando Florida to Honeywell for $185 million that year.

Mergers and Acquisitions

In a three-year span (2014 through 2016) Dover has spent over $2.9 billion to purchase 17 businesses. During 2016 it acquired six businesses for about $1.6 billion; these included Tokheim Group S.A.S. Fairbanks Environmental ProGauge and Wayne Fueling Systems to expand its fluids segment's retail fueling portfolio. Dover also obtained Alliance Wireless Technologies and Ravaglioli S.p.A. Group to complement the industrials platform within its engineered systems segment.

During 2015 Dover acquired four businesses for an aggregate purchase price of $568 million. These included Gala Industries and Reduction Engineering Scheer which expanded its fluids segment's plastics and polymers product and integrated systems portfolio. In addition the company snapped up the JK Group a global manufacturer and provider of digital inks for the textile printing market; that deal enhanced the printing and identification platform within its engineered systems segment.

HISTORY

George Ohrstrom a New York stockbroker formed Dover in 1955 and took it public that year. Originally headquartered in Washington DC Dover consisted of four companies: C. Lee Cook (compressor seals and piston rings) Peerless (space-venting heaters) Rotary Lift (automotive lifts) and W.C. Norris (components for oil wells). In 1958 Dover made the first of many acquisitions and entered the elevator industry by buying Shepard Warner Elevator.

EXECUTIVES

VP; President and CEO Dover Fluids, William W. (Bill) Spurgeon, age 59, $650,000 total compensation

President and CEO, Robert A. (Bob) Livingston, age 63, $1,030,000 total compensation
President and CEO Dover Energy, Sivasankaran (Soma) Somasundaram, age 52, $502,000 total compensation
SVP and CFO, Brad M. Cerepak, age 58, $670,000 total compensation
President and CEO Dover Engineered Systems, C. Anderson Fincher, age 46, $530,000 total compensation
President and CEO Refrigeration and Food Equipment, William T. Bosway
President Dover Business Services, S. Gary Kennon
Vice President Operations, Dan Giesecke
Vice President and Controller, Carrie Anderson
Chairman, Michael F. (Mike) Johnston, age 69
Board Of Directors, Michael Stubbs
Auditors: PricewaterhouseCoopers LLP

LOCATIONS

HQ: Dover Corp
  3005 Highland Parkway, Downers Grove, IL 60515
Phone: 630 541-1540
Web: www.dovercorporation.com

2016 Sales

	$ mil.	% of total
Americas		
United States	3,910	58
Other Americas	594	9
Europe	1,261	18
Asia	676	10
Other	351	5
Total	**6,794**	**100**

PRODUCTS/OPERATIONS

2016 Sales

	$ mil.	% of total
Engineered Systems	2,366	35
Fluids	1,700	25
Refrigeration & Food Equipment	1,620	24
Energy	1,108	16
Intra-segment eliminations	(1.3)	-
Total	**6,794**	**100**

COMPETITORS

Alfa Laval	Middleby
Brother Industries	Navistar
Carlisle Companies	Oshkosh Truck
Crane Co.	PACCAR
Danaher	Paul Mueller
Danfoss	RAKON LIMITED
Dayco Products	SPX
Domino Printing	Schlumberger
Fortive	Sequa
Franklin Electric	Siemens AG
Gardner Denver	Smith Bits
Hussmann International	Snap-on
IDEX	Swagelok
Illinois Tool Works	Tatung
Ingersoll-Rand	Thermador Groupe
KEMET	Vesuvius
KSB AG	Wastequip
Kaydon	Weatherford
Lufkin Industries	International
Manitowoc	Zebra Technologies

HISTORICAL FINANCIALS
Company Type: Public

Income Statement
FYE: December 31

	REVENUE ($ mil.)	NET INCOME ($ mil.)	NET PROFIT MARGIN	EMPLOYEES
12/17	7,830	811	10.4%	29,000
12/16	6,794	508	7.5%	29,000
12/15	6,956	869	12.5%	26,000
12/14	7,752	775	10.0%	27,000
12/13	8,729	1,003	11.5%	37,000
Annual Growth	**(2.7%)**	**(5.2%)**	**—**	**(5.9%)**

2017 Year-End Financials

Debt ratio: 33.48%
Return on equity: 19.84%
Cash ($ mil.): 753
Current ratio: 1.40
Long-term debt ($ mil.): 2,986

No. of shares (mil.): 154
Dividends
  Yield: 0.0%
  Payout: 35.3%
Market value ($ mil.): 15,636

	STOCK PRICE ($) FY Close	P/E High/Low	PER SHARE ($) Earnings	Dividends	Book Value
12/17	100.99	19 15	5.15	1.82	28.31
12/16	74.93	24 16	3.25	1.72	24.45
12/15	61.31	14 10	5.46	1.64	23.51
12/14	71.72	21 15	4.59	1.55	22.70
12/13	96.54	16 11	5.78	1.45	31.65
Annual Growth	**1.1%**	**— —**	**(2.8%)**	**5.8%**	**(2.7%)**

DowDuPont Inc

LOCATIONS

HQ: DowDuPont Inc
  c/o The Dow Chemical Company, 2030 Dow Center, Midland, MI 48674
Phone: 989 636-1000
Web: www.dow-dupont.com

HISTORICAL FINANCIALS
Company Type: Public

Income Statement
FYE: December 31

	REVENUE ($ mil.)	NET INCOME ($ mil.)	NET PROFIT MARGIN	EMPLOYEES
12/17	62,484	1,460	2.3%	98,000
12/16	48,158	4,318	9.0%	—
12/15	48,778	7,685	15.8%	52,000
Annual Growth	**13.2%**	**(56.4%)**	**—**	**37.3%**

2017 Year-End Financials

Debt ratio: 17.73%—
Return on equity: 2.31%
Cash ($ mil.): 13,438
Current ratio: 1.91
Long-term debt ($ mil.): 30,056

Dividends
  Yield: 0.0%
  Payout: 41.7%
Market value ($ mil.): —

	STOCK PRICE ($) FY Close	P/E High/Low	PER SHARE ($) Earnings	Dividends	Book Value
12/17	71.22	80 70	0.91	0.38	43.11
12/16	0.00	— —	3.52	1.84	21.46
12/15	0.00	— —	6.15	1.72	(0.00)
Annual Growth	**—**	**— —**	**(61.5%)**	**(53.0%)**	**—**

Dr Pepper Snapple Group Inc

For many soft drinkers it's a snap decision about which doctor to choose. Dr Pepper Snapple Group (DPS) is the bottler and distributor of Dr Pepper soda and Snapple drinks. Serving Canada Mexico and the US the company offers a vast portfolio of non-alcoholic beverages including flavored carbonated (non-cola) soft drinks and non-carbonated soft drinks along with ready-to-drink non-carbonated teas juices juice drinks and mixers. Alongside its namesake brands it owns 7 Up A&W Root Beer Hawaiian Punch Mott's and Schweppes among others. It made its first major acquisition in a decade with the purchase of antioxidant drink maker Bai Brands in 2017. DPS is the #3 soda business in North America after #1 Coke and #2 Pepsi.

Operations

As well as Dr Pepper Dr Pepper Snapple's four "core" brands are Canada Dry (the #1 ginger ale in the US); 7up (the #2 lemon-lime carbonated drink in the US); A&W (the #1 root beer in the US) and Sunkist (#1 orange carbonated drink in the US).

The company operates its business through three segments: Packaged Beverages Beverage Concentrates and Latin America Beverages.

The Packaged Beverages segment accounting for more than 70% of total sales makes and distributes finished beverages and other products. Serving the US and Canada products include own brands as well as third party brands sold through both direct-store and warehouse direct delivery.

The Beverage Concentrates segment (roughly 20% of total sales) sells branded concentrates and syrup to third-party bottlers primarily in the US and Canada. Most of the brands in this segment are carbonated soft drink brands.

The Latin America Beverages segment (less than 10% of sales) serves the Mexico and Caribbean markets making and distributing concentrates syrup and finished beverages. About 90% of the segment's net sales are generated in Mexico.

Geographic Reach

Plano Texas-based Dr Pepper Snapple (DPS) operates nearly 150 administrative manufacturing and distribution facilities across the US which supply customers in the US and Canada. In Mexico it has more than a dozen sites through which it serves its customers in that country. Around 90% of the company's net sales are generated in the US with Mexico Canada and the Caribbean accounting for the remainder.

While Dr Pepper-branded drinks can be bought internationally DPSis only licensed to sell it in the Americas; international Dr Pepper licenses are held by Coca-Cola (Europe) and PepsiCo (Canada and Oceania).

Sales and Marketing

DPS primarily serves bottlers (including quick-serve restaurants for syrups) and distributors as well as retailers. Retail channels include supermarkets fountains mass merchandisers club stores vending machines convenience stores gas stations and small grocery and dollar stores. Major distributors include Wal-Mart Kroger Safeway Target and Publix.

DPS also enjoys strong relationships with the largest bottlers and distributors such as PepsiCo and Coca-Cola the top customers of its Beverage Concentrates segment which generate about 25% and more than 20% respectively of the segment's sales. The company's largest foodservice customers include McDonald's Yum! Brands Burger King Sonic Wendy's Jack in the Box and Subway as well as convenience store customers the likes of 7-Eleven.

Its Beverage Concentrates brands are sold by its bottlers including its own Packaged Beverages segment through all major retail channels. Unlike the majority of its other carbonated soft drink brands 58% of DPS volumes in 2015 were distributed through the Coca-Cola- and PepsiCo-affiliated bottler systems. The company's Packaged Beverages' products are made in multiple facilities nationwide and sold or distributed to retailers and their warehouses by its own distribution network or by third party distributors.

DPS sells its Packaged Beverages' products both through a Direct Store Delivery (DSD) system supported by a large vehicle fleet and thousands of employees including sales representatives merchandisers drivers and warehouse workers as well as through its Warehouse Direct delivery system (WD) both of which include sales to all major retail channels.

In Mexico DPS makes and distributes its products through bottling operations and third-party bottlers and distributors. It also sells finished beverages through all major Mexican retail channels including local stores supermarkets hypermarkets and on premise channels. Further in Mexico it manufactures Aguafiel brand water through Acqua Minerale San Benedetto. In the Caribbean it distributes products through third-party bottlers and distributors.

Financial Performance

DPS has enjoyed steady revenue and profit growth for the past several years. In fiscal 2016 revenue increased 3% to $6.4 billionthanks to a favorable product and package mix and higher shipments and pricing partially offset by unfavorable foreign currency translation and segment mix. Growth was concentrated in the Packaged Beverages segment with new product sales from the Bai Brands acquisition compensating for falls across three of its four core brands (only Canada Dry grew) as well as its carbonated soft drinks in general.

Net income ticked up 11% to $847 million thanks to higher revenue lower commodity costs and stronger pricing.

Cash from operations fell 5% to $939 million due mostly to a $35 million multi-employer pension plan settlement.

Strategy

In response to an increase in health-consciousness among consumers Dr Pepper Snapple (DPS) made its first major acquisition in a decade with the purchase of Bai Brands. Bai's antioxidant drinks open up the company's product portfolio to the growing sugar-avoiding consumer segment. The extra muscle afforded by DPS helped Bai Brands grow revenue by 40% in 2017.

DPS also works to leverage the strength of its significant brands by launching innovations and brand extensions to its core brands (Dr. Pepper 7UP Sunkist soda A&W and Canada Dry). To support supply and sales growth in fast-growing Mexico the company in 2016 broke ground on a new manufacturing facility in the country.

Mergers and Acquisitions

In 2017 Dr Pepper Snapple (DPS) completed the $1.7 billion acquisition of Bai Brands LLC a maker of antioxidant drinks. The move represents the latest diversification away from soda which has been declining in recent years as consumer awareness increases of the negative effects of sugary beverages on health.

Company Background

DPS in 2013 inked a deal with Mondelez International to reacquire the distribution rights for Snapple and several other non-carbonated beverage brands in parts of the Asia/Pacific region to give DPS rights to distribute the Snapple brand in Australia Malaysia Singapore China Hong Kong Japan and South Korea. In Australia the company also will have distribution rights for Mott's Mr & Mrs T Clamato Mistic Holland House and Yoohoo. As part of the agreement DPS can explore opportunities for expanding the presence of Snapple and other non-carbonated brands.

In 2013 DPS acquired the assets and territory of Dr Pepper/7-Up Bottling Company of the West based in Reno Nevada. The purchase includes rights to the Dr Pepper/7-Up West territory and ownership of its distribution operation in Reno Chico California and Boise Idaho. The purchase is consistent with DPS's strategy of strengthening its route to market in the US.

EXECUTIVES

Executive Vice President Human Resources, Jaxie Alt
President and CEO, Larry D. Young, age 62, $1,132,692 total compensation
CFO, Martin M. (Marty) Ellen, age 63, $604,808 total compensation
EVP and Chief Commercial Officer, James R. (Jim) Trebilcock, age 59
President Packaged Beverages, Rodger L. Collins, age 59, $604,462 total compensation
EVP and General Counsel, James L. (Jim) Baldwin, age 56, $478,769 total compensation
EVP Supply Chain, Derry L. Hobson, age 66, $499,769 total compensation
President Beverage Concentrates and Latin American Beverages, James J. (Jim) Johnston, age 60, $604,462 total compensation
EVP Research and Development, David J. Thomas, age 55
CEO Bai Brands, Lain Hancock
Vice President Fleet, Ted Phillips
Senior Vice President Research Development and Engineering, Pam Way
Region Vice President, Brad Allbee
Senior Vice President Supply Chain Planning and Logistics, Fernando Cortes
Vice President Finance Packaged Beverages, Brian Shepherd
Vice President Human Resources, Stan Wood
Vice President Manufacturing, Dan Graham
Vice President Licensing Operations, Rick Maiella
Vice President and General Manager, Bryan Mazur
Vice President Regional Accounts, Jeff Vandenberg
Vice President Of Information Technology Bottling Group, Michael McKinney
Vice President East Zone, Mark Pickard
Zone Vice President, Dave Pitzer
Marketing Vice President, Mario Magro
Vice President Strategy, Travis Wade
Vice President Government Affairs, Randy Downing
Vice President, Roy Wright
Vice President of Sales, David McMichael
Vice President Corporate Audit and SOX and ERM, Kathy Beirnes
Sales Vice President Finance, Greg Collins
Senior Vice President Marketing, Jim Trebilcock
Vice President, Craig Piechotta
Vice President Human Resources Services, Deena Rembert-Neason
Vice President of Finance, Elvira Yankiv
Vice President Sales CASO East, Sean Beacom
Vice President Tax, Elaine Nelson
National Accounts Manager, Sherry Batts
Chairman, Wayne R. Sanders, age 69
Treasurer, Lisa Papageorge
Assistant Treasurer and Senior Director Treasury, Dan Morrell
Auditors: Deloitte & Touche LLP

LOCATIONS

HQ: Dr Pepper Snapple Group Inc
  5301 Legacy Drive, Plano, TX 75024
Phone: 972 673-7000
Web: www.drpeppersnapplegroup.com

2016 Sales

	$ mil.	% of total
U.S.	5,768	90
International	672	10
Total	**6,440**	**100**

PRODUCTS/OPERATIONS

2016 Sales

	$ mil.	% of total
Packaged Beverages	4,696	73
Beverage Concentrates	1,284	20
Latin America Beverages	460	7
Total	**6,440**	**100**

Selected Brands

7UP
A&W
Aguafiel (Mexico only)
Cadbury
Canada Dry
Clamato
Crush
Diet Rite
Dr Pepper
Hawaiian Punch
IBC
Margaritaville (licensed)
Mott's
Mr & Mrs T
Nantucket Nectars
Orangina
Pe?afiel (Mexico only)
RC Cola
Rose's (licensed)
Schweppes
Snapple
Squirt
Stewart's (licensed)
Sunkist (licensed)
Vernors
Yoo-Hoo

COMPETITORS

American Beverage
Austin Coca-Cola
Big Heart Pet Brands
Campbell Soup
Citrus World
Coca-Cola
Coca-Cola Bottling Consolidated
Coca-Cola Bottling company of southern california
Coca-Cola Bottling of Northern New England
Coca-Cola FEMSA
Coca-Cola North America
Coca-Cola Refreshments
Coca-Cola Tennessee
Coke United
Cott
Country Pure Foods
Dole Food
Faygo
G & J Pepsi-Cola Bottlers
Gatorade
Great Plains Coca-Cola
Great Western Juice
Hornell Brewing
IZZE
Jones Soda
Jugos del Valle
Lane Affiliated
Mondelez International
Monster Beverage
National Beverage
Nestl ©
Ocean Spray
Odwalla
Old Orchard

Pepsi Bottling Ventures
Pepsi-Cola Bottling Company of NY
Pepsi-Cola Bottling of Central Virginia
Pepsi-Cola of Ft. Lauderdale
PepsiCo
Philadelphia Coca-Cola
Red Bull
Reed's
South Beach Beverage
Sunny Delight
Swire Coca-Cola
Tree Top
Tropicana
Wet Planet Beverages
Wonderful Company

HISTORICAL FINANCIALS

Company Type: Public

Income Statement

	REVENUE ($ mil.)	NET INCOME ($ mil.)	NET PROFIT MARGIN	EMPLOYEES
12/16	6,440	847	13.2%	20,000
12/15	6,282	764	12.2%	19,000
12/14	6,121	703	11.5%	19,000
12/13	5,997	624	10.4%	19,000
12/12	5,995	629	10.5%	19,000
Annual Growth	1.8%	7.7%	—	1.3%

2016 Year-End Financials

Debt ratio: 45.74%
Return on equity: 39.13%
Cash ($ mil.): 1,787
Current ratio: 2.60
Long-term debt ($ mil.): 4,468

No. of shares (mil.): 183
Dividends
Yield: 0.0%
Payout: 46.7%
Market value ($ mil.): 16,603

	STOCK PRICE ($) FY Close	P/E High/Low	PER SHARE ($) Earnings	Dividends	Book Value
12/16	90.67	22 18	4.54	2.12	11.65
12/15	93.20	24 18	3.97	1.92	11.62
12/14	71.68	21 13	3.56	1.64	11.89
12/13	48.72	16 14	3.05	1.52	11.50
12/12	44.18	15 12	2.96	1.36	11.11
Annual Growth	19.7%	— —	11.3%	11.7%	1.2%

DTE Electric Company

Ford Motors is not the only powerhouse operating in Detroit — DTE Electric is another. The utility (formerly known as Detroit Edison) generates and distributes electricity to 2.2 million customers in Michigan mainly around Detroit with expansion north to Lake Huron and east to Ann Arbor. The company a unit of regional power player DTE Energy has more than 11000 MW of generating capacity from its interests in primarily fossil-fueled nuclear and hydroelectric power plants. It operates more than 46000 circuit miles of distribution lines and owns and operates more than 670 distribution substations.

Operations

The largest electric utility in Michigan DTE Electric has a 1 million utility poles 671 distribution substations and 430600 line transformers.

The utility operates nine fossil fuel-(coal and oil) fired generating plants and one nuclear power plant (which accounts for 30% of Michigan's nuclear power output). It also co-owns a hydroelectric pumped storage plant with Consumers Energy.

Geographic Reach

The company serves customers across a 7600-sq. ml. service area in southeastern Michigan.

Financial Performance

Reflecting a stronger economy and growing demand in 2012 DTE Electric's revenues increased by 3% to $5.3 billion due to an 8% jump in residential segment sales 11% growth in commercial segment revenues and a 13% increase in industrial segment sales. Net income increased 11% in 2012 due to stronger sales and a 13% jump in other income.

The company has seen consistent revenue growth over the past five years.

Strategy

To meet the state requirements for reducing carbon emissions in 2009 the company announced plans to add 1200 MW of renewable power by 2015 half through contracts with third-parties and the remainder through its own renewable energy projects (primarily wind farms). In 2011 the company was working on developing a 200 MW wind farm.

In 2010 the company began operating a 60-kW solar energy plant in Scio Township in Washtenaw County the first installation to produce power for the grid under DTE Electric's SolarCurrents program. Its 270 solar panels include 60 that track the sun's movement.

EXECUTIVES

EVP and CFO DTE Energy, David E. Meador, age 59
VP Corporate Secretary and Director, Susan M. Beale
Chairman, Anthony F. Earley Jr., age 66
SVP Customer Service, Joyce V. Hayes-Giles
Group President; President and Chief Operating Officer of Detroit Edison, Steven E. Kurmas, age 60
VP Distribution Operations DTE Energy, Trevor F. Lauer, age 51
Senior Vice President - Finance, Peter Oleksiak
Corporate Secretary, Lisa Muschong
Director, Bruce D. Peterson
SVP Electrical Operations DTE Energy, Paul Fessler, age 63
CIO DTE Energy, Steve Ambrose, age 50
EVP CFO and Director, David E. Meador, age 58
Director, Bruce D. Peterson
Auditors: PricewaterhouseCoopers LLP

LOCATIONS

HQ: DTE Electric Company
One Energy Plaza, Detroit, MI 48226-1279
Phone: 313 235-4000
Web: www.dteenergy.com

PRODUCTS/OPERATIONS

2016 Sales

	$ mil.	% of total
Residential	2,477	47
Commercial	1,754	34
Industrial	654	12
Interconnection sales	50	1
Other	290	6
Total	5,225	100

COMPETITORS

Consumers Energy	WEC Energy
Indiana Michigan Power	Xcel Energy

HISTORICAL FINANCIALS

Company Type: Public

Income Statement

FYE: December 31

	REVENUE ($ mil.)	NET INCOME ($ mil.)	NET PROFIT MARGIN	EMPLOYEES
12/16	5,225	622	11.9%	4,600
12/15	4,900	544	11.1%	4,500
12/14	5,282	532	10.1%	4,900
12/13	5,197	487	9.4%	4,800
12/12	5,291	486	9.2%	4,800
Annual Growth	(0.3%)	6.4%	—	(1.1%)

2016 Year-End Financials

Debt ratio: 29.05%
Return on equity: 10.63%
Cash ($ mil.): 13
Current ratio: 1.48
Long-term debt ($ mil.): 5,885

No. of shares (mil.): 138
Dividends
Yield: —
Payout: 67.5%
Market value ($ mil.): —

DTE Energy Co

Detroit's economy may be lackluster but DTE Energy still provides a reliable spark. The holding company's main subsidiary DTE Electric (formerly Detroit Edison) distributes electricity to some 2.2 million customers in southeastern Michigan. The utility's power plants have a generating capacity of more than 11900 MW. The company's DTE Gas unit distributes natural gas to 1.3 million customers. DTE Energy runs nonregulated businesses in gas storage & pipelines power & industrial operations and energy trading which together have a presence in more than 15 US states.

HISTORY

DTE Energy's predecessor threw its first switch in 1886 when George Peck and local investors incorporated the Edison Illuminating Company of Detroit. Neighboring utility Peninsular Electric Light was formed in 1891 and both companies bought smaller utilities until they merged in 1903 to form Detroit Edison. A subsidiary of holding company North American Co. Detroit Edison was incorporated in New York to secure financing for power plants.

Detroit's growth in the 1920s and 1930s led the utility to build plants and buy others in outlying areas. Detroit Edison acquired Michigan Electric Power which had been divested from its holding company under the Public Utility Holding Company Act of 1935 and was itself divested from North American in 1940.

The post-WWII boom prompted Detroit Edison to build more plants most of them coal-fired. In 1953 it joined a consortium of 34 companies to build Fermi 1 a nuclear plant brought on line in 1963. Still strapped for power Detroit Edison built the coal-fired Monroe plant which began service in 1970. In 1972 Fermi 1 had a partial core meltdown and was taken off line.

Detroit Edison began shipping low-sulfur Montana coal through its Wisconsin terminal in 1974 which reduced the cost of obtaining the fuel. The next year it began building another nuke Fermi 2. The nuke had cost more than $4.8 billion by the time it went on line in 1988. That year the utility began its landfill gas recovery operation (now DTE Biomass Energy).

A recession pounded automakers in the early 1990s leading to cutbacks in electricity purchases.

In 1992 Congress passed the Energy Policy Act allowing wholesale power competition. In 1993 a fire shut down Fermi 2 for almost two years. Michigan's public service commission (PSC) approved retail customer-choice pilot programs for its utilities in 1994. Detroit Edison and rival Consumers Energy (now CMS Energy) took the PSC to court.

DTE Energy became Detroit Edison's holding company in 1996. The next year it formed DTE Energy Trading (to broker power) and DTE-Co-Energy (to provide energy-management services and sell power to large customers). It also formed Plug Power with Mechanical Technology to develop fuel cells that convert natural gas to power without combustion.

In 1997 and 1998 the PSC bolstered by state court decisions issued orders to restructure Michigan's utilities. The transition to retail competition began in 1998. That year DTE Energy and natural gas provider Michigan Consolidated Gas (Mich-Con) began collaborating on some operations including billing and meter reading. DTE and GE formed a venture to sell and install Plug Power fuel cell systems.

A higher court shot down the PSC's restructuring orders in 1999 but DTE Energy and CMS Energy decided to implement customer choice using PSC guidelines. That year the US Department of Energy selected DTE Energy to install the world's first super power-cable which could carry three times as much electricity as conventional copper. Also in 1999 DTE Energy agreed to acquire MCN Energy MichCon's parent.

In 2000 DTE Energy formed subsidiary International Transmission (ITC) to hold Detroit Edison's transmission assets; the next year ITC joined the Midwest Independent System Operator which began to manage ITC's network. It also completed its $4.3 billion purchase of MCN Energy in 2001. Full deregulation of Michigan's electricity market was completed in 2002. International Transmission was sold in 2003 to affiliates of Kohlberg Kravis Roberts and Trimaran Capital Partners for $610 million.

In 2007 it sold its Michigan Antrim Shale gas exploration and production assets to Atlas Energy Resources (which later was acquired by Chevron) for about $1.3 billion. That year due to the expiration of synthetic fuel production tax credits DTE Energy exited the synfuels business. In 2010 it sold its rail service unit (DTE Rail Services) to FreightCar America for $23 million.

In 2012 DTE Energy signed a deal with Spectra Energy and Enbridge to jointly develop the NEXUS Gas Transmission system a 250-mile long pipeline project to transport the growing supplies of Ohio Utica shale gas to markets in Michigan Ohio and Ontario.

To raise cash to pay down debt and to focus on its core businesses in 2012 the company sold its Unconventional Gas Production business (88000 acres of gas and oil production assets in the western Barnett and Marble Falls shale areas of Texas) for $255 million.

In 2013 the company opened the northern portion of the Bluestone Project. The 44.5 mile pipeline (which interconnects with Millennium Pipeline in New York) transports up to 600000 million cu. ft. per day to both the Millennium Pipeline in Broome County New York and the Tennessee Gas Pipeline in Susquehanna County Pennsylvania. (The southern portion of Bluestone interconnects with Tennessee Pipeline).

In 2013 DTE Energy has reached an agreement to sell its historic Marysville Power Plant (an idled coal-fired plant on the St. Clair River) to Commercial Development Company.

EXECUTIVES

Chairman and CEO, Gerard M. Anderson, $1,293,519 total compensation
President DTE Gathering and Processing, Richard L. Redmond, age 60
Chairman and President DTE Energy Foundation, Faye A. Nelson, age 64
President and COO DTE Electric, Trevor F. Lauer, age 53
President and COO, Gerardo (Jerry) Norcia, $650,926 total compensation
President and COO DTE Gas, Mark W. Stiers, age 55
President DTE Energy Services, David Ruud, age 50
President DTE Biomass Energy, Mark Cousino
SVP and CFO, Peter B. Oleksiak, age 51, $553,519 total compensation
President DTE Energy Trading, Steven Mabry
VP and CIO, Steve Ambrose
President DTE Gas Stprage and Pipelines, David Slater
President DTE Energy Foundation, Lynette Dowler
Executive Vice President Major Enterprise Projects, Ron May
VP and Secretary Dte Energy Foundation And Manager C, Jennifer Whitteaker
Vice President And Chief Tax Officer, Joann Chavez
Vice President Regulatory Affairs, Daniel Brudzynski
Vice President Marketing, David Hicks
Vice President Corporate and Government Affairs, Renze Hoeksema
Vice President of Operations, Heather Rivard
Vice Chairman and Chief Administrative Officer, David E. (Dave) Meador, age 60
Secretary, Pam Dempsey
Auditors: PricewaterhouseCoopers LLP

LOCATIONS

HQ: DTE Energy Co
One Energy Plaza, Detroit, MI 48226-1279
Phone: 313 235-4000
Web: www.dteenergy.com

PRODUCTS/OPERATIONS

2016 Sales

	$ mil.	% of total
Electric utility	5,225	46
Gas utility	1,324	12
Energy trading	2,575	23
Power & industrial products	1,906	17
Gas storage & pipeline	302	2
Adjustments	(704)	—
Corporate and Other	2	-
Total	**10,630**	**100**

COMPETITORS

AEP	Indiana Michigan Power
CMS Energy	Nicor Gas
CMS Enterprises	PG&E Corporation
Consumers Energy	SEMCO ENERGY
DPL	WEC Energy
Dairyland Power	Xcel Energy
Exelon Energy	

HISTORICAL FINANCIALS

Company Type: Public

Income Statement

FYE: December 31

	REVENUE ($ mil.)	NET INCOME ($ mil.)	NET PROFIT MARGIN	EMPLOYEES
12/17	12,607	1,134	9.0%	10,200
12/16	10,630	868	8.2%	10,000
12/15	10,337	727	7.0%	10,000
12/14	12,301	905	7.4%	10,000
12/13	9,661	661	6.8%	9,900
Annual Growth	6.9%	14.4%	—	0.7%

2017 Year-End Financials

Debt ratio: 38.25%
Return on equity: 12.24%
Cash ($ mil.): 66
Current ratio: 1.10
Long-term debt ($ mil.): 12,185
No. of shares (mil.): 179
Dividends
　Yield: 0.0%
　Payout: 53.1%
Market value ($ mil.): 19,636

	STOCK PRICE ($) FY Close	P/E High/Low		PER SHARE ($) Earnings	Dividends	Book Value
12/17	109.46	18	15	6.32	3.36	53.03
12/16	98.51	21	16	4.83	3.06	50.22
12/15	80.19	23	18	4.05	2.84	48.88
12/14	86.37	18	13	5.10	2.69	47.05
12/13	66.39	19	16	3.76	2.59	44.73
Annual Growth	13.3%	—	—	13.9%	6.8%	4.3%

Duke Energy Carolinas LLC

Auditors: Deloitte & Touche LLP

LOCATIONS

HQ: Duke Energy Carolinas LLC
526 South Church Street, Charlotte, NC 28202-1803
Phone: 704 382-3853

HISTORICAL FINANCIALS

Company Type: Public

Income Statement

FYE: December 31

	REVENUE ($ mil.)	NET INCOME ($ mil.)	NET PROFIT MARGIN	EMPLOYEES
12/16	7,322	1,166	15.9%	—
12/15	7,229	1,081	15.0%	—
12/14	7,351	1,072	14.6%	—
12/13	6,954	976	14.0%	—
12/12	6,665	865	13.0%	—
Annual Growth	2.4%	7.8%		

2016 Year-End Financials

Debt ratio: 26.30%—
Return on equity: 10.39%
Cash ($ mil.): 14
Current ratio: 1.04
Long-term debt ($ mil.): 9,487
Dividends
　Yield: —
　Payout: —
Market value ($ mil.): —

Duke Energy Corp

Duke Energy Corporation keeps the machines humming and the lights burning for its millions of southeastern US customers. The company generates some 50000 MW of electricity primarily from coal nuclear and natural gas sources and serves it up to roughly 7.5 million residential commercial and industrial customers. Its natural gas operations use approximately 60000 miles of pipelines to supply fuel to 1.6 million customers. Duke performs its operations through regional government-regulated utilities: Duke Energy Carolinas Progress Energy Duke Energy Florida Duke Energy Ohio Duke Energy Progress Duke Energy Indiana and Duke Energy Kentucky. The company is also in investing solar and wind renewable sources.

HISTORY

Surgeon Gill Wylie founded Catawba Power Company in 1899; its first hydroelectric plant in South Carolina was on line by 1904. The next year Wylie and James "Buck" Duke (founder of the American Tobacco Company and Duke University's namesake) formed Southern Power Company with Wylie as president.

In 1910 Buck Duke became president of Southern Power and organized Mill-Power Supply to sell electric equipment and appliances. He also began investing in electricity-powered textile mills which prospered as a result of the electric power and continued to bring in customers. He formed the Southern Public Utility Company in 1913 to buy other Piedmont-region utilities. Wylie died in 1924 the same year the company was renamed Duke Power; Buck Duke died the next year.

Growing after WWII the company went public in 1950 and moved to the NYSE in 1961. It also formed its real estate arm Crescent Resources in the 1960s. Insulating itself from the 1970s energy crises Duke invested in coal mining and three nuclear plants the first completed in 1974.

In 1988 Duke began to develop power projects outside its home region and it also bought neighboring utility Nantahala Power and Light. The next year it formed a joint venture with Fluor's Fluor Daniel unit to provide engineering and construction services to power generators. Mill-Power Supply was sold in 1990.

By the 1990s Duke had moved into overseas markets acquiring an Argentine power station in 1992. It also tried its hand at telecommunications creating DukeNet Communications in 1994 to build fiber-optic systems and in 1996 it joined oil giant Mobil to create a power trading and marketing business. As the US power industry traveled toward deregulation Duke also sought natural gas operations. It targeted PanEnergy which owned a major pipeline system in the eastern half of the US. Duke Power bought PanEnergy in 1997 to form Duke Energy Corporation.

Seeing an opportunity in 1998 Duke formed Duke Communication Services to provide antenna sites to the fast-growing wireless communications industry. It also acquired a 52% stake in Electroquil an electric power generating company in Guayaquil Ecuador. That year it purchased a pipeline company in Australia from PG&E; it also bought three PG&E power plants to compete in California's deregulated electric utility marketplace.

Duke merged its pipeline business Duke Energy Trading and Transport with TEPPCO Partners and acquired gas processing operations from Union Pacific Resources. It sold Panhandle Eastern Pipe Line and gas-related assets in the Midwest to CMS Energy in 1999 to reduce operations in the region

and made plans to build a pipeline extending from Alabama to Florida (completed in 2002).

To further enhance natural gas operations in other regions Duke bought El Paso's East Tennessee Natural Gas pipeline unit in 2000 and a 20% stake in Canadian 88 Energy; it also purchased $1.4 billion in South American generation assets including assets from Dominion Resources and the gas trading operations of Mobil (now Exxon Mobil) in the Netherlands. Also in 2000 Duke and Phillips Petroleum (now ConocoPhillips) merged their gas gathering and processing and NGL operations into Duke Energy Field Services.

In 2001 Duke announced the $8 billion acquisition of Westcoast Energy; the purchase which was completed in 2002 added more than a million natural gas customers and 6900 miles of gas pipeline in Canada. That year Duke sold its Duke Engineering & Services unit to Framatome ANP and its DukeSolutions unit to Ameresco. Duke Energy Field Services purchased Chevron's 33% stake in Discovery Producer Services which operates a Gulf of Mexico gas pipeline and nearby processing facilities.

Duke set out to sell $1.5 billion in assets in 2003 to focus on core operations. The company sold its Empire State Pipeline subsidiary to National Fuel Gas for $240 million and sold its stakes in the Alliance Pipeline Alliance Canada Marketing and the Aux Sable refinery to Enbridge and Fort Chicago Energy Partners for $245 million. Also that year Duke sold its stake in Foothills Pipe Lines to TransCanada for $181 million and it sold $300 million in renewable energy facilities to privately owned Highstar Renewable Fuels.

In 2004 the company sold an Indonesian power plant to Freeport-McMoRan in a $300 million deal and it sold its 30% interest in the Vector Pipeline to Enbridge and DTE Energy for $145 million. It also sold the assets of its merchant finance business (Duke Capital Partners) and its stake in Canadian 88 Energy (now Esprit Exploration). Following this trend in 2005 Duke Energy sold its 620-MW Grays Harbor facility (Washington) to an affiliate of Invenergy for $21 million.

In 2006 Duke sold a 50% stake in its real estate subsidiary Crescent Resources to Morgan Stanley Real Estate. That year the company bought an 825-MW power plant in Rockingham County North Carolina from Dynegy for $195 million.

In a major industry power move in 2006 the company bought energy provider Cinergy in a $9 billion stock swap. Reorganizing its business lines to focus on its US power businesses that year Duke Energy sold its commercial marketing and trading businesses to Fortis and in 2007 it spun off its natural gas transmission business as Spectra Energy. The company also exited the European energy marketing business; it also left the proprietary (third-party) energy trading business in North America (primarily made up of Duke Energy North America or DENA sold to LS Power Equity Partners for a reported $1.5 billion). Duke also wound down its energy-trading joint venture with Exxon Mobil.

In 2008 Duke moved to strengthen its alternative energy assets by buying wind energy producer Catamount Energy for about $240 million plus assumed debt. Catamount had about 500MW of renewable energy in operation.

That year as part of its refocusing on its energy businesses the company stopped reporting on its Crescent Resources unit (a joint venture with Morgan Stanley Real Estate Fund which manages land holdings and develops real estate projects).

It acquired its first solar project Blue Wing Solar now a 14-MW solar farm in San Antonio from juwi solar in January 2010.

That year it formed a partnership with Integrys Energy Services and Smart Energy Capital to build

solar projects across the US. In 2010 Duke Energy also teamed up with Areva to build a $250 million biomass-fueled power plant in Shelton in Washington state.

To raise cash that year Duke Energy sold its 50% stake in DukeNet communications to investment firm Alinda Capital Partners for $137 million.

Boosting its role in the transmission sector in 2011 Duke Energy formed a transmission utility joint venture with American Transmission. Duke-American Transmission Co. builds owns and operates new power transmission infrastructure across North America.

In late 2011 the Renewables unit acquired three commercial solar projects in southwestern North Carolina. It bought the photovoltaic projects from ESA Renewables and the power from each solar farm is sold through Blue Ridge Mountain EMC to the Tennessee Valley Authority. The unit has four other commercial solar farms in North Carolina all located outside of Duke Energy's regulated service territories in the state. That year it also snapped up two solar farms in Arizona (in Ajo and Bagdad) from Recurrent Energy doubling its portfolio of commercial solar projects in operation and expanding its footprint further into the western US.

Not neglecting its international growth markets in 2012 Duke Energy International acquired CGE Group's Iberoamericana de Energa Ibener S.A. subsidiary in Chile including hydroelectric generating assets with 140 MW capacity for $415 million. Chile is Duke's the fourth largest non-US country in terms of generating capacity.

In a major US expansion in 2012 Duke acquired Progress Energy in a $32 billion deal. The acquisition created a more than $100 billion enterprise with the US' largest regulated customer base and was aimed at securing major costs savings in fuel purchasing power generating plant operations and other economies of scale benefits.

Growing its solar footprint in California in 2013 Duke Energy Renewables acquired a 4.5 MW solar project the largest solar generation facility in San Francisco from solar project developer Recurrent Energy. That year it also bought the 21-megawatt Highlander solar power projects in Twentynine Palms California. All told Duke Energy Renewables has more than 100 MW of solar generating capacity (16 solar farms in the US).

EXECUTIVES

EVP and CFO, Steven K. Young, age 57, $625,000 total compensation
SVP Global Risk Management and Insurance and Chief Risk Officer, Keith G. Butler, age 57
EVP Chief Legal Officer and Corporate Secretary, Julie S. Janson, age 52, $520,833 total compensation
EVP; President Natural Gas Business, Franklin H. Yoho, age 58
SVP and Chief Distriution Officer, Michael A. Lewis, age 55
EVP Market Solutions and President Carolinas Region, Lloyd M. Yates, age 56, $661,458 total compensation
Chairman President and CEO, Lynn J. Good, age 57, $1,291,667 total compensation
EVP and President Midwest and Florida, Douglas F. (Doug) Esamann, age 59
EVP and COO, Dhiaa M. Jamil, age 60, $737,500 total compensation
President Duke Energy Indiana, Melody Birmingham-Byrd
State President North Carolina, David B. Fountain
State President Ohio and Kentucky, James P. (Jim) Henning
SVP and Chief Nuclear Officer, John W. (Bill) Pitesa
VP and CIO, Christopher B. (Chris) Heck

EVP Administration and Chief Human Resources Officer, Melissa H. Anderson, age 52

State President South Carolina, Kodwo Ghartey-Tagoe

State President Florida, Harry K. Sideris

Vice President Of Marketing, Jack Farley

Vice President Generation Dispatch and Commodity Logistics, Gregory Cecil

Senior Vice President Stakeholder Strategy and President Duke Energy Foundation, Cari Boyce

Vice President, David Litchfield

Vice President, Preston Gillespie

Executive Vice President, John McArthur

Vice President Market and RTO Services, Lee Barrett

Vice President, Jay Alvaro

Senior Vice President, William Tyndall

Vice President, Toomey Peter

Vice President Regulated Combustion Turbine Operat, Al Smith

Vice President, John Barquin

Vice President Finance, Bill Dickey

VICE PRESIDENT FINANCE, Randy Brashier

Vice President, Angeline Clinton

Vice President Business Development, John Upchurch

Vice President And Controller, Stacey Schrader

Vice President, Thomasine Cannon

Vice President, Bryant Kinney

Vice President, John Stowell

Vice President, Jared Lawrence

Senior Vice President Government Relations, David Dave Marventano

Vice President Internal Audit and Chief Ethics and Compliance Officer, Jeffrey Stone

Vice President and Chief Communication Officer, Ginny Mackin

Senior Vice President and Chief Communications Officer, Selim Bingol

Vice President Asset Management, Ron Snead

Vice President Governance, Kim Maza

Board Member, Clark C Kovacs

Treasurer and Group Vice President Mergers and Acquisitions, Guy Buckley

Pac Treasurer, William Mayhew

Treasurer, Bryan Buckler

VICE CHAIRMAN, Garry Matocha

Board of Directors, John Herron

Auditors: DELOITTE & TOUCHE LLP

LOCATIONS

HQ: Duke Energy Corp
550 South Tryon Street, Charlotte, NC 28202-1803
Phone: 704 382-3853
Web: www.duke-energy.com

PRODUCTS/OPERATIONS

2016 Sales

	$ mil.	% of total
Electric Utilities and Infrastructure	21,366	93
Gas Utilities and Infrastructure	901	4
Commercial Renewables	484	2
Other	117	1
Eliminations	(125)	-
Total	**22,743**	**100**

2016 Sales

	$ mil.	% of total
Regulated electric	21,221	93
Regulated natural gas	863	4
Nonregulated electric and other	659	3
Total	**22,743**	**100**

COMPETITORS

AEP	Exelon
AES	PG&E Corporation
Avista	Piedmont Natural Gas
CenterPoint Energy	SCANA

Dynegy	Southern Company
Energy Future	TVA
Entergy	Williams Companies

HISTORICAL FINANCIALS

Company Type: Public

Income Statement

FYE: December 31

	REVENUE ($ mil.)	NET INCOME ($ mil.)	NET PROFIT MARGIN	EMPLOYEES
12/16	22,743	2,152	9.5%	28,798
12/15	23,459	2,816	12.0%	29,188
12/14	23,925	1,883	7.9%	28,344
12/13	24,598	2,665	10.8%	27,948
12/12	19,624	1,768	9.0%	27,885
Annual Growth	**3.8%**	**5.0%**	**—**	**0.8%**

2016 Year-End Financials

Debt ratio: 37.95%
Return on equity: 5.31%
Cash ($ mil.): 392
Current ratio: 0.70
Long-term debt ($ mil.): 45,576

No. of shares (mil.): 700
Dividends
Yield: 0.0%
Payout: 108.0%
Market value ($ mil.): 54,334

	STOCK PRICE ($) FY Close	P/E High/Low	PER SHARE ($)		
			Earnings	Dividends	Book Value
12/16	77.62	28 23	3.11	3.36	58.62
12/15	71.39	22 16	4.05	3.24	57.74
12/14	83.54	33 25	2.66	3.15	57.81
12/13	69.01	20 17	3.76	3.09	58.54
12/12	63.80	22 7	3.07	1.53	58.18
Annual Growth	**5.0%**	**— —**	**0.3%**	**21.7%**	**0.2%**

DUKE UNIVERSITY

Duke University is home to some 15000 Blue Devils who attend undergraduate- and graduate-level classes in 10 schools and colleges. Trinity College of Art and Sciences the Fuqua School of Business and the Pratt School of Engineering are among the most well known. Duke's law and medical schools are also highly regarded nationwide. The private institution boasts a student-teacher ratio of 8:1. Programs include arts and sciences engineering nursing allied health and public policy as well as schools in business divinity environment law medicine and nursing. Founded in 1838 as Trinity College Duke took its present name in 1924 after American Tobacco Co. magnate James Duke established the Duke Endowment.

Operations

Duke oversees several large scale programs including student academics (undergraduate and graduate) student athletics (27 NCAA Division I teams) Duke Medicine (education two hospitals and other medical operations) Duke Libraries (10 private research libraries) the Duke Marine Laboratory and Duke University Press (publishes about 120 new books annually).

Like most universities its it governed by a board of trustees which serves as the institution?s fiduciary. The board manages and oversees long-term financial health strategic direction educational policy finances and operations.

Geographic Reach

Most of Duke University?s academic operations occur in the heart of Durham North Carolina. It also operates research facilities and Duke University Health System (DUHS). DUHS consists of Duke University Hospital Durham Regional Hos-

pital Duke Raleigh Hospital and related health care clinics.

The university cooperates with other US-based institutions to support student exchanges in New York Washington D.C. Los Angeles Chicago Alaska and Silicon Valley in California. It also boasts programs abroad such as in Berlin Paris Glasgow Madrid St. Petersburg Venice Kunshan and Bangalore.

Sales and Marketing

Notable alumni include Richard Nixon Melinda French Gates Elizabeth Dole and Charlie Rose.

Financial Performance

In FY2017 (ended June 30 2017) Duke University generated consolidated operating revenue of $5.7 billion with more than half of that amount due to the Duke University Health System Patient Services. Operating revenue for the academic portion of Duke increased 8% on the year rising to $2.83 billion.

The university?s endowment was nearly $8.0 billion at the end of FY2017 up more than $1.0 billion from the prior year. FY2017 marked the end of the Duke Forward fundraising campaign which raised $3.85 billion over several years.

Strategy

Duke?s academic strategy pursues investment in its faculty improving the educational experience for all students building its capacity to address global challenges and supporting research learning and academia.

It is investing in its East West and Central campuses as well by building new facilities and improving on existing ones. Projects ongoing in 2017 are a new residence hall (Keohane Quad K-4) and the conversion of its Indoor Practice Facility into a Multi-Purpose Field House which will be used for varsity football practice soccer lacrosse band practice and intramural sports.

Duke is working toward several goals as part of its current expansion strategy. It has set aside an additional $100 million to recruit retain and support an outstanding and diverse faculty. While it's focused on existing fields such as humanities and social sciences the university is extending its reach into genome sciences ethics and global health as it addresses important world issues. To deepen engagement across its undergraduate and graduate student bodies Duke is reaching beyond its Focus Program for first-year students and its joint degree programs for professional students by creating new opportunities for students to make connection with the world outside the confines of the classroom. It's working in the arts to create opportunities for Duke students to interact with distinguished practitioners and create their own works.

To ensure that Duke maintains its commitment to diversity it has developed collaborative partnerships across Durham North Carolina the region and the world. Duke boasts that during the past 10 years the percentage of African-American faculty members has doubled. Indeed a third of all graduate and professional students are admitted from other countries. To ensure it's able to attract and retain a diverse student population Duke rolled out a major financial aid initiative which aims to strengthen its needblind admissions policy to keep Duke on the list of qualified applicants regardless of their family incomes.

EXECUTIVES

Vice President Nursing Pt Care, Mary Ann Fuchs

Chief Administrative Officer and CFO, Tallman Trask

President, Richard H. (Dick) Brodhead, age 70

VP Information Technology, Tracy Futhey

Dean Fuqua School of Business, William F. Boulding

Dean School of Medicine, Nancy C. Andrews
Dean Law School, David F. Levi
Provost, Sally Kornbluth
Chancellor Health Affairs; President and CEO Health System, A. Eugene Washington
President and CEO Duke Management Company, Neal Triplett
Interim Dean Divinity School, Ellen F. Davis
Dean Graduate School, Paula D. McClain
Dean Nicholas School of the Environment, Alan Townsend
Dean Pratt School of Engineering, George Truskey
Dean Sanford School of Public Policy, Kelly D. Brownell
Dean Trinity College of Arts and Sciences, Valerie S. Ashby
Dean School of Nursing, Marion E. Broome
Chancellor Duke Kunshan University, Liu Jingnan, age 74
Dean Duke-NUS Graduate Medical School, Thomas Coffman
Vice President ALUMNI Affairs and Development, Robert Shepard
Assistant Vice President Budget And Cost Allocations, John Clements
Vice President of Finance, Tim Walsh
Assistant Vice President Major Gifts, Juliette Ciani
Assistant Vice President Office Of Information Technology, Angel Wingate
Vice President, Judith Ruderman
Vice President And Director Of Athletics, Kevin White
Assistant Vice President Communications, Doug Stokke
Vice President, Jana Kovich
Vice Chairman, Jack O. Bovender, age 72
Vice Chairman, Robin A. Ferracone
Chairman, David M. Rubenstein, age 72
Secretary Staff Admissions And Financial Aid, Sandra Dillahunt
Executive Board Member, Kevin Kraft
GRS Secretary Treasurer Duke University School Of Law, Jennifer Behrens
Auditors: KPMG LLP GREENSBORO NC

LOCATIONS

HQ: DUKE UNIVERSITY
2200 W MAIN ST STE 710, DURHAM, NC 277054677
Phone: 919 684-3030

PRODUCTS/OPERATIONS

Selected Institutes

Center for the Study of Aging and Human Development
Duke Cancer Institute
Duke Global Health Institute
Duke Institute for Brain Sciences
Duke Science & Society Initiative
Duke University Energy Initiative
Institute for Genomic & Computational Biology
Interdisciplinary Studies
John Hope Franklin Humanities Institute
Kenan Institute for Ethics
Nicholas Institute for Environmental Policy Solutions
Trent Center for Bioethics Humanities and History of Medicine
Social Science Research Institute

Selected Schools and Colleges

Divinity School (Since 1926)
Duke Kunshan University (Since 2014; China)
Duke-NUS Medical School (Since 2005)
Fuqua School of Business (Since 1969)
Graduate School (Since 1926)
Nicholas School of the Environment (Since 1938)
Pratt School of Engineering (Since 1939)
Sanford School of Public Policy (Since 1971)
School of Law (Since 1904)
School of Medicine (Since 1930)
School of Nursing (Since 1931)
Trinity College of Arts & Sciences (Since 1859)

HISTORICAL FINANCIALS
Company Type: Private

Income Statement
FYE: June 30

	REVENUE ($ mil.)	NET INCOME ($ mil.)	NET PROFIT MARGIN	EMPLOYEES
06/12	4,611	(507)	—	26,000
06/05	1,832	246	13.5%	—
Annual Growth	14.1%	—	—	—

2012 Year-End Financials

Debt ratio: ——
Return on equity: (-11.00%)
Cash ($ mil.): 526
Current ratio: —
Long-term debt ($ mil.): —

Dividends
Yield: —
Payout: —
Market value ($ mil.): —

DXC Technology Co

LOCATIONS

HQ: DXC Technology Co
1775 Tysons Boulevard, Tysons, Virginia, VA 22102
Phone: 703 245-9700
Web: www.dxc.com

HISTORICAL FINANCIALS
Company Type: Public

Income Statement
FYE: October 31

	REVENUE ($ mil.)	NET INCOME ($ mil.)	NET PROFIT MARGIN	EMPLOYEES
10/16	18,112	(673)	—	112,900
10/15	19,032	(1,885)	—	
10/14	21,862	(1,408)	—	
Annual Growth	(9.0%)	—	—	

2016 Year-End Financials

Debt ratio: 21.27%—
Return on equity: (-61.15%)
Cash ($ mil.): 448
Current ratio: 1.05
Long-term debt ($ mil.): 1,570

Dividends
Yield: —
Payout: —
Market value ($ mil.): —

	STOCK PRICE ($) FY Close	P/E High/Low		PER SHARE ($) Earnings	Dividends	Book Value
10/16	0.00	—	—	(0.00)	0.00	(0.00)
10/15	0.00	—	—	(0.00)	0.00	(0.00)
Annual Growth	—		—	—	—	—

E*TRADE Financial Corp.

E*TRADE wants you to use its services for nearly everything financial. Known for its brokerage services the firm provides the products tools services and advice to individual investors and stock plan participants wanting to manage their own investments. For corporate clients it offers market making trade clearing and employee stock option plan administration services. Subsidiary E*TRADE Bank offers deposits savings and credit cards online and from 30 financial centers in major

US cities. E*TRADE Clearing offers securities clearing and settlement while E*TRADE Securities the bank's broker-dealer arm offers mutual funds options fixed income products exchange-traded funds and portfolio management services.

Operations

E*TRADE operates one unified segment. Its core brokerage business is split out into three product areas: Trading Investing and Corporate Services. It also offers banking and cash management offering debit cards online and mobile bill pay mobile check deposit and Apple Pay.

Trading products cover investment vehicles including US equities exchange-traded funds options bonds futures and non-proprietary mutual funds. It also provides margin solutions including calculators and requirement lookup and analysis. It serves self-directed investors and active traders with products delivered through web desktop and mobile digital channels.

Investing products and services include retirement accounts including Roth IRAs virtual advice managed investment portfolios and unified and separately managed accounts. It also offers retirement planning through teams at its 30 regional branches and through two national branches by phone and email.

Corporate Services provides stock plan administration and public and private companies. Its Equity Edge Online platform offers employee stock option management stock repurchase plans and accounting reporting and scenario modeling tools.

Geographic Reach

New York-based E*TRADE Financial has 30 branch offices across the US. E*TRADE currently maintains about a dozen retail brokerage websites in Europe the Middle East and the Pacific Rim in addition to the US.

Sales and Marketing

The company sells and provides customer support from its branches online and by telephone. Its financial advisors also promote the firm's products and services.

Financial Performance

After several years of decline E*TRADE's revenue picked up in fiscal 2016 climbing 30% to $2.0 billion. Growth was concentrated in non-interest income which returned to a level closer to previous years after the company incurred a $413 million charge on the termination of $4.4 billion of wholesale funding obligations in 2015. Net interest revenue increased $127 million mostly as a result of lower interest expense

Net income rose by 105% to $552 million due to a jump in gains on securities and higher net interest income offset by an increase in income tax expense. Cash from operations rose 95% to $1.6 billion on the back of higher net income and a 25% increase in customer payables relating to sales of securities to brokerage customer accounts.

Strategy

E*TRADE in 2016 reiterated its focus on growing its customer's wallet share in retirement investing and savings through its retail brokerage business by offering innovative solutions for trading margin lending and cash management. It also hopes its competitive pricing will attract new customers and that its wide variety of corporate services will allow it to build existing relationships via cross-selling.

E*TRADE continues its interest in mobile innovation to attract new customers as well. IT launched its custom Apple Watch market data app in 2015 following on from an iOS 8 app released the previous year that provides market and watch list information.

In order to spruce up its balance sheet E*TRADE shed $4.4 billion in legacy wholesale funding obligations in 2015 to cut its profits free.

Company Background

A disastrous decision to move more strongly into banking (originally aiming to triple its loan business) just as the credit crisis struck down banks and lenders around the world led to large losses at the company. The firm was forced to hoard reserves to counter loan losses and exited both its wholesale lending and direct lending operations. The company also shuttered its institutional brokerage business. Its strategy to do improve results revolves around focusing on its online brokerage business and enhancing its position in retirement and investing while continuing to mitigate credit losses in its loan portfolio.

HISTORY

In 1982 physicist William Porter created Trade Plus an electronic brokerage service for stockbrokers; clients included Charles Schwab & Co. and Fidelity Brokerage Services. A decade later subsidiary E*TRADE Securities became CompuServe's first online securities trader.

In 1996 E*TRADE moved from the institutional side to retail when it launched its website. Christos Cotsakos (a Vietnam and FedEx veteran) became CEO and took the firm public. But there were problems: E*TRADE covered $1.7 million in customer losses and added backup systems after computer failure stymied user access. In 1997 it formed alliances with America Online and BANK ONE and ended the year with 225000 accounts.

The firm began to position itself globally in 1997 and 1998 opening sites for Australian Canadian German Israeli and Japanese customers. It offered its first IPO (Sportline USA) in 1997. Volume grew as Internet trading increased but technical glitches dogged E*TRADE. In 1999 day trading became fashionable and the company began running ads promoting prudent trading to counter criticism that online trading fosters a get-rich-quick mentality.

The company also continued to add services. In 1999 it teamed with Garage.com to offer affluent clients venture capital investments in young companies and launched online investment bank E*OFFERING with former Robertson Stephens & Co. chairman Sanford Robertson. (E*TRADE sold its stake in the bank to Wit Soundview — which later became SoundView Technology Group — the next year.) It also bought TIR Holdings which executes and settles multi-currency securities transactions.

Retail banking was a major focus in 2000. The company bought Telebanc Financial (now E*TRADE Financial) owner of Telebank an online bank with more than 100000 depositors and started E*TRADE Bank which offers retail banking products on the E*TRADE website. To provide clients with "real-world" access to their money it bought Card Capture Services an operator of more than 9000 ATMs across the US.

Continuing to expand its global reach E*TRADE bought the part of its E*TRADE UK joint venture it didn't already own; acquired Canadian firm VERSUS Technologies a provider of electronic trading services; and teamed with UBS Warburg to allow non-US investors to buy US securities without needing to trade in dollars. Later its E*Trade International Capital announced plans to offer IPOs to European investors.

In 2001 E*TRADE entered consumer lending when it bought online mortgage originator LoansDirect (now E*TRADE Mortgage). Also that year the company bought online brokerage Web Street and moved to the NYSE. In late 2002 E*TRADE Bank purchased Ganis Credit Corp. (a US-based unit of Germany's Deutsche Bank) to boost its consumer finance business.

E*TRADE purchased the online trading operations of Tradescape in mid-2002. The deal which

cost E*TRADE $280 million was hashed out the previous April — just days after rival Ameritrade announced its acquisition of online brokerage Datek.

Cotsakos resigned in early 2003 days after the company issued a gloomy forecast (he also had been criticized for his 2001 pay of $80 million although he subsequently gave up about $20 million). He was replaced by company president Mitch Caplan who had been viewed as instrumental in the company's effort to integrate brokerage and banking operations.

In 2005 E*TRADE bought US-based online brokerage Harris direct from Bank of Montreal as well as the former J.P. Morgan Invest unit BrownCo which served experienced online traders. The acquisitions expanded its client base and helped the company to keep pace with TD Ameritrade (the result of the 2006 merger of rivals Ameritrade and TD Waterhouse).

E*TRADE built its wealth management operations in 2005 and 2006 by purchasing several money managers including Boston-area investment advisory firm Kobren Insight Management.

After E*TRADE got snared in the subprime mortgage crisis in 2007 Caplan stepped down. He was replaced in 2008 by Donald Layton a former executive with JPMorgan Chase.

Layton retired the following year. Company director Robert Druskin took over as chairman while Steven Freiberg became CEO. Freiberg was formerly a co-CEO of Citigroup's global consumer operations.

To raise additional cash it sold its Canadian operations to Scotiabank for more than $440 million in 2008. The following year it raised some $733 million in three separate stock offerings and exchanged another $1.7 billion in debt for convertible debentures.

EXECUTIVES

Chief Brokerage Officer, Michael J. Curcio, age 55, $450,000 total compensation
CEO, Karl A. Roessner, age 49, $800,000 total compensation
EVP and Chief Administrative Officer, Michael E. Foley, age 65, $592,308 total compensation
EVP and CFO, Michael A. Pizzi, $484,615 total compensation
EVP and Chief Risk Officer, Ellen Koebler
Chairman, Rodger A. Lawson, age 70
Auditors: Deloitte & Touche LLP

LOCATIONS

HQ: E*TRADE Financial Corp.
11 Times Square, 32nd Floor, New York, NY 10036
Phone: 646 521-4300
Web: www.etrade.com

PRODUCTS/OPERATIONS

2016 Sales

	$ mil.	% of total
Interest income	1,233	61
Commissions	442	22
Fees & service charges	268	13
Gains on loans and securities net	42	2
Other revenue	41	2
Total	**2,026**	**100**

Selected Subsidiaries

E*TRADE Bank (federally chartered savings bank)
E*TRADE Clearing LLC (clearing house)
E*TRADE Securities (registered broker-dealer)
G1 Execution Services LLC (registered broker-dealer and market maker)

COMPETITORS

Charles Schwab	ShareBuilder
FMR	Siebert Financial
Morgan Stanley	TD Ameritrade
Scottrade	UBS Financial Services

HISTORICAL FINANCIALS

Company Type: Public

Income Statement

				FYE: December 31
	ASSETS ($ mil.)	NET INCOME ($ mil.)	INCOME AS % OF ASSETS	EMPLOYEES
12/16	48,999	552	1.1%	3,600
12/15	45,427	268	0.6%	3,400
12/14	45,530	293	0.6%	3,200
12/13	46,279	86	0.2%	3,009
12/12	47,386	(112)	—	3,000
Annual Growth	**0.8%**	**—**		**4.7%**

2016 Year-End Financials

Debt ratio: 2.86%
Return on equity: 9.12%
Cash ($ mil.): 3,410
Current ratio: —
Long-term debt ($ mil.): —
No. of shares (mil.): 273
Dividends
  Yield: —
  Payout: —
Market value ($ mil.): 9,493

	STOCK PRICE ($) FY Close	P/E High/Low		PER SHARE ($)		
				Earnings	Dividends	Book Value
12/16	34.65	18	10	1.98	0.00	22.89
12/15	29.64	34	24	0.91	0.00	19.90
12/14	24.26	25	19	1.00	0.00	18.58
12/13	19.64	65	30	0.29	0.00	16.90
12/12	8.95	—	—	(0.39)	0.00	17.14
Annual Growth	**40.3%**			**—**	**—**	**7.5%**

Eagle Bancorp Inc (MD)

For those nest eggs that need a little help hatching holding company Eagle Bancorp would recommend its community-oriented EagleBank subsidiary. The bank serves businesses and individuals through more than 20 branches in Maryland Virginia and Washington DC and its suburbs. Deposit products include checking savings and money market accounts; certificates of deposit; and IRAs. Commercial real estate loans represent more than 70% of its loan portfolio while construction loans make up another more than 20%. The bank which has significant expertise as a Small Business Administration lender also writes business consumer and home equity loans. EagleBank offers insurance products through an agreement with The Meltzer Group.

Operations

Like other retail banks Eagle Bancorp makes the bulk of its money from loan interest. About 86% of its total revenue came from loan interest (including fees) during 2015 while another 4% came from interest on investment securities. The rest of its revenue came from deposit account service charges (2% of revenue) and non-recurring income sources.

The bank has two direct subsidiaries: Bethesda Leasing LLC which holds the bank's foreclosed real estate (owned and acquired); and Eagle Insurance Services LLC which provides commercial and retail insurance products through a referral arrangement with insurance broker The Meltzer Group.

Geographic Reach

The Bethesda Maryland-based bank operates 21 branches in Maryland Virginia and Washington DC (as of mid-2016) including nine in Northern Virginia seven in Montgomery County and five in the District of Columbia.

Sales and Marketing

Eagle Bancorp serves local businesses professional clients individuals sole proprietors small and medium-sized businesses non-profits and investors. Other clients are from the healthcare accountant and attorney markets.

The bank spent $2.7 million on marketing and advertising during 2015 up 38% from the $2 million it spent in 2014 mostly due to higher digital and print advertising and sponsorship costs.

Financial Performance

Eagle Bancorp's annual revenue has more than doubled since 2011 mostly thanks to strong loan growth with the addition of new branches. Meanwhile its net income has more than tripled as the bank has kept a lid on credit loss provisions and overhead costs.

The bank's revenue jumped 33% to $279.8 million during 2015 largely thanks to a rise in interest income as its loan assets grew 16%.

Strong revenue growth in 2015 coupled with an absence of merger expenses drove Eagle Bancorp's net income up 55% to $84.1 million. The bank's operating cash levels spiked 66% to $98.5 million for the year thanks to a strong rise in cash-based earnings.

Strategy

The company has been focused on growing within its existing markets. Its strategy for further growth includes continuing to seek opportunities to open or acquire new banking locations while waiting out record low interest rates. Eagle's strict loan underwriting standards — it didn't write subprime residential mortgages and didn't buy securities backed by subprime mortgages — has helped it have fewer problem loans the downfall for many banks.

Beyond its core lending and deposit businesses Eagle Bancorp continues to expand its other product offerings as well. In 2015 it introduced a Full Service Equipment Leasing program which provided alternative and convenient financing for all types of business equipment for customers.

Mergers and Acquisitions

In November 2014 Eagle Bancorp significantly expanded its presence in Northern Virginia after it purchased Fairfax County-based Virginia Heritage. The deal added six Virginia Heritage Bank branches (renamed as EagleBank) in northern Virginia along with $917.4 million in assets — including $715 million in loans and $737 million in deposits.

EXECUTIVES

EVP; SEVP and COO EagleBank, Susan G. Riel, age 68, $478,806 total compensation

Chairman President and CEO; Chairman and CEO EagleBank; President Ronald D. Paul Cos., Ronald D. Paul, age 62, $863,565 total compensation

EVP; EVP and Chief Credit Officer EagleBank, Janice L. Williams, age 60, $391,758 total compensation

EVP and General Counsel Eagle Bancorp and EagleBank, Laurence E. Bensignor, age 61

EVP; EVP and Chief Lending Officer Commercial Real Estate EagleBank, Antonio F. Marquez, age 59, $368,256 total compensation

EVP; EVP and Chief Lending Officer Commercial and Industrial EagleBank, Lindsey S. Rheaume, age 57

EVP and CFO, Charles D. Levingston, age 37

Executive Vice President, Susan Schumacher

Vice President Special Assets, Jodee Lichtenstein

Vice President Of Marketing, Jane Cornett

Senior Vice President Commercial Banking Team Leader, Derek Whitwer

Vice President Commercial Real Estate Lender, Timothy Annett

Senior Vice President, Elizabeth Ferrenz

Underwriting Manager Assistant Vice President, Cathy Clarke

Vice President, Samantha Perry

Vice President and Senior Portfolio Manager, Michael Benedict

Assistant Vice President Branch Service Manager, Rosalind Alexander

Vice President Facilities Operations Manager, Shawn Cox

Vice President, Jacqueline Ames

Vice President Senior Mortgage Banker, Deb Levy

Vice President Treasury Management, Mary Nord

Vice President Treasurer, Scott Clark

Auditors: Dixon Hughes Goodman LLP

LOCATIONS

HQ: Eagle Bancorp Inc (MD)
7830 Old Georgetown Road, Third Floor, Bethesda, MD 20814
Phone: 301 986-1800
Web: www.eaglebankcorp.com

PRODUCTS/OPERATIONS

Selected Subsidiaries
EagleBank
  Bethesda Leasing LLC
  Eagle Insurance Services LLC
  Fidelity Mortgage Inc.
Eagle Commercial Ventures LLC

COMPETITORS

BB&T	OBA Financial Services
Bank of America	PNC Financial
Capital One	Sandy Spring Bancorp
M&T Bank	SunTrust

HISTORICAL FINANCIALS

Company Type: Public

Income Statement

FYE: December 31

	ASSETS ($ mil.)	NET INCOME ($ mil.)	INCOME AS % OF ASSETS	EMPLOYEES
12/16	6,890	97	1.4%	469
12/15	6,076	84	1.4%	434
12/14	5,247	54	1.0%	427
12/13	3,771	47	1.2%	386
12/12	3,409	35	1.0%	393
Annual Growth	19.2%	29.0%	—	4.5%

2016 Year-End Financials

Debt ratio: 3.14%
Return on equity: 12.32%
Cash ($ mil.): 365
Current ratio: —
Long-term debt ($ mil.): —
No. of shares (mil.): 34
Dividends
Yield: —
Payout: —
Market value ($ mil.): 2,074

	STOCK PRICE ($) FY Close	P/E High/Low	PER SHARE ($) Earnings	Dividends	Book Value
12/16	60.95	22 15	2.86	0.00	24.77
12/15	50.47	22 13	2.50	0.00	22.07
12/14	35.52	18 15	1.95	0.00	20.60
12/13	30.63	18 11	1.76	0.00	15.22
12/12	19.97	14 10	1.46	0.00	13.86
Annual Growth	32.2%	— —	18.2%	—	15.6%

EAST BOSTON SAVING BANK

LOCATIONS

HQ: EAST BOSTON SAVING BANK
10 MERIDIAN ST, BOSTON, MA 021281963
Phone: 617 567-1500
Web: WWW.EBSB.COM

HISTORICAL FINANCIALS

Company Type: Private

Income Statement

FYE: December 31

	ASSETS ($ mil.)	NET INCOME ($ mil.)	INCOME AS % OF ASSETS	EMPLOYEES
12/11	1,974	11	0.6%	401
12/09	1,211	3	0.3%	—
12/08	1,024	0	0.0%	—
12/07	988	2	0.3%	—
Annual Growth	18.9%	42.0%	—	—

2011 Year-End Financials

Debt ratio: —
Return on equity: 12.70%
Cash ($ mil.): 506
Current ratio: —
Long-term debt ($ mil.): —
Dividends
Yield: —
Payout: —
Market value ($ mil.): —

East West Bancorp, Inc

East West Bancorp banks in both hemispheres of the world. It's the holding company for East West Bank which provides standard banking services and loans through more than 130 branches in major US metropolitan areas and about 10 offices across in China Hong Kong and Taiwan. Boasting $29 billion in assets East West Bank focuses on making commercial and industrial real estate loans which account for the majority of the company's loan portfolio. Catering to the Asian-American community it also provides international banking and trade financing to importers/exporters doing business in the Asia/Pacific region. East West Bank offers multilingual service in English Cantonese Mandarin Vietnamese and Spanish.

Operations

East West Bancorp operates two business segments. The commercial banking segment (which generated 62% of its total revenue in 2014) includes commercial industrial and commercial real estate primarily generates commercial and industrial real estate loans and offers a wide variety of international finance and trade services and products. The retail banking segment (33% of total revenue) focuses primarily on retail operations through the East West Bank's branch network. The bank also offers insurance products through East West Insurance.

Broadly speaking the bank made 93% of its revenue from loan interest (including fees) in 2014 and another 7% from interest on investment securities investment in Federal Home Loan Bank and Federal Reserve Bank Stock and short-term investments. It had a staff of roughly 2700 employees at the end of 2014.

Geographic Reach

East West's bank network in the US is mainly in California (in and around Los Angeles the San Francisco Bay area Orange County and Silicon Valley) and in the Atlanta Boston Houston New York and Seattle metropolitan areas. Internationally the bank has five branches in Hong Kong and Greater China (Shanghai Shantou and Shenzhen) and five representative offices in Beijing Chongqing Guangzhou Xiamen and Taiwan.

Sales and Marketing

East West Bancorp caters its banking and loan business to companies in the manufacturing wholesale trade and service sectors.

Financial Performance

The bank has struggled to consistently grow its revenues in recent years due to shrinking interest margins on loans amidst the low-interest environment. Its profits however have been rising thanks to declining loan loss provisions as its loan portfolio's credit quality has improved with higher property valuations in the strengthened economy.

East West had a breakout year in 2014 as its revenue climbed by 17% to $1.14 billion mostly thanks to an increase in non-covered loan volumes. Higher revenue in 2014 drove East West Bancorp's net income higher by 16% to $342.5 million. Lower income tax provisions resulting from additional purchases of affordable housing partnerships and tax-credited investments also help pad the bank's bottom line.

The bank's operating cash levels dipped by 8% to $392.9 million mostly due to unfavorable working capital changes related to accrued interest receivables and other asset balances.

Strategy

East West Bancorp's long-term vision reiterated in 2015 is to "serve as the financial bridge between the United States and Greater China" by reaching more customers with its cross-border products and capabilities. Its full-service branches in Greater China offer traditional letters of credit and trade finance between businesses while also providing the bank a way to serve existing clients and establish new business relationships.

Toward its international expansion plans the company opened two new branches in Greater China's Shenzhen and Shanghai Pilot Free Trade Zone during 2014 which would better position it to help its customers and facilitate their financial needs between Greater China and the US.

The bank may also occasionally pursue acquisitions of other banks to broaden its market reach and grow its loan and deposit business.

Mergers and Acquisitions

In 2014 East West Bancorp expanded its presence in Texas and California after it purchased Metrocorp along with its 19 MetroBank and Metro United Bank branches in the Houston Dallas and San Diego markets. The deal also added $1.7 billion in assets and $1.4 billion in new loan assets.

Company Background

East West Bancorp was founded in 1998.

In 2009 the company acquired more than 60 branches and most of the banking operations of larger rival United Commercial Bank which had been seized by regulators. The deal gave East West Bank about 40 more California branches plus some 20 additional US locations beyond the state.

EXECUTIVES

EVP Chief Risk Officer General Counsel and Secretary East West Bancorp and East West Bank, Douglas P. Krause, age 61, $403,090 total compensation

Chairman and CEO East West Bancorp and East West Bank, Dominic Ng, age 58, $1,000,000 total compensation

Vice Chairman East West Bancorp and East West Bank, John M. Lee, age 85

EVP and Head of International and Commercial Banking, Andy Yen, age 59, $370,977 total compensation

EVP and CFO East West Bancorp and East West Bank, Irene H. Oh, age 39, $403,090 total compensation

EVP and Chief Credit Officer East West Bank, Albert Sun, age 62

President and COO East West Bancorp and East West Bank, Gregory L. Guyett, age 53

EVP Head of U.S. Eastern and Texas Regions and Head of Consumer and Business Banking, Wendy Cai-Lee

Fvp And Recruiting Manager, Gary Teo

Vice President, Sue Chao

First Vice President Consumer Banking Regional Manager, Renee Chang

Senior Vice President, Bennett Chui

Vice President, Samsonz Lam

First Vice President Relationship Manager, Dorothy Zhao

Vice President Bus Relationship Manager, Chancellor Moy

Auditors: KPMG LLP

LOCATIONS

HQ: East West Bancorp, Inc
135 North Los Robles Ave., 7th Floor, Pasadena, CA 91101
Phone: 626 768-6000
Web: www.eastwestbank.com

PRODUCTS/OPERATIONS

2011 Sales

	$ mil.	% of total
Commercial lending	619	57
Retail banking	358	33
Other & adjustments	112	10
Total	**1,091**	**100**

COMPETITORS

Bank of America	Hanmi Financial
Bank of East Asia	Hope Bancorp
Cathay General Bancorp	JPMorgan Chase
Citibank	U.S. Bancorp
City National	Wells Fargo
Comerica	

HISTORICAL FINANCIALS

Company Type: Public

Income Statement   FYE: December 31

	ASSETS ($ mil.)	NET INCOME ($ mil.)	INCOME AS % OF ASSETS	EMPLOYEES
12/16	34,788	431	1.2%	2,873
12/15	32,350	384	1.2%	2,833
12/14	28,738	342	1.2%	2,709
12/13	24,730	295	1.2%	2,542
12/12	22,536	281	1.2%	2,306
Annual Growth	**11.5%**	**11.3%**	**—**	**5.6%**

2016 Year-End Financials

Debt ratio: 0.54%	No. of shares (mil.): 144
Return on equity: 13.14%	Dividends
Cash ($ mil.): 2,201	Yield: 0.0%
Current ratio: —	Payout: 26.9%
Long-term debt ($ mil.): —	Market value ($ mil.): 7,328

	STOCK PRICE ($) FY Close	P/E High/Low		PER SHARE ($) Earnings	Dividends	Book Value
12/16	50.83	17	9	2.97	0.80	23.78
12/15	41.56	17	13	2.66	0.80	21.70
12/14	38.71	16	13	2.38	0.72	19.85
12/13	34.97	17	10	2.10	0.60	17.18
12/12	21.49	13	10	1.89	0.40	16.98
Annual Growth	**24.0%**	**—**	**—**	**12.0%**	**18.9%**	**8.8%**

Eastman Chemical Co

Eastman Chemical Company is a major international producer of acetate tow for cigarette filters. From manufacturing sites in the US and six European countries (including the UK Germany and France) it also turns out chemicals fibers plastics rubber materials polymers and solvents. Eastman's products include such items as food and medical packaging films and toothbrushes. Its end markets include transportation building and construction tobacco consumer durables food and agriculture and health and wellbeing. The company was once part of film giant Eastman Kodak.

HISTORY

Eastman Chemical went public in 1994 but the company traces its roots to the 19th century. George Eastman after developing a method for dry-plate photography established the Eastman Dry Plate and Film Company in 1884 in Rochester New York (the name was changed to Eastman Kodak in 1892).

In 1886 Eastman hired scientist Henry Reichenbach to help create and manufacture new photographic chemicals. As time passed Reichenbach and the company's other scientists came up with chemicals that were either not directly related to photography or had uses in addition to photography.

Eastman bought a wood-distillation plant in Kingsport Tennessee in 1920 and formed the Tennessee Eastman Corporation to make methanol and acetone for the manufacture of photographic chemicals. The company by this time called Kodak introduced acetate yarn and Tenite a cellulose ester plastic in the early 1930s. During WWII the company formed Holston Defense to make explosives for the US armed forces.

Kodak began to vertically integrate Tennessee Eastman's operations during the 1950s acquiring A. M. Tenney Associates Tennessee Eastman's selling agent for its acetate yarn products in 1950. It also established Texas Eastman opening a plant in Longview to produce ethyl alcohol and aldehydes raw materials used in fiber and film production. At the end of 1952 Kodak created Eastman Chemical Products to sell alcohols plastics and fibers made by Tennessee Eastman and Texas Eastman. Also that year Tennessee Eastman developed cellulose acetate filter tow for use in cigarette filters. In the late 1950s the company introduced Kodel polyester fiber.

Kodak created Carolina Eastman Company in 1968 opening a plant in Columbia South Carolina to produce Kodel and other polyester products. It also created Eastman Chemicals Division to handle its chemical operations.

In the late 1970s Eastman Chemicals Division introduced polyethylene terephthalate (PET) resin used to make containers. It acquired biological and molecular instrumentation manufacturer International Biotechnologies in 1987.

Eastman Chemicals Division became Eastman Chemical Company in 1990. In 1993 it exited the polyester fiber business. When Kodak spun off Eastman Chemical in early 1994 the new company was saddled with $1.8 billion in debt.

Eastman's 1996 earnings were reduced when oversupply lowered prices for PET. Eastman opened plants in Argentina Malaysia and the Netherlands in 1998.

Eastman added to its international locations in 1999 by opening a plant in Singapore and an office in Bangkok. It also bought Lawter International (specialty chemicals for ink and coatings) with locations in Belgium China and Ireland. In 2000 the company began restructuring into two business segments (chemicals and polymers) and acquired resin and colorant maker McWhorter Technologies.

In 2001 Eastman acquired most of Hercules' resins business. In November the company announced that it had postponed plans to split into two companies (one focusing on specialty chemicals and plastics the other concentrating on polyethylene plastics and acetate fibers) until mid-2002 due to the weak economy. In early 2002 the company announced that it had cancelled those plans altogether and would operate the two as separate divisions.

The following year Eastman announced it would split off part of its coatings adhesives specialty polymers and inks (CASPI) segment. The division had been underperforming and had been hit particularly hard by the high costs of raw materials and a general overcapacity in the marketplace. Eastman sold a portion of CASPI to investment firm Apollo Management for $215 million. Businesses included in the sale were composites inks and graphic arts raw materials liquid and powder resins and textile chemicals. (Apollo called the acquired businesses Resolution Specialty Materials and then joined RSM with Resolution Performance Products and another of its chemical companies Borden Chemical to form the new Hexion Specialty Chemicals in 2005.)

It restructured its divisional alignment in 2006 in an attempt to group together related product groups and technologies. In the process Eastman disbanded its former Voridian Division.

At the end of 2007 the company decided to divest its PET facilities in the UK and the Netherlands as well as its Dutch PTA plants. Eastman sold the facilities to Indorama for about $330 million.

Chairman and CEO Brian Ferguson retired in 2009 after nearly seven years as CEO. James Rogers who had been president of the company and head of the chemicals and fibers group became his successor and Ferguson became executive chairman.

In 2009 the company joined with SK Chemicals in a joint venture to construct a cellulose acetate tow facility in Ulsan South Korea. Eastman owns 80% of the JV and operates the plant. It also bought a facility in China in 2010 in a joint venture with Mazzucchelli 1849 SPA. The previous year Eastman had expanded an acetate tow facility it owns in the UK.

Eastman Chemical acquired Genovique Specialties Corporation a global provider of benzoate plasticizers from Arsenal Capital Partners in 2010. Genovique produces benzoic acid sodium benzoate and specialty plasticizers with operations in North America Europe and Asia.

Eastman bought Houston-based Sterling Chemicals for $100 million in 2011. The company plans to use Sterling's plasticizers manufacturing plant to produce its own line of non-phthalate plasticizers Eastman 168 for its PCI segment. The non-phthalate plasticizers used to soften vinyl are an alternative to phthalates which have seen restrictions because of safety concerns.

To raise cash for core businesses in 2011 Eastman sold its Texas-based TX Energy unit to Zero Emission Energy Plants. The TX Energy facility will convert petroleum coke an oil refining waste product into hydrogen and pipeline-quality carbon dioxide.

Eastman Chemicals completed its exit of its Performance Polymers segment in 2011 by selling its polyethylene terephthalate (PET) business to DAK Americas LLC for about $600 million. Eastman Chemicals had been a top producer of PET a plastic used to make packaging for soft drinks food and water.

In a major move in 2012 Eastman acquired US-based chemicals firm Solutia in a $4.7 billion cash-and-stock deal. With the addition of Solutia Eastman became a top-tier specialty chemicals company. Its products include rubber materials specialty polymers (synthetic plastics) solvents adhesives plasticizers (additives to soften plastics such as PVC) and specialty fluids.

The Solutia purchase not only broadened Eastman Chemicals' portfolio but also its geographic reach. The addition was a significant step in the company's growth strategy particularly in the Asia/Pacific region and other emerging markets and the company expected the transaction to accelerate the expansion of its businesses worldwide.

That year Eastman also bought Dynaloy a specialty chemical company in Indianapolis. Dynaloy sells cleaning products used in the manufacture of semiconductors and the acquisition supports Eastman's efforts to expand its CASPI segment.

In 2012 Eastman's joint venture with Sinopec Yangzi Petrochemical announced plans to build a major hydrogenated hydrocarbon resin plant in Nanjing China capable of producing 50000 metric tons of Eastman's Adhesives and Plasticizers segment's Regalite hydrocarbon resins.

To meet customer growth in 2013 the company's Fibers segment joint venture with China National Tobacco completed a new 30000 metric ton acetate tow manufacturing facility in Hefei China.

EXECUTIVES

EVP and CFO, Curtis E. (Curt) Espeland, age 52, $736,887 total compensation
Chairman and CEO, Mark J. Costa, age 50, $1,102,895 total compensation
SVP and Chief International Ventures Officer, Michael H. K. Chung, age 63
SVP and CTO, Stephen G. (Steve) Crawford, age 52, $484,892 total compensation
EVP and Chief Commercial Officer, Brad A. Lich, age 49, $611,007 total compensation
SVP Chief Manufacturing and Engineering Officer, Mark K. Cox, age 51
Senior Vice President Fibers and Global Supply Chain, Richard Johnson
Vice President, Don Cleek
Treasurer, Mary Dean Hall
Auditors: PricewaterhouseCoopers LLP

LOCATIONS

HQ: Eastman Chemical Co
200 South Wilcox Drive, Kingsport, TN 37662
Phone: 423 229-2000
Web: www.eastman.com

2016 Sales

	$ mil.	% of total
US & Canada	4,025	45
Europe Middle East & Africa	2,305	24
Asia/Pacific	2,163	25
Latin America	515	6
Total	**9,008**	**100**

PRODUCTS/OPERATIONS

2016 Sales

	$ mil.	% of total
Additives & Functional Products	2,979	33
Chemical Intermediates	2,534	28
Advanced Materials	2,457	27
Fibers	992	11
Other	46	1
Total	**9,008**	**100**

Selected Brands and Products

ABALYN rosin resins
ABITOL hydroabietyl alcohols
ADMEX plasticizers
ASPIRA family of resins
BENZOFLEX plasticizers
BIOEXTEND high performance additives
CADENCE resins for calendered films
CELLOLYN synthetic resins
CHROMSPUN acetate yarn
CRYSTEX insoluble sulfur
CYPHREX microfibers
DRESINATE rosin soaps
DURASTAR polymer
DYMEREX rosins
EASTAPURE electronic chemicals
EASTAR copolyesters
EASTEK polymer dispersion
EASTMAN AQ polymers
EASTMAN cellulose esters
EASTMAN coalescents
EASTMAN G polymers
EASTMAN low volatile pure monomer resins
EASTMAN NPG glycol
EASTMAN plasticizers
EASTMAN solvents
EASTMAN TXIB formulation additive
EASTOFLEX amorphous polyolefins
EASTOTAC resins
ECDEL elastomers
EMBRACE family of resins
ENDEX hydrocarbon resins
ENERLOGIC low-e window film
ESTRON acetate yarn
FLEXVUE film
FORAL hydrogenated rosins
FORALYN hydrogenated rosin esters
FORMULAONE high performance auto tint
GILA DIY window film
HUPER OPTIK & DESIGN film
IQUE film
KRISTALEX hydrocarbon resins
LLUMAR window film
METALYN rosin esters
NANOLUX film
NEOSTAR elastomer
OPTIFILM family of products
PAMOLYN fatty acids
PENTALYN synthetic resins
PERENNIAL WOOD
PERMALYN resins
PICCO hydrocarbon resins
PICCOLASTIC hydrocarbon resins
PICCOTAC hydrocarbon resins
PICCOTEX hydrocarbon resins
PLASTOLYN hydrocarbon resins
POLY-PALE rosin resins
PROBENZ sodium benzoate
PROVISTA copolymer
REGALITE hydrocarbon resins
REGALREZ hydrocarbon resins
SAFLEX PVB polymers
SANTOFLEX antidegradants
SKYDROL aviation hydraulic fluids
SKYKLEEN solvents
SOLUS performance additive
SPECTAR copolyester
STAYBELITE-E hydrogenated rosins
SUN-X film
SUSTANE SAIB
TACOLYN resin dispersions
TENITE cellulosics
TENOX antioxidants
TEXANOL ester alcohol
THE GLASS POLYMER
THERMINOL heat transfer fluids
TiGLAZE copolyester
TMPD glycol
TRITAN copolyester

VANCEVA PVB polymers
VELATE coalescents
VISTA window film
V-KOOL film
XIR coated PET

COMPETITORS

Akzo Nobel	Dow Chemical
BASF SE	DuPont
Celanese	ExxonMobil Chemical
Clariant	Huntsman Corp
DIC Corporation	Solvay
DSM	

HISTORICAL FINANCIALS

Company Type: Public

Income Statement

FYE: December 31

	REVENUE ($ mil.)	NET INCOME ($ mil.)	NET PROFIT MARGIN	EMPLOYEES
12/16	9,008	854	9.5%	14,000
12/15	9,648	848	8.8%	15,000
12/14	9,527	751	7.9%	15,000
12/13	9,350	1,165	12.5%	14,000
12/12	8,102	437	5.4%	13,500
Annual Growth	2.7%	18.2%	—	0.9%

2016 Year-End Financials

Debt ratio: 42.66%
Return on equity: 20.10%
Cash ($ mil.): 181
Current ratio: 1.60
Long-term debt ($ mil.): 6,311

No. of shares (mil.): 146
Dividends
  Yield: 0.0%
  Payout: 32.8%
Market value ($ mil.): 11,014

	STOCK PRICE ($) FY Close	P/E High/Low		PER SHARE ($) Earnings	Dividends	Book Value
12/16	75.21	13	10	5.75	1.89	30.95
12/15	67.51	15	11	5.66	1.66	26.67
12/14	75.86	18	14	4.97	1.45	23.62
12/13	80.70	11	8	7.44	1.25	24.91
12/12	68.05	22	13	2.93	1.08	19.12
Annual Growth	2.5%		—	18.4%	15.0%	12.8%

eBay Inc.

eBay is a well-known e-commerce platform for online auctions. Trading goods every second of every day eBay offers an online forum for buying and selling merchandise worldwide from fine antiques to the latest video games. eBay generates revenue through listing and selling fees and through advertising and boasts more than 170 million users and more than 1 billion listings globally. Its e-commerce platforms include StubHub and Half.com. eBay also has a mobile version of its service and owns e-commerce services provider GSI Commerce as well as a minority stake in online classifieds service Craigslist.

HISTORY

Pierre Omidyar created a flea market in cyberspace when he launched online auction service Auction Web on Labor Day weekend in 1995. Making a name for itself largely through word of mouth the company incorporated in 1996 the same year it began to charge a fee to auction items online. That year it enhanced its service with Feedback Forum (buyer and seller ratings).

The company changed the name to eBay in 1997 and began promoting itself through advertising. By the middle of that year eBay was boasting nearly 800000 auctions each day and Benchmark Capital came on board as a significant financial backer.

Margaret ("Meg") Whitman a former Hasbro executive replaced Omidyar as CEO in early 1998. EBay made a blockbuster debut as a public company later that year. The company moved closer to household name status the same year by launching a national ad campaign and inking alliance deals with AOL and WebTV.

eBay showed its acquisitive streak in 1999 with purchases of Alando (online auctions in Germany) and Billpoint (person-to-person credit card technology). It also made one of its first investments in an outside company with the purchase of 6% of TradeOut.com an online seller of corporate surplus materials. The company set the jewel in its 1999 acquisition crown when it acquired upscale auction house Butterfield & Butterfield (now just Butterfields). eBay also expanded down under through a joint venture with Australia-based ecorp (formerly PBL Online). A bit of the bloom came off the rose in 1999 when online service interruptions (one "brownout" in June persisted for 22 hours) revealed a chink in eBay's armor. The company called its top 10000 users to convey its apologies and pledged to improve its website's performance.

In 2000 eBay agreed to develop person-to-person and merchant-to-person auction sites for Disney's GO Network began distributing information through wireless products and joined with banking giant Wells Fargo to offer eBay sellers the option of accepting online checks. Also that year the US Department of Justice began an investigation to determine if eBay had violated antitrust laws in its dealings with competitors. In other legal news a class-action lawsuit was filed against the company claiming that eBay was an auctioneer and therefore must authenticate the items on its site. (A trial court dismissed the case in early 2001.)

Also in 2000 the company expanded into Japan through eBay Japan with computer firm NEC acquiring 30% of the Japanese subsidiary and eBay owning the rest; it also launched Canadian and Austrian sites. In addition eBay took an equity stake in online used-car dealer AutoTrader.com and launched a co-branded used-car auction website and it acquired online trading community Half.com.

eBay strengthened its European position in 2001 through the purchase of French Internet auction firm iBazar. It also launched sites in Ireland New Zealand and Switzerland. eBay made a deal that year to provide its e-commerce capabilities to Microsoft developers and to add business-to-business auctions to its consumer operations. In addition the company began offering virtual storefronts for retailers to sell fixed-price items and purchased auctioneer of foreclosed property HomesDirect. In late 2001 eBay sold its iBazar's Brazilian subsidiary to MercadoLibre Latin America's leading auction site in exchange for a 19.5% stake (now 18%) in MercadoLibre.

Disappointed with the performance of eBay Premiere (fine art and other high-end merchandise) in 2002 the company partnered with Sotheby's in a deal that moved Sotheby's entire online business into the eBay website replacing eBay Premiere (Sotheby's later pulled out of the deal citing lagging sales). eBay also sold its traditional auction house Butterfields and shuttered its eBay Japan operations after its dismal performance in that market. In 2003 the company continued to grow through acquisitions with its purchases of EachNet (after acquiring a minority stake in the Chinese e-commerce company in 2002) FairMarket and Internet Auction.

In 2004 eBay took several steps toward diversifying its business. It expanded its international presence through acquisitions in China and India and spent heavily to establish operations there. Three years later eBay shifted its China strategy entering into a joint venture with Chinese Internet gaming firm TOM Online.

The company purchased about a 25% stake in online classifieds provider craigslist and announced plans to offer a music downloading service. Overall in 2004 more than 60% of eBay's new registered users were in the international business.

2005 was a particularly acquisitive year for eBay. That year it picked up Internet listing site Rent.com for about $415 million. Then eBay's international classifieds group Kijiji (Swahili for "village") acquired London-based Gumtree.com and Spain's LoQUo.com a community-based listings website that operates sites for several Spanish cities alongside ones for France Germany Norway Portugal and the UK. Kijiji next acquired opusforum a local classifieds website based in Germany for an undisclosed sum.

Later in 2005 eBay closed on three major deals. It acquired Shopping.com — a provider of online comparison shopping and consumer reviews with sites in France the UK and the US — for about $635 million. It also purchased PayPal VeriSign's payment gateway business for about $370 million. Also in 2005 eBay acquired start-up online telecom service provider Skype of Luxembourg for nearly $3 billion. Skype's Web-based software allowed its 220 million registered users to make phone calls over the Internet. The acquisition proved costly however. eBay took about $1.5 billion in Skype-related charges in the third quarter of 2007.

Keeping the acquisitions rolling in 2006 eBay snatched up the leading Swedish online auctioneer Tradera.com for $48 million; eBay made the purchase to strengthen its Swedish trading opportunities in the future. Later in 2006 Internet powerhouse Yahoo! and eBay entered an agreement to join forces on advertising Web searches online payments (through eBay's PayPal platform) and a co-branded toolbar. Key elements of the arrangement's design included Yahoo! providing advertisements throughout eBay's site and the integration of PayPal into Yahoo!'s e-commerce infrastructure.

eBay bought German auction management software company Via-Online in 2007. Via-Online operated sales tool Afterbuy.com and eBay made the deal to ramp up support for its Germany sellers. Looking to diversify its online marketplace operations also that year eBay acquired ticket seller StubHub for about $310 million. The company followed that up with the significant $900 million purchase of Bill Me Later in 2008.

In 2008 eBay settled its long-running patent dispute with MercExchange agreeing to buy the three MercExchange patents it had been accused of violating. MercExchange had sued eBay in 2001 claiming that eBay's "Buy It Now" option infringed on its patent technology. A federal judge ruled that eBay should pay MercExchange $30 million in damages in the case. Terms of the settlement were not disclosed.

Later in 2008 eBay announced it would end its arrangement with LiveAuctioneers.com that allowed customers to participate in live auctions hosted by other companies. eBay said ending the deal allowed it to better concentrate on growing listings in its core product.

To encourage further growth in its auctions the company reduced fees and rolled out an improved matching feature in 2008. The feature implemented a ranking system that took into account time remaining feedback scores quality of listing pictures and other criteria.

Whitman who led eBay for a decade stepped down as president and CEO of the company in 2008. She was succeeded by John Donahoe who previously led the company's highest revenue-producing unit eBay Marketplaces. Also that year eBay acquired the California-based visual media company VUVOX Network to further develop rich media capabilities in the eBay marketplace.

In a program that ran through the bulk of 2009 eBay partnered with resurrected automaker General Motors to sell new cars online. Prospective buyers could place bids for vehicles from more than 225 GM dealers in California at gm.ebay.com. The program did not move as many cars as anticipated however prompting the automaker to halt sales and shift its attention to marketing. eBay in 2009 paid about $1 billion for a majority stake (99.2%) in Gmarket a leading online marketplace in South Korea.

eBay also sold a majority of Skype in 2009. Four years after investing in the service eBay acknowledged that Skype did not complement the rest of its operations. It sold off a 70% stake in Skype to investors led by the private-equity firm Silver Lake in a deal involving $1.9 billion in cash and a $125 million note. As part of the agreement eBay retained a 30% interest in the Skype. (eBay had purchased Skype for nearly $3 billion but in 2007 it took a write-down for about half that amount.) eBay sold its share in Skype to Microsoft in 2011.

In 2010 eBay acquired popular German shopping site Brands4Friends for about $200 million. It made the deal to become a leading online fashion destination in Europe. The company continued its shopping spree in Germany the following year when it bolstered PayPal assets by acquiring the German company BillSAFE adding over 15 million accounts. The deal gave eBay purchase-on-invoice capabilities that are popular to merchants and consumers in Austria German the Netherlands and Switzerland.

eBay bought mobile software application developer Critical Path in 2010. Critical Path had worked with eBay to develop several of its applications for Apple's iPhone. The acquisition doubled the size of eBay's mobile team which is working to capitalize on the growing numbers of consumers who are shopping on their smart phones.

In its largest acquisition since purchasing Skype in 2011 eBay bought GSI Commerce a provider of such services as website development and maintenance order fulfillment and digital advertising for $2.4 billion.

In 2012 eBay sold Rent.com to PRIMEDIA. eBay spun off PayPal in 2015.

EXECUTIVES

President and CEO, Devin N. Wenig, age 50, $1,000,000 total compensation
President StubHub, Scott Cutler
SVP and General Counsel, Marie Oh Huber, age 56, $389,462 total compensation
SVP eBay North America, Harry A. (Hal) Lawton, age 43, $650,000 total compensation
SVP and CTO, Stephen (Steve) Fisher, age 52, $625,000 total compensation
SVP and CFO, Scott F. Schenkel, age 49, $650,000 total compensation
SVP Global Operations, Wendy Jones
SVP eBay Europe, Paul Todd
SVP eBay Asia Pacific, Jay Lee
SVP and Chief Product Officer, Raymond J. (R.J.) Pittman, age 47, $580,000 total compensation
SVP and Chief People Officer, Kristin Yetto
Vice President Intellectual Property, Jay Monahan
Senior Vice President Operations, Ryan Downs
Vice President eBay Customer Service Solutions and Technology, Scott Murray
Executive Vice President, Molly Smith

Vice President Talent Acquisition Management And Development, Lou Sanchez
Senior Vice President Information Technology, Andre Tozzi
Vice President and General Manager eBay Advertising, Bridget Davies
Vice President Marketing Ebay, Jody Ford
Vice President, Greg Fant
Vice President Sales, Todd Pearson
National Account Manager, Jessica Schrenker
Vice President Develop, Jay Hanson
Senior Vice President Finance Chief Financial Officer, Bob Swan
Vice President of Engineering, Dane Glasgow
Vice President, Don Albert
Vice President Global Customer Experience Ebay Europe, Jean-marc Codsi
Vice President Legal, John Muller
VICE PRESIDENT, DANIEL FAIN
Vice President of Compensation Benefits and Human Resources, Robin Colman
Vice President Information Technology, Omar Jabbar
VICE PRESIDENT NORTH AMERICA CUSTOMER EXPERIENCE, Denise Leleux
Vice President Engineering, Japjit Tulsi
Chairman, Thomas J. (Tom) Tierney, age 63
Vice President Treasurer, Anthony Glasby
Board Member, John Donahoe
Auditors: PricewaterhouseCoopers LLP

LOCATIONS

HQ: eBay Inc.
2025 Hamilton Avenue, San Jose, CA 95125
Phone: 408 376-7408
Web: www.ebay.com

2016 Sales

	$ mil.	% of total
US	3,866	43
UK	1,315	15
Germany	1,340	15
Rest of world	2,458	27
Total	**8,979**	**100**

2016 Sales

	$ mil.	% of total
Net transaction revenues:		
Marketplace	6,107	68
StubHub	937	10
Marketing services and other revenues:		
Marketplace	1,137	13
Classifieds	791	9
Corporate and other	7	-
Total	**8,979**	**100**

COMPETITORS

AKQA	HSN
Alibaba.com	NexTag
Amazon.com	OnlineAuction
Blast Radius Inc.	Overstock.com
Buy.com	PriceGrabber.com
Costco Wholesale	Shopzilla
Digital River	Spectrum Group
DigitasLBi	Target Corporation
Etsy	Tickets.com
Google	Walmart.com

HISTORICAL FINANCIALS

Company Type: Public

Income Statement

FYE: December 31

	REVENUE ($ mil.)	NET INCOME ($ mil.)	NET PROFIT MARGIN	EMPLOYEES
12/17	9,567	(1,016)	—	14,100
12/16	8,979	7,266	80.9%	12,600
12/15	8,592	1,725	20.1%	11,600
12/14	17,902	46	0.3%	36,500
12/13	16,047	2,856	17.8%	33,500
Annual Growth	**(12.1%)**	**—**		**(19.5%)**

2017 Year-End Financials

Debt ratio: 38.55%
Return on equity: (-10.92%)
Cash ($ mil.): 2,120
Current ratio: 2.19
Long-term debt ($ mil.): 9,234
No. of shares (mil.): 1,029
Dividends
Yield: —
Payout: —
Market value ($ mil.): 38,834

	STOCK PRICE ($) FY Close	P/E High/Low		PER SHARE ($) Earnings	Dividends	Book Value
12/17	37.74	—	—	(0.95)	0.00	7.84
12/16	29.69	5	3	6.35	0.00	9.70
12/15	27.48	46	17	1.42	0.00	5.55
12/14	56.12	1483	1197	0.04	0.00	16.26
12/13	54.87	26	22	2.18	0.00	18.27
Annual Growth	**(8.9%)**	**—**	**—**	**—**		**—(19.1%)**

Ecolab Inc

Ecolab cleans up by cleaning up. The company offers cleaning sanitation pest-elimination and maintenance products and services to the energy healthcare hospitality and industrial sectors among others. Its cleaning and sanitizing operations serve hotels schools commercial and institutional laundries and quick-service restaurants. Other units focus on products for textile care water care healthcare food and beverage processing and pest control. It also makes chemicals used in water treatment for industrial processes including in the paper and energy industries. The company is expanding its services to the offshore and international energy market.

HISTORY

Salesman Merritt Osborn founded Economics Laboratory in 1924 as a specialty chemical maker; its first product was a rug cleaner for hotels. It added industrial and institutional cleaners and consumer detergents in the 1950s. The company went public in 1957. By 1973 it had been organized into five divisions: industrial (cleaners and specialty chemical formulas) institutional (dishwasher products sanitation formulas) consumer (dishwasher detergent and laundry aids coffee filters floor cleaners) food-processing (detergents) and international (run by future CEO Fred Lanners).

At the time household dishwasher detergent was Economics Laboratory's top seller second to Procter & Gamble in the US and #1 overseas. The company began offering services and products as packages in the early 1970s including on-premise laundry services for hotels and hospitals and sanitation and cleaning services for the food industry.

E. B. Osborn son of the founder retired in 1978 and Lanners became the company's first CEO outside the Osborn family. Sales of dishwashing detergent had fallen while the institutional cleaning business had become its primary segment quadrupling in sales between 1970 and 1980. International sales were growing rapidly. In 1979 the company bought Apollo Technologies (chemicals and pollution-control equipment) to improve its share of the industrial market.

A depressed industrial sector caused Apollo's sales to drop in early 1980. The man expected to save Apollo Richard Ashley succeeded Lanners in 1982 but died in a car crash that year. Sandy Grieve became CEO in 1983 and shut down Apollo. Meanwhile debt was up the institutional market had shrunk and the company was slipping in the dishwashing-detergent market. Grieve sold the firm's coffee-filters unit and several plants laid off employees and began new packaging processes. The company changed its name to Ecolab in 1986 and in 1987 it sold its dishwashing-detergent unit and bought lawn-service provider ChemLawn. (ChemLawn was sold in 1992.)

As 1990 neared Grieve introduced what's now known as "Circle the Customer — Circle the Globe" the aim being to become a worldwide leader in core businesses and broaden product offerings. The company concentrated on building its presence in Africa the Asia/Pacific region Latin America and the Middle East. In 1991 Ecolab also began a highly successful joint venture Henkel-Ecolab with German consumer-products company Henkel to better exploit European markets.

Ecolab acquired Kay Chemical (cleaning and sanitation products for the fast-food industry 1994) Monarch (cleaning and sanitation products for food processing 1996) Huntington Laboratories (janitorial products 1996) and Australia-based Gibson (cleaning and sanitation products 1997). In 1995 Grieve stepped down and president Allan Schuman became CEO. Adding a few more degrees to its circle of services in 1998 Ecolab bought GCS Service (commercial kitchen equipment repair).

The company further secured footholds in Asia and South America in 2000 by acquiring industrial and institutional cleaning firms Dong Woo Deterpan (South Korea) Spartan de Chile and Spartan de Argentina. At home it bought kitchen-equipment companies ARR/CRS and Southwest Sanitary Distributing. Late in 2000 Ecolab sold its Johnson dish machines unit to Endonis and announced a restructuring that was soon followed by the departure of several top executives including president and COO Bruno Deschamps.

In 2001 Ecolab purchased the 50% of Henkel-Ecolab that it didn't own from Henkel for about $435 million; the move greatly expanded the company's international business.

Schuman stepped down as CEO in 2004 (retaining the chairman's role); president Doug Baker took over and became a director in addition to his role as president and CEO. Two years later Schuman retired as chairman ending his 49-year tenure with Ecolab. The company named Baker to replace him.

In 2007 Ecolab made an acquisition to expand its operations in the health care field buying Microtek Medical Holdings which makes infection control products for health care facilities for about $275 million. The next year it paid $210 million for Ecovation a company that treats wastewater solid waste and air pollution primarily for food and beverage companies.

In 2011 Ecolab completed its acquisition of O.R. Solutions a privately held Virginia company that makes warming and cooling systems for surgical fluids for $260 million. The business became part of the US Cleaning and Sanitizing segment.

The company began a major financial restructuring of its European operations in 2011 expecting to save about $120 million over a three-year period. The plan includes changes to the division's supply chain administrative operations and other functions as well as a 12% reduction in workforce. As a part of the restructuring it rolled out its Ecolab Business System platform a common set of business processes and systems for its European operations. The EBS platform is designed to streamline the organization improve efficiency and competitiveness and more rapidly improve the region's profitability.

In 2011 Ecolab acquired Nalco in a $5.4 billion cash and stock deal. Following this purchase Ecolab continued restructuring and cutting costs in 2012 including cutting back on its global workforce and streamlining its supply chain. With the merging of both companies' operations Ecolab emerged as a global leader in water hygiene and energy technologies and services.

In 2013 Ecolab bought Houston-based Champion Technologies for $2.3 billion. The acquisition of Champion Technologies and its related company Corsicana Technologies (collectively referred to as Champion Technologies) helps Ecolab to boost its technology and product strengths in North America and is very complementary to its innovative technology and services in the offshore and international energy markets. The deal is expected to yield $150 million in cost synergies by the end of 2015.

Other 2013 acquisitions included Quimiproductos (Mexico; cleaning sanitizing and water treatment products and services); Master Chemicals (Russia; oil field chemicals); and AkzoNobel's Purate business (Netherlands; water treatment services).

EXECUTIVES

Chairman and CEO, Douglas M. (Doug) Baker, age 59, $1,187,500 total compensation
CFO, Daniel J. (Dan) Schmechel, age 57, $581,250 total compensation
EVP and CIO, Stewart H. McCutcheon
President and COO, Thomas W. (Tom) Handley, age 62, $581,250 total compensation
EVP General Counsel and Assistant Secretary, Michael C. McCormick
EVP; President Global Institutional, Michael A. (Mike) Hickey, age 55, $543,125 total compensation
EVP and CTO, Larry L. Berger, age 56
EVP; President International Regions, Christophe Beck, age 49, $548,125 total compensation
VP and General Manager Healthcare North America, Paul B. Chaffin
EVP; President Global Water and Process Services, Timothy P. Mulhere, age 54
EVP Human Resources, Laurie M. Marsh, age 53
EVP; President Global Energy, Stephen M. (Steve) Taylor, age 55, $518,818 total compensation
EVP; President Global Services and Specialty, Roberto D. (Bobby) Mendez
EVP General Counsel and Secretary, James J. (Jim) Seifert, age 60
EVP Asia/Pacific, Darrell Brown
EVP Global Textile Care, Andreas Weilinghoff
EVP and President Global Food and Beverage and Global Healthcare, Jill S. Wyant, age 45
EVP and Chief Supply Chain Officer, Alex Blanco, age 56, $450,000 total compensation
SVP Global Marketing and Communications, Elizabeth A. (Beth) Simermeyer
SVP and President Middle East and Africa, Vishal Sharma
EVP Asia Pacific, Sean Toohey
EVP and General Manager Global Food and Beverage, Nicholas (Nick) Alfano
SVP and President Latin America, John Guttery
Vice President Information Technology Procurement, Glenn Thomson
Assistant Vice President Corporate Accounts, Cargile Kelly
ASSISTANT VICE PRESIDENT CORPORATE ACCOUNTS, Tom Wick
Vice President N.A. Global Business Services, David Mitchell
Vice President Of Finance, Anil Arcalgud
Vice President Corp Accounts Assistant, Cathy Schoeneck
Vice President Human Resources Talent, Sue Metcalf
VP Supply Chain, Gerald Denson
Assistant Vice President Corporate Accounts, Nick Degregorio
Vice President and GM, John Houghtby
Vice President Marketing Institute Strat PlnandCat Management, Tina Dear
Vice President Process Engineering and Quality, Keith Lokkesmoe
Assistant Vice President Corporate Accounts, Bill Clifford
Vice President Research Development and E, Steve Hatch
Assistant Vice President Field Sales and Operations Global Retail, Adam Johnson
Vice President Sales Swisher East, Dan Volker
Assistant Vice President Institutional Central Region Nalco Water, Heather Dubois
Auditors: PricewaterhouseCoopers LLP

LOCATIONS

HQ: Ecolab Inc
1 Ecolab Place, St. Paul, MN 55102
Phone: 800 232-6522
Web: www.ecolab.com

2016 Sales

	$ mil.	% of total
United States	7,035	53
Europe	2,361	18
Asia Pacific excluding Greater China	1,159	9
Latin America	852	7
MEA	667	5
Canada	576	4
Greater China	499	4
Total	**13,152**	**100**

PRODUCTS/OPERATIONS

2016 Sales

	$ mil.	% of total
Global Industrial	4,617	35
Global Institutional	4,495	34
Global Energy	3,035	23
Other	806	6
Effect of foreign currency translation	197	2
Total	**13,152**	**100**

Selected Services

Equipment Care
Facility Cleaning
Food Retail Solutions
Food Safety Specialties
Foodservice Water Management
Front and Back of House
Housekeeping ; Guest Rooms
HVAC Performance Services
Laundry
Pest Elimination
Pool and Spa
Restaurants
Water Safety
Water Treatment

COMPETITORS

3M Purification	ISS A/S
Ashland	Medline Industries
Chemed	Rollins Inc.
Diversey	STERIS
GE Water and Process Technologies	ServiceMaster
Healthcare Services	Zep Inc.

HISTORICAL FINANCIALS

Company Type: Public

Income Statement

FYE: December 31

	REVENUE ($ mil.)	NET INCOME ($ mil.)	NET PROFIT MARGIN	EMPLOYEES
12/16	13,152	1,229	9.3%	47,565
12/15	13,545	1,002	7.4%	47,000
12/14	14,280	1,202	8.4%	47,430
12/13	13,253	967	7.3%	45,415
12/12	11,838	703	5.9%	40,860
Annual Growth	2.7%	15.0%	—	3.9%

2016 Year-End Financials

Debt ratio: 36.48%
Return on equity: 17.76%
Cash ($ mil.): 327
Current ratio: 1.42
Long-term debt ($ mil.): 6,145

No. of shares (mil.): 291
Dividends
Yield: 0.0%
Payout: 34.3%
Market value ($ mil.): 34,208

	STOCK PRICE ($) FY Close	P/E High/Low		PER SHARE ($) Earnings	Dividends	Book Value
12/16	117.22	30	24	4.14	1.42	23.65
12/15	114.38	36	29	3.32	1.34	23.35
12/14	104.52	29	24	3.93	1.16	24.40
12/13	104.27	33	22	3.16	0.97	24.39
12/12	71.90	30	24	2.35	0.83	20.62
Annual Growth	13.0%	—	—	15.2%	14.4%	3.5%

Edison International

Edison International is a power player in Southern California through its largest subsidiary Southern California Edison (SCE) which distributes electricity to of about 14 million people in central coastal and southern California. It is also the top purchaser of renewable energy in the US. The utility's system consists of more than 12780 circuit miles of transmission lines and more than 91800 circuit miles of distribution lines. SCE also has about 6325 MW of generating capacity from interests in nuclear hydroelectric and fossil-fueled power plants. Through its Edison Energy subsidiary the company owns and operates solar power projects.

HISTORY

In 1896 a group including Elmer Peck and George Baker organized West Side Lighting to provide electricity in Los Angeles. The next year the company merged with Los Angeles Edison Electric which owned the rights to the Edison name and patents in the region and Baker became president. Edison Electric installed the first DC-power underground conduits in the Southwest.

John Barnes Miller took over the top spot in 1901. During his 31-year reign the firm bought many neighboring utilities and built several power plants. In 1909 it took the name Southern California Edison (SCE).

SCE doubled its assets by buying Southern California electric interests from rival Pacific Light & Power in 1917. However in 1912 the City of Los Angeles had decided to develop its own power distribution system and by 1922 SCE's authority in the city had ended. A 1925 earthquake and the 1928 collapse of the St. Francis Dam severely damaged SCE's facilities.

SCE built 11 fossil-fueled power stations (1948-1973) and moved into nuclear power in 1963

when it broke ground on the San Onofre plant with San Diego Gas & Electric (brought online in 1968). It finished consolidating its service territory with the 1964 purchase of California Electric Power. In the late 1970s SCE began to build solar geothermal and wind power facilities.

Edison Mission Energy (EME) was founded in 1986 to develop buy and operate power plants around the world. The next year investment arm Edison Capital was formed as well as a holding company for the entire group SCEcorp. EME began to build its portfolio in 1992 when it snagged a 51% stake in an Australian plant and bought hydroelectric facilities in Spain. In 1995 it bought UK hydroelectric company First Hydro; it also began building plants in Italy Turkey and Indonesia.

The 1994 Northridge earthquake that cut power to a million SCE customers was nothing compared to the industry's seismic shifts. In 1996 SCEcorp became the more worldly Edison International. California's electricity market opened to competition in 1998 and the utility began divesting SCE's generation assets; it sold 12 gas-fired plants. Overseas EME picked up 25% of a power plant being built in Thailand and a 50% stake in a cogeneration facility in Puerto Rico.

SCE got regulatory approval to offer telecom services in its utility territory in 1999. That year EME snapped up several plants in the Midwest from Unicom for $5 billion. Overseas it purchased two UK coal-fired plants from PowerGen (which it sold to American Electric Power in 2001 for $960 million). The next year EME CEO Edward Muller (who had held the post since 1994) abruptly resigned and Edison bought Citizens Power from the Peabody Group.

In 2000 SCE got caught in a price squeeze brought on in part by deregulation. Prices on the wholesale power market soared but the utility was unable to pass along the increase to customers because of a rate freeze. The company gained some prospect of relief in 2001 when California's governor signed legislation to allow a state agency to buy power from wholesalers under long-term contracts. In addition the California Public Utilities Commission (CPUC) approved a substantial increase in retail electricity rates and the Federal Energy Regulatory Commission approved a plan to limit wholesale energy prices during periods of severe shortage in 11 western states.

To reduce debt Edison International agreed to sell its transmission grid to the state for $2.8 billion. While the California legislature debated the agreement however the CPUC announced a settlement in which SCE would be allowed to keep its current high rates in place until its debts are paid off. The settlement which was approved in 2002 eliminated the need for the sale of the company's transmission grid.

Also in 2001 the company sold most of its Edison Enterprises businesses including home security services unit Edison Select which was sold to ADT Security Services.

In 2004 Edison International committed to taking a lead position in developing comprehensive national programs to reduce greenhouse gas emissions primarily carbon dioxide.

In 2006 SCE signed the largest wind energy deal ever completed by a US utility providing for 1500 MW of wind power from plants in the Tehachapi area of California.

EME marketed energy in the US and Turkey and had interests in more than 40 power plants in the US and one in Turkey that gave it a net physical generating capacity of about 10780 MW. EME filed for bankruptcy protection in 2012 citing high operating losses due to low realized energy and capacity prices high fuel costs and low generation at its Midwest Generation plants.

In 2013 SCE decided to permanently retire Units 2 and 3 of its San Onofre Nuclear Generating Station. Unit 2 was taken out of service January 2012 for a planned routine outage. Unit 3 was also taken offline a few weeks later after station operators found a small leak in a tube inside a steam generator.

In 2013 Edison Energy acquired SoCore Energy a Chicago-based solar portfolio development and commercial rooftop installation company focusing on the solar energy needs of multisite retailers REITs and industrial clients and bought a minority stake in Clean Power Finance a financial services and software provider for the solar industry.

EXECUTIVES

Vice President, John Finneran
President Edison Energy, Ronald L. Litzinger, age 58, $600,000 total compensation
President CEO and Director, Pedro J. Pizarro, age 52, $836,782 total compensation
VP and CIO Southern California Edison, Todd L. Inlander
CEO Southern California Edison Company (SCE), Kevin M. Payne, age 56, $421,171 total compensation
SVP Commercial Operations Edison Energy and President Edison Transmission LLC, Steven D. Eisenberg
EVP and CFO, Maria Rigatti, age 53, $392,891 total compensation
EVP and General Counsel, Adam S. Umanoff, age 57, $548,391 total compensation
President SoCore Energy, Rob Scheuermann
President Southern California Edison (SCE), Ronald O. Nichols, age 63
Vice President, Joseph Ruiz
Svp Corporate Communications, Janet Clayton
Vice President, PAUL JACOB
Vice President Human Resources, Jenene Wilson
Executive Vice President, David Schiada
Vice President, Cindy Creed
Vice President Of Information Technology, Jodi Collins
Vice President, Weston Williams
Vice President, Doug Kim
Senior Vice President Human Resources, John Kelly
Vice President, Mike Marelli
Vice President and Controller, Aaron Moss
Senior Vice President, Paul Grigaux
Senior Vice President, Drew Murphy
Vice President Local Public Affairs SCE and Vice President Government Affairs Edison International, Christopher Thompson
Chairman, William P. (Bill) Sullivan, age 67
Secretary, Beth Do
Auditors: PricewaterhouseCoopers LLP

LOCATIONS

HQ: Edison International
2244 Walnut Grove Avenue, P.O. Box 976, Rosemead, CA 91770
Phone: 626 302-2222
Web: www.edisoninvestor.com

PRODUCTS/OPERATIONS

Selected Subsidiaries
Edison Energy (solar power activities)
Southern California Edison Company (SCE electric utility)

COMPETITORS

AES
Avista
Berkshire Hathaway

NV Energy
NextEra Energy
PG&E Corporation

Energy
CMS Energy
Calpine
Constellation Energy
 Group
Electricit© de France
Los Angeles Water and
 Power

PacifiCorp
Portland General
 Electric
Sacramento Municipal
 Utility
Sempra Energy

HISTORICAL FINANCIALS
Company Type: Public

Income Statement
FYE: December 31

	REVENUE ($ mil.)	NET INCOME ($ mil.)	NET PROFIT MARGIN	EMPLOYEES
12/16	11,869	1,311	11.0%	12,390
12/15	11,524	1,020	8.9%	12,768
12/14	13,413	1,612	12.0%	13,690
12/13	12,581	915	7.3%	13,677
12/12	11,862	(183)	—	16,593
Annual Growth	0.0%	—	—	(7.0%)

2016 Year-End Financials

Debt ratio: 24.29%
Return on equity: 11.19%
Cash ($ mil.): 96
Current ratio: 0.36
Long-term debt ($ mil.): 10,175

No. of shares (mil.): 325
Dividends
 Yield: 0.0%
 Payout: 49.9%
Market value ($ mil.): 23,455

	STOCK PRICE ($) FY Close	P/E High/Low		PER SHARE ($) Earnings	Dividends	Book Value
12/16	71.99	20	14	3.97	1.98	36.82
12/15	59.21	22	18	3.10	1.73	34.89
12/14	65.48	14	9	4.89	1.48	33.64
12/13	46.30	19	16	2.78	1.37	30.50
12/12	45.19	—	—	(0.56)	1.31	28.95
Annual Growth	12.3%	—	—	—	10.9%	6.2%

EDUCATIONAL FUNDING OF THE SOUTH, INC.

Auditors: KRAFT CPAS NASHVILLE TENNESS

LOCATIONS

HQ: EDUCATIONAL FUNDING OF THE SOUTH, INC.
12700 KINGSTON PIKE, KNOXVILLE, TN 379340917
Phone: 865 342-0684
Web: WWW.EDSOUTHSERVICES.COM

COMPETITORS

Bank of America
Brazos Higher Education Service Corp.
College Loan Corporation
Discover
JPMorgan Chase
Nelnet
Sallie Mae

HISTORICAL FINANCIALS
Company Type: Private

Income Statement
FYE: September 30

	ASSETS ($ mil.)	NET INCOME ($ mil.)	INCOME AS % OF ASSETS	EMPLOYEES
09/12*	2,924	(20)	—	3
12/06	4,223	252	6.0%	—
12/05	4,484	26	0.6%	—
12/04	3,881	30	0.8%	—
Annual Growth	(3.5%)	—	—	—

*Fiscal year change

2012 Year-End Financials

Debt ratio: ——
Return on equity: (-12.10%)
Cash ($ mil.): 174
Current ratio: ——
Long-term debt ($ mil.): ——

Dividends
 Yield: —
 Payout: —
Market value ($ mil.): —

Electronic Arts, Inc.

Electronic Arts (EA) puts gamers in action on the gridiron the pitch the battlefield and in outer space with its most popular games. Its leading titles are Madden NFL (American football) FIFA (football) and Star Wars (all of which are licensed) and its own Battlefield Mass Effect and The Sims. EA is generates increasing sales of games for mobile devices but still makes most of its revenue from games played on consoles from Sony and Microsoft and on personal computers. EA also provides online social games such as those licensed from Hasbro which include Monopoly. The company is moving into competitive gaming and eSports with its Competitive Gaming Division.

Operations

Electronic Arts collects revenue from sales of its games on disc digital downloads (onto several platforms) subscription fees and in-game transactions.

Digital has become increasingly important for EA bringing in 60% of revenue in 2016 (ended March) and rising 10% for the year. Packaged games account for 40% of revenue. Its digital products and services are delivered via Sony's PlayStation Network Microsoft's Xbox Store Apple's App Store and the Google Play store. About a quarter of revenue comes from the sale of extra content.

EA's top three games generate nearly 60% of its revenue. Perennially popular games are FIFA Madden NFL Star Wars Titanfall Battlefield and Sim City.

Geographic Reach

Electronic Arts operates development studios in North America Europe Asia and Australia. North America is its largest market accounting for about 45% of sales with international customers supplying the rest.

Sales and Marketing

As Electronic Arts' business becomes increasingly digital more of its products and services are being purchased over the internet through Origin the company's direct-to-consumer platform or through digital downloads from third-party retailers or via mobile application storefronts. EA sells directly to console makers Sony and Microsoft; they each account for about 20% of revenue. The company also sells packaged games to retailers including mass merchants (Walmart) consumer electronics stores (Best Buy) and specialty game shops (GameStop). Direct sales to GameStop

stores have dropped under 10% of EA's annual sales. EA has partnerships with Tencent Holdings Limited and Nexon Co. Ltd. to sell FIFA Online 3 in China and Korea respectively.

Financial Performance

Electronic Arts? up-and-down revenue was up in 2017 (ended March) rising 10% to about $4.8 billion from 2016. Stronger sales of its FIFA franchise and first-person shooter titles drove the increase. Digital rose about 20% reflecting the trend of players purchasing games digitally and engaging with EA?s live services. Further full game download sales rose 44% year-over-year from a higher percentage of Battlefield 1 downloads in 2017 compared to the 2016 first-person shooter title Star Wars Battlefront. Another revenue driver: extra content which grew 16% in 2017 from 2016 from Ultimate Team services sales.

EA?s net income fell to $967 million down 16% in 2017 from 2016 year-over-year. The company had a tax benefit of some $450 million in 2016 that didn?t repeat in 2017.

A $385 million sales increase in the sale of FIFA 17 Battlefield 1 and Titanfall 2 drove cash flow from operations to $1.4 billion in 2017 from $1.2 billion in 2016.

Strategy

Electronic Arts has discovered the magic of the network effect. By connecting players with its games and with each through its Ultimate Team offerings and live events EA has captured more of its customers? time and drilled new revenue streams. The network effect means that the more people that use a product the more the valuable the product.

Providing avenues for players to reach other and venues in which they can engage with EA games and each other has helped drive the company?s revenue higher. Players can move from Battlefield game to Battlefield game through the game?s network. In FIFA 17 EA with the help of data and analytics created a story mode that brought new players to the title and drove many deeper into the game.

Live game services also opens sources of revenue for EA that include extra digital content subscriptions and advertising. The company draw a significant portion of revenue from the Ultimate Team game mode included in its FIFA Madden NFL and NHL games that are released every year.

Besides developing new games and ways to increase player engagement EA is building out a technology foundation to make sure play occurs without delays or breakdowns.

EA also is building out its competitive eSports programs in which game competitions are shown to spectators. The development is to gain more engagement and compete with Twitch which is owned by Amazon.

Looking ahead EA is investing in developing applications of virtual reality and augmented reality.

EXECUTIVES

EVP and CFO, Blake J. Jorgensen, age 57, $762,981 total compensation
EVP Business and Legal Affairs, Joel Linzner, age 66
CEO, Andrew Wilson, age 42, $1,083,846 total compensation
EVP EA Studios, Patrick S ¶derlund, age 43, $611,291 total compensation
CTO, Kenneth (Ken) Moss, age 51, $619,104 total compensation
EVP Global Publishing, Laura Miele, age 47
SVP General Counsel and Corporate Secretary, Jacob (Jake) Schatz
Chief People Officer, Mala Singh

Senior Vice President of Corporate Affairs, Regina Heenan
Vice President, Erika Peterson
Vice President And General Manager, Steve Papoutsis
Vice President Finance Worldwide Controller, Eric Kelly
Vice President Group GM Of Capital Games, Bill Mooney
Vice President Marketing, Katrina Strafford
Vice President Corporate Services and Facilities, Curt Wilhelm
Vice President Marketing, Jillian Goldberg
Senior Vice President Finance, David Carbone
Vice President General Counsel and Corporate Secretary, Steve Bena
Vice President of Mobile Publishing, Nick Rish
Vice President Apo Sales, Jason Slepecki
Vice President, Vivian MacDonald
Vice President Investor Relations, Chris Evenden
Vice President, Jesse Connell
Executive Vice President Of Human Resources, Greg Graybill
Vice President Of Mrktng, Kip Morgan
VICE PRESIDENT, Richard Garriott
Vice President and General Manager of APAC, Peter Tseng
Executive Chairman, Lawrence F. (Larry) Probst, age 68
Treasurer, Roch Leblanc
Auditors: KPMG LLP

LOCATIONS

HQ: Electronic Arts, Inc.
209 Redwood Shores Parkway, Redwood City, CA 94065
Phone: 650 628-1500
Web: www.ea.com

2017 Sales

	$ mil.	% of total
North America	2,119	44
Rest of world	2,726	56
Total	**4,845**	**100**

PRODUCTS/OPERATIONS

2017 sales

	% of total
Xbox One PlayStation 4	63
Xbox 360 PlayStation 3	7
Other consoles	-
PC / Browser	16
Mobile	13
Others	1
Total	**100**

COMPETITORS

Activision Blizzard	NCsoft
Atari	NEXON CO.LTD.
Big Fish Games	Namco Limited
Capcom	Nintendo
DIMG	Rovio Entertainment
Daybreak Game Company	SEGA
DeNA	Square Enix
GREE INC.	Take-Two
Gameloft	Tencent
Glu Mobile	Ubisoft
Konami	Valve Corporation
Lucasfilm	ZeniMax Media
Entertainment	Zynga
Microsoft	eGames

HISTORICAL FINANCIALS

Company Type: Public

Income Statement

FYE: March 31

	REVENUE ($ mil.)	NET INCOME ($ mil.)	NET PROFIT MARGIN	EMPLOYEES
03/17	4,845	967	20.0%	8,800
03/16	4,396	1,156	26.3%	8,500
03/15	4,515	875	19.4%	8,400
03/14	3,575	8	0.2%	8,300
03/13	3,797	98	2.6%	9,300
Annual Growth	**6.3%**	**77.2%**	**—**	**(1.4%)**

2017 Year-End Financials

Debt ratio: 12.83%
Return on equity: 25.94%
Cash ($ mil.): 2,565
Current ratio: 2.15
Long-term debt ($ mil.): 990
No. of shares (mil.): 308
Dividends
Yield: —
Payout: —
Market value ($ mil.): 27,605

	STOCK PRICE ($) FY Close	P/E High/Low	PER SHARE ($) Earnings	Dividends	Book Value
03/17	89.52	29 19	3.08	0.00	13.17
03/16	66.11	21 15	3.50	0.00	11.30
03/15	58.82	21 9	2.69	0.00	9.80
03/14	29.01	1008564	0.03	0.00	7.78
03/13	17.70	60 34	0.31	0.00	7.50
Annual Growth	**50.0%**	**— —**	**77.5%**	**—**	**15.1%**

EMC Insurance Group Inc.

EXECUTIVES

SVP and CFO, Mark E. Reese, age 59, $265,557 total compensation
EVP Corporate Development, Ronald W. Jean, age 67, $488,402 total compensation
President CEO and Director, Bruce G. Kelley, age 62, $845,070 total compensation
EVP and COO, Kevin J. Hovick, age 62, $406,419 total compensation
SVP Productivity and Technology, Rodney D Hanson, $235,620 total compensation
Chairman, Stephen A. Crane
Auditors: Ernst & Young LLP

LOCATIONS

HQ: EMC Insurance Group Inc.
717 Mulberry Street, Des Moines, IA 50309
Phone: 515 345-2902
Web: www.emcins.com

2016 Premiums Written by Pool Participants by State

	% of total
Iowa	13
Kansas	8
Wisconsin	6
Nebraska	5
Minnesota	5
Michigan	5
Illinois	4
Texas	4
North Carolina	4
Other states	46
Total	**100**

PRODUCTS/OPERATIONS

2016 Revenues

	$ mil.	% of total
Premiums earned	592	92
Net investment income	47	7
Realized investment gains	4	1
Other income	1	0
Total	**645**	**100**

2016 Premiums Earned

	% of total
Property/casualty	77
Reinsurance	23
Total	**100**

Selected Products

Property and Casualty Insurance
Commercial Lines
Automobile
Liability
Property
Workers' compensation
Other
Aircraft and marine
Fidelity and surety bonds
Theft protection
Personal Lines
Automobile
Liability
Property
Reinsurance

Selected Subsidiaries

Dakota Fire Insurance Company
EMC Reinsurance Company
EMCASCO Insurance Company
EMC Underwriters LLC
Illinois EMASCO Insurance Company

COMPETITORS

AIG	Nationwide
Allstate	Progressive
American Family	Corporation
Insurance	SECURA
Auto-Owners Insurance	State Farm
Farmers Group	The Hartford
GEICO	White Mountains
Liberty Mutual	Insurance Group

HISTORICAL FINANCIALS

Company Type: Public

Income Statement

FYE: December 31

	ASSETS ($ mil.)	NET INCOME ($ mil.)	INCOME AS % OF ASSETS	EMPLOYEES
12/16	1,588	46	2.9%	—
12/15	1,535	50	3.3%	—
12/14	1,497	29	2.0%	—
12/13	1,378	43	3.2%	—
12/12	1,290	37	2.9%	—
Annual Growth	**5.3%**	**5.0%**	**—**	**—**

2016 Year-End Financials

Debt ratio: —
Return on equity: 8.55%
Cash ($ mil.): 39
Current ratio: —
Long-term debt ($ mil.): —
No. of shares (mil.): 21
Dividends
Yield: 0.0%
Payout: 35.4%
Market value ($ mil.): 637

	STOCK PRICE ($) FY Close	P/E High/Low	PER SHARE ($) Earnings	Dividends	Book Value
12/16	30.01	14 10	2.20	0.78	26.07
12/15	25.30	15 9	2.43	0.69	25.26
12/14	35.46	24 18	1.49	0.94	24.72
12/13	30.62	15 11	2.22	0.86	22.81
12/12	23.88	12 10	1.97	0.81	20.72
Annual Growth	**5.9%**	**— —**	**2.8%**	**(0.9%)**	**5.9%**

EMCOR Group, Inc.

Electrical and mechanical construction specialist EMCOR Group is one of the world's largest specialty construction firms. It designs installs operates and maintains complex mechanical and electrical systems. These include systems for power generation and distribution lighting water and wastewater treatment voice and data communications fire protection plumbing and heating ventilation and air-conditioning (HVAC). EMCOR also provides facilities services including management and maintenance support. Through some 75 subsidiaries and joint ventures the company serves a range of commercial industrial institutional and utility customers.

HISTORY

EMCOR's forerunner Jamaica Water Supply Co. was incorporated in 1887 to supply water to some residents of Queens and Nassau Counties in New York. In 1902 it bought Jamaica Township Water Co. and by 1906 it was generating revenue — reaching $1.6 million by 1932. Over the next 35 years the company kept pace with the population of its service area.

In 1966 the enterprise was acquired by Jamaica Water and Utilities which then bought Sea Cliff Water Co. In 1969 and 1970 it acquired Welsbach (electrical contractors) and A to Z Equipment (construction trailer suppliers); it briefly changed its name in 1974 to Welsbach Corp. before becoming Jamaica Water Properties in 1976.

Diversification proved unprofitable however and in 1977 Martin Dwyer and his son Andrew took over the management of the struggling firm. Despite posting million-dollar losses in 1979 it was profitable by 1980.

The Dwyers acquired companies in the electrical and mechanical contracting security telecommunications computer energy and environmental businesses. In 1985 Andrew Dwyer became president and the firm changed its name the next year to JWP.

Between 1986 and 1990 JWP acquired more than a dozen companies including Extel (1986) Gibson Electric (1987) Dynalectric (1988) Drake & Scull (1989) NEECO and Compumat (1990) and Comstock Canada (1990).

In 1991 JWP capped its strategy of buying up US computer systems resellers by acquiring Businessland. It then bought French microelectronics distributor SIVEA. Later that year JWP bought a 34% stake in Resource Recycling Technologies (a solid-waste recycler).

JWP's shopping spree extended the firm's reach but the company began to struggle when several sectors turned sour. A price war in the information services business and a weak construction market led to a loss of more than $600 million in 1992. That year president David Sokol resigned after questioning JWP's accounting practices. He turned over to the SEC a report that claimed inflated profits.

Cutting itself to about half its former size the company sold JWP Information Services in 1993. (JWP Information Services later became ENTEX Information Services which was acquired by Siemens in 2000.) However JWP continued to struggle and in early 1994 it filed for bankruptcy. Emerging from Chapter 11 protection in December 1994 the reorganized company took the name EMCOR. That year Frank MacInnis former CEO of electrical contractor Comstock Group stepped in to lead EMCOR.

In 1995 the SEC using Sokol's information charged several former JWP executives with accounting fraud claiming they had overstated profits to boost the value of their company stock and their bonuses. EMCOR later reached a non-monetary settlement with the SEC. The company sold Jamaica Water Supply and Sea Cliff in 1996; it also achieved profitability that year.

Focusing on external growth EMCOR acquired a number of firms in 1998 and 1999 including Marelich Mechanical Co. and Mesa Energy Systems BALCO Inc. and the Poole & Kent group of mechanical contracting companies based in Baltimore and Miami. To meet increased demands for facilities services in 2000 EMCOR consolidated the operations of three of its mechanical contractors (BALCO J.C. Higgins and Tucker Mechanical) into one company EMCOR Services which operates in New England.

That year about six years after emerging from bankruptcy EMCOR began trading on the New York Stock Exchange. In 2002 EMCOR bought 19 subsidiaries from its financially troubled rival Comfort Systems USA including its largest unit Shambaugh & Son. Later that year it expanded its facilities services operations with the acquisition of Consolidated Engineering Services (CES) an Archstone-Smith subsidiary that operated in 20 states.

EMCOR broadened its facilities services operations by acquiring the US facility management services unit of Siemens Building Technologies in 2003; in 2005 it added Fluidics Inc. a mechanical services company based in Philadelphia.

In 2007 EMCOR acquired FR X Ohmstede Acquisitions Co. a leading provider of aftermarket maintenance and repair services and replacement parts for oil refinery equipment.

The company added to its industrial services operations by acquiring South Carolina-based facilities maintenance provider MOR PPM in 2008.

In 2009 EMCOR bought LT Mechanical of North Carolina a leading plumbing and mechanical contractor. The following year it bought Pennsylvania-based engineering and facilities services firm Scalise Industries broadening its mechanical services business.

EXECUTIVES

EVP and CFO, Mark A. Pompa, age 53, $670,000 total compensation
EVP Shared Services, R. Kevin Matz, age 59, $530,000 total compensation
CEO Emcor UK, Keith Chanter, age 58
President CEO and Director, Anthony J. (Tony) Guzzi, age 52, $1,071,000 total compensation
VP Marketing and Communications, Mava K. Heffler
President and CEO EMCOR Construction Services, Michael J. (Mike) Parry, age 68
President and CEO EMCOR Building Services, Michael P. (Mike) Bordes
President and CEO EMCOR Industrial Services and Ohmstede, Bill Reid
Executive Vice President General Counsel and Secretary, Shelly Cammaker
Vice President Of Sales And Marketing Emcor Group Inc, Jeff Budzinski
Vice President Information Systems and Technology, Peter Baker
Senior Vice President, Paul Gray
Vice President Massachusetts Operations, Gary Picco
Vice President Field Operations, Johnathan Doessel
Vice President, Maxine Mauricio
Vice President, Charlie Hadsell
Vice President and Controller, William Feher
Vice President Controls Division, John Schmitz
Chairman, Stephen W. Bershad, age 75
Treasurer, Joseph Serino
Board of Directors, Anthony R Triano
Auditors: Ernst & Young LLP

LOCATIONS

HQ: EMCOR Group, Inc.
301 Merritt Seven, Norwalk, CT 06851-1092
Phone: 203 849-7800
Web: www.emcorgroup.com

PRODUCTS/OPERATIONS

Selected Services

EMCOR Construction Services
Electrical Construction
Mechanical Construction
Fire Protection
EMCOR Building Services
EMCOR Facilities Services
EMCOR Mechanical Services
EMCOR Government Services
EMCOR Energy Services
Customer Solutions Centers
View our Fact Sheet
EMCOR Industrial Services
Turnarounds
Heat Exchangers
Towers
Refractory

2016 Sales

	% of total
United States mechanical construction and facilities services	35
United States building services	24
United States electrical construction and facilities services	23
United States industrial services	14
Less intersegment revenues	0
United Kingdom building services	4
Total	**100**

Selected Operations

Mechanical and Electrical Construction
Building plant and lighting systems
Data communications systems
Electrical power distribution systems
Energy recovery
Heating ventilation and air-conditioning (HVAC) systems
Lighting systems
Low-voltage systems (alarm security communications)
Piping and plumbing systems
Refrigeration systems
Voice communications systems
Facilities Services
Facilities management
Installation and support for building systems
Mobile maintenance and service
Program development and management for energy systems
Remote monitoring
Site-based operations and maintenance
Small modification and retrofit projects
Technical consulting and diagnostic services

Selected Subsidiaries

Dyn Specialty Contracting Inc.
EMCOR Construction Services Inc.
EMCOR-CSI Holding Co.
EMCOR Facilities Services Inc.
EMCOR Group (UK) plc
EMCOR International Inc.
EMCOR (UK) Limited
EMCOR Mechanical/Electrical Services (East) Inc.
EMCOR (UK) Limited
FR X Ohmstede Acquisitions Co.
MES Holdings Corporation

COMPETITORS

ABM Industries	Jacobs Technology
AECOM	Jones Lang LaSalle
APi Group	Limbach Facility
CBRE Group	Services
Carillion	MYR Group
Comfort Systems USA	MasTec
Dycom	Quanta Services
Fluor	Schneider Electric

Hoffman Corporation
Honeywell
 International
IES Holdings

Siemens AG
SteelFab
Trane Inc.
Tutor Perini

HISTORICAL FINANCIALS

Company Type: Public

Income Statement

FYE: December 31

	REVENUE ($ mil.)	NET INCOME ($ mil.)	NET PROFIT MARGIN	EMPLOYEES
12/16	7,551	181	2.4%	31,000
12/15	6,718	172	2.6%	29,000
12/14	6,424	168	2.6%	27,000
12/13	6,417	123	1.9%	27,000
12/12	6,346	146	2.3%	26,000
Annual Growth	4.4%	5.5%	—	4.5%

2016 Year-End Financials

Debt ratio: 10.87%
Return on equity: 12.04%
Cash ($ mil.): 464
Current ratio: 1.46
Long-term debt ($ mil.): 408

No. of shares (mil.): 59
Dividends
 Yield: 0.0%
 Payout: 10.7%
Market value ($ mil.): 4,242

	STOCK PRICE ($) FY Close	P/E High/Low	PER SHARE ($) Earnings	Dividends	Book Value
12/16	70.76	24 14	2.97	0.32	25.64
12/15	48.04	19 15	2.72	0.32	24.18
12/14	44.49	19 15	2.52	0.32	22.48
12/13	42.44	24 19	1.82	0.49	21.92
12/12	34.61	16 12	2.16	0.51	20.10
Annual Growth	19.6%	—	8.3%	(11.0%)	6.3%

Emerson Electric Co.

Emerson Electric goes with the flow and measure the flow as it goes. The company makes a range of electrical electromechanical and electronic products used to control gases liquids and electricity. Emerson also makes measurement and analytical instruments that provide data about the physical properties of gasses and liquids. Want another example of an Emerson product? Look in your kitchen sink. Its InSinkErator unit is a maker of food waste disposers and hot water dispensers. Emerson operates more than 200 manufacturing locations with about 130 outside of the US. International markets make up about 50% of Emerson's sales.

Operations

In 2017 Emerson Electric reconfigured its business segments to better focus its efforts. The company?s segments are Automation Solutions Climate Technologies and Tools & Home Products and Commercial & Residential Solutions.

Automation Solutions more than 60% of sales is made up of several product lines. Measurement & Analytical Instrumentation makes valves actuators and regulators; Industrial Solutions which makes fluid power and control mechanisms electrical distribution equipment and materials joining and precision cleaning products; and Process Control Systems & Solutions which provides digital systems that control plant processes by communicating with and adjusting the ?intelligent? plant devices that Emerson makes.

The Commercial & Residential Solutions business about 40% of revenue consists of the Climate Technologies and Tools & Home Products seg-

ments. This business provides products that promote energy efficiency enhance household and commercial comfort and protect food quality and sustainability through heating air conditioning and refrigeration technology.

Across all segments the company has dozens of brand names including AMS ASCO Bettis Damcos Fisher Go Switch Biffi Guardian El-O-Matic In-SinkErator RIDGID and TopWorx.

Geographic Reach

The US and Canada form Emerson Electric's largest market representing just more than half of its sales. Asia generates about 20% of its revenue while Europe accounts for about 15%. Other targeted markets include Latin America and the Middle East and Africa splitting the remaining revenue. The company has 200 manufacturing locations worldwide and a marketing presence in more than 150 countries.

Sales and Marketing

Emerson Electric sells its products through a variety of distribution channels including its direct sales force a network of independent sales representatives and distributors to end-users and original equipment manufacturers (OEMs). Emerson serves industries such as oil and gas pulp and paper chemicals power food and beverage and life sciences.

Financial Performance

After two years of declines Emerson Electric's revenue rose 5% to $15.3 billion in 2017 (ended September) from 2016. Most of the increase came from the acquisition of the valves and controls business which added 4% percent. Underlying sales rose 1%. Profit however dropped for the second year in a row falling 7% to $1.5 billion in 2016 from 2015.

Cash flow from operations was $1.9 billion in 2017 down from $2.8 billion in 2016. The 2016 cash flow was reduced by cash used for discontinued operations.

Strategy

Emerson has a history of achieving growth through acquisitions and by divesting underperforming non-core units. In early 2015 Emerson sold its power transmission solutions operations to Regal Beloit for $1.44 billion. In addition the company sold its InterMetro commercial storage business to Ali Group of Italy for $411 million.

Taking this strategy even further Emerson sold its network power segment for $4 billion in late 2016 to Platinum Equity and a group of co-investors. The company made the move to streamline its operations and focus on its remaining four core segments.

In 2017 Emerson switched from subtraction to addition buying Pentair Valves & Controls. The deal gives Emerson what company calls the most complete valves portfolio in the market. It enables the company to work with its customers on a wider range of projects.

Mergers and Acquisitions

Emerson bought Pentair's Valves & Controls business for $3.15 billion in a deal that closed in 2017. The complementary acquisition will establish Emerson's global presence in control isolation pressure relief valves and actuation as part of a larger strategy to build a broader automation product portfolio.

Throughout all of 2016 Emerson acquired six businesses. Of this total four were integrated into its process management segment's final control and measurement devices operations and two were combined with its climate technologies segment.

HISTORY

Emerson Electric was founded in 1890 in St. Louis by brothers Alexander and Charles Meston inventors who developed uses for the alternating-

current electric motor which was new at the time. The company was named after former Missouri judge and US marshal John Emerson who financed the enterprise and became its first president. Emerson's best-known product was an electric fan introduced in 1892. Between 1910 and 1920 the company helped develop the first forced-air circulating systems.

EXECUTIVES

SVP and CTO, Randall D. Ledford, age 68
Chairman and CEO, David N. Farr, age 62, $1,300,000 total compensation
Vice President Project Management Office, Chris Stephen
Vice President Global Logistics, Greg Fromknecht
EVP; Business Leader Commercial and Industrial Solutions, James J. (Jim) Lindemann, age 61
EVP Emerson Charitable Trust, Patrick J. (Pat) Sly
EVP and CFO, Frank J. Dellaquila, age 59, $620,000 total compensation
President, Edward L. Monser, age 66, $720,000 total compensation
VP Planning, Mark J. Bulanda
Chairman Automated Solutions, Steven A. (Steve) Sonnenberg, age 65
EVP and COO, Steve J. Pelch
EVP; Business Leader Emerson Climate Technologies, Robert T. (Bob) Sharp
EVP; Group Business Leader Automated Solutions, Michael H. Train
Vice President Engineering, Tim Graff
Vice President and General Manager Service and Aftermarket, Robert Brown
Senior Executive Vice President And Director Information Technology, Charles Peters
Vice President Marketing, Martin Leslie
Vice President Global Lifecycle Care, Don Fregelette
Vice President Residential Solutions, Steven Cox
Vice President Finance Embedded Computing, Trevor Zillwood
Vice President Product Safety, Steve Bryant
Vice President Business Development, Matthew Fox
Assistant Vice President, Frank Dejong
Vice President and Chief Financial Officer Middle East and Africa, Jonathan Peacock
Vice President Marketing, Jane Lansing
Vice President Finance, Brian McGinnis
Vice President Lp Gas Equipment, Tim Backs
Vice President Engineering, Scott Rose
Vice President And Managing Director, Pratap Chavan
Executive Vice President Global Sales, John Peterson
Vice President, Andy Wang
Vice President Fisher Global Parts Business, Doug Butler
Vice President, Steve Nahrup
Vice President and Sales Marketing Manager, Nick Norenberg
Vice President Southern Europe, Pascal Galant
Vice President Sales, Scott Whitley
Group Vice President, Terry Buzbee
Vice President of Pressure Operations, Ben Louwagie
Vice President of Human Resour, Barbara Gandy
Vice President Planning, David Bersaglini
Vice President Sales, Kevin Meyer
Vice President Marketing and E Business, Tim Flinn
Group Vice President Storage Solutions, Russ Kerstetter
Vice President General Manager Enterprise Solutions, Mark Bills
Vice President Business Development, Edward Blittschau
Vice President Marketing, Michael Johnson

Vice President Marketing O Z Gedney, Timothy Rooney
Executive Vice President, Mike-Mtown Mason
Vice President Market, Phil Niccolls
Vice President of Business Development, Wayne Wehber
VP Operations, Karen Isaacson
Vice President Building and Strategic Sales Building Division Closetmaid, Brian Dougherty
Vice President Product Development and Operations, Steve Santy
Vice President Global Sales And Marketing, Bruce Penning
Vice President Operations, Kent Schultz
National Account Manager, Traci Olmstead
Senior Vice President Materials and Logistics, Larry Lawrence
Vice President Global Supply Chain, Ken Poczekaj
Vice President Finance and E Business, Torsten Keller-Carnap
Vice President and Group Leader Intellectual Property, John Groves
Senior Vice President Information Technology Servicing Operations, Ana Victoria
Vice President Human Resources and General Manager, Phil Lamb
Assistant Vice President, John Bell
Vice President Planning and Development, Matt Whitener
Vice President Electronics Engineering, Sai Krishnan
Vice President and Chief Information Officer, Deb Miller
Vice President Employee Benefits, Jan L Bansch
Vice President Global Accounts, Craig Morris
Group Vice President, Pierre Sarre
Vice President Global Supply Chain, Justin Pete
Vice President Sales, Mark Downie
Vice President and Controller, Brian Harstad
Vice President, Denny Cahill
Vice President Sales and Marketing NA, Roger Hager
Vice President Project Management Office, Roger Freeman
Vice President Litigation and Arbitration, Michael Keating
Vice President of Quality and Lean Enterprise Regulator Technologies, Don Haugh
Vice President Employment Law, Charlie Morgan
Vice President Finance, Gerry R Lawrence
Vice President Sourcing Ridgid, Ed Kman
Vice President of Marketing, Dean M Landeche
Vice President And Chief Employment Counsel, J Caius
Vice President Controller Chief Accounting Officer, Rick Schlueter
Vice President General Manager, Tom McDowell
Vice President and General Manager Europe, Arjan Kolkman
Vice President Information Technology Motors Appliances, Terry Treadway
Vice President Technology, Bill Butler
National Account Manager, Kristina Schardijn
Vice President and Managing Director, John Ruese
Vice President Human Resources and Quality, Steve Shonka
Treasurer, Anita Cotton
Assistant Treasurer, Jim Thomasson
Secretary President, Amy Thomas
Secretary III Emerson Process Management, Susan Amberson
Treasurer, Alan Mielcuszny
Secretary Operations, Debbie Mangini
Assistant Treasurer and Director Investor Relations, Chris Tucker
Secretary Emerson Corporate, Paula Henkelman
Secretary President, Maureen Netzley
Auditors: KPMG LLP

LOCATIONS

HQ: Emerson Electric Co.
8000 W. Florissant Avenue, P.O. Box 4100, St. Louis, MO 63136
Phone: 314 553-2000
Web: www.emerson.com

2017 Sales

	$ mil.	% of total
United States and Canada	7,854	52
Asia	3,253	21
Europe	2,434	16
Latin America	767	5
Middle East/Africa	956	6
Total	**14,522**	**100**

PRODUCTS/OPERATIONS

2017 Sales

	$ mil.	% of total
Automation Solutions	9,418	62
Climate Technologies	4,212	28
Tools & Home Products	1,654	10
Commercial & Residential Solutions	5,857	38
Eliminations	(11)	-
Total	**15,264**	**100**

PRODUCTS

Automation Solutions
Density & Viscosity Measurement
Flame & Gas Detection
Flow Measurement
Gas Analysis
Level Measurement
Liquid Analysis
Marine Measurement & Analytical
Pipeline Integrity
Pressure
Tank Gauging System
Temperature Measurement
Wireless Acoustic & Discrete
Wireless Infrastructure
Commercial & Residential Solutions
Ceiling Fans & Lighting
Construction & Plumbing Tools
Food Waste Disposers
Grind2Energy
Heating & Air Conditioning
Home Repair & Maintenance
Indoor Outdoor Heating Cables
Instant Hot Water Dispensers
Monitoring Systems & Facility Control
Refrigeration
Sensing & Protection Devices
Thermostats
Vacuum Equipment
Industries

AUTOMATION SOLUTIONS INDUSTRIES

Automotive
Chemical
Downstream Hydrocarbons
Food & Beverage
Industrial Energy & Onsite Utilities
Life Sciences & Medical
Marine
Mining Minerals & Metals
Oil & Gas
Packaging
Power Generation
Pulp & Paper
Water & Wastewater

COMMERCIAL & RESIDENTIAL SOLUTIONS

Commercial Buildings & Construction
Energy & Utilities
Facility Management & Maintenance
Food Retail
Food Service & Hospitality
Residential Construction & Home Improvement
Transportation

Selected Brands

AMS Suite
Baumann
Bettis
Bristol
CSI
Emerson Process Management

COMPETITORS

ABB	Parker-Hannifin
AMETEK	Raytheon
Cummins	Rexnord
Dana	Rockwell Automation
Danaher	Rolls-Royce
Dayco Products	SPX
Endress + Hauser	Siemens AG
GE	Sino-American
Hitachi	Electronic
Honeywell	Snap-on
International	Stanley Black and
Illinois Tool Works	Decker
Ingersoll-Rand	TE Connectivity
Interpump	Tecumseh Products
Lennox	Toshiba
McDermott	Trippe Manufacturing
NEC	United Technologies
Nidec Kinetek	Yokogawa Electric

HISTORICAL FINANCIALS

Company Type: Public

Income Statement

FYE: September 30

	REVENUE ($ mil.)	NET INCOME ($ mil.)	NET PROFIT MARGIN	EMPLOYEES
09/17	15,264	1,518	9.9%	76,500
09/16	14,522	1,635	11.3%	103,500
09/15	22,304	2,710	12.2%	110,800
09/14	24,537	2,147	8.8%	115,100
09/13	24,669	2,004	8.1%	131,600
Annual Growth	(11.3%)	(6.7%)	—	(12.7%)

2017 Year-End Financials

Debt ratio: 23.77%
Return on equity: 18.64%
Cash ($ mil.): 3,062
Current ratio: 1.64
Long-term debt ($ mil.): 3,794

No. of shares (mil.): 641
Dividends
Yield: 0.0%
Payout: 81.7%
Market value ($ mil.): 40,324

	STOCK PRICE ($) FY Close	P/E High/Low		Earnings	PER SHARE ($) Dividends	Book Value
09/17	62.84	27	21	2.35	1.92	13.59
09/16	54.51	22	17	2.52	1.90	11.77
09/15	44.17	16	11	3.99	1.88	12.34
09/14	62.58	23	20	3.03	1.72	14.53
09/13	64.70	24	17	2.76	1.64	14.98
Annual Growth	(0.7%)	—	—	(3.9%)	4.0%	(2.4%)

Employers Holdings Inc

Because workers' compensation is nothing to gamble with small business owners can turn to Employers Holdings. The Reno-based holding company provides workers' compensation services including claims management loss prevention consulting and care management to small businesses in low and medium hazard industries including retailers and restaurants. The company provides workers' compensation through its Employer Insurance Company of Nevada (EICN) and Employers Compensation Insurance Company. Employers Holdings also operates Employers Assurance and Employers Preferred Insurance Company both of which also offer workers' compensation.

Geographic Reach

While Employers Holdings distributes its products in more than 35 states and the District of Columbia more than half of its premiums come from California.

Sales and Marketing

Employers Holdings uses a network of more than 5100 independent agencies to brings its wares to the public; these agencies bring in about three-fourths of the company's in-force premiums. The company also markets its products through brokers and local trade groups and associations. Furthermore it markets its products along with ADP's payroll services in several states. Employers Holdings is forging additional distribution partners in other markets.

Financial Performance

Employers Holdings' revenue has been relatively stable for the past few years. In fiscal 2016 revenue rose 4% to $779.8 million. That change was primarily driven by gains on investments as premiums earned saw just a modest increase.

The higher revenue and a drop in losses and loss adjustments led to higher profits that year. Employers Holdings' net income which has been recovering since taking a bit of a dip in 2013 increased 13% to $106.7 million in 2016. This in turn led to a 5% increase in operating cash flow which totaled $122.8 million.

Strategy

Employers Holdings targets small businesses as there are fewer competitors in that space. The firm operates in low-to-medium hazard industries to keep its losses under control. Its top sectors served include restaurants the clerical side of physician offices automobile service or repair centers and colleges (professional employees and clerical). The company also spreads its risk around and is not dependent upon any one customer for a significant portion of its income.Similarly although California is the firm's largest market it focuses on expanding geographically to diversify its revenue stream.

Additionally Employer Holdings is investing in its IT infrastructure to improve customer service increase efficiency and expand its operating capacity.

EXECUTIVES

President and CEO, Douglas D. Dirks, $927,569 total compensation
EVP Chief Legal Officer and General Counsel, Lenard T. Ormsby, $485,708 total compensation
EVP Corporate and Public Affairs, Ann W. Nelson, $354,501 total compensation
EVP and Chief Administrative Officer, John P. Nelson, $334,391 total compensation
EVP and COO, Stephen V. Festa, $488,299 total compensation
EVP and CIO, Tracey L. Berg
SVP and Chief Underwriting Officer, Lawrence S. (Larry) Rogers
EVP and CFO, Michael S. Paquette, age 54
Vice President Corporate Marketing, Ty Vukelich
Vice President Investor Relations, Vicki Erickson
Vice President Government and Regulatory Affairs, Jim Werbeckes
Vice President Customer Support, Dennis Dix
Vice President Sales East Region, Martha Collins
Vice President, Sam King
Vice President, James Cleymaet
Chairman, Michael D. (Mike) Rumbolz, age 64
Auditors: Ernst & Young LLP

LOCATIONS

HQ: Employers Holdings Inc
10375 Professional Circle, Reno, NV 89521
Phone: 888 682-6671

2015 Premiums In-force

	% of total
California	57
others	43
Total	**100**

PRODUCTS/OPERATIONS

2015 Sales

	$ mil.	% of total
Net premiums earned	690	91
Net investment income	72	9
Realized losses on investments	(10.7)	-
Other income	0	-
Total	**752**	**100**

Selected Products & Services

Claims Management
Fraud Prevention
Loss Control
Loss Run Report
Managed Care Services
PrecisePay (Pay-As-You-Go)
Premium Audit
Return to Work Program
Safety Promotion Programs
Workers' Compensation Insurance

Selected Subsidiaries

AmSERV Inc.
EIG Services Inc.
Elite Insurance Services Inc.
Employers Assurance Company
Employers Compensation Insurance Company
Employers Group Inc.
Employers Insurance Company of Nevada
Employers Occupational Health Inc.
Employers Preferred Insurance Company
Pinnacle Benefits Inc.

COMPETITORS

AMERISAFE	Republic Indemnity
AmTrust Financial	Safety Insurance
Baldwin & Lyons	SeaBright Insurance
Berkshire Hathaway	Selective Insurance
CNA Financial	State Auto Financial
Donegal	State Compensation
EMC Insurance	Insurance Fund
Liberty Mutual	The Hartford
Meadowbrook Insurance	TowerGroup
Navigators	Travelers Companies
ProAssurance	United Fire
RLI	Zurich Insurance Group

HISTORICAL FINANCIALS

Company Type: Public

Income Statement

FYE: December 31

	ASSETS ($ mil.)	NET INCOME ($ mil.)	INCOME AS % OF ASSETS	EMPLOYEES
12/16	3,773	106	2.8%	693
12/15	3,755	94	2.5%	716
12/14	3,769	100	2.7%	709
12/13	3,643	63	1.8%	723
12/12	3,511	106	3.0%	667
Annual Growth	**1.8%**	**(0.0%)**	**—**	**1.0%**

2016 Year-End Financials

Debt ratio: 0.85%	No. of shares (mil.): 32
Return on equity: 13.29%	Dividends
Cash ($ mil.): 67	Yield: 0.0%
Current ratio: —	Payout: 11.1%
Long-term debt ($ mil.): —	Market value ($ mil.): 1,272

	STOCK PRICE ($) FY Close	P/E High/Low		PER SHARE ($) Earnings	Dividends	Book Value
12/16	39.60	12	7	3.24	0.36	26.16
12/15	27.30	10	7	2.90	0.24	23.62
12/14	23.51	10	6	3.14	0.24	21.81
12/13	31.65	16	10	2.00	0.24	18.17
12/12	20.58	6	5	3.37	0.24	17.53
Annual Growth	**17.8%**	**—**	**—**	**(1.0%)**	**10.7%**	**10.5%**

Energy Transfer Equity LP

Energy Transfer Equity transfers natural gas and other energy resources through its massive network of US-based pipelines. The company?s operations occur primarily through subsidiaries Energy Transfer Partners (ETP) and Sunoco LP although it has interests in a number of LPs and other subsidiaries. Structured as a Master Limited Partnership it owns 71000 miles of pipelines that transport natural gas natural gas liquids refined products and crude oil across more than 35 US states. It also owns and operates associated terminalling storage and fractionation facilities. Sunoco supplies nearly 8 billion gallons of fuel to consumer and wholesale customers. An effort to purchase Tulsa-based Williams Companies in a $37.7 billion deal fell through in 2016.

Operations

Energy Transfer Equity (ETE) reports financial results according to its major investments in Energy Transfer Partners Sunoco LP and Lake Charles LNG.

Its largest segment is Energy Transfer Partners. ETP gathers processes compresses treats and transports natural gas. These midstream services occur in some of the most prolific shale plays in the US such as Eagle Ford Marcellus Utica Bone Spring and Avalon. ETP is one of the largest movers of natural gas in the country and does so through its 71000 miles of pipeline. It also possesses a controlling interest in a limited partnership that owns and operates a logistics business consisting of crude oil natural gas liquids (NGLs) and refined products pipelines. ETP generates roughly 60% of revenue.

Its investment in Sunoco LP brings in some 40% of revenue. Sunoco LP operates almost 50000 gas stations and convenience stores in the Eastern US. It produces revenue through fuel sales which typically top 2.5 billion gallons in a given year. It generates a few billion dollars from merchandise sales in its gas station convenience stores. Sunoco sells about 5 billion gallons of fuel wholesale through nearly 8000 dealers distributors and commercials customers. In 2017 this segment?s pipeline and product terminals were merged into the ETP entity.

Lake Charles LNG generates a small amount of total revenue by storing and re-gasifying natural gas in its facility in Lake Charles LA.

Geographic Reach

Dallas TX is home to Energy Transfer Equity?s and Energy Transfer Partners? headquarters. ETP along with the recently merged pipeline and terminal assets of Sunoco have significant operations in Texas Louisiana Oklahoma West Virginia Pennsylvania and New York. Its pipelines reach as far as North Dakota Arizona and Idaho.

The Sunoco LP subsidiary is headquartered in Philadelphia PA and operates nearly 5000 gas stations in 26 states mostly in the Eastern US and Texas.

Sales and Marketing

Energy Transfer Equity via Energy Transfer Partners sells natural gas to utilities industrial consumers other marketers and pipeline companies. Its Sunoco segment sells gasoline and diesel in addition to a broad mix of merchandise such as groceries fast foods and beverages at its convenience stores. A sizable portion of Sunoco?s gasoline and diesel sales are to wholesale customers.

Financial Performance

In recent years Energy Transfer Equity?s revenue growth has been excellent rising from a $5.4 billion low in 2009 to a $55.7 billion peak in 2014 (driven by the Sunoco acquisition) before sliding back to $37.5 billion in 2016. Net income was rangebound between 2010 and 2013 ($200 million - $300 million) before spiking to $1.2 billion in 2015 and then falling in 2016.

In 2016 revenue decreased 11% to $37.5 billion due to a 20% fall in crude oil sales and lower refined product sales both partially offset by higher NGL sales.

Net income in 2016 fell 17% to $983 million the result aided by a $954 million windfall from a noncontrolling interest adjustment. Without the adjustment net income from operations came in at a paltry $41 a 96% plummet from the prior year. Although in dollar terms operating expenses fell when viewed as a percent of revenue the expenses did not fall in line with revenue and therefore had a negative effect on earnings. Included in expenses was a goodwill impairment loss exceeding $1.0 billion.

Cash available at the end of 2016 was $483 million a decrease of $123 million from 2015. Large uses of cash came from $8.0 billion of capital expenditures and a $1.6 billion outlay for acquisitions. Operations contributed $3.4 billion to cash and financing activities added almost $6.0 billion mainly through issuance of debt and notes.

Strategy

Energy Transfer Equity has been busy in recent years. Its strategy is playing out through partnership restructuring divestitures capital raises and the build out of several midstream projects.

Announced in 2016 and closed in early 2017 ETE orchestrated a merger of its two primary subsidiaries ? Energy Transfer Partners and the midstream assets of its Sunoco LP ? into a surviving entity that kept the Energy Transfer Partners name. The deal cleans up its partnership structure and is anticipated to help with credit ratings going forward. Operational synergies are expected to be minimal.

Sunoco LP has been on an acquisition spree since 2014 spending over $700 million between then and mid-2017. Its retail acquisitions brought on board more than 120 new gas stations from previous owners Pico Petroleum Aziz Quick Stops Valentine Stores Denny Oil Aloha Petroleum among others. It purchased a wholesaler in the US Northeast and obtained midstream assets in Alabama Hawaii and Texas.

To help raise capital for its acquisitions and project expenses ETE sold in late 2017 half of its interests in ET Rover Pipeline to Blackstone Energy Partners for approximately $1.6 billion. ETE through its ETP subsidiary will remain operator of the Marcellus and Utica shale Rover Pipeline. ETE sold off partial interests in its Bakken holdings in late 2016 for $2 billion. ETE also issued perpetual preferred stock in late 2017 raising $1.5 billion.

ETE is building out its already expansive midstream network of assets. In the Permian Basin it brought online an additional 600 mm cubic feet/day in processing capacity and anticipates 200 mmcf/d more by mid-2018. Its Mariner East system in the Marcellus Shale is receiving capital to expand its NGLs transport line from Ohio & Western Pennsylvania to the Marcus Hook Industrial Complex on the Eastern Atlantic coast. ETE is also expanding its Mont Belvieu fractionation facility adding more than 250 mmbpd capacity by mid 2019. In total the company spent about $4.0 billion on capital expenditures in 2016 and is on track to spent $3.5 billion in 2017.

Mergers and Acquisitions

ETE?s ETP subsidiary purchased PennTex which provides natural gas gathering and processing and residue gas and natural gas liquids trans-

portation services to producers in the Terryville Complex in northern Louisiana.

ETE Sunoco retail division purchased a number of retail gas stations throughout mainland US and Hawaii between 2014 and 2017. The Sunoco Logistics division purchased in late 2016 for $760 million certain west Texas crude oil assets from Vitol Inc.

Company Background

In 2012 Energy Transfer Equity bought diversified gas player Southern Union for $9.4 billion (including $3.7 billion in debt). The acquisition made Energy Transfer Equity one of the largest natural gas infrastructure companies in the US.

That year the company also completed a $2 billion merger of a wholly owned Energy Transfer Partners subsidiary with and into Southern Union subsidiary CrossCountry Energy LLC which owns an indirect 50% interest in Citrus Corp. the owner of the Florida Gas Transmission pipeline system. After the merger CrossCountry Energy remained as the surviving entity a wholly owned subsidiary of Energy Transfer Partners.

In 2010 Energy Transfer Equity acquired the general partner stake of Regency Energy Partners and sold a 49.9% stake in its Midcontinent Express Pipeline to that company. The move was seen as a way for the company to diversify its general partner operations with the aim of getting a better return for shareholders. Regency Energy Partners focuses on the gathering processing marketing and transportation of natural gas and natural gas liquids in Arkansas Kansas Louisiana and Texas.

Energy Transfer Equity was formed in 2002 as La Grange Energy a Texas limited partnership. In early 2005 it changed its name to Energy Transfer Company. In August 2005 it converted from a Texas limited partnership to a Delaware limited partnership and became Energy Transfer Equity.

EXECUTIVES

President, John W. McReynolds, age 65, $577,280 total compensation

CFO, Thomas E. (Tom) Long, age 61, $454,154 total compensation

EVP and General Counsel, Thomas P. Mason, age 60, $571,729 total compensation

President and COO ETP, Marshall S. (Mackie) McCrea, $1,009,231 total compensation

EVP and Head Tax, Bradford D. (Brad) Whitehurst, $503,354 total compensation

Vice President Operations Support, Jeffrey Whippo

Vice President Refined Products Logistics Asset Marketing, Bob Young

Vice President Investor Relations, Renee Lorenz

Vice President Market Services, Bradley Holmes

Vice President Engineering, Charles Frey

Vice President Commercial, Steve Breckon

Auditors: Grant Thornton LLP

LOCATIONS

HQ: Energy Transfer Equity LP
8111 Westchester Drive, Suite 600, Dallas, TX 75225
Phone: 214 981-0700
Web: www.energytransfer.com

PRODUCTS/OPERATIONS

2016 Sales

	% of total
Investment in ETP	58
Investment in Sunoco LP	41
Investment in lake Charles LNG	1
Adjustments	-
Total	**100**

2016 Sales

	$ mil.	% of total
Refined product sales	14,020	37
Crude sales	6,766	18
NGL sales	4,841	13
Gathering transportation and other fees	4,172	11
Natural gas sales	3,619	10
Other	4,086	11
Total	**37,504**	**100**

Selected Subsidiaries and Operating Units

EASTERN GULF CRUDE ACCESS LLC
ETP- Energy Transfer Partners L.P.
ETP GP- Energy Transfer Partners GP L.P. the general partner of ETP
ETP LLC- Energy Transfer Partners L.L.C. the general partner of ETP GP
Holdco- ETP Holdco Corporation
Regency GP- Regency Energy Partners GP LP the general partner of Regency
Regency LLC- Regency Energy Partners GP LLC the general partner of Regency GP
Regency- Regency Energy Partners LP
Southern Union- Southern Union Company
Sunoco Logistics- Sunoco Logistics Partners L.P.
Sunoco- Sunoco Inc.

COMPETITORS

AmeriGas Partners	Exxon Mobil
Atmos Energy	Ferrellgas Partners
Chevron	Kinder Morgan
Crestwood Midstream Partners LP	Magellan Midstream
DCP Midstream Partners	ONEOK
Enbridge	Star Gas Partners
	Suburban Propane

HISTORICAL FINANCIALS

Company Type: Public

Income Statement

FYE: December 31

	REVENUE ($ mil.)	NET INCOME ($ mil.)	NET PROFIT MARGIN	EMPLOYEES
12/16	37,504	995	2.7%	30,992
12/15	42,126	1,189	2.8%	30,078
12/14	55,691	633	1.1%	27,605
12/13	48,335	196	0.4%	13,573
12/12	16,964	304	1.8%	14,433
Annual Growth	**21.9%**	**34.5%**	**—**	**21.1%**

2016 Year-End Financials

Debt ratio: 55.75%
Return on equity: 3,006.91%
Cash ($ mil.): 483
Current ratio: 0.96
Long-term debt ($ mil.): 42,858

No. of shares (mil.): 1,046
Dividends
  Yield: 0.0%
  Payout: 123.9%
Market value ($ mil.): 20,217

	STOCK PRICE ($) FY Close	P/E High/Low		PER SHARE ($) Earnings	Dividends	Book Value
12/16	19.31	21	4	0.92	1.14	(1.59)
12/15	13.74	63	10	1.11	1.02	(0.86)
12/14	57.38	146	69	0.58	0.75	0.65
12/13	81.74	471	260	0.18	0.65	0.99
12/12	45.48	169	122	0.28	0.63	1.95
Annual Growth	**(19.3%)**	**—**	**—**	**34.3%**	**16.2%**	**—**

Energy Transfer Partners LP (New)

Sunoco Logistics Partners acquires owns and operates a large swath of midstream and downstream assets primarily in tandem with former parent and current affiliate Sunoco. This includes ownership of more than 7900 miles of crude oil refined product and oil gathering pipelines and minority interests in four refined product pipelines as well as more than 40 terminals and other storage assets related to Sunoco's refining and marketing operations. In 2016 the company agreed to buy Vitol's crude oil assets in the Permian basin for $760 million. In 2017 the company bought Energy Transfer Partners in a deal valued at $19.9 billion.

Operations

Sunoco Logistics Partners operates in industry segments including crude oil acquisition and marketing refined products pipelines terminal facilities and crude oil pipeline. The company's refined products pipelines segment consists of 2500 miles of petroleum products pipeline and serves customers primarily in the Northeast and Midwest regions of the US. Through its terminal facilities unit Sunoco Logistics Partners is capable of storing 42 million barrels of refined products and crude oil. The crude oil pipeline segment consisting of about 4900 miles of crude oil pipelines primarily serves customers in Oklahoma and Texas. It also has 500 miles of crude oil gathering lines that supply the trunk pipelines.

The company gets the bulk of its revenues from crude oil acquisition and marketing activities.

Financial Performance

Higher oil and refined product prices helped to lift Sunoco Logistics Partners' revenue by 39% in 2011 thanks to an increase in revenues from terminal facilities (up 52%) crude oil pipelines (44%) and crude oil acquisition and marketing (40%) segments. Net income dropped by 7% in 2011 due to an increase in operating expenses other interest costs and debt expense.

Except for a revenue slump in 2009 (caused by the drop in demand for oil and oil products as a result of the global recession) Sunoco Logistics Partners saw an upward trend in revenues from 2007 to 2011.

Strategy

The company pursues a strategy of growing its businesses organically and through complementary acquisitions (more than 20 since 2002). Expanding its pipeline assets in 2011 the company acquired control of Inland Corp. (which has a 350-mile refined-products pipeline and related facilities) for $100 million. It also acquired the Eagle Point tank farm and related assets in Westville New Jersey from Sunoco for $100 million.

That year Sunoco Logistics Partners acquired a crude oil acquisition and marketing business from Texon. The purchase consists of a lease crude business and gathering assets in 16 states primarily in the western US. (It had acquired the butane blending business of Texon in 2010 for $140 million plus inventory).

EXECUTIVES

Vice President Operations, David Chalson
Auditors: Grant Thornton LLP

LOCATIONS

HQ: Energy Transfer Partners LP (New)
8111 Westchester Drive, Suite 600, Dallas, TX 75225
Phone: 214 981-0700
Web: www.energytransfer.com

PRODUCTS/OPERATIONS

2011 Sales

	% of total
Crude oil acquisition & marketing	92
Terminal facilities	4
Crude oil pipelines	3
Refined product pipelines	1
Total	**100**

COMPETITORS

Buckeye Partners	Magellan Midstream
CITGO	Marathon Petroleum
Enbridge Energy	Plains All American
Enterprise Products	Pipeline
Kinder Morgan Energy	RKA Petroleum
Partners	TransMontaigne
Kinder Morgan	TransMontaigne
Management	Partners

HISTORICAL FINANCIALS

Company Type: Public

Income Statement

FYE: December 31

	REVENUE ($ mil.)	NET INCOME ($ mil.)	NET PROFIT MARGIN	EMPLOYEES
12/16	9,151	705	7.7%	2,575
12/15	10,486	393	3.7%	2,500
12/14	18,088	291	1.6%	2,250
12/13	16,639	463	2.8%	2,000
12/12	3,194	139	4.4%	1,700
Annual Growth	**30.1%**	**50.1%**	**—**	**10.9%**

2016 Year-End Financials

Debt ratio: 38.80%
Return on equity: 239.96%
Cash ($ mil.): 41
Current ratio: 1.36
Long-term debt ($ mil.): 7,313
No. of shares (mil.): 331
Dividends
Yield: 0.0%
Payout: 201.8%
Market value ($ mil.): 7,970

	STOCK PRICE ($) FY Close	P/E High/Low	PER SHARE ($) Earnings	Dividends	Book Value
12/16	24.02	32 17	0.98	1.98	27.00
12/15	25.70	110 53	0.42	1.72	28.06
12/14	41.78	184 73	0.51	1.43	29.54
12/13	75.48	46 30	1.63	1.17	29.87
12/12	49.73	94 59	0.55	0.92	29.26
Annual Growth	**(16.6%)**	**— —**	**15.5%**	**21.2%**	**(2.0%)**

Entergy Corp

Entergy is into energy. The integrated utility holding company's subsidiaries distribute electricity to 2.9 million customers in four southern states (Arkansas Louisiana Mississippi and Texas) and provide natural gas to 200000 customers in Louisiana. The company has interests in regulated and non-regulated power plants in North America that have a combined generating capacity of about 30000 MW. Entergy is one of the largest nuclear power generators in the US and nearly 9000 MW of its power generation is from nuclear sources.

Operations

The company operates two business segments: Utility and Wholesale Commodities.

The Utility segment produces more than 80% of revenue by generating transmitting distributing and selling electric power to customers in its regulated service areas in the US Gulf States region. The segment is composed of several regulated utility companies including: Entergy Arkansas Inc. Entergy Louisiana LLC Entergy Mississippi Inc. Entergy New Orleans Inc. and Entergy Texas. Four nuclear power plant sites with capacity of some 5200 MW are owned and operated by corporations that roll up into this segment. It also runs a small natural gas distribution business. Of its generation capacity about 70% is from gas oil and hydroelectric sources 25% is from nuclear and the rest comes from coal-fired plants.

Entergy Wholesale Commodities segment produces just less than 20% of total revenue through its ownership and operation of nuclear power plants (3700 MW of capacity) and fossil fuel plants (400 MW of capacity) and the sale of its electricity on the wholesale market. The segment?s Indian Point nuclear site provides 25% of the electric power used in New York City distributed there by Entergy?s customer Con Edison. It also provides management services to Nebraska?s Cooper Nuclear Station (810 MW of capacity). More than 90% of this segment?s generation portfolio is nuclear-sourced.

Geographic Reach

Entergy?s Utility segments operates power plants in Arkansas Mississippi and Louisiana. It provides power to customers in those states plus Texas. Its transmission system covers 114000 square miles and is comprised of nearly 16000 circuit miles of transmission lines.

The Wholesale Commodities segment has power plants and customers in New York Michigan Massachusetts Nebraska Arkansas and Louisiana.

Sales and Marketing

Entergy delivers electricity to 700000 customers in Arkansas 1.2 million in Louisiana 450000 in Mississippi and 450000 in Texas. It provides natural gas to 100000 people in New Orleans and a further 100000 throughout the rest of Louisiana. Entergy?s retail business (mostly through the regulated utility companies) generates 40% of sales from industrial businesses 25% from commercial enterprises 30% from residential and the rest from government agencies.

Entergy Wholesale Commodities segment sells both energy and capacity from its nuclear plants to retail power providers utilities electric power cooperatives power trading organizations and other power generation companies. These customers include Consolidated Edison and Consumers Energy companies from which Entergy purchased plants with the promise to continue providing energy to them. It also sells to transmission-sharing entities such as ISO New England NYISO and MISO.

The company?s regulated utilities have little retail competition as they are deemed by state regulators as the sole providers of electricity in their service areas.

Financial Performance

In recent years Entergy?s revenue remained steadfast within a range of $10 billion and $12 billion with a $12.5 billion peak in 2014. Net income over the same period has generally been going down with extreme decreases in 2015 and 2016.

In 2016 the company generated $10.8 billion in revenue a 6% decline from the prior year. Electricity sales to residential customers slipped by almost 1000 GWh (about 3%) and billed energy sales from the Entergy Wholesale Commodities segment fell nearly 4000 GWh. The sales of a 50% owned wind farm triggered a $200 million hit to revenue.

Income in 2016 fell 130% to a net loss of $583 million compared to 2015?s loss of $176 million. Despite a significant fall in fuel costs and purchased power expense the decrease in revenue coupled with a $2.8 billion asset write down charge related to three of Entergy Wholesale Commodities? nuclear plants pushed income to the biggest loss of the past decade.

Cash on hand at the end of 2016 was $1.2 billion a decrease of $163 million from the prior year. Financing activities provided $688 million mainly from issuance of long-term debt. Operating activities added $3.0 billion in cash during the year while investing activities depleted the supply by $3.8 billion primarily from typical activities and the one-time $1.0 billion purchase cost of the Union Power Station in Arkansas.

Strategy

Entergy?s strategy involves continued investments in its utility firms and winding down the Entergy Wholesale Commodities segment. Following the change in its business portfolio it is expected that Entergy?s operations will be almost completely associated with its regulated utility firms.

Utility investments are projected to be $10.4 billion between 2017 and 2019. Generation plants will receive about 45% of that amount distribution & transmission is earmarked for about 50% and the remaining is for general support of the utility companies. It completed the Ninemile 6 plant at the recently acquired Union Power Station and received approval for work on its St. Charles Lake Charles and Montgomery County Power Stations. It is awaiting approval to build its new New Orleans Power Station. It joined and is working with the MISO transmission-sharing entity to expand the transmission network.

Entergy?s Wholesale Commodities business ran into significant headwinds in recent years including competitive pricing pressure from the shale boom (which means the price of its nuclear power is higher than that produced by plants running on shale-sourced natural gas) and to a lesser extent pressure from New York state to decommission its Indian Point Energy Center. The segment is on schedule to retire Indian Point between 2020 and 2021 and already sold its FitzPatrick plants. Entergy?s Vermont Yankee nuclear plant was decommissioned in 2014. Finally its Palisades nuclear operations are also targeted for closure in 2018 or 2022 depending on input from state regulators.

Mergers and Acquisitions

In early 2017 Entergy sold its FitzPatrick nuclear power plant to Exelon for $110 million.

In 2016 Entergy Arkansas Entergy Louisiana and Entergy New Orleans purchased the Union Power Station a 1980 MW power generation plant near El Dorado Arkansas consisting of four natural gas-fired combined-cycle gas turbine power blocks. Entergy Louisiana purchased two of the power blocks and a 50% stake and Entergy Arkansas and Entergy New Orleans each purchased one power block and a 25% undivided ownership interest in such related assets. The price for the Union Power Station was $948 million.

HISTORY

Arkansas Power & Light (AP&L founded in 1913) consolidated operations with three other Arkansas utilities in 1926. Also that year New Orleans Public Service Inc. (NOPSI founded in 1922) merged with two other Big Easy electric companies. Louisiana Power & Light (LP&L) and Mississippi Power & Light (MP&L) were both formed in 1927 also through consolidation of regional utilities.

AP&L LP&L MP&L NOPSI and other utilities were combined into a Maine holding company Electric Power and Light which was dissolved in 1949. A new holding company Middle South Utilities emerged that year to take over the four utilities' assets.

In 1971 the company bought Arkansas-Missouri Power. In 1974 it brought its first nuclear plant on line and formed Middle South Energy (now System Energy Resources) to develop two more nuclear facilities Grand Gulf 1 and 2. Unfortunately Grand Gulf 1 was completed behind schedule and about 400% over budget. When Middle South tried to pass on the costs to customers controversy ensued. Construction of Grand Gulf 2 was halted and the CFO Edwin Lupberger took charge in 1985. Two years later nuke-related losses took the company to the brink of bankruptcy.

The company moved to settle the disputes by absorbing a $900 million loss on Grand Gulf 2 in 1989. To distance itself from the controversy Middle South changed its name to Entergy. In 1991 NOPSI settled with the City of New Orleans over Grand Gulf 1 costs.

That year Entergy anticipating deregulation branched out into nonregulated industries and looked abroad for growth opportunities. In 1993 a consortium including Entergy acquired a 51% interest in Edesur a Buenos Aires electric utility. In 1995 Entergy agreed to buy a 20% stake in a power plant under construction in India but the state government soon halted the project accusing the participating US companies of exploiting India.

Entergy completed its acquisition of CitiPower an Australian electric distributor in 1996 and the next year it bought the UK's London Electricity.

But diversification had drained funds. Lupberger resigned in 1998 and a new management team began selling noncore businesses such as CitiPower and London Electricity. NYMEX began trading electricity futures in 1998 using Entergy and Cinergy as contract-delivery points.

EXECUTIVES

Group President Utility Operations, Theodore H. (Theo) Bunting, age 59, $607,806 total compensation

Chairman and CEO, Leo P. Denault, age 58, $1,191,462 total compensation

SVP and COO, Paul D. Hinnenkamp

EVP, Roderick K. (Rod) West, age 49, $654,514 total compensation

President and CEO Entergy Mississippi Inc, Haley R. Fisackerly, $248,346 total compensation

EVP Nuclear Operations and Chief Nuclear Officer, A. Christopher (Chris) Bakken, $426,990 total compensation

EVP and CFO, Andrew S. (Drew) Marsh, age 44, $553,284 total compensation

President and CEO Entergy New Orleans Inc, Charles Rice

President and CEO Entergy Arkansas Inc., Rick Riley

EVP and General Counsel, Marcus V. Brown, age 55, $563,208 total compensation

President and CEO Entergy Texas Inc, Sallie Rainer

President and CEO Entergy Louisiana LLC and Entergy Gulf States Louisiana L.L.C., Phillip R. May

EVP Shared Services and Human Resources; Chief Diversity Officer, Don Vinci

Senior Vice President Of Nuclear Business Development, Randy Hutchinson

Vice President Engineering, Michael Knight

Vice President, Charles Fink

Site Vice President, John Dent

Vice President Performance Management, Jeanne Kenney

Vice President Utility Support, Laura Mcmanus

Vice President, Bridgett Thomas

Vice President marketing and Corporate Communications, Tim Fitzpatrick

Vice President, Terry Roberts

Vice President, William Maguire

Vice President of Loss Prevention Services, Debbie Riggan

Vice President, Demetric Mercadel

Vice President Communication, Phil Miracle

Senior Vice President, Kimberly Despeaux

Vice President, Byron Young

Vice President, Robert Sloan

Vice President Information Technology Delivery, Christine Malmaron

Vice President Regulatory Affairs, Robert Hall

Vice President Public Affairs, Jody Montelaro

Site Vice President Waterford 3, Donna Jacobs

Vice President Planning And Financial Communications, Nancy Morovich

Vice President, Shelley Macnary

Vice President of Human Resour, Peter Proulx

Vice President; Vice President Operations production Manufacturing; Vice President O, Leo Denult

Senior Vice President and General Tax Counsel, Joseph Henderson

Vice President Federal Governmental Affairs, Daniel Turton

Vice President Finance, Bob Cushman

Vice President Finance, Alan Wright

Vice President, Michael R Kansler

Vice President, Derck Mills

Site Vice President, Bob Smith

Vice President Critical Infrastructur, Chris Peters

Senior Vice President Of Nuclear Business Development, Danny Hutchinson

Vice President and Associate Broker, Mike Wilson

Senior Vice President Shared Services, Jill Israel

Vice President, Lawrence Folks

Site Vice President, Charlie Arnone

Enior Vice President Operations And President And, John Herron

Secretary, Kim Leddy

Secretary, Cheryl Morse

Board Member, Perry Rodrigue

Board Of Directors, Dave McElwee

Board Member, Doris Minter

Auditors: Deloitte & Touche LLP

LOCATIONS

HQ: Entergy Corp
639 Loyola Avenue, New Orleans, LA 70113
Phone: 504 576-4000
Web: www.entergy.com

PRODUCTS/OPERATIONS

2016 Sales

	$ mil.	% of total
Utility	8,996	83
Entergy Wholesale Commodities	1,849	17
Eliminations	(0.1)	-
Total	**10,845**	**100**

2016 Sales

	$ mil.	% of total
Electric	8,866	82
Competitive businesses	1,849	17
Natural gas	129	1
Total	**10,845**	**100**

Selected Subsidiaries

Entergy Arkansas Inc. (electric utility)
Entergy Louisiana LLC. (electric utility)
Entergy Mississippi Inc. (electric utility)
Entergy New Orleans Inc. (electric and gas utility)
Entergy Nuclear Inc. (nuclear plant operation)
Entergy Operations Inc. (plant management and maintenance for Entergy utilities)
Entergy Services Inc. (management services for Entergy utilities)
System Energy Resources Inc. (plant management and supply to Entergy utilities)
System Fuels Inc. (fuel storage and delivery to Entergy utilities)

COMPETITORS

AEP	Edison International
AES	Energy Future
Atmos Energy	Exelon
Avista	NextEra Energy
Berkshire Hathaway Energy	OGE Energy
	PG&E Corporation
Brazos Electric	Peabody Energy
CenterPoint Energy	Progress Energy
Cleco	Sempra Energy
Constellation Energy Group	Southern Company
	TVA
Dominion Energy	Xcel Energy
Duke Energy	

HISTORICAL FINANCIALS
Company Type: Public

Income Statement
FYE: December 31

	REVENUE ($ mil.)	NET INCOME ($ mil.)	NET PROFIT MARGIN	EMPLOYEES
12/16	10,845	(564)	—	13,513
12/15	11,513	(156)	—	13,579
12/14	12,494	960	7.7%	13,393
12/13	11,390	730	6.4%	13,808
12/12	10,302	868	8.4%	14,625
Annual Growth	1.3%	—	—	(2.0%)

2016 Year-End Financials
Debt ratio: 33.27%
Return on equity: (-6.30%)
Cash ($ mil.): 1,187
Current ratio: 1.15
Long-term debt ($ mil.): 14,492
No. of shares (mil.): 179
Dividends
Yield: 0.0%
Payout: —
Market value ($ mil.): 13,161

	STOCK PRICE ($) FY Close	P/E High/Low		PER SHARE ($) Earnings	Dividends	Book Value
12/16	73.47	—	—	(3.26)	3.42	46.25
12/15	68.36	—	—	(0.99)	3.34	53.67
12/14	87.48	17	12	5.22	3.32	57.53
12/13	63.27	18	15	3.99	3.32	55.71
12/12	63.75	15	13	4.76	3.32	53.30
Annual Growth	3.6%	—	—	—	0.7%	(3.5%)

Enterprise Bancorp, Inc. (MA)

Enterprise Bancorp caters to more customers than just entrepreneurs. The holding company owns Enterprise Bank and Trust which operates more than 20 branches in north-central Massachusetts and southern New Hampshire. The $2 billion-asset bank offers traditional deposit and loan products specializing in lending to businesses professionals high-net-worth individuals and not-for-profits. About half of its loan portfolio is tied to commercial real estate while another one-third is tied to commercial and industrial and commercial construction loans. Subsidiaries Enterprise Investment Services and Enterprise Insurance Services provide investments and insurance geared to the bank's target business customers.

Operations

More than 50% of Enterprise Bancorp's $1.86 billion loan portfolio was tied to commercial real estate loans at the end of 2015 while commercial and industrial and commercial construction loans made up another 25% and 11% of the bank's loan assets. The rest of the bank's portfolio was tied to residential mortgages (9% of loan assets) home equity loans and lines of credit (4%) and consumer loans (less than 1%).

Nearly 80% of the bank's total revenue comes from loan interest while investment advisory fees and deposit and interchange fees each make up another 5%.

Geographic Reach

The Lowell Massachusetts-based bank operated 23 branches mostly located in the greater Merrimack Valley and North Central regions of Massachusetts and Southern New Hampshire at the end of 2015.

Sales and Marketing

Enterprise spent $2.7 million on advertising and public relations during 2015 down from $2.9 million in 2014.

Financial Performance

The bank's annual revenues have risen more than 40% since 2011 as its loan assets have swelled by 50% to $1.86 billion. Meanwhile its net income has grown more than 50% as it's kept a lid on loan loss provisions and operating costs.

Enterprise Bancorp's revenue climbed 8% to $98.4 million during 2015 thanks to 11% loan asset growth driven by a "seasoned" lending team a sales and service culture and geographic market expansion. Commercial construction loans grew the fastest rate during the year though all loans grew albeit at a slightly slower rate.

Revenue growth in 2015 drove the bank's net income up 10% to $16.1 million despite higher salary and employee benefit expenses. Enterprise Bancorp's operating cash levels nearly doubled to $25.7 million for the year largely thanks to positive changes in working capital mainly related to prepaid expenses and other assets.

Strategy

Enterprise Bancorp has traditionally expanded its loan and deposit business by opening new branches rather than by acquiring other banks. Enterprise hopes to take advantage of the trend to switch from larger banks to smaller community-oriented institutions. The company has also invested in upgrading its branches and operations systems.

EXECUTIVES

EVP and CFO Enterprise Bancorp and Enterprise Bank and Trust, James A. (Jim) Marcotte, age 59, $194,806 total compensation
CEO Enterprise Bancorp and Enterprise Bank and Trust, John P. (Jack) Clancy, age 59, $400,000 total compensation
President Enterprise Bancorp and Enterprise Bank and Trust, Richard W. (Dick) Main, age 69, $258,918 total compensation
EVP and COO Enterprise Bank and Trust, Stephen J. Irish, age 62, $194,804 total compensation
EVP and Chief Commercial Lending Officer Enterprise Bank and Trust, Brian H. Bullock, age 59
EVP and Chief Banking Officer Enterprise Bank and Trust, Steven R. Larochelle, age 53
EVP and Chief Sales and Marketing Officer Enterprise Bank and Trust, Chester J. (Chet) Szablak, age 59
Vice President, Paul Rousseau
Vice Chairman Enterprise Bancorp and Enterprise Bank and Trust, Arnold S. Lerner, age 87
Chairman Enterprise Bancorp and Enterprise Bank and Trust, George L. Duncan, age 76
Auditors: RSM US, LLP

LOCATIONS

HQ: Enterprise Bancorp, Inc. (MA)
222 Merrimack Street, Lowell, MA 01852
Phone: 978 459-9000

PRODUCTS/OPERATIONS

2015 Sales

	$ mil.	% of total
Interest and dividend income:		
Loans and loans held for sale	77	79
Investment securities	5	5
Other interest-earning assets	0	-
Non-interest income:		
Investment advisory fees	4	5
Deposit and interchange fees	4	5
Net gains on sales of investment securities	1	2
Income on bank-owned life insurance net	0	1
Gains on sales of loans	0	1
Other income	2	3
Total	**98**	**100**

Products and Services

Lending Products:
Residential Loans
Home Equity Loans and Lines of Credit
Consumer Loans
Credit Risk and Allowance for Loan Losses
Deposit Products:
Cash Management Services
Product Delivery Channels
Investment Services
Insurance Services

COMPETITORS

Bank of America	Peoples Federal
Citizens Financial	Bancshares Inc.
Group	Sovereign Bank
Eastern Bank	TD Bank USA

HISTORICAL FINANCIALS
Company Type: Public

Income Statement
FYE: December 31

	ASSETS ($ mil.)	NET INCOME ($ mil.)	INCOME AS % OF ASSETS	EMPLOYEES
12/16	2,526	18	0.7%	468
12/15	2,285	16	0.7%	426
12/14	2,022	14	0.7%	412
12/13	1,849	13	0.7%	398
12/12	1,665	12	0.7%	372
Annual Growth	11.0%	10.9%	—	5.9%

2016 Year-End Financials
Debt ratio: 0.59%
Return on equity: 9.47%
Cash ($ mil.): 50
Current ratio: —
Long-term debt ($ mil.): —
No. of shares (mil.): 11
Dividends
Yield: 0.0%
Payout: 30.5%
Market value ($ mil.): 431

	STOCK PRICE ($) FY Close	P/E High/Low		PER SHARE ($) Earnings	Dividends	Book Value
12/16	37.56	22	12	1.70	0.52	18.72
12/15	22.85	16	13	1.55	0.50	17.38
12/14	25.25	18	12	1.44	0.48	16.35
12/13	21.17	16	11	1.36	0.46	15.14
12/12	16.52	14	11	1.28	0.44	14.42
Annual Growth	22.8%	—	—	7.4%	4.3%	6.7%

Enterprise Financial Services Corp

Enterprise Financial Services wants you to boldly bank where many have banked before. It's the holding company for Enterprise Bank & Trust which mostly targets closely-held businesses and their owners but also serves individuals in the St. Louis Kansas City and Phoenix metropolitan areas. Boasting $3.8 billion in assets and 16 branches Enterprise offers standard products such as checking savings and money market accounts and CDs. Commercial and industrial loans make up over half of the company's lending activities while real estate loans make up another 45%. The bank also writes consumer and residential mortgage loans. Bank subsidiary Enterprise Trust offers wealth management services.

Operations

Enterprise Trust the company's wealth management unit targets business owners wealthy individuals and institutional investors providing financial planning business succession planning and related services. The unit also invests in Missouri state tax credits from funds for affordable housing development which it then sells to clients and others.

About 82% of Enterprise Financial's total revenue came from loan interest (including fees) in 2014 while another 7% came from interest on its taxable and tax-exempt investment securities. The rest of its revenue came from wealth management income (4%) service fees (3%) gains on state tax credits (1%) and other miscellaneous income sources. The bank had a staff of 452 full-time employees at the end of 2014.

Geographic Reach

Enterprise Bank & Trust operates eight banking locations in or around Kansas City six banking locations and a support center in the St. Louis area and two banking locations in the Phoenix metro area.

Financial Performance

The company has struggled to consistently grow its revenues in recent years mostly due to shrinking interest margins on its loans amidst the low-interest environment. Its profits however have mostly trended higher thanks to declining loan loss provisions as its loan portfolio's credit quality has improved with higher property valuations in the strengthened economy.

Enterprise Financials' revenue fell by 9% to $148.4 million in 2014 mostly due to double-digit declines in interest income as its purchased credit-impaired (PCI) loan balances and accelerated payments declined and as interest margins on its loans continued to shrink. The bank's portfolio loan balances increased however helping to offset some of its interest income decline.

Lower revenue and higher loan loss provisions (it received a loan loss benefit of $642 thousand in 2013) in 2014 caused the bank's net income to dive 18% to $27.2 million. Enterprise Financial's operating cash levels rose by 7% to $31.5 million despite lower earnings for the year mostly thanks to favorable changes in its working capital related to a $12-million change in other asset balances.

Strategy

Enterprise Financial Services planned in 2015 to continue its long-term strategy of keeping a "relationship-oriented distribution and sales approach"; growing its fee income and niche businesses; practicing "prudent" credit and interest rate risk management; and using advanced technology and controlled-expense growth. The company added that it planned on "operating branches with larger average deposits and employing experienced staff who are compensated on the basis of performance and customer service."

Though it just had two branches in Phoenix in 2015 the bank believes the fast-growing Phoenix market offers long-term growth opportunities for the company with its underlying demographic and geographic factors. Indeed at the end of 2014 the market had over 90000 privately-held businesses and 80000-plus households each with investable assets of more than $1 million.

Mergers and Acquisitions

In 2017 Enterprise Financial Services completed the acquisition of Jefferson County Bancshares the holding company of Eagle Bank and Trust Company in Missouri. The deal added 13 branches in metropolitan St. Louis and Perry County Missouri. The acquisition expanded EFS's assets to nearly $5 billion.

Company Background

In a restructuring move Enterprise Financial Services sold life insurance arm Millennium Brokerage in 2010 five years after investing in the company.

EXECUTIVES

President Enterprise Bank and Trust, Scott R. Goodman, age 53, $318,150 total compensation
EVP and CFO, Keene S. Turner, age 37, $333,125 total compensation
CEO, James B. Lally, age 49, $331,342 total compensation
Chief Credit Officer Enterprise Bank & Trust, Douglas N. Bauche, age 48, $253,270 total compensation
Senior Vice President Relationship Manager, Brian Hadican
Assistant Vice President Business Banking Special, Bill Forsythe
Senior Vice President Loan Review, Jeremy Jameson
Vice President Relationship Manager, Brian Glarner
Assistant Vice President Relationship Manager, Tom Noel
Assistant Vice President Business Banking Specialist, Arnold Otero
Assistant Vice President Relationship Manager, Aaron Wiens
AVP Relationship Manager, Bob Sivewright
Vice President Relationship Manager, Michael Hasenkamp
Senior Vice President Director of Commercial Real Estate, Adam Kilpatrick
Assistant Vice President Business Banking, Molly McKay
Senior Vice President Agriculture and Commercial Lending, Matthew Hardecke
Assistant Vice President Business Banking Specialist, Jessica Nollett
Vice President Treasury Management, Larry Fredette
Assistant Vice President Business Banking Specialist, Brandy Kimble
Senior Vice President, Eve Janis
Vice President Business Banking, Pam Hosty
Senior Vice President, Paul Stone
Vice President Resolution Management Group, Jeff Cook
Chairman, John S. Eulich, age 66
Vice Chairman, Robert Witterschein
Auditors: Deloitte & Touche LLP

LOCATIONS

HQ: Enterprise Financial Services Corp
150 North Meramec, Clayton, MO 63105
Phone: 314 725-5500
Web: www.enterprisebank.com

PRODUCTS/OPERATIONS

2011 Sales

	$ mil.	% of total
Interest		
Loans including fees	130	79
Securities	11	7
Other	0	1
Noninterest		
Wealth management	6	4
Service charges on deposit accounts	5	3
Gain on state tax credits net	3	2
Other service charges and fee income	1	1
Other	4	3
Adjustments	(3.5)	-
Total	**161**	**100**

Selected Acquisitions

COMPETITORS

BOK Financial	Midwest BankCentre
Bank of America	Pulaski Financial
Commerce Bancshares	U.S. Bancorp
First Clover Leaf Financial	Wells Fargo

HISTORICAL FINANCIALS

Company Type: Public

Income Statement

FYE: December 31

	ASSETS ($ mil.)	NET INCOME ($ mil.)	INCOME AS % OF ASSETS	EMPLOYEES
12/16	4,081	48	1.2%	479
12/15	3,608	38	1.1%	459
12/14	3,277	27	0.8%	452
12/13	3,170	33	1.0%	455
12/12	3,325	28	0.9%	450
Annual Growth	5.3%	14.6%	—	1.6%

2016 Year-End Financials

Debt ratio: 2.59%
Return on equity: 13.20%
Cash ($ mil.): 198
Current ratio: —
Long-term debt ($ mil.): —

No. of shares (mil.): 20
Dividends
  Yield: 0.0%
  Payout: 17.0%
Market value ($ mil.): 862

	STOCK PRICE ($) FY Close	P/E High/Low		Earnings	PER SHARE ($) Dividends	Book Value
12/16	43.00	18	10	2.41	0.41	19.31
12/15	28.35	16	10	1.89	0.26	17.53
12/14	19.73	15	12	1.35	0.21	15.94
12/13	20.42	12	7	1.73	0.21	14.47
12/12	13.07	11	7	1.37	0.21	13.09
Annual Growth	34.7%	—	—	15.2%	18.2%	10.2%

Enterprise Products Partners L.P.

Enterprise Products Partners has the energy to go the distance. The limited partnership?s primary operating subsidiary Enterprise Products Operating LLC (EPO) is a leading player in the North American midstream services to producers and consumers of natural gas natural gas liquids (NGL) crude oil petrochemicals and refined products. Operations include natural gas processing NGL fractionation petrochemical services and crude oil transportation. It owns 49000 miles of pipelines 14 billion cu. ft. of natural gas storage and 260 million barrels of storage for NGLs refined products and crude oil. It owns some 27 natural gas processing plants and 18 deep water docks used to export product. The hub of EPO?s business is Houston's Mont Belvieu refinery complex.

Operations

Enterprise has four business segments: NGL Pipelines and Services Crude Oil Pipelines and Services Petrochemical and Refined Products Services Natural Gas Pipelines and Services. It sold in 2015 a former fifth segment Offshore Pipelines and Services which ran its Gulf of Mexico operations.

The NGL Pipelines and Services segment produces some 45% of overall revenue with its natural gas processing plants and related natural gas liquid (NGL) marketing activities. At the core of its business are 25 processing plants that collect natural gas and remove NGLs and impurities in preparation for transportation and eventual end-user purchase. It owns nearly 20000 miles of NGL pipelines NGL and related product storage facilities and 15 NGL fractionators. The segment also includes the company's NGL import and LPG export terminal operations. NGL marketing activities use a fleet of roughly 900 railcars to deliver feedstocks to its facilities and distribute NGLs to customers throughout the US and Canada.

Crude Oil Pipelines & Services brings in about 30% of revenue and includes 5400 miles of crude oil pipelines and related operations crude oil storage and marine terminals and crude oil marketing activities. Of its pipelines the Seaway pipeline is notable in that it connects the Cushing OK crude oil hub (major industry hub where price settlement for West Texas Intermediate (WTI) occurs) with markets in southeast Texas.

The Petrochemical and Refined Products Services segment is engaged in petrochemical and refined products transportation and services. It fractionates propylene to create the building blocks of carpet fibers molded plastic parts for appliances cars and medical products and packaging film. It accounts for approximately 15% of revenue.

Natural Gas Pipelines and Services segment includes 19000 miles of pipeline used to gather and transport natural gas from shale plays Eagle Ford Haynesville Barnett Permian and others. It leases underground salt dome natural gas storage facilities in Texas and Louisiana. The segment is also home to natural gas marketing activities.

Geographic Reach

Houston TX-based Enterprise Products operates the vast majority of its facilities in Texas along the Gulf Coast with particular emphasis in the Mont Belvieu refinery and transport complex. Key locations from which it gathers natural gas and crude oil include Colorado Louisiana New Mexico Texas and Wyoming. It has a presence in shale plays: Eagle Ford Haynesville Barnett Permian Piceance San Juan and Greater Green River supply basins. Its NGL pipelines extend throughout the US Midwest and Gulf Coast including states such as Georgia New York Oklahoma and Minnesota.

Sales and Marketing

Enterprise Products sells product and services to refineries industrial companies commercial customers and regional natural gas processing plants. It generates much of its revenue from fees calculated by the volume of product it transports. No customer accounted for more than 10% of sales although Vitol accounted for about 9.8% in 2016.

The company performs significant intersegment sales to the degree that the value of intersegment sales exceeds the consolidated total revenue (sold to third parties).

Financial Performance

Like the entire oil and gas industry Enterprise Products was adversely affected by the extreme downturn in commodity pricing in 2014 although it has fared better than many others. Its revenue climbed steadily from $25.5 billion in 2010 to $47.9 billion in 2014 before taking some hits in the following two years. The company managed to keep net income steady throughout the cycle ranging between $2.4 billion and $2.8 billion.

In 2016 revenue fell 14% to $23.0 billion due largely to lower volumes and lower prices of its crude oil marketing business. Sales of natural gas petrochemicals and refined products experienced lower prices which more than offset volume increases. NGLs sales volumes increased notably but the overall effect on revenue was muted due to lower sales prices.

Net income in 2016 moved less than 1% from the 2015 result coming in at $2.5 billion despite the double-digit decrease in revenue. Enterprise did well managing its expenses firstly through the reduction of purchased crude oil whose volumes and prices declined and secondly through deft pricing management of NGLs.

Cash on hand at the end of 2016 was $63 million up $44 million from 2015. Cash from operations contributed $4.1 billion to the coffers mainly from net income and adjustments for depreciation

and amortization. Investing activities in capital projects (for example maintenance & expansion of pipelines and plants) was $3.0 billion and in business acquisitions was $1.0 billion. Financing activities netted out with a $320 million contribution to cash although it rolled more than $60 billion in debt during the year. It also issued $3.3 billion in dividends and issued $2.5 billion in secondary units (stock).

Strategy

Enterprise's strategy is focused on building and managing an integrated network of midstream energy assets (including salt domes and fractionation and natural gas processing plants) to take advantage of growing US market demand for natural gas NGLs crude oil and refined products.

The company's business strategies are to capitalize on expected increases in the production of natural gas NGLs and crude oil from development activities in various US production basins. Part of this strategy involves expansion through growth capital projects. It plans to continue to expand its assets through the construction of new facilities and to capitalize on expected increases in natural gas NGL and crude oil production resulting from development activities in the Rocky Mountains Mid-Continent Northeast and US Gulf Coast regions including the Niobrara Barnett Eagle Ford Permian Haynesville Marcellus and Utica Shale plays.

Enterprise began commercial service in 2016 on approximately $2.2 billion of growth capital projects. The projects included its Morgan?s Point Ethane Export Terminal Waha and South Eddy natural gas processing facilities and the completion of over 2 MMBbls of additional crude oil storage capacity at terminals in Houston and Mont Belvieu.

The company has approximately $6.7 billion of growth capital projects scheduled to be completed by 2020 including two processing facilities the Midland-to-Sealy segment of its Midland-to-ECHO Pipeline System and a joint venture-owned dock infrastructure project in Corpus Christi designed to accommodate crude oil volumes. In early 2017 it purchased assets from bankrupt Azure Midstream to extend its capabilities in East Texas and Northern Louisiana.

To raise cash to both weather the market downturn and fund capital expenditures Enterprise sold its entire Offshore Pipelines & Services segment to Genesis Energy for $1.5 billion. It also raised $2.5 billion with a secondary offering of its stock units.

Mergers and Acquisitions

In 2017 Enterprise Products purchased the midstream business and assets of bankrupt Azure Midstream which has operations in East Texas and Northern Louisiana. Enterprise gained nearly 1000 miles of natural gas gathering pipelines and three natural gas processing facilities.

Company Background

The company is investing heavily in serving shale plays especially the Eagle Ford in South Texas and is building midstream facilities to serve the surge in natural gas production. In 2012 it opened a fifth NGL fractionator at its Mont Belvieu facility to process Eagle Ford hydrocarbons and a fifth in 2012.

That year Enterprise joined Enbridge Energy Partners and Anadarko Petroleum in advancing development of the Texas Express Pipeline by the companies' joint venture. The 20-inch diameter pipeline will extend about 580 miles from Skellytown Texas to the Mont Belvieu NGL fractionation complex. The pipeline also provides access to other producers in several regions: West Texas the Rocky Mountains southern Oklahoma and the Mid-continent area.

In 2010 in a move to increase its footprint in the lucrative Haynesville/Bossier Shale play En-

terprise acquired two natural gas gathering and treating systems in northwest Louisiana and East Texas from M2 Midstream LLC for $1.2 billion.

In a major expansion move in 2009 the company acquired rival TEPPCO Partners L.P. in a $26 billion all-stock deal which boosted its pipelines and oil refined products and NGL storage capacity. The TEPPCO Partners purchase made the company the largest publicly traded energy partnership in the US. The expanded company's assets include 60 liquid storage terminals 25 natural gas storage facilities 17 fractionation facilities and six offshore hub platforms.

That year the company acquired Enterprise GP Holdings which controlled the general partner of Enterprise. The $8 billion deal was aimed at reducing long-term capital costs and simplifying the business structure of Enterprise Products Partners.

The family of Chairman Dan Duncan controls a 35% stake in Enterprise.

EXECUTIVES

President, W. Randall (Randy) Fowler, age 61, $521,178 total compensation
CEO, A. James (Jim) Teague, age 71, $800,000 total compensation
EVP Commercial, William (Bill) Ordemann, age 58, $451,150 total compensation
SVP and CFO, Bryan F. Bulawa, age 48
SVP and CIO, Paul G. Flynn
EVP Operations and Engineering, Graham W. Bacon, age 53, $375,000 total compensation
Vice President, Tony Chovanec
Group Senior Vice President, Leonard Mallett
Group Senior Vice President, Rudy Nix
Vice President Gulf Coast Distribution, Mark Youtsey
Vice President Project Management, Craig Roper
Senior Vice President Enterprise General Partner, James Cisrik
Vice President, Darrell Kainer
Vice President Operations and Finance MBD APAC, Troy A Rousse
Vice President Government Affairs, Delbert Fore
Senior Vice President of Engineering, Patty Gilmore
Senior Vice President, Charles Brabson
Executive Vice President and Chief Commercial Officer, Jim Teague
Vice President Human Resources, Karen Taylor
Vice President of Business Development, David Tucker
Vice President of Environmental Health and Training, Bryan Oliver
Senior Vice President, Carolyn Stone
Chairman, Randa D. Williams, age 55
Auditors: Deloitte & Touche LLP

LOCATIONS

HQ: Enterprise Products Partners L.P.
1100 Louisiana Street, 10th Floor, Houston, TX 77002
Phone: 713 381-6500
Web: www.enterpriseproducts.com

PRODUCTS/OPERATIONS

2016 Sales

	$ mil.	% of total
NGL Pipelines & Services	10,242	45
Crude Oil Pipelines & Services	6,515	28
Petrochemical & Refined Products Services	3,721	16
Natural Gas Pipelines & Services	2,543	11
Total	**23,022**	**100**

COMPETITORS

Anadarko Petroleum	Kinder Morgan
CenterPoint Energy	Magellan Midstream
Crestwood Midstream Partners LP	ONEOK
	Occidental Petroleum
Dominion Energy	Plains All American
Duke Energy	Pipeline
Dynegy	Spectra Energy
Enbridge	TRII
Energy Transfer Equity	Williams Companies
Exxon Mobil	

HISTORICAL FINANCIALS

Company Type: Public

Income Statement

FYE: December 31

	REVENUE ($ mil.)	NET INCOME ($ mil.)	NET PROFIT MARGIN	EMPLOYEES
12/16	23,022	2,513	10.9%	—
12/15	27,027	2,521	9.3%	—
12/14	47,951	2,787	5.8%	—
12/13	47,727	2,596	5.4%	—
12/12	42,583	2,419	5.7%	—
Annual Growth	(14.3%)	0.9%	—	—

2016 Year-End Financials

Debt ratio: 45.40%	No. of shares (mil.): 2,117
Return on equity: —	Dividends
Cash ($ mil.): 63	Yield: 0.0%
Current ratio: 0.79	Payout: 132.5%
Long-term debt ($ mil.): 21,120	Market value ($ mil.): 57,260

	STOCK PRICE ($) FY Close	P/E High/Low		PER SHARE ($) Earnings	Dividends	Book Value
12/16	27.04	25	16	1.20	1.59	10.41
12/15	25.58	29	17	1.26	1.51	10.08
12/14	36.12	53	21	1.47	1.43	9.32
12/13	66.30	45	35	1.41	1.35	8.13
12/12	50.08	39	33	1.36	1.27	7.30
Annual Growth	(14.3%)	—	—	(3.0%)	5.9%	9.3%

EOG Resources, Inc.

Large-scale shale is the Holy Grail for oil prospector EOG Resources. The independent oil and gas company engages in exploring for natural gas and crude oil in the Eagle Ford Shale and Barnett Shale in Texas and the Bakken formation in North Dakota which it develops produces and markets. EOG's boasts total estimated net proved reserves of 2.1 million barrels of oil equivalent of which nearly 1.1 million barrels was crude oil and condensate reserves and 3.8 billion cubic feet was natural gas reserves.

Operations

EOG is the largest oil producer in the lucrative Eagle Ford Shale play in South Texas.

In the wider Permian Basin's Delaware Basin the company has 160000 net acres in the Leonard Shale and 346000 net acres in the Wolfcamp Shale. Additionally EOG has acreage in the Wolfcamp Shale within the Midland Basin.

Sales of crude oil and crude condensates account for around 55% of total sales natural gas sales account for 10% and NGLs (natural gas liquids) 5%.

EOG also conducts gas gathering processing and marketing which together bring in a quarter of the company's sales. It sells oil and natural gas into local downstream markets transported either by pipeline or truck.

EOG operates its own sand mine and sand processing plants in Hood County Texas to reduce costs and to help fulfill EOG's sand needs for its well completion operations in Texas.

Geographic Reach

EOG major shale plays in the US are the Eagle Ford Shale and Barnett Shale in Texas and the Bakken Formation in North Dakota. EOG also has operations in Canada offshore Trinidad the UK North Sea and East Irish Sea and Sichuan Basin in China.

The US accounts for some 95% of the company's proved reserves.

Sales and Marketing

EOG sell its North American wellhead crude oil and condensate production to local markets and (by pipeline rail and truck) to downstream markets and its natural gas production to local markets or via pipeline to downstream markets.

EOG's major sales points include Cushing Oklahoma St. James Louisiana and other points along the Gulf Coast. Its three biggest customers each account for more than 10% of EOG's total revenue from wellhead crude oil and condensates NGLs and natural gas and gathering processing and marketing revenue.

All the natural gas produced by EOG's Trinidad operations was sold to the National Gas Company of Trinidad and Tobago and all natural gas from EOG's China operations was sold to PetroChina.

Major US sales areas included the Midwest the Permian Basin Cushing Oklahoma St. James Louisiana and other points along the Gulf Coast.

Financial Performance

EOG's revenue has been stunted by the drop in the oil price since 2014. In fiscal 2016 sales declined a further 13% to $7.7 billion amid falls in revenue from both hydrocarbon sales and gathering processing and marketing.

EOG lost $1.1 billion in 2015 an improvement on the $4.5 billion loss incurred in 2015. The improvement related mostly to a steep reduction in impairment costs and $206 million gains on asset sales in Texas Louisiana the Rocky Mountains and Oklahoma. However the low oil price continued to impact on profitability while EOG also lost $100 million derivatives versus a gain of $62 million the year before.

Cash from operations fell 34% to $2.4 billion due to decreases in oil revenue and from the settlement of financial commodity derivative contracts partially offset by a decrease in cash operating expenses.

Strategy

To return to profitability during the ongoing oil price depression EOG is selling off underperforming assets while only drilling new sites where it can generate returns of 30% when the oil price is at $40 per barrel. In 2016 EOG divested all its Haynesville natural gas assets as well as its Barnett Shale natural gas assets in Johnson County Texas. Since the price crash it has also sold assets in Canada as well as certain gathering and processing assets. Its drilling strategy is to buy up acreage adjacent to its current holdings where it can employ cheaper horizontal drilling techniques. To that end it acquired Yates Petroleum Company in 2016 which added 180000 acres in the Delaware Basin and 200000 acreas in the Powder River Basin.

Mergers and Acquisitions

In 2016 EOG acquired Yates Petroleum Corporation Abo Petroleum Corporation MYCO Industries Inc. and certain other entities (collectively Yates) in a deal valued at $2.5 billion.

HISTORY

In 1987 Enron formed Enron Oil & Gas from its existing InterNorth and Houston Natural Gas operations to concentrate on exploration for oil and natural gas and their production. Enron maintained full ownership until 1989 when it spun off 16% of Enron Oil & Gas to the public raising about $200 million. Later offerings reduced its holdings to just over 50%.

Enron Oil & Gas in 1992 was awarded a 95% working interest in three fields off Trinidad that previously had been held by government-owned companies. Two years later the company assumed the operations of three drilling blocks off Bombay (including the Tapti field) as well as a 30% interest in them. Natural gas prices fell in the winter of 1994 causing Enron Oil & Gas to focus its 1995 drilling on crude oil exploitation and the enhancement of its natural gas reserves. Natural gas prices rebounded in 1996. That year Enron Oil & Gas was awarded a 90% interest in an offshore area of Venezuela. In 1997 the company inked a 30-year production contract with China. The company made a major discovery of natural gas in offshore Trinidad in 1998. That year Mark Papa succeeded Forrest Hoglund as CEO (Papa became chairman in 1999).

In 1999 Enron traded most of its remaining stake in Enron Oil & Gas to the company in exchange for Enron Oil & Gas' operations and assets in India and China. Consequently the company changed its name from Enron Oil & Gas to EOG Resources.

The next year EOG won contracts to develop properties in Canada's Northwest Territories. It also moved into the Appalachian Basin in 2000 through the acquisition of Somerset Oil & Gas. Buoyed by a strong performance that year the company increased its capital spending on North American exploration by more than 30% and in 2001 it bought Energy Search a small natural gas exploration and production company that operated in the Appalachian Basin.

EXECUTIVES

Chairman and CEO, William R. Thomas, age 65, $925,000 total compensation

President and COO, Gary L. Thomas, age 68, $835,000 total compensation

SVP and Chief Information and Technology Officer, Sandeep Bhakhri

SVP and Chief Human Resources Officer, Patricia L. Edwards

EVP and CFO, Timothy K. Driggers, age 56, $480,000 total compensation

VP and General Manager Fort Worth, Kenneth E. Dunn

EVP Exploration and Production, Lloyd W. (Bill) Helms, age 59, $470,000 total compensation

VP Drilling, Robert C. Smith

Managing Director EOG Resources Trinidad Limited, Sammy G. Pickering

VP and General Manager Fort Worth, David W. Trice, age 46

VP and General Manager International, J. Pat Woods

VP and General Manager Midland, Ezra Y. Yacob

SVP Operations, John J. Boyd

VP Land, Steven D. Wentworth

EVP General Counsel and Corporate Secretary, Michael P. Donaldson, $475,000 total compensation

VP and General Manager Oklahoma City, Nathan J. Andrews

VP and General Manager Corpus Christi, Kenneth D. Marbach

VP and General Manager Denver, Kenneth W. Boedeker

VP and General Manager Artesia, Reese T. Lantrip

Vice President Engineering, Cory Helms
Vice President Marketing, Marc Eschenburg
Vice President of Financial Analysis, Allun Powell
Vice President Exploration, Charlie Sheppard
Auditors: Deloitte & Touche LLP

LOCATIONS

HQ: EOG Resources, Inc.
1111 Bagby, Sky Lobby 2, Houston, TX 77002
Phone: 713 651-7000
Web: www.eogresources.com

2016 sales

	$ mil.	% of total
United States	7,323	96
Trinidad	242	3
Other International	85	1
Total	**7,650**	**100**

PRODUCTS/OPERATIONS

2016 sales

	$ mil.	% of total
Crude oil & condensate	4,317	56
Natural Gas Liquids	437	5
Natural Gas	742	10
Gains on Mark-to-Market Commodity Derivative Contracts (99.6) (1)		
GatheringProcessing and Marketing	1,966	26
Gains on Asset DispositionsNet	205	3
OtherNet	81	1
Total	**7,650**	**100**

COMPETITORS

Adams Resources	Murphy Oil
Anadarko Petroleum	Occidental Petroleum
Apache	Pioneer Natural
BP	Resources
Cabot Oil & Gas	Repsol Oil & Gas
Chevron	Royal Dutch Shell
Exxon Mobil	

HISTORICAL FINANCIALS

Company Type: Public

Income Statement
FYE: December 31

	REVENUE ($ mil.)	NET INCOME ($ mil.)	NET PROFIT MARGIN	EMPLOYEES
12/16	7,650	(1,096)	—	2,650
12/15	8,757	(4,524)	—	2,760
12/14	18,035	2,915	16.2%	3,000
12/13	14,487	2,197	15.2%	2,800
12/12	11,682	570	4.9%	2,650
Annual Growth	**(10.0%)**	**—**	**—**	**0.0%**

2016 Year-End Financials

Debt ratio: 23.72%
Return on equity: (-8.12%)
Cash ($ mil.): 1,599
Current ratio: 1.75
Long-term debt ($ mil.): 6,979

No. of shares (mil.): 576
Dividends
Yield: 0.0%
Payout: —
Market value ($ mil.): 58,304

	STOCK PRICE ($) FY Close	P/E High/Low	Earnings	PER SHARE ($) Dividends	Book Value
12/16	101.10	— —	(1.98)	0.67	24.24
12/15	70.79	— —	(8.29)	0.67	23.54
12/14	92.07	35 15	5.32	0.51	32.30
12/13	167.84	46 28	4.02	0.73	28.23
12/12	120.79	117 79	1.06	0.67	24.45
Annual Growth	**(4.4%)**	**— —**	**—**	**(0.0%)**	**(0.2%)**

Equity Bancshares Inc

Auditors: Crowe Chizek LLP

LOCATIONS

HQ: Equity Bancshares Inc
7701 East Kellogg Drive, Suite 300, Wichita, KS 67207
Phone: 316 612-6000
Web: www.equitybank.com

HISTORICAL FINANCIALS

Company Type: Public

Income Statement
FYE: December 31

	ASSETS ($ mil.)	NET INCOME ($ mil.)	INCOME AS % OF ASSETS	EMPLOYEES
12/16	2,192	9	0.4%	415
12/15	1,585	10	0.6%	297
12/14	1,175	8	0.8%	262
12/13	1,140	7	0.7%	—
Annual Growth	**24.4%**	**6.0%**	**—**	**—**

2016 Year-End Financials

Debt ratio: 0.74%
Return on equity: 4.40%
Cash ($ mil.): 37
Current ratio: —
Long-term debt ($ mil.): —

No. of shares (mil.): 11
Dividends
Yield: 0.0%
Payout: —
Market value ($ mil.): 393

	STOCK PRICE ($) FY Close	P/E High/Low	Earnings	PER SHARE ($) Dividends	Book Value
12/16	33.64	34 19	1.07	0.00	22.09
12/15	23.39	16 15	1.54	0.00	20.37
12/14	0.00	— —	1.30	0.00	19.40
Annual Growth	**—**	**— —**	**(6.3%)**	**—**	**4.4%**

Erie Indemnity Co.

Erie Indemnity may be near a lake but it prefers pools. Founded in 1925 as an auto insurer it now provides management services that relate to the sales underwriting and issuance of policies of one customer: Erie Insurance Exchange. The Exchange is a reciprocal insurance exchange that pools the underwriting of several property/casualty insurance firms. It offers coverage ranging from homeowners to boat policies through independent representatives with a reach that extends to a dozen states east of the Mississippi River. Erie Indemnity charges a management fee of 25% of all premiums written or assumed by the Exchange.

Operations

Management fees account for more than 95% of Erie Indemnity's revenue; service agreements and investment income accounts for the remainder.

The Exchange and its subsidiaries (Erie Insurance Erie Insurance Company of New York Erie Insurance Property and Casualty and Flagship City Insurance) operate as a property/casualty insurer and are collectively referred to as the Property and Casualty Group. The group also owns Erie Family Life Insurance.

Personal lines — primarily private passenger automobile and homeowners products — comprise some 70% of the direct and assumed premiums written; commercial lines — primarily multi-peril workers' compensation and commercial automo-

bile — make up the rest. The Erie Insurance family of companies serves a total of some 5 million property/casualty policyholders.

Geographic Reach

Erie Indemnity operates in a dozen midwestern mid-Atlantic and southeastern states (Illinois Indiana Kentucky Maryland New York North Carolina Ohio Pennsylvania Tennessee Virginia West Virginia and Wisconsin) as well as in the District of Columbia.

Sales and Marketing Erie Indemnity's distribution network includes about 121000 independent agents.

Financial Performance Erie Indemnity's revenue dropped 74% to $1.5 billion in 2015 due to a change in the company's accounting policy; however when considering the restated figures of 2014 revenue increased 7% in 2015. Revenue rose 6% to $1.6 billion in 2016 as sales growth outpaced growth in operating expenses. Property/casualty premiums grew 6.2% while total life insurance and annuity premiums grew 4.5% that year. These increases were partially offset by a decrease in investment income Net income continued its rising trend in 2016 growing 20% to $210.4 million. Cash flow from operations which fell with revenue in 2015 rose 17% to $254.3 million.

Strategy

Through careful risk selection and pricing practices as well as by maintaining a diverse product mix Erie Indemnity seeks to maintain long-term underwriting profit growth for the Exchange. It also seeks to provide consistent support services to policyholders and agents. Towards that end the company is upgrading its technology platforms (such as its claims management system). Additionally it was an early adopter of drone technology to improve the insurance claims process.

Erie Indemnity plans for growth also include increasing its property/casualty group premiums and improving its competitive position in the marketplace by expanding the size of its agency force and increasing market penetration in existing territories. It also intends to expand geographically and broaden the types of products it offers. For example in 2015 it introduced new motorcycle coverage as well as expanded automobile insurance. Also that year the company launched such extras as eSignature capability an improved online marketing portal an online quoting platform and social media content.In 2016 it began providing small to midsized companies with protection against cloud computing risks.

Erie Indemnity develops innovative products to address new types of risks as the world increasingly modernizes. It was one of the first insurers to offer coverage for ride-sharing drivers. The company is keeping an eye on additional new opportunities presented by such areas as self-driving cars blockchain technology the Internet of Things big data and cybersecurity.

Company Background

Erie Indemnity's structure and relationship to other parts of the larger Erie Insurance Group are complex to say the least. The company operated as a property/casualty insurer through its wholly-owned subsidiaries Erie Insurance Co. Erie New York and Erie Insurance Property and Casualty throughout 2010. At year-end however Erie Indemnity sold all of its outstanding capital stock and voting shares of these subsidiaries to the Exchange. As a result now all of its former property/casualty insurance operations are owned by the Exchange and Erie Indemnity serves as the management company. The sale of the subsidiaries did not affect its pooling agreement. The company also sold its approximate 22% ownership in Erie Family Life to the Exchange which became its full parent.

EXECUTIVES

President and CEO, Timothy G. NeCastro, $492,085 total compensation
EVP and CIO, Robert C. (Bob) Ingram, age 58, $456,923 total compensation
EVP Claims and Customer Service, Lorianne Feltz
SVP and Chief Investment Officer, Bradley G. Postema, $418,558 total compensation
EVP and General Counsel, Sean J. McLaughlin, age 62, $426,923 total compensation
EVP and CFO, Gregory J. (Greg) Gutting, age 53, $406,885 total compensation
EVP Sales and Products, Doug Smith
Vice President and Claims Manager, Gregory Green
Executive Vice President Sales and Marketing, John Kearns
Vice President Information Technology Operations and Service Management, Andrew Abramczyk
Vice President Enterprise Project Management Office, Ferenc Csatlos
Vice Chairman, Jonathan Hirt Hagen, age 54
Chairman, Thomas B. Hagen, age 81
Auditors: Ernst & Young LLP

LOCATIONS

HQ: Erie Indemnity Co.
100 Erie Insurance Place, Erie, PA 16530
Phone: 814 870-2000
Web: www.erieinsurance.com

PRODUCTS/OPERATIONS

2016 Sales

	$ mil.	% of total
Operating revenue		
Net management fees	1,567	96
Service agreements	29	2
Investment income	27	2
Total	**1,624**	**100**

COMPETITORS

ACE USA	Old Republic
Alleghany Corporation	PMA Companies
Gallagher	Transatlantic Holdings
Marsh & McLennan	Travelers Companies
Navigators	

HISTORICAL FINANCIALS

Company Type: Public

Income Statement

FYE: December 31

	ASSETS ($ mil.)	NET INCOME ($ mil.)	INCOME AS % OF ASSETS	EMPLOYEES
12/16	1,548	210	13.6%	5,000
12/15	1,407	174	12.4%	4,800
12/14	17,758	168	0.9%	4,700
12/13	16,676	163	1.0%	4,450
12/12	15,441	160	1.0%	4,400
Annual Growth	**(43.7%)**	**7.1%**	**—**	**3.2%**

2016 Year-End Financials

Debt ratio: 1.60%
Return on equity: 26.45%
Cash ($ mil.): 189
Current ratio: —
Long-term debt ($ mil.): —
No. of shares (mil.): 46
Dividends
  Yield: 0.0%
  Payout: 54.6%
Market value ($ mil.): 5,194

	STOCK PRICE ($) FY Close	P/E High/Low		PER SHARE ($) Earnings	Dividends	Book Value
12/16	112.45	25	20	4.01	2.19	17.69
12/15	95.64	27	21	3.33	2.77	16.66
12/14	90.77	26	19	3.18	2.54	15.22
12/13	73.12	24	20	3.08	4.37	15.80
12/12	69.22	23	18	2.99	4.80	13.69
Annual Growth	**12.9%**	**—**	**—**	**7.6%**	**(17.8%)**	**6.6%**

ESSA Bancorp Inc

EXECUTIVES

Vice President Credit Administrator, Charles Hangen
Vice President Commercial Loan Officer III, Henry Kush
Auditors: S.R. Snodgrass, P.C.

LOCATIONS

HQ: ESSA Bancorp Inc
200 Palmer Street, Stroudsburg, PA 18360
Phone: 570 421-0531
Web: www.essabank.com

COMPETITORS

First National Community Bancorp	Norwood Financial
Fulton Financial	PNC Financial
	Sovereign Bank

HISTORICAL FINANCIALS

Company Type: Public

Income Statement

FYE: September 30

	ASSETS ($ mil.)	NET INCOME ($ mil.)	INCOME AS % OF ASSETS	EMPLOYEES
09/17	1,785	7	0.4%	323
09/16	1,772	7	0.4%	326
09/15	1,606	9	0.6%	303
09/14	1,574	8	0.5%	303
09/13	1,372	8	0.6%	282
Annual Growth	**6.8%**	**(4.5%)**		**3.5%**

2017 Year-End Financials

Debt ratio: 9.76%
Return on equity: 4.09%
Cash ($ mil.): 42
Current ratio: —
Long-term debt ($ mil.): —
No. of shares (mil.): 11
Dividends
  Yield: 0.0%
  Payout: 52.1%
Market value ($ mil.): 182

	STOCK PRICE ($) FY Close	P/E High/Low		PER SHARE ($) Earnings	Dividends	Book Value
09/17	15.70	24	19	0.69	0.36	15.76
09/16	13.83	19	17	0.73	0.36	15.48
09/15	12.96	14	12	0.93	0.34	15.09
09/14	11.30	15	13	0.79	0.26	14.44
09/13	10.42	15	13	0.76	0.20	13.93
Annual Growth	**10.8%**	**—**	**—**	**(2.4%)**	**15.8%**	**3.1%**

Essendant Inc

Essendant strives to make the workplace work. The company is a leading distributor of supplies and equipment for offices and other workplaces. Its more than 190000 products include janitorial and breakroom supplies; digital cameras printers data storage and other technology products; and traditional office supplies as well as paper products automotive products and office furniture. Essendant distributes products from major suppliers such as Hewlett-Packard Rubbermaid and Clorox and offers items under its own brand names which include Boardwalk Innovera Universal and Windsoft. It serves some 29000 customers mostly independent resellers.The company generates most of its sales in the US.

Operations

More than half of Essendant's total revenue comes from two categories: Janitorial Foodservice and Breakroom Supplies (cleaners food and beverages disposable plates and cups) and Technology Products (computer hardware and accessories). Traditional Office Products (pens calendars shipping supplies) and Industrial Supplies (hand tools safety and security items janitorial equipment) bring in another 25%.

The company also offers Cut Sheet paper Products (copy paper) Automotive Products (automotive aftermarket tools) and Office Furniture (desks filing cabinets seating).

Geographic Reach

Essendant generates nearly all of its sales from customers in the US. It has very limited operations in Canada and the United Arab Emirates.

The company has some 70 distribution centers across the US and in Canada as well as offices in California Georgia Illinois New York and Oklahoma.

Sales and Marketing

Essendant operates some 70 regional distribution centers and a fleet of nearly 500 trucks to deliver its products directly to resellers.

The company's reseller customers include independent dealers (about 75% of total revenue) internet retailers (15%) and big-box retailers (10%). W.B. Mason one of the nation's largest independent dealers accounts for about 10% of sales.

Financial Performance

Although Essendant's revenue has trended higher over the past decade growth has been slow particularly in the past two fiscal years. In 2016 revenue was up less than half a percent to $5.4 billion as the company contends with an increasingly digitized workplace environment and competitive pressures. Most product categories were flat that year with double-digit jumps in cut sheet paper and automotive product sales offset by parallel declines in janitorial technology and office furniture sales.

Net income was a slightly more positive story for Essendant in 2016 hitting $64 million compared to a loss of $44 million the prior year when the company was hit with a $130 million impairment charge. The 2016 profit however is still significantly lower than the company's profit from 2007 to 2014 which averaged $110 million.

Strategy

Essendant is struggling to return to growth as the office products industry undergoes significant changes related to digitization and other advancements as well as consolidation. It is also contending with challenges in its national accounts channel as it lost a contract with the world's #2 office supply chain (Office Depot) and the #1 chain (Staples) has changed its procurement model. In an effort to improve its financial standing the company is focused on three key areas: reducing costs accelerating growth in targeted sales channels and improving the supplier network.

Essendant is looking to open consolidation centers that will reduce supply chain costs and streamline or optimize its distribution network. The company anticipates it will consolidate some distribution facilities with locations in California and Arizona being evaluated first. It is also shifting resources from declining channels (office products paper technology) to those better positioned for future growth including online retail and the industrial and automotive channels. Lastly Essendant has launched a Preferred Supplier Network so that it can focus its time and resources on growing those most important national supplier relationships.

HISTORY

Morris Wolf and Harry Hecktman former office supply salesmen and Israel Kriloff a grocer purchased Utility Supply Company (founded in 1906) and began selling office supplies in downtown Chicago in 1921. Weathering the Depression Utility Supply's business grew steadily during the 1930s. In 1935 the company published its first catalog and it opened its first retail store in downtown Chicago two years later. The partners bought out Kriloff in 1939.

WWII created a scarcity of raw materials and Utility Supply had difficulty in obtaining merchandise. The company tried selling non-office products unsuccessfully. Fortunately the war's end brought an end to the inventory drought. During the postwar era Utility Supply began mailing a series of catalogs to retailers nationwide. By 1948 mail-order business accounted for 40% of sales. A wholesale division to sell products to independent resellers was created in the 1950s.

In 1960 the company adopted the name United Stationers Supply and the retail stores became the Utility Stationery Stores. Business increased as independent retailers began to appreciate the advantages of ordering through a wholesaler instead of a manufacturer — purchasing goods on an asneeded basis. Howard Wolf the founder's son became CEO in 1967 and began emphasizing computers and automation to track inventory and costs.

Wholesale trade accounted for about two-thirds of sales by 1970. United Stationers introduced a series of abridged catalogs targeting specific groups and marketing segments such as furniture and electronics. The following year United Stationers developed regional redistribution centers that offered overnight delivery. The company sold its retail outlets in 1978.

Three years later United Stationers went public. During the 1980s the advent of warehouse clubs and office supply superstores threatened independent retailers. The company developed marketing concepts to help its independent resellers even as it aggressively targeted mail-order houses and superstores. The downsizing trend in the late 1980s caused the corporate market to shrink and United Stationers lowered prices; it instituted a decentralization plan in 1990.

The next year the company expanded into Canada opening its first non-US subsidiary and it acquired archrival Stationers Distributing and its distribution centers across the US in 1992. In 1994 it established its United Facility Supply unit to distribute maintenance supplies.

Investment firm Wingate Partners which controlled rival Associated Stationers bought United Stationers in 1995 and combined the operations of the two companies under the United Stationers name. United Stationers acquired janitorial supplies wholesaler Lagasse Bros. in 1996. In 1998

the company acquired the US and Mexican operations of Abitibi-Consolidated including Azerty. (It acquired Azerty Canada in 2000.)

United Stationers launched a venture with E-Commerce Industries in 1999 to help customers sell products over the Internet. The next year the company started The Order People a third-party call center fulfillment business aimed at online retailers; however the dot-com bust and higher losses than planned led United Stationers to curtail operations in 2001. Also that year it bought Peerless Paper Mills (merging the wholesale distributor of janitorial and paper products into Lagasse).

The company sold its Canadian operations in 2006 following an accounting scandal. United Stationers discovered that its Canadian operation was incorrectly accounting for supplier allowances and other receivables.

United Stationers acquired ORS Nasco a wholesale distributor of industrial supplies for about $180 million in 2007.

In 2008 it purchased Emco Distribution a New Jersey-based business product distributor for $15 million.

United Stationers promoted P. Cody Phipps its president and COO to the position of CEO in May 2011 when CEO Richard Gochnauer retired.

In late 2012 Essendant purchased Ohio-based privately-owned welding safety and industry products wholesaler O.K.I. Supply Co. which joined the its ORS Nasco business for $90 million.

EXECUTIVES

President CEO and Director, Richard D. (Ric) Phillips, age 46, $386,458 total compensation
SVP and CFO, Janet Zelenka, age 58, $351,042 total compensation
President Business and Facility Essentials, Harry A. Dochelli, age 57
Senior Vice President Operations, Cody Phipps
Vice President Sales, Mike Miller
Senior Vice President Human Resource, Carole Tomko
Vice President of Supply Chain Analytics, Henrik Danford-Klein
Vice President, Peter Dehio
Senior Vice President of Human Resources, Barbara Kennedy
Senior Vice President Strategy and Business Development, Elizabeth Meloy
Vice President Human Resources and Talent Management, Jerry Williams
Vice President of Marketing and Merchandising, Oi Eng Crandus
Vice President, Dave Haugh
Vice President Business Integration, Mark Dangremond
Senior Vice President Marketing and Chief Digital, Girisha Chandraraj
Vice President Pricing and Business Integration, Ken Sauers
Chairman, Charles K. Crovitz, age 63
Auditors: Ernst & Young LLP

LOCATIONS

HQ: Essendant Inc
One Parkway North Boulevard, Suite 100, Deerfield, IL 60015-2559
Phone: 847 627-7000   **Fax:** 847 627-7001
Web: www.unitedstationers.com

PRODUCTS/OPERATIONS

2016 Sales

	$ mil.	% of total
Janitorial & break room supplies	1,435	27
Technology products	1,347	25
Traditional office products	860	16
Industrial supplies	560	10
Cut sheet paper	394	7
Automotive	316	6
Office furniture	298	6
Freight and other	155	3
Total	**5,369**	**100**

Selected Products

Technology products
  Computer monitors
  Copiers and fax machines
  Data storage
  Digital cameras
  Printers and printer cartridges
Traditional office products
  Calendars
  Organizers
  Paper products
  Writing instruments
Office furniture
  Computer furniture
  Leather chairs
  Vertical and lateral file cabinets
  Wooden and steel desks
Janitorial and sanitation products
  Food service disposables
  Janitorial and sanitation supplies
  Paper and packaging supplies
  Safety and security items
Industrial supplies
  Hand and power tools
  Safety and security supplies
  Janitorial equipment and supplies
  Maintenance repair and operations items
  Oil field and welding supplies

COMPETITORS

D & H Distributing	SED International
Genuine Parts	Staples
Gould Paper	Supplies Network
Ingram Micro	W.W. Grainger
Newell Brands	WESCO International
Office Solutions	

HISTORICAL FINANCIALS

Company Type: Public

Income Statement

FYE: December 31

	REVENUE ($ mil.)	NET INCOME ($ mil.)	NET PROFIT MARGIN	EMPLOYEES
12/16	5,369	63	1.2%	6,600
12/15	5,363	(44)	—	6,400
12/14	5,327	119	2.2%	6,500
12/13	5,085	123	2.4%	6,100
12/12	5,080	111	2.2%	6,100
Annual Growth	**1.4%**	**(13.1%)**	**—**	**2.0%**

2016 Year-End Financials

Debt ratio: 28.15%
Return on equity: 8.46%
Cash ($ mil.): 21
Current ratio: 2.36
Long-term debt ($ mil.): 608
No. of shares (mil.): 37
Dividends
  Yield: 0.0%
  Payout: 32.3%
Market value ($ mil.): 783

	STOCK PRICE ($) FY Close	P/E High/Low		PER SHARE ($) Earnings	Dividends	Book Value
12/16	20.90	20	9	1.73	0.56	20.84
12/15	32.51	—	—	(1.18)	0.56	19.43
12/14	42.16	15	12	3.05	0.56	22.11
12/13	45.89	15	10	3.06	0.56	20.78
12/12	30.99	13	9	2.73	0.53	18.31
Annual Growth	**(9.4%)**	—	—	**(10.8%)**	**1.4%**	**3.3%**

ESSEX PORTFOLIO, L.P.

Auditors: KPMG LLP SAN FRANCISCO CALIF

LOCATIONS

HQ: ESSEX PORTFOLIO, L.P.
925 E MEADOW DR, PALO ALTO, CA 943034299
Phone: 650 494-3700

HISTORICAL FINANCIALS

Company Type: Private

Income Statement

FYE: December 31

	ASSETS ($ mil.)	NET INCOME ($ mil.)	INCOME AS % OF ASSETS	EMPLOYEES
12/16	12,217	438	3.6%	869
12/15	12,005	248	2.1%	—
12/14	11,562	134	1.2%	—
12/13	5,186	172	3.3%	—
Annual Growth	33.1%	36.6%	—	—

2016 Year-End Financials

Debt ratio: ——
Return on equity: 33.90%
Cash ($ mil.): 64
Current ratio: ——
Long-term debt ($ mil.): —

Dividends
Yield: —
Payout: —
Market value ($ mil.): —

Eversource Energy

Eversource Energy uses Yankee ingenuity power and gas to keep its customers happy. The largest energy delivery company in New England Eversource serves 3.6 million electric and gas customers via its six distinct utility companies in Connecticut Massachusetts and New Hampshire. Eversource delivers its energy over nearly 4000 miles of power transmission lines 40000 miles of electric distribution lines and more than 6500 miles of gas distribution lines. Its electricity-focused utility companies include Public Service Company of New Hampshire (PNSH) and Western Massachusetts Electric. Eversource?s gas utilities are NSTAR Gas and Yankee Gas the latter of which supplies natural gas to nearly 230000 customers in more than 70 cities and towns in Connecticut. Although PNSH generates its own power Eversource buys most of its electricity from third parties before distributing it to its customers.

HISTORY

In 1966 three old intertwined New England utilities merged. One was The Hartford Electric Light Company (HELCO) founded in 1883 by Austin Dunham in Hartford Connecticut. In 1915 the company signed the first power exchange agreement in the US with Connecticut Power (CP) which HELCO acquired in 1920.

The second founded in 1886 was Western Massachusetts Electric (WMECO) which merged with Western Counties in the 1930s to become WMECO. The third was Connecticut Light and Power (CL&P). Founded as Rocky River Power in 1905 it took the CL&P name in 1917. In 1929 it built the US's first large-scale pumped-storage hydroelectric plant.

In the 1950s HELCO formed Yankee Atomic Electric with CL&P WMECO and others to build an experimental nuclear reactor. In 1965 members of the group began jointly building the Connecticut Yankee nuke (on line in 1968). After years of cooperation CL&P HELCO and WMECO merged in 1966 and Northeast Utilities (NU) was born. It was the first multistate utility holding company created since the Public Utility Holding Company Act of 1935 had broken up the old utility giants. Holyoke Water Power joined NU the following year.

The 1970s energy crisis spurred NU to continue building nukes including Maine Yankee Vermont Yankee and two Millstone units. But by the 1980s construction delays had raised the cost of the final unit Millstone 3.

Regulators forced CL&P to spin off its gas utility Yankee Energy System in 1989. The next year NU acquired bankrupt utility Public Service Company of New Hampshire (PSNH) and its new Seabrook nuke. (PSNH emerged from bankruptcy in 1991.)

The 1995 shutdown of Millstone 1 began NU's nuclear troubles. In 1996 regulators closed all of its nukes except Seabrook because of safety concerns and NU mothballed Connecticut Yankee. The next year Michael Morris replaced CEO Bernard Fox who left after federal regulators ordered NU to comply with regulations and fix management problems — NU managers had routinely retaliated against whistleblowers — the first time a utility had been given such an order. New managers came in including a former whistleblower but NU couldn't avoid a record-setting $2.1 million fine. NU received permission to restart the Millstone units in 1998-99. But it had to absorb the $1 billion in power replacement associated with the shutdown.

Meanwhile as deregulation loomed NU created a retail marketer (now Select Energy) and a telecommunications arm (Mode 1 Communications) in 1996. Two years later retail competition began in Massachusetts and deregulation legislation was passed in Connecticut (deregulation went into effect there in 2000).

In 1999 NU sold its Massachusetts plants to New York's Consolidated Edison and auctioned off its non-nuclear plants in Connecticut to its subsidiary Northeast Generation and Northern States Power (now Xcel Energy). NU agreed to plead guilty to 25 federal felony counts and pay $10 million in penalties for polluting water near Millstone and lying to regulators.

That year Consolidated Edison agreed to buy NU for $3.3 billion in cash and stock and $3.9 billion in assumed debt. The deal broke down in 2001 however; Con Edison charged NU with misrepresenting information about power-supply contracts and NU charged Con Edison with improperly attempting to renegotiate the terms of the acquisition.

Bringing an old family member home NU bought Yankee Energy System for $679 million in 2000. Later that year Dominion Resources which had helped NU restart Millstone 2 and Millstone 3 (Millstone 1 had been taken out of service) agreed to buy the Millstone complex for $1.3 billion. The sale closed in 2001.

Also in 2001 NU subsidiary Select Energy bought Niagara Mohawk's energy marketing unit NU sold the distribution business of its Holyoke Water Power utility to the City of Holyoke for $18 million and retail electric competition began in New Hampshire. The company agreed to sell CL&P's 10% stake in the Vermont Yankee nuclear facility to Entergy in 2001; the deal was completed the following year.

NU sold its 40% interest in the Seabrook Nuclear Generating facility in 2002 to FPL Group.

In 2006 NU sold nonregulated subsidiary Select Energy which marketed and traded energy to wholesale and retail customers to Hess Corporation. That year the company also sold its competitive generation assets in Connecticut and Massachusetts to Energy Capital Partners for $1.34 billion.

In 2007 Connecticut Light and Power Company completed the installation of electric service to Yankee Gas Services Company's new liquefied natural gas facility in Waterbury.

To give better access and service to its customers in 2009 NU relocated its headquarters from Berlin Connecticut to a larger building in downtown Hartford.

The 2012 acquisition of NSTAR (with 1.1 million power and 300000 gas customers) for $4.2 billion boosted the financial resources of Eversource to pay for planned transmission projects aimed at bringing cleaner power from northern New England and Canada to population centers in southern New England. The "merger of equals" (NSTAR and Eversource) created a major energy player in the US Northeast which serves more than half the total utility customers in New England. NSTAR shareholders hold about 44% of the expanded company.

EXECUTIVES

EVP and COO, Werner J. Schweiger, age 57, $592,108 total compensation

EVP and General Counsel, Gregory B. Butler, age 59, $514,494 total compensation

President and CEO, James J. (Jim) Judge, age 61, $959,690 total compensation

EVP Enterprise Energy Strategy and Business Development Eversource Energy and Eversource Service, Leon J. (Lee) Olivier, age 69, $1,232,250 total compensation

EVP Customer and Corporate Relations Eversource Energy and Eversource Service, Joseph R. (Joe) Nolan, age 53, $419,364 total compensation

EVP Human Resources and Information Technology Eversource Energy and Eversource Service, Christine M. (Chris) Carmody, age 54

SVP and CFO, Philip J. (Phil) Lembo, age 61, $439,208 total compensation

Chairman, Thomas J. (Tom) May, age 70

Board Member, Dennis Harrington

Secretary, Richard Morrison

Auditors: Deloitte & Touche LLP

LOCATIONS

HQ: Eversource Energy
300 Cadwell Drive, Springfield, MA 01104
Phone: 800 286-5000
Web: www.eversource.com

PRODUCTS/OPERATIONS

2016 Sales

	$ mil.	% of total
Electric:		
Residential	3,448	45
Commercial	2,465	32
Wholesale	426	4
Industrial	328	6
Other	93	1
Natural Gas	854	12
Other	23	-
Total	**7,639**	**100**

2016 Sales

	$ mil.	% of total
Electric distribution	5,594	66
Electric transmission	1,210	10
Natural gas distribution	857	14
Other	870	10
Eliminations	(893.3)	-
Total	**7,639**	**100**

Selected Subsidiaries & Affiliates

The Connecticut Light and Power Company (CL&P eletric utility)
NSTAR Electric Company (electric utility)
NSTAR Gas Company (natural gas utility)
Public Service Company of New Hampsire (PSNH electric utility)
Western Massachusetts Electric Company (WMECO electric utility)
Yankee Gas Services Company (natural gas utility)

COMPETITORS

Avangrid
Con Edison
Green Mountain Power
National Grid
New Hampshire Electric
NiSource
Public Service Enterprise Group
Unitil

HISTORICAL FINANCIALS

Company Type: Public

Income Statement

FYE: December 31

	REVENUE ($ mil.)	NET INCOME ($ mil.)	NET PROFIT MARGIN	EMPLOYEES
12/16	7,639	942	12.3%	7,762
12/15	7,954	878	11.0%	7,943
12/14	7,741	819	10.6%	8,248
12/13	7,301	786	10.8%	8,697
12/12	6,273	525	8.4%	8,842
Annual Growth	5.0%	15.7%	—	(3.2%)

2016 Year-End Financials

Debt ratio: 33.54%
Return on equity: 8.92%
Cash ($ mil.): 30
Current ratio: 0.68
Long-term debt ($ mil.): 8,829

No. of shares (mil.): 316
Dividends
Yield: 0.0%
Payout: 60.1%
Market value ($ mil.): 17,502

	STOCK PRICE ($) FY Close	P/E High/Low	PER SHARE ($) Earnings	Dividends	Book Value
12/16	55.23	20 17	2.96	1.78	33.80
12/15	51.07	20 16	2.76	1.67	32.64
12/14	53.52	22 16	2.58	1.57	31.47
12/13	42.39	18 16	2.49	1.47	30.49
12/12	39.08	21 18	1.89	1.60	29.41
Annual Growth	9.0%	— —	11.9%	2.7%	3.5%

Exchange Bank (Santa Rosa, CA)

Exchange Bank serves personal and business customers from some 20 branch offices throughout Sonoma County California. It also has a branch in nearby Placer County. The bank provides standard products including checking and savings accounts Visa credit cards online banking and a variety of real estate business and consumer loans. It also offers investment services such as wealth management personal trust administration employee benefits plans and individual retirement accounts. Effective early 2014 Exchange Bank is on its eighth president since its inception in 1890. The Doyle Trust which was established by co-founder Frank Doyle owns a majority of the bank.

Operations

Exchange Bank's lending activity is concentrated in Sonoma County. Commercial real estate loans represent more than half of its loan portfolio.

Exchange Bank believes it will continue to benefit from growth in the local technology and biomedical industries and lower unemployment increased tourism and a decline in commercial real estate vacancies in Sonoma County.

Geographic Reach

Based in Santa Rosa California Exchange Bank operates primarily in Sonoma County but also in Placer and Contra counties.

Sales and Marketing

Exchange Bank counts some 25000 customers among its clients serving them through about 20 branch offices. It caters to customers online as well through its website which in fiscal 2013 earned 1.5 million customer visits.

Financial Performance

Revenue dropped 4% in fiscal 2013 to $85.9 million as compared to $89.1 million in 2012. Exchange Bank attributes the decrease to lower interest income resulting from a decline in interest received on term loans offset in part by increased interest on securities. From $12.26 million in 2012 the firm's net income grew some 28% to $15.73 million. Exchange Bank points to noteworthy drops in the provision for loan and lease losses and a decrease in interest and non-interest income for the net income gains.

EXECUTIVES

Vice President and Employee Benefit Trust Business Development Officer, David Rapoport
Vice President And General Manager, Kenneth Taylor
Assistant Vice President and Real Estate Loan Administrative Specialist, Donna J Smith
Vice President and Branch Operations Coordinator, Cheryl Mays
Senior Vice President and Chief Credit Officer, Anthony V Ghisla
Vice President Human Resources, Diana Angell
AVP and REGULATORY and CREDIT RISK OFFICER, Glenna Yaple
Vice President Business Develo, Scott Dykstra
Assistant Vice President and BANK Operations Analyst, Byron Webb
Senior Vice President and Chief Credit Risk Officer, Gary Hartwick
Assistant Vice President And Application Support Manager, Linda Wilson
Assistant Vice President and Trust Operations Manager, Elisabeth Pellegrini
Senior Vice President and Manager Retail Banking, Rolf Nelson
Assistant Vice President and Bank Operations Analyst, Jane Daniel
Vice President Business Develo, Michael Arendt
Assistant Vice President and Controller, Shauna Lorenzen
Vice President, Lori Decosta
Vice President and Personal Trust Fiduciary Manager, Emily Menjou
Vice President and General Manager, Ken Taylor
Vice President Business Banking Credit Manager, Justin Hubbs
Senior Vice President, Tony Ghisla
Senior Vice President and Regional Manager Rosevil, Andrew Ware
Vice President and Real Estate Loan Officer, Jeffrey Owen
Assistant Vice President Regional Customer Service Manager, Cassandra Zorn
Assistant Vice President and Trust Officer, Denise Palmer
Vice President, Edie Cheda
Senior Vice President, Steve Herron
Vice President, Jason Hinde
Senior Vice President Real Estate Loan, Louise Mason
Vice President Sales, John Meislahn

Vice President and Product Manager, Carrie Brown
Senior Vice President And Chief Credit O, Ed Gomez
Vice President, Joseph Huang
Assistant Vice President Cash Management Sales, Kenn Cunningham
Vice President, Jennifer Robb
Vice President And Personal Trust Administration Officer, Linda Burille
Vice President, James Ruppert
Senior Vice President and Chief Investment Officer, Gregory S Jahn
Executive Vice President and Chief Credit Officer, Mark Crawford
Vice President, Cody Radelfinger
Vice President and Employee Benefit Trust Officer, Susan Preston
Assistant Vice President and Deposit Compliance and Operations Risk Officer, Cyndi Perez
Vice President Operations, Beth Pellegrini
Executive Vice President and Chief Operating Officer, William R Schrader
Vice President and Trust Operations and Compliance Manager, SungWon Kang
Senior Vice President, John Mackey
Vice President Investment Officer, Bill Sullivan

LOCATIONS

HQ: Exchange Bank (Santa Rosa, CA)
545 Fourth Street, Santa Rosa, CA 95401
Phone: 707 524-3301
Web: www.exchangebank.com

COMPETITORS

Bank of America
First Northern
JPMorgan Chase
MUFG Americas Holdings
U.S. Bancorp
Wells Fargo
Westamerica

HISTORICAL FINANCIALS

Company Type: Public

Income Statement

FYE: December 31

	ASSETS ($ mil.)	NET INCOME ($ mil.)	INCOME AS % OF ASSETS	EMPLOYEES
12/16	2,179	21	1.0%	—
12/15	2,062	21	1.0%	—
12/14	1,887	17	0.9%	—
12/13	1,783	15	0.9%	—
12/12	1,698	12	0.7%	—
Annual Growth	6.4%	15.1%	—	—

2016 Year-End Financials

Debt ratio: 0.37%
Return on equity: 11.84%
Cash ($ mil.): 144
Current ratio: —
Long-term debt ($ mil.): —

No. of shares (mil.): 1
Dividends
Yield: 0.0%
Payout: 22.3%
Market value ($ mil.): 214

	STOCK PRICE ($) FY Close	P/E High/Low	PER SHARE ($) Earnings	Dividends	Book Value
12/16	125.00	11 6	12.54	2.80	110.35
12/15	89.00	7 6	12.27	2.20	100.98
12/14	84.00	8 7	10.25	1.55	93.37
12/13	69.00	8 6	8.60	1.10	90.42
12/12	53.75	11 8	5.93	0.50	91.24
Annual Growth	23.5%	— —	20.6%	53.8%	4.9%

Exelon Corp

Exelon is lighting up the utility industry with high-powered energy generation and extensive electricity delivery. The utility holding company does enough of both to be designated one of the largest in the US. Its Exelon Generation subsidiary holds power-generating assets of almost 33000 MW (some 19500 MW is produced at 23 nuclear plants). Exelon distributes electricity and gas to 10 million customers in Illinois Maryland the District of Columbia Delaware New Jersey and Pennsylvania through its regulated utility companies. Its Constellation subsidiary provides energy products and services to 2 million business customers. In a major expansion Exelon acquired three regulated utilities for $7.1 billion in 2016

HISTORY

Thomas Dolan and local investors formed the Brush Electric Light Company of Philadelphia in 1881 to provide street and commercial lighting. Competitors sprang up and in 1885 Brush merged with the United States Electric Lighting Company of Pennsylvania to form a secret "electric trust" or holding company. Dolan became president in 1886 and bought four other utilities.

In 1895 Martin Maloney formed Pennsylvania Heat Light and Power to consolidate the city's electric companies. By the next year it had acquired among other businesses Columbia Electric Light Philadelphia Edison and the electric trust. In 1899 a new firm National Electric challenged Maloney by acquiring neighboring rival Southern Electric Light. Before retiring Maloney negotiated the merger of the two firms forming Philadelphia Electric in 1902.

Demand rose rapidly into the 1920s fueled in part by the company's promotion of electric appliances. In 1928 the year after it completed the Conowingo Hydroelectric Station Philadelphia Electric was absorbed by the much larger United Gas Improvement. United Gas avoided large layoffs during the Depression but passage of the Public Utility Holding Company Act (PUHCA) in 1935 sounded its death knell. (PUHCA was repealed in 2005.) In 1943 the SEC forced United Gas to divest Philadelphia Electric.

Philadelphia Electric built several plants in the 1950s and 1960s in response to a postwar electricity boom. A small experimental nuclear reactor was completed at Peach Bottom Pennsylvania in 1967 and in 1974 the company placed two nuclear units in service at the plant. The Salem (New Jersey) nuke (Unit 1) followed in 1977. The company relied on these plants during the OPEC oil crisis. Another one Limerick Unit 1 began operations in 1986 and Unit 2 went on line in 1990 but the Peach Bottom plant was shut down from 1989 to 1991 because of management problems (later resolved).

The company began reorganizing in 1993 and changed its name the next year to PECO Energy Company. It also sold Maryland retail subsidiary Conowingo Power retaining the hydroelectric plant. In 1995 rival PP&L rejected PECO's acquisition bid citing PECO's nuclear liabilities.

A year later PECO teamed with AT&T Wireless to offer PCS in Philadelphia (service was launched in 1997). EnergyOne a national venture formed in 1997 by PECO UtiliCorp United (now Aquila) and AT&T offered consumers a package of power phone and Internet services on one bill. However the slow deregulation process caused the venture to fail.

PECO also joined with British Energy in 1997 to form AmerGen hoping to buy nukes at rock-bottom prices from utilities eager to unload them. AmerGen purchased three nuclear facilities in 1999 and 2000: Unit 1 of the Three Mile Island (Pennsylvania) facility; a plant in Clinton Illinois; and an Oyster Creek (New Jersey) location.

In 1999 PECO announced plans to acquire Chicago's Unicom the parent company of Commonwealth Edison (ComEd). After the deal was completed in 2000 the combined company took the name Exelon and established its headquarters in Chicago.

Pennsylvania's utility markets were fully deregulated in 2000. To expand its power generation business Exelon that year bought 49.9% of Sithe Energies for $682 million. In 2001 Exelon agreed to buy two gas-fired power plants (2300 MW) in Texas from TXU for $443 million; the deal was completed in 2002.

Also in 2002 Exelon purchased Sithe Energies' stakes in six New England power plants with 2000 MW of capacity (plus 2400 MW under construction) for $543 million plus the assumption of $1.15 billion in debt. The company also sold its Philadelphia PCS venture interest to former partner AT&T Wireless Services (now part of AT&T Mobility). Sithe Energies was sold to Dynegy in 2005 for $135 million.

To focus on core utility operations the company sold its infrastructure construction business InfraSource and its facility and infrastructure management business Exelon Solutions. Exelon then completed the sale of its interest in telecommunications joint venture PECO TelCove which provides voice and data services to its partner TelCove and sold its district heating and cooling division (Thermal Chicago).

In 2008 in a move to expand its geographic reach Exelon made a $6.2 billion bid to buy NRG Energy. Though the offer to buy NRG met with resistance Exelon had kept up its pursuit of the company. Toward the end of 2008 it announced an exchange offer for NRG's shares. By the expiration date of the offer early the next year it had acquired just more than 50% of those shares. In addition to announcing another extension of the offer Exelon said it hoped NRG's Board would allow it to do due diligence and begin negotiations for an acquisition. But an NRG proxy vote rejection in 2009 led Exelon to terminate its offer.

In 2010 in a bid to grow its renewable energy segment and lower its carbon emissions the company acquired wind power developer John Deere Renewables for about $860 million. The deal added 735 MW of operating wind power capacity (and 230 MW under development) to Exelon's generation assets.

To meet stricter environmental regulations the company has been bulking up its non-fossil fuel generating assets. Growing its cleaner-burning plant fleet in Texas in 2011 the company bought Wolf Hollow a 720 MW combined-cycle natural gas-fired power plant in north Texas from Sequent Wolf Hollow for $305 million.

Expanding its green energy assets that year the company also acquired Antelope Valley Solar Ranch One from First Solar. The 230-MW solar power project is under development in northern Los Angeles County. The $1.4 billion investment complements Constellation Energy's solar power holdings and marks Exelon's first move into the California merchant power market.

In 2012 the company bought Constellation Energy in a $7.9 billion stock deal. The acquisition part of an industry-wide consolidation trend gives Exelon access to Constellation's major retail operations in Maryland enabling it to grow its retail profile.

The US Department of Justice required Exelon and Constellation to divest three electricity generating plants in Maryland to proceed with the merger. It contended that combining the companies' assets would potentially enable the merged firm to raise wholesale electricity prices and reduce output.

As part of the integration of Constellation Energy's assets in 2013 Exelon announced that three commercial nuclear power plants operated by the Constellation Energy Nuclear Group in New York and Maryland will be integrated into the Exelon Generation nuclear fleet.

EXECUTIVES

President and CEO, Christopher M. (Chris) Crane, age 58, $1,255,515 total compensation

SVP and Chief Information and Digital Officer, Mike Koehler, age 50

President Exelon Power, Ronald J. (Ron) DeGregorio, age 54

EVP; COO Excelon Generation, Michael J. Pacilio, age 56

SEVP and CFO, Jonathan W. (Jack) Thayer, age 45, $784,802 total compensation

EVP Customer Operations Regulatory and External Affairs ComEd, Anne R. Pramaggiore, age 58

SEVP and Chief Commercial Officer and President and CEO Exelon Generation, Kenneth W. (Ken) Cornew, age 51, $857,477 total compensation

EVP and CEO Constellation, Joseph (Joe) Nigro, age 52

SEVP and Chief Strategy Officer, William A. (Bill) Von Hoene, age 63, $831,350 total compensation

President and CEO Pepco Holdings, David M. (Dave) Velazquez, age 58

President and Chief Nuclear Officer Exelon Nuclear, Bryan C. Hanson, age 51

EVP; President and CEO PECO, Craig L. Adams, age 64

CEO Baltimore Gas and Electric, Calvin G. Butler, age 47

EVP and Chief Enterprise Risk Officer, Paymon Aliabadi, age 54

EVP Governmental and Regulatory Affairs and Public Policy, Joseph Dominguez, age 53

SEVP and CEO Exelon Utilities, Denis P. OÂ'Brien, age 56, $800,378 total compensation

EVP Corporate Operations, M. Bridget Reidy

Senior Vice President Operations Support, Christopher Mudrick

Vice President, Chris Symonds

Vice President Federal Regulatory Affairs and Policy, Kathleen Barron

Vice President Investor Relations, Stacie Frank

Vice President and General Counsel, Paul R Bonney

Vice President Engineering and Project Management, Michelle Blaise

Vice President Regulatory Policy and S, Michael Guerra

Vice President, Teresa Dismukes

Vice President, William Scott

Vice President and Chief Integration Officer, David Villa

Chairman, Mayo A. Shattuck, age 62

Auditors: PricewaterhouseCoopers LLP

LOCATIONS

HQ: Exelon Corp
10 South Dearborn Street, P.O. Box 805379, Chicago, IL 60680-5379
Phone: 800 483-3220
Web: www.exeloncorp.com

PRODUCTS/OPERATIONS

2016 Sales

	$ mil.	% of total
Generation	17,751	54
ComEd	5,254	16
PECO	2,994	9
BGE	3,233	10
PHI	3,643	11
Other	(1515)	-
Total	**31,360**	**100**

2016 Sales

	$ mil.	% of total
Competitive businesses revenues	16,324	52
Rate-regulated utility revenues	15,036	48
Total	**31,360**	**100**

Selected Operating Units Subsidiaries and Affiliates

Exelon Energy Delivery
Baltimore Gas and Electric (BGE electric and gas utility)
Commonwealth Edison Company (ComEd electric utility)
PECO Energy Company (PECO electric and gas utility)
Pepco Holdings LLC (PHI)
Potomac Electric Power Company (Pepco electric utility)
Delmarva Power & Light Company (DPL electric and gas utility)
Atlantic City Electric Company (ACE electric utility)
Exelon Generation Company LLC
  Constellation
  Exelon Power
  Exelon Hydro
  Exelon Solar
  Exelon Wind
  Exelon Power Team
  Exelon Energy (nonregulated retail power sales)
  Exelon Nuclear (nuclear power generation)
Exelon Transmission Company

COMPETITORS

AES	FirstEnergy
Alliant Energy	Green Mountain Energy
Ambit Energy	Jersey Central Power &
Ameren	Light
American Transmission	NextEra Energy
Dominion Energy	PPL Corporation
Duke Energy	Public Service
Duquesne Light	Electric and Gas
Holdings	UGI
Dynegy	

HISTORICAL FINANCIALS

Company Type: Public

Income Statement

FYE: December 31

	REVENUE ($ mil.)	NET INCOME ($ mil.)	NET PROFIT MARGIN	EMPLOYEES
12/17	33,531	3,770	11.2%	34,621
12/16	31,360	1,134	3.6%	34,396
12/15	29,447	2,269	7.7%	29,762
12/14	27,429	1,623	5.9%	28,993
12/13	24,888	1,719	6.9%	25,829
Annual Growth	**7.7%**	**21.7%**	**—**	**7.6%**

2017 Year-End Financials

Debt ratio: 30.49%
Return on equity: 13.54%
Cash ($ mil.): 898
Current ratio: 1.10
Long-term debt ($ mil.): 32,565
No. of shares (mil.): 963
Dividends
  Yield: 0.0%
  Payout: 33.0%
Market value ($ mil.): 37,965

	STOCK PRICE ($) FY Close	P/E High/Low		PER SHARE ($) Earnings	Dividends	Book Value
12/17	39.41	11	8	3.97	1.31	30.99
12/16	35.49	30	22	1.22	1.26	27.96
12/15	27.77	15	10	2.54	1.24	28.25
12/14	37.08	20	14	1.88	1.24	26.52
12/13	27.39	19	13	2.00	1.46	26.74
Annual Growth	**9.5%**	**—**	**—**	**18.7%**	**(2.6%)**	**3.8%**

Exelon Generation Co LLC

Exelon Generation Company has built an excellent reputation by generating electricity. The company a subsidiary of Exelon Corporation is one of the largest electric wholesale and retail power generation companies in the US. In 2013 Exelon Generation had a generation capacity of more than 44560 MW (primarily nuclear but also fossil-fired and hydroelectric and other renewable energy-based plants). Subsidiary Exelon Nuclear operates the largest fleet of nuclear power plants in the US. Exelon Generation's Exelon Power unit oversees a fleet of more than 100 fossil- and renewable-fueled plants (more than 15875 MW of capacity) in Illinois Maryland Massachusetts Pennsylvania and Texas.

Operations

The company operates as an integrated business leveraging its owned and contracted electric generation capacity to market and sell power to wholesale and retail customers. It has ownership interests in eleven nuclear generating stations currently in service consisting of 19 units with an aggregate of 17263 MW of capacity. It also owns a 50% interest in CENG a joint venture with EDF. CENG is governed by a board of ten directors five of which are appointed by Generation and five by EDF.

Geographic Reach

The Mid-Atlantic represents operations in the eastern half of PJM and accounted for 37% of Exelon Generation's generating capacity in 2013; Midwest (western half of PJM the entire US footprint of MISO 34%); New England (the operations within the ISO-NE 8%); New York (ISO-NY 3%); ERCOT (Texas) 12%; and Other areas 6%).

The Mid-Atlantic region includes Pennsylvania New Jersey Maryland Virginia West Virginia Delaware the District of Columbia and parts of North Carolina. Midwest includes portions of Illinois Indiana Ohio Michigan Kentucky and Tennessee; and the United States footprint of MISO excluding MISO's Southern Region which covers all or most of North Dakota South Dakota Nebraska Minnesota Iowa Wisconsin and the remaining parts of Illinois Indiana Michigan and Ohio not covered by PJM; and parts of Montana Missouri and Kentucky.New England represents the operations within ISO-NE covering the states of Connecticut Maine Massachusetts New Hampshire Rhode Island and Vermont. New York represents the operations within ISO-NY which covers the state of New York in its entirety. ERCOT represents operations within Electric Reliability Council of Texas covering most of the state of Texas. "Other Regions" is an aggregate of other geographic regions not considered individually significant.

Sales and Marketing

Exelon Generation's customers include distribution utilities municipalities cooperatives financial institutions and commercial industrial governmental and residential customers in competitive markets. The company also sells natural gas and renewable energy and other energy-related products and services and engages in natural gas exploration and production activities.

Financial Performance

The company's revenues increased by 8% in 2013 primarily due to increased capacity prices and higher nuclear volume partially offset by lower realized energy prices higher nuclear fuel costs and lower mark-to-market gains.

Net income increased by 90% in 2013 primarily due to higher revenues net of purchased power and fuel expense lower operating and maintenance expense and higher earnings from Exelon Generation's interest in CENG; partially offset by impairment of certain generating assets and higher depreciation costs property taxes and interest expenses.

Strategy

Exelon Generation leverages owned and contracted electric generation capacity to market and sell power wholesale. The company's integrated business operations include the physical delivery and marketing of power obtained through its generation capacity and through long-term intermediate-term and short-term contracts. Exelon Generation maintains an effective supply strategy through ownership of generation assets and power purchase and lease agreements. The company has also contracted for access to additional generation through bilateral long-term power agreements.

Exelon Generation's electricity generation strategy is to pursue opportunities that provide generation to load matching and that diversify the generation fleet by expanding Generation's regional and technological footprint. The company leverages its energy generation portfolio to ensure delivery of energy to both wholesale and retail customers under long-term and short-term contracts and in wholesale power markets.

In 2012 a subsidiary of Exelon Generation sold three coal-fired plants (Brandon Shores and H.A. Wagner generating station in Anne Arundel County Maryland and the C.P. Crane plant in Baltimore County Maryland) to Raven Power Holdings LLC a subsidiary of Riverstone Holdings LLC to comply with certain of the regulatory approvals required by the company's merger with Constellation Energy for net proceeds of $371 million which resulted in a pre-tax loss of $272 million.

Exelon Nuclear operates the largest nuclear fleet in the US (10 stations with 17 nuclear units) and has about 20% of the industry's total capacity. Exelon Generation has submitted an application to the Nuclear Regulatory Commission to build a new nuclear generating facility in Texas. The company hasn't made the decision to build the facility but wanted to get a start on the potentially onerous process. The last license to result in the construction of a new nuclear facility in the US was granted in 1973. However the Fukushima nuclear plant disaster in early 2011 placed nuclear power expansion plans under serious scrutiny from regulators.

Mergers and Acquisitions

In a major move to grow its retail operations in 2012 parent Exelon Corporation bought Constellation Energy in a $7.9 billion stock deal. The purchase of Constellation Energy (which gets 17% of its power from nuclear plants) helped the company boost its nuclear-generated power plant assets.

Company Background

Growing its cleaner-burning plant fleet in Texas in 2011 Exelon Corporation bought the 720 MW capacity Wolf Hollow plant in north Texas from Sequent Wolf Hollow for $305 million.

In 2010 to grow its renewable energy unit the company acquired wind power developer John Deere Renewables for about $860 million. The purchase adds 735 MW of operating wind power capacity to its generation capacity.

EXECUTIVES

Svp And President And Chief Nuclear Officer Exelon Nuclear, Bryan C Hanson, age 52
Auditors: PricewaterhouseCoopers LLP

LOCATIONS

HQ: Exelon Generation Co LLC
300 Exelon Way, Kennett Square, PA 19348-2473
Phone: 610 765-5959
Web: www.exeloncorp.com

PRODUCTS/OPERATIONS

2013 Sales

	% of total
Mid-Atlantic	33
Midwest	27
New England	8
ERCOT	8
Other Regions	6
New York	5
Others	13
Total	**100**

COMPETITORS

AES	Duke Energy
AMP	NextEra Energy
Buckeye Power	Wolverine Power Supply
CMS Energy	

HISTORICAL FINANCIALS

Company Type: Public

Income Statement

FYE: December 31

	REVENUE ($ mil.)	NET INCOME ($ mil.)	NET PROFIT MARGIN	EMPLOYEES
12/16	17,751	496	2.8%	14,717
12/15	19,135	1,372	7.2%	14,512
12/14	17,393	835	4.8%	14,370
12/13	15,630	1,070	6.8%	11,973
12/12	14,437	562	3.9%	12,116
Annual Growth	**5.3%**	**(3.1%)**	**—**	**5.0%**

2016 Year-End Financials

Debt ratio: 22.19%—
Return on equity: 4.28%
Cash ($ mil.): 290
Current ratio: 1.15
Long-term debt ($ mil.): 8,124

Dividends
Yield: —
Payout: —
Market value ($ mil.): —

Expedia Inc

Expediting your expedition often begins by accessing a travel web site. Expedia a market leader in online travel services (with rival Priceline Group) is often the go-to online trip-planner. It offers tools that allow users to book airline tickets hotel reservations car rentals cruises and vacation packages. Expedia's portfolio of brands could fill a boutique hotel. They include flagship Expedia.com online travel bookers Travelocity and Orbitz accommodations manager Hotels.com vacation rental site HomeAway travel discounter Hotwire hotel metasearcher trivago luxury package provider Classic Vacations and several sites focused on international destinations. More than 435000 hotels and alternative accommodations properties can be booked through Expedia.

Operations

Expedia books 80% of its revenue from its online travel agency (OTA) websites including Hotwire and Hotels.com. HomeAway the supplier of rental-by-owner properties accounts for less than 10% of revenue with Expedia's corporate travel booking unit Egencia generating about 5% of revenue. Trivago which supplies about 5% of revenue was spun out with an IPO in 2016; Expedia owns about 65% of trivago.

Geographic Reach

Based in Bellevue Washington Expedia has offices throughout the Americas Europe and Asia/Pacific regions and operates in about 200 countries. The company operates call centers around the world including outsourced centers in the Philippines El Salvador Egypt and India.

The US accounts for about 55% of revenue.

Financial Performance

Expedia has traveled a long way in the past decade with revenue rising from $2.6 billion in 2007 to $8.7 billion in 2016 which was 31% higher than 2015. The company?s profit has had a more up-and-down journey and arrived at about $282 million in 2016 a 63% drop from the previous year.

The 2016 revenue increase was driven by a strong contribution from acquisitions and growth in the Core OTA segment up 21% and trivago up 62%. The HomeAway acquisition completed in 2015 added about $690 million in its first full year as part of Expedia.

Expedia?s costs rose in 2016 from 2015 reducing profit for the year. The company spent a significant amount of money on technology in 2016 to support technology projects throughout the company including expansion into cloud computing environment and higher licensing and maintenance for its expanding technology platforms.

Cash flow from operations was $1.5 billion up from about $1.4 billion in 2015. The increase was due to higher operating income after adjusting for depreciation and amortization offset some by a decrease in benefits from working capital adjustments and a net refund of hotel occupancy and other taxes in 2015.

Strategy

International customers accounted for 42% of 2016 revenue up significantly from 30% in 2008. Building its image globally and expanding its brand portfolio have been key in its efforts to reach a wide slice of consumers (including budget-conscious luxury and business travelers). Expedia has international with the acquisition of several online travel sites around the world.

While it is the biggest online travel company Expedia still faces a lot of competition. Its main online rival is Priceline.com ($10.7 billion in 2016 revenue) which offers bookings and travel services through Priceline.com Booking.com Kayak Rentalcars.com and OpenTable (restaurant reservations) and other sites. Priceline is stronger than Expedia overseas with more than 80% of its revenue coming from customers outside the US. Expedia offers a range of booking options that help it compete throughout the hospitality industry. Through acquisitions it has assembled Hotels.com Travelocity and HomeAway. It offers booking services in the US and overseas.

The 2015 acquisition of HomeAway Expedia has an entity to compete against Airbnb which offers short-term rentals in what Expedia calls 'alternative accommodations.' The properties are more commonly known as homes and apartments. Under Expedia HomeAway has become a site where travelers can book rooms immediately rather than a site where owners can list properties and get a referral from the company. Expedia is also integrating HomeAway?s properties into main online booking brands. HomeAway has some 1.2 million vacation rentals on its sites.

Mergers and Acquisitions

Expedia isn't shy about acquiring parts of the travel planning experience that it doesn't already have. That has brought some well-recognized travel sites under its corporate umbrella.

In 2017 Expedia bought a majority stake in SilverRail a provider of technology for rail travel. The companies have worked together since 2010. SilverRail expands the number of travel products through Expedia adding rail travel to online options.

The company in 2015 paid $3.6 billion for HomeAway Inc. which has provided listings for owners of vacation rentals. Expedia has moved to shift HomeAway from a classified marketplace to an online transactional model. The shift according to Expedia would provide better experiences for HomeAway's travelers and the property owners and managers.

In another 2015 deal the company completed the purchase of Orbitz Worldwide and all of its brands that include Orbitz ebookers HotelClub and CheapTickets. The $1.8 billion deal enhanced the marketing and distribution capabilities that Expedia offers its suppliers.

Expedia in 2015 acquired key competitor Travelocity from its parent Sabre Corporation for $280 million in cash. The acquisition cemented a relationship Expedia and Travelocity had since 2013 in which Expedia provided technology platforms for Travelocity's US and Canadian websites and access to its supply and customer service program.

Company Background

Originally a division of Microsoft Expedia was sold to IAC/InterActiveCorp which acquired the computer maker's majority stake in 2002 and the minority interest it did not already own in 2003. Two years later IAC spun off Expedia into a separate publicly traded firm.

EXECUTIVES

President eCommerce Platform, J. Tucker Moodey
President Hotwire Group, Henrik V. Kjellberg, age 47
President Hotels.com and EAN, Johan Svanstrom, age 46
President Expedia Lodging Partner Services, Cyril Ranque
President Egencia, Rob Greyber
President CEO and Director, Mark D. Okerstrom, $750,000 total compensation
EVP General Counsel and Secretary, Robert Dzielak, $575,000 total compensation
President Brand Expedia Group, Aman Bhutani, age 41
Chief People Officer, Nikki Krishnamurthy
President HomeAway, John Kim
SVP and General Manager Expedia Affiliate Network, Ariane Gorin
Vice President Of Employee Engagement, Kristin Graham
Senior Vice President Marketing Packages And Canada, Sean C Shannon
Vice President And Associate Corporate Counsel, Angela Niemann
Vice President, Lisa Youel
Vice President and Associate General Counsel, Mark Rowland
Director of Pharmacy, Mark Moseley
Vice President Associate General Counsel, Ronen Elad
Vice President Transport Americas, Julie Kyse
Global Senior Vice President, Hari Nair
Senior Vice President Sales, Bruce Freeman

Vice President of Finance, Bank Rec
Vice President of Corporate Development, Patrick Thompson
Vice President Market Management, Mario Ribera
Vice President Global Marketing, Daniel Hest
Associate Vice President Lifecycle Manager, Nicole Jubie
Vice Chairman, Victor A. Kaufman, age 73
Chairman, Barry Diller, age 75
Auditors: Ernst & Young LLP

LOCATIONS

HQ: Expedia Inc
  333 108th Avenue N.E., Bellevue, WA 98004
Phone: 425 679-7200
Web: www.expediainc.com

2016 Sales

	$ mil.	% of total
United States	5,036	57
All other countries	3,737	43
Total	**8,773**	**100**

PRODUCTS/OPERATIONS

2016 Sales

	$ mil.	% of total
Core OTA	7,083	78
trivago	835	9
HomeAway	689	8
Egencia	462	5
Corporate & Eliminations	(297.3)	-
Total	**8,773**	**100**

2016 Sales

	% of total
Merchant	55
Agency	28
Advertising and media	9
HomeAway	8
Total	**100**

BRANDS

BRANDS
CarRentals.com
Classic Vacations
Egencia
Expedia
Expedia Affiliate Network (EAN)
Expedia CruiseShipCenters
Expedia Local Expert
Expedia Media Solutions
HomeAway
Hotels.com
Hotwire
Orbitz
SilverRail
Traveldoo
Travelocity
trivago
Wotif Group

SELECTED SUBSIDIARIES

Classic Vacations LLC
Cruise LLC
EAN.com LP
Egencia France SAS
Egencia LLC
EXP Holdings Luxembourg S.A.
Expedia Asia Holdings Mauritius
Expedia do Brasil Agencia de Viagens e Turismo Ltda.

COMPETITORS

American Express	Priceline
BCD Travel	Sabre
Carlson Wagonlit	Travelport
Concur Technologies	TripAdvisor
GetThere	Uniglobe Travel
Google	WorldRes
Pegasus Solutions	ebookers.com
Prestige Travel	last minute network

HISTORICAL FINANCIALS

Company Type: Public

Income Statement

FYE: December 31

	REVENUE ($ mil.)	NET INCOME ($ mil.)	NET PROFIT MARGIN	EMPLOYEES
12/17	10,059	377	3.8%	22,615
12/16	8,773	281	3.2%	20,075
12/15	6,672	764	11.5%	18,730
12/14	5,763	398	6.9%	18,210
12/13	4,771	232	4.9%	14,570
Annual Growth	**20.5%**	**12.9%**	**—**	**11.6%**

2017 Year-End Financials

Debt ratio: 22.95%
Return on equity: 8.73%
Cash ($ mil.): 2,846
Current ratio: 0.70
Long-term debt ($ mil.): 3,749

No. of shares (mil.): 151
Dividends
  Yield: 0.0%
  Payout: 47.9%
Market value ($ mil.): 18,174

	STOCK PRICE ($) FY Close	P/E High/Low		PER SHARE ($) Earnings	Dividends	Book Value
12/17	119.77	64	45	2.42	1.16	29.80
12/16	113.28	70	49	1.82	1.00	27.54
12/15	124.30	23	13	5.70	0.84	32.37
12/14	85.36	30	20	2.99	0.66	14.04
12/13	69.66	40	26	1.67	1.08	16.54
Annual Growth	**14.5%**	**—**	**—**	**9.7%**	**1.8%**	**15.9%**

Expeditors International of Washington, Inc.

As a freight forwarder Expeditors International of Washington purchases air and ocean cargo space on a volume basis and resells that space to its customers at lower rates than they could obtain directly from the carriers. The company also acts as a customs broker for air and ocean freight shipped by its customers and offers supply chain management services. Customers include global businesses engaged in retailing/wholesaling electronics and manufacturing. Founder Peter Rose used $55000 in seed money to establish Expeditors International of Washington in 1979.

Operations

Expeditors' airfreight services segment around 40% of revenue represents airlines as an agent in addition to providing freight consolidation for shippers. The consolidation of airfreight owned by several shippers is a valuable service because increasing the weight of an air shipment decreases its cost per pound/kilo or cubic inch/centimeter. Besides shipping on scheduled flights the company sometimes charters aircraft for the delivery of backlogs. By not purchasing its own aircraft the company avoids the costs of large capital expenditures and operating costs.

Ocean freight and ocean services roughly 30% of revenue operates as a non-vessel operating common carrier which is a contractor with ocean shipping lines for a set amount of containers. Expeditors also obtains less-than container load freight to fill containers. The segment additionally provides such order management services as document management and SKU visibility. Similar to the strategy of the airfreight services segment the ocean freight segment does not own its own vessels.

Customs brokerage and other services almost 30% of revenue aids in the movement of shipments across borders by providing such services as adding up duties and taxes and arranging inspections. Beyond the border entry the segment provides additional services including warehousing product distribution and time-definite transportation. Expeditors provides these services not only for its own shipping customers but also for businesses that have not hired the company as a forwarder a class of client that accounts for a significant portion of the segment's revenue.

Geographic Reach

Expeditors operates from more than 330 facilities in about 60 countries. Regional international headquarters reside in Beirut London Sao Paulo and Shanghai.Asia is its largest market generating 45% of revenue.

Sales and Marketing

Expeditors caters to its customers' supply chains. Therefore its marketing efforts target people in their company's logistics international and domestic transportation customs compliance and purchasing departments. It employes district managers who are responsible for marketing sales coordination and implementation in the area in which he or she is located. The company primarily targets the aviation and aerospace health care oil and energy and retail sectors.

Financial Performance

After posting record-setting revenues of $6.6 billion in 2015 Expeditors saw its revenues decline 8% to $6.1 billion in 2016. This was attributed to declines from its airfreight services (10%) and ocean freight and ocean services (13%) segments. These decreases were attributed to lowering average sell rates in response to competitive market conditions.

Its profits also declined 6% from $457 million in 2015 to $431 million in 2016 primarily due to a bump in overhead expenses. After experiencing a sharp increase in operating cash flow for 2015 Expeditors saw its operating cash flow decline by 6% in 2016 due to the lower profits and unfavorable changes in working capital.

Strategy

In its rapid development Expeditors has favored internal growth over expansion by acquisition (though it has also selectively made some strategic acquisitions) and the company continues to open new offices and to invest in its information technology infrastructure. By eschewing acquisitions as its main form of growth the company has been able to develop a common hardware platform that lets the entire company use the same accounting and transportation software.

Going forward in 2017 and beyond the company is focused on diversifying its product mix through focused investments in its distribution services transcon and ocean export products. It also aims to diversify its market verticals by investing further in the pharmaceutical and automotive markets.

EXECUTIVES

EVP Europe, Timothy C. Barber, age 57, $100,000 total compensation
President Global Services, Eugene K. Alger, age 56, $100,000 total compensation
SVP and CFO, Bradley S. (Brad) Powell, age 57, $100,000 total compensation
President Global Products, Daniel R. Wall, age 48, $100,000 total compensation
President and CEO, Jeffrey S. Musser, age 51, $100,000 total compensation

President Global Geographies and Operations, Richard H. Rostan
SVP and CIO, Christopher J. McClincy, age 42
SVP Global Sales and Marketing, J. Jonathan Song
Senior Vice President Corporate Controller
 Expeditors Int'l of Washington, Charles Lynch
Director, Robert R. Wright, age 57
Auditors: KPMG LLP

LOCATIONS

HQ: Expeditors International of Washington, Inc.
 1015 Third Avenue, 12th Floor, Seattle, WA 98104
Phone: 206 674-3400   **Fax:** 206 674-3459
Web: www.expeditors.com

2016 Sales

	$ mil.	% of total
Asia		
North Asia	2,263	36
South Asia	628	10
North America		
US	1,789	28
Other North America	237	4
Europe	959	15
Middle East Africa and India	360	6
Latin America	99	1
Eliminations	(240.3)	-
Total	**6,098**	**100**

PRODUCTS/OPERATIONS

2016 Sales

	$ mil.	% of total
Airfreight services	2,453	40
Ocean freight & ocean services	1,917	32
Customs brokerage & other services	1,727	28
Total	**6,098**	**100**

Selected Products and Services

Air consolidation
Air forwarding
Cargo insurance
Customs
Distribution management
Direct Ocean Forwarding
Ocean shipment
Order Management
Purchase order management
Risk Management
Supply Chain Solutions
Transcon
Transportation

COMPETITORS

APL Logistics
C.H. Robinson
 Worldwide
CEVA Logistics
DHL
FedEx Trade Networks
Kintetsu World Express
Kuehne + Nagel
 International
Mitsui-Soko

NYK Line
Nippon Express
Panalpina
Schenker
Sino-Global
Sinotrans
UPS Supply Chain
 Solutions
Yamato Holdings

HISTORICAL FINANCIALS

Company Type: Public

Income Statement

FYE: December 31

	REVENUE ($ mil.)	NET INCOME ($ mil.)	NET PROFIT MARGIN	EMPLOYEES
12/16	6,098	430	7.1%	16,000
12/15	6,616	457	6.9%	15,397
12/14	6,564	376	5.7%	14,670
12/13	6,080	348	5.7%	13,910
12/12	5,980	333	5.6%	13,700
Annual Growth	**0.5%**	**6.6%**	**—**	**4.0%**

2016 Year-End Financials

Debt ratio: —
Return on equity: 24.30%
Cash ($ mil.): 974
Current ratio: 2.39
Long-term debt ($ mil.): —

No. of shares (mil.): 179
Dividends
 Yield: 0.0%
 Payout: 33.9%
Market value ($ mil.): 9,525

	STOCK PRICE ($) FY Close	P/E High/Low		PER SHARE ($) Earnings	Dividends	Book Value
12/16	52.96	24	18	2.36	0.80	10.26
12/15	45.10	21	18	2.40	0.72	9.29
12/14	44.61	24	20	1.92	0.64	9.75
12/13	44.25	28	21	1.68	0.60	10.29
12/12	39.55	30	22	1.57	0.56	9.82
Annual Growth	**7.6%**	**—**	**—**	**10.7%**	**9.3%**	**1.1%**

Express Scripts Holding Co

Express Scripts Holding knows that its customers like their medicine delivered quickly. The company administers more than 1.4 billion prescription drug benefits of 85 million health plan members in the US and Canada. Members have access to a network of more than 69000 retail pharmacies as well as the company's own mail-order pharmacies. On behalf of its insurer clients Express Scripts processes claims for prescriptions designs drug benefit plans and offers such services as specialty drug delivery disease management programs and consumer drug data analysis.

Operations

Express Scripts provides services in four areas: benefit choices drug choices pharmacy choices and health choices. Its Health Decision Science method combines behavioral science clinical specialization and actionable data to help customers make the best choices. Additionally the firm's Therapeutic Resource Center provides access to specialist pharmacies and nurses to fill in gaps in health care.

The company operates in two segments: PBM (pharmacy benefit management which accounts for nearly all revenues) and Other Business Operations. The PBM segment covers an array of benefits services including personalized medicine case coordination specialized pharmacy care home delivery retail network pharmacy administration benefit design consultation and public exchange offerings such as Medicare and Medicaid. The Other Business Operations segment includes subsidiaries CuraScript Specialty Distribution (which distributes specialty medicines to treat rare and orphan diseases directly to providers and hospitals in the US) and United BioSource (scientific consulting services for pharmaceutical manufacturers).

The PBM acquires pharmaceuticals either directly from manufacturers or through wholesalers. Generics are typically acquired directly from the manufacturer.

Geographic Reach

Express Scripts has more than 90 owned or leased PBM facilities throughout the US and seven owned or leased PBM facilities in Canada. Of these eight domestic facilities are processing pharmacies for home delivery operations and five are mail-order dispensing pharmacies. The company also has more than 35 specialty branch pharmacies and eight contact centers in the US.

The Other Business Operations segment owns or leases 15 locations throughout the US and five more locations in Canada and Europe.

Sales and Marketing

Express Scripts' clients include HMOs and other health insurers self-insured businesses managed care organizations third-party administrators employers workers' compensation plans government health programs and union benefit plans throughout North America. The company's top two clients are Anthem (more than 15% of total revenues) and the Department of Defense (more than 10%). In all Express Scripts serves some 3000 customers.

Financial Performance

Express Scripts' revenues have remained fairly steady at around $100 billion for the past few years. In 2016 revenue fell 1% to $100.3 billion as network revenues and other PBM revenues dropped; this was partially offset by growth in home delivery and specialty revenues.

Net income has shown strong growth for the past five years. It rose 37% to $3.4 billion in 2016 as cost of revenues and selling general and administrative expenses declined. The company also set aside lower provisions for income taxes that year.

Cash flow from operations has held steady as of late; it rose 1% to $4.9 billion in 2016. A decline in accounts receivable and higher accrued expenses offset the sharp rise in net income.

Strategy

Express Scripts and the pharmacy benefit management (PBM) industry have grown rapidly in today's complex health care system. PBMs strive to save money for their customers by negotiating good deals for prescription drugs with networks of retail pharmacies (their primary source of revenue) as well as by encouraging the use of cheaper generic drugs and home-delivered medications. Express Scripts also saves clients' money by offering disease and medication management programs to help members avoid unnecessary medical expenses.

The PBM industry has also undergone rapid consolidation a factor that has allowed Express Scripts to grow its profits exponentially in recent years. Although it hasn't been acquisitive as of late Express Scripts historically expanded its PBM operations through smaller purchases. It has also grown through organic measures such as the addition of new customer contracts as well as the extension of existing contracts to add new services. The company has also been investing some $75 million in the improvement of two new data centers in Chicago and Piscataway New Jersey.

To serve consumers who are either uninsured or pay high out-of-pocket costs Express Scripts launched the Inside Rx partnership with pricing comparison service GoodRx in 2017. The program offers an average savings of 34% off of drugs' typical cash prices. Also that year the company agreed to participate in group purchasing organization (GPO) Walgreens Boots Alliance Development (WBAD). That move should allow Express Scripts to reduce the prices of generic prescriptions for patients.

Specialty pharmacy subsidiary CuraScript part of the Other Business Operations segment is experiencing higher consumer demand. Through its primary operating unit CuraScript Specialty Distribution (or CuraScript SD) the subsidiary provides home distribution of specialty prescriptions (primarily injectable biotech drugs that require special packaging and handling); the unit also delivers to doctors' offices and other health care providers.

In 2017 Express Scripts signed a new contract with its largest customer insurance giant Anthem. The insurer brings in more than 15% of Express Scripts' total revenues. However that contract expires in 2019 and Anthem plans to consider all potential providers (including Express Scripts) at that time.

Mergers and Acquisitions

In late 2017 Express Scripts bought medical benefit management firm eviCore for $3.6 billion. eviCore helps health plans and commercial customers to secure better health care costs; it manages medical benefits for 100 million individuals. The acquisition provided Express Scripts with an entry into the medical benefit management sector a growing market.

Company Background

Express Scripts merged with rival Medco Health Solutions in 2012 creating the largest pharmacy benefits management (PBM) company in North America.

EXECUTIVES

SVP and Chief Medical Officer, Steven (Steve) Miller, age 59
SVP Clinical Research and New Solutions and Chief Innovation Officer, Glen D. Stettin, age 53
President and CEO, Timothy (Tim) Wentworth, age 56, $1,214,231 total compensation
SVP and CIO, Neal Sample, $507,692 total compensation
EVP and COO, Christine Houston, age 54, $592,039 total compensation
SVP and Chief Marketing Officer, Phyllis Anderson, age 57
SVP Supply Chain, Everett Neville, age 52
EVP and CFO, James M. Havel
Chairman, George Paz, age 61
Auditors: PricewaterhouseCoopers LLP

LOCATIONS

HQ: Express Scripts Holding Co
One Express Way, St. Louis, MO 63121
Phone: 314 996-0900
Web: www.express-scripts.com

PRODUCTS/OPERATIONS

2016 Sales

Product	$ mil.	% of total
Network	51,402	51
Home delivery & specialty	43,685	44
Other	3,538	3
Service	1,661	2
Total	**100,287**	**100**

2016 Sales

	$ mil.	% of total
Pharmacy Benefit Management (PBM)	96,509	96
Other business operations	3,778	4
Total	**100,287**	**100**

Selected Products and Services

Pharmacy Benefits Management (PBM)
Benefit design consultation
Biopharma management
Compliance management programs for members
Drug formulary management
Drug utilization review
Electronic claims processing
Fertility drug distribution

COMPETITORS

Aetna	Magellan Health
Allscripts	MedImpact
Argus	NationsHealth
BioScrip	Omnicare
CIGNA	OptumRx
Caremark Pharmacy Services	PharMerica
	Prime Therapeutics
First Health Group	Rite Aid
HealthTrans	Wal-Mart
Humana	Walgreen

HISTORICAL FINANCIALS

Company Type: Public

Income Statement

FYE: December 31

	REVENUE ($ mil.)	NET INCOME ($ mil.)	NET PROFIT MARGIN	EMPLOYEES
12/16	100,287	3,404	3.4%	25,600
12/15	101,751	2,476	2.4%	25,900
12/14	100,887	2,007	2.0%	29,500
12/13	104,098	1,844	1.8%	29,975
12/12	93,858	1,312	1.4%	30,215
Annual Growth	**1.7%**	**26.9%**	**—**	**(4.1%)**

2016 Year-End Financials

Debt ratio: 30.09%
Return on equity: 20.20%
Cash ($ mil.): 3,077
Current ratio: 0.75
Long-term debt ($ mil.): 14,846
No. of shares (mil.): 605
Dividends
Yield: —
Payout: —
Market value ($ mil.): 41,652

	STOCK PRICE ($) FY Close	P/E High/Low		PER SHARE ($) Earnings	Dividends	Book Value
12/16	68.79	16	12	5.39	0.00	26.81
12/15	87.41	26	22	3.56	0.00	25.67
12/14	84.67	32	24	2.64	0.00	27.62
12/13	70.24	31	23	2.25	0.00	28.23
12/12	54.00	36	26	1.76	0.00	28.58
Annual Growth	**6.2%**	**—**	**—**	**32.3%**	**—**	**(1.6%)**

Exxon Mobil Corp

It's not necessarily the oil standard but Exxon Mobil is one of the world's largest integrated oil companies (with Royal Dutch Shell and BP) engaging in oil and gas exploration production supply transportation and marketing. It has proved reserves of 20 billion barrels of oil equivalent and refinery capacity of 4.9 million barrels per day. The corporation has 20 refineries spread across 14 countries and operates some 100 major exploration projects worldwide. Exxon Mobil supplies refined products to more than 19000 global gas stations and is a major petrochemical producer. In 2017 Exxon Mobil CEO Rex Tillerson resigned to accept the US government position of Secretary of State.

HISTORY

Exxon's 1999 acquisition of Mobil reunited two descendants of John D. Rockefeller's Standard Oil Company. Rockefeller a commodity trader started his first oil refinery in 1863 in Cleveland. Realizing that the price of oil at the well would shrink with each new strike Rockefeller chose to monopolize oil refining and transportation. In 1870 he formed Standard Oil and in 1882 he created the Standard Oil Trust which allowed him to set up new ostensibly independent companies including the Standard Oil Company of New Jersey (Jersey Standard); Rochester New York-based Vacuum Oil; and Standard Oil of New York (nicknamed Socony).

Initially capitalized at $70 million the Standard Oil Trust controlled 90% of the petroleum industry. In 1911 after two decades of political and legal wrangling the Supreme Court broke up the trust into 34 companies the largest of which was Jersey Standard.

Walter Teagle who became president of Jersey Standard in 1917 secretly bought half of Humble Oil of Texas (1919) and expanded operations into South America. In 1928 Jersey Standard joined in the Red Line Agreement which reserved most Middle East oil for a few companies. Teagle resigned in 1942 after the company was criticized for a prewar research pact with German chemical giant I.G. Farben.

The 1948 purchase of a 40% stake in Arabian American Oil Company combined with a 7% share of Iranian production bought in 1954 made Jersey Standard the world's #1 oil company at that time.

Meanwhile Vacuum Oil and Socony reunited in 1931 as Socony-Vacuum and the company adopted the Flying Red Horse (Pegasus — representing speed and power) as a trademark. The fast-growing diversifying company changed its name to Socony Mobil Oil in 1955 and became Mobil in 1976.

Other US companies still using the Standard Oil name objected to Jersey Standard's marketing in their territories as Esso (derived from the initials for Standard Oil). To end the confusion in 1972 Jersey Standard became Exxon a name change that cost $100 million.

Nationalization of oil assets by producing countries reduced Exxon's access to oil during the 1970s. Though it increased exploration that decade and the next Exxon's reserves shrank.

Oil tanker Exxon Valdez spilled some 11 million gallons of oil into Alaska's Prince William Sound in 1989. Exxon spent billions on the cleanup and in 1994 a federal jury in Alaska ordered the company to pay $5.3 billion in punitive damages to fishermen and others affected by the spill. (Exxon appealed and in 2001 the jury award was reduced to $2.5 billion and in 2008 to $507.5 million).

With the oil industry consolidating Exxon merged its worldwide oil and fuel additives business with that of Royal Dutch/Shell in 1996. The next year under FTC pressure Exxon agreed to run ads refuting claims that its premium gas enabled car engines to run more efficiently. Another PR disaster followed in 1998 when CEO Lee Raymond upset environmentalists by publicly questioning the global warming theory.

Still Exxon was unstoppable. It acquired Mobil for $81 billion in 1999; the new company had Raymond at the helm and Mobil's Lucio Noto as vice chairman. (Noto retired in 2001.) To get the deal done Exxon Mobil had to divest $4 billion in assets. It agreed to end its European gasoline and lubricants joint venture with BP and to sell more than 2400 gas stations in the US.

In 2000 Exxon Mobil sold 1740 East Coast gas stations to Tosco for $860 million. It sold a California refinery and 340 gas stations to Valero Energy for about $1 billion.

More than a decade after the Exxon Valdez wreaked environmental havoc off the shores of Alaska Exxon Mobil attempted to atone in 2001 by joining the California Fuel Cell Partnership a group studying possible alternatives to and supplements for gasoline in fuel-burning engines. That year Exxon Mobil also announced that it was proceeding with a $12 billion project (with Japanese Indian and Russian partners) to develop oil fields in the Russian Far East.

In 2002 Exxon Mobil sold its 50% stake in a Colombian coal mine as part of its strategy to divest coal assets in order to focus on its core businesses. That year the company sold its Chilean copper mining subsidiary (Disputada de Las Condes) to mineral giant Anglo American for $1.3 billion. Exxon Mobil sold its 3.7% stake in China Petroleum & Chemical Corp. (Sinopec) in early 2005. Later that year the company was ordered to pay $1.3 billion to about 10000 gas station owners for overcharges dating back to 1983; the average amount for each station owner was about $130000.

Shortages caused by Hurricane Katrina prompted Exxon Mobil to receive a 6 million barrel of crude oil loan primarily from the US Strategic Petroleum Reserve and increase gasoline production at its Baton Rouge facility.

Exiting the low-margin retail gasoline business in order to focus on its other operations in 2008 the company began to sell to distributors its remaining 820 company-owned US gas stations and another 1400 outlets operated by dealers.

In 2009 the company signed up to partner with TransCanada to jointly develop the $26 billion Alaska Pipeline Project. A long-term project if and when built the pipeline will deliver natural gas from Alaska's North Slope to US markets.

Also in 2009 it made its first major investment in developing biofuels agreeing to spend $600 million in an algae-to-fuel project with biotech firm Synthetic Genomics.

In a move to replace the decline of oil reserves from its mature fields in 2010 Exxon Mobil acquired XTO Energy. The $41 billion all-stock deal sharply boosted Exxon shale properties in the continental US including the Haynesville shale. Exxon followed up by acquiring Ellora Energy that same year for $695 million which further solidified Exxon's Haynesville position in Texas and Louisiana.

In 2010 in response to the BP oil rig disaster in the Gulf of Mexico Exxon Mobil joined forces with other US oil companies to create a $1 billion rapid-response joint venture capable of capturing and containing some 100000 barrels of oil in water depths of 10000 feet.

In 2011 the company reported a major oil find in the Gulf with potentially 700 million barrels of recoverable oil equivalent.

That year Exxon Mobil acquired two Pittsburgh-area natural gas producers (Phillips Resources and TWP) for $1.7 billion giving the company access to hundreds of thousands of leased acres of the Marcellus Shale in southwestern Pennsylvania.

In 2012 Saudi Basic Industries Corporation and Exxon Mobil agreed to build a world-scale specialty elastomers facility (to be completed in 2015) at the Al-Jubail Petrochemical Company manufacturing joint venture in Saudi Arabia.

To raise cash to pay down debt in 2012 the company sold its North Sea assets to Apache for $1.25 billion.

In 2013 Rosneft and Exxon Mobil agreed to expand their cooperation under their 2011 Strategic Cooperation Agreement to include an additional 150 million acres of exploration acreage in the Russian Arctic and potential participation by Rosneft in the Point Thomson project in Alaska. They also agreed to conduct a joint study on a potential LNG project in the Russian Far East. (In 2011 Exxon Mobil agreed to spend $1 billion in a joint venture with Rosneft to jointly explore oil and gas fields in the Black Sea.). However US economic sanctions on Russia in 2014 forced the company to suspend its operations in the Arctic with Rosneft.

In 2013 Exxon Mobil acquired Canada's Celtic Exploration for about $2.5 billion Exxon Mobil's largest transaction since it bought Texas' XTO Energy for a whopping $41 billion in 2010. The Celtic deal gives Exxon 545000 net acres in the liquids-rich Montney shale 104000 net acres in the Duvernay shale and other acreage in Alberta.

EXECUTIVES

SVP and Principal Financial Officer, Andrew P. (Andy) Swiger, age 61, $1,287,500 total compensation

President ExxonMobil Chemical Company, John R. Verity

President ExxonMobil Refining & Supply Company, Darren W. Woods, age 52, $1,000,000 total compensation

VP and President ExxonMobil Upstream Ventures, B. W. Corson

VP and General Counsel, R. M. Ebner

VP Human Resources, M. A. Farrant

President ExxonMobil Production Company, N. W. Duffin

President ExxonMobil Fuels Lubricants and Specialties Marketing Company, B. W. Milton

President ExxonMobil Refining and Supply Company, D. G. Wascom

President ExxonMobil Research and Engineering Company, T. J. Wojnar

President ExxonMobil Global Services Company, L. D. DuCharme

Vice President Information Technology, Nigel Searle

National Accounts Manager, Juan Rodriguez

Vice President Business Services, David Norwood

Vice President Drilling, Harry Newman

Indonesia Vice President For Public And Government Affairs, Erwin Maryoto

Process Vice President, Mike Coker

Financial Vice President, Gregory S Rogers

Vice President Legal Services, Dave Raaf

Vice President, Pat Doolan

Vice President Arctic And Eastern Canada, Jim K Flood

Vice President of Information Technology, Terri L Dosch

Vice President Land, Patrick Murphy

National Account Manager, Richard Bowen

Vice President, William Espegren

Department Head, Michael Hotaling

Senior Vice President, Michael Dolan

Vice President, Tristan Aspray

Senior Vice President Of Natural Gas Operations, Idora Abdulmalek

Vice President and President ExxonMobil Production Company, Thomas Walters

Vice President Investor Relations And Secretary, David Rosenthal

National Accounts Manager, Thomas Luzzi

Vice President Global Retail, Ben Soraci

Vice President Operations, John Fraser

Vice President Plastics and Resins, Cindy Shulman

Vice President, Lee Willis

Vice President, Tina Fitts

Vice President, David Cochrane

Treasurer, Alton Fleming

Assistant Treasurer exxonmobil Chemical America, Beth Casteel

Treasurer, Simeon Moats

Treasurer???s ??? Benefits Finance And Investments, Cindy Kessel

Secretary, Suzanne Manahan-smith

Upstream Treasurers, Tanya Gordon

Board Member, Pin Oak

Vice Chair, Harleen Chhabra

L And S Downstream Treasurers Credit Analyst, Patricia Beckwith

Financial Advisor Upstream Treasurers, Todd Norman

Assistant Treasurer, Kate Shae

Treasurer, Steven Kane

Upstream Treasurers, Michael Smith

Upstream Treasurer, Freda Bass

Treasurers Department, Rachel Reed

Auditors: PricewaterhouseCoopers LLP

LOCATIONS

HQ: Exxon Mobil Corp
5959 Las Colinas Boulevard, Irving, TX 75039-2298
Phone: 972 444-1000   **Fax:** 972 444-1505
Web: www.exxonmobil.com

2016 Sales

	% of total
U.S.	34
Non-U.S.	66
Total	**100**

PRODUCTS/OPERATIONS

2016 Sales

	% of total
Downstream	79
Chemical	12
Upstream	9
Total	**100**

2016 Sales

	$ mil.	% of total
Sales and Other Operating Revenue	218,608	97
Income From Equity Affiliates	4,806	2
Other Income	2,680	1
Total	**226,094**	**100**

COMPETITORS

7-Eleven	Marathon Oil
Ashland	Norsk Hydro ASA
BHP Billiton	Occidental Petroleum
BP	PEMEX
Chevron	PETROBRAS
ConocoPhillips	Petr⬚leos de
Costco Wholesale	Venezuela
Dow Chemical	Racetrac Petroleum
DuPont	Repsol
Eastman Chemical	Royal Dutch Shell
Eni	Saudi Aramco
Hess Corporation	Sinopec Corp.
Huntsman International	Sunoco
JXTG Holdings	TOTAL
Koch Industries Inc.	Valero Energy

HISTORICAL FINANCIALS
Company Type: Public

Income Statement
FYE: December 31

	REVENUE ($ mil.)	NET INCOME ($ mil.)	NET PROFIT MARGIN	EMPLOYEES
12/16	226,094	7,840	3.5%	71,100
12/15	268,882	16,150	6.0%	73,500
12/14	411,939	32,520	7.9%	75,300
12/13	438,255	32,580	7.4%	75,000
12/12	482,295	44,880	9.3%	76,900
Annual Growth	**(17.3%)**	**(35.4%)**	**—**	**(1.9%)**

2016 Year-End Financials

Debt ratio: 12.95%—
Return on equity: 4.62%
Cash ($ mil.): 3,657
Current ratio: 0.87
Long-term debt ($ mil.): 28,932

Dividends
Yield: 0.0%
Payout: 158.5%
Market value ($ mil.): —

	STOCK PRICE ($) FY Close	P/E High/Low		Earnings	Dividends	Book Value
12/16	90.26	51	39	1.88	2.98	40.34
12/15	77.95	24	18	3.85	2.88	41.10
12/14	92.45	14	11	7.60	2.70	41.51
12/13	101.20	14	12	7.37	2.46	40.14
12/12	86.55	10	8	9.70	2.18	36.84
Annual Growth	**1.1%**	**—**	**—**	**(33.6%)**	**8.1%**	**2.3%**

Facebook Inc

When it comes to social networking it's wise to put your best face forward. Facebook the social networking juggernaut lets users share information post photos and videos play games and otherwise connect with one another through online profiles. The site which allows outside developers to build apps that integrate with Facebook boasts more than a billion total users. The firm was launched in 2004 by Harvard student Mark Zuckerberg as an online version of the Harvard Facebook. (The name comes from books of freshmen's faces majors and hometowns that are distributed to students.) In 2012 Facebook began publicly trading after filing one of the largest IPOs in US history.

Operations

Facebook's primary products include the Facebook app Instagram Messenger WhatsApp and Oculus. Facebook enables people to connect share discover and communicate with each other on mobile devices and personal computers. Instagram enables people to take photos or videos customize them with filter effects and share them with friends and followers in a photo feed or send them directly to friends. Messenger allows for a rich and expressive way to communicate with people and businesses across a variety of platforms and devices. WhatsApp Messenger is a messaging application that is used by people around the world on a variety of mobile platforms. The Oculus virtual reality technology and content platform powers products that allow people to enter a completely immersive and interactive environment to play games consume content and connect with others.

Geographic Reach

Global in its reach Facebook generates more than half of its revenue from outside of the US. The majority of its international business comes from customers located in western Europe Australia Canada and China. Facebook sees India in particular as a key source of growth. The company has offices and data center facilities located all over the world.

Sales and Marketing

Facebook which has a global sales force earns more than 95% of its revenue from the sale of advertising (about $26 billion in fiscal 2016). The company spent $310 million on its own advertising and promotional expenses during 2016.

Financial Performance

Facebook has experienced exponential growth over the past few years enabling it to dominate the social networking world as the most trafficked site of its kind in the US. Its revenue was $27.64 billion in fiscal 2016 up 54% year-over-year. The company's advertising revenue was $26.89 billion in fiscal 2016 up 57% year-over-year.

Facebook's net income was $10.22 billion in fiscal 2016 up from $3.6 billion in fiscal 2015. The company has a surplus of cash on hand from operations. It ended fiscal 2016 with more than $16 billion in cash. Facebook's capital expenditures were $4.49 billion in fiscal 2016.

Strategy

Facebook owes the bulk of its growth to its ability to lure more and more visitors to its site and keeping them engaged. The site then stores data about its users and sells that info to advertisers and marketers. The growth in Facebook's advertising business driven by mobile ads customized for individuals has been staggering.

Since Facebook is a free service it relies almost completely on ads to make money. The company constantly needs creative new ways to let businesses sell their products and services through its applications. That is why the company has spread its advertising business beyond Facebook itself and onto the other popular messaging and photo-sharing apps it owns.

The company's strategy includes making key acquisitions to add specialized employees and complementary companies products or technologies. Facebook also continues to invest in its own core products and services to better serve its existing users and customers. The company spends considerable time and money on research and development. Its R&D expenses were $5.92 billion $4.82 billion and $2.67 billion in 2016 2015 and 2014 respectively.

Mergers and Acquisitions

Acquisitions to add specialized employees and complementary companies products or technologies has long been a part of Facebook's strategy. Even though the company has slowed down its pace of acquiring other companies somewhat Facebook did acquire three different companies in 2016.

In September 2016 Facebook acquired Nascent Objects a small California startup that focuses on creating a modular electronics system that consumers could use to build their own gadgets. The acquisition of Nascent is geared towards strengthening Facebook?s hardware offerings.

During 2016 Facebook also acquired facial recognition startup FacioMetrics. The acquisition of FacioMetrics enhanced Facebook's photo and video special effects. Facebook acquired social analytics service CrowdTangle during 2016 as well.

EXECUTIVES

COO, Sheryl K. Sandberg, age 48, $738,077 total compensation

Chairman and CEO, Mark Zuckerberg, age 33, $1 total compensation

CTO, Michael (Mike) Schroepfer, age 42, $658,846 total compensation

CIO, Atish Banerjea, age 51

CFO, David M. (Dave) Wehner, age 48, $662,692 total compensation

Chief Product Officer, Christopher K. (Chris) Cox, age 34, $658,846 total compensation

PARSE REGIONAL VICE PRESIDENT, Thomas Buerkle

PARSE REGIONAL VICE PRESIDENT, Thomas Oneill

Auditors: Ernst & Young LLP

LOCATIONS

HQ: Facebook Inc
1601 Willow Road, Menlo Park, CA 94025
Phone: 650 543-4800
Web: www.facebook.com

2016 Sales

	$ mil.	% of total
US	12,579	46
International	15,059	54
Total	**27,638**	**100**

PRODUCTS/OPERATIONS

2016 Sales

	$ mil.	% of total
Advertising	26,885	97
Payments & other fees	753	3
Total	**27,638**	**100**

Selected Products and Features

Products for Users
  Timeline
  News feed
  Photos & videos
  Messages
  Groups
  Lists
  Events
  Places
  Notifications
  Facebook Pages
Products for Developers
  Open Graph
  Social plugins
  Like button
  Recommendations
  Comments
  Facebook Payments
  Apps on Facebook
Products for Advertisers & Marketers
  Facebook Ads
  Sponsored Stories
  Ad analytics

COMPETITORS

Apple Inc.	Memory Lane
Bebo	Microsoft
Digg	Myspace
Friendster	TheSquare
Google	Tribe Networks
IAC	Twitter
LinkedIn	Yelp
LiveJournal	YouTube
Meetup	craigslist

HISTORICAL FINANCIALS

Company Type: Public

Income Statement

FYE: December 31

	REVENUE ($ mil.)	NET INCOME ($ mil.)	NET PROFIT MARGIN	EMPLOYEES
12/17	40,653	15,934	39.2%	25,105
12/16	27,638	10,217	37.0%	17,048
12/15	17,928	3,688	20.6%	12,691
12/14	12,466	2,940	23.6%	9,199
12/13	7,872	1,500	19.1%	6,337
Annual Growth	**50.7%**	**80.5%**	**—**	**41.1%**

2017 Year-End Financials

Debt ratio: —
Return on equity: 23.86%
Cash ($ mil.): 8,079
Current ratio: 12.92
Long-term debt ($ mil.): —

Dividends
  Yield: —
  Payout: —
Market value ($ mil.): —

	STOCK PRICE ($) FY Close	P/E High/Low	PER SHARE ($) Earnings	Dividends	Book Value
12/17	176.46	33 21	5.39	0.00	25.58
12/16	115.05	37 26	3.49	0.00	20.47
12/15	104.66	83 57	1.29	0.00	15.54
12/14	78.02	73 48	1.10	0.00	12.91
12/13	54.65	93 37	0.60	0.00	6.07
Annual Growth	**34.0%**	**— —**	**73.1%**	**—**	**43.3%**

Fannie Mae

The Federal National Mortgage Association or Fannie Mae has helped more than 50 million low-to middle-income families realize the American Dream of owning a home. Like its brother Freddie Mac the government-supported enterprise (GSE) provides liquidity in the mortgage market by buying mortgages from lenders and packaging them for resale transferring risk from lenders and allowing them to offer mortgages to those who may not otherwise qualify. It owns or guarantees more than $2.6 trillion in single family home loans (nearly 30% of US total) and about $230 billion in multifamily mortgages (nearly 20% of US total). Due to losses caused largely by the subprime mortgage crisis the government seized both Fannie and Freddie in 2008. Government plans to divest the firms into private ownership have proven difficult; they remain GSEs.

HISTORY

In 1938 President Franklin Roosevelt created Fannie Mae as part of the government-owned Reconstruction Finance Corporation; its mandate was to buy FHA (Federal Housing Administration) loans. Fannie Mae began buying VA (Veterans Administration) mortgages in 1948. It was rechartered as a public-private mixed-ownership corporation in 1954.

The Housing Act of 1968 divided the corporation into the Government National Mortgage Association (Ginnie Mae which retained explicit government backing) and Fannie Mae which went public (with only an implicit US guarantee). Fannie Mae retained its treasury backstop authority whereby the secretary of the treasury can purchase up to $2.24 billion of the company's obligations.

The company introduced uniform conventional loan mortgage documents in 1970 began to buy conventional mortgages in 1972 and started buying condo and planned-unit development mortgages in 1974. By 1976 it was buying more conventional loans than FHA and VA loans.

As interest rates rose in the 1970s Fannie Mae's profits declined and by 1981 it was losing more than $1 million a day. Then it began offering mortgage-backed securities (MBSs) — popular as an investment product because of their implicit guarantee from the government. By 1982 the company funded 14% of US home mortgages.

Fannie Mae began borrowing money overseas and buying conventional multifamily and co-op housing loans in 1984. The next year it tightened credit rules and began issuing securities aimed at foreign investors such as yen-denominated securities. Fannie Mae issued its first real estate mortgage investment conduit (REMIC) securities (shares in mortgage pools of specific maturities and risk classes) and introduced a program to allow small lenders to pool loans with other lenders to create MBSs in 1987.

After CEO David Maxwell's 1991 retirement with a reported $29 million pension package Fannie Mae's powerful Washington lobby squelched calls to limit executive salaries. Other attempts to make the company more competitive with private concerns were more successful. In 1992 Fannie Mae's capital requirements were raised; a new mandate also required the organization to lend greater support to inner-city buyers. A new client/server computer system helped the company handle the deluge of new and refinanced loans that came in 1993 (Fannie Mae had struggled to improve its information systems in the 1980s pouring more than $100 million into a mainframe system that was obsolete before it went online).

In 1997 Fannie Mae officially adopted its longtime nickname. The next year Fannie Mae named White House budget chief Franklin Raines to succeed CEO James Johnson.

Fannie Mae is no stranger to bad news or bad press. In 1999 the Department of Housing and Urban Development began investigating charges that the company's automated underwriting systems were racially biased. The next year the agency released a study that found it to be negligent in promoting homeownership in low-income neighborhoods. In response Fannie Mae eased credit requirements in an effort to boost minority homeownership (1999) and announced plans to loan some $2 trillion to minority and low-income home-

buyers (2000). This move however invoked criticism that the company was exposing itself to increased risk from buyers more likely to default.

Following the lead of rival Freddie Mac in 2000 Fannie Mae offered securities for sale over the Internet. In 2002 it tightened standards for mortgage refinance cash-out loans it would buy as mortgage defaults rose (even as home sales and mortgage refinancings were helping prop up the sagging US economy).

In response to those who thought it was in bed with the federal government Fannie Mae kicked off the covers and put one foot on the floor. In 2003 it fulfilled a voluntary commitment to register its common stock with the SEC and came permanently under that organization's disclosure and oversight requirements.

But the move did not stop controversy from swirling around the lender. Chairman and CEO Franklin Raines CFO Timothy Howard and auditor KPMG were ousted in December 2004 after the SEC determined Fannie Mae had violated accounting rules. The inquiry was prompted by accusations Fannie Mae had manipulated earnings; earnings from 2001 through 2003 were restated and those from 2004 and 2005 were each released more than a year late.

In 2006 federal regulators hit the firm with a whopping $400 million fine. Investigators claimed that its former executives willfully overstated earnings by more than $10 billion — and then tried to impede an investigation into the discrepancies — in order to reap performance bonuses. Chairman Stephen Ashley and CEO Daniel Mudd who'd been brought in to replace Franklin Raines in late 2004 were brought to task by the Senate Banking Committee in regard to accounting misdeeds.

Though the Justice Department eventually dropped criminal charges against the firm Fannie Mae agreed to major changes in its accounting internal controls and management practices. It additionally agreed to appoint an independent chief risk officer as well as an organizational review overseen by a compliance committee. Meanwhile the lender suspended its home construction loan program — worth about $10 billion — while it got its financial house in order.

Fannie suffered huge losses in 2007 and 2008 as a result of the subprime mortgage crisis which saw a tremenduose increase in loan defaults. The government stepped in loans and in 2008 seized both Fannie and Freddie. It also shuffled their management teams: Fannie CEO Mudd was replaced by Herbert Allison former TIAA-CREF. Allison was later tapped by the Obama administration to run the Treasury Department's financial recovery program. Former COO Michael Williams was named CEO in 2009.

The Federal Housing Finance Agency (FHFA) was created in 2008 to oversee both Fannie and Freddie as well as the 12 Federal Home Loan Banks. The FHFA was granted more authority than its predecessor agencies the Federal Housing Finance Board and the Office of Federal Housing Enterprise Oversight.

In an historic move the government in 2008 placed the two GSEs in conservatorship which is a legal status similar to bankruptcy rather than risk the possibility that the companies might fail. The government assumed a nearly 80% stake in the troubled companies in a $111 billion bailout (with a commitment of up to $400 billion). In 2011 the Obama administration proposed to restructure the housing market in a plan that will reduce the government's role and eventually eliminate the GSEs.

In 2009 the Making Home Affordable Program was introduced to provide assistance to borrowers in default through refinancings and other loan modifications.

EXECUTIVES

President CEO and Director, Timothy J. (Tim) Mayopoulos, age 58, $600,000 total compensation

EVP and Head Multifamily, Jeffery R. Hayward, age 61, $475,000 total compensation

EVP and CFO, David C. Benson, age 58, $600,000 total compensation

EVP Single-Family Underwriting Pricing and Capital Markets, Andrew Bon Salle, $500,000 total compensation

EVP General Counsel and Corporate Secretary, Brian P. Brooks, $500,000 total compensation

EVP and Chief Risk Officer, Kimberly H. Johnson

SVP Operations and Technology, Bruce Lee

Vice President of Benefits Compensation, Christine Wolf

Vice President, Steve Spies

Vice President Risk Management, Carlos Perez

Vice President Risk, Tracy L Glascoe

Vice President Human Resources Business Development, Karen Jez

Vice President Finance And Corporate Technology, Ramon Richards

Vice President Information Technology, Beth Applegate

Vice President Of Internal Audit Technology, Don Farineau

Vice President Business Unit Controller, Nigel D Brazier

Vice President Sales and Marketing, Nancy Liebermann

Chairman, Egbert L. J. Perry, age 61

Board Member, Kenneth Duberstein

Auditors: Deloitte & Touche LLP

LOCATIONS

HQ: Fannie Mae
   3900 Wisconsin Avenue, NW, Washington, DC 20016
Phone: 800 232-6643
Web: www.fanniemae.com

Selected Locations
Atlanta
Chicago
Dallas
Pasadena
Philadelphia
Washington DC

PRODUCTS/OPERATIONS

2016 Sales

	% of total
Interest income	
Mortgage loans	97
Available-for-sale securities	1
Trading securities	-
Others	-
Non interest income	
Investment gains net	1
Fair value losses net	-
Fee and other income	1
Total	**100**

2016 Sales

	% of total
Single-Family	88
Multifamily	12
Total	**100**

Selected Business Segments
Single-Family Credit Guaranty
Multifamily

COMPETITORS

Freddie Mac	VBA
Ginnie Mae	Wells Fargo

HISTORICAL FINANCIALS
Company Type: Public

Income Statement
FYE: December 31

	ASSETS ($ mil.)	NET INCOME ($ mil.)	INCOME AS % OF ASSETS	EMPLOYEES
12/16	3,287,968	12,313	0.4%	7,000
12/15	3,221,917	10,954	0.3%	7,300
12/14	3,248,176	14,208	0.4%	7,600
12/13	3,270,108	83,963	2.6%	7,400
12/12	3,222,422	17,224	0.5%	7,200
Annual Growth	0.5%	(8.0%)	—	(0.7%)

2016 Year-End Financials
Debt ratio: 99.22%
Return on equity: 243.13%
Cash ($ mil.): 25,224
Current ratio: —
Long-term debt ($ mil.): —
No. of shares (mil.): 1,158
Dividends
　Yield: —
　Payout: —
Market value ($ mil.): 4,517

	STOCK PRICE ($) FY Close	P/E High/Low	PER SHARE ($) Earnings	Dividends	Book Value
12/16	3.90	449 110	0.01	0.00	5.24
12/15	1.64	— —	(0.05)	0.00	3.48
12/14	2.06	— —	(0.19)	0.00	3.18
12/13	3.01	— —	(0.25)	0.00	8.24
12/12	0.26	2 1	0.24	0.00	6.20
Annual Growth	97.8%	— —	(54.8%)	—	(4.1%)

FARM CREDIT ILLINOIS, ACA

Auditors: PRICEWATERHOUSECOOPERS LLP MI

LOCATIONS
HQ: FARM CREDIT ILLINOIS, ACA
　1100 FARM CREDIT DR, MAHOMET, IL 618538532
Phone: 217 590-2222
Web: WWW.FCSILLINOIS.COM

HISTORICAL FINANCIALS
Company Type: Private

Income Statement
FYE: December 31

	ASSETS ($ mil.)	NET INCOME ($ mil.)	INCOME AS % OF ASSETS	EMPLOYEES
12/12	3,304	63	1.9%	210
12/11	2,843	56	2.0%	—
Annual Growth	16.2%	11.2%	—	—

FARM CREDIT OF THE VIRGINIAS ACA

LOCATIONS
HQ: FARM CREDIT OF THE VIRGINIAS ACA
　106 SANGERS LN, STAUNTON, VA 244016711
Phone: 540 899-0989

HISTORICAL FINANCIALS
Company Type: Private

Income Statement
FYE: December 31

	ASSETS ($ mil.)	NET INCOME ($ mil.)	INCOME AS % OF ASSETS	EMPLOYEES
12/15	1,757	44	2.5%	142
12/14	1,654	50	3.1%	—
12/13	1,560	51	3.3%	—
12/12	1,539	35	2.3%	—
Annual Growth	4.5%	7.3%	—	—

2015 Year-End Financials
Debt ratio: —
Return on equity: 40.50%
Cash ($ mil.): 2
Current ratio: —
Long-term debt ($ mil.): —
Dividends
　Yield: —
　Payout: —
Market value ($ mil.): —

FARM CREDIT SERVICES OF AMERICA, PCA

Auditors: PRICEWATERHOUSECOOPERS LLP M

LOCATIONS
HQ: FARM CREDIT SERVICES OF AMERICA, PCA
　5015 S 118TH ST, OMAHA, NE 681372210
Phone: 800 884-3276
Web: WWW.FCSAMERICA.COM

HISTORICAL FINANCIALS
Company Type: Private

Income Statement
FYE: December 31

	ASSETS ($ mil.)	NET INCOME ($ mil.)	INCOME AS % OF ASSETS	EMPLOYEES
12/15	24,772	514	2.1%	10,000
12/04	8,475	294	3.5%	—
12/03	7,633	114	1.5%	—
Annual Growth	10.3%	13.4%	—	—

2015 Year-End Financials
Debt ratio: —
Return on equity: 46.80%
Cash ($ mil.): 60
Current ratio: —
Long-term debt ($ mil.): —
Dividends
　Yield: —
　Payout: —
Market value ($ mil.): —

FARM CREDIT WEST

Auditors: PRICEWATERHOUSECOOPERS LLP SA

LOCATIONS
HQ: FARM CREDIT WEST
　3755 ATHERTON RD, ROCKLIN, CA 957653701
Phone: 916 724-4800
Web: WWW.FARMCREDITWEST.COM

HISTORICAL FINANCIALS
Company Type: Private

Income Statement
FYE: December 31

	ASSETS ($ mil.)	NET INCOME ($ mil.)	INCOME AS % OF ASSETS	EMPLOYEES
12/12	6,668	151	2.3%	165
12/11	6,282	176	2.8%	—
Annual Growth	6.1%	(14.3%)	—	—

2012 Year-End Financials
Debt ratio: —
Return on equity: 51.30%
Cash ($ mil.): 35
Current ratio: —
Long-term debt ($ mil.): —
Dividends
　Yield: —
　Payout: —
Market value ($ mil.): —

Farmers & Merchants Bancorp (Lodi, CA)

EXECUTIVES
Chb-pres-ceo, Kent A Steinwert
Vice President, Denise Goodell
Senior Vice President And Credit Administration, Tracy Muegge
Vice President Facilities Manager, Mario Eguiluz
Vice President, Chris Winek
Executive Vice President Senior Credit Officer, Ken Smith
Auditors: Moss Adams LLP

LOCATIONS
HQ: Farmers & Merchants Bancorp (Lodi, CA)
　111 W. Pine Street, Lodi, CA 95240
Phone: 209 367-2300
Web: www.fmbonline.com

HISTORICAL FINANCIALS
Company Type: Public

Income Statement
FYE: December 31

	ASSETS ($ mil.)	NET INCOME ($ mil.)	INCOME AS % OF ASSETS	EMPLOYEES
12/16	2,922	29	1.0%	339
12/15	2,615	27	1.0%	316
12/14	2,360	25	1.1%	310
12/13	2,076	24	1.2%	299
12/12	1,974	23	1.2%	299
Annual Growth	10.3%	6.2%	—	3.2%

2016 Year-End Financials
Debt ratio: 0.35%
Return on equity: 11.15%
Cash ($ mil.): 98
Current ratio: —
Long-term debt ($ mil.): —
No. of shares (mil.): 0
Dividends
　Yield: 0.0%
　Payout: 34.9%
Market value ($ mil.): 517

	STOCK PRICE ($) FY Close	P/E High/Low	PER SHARE ($) Earnings	Dividends	Book Value
12/16	640.00	17 13	37.44	13.10	346.80
12/15	540.00	17 13	34.82	12.90	318.46
12/14	463.00	14 13	32.64	12.70	297.39
12/13	417.00	16 12	30.93	12.50	269.84
12/12	405.00	14 11	29.99	12.10	263.58
Annual Growth	12.1%	— —	5.7%	2.0%	7.1%

Farmers & Merchants Bank of Long Beach (CA)

LOCATIONS

HQ: Farmers & Merchants Bank of Long Beach (CA)
302 Pine Avenue, Long Beach, CA 90802
Phone: 213 437-0011
Web: www.fmb.com

HISTORICAL FINANCIALS

Company Type: Public

Income Statement

FYE: December 31

	ASSETS ($ mil.)	NET INCOME ($ mil.)	INCOME AS % OF ASSETS	EMPLOYEES
12/16	6,729	71	1.1%	—
12/15	6,153	64	1.1%	—
12/14	5,581	62	1.1%	—
12/13	5,214	62	1.2%	—
12/12	4,988	63	1.3%	—
Annual Growth	7.8%	3.1%	—	—

2016 Year-End Financials

Debt ratio: —
Return on equity: 8.08%
Cash ($ mil.): 148
Current ratio: —
Long-term debt ($ mil.): —

No. of shares (mil.): 0
Dividends
  Yield: 0.0%
  Payout: 21.7%
Market value ($ mil.): 890

	STOCK PRICE ($) FY Close	P/E High/Low	PER SHARE ($) Earnings	Dividends	Book Value
12/16	6,800	13 11	546	119	6,952
12/15	6,240	13 12	496	119	6,532
12/14	6,060	13 11	47	114	6,160
12/13	5,226	11 9	474	114	5,798
12/12	4,310	9 8	484	114	5,478
Annual Growth	12.1%	— —	3.1%	1.1%	6.1%

Farmers Capital Bank Corp.

Farmers Capital has found some green in the Bluegrass State. Its four bank subsidiaries — Citizens Bank of Northern Kentucky Farmers Bank & Capital Trust First Citizens Bank and United Bank & Trust Company — operate more than 35 branches in northern and central Kentucky. Serving individuals and local businesses they offer standard retail services such as checking and savings accounts and CDs as well as trust activities. Real estate loans including (primarily) residential mortgages and commercial real estate loans account for around 90% of the company's loan portfolio. Nonbank subsidiaries of Farmers Capital provide insurance and data processing services.

Strategy

Until recently Farmers Capital Bank retained the names and brands of its acquired banks. However the bank has stepped away from that practice and has been merging its banks together. The mergers allow customers to access their accounts at more locations but also help cut regulatory costs for the company. In 2016 the company announced it would merge its four banks as well as its data processing unit FCB Services into one company to be named United Bank & Capital Trust. The single bank will be headquartered in Frankfort Kentucky and will be structured into four regional segments.

EXECUTIVES

VP Marketing, Janelda R. Mitchell
President and CEO, Lloyd C. Hillard, age 70, $400,000 total compensation
EVP Finance, C. Douglas Carpenter, $155,000 total compensation
President and CEO Farmers Bank, Rickey D. Harp, $200,000 total compensation
EVP CFO and Secretary, Mark A. Hampton
President and CEO United Bank, James L. Grubbs, $200,000 total compensation
EVP and Chief Credit Officer, James Barsotti
CEO First Citizens Bank, Scott T. Conway, $175,000 total compensation
SEVP and COO, J. David Smith
Vice President Special Assets Manager, John Pendergrass
Senior Vice President Human Resources, Carla Miles
Vice President, Kaye Hall
Vice President of Internal Audit, Anish Banker
Vice Chairman, J. Barry Banker, age 65
Chairman, R. Terry Bennett, age 70
Auditors: BKD, LLP

LOCATIONS

HQ: Farmers Capital Bank Corp.
202 West Main St., Frankfort, KY 40601
Phone: 502 227-1668
Web: www.farmerscapital.com

PRODUCTS/OPERATIONS

2016 Sales

	$ mil.	% of total
Interest Income:		
Interest and fees on loans	47	53
Interest on investment securities	11	13
Interest on deposits in other banks	0	0
Non Interest Income:		
Service charges and fees on deposits	7	9
Other service charges commissions and fees	5	6
Gain on debt extinguishment	4	4
Investment securities gains (losses) net	4	4
Allotment processing fees	3	4
Trust income	2	3
Legal settlement	1	2
Income from company-owned life insurance	1	1
Gains on sale of mortgage loans net	0	1
Other	0	0
Total	**90**	**100**

2016 Sales

	% of total
Real Estate	
Farmland and other commercial enterprises	41
Residential	36
Construction and land development	13
Commercial financial and agricultural	9
Installment	1
Total	**100**

COMPETITORS

BB&T	Premier Financial
Community Trust	Bancorp
Fifth Third	Republic Bancorp
Home Federal	U.S. Bancorp

HISTORICAL FINANCIALS

Company Type: Public

Income Statement

FYE: December 31

	ASSETS ($ mil.)	NET INCOME ($ mil.)	INCOME AS % OF ASSETS	EMPLOYEES
12/16	1,671	16	1.0%	472
12/15	1,775	14	0.8%	501
12/14	1,782	16	0.9%	510
12/13	1,809	13	0.7%	519
12/12	1,807	12	0.7%	518
Annual Growth	(1.9%)	8.1%	—	(2.3%)

2016 Year-End Financials

Debt ratio: 2.08%
Return on equity: 9.21%
Cash ($ mil.): 106
Current ratio: —
Long-term debt ($ mil.): —

No. of shares (mil.): 7
Dividends
  Yield: 0.0%
  Payout: 14.0%
Market value ($ mil.): 316

	STOCK PRICE ($) FY Close	P/E High/Low	PER SHARE ($) Earnings	Dividends	Book Value
12/16	42.05	20 11	2.21	0.31	24.51
12/15	27.11	16 11	1.95	0.00	23.43
12/14	23.29	13 10	1.94	0.00	23.09
12/13	21.75	17 8	1.54	0.00	22.74
12/12	12.25	10 3	1.37	0.00	22.49
Annual Growth	36.1%	— —	12.7%	—	2.2%

Farmers National Banc Corp. (Canfield, OH)

Farmers National Banc is willing to help even nonfarmers grow their seed income into thriving bounties of wealth. The bank provides commercial and personal banking from nearly 20 branches in Ohio. Founded in 1887 Farmers National Banc offers checking and savings accounts credit cards and loans and mortgages. Farmers' lending portfolio is composed of real estate mortgages consumer loans and commercial loans. The company also includes Farmers National Insurance and Farmers Trust Company a non-depository trust bank that offers wealth management and trust services.

Geographic Reach

Farmers National Banc operates 19 branches located throughout Mahoning Trumbull Columbiana Stark and Cuyahoga Counties. Farmers Trust Company operates two offices located in Boardman and Howland Ohio.

Financial Performance

The company's revenues have ranged from $40 million to $60 million in the past decade. In 2013 overall sales fell 1% to $54 million; the slight dip was due to lessened interest income on loans and taxable securities. (Financial institutions make their money on interest income from loans and non-interest income from fees.) Its non-interest income experienced growth from service charges insurance agency commissions and consulting fees for retirement planning.

Profits decreased by 22% to $8 million in 2013 due to increase in a provision for loan losses and non-interest expenses such as salary and employee benefits.

Mergers and Acquisitions

In 2013 the bank added retirement planning services to their portfolio with the acquisition of Cleveland-based National Associates Inc. for $4.4 million. The acquisition was part of its plan to boost noninterest income and complement its existing retirement services.

EXECUTIVES

Executive Vice President and Chief Credit Officer of Farmers Bank, Mark Graham
Vice President of Marketing, Linda Stanford
Assistant Vice President, Francis Gallagher
Branch Manager Assistant Vice President, Linda Jones
Vice President and Treasury Manager, Bobbi Harding
Assistant Vice President Small Business Lender, Dean Karhan
Assistant Vice President Branch Manager Downtown Massillon, Katherine Shultz
Auditors: Crowe Horwath LLP

LOCATIONS

HQ: Farmers National Banc Corp. (Canfield,OH)
20 South Broad Street, Canfield, OH 44406
Phone: 330 533-3341
Web: www.farmersbankgroup.com

PRODUCTS/OPERATIONS

Selected Products
Personal
Certificate of DepositChecking AccountsChildren's
  AccountsConsumer LoansHome Equity Loans &
  LinesMortgage LoansOnline BankingPersonal Credit
  CardPersonal Debit CardPhone
  BankingRetirementSavings Accounts
Business
Business Credit CardBusiness Debit CardBusiness
  DepositsBusiness LoansCash ManagementRemote
  Deposit Capture
Wealth Management and Insurance
Farmers Trust CompanyFarmers National
  InvestmentsFarmers National Insurance
On-line banking

COMPETITORS

CSB Bancorp	JPMorgan Chase
Central Federal	Killbuck Bancshares
Consumers Bancorp	National Bancshares
Cortland Bancorp	Ohio Legacy
FFD Financial	Tri-State 1st Banc
Fifth Third	United Community
First Financial	Financial
Bancorp	Wayne Savings
First Niles Financial	Bancshares
Home Loan Financial	

HISTORICAL FINANCIALS

Company Type: Public

Income Statement
FYE: December 31

	ASSETS ($ mil.)	NET INCOME ($ mil.)	INCOME AS % OF ASSETS	EMPLOYEES
12/16	1,966	20	1.0%	441
12/15	1,869	8	0.4%	432
12/14	1,136	8	0.8%	327
12/13	1,137	7	0.7%	328
12/12	1,139	9	0.9%	335
Annual Growth	14.6%	19.9%	—	7.1%

2016 Year-End Financials

Debt ratio: 0.76%	No. of shares (mil.): 27
Return on equity: 9.97%	Dividends
Cash ($ mil.): 41	Yield: 0.0%
Current ratio: —	Payout: 21.0%
Long-term debt ($ mil.): —	Market value ($ mil.): 384

	STOCK PRICE ($) FY Close	P/E High/Low	Earnings	PER SHARE ($) Dividends	Book Value
12/16	14.20	20 11	0.76	0.16	7.88
12/15	8.60	24 20	0.36	0.12	7.35
12/14	8.35	18 14	0.48	0.12	6.71
12/13	6.55	17 14	0.41	0.12	6.02
12/12	6.20	13 9	0.53	0.18	6.43
Annual Growth	23.0%	— —	9.4%	(2.9%)	5.2%

FB Financial Corp

LOCATIONS

HQ: FB Financial Corp
211 Commerce Street, Suite 300, Nashville, TN 37201
Phone: 615 564-1212
Web: www.firstbankonline.com

HISTORICAL FINANCIALS

Company Type: Public

Income Statement
FYE: December 31

	ASSETS ($ mil.)	NET INCOME ($ mil.)	INCOME AS % OF ASSETS	EMPLOYEES
12/16	3,276	40	1.2%	1,108
12/15	2,899	47	1.7%	1,038
12/14	2,428	32	1.3%	—
12/13	2,258	26	1.2%	—
Annual Growth	13.2%	14.7%	—	—

2016 Year-End Financials

Debt ratio: 0.94%	No. of shares (mil.): 24
Return on equity: 14.27%	Dividends
Cash ($ mil.): 123	Yield: 0.1%
Current ratio: —	Payout: 191.9%
Long-term debt ($ mil.): —	Market value ($ mil.): 626

	STOCK PRICE ($) FY Close	P/E High/Low	Earnings	PER SHARE ($) Dividends	Book Value
12/16	25.95	12 9	2.10	4.03	13.71
12/15	0.00	— —	2.79	1.37	13.78
Annual Growth	—	— —	(9.0%)	43.3%	(0.2%)

FBL Financial Group Inc

Insurance holding company FBL Financial Group (FBL) is the parent of Farm Bureau Life Insurance Company. Through its subsidiary the firm sells life insurance annuities and investment products to farmers ranchers and agricultural businesses. Farm Bureau Life sells insurance and annuities through an exclusive network of about 2000 agents across some 15 states in the Midwest and West. (In Colorado it operates as Greenfields Life Insurance.) The company markets its products through an affiliation with the American Farm Bureau Federation. FBL also manages for a fee two Farm Bureau-affiliated property/casualty insurance companies. The Iowa Farm Bureau Federation owns close to 60% of the company.

Operations

FBL divides its business into two segments annuity and life insurance. Traditional and universal life insurance products sold primarily in Iowa Kansas and Oklahoma account for about 60% of sales. Annuities including fixed rate and index are also big in Iowa and Kansas and account for about 30% of revenue.

The two Farm Bureau-affiliated property/casualty insurers that FBL manages are Farm Bureau Property & Casualty and Western Agricultural Insurance. The two affiliates underwrite auto crop and other property/casualty policies for individuals and groups under FBL's corporate and other segment which accounts for about 10% of revenue.

Geographic Reach
FBL offers its services in 15 western and midwestern states. Iowa Kansas Oklahoma and Wyoming are key markets.

Financial Performance
After a few rocky years FBL has been back on track the last two years. In 2013 it reported a 5% increase in revenue from $656 million to $691 million as both annuity and life segments reported increases in the volume of business. Net income has been on a steady rise and increased 36% in 2013 from $80 million to $109 million due to the improved revenue and increased equity income. Cash from operations however has been declining for years and continued its trend with a $24 million drop to $182 million due to cash used for paying out and administering claims.

Strategy
Strategically FBL expands its penetration in both the life and property/casualty markets by encouraging existing policyholders to purchase other insurance products through the agents they already know. Its cross-selling technique has led the industry as a whole. Additionally FBL depends on the talent of the agents it engages and its overall ability to provide products that meet changing needs as well as superior customer service and market knowledge. It continually invests in training and supporting existing agents and recruiting new ones. FBL also launches new products like index annuities in 2012 and takes steps like decreasing commissions for some products that aren't profitable during this time of low interest rates.

EXECUTIVES

CEO, James P. (Jim) Brannen, age 55, $700,000 total compensation
CFO and Treasurer, Donald J. (Don) Seibel, age 53, $360,706 total compensation
Chief Investment Officer, Charles T. Happel, age 55, $353,496 total compensation
COO Life Companies, Raymond W. Wasilewski, age 58
CIO, Casey Decker
COO Property Casualty Companies, Daniel D. Pitcher, age 55, $383,778 total compensation
Vice Chairman, Jerry L. Chicoine, age 74
Chairman, Craig D. Hill, age 61
Auditors: Ernst & Young LLP

LOCATIONS

HQ: FBL Financial Group Inc
5400 University Avenue, West Des Moines, IA 50266-5997
Phone: 515 225-5400
Web: www.fblfinancial.com

Selected Areas of Operation
Farm Bureau Life Insurance Company
Multi-line (life and property/casualty
Arizona
Iowa
Kansas
Minnesota
Nebraska

New Mexico
South Dakota
Utah
Life only
Idaho
Montana
North Dakota
Oklahoma
Wisconsin
Wyoming
Farm Bureau Property & Casualty Insurance Company
and Western Agricultural Insurance Company
Arizona
Iowa
Kansas
Minnesota
Nebraska
New Mexico
South Dakota
Utah

PRODUCTS/OPERATIONS

2015 Sales

	$ mil.	% of total
Life Insurance	409	57
Annuity	212	29
Gains on derivatives	10	1
Losses on investments	(2.7)	-
Corporate & other	93	13
Total	**722**	**100**

Selected Subsidiaries

Insurance
  Farm Bureau Life Insurance Company
Noninsurance
  5400 Holdings L.L.C.
  FBL Assigned Benefit Company
  FBL Financial Group Capital Trust
  FBL Financial Group Capital Trust II
  FBL Financial Services Inc.
  FBL Investment Management Services Inc.
  FBL Leasing Services Inc.
  FBL Marketing Services L.L.C.

COMPETITORS

AIG
Allstate
American Equity Investment Life Holding Company
American Farmers & Ranchers Mutual Insurance Co.
COUNTRY Financial
Farm Family Holdings
Farmers & Merchants Investment
Great American Financial Resources
MetLife
Midland National Life
Nationwide
Prudential
State Farm
Thrivent Investment Management

HISTORICAL FINANCIALS

Company Type: Public

Income Statement
FYE: December 31

	ASSETS ($ mil.)	NET INCOME ($ mil.)	INCOME AS % OF ASSETS	EMPLOYEES
12/16	9,566	107	1.1%	1,644
12/15	9,132	113	1.2%	1,637
12/14	9,064	109	1.2%	1,628
12/13	8,461	108	1.3%	1,589
12/12	8,417	79	0.9%	1,582
Annual Growth	**3.2%**	**7.6%**	**—**	**1.0%**

2016 Year-End Financials

Debt ratio: 1.01%	No. of shares (mil.): 24
Return on equity: 9.21%	Dividends
Cash ($ mil.): 33	Yield: 0.0%
Current ratio: —	Payout: 85.9%
Long-term debt ($ mil.): —	Market value ($ mil.): 1,945

	STOCK PRICE ($) FY Close	P/E High/Low	PER SHARE ($) Earnings	Dividends	Book Value
12/16	78.15	19 13	4.28	3.68	47.73
12/15	63.64	15 11	4.53	3.60	45.73
12/14	58.03	13 8	4.39	1.40	50.69
12/13	44.79	11 8	4.21	2.52	42.20
12/12	34.21	13 9	2.87	0.40	47.58
Annual Growth	**22.9%**	**— —**	**10.5%**	**74.2%**	**0.1%**

FCB Financial Holdings Inc

Auditors: GRANT THORNTON LLP

LOCATIONS

HQ: FCB Financial Holdings Inc
2500 Weston Road, Suite 300, Weston, FL 33331
Phone: 954 984-3313
Web: www.floridacommunitybank.com

HISTORICAL FINANCIALS

Company Type: Public

Income Statement
FYE: December 31

	ASSETS ($ mil.)	NET INCOME ($ mil.)	INCOME AS % OF ASSETS	EMPLOYEES
12/16	9,090	99	1.1%	644
12/15	7,331	53	0.7%	649
12/14	5,957	22	0.4%	638
12/13	3,973	17	0.4%	640
12/12	3,245	(4)	—	—
Annual Growth	**29.4%**	**—**	**—**	**—**

2016 Year-End Financials

Debt ratio: —	No. of shares (mil.): 41
Return on equity: 10.72%	Dividends
Cash ($ mil.): 83	Yield: —
Current ratio: —	Payout: —
Long-term debt ($ mil.): —	Market value ($ mil.): 1,963

	STOCK PRICE ($) FY Close	P/E High/Low	PER SHARE ($) Earnings	Dividends	Book Value
12/16	47.70	20 12	2.31	0.00	23.87
12/15	35.79	30 17	1.23	0.00	21.44
12/14	24.64	42 35	0.58	0.00	20.57
Annual Growth	**18.0%**	**— —**	**41.3%**		**3.8%**

Federal Agricultural Mortgage Corp

Farmer Mac (Federal Agricultural Mortgage Corporation) is Fannie Mae and Freddie Mac's country cousin. Like its city-slicker kin it provides liquidity in its markets (agricultural real estate and rural housing mortgages) by buying loans from lenders and then securitizing the loans into Farmer Mac Guaranteed Securities. Farmer Mac buys both conventional loans and those guaranteed by the US Department of Agriculture. Farmer Mac was created by Congress in 1987 to establish a secondary market for agricultural mortgage and rural utilities loans. It is a stockholder-owned publicly-traded corporation based in Washington DC with an underwriting office in Iowa.

Operations

Farmer Mac operates four segments: Farm & Ranch which accounted for 39% of revenue during 2015 purchases mortgage loans secured by first liens on agricultural real estate including part-time farms and rural housing; Institutional Credit (28% of revenue) which buys or guarantees general lender obligations secured by eligible pools of loans; the USDA Guarantees segment (18%) which buys USDA-backed agricultural rural development business and industry and community facilities loans; and Rural Utilities (10%) which buys mortgages tied to eligible rural utilities loans. The organization generates more than 90% of its revenue from interest income stemming from a roughly even mix of loans and backed loan securities. About 47% of its revenue came from interest on Farmer Mac Guaranteed or USDA securities during 2015 while another 41% came from interest on loans. The rest came from interest on other investments (5% of revenue) guarantee and commitment fees (5%) and gains on financial derivatives and hedging activities (1%).

Geographic Reach

The Washington DC-based group serves the US from satellite operations in Ames Iowa; Boise Idaho; Canton Michigan; Fresno California; Johnston Iowa; and Scottsdale Arizona.

Sales and Marketing

Farmer Mac markets its services personally and directly to agricultural lenders by participating regularly in events such as state and national banking conferences. It also has alliances with the American Bankers Association and the Independent Community Bankers of Alliances and has a business relationship with the members of the Farm Credit System.

Financial Performance

Farmer Mac's annual revenues have risen more than 25% since 2011 thanks to a stronger agricultural economy as well as product developments which have driven customer and overall loan asset growth over the years. Its annual profits have also trended higher but have fluctuated more due to the volatility of the gains it's made from financial derivatives hedging activities and other trading securities.

The group's revenue climbed 4% to $284 million during 2015 mostly thanks to double-digit interest income growth as its loan assets grew 12% to $3.96 billion and as its Farm & Ranch loans USDA Securities and AgVantage securities balances grew as well. Farmer Mac's non-interest income shrank 39% as it collected $37.4 million less in trading securities gains as it did in 2014.

Revenue growth and a decline in interest expenses in 2015 drove Farmer Mac's net income up 43% to $68.7 million. The lender's operating cash levels jumped 19% to $184 million as its cash-based earnings rose and as working capital increased with changes in other assets.

Strategy

Farmer Mac seeks to improve the availability of long-term credit at stable interest rates to rural communities. To this end its primary strategy for managing interest rate risk is to fund asset purchases with liabilities that have similar duration and cash flow characteristics so that they will perform similarly as interest rates change.

EXECUTIVES

President and CEO, Timothy L. (Tim) Buzby, age 48, $643,750 total compensation
EVP CFO and Treasurer, R. Dale Lynch, age 50, $375,950 total compensation
SVP Agricultural Finance, J. Curtis Covington, age 61
SVP General Counsel and Secretary, Stephen P. Mullery, age 50, $340,930 total compensation
Senior Vice President Agricultural Finance, Curt Covington
Vice President Financial Planning and Analysis, Brian Brinch
Chairman, Lowell L. Junkins, age 73
Vice Chairman, Myles J. Watts, age 66
Auditors: PRICEWATERHOUSECOOPERS LLP

LOCATIONS

HQ: Federal Agricultural Mortgage Corp
1999 K Street, N.W., 4th Floor, Washington, DC 20006
Phone: 202 872-7700   **Fax:** 202 872-7713
Web: www.farmermac.com

PRODUCTS/OPERATIONS

2015 Sales

	% of total
Interest income	
Farmer Mac Guaranteed Securities and USDA Securities	47
Loans	41
Investments and cash equivalents	5
Noninterest income	
Guarantee and commitment fees	5
Gains on financial derivatives and hedging activities	1
Other	1
Total	**100**

2015 Sales

	% of total
Farm & Ranch	39
USDA Guarantees	28
Rural Utilities	18
Institutional Credit	10
Corporate	4
Reconciling Adjustments	1
Total	**100**

Selected Operations

Farm & Ranch (Farmer Mac I)
USDA Guarantees (Farmer Mac II)
Rural Utilities

COMPETITORS

AgFirst	Fannie Mae
AgStar	Farm Credit Services
AgriBank	of Mid-America
Bank of America	Freddie Mac
Citigroup	

HISTORICAL FINANCIALS

Company Type: Public

Income Statement

FYE: December 31

	ASSETS ($ mil.)	NET INCOME ($ mil.)	INCOME AS % OF ASSETS	EMPLOYEES
12/16	15,606	77	0.5%	81
12/15	15,540	68	0.4%	71
12/14	14,287	48	0.3%	71
12/13	13,361	75	0.6%	67
12/12	12,622	46	0.4%	64
Annual Growth	**5.4%**	**13.4%**	**—**	**6.1%**

2016 Year-End Financials

Debt ratio: 87.55%
Return on equity: 12.89%
Cash ($ mil.): 265
Current ratio: —
Long-term debt ($ mil.): —
No. of shares (mil.): 10
Dividends
  Yield: 0.0%
  Payout: 17.4%
Market value ($ mil.): 604

	STOCK PRICE ($) FY Close	P/E High/Low		PER SHARE ($) Earnings	Dividends	Book Value
12/16	57.27	10	4	5.97	1.04	61.05
12/15	31.57	8	5	4.19	0.64	51.79
12/14	30.34	10	8	3.37	0.56	49.90
12/13	34.25	6	4	6.41	0.48	30.55
12/12	32.50	8	4	3.98	0.40	32.81
Annual Growth	**15.2%**			**10.7%**	**27.0%**	**16.8%**

Federal Home Loan Bank New York

Federal Home Loan Bank of New York (FHLBNY) provides funds for residential mortgages and community development to more than 330 member banks savings and loans credit unions and life insurance companies in New York New Jersey Puerto Rico and the US Virgin Islands. One of a dozen Federal Home Loan Banks in the US it is cooperatively owned by its member institutions and supervised by the Federal Housing Finance Agency. FHLBNY like others in the system is privately capitalized; it receives no taxpayer funding. The bank instead raises funds mainly by issuing debt instruments in the capital markets.

Operations

FHLBNY is a secured lender that requires collateral for its advances which are typically used by members to underwrite residential mortgages or to invest in US Treasury and agency securities mortgage-backed securities and other real estate-related assets.

A large part of FHLBNY's business is in making collateralized loans or advances to members. It serves the public through its mortgage programs. Three members — Citibank (25%) Met Life (14%) and New York Community Bank (11%) — accounted for half of total advances.

Geographic Reach

Based in New York FHLBNY serves not only New York but New Jersey Puerto Rico and the US Virgin Islands.

Sales and Marketing

FHLBNY caters to more than 330 member banks credit unions life insurance companies and savings and loans.

Financial Performance

Revenue dropped by 14% to $801 million in fiscal 2013 from 2012's $934.9 million. FHLBNY attributes the decline to a decrease in interest income and other income. Net income also dropped some 16% in 2013 to $304.6 million vs. $360.7 million in 2012. It attributes net income decreases to declining revenue and rising other expenses. Operating cash flow decreased in fiscal 2013 to $525.6 million compared to 2012's $678.9 million.

Strategy

Credit unions are a possible area of growth for FHLBNY. The bank has identified more than 50 credit unions and banks that are not members but are eligible. To be under consideration an institution must have more than $50 million in assets ($100 million for banks) be an established wholesale lender maintain a high deposit-to-loan ratio and have management that has done business with an FHLB in the past.

Beginning in 2014 it's also funding — with the help of $35.5 million in subsidies — 48 affordable housing initiatives throughout New Jersey New York Puerto Rico the US Virgin Islands Florida Maryland and Pennsylvania. The effort involves the creation or rehabilitation of more than 3000 affordable housing units.

EXECUTIVES

Vice President and Director Information Security, Ken Brothers
Assistant Vice President, Diahann Rothstein
Vice President of MIS IS, Robert Fusco
Assistant Vice President, Claudia Kim
Vice President, Edward Samson
Vice President, Edwin Bird
Vice President Director Of Trading, Philip Scott
Vice President Sales And Marketing And C, Alfred O'Connell
Vice President Manager Business Research and Devolpment, John Brandon
Vice President, Eugene Khesin
Assistant Vice President, Kristen Lalama
Assistant Vice President Financial Risk Management, Kimberly Whitenack
Auditors: PricewaterhouseCoopers LLP

LOCATIONS

HQ: Federal Home Loan Bank New York
101 Park Avenue, New York, NY 10178
Phone: 212 681-6000
Web: www.fhlbny.com

PRODUCTS/OPERATIONS

2013 Sales

	$ mil.	% of total
Interest		
Advances	444	55
Long-term securities	244	30
Mortgage loans held for portfolio	68	9
Available-for-sale securities	16	2
Other	14	2
Non-interest	13	2
Total	**801**	**100**

HISTORICAL FINANCIALS

Company Type: Public

Income Statement

FYE: December 31

	ASSETS ($ mil.)	NET INCOME ($ mil.)	INCOME AS % OF ASSETS	EMPLOYEES
12/16	143,606	401	0.3%	280
12/15	123,248	414	0.3%	273
12/14	132,825	314	0.2%	258
12/13	128,332	304	0.2%	258
12/12	102,988	360	0.4%	272
Annual Growth	**8.7%**	**2.7%**	**—**	**0.7%**

2016 Year-End Financials

Debt ratio: 59.04%
Return on equity: 5.58%
Cash ($ mil.): 151
Current ratio: —
Long-term debt ($ mil.): —
No. of shares (mil.): 63
Dividends
  Yield: —
  Payout: 67.3%
Market value ($ mil.): —

FEDERAL HOME LOAN BANK OF ATLANTA

Where do banks in the southeastern US bank? Federal Home Loan Bank of Atlanta. Known as FHLBank Atlanta for short the bank provides mortgage funding deposit community investment and cash management services to some 1100 commercial banks credit unions insurance companies and thrifts. Its territory includes Alabama Florida Georgia Maryland North Carolina South Carolina Virginia and Washington DC. The bank primarily provides funding to members to originate residential mortgages and community development loans. It also purchases mortgages on the secondary market to provide liquidity.

EXECUTIVES

Vice President and Director of Accounting Policy, William Shaw

Assistant Vice President Liquidity Management, Deandra Wulf

Vice President, Pam MacPhaul

Vice President Senior Vice President Finance, Leslie Schreiner

Vice President Assistant Director of Administrative Services, Connie Arnold

Support Center Manager Assistant Vice President, Tony Norsworthy

Senior Vice President Compliance, Kevin Ashburn

Senior Vice President, Melissa Hoggatt

Vice President, David Eckardt

Senior Vice President Corp SEC, Julia Brown

Vice President, Colin Gatewood

Assistant Vice President Senior Financial Business And Operations Analyst, Cindy Wilson

Soa Development Manager Assistant Vice President, Jerry Versteegh

Vice President Director Community Investment Services Production and Operations, Jennifer Robinson

Director of Government Relations, Kimani Little

LOCATIONS

HQ: FEDERAL HOME LOAN BANK OF ATLANTA
1475 PEACHTREE ST NE # 400, ATLANTA, GA 303093037
Phone: 404 888-8000
Web: WWW.FHLBANKS.COM

COMPETITORS

Fannie Mae · Ginnie Mae · Freddie Mac

HISTORICAL FINANCIALS
Company Type: Private

Income Statement · FYE: December 31

	ASSETS ($ mil.)	NET INCOME ($ mil.)	INCOME AS % OF ASSETS	EMPLOYEES
12/16	138,671	278	0.2%	339
12/15	142,253	301	0.2%	—
12/14	138,344	271	0.2%	—
12/13	122,316	338	0.3%	—
Annual Growth	4.3%	(6.3%)	—	—

2016 Year-End Financials

Debt ratio: ——
Return on equity: 22.80%
Cash ($ mil.): 12,077
Current ratio: ——
Long-term debt ($ mil.): ——
Dividends
Yield: —
Payout: —
Market value ($ mil.): —

FEDERAL HOME LOAN BANK OF CHICAGO

Federal Home Loan Bank of Chicago (FHLB Chicago) is a government-sponsored enterprises that provides secured loans and other support services to about 760 members including commercial banks credit unions insurance companies thrifts and community development financial institutions throughout Illinois and Wisconsin. It is cooperatively owned by its member institutions who use advances from the bank to originate residential mortgages invest in government or mortgage-related securities and promote affordable housing and community development in their respective communities. FHLB Chicago is one of a dozen federal banks that comprise the Federal Home Loan Bank System that was established by Congress in 1932.

Operations

The Federal Home Loan Banks are overseen by the Federal Housing Finance Agency. Other services offered include deposits wire transfers and check processing.

Strategy

Loan demand at the bank has fallen as its members have increased access to other forms of liquidity such as customer deposits and certain government programs. FHLB Chicago believes its restructuring efforts and investment activity have led the bank to a position of strength going forward.

EXECUTIVES

Vice President Financial Markets, Matthew Desmarais

Vice President, Matt Zimmerman

Vice President, Kimberly Cullotta

Managing Director, Steven Mosshamer

Vice President Develop, Thomas Ruggieri

Vice President of Sales, Carolyn Jaw

Vice President and Senior Manager Human Resources, Joaquin Fonte

Vice President Managing Director MPF Applications, Kathy Rasmussen

Assistant Vice President Community Investment Database Analyst, Sameera Ishaq

Senior Vice President Balance Sheet Strategy and Quantitative Analysis, Rene Cornejo

Senior Vice President Member Product Support, Christian Claffy

Vice President and Associate General Counsel, Judd Levy

Assistant Vice President of Development, Gary Engstrom

Vice President and Assistant General Counsel, Maryjane Hall

Vice President accounting policy, Claude Edelson

Auditors: PRICEWATERHOUSECOOPERS LLP CH

LOCATIONS

HQ: FEDERAL HOME LOAN BANK OF CHICAGO
200 E RANDOLPH ST # 1700, CHICAGO, IL 606016428
Phone: 312 565-5700
Web: WWW.FHLBC.COM

HISTORICAL FINANCIALS
Company Type: Private

Income Statement · FYE: December 31

	ASSETS ($ mil.)	NET INCOME ($ mil.)	INCOME AS % OF ASSETS	EMPLOYEES
12/16	78,692	327	0.4%	405
12/15	70,676	349	0.5%	—
12/14	71,841	392	0.5%	—
12/12	69,584	375	0.5%	—
Annual Growth	3.1%	(3.4%)	—	—

2016 Year-End Financials

Debt ratio: ——
Return on equity: 24.50%
Cash ($ mil.): 5,076
Current ratio: ——
Long-term debt ($ mil.): ——
Dividends
Yield: —
Payout: —
Market value ($ mil.): —

Federal Home Loan Bank Of Cincinnati

Auditors: PricewaterhouseCoopers LLP

LOCATIONS

HQ: Federal Home Loan Bank Of Cincinnati
600 Atrium Two, P.O Box 598, Cincinnati, OH 45201-0598
Phone: 513 852-7500
Web: www.fhlbcin.com

HISTORICAL FINANCIALS
Company Type: Public

Income Statement · FYE: December 31

	ASSETS ($ mil.)	NET INCOME ($ mil.)	INCOME AS % OF ASSETS	EMPLOYEES
12/16	104,635	268	0.3%	211
12/15	118,796	248	0.2%	203
12/14	106,640	244	0.2%	204
12/13	103,180	261	0.3%	—
12/12	0	234	—	—
Annual Growth	—	3.4%	—	—

2016 Year-End Financials

Debt ratio: 93.54%
Return on equity: 5.27%
Cash ($ mil.): 8
Current ratio: ——
Long-term debt ($ mil.): ——
No. of shares (mil.): 41
Dividends
Yield: —
Payout: 63.9%
Market value ($ mil.): —

Federal Home Loan Bank Of Dallas

LOCATIONS

HQ: Federal Home Loan Bank Of Dallas
8500 Freeport Parkway South, Suite 600, Irving, TX 75063-2547
Phone: 214 441-8500

HISTORICAL FINANCIALS
Company Type: Public

Income Statement
FYE: December 31

	ASSETS ($ mil.)	NET INCOME ($ mil.)	INCOME AS % OF ASSETS	EMPLOYEES
12/16	58,212	79	0.1%	218
12/15	42,083	67	0.2%	207
12/14	38,045	48	0.1%	192
12/13	30,221	87	0.3%	—
12/12	0	81	—	—
Annual Growth	—	(0.7%)	—	—

2016 Year-End Financials
Debt ratio: 46.38%
Return on equity: 3.16%
Cash ($ mil.): 27
Current ratio: —
Long-term debt ($ mil.): —

No. of shares (mil.): 19
Dividends
 Yield: —
 Payout: 22.2%
Market value ($ mil.): —

Federal Home Loan Bank Of Des Moines

Auditors: PricewaterhouseCoopers LLP

LOCATIONS
HQ: Federal Home Loan Bank Of Des Moines Financial Center, 666 Walnut Street, Des Moines, IA 50309
Phone: 515 281-1000
Web: www.fhlbdm.com

HISTORICAL FINANCIALS
Company Type: Public

Income Statement
FYE: December 31

	ASSETS ($ mil.)	NET INCOME ($ mil.)	INCOME AS % OF ASSETS	EMPLOYEES
12/16	180,605	649	0.4%	307
12/15	137,381	131	0.1%	279
12/14	95,523	121	0.1%	228
12/13	73,004	109	0.2%	—
12/12	0	111	—	—
Annual Growth	—	55.3%	—	—

2016 Year-End Financials
Debt ratio: 94.60%
Return on equity: 9.94%
Cash ($ mil.): 225
Current ratio: —
Long-term debt ($ mil.): —

No. of shares (mil.): 59
Dividends
 Yield: —
 Payout: —
Market value ($ mil.): —

Federal Home Loan Bank Of San Francisco

The city by the bay is the home to the Federal Home Loan Bank of San Francisco one ofÂ a dozenÂ regional banks in the Federal Home Loan Bank System chartered by Congress inÂ 1932 to provide credit to residential mortgage lenders. TheÂ government-sponsored enterpriseÂ is privately owned by its members which include some 400 commercial banks credit unions industrial loan companies savings and loans insurance companies and housing associatesÂ headquartered in Arizona California and Nevada. The bank links members to worldwide capital markets which provide them with low-cost funding. Members then pass these advances along to their customers in the form of affordable home mortgage and economic development loans.

EXECUTIVES
Senior Vice President Financial Risk Man, Kenneth Miller
Senior Vice President and CIO, Elena Andreadakis
Managing Director Mortgage Finance, John McCormack
Assistant Vice President Operations and Compliance Risk Management, Katy Liu
Auditors: PricewaterhouseCoopers LLP

LOCATIONS
HQ: Federal Home Loan Bank Of San Francisco
 600 California Street, San Francisco, CA 94108
Phone: 415 616-1000
Web: www.fhlbsf.com

PRODUCTS/OPERATIONS

2013

	$ mil.	% of total
Interest income	1,086	97
Other income	5	3
Total	**1,091**	**100**

HISTORICAL FINANCIALS
Company Type: Public

Income Statement
FYE: December 31

	ASSETS ($ mil.)	NET INCOME ($ mil.)	INCOME AS % OF ASSETS	EMPLOYEES
12/16	91,941	712	0.8%	274
12/15	85,707	638	0.7%	263
12/14	75,807	205	0.3%	255
12/13	85,774	308	0.4%	262
12/12	86,421	491	0.6%	264
Annual Growth	1.6%	9.7%	—	0.9%

2016 Year-End Financials
Debt ratio: 91.07%
Return on equity: 13.61%
Cash ($ mil.): 592
Current ratio: —
Long-term debt ($ mil.): —

No. of shares (mil.): 24
Dividends
 Yield: —
 Payout: 39.8%
Market value ($ mil.): —

FEDERAL-MOGUL HOLDINGS LLC

LOCATIONS
HQ: FEDERAL-MOGUL HOLDINGS LLC
 27300 W 11 MILE RD, SOUTHFIELD, MI 480346147
Phone: 248 354-7700
Web: WWW.FEDERALMOGUL.COM

HISTORICAL FINANCIALS
Company Type: Private

Income Statement
FYE: December 31

	REVENUE ($ mil.)	NET INCOME ($ mil.)	NET PROFIT MARGIN	EMPLOYEES
12/16	7,434	90	1.2%	53,700
12/15	7,419	(104)	—	—
12/14	7,317	(161)	—	—
Annual Growth	0.8%	—	—	—

2016 Year-End Financials
Debt ratio: —
Return on equity: 1.20%
Cash ($ mil.): 300
Current ratio: 0.90
Long-term debt ($ mil.): —

Dividends
 Yield: —
 Payout: —
Market value ($ mil.): —

FedEx Corp

Holding company FedEx hopes its package of subsidiaries will keep delivering significant market share. Its FedEx Express unit is the world's #1 express transportation provider delivering more than 4 million packages daily to more than 220 countries and territories from about 1800 FedEx Office shops. It maintains a fleet of more than 655 aircraft and roughly 58000 motor vehicles and trailers. To complement the express delivery business FedEx Ground provides small-package ground delivery in North America and less-than-truckload (LTL) carrier FedEx Freight hauls larger shipments. FedEx Office stores offer a variety of document-related and other business services and serve as retail hubs for other FedEx units.In addition its TNT Express subsidiary is an international express transportation and small-package ground delivery company.

Operations

FedEx offers a broad portfolio of transportation e-commerce and business services through subsidiary companies which operate independently and are managed collaboratively under the FedEx brand.

FedEx Express is the world's largest express transportation company. Its business operations include FedEx Trade Networks (international trade services) and FedEx SupplyChain Systems (supply chain solutions).

FedEx Ground is a North American provider of small-package ground delivery services. This segment includes FedEx SmartPost a business-to-consumer package delivery using the US Postal Service.

FedEx Freight offers less-than-truckload (LTL) freight services throughout Canada Mexico Puerto Rico and the US Virgin Islands. (LTL carriers consolidate freight from multiple shippers into a single truckload.) This unit's offerings include FedEx Freight Priority FedEx Freight Economy and FedEx Custom Critical.

FedEx Services provides sales marketing information technology communications and back-office support for other FedEx companies. This unit includes FedEx TechConnect (US billings and collections support) and FedEx Office and Print Services (document and business services for FedEx Express and FedEx Ground shipping services).

The company in 2016 added a new subsidiary to its operations through the purchase of TNT Express B.V. an international express transportation small-package ground delivery and freight transportation company. TNT Express operates road transportation networks and delivers to over 200 countries.

Geographic Reach

FedEx operates in or delivers goods to more than 220 countries and territories from over 1800 locations. Its sorting and handling facilities are located in Memphis Tennessee; Indianapolis Indiana; Fort Worth Texas; Newark New Jersey; Oakland and Los Angeles California; Greensboro North Carolina; Chicago Illinois; Anchorage Alaska; Paris France; Cologne Germany; Guangzhou China; and Osaka Japan. The US accounts for roughly 70% of net sales each year.

Sales and Marketing

FedEx promotes its brands through television print digital advertising sponsorships and special events. It also serves customers in more than 375 airports worldwide.

TNT Express?s customers are primarily large companies and multinationals as well as small and medium-sized enterprises. It mainly targets the industrial automotive high-tech and healthcare sectors.

Financial Performance

FedEx has achieved seven straight years of unprecedented growth. Revenues jumped from 20% from $50.4 billion in 2016 to peak at $60.3 billion in 2017 — a historic milestone for the company. The growth for 2017 was led by a 9% increase in FedEx Ground sales fueled by volume growth in its residential services coupled with rate increases and full-year results from its GENCO acquisition. FedEX also experienced a 3% bump in FedEx Express sales mainly due to its TNT Express acquisition.

Profits surged by 65% from $1.8 billion in 2016 to $3 billion in 2017 another landmark total. This was attributed to a $24 million gain on a retirement plans market-to-market adjustment compared to an almost $1.5 billion loss for this item the previous year. FedEx's cash flow from operating activities however decreased from $5.71 billion to $4.93 billion due to almost $1.7 billion it spent on pension plans in 2017 compared to $346 million in 2016.

Strategy

In addition to making strategic acquisitions FedEx has signaled that it is ready to enhance its automation infrastructure to compete with industry leaders like Amazon and Uber. In 2017 the company announced it is exploring launching driverless small vehicles that could drive around neighborhoods and make deliveries. It has partnered with several automakers that specialize in autonomous trucking and expects to see a major ramp-up of automated vehicles in the shipping industry within the next ten years. However it plans to be selective about where it invests its money and will deploy technology in areas it sees will provide the best payoff and value.

In the meantime e-commerce continues to be a crucial growth engine for FedEx. Even though the company's residential e-commerce revenues are much smaller than its business-to-business revenues it is still its fastest-growing market and FedEx will continue to enhance and extend its global transportation and technology networks. In 2017 FedEx announced it increased its ground facilities by 10 million sq. ft. or 15% during the past year to meet increased demand for orders over the internet.

Mergers and Acquisitions

FedEx has achieved historic growth over the years through the use of acquisitions. In 2016 it acquired rival TNT Express for a purchase price of $4.9 billion. The major deal was the largest in FedEx's history and vastly improved its European footprint and its strength in other regions including North America and Asia.The full integration of FedEx Express and TNT Express is projected to be completed by the end of 2020.

Previously in 2015 FedEx expanded its e-commerce and supply chain portfolio through the purchase of GENCO a leading North American third-party logistics provider for $1.4 billion. The deal bolstered FedEx's expertise in the targeted vertical markets of technology health care and retail.

HISTORY

From his undergraduate classes at Yale and his experience as a charter airplane pilot Fred Smith got the idea that increased automation of business processes would create the need for a reliable overnight delivery service and he presented his case in a term paper in 1965. After serving in the Marine Corps in Vietnam Smith began raising money to develop the overnight delivery idea. He founded Federal Express in 1971 with $4 million inherited from his father and $80 million from investors. Overnight and second-day delivery to two dozen US cities began in 1973.

Several factors contributed to FedEx's early success: Airlines turned their focus from parcels to passengers; United Parcel Service (UPS) union workers went on strike in 1974; and competitor REA Express went bankrupt. FedEx went public in 1978.

EXECUTIVES

EVP Market Development and Corporate Communications, T. Michael Glenn, age 61, $850,028 total compensation

EVP and CFO, Alan B. Graf, age 61, $920,840 total compensation

Chairman and CEO, Frederick W. (Fred) Smith, age 73, $1,279,632 total compensation

President and COO, David J. Bronczek, age 63, $960,936 total compensation

Senior Vice President, James Webb

Corporate Vice President Strategic Financial Planning and Control, James Hudson

EVP Information Services and CIO, Robert B. (Rob) Carter, age 57, $778,216 total compensation

President and CEO FedEx Freight, Michael L. Ducker, age 64

Corporate VP Customer and Business Transactions, Christine P. Richards, age 62, $617,640 total compensation

President and CEO FedEx Express, David L. Cunningham

President and CEO FedEx Ground, Henry J. Maier

Vice President Customer Services, Casey Zettler

Vice President, Don Fike

VP Admin, Chris Sniezak

Vice President Sales, Aimee DiCicco

Corp Vice President and Treasurer, Mike Lenz

Vice President Solutions, Chris Suhoza

Vice President Corporate Security, Bruce A Townsend

Vice President Administration, Stefanie Mouzon

Vice President of Operations, Karl Stingily

Vice President, Tayssir Awada

Vice President Strat Custmr Support, Troy Brock

Vice President Strategic Planning and Support, Dale Chrystie

Senior Vice President Administ, Kristi Emmons

Vice President Service Experience Leadership, Rebecca Yeung

Vice President Regional Operations, Craig Thompson

Vice President Operations, Robert Cooper

Corporate Vice President and Principal Accounting Officer, John Merino

Vice President Regional Operations West Region, Glen Corbin

Vice President Human Resources, Donna Humphreys

Vice President Operations Americas For Fedex Trade Networks, John Gazitua

Senior Vice President Transportation Systems and Chief Postal Officer FedEx Ground, Barbara Wallander

Vice President Finance, Jane Amaba

Vice President Administration EC Marketing, Shana Hyman

Executive Vice President, Rosa Rangel

Senior Vice President Human RE, Mark Bishop

Executive Vice President, Marilyn Dasilva

Senior Vice President Information Technology, Winn Stephenson

Vice President Corporate Sales, Michael Moriarty

Vice President Sales and LAC, Steven Goddard

Vice President Sales, Alan Grayson

Vice President, Shana Bertram

Vice President Information Technology EMEA, Michael Foster

Vice President Digital Access Marketing, Tom Wicinski

Vice President Sales, Larry Labelle

Vice President Marketing, Lawrence Lanier

Executive Vice President, Dottie Berry

Vice President of the Southern Region, Robert E Holcombe

VICE PRESIDENT ADMIN, Janice Gibbs

Vice President Senior Assistant Ii, Patricia Hofer

Senior Regional Vice President Of Logistics, Gerald Hart

Vice President Sales, Pat Finan

Vice President Administration, Deanna Davidson

Vice President Risk Management and Business Transactions (1993), Cary S Blancett

Marketing Vice President, Randy Pepper

Vice President Admin, Mary Bryant

Vice President Finance, Tom Holland

Senior Vice President, Leonard B Feiler

Executive Vice President and Global Sales Manager, Jim French

Senior Vice President Administ, Kristi Richardson

Vice President Senior Assistant II, Lisa Vinson

Senior Vice President Operations, Sev Mcmurtry

Vice President of Operations, Michael Murkowski

Vice President Regional Operations, Dale Davis

Vice President Worldwide Services, Glenda Welsh Corwin

Executive Vice President and Chief Operating Officer FedEx Office, Kim Dixon

National Account Manager, Kyle Rowden

Vice President Regulatory Affairs and Compliance, Cindy Allen

Vice President Administration, Clara Petty

CVP Human Resources, Judy Edge

Senior Vice President, George Silverman

Vice President of Human Resour, Sean McNamee

Senior Vice President Global Product Marketing, Jill Brown

Vice President, Michael Macyauski

Vice President Electronic Marketing, Karen Rodgers

Division Vice President Operations, Michael Zanolli

VP Admin, Kaye Farrah

Vice President, Ray Carroll

Treasurer, Elizabeth Crowder

Auditors: Ernst & Young LLP

LOCATIONS

HQ: FedEx Corp
942 South Shady Grove Road, Memphis, TN 38120
Phone: 901 818-7500
Web: www.fedex.com

2017 Sales

	$ mil.	% of total
US	40,269	67
Other countries	20,050	33
Total	**60,319**	**100**

PRODUCTS/OPERATIONS

2017 Sales

	$ mil.	% of total
FedEx Express	27,358	45
FedEx Ground	18,075	30
TNT Express	7,401	12
FedEx Freight	6,443	11
FedEx Services	1,621	2
Corporate eliminations and other	(579)	-
Total	**60,319**	**100**

Services
FedEx Trade Networks
FedEx Supply Chain Systems
FedEx SmartPost
GENCO

COMPETITORS

ABF Freight System	Pitney Bowes
Allegra Network	PostNL
AlphaGraphics	Ricoh USA
ArcBest	Ryder System
Canada Post	The UPS Store
DHL	UPS
Japan Post	US Postal Service
Nippon Express	Xerox
Office Depot	YRC Worldwide
Old Dominion Freight	

HISTORICAL FINANCIALS

Company Type: Public

Income Statement

FYE: May 31

	REVENUE ($ mil.)	NET INCOME ($ mil.)	NET PROFIT MARGIN	EMPLOYEES
05/17	60,319	2,997	5.0%	169,000
05/16	50,365	1,820	3.6%	168,000
05/15	47,453	1,050	2.2%	166,000
05/14	45,567	2,097	4.6%	162,000
05/13	44,287	1,561	3.5%	160,700
Annual Growth	**8.0%**	**17.7%**	**—**	**1.3%**

2017 Year-End Financials

Debt ratio: 30.75%
Return on equity: 20.08%
Cash ($ mil.): 3,969
Current ratio: 1.59
Long-term debt ($ mil.): 14,909
No. of shares (mil.): 268
Dividends
Yield: 0.8%
Payout: 22.5%
Market value ($ mil.): 51,999

	STOCK PRICE ($) FY Close	P/E High/Low		PER SHARE ($) Earnings	Dividends	Book Value
05/17	193.84	18	13	11.07	1.60	59.92
05/16	164.97	28	19	6.51	1.00	51.91
05/15	173.22	49	38	3.65	0.80	53.09
05/14	144.16	21	14	6.75	0.60	48.04
05/13	96.34	22	17	4.91	0.56	54.71
Annual Growth	**19.1%**	**—**	**—**	**22.5%**	**30.0%**	**2.3%**

Fidelity National Financial Inc

To make sure that buying a dream home doesn't become a nightmare Fidelity National Financial (also known as FNF) provides title insurance escrow home warranties and other services related to real estate transactions. It is now the biggest dog in the residential and commercial title insurance sectors (the next largest player is First American) and accounts for around 35% of all title in-surance policies in the US. The company operates through underwriters including Fidelity National Title Company Commonwealth Land Title Alamo Title and National Title of New York. It sells its products both directly and through independent agents. Fidelity National has been divesting its holdings in casual restaurant chains.

Operations

FNF is organized into two segments: FNF Core Operations which accounts for more than 85% of revenues and includes title insurance and related closing services; and Fidelity National Finance Ventures (FNFV) which includes its other investments.

Through Black Knight Financial and Ser-viceLink FNF provides mortgage technology and transaction services utilizing subsidiary Lender Processing Services' or LPS' MSP system (the largest residential mortgage servicing technology platform in the country).

Title insurance premiums account for about three-fourths of Fidelity National Financial's rev-enues but the company also maintains through FNFV a small handful of other operations com-pletely outside of the title insurance industry. These holdings include a 33% stake in Ceridian a payroll and HR services firm. It also has holdings in casual and upscale dining restaurants though its 55% ownership of American Blue Ribbon Holdings.

In late 2016 FNF announced plans to spin off Black Knight and FNFV to create three standalone public entities.

Geographic Reach

FNF's insurance businesses operate exclusively within the US. Naturally the biggest markets are in states with the greatest populations: California Texas New York and Florida combined account for some 45% of its title insurance premiums.

The company leases offices in more than 40 states and Washington DC as well as in Canada India and Puerto Rico.

Sales and Marketing

FNF uses direct sales representatives and inde-pendent agents to market its title and escrow prod-ucts to residential and commercial real estate cus-tomers. The company maintains some 1300 retail offices to provide residential title insurance. It mar-kets its commercial title insurance through a net-work of 5000 agents in major urban real estate markets.

Financial Performance

While the company is basically sound FNF's rev-enues can be hampered by stiffness in the residen-tial mortgage lending market. With the exception of 2014 revenue has been on the rise; it rose 5% to $9.6 billion in 2016 as closing volumes contin-ued to rebound. Increased agent remittances and growth in the Black Knight and OneDigital units also led to higher revenue that year. All told FNF saw 6% growth in escrow title-related and other fees; 15% growth in agency title insurance premi-ums; and 4% growth in direct title insurance pre-miums.

Net income on the other hand has been fluctu-ating for the past few years. Thanks largely to FNF's higher revenue net income rose 23% to $650 million in 2016. However higher agent com-missions expenses and personnel costs did cut into profits that year.

Cash flow from operations continued its upward trend in 2016 increasing 26% to $1.2 billion. That increase was driven by the higher net income as well as positive changes in assets and liabilities such as accounts payable.

Strategy

Title insurance is typically one of the most stable types of insurance written. It is folded into the piles of paperwork home buyers sign during closings with little or no fuss. Even when US home sales become sluggish FNF stays active from refinancing of existing mortgages. However when interest rates rise refinancing activities tend to slow down. In the current economic cycle FNF expects that mort-gage originations will slow down through 2019 but lower unemployment rates and rising con-sumer confidence should help offset the impact of higher interest rates. Additionally commercial real estate transactions tend to be less reliant on inter-est rates which should help boost the company's sales.

To stay at the top of the title insurance game FNF's core strategies include building on its vari-ous well-known brand names; delivering superior customer service; and maintaining operations that can withstand the cyclical title insurance industry. For the latter it monitors its corporate organization and office network (consolidating operations as necessary) and strikes a balance between residen-tial and commercial transactions. The company also introduces new products and technologies to remain competitive.

FNF's Black Knight technology services arm aims to deepen its existing customer relationships by cross-selling its various offerings including data and analytics. The unit has its eye on the mid-tier origination and servicing market for new business. Although Black Knight primarily pursues organic growth it is also open to making acquisitions to enter new geographic markets or add new prod-ucts and services.

In a similar vein transaction services unit Ser-viceLink entered the auction business when FNF acquired Hudson & Marshall in mid-2017. The new ServiceLink Auction offering will provide fore-closure and real estate owned auction services.

Historically FNF and its operating subsidiaries have grown through numerous acquisitions in the title insurance space as well as by adding new of-ferings to attract more customers. However FNF is now so dominant within the industry that any attempt to grow larger there would draw the scrutiny of regulators. While keeping its eye on strengthening its existing title insurance operations the company has made some moves to diversify by buying up non-insurance related businesses. In 2017 it acquired health care technology firm T-System for $200 million.

To raise cash for more diversification the com-pany sometimes sells its stakes in certain invest-ments. For example in 2015 it sold its 70% stake in Cascade Timberlands to Whitefish Cascade For-est Resources for $85 million. After a short stint investing in restaurants the company spun off its stake in J. Alexander's in 2015; it also announced plans to spin off American Blue Ribbon Holdings. In 2017 the company agreed to sell its 96% stake in health insurance distribution and management firm OneDigital to New Mountain Capital for $560 million.

Mergers and Acquisitions

In 2017 FNF bought Hudson & Marshall a lead-ing property and real estate auction firm. FNF sub-sidiary ServiceLink entered the auction business through that transaction; Hudson & Marshall now powers the new ServiceLink Auction offering.

Also in 2017 the company acquired Real Geeks which provides a customer relationship manage-ment (CRM) platform and other internet tools to the real estate industry. It then acquired control of Title Guaranty of Hawaii the state's oldest title in-surance company.

Further boosting its technology capabilities in 2016 FNF acquired Georgia-based Commissions (which provides web-based real estate marketing and CRM software) for $229 million. Also that year subsidiary Black Knight Financial Services acquired eLynx which provides electronic capture and document management services to the finan-cial and real estate sectors for $115 million.

Company Background

Like all title insurers Fidelity National Financial shivered when the big chill hit the real estate market in 2008. But while the company slowed it remained quick enough to take advantage of opportunities. When its ailing rival LandAmerica Financial Group filed Chapter 11 in 2008 the company bought up the choicer bits for $235 million. This purchase helped make it into the largest title insurer in the US and caught the attention of the FTC prompting the company to divest a few holdings to soothe the agency's nerves. The 2009 sale of Fidelity National Capital only brought in $50 million but took $214 million of debt off company ledgers. The 2010 sale of its 32% stake in Sedgwick Claims Management brought in some $225 million.

The current company arose in 2006 when a previous company also named Fidelity National Financial split apart its title insurance operations from its information services business. What had been Fidelity National Title Group took on its former parent's name while Fidelity National Information Services took on the former parent's remaining operations. The two companies share a history and some stray holdings but are otherwise separate.

EXECUTIVES

EVP and Chief Legal Officer, Peter T. Sadowski, age 63, $431,671 total compensation

CEO, Raymond R. (Randy) Quirk, age 71, $831,692 total compensation

Executive Vice President, Richard Cox

EVP General Counsel and Corporate Secretary, Michael L. (Mike) Gravelle, age 56, $550,500 total compensation

EVP Corporate Strategy, Brent B. Bickett, age 53, $550,500 total compensation

COO, Roger S. Jewkes, age 59, $630,000 total compensation

President Fidelity National Title Group National Agency Operations, Erika Meinhardt, age 59

EVP and CFO, Anthony J. (Tony) Park, age 51, $483,000 total compensation

President, Michael J. (Mike) Nolan, age 58, $557,308 total compensation

Vice President and Information Technology Director Senior Data Analyst, James Williams

Vice President and Assistant Corporate Secretary, Colleen Haley

Senior Vice President Finance and Controller Fidelity National Information Services, Steven Parker

Senior Vice President Government Relations, Sherwood Girion

Vice President Regional Controller, Sylvia Freyling

Assistant Vice President And Administrative Assistant, Jennifer Edwards

Vice President Business Development, Sue Jacobson

Escrow Officer Assistant Vice President, Sam Saravia

Assistant Vice President Sales Representative, Kelly McConnell

Vice President Employment Counsel, Patrick Mortimer

Assistant Vice President Special Projects Franchise Team Lead, Andrea McMahon

Vice President and Commercial Counsel, Sophie Stein

Vice President bound Sales, Terri Adamo

Assistant Vice President And Chair Of Citizenship Committee, Cathy Kennedy

Vice President And Counsel, Nathaniel Yingling

Assistant Vice President, Rhonda Evans

VP Tax Director, Carl Utter

AVP Director of Social Strategy Fidelity National Title Agency, Chelsea Peitz

Vice President and Area Counsel, Kevin Campbell

Vice President Digital Strategy Fidelity National Title, Bill Risser

Vice President, April Palmer

Vice President, David Golub

Assistant Vice President, Sandy Dow

Assistant Vice President Agency Auditor, Mary Rooney

Vice President, Tamara Strickland

Vice President Sales Executive FNTG Builder Services National Commercial Services, Alissa Vatter

Vice President, Terence Mullin

Vice President Kitsap Operations, Mary Schofield

Title Officer Assistant Vice President, Kevin Davis

Vice President Senior Commercial Escrow Officer Fidelity National Title, Tina Lucero

Assistant Vice President And Senior Claims Counsel, Stephanie Thomas

Vice President, George Tellez

Senior Vice President National Business Development, Mark Till

Senior Vice President, Kenji Kikuchi

Vice President Chicago Title and Fidelity National Title Santa Barbara County, Jennifer Lemert

Vice President Brand Director FNTG Commercial Operations, Karim Moullemaaz

Assistant Vice President Business Process and Automation Digital Solutions Manager, Pamela Williams

Assistant Vice President, Jason Dumas

Assistant Vice President and Agency Account Manager, John Stilla

Assistant Vice President, Suzy Pelshaw

Assistant Vice President Claims Counsel, Christine Amaro

Managing Counsel Vice President, Kathleen LaBarge

Vice President And Senior Claims Counsel, Lindsy Doucette

Assistant Vice President Branch Manager Fidelity National Title Agency, Jennifer Eaves

Assistant Vice President, Chris McGregor

Vice President Operations Manager, Cindy Wagner

Vice President, Lou Italiano

Assistant Vice President, Michele Clement

Assistant Vice President Of Human Resource, Carla Farmer

Vice President Regional Manager, Jeffrey Wolff

Assistant Vice President And Director 401K Plan, Eva Chavis

Certified Escrow Officer Assistant Vice President, Kathy Nelsen

Vice President, Amy Tueckes

Vice President And Associate Counsel, Kevin Reina

Assistant Vice President, David Scott

Vice President, Asher Fried

Senior Vice President Fidelity National Title, John Tonelli

Vice President And Senior Clams Counsel, Greg Foster

Senior Claims Counsel And Vice President, Scott Aronowitz

Assistant Vice President Corporate Accounting Manager, Joann L Jacks

Vice President and Associate Counsel, James H Duncan

Assistant Vice President and Claims Counsel, Alicia Buckley

Vice President, Debby Boyd

Assistant Vice President and Assistant Manager, Amy L Schaupeter

Executive Vice President Chief Operating Officer, Victoria Yee

Senior Managing Counsel Vice President, Chad A Dean

Vice President Sales and Major Accounts, Ginger McCully

Assistant Vice President, Brenda Eddy

Assistant Vice President, Kim Rugg

Assistant Vice President, Debbie Hortum

Senior Vice President Corporate Finance, David Ducommun

Vice President Of Business Development, Ryan Pulliam

Vice President, Tabitha Campbell

Vice President Senior Claims Counsel Central States, Jeffrey Deaver

Vice President, Darcy Marsh

Vice President Senior Commercial Counsel, Christopher Naughten

Vice President, Christine Rifkin

Vice President, Roger Shiffermiller

Vice President, Stacey Krone

Assistant Vice President Counsel, Natalie Bray

Vice President And Senior Trial Counsel, Donald Davis

Managing Counsel Vice President, Ray Aaronian

Assistant Vice President, Kristin Wyckoff

Vice President Of Operations, Christine Martin

Vice President And Trial Counsel, Jack P Wang

Executive Vice President, Phil Shea

Vice President And Litigation Attorney, Tiziana Scaccia

Senior Escrow Officer Assistant Vice President, Elizabeth Stoops

Assistant Vice President, Annie Grogan

Vice President, Joe Grealish

Vice President Sales, John Ravita

AVP Education and Marketing Services, Brian Boronat

Assistant Vice President, Staci Clayton

Assistant Vice President, Sue Davila

Assistant Vice President, Phyllis Miller

Assistant Vice President and Branch Manager and Escrow Officer Fidelity National Title, Lynda Garcia-McCutcheon

Assistant Vice President Escrow Closer, Vickie Zackery

Assistant Vice President Account Executive, Donna Nowlin

Assistant Vice President Associate Branch Counsel, Francis Hoffman

Executive Vice President Human Resources, Donnette Peacock

Assistant Vice President, Brandie Cho

Assistant Vice President and Senior Account Executive, Chris Newman

Vice President Counsel, Henry Hamilton

Vice President And Senior Litigation Counsel, Simone Kenyon

Assistant Vice President Analyst Corporate Compliance, Gina Stanley

Vice President And Ncs Counsel, Carol Martinelli

Vice President, Dominic Conetto

Assistant Vice President And Director Health And Welfare Benefits, Lori Simmons

Assistant Vice President, Christine Huff

Major Claims Counsel Vice President, Matthew Finniss

Vice President, Dorry Bragg

Vice President Sales, Betty Carter

Vice President, Gerry Grady

Assistant Vice President, Lois Watson

Vice President Business Development, Paul Jackson

Vice President, Sam Kitamura

Assistant Vice President; Program Manager Technology, Jason Bakes

Assistant Vice President, Cheryl Garrison

Senior Vice President, Morris Evans

Executive Vice President, Kevin Lutes

Assistant Vice President Production, Chris Rouly

Vice President Senior Escrow Officer, Marianne Platt

Vice President Statutory Reporting, Jan Wilson

Assistant Vice President, Mary Mendoza

Senior Recoupment Counsel Assistant Vice President and Team Lead, John Watson

Assistant Vice President And Agency Representative, Tiffany Mcdonough

Executive Vice President and National Sales Manager, Joey Mitchell
Vice President, Jeff Campbell
Vice President, Kerry Turner
Senior Vice President, Karen Highfield
Vice President Account Manager, Gordon Peterson
Vice President, Gary Forkel
Vice President and Title Officer, Rob Samuels
Vice President Commercial Group, Cheryl Mozinski
Assistant Vice President Branch Manager, Jodi Ayala
Vice President, Cheryl Barron
EVP National Agency Operations, John Obzud
AVP Senior Escrow Officer, Pam Teal
Vice President and Business Development Representative, Jorita Roberts
Vice President Escrow Manager, Lisa Wikert
Assistant Vice President, Lynn Riddle
Assistant Vice President Operations, Lance White
Auditors: Ernst & Young LLP

LOCATIONS

HQ: Fidelity National Financial Inc
601 Riverside Avenue, Jacksonville, FL 32204
Phone: 904 854-8100
Web: www.fnf.com

PRODUCTS/OPERATIONS

2016 Sales

	$ mil.	% of total
FNF Core		
Title operations	6,978	73
Black Knight	1,026	11
FNF Corporate & other	215	2
FNFV		
Restaurant group	1,152	12
FNF Corporate & other	183	2
Total	**9,554**	**100**

2016 Sales

	$ mil.	% of total
Escrow title-related and other fees	3,546	37
Agency title insurance premiums	2,626	28
Direct title insurance premiums	2,097	22
Restaurant revenue	1,158	12
Interest and investment income	129	1
Realized gains and losses net	(2)	-
Total	**9,554**	**100**

Selected Acquisitions

COMPETITORS

American Coast Title	Old Republic
American Home Shield	Old Republic National
Denny's	Title
DineEquity	Perkins & Marie
Equity Title Company	Callender's
First American	Stewart Information
Gracy Title A Stewart	Services
Company	Title Resource Group
Investors Title	United General Title
North American Title	Insurance
OSI Restaurant	
Partners	

HISTORICAL FINANCIALS

Company Type: Public

Income Statement

FYE: December 31

	ASSETS ($ mil.)	NET INCOME ($ mil.)	INCOME AS % OF ASSETS	EMPLOYEES
12/16	14,463	650	4.5%	55,219
12/15	13,931	527	3.8%	54,091
12/14	13,868	583	4.2%	56,883
12/13	10,524	402	3.8%	63,861
12/12	9,902	606	6.1%	60,451
Annual Growth	9.9%	1.7%	—	(2.2%)

2016 Year-End Financials

Debt ratio: 18.99%
Return on equity: 11.03%
Cash ($ mil.): 1,323
Current ratio: —
Long-term debt ($ mil.): —

No. of shares (mil.): 338
Dividends
Yield: 0.0%
Payout: 37.6%
Market value ($ mil.): 11,500

	STOCK PRICE ($) FY Close	P/E High/Low	PER SHARE ($) Earnings	Dividends	Book Value
12/16	33.96	16 12	2.34	0.88	17.71
12/15	34.67	21 17	1.89	0.80	16.53
12/14	34.45	47 34	0.75	0.37	16.12
Annual Growth	(0.4%)	— —	32.9%	24.2%	2.4%

Fidelity National Information Services Inc

At Fidelity National Information Services (FIS) the check will never get lost in the mail. FIS provides software outsourcing and IT consulting for the financial services industry. For banks and other financing entities the company's offerings address financial functions such as core processing decision and risk management and retail channel operations as well as payment services such as electronic funds transfer check and ticket processing and credit card production and activation. The company's 20000 customers aren't just the largest private financial institutions but also small businesses and government entities and are in more than 130 countries.

Operations

The Integrated Financial Solutions (IFS) supplies about half of Fidelity National Information Services? revenue. The unit provides services to regional and community banks and savings institutions in North America. Services include transaction and account processing payment tools lending and wealth management services mobile and digital banking technologies credit and debit card technologies and fraud risk management and compliance tools and services.

The Global Financial Solutions (GFS) provides about 45% of the company?s revenue. Its portfolio which includes the acquired SunGard businesses is bigger and broader than that of IFS in that its customers are large global financial institutions. GFS provides securities processing and finance technologies and services asset management and insurance and retail banking and payments services and strategic consulting.

The Corporate and Other segment 5% of revenue includes corporate overhead expense other functions and some non-strategic businesses.

Geographic Reach

Fidelity National Information Services operates through 280 owned or leased locations in Africa Asia Australia Europe the Middle East the Caribbean Latin America and the US. The company develops products and services in San Francisco London and Bangalore India.

FIS?s North American operations generate about three quarters of its revenue. Most of its international revenue comes from customers in Brazil the UK France and Germany.

Sales and Marketing

Fidelity National Information Services markets its products through direct and indirect field sales as well as inbound and outbound lead generation and telesales. Customers include Credit Suisse Atom Bank Centennial Bank Kitsap Bank and Landesbank Baden-Wuerttemberg.

Financial Performance

Fidelity National Information Services? revenue grew incrementally for about eight years but it jumped 40% from 2015 to 2016 with revenue from the SunGard acquisition.

In 2016 the company?s sales climbed to $9.2 billion from $6.6 billion in 2015. Besides the SunGard revenue FIS saw growth in consulting increased demand for output services and technologies higher card processing volumes in Brazil card production activities associated with the roll-out of EMV (chip-enabled) cards volume growth in debit payments and demand for regulatory and compliance solutions. The company experienced a negative impact of about $100 million on currency rates from the stronger US dollar against the British pound and the Brazilian real.

Despite the strong revenue gain FIS?s profit dropped 10% to $568 million in 2016 from $631 million in 2015. Its selling general and administrative expenses jumped 55% because of expenses associated with the SunGard acquisition and other acquisition-related costs. The SunGard acquisition also incurred higher interest expenses because of debt taken on to make the deal.

FIS generated about $1.9 billion in cash flow from operations in 2016 up from $1.1 billion the year before. The increase resulted from higher earnings after non-cash depreciation and amortization was added back from the inclusion of SunGard operations for the full year.

Strategy

Fidelity National Information Services (FIS) is working to run its businesses more efficiently as well as to obtain new customers and sell additional products to current customers.

On the efficiency side FIS is moving from a legacy server-based technology to cloud technologies to gain the benefits of speed efficiency and scale. The switch would help the company maintain and even increase margins. By the end of 2016 more than 20% of its server-based client systems were running in its private cloud and it expected the percentage to increase to 40% in 2017.

The acquisition of SunGard provides FIS with a more comprehensive product and services portfolio and resources that it intends to exploit. In the first full year with SunGard on board FIS has captured new business and expanded business through cross-selling and upselling.

FIS relies on strong free cash flow for flexibility in pursuing opportunities. The company had $1.5 billion in free cash flow in 2016 which it used to invest in the business pay down debt and return capital to shareholders.

On the product side FIS has gained revenue by supplying customers with EMV-enabled credit cards. The cards reply on a chip to provide security which is greater than that of the magnetic stripe on the cards it replaces. However FIS might have reached peak EMV. By the end of 2016 about half of its clients had EMV cards. The company expects the rest of its new EMV card business to follow the cycle of replacing cards as they expire.

In 2017 FIS sold majority ownership in Capco to Clayton Dubilier & Rice establishing Capco as an independent company. FIS is to receive about $477 million for the 60% of Capco it is selling. Capco offers business digital and technology consulting services for the financial services industry. The deal is expected to close in the 2017 third quarter.

Mergers and Acquisitions

The 2015 acquisition of SunGard Data Systems made Fidelity National Information Systems (FIS) the biggest financial services company. The SunGard assets cost about $9 billion and brought more than $4 billion in debt. The combined company produced $9.2 billion in revenue in 2015 its first full year. SunGard expanded FIS?s geographic reach and enriched its Global Financial Services unit with $1.8 billion in annual revenue. FIS was on track to clear about $257 million in savings by the end of 2017 as it consolidated and elimination duplicate functions.

EXECUTIVES

Corporate EVP and COO Institutional and Wholesale, Marianne C. Brown, age 58, $700,000 total compensation
CIO, Ido Gileadi
President Integrated Financial Solutions, Gary A. Norcross, age 52, $1,000,000 total compensation
Corporate EVP and COO Banking and Payments, Anthony M. Jabbour, age 49, $700,000 total compensation
Corporate EVP Chief Administrative Officer and Corporate Secretary, Michael P. Oates, age 58, $475,000 total compensation
EVP and CFO, James W. (Woody) Woodall, age 47, $605,000 total compensation
Corporate EVP and Chief Risk Officer, Gregory G. (Greg) Montana, age 48, $365,000 total compensation
EVP International Markets, Raja Gopalakrishnan
CEO Capco, Lance Levy
EVP and Chief Legal Officer, Marc Mayo
COO Integrated Financial Solutions, Bruce Lowthers
Senior Vice President Global Commercial Services Supply Chain and Real Estate, Kevin Gouin
Vice President Account Management and Product Portfolio, Jaspreet Kondal
Senior Vice President and Treasurer, Michael E Sax
Senior Vice President And Associate General Counsel, Pamela Phillips
Senior Vice President, Nikki Sunn
Vice President Marketing and Strategy, Linda Netherton
Vice President, Doug French
Assistant Vice President Chargeback Services, Christine Sterling
Assistant Vice President, Marie Storey
Vice President Human Resources, Mario Herranz
Senior Vice President Director, Steve Pierce
Executive Vice President, Steve Patterson
Vice President Product Management, Dominique Stevens
Vice President Sales And Marketing, Robert Boitano
Senior Vice President Loyalty Services, Robert Legters
Vice President Operations, John Oleon
Vice President Law, Debbie Segers
Assistant Vice President Director of Purchasing and Accounts Payable, Dawn Frye
Assistant Vice President Treasury, Alex Alley
Senior Vice President of Governance and Risk, Michael Weathers
Senior Vice President and Chief Division Counsel Check Services, Lynn Cravey
Vice President Advanced Technology Solutions, Hank Godwin
Vice President Business Recovery Services Advanced Technology Solutions, Ovid Babb
Assistant Vice President Global Midrange Applications, Alex Pisieczko
Senior Vice President Channel Architecture And Strategy, Bernie Schramm
Vice President New Solutions Architecture, Will Starnes
Vice President ACBS Global Sales, Gregg Cerniglia
Senior Vice President Operations, Mike Amble

Senior Vice President, Kim Snider
Vice President Channels Delivery, Sethu Thottikamath
Senior Vice President Business Development Enterprise Banking Solutions, Frank Krause
Senior Vice President And General Manager, Michelle Bowen
Assistant Vice President Senior Corporate Accounting Manager, Paula Orel
Vice President Client Relations, Jim Sheahan
Executive Vice President Customer Support, Cynthia Fitzgerald
Senior Vice President Mobile Financial Solutions, Douglas Brown
Vice President Product and Systems Development, Michael Lovett
Vice President Strategic Account Sales, Lucy Mills
Senior Vice President and Deputy General Counsel Corporate, Charles Curley
Senior Vice President Business Development, Chad Davis
Division Vice President Global Compensation, Gary Watts
Vice President, John Francis
Chairman, Frank R. Martire, age 69
Auditors: KPMG LLP

LOCATIONS

HQ: Fidelity National Information Services Inc
601 Riverside Avenue, Jacksonville, FL 32204
Phone: 904 438-6000
Web: www.fisglobal.com

PRODUCTS/OPERATIONS

2016 Sales

	$ mil.	% of total
IFS	4,566	49
GFS	4,250	46
Corporate & Other	425	5
Total	**9,241**	**100**

SOLUTIONS

SOLUTIONS
Banking and Wealth
Institutional and Wholesale
Management Consulting
Payments

COMPETITORS

ACI Worldwide	Infosys
Accenture	Jack Henry
Alliance Data Systems	MasterCard
D+H USA	Misys
DST Systems	Open Solutions
First Data	Oracle Financial
Fiserv	Services Software
Global Payments	SEI Investments
HP Enterprise Services	TEMENOS Group AG
Heartland Payment	TeleCheck
Systems	Total System Services
IBM	Visa Inc

HISTORICAL FINANCIALS

Company Type: Public

Income Statement
FYE: December 31

	REVENUE ($ mil.)	NET INCOME ($ mil.)	NET PROFIT MARGIN	EMPLOYEES
12/16	9,241	568	6.1%	55,000
12/15	6,595	631	9.6%	55,000
12/14	6,413	679	10.6%	40,000
12/13	6,070	493	8.1%	38,000
12/12	5,807	461	7.9%	35,000
Annual Growth	**12.3%**	**5.3%**	**—**	**12.0%**

2016 Year-End Financials

Debt ratio: 40.25%	No. of shares (mil.): 328
Return on equity: 5.94%	Dividends
Cash ($ mil.): 683	Yield: 0.0%
Current ratio: 1.36	Payout: 60.4%
Long-term debt ($ mil.): 10,146	Market value ($ mil.): 24,810

	STOCK PRICE ($) FY Close	P/E High/Low		PER SHARE ($) Earnings	Dividends	Book Value
12/16	75.64	46	32	1.72	1.04	29.70
12/15	60.60	33	26	2.19	1.04	28.72
12/14	62.20	27	21	2.35	0.96	23.01
12/13	53.68	31	20	1.68	0.88	22.64
12/12	34.81	23	17	1.55	0.80	22.58
Annual Growth	**21.4%**	**—**	**—**	**2.6%**	**6.8%**	**7.1%**

Fidelity Southern Corp

Fidelity Southern Corp. is the holding company for Fidelity Bank which boasts over $3 billion in assets and some 45 branches in the Atlanta metro and in northern Florida markets. The bank offers traditional deposit services such as checking and savings accounts CDs and IRAs. Consumer loans primarily indirect auto loans which the company purchases from auto franchises and independent dealers throughout the Southeast make up more than 50% of its loan portfolio. Real estate construction commercial real estate business residential mortgage and other consumer loans round out Fidelity Southern's lending activities. Subsidiary LionMark Insurance Company offers consumer credit-related insurance products.

Operations
About 50% of Fidelity Southern's total revenue came from loan interest (including fees) in 2014 while another 2% came from interest on its investment securities. The rest of its revenue came from mortgage banking income (28%) indirect lending activities (9%) SBA Lending (3%) service charges on deposit accounts (2%) and other miscellaneous income sources. The bank had a staff of roughly 1040 employees at the end of 2014.

Geographic Reach
While the company mostly has a branch presence in Georgia and Florida it also offers mortgage loans indirect auto loans and Small Business Administration (SBA) loans in a dozen Southern states.

Sales and Marketing
Fidelity Southern mostly serves individuals and small to medium-sized businesses. The company spent $2.34 million on advertising and promotions in 2014 up from $1.69 million and $1.13 million in 2013 and 2012 respectively.

Financial Performance
Fidelity Southern's revenues and profits have risen over the past several years thanks to growing loan and deposit business from branch openings and acquisitions lower interest expenses and declining loan loss provisions as its loan portfolio's credit quality has improved with higher property valuations in the strengthened economy.

The company's revenue inched higher by 1% to $197 million in 2014 mostly as its loan balances grew organically by 8% during the year with higher loan originations and market expansion.

Higher revenue and lower interest expenses in 2014 boosted Fidelity Southern's net income by 9% to a record $30 million. Its cash levels plummeted during the year with operations using a net $141 million for the year after adjusting its earnings for non-cash items related to its net proceeds from its loans held for sale.

Strategy

Fidelity Southern has focused on building and diversifying its loan portfolio including originating more residential mortgages commercial loans and consumer installment loans. The bank has been opening new branches as part of this organic growth strategy. During 2014 it opened 12 new branches including five in Georgia and seven in Florida.

It's also pursued small bank and branch acquisitions to grow its loan and deposit business while expanding its geographic reach in Florida and Georgia.

Mergers and Acquisitions

In October 2015 the Fidelity Bank agreed to purchase The Bank of Georgia including its $295 million in total assets $280 million in deposits and seven branches in Peachtree City Fayetteville Tyrone Sharpsburg Newnan and Fairburn.

September 2015 Fidelity Southern purchased eight branches in Florida from First Bank including $154 million in deposits and $31.6 million in loans. The deal expanded Fidelity's presence in counties surrounding Bradenton Palmetto and Longboat Key.

In September 2014 the company purchased six branches of CenterState Bank of Florida including $174.2 million in deposits. The deal expanded Fidelity's presence in counties surrounding Orlando and Jacksonville.

HISTORY

WWII veteran Clark Harrison and five others founded Fidelity National Bank in 1973. The first office opened in downtown Decatur Georgia the next year. Fidelity National Bank opened its second branch and formed Fidelity Southern Corporation as a holding company in 1979; it formed Fidelity National Mortgage a year later. In 1984 the company received trust powers opened two new branches and began a major credit card marketing program.

The acquisition of two branches from the Resolution Trust Corporation in 1992 brought the number of branches to 10 and increased assets to $257 million. Fidelity National Capital Investors a retail brokerage was incorporated that year. In 1993 Fidelity National Bank began a consumer sales finance department to buy auto loans from car dealers.

The company opened an office in Jacksonville in 1995 to offer mortgage car and construction lending. Also that year the firm changed the name of its holding company to Fidelity National Corporation.

Fidelity National acquired Friendship Community Bank in Florida and bought six branches from First Union and NationsBank in 1996; rapid expansion and unexpectedly high credit card chargeoffs that year slashed earnings and prevented Fidelity National from opening three of its newly acquired branches. Under the scrutiny of federal regulators the bank discontinued its high-default card program the next year and shored up its finances raising capital through a stock offering.

In 1998 Fidelity National focused on maintaining capital levels and recovering from its losses while other banks expanded. Fidelity National Bank finally gained regulatory approval to open the three remaining branches acquired from NationsBank and First Union later that year. Regulators released the bank from capital and dividend restrictions in 1999 but Fidelity National had to restate its earnings for 1997 citing overestimation of an asset's value.

Fidelity National experienced moderate growth in 2001. Inspections by the Federal Reserve Board

in 2000 and 2001 led to Fidelity National's adoption of a resolution that prohibits Fidelity National from redeeming its capital stock paying dividends on its common stock or incurring debt without prior approval of the Federal Reserve Board. In light of a softening economy in 2001 Fidelity National placed greater significance on credit risk management and building the secured portion of its consumer loan portfolio. The company sold its credit card business to Bank One in December.

In 2003 the company changed its name back to Fidelity Southern Corporation and its branches converted to the shortened Fidelity Bank; the bank also switched from a national to a state charter.

EXECUTIVES

President Fidelity Southern and Fidelity Bank, H. Palmer Proctor, age 49, $500,000 total compensation
Chairman and CEO, James B. Miller, age 77, $800,000 total compensation
VP; EVP Fidelity Bank; President LionMark Insurance, David Buchanan, age 59, $400,000 total compensation
CFO Fidelity Southern and Fidelity Bank, Stephen H. Brolly, age 54, $250,000 total compensation
Senior Vice President, Sam Mathis
Vice President Commercial Banking, Kevin Lubitz
Executive Vice President, Michael Pierson
Vice President Construction Lending, Ron Hendrix
Vice President, Mickey Parker
Vice President And Information and Systems Manager, Julie Mirts
Vice President, Josh Savage
Senior Vice President Regional Manager, John Andrews
Assistant Vice President Branch Manager, Kristina Hajzak
Vice President, David Mancuso
Vice President Fidelity Bank, Trice Dukes
Assistant Vice President Cash Management Officer, Kalea James
Vice President Senior Operations Manager, Regina Corker
Vice President Loan Operations Manager, Maria Becerra
Assistant Vice President, Jessie Fielder
Senior Vice President Wealth Management, Dave Johnston
Vice President, Christine Hobert
Senior Vice President Fidelity Bank, Bill Germany
Vice President Mortgage Servicing Manager, Jacque Williams
Vice President Customer Service and Digital Banking Manager Fidelity Bank, Dan Duchnowski
Vice President Corporate Insurance and Accounting Operations Manager Fidelity Bank, Laura Eastman
Vice President, Nina Efird
Auditors: Ernst & Young LLP

LOCATIONS

HQ: Fidelity Southern Corp
3490 Piedmont Road, Suite 1550, Atlanta, GA 30305
Phone: 404 639-6500
Web: www.FidelitySouthern.com

PRODUCTS/OPERATIONS

2014 Sales

	$ mil.	% of total
Interest		
Loans including fees	96	50
Investment securities	4	2
Federal funds sold & bank deposits	0	-
Noninterest		
Mortgage banking activities	55	28
Indirect lending activities	18	9
SBA lending activities	5	3
Service charges on deposit accounts	4	2

Bank owned life insurance	1	1
Other fees & charges	4	2
Other	5	3
Total	**197**	**100**

COMPETITORS

BB&T	SunTrust
Bank of America	Synovus
Citizens Bancshares	Wells Fargo
Regions Financial	

HISTORICAL FINANCIALS

Company Type: Public

Income Statement

FYE: December 31

	ASSETS ($ mil.)	NET INCOME ($ mil.)	INCOME AS % OF ASSETS	EMPLOYEES
12/16	4,389	38	0.9%	1,284
12/15	3,849	39	1.0%	1,242
12/14	3,085	30	1.0%	1,038
12/13	2,564	27	1.1%	890
12/12	2,477	25	1.0%	774
Annual Growth	**15.4%**	**11.2%**	**—**	**13.5%**

2016 Year-End Financials

Debt ratio: 2.74%   No. of shares (mil.): 26
Return on equity: 11.64%   Dividends
Cash ($ mil.): 129   Yield: 0.0%
Current ratio: —   Payout: 32.0%
Long-term debt ($ mil.): —   Market value ($ mil.): 623

	STOCK PRICE ($) FY Close	P/E High/Low		Earnings	PER SHARE ($) Dividends	Book Value
12/16	23.67	16	9	1.50	0.48	13.78
12/15	22.31	13	9	1.64	0.39	13.03
12/14	16.11	12	9	1.28	0.30	12.40
12/13	16.61	13	7	1.21	0.05	11.07
12/12	9.55	7	4	1.34	0.00	13.05
Annual Growth	**25.5%**	**—**	**—**	**2.9%**	**—**	**1.4%**

Fifth Third Bancorp (Cincinnati, OH)

Fifth Third Bancorp strives to be first in the hearts and minds of its customers. The holding company of Fifth Third Bank boasts assets of more than $140 billion and nearly 1200 branches across Ohio Michigan Florida and several other states in the Midwest and Southeast. Fifth Third offers branch banking (deposit accounts and loans for consumers and small businesses) commercial banking (lending leasing and syndicated and trade finance for corporations) consumer lending (residential mortgages home equity loans and credit cards) and wealth and asset management (private banking brokerage and asset management). Fifth Third owns part of Vantiv one of the country's largest payment processing firms.

Operations

The biggest chunk of Fifth Third's revenue comes from interest income on loans and leases at more than 45%. It makes 15% of revenue from interest on securities. Its non-interest income (at around 29% in total) consists of revenue from service charges on deposits (nearly 10%) wealth and asset management (5%) corporate banking income (5%) and mortgage banking revenue (5%) among other sources.

Geographic Reach

Fifth Third has 10 affiliates with around 1200 full-service branches and almost 2500 ATMs in the states of Ohio Kentucky Indiana Michigan Illinois Florida Tennessee West Virginia Pennsylvania Missouri Georgia and North Carolina.

Sales and Marketing

In addition to retail customers and affluent individuals Fifth Third targets provides financial services to agribusinesses dealers government agencies healthcare-related companies US financial institutions and to businesses seeking energy financing.

Financial Performance

Fifth Third has struggled to grow its annual revenues much past the $7 billion mark since 2011 despite slow and steady loan asset growth mostly as interest margins have been squeezed in the low-interest environment. The bank's profits have been steadily trending higher since 2011 as it's kept a handle on operating expenses.

In fiscal 2016 Fifth Third's revenue fell a modest 2% to $6.9 billion. An increase in securities and corporate banking revenue was outweighed by a fall in noninterest income: Fifth First made a $331 million exceptional gain in 2015 relating to the sale of Vantiv stock. Higher corporate banking revenue was down to increases in syndication and lease remarketing fees.

Net income fell 9% to $1.6 billion although much of the fall related to the aforementioned exceptional gain. Gain notwithstanding the company recorded higher net income in three of its core segments: commercial banking (up 39% to $995 million) branch banking (up 45% to $431 million) and wealth and asset management (up 60% to $93 million). Consumer lending profits fell sharply down to $20 million from $111 million in 2015.

Cash provided by operating activities fell 13% to $2.1 billion again due to proceeds from the Vantiv sale inflating the previous year's figures.

Strategy

Fifth Third Bancorp has been moving toward digital banking channels that are quickly taking the industry by storm allowing the bank to cut back its branch network and slash operating costs significantly while giving customers faster access to banking services. At the end of 2016 Fifth Third planned to consolidate and sell 64 branch locations and 35 undeveloped land parcels worth some $46 million and its consolidation and sale plan will result in total cost savings of $72 million.

Alongside the property and branch sales plan Fifth Third kicked off a growth plan with the intention of improving customer experience; strengthening brand value; expanding products solutions and services; and investing in sales. To those ends it has partnered with GreenSky a credit company to allow Fifth Third to originate loans through GreenSky's merchant network. (It will also be able to offer GreenSky's finance products to Fifth Thirds pre-exisisting customers.) Fifth Third has also upgraded its mortgage and teller systems expanded its credit card and treasury business and accelerated its automation and robotics initiatives.

Mergers and Acquisitions

Fifth Third (via its insurance agency subsidiary) acquired R.G. McGraw Insurance Agency. The acquisition will add to Fifth Third's insurance capability.

Company Background

Fifth Third spun off part of its payment processing unit formerly named Fifth Third Processing Solutions in 2009 as part of a plan to create a stand-alone payment processing business. Two years later Fifth Third Processing changed its name to Vantiv in preparation for taking itself public in 2012.

HISTORY

In 1863 a group of Cincinnati businessmen opened the Third National Bank inside a Masonic temple to serve the Ohio River trade. Acquiring the Bank of the Ohio Valley (founded 1858) in 1871 the firm progressed until the panic of 1907. Third National survived and in 1908 consolidated with Fifth National forming the Fifth Third National Bank of Cincinnati. The newly organized bank acquired two local banks in 1910.

A second bank consolidation in 1919 resulted in Fifth Third's affiliation with Union Savings Bank and Trust Company permitting the bank to establish branches theretofore forbidden by regulators. The company acquired the assets and offices of five more banks and thrifts that year operating them as branches.

In 1927 the bank merged its operations with the Union Trust Company forming the Fifth Third Union Trust. With its combined strength it weathered the Great Depression and acquired three more banks between 1930 and 1933. However the Depression also brought massive banking regulations to the industry limiting Fifth Third's acquisitions.

In the postwar years and during the 1950s and 1960s the bank expanded its consumer banking services offering traveler's checks. Under CEO Bill Rowe son of former CEO John Rowe the firm emphasized the convenience of its locations and increased hours of operations.

In the 1970s Fifth Third shifted its lending program's emphasis from commercial loans to consumer credit and launched its ATM and telephone banking services. Aware that the bank was technologically unprepared for the onslaught of electronic information Fifth Third expanded its data processing and information services resources forming the basis for its Midwest Payment Systems division.

The company formed Fifth Third Bancorp a holding company and began to branch within Ohio (branching had previously been limited to the home county) in 1975. Ten years later more deregulation allowed the bank to move into contiguous states. Focused on consumer banking and with cautious underwriting policies Fifth Third weathered the real estate bust and leveraged-buyout problems of the 1980s and acquired new outlets cheaply by buying several small banks as well as branches from larger banks. It acquired the American National Bank in Kentucky and moved further afield with its purchase of the Sovereign Savings Bank in Palm Harbor Florida in 1991.

The company continued to expand buying several banks and thrifts in Ohio in 1997 and 1998. In 1999 Fifth Third moved into Indiana in a big way with its purchase of CNB Bancshares then solidified its position in the state with the acquisition of Peoples Bank of Indianapolis. Fifth Third also moved into new business areas buying mortgage banker W. Lyman Case broker-dealer The Ohio Company (1998) and Cincinnati-based commercial mortgage banker Vanguard Financial (1999). The company began to offer online foreign exchange via its FX Internet Trading Web in 2000.

In 2001 Fifth Third bought money manager Maxus Investments and added some 300 bank branches with its purchase of Capital Holdings (Ohio and Michigan) and Old Kent Financial (Michigan Indiana and Illinois) its largest-ever acquisition.

Fifth Third exited the property/casualty insurance brokerage business in 2002 selling its operations to Hub International. Also that year Fifth Third arranged to enter Tennessee via its planned purchase of Franklin Financial. But the deal was stalled as industry regulators investigated Fifth Third's risk management procedures and internal controls. A moratorium on acquisitions was placed on the bank during the investigation. It was lifted in 2004 and the purchase of Franklin was completed not long afterwards. That opened the door for Fifth Third's acquisition of First National Bankshares of Florida in 2005. Two years later it continued growing with its purchase of R-G Crown Bank from R&G Financial which added some 30 branches in Florida in addition to locations in Georgia.

EXECUTIVES

Executive Vice President, Robert Sullivan
President CEO and Director, Greg D. Carmichael, age 55, $994,287 total compensation
EVP and COO, Lars C. Anderson, age 56, $675,002 total compensation
EVP and Chief Risk Officer, Frank R. Forrest, age 62, $519,713 total compensation
EVP, Philip R. McHugh, age 52
EVP and Chief Corporate Responsibility and Reputation Officer, Brian Lamb
EVP and Chief Administrative Officer, Teresa J. Tanner, age 48
EVP and CFO, Tayfun Tuzun, age 52, $519,342 total compensation
EVP, Chad M. Borton, age 46, $491,260 total compensation
EVP and Treasurer, James C. Leonard, age 47
EVP and Chief Strategy Officer, Timothy N. Spence, age 38, $450,008 total compensation
EVP and Chief Operations and Technology Officer, Aravind Immaneni
EVP Chief Legal Officer and Corporate Secretary, Jelena McWilliams
EVP, Richard Stein
Vice President Of Benefits, James Girton
Vice President Finance, Dan Flanigan
Vice President Information Technology, Ken Valentine
Assistant Vice President Principal Application Developer, Aaron Stockmeister
Director International Origination and Client Coverage Vice President, Annie Daniel
Senior Vice President, William Thurman
Assistant Vice President Residential Lending, Chris Fink
Vice President, Thomas Scarborough
Vice President, Fred Abblett
Assistant Vice President, Steve Hegele
Vice President Recruiting, Nancy Pinckney
Vice President, Robert Mancini
Portfolio Risk Segment Manager Assistant Vice President, Jason Arseneault
Senior Vice President, Jeffrey Leithauser
Vice President Acquisitions, Jim Rose
Assistant Vice President Branch Manager, Cory Kent
Vice President Treasury Management, Kevin Zgonc
Vice President Mortgage, Alisa Hunter
Assistant Vice President, Michelle Knight
Senior Vice President, Doug Riddle
Vice President, Thomas Merkle
Assistant Vice President Program Manager Call Center Technology, Charlie Licata
Senior Vice President, Randy Schwarzman
Vice President Marketing, Kathy Gelement
Vice President Commercial Lending, Jerry Hartley
Vice President Chief Operational Risk Officer, John Wallace
Mortgage Loan Originator Assistant Vice President Fifth Third Mortgage, Michael Cole
Assistant Vice President, Mark Zink
Vice President And Trust Officer, David Garber
Vice President, Timothy Pace
Assistant Vice President, Jason Youngman
Vice President of Enterprise Architecture, Gary Schnettler
Vice President, Greg Vollmer
Vice President, Tab Demita

Vice President And Director Commercial Analytics, Stephen Boras
Vice President Portfolio Manager, Keith McFarland
Assistant Vice President, Patrick Kavanaugh
Vice President, Charles Arkin
Vice President And Chief Financial Officer Of Eastern Michigan, John Worthington
Vice President Manager Financial Services, Terrence Lyons
Vice President And Market Manager, Lori Geier
Vice President, Alfred Mancuso
Vice President Dealer Development Representative, Steve Sudnick
Senior Vice President and Commercial Line of Business Manager, Gregory Dryden
Vice President Investments Executive, James Beckman
Vice President Treasury Management Officer, Alicia Mattice
Assistant Vice President Marketing Communications Manager, Ashley Duncan
Vice President Executive Consulting and Conversions, James Karas
Assistant Vice President Direct Lending Officer, Kevin Mull
Vice President Consumer Collections, Mona Erickson
Vice President, William Hummel
Vice President Regional Manager, Lynne Leece
Vice President Institutional Real Estate, Brad Boersma
Assistant Vice President Financial Cen, Brad Pinson
Vice President Retail Risk and Operations Oversight Manager, Arthur Bradley
Assistant Vice President and Counsel, David Love
Vice President, Libby Chapin
Senior Vice President, Steven Slee
Senior Vice President, David Pearce
Vice President Foreign Exchange, Joe Areddy
Vice President and Trust Officer, William Christensen
Vice President, Mark Telles
Assistant Vice President, Anoopa McKim
Vice President Middle Market, Kathleen Mekesa
Vice President and Team Lead, Kelly Soller
Vice President Indirect Originations, Edward Mcelveen
Vice President and Sales Manager Global Cash Solutions, Megan Anderson
Vice President And Senior Portfolio Manager, Jim Desmond
Vice President, Dan Driscoll
Vice President Global Payments, Jason Dement
Assistant Vice President Senior Market Intelligence Analyst, Ashley Wyant
Vice President, Donald Mitchell
Investment Executive Vice President, Jeffrey Noeker
Vice President Legal Counsel, Peter Jurs
Vice President, Jennifer Dunigan-wernke
Assistant Vice President, Chad Rudzik
Vice President Business Banking, Tracey Siarkowski
Vice President Commercial Banking, Tim Egloff
Vice President National Healthcare Finance, William Priester
Financial Center Manager vice Presiden, Mikki Smith
Vice President Commercial Banking, Mary Weldon
Vice President, Bill Szlinis
Vice President Commercial Portfolio Manager, Jonathan Roe
Vice President Product And Risk Manager, April Cothran
Vice President, Donald McGill
Vice President, Mark Ransom
Vice President, Joe Acito
Vice President Sales, Russ Schnurr
Vice President Structured Finance, Scott Unkraut

Vice President, Herbert Kidd
Assistant Vice President Portfolio Manager, Jean Phelan
Vice President, Tom Palermo
Vice President Professional Services, John Huber
Vice President, Rod Brown
Solutions Architect And Assistant Vice President, Michaela Schleifer
Executive Vice President, Steve Alonso
Vice President of Capital Markets Technology, Scott Patrick
Assistant Vice President, Debra L Guisinger
Senior Vice President Middle Market Group Head, Chip Reeves
Vice President Commercial Loan Operations, Margie Johnson
Senior Vice President Head Of Retail Banking, Mike Butera
Assistant Vice President Fiancial Center Manager I, Jim Goodfriend
Vice President, Phil Steenbergen
Vice President, William Krummen
Vice President Private Bank, David W Herrenbruck
Vice President, Maggie Sigler
Vice President And Team Lead, Louise Sorg
Vice President And Counsel, H Lind
Vice President, Joanne Hindel
Structured Finance Group Assistant Vice President, Paul Bahra
Vice President, Sonia Sonecha
Vice President, Roger Luksik
Vice President Treasury Management, Kate Nagy
Vice President, Jeff Tabler
Vice President, Joe Szymanowski
Assistant Vice President Remarketing Manager, Richard Steimer
Marketing Specialist Assistant Vice President, Angie Martin
Vice President, Patrick Farnan
Financial Center Manager Assistant Vice President, Archard Mathis
Vice President Enterprise Qa, William Nearhood
Vice President, John Sharp
Vice President, Leo Smith
Senior Vice President, Tom Plodzeen
Vice President Treasury Management Officer, Douglas Henderson
Vice President Commercial Lending, Glenn Nord
Vice President Sba Alternative Lending, Chris Intemann
Fifth Third Bank Vice President Manager Systems Engineering Middleware Engineering, Randall Gray
Vice President, Jason Fronheiser
Fcm Vice President, Rubia Marins
Vice President And Director Of Accounting, Glen Napolitano
Vice President of Capital Markets Accounting Group, Bryan Preston
Assistant Vice President Physician Loan Specialist, Rebecca Gray
Vice President, Thomas Begam
Vice President Group Manager, Tim Fergan
Assistant Vice President Portfolio Manager, Carolyn Dearmond
Vice President Online Strategy, Shannon Paul
Vice President, Maurice Williams
Auditors: Deloitte & Touche LLP

LOCATIONS

HQ: Fifth Third Bancorp (Cincinnati, OH)
Fifth Third Center, Cincinnati, OH 45263
Phone: 800 972-3030
Web: www.53.com

Selected Markets

Florida
Georgia
Indiana
Illinois
Kentucky
Michigan
Missouri
North Carolina
Ohio
Pennsylvania
Tennessee
West Virginia

PRODUCTS/OPERATIONS

2016 Sales

	$ mil.	% of total
Interest		
Loans & leases including fees	3,233	47
Securities & other	952	14
Interest on other short-term investments	8	-
Non-Interest		
Service charges on deposits	558	8
Wealth and asset management revenue	404	6
Corporate banking revenue	432	6
Mortgage banking net revenue	285	4
Card & processing revenue	319	5
Securities gains net	10	-
Other	688	10
Total	**6,889**	**100**

Selected Subsidiaries

Fifth Third Capital Trust VII
Fifth Third Financial Corporation
Fifth Third Bank
GNB Management LLC
GNB Realty LLC
Fifth Third Asset Management Inc.
Fifth Third Funding LLC
Fifth Third Holdings LLC
Fifth Third Insurance Agency Inc.
Fifth Third International Company
Fifth Third Trade Services Limited (Hong Kong)
Fifth Third Equipment Finance Company (formerly The Fifth Third Leasing Company)
The Fifth Third Auto Leasing Trust
Fifth Third Mortgage Company
Fifth Third Real Estate Investment Trust Inc.
Fifth Third Real Estate Capital Markets Company
Fifth Third Securities Inc.
Old Kent Mortgage Services Inc.
Fifth Third Community Development Corporation
Fifth Third New Markets Development Co. LLC
Fifth Third Investment Company
Fountain Square Life Reinsurance Company Ltd. (Turks and Caicos Islands)
Vista Settlement Services LLC

COMPETITORS

Bank of America	KeyCorp
Citigroup	Northern Trust
Comerica	PNC Financial
Harris	U.S. Bancorp
Huntington Bancshares	Wells Fargo
JPMorgan Chase	

HISTORICAL FINANCIALS

Company Type: Public

Income Statement

FYE: December 31

	ASSETS ($ mil.)	NET INCOME ($ mil.)	INCOME AS % OF ASSETS	EMPLOYEES
12/16	142,177	1,564	1.1%	17,844
12/15	141,082	1,712	1.2%	18,261
12/14	138,706	1,481	1.1%	18,351
12/13	130,443	1,836	1.4%	19,446
12/12	121,894	1,576	1.3%	20,798
Annual Growth	3.9%	(0.2%)	—	(3.8%)

2016 Year-End Financials

Debt ratio: 10.10%
Return on equity: 9.73%
Cash ($ mil.): 2,802
Current ratio: —
Long-term debt ($ mil.): —
No. of shares (mil.): 750
Dividends
Yield: 0.0%
Payout: 27.4%
Market value ($ mil.): 20,240

	STOCK PRICE ($) FY Close	P/E High/Low		PER SHARE ($) Earnings	Dividends	Book Value
12/16	26.97	14	7	1.93	0.53	21.59
12/15	20.10	11	8	2.01	0.52	20.18
12/14	20.38	14	11	1.66	0.51	18.96
12/13	21.03	10	7	2.02	0.47	17.06
12/12	15.20	9	7	1.66	0.36	15.55
Annual Growth	15.4%	—	—	3.8%	10.2%	8.6%

Financial Institutions Inc.

Financial Institutions may not have a luxurious name but they specialize in five star service. The holding company owns Five Star Bank which provides standard deposit products such as checking and savings accounts CDs and IRAs to retail and business customers through some 50 branches across western and central New York. Indirect consumer loans originated through agreements with area franchised car dealers account for the largest percentage of the company's loan portfolio (35%) followed by commercial mortgages. The company also sells insurance while its Five Star Investment Services subsidiary offers brokerage and financial planning services.

Operations

Financial Institutions operates through two business segments: banking which includes the bank's retail and commercial banking operations; and insurance which sells insurance to both personal and business clients through its Scott Danahy Naylon Co (SDN) subsidiary.

About 65% of the company's total revenue came from loan interest (including fees) in 2014 while another 15% came from interest on its investment securities. The rest of its revenue came from deposit account service charges (7%) ATM and debit card fees (4%) insurance income (2%) investment advisory (2%) and other miscellaneous income sources.

Geographic Reach

Five Star Bank boasts 50 branches and an ATM network across Western and Central New York in the counties of Allegany Cattaraugus Cayuga Chautauqua Chemung Erie Genesee Livingston Monroe Ontario Orleans Schuyler Seneca Steuben Wyoming and Yates.

Sales and Marketing

The company offers financial and banking services to individuals municipalities and businesses in Western and Central New York.

Financial Performance

Financial Institution's revenues and profits have been rising over the past few years thanks to growing loan business (organically and from 2012 acquisitions) lower interest expenses and rising fee-based revenue.

The company's revenue rose by 2% to $126.4 million in 2014 mostly thanks to the addition of insurance income from stemming from the bank's acquisition of SDN. Financial's loan interest grew by 1% on organic loan business growth while interest on investment securities grew by 7% as it purchased more interest-earning assets.

Higher revenue and a decline in loan loss provisions from a more credit-worthy loan portfolio in 2014 drove Financial Institution's net income higher by 15% to a record $29.4 million. The com-

pany's operating cash levels dipped by 5% to $35.2 million during the year due to unfavorable changes in working capital related to its contributions to its defined benefit pension plan.

Strategy

Financial Institutions' long-term strategy reiterated in 2015 has been to "maintain a community bank philosophy which consists of focusing on and understanding the individualized banking needs of individuals municipalities and businesses of the local communities surrounding their primary service area." The firm believes this focus will enable it to better respond to customer needs and provide a higher level of personalized services giving it a competitive advantage over larger competitors.

The company has also pursued acquisitions to bolster its service lines to grow its non-interest business. Its 2014 acquisition of a New-York based full-service insurance agency for example launched it beyond banking into the insurance business.

Mergers and Acquisitions

In January 2015 Financial Institutions bolstered its investment service business after acquiring Courier Capital which offers customized investment management investment consulting and retirement plan services to some 1100 individuals businesses and institutions.

In 2014 Financial Institutions expanded its services into the insurance business after acquiring Buffalo-based Scott Danahy Naylon Co. (SDN) a full-service insurance agency for a total of $16.9 million plus a promise of $3.4 million in future payments contingent on SDN meeting revenue performance goal targets through 2017.

Company Background

In 2012 Five Star Bank acquired four retail branches owned by HSBC Bank and four owned by First Niagara Bank in upstate New York.

Five Star Bank was formed in 2005 when the company consolidated its four banking subsidiaries (First Tier Bank & Trust National Bank of Geneva Wyoming County Bank and Bath National Bank) into a single entity. First Tier Bank & Trust absorbed the other three banks and changed its name to Five Star Bank.

EXECUTIVES

Vice President, Brenda Schell
Assistant Vice President Investment Services, David Macintyre
EVP CFO and Treasurer, Kevin B. Klotzbach, age 64, $230,000 total compensation
President and CEO, Martin K. Birmingham, $420,000 total compensation
EVP Commercial Executive and Regional President, Jeffrey P. Kenefick, $209,100 total compensation
SVP and Director of Human Resources and Enterprise Planning, Paula D. Dolan, $140,000 total compensation
EVP and Chief Risk Officer, Kenneth V. Winn
Vice President Information Technology, Raymond Knapp
Second Vice President, Allen Corey
Vice President, Christopher Bergeon
Senior Vice President And Manager Work, Steven Ambrose
Vice Presidenti Information Technology, R McLaughlin
Senior Vice President and Administrator Loan Revie, David Squire
Chairman, Robert N. Latella, age 74
Auditors: KPMG LLP

LOCATIONS

HQ: Financial Institutions Inc.
220 Liberty Street, Warsaw, NY 14569
Phone: 585 786-1100
Web: www.fiiwarsaw.com

PRODUCTS/OPERATIONS

2013 Sales

	$ mil.	% of total
Interest income		
Loans including fees	81	66
Investment securities	17	14
Noninterest income		
Service charges on deposits	9	9
ATM & debit card	5	4
Investment advisory	2	2
Other	7	5
Total	**123**	**100**

COMPETITORS

Astoria Financial	HSBC USA
Citibank	KeyCorp
Community Bank System	M&T Bank
ESL Federal Credit Union	

HISTORICAL FINANCIALS

Company Type: Public

Income Statement

FYE: December 31

	ASSETS ($ mil.)	NET INCOME ($ mil.)	INCOME AS % OF ASSETS	EMPLOYEES
12/16	3,710	31	0.9%	654
12/15	3,381	28	0.8%	691
12/14	3,089	29	1.0%	645
12/13	2,928	25	0.9%	645
12/12	2,764	23	0.8%	662
Annual Growth	7.6%	8.0%	—	(0.3%)

2016 Year-End Financials

Debt ratio: 1.05%	No. of shares (mil.): 14
Return on equity: 10.37%	Dividends
Cash ($ mil.): 71	Yield: 0.0%
Current ratio: —	Payout: 38.5%
Long-term debt ($ mil.): —	Market value ($ mil.): 497

	STOCK PRICE ($) FY Close	P/E High/Low		PER SHARE ($) Earnings	Dividends	Book Value
12/16	34.20	16	12	2.10	0.81	22.02
12/15	28.00	15	12	1.90	0.80	20.71
12/14	25.15	13	10	2.00	0.77	19.80
12/13	24.71	15	10	1.75	0.74	18.43
12/12	18.63	12	10	1.60	0.57	18.41
Annual Growth	16.4%	—	—	7.0%	9.2%	4.6%

First American Financial Corp

First American Financial knows that when you're buying real estate you'll probably want some insurance to go along with it. In addition to good old title insurance from its First American Title subsidiary the company's financial services arm also provides specialty property/casualty insurance and home warranties through First American Home Buyers Protection. Its First American Trust unit offers banking and trust services to the escrow and real estate industries. Other offerings include settlement title plant management valuation and investment advisory services.

Operations

First American Financial is one of the largest title insurers in the US. Its title insurance and services segment accounts for more than 90% of revenues. The unit is focused on issuing title insurance for commercial and residential real estate transactions in the US and abroad; it also provides escrow closing exchange documentation banking and other title insurance-related services. The company also provides real property-related data services to mitigate risk and facilitate transactions.

The remainder of revenue comes from the specialty insurance segment which offers property/casualty policies including homeowners renters and property hazard coverage. It also markets home warranties.

Geographic Reach

With headquarters in California First American Financial serves customers in over 40 countries around the globe. The US market where the specialty business is licensed in all 50 states and the District of Columbia accounts for about 95% of revenues.

The company has regional offices in countries including Australia Canada and the UK. Through acquisitions (partial and total) of existing businesses and through partnerships with local companies First American Financial is carefully moving into emerging markets in central and eastern Europe.

Sales and Marketing

First American Financial distributes its title insurance and related products through a direct sales force and via agent channels. For residential products it markets to real estate agents and brokers as well as mortgage originators and brokers real estate attorneys homebuilders and escrow service providers. Refinance business is marketed to mortgage originators and servicers and government-sponsored entities. Commercial lines are primarily marketed to investors including real estate investment trusts (REITs) as well as law firms banks investment banks mortgage brokers and commercial property owners.

Property/casualty insurance is marketed through direct distribution channels (including cross-selling to existing customers) and through a network of independent brokers.

Financial Performance

With the exception of 2014 First American Financial's net sales have been on the rise for the past five years. In 2016 net sales increased 8% to $5.6 billion as all lines of revenue (direct premiums and escrow fees agent premiums information and other net investment income and net realized investment gains) grew. In particular 9% increase in agent premiums drove the overall increase. Direct premiums and escrow fees rose 4% that year largely due to an increase in residential transactions.

Net income has been increasing since 2013. In 2016 the higher net sales helped net income rise 19% to $343 million but that was partially offset by an increase in most expenses.

Cash flow from operations slipped 11% to $489.4 million in 2016 primarily due to an $85 million contribution to the firm's termination of its legacy pension plan.

Strategy

First American Financial operates through three primary strategic lenses: growing its core title and settlement businesses strengthening its business with data and managing and buying complementary businesses that expand or support its core activities. In terms of growing its core operations the company works to bring greater efficiency to the business including seeking innovative growth drivers and making strategic acquisitions. To increase its stores of data First American Financial has made a number of purchases such as RedVision

Systems and TD Service Financial. Those and other acquisitions have helped the company streamline the title process and improve the services it offers clients. And with the sheer volume of data the company has at its disposal (its data covers 100% of the counties in the US for example) First American Financial is positioned to benefit from the improving economy and expected rise in real estate transactions.

Mergers and Acquisitions

First American Financial continues to grow through a number of strategic acquisitions. In 2015 it bought New York-based title agency TitleVest Holdings. Then in 2016 it acquired New Jersey-based title data firm RedVision Systems which became part of First American's Data and Mortgage Solutions division. Further adding to its mortgage solutions operations the company bought TD Service Financial Corporation and its subsidiaries including TD Service Company Security Connections and TD Quality Control Services. Those firms provide technology services such as lien releases audits document retrieval and post-closing services to the mortgage banking industry.

Company Background

Previously known as First American Corporation the company spun off its real estate information services into CoreLogic in 2010.

Chairman Parker Kennedy is a descendant of the founder of the company C. E. Parker.

HISTORY

In 1889 when Los Angeles was on its way to becoming a real city the more countrified residents to the south (including The Irvine Company's founding family) formed Orange County a peaceful realm of citrus groves where land transactions were assisted by title companies Orange County Abstract and Santa Ana Abstract. In 1894 the firms merged under the leadership of local businessman C. E. Parker. For three decades the resulting Orange County Title limited its business to title searches.

In 1924 as real estate transactions became more complex (in part because of mineral-rights issues related to Southern California's oil boom) Orange County Title began offering title insurance and escrow services. The company remained under Parker family management until 1930 when H. A. Gardner took over and guided it through the Depression. In 1943 the company returned to Parker family control.

In 1957 the company began a major expansion beyond Orange County. The new First American Title Insurance and Trust name acknowledged the firm's expansion into trust and custody operations. Donald Kennedy (C. E. Parker's grandson) took over in 1963 and took the company public the next year.

In 1968 First American Corporation was formed as a holding company for subsidiaries First American Title Insurance and First American Trust. This structure facilitated growth as the firm began opening new offices and buying all or parts of other title companies including Title Guaranty Co. of Wyoming Security Title & Trust (San Antonio) and Ticore Inc. (Portland Oregon) all purchased in 1968.

The 1970s were a quiet time for the company but it began growing again in the 1980s as savings and loan deregulation jump-started the commercial real estate market in Southern California. First American diversified into home warranty and real estate tax services. In 1988 on the brink of the California meltdown the company bought an industrial loan corporation to make commercial real estate loans.

EXECUTIVES

EVP, Kenneth D. DeGiorgio, age 45, $749,615 total compensation
CEO and Director, Dennis J. Gilmore, age 58, $949,231 total compensation
COO Mortgage Information Services Group, Christopher M. Leavell, age 54, $699,615 total compensation
EVP and CFO, Mark E. Seaton, age 41, $574,231 total compensation
Vice President of Operations, Shawna Mixon
VP and Chief Accounting Officer, Matthew F. Wajner, age 41, $274,769 total compensation
Vice President Southern California Area Operations Director, Chris Clemens
Vice President and Manager, Jordan Dunn
Vice President, Michael Kennedy
Vice President and State Counsel, Leonard Prescott
Senior Vice President, George Gauger
Vice President National Accounts, Valerie Kolytiris
Senior Vice President Sales, Caitlin Stearns
Vice President, Trish Brown
Assistant Vice President Trust Services, Kathy Vian
Vice President, Jack Hanrahan
Executive Vice President, Scott Callender
Vice President, Jeanne LaBelle
Vice President and Underwriting Counsel, Mitch Gluck
Vice President of Sales Miami, Keren Marti
Vice President of Sales, Tori Robinson
Chairman, Parker S. Kennedy
Auditors: PricewaterhouseCoopers LLP

LOCATIONS

HQ: First American Financial Corp
1 First American Way, Santa Ana, CA 92707-5913
Phone: 714 250-3000   **Fax:** 714 250-3151
Web: www.firstam.com

2016 Sales

	% of total
US	94
International	6
Total	**100**

PRODUCTS/OPERATIONS

2016 Sales

	$ mil.	% of total
Direct premiums & escrow fees	2,416	43
Agent premiums	2,286	41
Information & other	724	13
Net investment income	126	2
Net realized investment losses	23	1
Total	**5,575**	**100**

2016 Sales

	% of total
Title Insurance and Services	92
Specialty Insurance	8
Corporate	—
Eliminations	—
Total	**100**

Selected Services

Property/Casualty Insurance
  Home Warranty
Title Insurance and Services
  1031 Tax-Deferred Exchange Services
  Banking and Investment Management
  Default Services
  Homebuilder Services
  National Commercial Services
  Origination Services
  Professional Real Estate Services
  Property Information and Recorded Documents
  Title Insurance and Closing Services
  Title Technology Solutions
  UCC Insurance Search and Filing Services
  Valuation Services

HISTORICAL FINANCIALS

Company Type: Public

Income Statement

FYE: December 31

	ASSETS ($ mil.)	NET INCOME ($ mil.)	INCOME AS % OF ASSETS	EMPLOYEES
12/16	8,831	342	3.9%	19,531
12/15	8,254	288	3.5%	17,955
12/14	7,666	233	3.0%	17,103
12/13	6,520	186	2.9%	17,292
12/12	6,050	301	5.0%	17,312
Annual Growth	9.9%	3.3%	—	3.1%

2016 Year-End Financials

Debt ratio: 8.34%	No. of shares (mil.): 109
Return on equity: 11.86%	Dividends
Cash ($ mil.): 1,006	Yield: 0.0%
Current ratio: —	Payout: 38.8%
Long-term debt ($ mil.): —	Market value ($ mil.): 4,027

	STOCK PRICE ($) FY Close	P/E High/Low		PER SHARE ($) Earnings	Dividends	Book Value
12/16	36.63	14	10	3.09	1.20	27.36
12/15	35.90	16	12	2.62	1.00	25.28
12/14	33.90	16	11	2.15	0.84	23.92
12/13	28.20	16	12	1.71	0.48	23.16
12/12	24.09	9	5	2.77	0.36	21.90
Annual Growth	11.0%	—	—	2.8%	35.1%	5.7%

First Bancorp

Not to be confused with North Carolina's First Bancorp this First BanCorp is the holding company for FirstBank Puerto Rico which provides business and retail banking services through more than 50 branches in Puerto Rico and about two dozen more in Florida and the Virgin Islands. Puerto Rico's second-largest bank gets more than one-third of its business from its Commercial and Corporate Banking loans and services. Residential mortgages make up nearly one-third of FirstBank's $9 billion loan portfolio while commercial mortgages make up another one-fifth. First BanCorp also owns FirstBank Insurance Agency Firstbank Puerto Rico Securities and the consumer loan company Money Express La Financiera.

Operations

Generating more than 80% of its revenue from loan interest First BanCorp operates through six business segments: Commercial and Corporate Banking; Consumer (Retail) Banking; Mortgage Banking; Treasury and Investments; United States Operations; and Virgin Islands Operations.

Commercial and Corporate Banking which made up roughly 35% of the company's total revenue in 2014 provides lending and other services for organizations in the public sector as well as for large and specialized middle-market businesses operating in a variety of industries.

The Consumer (Retail) Banking segment (22% of revenue) provides consumer lending and deposit services mainly through FirstBank's branch network and loan centers in Puerto Rico. FirstBank's loans include auto boat and personal loans credit cards and lines of credit.

The Mortgage Banking (18% of revenue) business buys and sells home loans through FirstBank and the company's mortgage origination subsidiary First Mortgage.

Treasury and Investments (1% of revenue) manages securities and lends funds to the company's three banking segments to finance their respective lending activities. It also borrows from those segments and from the United States Operations segment.

United States Operations (20% of revenue) consists of FirstBank's 10 retail and corporate banking businesses in the US mainland mostly in southern Florida.

Virgin Islands Operations (3% of revenue) counts FirstBank's banking business (mostly consumer commercial lending and deposit account activities) in the US Virgin Islands (USVI) and British Virgin Islands (BVI) through 12 branches in the USVI (St. Thomas St. Croix and St. John and the islands) and the BVI (Tortola and Virgin Gorda).

Geographic Reach

San Juan-based FirstBank boasts more than 50 branches across Puerto Rico around a dozen branches in the USVI and BVI and 10 US branches in southern Florida. The bank also has 27 First First Federal Finance Corp (dba Money Express La Financiera) offices in Puerto Rico.

Financial Performance

First BanCorp ended its multi-year revenue decline in 2014 with revenue rebounding by 10% to $695.3 million for the year. This is mostly because the bank in 2013 had suffered more than $200 million from a combination of losses on sales from non-performing assets and losses from a write-off of assets pledged as collateral to Lehman Brothers Inc. Despite earning lower interest income during 2014 the bank's net interest income managed to climb slightly thanks to lower interest expenses on deposits amidst the continued low-interest environment.

The company's profit jumped sharply to $392.29 million in 2014 (compared to a net loss of $164.49 million in 2013) mostly thanks to a drop in loan loss provisions as its loan portfolio's credit quality improved as the economy strengthened but also thanks to a combination of higher revenue and lower interest and non-interest expenses.

Despite higher earnings in 2014 First BanCorp's operating cash declined as the company generated less cash from proceeds on its loans held for sale.

Strategy

First BanCorp has followed an acquisition strategy to grow its loan business and bank clientele in recent years. In early 2015 for example flagship subsidiary FirstBank purchased 10 bank branches in Puerto Rico from its rival Doral Bank which added some $600 million in new deposits $300 million in new mortgage loan business and 140000 new clients. The acquisition also grew FirstBanCorp's total branch network by 20% while expanding its market presence in geographic areas with room for deposit and mortgage loan business growth. The year before in 2014 FirstBank expanded its loan business through the purchase of a $242-million portfolio of mortgage loans from Doral for some $232.9 million.

Company Background

Scotiabank a Canadian bank with operations throughout the Caribbean acquired a 10% stake in First BanCorp in 2007.

EXECUTIVES

EVP Business Group Executive, Cassan Pancham, age 57, $399,815 total compensation

EVP and Chief Risk Officer, Nayda Rivera-Batista, age 43

President and CEO, Aurelio Aleman-Bermudez, $850,102 total compensation

EVP and CFO, Orlando Berges-Gonzalez, $600,101 total compensation

EVP and Florida Region Executive, Calixto Garcia-Velez, $486,115 total compensation

EVP and COO, Donald L. Kafka

EVP Retail and Business Banking Executive, Ginoris Lopez-Lay

EVP and Chief Lending Officer, Emilio Martino-Valdes

EVP and Business Group Director, Michael McDonald

EVP; General Counsel and Secretary, Lawrence Odell, $550,110 total compensation

EVP and Consumer Lending Business Executive, Carlos Power Pietrantoni

Assistant Vice President, Hiram Rivas

Vice President, Rafael Perez

Vice President Of Commercial Department, Francisco Pascual

Senior Vice President Commercial Lending, Alfred Massheder

Chairman, Roberto R. Herencia, age 57

Auditors: KPMG LLP

LOCATIONS

HQ: First Bancorp
1519 Ponce de Leon Avenue, Stop 23, Santurce 00908
Phone: 787 729 8200
Web: www.firstbankpr.com

PRODUCTS/OPERATIONS

2014 Sales

	$ mil.	% of total
Interest		
Loans	579	82
Investment securities	52	8
Money market investments	1	-
Noninterest		
Service charges on deposit accounts	16	2
Mortgage banking activities	14	2
Insurance income	6	1
Others	30	5
Adjustments	(7.7)	-
Total	695	100

2014 Sales by Segments

	% of total
Commercial and corporate banking	35
Consumer(Retail) banking	22
United State Operations	21
Mortgage Banking	18
Virgin Island Operations	3
Treasury and Investments	1
Total	100

Selected Subsidiaries

FirstBank Puerto Rico
FirstBank Overseas Corporation
FirstBank Puerto Rico Securities Corp.
First Federal Finance Corp. (d/b/a Money Express La Financiera)
First Insurance Agency Inc.
First Mortgage Inc.
FirstBank Insurance Agency Inc.
Grupo Empresas de Servicios Financieros (d/b/a PR Finance)

COMPETITORS

Citigroup	Popular Inc.
OFG Bancorp	Santander BanCorp

HISTORICAL FINANCIALS

Company Type: Public

Income Statement

FYE: December 31

	ASSETS ($ mil.)	NET INCOME ($ mil.)	INCOME AS % OF ASSETS	EMPLOYEES
12/16	11,922	93	0.8%	2,701
12/15	12,573	21	0.2%	2,758
12/14	12,727	392	3.1%	2,617
12/13	12,656	(164)	—	2,458
12/12	13,099	29	0.2%	2,512
Annual Growth	(2.3%)	33.0%	—	1.8%

2016 Year-End Financials

Debt ratio: 1.81%
Return on equity: 5.34%
Cash ($ mil.): 299
Current ratio: —
Long-term debt ($ mil.): —

No. of shares (mil.): 217
Dividends
  Yield: —
  Payout: —
Market value ($ mil.): 1,437

	STOCK PRICE ($) FY Close	P/E High/Low		PER SHARE ($) Earnings	Dividends	Book Value
12/16	6.61	16	5	0.43	0.00	8.21
12/15	3.25	67	31	0.10	0.00	7.88
12/14	5.87	3	2	1.87	0.00	7.85
12/13	6.19	—	—	(0.80)	0.00	5.87
12/12	4.58	30	22	0.14	0.00	7.20
Annual Growth	9.6%	—	—	32.4%	—	3.3%

HISTORICAL FINANCIALS

Company Type: Public

Income Statement

FYE: December 31

	ASSETS ($ mil.)	NET INCOME ($ mil.)	INCOME AS % OF ASSETS	EMPLOYEES
12/16	3,614	27	0.8%	861
12/15	3,362	27	0.8%	840
12/14	3,218	25	0.8%	825
12/13	3,185	20	0.6%	873
12/12	3,244	(23)	—	852
Annual Growth	2.7%	—	—	0.3%

2016 Year-End Financials

Debt ratio: 1.28%
Return on equity: 7.72%
Cash ($ mil.): 305
Current ratio: —
Long-term debt ($ mil.): —

No. of shares (mil.): 20
Dividends
  Yield: 0.0%
  Payout: 24.0%
Market value ($ mil.): 566

	STOCK PRICE ($) FY Close	P/E High/Low		PER SHARE ($) Earnings	Dividends	Book Value
12/16	27.14	21	13	1.33	0.32	17.66
12/15	18.74	15	12	1.30	0.32	17.33
12/14	18.47	16	13	1.19	0.32	19.67
12/13	16.62	17	12	0.98	0.32	18.90
12/12	12.82	—	—	(1.54)	0.32	18.11
Annual Growth	20.6%	—	—	—	(0.0%)	(0.6%)

First Bancorp (NC)

EXECUTIVES

EVP and CFO First Bancorp and First Bank, Eric P. Credle, age 48, $325,000 total compensation

President and Director First Bancorp and President and CEO First Bank, Michael G. Mayer, age 57, $425,000 total compensation

President CEO and Director, Richard H. Moore, age 56, $525,000 total compensation

Senior Vice President Legal Division, Kirsten Foyles

Vice President, Jason Williams

Assistant Vice President, Laurie Byrd

Chairman First Bancorp and First Bank, James C. Crawford, age 60

Auditors: Elliott Davis Decosimo, PLLC

LOCATIONS

HQ: First Bancorp (NC)
  300 S.W. Broad Street, Southern Pines, NC 28387
Phone: 910 246-2500
Web: www.localFirstbank.com

PRODUCTS/OPERATIONS

2016 Sales

	$ mil.	% of total
Interest Income	130	84
Non-interest Income	25	16
Total	**156**	**100**

COMPETITORS

BB&T	NewBridge Bancorp
BNC Bancorp	PNC Financial
Bank of America	South Street Financial
CommunityOne Bancorp	SunTrust
First Citizens	Wells Fargo
BancShares	

First Bancorp Inc (ME)

It may not actually be the first bank but The First Bancorp (formerly First National Lincoln) was founded over 150 years ago. It is the holding company for The First a regional bank serving coastal Maine from more than 15 branches. The bank offers traditional retail products and services including checking and savings accounts CDs IRAs and loans. Residential mortgages make up about 40% of the company's loan portfolio; business loans account for another 40%; and home equity and consumer loans comprise the rest. Bank subsidiary First Advisors offers private banking and investment management services. Founded in 1864 the bank now boasts more than $1.4 billion in assets.

Operations

Subsidiary First Advisors acts as the bank's Trust and Investment services division which managed some $740 million in investor assets as of late 2014.

The First Bancorp generated 57% of its total revenue from interest income on loans (including fees) while another 25% came from interest and dividends on its investments. Service charges on deposit accounts (4%) Fiduciary and investment management income (3%) mortgage origination (2%) and net securities gains (2%) made up most of the rest of its total revenue.

Geographic Reach

The Damariscotta-based bank boasts more than 15 branches in Mid-Coast Eastern and Down East regions of Maine in Lincoln Knox Hancock Washington and Penobscot counties.

Sales and Marketing

The community-oriented bank concentrates on marketing to small businesses and individuals within its local markets.

Financial Performance

The First Bancorp's revenues have slowly declined over the past few years mostly with as its loan business has stagnated and as its interest margins on loans and investments have been shrinking in the low-interest rate environment. Its profits however have been steadily rising thanks to declining loan loss provisions as its loan portfolio's credit quality has improved with the strengthened economy.

The company's revenue inched up by less than one-tenth of a percent to $62.07 million in 2014 mostly as the bank carried more interest-earning investment assets during the year. The bank's non-interest income however declined by 9% as it collected less from the origination and sale of refinanced mortgage loans into the secondary market.

The First Bancorp's net income jumped by 13% to $14.7 million in 2014 thanks primarily to a continued decline in loan loss provisions as its portfolio's credit quality improved. Slightly higher revenue and lower interest expenses on deposits also helped pad the company's bottom line. The bank's operating cash levels fell by 18% to $20.5 million after adjusting its earnings for non-cash items related to its loan loss provisions and its net proceeds from the sale of its mortgage loans held for sale.

Strategy

As management reiterated in early 2015 remaining well capitalized "remains a top priority for The First Bancorp" and has been key to its profit growth over the past several years. Indeed its de-risking initiatives for its loan portfolio assets have taken the bank's risk-based capital ratio from 11.13% in 2008 to 16.27% at the end of 2014 well above the FDIC's suggested threshold of 10%. As a result the bank's loan loss provisions have declined over the period and its profits have blossomed despite a lack of revenue growth.

Company Background

First National Lincoln acquired competitor FNB Bankshares and its First National Bank of Bar Harbor subsidiary in 2005. It merged that bank into its own subsidiary The First National Bank of Damariscotta which was renamed The First.

EXECUTIVES

Treasurer The First Bancorp Inc. and EVP and CFO First National Bank, F. Stephen Ward, age 64, $254,400 total compensation

EVP and Clerk The First Bancorp Inc. and EVP Banking Services and Senior Loan Officer The First National Bank, Charles A. Wootton, age 60, $241,100 total compensation

EVP and Chief Administrative Officer First National Bank, Susan A. Norton, age 57, $210,000 total compensation

EVP and Treasurer First National Bank, Richard M. Elder, age 51, $179,400 total compensation

EVP and CIO The First, Tammy L. Plummer, age 51

President and CEO The First Bancorp and The First N.A., Tony C. McKim, age 50, $430,000 total compensation

Vice President Regional Manager, Jennifer Stewart

Chairman, David B. Soule, age 72

Vice Chairman, Mark N. Rosborough, age 69

Auditors: Berry Dunn McNeil & Parker, LLC

LOCATIONS

HQ: First Bancorp Inc (ME)
  Main Street, Damariscotta, ME 04543
Phone: 207 563-3195
Web: www.thefirstbancorp.com

2007 Sales

	$ mil.	% of total
Interest		
Loans including fees	60	74
Investments & other	11	14
Noninterest		
Service charges on deposit accounts	2	3
Fiduciary & investment management income	1	1
Other	6	8
Total	**81**	**100**

COMPETITORS

Bangor Savings Bank	KeyCorp
Bar Harbor Bankshares	Northeast Bancorp
Camden National	TD Bank USA

HISTORICAL FINANCIALS

Company Type: Public

Income Statement

FYE: December 31

	ASSETS ($ mil.)	NET INCOME ($ mil.)	INCOME AS % OF ASSETS	EMPLOYEES
12/16	1,712	18	1.1%	235
12/15	1,564	16	1.0%	223
12/14	1,482	14	1.0%	235
12/13	1,463	12	0.9%	233
12/12	1,415	12	0.9%	228
Annual Growth	4.9%	9.2%	—	0.8%

2016 Year-End Financials

Debt ratio: 7.01%
Return on equity: 10.56%
Cash ($ mil.): 17
Current ratio: —
Long-term debt ($ mil.): —

No. of shares (mil.): 10
Dividends
  Yield: 0.0%
  Payout: 54.2%
Market value ($ mil.): 357

	STOCK PRICE ($) FY Close	P/E High/Low	PER SHARE ($) Earnings	Dividends	Book Value
12/16	33.10	20 11	1.66	0.90	15.98
12/15	20.47	15 11	1.51	0.86	15.58
12/14	18.09	13 11	1.37	0.83	15.06
12/13	17.42	15 13	1.20	0.78	13.69
12/12	16.47	15 11	1.22	0.78	15.85
Annual Growth	19.1%	— —	8.0%	3.6%	0.2%

First Busey Corp

First Busey Corporation keeps itself busy taking care of deposits and making loans. It's the holding company for Busey Bank which boasts $4 billion in assets and 40 branches across Illinois Florida and Indiana. The bank offers standard deposit products and services using funds from deposits to originate primarily real estate loans and mortgages. Subsidiary Busey Wealth Management which manages $5 billion in assets provides asset management trust brokerage and related services to individuals businesses and foundations while FirsTech provides retail payment processing services. Most of Busey Bank's branches are located in downstate Illinois.

Operations

First Busey Corporation operates three business segments Busey Bank which generated more than 99% of its total revenue in 2014 and serves retail and corporate customers; FirsTech which provides remittance processing for online bill payments lock box and walk-in payments; and Busey Wealth Management which provides asset management tax preparation philanthropic advisory services and investment and fiduciary services to individuals businesses and foundations.

Real estate loans including commercial and residential mortgages accounted for 70% of the bank's loan portfolio in 2014 while commercial loans (25%) construction loans (4%) and consumer installments and other loans (0.5%) comprised the rest.

About 55% of First Busey's total revenue came from loan interest (including fees) while another 10% came from interest income on taxable and non-taxable investment securities. The rest of its revenue came from trust fees (11%) deposit account service charges (7%) remittance processing fees (6%) commissions and brokers' fees (2%) and various types of gains on securities and loan sales.

Geographic Reach

Busey Bank has nearly 30 branches in Illinois seven locations in southwest Florida and another office in Indianapolis. Its FirsTech subsidiary accepts payments from its 3000 agent locations across 36 US states.

Sales and Marketing

The bank which staffed 801 employees at the end of 2014 serves individuals businesses and foundations.

Financial Performance

First Busey's revenues have declined in recent years due to shrinking interest margins on loans amidst the low-interest environment. Its profits however have been rising thanks to lower interest expenses on deposits and declining loan loss provisions as its loan portfolio's credit quality has improved with higher property valuations in the strengthened economy.

The bank's revenue dipped by 2% to $167 million mostly as it collected smaller gains from loan sales due to lower refinancing volumes as interest rates began to rise. The bank's loan interest income also continued to decline with lower yields on loan and security assets in the low-interest environment.

Despite generating less revenue in 2014 First Busey's net income jumped by 14% to $32.8 million thanks to continued declines in interest expenses on deposits and lower loan loss provisions. The company's operating cash levels fell by 31% to $68.1 million after adjusting its earnings for non-cash items related to its net proceeds from its loans held-for-sale.

Strategy

First Busey sometimes strategically acquires smaller banks in its target markets to boost its market share broaden its service offerings and boost its loan and deposit business.

Mergers and Acquisitions

In December 2015 First Busey Corporation expanded into Missouri for the first time after it agreed to buy Pulaski Financial Corporation—along with its $1.5 billion in assets (including $1.3 billion in loans $1.1 billion in deposits) and 13 Pulaski Bank branches in the St. Louis metro area — for around $210.7 million.

In January 2015 First Busey boosted its market share in Illinois after purchasing Pekin-based Herget Financial and its three Herget Bank branches in the area. The $34.1 million-deal extended Busey Bank's presence in Pekin and the greater Peoria market added Herget Financials "dominant" deposit market position in its community and bolstered its service offerings with trust estate and asset management services as well as competitive commercial loan and mortgage offerings.

EXECUTIVES

EVP and Chief Risk Officer, Barbara J. Harrington, age 57
President CEO and Director, Van A. Dukeman, age 58, $537,308 total compensation
Chief Credit Officer, Robert F. (Bob) Plecki, age 56, $268,654 total compensation
President and CEO FirsTech, Howard F. Mooney, age 52, $240,216 total compensation
EVP and President and CEO Busey Bank, Christopher M. (Chris) Shroyer, age 51, $268,654 total compensation
EVP and General Counsel, John J. Powers
COO and CFO, Robin N. Elliott, $256,731 total compensation
Executive Vice President, Dave Weber
Vice President Senior Retirement Plan Services Advisor, Charlee Seaton
Senior Vice President Commercial Real Estate, Kent Poli
Vice President, Kelly Dennemann
Senior Vice President, Cheryl Chisholm
Assistant Vice President, Emerson Schoonover
Vice President Retail Market Manager, Tami Crouch
Regional President, Stacia Peterson
Assistant Vice President, Chris Wilson
Vice President, Brenda Carlson
Senior Vice President, Delores Eagleson
Senior Vice President, Janice Wolters
Assistant Vice President Risk Management Analyst, Annie Feleccia
Vice President Senior Loan Officer, Brian Church
Senior Vice President Relationship Manager, David Bealke
Vice President, Michele Ringsdorf
Vice President, Briggett Carter
Assistant Vice President Wealth Advisor Assistant, Monya Russell
Vice President Retail Market Manager, Linda Smith
Senior Vice President Relationship Manager Middle Market, Karen Johnson
Assistant Vice President Wire Services Manager, Karen Aulph
Senior Vice President Cash Management Executive, Brian Hintz
Chairman, Gregory B. (Greg) Lykins, age 69
Auditors: RSM US LLP

LOCATIONS

HQ: First Busey Corp
100 W. University Ave., Champaign, IL 61820
Phone: 217 365-4544
Web: www.busey.com

PRODUCTS/OPERATIONS

2014 Sales

	$ mil.	% of total
Interest		
Loans including fees	92	55
Interest & dividends on securities	15	10
Noninterest		
Trust fees	19	11
Service charges on deposit accounts	12	7
Remittance processing	9	6
Gain on sales of loans	4	3
Commissions and broker's fees net	2	2
Other	10	6
Total	**167**	**100**

COMPETITORS

Bank of America	First Midwest Bancorp
CIB Marine Bancshares	JPMorgan Chase
Fifth Third	Mercantile Bancorp
First Mid-Illinois Bancshares	PNC Financial
	Wintrust Financial

HISTORICAL FINANCIALS
Company Type: Public

Income Statement
FYE: December 31

	ASSETS ($ mil.)	NET INCOME ($ mil.)	INCOME AS % OF ASSETS	EMPLOYEES
12/16	5,425	49	0.9%	1,295
12/15	3,998	39	1.0%	795
12/14	3,665	32	0.9%	801
12/13	3,539	28	0.8%	849
12/12	3,618	22	0.6%	948
Annual Growth	10.7%	22.1%	—	8.1%

2016 Year-End Financials

Debt ratio: 1.31%
Return on equity: 10.24%
Cash ($ mil.): 166
Current ratio: —
Long-term debt ($ mil.): —

No. of shares (mil.): 38
Dividends
  Yield: 0.0%
  Payout: 48.5%
Market value ($ mil.): 1,177

	STOCK PRICE ($) FY Close	P/E High/Low		PER SHARE ($) Earnings	Dividends	Book Value
12/16	30.78	22	13	1.40	0.68	15.54
12/15	20.63	17	5	1.32	0.17	13.01
12/14	6.51	6	5	1.11	0.57	14.98
12/13	5.80	7	5	0.87	0.36	14.36
12/12	4.65	8	6	0.66	0.00	14.15
Annual Growth	60.4%	—	—	20.7%	—	2.4%

First Business Financial Services, Inc.

Business comes first at First Business Financial Services which serves small and midsized companies entrepreneurs professionals and high-networth individuals through First Business Bank and First Business Bank - Milwaukee. The banks offer deposits loans cash management and trust services from a handful of offices in Wisconsin and Kansas. Over 60% of the company's loan portfolio is made up of commercial real estate loans. Subsidiary First Business Capital specializes in asset-based lending while First Business Equipment Finance provides commercial equipment financing. First Business Trust & Investments offers investment management and retirement services.

Operations
First Business Financial Services backs its subsidiaries with low-cost corporate services such as human resources finance IT and marketing. First Business Credit Cards provides revolving lines of credit and term loans for financial and strategic acquisitions capital expenditures working capital used to support rapid growth bank debt refinancing debt restructuring and other corporate financing needs.

The company generated 80% of its total revenue from interest on loans and leases in 2014 and another 5% from interest on its securities. About 7% of revenue came from trust and investment services fee income while service charges on deposits and loan fees made up 4% and 2% of revenue respectively.

Geographic Reach
The company's primary market areas are in Wisconsin Kansas and Missouri. First Business's loan production offices are in Wisconsin in Oshkosh Green Bay Appleton and Kenosha while its two Kansas offices are in Leawood and Overland Park. In Wisconsin it targets Madison Milwaukee Appleton Green Bay Oshkosh and their surrounding communities.

Sales and Marketing
Beyond individual customers the bank generally targets businesses with annual sales between $2 million and $75 million.

Financial Performance
The company has struggled to consistently grow its revenues in recent years due to shrinking interest margins on loans amidst the low-interest environment. Its profits however have been rising thanks to declining loan loss provisions as its loan portfolio's credit quality has improved with higher property valuations in a strengthened economy.

First Business had a breakout year in 2014 however as its revenue rose 9% to $67.8 million on higher loan interest as its commercial and industrial loans comercial real estate and other mortgage loans and direct financing leases businesses all enjoyed "favorable volume variances." The bank's non-interest income also jumped by 20% which was mostly driven by growth in trust and investment services fee income on higher assets under management.

Higher revenue and lower interest expenses on deposits in 2014 pushed the company's net income up by 3% to $14.1 million. First Business' operating cash levels fell by 25% to $11.9 million due to unfavorable changes in working capital related to an increase in accrued interest payable and other liabilities.

Strategy
First Business Financial Services continued in 2015 to focus on maintaining its loan asset quality while organically growing its loan and lease portfolio in addition to growing its customer account based to increase its fee-based revenues on its variety of treasury management trust and investment services and SBA loans. It also planned to boost its investment in utilizing technology to support these initiatives while staying efficient as the business grows.

The company occasionally opens new offices or strategically acquires other banks and financial companies to extend its reach into its target markets and to grow its loan and deposit business. In 2014 its FBB-Milwaukee bank subsidiary expanded more into the southeastern area of Wisconsin after opening a loan production office in Kenosha; while its acquisition of Aslin Group and Alterra Bank furthered its exposure to new markets and loan and deposit business in Kansas.

Mergers and Acquisitions
In November 2014 First Business Financial Services expanded its Midwest market and extended its reach into Kansas after its acquisition of Leawood-based Aslin Group including its Alterra Bank subsidiary. The deal added $223 million in total assets including $182 million in new loan assets and $192 million in new deposits.

EXECUTIVES

President and CEO, Corey A. Chambas, age 54, $416,000 total compensation
SVP and Chief Credit Officer, Michael J. Losenegger, age 59, $221,950 total compensation
President and CEO First Business Capital, Charles H. (Chuck) Batson, age 63, $242,927 total compensation
President and CEO First Business Bank - Madison, Mark J. Meloy, age 55, $201,800 total compensation
President First Business Trust & Investments, Joan A. Burke, age 65
President and CEO First Business Bank - Milwaukee, David J. (Dave) Vetta, age 62
CFO, Edward G. (Ed) Sloane, age 56
President Kenosha Region, Wesley Ricchio
SVP and COO First Business Capital Corp., Peter Lowney
COO and Interim President and CEO Alterra Bank, David R. Seiler
CIO, Daniel S. Ovokaitys, age 43
Vice President Business Development, Tom Rude
Senior Vice President and Division Manager, Gail Heldke
Vice President, Cymbre Van Fossen
Vice President, Josh Hoesch
Assistant Vice President Treasury Management, Natalie Glumm
Assistant Vice President Treasury Management, Wade Hanna
Vice President, Mark Buchert
Vice President, Paul Farrelly
Vice President Internal Loan Review, Gretchen Griffin
Chairman, Jerome R. (Jerry) Smith, age 66
Board Member, Jim Hartlieb
Auditors: KPMG LLP

LOCATIONS

HQ: First Business Financial Services, Inc.
  401 Charmany Drive, Madison, WI 53719
Phone: 608 238-8008
Web: www.firstbusiness.com

COMPETITORS

Associated Banc-Corp
Bank Mutual
Harris
TCF Financial
U.S. Bancorp

HISTORICAL FINANCIALS
Company Type: Public

Income Statement
FYE: December 31

	ASSETS ($ mil.)	NET INCOME ($ mil.)	INCOME AS % OF ASSETS	EMPLOYEES
12/16	1,780	14	0.8%	272
12/15	1,782	16	0.9%	258
12/14	1,629	14	0.9%	231
12/13	1,268	13	1.1%	164
12/12	1,226	8	0.7%	155
Annual Growth	9.8%	13.7%	—	15.1%

2016 Year-End Financials

Debt ratio: 3.91%
Return on equity: 9.52%
Cash ($ mil.): 77
Current ratio: —
Long-term debt ($ mil.): —

No. of shares (mil.): 8
Dividends
  Yield: 0.0%
  Payout: 28.0%
Market value ($ mil.): 207

	STOCK PRICE ($) FY Close	P/E High/Low		PER SHARE ($) Earnings	Dividends	Book Value
12/16	23.72	15	11	1.71	0.48	18.55
12/15	25.01	25	12	1.90	0.44	17.34
12/14	47.91	28	21	1.76	0.42	15.88
12/13	37.63	22	13	1.75	0.32	13.85
12/12	22.95	15	10	1.65	0.14	12.71
Annual Growth	0.8%	—	—	1.0%	36.1%	9.9%

First Citizens BancShares Inc (NC)

First Citizens BancShares owns First-Citizens Bank which operates more than 550 branches in 20 states mainly in the southeastern and western US and urban areas scattered nationwide. The $32 billion-asset bank provides standard services such as deposits loans mortgages and trust services in addition to processing and operational support to other banks. Real estate loans including commercial residential and revolving mortgages and construction and land development loans comprise most of its loan portfolio. Subsidiaries First Citizens Investor Services First Citizens Securities Corporation and First Citizens Asset Management offers investment and discount brokerage services to bank clients.

Operations

The company provides consumer business and commercial banking wealth investments and insurance through a network of branch offices internet banking mobile banking telephone banking and ATMs.

More than 60% of the bank's total revenue came from loan and lease interest during 2015 while another 6% came from interest income on investment securities. The rest of its revenue came from merchant services (6% of revenue) service charges on deposit accounts (6%) wealth management services (6%) cardholder services (4%) mortgage income (1%) insurance commissions (1%) and other miscellaneous income sources.

Geographic Reach

First Citizens BancShares has nearly 560 branches in almost 20 states (Arizona California Colorado Florida Georgia Kansas Maryland Missouri New Mexico North Carolina Oklahoma Oregon South Carolina Tennessee Texas Virginia Washington and West Virginia) and Washington DC.

Sales and Marketing

First Citizens BancShares serves both individuals and commercial entities operating in the healthcare dental practices legal services property management agribusiness nonprofit and trade association markets.

The bank has been ramping up its advertising spend in recent years. It spent $12.4 million in 2015 up from $11.4 million and $8.2 million in 2014 and 2013 respectively.

Financial Performance

First Citizens BancShares' annual revenues have risen more than 35% since 2013 thanks to growth in its variety of non-banking business. Its profits have also been trending higher thanks to declining loan loss provisions as its loan portfolio's credit quality has improved with higher property valuations in the strengthened economy.

The bank's revenue jumped 30% to $1.44 billion during 2015 mostly thanks to higher loan and lease interest income stemming from added loan business from the acquisition of First Citizens Bancorporation. Its non-interest income sources grew 36% during the year as well.

Strong revenue growth in 2015 drove First Citizen's net income up 52% to $210.3 million. The bank's operating cash levels rose 28% to $233 million with the rise in cash-based earnings.

Strategy

FCB has expanded its branch network into new markets while bolstering its loan and deposit business by acquiring small community banks in new territory.

Mergers and Acquisitions

In May 2016 the bank made an agreement with the FDIC to buy select assets and liabilities of First Cornerstone Bank of King of Prussia in Pennsylvania. It made a similar FDIC transaction to buy North Milwaukee State Bank in March 2016. Later that year the company acquired Cordia Bancorp and its six-branch subsidiary Bank of Virginia.

In February 2015 also through the FDIC First Citizens bought select assets and deposits of Capitol City Bank & Trust (CCBT) expanding into Georgia with eight branches in Atlanta Albany Augusta Stone Mountain and Savannah.

In January 2015 First Citizens BancShares expanded its loan business and expanded into South Carolina after buying First Citizens Bancorporation and its subsidiary First Citizens Bank and Trust Company.

Company Background

First Citizens BancShares has been fortifying its presence along the West Coast by snapping up failed financial institutions. Since 2009 it has acquired most of the banking operations of Temecula Valley Bank Washington-based Venture Bank and First Regional Bank in Southern California. It also acquired the failed Florida-based bank Sun American and entered Colorado through the acquisitions of United Western Bank and Colorado Capital Bank. All were FDIC-assisted transactions and each acquired institution became branches of First-Citizens Bank. The deals added about 50 branches to the bank's network. First Citizens BancShares continues to seek out acquisitions of other seized institutions.

Though the company has been able to grow geographically thanks to the economic downturn its IronStone Bank division which focused on business customers suffered from weakened markets in Florida and Georgia. (First Citizens Bancshares merged IronStone into First-Citizens Bank in 2011 to increase efficiency and unify the company's brand.) It has remained profitable thanks in part to its acquisitions which include loss-sharing agreements with the FDIC but has had to increase its provisions for loan losses each of the last five years.

The Holding family which occupies several positions in the company's board room and executive suite controls First Citizens BancShares.

EXECUTIVES

COO BancShares and First-Citizens Bank & Trust Company, Edward L. (Ed) Willingham, age 62, $585,125 total compensation
President and Corporate Sales Executive of BancShares and First-Citizens Bank & Trust Company, Peter M. Bristow, age 51
Chairman and CEO First Citizens BancShares First-Citizens Bank & Trust and IronStone Bank, Frank B. Holding, age 56, $902,875 total compensation
EVP Finance and CFO, Craig L. Nix, age 45
Vice Chairman and Vice Chairman EVP and Business Banking Segment Manager First-Citizens Bank and Trust and President IronStone Bank, Hope Holding Connell, age 54, $563,750 total compensation
Chief Human Resources Officer; Executive Vice President of FCB, Lou J. Davis, age 64
Chief Credit Officer and Executive Vice President of FCB, Ricky T. Holland, age 63
Executive Vice President and General Auditor of FCB, Donald Preskenis
Vice President, Rhonda Chapman
Vice President, Scott German
Assistant Vice President of Information Technology, Kim Whalen
Financial Sales Manager Assistant Vice President, Chris Rivera
Vice President Business Banking, Kevin Scott
Vice President, Ruth McNeal
Vice President Commercial Banking, Drew Schiavone
Vice President, Carl Pukin
Seniorvice President, Marcus White
Auditors: Dixon Hughes Goodman LLP

LOCATIONS

HQ: First Citizens BancShares Inc (NC)
4300 Six Forks Road, Raleigh, NC 27609
Phone: 919 716-7000
Web: www.firstcitizens.com

2013 Branches

	No.
North Carolina	253
Virginia	48
California	21
Florida	18
Georgia	14
Washington	7
Texas	7
Colorado	6
Tennessee	6
West Virginia	5
Arizona	2
New Mexico	2
Oklahoma	2
Oregon	2
District of Columbia	1
Kanas	1
Maryland	1
Missouri	1
Total	**397**

PRODUCTS/OPERATIONS

2013 Sales

	$ mil.	% of total
Interest		
Loans & leases	757	72
Investment securities including dividends	36	3
Overnight investments	2	-
Noninterest		
Service charges on deposit accounts	60	5
Wealth management services	59	5
Merchant services	56	4
Cardholder services	48	4
Fees from processing services	22	1
Other service charges and fees	15	1
Adjustments	(72.3)	-
Other	72	5
Total	**1,060**	**100**

COMPETITORS

BB&T	JPMorgan Chase
BBVA Compass Bancshares	PNC Financial
Bank of America	Regions Financial
Capital One	SunTrust
Citibank	Synovus
First Horizon	Wachovia Corp
	Wells Fargo

HISTORICAL FINANCIALS

Company Type: Public

Income Statement

FYE: December 31

	ASSETS ($ mil.)	NET INCOME ($ mil.)	INCOME AS % OF ASSETS	EMPLOYEES
12/16	32,990	225	0.7%	6,296
12/15	31,475	210	0.7%	6,232
12/14	30,075	138	0.5%	6,440
12/13	21,199	167	0.8%	4,875
12/12	21,283	134	0.6%	4,821
Annual Growth	**11.6%**	**13.8%**	**—**	**6.9%**

2016 Year-End Financials

Debt ratio: 2.52%	No. of shares (mil.): 12
Return on equity: 7.64%	Dividends
Cash ($ mil.): 2,412	Yield: 0.0%
Current ratio: —	Payout: 6.3%
Long-term debt ($ mil.): —	Market value ($ mil.): 4,264

	STOCK PRICE ($) FY Close	P/E High/Low		Earnings	PER SHARE ($) Dividends	Book Value
12/16	355.00	19	12	18.77	1.20	250.82
12/15	258.17	15	12	17.52	1.20	239.14
12/14	252.79	20	16	13.56	1.20	223.77
12/13	222.63	13	9	17.43	1.20	215.89
12/12	163.50	14	12	13.11	1.20	193.75
Annual Growth	21.4%	—	—	9.4%	(0.0%)	6.7%

First Citizens Bancshares, Inc. (Dyersburg, TN)

EXECUTIVES

Chb, Katie Winchester
Auditors: Alexander Thompson Arnold PLLC

LOCATIONS

HQ: First Citizens Bancshares, Inc. (Dyersburg, TN)
One First Citizens Place, Dyersburg, TN 38024
Phone: 731 285-4410
Web: www.firstCNB.com

HISTORICAL FINANCIALS

Company Type: Public

Income Statement

FYE: December 31

	ASSETS ($ mil.)	NET INCOME ($ mil.)	INCOME AS % OF ASSETS	EMPLOYEES
12/16	1,599	15	1.0%	—
12/15	1,532	15	1.0%	—
12/14	1,481	13	0.9%	348
12/13	1,174	13	1.2%	—
12/12	1,178	13	1.1%	—
Annual Growth	7.9%	3.9%	—	—

2016 Year-End Financials

Debt ratio: 1.45%
Return on equity: 10.26%
Cash ($ mil.): 53
Current ratio: —
Long-term debt ($ mil.): —

No. of shares (mil.): 3
Dividends
Yield: 0.0%
Payout: 35.2%
Market value ($ mil.): 203

	STOCK PRICE ($) FY Close	P/E High/Low		Earnings	PER SHARE ($) Dividends	Book Value
12/16	51.00	13	12	3.97	1.40	38.93
12/15	48.50	12	11	3.92	1.15	38.19
12/14	43.00	12	10	3.72	1.30	35.75
12/13	37.80	—	—	3.83	1.30	30.64
12/12	37.80	10	8	3.75	1.20	31.07
Annual Growth	7.8%	—	—	1.4%	3.9%	5.8%

First Commonwealth Financial Corp (Indiana, PA)

First Commonwealth Financial is the holding company for First Commonwealth Bank which provides consumer and commercial banking services from nearly 115 branches across 15 central and western Pennsylvania counties as well as in Columbus Ohio. The bank's loan portfolio mostly consists of commercial and industrial loans including real estate operating agricultural and construction loans. It also issues consumer loans such as education automobile and home equity loans and offers wealth management insurance financial planning retail brokerage and trust services. The company has total assets of some $6.7 billion with deposits of roughly $4.5 billion.

Operations

The bank made 65% of its total revenue from interest and fees on loans in 2014 while another 12% came from interest and dividends on its investments. Another 6% of First Commonwealth's revenue came from service charges on deposit accounts while trust income and insurance and retail brokerage commissions each made up 2% of the bank's total revenue.

Geographic Reach

The bank boasts nearly 115 branch offices in western and central Pennsylvania and Columbus Ohio. It also has loan production offices in downtown Pittsburgh Pennsylvania and Cleveland Ohio.

Sales and Marketing

First Commonwealth Financial spent $2.95 million on advertising in 2014 compared to $3.13 million and $4.16 million in 2013 and 2012 respectively.

Financial Performance

First Commonwealth's revenues have been slowly decline over the past few years due to shrinking interest margins on loans amidst the low-interest environment. The firm's profits however have been rising thanks to declining loan loss provisions as its loan portfolio's credit quality has been improving in the strengthening economy.

The bank's revenue dipped by more than 1% to $263.04 million in 2014 mostly as interest margins on loans continued to decline as it issued new loans with lower rates in the low-interest environment.

Despite lower revenue in 2014 the bank's net income jumped by 7% to $44.45 million for the year mostly thanks to further decreases in loan loss provisions with a strengthening credit portfolio and lower interest expenses on deposits. First Commonwealth's operating cash fell by 4% to $82.14 million despite higher earnings mostly as the bank collected less in cash proceeds from the sales of its mortgage loans held for sale.

Strategy

First Commonwealth Financial has historically expanded its branch reach through the acquisition smaller banks and thrifts in its market area. However in recent years the company has also been adding non-banking businesses such as insurance firms to bolster its existing non-banking service lines.

Mergers and Acquisitions

First Commonwealth Bank acquired 13 branches in Canton and Ashtabula Ohio from FirstMerit Bank in 2016. The acquisition related to FirstMerit's acquisition by Huntington Bancshares added some $735 million in deposits and some 34000 customers. It is also buying Ohio's DCB Financial parent company of Delaware County Bank & Trust for some $106 million. That deal will add nine full-service branches in central Ohio.

In 2014 First Commonwealth Bank entered the Columbus Ohio market for the first time with its purchase of the Ohio-based First Community Bank for $14.75 million cash.

Also in 2014 the bank bolstered its insurance business through its acquisition of Thompson/McLay Insurance Associates which boasted long-term client relationships in the home auto commercial and specialty insurance lines. The deal added the insurance firm's experienced sales and account management personnel as well as the popular Thompson/McLay Insurance Associates brand which it would keep as a division of its own insurance agency.

EXECUTIVES

EVP and Chief Revenue Officer, Jane Grebenc, $355,833 total compensation
EVP and Chief Credit Officer, I. Robert (Bob) Emmerich, $274,500 total compensation
President and CEO, Thomas Michael (Mike) Price, age 54, $435,567 total compensation
EVP CFO and Treasurer, James R. Reske, $237,372 total compensation
EVP and Chief Audit Executive, Leonard V. Lombardi, age 57
EVP Business Integration, Norman J. Montgomery, $261,792 total compensation
EVP Chief Risk Officer General Counsel and Secretary, Matthew C. (Matt) Tomb
EVP Human Resources, Carrie Riggle
Vice President Administration, Wendy Reynolds
Assistant Vice President, Scott Repine
Vice President Corporate Banking, Bowser Brian
Senior Vice President and Senior Operations Audit Manager, John M Heise
Vice President, Chuck Bennett
Vice President and Office Manager of Murrysville and Export Offices, John Mango
Vice President And Commercial Real Estate, Brian Pukylo
Vice President, David Hepler
Assistant Vice President Operations, Mona Straw
Vice President Human Resources Representative, Vicki Fox
Vice President Commercial Real Estate, John E Clingan
Executive Vice President, David Buckiso
Senior Vice President Relationship Manager, David McGowan
Assistant Vice President Benefits Administration, Natalie Felix
Assistant Vice President Office Manager, Jody Shepler
Office Manager Assistant Vice President, Jeffrey Sokolowski
Assistant Vice President, Sean Gabler
Business Banker Vice President, Susan Henigin
Assistant Vice President, Bradley Wojnar
Vice President Senior Corporate Banker First Commonwealth Bank, Matthew Zuro
Vice President, Linda Tasser
Vice President and Senior Investment Officer First Commonwealth Bank, Dona Denaro
Chairman, David S. (Dave) Dahlmann, age 67
Auditors: KPMG LLP

LOCATIONS

HQ: First Commonwealth Financial Corp (Indiana, PA)
601 Philadelphia Street, Indiana, PA 15701
Phone: 724 349-7220
Web: www.fcbanking.com

PRODUCTS/OPERATIONS

2014 Sales

	$ mil.	% of total
Interest		
Loans including fees	171	65
Taxable investments	31	12
Noninterest		
Service charges on deposit accounts	15	7
Insurance & retail brokerage commissions	6	2
Trust income	6	2
Others	32	12
Total	**263**	**100**

Selected Subsidiaries

First Commonwealth Bank
  First Commonwealth Insurance Agency
  First Commonwealth Home Mortgage LLC (49.9%)
First Commonwealth Financial Advisors Incorporated

COMPETITORS

Allegheny Valley	F.N.B. (PA)
Bancorp	Fidelity Bancorp (PA)
AmeriServ Financial	Northwest Bancshares
Citizens Financial	PNC Financial
Group	S&T Bancorp
Dollar Bank	

HISTORICAL FINANCIALS

Company Type: Public

Income Statement

FYE: December 31

	ASSETS ($ mil.)	NET INCOME ($ mil.)	INCOME AS % OF ASSETS	EMPLOYEES
12/16	6,684	59	0.9%	1,376
12/15	6,566	50	0.8%	1,311
12/14	6,360	44	0.7%	1,363
12/13	6,214	41	0.7%	1,437
12/12	5,995	41	0.7%	1,482
Annual Growth	**2.8%**	**9.2%**	**—**	**(1.8%)**

2016 Year-End Financials

Debt ratio: 1.08%	No. of shares (mil.): 89
Return on equity: 8.09%	Dividends
Cash ($ mil.): 115	Yield: 0.0%
Current ratio: —	Payout: 41.7%
Long-term debt ($ mil.): —	Market value ($ mil.): 1,262

	STOCK PRICE ($) FY Close	P/E High/Low		PER SHARE ($) Earnings	Dividends	Book Value
12/16	14.18	21	12	0.67	0.28	8.43
12/15	9.07	18	14	0.56	0.28	8.09
12/14	9.22	20	16	0.48	0.28	7.81
12/13	8.82	22	16	0.43	0.23	7.47
12/12	6.82	19	14	0.40	0.18	7.49
Annual Growth	**20.1%**	**—**	**—**	**13.8%**	**11.7%**	**3.0%**

First Community Bancshares, Inc. (NV)

First Community Bancshares doesn't play second fiddle to other area banks. The firm is the holding company for First Community Bank which provides traditional services like checking and savings accounts CDs and credit cards and serves communities through some 55 branches across Virginia West Virginia North Carolina and Tennessee. Commercial real estate loans make up 45% of its loan portfolio while commercial business

loans make up another 5%. First Community Bancshares offers insurance through subsidiary Greenpoint Insurance and wealth management and investment advisory services through Trust Services and First Community Wealth Management.

Operations

First Community Bancshares operates through four main business activities: commercial and consumer banking lending activities wealth management and insurance services. Its Trust Services and First Community Wealth Management subsidiary had managed assets with a market value of nearly $700 million in 2014.

The bank which had a staff of 678 employees at the end of 2014 generated 70% of its total revenue from loan interest (including fees and loans held for investment) in 2014 and another 8% from interest on taxable and non-taxable securities. The rest of its revenue came from deposit account service charges (9%) insurance commissions (4%) wealth management (1%) and other miscellaneous sources of income.

Sales and Marketing

The bank serves individuals and businesses across several industries including: manufacturing mining services construction retail healthcare military and transportation.

Financial Performance

The company has struggled to grow its revenues in recent years due to shrinking interest margins on loans amidst the low-interest environment. Its profits however have been rising thanks to falling interest expenses and declining loan loss provisions as its loan portfolio's credit quality has improved with higher property valuations in the strengthened economy.

First Community Bancshares's revenue dipped by 2% to $136.1 million in 2014 as its interest income on loans and securities declined with fewer assets and because it took on a $1.39 million loss from the sale of its investment securities during the year.

Despite revenue declines in 2014 the bank's net income jumped 9% to $25.5 million thanks to continued declines in interest expenses on deposits and loan loss provisions. First Community's operating cash levels fell by 6% to $41.7 million for the year after adjusting its earnings for non-cash items related to its loan loss provisions and the proceeds of its mortgage loan sales.

Strategy

Faced with shrinking revenues in recent years First Community has been strategically changing its geographic positioning selling off some of its branches in certain areas and acquiring new branches in others. In late 2014 it acquired seven branches from Bank of America in Southwestern Virginia and Central North Carolina and sold 13 of its branches to Charleston-based CresCom Bank including 10 of its branches in Southeastern North Carolina and three in South Carolina.

Mergers and Acquisitions

In 2014 First Community purchased seven branches from Bank of America including six branches in Southwestern Virginia and one in Central North Carolina. The deal also added $318.9 million in new deposits as well as real estate and assumed leases associated with the branches.

Company Background

After slowing its acquisition activity during the economic downturn First Community resumed in 2012 buying Peoples Bank of Virginia which added four branches in the Richmond area. The company also acquired the failed Waccamaw Bank in a FDIC-facilitated transaction. That deal brought in 16 branches in North Carolina.

EXECUTIVES

EVP and COO, E. Stephen (Steve) Lilly, age 58, $252,000 total compensation
Chairman and CEO, William P. Stafford, age 53, $200,013 total compensation
CFO, David D. Brown, age 42, $225,000 total compensation
President; CEO First Community Bank, Gary R. Mills, $300,000 total compensation
President First Community Bank, Martyn A. Pell, $255,000 total compensation
Vice President Director of Operations, Garry Stutts
Assistant Vice President Credit Administration, Jeff Noble
Senior Vice President On the Corporate Staff, John Spracher
Assistant Vice President Regulatory Compliance Officer, Jean Prazecky
Regional President, William C Hopkins
Vice President, Robert Partrea
Auditors: Dixon Hughes Goodman LLP

LOCATIONS

HQ: First Community Bancshares, Inc. (NV)
P.O. Box 989, Bluefield, VA 24605-0989
Phone: 276 326-9000
Web: www.fcbinc.com

PRODUCTS/OPERATIONS

2011 Sales

	$ mil.	% of total
Interest		
Loans including fees	80	61
Securities	13	10
Deposits in banks	0	-
Noninterest		
Service charges on deposit accounts	13	10
Insurance commissions	6	5
Net gains on sales of securities	5	4
Wealth management	3	3
Other service charges commissions & fees	5	4
Other	3	3
Adjustments	(2.3)	-
Total	**129**	**100**

COMPETITORS

BB&T	Huntington Bancshares
Bank of America	SunTrust
City Holding	United Bankshares
First Citizens	WesBanco
BancShares	
Highlands Bankshares	
Inc.	

HISTORICAL FINANCIALS

Company Type: Public

Income Statement

FYE: December 31

	ASSETS ($ mil.)	NET INCOME ($ mil.)	INCOME AS % OF ASSETS	EMPLOYEES
12/16	2,386	25	1.1%	580
12/15	2,462	24	1.0%	673
12/14	2,607	25	1.0%	678
12/13	2,602	23	0.9%	729
12/12	2,728	28	1.0%	760
Annual Growth	**(3.3%)**	**(3.2%)**	**—**	**(6.5%)**

2016 Year-End Financials

Debt ratio: 0.66%	No. of shares (mil.): 16
Return on equity: 7.35%	Dividends
Cash ($ mil.): 37	Yield: 0.0%
Current ratio: —	Payout: 41.3%
Long-term debt ($ mil.): —	Market value ($ mil.): 512

	STOCK PRICE ($)	P/E	PER SHARE ($)		
	FY Close	High/Low	Earnings	Dividends	Book Value
12/16	30.14	22 12	1.45	0.60	19.95
12/15	18.63	16 11	1.31	0.54	18.95
12/14	16.47	13 10	1.31	0.50	19.09
12/13	16.70	16 13	1.11	0.48	17.75
12/12	15.97	11 8	1.40	0.43	17.77
Annual Growth	17.2%	——	0.9%	8.7%	2.9%

First Connecticut Bancorp Inc. (MD)

One of the oldest states in the union also has some of the oldest banks in the union. First Connecticut Bancorp (FCB) is the holding company for Farmington Bank a Connecticut-based community bank tracing its roots back to the mid-1800s. The bank offers traditional deposit accounts and loan products to consumers businesses and government clients through about 25 branches in the suburban communities in central Connecticut and western Massachusetts. Its lending activity consists primarily of commercial and residential real estate loans. The bank also offers wealth management services.

Operations

The lender specializes in originating residential real estate loans (for one-to-four family homes) and commercial real estate loans (for office buildings multi-family residences industrial and warehouse facilities and retail outlets). About 55% of its loan portfolio consisted of commercial loans at the end of 2015 while another 36% was tied to residential loans. Real estate loans made up 75% of the loan portfolio.

The bank made 86% of its revenue from interest income in 2015 mostly from its mortgage loans. The rest came from customer service fees (6% of revenue) gains on loan sales (3%) and other miscellaneous income sources.

Geographic Reach

FCB had 23 branches across central Connecticut (including ones in Hartford County and Rocky Hill) and western Massachusetts (including ones in Hampden County West Springfield and East Longmeadow) as of early 2016.

Sales and Marketing

The company originates mortgages for developers licensed contractors and builders that work on commercial and residential properties. FCB serves a variety of sectors including the Insurance Health Services Finance Manufacturing Non-profit Education Government and Technology sectors.

FCB spent $2.1 million on marketing during 2015 up from $1.6 million in 2014.

Financial Performance

First Connecticut's annual revenues have risen 50% since 2011 mostly as its loan assets have nearly doubled to $2.34 billion. The bank has also seen its profits more the triple over that time as its loan loss provisions have receded with an improvement in portfolio credit quality.

The bank's revenue jumped 16% to $95.3 million during 2015 mostly thanks to a double-digit rise in organic loan growth. Its non-interest income increased by 48% on a combination of higher investment sale gains and more customer service fees with deposit account and debit card growth helping to buoy revenues further.

Strong revenue growth and a continued decline in loan loss provisions in 2015 drove FCB's net income up 35% to $12.6 million for the year. The bank's operating cash levels fell nearly 80% to $9.3 million in 2015 mainly as the bank used more cash to originate loans.

Strategy

First Connecticut Bancorp has been focused on expanding its commercial lending business. It has also been opening several new branches in recent years through de novo branching. The bank introduced two new de novo branches in western Massachusetts in late 2015 and planned to open two more in Connecticut in 2016. It also opened a new loan production office in Branford Connecticut with plans to open another in Fairfield Connecticut in early 2016.

In past years First Connecticut launched small business cash management and government banking divisions to draw in new customers.

Company Background

In 2011 FCB converted from a mutual holding structure to a public company. The conversion was a way for FCB to generate new capital and support the bank's strategy for continued growth.Also that year FCB formed an alliance with Essex Financial Services to offer wealth management services to high-net-worth individuals.

EXECUTIVES

Chairman President and CEO First Connecticut Bancorp and Farmington Bank, John J. Patrick, age 57, $409,692 total compensation
EVP CFO and Treasurer, Gregory A. White, age 52, $213,279 total compensation
EVP and Director Retail Banking, Kenneth F. Burns, age 53, $183,077 total compensation
EVP and Chief Risk Officer, Michael T. Schweighoffer, age 54, $232,673 total compensation
Assistant Vice President Branch Manager, Nikki Gleason
Auditors: PricewaterhouseCoopers LLP

LOCATIONS

HQ: First Connecticut Bancorp Inc. (MD)
One Farm Glen Boulevard, Farmington, CT 06032
Phone: 860 676-4600
Web: www.farmingtonbankct.com

PRODUCTS/OPERATIONS

2015 Sales

	% of total
Interest income	
Interest and fees on loans	
Mortgage	65
Other	18
Interest and dividends on investments	
United States Government and agency obligations	2
Corporate stocks	1
Other	-
Noninterest income	
Fees for customer services	6
Net gain on loans sold	3
Gain on sales of investments	1
Bank owned life insurance income	2
Other	2
Total	**100**

Selected Services

Business Borrowing
Business Deposit Accounts
Business Financing
Business Services
Cash Management
Cash Management
Checking Accounts
Commercial Home
Government Home
Home Loans
Interest-Bearing Accounts

International Services
Investment Services
Municipal Services
Personal Loans
Savings Accounts
Security Awareness

COMPETITORS

Bank of America	Sovereign Bank
Citizens Financial Corp.	TD Bank USA
Liberty Bank	U.S. Bancorp
People's United Financial	Webster Financial

HISTORICAL FINANCIALS

Company Type: Public

Income Statement

FYE: December 31

	ASSETS ($ mil.)	NET INCOME ($ mil.)	INCOME AS % OF ASSETS	EMPLOYEES
12/16	2,837	15	0.5%	339
12/15	2,708	12	0.5%	343
12/14	2,485	9	0.4%	328
12/13	2,110	3	0.2%	337
12/12	1,822	3	0.2%	326
Annual Growth	11.7%	40.3%	—	1.0%

2016 Year-End Financials

Debt ratio: —
Return on equity: 6.00%
Cash ($ mil.): 47
Current ratio: —
Long-term debt ($ mil.): —
No. of shares (mil.): 15
Dividends
　Yield: 0.0%
　Payout: 31.0%
Market value ($ mil.): 360

	STOCK PRICE ($)	P/E	PER SHARE ($)		
	FY Close	High/Low	Earnings	Dividends	Book Value
12/16	22.65	24 15	1.00	0.31	16.37
12/15	17.41	22 17	0.83	0.22	15.47
12/14	16.32	27 23	0.62	0.17	14.64
12/13	16.12	71 55	0.24	0.12	14.11
12/12	13.75	58 52	0.24	0.12	13.63
Annual Growth	13.3%	——	42.9%	26.8%	4.7%

First Data Corp (New)

Paper plastic or digital — in whatever form First Data moves the money. One of the world's largest electronic payments processors First Data serves roughly 6 million merchants and 4000 card issuers in some 100 countries. It provides a variety of secure funds transfer and related services including credit card payment processing fraud protection and authentication check guarantee (through subsidiary TeleCheck) electronic bill payment management and point-of-sale (POS) services. First Data takes part in merchant alliance partnerships with Bank of America and Wells Fargo. After being taken private for $30 billion by KKR in 2007 First Data went public in 2015 although KKR remained majority shareholder.

HISTORY

Both predecessors of today's First Data (First Financial Management and First Data Resources) developed from in-house data processing operations that became independent profit centers for their parent companies and were then spun off.

The older of the two companies First Financial Management arose out of the data processing department of the Georgia Railroad Bank & Trust. By the time it went public in 1983 First Financial was the largest banking data processor in the Southeast. It grew rapidly in a consolidating industry and in 1987 entered the credit card transaction processing business with the purchase of NaBANCO.

That year American Express created First Data Resources a separate unit for its transaction processing functions under the leadership of Henry Duques. Duques had built up the unit during the 1980s to process a variety of transactions for American Express' charge card processing business and its burgeoning financial services operations. While First Data was growing First Financial remained active buying Georgia Federal Bank in 1989 to facilitate the growth of its bank card business.

As the 1990s dawned American Express' dreams of a financial services empire were crumbling. The businesses did not fit well with American Express diverting attention from its core lines. However First Data had become the largest bank card processing company in the US and a significant power in mutual fund transactions. In 1992 it was spun off.

First Financial began sharpening its focus on merchant (rather than bank) services. It bought TeleCheck (check authorization) in 1992 and began divesting its banking and bank services holdings.

In 1994 First Data and First Financial Management went head-to-head vying for Western Union (founded 1855) from bankrupt parent New Valley. First Financial was the victor in the bruising bidding war (which also included Forstmann Little).

Although First Data's $6.5 billion merger with First Financial in 1995 raised antitrust concerns the deal went through with only the stipulation of selling the MoneyGram (money transfer) services business. The new union gave First Data a 30% share of the fragmented credit card processing market and moved it into new service areas many of which it began divesting in efforts to focus on financial support.

First Data won a 10-year contract in 1996 to process credit and debit transactions for retail giant Wal-Mart— more than 5 billion transactions each year. A 1997 pact with BANK ONE and its First USA subsidiary added another 6 million accounts. First Data also expanded its geographical presence that year agreeing to provide credit card processing for HSBC Holdings' banks in the UK the US and Hong Kong (First Data pulled out of Hong Kong the following year).

In 1999 First Data and BANK ONE strengthened their relationship: First Data took a stake in BANK ONE subsidiary Paymentech and folded it into an existing joint venture with BANK ONE (Banc One Payment Services). To refocus on its electronic payment and commerce services First Data sold its Investor Services Group.

In 2000 the company slashed some 400 management jobs and made other workforce cuts. First Data continued to grow through acquisitions (including Cardservice International and PaySys) and alliances (with such entities as JPMorgan Chase and Deutsche Post) in 2001.

The US Department of Justice challenged First Data's 2004 purchase of rival Concord EFS over antitrust concerns but later approved the deal when First Data agreed to divest ATM network NYCE in a sale to Metavante.

The Concord EFS acquisition was notable both because of its size and because it brought First Data's credit and debit processing strengths together with Concord EFS' PIN-debit network. However it did not bring about the expected syn-

ergies and First Data struggled for the next few years to absorb its new prize. CEO Charlie Fote left the company in 2005 and was replaced by his predecessor Ric Duques who had led the company from 1992 to 2002.

Duques led the company through a restructuring in 2006 spinning off its Western Union operations as well as related units Orlandi Valuta and Vigo Remittance to shareholders.

Investment firm KKR acquired First Data in 2007 and Duques handed over the company reins to former Compaq and MCI exec Michael Capellas following the acquisition. The $26 billion deal was the largest leveraged-buyout transaction to date but the timing was less than ideal. After the acquisition the economy took a nosedive and payments declined in volume and number. Consumers began using debit cards rather than credit cards another trend that lowered the company's revenues. Facing billions in debt from the buyout First Data sold some operations to raise capital and discontinued others that weren't performing. The company also restructured merging its commercial and financial services segments and cutting operational costs.

In 2008 First Data strengthened its European business by forming card processing joint venture AIB Merchant Services with Allied Irish Banks and through the acquisition of a 50% stake in the interbank processing business of multibank entity Trionis (formerly European Savings Banks Financial Services or EUFISERV). Also that year First Data announced plans to buy prepaid gift card provider Interactive Communications but purchase negotiations stalled and the company instead inked a distribution deal to sell InComm's cards.

In 2009 First Data moved its headquarters office back to Atlanta — near Banc of America Merchant Services and other payments industry companies including customers — after some eight years of being headquartered in the Denver area. First Data retained its Colorado office as its administrative headquarters.

EXECUTIVES

EVP and Head of EMEA Region, Michael K. (Mike) Neborak, age 60, $600,000 total compensation
Chairman and CEO, Frank J. Bisignano, age 57, $1,320,000 total compensation
EVP and Head of Latin America and Mexico (LATAM) Region, Gustavo C. Marin, age 59
EVP and Head of Human Resources, Anthony S. (Tony) Marino, age 53
EVP and Head of Network and Security Solutions, Barry C. McCarthy, age 53, $750,000 total compensation
President, Guy Chiarello, age 57, $1,000,000 total compensation
EVP and Head of Corporate and Business Development, Christopher M. Foskett, age 59
EVP and Head of Asia Pacific Region, Ivo M. Distelbrink, age 47
EVP General Counsel and Secretary, Adam L. Rosman, age 52
EVP and COO, Christine E. Larsen, age 55, $396,667 total compensation
EVP and CFO, Himanshu A. Patel, age 41, $600,000 total compensation
CIO, Christopher (Chris) Augustin
EVP and Co-Head of Global Financial Solutions, Andrew Gelb, age 46
EVP and Chief Control Officer, Cynthia (Cindy) Armine-Klein, age 55, $320,192 total compensation
EVP and Head of Global Business Solutions, Daniel J. (Dan) Charron, age 52, $750,000 total compensation
EVP and Chief Administrative Officer, Thomas (Tom) Higgins, age 58
Vice Chairman, Joseph J. (Joe) Plumeri, age 73
Auditors: Ernst & Young LLP

LOCATIONS

HQ: First Data Corp (New)
225 Liberty Street, 29th Floor, New York, NY 10281
Phone: 800 735-3362
Web: www.firstdata.com

2016 sales

	% of total
North America	85
Non-NA	15
Total	**100**

PRODUCTS/OPERATIONS

2016 sales

	$ mil.	% of total
Global Business Solutions	4,063	57
Global Financial Solutions	1,593	22
Network & Security Solutions	1,485	21
Total	**7,141**	**100**

COMPETITORS

Atos	Fiserv
Cardtronics	Global Payments
Chase Paymentech	MasterCard
Solutions	PayPal
Discover	Total System Services
ECHO Inc.	Vantiv
Elavon	Visa Inc
Fidelity National	
Information Services	

HISTORICAL FINANCIALS

Company Type: Public

Income Statement

FYE: December 31

	REVENUE ($ mil.)	NET INCOME ($ mil.)	NET PROFIT MARGIN	EMPLOYEES
12/16	11,584	420	3.6%	24,000
12/15	11,451	(1,481)	—	24,000
12/14	11,151	(457)	—	23,000
12/13	10,808	(869)	—	23,000
12/12	10,680	(700)	—	24,000
Annual Growth	2.1%	—	—	0.0%

2016 Year-End Financials

Debt ratio: 45.89%	No. of shares (mil.): 911
Return on equity: 44.37%	Dividends
Cash ($ mil.): 385	Yield: —
Current ratio: 1.04	Payout: —
Long-term debt ($ mil.): 18,131	Market value ($ mil.): 12,941

	STOCK PRICE ($) FY Close	P/E High/Low	Earnings	PER SHARE ($) Dividends	Book Value
12/16	14.19	34 18	0.46	0.00	1.34
12/15	16.02	— —	(7.70)	0.00	0.74
Annual Growth	(3.0%)	— —	—	—	15.8%

First Defiance Financial Corp

Named for its hometown not its attitude First Defiance Financial is the holding company for First Federal Bank of the Midwest which operates more than 30 branches serving northwestern Ohio western Indiana and southern Michigan. The thrift offers standard deposit products including checking savings and money market accounts and CDs.

Commercial real estate loans account for more than half of the bank's loan portfolio; commercial loans make up another quarter of all loans. The company's insurance agency subsidiary First Insurance Group of the Midwest which accounts for some 7% of the company's revenues provides life insurance property/casualty coverage and investments.

Strategy

First Defiance Financial has boosted its non-banking product lines via acquisitions. It bought the employee benefits insurance business of another local agency Andres O'Neil & Lowe in 2010; and property/casualty agency Payak-Dubbs Insurance Agency in 2011. Both additions became part of First Insurance Group of the Midwest (formerly named First Insurance & Investments).

In 2016 the company agreed to buy another bank serving northwest Ohio Commercial Bancshares. The deal is valued at some $63 million and adds seven branches and $342 million in assets.

EXECUTIVES

EVP Business Banking First Federal Bank, Dennis E. Rose, age 48, $144,077 total compensation

President and CEO First Defiance Financial and First Federal Bank, Donald P. Hileman, age 64, $400,000 total compensation

EVP General Counsel and Chief Risk Officer First Defiance Financial Corp and First Federal Bank, John R. Reisner, age 61, $180,147 total compensation

EVP and Community Banking President Â– First Federal Bank, Gregory R. Allen, age 53, $200,000 total compensation

EVP and President Western Market Area First Federal Bank, James R. Williams, age 49

EVP and President Eastern Market Area First Federal Bank, Timothy K. (Tim) Harris, age 58

EVP and Chief Credit Officer First Federal Bank, Michael D. Mulford, age 52, $149,387 total compensation

EVP and President Northern Market Area First Federal Bank, Marybeth Shunck, age 47

EVP and CFO First Defiance Financial Corp. and First Federal Bank, Kent T. Thompson, age 63, $218,360 total compensation

EVP and Director Human Resources First Defiance Financial Corp. and First Federal Bank, Sharon L. Davis, age 35

EVP and President Southern Market Area First Federal Bank, Amy L. Hackenberg, age 46

Vice President Sales and Marketing, Ken Wenner

Vice President, Gary Verhoff

Assistant Vice President Human Resources, Diane Beam

Senior Vice President, Lisa R Christy

Chairman, William J. (Bill) Small, age 66

Vice Chairman, Stephen L. Boomer, age 66

Auditors: Crowe Horwath LLP

LOCATIONS

HQ: First Defiance Financial Corp
601 Clinton Street, Defiance, OH 43512
Phone: 419 782-5015
Web: www.fdef.com

PRODUCTS/OPERATIONS

2016 Sales

	$ mil.	% of total
Interest		
Loans	80	66
Investment securities		
Taxable	3	3
Tax-exempt	3	2
Interest-bearing deposits	0	-
FHLB stock dividends	0	1
Non-interest		
Service fees & other charges	10	9
Insurance commissions	10	9
Mortgage banking income	7	6
Trust income	1	1
Gain on sale of non-mortgage loans	0	1
Income from bank owned life insurance	0	1
Gain on sale or call of securities	0	-
Other	1	1
Total	**121**	**100**

COMPETITORS

Farmers National	Huntington Bancshares
Fifth Third	KeyCorp
First Citizens Banc Corp	PNC Financial
First Financial Bancorp	SB Financial Group

HISTORICAL FINANCIALS

Company Type: Public

Income Statement

FYE: December 31

	ASSETS ($ mil.)	NET INCOME ($ mil.)	INCOME AS % OF ASSETS	EMPLOYEES
12/16	2,477	28	1.2%	581
12/15	2,297	26	1.2%	586
12/14	2,178	24	1.1%	555
12/13	2,137	22	1.0%	549
12/12	2,046	18	0.9%	553
Annual Growth	**4.9%**	**11.5%**	**—**	**1.2%**

2016 Year-End Financials

Debt ratio: 1.46%
Return on equity: 10.04%
Cash ($ mil.): 53
Current ratio: —
Long-term debt ($ mil.): —
No. of shares (mil.): 8
Dividends
Yield: 0.0%
Payout: 27.5%
Market value ($ mil.): 456

	STOCK PRICE ($) FY Close	P/E High/Low		PER SHARE ($)		
				Earnings	Dividends	Book Value
12/16	50.74	16	11	3.19	0.88	32.62
12/15	37.78	15	11	2.82	0.78	30.78
12/14	34.06	14	10	2.44	0.63	30.27
12/13	25.97	12	8	2.19	0.45	28.00
12/12	19.19	10	8	1.81	0.20	26.53
Annual Growth	**27.5%**	**—**	**—**	**15.2%**	**44.8%**	**5.3%**

First Financial Bancorp (OH)

First Financial Bancorp spreads itself thick. The holding company's flagship subsidiary First Financial Bank operates nearly 110 branches in Ohio Indiana and Kentucky. Founded in 1863 the bank offers checking and savings accounts money market accounts CDs credit cards private banking and wealth management services through its First Financial Wealth Management subsidiary. Commercial loans including real estate and construction loans make up more than 50% of First Financial's total loan portfolio; the bank also offers residential mortgage and consumer loans. First Financial Bancorp boasts more than $7 billion in assets including nearly $5 billion in loans.

Operations

The company's private banking business First Financial Wealth Management had $2.4 billion in assets under management in early 2015.

Sales and Marketing

First Financial spent $3.60 million on marketing in 2014 compared to $4.27 million and $5.55 million in 2013 and 2012 respectively.

Financial Performance

First Financial's revenue has been in decline in recent years due to shrinking interest margins on loans amidst the low-interest environment. The company has also struggled to grow its profits much past the $65 million-mark though profit levels are more than twice as high as they were prior to 2009.

The company's revenue dipped by 2% to $311.82 million in 2014 mostly as its loan interest income declined by nearly 4% as interest margins continued to shrink in the low-interest environment. First Financial's non-interest income fell by double-digits mostly due to lower FDIC loss sharing income lower income from the accelerated discount on prepaid covered loans and smaller gains on investment securities sales.

Despite lower revenue in 2014 First Financial's net income rebounded by 34% to $65 million for the year mostly thanks to an 80% reduction in loan and lease loss provisions as the bank's loan portfolio's credit quality improved with the strengthening economy. The company's non-interest expenses also declined by double-digits mostly because the bank in 2013 incurred a non-recurring $22.4 million FDIC indemnification valuation adjustment.

First Financial's operating cash declined by 66% to $56.65 million after adjusting its earnings for non-cash items related to the indemnification asset decrease and net sales proceeds on its loans held for sale.

Strategy

First Financial has been focusing on branch expansion (on its own or through acquisitions) in three core metropolitan markets: Cincinnati Dayton and Indianapolis. In 2014 for example First Financial acquired three Ohio-based banks and their branches in 2014 expanding its branch network in Central Ohio while adding new loan and deposit business at the same time.

Mergers and Acquisitions

In 2014 to expand further into key markets in Columbus and Central Ohio First Financial purchased The First Bexley Bank which served commercial and consumer bank clients from its one branch location in Bexley Ohio. Similarly that year it purchased Insight Bank operated a branch in Worthington Ohio and a mortgage origination office in Newark Ohio; and bought Worthington-based Guernsey Bancorp and its three branches in Central Ohio.

Company Background

In the past the bank acquired 16 branches in western Ohio from Liberty Savings Bank and bought 22 Indianapolis-area branches from Flagstar Bank in 2011. Together the two acquisitions furthered the bank's growth strategy for the key markets of Dayton and Indianapolis.

EXECUTIVES

President Western Markets Commercial Banking and Wealth Management, C. Douglas (Doug) Lefferson

President and CEO, Claude E. Davis

President and COO, Anthony M. (Tony) Stollings

Chief Credit Officer, Richard S. Barbercheck

SVP and CFO, John Gavigan

President Mortgage Banking, Jill A. Stanton

EVP and Chief Compliance Officer, Holly M. Foster

President Corporate Banking, Brad Ringwald

Executive Vice President and Chief Internal Auditor, Matthew B Burgess

Vice President Commercial Underwriter, Brian Englert

First Vice President Commercial Banking, Stephen Murphy

Assistant Vice President Sales Center Manager III, Diana Bravo

Assistant Vice President, Jeremy Fuller

First Vice President Information Technology, Bard Lowry

Assistant Vice President Sales Center Manager III, Cooley Andrew

Vice President Mortgage Operations Manager, Tammy Kinser

Vice President Of Mortgage Lending, Wade Spain

Vice President, Chris Peffly

Vice President Commercial Lending, Gary Kovach

Vice President Network, Brad Stroeh

F Vice President and Manager of Corporate Banking, Paul Silva

Regional Market Manager Vice President, Shane Wilken

Assistant Vice President Loan Operations, Barbara A Sensibaugh

Assistant Vice President Lockbox Services, Greg Rudolph

Vice President, Irene Tsen

Assistant Vice President Mortgage Lending, Michael Reeve

Banking Center Manager III Assistant Vice President, Ashley Dick

First Vice President Deposit Operations and Processing Services, Peter Beccaccio

Vice President Senior Commercial Underwriter, Christy Wooldridge

Vice President Digital Sales Channel Manager, Brano Tomic

Vice President, Mark Bicker

First Vice President Commercial Banking, Lisa Tsen

Vice President, Jim Osmon

Vice President Commercial Banking, Eric Evans

Vice President, Josh Riley

First Vice President Commercial Banking, Steve Murphy

Vice President Commercial Lending Barry.lampley Bankatfirst Www Bankatfirst.com, Barry Lampley

Assistant Vice President Mortgage Sales Manager, Mark Spangler

Vice President Commercial Banking First Financial Bank, Jason King

Vice President Commercial Market Manager, Zac Nelson

Chairman, Murph Knapke

Vice Chairman, J. Wickliffe Ach

Auditors: Crowe Horwath LLP

LOCATIONS

HQ: First Financial Bancorp (OH)
255 East Fifth Street, Suite 700, Cincinnati, OH 45202
Phone: 877 322-9530
Web: www.bankatfirst.com

PRODUCTS/OPERATIONS

2014 Sales

	$ mil.	% of total
Interest		
Loans including fees	208	66
Investment securities	44	14
(Adjustment)	(5.5)	
Noninterest		
Service charges on deposit accounts	20	7
Trust and wealth management fees	13	5
Bankcard income	10	3
Net gains from sales on loans	4	1
Accelerated discount on covered/formerly covered loans	4	1
Others	10	3
Total	**311**	**100**

COMPETITORS

AMB Financial
Commercial Bancshares
Farmers National
Fifth Third
First Defiance Financial
First Franklin
LCNB
Liberty Capital
Logansport Financial
MutualFirst Financial
PNC Financial
Peoples Community Bancorp
Peoples-Sidney
SB Financial Group
U.S. Bancorp

HISTORICAL FINANCIALS

Company Type: Public

Income Statement

FYE: December 31

	ASSETS ($ mil.)	NET INCOME ($ mil.)	INCOME AS % OF ASSETS	EMPLOYEES
12/16	8,437	88	1.0%	1,521
12/15	8,147	75	0.9%	1,471
12/14	7,217	65	0.9%	1,442
12/13	6,417	48	0.8%	1,422
12/12	6,497	67	1.0%	1,547
Annual Growth	**6.8%**	**7.1%**	**—**	**(0.4%)**

2016 Year-End Financials

Debt ratio: 1.41%
Return on equity: 10.54%
Cash ($ mil.): 204
Current ratio: —
Long-term debt ($ mil.): —

No. of shares (mil.): 61
Dividends
Yield: 0.0%
Payout: 44.7%
Market value ($ mil.): 1,763

	STOCK PRICE ($) FY Close	P/E High/Low		PER SHARE ($)		
				Earnings	Dividends	Book Value
12/16	28.45	20	10	1.43	0.64	13.96
12/15	18.07	17	13	1.21	0.64	13.13
12/14	18.59	17	14	1.09	0.61	12.76
12/13	17.43	21	17	0.83	0.94	11.86
12/12	14.62	16	12	1.14	1.18	12.24
Annual Growth	**18.1%**	**—**	**—**	**5.8%**	**(14.2%)**	**3.3%**

First Financial Bankshares, Inc.

Texas hold 'em? Well sort of. First Financial Bankshares is the holding company for eleven banks consolidated under the First Financial brand all of which are located in small and midsized markets in Texas. Together they have about 50 locations. The company maintains a decentralized management structure with each of the subsidiary banks having their own local leadership and decision-making authority. Its First Financial Trust & Asset Management subsidiary administers retirement and employee benefit plans in addition to providing trust services. First Financial Bankshares also owns an insurance agency.

EXECUTIVES

Chairman President and CEO; Chairman First Financial Bank N.A., F. Scott Dueser, age 64, $754,167 total compensation

EVP and CFO, J. Bruce Hildebrand, age 62, $445,000 total compensation

EVP and Chief Administrative Officer, Ronald D. (Ron) Butler, age 56, $405,000 total compensation

EVP Lending, Marna Yerigan

EVP Lending, T. Luke Longhofer

EVP and CIO, Thomas S. (Stan) Limerick

EVP and Lending Officer, Gary S.Gragg, age 57, $325,000 total compensation

EVP Retail and Training, Monica Houston

EVP Chief Risk Officer, Randy Roewe

Senior Vice President, Kay Berry

Assistant Vice President Human Resources, Racheal Carter

Senior Vice President Consumer Lending, Chris Schjetnan

Vice President, Wade Spain

Vice President, Isabel Montoya

Auditors: Ernst & Young LLP

LOCATIONS

HQ: First Financial Bankshares, Inc.
400 Pine Street, Abilene, TX 79601
Phone: 325 627-7155
Web: www.ffin.com

PRODUCTS/OPERATIONS

2015 sales

	$ mil.	% of total
Interest Income		
Interest and fees on loans	151	51
Interest on investment securities	69	24
Interest on federal funds sold and interest-bearinga deposits in banks	0	-
Non-Interest Income		
ATM interchange and credit card fees	21	7
Trust fees	19	6
Service charges on deposit accounts	17	6
Real estate mortgage operations	10	4
Net gain on sale of available-for-sale securities	0	-
Net gain on sale of foreclosed assets	0	-
Net loss on sale of assets	(0.8)	-
Other	4	2
Total	**295**	**100**

Products/ServicesPersonal
Learn
Online Banking
Mobile Banking
Consumer Education
FAQS
Privacy & Security Information
Resources
Testimonials
Tools
Bank
Checking
Savings
Invest
CDS & IRAS
Broker Services
Borrow
Mortgage Loans
Mortgage Lenders
Auto Loans
Recreational Loans
Home Equity Loans
Personal Line of Credit
CD Secured Loans
Banking with First Financial
Mobile Banking
Online Banking
Pay Bills
Get Cash
Make Deposit
Move Money
Keep Track
Business
Learn
Online Banking
Mobile Banking
Business Education
Starting your Business
Growing your Business
Tools
Business Banking Services
Manage Cash
Send Payments
Receive Payments
Manage Fraud and Risk
Other Services
Trust & Wealth Management

Investment Management
Trust Management
Estate Management
Oil & Gas Management
Real Estate and Property Management
Company Retirement Plans

Selected Subsidiaries

First Financial Bank National Association Abilene Texas.
First Technology Services Inc. Abilene Texas (wholly owned subsidiary of First Financial Bank National Association Abilene Texas).
First Financial Trust & Asset Management Company National Association Abilene Texas.
First Financial Insurance Agency Inc. Abilene Texas.
First Financial Investments Inc. Abilene Texas.

COMPETITORS

BBVA Compass Bancshares	JPMorgan Chase
Bank of America	Wells Fargo
Cullen/Frost Bankers	Woodforest Financial

HISTORICAL FINANCIALS

Company Type: Public

Income Statement

FYE: December 31

	ASSETS ($ mil.)	NET INCOME ($ mil.)	INCOME AS % OF ASSETS	EMPLOYEES
12/16	6,809	104	1.5%	1,300
12/15	6,665	100	1.5%	1,270
12/14	5,848	89	1.5%	1,140
12/13	5,222	78	1.5%	1,100
12/12	4,502	74	1.6%	1,000
Annual Growth	10.9%	9.0%	—	6.8%

2016 Year-End Financials

Debt ratio: —
Return on equity: 12.72%
Cash ($ mil.): 255
Current ratio: —
Long-term debt ($ mil.): —

No. of shares (mil.): 65
Dividends
Yield: 0.0%
Payout: 44.0%
Market value ($ mil.): 2,965

	STOCK PRICE ($) FY Close	P/E High/Low	PER SHARE ($) Earnings	Dividends	Book Value
12/16	45.20	29 15	1.59	0.70	12.78
12/15	30.17	23 16	1.54	0.62	12.30
12/14	29.88	47 20	1.39	0.55	10.72
12/13	66.11	54 31	1.24	1.03	9.26
12/12	39.01	35 26	1.18	0.99	8.92
Annual Growth	3.8%	— —	7.7%	(8.3%)	9.4%

First Financial Corp. (IN)

Which came first the First Financial in Indiana Ohio South Carolina or Texas? Regardless this particular First Financial Corporation is the holding company for First Financial Bank which offers traditional banking deposit accounts and loans as well as trust private banking wealth management and investment services through more than 70 branches in west-central Indiana and east-central Illinois. About 60% of its loan portfolio is tied to commercial loans while the rest is split between residential and consumer loans. Subsidiary Forrest Sherer sells personal and commercial insurance while subsidiary Morris Plan originates indirect auto loans through dealerships in the bank's market area.

Operations

About 59% of the bank's $1.76 billion loan portfolio was tied to commercial business loans to finance business asset purchases and expansion at the end of 2015 while the remainder of the portfolio was tied to 1-4 family residential real estate mortgages (25% of loan assets) and consumer loans (16%).

Nearly 75% of First Financial's revenue comes from interest income. About 57% of its total revenue came from loan interest (including fees) during 2015 while another 16% came from interest income on taxable and tax-exempt investment securities. The rest of its revenue came from deposit account service charges (7% of revenue) insurance commissions (5%) trust and financial services (4%) gains on mortgage loan sales (2%) and other miscellaneous income sources.

Geographic Reach

The Terre Haute Indiana-based bank operated 71 branches in west-central Indiana and east-central Illinois at the end of 2015.

Financial Performance

First Financial Corporation's annual revenues and profits have been trending lower over the past several years due to shrinking margins in the low-interest environment and as its loan assets have declined more than 5% since 2011.

The bank's revenue fell 4% to $147.86 million during 2015 mostly as its interest-earning loan and investment assets and the interest margins they command continued to decline. Its non-interest income tumbled at a similar rate due to reduced investment service and insurance agency income.

Revenue declines in 2015 caused First Financial's net income to dive nearly 11% to $30.2 million. The bank's operating cash levels plunged almost 30% to $41.26 million for the year as cash earnings shrank.

Strategy

First Financial Corporation continued in 2016 to expand its branch network in hopes to build its loan and deposit business. Indeed its branch network has steadily grown from 65 branches at the end of 2011 to 71 branches at the end of 2015.

Company Background

In 2011 First Financial bought Freestar Bank adding more than a dozen branches in central Illinois. It was the largest acquisition in the company's history.

With roots dating back to 1834 First Financial Bank is not only one of the oldest banks in Indiana but also the entire country. It is also one of the oldest continually operating businesses in its hometown of Terre Haute. Another local business Princeton Mining Company owns nearly 10% of First Financial Corporation.

EXECUTIVES

Vice Chairman and CEO, Norman D. Lowery, age 49, $630,297 total compensation
Vice President, Jim Nichols
Personal Trust Department Assistant Vice Presiden, Carol Myers
Vice President, Patrick R Ralston
Vice President Collections, Jeff Nickels
Vice President, Thom Frantz
Vice President Director of Consumer Lending, Carl Britton
Vice President, Eric Feathers
Chairman, B. Guille Cox
Auditors: Crowe Horwath LLP

LOCATIONS

HQ: First Financial Corp. (IN)
One First Financial Plaza, Terre Haute, IN 47807
Phone: 812 238-6000
Web: www.first-online.com

PRODUCTS/OPERATIONS

2011 Sales

	$ mil.	% of total
Interest		
Loans including related fees	91	61
Securities	22	15
Other	2	1
Noninterest		
Service charges & fees on deposit accounts	9	6
Other service charges & fees	8	6
Insurance commissions	7	5
Trust & financial services	4	3
Other	4	3
Total	**149**	**100**

COMPETITORS

FFW	Huntington Bancshares
Fifth Third	JPMorgan Chase
First Midwest Bancorp	MainSource Financial
First Robinson Financial	Old National Bancorp
	PNC Financial

HISTORICAL FINANCIALS

Company Type: Public

Income Statement

FYE: December 31

	ASSETS ($ mil.)	NET INCOME ($ mil.)	INCOME AS % OF ASSETS	EMPLOYEES
12/16	2,988	38	1.3%	846
12/15	2,979	30	1.0%	896
12/14	3,002	33	1.1%	952
12/13	3,018	31	1.0%	954
12/12	2,895	32	1.1%	928
Annual Growth	0.8%	4.0%	—	(2.3%)

2016 Year-End Financials

Debt ratio: —
Return on equity: 9.29%
Cash ($ mil.): 75
Current ratio: —
Long-term debt ($ mil.): —

No. of shares (mil.): 12
Dividends
Yield: 0.0%
Payout: 31.7%
Market value ($ mil.): 645

	STOCK PRICE ($) FY Close	P/E High/Low	PER SHARE ($) Earnings	Dividends	Book Value
12/16	52.80	17 10	3.12	0.99	33.92
12/15	33.97	16 14	2.35	0.98	32.21
12/14	35.62	14 12	2.55	0.97	30.46
12/13	36.56	16 12	2.37	0.96	28.94
12/12	30.24	15 11	2.48	0.95	28.01
Annual Growth	15.0%	— —	5.9%	1.0%	4.9%

First Foundation Inc

Auditors: Vavrinek, Trine, Day & Co., LLP

LOCATIONS

HQ: First Foundation Inc
18101 Von Karman Avenue, Suite 700, Irvine, CA 92612
Phone: 949 202-4160
Web: www.ff-inc.com

HISTORICAL FINANCIALS
Company Type: Public

Income Statement
FYE: December 31

	ASSETS ($ mil.)	NET INCOME ($ mil.)	INCOME AS % OF ASSETS	EMPLOYEES
12/16	3,975	23	0.6%	335
12/15	2,592	13	0.5%	295
12/14	1,355	8	0.6%	207
12/13	1,037	7	0.8%	187
12/12	830	5	0.7%	—
Annual Growth	47.9%	41.6%	—	—

2016 Year-End Financials
Debt ratio: 31.44%
Return on equity: 8.54%
Cash ($ mil.): 597
Current ratio: —
Long-term debt ($ mil.): —

No. of shares (mil.): 32
Dividends
　Yield: —
　Payout: —
Market value ($ mil.): 933

	STOCK PRICE ($) FY Close	P/E High/Low		PER SHARE ($) Earnings	Dividends	Book Value
12/16	28.50	41	28	0.70	0.00	8.69
12/15	23.59	41	29	0.58	0.00	8.13
12/14	18.14	37	33	0.52	0.00	6.34
Annual Growth	12.0%	—	—	8.0%	—	8.2%

First Guaranty Bancshares, Inc.

Auditors: Castaing, Hussey & Lolan, LLC

LOCATIONS
HQ: First Guaranty Bancshares, Inc.
　400 East Thomas Street, Hammond, LA 70401
Phone: 985 345-7685
Web: www.eguaranty.com

HISTORICAL FINANCIALS
Company Type: Public

Income Statement
FYE: December 31

	ASSETS ($ mil.)	NET INCOME ($ mil.)	INCOME AS % OF ASSETS	EMPLOYEES
12/16	1,500	14	0.9%	304
12/15	1,459	14	1.0%	289
12/14	1,518	11	0.7%	272
12/13	1,436	9	0.6%	278
12/12	1,407	12	0.9%	274
Annual Growth	1.6%	4.0%	—	2.6%

2016 Year-End Financials
Debt ratio: 2.45%
Return on equity: 11.59%
Cash ($ mil.): 17
Current ratio: —
Long-term debt ($ mil.): —

No. of shares (mil.): 8
Dividends
　Yield: 0.0%
　Payout: 34.6%
Market value ($ mil.): 200

	STOCK PRICE ($) FY Close	P/E High/Low		PER SHARE ($) Earnings	Dividends	Book Value
12/16	23.93	14	9	1.68	0.58	14.86
12/15	18.75	12	9	1.83	0.54	14.12
12/14	19.00	14	10	1.42	0.53	18.34
12/13	14.02	14	12	1.11	0.53	16.21
12/12	12.85	10	9	1.32	0.53	17.63
Annual Growth	16.8%	—	—	6.2%	2.4%	(4.2%)

First Hawaiian Inc

LOCATIONS
HQ: First Hawaiian Inc
　999 Bishop Street, 29th Floor, Honolulu, HI 96813
Phone: 808 525-7000
Web: www.fhb.com

HISTORICAL FINANCIALS
Company Type: Public

Income Statement
FYE: December 31

	ASSETS ($ mil.)	NET INCOME ($ mil.)	INCOME AS % OF ASSETS	EMPLOYEES
12/16	19,661	230	1.2%	2,200
12/15	19,352	213	1.1%	2,250
12/14	18,133	216	1.2%	—
Annual Growth	4.1%	3.1%	—	—

2016 Year-End Financials
Debt ratio: 0.00%
Return on equity: 8.81%
Cash ($ mil.): 1,052
Current ratio: —
Long-term debt ($ mil.): —

No. of shares (mil.): 139
Dividends
　Yield: 0.0%
　Payout: 12.3%
Market value ($ mil.): 4,858

	STOCK PRICE ($) FY Close	P/E High/Low		PER SHARE ($) Earnings	Dividends	Book Value
12/16	34.82	21	15	1.62	0.20	17.75
12/15	0.00	—	—	1.53	0.00	19.63
12/14	0.00	—	—	1.55	0.00	(0.00)
Annual Growth	—	—	—	2.2%	—	—

First Horizon National Corp

First Horizon National would like to be on banking consumers' horizons in the Volunteer State and beyond. The bank holding company operates more than 170 First Tennessee Bank branches in its home state and neighboring markets. Boasting roughly $26 billion in total assets it offers traditional banking services like loans deposit accounts and credit cards as well as trust asset management financial advisory and investment services. Subsidiary FTN Financial performs securities sales and trading fixed-income underwriting and other investment banking services through more than 25 offices in more than 15 states as well as in Hong Kong.

Operations

First Horizon operates two core business segments: Regional Banking and Capital Markets.

Regional Banking is the company's largest division (it generated 73% of the bank's total revenue in 2014) and provides traditional banking products and services to retail and commercial customers mostly in Tennessee but also in neighboring markets. The division also provides investments financial panning trust services and asset management as well as correspondent banking services such as credit depository and other banking related services for financial institutions.

The Capital Markets segment which contributed 18% to total revenues in 2014 serves mainly institutional clients in the US and overseas. Its services consist of fixed-income sales trading loan sales portfolio advisory and derivative sales.

First Horizon's two non-core segments include a Corporate division which collects gains and losses related to the bank's debt and investment activities; and the non-strategic segment (11% of total revenues in 2014) which consists of the wind down of the company's national consumer lending activities its legacy mortgage banking elements including service fees its trust preferred loan portfolio and exited businesses.

The company has diversified revenue streams generating about 56% of its total revenue from interest income (mostly from loans) in 2014 16% from capital markets-related fees nearly 10% from deposit transactions and cash management fees about 6% from its Mortgage Banking business and 6% from a combination of brokerage fees and trust services and management fees.

Geographic Reach

First Horizon National boasts more than 180 branch locations across seven US states. More than 90% of the branches are in Tennessee while just over a dozen are in the states of Georgia (northwestern) Mississippi (northwestern) North Carolina Virginia South Carolina and Florida. It also has more than 25 financial offices in 16 states across the US plus a financial office in Hong Kong.

Sales and Marketing

The company spent $18.68 million on advertising and public relations in 2014 up from $18.24 million and $17.44 million in 2013 and 2012 respectively.

Financial Performance

First Horizon's revenue has been in decline in recent years due to shrinking interest margins on loans amidst the low-interest environment. The firm's profits however have been rising thanks to declining loan loss provisions as its loan portfolio's credit quality has been improving in the strengthening economy.

The company's revenue fell by 4% to $1.26 billion in 2014 mostly as the Capital Markets business shrank by 26% as fixed-income markets suffered from low rates low market volatility and uncertainty around the Federal Reserve's monetary policy. The bank's interest income also fell by 3% despite rising commercial loan business mostly due to a combination of continued run-off of non-strategic loan portfolios lower-yielding commercial loans and lower strategic loan balances. Offsetting some of the top-line decline First Horizon's mortgage banking revenue more than doubled for the year mostly thanks to a nearly $40 million gain on the sale of its mortgage loans held-for-sale.

Despite revenue declines in 2014 First Horizon's net income skyrocket nearly seven-fold to $219.52 million thanks to a combination of lower interest and non-interest expenses and a significant decline in loan loss provisions as its loan portfolio's credit condition improved.

The company's operating cash also jumped by 63% to $704.7 million during the year as cash earnings rose and as net cash proceeds from the bank's mortgage loans held-for-sale increased.

Strategy

First Horizon National's flagship First Tennessee Bank has been expanding its geographic reach in recent years through both branch openings and strategic acquisitions of smaller banks and branches in target markets. In 2014 the bank opened its first office in Florida (in Jacksonville) as it continued its plans for growth in the Mid-Atlantic region which includes North Carolina South Carolina Virginia and northern parts of Florida. Also that year the bank agreed to purchase 13 bank branches located in the Middle and East Tennessee for a total of nearly $438 million which would add some $437 million worth of new deposits and expand its reach in its home state.

Mergers and Acquisitions

In 2014 First Horizon agreed to purchase TrustAtlantic Financial Corporation along with its five TrustAtlantic Bank branches in North Carolina (mostly in the Raleigh-Cary metro area). The deal matched First Horizon's objectives to expand in North Carolina's fast-growing Research Triangle region of the state.

In mid-2013 First Tennessee bank acquired Mountain National Bank from the FDIC adding 12 new branch locations in Sevier and Blount counties in Eastern Tennessee as well as $249 million in loan assets and $362 million in deposits.

In 2012 the company added to FTN Financial with the purchase of Las Vegas-based Main Street Capital Advisors which provides investment management and consulting services mainly to state and local municipalities.

Company Background

At the start of the recession First Horizon began selling non-core assets and refocused growth closer to home. First Horizon exited the Baltimore-Washington DC and Atlanta markets. The company also sold some 230 First Horizon Home Loan offices as well as the unit's loan origination and servicing operations outside of Tennessee to MetLife. After the sale First Horizon Financial outsourced some its mortgage origination processing and servicing operations within Tennessee to PHH Mortgage.

In 2008 the bank discontinued its specialty construction and consumer lending activities beyond Tennessee. It exited the institutional equity research business in 2010 and sold its First Horizon Insurance unit to Brown & Brown the following year. Also in 2011 First Horizon sold a subsidiary that provided administrative services for health savings accounts.

EXECUTIVES

EVP and Chief Human Resources Officer, John M. Daniel, age 62

President and COO First Tennessee Bank, David T. Popwell, age 56, $450,000 total compensation

Chairman President and CEO, D. Bryan Jordan, age 55, $815,000 total compensation

EVP and General Counsel, Charles T. Tuggle, age 68, $475,000 total compensation

EVP Corporate Communications, Kimberley C. (Kim) Cherry

EVP Technology and Operations and CIO, Bruce A. Livesay

EVP and CFO, William C. (BJ) Losch, age 46, $425,000 total compensation

EVP and Chief Risk Officer, Yousef A. Valine, age 57, $362,692 total compensation

President FTN Financial, Michael E. Kisber, age 57, $600,000 total compensation

EVP and Chief Credit Officer, Susan L. Springfield, age 52

EVP and Chief Operating and Financial Officer FTN Financial, Michael K. Waddell

EVP Consumer Banking First Tennessee Bank, David W. Miller

EVP Corporate Banking, Steve J. Hawkins

President First Tennessee Bank Mid-Atlantic Region, Billy Frank, age 46

President First Tennessee Bank Mid-Atlantic region, John Fox, age 64

Regional President First Tennessee Bank Tennessee Banking Group, Richard Shaffer, age 52

EVP and Chief Audit Executive, Vernon H. Stafford

Vice President Of Corporate Strategy, Dane P Smith

Vice President Risk Management, Kathleen Mooney

Senior Vice President and Chief Investment.., Karen Kruse

Senior Vice President and Counsel (2003), Keri Goldstein Unowsky

Senior Vice President and Counsel (2004), John Arthur Niemoeller

Senior Vice President Bank Operations, Janet Honeycutt

Senior Vice President, Christine Bland

Vice President, David Ward

Auditors: KPMG LLP

LOCATIONS

HQ: First Horizon National Corp
165 Madison Avenue, Memphis, TN 38103
Phone: 901 523-4444
Web: www.firsthorizon.com

PRODUCTS/OPERATIONS

2014 Sales

	$ mil.	% of total
Interest		
Loans including fees	571	45
Investment securities	93	7
Trading securities	32	3
Loans held for sale	11	1
Other	1	—
Noninterest		
Capital markets	200	16
Deposit transactions & cash management	112	9
Mortgage banking	71	6
Brokerage management fees & commissions	49	4
Trust services and investment management	27	2
Bankcard income	23	2
Bank owned life insurance	16	1
Other	49	4
Total	**1,259**	**100**

COMPETITORS

Athens Federal Community Bank	JPMorgan Chase
BB&T	Regions Financial
Bank of America	SunTrust
Citigroup	Trustmark
	Wells Fargo

HISTORICAL FINANCIALS

Company Type: Public

Income Statement

FYE: December 31

	ASSETS ($ mil.)	NET INCOME ($ mil.)	INCOME AS % OF ASSETS	EMPLOYEES
12/16	28,555	227	0.8%	4,288
12/15	26,195	85	0.3%	4,293
12/14	25,672	219	0.9%	4,310
12/13	23,789	29	0.1%	4,340
12/12	25,520	(27)	—	4,514
Annual Growth	**2.8%**	—	—	**(1.3%)**

2016 Year-End Financials

Debt ratio: 3.64%
Return on equity: 9.53%
Cash ($ mil.): 1,433
Current ratio: —
Long-term debt ($ mil.): —
No. of shares (mil.): 233
Dividends
  Yield: 0.0%
  Payout: 29.7%
Market value ($ mil.): 4,675

	STOCK PRICE ($) FY Close	P/E High/Low		Earnings	PER SHARE ($) Dividends	Book Value
12/16	20.01	22	12	0.94	0.28	10.31
12/15	14.52	48	36	0.34	0.24	9.83
12/14	13.58	15	12	0.91	0.20	9.80
12/13	11.65	126	97	0.10	0.20	9.33
12/12	9.91	—	—	(0.11)	0.04	9.09
Annual Growth	**19.2%**	—	—	—	**62.7%**	**3.2%**

First Internet Bancorp

EXECUTIVES

Vice President Treasury Management, Maria Bryce

Vice President Deposit Operations And BSA Officer, Jan Jones

Senior Vice President and Chief Financial Officer, Kenneth Lovik

Vice President Commercial Lender, Carl Osberg

Vice President Commercial Lending, Jim Laine

Vice President Commercial Lending, Kevin Lynch

VICE PRESIDENT, Thomas Smith

Auditors: BKD, LLP

LOCATIONS

HQ: First Internet Bancorp
11201 USA Parkway, Fishers, IN 46037
Phone: 317 532-7900
Web: www.firstinternetbancorp.com

COMPETITORS

Bank of America	Citibank
BofI	E*TRADE Bank

HISTORICAL FINANCIALS

Company Type: Public

Income Statement

FYE: December 31

	ASSETS ($ mil.)	NET INCOME ($ mil.)	INCOME AS % OF ASSETS	EMPLOYEES
12/16	1,854	12	0.7%	192
12/15	1,269	8	0.7%	152
12/14	970	4	0.4%	143
12/13	802	4	0.6%	130
12/12	636	5	0.9%	97
Annual Growth	**30.7%**	**21.1%**	—	**18.6%**

2016 Year-End Financials

Debt ratio: 1.97%
Return on equity: 9.32%
Cash ($ mil.): 39
Current ratio: —
Long-term debt ($ mil.): —
No. of shares (mil.): 6
Dividends
  Yield: 0.0%
  Payout: 10.4%
Market value ($ mil.): 207

	STOCK PRICE ($) FY Close	P/E High/Low		Earnings	PER SHARE ($) Dividends	Book Value
12/16	32.00	14	10	2.30	0.24	23.76
12/15	28.69	18	7	1.96	0.24	23.28
12/14	16.74	26	16	0.96	0.24	21.80
12/13	22.50	22	13	1.51	0.22	20.44
12/12	21.00	11	5	1.95	0.17	21.79
Annual Growth	**11.1%**	—	—	**4.2%**	**9.5%**	**2.2%**

First Interstate BancSystem Inc

This Treasure State bank wants to be your treasury. First Interstate BancSystem is the holding company for First Interstate Bank which has about 80 branches in Montana western South Dakota and Wyoming. Serving area consumers businesses and municipalities the bank provides traditional services including deposit accounts wealth management and loans. Commercial loans including mortgages make up more than half of the bank's loan portfolio; residential real estate agricultural and construction loans round out its lending activities. On the wealth management side the bank has more than $8 billion in trust assets held in a fiduciary or agent capacity.

Financial Performance

The company's revenue decreased in fiscal 2013 compared to the previous period. It reported $369.3 million in revenue for fiscal 2013 down from $388.8 million in fiscal 2012. However despite the decreased annual revenue the company's net income increased in fiscal 2013 to $86 million up from a net income of $58 million the prior fiscal year. Cash flow increased by about $15 million in fiscal 2013 compared to 2012 levels.

Strategy

The company is always looking for opportunities for expansion including organic growth as well as growth through acquisitions. It expanded into the northwest growth market with the acquisition of Cascade Bancorp for around $589 million.

EXECUTIVES

SVP and CIO, Kevin J. Guenthner, age 53, $205,385 total compensation

President and CEO, Kevin P. Riley, age 57, $307,270 total compensation

EVP and Chief Banking Officer, Bill Gottwals

EVP and CFO, Marcy D. Mutch, age 57

Executive Vice President and Chief Banking Officer, Michael Huston

Vice President Wealth Advisor, Kyle Geffre

Vice President Wealth Advisor, Troy Nearpass

Chairman, James R. Scott, age 67

Auditors: RSM US LLP

LOCATIONS

HQ: First Interstate BancSystem Inc
401 North 31st Street, Billings, MT 59116-0918
Phone: 406 255-5390
Web: www.fibk.com

PRODUCTS/OPERATIONS

Selected ServicesBanking
Checking Accounts
Credit Cards
Debit Cards
Escrow Services
Foreign Currency
Overdraft Protection
Personal Resources
Prepaid Cards
Savings Accounts
Borrowing
AdvanceLine
Auto & Recreation
Debt Consolidation
Home Equity
Home Mortgage
Personal Loans
Create & Build Wealth
Long-Term Planning
Planning for the Unexpected

Saving for College
Saving for Retirement
Wealth Resources
Protect & Preserve Wealth
Asset Management
Employee Exit Strategies
Health Concerns
Investment Services
Retirement Plan Services

Sales 2015

	$ mil.	% of total
Interest income	282	70
Non-interest income	121	30
Total	**403**	**100**

COMPETITORS

Bank of the West	Great Western Bancorp
Crazy Woman Creek	U.S. Bancorp
Eagle Bancorp	Wells Fargo
Glacier Bancorp	

HISTORICAL FINANCIALS

Company Type: Public

Income Statement

FYE: December 31

	ASSETS ($ mil.)	NET INCOME ($ mil.)	INCOME AS % OF ASSETS	EMPLOYEES
12/16	9,063	95	1.1%	1,721
12/15	8,728	86	1.0%	1,742
12/14	8,609	84	1.0%	1,705
12/13	7,564	86	1.1%	1,635
12/12	7,721	58	0.8%	1,683
Annual Growth	**4.1%**	**13.2%**	**—**	**0.6%**

2016 Year-End Financials

Debt ratio: 1.22%	No. of shares (mil.): 44
Return on equity: 9.87%	Dividends
Cash ($ mil.): 781	Yield: 0.0%
Current ratio: —	Payout: 41.3%
Long-term debt ($ mil.): —	Market value ($ mil.): 1,912

	STOCK PRICE ($) FY Close	P/E High/Low	Earnings	Dividends	Book Value
12/16	42.55	20 12	2.13	0.88	21.87
12/15	29.07	16 12	1.90	0.80	20.92
12/14	27.82	16 13	1.87	0.64	19.85
12/13	28.37	15 8	1.96	0.54	18.15
12/12	15.43	12 10	1.27	0.61	17.35
Annual Growth	**28.9%**	**— —**	**13.8%**	**9.6%**	**6.0%**

First Merchants Corp

First Merchants is the holding company that owns First Merchants Bank which operates more than 100 branches in Indiana Illinois and western Ohio. Along with its Lafayette Bank & Trust and Commerce National Bank divisions the bank provides standard consumer and commercial banking services including checking and savings accounts CDs check cards and loans and mortgages. First Merchants Corporation also owns First Merchants Trust Company which provides trust and asset management services and First Merchants Insurance Group which sells personal property/casualty and employee benefit coverage. Founded in 1982 First Merchants has nearly $6 billion worth of consolidated assets.

Operations

First Merchants operates under three different bank brands including: First Merchants Bank which serves Indiana Illinois and Ohio; Lafayette Bank & Trust serving customers in six Indiana counties; and Commerce National Bank which serves customers in Franklin county in Ohio.

Commercial real estate loans made up nearly 50% of the bank's loan portfolio while residential and commercial & consumer loans split the remaining 50%.

Geographic Reach

The Muncie Indiana-based holding company's 100-plus bank branches are located across Indiana and in two counties each in Illinois and Ohio.

Sales and Marketing

First Merchant spent $3.46 million on marketing in 2014 which is 55% more than in 2013 and 60% more than in 2012.

Financial Performance

Revenue jumped by 22% to a record-high of $274.6 million in 2014 mostly thanks to higher interest income from more loan business and more investment security income following the bank's recent acquisitions of CFS Bancorp and Community Bancshares. The bank also collected significantly more non-interest income from deposit account service charges electronic card fees and investment brokerage fees as it grew its customer base with the recent acquisitions.

Net income also spiked by 35% to a record-high $60.2 million in 2014 thanks mostly to higher revenue and lower provisions for loan losses as the credit of the bank's loan portfolio improved with a strengthening housing market.

Operations provided $75.84 million or 59% less cash than in 2013 returning to cash levels seen between 2010 and 2012. Cash from operations reached a recent high in 2013 as the bank was able to decrease its "other" receivables accounts by more than $110 million which was an non-occurring event.

Strategy

A key part of the bank holding company's growth strategy is to expand geographically through more branch openings in new areas. In 2014 the bank expanded its reach into Tennessee through opening a new branch in Davidson County and by purchasing land in Williamson County for another branch location in the future. In early 2014 the bank opened its second location in Shelbyville Indiana.

It's also been expanding through strategic acquisitions. In early 2015 First Merchants acquired C Financial Corporation and its handful of Cooper State Bank locations to create the second-largest financial holding company based in Indiana. In late 2014 the company bought Community Bancshares and acquired 10 more branches in the central Indiana region. In late 2013 First Merchants purchased CFS Bancorp. to increase its branch network in Indiana and Illinois by 20 branches. In 2012 it acquired certain loans and core deposits of Shelby County Bank which was seized by the FDIC. The deal included four branches in Shelby County Indiana a new market for First Merchants.

Mergers and Acquisitions

In January 2015 First Merchants agreed to purchase C Financial Corporation along with its handful of Cooper State Bank branches in exchange for $15.5 million in cash for all outstanding shares of C Financial common stock. Both C Financial and Cooper State Bank adopted the First Merchant brand name as part of the deal.

In November 2014 First Merchants purchased Community Bancshares for $49.2 million in cash and common stock which added 10 full-service branches in central Indiana to its network.

In November 2013 First Merchants Corp. (FMC) acquired Munster Indiana-based CFS Bancorp. a holding company for Citizens Financial Bank (CFB) with about 20 branches in Indiana and Illinois including parts of the Chicago metro area in a transaction valued at about $135.6 million. CFB branches were rebranded as First Merchants Bank in early 2014.

First Vice President Corporate Controller, Jeff Lorentson

EVP and CFO, Mark K. Hardwick, age 46, $317,347 total compensation

CTO, Stephan H. Fluhler, $205,268 total compensation

President and CEO, Michael C. (Mike) Rechin, age 58, $502,181 total compensation

EVP and Chief Banking Officer, Michael J. (Mike) Stewart, age 51, $310,077 total compensation

EVP and Chief Credit Officer, John J. Martin, age 50, $249,193 total compensation

SVP and Chief Risk Officer, Jeffery B. Lorentson

Vice President of the Mortgage Department, Tracie Simon

Vice President, Brad Wise

Vice President Business Banking Officer, Ryan Mooney

First Vice President and Director Investor Relations, David Ortega

Vice President oF marketing, Deanne Beard

Assistant Vice President Software Developer, Chris Horton

Vice President Trust and Insurance Marketing Director, Nichole Kinghorn

Vice President, Tom Dunson

Vice President of Loans, Christopher Allen

Senior Vice President Director of Retail Sales and Service, Carrie Valek

Vice President Account Executive, Shelley Campbell

Vice President Credit Manager, Christy Kessler

Vice President Marketing Manager, Dana Talaga

Vice President, Tonya Gooden

Vice President, Lentz Gregory

Senior Vice President Human RE, Leslie Holland

Regional President, James A Meinerding

Vice President and Purchasing Director, Lisa Brothers

Senior. Vice President Manager. Retail Banking Division, Dan Gick

Senior Vice President Chief Accounting Officer, Jami Bradshaw

Vice President, David Benjamin

Vice President, Joseph Keyler

Assistant Vice President Relationship Manager, Michael Kahne

Vice President, Margaret Hoke

Senior Vice President, John Ditmars

AVP Review Appraiser, Joanilla Barker

Senior Vice President, David E Mooney

Vice President Business Banking, Chris Chatfield

Senior Vice President Chief Sales Officer Lakeshore Region, Dale Clapp

Vice President Branch Center Manager, Stacy Stephens-Chemelewski

Vice President Special Assets Officer, Jeffrey Jex

Regional President, Daryl Pomranke

Vice President Retail Market Leader, Roberta Salway

Vice President Structured Finance, Dave Decraene

Vice President, Daniel J Gick

Senior Vice President and Director of Human Resources, Kim A Ellington

Executive Vice President, Mike Gilbert

Assistant Vice President, Tammy Hall

Avp Banking Center Manager, Andy Bowen

Vice President, Josh McKenney

Vice President, Adam Treibic

Vice President Relationship Manager III, Kevin Wagner

Senior Vice President of Treasury and Accounting, Michele Kawiecki

Vice President, Steve Moore

Vice President, Ben Hartings

First Vice President, Rene Martin

Vice President Wealth Advisor, Michael Daugherty

First Vice President General Counsel, Brian Hunt

VICE PRESIDENT, William Robertson

VICE PRESIDENT AND CLIENT ADVISOR, Rita K Smith

VICE PRESIDENT, Benjamin J Hartings

ASSISTANT VICE PRESIDENT MANAGER FACILITIES PROJECTS AND PLANNING, Lindsay S Sweet

VICE PRESIDENT RELATIONSHIP MANAGER III, Kevin M Orourke

VICE PRESIDENT RETIREMENT PLAN ADVISOR, Kristopher Feldmeyer

First Vice President, Scott Steinwart

Vice President, Bill Robertson

Chairman, Charles E. Schalliol, age 70

Auditors: BKD, LLP

LOCATIONS

HQ: First Merchants Corp
200 East Jackson Street, Muncie, IN 47305-2814
Phone: 765 747-1500

PRODUCTS/OPERATIONS

2016 Sales

	$ mil.	% of total
Interest		
Loans	216	68
Investment Securities	35	11
Federal Reserve and Federal Home Loan Bank stock	1	1
Deposits with financial institutions	0	-
Non-interest		
Service charges on deposits	17	6
Fiduciary activities	9	3
Other customer fees	19	6
Earnings on cash surrender value of life insurance	4	1
Net gains and fees on sales of loans	7	2
Net realized gains on sales of available for sale securities	3	1
Others	3	1
Total	**318**	**100**

COMPETITORS

Ameriana Bancorp	MutualFirst Financial
Bank of America	NorthWest Indiana
Citigroup	Bancorp
Harris	Old National Bancorp
JPMorgan Chase	STAR Financial Group
MainSource Financial	U.S. Bancorp

HISTORICAL FINANCIALS

Company Type: Public

Income Statement
FYE: December 31

	ASSETS ($ mil.)	NET INCOME ($ mil.)	INCOME AS % OF ASSETS	EMPLOYEES
12/16	7,211	81	1.1%	1,449
12/15	6,761	65	1.0%	1,529
12/14	5,824	60	1.0%	1,415
12/13	5,437	44	0.8%	1,449
12/12	4,304	45	1.0%	1,149
Annual Growth	13.8%	15.8%	—	6.0%

2016 Year-End Financials

Debt ratio: 1.78%
Return on equity: 9.23%
Cash ($ mil.): 152
Current ratio: —
Long-term debt ($ mil.): —

No. of shares (mil.): 40
Dividends
Yield: 0.0%
Payout: 27.2%
Market value ($ mil.): 1,540

	STOCK PRICE ($) FY Close	P/E High/Low		Earnings	PER SHARE ($) Dividends	Book Value
12/16	37.65	19	11	1.98	0.54	22.04
12/15	25.42	16	13	1.72	0.41	20.92
12/14	22.75	14	12	1.65	0.29	19.29
12/13	22.72	16	10	1.41	0.18	17.68
12/12	14.84	11	6	1.41	0.10	19.25
Annual Growth	26.2%	—	—	8.9%	52.4%	3.4%

First Mid-Illinois Bancshares Inc

EXECUTIVES

Vice President Marketing, Rodney Morris

Assistant Vice President, Jaci Manzella

Senior Management (Senior Vice President General Manager Director), Jason Tucker

Vice President And Chief Audit Executive, Melissa Wilhelm

Senior Vice President, Robert Weber

Senior Vice President Risk Management, Christopher Slabach

Assistant Vice President And Dep Statement Services, Joan Kirk

Assistant Vice President Mortgage Loan Administration, Sue Radloff

Vice President Regional Lending Manager, Dave Garrett

Vice President, Gant Harper

Assistant Vice President Human Resource Generalist II, Tyla Larson

Auditors: BKD, LLP

LOCATIONS

HQ: First Mid-Illinois Bancshares Inc
1421 Charleston Avenue, Mattoon, IL 61938
Phone: 217 234-7454 **Fax:** 217 258-0485
Web: www.firstmid.com

PRODUCTS/OPERATIONS

Selected Subsidiaries

The Checkley Agency Inc. (dba First Mid Insurance Group)
First Mid-Illinois Bank & Trust N.A.
First Mid-Illinois Statutory Trust I II
Mid-Illinois Data Services Inc.

COMPETITORS

Bank of America	Northern Trust
Fifth Third	PNC Financial
First BancTrust	U.S. Bancorp
First Busey	

HISTORICAL FINANCIALS

Company Type: Public

Income Statement
FYE: December 31

	ASSETS ($ mil.)	NET INCOME ($ mil.)	INCOME AS % OF ASSETS	EMPLOYEES
12/16	2,884	21	0.8%	598
12/15	2,114	16	0.8%	513
12/14	1,607	15	1.0%	400
12/13	1,605	14	0.9%	406
12/12	1,578	14	0.9%	400
Annual Growth	16.3%	11.7%	—	10.6%

2016 Year-End Financials

Debt ratio: 1.46%
Return on equity: 8.97%
Cash ($ mil.): 137
Current ratio: —
Long-term debt ($ mil.): —

No. of shares (mil.): 12
Dividends
Yield: 0.0%
Payout: 30.2%
Market value ($ mil.): 424

	STOCK PRICE ($) FY Close	P/E High/Low		Earnings	PER SHARE ($) Dividends	Book Value
12/16	34.00	17	11	2.05	0.62	22.51
12/15	26.00	14	10	1.81	0.59	24.25
12/14	18.55	13	9	1.85	0.55	23.45
12/13	22.00	14	12	1.73	0.46	25.39
12/12	22.75	17	11	1.62	0.42	26.24
Annual Growth	10.6%	—	—	6.1%	10.2%	(3.8%)

First Midwest Bancorp, Inc. (Naperville, IL)

There's a lot of cabbage in corn country. Just ask First Midwest Bancorp the holding company for First Midwest Bank. Through nearly 110 branches the bank mainly serves suburban Chicago though its market extends into central and western Illinois and neighboring portions of Iowa and Indiana. Focusing on area small to mid-sized businesses it offers deposit products loans trust services wealth management insurance and retirement plan services; it has $7.2 billion of client trust and investment assets under management. Commercial real estate loans account for more than half of the company's portfolio.

Operations

More than 85% of the company's loan portfolio consists of corporate loans (the majority of which are secured by commercial real estate) while the remainder of the portfolio consists of consumer loans (which include home equity loans lines of credit and 1-4 family mortgages). Illustrative of its commitment to business lending First Midwest does not originate sub-prime lending or investment banking activities.

The bank's subsidiaries include: equipment leasing and commercial financier First Midwest Equipment Finance Co.; investment security managers First Midwest Securities Management LLC and First Midwest Holdings Inc.; Section 8 housing venture investor LIH Holdings; and Synergy Property Holdings LLC which manages the bank's OREO properties.

Geographic Reach

The company operates 109 banking offices largely located in various communities throughout the suburban metropolitan Chicago market as well as central and western Illinois and eastern Iowa. It owns 145 automated teller machines most of which are housed at banking locations. First Midwest and Allpoint together provide access to more than 50000 free ATMs worldwide.

Sales and Marketing

The company serves different industry segments including manufacturing health care pharmaceutical higher education wholesale and retail trade service and agricultural. First Midwest spent about $8.2 million on advertising and promotions in 2014 up from $7.8 million in 2013 and $5.1 million in 2012.

Financial Performance

Following a modest rebound in 2013 First Midwest's revenue in 2014 dipped by less than 1% to $426.48 million mostly because of a 76% drop in net securities gains as the bank in 2013 was able to collect a non-recurring equity investment sale gain of $34 million. Lower mortgage banking income resulting from lower market pricing also contributed to the modest dip in revenue. The bank did however report higher interest income as its loan business grew higher wealth management fees with growth in assets under management and higher service charge fees as deposit accounts grew.

After healthy profit growth in 2013 net income fell by nearly 13% to $69.31 million in 2014 mostly as the bank incurred higher costs associated with the acquisition and integration of Popular and Great Lakes and because the bank had higher loan loss provision expenses. In 2013 First Midwest had posted a large jump in net income thanks to higher revenue a decrease in the provision for loan and covered loan losses and lower interest and non-interest expenses.

Continuing its annual cash declines the bank's operations provided $122.93 million (or 10% less cash than in 2013) mostly due to lower earnings.

Mergers and Acquisitions

In 2014 First Midwest acquired south suburban Chicago-based Great Lakes Financial Resources Inc. the holding company for Great Lakes Bank National Association. As part of the $58 million deal the company gained eight locations $490 million in deposits and $234 million in loans.

That year it also bought the Chicago banking operations of Popular Community Bank a subsidiary of Popular Inc. (12 full-service retail branches and its small business and middle market commercial lending activities in the Chicago metropolitan area which included $726 million in deposits and $562 million in loans).

In early 2017 the company completed the acquisition of another Chicago-area bank Standard Bancshares. The deal will add 35 branches $2.3 billion in assets $2.1 billion in deposits and $1.9 million in loans.

Company Background

First Midwest capitalized on the rash of bank failures that have occurred in the Chicago area amid the recessionary economy. Its relative financial soundness put it in a position to acquire three failed Illinois banks through separate FDIC-facilitated transactions in 2009 and 2010: First DuPage Bank Peotone Bank and Trust and Palos Bank and Trust. The deals which included loss-sharing agreements with the regulator added a total of nearly 10 branches. In 2012 the company acquired the deposits and loans of Waukegan Savings Bank in another FDIC-assisted deal that added two more branches to its network. First Midwest will continue to consider acquisitions of failed banks in the Chicago area.

EXECUTIVES

President CEO and Director; Chairman and CEO First Midwest Bank, Michael L. Scudder, age 56, $750,000 total compensation

EVP CIO and COO First Midwest Bank, Kent S. Belasco, age 66, $224,000 total compensation

EVP and CFO First Midwest Bancorp Inc. & First Midwest Bank, Paul F. Clemens, age 65, $376,000 total compensation

SEVP and COO; Vice Chairman and President First Midwest Bank, Mark G. Sander, age 58, $545,000 total compensation

EVP and Treasurer First Midwest Bancorp Inc. & First Midwest Bank, James P. Hotchkiss, age 60

EVP and Chief Risk Officer First Midwest Bancorp Inc. & First Midwest Bank, Kevin L. Moffitt

EVP Corporate Secretary and General Counsel, Nicholas J. Chulos

Executive Vice President and Director Wealth Management of the Bank, Robert Diedrich

Senior Vice President, Julie Mcgrath

Vice President Field, Phillip Tan

Vice President, Juan Cortez

Vice President, Theresa Yauger

Executive Vice President and Director Commercial Banking First Midwest Bank, Victor Carapella

Senior Vice President, Jim Schramm

Vice President, Beth Uhlir

Vice President, Ed Garner

Senior Vice President, Rob Schultz

Vice President, Cheri Rubocki

Senior Vice President, Carlos Touza

Vice President, Sue Barreto

Vice President, Susan Koski

Vice President, Terrence Briese

Senior Vice President Director Applic, John Hudak

Assistant Vice President Branch Manager, Josie Pacheco

Vice President, Tami Johnson

Senior Vice President, Stephen Clingen

Assistant Vice President Branch Manager, Evette Berryhill

Senior Vice President, Joe Monocchio

Vice President, Chris Sawyer

Senior Vice President, Connie Lavin

Senior Vice President, Roger Kallal

Vice President, Brian Ruos

Assistant Vice President Branch Manager II, Michael Barbari

Vice President Treasury Management, Ala Swais

Assistant Vice President, Megan Miller

Vice President, Gia Ormond

Vice President Community Banking Officer Community Real Estate Group, Richard Rischall

Executive Vice President CHRO, Michelle Hoskins

Senior Vice President, Sharon Carnaghi

Vice President Commercial Banking Officer, Sheela Prahlad

Assistant Vice President, Andrew Trasatt

Vice President Business Banking, Tony Martino

Vice President, Jay Dainas

Vice President, Rose Svoboda

Vice President Sales, Joe Creamons

Vice President, Tim Woodcock

Vice President, Michael Chin

Senior Vice President Senior Retail Project Manager Branch Transformation, Brad Brown

Vice President ABL Relationship Manager Business Credit, Thomas Brennan

Senior Vice President, Tom Neylon

Senior Vice President, Aaron Markos

Vice President, Shannon Stevens

Vice President CRA Manager, Mary Morstadt

Vice President Franchise Banking Group, Kara Symeonides

Vice President, Robert Rodie

Senior Vice President Manager Business Banking, Brian Burke

Chairman, Robert P. (Bob) O'Meara, age 79

Auditors: Ernst & Young LLP

LOCATIONS

HQ: First Midwest Bancorp, Inc. (Naperville, IL)
One Pierce Place, Suite 1500, Itasca, IL 60143-1254
Phone: 630 875-7463
Web: www.firstmidwest.com

PRODUCTS/OPERATIONS

2016

	$ mil.	% of total
Interest Income		
Loans	338	63
Investment securities - taxable	28	5
Investment securities - tax-exempt	8	2
Other short-term investments	2	0
Noninterest Income		
Service charges on deposit accounts	40	8
Wealth management fees	33	6
Card-based fees	29	5
Merchant servicing fees	12	2
Mortgage banking income	10	2
Capital market products income	10	2
Other service charges commissions and fees	9	2
Net gain on sale-leaseback transaction	5	1
BOLI income	3	1
Net securities gains	1	0
Other income	3	1
Total	**537**	**100**

COMPETITORS

Bank of America	Meta Financial Group
BankFinancial	Northern Trust
Cummins-Allison	PrivateBank
Fifth Third	QCR Holdings
First Busey	West Suburban Bancorp
Harris	Wintrust Financial
JPMorgan Chase	

HISTORICAL FINANCIALS
Company Type: Public

Income Statement
FYE: December 31

	ASSETS ($ mil.)	NET INCOME ($ mil.)	INCOME AS % OF ASSETS	EMPLOYEES
12/16	11,422	92	0.8%	1,882
12/15	9,732	82	0.8%	1,790
12/14	9,445	69	0.7%	1,788
12/13	8,253	79	1.0%	1,647
12/12	8,099	(21)	—	1,707
Annual Growth	9.0%	—	—	2.5%

2016 Year-End Financials
Debt ratio: 1.70%
Return on equity: 7.66%
Cash ($ mil.): 262
Current ratio: —
Long-term debt ($ mil.): —
No. of shares (mil.): 81
Dividends
  Yield: 0.0%
  Payout: 31.5%
Market value ($ mil.): 2,052

	STOCK PRICE ($) FY Close	P/E High/Low		PER SHARE ($) Earnings	Dividends	Book Value
12/16	25.23	22	14	1.14	0.36	15.46
12/15	18.43	19	15	1.05	0.36	14.70
12/14	17.11	19	17	0.92	0.31	14.17
12/13	17.53	17	11	1.06	0.16	13.34
12/12	12.52	—	—	(0.28)	0.04	12.57
Annual Growth	19.1%	—	—	—	73.2%	5.3%

First National Bank Alaska

First National Bank Alaska is a financial anchor in Anchorage. Founded in 1922 the bank is one of the state's oldest and largest financial institutions. With about 30 branches throughout The Last Frontier (and about 20 ATMs in rural communities) the bank offers traditional deposit products such as checking and savings accounts CDs and IRAs as well as loans and mortgages credit and debit cards and trust and investment management services. The family of longtime president Daniel Cuddy owns a majority of First National Bank Alaska; he took the helm of the bank in 1951.

Geographic Reach

In order to help serve clients in remote locales First National Bank Alaska opened its first branch with a full-service customer kiosk at a joint air force/army base outside of Anchorage where customers can make routine banking transactions without teller assistance. The bank may add such kiosks at other branches.

Financial Performance

The company's total annul revenue has slowly declining across recent fiscal years. However it has managed to stay profitable.

EXECUTIVES

Senior Vice President, David Stringer
Vice President Information Systems, Larry Chen
Senior Vice President Commercial Lending, Bill Inscho
Assistant Vice President, Becky Monterosso
Vice President, Dustin Hofeling
Senior Vice President and Chief Financial Officer, Michele Schuh

---

Vice President Corporate Lending, Joe Gelione
Vice President, Lita Beck
Auditors: Crowe Horwath LLP

LOCATIONS
HQ: First National Bank Alaska
  101 West 36th Avenue, Post Office Box 100720, Anchorage, AK 99510-0720
Phone: 907 777-4362   **Fax:** 907 265-3528
Web: www.FNBAlaska.com

COMPETITORS
Alaska Pacific Bancshares	KeyCorp
Alaska USA	Northrim BanCorp
	Wells Fargo

HISTORICAL FINANCIALS
Company Type: Public

Income Statement
FYE: December 31

	ASSETS ($ mil.)	NET INCOME ($ mil.)	INCOME AS % OF ASSETS	EMPLOYEES
12/16	3,609	41	1.1%	—
12/15	3,569	36	1.0%	—
12/14	3,312	32	1.0%	—
12/13	3,102	32	1.0%	—
12/12	3,015	40	1.3%	—
Annual Growth	4.6%	0.8%		

2016 Year-End Financials
Debt ratio: —
Return on equity: 8.41%
Cash ($ mil.): 79
Current ratio: —
Long-term debt ($ mil.): —
No. of shares (mil.): 0
Dividends
  Yield: 0.0%
  Payout: 65.2%
Market value ($ mil.): 555

	STOCK PRICE ($) FY Close	P/E High/Low		PER SHARE ($) Earnings	Dividends	Book Value
12/16	1,750.00	13	10	130.35	85.00	1,553
12/15	1,403.00	14	12	113.02	50.00	1,534
12/14	1,588.00	17	16	101.37	50.00	1,472
12/13	1,751.00	18	17	99.80	50.00	1,403
12/12	1,675.00	14	12	122.51	50.00	1,416
Annual Growth	1.1%	—	—	1.6%	14.2%	2.3%

First of Long Island Corp

When it comes to banking The First of Long Island wants to be the first thing on Long Islanders' minds. The company owns The First National Bank of Long Island which offers a variety of lending investment and deposit services through around 45 commercial and retail branches on New York's Long Island and the boroughs of Manhattan and Queens. Residential and Commercial Mortgages (particularly tied to multifamily properties) make up more than 90% of the bank's loan portfolio though the bank also writes revolving home equity business and consumer loans. Its two bank subsidiaries include insurance agency The First of Long Island Agency and investment firm FNY Service.

Operations

The First National Bank of Long Island also operates an investment management division that of-

---

fers trust and investment management estate and custody services.

The bank makes more than 90% of its revenue from interest income. About 70% of its total revenue came from loan interest during 2015 while another 21% came from interest income on taxable and non-taxable investment securities. The rest of its revenue came from deposit account service charges (3% of revenue) investment management division income (2%) gains on securities sales (1%) and other income sources.

Geographic Reach

The New York City-based bank operated 45 branches at the end of 2015 including 41 in Long Island and two each in Manhattan and Queens.

Sales and Marketing

First serves individuals professionals corporations institutions and governmental clients through its branches.

The bank markets its services through customer service personnel tele-sales lending relationships referral sources and advertisements. It spent $877000 on marketing during 2015 compared to $927000 and $670000 in 2014 and 2013 respectively.

Financial Performance

The First of Long Island's annual revenues have risen more than 20% since 2011 as its loan assets have more than doubled to $2.25 billion. Meanwhile the bank's profits have swelled more than 30% thanks to revenue growth and low interest expenses.

First's revenue jumped 13% to $101 million during 2015 mostly thanks to higher interest income as its average loan balances grew 26% and as its non-taxable security assets rose by 6%. The bulk of the loan asset growth was tied to residential mortgages while most of the rest came from multi-family commercial mortgage growth.

Double-digit revenue growth drove the bank's net income up 12% to $25.9 million. First's operating cash levels dipped 1% to $35 million despite the rise in earnings due to unfavorable working capital changes mostly related to a decrease in accrued expenses and other liabilities.

Strategy

The bank has been opening new branches utilizing "effective relationship management" using targeted solicitation efforts and expanding its product and service offerings to boost its loan and deposit business in recent years.

In early 2016 the company planned to open between eight and 12 more The First National Bank of Long Island branches in Queens after opening two branches there in Howard Beach and Whitestone in 2015. It also planned to open branches in Brooklyn. Expanding its branch network on Long Island the bank in 2015 launched new branches in Patchogue and Melville.

EXECUTIVES

SVP and EVP and Senior Lending Officer Commercial Lending The First National Bank Long Island, Donald L. Manfredonia, age 65, $222,500 total compensation
SVP, Richard Kick, age 59, $230,100 total compensation
SVP and Treasurer; EVP CFO and Cashier The First National Bank of Long Island, Mark D. Curtis, age 62, $242,700 total compensation
President and CEO The First of Long Island Corporation and The First National Bank of Long Island, Michael N. Vittorio, age 64, $468,000 total compensation
SVP and Secretary; SEVP The First National Bank of Long Island, Sallyanne K. Ballweg, age 61, $264,000 total compensation
EVP and Chief Risk Officer First National Bank of Long Island, Christopher Becker

Senior Vice President Of Commercial, Paul Daley
Vice President, Jane Reed
Vice President, Robert Eisen
Vice President Sales Manager, Rick Hughes
Vice President Director Of Human Resources, Sue Hempton
Vice President Of Marketing, Laura Ierulli
Chairman The First of Long Island Corporation and The First National Bank of Long Island, Walter C. Teagle, age 67
Auditors: Crowe Horwath LLP

LOCATIONS

HQ: First of Long Island Corp
10 Glen Head Road, Glen Head, NY 11545
Phone: 516 671-4900
Web: www.fnbli.com

PRODUCTS/OPERATIONS

2015 Sales

	$ mil.	% of total
Interest and dividend income:		
Loans	70	70
Investment securities		
Taxable	8	8
Nontaxable	13	13
Noninterest income		
Investment Management Division income	2	2
Service charges on deposit accounts	2	3
Net gains on sales of securities	1	1
Other	2	3
Total	**100**	**100**

Selected Services:

CheckingSavings
Saving for Retirement & Education
Online Banking & Bill Pay
FirstLink Online Banking
Quicken/Quickbooks
FirstPay Bill Pay
PopMoney
Account to Account Transfers

COMPETITORS

Astoria Financial	JPMorgan Chase
Bank of America	New York Community
Citibank	Bancorp
Dime Community	Ridgewood Savings Bank
Bancshares	Suffolk Bancorp
Flushing Financial	

HISTORICAL FINANCIALS

Company Type: Public

Income Statement

FYE: December 31

	ASSETS ($ mil.)	NET INCOME ($ mil.)	INCOME AS % OF ASSETS	EMPLOYEES
12/16	3,510	30	0.9%	314
12/15	3,130	25	0.8%	302
12/14	2,721	23	0.8%	284
12/13	2,399	21	0.9%	260
12/12	2,108	20	1.0%	255
Annual Growth	**13.6%**	**10.9%**	**—**	**5.3%**

2016 Year-End Financials

Debt ratio: 0.14%
Return on equity: 11.06%
Cash ($ mil.): 36
Current ratio: —
Long-term debt ($ mil.): —
No. of shares (mil.): 23
Dividends
 Yield: 0.0%
 Payout: 40.8%
Market value ($ mil.): 677

STOCK PRICE ($) FY Close	P/E High/Low	PER SHARE ($) Earnings	Dividends	Book Value
12/16	28.55	30 19	1.34	0.55	12.90
12/15	30.00	26 19	1.22	0.52	11.85
12/14	28.37	39 21	1.10	0.47	11.20
12/13	42.87	41 27	1.03	0.45	10.04
12/12	28.32	31 25	1.01	0.53	10.14
Annual Growth	**0.2%**	**— —**	**7.4%**	**0.8%**	**6.2%**

First Republic Bank (San Francisco, CA)

No not the original Roman Republic but rather a modern-day haven for the elite. Founded in 1985 First Republic Bank offers private banking wealth management trust and brokerage services for businesses and high-net-worth clients though about 75 branches. Its main geographic focus is on urban markets including San Francisco Los Angeles New York Boston Portland and San Diego. The bank's lending focuses on commercial and residential real estate and personal loans including vacation home mortgages and aircraft and yacht financing. Trust services are offered through the bank's First Republic Trust Company division. First Republic Bank has some $83.6 billion of assets under management.

Operations

First Republic's wealth management services consists of various investment strategies and products trust and custody services online brokerage financial and estate planning access to alternative investments (private equity venture capital hedge and real estate funds) socially responsible investing insurance and foreign exchange. First Republic has a number of operating subsidiaries: it operates its wealth management through First Republic Investment Management; brokerage through First Republic Securities; trust services through First Republic Trust (a division of the bank) and First Republic Trust Company.

Geographic Reach

First Republic operates some 75 offices around 70 of which are Preferred Banking locations in Boston; Los Angeles; New York; Palm Beach Florida; Palo Alto Newport Beach San Diego San Francisco and Santa Barbara California; and Portland Oregon. The other five locations offer lending wealth management or trust services.

California accounts for around 60% of First Republic's outstanding loans.

Sales and Marketing

First Republic Bank advertises via digital media and newspaper and radio ads; its primary marketing goal is to attract deposits in its Preferred Banking offices. The vast majority of new clients are referred by word of mouth from existing clients.

Financial Performance

First Republic has recorded steady interest and non-interest revenue growth since 2010. In fiscal 2016 revenue increased 19% to $2.4 billion due to higher loan origination (particularly in single and multifamily loans) and increases in investment income relating to purchases of new investments. Offsetting factors include lower interest rates and lower investment yields.

Net income rose 29% to $673.4 million on the back of strong performances in Commercial Banking and Wealth Management. Cash from operations increased 36% to $852.5 million thanks to higher net income and adjustments to other assets.

Strategy

First Republic takes a conservative approach to banking issuing loans to high-net-worth individuals that it can work with in the long term. To support this the company ensures a low employee turnover to create deep and long-lasting relationships with its clients. Top class service is essential to the growth of the business: the majority of First Republic's new clients are sourced by word-of-mouth from within high-net-worth networks.

Mergers and Acquisitions

In 2016 First Republic acquired Gradifi a Boston-based company that helps employers offer student-loan repayment as an employee perk.

EXECUTIVES

EVP Secretary and General Counsel, Edward J. Dobranski, age 66
President CEO and Director, James H. Herbert
EVP and Chief Credit Officer, David B. Lichtman
President First Republic Securities, David Tateosian
SEVP and Chief Banking Officer, Michael D. (Mike) Selfridge, age 49
Chairman First Republic Trust Company, Michael J. Harrington
EVP and President Private Wealth Management, Bob Thornton
EVP and Chief Marketing Officer, Dianne Snedaker
SVP Chief Deposit Officer and Chief Investment Officer, Hafize Gaye (Gaye) Erkan
EVP and CFO, Michael J. (Mike) Roffler
EVP; Chief BSA and AML and Security Officer, Bill Ward
EVP and CIO, Dale A. Smith
EVP and COO, Jason C. Bender
President First Republic Trust Company, Kelly Johnston
Senior Vice President Foreign Exchange, Kate Kent-Sheehan
CFA CPA Vice President Wealth Manager, Stephen Marotto
Vice President Compliance Risk Manager, Steven Sears
Vice President Residential Lending, Lionel Antunes
Vice President, Michael Curley
Vice President, Todd Brantley
Vice President and Assistant General Counsel, Janisha Sabnani
Vice President First Republic Investment Management, Reynolds Ospina
Executive Vice President, Brian Riley
Vice President of Retail Marketing, Gwenn Murphy
Vice President, Peter Chang
Executive Vice President, Susie Cranston
Vice President Of Operations, John Stone
Vice President Credit Risk Officer, Sean Callum
Senior Vice President and Chief Accounting Officer, Olga Tsokova
Vice President, DAVID WEITGENANT
Senior Vice President, Bradley Finn
Vice President Wealth Manager, Jeff Greene
Vice President, Justin Launer
Senior Vice President, Helene Jepson
Vice President Foreign Exchange, Alexandra Hall
CFA Vice President, Garret Giglia
Assistant Vice President, Scott Scrimager
Vice President and Associate General Counsel, Hilary Gevondyan
Senior Vice President Technology Strategy, Ken Chou
Vice President and Head of Digital Channels (Business Operations), Jonathan Kropf
Senior Vice President, David Breslin
Vice President Info Security Programs Information Security, David Estabrook

Vice Chair, Katherine August-deWilde, age 66
Assistant Treasurer, Thomas Lacher
Auditors: KPMG LLP

LOCATIONS

HQ: First Republic Bank (San Francisco, CA)
111 Pine Street, 2nd Floor, San Francisco, CA 94111
Phone: 415 392-1400
Web: www.firstrepublic.com

PRODUCTS/OPERATIONS

2016 Sales

	% of total
Interest income other	83
Noninterest income	17
Total	**100**

Selected Affiliates

First Republic Investment Management Inc.
First Republic Securities Company LLC
First Republic Trust Company

COMPETITORS

Bank of Marin	City National
Bank of New York	JPMorgan Private Bank
Mellon	MUFG Americas Holdings
Boston Private	Morgan Stanley
Citigroup Private Bank	TriState Capital

HISTORICAL FINANCIALS

Company Type: Public

Income Statement

FYE: December 31

	ASSETS ($ mil.)	NET INCOME ($ mil.)	INCOME AS % OF ASSETS	EMPLOYEES
12/16	73,277	673	0.9%	3,566
12/15	58,981	522	0.9%	—
12/14	48,353	487	1.0%	2,506
12/13	42,112	462	1.1%	2,388
12/12	34,387	402	1.2%	2,110
Annual Growth	**20.8%**	**13.7%**	**—**	**14.0%**

2016 Year-End Financials

Debt ratio: 1.11%	No. of shares (mil.): 154
Return on equity: 10.65%	Dividends
Cash ($ mil.): 2,107	Yield: 0.0%
Current ratio: —	Payout: 16.0%
Long-term debt ($ mil.): —	Market value ($ mil.): 14,217

	STOCK PRICE ($) FY Close	P/E High/Low	PER SHARE ($) Earnings	Dividends	Book Value
12/16	92.14	23 14	3.93	0.63	44.78
12/15	66.06	21 15	3.18	0.59	39.05
12/14	52.12	18 14	3.07	0.54	34.56
12/13	52.35	16 10	3.10	0.46	31.33
12/12	32.78	12 10	2.76	0.30	25.89
Annual Growth	**29.5%**	**—**	**9.2%**	**20.4%**	**14.7%**

FirstEnergy Corp

FirstEnergy's first goal is to generate and deliver power but its second goal is to stay profitable in a market undergoing deregulation. Its ten utilities provide electricity to 6 million customers in the Midwest and the Mid-Atlantic. The company's domestic power plants have a total generating capacity of more than 17000 MW an amount expected to diminish as the company winds down its deregulated business. Subsidiary FirstEnergy Solutions trades energy commodities in deregulated US markets. FirstEnergy's other nonregulated operations include electrical and mechanical contracting and energy planning and procurement.

Operations

FirstEnergy has three primary operating segments: Regulated Distribution Regulated Transmission and Competitive Energy Services (CES). About 65% of total revenue comes from Regulated Distribution roughly 30% from Competitive Energy Services and the rest from Regulated Transmission. The company is transitioning away from its competitive wholesale business and therefore the percent of revenue from CES is expected to dwindle.

The Regulated Distribution segment distributes electricity through FirstEnergy's ten utilities which serve 6 million customers in a service area with a total population of 13.3 million. It has a controlling interest in 38000 MWs of generation capacity in West Virginia Virginia and New Jersey. It fulfills the additional electricity needs of its customers through power purchase agreements.

The Competitive Energy Services segment through its subsidiaries FES and AE Supply supplies electricity through retail and wholesale arrangements including competitive retail sale to customers primarily in Ohio Pennsylvania Illinois Michigan New Jersey and Maryland. It controls some 13100 MW of capacity.

The Regulated Transmission segment transmits electricity through transmission facilities owned and operated by American Transmission Systems Trans-Allegheny Interstate Line Company and a number of FirstEnergy's utilities. Transmission operations include approximately 24000 miles of lines and two regional transmission operation centers.

Geographic Reach

FirstEnergy operates and serves customers in a service area of 65000 square miles in Illinois Maryland Michigan New Jersey New York Ohio Pennsylvania and West Virginia.

Its power generating assets are located in Pennsylvania Ohio West Virginia New Jersey and Indiana.

Sales and Marketing

The Regulated Distribution segment sells roughly equal amounts of electricity to its residential and industrial customers and slightly less to its commercial customers. Generally there is no competition for electric distribution service in its service territories in Ohio Pennsylvania West Virginia Maryland New Jersey and New York.

FirstEnergy's CES segment participates in deregulated energy markets in Ohio Pennsylvania Maryland Michigan New Jersey and Illinois through FES and AE Supply. CES competes to provide retail generation service directly to end users to provide wholesale generation service to utilities municipalities and co-operatives which in turn resell to end users and in the electricity wholesale market.

Over the next few years FirstEnergy is transitioning away from deregulated markets (served by its CES segment) and shoring up its regulated utility business. The change is due to shifting economics of supplying electricity with older format energy plants powered with coal oil etc. against that provided by newer sources such as natural gas wind and solar.

Financial Performance

Until 2016 the company?s financial performance was steady through trending slightly downward. Revenue peaked at $16.1 billion in 2011 and since slid to below $15 billion in 2016. Net income slipped from $885 million in 2011 to below $300 million in 2014 before an upward tick in 2015 which preceded a massive fall in 2016.

For the year 2016 revenue was $14.6 billion down 3% from the prior year as a result of expected lower energy contract sales in the CES segment partially offset by higher revenue from the Regulated Transmission segment (via cost recoveries and a higher rate base) and increased revenue from Regulated Distribution (via higher demand and increased customer-charged rates).

Net income plummeted on the back of a $10.6 billion pre-tax impairment charge. Although revenue slipped only 3% and expenses were held in check the impairment of its CES assets such as power plants and nuclear fuel drove 2016?s earnings to a $6.2 billion loss. Because CES is exiting its business by mid-2018 it will not receive the anticipated cash flows and earnings from its long-lived assets and therefore chose to take the significant charge.

Cash on hand at the end of 2016 was $200 million up nearly $70 million from 2015. Cash provided by operating activities was $3.4 billion mainly the result of the $6.2 billion loss adjusted by the $10.6 billion asset impairment. Financing activities largely balanced out while investing activities used $3.3 billion mostly for capital expenditures.

Strategy

The overriding long-term objective for FirstEnergy is to transition its business model from being a holding company of competitive energy wholesaler subsidiaries into one that holds solely regulated utilities. As an energy wholesaler the CES subsidiary is tossed about by the volatile pricing of energy products (oil coal etc.) and therefore carries a high risk with volatile financial results. The move to wind down CES and focus on regulated utilities brings with it a much lower risk profile and predictable steady cash flows.

Part of its plan includes divestitures. In 2017 FirstEnergy?s CES segment agreed to sell four natural gas generating plants in Pennsylvania its ownership interests in a Virginia hydroelectric power station and gas/oil-fired facility to a subsidiary of LS Power Equity Partners III LP for $925 million. In total it is selling off more than 1600 MW of generation capacity. Additionally it plans to retire by 2020 720 MW of capacity at its Sammis Plant and 136 MW at its Bay Shore plant both in Ohio.

Meanwhile First Energy continues to invest in its regulated companies. To date it?s installed 550000 smart meters across its Pennsylvania market and plans to replace them for all 2 million of the state?s customers by 2019. It is working with Ohio regulator agencies to pursue a similar grid modernization effort in that state. In total it plans to spend roughly $1 billion/year on its utilities companies between 2017 and 2020.

HISTORY

FirstEnergy came to light in 1893 as the Akron Electric Light and Power Company. After several mergers the business went bankrupt and was sold in 1899 to Akron Traction and Electric Company which became Northern Ohio Power and Light (NOP&L).

In 1930 Commonwealth and Southern (C&S) bought NOP&L and merged it with four other Ohio utility holding companies to form Ohio Edison. The new firm increased sales during the Depression by selling electric appliances.

The Public Utility Holding Company Act of 1935 (passed to rein in uncontrolled utilities) caught up with C&S in 1949 forcing it to divest Ohio Edison. Rival Ohio Public Service was also divested from its holding company and in 1950 Ohio Edison bought it.

In 1967 after two decades of expansion Ohio Edison and three other Ohio and Pennsylvania utilities formed the Central Area Power Coordination Group (CAPCO) to share new power-plant costs including the construction of the Beaver Valley nuclear plant (1970-76). Although the CAPCO partners agreed in 1980 to cancel four planned nukes in 1985 Ohio Edison took part in building the Perry Unit 1 and Beaver Valley Unit 2 nuclear plants.

The federal Energy Policy Act of 1992 allowed wholesale power competition and to satisfy new federal requirements Ohio Edison formed a six-state transmission alliance in 1996 with fellow utilities Centerior Energy Allegheny Power System and Dominion Resources' Virginia Power to coordinate their grids.

Ohio Edison paid about $1.5 billion in 1997 for Centerior Energy formed in 1986 as a holding company for Toledo Edison and Cleveland Electric. Ohio Edison and Centerior both burdened by high-cost generating plants merged to cut costs and the expanded energy concern was renamed FirstEnergy Corp.

Looking toward deregulation FirstEnergy began buying mechanical construction contracting and energy management companies in 1997 including Roth Bros. and RPC Mechanical. In 1998 it added nine more. FirstEnergy then ventured into natural gas operations by purchasing MARBEL Energy. The company also created separate subsidiaries for its nuclear and transmission assets.

In 2000 FirstEnergy agreed to acquire New Jersey-based electric utility GPU in an $11.9 billion deal; it became one of the largest US utilities in 2001 when it completed the acquisition which added three utilities (Jersey Central Power & Light Metropolitan Edison and Pennsylvania Electric) serving 2.1 million electricity customers.

Beefing up its generation assets in 2011 the company acquired Allegheny Energy in a $8.5 billion deal. The acquisition increased FirstEnergy's power generation capacity by 70% and its customer base by 35% dramatically boosting its position as a leading regional energy provider focused on both regulated utility operations and a competitive generation business.

EXECUTIVES

President Maryland Operations, James A. Sears
EVP Corporate Strategy Regulatory Affairs and Chief Legal Officer, Leila L. Vespoli, age 58, $758,606 total compensation
President FirstEnergy Solutions (FES), Donald R. (Donny) Schneider, age 56, $552,404 total compensation
SVP Corporate Services and CIO, Bennett L. Gaines, age 63
SVP Marketing and Branding, Dennis M. Chack, age 66
SVP and President Utilities Business, Steven E. (Steve) Strah, age 53, $553,286 total compensation
President CEO and Director, Charles E. (Chuck) Jones, age 62, $1,133,840 total compensation
EVP and CFO, James F. (Jim) Pearson, age 63, $659,884 total compensation
EVP and President FirstEnergy Generation, James H. (Jim) Lash, age 66, $583,187 total compensation
Regional President The Cleveland Electric Illuminating Company, John E. Skory
Regional President Metropolitan Edison Company, Edward L. Shuttleworth
Regional President Ohio Edison Company, Randall A. Frame
Regional President West Penn Power Company, David W. McDonald
President Jersey Central Power and Light, James V. Fakult
Regional President Pennsylvania Electric Company, Scott R Wyman
President West Virginia Operations, Holly C Kauffman

President Pennsylvania Operations, Linda L. Moss, age 52
SVP and COO FirstEnergy Nuclear Operating Company, Samuel L. Belcher
Regional President Toledo Edison Company, Richard S. Sweeney
Vice President Corporate Affairs, Dee Lowery
Executive Vice President, Charles Lasky
Regional Vice President, Jeffrey Elser
Senior Vice President Strategic Planning And Opera, Mark Clark
Vice President of Information System, Jeffrey Steiner
Vice President and Treasurer, Steve Staub
Vice President, Carl Bridenbaugh
Vice President and General Counsel, Robert Reffner
Chairman, George M. Smart, age 71
Auditors: PricewaterhouseCoopers LLP

LOCATIONS

HQ: FirstEnergy Corp
76 South Main Street, Akron, OH 44308
Phone: 800 736-3402
Web: www.firstenergycorp.com

PRODUCTS/OPERATIONS

2016 Sales

	$ mil.	% of total
Regulated Distribution	9,629	63
Competitive Energy Services	4,549	30
Regulated Transmission	1,151	7
Corporate/Other and Reconciling Adjustments	(767)	-
Total	**14,562**	**100**

COMPETITORS

AEP	Exelon
Avista	National Fuel Gas
CMS Energy	NiSource
Constellation Energy Group	PPL Corporation
	PSEG Energy Holdings
DPL	Peoples Natural Gas
Delmarva Power	Pepco Holdings
Dominion Energy	Public Service Enterprise Group
Duquesne Light	
Duquesne Light Holdings	TVA
	Vectren
Dynegy	WGL Holdings
EnergySolve	

HISTORICAL FINANCIALS

Company Type: Public

Income Statement

FYE: December 31

	REVENUE ($ mil.)	NET INCOME ($ mil.)	NET PROFIT MARGIN	EMPLOYEES
12/16	14,562	(6,177)	—	15,707
12/15	15,026	578	3.8%	15,781
12/14	15,049	299	2.0%	15,557
12/13	14,917	392	2.6%	15,754
12/12	15,303	770	5.0%	16,495
Annual Growth	(1.2%)	—	—	(1.2%)

2016 Year-End Financials

Debt ratio: 52.27%
Return on equity: (-66.02%)
Cash ($ mil.): 199
Current ratio: 0.41
Long-term debt ($ mil.): 18,192
No. of shares (mil.): 442
Dividends
  Yield: 0.0%
  Payout: —
Market value ($ mil.): 13,699

	STOCK PRICE ($) FY Close	P/E High/Low	PER SHARE ($) Earnings	Dividends	Book Value
12/16	30.97	— —	(14.49)	1.44	14.11
12/15	31.73	30 21	1.37	1.44	29.33
12/14	38.99	57 43	0.71	1.44	29.49
12/13	32.98	50 34	0.94	2.20	30.32
12/12	41.76	27 22	1.84	2.20	31.29
Annual Growth (18.1%)	(7.2%)	— —	— (10.1%)		

Fiserv Inc

Fiserv Inc. provides financial companies with the technology services they need to operate. The company provides core processing systems electronic billing and payment systems ATM management and loan processing services to banks thrifts credit unions and other financial institutions. It also provides licensed software consulting and other support services. Fiserv serves customers of all sizes but its bread and butter has traditionally been small to midsized banks without in-house processing units. Other clients include insurance companies merchants leasing firms and government agencies. Founded in 1984 Fiserv has more than 12000 clients in 80-plus countries.

Operations

Fiserve's Payments businesses which represent about 55% of its sales provide financial institutions and other companies with products and services needed to process electronic payments as well as offer their customers financial services through digital channels. The payments segment primarily provides electronic bill payments and presentment services debit and other card-based payment products and services Internet and mobile banking software and services and other products.

Fiserv's Financial businesses (about 45% of revenue) provide banks thrifts and credit unions with back office-related account processing services item processing and source capture services loan origination and service products cash management and consulting services.

The company also owns a 49% stake in StoneRiver Group made up of its former insurance services businesses.

Geographic Reach

Wisconsin-based Fiserv's operations are principally located in the US home to its data and transaction processing centers though it has data development item processing and support centers in about 110 cities and has customers in some 80 countries. The US is Fiserv's largest market providing about 95% of revenue with the rest generated by international customers.

Sales and Marketing

Fiserv serves about 12000 clients (including about 2400 mobile banking clients) worldwide and enjoys high contract renewal rates (excluding clients lost because they have been acquired). Banks typically stay with their service providers because the cost and work involved in changing providers is prohibitive.

More than 2500 financial institutions — including banks thrifts credit unions investment management firms leasing and finance companies retailers merchants mutual savings banks and building societies — have signed on to offer Fiserv's person-to-person payment services to their customers.

Financial Performance

Fiserv Inc. served up its seventh straight year of revenue increases in 2016 with a 5% gain to $5.5 billion from 2015. The Payments segment?s sales rose 8% driven by recurring the revenue businesses of processing and services. The company added customers and reported higher transaction volumes from existing clients in card services electronic payments and digital channels. Acquisitions also added revenue. Financial segment sales inched 1% higher in 2016 with higher processing and services revenue. The segment had lower international revenue for the year.

Net income jumped more than 30% in 2016 to $930 million on the higher revenue.

Cash flow from operations was $1.4 billion in 2016 up from $1.3 billion in 2015. This increase was attributed to improved operating results and an increase in cash dividends from its StoneRiver joint venture.

Strategy

Fiserv Inc. has deployed several product suites and products for offering managing and processing digital and mobile financial transactions. Packages of products include Corillian which enables to add and integrate applications such as electronic bill payment person-to-person payments and personal financial management tools. The Mobiliti product suite provides a variety of mobile banking and payments services. Specific products include Messenger Center for cash management Architect for online and mobile banking and Notifi for realtime communication between institutions and customers.

Besides driving revenue with new products Fiserv also seeks to maintain a handle on costs. The company has saved money by streamlining procurement and adjusting its workforce. It also is consolidating its data centers combining 18 in 2016.

Mergers and Acquisitions

In 2017 Fiserv Inc. acquired Online Banking Solutions Inc. (OBS) for $78 million. OBS provides secure online business banking services to financial institutions. The deal extends Fiserv?s cash management digital business banking and secure browser capabilities for large commercial and small business clients.

In March 2016 Fiserv expanded its product base for community banks and credit unions after buying ACI Worldwide's consumer financial services business for $200 million.

HISTORY

When First Bank System of Minneapolis bought Milwaukee-based Midland Bank in 1984 the head of Midland's data processing operation George Dalton bought the unit and then merged that operation with Sunshine State Systems a newly independent Florida processing company headed by Leslie Muma. Christened Fiserv the company went public in 1986. It grew by providing outsourcing services to small banks and thrifts.

In the 1990s Fiserv began targeting larger clients. But industry consolidation sometimes hurt the company as when the 12-year term of a 1995 contract with Chase Manhattan was reduced to three after Chase and Chemical Bank merged in 1996.

As banks moved into new areas Fiserv went along. In the late 1990s it acquired BHC Financial and Hanifen Imhoff Holdings (securities transaction processing). Other purchases that broadened its service list included Automated Financial Technology (credit union software) and Network Data Processing (administrative software for insurance companies). The push into software continued with 1999 purchases in the field of workers' compensation systems.

Also in 1999 Fiserv bolstered its client list by buying QuestPoint's check servicing business. It moved into retirement plan administration with the purchase of a unit from what is now SunAmerica Financial Group. In 2000 a deal to provide back-office services for American Express' online Membership Banking unit fell apart but Fiserv recovered its momentum with enhanced mortgage servicing offerings and an agreement to provide technology services to cahoot the online banking unit of the UK's Abbey National (which was acquired by Spanish group Banco Santander in 2004).

Fiserv continued its acquisitive activities in 2001 buying Benefit Planners (a leading employee benefit program administrator with operations in Europe the Middle East South America and the US) Facilities and Services Corporation (a Californiabased insurance software maker) NCSI (information and services targeting the flood insurance industry) and the bank processing operations of NCR Corporation. The company that year also sold its Human Resources Information Services unit to buyout firm Gores Group.

Fiserv boosted its ATM and electronic funds transfer (ETF) business with the 2002 purchase of the Consumer Network Services unit of Electronic Data Systems (now HP Enterprise Services).

The company embarked on a series of sales in the next few years. It sold its securities clearing operations to a unit of FMR in 2005. Three years later it sold most of its health business to UnitedHealth for some $480 million. The sale included Fiserv Health Plan Administration Fiserv Health Plan Management Innoviant Pharmacy Avidyn Health and other units but not WorkingRx (workers' compensation) and CareGain (technology) which remained with Fiserv.

The company also sold the bulk of its Fiserv Trust Company (also known as Fiserv Investment Support Services or Fiserv ISS) business including advisor services and institutional retirement services to TD AMERITRADE. In a separate transaction the newly formed Trust Institution Bank (headed by former Fiserv ISS management) acquired most of the company's investment administration services business.

Fiserv acquired one of the largest electronic payments firms CheckFree in 2007 boosting its capabilities in the payments landscape. In a smaller deal Fibought payment processor i_Tech from First Interstate BancSystem in 2008.

All of the acquisition activity led the company to higher debt levels which it began paying down through a combination of cost-cutting measures and divesting noncore operations. In 2008 it sold most of its health business to UnitedHealth and the bulk of Fiserv Trust Company to TD AMERITRADE. The following year it sold 51% of Fiserv Insurance Services (now StoneRiver) to investment firm Stone Point Capital for some $540 million. It also sold Loan Fulfillment Solutions a provider of mortgage-related services including settlement and title certification. As it added new operations and jettisoned others the company introduced a new marketing strategy in 2009 to unify its brands under the Fiserv banner.

In 2010 Fiserv acquired AdviceAmerica which provides desktop technology for financial advisers. It also introduced ZashPay a peer-to-peer platform available to consumers.

EXECUTIVES

EVP and COO, Mark A. Ernst, age 58, $600,000 total compensation

Chief Sales Officer; Group President International, Steven (Steve) Tait, age 57

President CEO and Director, Jeffery W. Yabuki, age 56, $840,000 total compensation

EVP Human Resources, Kevin P. Pennington

Group President Depository Institution Services, Byron C. Vielehr, age 53, $470,000 total compensation

EVP Corporate Development, James W. Cox, age 55, $450,000 total compensation

Group President Digital Banking, Kevin J. Schultz, age 59

CFO, Robert W. (Bob) Hau, age 51, $499,599 total compensation

EVP General Counsel and Secretary, Lynn S. McCreary, age 57

Group President Financial Institutions, Kevin P. Gregoire, age 49, $450,000 total compensation

President Billing and Payments Group, Devin B. McGranahan, $86,961 total compensation

CIO, Jim Grech

Senior Vice President, Amy Switalla

Vice President Institutional Retirement Plan Services, John Newman

Vice President, Rebekkah Wilson

Assistant Vice President, Jerome Linderman

Senior Vice President, Jed Delker

Executive Vice President, Cliff Skelton

Senior Vice President of Technology and Business Development, Oscar Mireles

Chairman, Daniel P. Kearney, age 77

Auditors: Deloitte & Touche LLP

LOCATIONS

HQ: Fiserv Inc
255 Fiserv Drive, Brookfield, WI 53045
Phone: 262 879-5000   Fax: 262 879-5013
Web: www.fiserv.com

PRODUCTS/OPERATIONS

2016 Sales

	$ mil.	% of total
Payments		
Processing & services	2,334	42
Products	756	14
Financial		
Processing & services	2,285	41
Product	192	3
Adjustments	(62)	-
Total	**5,254**	**100**

Selected Subsidiaries

BillMatrix Corporation
CheckFree Corporation
CheckFreePay Corporation
Corillian Corporation
Fiserv Global Services Inc.
Fiserv Automotive Solutions Inc.
Fiserv CIR Inc.
Fiserv (Europe) Limited (UK)
Information Technology Inc.
ITI of Nebraska Inc.
XP Systems Corp.

COMPETITORS

ACI Worldwide	Jack Henry
Accenture	MasterCard
Banc of America	NCR
Merchant Services	PayPal
CGI Group	Q2 Holdings
D+H USA	SunGard
DST Systems	Total System Services
Fidelity National	Vantiv
Information Services	Visa Inc
First Data	Western Union
Intuit	
Intuit Financial	
Services	

Company Type: Public

Income Statement

FYE: December 31

	REVENUE ($ mil.)	NET INCOME ($ mil.)	NET PROFIT MARGIN	EMPLOYEES
12/16	5,505	930	16.9%	23,000
12/15	5,254	712	13.6%	22,000
12/14	5,066	754	14.9%	21,000
12/13	4,814	648	13.5%	21,000
12/12	4,482	611	13.6%	20,000
Annual Growth	5.3%	11.1%	—	3.6%

2016 Year-End Financials

Debt ratio: 46.82%
Return on equity: 35.66%
Cash ($ mil.): 300
Current ratio: 0.95
Long-term debt ($ mil.): 4,467

No. of shares (mil.): 215
Dividends
Yield: —
Payout: —
Market value ($ mil.): 22,903

	STOCK PRICE ($) FY Close	P/E High/Low	PER SHARE ($) Earnings	Dividends	Book Value
12/16	106.28	26 21	4.15	0.00	11.79
12/15	91.46	32 23	2.99	0.00	11.81
12/14	70.97	24 18	2.98	0.00	13.71
12/13	59.05	46 23	2.44	0.00	13.97
12/12	79.03	36 26	2.22	0.00	12.81
Annual Growth	7.7%	— —	16.9%	—	(2.0%)

Flagstar Bancorp, Inc.

Flagstar Bancorp is the holding company for Flagstar Bank which operates around 110 branches (including 10 in retail stores) mostly in Michigan. Beyond offering traditional deposit and loan products Michigan's largest bank specializes in originating purchasing and servicing one-to-four family residential mortgage loans across all 50 states through a network of brokers and correspondents. Around 70% of the Flagstar's revenue is linked to mortgage origination and servicing while another 25% comes from its community banking business. Boasting $14 billion in assets Flagstar is one of the nation's 10 largest savings banks.

Operations

Flagstar Bancorp operates four business segments: Mortgage Originations which made up 58% of its total revenue during 2015 and acquires and sells one-to-four family residential mortgage loans; Mortgage Servicing (12% of revenue) which charges a fee to service and sub-service mortgage loans for its own community bank and other parties; and Community Banking (24%) which provides deposit and loan products (including warehouse lending) to businesses individuals government entities and held-for-investment portfolio groups.

Unlike traditional banks which focus on interest income Flagstar makes most of its revenue from its mortgage banking business. Only about 43% of its revenue came from interest during 2015 (mostly from loans) while most of the rest came from gains on mortgage loan sales (36% of revenue) loan fees and charges (8%) and other mortgage-banking related fees (10%).

Geographic Reach

The Troy Michigan-based company had 99 branches in Michigan and another 10 locations in retail locations in nine highly-populous states. Its mortgage banking business does business in all 50 states.

Sales and Marketing

Flagstar spent $9 million on advertising in 2015 compared to $10 million and $9 million in 2014 and 2013 respectively.

Financial Performance

As with other mortgage bankers Flagstar has struggled to grow its revenues over the past few years as many borrowers have already refinanced their loans to take advantage of low interest rates. The lender has also been in and out of the red in recent years suffering losses in 2014 and 2011.

Flagstar Bancorp's revenue rebounded 28% to $825 million during 2015 however thanks to a combination of higher interest income and mortgage sales. On the mortgage side a 40% jump in loan sale gains were driven by higher fallout-adjusted lock volumes improved margins and lower representation and warranty provisions. The company's interest income grew 24% as it continued to build its average loans held-for-sale loans held-for-investment and investment security assets.

Strong revenue growth in 2015 and a sharp decline in loan loss provisions on an improving quality credit portfolio drove the company's net income up 28% to $158 million (compared to a $70 million loss in 2014). Despite earnings growth Flagstar's operations used $9.55 billion in cash or about 17% more than in 2014 mostly as it used more cash to originate mortgage loans.

Strategy

While home mortgage lending remains key to Flagstar the company hopes to diversify its revenue streams so the business eventually accounts for about a third of sales. Over the past few years the company has been transforming its branches into full-service community banks and moving toward cross-selling an expanded suite of retail commercial and government banking services.

In February 2016 the company expanded and diversified more into commercial lending after launching its national homebuilder lending platform designed to offer financing to residential developers and homebuilders across the US. In past years it introduced a line of consumer loans such as credit cards and home equity lines of credit and added services for small and midsized businesses like treasury management and specialty lending.

Company Background

In 2011 to raise capital after suffering the effects of the housing bust the company sold 27 bank branches in the suburbs north of Atlanta along with their deposits to PNC. The company also sold its 22 Indiana branches to First Financial Bancorp later that year. In addition to bringing in some cash the divestitures help Flagstar focus on its Michigan operations.

MP Thrift an affiliate of private equity firm MatlinPatterson Global Advisors assumed a controlling stake of Flagstar in 2009. Today it owns 64% of the company.

EXECUTIVES

EVP and Director Performing Servicing, Mark Landschulz, age 52
President Mortgage Banking, Leonard (Len) Israel
President CEO and Director, Alessandro P. DiNello, age 62
EVP and Senior Deputy General Counsel, Paul D. Borja, age 56, $749,982 total compensation
EVP and Treasurer, Brian D.J. Boike, age 40
EVP and COO, Lee M. Smith
EVP and CFO, James K. Ciroli
EVP and Chief Risk Officer, Steve Figliuolo
EVP and Director MIS and Analytics, William D. Belekewicz
EVP and CIO, Tony Buttrick

EVP Secondary Marketing, Palmer T. Heenan
EVP and Director Mortgage Fulfillment, Donna M. Krall
EVP and Chief Lending Officer Commercial Banking, Thomas R. Kuslits
EVP and Chief Human Resources Officer, Cynthia M. Myers
EVP and Chief Credit Officer, Joseph M. Redoutey
EVP and Chief Compliance Officer, Karen A. Sabatowski
Chairman, John D. Lewis
Auditors: PricewaterhouseCoopers LLP

LOCATIONS

HQ: Flagstar Bancorp, Inc.
5151 Corporate Drive, Troy, MI 48098-2639
Phone: 248 312-2000
Web: www.flagstar.com

PRODUCTS/OPERATIONS

2015 Sales

	$ mil.	% of total
Interest income		
Loans	295	36
Investment securities	59	7
Interest-earning deposits and other	1	-
Non interest income		
Net gain on loan sales	288	36
Loan fees & charges	67	8
Deposit fees and charges	25	3
Loan administration income	26	3
Net return on mortgage serving assets	28	3
Net (loss) gain on sale of assets	(1)	-
Representation and warranty benefit (provision)	19	2
Other non-interest income	18	2
Total	**825**	**100**

2015 Sales

	% of total
Mortgage origination	58
Community Banking	24
Mortgage Servicing	12
Others	6
Total	**100**

Selected Products/Services

Personal Banking
Banking
Checking Accounts
Checking
Savings Accounts
Savings Accounts: Personal
Banking Goals
View All Rates
Online Banking Login: Personal Accounts
Mobile Banking
Detroit Red Wings Partnership
Foreign Currency
Loans
Home Loans
Refinance
Home Equity Solutions
Credit Cards
Money Market
Investment Accounts: Personal

COMPETITORS

Bank of America	JPMorgan Chase
Comerica	KeyCorp
Fifth Third	Northern Trust
Harris	PNC Financial
Huntington Bancshares	

Income Statement

FYE: December 31

	ASSETS ($ mil.)	NET INCOME ($ mil.)	INCOME AS % OF ASSETS	EMPLOYEES
12/16	14,053	171	1.2%	2,886
12/15	13,715	158	1.2%	2,713
12/14	9,839	(69)	—	2,739
12/13	9,407	266	2.8%	3,253
12/12	14,082	68	0.5%	3,328
Annual Growth	(0.1%)	25.8%	—	(3.5%)

2016 Year-End Financials

Debt ratio: 3.51%	No. of shares (mil.): 56
Return on equity: 11.90%	Dividends
Cash ($ mil.): 158	Yield: —
Current ratio: —	Payout: —
Long-term debt ($ mil.): —	Market value ($ mil.): 1,531

	STOCK PRICE ($) FY Close	P/E High/Low		PER SHARE ($) Earnings	Dividends	Book Value
12/16	26.94	11	6	2.66	0.00	23.51
12/15	23.11	11	6	2.24	0.00	27.07
12/14	15.73	—	—	(1.72)	0.00	24.37
12/13	19.62	5	3	4.37	0.00	25.40
12/12	19.40	22	1	0.87	0.00	20.75
Annual Growth	8.6%	—	—	32.2%	—	3.2%

Florida Power & Light Co.

Florida Power & Light (FPL) sheds extra light onto the Sunshine State. The company a subsidiary of utility holding company NextEra Energy serves some 5 million electricity customers in eastern and southern Florida. FPL has more than 74800 miles of transmission and distribution lines as well as interests in fossil-fueled nuclear and solar power plants that give it a generating capacity of about 26000 MW. FPL also purchases and sells energy commodities to wholesale customers. FPL's has one of the cleanest power plant fleets across the US.

Operations

FPL's power generations relies on a mix of fuel sources which includes Fossil Operations (primarily uses fossil fuels natural gas and a joint ownership interest in 3 coal units) Nuclear Operations (supply of uranium and the conversion enrichment and fabrication of nuclear fuel) and Solar Operations (utility-owned and customer-owned or leased). In Solar Operations the energy generated goes directly to the location it is serving. In addition FPL also purchases a small amount of power and capacity from non-utility generators and other utilities.

It generates about 70% of its energy with oil/gas-sourced power plants an additional roughly 20% from four nuclear plants and the rest from coal oil and solar.

Geographic Reach

Juno Beach FL-headquartered FPL serves retail customers along Florida?s Atlantic and southern Gulf Coasts.

Sales and Marketing

FPL provides service to its customers through an integrated transmission and distribution system that links its generation facilities to its customers. As a state-regulated utility its market is largely re-

stricted to other entrants although niche project such as rooftop solar provide negligible competition.

Financial Performance

FPL produced $10.9 billion in 2016 operating revenues down 6% from the prior year due to lower fuel cost recoveries.

Despite lower revenue the utility generated $1.7 billion in net income up 5% from 2015. Lower interest expense and tighter control over operating expenses boosted the year's earnings.

Strategy

Florida Power and Light has a 2017-2020 budget of some $18 billion to pursue its strategic endeavors. About half of the capital expenditures are targeted for improvements and expansion of its transmission and distribution segment. It plans to invest heavily into solar farms envisioning nearly $3.0 billion to construct new facilities the first of which is expected to open in early 2018. Capacity expansion and modernization of generation facilities will receive the remaining funds.

In 2016 FPL and the Daytona International Speedway completed FPL Solar Circuit a system of more than 7000 solar panels with capacity of 2.1 MW to generate power for the Speedway's operations. It is one of the largest solar panel installed for US professional sports. The company also intends to build three new solar photovoltaic power plants.

Mergers and Acquisitions

In 2015 FPL and Office of Public Counsel acquired the coal-fired Cedar Bay plant and phased out 90% of its operations to will eventually phase the plant out of service. This saved FPL about a $70 million in operating costs and avoids nearly 1 million tons of carbon dioxide emissions annually.

Company Background

In 2013 FPL began installing solar panels at about 100 schools in 23 counties. It also agreed to a plan whereby more than 400 homes being built or refurbished by Habitat for Humanity and other non-profits would be fitted with solar-powered water heaters.

Between 2011 to 2013 FPL invested $9 billion to strengthen and improve its electric generation and delivery system. The company has revived a $2 billion plan to convert a plant in Port St. John and a plant in Riviera Beach from heavy fuel to natural gas. It also got a further 510 MW of capacity from its Turkey Point and St. Lucie nuclear power plants in 2012 and 2013.

In 2010 the Florida Public Service Commission turned down the company's proposed 30% retail rate hike or $1.3 billion. FPL adjusted its expansion programs accordingly.

Moving further to meet federal requirements for green energy production in 2010 the company commissioned the Space Coast Next Generation Solar Energy Center at the Kennedy Space Center three solar farms built in tandem with NASA to produce 10 MW of clean energy enough to serve 1100 homes. It also brought into service the 75-MW Martin Next Generation Solar Energy Center designed to power about 11000 homes. The hybrid facility connects more than 190000 solar thermal mirrors to an existing combined-cycle natural gas power plant.

EXECUTIVES

EVP Engineering Construction and Corporate Services, Robert L. (Bob) McGrath, age 64
EVP Finance and CFO, Moray P. Dewhurst, age 62
EVP, Charles E. Sieving, age 44
President and CEO, Eric E. Silagy
EVP Human Resources, Shaun J. Francis
Chairman, Lewis (Lew) Hay, age 61
Auditors: Deloitte & Touche LLP

LOCATIONS

HQ: Florida Power & Light Co.
700 Universe Boulevard, Juno Beach, FL 33408
Phone: 561 694-4000
Web: www.nexteraenergy.com

PRODUCTS/OPERATIONS

2016 Operating Revenues

	% of total
Residential	89
Commercial	11
Total	**100**

2016 Sales

	$ mil.	% of total
Retail base	5,807	53
Fuel cost recovery	3,120	29
Other	1,962	18
Total	**10,114**	**100**

COMPETITORS

Clay Electric	Progress Energy
Florida Public	Florida
Utilities	Seminole Electric
Gulf Power	Southern Company Gas
JEA	Sumter Electric
Orlando Utilities	Tampa Electric
Commission	

HISTORICAL FINANCIALS
Company Type: Public

Income Statement

FYE: December 31

	REVENUE ($ mil.)	NET INCOME ($ mil.)	NET PROFIT MARGIN	EMPLOYEES
12/16	10,895	1,727	15.9%	8,900
12/15	11,651	1,648	14.1%	8,800
12/14	11,421	1,517	13.3%	8,700
12/13	10,445	1,349	12.9%	8,900
12/12	10,114	1,240	12.3%	9,700
Annual Growth	1.9%	8.6%	—	(2.1%)

2016 Year-End Financials

Debt ratio: 22.72%	No. of shares (mil.): 0
Return on equity: 10.72%	Dividends
Cash ($ mil.): 33	Yield: —
Current ratio: 0.81	Payout: —
Long-term debt ($ mil.): 9,705	Market value ($ mil.): —

Florida Power Corp.

Sometimes the sunshine state just isn't bright enough and that's when Florida Power (doing business as Progress Energy Florida) really shines. The utility transmits and distributes electricity to 1.6 million customers and oversees 10025 MW of generating capacity from interests in 14 nuclear and coal- oil- and gas-fired power plants. Additionally Florida Power purchases about 20% of the energy it provides. Florida Power operates 5100 miles of transmission lines and 52000 miles of overhead and 18700 miles of underground distribution cable. It also has 500 electric substations. A subsidiary of holding company Duke Energy the company also sells wholesale power to other utilities and marketers.

Operations

The company is a regulated public utility primarily engaged in the generation transmission distribution and sale of electricity. Its power grid is interconnected with 22 municipal power systems and with nine rural electric cooperative systems.

Geographic Reach

Florida Power's service territory covers 20000 square miles in west-central Florida and includes the densely populated areas around Orlando as well as the cities of St. Petersburg and Clearwater.

Sales and Marketing

The company's wholesale customers include Seminole Electric Cooperative Reedy Creek Improvement District the city of Gainesville the city of Winter Park and the city of Homestead.

Financial Performance

Revenue decreased by 17% in 2011 primarily due to the unfavorable impact of weather and lower wholesale base revenues. The unfavorable impact of weather was driven by 61% lower heating-degree days than in the previous year.

Net income decreased by 31% in 2011 primarily due to the charge for the amount to be refunded to customers through the fuel clause in accordance with a settlement agreement and the less favorable impact of weather.

EXECUTIVES

Vice President Power Generation Operations Florida, Jeffrey Swartz
Auditors: Deloitte & Touche LLP

LOCATIONS

HQ: Florida Power Corp.
299 First Avenue North, St. Petersburg, FL 33701
Phone: 704 382-3853   **Fax:** 727 866-4990

COMPETITORS

Florida Power & Light	Orlando Utilities
Florida Public	Commission
Utilities	Seminole Electric
Gulf Power	Southern Company Gas
JEA	Tampa Electric

HISTORICAL FINANCIALS

Company Type: Public

Income Statement

FYE: December 31

	REVENUE ($ mil.)	NET INCOME ($ mil.)	NET PROFIT MARGIN	EMPLOYEES
12/16	4,568	551	12.1%	—
12/15	4,977	599	12.0%	—
12/14	4,975	548	11.0%	—
12/13	4,527	325	7.2%	—
12/12	4,689	266	5.7%	—
Annual Growth	(0.7%)	20.0%	—	—

2016 Year-End Financials

Debt ratio: 36.87%—
Return on equity: 10.97%
Cash ($ mil.): 16
Current ratio: 0.83
Long-term debt ($ mil.): 5,799

Dividends
Yield: —
Payout: —
Market value ($ mil.): —

	STOCK PRICE ($) FY Close	P/E High/Low	PER SHARE ($) Earnings	Dividends	Book Value
12/16	0.00	— —	(0.00)	0.00	(0.00)
Annual Growth	—	— —	—	—	—

Fluor Corp.

Fluor is one of the world's largest international design engineering and contracting firms. Through subsidiaries it provides engineering procurement construction and maintenance (EPCM) as well as project management services for a variety of industrial sectors around the world. Its construction portfolio includes manufacturing plants refineries pharmaceutical facilities health care buildings power plants and telecommunications and transportation infrastructure. Energy chemicals and mining sector projects account for more than 50% of its revenue. The group also provides operations and maintenance services for its projects as well as administrative and support services to the US government.

Operations

The company is structured into four segments by sector.

Energy Chemicals & Mining (more than 50% of the revenue) targets the upstream downstream chemical petrochemical offshore and onshore oil and gas production liquefied natural gas pipeline metals and mining markets. It offers a full range of design engineering procurement construction fabrication and project management services.

The Industrial & Infrastructure (more than 20%) segment provides design engineering procurement and construction services for pharmaceutical and biotechnology facilities commercial and institutional buildings and mining telecommunications wind power and transportation projects. The unit also participates in public/private partnerships to oversee financing and management of roadway and railway projects. One ongoing significant project is the world's largest offshore wind farm development off the coast of the UK which is expected to help produce 25 gigawatts of wind energy by 2020.

Fluor's Government Services segment (roughly 15%) offers project management services primarily to the US Departments of Energy Defense and Homeland Security. It provides environmental restoration engineering and construction and operations and maintenance services.

The company?s Maintenance Modification & Asset Integrity segment (about 15%) provides facility start-up and management plant and facility maintenance operations support and asset management services to the oil and gas chemicals life sciences mining and metals consumer products and manufacturing industries. The segment includes Fluor's equipment temporary staffing and power services businesses as well as the recently acquired Stork business.

Geographic Reach

While Irving Texas-based Fluor has offices in 100 countries its largest markets are in the US and Europe which account for some 50% and almost 20% of its revenue respectively.

Sales and Marketing

Fluor performs its business through contracts which require payments as the projects progress. A primary provider of engineering construction and related services to the US government Fluor gleans about 15% of its revenue from the US. Its largest private-sector client is Exxon Mobil representing nearly 15% of revenue.

Financial Performance

After experiencing declining revenues in 2015 Fluor saw its revenues increase 5% to $19 billion in 2016. This was due to an 81% spike in Industrial Infrastructure & Power sales and a 73% surge in Maintenance Modification & Asset Integrity sales. These segments benefited from increased project execution activities for several power projects as well as revenue contributions from its acquired Stork business.

Its profits however declined 32% to $281 million in 2016 mainly due to the absence of a $240 million pension settlement charge it earned the previous year. The contractor's operating cash levels have also fluctuated over the last several years; after increasing in 2015 to $849 million cash flow decreased to $706 million mainly due to the decreased profits coupled with a decline in net working capital inflows.

Strategy

Broadly speaking the engineering and construction industry faces challenges with heavy competition and overcapacity. Due to its great size Fluor is well-positioned to survive in a variety of economic climates as it is active in diverse sectors as well as experienced in carrying out projects in difficult locations such as the Middle East. Its strong balance sheet also allows it to fund its strategic initiatives and pursue opportunities for growth.

Strengthening its position at the heart of the Asia/Pacific region in 2016 Fluor completed its joint venture investment in its COOEC-Fluor Heavy Industries (CFHI) fabrication yard in China. The move significantly expanded its fabrication ability for global onshore and offshore projects.

Mergers and Acquisitions

In March 2016 Fluor boosted its operations and maintenance business while enhancing its integrated solutions capabilities after buying Netherlands-based Stork Holding B.V. from UK-based private equity Arle Capital Partners for $755 million.Going forward Fluor is focused on Stork's expansion outside of its traditional footprint in Europe and South America.

HISTORY

Fluor's history began in 1890 when three Fluor brothers immigrants from Switzerland opened a Wisconsin lumber mill under the name Rudolph Fluor & Brothers. In 1912 John Simon Fluor formed a construction firm in Santa Ana California. Fluor's company soon began a relationship with Southern California Gas which led it to specialize in oil and gas construction. The company incorporated as Fluor Construction in 1924 later began making engine mufflers. In 1930 it expanded outside of California with a contract to build Texas pipelines.

After WWII Middle East oil reserves were aggressively developed by Western companies. Fluor cashed in on the stampede winning major contracts in Saudi Arabia. During the early 1960s it continued to emphasize oil and gas work establishing a contract drilling unit and in the 1970s it began work on giant energy projects.

In 1977 Fluor made its biggest purchase: Daniel International a South Carolina engineering and construction firm with more than $1 billion in annual revenues. The contracting firm founded by Charles Daniel in 1934 initially did construction work for the textile industry then later worked for the chemical pharmaceutical metal and power industries.

Flush with cash Fluor bought St. Joe Minerals in 1981. A drop in oil prices in the 1980s killed demand for the big projects that were its bread and butter. As metal prices fell St. Joe didn't help the bottom line either. John Robert Fluor the last of the founding family to head the firm died in 1984.

When David Tappan stepped in as CEO he faced a $573 million loss the first year. The white-haired son of missionaries to China Tappan — known as the Ice Man — dumped subsidiaries and halved the payroll. In 1986 he merged Daniel into Fluor's engineering unit forming Fluor Daniel.

Leslie McCraw succeeded Tappan as CEO in 1991. McCraw saw Fluor as overly conservative and three years later he began setting up offices around the world while decentralizing Fluor's structure and adding new business such as temporary staffing and equipment leasing. Fluor also shed some of its commodity companies including its lead business in 1994. In 1996 Fluor's environmental services unit merged with Groundwater Technology and was spun off as a public company Fluor Daniel GTI.

Fluor saw mixed results from its expansion. Amid fierce competition and pricing pressure Fluor Daniel began cutting its overhead in early 1997 by reorganizing and selling noncore businesses.

Ill with cancer McCraw stepped down in 1998 and Philip Carroll who had overhauled Shell Oil took over as CEO. Carroll reorganized Fluor into four business units and tagged $90 million to rebuild its internal information management systems. Fluor also unloaded its 52% stake in Fluor Daniel GTI to The IT Group for $36 million.

Fluor in 1999 cut 5000 jobs further streamlined operations and focused on growth industries such as biotechnology and telecommunications. The next year the company split its construction and coal mining operations into two separate publicly traded companies one to concentrate on engineering and construction and one on coal mining. Former Fluor subsidiary A. T. Massey Coal was spun off as Massey Energy.

Carroll his restructuring job complete announced in December 2001 that he would retire the following February. That year the company also made plans to dispose of noncore operations of the company's construction equipment and temporary staffing businesses. Alan Boeckmann who had been president and COO succeeded Carroll in 2002.

The next year Fluor acquired Del-Jen a provider of outsourced services to US military bases and to the US Department of Labor. It also picked up five specialty operations and maintenance business groups from Philip Services. And in 2003 the company decided to dissolve its Duke/Fluor Daniel joint venture.

Fluor moved its headquarters from California to Dallas in 2006. The move resulted in the elimination of about 100 jobs. That year the company also entered the health care construction market.

In 2007 the company saw growth in all of its business segments with the exception of its government contracts in part because of the conclusion of projects for FEMA and in Iraq. The following year Fluor formed Fluor Offshore Solutions which is dedicated to global oil and gas clients in the offshore market. The company's construction segment acquired two private engineering companies in Europe — Belgium's UNEC Engineering N.V. and Spain's Europea de Ingenieria y Asesoramiento — increasing Fluor's ability to support its clients from a local level.

In early 2011 Alan Boeckmann retired as CEO after nearly a decade at the helm. He was succeeded by longtime company executive David Seaton who previously led Fluor's energy and chemicals global sales and China operations among others.

EXECUTIVES

Senior Vice President of Infrastructure, Robert Prieto
Senior Vice President Corporate Strate, Ian Thomas
Executive Vice President Human Resources and Administration, Glenn Gilkey
EVP Chief Legal Officer and Secretary, Carlos M. Hernandez, age 62, $630,032 total compensation

President Power, Chris Tye
EVP and CFO, Biggs C. Porter, age 64, $841,318 total compensation
President Government, Bruce A. Stanski, age 56, $600,018 total compensation
EVP Systems and Supply Chain, Ray F. Barnard, age 59, $564,689 total compensation
President AMECO, Tracey Cook
EVP Project Support Services, Garry W. Flowers, age 66
Chairman and CEO, David T. Seaton, age 56, $1,295,029 total compensation
President Energy and Chemicals Americas, Jim Brittain
President Energy and Chemicals Asia/Pacific, Ken R. Choudhary
President Energy and Chemicals Europe Africa and Middle East, Taco de Haan
President Life Sciences and Advanced Manufacturing, Juan G. Hern ̃ndez
President Mining and Metals, Rick Koumouris
SVP Information Technology and CIO, Robert C. Taylor
EVP Business Development and Strategy, Jose L. M. Bustamante
President Infrastructure, Hans Dekker
President Construction and Fabrication, Jack Penley
Senior Vice President Project Management, Steve Andersen
Vice President Corporate Finance, Kenneth Lockwood
Senior Vice President Government Relations, David Marventano
Senior Vice President Global Projects, Joe McAneny
Vice President And Executive Project Director, Tony Umek
Executive Vice President, Johnathan Carlson
Vice President Business Development, Julio Miranda
Vice President and General Counsel Litigation, Paul Bruno
Senior Vice President, Jim Heavner
Vice President of Prime Contract Management, Eleanor Spector
Vice President Of Technology, Bonita Hamilton
Vice President, Jose Herrero
Vice President Sales and Marketing, Larry Bolander
Larry Bolander
Vice President, Paul Koppel
Vice President, Tom Siebenmorgen
Vice President China Operations, Leo Onderwater
Vice President and Treasurer, Joanna Oliva
Vice President Operation, Carl Fletcher
Vice President, Lee Tashjian
Vice President Commercial and Institutions, Terry Towle
Hanford Vice President, Pete Knollmeyer
Vice President Operations, Dewitt Porter
VICE PRESIDENT PROJECT DEVELOPMENT AND, Troy Ailshie
Vice President, Shawn West
Vice President, Lee Richardson
Vice President Project Management, Denis L Menegaz
Vice President of Power Group, James Mackey
Vice President Strategy, Dr Oscar
Vice President Fluor, Tom Hendricks
Senior Vice President Global Sales and Marketing, Michael Pears
Vice President, Michael Wolf
Vice President, Arnold Noriega
Vice President Corporate Communications, Lisa Bottle
Vice President Procurement, Sue Joner
Vice President, Michael Honeycutt
VICE PRESIDENT, Richard C Meserole

VICE PRESIDENT AND VC SUMMER CONSORTIUM PROJECT DIRECTOR, Frederick P Hughes
Treasurer, Edward Kowalchuk
Assistant Treasurer, Enrique Calderon
Assistant Treasurer, Mitch Stone
Auditors: Ernst & Young LLP

LOCATIONS

HQ: Fluor Corp.
6700 Las Colinas Boulevard, Irving, TX 75039
Phone: 469 398-7000
Web: www.fluor.com

2016 Sales

	$ mil.	% of total
United States	9,891	52
Europe	3,372	18
Canada	2,170	12
Middle East and Africa	1,586	8
Asia Pacific (includes Australia)	1,010	5
Central and South America	1,006	5
Total	**19,036**	**100**

PRODUCTS/OPERATIONS

2016 Sales

	$ mil.	% of total
Energy Chemicals & Mining	9,754	51
Industrial Infrastructure & Power	4,094	22
Government	2,720	14
Maintenance Modification & Asset Integrity	2,467	13
Total	**19,036**	**100**

Selected Services

Construction management
Design
Engineering procurement and construction (EPC)
Operations and maintenance
Program management
Project development and finance
Project management
Staffing

Selected Industries Served

Biotechnology
Chemicals and petrochemicals
Commercial and institutional
Equipment
Gas processing
Government
Manufacturing
Mining
Oil and gas production
Petroleum refining
Pharmaceuticals
Power generation
Telecommunications
Transportation

Selected Subsidiaries

American Equipment Company Inc.
American Construction Equipment Company Inc.
Fluor Constructors International Inc.
Fluor Enterprises Inc.
Daniel International Corporation
Del-Jen Inc.
Fluor Daniel Mexico S.A.
ICA-Fluor Daniel S. de R.L. de C.V. (49% Mexico)
Fluor Holding Company LLC
TRS Staffing Solutions Inc.

COMPETITORS

AECOM	JGC
Amec Foster Wheeler	Jacobs Engineering
Balfour Beatty	KBR
Construction	Kiewit Power
Bechtel	Constructors
CH2M HILL	Parsons Corporation
Chicago Bridge & Iron	Petrofac
Chiyoda Corp.	SNC-Lavalin
Granite Construction	WorleyParsons Corp.
Hyundai Engineering	
and Construction	

HISTORICAL FINANCIALS
Company Type: Public

Income Statement
FYE: December 31

	REVENUE ($ mil.)	NET INCOME ($ mil.)	NET PROFIT MARGIN	EMPLOYEES
12/16	19,036	281	1.5%	61,551
12/15	18,114	412	2.3%	38,758
12/14	21,531	510	2.4%	37,508
12/13	27,351	667	2.4%	38,129
12/12	27,577	456	1.7%	41,193
Annual Growth	(8.8%)	(11.4%)	—	10.6%

2016 Year-End Financials

Debt ratio: 17.36%	No. of shares (mil.): 139
Return on equity: 9.17%	Dividends
Cash ($ mil.): 1,850	Yield: 0.0%
Current ratio: 1.47	Payout: 42.0%
Long-term debt ($ mil.): 1,517	Market value ($ mil.): 7,314

	STOCK PRICE ($) FY Close	P/E High/Low		PER SHARE ($) Earnings	Dividends	Book Value
12/16	52.52	28	20	2.00	0.84	22.44
12/15	47.22	21	14	2.81	0.84	21.56
12/14	60.63	26	17	3.20	0.84	20.93
12/13	80.29	19	13	4.06	0.64	23.29
12/12	58.74	23	17	2.71	0.64	20.58
Annual Growth	(2.8%)	—	—	(7.3%)	7.0%	2.2%

Flushing Financial Corp.

Flush with cash? You could keep it at Flushing Financial Corp. (FFC). The holding company's Flushing Savings Bank operates more than 15 branches in the Brooklyn Manhattan and Queens boroughs of New York City and in nearby Nassau County. The bank offers services catering to the sizable populations of Asians and other ethnic groups in its market. Deposit products include CDs and checking savings passbook money market and NOW accounts. Mortgages secured by multifamily residential commercial and mixed-use real estate account for most of the company's loan portfolio.

Operations

The company's other offerings include single-family mortgages construction loans business loans and taxi medallion loans.

Financial Performance

The company's revenue decreased in fiscal 2013 compared to the previous fiscal period. It reported revenue of $210.1 million for fiscal 2013 down from $222.8 million in revenue for fiscal 2012.

However despite the dip in annual revenue the company's net income increased in fiscal 2013 compared to the prior year. FFC reported $37.75 million in net income for fiscal 2013 up from $34.3 million in net income for fiscal 2012.

The company's cash flow increased by about $3 million in fiscal 2013 compared to fiscal 2012 levels.

Strategy

The bank has shifted its strategy from operating as a traditional thrift to a more commercial slant focusing on such offerings as business lending and cash management services as well as commercial lending.

Flushing Savings tightened its lending practices after seeing a rise in bad loans during the financial crisis. It has also reduced the number of construc-

tion loans and commercial mortgages it originates as they typically carry a higher risk. As a result the bank has been originating and purchasing fewer loans than it did before the downturn started. However higher-yielding multifamily mortgages remain a key strategic focus for the company.

EXECUTIVES

SEVP and Chief of Real Estate Lending Flushing Financial and Flushing Savings Bank, Francis W. (Frank) Korzekwinski, age 54, $418,111 total compensation
President CEO and Director Flushing Financial and Flushing Savings Bank, John R. Buran, age 67, $899,176 total compensation
SEVP COO and Corporate Secretary Flushing Financial and Flushing Savings Bank, Maria A. Grasso, age 52, $481,222 total compensation
EVP Residential Mixed-Use and Small Multi-Family Real Estate Lending, Jeoung (A. J.) Jin, age 50
EVP and CIO, Allen M. Brewer, age 64
EVP and Chief Audit Officer, Robert G. (Bob) Kiraly, age 61
EVP and Director of Government Banking, Patricia Mezeul, age 57
EVP Commercial Real Estate Lending, Ronald Hartmann, age 61
EVP Business Banking Flushing Financial and Flushing Savings Bank, Theresa Kelly, age 55, $285,704 total compensation
EVP and Chief Risk Officer, Gary P. Liotta, age 57
EVP CFO and Treasurer, Susan Cullen
EVP and Director of Distribution and Client Development, Michael Bingold, age 54
EVP and Chief of Staff, John F. Stewart
SVP and Chief Investment Officer, Frank J. Akalski, age 62
Vice President, Astrid Burrowes
Vice President Flushing Bank, Joan Roche
Assistant Vice President Commercial Real Estate Loan Officer, Albert Bozzolo
Senior Vice President and Director of Strategic Development and Delivery, Caterina dePasquale
Assistant Vice President Internet Banking, Maria Meihoefer
Senior Vice President, Joanne Orelli
Assistant Vice President Investment Sales Manager, Maria Masi
Vice President Business Development, Steven Glass
Senior Vice President, James Jacovatos
Senior Vice President And Director of Op, Barbara Beckmann
Vice President, Rhonda Delorenzo
Assistant Vice President Loan Servicing, Marcia Witter
Vice President Branch Manager Springfield Branch, Ling Xu
Vice President Information Technology Project Management, Bruce Randall
Vice President Business Banking, Louis Matti
Vice President, Keith Nam
Senior Vice President, Michael Nedder
Vice President Business Banking, Denis Healy
Assistant Vice President Loan Officer, Anthony Montalbano
Vice President Business Banking, Jonathan Stern
Assistant Vice President BSA Department, Karen Williams
Senior Vice President Team Leader Business Banking, Gus Buitrago
Vice President Small Business Advisor Lending, Emil Temelkov
Chairman Flushing Financial and Flushing Savings Bank, John E. Roe, age 83
Board Member, Sam Han
Auditors: BDO USA, LLP

LOCATIONS

HQ: Flushing Financial Corp.
220 RXR Plaza, Uniondale, NY 11556
Phone: 718 961-5400
Web: www.flushingbank.com

PRODUCTS/OPERATIONS

2016 Sales

	$ mil.	% of total
Interest and dividend income:		
Interest and fees on loans	195	69
Interest and dividends on securities		
Interest	25	9
Dividends	0	-
Other interest income	0	-
Non-interest income:		
Banking services fee income	3	1
Net gain on sale of loans	0	-
Net gain on sale of securities	1	1
Net gain on sale of buildings	48	17
Net loss from fair value adjustments	(3.4)	-
Federal Home Loan Bank of New York stock dividends	2	1
Gains from life insurance proceeds	0	-
Bank owned life insurance	2	1
Other income	1	1
Total	**278**	**100**

2016 Loan Portfolio

	% of total
Mortgage Loans	87
Non-mortgage loans	13
Total	**100**

COMPETITORS

Apple Bank for Savings	First of Long Island
Astoria Financial	HSBC USA
Bank of America	JPMorgan Chase
Bank of New York Mellon	Korea Exchange Bank
Citigroup	New York Community Bancorp
Dime Community Bancshares	

HISTORICAL FINANCIALS
Company Type: Public

Income Statement
FYE: December 31

	ASSETS ($ mil.)	NET INCOME ($ mil.)	INCOME AS % OF ASSETS	EMPLOYEES
12/16	6,058	64	1.1%	470
12/15	5,704	46	0.8%	442
12/14	5,077	44	0.9%	424
12/13	4,721	37	0.8%	378
12/12	4,451	34	0.8%	385
Annual Growth	8.0%	17.3%	—	5.1%

2016 Year-End Financials

Debt ratio: 1.77%	No. of shares (mil.): 28
Return on equity: 13.12%	Dividends
Cash ($ mil.): 35	Yield: 0.0%
Current ratio: —	Payout: 30.3%
Long-term debt ($ mil.): —	Market value ($ mil.): 842

	STOCK PRICE ($) FY Close	P/E High/Low		PER SHARE ($) Earnings	Dividends	Book Value
12/16	29.39	13	8	2.24	0.68	17.95
12/15	21.64	14	11	1.59	0.64	16.41
12/14	20.27	14	12	1.48	0.60	15.52
12/13	20.70	17	12	1.26	0.52	14.36
12/12	15.34	14	11	1.13	0.52	14.39
Annual Growth	17.7%	—	—	18.7%	6.9%	5.7%

FNB Corp

F.N.B. Corporation is the holding company for First National Bank of Pennsylvania which serves consumers and small to midsized businesses though almost 290 bank branches in Pennsylvania northeastern Ohio and Maryland. The company also has more than 70 consumer finance offices operating as Regency Finance in those states as well as Tennessee and Kentucky. In addition to community banking and consumer finance F.N.B. also has segments devoted to insurance and wealth management. It also offers leasing and merchant banking services. F.N.B. has extended its reach in its target states through acquisitions of banks including Metro Bancorp Annapolis Bancorp and PVF Capital Corp.

Operations

F.N.B operates four segments. The Community Banking segment which made up almost 90% of the company's total revenue during 2015 provides commercial and consumer banking services including corporate banking small business banking investment real estate financing asset-based lending capital markets services and lease financing as well as traditional consumer banking products.

The company's Wealth Management segment (5% of revenue) offers trust and other fiduciary services while the Insurance segment (2% of revenue) offers commercial and personal insurance through major carriers. F.N.B.'s Consumer Finance segment (6% of revenue) which operates through subsidiary Regency Finance Company provides installment loans to individuals and buys installment loans from retail merchants.

Like other retail banks F.N.B. makes the bulk of its money from interest income. Nearly 70% of the bank's total revenue came from loan and lease interest (including fees) during 2015 while 9% came from interest on taxable and non-taxable securities. The rest of money came from service charges (10% of revenue) trust income (3%) insurance commissions and fees (2%) securities commissions and fees (2%) mortgage banking (1%) and other non-interest income sources.

Geographic Reach

Most of the Pittsburgh-based company's branches are concentrated in Pennsylvania with the next largest markets being in Ohio Maryland and West Virginia. Its consumer finance offices are mostly in Pennsylvania and Tennessee with others in Kentucky and Ohio.

Sales and Marketing

F.N.B. boosted its advertising and promotional spend by 7% to $8.4 million during 2015 mostly because of higher expenses associated with the bank's recent acquisitions as it worked to get the name out in new territories such as in Cleveland Ohio and Baltimore.

Financial Performance

F.N.B. Corporation's annual revenues have risen nearly 40% since 2011 as its loan assets have nearly doubled with new branch openings and acquisitions. Its profits have doubled as well over the period as the company has kept a lid on growing costs.

The bank's revenue climbed 6% to $709.21 million during 2015 thanks to continued loan business growth stemming from recent bank acquisitions.

Revenue growth in 2015 drove F.N.B.'s net income up 11% to $159.65 million. The company's operating cash levels plunged 50% to $223.48 million for the year due to unfavorable changes in working capital related to securities classified as trading in business combination and sold.

Strategy

F.N.B. Corporation grows its loan and deposit business while expanding into new markets by acquiring smaller banks and select bank branches. In 2016 it agreed to buy North Carolina-based Yadkin Financial for $1.4 billion. That deal will add around 100 banking locations in the Carolinas and some $7.5 billion in assets. The combined bank will have some 400 branches across the Mid-Atlantic and Southeast US.

Mergers and Acquisitions

In April 2016 the company bought 17 branch locations in the Pittsburgh area from Fifth Third Bank as well as $100000 in loans and over $300000 in deposits.

In February 2016 F.N.B. Corporation purchased Metro Bancorp along with its $3 billion in assets and more than 30 Metro Bank branches in south-central Pennsylvania. The deal effectively merged Metro Bank into F.N.B.'s First National Bank of Pennsylvania subsidiary.

In September 2015 the bank purchased five branches in southeastern Pennsylvania from Bank of America along with almost $155000 in associated deposits.

In October 2013 F.N.B. moved to expand its presence in the greater Cleveland area by purchasing PVF Capital Corp. which owned Park View Federal Savings Bank with some 20 offices in Cleveland and northeastern Ohio.

In April 2013 F.N.B. purchased Annapolis Bancorp the parent company of BankAnnapolis in an all-stock transaction valued at about $51 million. The deal expanded F.N.B.'s reach into Maryland.

Company Background

F.N.B. which moved its headquarters from Pennsylvania to Florida in 2001 spun off First National Bankshares of Florida at the start of 2004 and returned to the Pittsburgh area. F.N.B. still operates two loan offices in Florida but these primarily manage the company's legacy loan portfolio there.

The bank is again rooted firmly in the Keystone State and bordering markets. After returning it expanded via several acquisitions prior to the Parkvale deal including bank holding companies NSD Bancorp Slippery Rock Financial North East Bancshares Omega Financial and Iron and Glass Bancorp. In 2011 F.N.B. expanded in northeastern Pennsylvania through the acquisition of Comm Bancorp. The deal valued at some $70 million brought in 15 branches.

EXECUTIVES

SVP and Corporate Controller, Timothy G. Rubritz, age 64, $215,016 total compensation
Chief Legal Officer, James G. Orie, age 58, $165,000 total compensation
CFO, Vincent J. Calabrese, age 54, $385,008 total compensation
Chief Credit Officer, Gary Guerrieri, age 56, $350,016 total compensation
President and CEO; CEO First National Bank, Vincent J. (Vince) Delie, age 52, $770,016 total compensation
President First National Bank, John C. Williams, $385,008 total compensation
President Charlotte Region, Gregory L. (Greg) Heaton
Vice President Private Banking, Caren Renz
Vice President Business Development Officer, Leslie Harrison
AVP Special Lending Department Special Assets Officer II, Susan Mann
Vice President, Gregory Robb
Senior Vice President, Craig Muthler
Vice President Commercial Banking, Tim Moorstein
Vice President Private Banking Group, Nishant Bhattarai

Assistant Vice President Commercial Loan Review, Cynthia Jennings
Vice President, Mike DeRosa
Assistant Vice President Branch Manager II, Christie Rosario
Assistant Vice President Germantown Branch Merchant Services First National Bank, Jean Carpinone
Vice President, Zac Craig
Vice President Wealth Advisor Maryland Region, Nick Ey
Assistant Vice President, Mark Condrin
Public Square Assistant Vice President Relationship Manager Investment Real Estate, Dean Razek
Vice President Branch Manager III, Kevin Claggett
Vice President Business Development Officer, Sean Laurin
Chairman, Stephen J. (Steve) Gurgovits, age 73
Board Member, Stephen Martz
Auditors: Ernst & Young LLP

LOCATIONS

HQ: FNB Corp
One North Shore Center, 12 Federal Street, Pittsburgh, PA 15212
Phone: 800 555-5455
Web: www.fnbcorporation.com

PRODUCTS/OPERATIONS

2015 Sales by Segment

	$ mil.	% of total
Community banking	616	87
Consumer finance	42	6
Wealth management	35	5
Insurance	13	2
parent & other	1	-
Total	**709**	**100**

2015 Sales

	$ mil.	% of total
Interest		
Loans including fees	482	68
Securities including dividends	64	9
Other	0	-
Non-interest		
Service charges	70	10
Trust Services	20	3
Insurance commissions & fees	16	2
Securities commissions & fees	13	2
Other	40	6
Total	**709**	**100**

Selected Subsidiaries

F.N.B. Capital Corporation (merchant banking)
First National Bank of Pennsylvania
  Bank Capital Services LLC (also dba F.N.B. Commercial Leasing)
  First National Trust Company
  F.N.B. Investment Advisors
  First National Investment Services Company
First National Insurance Agency LLC
Regency Finance Company
  Citizens Financial Services Inc.
  F.N.B. Consumer Discount Company
  Finance and Mortgage Acceptance Corporation

COMPETITORS

Bank of America	Huntington Bancshares
Citizens Financial Group	M&T Bank
Dollar Bank	Northwest Bancshares
Fifth Third	PNC Financial
First Commonwealth Financial	S&T Bancorp
Fulton Financial	Sandy Spring Bancorp
Glen Burnie Bancorp	Sovereign Bank
	United Community Financial

Company Type: Public

Income Statement
FYE: December 31

	ASSETS ($ mil.)	NET INCOME ($ mil.)	INCOME AS % OF ASSETS	EMPLOYEES
12/16	21,844	170	0.8%	3,821
12/15	17,557	159	0.9%	3,205
12/14	16,127	144	0.9%	3,145
12/13	13,563	117	0.9%	3,103
12/12	12,023	110	0.9%	2,975
Annual Growth	16.1%	11.5%	—	6.5%

2016 Year-End Financials

Debt ratio: 1.07%
Return on equity: 7.30%
Cash ($ mil.): 371
Current ratio: —
Long-term debt ($ mil.): —
No. of shares (mil.): 211
Dividends
  Yield: 0.0%
  Payout: 61.5%
Market value ($ mil.): 3,383

	STOCK PRICE ($) FY Close	P/E High/Low		PER SHARE ($) Earnings	Dividends	Book Value
12/16	16.03	21	14	0.78	0.48	12.18
12/15	13.34	17	14	0.86	0.48	11.95
12/14	13.32	17	14	0.80	0.48	11.62
12/13	12.62	16	13	0.80	0.48	11.16
12/12	10.62	16	13	0.79	0.48	10.02
Annual Growth	10.8%		—	(0.3%)	(0.0%)	5.0%

Foot Locker, Inc.

Foot Locker leads the footrace to capture the biggest retail share of the global athletic footwear market. It is a leading retailer of athletic shoes and apparel with more than 3360 specialty stores mostly in US malls but also in 23 countries in North America and Europe as well as in Australia and New Zealand. Its 1796-store namesake Foot Locker chain is the #1 seller of name-brand (NIKE) athletic footwear in the US. Other store brands include Lady Foot Locker Kids Foot Locker Footaction Champs Sports SIX:02 Runners Point and Sidestep. Beyond its bricks-and-mortar business Foot Locker markets sports gear through direct-to-customer units (catalog retailer Eastbay and Footlocker.com).

HISTORY

With the idea of selling merchandise priced at no more than five cents Frank Woolworth opened the Great Five Cent Store in Utica New York in 1879; it failed. That year he moved to Lancaster Pennsylvania and created the first five-and-dime. Woolworth moved his headquarters to New York City (1886) and spent the rest of the century acquiring other dime-store chains. He later expanded to Canada (1897) England (1909) France (1922) and Germany (1927).

The 120-store chain with $10 million in sales incorporated as F.W. Woolworth & Company in 1905 with Woolworth as president. In 1912 the company merged with five rival chains and went public with 596 stores making $52 million in sales the first year. The next year paying $13.5 million in cash Woolworth finished construction of the Woolworth Building then the world's tallest building (792 feet). When he died in 1919 the chain had 1081 stores with sales of $119 million.

Woolworth became more competitive after WWII by advertising establishing revolving credit and self-service moving stores to suburbs and expanding merchandise selections. In 1962 it opened Woolco a US and Canadian discount chain.

From the 1960s through the 1980s the company grew by acquiring and expanding in the US and abroad. It picked up Kinney (shoes 1963) Richman Brothers (men's clothing 1969) Holtzman's Little Folk Shop (children's clothing 1983) Champs Sports (sporting goods 1987) and Mathers (shoes Australia 1988).

The company introduced Foot Locker the athletic shoe chain in 1974 later developing Lady Foot Locker (1982) and Kids Foot Locker (1987). In 1993 Woolworth launched an ambitious restructuring plan focusing on specialty stores (mostly apparel and shoes). It also closed 400 US stores and sold 122 Canadian Woolco stores to Wal-Mart that year. Former Macy's president Roger Farah became CEO in 1994. Farah eliminated 16 divisions and dozens of executives.

A year later the firm sold its Kids Mart/Little Folks children's wear chain. In 1996 Woolworth began a major remodeling program that included removing its venerable lunch counters. (Another alleged renovation at the Woolworth chain — the firing of older workers who were replaced by teenagers — led to an Equal Employment Opportunity Commission lawsuit against the company in 1999.) The changes failed and the next year the company closed its US Woolworth stores and bought athletic-products catalog company Eastbay.

In 1998 Woolworth changed its name to Venator Group and sold the Woolworth Building a national landmark (headquarters remained in the building). The company then shed itself of more than 1400 stores including Kinney shoes and Footquarters (both closed).

Internet site eVenator was launched in 1999 to sell Eastbay Champs and Foot Locker merchandise. Venator came out the champ in a proxy fight against investment group Greenway Partners in July 1999. Shortly thereafter Farah was replaced as CEO (he remained chairman) by president Dale Hilpert.

In 2000 Venator slashed 7% of its workforce in the US and Canada (a small part of the planned 30% cut) and closed 465 stores. COO Matt Serra became president and Hilpert became chairman when Farah resigned later that year.

In March 2001 Hilpert resigned replaced by Carter Bacot as chairman and Serra added CEO to his title. Venator later sold its Canadian Northern Group unit to investment firm York Management Services and closed its Northern Reflections stores in the US. Venator changed its name to Foot Locker in November. It also sold gift retailer San Francisco Music Box Co. and its hospitality division's fast-food franchises before the end of the year.

In early 2004 chairman Bacot become lead director and president and CEO Serra added chairman to his title.

In 2004 Foot Locker capitalizing on the Chapter 11 filing of Footstar Inc. purchased from the company 350 of its Footaction stores. The company also acquired 11 stores in Ireland from Champion Sports Group later in the same year.

The company's short-lived family footwear retail concept — called Footquarters — launched in early 2007 but was quickly discontinued due to poor performance. The locations were converted to Foot Lockers and Champs Sports outlet stores. Also in early 2007 Foot Locker made an unsolicited $1.2 billion bid for rival Genesco that was rejected by Genesco's board. Foot Locker closed about 275 mostly underperforming stores in 2007.

In 2008 the company reduced its store count by about 145 locations across its five chains in a bid to boost profitability by focusing on its most prof-

itable locations and improving operations. In November Foot Locker acquired the CCS brand from dELia*s for about $103 million. The CCS brand includes skateboarding and snowboarding equipment apparel and footwear targeting primarily teenage boys.

J.C. Penney executive Kenneth Hicks was recruited to succeed Serra as president and CEO in August 2009. Serra who had held the CEO title since 2001 retained the chairman's title until his retirement in January 2010. At that time Hicks became chairman.

In July 2013 Foot Locker acquired Germany's Runners Point Group a specialty athletic store and online retailer based in Recklinghausen in a deal valued at ?72 million Euros ($94 million). The move gave Foot Locker shops in Germany that operated under the Runners Point and Sidestep banners as well as stores in the Netherlands Austria and Switzerland.

EXECUTIVES

EVP and CFO, Lauren B. Peters, age 55, $657,500 total compensation
Chairman President and CEO, Richard A. (Dick) Johnson, age 59, $1,087,500 total compensation
EVP and CEO International, Lewis P. Kimble, age 58, $642,460 total compensation
EVP and CEO North America, Stephen D. (Jake) Jacobs, age 54, $844,445 total compensation
SVP and Chief Human Resources Officer, Paulette R. Alviti, age 46, $486,250 total compensation
SVP and CIO, Pawan Verma, age 40, $216,071 total compensation
Vice President HK Office, David Burke
Vice President Human Resources, Evelyn Ross
Auditors: KPMG LLP

LOCATIONS

HQ: Foot Locker, Inc.
330 West 34th Street, New York, NY 10001
Phone: 212 720-3700
Web: www.footlocker-inc.com

2017 Sales

	$ mil.	% of total
US	5,562	72
International	2,204	28
Total	**7,766**	**100**

PRODUCTS/OPERATIONS

2017 Stores

stores	No of stores
Foot Locker U.S.	948
Foot Locker Europe	622
Champs Sports	545
Kids Foot Locker	411
Footaction	261
Lady Foot Locker	124
Runners Point	122
Foot Locker Canada	119
Foot Locker Asia Pacific	95
Sidestep	86
SIX:02	30
Total	**3,363**

2017 Sales

	$ mil.	% of total
Athletic Stores	6,744	87
Direct-to-Customers	1,022	13
Total	**7,766**	**100**

COMPETITORS

Academy Sports
Caleres
DSW
Dick's Sporting Goods
Dillard's
Modell's
Pacific Sunwear
Quiksilver
Sears
Shoe Carnival

FGL Sports	Sports Authority
Finish Line	TJX Companies
Genesco	Target Corporation
Hibbett Sports	The Gap
J. C. Penney	Wal-Mart
Kmart	Zappos.com
L.L. Bean	shoebuy.com
Macy's	

HISTORICAL FINANCIALS

Company Type: Public

Income Statement

FYE: January 28

	REVENUE ($ mil.)	NET INCOME ($ mil.)	NET PROFIT MARGIN	EMPLOYEES
01/17	7,766	664	8.6%	50,168
01/16	7,412	541	7.3%	47,025
01/15*	7,151	520	7.3%	44,568
02/14	6,505	429	6.6%	43,518
02/13	6,182	397	6.4%	40,639
Annual Growth	5.9%	13.7%	—	5.4%

*Fiscal year change

2017 Year-End Financials

Debt ratio: 3.31%
Return on equity: 25.30%
Cash ($ mil.): 1,046
Current ratio: 4.30
Long-term debt ($ mil.): 127

No. of shares (mil.): 131
Dividends
  Yield: 0.0%
  Payout: 22.4%
Market value ($ mil.): 8,943

	STOCK PRICE ($) FY Close	P/E High/Low		PER SHARE ($) Earnings	Dividends	Book Value
01/17	68.01	16	10	4.91	1.10	20.61
01/16	67.56	19	13	3.84	1.00	18.64
01/15*	53.22	16	10	3.56	0.88	17.72
02/14	38.60	14	11	2.85	0.80	17.16
02/13	34.56	14	10	2.58	0.72	15.84
Annual Growth	18.4%	—	—	17.5%	11.2%	6.8%

*Fiscal year change

Ford Motor Co. (DE)

Ford Motor is striving to build smart vehicles for a smart world. One of the ?Big Three? automakers in the US (GM and Fiat Chrysler being the other two) the company manufactures cars trucks and SUVs under the Ford and Lincoln brands ? the F-150 the Escape and the Fusion among its most popular models ? and finances sales through Ford Motor Credit. Ford does business worldwide. It is making significant investments in line with a strategic shift to move the company from an auto company into its new business model as an auto and mobility company.

Operations

Ford?s Automotive segment representing more than 90% of revenue includes the sale of Ford and Lincoln brand vehicles. The Financial Services segment contributes more than 5% of revenue and includes vehicle-related financing and leasing through Ford Motor Credit Company; outside the US Europe is Ford Credit?s largest operation with about 65% of that region's receivables in the UK and Germany

Other operations include Central Treasury (which manages the company?s investment portfolio) and the growing Ford Smart Mobility (which invests in emerging technologies).

Geographic Reach

Ford's business units span the five regions of North America South America Europe the Middle East and Africa and Asia-Pacific. More than 45% of its 60-plus plants are in the US with about 25% in Europe.

The US accounts for more than 60% of Ford's revenue; other major markets include the UK and Canada (nearly 15% together) and Germany (about 5%).

Sales and Marketing

Ford's vehicles parts and accessories are sold through more than 11500 dealerships worldwide most independently-owned. In addition to retail sales these dealerships sell vehicles to commercial fleet customers rental car companies and governments.

Financial Performance

Ford has yet to reach its pre-recession highs but it has seen strong growth since 2009 with revenue up nearly 30% over that time. The company?s total revenue for 2016 amounted to $151.8 billion an increase of more than 1% from the previous year. The Automotive segment was up about 1% with Asian sales up 12% (powered by strong growth in China). Financial Services revenue jumped nearly 15% compared with 2015.

Net income dropped to $4.6 billion down more than 35% from 2015 due to a $3 billion pre-tax pension remeasurement loss. Cash flow from operations has increased steadily over the last three years to $19.8 billion in 2016.

Strategy

Three strategic priorities underpin Ford?s operations: fortifying its core strengths (primarily trucks and SUVs) shoring up its weaknesses (primarily small and luxury vehicles and emerging geographies) and investing in the technologies it thinks are going to transform the industry.

The company's F-150 truck has been the best-selling model in the US for decades. Ford keeps that momentum going with innovations; it is offering a diesel F-150 in 2018 and has plans for a hybrid version. Ford also plans to add the midsized Ranger to its North American pickup portfolio.

In other areas of its automotive business Ford has boosted its luxury Lincoln brand with a new Continental and an aluminum-body Navigator. It has also launched a smaller value model the India-made KA+. In 2017 Ford announced plans to introduce 15 electric or hybrid vehicles in China (the world?s biggest auto market) by 2025.

Ford is also making huge investments in emerging opportunities such as electrification autonomy and mobility. In addition to new electric vehicles models and hybrid versions of existing models the company is expanding its test fleet of 30 autonomous vehicles and has begun testing in Europe (it plans to have a fully autonomous vehicle in commercial production in 2021). Mobility services are being developed to increase transportation capacity in crowded cities and Ford has even established a City Solutions team to work with municipalities to propose pilot and develop mobility solutions tailored to individual communities. A 2017 partnership with Lyft ride sharing service and a $1 billion investment in artificial intelligence startup Argo AI will pave the way for the development of software for self-driving vehicles.

Mergers and Acquisitions

Ford's $65 million acquisition of app-based crowd-sourced shuttle service Chariot (completed in 2017) is allowing Ford to use its data algorithms to schedule trips in real time. Chariot uses 100 Ford Transit 15-seat vans; its 28 routes have been based on demand from riders. Ford is expanding the service from two cities (San Francisco and Austin) to eight with at least one outside the US.

HISTORY

Henry Ford started the Ford Motor Company in 1903 in Dearborn Michigan. In 1908 Ford introduced the Model T produced on a moving assembly line that revolutionized both carmaking and manufacturing. By 1920 some 60% of all vehicles on the road were Fords.

After Ford omitted its usual dividend in 1916 stockholders sued. Ford responded by buying back all of its outstanding shares in 1919 and didn't allow outside ownership again until 1956.

Ford bought Lincoln Motor Company in 1922 and discontinued the Model T in 1927. Its replacement the Model A came in 1932. With Henry Ford's health failing his son Edsel became president that year. Despite the debut of the Mercury (1938) market share slipped behind General Motors and Chrysler. After Edsel's death in 1943 his son Henry II took over and decentralized Ford following the GM model. Henry Ford died in 1947 at the age of 83. In 1950 the carmaker recaptured second place. Ford rolled out the infamous Edsel line in 1958 and launched the Mustang in 1964.

Ford acquired Hertz in 1994 and two years later bought #3 rental agency Budget Rent a Car (sold 1997). Also in 1996 it sold a 19% stake in finance unit Associates First Capital in an IPO and increased its stake in Mazda to one-third. The next year Ford sold its heavy-duty truck unit to Daimler's Freightliner subsidiary (since renamed Daimler Trucks North America) for about $200 million and spun off 19% of Hertz in an IPO. Also in 1997 it launched automotive systems supplier Visteon (formerly Ford Automotive Products Operations) at the Frankfurt Motor Show.

Decades later in order to focus on its struggling automotive operations Ford sold its Hertz car rental business in 2005 to a private equity group made up of Clayton Dubilier & Rice The Carlyle Group and Merrill Lynch Global Private Equity for $5.6 billion and the assumption of nearly $10 billion of Hertz debt.

In mid-2009 the US Department of Energy approved $5.9 billion in low-interest loans to Ford for converting its US plants to making cleaner more efficient engines transmissions and vehicles. As a result Ford reported it would spend $550 million to convert its Michigan Assembly Plant where Ford Expedition and Lincoln Navigator SUVs were produced into a modern facility for making its next-generation Focus small car. The new Focus rolled off the assembly line in 2010 with an all-electric version of the Focus to follow in 2011. Ford consolidated operations from its Wayne Assembly Plant as part of the project and worked with the UAW on more flexible work rules for the Michigan Assembly Plant. In addition Ford converted its Cuautitlan Assembly Plant in Mexico from SUV production to assembly of small cars commencing in 2011. The Mexican plant began building the new Fiesta subcompact in 2010.

With the automotive industry reeling from the Great Recession companies made decisions to streamline their operations for survival. In mid-2010 Ford sold all of Volvo Car Corporation to Geely Automotive a subsidiary of China-based Zhejiang Geely Holding Group. Volvo's headquarters and manufacturing operations remain in Sweden and Belgium with Stefan Jacoby (former CEO of Volkswagen Group of America) serving as president and CEO of Volvo Cars. At the onset of 2011 Ford's Mercury model production was discontinued.

EXECUTIVES

Group Vice President Human Resources and Corporate Services, Felicia J Fields
EVP and CFO, Robert L. (Bob) Shanks, age 64, $858,000 total compensation
President Ford Motor Company Fund & Community Services, James G. (Jim) Vella

Chairman and CEO Ford China, Jason Luo, age 51
EVP and President Global Markets, James D. (Jim) Farley, age 54, $918,750 total compensation
EVP and President Global Operations, Joseph R. (Joe) Hinrichs, age 51, $1,053,500 total compensation
VP Strategic Planning and CFO Ford of Europe, Dave L. (Dave) Schoch, age 65
VP and COO Ford Europe, Steven Armstrong
Chief Marketing Officer and President Lincoln, A. Kumar Galhotra
VP and President Global Ford Customer Service Division, Frederiek Toney, age 61
Group VP and President Asia Pacific, Peter Fleet
VP; President Changan Ford Automotive, Nigel Harris, age 56
EVP Product Development and CTO, Raj Nair, age 52
EVP and President Mobility, Marcy Klevorn, age 57
President Ford Middle East and Africa, Jacques Brent
President Ford South America, Lyle Watters
President and CEO Ford Motor Company of Canada Limited, Mark Buzzell
Group VP; Chairman and CEO Ford Motor Credit Company, Joy Falotico
CEO, Jim Hackett, age 62
President and CEO Ford Motor Company Southern Africa (FMCSA), Jeffery Nemeth
President ASEAN, Yukontorn (Vickie) Wisadkosin
VP Quality and New Model Launch, Linda Cash
Executive Director HR Global Markets, Kiersten Robinson
RIC PTE NAVP Portfolio Manager Vehicle Solutions, Mark Anders
Vice President Sales and Marketing, Gabriella Bruno
Vice President, Frank P Froio
Vice President Human Resources, Rex Johnson
Vice President, Linda Garrison
Vice President Quality Foe, Gunnar Herrmann
Senior Vice President, Greg Bell
Vice President of Retail Operations, Randy Houston
Global Vice President Cycle Plan Manager At Ford Motor Company, David Schaefer
Vice President Of Global Communications, Brenda Hines
Vice President, Craig Kuberski
National Account Manager, Rory Cashman
Vice President, Scott Collins
Vice President Global Quality Assurance, Ronald D Domas
Vice President of Purchasing, Sam Casabene
Vice President of Communications, Chris Pitchford
Vice President General Counsel and Secretary, Shawn Murphy
National Account Manager, Vic Kachel
Vice President Sales And Marketing, Robert Gerrard
Vice President Supply Chain, Estella Slone
Group Philippines Assistant Vice President, Anika Salceda-Wycoco
Senior Vice President Operations and Implementation, Jason Rau
Senior Vice President, David Reeves
GVP Marketing and Sales, Jim Farley
National Accounts Manager, Katherine Garland
Senior Vice President, Keith Sprain
Vice President Communications, David Scott
Vice President Finance, Bob Stein
Group Vice President Sustainability Environment and Safety Engineering, Kimberly Pittel
National Account Manager, Mark Lowrey
Manager Government Relations, Sam Scales
National Account Manager, Joel Nielsen
UAW Vice President and Bargaining Representative, Jeff Hodges
Executive Vice President Marketing and Sales
Executive Vice President Asia Pacific, David McClelland

GOVERNMENT RELATIONS, Marilee Chlebicki
NATIONAL ACCOUNT MANAGER, Wayne Boor
FCSD Vice President Buyer, Martha Tryba
Vice President Manufacturing Troy Design TDM, Steve Guido
Executive Chairman, William C. (Bill) Ford, age 59
SECRETARY TREASURER, Ed Hogan
Financial Strategy Treasurers Office, Mark Turner
Board Member, Wayne Conner
Board Member, Eldric Arnold
Auditors: PricewaterhouseCoopers LLP

LOCATIONS

HQ: Ford Motor Co. (DE)
One American Road, Dearborn, MI 48126
Phone: 313 322-3000
Web: www.corporate.ford.com

2016 Sales

	$ mil.	% of total
US	93,433	61
United Kingdom	10,041	7
Canada	10,028	7
Germany	7,322	5
All Others	30,976	20
Total	**151,800**	**100**

PRODUCTS/OPERATIONS

Selected Products

Cars
Fiesta
Focus
Fusion
Mustang
Taurus
Crossovers
Edge
Flex
Commercial trucks
Chassis Cab
E-Series Cutaway
E-Series Van
E-Series Wagon
F-650
F-750
Stripped Chassis
Super Duty Pickup
Transit Connect
Electric vehicles (EVs)
Transit Connect EV
Hybrids
Escape Hybrid
Fusion Hybrid
Sport utility vehicles (SUVs)
Escape
Expedition
Explorer
Trucks
E-Series Wagon
F-150
Ranger
Super Duty
Transit Connect

2016 Sales

	$ mil.	% of total
Automotive	141,546	93
Financial services	10,253	7
Adjustments	1	-
Total	**151,800**	**100**

COMPETITORS

BMW	Mitsubishi Motors
Daimler	Nissan
Fiat Chrysler	Peugeot
General Motors	Renault
Honda	Suzuki Motor
Hyundai Motor	Tata Motors
Isuzu	Toyota
Kia Motors	Volkswagen
Mazda	Volvo

HISTORICAL FINANCIALS

Company Type: Public

Income Statement

FYE: December 31

	REVENUE ($ mil.)	NET INCOME ($ mil.)	NET PROFIT MARGIN	EMPLOYEES
12/17	156,776	7,602	4.8%	202,000
12/16	151,800	4,596	3.0%	201,000
12/15	149,558	7,373	4.9%	199,000
12/14	144,077	3,187	2.2%	187,000
12/13	146,917	7,155	4.9%	181,000
Annual Growth	1.6%	1.5%	—	2.8%

2017 Year-End Financials

Debt ratio: 59.85%—
Return on equity: 23.73%
Cash ($ mil.): 18,492
Current ratio: 1.23
Long-term debt ($ mil.): 102,666

Dividends
Yield: 0.0%
Payout: 34.2%
Market value ($ mil.): —

	STOCK PRICE ($) FY Close	P/E High/Low		PER SHARE ($) Earnings	Dividends	Book Value
12/17	12.49	7	6	1.90	0.65	8.78
12/16	12.13	12	10	1.15	0.85	7.34
12/15	14.09	9	7	1.84	0.60	7.22
12/14	15.50	22	17	0.80	0.50	6.27
12/13	15.43	10	7	1.76	0.40	6.69
Annual Growth	(5.1%)	—	—	1.9%	12.9%	7.0%

Fortive Corp

LOCATIONS

HQ: Fortive Corp
6920 Seaway Blvd., Everett, WA 98203
Phone: 425 446-5000
Web: www.fortive.com

HISTORICAL FINANCIALS

Company Type: Public

Income Statement

FYE: December 31

	REVENUE ($ mil.)	NET INCOME ($ mil.)	NET PROFIT MARGIN	EMPLOYEES
12/16	6,224	872	14.0%	24,000
12/15	6,178	863	14.0%	22,000
12/14	6,337	883	13.9%	—
12/13	5,961	830	13.9%	—
Annual Growth	1.4%	1.6%	—	—

2016 Year-End Financials

Debt ratio: 41.00%
Return on equity: 22.11%
Cash ($ mil.): 803
Current ratio: 1.70
Long-term debt ($ mil.): 3,358

No. of shares (mil.): 345
Dividends
Yield: 0.0%
Payout: 5.5%
Market value ($ mil.): 18,551

	STOCK PRICE ($) FY Close	P/E High/Low		PER SHARE ($) Earnings	Dividends	Book Value
12/16	53.63	22	19	2.51	0.14	7.77
12/15	0.00	—	—	(0.00)	0.00	(0.00)
Annual Growth	—	—	—	—	—	—

Fortune Brands Home & Security, Inc.

Fortune Brands Home & Security (FBHS) holds the keys to the kitchen and the garden shed. With about 45 plants worldwide the consumer products manufacturer makes and sells kitchen and bathroom cabinets faucets entry doors trim and padlocks. Its well-known brands include Moen faucets MasterBrand Cabinets SentrySafe and Therma-Tru entry doors along with Master Lock and American Lock padlocks and other security products. Most of the company's products are the top sellers in their respective markets. FBHS was formed in 2011 when its former parent company Fortune Brands spun off its alcohol and home and security brands as separate businesses.

Operations

Fortune Brands Home & Security (FBHS) operates four business segments: Cabinets Plumbing Security and Doors.

The Cabinets segment generates nearly 50% of sales and ranks as the #1 maker of such cabinetry in North America. Its brands include Aristokraft Mid-Continent Diamond Kitchen Classics among others. The Plumbing business brings in around 30% of sales and manufactures Moen Cleveland Faucet Group and Waste King brand faucets the leading brands in North America and China. Doors accounts for 10% of sales and makes doors and vinyl windows; and Security which also brings in around 10% of sales is the #1 maker of padlocks in North America and Europe.

Geographic Reach

Illinois-based Fortune Brands Home & Security (FBHS) rang up almost 85% of its sales in the US in 2015. Canada is the company's largest international market representing about 10% of sales. China and other countries account for the rest. Other major markets for FBHS include Europe Southeast Asia South America and Mexico. The company operates some 30 US manufacturing facilities in 16 states and has around 15 international plant locations in Mexico Asia Europe and Canada.

Sales and Marketing

Fortune Brands Home & Security (FBHS) two largest customers are Home Depot and Lowe's Companies together accounting for about 30% of annual sales. The company sells directly through its own sales force and indirectly through independent manufacturers' representatives. Other sales channels include kitchen and bath dealers wholesalers catering to builders or professional remodelers industrial distributors and other retail outlets including mass merchants. Sales to all US home centers in the aggregate account for approximately 25% of net sales.

Financial Performance

The improving US home products market market share gains growth overseas and acquisitions have collectively driven Fortune Brands Home & Security (FBHS)'s sales up in recent years.

In fiscal 2016 sales grew a further 9% to $5.0 billion due to continued expansion in the housing market acquisitions in the Cabinets and Plumbing segments. and higher prices.

Net income grew 31% to $413.2 million as increases in revenue outpaced the relative increase in selling costs. The company achieved productivity gains and benefited from the positive contributions from the acquired businesses.

Cash from operations grew 52% to $650.5 million due to a reduction in working capital in 2016 and higher net income.

Strategy

Fortune Brands Home Security (FBHS) is focused on expanding internationally. It is developing its relationships with its dealers and distributors and their Moen branded stores throughout China India and South America. Master Lock expanded its presence further in Europe and Asia (primarily Japan) while Therma-Tru made inroads in Canada as consumers transitioned from traditional entry door materials to more advanced and energy-efficient fiberglass doors.

FBHS is also focused on expanding its product portfolio. Its Norcraft Companies expands regional market presence and enhances frameless cabinetry. In 2016 MasterBrand Cabinets launched new cabinet door designs color palettes and features in a range of styles; exclusive laminate door & finish options. Its Moen brand introduces hand showers featuring the Magnetix magnetic docking system a new line of garbage disposals Spot Resist finish touchless Motionsense electronic faucets and pull-out and pull-down faucets with Reflex self-retraction. Its Therma-Tru released a portfolio of on-trend door and glass collections.

Signaling its intent to boost its plumbing business the company in late 2016 created Global Plumbing Group. Its goal is to increase plumbing sales to $2.5 billion by 2020 (from $1.5 billion in 2016). The division will become a multi-brand -channel and -geography business and will grow organically and through acquisitions; its first such acquisitions were Riobel a Canadian premium showroom brand; ROHL a Californian luxury brand; and TCL Manufacturing which gave it control of Perrin & Rowe a UK manufacturer of luxury kitchen and bathroom plumbing products.

Mergers and Acquisitions

In 2016 Fortune Brands Home Security made a number of acquisitions to add meat to its new Global Plumbing Group division. It bought Riobel a Canadian premium showroom brand with annual sales of $40 million which it followed up with the acquisitions of ROHL and TCL Manufacturing. ROHL is a manufacturer of high-end faucets and TCL owns Perrin & Rowe a UK luxury kitchen plumbing company.

Company Background

Formed in 1988 as a Fortune Brands subsidiary the company was spun off in 2011.

In 2013 FBHS' Kitchen & Bath Cabinetry business acquired WoodCrafters a manufacturer of bathroom vanities and tops for about $302 million. The purchase expanded the company's bathroom cabinetry products offering.

EXECUTIVES

EVP, E. Lee Wyatt, age 64, $770,333 total compensation
President The Master Lock Co., Michael P. (Mike) Bauer, age 52
CEO, Christopher J. (Chris) Klein, age 53, $1,093,333 total compensation
President MasterBrand Cabinets, David M. Randich, age 55, $585,269 total compensation
President Therma-Tru, Brett Finley, age 46
SVP Global Growth and Development, Tracey Belcourt
President Global Plumbing Group, Nicholas I. Fink, age 42, $505,833 total compensation
President U.S. Businesses Moen, Troy Shay
SVP and CFO, Patrick D. Hallinan
Vice President Tax, Kathleen Weston
Senior Vice President Human Resources, Sheri R Grissom
Vice President, Gary Tobison
Vice President And Corporate Controller, Edward Wiertel
Chairman, David M. Thomas
Assistant Treasurer, Cory Kruse
Assistant Secretary, Angela Pla
Auditors: PricewaterhouseCoopers LLP

LOCATIONS

HQ: Fortune Brands Home & Security, Inc.
520 Lake Cook Road, Deerfield, IL 60015-5611
Phone: 847 484-4400
Web: www.fbhs.com

2016 Sales

	$ mil.	% of total
US	4,258	86
Canada	406	8
China & other international	320	6
Total	**4,984**	**100**

PRODUCTS/OPERATIONS

2016 Sales

	$ mil.	% of total
Cabinets	2,397	48
Plumbing	1,534	31
Security	579	12
Doors	473	9
Total	**4,984**	**100**

Selected Brands

Aristokraft
Diamond
Homecrest
Kitchen Classics
Kitchen Craft
Master Lock
MasterBrand Cabinets
Mid-Continent
Moen
Omega
Schrock
Sentry
Safe
Star
Mark
Therma-Tru Doors
Thomasville
Ultracraft

Selected Products

Cabinets
Stock cabinetry
Vanities
Plumbing Accessor

COMPETITORS

American Woodmark	Kwikset Corporation
Andersen Corporation	Masco
Armstrong World	Pella
Industries	Pfister
B.J. Tidwell	Republic National
Industries	Cabinet
Conestoga	Stanley Black and
Delta Faucet	Decker
Elkay Manufacturing	Sterilite
IKEA	US Home Systems
JELD-WEN	Wood-Mode
Kohler	

HISTORICAL FINANCIALS

Company Type: Public

Income Statement

FYE: December 31

	REVENUE ($ mil.)	NET INCOME ($ mil.)	NET PROFIT MARGIN	EMPLOYEES
12/16	4,984	413	8.3%	22,700
12/15	4,579	315	6.9%	21,400
12/14	4,013	158	3.9%	18,000
12/13	4,157	229	5.5%	19,500
12/12	3,591	118	3.3%	16,100
Annual Growth	**8.5%**	**36.6%**	**—**	**9.0%**

2016 Year-End Financials

Debt ratio: 27.90%
Return on equity: 17.13%
Cash ($ mil.): 251
Current ratio: 1.71
Long-term debt ($ mil.): 1,431

No. of shares (mil.): 153
Dividends
  Yield: 0.0%
  Payout: 24.4%
Market value ($ mil.): 8,201

	STOCK PRICE ($) FY Close	P/E High/Low	Earnings	PER SHARE ($) Dividends	Book Value
12/16	53.46	24 17	2.62	0.64	15.39
12/15	55.50	29 22	1.93	0.56	15.33
12/14	45.27	49 38	0.95	0.48	14.29
12/13	45.70	33 21	1.34	0.30	15.90
12/12	29.22	41 23	0.71	0.00	14.53
Annual Growth	16.3%	— —	38.6%	—	1.5%

Franklin Financial Network Inc

Auditors: Crowe Horwath LLP

LOCATIONS

HQ: Franklin Financial Network Inc
  722 Columbia Avenue, Franklin, TN 37064
Phone: 615 236-2265
Web: www.franklinsynergybank.com

HISTORICAL FINANCIALS

Company Type: Public

Income Statement

FYE: December 31

	ASSETS ($ mil.)	NET INCOME ($ mil.)	INCOME AS % OF ASSETS	EMPLOYEES
12/16	2,943	28	1.0%	268
12/15	2,167	16	0.7%	226
12/14	1,355	8	0.6%	220
12/13	796	4	0.6%	—
Annual Growth	54.6%	83.2%	—	—

2016 Year-End Financials

Debt ratio: 1.98%
Return on equity: 12.19%
Cash ($ mil.): 1,074
Current ratio: —
Long-term debt ($ mil.): —

No. of shares (mil.): 13
Dividends
  Yield: —
  Payout: —
Market value ($ mil.): 546

	STOCK PRICE ($) FY Close	P/E High/Low	Earnings	PER SHARE ($) Dividends	Book Value
12/16	41.85	17 10	2.42	0.00	20.73
12/15	31.38	20 11	1.54	0.00	17.86
12/14	17.30	17 13	1.27	0.00	15.70
12/13	12.90	11 11	1.10	0.00	13.40
/0.00			—(0.00)	0.00	(0.00)
Annual Growth	—	— —	—	—	—

Franklin Resources, Inc.

Franklin Resources believes your Benjamins can be put to better use than sitting in a bank account. Operating as Franklin Templeton Investments the firm manages more than 100 mutual funds that invest in international and domestic stocks taxable and tax-exempt money market instruments and corporate municipal and US government bonds. Franklin Resources also offers separately managed accounts closed-end funds insurance product funds and retirement and college savings plans. Its investment products are sold through more than 1200 banks securities firms and financial advisors under the Franklin Templeton Mutual Series Bissett Darby and Fiduciary Trust banners.

Operations

Most of Franklin Resources' revenue come from investment management fees which account for more than 65% of company revenue and are directly tied to its assets under management. Sales and distribution fees generate over 25% of revenue and are made up of sales charges and commissions derived from sales and distribution of the company's sponsored investment products (SIPs).

In addition to its core business Franklin Resources also provides shareholder services and manages investments for high-net-worth clients and institutional investors. These services make up less than 5% of overall revenue.

Retail banking private banking auto finance and trust services are offered through Franklin Templeton Bank & Trust Franklin Capital Fiduciary Trust Company International and other subsidiaries. Serving more than 24 million shareholder accounts Franklin Resources and its subsidiaries boast some $750 billion in assets under management.

Geographic Reach

Based in California Franklin Resources boasts an extensive global presence with offices in some 35 countries and clients reaching across 180-plus countries. The firm has operations in North America South America Europe Middle East and Africa (EMEA) and Asia Pacific.

Of its assets under management 65% are in the US and 15% are in EMEA. The majority of its revenue comes from the US ($4 billion annually) while a significant portion comes from Luxembourg ($2 billion) which together accounts for roughly 90% of total company revenue.

Sales and Marketing

Franklin Resources relies on a large network of independent financial intermediaries to be the front end of the sales process. In the US approximately 1200 local regional and national banks securities firms and financial advisor firms offer shares in Franklin?s US funds. Outside the US Franklin Resources leverages about 2900 banks securities firms and financial advisor firms to sell its non-US funds to the investing public.

The company sells its investment products and services under a variety of brand names such as Franklin Templeton Franklin Mutual Series Franklin Bissett Fiduciary Trust Darby Balanced Equity Management K2 and LibertyShares.

The company generates brand awareness through advertisements in major financial publications television internet through sporting event sponsorship and social media marketing.

Financial Performance

Franklin Resources? financial returns have slumped in recent years in contrast to the ascending value of US and global stock markets. After peaking in FY2014 at $8.5 billion revenue has retreated each year dipping below $6.4 billion in FY2017 (ended September 30). Net income followed a similar pattern falling from a FY2014 high of $2.4 billion to FY2017 result around $1.7 billion. The decline stems from underperformance (versus peers) across many of the company?s mutual funds leading large clients to redeem their shares in Franklin funds which in turns lowers Franklin?s assets under management (AUM) which puts downward pressure on its investment management fees.

For FY2017 revenue was slightly lower than $6.4 billion a 3% decline compared to the prior year. Across its three primary revenue categories shareholder servicing fees slid 7% sales and distribution fees fell 6% and investment management fees decreased 3%. Average assets under management fell 2% to $737 million a marginal difference considering the 14% decline experienced in the prior year.

Net income in FY2017 decreased 2% to $1.4 billion as the firm kept expenses in line with the lower revenue.

Cash at the end of FY2017 was $8.8 billion up $266 million from FY2016. Operating activities provided $1.1 billion while investing activities contributed $52 million. Financing activities used about $1.0 billion mainly through the issuance of stock dividends to Franklin shareholders and the repurchase of Franklin stock.

Strategy

Franklin Resources strategy includes stemming the tide of net fund redemptions by its clientele growing its distribution network outside the US taking advantage of a global return to value investing (as opposed to growth investing which has led the charge in recent years) and adjusting its fee structure in response to the US Department of Labor Fiduciary Rule.

A key tenet of the firm?s financial success it to sell more shares in its funds than it redeems. Based on its funds? performance it experienced net fund outflows in past years. To address the issue the company appointed a single head of Equities to shore up the performance of its equities-centered funds and match or exceed the average performance of fund peer groups. As well by expanding its distribution network (particularly outside the US) it anticipates an increased amount of fund sales. With fewer outflows and increased inflows (sales) Franklin expects its average assets under management (AUM) to rise stemming an increase in its investment management fees.

Another headwind buffeting Franklin recently is a widespread investment strategy focusing on growth stocks. Franklin?s equity funds typically are value oriented which have lagged the market in recent years. With the rising interest rate environment in the US and similar raises in other countries Franklin believes the headwind will turn into a tailwind as value investing returns to favor.

In the US the Department of Labor Fiduciary Rule is impacting the entire investment management industry. Franklin?s response is to shift from commission-based sales to fee-based management which contains the liability risk associated with the new Fiduciary Rule rollout.

In early 2018 the company agreed to purchase Edinburgh Partners a $10 billion fund management company.

Company Background

Rupert Johnson Sr. founded Franklin Distributors (capitalizing on Benjamin Franklin's reputation for thrift) in New York in 1947; it launched its first fund Franklin Custodian in 1948. Custodian grew into five funds including conservatively managed equity and bond funds. In 1968 Johnson's son Charles (who had joined the firm in 1957) became president and CEO. The company went public in 1971 as Franklin Resources.

EXECUTIVES

Chairman and CEO, Gregory E. Johnson, age 57, $783,633 total compensation
President, Jennifer M. Johnson, age 54, $527,356 total compensation
EVP and CFO, Kenneth A. Lewis, age 57, $527,356 total compensation

EVP Alternative Strategies, William Y. Yun, age 58, $525,000 total compensation
EVP Investment Management, John M. Lusk, $527,356 total compensation
EVP and General Counsel, Craig S. Tyle, age 58
SVP and CIO, Priscilla Moyer
Vice Chairman, Rupert H. Johnson, age 78
Auditors: PricewaterhouseCoopers LLP

LOCATIONS

HQ: Franklin Resources, Inc.
One Franklin Parkway, San Mateo, CA 94403
Phone: 650 312-2000   **Fax:** 650 312-3655
Web: www.franklinresources.com

FY2017 Sales by Geography

	$ mil.	% of total
United States	3,898	61
Luxembourg	1,652	26
Canada	281	5
Asia-Pacific	260	4
The Bahamas	205	3
Europe the Middle East and Africa excluding Luxembourg	83	1
Latin America	10	-
Total	**6,392**	**100**

PRODUCTS/OPERATIONS

FY2017 Sales by Type

	$ mil.	% of total
Investment management fees	4,359	68
Sales & distribution fees	1,705	27
Shareholder servicing fees	225	4
Other	101	1
Total	**6,392**	**100**

Selected Subsidiaries

Balanced Equity Management Pty. Limited
C&EE General Partner Ltd.
Darby Administração de Investimentos Ltda.
Darby Asia Founder Partner L.P.
Darby Asia Investors (HK) Ltd.
Darby Asia Investors (India) Private Limited
Darby Asia Investors Ltd.
Darby Asia Mezzanine Fund II Management Co. Ltd.
Darby Asia Opportunities Fund III GP L.P.

COMPETITORS

AllianceBernstein	Legg Mason
American Century	Morgan Stanley
BlackRock	Old Mutual (US)
Capital Group	PIMCO
Dodge & Cox	Principal Financial
FMR	Putnam
Invesco	T. Rowe Price
John Hancock Financial Services	The Vanguard Group

HISTORICAL FINANCIALS

Company Type: Public

Income Statement

FYE: September 30

	REVENUE ($ mil.)	NET INCOME ($ mil.)	NET PROFIT MARGIN	EMPLOYEES
09/17	6,392	1,696	26.5%	9,400
09/16	6,618	1,726	26.1%	9,100
09/15	7,948	2,035	25.6%	9,500
09/14	8,491	2,384	28.1%	9,300
09/13	7,985	2,150	26.9%	9,000
Annual Growth	**(5.4%)**	**(5.8%)**	**—**	**1.1%**

2017 Year-End Financials

Debt ratio: 6.26%
Return on equity: 13.82%
Cash ($ mil.): 8,749
Current ratio: 8.75
Long-term debt ($ mil.): 1,097

No. of shares (mil.): 554
Dividends
 Yield: 0.0%
 Payout: 26.5%
Market value ($ mil.): 24,697

	STOCK PRICE ($) FY Close	P/E High/Low		PER SHARE ($) Earnings	Dividends	Book Value
09/17	44.51	16	11	3.01	0.80	22.74
09/16	35.57	14	10	2.94	0.72	20.93
09/15	37.26	18	11	3.29	1.10	19.62
09/14	54.61	15	13	3.79	0.48	18.60
09/13	50.55	50	13	3.37	1.39	15.97
Annual Growth	**(3.1%)**	**—**	**—**	**(2.8%)**	**(12.9%)**	**9.2%**

Freddie Mac

These siblings know there's no place like home. Government-sponsored enterprises (GSEs) Freddie Mac (officially Federal Home Loan Mortgage Corporation) and Fannie Mae were established to buy residential mortgages and boost the housing market. They do so by purchasing mortgages from lenders and packaging them for resale thereby mitigating risk and allowing lenders to provide mortgages to those who may not otherwise qualify. The agency also provides assistance for affordable rental housing. Together Fannie and Freddie guarantee some 70% of all new home loans in the US. Due to losses related to the subprime mortgage crisis the government seized Fannie and Freddie in 2008. Government plans to divest the firms into private ownership have proven difficult; they remain GSEs.

HISTORY

Ah the '60s — free love great tunes and a war nobody wanted to pay for with taxes. By the '70s inflation was rising and real income was starting to fall. To divert a construction industry recession Congress created a new entity to buy home mortgages and boost the flow of money into the housing market.

Fannie Mae had been buying mortgages since 1938 but focused on Federal Housing Administration (FHA) and Veterans Administration loans. In 1970 Congress created Freddie Mac and enlarged Fannie Mae's field of action to include conventional mortgages. Still rising interest rates in the 1970s were brutal to the US real estate market.

In the early 1980s dealers devised a way to securitize the company's loans — seen as somewhat frumpy investments — by packaging them into more alluring bond-like investments made even sexier by the implicit government guarantee. When three major government securities dealers collapsed in 1985 ownership of some Freddie Mac securities was in doubt and the Federal Reserve Bank of New York quickly automated registration of government securities.

In 1984 Freddie Mac issued shares to members of the Federal Home Loan Bank (the overseer of US savings and loans). By 1989 the shares had been converted to common stock and were traded on the NYSE. Freddie Mac's board expanded from three political appointees to 18 members.

Nationwide real estate defaults (rampant in the wake of the late 1980s crash) kindled concern about Freddie Mac's reserve levels and whether it might need to tap its US Treasury line of credit. In response Congress in 1992 created the Office of Federal Housing Enterprise Oversight to regulate Freddie Mac and Fannie Mae. Initial examinations sounded no alarms. A 1996 Congressional Budget Office report questioned whether the government

should continue its implicit guarantees of the pair's debt securities.

In 1997 Freddie Mac officially adopted its long-time nickname. The next year it launched a system to cut loan approval time from weeks to minutes (it agreed to develop a similar version for the FHA). The streamlining was crucial to pacts in which mortgage lenders (including one of the US's largest Wells Fargo) promised to sell Freddie Mac their loan originations. In 1999 Freddie Mac hired former House Speaker Newt Gingrich as a consultant.

Freddie Mac made a major Internet push in 2000 with its first online taxable bond offering. A wired venture involving Freddie Mac Microsoft and such big lenders as Chase Manhattan (now part of JPMorgan Chase & Co.) Bank of America and Wells Fargo drew fire from small banks that said it would push them out of the online lending business.

In 2001 Freddie Mac bought Tuttle Decision Systems a loan-pricing software system provider. Critics responded that Freddie Mac overstepped its government charter with such a move.

In a move initiated by its auditor Freddie Mac re-audited its earnings from 2000 to 2003 uncovering accounting irregularities and employee misconduct. Further investigations executive oustings restructuring and numerous lawsuits followed. In late 2003 Freddie Mac announced the findings of its re-audit. The company admitted to understating earnings by $4.4 billion between 2000 and 2002 and overstating profits by $989 million in 2001 all in an attempt to smooth out results and show steady profit growth.

In 2006 the company paid a record $3.8 million fine to settle allegations by the Federal Election Commission that the company made illegal campaign contributions to members of the US House Financial Services Committee. It also agreed to pay $4.65 million to settle a lawsuit related to its employee 401(k) plan. Freddie Mac did receive good news that year though when the Department of Justice dropped criminal charges against the company for misstating earnings from 2000 to 2002.

As the subprime mortgage crisis began heating up in 2007 and 2008 Freddie Mac announced plans to stop purchasing risky subprime mortgages. However the company tried to help restore stability to the teetering mortgage market by investing in billions of dollars in new jumbo mortgages raising its loan limits to more than $700000.

Although the government stepped in with loans to help Freddie the company still struggled with subprime mortgage losses. The government seized Fannie Mae and Freddie Mac in 2008 and placed them in conservatorship. Freddie Mac's leadership was also shaken up. David Moffat resigned as CEO in 2009 and chairman John Koskinen stepped in to serve as his interim replacement. Later that year Charles Haldeman Jr. the former head of Putnam Investments was selected to lead the company.

The Federal Housing Finance Administration (FHFA) was created in 2008 to oversee Fannie and Freddie as well as the 12 Federal Home Loan Banks. The FHFA was granted more authority than its predecessor agencies the Federal Housing Finance Board and the Office of Federal Housing Enterprise Oversight.

EXECUTIVES

EVP General Counsel and Corporate Secretary, William H. (Bill) McDavid, age 69, $500,000 total compensation
CEO, Donald H. (Don) Layton, age 66, $600,000 total compensation
Vice President, James Bowden

EVP and Chief Administrative Officer, Jerry Weiss, age 56, $450,000 total compensation

EVP Multifamily Business, David M. Brickman

Chairman, Christopher S. Lynch, age 59

EVP and CIO, Stacey Goodman, age 54

EVP Single-Family Business, David B. (Dave) Lowman, age 56, $500,000 total compensation

EVP and CFO, James G. Mackey, age 50, $500,000 total compensation

EVP Investments and Capital Markets, Michael Hutchins

EVP and Chief Enterprise Risk Officer, Anil Hinduja, $500,000 total compensation

Senior Vice President and Chief Compliance Officer, Carol Wambeke

Senior Vice President Corporate Contro, Robert Mailloux

Vice President Call Centers, Jeanmarie Puglisi

Vice President, Glenn Errigo

Vice President Underwriting, Stephen Lansbury

Vice President Operations, Ruben Sanchez

National Account Manager, Edward Abbott

Vice President securities Strategy and Policy, Mark Pettit

Vice President quality Control, James J Johnson

Vice President Single Family Underwriting and Quality Control, Pamela Padgett

Vice President Sourcing, Sally W Baker

VP Compliance Regulatory Affairs, Joseph Evers

Vice President of Tax Accounting and Compliance, Michael Culhane

VICE PRESIDENT, Buckner Bill

ASSISTANT VICE PRESIDENT, Appou Thirumurugan

ASSISTANT VICE PRESIDENT, Rush Brandon

SENIOR VICE PRESIDENT AND CHIEF COMPLIANCE OFFICER, Tsang Cynthia

Vice President, Ty Miller

National Account Manager, Steve Pattee

Auditors: PricewaterhouseCoopers LLP

LOCATIONS

HQ: Freddie Mac
8200 Jones Branch Drive, McLean, VA 22102-3110
Phone: 703 903-2000
Web: www.freddiemac.com

PRODUCTS/OPERATIONS

2016 Revenue

	$ mil.	% of total
Interest Income	61,040	93
Investments in Securities	3,855	6
Other	270	—
Non-interest Income	500	1
Total	**65,665**	**100**

COMPETITORS

FHLB Atlanta

HISTORICAL FINANCIALS

Company Type: Public

Income Statement

FYE: December 31

	ASSETS ($ mil.)	NET INCOME ($ mil.)	INCOME AS % OF ASSETS	EMPLOYEES
12/16	2,023,376	7,815	0.4%	6,004
12/15	1,986,050	6,376	0.3%	5,462
12/14	1,945,539	7,690	0.4%	5,007
12/13	1,966,061	48,668	2.5%	5,112
12/12	1,989,856	10,982	0.6%	5,017
Annual Growth	**0.4%**	**(8.2%)**	**—**	**4.6%**

2016 Year-End Financials

Debt ratio: 98.94%	No. of shares (mil.): 650
Return on equity: 194.48%	Dividends
Cash ($ mil.): 22,220	Yield: —
Current ratio: —	Payout: —
Long-term debt ($ mil.): —	Market value ($ mil.): 2,431

	STOCK PRICE ($) FY Close	P/E High/Low		PER SHARE ($) Earnings	Dividends	Book Value
12/16	3.74	147	36	0.03	0.00	7.81
12/15	1.62	—	—	(0.01)	0.00	4.52
12/14	2.06	—	—	(0.72)	0.00	4.08
12/13	2.90	—	—	(1.09)	0.00	19.74
12/12	0.26	—	—	(0.64)	0.00	13.58
Annual Growth	**94.2%**	—	—	—	—	**(12.9%)**

Freeport-McMoRan Inc

Freeport McMoRan (FCX) is one of world?s major mining company with holdings in copper molybdenum and gold. It is a leading copper producer with proven or probable reserves of more than 85 billion pounds; the company also has more than 25 million ounces of gold reserves and about 3 billion pounds of molybdenum reserves. FCX?s mines are in the Americas and Indonesia. The company also has oil and gas assets (some 18 million barrels of oil equivalents) in the US and Gulf of Mexico. The US accounts for about 40% of company revenue.

HISTORY

The Freeport Sulfur Company was formed in Texas in 1912 by Francis Pemberton banker Eric Swenson and several investors to develop a sulfur field. The next year Freeport Texas was formed as a holding company for Freeport Sulfur and other enterprises.

During the 1930s the company diversified. In 1936 Freeport pioneered a process to remove hydrocarbons from sulfur. The company joined Consolidated Coal in 1955 to establish the National Potash Company. In 1956 Freeport formed an oil and gas subsidiary Freeport Oil.

Internationally Freeport formed an Australian minerals subsidiary in 1964 and a copper-mining subsidiary in Indonesia in 1967. The company changed its name to Freeport Minerals in 1971 and merged with Utah-based McMoRan Oil & Gas (formerly McMoRan Explorations) in 1982.

McMoRan Explorations had been formed in 1969 by William McWilliams Jim Bob Moffett and Byron Rankin. In 1973 McMoRan formed an exploration and drilling alliance with Dow Chemical and signed a deal with Indonesia to mine in the remote Irian Jaya region. McMoRan went public in 1978.

Moffett became chairman and CEO of Freeport-McMoRan in 1984. The company formed Freeport-McMoRan Copper in 1987 to manage its Indonesian operations. The unit assumed the Freeport-McMoRan Copper & Gold name in 1991. Two years later Freeport-McMoRan acquired Rio Tinto Minera a copper-smelting business with operations in Spain.

To support expansion in Indonesia Freeport-McMoRan spun off its copper and gold division in 1994. In 1995 Freeport-McMoRan Copper & Gold (FCX) formed an alliance with the UK's RTZ Corporation to develop its Indonesian mineral reserves. Local riots that year closed the Grasberg

Mine and FCX's political risk insurance was canceled. Despite these setbacks higher metal prices and growing sales in 1995 helped the company double its operating income.

An Indonesian tribal leader filed a $6 billion lawsuit in 1996 charging FCX with environmental human rights and social and cultural violations. The company called the suit baseless but offered to set aside 1% of its annual revenues or about $15 million to help local tribes. Tribal leaders rejected the offer and in 1997 a judge dismissed the lawsuit.

In 1997 FCX pulled out of Bre-X Minerals' Busang gold mine project which independent tests later proved to be a fraud of historic proportions. Amid widespread rioting Indonesia's embattled president Suharto was forced out of office in 1998. The new government investigated charges of cronyism involving FCX.

FCX received permission from the Indonesian government in 1999 to expand the Grasberg Mine and increase ore output up to 300000 metric tons per day. However the next year an overflow accident killed four workers in Grasberg and as a result of the accident the Indonesian government ordered FCX to reduce its production at the mine by up to 30%. Normal production at the mine resumed in early 2001.

FM Services (administrative legal and financial services) was added as a subsidiary in 2002. In 2003 FCX bought an 86% stake in PT Puncakjaya Power a supplier of power to PT-FI.

The $26 billion acquisition of Phelps Dodge in 2007 brought that company's global copper gold and molybdenum business into the fold. The deal placed FCX in a position to thrive as a global competitor in the rank just below metals and mining giants such as BHP Billiton Rio Tinto and Vale. A year later FCX sold the wire and cable business it acquired in the Phelps Dodge deal to General Cable Corporation for $735 million.

Following the acquisition — and benefiting from high copper prices and a good business climate — the company began to invest in its development projects. It was also able to retire a sizable portion of its debt much of it accumulated from the Phelps Dodge acquisition.

Political and environmental controversy in Indonesia has been a problem for FCX since its major protector former President Suharto was forced to resign in 1998 after more than 30 years in power. Sectarian violence in Indonesia where FCX is one of the largest employers also makes the company vulnerable to work stoppages. Anglo-Australian mining giant Rio Tinto is jointly involved with FCX in developing mineral properties in Indonesia's politically and environmentally sensitive Papua region. The company's Tenke Fungume copper and gold mine named Too is located in the Democratic Republic of Congo which also can be an unstable environment in which to do business. Tenke Fungume is jointly owned with Lundin Mining and the Congolese government. It began production in 2009.

Beginning in 2013 FCX has also moved into the oil and gas market to broaden its portfolio as a natural resource player though acquisitions.

In 2013 the company bought Plains Exploration & Production for $16.3 billion (including $9.7 billion of debt). Assets acquired included oil production facilities in California a production base in the Eagle Ford trend in Texas and deepwater Gulf of Mexico and onshore Haynesville assets.

That year to enhance FCX's cobalt marketing position it acquired 56% of a large scale cobalt chemical refinery in Kokkola Finland. The joint venture will operate under the name Freeport Cobalt FCX will be the operator. Other JV partners include Lundin Mining (24%) and La G ©n ©rale des Carri "res et des Mines (20%).

EXECUTIVES

EVP and Chief Administrative Officer, Michael J. Arnold, age 65, $550,000 total compensation
Vice Chairman President and CEO, Richard C. Adkerson, age 70, $1,250,000 total compensation
Vice President Taxes, Hugh O Donahue
EVP CFO and Treasurer, Kathleen L. Quirk, age 53, $650,000 total compensation
President Americas and Africa Mining, Harry M. (Red) Conger, age 85, $500,000 total compensation
VP and CIO, Bertrand (Bert) Odinet
Chairman, Gerald J. Ford, age 73
Auditors: Ernst & Young LLP

LOCATIONS

HQ: Freeport-McMoRan Inc
    333 North Central Avenue, Phoenix, AZ 85004-2189
Phone: 602 366-8100
Web: www.fcx.com

2016 Sales

	$ mil.	% of total
North America copper mines	4,374	24
Rod & Refining	3,862	22
Indonesia mining	3,295	18
South America mining	2,938	16
Atlantic Copper Smelting & Refining	1,830	10
U.S. Oil & Gas operations	1,513	9
Molybdenum mines	186	1
Other mining corporate other & eliminations	(3168)	-
Total	**14,830**	**100**

PRODUCTS/OPERATIONS

2016 Sales

	$ mil.	% of total
Refined copper products	5,888	40
Copper in concentrates	4,502	30
Gold	1,512	10
Oil	1,304	9
Molybdenum	651	4
Other products	973	7
Total	**14,830**	**100**

Selected Subsidiaries and Affiliates

Atlantic Copper Holding SA (smelting and refining Spain)
Chino Mines Company
Climax Molybdenum Company
FM Service Company (administrative and financial services)
Missouri Lead Smelting Company
Plains Exploration & Production (oil and gas US)
PT Freeport Indonesia Co. (91% mining)
    PT Smelting (Gresik) Co. (25% smelting Indonesia)
PT Irja Eastern Minerals Corp. (mining Indonesia)
PT Puncakjaya Power (86% supplies power to PT Freeport Indonesia)

COMPETITORS

Anadarko Petroleum	EOG
Anglo American	Encana Oil & Gas (USA)
Antofagasta	Inc.
Apache	Exxon Mobil
BHP Billiton	Goodrich Petroleum
BP	Newmont Mining
Barrick Gold	Regency Energy
Cabot Oil & Gas	Rio Tinto Limited
Chesapeake Energy	Royal Dutch Shell
Chevron Mining	Southern Copper
Codelco	Vale Limited
Devon Energy	

HISTORICAL FINANCIALS

Company Type: Public

Income Statement

FYE: December 31

	REVENUE ($ mil.)	NET INCOME ($ mil.)	NET PROFIT MARGIN	EMPLOYEES
12/16	14,830	(4,315)	—	30,000
12/15	15,877	(12,195)	—	34,500
12/14	21,438	(1,268)	—	35,000
12/13	20,921	2,680	12.8%	36,100
12/12	18,010	3,041	16.9%	34,000
Annual Growth	**(4.7%)**	**—**	**—**	**(3.1%)**

2016 Year-End Financials

Debt ratio: 42.95%
Return on equity: (-62.01%)
Cash ($ mil.): 4,245
Current ratio: 2.45
Long-term debt ($ mil.): 14,795

No. of shares (mil.): 1,445
Dividends
    Yield: —
    Payout: —
Market value ($ mil.): 19,060

	STOCK PRICE ($) FY Close	P/E High/Low	PER SHARE ($) Earnings	Dividends	Book Value
12/16	13.19	— —	(3.16)	0.00	4.19
12/15	6.77	— —	(11.31)	0.57	6.28
12/14	23.36	— —	(1.26)	1.25	17.60
12/13	37.74	14 10	2.64	2.25	20.17
12/12	34.20	15 10	3.19	1.19	18.49
Annual Growth	**(21.2%)**	**— —**	**—**	**—**	**(31.0%)**

Frontier Communications Corp

Serving city dwellers and country folk alike Frontier Communications provides phone internet video and satellite TV (through a partnership with DISH Network) services in about 30 US states. The company has more than 5.4 million residential and business voice subscribers about 4.35 million broadband internet customers and some 1.4 million video subscribers. Frontier is active mostly in rural and small to mid-sized markets where it is the incumbent local-exchange carrier (ILEC). About 7% of the company?s revenue comes from government support for serving rural areas. In 2016 Frontier acquired the wireline operations of Verizon Communications in California Texas and Florida for about $10.5 billion.

Operations

Frontier Communications' data and internet services contribute more than 40% of revenue while local and long distance services account for about a third of the company's revenue followed by switched access and subsidy revenue about 10% and other services less than 5%.

The company offers broadband video voice and other services and products to residential customers over a combination of fiber and copper-based networks. For business customers Frontier offers broadband Ethernet traditional circuit-based services and voice services. The company also sells customer premise equipment and related maintenance services.

Geographic Reach

Frontier Communications has operations in Alabama Arizona California Connecticut Florida Georgia Idaho Illinois Indiana Iowa Michigan Minnesota Mississippi Montana Nebraska Nevada New Mexico New York North Carolina Ohio Oregon Pennsylvania South Carolina Tennessee Texas Utah Washington West Virginia and Wisconsin. The acquisition of Verizon?s wireline operations in California Texas and Florida expanded Frontier?s activities in those states.

Sales and Marketing

Residential customers account for about 50% of Frontier Communications? revenue and business customers contribute more than 40% while the rest comes from the access and subsidy segment.

Financial Performance

For 2016 Frontier Communications reported $8.9 billion in revenue a 60% increase from 2015 boosted by the inclusion of the Verizon operations acquired in 2016. Not counting the acquired sales Frontier?s revenue fell 5% in 2016 from decreases in revenue from voice services and switched and non-switched access. Frontier continued to see lower voice revenue in the consumer and business segments as customers switch to wireless services. On the plus side data services revenue increased in 2016.

Costs associated with the acquisition led to a net loss of $373 million in 2016 which was greater than the $196 million loss posted in 2015.

Cash flow from operations increased to $1.7 million in 2016 from $1.4 billion in 2015. The addition of the Verizon operations helped raise cash flow but that was somewhat offset by negative changes in working capital along with higher interest expense and acquisition and integration costs.

Strategy

When Frontier Communications bought Verizon Communications properties in California Texas and Florida (CTF) in 2016 the deal brought opportunity and costs. The CTF operations added about $3.6 billion in revenue in 2016 as well as the expenses of integrating those widespread operations into Frontier. The company said it has worked through some service issues that occurred after the acquisition and that it was well on its way of finding some $250 million in savings through a thorough inventory of each company?s operations.

The acquisition brought Frontier opportunities in the three of the biggest — and still growing — US states and the company reconfigured some of its sales and marketing organizations to take a more customer-centric approach. Frontier concentrates field sales teams where its network and market opportunity offer the highest potential for growth among business customers. The company has identified more than 30000 fiber-fed multi-customer buildings and footprint for a sales push. Frontier?s call center and field operations also have been revamped (including relocating call centers in the US from overseas) to offer better service and customer experience.

Frontier continues to expand its network infrastructure to offer faster internet speeds to more customers. In 2016 about half of its capital expenditures went to broadband expansion speed upgrades and fiber-to-the-home expansions. The company enabled more than a million households with 50 mbps and higher speeds in 2016 and it added some 200000 copper broadband builds in the CTF areas.

Mergers and Acquisitions

The Frontier Communications acquisition of Verizon Communications? wireline operations in California Texas and Florida for $10.5 billion closed in 2016. The acquisition brought about 3.3 million voice connections 2.1 million broadband connections and 1.2 million FiOS video subscribers and the related incumbent local exchange carrier businesses to Frontier. The deal expanded Frontier?s presence large but still fast-growing states and improved the revenue mix by increasing the percentage of revenue generated by segments with promising potential.

EXECUTIVES

EVP Field Operations, John J. Lass, age 60, $436,156 total compensation

EVP Consumer Sales Marketing and Product, John Maduri

President and CEO, Daniel J. McCarthy, age 52, $981,251 total compensation

EVP and Chief People Officer, Kathleen Weslock, age 61

EVP General Counsel and Corporate Secretary, Mark D. Nielsen, age 52, $387,500 total compensation

EVP and CTO, Steve Gable, age 43, $458,750 total compensation

EVP and CFO, R. Perley McBride, $199,432 total compensation

EVP Commercial Sales Operations, Kenneth A. Arndt

EVP Operational Transformation, Tim Travaille

Senior Vice President Deputy General Counsel, Nancy Rights

Executive Vice President of Customer Service, Jennifer Brown

Assistant Vice President Training And Development, Gregg Barratt

Senior Vice President West Region, Denise Baumbach

Vice President Human Resources Labor And Employment Law, Richard Reice

Senior Vice President and General Manager Westside Teritory, Michelle Wolloff

Assistant Vice President Engineering, Kole Sanders

Chairman, Pamela D. A. Reeve, age 68

Auditors: KPMG LLP

LOCATIONS

HQ: Frontier Communications Corp
401 Merritt 7, Norwalk, CT 06851
Phone: 203 614-5600 **Fax:** 203 614-4602
Web: www.frontier.com

PRODUCTS/OPERATIONS

2016 Sales

	$ mil.	% of total
Customer revenue		
Business	4,383	49
Residential	3,716	42
Switched access and subsidy	797	9
Total	**8,896**	**100**

2016 Sales

	$ mil.	% of total
Customer Revenue		
Data and internet services 3693	42	
Voice Services	2,886	32
video services	1,244	14
Others	276	3
Switched access and subsidy	797	9
Total	**8,896**	**100**

COMPETITORS

AT&T	Integra Telecom
Altice USA	Time Warner Cable
CenturyLink	U.S. TelePacific
Charter Communications	Verizon
Comcast	Vonage
Cox Communications	XO Holdings
FairPoint Communications Inc.	

HISTORICAL FINANCIALS

Company Type: Public

Income Statement

FYE: December 31

	REVENUE ($ mil.)	NET INCOME ($ mil.)	NET PROFIT MARGIN	EMPLOYEES
12/16	8,896	(373)	—	28,300
12/15	5,576	(196)	—	19,200
12/14	4,772	132	2.8%	17,400
12/13	4,761	112	2.4%	13,650
12/12	5,011	136	2.7%	14,700
Annual Growth	15.4%	—	—	17.8%

2016 Year-End Financials

Debt ratio: 61.78%
Return on equity: (-7.34%)
Cash ($ mil.): 522
Current ratio: 0.68
Long-term debt ($ mil.): 17,560
No. of shares (mil.): 78
Dividends
Yield: 1.3%
Payout: —
Market value ($ mil.): 264

	STOCK PRICE ($) FY Close	P/E High	P/E Low	PER SHARE ($) Earnings	Dividends	Book Value
12/16	3.38	—	—	(7.65)	6.30	57.81
12/15	4.67	—	—	(4.35)	6.30	72.09
12/14	6.67	4	2	1.95	6.00	54.73
12/13	4.65	3	2	1.65	6.00	60.86
12/12	4.28	3	2	1.95	6.00	61.71
Annual Growth	(5.7%)			—	1.2%	(1.6%)

Fulton Financial Corp. (PA)

Fulton Financial is a $17 billion financial holding company that owns six community banks which together operate more than 250 branches in rural and suburban areas of Pennsylvania Maryland Delaware New Jersey and Virginia. The banks offer standard products such as checking and savings accounts CDs IRAs and credit cards. While commercial mortgage and construction loans account for about 45% of the company's loan portfolio home loans are also available through subsidiary Fulton Mortgage Company. Other non-bank units include investment management and trust services provider Fulton Financial Advisors and Fulton Insurance an agency selling life insurance and related products.

Operations

Fulton Financial's six subsidiary banks include the $9.5 billion Fulton Bank (Fulton's largest with more than 100 branches in Pennsylvania and Delaware) The Columbia Bank FNB Bank Fulton Bank of New Jersey Lafayette Ambassador Bank and Swineford National Bank.

Geographic Reach

Fulton Financial and its subsidiary banks operate more than 250 branches in suburban and semi-rural markets in the states of Pennsylvania Delaware Maryland New Jersey and Virginia.

Sales and Marketing

Fulton spent $7.7 million on advertising in 2013 or 6% less than it spent in 2012.

Financial Performance

Fulton Financial's revenue has been in decline since 2007 and fell by another 4% to $763.5 million in 2014 mostly from a combination of lower interest income from loans as interest margins shrunk less fee income from deposit service

charges and smaller gains from mortgage sales as the bank had a lower balance of loan commitments.

Lower revenue caused net income to dip by 2% to $157.9 million in 2014 but lower interest expenses on deposits less risk-related losses and lower salary and employee benefit costs from recent cost-savings initiatives all helped to buoy profits some.

Cash provided by operations fell by 30% to $210.4 million in 2014 mostly because the company generated smaller gains from the sales of its held-for-sale mortgage loans and used more cash toward other assets related to tax credit partnerships and commercial interest rate swaps.

Company Background

The company had owned more than a dozen banks as recently as 2007 but consolidated some of them in the hopes of creating operating and marketing efficiencies. Maryland-based Hagerstown Trust Company and The Peoples Bank of Elkton merged into The Columbia Bank in 2009 and Delaware National Bank which had a dozen branches in the state became part of Fulton Bank the following year. In 2011 Fulton Financial merged two more banks New Jersey-based The Bank and Skylands Community Bank to form Fulton Bank of New Jersey which has some 70 branches throughout the state.

EXECUTIVES

Senior Vice President Finance, Jeffrey Peeling

SEVP Community Banking, Craig A. Roda, $398,805 total compensation

SEVP COO and Interim CFO, Philmer H. (Phil) Rohrbaugh, age 65, $478,543 total compensation

SEVP; President and COO Fulton Bank, Curtis J. Myers, $371,347 total compensation

SEVP and Chief Credit Officer, Meg R. Mueller

SEVP and CIO, Angela M. Sargent

Chairman President and CEO, E. Philip (Phil) Wenger, $944,103 total compensation

SEVP and Chief Risk Officer, Beth Ann L. Chivinski

President Small Business Administration Lending, Lynn Ozer

President and COO Fulton Mortgage Company, Jeffrey J. Scheuren

Executive Vice President Marketing Corporate Communications, David Hostetter

Senior Vice President Talent Management Program Manager, Lori Berquist

Vice President Senior Leasing Sales Officer, Neil Wiker

Senior Executive Vice President Community Banking, Philip Wenger

Vice President Director Manager, Betty Hart

SENIOR VICE PRESIDENT AND RETAIL SALES LEADER, Smokey Glover

Vice President Ancillary Services Manager, Doug Tshudy

Vice President and Corporate Training Director, William Glover

Vice President, Constance Beck

Vice President Of Loan Administration, Patricia Royer

Executive Vice President Treasurer, James Radick

Vice President Senior Cash Management Sales Officer, Steve Schreiber Steve Schreiber

Sr Vice President, Forest Crigler

Vice President Information Technology Service and Support, Linda Baer

Senior Vice President Director of Retail, Randy Metz

Vice President, Marc Ryan

Vice President Residential and Consumer Defauls, Tonya Samuel

Senior Vice President Bank Controller, Linda Schroeder

Senior Vice President Funds Management, Keith Paich
Vice President And Records Manager, Robert Sandusky
Senior Vice President, Clint Miller
Vice President, Alan Brayman
Senior Vice President Information Technology Governance, Donna Braunschweig
Senior Vice President Regional Manager, Iwona Shillingford
Vice President Tax Accounting and Planning Officer, David Rorabaugh
Vice President, Michael Thompson
Vice President Consumer Loan Review, Domenick Vitale
Senior Vice President Trust Manager, Stuart Juppenlatz
Vice President Lending Compliance Officer, Eileen Moyer
Vice President and Regional Sales Manager, Becky Lanzino
Vice President Portfolio Manager, Theodore Walden
Vice President Relationship Manager Private Banking, Jessica Malone
Senior Executive Vice President Chief Human Resources Officer, Bernadette Taylor
SVP Small Business Segment Manager, Stephen Markley
SENIOR VICE PRESIDENT AND SENIOR PORTFOLIO MANAGER, Walter J Banta
SENIOR VICE PRESIDENT, Willie A Maddox
VICE PRESIDENT AND PORTFOLIO MANAGER, Laurie Bodisch
SENIOR VICE PRESIDENT, Richard J Mason
VICE PRESIDENT AND SENIOR LEASING SALES OFFICER, Sharon Wingenroth
VICE PRESIDENT VENDOR RISK AND RELATIONS, Gregory Lampe
SENIOR VICE PRESIDENT, John D Harding
VICE PRESIDENT AND SENIOR LEASING OFFICER, Jason D Ibach
EXECUTIVE VICE PRESIDENT AND CHIEF INVESTMENT OFFICER, Keith P Aleardi
VICE PRESIDENT, Debbie Truckermiller
Board Member, Joe Ballard
Auditors: KPMG LLP

LOCATIONS

HQ: Fulton Financial Corp. (PA)
One Penn Square, P.O. Box 4887, Lancaster, PA 17604
Phone: 717 291-2411
Web: www.fult.com

PRODUCTS/OPERATIONS

2016 Sales

	$ mil.	% of total
Interest		
Loans including fees	543	68
Investment securities	55	7
Other	3	1
Non interest		
Service charges on deposit accounts	51	6
Other service charges & fees	51	6
Investment management & trust services	45	6
Mortgage banking income	19	2
Investment securities gains	2	1
Other	20	3
Total	793	100

COMPETITORS

First Commonwealth Financial	Mid Penn Bancorp
Investors Bancorp	PNC Financial
M&T Bank	Sovereign Bank
	TD Bank USA

HISTORICAL FINANCIALS

Company Type: Public

Income Statement

FYE: December 31

	ASSETS ($ mil.)	NET INCOME ($ mil.)	INCOME AS % OF ASSETS	EMPLOYEES
12/16	18,944	161	0.9%	3,500
12/15	17,914	149	0.8%	3,460
12/14	17,124	157	0.9%	3,560
12/13	16,934	161	1.0%	3,620
12/12	16,528	159	1.0%	3,570
Annual Growth	3.5%	0.3%	—	(0.5%)

2016 Year-End Financials

Debt ratio: 1.91%
Return on equity: 7.74%
Cash ($ mil.): 352
Current ratio: —
Long-term debt ($ mil.): —
No. of shares (mil.): 174
Dividends
Yield: 0.0%
Payout: 44.0%
Market value ($ mil.): 3,273

	STOCK PRICE ($) FY Close	P/E High/Low	PER SHARE ($) Earnings	Dividends	Book Value
12/16	18.80	21 13	0.93	0.41	12.18
12/15	13.01	17 13	0.85	0.38	11.72
12/14	12.36	15 12	0.84	0.34	11.16
12/13	13.09	16 11	0.83	0.32	10.71
12/12	9.61	13 11	0.80	0.30	10.45
Annual Growth	18.3%	— —	3.8%	8.1%	3.9%

Gallagher (Arthur J.) & Co.

Arthur J. Gallagher knows all about risks in business. The company provides insurance brokerage and risk management services through a network of subsidiaries and agencies. It places traditional and niche property/casualty lines in addition to offering retirement solutions and managing employee benefits programs. Risk management services include claims management loss control consulting and workers' compensation investigations. Gallagher UK places insurance with the Lloyd's of London exchange. The global company operates more than 600 sales and service locations in more than 30 nations and through correspondent brokers and consultants does business in more than 110 countries.

Operations

Gallagher has grown to become one of the world's top five insurance brokers based on revenue as well as a top property/casualty claims administrator. It also ranks among the top employee benefits consulting firms.

The company operates through three reportable segments: Brokerage Corporate and Risk Management.

The Brokerage segment which provides both retail and wholesale services accounts for more than 60% of annual revenues. A majority of Gallagher's brokerage income comes from commissions paid by insurance companies (upon placement of their policies). Retail insurance brokerage accounts for more than 80% of the segment's revenues.

Gallagher's Corporate segment accounts for about a quarter of total revenues; it primarily generated income in 2016 from the consolidation of refined fuel operations. Its managed investments include a 46.5% stake in pollutant reduction firm Chem-Mod and a 12% stake in private carbon dioxide emissions reduction outfit C-Quest Technology.

The smaller Risk Management segment (more than 10% of sales) provides contract claim settlement and administration services for enterprises; it earns fees from insurance companies and self-insured clients. The segment's business is largely related to workers' compensation claims as well as auto liability and property claims.

Geographic Reach

Gallagher gets more than 75% of its revenues from the US but it is working to expand its international operations. The company operates in more than 30 nations and through a brokerage and consultant network serves more than 150 nations. Its largest overseas markets include Australia Bermuda Canada the Caribbean New Zealand Singapore and the UK.

Sales and Marketing

Most of Gallagher's brokerage business comes from retail customers which include commercial industrial not-for-profit government and religious organizations. Gallagher's wholesale brokerage centers provide insurance placement assistance to affiliated and independent agents.

The company manages its brokerage operations through a network of more than 600 sales and service offices. It manages its third-party claims adjusting operations through a network of 110 offices across the US and in Australia Canada New Zealand and the UK.

Financial Performance

Gallagher's growth efforts in both the brokerage segment and the risk management segment have helped the company to increase new customer volumes and has created substantial annual revenue increases in recent years. In 2016 revenue grew a more modest 4% to $5.6 billion. Most sources of income increased that year including commissions fees investment income and revenues from clean coal activities.

Net income has also been rising and in 2016 increased 16% to $414.4 million. This was largely due to the higher revenue and a decrease in operating costs such as technology expenses.

Cash flow from operations took its first dip in five years in 2016 falling 5% to $622.1 million. Negative adjustments to reconcile net earnings to net cash provided by operating activities such as accrued liabilities and premiums receivable led to that decline.

Strategy

Gallagher grows through the ongoing acquisition of small regional insurance agencies and benefits consulting firms. The company targets strong sales organizations with a focus on middle-market clients or expertise in niche property/casualty lines (such as aviation energy hospitality and health care).

In addition to growth through acquisitions Gallagher has influenced the growth of its business by expanding and strengthening its relationships with independent brokerage partners increasing cross-selling opportunities and pursuing niche markets such as employee benefit risk management. It also expands its geographic presence through organic and acquisitive growth efforts.

Mergers and Acquisitions

A core strategy of Gallagher is to expand through acquisitions. Purchases typically cost between $1 million and $50 million. In 2016 Gallagher completed more than 35 acquisitions spending nearly $400 million in the process. Some of the firms acquired in that period included Kane's Insurance Management Altman & Cronin Benefit Consultants McNeary and Victory Insurance Agency.

Company Background

Gallagher is led by J. Patrick Gallagher grandson of founder Arthur Gallagher who formed the company back in 1927.

EXECUTIVES

Corporate Vice President and President U.S. Wholesale Brokerage, David McGurn

Chairman Employee Benefits Consulting and Brokerage, James W. (Jim) Durkin, age 67, $725,000 total compensation

Chairman President and CEO, J. Patrick (Pat) Gallagher, age 64, $1,000,000 total compensation

CFO, Douglas K. (Doug) Howell, age 55, $850,000 total compensation

President U.S. Wholesale Brokerage, Joel D. Cavaness, age 55

Chairman Brokerage Services, James S. (Jim) Gault, age 65, $800,000 total compensation

President and CEO Risk Management Services, Scott R. Hudson, age 55

Corporate VP and Chairman International Brokerage, Thomas J. (Tom) Gallagher, age 59, $750,000 total compensation

Global Chief Service Officer, Vishal Jain

CEO Employee Benefits Consulting and Brokerage, William F. Ziebell, age 54

Managing Director Commercial Broking Arthur J Gallagher Australia, Sarah Lyons

AREA EXECUTIVE VICE PRESIDENT, John Ergastolo

Executive Vice President, Mike Temple

Senior Vice President, Diana Bertoni

Senior Area Vice President, Bill Dickenson

Area Vice President Marketing, Kevin Groba

Area Executive Vice President, Rich Stokluska

Vice President Information Technology, Steve Cius

Area Vice President Global Human Resources Services, Kristin M Sampson

Area Senior Vice President, David D Kempton

Area Executive Vice President, James Mandel

Area President, Brendan Gallagher

Area Senior Vice President, Barb Galuppi

Area Senior Vice President, Mike Mayo

Area Senior Vice President, David D White

Area Assistant Vice President, Nathan Mitzner

Area Vice President, Rob Erzen

Area Assistant Vice President, Paige Nabavian

Area Vice President Operations, Donna Dailly

Area Vice President Client Consultant, Nancy Kokenge

Area Vice President, Gary Duvall

Area Vice President, Peter Benshetler

Vice President of Claims and Loss Control Services, Toby Grist

Area Vice President, Neil C Cox

Area Senior Vice President, DAVID GHIRARDINI

Area Senior Vice President, Maureen O'Connell

Vice President, Bruce Beardsley

Vice President Corporate Ethics And Sustainability, Tom Tropp

Area Vice President, Eric J Ginsburg

Vice President Client Management, Craig Chisholm

EXECUTIVE VICE PRESIDENT, George Spanjers

Area Vice President, Paul Pellerito

Division Vice President, Michael McKee

Area Executive Vice President, Tim Gonsior

Area Senior Vice President, Kevin Gregory

Assistant Vice President Real Estate And Hospitality, Sandy Gilder

Area Vice President Employee Benefits Consultant, Lance Clemens

Area Vice President Marine, Marc Dunn

Area Vice President, Jack Zogg

Aavp And Director Of Operations Tampa Bay Branch, Randi Watson

Senior Vice President, Susan Ruvolo

Division President, Teresa Koster

Area Executive Vice President, Daniel Johnson

Area Executive Vice President, Eric Olson

Area Vice President, Kelly Bonanno

Area Vice President, Cindy Caslin

Vice President Sourcing and Services, Cara Richardson

Area Senior Vice President, Steven Beck

Area Vice President Of Business Insurance Sales And Risk Management Consulting, John Sence

Area Assistant Vice President Property Loss Control, Scott Quackenbush

AREA VICE PRESIDENT, Bob Murphy

Area Assistant Vice President, Lee Newmark

Area Vice President And Consultant, Janet Brendis

Area Vice President Human Capital And Employee Benefits, Bobby Desai

Area Vice Presidenta, Susan Blankenburg

Area Vice President, Jim Risk

Regional Executive Vice President, Bret VanderVoort

Area Assistant Vice President Compliance Counsel, Kat Lacy-Wilson

Area Senior Vice President, Nancy Webster

Area Vice President, Danny Bone

Area Vice President, Barbara Murray

AREA VICE PRESIDENT, Melissa Walsh

AREA ASSISTANT VICE PRESIDENT, Beth Ulrich

SENIOR VICE PRESIDENT AND AE, Cynthia Taylor

Area Executive Vice President, Robert Gigax

Area Vice President, Paul Nelson

Area Senior Vice President, Ron Seymour

Area Vice President, Judy Worrall

Senior Vice President, Daniel R'bibo

Area Assistant Vice President I Private Client Practice, Jason Coughlin

AREA EXECUTIVE VICE PRESIDENT, Mike Spaude

AREA ASSISTANT VICE PRESIDENT, Janet M Rushing

AREA SENIOR VICE PRESIDENT AND COMPLIANCE COUNSEL, Mandy Bartoshesky

AREA SENIOR VICE PRESIDENT, Chris Cammarata

Auditors: Ernst & Young LLP

LOCATIONS

HQ: Gallagher (Arthur J.) & Co.
2850 W. Golf Road, Rolling Meadows, IL 60008-4050
Phone: 630 773-3800
Web: www.ajg.com

2016 Sales

	$ mil.	% of total
US	4,272	76
UK	712	13
Australia	245	4
Canada	138	3
New Zealand	125	2
Other foreign	100	2
Total	**5,594**	**100**

PRODUCTS/OPERATIONS

2016 Sales

	$ mil.	% of total
Brokerage		
Commissions	2,439	44
Fees	775	14
Supplemental commissions	147	2
Contingent commissions	107	2
Investment income	58	1
Risk management		
Fees	717	13
Investment income	1	.
Corporate		
Clean energy & other investment income	1,348	24
Total	**5,594**	**100**

Selected Subsidiaries

AJG Financial Services Inc.
  AJG Coal Inc.
Arthur J. Gallagher & Co. (Bermuda) Limited (insurance & reinsurance placement captive risk services)

Artex Risk Solutions (Bermuda) Ltd.
Arthur J. Gallagher & Co. (Canada) Ltd.
Arthur J. Gallagher Australasia Holdings Pty Ltd (Australia)
  Australis Group (Underwriting) Pty Ltd
  Interpacific Underwriting Agencies Pty Ltd
Arthur J. Gallagher Brokerage & Risk Management Services LLC
  Arthur J. Gallagher Risk Management Services Inc.
  Manning & Smith Insurance Inc.
Arthur J. Gallagher Service Company
Arthur J. Gallagher (UK) Limited (Lloyd's of London brokerage)
  Risk Management Partners Ltd. (customized insurance & risk management)
Gallagher Bassett Services Inc. (risk analysis)
  Gallagher Bassett International Ltd. (UK)
  Gallagher Bassett Services Pty Ltd. (Australia)
Gallagher Benefit Services Inc. (employee benefit program management)
Heath Lambert Limited (Gallagher Heath UK)
Protected Insurance Company
Risk Placement Services Inc.

COMPETITORS

ACE USA	Hub International
AIG	Jardine Lloyd
AmWINS Group	Marsh & McLennan
Aon	Sedgwick Claims
Bollinger Inc.	Management Services
BroadSpire	The Hartford
Brown & Brown	The Lockton Companies
CRC Insurance	UMR
Fiserv	USI
Fortegra Financial	Willis Towers Watson
General Re	Zurich American

HISTORICAL FINANCIALS

Company Type: Public

Income Statement

FYE: December 31

	REVENUE ($ mil.)	NET INCOME ($ mil.)	NET PROFIT MARGIN	EMPLOYEES
12/17	6,159	463	7.5%	26,800
12/16	5,594	414	7.4%	24,800
12/15	5,392	356	6.6%	21,500
12/14	4,626	303	6.6%	20,200
12/13	3,179	268	8.4%	16,400
Annual Growth	**18.0%**	**14.6%**	**—**	**13.1%**

2017 Year-End Financials

Debt ratio: 24.29%
Return on equity: 12.03%
Cash ($ mil.): 681
Current ratio: 1.05
Long-term debt ($ mil.): 2,691

No. of shares (mil.): 181
Dividends
  Yield: 0.0%
  Payout: 61.4%
Market value ($ mil.): 11,454

	STOCK PRICE ($) FY Close	P/E High/Low	PER SHARE ($) Earnings	Dividends	Book Value
12/17	63.28	26 20	2.54	1.56	22.68
12/16	51.96	22 16	2.32	1.52	20.17
12/15	40.94	24 19	2.06	1.48	20.57
12/14	47.08	25 22	1.97	1.44	19.62
12/13	46.93	23 17	2.06	1.40	15.61
Annual Growth	**7.8%**	**— —**	**5.4%**	**2.7%**	**9.8%**

GameStop Corp

GameStop holds the top score in video game retailing. The largest retailer of new and used games hardware entertainment software and accessories boasts roughly 4000 GameStop EB Games and Micromania branded stores in the US and 2000-plus stores in Europe Australia and Canada. Its stores and e-commerce websites stock more than 6000 video game related items with more than half of its sales coming from new video game hardware and software. GameStop also sells downloadable add-on content from publishers operates 1400 smartphone retail locations (under the AT&T Cricket Wireless Simply Mac and Spring Mobile banners) and publishes video game magazine Game Informer .

HISTORY

NeoStar Retail Group resulted from the 1994 combination of software retailers Babbage's and Software Etc. Babbage's had been founded by James McCurry and Gary Kusin in 1983. Named for 19th-century mathematician Charles Babbage (considered the father of the computer) it went public in 1988.

Software Etc. began as a division of B. Dalton Bookseller in 1984. Bookstore chain Barnes & Noble and Dutch retailer Vendex acquired B. Dalton two years later. Software Etc. went public in 1992.

Both companies focused on mall retailing: Babbage's on game software and Software Etc. on a broader variety of PC software. Both saw growth spurred by the rising popularity of Nintendo and Sega game systems and by falling PC prices. The two merged in 1994 in an effort to stave off growing competition from big retail chains such as Best Buy and Wal-Mart. NeoStar opened 122 stores in 1995.

Amid flat sales the following year several senior executives left. Also in 1996 NeoStar lost its contract to operate software departments at 136 Barnes & Noble sites and it soon filed for Chapter 11. Late that year a group led by Barnes & Noble's head honcho Leonard Riggio purchased about 460 of NeoStar's 650 stores for $58.5 million and renamed the company Babbage's Etc. Former Software Etc. chief Dick Fontaine was named CEO.

By 1997 the company began concentrating on popular games and software and in 1999 it formed its e-commerce site GameStop.com. In late 1999 Barnes & Noble paid Riggio's group $210 million for Babbage's Etc. In June 2000 the company fortified its position and became the #1 US video game retailer with the purchase of rival game retailer Funco (about 400 stores) for $161.5 million. The company changed its name to GameStop in August 2001 and filed to go public which it accomplished in February 2002. Though public it was still under the majority control of Barnes & Noble until 2004 when GameStop bought back its shares.

GameStop bought rival Electronics Boutique in 2005 more than doubling its size from 2000 to about 4500 stores. Steven R. Morgan a former executive with Electronics Boutique became president of GameStop later that year.

A new CEO took the controls at GameStop in 2008 — its first CEO change since the company's inception in 1996. Dick Fontaine gave up the title of chief executive to Daniel DeMatteo who had served as COO since 1996 and vice chairman of the company since 2004. Also Paul Raines formerly with Home Depot joined the company as COO in September 2008. Fontaine retained the chairman's title and focused on international operations and acquisitions.

GameStop focused on international expansion in 2008 driven primarily by a pair of acquisitions. The largest of those was its $629 million purchase of video game retailer Micromania which brought with it some 330 stores in France. South of the equator GameStop acquired The Gamesman the largest independent gaming retailer in New Zealand. The deal included eight Gamesman video game stores and brought GameStop's total store count in the country to 38.

In June 2010 DeMatteo was promoted to executive chairman of the company while Raines was named CEO.

In late 2013 the company acquired the 50.1% of Simply Mac that it didn't already own boosting its Technology Brands segment. The $9.5 million deal added Apple specialty retail stores in Utah and Wyoming. Also that year GameStop bought Spring Communications for $62.6 million.

EXECUTIVES

COO, Tony D. Bartel, age 53, $924,923 total compensation
CEO, J. Paul Raines, age 53, $1,285,077 total compensation
CFO, Robert A. (Rob) Lloyd, age 55, $707,385 total compensation
EVP Strategic Business and Brand Development, Michael P. (Mike) Hogan, age 58, $613,923 total compensation
EVP; President U.S. Stores, Michael T. (Mike) Buskey, age 68
President Kongregate, Emily Greer
EVP; President GameStop International, Michael K. (Mike) Mauler, age 56, $571,846 total compensation
SVP Information Technology and CIO, Michael Cooper
Divisional Vice President Refurbishment Reverse Logistics, John Daugherty
Division Vice President Gamestop Mobile, Ram Krishnamurthy
Divisional Vice President Distribution, Pat Sweetall
Vice President Marketing And Sales, Art Doud
Vice President, Blayne White
Vice President Distribution And Logist, John Watson
Senior Vice President U.S. Stores, Jason Cochran
Vice President of Used Merchandising, Jon Haes
Chairman, Daniel A. DeMatteo, age 69
Treasurer, Sara Chho
Board Member, Asim Naqvi
Auditors: Deloitte & Touche LLP

LOCATIONS

HQ: GameStop Corp
625 Westport Parkway, Grapevine, TX 76051
Phone: 817 424-2000
Web: www.gamestop.com

2017 Sales

	% of total
US	64
Europe	15
Australia	7
Canada	4
Technology Brands	9
Total	**100**

PRODUCTS/OPERATIONS

2017 Sales

	% of total
New video game software	29
Pre-owned and value video game products	26
New video game hardware	16
Technology Brands	9
Video game accessories	8
Collectables	6
Digital	3
Other	3
Total	**100**

Selected Websites

www.ebgames.com.au
www.gamestop.ca
www.gamestop.co.uk

www.gamestop.com
www.gamestop.com/pcgames
www.gamestop.de
www.gamestop.es
www.gamestop.ie
www.gamestop.it
www.kongregate.com
www.micromania.fr

Selected Merchandise

Accessories
  PC entertainment accessories
  Video game accessories
  Other
Internet streaming technology & digital distribution
Online games
PC entertainment software & other software
Used video games
Video game hardware
Video game software

COMPETITORS

Amazon.com	Kmart
Best Buy	Target Corporation
Buy.com	Toys "R" Us
Carrefour	Wal-Mart
Costco Wholesale	Zones
Fry's Electronics	eBay
GameFly	

HISTORICAL FINANCIALS

Company Type: Public

Income Statement

FYE: January 28

	REVENUE ($ mil.)	NET INCOME ($ mil.)	NET PROFIT MARGIN	EMPLOYEES
01/17	8,607	353	4.1%	68,000
01/16	9,363	402	4.3%	82,000
01/15*	9,296	393	4.2%	73,000
02/14	9,039	354	3.9%	69,000
02/13	8,886	(269)	—	65,000
Annual Growth	(0.8%)	—	—	1.1%

*Fiscal year change

2017 Year-End Financials

Debt ratio: 16.38%
Return on equity: 16.34%
Cash ($ mil.): 669
Current ratio: 1.22
Long-term debt ($ mil.): 815

No. of shares (mil.): 101
Dividends
  Yield: 0.0%
  Payout: 43.5%
Market value ($ mil.): 2,455

	STOCK PRICE ($) FY Close	P/E High/Low		Earnings	PER SHARE ($) Dividends	Book Value
01/17	24.31	10	6	3.40	1.48	22.32
01/16	26.21	12	7	3.78	1.44	20.15
01/15*	35.25	13	9	3.47	1.32	19.20
02/14	35.07	19	8	2.99	1.10	19.53
02/13	24.69	—	—	(2.13)	0.80	19.34
Annual Growth	(0.4%)	—	—	—	16.6%	3.6%

*Fiscal year change

General Dynamics Corp

General Dynamics is a prime military contractor to the Pentagon (the US government accounts for about 60% of sales). The company's military operations include information systems and technology (information technology and collection as well as command control systems); marine systems (warships commercial tankers and nuclear submarines); and combat systems (battle tanks wheeled combat/tactical vehicles munitions and rockets and gun systems). Its aerospace unit which is composed of Gulfstream Aerospace and Jet Aviation designs makes and refurbishes business jets primarily for civilian customers.

Operations

Unlike some of its rivals who cater only to the military market that is at the mercy of government budgetary fluctuations General Dynamics caters to military and civilian sectors manufacturing both combat systems and high-tech systems with each side buffering the other in times of market downturn. The Combat Systems division is composed of Armament and Technical Products; European Land Systems; Land Systems; and Ordnance and Tactical Systems.

General Dynamic's Marine Systems group is a major shipbuilder for the US Navy and it provides MRO (maintenance/repair/overhaul) services to keep those vessels ship-shape. Marine Systems manufactures the Virginia-class nuclear-powered submarine the Arleigh Burke-class guided-missile destroyer (DDG-51) and the Lewis and Clark-class dry cargo/ammunition combat-logistics ship (T-AKE). Subsidiary Electric Boat builds nuclear submarines (Seawolf Ohio and Los Angeles classes) while Bath Iron Works builds DDG-51 and DDG-1000 destroyers.

On the civilian side of the business the company's Aerospace segment produces mid- and large-cabin business jet aircraft for which the company provides maintenance refurbishment and outfitting.

Last but not least — serving both the military and civilian sides — the company's Information Systems and Technology business unit provides cyber security tactical communication systems sensors and cameras ruggedized computers (for use in harsh environments such as those with strong vibrations extreme temperatures and wet or dusty conditions) and antennas to customers in the DoD the Department of Homeland Security the intelligence community federal civilian agencies and international customers.

Geographic Reach

General Dynamics operates around the world serving government and commercial customers on six continents spanning more than 45 countries. North America represents its largest market generating around 75% of sales.

Sales and Marketing

General Dynamics' main customer is the US Department of Defense (DoD). The company conducts business with government customers around the world with operations in Australia Brazil Canada France Germany Mexico Spain Switzerland and the UK. About 60% of its revenues stem from the US government and 15% come from US commercial customers.

Financial Performance

General Dynamics' revenues and profits remained static during 2015 and 2016 hovering around the $31 billion and $3 billion marks for both years respectively

The company's revenues for 2016 reflected fewer aircraft deliveries in its Aerospace group offset largely by additional US Navy engineering and ship construction work within its Marine Systems segment.

C4SIR (Command Control Communications Computers Intelligence Surveillance and Reconnaissance) sales surged in 2016 due to higher volume across the business including its Warfighter Information Network-Tactical (WIN-T) mobile communications program and several programs in Canada and the UK.

Strategy

With US defense spending changing with each administration General Dynamics' business strategy addresses programs that the military continues to emphasize including the need for warfighters

and the need to replace resources lost in Iraq and Afghanistan. As the first US submarine to be configured for a post-Cold War defense landscape General Dynamics' Virginia-class submarine continues to meet the needs of the US Navy.

The company in late 2017 received a $5 billion contract from the US Navy to complete the design of its next-generation ballistic missile submarine the Columbia-class submarine. The Columbia-class submarines are nuclear-armed ballistic missile submarines that are designed to ensure a second strike capability in the event of a nuclear attack on the US.

Mergers and Acquisitions

In 2018 General Dynamics agreed to acquire CRSA a provider of information technology services to the federal government for about $6.8 billion in cash and the assumption of $2.8 billion in debt. The acquisition would beef up the IT offerings of General Dynamics catapulting it to the No. 2 spot among large government IT contractors. The combined company would have close to $10 billion in revenue from government IT services. The move comes as government spending was expected to increase with a strong push from the White House and the US Congress. The deal was expected to close in 2018.

In 2016 it acquired Bluefin Robotics a manufacturer of unmanned undersea vehicles (UUVs) that perform a wide range of missions for the US military and commercial customers. Bluefin Robotics became part of General Dynamics Mission Systems' Maritime and Strategic Systems line of business.

HISTORY

In 1899 John Holland founded Electric Boat Company a New Jersey ship and submarine builder. The company built ships PT boats and submarines during WWII but when faced with waning postwar orders CEO John Jay Hopkins diversified with the 1947 purchase of aircraft builder Canadair. Hopkins formed General Dynamics in 1952 merging Electric Boat and Canadair and buying Consolidated Vultee Aircraft (Convair) a major producer of military and civilian aircraft in 1954.

EXECUTIVES

Senior Vice President Planning Develop, Robert Helm
Vice President Administration, Raymond Kozen
EVP Marine Systems, John P. Casey, age 62, $747,500 total compensation
Chairman and CEO, Phebe N. Novakovic, age 59, $1,585,000 total compensation
VP and President General Dynamics Mission Systems, Christopher (Chris) Marzilli, age 57
VP and President Electric Boat, Jeffrey S. Geiger, age 55
VP; President Bath Iron Works, Dirk Lesko
VP and President Gulfstream Aerospace Corp., Mark L. Burns, age 57
VP and President Jet Aviation, Robert E. (Rob) Smith
EVP Combat Systems, Mark C. Roualet, age 59, $747,500 total compensation
VP; President NASSCO, Kevin M. Graney
EVP General Dynamics Information Systems and Technology Group; President General Dynamics Information Technology, S. Daniel (Dan) Johnson, age 70, $713,750 total compensation
VP and President European Land Systems, Alfonso J. Ramonet
SVP and CFO, Jason W. Aiken, age 44, $701,250 total compensation
VP and President Land Systems, Gary L. Whited, age 56

President General Dynamics Information Technology, M. Amy Gilliland
Vice President of Human Resources, Amy Gilliland
Vice President Supply Chain Management, Kevin Mooney
Vice President President Land Systems, Mark Smith
Vice President And Deputy General Coun, Gregory Gallopoulos
Corporate Vice President for Communications and Government Relations, Teresa Gaines
Executive Vice President Information Systems And T, Gerard Demuro
Vice President Internal Audit, Wayne Maiers
Director of Government Relations and Submarine Programs, Ted Hack
Vice President, Phelecia Jefferson
Executive Vice President Information Systems and Technology, David Heebner
Vice President Strategic Planning, Marion T Davis
Director of Government Relations, Tomas R Madson
Vice President, Markeba Gregory
Vice President Information Technology, Tommy Augustsson
Vice President Information Technology, Kenneth Hill
Director of Surgery, Todd Tarby
Senior Vice President Service Delivery for AIS, Tom Carstenbrock
Vice President, Asha Wiethers
Vice President Communications Information Technology, Mark Meudt
Vice President and Treasurer, David H Fogg
Vice President International, William Schmieder
Executive Vice President Aerospace, Joseph T Lombardo
Vice President Information Technology and Infrastructure, Phillip Lacombel
Senior Vice President General Counsel Secretary, David A Savner
Vice President, David Pizzano
VP Engineering, Jack Manning
Vice President Planning And Development, Bob Helm
Vice President new Marketing, Chris Trella
Vice President Program Integration And C, Kenneth Perry
Vice President Program Integration and Concept Development, Ken Perry
Vice President, Vincent Shugrue
Board Member, William Fricks
Treasurer, Bob Selee
Assistant Treasurer, Chris Wood
Auditors: KPMG LLP

LOCATIONS

HQ: General Dynamics Corp
2941 Fairview Park Drive, Suite 100, Falls Church, VA 22042-4513
Phone: 703 876-3000
Web: www.generaldynamics.com

2016 Sales

	$ mil.	% of total
North America	24,122	77
Europe	2,355	8
Africa/Middle East	2,668	8
Asia/Pacific	1,914	6
South America	294	1
Total	31,353	100

PRODUCTS/OPERATIONS

2016 Sales

	$ mil.	% of total
Information Systems and Technology	9,187	29
Aerospace	8,362	27
Marine Systems	8,202	26
Combat Systems	5,602	18
Total	31,353	100

2016 Sales

	$ mil.	% of total
Products	19,885	63
Services	11,468	37
Total	**31,353**	**100**

COMPETITORS

Airbus	Leidos
BAE SYSTEMS	Lockheed Martin
Boeing	Motorola Solutions
Bombardier	Navistar International
Cisco Systems	Nokia
DRS Technologies	Northrop Grumman
Dassault Aviation	Orbital ATK
Day & Zimmermann	Peugeot
FLIR Systems	Raytheon
HP Enterprise Services	Renco
Harris Corp.	Rockwell Collins
ITT Corp.	Textron
L3 Technologies	United Technologies

HISTORICAL FINANCIALS

Company Type: Public

Income Statement

FYE: December 31

	REVENUE ($ mil.)	NET INCOME ($ mil.)	NET PROFIT MARGIN	EMPLOYEES
12/17	30,973	2,912	9.4%	98,600
12/16	31,353	2,955	9.4%	98,800
12/15	31,469	2,965	9.4%	99,900
12/14	30,852	2,533	8.2%	99,500
12/13	31,218	2,357	7.6%	96,000
Annual Growth	(0.2%)	5.4%	—	0.7%

2017 Year-End Financials

Debt ratio: 11.36%
Return on equity: 25.99%
Cash ($ mil.): 2,983
Current ratio: 1.40
Long-term debt ($ mil.): 3,980

No. of shares (mil.): 296
Dividends
  Yield: 0.0%
  Payout: 34.3%
Market value ($ mil.): 60,403

	STOCK PRICE ($) FY Close	P/E High/Low	PER SHARE ($) Earnings	Dividends	Book Value
12/17	203.45	22 18	9.56	3.28	38.52
12/16	172.66	18 13	9.52	2.97	36.29
12/15	137.36	17 14	9.08	2.69	34.31
12/14	137.62	19 12	7.42	2.42	35.61
12/13	95.55	14 10	6.67	2.19	41.03
Annual Growth	20.8%	— —	9.4%	10.6%	(1.6%)

General Electric Co

From turbines and oilfield equipment to aircraft engines and power plants General Electric (GE) is plugged in to industrial equipment businesses that shape the modern world. The company produces aircraft engines locomotives and other transportation equipment generators and turbines and oil and gas exploration and production equipment. GE also is a major healthcare products provider. GE still owns GE Capital but has gradually divested the majority of its non-industrial business assets. To accelerate growth for its oil and gas business in 2017 GE spent $25 billion to acquire Baker Hughes and merged it with its GE Oil & Gas division.

HISTORY

General Electric (GE) was established in 1892 in New York the result of a merger between Thomson-Houston and Edison General Electric. Charles Coffin was GE's first president and Thomas Edison who left the company in 1894 was one of the directors.

GE's financial strength (backed by the Morgan banking house) and its research focus contributed to its initial success. Early products included such Edison legacies as light bulbs elevators motors toasters and other appliances under the GE and Hotpoint labels. In the 1920s GE joined AT&T and Westinghouse in a radio broadcasting venture Radio Corporation of America (RCA) but GE sold off its RCA holdings in 1930 because of an antitrust ruling.

By 1980 GE had reached $25 billion in revenues from plastics consumer electronics nuclear reactors and jet engines. But it had become rigid and bureaucratic. Jack Welch became president in 1981 and shook up the company. He decentralized operations and adopted a strategy of pursuing only high-achieving ventures and dumping those that didn't perform. GE shed air-conditioning (1982) housewares (1984) and semiconductors (1988) and with the proceeds acquired Employers Reinsurance (1984); RCA including NBC (1986 but sold RCA in 1987); CGR medical equipment (1987); and investment banker Kidder Peabody (1990).

In the early 1990s GE grew its lighting business. It bought mutual fund wholesaler GNA in 1993 and GE Investment Management (now GE Financial Network) began selling mutual funds to the public.

GE sold scandal-plagued Kidder Peabody to Paine Webber in 1994. General Electric Capital Services (GECS) expanded its lines buying Amex Life Insurance (Aon's Union Fidelity unit) and Life Insurance Co. of Virginia in 1995 and First Colony the next year. The company sold its struggling GEnie online service in 1996 and formed an NBC and Microsoft venture the MSNBC cable news channel. In 1997 GE Engine Services bought aircraft engine maintenance firms Greenwich Air Services and UNC.

GE acquired Lockheed Martin's medical imaging unit in 1997 and added to the medical systems business with the 1998 purchase of Marquette Medical Systems. In 1998 GECS became the first foreign company to enter Japan's life insurance market when it bought assets from Toho Mutual Life Insurance and set up GE Edison Life.

In 1999 GECS bought the 53% of Montgomery Ward it didn't already own along with the retailer's direct-marketing arm as Montgomery Ward emerged from bankruptcy. (Ward declared bankruptcy again in 2000.) In 2000 it reorganized GE Information Systems to form an e-commerce unit Global eXchange Services (GXS). (GE sold 90% of GXS to buyout firm Francisco Partners in 2002.)

Later in 2000 the company announced its biggest acquisition of the Welch era. Moving in at the last minute GE trumped a rival bid from United Technologies and agreed to pay $45 billion in stock for manufacturing giant Honeywell International and to assume $3.4 billion in Honeywell debt.

Welch by then viewed as one of the best corporate leaders in the US had agreed to postpone his retirement from April 2001 until the end of that year in order to oversee the completion of the Honeywell acquisition. But European regulators concerned about the potential strength of the combined GE-Honeywell aircraft-related businesses blocked the Honeywell deal that summer. Welch then stepped down and Jeff Immelt formerly pres-

ident and CEO of GE Medical Systems succeeded him in September 2001.

Immelt initially set about reshaping GE by spinning off its life and mortgage insurance businesses into a new entity Genworth Financial which went public in 2004 (completely divested in 2006). GE acquired UK-based Amersham a medical diagnostics and life sciences company since renamed GE Healthcare Medical Diagnostics.

In 2006 GE sold off most of its remaining insurance businesses including GE Insurance Solutions and Employers Reinsurance in a sale to Swiss Re. The company kept its US life reinsurance business.

Citing rising commodities costs GE sold its advanced materials unit which produced silicone quartz and ceramics products to Apollo Management and sold its GE Plastics unit (now SABIC Innovative Plastics) to SABIC for more than $11 billion in 2007. Also that year GE shut down the operations of wholesale subprime lender WMC Mortgage.

At the same time GE built some of its traditional businesses through acquisitions. In early 2007 the company's aviation division acquired aircraft systems manufacturer Smiths Aerospace from Smiths Group. GE Energy bought oil and gas production equipment supplier Vetco Gray and the US retail natural gas distribution network of Knight (then named Kinder Morgan).

In 2011 GE sold a controlling stake in NBCUniversal to Comcast. GE retained a 49% stake in the media venture.

In 2013 GE sold its 49% stake in NBCUniversal for nearly $17 billion to Comcast as part of its strategy to focus on its industrial operations. There was already a structure in place for Comcast to eventually take full ownership of NBCUniversal but stronger than expected growth from the joint venture accelerated those plans.

GE in 2013 acquired Texas-based Lufkin Industries which specializes in providing artificial lift technologies for the oil and gas industry as well as making industrial gears. The $3.3 billion deal broadened the GE Oil & Gas unit and supports the company's plans to tighten its focus on industrial customers by providing services and equipment. In 2014 GE launched Predictivity a portfolio of web-based products to help oil and gas customers in the Asia/Pacific region improve operational and fiscal productivity.

To further boost its industrial operations the partnered with XD Electric Group in 2013 to combine GE's grid automation capabilities with XD's high-voltage power equipment. GE Energy Financial Services has also recently invested in Japan's largest solar power project to be built in Okayama Prefecture; it holds a 60% stake in the project.

In 2013 to boost its global reach GE's financial arm bought a $2.3 billion portfolio of commercial real estate loans from Deutsche Postbank that comprised 90% British as well as German and French properties. GE Capital also acquired MetLife's banking unit in 2013 adding some $6.4 billion in deposits and an established online banking platform.

That year the company also bought Italy-based industrial manufacturer Avio's aviation business which it renamed Avio Aero for $4.3 billion. The move expanded GE's activities in the appealing jet propulsion segment and strengthens its global supply chain.

In 2014 GE sold GE Money Bank AB business in Sweden Denmark and Norway to Santander for $2.3 billion. That year the company also announced plans to exit its North American Retail Finance operations.

EXECUTIVES

Chairman and CEO, John L. Flannery, age 55
SVP; Chairman and CEO GE Capital, Richard A. (Rich) Laxer
President and CEO GE Fanuc Intelligent Platforms Technology Infrastructure, Maryrose T. Sylvester
SVP and President and CEO GE Aviation, David L. Joyce, age 60, $1,333,333 total compensation
SVP and CTO, Victor (Vic) Abate, age 48
SVP and President and CEO GE Power, Steve Bolze, age 54
CFO, Jamie S. Miller, age 48
President and CEO GE Africa, Jay W. Ireland
President and CEO GE Europe and Alstom Integration Leader, Mark Hutchinson, age 57
President and CEO Central and Eastern Europe GE Money, Dmitri L. Stockton, age 53
President and CEO GE Korea, Chris Khang
SVP and President and CEO Power Services, Paul A. McElhinney
President and CEO Baker Hughes a GE company, Lorenzo Simonelli, age 44
SVP and President and CEO GE Power, Russell Stokes, age 46
SVP and Chief Digital Officer GE and CEO GE Digital, William (Bill) Ruh, age 56
President and CEO GE Renewable Energy, J©r´me P ©cresse
President and CEO Onshore Wind, Pete McCabe
CEO GE Malaysia, Datuk Mark Rozario
CEO GE Australia, Max York
CEO GE New Zealand and GE Papua New Guinea, Kevin Hart
President and CEO GE APAC, Wouter Van Wersch
CEO GE Japan, Eriko Asai
Vice President, Kevin Czarnecki
Assistant Vice President, Valerie Bouchereau
Vice President Of Sales, Michael Sylstra
Vice President For Clinical And Regulatory Affairs, Mei Barselou
Vice President Strategic Initiatives, Allison Garrigan
Senior Vice President Vice Public Relations, Rene Buhay
Senior Vice President, Kathleen Chomienne
Legal Secretary, Marlene Gerardi
Senior Vice President, Matthew Pauley
Senior Vice President, Thomas Costello
Vice President Engineering, Luciano Cerone
Vice President, John Laws
Vice President National Direct Sales, David Robinson
Vice President Risk, Dennis Duffany
Vice President Speciality Solutions Sales Southeast, Randy Goins
Assistant Vice President: Franchiefinance, Vince Malizia
Vice President Retail Finance, Stephen Motta
National Account Manager Sears, Gary Howard
Assistant Vice President, Dennis Leonard
Vice President Develop, Michael Dahlweid
Senior Vice President, Bob Vail
Senior Vice President, David Richman
National Account Manager, Jack Hodes
Board Member, Shannon Winlove-smith
Board Member, Heather Bunyard
Advisory Board Member, Jill Johnson
Board Member, Linda Reynolds
Board Member, Jessica Gee
Board Member, Jody Engel
Board Member, Brian Alexander
Board Member, Jiahong Wang
Board Member, Mike Klein
Board Member, Michael Tengelin
Vice Chairman, Jesse Rock
Board Member, Michele Zizzi
Board Member, Eric Denoyel
Auditors: KPMG LLP

LOCATIONS

HQ: General Electric Co
  41 Farnsworth Street, Boston, MA 02210
Phone: 617 443-3000
Web: www.ge.com

Sales 2016

	% of total
US	43
Europe	17
Asia	17
Americas	9
Middle East & Africa	14
Total	**100**

PRODUCTS/OPERATIONS

2016 Sales

	$ mil.	% of total
Power	26,827	22
Aviation	26,261	21
Healthcare	18,291	15
Oil & Gas	12,898	10
Energy Connections & Lighting	15,133	12
Capital	10,905	9
Renewable Energy	9,033	7
Transportation	4,713	4
Corporate items & eliminations	(368)	.
Total	**123,693**	**100**

COMPETITORS

ABB	Rockwell Automation
ALSTOM	Rolls-Royce
Agilent Technologies	Schneider Electric
Atlas Copco	Siemens AG
Caterpillar	Textron
Emerson Electric	ThyssenKrupp
FANUC	Toshiba
ITT Corp.	United Technologies
Raytheon	

HISTORICAL FINANCIALS

Company Type: Public

Income Statement

FYE: December 31

	REVENUE ($ mil.)	NET INCOME ($ mil.)	NET PROFIT MARGIN	EMPLOYEES
12/16	123,693	8,831	7.1%	295,000
12/15	117,386	(6,126)	—	333,000
12/14	148,589	15,233	10.3%	305,000
12/13	146,045	13,057	8.9%	307,000
12/12	147,359	13,641	9.3%	305,000
Annual Growth	(4.3%)	(10.3%)	—	(0.8%)

2016 Year-End Financials

Debt ratio: 37.19%—
Return on equity: 10.12%
Cash ($ mil.): 48,129
Current ratio: 1.69
Long-term debt ($ mil.): 105,080

Dividends
  Yield: 0.0%
  Payout: 104.4%
Market value ($ mil.): —

	STOCK PRICE ($) FY Close	P/E High/Low		Earnings	PER SHARE ($) Dividends	Book Value
12/16	31.60	37	31	0.89	0.93	8.67
12/15	31.15	—		(0.61)	0.92	10.48
12/14	25.27	19	16	1.50	0.89	12.74
12/13	28.03	22	16	1.27	0.79	12.98
12/12	20.99	18	14	1.29	0.70	11.82
Annual Growth	10.8%	—	—	(8.9%)	7.4%	(7.5%)

General Mills, Inc.

General Mills is high in the ranks of consumer packaged goods companies. Some of its #1 and #2 market-leading brands include Betty Crocker dessert mixes Gold Medal flour Pillsbury cookie dough and Yoplait yogurt. It competes with Kellogg to be the top cereal maker with a brand arsenal that includes Kix Chex Cheerios Lucky Charms and Wheaties. While most of the firm's sales come from the US General Mills is working to extend the reach and position of its brands globally. It picked up natural foods maker Annie's in 2014 and premium meat snack maker EPIC Provisions in 2016.

HISTORY

Cadwallader Washburn built his first flour mill in 1866 in Minneapolis which eventually became the Washburn Crosby Company. After winning a gold medal for flour at an 1880 exposition the company changed the name of its best flour to Gold Medal Flour.

In 1921 advertising manager Sam Gale created fictional spokeswoman Betty Crocker so that correspondence to housewives could go out with her signature. The firm introduced Wheaties cereal in 1924. James Bell named president in 1925 consolidated the company with other US mills in 1928 to form General Mills the world's largest miller. The companies operated independently of one another with corporate headquarters coordinating advertising and merchandising.

General Mills began introducing convenience foods such as Bisquick (1931) and Cheerios (1941). During WWII it produced war goods such as ordnance equipment and developed chemical and electronics divisions.

When Edwin Rawlings became CEO in 1961 he closed half of the flour mills and divested such unprofitable lines as electronics. This cost $200 million in annual sales but freed resources for such acquisitions as Kenner Products (toys 1967) and Parker Brothers (board games 1968) which made General Mills the world's largest toy company.

During the next 20 years the company made many acquisitions including Gorton's (frozen seafood 1968) Monet (jewelry 1968) Eddie Bauer (outerwear 1971) and The Talbots (women's clothing 1973). It bought Red Lobster in 1970 and acquired the US rights to Yoplait yogurt in 1977. When the toy and fashion divisions' profits fell in 1984 they were spun off as Kenner Parker Toys and Crystal Brands (1985). Reemphasizing food in 1989 the firm sold many businesses including Eddie Bauer and Talbots.

To expand into Europe General Mills struck two important joint ventures: Cereal Partners Worldwide (with Nestl © in 1989) and Snack Ventures Europe (with PepsiCo in 1992).

As part of a cereal price war in 1994 the company cut coupon promotion costs by $175 million and lowered prices on many cereals. But some retailers did not pass on the price cuts to consumers due to shortages that developed after the FDA found an unauthorized pesticide in some cereals. General Mills destroyed 55 million boxes of cereal at a cost of $140 million. Stephen Sanger became CEO in 1995. That year the company sold Gortons to Unilever and spun off its restaurant businesses as Darden Restaurants.

Focused on a food-only future in the late 1990s General Mills picked up several smaller businesses including Ralcorp Holdings' Chex snack and cereal lines and Gardetto's Bakery snack mixes as well as the North American rights to Olibra an appetite suppressant food additive made by Scotia Holdings. Entering the natural foods market in 2000 General Mills launched Sunrise organic cereal and bought organic foods producer Small Planet Foods.

Big changes came in 2001 when General Mills became the #1 cereal maker in the US overtaking Kellogg for the first time since 1906. The company then completed its $10.5 billion purchase of Pillsbury from Diageo in October 2001. A month later General Mills sold competing product lines to International Multifoods. Also that year the company launched a 50-50 joint venture with DuPont to develop soy beverages marketed under the 8th Continent brand name. While busily integrating Pillsbury in 2002 General Mills saw its income fall and watched as Kellogg regained the lead in the cereal market. In 2003 the SEC began an investigation into the company's sales and accounting practices (which it terminated in 2005 taking no action against General Mills).

In 2004 General Mills filed a universal shelf registration with the SEC the result of which is that Diageo had to register the common shares of General Mills that it owns before it could sell those shares in a public offering. Also as a result of the shelf registration two Diageo-designated members of General Mills' board (including Diageo CEO Paul Walsh) resigned as a result of a change in the two companies' stockholders agreement that terminated Diageo's right to designate two General Mills' board members. Diageo sold part of its approximate 20% stake in General Mills. General Mills in turn sold an $835 million stake to an affiliate of Lehman Brothers Holding and used $750 million to buy back the Diageo shares and $85 million to pay down debt.

Also in 2004 the company sold its US H ☐agen-Dazs ice cream shop franchise business to Dreyer's Grand Ice Cream. In 2005 it sold its stake in Snack Ventures Europe joint venture to PepsiCo for $750 million. That year the company introduced Yoplait Healthy Heart which contains cholesterol-lowering plant sterols.

Diageo sold two-thirds of its 20% stake in General Mills in 2005. Later that year General Mills announced the sale of Lloyd's barbecue business to Hormel Foods. In 2006 Cereal Partners Worldwide (its joint venture with Nestl ©) acquired the Australian breakfast cereal operations of Uncle Tobys from Burns Philp.

After more than 10 years of being ignored the Jolly Green Giant came out of retirement in 2005 as part of a multi-million dollar marketing campaign by General Mills to up its veggie sales. The next year General Mills declined to renew its licensing agreement with Archer Daniels Midland regarding the sale and marketing of Pillsbury Bakery Flour to the industrial and foodservice sectors. General Mills integrated the brand which consists of mixes and frozen bakery products into its bakery ingredients segment.

In order to develop healthier products in 2006 the company entered a supply agreement for DHA (an omega-3 fatty acid said to play a role in mental and cardiovascular health) with Martek Biosciences maker of DHA (which is already widely used in infant formula).

General Mills pulled its reduced-sugar children's cereal from the market in 2007 due to poor sales. Sweetened with SPLENDA the cereals never took off with consumers perhaps due to resistance to the sugar replacement. (Kellogg and Kraft use sugar in their reduced-sugar cereal offerings.) That year the company acquired UK chilled pastry company Saxby Bros.

Also in 2007 CEO Sanger stepped down. President and COO Ken Powell replaced him. The following year General Mills and DuPont sold their soy-milk joint venture 8th Continent to Stremicks Heritage Foods.

To better focus on its core brands and foodservice offerings the company in mid-2010 sold its Delicity chain of bakeries in Argentina to Tentissimo Group which also operates restaurants under the Tentissimo banner in the country. The deal included the Delicity brand five company-owned bakeries and franchiser rights which apply to the roughly 55 bakery locations operated by franchisees. General Mills also agreed to continue supplying dough products to the chain. It had owned Delicity since acquiring Pillsbury in 2001.

In 2008 the company sold its PopÂ·Secret operations to Diamond Foods for some $190 million in cash. PopÂ·Secret is the second-largest-selling branded popcorn in the US after Orville Redenbacher which is made by ConAgra. (ConAgra also makes Act II microwaveable popcorn.) While General Mills said it is concentrating its efforts on increasing the sales of its more lucrative core brands the high price of corn most probably also figured into the decision to jettison PopÂ·Secret.

General Mills made no divestures in 2009 but in 2010 the company ceased making Perfect Portions refrigerated biscuits and exited the kids' refrigerated yogurt beverage and microwave soup segments in its US retail operations; internationally it also stopped the manufacture of foodservice breadcrumbs with the sale of its Brazilian bread and pasta plant for $6 million. These product cessations were made in response to its declining financial results particularly in its international segment.

To better focus on its retail sales channels in late 2010 General Mills sold its Croissant King (acquired in 2005) and van den Bergh's (acquired in 1999) frozen bakery business in Australia to Ireland's Kerry Group. The sale includes frozen dough and pastry products sold to professional bakers.

Following that divestiture General Mills in 2011 acquired Australia's Pasta Master a maker of chilled Italian meals pasta and sauces. The purchase valued at nearly $40 million broadened General Mills' ready-to-cook pasta offerings.

To help offset weakness in its core cereal business General Mills is beefing up its yogurt empire through acquisitions such as its $1.2 billion purchase of a controlling stake in Yoplait in 2011 a brand that it had licensed for several decades. The company acquired the 50% stake in Yoplait owned by French investment firm PAI Partners plus 1% from dairy cooperative Social. Additionally General Mills acquired a 50% share of a related firm that owns Yoplait's global branding rights. General Mills aims to expand Yoplait's operations in France Europe and the rest of the world. Also in 2011 General Mills acquired Dean Foods' Mountain High all-natural yogurt business for about $85 million. The brand became part of General Mills' Yoplait USA division.

In line with its strategy to grow its business in global markets General Mills acquired Parampara's ready-to-cook spice and sauce mixes made and marketed in India and also exported to the US Canada and Japan. In 2012 it bought Brazilian food maker Yoki Alimentos which makes and markets more than 600 items under nine brands including Yoki and Kitano. The deal doubles General Mills' annual sales in Latin America.

EXECUTIVES

SVP; CEO Cereal Partners Worldwide, David P. (Dave) Homer

SVP and President Meals Division, Christopher D. (Chris) O'Leary, age 58, $730,133 total compensation

VP; President AnnieÂ's Foods, John M. Foraker, age 54

SVP External Relations; President General Mills Foundation, Kimberly A. (Kim) Nelson, age 54

SVP; President Greater China, Gary Chu

VP Treasurer, Donal L. (Don) Mulligan, age 57, $736,050 total compensation

SVP; President Big G Cereals, James H. (Jim) Murphy

EVP Supply Chain, John R. Church, age 51, $577,767 total compensation

SVP; President Meals, Michele S. Meyer

SVP; President Sales and Channel Development, Shawn P. O'Grady, age 53

CEO, Jeffrey L. Harmening, age 50, $775,000 total compensation

EVP Innovation Technology and Quality, Peter C. Erickson, age 56

SVP; President Latin America, Sean N. Walker

SVP; President Europe Australia and New Zealand, Jonathon J. (Jon) Nudi

VP; President Snacks, Anton Vincent

VP; President Yoplait International, Olivier Faujour

VP; President Asia Middle East and Africa, Christina Law

VP; President Yoplait USA, David Clark

VP; President Convenience and Foodservice, Bethany C. Quam

VP; President Baking, Elizabeth M. Nordlie

Vice President Corporate Services, Mike Nordstrom

Vice President and Chief Tax Officer, Gerald Morris

Vice President Information Technology, John Spylka

Vice President Global Internal Audit, Todd Leidahl

Senior Vice President Chief Human Resources Officer, Jacqueline Williams-Roll

Vice President and Deputy General Counsel, Eric Wedepohl

National Account Manager, Matt Thom

Vice President, Dave Dudick

Vice President Yoplait, Camille Gibson

National Account Manager, Kurt Schuitema

Vice President of Marketing Snacks, Doug McGillivray

Senior Vice President Finance, Keith Woodward

Executive Vice President, Roderick Palmore

Hrvp, Ruth Harris

Vice President Sales Strategy and Capabilities, David Wurm

Vice President And President General Mills Canada, Christianne Strauss

Vice President Of Human Resources, Victor Huang

Vice President and Chief Operations Officer, Missy Mound

Vice President Director, Herman Miller

Vice President, Glenn Krueger

Vice President, Becky Oagrady

Vice President of Maintenance and Engineering, Christophe Oleary

Vice President ww Engineering and Technology, Stephen Sanger

Vice President, Lex Arbesfeld

Vice President, Amina Aska

Vice President, Warren Boleware

Vice President, Glenn Augustine

Vice President, Marlene Simon

Vice President, Mike Trembley

Vice President, Michelle Randall

Vice President, Jonathan Dawidowski

Vice President, Justin Leigh

Vice President Trade Marketing, Bryant Johnson

Vice President Trade Marketing, Lohr Lesueur

National Account Manager, Lynn Vinnai

Vice President, Putnam D McMillan

Senior Vice President, Dan Malina

Vice President, Judy Boughton

Vice President of Human Resources, Joseph Mucha

National Sales Manager Foodservice, Esme Plessis

Chairman, Kendall J. (Ken) Powell, age 64

Secretary, Christopher Rauschl

Auditors: KPMG LLP

LOCATIONS

HQ: General Mills, Inc.
Number One General Mills Boulevard, Minneapolis,
MN 55426
Phone: 763 764-7600   **Fax:** 763 764-8330
Web: www.generalmills.com

2016 sales

	$ mil.	% of total
US	11,930	72
International		
Europe	1,998	12
Canada	929	6
Asia/Pacific	995	6
Latin America	709	4
Total	**16,563**	**100**

PRODUCTS/OPERATIONS

2016 sales

	$ mil.	% of total
Snacks	3,297	20
Yogurt	2,760	17
Cereal	2,731	17
Convenient meals	2,779	17
Baking mixes & integrates	1,704	10
Dough	1,820	11
Vegetables	532	3
Super-premium ice cream	731	4
Other	206	1
Total	**16,563**	**100**

2016 sales

	$ mil.	% of total
US Retail	10,007	60
International	4,632	28
Convenience Stores & Foodservice	1,923	12
Total	**16,563**	**100**

Selected Brands

Dessert and baking mixes
 Betty Crocker
 Bisquick
 Gold Medal
 SuperMoist
 Warm Delights
Dry dinners and shelf stable and frozen vegetable
 products
 Annie's
 Bac*O's
 Betty Crocker
 Chicken Helper
 Diablitos
 Green Giant
 Hamburger Helper
 Old El Paso
 Potato Buds
 Simply Steam
 Suddenly Salad
 Valley Selections
 Tuna Helper
 Wanchai Ferry
Frozen pizza and pizza snacks
 Jeno's
 Party Pizza
 Pillsbury Pizza Minis
 Pillsbury Pizza Pops
 Pizza Rolls
 Totino's
Grain fruit and savory snacks
 Annie's
 Bugles
 Chex Mix
 Fiber One
 Fruit By The Foot
 Fruit Roll-Ups
 Gardetto's
 Gushers
 Lärabar
 Nature Valley
 Stickerz
Ice cream and frozen desserts
 Hagen-Dazs
Organic products
 Annie's
 Cascadian Farm
 Muir Glen
Ready-to-eat cereals

Basic 4
Cheerios
Chex
Cinnamon Toast Crunch
Clusters
Cocoa Puffs
Cookie Crisp
Fiber One
Golden Grahams
Kix
Lucky Charms
Oatmeal Crisp
Reese's Puffs
Total
Trix
Wheaties
Ready-to-serve soup
 Progresso
Refrigerated and frozen dough products
 Big Deluxe
 Golden Layers
 Grands!
 Jus-Rol
 La Salte?a
 Latina
 Pasta Master
 Pillsbury
 Savorings
 Toaster Scrambles
 Toaster Strudel
 V.Pearl
 Wanchai Ferry
Refrigerated yogurt
 Go-GURT
 Fiber One
 Mountain High
 Trix
 Yoplait
 Yoplait Kids
 Yoplait Whips!
 YoPlus

COMPETITORS

B&G Foods	Hain Celestial
Barbara's Bakery	Hanover Foods
Bay State Milling	Heinz
Ben & Jerry's	Kellogg
Big Heart Pet Brands	King Arthur Flour
Birds Eye	Lakeside Foods
Blue Bell	MOM Brands
Bob's Red Mill Natural	Manischewitz Company
Foods	McKee Foods
Campbell Soup	Mondelez International
Carvel	Mrs. Fields
Chelsea Milling	Nature's Path
Cold Stone Creamery	Nestl©
ConAgra	Pinnacle Foods
Dairy Queen	Pro-Fac
Danone	Procter & Gamble
Dole Food	Ralston Food
Dreyer's	Seneca Foods
Fresh□«ns	Stonyfield Farm
Friendly's Ice Cream	Victoria Packing
Frito-Lay	YoCream
Gilster-Mary Lee	

HISTORICAL FINANCIALS

Company Type: Public

Income Statement

FYE: May 28

	REVENUE ($ mil.)	NET INCOME ($ mil.)	NET PROFIT MARGIN	EMPLOYEES
05/17	15,619	1,657	10.6%	38,000
05/16	16,563	1,697	10.2%	39,000
05/15	17,630	1,221	6.9%	42,000
05/14	17,909	1,824	10.2%	43,000
05/13	17,774	1,855	10.4%	41,000
Annual Growth	**(3.2%)**	**(2.8%)**	**—**	**(1.9%)**

2017 Year-End Financials

Debt ratio: 43.47%
Return on equity: 35.90%
Cash ($ mil.): 766
Current ratio: 0.76
Long-term debt ($ mil.): 7,642

No. of shares (mil.): 576
Dividends
 Yield: 0.0%
 Payout: 69.3%
Market value ($ mil.): 33,068

	STOCK PRICE ($) FY Close	P/E High/Low		PER SHARE ($) Earnings	Dividends	Book Value
05/17	57.32	26	20	2.77	1.92	7.50
05/16	62.87	23	19	2.77	1.78	8.26
05/15	56.15	28	24	1.97	1.67	8.35
05/14	53.81	19	16	2.83	1.55	10.67
05/13	48.98	18	13	2.79	1.32	10.41
Annual Growth	**4.0%**	**—**	**—**	**(0.2%)**	**9.8%**	**(7.9%)**

General Motors Co

General Motors (GM) one of the world's largest auto manufacturers makes cars and trucks with well known brands such as Buick Cadillac Chevrolet and GMC. GM also builds cars through its GM Daewoo and Holden units. The company operates through almost a half dozen business segments: GM North America GM Europe GM International Operations and GM South America. Financing activities are primarily conducted by General Motors Financial Company. In mid-2017 GM sold its European operations (consisting of its Opel and Vauxhuall businesses) to France-based PSA Group for $2.2 billion.

Operations

GM operates through the following segments: GM North America (GMNA) GM Europe (GME) GM International Operations (GMIO) GM South America (GMSA) and GM Financial. GM North America is its largest segment accounting for more than 70% of total revenue.

GM Financial is an automotive finance company and global provider of retail loan and lease lending products and services. Additionally GM Financial offers commercial products to dealers that include new and used vehicle inventory financing inventory insurance working capital capital improvement loans and storage center financing.

Geographic Reach

GM has more than 100 locations in the US (excluding automotive financing operations and dealerships). It has assembly manufacturing distribution office or warehousing operations in more than 60 other countries.

GM Financial has 50 facilities of which 25 are located in the US. Its major facilities outside the US reside in Canada China Germany the UK Brazil and Mexico. The US generates around 65% of its total sales.

Sales and Marketing

The company sells cars and trucks to fleet customers including daily rental car companies commercial fleet customers leasing companies and governments. GM markets its vehicles worldwide primarily through a network of independent distributors dealers and authorized sales service and parts outlets with a network of over 19500 dealerships. It spends about $5 billion each year on advertising.

Financial Performance

GM experienced historic growth in 2016 as revenues peaked at $166 billion its highest total since the recession. This was fueled by higher sales from GM Financial (48%) and GM North America (12%).

GM North America in 2016 experienced strong retail demand for the Chevrolet Malibu and Spark full-size trucks and SUVs and the Buick Envision. GM Financial's surge in sales stemmed from increased leased vehicle income of $3.1 billion due to a larger lease portfolio.

Two segments however experienced declines for 2016. GMSA sales dropped by 8% due to decreased wholesale volumes due to difficult economic conditions in Brazil and Venezuela that drove an industry reduction of 12% compared to the same period in 2015. In addition GMIO sales fell by 7% due to decreased wholesale volumes of pick-up trucks and passenger cars in Egypt and South Africa and full-size trucks and SUVs in the Middle East due to low oil prices.

GM's net income declined 3% from $9.69 billion in 2015 to $9.43 billion in 2016 mainly due income taxes paid in 2016 as opposed to tax benefits earned the previous year. GM's operating cash flow surged by 38% from $11.98 billion in 2015 to $16.55 billion in 2016. This was mostly due to the record-setting revenues for 2016 and a reduction in foreign currency transaction costs.

Strategy

The company's strategic plan includes several major initiatives to help to achieve 9-10% margins by the early 2020s. The initiatives include a strong product pipeline to retain customers; leading the industry in quality and safety; taking a lead in product design with light-weight and mixed material body structures and in leading edge technology; growing its brands (especially the Cadillac brand); divesting underforming operations; and continuing to develop GM Financial as its captive automotive financing company.

Adhering to this strategy in mid-2017 GM sold its Opel and Vauxhall businesses to European carmaker PSA Group for about $2.2 billion. The Opel/Vauxhall combination represented about $19 billion in annual revenue and included six assembly plants five parts facilities and an engineering center. The significant move of exiting a business it has controlled for nearly 90 years has followed unfruitful efforts since 1999 to make the Opel/Vauxhall subsidiary profitable again. The company has lost nearly $20 billion in Europe during that time.

Going forward GM will instead focus on investing in China and the Americas. In China it aims to increase the number of nameplates under the Buick Chevrolet and Cadillac brands in China and continue to grow its business under the Baojun Jiefang and Wuling brands.It has also singled out the luxury segment as a springboard for future growth in China buoyed by strong sales of Cadillac vehicles. In the electric car market GM aims to launch at least 10 clean-energy vehicles in China between 2016 and 2020; this includes its Cadillac CT6 plug-in Buick Velite 5 and Baojun E100 models.

GM's previous efforts to develop energy-saving models included the Chevrolet Volt an electric car powered by a lithium-ion battery able to drive 38 miles on one charge introduced in late 2010. In 2015 the auto maker introduced the second-generation Chevrolet Volt. It also launched the Chevrolet Bolt EV in 2016 which can drive 238 miles on a full charge.

To compete with up-and-coming competitors like Uber Google and Tesla GM in 2016 began offering a new car-sharing service called Maven which combines its multiple car-sharing programs under a single brand and expands its offerings to multiple cities and communities across the US. Operating in 17 cities with 100000 members so far Maven targets customers who don't want to own a car but still need a ride every now and then. The customer downloads the Maven app to their phone and provides their driver?s license number and other data. After Maven checks their driving record to make sure they're a safe driver he or she is then eligible to rent a GM vehicle for as long as they like be it an hour or a week. Since GM owns the vehicles to choose from it can insert whatever cars it wants in the Maven fleet which optimizes costs and efficiency.

Mergers and Acquisitions

GM often uses acquisitions as a means to fortify its technological expertise and grow rapidly in cutting-edge markets. As such the company in 2016 acquired California-based Cruise Automation Inc. (Cruise) an autonomous vehicle technology company. GM paid $581 million for Cruise in order to accelerate its development of autonomous vehicles. GM has recently tested autonomous vehicles on public roads in San Francisco; Scottsdale Arizona; and Warren Michigan.

Growing its financial services operations in 2015 GM Financial acquired Ally Financial's 40% stake in SAIC-GMAC in China for $1 billion. The strategic move was partially responsible for a 48% surge in GM Financial's sales from 2015 to 2016.

Company Background

In the early years of the auto industry hundreds of carmakers each produced a few models. William Durant who bought a failing Buick Motors in 1904 reasoned that manufacturers could benefit from banding together and formed the General Motors Company in Flint Michigan in 1908.

The auto giant went through a six-week period of bankruptcy protection in 2009. GM was split into two companies when it emerged from Chapter 11 — General Motors and Motors Liquidation (the name for leftover assets). In 2011 Motors Liquidation sold the majority of its assets which encompassed almost 90 industrial sites in 14 states which cleared the way for GM bondholders to receive stock in the new company.

EXECUTIVES

SVP; President and CEO GM Financial, Daniel E. (Dan) Berce, age 64

EVP Legal and Public Policy and General Counsel, Craig B. Glidden, age 59, $583,333 total compensation

EVP; President Europe; Chairman Management Board Opel Group, Karl-Thomas Neumann, age 56, $822,133 total compensation

EVP; President Cadillac, Carel Johannes de Nysschen, age 56

EVP Global Product Development Purchasing and Supply Chain, Mark L. Reuss, age 53, $1,100,000 total compensation

Chairman and CEO, Mary T. Barra, age 56, $1,750,000 total compensation

Executive Director Global Technology Engineering, Matthew (Matt) Tsien, age 56

EVP and President GM International, Barry Engle, age 54

EVP Global Manufacturing, Alicia Boler Davis

EVP; President North America, Alan S. Batey, age 53

President, Daniel (Dan) Ammann, age 45, $1,200,000 total compensation

SVP Global Information Technology and CIO, Randall D. (Randy) Mott

EVP and CFO, Charles K. (Chuck) Stevens, age 57, $1,000,000 total compensation

President and Managing Director General Motors India, Sanjiv Gupta

Vp Global Purchasing And Supply Chain, Robert E Socia, age 64

Vice President Public Relations and Media Communications, Paul Copses

Vice President, Daniel Nicholson

Vice President, Ken Morris

U.S. Vice President of Customer Experience, Alicia Bolerdavis

Executive Vice President, Dana Richardson

VP Quality, Tony Francavilla

Corporate Vice President and Chief Financial Officer, Michael Gaines

Vice President Labor Relations, Catherine Clegg

VP Information Security, Kevin Baltes

Vice President Of Operations, Jim Munofo

Vice President of Sales Marketing and Aftersales Service Chevrolet Sales Thailand, Antonio Zara

Group Vice President and President and Publisher, Serge St-Louis

Vice President, Travis Hester

National Account Manager, Steven Sheldon

Vice President Sales, Rajesh Singh

VP Manufacturing, Reinaldo Pereira

Vice President of Global Engineering, John Calabrese

Call Center customer Service Director Vice President, Rob Thwing

Vice President Finance Treasurer, Jim Davlin

Vice President, Carlos Diaz

Vice President Global Purchasing and Supply Chain, Steven Kiefer

Medical Director, Donna Smith

Vice President Legal Affairs South East Asia, Elizabeth Shaffer

VP Supply Chain, John Robertson

Global Vpo Airborne Noise, Alan Parrett

Vice President Global Purchasing and Supply Chain, Anirvan Coomer

Vice President and Human Resources Director, Michael Todd

Vice President Manufacturing South America, Jose Pinheiro

Vice President Tax, Marie Curry

Vice President, Michael Ableson

Board Member, Joe McHugh

Secretary, Guy Green

Board Member, Joe Dent

Assistant Treasurer, Rick Westenberg

Board Member, Chris Gibson

Auditors: DELOITTE & TOUCHE LLP

LOCATIONS

HQ: General Motors Co
300 Renaissance Center, Detroit, MI 48265-3000
Phone: 313 667-1500
Web: www.gm.com

PRODUCTS/OPERATIONS

2016 Sales

	$ mil.	% of total
GMNA	119,022	72
GME	18,707	11
GMIO	11,749	7
GM Financial	9,531	6
GMSA	7,223	4
Corporate	148	-
Total	**166,380**	**100**

2016 Sales

	$ mil.	% of total
Automotive		
U.S.	110,848	67
Non-U.S.	46,001	28
GM Financial		
U.S.	7,462	4
Non-U.S.	2,069	1
Total	**166,380**	**100**

Selected Brands

Buick
Cadillac
Chevrolet
GMC
Holden
Isuzu

COMPETITORS

BMW	Mitsubishi Motors
Daimler	Navistar International
FCA US	Nissan
Fiat Chrysler	Peugeot
Ford Motor	Renault
Honda	Subaru
Hyundai Motor	Suzuki Motor
Kia Motors	Tata Motors
Land Rover	Toyota
Mazda	Volkswagen

HISTORICAL FINANCIALS

Company Type: Public

Income Statement

FYE: December 31

	REVENUE ($ mil.)	NET INCOME ($ mil.)	NET PROFIT MARGIN	EMPLOYEES
12/17	145,588	(3,864)	—	180,000
12/16	166,380	9,427	5.7%	225,000
12/15	152,356	9,687	6.4%	215,000
12/14	155,929	3,949	2.5%	216,000
12/13	155,427	5,346	3.4%	219,000
Annual Growth	(1.6%)	—	—	(4.8%)

2017 Year-End Financials

Debt ratio: 44.34%	No. of shares (mil.): 1,402
Return on equity: (-9.80%)	Dividends
Cash ($ mil.): 23,825	Yield: 0.0%
Current ratio: 0.89	Payout: —
Long-term debt ($ mil.): 67,254	Market value ($ mil.): 57,494

	STOCK PRICE ($) FY Close	P/E High/Low		PER SHARE ($) Earnings	Dividends	Book Value
12/17	40.99	—	—	(2.60)	1.52	24.95
12/16	34.84	6	4	6.00	1.52	29.26
12/15	34.01	6	4	5.91	1.38	25.81
12/14	34.91	23	17	1.65	1.20	22.02
12/13	40.87	15	10	2.38	0.00	26.80
Annual Growth	0.1%	—	—	—	—	(1.8%)

Genesis Healthcare Inc

Genesis Healthcare helps seniors begin to thrive again after suffering a medical setback. Through some 500 skilled nursing facilities and assisted-living centers the company specializes in providing intensive medical care for weakened elderly patients such as those recovering from stroke or hip replacement therapy. Its facilities located in 34 states across the US house nearly 60000 beds in all. Genesis also has subsidiaries that provide third-party services including rehab and respiratory therapy administrative services and consulting. Rehab services include speech pathology physical therapy and occupational therapy. These units serve more than 1800 clients in 47 states and the District of Columbia.

Operations

Genesis operates through two primary segments — Inpatient Services and Rehabilitation Therapy Services. The larger segment Inpatient Services operates the group's skilled nursing centers and assisted-living facilities and accounts for nearly 90% of revenue. Rehabilitation Therapy Services provides third-party rehab and respiratory therapy services; it accounts for more than 10% of revenue.

The company also provides some specialized services including staffing management services physician services and other medical offerings.

Geographic Reach

Genesis is based in California and has an executive office in Kennett Square Pennsylvania. It has other corporate offices in California Maryland Massachusetts and New Mexico.

The company operates its own network of facilities in 34 states throughout the US. It provides third-party services in 45 states and the District of Columbia.

Financial Performance

Genesis revenues jumped significantly after its early 2015 merger with Skilled Healthcare Group. In 2016 revenue stayed relatively flat rising 2% to $5.7 billion. Inpatient Services revenue rose that year due to higher skilled nursing facilities income but that was offset by decreases in the rehabilitation therapy and other services businesses.

However the company has reported net losses for the past four years. In 2016 its net loss decreased to $64 million versus a loss of $426.2 million in 2015. That improvement was largely due to a more than $200 million increase in other income as well as a nearly $90 million decrease in transaction costs.

Cash flow from operations increased nearly 700% to $68.4 million in 2016 primarily due to the lower net loss that year.

Strategy

Genesis' growth strategies include continually improving the quality of care its facilities provide and focusing on providing skilled nursing care for elderly patients. The company has been positioning itself to take advantage of the growing need for post-acute care services as Medicare and other payors look to shift patients away from stays at costlier hospitals and long-term acute care facilities. Rehabilitation therapy is another area of focus for Genesis as the company works to expand the types of services it offers its existing patients.

Genesis is also focusing on increasing value through its conservative management strategy.It utilizes its network size to secure better prices from suppliers for example.

The company seeks strategic acquisitions of short-stay facilities to expand its presence geographically. In 2015 and 2016 it bought 24 skilled nursing facilities (including more than 3000 beds) from Revera for nearly $300 million. As the nation's largest operator of skilled nursing facilities it has somewhat of an advantage in its ability to acquire smaller competitors. Genesis is also open to establishing partnerships for further expansion.In early 2017 the company established a collaboration with Kindred Healthcare which is exiting its nursing home business to promote economies of scale through growth.

Faced with declining reimbursement rates paid by Medicare for its core skilled nursing business the company has worked to diversify its operations. Fast-growing areas such as hospice and home care helped fill the gap temporarily but the company sold those businesses in 2016 to pay down debt. The company also sold 40 underperforming facilities in 2016 and is exploring other strategic divestitures.

Company Background

In early 2015 Skilled Healthcare Group merged with Genesis Healthcare LLC to become one of the nation's largest long-term care providers. Prior to the merger Skilled Healthcare Group operated nearly 100 skilled nursing and assisted living facilities while Genesis specialized in long-term care and rehabilitation centers. The combined firm operated more than 500 facilities.

EXECUTIVES

CEO and Director, George V. Hager, age 62, $822,263 total compensation

EVP and President West Division, David C. (Dave) Almquist, age 63

EVP and President Northeast Division, Richard P. (Dick) Blinn, age 63

SVP and CIO, Richard L. (Rich) Castor

EVP and COO, Paul D. Bach, age 59

SVP and Chief Human Resources Officer, Jeanne Phillips

EVP Clinical Operations and Chief Nursing Officer, JoAnne Reifsnyder, age 58, $364,998 total compensation

SVP and CFO, Thomas (Tom) DiVittorio, age 48, $429,998 total compensation

SVP and General Counsel, Michael (Mike) Sherman

Vice President Brand Management, Lori Mayer

Vice President For Government Relations, Larry Lane

Vice President Treasury Services, Rick Edwards

Vice President Senior Centers Operations, Christopher Evans

Auditors: KPMG LLP

LOCATIONS

HQ: Genesis Healthcare Inc
101 East State Street, Kennett Square, PA 19348
Phone: 610 444-6350
Web: www.genesishcc.com

PRODUCTS/OPERATIONS

2016 Sales by Segment

	$ mil.	% of total
Inpatient Services	4,910	80
Rehabilitation Therapy Services	1,070	17
Other services	184	3
Corporate	0	—
Eliminations	(433.3)	—
Total	5,732	100

2016 Sales by Payer

	% of total
Medicaid	55
Medicare	24
Insurance	11
Private & other	10
Total	100

Selected Subsidiaries

SHG Resources LP
Signature Hospice and Home Health
Summit Care Corporation
SunBridge Healthcare LLC
Genesis Administrative Services LLC

COMPETITORS

Allied Healthcare International	Gentiva
Amedisys	Golden Horizons
American HomePatient	HealthSouth
Brookdale Senior Living	Kindred Healthcare
Covenant Care	LHC Group
Diversicare Healthcare Services	Life Care Centers
Enlivant	Lincare Holdings
Ensign Group	NHC
Extendicare	RehabCare
Five Star Senior Living	SavaSeniorCare
	Sunrise Senior Living
	Tenet Healthcare

Company Type: Public

Income Statement

FYE: December 31

	REVENUE ($ mil.)	NET INCOME ($ mil.)	NET PROFIT MARGIN	EMPLOYEES
12/16	5,732	(64)	—	82,000
12/15	5,619	(426)	—	88,700
12/14	833	(0)	—	13,025
12/13	842	(10)	—	15,050
12/12	872	21	2.5%	15,000
Annual Growth	60.1%	—	—	52.9%

2016 Year-End Financials

Debt ratio: 87.22%
Return on equity: ***,***.**%
Cash ($ mil.): 94
Current ratio: 1.23
Long-term debt ($ mil.): 5,011

No. of shares (mil.): 154
Dividends
  Yield: —
  Payout: —
Market value ($ mil.): 657

	STOCK PRICE ($) FY Close	P/E High/Low	PER SHARE ($) Earnings	Dividends	Book Value
12/16	4.25	— —	(0.82)	0.00	(3.17)
12/15	3.47	— —	(4.97)	0.00	(2.84)
12/14	8.57	— —	(0.02)	0.00	2.38
12/13	4.81	— —	(0.28)	0.00	2.32
12/12	6.37	14 9	0.57	0.00	2.59
Annual Growth	(9.6%)	— —	—	—	—

Genuine Parts Co.

What do spark plugs hydraulic hoses paper clips and magnet wire have in common? They're all Genuine Parts. The diversified company is the sole member and majority owner of National Automotive Parts Association (NAPA) a voluntary trade association that distributes auto parts nationwide. Genuine Parts Company (GPC) operates about 1100 NAPA Auto Parts stores in more than 45 US states. It also distributes parts through chains in Canada Mexico and across Europe. Other subsidiaries include auto parts distributor Balkamp industrial parts supplier Motion Industries and office products distributor S.P. Richards.

HISTORY

Genuine Parts Company (GPC) got its start in Atlanta in 1928 when Carlyle Fraser bought a small auto parts store. That year GPC had the only loss in its history. Three years earlier a group that included Fraser had founded the National Automotive Parts Association (NAPA) an organization of automotive manufacturers remanufacturers distributors and retailers.

The Depression was a boon for GPC because fewer new-car sales meant more sales of replacement parts. During the 1930s GPC's sales rose from less than $350000 to more than $3 million. One tool it developed to spur sales during the Depression was its monthly magazine Parts Pups which featured pretty girls and corny jokes (discontinued in the 1990s). GPC acquired auto parts rebuilder Rayloc in 1931 and established parts distributor Balkamp in 1936.

WWII boosted sales at GPC because carmakers were producing for the war effort but scarce resources limited auto parts companies to producing functional parts. GPC went public in 1948.

The postwar boom in car sales boosted GPC's sales in the 1950s and 1960s. It expanded during this period with new distribution centers across the country. GPC bought Colyear Motor Sales (NAPA's West Coast distributor) in 1965 and introduced a line of filters and batteries in 1966 that were the first parts to carry the NAPA name.

GPC moved into Canada in 1972 when it bought Corbetts a Calgary-based parts distributor. That acquisition included Oliver Industrial Supply. During the mid-1970s GPC began to broaden its distribution businesses adding S.P. Richards (office products 1975) and Motion Industries (industrial replacement parts 1976). In the late 1970s GPC acquired Bearing Specialty and Michigan Bearing as part of Motion Industries.

In 1982 the company introduced its now familiar blue-and-yellow NAPA logo. Canadian parts distributor UAP (formerly United Auto Parts) and GPC formed a joint venture UAP/NAPA in 1988 with GPC acquiring a 20% stake in UAP.

During the 1990s GPC diversified its product lines and its geographic reach. Its 1993 acquisition of Berry Bearing made the company a leading distributor of industrial parts. The next year GPC formed a joint venture with Grupo Auto Todo of Mexico.

NAPA formed an agreement in 1995 with Penske Corporation to be the exclusive supplier of auto parts to nearly 900 Penske Auto Centers. GPC purchased Horizon USA Data Supplies that year adding computer supplies to S.P. Richards' product mix.

A string of acquisitions in the late 1990s increased GPC's industrial distribution business (including Midcap Bearing Power Drives & Bearings and Amarillo Bearing).

GPC paid $200 million in 1998 for EIS a leading wholesale distributor of materials and supplies to the electrical and electronics industries. Late in 1998 after a 10-year joint venture it bought the remaining 80% of UAP it didn't already own. GPC continued to expand its auto parts distribution network in 1999 acquiring Johnson Industries an independent distributor of auto supplies for large fleets and car dealers. GPC also acquired Oklahoma City-based Brittain Brothers a NAPA distributor that serves about 190 auto supply stores in Arkansas Missouri Oklahoma and Texas.

In 2000 the company bought a 15% interest in Mitchell Repair Information (MRIC) a subsidiary of Snap-on Incorporated that provides diagnostic and repair information services. The next year Johnson Industries acquired Coach and Motors a distribution center in Detroit.

GPC acquired NAPA Hawaii which serves more than 30 independently owned NAPA stores and four company-owned ones in Hawaii and Samoa in 2003. Also that year the company sold its interest in the partnership that distributes industrial parts in Mexico Refacciones Industriales de M©xico.

President Thomas Gallagher became the company's fourth CEO in more than 75 years when he was named to the position in August 2004. Former CEO Larry Prince remained as chairman until early in 2005 when Gallagher was elected chairman; Prince remains on the board. Also during 2005 the company acquired a 25% interest in Altrom Canada Corp.

GPC subsidiary Motion Industries in mid-2006 acquired Lewis Supply Co. a provider of casters cutting tools machinery accessories and other general mill supplies. In October the company merged HorizonUSA Data Supplies previously a wholly owned subsidiary of S.P. Richards into S.P. Richards.

In early 2008 the company sold its Johnson Industries subsidiary which provided automotive supplies to fleets and new car dealers. In October GPC's S.P. Richards unit acquired ActionEmco's business assets in the midwestern US including its Grand Rapids Michigan distribution center. Also that year Motion Industries acquired Texas-based Drago Supply Company Mill Supply Corp. and Monroe Rubber and Plastic Supply.

In 2009 GPC added eight companies to its industrial and automotive operations for about $70 million and snapped up the remaining 11% interest in Balkamp that it did not already control for some $60 million making it a wholly owned subsidiary. These deals compare to a broader acquisition strategy in 2008 which added a dozen companies to all four of GPC's business segments (automotive industrial office products and electrical and electronic) for nearly $135 million.

Also in 2010 it acquired Canada's BC Bearing a distributor of bearing and power transmission components.

In late 2013 Motion acquired AST Bearings an industrial distributor specializing in high-precision miniature and specialty bearing with locations in New Jersey and California as well as Paragon Service & Supply (PS&S) of Lima Ohio. PS&S distributes industrial cutting tools abrasives and metalworking equipment.

In 2013 GPC acquired the remaining 70% of Melbourne-based Exego Group for approximately $800 million. (In January 2012 it purchased a 30% share in the company for around $150 million in cash). Exego an aftermarket distributor of automotive replacement parts and accessories has about 430 stores across Australia and New Zealand. The Exego stake allows GPC an entry point into Asia.

In 2012 GPC bought rival auto parts distributor Quaker City Motor Parts Co. for $343 million and thus became the only member of NAPA. Delaware-based Quaker was a long-standing NAPA distributor with annual sales of about $300 million and some 270 auto parts stores.

EXECUTIVES

EVP CFO and Corporate Secretary, Carol B. Yancey, age 54, $507,500 total compensation
SVP Human Resources, James R. (Jim) Neill, age 55, $319,000 total compensation
President and CEO, Paul D. Donahue, age 61, $840,000 total compensation
President and COO U.S. Automotive Parts Group, Lee A. Maher, $489,670 total compensation
President and CEO Motion Industries, Timothy P. (Tim) Breen, age 56, $456,000 total compensation
VICE PRESIDENT OF BUSINESS OPERATIONS SOFTWARE DIVISION, Wilcox Joshua
Chairman, Thomas C. (Tom) Gallagher, age 70
SECRETARY, Kent Guillaume
Auditors: Ernst & Young LLP

LOCATIONS

HQ: Genuine Parts Co.
2999 Wildwood Parkway, Atlanta, GA 30339
Phone: 678 934-5000
Web: www.genpt.com

2016 Sales

	$ mil.	% of total
US	12,822	83
Canada	1,390	9
Australasia	1,104	7
Mexico	112	1
Adjustments	(91.0)	-
Total	**15,339**	**100**

PRODUCTS/OPERATIONS

2016 Sales

	$ mil.	% of total
Automotive	8,111	52
Industrial	4,634	30
Office products	1,969	13
Electrical & electronic materials	715	5
Adjustments	(91.0)	-
Total	**15,339**	**100**

Selected Operations

Automotive Parts Group
  Altrom Canada Corp. (distribution of import automotive parts Canada)
  Balkamp (majority-owned subsidiary; distribution of replacement parts and accessories for cars heavy-duty vehicles motorcycles and farm equipment)
  Grupo Auto Todo S.A. de C.V. (Mexico)
  UAP Inc. (auto parts distribution Canada)
Electrical/Electronic Materials Group
  EIS Inc. (products for electrical and electronic equipment including adhesives copper foil and thermal management materials)
Industrial Parts Group
  Motion Industries (Canada) Inc.
  Motion Industries Inc.
Office Products Group
  S.P. Richards Company

COMPETITORS

Advance Auto Parts	General Parts
Applied Industrial Technologies	Gould Paper
	Graybar Electric
Arrow Electronics	Hahn Automotive
AutoZone	Ingersoll-Rand
Avnet	Kaman Industrial
CARQUEST	Technologies
Coast Distribution	MSC Industrial Direct
Cole Office Products	O'Reilly Automotive
Complete Office	Office Depot
D & H Distributing	Pep Boys
Essendant	Staples
Ford Motor	W.W. Grainger
General Motors	

HISTORICAL FINANCIALS

Company Type: Public

Income Statement

FYE: December 31

	REVENUE ($ mil.)	NET INCOME ($ mil.)	NET PROFIT MARGIN	EMPLOYEES
12/16	15,339	687	4.5%	40,000
12/15	15,280	705	4.6%	39,600
12/14	15,341	711	4.6%	39,000
12/13	14,077	684	4.9%	37,500
12/12	13,013	648	5.0%	31,900
Annual Growth	4.2%	1.5%	—	5.8%

2016 Year-End Financials

Debt ratio: 10.32%
Return on equity: 21.62%
Cash ($ mil.): 242
Current ratio: 1.40
Long-term debt ($ mil.): 589

No. of shares (mil.): 148
Dividends
  Yield: 0.0%
  Payout: 57.3%
Market value ($ mil.): 14,179

	STOCK PRICE ($) FY Close	P/E High/Low		PER SHARE ($) Earnings	Dividends	Book Value
12/16	95.54	23	17	4.59	2.63	21.52
12/15	85.89	23	17	4.63	2.46	20.97
12/14	106.57	23	17	4.61	2.30	21.56
12/13	83.19	19	14	4.40	2.15	21.78
12/12	63.58	16	14	4.14	1.98	19.36
Annual Growth	10.7%	—		2.6%	7.4%	2.7%

Genworth Financial, Inc. (Holding Co)

Insurance and investment specialist Genworth Financial specializes in life insurance and retirement investments in the US market. Internationally Genworth offers mortgage insurance and other payment protection products. The firm also provides private residential mortgage insurance in the US. Genworth focuses its retirement investment products including fixed annuities and mutual funds on affluent individuals. Genworth serves customers in 25 countries. Chinese conglomerate China Oceanwide Holdings is buying Genworth for $2.7 billion.

Change in Company Type

In October 2016 Genworth agreed to be acquired by China Oceanwide Holdings a family-owned holding company based in Beijing. China Oceanwide plans to contribute an additional $1.1 billion to support Genworth as it restructures its life insurance operations including divesting certain annuity businesses and meeting maturing debt obligations.

Operations

Genworth operates in five segments: US Life Insurance US Mortgage Insurance Canada Mortgage Insurance Australia Mortgage Insurance and Runoff.

The US Life Insurance segment is Genworth's largest unit bringing in some 75% of total revenue. It provides long-term coverage products and services traditional life insurance policies and fixed annuity products in the US.

The three mortgage insurance segments primarily offer prime mortgage insurance coverage for individually underwritten loans; they also offer selective bulk mortgage insurance. US Life Insurance provides long-term care coverage products and services traditional life insurance policies and fixed annuity products in the US. The runoff segment managed products that are no longer actively marketed including variable annuity variable life and corporate-owned life policies.

Geographic Reach

While US operations account for more than 85% of revenues Genworth's international operations include significant mortgage insurance businesses in Australia Canada and Mexico. The firm is looking to expand its mortgage insurance operations into emerging markets. For example it has a minority stake in a joint venture in India.

Sales and Marketing

Genworth's products are sold through direct sales brokerage general agencies and independent marketing organizations as well as by banks and financial advisors. Long-term care insurance products are sold through a variety of sales channels — independent producers financial intermediaries and sales specialists.

The company markets its mortgage products to financial groups and mortgage lenders that require mortgage insurance for customer financing. It has a field sales force throughout the US and a telephone sales force that primarily works with smaller lenders. Genworth also has a call center to support all customer segments.

Financial Performance

Genworth's revenue has been trending downward over the past five years. In 2016 it fell 2% to $8.4 billion as US life insurance and fixed annuities sales declined.

The company has been recovering from a $1.2 billion net loss in 2014 caused largely by an increase in benefits and other changes in policy reserves. In 2015 the company cut its losses to $629 million as expenses related to changes in policy reserves declined. Losses in 2016 totaled an even more palatable $277 million as losses from continuing operations declined. Genworth also had an $18 million gain that year from the sale of its European mortgage operations.

Cash flow from operations which fell 35% in 2015 rose 16% to $1.9 billion in 2016. This was primarily due to the decrease in net losses.

Strategy

Genworth is streamlining its operations through asset sales which allow the company to improve its cash position and focus on its core offerings. Additionally it is working to improve returns in the international mortgage units by reducing exposure in certain markets: It sold its European mortgage insurance business to AmTrust Financial in 2016 and sold part of the Australian unit in 2015. Also in 2015 it sold its European lifestyle protection insurance business to France's AXA for some $510 million. In early 2016 Genworth sold certain blocks of term life insurance policies to Protective Life Insurance Company.

The company is also restructuring its US life insurance segment. In early 2016 it announced it would suspend sales of its traditional life and fixed annuity products to cut expenses. It also began unwinding existing products from Bermuda-based subsidiary Brookfield Life and Annuity Insurance to its US life insurance units that year; it dissolved the Bermuda unit once that process was complete. Finally it has been separating its troubled long-term care insurance business for ultimate isolation.

To boost its core operations the company has realigned and expanded its sales team dedicated to serving mortgage originators. Genworth is also focused on increasing the value of new and existing policies through pricing initiatives and changes in product distribution and design practices across all of its business units.

In October 2016 the company agreed to be acquired by China Oceanwide Holdings for $2.7 billion. China Oceanwide has committed another $1.1 billion to help Genworth as it restructures its operations. The acquisition will assist Genworth as it tackles another strategic initiative — reducing debt.

HISTORY

The company was formed in 2004 to acquire certain insurance and financial services business from General Electric (GE). GE retained a controlling stake in Genworth Financial after its stock offering but sold its remaining stake in 2006.

During the downturn in the US housing market (starting in 2008) the company faced losses in its US mortgage insurance segment. After considering divestitures Genworth instead simply yanked hard on those operations making its underwriting criteria more stringent and restricting new business. The company also conducted extensive restructuring programs including a 15% workforce reduction in 2009 and a de-risking of its investment portfolio to recover from the economic downturn. Nonetheless the company saw income and cash flow losses during those years as a result of poor returns on investments.

In 2009 the company launched an IPO of its Canadian mortgage insurance business.

In late 2010 Genworth expanded its asset management operations with the purchase of hedge fund and managed futures producer Altegris Capital. The purchase brought in alternative investments and $2.2 billion in assets under management.

Despite steady growth in the sales of its Medicare supplemental products in 2011 the company sold the block of products (held by the former Continental Life Insurance Company unit) to Aetna for $290 million. In addition in 2011 the company stopped offering mortgage insurance policies in New Zealand.

EXECUTIVES

President and CEO, Thomas J. (Tom) McInerney, age 61, $996,804 total compensation
President and CEO US Mortgage Insurance, Rohit Gupta

EVP Human Resources, Michael S. Laming, age 66, $491,692 total compensation
EVP and CIO, Scott J. McKay, age 56
EVP and COO, Kevin D. Schneider, age 55, $722,683 total compensation
President and CEO Genworth Mortgage Insurance Canada, Stuart Levings
President and CEO U.S. Life Insurance, David OÂ'Leary
EVP and Chief Investment Officer, Daniel J. (Dan) Sheehan, age 51, $598,083 total compensation
EVP and Chief Risk Officer, Lori M. Evangel, age 54, $455,271 total compensation
EVP and General Counsel, Ward E. Bobitz, age 52, $423,642 total compensation
EVP and CFO, Kelly L. Groh, age 48, $538,657 total compensation
President and CEO Genworth Mortgage Insurance Australia, Georgette C. Nicholas
Regional Vice President, Erin Kirkeeng
Vice President Accounting Policy, Mitch Rosen
Executive Vice President and Chief Investment Officer, Dan Sheehan
Senior Vice President, Peter Hurst
DIVISIONAL VICE PRESIDENT, Stan J Mensing
VICE PRESIDENT PRODUCTS AND SERVICES MARKETING, Miller Tammy
ChFC CLTC Income Assurance Region Vice President, Scott Burkard
Vice President Corporate Accounts, David Stagnitti
Medical Director, James Wright
Commercial Senior Vice President Mortgage Insurance Manager Information Technology, Alejandro Espinosa
Commercial Real Estate Assistant Vice President Loan Origination SE Region, Duncan Hall
Chairman, James S. (Jim) Riepe, age 74
Auditors: KPMG LLP

LOCATIONS

HQ: Genworth Financial, Inc. (Holding Co)
6620 West Broad Street, Richmond, VA 23230
Phone: 804 281-6000
Web: www.genworth.com

2016 Revenues

	$ mil.	% of total
US	7,270	87
Canada	645	8
Australia	440	5
Other countries	14	-
Total	**8,369**	**100**

PRODUCTS/OPERATIONS

2016 Revenues

	$ mil.	% of total
US Life	6,250	74
U.S. Mortgage Insurance	726	9
Canada Mortgage Insurance	645	8
Australia Mortgage Insurance	440	5
Runoff	302	4
Corporate & other	6	-
Total	**8,369**	**100**

2016 Revenues

	$ mil.	% of total
Premiums	4,160	50
Net Investment income	3,159	37
Net investment losses	72	1
Policy fees and other income	978	12
Total	**8,369**	**100**

Selected Products and Services

Fixed annuities
Life insurance
Long-term care insurance
Mortgage
Retirement solutions
Wealth management solutions

COMPETITORS

AEGON USA	MetLife
AIG	Nationwide
Great American	New York Life
Financial Resources	Northwestern Mutual
John Hancock Financial	PMI Group
Services	Prudential
MGIC Investment	Radian Group
MassMutual	The Hartford
Medamerica Insurance	

HISTORICAL FINANCIALS

Company Type: Public

Income Statement

FYE: December 31

	ASSETS ($ mil.)	NET INCOME ($ mil.)	INCOME AS % OF ASSETS	EMPLOYEES
12/16	104,658	(277)	—	3,400
12/15	106,431	(615)	—	4,100
12/14	111,358	(1,244)	—	5,300
12/13	108,045	560	0.5%	5,000
12/12	113,312	323	0.3%	6,300
Annual Growth	**(2.0%)**	**—**	**—**	**(14.3%)**

2016 Year-End Financials

Debt ratio: 4.29%
Return on equity: (-2.17%)
Cash ($ mil.): 2,784
Current ratio: —
Long-term debt ($ mil.): —

No. of shares (mil.): 498
Dividends
Yield: —
Payout: —
Market value ($ mil.): 1,897

	STOCK PRICE ($) FY Close	P/E High/Low		PER SHARE ($) Earnings	Dividends	Book Value
12/16	3.81	—	—	(0.56)	0.00	25.39
12/15	3.73	—	—	(1.24)	0.00	25.75
12/14	8.50	—	—	(2.51)	0.00	30.03
12/13	15.53	14	7	1.12	0.00	29.08
12/12	7.51	14	6	0.65	0.00	33.61
Annual Growth	**(15.6%)**	**—**	**—**	**—**	**—**	**(6.8%)**

Georgia Power Co

Georgia Power is the largest subsidiary of US utility holding company Southern Company. The regulated utility provides electricity to about 2.4 million residential commercial and industrial customers throughout most of Georgia. It has interests in about 20 fossil-fueled 2 nuclear and 20 hydroelectric power plants that give it about 22000 MW of generating capacity. When necessary the company purchases excess power from nine small power producers. Georgia Power sells wholesale electricity to several cooperatives and municipalities in the region. The utility also offers energy efficiency surge protection and outdoor lighting products and services.

Operations

Georgia Power generates purchases transmits distributes and sells electricity in Georgia. It generates power from coal and natural gas as well as from renewable sources such as solar hydroelectric and wind.

In 2012 the company purchased about 440 kilowatt hours of power from other providers.

On the financing front the company invests in domestic equity international equity fixed income trust-owned life insurance special situations real estate investments and private equity.

Geographic Reach

The company serves retail customers in Georgia. It also sells power to wholesale customers across the US Southeast.

Financial Performance

Georgia Power's revenues grew by 3% in 2013 due to increase in retail base revenues as the result of higher rates (to help pay for placing new generating units at Plant McDonough-Atkinson in service and collecting financing costs related to the construction of Plant Vogtle Units 3 and 4 as well as higher market-driven contributions from commercial and industrial customers.

Net income was flat in 2013 at stayed at $1.2 million as an increase in operating expenses (the result of a 9.9% increase in the volume of KWHs generated as a result of higher prices for purchased power and an 8.1% increase in the average cost of fuel per KWH generated for all types of fuel generation) was offset by a decrease in other expenses due to the decline in interest expenses as a result of refinancing activity.

Strategy

As part of the company's integrated resource plan in addition to a renewables push it is looking to building two additional nuclear power units at its power plant in Vogtle near Waynesboro Georgia (the country's first nuclear power plants in more than 30 years). In 2012 it secured US Nuclear Regulatory Commission approval to go ahead and build these units.

To upgrade its coal plants between 1990 and 2015 Georgia Power plans to invest $7 billion on environmental control technologies.

The company is committed to diversifying its portfolio to include more green energy. To that end in 2013 it signed a contract with EDP Renewables North America for 250 MW of wind energy which it will begin receiving in 2016. That year Georgia Power opened its Water Research Center that will look for ways to reduce its power plant water use and improve the quality of water it releases from plants.

In 2012 it opened the Piedmont Green Power Plant in Barnesville Georgia and signed a 20-year agreement with Rollcast Energy to purchase about 54 MW of biomass energy.

Company Background

The company was founded in 1927.

EXECUTIVES

Vice President Distribution, Anthony Wilson
EVP CFO Treasurer and Comptroller, W. Ron Hinson, age 60
EVP and Chief Production Officer Southern Company Generation, Theodore J. (Ted) McCullough, age 54
Chairman President and CEO, Paul Bowers
SVP Marketing, Kenny Coleman
EVP External Affairs, Chris Cummiskey
EVP Customer Service and Operations, Pedro Cherry
Vice President Of Diversity, Moanica Caston
Vice President sales, Murry Weaver
Sales Vice President, Latanza Adjei
Vice President controller, Robert Morris
Vice President Of Corporate Communi, Jason Cuevas
Executive Vice President of Finance, Larry Westbrook
Vice President human Resources, Leonard Owens
Vice President and Director of Information Technology, Jeaneen Hunter
Vice President, Anne Kaiser
Vice President, Brian Ivey
Vice President Customer Services, Louise Scott
Senior Vice President of Operations, Bill Strang
Vice President of Security, Ken Lee
Executive Vice President of External Affairs, Christopher Womack

Vice President Information Resources, Clare Blalock
Vice President Field Services Region Distribution, Lamont Houston
Chief Financial Officer of Gulf Power and Vice President of Gulf Power, Philip Raymond
Senior Vice President, Anita Lemon
NORTHEAST REGION VICE PRESIDENT, Lenn H Chandler
Board Member, Allan Bense
Auditors: Deloitte & Touche LLP

LOCATIONS

HQ: Georgia Power Co
  241 Ralph McGill Boulevard, N.E., Atlanta, GA 30308
Phone: 404 506-6526
Web: www.georgiapower.com

PRODUCTS/OPERATIONS

Selected Services

Residential Customers
My Account
Pay My Bill
Turn On/Off Power
Payment Arrangements
Paperless Billing
Budget Billing
Prices/Rate
Save Money and Energy
Energy Audits
Money-Saving Tips
Rebates & Incentives
Electric Vehicles
Products & Programs
Water Heaters
Heat Pumps
Lighting
Power Credit
Green Energy
Smart Meter
Multifamily
Business Customers
My Account
Pay My Bill
Turn On/Off Power
Budget Billing
Prices/Rates
Save Money and Energy
Energy Audits
Money-Saving Tips
Rebates & Incentives
Electric Vehicles
Programs & Services
Water Heaters
Heat Pumps
Outdoor Lighting
Electric Cooking
Forklifts
Green Energy
Smart Meter
Energydirect

2016 Sales

	$ mil.	% of total
Retail		
Residential	3,318	40
Commercial	3,077	37
Industrial	1,291	15
Other retail	86	1
Wholesale	217	2
Other	394	5
Total	**8,383**	**100**

COMPETITORS

Atmos Energy	Progress Energy
Duke Energy Progress	SCANA
Inc.	Sawnee EMC
Energen	South Carolina
Entergy	Electric & Gas
Flint Energies	Southern Company Gas
MEAG Power	TECO Energy
Oglethorpe Power	Walton EMC

HISTORICAL FINANCIALS

Company Type: Public

Income Statement

FYE: December 31

	REVENUE ($ mil.)	NET INCOME ($ mil.)	NET PROFIT MARGIN	EMPLOYEES
12/16	8,383	1,347	16.1%	7,527
12/15	8,326	1,277	15.3%	7,989
12/14	8,988	1,242	13.8%	7,909
12/13	8,274	1,191	14.4%	7,886
12/12	7,998	1,185	14.8%	8,094
Annual Growth	1.2%	3.3%	—	(1.8%)

2016 Year-End Financials

Debt ratio: 31.80%
Return on equity: 11.88%
Cash ($ mil.): 3
Current ratio: 0.58
Long-term debt ($ mil.): 10,225
No. of shares (mil.): 9
Dividends
  Yield: 0.0%
  Payout: 98.1%
Market value ($ mil.): 237

	STOCK PRICE ($) FY Close	P/E High/Low	Earnings	Dividends	Book Value
12/16	25.59	— —	(0.00)	1.53	1,254
12/15	29.43	— —	(0.00)	1.53	1,186
12/14	27.55	— —	(0.00)	1.53	1,153
12/13	26.03	— —	(0.00)	1.53	1,064
12/12	26.66	— —	(0.00)	1.53	1,029
Annual Growth	(1.0%)	—	—	(0.0%)	5.1%

German American Bancorp Inc

EXECUTIVES

Vice President, Lisa Matheis
General technical; Senior Vice President, Floyd Alsman
Chairman and CEO, Mark A. Schroeder, age 64, $342,500 total compensation
President, Clay W. Ewing, age 62, $250,000 total compensation
EVP CFO and Senior Administrative Officer, Bradley M. Rust, age 51, $210,000 total compensation
SVP and Chief Credit Officer, Keith A. Leinenbach, age 58, $180,000 total compensation
SVP and Head of Retail Banking, Randall L. Braun, age 57, $180,000 total compensation
Senior Vice President Trust Officer, Dave Mitchell
Vice President Deposit Services Secruity, Dale Altstadt
Vice President Product Manager, Clay Barrett
Regional President, John Lamb
Vice President Commercial Banking, Dan Collignon
Senior Vice President Commercial Banking, Joe Hauersperger
Senior Vice President Commercial Banking, Julie Donham
Senior Vice President Sales Manager, David Pleiss
Regional Senior Vice President, Jim Thomas
Vice President, Christina Lebeau
Senior Vice President Commercial Lender, Jane Thoma
Vice President Trust Officer, Donna Sholtis
Vice President Wealth Advisor, Patti Evans
Regional President, Mark Franklin
Regional Vice President, Jean Emery
Vice President Private Banking, Sherri Alley
Vice President, John Schroeder

Vice President, Ashley McCreary
Regional Vice President Commercial Lending, Doug Bell
Vice President Commercial Banking, John Newcomer
Vice President, Eric Kehl
Senior Vice President Commercial Banking, Greg Cardinal
Senior Vice President Retail Banking, Brock Goggins
Vice President Commercial Banking, Randy Goodman
Senior Vice President Senior Wealth Advisor, Alan VanCleef
Vice President Agriculture and Commercial Banking, Gaven Oexmann
Vice President Agriculture and Commercial Banking, Joe Dickson
Auditors: Crowe Horwath LLP

LOCATIONS

HQ: German American Bancorp Inc
  711 Main Street, Box 810, Jasper, IN 47546
Phone: 812 482-1314
Web: www.germanamerican.com

COMPETITORS

Fidelity Federal	MainSource Financial
Fifth Third	Norwood Financial
Home Financial Bancorp	Old National Bancorp

HISTORICAL FINANCIALS

Company Type: Public

Income Statement

FYE: December 31

	ASSETS ($ mil.)	NET INCOME ($ mil.)	INCOME AS % OF ASSETS	EMPLOYEES
12/16	2,955	35	1.2%	597
12/15	2,373	30	1.3%	596
12/14	2,237	28	1.3%	484
12/13	2,163	25	1.2%	480
12/12	2,006	24	1.2%	440
Annual Growth	10.2%	10.0%	—	7.9%

2016 Year-End Financials

Debt ratio: 0.50%
Return on equity: 12.04%
Cash ($ mil.): 64
Current ratio: —
Long-term debt ($ mil.): —
No. of shares (mil.): 22
Dividends
  Yield: 0.0%
  Payout: 30.5%
Market value ($ mil.): 1,204

	STOCK PRICE ($) FY Close	P/E High/Low	Earnings	Dividends	Book Value
12/16	52.61	34 19	1.57	0.48	14.43
12/15	33.32	23 18	1.51	0.45	12.67
12/14	30.52	22 17	1.43	0.43	11.54
12/13	28.42	23 15	1.32	0.40	10.13
12/12	21.72	20 14	1.27	0.37	9.76
Annual Growth	24.8%	— —	5.6%	6.5%	10.3%

Gilead Sciences Inc

Gilead Sciences has biotech balms for infectious diseases including hepatitis HIV and infections related to AIDS. The company's HIV franchise includes Truvada a combination of two of its other drugs Viread and Emtriva. It co-promotes another HIV treatment called Atripla in the US and Europe with Bristol-Myers Squibb (BMS). Other products on the market include AmBisome used to treat systemic fungal infections such as those that accompany AIDS or kidney disease; and hepatitis B antiviral Hepsera. Beyond HIV/AIDS Gilead also markets cardiovascular drugs as well as respiratory and ophthalmic medicines and the Yescarta CAR-T cell therapy for cancer.

Operations

Gilead primarily focuses on producing treatments for HIV liver diseases including hepatitis B and hepatitis C cancer and inflammation and cardiovascular and respiratory conditions. Although the company is steadily working to expand in medicines in various fields its main source of revenue continues to be its antiviral franchise which contributes more than 90% of product sales and primarily consists of HIV medications.

Aside from the Atripla partnership with BMS Gilead has collaborations with other companies including Japan Tobacco which promotes HIV drugs Truvada Viread and Emtriva in Japan; and with GlaxoSmithKline which markets Hepsera Viread and Volbris in select international markets. Additionally Gilead receives royalties on influenza treatment Tamiflu which it developed with Roche and on Macugen an ophthalmologic drug developed by Eyetech using Gilead's technology. In addition to distributing AmBisome in Canada and the US Astellas Pharma pays royalties on US sales of Lexiscan which is used in stress tests for coronary artery disease.

Gilead continues to advance its R&D pipeline; the company had more than 165 active clinical studies at the end of 2016. It has more than 60 trials in Phase III.

The company's portfolio of more than 20 marketed products contains a number of firsts such as the first complete treatment regimens for HIV and chronic hepatitis C available in a once-daily single pill.

Geographic Reach

The US market accounts for some 65% of Gilead's annual revenues. The company operates in more than 30 countries worldwide with a significant presence in Europe (France the UK Spain Italy Germany and Switzerland); Europe accounts for more than 20% of its annual revenue. Gilead also operates in Africa South America and the Asia/Pacific region.

Gilead has R&D facilities in Oceanside and Fremont California; Alberta; and Seattle. It has manufacturing sites in San Dimas and La Verne California; Foster City Alberta; and Cork Ireland. Commercial operations are located in 20 offices throughout Europe 10 in North America seven in Asia two in South America and one each in the Middle East Australia and Africa.

Sales and Marketing

Gilead promotes its antiviral drugs through its own commercial infrastructure in North America some European and Asian countries and in Australia and New Zealand; products are promoted through third-party distributors and partnerships in other regions. Gilead sells and distributes products including Atripla Sovaldi and Viread exclusively through wholesale channels in the US; Letairis and Cayston are distributed through specialty pharmacies. Customers include physicians hospitals clinics and other health care facilities. The company's product distribution processes are handled primarily by wholesalers including McKessonAmerisourceBergen and Cardinal Health.

In 2016 Gilead spent $618 million on advertising versus $601 million in 2015 and $393 million.

Financial Performance

Increased sales of antiviral products have provided healthy revenue increases for Gilead in recent years. After rising 31% in 2015 revenue fell 7% to $30.4 billion in 2016 as antiviral product sales

dropped 7% and royalty contract and other revenue declined 10%. Top sellers Harvoni and Sovaldi had lower sales (by 34% and 24% respectively) that year as did Atripla (which fell by 17%). However these declines were offset by growing sales of other products including HIV treatments Genvoya and Odefsey and the launch of new hepatitis blockbuster Epclusa.

Net income has also seen significant growth in recent years more than tripling in 2014 and then rising another 50% in 2015. In 2016 net income fell 25% to $13.5 billion largely as a result of higher research and development expenses.

Like revenue and net income cash flow from operations dipped after seeing rapid growth. It declined 18% to $16.7 billion in 2016 due to the lower net income and negative changes in operating assets and liabilities.

Strategy

One of the pitfalls of the pharma manufacturing business is patent expirations where older medications see a decline in sales as they begin to face generic competition. Other medications struggle to penetrate highly saturated markets. To offset potential losses from these challenges Gilead is working to increase sales of top selling products in new territories. In addition Gilead works to get existing medications approved for new medical indications.

The company also works to launch new or next-generation drugs to freshen its lineup of patent-protected offerings. Although it is focused on remaining a leader in anti-virals treating HIV and hepatitis C Gilead is increasingly turning toward oncology and inflammation research. Non-alcoholic steatohepatitis (NASH) treatments present significant opportunity for the company which has already seen some success in related trials. In cancer research Gilead is focused on immuno-oncology cellular therapies and targeted therapies.

In 2015 the company launched Genvoya for the treatment of HIV-1 infections. The following year the company launched Epclusa (a single-table regiment for adults with genotype 1-6 chronic hepatitis C) Descovy (a combination for the treatment of HIV) and Odefsey (for HIV-1).

In 2016 Gilead partnered with Galapagos to develop and commercialize filgotinib which is being investigated for inflammatory disease.

In 2017 the company's Yescarta treatment was the second CAR-T cell therapy to be given FDA approval. These new therapies reprogram immune cells' DNA to attack cancers and could change the way certain cancers are treated going forward.

The company opened a new manufacturing campus in La Verne California in mid-2017.

Mergers and Acquisitions

As a way of fending off losses from patent expirations Gilead has diversified its product line through acquisitions. In 2015 Gilead acquired EpiTherapeutics a developer of novel cancer drugs based on epigenetics for $65 million.

Also in 2015 the company entered into an agreement with Phenex Pharmaceuticals in 2015; under the deal Gilead acquired Phenex's FXR program for the treatment of liver diseases for some $470 million. That transaction accelerated Gilead's efforts to develop new treatments for fibrotic liver diseases.

In 2016 the company bought Nimbus Therapeutics subsidiary Nimbus Apollo for $400 million; the deal included Nimbus' Acetyl-CoA Carboxylase (ACC) inhibitor program for the treatment of liver disease.

In 2017 the company bought Kite Pharma a leader in the development of cell therapy treatments for cancer for $11.9 billion. That purchase provided Gilead with a pipeline of CAR-T therapy products including Yescarta which was shortly

thereafter approved by the FDA. It was the second CAR-T cell therapy to receive approval in the US.

HISTORY

Dr. Michael Riordan started Gilead Sciences in 1987 backed by venture capital firm Menlo Ventures. The name was derived from the Biblical phrase "Is there no balm in Gilead?" In 1990 Glaxo Wellcome (now GlaxoSmithKline) agreed to fund Gilead's research into code-blocking treatments for cancer. Gilead went public in 1992.

In 1994 the company formed an alliance with American Home Products' Storz Instruments (now part of Bausch & Lomb) to develop and market a topical treatment for an ophthalmic virus. Two years later Gilead joined forces with Roche to develop treatments for influenza.

Vistide was approved in the US in 1996 and in Europe in 1997. But more-effective HIV therapies brought declining demand for Vistide.

The company bounced back with Tamiflu (the fruit of its Roche partnership) which was approved in 1999. Sales were brisk during that flu season. Also that year Gilead expanded its pipeline and geographic reach with the $550 million all-stock acquisition of NeXstar Pharmaceuticals which focused on antifungals antibiotics and cancer treatments.

In 2000 Gilead sought approval for Tamiflu in Japan and Europe (it withdrew the European application after regulators there asked for more information) and also sought approval for pediatric uses for the drug which was granted. The following year it resubmitted Tamiflu for approval in Europe.

Chairman Donald Rumsfeld resigned in 2001 to become US secretary of defense and was replaced by retired Sears Roebuck executive James Denny. Perhaps the Defense connection helped: Vistide became one of the many drugs that researchers began studying as possible alternatives to vaccines should a smallpox bio-attack occur in the US.

EXECUTIVES

EVP Pharmaceutical Development and Manufacturing, Taiyin Yang, age 63
EVP Research, William A. Lee, age 61, $363,333 total compensation
EVP Research and Development and Chief Scientific Officer, Norbert W. Bischofberger, age 61, $1,044,231 total compensation
President and CEO, John F. Milligan, age 56, $1,465,385 total compensation
COO, Kevin Young, $787,645 total compensation
EVP and CFO, Robin L. Washington, age 54, $900,385 total compensation
EVP Commercial and Access Operations (Asia Latin America and Africa) and Corporate and Medical Affairs, Gregg H. Alton, age 51, $925,385 total compensation
EVP Clinical Research and Development Operations, Andrew Cheng
EVP Clinical Research, John G. McHutchison
EVP Strategy, Martin B. Silverstein, age 62
EVP and General Counsel, Brett Pletcher
EVP Human Resources, Katie L. Watson
Vice President Of U S Marketing And Sales, Jean Kress
V P Risk Management, Marti Dodson
Vice President, Choung Kim
Chairman, John C. Martin, age 65
Auditors: Ernst & Young LLP

LOCATIONS

HQ: Gilead Sciences Inc
333 Lakeside Drive, Foster City, CA 94404
Phone: 650 574-3000
Web: www.gilead.com

2016 Sales

	$ mil.	% of total
US	19,354	64
Europe	6,365	21
Japan	2,527	8
Other countries & regions	2,144	7
Total	**30,390**	**100**

PRODUCTS/OPERATIONS

2016 Sales

	$ mil.	% of total
Antiviral products:		
Harvoni	9,081	30
Sovaldi	4,001	13
Truvada	3,566	12
Atripla	2,605	9
Stribild	1,914	6
Epclusa	1,752	6
Genvoya	1,484	5
Complera/Eviplera	1,457	5
Viread	1,186	4
Odefsey	329	1
Descovy	298	1
Other antiviral	72	–
Other products:		
Letaris	819	2
Ranexa	677	2
AmBisome	356	1
Zydelig	168	1
Other	188	1
Royalties Contract & other	437	1
Total	**30,390**	**100**

Selected Products

Antiviral
Atripla (HIV with Bristol-Myers Squibb)
Complera/Eviplera (HIV)
Emtriva (HIV)
Harvoni (HCV infection)
Hepsera (hepatitis B)
Sovaldi (HCV infection)
Stribild (HIV)
Tamiflu (flu treatment royalties from Roche)
Truvada (fixed-dose combination of Viread and
Emtriva for HIV)
Viread (HIV chronic hepatitis B with liver disease)
Vistide (AIDS-related cytomegalovirus retinitis)
Other products
AmBisome (antifungal with Astellas)
Cayston (cystic fibrosis)
Flolan (pulmonary hypertension)
Letairis (pulmonary arterial hypertension)
Lexiscan/Rapiscan (cardiovascular with Astellas)
Macugen (age-related macular degeneration royalties
from Eyetech)
Ranexa (chronic angina)
Products in development
Aztreonam (cystic fibrosis)
Cobicistat (HIV/AIDS)
Elvitegravir (HIV/AIDS)
GS-1101 (leukemia and lymphoma)
GS-7977 (hepatitis C)
Intesgrase (HIV)
Ranolazine (cardiovascular diabetes)

COMPETITORS

AbbVie	GlaxoSmithKline
Abbott Labs	Janssen
Actelion	Pharmaceuticals
AstraZeneca	Merck
BioCryst	Novartis
Pharmaceuticals	Pfizer
Boehringer Ingelheim	Roche Holding
Bristol-Myers Squibb	Shire
Enzon	

HISTORICAL FINANCIALS

Company Type: Public

Income Statement

FYE: December 31

	REVENUE ($ mil.)	NET INCOME ($ mil.)	NET PROFIT MARGIN	EMPLOYEES
12/16	30,390	13,501	44.4%	9,000
12/15	32,639	18,108	55.5%	8,000
12/14	24,890	12,101	48.6%	7,000
12/13	11,201	3,074	27.4%	6,100
12/12	9,702	2,591	26.7%	5,000
Annual Growth	**33.0%**	**51.1%**	**—**	**15.8%**

2016 Year-End Financials

Debt ratio: 46.24%
Return on equity: 71.96%
Cash ($ mil.): 8,229
Current ratio: 2.22
Long-term debt ($ mil.): 26,346
No. of shares (mil.): 1,310
Dividends
Yield: 0.0%
Payout: 18.5%
Market value ($ mil.): 93,809

	STOCK PRICE ($) FY Close	P/E High/Low		PER SHARE ($) Earnings	Dividends	Book Value
12/16	71.61	10	7	9.94	1.84	14.42
12/15	101.19	10	8	11.91	1.29	13.03
12/14	94.26	14	8	7.35	0.00	10.29
12/13	75.10	39	20	1.81	0.00	7.41
12/12	73.45	45	24	1.64	0.00	6.13
Annual Growth	**(0.6%)**	**—**	**—**	**56.9%**	**—**	**23.8%**

Glacier Bancorp, Inc.

Glacier Bancorp is on a Rocky Mountain high. The holding company owns about a dozen community bank divisions with about 100 locations in Montana Idaho Utah Washington Colorado and Wyoming. Serving individuals small to midsized businesses not-for-profits and public entities the banks offer traditional deposit products and credit cards in addition to retail brokerage and investment services through agreements with third-party providers. Its lending activities consist of commercial real estate loans (about half of the company's loan portfolio) as well as residential mortgages business loans and consumer loans.

Financial Performance
The company's revenue increased in fiscal 2013 compared to the prior fiscal period. It reported revenue of $356.6 million for fiscal 2013 up from $345.3 million in revenue for fiscal 2012. Net income also increased in fiscal 2013 compared to the prior year. The company reported net income of $95 million for fiscal 2013 up from $75 million in fiscal 2012.

Glacier Bancorp's cash on hand also increased in fiscal 2013 compared to fiscal 2012 levels.

Strategy
Glacier Bancorp hopes to capitalize on additional acquisition opportunities that it expects to arise as small banks deal with new industry regulations. To this end the bank agreed in 2014 to buy Montana Community Banks for $25 million to expand its Western Montana presence. In 2016 it acquired another Montana bank Treasure State Bank.

The company is also banking on organic growth with the populations of the states in its market area growing faster than the national average thanks to an influx of retiring Baby Boomers and an increase in energy- and natural resource-related jobs.

EXECUTIVES

EVP and CFO, Ron J. Copher, $352,651 total compensation
EVP and Chief Administrative Officer, Don J. Cherry, $299,950 total compensation
President and CEO, Randall M. (Randy) Chesler, age 59, $153,846 total compensation
Vice President CRA Compliance Officer, Lanette Marcum
Senior Vice President, Robert Taylor
Vice President Internal Auditor, Judy Overcast
Vice President Marketing North America, Martha Tannehill
Assistant Vice President and Corporate Auditor, Sonal Shah
Vice President Information Security, Chris Mauch
Senior Vice President Real Estate Manager, Michael Smith
Senior Vice President Business Development, Don Lloyd
Assistant Vice President, Judy Gohsman
Vice President, Donald Mccarthy
Executive Vice President Chief Admin Officer, Don Chery
Senior Vice President Human RE, Robin S Roush
Vice President Compliance CRA Officer, Karin Hergesheimer
Vice President of Human Resour, Christopher Murphy
Vice President Finance, Bob Nystuen
Vice President Internal Auditor, Leslie Thompson
Vice President, Melody Pieri
Vice President and Risk Manager, Emily Lamb
Vice President, Vanessa Barrett
Chairman, Dallas I. Herron, age 72
Auditors: BKD, LLP

LOCATIONS

HQ: Glacier Bancorp, Inc.
49 Commons Loop, Kalispell, MT 59901
Phone: 406 756-4200
Web: www.glacierbank.com

PRODUCTS/OPERATIONS

2016 Sales

	% of total
Interest income	
Commercial loans	42
Investment securities	20
Residential real estate loans	7
Consumer and other loans	7
Non-interest income	
Service charges and other fees	14
Gain on sale of loans	7
Miscellaneous loan fees and charges	1
(Loss) gain on sale of investments	–
Other income	2
Total	**100**

Selected Services

Commercial loan
Consumer loan
Deposits
Mortgage origination services
Real estate loan
Retail brokerage services
Transaction and savings

Selected Bank Divisions

1st Bank (Wyoming)
Bank of the San Juans (Colorado)
Big Sky Western Bank (Montana)
Citizens Community Bank (Idaho)
First Bank of Montana
First Bank of Wyoming
First Security Bank (Montana)
First State Bank (Wyoming)
Glacier Bank (Montana)
Mountain West Bank (Idaho)
North Cascades Bank (Washington)
Valley Bank of Helena (Montana)
Western Security Bank (Montana)

HISTORICAL FINANCIALS

Company Type: Public

Income Statement

FYE: December 31

	ASSETS ($ mil.)	NET INCOME ($ mil.)	INCOME AS % OF ASSETS	EMPLOYEES
12/16	9,450	121	1.3%	2,291
12/15	9,089	116	1.3%	2,245
12/14	8,306	112	1.4%	2,030
12/13	7,884	95	1.2%	1,919
12/12	7,747	75	1.0%	1,753
Annual Growth	5.1%	12.5%	—	6.9%

2016 Year-End Financials

Debt ratio: 1.33%	No. of shares (mil.): 76
Return on equity: 11.01%	Dividends
Cash ($ mil.): 152	Yield: 0.0%
Current ratio: —	Payout: 69.1%
Long-term debt ($ mil.): —	Market value ($ mil.): 2,773

	STOCK PRICE ($) FY Close	P/E High/Low	PER SHARE ($) Earnings	Dividends	Book Value
12/16	36.23	24 14	1.59	1.10	14.59
12/15	26.53	20 14	1.54	1.05	14.15
12/14	27.77	20 16	1.51	0.68	13.70
12/13	29.79	24 11	1.31	0.60	12.95
12/12	14.71	15 12	1.05	0.66	12.52
Annual Growth	25.3%	— —	10.9%	13.6%	3.9%

Global Partners LP

Global Partners imports petroleum products from global sources but its marketing is largely regional. The company wholesales heating oil residual fuel oil diesel oil kerosene distillates and gasoline to commercial retail and wholesale customers in New England and New York. A major player in the regional home heating oil market Global Partners operates storage facilities at 25 bulk terminals each with a storage capacity of more than 50000 barrels and with a collective storage capacity of 12.2 million barrels. It also owns and supplies a network of gasoline stations. Wholesale revenues accounts for the bulk of the company's sales.

Operations

Global Partners consists of three operating segments: Wholesale Gasoline Distribution and Station Operations (GDSO) and Commercial.

Wholesale accounts for around 50% of total sales and sells unbranded gasoline and diesel to unbranded gasoline customers and other resellers of transportation fuels. It also sells home heating oil diesel kerosene and residual oil to home heating oil retailers and wholesale distributors; as well as crude oil to refiners.

GDSO generates more than 40% of total sales and sells branded and unbranded gasoline to gasoline stations and other sub-jobbers such as gasoline convenience store car wash and other ancillary services at company operated stores and leased gas stations.

Commercial brings in the remaining nearly 10% of sales and sells unbranded gasoline custom blended fuels home heating oil diesel kerosene residual oil renewable fuels and natural gas. Its customers are public sector and large commercial and industrial end users. The segment also includes the sale of custom blended distillates and residual oil delivered by barge or from a terminal dock to ships through its bunkering activity.

The company owns storage facilities at 25 petroleum product bulk terminals each with the capacity of more than 50000 barrels including 22 refined product terminals located throughout the Northeast.

Through gas station company Global Montello Group the company sells food beverages snacks grocery and non-food merchandise at its convenience store locations.

Geographic Reach

Global Partners has a network of refined petroleum products and renewable fuels terminals throughout the Northeast region and into the Mid-Atlantic States (Connecticut Florida Georgia Indiana Louisiana Maine Maryland Massachusetts Michigan New Hampshire New Jersey New York North Dakota Ohio Oregon Pennsylvania Rhode Island Tennessee Texas Vermont and Virginia).

It has some 1460 owned leased and/or supplied gas stations including 248 convenience stores in the Northeast Maryland and Virginia. It also owns transload and storage terminals in North Dakota and Oregon.

Sales and Marketing

Global Partners gets its revenue primarily from convenience store sales at its directly operated stores and rental income from dealer leased or commission agent leased gasoline stations. Global Partners also is one of the largest distributors of gasoline distillates residual oil and renewable fuels to wholesalers retailers and commercial customers in New England and New York.

In the Commercial segment it serves customers in the public sector and large commercial and industrial end users of unbranded gasoline home heating oil diesel kerosene residual oil bunker fuel and natural gas. In the case of public sector commercial and industrial end user customers Global Partners sell products through a competitive bidding process or through contracts of various terms. It generally arranges for the delivery of the product to the customer's designated location and responds to publicly-issued requests for product proposals and quotes. The Commercial segment also includes sales of custom blended fuels delivered by barges or from a terminal dock to ships through bunkering activity.

Nearly 10% of the volume of home heating oil Global Partners sold to wholesale distributors is Heating Oil Plus. It sells home heating oil including Heating Oil Plus to about 790 wholesale distributors and retailers. About 35% of the home heating oil volume was sold using forward fixed price contracts.

Global Partners has a long term relationship with Exxon Mobil which accounts for about 15% of total sales.

Financial Performance

Global Partner's (GP) revenue has crashed since a high of $19.6 billion in 2013. In fiscal 2016 total sales of $8.2 billion represented a 20% fall on prior year. GP is vulnerable to changes in the global oil price and the sharp fall in prices beginning in 2014 is the primary factor in the sales decline. The company sold 5.1 billion gallons of product in 2016 versus 5.6 billion in 2015. The Wholesale segment's crude oil and gasoline blendstocks bore the brunt of the decline in volume sales while the Gasoline Distribution and Station Operations (GDSO) and Commercial segments grew product volume sales by 74 million and 72 million gallons respectively due to the full year contribution from the acquired Capitol business.

GP made a loss of $238.6 million in 2016 versus net income of $43.4 million in 2015. The poor performance was linked to the low oil price and resultant asset impairments in the Wholesale business.

GP used $119.9 million in its operating activities compared to net cash provided by operating activities of $62.5 million the previous year. The worsening was down to lower net income higher accounts receivable and $80.7 million lease exit expenses.

Strategy

Global Partner's management's primary concern is navigating the low oil price environment that has battered revenue and profits since 2014. To support profitability and better position for future growth the company has sold off a number of its less profitable assets. These include 31 gas stations and convenience stores its natural gas and electricity brokerage business and the termination of a sublease for more than 1600 rail cars. It is also seeking a buyer for six refined petroleum terminals.

Company Background

Through AE Holdings the Slifka family controls about 21% of Global Partners; Kayne Anderson Capital Advisors L.P 12%.

Global Partners was founded in 1933 as a one-truck heating oil retailer by current CEO Eric Slifka's grandfather Abraham Slifka.

In 2010 in order to expand its wholesale supply business the company acquired about 190 retail gas stations in three states in the Northeast from Exxon Mobil and some of its dealers for $202.3 million. Pursuing a strategy of growing its storage capacity in 2010 Global Partners also acquired three terminals in Newburgh New York from Warex Terminals for $47.5 million.

In 2012 the company signed a long-term lease agreement with Getty Realty to supply gasoline to and operate about 90 of Getty's gas station in Queens Manhattan and the Bronx as well as in Long Island and Westchester County.

Boosting its gas station network in 2012 Global Partners acquired Alliance Energy a gasoline distributor and gas stations/convenience store operator controlled by the Slifka family for $180 million.

Growing its portfolio in 2013 Global Partners acquired Cascade Kelly Holdings LLC (a crude oil and ethanol facility near Portland Oregon) for $95 million. That year it also acquired 60% of Basin Transload LLC (which operates two crude oil transloading facilities in Columbus and Beulah North Dakota with a combined rail loading capacity of 160000 barrels per day) for $85 million. The transaction complements its purchase of West Coast crude oil transload and ethanol facility near Portland.

EXECUTIVES

Senior Vice President, William Davidson
SVP Light Oil Supply and Distribution, Mark A. Romaine, age 48, $500,000 total compensation
EVP Chief Accounting Officer and Co-Director Mergers and Acquisitions, Charles A. (Chuck) Rudinsky, age 69, $273,000 total compensation
SVP Marketing, Joseph (Joe) DeStefano
President CEO and Director, Eric Slifka, age 51, $800,000 total compensation
EVP General Counsel and Secretary, Edward J. Faneuil, age 64, $450,000 total compensation
CFO, Daphne H. Foster, age 59, $400,000 total compensation
EVP Director and President Alliance Gasoline, Andrew Slifka, age 48, $425,000 total compensation
SVP Information Technology, Bill Gifford
Vice President of Marketing Information technology, Mary McCarty

Vice President of Business Development, Bruce Atkins

Vice President Project Management and Development, Jack Frost

Vice President Branded Wholesale Supply and Trading, Jeff Mansfield

Vice President Terminals and Information technology, Katherine McManmon

Senior Vice President Information Security and Compliance, Carl Stolfi

Executive Vice President of Information Technology, Gregory Rudoy

Vice President Heavy Oil Marketing, Dennis Bowersox

Senior Vice President, Mark Cosenza

Vice President of Terminal Operations, Dylan Remley

Senior Vice President Real Estate and Development, Larry Strain

Chairman, Richard Slifka, age 76

Treasurer, Greg Hanson

Senior Executive Assistant To Edward J. Faneuil

Vice President Group Chief Officer and Secretary, Lillian Santangelo

Auditors: Ernst & Young LLP

LOCATIONS

HQ: Global Partners LP
P.O. Box 9161, 800 South Street, Waltham, MA 02454-9161
Phone: 781 894-8800
Web: www.globalp.com

PRODUCTS/OPERATIONS

2016 Sales

	$ mil.	% of total
Wholesale	4,107	50
Gasoline distribution & station operations	3,443	42
Commercial	689	8
Total	**8,239**	**100**

Selected Products

Biofuels
Bunker oil
Diesel oil
Distillates
Gasoline
Home heating oil
Kerosene
Residual fuel oil

Selected Mergers and Acquisitions

COMPETITORS

Bayside Fuel
Exxon Mobil
George Warren
Gulf Oil
Highlands Fuel Delivery
Koch Industries Inc.
Sprague Resources
Tauber Oil
Warren Equities

HISTORICAL FINANCIALS

Company Type: Public

Income Statement

FYE: December 31

	REVENUE ($ mil.)	NET INCOME ($ mil.)	NET PROFIT MARGIN	EMPLOYEES
12/16	8,239	(199)	—	1,770
12/15	10,314	43	0.4%	1,890
12/14	17,269	114	0.7%	1,154
12/13	19,589	42	0.2%	943
12/12	17,626	46	0.3%	788
Annual Growth	**(17.3%)**	**—**	**—**	**22.4%**

2016 Year-End Financials

Debt ratio: 50.72%
Return on equity: —
Cash ($ mil.): 37
Current ratio: 1.35
Long-term debt ($ mil.): 1,025
No. of shares (mil.): 33
Dividends
Yield: 0.1%
Payout: —
Market value ($ mil.): 657

	STOCK PRICE ($) FY Close	P/E High/Low		PER SHARE ($) Earnings	Dividends	Book Value
12/16	19.45	—	—	(5.91)	1.85	11.63
12/15	17.57	37	14	1.11	2.74	19.20
12/14	32.99	11	8	3.95	2.53	19.03
12/13	35.39	28	18	1.42	2.34	15.10
12/12	25.35	16	12	1.71	2.06	15.85
Annual Growth	**(6.4%)**	**—**	**—**	**—**	**(2.6%)**	**(7.5%)**

Goldman Sachs Group Inc

Goldman Sachs has long possessed the Midas touch in the investment banking world. A global leader in mergers and acquisitions advice and securities underwriting Goldman offers a gamut of investment banking and asset management services to corporate and government clients worldwide as well as institutional and wealth individual investors. It owns Goldman Sachs Execution & Clearing one of the largest market makers on the NYSE & and a leading market maker for fixed income products currencies and commodities. Through affiliates Goldman Sachs is also one of the largest private equity investors in the world. Goldman Sachs was founded in 1869.

HISTORY

German immigrant-cum-Philadelphia retailer Marcus Goldman moved to New York in 1869 and began buying customers' promissory notes from jewelers to resell to banks. Goldman's son-in-law came aboard in 1882 and the firm became Goldman Sachs & Co. in 1885.

Two years later Goldman Sachs began offering US-UK foreign exchange and currency services. To serve such clients as Sears Roebuck it expanded to Chicago and St. Louis. In 1896 it joined the NYSE.

While the firm increased its European contracts Goldman's son Henry made it a major source of financing for US industry. In 1906 it co-managed its first public offering United Cigar Manufacturers (later General Cigar). By 1920 it had underwritten IPOs for Sears B.F. Goodrich and Merck.

Sidney Weinberg made partner in 1927 and stayed until his death in 1969. In the 1930s Goldman Sachs entered securities dealing and sales. After WWII it became a leader in investment banking co-managing Ford's 1956 IPO. In the 1970s it pioneered buying blocks of stock for resale.

Under Weinberg's son John Goldman Sachs became a leader in mergers and acquisitions. The 1981 purchase of J. Aron gave the firm a significant commodities presence and helped it grow in South America.

Seeking capital after 1987's market crash Goldman Sachs raised more than $500 million from Sumitomo for a 12% nonvoting interest in the firm (since reduced to 3%). The Kamehameha Schools/Bishop Estate of Hawaii an educational trust also invested.

The 1994 bond crash and a decline in new debt issues led Goldman Sachs to cut staffing for the first time since the 1980s. But problems went deeper. Partners began leaving and taking their equity. Cost cuts a stronger bond market and the long bull market helped the firm rebound; firm members sought protection through limited liability partnership status. The firm also extended the period during which partners can cash out (slowing the cash drain) and limited the number of people entitled to a share of profits. Overseas growth in 1996 and 1997 focused on the UK and Asia.

After three decades of resistance the partners in 1998 voted to sell the public a minority stake in the firm but market volatility led to postponement. Goldman Sachs also suffered from involvement with Long-Term Capital Management ultimately contributing $300 million to its bailout.

In 1999 Jon Corzine then co-chairman and co-CEO announced that he would leave the group after seeing it through its IPO and Goldman Sachs finally went public that year in an offering valued at close to $4 billion. In 2000 Corzine was elected to a US Senate seat. The New Jersey Democrat spent more than $64 million on his campaign (a record) nearly $61 million of it from his own personal wealth (also a record). Corzine went on to win New Jersey's gubernatorial race in 2005.

In early 2004 Goldman president and COO John Thain left the firm to assume the helm of the New York Stock Exchange. Lloyd Blankfein was named his successor and became chairman and CEO in 2006 when his predecessor Henry "Hank" Paulson was named secretary of the US Treasury.

At the height of the economic crisis Goldman Sachs converted to a bank holding company. It formed subsidiary Goldman Sachs Bank USA (GS Bank USA) to manage bank loan trading mortgage originations and other activities. The Federal Reserve mandated the change for Goldman Sachs and fellow investment bank Morgan Stanley. The shift marked a monumental change on Wall Street as it put an end to the independent brokerage firm model that had been a mainstay in the US since reform measures were implemented during the Great Depression. Rivals Merrill Lynch Lehman Brothers and Bear Stearns had already merged with larger banks or filed for bankruptcy. The bank holding company structure brought increased regulation but allowed Goldman Sachs to acquire commercial banks — all in an effort to shore up the company's balance sheet.

In the days following the Federal Reserve announcement Warren Buffett's Berkshire Hathaway invested $5 billion in Goldman Sachs and acquired an option to assume $5 billion more of the company's common shares. Goldman Sachs made an additional $5 billion worth of stock available in a public offering. Additionally the US government stepped in with funding for Goldman Sachs in late 2008 when it announced an economic stimulus plan to buy some $250 billion worth of preferred shares of the nation's top banks; approximately $10 billion went to Goldman Sachs.

The capital infusions helped but didn't completely shield Goldman Sachs from the financial crisis the effects of which were felt worldwide. To cut costs the company trimmed some 10% of its workforce. It eventually returned to profitability in 2009 and paid back the money it received from the government but still drew ire from politicians over what have been perceived to be extravagant pay packages for its top employees. (The firm's extravagant year-end bonuses had become the stuff of legend.)

Goldman Sachs opened a new $1.8-billion headquarters building in New York City's lower Manhattan in 2009.

In 2012 Goldman spent some $5.65 billion to buy back preferred shares that Warren Buffet's

Berkshire Hathaway acquired in 2008. The repurchase would save the firm money as it had been paying some 10% interest on the shares (or some $500 million annually).

Also in 2012 Goldman acquired the Bermuda-based insurance and reinsurance operations of Ariel Reinsurance; an addition that should bring in a steady stream of fees. Additionally that year the company arranged to sell hedge fund administrator Goldman Sachs Administration Services to State Street for some $550 million.

In 2013 Goldman Sachs Asset Management acquired the Global Treasury Funds assets which consists of a variety of money market funds from RBS Asset Management to strengthen its strong fixed income and liquidity management businesses in Europe and around the world.

Goldman bought the remaining 20% stake it didn't already own in Endesa Gas T&D in 2013. It purchased the natural gas transport firm from Spanish power utility Endesa for about $174 million.

In January 2013 Goldman sold approximately 45% of its ordinary shares of ICBC.

EXECUTIVES

Head Merchant Banking Division, Richard A. Friedman, age 59

EVP General Counsel and Secretary, Gregory K. Palm, age 68

Chairman Goldman Sachs Bank USA and Goldman Sachs International Bank, Esta E. Stecher, age 60

EVP and CFO, R. Martin Chavez, age 53

Chairman and CEO, Lloyd C. Blankfein, age 62, $2,000,000 total compensation

EVP and Head of Global Compliance, Sarah E. Smith

Vice Chairman CEO Goldman Sachs International and Co-Head Investment Banking Division, Richard J. Gnodde, age 57

President and Co-COO, David M. Solomon, age 55

President Goldman Sachs Japan, Masanori Mochida

President Asia/Pacific Outside Japan, Kenneth W. Hitchner

EVP Chief of Staff and Secretary, John F.W. Rogers, age 60

Global Co-Head Investment Management Division, Timothy J. O'Neill

EVP and Global Head Human Capital Management, Edith W. Cooper, age 55

Global Co-COO Equities Franchise, Michael D. Daffey

Head Conflicts Resolution Group, Gwen R. Libstag

President and Co-COO, Harvey M. Schwartz, age 52, $1,850,000 total compensation

Global Co-Head Securities Division, Isabelle Ealet

Vice Chairman and Global Co-Head Securities Division, Pablo J. Salame, age 51

Head Global Investment Research, Steven H. Strongin

Global Co-Head Investment Management Division, Eric S. Lane

Chief Strategy Officer and Head Latin America, Stephen M. Scherr

Global Co-Head Securities Division, Ashok Varadhan

Chief Risk Officer, Craig W. Broderick

Co-Head Investment Banking Division, John Waldron

Global Head Credit Trading, Justin G. Gmelich

Co-Head of Global Mergers and Acquisitions, Gregg R. Lemkau

Head of the Global Financing Group and Head of Latin America, Marc Nachmann

Chairman Global Financial Institutions Group (FIG), Mike Esposito

Co-Head Global Financial Institutions Group (FIG), Luke Sarsfield

Co-Head Global Financial Institutions Group, Todd Leland

Global Co-COO Equities Franchise, Paul M. Russo

Head of the Global Special Situations Group (GSSG), Julian Salisbury

CEO Goldman Sachs Singapore Pte., Jason Moo

Vice President and Portfolio Manager, Michael DeSantis

Vice President Technology, Ted Najjar

Vice President Of Network Architecture, Miruna Stratan

Vice President, Lawrence Zeng

Vice President, Nick Gelber

Vice President And Associate General Counsel, Mark Robertson

Vice President, Adam Rosenberg

Vice President, Robert Abreu

Vice President, Lindsay Quereau

Vice President of Workplace and Middleware Technology, John Stecher

Vice President Equity Research Brokers Market STR, Daniel Harris

Vice President In Technology, David Olivares

Vice President, Vijay Kalakoti

Vice President, Jeff Boyd

Vice President, Jonathan Fallin

Vice President Alternative Investments Product Services, Stephen Blumenfeld

Vice President, Roger Gardiner

Vice President, Tom Healy

Vice President Information Technology, Milind Sapre

Vice President And Assistant General C, Daniel Young

Vice President, Lindsay Chock

Vice President, Richard Case

Vice President, Douglas Tansey

Vice President, James Wilcox

Vice President, Anuraag Verma

Vice President, Curtis L Ambrose

Vice President, Neil Kaufman

Vice President Global Securities Services, Caitlin Walsh

Vice President, Temitayo Olajide

Vice President, Jim Gabriel

Vice President, Anisha Malhotra

Vice President, Richard Skidmore

Vice President FX Ecommerce Product Management, Soomin Hu

Vice President Private Wealth Management Investment Management Division, Cristin Dalecki

Vice President Leveraged Finance Investment Banking, Jamie Tam

Vice President, Tim Halladay

Vice President, Karen Ho

Vice President Information Technology, Chris Muller

Vice President, Manoj Susarla

Vice President, Nancy Benchoff

Vice President Of Legal Technology, Danielle Cherence

Vice President, Peter Pritchard

Vice President, Michael Parrish

Vice President, Albert Elkind

Vice President, Justin Portnoy

Vice President, Puneet Awasthi

Vice President, Carrie Gannon

Vice President, Gitika Gumbar

Vice President, Lindsey Morfin

Vice President, Andrew Dubinsky

Vice President, Daniel Goldberg

Vice President, Brian Krawczyk

Vice President, Matt Levin

Vice President Information Technology Manager, Greg Killeen

Vice President, Krishnan Narayanan

Vice President, Seth Greengrass

Vice President Securities Compliance Information Technology, Peter Ferns

Vice President, Barbara Williams

Vice President, Alex Topkins

Vice President, Dmitriy Furer

Vice President Investment Management Division, Ryan Sobeck

Vice President, Gary Godshaw

Vice President, Rafael Gonzalez

Vice President, Cynthia Klein

Vice President, Christopher Higgins

Vice President, Philip Vehec

Vice President, Dugan Lawrence

Vice President Global Mobility, Tim Dwyer

Vice President Investment Management Division, Dan Forman

Vice President, Narayanan Radhakrishnan

Vice President, Kevin Carmody

Vice President, Claira Kim

Vice President, Linda Avery

Vice President Critical Systems Operations, Carlos Hanco

Vice President, Anna Soderini

Vice President, Robert McDonald

Vice President, Jeremiah DeNonno

Vice President, Elton Andrews

Vice President International Equities, Simon Fennell

Vice President, Eric Riley

Vice President, Jared Abrams

Vice President, Jeffrey Frank

Vice President Technology, Eugene Gauthier

Vice President Private Wealth Management Investment Management Division, Neil Stone

Vice President, Matthew Korenberg

Vice President Technology, Stephen Chan

Vice President Equities Division, Tara Pardo

Vice President, Allison Marsh

Vice President of Information Technology, Michael Deninno

Vice President, Sean Butkus

Vice President Systems Management, Jeff Levine

Vice President, Christopher Wright

Vice President Investment Banking Division, Thomas Lynch

Vice President and Tax Counsel Tax Planning and Advisory, David Felman

Vice President, Jeffrey Gido

Vice President, Howard Epstein

Vice President IMD Infrastructure, Kirk Eide

Vice President, Kathryn Boyles

Vice President, Richard Jiang

Vice President and Tax Counsel, Kenneth Sheinman

Vice President Information Security, Anita Nandakumar

Vice President, JARRETT SCHUBE

Vice President, Bob Jones

Vice President, Allison Lucas

Vice President, Andrew Hartman

Vice President Marketing, Michael Moran

Vice President, Joe Mella

Vice President Investment Banking Division, Dave Park

Vice President, Tim Bridges

Vice President, David Bao

Vice President in Information Technology, Rizvan Gurmu

Vice President, Philip Pallone

Vice President Tax, Dean Sharpe

Vice President and Associate General Counsel, Neena Reddy

Vice President, Aileen Kriel

Vice President Global Security Services, Alicia Grippi-Virag

Vice President, Giovanni Sansalone

Software Architect Vice President, Moinuddin Qadir

Auditors: PricewaterhouseCoopers LLP

LOCATIONS

HQ: Goldman Sachs Group Inc
200 West Street, New York, NY 10282
Phone: 212 902-1000   **Fax:** 212 902-3000
Web: www.gs.com

2016 Sales

	% of total
Americas	60
Europe the Middle East & Africa	26
Asia	14
Total	**100**

Goodyear Tire & Rubber Co.

PRODUCTS/OPERATIONS

2016 Sales

	$ mil.	% of total
Interest income	9,691	26
Non Interest income		
Market making	9,933	26
Investment banking	6,273	17
Investment management	5,407	14
Commissions & fees	3,208	9
Other	3,200	8
Total	**37,712**	**100**

2016 Sales

	% of total
Institutional Client Services	47
Investment Banking	21
Investment Management	19
Investing & Lending	13
Total	**100**

Selected Subsidiaries

Goldman Sachs & Co.
Goldman Sachs Bank USA
Goldman Sachs Credit Partners L.P. (Bermuda)
Goldman Sachs Financial Markets L.P.
Goldman Sachs International (UK)
Goldman Sachs Japan Co. Ltd.
Goldman Sachs Mortgage Company
GSTM LLC
  Goldman Sachs Execution & Clearing L.P.
J. Aron & Company

COMPETITORS

BMO Capital Markets	FMR
Barclays	JPMorgan Chase
CIBC World Markets	Lazard
Citigroup Global	Merrill Lynch
Markets	Morgan Stanley
Credit Suisse	Nomura Securities
Credit Suisse (USA)	RBC Capital Markets
Deutsche Bank	UBS

HISTORICAL FINANCIALS

Company Type: Public

Income Statement

FYE: December 31

	ASSETS ($ mil.)	NET INCOME ($ mil.)	INCOME AS % OF ASSETS	EMPLOYEES
12/16	860,165	7,398	0.9%	34,400
12/15	861,395	6,083	0.7%	36,800
12/14	856,240	8,477	1.0%	34,000
12/13	911,507	8,040	0.9%	32,900
12/12	938,555	7,475	0.8%	32,400
Annual Growth	(2.2%)	(0.3%)	—	1.5%

2016 Year-End Financials

Debt ratio: 27.22%	No. of shares (mil.): 392
Return on equity: 8.50%	Dividends
Cash ($ mil.): 121,711	Yield: 0.0%
Current ratio: —	Payout: 15.9%
Long-term debt ($ mil.): —	Market value ($ mil.): 94,016

	STOCK PRICE ($) FY Close	P/E High/Low		PER SHARE ($) Earnings	Dividends	Book Value
12/16	239.45	15	8	16.29	2.60	221.31
12/15	180.23	18	14	12.14	2.55	206.75
12/14	193.83	11	9	17.07	2.25	192.44
12/13	177.26	11	8	15.46	2.05	175.79
12/12	127.56	9	6	14.13	1.77	162.78
Annual Growth	17.1%	—	—	3.6%	10.1%	8.0%

Goodyear Tire & Rubber is working to unseat tire industry leaders Bridgestone and Michelin (by total sales). Goodyear sells mainly new tires under the Goodyear Dunlop Kelly Fulda Debica Just Tires and Sava brand names. Goodyear makes markets and sells Dunlop tires across the Americas the EMEA and the Asia/Pacific. In Japan the tire makers own businesses that sell tires separately to OEMs and to aftermarket companies. Goodyear sells more than 55% of its products outside the US.

HISTORY

In 1898 Frank and Charles Seiberling founded a tire and rubber company in Akron Ohio and named it after Charles Goodyear (inventor of the vulcanization process 1839). The debut of the Quick Detachable tire and the Universal Rim (1903) made Goodyear the world's largest tire maker by 1916.

Goodyear began manufacturing in Canada in 1910 and over the next two decades it expanded into Argentina Australia and the Dutch East Indies. The company established its own rubber plantations in Sumatra (now part of Indonesia) in 1916.

Financial woes led to reorganization in 1921 and investment bankers forced the Seiberlings out. Succeeding caretaker management Paul Litchfield began three decades as CEO in 1926 a time in which Goodyear emerged to become the world's largest rubber company.

Goodyear blimps served as floating billboards nationwide by the 1930s. During that decade Goodyear opened company stores acquired tire maker Kelly-Springfield (1935) and began producing tires made from synthetic rubber (1937). After WWII Goodyear was an innovative leader in technologies such as polyester tire cord (1962) and the bias-belted tire (1967).

By 1980 Goodyear had introduced radial tire brands such as the all-weather Tiempo the Eagle and the Arriva as it led the US market.

Thwarting British financier Sir James Goldsmith's takeover attempt in 1986 CEO Robert Mercer raised $1.7 billion by selling the company's non-tire businesses (Motor Wheel Goodyear Aerospace) and by borrowing heavily.

Recession overcapacity and price-cutting in 1990 led to hard times for tire makers. After suffering through 1990 its first money-losing year since the Depression Goodyear lured Stanley Gault out of retirement. He ceased marketing tires exclusively through Goodyear's dealer network by selling tires through Wal-Mart Kmart and Sears. Gault also cut costs through layoffs plant closures and spending reductions and returned Goodyear to profitability in 1991.

The company increased its presence in the US retail market in 1995 when it began selling tires through 860 Penske Auto Centers and 300 Montgomery Ward auto centers. President Samir Gibara succeeded chairman Gault as CEO in 1996. That year Goodyear bought Poland's leading tire maker T C Debica and a 60% stake in South African tire maker Contred (acquiring the rest in 1998).

In 1997 Goodyear formed an alliance with Sumitomo Rubber Industries under which the companies agreed to make and market tires for one another in Asia and North America. The next year Goodyear sold its Celeron Oil subsidiary which operated the All American Pipeline and acquired the remaining 26% stake in tire distributor Brad Ragan (commercial and retail outlets in the US) for $20.7 million.

The company acquired Sumitomo Rubber Industries' North American and European Dunlop tire businesses in 1999. The acquisition returned Goodyear to its #1 position in the tire-making industry. However the company recorded drastically low profits that year because it had cut tire production and was unable to meet supplier demands.

To improve profitability Goodyear increased tire prices in 2000 and began consolidating its manufacturing operations. Goodyear also announced plans to combine its commercial tire service centers with those of Treadco through a joint venture named Wingfoot Commercial Tire Systems. Despite record sales in 2000 the company's profits hit some hard road prompting Goodyear to lay off 10% of its workforce and implement other cost-cutting efforts.

Early in 2001 the company announced that it would close its Mexican tire plant. The same year the company agreed to replace Firestone Wilderness AT tires with Goodyear tires for Ford owners as part of Ford's big Firestone tire recall.

Early in 2002 Goodyear announced that its recent job cuts and manufacturing consolidation resulted in an $85 million decrease in annual operating costs. Later in the year the tire maker became embroiled in an age discrimination lawsuit claiming unfair job evaluations for the company's older employees. Blaming a slow US economy Goodyear announced plans to cut 450 jobs at its Union City Tennessee manufacturing plant. The job cuts were just the beginning of what would be a series of operational adjustments made as part of a Capital Structure Improvement Plan formally launched in 2003.

Although Goodyear once owned about 10% of its Sumitomo Rubber Industries it sold more than 20 million shares of its Japanese counterpart stock back to the tire maker in 2003. Later in the year as the company was embroiled in a lengthy debate with the United Steelworkers union it was announced that the Huntsville Alabama tire manufacturing plant would be closed. Goodyear also announced that it would cut 500 non-union salaried employees in North America. Later that same year it was announced that Goodyear was chosen by Volvo to be the truck manufacturer's primary tire supplier in North America; Goodyear had a similar contract with Mack Trucks.

Qantas Airways announced in early 2004 that it chose Goodyear to provide tires for the Australia-based company's Jetstar Airways. Later in the year Goodyear acquired the shares of Slovenia-based Sava Tires it did not already own and the company's Goodyear Dunlop Tires Europe unit purchased the Sweden-based Dackia retail tire stores. The company announced more job cuts in the non-tire sector in 2004 affecting Goodyear's engineered products and chemical units.

In 2005 Goodyear sold its stake in Goodyear Sumatra Plantations (rubber plantations in Indonesia) to rival Bridgestone for $62 million. Later that year the company sold its Wingtack adhesive resin business to Sartomer Company Inc. (a subsidiary of France's TOTAL S.A.) for about $65 million. As 2005 wound to a close the company sold its farm tire business to Titan International for $100 million.

Goodyear called off plans to sell its Chemical Products division. Instead the company integrated its chemical operations with those of its North American Tire division to take greater advantage of operational synergies. The company did however move forward with plans to jettison its Engineered Products division. In 2005 Goodyear secured the services of J.P. Morgan Securities and Goldman Sachs to help it explore opportunities for the sale of Engineered Products. The company struck a deal for The Carlyle Group in 2007 to buy its Engineered Products division for about $1.5 billion.

In 2011 Goodyear sold its tire reinforcement wire business (located in Luxembourg and North Carolina) to South Korea-based Hyosung for $50 million. The same year it sold its farm tire business in Latin America to a Titan International unit for $99 million. In 2010 Goodyear had agreed to sell its farm tire business in Europe as well as Latin America to Titan but the European part of the deal fell through and Goodyear does not have a time frame for making that sale. (In 2005 Titan had purchased Goodyear's North American farm tire business.) Also in 2011 Goodyear closed a facility in Union City Tennessee.

Intent on making more tires at lower-cost facilities Goodyear relocated its tire-making operations from Dalian China to Pulandian China in 2012. Additionally Goodyear is expanding or modernizing plants in Brazil Chile Germany and the US.

EXECUTIVES

Chairman President and CEO, Richard J. (Rich) Kramer, age 53, $1,233,333 total compensation

SVP General Counsel and Secretary, David L. (Dave) Bialosky, age 60, $565,000 total compensation

EVP and CFO, Laura K. Thompson, age 52, $621,667 total compensation

President Americas, Stephen R. (Steve) McClellan, age 51, $610,000 total compensation

SVP Global Operations and Technology, Joseph (Joe) Zekoski, age 65

President North America Consumer, R. Scott Rogers, age 48

President Europe Middle East and Africa (EMEA), Chris Delaney, age 56

SVP Global Human Resources and Chief Human Resources Officer, John T. Lucas, age 57, $547,333 total compensation

SVP Global Sales and Marketing, Richard Kellam, age 56

VP and CTO, Christopher Helsel, age 52

President Asia Pacific, Ryan Patterson, age 43

Vice President Global Labor Relations, Jim Allen

Vice President Consumer Sales and Customer Development, Andy Traicoff

Vice President and Assistant Controller, Michael McNulty

Vice President Total Rewards At The Goodyear Tire And Rubber Company, Annie Granchi

Vice President and Chief Procurement Officer, Mark Purtilar

Secretary Marketing Department, Marilyn Chapanar

Assistant Treasurer, Ken Barfuss

Auditors: PricewaterhouseCoopers LLP

LOCATIONS

HQ: Goodyear Tire & Rubber Co.
200 Innovation Way, Akron, OH 44316-0001
Phone: 330 796-2121   **Fax:** 330 796-4099
Web: www.goodyear.com

2016 Sales

	$ mil.	% of total
Americas	8,172	54
Europe Middle East and Africa	4,880	32
Asia Pacific	2,106	14
Total	**15,158**	**100**

2016 Sales

	$ mil.	% of total
United States	6,724	44
Germany	1,853	12
Other international	6,581	44
Total	**15,158**	**100**

PRODUCTS/OPERATIONS

Selected Products

Automotive repair services
Chemical products
Natural rubber
Tires
  Automotive
  Aviation
  Buses
  Construction
  Farm
  Mining
  Motorcycles
  Trucks
Tread rubber
Wholesale tires

Selected Subsidiaries

Celeron Corporation
Dunlop Grund und Service Verwaltungs GmbH (Germany)
Dunlop Tyres Limited (UK)
Goodyear Canada Inc.
Goodyear Dalian Tire Company Ltd. (China)
Goodyear de Chile S.A.I.C.
Goodyear de Colombia S.A.
Goodyear do Brasil Produtos de Borracha Ltda (Brazil)
Goodyear Dunlop Tires Austria GmbH
Goodyear Dunlop Tires Belgium N.V.
Goodyear Dunlop Tires Czech s.r.o.
Goodyear Dunlop Tires Danmark A/S
Goodyear Dunlop Tires Espana S.A. (Spain)
Goodyear Dunlop Tires Finland OY
Goodyear Dunlop Tires Hellas S.A.I.C. (Greece)
Goodyear Dunlop Tires Hungary Ltd.
Goodyear Dunlop Tires Ireland Ltd
Goodyear Dunlop Tires Italia SpA (Italy)
Goodyear Dunlop Tires Polska Sp z.o.o. (Poland)
Goodyear Dunlop Tires Portugal Unipessoal Lda
Goodyear Dunlop Tires Slovakia s.r.o.
Goodyear Dunlop Tires Suisse S.A. (Switzerland)
The Kelly-Springfield Tyre Company Ltd (UK)
Wingfoot Corporation

COMPETITORS

Bridgestone	Pep Boys
Continental AG	Pirelli
Cooper Tire & Rubber	Sime Darby
Hankook Tire	Titan International
Kumho Tire	Toyo Tire & Rubber
Marangoni	Yokohama Rubber
Michelin	Zeon
Midas	

HISTORICAL FINANCIALS

Company Type: Public

Income Statement

FYE: December 31

	REVENUE ($ mil.)	NET INCOME ($ mil.)	NET PROFIT MARGIN	EMPLOYEES
12/17	15,377	346	2.3%	64,000
12/16	15,158	1,264	8.3%	66,000
12/15	16,443	307	1.9%	66,000
12/14	18,138	2,452	13.5%	67,000
12/13	19,540	629	3.2%	69,000
Annual Growth	**(5.8%)**	**(13.9%)**	**—**	**(1.9%)**

2017 Year-End Financials

Debt ratio: 33.57%
Return on equity: 7.60%
Cash ($ mil.): 1,043
Current ratio: 1.21
Long-term debt ($ mil.): 5,076
No. of shares (mil.): 240
Dividends
  Yield: 0.0%
  Payout: 32.1%
Market value ($ mil.): 7,759

	STOCK PRICE ($) FY Close	P/E High/Low		PER SHARE ($) Earnings	Dividends	Book Value
12/17	32.31	27	21	1.37	0.44	19.17
12/16	30.87	7	5	4.74	0.31	17.91
12/15	32.67	31	21	1.12	0.25	14.68
12/14	28.57	3	2	8.78	0.22	13.40
12/13	23.85	10	5	2.28	0.05	6.48
Annual Growth	**7.9%**	**—**	**—**	**(12.0%)**	**72.2%**	**31.1%**

Grainger (W.W.) Inc.

Grainger is no stranger to industrial products. W.W. Grainger distributes more than 1.9 million industrial products from supplies to equipment and tools. The short list has electrical devices fasteners fleet maintenance equipment hand tools hardware janitorial lighting office supplies power and plumbing tools and safety security and test instruments. Its 1.1 million customers are contractors maintenance and repair shops manufacturers and commercial government and educational facilities. Grainger sells through a network of branches distribution centers catalogs and websites.

Operations

Grainger's US business is its largest operating segment representing around 75% of net sales. The segment's product lines include lighting and electrical equipment power and hand tools pumps and plumbing and cleaning and maintenance supplies. The US business purchases products from more than 2600 key suppliers most of which are manufacturers.

Acklands-Grainger the company's core Canadian business focuses on distributing industrial and safety products via about 150 domestic branches and distribution centers.

Through a global sourcing operation Grainger procures competitively priced high-quality products produced outside the US from some 400 suppliers.

Besides a wide range of products Grainger also provides services that include inventory management and energy efficiency assistance for lower maintenance costs. The company's KeepStock program offers on-site services and vendor-managed inventory. Since the program's launch in 2006 KeepStock has grown to serve more than 21000 customers. It completes more than 11000 installations each year.

Geographic Reach

About 75% of Grainger's sales stem from the US 10% in Canada and the rest in Europe Asia and Latin America. With locations in all 50 states the US business has about 280 branches and almost 20 distribution centers and roughly 40 contact centers.

Sales and Marketing

Grainger offers its services to a range of industries such as manufacturing hospitality transportation government retail healthcare and education. It markets its products through sales representatives direct marketing materials catalogs and eCommerce and also through contact centers inventory management and its branches.

The company also operates its international business through Fabory a European distributor of fasteners tools and industrial supplies; and in Japan through its 51% stake in MonotaRO Co.

Its Zoro Tools unit is an online distributor serving US businesses and consumers through its website Zorotools.com.

Financial Performance

Grainger has enjoyed seven straight years (2010-2016) of unprecedented growth. Revenues increased 2% to peak at $10.1 billion in 2016. This was driven by 3% growth from acquisitions and 1% sales growth offset by a 2% decline in price deflation exceeding cost deflation and an unfavorable customer mix.

In addition to experiencing sales growth from government retail and light manufacturing customers during 2016 Grainger saw its eCommerce sales grow by 15%. This was driven by stronger sales via electronic purchasing platforms in the US and Japan.

Grainger's profits however declined 21% from $769 million in 2015 to $606 million in 2016 mainly due to a 2% rise in operating expenses. This percentage included almost $90 million collectively in restructuring and impairment charges.

Strategy

To grow its already burgeoning eCommerce operations Grainger is targeting global economies with robust IT systems and a developed infrastructure. These include North America Japan and Western Europe. Stating that more than 65% of its orders currently originate digitally (and that number will continue to surge) Grainger has also made investing in its own technological infrastructure a priority.

Grainger is also open to using acquisitions to strengthen its online operations. In 2015 the company bought Cromwell Group Limited a broad line distributor of MRO supplies in the UK for Â 310 million. The acquisition enhanced Grainger's supply chain and eCommerce offerings and will enable Grainger to profitably scale its single channel online business Zoro Germany.

HISTORY

In 1919 William W. Grainger a motor designer and salesman saw the opportunity to develop a wholesale electric-motor sales and distribution company. He set up an office in Chicago in 1927 and incorporated the business a year later. With sales generated primarily through postcard mailers and an eight-page catalog called MotorBook Grainger started shipping motors to mail-order customers.

Utilities and factories began to shift from direct-current to alternating-current power systems in the late 1920s. Uniform DC-powered assembly lines gave way to individual workstations each powered by a separate AC motor. This burgeoning market opened the way for distributors such as W.W. Grainger to tap into segments that high-volume manufacturers found difficult to reach. In the early 1930s W.W. Grainger opened offices in Atlanta Dallas Philadelphia and San Francisco; by 1936 it had 15 sales branches.

W.W. Grainger entered a boom period after WWII and by 1949 it had branches in 30 states. The company continued to expand in the 1950s and 1960s then went public in 1967.

William Grainger retired in 1968 and his son David succeeded him as CEO. The company expanded into electric motor manufacturing with the purchase of the Doerr Companies in 1969. Ten years later it opened its 150th branch.

Grainger's distribution became decentralized with the 1983 opening of its 1.4-million-sq.-ft. automated regional distribution center in Kansas City. The next year Grainger surpassed $1 billion in sales. The company sold its Doerr Electric subsidiary to Emerson Electric in 1986. It added 91 branches in 1987 and 1988.

After a 17-year hiatus the company started making acquisitions again buying Vonnegut Industrial Products in 1989; Bossert Industrial Supply and Allied Safety in 1990; Ball Industries a distributor of sanitary and janitorial supplies in 1991; and Lab Safety Supply in 1992. Grainger began integrating its sanitary supply business with its core activities in 1993.

For the first time in company history no Grainger held the CEO position when president Richard Keyser was appointed in 1995 replacing David Grainger. That year the company moved its headquarters to Lake Forest Illinois.

EXECUTIVES

SVP and General Counsel, John L. Howard, age 60, $673,828 total compensation

SVP and Chief People Officer, Joseph C. High, age 64, $495,250 total compensation

VP Finance Industrial Supply Division, Ronald L. Jadin, age 57, $721,885 total compensation

Chairman and CEO, Donald G. (D.G.) Macpherson, age 50, $875,000 total compensation

SVP Global Supply Chain Branch Network Contact Centers and Corporate Strategy, Paige K. Robbins, age 48, $441,769 total compensation

Vice President Manager Director, Patrick ONeal

Vice President of Corporate and Major Account Business, Michael DuBose

Regional Sales Vice President, Daniel Moscaritolo

Vice President Marketing, Jim Penvillo

Regional Sales Vice President, Lloyd Peterson

Vice President Corporate Strategy and Continuous Improvement, Elizabeth Ubell

Auditors: Ernst & Young LLP

LOCATIONS

HQ: Grainger (W.W.) Inc.
100 Grainger Parkway, Lake Forest, IL 60045-5201
Phone: 847 535-1000   **Fax:** 847 535-0878
Web: www.grainger.com

2016 Sales

	$ mil.	% of total
US	7,834	77
Canada	739	7
Other countries	1,563	16
Total	**10,137**	**100**

PRODUCTS/OPERATIONS

2016 Sales

	$ mil.	% of total
US-based businesses	7,522	74
Canada-based businesses	733	7
Other businesses	1,880	19
Total	**10,137**	**100**

Selected Products

Adhesives
Air compressors
Air-filtration equipment
Electric motors
Electrical products
Fasteners
Fleet and vehicle maintenance products
Hand tools
Heating and ventilation equipment
Janitorial and plumbing supplies
Lab supplies
Library equipment
Lighting equipment
Material handling
Pneumatics and hydraulics
Power tools
Pumps
Safety products
Security products
Spray paints
Test Instruments

COMPETITORS

Ace Hardware	International Library
Applied Industrial	Furniture
Technologies	Kaman Industrial
Fastenal	Technologies
Genuine Parts	Lowe's
Gexpro	MSC Industrial Direct
Graybar Electric	McMaster-Carr
Industrial	WESCO International
Distribution Group	Wilson

HISTORICAL FINANCIALS

Company Type: Public

Income Statement

FYE: December 31

	REVENUE ($ mil.)	NET INCOME ($ mil.)	NET PROFIT MARGIN	EMPLOYEES
12/16	10,137	605	6.0%	25,600
12/15	9,973	769	7.7%	25,800
12/14	9,964	801	8.0%	23,600
12/13	9,437	797	8.4%	23,700
12/12	8,950	689	7.7%	22,400
Annual Growth	**3.2%**	**(3.2%)**	**—**	**3.4%**

2016 Year-End Financials

Debt ratio: 39.46%
Return on equity: 29.73%
Cash ($ mil.): 274
Current ratio: 1.85
Long-term debt ($ mil.): 1,840

No. of shares (mil.): 58
Dividends
　Yield: 0.0%
　Payout: 48.9%
Market value ($ mil.): 13,657

	STOCK PRICE ($) FY Close	P/E High/Low	PER SHARE ($) Earnings	Dividends	Book Value
12/16	232.25	24 18	9.87	4.83	30.57
12/15	202.59	22 16	11.58	4.59	36.54
12/14	254.89	23 20	11.45	4.17	47.60
12/13	255.42	24 18	11.13	3.59	47.21
12/12	202.37	23 18	9.52	3.06	43.52
Annual Growth	**3.5%**	**— —**	**0.9%**	**12.1%**	**(8.4%)**

Graybar Electric Co., Inc.

Graybar Electric is one of the largest distributors of electrical products in the US. The employee-owned company distributes more than 1 million electrical communications and data networking products through a network of around 260 distribution facilities. Its diversified lineup includes a myriad of wire cable and lighting products from thousands of manufacturers and suppliers. It also offers supply chain management and logistics services. Affiliate Graybar Financial Services provides equipment leasing and financing. Graybar Electric sells to construction contractors industrial plants power utilities and telecommunications providers primarily in the US.

Operations

The company mainly operates through its subsidiaries of Graybar Canada Advantage Industrial Automation Cape Electrical Supply and Commonwealth Controls.

Geographic Reach

Graybar's business is primarily based in the US as its headquarters are located in St. Louis Missouri. Other operations include distribution facilities in Canada and Puerto Rico. The company serves its customers through a a network of over 260 locations across the US and Canada.

It also operates in 13 geographical districts in the US each of which maintains multiple distribution facilities that consist primarily of warehouse space. The number of facilities excluding distribution centers in its designated districts varies from 11 to 22 totaling 218 for all districts.

Sales and Marketing

Among the company's strengths is a diverse and large customer base with more than 140000 clients. Graybar gets nearly half of its sales from the construction sector. Other customers come from the institutional commercial and government (23%) and industrial and utility (21%) sectors. The company has expanded its sales presence to support its government business which continues to see strong growth.

Graybar distributes one million products purchased from more than 4600 manufacturers and suppliers. The company sells approximately 50% of the products from its top 25 suppliers.

Financial Performance

Graybar's revenue climbed 5% from $6.1 billion in 2015 to peak at a record-setting $6.4 billion in 2016. In addition Graybar's profits increased 2% from $91 million to $93 million during that same time period. The historic growth for 2016 was fueled by a 9% surge in sales from its construction vertical and a marginal uptick from the industrial and utility markets.It also generated additional revenue from previous acquisitions.

Strategy

Graybar plans to continue adding physical locations to expand its presence and service offerings. In addition Graybar is broadening its e-commerce and mobility capabilities to enhance its online presence and expand its digital marketing to grow sales with new and existing customers.

In 2015 Graybar established a branch in Utah and two branches in California. The company in 2014 opened a branch in Texas two in North Dakota and one in Oregon.

Mergers and Acquisitions

Graybar has achieved historic growth over the last few years through the help of acquisitions. In the summer of 2016 it purchased Cape Electrical Supply a regional distributor serving electrical contractors and large engineering construction firms as well as industrial institutional and utility customers. The previous year Graybar obtained Advantage Industrial Automation a provider of control and automation equipment catering to industrial users.

HISTORY

After serving as a telegrapher during the Civil War Enos Barton borrowed $400 from his widowed mother in 1869 and started an electrical equipment shop in Cleveland with George Shawk. Later that year Elisha Gray a professor of physics at Oberlin College who had several inventions (including a printing telegraph) to his credit bought Shawk's interest in the shop and the firm of Gray & Barton moved to Chicago where a third partner joined.

The company incorporated as the Western Electric Manufacturing Co. in 1872 with two-thirds of the company's stock held by two Western Union executives. As the telegraph industry took off the enterprise grew rapidly providing equipment to towns and railroads in the western US.

Western Electric then formed a new distribution business in 1926 Graybar Electric Co. (from "Gray" and "Barton") the world's largest electrical supply merchandiser. In 1929 employees bought the company from Western Electric for $3 million in cash and $6 million in preferred stock. During the

1930s it marketed a line of appliances and sewing machines under the Graybar name.

EXECUTIVES

Regional VP Western Region, Dennis E. DeSousa, age 59, $276,571 total compensation
Regional VP Eastern Region, Robert C. Lyons, age 61, $268,435 total compensation
SVP Sales and Marketing, William P. Mansfield, age 55, $256,288 total compensation
SVP and CFO, Randall R. Harwood, age 61, $280,000 total compensation
Regional VP Western Region and Director, David G. Maxwell
Chairman President and CEO, Kathleen M. Mazzarella, age 56, $854,921 total compensation
SVP Secretary and General Counsel, Matthew W. Geekie, age 55, $313,119 total compensation
SVP Human Resources and Director, Beverly L. Propst, age 47, $284,632 total compensation
VP and CIO, David Meyer
SVP Supply Chain Management, Scott S. Clifford, age 46
Vice President Education Graybar Electric, Chris Althauser
Vice President Of Marketing, Rob Bezjak
District Vice President, Joseph Lamotte
Auditors: Ernst & Young LLP

LOCATIONS

HQ: Graybar Electric Co., Inc.
34 North Meramec Avenue, St. Louis, MO 63105
Phone: 314 573-9200
Web: www.graybar.com

2015 Sales

	% of total
US	95
Other countries	5
Total	**100**

PRODUCTS/OPERATIONS

2015 Sales

	% of total
Construction	56
Commercial Institutional and Government	23
Utility & Industrial	21
Total	**100**

Selected Products

Ballasts
Batteries
Cable
Conduit
Connectors
Emergency lighting
Enclosures
Fiber-optic cable
Fittings
Fluorescent lighting
Fuses
Hand tools
Hangers/fasteners
Heating and ventilating equipment
Industrial fans
Lighting
Lubricants
Paints
Patch cords
Smoke detectors
Testing and measuring instruments
Timers
Transfer switches
Transformers
Utility products
Wire

Selected Subsidiaries

Commonwealth Controls Corporation
Distribution Associates Inc.
Graybar Business Services Inc.

Graybar Canada Limited
Graybar Commerce Corporation
Graybar Electric Canada Limited
Graybar Financial Services Inc.
Graybar International Inc.
Graybar Services Inc.

COMPETITORS

Anixter International	Rexel Canada
Border States Electric	Rexel Inc.
Communications Supply	Richardson Electronics
Consolidated	SUMMIT Electric Supply
Electrical	Sonepar USA
Gexpro	United Electric Supply
HD Supply	W.W. Grainger
HWC	WESCO International
Premier Farnell	

HISTORICAL FINANCIALS

Company Type: Public

Income Statement

FYE: December 31

	REVENUE ($ mil.)	NET INCOME ($ mil.)	NET PROFIT MARGIN	EMPLOYEES
12/16	6,385	93	1.5%	8,500
12/15	6,110	91	1.5%	8,300
12/14	5,978	87	1.5%	8,250
12/13	5,659	81	1.4%	7,600
12/12	5,413	86	1.6%	7,500
Annual Growth	4.2%	1.9%	—	3.2%

2016 Year-End Financials

Debt ratio: 7.24%	No. of shares (mil.): 17
Return on equity: 13.14%	Dividends
Cash ($ mil.): 43	Yield: —
Current ratio: 1.40	Payout: 56.0%
Long-term debt ($ mil.): 7	Market value ($ mil.): —

Great Southern Bancorp, Inc.

Despite its name Great Southern Bancorp is firmly entrenched in the heartland. It is the holding company for nearly 200-year-old Great Southern Bank which offers loans deposit accounts CDs IRAs and credit cards through more than 75 branches in Missouri plus more than two dozen locations in Iowa Kansas Nebraska Minnesota and Arkansas. The firm's Great Southern Travel division is one of the largest travel agencies in Missouri. It serves both leisure and corporate travelers through about a dozen offices. Great Southern Insurance offers property/casualty and life insurance while Great Southern Financial provides investment products and services through an agreement with Ameriprise.

Operations

Great Southern loan portfolio is mostly made up of real estate loans. Commercial real estate mortgages and construction and land development loans accounted for around half of its loan portfolio at the end of 2015 while single-family residential mortgages made up another roughly 15%. The bank also writes consumer (including home equity) construction and business loans.

The bank made 82% of its total revenue from loan interest during 2015 while the rest of its revenue came from service charges and fees (9% of revenue) and other non-interest income sources.

Sales and Marketing

The bank served more than 169000 households mostly in Missouri but also in Arkansas Iowa Kansas Minnesota and Nebraska. It spent $2.3 million on advertising during 2015 compared to $2.4 million and $2.17 million in 2014 and 2013 respectively.

Financial Performance

Great Southern has struggled to consistently grow its revenues in recent years despite a 30% rise in loan assets since 2011 mostly as it's been selling off more of its interest-earning mortgage-backed securities assets. Its profits have been rising thanks to declining loan loss provisions as its loan portfolio's credit quality has improved with higher property valuations in the strengthened economy.

The bank's revenue dipped less than 1% to $197.93 million during 2015 as the bank continued to sell more of its mortgage-backed securities which led to lower interest income. It also earned $2.14 million less in gains from security sales than it did in 2014.

Despite modest revenue declines in 2015 Great Southern's net income climbed 7% to $46.5 million mostly as in 2014 it incurred prepayment penalties when it repaid $130 million of its FHLB advances. The bank's operating cash levels rose 6% to $71.42 million thanks to the increase in cash-denominated earnings.

Strategy

Great Southern Bancorp continues to expand its bank network to grow its loan and deposit business either through new branch openings or by acquiring branches in new geographic markets. Its branch network has grown from 104 branches in 2011 to 110 at the end of 2015.

Mergers and Acquisitions

In 2015 the bank purchased 12 branches and related deposit and loan business in the St. Louis area from Cincinnati-based Fifth Third Bank more than doubling its branch presence in the St. Louis area.

EXECUTIVES

VP Operations and Secretary Great Southern Bank, Douglas W. (Doug) Marrs, age 59, $122,602 total compensation
SVP and Chief Lending Officer of the Bank, Steven G. Mitchem, age 65, $227,429 total compensation
President CEO and Director Great Southern Bancorp and Great Southern Bank, Joseph W. (Joe) Turner, age 52, $299,237 total compensation
SVP and CFO Great Southern Bank, Rex A. Copeland, age 52, $235,201 total compensation
VP Information Systems, Linton J. (Lin) Thomason, age 60
Vice President, Scott Brekke
Assistant Vice President, Denit Patrick
Vice President Operations, Tonia Tillman
Chairman Great Southern Bancorp and Great Southern Bank, William V. Turner, age 84
SECRETARY, Larry Lrimore
Board Member, Douglas Pitt
Auditors: BKD, LLP

LOCATIONS

HQ: Great Southern Bancorp, Inc.
1451 E. Battlefield, Springfield, MO 65804
Phone: 417 887-4400
Web: www.greatsouthernbank.com

COMPETITORS

Arvest Bank	Hawthorn Bancshares
BancorpSouth	NASB Financial
Bank of America	Scottrade
Commerce Bancshares	U.S. Bancorp
First Bancshares (MO)	UMB Financial
Guaranty Federal	Wells Fargo

HISTORICAL FINANCIALS

Company Type: Public

Income Statement

FYE: December 31

	ASSETS ($ mil.)	NET INCOME ($ mil.)	INCOME AS % OF ASSETS	EMPLOYEES
12/16	4,550	45	1.0%	1,263
12/15	4,104	46	1.1%	1,270
12/14	3,951	43	1.1%	1,252
12/13	3,560	33	0.9%	1,163
12/12	3,955	48	1.2%	1,164
Annual Growth	3.6%	(1.8%)	—	2.1%

2016 Year-End Financials

Debt ratio: 2.18%
Return on equity: 10.92%
Cash ($ mil.): 279
Current ratio: —
Long-term debt ($ mil.): —
No. of shares (mil.): 13
Dividends
 Yield: 0.0%
 Payout: 27.4%
Market value ($ mil.): 763

	STOCK PRICE ($) FY Close	P/E High/Low		PER SHARE ($) Earnings	Dividends	Book Value
12/16	54.65	17	11	3.21	0.88	30.77
12/15	45.26	16	11	3.28	0.86	28.67
12/14	39.67	13	9	3.10	0.80	30.52
12/13	30.41	13	9	2.42	0.72	27.84
12/12	25.45	9	6	3.54	0.90	27.20
Annual Growth	21.1%	—	—	(2.4%)	(0.6%)	3.1%

Great West Life & Annuity Insurance Co - Insurance Products

Great-West Life & Annuity Insurance is the southern arm of a northern parent. The company a subsidiary of Canada's Great-West Lifeco and a member of the Power Financial family represents the Great-West group's primary US operations. It offers life insurance and annuities to individuals and employer groups. Under the Great-West Retirement Services brand it administers employer-sponsored retirement products including defined-benefit pension and 401(k) plans. Additional Great-West services include investment consulting and fund management. Great-West Life & Annuity markets products through its sales representatives and regional offices as well as independent brokers.

Operations

Great-West Life & Annuity also distributes its individual life insurance and annuity products through partnerships with banking institutions and financial advisors including Bank of America Citigroup and Charles Schwab. Outside of its own retirement products which are marketed to corporate not-for-profit health care educational and government organizations the Great-West Retirement Services unit provides business services including record-keeping for plans offered by other financial institutions. Its recordkeeping subsidiary FASCore LLC serves 4.7 million participant accounts. Great-West Life & Annuity's Individual Markets Division offers individual retirement accounts (IRAs) individual term and single-premium life insurance individual annuity products as well as executive benefits and business-owned life insurance products.

In 2012 the company had 540000 individual accounts and had $201.5 billion in assets under administration.

Geographic Reach

Great-West Life & Annuity has offices in more than 50 locations throughout the US Puerto Rico Guam and the US Virgin Islands.

Sales and Marketing

Great-West Life & Annuity markets its products and services through sales and service professionals brokers consultants advisors financial institutions and third-party administrators.

Financial Performance

Great-West Life & Annuity's revenues grew by 3% in 2012 thanks to its portfolio of diverse products expanded partnerships and enhanced tools. IRA sales grew 50% as part of a push to provide enhanced distribution education services to terminated group plan participants. This initiative gained $916 million in roll-ins to existing plans.

The company's net income jumped by 18% in 2012 thanks to higher revenues and a drop in expenses.

Strategy

Growing it product portfolio in 2012 the company launched two retail retirement income products securing selling agreements with five distribution partners.

Company Background

In 2008 the company sold its Great-West Healthcare division to CIGNA for $1.5 billion; the segment offered group life and medical insurance products to US businesses with an emphasis on self-funded programs for small and midsized employers. The divestiture of its health care unit was part of Great-West's strategy of focusing its efforts in the financial services arena.

EXECUTIVES

EVP Individual Markets, Robert K. Shaw, age 62, $458,100 total compensation
SVP and Chief Investment Officer General Account, Ernie Friesen
SVP and Chief Investment Officer Separate Accounts, Catherine S. Tocher
President and CEO, Robert L. Reynolds
President Empower Retirement, Edmund F. Murphy
EVP Great West Lifeco U.S. Inc., Charles B. McDevitt
SVP and CIO, Jeffrey W. Knight
SVP and CFO, Louis J. Mannello
SVP Product Management, David G. McLeod
Senior Vice President and Chief Technology Officer, Jeff Knight
Assistant Vice President Information Systems, Camilla Langenfeld
Regional Vice President, Brian Sugrue
Assistant Vice President, Renee Graham
Senior Vice President Fin Svces, Scot A Miller
Vice President, Robert Onstad
Auditors: Deloitte & Touche LLP

LOCATIONS

HQ: Great West Life & Annuity Insurance Co - Insurance Products
8515 East Orchard Road, Greenwood Village, CO 80111
Phone: 303 737-3000
Web: www.greatwest.com

PRODUCTS/OPERATIONS

Selected Products and Services
Annuities
Life insurance
Retirement services
 Retirement plans for government corporate and not-for-profit employers

Communication and education services
Enrollment services
Investment options
Third-party administrative and record-keeping services
(FASCore)

COMPETITORS

AXA Financial
Allstate
Industrial Alliance Insurance and Financial Servic
John Hancock Financial Services
Liberty Mutual
Lincoln Financial Group
Manulife Financial
MetLife
Mutual of Omaha
Nationwide Financial
Pacific Mutual
Prudential
State Farm
Sun Life
The Hartford

HISTORICAL FINANCIALS

Company Type: Public

Income Statement

	ASSETS ($ mil.)	NET INCOME ($ mil.)	INCOME AS % OF ASSETS	EMPLOYEES
12/16	60,308	231	0.4%	5,800
12/15	57,899	190	0.3%	5,400
12/14	58,348	317	0.5%	4,500
12/13	55,323	128	0.2%	3,300
12/12	52,818	238	0.5%	3,300
Annual Growth	3.4%	(0.7%)		15.1%

2016 Year-End Financials

Debt ratio: 0.89%
Return on equity: 11.83%
Cash ($ mil.): 18
Current ratio: —
Long-term debt ($ mil.): —

No. of shares (mil.): 7
Dividends
  Yield: —
  Payout: 54.3%
Market value ($ mil.): —

Great Western Bancorp Inc

Auditors: Ernst & Young LLP

LOCATIONS

HQ: Great Western Bancorp Inc
225 South Main Avenue, Sioux Falls, SD 57104
Phone: 605 334-2548
Web: www.greatwesternbank.com

HISTORICAL FINANCIALS

Company Type: Public

Income Statement
FYE: September 30

	ASSETS ($ mil.)	NET INCOME ($ mil.)	INCOME AS % OF ASSETS	EMPLOYEES
09/17	11,690	144	1.2%	1,689
09/16	11,531	121	1.1%	1,649
09/15	9,798	109	1.1%	1,475
09/14	9,371	104	1.1%	1,492
09/13	9,134	96	1.1%	1,486
Annual Growth	6.4%	10.7%		3.3%

2017 Year-End Financials

Debt ratio: 6.43%
Return on equity: 8.47%
Cash ($ mil.): 360
Current ratio: —
Long-term debt ($ mil.): —

No. of shares (mil.): 58
Dividends
  Yield: 0.0%
  Payout: 30.2%
Market value ($ mil.): 2,429

	STOCK PRICE ($) FY Close	P/E High/Low		PER SHARE ($) Earnings	Dividends	Book Value
09/17	41.28	18	13	2.45	0.74	29.83
09/16	33.32	16	11	2.14	0.56	28.34
09/15	25.37	14	9	1.90	0.36	26.43
Annual Growth	12.9%	—	—	6.6%	19.7%	3.1%

Green Bancorp Inc

Auditors: Deloitte & Touche LLP

LOCATIONS

HQ: Green Bancorp Inc
4000 Greenbriar, Houston, TX 77098
Phone: 713 275-8220
Web: www.greenbank.com

HISTORICAL FINANCIALS

Company Type: Public

Income Statement
FYE: December 31

	ASSETS ($ mil.)	NET INCOME ($ mil.)	INCOME AS % OF ASSETS	EMPLOYEES
12/16	4,024	(0)	—	372
12/15	3,786	15	0.4%	353
12/14	2,196	14	0.7%	272
12/13	1,703	12	0.7%	216
12/12	1,674	8	0.5%	—
Annual Growth	24.5%	—		—

2016 Year-End Financials

Debt ratio: 4.91%
Return on equity: (-0.23%)
Cash ($ mil.): 388
Current ratio: —
Long-term debt ($ mil.): —

No. of shares (mil.): 36
Dividends
  Yield: —
  Payout: —
Market value ($ mil.): 562

	STOCK PRICE ($) FY Close	P/E High/Low		PER SHARE ($) Earnings	Dividends	Book Value
12/16	15.20	—	—	(0.03)	0.00	11.64
12/15	10.48	29	19	0.53	0.00	11.67
12/14	12.04	28	19	0.64	0.00	11.02
Annual Growth	6.0%			—		1.4%

Group 1 Automotive, Inc.

Group 1 Automotive is the third largest of a group of new and used car retailers (behind #1 AutoNation and #2 Penske Automotive Group) striving to consolidate US auto sales. The company owns more than 155 dealerships around 210 franchises and about 35 collision service centers oper-

ating under their own branding in the US UK and Brazil. The US is the biggest market and the company is present in 14 US states. Group 1 sells more than 30 car and light truck brands of which Toyota BMW and Ford are the biggest sellers. It also offers financing provides maintenance and repair services and sells replacement parts.

Operations

Group 1 Automotive's operations include five core business segments: New Vehicles (around 55% of sales) Used Vehicles (25%) Parts & Service (10%) Used Vehicles wholesale (5%) and Finance & Insurance (5%). In the UK the auto dealer operates through its subsidiary Group 1 Automotive UK Ltd.

Geographic Reach

The auto dealer rings up about 80% of its sales in the US; the remainder comes from the UK (15%) and Brazil (5%). More than half of Group 1's dealerships are located in Texas Oklahoma and California. In the UK Group 1 Automotive has about 40 franchises 30 dealerships and nearly 10 collision centers; and in Brazil nearly 25 franchises 20 dealerships and one collision center.

The company's US operations are located primarily major metropolitan areas. It is present 20 towns and cities in the UK and has a presence in Brazil in key metropolitan areas in the states of Sao Paulo Parana and Mato Grosso do Sul.

Financial Performance

Group 1's recent strong revenue growth continued in fiscal 2016 albeit at a slower pace than previously increasing 2% to $10.9 billion. Growth in the UK new car market relating to acquisitions and overall market strength was partially offset by new car declines in the US and Brazil. Weakness in the US was concentrated in Group 1's significant Houston market as the oil city's workers have reduced their spending as the industry-wide squeeze continued. Used car sales rose 5% due to good performance in the US and UK. The Parts & Services business also grew.

Net income ticked up 56% to $147 million due mostly to higher net sales.

Cash from operations climbed 172% to $384.9 million due to higher net income and an increase in accounts payable and inventories.

Strategy

Group 1 is looking to capitalize on growth opportunities in the UK (where it already has an established presence) and in Brazil a relatively new market for the company. It acquired 12 dealerships and opened two additional dealerships in the UK in fiscal 2016. The company's strategy also includes growing its higher margin parts and services business growing its share of the new and used vehicle market taking advantage of its size to boost efficiency and continuing to make strategic acquisitions. In recent years Group 1 has seen import and luxury brands account for an increased share of its business.

Mergers and Acquisitions

In 2016 Group 1 acquired London-based Spire Automotive Group's twelve dealerships including four Audi dealerships and three BMW/MINI dealerships which will continue to use the Spire brand name. The acquired dealerships are expected to bring in approximately $575 million per year. The acquisition could also further Group 1's relationships with BMW and the Volkswagen Group in the UK.

EXECUTIVES

President CEO and Director, Earl J. Hesterberg, age 64, $1,100,000 total compensation
VP Manufacturer Relations Financial Services and Public Affairs, Peter C. DeLongchamps, age 56, $456,300 total compensation

SVP Human Resources Training and Operations
Support, Frank Grese, age 65, $540,000 total
compensation
SVP and CFO, John C. Rickel, age 56, $583,500 total
compensation
VP and General Counsel, Darryl M. Burman, age 59,
$440,300 total compensation
VP Information Systems, James R. Druzbik
Vice President Information Technology Chief
Information Officer, Wade Hubbard
Vice President, Mark Iuppenlatz
Vice President, Larry Caudill
Chairman, Stephen D. Quinn, age 62
Corporate Treasurer, Kim Craig
Auditors: Ernst & Young LLP

LOCATIONS

HQ: Group 1 Automotive, Inc.
800 Gessner, Suite 500, Houston, TX 77024
Phone: 713 647-5700   **Fax:** 713 647-5858
Web: www.group1auto.com

2016 Sales

	$ mil.	% of total
U.S.	8,734	80
U.K.	1,723	16
Brazil	429	4
Total	**10,887**	**100**

Dealership presence

Dealership presence
United States
 Alabama
 California
 Florida
 Georgia
 Kansas
 Louisiana
 Maryland
 Massachusetts
 Mississippi
 New Hampshire
 New Jersey
 Oklahoma
 South Carolina
 Texas
United Kingdom
 Brighton
 Chelmsford
 Chingford
 Farnborough
 Hailsham
 Harold Wood
 Hindhead
 Southend
 Stansted
 Worthington
Brazil
 Sao Paolo
 Parana
 Mato Grosso do Sul

2015 Sales

	% of total
Driveline	47
Aerospace	32
Powder Metallurgy	12
Land Systems	9
Total	**100**

Selected Products

Aerospace
 Aerostructures (flight control assemblies fuselage and
 wings)
 Propulsion systems (engine and nacelle components)
Driveline
 Constant velocity jointed components
 Propshafts
 Traction control devices
Land Systems
 Axles
 High-speed & take-off shafts
 Tractor attachments
 Wheels
Powder Metallurgy
 Metal powders (raw material for sintered components)
 Sintered components (precision parts in automotive
 engines transmissions body and chassis)

Selected Subsidiaries

GKN Aerospace Services Ltd
GKN Automotive Ltd
Hoeganaes
Sinter Metals

PRODUCTS/OPERATIONS

2016 Sales

	$ mil.	% of total
New vehicle retail	6,046	55
Used vehicle retail	2,757	25
Used vehicle wholesale	401	4
Parts & service	1,261	12
Finance insurance & other	420	4
Total	**10,887**	**100**

Selected Brands

Domestic
 Ford
 Chevrolet
 Dodge
 Jeep
 GMC
 Chrysler
 Buick
 RAM
Import
 Toyota
 Nissan
 Honda
 Volkswagen
 Hyundai
 Mazda
 Subaru
 Scion
 Kia
 Peugeot
 Renault
Luxury
 BMW
 Acura
 MINI
 Land Rover
 Lexus
 Mercedes
 Audi
 Volvo
 Cadillac
 Lincoln
 Porsche
 Sprinter
 smart
 Jaguar

COMPETITORS

Ancira	Lookers
Asbury Automotive	Pendragon
AutoNation	Penske Automotive
CarMax	Group
David McDavid Auto	Phil Long Dealerships
Group	Sonic Automotive
Herb Chambers	Sytner
Lithia Motors	

HISTORICAL FINANCIALS

Company Type: Public

Income Statement

FYE: December 31

	REVENUE ($ mil.)	NET INCOME ($ mil.)	NET PROFIT MARGIN	EMPLOYEES
12/16	10,887	147	1.4%	13,500
12/15	10,632	94	0.9%	12,886
12/14	9,937	93	0.9%	11,978
12/13	8,918	113	1.3%	11,510
12/12	7,476	100	1.3%	9,343
Annual Growth	**9.9%**	**10.1%**	**—**	**9.6%**

2016 Year-End Financials

Debt ratio: 61.17%   No. of shares (mil.): 21
Return on equity: 15.87%   Dividends
Cash ($ mil.): 20   Yield: 0.0%
Current ratio: 1.05   Payout: 13.6%
Long-term debt ($ mil.): 1,212   Market value ($ mil.): 1,668

	STOCK PRICE ($) FY Close	P/E High/Low		PER SHARE ($) Earnings	Dividends	Book Value
12/16	77.94	12	7	6.67	0.91	43.46
12/15	75.70	25	19	3.90	0.83	39.22
12/14	89.62	24	16	3.60	0.70	40.18
12/13	71.02	17	12	4.32	0.65	43.77
12/12	61.99	15	10	4.19	0.59	39.28
Annual Growth	**5.9%**	**—**	**—**	**12.3%**	**11.4%**	**2.6%**

GROWMARK, INC.

Retail farm-supply and grain-marketing cooperative GROWMARK can mark its growth by the grain. A member-owed agricultural co-op GROWMARK has more than 100000 members. Under the FAST STOP name the co-op runs more than 250 fuel stations and convenience stores in the Midwest. Its Seedway subsidiary sells commercial vegetable seed and farm seed for turf and grains including alfalfa corn wheat and soybeans. GROWMARK also offers fertilizer seeds ethanol biodiesel and farm financing. Its MID-CO COMMODITIES subsidiary trades grain and offers advice regarding futures and options.

Geographic Reach

GROWMARK is headquartered in Bloomington Illinois and serves customers in more than 40 states and Ontario Canada. SEEDWAY maintains eight office and warehouse locations in Vermont New York Pennsylvania and Florida.

Strategy

Cooperation is important within and among agricultural cooperatives. A strong believer in the latter part of this principle GROWMARK has marketing agreements and alliances with among others fertilizer maker and distributor CF Industries pet-food producer PRO-PET agribusiness company Syngenta and rural financial services provider CoBank.

Mergers and Acquisitions

GROWMARK acquires fertilizer storage terminals and transportation infrastructure on a regular basis.

EXECUTIVES

Vice Chairman, John Reifsteck
CEO, Jeff Solberg
Vice President General Counsel, Brent Bostrom
VP Eastern Retail Operations, Steve Buckalew
VP and CFO, Marshall Bohbrink
VP Energy, Kevin Carroll
VP Midwest Retail and Acquisitions, Shelly Kruse
VP Grain, Brent Ericson
Vice President Human Resources & Compliance,
Gary Swango
VP Agronomy, Mark Orr
VP Financial and Risk Management, Mike Woods
VP Member Services, Denny Worth
Vice President Information TEC, George Key
Vice President Information TEC, George Mueller
Vice President, Ron Milby
Region Vice President, Barry Schmidt
Vice President, Richard Fiedler
Senior Vice President, Dennis Farmer

Vice President, Tom Dowell
Senior Vice President, Jeffrey M Solberg
Vice Chairman, Rick Nelson
Vice Chairman, Chet Esther
Assistant Treasurer, John Fruin
Auditors: ERNST & YOUNG LLP CHICAGO I

LOCATIONS

HQ: GROWMARK, INC.
1701 TOWANDA AVE, BLOOMINGTON, IL 617012057
Phone: 309 557-6000
Web: WWW.GROWMARK.COM

PRODUCTS/OPERATIONS

Selected Retail Products and Operations
COMFORT PRO (propane heating oil)
FAST STOP (fuel facilities)
FS (farm supplies)
Green Yard (turf seed fertilizer)
Seedway (farm turf and vegetable seed)

Selected Member Cooperatives and Subsidiaries
AgVantage FS Inc.
AgView Grain LLC
Evergreen FS Inc.
GROWMARK FS LLC
MID-CO COMMODITIES
Northern Grain Marketing LLC
Seedway LLC
Total Grain Marketing LLC
Western Grain Marketing LLC

COMPETITORS

ADM	Marathon Oil
AGRI Industries	NC Hybrids
Ag Processing Inc.	Orscheln Farm and Home
BP	Pfister Hybrid Corn
Barkley Seed	Pioneer Hi-Bred
Bayer CropScience	Rabo AgriFinance
CHS	Sakata Seed
Cargill	Seed Enterprises
Chevron	Southern States
Costco Wholesale	Terra Nitrogen
DeBruce Grain	Wal-Mart
Exxon Mobil	Wilbur-Ellis

HISTORICAL FINANCIALS

Company Type: Private

Income Statement

FYE: August 31

	REVENUE ($ mil.)	NET INCOME ($ mil.)	NET PROFIT MARGIN	EMPLOYEES
08/16	7,031	101	1.4%	1,036
08/15	8,727	113	1.3%	—
08/14	10,372	166	1.6%	—
08/13	10,171	189	1.9%	—
Annual Growth	(11.6%)	(18.8%)	—	—

2016 Year-End Financials

Debt ratio: ——
Return on equity: 1.40%
Cash ($ mil.): 143
Current ratio: 1.20
Long-term debt ($ mil.): —

Dividends
Yield: —
Payout: —
Market value ($ mil.): —

Guaranty Bancorp (DE)

Guaranty Bancorp holds Colorado's Guaranty Bank and Trust which operates 25-plus branches mostly in the metropolitan Denver and Front Range areas. Boasting $3.3 billion in assets the bank offers traditional retail and commercial banking including deposit accounts loans and trust services. Subsidiaries Private Capital Management and Cherry Hills Investment Advisors provide private banking investment management trust services and other wealth management services. The bank mostly targets small to medium-sized businesses. Over 30% of the bank's loan portfolio is made up of commercial and residential real estate property loans while another 15% consists of retail and industrial property loans.

Operations

An additional 25% of the bank's loan portfolio is made up of office other commercial real estate and multi-family property loans (as of early 2016).

The bank gets the bulk of its revenue from interest income. About 71% of Guaranty Bancorp's total revenue came from loan interest (including fees) during 2015 with an additional 11% of revenue coming from interest on taxable or tax-exempt investment securities. The rest of its revenue came from deposit services and other fees (9% of revenue) investment management and trust fees (5%) and other miscellaneous income sources.

Geographic Reach

Guaranty Bank operates 26 branches located in the Denver metro area and nine counties in Colorado: Adams Arapahoe Boulder Broomfield Denver Douglas Jefferson Larimer and Weld.

Sales and Marketing

In addition to retail consumers the bank mostly targets small to medium-sized businesses as well as their owners and employees.

Financial Performance

Guaranty Bank's revenue has been trending higher every year since 2012 as its loan assets have swelled around 70% (from 2011 through 2015). While more volatile the bank's net income has risen more than 25% over the same period thanks to declining loan loss provisions as its loan portfolio's credit quality has improved with less risky loan assets and higher property valuations.

The bank's revenue jumped 8% to $99.5 million during 2015 mostly as its loan assets grew 18% to $1.79 billion. Its non-interest income increased 3% thanks to steady growth in its investment management and trust businesses also helping to buoy the bank's top line.

Solid revenue growth and lower interest expenses from debt paydown in 2015 drove Guaranty Bank's net income up 6% to $22 million for the year. The bank's operating cash levels jumped 19% to $33 million thanks to the rise in cash earnings.

Strategy

Once known for its focus on energy-related property loans Guaranty Bank has been busy reducing its exposure to the energy industry to diversify into other industries over the past few years. Indeed as of late 2015 less than 1% of the bank's loan portfolio was tied to the energy industry.

The bank has also been expanding into new lines of business services mostly related to wealth management in recent years either on its own or through acquiring specialty finance companies. Guaranty is also open to acquiring small to medium-sized banks to expand its branch network and service lines. The community bank has historically emphasized superior service and relationships as opposed to transaction volume or low pricing.

Mergers and Acquisitions

In September 2016 the company merged with Home State Bancorp holding company of Home State Bank. Home State branches are to be rebranded under the Guaranty banner.

In July 2014 Guaranty Bank and Trust Co. and a wholly owned subsidiary of parent Guaranty Bancorp acquired privately-held Cherry Hills Investment Advisors LLC a Greenwood Village-based investment management firm serving the financial planning and investment management needs of individuals and families.

In June 2012 Guaranty Bank acquired the investment advisory firm Private Capital Management (PCM) a Denver-based firm providing investment advisory and financial planning services to wealthy individuals making it a subsidiary.

Company Background

The former Centennial Bank Holdings acquired Guaranty Corporation and its Guaranty Bank and Trust subsidiary in 2004. Four years later the company merged its Centennial Bank of the West subsidiary into Guaranty Bank and Trust and following suit changed its own name.

EXECUTIVES

President and CEO Guaranty Bancorp; CEO Guaranty Bank & Trust, Paul W. Taylor, age 56, $440,000 total compensation
EVP and Chief Credit Officer Guaranty Bank and Trust, Cathy P. Goss
EVP and CFO Guaranty Bancorp and Guaranty Bank & Trust, Christopher G. Treece
President Guaranty Bank & Trust Company, Michael B. Hobbs, $300,000 total compensation
Senior Vice President Marketing, Wes Sargent
Vice President, Gerad Bergrud
Vice President Manager Loan Operations, Debbie Culbertson
Vice President, Travis Houstoun
Senior Vice President Executive Vice President, Chris Erickson
Chairman, Edward B. Cordes, age 65
Auditors: Crowe Horwath LLP

LOCATIONS

HQ: Guaranty Bancorp (DE)
1331 Seventeenth St., Suite 200, Denver, CO 80202
Phone: 303 675-1194
Web: www.gbnk.com

Selected Locations
Arvada
Bennett
Berthoud
Boulder
Brighton
Byers
Castle Rock
Denver
Eaton
Englewood
Ft. Collins
Golden
Greeley
Ken Caryl
Longmont
Loveland
Strasburg
Westminster

PRODUCTS/OPERATIONS

2015 Sales

	$ mil.	% of total
Interest income		
Loans including fees	70	71
Investment securities:		
Taxable	8	8
Tax-exempt	2	3
Other	1	1
Noninterest income		
Deposit service and other fees	8	9
Investment management and trust	5	5
Increase in cash surrender value of life insurance	1	2
Other	1	1
Total	99	100

Selected Services
Auto
Cards

CD secured loans and unsecured loans
Checking
Guaranty 50 Club
Home Equity Loans and Lines of Credit
Jumbo Mortgage Loans
Overdraft Protection
Savings

COMPETITORS

BBVA Compass Bancshares	High Country Bancorp
BOK Financial	JPMorgan Chase
Bank of the West	KeyCorp
CoBiz Financial	Liberty Capital
Ent FCU	TCF Financial
FirstBank Holding Company	U.S. Bancorp
	UMB Financial
	Vectra Bank

HISTORICAL FINANCIALS

Company Type: Public

Income Statement

FYE: December 31

	ASSETS ($ mil.)	NET INCOME ($ mil.)	INCOME AS % OF ASSETS	EMPLOYEES
12/16	3,366	24	0.7%	521
12/15	2,368	22	0.9%	376
12/14	2,124	13	0.6%	389
12/13	1,911	14	0.7%	374
12/12	1,886	15	0.8%	378
Annual Growth	15.6%	13.2%	—	8.4%

2016 Year-End Financials

Debt ratio: 1.93%
Return on equity: 8.59%
Cash ($ mil.): 50
Current ratio: —
Long-term debt ($ mil.): —

No. of shares (mil.): 28
Dividends
  Yield: 0.0%
  Payout: 43.8%
Market value ($ mil.): 686

	STOCK PRICE ($) FY Close	P/E High/Low		PER SHARE ($) Earnings	Dividends	Book Value
12/16	24.20	23	14	1.05	0.46	12.44
12/15	16.54	17	13	1.06	0.40	10.21
12/14	14.44	25	19	0.64	0.20	9.57
12/13	14.05	23	3	0.67	0.08	8.89
12/12	1.95	3	2	0.70	0.00	8.89
Annual Growth	87.7%	—	—	10.7%	—	8.8%

Guaranty Bancshares Inc

EXECUTIVES

Vice President, Mick Trusty
Senior Vice President, Mary Munsinger
Senior Vice President of Audit, Terry Todd
Assistant Vice President, Joy Travis
Senior Vice President and Chief Risk Officer, Shalene Jacobson
Vice President, Susan Roberts
Senior Vice President, Paul Parkinson
Vice President Regional Sales Manager, Keri Price
Vice President, Jeffrey Harris
Assistant Vice President, Ryan Coaxum
Vice President, Kathy Kelly
Vice President, Natalie Kidd
Branch President, Jon Ruff
Vice Chairman, Chuck Cowell

LOCATIONS

HQ: Guaranty Bancshares Inc
201 South Jefferson Avenue, Mount Pleasant, TX 75455
Phone: 903 572-9881
Web: www.gnty.com

PRODUCTS/OPERATIONS

2008 Sales

	$ mil.	% of total
Interest		
Loans including fees	31	70
Securities	6	13
Other	1	2
Noninterest		
Service charges	4	8
Other	3	7
Total	46	100

COMPETITORS

BancorpSouth	Southside Bancshares
Bank of America	Wells Fargo
Capital One	Woodforest Financial
Cullen/Frost Bankers	

HISTORICAL FINANCIALS

Company Type: Public

Income Statement

FYE: December 31

	ASSETS ($ mil.)	NET INCOME ($ mil.)	INCOME AS % OF ASSETS	EMPLOYEES
12/16	1,828	12	0.7%	397
12/15	1,682	10	0.6%	—
12/14	1,334	9	0.7%	—
12/13	1,247	14	1.2%	—
12/12	1,160	15	1.3%	—
Annual Growth	12.0%	(5.9%)	—	—

2016 Year-End Financials

Debt ratio: 2.06%
Return on equity: 8.65%
Cash ($ mil.): 66
Current ratio: —
Long-term debt ($ mil.): —

No. of shares (mil.): 8
Dividends
  Yield: —
  Payout: 38.5%
Market value ($ mil.): 232

	STOCK PRICE ($) FY Close	P/E High/Low		PER SHARE ($) Earnings	Dividends	Book Value
12/16	26.50	—	—	1.35	0.52	16.22
12/15	26.50	—	—	1.15	0.50	15.47
12/14	26.50	—	—	1.25	1.50	14.01
12/13	26.50	—	—	2.40	1.90	13.25
12/12	26.50	—	—	(0.00)	0.40	13.67
Annual Growth	(0.0%)	—	—	—	6.8%	4.4%

Halliburton Company

One of the largest oilfield services companies in the world Halliburton serves the global upstream oil and gas industry with a broad array of products and services. It manufactures drill bits and other downhole and completion tools; provides pressure pumping services; locates hydrocarbons and manages geological data; drills new wells; and optimizes production once the well is operational. It maintains advantages in the highly competitive market by combining tried-and-true well drilling and optimization techniques with high-tech analysis and modeling software and services.

HISTORY

Erle Halliburton began his oil career in 1916 at Perkins Oil Well Cementing. He moved to oil boomtown Burkburnett Texas to start his Better Method Oil Well Cementing Company in 1919. Halliburton used cement to hold a steel pipe in a well which kept oil out of the water table strengthened well walls and reduced the risk of explosions. Though the contribution would later be praised his technique was considered useless at the time.

In 1920 Halliburton moved to Oklahoma. Incorporating Halliburton Oil Well Cementing Company in 1924 he patented its products and services forcing oil companies to employ his firm if they wanted to cement wells.

Erle died in 1957 and his company grew through acquisitions between the 1950s and the 1970s. In 1962 it bought Houston construction giant Brown & Root an expert in offshore platforms. After the 1973 Arab oil embargo Halliburton benefited from the surge in global oil exploration and later as drilling costs surged it became a leader in well stimulation.

When the oil industry slumped in 1982 the firm halved its workforce. Three years later a suffering Brown & Root coughed up $750 million to settle charges of mismanagement at the South Texas Nuclear Project.

In the 1990s Halliburton expanded abroad entering Russia in 1991 and China in 1993. The next year Brown & Root was named contractor for a pipeline stretching from Qatar to Pakistan. Halliburton drilled the world's deepest horizontal well (18860 ft.) in Germany in 1995.

That year Dick Cheney a former US defense secretary became CEO. Brown & Root began providing engineering and logistics services to US Army peacekeeping troops in the Balkans in 1995 and won a major contract to develop an offshore Canadian oil field the next year.

In 1997 Halliburton completed a major reorganization started in 1993 uniting 10 businesses under the Halliburton Energy Services umbrella. The company nearly doubled in size in 1998 with its $7.7 billion acquisition of oil field equipment manufacturer Dresser Industries. The purchase coupled with falling oil prices in 1998 and 1999 prompted Halliburton to ax more than 9000 workers. (Even after oil prices rebounded in 2000 Halliburton had to wait for the effects of the upturn to reach the oil field services sector.)

Brown & Root Energy Services won a contract to provide logistics support for the US Army in Albania in 1999. Halliburton also invested in oil field emergency-response firm Boots & Coots and took a stake in Japanese engineering firm Chiyoda.

The company began to sell off portions of its Dresser acquisition in 1999. Partner Ingersoll-Rand bought Halliburton's stake in Ingersoll-Dresser Pump for $515 million and bought its stake in Dresser-Rand (industrial compressors) for $579 million in 2000. Cheney resigned as chairman and CEO that year after he was chosen as George W. Bush's vice presidential running mate. President and COO David Lesar was named to succeed him.

A group consisting of investment firms First Reserve and Odyssey Investment Partners and Dresser managers paid $1.55 billion in 2001 for Dresser Equipment Group. That year a number of multimillion-dollar verdicts against Halliburton in asbestos cases sparked rumors that the company was going to file for bankruptcy (flatly denied by Halliburton) and caused the firm's stock price to tumble.

In 2002 in part to protect the company's assets from the unresolved asbestos claims issue Lesar announced plans to restructure Halliburton into two independent subsidiaries separating the Energy Services Group from Halliburton's KBR engineering and construction operations. Halliburton took a $483 million (pretax) charge against earnings in the second quarter of 2002 to cover its estimated asbestos liability.

Halliburton settled more than 300000 asbestos-related lawsuits by paying about $4 billion in cash and in stock. As a result Halliburton placed its subsidiaries Dresser Industries and Kellogg Brown & Root under Chapter 11 bankruptcy protection. Later that year in an effort to boost its newly formed Energy Services unit Halliburton purchased Pruett Industries a fiber optic sensor technology company.

In 2003 Halliburton announced plans to divest its noncore assets in an effort to return its focus to its main operating divisions. The company began its disposal of assets with the sale of its mono pumping businesses to National-Oilwell. The company sold its Wellstream business to European buyout firm Candover Partners for $136 million. It also completed the sale of its interests in European Marine Contractors Bredero-Shaw and its Subsea operations. The company's Halliburton Measurement Systems subsidiary was sold to NuFlo Technologies.

In 2004 the company's KBR subsidiary was awarded nearly $1.4 billion worth of contracts to aid in the repair and restoration of Iraq's oil fields during the US-led invasion of Iraq. The US Army Corps of Engineers later withdrew the contracts after allegations that they were awarded to the subsidiary due to Halliburton's relationship to Cheney. KBR also came under fire when the Pentagon claimed the company overcharged US taxpayers $61 million to supply fuel to Iraq. After an investigation by the US Army Corp of Engineers Halliburton was cleared of any wrongdoing. The investigation was picked up by the Pentagon's criminal investigative unit and the US State Department. Following an internal audit Halliburton repaid $6 million after discovering an overcharge from one of its subcontractor companies.

Later that year Halliburton enhanced its Fluids division by acquiring ITS Drilling Services' SU-PAVAC unit. It also restructured its Engineering and Construction group into two divisions: Energy and Chemicals and Government and Infrastructure. In anticipation of selling off its KBR unit the company reorganized its management team promoting KBR CEO Andrew Lane to COO for Halliburton and placing him in charge of all Halliburton subsidiaries.

The company agreed to pay more than $4 billion in cash and stock to settle more than 300000 asbestos and silica-related personal injury lawsuits filed against its DII Industries and KBR subsidiaries. Halliburton reorganized its DII and KBR subsidiaries and finalized its asbestos settlements. DII and KBR emerged from Chapter 11 bankruptcy protection in January 2005. The company also completed the sale of its 50% stake in Subsea 7 to joint venture partner Siem Offshore for $200 million.

In 2006 Halliburton was awarded a multimillion-dollar contract by Saudi Aramco as part of the Khurais oilfield development project the largest in the region since the 1950s. The same year it spun off KBR to the public.

Establishing a new product service line (intervention services and pressure control) in 2010 the company acquired well control specialist and industry innovator Boots & Coots for $240 million in cash and stock. Halliburton has combined its global hydraulic workover and coiled tubing deployed technologies with Boots & Coots' operations to provide customers with a wider range of services to help increase well production.

Earlier in 2010 the company was involved in cementing operations to cap a well on the ill-fated BP's Deepwater Horizon rig. The rig exploded and sank spewing oil into the Gulf of Mexico. A board of inquiry found fault with the company's cementing procedures.

In 2011 Halliburton acquired Multi-Chem a leading provider of oilfield production and completion chemicals and services.

In 2012 Halliburton signed a strategic agreement with Russian gas giant Gazprom to jointly develop new oil and gas technologies to support global exploration and production projects.

In 2012 the company formed a 40%-owned joint venture with Schlumberger OneSubsea to make and develop products systems and services for the subsea oil and gas market. Cameron will contribute its existing subsea division and receive $600 million from Schlumberger. Schlumberger will contribute its Framo Surveillance Flow Assurance and Power and Controls businesses.

Expanding its portfolio in 2012 Halliburton acquired Petris Technology a leading US-based global supplier of data-management and integration solutions.

In 2013 Halliburton opened the Completion Technology and Manufacturing Center in Singapore significantly expanding the Company's Completion Tools technology and manufacturing capacity. This additional capability allows Halliburton upgrade its delivery of high-quality products to a broad and growing customer base in the Eastern Hemisphere. That year it also expanded its Malaysia Manufacturing and Technology Centre in Senai Malaysia.

Similarly in 2013 Halliburton opened its Technology Center at the Federal University of Rio de Janeiro Technology Park to establish a global center of expertise for deepwater and mature fields and to support customers engaged in the deepwater drilling push in offshore Brazil.

In 2013 Halliburton entered into an agreement of cooperation with Gazprom Neft for the introduction of new technologies to improve operational efficiency in Gazprom Neft fields. The strategic objective of Gazprom Neft is to increase hydrocarbon production to 100 million tons of oil equivalent by 2020.

In 2013 subsidiary Landmark Software and Service acquired geoscience data company Neftex Petroleum Consultants. The deal allows geoscientists for the first time to use a single global platform to search discover analyze and integrate geoscience data and interpretations essential to understanding and managing subsurface risk.

EXECUTIVES

EVP Administration and Chief Human Resources Officer, Lawrence J. Pope, age 48, $535,000 total compensation
EVP and General Counsel, Robb L. Voyles, age 59
President Eastern Hemisphere, Joseph D. (Joe) Rainey, age 60, $809,950 total compensation
President Western Hemisphere, James S. (Jim) Brown, age 62, $873,000 total compensation
President and CEO, Jeffrey A. (Jeff) Miller, age 53, $970,000 total compensation
EVP and CFO, Christopher T. (Chris) Weber, age 44
EVP Global Business Lines, Eric Carre
RTA Vice President Commericalization, James Antilley
Vice President Manager Director, Kim Stark
Vice President Home and Hardlines, Larry Molnar
Vice President Mergers and Acquisitions, Michael Cheeseman
Vice President Drilling, David Field
Vice President of Business Development, David Prather
Vice President, Chuck Ervin
Chairman, David J. (Dave) Lesar, age 64
Auditors: KPMG LLP

LOCATIONS

HQ: Halliburton Company
3000 North Sam Houston Parkway East, Houston, TX 77032
Phone: 281 871-2699
Web: www.halliburton.com

2016 Sales

	$ mil.	% of total
North America	6,770	43
Middle East/Asia	4,264	27
Europe/Africa/CIS	2,993	19
Latin America	1,860	11
Total	**15,887**	**100**

PRODUCTS/OPERATIONS

2016 Sales

	$ mil.	% of total
Completion and Production	8,882	56
Drilling and Evaluation	7,005	44
Total	**15,887**	**100**

2016 Sales

	$ mil.	% of total
Services	11,140	70
Product sales	4,747	30
Total	**15,887**	**100**

Areas of Expertise

Areas of Expertise
Clean Energy
Deepwater
Heavy Oil
High Pressure/Temperature
Mature Fields
Unconventional Resources

Selected Products and Services

Artificial Lift
Cementing
Consulting
Coring
Drilling
Fluid Services
Formation Evaluation
Hole Enlargement
Pipeline & Process Services
Project Management
Real Time Services
Reservoir Testing / Analysis
Sand Control
Wellbore Service Tools
Software and Services
Stimulation
Subsea
Well Completions
Well Intervention
Wireline and Perforating

Selected Brands

Baroid
Boots & Coots
Landmark
Multi-Chem
Pinnacle
Sperry Drilling

COMPETITORS

Baker Hughes	Superior Energy
Cudd Energy Services	Transocean
GE Oil	Weatherford
RPC	International
Saipem	Wild Well Control
Schlumberger	

Income Statement
FYE: December 31

	REVENUE ($ mil.)	NET INCOME ($ mil.)	NET PROFIT MARGIN	EMPLOYEES
12/17	20,620	(463)	—	55,000
12/16	15,887	(5,763)	—	50,000
12/15	23,633	(671)	—	65,000
12/14	32,870	3,500	10.6%	80,000
12/13	29,402	2,125	7.2%	77,000
Annual Growth	(8.5%)	—	—	(8.1%)

2017 Year-End Financials

Debt ratio: 43.62%
Return on equity: (-5.22%)
Cash ($ mil.): 2,337
Current ratio: 2.22
Long-term debt ($ mil.): 10,430
No. of shares (mil.): 873
Dividends
Yield: 0.0%
Payout: —
Market value ($ mil.): 42,664

	STOCK PRICE ($) FY Close	P/E High/Low	PER SHARE ($) Earnings	Dividends	Book Value
12/17	48.87	— —	(0.53)	0.72	9.53
12/16	54.09	— —	(6.69)	0.72	10.86
12/15	34.04	— —	(0.79)	0.72	18.06
12/14	39.33	18 9	4.11	0.63	19.18
12/13	50.75	24 15	2.36	0.53	16.00
Annual Growth	(0.9%)	— —	—	8.2%	(12.1%)

Hancock Holding Co.

EXECUTIVES

President CEO and Director, John M. Hairston, age 54, $707,000 total compensation
COO, D. Shane Loper, age 51, $400,000 total compensation
CFO, Michael M. Achary, age 56, $400,000 total compensation
President Whitney Bank, Joseph S. Exnicios, age 61, $375,000 total compensation
Chief Credit Officer Whitney Bank, Suzanne C. Thomas, age 62
Chief Credit Risk Officer, Samuel B. Kendricks, age 57
Chief Investment Officer, David J. Lundgren
Vice President And Private Banker, Larry Cuervo
Senior Vice President Financial And Estate Planner, Emile Koury
Assistant Vice President, Kim Gibson
Assistant Vice President, Jimmy Campbell
Vice President Senior Product Manager, John Fox
Vice President, Kristy Oehms
Assistant Vice President Technology, Roland Pittman
Vice President Production Manager, Owen Munton
Human Resources Compliance Manager Assistant Vice President, Katherine C Widdows
Assistant Vice President andamp; Senior Asset Liability Management Analyst, George Mckinney
Vice President, Debbie Renfroe
Vice President, Jim Drummond
Chairman, James B. Estabrook, age 73
Auditors: PricewaterhouseCoopers LLP

LOCATIONS

HQ: Hancock Holding Co.
One Hancock Plaza, 2510, 14th Street, Gulfport, MS 39501
Phone: 228 868-4000
Web: www.hancockbank.com

PRODUCTS/OPERATIONS

2015 Sales

	$ mil.	% of total
Interest income		
Loans including fees	583	64
Securities	94	10
Other	2	.
Non interest income		
Service charges on deposit accounts	72	8
Bank card and ATM fees	46	5
Trust fees	45	5
Investment and annuity fees	20	2
Secondary mortgage market operations	12	1
Insurance commissions and fees	8	1
Other	30	4
Total	**916**	**100**

Selected Services

Banking
Checking
Credit Cards
Currency Exchange
Home Equity Loans and Lines
Investment Services
Investments
Loans & Credit
Mobile Banking
Mortgage
Online & Mobile Banking
Online Banking
Personal Loans and Lines
Savings
Subsidiaries
Berwick LLC
Community First Inc.
Dudley Ventures Hancock Fund LLC
Gulf South Technology Center LLC
The Gulfport Building Inc.
Hancock Bank
Hancock Bank of Alabama
Hancock Bank Securities Corporation II
Hancock Community Investment Corporation
Hancock Enterprise Investment Fund LLC
Hancock Insurance Agency
Hancock Insurance Agency of Alabama
Hancock Insurance Agency of Florida
Hancock Investment Services of Alabama Inc.
Hancock Investment Services of Florida Inc.
Hancock Investment Services of Louisiana Inc.
Hancock Investment Services of Mississippi Inc.
Hancock Investment Services Inc.
Harrison Finance Company
Harrison Loan Company
HBSC LLC
HMC LLC
Invest-Sure Inc.
J Everett Eaves Inc.
Lighthouse Services Corporation
Peoples First Transportation Inc.
Town Properties Inc.
Whitney Bank

COMPETITORS

BancorpSouth	MidSouth Bancorp
Capital One	Regions Financial
First Horizon	Renasant
IBERIABANK	Trustmark
Investar	

Income Statement
FYE: December 31

	ASSETS ($ mil.)	NET INCOME ($ mil.)	INCOME AS % OF ASSETS	EMPLOYEES
12/16	23,975	149	0.6%	3,724
12/15	22,839	131	0.6%	3,921
12/14	20,747	175	0.8%	3,794
12/13	19,009	163	0.9%	3,978
12/12	19,464	151	0.8%	4,235
Annual Growth	5.3%	(0.4%)	—	(3.2%)

2016 Year-End Financials

Debt ratio: 1.82%
Return on equity: 5.80%
Cash ($ mil.): 449
Current ratio: —
Long-term debt ($ mil.): —
No. of shares (mil.): 84
Dividends
Yield: 0.0%
Payout: 51.3%
Market value ($ mil.): 3,631

	STOCK PRICE ($) FY Close	P/E High/Low	PER SHARE ($) Earnings	Dividends	Book Value
12/16	43.10	24 11	1.87	0.96	32.29
12/15	25.17	20 15	1.64	0.96	31.14
12/14	30.70	18 14	2.10	0.96	30.74
12/13	36.68	19 14	1.93	0.96	29.49
12/12	31.73	21 16	1.75	0.96	28.91
Annual Growth	8.0%	— —	1.7%	(0.0%)	2.8%

HanesBrands Inc

Hanesbrands can't wait 'til it gets its Hanes on you. The company designs makes and sells bras hosiery men's boxers socks and other intimate apparel under brand names such as Bali Champion barely there Just My Size Hanes L'eggs Playtex and Wonderbra. Its bras are tops in the US and its underwear legwear and activewear units are market leaders as well. Hanesbrands also makes basic outerwear such as T-shirts and licensed logo apparel for collegiate bookstores legwear for Donna Karan and underwear for Polo Ralph Lauren. The lineup is sold to wholesalers major retail chains (Wal-Mart Target and Kohls) and through Hanesbrands' value outlets and Internet site.

Operations

Hanesbrands divides its operations into four segments including innerwear (intimate apparel men's and children's underwear and socks) activewear direct to consumer and international. Innerwear is the largest by far accounting for more than 50% of revenue in 2015 while Activewear generated more than 25%.

The company operates nearly 40 distribution centers with 16 in the US and 21 located internationally near manufacturing regions.

Geographic Reach

Hanesbrands sells in roughly 35 countries and rings up roughly 80% of its sales in the US (during 2015). Its largest international markets include Europe (12% of sales) Canada Japan Mexico Brazil and China.

Sales and Marketing

Wal-Mart Target and Kohls are the company's largest customers accounting for 23% 15% and 5% of 2015 sales respectively. Mass merchandise stores are vital to the company's performance accounting for about half of Hanesbrands' total sales. Hanesbrands also allies with mid-tier stores including J. C. Penney Macy's and Kohls which are adding its lower-priced labels. It's L'eggs and Hanes brand underwear are also sold in food drug and variety stores. Hanesbrands also sell apparel to the US military for sale to soldiers and through discount chains including Dollar General and Family Dollar Stores.

Financial Performance

Hanesbrands' annual sales and profits have been growing over the past few years as new brand acquisitions have spurred more sales in more geographic markets.

The company's sales rose nearly 8% to $5.73 billion during fiscal 2016 (ended January 2016) mostly thanks to 40%-plus International segment growth. The International segment's Europe operation was boosted by its late 2014 acquisition of DBApparel. Its Activewear sales also grew as its Knights Apparel acquisition led to higher sports apparel sales.

Sales growth in FY2016 drove Hanesbrands' net income up 6% to $428.2 million despite higher selling general and administration costs associated with acquisition and integration charges. The apparel maker's operating cash levels plunged 55% to $227 million for the year as it used more cash to build its inventory levels paid $100 million in pension contributions and decreased its accounts receivables collections due to the timing of sales in the fourth quarter.

Strategy

Hanesbrands has been expanding its business overseas by acquiring top brands in its less-tapped markets. In 2016 for example the company expanded in Australia after buying top intimates maker Pacific Brands in Australia. Pacific Brands adds to the 2014 acquisition of DBApparel Group of France licensed to sell the Wonderbra and Playdex trademarks in the EU and South Africa.

The company also hopes to identify and capitalize on the long-term megatrends related to their top product lines over the next five to 10 years. To this end in early 2015 the company purchased Knights Apparel to expand its sports licensed collegiate apparel business with a goal of appealing to college students as that market grows over the next years and decades.

Beyond growth Hanesbrands has been reducing production costs by improving operating efficiencies in using a low-cost global supply chain based upon a combination of owned contracted and sourced manufacturing.

Mergers and Acquisitions

In 2016 the company acquired leading Australian undergarment company Pacific Brands Limited in a cash deal valued at $800 million. The acquisition gave Hanesbrands the top market position in Australia for intimate apparel. In addition to its core products Pacific Brands Limited also operates pillow business Tontine and flooring business Dunlop. Hanesbrands intends to divest both businesses.

Hanesbrands also acquired Champion Europe which owned the Champion brand in Europe Middle East and Africa in 2016 for $228 million in cash. The company operates Champion Europe as a division of Hanes' global Champion organization.

In 2015 the company bought Knights Apparel a leading retailer of licensed collegiate logo apparel to enrich its own Gear for Sports licensed collegiate apparel business.

EXECUTIVES

CEO, Gerald W. Evans, age 57, $912,500 total compensation
Group President Innerwear Americas, W. Howard Upchurch, age 53, $525,000 total compensation
CFO, Barry A. Hytinen, age 42

President Chief Supply Chain and Information Technology Officer, Michael E. Faircloth, age 51, $510,000 total compensation
President Activewear, John T. Marsh, age 51
Vice President Marketing, Richard Heller
Vice President Distribution, Chuck Allen
Vice President Textiles E Hilos, Keith Huskins
Chairman, Richard A. (Rich) Noll, age 60
Auditors: PricewaterhouseCoopers LLP

LOCATIONS

HQ: HanesBrands Inc
  1000 East Hanes Mill Road, Winston-Salem, NC 27105
Phone: 336 519-8080
Web: www.Hanes.com

2016 Sales

	$ mil.	% of total
US	4,489	74
France	290	5
Austrila	278	5
Japan	182	3
Italy	174	3
Germany	110	2
Europe (other)	96	2
Canada	90	1
Spain	65	1
Mexico	60	1
United Kingdom	32	1
Brazil	28	0
China	5	0
Central America & the Caribbean Basin	3	0
Other	120	2
Total	**6,028**	**100**

2016 Sales

	$ mil.	% of total
Innerwear	2,609	43
Activewear	1,570	26
Direct to Consumer	315	5
International	1,531	26
Total	**6,028**	**100**

PRODUCTS/OPERATIONS

Selected Brands
Bali
barely there
C9 by Champion
Champion
Gear for Sports
Just My Size
Hanes
L'eggs
Maidenform
Outer Banks
Playtex
Rinbros
Sol y Oro
Wonderbra
Zorba

COMPETITORS

Calvin Klein	Russell Brands
Frederick's of	The Gap
Hollywood Group	Tommy Hilfiger
Fruit of the Loom	Top Form
Gerber Childrenswear	Triumph Apparel
Gildan Activewear	Under Armour
J. Crew	Victoria's Secret
Jockey International	Stores
L Brands	Wacoal
PremiumWear	Warnaco Group
Redcats USA	Warnaco Swimwear

HISTORICAL FINANCIALS
Company Type: Public

Income Statement
FYE: December 30

	REVENUE ($ mil.)	NET INCOME ($ mil.)	NET PROFIT MARGIN	EMPLOYEES
12/17	6,471	61	1.0%	67,200
12/16*	6,028	539	8.9%	67,800
01/16	5,731	428	7.5%	65,300
01/15	5,324	404	7.6%	59,500
12/13	4,627	330	7.1%	49,700
Annual Growth	**8.7%**	**(34.2%)**	**—**	**7.8%**

*Fiscal year change

2017 Year-End Financials
Debt ratio: 57.49%
Return on equity: 6.50%
Cash ($ mil.): 421
Current ratio: 1.90
Long-term debt ($ mil.): 3,702

No. of shares (mil.): 360
Dividends
  Yield: 0.0%
  Payout: 352.9%
Market value ($ mil.): 7,530

	STOCK PRICE ($) FY Close	P/E High/Low	PER SHARE ($) Earnings	Dividends	Book Value
12/17	20.91	151 112	0.17	0.60	1.91
12/16*	21.57	22 15	1.40	0.44	3.23
01/16	29.43	120 25	1.06	0.40	3.26
01/15	110.61	86 48	1.32	0.30	4.61
12/13	69.35	64 32	1.08	0.15	4.12
Annual Growth	**(25.9%)**	**—**	**—(37.1%)**	**41.4%**	**(17.6%)**

*Fiscal year change

Hanmi Financial Corp.

No hand-me-down operation Hanmi Financial is headquartered in a penthouse suite along Los Angeles' Wilshire Boulevard. The company owns Hanmi Bank which serves California's Korean-American community and others in the multi-ethnic Los Angeles San Diego San Francisco Bay and Silicon Valley areas. Hanmi Bank offers retail and small business banking with an emphasis on the latter from more than 25 California branches and loan offices throughout the US. Commercial and industrial loans including SBA and international trade finance loans account for about 60% of its loan portfolio; real estate loans make up most of the rest.

Financial Performance

After five straight years of declines Hanmi's revenue grew 6% in 2013 to $153 million. The financial and housing crises particularly acute in California hurt Hanmi's customers many of whom operate small businesses and consequently the bank's finances. As loan volume begins to increase and bring higher yields on investment securities the company's interest income has slowly risen. While non-interest income such as insurance commissions is also on the rise other types of non-interest income such as service charges on deposit accounts is declining as customers demand lower-cost banking products and services.

In 2013 it earned $39.9 million in profit down from $90.4 million in 2012. The decrease was due to the absence of the reversal of the deferred tax asset valuation allowance which contributed an income tax benefit of $47.4 million in 2012.

Strategy

Hanmi and Korean bank Woori Finance called off plans to merge in mid-2011 instead forming a business alliance. Two years later Hanmi is still actively looking for a partner to merge with. It hopes to find a South Korean financial institution looking to establish a presence in the US.

In order to focus on its business banking in 2014 the bank sold its insurance subsidiaries Chun-Ha Insurance Services and All World Insurance Services to Chunha Holding Corporation. The two companies sold life and property/casualty insurance plans.

Mergers and Acquisitions

In its first foray outside of California in late 2013 Hanmi agreed to acquire Central Bancorp Inc. the parent of Texas-based United Central Bank. United Central Bank serves multi-ethnic communities in Texas Illinois Virginia California New York and New Jersey through some two dozen branches. Once the acquisition is complete Hanmi will have about 50 branches and two loan production offices serving a broad range of ethnic communities in California Texas Illinois New York New Jersey Virginia and Georgia.

EXECUTIVES

SEVP and COO, Bonita I. (Bonnie) Lee, age 54
Chief Compliance and BSA Officer, Jean Lim
EVP and CFO, Michael W. McCall
President CEO and Director, Chong Guk (C. G.) Kum
EVP and Chief Credit Officer, Randall G. Ewig
EVP and Chief Administrative Officer, Greg D. Kim
EVP and Chief Banking Officer, Peter Yang
EVP and Chief Lending Officer, Anthony Kim
Senior Executive Vice President, Romolo C Santarosa
First Vice President And Loan Manager, Richard Son
Vice President and Loan Officer, Yong Park
Assistant Vice President Compliance Officer, Michael Santiago
Vice President, Joonhyok Shin
Vice President, Maheboob Kurani
Vice President Loss Share Accounting Manager, Brian Rogers
Assistant Vice President andamp; Credit Analyst, Daniel Park
Assistant Vice President andamp; SBA Loan Officer, Sharon Min
First Vice President and Branch Manager, Annie Chung
Vice President andamp; LOAN OFFICER, Paul Rhee
Senior Vice President Corporate Banking Manager, Chris Cho
Vice President, Mark Flannery
Vice President and Accounting Officer Accounting Department, Jin Shin
Chairman, Joseph K. Rho, age 76
Auditors: KPMG LLP

LOCATIONS

HQ: Hanmi Financial Corp.
3660 Wilshire Boulevard, Penthouse Suite A, Los Angeles, CA 90010
Phone: 213 382-2200
Web: www.hanmi.com

PRODUCTS/OPERATIONS

2013 Sales

	$ mil.	% of total
Interest income	122	80
Non-interest income	31	20
Total	**153**	**100**

COMPETITORS

Bank of America	Far East National Bank
Broadway Financial	Hope Bancorp
Cathay General Bancorp	JPMorgan Chase
East West Bancorp	Woori

HISTORICAL FINANCIALS

Company Type: Public

Income Statement

FYE: December 31

	ASSETS ($ mil.)	NET INCOME ($ mil.)	INCOME AS % OF ASSETS	EMPLOYEES
12/16	4,701	56	1.2%	638
12/15	4,234	53	1.3%	622
12/14	4,232	49	1.2%	699
12/13	3,055	39	1.3%	499
12/12	2,882	90	3.1%	470
Annual Growth	13.0%	(11.1%)	—	7.9%

2016 Year-End Financials

Debt ratio: 0.40%
Return on equity: 10.99%
Cash ($ mil.): 147
Current ratio: —
Long-term debt ($ mil.): —

No. of shares (mil.): 32
Dividends
Yield: 0.0%
Payout: 37.7%
Market value ($ mil.): 1,128

	STOCK PRICE ($) FY Close	P/E High/Low		PER SHARE ($) Earnings	Dividends	Book Value
12/16	34.90	20	11	1.75	0.66	16.42
12/15	23.72	16	12	1.68	0.47	15.45
12/14	21.81	16	12	1.56	0.28	14.21
12/13	21.89	18	11	1.26	0.14	12.63
12/12	13.59	5	3	2.87	0.00	12.01
Annual Growth	26.6%	—	—(11.6%)		—	8.1%

Hanover Insurance Group Inc

The Hanover Insurance Group is an all-around property/casualty insurance holding company. Through Hanover Insurance Company it provides personal and commercial automobile homeowners and workers' compensation coverage as well as commercial multi-peril insurance and professional liability coverage. The group sells its products through a network of 2000 independent agents throughout the US but Michigan Massachusetts and New York account for about 40% of its business. In Michigan it operates as Citizens Insurance Company. Hanover's Opus Investment Management subsidiary provides institutional investment management services; the group operates internationally through UK subsidiary Chaucer Holdings.

Operations

Hanover's primary domestic segments are Commercial Lines Personal Lines and Other while its international segment is Chaucer.

Primarily through the Hanover Insurance Company unit Hanover writes more than $5 billion in gross premiums and handles about 200000 claims each year. Commercial policies account for nearly half of annual revenues while personal lines account for 30%. Subsidiary Chaucer operates two Lloyd's of London syndicates which manage and underwrite global property/casualty policies; the subsidiary also offers specialty insurance and reinsurance coverage. Chaucer generates about 20% of the group's revenues.

Hanover's Other segment comprises Opus Investment Management which provides investment advisory services to affiliates; it also manages assets for unaffiliated clients including insurance companies retirement plans and foundations.

Geographic Reach

Hanover is licensed to sell property/casualty insurance in all 50 US states and the District of Columbia. It actively markets commercial policies in 37 states and personal lines policies in 18 states. Michigan is the company's largest market accounting for some 20% of all commercial and personal lines. Massachusetts and New York account for about 10% each. Altogether US operations account for some 85% of annual premiums.

In addition to its headquarters in Worcester Massachusetts the company has more than 40 regional offices in cities across the US and about 10 overseas locations including those in Denmark (Copenhagen) Norway (Oslo) the UK (London) and Singapore.

Sales and Marketing

Hanover sells through a network of agents and brokers including some 2000 independent representatives. The company's customers include individuals families and businesses.

Chaucer the international segment distributes primarily via Lloyd's as well as through underwriting agencies.

Financial Performance

Hanover reported several years of growth until 2015 when revenue declined less than 1% to $5.03 billion. Revenue fell another 2% to $4.95 billion in 2016 as premiums dropped for the second year in a row.

Net income which had risen for four straight years fell 53% to $155.1 million in 2016. This decline was driven by factors including increased losses and loss adjustment expenses lower gains on Chaucer's 2015 sale of its UK motor business and higher net loss from repayment of debt. Cash flow from operations increased 68% to $737.6 million that year largely due to changes in loss loss adjustment expenses and unearned premium reserves.

Strategy

One of Hanover's strategies is to build partnerships with other insurers and agents while expanding its product offerings and geographic presence beyond its three historical core markets of Massachusetts New York and Michigan. The company pursues growth in a conservative manner to preserve long-term financial and operational stability. In addition Hanover is working to increase efficiencies through technology upgrades.

Written premiums are balanced between personal and commercial products but competition is fierce in personal insurance so the company has placed more emphasis on expanding its commercial offerings. It does this by deepening its relationships with agents through diverse product offerings.

Wriggling into a niche is one method of expanding and Hanover has moved into several areas of specialty insurance in recent years such as health care and engineering. The company has launched several niche insurance programs such as coverage for not-for-profit youth organizations community services organizations and religious institutions. In 2015 it launched a suite of cyber products to protect mid-sized business from data breaches and cyberattacks. It also introduced its Fidelity & Crime Advantage program to protect employers from crimes committed by their own employees. In 2017 the company launched Hanover Fusion a life sciences product that includes coverage for errors and omissions information security media and content and operations liability. Also that year Chaucer established Chaucer Dublin to write international specialty insurance.

In 2015 the company sold its UK motor business for $64.9 million.

Mergers and Acquisitions

In 2017 Hanover's international subsidiary Chaucer acquired SLE Holdings a Lloyd's managing general underwriting agency operating in Australia. SLE focuses on the sports entertainment and leisure sectors. The purchase broadened Chaucer's Australian operations as well as widening its specialty product lines.

HISTORY

In 1842 a group of Worcester Massachusetts businessmen tried to form a mutual life insurance company. After a failed first attempt they succeeded with the help of lobbyist Benjamin Balch. In 1844 the State Mutual Life Assurance Co. of Worcester set up business in the back room of secretary Clarendon Harris' bookstore. The first president was John Davis a US senator. The company issued its first policy in 1845.

In the early years State Mutual reduced risk by issuing policies only for residents of such "civilized" areas as New England New Jersey New York Pennsylvania and Ohio. It also restricted movement requiring policyholders to get permission for travel outside those areas. By the 1850s the company had begun issuing policies in the Midwest (with a 25% premium surcharge) the South (for 30% extra) and California (for a pricey extra $25 per $1000) with a maximum coverage of $5000.

The Civil War was a problem for many insurers who had to decide what to do about Southern policyholders and payment on war-related claims. State Mutual chose to pay out its Northern policyholders' benefits despite the extra cost. In 1896 the firm began offering installment pay-out plans for policyholders concerned that their beneficiaries would fritter away the whole payment.

The first 30 years of the 20th century were for the company a time of growth that was stopped short by the Depression. But despite a great increase in the number of policy loans and surrenders for cash value State Mutual's financial footing remained solid.

After WWII the company entered group insurance and began offering individual sickness and accident coverage. In 1957 it was renamed State Mutual Life Assurance Co. of America. The firm added property/casualty insurance in the late 1950s through alliances with such firms as Worcester Mutual Fire Insurance. During the 1960s State Mutual continued to develop property/casualty buying interests in Hanover Insurance and Citizens Corp.

The firm followed the industrywide shift into financial services in the 1970s adding mutual funds a real estate investment trust and an investment management firm. This trend accelerated in the 1980s and State Mutual began offering financial planning services as well as administrative and other services for the insurance and mutual fund industries (the mutual fund administration operations were sold in 1995). Managing this growth was another story: Its acquisitions left it bloated and disorganized. Technical systems were in disarray by the early 1990s and the agency force had grown to more than 1400. In response the company began a five-year effort to upgrade systems cut fat and reduce sales positions.

In view of its shifting focus State Mutual became Allmerica Financial in 1992. Three years later it demutualized. In 1997 it bought the 40% of Allmerica Property & Casualty it didn't already own.

EXECUTIVES

EVP General Counsel and Assistant Secretary, J. Kendall Huber, age 62, $498,077 total compensation
EVP and CFO, Jeffrey M. (Jeff) Farber, age 52, $150,000 total compensation
SVP and Chief Claims Officer, Mark Welzenbach, age 57

President and CEO, John C. (Jack) Roche, age 53, $470,385 total compensation
Chief Growth Innovation Officer, Richard W. (Dick) Lavey
Chief Investment Officer; President Opus Investment Management, Ann K. Tripp, age 58
CEO and Chief Underwriting Officer Chaucer, John Fowle, age 47
Chief Technology Innovation Officer, Mark L. Berthiaume, age 60
EVP and Chief Human Resources Officer, Christine Bilotti-Peterson, age 46
EVP Corporate Development and Strategy, Mark L. Keim, age 51
EVP; President Specialty, Bryan J. Salvatore
Vice President Management Liability of Commercial Lines Business, Helen Savaiano
Regional President, John Casper
Vice President Investor Relations, Oksana Lukasheva
Vice President Personal Lines, Tammy Hessberger
Senior Vice President and Treasurer, Mark Canfield
Regional Vice President Commercial Lines Downstate NY, Frank Vetrano
RVP, George Agyen
Regional Vice President, John Buckalew
Vice President, Roger Pare
Regional President Midwest, Paul Mueller
Vice President of Corporate Real Estate, James Johnson
Regional Vice President, SCOTT BETLESKY
Executive Vice President and Chief Financial Officer, David B Greenfield
Assistant Vice President Management Liability, Matt Tusinski
Vice President Distribution, Michael Lewis
Assistant Vice President Business Integration, Kevin D Pray
AVP Network Telecommunications Pc Services Collabo, Steve White
Assistant Vice President Marine Uw Development, Mary Corcoran
Assistant Vice President Cl Uw Processes, Erin A Fenlon
Assistant Vice President Product Management, Joseph Brophy
Vice President MARKETING and COMM., Jennifer F Luisa
Assistant Vice President Community Relations, Paul A Belsito
Vice President of Information Technology, Patty Kularski
Branch Vice President, Mark E Mcgregor
Regional Vice President, Gregory L Parr
Assistant Vice President, Lisa Binnie
Regional President Northeast, Kelly Stacy
Branch Vice President, Carla Northcutt
Assistant Vice President Human Resources, Liz Berry
Vice President Chief Information Security Officer, Brian Haugli
Regional Vice President, Scott Couger
Assistant Vice President Human Resources Business Partner, Tina Achorn
Assistant Vice President Human Resources Strategic Business Partner, Kelly Villanueva
Assistant Vice President Enterprise Architecture, Brian Kane
Assistant Vice President Strategic Initiatives, Taylor MacFarlane
Assistant Vice President Senior Counsel, Matthew Frascella
Assistant Vice President Commercial Umbrella, John Lyons
Regional Vice President CL, Angela Roman-Grimaldi
Assistant Vice President CL Agency Services, Karen Jenkins
Chairman, Michael P. Angelini, age 74
Auditors: PricewaterhouseCoopers LLP

LOCATIONS

HQ: Hanover Insurance Group Inc
440 Lincoln Street, Worcester, MA 01653
Phone: 508 855-1000   **Fax:** 508 855-6332
Web: www.hanover.com

PRODUCTS/OPERATIONS

2016 Revenue

	$ mil.	% of total
Premiums	4,628	93
Net investment income	279	6
Net realized investment gains	8	—
Fees and other income	29	1
Total	**4,945**	**100**

2016 Revenue

	$ mil.	% of total
Insurance		
Commercial lines	2,485	48
Personal lines	1,552	30
Chaucer	891	22
Other	8	-
Investment gains	8	-
Total	**4,945**	**100**

Selected Products

Personal Lines
  Auto Insurance
  Companion Products
  Dwelling Fire
  Home Care Services
  Homeowners Insurance
  Identity Integrity
  Umbrella
  Valuable Items
  Watercraft
Small Commercial and Middle Market Core Products
  Business Owner's Policy
  Commercial Automobile
  Commercial Package
  General Liability
  Property
  Umbrella
  Workers' Compensation
Specialized Products
  AIX Specialty Programs
  Commercial Umbrella and Excess
  Healthcare
  Industrial Property Risk
  Management Liability
  Marine (inland and ocean)
  Professional Liability
  Surety (commercial and contract)

COMPETITORS

Alleghany Corporation	Liberty Mutual
Allstate	Markel Insurance
American Automobile	Nationwide
Association (AAA)	Progressive
American Financial	Corporation
Group	State Farm
Auto-Owners Insurance	Travelers Companies
GEICO	USAA

HISTORICAL FINANCIALS

Company Type: Public

Income Statement

FYE: December 31

	ASSETS ($ mil.)	NET INCOME ($ mil.)	INCOME AS % OF ASSETS	EMPLOYEES
12/16	14,220	155	1.1%	4,900
12/15	13,790	331	2.4%	4,800
12/14	13,759	282	2.0%	5,100
12/13	13,378	251	1.9%	5,100
12/12	13,484	55	0.4%	5,100
Annual Growth	**1.3%**	**29.1%**	**—**	**(1.0%)**

2016 Year-End Financials

Debt ratio: 5.53%
Return on equity: 5.43%
Cash ($ mil.): 282
Current ratio: —
Long-term debt ($ mil.): —

No. of shares (mil.): 42
Dividends
Yield: 0.0%
Payout: 52.3%
Market value ($ mil.): 3,859

	STOCK PRICE ($) FY Close	P/E High/Low		PER SHARE ($) Earnings	Dividends	Book Value
12/16	91.01	25	20	3.59	1.88	67.39
12/15	81.34	11	9	7.40	1.69	66.15
12/14	71.32	11	8	6.28	1.52	64.78
12/13	59.71	11	7	5.59	1.36	59.37
12/12	38.74	33	27	1.23	1.23	58.59
Annual Growth	23.8%			30.7%	11.2%	3.6%

HarborOne Bancorp Inc

LOCATIONS

HQ: HarborOne Bancorp Inc
770 Oak Street, Brockton, MA 02301
Phone: 508 895-1000
Web: www.harborone.com

HISTORICAL FINANCIALS

Company Type: Public

Income Statement

FYE: December 31

	ASSETS ($ mil.)	NET INCOME ($ mil.)	INCOME AS % OF ASSETS	EMPLOYEES
12/16	2,448	5	0.2%	614
12/15	2,163	5	0.3%	387
12/14	2,041	2	0.1%	—
Annual Growth	9.5%	51.9%	—	—

2016 Year-End Financials

Debt ratio: 7.97%
Return on equity: 2.27%
Cash ($ mil.): 50
Current ratio: —
Long-term debt ($ mil.): —

No. of shares (mil.): 32
Dividends
Yield: —
Payout: —
Market value ($ mil.): 621

	STOCK PRICE ($) FY Close	P/E High/Low		PER SHARE ($) Earnings	Dividends	Book Value
12/16	19.34	—	—	(0.00)	0.00	10.25
12/15	0.00	—	—	(0.00)	0.00	(0.00)
12/14	0.00	—	—	(0.00)	0.00	(0.00)
Annual Growth						

Harley-Davidson Inc

Harley-Davidson is a major US maker of motorcycles and seller of heavyweight cruisers. The company offers touring and custom Harleys through a worldwide network of more than 1460 dealers. The company manufactures and markets six families of motorcycles: Touring Dyna Softail Street Sportster and V-Rod. It also makes three-wheeled motorcycles. Harley-Davidson sells attitude with its brand-name products which include a line of clothing and accessories (MotorClothes). Harley-Davidson Financial Services (HDFS) offers financing to dealers and consumers in the US and Canada.

Operations

The company operates through two segments. Its core motorcycle manufacturing operations generate around 90% of its revenue each year; Harley-Davidson Financial Services contributes the remainder of revenue.

Harley-Davidson's Touring Dyna Softail Street and Sportster are equipped with air-cooled twin-cylinder engines (in a 45-degree "V" configuration) while its V-Rod sports a 60-degree "V" configuration twin-cylinder engine that is liquid cooled.

The company also makes special editions for peace officers and firefighters. Its products and related lifestyle are supported by H.O.G. (Harley Owners Group). Harley also supports a rental and tour program market and a rider training program known as Riders Edge.

Geographic Reach

Harley-Davidson generates 60% of its total sales from the US. Its operations are located in the Asia/Pacific Europe the Middle East Africa Latin America and the US. Manufacturing and regional offices reside in Brazil India Australia New Zealand Singapore and the UK.

Sales and Marketing

Harley-Davidson's motorcycles are sold to customers through a network of independent distributors. The company spends around $130 million each year on advertising. Its products are marketed to retail customers worldwide primarily through advertising and promotional activities via various broadcast print and electronic channels. The company targets young adults ages 18-34 women African-Americans and Hispanics as well as Caucasian men ages 35-plus.

Financial Performance

Harley-Davidson's revenues remained static for both 2015 and 2016 hovering around the $6 billion mark for both years. The company's profits also fell 8% from $752 million in 2015 to $692 million in 2016. Cash flow from operations increased from $1.1 billion to $1.17 billion during that same time period due to lower net cash outflows from wholesale lending and favorable changes in working capital driven by a reduction in inventory.

Wholesale shipments of Harley-Davidson motorcycles were down 2% in 2016 compared to the prior year; this was in line with a 2% decrease in dealer retail sales of new Harley-Davidson motorcycles. Its motorcycles segment was also affected by unfavorable manufacturing costs and unfavorable foreign currency exchange rates. In addition its Financial Services segment experienced decreased sales primarily due to a higher provision for credit losses.

Strategy

In the midst of a soft US industry driven by weak oil-dependent region sales Harley-Davidson is focused on growing internationally. To support this initiative it has two CKD (complete knock down) assembly plants which assemble motorcycles from component kits produced by its US plants and by its suppliers. Its first CKD plant is located in Brazil and has been in operation since 1999 and its second CKD resides in India and has been in operation since 2011.

As a primary means of growth the company adds new dealerships to its network each year. In 2016 it added 40 new international dealerships and it plans to add a total of 150 to 200 from 2016 through 2020.

Tapping an important new market Harley-Davidson has introduced its prototype Livewire electric bike and has plans to launch it to the market within the next five years. In total the company plans to introduce 100 new motorcycles over the next 10 years including an entire range of electric vehicles.

HISTORY

In 1903 William Harley and the Davidson brothers (Walter William and Arthur) of Milwaukee sold their first Harley-Davidson motorcycle which essentially was motor-assisted bicycle that required pedaling uphill. Demand was high and most sold before leaving the factory. Six years later the company debuted its trademark two-cylinder V-twin engine. By 1913 it had 150 competitors.

EXECUTIVES

VP Communications; President Harley-Davidson Foundation Inc., Joanne M. Bischmann, age 55
President and COO Harley-Davidson Financial Services, Lawrence G. Hund, age 60, $596,668 total compensation
VP General Counsel and Secretary, Paul J. Jones, age 47, $546,667 total compensation
President and CEO, Matthew S. (Matt) Levatich, age 52, $1,041,667 total compensation
SVP and CFO, John A. Olin, age 56, $651,500 total compensation
COO Harley-Davidson Motor Company, Michelle A. Kumbier, $560,000 total compensation
SVP Global Demand, Sean J. Cummings, age 54
Chairman, Michael J. (Mike) Cave, age 57
Auditors: Ernst & Young LLP

LOCATIONS

HQ: Harley-Davidson Inc
3700 West Juneau Avenue, Milwaukee, WI 53208
Phone: 414 342-4680
Web: www.harley-davidson.com

2016 Sales

	$ mil.	% of total
US	3,579	60
EMEA	798	13
Canada	212	4
Australia	181	3
Japan	200	3
Other	299	5
Financial Services	725	12
Total	**5,996**	**100**

PRODUCTS/OPERATIONS

2016 Sales

	$ mil.	% of total
Motorcycle & related parts	5,271	88
Financial services	725	12
Total	**5,996**	**100**

Selected Motorcycles

Harley-Davidson
CVO (custom vehicle operations)
Road Gllide Ultra
Softail Convertible
Street Glide
Ultra Classic Electroglide
Dyna
Fat BOB
Street BOB
Super Glide Custom
Wide Glide
Softail
Black Line
Cross Bones
Fat Boy
Heritage Softail Classic
Night Train
Rocker C
Softail Deluxe
Sportster
883 (Low and Custom)
1200 (Custom and Low)
Forty Eight
Iron 883
Nightster
SuperLow
XR1200X
Touring

Electra Glide (Standard Classic and Ultra Classic)
Road Glide Ultra
Road King (and Classic)
Street Glide
Tri Glide Ultra Classic
Trike
Street Glide Trike
Tri Glide Ultra Classic
VRSC
Night Rod Special
V-Rod (and V-Rod Muscle)

Selected Operations

Motorcycles
 Harley-Davidson Motor Company
Financial services
 Harley-Davidson Financial Services Inc.
 Harley-Davidson Credit
 Harley-Davidson Insurance

COMPETITORS

BMW	Polaris Industries
Ducati	Triumph Motorcycles
Honda	Ultra Motorcycle
Indian Motorcycle	Viper Motorcycle

HISTORICAL FINANCIALS

Company Type: Public

Income Statement

FYE: December 31

	REVENUE ($ mil.)	NET INCOME ($ mil.)	NET PROFIT MARGIN	EMPLOYEES
12/16	5,996	692	11.5%	6,000
12/15	5,995	752	12.5%	6,300
12/14	6,228	844	13.6%	6,500
12/13	5,899	733	12.4%	6,400
12/12	5,580	623	11.2%	5,800
Annual Growth	1.8%	2.6%	—	0.9%

2016 Year-End Financials

Debt ratio: 68.83%	No. of shares (mil.): 175
Return on equity: 36.72%	Dividends
Cash ($ mil.): 759	Yield: 0.0%
Current ratio: 1.35	Payout: 36.5%
Long-term debt ($ mil.): 4,666	Market value ($ mil.): 10,265

	STOCK PRICE ($) FY Close	P/E High/Low	PER SHARE ($) Earnings	Dividends	Book Value
12/16	58.34	16 10	3.83	1.40	10.91
12/15	45.39	18 12	3.69	1.24	9.96
12/14	65.91	19 14	3.88	1.10	13.73
12/13	69.24	21 15	3.28	0.84	13.68
12/12	48.83	19 14	2.72	0.62	11.31
Annual Growth	4.5%	— —	8.9%	22.6%	(0.9%)

Harris Corp.

Harris Corp. keeps customers communicating on the battlefield in the air and space and just about everywhere else. The company develops communications products for government and commercial customers in more than 100 countries. It makes radio-frequency (RF) and satellite communications and other wireless network transmission equipment; air traffic control systems; and digital network management systems. About three-quarter of Harris' revenue comes from US government agencies. Its commercial clients come from the construction energy health care maritime oil transportation and utilities industries. One of its biggest customers is the US Department of Defense.

Operations

Harris Corp. has reorganized its divisions following divestitures and to better reflect its operations.

Its Communication Systems segment about 30% of revenue develops and makes tactical communications and defense products including tactical ground and airborne radio communications equipment and night vision technology and equipment for public safety networks.

The Electronic Systems 40% of revenue provides electronic warfare avionics and command control communications computers intelligence surveillance and reconnaissance equipment for the defense industry. It also makes air traffic management systems for civil aviation.

Space and Intelligence Systems 30% of revenue provides intelligence space protection geospatial complete Earth observation universe exploration positioning navigation and timing and environmental equipment for national security defense civil and commercial customers. Among its products are advanced sensors antennas and payloads as well as ground processing and information analytics.

Geographic Reach

Harris Corp. operates some 170 locations in Canada Europe the Middle East Central and South America Africa Asia Caribbean Latin American and the US. Exports account for about 20% of revenue; no foreign customer accounts for more than 5% of revenue.

Sales and Marketing

Harris Corp.?s primary customers are US government agencies including prime contractors and supported foreign defense organizations accounting for about 75% of sales.

Financial Performance

Harris Corp.?s revenue fell is 2017 (ended June) no matter how it?s figured. The company has made divestitures and made its past financials reflect current operations. Without that refiguring revenue fell 21% in 2017 from 2016. With the company?s recalculation revenue dropped just 2%. The rest of this report will use Harris? recalculated numbers.

The decrease company attributed the revenue drop to lower Tactical Communications revenue in the Communication Systems segment and lower revenue due to the impact of the divestiture of the Aerostructures business in the fourth quarter of 2016. Other factors were environmental and commercial space programs in the Space and Intelligence Systems segment that moved from build-out to sustainment. Bringing in more revenue were the ramp up of the United Arab Emirates integrated battle management system program electronic warfare in the Electronic Systems segment and a $36 million revenue increase from classified customers in the Space and Intelligence Systems segment.

Harris reported a 70% jump in net income to $553 million in 2017 from 2016. The big difference was a lower loss from discontinued operations in 2017 $85 million compared to loss of $287 million in 2016.

Cash flow from operations fell to $569 million in 207 from $924 million in 2016 because of a $415 million payment to the company pension plan and $127 million less of impairment of goodwill and other assets.

Strategy

Harris Corp. has reconfigured its operations through a series of five divestitures in the past four years. That has provided the company with the resources to focus on what it considers growth opportunities: managed satellite communications public safety and professional communications health care IT and emerging national markets par-

ticularly in the energy maritime and government sectors.

The company has rolled out several products that reflect the new focus. They include an HF manpack radio that provides soldiers with 10 times faster data rates than other equipment an advanced wideband phased-array antenna with improved anti-jamming electronic warfare capabilities and an environmental sensor that more precisely detects greenhouse gas emissions and a robotic system with human-like dexterity for ease of use in bomb disposal and other applications.

Harris? changes have increased its sales to and dependence on government and particularly defense-related customers. Sales to federal agencies account for about three-quarters of revenue up from about two-thirds in 2015. Not all of it is defense however. Some government work is related to civil agencies in law enforcement and aviation.

Mergers and Acquisitions

While most of Harris Corp.?s focus has been on divesting operations that no longer fit into its product mix it has made one significant acquisition. In 2015 it bought Exelis provider of communications products catering to the government in a transaction worth $4.7 billion. The deal beefed up Harris' presence in the government sector.

EXECUTIVES

Vice President Harris Caprock General Counsel, Alan Aronowitz

Chairman President and CEO, William M. (Bill) Brown, age 54, $1,172,913 total compensation

SVP and Chief Global Business Development Officer, Dana A. Mehnert, age 55, $527,770 total compensation

SVP Integration and Engineering, Sheldon J. Fox, age 59, $521,346 total compensation

President Critical Networks, Carl D'Alessandro, age 53

SVP Human Resources and Administration, Robert L. Duffy, age 49, $459,885 total compensation

CIO, Henry Debnam

President Electronic Systems, Edward J. (Ed) Zoiss, age 51

President Space and Intelligence Systems, William H. (Bill) Gattle, age 55

President Communication Systems, Christopher D. (Chris) Young, age 56, $411,749 total compensation

SVP and CFO, Rahul Ghai, age 45, $376,238 total compensation

Senior Vice President Of Business Development, Alex Heidt

Vice President Corporate Technology, Kent Buchanon

Vice President Operations, Paul North

Vice President Sales, John Koening

Broker And Vice President, George Hurst

Vice President Products And Systems, Shawn Baerlocher

Vice President Large Account Sales, Kevin Lombardo

Senior Vice President, Neal Serven

Vice President Information Technology, Michele St Mary

Vice President General Counsel, Eugene Cavallucci

Vice President Information Technology, Mark Gawron

Vice President, Paul Eisner

Vice President Human Resources, Ken Laprade

Vice President Lean Six Sigma, Phil Burroughs

Vice President Finance Public Safety And Professional Communications, William Cullen

Vice President, Erick Sanz

Engineering Team Manager Treasurer, David Bruder

Treasurer, Steve Thompson

Treasurer, Harmon David

Auditors: Ernst & Young LLP

LOCATIONS

HQ: Harris Corp.
  1025 West NASA Boulevard, Melbourne, FL 32919
Phone: 321 727-9100
Web: www.harris.com

2017 sales

	$ mil.	% of total
US	5,639	95
Other countries	261	5
Total	**5,900**	**100**

PRODUCTS/OPERATIONS

2017 sales

	$ mil.	% of total
Communication systems	1,753	30
Space and intelligence systems	1,902	30
Electronic systems	2,251	40
Adjustments	(6)	-
Total	**5,900**	**100**

Selected Product Groups

Government Communications Systems
  Civil programs
  Aviation
  Weather
  IT services
  Mission command-and-control
  National intelligence programs
Radio-frequency (RF) Communications
  Antennas and accessories
  Information assurance
  Internet protocol voice and data networks
  Public safety
  Tactical radio communications

COMPETITORS

Advisory Board	Lockheed Martin
Airbus Group	ManTech
Alcatel-Lucent	Motorola Solutions
Amper	NCI
Avid Technology	NEC
BAE Systems Inc.	NSN
Boeing	Nortel Networks
CACI International	Northrop Grumman
Ceragon Networks	Orion HealthCorp
ChyronHego	Pilat Media
Cisco Systems	Raytheon
Computer Sciences	RigNet
Corp.	Rockwell Collins
Dell	Rohde & Schwarz
Elbit Systems	SELEX SI
Ericsson	Sony
General Dynamics	Technicolor
Globecomm	Tektronix
HP	Telos
Harmonic	Thales
IBM	UNICOM Government
L3 Technologies	Vizrt
Leidos	WideOrbit

HISTORICAL FINANCIALS

Company Type: Public

Income Statement

FYE: June 30

	REVENUE ($ mil.)	NET INCOME ($ mil.)	NET PROFIT MARGIN	EMPLOYEES
06/17*	5,900	553	9.4%	17,000
07/16	7,467	324	4.3%	21,000
07/15	5,083	334	6.6%	22,300
06/14	5,012	534	10.7%	14,000
06/13	5,111	113	2.2%	14,000
Annual Growth	**3.7%**	**48.7%**	**—**	**5.0%**

*Fiscal year change

2017 Year-End Financials

Debt ratio: 39.94%
Return on equity: 18.53%
Cash ($ mil.): 484
Current ratio: 1.08
Long-term debt ($ mil.): 3,396

No. of shares (mil.): 119
Dividends
  Yield: 1.9%
  Payout: 45.6%
Market value ($ mil.): 13,049

	STOCK PRICE ($) FY Close	P/E High/Low	PER SHARE ($) Earnings	Dividends	Book Value
06/17*	109.08	25 18	4.44	2.12	24.48
07/16	82.59	34 27	2.59	2.00	24.52
07/15	77.74	26 20	3.11	1.88	27.47
06/14	75.98	16 10	4.95	1.68	17.31
06/13	49.25	51 40	1.01	1.48	14.60
Annual Growth	**22.0%**	**— —**	**44.8%**	**9.4%**	**13.8%**

*Fiscal year change

Hartford Financial Services Group Inc.

The Hartford Financial Services Group is an insurer offering a range of commercial and personal property/casualty insurance and financial products. Its commercial operations include auto liability and workers' compensation policies as well as group benefits and specialty commercial coverage for large companies. The Hartford also offers consumer homeowners and auto coverage. The group has been the direct auto and home insurance writer for AARP's members for more than 30 years. Through its mutual fund division the company offers wealth management products and services. The Hartford in business since 1810 serves some 18 million individuals.

HISTORY

In 1810 a group of Hartford Connecticut businessmen led by Walter Mitchell and Henry Terry founded the Hartford Fire Insurance Co. Frequent fires in America's wooden cities and executive ignorance of risk assessment and premium-setting often left the firm on the edge of insolvency. (In 1835 stockholders staged a coup and threw management out.) Still each urban conflagration — including the Great Chicago Fire of 1871 — gave The Hartford an opportunity to seek out and pay all its policyholders thus teaching the company to underwrite under fire as it were and to use such disasters to refine its rates.

The company's stag logo was initially a little deer as shown on a policy sold to Abraham Lincoln in 1861. A few years later however Hartford began using the majestic creature (from a Landseer painting) now familiar to customers. By the 1880s Hartford operated nationwide as well as in Canada and Hawaii.

The company survived both world wars and the Depression but emerged in the 1950s in need of organization. It set up new regional offices and added life insurance buying Columbian National Life (founded 1902) which became Hartford Life Insurance Co.

In 1969 Hartford was bought by ITT (formerly International Telephone and Telegraph) whose CEO Harold Geneen was an avid conglomerateur. Consumer advocate Ralph Nader strongly opposed the acquisition — he fought the merger in court for years and felt vindicated when ITT spun off Hartford in 1995. Others opposed it too because

ITT had engineered the merger based on an IRS ruling (later revoked) that Hartford stockholders wouldn't have to pay capital gains taxes on the purchase price of their stock.

Insurance operations consolidated under the Hartford Life Insurance banner in 1978. Through the 1980s Hartford Life remained one of ITT's strongest operations. A conservative investment policy kept Hartford safe from the junk bond and real estate manias of the 1980s.

Hartford reorganized its property/casualty operations along three lines in 1986 and in 1992 it organized its reinsurance business into one unit. The company faced some liability in relation to Dow Corning's breast-implant litigation but underwriting standards after 1985 reduced long-term risk. In 1994 the company began selling insurance products to AARP members under an exclusive agreement. In 1996 the company finished its spin-off from ITT which was acquired by Starwood Hotels & Resorts two years later.

To grow its reinsurance operation Hartford acquired the reinsurance business of Orion Capital (now Royal & SunAlliance USA) in 1996. It posted a loss of $99 million due in large part to asbestos and pollution liabilities. Late that year the firm changed its name to The Hartford Financial Services Group.

To shore up reserves and fund growth in 1997 the company spun off 19% of Hartford Life. The Hartford expanded into nonstandard auto insurance in 1998 by buying Omni Insurance Group (since sold in 2006). The company also sold its London & Edinburgh Insurance Group in 1998 to Norwich Union (now part of Aviva formerly CGNU). In 1999 The Hartford acquired the reinsurance business of Vesta Fire Insurance a subsidiary of Vesta Insurance Group.

In 2000 Hartford bought back the part of Hartford Life it had spun off. The Hartford also bought the financial products and excess and surplus specialty insurance lines of Reliance Group Holdings. Assurances G ©n ©rales de France bought the company's Dutch subsidiary Zwolsche Algemeene. In 2001 the company bought Fortis Financial a US subsidiary of Belgian insurer Fortis and sold Hartford Seguros its Spanish subsidiary to Liberty Mutual.

Before the financial crisis hit Hartford Life invested in its data management with the acquisition of a defined contribution recordkeeping business (Princeton Retirement Group 2007) and a web-based technology company (TopNoggin 2008). Following the same strategy The Hartford acquired Sun Life's US 401K plan administration business.

Like so many others in the insurance and financial services industry The Hartford had its share of losses during the 2008 financial crisis due to its investment holdings in Fannie Mae Freddie Mac and Lehman Brothers. In mid-2009 the US Treasury stepped in and offered The Hartford and other major life insurers access to its Troubled Asset Relief Program (TARP). The Hartford borrowed $3.4 billion to shore up its capital reserves. As the company and the economy stabilized the loan was repaid by early 2010 including an additional $21.7 million dividend payment.

Prior to the creation of TARP funds the Treasury first made money available to banks through its Capital Purchase Program (CPP). To make itself more eligible The Hartford worked quickly to transform itself into a bank — at least on paper. In 2009 The Hartford acquired Federal Trust Corporation a regional bank holding company for $10 million. However shortly thereafter TARP funds became available and The Hartford readily accepted them and the strings attached. Two years later the company recognized that banking was not among its core competencies or passions and made arrangements to sell Federal Trust Corporation to CenterState Banks.

Chairman and CEO Ramani Ayer had planned on retiring at the end of 2008 but agreed to stay at the helm through 2009. His final year was marked by efforts to stem the company's losses stemming from the global economic and financial crisis that began in 2008. Former head of consumer banking at Bank of America Liam McGee was appointed as the company's new CEO in late 2009.

The Hartford then conducted restructuring measures including exiting international markets and disposing of non-core assets. It ended sales of variable annuities in Japan and the UK in 2009 and sold its Canadian mutual funds business and its Brazilian joint venture in 2010. In early 2011 The Hartford also sold off its third-party claims administration business Specialty Risk Services (SRS) unit to Sedgwick Claims Management Services for $278 million. In addition in late 2011 the company formed an agreement with Wellington Management which took over management of several of Hartford's mutual funds.

During 2010 the company reshaped its reporting segments into the commercial markets consumer markets and wealth management categories. In 2011 it also also placed a number of operations into a separate runoff segment including its exited international operations and its discontinued institutional annuities and private placement life insurance operations.

Despite all of its efforts to recover from the financial crisis of 2008-2009 (which caused heavy investment losses for The Hartford) via cost-cutting and restructuring measures in early 2012 the company began facing investor pressure to separate its life and property/casualty operations through spinoff or asset sale transactions. After reviewing its options The Hartford soon gave in to the demands. While it retained its mutual funds business the firm exited its annuity business and sold the bulk of its life insurance operations (including individual life retirement plans and Woodbury Financial Services units) in 2012 and 2013. It also sold Hartford Life Insurance KK in 2014.

EXECUTIVES

President, Douglas G. (Doug) Elliot, age 57, $918,750 total compensation

EVP Group Benefits, Michael (Mike) Concannon, age 55

Chairman and CEO, Christopher J. Swift, age 56, $1,075,000 total compensation

Chief Investment Officer; President Hartford Investment Management and Talcott Resolution, Brion Johnson, age 57, $525,000 total compensation

EVP Digital Commerce and Customer Analytics, Jonathan R. Bennett, age 53

EVP and Property and Casual Chief Underwriting Officer, A. Morris (Mo) Tooker

CFO, Beth A. Bombara, age 49, $687,500 total compensation

EVP Human Resources, Martha (Marty) Gervasi, age 55

SVP U.S. Wealth Management Group, James E. (Jim) Davey, age 52

EVP and Chief Risk Officer, Robert R. Rupp, age 64, $600,000 total compensation

EVP Operations Technology and Data, William A. (Bill) Bloom, age 53

SVP and Secretary, David C. Robinson, age 52

EVP Personal Lines, Raymond J. (Ray) Sprague, age 58

EVP Small Commercial, Stephanie Bush

Chief Claims Officer, John Kinney

Vice President Brand And Advertising, Michael Johnson

Senior Vice President and Head of Field Sales and Execution, Tracey Ant

Vice President, Debra Fox

Assistant Vice President Human Resources, Daniel O'Shea

Assistant Vice President Corporate Communications, Paula McGinley

Assistant Vice President Loss Control Product and Strategy, Dorothy Doyle

Assistant Vice President Finance Shared Services, Stephanie Radinieri

Assistant Vice President and LOB Manager Workers Compensation, Sashi Aiyathurai

Assistant Vice President Claim Account Management, Sean Faherty

Vice President and Assistant General Counsel, Richard Keough

Regional Vice President, Brian Carey

Vice President and Chief Marketing Officer Individual Life Insurance, Wade Seward

Vice President Market Risk Officer, Christopher Abreu

Vice President and Actuary ERM, John Brady

Assistant Vice President Assistant General Counsel, Stephen Harris

Assistant Vice President and Counsel, Andrew Golden

National Account Manager group Benefits, Kevin Goff

Assistant Vice President Group Benefits Relationship Management, Alison Colli

Assistant Vice President Workers Compensation Product Manager, Matt Lyon

Senior Vice President And General Auditor, Michael Hession

Assistant Vice President UW Small Comm, Kenneth Zygiel

Senior Vice President Procurement, Jahn Surette

Assistant Vice President Napc Strategic Initiatives, Jeffrey Lange

Mbr 1St Vice President, Mayer Goldberger

Assistant Vice President and Senior Risk Manager, Xiangrong Cai

Division Manager Vice President, Robert Larence

Assistant Vice President and Senior Counsel, Jason Kuselias

Assistant Vice President Assistant General Counsel, Liz Steigman

Senior Vice President Sales and Distribution Commercial Markets Division, Mathew Kirk

Assistant Vice President Commercial Markets Technology, Ann Nemphos

Vice President, Renee Johnson

Vice President and Director of Tax Planning, Keith Percy

Assistant Vice President Head of Quantitative Analysis Market Risk Management, Greg Slone

Assistant Vice President Project Management Office, Bill Lombardi

Vice President Claims CIO for Commercial Markets Technology, Michael Lipka

Assistant Vice President Counsel, Brian Fresher

Senior Tax Counsel Assistant Vice President, William Elwell

Vice President and General Cou, Danielle Woolsey

Assistant Vice President Senior Counsel, Cedric Delacruz

Assistant Vice President Finance Business Lead, Steven Paccioretti

Assistant Vice President and Senior Risk Manager, Michael Nguyen

Assistant Vice President and Counsel, Deborah A Millum

Vice President Auto and Property Strategy, Mike Lawlor

Executive Vice President, David Johnson

Assistant Vice President and Assistant Treasurer, Mike Fixer

Senior Vice President, Kevin Harnetiaux

Senior Counsel And Assistant Vice President, Elia Walsh

Assistant Vice President Information Technology Program Management, Steven Hatch

Vice President, Joe Coray

Assistant Vice President And Chief Financial Officer, Steven Penn

Assistant Vice President Counsel, Catherine Gregory

Assistant Vice President Financial Planning and Analysis, Stephen Logan

Regional Vice President Hartford Mutual Funds, Curtis Ranta

Senior Vice President Investor Relations, Richard Costello

Assistant Vice President Information Security, Timothy Carling

Assistant Vice President, Gurunatham Pellakuru

Assistant Vice President Information Technology, Len Fiorilli

Assistant Vice President Product Management, Chad Mirock

Divisional Vice President, Brian Garrette

Assistant Vice President Product Management, Chris DiMartino

Vice President and Assistant General Counsel, Kevin LaFreniere

Assistant Vice President and Counsel, Andrew Daly

Vice President And Actuary, Thomas A Campbell

Assistant Vice President Internal Communication, Kristin Tetreault

Vice President Project Management Office, Ellen Below

Assistant Vice President Middle Market and Specialty Commercial Project Management and Execution, Bob Leyden

Assistant Vice President Product Management, Sean Meehan

Assistant Vice President Information Technology Program Management and Delivery (Middle Market Technology), Michael Boudreau

Assistant Vice President and Actuary, Greg Larsson

Senior Vice President and Controller, Scott Lewis

Assistant Vice President Reinsurance, Salvatore Morelli

Vice President Raw Materials Procurement, Phillip Koch

Senior Vice President Middle Market, Lisa Morgan

Vice President Finance, Thomas Peloquin

Vice President Liquidity and Market Risk Management, Nancy O'Connor

Vice President Eso, Srini Krishnamurthy

Assistant Vice President Information Technology, Carolyn Small

Assistant Vice President Small Commercial Information Technology, Brian Pierz

Vice President Product Management, Brent Radeloff

Assistant Vice President Specialty Business, Steve Basson

Assistant Vice President Infrastructure Solutions, Kathy Kmietek

Assistant Vice President Business Development and Strategic Marketing, Daniel Campany

Vice President Retirement Plans Mid Market, Denise Diana

Assistant Vice President Small Commercial Sales, Kim Stuhr

Assistant Vice President Agency Compensation, Keith Lawler

Vice President Claims Operations, Matthew Scott

Vice President Energy, Ric Pena

Regional Vice President, Henry Dominioni

Regional Senior Vice President, Michael Parker

Assistant Vice President, Pat Wright

Vice President of Information Delivery Services, Rich Filthaut

Assistant Vice President Finance Executive Management, Anthony Horvath

AVP Enterprise Process Improvement, Doug Muzzy
AVP Personal Auto Data Science, Josh Grunin
Senior Vice President, David McElroy
ASSISTANT VICE PRESIDENT SECURITY, Daniel J Lewis
VICE PRESIDENT LIABILITY FIELD CLAIMS, Richard Bowman
RVP CLAIMS GROUP BENEFITS MINN, Christopher Lancaster
Vice President and Actuary, Robert FSA
Assistant Vice President Group Benefits Claim Practices, Sally Monson
Avp Enterprise Strategy and Business Development, Ariadna Khafizova
Treasurer Administrative Assistant, Grace-Lynn Kingsbury
Auditors: Deloitte & Touche LLP

LOCATIONS

HQ: Hartford Financial Services Group Inc.
One Hartford Plaza, Hartford, CT 06155
Phone: 860 547-5000
Web: www.thehartford.com

PRODUCTS/OPERATIONS

2016 Revenue

Earned premiums fees & other

	$ mil.	% of total
Commercial lines	6,651	36
Personal lines	3,898	21
Group benefits	3,223	17
Talcott Resolution (runoff)	1,044	6
Mutual funds	701	4
Property/casualty other products	0	0
Corporate	4	0
Net investment income	2,961	16
Net realized capital gains (losses)	(268)	—
Other revenues	86	0
Total	**18,300**	**100**

COMPETITORS

AIG	Nationwide
Allstate	New York Life
Berkshire Hathaway	Prudential
CNA Financial	State Farm
Liberty Mutual	Travelers Companies
MetLife	Zurich Insurance Group

HISTORICAL FINANCIALS

Company Type: Public

Income Statement

FYE: December 31

	ASSETS ($ mil.)	NET INCOME ($ mil.)	INCOME AS % OF ASSETS	EMPLOYEES
12/16	223,432	896	0.4%	16,900
12/15	228,348	1,682	0.7%	17,400
12/14	245,013	798	0.3%	17,500
12/13	277,884	176	0.1%	18,800
12/12	298,513	(38)	—	22,500
Annual Growth	**(7.0%)**	**—**		**(6.9%)**

2016 Year-End Financials

Debt ratio: 2.07%
Return on equity: 5.17%
Cash ($ mil.): 882
Current ratio: —
Long-term debt ($ mil.): —

No. of shares (mil.): 373
Dividends
Yield: 0.0%
Payout: 37.8%
Market value ($ mil.): 17,819

	STOCK PRICE ($) FY Close	P/E High/Low	PER SHARE ($) Earnings	Dividends	Book Value
12/16	47.65	21 16	2.27	0.86	45.20
12/15	43.46	12 10	3.96	0.78	43.91
12/14	41.69	23 18	1.73	0.66	44.11
12/13	36.23	99 61	0.34	0.50	41.71
12/12	22.44	— —	(0.18)	0.40	51.45
Annual Growth	**20.7%**	**— —**	**—**	**21.1%**	**(3.2%)**

Hartford Life Insurance Co

Auditors: Deloitte & Touche LLP

LOCATIONS

HQ: Hartford Life Insurance Co
One Hartford Plaza, Hartford, CT 06155
Phone: 860 547-5000
Web: www.thehartford.com

HISTORICAL FINANCIALS

Company Type: Public

Income Statement

FYE: December 31

	ASSETS ($ mil.)	NET INCOME ($ mil.)	INCOME AS % OF ASSETS	EMPLOYEES
12/16	170,346	282	0.2%	—
12/15	175,350	500	0.3%	—
12/14	191,775	676	0.4%	—
12/13	202,715	465	0.2%	—
12/12	215,891	554	0.3%	—
Annual Growth	**(5.8%)**	**(15.5%)**	**—**	**—**

2016 Year-End Financials

Debt ratio: —
Return on equity: 3.52%
Cash ($ mil.): 554
Current ratio: —
Long-term debt ($ mil.): —

No. of shares (mil.): 0
Dividends
Yield: —
Payout: —
Market value ($ mil.): —

Hasbro, Inc.

It's all fun and games at Hasbro the #2 toy maker in the US (after Mattel) and the producer of such childhood favorites as G.I. Joe Play-Doh Tonka toys Transformers Mr. Potato Head Nerf balls and My Little Pony. Hasbro has a significant relationship with Disney producing merchandise for the entertainment giant's megabrands including Star Wars Marvel (including Spider-Man Thor and Captain America) and Frozen and other Dreamworks features. Besides toys Hasbro makes board games such as Scrabble Monopoly and Trivial Pursuit as well as trading cards including Magic: The Gathering (through its Wizards of the Coast unit) and Dungeons & Dragons .

Operations

Hasbro divides its products into four brand categories: Franchise Brands Partner Brands Hasbro Gaming and Emerging Brands.

Franchise Brands are the company's core growth drivers and consist of seven brands that offer sustained revenue for the long term: Littlest Pet Shop Magic: the Gathering Monopoly My Little Pony Nerf Play-Doh and Transformers. Franchise Brands account for around half of total revenue.

Partner Brands encompasses Hasbro's licensed brands (principally from Disney) for which it makes toys and games. These include Marvel Star Wars Disney's Descendants Dreamworks' Trolls and Sesame Street.

Hasbro's Gaming portfolio counts such well known board games as Pie Face Connect 4 Elefun & Friends Jenga The Game of Life Operation Scrabble Trivial Pursuit and Twister. The category also includes trading cards and digital games.

Emerging Brands consists of those brands Hasbro believes have potential to become Franchise Brands but need further development and investment. These include Baby Alive Furby Furreal Friends Playskool and Playskool Heroes.

Geographic Reach

More than 50% of Rhode Island-based Hasbro's total sales come from the US and Canada. Europe is its largest international market accounting for nearly two-thirds of overseas sales while emerging markets (including Brazil China and Russia) made up the rest. The toy maker operates in 40-plus countries across the Americas Europe and Asia though almost all of its products were sourced from third-party facilities the Far East (mostly in China).

Sales and Marketing

Hasbro's products are sold through wholesalers distributors chain stores discount stores drug stores mail order houses catalog stores and department stores among other outlets. The company's top three customers are Wal-Mart (which accounts for nearly 20% of sales) Toys "R" Us (nearly 10%) and Target (nearly 10%). In the US around 60% of the toy maker's revenue is derived from these top three chains.

Hasbro markets products via television and digital devices (including Netflix and iTunes). It also showcases certain new products at the American International Toy Fair held each February in New York City.

Financial Performance

Hasbro's sales and profits have been steadily rising in recent years as demand for toys (especially preschool brands) has been buoyed by strong economic and population growth in North America and abroad.

In fiscal 2016 sales grew a further 13% to $5.0 billion amid growth in almost all segments and geographies. Particular highlights include 15% growth in the US and Canada 9% growth in Gaming and 28% growth in Partner Brands. The important Franchise Brands segment recorded 2% growth. The only product category to decline was Preschool which fell by $7.6 million or about 1%.

Net income grew 22% to $551.4 million due to higher revenue and improved margins partially offset by a $32.9 million impairment charge relating to Hasbro's investment in Backflip.

Cash from operations increased 40% to $774.9 million due to higher net income and changes in impairment deferred income taxes and accounts receivable.

Strategy

Hasbro recently extended its Marvel and Star Wars licenses when it signed deals for all properties through 2020. The move has paid off big: the two franchises continue to generate box office-topping sales figures with the annual December Star Wars release now all but assured to be that year's highest-grossing feature. The success of Disney's motion picture IPs has driven consistent year-on-year growth in Hasbro's Partner Brands segment.

Hasbro has also entirely revised its advertising approach. The company de-emphasised its advertising stalwart — television — in favor of digital channels. The social media platforms of Facebook Instagram Twitter and others have helped Hasbro create communities of millions of fans and subscribers. Additionally in 2016 Hasbro increased its ownership stake in mobile game maker Backflip from 70% to 100% to further increase its brand touchpoints; and has teamed up with gaming titan Electronic Arts to create digital versions of Monopoly Scrabble and Yahtzee. Hasbro has also pivoted away from its famous mantra of "to sell to the parents market to the kids" — the wealth of data produced by digital showed that millennials now entering parenthood were likely to buy toys they themselves used as kids.

Mergers and Acquisitions

In 2016 Hasbro acquired Dublin-based Boulder Media an animation company. Hasbro lacked an in-house cartoon creator; the acquisition will allow the company to expand its animation and storytelling.

In 2017 Hasbro increased its ownership in mobile games company Backflip from 70% to 100%.

HISTORY

Henry and Helal Hassenfeld formed Hassenfeld Brothers in Pawtucket Rhode Island in 1923 to distribute fabric remnants. By 1926 the company was manufacturing fabric-covered pencil boxes and shortly thereafter pencils.

Hassenfeld Brothers branched into the toy industry during the 1940s by introducing toy nurse and doctor kits. The company's toy division was the first to use TV to promote a toy product (Mr. Potato Head in 1952).

Expansion continued in the mid-1960s with the introduction of the G.I. Joe doll which quickly became its primary toy line. Hassenfeld Brothers went public in 1968 and changed its name to Hasbro Industries. It bought Romper Room (TV productions) the next year.

In the 1970s the toy and pencil divisions led by different family members disagreed over the company's finances future direction and leadership. The dispute caused the company to split in 1980. The toy division continued to operate under the Hasbro name; the pencil division (Empire Pencil Corporation in Shelbyville Tennessee led by Harold Hassenfeld) became a separate corporation.

EXECUTIVES

Chairman and CEO, Brian D. Goldner, age 54, $1,300,000 total compensation
President Worldwide Marketing and Brand Development, Duncan J. Billing, age 59, $545,910 total compensation
EVP and Chief Content Officer, Stephen J. Davis, age 55
President, Johnathan A. (John) Frascotti, age 56, $772,308 total compensation
President Wizards of the Coast, Chris Cocks
EVP and CFO, Deborah M. (Deb) Thomas, age 53, $690,385 total compensation
EVP and Chief Human Resources Officer, Dolph Johnson
EVP Chief Legal Officer and Secretary, Barbara Finigan, age 56
EVP and Chief Commercial Officer, Wiebe Tinga, age 56, $592,787 total compensation
EVP Global Operations, Tom Courtney
Vice President Of Marketing, Jerry Perez
Senior Vice President of Hasbro Gaming, Jonathan Berkowitz
Senior Vice President and CIO, Steve Zoltick
Vice President Finance, Joanne Haworth
Vice President Tax, Edward Houde

Senior Vice President, Arthur Kazianis
Vice President Business Development, Ted Fischer
Vice President, David Fergenbaum
Vice President Global Planning, Ramesh Murthy
Vice President Technical Services, Jack Popp
Vice President of Development Services, Marc Millspaugh
Vice President Finance, Paul Alexander
Senior Vice President Global Brand Finance, David Holmes
Vice President of Design, Brian Wilk
Vice President Marketing and Sales, Oscar Miranda
Vice President Product Design, John Reale
Executive Vice President of Sales and Marketing, Julie Duffy
Vice President Benefits And Hris, Briana Sullivan
Vice President Legal, Lisa Fasoldt
Vice President, Kathrin Belliveau
Executive Vice President of Sales and Marketing, Jackie Fradin
Vice President of Design and Development, Daizo Uehara
Vice President Finance and Operations, Melanie Renaud
Vice President of Global Brand Marketing and Strategy, Greg Lombardo
VICE PRESIDENT MARKETING, Greg Ferguson
NATIONAL ACCOUNT MANAGER, Courtney I Chahal
Secretary, Pauline Casey
ABM New Business Development and Strategy Health and Wellness, Tom Canterino
Auditors: KPMG LLP

LOCATIONS

HQ: Hasbro, Inc.
   1027 Newport Avenue, Pawtucket, RI 02861
Phone: 401 431-8697
Web: www.hasbro.com

2016 Sales

	$ mil.	% of total
US & Canada	2,559	51
International	2,194	44
Entertainment & licensing	265	5
Global operations	0	-
Total	**5,019**	**100**

PRODUCTS/OPERATIONS

2016 Sales

	$ mil.	% of total
Boys	1,849	37
Games	1,387	27
Girls	1,193	24
Preschool	589	12
Total	**5,019**	**100**

Selected Product Categories

Action Battling
Action Figures & Collectibles
Apparel
Arts & Crafts
Books & Comics
Creative & Pretend Play
Dolls & Plush
Electronic Toys & Games
Games
Parts & Refills
Party Supplies
Sports & Outdoor Play
Vehicles

Selected BrandsHASBRO
GAMINGClueMonopolyScrabbleTwisterYahtzee
GIRLSNerf RebelleMy Little PonyMy Little Pony
Equestria GirlsLittlest Pet ShopFurby
BOYSNerfBeybladeStar WarsB-
DamanTransformersPRESCHOOLPlay-

DohPlayskoolFurReal FriendsBaby AliveElefun and F

COMPETITORS

Build-A-Bear	Playmates Toys
Cartoon Network	Playmobil
Enesco	Poof-Slinky
Graco Children's	RC2 Corporation
Products	Radio Flyer
JAKKS Pacific	Sanrio
LEGO	Simba Dickie Group
LeapFrog	Smoby
MGA Entertainment	Spin Master
Marvel Entertainment	TakaraTomy
Mattel	Toy Quest
Nakajima USA	Ty
Namco Bandai	VTech Holdings
Nickelodeon	WHAM-O
Ohio Art	

HISTORICAL FINANCIALS

Company Type: Public

Income Statement   FYE: December 25

	REVENUE ($ mil.)	NET INCOME ($ mil.)	NET PROFIT MARGIN	EMPLOYEES
12/16	5,019	551	11.0%	5,400
12/15	4,447	451	10.2%	5,000
12/14	4,277	415	9.7%	5,200
12/13	4,082	286	7.0%	5,000
12/12	4,088	336	8.2%	5,500
Annual Growth	**5.3%**	**13.2%**	**—**	**(0.5%)**

2016 Year-End Financials

Debt ratio: 33.80%
Return on equity: 31.36%
Cash ($ mil.): 1,282
Current ratio: 1.99
Long-term debt ($ mil.): 1,198

No. of shares (mil.): 124
Dividends
   Yield: 0.0%
   Payout: 45.8%
Market value ($ mil.): 9,755

	STOCK PRICE ($) FY Close	P/E High/Low	PER SHARE ($) Earnings	Dividends	Book Value
12/16	78.36	20 15	4.34	1.99	14.96
12/15	67.62	23 14	3.57	1.81	13.33
12/14	55.54	18 15	3.20	1.69	11.77
12/13	54.40	25 16	2.17	1.20	12.84
12/12	35.31	15 12	2.55	1.74	11.69
Annual Growth	**22.1%**	**— —**	**14.2%**	**3.4%**	**6.4%**

HCA Healthcare Inc

HCA dispenses TLC for a profit. HCA Healthcare (formerly HCA Holdings) through its HCA Inc. (Hospital Corporation of America) unit operates more than 170 hospitals — mostly acute care centers as well as three psychiatric facilities and one rehabilitation hospital — located in the US and UK. It also runs about 120 ambulatory surgery centers — as well as cancer treatment urgent care and outpatient rehab centers — that form health care networks in many of the communities it serves. In total its hospitals are home to some 44300 beds. HCA's facilities are located in 20 states; roughly half of its hospitals are in Florida and Texas. The HCA International unit operates the company's hospitals and clinics in the UK.

HISTORY

In 1987 Dallas lawyer Rick Scott and Fort Worth Texas financier Richard Rainwater founded Columbia Hospital Corp. to buy two hospitals in El Paso Texas. The partners eventually sold 40% of the hospitals to local doctors hoping that ownership would motivate physicians to increase productivity and efficiency.

The company entered the Miami market the next year and by 1990 had four hospitals. After merging with Smith Laboratories that year Columbia went public and then acquired Sutter Laboratories (orthopedic products). By the end of 1990 it had 11 hospitals.

Columbia moved into Florida in 1992 with the purchase of several hospitals and facilities. The next year it acquired Galen Health Care which operated 73 hospitals and had been spun off from health plan operator Humana earlier in the year. The merger thrust the hospital chain into about 15 new markets.

Columbia bought Hospital Corporation of America (HCA) in 1994. Thomas Frist his son Thomas Frist Jr. and Jack Massey (former owner of Kentucky Fried Chicken now part of TRICON) founded HCA in Nashville Tennessee in 1968. By 1973 the company had grown to 50 hospitals.

Meanwhile the medical industry was changing — insurers Medicare and Medicaid began scrutinizing payment procedures while the growth of HMOs (which aimed to restrict hospital admissions) cut hospital occupancy rates. HCA began paring operations in the late 1980s selling more than 100 hospitals. In 1989 the younger Frist led a $5.1 billion leveraged buyout of the company. He sold more assets and in 1992 took HCA public again but losses and a tumbling stock price made it a takeover target.

Later in 1994 the newly christened Columbia/HCA acquired the US's largest operator of outpatient surgery centers Dallas-based Medical Care America. A year later it bought 117-hospital HealthTrust a 1987 offshoot of HCA. Columbia/HCA was unstoppable in 1996 with some 150 acquisitions.

In 1997 the government began investigating the company's business practices. After executive indictments the company fired Scott and several other top officers. Frist Jr. became chairman and CEO pledging to shrink the company and tone down its aggressive approach. Columbia/HCA sold its home care business more than 100 of its less-desirable hospitals and almost all the operations of Value Health a pharmacy benefits and behavioral health care management firm it had recently bought.

The trimming continued in 1998: The company sold nearly three dozen outpatient surgery centers and more than a dozen hospitals. That year Columbia/HCA sued former financial executive Samuel Greco and several vendors accusing them of defrauding the company of several million dollars. In 1999 it spun off regional operators LifePoint Health (23 facilities) and Triad Hospitals (34) to trim its holdings. The next year it sold some 120 medical buildings to MedCap Properties a joint venture formed with First Union Capital Partners.

During 2000 the company bought out partner Sun Life and Provincial Holdings' (now AXA UK) interest in several London hospitals and bought three hospitals there from St. Martins Healthcare. It also renamed itself HCA - The Healthcare Company. While continuing a strategy of consolidating and streamlining operations (and resolving remaining legal matters) in 2001 the company streamlined its name even further to simply HCA Inc.

By 2002 HCA began shaking off its shaky past. Profits stabilized allowing it to reinvest millions into modernizing facilities and equipment at its hospitals and surgery centers. It entered the Kansas City market in 2003 by acquiring a local hospital chain.

The company finally closed the books during 2003 on the numerous government investigations launched in 1997 into its business practices. In the five years leading up to 2003 HCA paid out some $2 billion in settlements for Medicare fraud and other claims. These settlements took their toll on the firm's bottom line.

To expand its outpatient services HCA beginning in 2004 began purchasing imaging centers. In early 2005 the firm acquired Tampa Florida's Total I Imaging and its five centers that offer diagnostic services. In 2005 HCA's iMage1 Network part of HCA's outpatient services group bought more than a handful of imaging centers located in the Tampa Florida area from Ultra Open MRI Corp.

The devastating hurricane season of 2005 hit HCA's operations hard as they are concentrated in the southern US. When Hurricane Katrina hit HCA evacuated its Tulane University Hospital and Clinic (it reopened in early 2006). Hurricane Rita spurred HCA to evacuate three Houston-area hospitals (Mainland Medical Center in Texas City East Houston Regional Medical Center in Houston and Clear Lake Regional Medical Center in Webster) and partially evacuate two others.

In 2006 a group of investors — including Thomas Frist Jr. as well as Bain Capital Kohlberg Kravis Roberts and the private equity arm of Merrill Lynch— took HCA private in a $30 billion leveraged buyout. In 2009 Richard Bracken became CEO of the company.

The hospital operator maintained its private status for several years until it once again went public in 2011 as a way to pay off some debt.

EXECUTIVES

Chairman and CEO, R. Milton Johnson, age 60, $1,391,667 total compensation
President and COO, Samuel N. (Sam) Hazen, age 57, $995,834 total compensation
President Service Line and Operations Integration, A. Bruce Moore, age 57, $574,989 total compensation
EVP and CFO, William B. (Bill) Rutherford, age 53, $793,750 total compensation
President American Group, Jon M. Foster, age 55, $762,781 total compensation
President Clinical Services and Chief Medical Officer, Jonathan B. (Jon) Perlin, age 56, $795,833 total compensation
President National Group, Charles J. (Chuck) Hall, age 64, $797,088 total compensation
SVP Marketing and Corporate Affairs, Jana J. Davis, age 58
SVP and CIO, P. Martin (Marty) Paslick, age 57
President Physician Services Group, Michael S. Cuffe, age 51
SVP and Chief Nursing Officer, Jane D. Englebright, age 58
Director Of Physical Therapy Physical Therapy Director, Angie Brown
Physical Therapy Director, Mary B Peterson
Vice President, Valencia Hooper
Assistant Vice President Risk Management, Joseph Haase
Vice President, Michael Marotta
Director Of Radiology Services, Phyllis Barker
Assistant Vice President Technical Services, Bill Fitzgerald
Assistant Vice President Development, Bobby Stokes
Assistant Vice President Owned Hospitals, Ron Redding
Vice President, Kim F Hatley
Vice President, Sam Coulter
Director Of Pharmacy, Ron Nagata
Assistant Vice President Information Technology Strategy and Planning, David Catino
Assistant Vice President Clinical Systems, Frank Wolf
Vice President Human Resources Operations Support, Yonnie Chesley
Vice President Human Resources Midwest Division, Rich Lowe
Vice President Information Technology, Cyndi Talley
Auditors: Ernst & Young LLP

LOCATIONS

HQ: HCA Healthcare Inc
One Park Plaza, Nashville, TN 37203
Phone: 615 344-9551
Web: www.hcahealthcare.com

2016 Locations

	No.
US	
Florida	43
Texas	40
Tennessee	13
Virginia	11
Utah	8
Colorado	7
Georgia	7
Missouri	5
California	5
Kansas	4
Louisiana	4
Nevada	3
South Carolina	3
Idaho	2
Kentucky	2
New Hampshire	2
Oklahoma	2
Alaska	1
Indiana	1
Mississippi	1
UK	6
Total	**168**

Selected US Facilities

Alaska
  Alaska Regional Hospital (Anchorage)
California
  Good Samaritan Hospital (San Jose)
  Los Robles Medical Center (Thousand Oaks)
  Regional Medical Center of San Jose
  Riverside Community Hospital
  West Hills Hospital & Medical Center
Colorado
  Centrum Surgical Center (Greenwood Village)
  Medical Center of Aurora
  North Suburban Medical Center (Thornton)
  Presbyterian/St. Luke's Medical Center (Denver)
  Rose Medical Center (Denver)
  Sky Ridge Medical Center (Lone Tree)
  Spalding Rehabilitation Hospital (Aurora)
  Swedish Medical Center (Englewood)
Florida
  Aventura Hospital and Medical Center
  Blake Medical Center (Bradenton)
  Brandon Regional Hospital
  Capital Regional Medical Center (Tallahassee)
  Central Florida Regional Hospital (Sanford)
  Columbia Hospital (West Palm Beach)
  Doctors Hospital of Sarasota
  Edward White Hospital (St. Petersburg)
  Fawcett Memorial Hospital (Port Charlotte)
  Gulf Coast Medical Center (Panama City)
  JFK Medical Center (Atlantis)
  Kendall Regional Medical Center (Miami)
  Lake City Medical Center
  Largo Medical Center
  Memorial Hospital Jacksonville
  Memorial Hospital of Tampa
  North Florida Regional Medical Center (Gainesville)
  Northwest Medical Center (Margate)
  Ocala Regional Medical Center
  Osceola Regional Medical Center (Kissimmee)
  Palms of Pasadena Hospital (St. Petersburg)
  Palms West Hospital (Loxahatchee)
  South Bay Hospital (Sun City Center)
  St. Lucie Medical Center (Port St. Lucie)
  Town and Country Hospital (Tampa)

Twin Cities Hospital (Niceville)
University Hospital and Medical Center (Tamarac)
West Florida Hospital (Pensacola)
Westside Regional Medical Center (Plantation)
Georgia
Atlanta Outpatient Surgery Center (Atlanta)
Cartersville Medical Center
Coliseum Medical Centers (Macon)
Doctors Hospital (Augusta)
Eastside Medical Center (Snellville)
Fairview Park Hospital (Dublin)
Northlake Surgical Center (Tucker)
Polk Medical Center (Cedartown)
Redmond Regional Medical Center (Rome)
Idaho
Eastern Idaho Regional Medical Center (Idaho Falls)
West Valley Medical Center (Caldwell)
Indiana
Terre Haute Regional Hospital
Kansas
Allen County Hospital (Iola)
Galichia Heart Hospital (Wichita)
Menorah Medical Center (Overland Park)
Overland Park Regional Medical Center
Wesley Medical Center (Wichita)
Kentucky
Frankfort Regional Medical Center
Greenview Regional Hospital (Bowling Green)
Louisiana
Dauterive Hospital (New Iberia)
Lafayette Surgicare
Lakeview Regional Medical Center (Covington)
Rapides Regional Medical Center (Alexandria)
Tulane Medical Center (Metarie)
Tulane University Hospital & Clinic (New Orleans)
Women's & Children's Hospital (Lafayette)
Mississippi
Garden Park Medical Center (Gulfport)
Missouri
Centerpoint Medical Center (Independence)
Lafayette Regional Health Center (Lexington)
Lee's Summit Hospital
Research Medical Center (Kansas City)
Research Psychiatric Center (Kansas City)
Nevada
Flamingo Surgery Center (Las Vegas)
MountainView Hospital (Las Vegas)
Southern Hills Hospital and Medical Center (Las Vegas)
Sunrise Hospital and Medical Center (Las Vegas)
New Hampshire
Parkland Medical Center (Derry)
Portsmouth Regional Hospital
Salem Surgery Center
Oklahoma
Edmond Medical Center
Oklahoma Surgicare (Oklahoma City)
Oklahoma University Medical Center (Oklahoma City)
South Carolina
Colleton Medical Cemter (Walterboro)
Grand Dunes Surgery Center (Myrtle Beach)
Grand Strand Regional Medical Center (Myrtle Beach)
Summerville Medical Center
Trident Regional Medical Center (Charleston)
Tennessee
Centennial Medical Center (Nashville)
Hendersonville Medical Center
Horizon Medical Center (Dickson)
Parkridge East Hospital (Chattanooga)
Parkridge Valley Hospital (Chattanooga)
Skyline Medical Center (Nashville)
StoneCrest Medical Center (Smyrna)
Summit Medical Center (Hermitage)
Texas
Bailey Square Surgery Center (Austin)
Bayshore Medical Center (Pasadena)
Clear Lake Regional Medical Center (Webster)
Conroe Regional Medical Center
Corpus Christi Medical Center
Del Sol Medical Center (El Paso)
Denton Regional Medical Center
Green Oaks Hospital (Dallas)
Kingwood Medical Center
Las Colinas Medical Center (Irving)
Mainland Medical Center (Texas City)
Medical Center of Arlington
Medical Center of Lewisville
Medical Center of McKinney
Medical Center of Plano
Medical City Dallas Hospital
Methodist Hospital (San Antonio)

Metropolitan Methodist Hospital (San Antonio)
North Austin Medical Center
North Hills Hospital (North Richland Hills)
Plaza Medical Center of Fort Worth
Rio Grande Regional Hospital (McAllen)
Round Rock Medical Center
South Austin Hospital
St. David's Medical Center (Austin)
Valley Regional Medical Center (Brownsville)
West Houston Medical Center
Woman's Hospital of Texas (Houston)
Utah
Brigham City Community Hospital
Lakeview Hospital (Bountiful)
Ogden Regional Medical Center
St. Mark's Hospital (Salt Lake City)
Timpanogos Regional Hospital (Orem)
Virginia
CJW Medical Center (Richmond)
Dominion Hospital (Falls Church)
Henrico Doctors' Hospital (Richmond)
John Randolph Medical Center
LewisGale Medical Center (Salem)
Pulaski Community Hospital
Reston Hospital Center
Spotsylvania Regional Medical Center (Fredricksburg)

Selected International Facilities
UK
Harley Street Clinic (London)
Lister Hospital (London)
London Bridge Hospital (London)
The Portland Hospital for Women and Children (London)
Princess Grace Hospital (London)
The Wellington Hospital (London)

PRODUCTS/OPERATIONS

2016 Revenue

	$ mil.	% of total
Payer sources		
Managed care & other insurers	23,441	52
Medicare	8,895	20
Managed Medicare	4,355	10
Managed Medicaid	2,478	5
Medicaid	1,597	4
International (managed care & other insurers)	1,195	3
Uninsured	1,135	2
Other	1,651	4
Provisions for doubtful accounts)	(3257)	-
Total	**41,490**	**100**

2016 Revenues

	$ mil.	% of total
National Group	19,845	48
American Group	19,648	47
Corporate & other	1,997	5
Total	**41,490**	**100**

COMPETITORS

Adventist Health System Sunbelt Healthcare
Adventist Health System West
Ascension Health
Banner Health
CHRISTUS Health
Catholic Health Initiatives
Children's Medical Center of Dallas
Community Health Systems
HealthSouth
LifePoint Health
SSM Health Care
Saint Thomas Midtown Hospital
Sutter Health
Tenet Healthcare
Texas Health Resources
Trinity Health (Novi)
United Surgical Partners
Universal Health Services

HISTORICAL FINANCIALS
Company Type: Public

Income Statement
FYE: December 31

	REVENUE ($ mil.)	NET INCOME ($ mil.)	NET PROFIT MARGIN	EMPLOYEES
12/16	41,490	2,890	7.0%	241,000
12/15	39,678	2,129	5.4%	233,000
12/14	36,918	1,875	5.1%	225,000
12/13	34,182	1,556	4.6%	215,000
12/12	33,013	1,605	4.9%	204,000
Annual Growth	5.9%	15.8%	—	4.3%

2016 Year-End Financials

Debt ratio: 92.94%
Return on equity: ***,***.**%
Cash ($ mil.): 646
Current ratio: 1.56
Long-term debt ($ mil.): 31,160

No. of shares (mil.): 370
Dividends
  Yield: —
  Payout: —
Market value ($ mil.): 27,427

	STOCK PRICE ($) FY Close	P/E High/Low		PER SHARE ($) Earnings	Dividends	Book Value
12/16	74.02	11	8	7.30	0.00	(19.71)
12/15	67.63	18	13	4.99	0.00	(19.06)
12/14	73.39	17	11	4.16	0.00	(18.77)
12/13	47.71	14	9	3.37	0.00	(18.81)
12/12	30.17	9	6	3.49	6.50	(21.80)
Annual Growth	25.2%	—	—	20.3%	—	—

HD Supply Holdings Inc

Do-it-yourselfers shop Home Depot or Lowe's but many pros do business at HD Supply. One of the largest industrial distributors in North America (and formerly the professional services division of Home Depot) HD Supply provides building materials tools and installation services to professionals in the specialty construction; maintenance repair and operations (MRO); and infrastructure markets through about 500 locations across 48 US states and six Canadian provinces. After selling parts of its business HD Supply operates through two units: HD Supply Facilities Maintenance and Construction & Industrial.

Operations

HD Supply had operated through three segment: Facilities Maintenance (nearly 40% of revenue) Waterworks (more than a third of revenue); and Construction & Industrial (about 30% of revenue). In 2017 however it sold the Waterworks business.

Top segment Facilities Maintenance distributes maintenance repair and operations (MRO) products provides value-add services and fabricates custom products to multifamily hospitality healthcare and institutional facilities. Within the segment products include electrical and lighting items plumbing HVAC products appliances janitorial supplies hardware kitchen and bath cabinets window coverings textiles and guest amenities and healthcare maintenance.

The Construction & Industrial segment distributes specialized hardware tools engineered materials and safety products to non-residential and residential contractors. It also offers services that range from pre-bid assistance and product submissions to engineering and tool repair. The unit also includes Home Improvement Solutions which offers light remodeling and construction supplies electrical equipment and fixtures to small remodeling contractors and trade professionals through local retail outlets.

The company's Waterworks segment which it sold to a private investment firm in 2017 focused on water distribution and wastewater transmission products. Its customer were contractors and municipalities in the water and wastewater industries for non-residential and residential uses. The unit supplied more than a third of HD Supply?s revenue in 2016.

Geographic Reach

HD Supply primarily operates its business in the US but extends its reach into Canada through its Facilities Maintenance segment. The company operates through about 550 locations across 48 US states and six Canadian provinces.

Sales and Marketing

HD Supply which boasts 14000 associates and carries a broad range of products and offers value-added services serves some 500000 professional customers. As part of its services HD Supply provides jobsite delivery will call or direct-ship of its products as well as diversified logistics. It ships products through an internal fleet or to a lesser extent by third-party carriers.

The company markets its products and services through a range of sales channels including through its outside and inside sales forces call centers various business unit websites and branch-supported direct marketing programs that utilize market-tailored product catalogs.

Financial Performance

HD Supply?s revenue rose $316 million in 2016 (ended January 2017) from 2015 (ended January 2016) as each segment reported higher sales boosted by growth initiatives and greater market volume. Construction & Industrial posted the biggest increase of 7% for the year driven by the impact of its Managed Sales Approach which uses analysis tools and sales management to drive sales at regional levels. It also benefited from improvement in non-residential and residential housing markets.

The company?s net income tumbled about 87% to $196 million in 2016 from 2015 when profit swelled from a big tax benefit.

Cash flow from operations rose to $513 million in 2016 from $422 million in 2015. The company paid less cash interest in 2016 than in 2015.

Strategy

HD Supply's strategy includes entering new markets and expanding its product lines to grow its customer base. It also seeks to streamline and upgrade its supply chain processes and technological capabilities. Aside from its focus on organic growth HD Supply works to expand its business by seeking tuck-in acquisitions in core and adjacent markets to supplement its product set geographic footprint and other capabilities.

To boost profitability and free up resources HD Supply has also strategically sold off its non-core business lines in recent years as well as combined some units. The company got closer to its core in 2017 with the sale of the Waterworks business a distributor of water sewer storm and fire protection products to Clayton Dubilier & Rice a private investment firm for about $2.5 billion in cash. The deal simplifies HD Supply?s business mix and focus and it helps pay down debt. The unit provided more than a third of HD Supply?s sales.

In late 2016 the company combined the Home Improvement Solutions business with the Construction & Industrial business. Also in 2016 HD Supply sold its Interior Solutions business.

In October 2015 HD Supply sold its Power Solutions business to Anixter for $825 million. Also in 2015 HD Supply sold its Hardware Solutions business which sold fasteners business hardware plumbing and other supplies to Home Depot for $198 million.

HISTORY

HD Supply went public in 2013. It aimed to raise $1 billion in the IPO but it walked away with $957 million which would be used to pay down debt.

In mid-2013 it opened a 50000-sq.-ft. facility in Secaucus New Jersey as well as a distribution center in Calera Alabama to improve its local support for customers in the Southeast including Alabama Tennessee Mississippi Louisiana and the Florida panhandle.

In 2012 the company's HD Supply Waterworks division purchased RAMSCO a waterworks distributor specializing in water sanitary and storm sewer materials and services. The addition of RAMSCO which is based in New York State extended Waterworks' service to customers in the US Northeast.

Also in 2012 HD Supply purchased Water Products of Oklahoma Arkansas Water Products and Municipal Water Works Supply for $48 million. Additionally it bought Georgia-based Peachtree Business Products (a specialist in customizable business and property marketing supplies serving residential and commercial property managers medical facilities schools and universities churches and funeral homes) for $196 million.

HD Supply was formed in 1997 when Home Depot acquired Maintenance Warehouse. Before going public in 2013 it was owned by three of the world's leading private equity firms: Bain Capital The Carlyle Group and Clayton Dubilier & Rice each held about a 19% stake in the company.

EXECUTIVES

Chairman and CEO, Joseph J. (Joe) DeAngelo, age 55, $1,000,000 total compensation
Executive President HD Supply and President HD Supply Construction and Industrial; White Cap, John A. Stegeman, age 56, $788,677 total compensation
President HD Supply Waterworks, Stephen O. (Steve) LeClair, age 48, $442,280 total compensation
SVP CFO and Chief Administrative Officer, Evan J. Levitt, age 47, $461,778 total compensation
COO HD Supply Waterworks, Brad Cowles
President and CEO HD Supply Facilities Maintenance, William P. (Will) Stengel, age 39
Auditors: PricewaterhouseCoopers LLP

LOCATIONS

HQ: HD Supply Holdings Inc
3100 Cumberland Boulevard, Suite 1480, Atlanta, GA 30339
Phone: 770 852-9000
Web: www.hdsupply.com

PRODUCTS/OPERATIONS

2016 Sales

	% of total
Facilities maintenance	37
Waterworks	35
Construction & Industrial;White Cap	28
Corporate & others	0
Total	**100**

Selected Businesses

Creative Touch Interiors
HD Supply Canada
HD Supply Crown Bolt
HD Supply Electrical
HD Supply Industrial PVF
HD Supply Facilities Maintenance
HD Supply Repair & Remodel
HD Supply Utilities
HD Supply Waterworks
HD Supply White Cap

Selected Products:

WATERWORKS:
Pipe - Water Sewer Storm PVC Ductile iron Concrete HDPE
Valves
Hydrants
Fittings
Restraints
FACILITIES MAINTENANCE:
Plumbing
HVAC
Electrical
Lighting
Appliances
CONSTRUCTION & INDUSTRIAL - WHITE CAP:
Concrete additives and cementitious products
Decorative and stamped concrete accessories
Forming lumber
Rebar and wire mesh
3M fire protection products
Drywall accessories
HOME IMPROVEMENT SOLUTIONS:
Cabinets
Cleaning Supplies
Countertops
Doors
Fencing
Flooring

COMPETITORS

84 Lumber
ABC Supply
BMC Stock
BlueLinx
Builders FirstSource
Fastenal
Ferguson Enterprises
Guardian Building Products Distribution
MSC Industrial Direct
PrimeSource Building
Rexel Inc.
W.W. Grainger
Watsco
Wesco
WinWholesale

HISTORICAL FINANCIALS

Company Type: Public

Income Statement

FYE: January 29

	REVENUE ($ mil.)	NET INCOME ($ mil.)	NET PROFIT MARGIN	EMPLOYEES
01/17	7,439	196	2.6%	14,000
01/16*	7,388	1,472	19.9%	14,000
02/15	8,882	3	0.0%	15,000
02/14	8,487	(218)	—	15,500
02/13	8,035	(1,179)	—	15,000
Annual Growth	(1.9%)	—	—	(1.7%)

*Fiscal year change

2017 Year-End Financials

Debt ratio: 66.80%
Return on equity: 23.07%
Cash ($ mil.): 75
Current ratio: 2.19
Long-term debt ($ mil.): 3,798

No. of shares (mil.): 201
Dividends
  Yield: —
  Payout: —
Market value ($ mil.): 8,598

	STOCK PRICE ($) FY Close	P/E High/Low		PER SHARE ($) Earnings	Dividends	Book Value
01/17	42.69	45	23	0.97	0.00	4.77
01/16*	26.27	5	3	7.31	0.00	3.72
02/15	28.83	1509	1045	0.02	0.00	(3.88)
02/14	21.47	—		(1.31)	0.00	(3.97)
Annual Growth	18.7%			—	—	—

*Fiscal year change

HEALTHPARTNERS, INC.

Auditors: KPMG LLP MINNEAPOLIS MN

LOCATIONS

HQ: HEALTHPARTNERS, INC.
8170 33RD AVE S, BLOOMINGTON, MN 554254516
Phone: 952 883-6000

HISTORICAL FINANCIALS

Company Type: Private

Income Statement

	REVENUE ($ mil.)	NET INCOME ($ mil.)	NET PROFIT MARGIN	EMPLOYEES
12/13	5,223	365	7.0%	22,000
12/97	1,247	(2)	—	—
12/96	1,178	9	0.8%	—
12/95	0	0	—	—
Annual Growth	—	—	—	—

2013 Year-End Financials

Debt ratio: ——
Return on equity: 7.00%
Cash ($ mil.): 546
Current ratio: 1.30
Long-term debt ($ mil.): —

Dividends
Yield: —
Payout: —
Market value ($ mil.): —

Heartland Financial USA, Inc. (Dubuque, IA)

Heartland Financial USA brings heart-felt community banking to nation's heartland. The $5.9 billion multi-bank holding company owns flagship subsidiary Dubuque Bank & Trust and nine other banks that together operate more than 75 branches in 55-plus communities in the Midwest and Southwest US. In addition to standard deposit loan and mortgage services the banks also offer retirement wealth management trust insurance and investment services including socially responsible investing. Heartland Financial USA also owns consumer lender Citizens Finance which has about a dozen offices in Illinois Iowa and Wisconsin.

Operations

Heartland operates two main segments: Community and Other Banking and Retail Mortgage Banking. The Community and Other Banking business generates revenue from interest earned on loans and investment securities and fees from deposit services. Its Retail Mortgage Banking collects revenue from interest from mortgage loans held for sale gains on sales of loans on the secondary market the servicing of mortgage loans for investors and loan origination fee income.

Approximately 70% of Heartland Financial's loan portfolio comes from commercial loans and mortgages but in keeping with the bank's Midwestern identity it also makes agricultural residential mortgage and consumer loans.

Heartland Financial USA's subsidiaries include: Dubuque Bank and Trust Company Galena State Bank & Trust Co. Illinois Bank & Trust Wisconsin Bank & Trust Morrill & Janes Bank and Trust New Mexico Bank & Trust Arizona Bank & Trust. It also owns multi-line insurance company DB&T

Insurance Inc. and runs the community development company DB&T Community Development Corp.

Geographic Reach

Heartland operates more than 75 branches in local communities in Arizona Colorado Illinois Iowa Kansas Montana Minnesota Missouri New Mexico and Wisconsin. It also has loan production offices in California Idaho Nevada North Dakota Oregon Washington and Wyoming. About 40% of the company's assets are based in Western markets.

Sales and Marketing

Heartland offers its banking services to businesses public sector and non-profit entities and individuals. In total the bank serves some 120000 business and consumer households.

Heartland spent $5.52 million on advertising in 2014 about 4% more than it spent in 2013.

Financial Performance

Heartland's revenue was up for a second straight year jumping by 10% to $319.3 million in 2014. The boost was mostly driven by interest income from loan growth and additional investment security income as the company increased its earning assets by 18% during the year. The bank's non-interest income sources however lagged as the bank netted fewer gains on its loans held for sale and its investment security sales.

The company's net income also rose in 2014 by 14% to $41.9 million rebounding from last year's dip thanks to higher revenue and because it paid lower interest on its deposits.

Operations provided $80.4 million or 40% less cash than in 2013 mostly as the bank collected less in proceeds from the net sales of its loans-held-for-sale and because it used more cash toward its prepaid expenses.

Strategy

Heartland Financial's main growth strategy is to expand its presence in the West with the goal of making the region home to half of its total assets and balancing growth in those markets with the stability of the Midwest. In line with this the bank seeks to expand its subsidiaries through acquisitions and grow its customer base organically in its existing markets.

Consistent with this strategy in early 2015 Heartland purchased the Community Banc-Corp of Sheboygan Inc. (the parent company of Community Bank & Trust) which added 10 branches in Wisconsin and some $410 million worth of loan assets. In 2013 Heartland purchased Morrill Bancshares Inc. along with its Morrill & Janes Bank and Trust Company subsidiary effectively expanding its reach into Kansas and growing its loan assets and deposits by nearly $378 million and $665 million respectively. That year Heartland also bought Freedom Bank and its three branches which expanded its reach into Illinois and enriched its service offerings to business agri-business and consumer banking clients.

Mergers and Acquisitions

In January 2015 Heartland acquired the Community Banc-Corp of Sheboygan Inc. along with all 10 of its Community Bank & Trust branches along with $530.4 million worth of assets $410 million in loans and $429 million in deposits; in exchange for $52 million in an all-stock transaction. The Community Bank & Trust bank was folded into Wisconsin Bank & Trust under the deal.

In 2013 the company acquired Morrill Bancshares Inc. the holding company of the Kansas-based Morrill & Janes Bank and Trust Company along with $377.7 million in total loans and $665.3 million worth of deposits. The Morrill & Janes Bank and Trust Company became one of Heartland's independent bank subsidiaries.

In 2012 Heartland Financial acquired Heritage Bank N.A. a Phoenix-based commercial bank in an all-cash deal valued at about $16 million consistent with its goal of expansion in the West.

EXECUTIVES

Vice President Marketing, Dawn Oelke
President and CEO Minnesota Bank & Trust, Catherine T. (Kate) Kelly
Chairman President and CEO Heartland Financial USA Inc.; Vice Chairman Dubuque Bank & Trust Wisconsin Bank & Trust New Mexico Bank & Trust Arizona Bank & Trust Rocky Mountain Bank Centennial Bank and Trust(1) Minnesota Bank & Trust and Premier Valley Bank, Lynn B. Fuller, age 67, $486,388 total compensation
EVP Lending, Douglas J. Horstmann, age 63, $275,156 total compensation
President and CEO New Mexico Bank & Trust, R. Greg Leyendecker
President and CEO Wisconsin Bank & Trust, Kevin S. Tenpas
President of Heartland Director Rocky Mountain Bank and President Heartland Financial USA Inc. Insurance Services, Bruce K. Lee, age 56, $383,519 total compensation
EVP Human Resources and Organizational Development, Mark G. Murtha, age 55
SVP Chief Accounting Officer, Janet M. Quick
President and CEO Riverside Community Bank, Steven E. Ward
SVP and COO Wealth management Group, Bruce C. Rehmke
EVP Commercial Sales, Frank E. Walter, age 70
EVP Senior General Counsel and Corporate Secretary, Michael J. Coyle, age 71
EVP Operations, Brian J. Fox, age 68, $190,000 total compensation
EVP and Chief Risk Officer, Rodney L. Sloan, age 57
EVP and CFO Heartland Financial USA Treasurer Citizens Finance Parent Co.. and Director Heartland Financial USA Inc. Insurance Services, Bryan R. McKeag, age 56, $305,625 total compensation
EVP Finance and Corporate Strategy, David L. Horstmann, age 67
President and CEO Arizona Bank & Trust, Jerry L. Schwallier
President and CEO Rocky Mountain Bank, Curtis Chrystal
President and CEO Morrill & Janes Bank and Trust Co., Kurt M. Saylor
EVP Private Client Services, Kelly J. Johnson, age 55
President and CEO Illinois Bank and Trust, Jeff Hultman
Chief Investment Officer, Nancy Tengler
EVP and Chief Credit Officer, Drew Townsend
EVP and Private Wealth Management Director, Rick O. Terry
President and CEO Heartland Mortgage, Paul Johnstun
CEO Centennial Bank and Trust, Jim Basey
President Heartland Mortgage, Jack Lloyd
Vice President Administrative Services, Joseph V Berretta
Senior Vice President Corporate Secretary, Lois K Pearce
Vice President, Jean Harkey
Vice President Loan Imaging Manager, Marie Koerperich
Vice President Information Technology, Les Oelke
Vice President Credit Administration, Ted Kraft
Senior Vice President, Julie Shanahan
Senior Vice President Special Assets REO, John Hawkins
Vice President, Troy Steger

Senior Vice President Credit Administration, Brian McCarthy
Senior Vice President Head of Loan Operations, Dan Tabraham
Assistant Vice President Information Services, Brent Wilke
CREDIT ADMIN OFFICER IV SENIOR VICE PRESIDENT, Jeffery Viviano
PCS DIRECTOR OF FINANCIAL PLANNING VICE PRESIDENT, Chrisanna Elser
HUMAN RESOURCES GENERALIST SENIOR ASSISTANT VICE PRESIDENT, Dana Rosebrook
MORTGAGE CHIEF FINANCIAL OFFICER SENIOR VICE PRESIDENT, Dave Wallace
Vice Chairman of the Board of Heartland Financial USA Inc.; Chairman and Director of Dubuque Bank and Trust, Mark C. Falb, age 69
Vice Chairman of the Board of Heartland Financial USA Inc.; Director and Vice Chairman of the Board of Dubuque Bank and Trust, Thomas L. Flynn, age 61
Auditors: KPMG LLP

LOCATIONS

HQ: Heartland Financial USA, Inc. (Dubuque, IA)
1398 Central Avenue, Dubuque, IA 52001
Phone: 563 589-2000   **Fax:** 563 589-2011
Web: www.htlf.com

PRODUCTS/OPERATIONS

2014 Sales

	$ mil.	% of total
Interest		
Loans & leases including fees	194	61
Securities & other	43	13
Noninterest		
Gains on sales of loans	31	10
Service charges and fees	20	7
Trust fees	13	4
Loan serving income	5	2
Brokerage & insurance commissions	4	1
Security gains	3	1
Other	4	1
Total	**319**	**100**

Selected Subsidiaries

Arizona Bank & Trust
Citizens Finance Co. (consumer lending)
Dubuque Bank and Trust (IA)
  DB&T Insurance Inc.
  DB&T Community Development Corp.
First Community Bank (IA)
Galena State Bank & Trust Co. (IL)
New Mexico Bank & Trust
Minnesota Bank & Trust (80%)
Riverside Community Bank (IL)
Rocky Mountain Bank (MT)
Summit Bank & Trust (87% CO)
Wisconsin Community Bank

COMPETITORS

Associated Banc-Corp	First Banks
BBVA Compass	U.S. Bancorp
Bancshares	Wells Fargo
Bank of America	Zions Bancorporation
Bank of the West	

HISTORICAL FINANCIALS

Company Type: Public

Income Statement

FYE: December 31

	ASSETS ($ mil.)	NET INCOME ($ mil.)	INCOME AS % OF ASSETS	EMPLOYEES
12/16	8,247	80	1.0%	1,864
12/15	7,694	60	0.8%	1,799
12/14	6,052	41	0.7%	1,631
12/13	5,923	36	0.6%	1,676
12/12	4,990	49	1.0%	1,498
Annual Growth	**13.4%**	**12.7%**	**—**	**5.6%**

2016 Year-End Financials

Debt ratio: 3.41%	No. of shares (mil.): 26
Return on equity: 11.41%	Dividends
Cash ($ mil.): 160	Yield: 0.0%
Current ratio: —	Payout: 15.5%
Long-term debt ($ mil.): —	Market value ($ mil.): 1,254

	STOCK PRICE ($) FY Close	P/E High/Low		PER SHARE ($) Earnings	Dividends	Book Value
12/16	48.00	15	8	3.22	0.50	28.37
12/15	31.36	14	9	2.83	0.45	29.56
12/14	27.10	13	10	2.19	0.40	26.81
12/13	28.79	14	11	2.04	0.50	23.88
12/12	26.15	10	5	2.77	0.50	23.88
Annual Growth	**16.4%**			**3.8%**	**(0.0%)**	**4.4%**

Heritage Commerce Corp

EXECUTIVES

EVP and CFO, Lawrence D. McGovern, age 62, $260,753 total compensation
President and CEO, Walter T. (Walt) Kaczmarek, age 65, $368,509 total compensation
EVP and Director Business Development, Robert P. (Bob) Gionfriddo, age 71
EVP Banking Division, Michael E. Benito, $244,826 total compensation
COO, Keith A. Wilton, $243,025 total compensation
EVP and Chief Credit Officer, David E. Porter, $260,738 total compensation
EVP and Corporate Secretary, Deborah K. (Debbie) Reuter
EVP HOA and Deposit Services, Teresa Powell
Chairman, Jack W. Conner, age 77
Auditors: Crowe Horwath LLP

LOCATIONS

HQ: Heritage Commerce Corp
150 Almaden Boulevard, San Jose, CA 95113
Phone: 408 947-6900
Web: www.heritagecommercecorp.com

PRODUCTS/OPERATIONS

2015 Sales

	$ mil.	% of total
Interest		
Loans including fees	68	78
Taxable securities	6	8
Other	3	4
Noninterest		
Service charges & fees on deposit accounts	2	3
Increase in cash surrender value of life insurance	1	2
Servicing income	1	1
Gain on sales of securities	0	1
Other	2	3
Total	**0**	**100**

COMPETITORS

Bank of America	JPMorgan Chase
Bank of the West	MUFG Americas Holdings
Citibank	SVB Financial
Comerica	U.S. Bancorp
First Republic (CA)	Wells Fargo

HISTORICAL FINANCIALS

Company Type: Public

Income Statement

FYE: December 31

	ASSETS ($ mil.)	NET INCOME ($ mil.)	INCOME AS % OF ASSETS	EMPLOYEES
12/16	2,570	27	1.1%	263
12/15	2,361	16	0.7%	260
12/14	1,617	13	0.8%	242
12/13	1,491	11	0.8%	193
12/12	1,693	9	0.6%	190
Annual Growth	**11.0%**	**28.9%**	**—**	**8.5%**

2016 Year-End Financials

Debt ratio: —	No. of shares (mil.): 37
Return on equity: 10.81%	Dividends
Cash ($ mil.): 266	Yield: 0.0%
Current ratio: —	Payout: 50.0%
Long-term debt ($ mil.): —	Market value ($ mil.): 547

	STOCK PRICE ($) FY Close	P/E High/Low		PER SHARE ($) Earnings	Dividends	Book Value
12/16	14.43	20	13	0.72	0.36	6.85
12/15	11.96	26	17	0.48	0.32	7.64
12/14	8.83	21	19	0.42	0.18	6.96
12/13	8.24	23	18	0.36	0.06	6.58
12/12	6.98	26	17	0.27	0.00	6.45
Annual Growth	**19.9%**			**27.8%**	**—**	**1.5%**

Heritage Financial Corp. (WA)

Heritage Financial is ready to answer the call of Pacific Northwesterners seeking to preserve their heritage. Heritage Financial is the holding company for Heritage Bank which operates more than 65 branches throughout Washington and Oregon. Boasting nearly $4 billion in assets the bank offers a range of deposit products to consumers and businesses such as CDs IRAs and checking savings NOW and money market accounts. Commercial and industrial loans account for over 50% of Heritage Financial's loan portfolio while mortgages secured by multi-family real estate comprise about 5%. The bank also originates single-family mortgages land development construction loans and consumer loans.

Operations

The bank also does business under the Central Valley Bank name in the Yakima and Kittitas counties of Washington and under the Whidbey Island Bank name on Whidbey Island.

About 79% of Heritage Financial's total revenue came from loan interest (including fees) in 2014 while another 7% came from interest on its investment securities. The rest of its revenue came from service charges and other fees (8%) Merchant Visa income (1%) and other miscellaneous fees. The company had a staff of 748 employees at the end of that year.

Geographic Reach

The Olympia-based bank operates more than 65 branches across Washington and the greater Portland area. It has additional offices in eastern Washington mostly in Yakima county.

Sales and Marketing

Heritage targets small and medium-sized businesses along with their owners as well as individuals.

Financial Performance

Fueled by loan and deposit growth from a series of bank acquisitions Heritage Financial's revenues and profits have been on the rise in recent years.

The company's revenue jumped 70% to a record $137.6 million in 2014 mostly thanks to new loan business stemming from its acquisition of Washington Banking Company. Deposit service charge income also increased thanks to new deposit business from the acquisition.

Higher revenue in 2014 allowed Heritage Financial's net income to more than double to a record $21 million while its operating cash levels rose 66% to $51.3 million on higher cash earnings and net proceeds from the sale of its loans.

Strategy

The bank reiterated in 2015 that it would continue to pursue strategic acquisitions of community banks to grow market share across the Pacific Northwest (its region of expertise) expand its business lines and grow its loan and deposit business.

With its focus on business and commercial lending the bank also in 2015 emphasized the importance of seeking high asset quality loans lending to familiar markets that have a historical record of success. Recruiting and retaining "highly competent personnel" to execute its strategies was also key to its long-term agenda.

Mergers and Acquisitions

In May 2014 Heritage acquired Washington Banking Company and its Whidbey Island Bank subsidiary for $265 million which "significantly expanded and enhanced" its product offerings across its core geographic market.

In July 2013 the bank acquired Puyallup Washington-based Valley Community Bancshares and its eight Valley Bank branches for $44 million.

In January 2013 the company purchased Lakewood Washington-based Northwest Commercial Bank along with its two branch locations in Washington state for $5 million.

EXECUTIVES

President CEO and Director Heritage Financial and CEO Heritage Bank, Brian L. Vance, age 62, $494,316 total compensation

EVP and CFO Heritage Financial and Heritage Bank, Donald J. Hinson, age 56, $255,084 total compensation

EVP and Chief Credit Officer Heritage Bank, David A. Spurling, age 64, $237,342 total compensation

EVP Heritage Financial and President and COO Heritage Bank, Jeffrey J. (Jeff) Deuel, $291,516 total compensation

EVP and Chief Lending Officer Heritage Bank, Bryan D. McDonald, age 45, $261,374 total compensation

Vice President And Financial Reporting Manager, Patrice Hernandez

Chairman, Brian S. Charneski, age 55

Auditors: Crowe Horwath LLP

LOCATIONS

HQ: Heritage Financial Corp. (WA)
201 Fifth Avenue S.W., Olympia, WA 98501
Phone: 360 943-1500
Web: www.HF-WA.com

PRODUCTS/OPERATIONS

2014 Sales

	$ mil.	% of total
Interest income		
Interest and fees on loans	110	79
Investment securities	10	7
Others	0	-
Non-interest income		
Service charges and others	11	8
Merchant Visa income	1	1
Others	4	5
Total	**137**	**100**

COMPETITORS

Bank of America	U.S. Bancorp
Columbia Banking	Washington Federal
FS Bancorp	Wells Fargo
KeyCorp	

HISTORICAL FINANCIALS
Company Type: Public

Income Statement
FYE: December 31

	ASSETS ($ mil.)	NET INCOME ($ mil.)	INCOME AS % OF ASSETS	EMPLOYEES
12/16	3,878	38	1.0%	760
12/15	3,650	37	1.0%	717
12/14	3,457	21	0.6%	748
12/13	1,659	9	0.6%	373
12/12	1,345	13	1.0%	363
Annual Growth	**30.3%**	**30.9%**	**—**	**20.3%**

2016 Year-End Financials

Debt ratio: 0.51%	No. of shares (mil.): 29
Return on equity: 8.16%	Dividends
Cash ($ mil.): 103	Yield: 0.0%
Current ratio: —	Payout: 55.3%
Long-term debt ($ mil.): —	Market value ($ mil.): 771

	STOCK PRICE ($) FY Close	P/E High/Low	PER SHARE ($) Earnings	Dividends	Book Value
12/16	25.75	20 13	1.30	0.72	16.08
12/15	18.84	16 12	1.25	0.69	15.68
12/14	17.55	23 19	0.82	0.50	15.02
12/13	17.10	29 22	0.61	0.42	13.31
12/12	14.69	18 14	0.87	0.80	13.16
Annual Growth	**15.1%**	**— —**	**10.6%**	**(2.6%)**	**5.1%**

Hershey Company (The)

The Hershey Company works to spread Almond Joy and lots of Kisses. With its portfolio of more than 80 global brands the #1 chocolate producer in North America has built a big business manufacturing such well-known chocolate and candy brands as Hershey's Kisses Reese's peanut butter cups Twizzlers Mounds and Almond Joy candy bars (under a license) York peppermint patties and Kit Kat wafer bars. Hershey also makes grocery goods including baking chocolate chocolate syrup cocoa mix cookies snack nuts breath mints and bubble gum. Products from the chocolate king are sold to a variety of wholesale distributors and retailers throughout North America and exported overseas.

Operations

Hershey's operations consist of two business segments (North America; and International and Other) in which more than 80 name brands are made marketed sold and distributed. Many product types sold under the Hershey's Kisses and Reese's names are included in the company's chocolate business unit. Other popular brand franchises — such as Twizzlers Mounds York Kit Kat Ice Breakers and Bubble Yum — fall within the company's sweets and refreshment business unit.

Geographic Reach

Hershey has two reportable segments: North America and International and Other. North America is the largest segment (accounting for 88% of the total revenue) and caters to the traditional chocolate and non-chocolate confectionery market as well as grocery and growing snacks markets within the US and Canada.

International and Other (12%) has operations in China Mexico Brazil India and Malaysia primarily for consumers in these regions. The segment also distributes and sells confectionery products in export markets within Asia Latin America Middle East Europe Africa and other regions. It also includes global retail operations including Hershey's Chocolate World stores in Hershey Pennsylvania; New York; Las Vegas; Shanghai; Niagara Falls (Ontario); Dubai; and Singapore as well as operations associated with licensing the use of certain of Hershey's trademarks and products to third parties around the world.

Sales and Marketing

Among its significant customers wholesale distribution giant McLane Company accounts for 25% of Hershey's sales each year. It's the primary distributor of Hershey products to Wal-Mart. Hershey leverages a staff of full-time sales representatives and food brokers to peddle its products to customers. In general the confectionery company counts wholesale distributors chain drug stores vending companies wholesale clubs convenience stores dollar stores concessionaires and department stores among its vast customer set. Hershey's distribution network ships its products from its manufacturing plants to strategically located distribution centers using common carriers to deliver products from there to customers.

The company makes a point to launch new versions of old favorites such as Jolly Rancher lollipops and bite-size bits of chocolate bars. Although chocolate bars take center stage most recently premium dark varieties it introduced sugar-free chocolate to tempt the growing number of diabetic and overweight consumers. Moving into the snack aisle Hershey has rolled out cookies 100-calorie treats and granola bars.

Financial Performance

Hershey achieved historic growth in 2016 with revenues peaking at a record-setting $7.44 billion. The growth was driven by higher North America volumes largely in products supported by increased high-profile promotional programming such as NCAA March Madness the Summer Olympics and NCAA Football College Game Day. It was also helped by new product launches for Snack Mix Snack Bites and Hershey's Cookie Layer Crunch bars.

After experiencing a drop in profits for 2015 Hershey posted profit growth of 40% in 2016. This was mainly due to a major decrease in the amount of impairment and realignment charges it paid compared to the previous year.

In addition Hershey's operating cash flow has fluctuated wildly over the years after spiking in 2015 to $1.21 billion cash flow declined 19% to $983 million in 2016; this was attributed to unfavorable changes in working capital and additional prepaid expenses associated with higher payments on commodity futures contracts in 2016 as the market price of cocoa declined.

Strategy

Hershey's growth strategy includes expanding its snack foods business while continuing to invest in its core confectionery business. The chocolate maker is bolstering its snack food line up to capitalize on US consumers' growing appetite for healthier snacks. With consumers in the US snacking more than in years past Hershey has begun offering more mixed snack options including nut pretzel and chocolate mixes. The company plans to introduce additional snack categories and may pursue acquisitions of companies that produce protein-based and other types of snacks it hasn't traditionally offered. Hershey also continues to invest in its iconic brands including Hershey's Reese's and Hershey's Kisses.

In order to compete with online competitors Hershey in 2017 announced plans to significantly ramp up its e-commerce operations through potential collaborations with brick-and-mortar retailers and investing significantly more in its technological infrastructure.

In addition to its growth initiatives the company is also cutting costs to improve profitably particularly in international markets. In 2017 Hershey announced it was laying off about 15% of its global workforce. The employee reduction intended to improve operating margins between 2017 and 2019 will affect about 2700 mostly hourly workers outside of the US.

Mergers and Acquisitions

Hershey's strategic focus is on expanding its global presence as it jockeys for market share from rivals Mars and Kraft which owns Cadbury.

In late 2017 Hershey agreed to acquire Amplify Snack Brands a high-growth snack food company that makes SkinnyPop its market leading healthy popcorn brand. The transaction is valued at $1.6 billion and will help Hershey develop a broader portfolio of consumer snacking brands especially as they pertain to "better-for-you" products that feature clean simple and transparent ingredients.

In 2016 the company acquired Ripple Brand Collective LLC a privately held company based in Congers New York that owns the barkTHINS mass premium chocolate snacking brand for approximately $285 million. The acquisition was undertaken in order to broaden the company?s product offerings in the premium and portable snacking categories.

In 2015 Hershey picked up KRAVE Pure Foods headquartered in Sonoma California. KRAVE is a manufacturer of KRAVE jerky an all-natural snack brand of premium jerky products. The transaction allowed Hershey to tap into the rapidly growing meat snacks category and further expand into the broader snacks space.

HISTORY

The Hershey Company is the legacy of Milton Hershey of Pennsylvania Dutch origin. Apprenticed in 1872 at age 15 to a candy maker Hershey started Lancaster Caramel Company at age 30. In 1893 at the Chicago Exposition he saw a new chocolate-making machine and in 1900 he sold the caramel operations for $1 million to start a chocolate factory.

The factory was completed in 1905 in Derry Church Pennsylvania and renamed Hershey Foods the next year. Chocolate Kisses individually hand-wrapped in silver foil were introduced in 1907. Two years later the candy man founded the Milton Hershey School an orphanage; the company was donated to a trust in 1918 and for years existed solely to fund the school. Hershey went public in 1927.

EXECUTIVES

Vice President and Chief Accou, David Tacka
Senior Vice President, Thomas Hernquist
President and CEO, Michele G. Buck, age 56
SVP and Chief Product Supply and Technology Officer, Terence L. O'Day, age 67, $590,061 total compensation
SVP and CFO, Patricia A. Little, age 57, $629,412 total compensation
Regional President AEMEA, Steven C. Schiller
President U.S., Todd W. Tillemans
Vice President Us Finance, Todd Cunfer
Vice President, Joe Beck
National Account Manager, Mike Jauch
Vice President US Supply Chain, Wade Latz
Senior Vice President Chief Research and Development Officer, William Papa
Vice President Technology and Operations Information, Simon Viltz
Vice President and General Manager Americas Region, Hector de la Barreda
Chairman, John P. (J.P.) Bilbrey, age 60
VP Treasurer, Rosa Stroh
Vice Chairman For Finance And Informatics, Doug Eggli
Assistant Secretary, Kathleen Purcell
Assistant Treasurer, John Dourdis
Treasurer, Wendy Mcclintock
Auditors: KPMG LLP

LOCATIONS

HQ: Hershey Company (The)
100 Crystal A Drive, Hershey, PA 17033
Phone: 717 534-4200   **Fax:** 717 531-6161
Web: www.hersheys.com

2016 Sales

	$ mil.	% of total
North America	6,533	88
International and Other	907	12
Total	**7,440**	**100**

2016 Sales

	$ mil.	% of total
United States	6,196	83
Other	1,243	17
Total	**7,440**	**100**

COMPETITORS

Annabelle Candy
Anthony-Thomas Candy
Asher's Chocolates
Betsy Ann Candies
Chase General
Chocolates □ la Carte
Chupa Chups
Endangered Species Chocolate
Enstrom
Fazer Konfektyr
Ferrero
Flowers Foods
Ghirardelli Chocolate
Godiva Chocolatier
Goetze's Candy
Guittard
Harry London Candies
Jelly Belly Candy
Kellogg
Laura Secord
Lindt & Sprüngli
Mars Incorporated
Mondelez International
Nestl©
Otis Spunkmeyer
Perfetti Van Melle
Purdy's Chocolates
Rocky Mountain Chocolate
Russell Stover
See's Candies
Smucker
Spangler Candy
Sweet Shop USA
Tootsie Roll
Warrell Corporation
World's Finest Chocolate
Wrigley
Zachary Confections

HISTORICAL FINANCIALS

Company Type: Public

Income Statement

FYE: December 31

	REVENUE ($ mil.)	NET INCOME ($ mil.)	NET PROFIT MARGIN	EMPLOYEES
12/16	7,440	720	9.7%	17,980
12/15	7,386	512	6.9%	20,710
12/14	7,421	846	11.4%	22,450
12/13	7,146	820	11.5%	14,800
12/12	6,644	660	9.9%	14,200
Annual Growth	2.9%	2.2%	—	6.1%

2016 Year-End Financials

Debt ratio: 53.95%
Return on equity: 80.51%
Cash ($ mil.): 296
Current ratio: 0.95
Long-term debt ($ mil.): 2,347
No. of shares (mil.): 212
Dividends
  Yield: 0.0%
  Payout: 71.9%
Market value ($ mil.): 21,954

	STOCK PRICE ($) FY Close	P/E High/Low	Earnings	Dividends	Book Value
12/16	103.43	33 24	3.34	2.40	3.70
12/15	89.27	46 35	2.32	2.24	4.60
12/14	103.93	28 23	3.77	2.04	6.58
12/13	97.23	27 19	3.61	1.81	7.17
12/12	72.22	25 20	2.89	1.56	4.63
Annual Growth	9.4%	— —	—	3.7% 11.4%	(5.5%)

Hertz Global Holdings Inc (New)

LOCATIONS

HQ: Hertz Global Holdings Inc (New)
8501 Williams Road, Estero, FL 33928
Phone: 239 301-7000
Web: www.hertz.com

HISTORICAL FINANCIALS

Company Type: Public

Income Statement

FYE: December 31

	REVENUE ($ mil.)	NET INCOME ($ mil.)	NET PROFIT MARGIN	EMPLOYEES
12/16	8,803	(491)	—	36,000
12/15	9,017	273	3.0%	—
12/14	9,475	(82)	—	—
Annual Growth	(3.6%)	—	—	—

2016 Year-End Financials

Debt ratio: 70.69%
Return on equity: (-31.65%)
Cash ($ mil.): 816
Current ratio: 1.21
Long-term debt ($ mil.): 13,541
No. of shares (mil.): 83
Dividends
  Yield: —
  Payout: —
Market value ($ mil.): 1,789

	STOCK PRICE ($) FY Close	P/E High/Low	Earnings	Dividends	Book Value
12/16	21.56	— —	(5.85)	0.00	12.95
12/15	0.00	— —	3.00	0.00	4.77
12/14	0.00	— —	(0.09)	0.00	(0.00)
Annual Growth		— —			

Hess Corp

Oil and gas company Hess can profess to owning no less than 1.1 billion barrels of oil equivalent worldwide. Crude oil is the company's primary output resource but it also produces natural gas and NGLs (natural gas liquids). Its primary operations are in the US but it also has producing interests in Denmark Equatorial Guinea Malaysia and Thailand. It also offers midstream services including gathering compressing and transporting hydrocarbons as well as propane storage. Hess has been prospecting for oil since the 1920s.

HISTORY

In 1919 British oil entrepreneur Lord Cowdray formed Amerada Corporation to explore for oil in North America. Cowdray soon hired geophysicist Everette DeGolyer a pioneer in oil geology research. DeGolyer's systematic methods helped Amerada not only find oil deposits faster but also pick up fields missed by competitors. DeGolyer became president of Amerada in 1929 but left in 1932 to work independently.

After WWII Amerada began exploring overseas and during the 1950s entered pipelining and refining. It continued its overseas exploration through Oasis a consortium formed in 1964 with Marathon Shell and Continental to explore in Libya.

Leon Hess began to buy stock in Amerada in 1966. The son of immigrants he had entered the oil business during the Depression selling "resid" — thick refining leftovers that refineries discarded — from a 1929 Dodge truck in New Jersey. He bought the resid cheap and sold it as heating fuel to hotels. Hess also speculated buying oil at low prices in the summer and selling it for a profit in the winter. He later bought more trucks a transportation network refineries and gas stations and went into oil exploration. Expansion pushed up debt so in 1962 Leon's company went public as Hess Oil and Chemical after merging with Cletrac Corporation.

Hess acquired Amerada in 1969 after an ownership battle with Phillips Petroleum. During the Arab oil embargo of the 1970s Amerada Hess began drilling on Alaska's North Slope. Oilman T. Boone Pickens bought up a chunk of Amerada Hess stock during the 1980s spurring takeover rumors. They proved premature.

Amerada Hess completed a pipeline in 1993 to carry natural gas from the North Sea to the UK. In 1995 Leon Hess stepped down as CEO (he died in 1999) and his son John took the position. Amerada Hess sold its 81% interest in the Northstar oil field in Alaska to BP and the next year Petro-Canada bought the company's Canadian operations. In 1996 the company acquired a 25% stake (sold in 2002) in UK-based Premier Oil.

The company teamed with Dixons Stores Group in 1997 to market gas in the UK. It also purchased 66 Pick Wick convenience store/service stations.

In 1998 Amerada Hess signed production-sharing contracts with a Malaysian oil firm as part of its strategy to move into Southeast Asia and began to sell natural gas to retail customers in the UK.

To offset losses brought on by depressed oil prices Amerada Hess sold assets worth more than $300 million in 1999 including its southeastern pipeline network gas stations in Georgia and South Carolina and Gulf Coast terminals. It also moved into Latin America acquiring stakes in fields in offshore Brazil.

In 2000 Amerada Hess acquired Statoil Energy Services which markets natural gas and electricity to industrial and commercial customers in the northeastern US. It also announced its intention to buy LASMO a UK-based exploration and production company before Italy's Eni topped the Amerada Hess offer.

Undeterred in 2001 the company bought Dallas-based exploration and production company Triton Energy for $2.7 billion in cash and $500 million in assumed debt. Amerada Hess also acquired the Gulf of Mexico assets of LLOG Exploration Company for $750 million. That year however stiff competition prompted Amerada Hess to put its UK gas and electricity supply business on the auction block. The unit was sold to TXU (now Energy Future Holdings) in 2002.

In 2003 Amerada Hess sold 26 oil and gas fields in the Gulf of Mexico to Anadarko Petroleum. Amerada Hess was granted permission by the Equatorial Guinea government in 2004 to develop 29 new wells in that country. That year Amerada Hess acquired a 65% stake in Trabant Holdings International a Russia-based production and exploration company.

The company re-entered its former oil and gas production operations in the Waha concessions in Libya in 2006. Also that year it changed its name to Hess Corporation.

Looking to grow its position in the lucrative Bakken oil shale play in North Dakota in 2010 the company acquired American Oil and Gas in a $450 million stock deal that added 85000 net acres to Hess' holdings. It also bought 167000 acres in the Bakken play from TRZ Energy LLC for $1 billion.

Hess' former refinery in the US Virgin Islands was operated as a joint venture with Venezuela's state oil company Petr leos de Venezuela S.A (PDVSA). However the loss-making HOVENSA refinery was shut down in 2012 and converted to an oil storage terminal. In 2013 Hess announced that it completed its exit from the refining business by closing its Port Reading New Jersey refinery.

As part of its strategy of unwinding its refining and marketing assets in 2013 Hess sold Russian subsidiary Samara-Nafta to LUKOIL for $2.05 billion. It also sold its energy marketing business to Direct Energy for a $1.2 billion.

To raise cash it also sold its 2.7% interest in India's Azeri Chirag and Guneshli Fields and its 2.4% stake in the associated BTC pipeline to ONGC Videsh for $1 billion. It also sold its Indonesian oil and gas assets for $1.3 billion.

That year it also sold 20 liquid petroleum products terminals along the US East Coast with total storage capacity of 39 million barrels to Buckeye Partners for $850 million.

The Utica Shale in Ohio was a growth area. However in 2014 low gas prices prompted Hess agreed to sell 74000 acres of dry gas acreage in the Utica Shale for $924 million in order to focus on more lucrative oil plays.

That year it also sold its oil and gas assets in Thailand to PTT Exploration and Production for $1 billion.

EXECUTIVES

CEO, John B. Hess, age 63, $1,500,000 total compensation
SVP and CFO, John P. Rielly, age 54, $775,000 total compensation
President and COO, Gregory P. (Greg) Hill, age 55, $1,100,000 total compensation
SVP Global Production, Michael R. (Mike) Turner, age 57, $575,000 total compensation
SVP Global Services, Brian D. Truelove, age 58
SVP Developments Drilling and Completions, Richard Lynch
SVP Exploration, Barbara Lowery-Yilmaz, age 60

Senior Vice President of Human Resources, Mykel Ziolo
Executive Vice President, David Chaimengyew
Vice President and General Counsel Worldwide E and P, Toni Hennike
Senior Vice President Operations and Marketing, Joseph Serafino
Vice President Global Supply Chain, Dennis Creech
Senior Vice President Services and CIO, Zhanna Golodryga
Vice President Controller, Dan Devine
Vice President Exploration Capture, Timothy Chisholm
Vice President Corporate Planning and Strategy, Colin Davies
Vice President Natural Gas Sales, Todd Porter
Executive Assistant Vice President Global Supply Chain, Robin T Hensley
Vice President Projects Asia Pacific, Brock Hajdik
Vice President Land Global Exploration, John Y Christopher
Senior Vice President, Timothy Goodell
Senior Vice President Retail and Energy Marketing, Christopher Baldwin
Vice President, Jay Wilson
Vice President Human Resources Operations, Helena Deal
Vice President Talent and Organization Development, Jamie Lane
Vice President Finance and Administration, Luz Gutierrez
Executive Vice President Exploration And Productio, Eloise Castillo
Vice President Information Technology and Knowledge Management, Marfiza Muhammad
Vice President Retail Field Operations, David Klavsons
Senior Vice President Development And Technical Su, Janice Flaherty
Vice President International Exploration, Grant Gilchrist
Vice President Mobile Communications, Bambang Prasodjo
Vice President Bakken WF Execution, David Mckay
Executive Vice President, Barclay Collins
Vice President Secretary and Deputy General Counsel, George Barry
Vice President CIO, Peter Walton
Vice President, Eka Marina
Vice President Retail Operations, Richard Lawlor
Assistant Vice President, Benjamin Yau
Senior Vice President Strategy Commercial and New Business Development, Scott Sloan
Executive Vice President, Andrew Chang
Director, James H. (Jim) Quigley, age 65
Secretary, Grace Garcia
Assistant Treasurer, Bob Franzino
Auditors: Ernst & Young LLP

LOCATIONS

HQ: Hess Corp
1185 Avenue of the Americas, New York, NY 10036
Phone: 212 997-8500
Web: www.hess.com

2016 sales

	% of total
US	65
Europe	13
Africa	12
Asia & other regions	10
Total	**100**

PRODUCTS/OPERATIONS

2016 sales

	% of total
Exploration and Production	90
Bakken Midstream	10
Total	**100**

2016 Sales

	% of total
Crude oil	76
Natural gas	16
Natural gas liquids	6
Other	2
Total	**100**

COMPETITORS

Abraxas Petroleum	Gastar Exploration
BP	Koch Industries Inc.
CMA CGM	Marathon Oil
Chevron	Norsk Hydro ASA
ConocoPhillips	Occidental Petroleum
Continental Energy	PEMEX
Devon Energy	PETROBRAS
Dominion Energy	Petr□□eos de
Double Eagle Petroleum	Venezuela
ERHC	Pioneer Oil and Gas
Encana Oil & Gas (USA)	Royal Dutch Shell
Inc.	Serica Energy
Eni	TOTAL
Exxon Mobil	

HISTORICAL FINANCIALS

Company Type: Public

Income Statement

FYE: December 31

	REVENUE ($ mil.)	NET INCOME ($ mil.)	NET PROFIT MARGIN	EMPLOYEES
12/16	4,844	(6,132)	—	2,304
12/15	6,561	(3,056)	—	2,770
12/14	11,439	2,317	20.3%	3,045
12/13	24,421	5,052	20.7%	12,225
12/12	38,373	2,025	5.3%	14,775
Annual Growth	**(40.4%)**	—	—	**(37.2%)**

2016 Year-End Financials

Debt ratio: 23.78%
Return on equity: (-36.06%)
Cash ($ mil.): 2,732
Current ratio: 1.90
Long-term debt ($ mil.): 6,694

No. of shares (mil.): 316
Dividends
Yield: 0.0%
Payout: —
Market value ($ mil.): 19,716

	STOCK PRICE ($) FY Close	P/E High/Low		PER SHARE ($) Earnings	Dividends	Book Value
12/16	62.29	—	—	(19.92)	1.00	45.92
12/15	48.48	—	—	(10.78)	1.00	67.77
12/14	73.82	13	9	7.53	1.00	77.68
12/13	83.00	6	4	14.82	0.70	75.99
12/12	52.96	11	7	5.95	0.40	61.75
Annual Growth	**4.1%**	—	—	—	**25.7%**	**(7.1%)**

Hewlett Packard Enterprise Co

HP Enterprise (HPE) once part of the storied Hewlett-Packard Corporation has whittled itself down to focus its business on what it calls HybridIT. It recently spun off its $9 billion Software division and its 100000-person $13.5 billion Enterprise Services business. The remaining business designs manufactures and sells servers storage and networking equipment and provides technology services to help its large enterprise customers architect and deploy IT solutions. HPE focuses its efforts on software-defined IT offerings for private and public cloud environments as well as solutions for industrial Internet of Things (IoT) applications. HPE is a global company and about two thirds of its revenue comes from outside the US. Its technology has a rich history and maintains a cache of nearly 11000 patents.

Operations

HPE operates a corporate investments segment and two business segments. The Enterprise Group is the primary operational segment and within it are its server storage networking and technology services divisions. Financial Services offers leasing financing and other means to help customers pay for HPE purchases. Corporate Investments include the research organization HP Labs and certain cloud-related business incubation projects.

The Enterprise Group generates a little more than 85% of total revenue and within the segment the server division accounts for nearly 50% of revenue while technology services brings in 30%. The segment provides secure software-defined technology and services that enable customers to move data seamlessly across hybrid IT environments (private & public cloud connected to traditional data centers for example) and to provide solutions for non-core computing environments that run campus branch and Internet of Things (IoT) applications.

The Financial Services segment provides flexible investment solutions such as leasing financing IT consumption and utility programs and asset management services. It helps customers create unique technology deployment models and acquire complete IT solutions including hardware software and services from Hewlett Packard Enterprise and others. The segment accounts for roughly 15% of total revenue.

Corporate Investments is a cost-centered segment focused on research & development projects. From its efforts come new technologies and ideas that HPE eventually turns into products and services. Its revenue is negligible and earnings are typically small losses.

Geographic Reach

Palo Alto CA-based HPE is a global organization with a global customer base. Its physical operations include offices manufacturing facilities and HP Labs R&D centers. It has nearly 20 locations in the US and Puerto Rico and about 10 outside the US such as in the UK India Brazil China and Taiwan. As part of its HPE Next 2020 initiative it appears poised to shutter some sites.

Approximately two thirds of revenue originate outside the US.

Sales and Marketing

HPE customers are mostly large companies and government agencies. The company reaches them through its own sales staff and resellers distribution partners OEMs independent software vendors system integrators and consulting services companies. HPE account managers maintain relationships between the company's businesses and large enterprise customers.

HPE not only sells its own products and services but partners with a plethora of technologies companies to supplement its own offerings when designing and deploying customer solutions.

Financial Performance

HPE?s size and revenue generation dwindled along with the divestiture of its two large segments HP Software and HP Enterprise Services. In reviewing the remaining continuing operations of HPE revenue decreased marginally in each of FY2016 and FY2017 (fiscal year ends October 31).

For FY2017 revenue fell 4% to $28.9 billion. HPE?s largest segment Enterprise Group saw its revenue decline nearly 6% due to across-the-board decreases in its servers storage networking and technical services divisions. The greatest impacts came from a decline in the number of servers sold and the loss of revenue from its divested H3C network products operations. Those actions were partially offset by new revenue from two acquisitions SGI and Nimble Storage. A positive contribution came from HPE?s Financial Services segment whose revenue increased 13% compared to FY2016.

Net income in FY2017 crashed to $344 million from $3.2 billion the prior year. The fall was the result of various extraneous charges including $93 million in costs related to damages to its Puerto Rico and Houston facilities from Hurricane Harvey. It also spent nearly $800 million on restructuring and transformation charges. Finally the prior year had a $2.4 billion gain on divestitures causing an unfavorable comparison between FY2017 and FY2016.

Cash on hand at the end of FY2017 was $9.6 billion down $3.4 billion from the previous year. Operating activities contributed some $900 million to cash through net earnings and large adjustments for depreciation and amortization. Investing activities used nearly $5.0 billion of cash due primarily to $2.5 billion of investments in property plant and equipment along with $2.2 for business acquisitions. Despite large layouts for stock repurchases and debt repayment financing activities provided $600 million due to large dividend payments to HPE from the sale of its Software and Enterprise Services segments.

Strategy

HPE has undergone tremendous change in the past few years first split off from Hewlett Packard Corporation followed by its subsequent divestitures of large entities HP Software and HP Enterprise Services. In 2014 it was part of a 350000 person $120 billion conglomerate and by the end of 2017 HPE employed less than 50000 people and generated just under $30 billion in revenue.

With the corporate reshaping largely complete the company is focused on transforming itself to match the demands of its customers ? from a product portfolio perspective a geographic presence perspective and from a competitive posture perspective.

Its Enterprise Group continues to experience challenges with revenue growth due to the shifting of computing workloads to cloud deployment models instead of in-house data centers the emergence of software-defined architectures which reduces the needs for server and networking hardware and an increasingly competitive pricing environment. It is combating these trends with investments in its portfolio of solutions for the data center cloud and edge computing environments; all with an emphasis on software-defined infrastructure which is aided by its 2017 acquisition of SimpliVity. It has a sweeping set of technologies and services making it an ideal candidate for customers who want a one-stop-shop for all things enterprise computing.

In 2017 the company launched an initiative called HPE Next through which it plans to simplify its operating model by streamlining its offerings and business processes to support investments in high growth and higher margin solutions & services. It includes consolidating its manufacturing and support services locations streamlining its business systems and reducing the number of countries in which it has a direct sales presence while migrating to a channel-only model in the remaining countries. The initiative will continue through FY2020 and will incur expenses for staff reductions upgrading its IT infrastructure and plant closures. It expects to partially offset the expenses with proceeds from real estate sales. When it is complete HPE expects the initiative will drive down annual costs by $800 million.

HPE doesn't lack for competitors in enterprise IT. Longtime rival Dell is in the process of buying storage system company EMC to get even bigger.

Other competitors across HPE's portfolio include Cisco Systems Lenovo Group Ltd. Oracle Fujitsu Ltd. Inspur Co. Huawei Technologies NetApp Hitachi Ltd. Juniper Networks and Arista Networks.With the wave of cloud services changing the way customers implement their computing solutions HPE is also competing against Amazon and Google.

Mergers and Acquisitions

HPE acquired three companies in FY2017: Cloud Technology Partners a cloud consulting design and advisory services company; Nimble Storage a provider of all-flash and hybrid storage solutions for a little more than $1 billion; SimpliVity a provider of software-defined computing infrastructure solutions for $650 million.

In August 2016 HPE bought SGI (formerly Silicon Graphics) for $275 million. SGI's high performance computing products are used for data analytics and data management. The plan is to combine SGI's supercomputing capabilities to beef up HPE's enterprise offerings to provide faster and higher capacity analytics to customers. The deal is expected to close in early 2017. SGI reported a loss of $39 million on revenue of $529 million in 2015.

EXECUTIVES

President and CEO, Margaret C. (Meg) Whitman, age 61, $1,500,058 total compensation

EVP and Chief Marketing and Communications Officer, Henry Gomez, age 54

EVP General Counsel and Secretary, John F. Schultz, age 53

EVP and COO, Christopher P. (Chris) Hsu, age 46, $675,026 total compensation

EVP Human Resources, Alan May, age 59

EVP and General Manager Enterprise Group, Antonio Neri, age 50, $725,028 total compensation

EVP and CFO, Timothy C. (Tim) Stonesifer, age 50, $675,026 total compensation

Senior Vice President Finance and Treasurer, Kirt Karros

Executive Vice President and General Manager HP Enterprise Services, Mike Nefkens

Vice President, Mark Collins

Senior Vice President, Cliff Henson

Vice President and General Manager, Bill Mannel

Vice President, Anthony Delisio

Vice President WW Channels Enterprise Servers Storage and Networking, Jesse Chavez

Vice President, James McAnally

Vice President Information Technology, Carl Fetzner

Vice President, Sunil Pandita

Vice President Strategic Alliances, Steve McGuinness

Vice President Global Healthcare Services, Mary Mirabelli

Vice President and General Manager World Wide Travel and Transportation, Brian Cook

Vice President ISS Supply Chain, Colin Todd

Vice President Global Accounts, Gerri Gold

Vice President Strategic Alliances, Carrie Francey

Vice President, Rhonda Rubinstein

Senior Vice President Experience Marketing, Susan Popper

Vice President, Jeff Nuckols

Vice President, Victor Ferreira

Senior Vice President, Parvesh Sethi

Senior Vice President and General Manager, Ric Lewis

Vice President, Mark Colaluca

Vice President, Earl Matthews

Vice President, Dominic Wilde

Vice President, Hugh Rivers

Vice President Global Pursuits, Dan Zankman

Vice President, Peter Quirk

Senior Vice President Marketing and Events, Rob Pace

Vice President, Lou Berger

Vice President Channels North America, Jim Harold

Vice President, Vishal Lall

Vice President Chief of Staff To Executive Office, Paul Hunter

Vice President Healthcare Recruiter DCIG, Kathy Eastwood

Vice President Global Pursuit Strategist, Ron Knauer

Vice President DXC Technology, Barry Weiss

Vice President and General Manager, Scott McNinch

Vice President Executive Assistant, Jeff Dolce

Vice President, Swetal Desai

Vice President Business Operations DCHC Network Analyst, Jas Sood

Senior Vice President, Lee Tan

Senior Vice President and General Manager, Ana Pinczuk

Vice President Global Marketing Aruba, Janice Le

Vice President Strategic Sales User. Public Sector Hewlett Packard Enterprise Services, Rolf Holman

Vice President, Greg Robins

National Sales Manager, Mark McBroom

Vice President Sales, Mark Fazio

Vice President Transformation, Jonathan Ford

Vice President and General Manager, Leslie Maher

Vice President and Global Account Executive Client HP, Phillip Myers

Vice President Global Functions Legal, Kristin Major

Vice President and Deputy General Counsel, Gregorio Hernandez

VP Communications and Media Solutions Research and Development, Paul Mitalas

WW Vice President Sales Big Data, Bruce Jones

Vice President of Sales Technology Value Solutions, John Tyros

Vice President Global Practices, Rick Sullivan

Senior Vice President, Vishal Bhagwati

Vice President, Nick Caller

Sales Vice President and General Manager, Keerti Melkote

Vice President Central, John Jankowski

Vice President Hewlett Packard Federal Business Organization, Tom Hempfield

Chairman, Patricia F. (Pat) Russo, age 64

Auditors: Ernst & Young LLP

LOCATIONS

HQ: Hewlett Packard Enterprise Co
3000 Hanover Street, Palo Alto, CA 94304
Phone: 650 687-5817
Web: www.hpe.com

COMPETITORS

Amazon.com	IBM
Arista Networks	Juniper Networks
Brocade Communications	Lenovo
Cisco Systems	Microsoft
Dell	NetApp
Fujitsu	Oracle
Hitachi	salesforce.com

HISTORICAL FINANCIALS

Company Type: Public

Income Statement

FYE: October 31

	REVENUE ($ mil.)	NET INCOME ($ mil.)	NET PROFIT MARGIN	EMPLOYEES
10/17	28,871	344	1.2%	66,000
10/16	50,123	3,161	6.3%	195,000
10/15	52,107	2,461	4.7%	240,000
10/14	55,123	1,648	3.0%	252,000
10/13	57,371	2,051	3.6%	—
Annual Growth	(15.8%)	(36.0%)	—	—

2017 Year-End Financials

Debt ratio: 22.85%
Return on equity: 1.25%
Cash ($ mil.): 9,579
Current ratio: 1.13
Long-term debt ($ mil.): 10,182

No. of shares (mil.): 1,595
Dividends
Yield: 2.2%
Payout: 572.7%
Market value ($ mil.): 22,205

	STOCK PRICE ($) FY Close	P/E High/Low		PER SHARE ($) Earnings	Dividends	Book Value
10/17	13.92	118	62	0.21	0.32	14.71
10/16	22.47	13	7	1.82	0.22	18.87
10/15	14.72	13	11	1.34	0.00	19.25
Annual Growth	(1.4%)	—	—	(37.1%)	—	(6.5%)

HILL/AHERN FIRE PROTECTION, LLC

LOCATIONS

HQ: HILL/AHERN FIRE PROTECTION, LLC
11045 GAGE AVE, FRANKLIN PARK, IL 601311437
Phone: 847 288-5100
Web: WWW.HILLGRP.COM

HISTORICAL FINANCIALS

Company Type: Private

Income Statement

FYE: December 31

	REVENUE ($ mil.)	NET INCOME ($ mil.)	NET PROFIT MARGIN	EMPLOYEES
12/11	5,669	185	3.3%	100
12/10	2,568	80	3.1%	—
Annual Growth	120.7%	130.7%	—	—

2011 Year-End Financials

Debt ratio: ——
Return on equity: 3.30%
Cash ($ mil.): 480
Current ratio: 2.30
Long-term debt ($ mil.): —

Dividends
Yield: —
Payout: —
Market value ($ mil.): —

Hills Bancorporation

EXECUTIVES

Senior Vice President Director Of Retail, Tracy Stotler

Vice President, Kenneth Hinrichs

Auditors: BKD, LLP

LOCATIONS

HQ: Hills Bancorporation
131 Main Street, Hills, IA 52235
Phone: 319 679-2291
Web: www.hillsbank.com

COMPETITORS

Ames National	MidWestOne
Bank of America	Regions Financial
Citigroup	U.S. Bancorp
Iowa First	Wells Fargo
Meta Financial Group	West Bancorporation

HISTORICAL FINANCIALS

Company Type: Public

Income Statement

FYE: December 31

	ASSETS ($ mil.)	NET INCOME ($ mil.)	INCOME AS % OF ASSETS	EMPLOYEES
12/16	2,655	31	1.2%	503
12/15	2,493	28	1.1%	464
12/14	2,334	26	1.2%	428
12/13	2,167	25	1.2%	421
12/12	2,099	26	1.3%	423
Annual Growth	6.0%	4.1%	—	4.4%

2016 Year-End Financials

Debt ratio: —	No. of shares (mil.): 9
Return on equity: 9.84%	Dividends
Cash ($ mil.): 38	Yield: 0.0%
Current ratio: —	Payout: 19.1%
Long-term debt ($ mil.): —	Market value ($ mil.): 446

	STOCK PRICE ($) FY Close	P/E High/Low	Earnings	PER SHARE ($) Dividends	Book Value
12/16	48.11	17 13	3.40	0.65	35.63
12/15	45.00	27 14	3.04	0.63	33.23
12/14	82.50	29 25	2.87	0.58	30.93
12/13	72.00	26 25	2.75	0.55	28.91
12/12	67.00	24 22	2.84	0.53	27.02
Annual Growth	(7.9%)	— —	4.6%	5.5%	7.2%

Hilton Worldwide Holdings Inc

If you need a bed for the night Hilton has a few hundred thousand of them. The company is one of the world's largest hoteliers with a lodging empire that includes about 4900 hotels and resorts in more than 100 countries operating under such names as Doubletree Embassy Suites and Hampton Inn as well as its flagship Hilton brand. Many of its hotels serve the mid-market segment though its Hilton and Conrad hotels offer full-service upscale lodging. In addition its Homewood Suites chain offers extended-stay services. The company franchises many of its hotels; it owns the Waldorf-Astoria brand and the New York Hilton. Hilton became a public company again in 2013.

Operations

With its extensive portfolio of brands Hilton seeks to serve multiple segments within the lodging sector. The company's largest chains Hampton Inn and Hampton Inn & Suites include about 2200 locations and target mid-market travelers with moderately priced rooms and limited amenities. Nearly all its Hampton hotels are operated by fran-

chisees or by the company under management contracts with third-party owners.

At the other end of the scale the company's Conrad chain offers luxury services and distinctive locations while its Waldorf-Astoria Collection is a prestigious collection of hotels inspired by the New York landmark. The company's Hilton Grand Vacations subsidiary operates about 45 time-share vacation resorts with a concentration located in Florida.

Geographic Reach

Even though the company has hotels all over the world it generates about 80% of its sales in the US.

Sales and Marketing

Hilton relies on traditional advertising and promotions along with a variety of direct marketing techniques such as email social media marketing and postal mailings to drum up business. A fair amount of the company's hotel rooms get booked through internet travel intermediaries. Hilton pays commissions and transaction fees for sales of rooms through such services. The company also has a robust customer loyalty program it uses to try to generate return business.

Financial Performance

Hilton has maintained steady revenue growth for the past several years. In fiscal 2016 revenue increased by slightly compared to fiscal 2015. The company reported revenue of $11.66 billion for fiscal 2016 after reporting $11.27 billion in revenue the prior fiscal year.

The company's net income was $1.4 billion in fiscal 2015 but it dropped to just under $350 million in fiscal 2016. The decreased net income was the result of increased operating expenses. Hilton's cash flow remained strong in fiscal 2016 despite the dip in net income.

Strategy

The company continues to expand its global footprint and its timeshare business. In January 2016 Hilton launched its newest midscale brand Tru by Hilton. Each Tru by Hilton property includes various social spaces in a large first floor lobby.

In February 2016 the company announced a plan to separate a substantial portion of its ownership business consisting primarily of its owned hotels located in the US along with its timeshare business from Hilton to form two additional new publicly traded companies.

Mergers and Acquisitions

In 2015 Hilton sold its Waldorf Astoria New York hotel for $1.95 billion. The company used the proceeds from the sale to acquire five other hotel properties.

HISTORY

Conrad Hilton got his start in hotel management by renting out rooms in his family's New Mexico home. He served as a state legislator and started a bank before leaving for Texas in 1919 hoping to make his fortune in banking. Hilton was unable to shoulder the cost of purchasing a bank however but recognized a high demand for hotel rooms and made a quick change in strategy buying his first hotel in Cisco Texas. Over the next decade he bought seven more Texas hotels.

Hilton lost several properties during the Depression but began rebuilding his empire soon thereafter through the purchase of hotels in California (1938) New Mexico (1939) and Mexico (1942). He even married starlet Zsa Zsa Gabor in 1942 (they later divorced of course). Hilton Hotels Corporation was formed in 1946 and went public. The company bought New York's Waldorf-Astoria in 1949 (a hotel Hilton called "the greatest of them all") and opened its first European hotel in Madrid

in 1953. Hilton paid $111 million for the 10-hotel Statler chain the following year.

Hilton took his company out of the overseas hotel business in 1964 by spinning off Hilton International and began franchising the following year to capitalize on the well-known Hilton name. Barron Hilton Conrad's son was appointed president in 1966 (he became chairman upon Conrad Hilton's death in 1979). Hilton bought two Las Vegas hotels (the Las Vegas Hilton and the Flamingo Hilton) in 1970 and launched its gaming division. The company returned to the international hotel business with Conrad International Hotels in 1982 and opened its first suite-only Hilton Suites hotel in 1989.

In the 1990s Hilton expanded its gaming operations buying Bally's Casino Resort in Reno in 1992 and launching its first riverboat casino the Hilton Queen of New Orleans in 1994. Two years later it acquired all of Bally Entertainment making it the largest gaming company in the world. Also that year Stephen Bollenbach the former Walt Disney CFO who had negotiated the $19 billion acquisition of Capital Cities/ABC was named CEO — becoming the first nonfamily-member to run the company.

Hilton formed an alliance with Ladbroke Group in 1997 (later Hilton Group owner of Hilton International and the rights to the Hilton name outside the US) to promote the Hilton brand worldwide. Hilton also put in a bid that year to acquire ITT owner of Sheraton hotels and Caesars World but was thwarted when ITT accepted a higher offer from Starwood Hotels & Resorts. Hilton was foiled once again in 1998 when a deal with casino operator Circus Circus (now part of MGM Resorts International) that would have separated Hilton's hotel and casino operations fell through. With a downturn in the gambling industry translating into sluggish results in Hilton's gaming segment the company spun off its gaming interests as Park Place Entertainment later that year.

In 1999 Hilton made a massive acquisition with the $3.7 billion purchase of Promus Hotel Corp. The following year Hilton sold its Flamingo Casino-Kansas City a remaining casino property left over from the Park Place spinoff to Isle of Capri Casinos for $33.5 million. In 2001 it sold 56 of its leases and management contracts to RFS Hotel Investors for about $60 million.

Hilton continued selling properties in 2002 with the sales of two Doubletree hotels and all 41 Red Lion locations to WestCoast Hospitality (now Red Lion Hotels) for about $51 million. It also sold its Harrison Conference Center portfolio (14 conference centers and university hotels) to ARAMARK for $55 million. At the end of that same year the company formed a $400 million venture with CNL Hospitality (now CNL Hotels & Resorts) to buy and refurbish hotel properties.

Following an extended downturn in the hospitality business brought on by recession and post-9/11 fears about terrorism Hilton began to invest in refurbishments for many of its properties and added about 150 locations in 2004.

Hilton Hotels acquired Hilton International from Hilton Group (now Ladbrokes) for about $5.7 billion in 2006. The deal re-unified the Hilton brand globally and added about 400 new locations to the company's portfolio. The year after the acquisition Hilton Hotels sold its Scandic Hotels business to private equity firm EQT for $1.1 billion and later sold LivingWell Health Clubs to Bannatyne Fitness; both brands had been included in the Hilton International transaction.

Also in 2007 the company was taken private by The Blackstone Group through a $26 billion buyout. The acquisition included about $6 billion in debt. Christopher Nassetta later replaced Bollenbach as CEO. Hilton Hotels was renamed Hilton

Worldwide in 2009. Through a financial restructuring in 2010 Hilton was able to cut about $4 billion of its $20 billion debt. In early 2011 its newest brand Home2 Suites by Hilton opened its first property.

Hilton sold its Waldorf Astoria New York hotel for $1.95 billion in 2015.

EXECUTIVES

EVP and President Development Architecture and Construction, Ian R. Carter, age 55, $739,302 total compensation

President CEO and Director, Christopher J. (Chris) Nassetta, age 55, $1,200,000 total compensation

EVP and Chief Human Resources Officer, Matthew W. (Matt) Schuyler, age 51

EVP and General Counsel, Kristin A. Campbell, age 55, $638,308 total compensation

EVP Global Brands, James E. (Jim) Holthouser, age 58, $600,000 total compensation

EVP and CFO, Kevin J. Jacobs, age 44, $743,404 total compensation

EVP and President Americas, Joe Berger

EVP and President Europe Middle East and Africa, Simon Vincent

EVP and Chief Commercial Officer, Chris Silcock

Head Architecture Design and Construction, Matt Richardson

EVP and President Asia Pacific (APAC), Alan Watts

Chairman, Jonathan D. Gray, age 47

Auditors: Ernst & Young LLP

LOCATIONS

HQ: Hilton Worldwide Holdings Inc
7930 Jones Branch Drive, Suite 1100, McLean, VA 22102
Phone: 703 883-1000
Web: www.hiltonworldwide.com

2016 sales

	% of total
U.S.	80
All other	20
Total	**100**

PRODUCTS/OPERATIONS

2016 sales

	% of total
Owned and leased hotels	35
Management and franchise fees and other	15
Timeshare	12
Other revenues from managed and franchised properties	38
Total	**100**

Selected Brands

Conrad Hotels & Resorts
Doubletree
Embassy Suites Hotels
Hampton Inn
Hampton Inn & Suites
Hilton
Hilton Garden Inn
Hilton Grand Vacations Club
Homewood Suites by Hilton

Selected Hotels

Chicago's Palmer House Hilton
Hilton Barcelona
Hilton Bora Bora Nui Resort & Spa
The Hilton Hawaiian Village on Waikiki Beach
Hilton Manchester Deansgate
Hilton Orlando
Hilton San Francisco on Union Square
Hilton Sedona
The New York Hilton
The Waldorf Astoria

COMPETITORS

Accor	Interstate Hotels
Best Western	Loews
Carlson Hotels	Marriott
Choice Hotels	Omni Hotels
FRHI Hotels and Resorts	Red Lion Hotels
	Ritz-Carlton
Four Seasons Hotels	Starwood Hotels & Resorts
Hyatt	
InterContinental Hotels	Wyndham Worldwide

HISTORICAL FINANCIALS

Company Type: Public

Income Statement

FYE: December 31

	REVENUE ($ mil.)	NET INCOME ($ mil.)	NET PROFIT MARGIN	EMPLOYEES
12/17	9,140	1,259	13.8%	163,000
12/16	11,663	348	3.0%	169,000
12/15	11,272	1,404	12.5%	164,000
12/14	10,502	673	6.4%	157,000
12/13	9,735	415	4.3%	152,000
Annual Growth	(1.6%)	32.0%	—	1.8%

2017 Year-End Financials

Debt ratio: 46.14%
Return on equity: 31.59%
Cash ($ mil.): 570
Current ratio: 0.90
Long-term debt ($ mil.): 6,556

No. of shares (mil.): 317
Dividends
Yield: 0.0%
Payout: 15.5%
Market value ($ mil.): 25,349

	STOCK PRICE ($) FY Close	P/E High/Low		PER SHARE ($) Earnings	Dividends	Book Value
12/17	79.86	21	7	3.85	0.60	6.53
12/16	27.20	26	16	1.05	0.84	17.91
12/15	21.40	7	5	4.26	0.42	18.18
12/14	26.09	13	10	2.04	0.00	14.48
12/13	22.25	17	16	1.35	0.00	13.29
Annual Growth	37.6%	—	—	30.0%	—	(16.3%)

Hingham Institution for Savings

The Hingham Institution for Savings serves businesses and retail customers in Boston's south shore communities operating more than 10 branches in Massachusetts in Boston Cohasset Hingham Hull Norwell Scituate South Hingham and South Weymouth. Founded in 1834 the bank offers traditional deposit products such as checking and savings accounts IRAs and certificates of deposit. More than 90% of its loan portfolio is split between commercial mortgages and residential mortgages (including home equity loans) though the bank also originates construction business and consumer loans. More than 95% of the company's revenue comes from loan interest.

Operations

The Hingham Institution for Savings made 96% of its total revenue from loan interest during 2015 while about 2% came from interest in equities CODs and other investments. The rest of its revenue mostly came from service fees on deposit accounts.

Of its $1.4 billion loan portfolio (at the end of 2015) about 48% was made up of commercial real estate mortgages (including multi-family housing)

while 45% was tied to residential mortgages (including home equity). The remainder of the portfolio was made up of residential and commercial construction loans (7% of loan assets) and commercial business loans and consumer loans (1%).

Subsidiary Hingham Unpledged Securities Corporation holds title to certain securities available for sale.

Geographic Reach

The company mostly serves clients in Boston the South Shore and the island of Nantucket. Its branches are in Boston Cohasset Hingham Hull Nantucket Norwell Scituate South Hingham and South Weymouth Massachusetts.

Sales and Marketing

The Hingham Institution for Savings serves both individuals and small businesses in its three target markets in Massachusetts. Some of its clients (as of mid-2016) include Lyons Associates The Hub TCR Development SYA+FH Steven Young Architect + Fine Home Builder and Park Drive Inc.

The bank spent $489000 on marketing expenses during 2015 down from $557000 in each of 2014 and 2013.

Financial Performance

The bank's annual revenues have slowly trended higher over the past several years as the promising Boston real estate market has fueled its commercial real estate and residential loan business growth.

Hingham's revenue dipped 1% to $64.34 million during 2015 despite 13% mortgage loan growth mostly because in 2014 it earned a gains on life insurance distributions. The bank also continued to lose fee income as it has eliminated many fees on its deposit products to simplify offerings and attract customer deposits.

Revenue declines and higher income tax provisions in 2015 (in 2014 it earned non-taxed death benefit proceeds) caused the bank's net income to fall 13% to $19.34 million. Hingham's operating cash levels rose 11% to $20.2 million for the year thanks to a jump in cash-based earnings.

Strategy

The Hingham Institution for Savings continued in 2016 to focus on originating commercial multi-family and single-family mortgage loans in its target markets of Boston the South Shore and the island of Nantucket in Massachusetts especially as the healthy real estate market in and around Boston has provided a tailwind for its lending business.

EXECUTIVES

Chief Executive Officer; President; Director, Robert H. Gaughen, $319,615 total compensation
Assistant Vice President Branch Manager, Paula Stookey
Auditors: Wolf & Company, P.C.

LOCATIONS

HQ: Hingham Institution for Savings
55 Main Street, Hingham, MA 02043
Phone: 781 749-2200   **Fax:** 781 740-4889
Web: www.hinghamsavings.com

COMPETITORS

Bank of America	Independent Bank (MA)
Citizens Financial Group	Peoples Federal Bancshares Inc.
Eastern Bank	Sovereign Bank

Income Statement

FYE: December 31

	ASSETS ($ mil.)	NET INCOME ($ mil.)	INCOME AS % OF ASSETS	EMPLOYEES
12/16	2,014	23	1.2%	103
12/15	1,768	19	1.1%	111
12/14	1,552	22	1.4%	121
12/13	1,356	13	1.0%	131
12/12	1,205	13	1.1%	126
Annual Growth	13.7%	15.2%	—	(4.9%)

2016 Year-End Financials

Debt ratio: 0.04%	No. of shares (mil.): 2
Return on equity: 15.62%	Dividends
Cash ($ mil.): 7	Yield: 0.0%
Current ratio: —	Payout: 13.9%
Long-term debt ($ mil.): —	Market value ($ mil.): 420

	STOCK PRICE ($) FY Close	P/E High/Low		PER SHARE ($) Earnings	Dividends	Book Value
12/16	196.78	18	11	10.89	1.52	75.50
12/15	119.80	15	9	9.02	2.14	64.83
12/14	87.01	9	7	10.44	1.37	57.08
12/13	78.49	13	10	6.28	1.32	48.49
12/12	62.60	11	8	6.25	1.28	43.65
Annual Growth	33.2%	—	—	14.9%	4.4%	14.7%

HollyFrontier Corp

HollyFrontier refines crude oil to produce gasoline diesel and jet fuel and sells it in erstwhile American frontier territories: the Southwest northern Mexico Kansas and the Rockies. Its major assets are a 52000 barrels-per-day (bpd) refinery in Wyoming; the 135000 bpd El Dorado Kansas refinery; a45000 bpd Utah refinery; a 125000 bpd Tulsa refinery; and subsidiary Navajo Refining (New Mexico) which has a capacity of 100000 bpd. The company also has a 36% stake in Holly Energy Partners (HEP) which operates crude oil and petroleum product pipelines. .

Operations

HollyFrontier operates two businesses: the refining business which accounts for the vast majority of total revenue and HollyFrontier Energy Partners (HEP).

The refining segment produces products such as gasoline diesel fuel jet fuel specialty lubricant products and specialty and modified asphalt. It turns out around 46000 barrels per day of product from its El Dorado Tulsa Navajo Cheyenne and Woods Cross refineries. It also produces asphalt via the HFC Asphalt business that makes asphalt in Arizona New Mexico and Oklahoma.

By product gasoline accounts for half its HollyFrontier's sales volume; diesel fuel accounts for around 35%; and jet fuel and specialty lubricants less than 5% each.

The HEP segment generates revenues by charging tariffs for transporting petroleum products and crude oil through its pipelines.

Geographic Reach

Dallas-based HollyFrontier's refinery operations (Cheyenne Wyoming; El Dorado Kansas; Navajo New Mexico; Tulsa Oklahoma; and Woods Cross Utah) serve customers in the US Mid-Continent Rocky Mountain and Southwest regions of the US.

Sales and Marketing

HollyFrontier's principal customers for gasoline include other refiners convenience store chains independent marketers and retailers. Diesel fuel is sold to other refiners truck stop chains wholesalers and railroads. Jet fuel is sold for commercial airline use. Specialty lubricant products are sold in both commercial and specialty markets. LPG's are sold to LPG wholesalers and LPG retailers. They produce and purchase asphalt products that are sold to governmental entities paving contractors or manufacturers. Asphalt is also blended into fuel oil and is either sold locally or is shipped to the Gulf Coast.

Sales to Shell Oil represented 10% of HollyFrontier's sales as did sales to Sinclair Oil.

The primary markets for the El Dorado Refinery's refined products are Colorado and the Plains States. The Woods Cross Refinery's primary market is Utah. The Cheyenne Refinery primarily markets its products in eastern Colorado including metropolitan Denver eastern Wyoming and western Nebraska. It also sells a significant portion of its diesel directly from the truck rack at the refinery eliminating transportation costs.

Asphalt products are marketed in Arizona New Mexico Oklahoma Kansas Missouri Texas and northern Mexico. Products are shipped via third-party trucking companies to commercial customers that provide asphalt based materials for commercial and government projects.

Financial Performance

The collapse in the global oil price since 2014 has reduced net revenue by nearly half and pushed HollyFrontier into the red.

In fiscal 2016 revenue fell a further 20% to $10.5 billion relating to lower average prices across the year while a curtailing of activity at its Woods Cross refinery due to insufficient crude supply from the Plains Rocky Mountain Pipeline was also a factor.

The company lost $260.5 million mostly as a result of non-cash good will and asset impairment charges totaling $654.1 million. Additionally margins were eroded 48% as selling prices fell further than raw material costs.

Cash from operations fell 29% to $602.3 million on the back of lower net income and revenue.

Strategy

With the refining business suffering under the low oil price HollyFrontier is diversifying its operations and seeking higher margins. In 2017 it closed the acquisition of Canadian lubricants business Suncor Energy increasing its lubricants position — particularly in high-margin Group III base oils of which Suncor is the only North American producer. It is now the fourth-larges lubricants producers on the continent.

To raise cash the company on occasion carries out "drop-down" asset sales to subsidiary HollyFrontier Energy Partners. In 2016 it sold Woods Cross Refinery Units — including crude fluid catalytic cracking and polymerization units — constructed as part of the Woods Cross expansion for $275 million.

Mergers and Acquisitions

In 2017 HollyFrontier completed the $1.1 billion acquisition of Canadian lubricants company Petro-Canada Lubricants a subsidiary of Suncor. The company produces 15600 barrels per day of lubricants including specialty lubricants and white oils.

HISTORY

HollyFrontier was founded in 1947 as General Appliance Corp. to process other companies' crude oil; the current name was adopted in 1952. As Holly the company grew with the number of gas-guzzling cars in the 1950s and 1960s and in the 1970s it developed its Navajo refinery in New Mexico. In 1981 Holly began producing higher-grade gasoline and started an asphalt company at Navajo.

In 1984 Holly became a partner in Montana Refining and later bought the entire business. It upgraded the Navajo refinery in the early 1990s to meet the demand for unleaded gasoline. In 1995 Amoco Mapco and Holly formed a joint venture the 265-mile Rio Grande Pipeline (completed in 1997) to transport natural gas liquids to Mexico.

Also in 1997 FINA and Holly allied to expand and use Holly's pipelines in the southwestern US. A proposed merger with another southwestern refiner Giant Industries died in 1998 because of federal antitrust concerns and a billion-dollar lawsuit filed against Holly by Longhorn Partners Pipeline. Court papers revealed in 2000 that Holly had paid $4 million to fight Longhorn's request for a permit to transport gasoline in its Houston-to-El Paso pipeline. The permit if approved would compete with Holly's own interests in western Texas.

Later in 2000 Holly cut its workforce by about 10% mostly at Navajo Refining. The next year Navajo Refining secured a $122 million contract to provide JP-8 jet fuel to the Defense Department.

In a move to expand its production capacity in 2003 Holly acquired ConocoPhillips' Woods Cross refinery and related assets for $25 million. Holly agreed to be acquired by Frontier Oil for about $450 million that year but the companies terminated the agreement and litigation between the parties resulted.

In 2004 the company spun off its Navajo refinery-related refined petroleum pipeline and other distribution assets as Holly Energy Partners L.P.; it retains a 45% interest in the company.

In 2005 the Delaware Chancery Court ruled that Frontier Oil had not proved that Holly had repudiated the merger agreement and awarded Frontier Oil only $1 in damages. Also that year Holly acquired the remaining 51% of NK Asphalt Producers that it did not already own. The company sold its intermediate feedstock pipelines connecting two refining facilities in Lovington and Artesia New Mexico to Holly Energy Partners for $81.5 million.

To free up cash in 2008 it sold 136 miles of crude oil trunk lines and some tankage assets to Holly Energy Partners for $180 million.

To expand market share in 2011 the company acquired regional rival Frontier Oil and Holly changed its corporate name to HollyFrontier.

The all-stock deal created an enterprise valued at $7 billion and added Frontier's Kansas and Wyoming refineries to the company's portfolio. The acquisition which boosted HollyFrontier's refining capacity to 443000 barrels a day is expected to create cost savings of at least $30 million per year.

The purchase was part of a multi-year strategy of expanding refinery capacity through selective acquisitions of complementary assets. (Earlier the company bought Sunoco's 85000-barrels-per-day Tulsa refinery. Building the largest refinery complex in the Midcontinent the company also acquired Sinclair Oil's 75000-barrels-per-day Tulsa refinery for $128.5 million).

Responding to increased demand in 2012 HollyFrontier announced planned to expand the capacity of its Woods Cross Utah refinery from 31000 barrel per day to 45000 barrel per day.

Building up its infrastructure to create greater efficiencies in 2013 HollyFrontier and Holly Energy Partners agreed to build a rail facility to enable crude oil loading and unloading near HollyFrontier's Artesia and/or Lovington New Mexico refining facilities. The rail project which will be connected to Holly Energy's crude oil pipeline transportation system in southeastern New Mexico will have a capacity of up to 70000 barrels per day and will enable access to a variety of crude oil types.

EXECUTIVES

Vice President Operations Holly Logist, Mark Cunningham
SVP Refining Operations, James M. Stump, age 50, $510,000 total compensation
President and CEO, George J. Damiris, age 57, $1,100,000 total compensation
SVP Commercial and President HollyFrontier Refining & Marketing LLC, Thomas G. Creery, age 58
SVP General Counsel and Secretary, Denise C. McWatters, age 57, $470,000 total compensation
VP Information Technology, Nellson D. Burns
EVP and CFO, Richard L. Voliva, age 39
Vice President Marketing, Fred Nley
Assistant Vice President, Margaret Schieffer
Vice President, Patrick Gribbin
Vice President Human Resources, Nancy Hartmann
Vice President IR, Neale Hickerson
Senior Vice President Capital Projects And Purchasing, James E Resinger
Vice President, Scott Surplus
Vice President Engineering and Process Development Holly Refining and Marketing, Janusz Siwek
Vice President of Information Technology, Ryan Kiernan
Vice President Accounting, Kathryn Walker
VP Operations, Michael McKee
Vice President Investor Relations, Marcus Hickerson
Vice President And Project Manager, Conrad Jenson
Vice President Acquisitions and Corporate Development, Paige Kester
Vice President of Information Technology, Nelson Burns
Vice President and Controller, JW Gann
SENIOR VICE PRESIDENT DIRECT, Gavin T Brady
Vice President and Refinery Manager, Tony Conetta
Vice President, Ajay Seth
Chairman, Michael C. Jennings, age 52
Board Member, William Gray
Board Member, Dean Ridenour
Treasurer, Steve Wise
Auditors: Ernst & Young LLP

LOCATIONS

HQ: HollyFrontier Corp
2828 N. Harwood, Suite 1300, Dallas, TX 75201
Phone: 214 871-3555
Web: www.hollyfrontier.com

PRODUCTS/OPERATIONS

2016 Sales

	$ mil.	% of total
Refining	10,467	96
HEP	402	4
Corporate & other	0	-
Elimination	(333.7)	-
Total	**10,535**	**100**

COMPETITORS

BP	Sunoco
Crown Central	Tesoro
Exxon Mobil	Valero Energy
George Warren	Williams Companies
Marathon Petroleum	

HISTORICAL FINANCIALS

Company Type: Public

Income Statement

FYE: December 31

	REVENUE ($ mil.)	NET INCOME ($ mil.)	NET PROFIT MARGIN	EMPLOYEES
12/16	10,535	(260)	—	2,676
12/15	13,237	740	5.6%	2,704
12/14	19,764	281	1.4%	2,686
12/13	20,160	735	3.6%	2,662
12/12	20,090	1,727	8.6%	2,534
Annual Growth	(14.9%)	—	—	1.4%

2016 Year-End Financials

Debt ratio: 23.69%
Return on equity: (-5.23%)
Cash ($ mil.): 710
Current ratio: 2.63
Long-term debt ($ mil.): 2,235
No. of shares (mil.): 177
Dividends
  Yield: 0.0%
  Payout: —
Market value ($ mil.): 5,810

	STOCK PRICE ($) FY Close	P/E High/Low		Earnings	PER SHARE ($) Dividends	Book Value
12/16	32.76	—	—	(1.48)	1.32	26.40
12/15	39.89	14	8	3.90	1.31	29.15
12/14	37.48	37	25	1.42	3.26	28.17
12/13	49.69	16	11	3.64	3.20	30.17
12/12	46.55	6	3	8.38	3.10	29.74
Annual Growth	(8.4%)	—	—	—	(19.2%)	(2.9%)

Home Bancorp Inc

Making its home in Cajun Country Home Bancorp is the holding company for Home Bank a community bank which offers deposit and loan services to consumers and small to midsized businesses in southern Louisiana. Through about two dozen branches the bank offers standard savings and checking accounts as well as lending services such as mortgages consumer loans and credit cards. Its loan portfolio includes commercial real estate commercial and industrial loans as well as construction and land loans. Home Bancorp also operates about half a dozen bank branches in west Mississippi which were formerly part of Britton & Koontz Bank.

Geographic Reach

Home Bancorp serves the Louisiana areas of Greater Lafayette Baton Rouge Greater New Orleans and Northshore (of Lake Pontchartrain). Its markets in Mississippi include Vicksburg and Natchez.

Financial Performance

Although the company saw assets and loans grow in 2013 net income fell 20% that year to $7.3 million on lower operating income.

Mergers and Acquisitions

In early 2014 Home Bancorp spent about $35 million on Britton & Koontz Capital Corporation the holding company of Britton & Koontz Bank; the deal added five branches in west Mississippi to Home Bancorp's operations.

EXECUTIVES

Executive Vice President, Darren Guidry
Assistant Vice President Mortgage Loan Officer, Flori Hicks
Auditors: Porter Keadle Moore, LLC

LOCATIONS

HQ: Home Bancorp Inc
503 Kaliste Saloom Road, Lafayette, LA 70508
Phone: 337 237-1960   **Fax:** 337 264-9280
Web: www.home24bank.com

COMPETITORS

Capital One	MidSouth Bancorp
IBERIABANK	Regions Financial
JPMorgan Chase	Teche Holding
Louisiana Bancorp	

HISTORICAL FINANCIALS

Company Type: Public

Income Statement

FYE: December 31

	ASSETS ($ mil.)	NET INCOME ($ mil.)	INCOME AS % OF ASSETS	EMPLOYEES
12/16	1,556	16	1.0%	—
12/15	1,551	12	0.8%	—
12/14	1,221	9	0.8%	—
12/13	984	7	0.7%	—
12/12	962	9	1.0%	—
Annual Growth	12.8%	14.9%	—	—

2016 Year-End Financials

Debt ratio: —
Return on equity: 9.26%
Cash ($ mil.): 31
Current ratio: —
Long-term debt ($ mil.): —
No. of shares (mil.): 7
Dividends
  Yield: 0.0%
  Payout: 18.2%
Market value ($ mil.): 284

	STOCK PRICE ($) FY Close	P/E High/Low		Earnings	PER SHARE ($) Dividends	Book Value
12/16	38.61	17	10	2.25	0.41	24.47
12/15	25.98	14	11	1.79	0.37	22.80
12/14	22.94	15	12	1.42	0.07	21.64
12/13	18.85	17	15	1.06	0.00	19.99
12/12	18.25	14	12	1.28	0.00	19.03
Annual Growth	20.6%	—	—	15.1%	—	6.5%

Home BancShares Inc

At this Home you don't have to stash your cash under the mattress. Home BancShares is the holding company for Centennial Bank which operates about 180 branches in Arkansas Alabama and Florida. The bank offers traditional services such as checking savings and money market accounts; IRAs; and CDs. It focuses on commercial real estate lending including construction land development and agricultural loans which make up more than 55% of its lending portfolio. The bank also writes residential mortgage business and consumer loans. Nonbank subsidiaries offer trust and insurance services. Investments are available to customers through an agreement with third-party provider LPL Financial.

Geographic Reach

The Arkansas-based bank holding company's Centennial Bank operates more than 75 branches in Arkansas about 90 branches in Florida six in Southern Alabama and one in New York City.

Financial Performance

Home BancShares reported $257.5 million in revenue in 2013 up 14% versus 2012. The rise in revenue was due primarily to increased interest income from a higher level of earning assets combined with higher yields on their covered loans.

Net income rose 6% over the same period to $66.5 million. The increase was primarily due to additional net income and other non-interest income resulting from acquisitions completed in 2012.

Strategy

The acquisitive bank holding company is expanding in its core Florida and Arkansas markets through the purchase of local managed community banks. Home continues to look for additional acquisitions including institutions seized by regulators in and contiguous to its geographical markets.

Mergers and Acquisitions

In 2017 Home BancShares acquired Giant Holdings Inc and its subsidiary bank Landmark Bank for $96 million. In that same year Home BancShares purchased Stonegate Bank and its more than 20 Florida branches for $820 million.

In 2015 Home BancShares made three acquisitions: the Florida Panhandle operations of the failed Doral Bank $290 million in commercial real estate loans from Doral Bank and the Florida Business BancGroup Inc. and its subsidiary Bay Cities Bank.

EXECUTIVES

CFO and Treasurer and Director, Randy E. Mayor, age 52, $300,000 total compensation

President and CEO, C. Randall (Randy) Sims, age 62, $390,000 total compensation

Regional President Centennial Bank, Robert F. Birch, age 67, $290,000 total compensation

President and CEO Centennial Bank, Tracy M. French, age 55, $290,000 total compensation

Chief Lending Officer, Kevin D. Hester, age 53

COO Home BancShares Inc. and Centennial Bank, John (Stephen) Tipton

Vice President Security, Jenni Holbrook

Vice President, Brian Jackson

Chairman, John W. Allison, age 70

Vice Chairman, Robert H. Adcock, age 68

Auditors: BKD, LLP

LOCATIONS

HQ: Home BancShares Inc
719 Harkrider, Suite 100, Conway, AR 72032
Phone: 501 339-2929
Web: www.homebancshares.com

PRODUCTS/OPERATIONS

2015 Sales

	$ mil.	% of total
Interest		
Loans	344	76
Investment securities	33	7
Non-interest		
Other service charges & fees	26	6
Service charges on deposit accounts	24	5
Other	15	6
Total	**442**	**100**

Selected Services

Personal Banking
Business Banking
ebanking
Investment & insurance
Trust Services

COMPETITORS

Arvest Bank
BB&T
BBX Capital
Bank of America
Bank of the Ozarks

Bear State Financial
Regions Financial
Simmons First
Woodforest Financial

HISTORICAL FINANCIALS

Company Type: Public

Income Statement

FYE: December 31

	ASSETS ($ mil.)	NET INCOME ($ mil.)	INCOME AS % OF ASSETS	EMPLOYEES
12/16	9,808	177	1.8%	1,503
12/15	9,289	138	1.5%	1,424
12/14	7,403	113	1.5%	1,376
12/13	6,811	66	1.0%	1,497
12/12	4,242	63	1.5%	926
Annual Growth	**23.3%**	**29.5%**	**—**	**12.9%**

2016 Year-End Financials

Debt ratio: 0.62%
Return on equity: 13.98%
Cash ($ mil.): 216
Current ratio: —
Long-term debt ($ mil.): —

No. of shares (mil.): 140
Dividends
Yield: 0.0%
Payout: 27.1%
Market value ($ mil.): 3,901

	STOCK PRICE ($) FY Close	P/E High/Low	Earnings	PER SHARE ($) Dividends	Book Value
12/16	27.77	35 15	1.26	0.34	9.45
12/15	40.52	46 28	1.01	0.28	8.55
12/14	32.16	44 33	0.85	0.18	7.51
12/13	37.35	75 36	0.57	0.18	6.46
12/12	33.02	63 44	0.56	0.15	4.58
Annual Growth	**(4.2%)**	**— —**	**22.6%**	**24.0%**	**19.8%**

Home Depot Inc

When embarking on household projects many start their journey at The Home Depot. As the world's largest home improvement chain and one of the largest US retailers the company operates nearly 2275 stores in the US Canada and Mexico as well as an online business. It targets the do-it-yourself (DIY) and professional markets with its selection of some 40000 items including lumber flooring plumbing supplies garden products tools paint and appliances. Home Depot also offers installation services for carpeting cabinetry and other products. One-third of Home Depot's total sales in FY2016 came from business in the states of California Florida New York and Texas.

HISTORY

Bernard Marcus and Arthur Blank founded The Home Depot in 1978 after they were fired (under disputed circumstances) from Handy Dan Home Improvement Centers. They joined Handy Dan coworker Ronald Brill to launch a "new and improved" home center for the do-it-yourselfer (DIY). In 1979 they opened three stores in the fast-growing Atlanta area and expanded to four stores in 1980.

Home Depot went public opened four stores in South Florida and posted sales of $50 million in 1981. The chain entered Louisiana and Arizona next. By 1983 sales were more than $250 million.

In 1984 Home Depot's stock was listed on the NYSE and the company acquired nine Bowater Home Centers in the South. Through subsequent stock and debenture offerings Home Depot continued to grow entering California (Handy Dan's home turf) with six new stores in 1985.

Back on track in 1986 sales exceeded $1 billion in the firm's 60 stores. Home Depot began the current policy of "low day-in day-out pricing" the following year achieving Marcus' dream of elimi-

nating sales events. The company entered the competitive northeastern market with stores in Long Island New York in 1988 and opened its first EXPO Design Center in San Diego.

Home Depot's sales continued to rise during the 1990-92 recession and the retailer kept opening stores. It entered Canada in 1994 when it acquired a 75% interest in Aikenhead's a DIY chain that it converted to the Home Depot name (it bought the remaining 25% in 1998).

A series of gender-bias lawsuits plagued the company in 1994 as female workers claimed they were not treated on an equal basis with male employees. Home Depot reached a $65 million out-of-court settlement in 1997 but not before the company was ordered to pay another female employee $1.7 million in a case in California.

Troubles aside Home Depot roared past the 500-store mark in 1997. That year Blank succeeded Marcus as the company's CEO; Marcus remained chairman. Home Depot bought National Blind & Wallpaper Factory (a mail-order firm) and Maintenance Warehouse (a direct-mail marketer) that year.

The company introduced its 40000-sq.-ft. Villager's Hardware stores designed to compete with smaller hardware shops in 1999 in New Jersey. It also bought Georgia Lighting an Atlanta lighting designer distributor and retailer. Home Depot later began adding large appliances to some stores following competitor Lowe's (most stores had them by 2000).

In 2000 Home Depot bought Apex Supply (a 20-plus-location plumbing distributor in Georgia South Carolina and Tennessee) and opened a flooring-only test store in Texas. Later that year the company named General Electric executive Robert Nardelli as its president and CEO. Marcus and Blank were named co-chairmen.

The company opened 200 new stores in 2001 and bought Total HOME a home improvement chain with four stores in Mexico. Additionally Marcus was named chairman after Blank stepped down. Later in the year Marcus retired and Nardelli became chairman. Also that year the company said it was scrapping its Villager's Hardware experiment to test a small-store concept in urban areas.

In 2002 Home Depot opened its first small store a 61000-sq.-ft. outlet in New York City. Further increasing its presence in Mexico the company acquired the four-store Del Norte chain in Ciudad Juárez that year.

Also in 2002 Home Depot created a new subsidiary HD Builder Solutions through the acquisition of Floors Inc. Arvada Hardwood Floor Company and FloorWorks Inc. The next year the company acquired roofing installer IPUSA and replacement windows and siding installer RMA Home Services.

Home Depot expanded its business in the home-builder market in January 2004 by purchasing Creative Touch Interiors a floor and counter installer in California and Nevada. Additionally early that year Home Depot opened its largest store ever — 205000 sq. ft. — in wealthy Anaheim Hills California. It also announced in February 2004 that it had partnered with AARP to hire people older than 50.

In addition that month Home Depot became the exclusive retailer of Maytag's SkyBox a home beverage dispenser. It acquired Home Mart a 20-unit Mexican chain in March that June giving it a total of more than 40 stores in Mexico. Also in 2004 the company acquired White Cap Construction Supply; agreed to settle discrimination claims of some Colorado employees for $5.5 million; opened two trend-setting urban-oriented stores in Manhattan; and bought 18 stores from Kmart.

In mid-2005 Home Depot acquired National Waterworks Holdings (now National Waterworks Inc.)

and Williams Bros. Lumber of Georgia and folded them both into its The Home Depot Supply business (called HD Supply until it was sold). In September Home Depot Direct launched 10 Crescent Lane a high-end home decorating catalog and Web site offering furniture lighting and decorative accessories housewares and more. While some Home Depot locations in Louisiana and Texas were temporarily shut down by hurricanes Katrina and Rita its stores (and those of rival Lowe's and other building suppliers) are among the first places people visited in the wake of the disaster. In the immediate aftermath of the storms Home Depot stocked nontraditional items such as food and diapers in affected areas. Also in 2005 the company shuttered 15 EXPO Design Center stores which cater to affluent homeowners and converted five others to The Home Depot format. In all in 2005 Home Depot spent about $2.5 billion to acquire 21 companies.

The company's direct-to-consumer division launched a pair of high-end catalogs in 2005: 10 Crescent Lane and Paces Trading Company. However the catalogs which featured home furnishings and lighting products were discontinued in 2006 and selected products were folded back into the main Home Depot store catalog and website.

In January 2006 Home Depot acquired carpet and upholstery cleaning franchisor Chem-Dry and folded it into its At-Home Services division. (Chem-Dry has some 4000 franchises worldwide including 2500 in the US). In March the company completed its largest acquisition to date: the construction repair and maintenance products distributor Hughes Supply Inc. for $3.2 billion. That purchase was followed in May by the acquisition of Cox Lumber Co. a Tampa-based provider of trusses doors and lumber-related products. Also Home Depot acquired Home Decorators Collection a company specializing in catalog and online sales of home decor merchandise in 2006. Lured by the growth potential of the vast Chinese market the retailer purchased a majority stake in Taiwan-based Home-Way for about $100 million in late 2006. Home-Way operates DIY warehouse stores in northern China.

Joining the trend of big-box retailers adding gasoline and convenience store services to fuel sales Home Depot opened its first Home Depot Fuel locations in Tennessee and Georgia in 2006.

In early 2007 Nardelli left the company and vice chairman and EVP Frank Blake took the top spot. Home Depot decided to close its handful of flooring-only stores that year. The apparent nail in Nardelli's coffin was his autocratic management style and hefty compensation package (strategically based on options rather than shareholder returns and estimated at $245 million over five years). Nardelli left Home Depot with a $210 million severance package.

The company sold its HD Supply business in 2007 to Bain Capital Carlyle Group and Clayton Dubilier & Rice. The retailer used the proceeds to help it make a $10 billion stock repurchase of more than 15% of its market capitalization.

The Home Depot closed two stores in China in fiscal 2011. In fiscal 2013 it closed the last of its big-box stores there.

EXECUTIVES

President Southern Division, Tim Hourigan
EVP Corporate Services and CFO, Carol B. Tom ©, age 60, $1,079,231 total compensation
President The Home Depot Mexico, Ricardo E. Saldivar, age 64
Chairman President and CEO, Craig A. Menear, age 59, $1,300,000 total compensation

EVP Supply Chain and Product Development, Mark Q. Holifield, age 60, $775,385 total compensation
EVP and CIO, Matthew A. (Matt) Carey, age 52, $730,385 total compensation
SVP Talent Organization and Performance Systems, Timothy M. (Tim) Crow, age 61, $586,308 total compensation
EVP U.S. Stores, Ann-Marie Campbell, age 51, $665,385 total compensation
President The Home Depot Canada, Jeff Kinnaird
EVP Outside Sales and Service, William G. (Bill) Lennie, age 61
EVP General Counsel and Corporate Secretary, Teresa W. Roseborough, age 58
President Western Division, Aaron Flowe
SVP and President Online, Kevin Hofmann
EVP Merchandising, Edward P. (Ted) Decker, age 54
President Northern Division, Crystal Hanlon
Vice President Of Marketing, Lyne Castonguay
Vice President Supply Chain Development, John Deaton
Vice President Planning and Enterprise Architecture, Michael Goodell
Regional Vice President, Christopher Waits
Vice President Human Resources, Michael Hagan
National Sales Manager, Steve Siegler
Vice President Employment Practices and Associate Relations, Derek W Bottoms
Vice President, Monica Gosnell
Executive Vice President Corporate Development, Richard McPhail
Vice President, Kelly Barrett
Vice President of Talent Management and Diversity, Thomas Spahr
Senior Vice President Of Merchandising, Giles Bowerman
Regional Vice President South Florida, Donny Sanchez
Vice President and General Manager of Eastern South Carolina Information technology Branch, Jason Rice
Vice President of Operations, Haydn Chilcott
Regional Vice President, Quonta Vance
Vice President Merchandising Online, Mark Veeder
Vice President Marketing and Merchandising, Robin Soehl
Merchandising Vice President, Mike Hogenmiller
Senior Vice President Supply Chain, Thomas Shortt
Division President, Ann Campbell
Senior Vice President Supply Chain, Tom Shortt
Vice President Of Merchandising Mexico Division, Ed Orona
Vice President of PRO Business, JT Rieves
Senior Vice President of Operations, Tim Applebee
Area Vice President, Randy Weber
National Sales Manager, Jeff Capone
Vice President Marketing, Lisa DeStefano
Vice President and General Manager Home Depot Exteriors, Aaron Carmack
National Account Manager, Sherry Gagne
Vice President Online, Prat Vemana
Executive Vice President CIO, Matt Carey
Vice President Sales Strategy and Integration, Juan Bueno
Vice President Learning and Development, Tom Spahr
Regional Vice President Midwest Region, Kelly Mayhall
Vice President, David Abbott
Auditors: KPMG LLP

LOCATIONS

HQ: Home Depot Inc
2455 Paces Ferry Road, Atlanta, GA 30339
Phone: 770 433-8211   Fax: 770 431-2707
Web: www.homedepot.com

2017 Store

	No.
US	1,977
Canada	182
Mexico	119
Total	**2,278**

PRODUCTS/OPERATIONS

2017 Sales

	$ mil.	% of total
Indoor garden	9,204	10
Paint	7,666	8
Appliances	7,362	8
Kitchen and bath	7,184	8
Plumbing	6,985	7
Lumber	6,828	7
Outdoor Garden	6,789	7
Building materials	6,774	7
Tools	6,668	7
Flooring	6,477	7
Electrical	6,090	6
Hardware	5,629	6
Millwork	5,139	6
Dé;cor	2,906	3
Lighting	2,894	3
Total	**94,595**	**100**

Selected Private Labels and Proprietary Brands

Glacier Bay (fixtures)
Hampton Bay (lighting)
Husky (hand tools)
Thomasville®; (cabinets)
Vigoro (lawn care products)

COMPETITORS

84 Lumber
Abbey Carpet
Ace Hardware
Amazon.com
B&Q
BMC Stock
Best Buy
CCA Global
Costco Wholesale
Do it Best
F.W. Webb
Guardian Building Products Distribution
Improvement Direct
Kelly-Moore
Lowe's
Menard
Northern Tool
Pacific Coast Building Products
RONA
Sears Holdings
Sherwin-Williams
Sutherland Lumber
Target Corporation
Tractor Supply
True Value
W.E. Aubuchon
Wal-Mart
WinWholesale
Wolseley

HISTORICAL FINANCIALS

Company Type: Public

Income Statement

FYE: January 29

	REVENUE ($ mil.)	NET INCOME ($ mil.)	NET PROFIT MARGIN	EMPLOYEES
01/17	94,595	7,957	8.4%	406,000
01/16*	88,519	7,009	7.9%	385,000
02/15	83,176	6,345	7.6%	371,000
02/14	78,812	5,385	6.8%	365,000
02/13	74,754	4,535	6.1%	340,000
Annual Growth	6.1%	15.1%	—	4.5%

*Fiscal year change

2017 Year-End Financials

Debt ratio: 54.93%
Return on equity: 149.85%
Cash ($ mil.): 2,538
Current ratio: 1.25
Long-term debt ($ mil.): 22,349

No. of shares (mil.): 1,203
Dividends
  Yield: 0.0%
  Payout: 42.7%
Market value ($ mil.): 166,411

	STOCK PRICE ($) FY Close	P/E High/Low	PER SHARE ($) Earnings	Dividends	Book Value
01/17	138.33	21 17	6.45	2.76	3.60
01/16*	125.76	25 19	5.46	2.36	5.04
02/15	104.42	23 16	4.71	1.88	7.13
02/14	76.85	22 17	3.76	1.56	9.07
02/13	67.30	22 15	3.00	1.16	11.98
Annual Growth	19.7%	— —	21.1%	24.2%	(26.0%)

*Fiscal year change

HOME PROPERTIES, LIMITED PARTNERSHIP

LOCATIONS

HQ: HOME PROPERTIES, LIMITED PARTNERSHIP
850 CLINTON SQ, ROCHESTER, NY 146041730
Phone: 585 546-4900

HISTORICAL FINANCIALS

Company Type: Private

Income Statement

FYE: December 31

	ASSETS ($ mil.)	NET INCOME ($ mil.)	INCOME AS % OF ASSETS	EMPLOYEES
12/07	3,216	61	1.9%	1,000
12/06	3,240	110	3.4%	—
12/05	2,977	26	0.9%	—
12/01	1,346	2	0.2%	—
Annual Growth	15.6%	75.1%		

2007 Year-End Financials

Debt ratio: —
Return on equity: 12.20%
Cash ($ mil.): 37
Current ratio: —
Long-term debt ($ mil.): —

Dividends
  Yield: —
  Payout: —
Market value ($ mil.): —

HomeStreet Inc

HomeStreet aims to offer home and business mortgages to all in the Pacific Northwest and Hawaii. Its subsidiary HomeStreet Bank offers traditional consumer banking accounts as well as commercial and private banking investment and insurance products and services through 45 branches and 65 loan offices in the Pacific Northwest California and Hawaii. Specializing in residential and commercial mortgages the bank and fellow subsidiary Homestreet Capital Corp originate home loans both directly and through a joint venture Windermere Real Estate which operates about 40 offices in Washington and Oregon. HomeStreet also provides specialty financing for income-producing properties.

Operations

HomeStreet operates two lines of business: Commercial and Consumer Banking and Mortgage Banking which originates residential mortgage loans for wale in the secondary markets to be securitized by GSAs. Its primary subsidiaries are HomeStreet Bank and HomeStreet Capital Corp. (HCC). HCC sells and services multifamily mortgage loans in conjunction with HomeStreet Bank.

HomeStreet gets most of its business from mortgage originations and sales. About 53% of the company's revenue came from its mortgage banking business (origination and sales) during 2015 while another 6% came from mortgage servicing income. Another 34% of its revenue came from loan interest.

Geographic Reach

Seattle-based HomeStreet operates bank branches in Arizona California Colorado Hawaii Idaho Oregon Utah and Washington.

Sales and Marketing

HomeStreet provides financial services for small- and middle-market businesses as well as consumers.

Financial Performance

HomeStreet's annual revenues and profits have more than doubled since 2011 thanks to strong mortgage banking and loan business growth driven by a strengthening housing market.

The company's revenue spiked 50% to $446.35 million during 2015 mostly thanks to a 64% increase in gains on mortgage loan origination sales resulting from a rise in single family mortgage interest rate lock commitments.

Strong revenue growth in 2015 caused HomeStreet's net income to nearly double to $41.32 million. The company's operating cash levels spiked to $8.31 million for the year (operations had used $348.6 million in 2014) mostly because it collected more in cash-denominated proceeds from its mortgage loan sales than it did in 2014.

Strategy

HomeStreet has been moving more toward commercial mortgage and SBA originations in recent years launching its HomeStreet commercial capital business in Orange County California in 2015. It also continues to acquire other small community banks in its region to grow its loan and deposit business and expand into new geographic markets.

Additionally it's been expanding its retail operations its own opening two new branches in San Diego's Mission Gorge and Kearny Mesa markets in March 2016. To boost profitability HomeStreet looked in 2016 to enhance productivity and cut costs by streamlining operations.

Mergers and Acquisitions

The company plans to buy two Southern California banks from Boston Private Bank & Trust. Through that acquisition HomeStreet will gain some $110 million in deposit accounts. It will then have a dozen retail branches in Southern California.

In February 2016 the company purchased Orange County Business Bank for $55 million extending its reach into "one of the premier commercial and consumer banking markets in the country" according to HomeStreet CEO and chairman Mark Mason.

In March 2015 HomeStreet expanded into Southern California's retail banking market after acquiring Simplicity Bancorp and its seven Simply Bank retail deposit branches in the greater Los Angeles area. Beyond geographic expansion the deal added valuable retail deposit and loan assets.

In November 2013 HomeStreet acquired Fortune Bank a community bank with two branches in Seattle and Bellevue for about $27 million. Concurrently it purchased YNB Financial Services Corp. the parent company of Yakima National Bank which operates four branches in Yakima Selah Sunnyside and Kennewick for about $10.3 million. The twin purchases along with the acquisition of two branches from AmericanWest Bank increased the number of retail deposit branches operates by HomeStreet to 29.

Company Background

HomeStreet went public in February 2012 with an offering worth $55 million. The company sold 1.6 million shares priced at $44 each. HomeStreet had postponed two previous attempts to go public in 2011 that had planned to sell many more shares. Proceeds from the 2012 IPO were used to meet capital-ratio requirements required by regulators in the wake of allegations that the bank engaged in unsafe practices.

HomeStreet was hit hard by the economic downturn and slowdown in the housing market. Trouble in its core mortgage lending business led to losses in 2009 and 2010 and the bank entered into agreements with regulators to improve its capital position earnings and management. It brought in a new management team and launched a turnaround plan to stabilize the business which included tightening its lending standards restructuring troubled loans when necessary and the sale of real estate backed by nonperforming loans. The measures helped HomeStreet return to profitability in 2011 and remain in the black for several years thereafter.

EXECUTIVES

Chairman President and CEO HomeStreet Inc. and HomeStreet Bank, Mark K. Mason, age 57, $537,500 total compensation
EVP Chief Administrative Officer General Counsel and Corporate Secretary Homestreet Inc. and Homestreet Bank, Godfrey B. Evans, age 63, $247,200 total compensation
SEVP Commercial Banking HomeStreet Bank, David H. Straus, age 70
EVP HomeStreet Inc. and EVP Residential Construction and Affiliated Businesses HomeStreet Bank, Richard W. H. (Rich) Bennion, age 67, $203,000 total compensation
EVP and Retail Banking Director HomeStreet Bank, Paulette Lemon, age 60
EVP and Human Resources Director Homestreet Bank, Pamela J. (Pam) Taylor, age 65
EVP Chief Risk Officer and Chief Credit Officer HomeStreet Inc. and Homestreet Bank, Jay C. Iseman, age 57, $200,000 total compensation
SEVP Mortgage Lending Director, Rose Marie David, age 53, $200,000 total compensation
EVP Commercial Real Estate and Commercial Capital President HomeStreet Bank, William D. Endresen, age 62
EVP and Residential Construction Lending Director HomeStreet Bank, Jeff Todhunter
EVP Chief Investment Officer and Treasurer HomeStreet Inc. and HomeStreet Bank, Darrell S. van Amen, age 51
Vice President Income Property Loan Officer, Katie Plett
Vice President Commercial Lending Manager, George Brace
Vice President Loan Officer, Carmen Esteban
Assistant Vice President Senior Marketing Manager Analytics And Digital, Katharine Czechowski
Auditors: Deloitte & Touche LLP

LOCATIONS

HQ: HomeStreet Inc
601 Union Street, Suite 2000, Seattle, WA 98101
Phone: 206 623-3050
Web: www.homestreet.com

PRODUCTS/OPERATIONS

2015 Sales

	$ mil.	% of total
Interest		
Loans	152	34
Investment securities available for sale	11	3
Other	0	-
Non-interest		
Net gains on mortgage origination & sales activities	236	53
Mortgage servicing	24	6
Depositor & other retail banking fees	5	1
Gain on sale of investment securities available for sale	2	1
Bargain purchase gain	7	2
Insurance agency commission Income from WMS Series LLC and other		4
Total	446	100

Selected Services

Personal Banking
Home LoansInvestmentInsurancePrivate Bank
Commercial Banking
Builder Financing/Residential ConstructionCommercial
  LendingCommercial Real EstatePartnership Programs

COMPETITORS

American Savings Bank	KeyCorp
Bank of America	Sound Financial
Bank of Hawaii	U.S. Bancorp
Banner Corp	Umpqua Holdings
First Hawaiian	Washington Federal
JPMorgan Chase	Wells Fargo

HISTORICAL FINANCIALS

Company Type: Public

Income Statement

FYE: December 31

	ASSETS ($ mil.)	NET INCOME ($ mil.)	INCOME AS % OF ASSETS	EMPLOYEES
12/16	6,243	58	0.9%	2,552
12/15	4,894	41	0.8%	2,139
12/14	3,535	22	0.6%	1,611
12/13	3,066	23	0.8%	1,502
12/12	2,631	82	3.1%	1,099
Annual Growth	24.1%	(8.3%)	—	23.4%

2016 Year-End Financials

Debt ratio: 2.00%
Return on equity: 10.60%
Cash ($ mil.): 53
Current ratio: —
Long-term debt ($ mil.): —

No. of shares (mil.): 26
Dividends
  Yield: —
  Payout: —
Market value ($ mil.): 847

	STOCK PRICE ($) FY Close	P/E High/Low		PER SHARE ($) Earnings	Dividends	Book Value
12/16	31.60	14	8	2.34	0.00	23.48
12/15	21.71	12	9	1.96	0.00	21.08
12/14	17.41	14	11	1.49	0.44	20.34
12/13	20.00	17	11	1.61	0.33	17.97
12/12	25.55	9	3	5.98	0.00	18.34
Annual Growth	5.5%	—	—	(20.9%)	—	6.4%

HOMETOWN AMERICA MANAGEMENT CORP.

LOCATIONS

HQ: HOMETOWN AMERICA MANAGEMENT CORP.
150 N WACKER DR STE 2800, CHICAGO, IL
606061610
Phone: 312 604-7500
Web: WWW.HOMETOWNAMERICA.COM

HISTORICAL FINANCIALS

Company Type: Private

Income Statement

FYE: December 31

	ASSETS ($ mil.)	NET INCOME ($ mil.)	INCOME AS % OF ASSETS	EMPLOYEES
12/07	3,059	56	1.9%	1,000
12/06	2,815	55	2.0%	—
12/05	2,454	55	2.3%	—
12/04	2,288	18	0.8%	—
Annual Growth	10.2%	44.8%	—	—

2007 Year-End Financials

Debt ratio: 15.80%
Return on equity: 15.80%
Cash ($ mil.): 3
Current ratio: 0.20
Long-term debt ($ mil.): —

Dividends
  Yield: —
  Payout: —
Market value ($ mil.): —

HomeTrust Bancshares Inc.

Auditors: Dixon Hughes Goodman LLP

LOCATIONS

HQ: HomeTrust Bancshares Inc.
  10 Woodfin Street, Asheville, NC 28801
Phone: 828 259-3939
Web: www.hometrustbancshares.com

HISTORICAL FINANCIALS

Company Type: Public

Income Statement

FYE: June 30

	ASSETS ($ mil.)	NET INCOME ($ mil.)	INCOME AS % OF ASSETS	EMPLOYEES
06/17	3,206	11	0.4%	486
06/16	2,717	11	0.4%	465
06/15	2,783	8	0.3%	505
06/14	2,074	10	0.5%	471
06/13	1,583	9	0.6%	328
Annual Growth	19.3%	7.0%	—	10.3%

2017 Year-End Financials

Debt ratio: 0.06%
Return on equity: 3.13%
Cash ($ mil.): 369
Current ratio: —
Long-term debt ($ mil.): —

No. of shares (mil.): 18
Dividends
  Yield: —
  Payout: —
Market value ($ mil.): 463

	STOCK PRICE ($) FY Close	P/E High/Low		PER SHARE ($) Earnings	Dividends	Book Value
06/17	24.40	41	27	0.65	0.00	20.96
06/16	18.50	32	26	0.65	0.00	20.00
06/15	16.76	40	35	0.42	0.00	19.04
06/14	15.77	31	28	0.54	0.00	18.28
06/13	16.96	38	26	0.45	0.00	17.65
Annual Growth	9.5%	—	—	9.6%	—	4.4%

Honeywell International Inc

Thermostats and jet engines seem worlds apart but they coexist at Honeywell International. More than a century old the company is a diverse industrial conglomerate with four segments; the largest are Aerospace (turbo engines and flight safety and landing systems) and Home and Building Technologies (smart controls and displays). Additional segments include Performance Materials and Technology (thermal switches fibers and chemicals) and Safety and Productivity Solutions (gas detection technology and mobile devices and software for computing data collection and thermal printing).In late 2017 Honeywell announced it will spin off its turbo charger operations and home heating and security businesses to create two new publicly listed companies.

Change in Company Type

In order to streamline its operations Honeywell in late 2017 announced it was spinning off its turbo charger unit and home heating and security businesses to create two new publicly listed companies. The new business featuring its turbo chargers will be known under the Transportation Systems moniker while home security and heating products will fall under its new Homes and Global Distribution business. After the spin-offs Honeywell believes its remaining portfolio will consist of six high-growth businesses each aligned to the global mega trends of energy efficiency infrastructure investment urbanization and safety.

Operations

Honeywell is organized across four segments: Aerospace (almost 40% of net sales) Home and Building Technologies (roughly 25%) Performance Materials and Technologies (more than 20%) and Safety and Productivity Solutions (more than 10%).

Geographic Reach

Honeywell has more than 1300 manufacturing research and sales offices and facilities; more than 40% of its products are manufactured in Asia and Europe and the US represents about 60% of sales. Other key international markets are Canada and Latin America.

Sales and Marketing

Honeywell sells its products and services to original equipment manufacturers (OEMs) and other end markets like air transport regional aircraft airlines aircraft operators defense and space contractors and automotive and truck manufacturers. It also caters to the petroleum refining gas processing and petrochemical sectors.

Financial Performance

Honeywell's revenues increased 2% from $38.6 billion in 2015 to $29.3 billion in 2016. This growth was led by a 16% spike in Home and Building Technologies sales due to organic growth and additional sales from acquisitions. The organic growth was attributed to new product introductions from its Environmental and Energy Solutions business and volume growth within its Security and Fire operations.

Honeywell's net income however remained static for both 2015 and 2016 hovering around the $4.8 billion mark for both years. This was mostly due to a spike in cost of products and services principally due to increased direct material costs of $380 million driven primarily by acquisitions.

Strategy

For all its segments Honeywell is focused on several issues and initiatives including expanding in China India Eastern Europe Latin America and the Middle East; managing raw material costs through hedging; staying alert for liquidity issues among suppliers and customers; and controlling costs related to asbestos and environmental matters. Over the last few years it has launched new facilities in China Malaysia and India.

Honeywell's strategy for this growth also includes both acquisitions and the divestiture of under-performing units. In 2016 the company sold Honeywell Technology Solutions to KBR for some $300 million.Also that year Honeywell spun off its former resins and chemicals business (within Performance Materials and Technologies) into a standalone publicly traded company named AdvanSix.

Mergers and Acquisitions

Spurred by an aggressive acquisition strategy (possibly spending $10 billion or more through 2018) the company hopes to increase its revenues to $59 billion by 2018.These acquisitions specifically enhance Honeywell's software and technology infrastructure and increase its position within the growing trends involving energy efficiency clean energy generation safety security and global urbanization.

In 2016 Honeywell acquired Intelligrated for $1.5 billion. Intelligrated made and installed automated material handling equipment including conveyors sorters and airport baggage handling equipment as well as ordered fulfillment and warehouse control software. Its operations were added to Honeywell's Safety and Productivity Solutions segment and the deal bolstered Honeywell's industrial Internet of Things expertise to optimize productivity and increase fulfillment speed for its customers.

Looking to fortify its Aerospace segment Honeywell in 2016 purchased Canada-based COM DEV International a satellite and space components provider of switches and multiplexers. The $347 million acquisition extended Honeywell's connectivity capabilities with proven satellite component technologies and granted it access to additional international customers.

Its Safety and Productivity Solutions segment also received a boost in 2016 through the $480 million purchase of New York-based Xtralis a provider of smoke detection products advanced perimeter security technologies and video analytics software. The transaction added products to Honeywell that remotely verify fire and intrusion risks and enhanced its own Critical Infrastructure Protection (CIP) operations.

In 2015 Honeywell completed its $185 million acquisition of Datamax-O'Neil a global manufacturer of fixed and mobile printers used in a variety of retail warehouse and distribution and health care applications. The addition of Datamax-O'Neil to its portfolio enhanced its position within the global barcode printing segment.

HISTORY

During WWI Germany controlled much of the world's chemical industry causing dye and drug shortages. In response Washington Post publisher Eugene Meyer and scientist William Nichols organized the Allied Chemical & Dye Corporation in 1920.

Allied opened a synthetic ammonia plant in 1928 near Hopewell Virginia and became the world's leading producer of ammonia. After WWII Allied began making nylon refrigerants and other products. The company became Allied Chemical Corporation in 1958.

Seeking a supplier of raw materials for its chemical products Allied bought Union Texas Natural Gas in 1962. In the early 1970s CEO John Connor sold many of the firm's unprofitable businesses and invested in oil and gas exploration. By 1979 when Edward Hennessy became CEO Union Texas produced 80% of Allied's income.

Hennessy led the company into the electronics and technical markets. Under a new name Allied Corporation (1981) it bought the Bendix Corporation an aerospace and automotive company in 1983. In 1985 Allied merged with Signal Companies (founded by Sam Mosher in 1922) to form AlliedSignal. The company spun off more than 40 unprofitable chemical and engineering businesses over the next two years.

Larry Bossidy hired from General Electric in 1991 as the new CEO began to cut waste and buy growth businesses. In 1998 alone the company made 13 acquisitions. Late in 1999 the company acquired Honeywell (which dated back to 1906) in a deal valued at $15 billion and changed its name to Honeywell International. Honeywell after trying to make a go of it in the computer and telecommunications industries had refocused on its core products lines — thermostats security systems and other automation equipment.

In 2016 Honeywell was engaged in talks to merge with industry powerhouse United Technologies Corp. in a merger valued at around $90 billion. The talks ended however after United Technologies refused to explore the deal further fearing that the massive transaction could not clear steep regulatory hurdles.

EXECUTIVES

President and CEO Aerospace, Timothy O. (Tim) Mahoney, age 60, $917,019 total compensation
CEO Honeywell China and India, Shane Tedjarati
President and CEO Home and Building Technologies (HBT), Terrence S. Hahn, age 51
SVP Engineering Operations and Information Technology, Krishna Mikkilineni, age 57, $717,678 total compensation
President and CEO Performance Materials and Technologies, Rajeev Gautam, age 64
President and CEO Safety and Productivity Solutions (SPS), John Waldron, age 41
SVP and CFO, Thomas A. (Tom) Szlosek, age 53, $840,000 total compensation
President and CEO, Darius Adamczyk, age 51, $1,120,383 total compensation
President and CEO Honeywell Transportation Systems, Olivier Rabiller
President Honeywell Intelligrated, Pieter Krynauw
President Honeywell Thailand, Mai Trang Thanh
Vice President General Manager Resins And Chemicals, Qamar S Bhatia
Vice President Marketing, Brian Holliday
Vice President Electrical Sourcing, Lawrence Polizzotto
Vice President Marketing, Athanasios Karras
Vice President Americas Htt, Anthony Schultz
Vice President Marketing, Jeff Klein
Vice President Global Operations Integrated Supply Chain COE, Stan St John
Senior Vice President Global Govt Relations, Jim Carroll
Chairman, David M. (Dave) Cote, age 64
Auditors: Deloitte & Touche LLP

LOCATIONS

HQ: Honeywell International Inc
115 Tabor Road, Morris Plains, NJ 07950
Phone: 973 455-2000   **Fax:** 973 455-4807
Web: www.honeywell.com

2016 Sales

	$ mil.	% of total
US	22,652	68
Europe	9,966	25
Rest of world	6,684	17
Total	**39,302**	**100**

PRODUCTS/OPERATIONS

2016 Sales

	$ mil.	% of total
Aerospace	14,751	38
Home and Building Technologies	10,654	27
Performance Materials and Technologies	9,272	23
Safety and Productivity Solutions	4,625	12
Total	**39,302**	**100**

2016 Sales

	$ mil.	% of total
Product sales	31,362	80
Service sales	7,940	20
Total	**39,302**	**100**

Selected Services

Aerospace
 Ground support
 Repair and overhaul
 Spare parts
 Training
Automation and Control Solutions
 Building information and energy management
 HVAC maintenance and repair

COMPETITORS

3M	KVH Industries
Albemarle	Kion Group
BorgWarner	Kyocera
Dow Chemical	Rockwell Automation
DuPont	Schneider Electric
Emerson Electric	Siemens AG
GE	TE Connectivity
Garmin	Teijin
ITT Corp.	United Technologies
Jeppesen Sanderson	Zebra Technologies

HISTORICAL FINANCIALS

Company Type: Public

Income Statement

FYE: December 31

	REVENUE ($ mil.)	NET INCOME ($ mil.)	NET PROFIT MARGIN	EMPLOYEES
12/17	40,534	1,655	4.1%	131,000
12/16	39,302	4,809	12.2%	131,000
12/15	38,581	4,768	12.4%	129,000
12/14	40,306	4,239	10.5%	127,000
12/13	39,055	3,924	10.0%	131,000
Annual Growth	**0.9%**	**(19.4%)**	**—**	**0.0%**

2017 Year-End Financials

Debt ratio: 30.11%
Return on equity: 9.03%
Cash ($ mil.): 7,059
Current ratio: 1.38
Long-term debt ($ mil.): 12,573

No. of shares (mil.): 750
Dividends
 Yield: 0.0%
 Payout: 128.0%
Market value ($ mil.): 115,158

	STOCK PRICE ($) FY Close	P/E High/Low		PER SHARE ($) Earnings	Dividends	Book Value
12/17	153.36	72	54	2.14	2.74	23.01
12/16	115.85	19	15	6.20	2.45	25.46
12/15	103.57	18	15	6.04	2.15	24.11
12/14	99.92	19	16	5.33	1.87	22.85
12/13	91.37	18	13	4.92	1.68	22.50
Annual Growth	**13.8%**	**—**	**—**	**(18.8%)**	**13.0%**	**0.6%**

Hope Bancorp Inc

EXECUTIVES

Evp And Chief Lending Officer Bbcn Bank, Jason K Kim

Executive Vice President Chief Operations Administrator, Sook Goo

Vice President And Systems Support Manager, Joshua Chu

Senior Vice President and Chief Credit Officer, Peter Koh

FVP and Manager General Services Department, Brandon Lee

Vice President Desktop Manager We Are Now Bank of Hope, Charles Yoo

Senior Vice President Institutional Banking Director Business Aircraft, Scott Schaidle

Senior Vice President 8c Branch Manager, Cindy Chi

Senior Vice President Manager Vendor Risk Management, Bradley Martin

AAP Senior Vice President TMS Operations Manager, Rachel Lim

Senior Vice President and Director of Investment Banking Operations, Charuka Sinhabahu

Vice President and Operational Risk Management Assistant, Katelyn Kang

First Vice President and Senior Financial Analyst, Joonhyok Shin

Vice President International Operations, Lisa Lee

AVP and Loan Officer Bank of Hope, James Chong

Auditors: Crowe Horwath LLP

LOCATIONS

HQ: Hope Bancorp Inc
3200 Wilshire Boulevard, Suite 1400, Los Angeles, CA 90010
Phone: 213 387-3200   **Fax:** 213 235-3033
Web: www.bankofhope.com

PRODUCTS/OPERATIONS

2015 Sales

	$ mil.	% of total
Interest income	313	88
Non-interest income	43	12
Total	**357**	**100**

COMPETITORS

Bank of America	Grandpoint
Broadway Financial	Hanmi Financial
Cathay General Bancorp	U.S. Bancorp
East West Bancorp	Wells Fargo
Far East National Bank	Woori

HISTORICAL FINANCIALS

Company Type: Public

Income Statement

FYE: December 31

	ASSETS ($ mil.)	NET INCOME ($ mil.)	INCOME AS % OF ASSETS	EMPLOYEES
12/16	13,441	113	0.8%	1,372
12/15	7,912	92	1.2%	938
12/14	7,140	88	1.2%	915
12/13	6,475	81	1.3%	835
12/12	5,640	83	1.5%	704
Annual Growth	**24.2%**	**8.1%**	**—**	**18.2%**

2016 Year-End Financials

Debt ratio: 0.74%
Return on equity: 8.12%
Cash ($ mil.): 437
Current ratio: —
Long-term debt ($ mil.): —
No. of shares (mil.): 135
Dividends
Yield: 0.0%
Payout: 40.9%
Market value ($ mil.): 2,960

	STOCK PRICE ($) FY Close	P/E High/Low	PER SHARE ($) Earnings	Dividends	Book Value
12/16	21.89	20 13	1.10	0.45	13.72
12/15	17.22	17 11	1.16	0.42	11.79
12/14	14.38	16 12	1.11	0.35	11.10
12/13	16.59	16 11	1.03	0.25	10.19
12/12	11.57	13 10	0.99	0.05	9.62
Annual Growth	**17.3%**	**— —**	**2.7%**	**73.2%**	**9.3%**

Horace Mann Educators Corp.

Naming itself in honor of Horace Mann considered the father of public education Horace Mann Educators is an insurance holding company that primarily serves K-12 school teachers and other public school employees throughout the US. Through its operating subsidiaries the company offers homeowners auto (majority of revenue) and individual and group life insurance as well as retirement annuities. Horace Mann employs some 735 agents many of whom are former teachers themselves. Writing business in 48 states and Washington DC the company derives about a third of its direct premiums and contract deposits from five states — California Illinois Texas North Carolina and Florida.

Operations

Horace Mann maintains a long-standing relationship with the country's biggest education association the National Education Association which has around 3.2 million members. It has also established a number of advertising and sponsorship agreements with a host of smaller educator groups as a way to drum up new business leads.

The company divides it business into property and casualty insurance annuities and life insurance. Property casualty is the largest contributor to revenue with auto being the largest component of that group. The property and casualty annuity and life segments account for some 48% 44% and 8% respectively of the company's insurance premiums and contract deposits.

Geographic Reach

The company is based in Springfield Illinois.

Financial Performance

Horace Mann's net revenue has been increasing steadily in recent years and in fiscal 2015 climbed a further 2% to $1.1 billion. The company was able to charge higher average premiums per policy for homeowners and automobiles.

Net income however has been falling consistently in the past five years and in fiscal 2015 fell 10% to $93.5 million due to an increase in property and casualty loss severity (particularly in automobile) as well as catastrophe costs and life mortality costs. Cash from operating activities fell 7% to $207.0 million due to an increase in claims and policyholder benefits paid.

Strategy

In recent years the company has moved away from single-person agency operations to an agency business model (ABM) with multiple sales agents licensed product specialists and other support personnel based together in outside offices. The company saw enough success with the ABM model that it began migrating agents over to an exclusive agent agreement through which the agents become independent contractors that only sell Ho-

race Mann products. Nearly all its agents now operate in this manner.

EXECUTIVES

Executive Vice President Service and Technology Operations and Financial Services, George J Zock

EVP and CFO, Dwayne D. Hallman, age 54, $444,000 total compensation

President and CEO, Marita Zuraitis, age 56, $742,333 total compensation

EVP Annuity and Life, Matthew P. Sharpe, $394,000 total compensation

EVP Property and Casualty, William J. Caldwell, $325,000 total compensation

Assistant Vice Presi, Paul Wappel

Vice President Information Technology, Eshwar Pastapur

Vice President Human Resources, Kathi Karr

Vice President Chief Actuary, Robert Rich

Assistant Vice President Product Management, Joel Abrahamson

Assistant Vice President Product Management, Adam Wendling

Assistant Vice President Claims Training, Jill Kilroy

Chairman, Gabriel L. Shaheen, age 64

Auditors: KPMG LLP

LOCATIONS

HQ: Horace Mann Educators Corp.
1 Horace Mann Plaza, Springfield, IL 62715-0001
Phone: 217 789-2500
Web: www.horacemann.com

PRODUCTS/OPERATIONS

2016 Sales

	$ mil.	% of total
Insurance premiums & contract charges earned	759	67
Net investment income	361	32
Net realized investment gains	4	-
Other income	4	1
Total	**1,128**	**100**

COMPETITORS

AIG	Nationwide
AXA	Progressive
Allstate	Corporation
Farmers Group	Security Benefit Group
GEICO	State Farm
ING Americas	TIAA
LSW	USAA
Liberty Mutual Agency	VALIC
MetLife	

HISTORICAL FINANCIALS

Company Type: Public

Income Statement

FYE: December 31

	ASSETS ($ mil.)	NET INCOME ($ mil.)	INCOME AS % OF ASSETS	EMPLOYEES
12/16	10,576	83	0.8%	2,061
12/15	10,059	93	0.9%	2,034
12/14	9,768	104	1.1%	2,008
12/13	8,826	110	1.3%	2,095
12/12	8,167	103	1.3%	2,058
Annual Growth	**6.7%**	**(5.2%)**	**—**	**0.0%**

2016 Year-End Financials

Debt ratio: 2.34%
Return on equity: 6.53%
Cash ($ mil.): 16
Current ratio: —
Long-term debt ($ mil.): —
No. of shares (mil.): 40
Dividends
Yield: 0.0%
Payout: 52.4%
Market value ($ mil.): 1,722

	STOCK PRICE ($) FY Close	P/E High/Low	PER SHARE ($) Earnings	Dividends	Book Value
12/16	42.80	21 14	2.02	1.06	32.15
12/15	33.18	17 14	2.20	1.00	31.18
12/14	33.18	13 11	2.47	0.92	32.65
12/13	31.54	11 7	2.66	0.78	27.14
12/12	19.96	8 5	2.51	0.55	31.65
Annual Growth	21.0%	— —	(5.3%)	17.8%	0.4%

Horizon Bancorp (Michigan City, IN)

For those in Indiana and Michigan Horizon Bancorp stretches as far as the eye can see. The company is the holding company for Horizon Bank (and its Heartland Community Bank division) which provides checking and savings accounts IRAs CDs and credit cards to customers through more than 50 branches in north and central Indiana and southwest and central Michigan. Commercial financial and agricultural loans make up the largest segment of its loan portfolio which also includes mortgage warehouse loans (loans earmarked for sale into the secondary market) consumer loans and residential mortgages. Through subsidiaries the bank offers trust and investment management services; life health and property/casualty insurance; and annuities.

Operations

Horizon boasted more than $2.08 billion in total assets and $1.48 billion in deposits in 2014. Commercial loans made up 49% of the bank's total loan portfolio. The bank employed nearly 450 full and part time employees that year.

Horizon's subsidiaries include: Horizon Investments which manages the bank's investment portfolio; Horizon Properties which manages the real estate investment trust; Horizon Insurance Services which sells through the company's Wealth Management; and Horizon Grantor Trust which holds title to certain company-owned life insurance policies.

The bank generated 61% of its revenue from interest income on loans in 2014 while another 13% came from interest on its taxable and tax-exempt investments. About 8% of revenues came from gains on its mortgage sales while the remainder of revenues were mostly generated by a mix of service charges on deposit accounts interchange fees and fiduciary activities fees.

Geographic Reach

The bank's more than 30 branches serve customers in north and central Indiana and southwest and central Michigan. Its mortgage-banking services are offered across the Midwest.

Financial Performance

Horizon Bancorp's revenues and profits have been trending higher over the past few years mostly as it's continued to grow its loan business and deposit customer base through acquisitions.

The bank's revenue rose by 2% to $102.5 million in 2014 mostly as the bank increased its interest-earning assets during the year. Its non-interest income also increased thanks to higher service charges on deposits and interchange fee income resulting from the growth in transactional deposit accounts and volume.

Despite higher revenue in 2014 the company's net income fell by 9% to $18.1 million for the year on higher provisions for loan losses due to loan growth and a write off of a commercial account coupled with an increase in transaction costs related to its Summit acquisition and an increase in salaries and employee benefits due to growth. Horizon's operating cash levels fell by 62% to $17.7 million after adjusting its earnings for non-cash items related to its net proceeds on the sale of its held-for-sale loans.

Strategy

Horizon Bancorp continues to expand its geographic reach and loan business through acquisitions and new branches. It acquired several banks and opened new branches throughout 2016 and 2017.

Mergers and Acquisitions

In 2017 Horizon Bancorp agreed to buy Wolverine Bancorp for $92 million and Lafayette Community Bancorp for $32 million

In 2016 Horizon Bancorp bought LaPorte Bancorp for $98.9 million boosting its total assets by 20% to more than $3.24 billion while expanding its branch reach into the LaPorte area of Indiana. It also agreed to buy CNB Bancorp which operates Central National Bank & Trust in Attica Indiana.

In 2015 Horizon Bancorp agreed to buy Peoples Bancorp and subsidiary Peoples Federal Savings Bank of DeKalb County.

In April 2014 the company purchased SCP Bancorp including subsidiary Summit Community Bank and its two branches.

EXECUTIVES

President CEO Chief Administrative Officer and Director; Chairman and CEO Horizon Bank, Craig M. Dwight, age 60, $300,000 total compensation
EVP; President and COO Horizon Bank, Thomas H. Edwards, age 64, $187,000 total compensation
CFO, Mark E. Secor, age 51, $131,921 total compensation
President LaPorte County Indiana Horizon Bank, Steven C. Kring
President Southwest Michigan Horizon Bank, Donald E. (Don) Radde, age 64, $166,000 total compensation
President Porter County Indiana Horizon Bank, David G. Rose
Vice President Consumer Loan Manager, Jill Sandilla
Vice President Data Processing, Bradford Smith
Chairman, Robert C. Dabagia, age 78
Auditors: BKD, LLP

LOCATIONS

HQ: Horizon Bancorp (Michigan City, IN)
515 Franklin Square, Michigan City, IN 46360
Phone: 219 879-0211
Web: www.accesshorizon.com

PRODUCTS/OPERATIONS

Selected Subsidiaries
Horizon Bank National Association
Horizon Insurance Services Inc.
Horizon Investments Inc.
Horizon Trust & Investment Management N.A.

COMPETITORS

1st Source Corporation	Farmers Mutual of NE
American United Mutual	Fifth Third
Bank of America	First Merchants
Brotherhood Mutual	Indiana Farmers Mutual

HISTORICAL FINANCIALS

Company Type: Public

Income Statement

FYE: December 31

	ASSETS ($ mil.)	NET INCOME ($ mil.)	INCOME AS % OF ASSETS	EMPLOYEES
12/16	3,141	23	0.8%	665
12/15	2,652	20	0.8%	558
12/14	2,076	18	0.9%	448
12/13	1,758	19	1.1%	421
12/12	1,848	19	1.1%	419
Annual Growth	14.2%	5.2%	—	12.2%

2016 Year-End Financials

Debt ratio: 1.81%
Return on equity: 7.85%
Cash ($ mil.): 70
Current ratio: —
Long-term debt ($ mil.): —
No. of shares (mil.): 22
Dividends
  Yield: 0.0%
  Payout: 33.6%
Market value ($ mil.): 621

	STOCK PRICE ($) FY Close	P/E High/Low	PER SHARE ($) Earnings	Dividends	Book Value
12/16	28.00	27 18	1.19	0.40	15.37
12/15	27.96	22 17	1.26	0.38	14.90
12/14	26.14	20 15	1.27	0.34	14.07
12/13	25.33	17 13	1.45	0.28	12.71
12/12	19.65	18 10	1.53	0.25	12.30
Annual Growth	9.3%	— —	(6.1%)	12.6%	5.7%

Hormel Foods Corp.

The maker of such thrifty pantry staples as SPAM lunch meat and Dinty Moore stew Hormel Foods produces a slew of refrigerated processed meats and deli items ethnic entrees and frozen foods sold under the flagship Hormel brand as well as Don Miguel and MegaMex (Mexican) and Lloyd's (barbeque). Food service offerings include Hormel Natural Choice meats Caf © H Austin Blues and Bread Ready pre-sliced meats. Hormel is also a major US turkey and pork processor churning out Jennie-O turkey Cure 81 hams and Always Tender pork. More than 30 Hormel brands are ranked #1 or #2 in their respective markets.

HISTORY

George Hormel opened his Austin Minnesota slaughterhouse in an abandoned creamery in 1891. By 1900 Hormel had modernized his facilities to compete with larger meat processors. In 1903 the enterprise introduced its first brand name (Dairy Brand) and a year later began opening distribution centers nationwide. The scandal that ensued after the discovery in 1921 that an assistant controller had embezzled over $1 million almost broke the company causing Hormel to initiate tighter controls. By 1924 it was processing more than a million hogs annually. Hormel introduced canned ham two years later.

Jay Hormel George's son became president in 1929; under his guidance Hormel introduced Dinty Moore beef stew (1936) and SPAM (1937). A Hormel executive won a contest and $100 by submitting the name a contraction of "spiced ham." During WWII the US government bought over half of Hormel's output; it supplied SPAM to GIs and Allied forces.

In 1959 Hormel introduced its Little Sizzlers pork sausage and sold its billionth can of SPAM. New products rolled out in the 1960s included

Hormel's Cure 81 ham (1963). By the mid-1970s the firm had more than 750 products.

The company survived a violent nationally publicized strike triggered by a pay cut in 1985. In the end only 500 of the original 1500 strikers returned to accept lower pay scales.

Sensing the consumer shift toward poultry Hormel purchased Jennie-O Foods in 1986. Later acquisitions included the House of Tsang and Oriental Deli (1992) Dubuque (processed pork 1993) and Herb-Ox (bouillon and dry soup mix 1993). After more than a century as Geo. A. Hormel & Co. the company began calling itself Hormel Foods in 1993 to reflect its expansion into non-pork foods. Former General Foods executive Joel Johnson was named president and CEO that year (and chairman two years later).

Hormel proved it could take a joke with the 1994 debut of its tongue-in-cheek SPAM catalog featuring dozens of SPAM-related products. But when a 1996 Muppets movie featured a porcine character named Spa'am Hormel sued Jim Henson Productions; a federal court gave Spa'am the go-ahead.

Also in 1996 Hormel teamed up with Mexican food processor Grupo Herdez to sell Herdez sauces and other Mexican food products in the US. It then formed a joint venture with Indian food producer Patak Spices (UK) to market its products in the US. Late that year Hormel paid $64 million for a 21% interest in Spanish food maker Campofrio Alimentacion.

Earnings fell in 1996 due in part to soaring hog prices. The company was hit hard again in 1998 when production contracts with hog growers meant it wound up paying premium rates despite a market glut. In 1998 the Smithsonian Institution accepted two cans of SPAM (one from 1937 the other an updated 1997 version) for its History of Technology collection.

SPAM sales soared in 1999 as nervous consumers stockpiled provisions for the millennium. To build its growing HealthLabs division Hormel acquired Cliffdale Farms (2000) and Diamond Crystal Brands nutritional products (a division of Imperial Sugar) in 2001 — boosting its share of the market for easy-to-swallow foods sold to hospitals and nursing homes.

In early 2001 Hormel acquired family-owned The Turkey Store for approximately $334 million and folded it into its Jennie-O division.

Hormel produced its 6 billionth can of SPAM in 2002 and traded $115 million in stock to acquire the rest of Imperial Sugar's Diamond Crystal Brands unit which packages single-serve packets of sugar sweeteners seasonings and plastic cutlery for the foodservice industry.

To further diversify in 2003 Hormel acquired food manufacturer Century Foods International (whey-based protein powders beverages and nutrition bars) and added it to its burgeoning specialty foods group. In 2004 Hormel sold off its stake in Campofrio to Smithfield Foods.

Its last act of business in 2004 was to purchase Southern California's Clougherty Packing for about $186 million. The pork processor's facilities help extend Hormel's capacity for further-processed foods in the southwestern US.

In 2005 the company purchased Mexican food manufacturer Arriba Foods for $47 million in cash. Later that year it bought Lloyd's Barbecue Company from General Mills.

Responding to the growing trend of the US population to dine out Hormel expanded its foodservice segment (which it refers to as its specialty foods business) with the 2005 purchase of foodservice food manufacturer and distributor Mark-Lynn Foods. Mark-Lynn's products include salt and pepper packets ketchup mustard sauces and

salad dressings creamers and sugar packets as well as jellies desserts and drink mixes.

Adding to its grocery product offerings in 2006 the company acquired canned ready-to-eat chicken producer Valley Fresh Foods for $78 million. It also bought pepperoni and pasta maker Provena Foods and sausage and sliced meat maker Saag's Products. It added another to its list of countries in which it has joint ventures in 2006 when it formed a JV with San Miguel to raise and market hogs and animal feed in Vietnam. The JV is 49%-owned by Hormel.

Hormel acquired Burke Corporation a maker of pizza toppings and other fully cooked meat items in 2007 for $115 million in cash. The acquisition allowed Hormel to extend its pizza-topping operations into the foodservice sector. The following year it acquired Boca Grande Foods for $23.5 in cash. Boca Grande makes Poco Pac branded jams jellies and pancake syrup portion-control products for foodservice operators.

EXECUTIVES

Vice President Marketing, Ronald W Fielding
Group Vice President; President Hormel Foods International, Richard A Bross
Vice President Legislative Affairs, Joe Swedberg
EVP and President Hormel Business Units, Steven G. Binder, age 60, $500,965 total compensation
Group VP and President Hormel Foods International, Larry L. Vorpahl, age 54
VP and Chief Accounting Officer, James N. Sheehan, age 62
Group VP Refrigerated Foods, Thomas R. Day, age 59, $337,900 total compensation
SVP Supply Chain, Bryan D. Farnsworth, age 60
Group VP and President Consumer Products Sales, Deanna T. Brady, age 52
Group VP Specialty Foods, Donald H. (Don) Kremin, age 57
Chairman President and CEO, James P. Snee, age 49, $509,595 total compensation
Group VP and President Jennie-O Turkey Store, Glenn R. Leitch, age 56, $380,500 total compensation
Group VP Foodservice, Jeffrey R. Baker, age 52
Group VP Grocery Products, Luis G. Marconi, age 50
VP Information Technology Services, Mark D. Vaupel
Vice President, Alan Rasell
Vice President of Retail Marketing, Jeff Frank
Vice President, Patrick Connor
Vice President, Brett Asleson
Vice President Business Planning, Steve Althaus
National Sales Manager, Mark Engelhardt
National Sales Manager, Michael Dougherty
Senior Vice President External Affairs and General Counsel, Lori Marco
Vice President Corp SEC, Brian Johnson
Vice President Corporate Communications, Juile Craven
Vice President Farm Operations, Jose Rojas
Vice President Affiliated Business Units Refrigerated Foods, Jim Snee
Vice President Sales and Marketing, Debra DiCarlo
Senior Vice President Sales, Dan Hartzog
Vice President and Director of Marketing and Administration, Tim Barinka
Vice President Supply Chain, Bill Snyder
Treasurer, Michael Mccoy
Vice Chairman, Kim Bruggeman
Auditors: Ernst & Young LLP

LOCATIONS

HQ: Hormel Foods Corp.
1 Hormel Place, Austin, MN 55912-3680
Phone: 507 437-5611   **Fax:** 507 437-5489
Web: www.hormel.com

2016 sales

	$ mil.	% of total
US	9,012	95
Foreign	510	5
Total	**9,523**	**100**

PRODUCTS/OPERATIONS

2016 sales

	$ mil.	% of total
Grocery Products	1,684	18
Refrigerated Foods	4,647	49
Jennie-O Turkey Store	1,740	18
Specialty Foods	939	10
International & Other	511	5
Total	**9,523**	**100**

Selected Products and Brands

Refrigerated
  Country Crock Side Dishes
  Hormel
  Hormel Always Tender flavored pork and beef products
  Hormel Black Label and Microwave Ready bacon
  Hormel Cure 81 ham
  Hormel Fresh Pantry meats
  Hormel Little Sizzlers pork sausage
  Hormel Natural Choice meats
  Hormel pepperoni minis and stix
  Hormel refrigerated entrees
  Hormel Wranglers franks
  Hormel Snac Cups
  Lloyd's Barbeque products
  Saag's sausages
Jennie-O Turkey Store
  Bratwursts and breakfast/dinner sausages
  Breast meat products
  Deli
  Di Lusso deli meats
  Farmer John deli meats
  Hormel 100 percent natural deli meats
  Hormel Deli beef dry sausage ham and turkey
  Hormel party trays
  Ground turkey
  Marinated turkey tenderloins
  So-Easy Entrees
  Turkey burger patties and franks
  Whole turkeys
Grocery products
  Dinty Moore stew Hearty Meals varieties microwave-ready products
  Herb-Ox bouillon
  Herdez Salsa
  Hormel
  Hormel bacon toppings
  Hormel Chili Master
  Hormel chunk meats
  Hormel Compleats microwave meals
  Hormel corned beef and roast beef with gravy
  Hormel dried beef
  Hormel Kid's Kitchen microwave cups
  Hormel Mary Kitchen hash
  Hormel microwave cups
  Not-So-Sloppy-Joe sloppy joe sauce
  Skippy peanut butter
  SPAM products (classic hickory smoke flavored hot and spicy lite low-sodium spread singles and oven-roasted turkey)
  Stagg chili
  Valley Fresh chunk meats and broths
Specialty Foods
  Century Foods International (dairy and vegetable proteins nutraceuticals)
  Diamond Crystal Brands (salts sugar substitutes)
  Hormel Foods Ingredients (sauces powders broths oils Omega-3 additives)
  Private Label products (canned meats prepared foods and desserts bouillon sweeteners salts seasonings)
Other
  MegaMex Mexican brands
  Bufalo hot sauces
  CHI-CHI'S Mexican hot sauces taco tubs dips seasoning mixes and tortillas
  Do?a Marí;a Authentic Mexican products
  Don Miguel burritos appetizers empanadas taquitos tacos flautas chimichangas enchiladas
  El Torito sauces dressings and corn cakes
  Embasa Mexican peppers salsas
  Herdez imported salsas

La Victoria Mexican salsas taco sauces enchilada sauces green chile peppers
Wholly Guacamole
World Food ethnic brands
House of Tsang sauces and oils
Marrakesh Express Mediterranean products (couscous risotto)
Peloponnese Greek foods olives

Selected Foodservice Brands

Always Tender Pork
Austin Blues barbeque meats
Authentic Barbeque
Bread Ready pre-sliced meats
Café; H ethnic meats
Cure 81 Ham
Dry Sausage
Fast 'N Easy Fully Cooked Meats
Hormel Chili
Masterpieces Toppings
Natural Choice meats
Old Smokehouse bacon
Old Tyme breakfast sausage
Old Tyme ham
Special Recipe Sausage
Stagg Chili

COMPETITORS

B&G Foods	H. J. Heinz Limited
Boar's Head	JBS USA
Bob Evans	Perdue Incorporated
Bridgford Foods	Pilgrim's Pride
Bush Brothers	Pinnacle Foods
Butterball	Plainville Farms
Campbell Soup	Sanderson Farms
Cargill	Seaboard
ConAgra	Smithfield Foods
Cooper Farms	Smucker
Eberly Poultry	The Dial Corporation
Foster Farms	Tyson Foods
General Mills	

HISTORICAL FINANCIALS

Company Type: Public

Income Statement

FYE: October 29

	REVENUE ($ mil.)	NET INCOME ($ mil.)	NET PROFIT MARGIN	EMPLOYEES
10/17	9,167	846	9.2%	20,200
10/16	9,523	890	9.3%	21,100
10/15	9,263	686	7.4%	20,700
10/14	9,316	602	6.5%	20,400
10/13	8,751	526	6.0%	19,800
Annual Growth	1.2%	12.6%	—	0.5%

2017 Year-End Financials

Debt ratio: 3.58%
Return on equity: 18.05%
Cash ($ mil.): 444
Current ratio: 1.92
Long-term debt ($ mil.): 250

No. of shares (mil.): 528
Dividends
Yield: 0.0%
Payout: 43.3%
Market value ($ mil.): 16,054

	STOCK PRICE ($) FY Close	P/E High/Low	PER SHARE ($) Earnings	Dividends	Book Value
10/17	30.38	24 19	1.57	0.68	9.34
10/16	38.22	49 20	1.64	0.58	8.42
10/15	68.33	53 39	1.27	0.50	7.57
10/14	52.54	46 37	1.12	0.40	6.84
10/13	43.62	44 30	0.98	0.34	6.28
Annual Growth	(8.6%)	— —	12.6%	18.9%	10.4%

Horton (DR) Inc

When this Horton heard a Who it built the little guy a house. One of the largest homebuilding companies in the US D.R. Horton constructs single-family homes that range in size from 1000 sq. ft. to 4000 sq. ft. and sell for an average price of about $300000 under the D.R. Horton and other brand names. Texas-based D.R. Horton is active in nearly 80 markets in 26 states and generates more than 75% of its revenue in the Southeast South Central and Western regions of the US. Beyond single-family detached homes which account for some 90% of sales D.R. Horton builds duplexes townhomes and condominiums. It also provides mortgage title and closing services.

Operations

The primary activity of D.R. Horton is acquiring land developing infrastructure on the land (utilities roads) and building residential homes. Its homes range in size from 1000 square feet to more than 4000 square feet and in price from $100000 to more than $1000000. In a typical year the builder sells more than 40000 homes.

Most of its direct homebuilding activities are decentralized to provide operational flexibility to its nearly 40 local management teams who are familiar with local conditions. The divisions report to one of six regional offices. Generally each operating division consists of a division president; a controller; land entitlement acquisition and development personnel; sales and marketing personnel; a construction manager and construction superintendents; customer service personnel; a purchasing manager and office staff.

Geographic Reach

Arlington TX-based D.R. Horton is hammering away in 26 states. On a regional basis the homebuilder generates about 30% of its sales in the Southeast (Florida Georgia among others) 25% in the South Central US (in states such as Texas Louisiana and Oklahoma) and 25% in the West (including California Oregon Washington Hawaii).

Sales and Marketing

The builder markets and sells its homes under the D.R. Horton Emerald Homes Express Homes and Freedom Homes brand names in most of its markets. As part of a recent acquisition it sells homes in the Seattle market under the Pacific Ridge Homes moniker. In FY2017 (ended September) homes marketed under Express Homes brand represented 31% of closings and 24% of home sales revenue while Emerald Homes brand represented 4% of home closings and 8% of home sales revenue.

D.R. Horton markets and sells homes mostly through commissioned employees and independent real estate brokers. It also markets through digital media (such as email search engine marketing social networking sites and the company website) and print media and advertisement formats such as billboards radio television magazine and newspaper advertising in local markets.

Financial Performance

D.R. Horton has enjoyed growing revenue and higher profits over the past several years thanks to a strengthening housing market and higher demand for higher-end homes. The builder's FY2017 revenues are closing in on the $15 billion mark posted in 2006 the high-water point achieved just prior to the 2008-2009 Financial Crisis.

In FY2017 (ended September 30 2017) revenue rose to $14 billion 16% higher than FY2016 on increased home sales (up 14% year over year) and higher average selling prices. Its financial services albeit a small portion of overall revenue posted an 18% increase in sales generating nearly $350 million.

The rise in sales along with marginally better operating margins boosted net income 17% to $1.0 billion in 2016 from 2015. It was the first time it exceeded the $1 billion profit threshold since 2006.

Cash on hand at the end of FY2017 was $1.0 billion down about $300 million from the prior year. Operating activities contributed $435 million including the $1.0 billion in net income reduced by investments in work-in-progress homes and residential lots. Investing activities used $171 million and financing activities used $560 million mostly for debt repayments.

Strategy

D.R. Horton?s strategy is hitting on all cylinders lately. Its ability to weather the Great Recession (2008-2009) which hit home builders particularly hard allowed it to make long-term investments that are now paying off. As the US economy continues its multi-year growth trend the housing market continues to climb upward creating a welcome tailwind for the fortunes of D.R. Horton.

In recent years it has focused on expanding its product offerings to more consistently include a broad range of homes for entry-level move-up and luxury buyers across most of its geographic markets. Its entry-level homes have experienced very strong demand from homebuyers as the entry-level segment of the new home market remains under-served with low inventory levels relative to demand. Beginning in late 2016 D.R. Horton started introducing affordable homes in communities designed for active adult buyers seeking a low-maintenance lifestyle.

The company continues to acquire regional builders and their brands assets and home/lot inventories to grow looking to sell more homes at higher prices. The late 2017 acquisition of Texas-based Forestar Group Inc. (Forestar) advanced D.R. Horton?s strategy of increasing its access to high-quality optioned land and lot positions.

Mergers and Acquisitions

In October 2017 D.R. Horton acquired a controlling 75% stake in AustinTX-based home builder Forestar for some $550 million. The acquisition added to D.R. Horton's supply of developed lots and granted it rights to influence Forestar's strategic direction. Forestar's eleven-state operations include ownership of gas oil and timber real estate rights though its home building operations are primarily in Texas.

In September 2016 the company acquired the homebuilding operations of Wilson Parker Homes including some 490 lots and 700 homes in inventory and backlog plus control of around 1850 lots through option contracts. Wilson Parker operated primarily in the Atlanta area but also had holdings in August Georgia; the Carolinas; and Arizona.

In May 2015 D.R. Horton purchased Seattle-based builder Pacific Ridge Homes — including its 350 lots 90 homes in inventory and 40 homes in sales order backlog — for some $72 million in cash. D.R. Horton also bought control of some 400 lots through option contracts. Pacific Ridge would operate as a separate division within D.R. Horton.

In May 2014 D.R. Horton acquired the home-building assets of Crown Communities — including roughly a thousand homes that had been sold or remained in inventory as well as more than 2000 lots in Georgia South Carolina and Alabama — for $210 million.

Company Background

Chairman Donald R. Horton founded the business in 1978.

HISTORY

Donald R. Horton was selling homes in Fort Worth Texas when he hit upon a strategy for increasing sales — add options to a basic floor plan. In 1978 he borrowed $33000 to build his first home added a bay window for an additional charge and sold the home for $44000. Donald soon added floor plans and options that appealed to regional preferences.

The depressed Texas market drove the company to expand beyond the Dallas/Fort Worth area in 1987 when it entered the then-hot Phoenix market. It continued to expand into the Southeast Mid-Atlantic Midwest and West in the late 1980s and early 1990s. By 1991 Horton and his family owned more than 25 companies that were combined as D.R. Horton which went public in 1992.

D.R. Horton acquired six geographically diverse construction firms in 1994 and 1995. In 1996 the company started a mortgage services joint venture expanded its title operations and added three more firms.

In 1998 the company bought four builders including Scottsdale Arizona-based Continental Homes. Continental had been expanding beyond its Arizona and Southern California base and had entered the lucrative retirement community market. After the Continental purchase Donald Horton stepped down as president remaining chairman. Richard Beckwitt took over as president and Donald Tomnitz became CEO. In 1999 the company acquired Century Title and Midwest builder Cambridge Properties.

D.R. Horton sold its St. Louis assets to McBride & Son Enterprises in 2000 after spending five years trying to break into the St. Louis homebuilding market. Tomnitz also took over the duties of president in 2000 when Beckwitt retired.

D.R. Horton gained homebuilding operations in Houston and Phoenix when it bought Emerald Builders in 2001. In February 2002 the company acquired Schuler Homes for $1.2 billion including debt.

Sales continued to climb in fiscal 2003 and 2004. D.R. Horton experienced its 27th consecutive year of earnings and revenue growth in 2004 and broke records by being the first residential homebuilder to sell more than 45000 homes in the US in a fiscal year; in fiscal 2005 the company closed 51172 homes. By 2007 however it was evident that the heady days were over with a rise in cancellations and a larger value of backlog orders.

CEO Donald Tomnitz summed up the housing market crash when he said "I don't want to be too sophisticated here but '07 is going to suck all 12 months of the calendar year." Indeed the company suffered a loss that year and the next when sales orders declined and cancellation rates rose due to tightened mortgage markets and severe liquidity shortages. Adding to homebuilders' difficulties an influx of foreclosed homes on the market brought down the demand for new homes.

D.R. Horton responded to the downturn in 2008 by reducing land and housing inventory controlling construction and inventory costs and using its cash to reduce debt. Despite drops in many markets D.R. Horton saw improvements in its eastern market where home affordability and employment led to a higher demand for new homes.

EXECUTIVES

President West Region, J. Matt Farris
EVP and CFO, William W. (Bill) Wheat, age 51, $500,000 total compensation
President Financial Services, Randall C. (Randy) Present
VP and CIO, Rick Rawlings
President Central Region, Rick Horton

President and CEO, David V. Auld, age 60, $700,000 total compensation
SVP Busienss Development, Michael Murray, $500,000 total compensation
President East Region, Tom Hill
President North Region, Doug Brown
President Florida Region, Paul Romanowski
Vice President And Division Counsel, Carolyn Mitchell
Vice President of Construction, David Gude
Chairman, Donald R. Horton, age 67
Auditors: PricewaterhouseCoopers LLP

LOCATIONS

HQ: Horton (DR) Inc
   1341 Horton Circle, Arlington, TX 76102
Phone: 817 390-8200
Web: www.drhorton.com

FY2017 Homebuilding Sales by Region

	% of total
West	24
South central	24
Southeast	330
East	12
Midwest	5
Southwest	4
Total	**100**

PRODUCTS/OPERATIONS

FY2017 Sales by Service

	$ mil.	% of total
Home building		
Home sales	**13653.2**	**97**
Land/lot sales	88	-
Financial services	349	3
Total	**14,091**	**100**

COMPETITORS

Beazer Homes	Meritage Homes
Brookfield Residential Properties	NVR
David Weekley Homes	PulteGroup
Gehan Homes	Ryan Building
Highland Homes	TRI Pointe
Hovnanian Enterprises	Taylor Morrison
KB Home	Toll Brothers
Lennar	Weyerhaeuser Real Estate
M.D.C.	William Lyon Homes
M/I Homes	

HISTORICAL FINANCIALS

Company Type: Public

Income Statement

FYE: September 30

	REVENUE ($ mil.)	NET INCOME ($ mil.)	NET PROFIT MARGIN	EMPLOYEES
09/17	14,091	1,038	7.4%	7,735
09/16	12,157	886	7.3%	6,976
09/15	10,824	750	6.9%	6,230
09/14	8,024	533	6.6%	5,621
09/13	6,259	462	7.4%	4,609
Annual Growth	**22.5%**	**22.4%**	**—**	**13.8%**

2017 Year-End Financials

Debt ratio: 23.57%
Return on equity: 14.28%
Cash ($ mil.): 1,007
Current ratio: 11.37
Long-term debt ($ mil.): 2,871

No. of shares (mil.): 374
Dividends
   Yield: 0.0%
   Payout: 14.6%
Market value ($ mil.): 14,973

	STOCK PRICE ($) FY Close	P/E High/Low		PER SHARE ($) Earnings	Dividends	Book Value
09/17	39.93	14	10	2.74	0.40	20.66
09/16	30.20	14	10	2.36	0.32	18.21
09/15	29.36	16	10	2.03	0.25	15.99
09/14	20.52	16	11	1.50	0.14	14.03
09/13	19.43	19	12	1.33	0.30	12.57
Annual Growth	**19.7%**	**—**	**—**	**19.8%**	**7.5%**	**13.2%**

Host Hotels & Resorts Inc

Host Hotels & Resorts is home to luxury hotel properties around the world. It's the largest hospitality real estate investment trust (REIT) in the US and one of the top owners of luxury and upscale hotels. It owns more than 95 luxury and "upper upscale" hotels mostly in the US but also in Canada Australia Mexico and Brazil totaling some 53900 rooms. Properties are managed by third parties; most operate under the Marriott brand and are managed by sister firm Marriott International. Other brands include Hyatt Ritz-Carlton Sheraton and Westin. To maintain its status as a REIT which carries tax advantages Host operates through majority-owned Host Hotels & Resorts LP.

HISTORY

That's right — The Four Seasons started as a root beer stand.

Newlyweds John and Alice Marriott left Marriott Utah (founded by John's grandparents) in 1927 and opened a root beer stand in Washington DC. As a way to attract customers during the winter they began selling tamales and tacos — recipes came from a cook at the Mexican Embassy. Dubbed the Hot Shoppe the Marriotts built the business into a regional chain.

In 1937 the Marriotts began providing boxed lunches for airlines. Hot Shoppes entered the hospital food service business in 1955 and two years later opened its first hotel in Arlington Virginia. John and Alice's son Bill became president in 1964. The company which operated four hotels 45 Hot Shoppes and the airline catering business became Marriott-Hot Shoppes.

In the 1960s the company acquired Bob's Big Boy restaurant chain (sold 1987) started Roy Rogers fast-food restaurants (sold 1990) and changed its name to Marriott Corp. Later Marriott bought an Athenian cruise line (Oceanic; sold 1987). Bill became CEO in 1972.

Marriott diversified its hotel operations in the 1980s moving into limited-service middle-priced hotels with the launch of Courtyard by Marriott in 1983. To accelerate growth the company began building hotels for sale retaining their control through management contracts. In 1987 it acquired Residence Inn Co. which targeted extended-stay travelers. The company also expanded its airline catering business and moved into retirement facilities. To fund the expansion Marriott formed limited partnerships and issued corporate bonds; when the late 1980s recession hit the company was deeply in debt.

In 1993 Marriott Corp. divided into Marriott International (hotel management services) and Host Marriott (real estate and food service) leaving Host

Marriott with most of the corporation's debt. Host Marriott began focusing on full-service hotels. It raised money to buy more hotels (many of which belonged to its old limited partnerships) by taking loans from Marriott International and selling assets (including 14 retirement properties and 30 Fairfield Inns). In late 1995 the company further refined its focus by spinning off its food service and concessions business as Host Marriott Services (later acquired by Italy-based restaurant operator Autogrill).

Host Marriott acquired three Ritz-Carlton hotels in 1995 through Marriott International which owns the Ritz-Carlton name and in 1997 acquired the Forum Group owner of 29 retirement communities. The next year it spun off Crestline Capital (now Barcelo Crestline Corp.) to own its retirement properties and to lease its hotels.

In 1999 the company expanded its hotel brands adding controlling stakes in 13 luxury Ritz-Carlton Four Seasons Swiss ´tel and Hyatt properties bought from the Blackstone Group investment firm in exchange for a stake in Host Marriott. It also restructured as a real estate investment trust or REIT.

Host Marriott and Marriott International were slapped with an investor fraud lawsuit in 2000 relating to its capital-raising efforts in the late 1980s; they reached a tentative settlement under which they would buy back the partnerships. The bulk of the settlements were awarded to about 2000 investors in two of the six limited partnerships in question. That year Marriott matriarch Alice died.

Host Marriott's New York Marriott World Trade Center hotel located at Three World Trade Center was completely devastated on September 11 2001. Two blocks south the New York Marriott Financial Center hotel sustained heavy damage.

Even before September 11 brought the hotel industry to a screeching halt the company had curtailed the buying binge that saw it add more than 100 hotels to its portfolio since 1994. It decided to sell less posh noncore hotels and focus on renovating remaining holdings. Crashing per-room revenue had the company waiting for the slow return of the health of the industry and when it had the company began a cautious acquisition spree.

After a tourism industry downturn made worse by the September 11 2001 terrorist attacks the company made a key acquisition in 2006: It purchased a portfolio of 25 domestic and 3 international hotels from Starwood Hotels & Resorts for more than $4 billion and changed its name to Host Hotels & Resorts in conjunction with that buy. The package expanded the company's reach into Europe South America and the South Pacific.

In 2009 Host sold its leasehold interest in CBM Joint Venture Partnership which owned 115 Courtyard by Marriott hotels. The deal earned Host about $13 million.

In late 2011 the company sold its 95% interest in the Toronto Airport Marriott Hotel for CAD$30.6 million ($30.7 million).

Host in 2011 bought the New York Helmsley Hotel from Helmsley Enterprises and announced plans to renovate the 775-room property and reopen it under the Westin brand. In a separate deal Host acquired the Manchester Grand Hyatt San Diego's largest hotel for $570 million.

In 2012 it bought 888-room Grand Hyatt Washington for about $400 million and its acquisition of land in Rio de Janeiro to develop two hotels with a total count of 405 rooms that opened in time for the FIFA World Cup in 2014.

In 2013 the company acquired fee-simple interest in the 426-room Hyatt Place Waikiki Beach in Honolulu Hawaii from an affiliate of Chartres Lodging Group and Morgan Stanley Real Estate Fund VII Global for $138.5 million.

EXECUTIVES

CEO, James F. Risoleo, age 61, $576,800 total compensation
EVP and CFO, Gregory J. (Greg) Larson, age 52, $503,950 total compensation
EVP General Counsel and Secretary, Elizabeth A. Abdoo, age 58, $488,050 total compensation
EVP Asset Management, Minaz B. Abji, age 63, $546,400 total compensation
Managing Director Investments East Coast, Nathan S. Tyrrell, age 44
EVP Human Resources, Joanne G. Hamilton, age 59
Managing Director Development, Mike E. Lentz
Vice President National Account Sales, Carmen Hui
Vice President Feasibility and Strategic Analysis, Patrick Li
Vice President Asset Management, Georgina Sussan
Senior Vice President International Cap Ex, Alastair McPhail
Vice President Asset Management, Rick Werber
Vice President Asset Management, Patrick Webber
Vice President Capital Expenditures, Bryan Thrush
Vice President and Assistant General Counsel, Karen Grubber
Vice President Asset Management, Jeff Gross
Senior Vice President, Craig A Mason
Vice President Investments, Linda Laniado
Vice President Asset Management, Greg Fang
Vice President Controller, Alison Gendron
Vice President Risk Management, Gus Napoli
Vice President and Assistant Treasurer, Bret Mcleod
Vice President And Assistant General Counsel, Marlo Goldstein
Senior Vice President Tax, Jeff Clark
Vice President Asset Management, Kerry Gaber
Vice President, Raj Patel
Vice President Capital Expenditures Design Development and Construction, Larry Oleck
Senior Vice President and Assistant General Counsel, David Buckley
Senior Vice President Acquisitions, Doug Henry
Vice President of Tax, Doug Link
Vice President Asset Management, Christopher Ostapovicz
Senior Vice President and Corporate Controller, Brian Macnamara
Vice President of Tax Compliance and Accounting, Jeff Kaufman
Chairman, Richard E. Marriott, age 78
Auditors: KPMG LLP

LOCATIONS

HQ: Host Hotels & Resorts Inc
6903 Rockledge Drive, Suite 1500, Bethesda, MD 20817
Phone: 240 744-1000
Web: www.hosthotels.com

2016 Sales

	$ mil.	% of total
US	5,259	97
Canada	54	1
Others	117	2
Total	**5,430**	**100**

2016 Hotel Locations

	Nos
United States	89
Brazil	3
Canada	2
Mexico	1
Australia	1
Total	**96**

PRODUCTS/OPERATIONS

2016 Sales

	$ mil.	% of total
Rooms	3,492	64
Food & Beverage	1,599	30
Other	339	6
Total	**5,430**	**100**

2016 Brands

	No. of hotels
Marriott:	
Marriott	38
Westin	13
Ritz-Carlton	6
Sheraton	6
JW Marriott	5
W	3
Autograph Collection	1
St. Regis	1
Luxury Collection	1
Residence Inn	1
Courtyard	1
Hyatt:	
Hyatt Regency	5
Grand Hyatt	3
Hyatt Place	1
Hilton:	
Hilton	2
Curio	1
Embassy Suites	1
AccorHotels:	
Swissôtel	1
Fairmont	1
ibis	1
Novotel	1
Other/Independent	3
Total	**0** 96

COMPETITORS

Ashford Hospitality Trust	LaSalle Hotel Properties
Carlson Companies	Lodgian
FelCor	Pebblebrook
Hospitality Properties Trust	Strategic Hotels
InterContinental Hotels	Sunstone Hotel Investors

HISTORICAL FINANCIALS

Company Type: Public

Income Statement

FYE: December 31

	REVENUE ($ mil.)	NET INCOME ($ mil.)	NET PROFIT MARGIN	EMPLOYEES
12/16	5,430	762	14.0%	220
12/15	5,387	558	10.4%	240
12/14	5,354	732	13.7%	251
12/13	5,166	317	6.1%	242
12/12	5,286	61	1.2%	233
Annual Growth	**0.7%**	**88.0%**	**—**	**(1.4%)**

2016 Year-End Financials

Debt ratio: 31.99%
Return on equity: 10.81%
Cash ($ mil.): 372
Current ratio: 1.35
Long-term debt ($ mil.): 3,649

No. of shares (mil.): 737
Dividends
 Yield: 0.0%
 Payout: 83.3%
Market value ($ mil.): 13,900

	STOCK PRICE ($) FY Close	P/E High/Low		PER SHARE ($) Earnings	Dividends	Book Value
12/16	18.84	19	12	1.02	0.85	9.48
12/15	15.34	33	21	0.74	0.80	9.41
12/14	23.77	25	19	0.96	0.75	9.71
12/13	19.44	45	36	0.42	0.46	9.58
12/12	15.67	216	172	0.08	0.30	9.42
Annual Growth	**4.7%**			**89.0%**	**29.7%**	**0.2%**

HOUCHENS INDUSTRIES, INC.

Houchens Industries is a supermarket of businesses as well as an operator of supermarkets. The diversified company runs some 400 retail grocery convenience and neighborhood markets across the US. That includes more than 180 conventional supermarkets under the Houchens Food Giant IGA Piggly Wiggly Buehler Foods and Mad Butcher banners. It hass more than 200 Save-A-Lot discount grocery stores in a dozen states that offer limited selections and cover 15000 sq. ft. or less. Outside the grocery store Houchens operates Cohen's Fashion Optical franchise stores and several Sheldon's Express Pharmacy stores. Other businesses include construction financial services real estate restaurants and recycling. Houchens is 100%-owned by its employees.

Operations

Houchens Industries has amassed a diverse portfolio of more than 35 businesses over the years through acquisitions. Beyond the grocery segment Houchen also serves customers in the construction insurance wealth management technology and healthcare industries.

Houchens is the largest franchisee of limited-assortment Save-A-Lot stores in the US. (Grocery retailer and wholesaler SUPERVALU is the parent company of Save-A-Lot.) The company's manufacturing businesses include Stephens Pipe & Steel a leading maker and distributor of fence materials. Southern Recycling collects and processes metals paper glass and plastics. The company also franchises Sonic and Subway quick-serve restaurants. It also operates the Taco Del Mar restaurant chain and Price Less Foods which sells groceries at cost plus 10%.

Geographic Reach

Based in Kentucky Houchens Industries operates grocery stores in Alabama Arkansas Florida Georgia Indiana Illinois Kentucky Mississippi Missouri Tennessee and Virginia. Its diverse other businesses are active almost every US state and about 30 other countries worldwide.

Strategy

Houchens Industries looks to buy assets that have sound management and a history of providing good cash flow that can be bought at a reasonable price. Recent acquisitions include the 14-store family-run White's Fresh Foods chain which operates grocery stores in Tennessee and Virginia and the Bowling Green Kentucky-based two-store drug retailer Sheldon's Express Pharmacy thereby expanding into the drugstore business. Houchens plans to leverage the acquisition to create a regional drugstore chain. The Whites purchase followed the acquisition of Chicago-based Tampico Beverages a maker of refrigerated juice drinks and punches sold in more than 36 countries for an undisclosed amount. Tampico supplies beverages to grocery and convenience stores as well as quick-serve restaurants.

In new version of IGA stores Houchens has made convenience a watchword. The IGA Crossroads brand is set up to help customers get in and out quickly. The stores also contain quick service restaurants. In those and other stores Houchens added to the sandwich mix available bringing Which Wich into its lineup joining Schlotzsky's and Subway.

Company Background

Founded by Ervin Houchens as BG Wholesale in rural Kentucky in 1917 Houchens has been owned by its employees since 1988.

EXECUTIVES

Chairman and CEO, James (Jimmie) Gipson, age 76
President, Spencer A. Coates
CEO Tampico Beverages, Scott Miller
CFO, Gordon Minter
President Cohen's Fashion Optical, Bob Cohen
President hitcents.com, Chris Mills
President and CEO Food Giant Supermarkets, Ron Watkins
Head Pan Oston, Jim Vance
Head Save a Lot, David Burnett
Vice President Produce, John Mudd
Auditors: BKD LLP BOWLING GREEN KENTU

LOCATIONS

HQ: HOUCHENS INDUSTRIES, INC.
  700 CHURCH ST, BOWLING GREEN, KY 421011816
Phone: 270 843-3252
Web: WWW.SAVE-A-LOT.COM

PRODUCTS/OPERATIONS

Selected Operations

American Sun Systems (tanning salon supplier)
Blake Hart Taylor & Wiseman (insurance)
Buehler's Buy Low (grocery retail)
Cohen's Fashion Optical (optical stores)
Food Giant (grocery retail)
Hilliard Lyons (financial services)
Houchens Markets (grocery retail)
IGA (licensed grocery retail)
Insurance Specialists (insurance)
Jr. Food Stores (convenience stores)
Price Less Foods (grocery retail)
Save-A-Lot (licensed grocery retail)
Scotty's (asphalt paving)
Sheldon's Express Pharmacy (drugstores)
Southern Recycling Inc. (recycling)
Stewart-Richey Construction Inc. (construction management)
Taco Del Mar (fast-food)
Tampico (juice)
TS Trucking (hauling)
Van Meter Insurance (insurance benefits)
White's Fresh Foods (grocery retail)

COMPETITORS

7-Eleven	Meijer
ALDI	Mott's
Ameriprise	Nestl ©
CVS	Ocean Spray
Charles Schwab	Odwalla
Citigroup	Old Orchard
Citrus World	Raymond James
Cumberland Farms	Financial
Dole Food	Rite Aid
Dr Pepper Snapple	Sheetz
Group	Southeastern Grocers
E*TRADE Financial	Sunkist
E. W. James	Sunny Delight
Edward D. Jones	TD Ameritrade
FMR	Thorntons Inc.
Faygo	Tree Top
Goya	Tropicana
John Hancock Financial	Visionworks of America
Services	Wal-Mart
Jugos del Valle USA	Walgreen
K-VA-T Food Stores	Weis Markets
Kroger	Welch's
Luxottica Retail	

HISTORICAL FINANCIALS

Company Type: Private

Income Statement

FYE: October 1

	ASSETS ($ mil.)	NET INCOME ($ mil.)	INCOME AS % OF ASSETS	EMPLOYEES
10/16	1,976	104	5.3%	16,000
10/15*	2,014	99	5.0%	—
09/14	1,993	84	4.2%	—
09/13	1,969	110	5.6%	—
Annual Growth	0.1%	(1.9%)	—	—

*Fiscal year change

2016 Year-End Financials

Debt ratio: ——
Return on equity: 3.50%
Cash ($ mil.): 259
Current ratio: 0.90
Long-term debt ($ mil.): —

Dividends
  Yield: —
  Payout: —
Market value ($ mil.): —

HP Inc

Just about every office — from home to big business — has two basic items: a computer and printer. That's pretty much the business of HP Inc. one of two companies created from the breakup of Hewlett-Packard Co. HP makes a full line of computing devices from desktops and laptops for commercial and consumer use to tablets and point-of-sale systems. Its printers include large format commercial printers and inkjet and laser printers as well as 3D printers. And don't forget printer supplies such as ink cartridges. HP Inc. is the No. 1 printer company and No. 1 maker of PCs for commercial use in the world (Lenovo is the No. 1 PC maker overall).

Operations

HP Inc. reports its operations through three business segments: Personal Systems Printing and Corporate Investments.

Personal Systems makes and sells commercial PCs consumer PCs workstations thin clients commercial tablets and mobility devices retail point-of-sale systems displays and accessories software and support. The segment generates more than 60% of HP?s revenue.

Printing produces consumer and commercial printers supplies media services as well as scanning devices. About 40% of the company?s revenue rolls out of the unit.

Corporate Investments includes HP Labs and business incubation projects. As a research-oriented unit it contributes a negligible amount of revenue.

HP Inc. buys some components from other companies. That includes the laser printer engines and laser toner cartridges it obtains from Canon. Processors for the company?s computers come from Intel and AMD and the machines runs on Microsoft software. Most of HP?s mobile devices are based on the Android operating system.

While the company operates some of its own manufacturing it outsources a significant portion of the work to third party companies.

Geographic Reach

Although about 60% of HP Inc.'s revenue comes from customers outside the US no one country accounts for more than 10% of revenue. The company has operations throughout the world with significant facilities in the Singapore Malaysia and Israel as well its US operations.

Sales and Marketing

HP Inc. markets its products directly as well as through a wide range of third-party channels including retailers resellers and distributors and original equipment manufacturers and systems integrators.

Financial Performance

As the successor to the former Hewlett-Packard Company HP Inc.'s fiscal 2016 (ended October) revenue fell nearly 50% without the inclusion of the enterprise technology and software business that was spun off. However looking at only the comparable business results HP's 2016 sales fell just some 5% to about $48 billion from some $51 billion in 2015. One factor was the unfavorable currency exchange rates that affected many companies during the year. More specifically for HP Inc. consumer and commercial computer sales fell 5% primarily with weak demand — although there was an uptick in sales of commercial notebooks and PC services. Competitive pressure drove down average selling prices. Printing revenue fell 15% on weaker demand the impact of the change in the supplies sales model and pricing pressures. While unit volume of sales declined the average selling price increased because of a shift to high-value printers.

Net income fell to $2.5 billion in 2016 from $4.5 billion in 2015 mainly on the lower revenue.

Cash flow from operations fell to $3.2 billion in 2016 from $6.5 billion in 2015 because cash from discontinued operations was not included in the 2016 figure.

Strategy

In 2015 Hewlett-Packard split into two companies. Hewlett-Packard Enterprise took the computer systems and software products and services for large corporate customers while HP Inc. took the PC and printer business. The reasoning behind the separation was that the independent companies would be more nimble and responsive in developing products and services for their different markets. The 2016 fiscal year which ended in October was their first as separate companies.

Although ink has been a gusher of black gold (as well as cyan and magenta) for HP Inc. the company in 2016 made a significant change in its sales model for printer supplies going from push to pull. Instead of stuffing the supply line with ink and toner it changed to making ink cartridges and shipping them as demand occurred. At the same time the company said it would end price promotions in favor of consistent pricing. HP Inc.'s supplies business has been under pressure from competitors? prices and reduced printing by businesses and consumers. HP?s supplies business is based on what it calls the ?four box model.? The boxes are: increase the installed base drive use increase its share of supplies and optimize pricing.

The company has taken steps to check each of those boxes. It has extended a proprietary ink from commercial use to its office printers. The ink is a special formula available only from HP Inc. which says is better faster to print and cheaper. It is used in the new PageWide and OfficeJet Pro printers. The company also began offering quick delivery of ink to offices. Part of the shift to providing supplies through a service-oriented model is to satisfy the preference of millennials for services.

A printer area in which HP Inc. is investing is 3D printing for design and manufacturing applications. It is pumping about $65 million a year into a 3D printing research center in Spain and making other investments.

While HP Inc. saw an uptick in PC sales in its 2016 fourth quarter the long-term outlook for notebooks and desktops isn't bright as worldwide sales decrease. In 2016 the company instituted a device-as-a-service program designed to let customers rent computers and software which HP Inc. controls from the cloud.

The company started a restructuring in late 2016 that would include cutting some 4000 jobs — a bit less than 10% of its workforce. The cuts should save up to $300 million a year.

HP Inc. sold its Customer Communications Management business to Open Text for $315 million in 2016. The unit included products and services for customer communications management process automation and document solutions.

Mergers and Acquisitions

HP Inc. in September 2016 agreed to buy Samsung's printer business for about $1 billion. HP gets Samsung's laser printer portfolio and thousands of patents for printing technologies as well as an increased presence in Asia. The deal particularly strengthens HP in combination printer-copier machines which helps it compete with companies such as Xerox and Canon in the enterprise and office markets. The companies expect the deal to close in 2017.

In related 2016 deals HP Inc. bought David Vision Systems GmbH and David 3D Solutions which make 3-D scanning technology.

EXECUTIVES

Chief Supply Chain Officer, Stuart C. Pann, age 58
COO, Jon E. Flaxman, age 60, $700,027 total compensation
SVP; General Manager Graphics and Imaging HP Imaging and Printing Group, Stephen (Steve) Nigro
CTO, Shane D. Wall, age 52
President Personal Systems Business, Ron Coughlin
EVP and CFO, Catherine A. (Cathie) Lesjak, age 58, $850,033 total compensation
VP and General Manager Inkjet Commercial Division HP Imaging and Printing Group; Site Manager Barcelona, Enrique Lores, age 52
President Americas, Christoph Schell
President Asia Pacific and Japan (APJ), Richard Bailey
President and CEO, Dion J. Weisler, $1,200,046 total compensation
President Europe Middle East and Africa (EMEA), Nick Lazaridis
Chief Human Resources Officer, Tracy S. Keogh, $600,023 total compensation
Managing Director and General Manager HP India, Sumeer Chandra
Vice President Big Data, Pankaj Dugar
Vice President Americas Channels And Alliances, Archie Miller
Vice President World Wide Channel Marketing Printing and Personal Systems, Vincent Brissot
Vice President And General Manager Laserjet HW Portfolio And Quality, Jim Nottingham
National Account Manager, Amy Hilfiker
Assistant Vice President Senior Systems Administrator, Van Munoz
Vice President of Mobility Products, Keith Hartsfield
Assistant Vice President Operations, Sushanto Das
Vice President WW Commercial PC Marketing, Carol Hess
Chairman, Charles V. (Chip) Bergh, age 59
Board Member, Laurel Krieger
Auditors: Ernst & Young LLP

LOCATIONS

HQ: HP Inc
  1501 Page Mill Road, Palo Alto, CA 94304
Phone: 650 857-1501
Web: www.hp.com

2016 Sales

	$ mil.	% of total
US	18,042	37
Other countries	30,196	63
Total	**48,238**	**100**

PRODUCTS/OPERATIONS

2016 Sales

	$ mil.	% of total
Notebook PCs	16,982	35
Desktop PCs	9,956	21
Workstations	1,870	4
Other	1,179	2
Supplies	11,875	25
Commercial Hardware	5,131	11
Consumer Hardware	1,254	2
Adjustments	(9000)	-
Total	**48,238**	**100**

Selected Products and Services

Personal Systems
  Calculators
  Desktop PCs
  Digital entertainment centers
  DVD writers
  Handheld computers
  Notebook computers
  Televisions (LCD plasma)
  Workstations
Imaging and Printing
  Commercial printing
  Digital presses
  Printers
  Digital imaging
  Projectors
  Scanners
  Personal printing
  All-in-ones (copier fax printer scanner)
  Ink jet printers
  Laser printers
  Shared printing
  Networked inkjet laser and multifunction printers
  Office all-in-ones
  Services
  Supplies

Selected Acquisitions2011 Autonomy (UK; data repurposing software)Printelligent (managed print services)**2010**ArcSight (security software)3PAR (storage software and hardware)Fortify Software (data security software)Stratavia (database and application automa

COMPETITORS

ADP	Hitachi
ASUSTeK	Konica Minolta
Acer	Lenovo
Apple Inc.	Lexmark
Brother Industries	NCR
CACI International	NEC
CGI Group	Oc©@
Canon	Oki Electric
Dell	Panasonic Corp
Eastman Kodak	Ricoh Company
Epson	Samsung Electronics
First Data	Sharp Corp.
Fiserv	Sony
Fuji Xerox	Symantec
Fujitsu	Teradata
Fujitsu Technology Solutions	Toshiba
Heidelberger Druckmaschinen	Unisys
	Wipro Technologies
	Xerox

HISTORICAL FINANCIALS

Company Type: Public

Income Statement

FYE: October 31

	REVENUE ($ mil.)	NET INCOME ($ mil.)	NET PROFIT MARGIN	EMPLOYEES
10/17	52,056	2,526	4.9%	49,000
10/16	48,238	2,496	5.2%	49,000
10/15	103,355	4,554	4.4%	287,000
10/14	111,454	5,013	4.5%	302,000
10/13	112,298	5,113	4.6%	317,500
Annual Growth	**(17.5%)**	**(16.2%)**	**—**	**(37.3%)**

2017 Year-End Financials

Debt ratio: 23.76%
Return on equity:
Cash ($ mil.): 6,997
Current ratio: 1.00
Long-term debt ($ mil.): 6,747

No. of shares (mil.): 1,650
Dividends
Yield: 2.4%
Payout: 38.4%
Market value ($ mil.): 35,558

	STOCK PRICE ($) FY Close	P/E High/Low		PER SHARE ($) Earnings	Dividends	Book Value
10/17	21.55	15	10	1.48	0.53	(2.07)
10/16	14.49	11	6	1.43	0.50	(2.27)
10/15	26.96	16	10	2.48	0.67	15.39
10/14	35.88	14	9	2.62	0.61	14.53
10/13	24.37	10	4	2.62	0.55	14.29
Annual Growth	(3.0%)	—	—	(13.3%)	(1.1%)	

HRG Group Inc

As a holding company of other businesses HRG Group (formerly Harbinger Group) has seen its fortunes diminish recently. Seemingly triggered by the plunge in oil prices that caused large losses in its oil and gas company HRG now seems on the defensive. While its flagship company Spectrum Brand Holdings Inc. continues to perform well in its consumer products businesses HRG has sold off all its remaining investments including Compass Production Partners (oil & gas) Fidelity & Guarantee Life (insurance) and Front Street RE (re-insurance). Spectrum Brand owns many companies itself and operates such recognizable brands as Black+Decker Armor All and Farberware. HRG was co-founded in 1953 by former US President George H. W. Bush under the name Zapata.

Operations

Following divestitures of its insurance and oil & gas businesses HRG Group operates a single segment focused on consumer products. Its Spectrum Brand Holdings Inc. subsidiary which is 60% owned by HRG and 40% publicly owned (it trades under symbol SPB) manufactures markets and distributes its products in some 160 countries. It sells through a variety of trade channels including retailers wholesalers and distributors original equipment manufacturers (OEMs) construction companies and hearing aid professionals. Spectrum manages its businesses across five product lines: Global Batteries & Appliances Hardware & Home Improvement Global Pet Supplies Home and Garden and Global Auto Care. Spectrum benefits from strong product name recognition including: Kwikset Stanley Black+Decker Farberware Amor All STP HotShot and Cutter among many others.

Geographic Reach

New York-based HRG Group enjoys a global reach with operations in North America Latin America and Europe. Its customers span over 160 countries.

Sales and Marketing

HRG's sole business is now consumer products. Its Spectrum Brand products are sold through a limited group of retailers such as Wal-Mart The Home Depot Lowe's Target Carrefour PetSmart PetCo Canadian Tire and Gigante.

A significant percentage of Spectrum?s sales are attributable to a limited group of retailers including Amazon Autozone Dollar General Lidl Lowe?s PetSmart O?Reilly Target The Home Depot and Wal-Mart. Sales to its largest customer Wal-Mart represent about 15% of total revenue (in FY2017).

Financial Performance

HRG Group has enjoyed rising revenues from its portfolio holdings over the past several years thanks to organic growth and growth through acquisitions. However impairment charges including ones on its energy holdings and FGL insurance business have led the group to losses in recent years.

HRG?s revenue in FY2017 (ended September 30) decreased 4% to $5.0 billion. Its Spectrum Brands company generally maintained its revenue level from the prior year with marginal slips in Pet Supplies Home & Garden and Auto Care. HRG?s revenue reduction came from its now divested operations. Its Compass oil & gas operations were sold off causing an absence of revenue from that enterprise. Its FGL insurance business saw a 25% revenue growth mainly through investment gains and income but the rise was still too small to offset lower performance in other areas.

The group's net income in FY2017 rose almost 300% to $106 million up from the prior year?s $199 million loss. The comparison to prior year is skewed due to a more than $350 million impairment charge taken in FY2016 related to HRG?s now-divested FGL Insurance business. HRG?s Spectrum Brands subsidiary saw net income drop 17% from FY2016 due in large part to employee severance costs.

Cash at the end of FY2017 was $270 million down nearly $200 million from FY2016. Operating activities contributed $840 million some from the net income of Spectrum Brands and some from adjustments related to depreciation and amortization and some from divestiture of cash associated with sold businesses.

Strategy

HRG?s financial performance in recent years has pinched its growth trajectory. While its Spectrum Brands continues to perform well its oil and gas results in 2014 and 2015 put the company on the defensive. It sold its Fidelity Guarantee Life and First Street insurance businesses in 2017 to raise cash of approximately $2.0 billion. It stated that it is seeking strategic alternatives a phrase commonly used when a company is looking to sell itself or in HRG?s case its subsidiaries.

Despite HRG?s circle-the-wagons posture the Spectrum Brands company continues to acquire new products lines and businesses. In 2017 it purchased PetMatrix (rawhide-free dog chews) GloFish (fluorescent fish) and the remaining 44% of Shaser (skin care) that it didn?t already own.

HISTORY

Named for the movie Viva Zapata! Zapata was formed by the 1953 merger of the young George H. W. Bush's Bush-Overby oil company and another oil firm run by Hugh and Bill Liedtke. After going public in 1955 Bush and the Liedtkes split the company in 1959 with Bush taking over Zapata Off-Shore. He sold his stake in Zapata in 1966 after being elected to Congress. In 1973 the company bought fish processor Haynie Products. Zapata struggled through the oil slump of the 1980s sold assets and converted debt to stock to avoid bankruptcy.

Investor Malcolm Glazer took control of the company in 1993. He became CEO and chairman the following year and shifted the company's focus away from energy. In 1995 Zapata sold the natural gas compression business and acquired Glazer's 31% share of money-losing food packaging manufacturer Envirodyne (increased to 40% in 1996 and renamed Viskase Companies in 1998). In 1997 it sold its Bolivian operations the last of its energy holdings to Tesoro.

The company expanded its fishing business by purchasing two competitors in 1997 but it didn't hold them for long. The next year it spun off its fishing businesses to the public as Omega Protein retaining a majority stake.

Excited by the Internet's possibilities Zapata in 1998 resuscitated two e-zines that had been spiked by Icon CMT and it formed Zap.com to hold those and other Web sites that it planned to buy. Despite having few significant assets and no revenues in 1999 the company spun off Zap.com to its shareholders; Zapata retained nearly 98%. Also that year the company moved its headquarters from Houston to Rochester New York.

Zapata recorded big losses in 1999 mostly due to sluggish sales at Omega Protein which suffered from a glut in the protein meal and edible oil markets. In addition Viskase which has been struggling and selling operations for a few years sold its shrink film business in 2000 to help retire debt. Also that year Viskase announced that it was selling its plastics business. Zapata announced in 2000 that it would begin a new focus for Charged including expansion into wireless animation and creative multimedia. In 2001 however the company shut down both Zap.com and its Charged Productions operations. In September 2001 Zapata sold its interest in Viskase.

In 2003 Zapata rejected an unsolicited $108 million cash take-over bid from merger and acquisition group Hollingsworth Rothwell & Roxford. Later that year Zapata bought additional shares of Safety Components International bringing its ownership of the company to about 80%; however it sold its shares in Safety Components in 2005.

In late 2006 it began selling its holdings in Omega Protein. Omega bought back 36% of Zapata's shares for $47.5 million in November of that year. Zapata announced the sale of the last of its Omega holdings to a group of private investors for about $29 million in December 2006.

In 2009 the company changed its name to Harbinger Group.

HRG Group acquired a majority interest in consumer goods firm Spectrum Brands in 2011.

Spectrum Brands expanded its business in 2012 by acquiring the residential hardware and home improvement business of Stanley Black & Decker. The move gave the consumer products company additional brands names such as Kwikset Weiser Baldwin and National Hardware.

It also purchased certain assets of Tong Lung Metal Industry Co. Ltd. a Taiwan company that specializes in producing residential locks in 2013.

The company purchased Old Mutual U.S. Life Holdings from Old Mutual for $350 million rebranding them as Fidelity & Guaranty Life Insurance Company and Fidelity & Guaranty Life Insurance Company of New York. Harbinger Group then acquired a minority stake in North American Energy Partners which primarily provides construction and pipeline services to the Canadian oil sands market.

EXECUTIVES

Chairman and CEO, Joseph S. Steinberg, age 73
SVP Chief Accounting Officer and CFO, George C. Nicholson, age 58, $275,000 total compensation
EVP COO General Counsel and Corporate Secretary, Ehsan Zargar
Auditors: KPMG LLP

LOCATIONS

HQ: HRG Group Inc
450 Park Avenue, 29th Floor, New York, NY 10022
Phone: 212 906-8555
Web: www.harbingergroupinc.com

2016 Sales

	% of total
United States	64
EuropeMiddle east and Africa (EMEA)	22

Latin America	7
North America-other	4
Asia-Pacific	3
Total	**100**

PRODUCTS/OPERATIONS

FY2016 Revenue

	% of total
Net consumer product sales	97
Net investment (losses) gains	2
Net investment income	1
Insurance and investment product fees and other	-
Total	**100**

FY2016 Revenue by Segment

FY2016 Revenue by Segment

	$ mil.	% of total	
Consumer products	5039.7		97
Insurance	150.4	3	
Corporate and Other	16.4	-	
Elimination	8.9	-	
Total	5215.4	100	

COMPETITORS

Berkshire Hathaway	Leucadia National
Energizer Holdings	Mars Incorporated
GE	Onex
Hellman & Friedman	Procter & Gamble

HISTORICAL FINANCIALS

Company Type: Public

Income Statement

FYE: September 30

	REVENUE ($ mil.)	NET INCOME ($ mil.)	NET PROFIT MARGIN	EMPLOYEES
09/17	5,008	106	2.1%	17,113
09/16	5,215	(198)	—	16,021
09/15	5,815	(556)	—	15,922
09/14	5,963	(10)	—	14,427
09/13	5,543	(45)	—	13,742
Annual Growth	(2.5%)	—		5.6%

2017 Year-End Financials

Debt ratio: 16.11%	No. of shares (mil.): 200
Return on equity: 15.19%	Dividends
Cash ($ mil.): 270	Yield: —
Current ratio: 1.45	Payout: —
Long-term debt ($ mil.): 5,774	Market value ($ mil.): 3,132

	STOCK PRICE ($) FY Close	P/E High/Low	Earnings	PER SHARE ($) Dividends	Book Value
09/17	15.61	38 27	0.53	0.00	3.78
09/16	15.70	— —	(0.99)	0.00	3.18
09/15	11.73	— —	(2.81)	0.00	2.91
09/14	13.12	— —	(0.51)	0.00	7.13
09/13	10.37	— —	(0.67)	0.00	7.40
Annual Growth	10.8%	— —	—	—	(15.5%)

HSBC Finance Corp

Auditors: PricewaterhouseCoopers LLP

LOCATIONS

HQ: HSBC Finance Corp
1421 W. Shure Drive, Suite 100, Arlington Heights, IL 60004
Phone: 224 880-7000
Web: www.us.hsbc.com

HISTORICAL FINANCIALS

Company Type: Public

Income Statement

FYE: December 31

	ASSETS ($ mil.)	NET INCOME ($ mil.)	INCOME AS % OF ASSETS	EMPLOYEES
12/16	13,882	(529)	—	1,200
12/15	24,145	(431)	—	1,600
12/14	31,960	523	1.6%	1,700
12/13	37,872	536	1.4%	2,200
12/12	46,778	(845)	—	2,537
Annual Growth	(26.2%)	—	—	(17.1%)

2016 Year-End Financials

Debt ratio: 55.04%	No. of shares (mil.): 0
Return on equity: (-8.74%)	Dividends
Cash ($ mil.): 1,628	Yield: 0.0%
Current ratio: —	Payout: —
Long-term debt ($ mil.): —	Market value ($ mil.): —

	STOCK PRICE ($) FY Close	P/E High/Low	Earnings	PER SHARE ($) Dividends	Book Value
12/16 79,911,764.00	0.00	— —	(0.00)	0.86	
12/15 97,573,529.00	25.67	— —	(0.00)	1.59	
12/14 104,750,000.00	25.34	— —	(0.00)	1.59	
12/13 97,955,882.00	22.90	— —	(0.00)	1.59	
Annual Growth	—	— —	—	(14.2%)	(5.0%)

HSBC USA, Inc.

HSBC USA a subsidiary of British banking behemoth HSBC Holdings operates HSBC Bank USA one of the largest foreign-owned banks in the country. Boasting $200 billion in assets and 230-plus branches across 10 US states (including 145 in New York making it one of the state's largest banks by branches) the bank offers personal commercial and mortgage banking services as well as wealth management investment banking private banking brokerage and trust services. Its largest markets are in New York California New Jersey and Florida. Roughly 75% of HSBC USA's loan portfolio is made up of commercial loans and around 70% of its total revenue comes from interest income.

Operations

The company operates four business segments: Retail Banking and Wealth Management (RBWM); Commercial Banking which serves small and multinational businesses in five hubs where 50% of US corporate imports and exports happen (California Florida Illinois New York and Texas); Global Banking and Markets which offers advisory services and trading services for major government corporate and institutional clients; and Private Bank which serves high net worth and ultra-high net worth individuals and their families particularly focusing on multi-generational families business owners and entrepreneurs.

About 75% of HSBC USA's $82.92 billion-loan portfolio was made up of commercial loans (including global banking business and corporate banking and construction and other real estate loans) at the end of 2015. The rest of its portfolio was made up of consumer loans especially residential mortgages with some home equity credit card and other loans.

The bank makes around 70% of its revenue from interest income. About 41% of its total rev-

enue came from loan interest during 2015 while another 27% came from interest on securities trading securities and short-term investments. The rest of its revenue came from trust and investment management fees (3% of revenue) credit card fees (1%) trading revenue (1%) residential mortgage banking revenue (1%) other fees and commissions (15%) gains on securities at fair value (5%) and other miscellaneous sources.

Geographic Reach

HSBC USA serves customers nationwide with the highest concentration of its bank branches located in New York City Los Angeles San Francisco Chicago Atlanta Houston Seattle Miami and Washington DC. The company operates foreign branches and representative offices in the Caribbean Canada Latin America Europe and Asia.

Sales and Marketing

HSBC USA serves a variety of customers such as individuals (including high net worth individuals) small businesses corporations institutions and governments. It boasted 2.4 million customers at the end of 2015 30% of which live in New York and 29% in California.

The bank has been ramping up its advertising spend in recent years. It spent $60 million on advertising in 2015 up from $53 million and $43 million in 2014 and 2013 respectively.

Financial Performance

The US division of HSBC has been struggling to grow its revenue over the past several years as low interest rates have continued to eat away at its interest margins and as its non-interest revenues have been in decline. The bank has been recovering from losses in 2013 and 2012 caused by goodwill impairments and regulatory expenses.

HSBC USA's revenue turned a corner in 2015 jumping 11% to $5.17 billion during the year mostly thanks to higher interest income on 8% commercial loan asset growth and double-digit security asset growth.

Despite strong revenue growth in 2015 the company's net income fell 7% to $330 million mainly because its credit loss provisions increased by $173 million mostly as it made more commercial loans with exposure to the oil and gas industry. HSBC USA's operating cash levels dropped 22% to $4.65 billion for the year due to unfavorable working capital changes primarily related to changes in trading assets and liabilities.

Strategy

HSBC USA as part of the broader HSBC group aims to become the world's leading international bank and seeks to connected emerging economies with developed markets. The US division like parent HSBC also continued in 2016 to look for ways to cut operating costs to boost efficiency and overall profits.

In 2014 HSBC USA became one of the nation's first major banks to roll out a new fraud protection device which employs two-factor authentication for its personal Internet customers.

Company Background

HSBC and HSBC USA restructured their operations in 2011 which included divesting operations and cutting staff. As part of the restructuring HSBC sold 195 retail branches in New York and Connecticut to First Niagara for $1 billion. Through HSBC USA and its HSBC Finance affiliate HSBC also sold its card and retail services business to Capital One Financial. In 2010 HSBC USA exited its noncore wholesale banknotes business. The company also closed and consolidated about a dozen branches in Connecticut and New Jersey. The moves are part of the company's strategy to focus more on commercial and corporate banking in New York and other key urban markets itself part of HSBC's restructuring to create a leaner group.

EXECUTIVES

Chairman President and CEO HSBC North America Holdings Inc. and HSBC Bank USA, Patrick J. (Pat) Burke, age 55
SEVP and CFO, Mark A. Zaeske
SEVP and COO USA, Vittorio M. Severino
SEVP and Head of Global Banking and Markets Americas, Thierry Roland
SEVP and Head of Strategy and Planning, Loren C. Klug, age 56
EVP and Head of Private Banking Americas, Marlon Young, age 61, $389,423 total compensation
SEVP and Chief Risk Officer, Rhydian H. Cox
SEVP and Head of Commercial Banking, Wyatt E Crowell
EVP and Head of Human Resources USA, Maureen A. Gillan-Myer
EVP and Head of Regulatory Remediation, Stephen R. Nesbitt
SEVP and Chief Auditor, Richard E. O'Brien
EVP and Corporate Secretary, Karen Pisarczyk
SEVP and Head of Retail Banking and Wealth Management, Pablo Sanchez
SEVP and General Counsel, Mark Steffensen
EVP and Chief Accounting Officer, William Tabaka
Senior Vice President Compensation, Deanna Larkin
Auditors: PricewaterhouseCoopers LLP

LOCATIONS

HQ: HSBC USA, Inc.
452 Fifth Avenue, New York, NY 10018
Phone: 212 525-5000

PRODUCTS/OPERATIONS

2013 Sales

	$ mil.	% of total
Interest		
Loans	1,876	39
Securities	876	19
Other	227	4
Non-interest		
Other fees & commissions	706	14
Trading revenue	474	9
Servicing and other fees from HSBC affiliates	202	4
Other securities gains	202	4
Trust income	123	3
Other	150	4
Total	**4,836**	**100**

COMPETITORS

Astoria Financial	KeyCorp
Bank of America	M&T Bank
Capital One	New York Community
Citibank	Bancorp
Citizens Financial	PNC Financial
Group	TD Bank USA
JPMorgan Chase	Wells Fargo

HISTORICAL FINANCIALS

Company Type: Public

Income Statement

FYE: December 31

	ASSETS ($ mil.)	NET INCOME ($ mil.)	INCOME AS % OF ASSETS	EMPLOYEES
12/16	201,301	129	0.1%	6,114
12/15	188,278	330	0.2%	6,173
12/14	185,539	354	0.2%	6,400
12/13	185,487	(338)	—	6,500
12/12	196,567	(1,045)	—	7,000
Annual Growth	**0.6%**	**—**		**(3.3%)**

2016 Year-End Financials

Debt ratio: 15.92%	No. of shares (mil.): 0	
Return on equity: 0.63%	Dividends	
Cash ($ mil.): 38,323	Yield: 0.0%	
Current ratio: —	Payout: —	
Long-term debt ($ mil.): —	Market value ($ mil.): —	

	STOCK PRICE ($) FY Close	P/E High/Low	Earnings	Dividends	Book Value
12/16	0.00 28,508,403.00	— —	(0.00)	0.49	
12/15	23.99 28,746,498.00	— —	(0.00)	1.02	
12/14	23.25 23,796,633.00	— —	(0.00)	1.01	
12/13	20.28 23,091,164.00	— —	(0.00)	1.01	
Annual Growth	—	— —	—	(16.4%)	5.4%

Humana Inc.

Medicare has made Humana a big-time player in the insurance game. One of the largest Medicare providers and a top health insurer Humana provides Medicare Advantage plans and prescription drug coverage to more than 7.7 million members throughout the US. It also administers managed care plans for other government programs including Medicaid plans in Florida and Puerto Rico and TRICARE (for military personnel) in the South. Additionally Humana offers commercial health plans and specialty (life dental and vision) coverage; it also provides health management services and operates outpatient care clinics. All told it covers more than 21 million members in the US.

HISTORY

In 1961 Louisville Kentucky lawyers David Jones and Wendell Cherry bought a nursing home as a real estate investment. Within six years their company Extendicare was the largest nursing home chain in the US (with only eight homes).

Faced with a glutted nursing home market the partners noticed that hospitals received more money per patient per day than nursing homes so they took their company public in 1968 to finance hospital purchases (one per month from 1968 to 1971). The company then sold its 40 nursing homes. Sales rose 13 times over in the next five years and in 1973 the firm changed its name to Humana.

By 1975 Humana had built 27 hospitals in the South and Southwest. It targeted young privately insured patients and kept its charity caseload and bad-debt expenses low. Three years later #3 for-profit hospital operator Humana moved up a notch when it bought #2 American Medicorp.

In 1983 the government began reimbursing Medicare payments based on fixed rates. Counting on its high hospital occupancy in 1984 the company launched Humana Health Care Plans rewarding doctors and patients who used Humana hospitals. However hospital occupancy dropped and the company closed several clinics. When its net income fell 75% in 1986 the firm responded by lowering premiums to attract employers.

In 1991 co-founder Cherry died. With hospital profits down in 1993 Jones spun off Humana's 76 hospitals as Galen Healthcare which formed the nucleus of what is now HCA - The Healthcare Company. Humana used the cash to expand its

HMO membership buying Group Health Association (an HMO serving metropolitan Washington DC) and CareNetwork (a Milwaukee HMO). The next year Humana added 1.3 million members when it bought EMPHESYS and the company's income which had stagnated since the salad days of the late 1980s and early 1990s seemed headed in the right direction.

In the mid-1990s cutthroat premiums failed to cover rising health care costs as members' hospital use soared out of control particularly in the company's new Washington DC market. Profits dropped 94% and Humana's already tense relationship with doctors and members worsened. President and COO Wayne Smith and CFO Roger Drury resigned as part of a management shake-up and newly appointed president Gregory Wolf offered to drop the company's gag clause after the Florida Physicians Association threatened to sue.

A reorganized Humana rebounded in 1997. The company pulled out of 13 unprofitable markets including Alabama (though it did not drop TRICARE its military health coverage program in that state) and Washington DC. Refocusing on core markets in the Midwest and Southeast Humana bought Physician Corp. of America (PCA) and ChoiceCare a Cincinnati HMO. Wolf replaced Jones as CEO in 1997.

To cut costs Humana agreed in 1998 to be bought by United HealthCare (now UnitedHealth Group). The deal was abandoned however when United HealthCare took a $900 million charge in advance of the purchase. Humana found savings by pruning its Medicare HMO business.

Humana did everything but party in 1999. The company faced RICO charges for allegedly overcharging members for co-insurance; it agreed to repay $15 million in Medicare overpayments to the government; and it became the first health insurance firm to be slapped with a class-action suit over its physician incentives and other coverage policies.

Humana sold PCA in 2000 saying that it had paid too much for the company; subsidiary PCA Property & Casualty was also sold marking the company's exit from the workers' compensation business. That year Humana also sold its underperforming Florida Medicaid HMO to Well Care HMO and agreed to pay more than $14 million to the government for submitting false Medicare payment information.

In 2001 Humana bought a unit of Anthem that provides health benefits to the military. Expanding its holdings in the southeast Humana acquired Louisiana's Ochsner Health Plan in 2004.

It further grew its product line with the 2007 acquisition of Atlanta-based CompBenefits a provider of dental and vision benefits to nearly 5 million members. The acquisition gave Humana a full-service vision offering and expanded its dental benefits operations. Later that year the company bought KMG America a life and health insurer and third-party administrator for more than 1 million members. Humana combined CompBenefits KMG America and its previous dental benefits operations into a new unit in 2008 called Humana Specialty Benefits.

In 2008 Humana acquired about 25000 Medicare Advantage members in Nevada from UnitedHealth which was divesting the operations as part of its merger deal with Sierra Health Services for $225 million. And later that year it acquired smaller Florida-based Medicare Advantage provider Metcare Health Plans from Metropolitan Health Networks.

Additional acquisitions include the 2008 acquisition of OSF HealthPlans an Illinois-based managed care company belonging to OSF Healthcare. The deal worth about $90 million gave Humana another 60000 commercial members as well as some new Medicare customers in Illinois. The company had already wrapped up its acquisition of Tennessee-based PHP Companies (which does business as Cariten Healthcare) from Covenant Health. Humana spent $250 million in late 2008 to gain Cariten's managed care operations in East Tennessee adding 70000 commercial customers and 45000 Medicare members.

One of Humana's competitive TRICARE contracts was awarded to another party in 2009; however after Humana objected and bids were re-evaluated the decision was reversed in 2011 (with no negative impact on the company's operations).

In 2010 Humana moved into an all new specialty business area with its acquisition of Concentra a provider of occupational medicine urgent care and wellness programs from Welsh Carson Anderson & Stowe for some $790 million. Humana made the purchase to bolster its consumer-focused initiatives and provide a platform for future service-offering expansion efforts.

To widen its cost-control services and advance its IT offerings Humana partnered with software firm Anvita Health in 2010. The analytics firm provided analytics capabilities to identify at-risk members and also served other insurers benefit managers health care professionals and electronic health record providers. (Humana wound up acquiring Anvita in late 2011.)

Early in 2012 Humana purchased MD Care a Medicare Advantage provider serving some 15000 members in four Southern California counties. It also acquired Arcadian Management Services a Medicare Advantage HMO with some 64000 members in 15 states including California. To complete its acquisition of Arcadian Humana was required to sell select Medicare Advantage plans serving some 12000 former Arcadian members to CIGNA (in Texas and Arkansas) and WellCare Health Plans (in Arizona).

EXECUTIVES

Vice President Marketing, Thomas Noland
President and CEO, Bruce D. Broussard, age 54, $1,235,446 total compensation
SVP and Chief Consumer Officer, Jody L. Bilney, age 55, $573,452 total compensation
SVP and Chief Medical Officer, Roy A. Beveridge, age 59
SVP and CIO, Brian P. LeClaire, age 56
SVP and Chief Human Resources Officer, Timothy S. (Tim) Huval, age 50, $573,453 total compensation
SVP and CFO, Brian A. Kane, age 44, $636,254 total compensation
SVP and Chief Strategy Officer, Christopher H. (Chris) Hunter, age 48, $465,865 total compensation
President and Intermountain Region Market Leader Senior Products, Catherine Field
Segment Vice President, Mark A McCullough
Vice President, William Hauser
Vice President MarketPOINT Sales, Jim Van Valin
Market Vice President, Jordan Swanson
Vice President, Rachel Horton
Vice President of Provider Connectivity, Marisa Maxwell
Vice President Investment Management, Mark Preston
Director of Pharmacy Operations, Kathy Bowman
Vice President, Douglas Stoss
Vice President, Tim Moorhead
Vice President, John Montgomery
Assistant Vice President, Kimberly Brown
Regional Vice President of Market Development, Jeremy Gaskill
Medical Director, Joseph Migliozzi
National Account Manager, Aimee Walter
Vice President Information Technology, Michael Richmond
Vice President Sales, Nelson Tawasha

Third Vice President, Tom Ryan
Health Care Director, C Robertson
Health Services Director, Marlene Spicer
Vice President Public Sector, Tim Snyder
Vice President Compensation, Matthew Saxon
Vice President Group Sales, Rick Remmers
Vice President and Assistant General Counsel (2000), Ralph Martin Wilson
Health Services Director, Yvonne Shell
Executive Vice President Marketing, Jennifer Bazante
Regional President North And South Florida, Fernando Valverde
Executive Vice President Digital, Jeff Reid
Segment Vice President, John Delorimier
Health Services Director, Ricardo Menchaca
Market Vice President, Anita Holloway
National Account Manager, Melissa Staton
Vice President Information Technology Transformation And Shared Services, Faheem Zuberi
Enterprise Vice President Talent And Org, Roger Cude
National Sales Manager, Michael Chinigo
Regional President Senior Products, Kevin Meriwether
Vice President, Gary Williams
Ohio Indiana Vice President Network Contracting, Rich Gunza
Pharmacy Manager, Kenneth Tse
Regional Director Government Relations, Jenny Fowler
Medical Director, Mark Pierson
Medical Director, Amy Fendrich
Market Vice President, Giselle Cushing
Enterprise Vice President, Amin Kassem
Vice President And Chief Financial Officer Of Senior Products, Alisa Coppock
Market Vice President, Barry Boster
Medical Director, Bryan Carr
Srvpnr LAN Operating Systems, Wes Johnson
Medical Director, Donn Perisee
Vice President Retail Service Operations Contact Centers, Alyssa Reynolds
VICE PRESIDENT, Willia Densford
MARKET VICE PRESIDENT DFW AND HOUSTON SENIOR PRODUCTS, Lesli C Young
VICE PRESIDENT OF CLINICAL COMPLIANCE, Meliss A Koellner
MEDICAL DIRECTOR, Pegg Vaughan
FIELD VICE PRESIDENT, Patric Hollister
MEDICAL DIRECTOR, Rebecc Colon
VICE PRESIDENT SPECIALTY PHARMACY STRATEGY, Rand Falkenrath
SEGMENT VICE PRESIDENT, Thoma P Klammer
MEDICAL DIRECTOR, Jud Shaw-rice
VICE PRESIDENT, Kristin Martin
REGIONAL PRESIDENT, Charle Dow
MEDICAL DIRECTOR, Cind M Dunn
MEDICAL DIRECTOR, Davi Annand
VICE PRESIDENT HEAD OF WORKPLACE SOLUTIONS, Dougla Edwards
Chairman, Kurt J. Hilzinger, age 56
Board Member, Martha Northcutt
Board Member, Cathy McDaniel
Secretary Treasurer, Jeff Fernandez
Auditors: PricewaterhouseCoopers LLP

LOCATIONS

HQ: Humana Inc.
500 West Main Street, Louisville, KY 40202
Phone: 502 580-1000
Web: www.humana.com

PRODUCTS/OPERATIONS

2016 Sales

	$ mil.	% of total
Premiums		
Individual Medicare Advantage	31,863	59
Fully insured commercial	8,897	16
Group medicare advantage	4,283	8
Medicare stand-alone PDP	4,009	7
Specialty commercial	1,279	2
Medicaid & other premiums	2,690	5
Services	969	2
Investment income	389	1
Total	**54,379**	**100**

2016 Sales by Segment

	$ mil.	% of total
Retail	46,655	59
Healthcare Services	25,122	32
Group	7,249	19
Other	114	-
Adjustments	(24761)	-
Total	**54,379**	**100**

Selected Products and Services

Government
  Medicaid managed care plans
  Medicare Advantage plans
  Medicare prescription drug plans
  TRICARE (military personnel)
Commercial
  Administrative services only (ASO)
  HMO plans
  HumanaOne (individual insurance)
  POS (point-of-service) plans
  PPO plans
  Specialty products
  Dental insurance
  Life insurance
  Short-term disability insurance

COMPETITORS

AMERIGROUP	First Health Group
Aetna	Florida Blue
Anthem	HCSC
Assurant	Health Net
Blue Cross and Blue Shield of Texas	HealthSpring
	Highmark
CIGNA	Kaiser Foundation
Caremark Pharmacy Services	Health Plan
	Molina Healthcare
Centene	UnitedHealth Group
Coventry Health Care	Universal American
Express Scripts	WellCare Health Plans

HISTORICAL FINANCIALS

Company Type: Public

Income Statement

FYE: December 31

	ASSETS ($ mil.)	NET INCOME ($ mil.)	INCOME AS % OF ASSETS	EMPLOYEES
12/16	25,396	614	2.4%	54,200
12/15	24,705	1,276	5.2%	51,700
12/14	23,466	1,147	4.9%	57,000
12/13	20,735	1,231	5.9%	52,000
12/12	19,979	1,222	6.1%	43,400
Annual Growth	**6.2%**	**(15.8%)**	**—**	**5.7%**

2016 Year-End Financials

Debt ratio: 15.77%
Return on equity: 5.82%
Cash ($ mil.): 3,877
Current ratio: —
Long-term debt ($ mil.): —
No. of shares (mil.): 149
Dividends
  Yield: 0.0%
  Payout: 21.3%
Market value ($ mil.): 30,463

	STOCK PRICE ($)	P/E	PER SHARE ($)		
	FY Close	High/Low	Earnings	Dividends	Book Value
12/16	204.03	53 37	4.07	0.87	71.56
12/15	178.51	25 16	8.44	1.15	69.77
12/14	143.63	20 13	7.36	1.11	64.48
12/13	103.22	13 8	7.73	1.07	60.48
12/12	68.63	13 8	7.47	1.03	55.88
Annual Growth	31.3%	— —	(14.1%)	(4.1%)	6.4%

Hunt (J.B.) Transport Services, Inc.

When it comes to hauling freight J.B. Hunt Transport Services knows how to deliver. Its intermodal unit the company's largest maintains about 4580 tractors; 5400 drivers; and more than 84500 pieces of trailing equipment and moves customers' cargo by combinations of truck and train. JBI's dedicated contract services unit supplies customers with drivers and equipment; it operates about 6970 company-owned trucks. The company's truckload transportation unit provides dry freight transportation with a fleet of about 1460 tractors. A fourth business segment integrated capacity solutions (ICS) manages freight transportation via third-party carriers as well as J.B. Hunt equipment.The company traces its roots back to 1961 when it was founded by Johnnie Bryan (J.B.) Hunt.

Operations

Freight transported by J.B. Hunt includes automotive parts building materials chemicals electronics food and beverages forest and paper products and general merchandise. The company divides its operations across four segments. JBI offers intermodal freight services to customers in Canada Mexico and the US and generates almost 60% of the company's net sales.

Dedicated contract services (DCS) provides supply chain services supplementing a variety of different types of transportation and accounted for almost 25% of total sales. Other segments include JBT (trucking) and ICS (integrated capacity solutions). The latter segment often arranges specialty trucking services such as transporting freight that requires the use of flatbed or refrigerated trailers.

Geographic Reach

J.B. Hunt is headquartered in Lowell Arkansas and its principal facilities are located throughout the US. Its JBI segment offers intermodal freight services to customers in the US Canada and Mexico.

Sales and Marketing

J.B. Hunt markets its services through a nationwide sales and marketing network. It uses a specific sales force within its DCS segment due to the length and complexity of the sales cycle. In addition the ICS segment utilizes its own local branch of salespeople.

Financial Performance

J.B. Hunt has enjoyed unprecedented growth in the receding wake of the recession. From 2015 to 2016 revenues increased 6% from $6.19 billion in 2015 to $6.56 billion in 2016 a company milestone. The recent growth was due to overall increased load volume partially offset by lower revenue per load in its JBI ICS and JBT segments. Its ICS segment revenue increased the most (22%) due to an overall volume increase of 57% mainly due to new offerings.

Profits also surged from $427 million in 2015 to peak at a record-setting $432 million in 2016.

Strategy

J.B. Hunt hopes to continue its pathway to growth by concentrating on its operating segments as separate but overlapping businesses and by selling more value-added services to its customers. It has continued to expand its intermodal unit which has agreements with major North American railroads including Burlington Northern Santa Fe and Norfolk Southern railways. The arrangement also allows J.B. Hunt to cut down on costs.

To keep pace with the rapid progress of technology and meet modern-day customer demands J. B. Hunt plans to invest heavily in its operating infrastructure. In 2016 it announced plans to fully equip its highway trailer and intermodal container fleets with tracking systems by the end of 2018. These systems will provide location tracking services and load information services for each of its trailers and containers. J.B. hunt believes the initiative will give it a competitive edge providing improvements in areas of asset utilization as well as providing meaningful advances in customer service load management and planning. Throughout 2016 it also launched multiple mobile applications for its drivers carrier partners and customers.

HISTORY

Johnnie Bryan (J.B.) Hunt's life was a classic tale of rolling from rags to riches — with a little help from a Rockefeller. Hunt grew up in a family of sharecroppers during the Depression and he left school at age 12 to work for his uncle's Arkansas sawmill. In the late 1950s after driving trucks for more than nine years Hunt noticed that the rice mills along his eastern Arkansas route were burning rice hulls. Believing the hulls could be used as poultry litter Hunt got a contract to haul away the hulls and began selling them to chicken farmers.

In 1961 he began the J.B. Hunt Company with help from future Arkansas governor Winthrop Rockefeller who owned Winrock grass company where Hunt bought sod for one of his side businesses. Hunt developed a machine to compress the rice hulls which made their transportation profitable and within a few years the company was the world's largest producer of rice hulls for poultry litter.

Still looking for new opportunities Hunt bought some used trucks and refrigerated trailers in 1969 though the company continued to focus on its original business. In the 1980s J.B. Hunt's trucking division grew dramatically and became lucrative as the trucking industry was being deregulated. In 1981-82 the Hunt trucking business had higher margins than most trucking firms. In 1983 when J.B. Hunt Transport Services went public Hunt sold the rice hull business to concentrate on trucking.

EXECUTIVES

EVP Operations and COO, Craig Harper, age 60, $375,000 total compensation

President and CEO, John N. Roberts, age 52, $807,747 total compensation

Vice President Finance, Richie Henderson

EVP and CIO, Stuart L. Scott, age 51

EVP; President Intermodal, Terrence D. (Terry) Matthews, age 59, $478,819 total compensation

EVP Finance and Administration CFO and Corporate Secretary, David G. Mee, age 57, $480,660 total compensation

EVP and Chief Commercial Officer; President Highway Services, Shelley Simpson, age 45, $476,923 total compensation

EVP; President Dedicated Contract Services, Nicholas (Nick) Hobbs, age 54, $454,808 total compensation

Vice President Sales National Accounts, Mark Calcagni

National Account Manager, Korey Christian

Vice President of Transportation, Tami Allensworth

Vice President of Transportation, Nick Gowen

Vice President of Operations, Andrew DeBlock

Senior Vice President, Brian Webb

Vice President Intermodal Pricing, Darren Field

Vice President Finance, Erin Taylor

Vice President of Sales, Chris Sandor

Vice President Of Trans, Greg Price

National Account Manager, Chris Putnam

Senior Vice President of Transportation, Eric McGee

National Sales Manager, Ed Page

Vice President of IS, Jay Davidson

Vice President Strategic Accounts, Clay Cox

National Account Manager, Kevin Boortz

Senior Vice President, Paul Bingham

Vice President of Business Development, Rodney Nye

National Sales Manager, Brandon Parker

Vice President Of Maintenance, Derek Kennemer

Vice President Intermodal Operations, Michael Brothers

Vice President of Sales and Marketing, Jessica Brooks

Vice President Claims and Litigation Management, Mark Whitehead

Vice President Transportation, Brandon Taylor

Senior Vice President, Thomas Lastovica

Vice President Intermodal Operations, John Mckuin

Senior Vice President Marketing, Tom Williams

Vice President Sales, Jason Bohannon

National Account Manager, Kim Armstrong

National Account Manager, Christopher Trout

Vice President, Shawn Graves

Vice President National Accounts, Bill Copelin

Vice President of Maintenance, Michael Ralston

Vice President Maintenance Maintenance Manager, Charles Radcliffe

National Account Manager, Sonya Cates

National Sales Manager, Scott Coleman

Senior Vice President Sales, Spencer Frazier

National Sales Manager, Bill Gasaway

Vice President, John Kuhlow

Vice President of Technical Services, Ken Mangold

Vice President Sales Southern Region, Shannon Foley

Vice President Of Operations, Brian Dieringer

National Account Manager, Tommie Wood

Vice President Sales Eastern Region, Bill Fedorchak

National Sales Manager, Markis Randall

Vice President of Strategic Accounts, Gabe Waldrop

National Sales Manager, Anton Olson

National Sales Manager, Ben Mallard

Vice President of Sales, Bill Carver

Vice President, Steve Guthrie

Vice President of Transportation, Clint Elcan

Chairman, Kirk Thompson, age 64

Auditors: Ernst & Young LLP

LOCATIONS

HQ: Hunt (J.B.) Transport Services, Inc.
615 J.B. Hunt Corporate Drive, Lowell, AR 72745
Phone: 479 820-0000
Web: www.jbhunt.com

PRODUCTS/OPERATIONS

2016 Sales

	$ mil.	% of total
Intermodal (JBI)	3,796	58
Dedicated contract services (DCS)	1,533	23
Integrated capacity solutions (ICS)	852	13
Trucking (JBT)	388	6
Adjustments	(14)	-
Total	**6,555**	**100**

Selected Trucking Services

Dedicated
Expedited
Final Mile
Flatbed
Intermodal
Less Than Truckload
Refrigerated
Truckload

COMPETITORS

APL Logistics	Ryder System
CSX	Schneider National
Canadian National	Swift Transportation
Railway	U.S. Xpress
Hub Group	Union Pacific
Kansas City Southern	Werner Enterprises
Landstar System	YRC Worldwide
Old Dominion Freight	

HISTORICAL FINANCIALS

Company Type: Public

Income Statement

FYE: December 31

	REVENUE ($ mil.)	NET INCOME ($ mil.)	NET PROFIT MARGIN	EMPLOYEES
12/16	6,555	432	6.6%	22,190
12/15	6,187	427	6.9%	21,562
12/14	6,165	374	6.1%	20,158
12/13	5,584	342	6.1%	18,467
12/12	5,054	310	6.1%	16,475
Annual Growth	**6.7%**	**8.6%**	**—**	**7.7%**

2016 Year-End Financials

Debt ratio: 25.76%	No. of shares (mil.): 111
Return on equity: 31.75%	Dividends
Cash ($ mil.): 6	Yield: 0.0%
Current ratio: 1.65	Payout: 23.1%
Long-term debt ($ mil.): 986	Market value ($ mil.): 10,804

	STOCK PRICE ($) FY Close	P/E High/Low	PER SHARE ($) Earnings	Dividends	Book Value
12/16	97.07	26 17	3.81	0.88	12.70
12/15	73.36	25 19	3.66	0.84	11.41
12/14	84.25	27 22	3.16	0.80	10.33
12/13	77.30	27 20	2.87	0.60	8.64
12/12	59.71	23 17	2.59	0.71	6.74
Annual Growth	**12.9%**	**— —**	**10.1%**	**5.5%**	**17.2%**

Huntington Bancshares Inc

Huntington Bancshares is the holding company for The Huntington National Bank which operates around 1100 branches in Ohio Michigan Illinois Indiana Kentucky Pennsylvania West Virginia and Wisconsin. In addition to traditional retail and commercial banking services the bank offers mortgage banking capital market services equipment leasing brokerage services investment management recreational vehicle and marine financing and trust and estate services. The company's automobile finance business provides car loans to consumers and real estate and inventory finance to car dealerships throughout the Midwest and Northeast. Founded in 1966 the company boasts total assets of more than $70 billion.

Operations

Huntington Bancshares operates through five main business segments: Consumer and Business Banking Commercial Banking Commercial Real Estate and Vehicle Finance Regional Banking and The Huntington Private Client Group (RBHPCG) and Home Lending.

Huntington's Consumer and Business Banking division which contributes more than 40% to total sales provides traditional banking products and services to consumer and small business customers as well as investment insurance foreign exchange hedging and treasury management services.

Its Commercial Banking division (almost 25% of total sales) is made up of seven business units: middle-market large corporate government public sector specialty banking asset finance capital markets treasury management and insurance brokerage.

The Commercial Real Estate and Vehicle Finance division (nearly 25%) provides lending and other banking services to customers outside of its traditional retail and commercial banking segments mostly offering new and used car financing for franchised automotive dealerships as well as their customers. Other vehicles include light-duty trucks and boats. The segment also offers financing for land buildings and other commercial real estate owned or constructed by real estate developers automobile dealerships or other customers needing real estate project financing.

RBHPCG (Regional Banking and The Huntington Private Client Group) accounts for under 10% of sales and provides specialized private banking trust investment and financial services for high net-worth customers under the Huntington brand name. The Home Lending division originates and services consumer loans and mortgages for the bank's retail and business banking divisions.

The small Home Lending segment (2% of sales) originates loans and mortgages for customers mainly in its primary banking markets.

Geographic Reach

Huntington Bancshares operates around 25 private client offices and nearly 1100 branches in the Midwest and Northeast US. Over 50% of the bank's branches were located in Ohio with Michigan hosting another 30%-plus.

Sales and Marketing

In addition to traditional bank branches Huntington distributes its products and services through convenience branches (in grocery stores and retirement centers for example) and an expansive ATM network as well as via internet and mobile services. The bank's branches can be found in Michigan's Meijer and Ohio's Giant Eagle grocery stores.

Financial Performance

A blip in 2013 aside Huntington has recorded steadily climbing growth for more than five years. In fiscal 2016 revenue climbed 16% to $3.8 billion. The company's interest income grew by over $500 million while non-interest income rose by $111 million.

Interest income was boosted by 21% earning asset growth and 22% interest-bearing liability growth largely down to the acquisition of First-Merit during the year. Non-interest income grew amid higher service charges on deposit accounts and card and payment processing due to new customer acquisition. Mortgage banking was also up due to higher mortgage origination.

Net income increased 3% to $712 million due to higher revenue partially offset by outsized growth in non-interest expense (i.e. expense grew faster than revenue). The increase was down to acquisition related expenses totaling $282 million.

Cash from operations rose 18% to $1.2 billion due to higher provision for credit losses and net changes in accrued income and other assets.

Strategy

Huntington is focused on expanding its market share through branch openings and strategic acquisitions to better compete in its target markets. In 2016 the company bought FirstMerit Corporation boosting total assets by 41% swelling its branch network by nearly 50% and making it Ohio's largest bank. Prior to the FirstMerit acquisition the bank opened 67 branches in Michigan and increased its deposit business by $750 million.

Mergers and Acquisitions

In August 2016 Huntington Bancshares paid $3.7 billion to buy Akron-based rival FirstMerit Corporation making it Ohio's largest bank and boosting its total assets by 41% to $100 billion. The acquisition also expanded Huntington's branch network by nearly 50% to some 1000 branches extending into the surrounding states of Michigan and Pennsylvania.

Company Background

With the economy in the Midwest wracked by the recession Huntington posted losses in 2008 and 2009 — more than $3 billion in the latter year alone — mainly attributable to credit losses due to nonperforming assets and the write down of goodwill related to past acquisitions. It returned to profitability in 2010 thanks in part to higher interest margins as a result of the company's focus on lower-cost customer checking accounts.

HISTORY

Pelatiah Webster (P. W.) Huntington descendant of both a Revolutionary War leader and a Declaration of Independence signer went to work at sea in 1850 at age 14. He returned to go into banking and in 1866 founded what would become Huntington National Bank of Columbus. As the business grew he conscripted four of his five sons. The bank took a national charter in 1905 and became The Huntington National Bank of Columbus. It survived the hard times of 1907 and 1912 through the Huntington philosophy of sitting on piles of cash.

P. W. died in 1918 and his son Francis became president. Francis expanded the company into trust services. Unlike many bankers in the 1920s he refused to make speculative loans based on the stock market. Francis died in 1928 and was succeeded by brother Theodore. By 1930 Huntington's trust assets accounted for more than half of the total. The family's conservative philosophy helped the bank sail through the 1933 bank holiday although when it reopened the amount of cash it could pay out was restricted to 10% of deposits.

P. W.'s son Gwynne chaired the bank during its post-WWII expansion. His death in 1958 ended the Huntington family reign. The bank began opening branches and adding new services such as mortgage and consumer loans. In 1966 in order to expand statewide the bank formed a holding company Huntington Bancshares. In the 1960s and 1970s the corporation added new operations including mortgage and leasing companies and an international division to help clients with foreign exchange.

In 1979 the company consolidated its 15 affiliates into The Huntington National Bank. Three years later the company bit off more than it could chew with the acquisitions of Reeves Banking and Trust Company of Dover and Union Commerce Corporation of Cleveland. The latter purchase loaded the company with debt. Nevertheless it continued to expand particularly after 1985 when banking regulations allowed interstate branch banking and it soon had operations in Florida Indiana Kentucky Michigan and West Virginia.

Huntington Bancshares was largely insulated from the real estate problems of the late 1980s and early 1990s thanks to its continuing conservative lending policies. But the company was at risk from the nationwide consolidation of the banking industry which made it a potential takeover target. It increased its service offerings and bolstered its place in the market through acquisitions. In 1996 Huntington Bancshares bought life insurance agency Tice & Associates and began cross-selling bank and insurance products. Important banking acquisitions in 1997 included First Michigan Bank and several Florida companies.

Also in 1997 the company took advantage of deregulation to consolidate its interstate operations (except for The Huntington State Bank) into a single operating company. In 1998 Huntington Bancshares continued to build its Huntington insurance services unit with the acquisition of Pollock & Pollock. In 1999 the bank launched a mortgage program aimed at wealthy clients and sold its credit card receivables portfolio to Chase Manhattan (now JPMorgan Chase & Co.). In 2000 the company bought Michigan's Empire Banc Corporation.

Former BANK ONE executive Thomas Hoaglin was named president and CEO in 2001. Later that year he became chairman when Frank Wobst retired after leading the company for 20 years.

In 2002 the company consolidated some branches in the Midwest to cut costs and exited the retail banking market in Florida selling some 140 retail branches there to SunTrust. After the mid-2007 acquisition of Sky Financial Sky's CEO Marty Adams became president and COO of Huntington Bancshares. He retired at the end of 2007 and Hoaglin resumed the president's role until his own retirement in 2009; Stephen Steinour then took the helm.

EXECUTIVES

President Northwest Ohio The Huntington National Bank, Sharon S. Speyer
EVP General Counsel and Secretary, Richard A. Cheap, age 65, $279,833 total compensation
Chairman President and CEO, Stephen D. (Steve) Steinour, age 59, $1,061,538 total compensation
SEVP and Managing Director Auto Finance Commercial Real Estate and Community Development Lending and Investment, Nicholas G. (Nick) Stanutz, age 62, $465,000 total compensation
SEVP Retail and Business Banking, Mary W. Navarro, age 61, $541,154 total compensation
SEVP and Chief Risk Officer, Helga S. Houston, age 56, $542,308 total compensation
SEVP and Director Regional Banking and The Huntington Private Client Group, James E. (Jim) Dunlap, age 64, $518,333 total compensation
President Central Ohio and Columbus Region, James E. Kunk
SEVP and Director Corporate Operations and Corporate Services, Mark E. Thompson, age 58, $315,340 total compensation
President Central Ohio Region, Sue E. Zazon
President West Virginia Region, Andrew J. Paterno
President Western Pennsylvania and Ohio Valley Region, Susan (Susie) Baker Shipley
SEVP and CFO, Howell D. (Mac) McCullough, age 59, $596,538 total compensation

President Greater Cleveland Region, Sean P. Richardson
President Chicago Region, Peter K. Gillespie
VP Commercial Banking Greater Akron/Canton Region, William C. Shivers
SEVP and Chief Credit Officer, Daniel J. Neumeyer, age 57
SEVP Chief Technology and Operations Officer, Paul G. Heller, age 53, $590,385 total compensation
President West Michigan Region, John Irwin
President Southern Ohio and Northern Kentucky Region, Kevin Jones
SEVP and Director Commercial Banking, Richard (Rich) Remiker, age 59
SEVP and Chief Human Resources Officer, Rajeev (Raj) Syal, age 51
President Akron Region, Nicholas Browning
President Indiana Region, John Corbin
President Wisconsin Region, Kevin Leissring
President East Michigan, David Lochner
SEVP Private Bank; Regional Banking Director and Chair Michigan, Sandra E. Pierce, $222,789 total compensation
EVP and Chief Communications and Marketing Director, Julie C. Tutkovics
Senior Vice President Treasury Management Sales Manager, Robin Triplett
Senior Counsel Vice President and Assistant Secretary (1996), Elizabeth Berner Moore
Senior Vice President, Andy Arduini
Senior Vice President, Richard Waldman
Vice President, Bill Cosby
Vice President, Paul Regoni
Vice President Relationship Manager, Stephen Delaney
Senior Vice President Chief Sourcing Officer, Debbie Manos-Mchenry
Vice President Sales And Service Special, Natalie Johns
Vice President Employee Benefits at Huntington National Bank, Kristin Janutolo
Vice President of Human Resour, Rob Nussbaum
Vice President, Bruce Sautter
Vice President, Couturier Jan
Assistant Vice President and Senior Product Manage, Amy Beck
Vice President, Geoffrey Mowery
Vice President, Brian Hair
Vice President; Energy Team, Maggie Niekrash
Assistant Vice President Non Distributed Platforms Mainframe, John Viola
Vice President SEC Reporting Manager, Jeff Endres
Business Systems Analyst Assistant Vice President, Michael Roach
Assistant Vice President Principal Architect, Tom Hill
Senior Vice President, Clint Sommer
Vice President, James Matousek
Senior Vice President Retail Sales and Service Support, Melana Ackerman
Vice President Trust Officer, Philip L Francis
Vice President Corporate Trust Department, James Schultz
Vice President and Community Development Director, Staci Glenn
Vice President of Retail Distribution, Tom Wesolowski
Vice President National Sales Manager And Key Accounts, Patrick Prato
Vice President Senior SBA Lender, Paul Collinsworth
Assistant Vice President mortgage Lending, James Boots
Vice President Senior Sales Executive, Bret Haggy
Vice President I Treasury Management Industry Solutions, Brett Bailey
Vice President Enterprise Technology Systems, Carolyn Jones
Assistant Vice President, Diane Clingerman

Senior Vice President Market Manager, Geoffrey Sale
Senior Vice President and Director Government Relations, Todd Bailey
Senior Vice President Credit Card Services, Scott Abramowitz
Senior Vice President Marketing, Tony Monago
Assistant Vice President, Jenny Nickles
Assistant Vice President Project Management, Regis Martin-Fuller
Assistant Vice President 1 Portfolio Manager, Nick Markovich
Assistant Vice President, Cary J Hager
Assistant Vice President Aml Bsa, Katherine Orkis
Senior Vice President Regional Banking Process Solutions, Steven Clemens
Vice President, Sheryl Palmer
Senior Vice President, Neil S Clark, age 65
Vice President and Manager eCommerce Channel, Tenzin Alexander
Assistant Vice President Treasury Group Finance Manager, Erik Kyre
Senior Vice President, Thomas Cirincione
Vice President Region Marketing Manager, Patricia Barton
Vice President, Todd Sawyers
Vice President General Manager, Kendra Musgrave
Assistant Vice President Senior Product Manager, Shannon Gardner
Vice President, Robin Washienko
Assistant Vice President, Karissa Hendricks
Assistant Vice President Manager Trust Application Support, Susan DiSanza
Credit Risk Executive Vice President, Fred Manning
Senior Vice President Sales, Jon Greenwood
Vice President, Howard Walters
Senior Vice President, David Carcy
Senior Vice President Credit Risk Management, Tim Barber
Vice President And Trust Officer, Carla D Parsons
Vice President Tm Liquidity and Fraud Group Product Manager, Ashley Sanders
Vice President Commercial Banking, Lance Rapp
Nonprofit and University Specialist Vice President CTP, Karen Rath
Vice President Business Unit Controller, Scott Dupler
Vice President, Walt Tomich
Assistant Vice President, Sandra Clarke
Vice President, Rob Koogler
Vice President, Theresa FR Davis
Vice President, Mike Flis
Senior Vice President, Jay Plum
Vice President, Michael Crawford
Assistant Vice President Senior Human Resources Generalist, Susan Lelonek
Executive Vice President and Chief Auditor, Harry Farver
Vice President, Bill Leemhuis
Vice President Collections MIS, Willie Tackett
Vice President, Joseph Ahee
Executive Vice President Senior Commercial Credit Approval Officer, Josh Eichenhorn
Senior Vice President Treasury Management, Steve Veach
Senior Vice President Commercial Lending, Daniel Erlandson
Vice President, Terry Kuney
Vice President, Diana Ferrara
Assistant Vice President Home Lending Compliance Section Manager, Omar Ramsay
Vice President, Josh Bond
Vice President Loan Syndications, Chad Lowe
Business Banking Specialist Assistant Vice President, Tara Murphy
Senior Vice President Deposit Product Pricing and Fees Director, David Schamer
Vice President commercial dealer Services portfolio Manager, Dan Hewitt

Vice Presicent Business Analyst 3, Andrew Mace
Senior Financial Advisor Assistant Vice President, Nick Brown
Vice President Human Resources Senior Staffing Specialist, Karis Spence
Vice President Senior Sourcing Manager, Jay Gomer
Vice President Business Banking, Lesley Burt
Senior Vice President, Bob Redfield
Assistant Vice President Branch Manager, Glen Shtjefni
Senior Vice President Retail Marketing, Karen Maruna
Vice President, Kimberly Harrison
Assistant Vice President, Tony Ruberg
Vice President commercial Banking, Michael Price
Vice President Change and Capacity Management, Tim Dirrim
Vice President Front End Collections, Dave Mortenson
Assistant Vice President Regional Property Manager, Cheryl Pitzer
Vice President of the Mortgage Group, Linda Zack
Vice President, Andy Ohler
Vice President, Renee Ross
Vice President, William Mokma
Vice President, Dan Lowrie
Assistant Vice President, Schlosser James
Vice President, Terri Whitman
Vice President, William Denehy
Executive Vice President Marketing, Chandra Kimble
Vice President Commercial Loans, John Leuhmann
Vice President digital business architect, Rick Gonzalez
Vice President Portfolio Manager, Matthew Alexander
Vice President Senior Commercial Relationship Manager, Kevin Contat
Vice President Treasury Management Customer Care Manager, Raquel Ribe
Vice President, David Konik
Vice President, Steve McNeil
Vice President Business Banking, Herb Sawtell
Assistant Vice President And Branch Manager, Amber Babik
Vice President Retirement Plan Services Consultant, Douglas Scharphorn
Auditors: PricewaterhouseCoopers LLP

LOCATIONS

HQ: Huntington Bancshares Inc
41 South High Street, Columbus, OH 43287
Phone: 614 480-8300
Web: www.huntington.com

2016 Bank Branches

	No.
Ohio	523
Michigan	353
Pennsylvania	53
Indiana	46
Illinois	39
Wisconsin	37
West Virginia	30
Kentucky	10
Total	**1,091**

2016 sales

	No.
Consumer and Business Banking	43
Commercial Banking	23
Commercial Real Estate and Vehicle Finance	24
Regional Banking and The Huntington Private Client Group	8
Home Lending	2
Total	**100**

PRODUCTS/OPERATIONS

2016 Sales

	$ mil.	% of total
Interest		
Loans & leases	2,178	58
Available-for-sale and other securities	280	7
Held-to-maturity securities	138	4
Other	35	1
Noninterest		
Service charges on deposit accounts	324	9
cards and payment processing income	169	4
Mortgage banking income	128	3
Trust services	108	3
Insurance income	64	2
Brokerage income	61	2
Capital markets fees	59	2
Bank owned life insurance income	57	2
Gain on sales of loans	47	1
Net gains on sales of securities	2	
Other	129	3
Impairment losses recognized in earnings on available-for-sale securities	(2.1)	
Total	**3,781**	**100**

COMPETITORS

Citizens Financial Group	PNC Financial
Comerica	Park National
Fifth Third	Regions Financial
JPMorgan Chase	TFS Financial
KeyCorp	U.S. Bancorp
	Wells Fargo

HISTORICAL FINANCIALS

Company Type: Public

Income Statement

FYE: December 31

	ASSETS ($ mil.)	NET INCOME ($ mil.)	INCOME AS % OF ASSETS	EMPLOYEES
12/17	104,185	1,186	1.1%	15,770
12/16	99,714	711	0.7%	15,993
12/15	71,044	692	1.0%	12,243
12/14	66,298	632	1.0%	11,873
12/13	59,476	638	1.1%	11,964
Annual Growth	**15.0%**	**16.7%**	**—**	**7.1%**

2017 Year-End Financials

Debt ratio: 8.83%	No. of shares (mil.): 1,072
Return on equity: 11.23%	Dividends
Cash ($ mil.): 1,567	Yield: 0.0%
Current ratio: —	Payout: 35.0%
Long-term debt ($ mil.): —	Market value ($ mil.): 15,609

	STOCK PRICE ($) FY Close	P/E High/Low		PER SHARE ($) Earnings	Dividends	Book Value
12/17	14.56	15	12	1.00	0.35	10.09
12/16	13.22	19	11	0.70	0.29	9.49
12/15	11.06	14	12	0.81	0.25	8.30
12/14	10.52	15	12	0.72	0.21	7.80
12/13	9.65	13	9	0.72	0.19	7.34
Annual Growth	**10.8%**	**—**	**—**	**8.6%**	**16.5%**	**8.3%**

Huntington Ingalls Industries, Inc.

For 40 years Huntington Ingalls Industries (HII) has been the sole builder of the US Navy's nuclear aircraft carriers. Rivaling nuclear submarine builder General Dynamics HII is the largest naval shipbuilder in the world; it also maintains refuels and repairs nuclear aircraft carriers and sub-marines. In addition HII supplies expeditionary warfare ships surface combatants submarines commercial oil hull tankers and Coast Guard surface ships as well as provides aftermarket fleet support. Almost all its offerings are sold to the US government.

Operations

The shipbuilder divides its work between a few divisions: Newport News (nuclear-powered submarines; almost 60% of net sales) Ingalls (warship production for the US Navy; roughly 30%) and Technical Solutions (fleet support services; 10%). In addition subsidiary AMSEC offers a wide variety of naval architecture and marine engineering services.

Its carrier Gerald R. Ford (CVN 78) is the first ship of its class and is scheduled for delivery to the Navy in 2017. Its last-of-the- Nimitz -class predecessor the USS George H.W. Bush was commissioned in early 2009.

Geographic Reach

Headquartered in Newport News Virginia HII has offices in Huntsville Alabama; San Diego California; Broomfield Colorado; Avondale (New Orleans) Louisiana; Pascagoula Mississippi; Houston; Fairfax Hampton Newport News Suffolk and Virginia Beach Virginia; and Washington DC.

Sales and Marketing

HII provides services to the governmental energy oil and gas private sector companies in addition to commercial industries. The US government is its largest customer with the US Navy accounting for almost 90% of its net sales. The US Coast Guard generates around 5%.

Financial Performance

HII has achieved unprecedented growth over the years with revenues climbing 1% to peak at a record-setting $7.07 billion in 2016. Profits also surged 42% to reach $573 million in 2016 another company milestone.

The historic growth for 2016 was attributed to a 9% rise in Ingalls sales and a 12% spike in Technical Solutions sales. Ingalls experienced higher revenues in surface combatants and amphibious assault ships in 2016. Its Technical Solutions posted higher nuclear and environmental and fleet support revenues as well as additional revenue from its Camber acquisition.

The surge in profits for 2016 was driven by the absence of about $75 million in goodwill and intangible asset impairment charges stemming from its Technical Solutions segment it posted the previous year.

Strategy

One way HII grows is by signing multi-year contracts. The company bets on the fact that the longer a contract runs the more likely contract modifications for certain upgrades will occur resulting in enhanced contract value. In 2013 HII was awarded a multi-year contract totaling $3.3 billion for the construction of five additional DDG-51 Arleigh Burke-class destroyers as a part of a larger US Navy order for nine DDG-51 Arleigh Burke-class destroyers. HII indeed received a modification for this contract in mid-2017 to incorporate some of the latest radar upgrades.

Adhering to this strategy further in late 2017 HII's Newport News segment clinched a $2.8 billion contract to support the refueling and complex overhaul of the USS George Washington. This ship is a Nimitz-class aircraft and is one of the largest nuclear-powered warships that can accommodate up to 6000 personnel on board. HII manages the only private shipyard capable of refueling and overhauling nuclear-powered aircraft carriers. Work for this deal will be completed by August 2021.

Mergers and Acquisitions

HII often uses acquisitions in order to bolster its core offerings.

In late 2016 HII picked up Camber Corporation a provider of information technology and training services to the armed services for $372 million. The acquisition allowed it to form HII Technical Solutions a professional services segment catering to a wide variety of government and commercial customers worldwide. The division offers expertise in agile software development and network engineering training systems logistics support information technology fleet maintenance and modernization and unmanned undersea systems.

In mid-2015 HII acquired the engineering solutions division of The Columbia Group in a deal that enabled it to compete more strongly in the unmanned underwater vehicle market.

EXECUTIVES

President and CEO, C. Michael (Mike) Petters, age 57, $328,847 total compensation
EVP Communications, Jerri Fuller Dickseski
EVP; President Newport News Shipbuilding, Matthew J. (Matt) Mulherin, age 57, $515,000 total compensation
EVP and General Counsel, Kellye L. Walker, age 50, $505,096 total compensation
EVP and Chief Human Resources Officer, William R. (Bill) Ermatinger
EVP and President Technical Solutions, Andy Green
EVP; President Ingalls Shipbuilding, Brian Cuccias, $514,906 total compensation
EVP Business Management and CFO, Christopher D. Kastner, age 53, $463,462 total compensation
EVP Government and Customer Relations, Mitchell B. (Mitch) Waldman
EVP Strategy and Development, Michael S. Smith
Corporate Vice President Litigation, Chad N Boudreaux
Corp Vice President Benefits and Compensatio, Jim Taylor
Corporate Vice President, William Ebbs
Corporate Vice President Deputy General Counsel, George Simmerman
Corporate Vice President Government and Customers Relations, Mitch Waldman
Vice President Senior Vice President, Thomas Johnston
Vice President Submarines And Fleet Support, Jim Hughes
VP Operations And President, Harris Leonard
Chairman, Thomas B. Fargo, age 69
Auditors: Deloitte & Touche LLP

LOCATIONS

HQ: Huntington Ingalls Industries, Inc.
4101 Washington Avenue, Newport News, VA 23607
Phone: 757 380-2000
Web: www.huntingtoningalls.com

PRODUCTS/OPERATIONS

2016 Sales

	$ mil.	% of total
Newport News	4,089	57
Ingalls	2,389	33
Technical Solutions	691	10
Intersegment eliminations	(101)	-
Total	**7,068**	**100**

2016 Sales

	$ mil.	% of total
Product sales	5,631	80
Service revenues	1,437	20
Total	**7,068**	**100**

Selected Products

Aircraft carriers (nuclear-powered)
Amphibious assault ships
Coast Guard cutters
Destroyers
Fleet services
Submarines (nuclear-powered)

COMPETITORS

BAE SYSTEMS
Direction des Constructions Navales
Electric Boat
General Dynamics
Northrop Grumman
Todd Shipyards

HISTORICAL FINANCIALS

Company Type: Public

Income Statement
FYE: December 31

	REVENUE ($ mil.)	NET INCOME ($ mil.)	NET PROFIT MARGIN	EMPLOYEES
12/16	7,068	573	8.1%	37,000
12/15	7,020	404	5.8%	36,000
12/14	6,957	338	4.9%	38,000
12/13	6,820	261	3.8%	3,800
12/12	6,708	146	2.2%	37,000
Annual Growth	**1.3%**	**40.8%**	**—**	**0.0%**

2016 Year-End Financials

Debt ratio: 20.12%
Return on equity: 36.36%
Cash ($ mil.): 720
Current ratio: 1.59
Long-term debt ($ mil.): 1,278
No. of shares (mil.): 46
Dividends
　Yield: 0.0%
　Payout: 17.3%
Market value ($ mil.): 8,510

	STOCK PRICE ($) FY Close	P/E High/Low	PER SHARE ($) Earnings	Dividends	Book Value
12/16	184.19	15 10	12.14	2.10	35.78
12/15	126.85	17 12	8.36	1.70	31.77
12/14	112.46	17 13	6.86	1.00	28.26
12/13	90.01	17 8	5.18	0.50	31.23
12/12	43.34	15 11	2.91	0.10	13.45
Annual Growth	**43.6%**	**— —**	**42.9%**	**114.1%**	**27.7%**

Huntsman Corp

Operating its businesses through subsidiary Huntsman International global chemical manufacturer Huntsman Corporation makes a broad range of products that include MDI (methylene diphenyl diisocyanate) amines surfactants epoxy-based polymers and polyurethanes. Huntsman's chemicals are sold worldwide to a variety of customers in the adhesives construction products electronics medical and packaging industries. Huntsman operates manufacturing and research and development facilities in about 30 countries worldwide. In 2017 the company agreed to merge with Clariant AG in a $20 billion deal; however both companies mutually terminated the merger later in the year.

Operations

Huntsman makes differentiated organic chemical products and inorganic chemical products. Its products comprise a broad range of chemicals and formulations which it markets globally to a diversified group of consumer and industrial customers. Its key product lines include MDI (methylene diphenyl diisocyanate) amines surfactants maleic anhydride epoxy-based polymer formulations textile chemicals dyes titanium dioxide and color pigments.

The company operates through five business segments: Advanced Materials (10% of net sales) Performance Products (more than 20%) Pigments and Additives (almost 20%) Polyurethanes (almost 40%) and Textile Effects (roughly 10%).

The largest segment is the Polyurethanes unit which makes MDI propylene oxide and propylene glycol for automotive interiors footwear and furniture cushioning. It is one of the largest producers of MDI which is used in producing rigid and other types of polyurethanes.

Other segments are Advanced Materials (epoxy acrylic and polyurethane-based polymers) Textile Effects (epoxy resins and adhesives) Performance Products (mostly ethylene-based chemicals used in detergents paints and fuel additives) and Pigments and Additives (the whitening agent titanium dioxide).

Geographic Reach

Huntsman operates more than 100 manufacturing and R&D facilities in more than 30 countries.

The company's MDI production facilities are located in Geismar Louisiana; Rotterdam The Netherlands; and through joint ventures in Caojing China. It operates synthesis formulating and production facilities in North America Europe Asia South America and Africa.

Pigments and Additives operate more than 25 manufacturing facilities have ten titanium dioxide manufacturing plants in Europe and roughly 20 color pigments manufacturing and processing facilities in the US. It also operates five facilities producing water treatment timber treatment chemicals and functional additives.

Sales and Marketing

Huntsman markets polyurethane chemicals to more than 3500 customers in about 90 countries. Major customers include companies in the appliance automotive footwear furniture and coatings construction products adhesives sealants and elastomers industries. It sells more than 1500 products to more than 3000 customers though the Performance Products marketing groups.

Huntsman sells iron oxides through its global sales force. The company's ultramarine sales are predominantly through specialty distributors. It sell the majority of its timber treatment products directly to end customers via Viance.

About 75% of Hunstman's sales are generated from 2050 direct customers through its global sales and technical services network and the remaining 25% is generated through distribution partners.

Financial Performance

Huntsman's revenues have declined the last two years dipping 6% from $10.3 billion in 2015 to $9.7 billion in 2016 due to lower average selling prices in all its segments and lower sales volumes in its Performance Products and Advanced Materials segments.

The decrease in revenues in Performance Products segment was primarily due to lower average selling prices and lower sales volumes. Sales volumes decreased due to competitive market conditions softer demand in China and for oilfield applications and the impact of weather related and other production outages.

The Advanced Materials segment revenue drop was due to lower sales volumes and lower average selling prices. Sales volumes decreased primarily in the Americas region due to competitive pressure and soft demand. Asia Pacific and European sales decreased primarily due to price concessions in its electrical electronic and wind markets and the foreign currency exchange impact of a stronger US dollar against major international currencies.

Huntsman's net income has fluctuated wildly over the years; after declining to $93 million in 2015 net income skyrocketed by more than 250% to $326 million in 2016. This was due to a 6% decline in operating expenses related to the impact of translating foreign currency amounts to the US dollar and a decrease in selling general and administrative expenses as a result of cost savings from restructuring programs within its Pigments and Additives segment.

Similarly cash from operating activities almost doubled from $575 million in 2015 to $1.1 billion in 2016. This was attributed to the massive net income growth coupled with a $473 million favorable variance in operating assets and liabilities for 2016.

Strategy

In mid-2017 Huntsman agreed to merge with Clariant AG one of the world's largest specialty chemicals companies in a $20 billion deal; however both companies mutually terminated the merger later in the year as a block of shareholders were not satisfied with the terms of the transaction. Clariant and Huntsman initially planned the merger to give Clariant 52% of the combined entity stating the combination would produce around $400 million in annual cost synergies and establish itself as the world's second-biggest specialty chemicals maker behind Germany's Evonik.

Moving forward Huntsman's strategy is to increase sales to its current customers while seeking growth in emerging international markets such as India and China. Huntsman has relocated the headquarters of some of its divisions overseas to be closer to critical markets putting its Polyurethanes operation in Hong Kong and its Textile Effects unit in Singapore. Huntsman has also expanded its manufacturing capabilities overseas by expanding its current operations and acquiring other companies. The company believes that by integrating its different product operations in large facilities close to its customers it can cut transportation costs and exposure to cyclical prices.

In 2016 Huntsman sold its European Differentiated Surfactants business valued at about $225 million to Innospec. It is still focused on its global surfactants business primarily in the US and Australia.

EXECUTIVES

EVP Strategy and Investment, J. Kimo Esplin, age 55, $686,575 total compensation
President and CEO, Peter R. Huntsman, age 54, $1,700,000 total compensation
EVP and CFO, Sean Douglas, age 53
Division President Performance Products, Monte G. Edlund, age 62
VP and CIO, Delaney M. Bellinger
CEO Asia/Pacific; Division President Polyurethanes, Anthony P. Hankins, age 60, $865,650 total compensation
EVP General Counsel Chief Compliance Officer and Secretary, David M. Stryker, age 59, $505,900 total compensation
Division President Pigments, Simon Turner, age 54, $544,616 total compensation
Division President Advanced Materials, Scott J. Wright
Division President Textile Effects, Rohit Aggarwal
Managing Director Indian Subcontinent, Harshad Naik
Vice President, David Hester
Vice President And General Manager, Eric Phillips
Division President Performance Products, Stewart Monteith
Executive Vice President Strategy and Investment, J Kimo Esplin
Vice President, Russell Healy
Vice President, Thomas Muir
Vice President, Parthiv Bhakta
Vice President, Brian Pellon
Global Vice President of Manufacturing and Upstream Business, Alastair Port

National Sales Manager, Katy Zukis
Vice Chairman, Nolan D. Archibald
Executive Chairman, Jon M. Huntsman, age 80
Auditors: Deloitte & Touche LLP

LOCATIONS

HQ: Huntsman Corp
10003 Woodloch Forest Drive, The Woodlands, TX 77380
Phone: 281 719-6000
Web: www.huntsman.com

2016 Sales

	$ mil.	% of total
US	3,005	31
China	1,021	10
Germany	676	7
Mexico	453	5
Other	4,502	47
Total	**9,657**	**100**

PRODUCTS/OPERATIONS

2016 Sales

	$ mil.	% of total
Polyurethanes	3,667	38
Performance Products	2,126	22
Pigments and Additives	2,139	22
Advanced Materials	1,020	10
Textile Effects	751	8
Corporate and eliminations	(46)	-
Total	**9,657**	**100**

Segments & Selected Products
Polyurethanes
  Aniline
  MDI (methylene diphenyl diisocyanate)
  MTBE (methyl tertiary-butyl ether)
  PG (propylene glycol)
  PO (propylene oxide)
  Polyols
  TPU (thermoplastic polyurethane)
Performance Products
  Ethylene glycol
  Ethylene oxide
  Ethanolamines
  Ethyleneamines
  Maleic anhydride
  Polyetheramines
  Surfactants
Materials & Effects
  Adhesives
  Acrylic
  Polyurethane-based
  Epoxy
  Epoxy resin compounds
Pigments
  Titanium dioxide

COMPETITORS

Akzo Nobel	DuPont
BASF SE	Evonik Degussa
Bayer AG	LyondellBasell
Covestro	Wanhua Chemical Group
Dow Chemical	Co. Ltd.

HISTORICAL FINANCIALS

Company Type: Public

Income Statement

FYE: December 31

	REVENUE ($ mil.)	NET INCOME ($ mil.)	NET PROFIT MARGIN	EMPLOYEES
12/16	9,657	326	3.4%	15,000
12/15	10,299	93	0.9%	15,000
12/14	11,578	323	2.8%	16,000
12/13	11,079	128	1.2%	12,000
12/12	11,187	363	3.2%	12,000
Annual Growth	**(3.6%)**	**(2.7%)**	**—**	**5.7%**

2016 Year-End Financials

Debt ratio: 45.66%	No. of shares (mil.): 236
Return on equity: 23.83%	Dividends
Cash ($ mil.): 414	Yield: 0.0%
Current ratio: 2.00	Payout: 36.7%
Long-term debt ($ mil.): 4,136	Market value ($ mil.): 4,510

	STOCK PRICE ($) FY Close	P/E High/Low		PER SHARE ($) Earnings	Dividends	Book Value
12/16	19.08	15	6	1.36	0.50	5.44
12/15	11.37	64	25	0.38	0.50	6.08
12/14	22.78	22	16	1.31	0.50	7.30
12/13	24.60	46	30	0.53	0.50	8.24
12/12	15.90	11	6	1.51	0.40	7.44
Annual Growth	**4.7%**	**—**	**—**	**(2.6%)**	**5.7%**	**(7.5%)**

HY-VEE, INC.

Give Hy-Vee a high five for being one of the largest privately owned US supermarket chains despite serving some modestly sized towns in the Midwest. The company runs some 235 stores in eight Midwestern states. About half of its supermarkets are in Iowa as are most of its 20-plus Hy-Vee drugstores. It distributes products to its stores through several subsidiaries including Lomar Distributing (specialty foods) and Perishable Distributors of Iowa (fresh foods). Other activities include construction and specialty pharmacies. Charles Hyde and David Vredenburg founded the employee-owned firm in 1930. It takes its name from a combination of its founders' names.

Operations

In addition to its food and drug retail operations Hy-Vee offers customers financial products. Adding to its menu of financial services Hy-Vee subsidiary Midwest Heritage Bank in 2011 acquired Iowa-based L&K Insurance a full-line insurance agency. L&K changed its name to Midwest Heritage Insurance Services post sale.

Geographic Reach

Hy-Vee's stores are located in Illinois Iowa Kansas Minnesota Missouri Nebraska South Dakota and Wisconsin. The company supplies its stores from distribution centers in Chariton and Cherokee Iowa.

Financial Performance

Hy-Vee's 235 stores ring up more than $8 billion in annual sales.

Strategy

Hy-Vee is gradually expanding in several key markets in the Midwest including Chicago Minneapolis-St. Paul and Madison Wisconsin. To that end the regional grocery chain in 2014 announced plans to enter the Twin Cities market. In 2013 the chain opened its second supermarket in Madison after entering the Madison market in 2009. To cater to local tastes the company says the 80000-sq.-ft. Madison store has the largest cheese selection of any Hy-Vee supermarket. Hy-Vee is also testing a smaller-format store (about 20000-25000 sq. ft. with no pharmacies) in select locations. It's also adding stores in its core Iowa market with a supermarket slated to open in Winterset in 2014.

Going beyond traditional grocery fare Hy-Vee in 2013 acquired its joint venture partner's stake in Hy-Vee Weitz Company a construction firm based in Des Moines. The grocery store operator renamed the company Hy-Vee Construction and plans to expand the in-house construction management group. The company also teamed up with specialty pharmacy operator Amber Pharmacy to form a new company (called Hy-Vee Pharmacy Solutions) to provide services for patients with complex and chronic health problems including Crohn's disease hemophilia psoriasis and other chronic ailments. The grocery chain has also been focusing on adding Hy-Vee Gas convenience units (some 80 locations include these) wine and spirits stores pharmacies and Hy-Vee HealthMarket departments.

Ric Jurgens in 2012 retired as chairman and CEO after 43-years with Hy-Vee. He was succeeded by president and COO Randy Edeker.

EXECUTIVES

Assistant Vice President Media Relations, Ruth Comer

EVP and Chief Merchandising Officer, Jon S. Wendel, age 54

Chairman President and CEO, Randy Edeker, age 55

EVP and Chief Customer Officer, Sheila Laing

EVP CFO and Treasurer, Mike Skokan

Vice Chairman EVP and Chief Administrative Officer, Andy McCann

EVP Western Region, Brett Bremser

EVP and COO, Jay Marshall

EVP Eastern Region, Darren Baty

Rph, Helen Eddy

Vice President Retail Information Technology, Julie Proffitt

Senior Vice President and Chief Health Officer, Kristin Williams

Pharmacy Manager, Marrianne Ryno

VICE PRESIDENT, BILL KELLEY

Assistant Vice President Sec, Angie Rosenberger

Assistant Vice President Operations, Rob Eslick

Group Vice President, Jason Pride

Assistant Vice President Engineering and Construction, Dave Kozak

Assistant Vice President Meat Operations, Kenan Judge

Director of Pharmacy Technology, Michael Wilson

Assistant Vice President Health and Wellness Marketing, Erin Bailey

Assistant Vice President operations, Dan Wampler

Assistant Vice President, Tony Kaska

Assistant Vice President Western Region, Pat Hensley

AIA Assistant Vice President Store Development Engineering, Andrew Reich

Assistant Vice President Government Relations, Noreen Otto

VICE PRESIDENT, TIM HOPSON

Vice President, Nate Stewart

Assistant Vice President Store Setup, Mark Millsap

Vice President Distribution, Tod Hockenson

Assistant Vice President Human Resources, Linda Threlkeld

Vice President Education and Training, Denise Broderick

SENIOR VICE PRESIDENT SUPPLY CHAIN, Karl Kruse

VICE PRESIDENT, JASON MIKESELL

Vice President Human Resources, Leigh Walters

Group Vice President Information Technology, Tom Settle

Assistant Vice President, Marshall Sanders

Assistant Vice President Human Resources, Kate Wolfe

Assistant Vice President Brand Image, Wendy Hiatt

VICE PRESIDENT, JULIE MCMILLIN

Assistant Vice President for Engineering and Construction, Jeff Markey

Assistant Vice President Employee Benefits, Kristine Jones

Assistant Vice President Risk Management, John Brummit

Vice President Convenience Stores, Tonia Petterson

Pharmacy Manager, Brad Moriarty

Pharmacy Manager, Heather Yennie

Pharmacy Manager, Jessica Wonderlich

Vice President Business Development, Kevin Sherlock

Assistant Vice President Food Service, Blane Jones

Assisant Treasurer, Jeff Pierce

Secretary to Greg Frampton, Stacey Groff

LOCATIONS

HQ: HY-VEE, INC.
5820 WESTOWN PKWY, WEST DES MOINES, IA 502668223
Phone: 515 267-2800
Web: WWW.HY-VEE.COM

PRODUCTS/OPERATIONS

2012 Stores

	No.
Supermarkets	212
Drugstores	22
Total	**234**

Selected Subsidiaries

D & D Foods Inc. (salads dips and meats)
Florist Distributing Inc. (flowers plants and florist supplies)
Hy-Vee Construction L.C. (construction)
Hy-Vee Pharmacy Solutions (specialty pharmacy services)
Hy-Vee Weitz Construction L.C. (construction)
Lomar Distributing Inc. (specialty foods)
Midwest Heritage Bank FSB (banking)
Perishable Distributors of Iowa Ltd. (meat fish seafood and ice cream)

COMPETITORS

ALDI	Niemann Foods
Associated Wholesale Grocers	Rite Aid
Ball's Food	Roundy's
CVS	SUPERVALU
Casey's General Stores	Save-A-Lot Food Stores
Fareway Stores	Target Corporation
Kmart	Wal-Mart
Kroger	Walgreen

HISTORICAL FINANCIALS

Company Type: Private

Income Statement

FYE: December 31

	REVENUE ($ mil.)	NET INCOME ($ mil.)	NET PROFIT MARGIN	EMPLOYEES
12/16*	9,842	0	—	84,000
09/13	8,014	0	—	—
09/12	7,682	0	—	—
Annual Growth	**6.4%**	—	—	—

*Fiscal year change

2016 Year-End Financials

Debt ratio: ——
Return on equity: —
Cash ($ mil.): 17
Current ratio: 0.30
Long-term debt ($ mil.): —

Dividends
Yield: —
Payout: —
Market value ($ mil.): —

IBERIABANK Corp

IBERIABANK Corp. serves up financial services with a Cajun flare. Through its flagship bank subsidiary also called IBERIABANK the holding company operates some 267 branches in Louisiana and five other southern states. It also has about 21 title insurance offices in Louisiana and Arkansas in addition to some 61 mortgage loan offices in a dozen states. Offering deposit products such as checking and savings accounts CDs and IRAs the bank uses funds gathered mainly to make loans. Commercial real estate and business loans make up nearly three-quarters of the company's loan portfolio which also includes consumer loans and residential mortgages. IBERIABANK Corp. has $13.4 billion in assets.

Operations

IBERIABANK Corp. has eight wholly-owned nonbank subsidiaries including brokerage unit Iberia Financial Services IBERIABANK Insurance Services Acadiana Holdings IBERIABANK Mortgage Company Little Rock Arkansas-based Lenders Title Company and several investment funds.

IB Aircraft Holdings LLC owns a fractional share of an aircraft used by management of the company and its subsidiaries. IAM provides wealth management and trust services for commercial and private banking clients. CDE is engaged in the purchase of tax credits.

Geographic Reach

The company operates 267 combined offices including 172 bank branch offices and four loan production offices in Louisiana Arkansas Florida Alabama Tennessee Georgia and Texas 21 title insurance offices in Arkansas and Louisiana and mortgage representatives in 61 locations in 12 US states.

Financial Performance

After enjoying two straight years of revenue increase in 2013 IBERIABANK Corp.'s revenues decreased by 2% due to lower interest and noninterest income. Noninterest income decreased as a result of a drop in the valuation of the company's mortgage-related derivatives and a lower margin on the sales of mortgage loans both of which negatively impacted mortgage income. However IBERIABANK Corp. had a $2.9 million increase in broker commissions as well as a growth of $2 million in service charges that partially offset the mortgage income decrease.

After experiencing a huge net income increase in 2012 due to a decrease in the provision for loan loss and interest expenses in 2013 the company's net income declined by 15% to $65.1 million due to increased noninterest expenses as a result of a higher impairment of FDIC loss share receivables and other long-lived assets. This was partially offset by a decline in the provision for loan losses and interest expenses.

In 2013 IBERIABANK Corp.'s operating cash inflow increased to $309.8 million (compared to cash out flow of $12.2 million in 2012) primarily due to a huge decline in the provision for loan losses and change in the assets and liabilities.

Strategy

Acquisitions have been a big part of IBERIABANK Corp.'s growth strategy since 2003. All of the acquisition activity has expanded the company's assets and branch network helped it enter new markets such as Florida and Texas and strengthen its presence in existing ones.

As part of IBERIABANK's growth through acquisition strategy in late 2014 it purchased Georgia Commerce Bank as part of a merger deal for $195 million which expanded IBERIABANK's reach into the Atlanta Georgia market for the first time. Earlier that same year the bank also acquired First Private Holdings Inc. the holding company of First Private Bank of Texas a Dallas Texas-based bank with two branch locations; Florida Bank Group; and certain assets of the Memphis Tennessee operations of Trust One Bank a division of Synovus Bank.

Company Background

In 2012 IBERIABANK Corp. struck an agreement to buy Florida Gulf Bank. In 2011 the bank completed three acquisitions: OMNI Bank with 14 offices in New Orleans and Baton Rouge Louisiana; Cameron State Bank with 22 offices in Lake Charles Louisiana; and the assets of Florida Trust Company a subsidiary of the failed Bank of Florida Corporation. (Between 2003 and 2010 the bank completed 13 acquisitions with combined total assets of more than $6 billion.)

The company was founded in 1887.

EXECUTIVES

President and CEO, Daryl G. Byrd, age 62, $1,015,000 total compensation

SEVP Mergers and Acquisitions Finance and Investor Relations; Director Financial Strategy and Mortgage, John R. Davis, age 56, $456,154 total compensation

Vice Chairman and Managing Director of Brokerage Trust and Wealth Management, Jefferson G. (Jeff) Parker, age 64, $480,192 total compensation

SEVP and Director Communications Facilities and Human Resources, Elizabeth A. (Beth) Ardoin, age 48

SEVP and CFO, Anthony J. Restel, age 47, $480,385 total compensation

Vice Chairman; SEVP and COO, Michael J. (Mike) Brown, age 53, $598,269 total compensation

President and CEO IberiaBank Mortgage, Bill Edwards

EVP and Director Retail Small Business and Mortgage, Robert M. (Bob) Kottler, age 58

EVP and Executive Credit Officer, H. Spurgeon Mackie, age 66

EVP and Chief Risk Officer, J. Randolph Bryan, age 49

EVP Corporate Secretary and General Counsel, Robert B. Worley, age 57

President and CEO Lender's Title Company, David B. Erb

Vice President Human Resources and Employee Development and Training, Mike Pelletier

Assistant Vice President Retail Support Specialist, Sheila Montgomery

Assistantvice President Business Banking Relationship Manager, Brian Wilkinson

Vice President Business Banker, Lori Buhs

Senior Vice President and Security Officer, Charles Montelaro

Vice President, Scott Becker

Vice President, Harold Simmons

Assistant Vice President, Dolores Hernandez

Vice President, Tom Chelewski

Vice President Commercial Relationship Manager, Douglas Webster

Vice President Bcs Ore Officer, Neel Stacy

Vice President Human Resources Manager, Kevin Robinson

Vice President Mortgage Executive, Judy Jackson

Vice President, Bruce Reid

Vice President Support Services, Jerry Prejean

Vice President And Senior Business Relationship Manager, Ty Powell

Executive Vice President, Ken Brown

Vice President Commercial Lending, Jeremy Young

Assistant Vice President, Misty Labat

Vice President, Mary Rice

Vice President, Nancy Dost

Vice President Business Banking, Shannon Pemberton

Senior Vice President, John Troyan

Senior Vice President, Missy S Krantz

Vice President, Craig Peak

Vice President Treasury Management Sales, Kelli Johnson

Senior Vice President, Greg Mendez

Vice President Community Banking, Randall Rojas

Vice President Of Product Management, Paula Allred

Vice President and Treasurer, Eric Movassaghi

Vice President Business Banking, Angela Velardi

Vice President Retail Administration, Linda Swinkey

Vice President, Steve Barnes

Vice President Ore Property Manager, Brian Buczko

Vice President Manager of Financial Analytics, Stephanie Verret

Vice President, Nancy H Wooten

Senior Vice President Corporate Banking, C Mizelle

Vice President, Michael Hallmark

Assistant Vice President, Andy Gaines

Assistant Vice President And Branch Manager, Candace Hoggatt

Vice President Branch Manager Business Development Officer, Pedro Diaz

Vice President Business Credit Services, Timothy Wilson

Executive Vice President Director of Organizational Deve, Donna Domick

Vice President, Janet Patton

Vice President Human Resources, Jayne Socotch

Vice President, Howard Mary

Vice President, Pamela Blanchet

Senior Vice President Project Management, Gina Stritzinger

Senior Vice President and Associate General Counsel, Beth Trotter

Vice President, Kelly M Casey

Senior Vice President, Steve Kelly

Assistant Vice President Branch Manager, Melissa Krackenberger

Executive Vice President Retail Segment Leader, Don Ledet

Senior Vice President, Pat Yates

Bank Manager Vice President, Melanie Savell

Vice President, Jeffrey Forte

Executive Vice President And Director Enterprise Risk Ma, Elise Latimer

Senior Vice President And Commercial Rel, Jamey Vaught

Assistant Vice President And Senior Relationship Banker, Darlene Nicks

Executive Vice President, Michael Naquin

Vice President, Beth Ardoin

Executive Vice President Capital Markets Manager, David Shutley

Senior Vice President, Richard Perdue

Branch Manager AVP, Ben Castillo

Executive Vice President, Norman Vascocu

Vice President, Shelia Thibodeaux

Vice President Business Banking, William Biossat

Treasury Management Consultant And Vice President, Steven Perez

Vice President, Sean Friend

Vice President and Coml Rel Manager Ii, Elizabeth Bodin

Vice President of Loans, James Cooper

Senior Vice President And Business And Retail Market Manger, Maurice Butler

VICE PRESIDENT, Elizabeth Viator

VICE PRESIDENT, Kathy Young

Senior Vice President Business Credit Se, Fred Malzahn

Senior Vice President and Manager of Financial Analytics, Shawn Jordan

Vice President Mortgage Executive, Mark Young

Vice President Mortgage Executive, Connie Fernandez

Assistant Vice President Information Technology Business Analyst, Brian Spahr

Senior Vice President Treasury Management, Kathaleen Parks

Vice President Central Retail Administration, Donna Pye

Vice President Corporate Counsel, Lynn Dodd

Assistant Vice President Branch Manager, Amaris Diaz

Vice President Private Banking, Brian Abshire

Assistant Vice President Relationship Manager, Millard Morrison

Senior Vice President, Mary Morgan

Assistant Vice President Branch Manager, Rob Wiles

Avp; Branch Manager, Michelle Schellinger

Senior Vice President Commercial Relationship Manager, Ben Lalikos

Vice President, Grant Spreter

Vice President, Linda Rodriguez

Vice President Business Banking, Tim Finn

Vice President, Cody Walker

Senior Vice President, Holly Brown

Senior Vice President, Skip McPheeters

Senior Vice President, Kevin Hagan

Vice President Deposit Operations, Felicia Weeks

Senior Vice President, Doug Woodman

Vice President Quality Control, Cheryl Terry

Vice President, Marc Massad

Assistant Vice President Branch Manager Leap Mentor, Kirstin Wicker

Senior Vice President Commercial Relationship Manager Assistant Rebecca Oberg, Kelly Gegerson

Senior Vice President C and I, Clay Thomas

Vice President, Karen Hardy

Vice President Manager Commercial Cash Vault, Anna Taylor

Business Intelligence Analyst Assistant Vice President, Kevin Cagle

Vice President of Treasury Management Product, William Watson

VICE PRESIDENT, Werner Erickson

VICE PRESIDENT, Donald Kessler

VICE PRESIDENT, Connie Larson

VICE PRESIDENT COMMERCIAL, Darris Waren

Network Operations Center Manager AVP, Harper Tadlock

Assistant Vice President Retail Support Specialist, Heather Wade

Assistant Vice President, Christie Bell

Asst. Vice President Branch Manager, Tamela Leger

Senior Vice President, Donald Dobbins

Assistant Vice President, Erica Murphy

Vice President Private Banking, Casey Lawhead

Assistant Vice President, Anita Jordan

Vice President Treasury Management Product Management, Cindy Wolbach

Assistant Vice President Branch Manager, Colleen Lemoine

Vice President Retail Support Lead, Terri Bridges

Executive Vice President and Commercial Group Manager, John Reingardt

Senior Vice President Compliance Manager Central Florida CRA Liaison, Susan DeFreese

Assistant Vice President Branch Manager II Barrow Branch, Brandon Boudreaux

Vice President, Glenn O'Leary

Vice President Human Resources Manager, Karla Newan

Vice President, Kim Leech

Vice President, Shelly Verbos-Ford

Vice President Treasury Management Implementations Manager, Megan Alesci

Vice President, Sheila Parfait-cooley

Chairman, William H. Fenstermaker, age 68

Vice Chairman, E. Stewart Shea, age 65

Auditors: Ernst & Young LLP

LOCATIONS

HQ: IBERIABANK Corp
200 West Congress Street, Lafayette, LA 70501
Phone: 337 521-4003
Web: www.iberiabank.com

PRODUCTS/OPERATIONS

2016 Sales

	$ mil.	% of total
Interest and Dividend Income:		
Loans including fees	663	69
Mortgage loans held for sale including fees	6	1
Investment Securities:		
Taxable interest	52	5
Tax-exempt interest	7	1
Amortization of FDIC loss share receivable	(16.0)	.
Other	4	.
Noninterest		
Mortgage income	83	9
Service charges on deposit accounts	44	5
Title revenue	22	2
Brokerage Commissions	15	2
ATM/debit card fees	14	1
Credit card and merchant-related income	12	1
Income from bank owned life insurance	5	.
Gain on sale of available for sale securities	2	.
Trust income	7	1
Other non-interest income	27	3
Total	**950**	**100**

Selected Mergers and Acquisitions

COMPETITORS

Bank of America	JPMorgan Chase
Bank of the Ozarks	Louisiana Bancorp
Capital One	MidSouth Bancorp
Hancock Holding	Regions Financial
Home Banc	Teche Holding
Investar	

HISTORICAL FINANCIALS

Company Type: Public

Income Statement

FYE: December 31

	ASSETS ($ mil.)	NET INCOME ($ mil.)	INCOME AS % OF ASSETS	EMPLOYEES
12/16	21,659	186	0.9%	3,155
12/15	19,504	142	0.7%	3,216
12/14	15,758	105	0.7%	2,825
12/13	13,365	65	0.5%	2,638
12/12	13,129	76	0.6%	2,758
Annual Growth	13.3%	25.0%	—	3.4%

2016 Year-End Financials

Debt ratio: 0.69%	No. of shares (mil.): 44
Return on equity: 6.85%	Dividends
Cash ($ mil.): 1,362	Yield: 0.0%
Current ratio: —	Payout: 32.5%
Long-term debt ($ mil.): —	Market value ($ mil.): 3,752

	STOCK PRICE ($) FY Close	P/E High/Low		PER SHARE ($) Earnings	Dividends	Book Value
12/16	83.75	21	10	4.30	1.40	65.62
12/15	55.07	19	15	3.68	1.36	60.74
12/14	64.85	22	18	3.30	1.36	55.39
12/13	62.85	29	20	2.20	1.36	51.40
12/12	49.12	21	17	2.59	1.36	51.88
Annual Growth	14.3%	—	—	13.5%	0.7%	6.1%

Icahn Enterprises LP

Icahn Enterprises has a can-do attitude when it comes to making money. The holding company has stakes in firms in a diverse array of industries including metals manufacturing energy real estate gaming and home fashion. Holdings include car parts maker Federal-Mogul; energy refinery and production company CVR; PSC Metals one of the largest scrap yard operators in the US; residential developer Bayswater which is active in Florida and Massachusetts; and WestPoint Home a maker of bed bath and other home products. Billionaire corporate raider Carl Icahn and his affiliates control his namesake firm.

Operations

Icahn Enterprises holds and operates companies across several industries each of which is called out as a distinct segment in its financial statements. Automotive Energy and Railcar segments comprise nearly 85% of annual company revenue. The remaining industry segments each generate between 0.5% and 4% of revenue and are: Gaming/Casinos Metals Mining Food Packaging Real Estate and Home Fashion. Icahn Enterprises also runs an Investment segment which invests money in private investment funds for the benefit of Mr. Icahn and his affiliates.

The Automotive segment generates about 45% of revenue and operates mainly through its Federal-Mogul holding. It also owns IEH Auto and Pep Boys. The Energy segment (25% of revenue) is conducted through its CVR Energy Inc. subsidiary and is engaged in petroleum refining and nitrogen fertilizer manufacturing. The Railcar segment is run through the American Railcar Industries Inc. subsidiary which designs and manufactures hopper and tank railcars and then sells or leases them to customers.

Geographic Reach

The New York-headquartered company owns stakes in a number of companies operating worldwide. Federal-Mogul operates more than 250 facilities globally including manufacturing technical and distribution centers. Its Pep Boys automotive retail chain operates more than 800 stores across the US. Icahn Enterprises? Energy segment holdings are mainly in Kansas and Oklahoma and its Railcar operations are in Missouri Arkansas and Texas.

Sales and Marketing

The firm's Federal-Mogul customers include automotive and heavy-duty vehicle manufacturers agricultural off-highway marine railroad aerospace high performance and industrial application manufacturers. The subsidiary has well-established relationships with nearly all major American European and Asian automotive OEs.

Its CVR subsidiary's petroleum customers include retailers railroads and farm cooperatives while its nitrogen fertilizer customers include retailers and distributors (for UAN products) and agricultural and industrial businesses (for ammonia products). Some of its largest customers in 2015 included Gavilan Fertilizer United Suppliers Crop Production Services J.R. Simplot Interchem and MFA.

Financial Performance

Over the past decade Icahn Enterprise revenue jumped higher year after year until it peaked in 2013 and slid back down. Over the same period net income was volatile within a wide band ranging from break-even to over $1 billion and after 2013 it fell precipitously.

In 2016 financial performance broke the recent downtrend. Revenue ticked up 7% to $16 billion from the prior year thanks to a $2.2 billion jump in Automotive segment revenue due to swelling demand for auto production countered by the Investment segment?s 20% loss in stock market short positions ($350 million larger than in 2015) and a $670 million reduction in Energy revenue due to significantly lower sales prices of oil and gas.

Earnings failed to achieve profitability in 2016 registering a $1.1 billion loss only 5% better than 2015?s loss. Although revenue improved in the year expenses took a big bite out of financial performance rising more than 20% over the prior year. A $1.0 billion increase in cost of goods sold for the automotive segment and much higher selling general and administrative (SG&A) costs for the gaming and automotive segments were primary contributors.

Cash at 2016 year-end was $1.8 billion a decrease of $250 million compared to 2015. Cash provided by operations was $1.7 billion aided by proceeds from sales of securities. Cash used by investing activities was $1.8 billion ($800 million for capital expenditures and $1.0 billion for acquiring Pep Boys automotive and Trump?s Taj Mahal casino).

Strategy

The company's strategy known as The Icahn Formula and named after its lead investment strategist is to seek undervalued or bankrupt assets improve their operations enhance their valuation and sell them for a profit. The firm typically purchases substantial stakes in companies with an eye toward gaining control of them often by waging proxy battles for seats on their boards of directors. Mr. Icahn — famous for his activism — is known for his ability to force underperforming management teams to maximize value for shareholders.

In recent years Icahn Enterprises increased its holdings in the Automotive and Energy businesses and repositioned its investment in its Railcar segment.

Icahn Enterprises' diversification across multiple industries and geographies acts as a natural hedge against cyclical and general economic swings. Through its investment segment the firm has held significant positions in various companies including Dell Inc. Herbalife Chesapeake Energy Hain Celestial Group Forest laboratories and Transocean.

Mergers and Acquisitions

In mid-2017 Icahn Enterprises sold for $2.8 billion its American Railcar Leasing LLC to a subsidiary of Sumitomo Mitsui Banking Corporation. Icahn still owns its American Railcar Industries subsidiary.

In February 2016 Icahn Enterprises purchased the Trump Taj Mahal Atlantic City casino fresh out of bankruptcy. Citing New Jersey political gamesmanship and workers? compensation demands as the cause Icahn shuttered the casino later that year and sold the property to Hard Rock Caf © in early 2017.

In February 2016 the firm acquired The Pep Boys for some $1.03 billion which provided "excellent synergistic opportunities for Auto Plus" its automotive aftermarket company.

In June 2015 subsidiary IEH Auto bought Uni-Select USA (the US auto parts assets of auto parts distributor Uni-Select Inc.) and Beck/Arnley Worldparts Inc. for a purchase price of $340 million. The firm acquired all 39 distribution centers and satellite locations and 240 corporate-owned jobber stores in the US. The business became part of Icahn Enterprises' automotive segment with Federal-Mogul.

EXECUTIVES

CFO and Director, SungHwan Cho, age 42, $822,616 total compensation
Chief Accounting Officer, Peter Reck, age 50, $300,000 total compensation
President CEO and Director, Keith Cozza, age 38, $1,557,736 total compensation
Chairman, Carl C. Icahn, age 81
Treasurer, John Saldarelli
Auditors: Grant Thornton LLP

LOCATIONS

HQ: Icahn Enterprises LP
767 Fifth Avenue, Suite 4700, New York, NY 10153
Phone: 212 702-4300
Web: www.ielp.com

2016 Sales

	% of total
United States	68
Germany	9
Other countries	23
Total	**100**

PRODUCTS/OPERATIONS

2016 Sales

	% of total
Automotive	57
Energy	27
Railcar	5
Gaming	5
Food packing	2
Metal	2
Home Fashion	1
Mining	1
Real Estate	1
Holding company	-
Investment	-
Total	**100**

Selected Subsidiaries

Ace Nevada Corp.
American Entertainment Properties Corp.
American Railcar Industries
AREP Oil & Gas Holdings LLC
AREP Real Estate Holdings LLC
Atlantic Coast Entertainment Holdings Inc.
Bayswater Development LLC
Federal-Mogul Corporation
Icahn Capital LP
Icahn Capital Management LP
Icahn Enterprises Holdings L.P.
Icahn Offshore LP
Icahn Onshore LP
New Seabury Properties L.L.C.
PEP Boys Automotive
PSC Metals Inc.
Tropicana Entertainment Inc.
Trump Taj Mahal
Viskase Companies Inc.
WestPoint Home LLC

COMPETITORS

Apollo Global Management	Leucadia National MSD Capital
Berkshire Hathaway	Soros Fund Management
Blackstone Group	The Trump Organization
Clark Enterprises	Vulcan
D. E. Shaw	Wesco Financial
KKR	

HISTORICAL FINANCIALS

Company Type: Public

Income Statement

FYE: December 31

	REVENUE ($ mil.)	NET INCOME ($ mil.)	NET PROFIT MARGIN	EMPLOYEES
12/16	16,348	(1,128)	—	90,960
12/15	15,272	(1,194)	—	73,786
12/14	19,157	(373)	—	66,559
12/13	20,682	1,025	5.0%	59,565
12/12	15,654	396	2.5%	60,665
Annual Growth	**1.1%**	**—**	**—**	**10.7%**

2016 Year-End Financials

Debt ratio: 33.36%	No. of shares (mil.): 144
Return on equity: —	Dividends
Cash ($ mil.): 2,637	Yield: 0.1%
Current ratio: 1.31	Payout: —
Long-term debt ($ mil.): 11,119	Market value ($ mil.): 8,673

	STOCK PRICE ($) FY Close	P/E High/Low	Earnings	Dividends	Book Value
12/16	59.92	— —	(8.07)	6.00	14.88
12/15	61.30	— —	(9.29)	6.00	30.32
12/14	92.47	— —	(3.08)	6.00	44.21
12/13	109.41	16 5	9.07	4.50	52.56
12/12	44.70	13 10	3.75	0.40	44.53
Annual Growth	**7.6%**	**— —**	**—**	**97.2%**	**(24.0%)**

---

iHeartMedia Inc

iHeartMedia is the #1 radio company in the US. The firm formerly known as CC Media owns and operates more than 855 radio stations in about 160 markets through iHeartCommunications. With more than 245 million listeners a month its stations generate revenue by selling advertising and subscriptions. The company also owns outdoor advertising giant Clear Channel Outdoor Holdings. Clear Channel Outdoor Holdings sells advertising space on billboards public transportation buildings and other outdoor environments throughout the US and more than 35 other countries.

Operations

iHeartMedia operates in three reportable segments. Its iHM segment (54% of total revenue in fiscal 2016) provides media and entertainment services via broadcast and digital delivery. It also includes the company's national syndication business. iHeartMedia's America?s outdoor advertising segment and its International outdoor advertising segment both provide outdoor advertising services.

Geographic Reach

Headquartered in San Antonio Texas United States iHeartMedia's broadcast stations are available on AM/FM HD digital radio satellite radio Internet smartphones iPads and tablets auto dashboards smart TVs and gaming consoles. Its iHeartRadio has more than 100 million registered users.

The company does business throughout North and South America Europe and the Asia/Pacific region. The majority of revenue comes from the Americas.

Sales and Marketing

iHeartMedia's top five customers in Americas outdoor were from the business services automotive technology beverage and travel industries. The company's top five customers in International outdoor were in the retail entertainment telecommunications food and food products automotive accessories and equipment industries.

Advertising partners are the iHeartRadio Music Festival the iHeartRadio Music Awards the iHeartRadio Ultimate Pool Party and the iHeartRadio Jingle Ball Tour. The company's advertising expenses were $132.7 million in fiscal 2016.

Financial Performance

iHeartMedia's revenue has been consistent across recent fiscal years. It reported $6.2 billion in revenue for fiscal 2016 after claiming $6.2 in revenue the prior fiscal year.

Even with billions in revenue the company has suffered net losses in recent fiscal periods. iHeartMedia claimed a net loss of $296 million in fiscal 2016 which was an improvement compared to the roughly $755 million net loss the company reported in fiscal 2015. The net losses have been caused by the iHeartMedia's extremely high cost of doing business.

Strategy

iHeartMedia's growth strategy includes investing in digital platforms. It is developing the next generation of iHeartRadio an integrated digital radio platform. The company is also working on the ongoing deployment of more digital outdoor displays.iHeartMedia expects to continue to expand its reach deeper into mobile social live events and on-demand entertainment.

EXECUTIVES

Senior Vice President Urban Operations, Earl Jones
President COO and CFO, Richard J. Bressler, age 59, $1,200,000 total compensation
President Entertainment Enterprises, John Sykes, age 56
Chairman and CEO, Robert W. (Bob) Pittman, age 63, $1,200,000 total compensation
CEO Clear Channel International, C. William Eccleshare, age 61, $927,601 total compensation
CEO Clear Channel Outdoor America, Scott R. Wells, age 48, $750,000 total compensation
EVP and Chief Communications Officer, Wendy Goldberg, age 53
EVP and General Counsel, Robert H. Walls, age 56, $750,000 total compensation
EVP and Chief Marketing Officer, Gayle Troberman
Global CIO, Steve Mills
Senior Vice President Sales Connections, Adrienne Pabst
Senior Vice President Real Estates, Chad Dan
Vice President Of Information Technology, Jeff Cage
Vice President Sales, Brian Duffell
Vice President Business Operations, Barbara Caraballo
Vice President Sales, Adam Pullman
Executive Vice President Regional Managing Director, John Duong
Vice President iHeartMedia, Debbie Cerrito
Vice President of Human Resources, Scott Logeman
Senior Vice President Human RE, William Feehan
I Vice President National Sales, David Steiner
Vice President, Elizabeth Bethea
Vice President and Information Technology Sales, Trisha Dall
National Sales Manager, Nicolette Kelly
Vice President Finance, Dina Odak
Vice President Product Management, R O Catalfo
Vice President And Market Manager, Jackie Rinker
Vice President Marketing Solutions, Tara Adamos
Vice President Of Marketing, Eileen Woodbury
Vice President of Sales Denver Market, Tim Hager
Vice President of Marketing, Justin Tanis
Senior Vice President Corporate Relations, Kathryn Johnson
Senior Vice President And Chief Accounting Officer, Herbert Hill
Senior Vice President Strategic Dev, John Tippit
Vice President Corporate Reporting, Bill Armstrong
Vice President Level, Vice president sales Diane Veres
SVP and President CC Media Holdings Inc., John Hogan
Vice President, Susan Holshouser
Senior Vice President of Sales, Tom Libby
Vice President Sales Digital and Alternative, Dean Peterson
National Sales Manager, Guy Goldschmidt
National Account Manager, Michelle Dannaher
Vice President, Scott Miller
Vice President and Associate General Counsel, Lauren Wood
Vice President Sales, Scott Clark

Executive Vice President General Counsel, Sara Lee Keller

Vice President and Market Manager, Kim Pyle

Vice President Director of Sales, Michael Newman

Vice President Director of Sales, Michelle Olivera

Vice President and Regional Market Manager, Kristen Delaney

Vice President and Market Manager, George Allen

Vice President, Britt Levine

Vice President Director of Sales, Jean Mihalek

Executive Vice President Of Strategic Development, Joe Robinson

Vice President Director of Sales, Staci Verzera-Fair

Vice President Sales, Lisa Neugarten

Vice President Director of Sales, Dan Smith

Vice President, Bill Mcmartin

Vice President Sales, Michael T Boyle

Senior Vice President of Sales, Kahilla Hakimzadeh

Vice President of Business Development, Greg Yelverton

Vice President of Sales, Jeff Luckoff

Senior Vice President Sales, Laurie Foster

Vice President of Sales, Ben Taylor

National Sales Manager, Josh Brooks

Vice President of Sales, Jason Mosher

Senior Vice President of Sales and Marketing, Rhetta Cloyd

Vice President of Sales, Melody Caldwell

Senior Vice President of Sales, Greg Alexander

Vice President of Sales, Joel Kelly

Vice President Sales, Ray Tejeda

Senior Vice President and General Manager iHeartRadio, Owen Grover

Senior Vice President of Sales, Marlon George

Vice President Finance, Steve Trubiano

Executive Vice President Programming Operations, Jon Zellner

Executive Vice President, Gary Larkin

Vice President Client Relations + Industry Marketing, Cammy Grusd

Senior Vice President of Sales, Claudia Bays

Senior Vice President of Sales, Dave Litteral

Senior Vice President Sales, Sabrena Martin

National Sales Manager, Jeff Howard

Senior Vice President Sales, Chris Aldrich

Vice President Sales Operations, Carol Chen

Senior Vice President of Sales, Tim Etes

Senior Vice President Strategic Partnerships, Michael Preacher

Vice President General Manager, Charles Cotton

Vice President Strategic Partnerships, Heather Baumli

Vice President and Associate General Counsel, Christopher Cain

Vice President of Revenue Management, Daniel Ballard

Vice President Media Planning, Kevin Ryan

Sales Vice President, Nicholas Garcia

Vice President West Coast Digital Sales, Melanie Gensler

Vice President of Real Estate, Cody Rutschman

Vice President of Real Estate, Stewart Howe

Vice President of Real Estate, Bruce Qualls

Senior Vice President Revenue Strategy and Analytics, James Liao

Branch President, Dave Lamberger

Senior Vice President of Sales, Judy Copier

Senior Vice President Corporate Accounting and Regulatory Comp, Christopher Harrington

Senior Vice President Accounting, Jason Dilger

Vice President Of Sales, Catherine Nye

Vice President Of Automotive, Larry Barditch

Vice President of Sales Las Vegas West Division, Stacey Eisenberg

Vice President Connections, TJ Sullivan

Senior Vice President I Programmatic, Ross Geier

Reg Vice President of Sales, Rick Westerfield

Vice President of Hispanic Operations, Hector Marcano

Vice President Content Partnerships Entertainment Enterprises, Rachel Herskovitz

Vice President National Sales Premiere Networks, John Buckley

National Sales Manager, Sharon Moses

Vice President Sales, James Feick

Executive Vice President Tech, Lasse Hamre

Vice President Corporate Accounting, Steve Brunner

Vice President Finance, Marc Goldstein

Senior Vice President Marketing and Promotions, Beth Tepper

Senior Vice President of Business Development Shopper Marketing, Joe Schembri

Executive Vice President National Platforms, Alan Korowitz

Executive Vice President, Jim Donovan

Vice President of Financial Planning and Analysis, Brennan Gerster

Regional Vice President Programming, Greg Swedberg

Vice President Landlease Div, Mary Groves

Board Member, Gary Sullivan

VICE PRESIDENT TREASURER, Brian Coleman

BOARD MEMBER, David Abrams

Treasurer, Jerry Burnham

BOARD MEMBER, GINA KEEL

Auditors: Ernst & Young LLP

LOCATIONS

HQ: iHeartMedia Inc
200 East Basse Road, Suite 100, San Antonio, TX 78209
Phone: 210 822-2828
Web: www.iheartmedia.com

PRODUCTS/OPERATIONS

2016 Sales

	$ mil.	% of total
iHM	3,403	54
Americas Outdoor Advertising	1,278	20
Internationl Outdoor Advertising	1,423	23
Other	171	3
Eliminations	(3.4)	-
Total	**6,273**	**100**

Sales - 2016

Source of revenue	% of total
Billboards:	
Bulletins	59
Posters	10
Street furniture displays	7
Transit displays	16
Spectaculars/walls capes	4
Other	4
Total	**100**

COMPETITORS

CBS Corp
Cumulus Media
JCDecaux
Lamar Advertising
Live Nation Entertainment
Radio One Inc.

HISTORICAL FINANCIALS

Company Type: Public

Income Statement

FYE: December 31

	REVENUE ($ mil.)	NET INCOME ($ mil.)	NET PROFIT MARGIN	EMPLOYEES
12/16	6,273	(296)	—	18,700
12/15	6,241	(754)	—	18,700
12/14	6,318	(793)	—	19,200
12/13	6,243	(606)	—	20,800
12/12	6,246	(424)	—	20,800
Annual Growth	**0.1%**	**—**	—	**(2.6%)**

2016 Year-End Financials

Debt ratio: 158.33%
Return on equity: ***.***.**%
Cash ($ mil.): 845
Current ratio: 1.48
Long-term debt ($ mil.): 20,022

No. of shares (mil.): 90
Dividends
Yield: —
Payout: —
Market value ($ mil.): 101

	STOCK PRICE ($) FY Close	P/E High/Low	PER SHARE ($) Earnings	Dividends	Book Value
12/16	1.11	— —	(3.50)	0.00	(121.59)
12/15	0.90	— —	(8.95)	0.00	(120.38)
12/14	7.35	— —	(9.46)	0.00	(111.61)
12/13	6.53	— —	(7.31)	0.00	(102.05)
12/12	3.40	— —	(5.23)	6.08	(96.88)
Annual Growth	**(24.4%)**	— —	—	—	—

Illinois Tool Works, Inc.

Illinois Tool Works (ITW) hammers out more than just basic tools. With operations in about 55 countries ITW manufactures and services equipment for the automotive construction electronics food beverage power system decorative surfaces and medical (adhesives) industries. The largest of its segments is Automotive OEM which provides metal and plastic fasteners components and chassies used in light vehicles automobiles and industrial applications. Other major segments include Food Equipment (cooking equipment such as ovens ranges and broilers) and Test & Measurement and Electronics (equipment and software for testing and measuring of materials structures gases and fluids). ITW traces its historical roots back to 1912.

Operations

ITW operates through the following segments: Test & Measurement and Electronics; Automotive OEM; Polymers & Fluids; Food Equipment; Construction Products; Welding; and Specialty Products.

Subsidiaries include Acme Packaging Foilmark Instron Vulcan-Hart CFC International Quipp FB Johnston Graphics Miller Electric Manufacturing Hobart Corporation Speedline Technologies Wynn's Avery Weigh-Tronix and Vitronics Soltec.

Innovation is a big selling point for ITW's myriad of products. The company holds about 11000 US and foreign patents as well as 6500 patents pending. R&D is executed cooperatively with customers seeking specific applications.

Geographic Reach

ITW has operations in 55 countries. The company operates more than 300 international plants and office facilities in China France Germany and the UK. The US represents ITW's largest market generating 45% of net sales. Other major markets include Europe/Africa/Middle East (EMEA almost 30%) and Asia/Pacific (roughly 15%).

Sales and Marketing

ITW distributes its products directly to industrial manufacturers and through independent distributors. It serves customers in a range of industries including automotive OEM/tiers automotive aftermarket general industrial commercial food equipment and construction.

Financial Performance

ITW's revenues increased marginally by 1% from $13.4 billion in 2015 to $13.6 billion in 2016. The revenue bump was fueled by organic growth of 1% as six of seven of its segments generated worldwide organic revenue growth primarily due to penetration gains higher end market demand and product innovation.

Specifically its Automotive OEM segment experienced a surge in revenue mainly due to a 10% increase in revenue stemming from its 2016 acquisition of EF&C. The overall growth for 2016 however was offset by declines from its Welding segment primarily due to lower capital spending in the industrial end markets and sluggish demand in the oil and gas end market.

In addition to revenues ITW's 's profits jumped 7% from $1.9 billion in 2015 to $2.04 billion in 2016 mainly due to decreased expenses associated with foreign currency translations.

Strategy

The company focuses on a five-year enterprise strategy that includes a few key initiatives: portfolio management business structure simplification and strategic sourcing. This also entails making internal investments that support organic growth to sustain its core businesses.

ITW's portfolio management initiative includes divesting businesses that are no longer aligned with the company's long-term objectives. This strategy has also trimmed the company's global workforce from 59000 at the end of 2009 to 50000 at the end of June 2017 which has reduced expenses and increased operating income despite slowly shrinking revenue totals.

Mergers and Acquisitions

In addition to using organic growth ITW has grown its portfolio through the use of acquisitions. In 2016 it acquired the Engineered Fasteners and Components (EF&C) business from ZF TRW for approximately $450 million. EF&C is a global supplier of engineered fastening systems and interior technical components to the automotive OEM market and operates 13 manufacturing facilities globally.The deal bolstered the company's Automotive OEM segment.

EXECUTIVES

EVP Test and Measurement and Electronics, Steven L. (Steve) Martindale, age 60
Chairman and CEO, E. Scott Santi, age 55, $1,205,313 total compensation
EVP Specialty Products, Roland M. Martel, age 63, $534,434 total compensation
EVP Polymers and Fluids, Juan Valls, age 56
SVP and CFO, Michael M. Larsen, age 48, $702,152 total compensation
EVP Automotive OEM, Sundaram (Naga) Nagarajan, age 54, $520,456 total compensation
EVP Welding, John R. Hartnett, age 57
VP and CIO, Mike Parisi
EVP Construction Products, Michael R. Zimmerman, age 56
EVP Food Equipment, Lei Zhang Schlitz, age 50
Vice President, James H Wooten
Executive Vice President, Jane Warner
Vice President and General Manager, Monte Hammouri
Vice Chairman, Christopher (Chris) O'Herlihy, age 53
Auditors: DELOITTE & TOUCHE LLP

LOCATIONS

HQ: Illinois Tool Works, Inc.
155 Harlem Avenue, Glenview, IL 60025
Phone: 847 724-7500
Web: www.itw.com

2016 Sales

	$ mil.	% of total
North America		
United States	6,176	45
Canada/Mexico	923	7
Europe Middle East and Africa	3,787	28
Asia Pacific	2,361	17
South America	352	3
Total	**13,599**	**100**

PRODUCTS/OPERATIONS

2016 Sales

	$ mil.	% of total
Automotive OEM	2,864	21
Food Equipment	2,110	15
Test & Measurement and Electronics	1,974	15
Specialty Products	1,885	14
Polymers & Fluids	1,691	12
Construction Products	1,609	12
Welding	1,486	11
Intersegment revenue	(20)	-
Total	**13,599**	**100**

Selected Products

Construction products
 Anchors for concrete applications
 Anchors for retail
 Fasteners concrete applications
 Fasteners for retail
 Fasteners for wood and metal applications
 Metal plate truss components
 Packaged hardware for retail
Decorative surfaces
 Decorative high-pressure laminate for furniture office and retail space and countertops
 High-pressure laminate worktops
Food equipment
 Cooking equipment
 Ovens
 Ranges
 Broilers
 Food processing equipment
 Slicers
 Mixers
 Scales
 Kitchen exhaust systems
 Pollution-control systems
 Refrigeration equipment
 Refrigerators
 Freezers
 Prep tables
 Ventilation Systems
 Warewashing equipment
Industrial packaging
 Metal jacketing
 Paper products that protect goods in transit
 Plastic products that protect goods in transit
 Plastic strapping
 Plastic stretch film
 Steel strapping
Polymers and fluids
 Adhesives
 Industrial
 Construction
 Consumer
 Chemical fluids that clean or add lubrication to machines
 Epoxy and resin-based coating products for industrial applications
 Hand wipes and cleaners for industrial applications
 Pressure-sensitive adhesives and components
 Telecommunications
 Electronics
 Medical
 Transportation
 Resin-based coating products for industrial applications
Power systems and electronics
 Airport ground support equipment
 Arc welding equipment
 Component packaging
 Electronic components
 Equipment for microelectronics assembly
 Metal arc welding consumables
 Metal solder materials for PC board fabrication
Transportation
 Fillers for auto body repair
 Fluids for auto aftermarket maintenance and appearance
 Metal components for automobiles and light trucks
 Patch products for the marine industry
 Plastic components for automobiles and light trucks
 Polyester coatings for the marine industry
 Polymers for auto aftermarket maintenance and appearance
 Putties for auto body repair
Other
 Equipment and related software for testing and measuring of materials and structures

Film used to decorate consumer products
Foil used to decorate consumer products
Plastic reclosable packaging for consumer food storage
Plastic consumables that multi-pack cans and bottles and related equipment
Plastic for appliances and industrial applications
Metal fasteners for appliances and industrial applications

COMPETITORS

3M	Marmon Group
BASF SE	NCH
Cummins	Nordson
DuPont	Park-Ohio Holdings
ESAB	PennEngineering
Emerson Electric	Snap-on
Federal Screw Works	Stanley Black and
GE	Decker
Graco	Textron
IBIDEN	TriMas
Koch Enterprises	Victor Technologies
Lincoln Electric	W. R. Grace
Manitowoc	

HISTORICAL FINANCIALS

Company Type: Public

Income Statement

FYE: December 31

	REVENUE ($ mil.)	NET INCOME ($ mil.)	NET PROFIT MARGIN	EMPLOYEES
12/17	14,314	1,687	11.8%	50,000
12/16	13,599	2,035	15.0%	50,000
12/15	13,405	1,899	14.2%	48,000
12/14	14,484	2,946	20.3%	49,000
12/13	14,135	1,679	11.9%	51,000
Annual Growth	0.3%	0.1%	—	(0.5%)

2017 Year-End Financials

Debt ratio: 49.63%
Return on equity: 38.17%
Cash ($ mil.): 3,094
Current ratio: 2.38
Long-term debt ($ mil.): 7,478

No. of shares (mil.): 341
Dividends
 Yield: 0.0%
 Payout: 58.8%
Market value ($ mil.): 56,979

	STOCK PRICE ($) FY Close	P/E High/Low	PER SHARE ($) Earnings	Dividends	Book Value
12/17	166.85	35 25	4.86	2.86	13.43
12/16	122.46	22 14	5.70	2.40	12.26
12/15	92.68	19 16	5.13	2.07	14.36
12/14	94.70	13 10	7.28	1.81	17.81
12/13	84.08	22 16	3.74	1.60	22.55
Annual Growth	18.7%	— —	6.8%	15.6%	(12.2%)

Independent Bank Corp (MA)

Independent Bank wants to rock the northeast. Its banking subsidiary Rockland Trust operates almost 75 retail branches as well as investment and lending offices in Eastern Massachusetts and Rhode Island. Serving area individuals and small to midsized businesses the bank offers standard services such as checking and savings accounts CDs and credit cards in addition to insurance products financial planning trust services. Commercial loans including industrial construction and small business loans make up more than 70% of Rockland Trust's loan portfolio. Incorporated in 1985 the bank boasts total assets of some $7.5 billion.

Operations

About 28% of Independent Bank's loan portfolio is made up of consumer real estate loans which include residential mortgages and home equity loans and lines; while personal loans and auto loans make up around 1% of the portfolio. Through an agreement with LPL Investment Holdings Rockland Trust offers investment products such as securities and insurance.

Independent Bank generated 70% of its total revenue from interest and fee income on loans in 2014 and another 6% from interest and dividends on investment securities. Investment management fees made up 6% of total revenue for the year while deposit account fees and interchange and ATM fees combined made up 11%.

Geographic Reach

Rockland Trust boasts nearly 75 retail branches and three limited-services branches located in Eastern Massachusetts in the counties of Barnstable Bristol Middlesex Norfolk Plymouth and Worcester.

Sales and Marketing

The company's borrowers include consumers and small-to-medium sized businesses with credit needs up to $250000 and revenues of less than $2.5 million. Independent Bank spent $3.86 million on advertising in 2014 compared to $4.28 million and $3.95 million in 2013 and 2012 respectively.

Financial Performance

Independent Bank Corp's revenues and profits have trended higher in recent years thanks to continued loan business growth from both acquisitions and through organic expansion higher deposit account and ATM fee income from customer base growth and thanks to a decline in loan loss provisions as the credit quality of its loan portfolio has improved with the strengthened economy.

The bank's revenue rose by 5% to $286.40 million in 2014 mostly thanks to higher interest income as its loan business growth continued to outpace the margin-eating impacts of low interest rates. Independent's non-interest income also rose by 3% thanks to a combination of higher interchange and ATM fees and investment management fees.

Higher revenue and lower interest expenses on deposits in 2014 drove Independent Bank Corp's net income up by 19% to $59.85 million. Despite higher earnings the company's operating cash dove sharply primarily because of working capital changes related to its loans held for sale and changes in other assets.

Strategy

Independent Bank planned in 2015 to grow its loans organically between 4-6% for the year while growing its deposits between 3% and 4%. The company has also been expanding its fee-based revenue business especially in its investment management segment with expectations of growing the business by another 3% to 4% in 2015.

In addition to organic growth in other financial services areas Independent Bank has expanded via acquisitions.

Mergers and Acquisitions

In October 2016 the company agreed to buy Island Bancorp and its Edgartown National Bank subsidiary which operates four branches on Massachusetts' Martha's Vineyard island. The transaction is valued at some $24.5 million.

In 2015 in expanding its Eastern Massachusetts presence and strengthening its position in the greater Boston market Independent Bank Corp purchased Peoples Federal Bancshares along with its flagship subsidiary Peoples Federal Savings Bank for $130.6 million. The deal added $606 million in total assets $435 million in deposits and $497 million in new loan business.

In November 2013 Independent Bank acquired Mayflower Bancorp along with Mayflower Co-operative Bank for a total of $40.3 million adding deposits and loan assets and expanding its product and service offerings.

In 2012 the company agreed to buy Central Bancorp parent of Central Bank. That deal added nine branches in Maryland's Middlesex County.

Company Background

In past years Independent Bank launched institutional asset managers Bright Rock Capital Management (2010) and Compass Exchange Advisors (2006) and formed a handful of mutual funds.

EXECUTIVES

Executive Vice President Director of Retail Delivery Business Banking & Home Equity Lending, Jane L. Lundquist, age 60, $262,981 total compensation
President CEO and Director Independent Bank Corp. and Rockland Trust, Christopher (Chris) Oddleifson, age 58, $589,616 total compensation
CFO, Robert D. Cozzone
Executive Vice President Commercial Banking, Gerard F. Nadeau, age 59, $322,308 total compensation
Chief Information Officer, Barry Jensen
Senior Vice President, Kyle Spears
Assistant Vice President Credit and Collections, Bruce Bumpus
Chairman, Donna L. Abelli
Auditors: Ernst & Young LLP

LOCATIONS

HQ: Independent Bank Corp (MA)
2036 Washington Street, Hanover, MA 02339
Phone: 781 878-6100
Web: www.RocklandTrust.com

PRODUCTS/OPERATIONS

2012 Sales

	$ mil.	% of total
Interest		
Loans	178	69
Taxable securities including dividends	16	6
Other	1	-
Noninterest		
Service charges on deposit accounts	16	6
Wealth management	14	6
Interchange & ATM fees	9	4
Other	21	9
Adjustments	(0.1)	-
Total	**258**	**100**

COMPETITORS

Bank of America	Hingham Institution
Citizens Financial	for Savings
Group	Sovereign Bank
Eastern Bank	TD Bank USA

HISTORICAL FINANCIALS

Company Type: Public

Income Statement

FYE: December 31

	ASSETS ($ mil.)	NET INCOME ($ mil.)	INCOME AS % OF ASSETS	EMPLOYEES
12/16	7,709	76	1.0%	1,103
12/15	7,210	64	0.9%	1,051
12/14	6,364	59	0.9%	980
12/13	6,099	50	0.8%	984
12/12	5,756	42	0.7%	998
Annual Growth	**7.6%**	**15.8%**	**—**	**2.5%**

2016 Year-End Financials

Debt ratio: 1.40%
Return on equity: 9.34%
Cash ($ mil.): 289
Current ratio: —
Long-term debt ($ mil.): —
No. of shares (mil.): 27
Dividends
Yield: 0.0%
Payout: 40.0%
Market value ($ mil.): 1,903

	STOCK PRICE ($) FY Close	P/E High/Low	Earnings	Dividends	Book Value
12/16	70.45	24 14	2.90	1.16	32.02
12/15	46.52	21 15	2.50	1.04	29.40
12/14	42.81	17 14	2.49	0.96	26.69
12/13	39.12	18 13	2.18	0.88	24.85
12/12	28.95	16 13	1.96	0.84	23.24
Annual Growth	**24.9%**	**— —**	**10.3%**	**8.4%**	**8.3%**

Independent Bank Corporation (Ionia, MI)

Independent Bank Corporation is the holding company for Independent Bank which serves rural and suburban communities of Michigan's Lower Peninsula from more than 100 branches. The bank offers traditional deposit products including checking and savings accounts and CDs. Loans to businesses account for about 40% of the bank's portfolio; real estate mortgages are more than a third. Independent Bank also offers additional products and services like title insurance through subsidiary Independent Title Services and investments through agreement with third-party provider PrimeVest.

Operations

The company also owns Mepco Finance which acquires and services payment plans for extended automobile warranties.

Financial Performance

The company's revenue has been trending down year-over-year. However its net income and cash on hand have both been spiking up across recent fiscal years.

Strategy

As Michigan's economy has exhibited signs of stabilizing and the company's results have relatively improved as well. Independent Bank has reduced its number of high-risk loans non-performing loans and delinquency rates.

EXECUTIVES

Vice President And Quality Control, Deborah Herman
Assistant Vice President Marketing Specialist, Erin McManus
Assistant Vice President Senior Business Analyst, Phil Hamlin
Senior Vice President, Richard Butler
Executive Vice President and Chief Risk Officer, Stefanie Kimball
Vice President Commercial Lending, Phil Clacko
Vice President Sales Manager, Sue Fulk
Assistant Vice President Loan Servicing Risk Managa, Gayle Brooke
Senior Vice President, Hank B Risley
Assistant Vice President Product Develop, Elizabeth Rose
Auditors: Crowe Horwath LLP

LOCATIONS

HQ: Independent Bank Corporation (Ionia, MI)
4200 East Beltline, Grand Rapids, MI 49525
Phone: 616 527-5820
Web: www.ibcp.com

COMPETITORS

Bank of America	Flagstar Bancorp
Chemical Financial	Huntington Bancshares
Fifth Third	JPMorgan Chase
Firstbank	Mercantile Bank

HISTORICAL FINANCIALS

Company Type: Public

Income Statement

FYE: December 31

	ASSETS ($ mil.)	NET INCOME ($ mil.)	INCOME AS % OF ASSETS	EMPLOYEES
12/16	2,548	22	0.9%	885
12/15	2,409	20	0.8%	831
12/14	2,248	18	0.8%	876
12/13	2,209	77	3.5%	896
12/12	2,023	26	1.3%	934
Annual Growth	5.9%	(3.4%)	—	(1.3%)

2016 Year-End Financials

Debt ratio: 1.40%
Return on equity: 9.08%
Cash ($ mil.): 88
Current ratio: —
Long-term debt ($ mil.): —
No. of shares (mil.): 21
Dividends
  Yield: 0.0%
  Payout: 32.3%
Market value ($ mil.): 461

	STOCK PRICE ($) FY Close	P/E High/Low	PER SHARE ($) Earnings	Dividends	Book Value
12/16	21.70	21 13	1.05	0.34	11.71
12/15	15.23	18 14	0.86	0.26	11.28
12/14	13.05	18 15	0.77	0.18	10.91
12/13	12.00	2 1	3.55	0.00	10.15
12/12	3.50	2 1	0.80	0.00	14.84
Annual Growth	57.7%	— —	7.0%	—	(5.7%)

Independent Bank Group Inc.

It makes sense that a company that calls itself Independent Bank Group (IBG) would do business in a state that was once its own country. The bank holding company does business through subsidiary Independent Bank which operates about 40 banking offices and 70 branches in North and Central Texas Houston and Colorado. The banks offer standard personal and business accounts and services including some focused on small business owners. IBG has total assets of nearly $8.9 billion and loans of about $6.4 billion. The company traces its roots back 100 years but took its current shape in 2002.

Operations

In addition to its banking activities Independent Bank Group (IBG)also owns IBG Adriatica a mixed use development in the Dallas-Fort Worth area. The company does not intend to move into real estate but purchased the development where one of its branches is located to help maintain business in the area. It had also made commercial loans to several tenants of the development and saw the purchase as a way to protect its investments rather than have the entire property go into foreclosure.

Financial Performance

Independent Bank Group has shown increasing net income for several years and in fiscal 2016 grew revenue a further 20% to $210.0 million. Net income has likewise been consistently growing reaching $53.5 million up 39%. Cash from operations increased 85% to $80.3 million.

Strategy

Independent Bank Group's strategy is all about growth. It seeks organic growth in loans and deposits in existing locations by developing customer relationships while maintaining the quality of its loan portfolio. It also makes acquisitions: since 2010 it has made nine acquisitions most recently of Carlile Bancshares and its subsidiary Northstar Bank and Grand Bank in Dallas.

Mergers and Acquisitions

Independent Bank Group acquired Carlile Bancshares and its subsidiary Northstar Bank for around $434 million in 2017.

EXECUTIVES

Chairman President and CEO, David R. Brooks, age 59, $650,000 total compensation
EVP and COO, James C. (Jim) White, age 52
Vice Chairman and Chief Lending Officer and President Independent Bank Central Texas, Brian E. Hobart, age 52, $350,000 total compensation
Executive Vice President and Chief Financial Officer, Michelle S. Hickox, age 50, $265,000 total compensation
EVP and Secretary and EVP and Senior Operations Officer Independent Bank, Jan C. Webb, age 59
Senior Vice President Controller, Amy Feagin
Senior Vice President Technology Services, Hector Salazar
Executive Vice President, Patrick Blossom
Senior Vice President, Randy Masters
Vice President Commercial Lending, Chris Bielss
Executive Vice President And Credit Officer, Mike Phillips
Executive Vice President, Tim Baker
Vice President Market Manager, Tisha Reyes
Vice Chairman and Chief Risk Officer, Daniel W. Brooks, age 57
Auditors: RSM US LLP

LOCATIONS

HQ: Independent Bank Group Inc.
1600 Redbud Boulevard, Suite 400, McKinney, TX 75069-3257
Phone: 972 562-9004
Web: www.ibtx.com

PRODUCTS/OPERATIONS

2012 Loan Portfolio

	% of total
Real estate	
Commercial	47
Residential	23
Construction land & land development	7
Single-family interim construction	5
Commercial	12
Agricultural	3
Consumer	3
Total	**100**

Selected Acquisition

Town Center Bank (2010 North Texas)
Farmersville Bancshares Inc. (2010 North Texas)
I Bank Holding Company Inc. (2012 Austin/Central Texas)
The Community Group Inc. (2012 Dallas/North Texas)

COMPETITORS

BBVA Compass Bancshares	HSBC International Bancshares
Bank of America	JPMorgan Chase
Broadway Bancshares	Lone Star Bank
Capital One	PlainsCapital
Citigroup	Prosperity Bancshares
Comerica	Texas Capital
Cullen/Frost Bankers	Bancshares
Extraco	Wells Fargo
First Financial Bankshares	Woodforest Financial

HISTORICAL FINANCIALS

Company Type: Public

Income Statement

FYE: December 31

	ASSETS ($ mil.)	NET INCOME ($ mil.)	INCOME AS % OF ASSETS	EMPLOYEES
12/16	5,852	53	0.9%	577
12/15	5,055	38	0.8%	587
12/14	4,132	28	0.7%	511
12/13	2,163	19	0.9%	340
12/12	1,740	17	1.0%	335
Annual Growth	35.4%	32.5%	—	14.6%

2016 Year-End Financials

Debt ratio: 2.14%
Return on equity: 8.22%
Cash ($ mil.): 495
Current ratio: —
Long-term debt ($ mil.): —
No. of shares (mil.): 18
Dividends
  Yield: 0.0%
  Payout: 11.8%
Market value ($ mil.): 1,178

	STOCK PRICE ($) FY Close	P/E High/Low	PER SHARE ($) Earnings	Dividends	Book Value
12/16	62.40	22 9	2.88	0.34	35.63
12/15	32.00	21 13	2.21	0.32	34.09
12/14	39.06	33 21	1.85	0.24	31.75
12/13	49.66	28 16	1.77	0.12	18.96
Annual Growth	5.9%	— —	12.9%	29.7%	17.1%

Infinity Property & Casualty Corp

Infinity Property and Casualty specializes in providing insurance coverage to high-risk drivers. The insurer primarily provides personal non-standard auto policies and is a leading writer of policies for high-risk drivers in the US. The company also offers standard and preferred personal auto commercial small fleet and classic collector auto insurance. Licensed in all 50 states the company currently focuses its business on targeted urban areas of a handful of states. Personal non-standard auto insurance accounts for more than 90% of its premiums; California accounts for about half of that business. Infinity distributes its products through more than 11800 independent agents.Kemper Corporation is buying Infinity for $1.4 billion.

Change in Company Type

In early 2018 Infinity agreed to be acquired by Chicago-based insurer Kemper Corporation for $1.4 billion. Through the acquisition Kemper will expand in terms of financial strength diversity and its ability to serve policyholders.

Operations

Personal automobile (liability and property damage) coverage is Infinity's bread and butter but the company also offers commercial vehicle coverage which accounts for nearly 10% of total gross written premiums. Classic collector protection brings in about 1% of written premiums.

Geographic Reach

Infinity's primary markets (or "Focus States" as it calls them) are Arizona California Florida and Texas. Other markets in which it operates include Georgia Nevada and Pennsylvania. Additionally Infinity is running down operations in other states.

Sales and Marketing

Infinity sells its products through independent agencies and brokers in more than 15000 locations. It also sells directly to customers from company-owned sales centers and via the internet. Targeted customers are urban and Hispanic drivers. Its largest market is California followed by Florida.

The company has increased advertising spending and agency incentives including commissions to stimulate growth. Advertising costs totaled $9.1 million in 2015 up from $8.7 million in 2014 and $8.4 million in 2013.

Financial Performance

Net sales have been growing for the past few years and in 2015 they rose 2% to $1.4 billion. This was largely due to growth in California-based personal auto lines and commercial vehicle coverage throughout its operating markets. However net income (which has been up and down as of late) declined 11% to $51.4 million as Infinity had increased losses and increased loss adjustment expenses.

Cash flow from activities fell 46% to $72.5 million in 2015 largely due to changes in assets and liabilities.

Strategy

By targeting a narrow group of potential customers (urban and Hispanic drivers in Focus States) Infinity is able to specialize concentrating its resources toward a very specific demographic. It does so by offering lower prices to traditionally underserved markets. It depends on meeting customers' lifestyle and budget needs by providing flexible product offerings and pricing options. The company is also committed to building relations with its agents and brokers by investing in agency productivity lead generation and training.

Company Background

Before going public in 2003 Infinity was owned by property/casualty giant American Financial Group (AFG). AFG transferred the personal insurance business of its property/casualty subsidiary Great American Financial Resources to Infinity but that business is now in runoff with no new policies being written.

EXECUTIVES

Senior Vice President and Controller, Amy Jordan
President and General Counsel, Samuel J. Simon, age 60, $420,000 total compensation
SVP Product Management, Scott C. Pitrone, age 54, $265,000 total compensation
CEO and Director, Glen N. Godwin, age 59, $295,385 total compensation
EVP and CFO, Robert H. Bateman, $400,000 total compensation
Vice President Head of Internal Audit, Stanton Kelley
Assistant Vice President Management Reporting, Gena Miller
Chairman, James R. Gober, age 65
Auditors: Ernst & Young LLP

LOCATIONS

HQ: Infinity Property & Casualty Corp
2201 4th Avenue North, Birmingham, AL 35203
Phone: 205 870-4000
Web: www.infinityauto.com

PRODUCTS/OPERATIONS

2015 Gross Written Premiums

	% of total
Personal automobile	90
Commercial vehicle	9
Classic collector	1
Total	**100**

Vehicle Insurance

Vehicle Insurance
Auto
Motorcycle
ATV
RV
Boat
Classic Car
Business Insurance
Commercial Auto
General Liability
Property Insurance
Home
Renters
Mobile Home
Flood
Condo
Other Products
Life Insurance
Umbrella Insurance
Infinity DriverClub®;

2015 Sales

	$ mil.	% of total
Earned premium	1346.6	91
Installment and other fee income	96.7	7
Net investment income	36.8	2
Net realized gains on investments	2.8	-
Other income	1.1	-
Total	**1484.0**	**100**

COMPETITORS

Affirmative Insurance	National General
Direct General	Holdings
First Acceptance	Permanent General
Corporation	Progressive
Hagerty Insurance	Corporation
Kingsway America	Safe Auto

HISTORICAL FINANCIALS

Company Type: Public

Income Statement

FYE: December 31

	ASSETS ($ mil.)	NET INCOME ($ mil.)	INCOME AS % OF ASSETS	EMPLOYEES
12/16	2,402	43	1.8%	2,300
12/15	2,386	51	2.2%	2,300
12/14	2,384	57	2.4%	2,200
12/13	2,317	32	1.4%	2,400
12/12	2,303	24	1.1%	2,200
Annual Growth	**1.1%**	**15.4%**	**—**	**1.1%**

2016 Year-End Financials

Debt ratio: 11.39%
Return on equity: 6.20%
Cash ($ mil.): 92
Current ratio: —
Long-term debt ($ mil.): —
No. of shares (mil.): 11
Dividends
 Yield: 0.0%
 Payout: 53.6%
Market value ($ mil.): 971

	STOCK PRICE ($) FY Close	P/E High/Low	PER SHARE ($) Earnings	Dividends	Book Value
12/16	87.90	23 19	3.88	2.08	63.31
12/15	82.23	19 15	4.51	1.72	61.66
12/14	77.26	16 13	4.95	1.44	60.75
12/13	71.75	25 19	2.80	1.20	57.09
12/12	58.24	30 24	2.04	0.90	56.55
Annual Growth	**10.8%**	**— —**	**17.4%**	**23.3%**	**2.9%**

Ingredion Inc

Sweet sodas and diet desserts alike get their taste and feel from Ingredion's ingredients. The company makes food ingredients and industrial products from corn and other starch-based raw materials. It serve customers in some 60 markets including food brewing and paper companies. Ingredion's largest product line is starches used in food for stabilization feel and texture and in paper packaging and other materials for quality strength and a host of other attributes. Its other product lines include sweeteners (high-fructose corn syrup dextrose) specialty ingredients (products focused on health affordability and sustainability) and co-products (refined corn oil corn gluten feed and meal). Ingredion operates worldwide but generates most of its sales in North America.

Operations

Cornstarch and other starch products account for about 45% of Ingredion's revenue and are used in processed foods as well as in paper and packaging adhesives textiles pharmaceuticals make-up and other products.

Sweeteners used in a wide range of foods — from condiments to candy — generate another 40% of sales with specialty ingredients designed to capitalize on consumer trends bringing in about a quarter.

The company's smallest product segment co-products includes refined corn oil sold to a variety of food producers and corn gluten feed and meal used for pet food. It accounts for about 15% of revenue.

Geographic Reach

Well-covered geographically Ingredion serves customers in more than 100 countries worldwide. North America is its largest market accounting for some 60% of sales. South America represents about 20% of sales followed by the Asia Pacific and EMEA (Europe Middle East and Africa) regions which each contribute about 10%.

Ingredion has some 45 manufacturing plants in about a dozen countries (the US is home to about a third of them).

Sales and Marketing

Ingredion exploits the versatility of corn in supplying a customers across some 60 industries. Food is the company's largest industry segment generating more than 50% of revenue; however the beverage animal nutrition paper and brewing industries each contribute about 10%.

Ingredion sells its products through its own sales force directly to manufacturers and distributors.

Financial Performance

Although Ingredion's revenue stabilized slightly in 2016 and net income rose more substantially the company has seen a general decline in both measures since 2012. Revenue has fallen nearly $1 billion in the past four years.

The company reported revenue of $5.7 billion in 2016 up 1% on improved performance in North

America where price increases and a more favorable product mix offset a slight decline in volume. Reduced cost of sales because of the effects of currency translation and lower resrructuring/impairment charges allowed Ingredion to post net income of $485 million up 20% from the from $402 million reported in 2015.

Cash provided by operations also rose in 2016 increasing 12% to $771 million primarily as a result of the company's improved net income.

Strategy

Ingredion's "Strategic Blueprint" for growth is built around six areas: market relevance innovation broadening ingredient portfolio continuous improvement sustainability and geographic diversity.

Three of those areas — market relevance innovation and broadening portfolio — are focused on the company's desire to adapt to changing consumer tastes and capitalize on trends such as simplicity health convenience and affordability. To that end Ingredion employs some 350 scientists in more than two dozen Ingredion Idea Labs across the globe and spends about $40 million on research and development.

In 2016 the company expanded its portfolio of gums and resins. It also partnered with Alliance Grain Traders to market pulse flours and plant protein ingredients and became a global distributor of stevia sweetener SweeGen.

Through acquisitions investments and product launches Ingredion also bolstered its global presence. It acquired businesses in China and Thailand in 2017 and 2016 launched a new sweetener (SWEETIS) across the Asia-Pacific region and invested some $300 million in plant improvements worldwide.

Mergers and Acquisitions

Ingredion bought the rice starch and flour business of Thailand's Sun Flour Industries in 2017 which boosts the company's specialty ingredients segment.

In late 2016 it paid nearly $400 million for Maryland-based TIC Gums which provides gums and resins to improve the texture of foods and beverages. The deal expands Ingredion's customer base and again adds to its specialty ingredients segment. Also that year the company acquired state-owned Shandong Huanong Specialty Corn Development Co. in China's Shandong Province to increase its manufacturing capacity in the country.

Ingredion in March 2015 acquired Iowa-based Penford Corp. a maker of carbohydrate-based specialty starches used by the paper packaging and food industries. The deal was valued at around $330 million and extended Ingredion's core offerings and geographical footprint; Penford has offices and plants in Colorado Idaho Iowa Pennsylvania South Carolina Washington and Wisconsin.

EXECUTIVES

SVP and Chief Innovation Officer, Anthony P. (Tony) Delio, age 61
President CEO and Director, James P. Zallie, age 55, $600,000 total compensation
SVP Operating Excellence Sustainability Information Technology and Chief Supply Chain Officer, Robert J. (Bob) Stefansic, age 55
SVP and President Asia/Pacific and EMEA, Jorgen Kokke, age 48, $403,340 total compensation
EVP and CFO, James D. (Jim) Gray, age 50
Vice President, Kevin Wilson
Vice President Global Procurement, Amy Pflueger
Vice President Marketing Us and Canada, Jim Low
Vice President and Corporate Controller, Steve Latreille
Vice President Manufacturing NA, Mark Madsen
Director of Pharmacy, Paul Bratley
Vice President Applications Research And Technical Services, Ron Deis

Senior Vice President President South America Ingredient Solutions, Ricardo Souza
Vice President Health and Safety, Ron McCrimmond
Vice President Talent Management, Henry Artalejo
Vice President and Managing Director Canada, Rob Kee
Chairman, Ilene S. Gordon, age 63
Auditors: KPMG LLP

LOCATIONS

HQ: Ingredion Inc
5 Westbrook Corporate Center, Westchester, IL 60154
Phone: 708 551-2600   **Fax:** 708 551-2700
Web: www.ingredion.com

2016 Sales

	$ mil.	% of total
North America	3,447	60
South America	1,010	18
Asia Pacific	709	12
EMEA	538	10
Total	**5,704**	**100**

PRODUCTS/OPERATIONS

2016 Sales

	% of total
Starch products	46
Sweetener products	37
Co-products & others	17
Total	**100**

Selected Products

Sweetener products
  Dextrose
  Glucose corn syrups
  High fructose corn syrup
  High maltose corn syrup
  Maltodextrins
  Polyols
Starch products
  Corn starch (consumer and industrial)
  Specialty Starches
Co-products and others
  Corn gluten feed
  Corn gluten meal
  Refined corn oil
Specialty Ingredients
  Delivery systems
  Green Solutions
  Nutrition
  Sweetness
  Texture
  Wholesome

COMPETITORS

ACH Food Companies	Malt Products
ADM	Corporation
Ajinomoto	Merisant
Cargill	NutraSweet
Cumberland Packing	PureCircle
DSM	Roquette Frères
Global Bio-chem	Sweet Green Fields
Grain Processing	Südzucker
Corporation	Tate & Lyle
Imperial Sugar	Ingredients

HISTORICAL FINANCIALS

Company Type: Public

Income Statement

FYE: December 31

	REVENUE ($ mil.)	NET INCOME ($ mil.)	NET PROFIT MARGIN	EMPLOYEES
12/16	5,704	485	8.5%	11,000
12/15	5,621	402	7.2%	11,000
12/14	5,668	355	6.3%	11,400
12/13	6,328	396	6.3%	11,300
12/12	6,532	428	6.6%	11,200
Annual Growth	**(3.3%)**	**3.2%**	**—**	**(0.4%)**

2016 Year-End Financials

Debt ratio: 33.83%	No. of shares (mil.): 72
Return on equity: 20.54%	Dividends
Cash ($ mil.): 512	Yield: 0.0%
Current ratio: 2.30	Payout: 29.0%
Long-term debt ($ mil.): 1,850	Market value ($ mil.): 9,049

	STOCK PRICE ($) FY Close	P/E High/Low		PER SHARE ($) Earnings	Dividends	Book Value
12/16	124.96	21	13	6.55	1.90	35.42
12/15	95.84	18	14	5.51	1.74	29.94
12/14	84.84	18	12	4.74	1.68	30.52
12/13	68.46	14	12	5.05	1.56	32.35
12/12	64.43	12	8	5.47	0.92	31.64
Annual Growth	**18.0%**	**—**	**—**	**4.6%**	**19.9%**	**2.9%**

Insight Enterprises Inc.

With Insight Enterprises around the end of a customer's technology woes could be in sight. The company distributes computer hardware and software and provides IT services for businesses schools and government agencies and departments. Insight offers thousands of products from major manufacturers (including Hewlett-Packard IBM and Cisco) and provides networking and communications services through subsidiaries Insight Networking in the US and UK-based MINX. The company uses direct telesales field sales agents and an e-commerce site to reach its clients in North America and about 200 other countries across Europe the Middle East Africa and the Asia-Pacific region.

Operations

In North America and Western Europe Insight sells hardware software and services. In the rest of the world it sells just software and related services.

Hardware accounts for more than half of the company's revenue and software 40%. Services revenue accounts for the remainder.

Insight purchases products and software from over 5100 partners. These include Cisco HP Lenovo Dell EMC NetApp Apple and IBM. More than 65% were from manufacturers and software publishers; the remainder was bought through distributors.

Geographic Reach

Insight rings up more than 70% of its sales in the US and Canada. The EMEA region (Europe the Middle East and Africa contributes almost 25% of which the UK brings in 10%. The Asia-Pacific (APAC) region accounts for the rest. The company has locations in the US Canada and the UK.

Sales and Marketing

Microsoft accounts for over 25% of Insight's revenue; HP 10%; and Cisco 10%.

Its five biggest manufacturers/publishers combined (including Lenovo and Dell) account for 60% of total sales.

Financial Performance

Insight has struggled to add pep to its top line in recent years. In fiscal 2016 revenue grew 2% to $5.5 billion. The only region to record growth was North America which grew 4% due to the BlueMetal acquisition and high demand for client devices servers and storage products. The EMEA and APAC regions both recorded 2% falls. Currency movements played a role: adjusting for FX fluctuations EMEA grew 4% and APAC was flat.

Net income increased 12% to $84.7 million due to higher revenue and better margins. Cash from operating activities fell 47% to $95.8 million due to a large ($160 million) receivable collected by a client in Q4 2016 offset by higher sales.

Strategy

Insight is growing at home and abroad by upgrading its technology expanding its product line entering new markets and making acquisitions.

To maintain a local market presence in select cities the company has invested in sales technical and service delivery resources (particularly in the large account client space).

The company is also focusing on growing its business with mid-sized and large clients in select vertical markets (including Federal government state and local K-12 education healthcare and service providers).

In EMEA and APAC the company is looking to increase its share in the mid-market and public sector including leveraging strategic relationships with partners and service delivery vendors to bring additional software Cloud and collaboration solutions to clients.

In APAC the company is growing its sales in the mid-market and enterprise space and on the developing specialized software services particularly in the areas of software license optimization and the Cloud.

Insight is putting more energy (and money) into its services offerings as hardware sales naturally ease amid market maturity. The company is advancing its Cloud-based solutions to help with the assessment migration integration of Cloud uptake.

Mergers and Acquisitions

In 2017 Insight acquired Datalink a Minnesota-based IT service and enterprise data center solutions provider for $257.5 million. The acquisition addresses market opportunities in hybrid cloud and other data center categories.

In 2016 it acquired Ignia an Australian digital mobile and cloud company with a foot in application design digital solutions cloud mobility and business analytics. The acquisition will also further Insight's reach into the APAC market.

In 2015 Insight acquired Boston-based BlueMetal (an interactive design and technology architecture firm with offices in Chicago and New York) for $44 million. This acquisition helped the company to expand its service capabilities in the area of application design mobility and big data.

HISTORY

Eric Crown worked for a small computer retail chain in the mid-1980s before leaving to market PCs. In 1986 he and his brother Tim pooled $2000 from credit cards and $1300 in savings and anticipating a drop in hard drive prices placed an ad for low-cost hard drives in a computer magazine. The ad pulled in $20000 worth of sales and since costs did indeed drop the profit was enough to start a new company Hard Drives International. In 1988 they changed the name to Insight Enterprises; by 1991 the Crowns also sold Insight-branded PCs software and peripherals (discontinued in 1995). The company passed the $100 million revenue mark in 1992.

Insight shifted its marketing focus to catalogs in 1993 and had a circulation of more than 7 million by 1995. The company went public that year and entered an alliance with Computer City (acquired by CompUSA in 1998) to handle its mail-order fulfillment. It also launched its website. The next year subsidiary Insight Direct began to offer on-site service warranties and in 1997 retailing subsidiary Direct Alliance was chosen to provide product fulfillment for Internet software firm Geo Publishing. That year the company began sponsoring the Copper Bowl a college football game played in Arizona which was renamed the Insight.com Bowl (and later the Insight Bowl).

Looking beyond the US in 1998 Insight established operations in Canada and acquired direct marketers Choice Peripherals (UK) and Computerprofis Computersysteme (Germany). At home it added direct marketer Treasure Chest Computers. Sales passed the billion-dollar mark that year.

The company formed an alliance with Daisytek International in 1999 that expanded its product line by more than 10000. Soon thereafter Insight walked away from a merger with UK-based computer wholesaler Action Computer Supplies when Action's profits slumped.

Insight withdrew its planned IPO and spinoff of Direct Alliance in 2001 due to poor market conditions. Also that month Eric became chairman and Tim became CEO (they had previously shared the title of co-CEO). Insight ended up buying Action Computer Supplies in 2001. It also shut down its German operations and acquired computer direct marketers in both the UK and Canada in late 2001.

In April 2002 Insight acquired Comark a leading private reseller of computers peripherals and computer supplies in the US and began integrating its operations into Insight North America's existing operational structure.

Tim stepped down as president and CEO and became chairman in late 2004 while Eric assumed the title of chairman emeritus. The company appointed IBM veteran Richard Fennessy to the position of president and CEO. That year Insight spun off its UK-based Internet service provider PlusNet.

In 2006 Insight Enterprises bought software and mobile solutions firm Software Spectrum.

EXECUTIVES

President and CEO, Kenneth T. (Ken) Lamneck, age 62, $800,000 total compensation
CIO, Michael Guggemos, age 52, $398,989 total compensation
CFO, Glynis A. Bryan, age 58, $466,140 total compensation
President Insight US, Steven W. Dodenhoff, age 54, $488,625 total compensation
President Insight EMEA, Wolfgang Ebermann, age 52, $578,726 total compensation
Vice President Marketing, David Locker
Vice President Sales, Rob McConnell
Vice President Sales, Collin Ryan
Vice President Marketing, Bill Daly
Vice President Sales, Kristopher Blasi
Vice President Sales, Jason Sullivan
Vice President of Finance, John Carnahan
Assistant Vice President Marketing Div, Karla Herder
Senior Vice President Na And Apac Software, Andrea Mattea
Vice President Infrastructure and Security, Curt Cornum
Vice President Sales, Mark Zawacki
Vice President and General Manager Insight Benelux, Frank Hoekstra
Chairman, Timothy A. (Tim) Crown, age 53
Auditors: KPMG LLP

LOCATIONS

HQ: Insight Enterprises Inc.
6820 South Harl Avenue, Tempe, AZ 85283
Phone: 480 333-3000
Web: www.insight.com

2016 Sales

	$ mil.	% of total
North America	3,971	73
Europe Middle East & Africa	1,338	24
Asia/Pacific	175	3
Total	**5,485**	**100**

2016 Sales

	$ mil.	% of total
United States	3,776	69
United Kingdom	672	12
Others Foreign	1,037	19
Total	**5,485**	**100**

PRODUCTS/OPERATIONS

2016 Sales

	$ mil.	% of total
Hardware	2,955	54
Software	2,189	40
Services	340	6
Total	**5,485**	**100**

Selected Products

Computer memory and processors
Desktop computers
Monitors
Networking equipment
Notebook computers
Printers and printing consumables
Servers
Software
Storage devices
Tablet computers

Selected Services

Business optimization software
  Business productivity
  Core infrastructure
  Software asset management
Collaboration
  Call/contact center
  Unified communications/messaging
  Video collaboration/conferencing
Cloud services
  Collaboration
  Infrastructure
  Messaging
  Security
Data center
  Infrastructure solutions
  Server solutions
  Storage solutions
Infrastructure and security
  Network infrastructure
  Security infrastructure
Managed services
  Business process outsourcing
  Connected real estate and sports
  Financing and leasing
  IT asset disposal
  Maintenance
  Product provisioning
  Remote network operations
  Telecom expense management
  Warehouse/integration
  Mobility
  Big Data
  Creativity
  Data protection

COMPETITORS

Amazon.com	Microsoft
Best Buy	Newegg
Buy.com	Office Depot
CDW	OfficeMax
CompuCom	PC Connection
Convergys	PC Mall
Dell	PFSweb
Digital River	RadioShack
Fry's Electronics	SHI International
Gateway Inc.	Softchoice
HP	Staples
HP Enterprise Services	Symantec
IBM	Systemax
Lenovo	Zones
Micro Electronics	

Company Type: Public

Income Statement

FYE: December 31

	REVENUE ($ mil.)	NET INCOME ($ mil.)	NET PROFIT MARGIN	EMPLOYEES
12/16	5,485	84	1.5%	5,930
12/15	5,373	75	1.4%	5,761
12/14	5,316	75	1.4%	5,406
12/13	5,144	71	1.4%	5,202
12/12	5,301	92	1.7%	5,045
Annual Growth	0.9%	(2.3%)	—	4.1%

2016 Year-End Financials

Debt ratio: 1.84%	No. of shares (mil.): 35
Return on equity: 12.07%	Dividends
Cash ($ mil.): 202	Yield: —
Current ratio: 1.38	Payout: —
Long-term debt ($ mil.): 40	Market value ($ mil.): 1,435

	STOCK PRICE ($) FY Close	P/E High/Low		PER SHARE ($) Earnings	Dividends	Book Value
12/16	40.44	18	9	2.32	0.00	20.11
12/15	25.12	16	12	1.98	0.00	18.48
12/14	25.89	17	11	1.83	0.00	17.96
12/13	22.71	15	10	1.64	0.00	17.06
12/12	17.37	11	7	2.07	0.00	15.82
Annual Growth	23.5%	—	—	2.9%	—	6.2%

Intel Corp

Intel Corp. is the brains of the operation. One the biggest computer chip companies the company controls 80% of the market for microprocessors that act as the brains of desktop notebook and server computers. It has dominated the PC chip market from the early x86 processors to Pentiums to today?s Core technology. Intel also makes chips for smartphones and tablets as well as embedded semiconductors for the industrial medical and automotive markets. The company develops its chips and makes most of them itself in one of the industry's biggest manufacturing systems. As PC sales have declined Intel has shifted focus and resources to chips for the data centers that power cloud computing.

Operations

Intel Corp.?s Client Computing Group is the company?s workhorse and cash generator delivering about 55% of its revenue. The business churns out chips for notebooks 2-in-1 systems desktops tablets phones wireless and wired connectivity products and mobile communication components.

The Data Center Group generates about 30% of Intel?s revenue with chips for server-platforms and related products designed for the enterprise cloud and communication infrastructure market.

The Internet of Things Group which make chips for connected devices in retail transportation industrial video buildings smart cities and other market. It accounts for about 5% of revenue.

Taken together the Intel Security the Programmable Solutions and Non-Volatile Memory Solutions groups provide about 10% of the company?s revenue. The company divested the security group in 2016.

Intel makes most of its products in its own manufacturing facilities which allows the company to control the process for quality speed and flexibility.

For some communications connectivity networking field programmable and memory components the company outsources manufacturing to third parties. Intel handles test and assembly in-house and through contractors.

Geographic Reach

Intel Corp. has more than 150 locations around the globe with assembly and test facilities in China Costa Rica Malaysia and Vietnam. Customers in China (including Hong Kong) generate about a quarter of Intel's sales followed by customers in the US and Singapore which supply a bit more than 20% of revenue and customers in Taiwan who kick in more than 15% of revenue.

Sales and Marketing

Intel sells its products primarily to original equipment manufacturers (OEMs) and original design manufacturers (ODMs). ODMs provide design and manufacturing services to branded and unbranded private label resellers. In addition Intel products are sold to makers of industrial and communications equipment.

Its customers also include those who buy PC components and other products through distributor reseller retail and OEM channels. Intel's worldwide reseller sales channel consists of thousands of indirect customers who are systems builders that purchase microprocessors and other products from distributors.

Intel?s three largest customers account for nearly 40% of the total revenue led by Dell Technologies with 15% with Lenovo Group and HP Inc. accounting for more than 10% each.

Financial Performance

Intel Corp. reported record revenue of about $59 billion in 2016 a 7% increase from $55 billion in 2015. The company?s revenue has grown 55% over the past decade in a pattern of a year or two of growth followed a year reduced revenue.

Intel?s two biggest groups drove growth in 2017 with assists from its smaller emerging businesses. The Client Computing Group?s (CCG) revenue rose 2% despite the continuing decline in PC sales around the world. CCG posted about $33 billion in revenue on an 11% increase in average selling prices for chips for notebook and desktop computers while volume fell 10%. For the Data Center Group a volume increase of 8% more than offset a 1% drop in average selling prices resulting in an 8% revenue increase to about $17 billion.

Revenue from the Internet of Things Group one of the company?s bets for the future rose 15%. But for now the unit accounts for just 5% of revenue. The Programmable Solutions Group new to the company with the 2016 acquisition of Altera had revenue of $1.7 billion. The discontinued security business reported a 9% sales increase for the year.

Intel?s net income dropped a billion dollars to $10 billion from 2015 to 2016. The company spent more on research and development and increased spending on restructuring by almost six-fold over the previous year.

Cash generated by operations rose about $3 billion to $22 billion in 2016 from 2015. The increase came from adjustments for non-cash items related to restructuring and changes in working capital which were somewhat offset by the decrease in net income.

Strategy

Although the PC market is shrinking Intel Corp. maintains a level of investment in its Client Computing Group to squeeze as much revenue as it can out of its biggest business. With a mix of more expensive and more powerful chips the company produced higher sales from PC chips in 2016.

However Intel began a restructuring program in 2016 to shift some resources from the PC business by reducing the number of employees and closing facilities. The company spent about $1.8

billion on restructuring in 2016. The company is reallocating the savings to data center and Internet of Things developments as well as memory and autonomous driving.

The company is adding new technologies to its wafer fabrication facilities to turn out more complex chips. The company spent most of its 2016 capital expenditures of about $10 billion on its factories to improve performance cost and power consumption.

Intel's pending acquisition of Mobileye stakes out a prominent position for providing technology for self-driving cars. Mobileye's sensor technologies combined with Intel's semiconductors should make for a formidable competitor in developing autonomous vehicles. Intel has teamed with BMW AG and Delphi Automotive for developing driverless vehicle technology and had an ongoing relationship with Mobileye.

Intel has devoted R&D dollars to develop chips for new applications. It tries to adapt technology from one processor to another to get as much revenue from a design as it can. It intends to exploit its $16.7 billion acquisition of Altera in 2015 to field a range of data center-ready chips for computing and storage purposes. That business generated about $1.7billion in revenue for Intel in 2016.

In 2016 Intel got out of the security software business. It teamed up with TPG a private investment firm to spin out Intel's security assets as an independent cybersecurity company under the McAfee name. TPG owns 51% and Intel 49% in the security company. TPG is investing more than $1 billion to boost McAfee's start as an independent firm. Intel bought McAfee in 2011 for about $7.7 billion.

Intel faces challenges from other semiconductor companies. Samsung Electronics' chip business has grown in recent years and the company is challenging Intel for the title of biggest chipmaker. Longtime rival AMD has released high-performance chips at price points that could undercut Intel's offerings. NVIDIA is growing quickly from its graphics chips that are well-suited to artificial intelligence applications.

Mergers and Acquisitions

In 2017 Intel acquired Mobileye for more than $15 billion. Mobileye based in Israel develops sensors and cameras for vehicles. The acquisition broadens Intel?s offerings for makers of driverless vehicles beyond the chips that are brains of such vehicles. Mobileye's technologies provide more of the critical capabilities that autonomous autos need to maneuver safely. The deal closed in August 2017.

The acquisition of Altera provides Intel with key technology for dealing with data center cloud and the Internet of Things. Altera makes chips that can be reprogrammed after installation. Intel will combine its powerful Xeon processors which handle dedicated tasks with Altera's more chips to give customers more flexibility.

In 2105 Intel completed the acquisition of Lantiq a supplier of broadband access and home networking technologies. With the acquisition Intel moves further into DSL and fiber markets. It made two other acquisitions of companies with IOT-related technologies.

Also in 2015 Intel invested nearly $1 billion in Beijing UniSpreadtrum Technology a subsidiary of Tsinghua Holdings to jointly develop chips for mobile phones based on Intel architectures.

EXECUTIVES

Corporate Vice President and General Manager Data Center Engineering Group, Stephen Smith
Evp Corporate Strategy, Thomas M Kilroy, age 60

EVP and CFO, Robert H. (Bob) Swan, age 57, $194,800 total compensation

CEO, Brian M. Krzanich, age 57, $1,250,000 total compensation

VP Sales and Marketing Group; President Intel Americas, Gregory R. (Greg) Pearson, age 57, $545,000 total compensation

EVP Sales Marketing and Operations, Stacy J. Smith, age 55, $800,000 total compensation

SVP; General Manager Automated Driving Group, Douglas L. (Doug) Davis, age 56

SVP; General Manager Technology and Manufacturing Group, Sohail U. Ahmed

SVP; General Manager Non-Volatile Memory Solutions Group, Robert B. Crooke

Group President Data Center Group, Diane M. Bryant, age 56, $618,700 total compensation

Corporate VP; Managing Director Intel Labs, Michael C. (Mike) Mayberry, age 60

SVP; General Manager New Technology Group, Joshua M. (Josh) Walden, age 55

SVP; General Manager Platform Engineering Group, Amir Faintuch

SVP; General Manager Software and Services Group, Douglas W. (Doug) Fisher

EVP and General Counsel, Steven R. (Steve) Rodgers

SVP; General Manager Client Computing Group, Navin Shenoy

SVP and Chief Marketing Officer, Steven L. Fund

SVP and Chief Strategy Officer, Aicha S. Evans

SVP; General Manager Internet of Things Group, Thomas P. (Tom) Lantzsch

SVP; President Intel Capital, Wendell M. Brooks

Corporate VP and CIO, Paula Tolliver

President Client and Internet of Things Businesses and Systems Architecture and Chief Engineering Officer, Venkata M. (Murthy) Renduchintala, age 52, $900,000 total compensation

Corporate VP; General Manager Technology and Manufacturing Group, Ann B. Kelleher

Corporate VP; General Manager Programmable Solutions Group, Daniel R. (Dan) McNamara

VP; General Manager Artificial Intelligence Products Group, Naveen G. Rao

Intel Information Technology vPro AMT Product Manager, Omer Livne

Corporate Vice President and Treasurer, Ravi Jacob

Vice President Technology And Manufacturing Group And Director Yield Technology, Melton C Bost

Senior Vice President, Arun Chandrasekhar

Northeast Regional Vice President, Praveen Kundurthy

Senior Vice President, Davidx Oh

Vice President and General Manager of Notebook Product Group, Chris Walker

Vice President, Lei Shao

Vice President Of Programs, Michael DeAngelis

Vice President Of Sales, Michael S Jakubowski

Vice President of Industrial and Motor Services, James A Kovacs

Vice President, Sanjiv Shah

Medical Director, Christopher Baruffi

Vice President of Human Resour, Michael Hill

Executive Vice President, Russell Haugan

Vice President of Finance and Treasurer, Aaron Blawn

Vice President Technology and Manufacturing Group Director Portl, Niraj Anand

Legal Secretary, Eyal Laufer

VPG Hardware, Anita Rao

Vice President Sustainability Initiatives, Joan C Garcia

Vice President Of Interactive Merchandising, Roshni Das

Vice President Data Center Group, Dave Patterson

Technical Advisor To Intel Vice President (Sales Marketing Group), Iris WU

vPro Product Specialist, Tal Elgar

Corporate Vice President and President Intel China, Ian Yang

Vice President Applications And Support, John Kreatsoulas

Vice President Tmg Plant Manager Nm Site Fab 11X, Kirby Jefferson

Vice President, Marcin Hejka

Vice President, Peter Cleveland

Vice President IC and MD Manufacturing. Memory and Digital Health Sector Intel Corporation, Keith Larson

Vice President, Ronald Dickel

Vice President, Rosalind Hudnell

Vice President Piston Pin Operations, Lornax Egan

Vice President Sales and Marketing, Dan Ferber

Vice President Global Creative Director, Teresa Herd

Vice President Events, Stephen Logan

Vice President Program Management, Yuri Tsuchitani

Assistant Vice President Business Development, Howard Wright

Vice President, Armin Sarstedt

Vice President Consumer Product Management, Alan LeFort

Vice President and Counsel To the President, Greg Slater

Vice President Global Marketing and Communications, Alyson Griffin

Corporate Vice President and GM Global Accounts Sales and Marketing Group, Christopher J Bruno

Vice President, Anil Rao

Vice President Engineering, Raheel Khan

Vice President of Visual Technology Architecture Group, Martin Ashton

Vice President Information Technology, David Allen

Chairman, Andy D. Bryant, age 66

Board Member, Harald Gossner

Treasurer, Lloyd Herring

Treasurer, Amanda Hamlin

Treasurer, Sharad Khetan

Board Member, Haripriya Prakasam

Treasurer, Mahendra Malliwal

Board Treasurer, Jacqueline Tan

Board Member, Prakash Sarangapani

Board Member, Gary Berger

Vice Chairman, Nelson Clark

Board Member, Edison F Rodrigues

Secretary, Rosidah Ahmad

Auditors: Ernst & Young LLP

LOCATIONS

HQ: Intel Corp
2200 Mission College Boulevard, Santa Clara, CA 95054-1549
Phone: 408 765-8080   Fax: 408 765-2633
Web: www.intc.com

2016 Sales

	$ mil.	% of total
China (including Hong Kong)	13,977	23
Singapore	12,957	22
US	12,780	22
Taiwan	9,953	17
Other	9,720	16
Total	**59,387**	**100**

PRODUCTS/OPERATIONS

2016 Sales

	$ mil.	% of total
Client computing Group	32,908	55
Data Center Group	17,236	29
internet of Things Groups	2,638	5
Non-Volatile Memory Solutions Group	2,576	4
Intel Security Group	2,161	4
Programmable Solutions Group	1,669	3
All others	199	-
Total	**59,387**	**100**

Selected Products

Chipsets (communications consumer electronics desktop embedded handheld netbook notebook server storage workstation)
Communication infrastructure components
　Network processors
　Networked storage products
Device software optimization products (embedded handheld)
Digital home (chips for cable modems digital TVs high-definition media players set-top boxes and home network integration)
Microprocessors (communications consumer electronics desktop embedded handheld network netbook notebook server storage workstation)
　Atom
　Celeron
　Centrino
　Core i3 i5 i7
　Core Duo
　Core Quad
　Itanium
　Pentium
　Xeon
Motherboards (desktop server workstation)
NAND flash memory (all-in-one desktop digital camera memory card portable memory storage device solid-state drive tablet computer)
Software products (software development tools middleware operating systems software tools)
Ultra-Mobility (chips for high-end smartphones handheld devices)
Wired and wireless connectivity components (embedded wireless cards network adapters)

COMPETITORS

AMD	Oracle
ARM Holdings	QUALCOMM
Apple Inc.	SK Hynix
Atmel	STMicroelectronics
Cisco Systems	Samsung Electronics
Conexant Systems	SanDisk
Fujitsu Semiconductor	Silicon Integrated
GLOBALFOUNDRIES	Systems
IBM	Sony
Maxim Integrated	Symantec
Products	TSMC
MediaTek	Texas Instruments
Microchip Technology	Toshiba Semiconductor
Micron Technology	& Storage Products
NVIDIA	VIA Technologies

HISTORICAL FINANCIALS

Company Type: Public

Income Statement

FYE: December 30

	REVENUE ($ mil.)	NET INCOME ($ mil.)	NET PROFIT MARGIN	EMPLOYEES
12/17	62,761	9,601	15.3%	102,700
12/16	59,387	10,316	17.4%	106,000
12/15	55,355	11,420	20.6%	107,300
12/14	55,870	11,704	20.9%	106,700
12/13	52,708	9,620	18.3%	107,600
Annual Growth	**4.5%**	**(0.0%)**	**—**	**(1.2%)**

2017 Year-End Financials

Debt ratio: 21.76%—
Return on equity: 14.06%
Cash ($ mil.): 3,433
Current ratio: 1.69
Long-term debt ($ mil.): 25,037

Dividends
　Yield: 0.0%
　Payout: 54.1%
Market value ($ mil.): —

	STOCK PRICE ($) FY Close	P/E High/Low		PER SHARE ($) Earnings	Dividends	Book Value
12/17	46.16	23	16	1.99	1.08	14.91
12/16	36.27	17	13	2.12	1.04	14.19
12/15	34.98	16	11	2.33	0.96	13.12
12/14	37.55	16	10	2.31	0.90	11.96
12/13	25.60	13	10	1.89	0.90	11.73
Annual Growth	**15.9%**	**—**	**—**	**1.3%**	**4.6%**	**6.2%**

Intercontinental Exchange Inc

Intercontinental Exchange (ICE) is a leading provider of online marketplaces and clearing services for global commodity trading primarily of electricity natural gas crude oil refined petroleum products precious metals and weather and emission credits. It manages a handful of global over-the-counter (OTC) markets and regulated futures exchanges. The firm also owns ICE Futures Europe a leading European energy futures and options platform as well as NYSE Holdings (including the New York Stock Exchange). ICE Data provides real-time daily and historical market data reports. The company serves clients in more than 120 countries.

Operations

Beginning in early 2016 ICE began operating two distinct business segments: Trading and Clearing and Data and Listings with total revenue split between the two about 47%/53% respectively.

The Trading and Clearing segment performs trade execution trade processing clearing and benchmark administration. Its exchanges host nearly 50% of the world?s traded crude and refined oil futures contract volume. It holds global benchmarks in energy agricultural commodities interest rates currency exchange rates and equity indexes. The segment clears more than 6 million futures and OTC contracts daily. The NYSE one of its 12 exchanges lists more than 2400 companies of which roughly 40 were new IPOs in 2016.

The Data and Listings segment known as ICE Data Services or IDS distributes data created from ICE?s exchanges and clearing houses to asset managers financial institutions commercial hedge managers corporations and others. Its data activities span nine asset classes across 11 exchanges and six clearing houses. The data supports market-wide liquidity price discovery compliance reporting and other activities. IDS incorporated operations from recent acquisitions: Interactive Data SuperDerivatives and assets from S&P Global.

Across all its operations the mix of products and services revenue breaks down to 45% for data services just less than 40% for global derivatives trading and clearing about 10% for listing new issues and the rest for cash-related and other activities.

Geographic Reach

ICE is based in AtlantaGA and has offices in Calgary Chicago Houston London New York San Francisco Singapore Stamford Washington DC; and Winnipeg. Its assets are primarily located in the US and the UK and to a lesser extent in Continental Europe Israel Canada and Singapore.

The company makes some 60% of revenue from its US activities.

Sales and Marketing

ICE serves industries such as energy financial services and agricultural markets which generally use ICE?s commodities exchanges to perform commodities trading and leverage futures contracts for hedging and other purposes. Clients range from financial institutions and trading firms to commodity producers and retail investors.

Financial Performance

Following steady upward financial growth after the 2009 Financial Crisis ICE?s revenue and net income have soared higher in each year since 2013. Revenue over that time went from $1.7 billion to almost $6.0 billion in 2016 and net income jumped from $254 million to $1.4 billion.

For the year 2016 revenue grew 27% to $5.96 billion primarily due to the inclusion of revenue from recent acquisitions Interactive Data Securities Evaluations and Credit Market Analysis and to a lesser extent from increased revenues in its data services and commodities transactions.

In 2016 net income ticked up 12% to $1.42 billion from the prior year. The higher revenue supported higher earnings although increased expenses related to acquisitions and an asset impairment charge (related to its Creditex customer relationship) subdued the upswing.

Cash on hand at the end of 2016 was $407 million down $220 million from the prior year. Cash from operations was $2.1 billion most of which came from net income and the rest largely from adjustments for depreciation and amortization. Cash used by investing activities neared $900 million with about half of that going towards acquisition costs. Financing activities used $1.5 billion with most of it going to repay short-term debt and dividend payments to stockholders.

Strategy

ICE is focused on growing its core exchange clearing and data business operations both organically and through acquisitions. To address the rising demand for more information it aims to expand its data offerings. ICE has plans to expand its trading and clearing capabilities while maintaining its leadership position in its new listings business.

The company meaningfully expanded its data offerings in 2016 mostly through acquisitions. Interactive Data increased the number of markets ICE serves added new kinds of data to its offerings and brought improvements in both connectivity and valuation services. With the addition ICE produces daily prices for more than 2.7 million fixed income securities. The Trayport acquisition targeted enhanced offerings to ICE?s energy customers particularly with electronic and hybrid trade execution. However UK regulators ordered ICE to divest Trayport to preserve healthy competition in the energy trading sector and in late 2017 ICE sold it to TMX. From S&P Global ICE acquired a suite of pricing and analytic products.

The derivatives trading market is requiring increased risk management and counterparty credit management as well as other capabilities related to regulatory needs. ICE is meeting these needs through new product development but also with licensing others? products (that it then serves to its customers) and through strategic acquisitions. It also maintains and enhances its own geographically diverse clearing operations whereby it is better able to respond to market demands and related risk management requirements from its customers.

In ICE?s NYSE listings business the company intends to keep its leadership position. In 2016 the NYSE saw more than 500 new issuers join its ranks most by companies switching from other exchanges. NYSE listed 38 IPOs in 2016 raising proceeds for those companies on the order of $13 billion. Between 2013 and 2017 NYSE has listed 27 of the 30 largest IPOs. ICE also plays well in the Exchange Traded Funds (ETF) market with its NYSE Arca exchange listing ETFs whose total assets under management approached $2.4 trillion which represented more than 90% of all US ETF AUM.

Mergers and Acquisitions

The company entered into a purchase agreement in late 2017 to buy Virtu BondPoint for $400 million. The target acquisition provides electronic fixed income trading solutions for more than 500 financial services firms.

In 2017 ICE purchased 100% of TMX Atrium a company that provides low-latency access to markets and market data across 12 countries and 30 trading venues including in Toronto New Jersey and Chicago.

In late 2016 the group acquired for $430 million S&P Global's Securities Evaluations (which provides fixed income evaluated pricing) and Credit Market Analysis (which provides data for OTC markets). Those operations were integrated into ICE Data Services.

In mid 2016 ICE acquired a majority equity position in MERSCORP Holdings Inc. and owner of Mortgage Electronic Registrations Systems which facilitates mortgage transactions by bringing together (digitally) lenders mortgage servicers investors and government institutions.

In late 2015 the company acquired 100% of Interactive data for $5.6 billion. It is a leading provider of financial market data and analytics. In 2017 it divested a small part of the acquisition Interactive Data Managed Solutions which serves the global wealth management industry.

Also in 2015 the company completed its acquisition of UK-based electronic trading platform developer Trayport for $620 million expanding the exchange operator's OTC energy markets service offerings. In late 2017 adhering to UK regulators? directive ICE was forced to sell Trayport to preserve healthy competition in the energy trading sector. ICE sold it to TMX which in return gave ICE Shorcan Energy (brokerage for North American crude oil markets) NGX (energy contracts clearing house) and $470 million in cash.

Company Background

ICE has grown rapidly through a series of acquisitions and portfolio diversification. In 2010 it acquired Climate Exchange a leader in the development of traded emissions markets. Expanding its options market portfolio in 2011 the company acquired broker/dealer Ballista which offers an electronic options platform for the execution of large and complex multi-leg options transactions. Also that year it bought 12% of Brazilian clearinghouse operator Cetip SA for $514 million. In 2012 ICE bought WhenTech a provider of options technology including valuation analytics and risk management.

The company has also added to its OTC contracts offerings through the recently formed ICE Clear Europe. In 2011 alone it launched more than 250 new contracts for oil natural gas power emissions and refined petroleum products. ICE that year also launched new futures contracts including currency futures contracts and coal and natural gas option contracts. In Canada in early 2012 the company began trading new futures contracts on wheat and barley.

EXECUTIVES

Vice President Investor Relations And Corporate Communications, Kelly Loeffler

Chairman and CEO, Jeffrey C. (Jeff) Sprecher, age 61, $1,050,000 total compensation

SVP and Chief Strategic Officer, David S. (Dave) Goone, age 56, $664,583 total compensation

President and COO, Charles A. (Chuck) Vice, age 53, $764,583 total compensation

President and COO ICE Futures Canada, E. Bradley (Brad) Vannan

President ICE Futures Europe, David J. Peniket, age 51

CTO, Mayur V. Kapani

President and COO ICE Clear U.S., Hester Serafini

President NYSE Group, Thomas W. (Tom) Farley, age 41, $664,583 total compensation

CFO, Scott A. Hill, age 49, $714,583 total compensation

President and Managing Director ICE Clear Europe, Paul Swann

Chief Commercial Officer, Benjamin R. (Ben) Jackson

President ICE Clear Credit, Stanislav (Stan) Ivanov

President ICE Benchmark Administration
Limited, Finbarr Hutcheson
President and COO ICE Data Services, Lynn
Martin
President ICE Futures U.S., Trabue Bland
Vice President Government Affairs, Peter Roberson
Executive Vice President, Michael Walsh
Assistant Vice President Information Technology
Security, David Jonas
Auditors: Ernst & Young LLP

LOCATIONS

HQ: Intercontinental Exchange Inc
5660 New Northside Drive, Atlanta, GA 30328
Phone: 770 857-4700 **Fax:** 770 937-0020
Web: www.theice.com

2016 Sales

	$ mil.	% of total
Transaction & clearing fees net	3,384	57
Data services fees	1,978	33
Listing fees	419	7
Other revenues	177	3
Total	**5,958**	**100**

2016 Sales

	% of total
US	61
Other countries	39
Total	**100**

2016 Sales

	% of total
Trading and clearing segment	47
Data and Listing segment	53
Total	**100**

PRODUCTS/OPERATIONS

Founding Partners

BP p.l.c.		
Deutsche Bank AG		
The Goldman Sachs Group Inc.		
Morgan Stanley Dean Witter & Co.		
Royal Dutch Shell plc		
Socié;té; Gé;né;rale		
Total	**0**	**0**

COMPETITORS

APX	GFI Group
BGC Partners	NEX
Bloomberg L.P.	NYMEX Holdings
CBOE	Nasdaq
CHOICE! Energy	Reuters
CME	Unitil
Enporion	

HISTORICAL FINANCIALS

Company Type: Public

Income Statement

FYE: December 31

	REVENUE ($ mil.)	NET INCOME ($ mil.)	NET PROFIT MARGIN	EMPLOYEES
12/17	5,834	2,514	43.1%	4,952
12/16	5,958	1,422	23.9%	5,631
12/15	4,682	1,274	27.2%	5,549
12/14	4,221	981	23.2%	2,902
12/13	1,795	254	14.2%	4,232
Annual Growth	**34.3%**	**77.4%**	**—**	**4.0%**

2017 Year-End Financials

Debt ratio: 7.79%	No. of shares (mil.): 583
Return on equity: 15.40%	Dividends
Cash ($ mil.): 535	Yield: 0.0%
Current ratio: 0.99	Payout: 18.9%
Long-term debt ($ mil.): 4,267	Market value ($ mil.): 41,136

	STOCK PRICE ($)	P/E		PER SHARE ($)		
	FY Close	High/Low	Earnings	Dividends	Book Value	
12/17	70.56	17 13	4.23	0.80	29.03	
12/16	56.42	119 22	2.37	0.68	26.42	
12/15	256.26	115 89	2.28	0.58	24.89	
12/14	219.29	132107	1.71	0.52	21.88	
12/13	224.92	349191	0.64	0.13	21.88	
Annual Growth	(25.2%)	— —	60.2%	57.5%	7.3%	

INTERMOUNTAIN HEALTH CARE INC

If you whoosh down the side of one of Idaho's majestic mountains and take a nasty spill Intermountain Health Care (dba Intermountain Healthcare) can pick you up and put you back together. From air ambulance services to urgent care clinics and general hospitals Intermountain has all the tools to mend skiers (and non-skiers alike) in Utah and southern Idaho. With about 1600 physicians the not-for-profit health system operates 22 hospitals and some 180 clinics as well as urgent care centers and rehabilitation centers. Intermountain also has an insurance arm named SelectHealth.

Operations

Intermountain Healthcare's hospitals range from general surgical to specialty care including orthopedic and pediatric facilities. Along with the full spectrum of physical health care services Intermountain also offers comprehensive mental health and substance abuse programs for patients of all ages. The organization's spectrum of care includes acute inpatient residential treatment day treatment chemical dependency inpatient/detoxification and intensive outpatient programs.

The system conducts cancer research through its partnership with Huntsman Cancer Institute at the University of Utah. The two share data best practices funding and co-conduct clinical trials. They also operate a number of cancer-specific treatment centers including multi-disciplinary tumor-specific clinics designed to provide one-stop service for cancer patients to meet with different cancer specialists on the same day for a more comprehensive treatment plan. Other areas of research include cardiovascular intensive medicine surgical care and behavioral health.

On the physician side the Intermountain Medical Group administers multi-specialty health care services in clinics located throughout the region. The group also operates urgent care clinics under the InstaCare and KidsCare banners.

Entering itself into the "what doesn't Intermountain do?" category the health system also provides health and dental insurance plans through its SelectHealth division.

Geographic Reach

Intermountain Healthcare serves the health care needs of Utah and Idaho residents.

Financial Performance

In 2016 Intermountain Healthcare's revenue grew 14% to $7.6 billion in fiscal 2016. This was due to increases in net patient services income non-patient activity income and investment income. Net patient services accounted for 63% of the system's total revenue that year.

The company used $7 billion of that revenue towards operating expenses including salaries and benefits medical supplies and facilities maintenance

and other business services as well as towards funds dedicated to future needs.

Strategy

Intermountain Healthcare uses its dedicated supply chain organization to continuously improve system efficiency. In addition to delivering medical supplies the unit also oversees hospital vehicles.

The system partners with several leading IT companies (including Xi3 Intel Dell and NetApp) to operate its Healthcare Transformation Lab on the campus of its flagship hospital Intermountain Medical Center in Murray Utah. The lab researches develops and measures new ideas to improve patient care.

In 2016 the system launched Navican Genomics its genomics research and testing arm. Also that year it partnered with the Stanford Genome Technology Center to establish a collaborative research program.

Intermountain has a number of projects underway to add expand or replace existing facilities.

Company Background

Intermountain was formed in 1975 when the Church of Jesus Christ of Latter Day Saints donated 15 hospitals to local communities.

EXECUTIVES

CEO Intermountain Medical Group and VP Physician Division, Linda C. Leckman
President and CEO SelectHealth, Patricia R. Richards
EVP and CFO, Bert R. Zimmerli
EVP and COO, Laura S. Kaiser
Regional VP Central Region, Moody L. Chisholm
VP and CIO, Marc Probst
President and CEO, A. Marc Harrison, age 53
Regional VP Soutwest Region, Terri Kane
SVP and COO, Robert Allen
VP Clinical Operations and Chief Nursing Officer, Kim Henrichsen
CEO Urban North Region and McKay-Dee Hospital Center, Timothy T. Pehrson
Chief Medical Officer, Brent E. Wallace
CEO Primary ChildrenÂ's Medical Center, Katherine A. (Katy) Welkie
Regional VP South Region, Steve Smoot
VP Supply Chain and Support Services, Joe Walsh
Medical Director Neurovascualar Medicine, Dean Roller
Assistant Vice President Of Risk Management Services, Harlan Hammond
Assistant Vice President Communications, Tom Vitelli
Director of Pharmacy, Alan Lodder
Vice President Management, Jim Darrington
Vice President Marketing and Communication, Todd Frehse
Medical Director Utah County Region Intermountain Medical Group, Gordon Harkness
Vice President Healthcare Transformation, Joe Mott
Medical Director, James Orme
Pharmacy Manager, Bruce Leavitt
Medical Director, Justin Abbott
Director Media Relations, Daron Cowley
Assistant Vice President Research, Raj Srivastava
Medical Director Epilepsy Program, Tawnya Constantino
Medical Director, Kristian Kemp
Clinic Manager, Gay Tregaskis
Medical Records Director, Connie Sawyer
Vice President Business Ethics and Compliance, Suzie Draper
Vice President Human Resources, Dan Zuhlke
Vice President And General Counsel, Doug Hammer
Assistant Vice President Financial and Administration System Intermountain Health Care Inc, Craig Jacobsen

Associate Medical Director, Chris Maloney
Cota L, Celeste Marsh
Assistant Vice President Telehealth Services,
 Brian Wayling
**Clinical Director Primary Children's Pediatric
 Behavioral Health Clinic,** Nancy Cantor
Vice President Of Underwriting, Mike Brown
Occupational Therapy Director, Andrew Bracken
Medical Director Information Technology, Ed
 Clark
Vice President of Operational Finance, Mark
 Runyon
Pharmacy Manager, Andrew Buckley
Operating Room Dir, DEBRA ESPLIN
Vice Chairman, Bruce T. Reese
Chairman, A. Scott Anderson
Board Member, Kim Bennion
Secretary, Stephanie Stromberg
Secretary, Jodi Simmons
Auditors: KPMG LLP SALT LAKE CITY UT

LOCATIONS

HQ: INTERMOUNTAIN HEALTH CARE INC
36 S STATE ST STE 1600, SALT LAKE CITY, UT
841111633
Phone: 801 442-2000
Web: WWW.INTERMOUNTAINHEALTHCARE.ORG

PRODUCTS/OPERATIONS

2016 Sales

	$ mil.	% of total
Net patient services	4,368	57
Non-patient activities	3,010	40
Non-operating income	237	3
Total	**7,617**	**100**

Selected Hospitals

Alta View Hospital (Sandy UT)
American Fork Hospital (Utah)
Bear River Valley Hospital (Tremonton UT)
Cassia Regional Medical Center (Burley ID)
Delta Community Medical Center (Utah)
Dixie Regional Medical Center (St. George UT)
Fillmore Community Medical Center (Utah)
Garfield Memorial Hospital (Panguitch UT)
Heber Valley Medical Center (Heber City UT)
Intermountain Medical Center (Murray UT)
LDS Hospital (Salt Lake City)
Logan Regional Hospital (Orem UT)
McKay-Dee Hospital Center (Ogden UT)
 McKay-Dee Behavioral Health Institute
Orem Community Hospital (Utah)
Park City Medical Center (Park City UT)
Primary Children's Medical Center (Salt Lake City)
Riverton Hospital (Riverton UT)
Sanpete Valley Hospital (Mt. Pleasant UT)
Sevier Valley Hospital (Richfield UT)
TOSH - The Orthopedic Specialty Hospital (Murray UT)
Utah Valley Regional Medical Center (Provo UT)
Valley View Medical Center (Cedar City UT)

COMPETITORS

CHRISTUS Health
HCA
HealthSouth
LifePoint Health
Ogden Regional Medical
 Center

Regence BlueCross
 BlueShield of Utah
St. Mark's
University of Utah
 Hospitals & Clinics

HISTORICAL FINANCIALS

Company Type: Private

Income Statement

FYE: December 31

	REVENUE ($ mil.)	NET INCOME ($ mil.)	NET PROFIT MARGIN	EMPLOYEES
12/15	6,058	155	2.6%	36,000
12/14	5,573	(156)	—	—
12/13	5,041	1,546	30.7%	—
12/12	4,700	546	11.6%	—
Annual Growth	**8.8%**	**(34.2%)**	—	—

2015 Year-End Financials

Debt ratio: —
Return on equity: 2.60%
Cash ($ mil.): 421
Current ratio: 0.50
Long-term debt ($ mil.): —

Dividends
 Yield: —
 Payout: —
Market value ($ mil.): —

International Bancshares Corp.

International Bancshares Corp. is leading post-NAFTA banking in South Texas. One of the largest bank holding companies in Texas it does business through International Bank of Commerce (IBC) and Commerce Bank in Texas and Oklahoma through nearly 220 locations. The company facilitates trade between the US and Mexico and serves Texas' growing Hispanic population; about 30% of its deposits come from south of the border. In addition to commercial and international banking services International Bancshares provides retail deposit services insurance and investment products and mortgages and consumer loans. The bulk of the company's portfolio is made up of business and construction loans.

Geographic Reach
Based in the border city of Laredo Texas IBC has many customers living in Mexico especially northern Mexico.

Financial Performance
IBC's 2011 revenue declined nearly 9% vs. 2010 on a decrease in both interest and non-interest income. Net income fell by about 2% over the same period. Indeed 2011 was the fourth consecutive year of falling revenue for the bank as interest and fees declined on its shrinking loan portfolio. Income on taxable investment securities declined as well in 2011 vs. 2010.

Cash flow increased by nearly $92 million is 2011 vs. 2010 due to cash provided by investing activities as compared to cash used in 2010.

Strategy
IBC maintains a decentralized structure in which local advisory boards made up of members of the communities in the bank is located direct operations of its branches including recruiting prospective clients and developing products and services to meet local customers' needs However in 2012 IBC closed most of its bank branches inside grocery stores (H-E-B Kroger Randalls) in response to an amendment to the Dodd-Frank Act that gutted overdraft charges and interchange fees that banks charge when a consumer swipes a debit card suppressing revenue at fee-focused in-store branches. The company is replacing the unprofitable grocery store branches with more expensive but lucrative brick-and-mortar branches in Houston and other cities.

In addition to the tougher regulatory environment the increasing preference by consumers for online and mobile banking is causing IBC to shrink it branch network in Texas and Oklahoma.

EXECUTIVES

**VP and Director; President and CEO
 International Bank of Commerce McAllen,** R.
 David Guerra, age 64, $245,668 total compensation
**Chairman and CEO; CEO International Bank of
 Commerce Laredo,** Dennis E. Nixon, age 74,
 $659,632 total compensation
**President COO and CFO International Bank of
 Commerce Laredo,** Imelda Navarro, age 59,
 $235,960 total compensation
**President and CEO Commerce Bank Laredo
 Texas,** Ignacio Urrabazo
**President and CEO International Bank of
 Commerce Eagle Pass Texas,** Hector J. Cerna
**Chairman and CEO International Bank of
 Commerce Houston Texas,** Jay Rogers
**Chairman and CEO International Bank of
 Commerce Zapata Texas,** Renato Ramirez
**President and CEO International Bank of
 Commerce Austin Texas,** Robert B. (Bob) Barnes
SVP, Eliza Gonzalez
**President International Bank of Commerce
 Houston Texas,** Jeff Samples
**President and CEO International Bank of
 Commerce San Antonio,** Mike K. Sohn
**President and CEO International Bank of
 Commerce Port Lavaca,** Derek Schmidt
President and CEO Corpus Christi, Harold
 Shockley
**President and CEO International Bank of
 Commerce Brownsville,** Al Villareal
CEO San Antonio Service Center, Julie Tarvin
**President Southwest Region International Bank
 of Commerce,** Brian Henry
President International Bank of Commerce Tulsa,
 Andrew Levinson
**President International Bank of Commerce
 Zapata,** Ricardo Ramirez
EVP Corporate International, Gerardo (Gerald)
 Schwebel
**President and CEO International Bank of
 Commerce Oklahoma,** Bill Schonacher
EVP and International Loan Officer, Natividad
 Lozano
Senior Vice President of Commercial Lending,
 Craig Bunk
Vice President Of Accounting, Alvaro Martinez
Senior Vice President of Electronic Services,
 Kevin Mullins
Vice President Accounting and Operations, David
 Shinn
Executive Vice President Finance, Gerald Schwebel
Executive Vice President, Dalia Martinez
Assistant Vice President Support Services,
 Fernando Santos
Vice President, Richard Capps
Vice President, Fernando Garza
Vice President, Juan Gamez
Vice President, Mirta Salcedo
Executive Vice President, Lee Reed
Vice President Life Sales, Markham Benn
Assistant Vice President Commercial Lending,
 Jose Palafox
Auditors: RSM US LLP

LOCATIONS

HQ: International Bancshares Corp.
1200 San Bernardo Avenue, Laredo, TX 78042-1359
Phone: 956 722-7611
Web: www.ibc.com

2015 Sales

	$ mil.	% of total
Interest income		
Loans including fees	297	54
Investment securities	99	18
Other	0	-
Non interest income		
Service charges on deposit accounts	78	14
Other service charges commissions & fees	52	9
Other investments net	17	3
Other	11	2
Net investment securities transactions	(3.7)	-
Total	**552**	**100**

Selected Services

Business Investors
Business Online Banking Services
Checking Options
Commercial Insurance
Home and Personal Loans
IBC First Equity
IBC Investment Services
Individual Investors
Life And Health
Manage Your Account
Mobile Banking
Online Banking Center
Online Banking Services
Other Personal Services
Overdraft Courtesy
Personal
Personal Insurance

COMPETITORS

BancFirst	JPMorgan Chase
Bank of America	Lone Star National
Broadway Bancshares	Bancshares
Citigroup	Midland Financial
Cullen/Frost Bankers	Wells Fargo
Falcon Bancshares	
First Victoria	
National Bank	

HISTORICAL FINANCIALS

Company Type: Public

Income Statement

FYE: December 31

	ASSETS ($ mil.)	NET INCOME ($ mil.)	INCOME AS % OF ASSETS	EMPLOYEES
12/16	11,804	133	1.1%	3,216
12/15	11,772	136	1.2%	3,218
12/14	12,196	153	1.3%	3,256
12/13	12,079	126	1.0%	3,223
12/12	11,882	107	0.9%	3,259
Annual Growth	(0.2%)	5.6%	—	(0.3%)

2016 Year-End Financials

Debt ratio: 7.57%
Return on equity: 7.88%
Cash ($ mil.): 269
Current ratio: —
Long-term debt ($ mil.): —

No. of shares (mil.): 65
Dividends
  Yield: 0.0%
  Payout: 29.7%
Market value ($ mil.): 2,692

	STOCK PRICE ($) FY Close	P/E High/Low	PER SHARE ($) Earnings	Dividends	Book Value
12/16	40.80	21 11	2.02	0.60	26.14
12/15	25.70	15 11	2.05	0.58	25.13
12/14	26.54	12 9	2.28	0.52	23.78
12/13	26.36	14 10	1.88	0.43	21.19
12/12	18.09	16 12	1.39	0.40	21.37
Annual Growth	22.5%	— —	9.8%	10.7%	5.2%

International Business Machines Corp

International Business Machines (IBM) bets that cognition is the ignition for growth. The company the world's top provider of computer products and services is increasingly investing in its cognitive computing system Watson. The artificial intelligence system helps customers in a wide range of businesses analyze massive amounts of data to make better decisions. The company's information technology business services and software units are among the largest in the world. While it has moved from hardware to a large degree the company maintains enterprise server and data storage product lines that are among industry leaders. IBM is moving to transform its operations as it deals with a rapidly changing technology environment.

Operations

IBM manages its sprawling operations in five segments.

Technology Services and Cloud Platforms about 45% of revenue provides a portfolio of cloud outsourcing and other managed services focused on clients? enterprise IT infrastructure. Offerings include maintenance for IBM products and other technology platforms as well as support.

Cognitive Solutions which provides about a quarter of revenue includes Watson IBM?s cognitive computing project. Major Watson initiatives are Watson Platform Watson Health and Watson Internet of Things. Another part of the unit is the company?s security platform which provides detection and protection against cyber threats across a customer?s operations.

Global Business Services about 20% of revenue provides consulting application management services and global process services to help customers move their businesses to digital platforms.

Systems about 10% of revenue is IBM?s hardware business. It provides technologies for hybrid cloud and cognitive workloads. The unit sells servers storage systems and operating systems software.

Global Financing provides credit arrangements for customers to buy IBM products. It accounts for about 2% of revenue.

Geographic Reach

The international in IBM has become increasingly important to its bottom line. With clients in about 175 countries sales outside the US account for more than 60% of revenue. Customers in Europe the Middle East and Africa (EMEA) generate about 30% of sales and Asia/Pacific about 20%.

Sales and Marketing

IBM operates country-based units where consultants product specialists and other workers (most hired locally) facilitate the adoption and fulfillment of its products and services. It serves clients across most industries; leading industry groups include financial services industrial and communications.

Financial Performance

As IBM works to reposition itself to capitalize on data analytics and cloud computing (all parts of its cognitive initiatives) among other areas its revenue has dropped for five straight years.

Revenue dipped 2% to $80 billion in 2016 from $82 billion in 2015. The businesses the company depends on for growth Global Technology and Cloud Services and Cognitive Solutions managed to increase sales 2% and 1% respectively. Within the Cognitive unit Solutions Software revenue rose about 5% in 2016 from security and analytics which includes Watson products and services.

Other segments however brought in significantly less money in 2016. Revenue from Z Systems Power Systems and Storage Systems dropped about 30%. Sales fell in all regions but the company reported higher sales in some countries including Japan and India.

IBM posted about $12 billion in net income in 2016 about a billion less than in 2015. The company had higher expenses including a doubling of costs for workforce rebalancing.

Cash generated by operating activities was about $17 billion in 2016 about $50 million less than the 2015 figure. The drop was due to lower net income which was somewhat offset by lower cash income tax payments.

Strategy

IBM is trying to bridge its operations from the days of high margin hardware and long-term service contracts to the lower margin model of selling subscription-based use of software stored in the cloud. The company has developed a broad strategy around the trends of big data and analytics cloud computing and social and mobile applications. It sees these areas as major growth opportunities and brings to bear homegrown initiatives and acquisitions to cultivate them.

A key element in IBM's plans is its Watson cognitive computing system which can assimilate and process complex information and deliver answers to questions across a range of industries. It is one of the initiatives in which IBM is investing about $4 billion over several years. The company has established Watson units focused on health and the Internet of Things. IBM has made Watson more widely available through a series of application programming interfaces for a number of uses.

The Watson Health group has partnered with health and medical institutions and companies to collect analyze and find patterns in health-related data from cancer to exercise. Partners include Memorial Sloan-Kettering the American Heart Association Under Armour Novo Nordisk and Teva Pharmaceuticals.

The company also is investing in cloud computing. It's trying to compete with Amazon Google (a unit of Alphabet) and Microsoft in offering cloud-based computing infrastructure services. The company focuses on hybrid cloud the mixture of keeping data on IBM computers and the customer's own systems. Other areas IBM has identified are security and mobility. In 2017 the company introduced a Z series mainframe with encryption capabilities.

In addition IBM is focused on emerging markets where the populations and companies that serve them are embracing mobile social cloud and big data at faster rates in some cases than mature countries.

Mergers and Acquisitions

IBM continues to use an aggressive acquisition strategy to augment its own R&D as it expands and refines its mix of business software and IT services. Many of the acquisitions have been made to provide data and services for the Watson system. IBM has earmarked $100 million to acquire startups that could expand Watson's capabilities.

In 2016 the company made nearly 15 acquisitions and continued at a somewhat slower pace with two purchases in the first half of 2017. The biggest acquisition of 2017 was of Truven Health Analytics which provides data and analysis technologies for $2.6 billion. IBM seeks to put data and analysis together with Watson?s cognitive capabilities to help health care professionals accomplish better patient outcomes.

In another Watson-related acquisition that closed in 2016 was of the Weather Company. IBM bought the company's business-to-business mobile and cloud-based web-properties weather.com Weather Underground The Weather Company brand and WSI its global business-to-business brand. The transaction did not include the Weather Channel but it licenses weather forecast data and analytics from IBM under a long-term contract. The deal provides a wealth of data for processing through Watson to help companies make better decisions that are affected by the weather.

EXECUTIVES

SVP IBM Watson and Cloud Platform, David W. Kenny, age 55

Vice President Of Legal, Martha Rendeiro

SVP Solutions Portfolio and Research, John E. Kelly, age 64, $754,000 total compensation

Chairman President and CEO, Virginia M. (Ginni) Rometty, age 59, $1,600,000 total compensation

SVP IBM Cloud, Robert J. LeBlanc, age 58

SVP Global Business Services, Mark Foster, age 58

SVP Global Markets and Chairman IBM Europe, Erich Clementi, age 58, $703,500 total compensation

SVP Global Markets, Martin J. Schroeter, age 52, $754,000 total compensation

SVP IBM Watson Group, Michael D. (Mike) Rhodin, age 56, $630,000 total compensation

SVP IBM Systems, Thomas W. (Tom) Rosamilia, age 56

SVP Global Markets, Bruno V. Di Leo, age 59

SVP IBM Analytics, Robert J. (Bob) Picciano, age 58

SVP and CFO, James J. Kavanaugh, age 50

SVP IBM Industry Platforms, Bridget A. van Kralingen, age 53, $665,000 total compensation

SVP IBM Global Technology Services, Martin Jetter, age 57, $650,000 total compensation

CIO, Fletcher Previn

Vice President Product Management, Rick Boldt

Vice President of Marketing, Anne Gray

Vice President Systems, Bryan Adair

Vice President Strategic Alliance and Chief Technologist Officer, Bernard Meyerson

Vice President, John Kirkwood

Vice President and Chief Technology Officer Distribution sector, Cathy Lasser

Vice President Human Resources, Mary Sue Rogers

Vice President of Integrated Technology Services, Cathy Lewis

Vice President Mergers And Acquisitions, Kareem Yusuf

Vice President Enterprise Operations, Stephanie Carmel

Vice President Finance And Operations Ibm Channels, David Colistra

Vice President Technology, Alex Cocq

Executive Vice President, Pari Sadasivan

Vice President Finance And Director, James W Boyken

Vice President of Marketing and Strategy, Scott Hebner

Vice President of Web Services, Michael Clark

Vice President, Moshe Cohen

Vice President, Steven Canepa

Vice President Solution Provider Sales, Cecelia Marrese

Senior Vice President Application Management Services, Colleen F Arnold

Vice President Sales, Robert Schneider

Vice President Marketing, Surjit Chana

Vice President Marketing, Annie Cheung

Vice President Marketing, E Rogers

Vice President and Partner, Srinivas Attili

Vice President Of Business Development Establishing Solutions And Reselling Agreements, Rich Schatzel

Vice President Technical Sales and Deployment, Lauren States

Vice President of Sales for Global Telecommunications Industry, John Polly

Vice President Strategic Services, Randall Dalia

Vice President of North American Sales, Paul Resten

Vice President Telecommunications Industry Americas, Dave Mancl

Vice President for Worldwide Information Management Marketing, David Laverty

Vice President Global Channels and Solutions Marketing, Michael Gerentine

Vice President Emerging Business Markets IBM Systems Group, Kathleen Smith

Vice President Pseries Sales Americas, Bill Donohue

Senior Vice President Legal And Regulatory Affairs General Counsel, Robert Weber

Vice President of Retail Store Solutions, Gregory Tavalsky

Vice President Software Business Partners And Midmarket, Mark Register

Vice President, Veronica Dwyer

Vice President Marketing and Channels Websphere Po, Kristen Lauria

Vice President Operations, Emilio Griman

Vice President North America Microelectronics Sales, David Faircloth

Vice President MODULAR and BLADE CENTER Program Ma, Terri Mitchell

Vice President Sales, Arlene Garcia

Vice President, Gilbert Molinar

Vice President Human Resource, Obed Louissaint

Vice President Ratinal Sales Americas, Rob Lamb

Vice President, Sal Vella

Vice President, Mike Cowan

Executive Vice President, Kari Barbar

Vice President Business Development, Mark Bytner

Vice President and Assistant General Counsel, Richard Kaplan

Vice President Marketing And Communications, Robyn Bennett

Vice President, Michael Healy

Vice President, Rosanne Mehelas

Vice President For Information Technology And Wireless Convergence, Radha Ratnaparkhi

Vice President Human Resources, Annette Favorite

Vice President Strategic Services, Brett Flory

Vice President Semiconductor Research And Development Center, Gary Patton

Vice President of Corporate Security, Joe Morton

Vice President of Marketing, Ann Rubin

Vice President Technology, Jay Cook

Vice President of Products and Solutions, Timothy Parish

Vice President of Business Development and Licensing, Tom Reeves

Vice President Global Sales Operations, Will Meikle

Vice President Strategy, Jessica Murillo

Vice President, David Simms

Vice President Network And Systems Operations, Simon Alves

Vice President Integrated Marketing Communications, Ed Abrams

Vice President Human Resources, Jill Maunder

Vice President Worldwide Sales, Ken Stoffregen

Vice President, Steve Jennings

Vice President Marketing And Communications, Maria Reeves Hayes

Vice President Sales, Janet Schultz

Vice President Technology Development, Percy Gilbert

Vice President of Technology Distinguished Engineer, Andrew Welleck

Senior Vice President Marketing Storage Technologies, Jim Kely

Information Technolgy Vice President, Mark Farabaugh

Vice President Corporate Development Growth Market, Harsh Chugh

Group Vice President of the Transportation Unit, Lillian Hanson

Vice President Partner Enablement, William Bill Liebler

Senior Vice President, Bob Moffat

Vice President Iseries Marketing, Peter Bingaman

Vice President Marketing, Linda Ryan

Vice President Information Security Strategy, John Hsieh

Vice President Workforce Strategy, Domenic Tripoli

Vice President Federal Systems Integrators, Kevin Costello

International Leader Vice President Worldwide Sales, David Valovcin

Vice President, Julie Curry

Senior Vice President Human Resources, Jonathan R Zalisk

Vice President, Laura Guio

Vice President Global Technology Services, Leslie Keating

VP Operations, John Sangalli

Vice President Marketing, Ray Cox

Vice President of Storage, Terri Green

Vice President Information Based Medicine, Mike Svinte

Information Technology Information Systems Vice President Director, Sadie Williams

Vice President of Sales and Marketing, Craig Rhinehart

Vice President Manager Director, Christopher Goudreau

Vice President Sales, Tom Waun

Vice President Marketing and Business Development, Gregory Adams

Vice President Of Global Business, Peggy Vaughan

Vice President Of Global Community Initiatives, Paula Baker

Vice President Marketing, Mark Seaver

Vice President Global Infrastructure and Resource Management, Joseph Dzaluk

Vice President Information Technology, Dennis Jay

Assistant Vice President Services Overall, Jen Noble

Vice President of Business Development, Janine Grasso

Worlwide Vice President Of Sales Systems And Tech, Bob Hoey

VP Sales, Bill Luse

Vice President Business Operations, John White

Worldwide Vice President Business Partners Sales IBM Software Group, Vincent Zandvliet

Vice President Sales, Peter Andino

Vice President Product Management Watson Health, Cory Wiegert

Vice President Life Systems, Dave Litschgi

Vice President Marketing, Kevin Taylor

Vice President of Worldwide Marketing, William Scull

Vice President worldwide Smarter Commerce Software Services, David Sawatzky

Vice President Security Growth Initiatives Security Services, Shelley Westman

Vice President Sales Western Region, Scott Ferber

Vice President Sales, Michael Connolly

Vice President And Senior Project Executive, Luis Fernandez

Vice President Databases and Data Warehousing, Sean Poulley

Vice President, Tony Ciro

Vice President Electronic Design Automation Techn, Leon Stok

Vice President For Software Standards And Cloud Co, Angel Thompson

Vice President Of Marketing Communication, Lisa Baird

Vice President Human Resource, James Carney

Vice President Marketing, Steve Solazzo

Vice President Partner Enablement, Bill Liebler

IBM Vice President of Science and Technology, Tze-Chiang Chen

Vice President Sales and Marketing, Steve Grove

Vice President and Leader Provider, Sean Hogan

Vice President of Global Sales Operations, P J Mitchell

Auditors: PricewaterhouseCoopers LLP

LOCATIONS

HQ: International Business Machines Corp
One New Orchard Road, Armonk, NY 10504
Phone: 914 499-1900   **Fax:** 914 765-4190
Web: www.ibm.com

2016 Sales

	$ mil.	% of total
US	30,194	38
Other countries	41,386	52
Japan	8,339	10
Total	**79,919**	**100**

PRODUCTS/OPERATIONS

2016 Sales

	$ mil.	% of total
Services	51,268	64
Sales	26,942	34
Financing	1,709	2
Total	**79,919**	**100**

2016 Sales

% of total	$ mil
Technology Services & Cloud Platforms	44
Cognitive Solutions	23
Global Business Services	21
Systems	10
Global financing	2
Other	-
Total	**100**

Selected Services

Business services
  Application management
  E-business
  Strategic consulting
  Systems integration
Financing
Technology services
  Business process outsourcing
  Infrastructure
  Maintenance
  Outsourcing
  Software integration
  Systems management
  Web hosting
  Training

Selected Products

Printing systems
Servers
Software
  Application development
  Database and data management
  E-commerce
  Graphics and multimedia
  Groupware
  Networking and communication
  Operating systems
  Product life cycle management
  Security
  Speech recognition
  System management
  Transaction system
  Web application servers
Storage
  Hard drive systems
  Optical libraries
  Storage networking
  Tape drives systems and libraries

Selected Acquisitions

Alchemy API (2015 data collection and analysis)
Lighthouse Security (2014 cloud computing)
Cloudant (2014 cloud computing)
Silverpop (2014 cloud computing)
CrossIdeas (2014 security software)
Aspera (2013 high-speed data transfer)
SoftLayer (2013 cloud-computing infrastructure)
Fiberlink Communications (2013 mobile management)
Xtify (2013 cloud-based mobile messaging)
Kenexa (2012 cloud-based recruiting and talent
  management)
Tealeaf Technology (2012 customer experience analytics
  software)
Vivisimo (2012 analytics software)

TRIRIGA (2011 real estate management software)
Netezza (2010 data storage and analysis devices)
BLADE Network Technologies (2010; network servers
  switches and software)
OpenPages (2010 financial risk and compliance
  management software)
Clarity Systems (2010 financial data management
  software)
PSS Systems (2010 legal software)
Unica (2010 enterprise marketing software)
Storwize (2010 data compression software)
Sterling Commerce (2010 business integration software)
Datacap (2010 document digitization and data
  management software)
Coremetrics (2010 Web analytics software)
BigFix (2010 corporate security software)
Lombardi (2010 business process management software)
SPSS (2009 enterprise data analysis software)
ILOG (2008 enterprise resource management software)
Telelogic (2008 embedded systems software)
Cognos (2008 business intelligence software)
Softek Storage Solutions (2007 storage management
  software)
NovusCG (2007 enterprise resource planning software)
DataMirror (2007 data integration software)
WebDialogs (2007 Web conferencing services)
Princeton Softech (2007 data management software)
Watchfire (2007 website management software)
Vallent (2007 network management software)
Consul Risk Management (2007 risk management
  software)

COMPETITORS

AWS	Hewlett Packard
Accenture	Enterprise
Alcatel-Lucent	Hitachi
Apple Inc.	Infosys
BMC Software	Intel
CA Inc.	Lexmark
Capgemini	Microsoft
Cisco Systems	Motorola Solutions
Cognizant Tech	NEC
Solutions	NTT DATA
Computer Sciences	Novell
Corp.	Oracle
Dell	Panasonic Corp
Deloitte Consulting	Ricoh Company
Deloitte Global	SAP
Services	Sony
EMC	TSMC
Epson	Tata Consultancy
Ericsson	Texas Instruments
Fujitsu	Toshiba
GE	Unisys
Google	Wipro Technologies
HCL Technologies	

HISTORICAL FINANCIALS

Company Type: Public

Income Statement

FYE: December 31

	REVENUE ($ mil.)	NET INCOME ($ mil.)	NET PROFIT MARGIN	EMPLOYEES
12/16	79,919	11,872	14.9%	380,300
12/15	81,741	13,190	16.1%	377,757
12/14	92,793	12,022	13.0%	379,592
12/13	99,751	16,483	16.5%	431,212
12/12	104,507	16,604	15.9%	434,246
Annual Growth	**(6.5%)**	**(8.0%)**	**—**	**(3.3%)**

2016 Year-End Financials

Debt ratio: 35.90%
Return on equity: 72.84%
Cash ($ mil.): 7,826
Current ratio: 1.21
Long-term debt ($ mil.): 34,655

No. of shares (mil.): 945
Dividends
  Yield: 0.0%
  Payout: 44.4%
Market value ($ mil.): 157,005

STOCK PRICE ($) FY Close	P/E High/Low		PER SHARE ($) Earnings	Dividends	Book Value
12/16	165.99	14	9	12.38	5.50	19.29
12/15	137.62	13	10	13.42	5.00	14.77
12/14	160.44	17	13	11.90	4.25	11.98
12/13	187.57	14	11	14.94	3.70	21.62
12/12	191.55	15	12	14.37	3.30	16.88
Annual Growth	**(3.5%)**	**—**	**—**	**(3.7%)**	**13.6%**	**3.4%**

International Paper Co

International Paper (IP) is one of the world's largest manufacturers of printing papers. Products include uncoated paper used in printers market pulp for making towels and tissues and coated paper and uncoated bristols (heavyweight art paper). In the US IP is #1 in containerboard production 80% of which is used in industrial corrugated boxes. A consumer packaging arm makes board to box cosmetics and food. IP owns recycling plants mainly in the US and a pulp and paper business in Russia via a 50/50 venture with Ilim Holding.

Operations

IP operates in four segments: Industrial Packaging (67% of net sales) Printing Papers (19%) Consumer Packaging (9%) and Global Cellulose Fibers (5%).

Industrial Packaging is the largest manufacturer of containerboard in the US with a production capacity of more than 13 million tons annually. Products include linerboard medium whitetop recycled linerboard recycled medium and saturating kraft.

Printing Papers produces printing and writing papers and Consumer Packaging makes solid bleached sulfate board with an annual US production capacity of about 1.2 million tons. Global Cellulose Fibers' product portfolio includes fluff market and specialty pulps.

Geographic Reach

IP has manufacturing operations in Asia Europe Latin America North America Africa the Middle East and Russia. In the US it operates nearly 30 pulp paper and packaging mills roughly 170 converting and packaging plants more than 15 recycling plants and three bag facilities. In Europe Asia Latin America and South America the company operates 16 pulp paper and packaging mills roughly 70 converting and packaging plants and two recycling plants.

The US is by far its largest market representing nearly 75% of its total sales each year. EMEA is its second-largest market generating around 15% followed by the Asia/Pacific almost 5%.

Sales and Marketing

IP?s products are used in copiers desktop and laser printers and digital imaging food cosmetics pharmaceuticals filtration construction material paints and coatings. End-use applications include advertising and promotional materials such as brochures pamphlets greeting cards books annual reports and direct mail.

Financial Performance

IP has experienced revenue declines the last three years. Its revenues dipped 6% from $22.4 billion in 2015 to $21.1 billion in 2016. The declines were driven by a 34% drop in Consumer Packaging sales. In North America coated paperboard sales volumes in 2016 for this segment were lower than in 2015 primarily due to IP's exit from the coated bristols market. Average sales price realizations also decreased year over year due to competitive pressures.

IP's profits have fluctuated over the years; after rising in $938 million in 2015 profits declined 5% to $904 million in 2016. The erosion of profits was attributed to an operating loss of $180 million stemming from its Global Cellulose Fibers segment which recognized lower average sales price realizations and mix higher operating costs and higher maintenance outage costs throughout 2016.

While changes in key cash operating costs — such as energy raw material and transportation costs — do have an effect on IP's operating cash flow the company believes its focus on pricing and cost controls has improved its cash flow generation over an operating cycle. Focusing on these key factors IP's cash flows from operations remained consistent in 2015 and 2016 hovering around the $2.5 billion mark for both years.

Strategy

As the world's biggest paper company IP has experienced a sharp decline in demand as more media is consumed digitally. In order to get back on track IP is focused on products that are spiking in other markets. It has zeroed in on the aging baby boomers generation as the adult diaper market is predicted to explode in the years ahead. As a global maker of fluff — a primary ingredient in adult incontinence products — IP is poised to take advantage of this swiftly growing market. It already took steps to strengthen its capabilities in this area through the $2.2 billion purchase of Canada-based Weyerhaeuser's pulp business in late 2016. After the purchase it formed its new Global Cellulose Fibers segment as a springboard for future growth.

Mergers and Acquisitions

In late 2016 IP added a new operating segment when it purchased Canada-based Weyerhaeuser's pulp business for $2.2 billion in cash. The company combined the newly acquired business with its own legacy pulp operations to form its Global Cellulose Fibers segment. The acquisition included five pulp mills and two converting facilities that produce fluff pulp softwood pulp and specialty pulp products for a number of consumer applications including diapers other hygiene products tissue and textiles. Perhaps more importantly the purchase strengthened IP's position in the rapidly growing adult incontinence products market.

HISTORY

In 1898 nearly 20 northeastern pulp and paper firms consolidated to lower costs. The resulting International Paper had 20 mills in Maine Massachusetts New Hampshire New York and Vermont. The mills relied on forests in New England and Canada for wood pulp. When Canada enacted legislation to stop the export of pulpwood in 1919 International Paper formed Canadian International Paper.

During the 1940s and 1950s the company bought Agar Manufacturing (shipping containers 1940) Single Service Containers (Pure-Pak milk containers 1946) and Lord Baltimore Press (folding cartons 1958). It diversified in the 1960s and 1970s buying Davol (hospital products 1968; sold to C. R. Bard 1980) American Central (land development 1968; sold to developers 1974) and General Crude Oil (gas and oil 1975; sold to Mobil Oil 1979).

Decades later International Paper picked up Shorewood Packaging for $850 million in 2000. That year it made an unsolicited $6.2 billion bid for Champion International— which had previously agreed to be acquired by UPM-Kymmene— igniting a bidding war. UPM withdrew its offer however and International Paper acquired Champion for about $9.6 billion.

After surviving the Great Recession IP made one of its most significant acquisitions to date in 2012 when it acquired Temple-Inland one of North America's top producers of corrugated packaging in a transaction valued at $4.5 billion.

EXECUTIVES

SVP Human Resources Government Relations and Global Citizenship, Thomas G. (Tom) Kadien, age 61, $629,167 total compensation

SVP Consumer Packaging, Catherine I. Slater, age 53

SVP Industrial Packaging The Americas, Timothy S. (Tim) Nicholls, age 56, $710,000 total compensation

Chairman and CEO, Mark S. Sutton, age 56, $1,200,000 total compensation

SVP Manufacturing Technology EHS and Global Sourcing, Tommy S. Joseph, age 57, $600,000 total compensation

SVP Pulp, Jean-Michel Ribieras, age 54, $420,000 total compensation

SVP and CFO, Glenn R. Landau, age 48

SVP Paper the Americas, W. Michael Amick, age 53, $500,000 total compensation

SVP and President Europe the Middle East Africa and Russia, John V. Sims, age 54

SVP North American Container, Gregory T. Wanta, age 51

SVP Global Cellulose Fibers, Jean-Michel Ribi ©ras, age 54

VP Information Technology, Frank Bevan

VP Supply Chain, Fred Towler

Senior Vice President, Maximo Pacheco

National Account Manager, Doug Arters

Vice President And General Manager Xpedx Illinois Division, Thomas Plath

Vice President Pulp, John Fisher

Senior Vice President Human Resources and Communications, Paul Karee

Vice President, Pamela Hollingsworth

National Account Manager, Jenae Lewis

VP Supply Chain, Atanu Chakrabarti

Vice President Mill Operations, Anitra Collins

Vice President Talent Management and Corporate Human Resources, Shiela P Vinczeller

Vice President, September Blane

NATIONAL ACCOUNTS MANAGER, Michael T Murphy

SENIOR VICE PRESIDENT CONSUMER PKG, Catherine I Slater

Senior Vice President, Debbie Ellington

Auditors: Deloitte & Touche LLP

LOCATIONS

HQ: International Paper Co
6400 Poplar Avenue, Memphis, TN 38197
Phone: 901 419-7000
Web: www.internationalpaper.com

2016 Sales

	$ mil.	% of total
Americas		
US	15,918	76
Other countries	1,581	7
EMEA	2,862	14
Pacific Rim & Asia	718	3
Total	**21,079**	**100**

PRODUCTS/OPERATIONS

2016 Sales

	$ mil.	% of total
Industrial packaging	14,191	67
Printing papers	4,058	19
Consumer packaging	1,954	9
Global Cellulose Fibers	1,092	5
Adjustments	(216)	-
Total	**21,079**	**100**

Selected Operations and Products

Consumer Packaging
  Cold cups and lids
  Consumer-ready packaging (Shorewood Packaging folding carton set-up box)
  Folding carton board
  Food buckets and lids
  Hot cups and lids
  Milk container and lids
  Starcote tobacco board
Distribution North America (xpedx)
  Building services and away-from-home markets with facility supplies
  Commercial printers with printing papers and graphic pre-press printing presses post press equipment
  Manufacturers with packaging supplies and equipment
  Warehousing and delivery services
Industrial Packaging
  Automotive packaging
  Corrugated pallet
  Die-cut package
  Flapless
  Kraft linerboard
  Laminated bulk bin
  Liquid bulk
  Litho lamination
  Medium paper
  Retail displays
  Saturating kraft
  Slotted container
  White top liner
Papers
  HP (Hewlett-Packard) home and commercial papers
  Office papers
Pulp
  Fluff pulp
  Paper and tissue pulp
Recycling products
  Old corrugated containers and kraft corrugated cuttings
  Old newspaper

COMPETITORS

Amcor	M-real
Cascades Inc.	Mondi
Domtar	Nippon Paper
ENCE Energia y Celulosa SA	Packaging Corp. of America
Environmental Mill & Supply	Smurfit Kappa
Georgia-Pacific	Stora Enso
Louisiana-Pacific	UPM-Kymmene

HISTORICAL FINANCIALS

Company Type: Public

Income Statement

FYE: December 31

	REVENUE ($ mil.)	NET INCOME ($ mil.)	NET PROFIT MARGIN	EMPLOYEES
12/16	21,079	904	4.3%	55,000
12/15	22,365	938	4.2%	56,000
12/14	23,617	555	2.4%	58,000
12/13	29,080	1,395	4.8%	69,000
12/12	27,833	794	2.9%	70,000
Annual Growth	**(6.7%)**	**3.3%**	**—**	**(5.9%)**

2016 Year-End Financials

Debt ratio: 33.93%	No. of shares (mil.): 411
Return on equity: 21.92%	Dividends
Cash ($ mil.): 1,033	Yield: 0.0%
Current ratio: 1.71	Payout: 81.7%
Long-term debt ($ mil.): 11,075	Market value ($ mil.): 21,821

	STOCK PRICE ($) FY Close	P/E High/Low		PER SHARE ($) Earnings	Dividends	Book Value
12/16	53.06	25	15	2.18	1.78	10.56
12/15	37.70	26	16	2.23	1.64	9.24
12/14	53.58	43	35	1.29	1.45	12.18
12/13	49.03	16	13	3.11	1.25	18.58
12/12	39.84	22	15	1.80	1.09	14.33
Annual Growth	**7.4%**		**—**	**4.9%**	**13.1%**	**(7.4%)**

Interpublic Group of Companies Inc.

The Interpublic Group of Companies is one of the world's largest advertising and marketing services conglomerates. Its flagship creative agencies include McCann Worldgroup and Lowe & Partners while such firms as Deutsch and Hill Holliday are leaders in the US advertising business. Interpublic also offers direct marketing media services and public relations through such agencies as Initiative and Weber Shandwick. Its largest have clients included General Motors Johnson & Johnson Microsoft Samsung and Unilever.

HISTORY

Standard Oil advertising executive Harrison Mc-Cann opened the H. K. McCann Company in 1911 and signed Standard Oil of New Jersey (later Exxon) as his first client. McCann's ad business boomed as the automobile became an integral part of American life. His firm merged with Alfred Erickson's agency (created 1902) in 1930 forming the McCann-Erickson Company. At the end of the decade the firm hired Marion Harper a top Yale graduate as a mailroom clerk. Harper became president in 1948.

Harper began acquiring other ad agencies and by 1961 controlled more than 20 companies. That year he unveiled a plan to create a holding company that would let the ad firms operate separately allowing them to work on accounts for competing products but giving them the parent firm's financial and information resources. He named the company Interpublic Inc. after a German research company owned by the former H. K. McCann Co. The conglomerate continued expanding and was renamed The Interpublic Group of Companies in 1964. Harper's management capabilities weren't up to the task however and the company soon faced bankruptcy. In 1967 the board replaced him with Robert Healy who saved Interpublic and returned it to profitability. The company went public in 1971.

The 1970s were fruitful years for Interpublic; its ad teams created memorable campaigns for Coke ("It's the Real Thing" and "Have a Coke and a Smile") and Miller Beer ("Miller Time" and Miller Lite ads). After Philip Geier became chairman in 1980 the company gained a stake in Lowe Howard-Spink (1983; it later became The Lowe Group) and bought Lintas International (1987). Interpublic bought the rest of The Lowe Group in 1990.

Interpublic bought Western International Media (now known as Initiative) and Ammirati & Puris (which was merged with Lintas to form Ammirati Puris Lintas) in 1994. As industry consolidation picked up in 1996 Interpublic kept pace with acquisitions of PR company Weber Group and Draft-Worldwide. Interpublic bought a majority stake in artist management and film production company Addis-Wechsler & Associates (now Industry Entertainment) in 1997 and later formed sports marketing and management group Octagon.

Interpublic acquired US agencies Carmichael Lynch and Hill Holliday Connors Cosmopulos in 1998. It also boosted its PR presence with its purchase of International Public Relations (UK) the parent company of public relations networks Shandwick and Golin/Harris. Interpublic strengthened its position in the online world in 1999 when it bought 20% of Stockholm-based Internet services company Icon Medialab International. That year the company merged agencies Ammirati and Lowe & Partners Worldwide to form Lowe Lintas & Partners Worldwide (in 2002 they changed the name to just Lowe & Partners Worldwide).

Interpublic bought market research firm NFO Worldwide for $580 million in 2000 and merged Weber Public Relations with Shandwick International to form Weber Shandwick Worldwide one of the world's largest PR firms. Later that year the company bought ad agency Deutsch for about $250 million. John Dooner took the position of chairman and CEO at the end of the year after Geier resigned. His first move proved a big one: Interpublic acquired True North Communications for $2.1 billion in stock in 2001.

The honeymoon was short lived; facing a recession the mounting debt from its buying spree and with the revelation of accounting discrepancies at McCann-Erickson WorldGroup (renamed McCann Worldgroup in 2004) Dooner stepped aside as chairman and CEO in 2003. Interpublic chose vice chairman David Bell (former CEO of True North) as Dooner's replacement. After almost two years of work to improve Interpublic's balance sheet Bell was replaced by former MONY Group chief Michael Roth.

In 2005 Roth was tasked with straightening out Interpublic's financial controls and improving its balance sheet. Later that year the company revealed extensive bookkeeping problems primarily in its overseas operations leading to a financial restatement going back to 2000.

In order to simplify its operating structure in 2006 Interpublic integrated direct marketer Draft Inc. with advertising agency Foote Cone & Belding (forming DraftFCB). A year later it restructured its vast network of media brands to report under a single management structure (Mediabrands).

Looking to India in mid-2007 Interpublic bought all the shares of FCB Ulka a top-five ad agency in the country that operated from six offices. Interpublic integrated the Indian agency with its DraftFCB operations. At the same time it acquired the remaining 51% stake it didn't hold in Lintas India Private Limited at a cost of $50 million in cash and integrated it into its Lowe Worldwide network.

In 2010 Interpublic acquired Brazilian creative advertising strategy firm CUBOCC and London-based marketing agency Delaney Lund Knox Warren & Partners (DLKW). During 2011 the company acquired several marketing agencies. In early 2012 Interpublic obtained German consumer lifestyle agency Nicole Weber Communications (NWC) and UK-based digital and interactive agency FUSE.

EXECUTIVES

Senior Vice President Business Development, David J Weiss

SVP and Managing Director, Terry D. Peigh

Chairman and CEO, Michael I. Roth, age 71, $1,500,000 total compensation

EVP and CFO, Frank Mergenthaler, age 56, $1,000,000 total compensation

EVP and Chief Strategy and Talent Officer, Philippe Krakowsky, age 55, $1,000,000 total compensation

SVP and Managing Director, Peter Leinroth

SVP General Counsel and Secretary, Andrew Bonzani, age 53, $800,000 total compensation

SVP Controller and Chief Accounting Officer, Christopher F. Carroll, age 50, $587,714 total compensation

SVP and CIO, John Halper

Auditors: PricewaterhouseCoopers LLP

LOCATIONS

HQ: Interpublic Group of Companies Inc.
909 Third Avenue, New York, NY 10022
Phone: 212 704-1200
Web: www.interpublic.com

2016 Sales

	$ mil.	% of total
Domestic	4,684	60
International:		
Asia Pacific	923	12
United Kingdom	695	9
Continental Europe	699	9
Latin America	372	5
Other	470	5
Total	**7,846**	**100**

PRODUCTS/OPERATIONS

2016 Sales

	% of total
IAN	81
CMG	19
Total	**100**

COMPETITORS

Dentsu	Omnicom
Dentsu Aegis	Publicis Groupe
Hakuhodo	WPP
Havas	

HISTORICAL FINANCIALS

Company Type: Public

Income Statement

FYE: December 31

	REVENUE ($ mil.)	NET INCOME ($ mil.)	NET PROFIT MARGIN	EMPLOYEES
12/16	7,846	608	7.8%	49,800
12/15	7,613	454	6.0%	49,200
12/14	7,537	477	6.3%	47,400
12/13	7,122	267	3.8%	45,400
12/12	6,956	446	6.4%	43,300
Annual Growth	3.1%	8.0%	—	3.6%

2016 Year-End Financials

Debt ratio: 13.54%
Return on equity: 30.47%
Cash ($ mil.): 1,097
Current ratio: 0.97
Long-term debt ($ mil.): 1,280
No. of shares (mil.): 391
Dividends
 Yield: 0.0%
 Payout: 40.2%
Market value ($ mil.): 9,167

	STOCK PRICE ($) FY Close	P/E High/Low		PER SHARE ($) Earnings	Dividends	Book Value
12/16	23.41	16	13	1.49	0.60	5.15
12/15	23.28	21	16	1.09	0.48	4.87
12/14	20.77	18	14	1.12	0.38	5.11
12/13	17.70	28	18	0.61	0.30	5.22
12/12	11.02	12	9	0.94	0.24	5.80
Annual Growth	20.7%	—	—	12.2%	25.7%	(2.9%)

INTL FCStone Inc.

Going global is the name of the game for commodities broker INTL FCStone. The company specializes in the physical trade of commodities such as corn gold renewable fuels and livestock though it makes most of its money through hedging securities trading and clearing activities. It offers clearing and execution services of listed futures and options on futures and serves as a wholesale market-maker for some 800 foreign securities. It operates in niche international markets offering commodity risk management consulting asset management and commodity financing and facilitation. Its clients base includes financial institutions corporations and charitable organizations in the US and abroad.

Operations

INTL FCStone runs five operating segments: Commercial Hedging Global Payments Securities Physical Commodities and Clearing & Execution Services. It supports its customers with a global platform that provides efficient and transparent execution market intelligence and post-trade services across all its asset classes and markets.

Although the Physical Commodities segment accounts for 99% of overall revenue it is the only segment that has significant operating costs (the costs of traded commodities) and therefore it contributes only about 5% of operating revenue. It provides a full range of trading and hedging capabilities for Precious Metals and Physical Agriculture & Energy commodities and acts as a principal by committing its own capital to buy and sell commodities on a spot and forward basis.

Commodity pricing is susceptible to a great many variables and therefore producers consumers and investors institute hedging strategies to soften the vagaries of the financial risk. The Commercial Hedging segment provides high-value-added services to its clients to assess risk design hedging strategies and execute those strategies. Its sweet spot is with agricultural and energy commodities and base metals. The segment produces about one third of INTL FC Stone?s operating revenue and at least that much of its net income.

The Clearing & Execution Services segment matches customer trades with the relevant commodity or stock exchange collects and manages the customer margin deposits needed for a transaction and accounts for and reports on the transaction to the customer. It does this for all major futures and securities exchanges globally. This segment was boosted in 2016 with the purchase and integration of Sterne Agee?s independent brokerage clearing and RIA businesses. CES generates about 30% of operating revenue.

The Securities segment facilitates cross-border trading in currencies stock shares (particularly foreign-listed depository receipts) and debt instruments. Global Payments services organizations such as banks commercial businesses and charities with their need to transact cross-border money movement commonly involving currency exchange; it does so in more than 175 countries and 140 currencies.

Geographic Reach

New York NY-headquartered INTL FCStone serves 20000 customers in about 130 countries around the world. The company operates through a network of more than 20 offices in the US. Just as many international offices support the company?s business in the rest of the world with half of them in the commodity-active region of South America. London and Dublin house its European facilities Sydney hosts its Australian operations and Shanghai Beijing Singapore and Hong Kong are home to its Asia offices.

Sales and Marketing

Customers are served through a direct sales force of risk management consultants who are organized by commodity verticals such as agriculture energy metals and livestock as well as geographic areas such as Latin America/Brazil or China.

Its clients include commercial customers asset managers broker-dealers insurance companies brokers institutional and professional investors commercial and investment banks and governmental and non-governmental organizations.

Customer types include corporations nonprofits financial institutions commercial hedger corporation cooperative introducing broker institutional trader professional trader and commercial hedger.

Financial Performance

While INTL FCStone produces eye-popping revenue numbers such as more than $70 billion in FY2011 (ended September 30 2011) and nearly $30 billion in FY2017 a preferred performance metric is operating revenue as it removes dramatic multi-year price swings in commodities. Operating revenue has risen year after year for almost a decade from roughly $80 million in FY2009 to more than $780 million in FY2017.

For the fiscal year 2017 (ended September 30 2017) revenue was $29.4 billion and operating revenue was $784 million. Operating revenue grew 17% from the prior year boosted by a massive 70% increase from the Clearing & Execution Services segment (in large part to the 2016 Sterne Agee business acquisition) and more than 20% upswings from Physical Commodities and Global Payments.

Net income for FY2017 fell dramatically from $55 million the prior year to $6.4 million due mostly to a business gone bad as INTL FCStone took at $47 million loss on a bad debt in its physical coal business in Singapore (which the company has since exited).

Cash at the end of the year was $315 million a decrease of $1 million from the prior year. Operating activities contributed $14 million and financing activities added $5.7 million. Investing activities used $22 million and currency fluctuations created a marginal change in cash reported in US dollars.

Strategy

INTL FCStone is focused on broadening its customer base in new markets by offering more services. The company is zeroing in on midsized commercial entities as many are relatively underserved by larger financial institutions. It continues to improve platforms and tools for internal and customer-facing functions. In early 2017 it launched its PMXecute+ platform the connects global buyers and sellers of physical gold and automates the trading process; it supported the trading of 49.5 tons of gold in its first year. Later that year it made available its Structured Products Online Calculator (SPOC) which enables its brokers and OTC customers to view real-time OTC structured product indications and request quotes 24/7; the release upgrades a largely manual process to one that is now automated.

Key geographic growth areas for INTL FCStone include Latin America Asia and Europe. In 2016 the company acquired Sterne Agee a securities clearing and wealth management business from Stifel Financial Corp. The acquisition added 50 correspondent clearing relationships with over 120000 accounts. Also in 2016 it acquired London-based oil broker ICAP plc which has operations in Europe the Middle East and Africa.

The company received its Capital Markets Services License from the Monetary Authority of Singapore significantly broadening its capacity to meet increasing demand for commodity risk management services.

Macro-economic influencers in coming years are expected to arise from the US Federal Reserve (FED) interest rate policy and Britain?s exit (BREXIT) from the European Union. The FED is in a tightening phase which will increase interest rates over time and with each 25-basis point rise (0.25%) INTL FC Stone anticipates earning an additional $5.8 million in net interest. Because the company has significant operations on London?s commodities exchange and that exchange underlies products being traded throughout the EU the functioning of the trades is known today. BREXIT adds a high degree of uncertainty about regula-

tions policies and rules that will apply to the exchange.

Mergers and Acquisitions

Acquisitions play a big part in INTL FCStone's growth strategy. In the past several years the company has bought other firms that have helped broaden its geographic reach and service capabilities. In 2016 the company made two acquisitions: Sterne Agee a securities clearing and wealth management firm; and ICAP plc an oil trader working in fuel crude middle distillates futures and options. ICAP was acquired for around $6 million.

In 2015 the company acquired G.X. Clarke & Co. a New Jersey-based dealer in fixed income securities for around $25.9 million. Its client base consists of asset managers commercial bank trust and investment departments broker-dealers and insurance companies.

Company Background

INTL FCStone which traces its roots to 1924 was created after the 2009 merger of FCStone Group and International Assets Holding.

EXECUTIVES

President and CEO, Sean M. O'Connor, age 55, $400,000 total compensation
CFO, William J. (Bill) Dunaway, age 46, $275,000 total compensation
COO, Xuong Nguyen, age 49, $325,000 total compensation
Chief Risk Officer, Tricia Harrod, age 58
CEO Europe Middle East Africa and Asia, Philip A. Smith, age 45, $324,105 total compensation
Executive Chairman Europe Middle East Africa and Asia, Malcolm Wilde, age 66
CEO INTL FCStone Markets, Mark Maurer, age 41
Vice President Sales, John Murphy
Vice President Equity Trading, Thomas Moore
Assistant Vice President Financial Operations, Marcelo Taborda
Assistant Vice President Trading, Gary Esterman
Vice President Asian Trading, Shaun Finnerty
Vice President Equity Trading, AL Barbella
Senior Vice President Base Metals Lead, Tom Gramlich
Vice President, Ryan Smith
Vice President Energy, Jonathan Kist
Chairman, John Radziwill
Board Member, Bruce Krehbiel
Board Member, Brent Bunte
Auditors: KPMG LLP

LOCATIONS

HQ: INTL FCStone Inc.
708 Third Avenue, Suite 1500, New York, NY 10017
Phone: 212 485-3500
Web: www.intlfcstone.com

2016 Sales

	% of total
US	6
Asia	91
Europe	3
South America	0
Total	**100**

PRODUCTS/OPERATIONS

FY2017 Net Operating Revenue by Segment

	% of total
Commercial Hedging	38
Global Payments	16
Securities	19
Clearing & Execution Services	20
Physical Commodities	7
Total	**100**

Selected Subsidiaries

Blackthorn Mult-Advisor Fund LP

FCC Futures Inc.
FCC Investments Inc.
FCStone Advisory Inc.
FCStone Asia Pte. Ltd.
FCStone Australia Pty Ltd.
FCStone Canada ULC
FCStone Carbon LLC
FCStone Commodities Services (Europe) Ltd.
FCStone do Brazil Ltda.
FCStone Financial Inc.
FCStone Forex LLC
FCStone Group
FCStone Information LLC
FCStone International LLC
FCStone Investments Inc.
FCStone Merchant Services LLC
FCStone Paraguay S.R.L.
FCStone LLC
Gainvest Asset Management Ltd.
Gainvest S.A. Sociedad Gerente de Fondos Comunes de
   Inversion
Gainvest Uruguay Asset Management S.A.
Gletir S.A.
Hanley Alternative Trade Group LLC
HGC Advisory Services LLC
HGC Asset Management LLC
HGC Office Services LLC
HGC Trading LLC
IAHC Bermuda Ltd
INTL Advisory Consultants Inc.
INTL Asia Pte. Ltd
INTL Capital and Treasury Global Services Ltd. (Nigeria)
INTL Capital Limited (Dubai UAE)
INTL Capital S.A. (Argentina)
INTL CIBSA Sociedad de Bolsa S.A.
INTL Colombia Ltda.
INTL Commodities DMCC
INTL Commodities Inc.
INTL Commodities Mexico S de RL de CV
INTL Custody & Clearing Solutions Inc.
INTL FCStone Commodities Inc.
INTL FCStone (Europe) Ltd.
INTL FCStone Financial
INTL FCStone (Netherlands) B.V.
INTL FCStone SA
INTL Gainvest Capital Assessoria Financeira Ltda.
   (formerly Gainvest do Brasil Ltda.).
INTL Global Currencies Ltd.
INTL Hanley LLC
INTL Hencorp Futures LLC
INTL Holding (U.K.) Limited
INTL Netherlands B.V.
INTL Participacoes Ltda.
INTL Provident Inc.
INTL Sieramet LLC
INTL Trading Inc.
INTL Universal Commercial (Shanghai) Co. Ltd.
Risk Management Incorporated
RMI Consulting Inc.
SA Stone Investment Advisors Inc.
SA Stone Wealth Management Inc.
Westown Commodities LLC

COMPETITORS

ADM
BGC Partners
CAPIS
Citigroup Global Markets
Credit Suisse (USA)
Glencore
Goldman Sachs
Interactive Brokers
J.P. Morgan Clearing
Morgan Stanley
NEX
R.J. O'Brien
Rosenthal Collins
Susquehanna International Group LLP
Wedbush Securities

HISTORICAL FINANCIALS

Company Type: Public

Income Statement

FYE: September 30

	REVENUE ($ mil.)	NET INCOME ($ mil.)	NET PROFIT MARGIN	EMPLOYEES
09/17	29,381	6	0.0%	1,607
09/16	14,726	54	0.4%	1,464
09/15	34,676	55	0.2%	1,231
09/14	34,011	19	0.1%	1,141
09/13	43,755	19	0.0%	1,094
Annual Growth	(9.5%)	(24.1%)	—	10.1%

2017 Year-End Financials

Debt ratio: 3.69%
Return on equity: 1.45%
Cash ($ mil.): 721
Current ratio: 0.73
Long-term debt ($ mil.): —

No. of shares (mil.): 18
Dividends
   Yield: —
   Payout: —
Market value ($ mil.): 718

	STOCK PRICE ($) FY Close	P/E High/Low		PER SHARE ($) Earnings	Dividends	Book Value
09/17	38.32	138	107	0.31	0.00	24.02
09/16	38.85	13	8	2.90	0.00	23.53
09/15	24.69	13	6	2.87	0.00	21.11
09/14	17.32	21	17	0.98	0.00	18.29
09/13	20.45	20	16	0.97	0.00	17.46
Annual Growth	17.0%	—	—	(24.8%)	—	8.3%

Intuit Inc

Intuit?s fact is: It handles other people?s taxes ? and their bookkeeping and other financial management tasks. The company is a leading developer of software used for small business accounting (QuickBooks) and consumer tax preparation (TurboTax). Mint the online service helps manage personal finances and budgeting. Professional accountants boot up Intuit?s Lacerte ProSeries and Intuit Tax Online products. More than 70% of revenue comes from products hosted on Intuit?s servers what the company calls connected services. Intuit claims more than 61 million users for its products and services. Not surprisingly about half of annual revenue comes in the quarter that includes April 15.

Operations

Intuit generates half its sales from small business clients with consumers representing another 42%. Professional accountants — who use the company's Lacerte ProSeries and Intuit Tax Online products — account for the remainder of revenue.

Geographic Reach

California-based Intuit has offices in the US Australia Canada India Singapore and the UK. The company's software and services are available in the US Canada the UK Australia India and Singapore. International sales consistently account for less than 5% of Intuit's sales.

Sales and Marketing

Intuit relies on web marketing and targeted advertising such as search engine optimization and purchasing key words from major search engine companies; placing its mobile application in proprietary online stores (including Google's Play Store and Apple's App Store) direct-response mail and email campaigns telephone solicitations TV radio and print advertisements social media and coordinated promotional offers with major retailers. Its TurboTax tax preparation software is dis-

played prominently in stores such as Office Depot Best Buy and Sam's Club through April 15 each year. Intuit ramped up advertising spending to $480 million in 2017 (ended July) from $394 million in 2016.

Financial Performance

Intuit reported 2017 (ended July) sales of $5.2 billion up 10% from the prior year. Each segment posted revenue gains in 2017 paced by a 13% increase in the Small Business segment?s sales because of a 30% rise in Small Business Online Ecosystem revenue and changes to QuickBooks Desktop software products that were implemented in 2015. Consumer Tax sales increased 9% in 2017 on growth in TurboTax federal units and a shift to higher end products. ProConnect segment?s sale rose 2% in 2017.

Intuit?s net income fell to $971 million in 2017 from $979 million in 2016. The company had about $170 million income in 2015 from discontinued operations that was not repeated in 2016. Operating income rose 12% in 2017 from the year before.

Cash flow from operations rose to about $1.6 billion in 2017 from $1.5 billion in 2016.

Strategy

Intuit has declared it intends to double its small business customer base by 2019 and it wants to make sure that its products are accessible online and can be accessed via desktops laptops and mobile devices. It also wants accessibility through social websites such as online forums and social media sites. The company generated nearly three-quarters of its revenue from connected services in 2017 up from 50% nine years ago.

Intuit has turned its applications into platforms open its products to third-party applications that users can integrate with Intuit software such as QuickBooks to more closely meet their specific needs. American Express for example offers an app for its business credit card holders that transfers transactions automatically to the user?s QuickBooks Online account.

While the company sells more than 37 million units of its TurboTax do-it-yourself software Intuit wants to carve out a bigger spot in the assisted tax preparation market. Of the nearly 180 million annual returns filed in the US and Canada some 82 million are filed by professional accountants on behalf of clients. The company has added its own assistance to tax preparation with its SmartLook service which connects preparers with Intuit experts. The company also offered a feature that connects small businesses that use QuickBooks with accountants. That has helped customer retention.

Further Intuit is investing more in artificial intelligence and machine learning to take advantage of the massive amounts of data in its systems to help consumer and businesses prepare tax returns more effectively.

Mergers and Acquisitions

In 2017 Intuit agreed to buy TSheets a platform that small and medium businesses self-employed and accountants use to automate time tracking and scheduling. The deal formalizes a deal that some customers of both companies have already done: about 12000 customers use QuickBooks and TSheets in tandem. By buying TSheets Intuit will create a more seamless experience for those users.

HISTORY

After earning his MBA from Harvard founder Scott Cook spent three years in marketing at Procter & Gamble and four years with consultancy Bain & Company before establishing Intuit in 1983. Research showed that consumers wanted an easy-to-use personal finance software package. Quicken was introduced in 1984.

Intuit was near collapse in 1986 when it received its first big order from software retailer Egghead.com. Intuit released QuickBooks in 1992 and went public in 1993. The next year it acquired a number of firms including tax preparation software developer ChipSoft which brought TurboTax onboard.

In 1995 Microsoft's $2 billion bid to buy Intuit was halted by a Justice Department antitrust lawsuit. Also that year Intuit launched an online banking service and forged its first ties with the Web by bundling a browser and free Internet access with Quicken. It sold its online banking and bill presentation business to CheckFree in 1997. In 1998 the company bought Lacerte Software a provider of software and services to tax professionals.

EXECUTIVES

EVP and Chief People Officer, Sherry Whiteley
Chairman and CEO, Brad D. Smith, age 53, $1,000,000 total compensation
EVP General Counsel and Secretary, Laura A. Fennell, age 56, $575,000 total compensation
EVP and General Manager Small Business Group, Sasan K. Goodarzi, age 49, $625,000 total compensation
EVP and General Manager ProConnect Group, CeCe Morken
EVP and CTO, H. Tayloe Stansbury, age 56, $625,000 total compensation
EVP and General Manager Consumer Tax Group, Daniel A. (Dan) Wernikoff, age 45, $725,000 total compensation
SVP and General Manager Consumer Ecosystem Group, Al Ko
EVP and Chief Marketing and Sales Officer, Lucas Watson
EVP and CFO, Michelle Clatterbuck, age 49
Vice President Corporate Communications, Rob Lanesey
Vice President, Leah Abad
SP Senior Vice President, Melani Armstrong
Vice President of Network Administration, Elisabeth Gettelman
Vice President Corporate Strategy and Development, Holger Wenzky
Senior Vice President Product Development, Marilyn Jones
Vice President WebSphere Technical Sales, Nitin Kant
VP Operations, Christopher Glennon
Vice President Corporate Controller, Jeffrey P Hank
Vice President Of Product Management, Barry Saik
Vice President Of Finance Operations, Scott Beth
Vice President Platform Chief Architect, Brian Ellison
Vice President of QuickBooks Product Marketing, Rob Lips
Vice President Corporate Development, Erika Swanson
Vice President General Manager, Bruce Johnson
Senior Vice President and Chief Technology Officer, Tayloe Stansbury
Auditors: Ernst & Young LLP

LOCATIONS

HQ: Intuit Inc
2700 Coast Avenue, Mountain View, CA 94043
Phone: 650 944-6000
Web: www.intuit.com

PRODUCTS/OPERATIONS

2017 Sales

	$ mil.	% of total
Small Business	2,597	50
Consumer Tax	2,143	41
ProConnect	437	9
Total	**5,177**	**100**

2017 Sales

	$ mil.	% of total
Product	1,376	27
Service and other	3,808	73
Total	**5,177**	**100**

Products and services
Individuals
Manage budgeting and taxes with confidence
Mint Budgeting
Quicken Personal Finance
QuickBooks Self-Employed
TurboTax Tax Preparation
Small Businesses
The tools you need to run your company
Checks & Supplies
Demandforce Marketing
Intuit Payroll Services
QuickBooks Business Finance
QuickBooks Payments
Accountants
Pro software for the range of client needs
Intuit Tax Online
Lacerte Pro Tax Software
ProSeries Pro Tax Software
QuickBooks for Accountants

COMPETITORS

ADP	JPMorgan Chase
Bank of America	Jackson Hewitt
CA Inc.	MYOB
CCH Incorporated	Microsoft Dynamics
Elavon	NetSuite
Fidelity National	Paychex
Information Services	SAP
First Data	Sage Group
Fiserv	Thomson Reuters
Global Payments	Universal Tax
H&R Block	Wells Fargo

HISTORICAL FINANCIALS

Company Type: Public

Income Statement

FYE: July 31

	REVENUE ($ mil.)	NET INCOME ($ mil.)	NET PROFIT MARGIN	EMPLOYEES
07/17	5,177	971	18.8%	8,200
07/16	4,694	979	20.9%	7,900
07/15	4,192	365	8.7%	7,700
07/14	4,506	907	20.1%	8,000
07/13	4,171	858	20.6%	8,000
Annual Growth	**5.6%**	**3.1%**	**—**	**0.6%**

2017 Year-End Financials

Debt ratio: 12.00%
Return on equity: 77.22%
Cash ($ mil.): 529
Current ratio: 0.73
Long-term debt ($ mil.): 438

No. of shares (mil.): 255
Dividends
  Yield: 0.9%
  Payout: 38.7%
Market value ($ mil.): 35,080

	STOCK PRICE ($) FY Close	P/E High/Low		PER SHARE ($) Earnings	Dividends	Book Value
07/17	137.21	38	28	3.72	1.36	5.30
07/16	110.99	31	21	3.69	1.20	4.50
07/15	105.77	83	60	1.28	1.00	8.40
07/14	81.97	26	20	3.12	0.76	10.80
07/13	63.92	24	20	2.83	0.68	11.79
Annual Growth	**21.0%**	**—**	**—**	**7.1%**	**18.9%**	**(18.1%)**

Investors Bancorp Inc (New)

Investors Bancorp is the holding company for Investors Savings Bank which serves New Jersey and New York from more than 130 branch offices. Founded in 1926 the bank offers such standard deposit products as savings and checking accounts CDs money market accounts and IRAs. Nearly 40% of the bank's loan portfolio is made up of residential mortgages while multi-family loans and commercial real estate loans make up more than 50% combined. The bank also originates business industrial and consumer loans. Founded in 1926 Investors Bancorp's assets now exceed $20 billion.

Operations

About 86% of Investors Bancorp's revenue came from interest income from loans and loans held-for sale in 2014 while another 8% came from interest income on the bank's mortgage-backed securities municipal bonds and other debt. The remainder of its revenue came from fees and service charges (3%) and other miscellaneous income sources. Investors Bancorp boasted a staff of more than 1700 at the end of 2014.

Geographic Reach

Based in Short Hills New Jersey Investors Bancorp has more than 130 branches across New Jersey and New York. It also has lending offices in New York City Short Hills Spring Lake Newark Astoria and Brooklyn. Its operation center is in Iselin New Jersey.

Sales and Marketing

The company offers retail and commercial banking services to individuals professional service firms municipalities small and middle-market companies commercial and industrial firms and other businesses.

Financial Performance

Investors Bancorp's revenues and profits have been rising thanks to strong loan growth from bank acquisitions falling interest expenses on deposits and declining loan loss provisions as its loan portfolio's credit quality has improved with higher property valuations in the strengthened economy.

The bank's revenue jumped by 21% to a record $702.7 million in 2014 mostly thanks to loan asset growth stemming from the bank's 2014 acquisition of Gateway Community Financial.

Higher revenue and a continued decline in loan loss provisions in 2014 drove the bank's net income higher by 18% to a record $131.7 million. Investor Bancorp's operating cash levels spiked by 58% to $277.4 million for the year on higher cash earnings and favorable changes in its working capital.

Strategy

Investors Bancorp continues to expand its geographic reach in its core New Jersey and New York markets and boost its loan and deposit business mainly through select bank and branch acquisitions. Indeed the bank noted in 2015 that it had made eight bank or branch acquisitions since 2008 adding that they have counted for "a significant portion" of the bank's historic growth.

The company's 2014 and 2013 bank acquisitions bolstered its expansion in New Jersey into the suburbs of Philadelphia the boroughs of New York City the Nassau and Suffolk Counties on Long Island and historic markets throughout New Jersey.

Mergers and Acquisitions

In May 2016 Investors Bancorp agreed to purchase the $1 billion-asset The Bank of Princeton along with its 13 branches in the greater Princeton

New Jersey and Philadelphia Pennsylvania areas. The added locations would grow Investors Bancorp's branch network by almost 10% to 156 branches in the Philadelphia to New York City corridor.

In January 2014 Investors Bancorp purchased Gateway Community Financial Corp along with its four branches in Gloucester County New Jersey. The deal added nearly $255 million in customer deposits and $195 million in new loan business to its books.

In December 2013 the company bought Roma Financial Corporation and its 26 branches in Burlington Ocean Mercer Camden and Middlesex counties in New Jersey. The deal added $1.34 billion in deposits and $991 million in loan assets while expanding the company's reach into the Philadelphia suburbs of New Jersey.

Company Background

In late 2012 the company acquired Marathon Banking Corporation (a subsidiary of Greece-based Piraeus Bank) for $135 million adding 13 branches in the New York metro area and more than doubling its branches in New York. The deal also would mark Investors Bancorp's entry into Manhattan and Staten Island.

EXECUTIVES

SEVP and COO, Domenick A. Cama, age 61, $621,000 total compensation
President and CEO, Kevin Cummings, age 62, $935,000 total compensation
EVP and Chief Lending Officer, Richard S. Spengler, age 55, $400,000 total compensation
EVP and Chief Retail Banking Officer, Paul Kalamaras, $375,000 total compensation
SVP and CFO, Sean Burke
Vice President Payroll Manager, Mary Ward
Senior Vice President, William Cosgrove
Senior Vice President Information Technology, Sergio Alonso
Senior Vice President, Jawad Chaudhry
Vice President Business Development Officer, Terry Delorenzo
Vice President Information Security Officer Director of Information Security, David Van
Vice President Systems, Charles Little
Vice President and Electronic Banking Manager, ROBERT MAWSON
Chairman, Robert M. Cashill, age 74
Auditors: KPMG LLP

LOCATIONS

HQ: Investors Bancorp Inc (New)
101 JFK Parkway, Short Hills, NJ 07078
Phone: 973 924-5100
Web: www.myinvestorsbank.com

PRODUCTS/OPERATIONS

2014 Sales

	$ mil.	% of total
Interest		
Loans receivable and held-for-sale	603	86
Mortgage-backed securities	44	6
Federal Home Loan Bank stock	6	1
Municipal bonds & other debt	5	1
Other	0	-
Non-interest		
Fees & service charges	19	3
Gain on loan transaction	5	2
Others	17	1
Total	702	100

COMPETITORS

Bank of America
Bank of New York Mellon
M&T Bank
New York Community Bancorp

Citigroup
ConnectOne Bancorp
Fulton Financial
OceanFirst Financial
PNC Financial

HISTORICAL FINANCIALS

Company Type: Public

Income Statement

FYE: December 31

	ASSETS ($ mil.)	NET INCOME ($ mil.)	INCOME AS % OF ASSETS	EMPLOYEES
12/16	23,174	192	0.8%	1,829
12/15	20,888	181	0.9%	1,768
12/14	18,773	131	0.7%	1,708
12/13	15,623	112	0.7%	1,597
12/12	12,722	88	0.7%	1,219
Annual Growth	16.2%	21.3%		10.7%

2016 Year-End Financials

Debt ratio: 19.62%
Return on equity: 5.96%
Cash ($ mil.): 164
Current ratio: —
Long-term debt ($ mil.): —
No. of shares (mil.): 309
Dividends
  Yield: 0.0%
  Payout: 40.6%
Market value ($ mil.): 4,317

	STOCK PRICE ($) FY Close	P/E High/Low	PER SHARE ($) Earnings	Dividends	Book Value
12/16	13.95	22 16	0.64	0.26	10.09
12/15	12.44	24 19	0.55	0.25	9.89
12/14	11.23	74 26	0.38	0.08	9.99
12/13	25.58	64 44	0.40	0.00	3.78
12/12	17.78	58 42	0.32	0.00	3.74
Annual Growth	(5.9%)	— —	18.8%	—	28.2%

IOWA FINANCE AUTHORITY

Auditors: KPMG LLP DES MOINES IA

LOCATIONS

HQ: IOWA FINANCE AUTHORITY
2015 GRAND AVE STE 200, DES MOINES, IA 503124903
Phone: 515 725-4900
Web: WWW.IOWAFINANCEAUTHORITY.GOV

HISTORICAL FINANCIALS

Company Type: Private

Income Statement

FYE: June 30

	ASSETS ($ mil.)	NET INCOME ($ mil.)	INCOME AS % OF ASSETS	EMPLOYEES
06/10	2,914	63	2.2%	89
06/09	2,519	85	3.4%	—
Annual Growth	15.7%	(26.0%)	—	—

2010 Year-End Financials

Debt ratio: —
Return on equity: 23.10%
Cash ($ mil.): 789
Current ratio: 1.60
Long-term debt ($ mil.): —
Dividends
  Yield: —
  Payout: —
Market value ($ mil.): —

IOWA STUDENT LOAN LIQUIDITY CORPORATION

Auditors: KPMG LLP DES MOINES IOWA

LOCATIONS

HQ: IOWA STUDENT LOAN LIQUIDITY CORPORATION
6775 VISTA DR, WEST DES MOINES, IA 502669305
Phone: 515 243-5626
Web: WWW.STUDENTLOAN.ORG

HISTORICAL FINANCIALS

Company Type: Private

Income Statement

FYE: June 30

	ASSETS ($ mil.)	NET INCOME ($ mil.)	INCOME AS % OF ASSETS	EMPLOYEES
06/16	1,659	7	0.5%	214
06/10	3,748	(28)	—	—
06/09	4,046	17	0.4%	—
Annual Growth	(12.0%)	(10.9%)		

2016 Year-End Financials

Debt ratio: —
Return on equity: 8.40%
Cash ($ mil.): 8
Current ratio: 0.10
Long-term debt ($ mil.): —
Dividends
  Yield: —
  Payout: —
Market value ($ mil.): —

IQVIA Holdings Inc

Quintiles IMS Holdings (formerly Quintiles Transnational) has plenty to CRO about. One of the world's largest contract research organizations (CROs) it helps pharmaceutical biotechnology and medical device companies develop and sell their products. The firm provides a comprehensive range of clinical trials management services including patient recruitment data analysis laboratory testing and regulatory filing assistance. Its consulting unit offers strategic advice at every stage of drug discovery and development and its capital and commercial divisions assist with project funding and sales and marketing efforts. Quintiles merged with IMS Health in October 2016 to create a $23 billion life science company.

Operations

Quintiles IMS provides consulting on product development and commercialization services for drugs that are ready to go to market. Services include conducting late-phase clinical trials on drugs after they've been released (post-marketing research) and setting up the information technology a drug maker needs to support a marketed drug. Additionally the company provides financing and partnering support which invests in client companies (either through cash or services) in return for royalties on sales of approved products.

The company operates through three primary segments: Research & Development Solutions Commercial Solutions and Integrated Engagement Services.

Research & Development the largest segment (some two-thirds of total revenue) comprises Quintiles' legacy product development operations. Commercial Solutions which brings in about 20% of total sales is the combination of IMS Health's legacy business plus Quintiles' real-world late phase payer/provider and advisory businesses. Integrated Engagement Services (about 15% of revenue) is composed of Quintile's former integrated health care services (real-world research market access and consulting and analytics and technology consulting) segment.

Geographic Reach

Quintiles IMS is co-headquartered in Durham North Carolina and Danbury Connecticut. It has some 275 offices in more than 80 countries in the Americas Europe Africa and the Asia/Pacific region. In recent years the company has been focusing on international expansion especially in Asia. It has a presence in all major biopharmaceutical markets including the US Japan and Europe as well as Russia India and China. In 2015 it opened a regional headquarters in China to better serve customers in the area.

The Americas account for about a third of all revenues.

Sales and Marketing

Quintiles IMS serves large multinational and regional/domestic biopharmaceutical firms in the US Europe Asia Japan Canada and Latin America.It markets its offerings through a number of channels including retail hospital and mail order.

Financial Performance

Quintiles' (and now Quintiles IMS') revenues have been on the rise for the past five years. The company's revenue rose 20% to $6.9 billion in 2016 largely due to growth in the Commercial Solutions segment. This was offset by a decline in Quintiles' legacy integrated health care service offerings. Sales increased in all geographic regions (Americas Europe and Africa and the Asia/Pacific region).

However expenses from the merger between Quintiles and IMS Health cut into profits which had been on the rise. Net income fell 70% to $115 million in 2016 as operating expenses (including merger-related costs) and cost of revenue increased.

On the other hand cash flow from operations continued its upward trend in 2016 rising 81% to $860 million that year. This increase was largely due to a positive adjustment in depreciation and amortization as a result of the IMS Health merger as well as an adjustment in provisions for deferred income taxes (related to reinvested foreign earnings) and changes in accounts receivable.

Strategy

The newly established Quintiles IMS is poised to benefit from its expertise in clinical trials and its information and technology capabilities. It plans to tap into these assets to continue innovating and offering its clients new ways to bring their drugs to market quickly and efficiently. The company also plans to take advantage of acquisition opportunities to further build out its platform. It is working to leverage that growth to expand into a broader swath of the health care market with a focus on connected health care.

To its benefit demand for outsourced clinical development services has been growing: Belt-tightening pharma and biotech companies look to trim costs even as they are desperate to find and develop new products. Key to its success Quintiles IMS has focused efforts on developing services that help its clients reduce risk and time-to-market. For instance its Cenduit subsidiary a joint venture with Thermo Fisher Scientific helps control clinical trials costs by automating delivery of supplies among other things. In 2015 Quintiles partnered with Quest Diagnostics to launch Q2 Solutions a

clinical trials lab services provider. It also began working with IMS Health to provide next-generation real-world results in late-stage clinical research. And in 2017 the company began offering a social media technology service which monitors hundreds of thousands of outlets to identify and validate any adverse events on its clients' products.

Additionally the company continues to invest in quality data and electronic health records. It has acquired data analytics products and services as well as personnel and created a proprietary data integration tool to manage data from multiple sources.Altogether the group owns more than 20 petabytes (one petabyte is equal to a million gigabytes) of unique data.

The company is also trimming itself of non-core operations after the merger. It has closed certain facilities cut some staff and is exploring opportunities to divest other assets. One area it may exit is its contract sales business as pharmaceuticals companies increasingly use their own sales teams.

Mergers and Acquisitions

In October 2016 Quintiles joined forces with health care data firm IMS Health Holdings in what it described as a merger of equals. (Upon closure of the deal IMS Health shareholders owned 51.4% of the merged company while Quintiles shareholders owned 48.6%.) The combined firm Quintiles IMS Holdings benefits from increased efficiencies and cost savings. For example IMS data is being utilized to improve Quintiles' clinical trial processes.

HISTORY

Quintiles was founded by Dennis Gillings a British biostatistician who had worked with Hoechst (later part of Sanofi) on data analysis in the 1970s. Gillings set up Quintiles (Quantitative Information Technology In The Life and Economic Sciences) in 1982 at the University of North Carolina where he was then teaching. The company grew as drug companies began outsourcing some of the more irksome tasks of drug development. Quintiles went public in 1994.

The company used the proceeds of the IPO to expand its health economics segment with the purchases of Benefit International (1995) and Lewin Group (1996). These purchases introduced it to such new clients as governments and HMOs. Quintiles' 1996 purchase of Innovex (unrelated to the computer hardware maker of the same name) made it the world's largest CRO. The buying spree continued in 1997 and 1998. Among the purchases were some intended to strengthen Quintiles' marketing services (Data Analysis Systems Inc. Q.E.D. International and France-based Serval). The firm also formed new collaborations with such academic research organizations as Johns Hopkins Medicine.

In 1999 Quintiles expanded its marketing arm with the purchase of Pharmaceutical Marketing Services (parent of the leading pharmaceuticals industry research company Scott-Levin) and jumped headlong into data mining with its purchase of ENVOY — which processed insurance claims. Quintiles found the core business uninspiring and sold it to Healtheon (now Emdeon formerly WebMD) the next year. But it kept rights to ENVOY's stream of treatment outcome and insurance data gleaned from health care providers hospitals payers and pharmacies — a treasure house of information useful to salespeople and health providers.

The company continued in 2000 to add offices in Europe Asia and Latin America. It also opened additional offices in the US and Europe to help Japanese pharmaceutical companies market their products in those regions. Late in the year Quin-

tiles bought the clinical development unit of Pharmacia.

In 2001 Quintiles became embroiled in a legal dispute with WebMD involving the availability of data associated with ENVOY; the company challenged WebMD's efforts to withhold such data. The two companies settled the squabble later that year and agreed to sever all ties. Also in 2001 Quintiles streamlined operations and cut about 5% of its workforce.

The future structure of the CRO came into question at the end of 2002. Gillings presented the company with a buyout offer; he planned to take the company private so he could pursue a new growth strategy Wall Street would surely find risky. The board rejected that offer in October 2002 but it opened up an auction. Some leading equity firms reportedly made offers but Gillings — with backing from Blackstone Group and BANK ONE's One Equity Partners (later part of JPMorgan Chase) — placed another offer for Quintiles and won the prize in April 2003. Some five months later Quintiles went private.

EXECUTIVES

Chairman and CEO, Ari Bousbib, age 55, $390,137 total compensation

CFO, Michael R. (Mike) McDonnell, age 53, $650,000 total compensation

SVP and Executive Director QuintilesIMS Institute, Murray L. Aitken

President Novella Clinical, W. Richard Staub, age 54, $485,923 total compensation

President Clinical Operations Research and Development Solutions, Cynthia L. Verst

EVP and Chief Customer Officer, Paul Spreen

President Information and Technology Solutions, Kevin C. Knightly, age 55, $119,399 total compensation

President Asia/Pacific, Anand Tharmaratnam

President Central East and South Europe, Elisabeth Beck

President Latin America, Nilton Paletta

EVP and General Counsel, James H. (Jim) Erlinger, age 58, $468,333 total compensation

President Real-World Insights (RWI), Jon Resnick

President Integrated Engagement Services, W. Scott Evangelista

SVP and CIO, Karl Guenault

President United States and Canada, Hossam Sadek

President Data Sciences Safety and Regulatory Research and Development Solutions, Margaret Keegan

CEO QÂ₂ Solutions, Costa Panagos

VP Administration and Chief of Staff to the CEO IMS Health, Trudy Stein

SVP Strategy Marketing and Communications, Marla Kessler

President Global Services, Jos © Luis Fern ¯ndez

Vice President And Global Head Of Risk Management, Stella Blackburn

Auditors: PricewaterhouseCoopers LLP

LOCATIONS

HQ: IQVIA Holdings Inc
4820 Emperor Blvd., Durham, NC 27703
Phone: 919 998-2000
Web: www.quintiles.com

PRODUCTS/OPERATIONS

2016 Sales

	% of total
Research & Development Solutions	65
Commercial Solutions	20
Integrated Engagement Services	15
Total	**100**

2016 Sales

	$ mil.	% of total
Americas:		
United States	2,145	31
Other	233	3
Europe and Africa:		
United Kingdom	461	7
Other	1,594	23
Asia-Pacific:		
Japan	587	9
Other	344	5
Reimbursed expenses	1,514	22
Total	**6,878**	**100**

Selected Products and Services

Capital services
  Funding assistance
  Managed partnerships
Clinical Services
  Biostatistics
  Central laboratory services
  Lifecycle safety monitoring
  Medical writing
  Pharmacokinetic studies
  Patient recruitment
  Phase I-III clinical trial design
Commercial Services
  Post-approval programs
  Regulatory services
  Safety monitoring

Selected Therapeutic Specialties

Cardiovascular
Central nervous system
Endocrinology
Infectious diseases
Internal medicine
Oncology
Pediatrics
Public health government services
Women's health

COMPETITORS

Albany Molecular Research	PRA Health Sciences
Charles River Laboratories	PharmaNet Development Group
Covance	Pharmaceutical Product Development
GlaxoSmithKline R & D	Premier Research Group
ICON	Quest Diagnostics
INC Research	UDG Healthcare
Nordion	WuXi PharmaTech
PAREXEL	inVentiv Health
PDI Inc.	

HISTORICAL FINANCIALS

Company Type: Public

Income Statement
FYE: December 31

	REVENUE ($ mil.)	NET INCOME ($ mil.)	NET PROFIT MARGIN	EMPLOYEES
12/16	6,878	115	1.7%	50,000
12/15	5,737	387	6.7%	36,100
12/14	5,460	356	6.5%	32,600
12/13	5,099	226	4.4%	28,200
12/12	4,865	177	3.6%	—
Annual Growth	**9.0%**	**(10.3%)**	**—**	**—**

2016 Year-End Financials

Debt ratio: 33.95%
Return on equity: 2.84%
Cash ($ mil.): 1,198
Current ratio: 1.23
Long-term debt ($ mil.): 7,108
No. of shares (mil.): 235
Dividends
  Yield: —
  Payout: —
Market value ($ mil.): 17,902

	STOCK PRICE ($) FY Close	P/E High/Low	PER SHARE ($) Earnings	Dividends	Book Value
12/16	76.05	105 73	0.76	0.00	36.67
12/15	68.66	25 18	3.08	0.00	(4.73)
12/14	58.87	22 16	2.72	0.00	(5.67)
12/13	46.34	25 23	1.77	0.00	(5.15)
Annual Growth	**13.2%**	**— —**	**(19.1%)**	**—**	**—**

IRC RETAIL CENTERS LLC

IRC Retail Centers (formerly Inland Real Estate Corporation) buys leases and operates retail properties mainly in the Midwest with a concentration in the Chicago and Minneapolis/St. Paul metropolitan markets. The self-managed real estate investment trust (REIT) owns about 150 properties most of which are strip shopping centers anchored by a grocery or big-box store. It also invests in single-tenant retail properties and develops properties usually through joint ventures. The REIT's portfolio totals about 14 million sq. ft. of leasable space in a dozen states. IRC Retail Centers was acquired by DRA Advisors in early 2015.

Operations

As a REIT IRC Retail Centers is exempt from paying federal income tax so long as it distributes quarterly dividends to shareholders. Most tenants of its investment properties are responsible for paying real estate taxes as insurance as well as maintaining the properties.

Financial Performance

Overall revenues fell 4% in 2012 to $160 million. That year the company had decreased income across the board from rent property fees and joint venture fees despite buying 20 new properties and divesting eight. However it posted profits of almost $18 million in 2012 thanks to one-time earnings on continuing operations and a gain on equity in joint ventures.

Strategy

In 2013 the company announced plans for a new joint venture with an affiliate of Australia-based MAB Corporation. The project calls for developing about 20 grocery-anchored shopping centers that would include a 50000-sq.-ft. supermarket with another 20000 sq. ft. of retail space. The JV will extend IRC Retail's reach to the eastern US namely Florida Georgia North and South Carolina Virginia and Washington DC.

Another joint venture with Dutch pension fund administrator PGGM (established 2010) calls for acquiring grocery-anchored and community retail centers in the Midwest. In 2013 the JV bought three Wal-Mart shopping centers in the Milwaukee area for $24.2 million a 139000-sq.-ft. Whole Foods/CVS shopping center in Cleveland for $25 million and is building a 92000-sq.-ft. shopping center in Evergreen Park Illinois.

EXECUTIVES

Senior Vice President, William Anderson
Assistant Vice President, Pam Reifke
Vice President Finance, Angela C Blaising
Assistant Vice President Senior Leasing Represen, Allison Kuchny
Assistant Vice President, Sharon Unger
Vice President Controller, Donna Urbain

Vice Chairman, Joe Cosenza
Auditors: KPMG LLP CHICAGO ILLINOIS

LOCATIONS

HQ: IRC RETAIL CENTERS LLC
  814 COMMERCE DR STE 300, OAK BROOK, IL
  605238823
Phone: 877 206-5656
Web: WWW.INLANDREALESTATE.COM

2015 Properties (excluding joint ventures)

	No.
Illinois	62
Minnesota	16
Wisconsin	7
Indiana	5
Ohio	2
Alabama	1
Florida	1
Nebraska	1
North Carolina	1
Total	**96**

PRODUCTS/OPERATIONS

2015 Sales

	$ mil.	% of total
Rents	135	66
Tenant recoveries	57	28
Other property income	5	3
Fee income from unconsolidated joint ventures	5	3
Total	**203**	**100**

COMPETITORS

Brixmor	Noddle Development
CBL & Associates Properties	Pennsylvania Real Estate
Canal Capital	Ramco-Gershenson
DDR	Realty Income
Federal Realty Investment	Retail Properties of America
Horizon Group Properties	Rubloff Development
Kimco Realty	Schottenstein
Macerich	Taubman Centers
	Weingarten Realty

HISTORICAL FINANCIALS

Company Type: Private

Income Statement
FYE: December 31

	ASSETS ($ mil.)	NET INCOME ($ mil.)	INCOME AS % OF ASSETS	EMPLOYEES
12/15	1,521	25	1.7%	129
12/14	1,572	39	2.5%	—
12/13	1,529	111	7.3%	—
12/12	1,243	17	1.4%	—
Annual Growth	**7.0%**	**13.0%**	**—**	**—**

2015 Year-End Financials

Debt ratio: ——
Return on equity: 12.50%
Cash ($ mil.): 9
Current ratio: —
Long-term debt ($ mil.): —
Dividends
  Yield: —
  Payout: —
Market value ($ mil.): —

Isabella Bank Corp

EXECUTIVES

President - Breckenridge Division Of Isabella Bank, Timothy Miller
Auditors: Rehmann Robson LLC

HQ: Isabella Bank Corp
401 N. Main St., Mt. Pleasant, MI 48858
Phone: 989 772-9471
Web: www.isabellabank.com

HISTORICAL FINANCIALS

Company Type: Public

Income Statement

FYE: December 30

	ASSETS ($ mil.)	NET INCOME ($ mil.)	INCOME AS % OF ASSETS	EMPLOYEES
12/16	1,732	13	0.8%	372
12/15	1,668	15	0.9%	374
12/14	1,549	13	0.9%	361
12/13	1,493	12	0.8%	360
12/12	1,430	12	0.9%	356
Annual Growth	4.9%	3.1%	—	1.1%

2016 Year-End Financials

Debt ratio: —
Return on equity: 7.42%
Cash ($ mil.): 22
Current ratio: —
Long-term debt ($ mil.): —

No. of shares (mil.): 7
Dividends
Yield: 3.5%
Payout: 53.8%
Market value ($ mil.): 218

	STOCK PRICE ($) FY Close	P/E High/Low	PER SHARE ($) Earnings	Dividends	Book Value
12/16	27.85	17 15	1.73	0.98	24.02
12/15	29.90	14 11	1.90	0.94	23.59
12/14	22.50	14 12	1.74	0.89	22.45
12/13	23.85	16 13	1.59	0.84	20.80
12/12	21.75	16 14	1.56	0.80	21.44
Annual Growth	6.4%	— —	2.6%	5.2%	2.9%

Jabil Inc

Jabil Circuit makes a jabillion different kinds of electronics. The company is one of the leading providers of outsourced electronics manufacturing services (EMS) in the world. It makes electronics components and parts on a contract basis for computers smartphones printers and other consumer electronics as well as more complex specialized products for the aerospace automotive and healthcare industries. The company's services range from product design and component procurement to product testing order fulfillment and supply chain management. Jabil Circuit operates more than 100 plants in about 30 countries.

Operations

Jabil Circuit conducts business in two segments: Electronics Manufacturing Services (EMS) and Diversified Manufacturing Services (DMS).

The EMS segment (about 60% of revenue) focuses on IT supply chain design and engineering for all things electronic. Customers' products are used in applications for automotive digital home industrial and energy networking and telecommunications point of sale printing and storage.

The DMS segment (about 40% of revenue) focuses on manufacturing services for material sciences and technologies. It works with customers to develop and manufacture products for consumer lifestyles and wearable technologies defense and aerospace emerging growth healthcare mobility and packaging.

Geographic Reach

Jabil Circuit's plants are in Argentina Brazil China Finland Hungary India Japan Malaysia Mex-

ico Poland Russia Singapore South Africa South Korea Spain Taiwan Ukraine and Vietnam as well as in Austria Belgium Canada France Germany Ireland Israel Italy Scotland the Netherlands and the US.

Singapore and China are its largest markets accounting for about 30% and about 20% of sales respectively. Customers in Mexico and the US generate about 20% and less than 10% of revenue respectively.

Sales and Marketing

Jabil Circuit depends on a small number of customers for a significant percentage of revenue - five customers account for just less than 50% of sales. Its top customer is Apple (25% of sales) and other significant customers are Cisco Systems Dell Technologies HP Inc. LM Ericsson General Electric Ingenico NetApp Valeo and Zebra Technologies.

Financial Performance

Jabil Circuit posted a 4% revenue increase to about $19 billion in 2017 (ended August) from 2016. It was the third straight year of higher sales. A 9% revenue increase in the DMS segment drove the overall rise due to stronger sales in consumer lifestyles and wearable technologies healthcare and mobility. Most of the increases came from new business for existing customers. The EMS segment?s revenue was flat year-to-year.

Jabil took about $160 million in restructuring charges in 2017 which cut its net income from 2016 in about half to about $129 million.

Cash flow from operations rose to $1.2 billion in 2017 from about $916 million in 2016. The company reported an increase in non-cash expenses accounts payable and accrued expenses and other liabilities. Those were somewhat countered by an increase in inventories and accounts receivable.

Strategy

To compete in a rapidly consolidating industry Jabil provides production on a global scale and operates through semi-autonomous business units that are dedicated to individual customers. The company continues to add services and to expand globally through acquisitions including deals to acquire manufacturing operations from customers looking to reduce costs through outsourcing. The company tends to place manufacturing plants close to its customers.

Jabil had expanded its work in the health care device market and it has been a strong performer for the company. Operating income from production for health-related products which include drug-delivery systems has grown about 20% a year.

Apple has been a long and profitable customer for Jabil and the company counts on that to continue in 2018. Jabil has been a key supplier for Apple?s iPhone and that includes the iPhone 8 and X released in late 2017.

Jabil implemented a restructuring program in 2017 (ended August) to realign costs and consolidate manufacturing in lower cost areas. The program included job cuts and cost the company about $160 million in 2017. It plans to save up to $90 million a year with the moves.

Mergers and Acquisitions

Acquisitions have extended Jabil's product portfolio and its geographic reach.

In January 2016 Jabil acquired Inala a South African energy products provider and systems integrator. The deal acquisition expanded Jabil's presence in the market for remote location energy products and marked its first venture in Africa.

In June 2015 Jabil acquired Clothing+ which makes the sensor fabric in the Victoria's Secret smart bra. It has been integrating electronics into textiles for almost two decades.

In August 2015 Jabil acquired Kasalis which makes sophisticated systems used in the assembly high-precision optical equipment.

In 2015 Jabil's healthcare and packaging division Nypro acquired Plasticos Castella a molder of plastic lids for condiments. Nypro's acquisition of Plasticos Castella expands smart packaging capabilities by combining design engineering and manufacturing facilities in Spain and Hungary with the services of Nypro's six North American plants.

EXECUTIVES

CEO and Director, Mark T. Mondello, age 53, $1,100,000 total compensation
EVP and COO, William D. (Bill) Muir, age 49, $700,000 total compensation
EVP Corporate Development and Chief of Staff, Courtney J. Ryan, age 47
CFO, Forbes I. J. Alexander, age 57, $700,000 total compensation
VP Business Development, Steven D. (Steve) Borges, age 48
EVP General Counsel and Corporate Secretary, Robert L. (Bobby) Katz, age 55
EVP and CEO Green Point, Hwai Hai (HH) Chiang, $445,000 total compensation
SVP and Chief Supply Chain Officer Manufacturing Services, Erich Hoch, age 47
EVP and CEO Engineered Solutions Group, Michael J. Loparco, age 46
EVP and CEO Enterprise and Infrastructure, Alessandro Parimbelli, age 49, $444,392 total compensation
President, William E. (Bill) Peters, age 54, $700,000 total compensation
SVP and CIO, Gary L. Cantrell
Evp Human Resources And Human Development, Scott D Slipy, age 50
Executive Vice President National Operations, Mark Butler
Vice President Of Finance After Market Services Division, Brian Greff
Vice President Real Estate and Construction, Jacky Lau
Vice President After Market Services, Hartmut Liebel
Assistant Vice President Sales National Accounts, Dennis Maddock
Chairman, Timothy L. (Tim) Main, age 60
Vice Chairman, Thomas A. Sansone, age 68
Auditors: Ernst & Young LLP

LOCATIONS

HQ: Jabil Inc
10560 Dr. Martin Luther King, Jr. Street North, St. Petersburg, FL 33716
Phone: 727 577-9749
Web: www.jabil.com

2017 Sales

	$ mil.	% of total
Singapore	5	29
China	4,012	21
Mexico	3,207	17
U.S.	1,645	9
Hungary	1,119	6
Malaysia	944	5
Other	2,547	13
Total	19,063	100

PRODUCTS/OPERATIONS

2017 Sales

	$ mil.	% of total
Electronics Manufacturing Services	11,077	58
Diversified Manufacturing Services	7,985	42
Total	19,063	100

Services
Component selection sourcing and procurement

Design and prototyping
Engineering
Order fulfillment
Printed circuit board and backplane assembly
Product testing
Repair and warranty
Systems assembly
Test development
Tooling design (molds and dies)

COMPETITORS

ASUSTeK	Key Tronic
BenQ	Plexus
Benchmark Electronics	SMTC Corp.
Celestica	Sanmina
Compal Electronics	Sparton
Flextronics	Venture Corp.
Hon Hai	Wistron
Inventec	

HISTORICAL FINANCIALS

Company Type: Public

Income Statement

FYE: August 31

	REVENUE ($ mil.)	NET INCOME ($ mil.)	NET PROFIT MARGIN	EMPLOYEES
08/17	19,063	129	0.7%	170,000
08/16	18,353	254	1.4%	138,000
08/15	17,899	284	1.6%	161,000
08/14	15,762	241	1.5%	142,000
08/13	18,336	371	2.0%	177,000
Annual Growth	1.0%	(23.2%)	—	(1.0%)

2017 Year-End Financials

Debt ratio: 18.73%	No. of shares (mil.): 177
Return on equity: 5.39%	Dividends
Cash ($ mil.): 1,189	Yield: 1.0%
Current ratio: 0.96	Payout: 46.3%
Long-term debt ($ mil.): 1,632	Market value ($ mil.): 5,572

	STOCK PRICE ($) FY Close	P/E High/Low		PER SHARE ($) Earnings	Dividends	Book Value
08/17	31.35	44	29	0.69	0.32	13.24
08/16	21.19	19	13	1.32	0.32	13.04
08/15	19.35	17	12	1.45	0.32	12.05
08/14	21.58	20	13	1.19	0.32	11.55
08/13	22.82	13	9	1.79	0.32	11.49
Annual Growth	8.3%	—	—	(21.2%)	(0.0%)	3.6%

Jacobs Engineering Group, Inc.

Jacobs Engineering provides technical professional and construction services for industrial government and commercial clients throughout the world. Jacobs handles project design and engineering construction operations maintenance and scientific consultation. Typical projects include oil refineries manufacturing plants infrastructure & telecommunications and aerospace facilities. More than half of revenue comes from the US while the rest originates in numerous other countries. Founded in 1947 Jacobs Engineering has more than 200 global offices.

HISTORY

Joseph Jacobs graduated from the Polytechnic Institute of Brooklyn in 1942 with a doctorate in engineering. He went to work for Merck designing processes for pharmaceutical production. Later he moved to Chemurgic Corp. near San Francisco where he worked until 1947 when he founded Jacobs Engineering as a consulting firm. Jacobs also sold industrial equipment avoiding any apparent conflict of interest by simply telling his consulting clients.

When equipment sales outstripped consulting work by 1954 Jacobs hired four salesmen and engineer Stan Krugman who became his right-hand man. Two years later the company got its first big chemical design job for Kaiser Aluminum. Jacobs incorporated his sole proprietorship in 1957.

In 1960 the firm won its first construction contract to design and build a potash flotation plant and Jacobs Engineering became an integrated design and construction firm. In 1967 it opened its first regional office but kept management decentralized to replicate the small size and hard-hitting qualities of its home office. Three years later Jacobs Engineering went public.

The firm merged with Houston-based Pace Companies which specialized in petrochemical engineering design in 1974. Also that year the firm became Jacobs Engineering Group and began building its first major overseas chemical plant in Ireland.

By 1977 sales had reached $250 million. A decade of lobbying paid off that year when the firm won a contract for the Arab Potash complex in Jordan. Jacobs began to withdraw from his firm's operations in the early 1980s but the 1982-83 recession and poor management decisions pounded earnings. Jacobs returned from retirement in 1985 fired 14 VPs cut staff in half and pushed the firm to pursue smaller process-plant jobs and specialty construction.

After abandoning a 1986 attempt to take the company private Jacobs began making acquisitions to improve the firm's construction expertise. In 1992 he relinquished his role as CEO to president Noel Watson. The next year the company expanded its international holdings by acquiring the UK's H&G Process Contracting and H&G Contractors.

The firm's $38 million purchase of CRS Sirrine Engineers and CRSS Constructors in 1994 was the company's largest buy at that point and added new markets in the paper and semiconductor industries. By 1995 Jacobs Engineering was working on a record backlog.

Continuing its acquisition drive the company bought a 49% interest in European engineering specialist Serete Group in 1996; it bought the rest the next year. Also in 1997 it gained control of Indian engineering affiliate Humphreys & Glasgow (now Jacobs H&G) increasing its 40% stake to 70% and bought CPR Engineering a pulp and paper processing specialist. It also formed a joint venture with Krupp UHDE to provide design engineering and construction management services in Mexico.

In 1999 the company paid $198 million for St. Louis construction and design firm Sverdrup which had completed projects in some 65 countries. The next year Jacobs Engineering purchased half of Dutch firm Stork Engineering's business (it acquired the rest in 2001). But the company's bid to buy the assets of bankrupt power plant construction company Stone & Webster in 2000 was topped by Shaw Group.

After being accused of overcharging the US government Jacobs Engineering settled a whistleblower lawsuit (for $35 million) in 2000 while continuing to deny the allegations. However the next year Jacobs continued to receive federal contracts including contracts for boosting security at the US Capitol complex and providing logistics to the US Special Operations Command. Jacobs completed its acquisition of the UK-based GIBB unit of engineering consulting firm LawGibb Group in 2001 as well as the purchase of McDermott Engineers and Constructors (Canada).

EXECUTIVES

Group Vice President, Walter Barber
SVP Information Technology, Cora L. Carmody, age 60
Chairman President and CEO, Steven J. Demetriou, age 58, $125,000 total compensation
EVP and CFO, Kevin C. Berryman, age 58, $544,832 total compensation
President Industrial, Robert V. (Bob) Pragada, age 49
President Petroleum and Chemicals, Joseph G. Mandel, age 57, $699,996 total compensation
EVP Operations, Phillip J. Stassi, age 62, $639,423 total compensation
President Aerospace and Technology, Terence D. Hagen, age 52
Gvp Consulting Operations, Robert McWhinney
Vice President Information Technology, Pete Young
Division Vice President Director Construction Services, Joseph Franco
Vice President, Albert Pozotrigo
Gvp Federal Operations, James Thiesing
Vice President Global Cyber Security, George Hull
Auditors: Ernst & Young, LLP

LOCATIONS

HQ: Jacobs Engineering Group, Inc.
1999 Bryan Street, Suite 1200, Dallas, TX 75201
Phone: 214 583-8500
Web: www.jacobs.com

2016 Sales

	$ mil.	% of total
United States	5,823	58
Europe	2,262	23
Canada	590	6
Australia and New Zealand	629	6
Middle East and Africa	226	2
Asia	253	3
India	165	2
South America and Mexico	74	1
Total	**10,022**	**100**

PRODUCTS/OPERATIONS

Selected Services
Architecture & interiors
Construction
Engineering
Environmental
Information technology
Operations & maintenance
Planning
Procurement
Program & construction management
Scientific research & testing

FY2017 Sales by Line of Business

	$ mil.	% of total
Aerospace & Technology	2,360	24
Buildings & Infrastructure	2,452	24
Industrial	2,744	27
Petroleum & Chemicals	2,466	25
Total	**10,022**	**100**

Selected Product
Chemetics
Comprimo sulfur solutions
Modular construction
Test SLATE Test Automation Software

COMPETITORS

AECOM	HOK
Aker Solutions	KBR
Amec Foster Wheeler	Leidos
BWX Technologies	Lockheed Martin

Bechtel
Fluor
HDR
HNTB Companies

Tetra Tech
Turner Construction
WS Atkins
WorleyParsons Corp.

HISTORICAL FINANCIALS

Company Type: Public

Income Statement

FYE: September 29

	REVENUE ($ mil.)	NET INCOME ($ mil.)	NET PROFIT MARGIN	EMPLOYEES
09/17	10,022	293	2.9%	54,700
09/16*	10,964	210	1.9%	54,900
10/15	12,114	302	2.5%	64,000
09/14	12,695	328	2.6%	66,300
09/13	11,818	423	3.6%	66,500
Annual Growth	(4.0%)	(8.7%)	—	(4.8%)

*Fiscal year change

2017 Year-End Financials

Debt ratio: 3.23%
Return on equity: 6.78%
Cash ($ mil.): 774
Current ratio: 1.56
Long-term debt ($ mil.): 235

No. of shares (mil.): 120
Dividends
Yield: 0.7%
Payout: 23.8%
Market value ($ mil.): 7,015

	STOCK PRICE ($) FY Close	P/E High/Low	PER SHARE ($) Earnings	Dividends	Book Value
09/17	58.27	26 20	2.42	0.45	36.78
09/16*	51.72	32 20	1.73	0.00	35.26
10/15	37.40	20 15	2.40	0.00	34.85
09/14	49.68	27 20	2.48	0.00	33.92
09/13	57.79	19 12	3.23	0.00	32.00
Annual Growth	0.2%	— —	(7.0%)	—	3.5%

*Fiscal year change

JetBlue Airways Corp

Airline JetBlue Airways offers one-class service — with leather seats satellite TV from DIRECTV satellite radio from XM and movies — to more than 38 million passengers a year and taking them to more than 100 cities. It has 1000 daily flights in nearly 30 US states Puerto Rico and 21 countries in the Caribbean and Latin America. Most of its flights arrive or depart from Boston; Los Angeles; New York; Orlando and Fort Lauderdale Florida; and San Juan Puerto Rico. JetBlue's fleet of about 230 aircraft consists mainly of Airbus A320s and A321s but also includes Embraer 190s.

Operations

The New York-based carrier is the largest domestic airline at New York's JFK International Airport — the US's biggest travel market. Operating primarily out of Terminal 5 or T5 JetBlue also serves New Jersey's Newark Liberty International Airport New York's LaGuardia Airport Newburgh New York's Stewart International Airport and White Plains New York's Westchester County Airport.

The company operates a fleet consisting of 37 Airbus A321 aircraft 130 Airbus A320 aircraft and 60 Embraer 190 aircraft. Its in-flight entertainment system include 36 channels of free DIRECTV 100 channels of free SiriusXM satellite radio and premium movie channel offerings from JetBlue Features a source of first run films.

Geographic Reach

JetBlue flies to more than 100 cities with 1000 daily flights to 100 cities in 21 countries through-out the Americas with one-third of its route network in the Caribbean and Latin America. It concentrates primarily on the cities of Boston; New York; Long Beach California; Fort Lauderdale and Orlando Florida; and San Juan Puerto Rico.

The US represents nearly 70% of total sales while Latin America and the Caribbean account for the remainder.

Sales and Marketing

JetBlue markets its services through advertising and promotions in various media forms including social media outlets. It also engages in large multi-market programs local events and sponsorships across route network as well as mobile marketing programs. The company sells its services across several major global distribution systems and on-line travel agents. It also sells vacation packages through JetBlue Vacations a one-stop value-priced vacation service for self-directed packaged travel planning.

Financial Performance

JetBlue has experienced unprecedented revenue growth over the years. In 2016 its revenues jumped 4% to peak at a record-setting $6.6 billion. Its profits also surged by 12% to reach $759 million another company milestone primarily due to a major decrease in fuel prices and the higher passenger revenue.

The historic growth for 2016 was due to higher passenger revenues mainly attributable to increased capacity and yield. Ancillary revenue continues to be a source of significant revenue growth primarily driven by customer demand for JetBlue's Even More Space products as well as changes to its fee structure.

Strategy

Traditionally focused on the leisure traveler JetBlue has been developing more service for the business customer to offset the seasonal limitations of the vacation market. Also to develop more business beyond vacation travelers JetBlue has been growing its operations in Latin America and the Caribbean (LACA) which has a strong presence of visiting-friends-and-relatives (VFR) travelers in addition to vacationers. LACA now accounts for about 30% of JetBlue's revenues.

During 2016 JetBlue launched its first commercial US flight to Cuba in 50 years with its inaugural flight from Fort Lauderdale-Hollywood to Santa Clara. It also launched services to Camag ey and Holguin Cuba. Overall in 2016 JetBlue commenced service to eight new cities including four destinations in Cuba and Quito Ecuador.

JetBlue entered an agreement with Airbus in mid-2016 to add 30 incremental Airbus A321 aircraft to its order book. The aircraft are scheduled to be delivered between 2017 and 2023. The carrier believes the aircraft will allow it to continue to grow profitably particularly in the transcontinental market.

HISTORY

JetBlue took to the skies in 2000 as the third airline start-up for founder and CEO David Neeleman. The first airline Neeleman helped create Morris Air was formed in 1984. Named after his business partner June Morris the discount airline was operating 22 planes out of Salt Lake City by 1993. While with Morris Air Neeleman pioneered ticketless travel which a decade later would become an industry standard.

Impressed with Morris Air's efficient and strategic network its e-ticket system and Neeleman Southwest Airlines acquired its smaller rival in 1993. Neeleman left Southwest after just six months but not without signing a non-compete clause that prevented him from attempting to repeat his Morris Air success in the US for five years.

Not willing to sit still for long (a characteristic he attributes to attention deficit disorder) Neeleman partnered with David Evans to create Open Skies an integrated e-ticket Internet booking and sales management tool that they began to market to smaller airlines.

Meanwhile Neeleman had skirted the terms of his non-compete agreement to help the founders of Canadian low-fare carrier WestJet get their project off of the ground serving as a consultant and a board member.

In 1999 a year after his non-compete agreement expired Neeleman sold Open Skies to Hewlett-Packard and set to work creating a new airline. In a matter of weeks he had managed to gather $130 million the most ever raised for a start-up airline from investors that included Chase Capital and financier George Soros. Neeleman immediately began acquiring new Airbus A320 jets and fitting them with satellite TV.

JetBlue's first flight was from New York to Fort Lauderdale in 2000. During the year the airline added nine more destinations in California Florida New York Utah and Vermont. By 2001 the airline was operating 20 new A320s with an ambitious 131 on order.

On September 11 of that year terrorists commandeered four passenger aircrafts and turned them into instruments of destruction killing some 3000 people. The events shocked the world and crippled the airline industry. Despite the climate however JetBlue continued to expand its network and it went public in 2002.

The industry star took some heat in 2003 for violating its own privacy policy when it gave the personal information of 1.1 million customers to the Department of Defense as part of anti-terrorism project.

JetBlue added nine new destinations in 2004 including Boston — a major market not dominated by a single carrier and lacking what the company deemed to be sufficient low-fare domestic service.

Consecutive losses in the fourth quarter of 2005 and the first quarter of 2006 — caused in part by rising fuel costs— led the carrier to raise fares on some routes redouble its efforts to keep expenses down and slow some of its expansion plans.

As part of the effort to improve the company's operations JetBlue's board in May 2007 asked David Neeleman to step down as CEO in favor of former president Dave Barger. Neeleman remained with the company as nonexecutive chairman until May 2008.

To grow JetBlue increased capacity at its base at New York's JFK airport with the opening of a new terminal in October 2008. The 630000 sq. ft. Terminal 5 has 26 gates solely used by JetBlue and can accommodate 250 daily departures. The $875 million renovation took three years; it has the largest single security checkpoint in the US and an adjacent 1500-space parking lot.

JetBlue expanded service in 2009 to Bogota Colombia and the Caribbean islands of St. Maarten and Jamaica.

In 2010 JetBlue ink a limited partnership with AMR Corp.'s legacy airline American; the two are sharing activities in New York and Boston including customer "interline" service one-stop booking and check-in and bag transfers for connecting flights. The partnership gives the younger low-cost carrier eight pairs of the Texas-based carrier's take-off and landing slots at Ronald Reagan Washington National Airport and swells American Airlines' New York market with 12 pairs of JetBlue's slots at John F. Kennedy International Airport.

In early 2011 the airline signed an interline agreement with Virgin Atlantic that allows passengers to make connecting flights on transatlantic routes using a single itinerary and baggage check.

JOHNS HOPKINS UNIVERSITY

Founded in 1876 with a $7 million bequest from its namesake The Johns Hopkins University has established its reputation by molding itself in the image of a European research institution. While renowned for its School of Medicine the private university offers 260 academic programs spanning fields of study including arts and sciences business and international studies. The university enrolls more than 24000 full- and part-time students. Johns Hopkins has about a half-dozen campuses in Maryland and Washington DC as well as facilities in China and Italy. The student-teacher ratio is 13:1. The affiliated Johns Hopkins Health System provides health care from its three Baltimore-area hospitals.

Operations

Johns Hopkins University a private and non-profit institution with 1700 non-medical and 2800 medical faculty members offers education research and professional medical services. Its research and related services are offered through about 1800 government and private sponsors.

Keenly focused on research Johns Hopkins is engaged in a range of disciplines including health and medicine social sciences humanities the arts natural sciences engineering and technology. Projects include researching alternatives to animal testing disease treatments and chemical and biomolecular engineering topics among others.

The Johns Hopkins University offers graduate programs in business finance and real estate through its relatively new Carey Business School. Trustee emeritus William Polk Carey chairman of W. P. Carey & Co. partially funded the $100 million development of the school with $50 million which was completed in 2007.

Notable alumni of the school include 28th US president Woodrow Wilson Michael Bloomberg and horror film director Wesley Craven.

Geographic Reach

The university boasts three major campuses in Baltimore as well as single campus locations in (Montgomery County) Maryland and Washington DC. Johns Hopkins also operates facilities in the Baltimore-Washington area and abroad in China and Italy.

Strategy

Johns Hopkins is mid-way through its Ten By Twenty program — comprising 10 goals to achieve by 2020 — launched in 2013. The 10 goals are divided into four categories: One University (forging collaboration across disciplines); Individual Excellence (supporting faculty students and staff); Commitment to Our Communities (enriching ties to Baltimore the US and the world); and Institution Building (building a stronger university). In its 2017 progress report some of the achievements listed are more robust mental health resources; smaller class sizes; around 25 (out of a goal of 50) hires of interdisciplinary scholars; improved diversity and inclusion; and raised $4.6 billion in donations.

EXECUTIVES

CIO and Vice Provost Information Technology, Stephanie L. Reel
President, Ronald J. (Ron) Daniels
SVP Finance and Administration, Daniel G. Ennis
SVP Academic Affairs and Provost, Sunil Kumar
Vice President, Thomas Lewis
Vice President, Fred Newman
Clinic Manager, Gerardine Finn
Vice President Finance, Debbie Palmerino
Education Department Chairperson, Anita Stone
Vice President Information Technology Secutiry and Corporate Compliance, Daniel Shealer
Medical Director, Haig Kazazian
Nursing Director Percutaneous Tracheostomy Program, Vinciya Pandian
Legal Secretary, Carolyn Mack
Pharmacy Manager, Michael Brown
Vice President and Chief Information Officer, John McLendon
Clinical Director, Peter Hill
Pharmacy Manager, Charles Wells
Vice President, Keith Hill
Medical Director of Care Coordination, Joseph Perno
Vice President For Population Health and Advancement, Elizabeth Kromm
Vice President For Quality, Renee Demski
Executive Vice President Information Technology, Mabel Chiu
VICE PRESIDENT AND CHIEF ADMINISTRATOR, Sowell Ashlyn
Director of Admissions, Valerie Mazza
Clinical Director Division of Allergy and Clinical Immunology, Peter Creticos
Director of Nursing, Laurie Saletnik
Director of Nursing, Deborah Baker
Vice Presidenttreasurer, Stephen Villanyi
Medical Director, Ekaterina Stepanova
Vice President Human Resources, Jon Oravec
Assistant Vice President, Kristen Pruski
Vice President, Carol Shannon
Board Member, Jim Fackler
Secretary To Doctor Roger Blumnethal, Frances Karas
Secretary, Beth Six
Assistant Secretary, Judith Moss
Medchi Vice Chair, Pranjal Gupta

LOCATIONS

HQ: JOHNS HOPKINS UNIVERSITY
  3400 N CHARLES ST, BALTIMORE, MD 212182680
Phone: 410 516-8000
Web: WWW.JHU.EDU

PRODUCTS/OPERATIONS

Selected Schools and Colleges
Bloomberg School of Public Health
Carey Business School
Krieger School of Arts and Sciences
Peabody Institute
School of Advanced International Studies
School of Education
School of Medicine
School of Nursing
Whiting School of Engineering

Selected Centers and Institutes
American Institute for Contemporary German Studies
Bloomberg School of Public Health Department of Health Policy and Management Fall Institute in Barcelona Spain
Bloomberg School of Public Health Research Centers

Center for Africana Studies
Center for Communication Programs
Center for Constitutional Studies and Democratic Development
Center for Clinical Global Health Education
Center for Global Health
Center for International Business and Public Policy
Center for Language Education
Center for Talented Youth
Center for Transatlantic Relations
Central Asia Caucasus Institute
Foreign Policy Institute
Hopkins Nanjing Center
Institute for Global Studies in Culture Power and History
Institute for Policy Studies
Johns Hopkins SAIS Bologna Center
Office of Global Nursing
SAIS Research Centers
Summer Language Institute
The Institute for Johns Hopkins Nursing
Yeung Center for Collaborative China Studies

Selected Campuses

Columbia Center - Columbia Maryland
East Baltimore Campus - Baltimore
Harbor East - Downtown Baltimore
Homewood Campus - Baltimore
Hopkins-Nanjing Center - Nanjing Jiangsu Province People's Republic of China
Johns Hopkins University Applied Physics Laboratory - Laurel MD; Baltimore and Washington
Johns Hopkins University Zanvyl Krieger School of Arts & Sciences Advanced Academic Programs - Washington DC
Montgomery County Center - Rockville Maryland
Nitze School of Advanced International Studies (SAIS) - Washington D.C
Peabody Campus - Baltimore
School of Advanced International Studies - Bologna Italy

HISTORICAL FINANCIALS

Company Type: Private

Income Statement

FYE: June 30

	REVENUE ($ mil.)	NET INCOME ($ mil.)	NET PROFIT MARGIN	EMPLOYEES
06/13	4,793	526	11.0%	30,228
06/11	4,369	826	18.9%	—
06/05	788	0	—	—
Annual Growth	25.3%	—	—	—

2013 Year-End Financials

Debt ratio: —
Return on equity: 11.00%
Cash ($ mil.): 235
Current ratio: —
Long-term debt ($ mil.): —

Dividends
Yield: —
Payout: —
Market value ($ mil.): —

Johnson & Johnson

It's difficult to get well without Johnson & Johnson (J&J). The diversified health care giant operates in three segments through more than 250 operating companies located in some 60 countries. Its Medical Devices division offers surgical equipment monitoring devices orthopedic and insulin delivery products and contact lenses among other things. J&J's Pharmaceuticals division makes drugs for an array of ailments such as neurological conditions blood disorders autoimmune diseases and pain. Top sellers are psoriasis drug Remicade and cancer medication Velcade. Finally J&J's Consumer business makes over-the-counter (OTC) drugs and products for baby skin and oral care as well as first-aid and nutritional uses.

HISTORY

Brothers James and Edward Mead Johnson founded their medical products company in 1885 in New Brunswick New Jersey. In 1886 Robert joined his brothers to make the antiseptic surgical dressings he developed. The company bought gauze maker Chicopee Manufacturing in 1916. In 1921 it introduced two of its classic products the Band-Aid and Johnson's Baby Cream.

Robert Jr. became chairman in 1932 and served until 1963. A WWII Army general he believed in decentralization; managers were given substantial freedom a principle still used today. Product lines in the 1940s included Ortho (birth control products) and Ethicon (sutures). In 1959 Johnson & Johnson bought McNeil Labs which launched Tylenol (acetaminophen) as an OTC drug the next year. Foreign acquisitions included Switzerland's Cilag-Chemie (1959) and Belgium's Janssen (1961). The company focused on consumer products in the 1970s gaining half the feminine protection market and making Tylenol the top-selling painkiller.

J&J bought Iolab a developer of intraocular lenses used in cataract surgery in 1980. Trouble struck in 1982 when someone laced Tylenol capsules with cyanide killing eight people. The company's response is now a damage-control classic: It immediately recalled 31 million bottles and totally redesigned its packaging to prevent future tampering. The move cost $240 million but saved the Tylenol brand. The next year prescription painkiller Zomax was linked to five deaths and was pulled.

New products in the 1980s included ACUVUE disposable contact lenses and Retin-A. The company bought LifeScan (blood-monitoring products for diabetics) in 1986. In 1989 it began a joint venture with Merck to sell Mylanta and other drugs bought from ICI Americas.

The firm continued its acquisition and diversification strategy in the 1990s. After introducing the first daily-wear disposable contact lenses in 1993 it bought skin-care product maker Neutrogena (1994) to enhance its consumer lines. To diversify its medical products and better compete for hospital business it bought Mitek Surgical Products (1995) and heart disease product maker Cordis (1996). The FDA cleared J&J's Renova wrinkle and fade cream in 1996. The company also began selling at-home HIV test Confide but pulled it the next year after low sales and other problems.

EXECUTIVES

VP Group Finance, Dominic J. Caruso, age 60, $909,500 total compensation
EVP and Worldwide Chairman Consumer Group, Jorge S. Mesquita, age 55
EVP and Group Worldwide Chairman, Sandra E. Peterson, age 59, $963,462 total compensation
Chairman and CEO, Alex Gorsky, age 56, $1,600,000 total compensation
Company Group Chairman Consumer Medical Devices, Ashley A. McEvoy
EVP and Chief Scientist Officer, Paulus (Paul) Stoffels, age 55, $1,144,000 total compensation
EVP and Worldwide Chairman Pharmaceuticals, Joaquin Duato, age 54, $875,000 total compensation
EVP and Chief Human Resources Officer, Peter M. Fasolo, age 54
EVP and General Counsel, Michael H. Ullmann, age 58, $645,385 total compensation
EVP and World Chairman Medical Devices, Gary Pruden, age 55
Company Group Chairman Pharmaceuticals The Americas, Jennifer Taubert
Vice President and Group CIO, Georgia Papathomas
Corporate Vice President Worldwide Government Affairs And Policy, Clifford Holland
Vice President North America for Global Marketing Group, Darryl Nicholson
Vice President of Human Resources, Valerie Love
VP Supply Chain, Steve Trozinski
Vice President Oncology Sci Innovation, Pamela Carroll
Vice President Research and Development, Steven Catani
VP Supply Chain, Michael Ehret
Vice President Research And Development Healthcare Compliance, Frank Konings
Vice President Global Medical Affairs, Craig Tendler
Vice President Comm And Public Affairs Med Dev, Tom Sanford
Vice President Human Resources, Sandra Heymann
Vice President Global Engineering, Michael Maggio
Vice President Business Transformation, Angie Caswell
Area Vice President Northeast, Travis Williams
Ww Vice President Research And Development McNeil Nutritionals, Tom Ells
Vice President Of Global Health, Scott Ratzan
Vice President Prod Stewardship, Susan Nettesheim
VP Supply Chain, Gerson Montenegro
Scientific Vice President, Wayne Drevets
Vice President Quality Assurance J And J Consumer Group Of Companies, Teresa Gorecki
Vice President Global Account Management, Jack Gelman
Vice President Global Pharmaceutical Communications, Craig Rothenberg
Vice President Sterile Process Technolog, Rainer Newman
Vice President Strategic Business Support, James Rider
Vice President Business Development, Robert Havard
Vice President, George Tarantino
VP Supply Chain, Michelle Dejonge
Vice President Enterprise Customers, Ruben Taborda
VP Supply Chain, Tom Glover
VP Supply Chain, Paul Lawrance
VP Supply Chain, Mark Edgerton
VP Supply Chain, Paul Pandiscio
VP Supply Chain, Scott Robertson
Vice President Customer Management, Scott Chilson
Vice President eCommerce, Sri Rajagopalan
Vice President Communication and Public Affairs, Efen Huang
Vice President Marketing, Ganesh Bangalore
Vice President Alliance Management, Cindy Warren
Vice President Human Resources Worldwide, Mary Fink
Ww Vice President Marketing, Timothy Czartoski
Vice President Immunology Research and Development, Dan Baker
Regional Vice President, Mark Sienkiewicz
Vice President Integrated Networks, Donald Delaney
Vice President Research and Development Communications, Oliver Stohlmann
Senior Vice President, Instructor Sunywcc
VP Global Clinical Pharmacology, Heald Donald
VP Supply Chain, Ivette Franco
VP Supply Chain, Christine Kowalski
VP Supply Chain, Meri Stevens
VP Supply Chain, Zenon Zdunek
VP Supply Chain, Debora Kawanami
VP Supply Chain, Sylvia Fouhy
VICE PRESIDENT SUPPLY CHAIN NORTH AMERICA OTC, Gaspar Zuniga
VP Customer Development (focused on Walmart), Michael Charette
Treasurer, John Papa
Board Member, Dirk Collier
Auditors: PricewaterhouseCoopers LLP

LOCATIONS

HQ: Johnson & Johnson
One Johnson & Johnson Plaza, New Brunswick, NJ
08933
Phone: 732 524-0400 **Fax:** 732 214-0332
Web: www.jnj.com

2017 Sales

	$ mil.	% of total
US	37,811	53
Europe	15,770	22
Asia/Pacific & Africa	12,575	17
Western Hemisphere excluding US	5,734	8
Total	**71,890**	**100**

2017 Sales

	$ mil.	% of total
US	37,811	53
International	34,079	47
Total	**71,890**	**100**

PRODUCTS/OPERATIONS

2017 Sales

	$ mil.	% of total
Pharmaceuticals	33,464	47
Medical Devices	25,119	35
Consumer	13,307	18
Total	**71,890**	**100**

Selected Products

Medical devices
  AcuVue contact lenses (Vistakon)
  Advanced sterilization products
  Animas insulin pump (LifeScan)
  DePuy Mitek sports medicine products
  DePuy Orthopaedics hip and knee replacement
  products
  DePuy Spine repair products
  Electrophysiology products (Biosense Webster)
  Ethicon women's health and urology
  Harmonic scalpel (plastic surgery)
  OneTouch blood glucose monitor (LifeScan)
  Vitros diagnostic instrumentation systems (Ortho-
  Clinical)
Pharmaceuticals
  Aciphex/Pariet (acid reflux)
  Concerta (ADHD)
  Duragesic/Fentanyl transdermal (pain management)
  Durogesic outside the US)
  Edurant (HIV)
  Intelence (HIV)
  Invega (schizophrenia)
  Invega Sustenna (injectable Invega)
  Levaquin/Floxin (anti-infective)
  Nucynta (pain)
  Ortho Evra (patch contraceptive)
  Ortho Tri-cyclen (oral contraceptive)
  Prezista (HIV)
  Procrit/Eprex (anemia Eprex outside the US)
  Remicade (rheumatoid arthritis psoriasis and Crohn's
  disease)
  Risperdal (schizophrenia and bipolar)
  Risperdal Consta (injectable Risperdal)
  Simponi (rheumatoid arthritis)
  Stelara (psoriasis)
  Topamax (epilepsy and migraines)
  Velcade (multiple myeloma)
  Xarelto (blood clots)
  Zytiga (prostate cancer)
Consumer
  Aveeno skin care products
  Band-Aid bandages
  Benecol food products
  Clean & Clear skin care products
  Imodium A-D antidiarrheal
  Johnson's adult skin care products
  Johnson's baby care products
  Lactaid nutritional products
  Listerine mouthwash
  Motrin IB analgesic
  Mylanta gastrointestinal aid
  Neutrogena skin and hair care products
  Pepcid AC gastrointestinal aid (marketed with Merck)
  Reach toothbrushes
  Rembrandt toothpaste
  RoC skin care products
  Splenda non-caloric sugar substitute

Sudafed cold flu and allergy medications
Tylenol acetaminophen pain medicines
Viactiv calcium supplements
Zyrtec allergy products

Selected Acquisitions

COMPETITORS

3M Health Care	Genzyme
Abbott Labs	GlaxoSmithKline
Alcon	Kimberly-Clark Health
Allergan plc	L'Or✺al USA
Amgen	Medtronic
ArthroCare	Mentholatum Company
AstraZeneca	Merck
B. Braun Melsungen	Mylan
Bard	Novartis
Bausch & Lomb	NutraSweet
Baxter International	Perrigo
Bayer AG	Pfizer
Beckman Coulter	Procter & Gamble
Becton Dickinson	Roche Holding
Biogen	Sanofi
Boehringer Ingelheim	Shire
Boston Scientific	Smith & Nephew
Bristol-Myers Squibb	St. Jude Medical
Chattem	Stryker
Colgate-Palmolive	Terumo
Cook Incorporated	Teva
Dr. Reddy's	The Dial Corporation
Edwards Lifesciences	UCB
Eli Lilly	Zimmer Biomet

HISTORICAL FINANCIALS

Company Type: Public

Income Statement

FYE: January 1

	REVENUE ($ mil.)	NET INCOME ($ mil.)	NET PROFIT MARGIN	EMPLOYEES
01/17	71,890	16,540	23.0%	126,400
01/16*	70,074	15,409	22.0%	127,100
12/14	74,331	16,323	22.0%	126,500
12/13	71,312	13,831	19.4%	128,100
12/12	67,224	10,853	16.1%	127,600
Annual Growth	**1.7%**	**11.1%**		**(0.2%)**

*Fiscal year change

2017 Year-End Financials

Debt ratio: 19.21%—
Return on equity: 23.43%
Cash ($ mil.): 18,972
Current ratio: 2.47
Long-term debt ($ mil.): 22,442

Dividends
  Yield: 0.0%
  Payout: 53.1%
Market value ($ mil.): —

	STOCK PRICE ($) FY Close	P/E High/Low	PER SHARE ($) Earnings	Dividends	Book Value
01/17	115.21	21 16	5.93	3.15	26.02
01/16*	102.72	19 16	5.48	2.95	25.82
12/14	105.06	19 15	5.70	2.76	25.06
12/13	92.35	19 14	4.81	2.59	26.25
12/12	69.48	18 16	3.86	2.40	23.33
Annual Growth	**13.5%**	**— —**	**11.3%**	**7.0%**	**2.8%**

*Fiscal year change

Jones Financial Companies LLLP

LOCATIONS

HQ: Jones Financial Companies LLLP
  12555 Manchester Road, Des Peres, MO 63131
Phone: 314 515-2000

HISTORICAL FINANCIALS

Company Type: Public

Income Statement

FYE: December 31

	REVENUE ($ mil.)	NET INCOME ($ mil.)	NET PROFIT MARGIN	EMPLOYEES
12/16	6,557	746	11.4%	43,000
12/15	6,619	838	12.7%	41,000
12/14	6,278	770	12.3%	40,000
12/13	5,656	674	11.9%	39,000
12/12	4,965	555	11.2%	—
Annual Growth	**7.2%**	**7.7%**		**—**

2016 Year-End Financials

Debt ratio: —
Return on equity: —
Cash ($ mil.): 1,939
Current ratio: 1.10
Long-term debt ($ mil.): —

No. of shares (mil.): 0
Dividends
  Yield: —
  Payout: —
Market value ($ mil.): —

Jones Lang LaSalle Inc

Jones Lang LaSalle (JLL) provides real estate without borders. Its services include commercial leasing real estate brokerage management advisory and financing through nearly 300 corporate offices in more than 80 countries around the world; almost 45% of its business is in the US. The company's LaSalle Investment Management arm is a diversified real estate management firm with about $60 billion in assets under management. JLL has commercial real estate expertise across office retail hotel health care industrial cultural and multifamily residential properties. It manages more than 4 billion sq. ft. worldwide.

Operations

JLL's real estate services are divided across six product categories: Property & Facility Management (almost 30% of net sales); Leasing (some 25%); Project & Development Services (almost 20%); Capital Markets & Hotels (15%); Advisory Consulting and Other (nearly 10%); and LaSalle Investment Management (more than 5%).

Geographic Reach

Chicago-based JLL generates about 45% of its annual revenue from the US while more than 30% comes from the Europe Middle East and Africa (EMEA) region. About 20% of revenue comes from the Asia Pacific region.

Sales and Marketing

JLL serves roughly half of the Fortune 500 companies and about 80% of the Fortune 100 companies.

Financial Performance

JLL has enjoyed consistent revenue growth over the past several years as both its managed property portfolio and its assets under management continue to grow.

In a historic milestone revenue in 2016 jumped 14% to $6.8 billion due to growth across all regions and segments. Property & Facility Management sales spiked in 2016 mainly due to incremental revenue from recent acquisitions most notably in the EMEA region. Its Project & Development Services division also experienced growth in the EMEA and Americas regions.

Despite the historic revenue total JLL's profits plummeted by 27% to $318 million in 2016. This was attributed to additional fee-based operating expenses from recent acquisitions and nearly $60 million of increased data and technology related expenditures.

In addition to profits operating cash flow fell from $376 million in 2015 to $215 million in 2016 due to an increase in working capital (mostly incentive compensation payments) and the profit decrease.

Strategy

JLL has grown by opening new offices and by buying up other companies; indeed the firm has completed more than 100 acquisitions around the world.

Throughout 2016 JLL completed almost 30 acquisitions in Australia Canada Germany Ireland Japan Poland Sweden Turkey the UK and the US. Of particular note was its purchase of Integral UK Ltd. a provider of mechanical and electrical property maintenance services. The deal strengthened JLL's integrated facilities management capabilities and made it one of the largest providers of mobile engineering services for property worldwide. The acquisition also contributed to JLL's historic revenues for 2016.

Other priorities for JLL include growing its local and regional service operations developing its ability to provide global capital markets services and strengthening LaSalle Investment Management's position by developing new products and extending its portfolio capabilities.

HISTORY

Jones Lang Wootton had roots in London's Paternoster Row auction houses in 1783. LaSalle Partners originally known as IDC Real Estate was founded in El Paso Texas in 1968. The two companies could not have started out in a more disparate fashion yet their combined force is now one of the largest real estate services firms in the world.

Richard Winstanley opened an auction house in 1783 and his son James joined him in that business in 1806. In 1840 the Joneses entered the picture — the Winstanleys created a partnership with one James Jones. The business moved to King Street (in the Guildhall section of London) in 1860 and remained in that location for some 100 years in various incarnations — James' son Frederick took over the business renaming it Frederick Jones and Co. When James retired in 1872 the firm was again renamed to Jones Lang and Co. and was controlled by C. A. Lang. Jones Lang merged with Wootton and Son in 1939 becoming Jones Lang Wootton and Sons.

Jones Lang Wootton was active in redrawing the property lines in London after the Blitz. In 1945 the firm began contacting small landowners and by combining small parcels of land secured development leasing and/or purchase contracts. When the rebuilding of London began in 1954 Jones Lang Wootton was in a secure place to be right at the forefront of that new development. The firm began engaging in speculative development in the West End and in the City of London.

The year 1958 saw the expansion of Jones Lang Wootton into Australia; the firm had offices throughout the Asia/Pacific region by 1968. Further expansion took place closer to home in Scotland (1962) and Ireland (1965) and the first continental European office in Brussels (also 1965). The firm moved into the Manhattan market in 1975.

On the other side of the story IDC Real Estate (the name change to LaSalle Partners came in 1977) was a group of partnerships initially focused on investment banking investment management and land. The firm began offering development management services in 1975; it moved into property management leasing and tenant representation in 1978 and facility management operations in 1980.

It built market share by buying other firms including Kleinwort Benson Realty Advisors Corp. (1994) and UK-based investment adviser CIN Property Management (1996).

The firm leveraged its experience and long-term client base to pursue an acquisition strategy taking advantage of trends shaping commercial real estate — globalization consolidation and merchant banking. LaSalle went public in 1997 amalgamating the Galbreath Company (a property and development management firm with which it merged that year) with its other partnerships and becoming a corporation.

In 1998 it acquired the project management business of Satulah Group and two retail management business units from Lend Lease and took real estate investment trust LaSalle Hotel Properties public. In 1999 the firm strengthened its world position by merging with Jones Lang Wootton; the company was renamed Jones Lang LaSalle.

The merger with Jones Lang Wootton combined Wootton's strength in Asia and Europe with LaSalle Partners' large presence in North America to create a worldwide real estate services firm. In 2006 the company acquired Spaulding & Slye strengthening operations in the Mid-Atlantic and New England. Also that year it opened an office in Dubai and acquired RSP Group which operates in North Africa and the Middle East. In 2007 Jones Lang LaSalle bought German property advisory firm Kemper's Holding and took a stake in the former Trammell Crow Meghraj one of the largest private real estate companies in India.

The company broadened its presence in key North American markets when it acquired The Staubach Company in 2008. Jones Lang LaSalle paid $613 million for the rival real estate services firm which was founded by football legend and former Dallas Cowboys quarterback Roger Staubach.

Jones Lang LaSalle slowed its acquisition pace during the economic recession. But managed to cut a few deals. In 2009 Jones Lang LaSalle teamed up with Real Estate Disposition to begin offering online auction sales a product to help customers quickly sell commercial property and other distressed assets.

In another deal Jones Lang LaSalle acquired the third-party leasing and management duties of General Growth Properties in 2010 as part of the mall owner's restructuring efforts. The deal added about 20 shopping centers to Jones Lang LaSalle's management portfolio.

EXECUTIVES

Executive Vice President, David Hendrickson
CEO Americas, Gregory P. (Greg) O'Brien, age 54, $400,000 total compensation
CEO LaSalle Investment Management, Jeff A. Jacobson, age 55, $400,000 total compensation
Executive Vice President, David Ottenjohn
CIO, David A. Johnson, age 54
President CEO and Director, Christian Ulbrich, age 51, $481,619 total compensation
CFO, Christie B. Kelly, age 55, $400,000 total compensation

CEO Europe Middle East and Africa, Guy Grainger
Managing Director Shanghai and East China, Anthony Couse, $420,902 total compensation
CEO Americas Corporate Solutions, John Forrest
EVP and Chief Human Resources Officer, Patricia (Trish) Maxson, age 58
Global Head Capital Markets, Richard Bloxam
CEO JLL Netherlands, Pieter Hendrikse
Vice President, Paige Morgan
Vice President, John Walters
Vice President Finance, Bill Grice
Vice President, Aaron Ellison
Vice President, Mia Eglinton
Senior Vice President, Bob Gross
Vice President and Director Marketing, Ray Bouley
Executive Vice President, Philip Lipper
Vice President Multifamily, Ray White
Vice President Clinical Projects Enterprise Real Estate Services, Scott Becker
Senior Vice President Of Engineering, Miles Anderson
Senior Vice President, Mike Chionchio
Vice President Hotels and Hospitality, Truitt Alday
Vice President of Sponsorship Marketing, Sally Hertz
Executive Vice President Capital Markets, Jason Schmidt
Senior Vice President Tenant Representation, Alex Lassar
Senior Vice President Investment Sales, Nihat Ercan
Senior Vice President, Cara Trani
Vice President West Region Manager Energy and Sustainability Services, Frank Teng
Vice President, Christine Tong
Vice President Global Client Applications Senior Business Analyst, Craig Parrish
Vice President, Rick Benoy
Senior Vice President Project and Development Services, Louis Molinini
Vice President and Leed AP Office Leasing, Michael Case
Vice President, Brooke Dewey
Assistant Vice President, Clayton Kline
Executive Vice President, Dan Adamski
Vice President, Ned Tarbox
Vice President, Kathryn Fudge
Executive Vice President, Mark Brandenburg
Vice President And General Manager, Amarjit Bains
Vice President Jones Lang Lasalle Americas, Matt Perrigue
Vice President, John Worthen
Vice President, Dean Brody
Vice President, Brian J Means
Senior Vice President, George Gemelos
Senior Vice President, Ned Roberts
Senior Vice President Broker License, Matthew Berres
Executive Vice President and Chief Corporate Counsel, Mackenzie Phillips
Senior Vice President, Scott Vinett
Vice President Denver Market Leader, Tracy Lopez
Vice President, John Ream
Senior Vice President Hotels and Hospitality, Nick Baer
Vice President Public Relations, Paige Steers
Senior Vice President Strategic Consulting, James Rice
Senior Vice President, Pete Kostroski
Executive Vice President Industrial, Robert Kossar
Vice President, James Stockdale
Vice President Retail Leasing, Charlie Owens
Senior Vice President, Jimmy Appich
Executive Vice President, Dan Jessup
Executive Vice President, Jeff Adkison
Vice President Finance, Greg Sheehan
Senior Vice President, Marti Nemer
Senior Vice President, Ryan Matthews
Executive Vice President, Shawn McDonald

Vice President Strategic Sourcing West Region, Tim Hamill
Vice President And General Manager, Jennifer Christakes
Vice President Project and Development Services, Pam Heckman
Senior Vice President, Alex Holton
Vice President of Training Coordinator, Ann Nance
Vice President, Gregg Christoffersen
Vice President, Anu Rao
Vice President, Cliff West
Vice President, Brad Crosley
Vice President Hotels and Hospitality, Melvin Chu
Vice President Regional Manager., Mary Stanton
Senior Vice President Hotels, John L Strauss
Executive Vice President, Julia Wilhelm
Vice President, Michele Barkinge
Vice President, Tarik Bateh
Executive Vice President, Pat McDowell
Senior Vice President, Jorg Mast
Vice President, Chester Ellis
Vice President, Tony Haning
Vice President Of Investment Sales, Steven Echelson
Vice President Hotels and Hospitality, Carolina Lacerda
Vice President Industrial Property Management, Ben Bischmann
Senior Vice President, Jodi Prentice
Senior Vice President, Tom Fox
Vice President Industrial Services, Scott Duerkop
Senior Vice President, Henry Voges
Executive Vice President, Brian Harris
Associate Vice President, Jason Benson
Senior Vice President Brokerage, Dean Stiles
Vice President Capital Markets Group, Bret Felberg
Vice President, Zach Anderson
Vice President, Matt Kiehne
Vice President, Steve Borup
Vice President, Tiffany Munro
Senior Vice President, Brian Tisbert
Vice President, Crissy Haley
Senior Vice President, Anneke Greco
Vice President, Teri Bell
Vice President And General Manager, Bryan Oyster
Vice President Brokerage, Diana Bridger
Vice President Director of Finance, Cliff Marnick
Executive Vice President, Patrick Devereaux
Vice President, Tom Doupe
Senior Vice President, Craig Eisenhardt
Senior Vice President, Robert Leiding
Executive Vice President, Rich Thompson
Vice President, Ben Stapleton
Senior Vice President, Keith Largay
Senior Vice President, Lyle Patterson
Executive Vice President, Mike McKeever
Executive Vice President Supply Chain Management, Gerald Donovan
Vice President, Scott Ohlander
Executive Vice President, Dominic Carbonari
Vice President, Christopher Ostop
Senior Vice President of Development and Asset Strategy, Jeffrey Adkison
Executive Vice President, Steve Burkett
Executive Vice President, Cameron Driscoll
Executive Vice President, John Davis
Vice President, Tom Taylor
Senior Vice President Tenant Representation, Patrick Bolick
Executive Vice President, Michael Diaz
Senior Vice President, Scott D Cahaly
Vice President, Lakshmi Nalluri
Vice President, Derek Ruterman
Vice President, Wesley Edwards
Vice President, Kurt Liss
Vice President, John A Starke
Senior Vice President, Stephen Steinberg
Executive Vice President, Rob Nielsen
Vice President Jones Lang Lasalle Americas, Nicole Mouren-Laurens

Senior Vice President Director of Public Relations, Gayle Kantro
Vice President, Jim McCahon
Senior Vice President, Alvin Magner
Vice President, Denise Delisser
Executive Vice President, Gregg Raus
Executive Vice President, Gregg Walker
Senior Vice President, Janet Kissel
Vice President, Chris Wagner
Senior Vice President, Eric Haskins
Senior Vice President National Director Business Consulting, Shannon Curley
Vice President, Weilin Koo
Vice President And Associate Director, Kristen Schneider
Auditors: KPMG LLP

LOCATIONS

HQ: Jones Lang LaSalle Inc
200 East Randolph Drive, Chicago, IL 60601
Phone: 312 782-5800   Fax: 312 782-4339
Web: www.jll.com

2016 Sales by Segment

	$ mil.	% of total
Americas	2,965	44
Europe Middle East Africa	2,077	30
Asia Pacific	1,352	20
Investment management	407	6
Total	**6,803**	**100**

PRODUCTS/OPERATIONS

2016 Sales

	$ mil.	% of total
Real Estate Services		
Property and facility management	1,902	28
Leasing	1,759	26
Project and development services	1,195	18
Capital Markets & Hotels	972	14
Advisory Consulting and Other	567	8
LaSalle Investment Management	407	6
Total	**6,803**	**100**

Selected Services

Investor services
  Agency leasing
  Property management
  Valuations and consulting
Occupier services
  Facilities management
  Project and development services
  Tenant representation
Construction management
Capital markets
Energy and sustainability services
Hotel advisory
Money management
Strategic consulting

COMPETITORS

BGC Partners	Cushman & Wakefield
CBRE Group	Hines
Colliers International	Lend Lease
Colliers International Group	Newmark Knight Frank
	Savills

HISTORICAL FINANCIALS

Company Type: Public

Income Statement

FYE: December 31

	REVENUE ($ mil.)	NET INCOME ($ mil.)	NET PROFIT MARGIN	EMPLOYEES
12/16	6,803	318	4.7%	77,300
12/15	5,965	438	7.4%	61,500
12/14	5,429	386	7.1%	58,100
12/13	4,461	269	6.0%	52,700
12/12	3,932	208	5.3%	48,000
Annual Growth	**14.7%**	**11.2%**	**—**	**12.7%**

2016 Year-End Financials

Debt ratio: 24.22%
Return on equity: 11.58%
Cash ($ mil.): 258
Current ratio: 1.11
Long-term debt ($ mil.): 1,178
No. of shares (mil.): 45
Dividends
Yield: 0.0%
Payout: 9.1%
Market value ($ mil.): 4,568

	STOCK PRICE ($) FY Close	P/E High/Low	PER SHARE ($) Earnings	Dividends	Book Value
12/16	101.04	23 13	6.98	0.64	61.70
12/15	159.86	18 15	9.65	0.56	59.68
12/14	149.93	18 12	8.52	0.48	53.24
12/13	102.39	17 13	5.98	0.44	49.04
12/12	83.94	18 13	4.63	0.40	44.29
Annual Growth	**4.7%**	**— —**	**10.8%**	**12.5%**	**8.6%**

JPMorgan Chase & Co

Boasting some $2.5 trillion in assets JPMorgan Chase is the largest bank holding company in the US and among the largest half-dozen in the world. With some 5250 branches in about two dozen states it is among the nation's top mortgage lenders and credit card issuers (it holds some $141 billion in credit card loans). Active in 60 countries the bank also boasts formidable investment banking and asset management operations through its subsidiaries JPMorgan Private Bank and institutional investment manager JPMorgan Asset Management which has $2.5 trillion in assets under supervision. The company can trace its history back to the Bank of Manhattan Company founded in 1799.

HISTORY

JPMorgan Chase & Co.'s roots are in The Manhattan Company created in 1799 to bring water to New York City. A provision buried in its incorporation documents let the company provide banking services; investor and future US Vice President Aaron Burr brought the company (eventually the Bank of Manhattan) into competition with The Bank of New York founded by Burr's political rival Alexander Hamilton. JPMorgan Chase still owns the pistols from the notorious 1804 duel in which Burr mortally wounded Hamilton.

In 1877 John Thompson formed Chase National naming it for Salmon Chase Abraham Lincoln's secretary of the treasury and the architect of the national bank system. Chase National merged with John D. Rockefeller's Equitable Trust in 1930 becoming the world's largest bank and beginning a long relationship with the Rockefellers. Chase National continued growing after WWII and in 1955 it merged with the Bank of Manhattan. Christened Chase Manhattan the bank remained the US's largest into the 1960s.

When soaring 1970s oil prices made energy loans attractive Chase invested in Penn Square an obscure oil-patch bank in Oklahoma and the first notable bank failure of the 1980s. (The legal aftereffects of Penn Square's 1982 failure dragged on until 1993.) Losses following the 1987 foreign loan crisis hit Chase hard as did the real estate crash. In 1995 the bank went looking for a partner. After talks with Bank of America it settled on Chemical Bank.

Chemical Bank opened in 1824 and was one of the US's largest banks by 1900. As with Chase Chemical Bank began as an unrelated business (New York Chemical Manufacturing) in 1823 largely in order to open a bank (it dropped its chemical operations in 1844). Chemical would merge with Manufacturers Hanover in 1991.

After its 1996 merger with Chase Chemical Bank was the surviving entity but assumed Chase's more prestigious name. Initial cost savings from the merger were substantial as jobs and branch offices were eliminated. In 1997 Chase acquired the credit business of The Bank of New York and the corporate trustee business of Mellon Financial but underwent another round of belt-tightening the next year when it took a $320 million charge and cut 4500 jobs. The bank also suffered losses related to its involvement with the ill-starred Long-Term Capital Management hedge fund.

In 1999 Chase focused on lending buying two mortgage originators and forming a marketing alliance with subprime auto lender AmeriCredit (now General Motors Financial Company). Chase also bought Mellon Financial's residential mortgage unit and Huntington Bancshares' credit card portfolio. It bought UK investment bank Robert Fleming Holdings in 2000.

In 2001 it closed its $30 billion buy of J.P. Morgan and renamed itself JPMorgan Chase & Co. The new firm eliminated some 10% of its combined workforce as a result of the merger. Chairman Sandy Warner (who ran J.P. Morgan) retired at year-end and was replaced by former Chase Manhattan leader CEO William Harrison.

JPMorgan Chase had more than $1 billion in exposure to Enron but in 2003 recovered some $600 million after a court battle with the failed energy trader's insurers which claimed the losses stemmed from loans by JPMorgan Chase disguised as oil and gas transactions. Nonetheless JPMorgan Chase ended up paying some $135 million to settle actions relating to the questionable loans.

In 2004 JPMorgan Chase joined forces with venerable investment bank Cazenove; the joint venture called JPMorgan Cazenove handles corporate finance and capital markets activities in the UK.

The next year JPMorgan Chase and its investment banking arm J.P. Morgan Securities avoided a trial by paying some $2 billion to settle claims from investors who lost money on bonds that the firm underwrote in 2000 and 2001 for scandal-ridden WorldCom which eventually declared bankruptcy (WorldCom became MCI and later was acquired by Verizon Communications).

On the heels of the its massive BANK ONE buy in 2004 JPMorgan Chase made several smaller purchases including global trade management and logistics software maker Vastera (renamed JPMorgan Chase Vastera) trading technology firm Neovest and the credit card business of Sears Canada. JPMorgan Chase also sold online brokerage subsidiary J.P. Morgan Invest and its BrownCo unit to E*TRADE. The following year the company acquired student lender Collegiate Funding Services which JPMorgan Chase combined with its existing Chase Education Finance division. The company also got the go-ahead from the FTC and bought Kohl's $1.6 billion credit card portfolio.

Enron continued to haunt the company: in 2005 it forked over $2.2 billion to settle part of an investor class-action suit over fraud charges related to the Enron debacle and paid another $350 million to the infamous energy trading firm which asserted that JPMorgan Chase and about 10 other banks aided and abetted the company's collapse. However the next year the company got some good news regarding its alleged involvement with the collapse of Enron when the class action suit against it was dismissed.

Also in 2006 the company cut ties with private equity investment arm J.P. Morgan Partners which divided into two companies CCMP Capital and Panorama Capital. JPMorgan Chase retained the former private equity operations of BANK ONE One Equity Partners.

In keeping with the lesson learned regarding its $2 billion fine to settle claims in the WorldCom debacle in 2006 the bank was quick to settle its part of another class-action lawsuit this time brought by investors claiming they were cheated in the dot-com IPO boom. JPMorgan Chase paid $425 million to settle that case. It paid a much smaller settlement of $3.8 million for its part in the demise of the ill-fated telecom Global Crossing.

All was not lawsuits and settlements in 2006 however: that year it swapped its corporate trust business for Bank of New York's nearly 340-branch network in the New York metropolitan area. Both units were valued at about $2 billion with JPMorgan Chase paying Bank of New York around $150 million more to make up the difference.

William Harrison retired as chairman at the end of 2006; he was succeeded by president and CEO (and the CEO of BANK ONE when it was acquired) Jamie Dimon.

As one of the largest mortgage and home equity providers in the country JPMorgan Chase was hurt by the subprime mortgage crisis and subsequent fall in home values in 2007. About a third of its loans were home equity loans and it had to write off more than $500 million in home equity loans that year.

In 2008 the bank assumed full ownership of payments processor Chase Paymentech Solutions which had been a joint venture with First Data. First Data assumed 49% of Chase Paymentech's assets and clients in the deal.

Also that year as part of a plan to stimulate the economy the US government invested in JPMorgan Chase and other banks. The bank got $25 billion of the $700 billion taxpayer-funded bailout package that was approved in late 2008 with the stipulation that the banks use the money and not hoard it. The investment came with restrictions on executive pay and other rules and JPMorgan returned the money the following year saying it was doing just fine without it.

Led by CEO Jamie Dimon JPMorgan Chase closed a couple of very high profile deals as the economic crisis claimed numerous victims. It acquired Bear Stearns one of Wall Street's top investment banks and the operations of Washington Mutual (WaMu) the largest bank to fail in US history. Both deals closed in 2008.

Initially JPMorgan Chase made a bargain-basement offer of $270 million (around $2 a share) for the struggling Bear Stearns which was drowning in subprime mortgage investment debt. It ultimately raised its offer to around $10 a share or some $1.2 billion. The deal came after the Fed extended a $30 billion lifeline to Bear Stearns to keep the firm afloat; JPMorgan Chase was one of the lenders.

The company also stepped in to buy WaMu when that bank failed and was seized by regulators. It paid $1.9 billion for the bank's operations and assumed some $31 billion in losses. JPMorgan began integrating WaMu's branches with its own retail network phasing out the WaMu brand and closing about 10% of the combined branches (especially in markets where there was overlap). Shortly after the acquisition JPMorgan cut 9200 WaMu jobs — about 20% of its workforce.

In 2009 JPMorgan Chase sold specialist firm Bear Wagner acquired in the Bear Stearns deal to Barclays Capital.

JPMorgan Chase agreed to pay more than $153 million to the Securities and Exchange Commission in order to settle a claim that it misled investors during the 2007 housing market crash.

The company was among others that were investigated for improper sales practices.

In 2010 JPMorgan acquired the European and Asian segments of RBS Sempra Commodities the energy trading joint venture between Royal Bank of Scotland and Sempra Energy. The $1.6 billion deal did not include RBS Sempra's more valuable North American segment. JPMorgan integrated the business into the bank's existing global commodities business doubling its corporate client numbers.

Also in 2010 the company bought the private equity administration services of Schroders. That deal added more than $6 billion in committed capital. J.P. Morgan Worldwide Securities Services already had some $15.3 trillion in assets under custody. In 2011 the company sold its 41% stake in mutual fund company American Century to CIBC for some $848 million.

EXECUTIVES

Assistant Vice President Business, James Lee
Vice President of Facilities Vip, Gerard Vanella
Vice President, Brian Coats
Vice President Information Technology Architecture, Douglas Schwarz
Vice President, John Bradley
Senior Vice President, Steven Smith
Chairman and CEO, James (Jamie) Dimon, age 60, $1,500,000 total compensation
CEO Card Services, Gordon A. Smith, age 58, $500,000 total compensation
CEO Corporate and Investment Bank, Daniel E. Pinto, age 54, $8,303,234 total compensation
CIO, Lori A. Beer, age 49
CEO Commercial Banking and Executive Committee Member, Douglas B. (Doug) Petno, age 51
CEO Asset and Wealth Management, Mary Callahan Erdoes, age 49, $750,000 total compensation
CFO, Marianne Lake, age 47, $750,000 total compensation
Chief Risk Officer, Ashley Bacon, age 47
Deputy CEO JPMorgan EMEA Operations, Vis Raghavan
Vice President, Josephine Norris
First Vice President District Manager, Sean Cummings
Vice President Central Technology, Albert Morgillo
Vice President Human Resources, Jim Odonnell
Vice President Information Technology, Dennis Ramawy
Vice President of Information Technology, Paul Rosenberg
Vice President of IT, Alex Kayzerman
Vice President Assistant General Counsel, Catherine Hasenzahl
Vice President, Michael Green
Executive Vice President Administration and Chief Information Officer, Jeff Morgan
Vice President Of Technology, Tracey Ball
Vice President Market Risk Technology, Kevin Ford
Vice President Of Public Finance, David Elmquist
Vice President Trading Technologies, Ann Billak
Vice President Talent and Development Operations, Ning Ham
Senior Vice President Middle Market Banking, Jim Nicholas
Vice President Controller, Michael Bourke
Vice President Information Technology, Judy Zito
Vice President Sourcing and Procurement Services, Benjamin Lamboy
Vice President, Alvin Lam
VICE PRESIDENT, CARLOS LEDET
Vice President Information Technology, Eric Bowers
Vice President, Richard Hixson
Vice President Technology Director, Ed White

Senior Vice President and Head of Digital Channel Marketing, Steve Ireland
Assistannt Vice President, Jason Silbaugh
Vice President, Diane Genovesi
Vice President Marketing China, James Katek
Senior Vice President Technology Director, Richard Ward
Vice President, Douglas Savage
Senior Vice President, Dan Howat
Vice President, Anatoly Morosov
Vice President, Kelley Simpson
Vice President Information Technology Operations Support, Sekou H Kaalund
Vice President, Gene Huang
Vice President, Mihir Agochiya
Vice President, Nancy Panetta
Vice President, Harvey Klyce
Senior Vice President Dealer Commercial Services, Jeff Johns
Senior Vice President, Nancy McDonnell
Vice President Global Infrastructure, Chris Head
Vice President Architecture, Prasad Chaubal
Vice President Accounting Manager, Jeanne Higgins
Vice President, Lewis Rieck
First Vice President, Michael V McCann
Vice President, Curt Barrentine
Vice President Client Advisor, Dan Brown
Vice President, Sahil Agarwal
Assistant Vice President Banker, Javier Varela
Vice President of Architecture, Adam Goldin
Vice President, Ellen Avrutis
Vice President Marketing Analysis Manager, Matthew Reynolds
Assistant Vice President Business Banker, Rakhee Singh
Vice President, Bruce Goldberg
Vice President, Donna Kopelman
Vice President Equity Prime Brokerage, Andrew Hannigan
Vice President Mortgage Advisory, Claudia Castillo
Vice President Senior P and A Manager, Charles Chiappone
Vice President Finance, Laurie Goodman
Senior Vice President, Gerry Murphy
Executive Vice President Staffing, Barbara Bernstein
Vice President, Michelle Erny
Assistant Vice President and Fixed Income Trading Operations, Joy Hayes
Vice President, Nazli Beirne
Executive Vice President, Bryne Hurley
Vice President, John Mathai
Vice President, Bob Cummings
Vice President Portfolio Manager, Thad Paskell
Vice President, Marc Genovese
Vice President Credit Risk Manager, Dan Wang
Vice President of Infrastructure, Michael Knight
Vice President Real Estate, Cavarly Garrett
Executive Vice President Customer Service, Deborah Walden
Vice President Crm Retention Management, Gail Timmerman
Vice President, Luc Droal
Vice President Banker, David Sagers
Vice President Client Satisfaction, Giovanna Pape
Vice President and Banker, Peggy C Murphy
Vice President, Gregory Walker
Senior Vice President Special Credits Group, Phil Martin
Vice President Application DEVPMT, David Overmyer
Assistant Vice President, John R Chalmers
Vice President, Kelli Wehrwein
Vice President, Greg Schmidt
Vice President, Greg Martin
Assistantvice President Business Banker, Jason Lee
Vice President Commercial Banking, Bill Cook
Vice President, Chris Collins
Vice President, Keith Jia

Vice President Customer Analytics, Stella Ng
Chaseside Assistant Vice President, Mike Howe
Vice President, Matthew Green
Vice President, Fariah Feinstein
Vice President of Technology, Miguel Choto
Vice President Architect Lead, Rajiv Kewalramani
Vice President Digital Marketing, Lauren Coulston
Vice President, Alice Lo
Vice President, Luis Oganes
Private Client Advisor Vice President, Jeff Williams
Vice President Human Resources Program Management, Jenny Blanco
Senior Vice President, Elli Thermos
Global Technology Vice President, Tom Pryor
Vice President Information Technology, Jason Tucker
Assistant Vice President Information Technology Production Assurance Analyst, Jarrod Holt
Vice President, Denise Connors
Senior Vice President, Mary Reilly
Vice President, Kevin Connor
Vice President Enterprise Technology Services, Josiah Lam
Vice President Area Manager, Sherry Minda
Assistant Vice President Business Relationship Manager, Carlo Condong
Senior Vice President, Bill W Handley
Vice President Treasury Services Manager, Jenny Chan
Vice President Generalist, Julie Bohan
Senior Vice President, John Ireton
Vice President in Technology, Michael Taylor
Vice President, John Friedman
Senior Vice President, Randolph Lopez
Vice President Chase Franchise Finance, Alma Winkel
Vice President, Gina Shera
Quality Assurance Analyst III And Assistant Vice President, Lisa Witcher
Vice President, Alessandro Bagnara
Assistant Vice President, Brian Anderson
Senior Vice President And Division Manager, Nick Klym
Vice President, Cherie Ward
Vice President, Amy Huelskamp
First Vice President, Heidi Scobell
Vice President, Gail Philips
Senior Vice President Middle Market Banking, Corey Limbaugh
Vice President, Luz Escarraman
Vice President, Diane Buschur
Vice President Appraisal Escalation Desk, Eric Gill
Vice President, Fiore Petrassi
Assistant Vice President, Christopher Bowman
Vice President, Joseph Pichla
Vice President, Todd Bruggeman
Vice President, Deb Vincent
Auditors: PricewaterhouseCoopers LLP

LOCATIONS

HQ: JPMorgan Chase & Co
270 Park Avenue, New York, NY 10017
Phone: 212 270-6000
Web: www.jpmorganchase.com

PRODUCTS/OPERATIONS

2016 Sales

	$ mil.	% of total
Interest		
Loans	36,634	35
securities	7,304	7
Trading assets	7,292	7
Federal funds sold & securities purchased under resale agreements	2,265	2
Deposits with banks	1,863	2
Securities borrowed	(332)	-
Other	875	1
Non-interest		
Asset management administration & commissions	14,591	14
Principal transactions	11,566	11
Investment banking fees	6,448	6
Lending- and deposit-related fees	5,774	5
Credit card income	4,779	4
Mortgage fees and related income	2,491	2
Securities gains	141	-
Other	3,795	4
Total	**101,006**	**100**

COMPETITORS

American Express	Goldman Sachs
Bank of America	HSBC
Bank of New York Mellon	Morgan Stanley
Barclays	PNC Financial
CIBC	RBC Financial Group
Capital One	State Bank Financial Corporation
Citigroup	SunTrust
Citigroup Global Markets	TD Bank USA
Credit Suisse (USA)	UBS
Deutsche Bank	Wells Fargo

HISTORICAL FINANCIALS

Company Type: Public

Income Statement
FYE: December 31

	ASSETS ($ mil.)	NET INCOME ($ mil.)	INCOME AS % OF ASSETS	EMPLOYEES
12/16	2,490,972	24,733	1.0%	243,355
12/15	2,351,698	24,442	1.0%	234,598
12/14	2,573,126	21,762	0.8%	241,359
12/13	2,415,689	17,923	0.7%	251,196
12/12	2,359,141	21,284	0.9%	258,965
Annual Growth	**1.4%**	**3.8%**	**—**	**(1.5%)**

2016 Year-End Financials

Debt ratio: 10.23%—
Return on equity: 9.83%
Cash ($ mil.): 389,635
Current ratio: —
Long-term debt ($ mil.): —

Dividends
Yield: 0.0%
Payout: 29.7%
Market value ($ mil.): —

	STOCK PRICE ($) FY Close	P/E High/Low		PER SHARE ($) Earnings	Dividends	Book Value
12/16	86.29	14	9	6.19	1.84	71.38
12/15	66.03	12	9	6.00	1.68	67.58
12/14	62.58	12	10	5.29	1.56	62.47
12/13	58.48	13	10	4.35	1.36	56.22
12/12	43.97	9	6	5.20	1.15	53.65
Annual Growth	**18.4%**	**—**		**4.5%**	**12.5%**	**7.4%**

Juniper Networks Inc

Juniper Networks helps its customers branch out and up all the way to the cloud. The company makes infrastructure hardware and software for large-scale networks for cloud-computing providers (including for data centers) telecommunications companies and large organizations in business government and education. Its routers and switches move traffic around networks and its software helps manage networks. Juniper also develops security products to protect from cyberattacks. Juniper sells directly and through resellers and distributors including Ingram Micro and Hitachi. More than half of sales are made to customers based in the US.

Operations

Juniper gets about 70% of its revenue from its networking equipment products and the rest from services. Routing products such as the ACX MX and Cloud Customer Platform series generate more than 45% of revenue. Services which include support professional and educational services account for about 30% of revenue with switching products ? the EX and QFX series ? providing about 15% and security products the SRX series among others less than 10%.

To get its products made Juniper relies on contract manufacturers - Celestica; Flex Ltd. Accton Technology and Alpha Networks.

Geographic Reach

The company does business in more than 100 countries. The US represents its largest market accounting for more than half of sales. Europe the Middle East and Africa combined account for about 25% of sales and Asia/Pacific makes up for about 15%

Sales and Marketing

Juniper sells its products directly and through distributors resellers and original equipment manufacturers (OEMs). About 70% of revenue came from telecom cable and cloud service providers with the rest from corporate customers. Juniper has resale agreements with Ericsson Dimension Data NEC Corp. and IBM.

Financial Performance

In 2016 Juniper posted its best-ever revenue but profit slipped below 2015?s figure.

The company's revenue rose 3% to about $5 billion from 2015 driven by the Switching and Services segments. Switching sales rose 12% boosted by a 50% increase of sales of the company?s QFX products. Service revenue rose 13% from being packaged with other products and contract renewals. Lower demand from telecommunications customers reduced the Routing segment?s revenue 6%. Security sales fell nearly 120% with the refresh of the MRX products underway and the phase-out of the Screen OS and other legacy products. The Europe/Middle East/Africa region was the only geographic segment to post lower revenue for 2016 due to reduced sales to companies moving to cloud computing and the timing of deployments for large telecom companies. Juniper also noted that macroeconomic uncertainties in the region and pricing pressures contributed to the revenue decline.

Juniper?s net income dropped 6% to $593 million in 2016 from 2015 because of pricing pressures and product mix. The company also set aside about $11 million to pay for remediation of defective components from a third-party supplier. Juniper had lower expenses as a percentage of revenue in 2016 from 2015.

Operating cash flow rose to $1.1 billion in 2016 from $892 million in 2015 as a result of timing differences in working capital.

Strategy

Juniper Networks is betting that helping customers move to cloud computing is the path to growth in the networking business. Beyond its traditional hardware products the company has added a range of software applications to meet the industrywide shift to software management of networks. In its router business the company offers the NorthStar WAN SDN (software defined network) controller for optimizing traffic on a network and it integrated its Contrail Networking SDN controller into its edge networking products.

Further strengthening Juniper's software portfolio was the acquisition of AppFormix. The software from AppFormix complements the analytics and machine learning capabilities of the Contrail product.

After a down year in 2016 for its security products Juniper looks for a rebound with products like Junos Space Security Director for security management and Sky ATP its first software-as-a-service offering.

Juniper faces competition on all sides as its tries to generate revenue from cloud computing. Competitors include industry giants such as Huawei Cisco Systems and Nokia as well as smaller companies like Arista Networks and Brocade Communications Systems which is being acquired by Broadcom. Other competitors are Hewlett Packard Enterprise and Dell Technologies (because of its acquisition of EMC).

Mergers and Acquisitions

In 2016 Juniper acquired AppFormix Inc. an optimization and management software platform for public private and hybrid clouds for about $50 million.

Also in 2016 Juniper bought the 88% interest it didn?t own of BTI Systems Inc. an optical equipment provider for about $25 million. The acquisition provides Juniper with optical transport solutions.

In a third 2016 deal Juniper paid about $74 million for 100% ownership of Aurrion Inc. a provider of fabless silicon photonic technology. The acquisition also bolsters Juniper?s optical portfolio.

EXECUTIVES

CTO and Chief Scientist, Pradeep S. Sindhu, age 64, $600,000 total compensation
SVP and CIO, Robert (Bob) Worrall, age 56
CEO, Rami Rahim, age 46, $1,000,000 total compensation
EVP and Chief Customer Officer, Vince Molinaro, $585,000 total compensation
EVP and General Manager Juniper Development and Innovation, Jonathan Davidson, $610,000 total compensation
EVP and CFO, Ken Miller, age 45, $499,755 total compensation
SVP and Chief Marketing Officer, Michael (Mike) Marcellin
SVP; GM APAC, Daniel Hua
Chief Development Officer, Anand (Andy) Athreya
SVP and General Manager Europe Middle East and Africa (EMEA), Marcus Jewell
Evp And General Manager Fabric And Switching Technologies Business Group, David Yen
Vice President and Managing Director Govedumed Americas Enterprise, John Orbe
Vice President Of Supply Chain, Joe Carson
Corporate Vice President Partners and Alliances, Brian Rosenberg
Executive Vice President Chief Sales Officer, Gerri Elliott
Vice President and Chief Compliance Officer, Michael Ward
Vice President Manufacturing Operations, Brad Tallman
Vice President of Service Provider Marketing, Paul Obsitnik
Chairman, Scott G. Kriens, age 59
Auditors: Ernst & Young LLP

LOCATIONS

HQ: Juniper Networks Inc
1133 Innovation Way, Sunnyvale, CA 94089
Phone: 408 745-2000 **Fax:** 408 745-2100
Web: www.juniper.net

2016 Sales

	$ mil.	% of total
Americas		
US	2,737	55
Others	231	4
Europe Middle East & Africa	1,238	25
Asia Pacific	783	16
Total	**4,990**	**100**

PRODUCTS/OPERATIONS

2016 Sales

	$ mil.	% of total
Products		
Routing	2,352	47
Switching	858	17
Security	318	7
Services	1,461	29
Total	**4,990**	**100**

2016 Sales by Market

	$ mil.	% of total
Service Provider	3,452	69
Enterprise	1,537	31
Total	**4,990**	**100**

Selected Products

Application Acceleration
Content and Media Delivery
Data Center Fabric
Identity and Policy Control
Juniper Developer Network
Mobile Infrastructure
Network Management
Network Operating System
Routers
Security
Software
Switches
Time Synchronization
Wireless
End-of-Sale Products

COMPETITORS

ADTRAN	Hewlett Packard
Arista Networks	Enterprise
Brocade Communications	Huawei Technologies
Check Point Software	IBM Internet Security
Cisco Systems	Systems
Citrix Systems	MRV Communications
Dell	NSN
Ericsson	Palo Alto Networks
Extreme Networks	Riverbed Technology
F5 Networks	Sycamore Networks
Fortinet	Solutions

HISTORICAL FINANCIALS

Company Type: Public

Income Statement   FYE: December 31

	REVENUE ($ mil.)	NET INCOME ($ mil.)	NET PROFIT MARGIN	EMPLOYEES
12/16	4,990	592	11.9%	9,832
12/15	4,857	633	13.0%	9,058
12/14	4,627	(334)	—	8,806
12/13	4,669	439	9.4%	9,483
12/12	4,365	186	4.3%	9,234
Annual Growth	3.4%	33.5%	—	1.6%

2016 Year-End Financials

Debt ratio: 22.10%
Return on equity: 12.40%
Cash ($ mil.): 1,833
Current ratio: 2.29
Long-term debt ($ mil.): 2,133
No. of shares (mil.): 381
Dividends
Yield: 0.0%
Payout: 26.1%
Market value ($ mil.): 10,770

	STOCK PRICE ($) FY Close	P/E High/Low	PER SHARE ($) Earnings	Dividends	Book Value
12/16	28.26	19 14	1.53	0.40	13.02
12/15	27.60	20 13	1.59	0.40	11.91
12/14	22.32	— —	(0.73)	0.20	11.82
12/13	22.57	26 18	0.86	0.00	14.75
12/12	19.67	66 40	0.35	0.00	13.77
Annual Growth	9.5%	— —	44.6%	—	(1.4%)

KAISER FOUNDATION HOSPITALS INC

Kaiser Foundation Hospitals is on a roll. The hospital group operates nearly 40 acute care hospitals and 680 medical offices in eight states (California Colorado Georgia Hawaii Maryland Oregon Virginia and Washington) and Washington D.C. The company's largest presence is in California where the majority of its hospitals are located. Kaiser Foundation Hospitals employs more than 21000 physicians representing all medical specialties. Kaiser Foundation Hospital's doctors group is controlled by Permanente Medical Groups and its HMO is offered through Kaiser Foundation Health Plan. Altogether the group provides care for about 11.7 million members.

Operations

Kaiser Foundation Hospitals works with other organizations to tackle such issues as obesity access to care and violence. It also works to promote health in the communities it serves through wellness programs.

In 2016 Kaiser Foundation Hospitals logged 44 million office visits. It facilitated 106000 births performed 129000 surgeries and filled 90 million prescriptions.

Company Background

Kaiser Foundation Hospitals was founded in 1945.

EXECUTIVES

EVP Kaiser Foundation Hospitals and Health Plan; Group President Kaiser Permanente Northern California and Mid-Atlantic States; President Kaiser Permanente Northern California, Gregory A. Adams

EVP Kaiser Foundation Hospitals and Health Plan; Group president Kaiser Permanente Southern California and Hawaii; President Kaiser Permanente Southern California, Benjamin K. Chu

Chairman Southern California Permanente Medical Group and Executive Medical Director, Edward Ellison

Vice President Of Information Technology, Lynn Fisher

Senior Vice President National Sales And Account Management, Thomas Curtin

Area Vice President Regional Teams, Neal Miller

Senior Management Senior Vice President General Manager Director, Anne Mcnealis

LOCATIONS

HQ: KAISER FOUNDATION HOSPITALS INC
1 KAISER PLZ, OAKLAND, CA 946123610
Phone: 510 271-6611
Web: WWW.HEALTHY.KAISERPERMANENTE.ORG

PRODUCTS/OPERATIONS

Selected Hospitals
Antioch Medical Center
Fremont Medical Center
Fresno Medical Center
Hayward Medical Center
Manteca Medical Center
Modesto Medical Center
Oakland Medical Center
Redwood City Medical Center
Richmond Medical Center
Roseville Women and Children's Center
San Jose Medical Center
Santa Clara Medical Center
Sacramento Medical Center

South San Francisco Medical Center
South Sacramento Trauma Center
Santa Rosa Medical Center
San Francisco Medical Center
San Rafael Medical Center
Vacaville Medical Center
Vallejo Medical Center
Walnut Creek Medical Center
Baldwin Park Medical Center
Downey Medical Center
Fontana Medical Center
Los Angeles Medical Center
Moreno Valley Community Hospital
Orange County - Anaheim Medical Center
Orange County - Irvine Medical Center
Panorama City Medical Center
Riverside Medical Center
San Diego Medical Center
Harbor City (South Bay Medical Center)
Woodlands Hills Medical Center
West Los Angeles Medical Center
Sunnyside Medical Center (Portland Oregon area)
Moanalua Medical Center (Hawaii)

COMPETITORS

Adventist Health System West	Dignity Health
Ascension Health	HCA
Banner Health	LifePoint Health
CHRISTUS Health	Mercy Health (OH)
Catholic Health Initiatives	Sutter Health
Community Health Systems	Tenet Healthcare
	The Cleveland Clinic
	Universal Health Services

HISTORICAL FINANCIALS

Company Type: Private

Income Statement

FYE: December 31

	REVENUE ($ mil.)	NET INCOME ($ mil.)	NET PROFIT MARGIN	EMPLOYEES
12/09	14,795	429	2.9%	175,668
12/08	0	0	99.0%	—
12/05	9,852	774	7.9%	—
Annual Growth	10.7%	(13.7%)	—	—

2009 Year-End Financials

Debt ratio: ——
Return on equity: 2.90%
Cash ($ mil.): 57
Current ratio: ——
Long-term debt ($ mil.): —

Dividends
Yield: —
Payout: —
Market value ($ mil.): —

Kansas City Life Insurance Co (Kansas City, MO)

Kansas City Life Insurance and subsidiary Sunset Life provide insurance products throughout the US to individuals (life and disability coverage and annuities) and to groups (life dental vision and disability insurance). Subsidiary Old American Insurance focuses on burial and related insurance. The insurance companies sell through more than 2500 independent agents brokers and third-party marketers. Kansas City Life also operates its own insurance and investment brokerage network through its Sunset Financial Services unit. Chairman and CEO R. Philip Bixby and his family control the company.

Operations

Kansas City Life offers both universal and variable life policies. The company operates in three business segments: Individual Insurance Group Insurance and Old American.

The Individual Insurance segment (68% of the company's revenues in 2014) consists of individual insurance products for both Kansas City Life and Sunset Life as well as the coinsurance and reinsurance transactions.

Old American (19% of Kansas City Life's revenues in 2014) sells final expense traditional life insurance products for the senior market (50-85 years old) principally through final arrangements planning (burial and related insurance).

The Group Insurance segment (13% of the company's revenues in 2014) is operated as part of Kansas City Life and its administrative and accounting operations are part of the company's home office. It has two primary markets: groups with between two and nine employees and groups with 10 or more employees.

Geographic Reach

The company operates in 49 US states and Washington DC. Some of its largest state markets include Missouri Texas Kansas California and Colorado.

Sales and Marketing

Kansas City Life markets its products through a nationwide sales force of independent general agents agents brokers and third-party marketing arrangements. Old American uses direct response marketing to supply agents with leads.

Financial Performance

The company saw marginal revenue increases in 2012 and 2013 followed by a 4% decline to $465 million in 2014. That decline was primarily due to declines in individual insurance premiums new immediate annuity premiums fixed annuity renewal deposits and universal life renewal deposits. However the company saw increases in group insurance and Old America premiums as well as renewal premiums.

Kansas City Life reached its historic peak of $40 million in net income in 2012 but that was followed by a 26% decline in 2013 due to a reduction in net realized investment gains. In 2014 net income remained relatively flat due to revenue declines (partially offset by declines in income taxes paid).

Cash flows from operations have also declined as of late — except in 2013 when cash flow increased by $41 million and touched its historic peak of $56 million as a result of cash generated from future policy benefits. In 2014 cash flow from operations fell 32% to $38 million due to an increase in cash used in reinsurance recoverables and a decline in cash provided by future policy benefits.

Strategy

The company is looking to grow by acquiring other life insurance companies expanding its product portfolio moving into new markets and by enhancing technology.

It also targets strategic growth opportunities through assumed reinsurance. In 2013 the Company completed a 100% modified coinsurance agreement for separate accounts a 100% coinsurance agreement for the fixed fund general account and a servicing agreement for a block of variable universal life insurance policies and variable annuity contracts from American Family.

The company is focused on expanding its individual life insurance operations by widening its distribution network and enhancing its marketing efforts. For instance it has marketing agreements with health plan provider American Republic Insurance and property/casualty firm GuideOne Insurance which distribute the life policies of Kansas City Life to their respective members and policyholders.

Expanding its individual insurance product portfolio in 2013 the company began to offer an indexed universal life product.

Old American is expanding its sales territories with a focus on the recruitment and development of new agencies and agents.

Group Insurance is looking to deliver more effective electronic and automated support through interactive delivery sites.

Company Background

The Bixby family owns about 60% of the company through trusts and investment partnerships.

Founded in 1895 the company built up its operations through a number of historical acquisitions including GuideOne Life (2003) Old American (1991) and Sunset Life (1974). The company exited its banking operations (Generations Bank) in 2007.

EXECUTIVES

SVP and Actuary Kansas City Life and VP and Actuary Sunset Life Insurance Company of America, Mark A. Milton, age 58, $325,812 total compensation

Chairman President and CEO, R. Philip Bixby, age 63, $779,160 total compensation

Director; President Old American Insurance, Walter E. (Web) Bixby, age 58, $347,088 total compensation

SVP Finance CFO and Director, Tracy W. Knapp, age 54, $322,344 total compensation

SVP Sales and Marketing Kansas City Life; VP Sales and Marketing Sunset Life, Donald E. (Don) Krebs, age 59, $300,060 total compensation

SVP Operations, Stephen E (Steve) Ropp, age 57

Assistant Vice President and Chief Underwriter, Mike Augustine

Regional Vice President, Bill Browning

Assistant Vice President, Dawn Roy

Vice President, Timothy Knott

Vice President Securities, Phil Williams

Vice President Of Customer Service, Richard Ropp

Assistant Vice President Of Marketing, Kris Jones

Medical Director, Charlotte Lee

Assistant Vice President, Stephen Mack

Assistant Vice President and Associate Actuary, Jill Daniel

Vice President Information Technology, Rob Fisher

Assistant Vice President Corporate Communications, Holly Ropp

Assistant Vice President Treasurer andamp; Assistant Controller, Paul Knoblauch

Assistant Vice President Marketing Services, Jim Wilcox

Assistant Vice President, Steve Mack

Senior Vice President Sales and Marketing, Don Krebs

Auditors: BKD, LLP

LOCATIONS

HQ: Kansas City Life Insurance Co (Kansas City, MO)
3520 Broadway, Kansas City, MO 64111
Phone: 816 753-7000   **Fax:** 816 753-4902
Web: www.kclife.com

PRODUCTS/OPERATIONS

2016 sales

	$ mil.	% of total
Individual Insurance	141	50
Group Insurance	56	20
Old American	84	30
Total	**282**	**100**

Selected Subsidiaries

Old American Insurance Company
Sunset Financial Services
Sunset Life Insurance Company of America

COMPETITORS

AEGON USA	MassMutual
Advance Insurance of Kansas	MetLife
	National Western
American Equity Life	Nationwide
American Heritage Life Insurance	New York Life
	Northwestern Mutual
American National Insurance	Phoenix Companies
	Primerica
Americo	Protective Life
Citizens Inc.	Prudential
Delphi Financial Group	Security Benefit Group
FBL Financial	The Hartford
Homesteaders Life	Torchmark
Kemper Corp	Universal American

HISTORICAL FINANCIALS

Company Type: Public

Income Statement

FYE: December 31

	ASSETS ($ mil.)	NET INCOME ($ mil.)	INCOME AS % OF ASSETS	EMPLOYEES
12/16	4,449	22	0.5%	—
12/15	4,421	29	0.7%	441
12/14	4,571	29	0.7%	436
12/13	4,514	29	0.7%	446
12/12	4,525	39	0.9%	443
Annual Growth	**(0.4%)**	**(13.5%)**	**—**	**—**

2016 Year-End Financials

Debt ratio: —
Return on equity: 3.30%
Cash ($ mil.): 9
Current ratio: —
Long-term debt ($ mil.): —

No. of shares (mil.): 9
Dividends
  Yield: 0.0%
  Payout: 46.9%
Market value ($ mil.): 460

	STOCK PRICE ($) FY Close	P/E High/Low		PER SHARE ($) Earnings	Dividends	Book Value
12/16	47.50	21	15	2.30	1.08	70.80
12/15	38.29	18	15	2.75	1.08	68.55
12/14	48.03	18	15	2.75	1.08	68.61
12/13	47.74	19	13	2.70	1.08	66.13
12/12	38.16	11	9	3.60	1.35	68.02
Annual Growth	**5.6%**	—	—	**(10.6%)**	**(5.4%)**	**1.0%**

Kearny Financial Corp (MD)

LOCATIONS

HQ: Kearny Financial Corp (MD)
120 Passaic Avenue, Fairfield, NJ 07004
Phone: 973 244-4500
Web: www.kearnybank.com

HISTORICAL FINANCIALS

Company Type: Public

Income Statement

FYE: June 30

	ASSETS ($ mil.)	NET INCOME ($ mil.)	INCOME AS % OF ASSETS	EMPLOYEES
06/17	4,818	18	0.4%	466
06/16	4,500	15	0.4%	459
06/15	4,237	5	0.1%	491
06/14	3,510	10	0.3%	474
06/13	0	6		
Annual Growth	**—**	**30.0%**		

2017 Year-End Financials

Debt ratio: 16.73%
Return on equity: 1.69%
Cash ($ mil.): 78
Current ratio: —
Long-term debt ($ mil.): —

No. of shares (mil.): 84
Dividends
  Yield: 0.6%
  Payout: 45.4%
Market value ($ mil.): 1,253

	STOCK PRICE ($) FY Close	P/E High/Low		PER SHARE ($) Earnings	Dividends	Book Value
06/17	14.85	73	57	0.22	0.10	12.53
06/16	12.58	74	62	0.18	0.08	12.50
06/15	11.16	191	179	0.06	0.00	12.48
Annual Growth	**7.4%**	—	—	**38.4%**	—	**0.1%**

Kellogg Co

This Special K is a cereal winner. From the company's home base in Battle Creek Michigan Kellogg Company battles with rival General Mills for the #1 spot in the US cereal market. Kellogg founded in 1906 boasts many familiar cereal brands including Kellogg's Corn Flakes Frosted Flakes Froot Loops Special K and Rice Krispies. While the company works to fill the world's cereal bowls it actually makes more money these days from its snacks and convenience brands such as Kashi Pringles Keebler Cheez-It and Famous Amos (snacks) and Eggo waffles and Nutri-Grain and Bear Naked cereal bars (convenience). Its products are sold worldwide.

Operations

Kellogg operates through several segments based on product category and geographic location. They include US Snacks (around 25% of sales) US Morning Foods (another 25% of sales) and US Specialty (around 10%). Kellogg rings up nearly 20% of sales in its Europe segment 12% in other North America (Canada) and around 5% each in Asia and Latin America.

US Snacks includes cookies crackers cereal bars savory snacks and fruit-flavored snacks. The US Morning Foods segment includes cereal toaster pastries health and wellness bars and beverages. US Specialty primarily represents non-residential food operations including food service convenience vending Girl Scouts (Kellogg produces Girl Scout Cookies for the Girl Scouts of the USA who sell them as a fundraiser) and food manufacturing.

Geographic Reach

The food company manufactures its products in over 20 countries and markets them in more than 180. It generates around 65% of its revenue in the US.

The company's manufacturing facilities in the US include four cereal plants and warehouses in Battle Creek Michigan; Lancaster Pennsylvania; Memphis Tennessee; and Omaha Nebraska. Its other facilities are mostly in Georgia Kentucky Michigan and Ohio.

Outside the US Kellogg has additional manufacturing locations (some with warehousing facilities) in about 20 countries in Europe Asia Africa and South America. The company has joint ventures in China Nigeria and Turkey.

Sales and Marketing

Kellogg's top five customers generate some 35% of Kellogg's total sales and over 45% of US sales.

The company markets its cereal products in general under the recognizable Kellogg's name as well as its "healthy" brand Kashi. Products are sold to supermarkets through a direct sales force model for resale to consumers. Kellogg uses broker and distributor arrangements for certain products in retail stores restaurants and other food service establishments. These particular arrangements are leveraged to market its products in less-developed areas or in markets outside its focus.

Financial Performance

Kellogg continued a four-year slide in revenue in fiscal 2016 (ended December).

Revenue fell a further 4% to $13 billion. By comparison it made not far off $15 billion in 2013. Kellogg's North America Other segment declined due to weakness in Kashi and Morningstar Farms a poor first half of 2016 pushed US Snacks revenue down and US Morning Foods' non-core categories fell sharply.

Net income climbed for the first time in a few years climbing 13% to $694 million. The increase came from the success of Kellogg's "Project K" cost cutting program.

Cash from operating activities was down 4% to $1.6 billion due to $97 million of after-tax costs relating to redeemed debentures.

Strategy

Kellogg is working at cutting costs and expanding revenue as consumers are turning away from its old reliable cereal lines as awareness of the health risks of sugar increases.

Its ongoing "Project K" efficiency and effectiveness program began in 2013 and will continue through to 2018. This program is designed to help the company focus on core products with increased level of value-added innovation.

Kellogg has adopted a zero-based budgeting (ZBB) program whereby all expenses must be rejustified each period in its North America business. The process helped slice $100 million in annual savings in North America in 2016. The company plans to expand ZBB program to international market.

On the product side Kellogg is extending and repositioning several brands. Kellogg reformulated Special K to create Special K Nourish with probiotic qualities. The company believes probiotics have greater appeal than low calories. Other product extensions include Mini-Wheats Harvest Delights Smorz and Dory-themed cereal (in line with the Disney Pixar movie "Finding Dory.")

In the cookie aisle Kellogg advertising is bringing back the Keebler Elves to push cookies. The company also is putting attention and muscle behind the Kashi brand. It intends to promote Kashi Go-Lean products which have been Non-GMO Project Verified and Kashi Heart-to-Heart products which have been fashioned to meet the USDA's organic standard.

In 2016 Kellogg was ready to open a cereal restaurant in Times Square in New York City to showcase its traditional offerings as well as more adventurous concoctions developed by chefs.

Mergers and Acquisitions

In 2016 Kellogg acquired Ritmo Investments a Brazilian food group that owns the Parati Zoo Cartoon Hot Cracker and Padua brands. The acquisition strengthens its snacking and emerging market businesses.

HISTORY

Will Keith (W. K.) Kellogg first made wheat flakes in 1894 while working for his brother Dr. John Kellogg at Battle Creek Michigan's famed homeopathic sanitarium. While doing an experiment with grains (for patients' diets) the two men were interrupted; by the time they returned to the dough it had absorbed water. They rolled it anyway toasted the result and accidentally created the first flaked cereal. John sold the flakes via mail order (1899) in a partnership that W. K. managed. In 1906 W. K. started his own firm to produce corn flakes.

As head of the Battle Creek Toasted Corn Flake Company W. K. competed against 42 cereal companies in Battle Creek (one run by former patient C. W. Post) and roared to the head of the pack with his innovative marketing ideas. A 1906 Ladies' Home Journal ad helped increase demand from 33 cases a day earlier that year to 2900 a day by year-end. W. K. soon introduced Bran Flakes (1915) All-Bran (1916) and Rice Krispies (1928). International expansion began in Canada (1914) and followed in Australia (1924) and England (1938).

EXECUTIVES

CEO and Director, Steven A. (Steve) Cahillane, age 52

Vice Chairman Corporate Development and Chief Legal Officer, Gary H. Pilnick, age 53, $719,092 total compensation

SVP; President Kellogg North America, Paul T. Norman, age 53, $783,319 total compensation

Chief Growth Officer, Clive Sirkin

President U.S. Specialty Channels, Wendy Davidson, age 46

SVP and CFO, Fareed A. Khan, age 52

President U.S. Morning Foods, Craig Bahner, age 52

SVP Global Snacks Category, Jim Cali, age 56

President Asia/Pacific, Amit Banati, age 48

SVP and CIO, Brian S. Rice, age 54

President US Snacks Division, Deanie Elsner

President Kellogg Canada, Carol Stewart

CEO Kashi Company, David J. Denholm

SVP Global Supply Chain, Alistair D. Hirst, age 57, $552,770 total compensation

SVP; President Kellogg Latin America, Maria F. Mejia

President Kellogg Europe, Chris Hood, $540,896 total compensation

President U.S. Frozen Foods, Andrew Loucks

SVP Global Breakfast Category, Doug VanDeVelde

Vice President Nutrition, Guy Johnson

Vice President, Margaret Bath

Vice President Sales, Kristina Geier

National Accounts Manager, Scott Abajian

Vice President Supply Chain, Gerry McMahon

National Account Manager, Laura Scherer

Senior Vice President Integrated Marketing, Gail Horwood

VP Supply Chain, Jeffrey Arnold

Vice President, Pablo Lewin

Vice President and Chief Sustainability Officer, Diane Holdorf

Chairman, John A. Bryant, age 52

ABM, Eric Hines

Auditors: PricewaterhouseCoopers LLP

LOCATIONS

HQ: Kellogg Co
One Kellogg Square, P.O. Box 3599, Battle Creek, MI 49016-3599
Phone: 269 961-2000
Web: www.kelloggcompany.com

2016 Sales

	$ mil.	% of total
United States	8,560	63
International	4,965	37
Total	**13,525**	**100**

2016 Sales

	$ mil.	% of total
United States	8,438	65
International	4,576	35
Total	**13,014**	**100**

PRODUCTS/OPERATIONS

2016 Sales

	$ mil.	% of total
U.S. Snacks	3,198	25
U.S. Morning Foods	2,931	23
Europe	2,377	18
North America Other	1,598	12
U.S. Specialty	1,214	9
Asia Pacific	916	7
Latin America	780	6
Total	**13,014**	**100**

2016 Sales

	$ mil.	% of total
Cereal	5,440	42
Snacks	6,660	51
Frozen	914	7
Total	**13,014**	**100**

Selected Cereal Brands

Asia and Australia
BeBig
Cerola
Chex
Frosties
Goldies
Kellogg's Iron Man Food
Nutri-Grain
Rice Bubbles
Sultana Bran
Canada
Vector
Vive
Europe
Choco Pops
Chocos
Country Store
Frosties
Fruit ‘n' Fibre
Honey Loops
Kellogg's Crunchy Nut Corn Flakes
Kellogg's Crunchy Nut Red Corn Flakes
Kellogg's Extra
Muslix
Optima
Pops
Ricicles
Smacks
Start
Sustain
Latin America
Choco Krispis
Choco Zucaritas
Crusli Sucrilhos
Musli
NutriDia
Sucrilhos Chocolate
Vector
Zucaritas
US
All-Bran
Apple Jacks
Bran Buds
Cinnamon Crunch
Cocoa Krispies
Complete Bran Flakes
Complete Wheat Flakes
Corn Pops
Cracklin' Oat Bran
Crispix
Crunch
Cruncheroos
Froot Loops
Frosted Krispies
Frosted Mini-Wheats
Just Right
Kellogg's Corn Flakes
Kellogg's Frosted Flakes
Kellogg's Low-Fat Granola
Kellogg's Raisin Bran
Mueslix
Pops
Product 19
Raisin Bran
Rice Krispies
Smacks/Honey Smacks
Smart Start
Special K
Special K Red Berries

Selected Other Brands

Cereal Bars and Granola
- All-Bran
- Bear Naked
- Choco Krispies
- Froot Loops
- GoLean
- Kashi

Convenience Foods
- Austin
- Cheez-It
- Chips Deluxe
- Club
- Croutettes Croutons
- E. L. Fudge
- Famous Amos
- Fudge Shoppe
- Hi-Ho
- Keebler
- Kellogg's Corn Flake Crumbs
- Krispy Munch'Ems
- Murray
- Pop-Tarts
- Pop-Tarts Pastry Swirls
- Pop-Tarts Snak-Stix
- Pringles
- Ready Crust
- Rice Krispies Squares
- Rice Krispies Treats
- Right Bites
- Sandies
- Soft Batch
- Stretch Island
- Sunshine
- Toasteds
- Town House

Frozen Waffles and Pancakes
- Eggo
- Froot Loops
- Nutri-Grain
- Special K

Water and Water Mixes
- Special K
- Special K2O

Meat and Egg Alternatives
- Gardenburger
- Loma Linda
- Morningstar Farms
- Natural Touch
- Worthington

COMPETITORS

Amy's Kitchen	McKee Foods
Barbara's Bakery	Mondelez International
Bob's Red Mill Natural Foods	Nestlé
Boca Foods	Patty King
Campbell Soup	PepsiCo
ConAgra	Pinnacle Foods
Frito-Lay	PowerBar
General Mills	Ralston Food
Gilster-Mary Lee	Schulze and Burch
Goodman Fielder	Snyder's-Lance
Hain Celestial	Weetabix
J & J Snack Foods	Wellness Foods
Jordans & Ryvita	Wessanen
MOM Brands	granoVita

HISTORICAL FINANCIALS

Company Type: Public

Income Statement

FYE: December 31

	REVENUE ($ mil.)	NET INCOME ($ mil.)	NET PROFIT MARGIN	EMPLOYEES
12/16*	13,014	694	5.3%	37,369
01/16	13,525	614	4.5%	33,577
01/15	14,580	632	4.3%	29,790
12/13	14,792	1,807	12.2%	30,277
12/12	14,197	961	6.8%	31,006
Annual Growth	(2.2%)	(7.8%)	—	4.8%

*Fiscal year change

2016 Year-End Financials

Debt ratio: 51.40%
Return on equity: 34.47%
Cash ($ mil.): 280
Current ratio: 0.66
Long-term debt ($ mil.): 6,698

No. of shares (mil.): 351
Dividends
Yield: 0.0%
Payout: 104.0%
Market value ($ mil.): 25,877

	STOCK PRICE ($) FY Close	P/E High/Low		PER SHARE ($) Earnings	Dividends	Book Value
12/16*	73.71	44	35	1.96	2.04	5.44
01/16	72.27	42	35	1.72	1.98	6.08
01/15	65.48	39	32	1.75	1.90	7.83
12/13	60.98	14	11	4.94	1.80	9.77
12/12	55.33	21	17	2.67	1.74	6.70
Annual Growth	7.4%	—	—	(7.4%)	4.1%	(5.1%)

*Fiscal year change

Kelly Services, Inc.

Staffing firm Kelly Services supplies temporary employees primarily across the light industrial technical and professional sectors including information technology specialists engineers and accountants. It also places lawyers (Kelly Law Registry) scientists (Kelly Scientific Resources) substitute teachers (Kelly Educational Staffing) nurses and other medical staff (Kelly Healthcare Resources) and teleservices personnel (KellyConnect). Kelly Services assigns some 500000 temporary employees around the world each year.

Operations

Kelly provides additional personnel in areas such as electronics (Kelly Electronic Assembly Services) merchandising (Kelly Marketing Services) and catering (Kelly Catering and Hospitality). It also offers career transition outplacement and human resources consulting services through its Ayers Group division (which makes up its Outsourcing and Consulting Group segment or OCG).

Geographic Reach

Kelly caters to customers in three chief regions: the Americas (more than 65% of total sales); Europe the Middle East and Africa (EMEA nearly 20%); and the Asia/Pacific (more than 15%).

Sales and Marketing

Kelly spent $7.6 million on advertising in fiscal 2017. The company?s 100 largest customers account for more than 50% of its revenue and its top customer accounts for nearly 5% of its revenue.

Financial Performance

Kelly's revenues have remained relatively consistent in recent years. However in fiscal 2017 revenue dropped to $5.28 billion from $5.52 billion in fiscal 2016.

Despite the dip in revenue during fiscal 2017 the company's net income increased compared to the prior fiscal period. Kelly reported a net income of $120 million for fiscal 2017 up from $53.8 million in fiscal 2016. Cash flow from operations also increased in fiscal 2017 compared to the prior fiscal year. The company ended fiscal 2017 with $37 million up from $23.5 million at the conclusion of fiscal 2016.

Strategy

Kelly's strategy for growth entails maintaining its core strengths in the commercial staffing market while also growing its professional and technical staffing capabilities. Kelly also plans to recognize additional revenue by growing its Outsourcing and Consulting Group segment and by targeting specialized niche markets which require staffing services.

HISTORY

William Russell Kelly a college dropout and former car salesman went to Detroit after WWII to seek his fortune. An owner of modern business equipment he set up Russell Kelly Office Service in 1946 to provide copying typing and inventory services for other businesses; first-year sales from 12 customers totaled $848.

Although companies began to acquire their own machines Kelly knew that they still needed people to work at their offices. He reincorporated his rapidly expanding business as Personnel Service in 1952 and opened the company's first branch office in Louisville Kentucky in 1955; by the end of that year he had 35 offices throughout the US. In 1957 the company was renamed Kelly Girl Service to reflect its all-female workforce.

In the 1960s Kelly ventured beyond office services and began placing convention hostesses blue-collar workers data processors door-to-door marketers and drafters among others. Kelly Girl went public in 1962 boasting 148 branches at the time. In 1966 the company adopted the name Kelly Services. It opened its first non-US office in Toronto in 1968 and one in Paris followed in 1972.

EXECUTIVES

Vice President, Tami Troxell
SVP and General Manager Global Business Services (GBS, James H. Bradley
President and CEO, George S. Corona, age 58, $655,000 total compensation
SVP and General Manager US Operations, Steven S. (Steve) Armstrong, age 59
SVP Centers of Excellence and General Manager Outsourcing and Consulting Group, Teresa S. Carroll, age 51, $500,000 total compensation
EVP Kelly Services and President Global Staffing and General Manager Global Information Technology Global Business Services and Global Service, Peter W. Quigley, age 55, $500,000 total compensation
SVP and CIO, Judy Snyder
SVP and CFO, Olivier G. Thirot, age 55, $515,000 total compensation
SVP Global Solutions, Myke Hawkins
Chief Legal Officer, Hannah Lim-Johnson
Chief Human Resources Officer, Kristin Supancich
SVP Centralized Operations Management (COM), Debra (Deb) Thorpe
Vice President Kelly Human Resources Solutions, Sandy Fitzpatrick
Vice President and Managing Director, John Healy
Vice President Tax And Purchasing, Mike Orsini
Territory Vice President, Brittna Valenzuela
Vice President Regional Sales and Account Services, Brian Pauley
Vice President, Donna Chantos
Vice President Pro Practice Lead, Tom Kaminsky
Vice President and Sector Lead, David Weeks
National Sales Manager, Yasikaan Chairoongrojsakul
Vice President Global Infrastructure, Darryl Staskowski
Vice President and District Manager Ak, Rich Struble
Vice President, Michelle Brown
Vice President and District Manager, Eileen Candels
Vice President Chicago, Brad Beckner
Vice President, John Drew
Chairman, Terence E. (Terry) Adderley, age 83
Board Member, Elizabeth Gonzalez-Benedict
Board Member, Lisa LaCrosse
Auditors: PricewaterhouseCoopers LLP

LOCATIONS

HQ: Kelly Services, Inc.
999 West Big Beaver Road, Troy, MI 48084
Phone: 248 362-4444
Web: www.kellyservices.com

2017 Sales

	$ mil.	% of total
US	3,722	71
International	1,554	29
Total	**5,276**	**100**

PRODUCTS/OPERATIONS

2017 Sales

	$ mil.	% of total
Americas		
Commercial	2,548	48
Professional & Technical	941	18
EMEA		
Commercial	769	15
Professional & Technical	168	3
APAC		
Commercial	170	3
Professional & Technical	18	-
Outsourcing & Consulting Group	706	13
Adjustments (-51.8) -		
Total	**5,276**	**100**

Selected Services

CGR/seven (creative services staffing)
Kelly Catering and Hospitality (chefs porters)
Kelly Educational Staffing (substitute teachers)
Kelly Electronic Assembly Services
Kelly Engineering Resources (engineers)
Kelly Financial Resources (accounting analysts)
Kelly Government Solutions (US federal government staffing)
Kelly Healthcare Resources (nurses medical technicians)
Kelly Information Technology Resources
Kelly Law Registry
Kelly Light Industrial
Kelly Marketing Services
Kelly Office Services (clerical staffing)
Kelly Scientific Resources (science staffing)
KellyConnect (call center staffing)
KellyDirect (permanent placement service)
KellySelect (temporary-to-hire service)

COMPETITORS

ATC Healthcare	Randstad Holding
Adecco	Robert Half
Allegis Group	Technical Aid
Insperity	Corporation
ManpowerGroup	TrueBlue
On Assignment	Volt Information

HISTORICAL FINANCIALS

Company Type: Public

Income Statement

FYE: January 1

	REVENUE ($ mil.)	NET INCOME ($ mil.)	NET PROFIT MARGIN	EMPLOYEES
01/17	5,276	120	2.3%	507,500
01/16*	5,518	53	1.0%	558,100
12/14	5,562	23	0.4%	563,300
12/13	5,413	58	1.1%	548,100
12/12	5,450	50	0.9%	568,100
Annual Growth	**(0.8%)**	**24.6%**	**—**	**(2.8%)**

*Fiscal year change

2017 Year-End Financials

Debt ratio: —	No. of shares (mil.): 38
Return on equity: 12.70%	Dividends
Cash ($ mil.): 29	Yield: 0.0%
Current ratio: 1.58	Payout: 8.9%
Long-term debt ($ mil.): —	Market value ($ mil.): 877

	STOCK PRICE ($) FY Close	P/E High/Low		PER SHARE ($)		
				Earnings	Dividends	Book Value
01/17	22.92	8	5	3.08	0.28	26.46
01/16*	16.15	13	10	1.39	0.20	23.57
12/14	17.00	42	25	0.61	0.20	22.10
12/13	25.29	17	10	1.54	0.20	21.98
12/12	15.55	13	9	1.32	0.20	19.93
Annual Growth	**10.2%**	—	—	**23.6%**	**8.3%**	**7.3%**

*Fiscal year change

Kemper Corp (DE)

Kemper is among the largest property/casualty insurance groups in the US. The company operates through two operating segments: Property and Casualty Insurance and Life and Health Insurance. The Property and Casualty Insurance segment's principal products are personal automobile insurance (both standard and non-standard risk) homeowners insurance other personal insurance and commercial automobile insurance. The smaller Life and Health Insurance segment's principal products are individual life accident health and property insurance. The company operates in the southern midwestern and western US.

Operations

The Kemper family of companies specializes in property/casualty insurance and life and health insurance products for individuals families and small businesses. Property and Casualty Insurance accounts for about two-thirds of the company's revenues while Life and Health Insurance accounts for the other third. It primarily does business through Kemper Home Service Companies which provides individual life and supplemental accident and health insurance products to customers of limited incomes. The smaller Reserve National unit sells specialty individual accident life and health insurance policies including illness and hospitalization plans.

Geographic Reach

Kemper sells its policies in 50 US states and Washington DC. Its largest markets include Alabama California Florida Louisiana Mississippi New York North Carolina Oregon and Texas. The Kemper Home Services Companies unit operates in 28 states.

Sales and Marketing

Kemper offers its services through independent agents and brokers. The Property and Casualty Insurance segment's products are offered by 18000 independent insurance agents and brokers. Kemper Direct sells auto and home coverage by phone and online. Kemper Home Services uses a network of some 2200 career agents while Reserve National uses about 400 independent agents.

Financial Performance

Kemper's revenues have been climbing the past couple of years; in 2016 revenue increased 8% to $2.5 billion. This was largely due to higher earned premium income but offset by lower net investment income other income and net realized gains on sales of investments. Earned premiums rose in the categories of personal automobile life and accident and health that year. The largest single business personal automobile increased 21% in terms of earned premiums.

However overall net income has been falling and in 2016 it dropped 80% to $16.8 million. This was driven by higher incurred catastrophe losses and underlying losses.

Cash flow from operations which has increased every year since 2012 rose another 12% to $240.5 million in 2016 (despite the lower net income). Positive adjustments to reconcile net income to net cash provided by operating activities especially an increase in insurance reserves led to that increase.

Strategy

In mid-2017 Kemper took a step back and decided that changes were needed to rejuvenate the company and that's just what it set out to do going forward. Its primary goals included making its recently acquired Alliance United unit profitable again investing in new technologies to support and improve operations and implementing new claims processes in its life insurance businesses.

Other areas of focus are increasing brand awareness diversifying operations and growing through acquisitions. The company also seeks to reduce catastrophe exposure through reinsurance (risk-sharing) agreements and selective underwriting practices.

Mergers and Acquisitions

In 2018 Kemper agreed to buy non-standard auto insurer Infinity Property and Casualty for $1.4 billion. Infinity does most of its business in California Florida and Texas and one of its key target markets is Hispanic consumers.

Company Background

The company changed its name from Unitrin to Kemper in August 2011; it also rebranded several of its business units under the Kemper name. The name change followed a downsizing where the company shed or shuttered several operations. Its Fireside Bank subsidiary which purchased subprime loan contracts from used automobile dealers halted lending activities in 2009 and ceased banking operations in 2012. Kemper also explored options to sell its Reserve National subsidiary but instead narrowed the unit's focus on specialized life and health policies.

Kemper's disposal-heavy strategy followed a period of expansion in its traditional consumer insurance options. The company enriched its property/casualty business segment through acquisitions of smaller companies.

James Kemper founded National Underwriters insurance exchange in 1913 to provide supplementary fire insurance for lumbermen.

EXECUTIVES

Executive Vice President Chief Financial Officer A, Eric Draut
VP and Chief Accounting Officer, Richard Roeske, age 57, $371,000 total compensation
EVP Kemper Preferred, Naimish Patel
SVP and Chief Investment Officer, John M. Boschelli, age 49, $400,000 total compensation
President and CEO, Joseph P. (Joe) Lacher, age 48, $750,000 total compensation
President Property and Casualty, George D. (Chip) Dufala, age 45, $214,519 total compensation
EVP; General Manager Kemper Specialty California, Timothy D. Bruns
President Kemper Home Service, Thomas D. Myers
Chief Risk Officer, Shekar G. Jannah
SVP Operations and Systems, Charles T. Brooks, age 51
SVP; President Life and Health, Mark A. Green, age 50, $240,692 total compensation
SVP and CFO, James J. McKinney, age 38
Vice President, Brad Andrekus
Vice President Human Resources Kemper Division, Scott Tomlinson
Vice President, Elizabeth Lupetini
Vice President and Treasurer, Christopher Moses
Avp Is, Brenda Williamson
Vice President Of Actuarial Services, Bradley Andrekus

Vice President Information Technology, Ray Gordon

Regional Vice President Adminstrative Assistant, Threnn Kim

Senior Vice President Product Underwriting and Pricing, Eric Neely

Assistant Vice President Property Claims HSIS, Greg Warnock

Associate Vice President Financial Analysis and Planning, Edward Aguirre

Senior Vice President and Chief Data and Analytics Officer, Andy Lau

Secretary, Scott Renwick

Chairman, Robert J. (Bob) Joyce

Senior Vice President Secretary and General Counsel, C Thomas Evans

Board Member, Wayne Kauth

Auditors: DELOITTE & TOUCHE LLP

LOCATIONS

HQ: Kemper Corp (DE)
One East Wacker Drive, Chicago, IL 60601
Phone: 312 661-4600
Web: www.kemper.com

PRODUCTS/OPERATIONS

2016 sales

	$ mil.	% of total
Property/casualty insurance	1,688	66
Life & health insurance	821	32
Net realized gains on the sales of investments	33	1
Net impairment losses recognized in earning	(33)	-
Other	13	1
Total	**2,522**	**100**

Selected Insurance Options

Auto
Boat
Collectibles
Commercial Auto
Condo
Home
Identity Fraud
Life and Health
Package
Personal Catastrophe Liability
Personal Valuables
Renters

COMPETITORS

Allstate
Citizens Financial
Citizens Inc.
GEICO
Liberty Mutual Agency
Nationwide

Penn-America
Security National
Financial
State Farm
USAA

HISTORICAL FINANCIALS

Company Type: Public

Income Statement

FYE: December 31

	ASSETS ($ mil.)	NET INCOME ($ mil.)	INCOME AS % OF ASSETS	EMPLOYEES
12/16	8,210	16	0.2%	5,750
12/15	8,036	85	1.1%	5,600
12/14	7,833	114	1.5%	5,350
12/13	7,656	217	2.8%	6,100
12/12	8,009	103	1.3%	6,075
Annual Growth	**0.6%**	**(36.5%)**	**—**	**(1.4%)**

2016 Year-End Financials

Debt ratio: 9.15%
Return on equity: 0.84%
Cash ($ mil.): 115
Current ratio: —
Long-term debt ($ mil.): —

No. of shares (mil.): 51
Dividends
  Yield: 0.0%
  Payout: 290.9%
Market value ($ mil.): 2,271

	STOCK PRICE ($) FY Close	P/E High/Low	PER SHARE ($) Earnings	Dividends	Book Value
12/16	44.30	138 72	0.33	0.96	38.52
12/15	37.25	25 21	1.65	0.96	38.82
12/14	36.11	19 16	2.12	0.96	39.88
12/13	40.88	11 8	3.80	0.96	36.86
12/12	29.50	19 16	1.74	0.96	36.98
Annual Growth	**10.7%**	**— —**	**(34.0%)**	**(0.0%)**	**1.0%**

KeyCorp

Financial services giant KeyCorp unlocks its customers' monetary potential. With a focus on retail operations flagship subsidiary KeyBank operates more than 1200 branches and 1500 ATMs in 15 states in the Northeast the Midwest the Rocky Mountains and the Pacific Northwest including Alaska. Its operations are divided into two groups: Key Community Bank offers traditional services such as deposits loans credit cards and financial planning; Key Corporate Bank provides investment banking services real estate capital equipment financing and capital markets services to large corporate clients nationwide. KeyCorp is also the US' third-largest servicer of commercial and multifamily loans.

Operations

The bank makes around 50% of its revenue from loan interest mostly from commercial financial and agricultural and commercial real estate loans (including commercial mortgage and construction loans) as well as commercial leases. Another roughly 20% of its revenue comes from trust and investment services fee income and investment banking and debt placement fee income.

Geographic Reach

Cleveland-based KeyCorp has 1500 US branches in Ohio Alaska Indiana Michigan New York Oregon Washington and throughout New England. Around a quarter of its branches are concentrated in the Pacific states while about one-third is split between the Eastern New York and Eastern Ohio regions. The acquisition of First Niagara Financial in mid-2016 added nearly 400 branches in upstate New York Connecticut Massachusetts and Pennsylvania.

Sales and Marketing

Key Community Bank provides traditional banking services to individuals and small to mid-sized businesses while Key Corporate Bank provides its investment banking services to middle-market clients in seven industry sectors including consumer energy healthcare industrial public sector real estate and technology.

Financial Performance

In fiscal 2016 revenue increased 20% to $5.4 billion as the acquisition of First Niagara gave a boost to interest income. The First Niagara acquisition also pushed up non-interest revenue by 10%; card and payments income and corporate services also contributed.

Net income ticked down 16% to $754 million as an increase non-interest expenses outstripped non-interest revenue growth. KeyCorp incurred various expenses relating to the First Niagara acquisition including a $494 million M&A cost and a $421 million personnel expense increase. The acquisition also pushed up non-personnel expense to the tune of $495 million.

Cash from operating activities increased 49% to $1.7 billion due to an increase in proceeds from loans held for sale.

Strategy

KeyCorp's new and existing business growth strategy is based on leveraging and cross-selling its variety of financial products and services. In addition to hit its 60% cash efficiency ratio Keycorp has been focusing on controlling costs and reducing expenses from the front to the back office embracing digital banking platforms and cutting costly branch operations. Indeed the bank has been cutting its branch network from 1088 branches in 2012 to 966 at the end of 2015. The First Niagara acquisition pushed up KeyCorp?s branch network to 1322 but the cull continues: in Q4 2016 the bank shed a further 105 branches (some of the closures are due to branch overlaps too).

Mergers and Acquisitions

In July 2016 KeyCorp purchased First Niagara Financial and its bank subsidiaries. The $3.7 billion deal added nearly 400 new branches to KeyCorp's network in New York state (boosting its existing total branch network by about 40%) and led to annual cost savings of $400 million beginning in 2017. KeyCorp also estimated that the deal would lead to an internal rate of return of around 15%.

HISTORY

KeyCorp predecessor Commercial Bank of Albany was chartered in 1825. In 1865 it joined the new national banking system and became National Commercial Bank of Albany. After WWI National Commercial consolidated with Union National Bank & Trust as National Commercial Bank and Trust which then merged with First Trust and Deposit in 1971.

In 1973 Victor Riley became president and CEO. Under Riley National Commercial grew during the 1970s and 1980s through acquisitions. Riley sought to make the company a regional powerhouse but was thwarted when several New England states passed legislation barring New York banks from buying banks in the region.

As a result the company renamed Key Bank in 1979 turned west targeting small towns with less competition. Thus situated it prospered despite entering Alaska just in time for the 1986 oil price collapse. Its folksy image and small-town success earned it a reputation as the "Wal-Mart of banking."

Meanwhile in Cleveland Society for Savings followed a different path. Founded as a mutual savings bank in 1849 the institution succeeded from the start. It survived the Civil War and postwar economic turmoil and built Cleveland's first skyscraper in 1890. It continued to grow even during the Depression and became the largest savings bank outside the Northeast in 1949.

In 1955 the bank formed a holding company Society National. Society grew through the acquisitions of smaller banks in Ohio until 1979 when Ohio allowed branch banking in contiguous counties. Thereafter Society National opened branches as well. In the mid-1980s and the early 1990s the renamed Society Corporation began consolidating its operations and continued growing.

A 1994 merger of National Commercial with Society more than doubled assets for the surviving KeyCorp; compatibility of the two companies' systems and software simplified consolidation. KeyCorp sold its mortgage-servicing unit to NationsBank (now Bank of America) in 1995 and over the next year bought investment management finance and investment banking firms.

In 1997 KeyCorp began trimming its branch network divesting 200 offices including its 28-branch KeyBank Wyoming subsidiary. It expanded its consumer lending business that year by buying

Champion Mortgage. In cooperation with USF&G (now part of The St. Paul Travelers Companies) and three HMOs KeyCorp began offering health insurance to the underserved small-business market.

In 1998 the company bought Leasetec which leases computer storage systems globally through its StorageTek subsidiary; it also bought McDonald & Company Investments (now McDonald Investments; sold in 2007) with an eye toward reaching its goal of earning half of its revenues from fees. Also in 1998 KeyCorp began offering business lines of credit to customers of Costco Wholesale the nation's largest wholesale club.

As part of a restructuring effort KeyCorp sold 28 Long Island New York branches to Dime Bancorp in 1999. The next year the company sold its credit card portfolio to Associates First Capital (now part of Citigroup) and bought National Realty Funding a securitizer of commercial mortgages. In 2001 it acquired Denver-based investment bank The Wallach Company.

The company expanded further in the Denver area with its 2002 purchase of Union Bankshares. Two years later KeyCorp bought Seattle-area bank EverTrust Financial Group.

In 2007 the company bought Tuition Management Systems which provides outsourced tuition billing accounting and counseling services for schools and colleges; the unit was later merged into its Key Education Resources operations. Also that year KeyCorp sold investment bank and brokerage McDonald Investments to UBS Financial Services.

The company bought New York-based U.S.B. Holding Co. and its Union State Bank subsidiary for some $550 million in early 2008. The deal added more than 30 branches nearly doubling KeyCorp's presence in the Hudson River Valley region.

EXECUTIVES

Executive Vice President of IT Devlopment, Vernon L Patterson

Senior Vice President, Bryon Pike

Vice Chairman and President Banking, Christopher M. (Chris) Gorman, age 56, $638,462 total compensation

Secretary and General Counsel, Paul N. Harris, age 58

Vice Chairman and CFO, Donald R. Kimble, age 57, $638,462 total compensation

Co-President Key Community Bank, Edward J. (E.J.) Burke, $550,000 total compensation

SEVP and Chief Risk Officer, William L. (Bill) Hartmann, $500,000 total compensation

Chairman and CEO, Beth E. Mooney, age 61, $1,000,000 total compensation

Co-President Key Community Bank, Dennis A. Devine, $571,154 total compensation

CIO, Amy G. Brady

EVP and Director Corporate Center, Katrina M. (Trina) Evans

Chief Human Resources Officer, Craig A. Buffie

EVP; Head Real Estate Capital, Angela G. Mago

EVP; President KeyBank Capital Markets, Andrew J. (Randy) Paine, $500,000 total compensation

Executive Vice President Marketing, Bonnie Squadere

Vice President Database Marketing, Jonathan Boyer

Senior Vice President and National Sales Manager Middle Market and Healthcare, Peter Wheeler

Vice President, Alison Sammon

Assistant Vice President, Grace Moyano

Assistant Vice President, Paul Pace

Executive Vice President and Corporate Tax Director, Clark Wulf

Vice President Healthcare Products, Victoria Terekhova

Vice President Information Technology Ri, Shamus McMahon

Vice President International marketing, Robert Kurek

Vice President virtual Banking manager, Theresa Shepherd

Vice President Information Technology, Anurag Sharma

Vice President, Victor Alexander

Senior Vice President, Kim Monson

Vice President Senior Business Analyst, Karen Mahoney

Executive Vice President Marketing, Darlene Kohring

Vice President Information Technology Project Management, Lari Greenleaf

Vice President and Underwriting Team Leader, David Navy

Vice President, John Dravenstott

Executive Vice President and National Executive, William Lettig

Vice President Business Development, Carol Schafer

Marketing Vice President, Paul Ridzon

Vice President And Manager Regional Reporting, Melissa Werner

Senior Vice President and Senior Tax Manager II, Beth Adams

Senior Vice President, Henry Alonso

Vice President, Kathy Mizener

Vice President and Senior Counselor, Richard Zeiger

Senior Vice President Central Ohio District, Thomas Spilman

Vice President, Marcella Pardo

Assistant Vice President Corporate Information Security, Rick Snevel

Vice President manager payment and Deposit Operations, Dominic Cugini

Senior Vice President, Clay Sublett

Senior Vice President of Marketing Strategy, Marta Blase

EVP Real Estate Capital KeyBank, Ej Burke

Senior Vice President Business Banking Market Executive, Randy Riffle

Senior Vice President Capital Planning, Jay Luzar

Senior Vice President, Karen Grexa

KCM Vice President, Kelly Crawford

Vice President, Laura Krusinski

Vice President Mainframe Change Coordination and Special Projects, Phil Wetter

Vice President Client Relations Manager, Laura Karter

Vice President Commercial Banker, Yong Lee

Vice Preseident, Dora Johnson

Assistant Vice President AND R, Daniel Jacques

Vice President Consumer Channel Sales, Colleen Dugarte

Vice President Oil and Gas Group, Nicholas Stuart

Vice President and Sales Officer, Debbie Rivetts

Vice President Meeting Marketing Manager, Laurie Masters

Executive Vice President, George Emmons

Senior Vice President Enterprise Architecture, Dale Jablonski

Marketing Vice President, Bradley Thomas

Vice President Of Training, Nitra Rucker

Assistant Vice President Services Officer, Stephanie Jackson

Senior Vice President, Patrick Fish

Senior Vice President and Chief Underwriter CMBS, Alan Williams

Vice President Senior Credit Officer, Katie Raco

Vice President Consumer Finance, Dan Sukys

Senior Vice President and District Retail Leader, John Roehm

Vice President Corporate Communications, Alison Altre-Kerber

Vice President Product Manager, Brian Guess

Vice President and Trust Team Lead Real Estate, Emily Mogen

Credit Executive Senior Vice President, Brett Swanson

Vice President Interest Rate and Energy Derivatives, Dusko Djukic

Vice President of Marketing Strategist, Jill Dalton

Vice President Senior Business Banker, John Marriott

Vice President Credit Officer, Kellie Whelan

Senior Vice President Manager, Robert Likes

Assistant Vice President and Trust Officer, Amy Keirsey

Assistant Vice President Retail Banking, Michael Emerson

Senior Vice President And Finance Director, William Shaw

Vice President and Manager, Janet Jaros

Vice President Credit Risk Reviewer, Greg Newhouse

Senior Vice President Commercial Banking, Stephen Markley

Vice President Private Banking, Andrew Bowen

Executive Vice President and Treasurer, Joseph Vayda

Vice President Senior Asset Manager, Thomas Wainscott

Senior Vice President, James Harnett

Vice President and Senior SBA Specialist, Jennifer Prouser

Vice President Foreign Exchange Sales, Rick Moskowitz

Vice President Credit Officer, Jay Coleman

Vice President And Senior Treasury Advisor, Susie Todaro

Senior Vice President Finance Director, Deborah Brady

Vice President Division Manager zEnterprise Systems Management, Robert Bellanti

Vice President Senior Portfolio Manager, Jeff Stegeman

Vice President, Brice Stammen

Vice President and Senior Banker, Brian Heagler

Vice President Senior Portfolio Manager, Paul Olszewski

Senior Vice President Enterprise Architecture, Mike Onders

Vice President Senior Appraisal Officer, Scott Tomak

Senior Vice President Private Bank Sales Leader, Lucia Pileggi

Vice President Senior Treasury Advisor Institutional Banking, Michael Thomas

Learning Consultant Assistant Vice President (Metrics and Analytics), Rebecka Johnston

Vice President Client Services Consumer Segment, Cheryl Towns

Senior Business Training Specialist Assistant Vice President, Candice Pizzuti

Vice President Risk Program and Policy Manager Enterprise Risk Management, Kandy Hricik

Vice President District Operations Manager, Monica Cichon

Senior Cash Management Advisor And Assistant Vice President Treasury Services, Kristina Simpson

Vice President Corporate Procurement and Sourcing, Tom Fourmas

Vice President Compliance and Security Operations, Anthony Rini

Vice President and Senior Trust Real Estate Officer, Michael Gillespie

Senior Vice President Real Estate Finance, Craig Younggren

Vice President and District Operations Manager, Laurie Dickinson

Vice President Community Bank Sales Systems, Robert Brzezinski

Senior Vice President Corporate Bank Technology And Sales Tool Team Manager, Brian Utrup

Vice President and Trust Officer, Chris Dietz

Vice President Senior Commercial Reviewer, Caryn Blauser

Anti Money Laundering Vice President, Jackie Koellner

Senior Asset Manager Assistant Vice President, Daniel Last

Vice President Senior Human Resources Bu, Amy Schrameck

Senior Vice President District Retail Leader, Curtis Hollis

Senior Vice President And Manager Instit, Flavio Giust

Senior Vice President Key Private Bank, Michael Schneider

Vice President and AML BSA Risk Review Auditor IV, Monique Johnson

E C Manager Assistant Vice President System Administrator, Margaret Mason

Assistant Vice President Procurement Strategist, Michael Hancock

Vice President Senior Equity Analyst, Robert Plaza

Vice President and Senior Associate Counsel, Mark Freeman

Senior Vice President Credit Card Group Manager, Mark Kolar

Vice President Network Solutions Engineering, Daniel Godlewski

Assistant Vice President Portfolio Manager, Sara Smith

Senior Vice President and Chief Learning Officer, Carole Torres

Senior Vice President Commerical Banking, Ben Rechkemmer

Executive Vice President and CIO, Steve Yates

Facilities Human Resources Executive Vice President, Renee Csuhran

Vice President, David Brown

Vice President Finance, John Bahr

Risk Management Vice President, Shawn Riley

Vice President sourcing, Stacey Starnes

Senior Vice President, Mark Morrison

Vice President Consumer Credit Risk Management, Kevin Takac

Executive Vice President Human Resources, Beth Yates

Executive Vice President Marketing, David Odell

Vice President Corporate Communications, Laura Mimura

Vice President and Senior Counsel, Howard Coburn

Vice President and Senior Lit Counsel, Michelle Deshon

Senior Vice President, Charlie Shoop

Senior Vice President, Peter Scharich

Auditors: Ernst & Young LLP

LOCATIONS

HQ: KeyCorp
127 Public Square, Cleveland, OH 44114-1306
Phone: 216 689-3000
Web: www.key.com

PRODUCTS/OPERATIONS

2016 Sales

	$ mil.	% of total
Interest		
Loans	2,773	51
Securities available for sale	329	6
Held-to-maturity securities	122	2
Loans held for sale	34	1
Trading account assets	23	1
Short-term investments	22	1
Other investments	16	-
Noninterest		
Trust & investment services	464	9
Investment banking and debt placement fees	482	9
Service charges on deposits	302	6
Corporate Service income	215	4
Cards and payments income	233	4
Corporate owned life insurance income	125	2
Operating lease income and other leasing gains	62	1

Mortgage servicing fees	57	1
Consumer mortgage income	17	0
Net gains (losses) from principal investing	20	0
Other income	94	2
Total	**5,390**	**100**

COMPETITORS

Bank of America	Huntington Bancshares
Citigroup	JPMorgan Chase
Citizens Financial Group	M&T Bank
Comerica	Northern Trust
Fifth Third	PNC Financial
Flagstar Bancorp	Sovereign Bank
HSBC USA	U.S. Bancorp
	Wells Fargo

HISTORICAL FINANCIALS

Company Type: Public

Income Statement
FYE: December 31

	ASSETS ($ mil.)	NET INCOME ($ mil.)	INCOME AS % OF ASSETS	EMPLOYEES
12/16	136,453	791	0.6%	15,700
12/15	95,133	916	1.0%	13,359
12/14	93,821	900	1.0%	13,853
12/13	92,934	910	1.0%	14,783
12/12	89,236	858	1.0%	15,589
Annual Growth	11.2%	(2.0%)	—	0.2%

2016 Year-End Financials

Debt ratio: 8.98%
Return on equity: 6.07%
Cash ($ mil.): 1,544
Current ratio: —
Long-term debt ($ mil.): —

No. of shares (mil.): 1,079
Dividends
  Yield: 0.0%
  Payout: 41.2%
Market value ($ mil.): 19,719

	STOCK PRICE ($) FY Close	P/E High/Low	Earnings	PER SHARE ($) Dividends	Book Value
12/16	18.27	23 12	0.80	0.33	14.12
12/15	13.19	15 11	1.05	0.29	12.86
12/14	13.90	14 12	0.99	0.25	12.25
12/13	13.42	14 9	0.97	0.22	11.57
12/12	8.42	10 8	0.89	0.18	11.09
Annual Growth	21.4%	— —	(2.6%)	16.4%	6.2%

KIEWIT CORPORATION

Auditors: KPMG LLP OMAHA NE

LOCATIONS

HQ: KIEWIT CORPORATION
3555 FARNAM ST STE 1000, OMAHA, NE 681313302
Phone: 402 342-2052

HISTORICAL FINANCIALS

Company Type: Private

Income Statement
FYE: December 29

	REVENUE ($ mil.)	NET INCOME ($ mil.)	NET PROFIT MARGIN	EMPLOYEES
12/12	11,220	512	4.6%	10,441
12/11	10,381	796	7.7%	—
Annual Growth	8.1%	(35.7%)	—	—

2012 Year-End Financials

Debt ratio: —
Return on equity: 4.60%
Cash ($ mil.): 1,763
Current ratio: 1.20
Long-term debt ($ mil.): —

Dividends
  Yield: —
  Payout: —
Market value ($ mil.): —

KILROY REALTY, L.P.

Auditors: DELOITTE & TOUCHE LLP LOS AN

LOCATIONS

HQ: KILROY REALTY, L.P.
12200 W OLYMPIC BLVD # 200, LOS ANGELES, CA 900641044
Phone: 310 481-8400

HISTORICAL FINANCIALS

Company Type: Private

Income Statement
FYE: December 31

	ASSETS ($ mil.)	NET INCOME ($ mil.)	INCOME AS % OF ASSETS	EMPLOYEES
12/16	6,706	303	4.5%	226
12/15	5,939	238	4.0%	—
12/14	5,633	183	3.3%	—
12/13	5,111	44	0.9%	—
Annual Growth	9.5%	89.6%	—	—

2016 Year-End Financials

Debt ratio: —
Return on equity: 47.30%
Cash ($ mil.): 193
Current ratio: —
Long-term debt ($ mil.): —

Dividends
  Yield: —
  Payout: —
Market value ($ mil.): —

Kimberly-Clark Corp.

One of the world's largest makers of personal paper products Kimberly-Clark operates through three business segments: Personal Care Consumer Tissue and K-C Professional. Kimberly-Clark's largest unit Personal Care makes products such as diapers (Huggies Pull-Ups) feminine care items (Kotex) and incontinence care products (Poise Depend). Through its Consumer Tissue segment the manufacturer offers facial and bathroom tissues paper towels and other household items under the names Cottonelle Kleenex Viva and Scott (plus the Scott Naturals line). Kimberly-Clark's K-C Professional unit makes WypAll commercial wipes among other items.

Operations

Kimberly-Clark operates in three reportable segments: Personal Care (50%) Consumer Tissue (almost 35%) and K-C Professional (nearly 15%).

Personal Care offers products such as disposable diapers training and youth pants swimpants baby wipes feminine and incontinence care products and other related products. Its products are sold under the Huggies Pull-Ups Little Swimmers GoodNites DryNites Kotex U by Kotex Intimus Depend Plenitud Poise and other brands.

Consumer Tissue's products include facial and bathroom tissue paper towels napkins and related products and are sold under the Kleenex Scott Cottonelle Viva Andrex Scottex Neve and other brand names.

K-C Professional (KCP) partners with businesses and provides supporting products such as wipers tissue towels apparel soaps and sanitizers sold under the Kleenex Scott WypAll Kimtech and Jackson Safety brands.

Consumer tissue and KCP products are produced in 55 facilities and personal care products are produced in 49 facilities.

Geographic Reach

Kimberly-Clark maintains a broad global presence as part of its growth strategy. It boasts around 100 manufacturing facilities in about 40 countries across the US Canada Europe Asia and Latin America. Products reach more than 175 countries.Developing regions such as Asia Latin America and others generated more than 35% of the company's net sales in 2016. North America accounted for 50% while Europe accounted for the remainder.

Sales and Marketing

Kimberly-Clark sells its household items directly to supermarkets mass merchandisers drugstores warehouse clubs variety and department stores and other retail outlets as well as through distributors and e-commerce. For the away-from-home market it serves the company sells through distributors and directly to high-volume public facilities and to manufacturing lodging office building food service and health care establishments.

Its largest customer worldwide retailer Wal-Mart represented about 14% of net sales in 2016.

Financial Performance

Kimberly-Clark's revenues have decreased the last three years dipping 2% from $18.6 billion in 2015 to $18.2 billion in 2016 due to decreases across all its segments. Unfavorable currency rates decreased sales by 4% in 2016 which was offset by a 2% increase in sales volumes.

With the help of major restructuring efforts Kimberly-Clark's profits more than doubled from $1 billion in 2015 to $2.2 billion in 2016. Profits also surged in 2016 due to the absence of nearly $1.6 billion in pension settlement expenses that were recognized the previous year.

Kimberly-Clark's net cash provided by operating activities surged by 40% from $2.3 billion in 2015 to $3.2 billion in 2016 due to favorable decreases from working capital and benefits from its cost savings initiative.

Strategy

Like many players in its industry Kimberly-Clark is utilizing sustainable packaging to refresh its image and sustainability reputation without necessarily having to revamp its product portfolio. In 2017 the company stated it was diverting 95% of manufacturing waste from landfills and diverting over 5000 metric tons of post-consumer waste through partnership programs around the world.

HISTORY

John Kimberly Charles Clark Havilah Babcock and Frank Shattuck founded Kimberly Clark & Company in Neenah Wisconsin in 1872 to manufacture newsprint from rags. The company incorporated as Kimberly & Clark Company in 1880 and built a pulp and paper plant on the Fox River in 1889.

In 1914 the company developed cellu-cotton a cotton substitute used by the US Army as surgical cotton during WWI. Army nurses used cellu-cotton pads as disposable sanitary napkins and six years later the company introduced Kotex the first disposable feminine hygiene product. Kleenex the first throwaway handkerchief followed in 1924. Kim-

berly & Clark joined with The New York Times Company in 1926 to build a newsprint mill (Spruce Falls Power and Paper) in Ontario Canada. Two years later the company went public as Kimberly-Clark.

EXECUTIVES

Chairman President and CEO, Thomas J. (Tom) Falk, age 59, $1,318,750 total compensation
SVP and CFO, Maria G. Henry, age 50, $772,500 total compensation
President Latin America, Sergio Cruz
President Global Brands and Innovation, Anthony J. (Tony) Palmer, age 57, $655,000 total compensation
President COO and Director, Michael D. Hsu, age 53, $833,750 total compensation
SVP and Chief Supply Chain Officer, Sandra J. MacQuillan, age 50, $392,424 total compensation
President Asia-Pacific Region, Achal Agarwal
President Europe Middle East and Africa, Gustavo Calvo Paz
President Kimberly-Clark Professional, Kim Underhill
Vice President Government Relations, Susan Phillips
Vice President Walmart International Development, John Scholes
Vice President Human Resources, Rick Purdy
Vice President and Treasurer, Karen Leets
VP Human Resources, Sylvia Fong
Auditors: DELOITTE & TOUCHE LLP

LOCATIONS

HQ: Kimberly-Clark Corp.
P.O. Box 619100, Dallas, TX 75261-9100
Phone: 972 281-1200
Web: www.kimberly-clark.com

2016 Sales

	$ mil.	% of total
North America	9,545	51
Asia Latin America & other	6,786	37
Europe	2,178	12
Intergeographic sales	(307)	-
Total	**18,202**	**100**

PRODUCTS/OPERATIONS

2016 Sales

	$ mil.	% of total
Personal Care	9,046	50
Consumer Tissue	5,967	33
K-C Professional	3,150	17
Corporate & other	39	-
Total	**18,202**	**100**

Selected Products and Brands

Medical
  Closed-suction respiratory products
  Examination gloves
  Safeskin
  Face masks
  Infection-control products
  Scrub suits and apparel
  Sterile wrap
  Kimguard
  Surgical drapes and gowns
Personal Care
  Baby wipes
  Huggies
  Disposable diapers
  GoodNites
  Huggies
  Pull-Ups
  Feminine hygiene products
  Kotex
  Lightdays
  New Freedom
  Incontinence products
  Depend
  Poise

  Swimpants
  Little Swimmers
Tissue-Based
  Bathroom tissue
  Cottonelle
  Scott
  Commercial wipes
  Kimwipes
  WypAll
  Facial tissue
  Kleenex
  Paper napkins
  Scott
  Paper towels
  Kleenex
  Scott
  Viva

COMPETITORS

3M	Johnson & Johnson
Ansell	Medline Industries
Becton Dickinson	Nice-Pak Products
Bristol-Myers Squibb	Potlatch
CCA Industries	Procter & Gamble
DSG International Ltd	SSI Surgical Services
Edgewell Personal Care	Suominen
Georgia-Pacific	

HISTORICAL FINANCIALS

Company Type: Public

Income Statement

FYE: December 31

	REVENUE ($ mil.)	NET INCOME ($ mil.)	NET PROFIT MARGIN	EMPLOYEES
12/17	18,259	2,278	12.5%	42,000
12/16	18,202	2,166	11.9%	42,000
12/15	18,591	1,013	5.4%	43,000
12/14	19,724	1,526	7.7%	43,000
12/13	21,152	2,142	10.1%	57,000
Annual Growth	(3.6%)	1.6%	—	(7.4%)

2017 Year-End Financials

Debt ratio: 49.01%
Return on equity: 705.26%
Cash ($ mil.): 616
Current ratio: 0.89
Long-term debt ($ mil.): 6,472
No. of shares (mil.): 351
Dividends
  Yield: 0.0%
  Payout: 60.6%
Market value ($ mil.): 42,364

	STOCK PRICE ($) FY Close	P/E High/Low		PER SHARE ($) Earnings	Dividends	Book Value
12/17	120.66	21	17	6.40	3.88	1.97
12/16	114.12	23	19	5.99	3.68	(0.12)
12/15	127.30	47	37	2.77	3.52	(0.30)
12/14	115.54	29	25	4.04	3.36	2.19
12/13	104.46	20	15	5.53	3.24	12.94
Annual Growth	3.7%			3.7%	4.6%	(37.6%)

Kinder Morgan Inc.

Kinder Morgan Inc. (KMI) one of the largest energy infrastructure companies in North America operates 84000 miles of pipelines that transport natural gas refined petroleum products crude oil condensate CO_2 and other products along with more than 150 terminals that transload and store petroleum and chemical products. The company is also a leading producer of CO_2 used in oilfield operations. It generates most of its sales in the US.

Operations

KMI reports via five segments: Natural Gas Pipelines Terminals Products Pipelines CO_2 and Kinder Morgan Canada.

Natural Gas Pipelines is KMI?s most significant business segment accounting for 60% of total revenue. It?s 70000 miles of pipelines and storage facilities account for 40% of all consumed natural gas in the US.

Terminals is the transportation arm of KMI and brings in about 15% of annual sales. With more than 50 liquid terminals 40 bulk terminals and some 10 Jones Act approved tankers KMI is the largest independent terminal operator in North America. (Jones Act restricts US point-to-point maritime shipping to vessels that?s are 75% US-owned.) The terminals transload store or blend refined petroleum products crude oil chemicals ethanol and bulk products to US and parts of Canada.

The Products Pipelines segment includes 9000 miles of pipelines and 60 terminals making this sector the largest independent transporter of petroleum products (more than 2 million barrels per day). Moving gasoline jet fuel diesel crude and NGL products this sector brings in just under 15% of annual sales.

Although KMI is the largest CO_2 transporter in North America (1.3 billion cubic feet/ day) this segment only accounts for about 10% of the company?s total revenues.

Kinder Morgan Canada (3% revenue) owns several pipeline systems and terminals including the Trans Mountain and Cochin pipeline that transports crude oil and refined petroleum products from Alberta Canada to various marketing terminals and refineries of western US and Canada.

Geographic Reach

KMI has operations in the US Canada and Mexico. KMI buys and sells significant volumes of natural gas in Texas.

US customers account for some 95% of the company's revenue.

Sales and Marketing

KMI serves customers in the western US Louisiana Texas the Midwest and the Southeast. The company's customers include major oil companies energy producers and shippers local distribution companies and companies representing a range of industries.

Most customers of KMI especially natural gas pipeline & products are under extended transport and sales contracts; midstream assets are fee-based and CO_2 has third-party contracts with minimum volume requirements.

Financial Performance

KMI reported annual revenue of $13 billion in 2016 a 9% reduction from the year prior. In just the last two years revenues have decreased by more than $3 billion. Depressed commodity prices and lower demand were primarily responsible. The natural gas segment saw revenue fall by $706 million followed by a $478 million reduction in the CO_2 segment. The CO_2 segment has seen revenue fall by almost 40% in just two years.

KMI remains profitable despite revenue reduction with net income increasing 185% to $721 million. Three factors were involved. First there was an absence of $1.1 billion charge over 2015 for losses on impairment of goodwill. There was also a $600 million reduction in cost of sales over the previous year as well as about $590 million decrease in losses on impairments and divestitures in its CO_2 sector from the previous year. Although KMI profits improved in 2013 and 2014 it posted nearly $2 billion more in profits.

Meanwhile KMI?s operating cash flow decreased by 10% to $4.8 billion primarily because of a sharp decline in accounts and income tax receivables.

Strategy

Despite a severely compressed commodity market Kinder Morgan a market leader in each of its business segments is paying down debt while re-maining profitable thanks to its fees being largely independent of underlying commodity prices.

The company has strengthened its balance sheet by reducing net debt by almost $6 billion since the third quarter of 2015. In 2016 KMI also reduced operating expenses by almost $2.5 billion from the year prior.

Its broader strategy remains the same — to leverage its asset footprint by acquiring or building stable fee-based energy transportation storage and gathering and processing assets across North America as demonstrated by the completions of the Southern Natural Gas pipeline and Elba Express Company expansion the South System Flexibility project and the Cortez Pipeline expansion as well as the delivery of the American Endurance tanker.

Also in Nov 2016 the Canadian government granted approval for the $7.4 billion Trans Mountain Expansion Project which will increase capacity by 890000 barrels per day by 2019.

These developments come at a crucial time for KMI given the decline in returns from its Natural Gas and CO_2 segments in the last few years. The company predicts energy demands to improve dramatically in the coming years except for the CO_2 sector where it plans to hold investment at current levels.

Mergers and Acquisitions

Growing its assets in 2016 the company acquired 15 products terminals and associated infrastructure from BP for $349 million.

EXECUTIVES

President and CEO, Steven J. (Steve) Kean, age 56, $1 total compensation
VP and CFO, Kimberly A. (Kim) Dang, age 48, $375,000 total compensation
President Kinder Morgan Canada, Ian D. Anderson, age 60
VP; President Natural Gas Pipelines, Thomas A. (Tom) Martin, $375,000 total compensation
VP Corporate Development, Dax Sanders, $375,000 total compensation
President Products Pipelines, Ronald G. (Ron) McClain
President Terminals, John W. Schlosser
VP and CIO, Mark Huse
President CO2, Jesse Arenivas, $325,000 total compensation
Information Technology Vice President Scada Systems, Greg Vaughn
Vice President Pipeline Scheduling, Holly Breaux
Vice President and Controller, Gary Bohnsack
Executive Vice President And Chief Operating Officer, Scott Stoness
Vice President Regulatory Affairs Products Pipelines, Randy P Parker
Vice President Corporate Security and Business Continuity, Jay Montgomery
Vice President Employee Benefits, Mark Smith
Vice President Financial Planning Midstream, Joe Joyce
Vice President Kinder Morgan Natural Gas Pipelines, Kevin Howard
Vice President Logistic, James Holland
Vice President and Treasurer, Anthony Ashley
Vice President, David Barrow
Vice President and Chief Compliance Officer, Charles Schwager
Vice President Pacific Business Development And Marketing, Mary Morgan
Vice President, James Saunders
Vice President, Scott Clapham
Executive Chairman, Richard D. (Rich) Kinder, age 73
Auditors: PricewaterhouseCoopers LLP

LOCATIONS

HQ: Kinder Morgan Inc.
1001 Louisiana Street, Suite 1000, Houston, TX 77002
Phone: 713 369-9000
Web: www.kindermorgan.com

2016 Sales

	$ mil.	% of total
U.S.	12,459	95
Canada	483	4
Mexico	116	1
Total	**13,058**	**100**

PRODUCTS/OPERATIONS

2016 Sales

	$ mil.	% of total
Natural Gas Pipelines	8,005	61
Terminals	1,922	15
Products Pipelines	1,649	13
CO2	1,221	9
Kinder Morgan Canada	253	2
Corporate and intersegment eliminations	8	-
Total	**13,058**	**100**

2016 Sales

	$ mil.	% of total
Services	8,146	62
Natural gas sales	2,454	19
Product sales and other	2,458	19
Total	**13,058**	**100**

COMPETITORS

AltaGas	K-Sea Transportation
Buckeye Partners	Koch Industries Inc.
Canadian Utilities	Plains All American
EnLink Midstream	Pipeline
Partners	TRII
Enbridge	TransMontaigne
Energy Transfer Equity	Williams Companies
Enterprise Products	

HISTORICAL FINANCIALS

Company Type: Public

Income Statement

FYE: December 31

	REVENUE ($ mil.)	NET INCOME ($ mil.)	NET PROFIT MARGIN	EMPLOYEES
12/17	13,705	183	1.3%	10,897
12/16	13,058	708	5.4%	11,121
12/15	14,403	253	1.8%	11,290
12/14	16,226	1,026	6.3%	11,535
12/13	14,070	1,193	8.5%	11,075
Annual Growth	(0.7%)	(37.4%)	—	(0.4%)

2017 Year-End Financials

Debt ratio: 47.87%—
Return on equity: 0.54%
Cash ($ mil.): 264
Current ratio: 0.44
Long-term debt ($ mil.): 35,015

Dividends
Yield: 0.0%
Payout: 5,000.0%
Market value ($ mil.): —

	STOCK PRICE ($) FY Close	P/E High/Low	PER SHARE ($) Earnings	Dividends	Book Value
12/17	18.07	2294 1676	0.01	0.50	15.17
12/16	20.71	93 48	0.25	0.50	15.44
12/15	14.92	446 145	0.10	1.93	15.75
12/14	42.31	48 35	0.89	1.70	16.03
12/13	36.00	36 28	1.15	1.56	12.70
Annual Growth	(15.8%)	—	— (69.5%)	(24.8%)	4.5%

Kindred Healthcare Inc

Families unable to provide 24-hour care to their kin can at least turn to Kindred Healthcare. As a leading provider of long-term health care Kindred operates about more than 80 transitional care hospitals about 20 inpatient rehabilitation hospitals 20 sub-acute units and 615 home health hospice and non-medical home care centers throughout the US. Its Kindred's RehabCare business provides contract rehabilitation therapy services at more than 1700 facilities. Its facilities have a combined capacity of about 19000 beds and span 45 states. A consortium of investors is taking Kindred private in a $4.1 billion transaction.

Change in Company Type

In late 2017 Kindred agreed to be taken private by three buyers — investment firms TPG Capital and Welsh Carson Anderson & Stowe and insurance company Humana. After the acquisition Kindred's home health hospice and community care businesses will be spun off into a separate company named Kindred at Home.Its long-term acute care hospitals inpatient rehab facilities and contract rehabilitation services businesses will operate as Kindred Healthcare.

Operations

Kindred is composed of five divisions: hospital home health services (including community care reporting) hospice services hospital rehabilitation services and rehab care. It sold its nursing division in 2017 to focus on its other operations.

The hospital division which brings in a third of Kindred's yearly income includes both free-standing long term acute care hospitals and "hospitals-within-hospitals" which are co-located with short-term acute care facilities and sometimes receive patients as they are discharged from the host facility. All of Kindred's hospitals care for patients with complex medical conditions — those who are recovering from major surgery are experiencing multiple organ failure or have brain or spinal cord injuries for instance.

The home health services division offers medical and related services for patients in residential settings. Kindred at Home provides services in more than 600 locations across 40 states.Its hospice division provides family oriented care and services in the home nursing centers assisted living facilities hospitals and inpatient hospice units.

Kindred hospital rehabilitation services includes both hospital and inpatient rehab hospitals including acute rehab units. The rehab care division provides therapy management services.

Geographic Reach

Kindred Healthcare operates around 2540 facilities in about 45 states across the US.

Sales and Marketing

Medicare and Medicaid reimbursements make up more than 60% of Kindred's revenue.

Financial Performance

Kindred's revenues reached $7.2 billion in 2016 its highest total in at least 10 years. The milestone was fueled by increased sales from its home health hospice and hospital rehabilitation services divisions.

Home health sales jumped 12% due to additional revenues from a previous acquisition coupled with growth in both home health admissions and episodes and a rise in community care revenues. Hospice sales also spiked due to a previous acquisition and hospital rehabilitation services growth was primarily attributable to two freestanding inpatient rehabilitation hospitals (IRFs) that opened during 2016 and two freestanding IRFs that opened during 2015.

Despite the revenue growth Kindred has suffered six straight years of net losses posting its largest net loss of $664 million in 2016. The recent was attributed to impairment charges of more than $340 million and increased restructuring charges during 2016 that were related to a handful of hospital closures and divestitures.

Cash flow from operations however has risen the last two years climbing from $163 million in 2015 to $185 million in 2016. Its operating cash flows each year are affected by changes in accounts receivable collections the timing of income tax payments the payment of one-time bonuses lease cancellations and litigation and financing payments.

Strategy

Kindred's strategy involves dominating the post-acute care sector and it has diversified accordingly. It has clustered its services in certain markets where it can provide rehabilitation services across several possible sites: hospital inpatient center outpatient center or private homes. In those geographic areas no matter where a patient needs to receive rehabilitation (or where Medicare is willing to pay for it) Kindred will have a means of providing that care.

In a large move to focus on its higher grossing operations Kindred sold its skilled nursing facility business for $700 million in cash. The deal included 12 skilled nursing facilities and four assisted living facilities and will help by cutting down on capital expenditures and rent obligations. Kindred expects to eventually get about half of its revenue from its Kindred at Home business and the rest from its long-term acute care hospital and rehabilitation services businesses.

Mergers and Acquisitions

In recent years Kindred's home care and hospice business has grown steadily through acquisitions of smaller regional operations.

In 2016 the company acquired the in-home health care operations (the Agency) from Arkansas Department of Health (ADH) which includes licenses to provide home health hospice and personal care services throughout the state of Arkansas for approximately $39 million. This acquisition expanded the company?s Home operations in Arkansas.

In a massive transaction the company in 2015 bought Gentiva Health Services for some $1.8 billion. The deal nearly doubled Kindred's size. The combined company which does business as Kindred at Home and Kindred Hospice operates in 45 states serving more than 1 million patients per year.

HISTORY

After a stint as Kentucky's commerce secretary in the 1980s Bruce Lunsford was approached by respiratory therapist Michael Barr with the idea of establishing long-term hospitals for ventilator-dependent patients. Barr said these hospitals would be cheaper to run than full-service facilities which require additional equipment. Lunsford (who became chairman president and CEO) and Barr (who was COO) founded Vencare in 1983 with backing from Gene Smith (a wealthy political associate of Lunsford). They bought a money-losing 62-bed Indiana hospital and soon turned the operation around.

Vencare expanded into Florida and Texas and by the end of the 1980s operated more than 420 beds in seven facilities. Revenues jumped from less than $1 million in 1985 to $54 million by 1989 the year it changed its name to Vencor.

During the early 1990s Vencor added facilities in Arizona California Colorado Georgia and Missouri. Vencor ran 29 facilities by the end of 1993 the same year it launched its Vencare respiratory care program.

Vencor acquisitions in 1995 included hospital respiratory and cardiopulmonary departments in seven states. Later that year it bought the much-larger Hillhaven the US's #2 nursing home operator at that time. (In 1990 Hillhaven had been spun off from what is now Tenet Healthcare.) When Vencor bought it Hillhaven owned 310 nursing homes 60 pharmacies and 23 retirement communities. The buy furthered Lunsford's vision of creating a network of long-term-care facilities and services. Vencor also debuted VenTouch an electronic-pad-based record-keeping system for its facilities in 1995.

In 1996 Vencor spun off its assisted and independent living properties as Atria Communities; as part of the Hillhaven assimilation it also consolidated its MediSave pharmacy unit into its hospital operations and sold 34 nursing homes to Lennox Healthcare.

Vencor's 1997 buys included TheraTx (216 rehabilitation centers 28 nursing centers 16 occupational health clinics) and Transitional Hospitals (long-term acute care hospitals). That year Vencor formed an alliance with insurer CNA to develop an insurance product for long-term care.

In 1998 the company split into Ventas (real estate) and Vencor (operations). It also sold most of its remaining interest in an assisted living company (now called Atria Senior Quarters) it had spun off in 1996. To attract wealthier residents it also launched a program in 1998 to turn away — and turn out — Medicaid patients. Vencor soon abandoned the plan amid heated attacks from advocacy groups. (Welcoming back the evictees didn't stop Florida regulators from fining Vencor.) Several other states and the federal government also began probing Vencor's practices; in 1999 the affair prompted Congressional action designed to protect Medicaid patients. Lunsford and Barr were ousted in the turmoil. The government also demanded that Vencor return $90 million in overpayments over 60 months ($2 million a month) or risk losing Medicare payments.

The company filed for Chapter 11 bankruptcy later in 1999. Despite bankruptcy protection the Justice Department in 2000 filed claims for more than $1 billion from Vencor for Medicare fraud since 1992. Vencor settled the majority of these claims the next year. The company emerged from bankruptcy in April 2001 and changed its name to Kindred Healthcare. In 2003 the company sold all of its Texas and Florida nursing center operations. Kindred Healthcare began operating its contract rehabilitation business as a separate division in 2004.

In 2006 the company bought the long-term care operations of Commonwealth Communities Holdings gaining six long-term acute care hospitals and 11 nursing homes in Massachusetts. The company entered lease agreements for eight nursing homes in San Francisco in 2007.

In 2007 Kindred spun off its Kindred Pharmacy Services unit which distributed drugs to long-term care facilities. The unit was combined with the institutional pharmacy unit of AmerisourceBergen to form a new entity named PharMerica. Kindred Pharmacy Services contributed more than 40 institutional pharmacies in 26 states to the combined company.

EXECUTIVES

Vice President and Chief Counsel, Ronald Lazas
EVP Strategy and Chief of Staff, William M. Altman, age 58, $402,278 total compensation
EVP and CFO, Stephen D. Farber, age 43, $605,798 total compensation
General Counsel and Corporate Secretary, Joseph L. Landenwich, age 53, $413,845 total compensation

President CEO and Director, Benjamin A. Breier, age 46, $1,045,098 total compensation
EVP and COO, Kent H. Wallace, age 62, $706,743 total compensation
President Nursing Center Division, Michael W. Beal
President Hospital Division, Peter K. Kalmey
EVP and President Kindred at Home, David A. Causby, $563,417 total compensation
COO Kindred Rehabilitation Services (KRS), Jason Zachariah
Chief Administrative Officer and Chief People Officer, Stephen R. Cunanan
President Kindred Innovations, Brian Holzer
Director of Health Information, Debra Patterson
Vice President Business Development, Michael Moody
Vice President Corporate Finance, Mark Laemmle
Division Vice President IS Operations, Vance Collins
Vice President of Information Technology, Douglas Curnutte
Division Vice President Government Affairs and Constituent Relations, Steve Albrecht
Cota, Janice Paradise
Director of Medical Records, Roxanne Keith
Division Vice President of Case Management, Tami Johnson
Nursing Services Director, Catherine Deane
Vice President of Liability Claims, Hans Koehler
Director of Respiratory Therapy, Daniel Simon
Vice President and Chief Information Security Officer, Charles Lebo
Vice President and Chief Counsel Nursing Center Division, Kelly Priegnitz
Vice President And Corporate Counsel, Jeffrey P Stodghill
Vice President of Labor Relations, Edward Goddard
Division Vice President Human Resources, Jane Mathews
Vice President Corporate Communications and Events, Susan Moss
Cota, Barbara Stewart
Vice President Of Facilities, Tony Dickamore
Director Of Nursing, Kellie Kennedy
Director Of Physical Therapy, Adila Millwala
Nursing Director, Phillip Lindsay
Vice President Internal Audit, Anne Woods
Corporate Vice President Finance I S And Administration, Stephen Dobler
Division Vice President and Litigation Counsel, Matthew Steinberg
Vice President of Rehab, Vonda Black
Vice President and Real Estate Counsel, Cristina E O'Brien
Division Vice President Human Resources, Jeffrey Sopko
Director of Radiology, Charles Cook
Director of Radiology Services, Jenny Hicks
Assistant Vice President Regulatory Affairs, Cindy Brock
Senior Vice President of Enterprise Sales, Dean Johnson
Vice President, Claire Willman
Divisional Vice President, Mark LaRoche
Senior Vice President, Michael Warrington
Director of Pharmacy, Catherine Waltz
Vice President of Compliance, John Hamilton
Vice President Corporate Finance and Treasury, Todd Flowers
Area Vice President Corporate Human Resources, Regina Evans
Regional Vice President of Operations, Robert Koch
Division Vice President Of Learning And Professional Development, Jere Dye
SENIOR VICE PRESIDENT HUMAN RESOURCES OPERATIONS, Jeffrey M Jasnoff
Chairman, Phyllis R. Yale, age 60
Auditors: PricewaterhouseCoopers LLP

LOCATIONS

HQ: Kindred Healthcare Inc
680 South Fourth Street, Louisville, KY 40202-2412
Phone: 502 596-7300
Web: www.kindredhealthcare.com

PRODUCTS/OPERATIONS

2016 Sales

	$ mil.	% of total
Medicare	3,743	50
Medicaid	821	11
Medicare Advantage	548	7
Medicaid Managed	260	4
Other	2,055	28
Eliminations -209.8 -		
Total	**7,219**	**100**

2016 Sales

	$ mil.	% of total
Hospital division	2,383	32
Kindred at home		
Home health	1,762	24
Hospice	736	10
Nursing center division	1,087	15
Kindred Rehabilitation Services		
Rehabcare	784	10
Kindred hospital rehabilitation services	674	9
Eliminations	(209.8)	-
Total	**7,219**	**100**

COMPETITORS

Ascension Health	NHC
Covenant Care	Omnicare
Ensign Group	Paradigm Management
Extendicare	Services
Five Star Senior Living	Physiotherapy Associates
Genesis Healthcare	SavaSeniorCare
Golden Horizons	Select Medical
HCA	Sunrise Senior Living
HealthSouth	Tenet Healthcare
Mercy Health (OH)	U.S. Physical Therapy

HISTORICAL FINANCIALS
Company Type: Public

Income Statement
FYE: December 31

	REVENUE ($ mil.)	NET INCOME ($ mil.)	NET PROFIT MARGIN	EMPLOYEES
12/16	7,219	(664)	—	100,100
12/15	7,054	(93)	—	102,000
12/14	5,027	(79)	—	61,500
12/13	4,900	(168)	—	63,300
12/12	6,181	(40)	—	78,000
Annual Growth	**4.0%**	**—**		**6.4%**

2016 Year-End Financials

Debt ratio: 53.05%
Return on equity: (-57.29%)
Cash ($ mil.): 137
Current ratio: 1.51
Long-term debt ($ mil.): 3,215
No. of shares (mil.): 85
Dividends
  Yield: 0.0%
  Payout: —
Market value ($ mil.): 669

	STOCK PRICE ($) FY Close	P/E High/Low		PER SHARE ($) Earnings	Dividends	Book Value
12/16	7.85	— —		(7.65)	0.48	9.54
12/15	11.91	— —		(1.11)	0.48	17.90
12/14	18.18	— —		(1.36)	0.48	20.60
12/13	19.74	— —		(3.23)	0.24	19.99
12/12	10.82	— —		(0.78)	0.00	23.58
Annual Growth	**(7.7%)**	**— —**		**—**	**—**	**(20.2%)**

KNIGHTS OF COLUMBUS

Good Knight! The Knights of Columbus is a formidable volunteer group boasting more than 15300 councils made up of 1.9 million Roman Catholic male members in the US Canada Mexico Cuba the Philippines Poland and several other countries. The fraternal organization is also a force to be reckoned with in the insurance world providing life insurance annuities and long-term care insurance to its members and their families. In addition the group manages the Knights of Columbus Museum in New Haven Connecticut featuring exhibits of religious art and history. The group was founded in 1882 by Father Michael J. McGivney.

Operations

The Knights of Columbus (KoC) was formed to render financial aid to members and their families. Mutual aid and assistance are offered to sick disabled and needy members and their families. Social and intellectual fellowship is promoted among members and their families through educational charitable religious social welfare war relief and public relief works. KoC is also engaged in religious education the support of public policy issues (including immigration reform marriage protection opposing abortion) and charitable activities such as disaster relief.

The entity is a Catholic family fraternal service organization. This theme permeates the entire Service Program: all Church community council family culture of life and youth activities. The Service Program is designed to establish each council as an influential and important force within the community elevate the status of the programming personnel provide more meaningful and relevant programs of action establish direct areas of responsibility build leadership and ensure the success of council programs.

The group's supreme council has more than 75 state council organizations.

The Knights of Columbus has partnered with Special Olympics the Global Wheelchair Mission and Habitat for Humanity to its Food for Families and Coats for Kids projects to work together with together with fellow Knights and their families. The group's other activities also include supporting people with intellectual disabilities and aiding victims of natural disasters and other catastrophic events (local and worldwide).

Geographic Reach

The Knights of Columbus is made up of local councils throughout the US Canada Mexico Puerto Rico Guam and the US Virgin Islands. It also has councils in the Bahamas Cuba the Dominican Republic Guatemala Panama the Philippines Poland and Saipan.

Company Background

The Knights of Columbus was founded in New Haven by Father Michael J. McGivney in 1882 and has been selling insurance since its founding.

EXECUTIVES

Supreme Knight, Carl A. Anderson
Supreme Secretary, Michael J. (Mike) O'Connor
Supreme Chaplain, William E. Lori
Deputy Supreme Knight, Patrick E. Kelly
Supreme Treasurer, Ronald F. Schwarz
Assistant Vice President of Application Development, Niki Kratzert
Vice President For Communications, Patrick Korten
Vice President Certified and Support Services, Lynn Hussey
Vice President, Anthony Minopoli

LOCATIONS

HQ: KNIGHTS OF COLUMBUS
1 COLUMBUS PLZ STE 1700, NEW HAVEN, CT 065103326
Phone: 203 752-4000
Web: WWW.KOFC.ORG

HISTORICAL FINANCIALS

Company Type: Private

Income Statement

FYE: December 31

	ASSETS ($ mil.)	NET INCOME ($ mil.)	INCOME AS % OF ASSETS	EMPLOYEES
12/13	20,534	113	0.6%	2,300
12/12	19,401	127	0.7%	—
12/11	18,026	81	0.4%	—
12/10	16,861	86	0.5%	—
Annual Growth	6.8%	9.5%	—	—

2013 Year-End Financials

Debt ratio: ——
Return on equity: 5.40%
Cash ($ mil.): 192
Current ratio: ——
Long-term debt ($ mil.): ——

Dividends
Yield: ——
Payout: ——
Market value ($ mil.): ——

Kohl's Corp.

Kohl's wants its prices to be easy on shoppers and tough on competition. The clothing retailer operates about 1150 department stores in 49 states with nearly half of stores in the Midwest and West. Competing with discount and mid-level department stores it sells moderately priced name-brand and private-label apparel shoes accessories and housewares through centrally located cash registers designed to speed checkout and keep staff costs down. Merchandising relationships allow Kohl's to carry top brands (NIKE Levi's OshKosh B'Gosh) not always available to discounters; it's able to sell them for lower prices by controlling costs. A typical store spans 88000 sq. ft. and serves markets with 150000 to 200000 people.

Operations

By product Kohl's generates about 30% of sales from women's clothing while more than 20% of sales come from men's clothing. The rest of the retailer's sales come from home products (about 20% of sales) children's clothing (about 15%) and accessories and footwear (about 10% each). More than half of its sales are of products tied to national brands while the rest is tied to private and exclusive brands.

Besides Kohl?s stores the company operates a dozen FILA Outlets and three Off-Aisle clearance centers.

Geographic Reach

While Kohl's operates in 49 US states nearly one-third of its stores are in the states of California Texas Illinois Ohio and Florida. To support its brick-and-mortar and online businesses Wisconsin-based Kohl's maintains a network of more than a dozen distribution centers nationwide in Findlay Ohio; Winchester Virginia; Blue Springs Missouri; Corsicana Texas; Mamakating New York; San Bernardino California; Macon Georgia; Patterson California; and Ottawa Illinois.

Facilities that serve Kohl's e-commerce business are in Monroe Ohio; San Bernardino California; Edgewood Maryland; Plainfield Indiana and DeSoto Texas. The company also operates design studios in New York City and Santa Monica California.

Sales and Marketing

Kohl's has been boosting its ad spending in recent years particularly on promotional activities as well as television and radio commercials direct mail and newspaper circulars. It typically spends around $1 billion on advertising each year.

The company sells its products through its stores (90% of sales) online (about 10%) and through in-store kiosks that offer customers free shipping to their homes. Kohl's purchases its merchandise from both domestic and foreign suppliers. A third-party purchasing agent supplies about 30% of the company's merchandise.

Financial Performance

Kohl's revenues have been flat over the past few years with few new store openings and sluggish comparable store sales growth. Its profits have also been in a slow decline as rising merchandise costs have caused margins to shrink and as it's been spending more on investments in IT and marketing to support growth.

The retailer's revenue slipped 3% to $18.7 billion in 2017 (ended January) due to higher prices per unit but lower sales per square foot (down 2%). Stores in the West Southeast and Midwest outperformed the company average in 2017 while in lines of business Footwear and Men's were the better-than-average performers in 2017.

Net income slumped 17% to $556 million in 2017 from 2016 due to an increase in expenses.

Cash flow from operations rose to $2.15 billion in 2017 from $1.47 billion in 2016 reflecting a 5% decrease in inventory per store from inventory reduction initiatives increases in accounts payable due to timing of spring merchandise receipts and extended payment terms with vendors.

Strategy

Is Kohl?s selling with the enemy? Or is it wholeheartedly embracing online sales? Those are questions asked by other retailers and retail analysts about Kohl?s deal to bring Amazon.com into its stores. In an agreement with the online retailer Kohl?s will accept Amazon.com returns in its stores as well as open Amazon smart home boutiques in its stores. Kohl?s defends the moves as the way of the future. Kohl?s is betting that the partnership will bring more customers into its stores. Falling customer count has bedeviled the company as it has most retailers. It also joins other retailers such as Best Buy and Sears that have arrangements with Amazon.com.

Kohl?s own digital sales efforts are showing some payoff in store traffic. About a third of digital sales units were either shipped from a store or picked up in stores in the 2017 fourth quarter.

Kohl?s continues to invest in its omnichannel initiatives. Online demand improved in 2017 (ended January) and shipping and fulfillment expenses improved as a percentage of digital sales and it got shipments to customers half a day faster. It is set to open a fifth ecommerce fulfillment center in 2017 to further reduce delivery time.

As for merchandise Kohl?s began selling Under Armour products in 2017 which it expected would boost sales.

Company Background

Kohl's own brands were key to Kohl's merchandising strategy in past years. In 2012 in a bid to emulate its "cheap chic" rival Target and also longtime competitor J. C. Penney Kohl's began enlisting big-name designers to produce merchandise exclusively for its stores. In building its "Available Only at Kohl's" business the discounter offered a low-cost collection named Simply Vera in stores and online as the result of the deal with designer Vera Wang. It inked a similar alliance with upscale jeans maker Rock & Republic Food Network LC Lauren Conrad and FILA Sport as well as "Design-Nation" limited-edition collections from designers Narciso Rodriguez in 2012 Derek Lam in spring 2013 and Catherine Malandrino in fall 2013.

HISTORY

Max Kohl (father of Sen. Herbert Kohl of Wisconsin) opened his first grocery store in Milwaukee in the late 1920s. Over the years he and his three sons developed it into a chain and in 1938 Kohl's incorporated.

Kohl opened a department store (half apparel half hard goods) in 1962 next door to a Kohl's grocery. In the mid-1960s he hired William Kellogg a twentysomething buyer in the basement discount department at Milwaukee's Boston Store for his expertise in budget retailing. Kellogg came from a retailing family (his father was VP of merchandising at Boston Store; the younger Kellogg had joined that firm out of high school). Kohl and Kellogg began developing the pattern for the store carving out a niche between upscale department stores and discounters (offering department store quality at discount store prices).

EXECUTIVES

Executive Vice President General Merchandise Manager, Jack Boyle
Senior Executive Vice President, John Worthington
Senior Executive Vice President Logistics, Kenneth Bonning
Senior Vice Presiden, Julie Gardner
Chairman President and CEO, Kevin B. Mansell, age 64, $1,400,441 total compensation
SEVP and Chief Administrative Officer, Richard D. (Rick) Schepp, age 56, $911,250 total compensation
CFO, Bruce H. Besanko, age 58
CEO-elect, Michelle Gass, age 48, $1,113,750 total compensation
President, Sona Chawla, age 50, $1,113,750 total compensation
Vice President Customer Relationship Management, Brian Miller
Vice President Information Technology Planning and Development, Dale Trafton
Vice President Customer Experience, Brian Dennis
Senior Vice President Human RE, Genny Shields
Vice President Application Development, Lawrence Mikels
Vice President of Human Resources Stores, Kate Beck
Vice President dmm, Suzanne Dawson
Vice President of Distribution, Jeff Kellan
Vice President Marketing, James Burns
Vice President Marketing Communications, Brad Simmons
eCommerce Call Center Vice President, Troy Crougthers
Vice President of Product Services, Richard Zielinski
Vice President Credit Marketing, Brent Cook
Senior Vice President DMM Jewelry, Laura Swan
Vice President, Richard Suhar
Executive Vice President, Sarah Masterson
Vice President, Andy Jaskaniec
Territory Vice President of Loss Prevention, David Ruffing
Vice President Of Finance And Assistan, Gary Stoltmann
Vice President Management Information Systems, Linn Allison
Vice President of Digital, Becky Ploeger

Vice President Merchandise Planning and Aallocation, John Futhey
Vice President Information Systems, Peter Ciriscioli
Vice President Executive, Julie Persich
Regional Vice President, Blaine Predmore
Vice President Internal Communication, Lynn Loignon
Vice President Product Development, Scott Conant
Vice President Operations and Analytics Product Development, Charlie Holmes
Vice President of Distribution, Reggie Davis
Executive Vice President Marketing, William Setliff
Executive Vice President GMM of Ladies, Nancy Feldman
Vice President District Manager, Randy Blackburn
Vice President of Marketing, Eric Kirkhofer
Vice President Internal Audit, Steve Zamansky
Senior Vice President Fraud Operations, Troy Carrothers
Senior Vice President DMM Womens, Marianne Stone
Executive Vice President Marketing, Debby Fisher
Vice President dmm E Commerce, Chad Melnick
Exectuvie Vice President Product Development, Carol Williams
Vice President Ecommerce Development, Sunil S Bhardwaj
Vice President of Finance and Operations, Santa Paul
Vice President Information Technology, Greg Heinz
Senior Vice President Planning And AL, Dan Newman
Vice President Merchandising E Commerce, Chris Cavalline
Senior Vice President Logistics, Greggory Barta
Vice President Of Logistics And Stores (Information Technology), Scott Vifquain
Vice President of Strategic Sourcing and Procurement, David Maley
Senior Vice President Of Product Development, Judi Langley
Executive Vice President, Will Setliff
Vice President Tax, Tom Taugher
Vice President of Finance, Mike Baughn
Vice President District Manager, Shane Knoy
Senior Vice President Assistant General Counsel, Steve Thomas
Vice President Production, Ron Katanick
Vice President E Commerce Planning and Allocation, Brian Toy
Vice President, Deb Kuczora
Vice President of Brand, Richard Vollmer
Vice President Product Management Intern, Amanda Travis
Senior Executive Vice President In Charge Of Store Operations And Information Technology, Tom Kingsbury
Vice President, Annette Adams
Vice President of Property Development Law, Steven Karl
Regional Vice President, Mark Grudecki
Vice President DMM, Chris Candee
Vice President Administration, Gregg Bartel
Vice President Information Technology, Lana D Ross
Senior Vice President Direct Marketing, Michael Stanley
Vice President, Tim Mclarty
Executive Vice President Human Resources, Telvin Jeffries
Executive Vice President of Administration, Johnathan Lesko
Vice President Finance, Kelli Johnson
Vice President Marketing Strategy, Mary Benedum
Executive Vice Presi, Ken Bonning
Vice President And District Manager, Dave Schmidt
Regional Vice President, Loretta Roszczewski
Vice President District Manager, Dave Schmit

Vice President of Corporate Sustainability, Jack Fojut
Senior Vice President Design, Chris Kolbe
Senior Vice President of Marketing, Eleanor E Hong
Vice President Information Technology, Adam Brundage
Vice President of Sales, Brenda Thompson
Executive Vice President, J Lesko
Vice President of Human Resources, Kate Anderson
Auditors: Ernst & Young LLP

LOCATIONS

HQ: Kohl's Corp.
N56 W17000 Ridgewood Drive, Menomonee Falls, WI 53051
Phone: 262 703-7000   **Fax:** 262 703-6373
Web: www.kohls.com

2017 stores

	No.
California	116
Texas	84
Illinois	67
Ohio	58
Florida	51
New York	51
Pennsylvania	50
Michigan	46
Wisconsin	41
Indiana	39
New Jersey	37
Georgia	32
North Carolina	30
Virginia	31
Missouri	27
Arizona	26
Minnesota	27
Massachusetts	25
Colorado	24
Maryland	23
Connecticut	22
Tennessee	20
Washington	19
Iowa	18
Kentucky	17
South Carolina	16
Alabama	14
Utah	12
Nevada	12
Kansas	12
Oklahoma	11
Oregon	11
New Hampshire	11
Louisiana	8
Arkansas	8
Nebraska	7
West Virginia	7
Delaware	5
Idaho	5
Maine	5
Mississippi	5
New Mexico	5
North Dakota	4
Rhode Island	3
South Dakota	4
Montana	3
Wyoming	2
Alaska	1
Vermont	2
Total	**1,154**

PRODUCTS/OPERATIONS

2017 Sales

	% of total
Women's	30
Men's	20
Home	19
Children's	13
Accessories	9
Footwear	9
Total	**100**

Store Locations

	No.
Strip centers	777
Freestanding	294
Community & regional malls	83
Total	**1154**

Selected National Brands

adidas
apt. 9
Arrow
Calphalon
Candies
Carter's
Chaps
Columbia
Cuisinart
Daisy Fuentes
Dickies
Dockers
everGirl
George Foreman
Gloria Vanderbilt Home
Gold Toe
Haggar
Hanes
Healthtex
Henckels
HoMedics
Jockey
Jumping Beans
KitchenAid
Krups
Laura Ashley Lifestyles
Lee
l.e.i.
Levi's
Mudd
NIKE
Nine & Company
Oneida
OshKosh B'Gosh
Pfaltzgraff
Pyrex
Reebok
Skechers
Speedo
Unionbay
Urban Pipeline
Villager

Selected Private-label Brands

Apt. 9
Bobby Flay
ELLE
Jennifer Lopez
Jumping Beans
Marc Anthony

COMPETITORS

Amazon.com	Ross Stores
BJ's Wholesale Club	Saks
Bed Bath & Beyond	Sears
Belk	Shopko Stores
Dillard's	TJX Companies
J. C. Penney	Tailored Brands
Kmart	Target Corporation
Macy's	Wal-Mart
Old Navy	

HISTORICAL FINANCIALS

Company Type: Public

Income Statement

FYE: January 28

	REVENUE ($ mil.)	NET INCOME ($ mil.)	NET PROFIT MARGIN	EMPLOYEES
01/17	18,686	556	3.0%	138,000
01/16	19,204	673	3.5%	140,000
01/15*	19,023	867	4.6%	137,000
02/14	19,031	889	4.7%	137,000
02/13	19,279	986	5.1%	135,000
Annual Growth	(0.8%)	(13.3%)	—	0.6%

*Fiscal year change

2017 Year-End Financials

Debt ratio: 33.97%	No. of shares (mil.): 174
Return on equity: 10.45%	Dividends
Cash ($ mil.): 1,074	Yield: 0.0%
Current ratio: 1.76	Payout: 64.3%
Long-term debt ($ mil.): 4,480	Market value ($ mil.): 6,786

	STOCK PRICE ($) FY Close	P/E High/Low	PER SHARE ($) Earnings	Dividends	Book Value
01/17	39.00	19 11	3.11	2.00	29.75
01/16	49.75	23 12	3.46	1.80	29.52
01/15*	59.72	15 11	4.24	1.56	29.81
02/14	50.63	14 11	4.05	1.40	28.33
02/13	46.01	13 10	4.17	1.28	27.24
Annual Growth	(4.0%)	—	(7.1%)	11.8%	2.2%

*Fiscal year change

Kraft Heinz Co (The)

Bringing together packaged food giants Kraft Foods and H.J. Heinz The Kraft Heinz Company is one of the largest food and beverage companies in the world. In addition to its two namesakes the company's portfolio of iconic brands (four of them billion-dollar brands) include such names as Cracker Barrel Oscar Meyer Capri Sun Ore-Ida Kool-Aid Jell-O Planters Philadelphia Lunchables Maxwell House and Velveeta. Kraft Heinz has employees in more than 45 countries and sells its products in some 190. The company was formed in mid-2015 when Heinz and Kraft merged. In early 2017 Kraft Heinz withdrew a $143 billion bid for consumer products giant Unilever after Unilever management and shareholders resisted.

Operations

Kraft Heinz's operations are organized across some half a dozen specific product categories. Its largest segments are condiments and sauces (about a quarter of sales) and cheese and dairy (about 20%). Other segments include meats and seafood and ambient or shelf-stable meals (both at about 10%); as well as frozen and chilled meals refreshment beverages and coffee.

Geographic Reach

Unlike many of its major competitors Kraft Heinz counts the US as its largest market by far accounting for about 70% of total revenue. Canada and Europe together contribute more than 15% with the remaining revenue coming from Latin America the Asia-Pacific region the Middle East and Africa.

Sales and Marketing

Kraft Heinz's products are sold through its sales organizations and through independent brokers agents and distributors. This network sells to chain wholesale cooperative and independent grocery accounts as well as drug stores and pharmacies value and club stores and foodservice distributors. It also caters to hotels restaurants hospitals health care facilities and certain government agencies.

Kraft Heinz is heavily reliant on its largest customer Wal-Mart Stores which represents more than 20% of sales.

Financial Performance

Kraft Heinz enjoyed a 44% spike in revenues from $18.3 billion in 2015 to $26.5 billion in 2016 primarily due to the results of its 2015 merger. This growth was offset by an 11% drop in European sales which reflected the unfavorable impacts of foreign currency divestitures and an additional 53rd week of shipments that occurred in 2015.

Kraft Heinz's net income skyrocketed by more than 470% from $634 million in 2015 to $3.6 billion in 2016 as a result of the merger and savings from the integration program and other restructuring activities (plant closings and layoffs). Following the trajectory of net income the company's cash flow from operations surged by $2.5 billion in 2015 to $5.2 billion in 2016.

Strategy

Like many of its competitors in the packaged foods space Kraft Heinz is focused on core brands cost-cutting and consolidation through acquisitions.

The company continues to work around its 'fewer bigger better' philosophy focusing its new products and innovations on a core group of top brands. In 2017 and 2016 for example it introduced new products and product innovation for a handful of key brands including Velveeta Philadelphia Cream Cheese and the Classico line of pasta sauces.

Kraft Heinz's strategy also includes reducing expenses. The company's management steered by Brazilian private equity firm and stakeholder 3G Capital has implemented multiyear cost-cutting measures across the business to reduce overhead by streamlining operations. Measures include closing seven plants in North America and consolidating operations in both existing and newly built modernized plants. Reducing employee headcount which has fallen from about 46000 at the time of the Kraft-Heinz merger to 41000 at the end of December is another key element of its strategy.

In line with 3G's approach to growth (centered on buying and consolidating large companies) the company is expected by some industry experts to leverage acquisitions of other major players in the food and beverage industry to expand internationally and bolster its product portfolio. Adhering to this strategy in early 2017 Kraft Heinz placed an unsolicited bid to purchase consumer goods manufacturing giant Unilever for $143 billion; however Unilever quickly rebuffed the bid claiming it underestimated its value and Kraft Heinz withdrew. The deal would have created one of the largest corporate takeovers in history and combined more than dozens of household brands. Kraft Heinz has indicated it will continue to pursue Unilever although it is prohibited by British corporate law from placing another bid until six months after its first bid.

EXECUTIVES

Head U.S. Meat and Dairy Business, Howard Friedman
CEO and Director, Bernardo V. Hees, age 48, $1,000,000 total compensation
EVP Global Operations, Eduardo Pelleissone, age 43, $600,000 total compensation
EVP Global Foodservice, Emin Mammadov, age 40
Head U.S. Meals and Sauces Business, Eduardo Luz, age 44
Zone President United States, Paulo Basilio, age 42, $600,000 total compensation
Zone President AMEA, Marcos Romaneiro, age 34, $395,437 total compensation
Zone President Latin America, Francisco Sa, age 51
Head U.S. Beverages and Snack Nuts Business, Tom Lopez
President U.S. Foodservice, David Toy
SVP Marketing Innovation Research and Development, Nina Barton
President Kraft Heinz Canada, Carlos Piani, $169,481 total compensation
SVP Global People Performance and Information Technology, Melissa Werneck
Zone President Europe, Rafael Oliveira
Head U.S. Commercial Finance, Andre Maciel
EVP and CFO, David Knopf, age 29
Vice Chairman, John T. Cahill, age 60
Chairman, Alexandre (Alex) Behring, age 50

LOCATIONS

HQ: Kraft Heinz Co (The)
One PPG Place, Pittsburgh, PA 15222
Phone: 412 456-5700
Web: www.kraftheinzcompany.com

2016 Sales

	$ mil.	% of total
United States	18,641	70
Canada	2,309	9
United Kingdom	1,055	4
Other	4,482	17
Total	26,487	100

PRODUCTS/OPERATIONS

2016 Sales

	$ mil.	% of total
Condiments and sauces	6,781	26
Cheese and dairy	5,661	21
Meats and seafood	2,710	10
Ambient meals	2,283	9
Frozen and chilled meals	2,251	8
Refreshment beverages	1,529	6
Coffee	1,496	5
Desserts toppings and baking	980	4
Nuts and salted snacks	1,051	4
Infant and nutrition	762	3
Other	983	4
Total	26,487	100

COMPETITORS

B&G Foods	Hormel
Bush Brothers	Kellogg
Campbell Soup	McCormick & Company
ConAgra	McIlhenny
Frito-Lay	Nestl© USA
General Mills	Unilever NV
Hershey	Unilever PLC
Hillshire Brands	

HISTORICAL FINANCIALS

Company Type: Public

Income Statement

FYE: December 30

	REVENUE ($ mil.)	NET INCOME ($ mil.)	NET PROFIT MARGIN	EMPLOYEES
12/17	26,232	10,999	41.9%	39,000
12/16*	26,487	3,632	13.7%	41,000
01/16	18,338	634	3.5%	42,000
12/14	10,922	657	6.0%	—
12/13	6,240	(77)	—	—
Annual Growth	43.2%	—	—	—

*Fiscal year change

2017 Year-End Financials

Debt ratio: 26.23%	No. of shares (mil.): 1,219
Return on equity: 17.88%	Dividends
Cash ($ mil.): 1,629	Yield: 0.0%
Current ratio: 0.72	Payout: 27.3%
Long-term debt ($ mil.): 28,333	Market value ($ mil.): 94,789

	STOCK PRICE ($) FY Close	P/E High/Low	PER SHARE ($) Earnings	Dividends	Book Value
12/17	77.76	11 8	8.95	2.45	54.17
12/16*	87.32	32 24	2.81	2.35	47.15
01/16	72.76	—	(0.34)	1.70	54.37
Annual Growth	1.7%	—	—	9.6%	(0.1%)

*Fiscal year change

Kroger Co (The)

Kroger is still the US's largest traditional grocer despite Wal-Mart overtaking the chain as the nation's largest seller of groceries years ago. It operates some 3900 stores under various banners including 2800 supermarkets and multi-department stores nearly 800 convenience stores and around 320 jewelry stores. It also has over 35 food processing plants in the US. Kroger's Fred Meyer Stores subsidiary operates around 130 supercenters that offer groceries merchandise and jewelry in the western US.

Operations

Kroger (either directly or through its subsidiaries) operates a wide variety of store formats and banners that divvy up the retail market by size price point and geography. Roughly 50% of its supermarket and multi-department stores have a fuel center. Its combination-food-and-drug stores account for 85% of its stores base followed by price-impact warehouse stores (5%) large multi-department stores (5%) and Marketplace stores (5%).

The company's 150 Marketplace stores which trade under the Dillon's Fry's Kroger and Smith's banners capitalize on Fred Meyer's general merchandise expertise. While similar to multi-department stores Marketplace stores are generally smaller and don't stock apparel. Kroger's 130 price-impact warehouse-style stores operate under the Food 4 Less and Foods Co. banners and cater to the thrifty with no-frills low-cost shopping for grocery and health and beauty care items.

Kroger's 780-plus convenience stores (C-Stores) generate around 20% of its revenue and operate under six main banners including Kwik Shop Loaf 'N Jug Quik Stop Tom Thumb Turkey Hill Minit Markets and Smith's Express. The company operates 35-plus manufacturing plants under the Kroger Ralphs and King Scooper's banners. Of these 17 are dairies ten are bakeries five grocery plants two beverage plants two meat plants and two cheese plants.

Kroger's supermarkets typically stock more than 14000 of its own-brand products (under the Kroger Ralphs Fred Meyer King Soopers and other brands) about 35% of which the company manufactures. Kroger is also a major pharmacy operator in the US (most of its stores have one) though its pharmacy products and services contribute just under 10% of its revenue.

Geographic Reach

Cincinnati-based Kroger operates supermarkets in about 35 US states from coast to coast. Key markets include California Ohio Texas and Georgia which combined are home to more than a third of its supermarkets. Its Fred Meyer subsidiary does business in the Pacific Northwest and Alaska. All of Kroger's sales are rung up in the US.

Financial Performance

Kroger's revenues and profits have been rising over the past several years thanks to new store openings and acquisitions and a steady increase in same-store sales revenue.

In fiscal 2017 (ended January) sales bumped up 5% to $115.3 billion due to an increase in comparable (excluding fuel) sales store openings and the contribution from the acquired ModernHEALTH business. Food price deflation weighed on growth. Weakness in the fuel price triggered a 6% decrease in fuel sales to $14.0 billion although the lower price pushed up volume sales by 4%.

Net income fell 5% to $2.0 billion due to the restructuring of multi-employer pension obligations. Cash from operating activities fell 13% to $4.3 billion due to lower net income and changes in working capital partially offset by higher non-cash expenses.

Strategy

Amid an intensely competitive grocery market that has seen Amazon's acquisition of Whole Foods and a European invasion of discount grocery chains such as Aldi and Lidl Kroger is looking to both accentuate and move beyond its traditional grocery store roots.

Announced in 2017 the company's Restock Kroger plan includes some $9 billion in capital investments over the following three years dedicated to technology (including the "Scan Bag Go" hand-held scanner initiative and online ordering) as well as training and higher pay. The strategic plan also includes an increased focus on Kroger's private-label brands which hit more than $20 billion in sales in 2017.

The grocery giant also announced as part of Restock Kroger that it would launch an everyday activewear apparel line in 2018 to make its stores more of a shopping destination. It also said it was considering strategic alternatives for its $4 billion convenience store business.

Mergers and Acquisitions

In early 2017 Kroger?s acquired Murray's Cheese a New York-based specialty cheesemaker. This acquisition bolsters Kroger's push into upscale and organic foods.

In July 2016 Kroger's subsidiary Axium Pharmacy Holdings acquired Modern HC Holdings a leading specialty pharmacy. The purchase created a combined specialty pharmacy that operate as a wholly-owned subsidiary of Kroger's.

In 2016 Kroger's invested in Lucky a Colorado-based chain that offers organic foods. The company's store are mostly in college towns in the Midwest and Southeast US.

In December 2015 the retailer closed its purchase of buy Milwaukee-based grocer Roundy's for $178 million. The deal expanded Kroger's reach into the Midwest adding 151 Copps Mariano's Metro Market and Pick 'n Save stores in Wisconsin and Illinois.

HISTORY

Bernard Kroger was 22 when he started the Great Western Tea Company in 1883 in Cincinnati. Kroger lowered prices by cutting out middlemen sometimes by making products such as bread. Growing to 40 stores in Cincinnati and northern Kentucky the company became Kroger Grocery and Baking Company in 1902. It expanded into St. Louis in 1912 and grew rapidly during the 1910s and 1920s by purchasing smaller cash-strapped companies. Kroger sold his holdings in the company for $28 million in 1928 the year before the stock market crash and retired.

The company acquired Piggly Wiggly stores in the late 1920s and bought most of Piggly Wiggly's corporate stock which it held until the early 1940s. The chain reached its largest number of stores — a whopping 5575 — in 1929. (The Depression later trimmed that total.) A year later Kroger manager Michael Cullen suggested opening self-service low-price supermarkets but company executives demurred. Cullen left Kroger and began King Kullen the first supermarket. If he was ahead of his time at Kroger it wasn't by much; within five years the company had 50 supermarkets.

During the 1950s Kroger acquired companies with stores in Texas Georgia and Washington DC. It added New Jersey-based Sav-on drugstores in 1960 and it opened its first SuperRx drugstore in 1961. The company began opening larger supermarkets in 1971; between 1970 and 1980 Kroger's store count grew just 5% but its selling space nearly doubled.

In 1983 the grocer bought Kansas-based Dillons Food Stores (supermarkets and convenience stores) and Kwik Shop convenience stores. Kroger sold most of its interests in the Hook and SupeRx drug chains (which became Hook-SupeRx) in 1987 and focused on its food-and-drugstores. (It sold its remaining stake to Revco in 1994.) The next year it faced two separate takeover bids from the Herbert Haft family and from Kohlberg Kravis Roberts. The company warded off the raiders by borrowing $4.1 billion to pay a special dividend to shareholders and to buy shares for an employee stock plan.

To reduce debt Kroger sold most of its equity in Price Saver Membership Wholesale Clubs and its Fry's California stores. In 1990 the company made its first big acquisition since the 1988 restructuring by buying 29 Great Scott! supermarkets. Joseph Pichler became CEO that year.

Kroger sold its Time Saver Stores unit in 1995. In 1999 Kroger acquired Fred Meyer operator of about 800 stores mainly in the West in a $13 billion deal. Late in 1999 it announced it was buying nearly 75 stores (mostly in Texas) from Winn-Dixie Stores; the deal was called off in 2000 shortly after the FTC withheld its approval. But the company kept buying — acquisitions included 20 former Hannaford stores in Virginia in 2000 as well as 16 Nebraska food stores bought from food distributor Fleming and seven New Mexico stores bought from Furrs Supermarkets in 2001.

Kroger acquired 17 supermarkets (16 in the Houston area) from Albertson's (now Albertsons LLC) and another seven stores from Winn-Dixie in the Dallas/Fort Worth area in 2002.

In April 2003 Kroger introduced Naturally Preferred its own brand of some 140 natural and organic items including baby food pastas cereal snacks milk and soy products.

In 2012 with pharmacies in many of its stores nationwide Kroger purchased specialty pharmacy company Axium Pharmacy Holdings based in Florida. The move satisfied Kroger's long-term growth plans and allowed the grocery chain to serve customers that require complex drug therapies.

EXECUTIVES

Group Vice President Logistics, Kevin Dougherty
Chairman and CEO, W. Rodney McMullen, age 56, $1,251,781 total compensation
EVP and CFO, J. Michael Schlotman, age 59, $850,360 total compensation
President Harris Teeter Supermarkets, Frederick J. (Fred) Morganthall, age 65, $691,487 total compensation
Sr V Pres, James Thorne
EVP and CIO, Christopher T. (Chris) Hjelm, age 55, $703,367 total compensation
EVP Merchandising, Michael J. (Mike) Donnelly, age 58, $757,036 total compensation
VP Grocery Products Group, Katie Wolfram, age 62
President Mid-Atlantic Division, Jerry L. Clontz
President Houston Division, Marlene Stewart, age 61
President Kroger's Columbus division, Dan De La Rosa
VP Manufacturing, Erin S. Sharp, age 59
President Dillons division, Joe Grieshaber
President Nashville Division, Zane Day
President Roundy's Supermarkets Wisconsin, Michael Marx
EVP Operations Roundy's, Don Rosanova
President Smith's, Kenny Kimball
President Dillons Division, Colleen Juergensen
Group VP and Chief Digital Officer, Yael Cosset, age 43
Senior Vice President, R Williams
Vice President, Jeremy Stover

Vice President, Nancy Moon-Eilers
Group Vice President Ret Oprs, Mary E Adcock
Vice President Store Development, Patti L Taylor
Vice President, Matt Thompson
Director Of Surgery, Frank Zagar
Vice President Risk and Collectons, William A Douglas
Vice President Engineering, Robin Debuke
Vice President, Bruce Gack
Vice President Distribution, Scott Palmer
Senior Vice President, Mark Tuffin
Vice President of Marketing, Barbara White
Vice President Of Tax, Joe Bradley
Vice President Engineering, Mike Kurzendoerfer
Vice President Store Development, Bryan S Smith
Vice President of Retail Operations, Mike Purdum
Department Head, JESSE KILE
Vice President and Controller, Elizabeth Van Olfen
Vice President Meat and Seafoo, Dan D Rosa
Vice President, Heather Coleman
Vice President Non Foods, Jim Wetta
Vice President of Talent Development, Tim Massa
Vice President Human Resource, Steve Jones
Pharmacy Manager, Peggy Gilligan
Associate Vice President Development, Rebecca Thompson
Vice Presidednt, Jeff Talbot
Pharmacy Manager, Diane Chance
Information technology Vice President, Charles Mitchell
Vice President, Deanna Golden
Vice President of Operations of the New Nashville Division, Laurie King
Vice President, Cindy Rantanen
Vice President, Joe Rother
RPH, Hattie Davis
Vice President Merchandising, Ruben Fernandez
Senior Vice President, Gary Bernardo
Executive Vice President Chief Financial Officer, Chris Hjelm
Merchandising Vice President, Chris Albi
Vice President, Will Baird
Group Vice President Information technology, Jeff Abate
Vice President, Angela Tracy
Vice President and Chief Ethics and Compliance Officer, Martha Sarra
Executive Vice President Secretary And General C, Paul Heldman
Pharmacy Manager, Mary Travis
Vice President Loss Prevention, Scott Bringhurst
Vice President Loyalty, Mark R Belleville
Pharmacy Manager, Janet Ballard
Pharmacy Manager, Mandy Brennaman
Vice President of Marketing, Trey Powell
Vice President Talent Management, Stephen Jones
Pharmacy Manager, Jennifer Strapp
Vice President Operations, Domonic Pacheco
Vice President of Brand Management, James Jenson
Vice President and Treasurer, Aaron Parra
Pharmacy Manager, David Le
Department Head, Val Smith
pharmacy manager, Vicci Lehman
Pharmacist Manager, Kenneth Letchworth
Pharmacy Manager, Jimmy Byun
Department head, Rochelle Hatcher
Pharmacy Manager, Sarah Fochtman
Pharmacy manager, Monique Laguerre
RPh, Vijay Chenna
RPH, Doreen Mwangi
Pharmacy Manager, Lanier Mull
Pharmacy Manager, Lauren Bryant
Vice President, Nancy Riggs
Pharmacy Manager, Kristin Perry
Pharmacy Manager, Stacey Dust
PharmD, Ashley Rhodes
Pharmacy Manager, Gabriel Stillabower
Pharmacy Manager, Julie Cymbola
Pharmacy Manager, Courtney Tran

DEPARTMENT HEAD, Curtis Bruns
Pharmacy Manager, Gayle Townsend
Pharmacy Manager, Turen Pang
Pharmacy Manager, Avi Bhatia
Pharmacy Manager, Steve Blackwell
Pharmacist Manager, Morgan Meade
Pharmacy manager, Natalie Lenfert
Pharmacy Manager, Abdurahman Ahmed
Department head, Brian Weisenberger
Vice President, Stuart Aitkin
Pharmacy Manager, Benjamin Azizi
Vice President Sales and Marketing, Norm Carhill
Pharmacy Manager, Barb Judge
Pharmacy Manager, Cc Hepburn
Department Head, Jeffrey Everling
Pharmacist (Manager), Lauren Luken
Board Member, Carol Mclemore
Assistant Treasurer, Kathy Hanna
Vice Chair, Rodney McMullen
Auditors: PricewaterhouseCoopers LLP

LOCATIONS

HQ: Kroger Co (The)
1014 Vine Street, Cincinnati, OH 45202
Phone: 513 762-4000   Fax: 513 762-1400
Web: www.thekrogerco.com

PRODUCTS/OPERATIONS

2017 Sales

	$ mil.	% of total
Supermarket	96,900	84
Supermarket fuel sales	13,979	12
Other stores & manufacturing	4,458	4
Total	**115,337**	**100**

2017 Stores

	No.
Supermarkets & multidepartment stores	2,796
Convenience stores	784
Jewelry	319
Total	**3,899**

2017 Sales

	$ mil.	% of total
Non-perishable	60,220	52
Perishable	27,666	24
Fuel	13,979	12
Pharmacy	10,432	9
Other	3,040	3
Total	**115,337**	**100**

Selected Kroger Stores

Multidepartment stores
  Fred Meyer
Supermarkets
  Baker's
  City Market Food & Pharmacy
  Dillon Food Stores
  Fry's Food & Drug Stores
  Gerbes Supermarkets
  Harris Teeter Supermarkets
  Jay C Food Stores
  King Soopers
  Kroger
  Kroger Fresh Fare
  Owen's
  Pay Less Super Markets
  Quality Food Centers (QFC)
  Ralphs
  Scott's Food & Pharmacy
  Smith's Food & Drug Centers
Warehouse stores
  Food 4 Less
  FoodsCo
Convenience stores
  Kwik Shop
  Loaf 'N Jug
  Quik Stop Markets
  Tom Thumb Food Stores
  Turkey Hill Minit Markets
Jewelry stores
  Barclay Jewelers
  Fox's Jewelers

Fred Meyer Jewelers
Littman Jewelers
Food Production
Bread and other baked goods
Cheese
Coffee
Crackers
Cultured products (cottage cheese yogurt)
Deli products
Fruit juices and fruit drinks
Ice cream
Juice
Meat
Milk
Nuts
Oatmeal
Peanut butter
Snacks
Soft drinks
Spaghetti sauce
Water

Selected Private-Label Brands

Bath & Body Therapies (body and bath)
Banner brands (Kroger Ralphs King Soopers)
Everyday Living (kitchen gadgets)
FMV (For Maximum Value)
HD Design (upscale kitchen gadgets)
Moto Tech (automotive)
Naturally Preferred (premium quality natural and organic brand)
Office Works (office and school supplies)
Private Selection (premium quality brand)
Splash Spa (body and bath)
Splash Sport (body and bath)

COMPETITORS

7-Eleven	Publix
99 Cents Only	Raley's
A&P	Randall's
Albertsons	Rite Aid
CVS	SUPERVALU
Chevron	Safeway
Costco Wholesale	Save Mart
Dollar General	Stater Bros.
Exxon Mobil	Sterling Jewelers
Family Dollar Stores	Target Corporation
GNC	Tesco
Giant Eagle	Valero Energy
H-E-B	Vitamin Shoppe
Hy-Vee	Wal-Mart
IGA	Walgreen
Kmart	Wegmans
Marsh Supermarkets	Whole Foods
Meijer	Winn-Dixie
NBTY	Zale

HISTORICAL FINANCIALS

Company Type: Public

Income Statement

FYE: January 28

	REVENUE ($ mil.)	NET INCOME ($ mil.)	NET PROFIT MARGIN	EMPLOYEES
01/17	115,337	1,975	1.7%	443,000
01/16	109,830	2,039	1.9%	431,000
01/15*	108,465	1,728	1.6%	400,000
02/14	98,375	1,519	1.5%	375,000
02/13	96,751	1,497	1.5%	343,000
Annual Growth	**4.5%**	**7.2%**	—	**6.6%**

*Fiscal year change

2017 Year-End Financials

Debt ratio: 38.56%	No. of shares (mil.): 924
Return on equity: 29.30%	Dividends
Cash ($ mil.): 322	Yield: 0.0%
Current ratio: 0.80	Payout: 21.9%
Long-term debt ($ mil.): 11,825	Market value ($ mil.): 30,825

| STOCK PRICE ($) | P/E | PER SHARE ($) | | |
FY Close	High/Low	Earnings	Dividends	Book Value
01/17	33.36	20 14	2.05	0.45	7.25
01/16	38.81	37 16	2.06	0.40	7.05
01/15*	69.05	40 20	1.72	0.34	5.56
02/14	36.10	30 19	1.45	0.31	5.30
02/13	27.89	20 15	1.39	0.25	4.09
Annual Growth	4.6%	— —	10.3%	16.1%	15.4%

*Fiscal year change

L Brands, Inc

L Brands (formerly Limited Brands) is as much of a shopping-mall mainstay as food courts and teenagers. The company operates 3005 specialty stores in North America and the UK primarily under the Victoria's Secret Bath & Body Works (BBW) and La Senza (in Canada) banners as well as corresponding websites and catalogs. Originally focused on apparel L Brands sold its ailing Limited and Express chains — leaving the company free to focus on its core businesses. L Brands also owns apparel importer MAST Industries accessories boutique operator Henri Bendel apothecary C.O. Bigelow and The White Barn Candle Co.

Operations

L Brands has realigned its reportable segments into Victoria's Secret Bath & Body Works (BBW) and Victoria's Secret and Bath and Body Works International. More than 60% of sales come from domestic Victoria's Secret stores driven by its eponymous and PINK brands. More than 30% of sales come from the BBW segment which also includes White Barn Candle and C.O. Bigelow brands. The remaining revenue comes from Victoria?s Secret and BBW International and others.

MAST Industries (dba Mast Global Fashions) is the company's production sourcing and logistics arm - it accounts for the rest of sales. Mast is one of the world's largest contract manufacturers importers and distributors of apparel. Mast has manufacturing operations and joint ventures in more than a dozen countries including China Israel Mexico and Sri Lanka.

The Victoria's Secret segment sells women's intimate and other apparel personal care and beauty products under the Victoria's Secret and PINK brand names.

The Bath & Body Works segment sells personal care soaps sanitizers and home fragrance products under the Bath & Body Works White Barn Candle Company C.O. Bigelow and other brand names.

Victoria's Secret and Bath & Body Works International segments include the Victoria's Secret and Bath & Body Works company-owned and partner-operated stores.

Geographic Reach

In addition to its 3078 US stores L Brands has retail stores in Canada the UK china and the Middle East. International sales totaled $1.4 billion in fiscal 2017 (ended January). The company has a partnership with M.H. Alshaya (a popular franchise partner for many American retailers including American Eagle Outfitters and Pottery Barn) to operate stores in the Middle East.

Sales and Marketing

L Brands spent $325 million on advertising expenses in fiscal 2017 down from $414 million and $436 million in 2016 and 2015 respectively. The company sells its La Senza products at more than 120 La Senza stores in Canada and online at www.LaSenza.com. Henri Bende sells its products through New York flagship and online at www.HenriBendel.com.

Financial Performance

The company's net revenues have been increasing over the last five years. In fiscal 2016 L Brands' net revenues increased by 6% due to increase in all of its segments particularly Victoria's Secret.

Victoria's Secret segment revenues increased due to higher Victoria's Secret Stores and Victoria's Secret Direct sales resulting from the performance of PINK brands core lingerie and sport driven by a compelling merchandise assortment that incorporated newness innovation and fashion as well as in-store execution.

In fiscal 2016 the company's net income increased by 20% due to higher net revenues and other income driven by a pre-tax gain due to the divestiture of remaining ownership interest in third-party apparel sourcing business to Sycamore Partners.

L Brands' operating cash inflow increased by 5% to $1.87 billion compared to $1.79 billion in fiscal 2015.

Strategy

The company's goal was for Victoria's Secret to blossom into a $10-billion brand but the global financial crisis decline in consumer confidence and poor performance of the La Senza business in Canada conspired to delay the growth strategy for the bra-and-panty business. The strategy at Victoria's Secret is to capture the teen and college-age female customer with its youth-oriented PINK brand with the hope that as she matures she will shop for sexier styles such as Angels and Very Sexy sold in Victoria's Secret stores. PINK is sold in freestanding stores as well as Victoria's Secret shops. While the retailer doesn't break out PINK sales the brand is meeting stiff competition from American Eagle's Aerie brand and Gilly Hicks by Abercrombie & Fitch. Both target the youth market. L Brands has been closing La Senza stores and repositioning the brand.

While the company's first focus is on major growth in North America it plans to further expand into international markets including mainland China and other countries through partner arrangements or company-owned stores.

HISTORY

After a disagreement with his father in 1963 over the operation of the family store (Leslie's) Leslie Wexner then 26 opened the first Limited store in Columbus Ohio with $5000 borrowed from his aunt. The company was named from Wexner's desire to do one product line well — moderately priced fashionable attire for teenagers and young women.

When The Limited went public in 1969 it had only five stores but the rapid development of large covered malls spurred growth to 100 stores by 1976. Two years later The Limited acquired MAST Industries an international apparel purchasing and importing company. The company opened Express in 1980 to serve the teen market.

The Limited grew with acquisitions including the 1982 purchases of Lane Bryant (large sizes) and Victoria's Secret (lingerie). That year it formed the Brylane fashion catalog division and acquired Roaman's a bricks-and-mortar and catalog merchandiser of plus sizes.

Wexner bought The Lerner Stores (budget women's apparel) and Henri Bendel (high fashion) in 1985 sportswear retailer Abercrombie & Fitch (A&F) in 1988 and London-based perfumer Penhaligon's in 1990 (sold in 1997). The Limited introduced several in-store shops including Cacique (French lingerie) in 1988 and Limited Too (girls' fashions) which were later expanded into standalone stores. It also launched Structure (men's sportswear) in 1989 and Bath & Body Works shops in 1990. All of these stores were in malls often strategically clustered together.

The company closed many The Limited and Lerner stores in 1993 and sold 60% of its Brylane catalog unit to Freeman Spogli (Brylane went public in 1997). It opened four Bath & Body Works stores in the UK (its first non-US stores) to compete with British rival The Body Shop.

In 1994 The Limited bought Galyan's Trading Company a chain of sporting goods superstores. The company began spinning off its businesses while keeping controlling stakes; it spun off Intimate Brands (Victoria's Secret Cacique and Bath & Body Works) in 1995 and A&F in 1996. (The Limited sold its remaining 84% in A&F in 1998.)

The Limited closed more than 100 of its women's apparel stores in 1997 and Intimate Brands shuttered the Cacique chain; the next year The Limited closed nearly 300 more stores companywide (excluding the Intimate Brands chains) and the majority of its Henri Bendel stores.

In 1998 The Limited launched White Barn Candle Co. (candle and home fragrance stores). The following year the company spun off Limited Too its most successful chain as Too Inc. and reduced its interest in Galyan's to 40%. (Galyan's management and buyout firm Freeman Spogli bought the remaining 60% of the sporting goods chain.) The Limited (as well as Intimate Brands) declared a two-for-one stock split in 2000.

To boost profits in 2001 The Limited folded the Structure brand into the Express unit and spun off its Galyan's and Alliance Data Systems subsidiaries retaining 22% and 20% respectively. The Limited sold its Lane Bryant unit to Charming Shoppes for $335 million that year.

The Limited bought back the remaining shares of Intimate Brands it did not already own in March 2002 and over the course of the year phased it into a business segment. In May 2002 the company changed its name to Limited Brands from The Limited. Later that year Limited Brands sold off its remaining stake in Lerner New York and in late 2003 sold its Structure label (which it had rebranded as Express Men's) to Sears Roebuck and Co.

In 2007 Limited Brands completed its acquisition of lingerie maker and retailer La Senza based in Montreal for about $600 million. It also sold a 75% stake in its 251-store Limited Stores business to Sun Capital Partners taking a loss on the sale. In mid-2010 it sold the rest. Three years later in 2013 it finally changed the company name from The Limited to L Brands.

EXECUTIVES

SVP and Controller, Stuart B. Burgdoerfer, age 53, $890,923 total compensation

Chairman and CEO, Leslie H. Wexner, age 79, $2,000,000 total compensation

EVP and CIO, Steven M. Stone, age 56

COO, Charles C. (Charlie) McGuigan, age 60, $1,290,385 total compensation

President and CEO Bath & Body Works, Nicholas P.M. (Nick) Coe, age 54, $1,080,769 total compensation

Senior Vice President And Chief Techno, Kurt Schnieders

Senior Vice President Procurement, Lauren Richardson

Associate Vice President Finance, Matt Lemon

Vice President Project Management, Beth Knuckles

Assistant Vice President Compensation, Gina Johnson

Senior Vice Presiden, Wendy Arlin

Vice President Consumer Services, Mike Underhill

Vice President, Vincent Null Russo

Associate Vice President Of Communicat, Christy Tostevin
Vice President Human Resources, Mike Kiida
Auditors: Ernst & Young LLP

LOCATIONS

HQ: L Brands, Inc
Three Limited Parkway, Columbus, OH 43230
Phone: 614 415-7000
Web: www.lb.com

PRODUCTS/OPERATIONS

2017 Stores

	No.
Bath & Body Works U.S.	1,591
Victoria's Secret U.S.	1,131
La Senza Canada	122
Bath & Body Works Canada	102
Victoria's Secret Canada	46
Victoria's Secret Beauty and Accessories	31
Henri Bendel	29
Victoria's Secret U.K.	18
La Senza U.S.	4
Total	**3,074**

2017 Sales

	$ mil.	% of total
Victoria's Secret	7,781	62
Bath & Body Works	3,852	31
Victoria's Secret and Bath & Body Works International	423	3
Other	518	4
Total	**12,574**	**100**

Selected Retail Brands

Bath & Body Works
C.O. Bigelow
Henri Bendel
La Senza
Pink
The White Barn Candle Company
Victoria's Secret

COMPETITORS

Abercrombie & Fitch	Macy's
American Eagle	Mary Kay
Outfitters	Natori
Avon	Nordstrom
Body Shop	Revlon
CVS	Saks
Dillard's	Sephora USA
Est©e Lauder	Shiseido Americas
Frederick's of	Target Corporation
Hollywood	The Gap
Fruit of the Loom	Ulta
Hanesbrands	VF Corporation
J. C. Penney	Wal-Mart
Jockey International	Warnaco Group
Kiehl's	

HISTORICAL FINANCIALS

Company Type: Public

Income Statement

FYE: January 28

	REVENUE ($ mil.)	NET INCOME ($ mil.)	NET PROFIT MARGIN	EMPLOYEES
01/17	12,574	1,158	9.2%	93,600
01/16	12,154	1,253	10.3%	87,900
01/15*	11,454	1,042	9.1%	80,100
02/14	10,773	903	8.4%	94,600
02/13	10,459	753	7.2%	99,400
Annual Growth	**4.7%**	**11.4%**	**—**	**(1.5%)**

*Fiscal year change

2017 Year-End Financials

Debt ratio: 70.21%
Return on equity: ***,***.**%
Cash ($ mil.): 1,934
Current ratio: 1.72
Long-term debt ($ mil.): 5,700

No. of shares (mil.): 286
Dividends
  Yield: 0.0%
  Payout: 110.5%
Market value ($ mil.): 16,877

	STOCK PRICE ($) FY Close	P/E High/Low	PER SHARE ($) Earnings	Dividends	Book Value
01/17	59.01	24 15	3.98	4.40	(2.55)
01/16	96.15	23 18	4.22	4.00	(0.89)
01/15*	84.63	24 14	3.50	2.36	0.06
02/14	52.36	21 14	3.05	1.20	(1.27)
02/13	47.25	20 16	2.54	5.00	(3.51)
Annual Growth	**5.7%**	**— —**	**11.9%**	**(3.1%)**	**—**

*Fiscal year change

L3 Technologies Inc

EXECUTIVES

VP; President Microwave Group, John S. Mega, age 63
Chairman President and CEO, Michael T. Strianese, age 60, $1,284,231 total compensation
EVP Corporate Strategy and Development, Curtis Brunson, age 68, $562,846 total compensation
SVP; President Sensors and Simulation Group, James W. Dunn, age 72, $534,462 total compensation
SVP and CFO, Ralph G. D'Ambrosio, age 48, $560,423 total compensation
SVP; President Services, Steven (Steve) Kantor, age 71
SVP Corporate Secretary and General Counsel, Steven M. (Steve) Post, age 63
SVP; President Integrated Systems Group, John C. McNellis, age 63
SVP Washington Operations, Gen. Richard A. Cody, age 66
VP; President Communications Systems Group, Susan D. Opp
VP Controller and Principal Accounting Officer, Dan Azmon, age 52
VP; President Marine and Power Systems, Robert E. (Bob) Leskow, age 57
VP; President of National Security Solutions Group, Les Rose
Investor Relations, Matt Steinberg
SVP and CFO, Ralph DAmbrosio
Director, Alan H. Washkowitz, age 75
Director, Robert B. Millard, age 65
Director, Arthur L. Simon, age 84
Director, Thomas A. (Tom) Corcoran, age 72
Director, Gen. Henry H. (Hugh) Shelton, age 74
Director, Claude R. Canizares, age 70
Director, John P. White, age 79
Director, Lewis Kramer, age 68
Independent Director, Lloyd Newton
Auditors: PricewaterhouseCoopers LLP

LOCATIONS

HQ: L3 Technologies Inc
600 Third Avenue, New York, NY 10016
Phone: 212 697-1111
Web: www.l-3com.com

COMPETITORS

BAE SYSTEMS	ITT Corp.
CACI International	Lockheed Martin
CAE Inc.	Meggitt
Cubic Corp.	Northrop Grumman
DRS Technologies	Orbital Sciences
DynCorp International	Raytheon
FLYHT Aerospace	Rockwell Collins
Solutions	Sierra Nevada Corp
General Dynamics	Thales
Harris Corp.	Trimble Navigation
Herley Industries	United Technologies
Honeywell	telent
International	

HISTORICAL FINANCIALS

Company Type: Public

Income Statement

FYE: December 31

	REVENUE ($ mil.)	NET INCOME ($ mil.)	NET PROFIT MARGIN	EMPLOYEES
12/16	10,511	710	6.8%	38,000
12/15	10,466	(240)	—	38,000
12/14	12,124	664	5.5%	45,000
12/13	12,629	778	6.2%	48,000
12/12	13,146	810	6.2%	51,000
Annual Growth	**(5.4%)**	**(3.2%)**	**—**	**(7.1%)**

2016 Year-End Financials

Debt ratio: 28.13%
Return on equity: 15.90%
Cash ($ mil.): 363
Current ratio: 1.73
Long-term debt ($ mil.): 3,338

No. of shares (mil.): 77
Dividends
  Yield: 0.0%
  Payout: 31.0%
Market value ($ mil.): 11,748

	STOCK PRICE ($) FY Close	P/E High/Low	PER SHARE ($) Earnings	Dividends	Book Value
12/16	152.11	18 12	9.01	2.80	58.95
12/15	119.51	— —	(2.93)	2.60	55.74
12/14	126.21	16 13	7.56	2.40	64.42
12/13	106.86	12 9	8.54	2.20	70.17
12/12	76.62	9 8	8.30	2.00	60.41
Annual Growth	**18.7%**	**— —**	**2.1%**	**8.8%**	**(0.6%)**

Laboratory Corporation of America Holdings

This company pricks and prods for profit. Laboratory Corporation of America (LabCorp) is a top provider of clinical laboratory services performing blood and other tests on more than 500000 specimens daily for some 220000 clients including managed care organizations contract research organizations (CROs) hospitals doctors government agencies drug companies independent clinical labs food and nutritional companies and employers. Services range from routine urinalyses HIV tests and Pap smears to specialty testing for diagnostic genetics disease monitoring forensics identity clinical drug trials and allergies. Through Covance it provides end-to-end drug development support. LabCorp operates more than 1750 service sites that collect specimens and 40 primary labs where tests are performed.

Operations

LabCorp operates through two primary segments: LabCorp Diagnostics (LCD) and Covance Drug Development (CCD).

The LCD segment which accounts for some 70% of LabCorp's annual revenues offers more than 4800 different tests. Many of the tests it performs each year are routine tests (including blood chemistry analyses blood cell counts and HIV tests) and nutritional chemistry and safety tests. It also offers specialty testing services for women's health allergies infectious disease oncology pain management and other areas. LCD's genomic and esoteric testing operations include subsidiaries Esoterix Monogram Biosciences and Integrated Genetics while specialty testing units include Cellmark Forensics Dianon Pathology and MedTox Laboratories.

CDD (30% of revenue) provides early drug development associated laboratory testing efficacy studies and clinical trial services to biopharmaceutical clients.

Geographic Reach

Most of LabCorp's operations are conducted through its extensive network of facilities throughout the US (which accounts for more than 80% of total revenue). The company also has joint ventures in Canada where it provides diagnostic testing services in several provinces and it has established presences in China Japan Singapore the United Arab Emirates and the UK.

CDD operates a network of laboratories in the US Switzerland Belgium Singapore and China. Covance has pre-clinical laboratories in Wisconsin Virginia Michigan and Indiana. It also operates labs in the UK (3) Germany China and Singapore.

Altogether LabCorp operates in approximately 60 countries.

Sales and Marketing

LabCorp uses a direct sales force to promote its products and services to customers including doctors hospitals clinical labs drugmakers managed care companies and government agencies. As payments from managed care entities (HMOs and PPOs) make up a significant part of LabCorp's net patient revenue gaining and maintaining contracts with these clients is a main thrust of the company's strategy. For instance LabCorp has a multi-year contract with UnitedHealth that makes LabCorp the insurer's exclusive national laboratory services provider.

LabCorp's LCD segment receives about 15% of its net revenue from Medicare and Medicaid programs.

Financial Performance

All of LabCorp's efforts towards expanding its offerings and geographic presence have helped keep the company's finances healthy for several consecutive years with its revenue growing each year since 2008. In 2016 the group reported an 11% increase in sales to some $9.6 billion. Both the LCD and CDD segments saw growth that year: LCD rose 6% due to organic volume growth and CDD rose 23% thanks to the addition of revenues from the recently acquired Covance.

After years of falling net income rose 68% to $732.1 million in 2016. A decline in restructuring and other special charges as well as a relatively low increase in selling general and administrative expenses helped boost the company's bottom line.

With the higher net income cash flow from operations increased 20% to $1.2 billion that year.

Strategy

Over the past seven years LabCorp has invested some $6.3 billion in strategic acquisitions. The company is focused on expanding its advanced testing capabilities especially in the areas of genetic and cancer testing. One particular area of interest for the company's product development efforts is the field of personalized medicine. It has introduced a number of "companion" diagnostic tests that determine whether a patient will react well or poorly to certain drugs. LabCorp is developing such tests internally as well as through partnerships with life science entities such as Duke University and Johns Hopkins University. Additional areas of focus are molecular diagnostics and the introduction of new assay platforms (both developed and acquired).

LabCorp strives to capitalize on its nationwide presence to strengthen managed care partnerships. In addition LabCorp looks to keep its physician customers happy with education tools and integrated information management systems including eLabCorp a web-based tool that allows doctors to access testing services online and its electronic health record (EHR) solution.

The company is also expanding consumer-focused tools such as its LabCorp Beacon patient portal. In 2017 it partnered with Walgreens to develop and operate patient service centers within Walgreens stores. These centers will offer lab testing to provide patients with a broader range of health care services.

Meanwhile LabCorp's specialty subsidiaries such as kidney stone analysis firm Litholink work to control costs for payers by focusing on providing patient-specific tools to manage chronic conditions.

Mergers and Acquisitions

In 2015 LabCorp bought New Jersey-based Covance one of the world's largest contract research organizations and a leader in nutritional analysis for approximately $5.7 billion. The deal provided LabCorp with new revenue sources and a broader international presence which has long been a goal for the company. The company also completed the $85 million acquisition of diagnostic testing firm LipoScience; that move strengthened LabCorp's position in the cardiovascular and metabolic disorder testing market. LabCorp additionally purchased Bode Technology Group which provides specialized forensic DNA collection analysis and relationship testing.

In 2016 LabCorp acquired Sequenom a specialist in tests for the prenatal and women's health markets. The deal was valued at $371 million. It also purchased women's health laboratory Pathology further building on its women's health offerings.

In mid-2017 the company bought UK-based CRO Chiltern International for $1.2 billion. With that deal it expanded its oncology operations as well as growing its international business.

EXECUTIVES

EVP CFO and Treasurer, Glenn A. Eisenberg, age 55, $653,438 total compensation
CEO Covance Drug Development, John D. Ratliff, age 57
SVP Chief Legal Officer Secretary and Chief Compliance Officer, F. Samuel Eberts, age 57, $486,875 total compensation
Chairman President and CEO, David P. (Dave) King, age 59, $1,133,333 total compensation
SVP and CIO, Lance V. Berberian, age 54, $396,112 total compensation
Senior Vice President, Devin Lorsson
Auditors: PricewaterhouseCoopers LLP

LOCATIONS

HQ: Laboratory Corporation of America Holdings
358 South Main Street, Burlington, NC 27215
Phone: 336 229-1127
Web: www.labcorp.com

2016 Sales

	% of total
US	81
Switzerland	5
Canada	3
United Kingdom	3
Other	8
Total	100

PRODUCTS/OPERATIONS

2016 Sales

	$ mil.	% of total
LCD	6,593	68
CDD	2,844	30
Reimbursable out-of-pocket expenses	204	2
Intercompany eliminations	-0.8	-
Total	9,641	100

Selected Subsidiaries

DIANON Systems Inc. (pathology Connecticut)
Dynacare Laboratories Inc. (clinical labs; Tennessee Washington Wisconsin Canada)

Esoterix Inc. (esoteric testing Colorado)
Integrated Genetics (formerly Genzyme Genetics fertility testing labs across the US)
Integrated Oncology (formerly US Labs esoteric oncology tests US)
Litholink Corporation (kidney patient testing Illinois)
Monogram Biosciences Inc. (HIV resistance testing and personalized medicine California)
National Genetics Institute (NGI infection testing and blood screening California)
Viro-Med Laboratories Inc. (molecular microbial testing Minnesota)

Selected Acquisitions

COMPETITORS

Arup Laboratories	NeoGenomics
Bio-Reference Labs	Oncolab
Celera	Orchid Cellmark
CompuNet Clinical	Pathology Associates
Laboratories	Medical Laboratories
HedgePath	Pharmaceutical Product
IDENTIGENE	Development
Kroll Background	Psychemedics
America	Quest Diagnostics
Laboratory Sciences of	Solstas
Arizona	Sonic Healthcare
MEDTOX Laboratories	eScreen
Medtox Scientific	
Mid America Clinical	
Laboratories	

HISTORICAL FINANCIALS

Company Type: Public

Income Statement

FYE: December 31

	REVENUE ($ mil.)	NET INCOME ($ mil.)	NET PROFIT MARGIN	EMPLOYEES
12/16	9,641	732	7.6%	52,000
12/15	8,680	436	5.0%	50,000
12/14	6,011	511	8.5%	36,000
12/13	5,808	573	9.9%	34,000
12/12	5,671	583	10.3%	34,000
Annual Growth	14.2%	5.9%	—	11.2%

2016 Year-End Financials

Debt ratio: 41.06%
Return on equity: 13.97%
Cash ($ mil.): 433
Current ratio: 1.36
Long-term debt ($ mil.): 5,300
No. of shares (mil.): 102
Dividends
  Yield: —
  Payout: —
Market value ($ mil.): 13,185

	STOCK PRICE ($) FY Close	P/E High/Low		PER SHARE ($) Earnings	Dividends	Book Value
12/16	128.38	20	14	7.02	0.00	53.61
12/15	123.64	29	24	4.34	0.00	48.81
12/14	107.90	18	15	5.91	0.00	33.34
12/13	91.37	17	14	6.25	0.00	29.07
12/12	86.62	16	14	5.99	0.00	29.06
Annual Growth	10.3%	—	—	4.0%	—	16.5%

Lakeland Bancorp, Inc.

Lakeland Bancorp is shoring up in the Garden State. It's the holding company for Lakeland Bank which serves northern New Jersey from more than 50 branch offices. Targeting individuals and small to midsized businesses the bank offers standard retail products such as checking and savings accounts money market and NOW accounts and CDs. It also offers financial planning and advisory services for consumers. The bank's lending activities primarily consist of commercial loans and mortgages (more than half of the company's loan portfolio) and residential mortgages. Lakeland also offers commercial lease financing for office systems and heavy equipment.

Operations

Lakeland boasts more than 50 banking offices across the New Jersey counties of Bergen Essex Morris Ocean Passaic Somerset Sussex Union and Warren.

Geographic Reach

Lakeland serves customers located in New Jersey.

Sales and Marketing

The financial institution serves a variety of customers from individuals to businesses to municipalities.

Strategy

While the company is looking to expand its operations through strategic acquisitions Lakeland is also focused on providing its customers with less traditional banking delivery channels. To this end the company offers Internet banking mobile banking and cash management services.

Mergers and Acquisitions

Lakeland acquired Bernardsville New Jersey-based Somerset Hills Bancorp which operates Somerset Hills Bank Sullivan Financial Services and Somerset Hills Investment Holdings and folding the company into its operations. The 2013 purchase allowed Lakeland to extend its reach into Somerset Union and Morris counties.

In 2016 the company acquired Harmony Bank a three-branch institution headquartered in Jackson New Jersey. The $32 million transaction expanded Lakeland's operations into Ocean County.

Company Background

The company has been minimizing its exposure to commercial leases though as its leasing portfolio contributed to Lakeland's first reported annual loss in 2009. The company cut its leasing portfolio by about half — a move made to de-emphasize that line of business. Instead Lakeland has focused on strengthening its mortgage and commercial loan portfolios. In fact commercial loans have recently been the area of greatest growth for the bank.

EXECUTIVES

SVP AND CONTROLLER, Rita Myers
Evp And Cfo, Joseph F Hurley, age 67
President and CEO Lakeland Bancorp and Lakeland Bank, Thomas J. Shara, age 59, $650,000 total compensation
SEVP and COO, Ronald E. (Ron) Schwarz, age 60, $266,769 total compensation
EVP and Chief Lending Officer; President National Bank of Sussex County, Robert A. Vandenbergh, age 65, $360,212 total compensation
EVP and Senior Government Banking and Financial Services Officer, Jeffrey J. Buonforte, age 65, $205,075 total compensation
SVP and Chief Credit Officer Lakeland Bank, James R. Noonan, age 65
EVP and Chief Risk Officer, James M. Nigro
CFO, Thomas F. Splaine, age 52
First SVP and Chief Technology and Information Security Officer, Mary Kaye Nardone
EVP and Chief Retail Officer, Ellen Lalwani
EVP and Chief Lending Officer, David S. Yanagisawa, $220,000 total compensation
EVP Chief Administrative Officer General Counsel and Corporate Secretary, Timothy J. Matteson, age 47
EVP and Regional President, Michael A. Schutzer
Senior Vice President and Team Leader of Commercial Lending, Michael Vessa
Vice President Asset Based Lending, Steven Breeman
Vice President, Russell Dunn

Vice President Commercial Lending, Bruce Bready
Vice President, Scott Heiman
Vice President Area Manager, Hafeza Mohammed
Vice President Director of Hurman Resource, Connie Meehan
Vice President, Jessalyn Mahan
Senior Vice President and Director of Marketing, Maureen Martin
Assistant Vice President Commercial Loan Officer, Jason Fischer
Senior Vice President, Laura Ferraro
Vice President, Elaine Petit
Vice President And Senior Loan Officer, Mary Karakos
Vice President, Rasiel Kleiner
Senior Vice President of Loan Operations, Gail Martin
Vice President Audit, Stephanie Dikovics
Vice President Information Technology, Maureen Mccully
Vice President, Betsy Kalman
Vice President In the Investment Program, Joseph P Dolan
Vice President, Cynthia SanPhillip
Vice President, Jane Quinn
Assistant Vice President Branch Manager, Kim Trimmer
Vice President and Business Development Officer, Mark McCoy
Vice President and Associate Counsel, Saily Avelenda
Assistant Vice President, Robert Surovich
Vice President Compliance Officer, Lisa Nienaber
Vice President of Management Accounting, Carl Ferraro
Assistant Vice President, Max Custer
Vice President Relationship Manager, Christina Paccione
Vice President Data Operations and Data Security Officer, Elizabeth Martin
Vice President and Compliance Officer, Lisa Mills
Vice President, David Heinmets
Vice President, John Allen
Senior Vice President, Robert Ravaschiere
Senior Vice President, Samuel Wilson
ASSISTANT VICE PRESIDENT, Diane Rallo
VICE PRESIDENT, Larry D Smith
First Senior Vice President, John Rath
Assistant Vice President, Maura Lapinski
Vice President Relationship Manager Commercial and Middle Market Lending, Brian Joyce
Vice Chairman, Bruce G Bohuny
Chairman Lakeland Bancorp and Lakeland Bank, Mary Ann Deacon, age 65
Assistant Treasurer, Rochelle Leonardo
Assistant Treasurer Branch Manager, Carianne Reeber
Auditors: KPMG LLP

LOCATIONS

HQ: Lakeland Bancorp, Inc.
250 Oak Ridge Road, Oak Ridge, NJ 07438
Phone: 973 697-2000
Web: www.lakelandbank.com

PRODUCTS/OPERATIONS

2015 Sales

	$ mil.	% of total
Interest		
Loans & fees	115	78
Investment securities and other	12	8
Non-interest		
Service charges on deposit accounts	10	7
Commissions & fees	4	3
Income on bank owned life insurance	2	1
Gains on debt extinguishment	1	1
Other	2	2
Total	**148**	**100**

Selected Services

401K and IRA Rollovers
Certificates of deposit & individual retirement accounts
Checking accounts
Consumer loans
Home loans
Insurance
Investment management
Online services
Retirement income planning
Savings and money market accounts

COMPETITORS

Bank of America
Bank of New York Mellon
Capital One
Clifton Bancorp
Hudson City Bancorp
Investors Bancorp
JPMorgan Chase
New York Community Bancorp
PNC Financial
Sovereign Bank
Sussex Bancorp
TD Bank USA
Valley National Bancorp
Wells Fargo

HISTORICAL FINANCIALS

Company Type: Public

Income Statement

	ASSETS ($ mil.)	NET INCOME ($ mil.)	INCOME AS % OF ASSETS	EMPLOYEES
				FYE: December 31
12/16	5,093	41	0.8%	592
12/15	3,869	32	0.8%	551
12/14	3,538	31	0.9%	566
12/13	3,317	24	0.8%	550
12/12	2,918	21	0.7%	522
Annual Growth	**14.9%**	**17.6%**	**—**	**3.2%**

2016 Year-End Financials

Debt ratio: 7.18%
Return on equity: 8.71%
Cash ($ mil.): 175
Current ratio: —
Long-term debt ($ mil.): —
No. of shares (mil.): 47
Dividends
Yield: 0.0%
Payout: 38.9%
Market value ($ mil.): 921

	STOCK PRICE ($) FY Close	P/E High/Low		PER SHARE ($) Earnings	Dividends	Book Value
12/16	19.50	21	10	0.95	0.37	11.65
12/15	11.79	15	12	0.85	0.33	10.57
12/14	11.70	15	12	0.82	0.29	10.01
12/13	12.37	18	13	0.71	0.27	9.28
12/12	10.18	15	12	0.72	0.24	9.00
Annual Growth	**17.6%**	**—**	**—**	**7.0%**	**12.0%**	**6.7%**

Lakeland Financial Corp

EXECUTIVES

EVP and Retail Banking Manager, Kevin L. Deardorff, age 56, $217,963 total compensation
President and CEO Lakeland Financial and Lake City Bank, David M. Findlay, age 55, $493,360 total compensation
EVP and Chief Credit Officer, Michael E. Gavin
EVP and CFO, Lisa M. O'Neill, age 49, $206,286 total compensation
Corporate Secretary, Kristin L. Pruitt, age 45

SVP Wealth Advisory, Eric H. Ottinger, $218,263
total compensation
Vice President And Trust Officer, Patricia Culp
Vice President Controller, Teresa Bartman
Senior Vice President Human Resources Training,
Jill DeBatty
**Senior Vice President and Commercial
Indianapolis Regional Manager,** Bill Redman
Chairman Lakeland Financial and Lake City Bank,
Michael L. Kubacki, age 65
Auditors: Crowe Horwath LLP

LOCATIONS

HQ: Lakeland Financial Corp
202 East Center Street, P.O. Box 1387, Warsaw, IN
46581-1387
Phone: 574 267-6144
Web: www.lakecitybank.com

PRODUCTS/OPERATIONS

2015 Sales

	$ mil.	% of total
Interest		
Loans	110	72
Securities	12	8
Noninteresst		
Service charges on deposit accounts	10	7
Loan insurance and service fees	7	4
Wealth advisory fees	4	3
Investment brokerage fees	1	1
Other	7	5
Total	**154**	**100**

COMPETITORS

1st Source Corporation	PNC Financial
KeyCorp	
Northeast Indiana	
Bancorp	

HISTORICAL FINANCIALS

Company Type: Public

Income Statement

FYE: December 31

	ASSETS ($ mil.)	NET INCOME ($ mil.)	INCOME AS % OF ASSETS	EMPLOYEES
12/16	4,290	52	1.2%	524
12/15	3,766	46	1.2%	518
12/14	3,443	43	1.3%	496
12/13	3,175	38	1.2%	497
12/12	3,064	35	1.2%	493
Annual Growth	8.8%	10.1%	—	1.5%

2016 Year-End Financials

Debt ratio: 0.72%
Return on equity: 12.67%
Cash ($ mil.): 167
Current ratio: —
Long-term debt ($ mil.): —
No. of shares (mil.): 24
Dividends
Yield: 0.0%
Payout: 35.4%
Market value ($ mil.): 1,181

	STOCK PRICE ($) FY Close	P/E High/Low	PER SHARE ($) Earnings	Dividends	Book Value
12/16	47.36	26 16	2.05	0.73	17.12
12/15	46.62	26 20	1.83	0.95	15.83
12/14	43.47	25 20	1.74	0.82	14.63
12/13	39.00	25 15	1.55	0.74	13.10
12/12	25.84	20 16	1.43	0.84	12.18
Annual Growth	16.4%	— —	9.4%	(3.4%)	8.9%

Lam Research Corp

Lam Research is a top maker of the equipment used to make semiconductors. The company's products address two key steps in the chip-making process. Its market-leading plasma etch machines are used to create tiny circuitry patterns on silicon wafers. Lam also makes cleaning equipment that keeps unwanted particles from contaminating processed wafers. The company's Customer Support Business Group provides products and services to maximize installed equipment performance. Lam's customers include many of the world's large chip makers; customers outside the US primarily in Asia represent the majority of sales. Lam's products are installed in more than 45000 semiconductor processing chambers around the world.

Operations

About two-thirds of Lam Research?s revenue comes from customers who make memory chips with another quarter of revenue generated by silicon foundries. Logic and integrated device manufacturers account for the remaining revenue.

Geographic Reach

South Korea is Lam Research's largest market accounting for about 30% of sales while customers in Taiwan account for about 25%. Other significant geographic markets are Japan and China each generating about 15% of Lam?s sales.

The company has manufacturing facilities in the US China Europe Korea Southeast Asia and Taiwan.

Sales and Marketing

Lam Research has five customers that each account for more than 10% of its revenue. They are Micron Technology Samsung Electronics Company SK Hynix Taiwan Semiconductor Manufacturing Company and Toshiba.

Financial Performance

Lam Research rode a wave of capital spending by its customers in 2017 (ended June) to post a 36% leap in revenue to about $8 billion. The company marked a fifth straight year of higher revenue as it said customers continued to invest in technology and capacity to meet increased computing demand from devices and applications for the Internet of Things cloud computing and other technologies. Sales were significantly higher in South Korea and to a lesser extent Taiwan.

The company?s net income skyrocketed about 86% higher to about $1.7 billion in 2017 compared to 2016. Lam credited the jump to higher revenue and more efficient factory use because of increased production volume. Net profit margin reached 21% in 2017 the highest since 2011?s 22%.

Lam?s cash flow from operations rose to about $2 billion in 2017 from about $1.3 billion in 2016 on significant changes in operating asset and liability accounts.

Strategy

The semiconductor business is notoriously cyclical rising and falling according to the strength of the overall economy. When the economy improves people buy more products with semiconductors in them. That's playing out at Lam where the value of shipments rose 45% in 2017 (ended June) from 2016.

The high expense of semiconductor manufacturing equipment however has resulted in consolidation of manufacturers. Samsung and Intel are among the few companies left that make their own products. So far Lam has maintained a mix of sales to manufacturers such as Samsung and to contract chip makers such as Taiwan Semiconductor.

A heavy investor in innovation the company's R&D expenses reached $1 billion in 2017 (ended June) up from $913 million in 2016 and $825 million in 2015. Particular research areas are deposition etch and single-wafer clean processes and technologies.

Mergers and Acquisitions

In 2017 Lam Research acquired Coventor which develops simulation and modeling software for the semiconductor industry. Coventor's software helps manufacturers predict structures and behaviors of design before committing to production.

The acquisition of KLA-Tencor which the companies agreed to in 2015 would have created a company with complementary products and something of a one-stop shop for companies that make semiconductors. Throughout the process the companies struggled to persuade regulators that the deal would not harm competition in the industry. Unable to make their case to the satisfaction of regulators Lam and KLA-Tencor called off the deal in October 2016.

EXECUTIVES

EVP Global Products Group, Richard A. (Rick) Gottscho, age 66, $545,296 total compensation
SVP and CTO Corporate Technology Development, David J. (Dave) Hemker
President and CEO, Martin B. Anstice, age 50, $937,789 total compensation
EVP and CFO, Douglas R. (Doug) Bettinger, age 50, $548,827 total compensation
EVP and COO, Timothy M. (Tim) Archer, age 50, $624,061 total compensation
SVP Chief Legal Officer and Secretary, Sarah A. O'Dowd, age 67, $434,488 total compensation
SVP Strategic Development Corporate Marketing and Communications, Gary Bultman
Vp Pl, Thorsten Lill
Corporate Vice President, Harmeet Singh
Vice President, Mohsen Salek
Vice President, Rangesh Raghavan
Vice President Regional Operations, Vince Brigman
Group Vice President Global Sales and Corporate Marketing, Steven Lindsay
Vice President of Etch Product Development and Engineering, John Daugherty
Vice President Director Manager, Robert Dunsford
Vice President and General Manager Etch, Pat Lord
Chairman, Stephen G. (Steve) Newberry, age 63
Auditors: Ernst & Young LLP

LOCATIONS

HQ: Lam Research Corp
4650 Cushing Parkway, Fremont, CA 94538
Phone: 510 572-0200   **Fax:** 510 572-6454
Web: www.lamresearch.com

2017 Sales

	$ mil.	% of total
Asia/Pacific		
Korea	2,480	31
Taiwan	2,096,669	26
Japan	1,041,969	13
China	1,023,195	13
Southeast Asia	401,877	5
United States	629,937	8
Europe	340,644	4
Total	**8,013,620**	**100**

PRODUCTS/OPERATIONS

Selected Products

Plasma ("dry") wafer-etching equipment
Plasma-based bevel clean system
Single-wafer spin and linear clean products
Three-dimensional integrated circuit etch equipment
Transformer Coupled Plasma (TCP) silicon etch equipment

COMPETITORS

ASM International	Plasma Etch
Applied Materials	Rennova Health
Ebara	SCREEN Holdings
Hitachi	Suss MicroTec
High-Technologies	Tokyo Electron
Intevac	Veeco Instruments
Mattson Technology	

HISTORICAL FINANCIALS

Company Type: Public

Income Statement
FYE: June 25

	REVENUE ($ mil.)	NET INCOME ($ mil.)	NET PROFIT MARGIN	EMPLOYEES
06/17	8,013	1,697	21.2%	9,400
06/16	5,885	914	15.5%	7,500
06/15	5,259	655	12.5%	7,300
06/14	4,607	632	13.7%	6,500
06/13	3,598	113	3.2%	6,600
Annual Growth	22.2%	96.5%	—	9.2%

2017 Year-End Financials

Debt ratio: 22.22%	No. of shares (mil.): 161
Return on equity: 26.01%	Dividends
Cash ($ mil.): 2,377	Yield: 0.0%
Current ratio: 3.10	Payout: 17.8%
Long-term debt ($ mil.): 1,784	Market value ($ mil.): 24,546

	STOCK PRICE ($) FY Close	P/E High/Low	PER SHARE ($) Earnings	Dividends	Book Value
06/17	151.78	16 8	9.24	1.65	43.21
06/16	82.28	15 11	5.22	1.20	38.09
06/15	82.86	21 16	3.70	0.84	33.72
06/14	66.95	18 12	3.62	0.18	30.98
06/13	44.34	72 47	0.66	0.00	27.56
Annual Growth	36.0%	— —	93.4%	—	11.9%

Las Vegas Sands Corp

Las Vegas Sands brings a touch of Venice to the US and China. Replete with gondoliers and a replica of the Rialto Bridge the company's Venetian Las Vegas Hotel Resort & Casino offers a 120000-sq.-ft. casino and a 4000-suite hotel as well as a shopping dining and entertainment complex. Through its majority-owned Sands China subsidiary the firm operates The Venetian Macao on the Cotai Strip (the Chinese equivalent of the Las Vegas Strip) as well as two other properties in Macao. Properties also include the Marina Bay Sands in Singapore and the partially-owned Sands Bethlehem in Bethlehem Pennsylvania.

Operations

The company's collection of resorts in Asia and the US feature state-of-the-art convention and exhibition facilities premium accommodations world-class gaming and entertainment destination retail and dining including celebrity chef restaurants and many other amenities. More than 70% of Las Vegas Sands' revenue comes from its casino operations.

Geographic Reach

Outside of Nevada Las Vegas Sands operates in Macao Singapore and Pennsylvania. Macao accounted for about 60% of the company's total revenue in fiscal 2016.

Sales and Marketing

Las Vegas Sands advertises on television internet radio newspapers magazines and billboards. Its advertising costs were $121 million in fiscal 2016. The Paiza Club located at the company?s properties is an important part of Las Vegas Sands' VIP gaming marketing strategy.

Financial Performance

Las Vegas Sands reported $11.4 billion in revenue for fiscal 2016 a slight decrease compared to the $11.6 billion the company claimed in revenue for fiscal 2015. The drop in revenue was largely attributed to the casino segment's revenue decrease of $312 million in fiscal 2016 (compared to previous fiscal year). The decrease in casino segment revenue was primarily caused by revenue decreases of $522 million at Las Vegas Sands' Macao properties and $152 million at Marina Bay Sands.

Las Vegas Sands' net income was $11.41 billion for fiscal 2016 a decrease of $278 million compared to the $11.69 billion the company claimed in revenue for the prior fiscal period. The decrease in net income was driven by decreases of $168 million at the company's Macao operations and $153 million at Marina Bay Sands primarily due to decreased casino revenues.

Las Vegas Sands ended fiscal 2016 with about $2.1 million in cash. That was roughly the same amount of cash as it had at the end of fiscal 2015. The company's capital expenditures totaled $1.4 billion during fiscal 2016 including $1.19 billion for construction and development activities in Macao.

Strategy

Las Vegas Sands is in the middle of a major international growth initiative with several projects in various stages of development. Despite the ambitious expansion plans abroad the company remains somewhat cautious in Las Vegas. Las Vegas Sands will explore opportunities to further expand its presence in Asia.

In May 2016 the company announced plans to work with the Madison Square Garden Company to construct a 17500-seat venue in Las Vegas built specifically for music and entertainment.

All Las Vegas Sands properties are participating in sustainability program aimed at reducing food waste.

EXECUTIVES

Chairman and CEO, Sheldon G. Adelson, age 83, $1,000,000 total compensation
President and COO, Robert G. (Rob) Goldstein, age 61, $3,400,000 total compensation
EVP Global General Counsel and Secretary, Lawrence A. (Lon) Jacobs, age 62, $284,800 total compensation
President Sands Bethlehem, Mark Juliano, age 62
President and CEO Marina Bay Sands, George Tanasijevich, age 56, $864,140 total compensation
President and COO The Venetian The Palazzo and Sands Expo & Convention Center, George M. Markantonis, age 59, $863,077 total compensation
EVP and CFO, Patrick Dumont, age 42, $1,200,000 total compensation
President and COO Sands China, Wilfred Wong
Vice President Global Head Of Infrastructure And Operations, Edwin Grogan
Vice President, Robert Cilento
Vice President Of Interiors Las Vegas Sa, Mark Signorio
Vice President Communi, Ron Reese
Vice President And General Counsel, Frederick Kraus
Global Vice President Of Marketing, Michael Volkert
Vice President Engineering and Facilities Management, Daniel Briggs
Senior Vice President Government Relations, Andrew Abboud
Vice President of Gaming Operations, Mia Banks
Vice President of Security, Jerry Markling
Vice President Casino Marketing, Kathy Mccracken
Senior Vice President Global Business Development, Wilson Ning
Vice President of Hotel Operations, Max Tappeiner
Vice President of Convention Sales, Tyler Stewart
National Sales Manager, Mikki Dejurnett
Senior Vice President and Global Chief Compliance Officer, Matthew Frank
National Sales Manager, Melissa Wilson
National Sales Manager, Ashley Reimer
Auditors: Deloitte & Touche LLP

LOCATIONS

HQ: Las Vegas Sands Corp
3355 Las Vegas Boulevard South, Las Vegas, NV 89109
Phone: 702 414-1000
Web: www.sands.com

PRODUCTS/OPERATIONS

2016 Sales

	$ mil.	% of total
Macao		
The Venetian Macao	2,895	25
Sands Cotai Central	1,965	17
The Parisian Macao	413	4
Four Seasons Macao	597	5
Sands Macao	688	6
Ferry Operations and Other	174	1
Marina Bay Sands	2,799	24
United States		
Las Vegas Operating Properties	1,537	13
Sands Bethlehem	571	5
Intersegment eliminations	(229)	-
Total	**11,410**	**100**

2016 Sales

	$ mil.	% of total
Casino	8,771	72
Rooms	1,527	13
Food and beverage	774	6
Mall	591	5
Convention retail and other	533	4
Promotional allowances	(786)	-
Total	**11,410**	**100**

Selected Properties

Sands Expo & Convention Center
THE Venetian Vegas
Sands Macao
The Venetian Macao
The Palazzo Las Vegas
The Plaza Macao
Sands Bethlehem
Marina Bay Sands
Sands Cotai Central
The Parisian Macao

COMPETITORS

Boyd Gaming	Penn National Gaming
Caesars Entertainment	Pinnacle Entertainment
Galaxy Entertainment	Rio All-Suite Hotel &
Genting Singapore	Casino
MGM Resorts	Tropicana
Melco Crown	Entertainment
Entertainment	Wynn Resorts

HISTORICAL FINANCIALS

Company Type: Public

Income Statement
FYE: December 31

	REVENUE ($ mil.)	NET INCOME ($ mil.)	NET PROFIT MARGIN	EMPLOYEES
12/16	11,410	1,670	14.6%	49,000
12/15	11,688	1,966	16.8%	46,500
12/14	14,583	2,840	19.5%	48,500
12/13	13,769	2,306	16.7%	48,500
12/12	11,131	1,524	13.7%	46,000
Annual Growth	0.6%	2.3%	—	1.6%

Debt ratio: 46.88% No. of shares (mil.): 794
Return on equity: 25.63% Dividends
Cash ($ mil.): 2,128   Yield: 0.0%
Current ratio: 1.10   Payout: 137.1%
Long-term debt ($ mil.): 9,428 Market value ($ mil.): 42,459

	STOCK PRICE ($) FY Close	P/E High/Low	PER SHARE ($) Earnings	Dividends	Book Value
12/16	53.41	30 18	2.10	2.88	7.77
12/15	43.84	25 15	2.47	2.60	8.58
12/14	58.16	25 15	3.52	2.00	9.04
12/13	78.87	28 16	2.79	1.40	9.36
12/12	46.16	32 19	1.85	3.75	8.57
Annual Growth	3.7%	— —	3.2%	(6.4%)	(2.4%)

Lauder (Estee) Cos., Inc. (The)

Auditors: KPMG LLP

LOCATIONS

HQ: Lauder (Estee) Cos., Inc. (The)
767 Fifth Avenue, New York, NY 10153
Phone: 212 572-4200
Web: www.elcompanies.com

HISTORICAL FINANCIALS

Company Type: Public

Income Statement

FYE: June 30

	REVENUE ($ mil.)	NET INCOME ($ mil.)	NET PROFIT MARGIN	EMPLOYEES
06/17	11,824	1,249	10.6%	46,000
06/16	11,262	1,114	9.9%	46,000
06/15	10,780	1,088	10.1%	44,000
06/14	10,968	1,204	11.0%	42,400
06/13	10,181	1,019	10.0%	40,200
Annual Growth	3.8%	5.2%	—	3.4%

2017 Year-End Financials

Debt ratio: 30.88% No. of shares (mil.): 368
Return on equity: 31.40% Dividends
Cash ($ mil.): 1,136   Yield: 1.3%
Current ratio: 1.76   Payout: 44.1%
Long-term debt ($ mil.): 3,383 Market value ($ mil.): 35,331

	STOCK PRICE ($) FY Close	P/E High/Low	PER SHARE ($) Earnings	Dividends	Book Value
06/17	95.98	29 22	3.35	1.32	11.91
06/16	91.02	32 25	2.96	1.14	9.71
06/15	86.66	31 25	2.82	0.92	9.72
06/14	74.26	25 21	3.06	0.78	10.07
06/13	65.77	27 19	2.58	1.08	8.47
Annual Growth	9.9%	— —	6.7%	5.1%	8.9%

Lear Corp.

Lear doesn't take a back seat to anyone when it comes to manufacturing automotive seats. The company's Seating business by far its most lucrative segment is a leader in the global market for manufacturing car seat systems and their components. The company's E-Systems segment produces automotive electronics and manufactures wire harnesses junction boxes terminals and connectors and body control modules. It operates from 245 facilities in 36 countries. Its largest customers include BMW Ford and General Motors Fiat Chrysler and Daimler. Lear traces its history back to 1917 when it was founded in Detroit as American Metal Products.

Operations

Lear has around 245 facilities; this includes 82 manufacturing facilities 114 dedicated component manufacturing locations seven sequencing and distribution sites 32 administrative/technical support facilities and eight advanced technology centers.

Lear's operations are split between Seating (77% of sales) and E-Systems (23%). Seating makes complete seat systems and major seat components including seat covers and surface materials such as leather and fabric seat structures and mechanisms seat foam and headrests. E-Systems makes complete electrical distribution systems that route electrical signals and manage electrical power within the vehicle for traditional vehicle architectures as well as high power and hybrid electric systems.

Products and brands include ProTec head restraints; leather (Aventino brand) and fabrics; interior materials like Lear's SoyFoam Seating; adjusters; and mechanisms. Lear produces a modular design seating system so they can be used over multiple segments thus minimizing investment costs. The company's seating systems are supported by its Lear-made electronics that power the adjusters and mechanisms but also other features like power heating and ventilation.

Geographic Reach

Lear operates from some 240 facilities in 36 countries. The US generates about 23% of its total sales each year while Mexico Germany and China contribute 14% 11% and 12% respectively.

Sales and Marketing

Lear serves the worldwide automotive and light truck market and produced about 90 million vehicles in 2016. General Motors and Ford accounted for 21% and 20% of Lear's total revenues in 2016 respectively. BMW also accounted for 10%.

Financial Performance

Lear has enjoyed unprecedented growth over the years with revenues peaking at a record-setting $18.6 billion in 2016. The historic growth was fueled by a 6% surge in Seating sales. This was attributed to positive impact from its acquisition of Eagle Ottawa new business and higher production volumes on key Lear platforms.

In addition to its revenue Lear's net income surged 31% to $975 million in 2016. New business and higher production volumes on key Lear platforms positively impacted profits in 2016. This more than offset the impact of selling price reductions and unfavorable foreign exchange rate fluctuations during the year.

Its net cash provided by operating activities also increased from $1.3 billion in 2015 to $1.6 billion in 2016. This was the result of increases in accounts receivable inventories and accounts payable.

Strategy

Where Lear stays ahead of the game with its E-Systems segment is by keeping an eye on the future of the automotive industry. The company cranks up the amperage on its competitors by manufacturing electrical distribution systems not just for traditional powertrain vehicles but for hybrid and electric vehicles as well.

It designs products that require less wiring and are therefore cheaper to make and are lighter in weight. Lear also follows the trends of customers who are showing an increased desire for additional functioning features in vehicles. Industry research indicates that electronic components account for about 35% of a car's total value. The company has exited non-core product lines such as switches and tire pressure monitoring systems opting instead to focus on an automobile's electrical distribution system with wired as well as wireless systems.

Mergers and Acquisitions

One way Lear has achieved milestone revenue growth recently is through the use of acquisitions. In 2017 it purchased Grupo Antolin's automotive seating business. The business has operations in five countries in Europe and North Africa and makes just-in-time seat assembly seat structures and mechanisms and seat covers. It also has partnerships with the largest European automakers including Daimler Peugeot Citroen Renault Nissan and Volkswagen.

In early 2015 the company bought Canadian premium automotive leather supplier Eagle Ottawa in a deal valued at about $850 million. The additional revenue from Eagle Ottawa along with other factors allowed Lear to post record-setting revenues of $18.2 billion during 2015.

Adding to its software offerings Lear in 2015 acquired intellectual property and technology from Autonet Mobile a developer of software and devices for automotive applications. It also purchased Arada Systems an automotive technology company that specializes in vehicle-to-vehicle and vehicle-to-infrastructure communications. Both acquisitions added software and hardware capabilities that will improve connectivity and communication features in vehicles as well as provide growth opportunities for its E-Systems segment.

EXECUTIVES

President CEO and Director, Raymond E. (Ray) Scott, age 51, $855,098 total compensation
President and CEO, Matthew J. Simoncini, age 56, $1,354,500 total compensation
SVP; President Asia/Pacific Operations, Jay K. Kunkel, age 57
EVP Business Development and General Counsel, Terrence B. (Terry) Larkin, age 62, $855,098 total compensation
SVP and CFO, Jeffrey H. Vanneste, age 57, $787,437 total compensation
SVP; President E-Systems, Frank C. Orsini, age 44, $736,375 total compensation
Vice President Korea, Dean M Ackerman
Multi Cultural Vice President, Jolito Bustamante
Chairman, Henry D. G. Wallace, age 71
Auditors: Ernst & Young LLP

LOCATIONS

HQ: Lear Corp.
21557 Telegraph Road, Southfield, MI 48033
Phone: 248 447-1500   **Fax:** 248 447-5250
Web: www.lear.com

2016 Sales

	$ mil.	% of total
US	4,186	23
Mexico	2,684	14
China	2,277	12
Germany	2,076	11
Other countries	7,333	40
Total	**18,557**	**100**

2016 Sales

	% of total
North America	40
Europe and Africa	38
Asia	19
South America	3
Total	**100**

PRODUCTS/OPERATIONS

2016 Sales

	$ mil.	% of total
Seating	14,356	77
E-Systems	4,200	23
Total	**18,557**	**100**

2016 Sales by Customer

	% of total
General Motors	21
Ford	20
BMW	10
Others	49
Total	**100**

Selected Products

Seating
  Adjusters
  Automotive seats
  Fabrics
  Head restraints
  Mechanisms
  Seat foam
  Structure systems
  Trim covers
Electrical power management
  Electrical distribution and power management
   systems
  Fuse boxes
  Junction boxes
  Terminals and connectors
  Wire harness assemblies
  High-power electrical systems
  Hybrid electrical systems
  Specialty electronics
  Audio sound systems
  In-vehicle television tuner module
  LED electronics (interior/exterior)
  Lighting control module
  Media console
  Radio amplifiers
  Wireless systems
  Keyless entry systems
  Passive entry systems
  Tire pressure monitoring systems

COMPETITORS

DENSO	Robert Bosch
Delphi Automotive	Stoneridge
Systems	Sumitomo
Faurecia	TS TECH CO
LEONI	Toyota Boshoku
Magna International	Valeo
Methode Electronics	Visteon
Mitsubishi Electric	Yazaki

HISTORICAL FINANCIALS

Company Type: Public

Income Statement

FYE: December 31

	REVENUE ($ mil.)	NET INCOME ($ mil.)	NET PROFIT MARGIN	EMPLOYEES
12/17	20,467	1,313	6.4%	165,000
12/16	18,557	975	5.3%	148,400
12/15	18,211	745	4.1%	136,200
12/14	17,727	672	3.8%	125,200
12/13	16,234	431	2.7%	122,300
Annual Growth	**6.0%**	**32.1%**	**—**	**7.8%**

2017 Year-End Financials

Debt ratio: 16.41%
Return on equity: 36.44%
Cash ($ mil.): 1,500
Current ratio: 1.36
Long-term debt ($ mil.): 1,951

No. of shares (mil.): 66
Dividends
  Yield: 0.0%
  Payout: 10.7%
Market value ($ mil.): 11,814

	STOCK PRICE ($) FY Close	P/E High/Low		PER SHARE ($) Earnings	Dividends	Book Value
12/17	176.66	10	7	18.59	2.00	62.06
12/16	132.37	10	7	13.33	1.20	44.03
12/15	122.83	13	10	9.59	1.00	39.31
12/14	98.08	12	9	8.23	0.80	37.92
12/13	80.97	16	9	4.99	0.68	37.72
Annual Growth	**21.5%**	**—**	**—**	**38.9%**	**31.0%**	**13.3%**

LegacyTexas Financial Group Inc

With its eye on the Lone Star State LegacyTexas Financial (formerly ViewPoint Financial) provides retail and commercial banking through its LegacyTexas Bank subsidiary which operates about 50 branches located mostly in the Dallas/Fort Worth area. LegacyTexas offers standard deposit products such as checking and savings accounts and CDs and uses deposit funds to originate primarily real estate loans: Commercial Real Estate loans account for nearly 50% of its lending portfolio while consumer real estate loans make up another nearly 20%. Non-real estate commercial loans make up almost 30% of its loan portfolio.

Operations

Outside of banking services the LegacyTexas offers brokerage services to buy and sell investments and insurance products through a third-party brokerage arrangement.

About 82% of the company's total revenue came from loan interest (including fees) in 2014 and another 6% came from interest on its taxable and non-taxable securities. Most of LegacyTexas' remaining revenue came from service charges and fees on deposit accounts.

Geographic Reach

The Plano-based company boasts 51 Texas branches with 48 of them located in the Dallas-Fort Worth Metroplex. Its two First National Bank of Jacksboro branches are in Jack in Wise counties in Texas.

Sales and Marketing

LegacyTexas' serves a diverse market of management professional and sales personnel office employees manufacturing and transportation workers service industry workers government employees and self-employed individuals. It spent $1.54 million on advertising in 2014 compared to $2.69 million and $1.75 million in 2013 and 2012 respectively.

Financial Performance

The company has struggled to consistently grow its revenues and profits in recent years despite growing loan business mostly stemming from lost revenues from the sale of its mortgage-banking subsidiary in 2012.

LegacyTexas' revenue rebounded by 7% to $31.3 million in 2014 primarily thanks to double-digit growth in its loan interest income driven by higher commercial loan volume.

Despite higher revenue in 2014 the company's net income dipped by 1% to $31.3 million mostly due to higher loan loss provisions as commercial loan production picked up. LegacyTexas' operating cash levels fell by 21% to $52 million mostly from unfavorable changes in working capital related to its assets and liabilities.

Strategy

The company formerly known as ViewPoint Financial significantly boosted its loan and deposit business and the size of its branch network through its early 2015 acquisition LegacyTexas Group. The deal made its branch network swell to 48 offices from just 31 before while adding some $1.63 billion in deposits and $1.4 billion in new loan business. The new LegacyTexas Group planned in 2015 to organically grow its loan portfolio focusing especially on making commercial real estate commercial and industrial and energy loans tied to high-quality assets. To cheaply raise funding for loans the bank plans to promote its non-interest-bearing demand deposit accounts especially in the commercial sector and using its treasury management services to provide a "catalyst for deposit growth."

Mergers and Acquisitions

In January 2015 the former ViewPoint Financial acquired LegacyTexas Group in a $300 million deal to create one of the largest independent banks in Texas with assets of nearly $6 billion. The parent company then changed its name to LegacyTexas Financial and the bank changed its name to LegacyTexas Bank.

Company Background

LegacyTexas Financial converted from a mutual holding company to a stock holding company in 2010. It sold its mortgage subsidiary VPM which operated a dozen loan production offices in Texas and Oklahoma in late 2012.

EXECUTIVES

EVP Chief Lending Officer, Thomas S. Swiley, age 67, $277,300 total compensation
EVP COO Chief Risk Officer and General Counsel, Scott A. Almy, age 50, $277,300 total compensation
President CEO and Director, Kevin J. Hanigan, age 60, $549,450 total compensation
EVP Community Banking, Charles D. Eikenberg, age 62, $277,300 total compensation
EVP and CFO, J. Mays Davenport, age 49
Vice President, Kelly Geer
Senior Vice President, Jeff Bundy
Vice President Business Development, Ginger Johnson
Senior Vice President Chief Information Officer, Ian McKintosh
Vice President Warehouse Lending, Michelle Marrapodi
Chairman, Anthony J. LeVecchio, age 70
Vice Chairman, George Fisk
Auditors: Ernst & Young LLP

LOCATIONS

HQ: LegacyTexas Financial Group Inc
5851 Legacy Circle, Plano, TX 75024
Phone: 972 578-5000
Web: www.legacytexasfinancialgroup.com

PRODUCTS/OPERATIONS

2014 Sales

	% of total
Interest and dividend income	88
Non interest income	12
Total	**100**

COMPETITORS

Amegy	PlainsCapital
BBVA Compass	SP Bancorp
Bancshares	Texas Capital
Bank of America	Bancshares
Cullen/Frost Bankers	Wells Fargo
North Dallas Bank	

HISTORICAL FINANCIALS

Company Type: Public

Income Statement
FYE: December 31

	ASSETS ($ mil.)	NET INCOME ($ mil.)	INCOME AS % OF ASSETS	EMPLOYEES
12/17	9,086	89	1.0%	869
12/16	8,362	97	1.2%	896
12/15	7,691	70	0.9%	856
12/14	4,164	31	0.8%	530
12/13	3,525	31	0.9%	576
Annual Growth	26.7%	29.6%	—	10.8%

2017 Year-End Financials

Debt ratio: 1.48%
Return on equity: 9.70%
Cash ($ mil.): 293
Current ratio: —
Long-term debt ($ mil.): —

No. of shares (mil.): 48
Dividends
  Yield: 0.0%
  Payout: 32.2%
Market value ($ mil.): 2,031

	STOCK PRICE ($) FY Close	P/E High/Low		PER SHARE ($) Earnings	Dividends	Book Value
12/17	42.21	23	18	1.89	0.61	19.95
12/16	43.06	21	8	2.09	0.58	18.49
12/15	25.02	21	13	1.53	0.54	16.88
12/14	23.85	36	26	0.81	0.48	14.20
12/13	27.45	33	22	0.83	0.42	13.63
Annual Growth	11.4%	—	—	22.8%	9.8%	10.0%

Leidos Holdings Inc

Leidos Holdings provides national security-related services to civil agencies of the US government all branches of the military and the intelligence community. The company's areas of expertise include cybersecurity; mission support; logistics; and intelligence surveillance and reconnaissance. It also operates one of the country's largest health system integrators and offers engineering services for energy (oil gas and electric) and industrial clients. In 2016 Leidos merged with Lockheed Martin's Information Systems & Global Solutions segment expand the scale and scope the IT and intelligence services it provides. The deal was valued at about $4.6 billion.

Change in Company Type
The combination with Lockheed Martin's Information Systems & Global Solutions unit created a company with a $10 billion portfolio of products and services. Leidos said the combined company serves more diverse markets with greater scale. The transaction included a special cash payment of approximately $1.8 billion to Lockheed Martin.

Operations
Leidos Holdings operates through four reportable segments: The largest segment National Security Solutions accounts for more than 50% of its revenue followed by the Information Systems & Global Solutions account with about 30% and Health and Infrastructure with more than 20% of company?s total revenue. The company's activities gathered in the corporate and other segment produces neglible revenue.

Geographic Reach
Leidos has some 340 offices in about 40 states across the US as well as in more than a dozen international locations where it works with US customers.

Sales and Marketing

The US government accounts for about 80% of Leidos Holdings' revenue with the US Department of Defense accounting for more than 50% of overall revenue. Within the government the company's major customers include the US Army Navy and Air Force the Defense Advanced Research Projects Agency the Department of Homeland Security and NASA. International customers account for about 5% of revenue

Financial Performance
Leidos Holdings reported $7 billion in revenue in 2016 a 50% increase from the year before. The Information Systems and Global Solutions group acquired in August 2016 added $1.5 billion in revenue. Sales for the National Security Solutions business rose 12% on international business and higher fees earned by reaching contract milestones. Revenue from the Health and Infrastructure segment dropped 2% with the divestiture of a design-build-construction engineering services business and the sale of a plant. Not counting the divested business the group?s revenue increased about 19% due to growth in federal and commercial health.

Leidos?s net income inched 1% higher to about $246 million in 2016 from the year before. The company spent about $90 million on the acquisition and integration of the IS&GS business. With the acquisition the company began a restructuring program to reduce headcount and consolidate facilities. The cost was about $12 million in 2016.

Cash flow from operating activities rose to $446 million in 2016 from $399 million the year before. The increase was due to timing of collections of receivables and early funding for employee benefit programs in the prior year that did not recur in 2016.

Strategy
The acquisition of Lockheed?s Information Systems and Global Solutions group in 2016 provided with the Leidos Holdings resources and capabilities that enable it to go after business it would not have qualified before. In one example IS&GS brought biometrics capabilities that improve its competitive position. Leidos has worked on bidding for contracts that total more than half a billion dollars as a result of the acquisition.

Leidos is putting its capabilities on the line with the multi-company project to modernize health records for the US Department of Defense. Working with Cerner Accenture and Henry Schein Leidos is putting together a modern EHR system that helps health systems run more efficiently and provide better care while protecting the privacy of patients.

In 2016 Leidos sold its heavy construction business to Haskell an engineering procurement and construction firm. Leidos sold the unit to focus more on market opportunities in the integration of physical and digital worlds.

Mergers and Acquisitions
The 2016 acquisition of Lockheed Martin's Information Systems and Global Solutions business for about $4.6 billion added multiple capabilities to the Leidos portfolio.The increased resources enable Leidos to go after projects with bigger scope than it had in the past.

EXECUTIVES

Chairman and CEO, Roger A. Krone, age 61, $988,462 total compensation
EVP and CFO, James C. (Jim) Reagan, age 58, $561,538 total compensation
EVP and Chief Human Resources Officer, Ann M. Addison, age 55
President Technology Group and CTO, John J. Fratamico, age 59
EVP and Chief of Business Development and Strategy, Gerard A. (Gerry) Fasano, age 51

President Health Group, Jonathan W. Scholl, age 55
EVP and General Counsel, Vincent A. (Vince) Maffeo, age 66, $575,000 total compensation
President Civil Group, Angela L. Heise, age 42
President Defense and Intelligence Group, Timothy J. Reardon, age 52, $162,240 total compensation
President Advanced Solutions Group, Michael L. Chagnon
VP Strategic Accounts and Government Relations, Rob Thomas
Vice President, Jack Gumbert
Vice President, Steve Ventsam
Senior Vice President Chief Human Resour, Marjorie Bailey
Senior Vice President Corporate Controller and Chief Accounting Officer, Ken Sharp
Vice President And Senior Pricing Director, Mark Achenbach
Vice President Senior Proposal Manager, Chris Overson
Assistant Vice President Senior Program Manager Fo, Richard Deason
Vice President Security Solutions, Jeffrey Murter
Vice President For Cybersecurity, Robert Pate
Vice President Production, Paul Dickinson
Vice President Information Technology, Chris Russeau
Vice President Lso Ssei Pm, Debbie Kerr
Director of Pharmacy, Stephen Bivona
Vice President of Strategy, Michael Leiter
Vice President Director of Human Resources Shared Services, Gayle Connatser
Svp Treasurer, Marc Crown
Vice President Executive Compensation and Compliance Director, Karen Kanjian
Senior Vice President Operations Manager, David Radcliffe
Vice President Division Manager, Brock Harris
Vice President Business Development, Robert Foster
Senior Vice President, James Baxter
Senior Vice President and Operations Manager Information Technology, Rick Jackson
Senior Vice President Government Affairs, Jay Killeen
Vice President, Robert Scott
Senior Vice President Enterprise Shared Service Director, Chris Buffoni
Vice President Enforcement and Public Safety Solutions, Jay Winkeler
Vice President Government Compliance, Matthew Popham
Vice President Business Development Veteran Health, Theresa Holder
Vice President Veterans Health, Jermon Bafaty
Auditors: Deloitte & Touche LLP

LOCATIONS

HQ: Leidos Holdings Inc
11951 Freedom Drive, Reston, VA 20190
Phone: 571 526-6000
Web: www.leidos.com

PRODUCTS/OPERATIONS

2016 Sales

	$ mil.	% of total
National Security solutions	3,610	51
Information Systems & Global Solutions	1,971	28
Health and engineering	1,463	21
Adjustments (-1) -		
Total	**7,043**	**100**

Selected Capabilites:

Civil:
Aviation
Cyber Solutions
Energy
Environment & Infrastructure

Exploration & Mission Support
Financial Solutions
Homeland & Transportation Security
Defense & Intelligence:
Airborne
Command & Control
Data Analytics
Enterprise IT
Federal Cybersecurity
Intelligence Services
Operations & Logistics
Sensors
Training
Health:
Federal Health IT
Hospitals & Health Systems
Life Sciences
Advanced Solutions:
Airborne Systems Integration
Maritime

COMPETITORS

Accenture
American Science and Engineering
BAE Systems Technology Solutions
Battelle Memorial
Boeing
Booz Allen
CACI International
CH2M HILL
Computer Sciences Corp.
Engility
Exelis
General Dynamics
HP Enterprise Services
Honeywell Technology Solutions
IBM Global Services
KBR
KEYW
Kratos Defense & Security Solutions
L3 Technologies
ManTech
OSI Systems
Raytheon Intelligence Information and Services
Serco
Unisys

HISTORICAL FINANCIALS

Company Type: Public

Income Statement

	REVENUE ($ mil.)	NET INCOME ($ mil.)	NET PROFIT MARGIN	EMPLOYEES
12/16*	7,043	244	3.5%	32,000
01/16	4,712	242	5.1%	18,000
01/15	5,063	(323)	—	19,000
01/14	5,772	164	2.8%	22,000
01/13	11,173	525	4.7%	40,000
Annual Growth	(10.9%)	(17.4%)	—	(5.4%)

*Fiscal year change

2016 Year-End Financials

Debt ratio: 35.99%
Return on equity: 11.64%
Cash ($ mil.): 376
Current ratio: 1.18
Long-term debt ($ mil.): 3,225

No. of shares (mil.): 150
Dividends
  Yield: 29.1%
  Payout: 441.4%
Market value ($ mil.): 7,671

	STOCK PRICE ($) FY Close	P/E High/Low		PER SHARE ($) Earnings	Dividends	Book Value
12/16*	51.14	24	16	2.35	14.92	20.90
01/16	56.26	18	11	3.27	1.28	14.83
01/15	41.40	—	—	(4.36)	1.28	13.49
01/14	45.34	25	6	1.94	0.64	19.94
01/13	12.10	2	2	6.16	1.92	30.62
Annual Growth	43.4%		—	— (21.4%)	67.0%	(9.1%)

*Fiscal year change

Leidos, Inc.

EXECUTIVES

Chb-ceo, Roger A Krone
Group Vice President, Vincent Maffeo
Vice President Division Manager, Edward Whitehouse
Senior Vice President Business Development and Strategy, Michael Molino
Executive Vice President and Chief Technology Officer, Gulu Gambhir
Vice President and Information Technology Quality User Experience Director, Gisele Moro
Assistant Vice President And Principal Systems Engineer, Michael Donovan
Vice President, Mark Podgorski
Senior Vice President, Marc Crown
Vice President of Marketing and Business Development, Brandon Ginsburg
Vice President and Director Business Development, Richard Waterman
Group Vice President Of Finance, Cindy P Tank
Vice President Distribution Planning And, Joni Batson
Senior Vice President and Deputy General Counsel, Michele Brown
Executive Vice President, Julianne Miller
Senior Vice President Director Business Development and Strategy, David Radcliffe
Vice President Director of Design, Mauro Dallabattista
Assistant Vice President Finance Operations Manager, Dale Napier
Vice President Pre Construction, Wallace Hunt
Vice President Strategic Regulatory Finance, Joe Kozsurek
Vice President, Jonathan Michel
Vice President, Pamela Saunders
Vice President, Steve Schneider
Assistant Vice President And Deputy Division Manager And Prgm Manager, Paul Desantis
Vice President Sales Operations and Corporate Accounts, Jessica Barnett Campbell
Senior Vice President for Operations, Gary Rosen
Senior Vice President Investor Relations, John Sweeney
Associate Vice President Chief Systems Architect, Roberto Estrada
Vice President, Mark Achenbach
Vice President, Joe Harrison
Vice President Division Manager, Robert Mullen
Vice President, Jack Walker
Assistant Vice President, Josh Wepman
Vice President Group Contracts Director, Tony Giuseppe
Assistant Vice President Senior Pricing Analyst, Evelyn Harrell
Vice President Program Execution, Jim Everett
Senior Vice President, Barbara Doornink
Vice President, Brian Thompson
Vice President, Michael Simms
Vice President Of Sales, Steven Russell
Vice President, Michael Hile
Vice President Division Manager, Doug Kumbalek
Senior Vice President of Investor Relations, Kelly Hernandez
Senior Vice President, Horace Blackman
Senior Vice President, Roy Stevens
Vice President, Michael Swan
Senior Vice President, Bob Mason
Senior Vice President, Karoom Brown
Vice President and Assistant Controller, Bernard Wanjara
Vice President, Ronald Moe
Senior Vice President, Jason McCarthy
Auditors: Deloitte & Touche LLP

LOCATIONS

HQ: Leidos, Inc.
11951 Freedom Drive, Reston, VA 20190
Phone: 571 526-6000
Web: www.leidos.com

HISTORICAL FINANCIALS

Company Type: Public

Income Statement

FYE: January 1

	REVENUE ($ mil.)	NET INCOME ($ mil.)	NET PROFIT MARGIN	EMPLOYEES
01/16	4,712	248	5.3%	18,000
01/15	5,063	(317)	—	19,000
01/14	5,772	166	2.9%	22,000
01/13	11,173	526	4.7%	40,000
01/12	10,587	56	0.5%	41,000
Annual Growth	(18.3%)	45.1%	—	(18.6%)

2016 Year-End Financials

Debt ratio: 22.60%
Return on equity: 4.80%
Cash ($ mil.): 673
Current ratio: 1.72
Long-term debt ($ mil.): 1,121

No. of shares (mil.): 72
Dividends
  Yield: —
  Payout: —
Market value ($ mil.): —

LendingClub Corp

Auditors: Deloitte & Touche LLP

LOCATIONS

HQ: LendingClub Corp
71 Stevenson Street, Suite 300, San Francisco, CA 94105
Phone: 415 632-5600
Web: www.lendingclub.com

HISTORICAL FINANCIALS

Company Type: Public

Income Statement

FYE: December 31

	ASSETS ($ mil.)	NET INCOME ($ mil.)	INCOME AS % OF ASSETS	EMPLOYEES
12/16	5,562	(145)	—	1,530
12/15	5,793	(5)	—	1,382
12/14	3,890	(32)	—	843
12/13	1,943	7	0.4%	742
12/12	850	(4)	—	
Annual Growth	59.9%	—	—	—

2016 Year-End Financials

Debt ratio: 77.68%
Return on equity: (-14.43%)
Cash ($ mil.): 515
Current ratio: —
Long-term debt ($ mil.): —

No. of shares (mil.): 397
Dividends
  Yield: —
  Payout: —
Market value ($ mil.): 2,089

	STOCK PRICE ($) FY Close	P/E High/Low		PER SHARE ($) Earnings	Dividends	Book Value
12/16	5.25	—	—	(0.38)	0.00	2.45
12/15	11.05	—	—	(0.01)	0.00	2.74
12/14	25.30	—	—	(0.44)	0.00	2.62
Annual Growth	(32.5%)	—	—	—	—	(1.6%)

Lennar Corp

Lennar is one of the largest homebuilding land-owning loan-making leviathans in the US along with D.R. Horton and Pulte Homes. The company builds single- and multi-family attached and detached homes in 18 states under brand names including Lennar Camelot NuHome and Greystone. Lennar targets first-time move-up and active adult buyers and markets its homes as "everything included." The company also provides financial services including mortgage financing title and closing services. Lennar's homes are delivered at an average price of $360000.In 2017 Lennar purchased Florida homebuilder WCI Communities and later that year announced a significant $6 billion deal to purchase rival CalAtlantic.

HISTORY

Lennar is the creation of Leonard Miller and Arnold Rosen and the name of the company is a combination of their given names. Rosen a Miami homebuilder formed F&R Builders in 1954. A year later Miller graduated from Harvard with no firm career plans. Having worked summers in Florida Miller decided it would be a good place to make his fortune and the 23-year-old began selling real estate there.

With $10000 earned from commissions Miller bought 42 lots and in 1956 entered a joint venture with Rosen to build homes on the lots. They worked well together and Miller soon joined F&R. The operation grew emphasizing marketing and concentrating on low- and medium-priced single-family homes for first-time buyers and retirees.

After expanding into commercial real estate in the late 1960s the duo folded F&R into a new company — Lennar Corporation — in 1971 and went public. During the 1970s and 1980s the company hawked Jacuzzi tubs and designer homes (such as the Calvin and the Liz) and promised customers "$10000 worth of extras" free at Midnight Madness shopping mall sales. Lennar also began expanding acquiring land and builders in the Phoenix area in 1973. Rosen retired in 1977.

Spurred by a recession Lennar began offering mortgage services nationwide in 1981 keeping the potentially lucrative servicing for itself and selling its mortgages to Fannie Mae Ginnie Mae and Freddie Mac among others. In 1984 it dissolved its construction operations and began subbing out its work (a practice that it continues today). Lennar was relatively unscathed by the recession of the late 1980s in part because Miller had foreseen a slump and had cut corporate debt and overhead. When other builders were overextending themselves by buying land in good times Miller had used profit to pay down debt so he would have the resources to buy land cheap when bad times arrived.

During the 1990s Lennar targeted other Sun Belt markets and began buying portfolios of distressed property in partnership with heavy hitters like Morgan Stanley. Although Miller had looked at Texas as a development site since 1987 it was not until 1991 that Lennar entered the state beginning in Dallas.

The company bought up the secured debt of Bramalea Homes in Southern California in 1995 and entered Northern California with its acquisition of Renaissance Homes. Lennar's acquisition of Village Homes and Exxon's Friendswood Development in 1996 made it Houston's top home builder and Lennar surpassed $1 billion in sales.

In 1997 Stuart Miller became president and CEO (Leonard his father remained chairman).

That year Lennar also spun off its commercial real estate operations as LNR Property a separately traded public company and acquired Pacific Greystone a Los Angeles builder.

The following year the company strengthened its position in the western US acquiring three California homebuilders: Winncrest Homes (Sacramento) ColRich Communities (San Diego) and Polygon Communities (Southern California and Sacramento). Lennar also purchased North American Title an escrow and title services company operating in Arizona California and Colorado.

In 2000 Lennar bought fellow builder U.S. Home for about $1.1 billion in a deal that expanded its operations into 13 states. The company acquired the North and South Carolina operations of The Fortress Group in late 2001 giving Lennar the Don Galloway Homes and Sunstar Homes brands. Through its FG Acquisition Corporation subsidiary Lennar acquired 93% of The Fortress Group in 2002; it also added Maryland-based Patriot Homes and assets of California homebuilders Pacific Century Homes and Cambridge Homes to bring its homebuilding operations to 16 states.

In July 2002 Leonard Miller died of liver cancer. Stuart Miller continues to lead the company as its president and CEO. The company acquired nine homebuilders that year which expanded its operations into markets in Chicago (Concord Homes and Summit Homes) Baltimore the Carolinas and California's Central Valley; some of the acquisitions strengthened Lennar's position in its existing markets. Lennar subsidiary North American Title Group acquired The Sentinel Title Corporation with nine branches in Maryland Virginia and Washington DC.

Lennar continued to acquire in 2003 adding Seppala Homes and Coleman Homes (with a backlog of about 300 homes and 3000 owned or controlled homesites) expanding its positions respectively in South Carolina and the Central Valley of California. The company's North American Title Group Inc. subsidiary acquired Mid America Title Company (Waukegan Illinois) which strengthened Lennar's homebuilding operations in the Chicago market.

In mid-2003 an entity jointly owned by Lennar and LNR Property Corporation (real estate investment finance and management) agreed to acquire The Newhall Land and Farming Company (master-planned communities) for about $1 billion. The deal closed in January 2004 enabling LNR to buy existing income-producing commercial assets from the venture and Lennar to option certain current homesites. Also that year Lennar's Texas operations grew with its cash purchase of San Antonio-based Connell-Barron Homes and the company expanded into Jacksonville by acquiring Classic American Homes for an undisclosed cash price. Lennar closed out the year with increased revenues and earnings of 18% and 26% respectively over the previous year and a strong backlog of about 15550 homes valued at about $5 billion.

As the real estate market continued to thrive Lennar acquired regional builders mortgage operations and title and closing businesses. During 2005 Lennar entered the Boston New York City and Reno markets; it also expanded its Jacksonville operations by acquiring Admiral Homes. The condo and apartment buildings in New York and Boston were valued at more than $2 billion.

Along with the rest of the homebuilding industry Lennar started to see trouble in 2006 as interest rates rose and years of overbuilding began taking their toll. Fallout from the subprime mortgage crisis and global credit crunch further unraveled the market. Lennar's average price per home fell by $40000 and the number of homes delivered fell by approximately 40000 (in 2009 as compared with fiscal 2005).

In early 2007 Lennar and its spun-off investment unit LNR Properties reduced their stakes in LandSource a joint venture that invests in raw land (among the riskiest of real estate investments particularly vulnerable to market downturns). MW Housing Partners an investment vehicle of the California Public Employees' Retirement System bought 68% of LandSource for $900 million in cash and property; Lennar lowered its stake from 50% to 16%. The sale proved to be fortuitous for Lennar: Not only did it bring the company much-needed cash but it also reduced Lennar's exposure to the debt-laden LandSource which filed for Chapter 11 bankruptcy protection a year later. LandSource emerged from bankruptcy as the debt-free Newhall Land Development. In 2009 Lennar bought back a 15% stake in the reorganized company for $140.

Lennar survived the economic downturn by shifting its focus and tightening its belt. As one of the larger builders it weathered the downturn by exiting slower markets lowering prices and reducing staff. The company also bought fewer home sites and tightened its lending standards to reduce its exposure to loan defaults. Lennar also increased its focus on the first-time buyer and limited the number of home plans offered.

EXECUTIVES

Vice President and Treasurer, Diane J Bessette

Vice President of Taxation, Michael Petrolino

VP and COO, Jonathan M. (Jon) Jaffe, age 57, $800,000 total compensation

VP and CFO, Bruce E. Gross, age 58, $650,000 total compensation

CEO, Stuart A. Miller, age 59, $1,000,000 total compensation

President, Richard (Rick) Beckwitt, age 57, $800,000 total compensation

CEO Rialto Capital Management, Jeffrey P. (Jeff) Krasnoff

Regional President Lennar Land and Homebuilding, Jeff Roos

Regional President Lennar Land and Homebuilding, Rob Hutton

President Lennar Ventures; CEO Sunstreet Energy Group, David J. Kaiserman

President North American Title Group, Thomas J. (Tom) Fischer

President Rialto Capital Management, Jay Mantz

Secretary and General Counsel, Mark Sustana, age 56, $450,000 total compensation

President Universal American Mortgage and Eagle Home Mortgage, James T. (Jimmy) Timmons

Regional President Lennar Land and Homebuilding, Fred Rothman

President Lennar Multifamily Communities, Todd Farrell

Regional President Lennar Multifamily Communities, Ed Easley

CIO, Laura Lete

Regional President Lennar Homebuilding and Land, Greg McGuff

President Lennar International, Chris Marlin

Vice President of Construction, Joe Barwinski

Executive Vice President, Al Lee

Division President, Mark Torres

Vice President of Sales and Marketing, Ericka Pace

Division President, Mike Zakrzewski

Vice President Of Operations, Chris Recker

Regional Vice President Land, Matthew Wineman

Vice President Land Acquisitions and Development, Jim Bowersox

West Region Vice President of Marketing, Janice Hinshaw

Vice President Land Division, Anthony Mignone

Vice President Marketing and Sales, Sheryl McKibben

Division President, Frank Walker

Vice President Purchasing, Scott Handt
Division President, Brad Reisinger
Vice President of Sales, Lori Pennebaker
Vice President Research And Development, Jim Petersen
Vice President Controller, Ryan Gatchalian
Division President, JJ Abraham
Vice President of Land and Acquisitions, Greg Urech
National Account Manager, Joe Sabella
Regional Vice President Land, Jim Bavouset
Senior Vice President of Operations and Technology, Alex Burris
Vice President Land Acquisitions, David Stearn
Division President, Blake Seeberger
Division President, MARK METHENY
Division President, WORTH JENKINS
Vice President Of Operations, Charles Webb
Vice President Government Relations, Dave Williams
Vice President of Construction, John Bishop
Vice President Quality Assurance, Norm Greuel
Vice President of Construction, Kevin Stream
Vice President Corporate Development, Christian Falk
Vice President Supply Chain Management and Strategic Initiatives, Paul Dodge
Vice President of Marketing, Stacy Sanders
Division President, Jon Hardy
Division President, John Merlino
Vice President Sales and Marketing, Garrett Chan
Assistant Treasurer, Gerry Rodriguez
Auditors: DELOITTE & TOUCHE LLP

LOCATIONS

HQ: Lennar Corp
700 Northwest 107th Avenue, Miami, FL 33172
Phone: 305 559-4000
Web: www.lennar.com

Selected Markets

Arizona
  Phoenix
  Tucson
California
  Bakersfield
  Fresno
  Los Angeles/Valencia
  Orange County
  Palm Springs
  Riverside County
  Sacramento
  San Bernardino
  San Diego
Colorado
  Denver
Florida
  Clermont
  Ft. Lauderdale
  Jacksonville
  Lakeland
  Miami
  Naples
  Orlando
  Sarasota
  Tampa
Illinois
  Chicago
Maryland
  Baltimore
  Maryland/DC Metro
New Jersey
  Edison Township
  Mays Landing
  Rockaway Township
North Carolina
  Charlotte
  Raleigh
South Carolina
  Charleston
  Greenville
  Myrtle Beach
Texas
  Austin
  Dallas/Fort Worth

Houston
San Antonio
Virginia
  Maryland/Virginia/Washington DC Metro
  Williamsburg

PRODUCTS/OPERATIONS

2016 Sales

	$ mil.	% of total
Homebuilding East	3,941	36
Homebuilding West	2,757	25
Homebuilding Central	2,283	21
Homebuilding Other	758	7
Lennar Financial Services	687	6
Rialto	234	2
Lennar Multifamily	287	3
Total	10,950	100

Selected Subsidiaries

360 Developers LLC
Camelot Ventures LLC
Eagle Bend Commercial LLC
Eagle Home Mortgage LLC
Heritage of Auburn Hills LLC
Lennar Associates Management LLC
Lennar Homes of California Inc.
Lennar Homes of Texas Sales and Marketing Ltd.
Lennar Ventures LLC
LH-EH Layton Lakes Estate LLC
Majestic Woods LLC
North American Title Company (MD)
Raintree Village L.L.C.
Savell Gulley Development LLC
Universal American Mortgage Company LLC
U.S. Home of Arizona Construction Co.

COMPETITORS

Beazer Homes
CalAtlantic
D.R. Horton
Hovnanian Enterprises
KB Home
M.D.C.
NVR
PulteGroup
Toll Brothers
Weyerhaeuser Real Estate

HISTORICAL FINANCIALS

Company Type: Public

Income Statement

FYE: November 30

	REVENUE ($ mil.)	NET INCOME ($ mil.)	NET PROFIT MARGIN	EMPLOYEES
11/17	12,646	810	6.4%	9,111
11/16	10,950	911	8.3%	8,335
11/15	9,474	802	8.5%	7,749
11/14	7,779	638	8.2%	6,825
11/13	5,935	479	8.1%	5,741
Annual Growth	20.8%	14.0%	—	12.2%

2017 Year-End Financials

Debt ratio: 34.20%
Return on equity: 10.88%
Cash ($ mil.): 2,673
Current ratio: 22.75
Long-term debt ($ mil.): 6,410

No. of shares (mil.): 239
Dividends
  Yield: 0.2%
  Payout: 4.7%
Market value ($ mil.): 15,065

	STOCK PRICE ($) FY Close	P/E High/Low		PER SHARE ($) Earnings	Dividends	Book Value
11/17	62.78	18	12	3.38	0.16	32.81
11/16	42.54	13	9	3.85	0.16	29.38
11/15	51.21	15	11	3.39	0.16	26.23
11/14	47.24	16	11	2.75	0.16	23.08
11/13	35.76	18	13	2.11	0.16	19.99
Annual Growth	15.1%	—	—	12.5%	(0.0%)	13.2%

Leucadia National Corp.

Leucadia National has a large investment stake in the US beef industry. Its National Beef Packaging Company is the corporate cash cow generating the majority of revenues. However the company?s primary functions are in financial services and merchant banking. Leucadia has partial or full ownership in companies operating in industries such as energy industrials financial services and healthcare. Leucadia typically seeks out troubled companies that it believes are undervalued buys in with equity or debt provides leadership assistance and lets company management handle the day-to-day operations. Some of its largest holdings include National Beef Idaho Timber Vitesse Energy Berkadia and HomeFed. It also has interests in a gold and silver mining company a telecommunications business in Italy and an automobile dealership holding company.

Operations

Leucadia's two reportable segments are National Beef its beef processing business and Jefferies its investment banking business.

Leucadia's National Beef Packing Company subsidiary one of the largest beef producers in the US is responsible for around 70% of Leucadia's total revenue each year. The company processes packages and delivers fresh and frozen beef and beef by-products for sale to customers in the US and international markets. Some 90% of the segment?s revenue comes from the sale of boxed beef products to supermarket chains independent grocers wholesales U.S. military and others. It also owns Kansas City Steak Company which sells beef directly to consumers through the internet and direct mail. It owns two processing facilities each of which can process 6000 cattle per day.

The company's Jeffries subsidiary a securities and investment banking business brings in around 25% of Leucadia's total revenue each year. Jefferies' capital markets business includes the firm's securities commodities futures and foreign exchange brokerage trading activities as well as investment banking consisting of underwriting and financial advisory activities. The subsidiary also provides the sales trading and origination support for various fixed income equity and advisory products and services. Jefferies also provides asset and investment management services.

All of Leucadia's other businesses and investments are contained in its Other Financial Services Businesses and its Other Merchant Banking Businesses. The former is active in asset management specialty finance commercial mortgage banking businesses and it owns a 65% stake in real estate developer HomeFed; while the latter operates oil and gas exploration and production automobile dealerships real estate fixed wireless services in Italy and a gold and silver mining business in California.

The company also has a 50% stake in Berkadia Commercial Mortgage in a joint venture with Berkshire Hathaway.

Geographic Reach

New York NY-based Leucadia National maintains offices in 30 cities throughout the world including a European headquarters in London and an Asia headquarters in Hong Kong.

Its Idaho Timber unit has a presence in North Carolina Florida New Mexico and Texas.

National Beef?s corporate head office is in Kansas City MO. It has three consumer-ready facilities in Pennsylvania Georgia and Kansas and two processing facilities in Kansas.

Leucadia?s Golden Queen investment operates a gold and silver mining project in California.

Sales and Marketing

Leucadia offers to a variety of financial services such as debt financing financial advisement capital injections equity investment etc. It markets these services through its network of business relationships and advisors in its global investment banking firm Jeffries.

The company is mostly hands-off when it comes to managing the businesses in its private equity portfolio leaving the day-to-day operations for the leadership of each individual business.

Financial Performance

Big changes in financial numbers occurred with Leucadia?s acquisition of National Beef in late 2011. Revenue jumped the following year from under $1 billion in 2011 to over $9 billion due to National Beef?s sales. Net income over the same period dwindled from a high mark exceeding $800 million to more recent results nearing $100 million. Much of Leucadia?s money is tied up in businesses it owns so financial results are volatile year over year; sometimes they spike higher due to sales of its businesses and investments sometimes they fall precipitously due to mark-to-market valuation adjustments. In recent years the swings have not been too large however the results are trending downward.

In 2016 the company produced $10.9 billion in revenue 70% of it from National Beef operations. Compared to the prior year revenue fell 7%. The volatile financial markets of early 2016 took its toll on the Jeffries businesses including its investment in HRG and its reduced level of investment banking activity. As well lower average selling prices for beef took a bite out of National Beef?s results.

Net income in 2016 fell 55% from the prior year to $126 million. Lower revenues of $800 million a slightly higher tax bill along with payouts to minority shareholders of owned businesses (mainly National Beef) were the primary causes. The company kept expenses as a percent of revenue in line with previous years.

Cash at the end of 2016 was $3.8 billion just $170 million higher than at the end of 2015. The biggest use of cash was loans and investments to Leucadia?s associated companies. The firm produced $608 million in cash from operating activities and some $230 million from financing activities (primarily debt issuance and contributions from noncontrolling interests).

Strategy

Leucadia?s strategies differ based on the line of business. For its Jeffries investment banking operation it is focused on revenue growth and margin expansion. For its majority- and minority-owned operating portfolio of companies it provides the funding and executive advisement to help turn-around and grow the businesses.

Jeffries? investment banking is looking to increase the average size of its M&A transactions thereby increasing its fee revenue. It wants to selectively enter new industry sub-sectors where it sees opportunities to outshine competitors. Its Equities branch in which it trades (mostly public) stocks is expectedly looking for ways to get an edge such as using event-driven trading strategies and leveraging data science.

Leucadia sold in 2016 its 100% ownership of manufacturer Conwed Plastics for $295 million. In mid-2017 the company sold its remaining holdings in KCG (previously Knight Capital Group) in which it had held a losing position for some time. It divested its 49% interest in Jeffries LoanCore in late 2017 for $170 million.

Mergers and Acquisitions

In 2016 Leucadia has agreed to acquire ITG Investment Research from Investment Technology Group. ITG Investment Research will be renamed M Science.

EXECUTIVES

CEO, Richard B. Handler, age 55, $1,000,000 total compensation

President, Brian P. Friedman, age 61, $1,000,000 total compensation

EVP and General Counsel, Michael J. Sharp, age 61, $1,000,000 total compensation

VP and CFO, Teresa S. Gendron, age 47, $500,000 total compensation

Assistant Vice President Information Systems, Lauren Hayer

Executive Vice President, Thomas Mara

Chairman, Joseph S. Steinberg, age 73

Auditors: Deloitte & Touche LLP

LOCATIONS

HQ: Leucadia National Corp.
520 Madison Avenue, New York, NY 10022
Phone: 212 460-1900   **Fax:** 212 598-4869
Web: www.leucadia.com

PRODUCTS/OPERATIONS

2016 Sales

	$ mil.	% of total
Beef Processing services	7,021	65
Investment banking	1,194	11
Interest income	926	8
Commissions	611	6
Principal transactions	603	6
Net realized security gains	29	0
Others	488	4
Interest expense	(812.6)	-
Total	**10,062**	**100**

2016 Sales

	$ mil.	% of total
National Beef	7,027	70
Jefferies	2,421	24
Corporate	88	1
all others	525	5
Total	**10,062**	**100**

COMPETITORS

Apollo Investment	H Group Holding
Berkshire Hathaway	Heico Companies
Berwind	Sun Capital
Blackstone Group	Tyson Foods
Cargill Meat Solutions	Veritas Capital
Castle Harlan	Wesco Financial

HISTORICAL FINANCIALS

Company Type: Public

Income Statement

FYE: December 31

	REVENUE ($ mil.)	NET INCOME ($ mil.)	NET PROFIT MARGIN	EMPLOYEES
12/16	10,062	130	1.3%	13,000
12/15	10,886	283	2.6%	13,300
12/14	11,486	208	1.8%	13,082
12/13	10,429	372	3.6%	14,647
12/12	9,193	854	9.3%	10,943
Annual Growth	**2.3%**	**(37.5%)**	**—**	**4.4%**

2016 Year-End Financials

Debt ratio: 19.82%
Return on equity: 1.25%
Cash ($ mil.): 8,527
Current ratio: 1.55
Long-term debt ($ mil.): 7,380
No. of shares (mil.): 359
Dividends
  Yield: 0.0%
  Payout: 73.5%
Market value ($ mil.): 8,357

	STOCK PRICE ($) FY Close	P/E High/Low		PER SHARE ($) Earnings	Dividends	Book Value
12/16	23.25	71	43	0.34	0.25	28.53
12/15	17.39	34	22	0.74	0.25	29.03
12/14	22.42	53	39	0.54	0.25	28.37
12/13	28.34	30	22	1.06	0.25	28.06
12/12	23.79	8	6	3.44	0.25	27.67
Annual Growth	**(0.6%)**	**—**	**—**	**(43.9%)**	**(0.0%)**	**0.8%**

Levi Strauss & Co.

Pioneering American apparel maker Levi Strauss & Co. (LS&CO.) has jeans in its genes. A global manufacturer of brand-name clothing LS&CO. sells jeans and sportswear under the Levi's Dockers Signature by Levi Strauss and Denizen labels in more than 110 countries. It also markets men's and women's underwear and loungewear. The Haas family (descendants of founder Levi Strauss) controls LS&CO. LS&CO. distributes its brand products through more than 695 company-operated stores located in over 30 countries and through the third-party and first-party online stores. LS&CO. makes more than 75% of its revenue from Levi's branded men's pants.

Operations

Directly or through third parties LS&CO. designs markets and sells jeans casual and dress pants tops shorts skirts jackets footwear and related accessories for men women and children. Company-operated and online stores generated about 30% of revenues in fiscal 2016.

LS&CO. distributes its Levi's and Dockers products through more than 695 company-operated stores located in more than 30 countries including the US and through the third-party and first-party online stores. The company distributes its Levi's and Dockers products nationwide through chain retailers and department stores. Outside the US it distributes products primarily to department stores specialty retailers and approximately 2200 franchised and other brand-dedicated stores.

By product LS&CO. generated more than 75% of its total revenue from men's products during fiscal 2016. Pants made about 75% of total revenue and the Levis' branded products generated more than 85% of total revenue.

Geographic Reach

Iconic LS&CO. sells its products in more than 110 countries. It operates manufacturing distribution and finishing facilities in the Americas Europe and Asia/Pacific regions. The company's Americas segment contributed about 60% to its total revenue during fiscal 2016 while its Europe and Asia (which counts the Middle East and North Africa) segments contributed about 25% and 15% respectively. Its key markets are the US France Germany Mexico and the UK.

Sales and Marketing

A multi-channel marketer LS&CO. sells its products in more than 50000 retail locations worldwide. Its brands lend themselves to a variety of retail formats including chain retailers (JCPenney Kohl's Wal-Mart and Target) department stores (Macy's Nordstrom and Barney's) and company-operated e-commerce sites and online stores of other retailers. Sales to its top 10 wholesale customers have accounted for approximately 30% of revenues.

The company distributes its products through a wide variety of retail formats around the world including chain and department stores franchise stores and shop-in-shops company-operated retail network multi-brand specialty stores mass channel retailers and both company-operated and retailer ecommerce sites.

Altogether LS&CO. spent $284.0 million on advertising in fiscal 2016 up from $276.4 million the prior fiscal period.

Financial Performance

The company's revenue was $4.5 billion during fiscal 2016 up slightly compared to the prior fiscal year. The small increase was largely driven by an increase in revenue from Europe. LS&CO. reported net income of about $291 million for fiscal 2016 which was a slight spike compared to the $209 million the company reported for net income in fiscal 2015. The high cost of producing the goods the company sells along with its selling general administrative and interest expenses resulted in LS&CO.'s modest net income on $4.5 billion in revenue.

Strategy

LS&CO continued in 2016 to follow a handful of growth-oriented measures including: driving profitable growth of its core men's pants brands (Dockers and Levi's); expanding its brand reach and diversifying into new or undertapped geographic markets including China India Russia and Brazil; becoming omni-channel through online stores franchises and company-operated stores; and improving its cost structure to ensure long-term profitable growth.

HISTORY

Levi Strauss arrived in New York City from Bavaria in 1847. In 1853 he joined his brother-in-law David Stern selling dry goods to the gold rushers. Shortly after a prospector told Strauss of miners' problems in finding sturdy pants. Strauss made a pair out of canvas for the prospector; word of the rugged pants spread quickly.

Strauss continued his dry-goods business in the 1860s. During this time he switched the pants' fabric to a durable French cloth called serge de Nimes soon known as denim. He colored the fabric with indigo dye and adopted the idea from Nevada tailor Jacob Davis of reinforcing the pants with copper rivets. In 1873 Strauss and Davis produced their first pair of waist-high overalls (later known as jeans). The pants soon became de rigueur for lumberjacks cowboys railroad workers oil drillers and farmers.

Strauss continued to build his pants and wholesaling business until he died in 1902. Levi Strauss & Co. passed to four Stern nephews who carried on their uncle's jeans business while maintaining the company's philanthropic reputation.

After WWII Walter Haas and Peter Haas (a fourth-generation Strauss family member) assumed leadership of LS&CO. In 1948 they ended the company's wholesaling business to concentrate on Levi's clothing. In the 1950s Levi's jeans ceased to be merely functional garments for workers; they became the uniform of American youth. In the 1960s LS&CO. added women's attire and expanded overseas.

The company went public in 1971. That year it added a women's career line and bought Koret sportswear (sold in 1984). By the mid-1980s profits declined. Peace Corps-veteran-turned-McKinsey-consultant Robert Haas (Walter's son) grabbed the reins of LS&CO. in 1984 and took the company private the next year (he became chairman in 1989). He also instilled a touchy-feely corporate culture often at odds with the bottom line.

In 1986 LS&CO. introduced Dockers casual pants. The company's sales began rising in 1991 as consumers forsook the designer duds of the 1980s for more practical clothes. LS&CO. says seven out of every 10 American men own a pair of Dockers. However LS&CO. missed out on the birth of another trend: the split between the fashion sense of US adolescents and their Levi's-loving baby boomer parents.

In 1996 the company introduced Slates dress slacks. That year LS&CO. bought back nearly one-third of its stock from family and employees for $4.3 billion. Grappling with slipping sales and debt from the buyout in 1997 LS&CO. closed 11 of its 37 North American plants laying off 6400 workers and 1000 salaried employees; it granted generous severance packages even to those earning minimum wage.

In 1998 citing improved labor conditions in China LS&CO. announced it would step up its use of Chinese subcontractors. Further restructuring added a third of its European plants to the closures list that year. LS&CO.'s sales fell 13% in fiscal 1998. Also that year Haas handed his CEO title to Pepsi executive Philip Marineau; Haas remained chairman.

LS&CO. closed 11 of 22 remaining North American plants in 1999. It also unleashed several new jeans brands that eschewed the company's one-style-fits-all approach of old.

In April 2002 LS&CO. announced it would close six of its last eight US plants and cut 20% of its worldwide staff (3300 workers). In September 2003 it cut another 5% of its global staff (650 workers). That month the company opened its first girls-only store located in Paris. In December LS&CO. replaced CFO Bill Chiasson with an outside turnaround specialist.

Pinpointing 2006 as the best time to step down as the company's chief executive Philip Marineau retired at the end of 2006. John Anderson president of LS&CO.'s Asia/Pacific division and head of the firm's global supply chain unit replaced Marineau as president and CEO.

Levi Strauss chairman Robert Haas retired in 2008 after 18 years in that role. His successor was Dryer's ice cream executive T. Gary Rogers who became the first leader in the company's history who was not a descendant of the founder. In August 2008 CFO Hans Ploos van Amstel left the company the and was replaced by Heidi Manes its corporate controller and principal accounting officer.

Looking to gain a more active role in its store business LS&CO. in July 2009 bought the operating rights for more than 70 Levi's and Dockers Outlet locations from store operator Anchor Blue Retail Group which had filed for bankruptcy for $72 million. Anchor Blue said the US recession and drop in consumer spending especially among teens severely affected its financial performance. LS&CO. said the acquisition will enable it to better manage its brands' positioning.

Rogers retired in late 2009 and Richard Kauffman became chairman.

EXECUTIVES

EVP; President Europe, Seth M. Ellison, age 58, $609,808 total compensation
President and CEO, Charles V. (Chip) Bergh, age 59, $1,343,077 total compensation
EVP and CFO, Harmit J. Singh, age 53, $746,538 total compensation
EVP and President Global e-Commerce, Marc Rosen, age 48
SVP and Chief Supply Chain Officer, David Love, age 54, $580,387 total compensation

EVP; President Americas, Roy Bagattini, age 53, $690,433 total compensation
EVP; President Levis Brand, James Curleigh, age 51, $523,269 total compensation
EVP; President Global Retail, Carrie Ask, $392,308 total compensation
SVP and Chief Supply Chain Officer, Liz O'Neill
VP Manufacturing, Patty Kimball
Global Vice President Of Women's Design, Jill Guenza
Senior Vice President PA and MARKETING COORDINATOR, Manuela Bellini
Vice President Marketing, Stacy Doren
Vice President Human Resources, Karthik Sarma
Senior Vice President Chief Information Officer, Roland Paanakker
Vice President Human Resources Europe, Hubert Van Nuvel
Vice President Global Logistics, Doug Flores
VICE PRESIDENT INFORMATION TECHNOLOGY, Ramiya Lyer
Chairman, Stephen C. Neal, age 67
Auditors: PricewaterhouseCoopers LLP

LOCATIONS

HQ: Levi Strauss & Co.
1155 Battery Street, San Francisco, CA 94111
Phone: 415 501-6000
Web: www.levistrauss.com

2016 Stores

	% of total
Americas region	234
Europe region	267
Asia/Pacific region	196
Total	**697**

2016 Sales

	$ mil.	% of total
Americas	2,683	59
Europe	1,091	24
Asia/Pacific region	778	17
Total	**4,552**	**100**

PRODUCTS/OPERATIONS

2016 Sales

	% of total
Levi's brand	85
Dockers brand	10
Signature by Levi Strauss & Denizen brands	5
Total	**100**

Selected Brands

Denizen
Dockers
  Dockers Alpha Khaki
  Dockers for Men
  Dockers for Women
Levi's
  Levi's 501 Original
  Levi's 505 Straight
  Levi's 511 Skinny
  Levi's 513 Slim
  Levi's 514 Slim Straight
  Levi's Curve ID
Signature by Levis Strauss & Co.
Intro
Waterless
Wellthread
Wasteless

COMPETITORS

Abercrombie & Fitch	NIKE
Abercrombie & Fitch	Nautica Apparel
American Eagle Outfitters	Nautica Apparel
American Eagle Outfitters	Nine West
Benetton	Nine West
Benetton	OshKosh B'Gosh
Calvin Klein	OshKosh B'Gosh
	Oxford Industries
	Oxford Industries

Calvin Klein	PVH
Diesel SpA	PVH
Diesel SpA	Perry Ellis
FUBU	International
FUBU	Perry Ellis
Fast Retailing	International
Fast Retailing	Ralph Lauren
Fruit of the Loom	Ralph Lauren
Fruit of the Loom	Sean John
Guess?	Sean John
Guess?	Sears
Haggar	Sears
Haggar	Target Corporation
Hugo Boss	Target Corporation
Hugo Boss	The Gap
Inditex	The Gap
Inditex	True Religion Apparel
J. C. Penney	True Religion Apparel
J. C. Penney	Under Armour
J. Crew	Under Armour
J. Crew	VF Corporation
Jockey International	VF Corporation
Jockey International	Victoria's Secret
Joe's Jeans	Stores
Joe's Jeans	Victoria's Secret
Kmart	Stores
Kmart	Wacoal
Kohl's	Wacoal
Kohl's	Wal-Mart
Lands' End	Wal-Mart
Lands' End	Warnaco Group
Macy's	Warnaco Group
Macy's	adidas
NIKE	adidas

HISTORICAL FINANCIALS

Company Type: Public

Income Statement

FYE: November 27

	REVENUE ($ mil.)	NET INCOME ($ mil.)	NET PROFIT MARGIN	EMPLOYEES
11/16	4,552	291	6.4%	13,200
11/15	4,494	209	4.7%	12,500
11/14	4,753	106	2.2%	15,000
11/13	4,681	229	4.9%	16,000
11/12	4,610	143	3.1%	17,000
Annual Growth	(0.3%)	19.3%	—	(6.1%)

2016 Year-End Financials

Debt ratio: 35.50%	No. of shares (mil.): 37
Return on equity: 59.08%	Dividends
Cash ($ mil.): 375	Yield: —
Current ratio: 2.21	Payout: 20.6%
Long-term debt ($ mil.): 1,021	Market value ($ mil.): —

LEVI STRAUSS & CO.

Pioneering American apparel maker Levi Strauss & Co. (LS&CO.) has jeans in its genes. A global manufacturer of brand-name clothing LS&CO. sells jeans and sportswear under the Levi's Dockers Signature by Levi Strauss and Denizen labels in more than 110 countries. It also markets men's and women's underwear and loungewear. The Haas family (descendants of founder Levi Strauss) controls LS&CO. LS&CO. distributes its brand products through more than 695 company-operated stores located in over 30 countries and through the third-party and first-party online stores. LS&CO. makes more than 75% of its revenue from Levi's branded men's pants.

Operations

Directly or through third parties LS&CO. designs markets and sells jeans casual and dress pants tops shorts skirts jackets footwear and related accessories for men women and children. Company-operated and online stores generated about 30% of revenues in fiscal 2016.

LS&CO. distributes its Levi's and Dockers products through more than 695 company-operated stores located in more than 30 countries including the US and through the third-party and first-party online stores. The company distributes its Levi's and Dockers products nationwide through chain retailers and department stores. Outside the US it distributes products primarily to department stores specialty retailers and approximately 2200 franchised and other brand-dedicated stores.

By product LS&CO. generated more than 75% of its total revenue from men's products during fiscal 2016. Pants made about 75% of total revenue and the Levis' branded products generated more than 85% of total revenue.

Geographic Reach

Iconic LS&CO. sells its products in more than 110 countries. It operates manufacturing distribution and finishing facilities in the Americas Europe and Asia/Pacific regions. The company's Americas segment contributed about 60% to its total revenue during fiscal 2016 while its Europe and Asia (which counts the Middle East and North Africa) segments contributed about 25% and 15% respectively. Its key markets are the US France Germany Mexico and the UK.

Sales and Marketing

A multi-channel marketer LS&CO. sells its products in more than 50000 retail locations worldwide. Its brands lend themselves to a variety of retail formats including chain retailers (JCPenney Kohl's Wal-Mart and Target) department stores (Macy's Nordstrom and Barney's) and company-operated e-commerce sites and online stores of other retailers. Sales to its top 10 wholesale customers have accounted for approximately 30% of revenues.

The company distributes its products through a wide variety of retail formats around the world including chain and department stores franchise stores and shop-in-shops company-operated retail network multi-brand specialty stores mass channel retailers and both company-operated and retailer ecommerce sites.

Altogether LS&CO. spent $284.0 million on advertising in fiscal 2016 up from $276.4 million the prior fiscal period.

Financial Performance

The company's revenue was $4.5 billion during fiscal 2016 up slightly compared to the prior fiscal year. The small increase was largely driven by an increase in revenue from Europe. LS&CO. reported net income of about $291 million for fiscal 2016 which was a slight spike compared to the $209 million the company reported for net income in fiscal 2015. The high cost of producing the goods the company sells along with its selling general administrative and interest expenses resulted in LS&CO.'s modest net income on $4.5 billion in revenue.

Strategy

LS&CO continued in 2016 to follow a handful of growth-oriented measures including: driving profitable growth of its core men's pants brands (Dockers and Levi's); expanding its brand reach and diversifying into new or undertapped geographic markets including China India Russia and Brazil; becoming omni-channel through online stores franchises and company-operated stores; and improving its cost structure to ensure long-term profitable growth.

HISTORY

Levi Strauss arrived in New York City from Bavaria in 1847. In 1853 he joined his brother-in-law David Stern in San Francisco selling dry goods to the gold rushers. Shortly after a prospector told Strauss of miners' problems in finding sturdy pants. Strauss made a pair out of canvas for the prospector; word of the rugged pants spread quickly.

Strauss continued his dry-goods business in the 1860s. During this time he switched the pants' fabric to a durable French cloth called serge de Nimes soon known as denim. He colored the fabric with indigo dye and adopted the idea from Nevada tailor Jacob Davis of reinforcing the pants with copper rivets. In 1873 Strauss and Davis produced their first pair of waist-high overalls (later known as jeans). The pants soon became de rigueur for lumberjacks cowboys railroad workers oil drillers and farmers.

Strauss continued to build his pants and wholesaling business until he died in 1902. Levi Strauss & Co. passed to four Stern nephews who carried on their uncle's jeans business while maintaining the company's philanthropic reputation.

After WWII Walter Haas and Peter Haas (a fourth-generation Strauss family member) assumed leadership of LS&CO. In 1948 they ended the company's wholesaling business to concentrate on Levi's clothing. In the 1950s Levi's jeans ceased to be merely functional garments for workers; they became the uniform of American youth. In the 1960s LS&CO. added women's attire and expanded overseas.

The company went public in 1971. That year it added a women's career line and bought Koret sportswear (sold in 1984). By the mid-1980s profits declined. Peace Corps-veteran-turned-McKinsey-consultant Robert Haas (Walter's son) grabbed the reins of LS&CO. in 1984 and took the company private the next year (he became chairman in 1989). He also instilled a touchy-feely corporate culture often at odds with the bottom line.

In 1986 LS&CO. introduced Dockers casual pants. The company's sales began rising in 1991 as consumers forsook the designer duds of the 1980s for more practical clothes. LS&CO. says seven out of every 10 American men own a pair of Dockers. However LS&CO. missed out on the birth of another trend: the split between the fashion sense of US adolescents and their Levi's-loving baby boomer parents.

In 1996 the company introduced Slates dress slacks. That year LS&CO. bought back nearly one-third of its stock from family and employees for $4.3 billion. Grappling with slipping sales and debt from the buyout in 1997 LS&CO. closed 11 of its 37 North American plants laying off 6400 workers and 1000 salaried employees; it granted generous severance packages even to those earning minimum wage.

In 1998 citing improved labor conditions in China LS&CO. announced it would step up its use of Chinese subcontractors. Further restructuring added a third of its European plants to the closures list that year. LS&CO.'s sales fell 13% in fiscal 1998. Also that year Haas handed his CEO title to Pepsi executive Philip Marineau; Haas remained chairman.

LS&CO. closed 11 of 22 remaining North American plants in 1999. It also unleashed several new jeans brands that eschewed the company's one-style-fits-all approach of old.

In April 2002 LS&CO. announced it would close six of its last eight US plants and cut 20% of its worldwide staff (3300 workers). In September 2003 it cut another 5% of its global staff (650 workers). That month the company opened its first girls-only store located in Paris. In December

LS&CO. replaced CFO Bill Chiasson with an out-side turnaround specialist.

Pinpointing 2006 as the best time to step down as the company's chief executive Philip Marineau retired at the end of 2006. John Anderson president of LS&CO.'s Asia/Pacific division and head of the firm's global supply chain unit replaced Marineau as president and CEO.

Levi Strauss chairman Robert Haas retired in 2008 after 18 years in that role. His successor was Dryer's ice cream executive T. Gary Rogers who became the first leader in the company's history who was not a descendant of the founder. In August 2008 CFO Hans Ploos van Amstel left the company the and was replaced by Heidi Manes its corporate controller and principal accounting officer.

Looking to gain a more active role in its store business LS&CO. in July 2009 bought the operating rights for more than 70 Levi's and Dockers Outlet locations from store operator Anchor Blue Retail Group which had filed for bankruptcy for $72 million. Anchor Blue said the US recession and drop in consumer spending especially among teens severely affected its financial performance. LS&CO. said the acquisition will enable it to better manage its brands' positioning.

Rogers retired in late 2009 and Richard Kauffman became chairman.

EXECUTIVES

EVP; President Europe, Seth M. Ellison, age 58, $609,808 total compensation
President and CEO, Charles V. (Chip) Bergh, age 59, $1,343,077 total compensation
EVP and CFO, Harmit J. Singh, age 53, $746,538 total compensation
EVP and President Global e-Commerce, Marc Rosen, age 48
SVP and Chief Supply Chain Officer, David Love, age 54, $580,387 total compensation
EVP; President Americas, Roy Bagattini, age 53, $690,433 total compensation
EVP; President Levis Brand, James Curleigh, age 51, $523,269 total compensation
EVP; President Global Retail, Carrie Ask, $392,308 total compensation
SVP and Chief Supply Chain Officer, Liz O'Neill
VP Manufacturing, Patty Kimball
Global Vice President Of Women's Design, Jill Guenza
Senior Vice President PA and MARKETING COORDINATOR, Manuela Bellini
Vice President Marketing, Stacy Doren
Vice President Human Resources, Karthik Sarma
Senior Vice President Chief Information Officer, Roland Paanakker
Vice President Human Resources Europe, Hubert Van Nuvel
Vice President Global Logistics, Doug Flores
VICE PRESIDENT INFORMATION TECHNOLOGY, Ramiya Iyer
Chairman, Stephen C. Neal, age 67
Auditors: PRICEWATERHOUSECOOPERS LLP SA

LOCATIONS

HQ: LEVI STRAUSS & CO.
1155 BATTERY ST, SAN FRANCISCO, CA 941111264
Phone: 415 501-6000
Web: WWW.LEVISTRAUSS.COM

2016 Stores

	% of total
Americas region	234
Europe region	267
Asia/Pacific region	196
Total	**697**

2016 Sales

	$ mil.	% of total
Americas	2,683	59
Europe	1,091	24
Asia/Pacific region	778	17
Total	**4,552**	**100**

PRODUCTS/OPERATIONS

2016 Sales

	% of total
Levi's brand	85
Dockers brand	10
Signature by Levi Strauss & Denizen brands	5
Total	**100**

Selected Brands

Denizen
Dockers
   Dockers Alpha Khaki
   Dockers for Men
   Dockers for Women
Levi's
   Levi's 501 Original
   Levi's 505 Straight
   Levi's 511 Skinny
   Levi's 513 Slim
   Levi's 514 Slim Straight
   Levi's Curve ID
Signature by Levis Strauss & Co.
Intro
Waterless
Wellthread
Wasteless

COMPETITORS

Abercrombie & Fitch	NIKE
Abercrombie & Fitch	Nautica Apparel
American Eagle Outfitters	Nautica Apparel
	Nine West
American Eagle Outfitters	Nine West
Benetton	OshKosh B'Gosh
Benetton	OshKosh B'Gosh
Calvin Klein	Oxford Industries
Calvin Klein	Oxford Industries
Diesel SpA	PVH
Diesel SpA	PVH
FUBU	Perry Ellis International
FUBU	Perry Ellis International
Fast Retailing	Ralph Lauren
Fast Retailing	Ralph Lauren
Fruit of the Loom	Sean John
Fruit of the Loom	Sean John
Guess?	Sears
Guess?	Sears
Haggar	Target Corporation
Haggar	Target Corporation
Hugo Boss	The Gap
Hugo Boss	The Gap
Inditex	True Religion Apparel
Inditex	True Religion Apparel
J. C. Penney	Under Armour
J. C. Penney	Under Armour
J. Crew	VF Corporation
J. Crew	VF Corporation
Jockey International	Victoria's Secret Stores
Jockey International	Victoria's Secret Stores
Joe's Jeans	Wacoal
Joe's Jeans	Wacoal
Kmart	Wal-Mart
Kmart	Wal-Mart
Kohl's	Warnaco Group
Kohl's	Warnaco Group
Lands' End	adidas
Lands' End	adidas
Macy's	
Macy's	
NIKE	

HISTORICAL FINANCIALS

Company Type: Private

Income Statement

FYE: November 27

	REVENUE ($ mil.)	NET INCOME ($ mil.)	NET PROFIT MARGIN	EMPLOYEES
11/16	4,552	291	6.4%	13,200
11/15	4,494	209	4.7%	—
11/14	4,753	104	2.2%	—
11/13	4,681	228	4.9%	—
Annual Growth	(0.9%)	8.5%	—	—

2016 Year-End Financials

Debt ratio: ——
Return on equity: 6.40%
Cash ($ mil.): 375
Current ratio: 1.10
Long-term debt ($ mil.): —
Dividends
  Yield: —
  Payout: —
Market value ($ mil.): —

Liberty Interactive Corp

Liberty Interactive Corp. stands by your right to shop at home and online. The company owns and operates market-leading home shopping channel QVC which sells 770 products each week across the home apparel beauty and accessories jewelry and electronics categories. QVC also sells online. Liberty Interactive also runs online businesses including Zulily and online invitation site Evite. It also holds equity stakes in FTD Companies HSN Interval Leisure and LendingTree among others. Liberty Interactive acquired the long-standing rival of its QVC business HSN Inc. for around $2.1 billion in 2017. Liberty Interactive Corp. was formed in 2011 when its predecessor restructured and split off its Liberty Capital and Liberty Starz businesses as Liberty Media.

Operations

Liberty Interactive operates through two main business divisions: QVC Group and Liberty Ventures.

The QVC Group consists of QVC Zulily and Liberty's interest in HSN. QVC is the company's cash cow subsidiary accounting about 80% of its sales. The television brand broadcasts live shopping programs and sells merchandise online in the US and abroad. QVC classifies its products into six groups: home beauty apparel jewelry accessories and electronics. Home is the biggest earner at around one third of sales followed by apparel at nearly 20% and beauty at more than 15%.

Zulily brings in 15% of sales sells products in the US and elsewhere online through flash sales events primarily through its desktop and mobile websites and mobile applications.

Liberty Ventures consists of e-card website Evite and interests in Liberty Broadband FTD Interval Leisure Group Time Warner Charter Communications Britco and LendingTree.

Geographic Reach

Liberty Interactive rings up around 75% of its sales in the US. Japan and Germany each account for less than 10% of sales. QVC has shopping channels in Germany Italy Japan France and the UK. The company also has a joint venture in China.

Sales and Marketing

Flagship subsidiary QVC distributes its television programs through satellite and optical fiber to cable and satellite system providers in the US Germany Japan the UK and neighboring countries. It also transmits programs via digital terrestrial broadcast television to viewers in Italy the UK and certain parts of the US and Germany. Additionally QVC offers a web-based catalog for retailers.

Some of QVC's clients include Comcast Time Warner Cable Cox Dish Network DirecTV Verizon and AT&T.

Financial Performance

After a bad 2015 Liberty Interactive's revenue bounced back in fiscal 2016 growing 7% to $10.6 billion. Growth was concentrated in Zulily which gained more than $1 billion due to its first full-year contribution. QVC's sales declined $61 million while the sales of Backcountry and Bodybuilding in 2015 and 2016 also weighed on sales.

Net income increased 40% to $1.3 billion thanks to higher revenue decreases in stock-based compensation and gains on the Right Start sale in January 2016.

Cash form operations increased 39% to $1.4 billion due to higher net income and changes in deferred income tax expense offset by realized losses on financial instruments.

Strategy

Liberty Interactive has been busy reshaping its business. In the last few years it has pared down its number of activities particularly in online retail — in 2015-16 it has sold or spun off Backcountry.com Bodybuilding.com Expedia and CommerceHub.com; the year before that it sold Provide Commerce to floral and gift retailer FTD Companies and spun off TripAdvisor and the Buy-Seasons group as TripAdvisor Holdings.

The sales paved the way for the $2.1 billion acquisition of QVC's archrival HSN Inc. agreed in 2017. With both QVC and HSN recording unfavorable revenue trends in recent years the acquisition reflects that the former rivals' biggest competitors are no longer each other but e-commerce giants such as Amazon. QVC HSN and Zulily will be bundled up as QVC Group.

Mergers and Acquisitions

Liberty Interactive agreed to buy the 62% of the Home Shopping Network Inc. (HSNi) that it didn't own for about $2.1 billion in stock. The deal would unite HSNi with Liberty's QVC in an effort to combat Amazon.com and other online retailers. Liberty plans to package QVC HSNi and Zulily.com into an asset-backed spinoff in late 2017. The acquisition of HSNi was expected to close by the end of the year.

HISTORY

The man who would be king of cable programming got his start on the hardware end of the business. In 1970 John Malone became president of General Instrument's Jerrold Communications subsidiary which supplied equipment to the then-new cable TV industry. One of Jerrold's customers was Bob Magness a former Texas rancher who in the 1950s started the company that eventually became Denver-based cable operator Tele-Communications Inc. (TCI). In the early 1970s TCI struggled in need of leadership. In 1973 the 32-year-old Malone was named CEO of TCI.

Malone restructured TCI's debt in 1977 paving the way for expansion into bigger cable markets after deregulation in 1984. He also acquired programming buying stakes in Black Entertainment Television (33% 1979 sold to Viacom in 2001) the Discovery Channel (14% 1986) and American Movie Classics (50% 1986). In 1987 TCI helped save debt-plagued Turner Broadcasting and came away with 12% of Turner Broadcasting's stock.

Due in part to antitrust pressure from government regulators in 1991 TCI spun off much of its programming assets along with interests in 14 cable systems as Liberty Media. Malone became chairman and principal shareholder. In its first year the company launched Court TV in a joint venture and introduced film channel Encore. The next year

it bought an interest in the Home Shopping Network (which became USA Networks in 1998 and later changed names to USA Interactive in 2002 InterActiveCorp in 2003 and finally IAC/InterActiveCorp in 2004).

In 1994 TCI reacquired Liberty Media; it issued a tracking stock the next year to reflect the value of Liberty's program assets. Also in 1995 Liberty Media and News Corp. joined forces to create FOX/Liberty Networks a national sports network designed to compete with Disney's ESPN.

In 2011 Liberty Media Corp. changed its name to Liberty Interactive Corp. following the split-off of its Liberty Capital and Liberty Starz tracking stocks.

EXECUTIVES

President and CEO, Gregory B. (Greg) Maffei, age 56, $1,045,739 total compensation
Chief Corporate Development Officer, Albert E. Rosenthaler, age 57, $336,031 total compensation
Chief Legal Officer, Richard N. (Rich) Baer, age 60, $327,307 total compensation
CFO Liberty Media Corporation Liberty Interactive Corporation and Liberty Broadband Corporation, Mark D. Carleton, age 56, $127,147 total compensation
Chairman, John C. Malone, age 76
Auditors: KPMG LLP

LOCATIONS

HQ: Liberty Interactive Corp
  12300 Liberty Boulevard, Englewood, CO 80112
Phone: 720 875-5300
Web: www.libertyinteractive.com

2016 Sales

	$ mil.	% of total
US	7,979	75
Japan	900	8
Germany	866	8
Other countries	902	9
Total	**10,647**	**100**

PRODUCTS/OPERATIONS

2016 Sales

	$ mil.	% of total
QVC	8,682	81
zulily	1,547	15
Ventures Group	428	4
eliminations	(10)	-
Total	**10,647**	**100**

2016 Sales

	% of total
Home	33
Apparel	19
Beauty	17
Accessories	13
Jewelry	9
Electronics	9
Total	**100**

COMPETITORS

Access TV	Orbitz Worldwide
Amazon.com	Priceline
American Express	Travelocity
EVINE Live	Wal-Mart
IAC	

Income Statement

FYE: December 31

	REVENUE ($ mil.)	NET INCOME ($ mil.)	NET PROFIT MARGIN	EMPLOYEES
12/16	10,647	1,235	11.6%	21,080
12/15	9,989	869	8.7%	22,080
12/14	10,499	537	5.1%	20,078
12/13	11,252	501	4.5%	23,079
12/12	10,054	1,530	15.2%	22,078
Annual Growth	**1.4%**	**(5.2%)**	**—**	**(1.1%)**

2016 Year-End Financials

Debt ratio: 39.51%
Return on equity: 18.17%
Cash ($ mil.): 825
Current ratio: 1.25
Long-term debt ($ mil.): 7,166

No. of shares (mil.): 543
Dividends
  Yield: —
  Payout: 39.9%
Market value ($ mil.): 10,865

	STOCK PRICE ($) FY Close	P/E High/Low		PER SHARE ($) Earnings	Dividends	Book Value
12/16	19.98	28	18	0.98	0.00	12.45
12/15	27.32	10	9	2.93	0.00	10.73
12/14	29.42	—	—	(0.00)	0.00	9.18
12/13	29.35	—	—	(0.00)	0.00	12.08
12/12	19.68	—	—	(0.00)	0.00	12.23
Annual Growth	**0.4%**	**—**		**—**	**—**	**0.5%**

Liberty Interactive Corp

LOCATIONS

HQ: Liberty Interactive Corp
  12300 Liberty Boulevard, Englewood, CO 80112
Phone: 720 875-5400
Web: www.libertymedia.com

HISTORICAL FINANCIALS

Company Type: Public

Income Statement

FYE: December 31

	REVENUE ($ mil.)	NET INCOME ($ mil.)	NET PROFIT MARGIN	EMPLOYEES
12/16	10,219	473	4.6%	21,080
12/15	9,169	640	7.0%	22,080
12/14	10,028	520	5.2%	20,078
12/13	10,307	438	4.2%	23,000
12/12	10,018	466	4.7%	22,078
Annual Growth	**0.5%**	**0.4%**	**—**	**(1.1%)**

2016 Year-End Financials

Debt ratio: 44.40%
Return on equity: 9.38%
Cash ($ mil.): 338
Current ratio: 1.50
Long-term debt ($ mil.): 6,361

No. of shares (mil.): 29
Dividends
  Yield: —
  Payout: —
Market value ($ mil.): 595

	STOCK PRICE ($) FY Close	P/E High/Low		PER SHARE ($) Earnings	Dividends	Book Value
12/16	20.25	28	18	0.98	0.00	165.54
12/15	27.16	23	19	1.33	0.00	177.80
12/14	29.69	29	22	1.06	0.00	148.21
12/13	29.39	35	23	0.83	0.00	220.81
12/12	19.50	53	41	0.38	0.00	242.24
Annual Growth	**0.9%**	**—**	**—**	**26.7%**	**—**	**(9.1%)**

Liberty Interactive Corp

LOCATIONS

HQ: Liberty Interactive Corp
12300 Liberty Boulevard, Englewood, CO 80112
Phone: 720 875-5300
Web: www.libertymedia.com

HISTORICAL FINANCIALS

Company Type: Public

Income Statement
FYE: December 31

	REVENUE ($ mil.)	NET INCOME ($ mil.)	NET PROFIT MARGIN	EMPLOYEES
12/16	10,219	473	4.6%	21,080
12/15	9,169	640	7.0%	22,080
12/14	10,028	520	5.2%	20,078
12/13	10,307	438	4.2%	23,079
12/12	10,018	466	4.7%	22,078
Annual Growth	0.5%	0.4%	—	(1.1%)

2016 Year-End Financials

Debt ratio: 44.40%
Return on equity: 9.38%
Cash ($ mil.): 338
Current ratio: 1.50
Long-term debt ($ mil.): 6,361

No. of shares (mil.): 458
Dividends
Yield: —
Payout: —
Market value ($ mil.): 9,158

	STOCK PRICE ($) FY Close	P/E High/Low	Earnings	Dividends	Book Value
12/16	19.98	28 18	0.98	0.00	10.60
12/15	27.32	23 19	1.33	0.00	10.59
12/14	29.42	28 22	1.06	0.00	8.99
12/13	29.35	35 23	0.83	0.00	12.74
12/12	19.68	53 41	0.38	0.00	12.87
Annual Growth	0.4%	— —	26.7%	—	(4.7%)

Liberty Media Corp (DE)

Auditors: KPMG LLP

LOCATIONS

HQ: Liberty Media Corp (DE)
12300 Liberty Boulevard, Englewood, CO 80112
Phone: 720 875-5400
Web: www.libertymedia.com

HISTORICAL FINANCIALS

Company Type: Public

Income Statement
FYE: December 31

	REVENUE ($ mil.)	NET INCOME ($ mil.)	NET PROFIT MARGIN	EMPLOYEES
12/16	5,276	680	12.9%	3,626
12/15	4,795	64	1.3%	3,503
12/14	4,450	178	4.0%	3,690
12/13	4,002	8,780	219.4%	3,893
12/12	1,999	1,414	70.7%	2,178
Annual Growth	27.5%	(16.7%)	—	13.6%

2016 Year-End Financials

Debt ratio: 25.55%
Return on equity: 5.98%
Cash ($ mil.): 562
Current ratio: 0.36
Long-term debt ($ mil.): 8,013

No. of shares (mil.): 468
Dividends
Yield: —
Payout: —
Market value ($ mil.): 14,676

	STOCK PRICE ($) FY Close	P/E High/Low	Earnings	Dividends	Book Value
12/16	31.33	34 16	1.12	0.00	25.10
12/15	38.08	212 175	0.19	0.00	32.68
12/14	35.03	95 64	0.52	0.00	33.21
Annual Growth	(2.8%)	— —	21.1%	—	(6.8%)

Liberty Media Corp (DE)

LOCATIONS

HQ: Liberty Media Corp (DE)
12300 Liberty Boulevard, Englewood, CO 80112
Phone: 720 875-5400
Web: www.libertymedia.com

HISTORICAL FINANCIALS

Company Type: Public

Income Statement
FYE: December 31

	REVENUE ($ mil.)	NET INCOME ($ mil.)	NET PROFIT MARGIN	EMPLOYEES
12/16	5,014	413	8.2%	3,626
12/15	4,552	259	5.7%	—
12/14	4,141	231	5.6%	—
Annual Growth	10.0%	33.7%	—	—

2016 Year-End Financials

Debt ratio: 22.58%
Return on equity: 4.18%
Cash ($ mil.): 287
Current ratio: 0.27
Long-term debt ($ mil.): 6,102

No. of shares (mil.): 335
Dividends
Yield: —
Payout: —
Market value ($ mil.): 11,571

	STOCK PRICE ($) FY Close	P/E High/Low	Earnings	Dividends	Book Value
12/16	34.52	44 33	0.88	0.00	30.09
12/15	39.25	— —	(0.00)	0.00	(0.00)
12/14	35.27	— —	(0.00)	0.00	(0.00)
/0.00	—	—	(0.00)	0.00	(0.00)
/0.00	—	—	(0.00)	0.00	(0.00)
Annual Growth	—	—	—	—	—

Liberty Media Corp (DE)

LOCATIONS

HQ: Liberty Media Corp (DE)
12300 Liberty Boulevard, Englewood, CO 80112
Phone: 720 875-5400
Web: www.libertymedia.com

HISTORICAL FINANCIALS

Company Type: Public

Income Statement
FYE: December 31

	REVENUE ($ mil.)	NET INCOME ($ mil.)	NET PROFIT MARGIN	EMPLOYEES
12/16	5,014	413	8.2%	3,626
12/15	4,552	259	5.7%	—
12/14	4,141	231	5.6%	—
Annual Growth	10.0%	33.7%	—	—

2016 Year-End Financials

Debt ratio: 22.58%
Return on equity: 4.18%
Cash ($ mil.): 287
Current ratio: 0.27
Long-term debt ($ mil.): 6,102

No. of shares (mil.): 222
Dividends
Yield: —
Payout: —
Market value ($ mil.): 7,562

	STOCK PRICE ($) FY Close	P/E High/Low	Earnings	Dividends	Book Value
12/16	33.92	41 33	0.88	0.00	45.24
12/15	0.00	— —	(0.00)	0.00	(0.00)
12/14	0.00	— —	(0.00)	0.00	(0.00)
Annual Growth	—	—	—	—	—

Liberty Media Corp (DE)

LOCATIONS

HQ: Liberty Media Corp (DE)
12300 Liberty Boulevard, Englewood, CO 80112
Phone: 720 875-5400
Web: www.libertymedia.com

HISTORICAL FINANCIALS

Company Type: Public

Income Statement
FYE: December 31

	REVENUE ($ mil.)	NET INCOME ($ mil.)	NET PROFIT MARGIN	EMPLOYEES
12/16	5,014	413	8.2%	3,626
12/15	4,552	259	5.7%	—
12/14	4,141	231	5.6%	—
Annual Growth	10.0%	33.7%	—	—

2016 Year-End Financials

Debt ratio: 22.58%
Return on equity: 4.18%
Cash ($ mil.): 287
Current ratio: 0.27
Long-term debt ($ mil.): 6,102

No. of shares (mil.): 9
Dividends
Yield: —
Payout: —
Market value ($ mil.): 345

	STOCK PRICE ($) FY Close	P/E High/Low	Earnings	Dividends	Book Value
12/16	34.94	42 32	0.88	0.00	
1,021.69					
12/15	0.00	— —	(0.00)	0.00	(0.00)
12/14	0.00	— —	(0.00)	0.00	(0.00)
Annual Growth	—	—	—	—	—

LifePoint Health Inc

LifePoint Health helps folks who get sick in the country get well. The company operates more than 70 hospitals located in non-urban areas. In most cases the hospitals (which combined house more than 9400 beds) are the only available acute care facilities in the region. LifePoint operates its hospitals in 22 states through its subsidiaries with a concentration in the southeastern US. In many markets LifePoint also operates outpatient clinics that provide family care diagnostic surgical and therapeutic services.

Operations

Unlike major urban medical centers the hospitals that LifePoint Health operates don't usually engage in extensive medical research train legions of new doctors or perform complex surgeries. The facilities do provide a spectrum of health care services that include emergency care general surgery obstetrics oncology cardiology coronary care rehabilitation services pediatric services and diagnostic care.

The company has nearly 40 post-acute service providers and facilities as well as more than 30 outpatient centers. Its Duke LifePoint Healthcare partnership with Duke University Health System works to strengthen and improve the delivery of health care.

Geographic Reach

LifePoint Health has the heaviest concentration of facilities in Georgia Kentucky Virginia New Mexico Michigan Pennsylvania and North Carolina.

North Carolina is the group's largest market bringing in some 15% of its total revenue; Kentucky and Virginia each account for more than 10%.

Sales and Marketing

Some 45% of LifePoint Health's annual revenues come from Medicare and Medicaid while around 40% come from private insurers (including HMO and PPO plans). Most of the rest of the company's revenues come from self-pay patients.

Financial Performance

LifePoint's revenues have been steadily rising over the past few years. In 2016 revenue rose 22% to $6.4 billion thanks to a number of recent hospital acquisitions.

Net income which has been more turbulent fell 33% to $121.9 million in 2016 due to higher operating expenses and certain non-recurring charges. Among those was a $24.7 million charge to settle lawsuits. Following suit operating cash flow fell 31% to $435.2 million.

Strategy

LifePoint Health has its eye on a number of important business areas including tracking and improving the quality of care its hospitals provide pursuing targeted physician recruitment activities and retaining its physician and non-physician staffs through improved employee satisfaction. It invests capital for new technologies and facility upgrades while improving the management of its expenses. Other efforts include increasing reimbursement payments from private payers acquiring hospitals and other health care facilities and partnering with not-for-profit care providers to enter new markets.

The company maintains a competitive edge in many of its regional markets by being the sole provider of many of the health care services it offers. Even so LifePoint is working to increase the breadth of services provided by its hospitals in an effort to keep patients from having to travel outside the community for care especially in fields such as open-heart surgery psychiatric care and neurosurgery. The company also manages procurement expenses by participating (and owning a 6% stake) in HealthTrust a group purchasing organization.

LifePoint struggles with containing expenses from serving charity care and self-pay customers that are part and parcel of running a health care system. To help offset losses related to caring for uninsured patients the company strives to negotiate favorable contracts with managed care and other private payers at each of its facilities.

To raise cash and save costs in 2015 the company sold Lakeland Hospital Northwest Hospital and Russellville Medical Center in Alabama as well as the Putnam Community Medical Center in Florida.

LifePoint Hospitals changed its name to LifePoint Health in 2015 to reflect its growing focus on comprehensive health care including physician practices post-acute and outpatient services and wellness programs.

Mergers and Acquisitions

In addition to organic growth measures LifePoint Health expands through regular acquisitions. The company targets small non-urban hospitals where it sees an opportunity for improved financial performance and LifePoint typically invests in facility upgrades once its purchases are complete. In 2016 the system acquired three hospitals (Frye Regional Medical Center and Central Carolina Hospital in North Carolina and St. Francis Hospital in Georgia) adding some 870 beds to its operations for a combined $448 million. It also acquired South Carolina-based Providence Hospitals adding two hospitals 13 physician practices rehab centers sleep centers and a chest pain center.

In 2015 through a joint venture with Norton Healthcare LifePoint added Indiana's 241-bed Clark Memorial Hospital; LifePoint also acquired the 52-bed Fleming County Hospital in Kentucky.In another purchase it bought Nason Hospital in Pennsylvania which became part of the Duke LifePoint Healthcare joint venture's Conemaugh Health System.

Company Background

LifePoint was born when hospital giant HCA spun off a group of about two dozen hospitals in 1999. It wasn't until its 2005 merger with Province Healthcare Company that LifePoint became the hulking presence it is today.

EXECUTIVES

Chairman and CEO, William F. (Bill) Carpenter, age 62, $1,179,000 total compensation

President and COO, David M. Dill, age 48, $687,000 total compensation

EVP and CFO, Michael S. (Mike) Coggin, age 47, $420,000 total compensation

President Eastern Group, Victor E. Giovanetti, age 53

President Central Group, R. Scott Raplee, age 52, $412,000 total compensation

Chief Medical Officer, Russell L. (Rusty) Holman, age 49

President Western Group, Robert N. Klein, age 57

EVP and Chief Administrative Officer, John P. Bumpus, age 57, $449,000 total compensation

SVP and CIO, Sean Tuley

CEO SageWest Health Care, Alan Daugherty

President Ambulatory and Operations Services, Melissa O. Waddey, age 41

Medical Director Sumner Regional Medical Center Emergency Department, Ray Pinkston

Clinical Director Meaningful Use, Kelly Lester

Vice President, Mary Kiger

Director Government Relations, Osei Mevs

Vice President Capital Asset and Construction Management, Ed O'Dell

Treasurer, Phillip Gilbertson

Auditors: Ernst & Young LLP

LOCATIONS

HQ: LifePoint Health Inc
330 Seven Springs Way, Brentwood, TN 37027
Phone: 615 920-7000
Web: www.lifepointhospitals.com

Selected Hospitals

Alabama
Andalusia Regional Hospital
Lakeland Community Hospital (Haleyville)
Northwest Medical Center (Winfield)
Russellville Hospital
Vaughan Regional Medical Center (Selma)
Arizona
Havasu Regional Medical Center (Lake Havasu City)
Valley View Medical Center (Ft. Mohave)
Colorado
Colorado Plains Medical Center (Fort Morgan)
Florida
Putnam Community Medical Center (Palatka)
Georgia
Rockdale Medical Center (Conyers)
Indiana
Scott Memorial Hospital (Scottsburg)
Kansas
Western Plains Medical Complex (Dodge City)
Kentucky
Bluegrass Community Hospital (Versailles)
Bourbon Community Hospital (Paris)
Clark Regional Medical Center (Winchester)
Georgetown Community Hospital
Jackson Purchase Medical Center (Mayfield)
Lake Cumberland Regional Hospital (Somerset)
Logan Memorial Hospital (Russellville)
Meadowview Regional Medical Center (Maysville)
Spring View Hospital (Lebanon)
Louisiana
Acadian Medical Center (Eunice)
Mercy Regional Medical Center (aka Ville Platte Medical Center)
Minden Medical Center
River Parishes Hospital (LaPlace)
Teche Regional Medical Center (Morgan City)
Michigan
Marquette General Health System
Mississippi
Bolivar Medical Center (Cleveland)
Nevada
Northeastern Nevada Regional Hospital (Elko)
New Mexico
Los Alamos Medical Center
Memorial Medical Center of Las Cruces
North Carolina
Maria Parham Medical Center (80% owned by Duke LifePoint Healthcare joint venture Henderson)
Person Memorial Hospital (owned by Duke LifePoint Healthcare joint venture Roxboro)
Tennessee
Athens Regional Medical Center
Crockett Hospital (Lawrenceburg)
Emerald-Hodgson Hospital (Winchester)
High Point Health System (formerly Sumner Regional Health Systems)
Sumner Regional Medical Center (Gallatin)
Hillside Hospital (Pulaski)
Livingston Regional Hospital
Riverview Regional Medical Center North and South (Carthage)
Southern Tennessee Medical Center (Winchester)
Trousdale Medical Center (Hartsville)
Texas
Ennis Regional Medical Center
Palestine Regional Medical Center
Parkview Regional Hospital (Mexia)
Utah
Ashley Regional Medical Center (Vernal)
Castleview Hospital (Price)
Virginia
Clinch Valley Medical Center (Richlands)
Danville Regional Medical Center
Fauquier Hospital (Warrenton)
Memorial Hospital of Martinsville and Henry County (Martinsville)
Twin County Regional Healthcare (owned by Duke LifePoint Healthcare joint venture)
Twin County Regional Hospital (Galax)
Wythe County Community Hospital (Wytheville)
West Virginia
Logan Regional Medical Center
Raleigh General Hospital (Beckley)

Wyoming
Lander Regional Hospital
Riverton Memorial Hospital

PRODUCTS/OPERATIONS

2016 Sales

	$ mil.	% of total
HMOs PPOs and other private insurers	3,015	41
Medicare	2,372	33
Medicaid	922	13
Self-pay	832	11
Other	130	2
Provision for doubtful accounts	(909.6)	-
Total	**6,364**	**100**

COMPETITORS

Ascension Health	Mercy Health (OH)
CHRISTUS Health	Methodist Healthcare
Catholic Health	Sisters of Charity of
Initiatives	Leavenworth
Community Health	SunLink Health Systems
Systems	Tenet Healthcare
Covenant Health	Tennova Healthcare
HCA	Universal Health
Intermountain Health	Services
Care	Wellmont Health System
Kaiser Foundation	West Tennessee
Hospitals	Healthcare
Mercy Health	

HISTORICAL FINANCIALS

Company Type: Public

Income Statement
FYE: December 31

	REVENUE ($ mil.)	NET INCOME ($ mil.)	NET PROFIT MARGIN	EMPLOYEES
12/16	6,364	121	1.9%	47,000
12/15	5,214	181	3.5%	40,000
12/14	4,483	126	2.8%	38,000
12/13	3,678	128	3.5%	31,000
12/12	3,391	151	4.5%	28,000
Annual Growth	**17.0%**	**(5.4%)**	**—**	**13.8%**

2016 Year-End Financials

Debt ratio: 46.12%
Return on equity: 5.47%
Cash ($ mil.): 96
Current ratio: 1.67
Long-term debt ($ mil.): 2,892

No. of shares (mil.): 39
Dividends
Yield: —
Payout: —
Market value ($ mil.): 2,269

	STOCK PRICE ($) FY Close	P/E High/Low	PER SHARE ($) Earnings	Dividends	Book Value
12/16	56.80	25 18	2.82	0.00	54.59
12/15	73.40	21 15	3.95	0.00	52.49
12/14	71.91	27 18	2.69	0.00	48.34
12/13	52.84	19 14	2.69	0.00	46.88
12/12	37.75	13 11	3.14	0.00	43.69
Annual Growth	**10.8%**	**— —**	**(2.7%)**	**—**	**5.7%**

Lilly (Eli) & Co

Best known for its neuroscience products pharmaceutical firm Eli Lilly also makes endocrinology oncology and cardiovascular care medicines. Its top-selling drugs include Cymbalta for depression and pain Alimta for lung cancer Humalog and Humulin insulin for diabetes and Cialis for erectile dysfunction. Lilly also makes medications to treat schizophrenia and bipolar disorder (Zyprexa) os-teoporosis (Evista and Forteo) heart conditions (Effient) ADHD (Strattera) gastric and lung cancer (Cyramza) and diabetes (Jardiance and Trulicity) as well as anti-infective agents and a growing line of animal health products.

HISTORY

Colonel Eli Lilly pharmacist and Union officer in the Civil War started Eli Lilly and Company in 1876 with $1300. His process of gelatin-coating pills led to sales of nearly $82000 in 1881. Later the company made gelatin capsules which it still sells. Lilly died in 1898 and his son and two grandsons ran the business until 1953.

Eli Lilly began extracting insulin from the pancreases of hogs and cattle in 1923; 6000 cattle glands or 24000 hog glands made one ounce of the substance. Other products created in the 1920s and 1930s included antiseptic Merthiolate sedative Seconal and treatments for pernicious anemia and heart disease. In 1947 the company began selling diethylstilbestrol (DES) a drug to prevent miscarriages. Eli Lilly researchers isolated the antibiotic erythromycin from a species of mold found in the Philippines in 1952. Lilly was also the major supplier of Salk polio vaccine.

The company enjoyed a 70% share of the DES market by 1971 when researchers noticed that a rare form of cervical cancer afflicted many of the daughters of women who had taken the drug. The FDA restricted the drug's use and Lilly found itself on the receiving (and frequently losing) end of a number of trailblazing product-liability suits that stretched into the 1990s.

The firm diversified in the 1970s buying Elizabeth Arden (cosmetics 1971; sold 1987) and IVAC (medical instruments 1977). It launched such products as analgesic Darvon and antibiotic Ceclor.

Lilly's 1982 launch of Humulin a synthetic insulin developed by Genentech made it the first company to market a genetically engineered product. In 1986 the company introduced Prozac; that year it also bought biotech firm Hybritech for $300 million (sold in 1995 for less than $10 million). In 1988 Lilly introduced anti-ulcerative Axid. It founded pesticides and herbicides maker DowElanco with Dow Chemical in 1989.

Trying to find a new product outlet the firm bought pharmacy benefit management company PCS Health Systems from what is now McKesson in 1994. But an FTC mandate to offer rival drugs and a lack of mail-order sales contributed to poor results which ultimately led Lilly to sell PCS to Rite Aid and exit this arena completely in 1998.

Eli Lilly in 1995 bought medical communications network developer Integrated Medical Systems. That year the firm and developer Centocor introduced ReoPro a blood-clot inhibitor used in angioplasties. The next year it launched antipsychotic Zyprexa Humalog and Gemzar and Prozac was approved to treat bulimia nervosa.

In 1997 the firm sold its DowElanco stake to Dow. In 1998 the Lilly Endowment passed the Ford Foundation as the US's largest charity largely due to Prozac (it has since been passed by the Bill & Melinda Gates Foundation). That year Lilly began trying to stop Chinese drugmakers from infringing on its patents for Prozac's active ingredient.

In 1999 a US federal judge found the firm illegally promoted osteoporosis drug Evista as a breast cancer preventative similar to AstraZeneca's Nolvadex. Lilly halted tests on its variation of heart drug Moxonidine after 53 patients died. Also that year Zyprexa was approved to treat bipolar disorder.

In 2000 the firm began marketing Prozac under the Sarafem name for severe premenstrual syndrome. A federal appeals court knocked more than two years off Prozac's patent reducing the expected 2003 expiration date to 2001 creating a negative impact on Lilly's annual sales (Prozac had accounted for 30% of revenues). Lilly suffered another blow when a potential successor to Prozac failed in clinical trials and became embroiled in legal maneuverings with generics maker Barr Pharmaceuticals.

While the firm fretted over Prozac and its patents it continued work to find its next blockbuster. In 2000 Lilly and partner ICOS announced favorable results from a study of erectile dysfunction treatment Cialis which was approved in Europe in 2002 and in the US in 2004. (Several years later Lilly acquired ICOS and with it full ownership of the Cialis franchise.)

In 2001 Lilly bought a minority stake in Isis Pharmaceuticals a developer of antisense drugs and licensed from it an antisense lung cancer drug. Also that year the firm launched Lilly BioVentures a venture fund aimed at private biotech startup companies. In 2002 the company settled with eight states in an infringement-of-privacy case involving the company's accidental disclosure of e-mail addresses for more than 600 Prozac patients.

In late 2004 the druggernaut was one of several pharmas hit by bad news about drug side effects. Lilly announced its attention-deficit disorder drug Strattera had been linked to rare liver problems. The company agreed to add warning labels about the potential side effects to the drug's packaging and advertisements. The company also began facing trouble over Zyprexa as consumer lawsuits claiming diabetes and high blood pressure began pouring in. The majority of suits were settled in 2005 and 2007 for some $1.2 billion.

Generalized anxiety disorder drug Cymbalta was approved by the FDA and released in 2006 and osteoporosis drug Evista was approved for an expanded indication as a breast cancer preventative for postmenopausal women in 2007.

Also in 2007 the company acquired and absorbed development partner ICOS for $2.1 billion; the deal gave Lilly full ownership of Viagra-competitor Cialis. Lilly dropped a joint-development effort with another partner Alkermes for an inhaled insulin device in 2008.

The company gradually reduced its workforce by more than 10% between 2003 and 2008 to fight off the effects of generic competition and other challenges. Other restructuring measures included an employee attrition plan announced in 2007 a management restructuring in 2008 and a manufacturing consolidation program launched in 2008.

After a lengthy lawsuit regarding its patents for its top seller Zyprexa a federal judge ruled in Lilly's favor in 2008 against generic manufacturers IVAX Dr. Reddy's Laboratories and Teva Pharmaceutical Industries. Federal courts ruled that the drug's patents would remain valid until October 2011.

To fuel growth in the biopharmaceuticals market the firm completed a $1 billion biotech research facility in Indianapolis in 2008. It further expanded through the 2008 acquisition of biotech firm ImClone for about $6.5 billion; ImClone began operating as a research subsidiary of Lilly following the transaction. ImClone already had one approved blockbuster therapy Erbitux for colorectal and head/neck cancers and was developing numerous other cancer therapy candidates. Lilly also expanded its biotech oncology program earlier that year by purchasing development partner SGX Pharmaceuticals for $64 million. SGX was absorbed into Lilly's research operations.

EXECUTIVES

SVP and President Elanco Animal Health, Jeffrey N. (Jeff) Simmons, age 50
SVP and President Diabetes Business Unit and Lilly USA, Enrique A. Conterno, age 50, $727,960 total compensation
President Manufacturing Operations, Maria Crowe, age 57
SVP and President Lilly International, Alfonso G. (Chito) Zulueta, age 54
SVP and President Lilly Oncology, Susan (Sue) Mahony, age 52
President and CEO, David A. Ricks, age 49
SVP and President Lilly Bio-Medicines, Christi Shaw
SVP and President Manufacturing Operations, Myles O'Neill
SVP Enterprise Risk Management and Chief Ethics and Compliance Officer, Melissa Stapleton Barnes, age 48
SVP and General Counsel, Michael J. Harrington, age 54, $827,400 total compensation
SVP and CIO, Aarti Shah
SVP and CFO, Josh Smiley
SVP Science and Technology and President Lilly Research Labs, Daniel (Dan) Skovronsky
Chief Marketing Officer Vice President Global Medi, Timothy Garnett
Vice President, Scott Slavens
Executive Vice President, Kelly Collett
Senior Vice President Product Research and Development, William Heath
Medical Director, Albert Allen
Vice President Medical Affiars, Robert Heine
Vice President of Finance, Dominic J Montani
Vice President and Deputy General Counsel, Alonzo Weems
Vice President Global Health Programs and Access, Michael J Martin
Senior Vice President Corporate Business Development, Darren Carroll
Vice President, Mary J Sashegyi
Vice President Finance, Bob Kaz
Senior Vice President Marketing and Communications, John M McGill
Vice President, David Clifford
Vice President New Media, Paula Garrett
Vice President Marketing, Michael Stone
Vice President, Wafaa Mamilli
Medical Director, Anurita Majumdar
Executive Vice President Finance and Chief Financial Officer, Matthew Yates
Vice President of Research and Development, Michele Oshman
Vice President Manufacturing, Myles Oneill
Vice President And Medical Director China, Li Wang
Senior Vice President Human RE, Tony Murphy
Chief Medical Officer Senior Vice President Drug Development Center of Excellence, Tim Garnett
Vice President, Jeff Emmick
Government Relations, Joel Worthington
Vice President of World Wide Marketing and Sales, Michele Y Hill
Vice President Manufacturing Science and Technology Global Packaging, Jeffrey Levy
Vice President Oncology Research, Greg Plowman
Vice President of Operations, David Gall
Vice President, Daniel W Collins
Chief Sales Officer, Julian Davies
MEDICAL DIRECTOR CEC, Andras Torocsik
Medical Director, Axel Haupt
Vice President, Julie Xing
Associate Vice President Project and Portfolio Management, Michael Dowd
Vice President, Susan J Kurkowski
Medical Director, Susan Kindig
Associate Vice President, Anthony Lonardo
Department Head, Brian Croxford

Vice President, T Dixon
Vice President of Marketing and Saless, Elvira Gord
Vice President of Oncology Research, Karen Oie
Chairman, John C. Lechleiter
Board Member, Amparo De La Pena
Board Member, Kathryn E Broderick
Board Member, Stacey Bledsoe
Secretary, Tim Conrad
Advisory Board Member, Ganesh Sharma
Board Member, ED Parrish
Board Member, Mark Miklinski
Auditors: Ernst & Young LLP

LOCATIONS

HQ: Lilly (Eli) & Co
   Lilly Corporate Center, Indianapolis, IN 46285
Phone: 317 276-2000
Web: www.lilly.com

2016 Sales

	$ mil.	% of total
US	11,506	54
Europe	3,768	18
Japan	2,330	11
Other regions & countries	3,616	17
Total	**21,222**	**100**

PRODUCTS/OPERATIONS

2016 Sales

	$ mil.	% of total
Endocrinology	8,082	38
Oncology	3,721	18
Cardiovascular	3,225	15
Neurosciences	2,720	13
Other human pharmaceuticals	313	1
Animal health	3,158	15
Total	**21,222**	**100**

2016 Sales

	$ mil.	% of total
Human Pharmaceutical products		
Humalog	2,768	13
Cialis	2,471	12
Alimta	2,283	11
Forteo	1,500	7
Humulin	1,365	7
Cymbalta	930	4
Trulicity	925	4
Strattera	854	4
Zyprexa	725	3
Erbitux	687	3
Cyramza	614	3
Effient	535	3
Trajenta	436	2
Other human pharmaceuticals	1,965	9
Animal health products	3,158	15
Total	**21,222**	**100**

Selected Products and Indications

Neuroscience
   Amyvid (florbetapir F 18 injection)
   Cymbalta (duloxetine hydrocholoride; depression anxiety pain; also for managing fibromyalgia and chronic musculoskeletal pain in the US)
   Prozac (fluoxetine hydrochloride; depression panic disorder obsessive-compulsive disorder and bulimia nervosa)
   Strattera (atomoxetine hydrochloride ADHD)
   Symbyax (olanzapine and fluoxetine hydrochloride bipolar and treatment-resistant depression)
   Zyprexa (olanzapine schizophrenia and bipolar)
   Zyprexa Relprevv (Zypadhera in the EU long-acting injectable Zyprexa)
Endocrinology (including diabetes)
   Actos (pioglitazone hydrochloride type 2 diabetes)
   Alimta (non-small cell lung cancer)
   Axiron (testosterone topical for testosterone deficiency)
   Erbitux (colorectal cancers head and neck cancers)
   Evista (raloxifene hydrochloride osteoporosis and breast cancer prevention in postmenopausal women)
   Forteo (osteoporosis)
   Gemzar (pancreatic cancer metastatic breast cancer non-small cell lung cancer; bladder cancer in the EU)

Glucagon (injection rDNA origin)
   Humalog (insulin lispro injection rDNA origin; diabetes)
   Humalog Mix 75/25 (75% Insulin lispro protamine suspension 25% insulin lispro injection rDNA origin; diabetes)
   Humalog Mix 50/50 (50% Insulin lispro protamine suspension 50% insulin lispro injection rDNA origin; diabetes)
   Humalog Pen (insulin lispro rDNA origin; diabetes)
   Humatrope (somatropin for injection rDNA origin; growth disorders)
   Humulin (human insulin rDNA origin; diabetes)
   Humulin Pen (human insulin rDNA origin; diabetes)
   Tradjenta (type 2 diabetes)
Oncology (cancer)
   Alimta (pemetrexed non-small cell lung cancer and malignant pleural mesothelioma)
   Erbitux (colorectal head and neck cancers; from ImClone)
   Gemzar (gemcitabine hydrochloride; pancreatic breast lung bladder and ovarian cancers)
Cardiovascular
   Adcirca (pulmonary arterial hypertension)
   Cialis (tadalafil erectile dysfunction; benign prostatic hyperplasia in US)
   Efient/Effient (atherothrombotic events)
   Livalo (statin high cholesterol)
   ReoPro (percutaneous coronary intervention)
Animal Health (Elanco)
   Apralan (antibiotic to control enteric infections in calves and swine)
   Coban Monteban and Maxiban (anticoccidial for poultry)
   Comfortis (flea infestation prevention tablets for dogs)
   Micotil Pulmotil and Pulmotil AC (antibiotics for respiratory disease in cattle swine and poultry respectively)
   Paylean Optaflexx (leanness and performance enhancers for swine and cattle respectively)
   Posilac (protein supplement for enhanced milk productivity in cows)
   Reconcile (separation anxiety for dogs)
   Rumensin (feed additive)
   Surmax/Maxus (performance enhancer for swine and poultry)
   Trifexis (chewable tablet for dogs to prevent flea infestations and heartworm disease and control intestinal parasite infections)
   Tylan (antibiotic)
Other pharmaceuticals (including anti-infectives)
   Ceclor (bacterial infections)
   Vancocin (staphylococcal infections)

COMPETITORS

Abbott Labs	Mylan
Amgen	Myriad Genetics
AstraZeneca	Novartis
Bayer AG	Novo Nordisk
Boehringer Ingelheim	Pfizer
Bristol-Myers Squibb	Roche Holding
Dr. Reddy's	Sanofi
GlaxoSmithKline	Shire
Johnson & Johnson	Takeda Pharmaceutical
Merck	Teva
Merck KGaA	

HISTORICAL FINANCIALS

Company Type: Public

Income Statement

FYE: December 31

	REVENUE ($ mil.)	NET INCOME ($ mil.)	NET PROFIT MARGIN	EMPLOYEES
12/16	21,222	2,737	12.9%	41,975
12/15	19,958	2,408	12.1%	41,275
12/14	19,615	2,390	12.2%	39,135
12/13	23,113	4,684	20.3%	37,925
12/12	22,603	4,088	18.1%	38,350
Annual Growth	(1.6%)	(9.5%)	—	2.3%

2016 Year-End Financials

Debt ratio: 26.56%
Return on equity: 19.11%
Cash ($ mil.): 6,038
Current ratio: 1.37
Long-term debt ($ mil.): 8,367

No. of shares (mil.): 1,100
Dividends
Yield: 0.0%
Payout: 79.0%
Market value ($ mil.): 80,969

	STOCK PRICE ($) FY Close	P/E High/Low		PER SHARE ($) Earnings	Dividends	Book Value
12/16	73.55	33	25	2.58	2.04	12.72
12/15	84.26	40	30	2.26	2.00	13.18
12/14	68.99	33	23	2.23	1.96	13.84
12/13	51.00	13	11	4.32	1.96	15.79
12/12	49.32	15	11	3.66	1.96	12.91
Annual Growth	10.5%	—	—	(8.4%)	1.0%	(0.4%)

LIMETREE BAY TERMINALS LLC

HOVENSA brings together US and Latin American know-how and operations to handle oil products in the US Virgin Islands. HOVENSA is a joint venture of Hess and Venezuelan oil giant PDVSA (its major crude oil supplier). Once the largest private employer in the US Virgin Islands the company operated a 500000-barrels-per-day crude oil refinery on St. Croix along with two specialized oil processing complexes a 150000-barrels-per-day fluid catalytic cracking unit and a 58000-barrels-per-day delayed coker unit. However the St. Croix refinery had run up losses for years; it was shut down in 2012 and was put up for sale in 2013.

Strategy

Citing high operating and maintenance costs (the refinery was fueled by oil not the cheaper natural gas) and the growth of lower-cost refineries in emerging markets HOVENSA has posted $1.3 billion in losses since 2009. As a result the company decided to cut its losses by converting the refinery into an oil storage terminal which can take advantage of St. Croix's strategic location. Its 55-ft. deep harbor enables it to receive crude oil tanker deliveries from Venezuela and around the world. The storage terminal employs about 100 workers. The shutdown of the refinery resulted in more than 2000 employes being laid off.

Company Background

In 2009 the global economic downturn depressed demand for oil caused a dip in production and prompted the company to lay off 270 employees (about 21% of its total contract workers).

Crude thoughput has declined steadily at HOVENSA due to weaker refining margins and planned and unplanned maintenance from 402000 barrels per day (bpd) in 2009 to 390000 bpd in 2010 to 284000 bpd in 2011.

EXECUTIVES

President and COO, Lawrence J. (Larry) Kupfer
EVP, Alexander A. (Alex) Moorehead
VP and Deputy COO, Marco Crovesi
VP Environmental Health and Safety, Richard (Dick) Smullen
VP Refinery Operations, Peter (Pete) Barba
Finance Manager, Mike Fennessey
Purchasing Manager, Gary Miller
President Chief Operating Officer of HOVENSA, Brian K. Lever
Auditors: ERNST & YOUNG LLP NEW YORK N

LOCATIONS

HQ: LIMETREE BAY TERMINALS LLC
1 ESTATE HOPE, CHRISTIANSTED, VI 00820
Phone: 340 692-3000

COMPETITORS

Chevron
ConocoPhillips
Exxon Mobil
Marathon Oil

Royal Dutch Shell
Sunoco
Valero Energy

HISTORICAL FINANCIALS

Company Type: Private

Income Statement

FYE: December 31

	REVENUE ($ mil.)	NET INCOME ($ mil.)	NET PROFIT MARGIN	EMPLOYEES
12/09	10,048	(451)	—	1,300
12/08	17,479	94	0.5%	—
Annual Growth	(42.5%)			

2009 Year-End Financials

Debt ratio: ——
Return on equity: (-4.50%)
Cash ($ mil.): 77
Current ratio: 0.20
Long-term debt ($ mil.): ——

Dividends
Yield: —
Payout: —
Market value ($ mil.): —

Lincoln National Corp.

Lincoln National which operates as Lincoln Financial Group provides retirement planning and life insurance to individuals and employers in the form of annuities 401k and savings plans and a variety of life dental and disability insurance products. The company does business through such subsidiaries as Lincoln National Life Insurance and Lincoln Life & Annuity Company of New York. Lincoln Financial is also active in the investment management business offering individual and institutional clients such financial services as pension plans trusts and mutual funds through its subsidiaries.

Operations

Lincoln Financial operates through four segments: Life Insurance Annuities Group Protection and Retirement Plan Services. The group serves more than 90000 group insurance and retirement plan contracts which have a total of some 17 million participants. It has a total of $236 billion in assets under management.

The company's largest segment Life Insurance (about 45% of sales) offers term products a linked benefit product and a critical illness rider. The Annuities segment (some 30% of sales) offers fixed and variable annuities. Group Protection (about 15% of sales) offers non-medical policies primarily term life dental and disability products to the employer market. Retirement Plan Services (nearly 10% of sales) provides employers with plans and services primarily in the defined contribution retirement plan marketplace.

Geographic Reach

Headquartered in Radnor Pennsylvania Lincoln Financial also has offices in Atlanta; Concord New Hampshire; Fort Wayne Indiana; Greensboro North Carolina; Hartford Connecticut; Omaha Nebraska; Philadelphia; and Rolling Meadows Illinois.

Sales and Marketing

Lincoln Financial Network distributes Lincoln Financial products through a network of more than 1200 agents while Lincoln Financial Distributors is the company's wholesale distributor serving brokers planners agents third party administrators financial advisors and other intermediaries.

The company also markets its products through online print and television advertising.

Lincoln Financial serves more than 17 million customers.

Financial Performance

Lincoln Financial has seen revenue growth over the past five years but saw a slight decline in 2016. That year revenue fell 2% to $13.3 billion as insurance premiums and other revenue declined and total realized losses more than doubled.

Net income which peaked in 2014 but then fell in 2015 as legal expenses increased rose 3% to $1.2 billion in 2016. This was primarily due to a decrease in benefits expenses. Cash flow from operations also peaked in 2014 but has since declined. It dropped 43% to $1.3 billion in 2016 as a result of negative adjustments provided by operating activities chiefly changes in future contract benefits and other contract holder funds.

Strategy

To meet the challenges of difficult economic times in the market Lincoln Financial has adopted a strategy to strengthen its business that includes investing in high-quality corporate securities to reduce asset risk; escalating share repurchases and debt repayment; repricing life and annuity products to guarantee new business that is profitable; and making significant investments in businesses to increase its future earning power.It is investing in product innovations and distribution channels to drive up revenues. The company leverages its powerful distribution network to enter new markets while maintaining its position in existing markets. It targets the fastest-growing industry segments while steering away from long-term guarantee products.

The company is also investing in technology to increase margins.Its current enterprise-wide digitization initiative is designed to improve customer experiences and provide for ease in meeting changing marketplace shifts.

Going forward Lincoln Financial will explore additional financial strategies to address the statutory reserve strain that comes with its term and universal life products that contain secondary guarantees. It will shift its business to focus on products with shorter duration liabilities and more limited liabilities.

The company sold its Lincoln Financial Media subsidiary which included 15 radio stations to Entercom Communications in 2015. The media arm was a legacy from its acquisition of Jefferson-Pilot but Lincoln exited the industry to focus on insurance.

EXECUTIVES

President and CEO; President Lincoln Financial Group, Dennis R. Glass, age 67, $1,200,000 total compensation
EVP Chief Human Resources Officer and Head Brand and Enterprise Communications, Lisa M. Buckingham, age 51, $578,448 total compensation
President Annuity Solutions Lincoln Financial Distributors and Lincoln Financial Network, Wilford H. (Will) Fuller, age 46, $650,000 total compensation
EVP and CFO, Randal J. Freitag, age 54, $669,708 total compensation
EVP and Chief Investment Officer, Ellen Cooper, age 52
EVP and General Counsel, Kirkland L. Hicks, age 46, $575,000 total compensation
EVP CIO and Head of Administrative Services, Kenneth S. Solon, age 56

Vice President Of Corporate Branding And Advertising, David Wozniak
Vice President Of Sales, Robert Risk
Senior Vice President, Beth O'Brien
Assistant Vice President and Director, Linda Fairbanks
Assistant Vice President Life Financial Planning and Analysis, Christopher Potochar
Assistant Vice President, Marlene Hammond
Senior Vice President Account Executive, Michael Herron
Assistant Vice President And Associate Counsel, Carl Semmler
Assistant Vice President, James M Gasparotto
Assistant Vice President and Associate Actuary, Lance Schulz
VICE PRESIDENT, Paul Spurr
Assistant Vice President Information Technology Shared Services, Dave Vachon
Assistant Vice President And Program Officer, Byron Champlin
Associate Vice President Enrollment Services, Joe Mitchell
Vice President: National Sales Manager, Bill Nash
Vice President Managing Director Tactical Strategies Fixed Inc, Jayson Bronchetti
Assistant Vice President Senior Employee Relations, Mary Carruth
ASSISTANT VICE PRESIDENT, Randy Gilbert
Vice President Human Resources, Audrey Im
Assistant Vice President Expense Management and Analysis, Jeff Kafel
Senior Vice President, Andrew Yorks
Assistant Vice President Procurement Technology and Operations, Jennifer Sheriff
Assistant Vice President And Senior Counsel, Jennifer Petruccelli
Assistant Vice President And Valuation Actuary, William Panyard
Assistant Vice President Senior Counsel Retirement Plan Services, Philip Lozano
Senior Vice President, Gene Mulligan
NATIONAL ACCOUNT MANAGER, Shannon Green
Assistant Vice President, Mike Link
Assistant Vice President, Stephen Turer
Regional Vice President, Laura Degnon
VICE PRESIDENT BUSINESS LEADER, John Weber
Assistant Vice President Customer Service, Jim Rooney
Assistant Vice President Financial Reporting And Expense Controls, Kathy Tibke
Vice President of Sales, Marie Cochrane
Divisional Vice President LFA, Matthew Echaniz
Vice President and Chief Counsel Supporting Distribution, Carrie Chelko
Assistant Vice President Treasury, Brad Jeffrey Brad Jeffrey
Vice President and Branch Manager, Melissa Hidalgo
Vice President Corporate Supply Chain And Manufacturing, Sharon Leggette
Assistant Vice President, Loraine Bernard
Vice President, Brian Jenkins
Vice President, Nancy Smith
Vice President Operations, Emma Ladd
Assistant Vice President Senior Product Manager, Brian Wilson
Assistant Vice President Digital, James Tierney
Assistant Vice President Senior Human Resources Business Partner, Kelly Pippett
Assistant Vice President, Laurie Scotti
Vice President Product Compliance, Pamela Telfer
Vice President Asset Liability Management, Nathan Hardiman
Second Vice President Corporate Actuary, Mike Antrobus
Assistant Vice President Group Underwriting, Steve Chamlee

Assistant Vice President Market Intelligence, Jamie Ranicar
Assistant Vice President Internal Audit, Wanda Pritchett
Vice President Talent Management, Nancy Rogers
Vice President, Nicole Delimitros
Vice President It, Scott Hardin
Senior Counsel And Assistant Vice President, Wayne Mcclain
Assistant Vice President Life and Annuity Strategy, Thomas Goas
Vice President and Head of Strategy for Retirement Solutions Distribution Business, Kathy Leckey
Assistant Vice President Meetings And Incentives, Richard Gladson
Vice President Large Market Defined Contribution, Sharon Scanlon
Vice President of Human Resources Administration, Stephen Dovey
Senior Vice President Head of Talent, Jen Warne
SENIOR VICE PRESIDENT, Matt Geis
Sales Vice President, Ryan D Lommel
Assistant Vice President, Marc Tomlinson
Assistant Vice President Internal Audit, Claude Campbell
Assistant Vice President Program Manager, Colette Reinhard
Sales Vice President, David Duckworth
Vice President And Associate General Counsel, Deborah Hayes
Vice President, James Sorey
Assistant Vice President Regional Manager, John Tognoli
Senior Vice President, Jon Kimmel
Assistant Vice President Senior Counsel, Joseph Gallo
Assistant Vice President Continuous Improvement, Martin Koritko
Sales Vice President, Valerie Staublin
Senior Vice President, William Conrad
Assistant Vice President Field Development, Angela Whitcher
Assistant Vice President Business Operations Pricing And Underwriting Solutions, Lorrie Zakrzewski
Assistant Vice President Digital Content Services, Christopher O'Connor
Assistant Vice President Individual Annuity Operations, Jeff Hamilton
Tax Assistant Vice President, Jan Webb
ASSISTANT VICE PRESIDENT, Martha Bradberry
Assistant Vice President Finance, Chris Reed
Fraud Vice President, Kenneth Elder
Vice President Commercial Real Estate Investments, Nick Heinzelmann
ASSISTANT VICE PRESIDENT AND ASSOCIATE ACTUARY, Jeffrey Curley
Vice President of Purchasing, Bill Flory
Second Vice President, Dave Furman
Vice President, James Thompson
Senior Vice President Finance, Roger Martin
Vice President Marketing, Tara Harkins
Assistant Vice President And Legal Services, Molly Graham
Assistant Vice President Consumer and Product Marketing, Nandita Dalal
National Account Manager, Tracey Lemelin
Assistant Vice President, Ray Fortier
Vice President, Peter A Foley
Assistant Vice President Human Resources, Kelly Rodeghiero
Assistant Vice President Financial Reporting, Ronda Kitchen
Assistant Vice President Group Finance, Angela Cobble
Assistant Vice President Data Science and Application Architecture, Bernard Ong
Assistant Vice President Organization and Leadership Effectiveness, Nicole Reilly

REGIONAL VICE PRESIDENT, Jonathan Paris
VICE PRESIDENT, Josh Durand
VICE PRESIDENT, Del Campbell
VICE PRESIDENT AND CORPORATE CHIEF ACTUARY, Rick Klenk
Chairman, William H. Cunningham, age 73
Board Member, Marilyn Ondecker
Treasurer, Michael Conte
Board Member, David McDunn
Auditors: Ernst & Young LLP

LOCATIONS

HQ: Lincoln National Corp.
150 N. Radnor Chester Road, Suite A305, Radnor, PA 19087
Phone: 484 583-1400
Web: www.lfg.com

PRODUCTS/OPERATIONS

2016 Revenues

	$ mil.	% of total
Insurance		
Life insurance	6,246	45
Group protection	2,130	15
Retirement		
Annuities	4,033	29
Retirement plan services	1,103	8
Other operations	332	3
Realized losses	(515)	-
Total	**13,330**	**100**

Selected Subsidiaries

First Penn-Pacific Life Insurance Company
Hampshire Funding Inc.
Jefferson-Pilot Investments Inc.
Lincoln Financial Investment Services Corporation
Lincoln Financial Securities Corporation
Lincoln Investment Management Company
The Lincoln National Life Insurance Company
Lincoln National Management Corporation
Lincoln National Reinsurance Company (Barbados) Limited
Lincoln Reinsurance Company of Bermuda Limited

COMPETITORS

AEGON
AIG
AXA Financial
American Equity Investment Life Holding Company
Guardian Life
ING
John Hancock Financial Services
MassMutual
MetLife
Nationwide Financial
New York Life
Northwestern Mutual
Pacific Mutual
Principal Financial
Prudential
TIAA
The Hartford
Torchmark
Unum Group

HISTORICAL FINANCIALS

Company Type: Public

Income Statement

FYE: December 31

	ASSETS ($ mil.)	NET INCOME ($ mil.)	INCOME AS % OF ASSETS	EMPLOYEES
12/16	261,627	1,192	0.5%	10,282
12/15	251,937	1,154	0.5%	10,535
12/14	253,377	1,515	0.6%	11,046
12/13	236,945	1,244	0.5%	10,539
12/12	218,869	1,313	0.6%	9,742
Annual Growth	4.6%	(2.4%)	—	1.4%

Lithia Motors Inc

Lithia Motors has its foot on the growth pedal. The auto dealer specializes in famed US auto brands such as Chevrolet Cadillac Chrysler and Dodge through about 155 stores in select markets in more than a dozen states. The firm sells some 30 brands of new domestic and imported vehicles and all brands of used cars and trucks through its stores and online. It also offers financing and replacement parts and operates more than 20 collision-repair centers. It also offers financing vehicle protection products and credit insurance. Chairman Sidney DeBoer controls Lithia Motors through Lithia Holding Co.

Operations

Lithia has three segments: Import (more than 40% of sales) Domestic (around 40%) and Luxury (almost 20%).

The Domestic segment comprises retail automotive franchises that sell new vehicles manufactured by Chrysler General Motors and Ford. The Import segment covers retail automotive franchises that sell new vehicles made by Honda Toyota Subaru Nissan and Volkswagen. The Luxury segment sells new vehicles manufactured made by BMW Mercedes-Benz and Lexus.

The franchises in each segment also sell used vehicles parts and automotive services and automotive finance and insurance products.

The company also operates three e-commerce websites: Lithia.com DCHauto.com and CarboneCars.com

Lithia sells in the region of 145000 new vehicles and 110000 used vehicles each year.

Geographic Reach

Medford Oregon-based Lithia sells 30 brands of new vehicles and all brands of used vehicles across 15 US states. Its dealerships are primarily located in the West and Midwest including more than a half a dozen dealerships in Alaska and nearly two dozen in Oregon. California is Lithia's biggest market accounting for more than 20% of the company's total sales followed by Oregon and Texas. It has no international business.

The company operates +20 collision repair centers: five each in Oregon and Texas; two each in Idaho New York and Washington; and one each in Alaska Iowa Montana Nevada Vermont and Wyoming.

Sales and Marketing

Lithia sells through its stores and online website. It also maintains mobile versions of its websites and a mobile application in anticipation of greater adoption of mobile technology.

It posts its inventory on major new and used vehicle listing services (cars.com autotrader.com kbb.com edmunds.com craigslist etc.) to reach online shoppers. It also employs search engine optimization search engine marketing and online display advertising (including re-targeting) to reach more online prospects.

Financial Performance

In fiscal 2016 Lithia kept its foot hard on the growth gas continuing the acquisition-fueled growth trend seen since 2010. Revenue rose 10% to $8.7 billion due mostly to dealership acquisitions. Lithia acquired 15 dealerships and 1 franchise in the year an increase on the 6 dealerships and 1 franchise in 2015. However even excluding acquisition-related revenue the company recorded 3.3% organic growth amid unit volume growth and higher selling prices. The best performing brands were the Japanese import brands Honda and Nissan while BMW Acura and Mercedes lagged.

Net income increased 8% to $197.1 million in line with the increase in revenue. Margins remained roughly the same.

Cash from operations was up 16% to $86.5 million due to higher net income.

Strategy

Lithia Motors relies on acquisitions to increase its revenue and diversify its brand portfolio. Indeed the company has completed more than 100 acquisitions since it went public in 1996. Historically the auto dealer has bought about 10 franchises a year expanding mostly in its western base.

Recently the company has shifted its acquisition strategy towards new markets in the US and larger multi-store dealerships. Lithia expanded into Pittsburgh Pennsylvania in 2017 and into New England in 2016 via Carbone Auto Group. Its preference for larger organizations resulted from the assessment that they take less manpower to integrate than smaller "mom and pop" dealerships due to a more established corporate culture.

Mergers and Acquisitions

In 2017 Lithia acquired Downtown Los Angeles Auto Group. The company owns Audi Mercedes-Benz Nissan Porsche Toyota and Volkswagen stores in Los Angeles as well as a Nissan store in nearby Carson. The company brings in more than $1 billion a year in revenue.

In the same year Lithia acquired Pittsburgh-based Baeirl Auto Group that sells Toyota Honda Subaru Ford Chevrolet Acura Kia and Cadillac in the affluent Cranberry Township area. Baeirl makes $500 million a year in revenue.

Company Background

Lithia Motors was founded in 1946 by Walt DeBoer as a Chrysler-Plymouth-Dodge dealership in Ashland Oregon. Walt's son Sidney is its chairman and grandson Bryan is president and CEO of the growing auto dealer.

EXECUTIVES

President and CEO, Bryan B. DeBoer, age 50, $950,000 total compensation

VP Financial Planning, Christopher (Chris) Holzshu, age 43, $485,100 total compensation

SVP Retail Operations, Scott A. Hillier, age 54, $485,100 total compensation

SVP and CFO, John F. North, age 40, $302,500 total compensation

VP Information Technology and CIO, Mark Smith

SVP Operations DCH Operations, George C. Liang, age 61, $378,000 total compensation

EVP, Brad Gray

VICE PRESIDENT, TIM FREEBORN

Chairman, Sidney B. (Sid) DeBoer, age 73

Auditors: KPMG LLP

LOCATIONS

HQ: Lithia Motors Inc
150 N. Bartlett Street, Medford, OR 97501
Phone: 541 776-6401
Web: www.lithia.com

2016 Stores

	No.
California	35
Oregon	25
Texas	16
Montana	11
New Jersey	11
New York	10
Alaska	9
Washington	8
Iowa	7
Hawaii	5
Nevada	4
Idaho	4
North Dakota	3
New Mexico	2
Vermont	2
Massachusetts	1
Wyoming	1
Total	**154**

PRODUCTS/OPERATIONS

2016 Sales

	$ mil	%
Import	3,764	43
Domestic	3,381	39
Luxury	1,528	18
Corporate and other	3	-
Total	**8,678**	**100**

2016 Sales

	$ mil.	% of total
New vehicles	4,938	57
Used vehicle retail	2,227	25
Service body & parts	844	10
Finance & insurance	330	4
Used vehicle wholesale	276	3
Fleet & other	60	1
Total	**8,678**	**100**

COMPETITORS

Ancira	Group 1 Automotive
AutoNation	Internet Brands
Autobytel	McCombs Enterprises
CarMax	Penske Automotive
David McDavid Auto	Group
Group	Sonic Automotive
Gillman Auto	

HISTORICAL FINANCIALS

Company Type: Public

Income Statement

FYE: December 31

	REVENUE ($ mil.)	NET INCOME ($ mil.)	NET PROFIT MARGIN	EMPLOYEES
12/16	8,678	197	2.3%	11,170
12/15	7,864	183	2.3%	9,574
12/14	5,390	138	2.6%	8,827
12/13	4,005	106	2.6%	5,700
12/12	3,316	80	2.4%	5,403
Annual Growth	27.2%	25.1%	—	19.9%

	STOCK PRICE ($) FY Close	P/E High/Low		PER SHARE ($) Earnings	Dividends	Book Value
12/16	96.83	14	9	7.72	0.95	36.22
12/15	106.67	18	12	6.91	0.76	31.59
12/14	86.69	18	10	5.26	0.61	25.66
12/13	69.42	18	9	4.05	0.49	20.65
12/12	37.42	12	7	3.07	0.47	16.67
Annual Growth	26.8%	—	—	25.9%	19.2%	21.4%

Live Nation Entertainment Inc

Live Nation Entertainment holds center stage as the world's largest ticket seller and promoter of live entertainment. The company significantly expanded its ticketing services with the purchase of Ticketmaster Entertainment. The firm owns or operates about 195 venues in North America and Europe. Annually about 550 million people attend some 250000 Live Nation events. Live Nation also owns House of Blues venues through HOB Entertainment and dozens of prestigious concert halls. In addition Live Nation owns a stake in more than 500 artists' music including albums tours and merchandise.

Operations

Live Nation's reportable segments are Concerts Ticketing Artist Nation and Sponsorship & Advertising. About 90% of its revenue comes from its Concerts and Ticketing segments.

Its Concerts segment involves global promotion of live music events in its owned and operated venues and in rented third-party venues the operation and management of music venues and the production of music festivals across the world.

The Ticketing segment is primarily an agency business that sells tickets for events on behalf of its clients and retains a convenience charge and order processing fee for its services.

The company's Artist Nation segment provides management services to music artists in exchange for a commission on the earnings of these artists.

Its Sponsorship & Advertising segment employs a sales force that creates and maintains relationships with sponsors that allow businesses to reach customers through Live Nation's concert venue artist relationship and ticketing assets including advertising on its websites.

Geographic Reach

Live Nation owns operates or leases more than 195 venues located throughout the world. The company generates about 70% of revenue from domestic operations.

Sales and Marketing

Live Nation promotes its events and sells tickets through websites (www.livenation.com and www.ticketmaster.com) they also sell tickets in numerous retail outlets and call centers and sold over 480 million tickets in 2015. Ticketmaster serves more than 12000 clients worldwide.

The company spent about $312 million on advertising and promotions during fiscal 2016. That was an increase compared to the $275 million Live Nation spent on advertising during 2015.

Financial Performance

Live Nation's revenue has been trending up across recent fiscal years. It reported $8.35 billion in revenue for fiscal 2016 up from $7.25 billion in fiscal 2015 and $6.87 billion in fiscal 2014. The company's net income was $2.94 million in fiscal 2016 which was a big improvement compared to the $32.5 million net loss Live Nation suffered in fiscal 2015. The company ended fiscal 2016 with $760 million in cash from operations.

Strategy

Live Nation has used joint ventures to expand its operations. The company continues to strengthen its core operations further expanding into additional global markets and optimizing cost structure. Its strategy is to expand its concert platform by adding artists and venues drive conversion of ticket sales through social and mobile channels and work to grow its sponsorship and advertising revenue.

Mergers and Acquisitions

In 2017 Ticketmaster acquired Ticketpro based in Halifax Nova Scotia Canada. Ticketpro is a leading provider of ticketing services with active operations in Belarus Bulgaria Canada Chile the Czech Republic Greece Hungary Malaysia Poland and the Slovak Republic. The acquisition offered Ticketmaster the opportunity to extend its international ticketing business activities into another key Central European market within the Czech Republic as well as complement the development of its existing business in neighboring Poland.

In 2017 the firm acquired Cuffe & Taylor one of the UK?s fastest-growing promoters focused on festivals and promoting artists in novel and non-traditional outdoor venues. The acquisition will help Live Nation expand its overall presence across the UK regional markets.

HISTORY

Robert Sillerman began his career teaching advertisers how to reach young consumers. He started investing in radio and TV stations and founded SFX Broadcasting (named for a scrambling of his initials) in 1992. In early 1997 the firm entered the live entertainment field with the formation of SFX Concerts and the purchase of concert promoter Delsener/Slater.

When SFX Broadcasting agreed to be bought in 1997 by Capstar Broadcasting 87% controlled by investment firm Hicks Muse Tate & Furst (now HM Capital) SFX Entertainment was formed to house the live entertainment operations (it was spun off in 1998). In 1998 the company continued its rapid acquisition rate with the purchases of sports marketing and management team FAME New England concert promoter Don Law and national concert producer PACE Entertainment.

In 1999 the company bought concert promoter The Cellar Door Companies (which almost doubled SFX's size) sports marketing firm Integrated Sports International sporting event management company The Marquee Group sports talent agency Hendricks Management 50% of urban-music producer A.H. Enterprises and troubled theatrical producer Livent. SFX also made its first foray abroad through its purchase of Apollo Leisure a UK-based live entertainment firm. The company rolled all of its sports talent and marketing businesses into a new division SFX Sports Group that year.

In 2000 SFX jumped on the other side of the acquisition train when it was bought by radio station owner Clear Channel Communications for about $4 billion. Sillerman stepped down as chairman and CEO and was replaced by Clear Channel EVP Brian Becker. Later that year SFX acquired Philadelphia-based concert promoter and venue operator Electric Factory Concerts; Core Audience Entertainment Canada's second-largest concert promoter and events marketer; and the Cotter Group a North Carolina-based motorsports marketing agency.

In 2001 SFX acquired a majority interest in the International Hot Rod Association. It also bought professional golf talent agency Signature Sports Group. Later that year the company changed its name to Clear Channel Entertainment. It also continued expansion into Europe with the acquisition of Trident Agency and Milano Concerti music promotion businesses in Italy.

While operating as Clear Channel Entertainment Live Nation spent nearly $2 billion on acquisitions (Pace Entertainment Livent) almost single-handedly consolidating the live entertainment industry.

Before being spun off in December 2005 the company changed its name to CCE Spinco then Live Nation. Also that year Randall Mays became chairman and Michael Rapino replaced Becker as CEO. As part of the Clear Channel spinoff the company relocated from Houston to headquarters in tony Beverly Hills. It trimmed the fat by shutting down operating divisions such as museum exhibitions and music publishing (and laying off about 400 employees in the process) in order to focus on its core businesses of live music concerts venue management and website brand development.

In 2006 the company acquired rival HOB Entertainment for $354 million. Live Nation used the acquisition to expand its presence in the midsized venue business and fill in geographic gaps in its existing amphitheater network. As part of the deal Live Nation gained high-profile House of Blues-branded music venues such as San Francisco's Fillmore Auditorium Jones Beach in New York and London's Apollo Theatre and Wembley Arena. The company subsequently began re-branding many of its midsize clubs "Fillmore" after the San Francisco venue.

The company had in 2005 formed Delirium Concert LP a joint venture with Cirque du Soleil. The Delirium tour began in 2006. The following year Live Nation signed a $120 million deal with pop icon Madonna. Through its North American Music segment in 2007 Live Nation promoted or produced some 10000 live music events including tours for Van Halen Dave Matthews Band and Kenny Chesney. International Music operations for the year included Cirque De Soleil's Delirium as well as UK's Reading Festival . Also in 2007 the company produced global tours for legends such as The Police The Rolling Stones Genesis and The Who and presented some 5000 theatrical performances such as the UK touring production of Chicago through its Global Theater operations.

In 2008 the company divested itself of its North American theatrical assets. Later that year the company signed pacts with U2 and Jay-Z. Michael Cohl chairman and Live Nation Artists chief who spearheaded the deals later resigned over conflicts with CEO Rapino. Also in 2008 the company sold its motor sports operations. In early 2010 the company acquired Ticketmaster Entertainment and Live Nation changed its name to Live Nation Entertainment.

EXECUTIVES

President House of Blues Entertainment, Ronald (Ron) Bension, age 62

EVP General Counsel and Secretary, Michael G. Rowles, age 52, $750,000 total compensation

Co-President North America Concerts, Mark Campana, age 59

CEO and Director, Michael (Mike) Rapino, age 52, $2,300,000 total compensation

Chairman Global Music and President Global Touring, Arthur Fogel, age 64

President and COO, Joe Berchtold, age 52, $1,100,000 total compensation

President International and Emerging Markets, Alan Ridgeway, age 50, $730,025 total compensation

CFO, Kathy Willard, age 51, $850,000 total compensation

President Media and Sponsorship, Russell Wallach, age 51
President Live Nation Europe - Concerts, John Reid, age 55
EVP Mergers and Acquisitions and Strategic Finance, John Hopmans, age 58
President Ticketmaster North America, Jared Smith, age 39
Co-President North America Concerts, Bob Roux, age 59
President Ticketmaster International, Mark Yovich, age 42
CIO, David Huckabay
President Production Film and Television, Heather Parry
Regional Vice President, Marc Abend
Vice President National Sales, Craig Hoover
Vice President Finance, Katherine Porter
Vice President Finance West Coast, Reuben Sanchez
Vice President Marketing, Danielle Engel
Regional Vice President Northeast Sales, Jeff Wallace
Vice President Legal Affairs, Ellie Schwimmer
Senior Vice President of Global Information Technology Financial Systems, Tim Moran
Senior Vice President Audit and Compliance, Brad Nelson
Regional Vice President, Robert Scolaro
Vice President, Stacie George
Vice President Production New York Music, Craig Goetsch
Vice President of Finance and Accounting House of Blues, Nathan Scott
Senior Vice President Finance, Jeremy Lawson
Vice President Accounting, Maria Moy
Vice President Latin Programming Touring, Manuel Moran
Vice President Planning, George Duran
Senior Vice President, Jorge Ferradas
Vice President Sponsorship Sales, Tobias Ekman
Regional Vice President of Finance, Frank Brayer
Senior Vice President Chief Information Security Officer, Jonathan Chow
Vice President Production, Leslie Holland
Senior Vice President Human Resources, Laura Morton-rowe
Vice President Information Technology Services, David Lucas
Executive Vice President, Felix Mussenden
Senior Vice President of Production, Stacey Harper
Senior Vice President and Treasurer, Bill Lowe
Executive Vice President Operations, Robert Simeone
Senior Vice President Marketing, Jackie Wilgar
Vice President Marketing Midwest, Jon Reens
Senior Vice President, Matt Prieshoff
Senior Vice President, Rich Levy
Executive Vice President Strategic Alliances, Kevin Chernett
Senior Vice President Administration, Linda Gross
Vice President of Marketing, Dave Niedbalski
Vice President Marketing, Kim Shiver
Executive Vice President, John Carnahan
Regional Vice President, Rob Scolaro
Vice President Midwest Music, Dan Kemer
Vice President, Michael McGaw
Vice President of Business Development and Strategy, Christopher Sumner
Regional Vice President, Louis Giangola
Vice President Business Development, Patti Kim
Vice President Pricing and Distribution, John Ketchum
Vice President, Brandon Martinez
Senior Vice President, Greg Gillin
Senior Vice President Sales and Special Events, Deirdre McCready
Senior Vice President, Bryan Dockett
Vice President, Harvey Cohen
Vice President Brand Strategist, Denise Quattrochi

Vice President of Foundation Room House of Blues, Victor Sutter
Vice President, Julie Jin
SENIOR VICE PRESIDENT BOOKING, Jon Hampton
Senior Vice President Media and Sponsorship, Jon Landa
Chairman, Gregory B. (Greg) Maffei, age 56
Auditors: Ernst & Young LLP

LOCATIONS

HQ: Live Nation Entertainment Inc
9348 Civic Center Drive, Beverly Hills, CA 90210
Phone: 310 867-7000
Web: www.livenation.com; www.ticketmaster.com

2016 Sales

	$ mil.	% of total
Domestic operations	5,788	69
Foreign operation:		
UK operations	683	8
Other operations	1,882	23
Total	**8,354**	**100**

PRODUCTS/OPERATIONS

2016 Sales

	$ mil.	% of total
Concerts	5,874	69
Ticketing	1,827	22
Artist Nation	421	5
Sponsorship & advertising	377	4
Other revenue	8	-
Eliminations	(154.4)	
Total	**8,354**	**100**

COMPETITORS

Brillstein
CAA
Dodger Properties
Feld Entertainment
IMG
International Creative Management
Jujamcyn Theaters
MSG Networks
Nederlander Producing Company
Octagon
On Stage Entertainment
Palace Sports & Entertainment
Ryman
SMG Management
Shubert Organization
TBA Global
United Talent
Universal Music Group
Warner Music
WestwoodOne
William Morris Endeavor Entertainment

HISTORICAL FINANCIALS

Company Type: Public

Income Statement

FYE: December 31

	REVENUE ($ mil.)	NET INCOME ($ mil.)	NET PROFIT MARGIN	EMPLOYEES
12/16	8,354	2	0.0%	8,300
12/15	7,245	(32)	—	7,700
12/14	6,866	(90)	—	14,000
12/13	6,478	(43)	—	7,400
12/12	5,819	(163)	—	7,100
Annual Growth	**9.5%**	**—**	**—**	**4.0%**

2016 Year-End Financials

Debt ratio: 34.20%
Return on equity: 0.25%
Cash ($ mil.): 1,526
Current ratio: 1.09
Long-term debt ($ mil.): 2,259
No. of shares (mil.): 204
Dividends
Yield: —
Payout: —
Market value ($ mil.): 5,428

	STOCK PRICE ($) FY Close	P/E High/Low	Earnings	PER SHARE ($) Dividends	Book Value
12/16	26.60	— —	(0.23)	0.00	5.52
12/15	24.57	— —	(0.33)	0.00	6.11
12/14	26.11	— —	(0.49)	0.00	6.45
12/13	19.76	— —	(0.22)	0.00	7.06
12/12	9.31	— —	(0.87)	0.00	7.10
Annual Growth	**30.0%**	**— —**			**(6.1%)**

Live Oak Bancshares Inc

Auditors: Dixon Hughes Goodman LLP

LOCATIONS

HQ: Live Oak Bancshares Inc
1741 Tiburon Drive, Wilmington, NC 28403
Phone: 910 790-5867
Web: www.liveoakbank.com

HISTORICAL FINANCIALS

Company Type: Public

Income Statement

FYE: December 31

	ASSETS ($ mil.)	NET INCOME ($ mil.)	INCOME AS % OF ASSETS	EMPLOYEES
12/16	1,755	13	0.8%	425
12/15	1,052	20	2.0%	366
12/14	673	10	1.5%	263
12/13	430	28	6.5%	
12/12	342	16	4.7%	
Annual Growth	**50.5%**	**(3.8%)**	**—**	**—**

2016 Year-End Financials

Debt ratio: 1.59%
Return on equity: 6.50%
Cash ($ mil.): 245
Current ratio: —
Long-term debt ($ mil.): —
No. of shares (mil.): 34
Dividends
Yield: 0.0%
Payout: 17.9%
Market value ($ mil.): 634

	STOCK PRICE ($) FY Close	P/E High/Low	Earnings	PER SHARE ($) Dividends	Book Value
12/16	18.50	50 30	0.39	0.07	6.51
12/15	14.20	31 20	0.65	0.02	5.84
Annual Growth	**6.8%**	**— —**	**(12.0%)**	**36.8%**	**2.8%**

LKQ Corp

LKQ distributes replacement parts and components needed to repair passenger cars and trucks. It's one of the leading aftermarket parts suppliers in the US through subsidiary Keystone Automotive. LKQ also offers reconditioned remanufactured and refurbished parts including wheels bumpers mirrors and engines as well as recycled parts that are reclaimed from salvage vehicles. Customers include collision repair and mechanical repair shops. Additionally LKQ operates self-service retail yards that allow customers to come in search through and buy recycled auto parts. LKQ was formed in 1998.

Operations

LKQ operates through three reportable segments: North America (more than 50%) Europe (almost 35%) and Specialty (15%).

North America is composed of its wholesale operations which consist of aftermarket and salvage operations and self service retail operations.

Europe capitalizes on the large and fragmented aftermarket mechanical replacement parts market in Europe and also complements its existing operations in the UK and the Benelux region.

Specialty serves major markets in the US and Canada focusing on the following six product segments: truck and off-road; speed and performance; RV; towing; wheels tires and performance handling; and miscellaneous accessories.

Geographic Reach

Headquartered in Chicago LKQ operates through roughly 1340 facilities including 550 facilities in the US and 790 facilities in 20 other countries. The majority of LKQ?s operations are conducted in the US and its European operations are located in the UK the Netherlands Belgium France Sweden and Norway. The US is its largest market accounting for more than 60% of total revenue.

Sales and Marketing

LKQ sells its products to wholesale customers that include collision and mechanical repair shops and new and used car dealerships as well as to retail customers. Customers of self service yards are frequently do-it-yourself mechanics small independent repair shops auto rebuilders and resellers.

The company markets its products directly to customers through sales personnel e-commerce partners and distributors who in turn sell to customers. LKQ promotes through marketing programs which include: catalogs advertising sponsorships and promotional activities product level marketing and online initiatives.

Financial Performance

LKQ has achieved unprecedented growth over the years with revenues jumping 19% to peak at a record-setting $8.6 billion in 2016. The growth was fueled by a 21% spike in parts and services revenues. This was attributed to contributions from acquisitions and organic growth.

Along with its revenues net income grew 10% to reach $464 million in 2016 another company milestone. This was attributed to the higher revenues about $8 million it earned from discontinued operations (net of tax) and a more marginal loss from unconsolidated subsidiaries compared to the previous year.

Similarly cash flow from operating activities has increased the last few years jumping 20% to $635 million in 2016. This was the result of acquisition-related growth and organic growth.

Strategy

Key to the company's growth strategy are acquisitions. Indeed LKQ has completed more than 200 acquisitions in the US and abroad since its founding in 1998.

The company has also worked on its supply chain expanding its network of parts warehouses and dismantling plants in major metros and operating a distribution system that allows for order fulfillment from regional warehouses located across the US and Canada. It also is expanding its branch network in the UK.

In North America the company has expanded its network of parts warehouses and dismantling plants in major metropolitan areas. In Europe the company focuses on the development of existing branch networks in the UK and Benelux and also looks to add locations. The company has undertaken a major project to expand its distribution

capabilities in Tamworth UK. The project is expected to be completed in 2018.

Mergers and Acquisitions

In one of its largest acquisitions to date LKQ paid $1.1 billion for Rhiag-Inter Auto Parts Italia S.p.A (Rhiag) a distributor of aftermarket spare parts for passenger cars and commercial vehicles in Italy Czech Republic Slovakia Switzerland Hungary Romania Ukraine Bulgaria Poland and Spain. The acquisition significantly expanded LKQ?s geographic presence in continental Europe by expanding its footprint by 10 countries.

In 2016 the company acquired 27% of Mekonomen AB for $181 million. Headquartered in Sweden Mekonomen is an independent car parts and service chain in the Nordic region of Europe offering a range of quality products including spare parts and accessories for cars and workshop services for consumers and businesses. The deal gave LKQ a strong brand and a diverse operating model for selling aftermarket automotive parts and accessories in Europe.

LKQ also in 2016 acquired Pittsburgh Glass Works (PGW) for $635 million. PGW is a global distributor and manufacturer of automotive glass products. With the acquisition the company entered into the sizable automotive glass market.

EXECUTIVES

CEO and Managing Director European Operations, John S. Quinn, age 58, $565,000 total compensation
SVP Development, Walter P. Hanley, age 51, $400,000 total compensation
President and CEO, Dominick P. (Nick) Zarcone, age 58, $1,000,000 total compensation
SVP and CIO, Ashley T. Brooks
SVP Operations Wholesale Parts Division, Justin L. Jude, age 40
EVP and CFO, Varun Laroyia
Vice President Finance And Chief Accounting Officer, Michael S Clark
National Account Manager, David Bowers
National Account Manager, Tom Flood
National Account Manager, Paul Houston
Chairman, Joseph M. Holsten, age 64
Auditors: Deloitte & Touche LLP

LOCATIONS

HQ: LKQ Corp
500 West Madison Street, Suite 2800, Chicago, IL 60661
Phone: 312 621-1950
Web: www.lkqcorp.com

2016 Sales

	$ mil.	% of total
United States	5,226	61
United Kingdom	1,390	16
Other countries	1,966	23
Total	**8,584**	**100**

PRODUCTS/OPERATIONS

2016 Sales

	$ mil.	% of total
North America	4,471	52
Europe	2,920	34
Specialty	1,196	14
Eliminations	(4.8)	-
Total	**8,584**	**100**

2016 Sales

	$ mil.	% of total
Aftermarket other new and refurbished products	6,441	75
Recycled remanufactured and related products and services	1,703	20
Other	439	5
Total	**8,584**	**100**

Products & Services

Accessories
Fleet Service
Refinishing
Vehicle & Salvage Disposal
Warranty
Wheels

COMPETITORS

Cardone Industries	Halfords
Copart	Jasper Engines
Delphi Automotive Systems	Kirk's Automotive
	O'Reilly Automotive
Federal-Mogul	Titan International
Fred Jones Enterprises	U.S. Auto Parts
Genuine Parts	Valeo
Hahn Automotive	

HISTORICAL FINANCIALS

Company Type: Public

Income Statement

FYE: December 31

	REVENUE ($ mil.)	NET INCOME ($ mil.)	NET PROFIT MARGIN	EMPLOYEES
12/16	8,584	463	5.4%	42,500
12/15	7,192	423	5.9%	31,100
12/14	6,740	381	5.7%	29,500
12/13	5,062	311	6.2%	23,800
12/12	4,122	261	6.3%	20,300
Annual Growth	**20.1%**	**15.4%**	**—**	**20.3%**

2016 Year-End Financials

Debt ratio: 40.25%	No. of shares (mil.): 307
Return on equity: 14.11%	Dividends
Cash ($ mil.): 227	Yield: —
Current ratio: 2.95	Payout: —
Long-term debt ($ mil.): 3,275	Market value ($ mil.): 9,426

	STOCK PRICE ($) FY Close	P/E High/Low		PER SHARE ($) Earnings	Dividends	Book Value
12/16	30.65	24	16	1.50	0.00	11.19
12/15	29.63	23	17	1.38	0.00	10.19
12/14	28.12	26	20	1.25	0.00	8.97
12/13	32.90	33	19	1.02	0.00	7.81
12/12	21.10	45	21	0.87	0.00	6.60
Annual Growth	**9.8%**	**—**	**—**	**14.6%**	**—**	**14.1%**

Lockheed Martin Corp

Auditors: Ernst & Young LLP

LOCATIONS

HQ: Lockheed Martin Corp
6801 Rockledge Drive, Bethesda, MD 20817-1877
Phone: 301 897-6000
Web: www.lockheedmartin.com

HISTORICAL FINANCIALS

Company Type: Public

Income Statement

FYE: December 31

	REVENUE ($ mil.)	NET INCOME ($ mil.)	NET PROFIT MARGIN	EMPLOYEES
12/17	51,048	2,002	3.9%	100,000
12/16	47,248	5,302	11.2%	97,000
12/15	46,132	3,605	7.8%	126,000
12/14	45,600	3,614	7.9%	112,000
12/13	45,358	2,981	6.6%	115,000
Annual Growth	**3.0%**	**(9.5%)**	**—**	**(3.4%)**

2017 Year-End Financials

Debt ratio: 30.66%
Return on equity: 483.57%
Cash ($ mil.): 2,861
Current ratio: 1.38
Long-term debt ($ mil.): 13,513

No. of shares (mil.): 284
Dividends
  Yield: 0.0%
  Payout: 108.2%
Market value ($ mil.): 91,178

	STOCK PRICE ($) FY Close	P/E High/Low		PER SHARE ($) Earnings	Dividends	Book Value
12/17	321.05	46	36	6.89	7.46	(2.40)
12/16	249.94	15	12	17.49	6.77	5.23
12/15	217.15	19	16	11.46	6.15	10.22
12/14	192.57	17	13	11.21	5.49	10.83
12/13	148.66	16	9	9.13	4.78	15.42
Annual Growth	21.2%	—	—	(6.8%)	11.8%	—

Loews Corp.

When it comes to diversification Loews definitely has the low-down. The holding company's main interest is insurance through publicly traded subsidiary CNA Financial which offers commercial property/casualty coverage. Other wholly owned and partially owned holdings include hotels in the US and Canada through its Loews Hotels subsidiary. Its energy holdings include contract oil-drilling operator Diamond Offshore Drilling (which operates roughly 25 offshore oil rigs) and interstate natural gas transmission pipeline systems operator Boardwalk Pipeline. Loews is controlled and run by the Tisch family including co-chairmen and cousins Andrew and Jonathan.

Operations

Loews' flagship unit CNA Financial is the company's cash cow accounting for more than 70% of its annual revenue. Rig operator Diamond Offshore Drilling represents more than 10% of annual sales while pipeline systems operator Boardwalk Pipeline accounts for most of the rest. Hotels contribute just 5% of annual sales.

CNA is organized into four divisions: Specialty (professional financial and specialty property/casualty products) Commercial (property/casualty coverage for businesses) International and Other Non-Core (primarily run-off long-term care businesses). CNA's affiliates include The Continental Insurance Company and CNA Surety. While commercial insurance is generally stable stuff CNA has faced the same downturn other big insurers have seen over the past few years. With commercial lending still sluggish businesses have less to insure and fewer workers to cover.

Diamond Offshore Drilling owns and operates rigs located offshore of six countries including the US. Boardwalk Pipeline consists of interstate natural gas pipeline systems originating in the Gulf Coast region Oklahoma and Arkansas and extending north and east; natural gas storage facilities in four states; and natural gas liquids pipelines and storage facilities in Louisiana and Texas.

Loews Hotels operates a chain of 25 hotels — 24 in the US and one in Canada.

Geographic Reach

Through its subsidiaries diversified Loews has operations in Canada and beyond. Its CNA Financial unit operates primarily in the US. Loews Hotels has 24 properties in the US and one property in Canada while Diamond Offshore has drilling rigs located off the coasts of about five countries in addition to the US and markets its products worldwide. Boardwalk Pipeline operates more than 14000 miles of pipelines in 13 US states and serves customers in the northeastern and southeastern US.

Sales and Marketing

Loews' largest division CNA Financial markets its products through independent brokers agents and managing general underwriters. CNA Financial targets professionals and small to large businesses as well as insurers associations and other groups.

Diamond Offshore's main customers include oil and gas companies ranging from large corporations to independent businesses as well as government-owned entities. Major customers include Petrobras Anadarko and Exxon Mobil . Boardwalk Pipeline serves gas producers distributors transporters and marketers as well as electric and industrial plants.

Financial Performance

Loews' revenue has been slipping since 2013. It fell 2% to $13.1 billion in 2016 primarily as a result of lower contract drilling revenues. Otherwise insurance premiums remained flat and net investment income rose while total investment gains returned to the black..

Net income which had taken a big hit in 2015 rebounded and then some the following year. It rose 151% to $654 million. This was largely due to a decline in contract drilling expenses.

Cash flow from operations which has fluctuated declined 37% to $2.3 billion in 2016 (despite the higher net income). This was driven by negative net changes in operating assets and liabilities such as trading securities as well as adjustment to net cash providing by operating activities including provisions for deferred income taxes.

Strategy

Each Loews business pursues customer growth in their various industries. CNA Financial for instance is working to grow its base of commercial customers in each of the small midsized and large account categories. It has been strengthening its core property/casualty operations while exiting underperforming segments. As a group Loews has been conservative lately with its acquisition activity. It completed its first purchase in a while when it bought Consolidated Container Company in 2017.

Mergers and Acquisitions

In 2017 Loews Corporation acquired Consolidated Container Company (CCC) a Georgia-based rigid plastic packaging manufacturer for $1.2 billion. With nearly 60 manufacturing facilities CCC serves the food beverage and household chemical industries in North America. After the purchase the group created a new segment named Loews Packaging Group.

HISTORY

In 1946 Larry Tisch who earned a business degree from New York University at age 18 dropped out of Harvard Law to run his parents' New Jersey resort. Younger brother Bob joined him in creating a new entity Tisch Hotels. The company bought two Atlantic City hotels in 1952 quickly making them profitable. Later Tisch purchased such illustrious hotels as the Mark Hopkins The Drake the Belmont Plaza and the Regency.

Moving beyond hotels the brothers bought money-losing companies with poor management. Discarding the management along with underperforming divisions they tightened operational control and eliminated such frills as fancy offices company planes and even memos.

In 1960 Tisch Hotels gained control of MGM's ailing Loew's Theaters to take advantage of their desirable city locations. The company then began demolishing more than 50 stately movie palaces and selling the land to developers. In 1968 the company bought Lorillard the oldest US tobacco company; it shed Lorillard's unprofitable pet food and candy operations and reversed its slipping tobacco market share.

Taking the Loews name in 1971 the company bought CNA Financial in 1974. The Tisch method turned losses of more than $200 million to profits of more than $100 million the very next year. It bought Bulova Watch in 1979 and guided by Larry's son Andrew it gradually returned to profitability.

In the early 1980s Loews entered the energy business by investing in oil supertankers. The company sold its last movie theaters in 1985. Then in 1987 Loews helped CBS fend off a takeover attempt by Ted Turner and ended up with about 25% of the company. Larry became president of the broadcaster.

In 1989 Loews acquired Diamond M Offshore a Texas drilling company and with the acquisition of Odeco Drilling in 1992 the company amassed the world's largest fleet of offshore rigs. The next year Loews grouped its drilling interests as Diamond Offshore Drilling.

In 1994 CNA expanded its insurance empire buying The Continental Corp. The next year Loews sold its interest in CBS and the following year Diamond Offshore Drilling merged with Arethusa (Off-Shore) Limited.

As deft as the Tisch brothers had been in accumulating their riches Larry's bearish investment strategy (short-selling stocks) cost Loews in the late 1990s (more than $900 million alone during 1997's bull market). Larry and Bob retired as co-CEOs at the end of 1998; Larry's son James already president and COO became CEO.

That year Lorillard signed on to the 46-state tobacco lawsuit settlement; the first payment cost the company $325 million (payments continue until 2025). Facing a softened insurance market CNA sold unprofitable lines to focus on commercial insurance; in 1999 it transferred its auto and homeowners lines to Allstate (it continues writing and renewing these policies) and put its life and life reinsurance units up for sale in 2000. Also that year Lorillard was hit with $16 billion of a record-breaking $144 billion punitive damage award in a smokers' class-action suit in Florida. CNA Financial paid out over $450 million in 2001-02 for claims related to the attacks on the World Trade Center.

In 2004 the company continued to expand its natural resource offerings when its subsidiary Boardwalk Pipelines (formerly known as TGT Pipeline) acquired Gulf South Pipeline which operates natural gas pipeline and gathering systems in Texas Louisiana Mississippi Alabama and Florida including several major supply hubs. Loews had acquired gas pipeline operator Texas Gas Transmission in 2003. Texas Gas operates natural gas pipeline systems reaching from the Louisiana Gulf Coast and East Texas north through Louisiana Arkansas Mississippi Tennessee Kentucky Indiana and into Ohio and Illinois.

Tobacco had long been a staple in Loews' portfolio until the company kicked the habit. Prior to quitting the company kept its 62% ownership of Lorillard rolled up as Carolina Group and traded it as a tracking subsidiary. Lorillard which included the Kent Newport and True cigarette brands in the US accounted for more than 20% of Loews' revenues. However after a steady stream of tobacco-related litigation the company spun Lorillard off into an independent public company in 2008 eliminating the Carolina Group and exiting the industry. Additionally while accessories make the outfit in 2008 Loews slipped its Bulova subsidiary off of its wrist and handed it to competitor Citizen Watch for $250 million.

Larry Tisch died at the age of 80 in 2003. Chairman Bob Tisch died of cancer in late 2005. Tisch also was co-owner of the New York Giants of the National Football League.

In keeping with the Loews strategy of acquiring what can be turned around letting go of what can't and the wisdom to know the difference the company spent $4 billion to acquire oil and gas exploration operator HighMount Exploration & Production and disposed of its tobacco interests and Bulova subsidiary in 2008.

EXECUTIVES

Vice President, Herbert Hofmann
Co-Chairman Loews Corporation and Chairman and CEO Loews Hotels, Jonathan M. Tisch, age 63, $975,000 total compensation
President and CEO, James S. Tisch, age 65, $975,000 total compensation
SVP and CFO, David B. Edelson, age 57, $975,000 total compensation
SVP and Chief Investment Officer, Richard W. Scott, age 63
SVP, Kenneth I. Siegel, age 60, $975,000 total compensation
VP Information Technology, Herb E. Hofmann
Senior Vice President Food and Beverage, Mark Weiss
Senior Vice President, Gail Gordon
National Sales Manager, Jay Heiskell
Vice President Talent Management, Jenny Duos
Vice President Loews Cna Holdings Investments, Winifred Harrison
Senior Vice President of Sales, David Wiener
Senior Vice President, Marc Shapiro
Vice President, Ramu Venkatachalam
Vice President Of Information Technology, Imelda Liddiad
National Sales Manager, David Brokaw
National Sales Manager, Susan Mack
National Sales Manager, Jay Smith
National Sales Manager, Christopher McLaren
National Sales Manager, Rania Hammad
Vice President of Sales and Marketing, Christopher Cawley
Vice President Operations Loews Hotels Universal Orlando, David Bartek
Vice President Accounting and Assistant Corporate Controller, Tracy Bress
National Sales Manager, Adam Crow
National Sales Manager, Cristina Godwin
National Sales Manager, Danielle Kroungold
National Sales Manager, Mike Westfield
National Sales Manager, Anthony Nelson
National Sales Manager, Melanie Lee
National Sales Manager, Jey Dutertre
Co-Chairman, Andrew H. Tisch, age 68
Vice Chairman Loews Hotels And Resorts, Paul W Whetsell
Treasurer, Andrew Stegen
Auditors: DELOITTE & TOUCHE LLP

LOCATIONS

HQ: Loews Corp.
667 Madison Avenue, New York, NY 10065-8087
Phone: 212 521-2000
Web: www.loews.com

PRODUCTS/OPERATIONS

2016 Revenues

	$ mil.	% of total
Insurance premiums	6,924	53
Net investment income	2,135	16
Contract drilling revenues	1,525	12
Other	2,471	19
Investment gains	50	-
Total	**13,105**	**100**

2016 Revenues

	$ mil.	% of total
CNA Financial	9,384	72
Diamond Offshore	1,589	12

Boardwalk Pipeline	1,316	10
Loews Hotels	667	5
Corporate & other	149	1
Total	**13,105**	**100**

Selected Subsidiaries

Boardwalk Pipeline Partners LP (51%)
CNA Financial Corporation (90%)
Diamond Offshore Drilling Inc. (53%)
Loews Hotels Holding Corporation (100%)

COMPETITORS

AIG	Noble
American Financial Group	Statoil
Berkshire Hathaway	The Hartford
Chubb Limited	Travelers Companies
Cincinnati Financial	W. R. Berkley

HISTORICAL FINANCIALS
Company Type: Public

Income Statement
FYE: December 31

	ASSETS ($ mil.)	NET INCOME ($ mil.)	INCOME AS % OF ASSETS	EMPLOYEES
12/17	79,586	1,164	1.5%	18,100
12/16	76,594	654	0.9%	15,800
12/15	76,029	260	0.3%	16,700
12/14	78,367	591	0.8%	17,510
12/13	79,939	595	0.7%	18,175
Annual Growth	**(0.1%)**	**18.3%**	**—**	**(0.1%)**

2017 Year-End Financials
Debt ratio: 14.14%
Return on equity: 6.23%
Cash ($ mil.): 472
Current ratio: —
Long-term debt ($ mil.): —
No. of shares (mil.): 332
Dividends
 Yield: 0.0%
 Payout: 7.2%
Market value ($ mil.): 16,614

	STOCK PRICE ($) FY Close	P/E High/Low		PER SHARE ($) Earnings	Dividends	Book Value
12/17	50.03	15	13	3.45	0.25	57.83
12/16	46.83	25	18	1.93	0.25	53.96
12/15	38.40	59	49	0.72	0.25	51.67
12/14	42.02	31	25	1.55	0.25	51.70
12/13	48.24	32	27	1.53	0.25	50.28
Annual Growth	**0.9%**	**—**	**—**	**22.5%**	**(0.0%)**	**3.6%**

LORD BALTIMORE CAPITAL CORPORATION

LOCATIONS

HQ: LORD BALTIMORE CAPITAL CORPORATION
6225 SMITH AVE STE B100, BALTIMORE, MD
212093623
Phone: 410 415-7600
Web: WWW.LORDBALTIMOREPROP.COM

HISTORICAL FINANCIALS
Company Type: Private

Income Statement
FYE: December 31

	ASSETS ($ mil.)	NET INCOME ($ mil.)	INCOME AS % OF ASSETS	EMPLOYEES
12/07	1,803	(3)	—	40
12/05	1,532	59	3.9%	—
12/04	1,469	0	0.0%	—
12/03	1,235	62	5.0%	—
Annual Growth	**9.9%**	**—**	**—**	**—**

2007 Year-End Financials
Debt ratio: ——
Return on equity: (-5.10%)
Cash ($ mil.): 8
Current ratio: ——
Long-term debt ($ mil.): ——
Dividends
 Yield: —
 Payout: —
Market value ($ mil.): —

Lowe's Companies Inc

Lowe's Companies has evolved from a regional hardware store into a nationwide chain of home improvement superstores bent on international expansion. The #2 US home improvement chain (after The Home Depot) Lowe's operates 1820 stores in the US along with some 300 in Canada and 10 in Mexico as well as an e-commerce site. Its stores sell roughly 37000 products for DIY-ers and professionals for home improvement and repair projects such as lumber paint plumbing and electrical supplies tools and gardening products as well as appliances outdoor power equipment home fashions and furniture. Lowe's is also the second-largest US home appliance retailer after Sears.

HISTORY

Lowe's Companies was founded in 1921 as Mr. L. S. Lowe's North Wilkesboro Hardware in North Wilkesboro North Carolina. A family operation by 1945 Mr. Lowe's store (which also sold groceries snuff and harnesses) was run by his son Jim and his son-in-law H. Carl Buchan. Buchan bought Lowe's share of the company in 1956 and incorporated as Lowe's North Wilkesboro Hardware; he wanted Lowe's as part of the company name because he liked the slogan "Lowe's Low Prices." The chain expanded from North Carolina into Tennessee Virginia and West Virginia. By 1960 Buchan had 15 stores and sales of $31 million — up $4 million from a decade before.

Buchan planned to create a profit-sharing plan for Lowe's employees but in 1960 he died of a heart attack at age 44. In 1961 Lowe's management and the executors of Buchan's estate established the Lowe's Employees Profit Sharing and Trust which bought Buchan's 89% of the company (later renamed Lowe's Companies). That year they financed the transaction through a public offering which diluted the employees' stock. Lowe's was listed on the NYSE in 1979.

Robert Strickland who had joined the company in 1957 became chairman in 1978. Revenues increased from $170 million in 1971 to more than $900 million with a net income of $25 million in 1979. Traditionally the majority of Lowe's business was in sales to professional homebuilders but in 1980 housing starts fell and company profits dropped. Concurrently The Home Depot introduced its low-price warehouse concept. Instead of building warehouse stores of its own Strickland changed the stores' layouts and by 1982 had redesigned half of the 229 stores to be more oriented toward do-it-yourself (DIY) consumers. The new designs featured softer lighting and displays of entire room layouts to appeal to women who made up over half of all DIY customers. In 1982 Lowe's made more than half of its sales to consumers for the first time in its history.

Although Lowe's had more than 300 stores by 1988 its outlets were only about 20000 sq. ft. (one-fifth the size of Home Depot's warehouse stores). By 1989 Lowe's which had continued to target contractors as well as DIYers was overtaken by Home Depot as the US's #1 home retail chain.

Since 1989 the company has focused on building larger stores taking a charge of $71 million in 1991 to phase out smaller stores and build warehouse outlets. In 1993 Lowe's opened 57 large stores (half were replacements for existing stores) almost doubling its total floor space.

The retailer opened 29 new stores in 1995. During 1996 Lowe's added a net of 37 stores and in 1997 it opened 42 stores in new markets. Also that year president and CEO Leonard Herring retired and was replaced by former COO Robert Tillman who also took the post of chairman when Strickland stepped down in 1998.

Also in 1998 the company entered a joint venture to sell an exclusive line of Kobalt-brand professional mechanics' tools produced by Snap-on and to better serve commercial customers began allowing them to special order items not stocked in stores. In addition Lowe's announced it would spend $1.5 billion over the next several years on a 100-store push into the western US. Lowe's westward expansion was fueled when it purchased Washington-based 38-store Eagle Hardware & Garden in 1999 in a stock swap deal worth $1.3 billion. The company gradually converted the Eagle stores into Lowe's.

In 2001 the company earmarked $2.4 billion of its $2.7 billion capital budget for store expansions and new distribution centers.

Robert Niblock was promoted from CFO to president in March 2003. Lowe's sold its some 30 outlets operating as The Contractor Yard to The Strober Organization in February 2004. In April 2004 the company opened its first predominantly urban-oriented store suited to the needs of city dwellers and building superintendents in Brooklyn.

Chairman and CEO Robert Tillman retired in January 2005. He was succeeded by president Robert Niblock.

Lowe's entered the Canadian market in 2007.

The home improvement chain expanded its distribution footprint in 2008 opening a regional distribution center in Pittston Pennsylvania and a flatbed distribution center in Purvis Mississippi.

During 2010 Lowe's opened its first location in Mexico (in Monterrey). In 2011 the company made a rare acquisition: online home-improvement retailer ATG Stores based in Kirkland Washington.

In 2013 the company acquired a majority stake of California-based Orchard Supply Hardware (OSH) adding 70 stores to the 110 stores that Lowe's already operated in California.

EXECUTIVES

Chairman President and CEO, Robert A. Niblock, age 54, $1,300,000 total compensation
Senior Vice President Store Operations South Central, Dennis Knowles
Vice President, Melissa Birdsong
CFO, Marshall A. Croom, age 56
President Orchard Supply Hardware, Lara L. Lee
Chief Supply Chain Officer, Brent G. Kirby

Chief Development Officer and President International, Richard D. Maltsbarger, age 41
Chief Customer Officer, Michael P. McDermott
CIO, Paul D. Ramsay, age 52
Managing Director LoweÂ's India, James A. Brandt
President and Managing Director LoweÂ's Mexico, Juan L. Pier Castell
President ATGStores.com, Michelle M. Newbery
President and CEO LoweÂ's Canada, Sylvain PrudÂ'homme
Vice President Public Affairs, Chris Ahearn
Senior Vice President, Troy Dally
Senior Vice President Store Operations, Kevin Measel
Call Center customer Service Director Vice President, Michael Jones
Senior Vice President, Michael Tummillo
Vice President Risk Management, Valerie Franco
Vice President Installed and Special Order Sales, Gary Gross
Vice President And Assistant General Counsel, Thomas Yih
Vice President Assistant General Counsel, Jeff Gray
Vice President Corporate Controller, Staci Dennis
Vice President of Client Services, Marian Craig
Merchandising Vice President Rough Plumbing and Electrical, Zach Miller
Senior Vice President, Belinda Rumple
Regional Vice President Distribution, Calvin Adams
Vice President and Assistant General Counsel, Reginald Henderson
Vice President Customer Experience, Brian Wolf
Vice President Of Store Operations, Stacey Ryan
Vice President Vendor Service Management, Ron Lutz
Vice President and General Man, Kevin Meagher
Senior Vice President Store Information technology, Robert F Wagner
Vice President Corporate Communication, Tracey Ahearn
Merchandising Vice President Flooring Division, Joseph Thomas
Vice President And Assistant General Counsel, Robert Oneale
Vice President Corporate Facilities, Troy Saunders
Vice President Real Estate Operations, Richard Goodman
Legal Secretary, Cindy Castine
Vice President of Merchandising, Ann Haines
Vice President of Transportation, Rick Gabrielson
Vice President of Operations, Jeffrey Blocker
Vice President Merchandising, Jeff Sain
Vice President, Joey Boley
Vice President Store Operations, Del Dryden
Vice President, Mike Riley
Vice President eCommerce and Digital Tech, Neelima Sharma
Svp Corp Finance-treasurer, Tiffany Mason
Auditors: Deloitte & Touche LLP

LOCATIONS

HQ: Lowe's Companies Inc
1000 Lowe's Blvd., Mooresville, NC 28117
Phone: 704 758-1000
Web: www.lowes.com

2017 Stores

	No.
United States	1,820
Canada	299
Mexico	10
Total	**2,129**

PRODUCTS/OPERATIONS

2017 Sales

	$ mil.	% of total
Lumber & Building Materials	8,399	13
Tools & Hardware	7,220	11
Appliances	7,037	11
Fashion Fixtures	6,307	10
Rough Plumbing & Electrical	5,744	9
Seasonal Living	4,253	7
Lawn & Garden	4,192	6
Paint	4,053	6
Millwork	3,729	6
Flooring	3,662	6
Kitchens	3,524	5
Outdoor Power Equipment	3,493	5
Home Fashions	2,611	4
Other	793	1
Total	**65,017**	**100**

Selected Product Categories

Appliances
Fashion Fixtures
Flooring
Home Fashions
Kitchens
Lawn & Garden
Lumber & Building Materials
Millwork
Outdoor Power Equipment
Paint
Rough Plumbing & Electrical
Seasonal Living
Tools & Hardware

Selected Services

Extended Protection Plans and Repair Services
Installed Sales

Selected Proprietary Brands

allen+roth
Aquasource
Garden Treasures
Harbor Breeze
Kobalt
Portfolio
Reliabilt
Top Choice
Utilitech

COMPETITORS

84 Lumber	Menard
Abbey Carpet	Northern Tool
Ace Hardware	RONA
Best Buy	Sears
CCA Global	Sherwin-Williams
Canadian Tire	Sutherland Lumber
Do it Best	True Value
HD Supply	Wal-Mart
Home Depot	Wolseley
McCoy Corp.	

HISTORICAL FINANCIALS

Company Type: Public

Income Statement

FYE: February 3

	REVENUE ($ mil.)	NET INCOME ($ mil.)	NET PROFIT MARGIN	EMPLOYEES
02/17*	65,017	3,093	4.8%	290,000
01/16	59,074	2,546	4.3%	270,000
01/15	56,223	2,698	4.8%	266,000
01/14	53,417	2,286	4.3%	262,000
02/13	50,521	1,959	3.9%	245,000
Annual Growth	**6.5%**	**12.1%**	**—**	**4.3%**

*Fiscal year change

2017 Year-End Financials

Debt ratio: 45.63%
Return on equity: 43.20%
Cash ($ mil.): 558
Current ratio: 1.00
Long-term debt ($ mil.): 14,394

No. of shares (mil.): 866
Dividends
　Yield: 1.8%
　Payout: 38.3%
Market value ($ mil.): 63,469

STOCK PRICE ($)		P/E	PER SHARE ($)		
FY Close		High/Low	Earnings	Dividends	Book Value
02/17*	73.29	24 18	3.47	1.33	7.43
01/16	71.66	28 24	2.73	1.07	8.41
01/15	67.76	26 16	2.71	0.87	10.38
01/14	46.29	24 17	2.14	0.70	11.51
02/13	38.56	23 15	1.69	0.62	12.48
Annual Growth	17.4%	— —	19.7%	21.0%	(12.2%)

*Fiscal year change

LUKOIL PAN AMERICAS, LLC

LOCATIONS

HQ: LUKOIL PAN AMERICAS, LLC
1095 AVE OF THE A, NEW YORK, NY 10036
Phone: 646 562-3600
Web: WWW.LUKOIL.COM

HISTORICAL FINANCIALS

Company Type: Private

Income Statement
FYE: December 31

	REVENUE ($ mil.)	NET INCOME ($ mil.)	NET PROFIT MARGIN	EMPLOYEES
12/08	4,745	5	0.1%	58
12/07	4,717	3	0.1%	—
12/06	3,021	23	0.8%	—
12/05	2,788	21	0.8%	—
Annual Growth	19.4%	(37.8%)	—	—

2008 Year-End Financials

Debt ratio: —
Return on equity: 0.10%
Cash ($ mil.): 1
Current ratio: 0.40
Long-term debt ($ mil.): —

Dividends
Yield: —
Payout: —
Market value ($ mil.): —

M & T Bank Corp

M&T Bank Corporation is making a splash in the mid-Atlantic region. It is the holding company of M&T Bank which offers deposit loan trust investment brokerage and insurance services to more than two million individuals and small- and mid-sized businesses. With about $123 billion in total assets and $95.5 billion in deposits the bank operates more than 775 branches and 1800 ATMs in New York Pennsylvania and other eastern states and Washington DC in addition to Canada and the Cayman Islands. Its residential mortgage origination unit spans more than a dozen states in the South and West. The firm also manages a proprietary line of mutual funds the Wilmington Funds.

Operations

M&T Bank comprises two wholly-owned bank subsidiaries: M&T Bank and Wilmington Trust N.A. (M&T Bank represents 99% of the company's consolidated assets.) M&T Bank operates through six reportable segments: Retail Banking Commercial Banking Commercial Real Estate Residential Mortgage Banking Business Banking and Discretionary Portfolio.

The Retail Banking segment which generates more than 25% of the bank's total revenue offers a variety of services to consumers through banking offices ATMs telephone banking and Internet banking.

The Commercial Banking segment brings in about 20% of revenue and offers a variety of credit products and banking services to middle-market and large commercial customers primarily within the markets it already serves.

M&T Bank's Commercial Real Estate segment generates another 15% of revenue and provides credit services which are secured by several types of multifamily residential and commercial real estate and deposit services to its customers.

Its Residential Mortgage Banking unit makes up nearly 10% of revenue and originates and services residential mortgage loans for consumers and sells substantially all of the loans in the secondary market to investors or to the Discretionary Portfolio segment.

The Business Banking segment brings in another nearly 10% of revenue and provides deposit lending cash management and other financial services to small businesses and professionals through its banking office network and other delivery channels including business banking centers telephone banking online banking and ATMs. The Discretionary Portfolio segment focuses on securities residential mortgage loans and other assets; short-term and long-term borrowed funds; brokered certificates of deposit and interest rate swap agreements; and Cayman Islands branch deposits. The segment also provides customers with foreign exchange services.

Geographic Reach

Buffalo-based M&T Bank operates in New York Pennsylvania Maryland Delaware New Jersey Connecticut Virginia West Virginia and the District of Columbia. It also boasts a full-service commercial banking office in Ontario Canada and an office in George Town Cayman Islands. Its regional headquarters is in Albany.

Sales and Marketing

M&T Bank caters to customers through multiple channels such as its business banking centers telephone banking online banking and ATMs. It serves individuals and small- and mid-sized business customers.

Financial Performance

M&T Bank's annual revenues and profits have been trending higher over the past few years mostly thanks to growing loan business stemming largely from bank acquisitions (including its large acquisition of Hudson City Bank).

Revenue climbed 14% to $5.7 billion in fiscal 2016 with growth concentrated in interest income which grew $727 million due to the first full year contribution of the Hudson City acquisition. Other income was unchanged from 2015.

Net income climbed 22% to $1.3 billion due to the absence from the books of acquisition expenses incurred in 2015.

Cash from operations fell 32% to $1.2 billion due to changes in provision for deferred income taxes and a net change in loans originated for sale offset by higher net income.

Strategy

M&T Bank's strategy is to achieve dominance in its relatively small geographic market. It does this through the acquisition of smaller rivals that has the dual effect of taking out competitors while putting off prospective market entrants by its stranglehold over the local market.

The biggest recent acquisition was of Hudson City a venerable New York-area bank that it acquired in 2015 after a long-running saga with regulators. It took three years before regulators were satisfied with M&T's efforts to improve its anti-money-laundering processes costing the company hundreds of millions of dollars. Hudson City had 725 branches.

While the regulator-imposed block on acquisitions was in place the company turned its efforts to increasing its advertising particularly in Western New York.

Mergers and Acquisitions

M&T Bank has historically purchased smaller banks to expand its reach or strengthen its presence in existing markets.

In November 2015 the bank completed the acquisition of New Jersey's Hudson City Bancorp for $3.7 billion after originally announcing its intentions to buy the bank back in August 2012. The Hudson City acquisition added some $19 billion in new loans and bring in branches in the New York City metropolitan area while greatly expanding M&T Bank's presence in New Jersey.

Company Background

M&T Bank traces its roots to the founding of Manufacturers and Traders Bank in Buffalo New York. M&T Bank reorganized under a bank holding company in 1969 called First Empire State Corp. The name was changed in 1998 to M&T Bank Corporation.

EXECUTIVES

EVP Wealth and Institutional Services Division M&T Bank Corp and M&T Bank, William J. (Bill) Farrell, age 59

EVP M&T Bank Corporation and EVP and Co-Head Commercial Banking M&T Bank, Brian E. Hickey, age 65, $299,231 total compensation

EVP M&T Bank Corporation and Vice Chairman and EVP M&T Bank, Kevin J. Pearson, age 56, $725,000 total compensation

EVP and Chief Credit Officer M&T Bank Corporation and M&T Bank, Robert J. Bojdak, age 62

EVP and CIO M&T Bank Corporation and M&T Bank, Michele D. Trolli, age 56

Chairman and CEO M&T Bank Corporation and M&T Bank, Ren © F. Jones, age 53, $725,000 total compensation

President COO and Director M&T Bank Corporation and M&T Bank, Richard S. Gold, age 57, $725,000 total compensation

EVP and Treasurer M&T Bank Corporation and M&T Bank, D. Scott N. Warman, age 51

EVP Retail Banking Division M&T Bank Corporation and M&T Bank, Darren J. King, age 47, $600,000 total compensation

EVP and Area Executive M&T Bank Corporation and M&T Bank, Gino A. Martocci, age 51

EVP Human Resources M&T Bank Corp and M&T Bank, Janet M. Coletti, age 53

EVP M&T Bank Corporation and EVP Wilmington Trust Wealth Management M&T Bank, Doris P. Meister, age 61

EVP Retail and Business Banking M&T Bank, Neil J. Hosty

EVP M&T Bank Corporation and EVP Mortgage and Customer Asset Management M&T Bank, Michael J. Todaro, age 55

Regional President Western New York and President M&T Charitable Foundation, Shelley Drake

Vice President, Jim DiStefano

Assistant Vice President Technology Infrastructure Operations, Zana Vernon

Assistant Vice President Operations, Katie Schultz

Senior Vice President and Enterprise Security Officer, David Stender

Vice President Lead Credit Review Officer, Betsy Mallon

Assistant Vice President Branch Manager, Linda Jones

Commercial Branch Manager Vice President, Keith Snyder

Executive Vice President Information Security, Manish Gupta

Assistant Vice President Branch Manager, Mary Moore

Assistant Vice President Senior Software Engineering, Ashish Vikram

Vice President Credit Analyst, Eric Swoboda

Vice President Trust Risk Manager, Dawn Snelling

Vice President Human Resources Business Partner Mortgage and Consumer Lending, Donna Harlacher

Administrative Vice President Bankwide Transformation Department Vice President, John Sexton

Assistant Vice President Construction Administration, Gavin Musynske

Associate Vice President Information Technology, Ivan Aguilera

Assistant Vice President Talent Acquisition Senior Recruiter, Roni Thomas

Assistant Vice President Team Lead, Bemina Rohde

Assistant Vice President Relationship Manager, Sam Higgins

Vice President Commercial Real Estate, Tom Daly

Vice President Business and Professional Banking, Scott Boli

Vice President, Christa DeSpirt

Vice President Senior Branch Manager, Kellyann O'Mara

Vice President Accounting Policy, Timothy Cahlstadt

Regional Vice President and Middle Market Group Manager, Daniel Liberty

Assistant Vice President Branch Manager, Lauren Perrone

Vice President Commercial Branch Manager, Romaine Johnson

Vice President Construction, Jean Sortino

Assistant Vice President Branch Sales Manager, Mary Leager

Branch Manager Assistant Vice President, Doreen Makara

Vice President, Leslie Wallace

Vice President, Juliet Alexander

Vice President of Corporate Communications, Chet Bridger

Vice President of Information Technology Project Management, David Lee

Administrative Vice President Retail Banking, Matt Calhoun

Vice President Portfolio Manager, Courtney Herbert

Vice President Product Manager, Brian Marzec

Vice President, John Lewis

Assistant Vice President Service Desk Operations, Kyle Obear

Supervising Senior Information Technology Auditor Assistant Vice President, James Bandinelli

Group Vice President Telephone Banking Center, Lisa Stchelski

Assistant Vice President Manager Information Systems, Steven McCormack

Vice President, Eric Goodwin

Assistant Vice President Emerging Channels, Kristen Cronyn

Vice President and Legal Counsel, Demario Carswell

Vice President, Laurie Benard

Vice President, Jerry Laspisa

Vice President, Steven Wendelboe

Vice President, Gary Gaudioso

Assistant Vice President, Lakendra McNair

Vice President Business and Professional Banking, Sue Simpson

Vice President and Sr. Employee Relations Specialist, Vivian Williams

Vice Chairman, Robert T. (Bob) Brady, age 76

abm, Robyn Cargill

Auditors: PricewaterhouseCoopers LLP

LOCATIONS

HQ: M & T Bank Corp
One M & T Plaza, Buffalo, NY 14203
Phone: 716 635-4000
Web: www.mtb.com

PRODUCTS/OPERATIONS

Selected Subsidiaries
M&T Life Insurance Company
M&T Insurance Agency Inc
M&T Mortgage Reinsurance Company Inc.
M&T Real Estate Trust
M&T Realty Capital Corporation
M&T Securities Inc.
Wilmington Trust Company
Wilmington Trust Investment Advisors Inc.
Wilmington Funds Management Corporation
Wilmington Trust Investment Management LLC

2016 Sales

	$mil.
% of total	
Interest income	
Loans and leasesincluding fees	61
Investment Securities	6
Deposits at banks	1
Others	0
Non interest income	
Trust income	8
Service charges on deposit accounts	7
Mortgage banking revenue	7
Brokerage services income	1
Others	9
Total	**100**

2016 Sales

	% of total
Retail Banking	26
Commercial Banking	20
Commercial Real Estate	15
Business Banking	9
Residential Mortgage	8
Discretionary Portfolio	7
All others	15
Total	**100**

COMPETITORS

Citigroup	KeyCorp
Citizens Financial Group	Northwest Bancshares
Fulton Financial	PNC Financial
HSBC USA	Sovereign Bank
JPMorgan Chase	SunTrust
	TriState Capital

HISTORICAL FINANCIALS

Company Type: Public

Income Statement

				FYE: December 31
	ASSETS ($ mil.)	NET INCOME ($ mil.)	INCOME AS % OF ASSETS	EMPLOYEES
12/16	123,449	1,315	1.1%	16,973
12/15	122,787	1,079	0.9%	17,476
12/14	96,685	1,066	1.1%	15,782
12/13	85,162	1,138	1.3%	15,893
12/12	83,008	1,029	1.2%	14,943
Annual Growth	10.4%	6.3%	—	3.2%

2016 Year-End Financials

Debt ratio: 6.76%	No. of shares (mil.): 156
Return on equity: 8.03%	Dividends
Cash ($ mil.): 6,645	Yield: 0.0%
Current ratio: —	Payout: 35.9%
Long-term debt ($ mil.): —	Market value ($ mil.): 24,431

	STOCK PRICE ($) FY Close	P/E High/Low		PER SHARE ($)		
			Earnings	Dividends	Book Value
12/16	156.43	20 13	7.78	2.80	105.56
12/15	121.18	18 16	7.18	3.50	101.36
12/14	125.62	17 15	7.42	2.80	93.23
12/13	116.42	14 12	8.20	2.80	86.62
12/12	98.47	14 10	7.54	2.80	79.60
Annual Growth	12.3%	— —	0.8%	(0.0%)	7.3%

Macatawa Bank Corp.

Macatawa Bank Corporation is the holding company for Macatawa Bank. Since its 1997 founding the company has grown into a network of more than 25 branches serving western Michigan's Allegan Kent and Ottawa counties. The bank provides standard services including checking and savings accounts CDs safe deposit boxes and ATM cards. It also offers investment services and products through an agreement with a third-party provider. With deposit funds the bank primarily originates commercial and industrial loans and mortgages which account for nearly 75% of its loan book. Macatawa Bank also originates residential mortgages and consumer loans.

Operations

The bank carries total assets of $1.58 billion total loans of $1.12 billion and total deposits of $1.31 billion.

Through its Infinex affiliate the bank provides various brokerage services (including discount brokerage) personal financial planning and consultation regarding mutual funds.

The firm's Trust Department manages assets of approximately $648 million and offers retirement plan and personal trust services. Its personal trust services include financial planning investment management services trust and estate administration and custodial services.

Geographic Reach

Macatawa Bank operates more than 25 branches along with a lending and operation service facility in its primary market in western Michigan which includes the counties of Ottawa Kent and northern Allegan.

Sales and Marketing

Macatawa Bank targets small businesses mission-driven (non-profit) organizations builders manufacturers and service industry companies. Some of its clients include associations businesses churches financial institutions government authorities individuals and non-profit organizations.

Financial Performance

Macatawa's revenue has been declining ever since its peak in 2007. Revenue in fiscal 2014 fell by 2% to $63 million as the bank collected lower interest margins on its commercial residential and consumer loan portfolios amidst customer refinancing in the low interest-rate environment. The bank also generated less income from its short-term investments which hindered top line growth further.

Despite falling revenue the bank enjoyed its highest profit since 2007 as net income jumped by 10% to $10.47 million in 2014. This was thanks to a combination of lower interest expense on deposits and an improving real estate market which led to fewer losses from non-performing assets and fewer provisions for credit losses as real estate values improved.

Operations provided $16.62 million or 2% more cash than in 2013 thanks to higher earnings and because the bank wrote off more in non-cash accrued expenses and other liabilities.

EXECUTIVES

Assistant Vice President Secondary Market Mortgage Manager, Ron Buit
Vice President Treasury Management, Stephanie Jamrog Stephanie Jamrog
Vice President, Jason Coney
Vice President Mortgage Loan Officer, Bob Martin
Vice President Commercial Real Estate, Andrew Meelberg
Vice President Treasury Management Sales, Kristin Timmer
Vice President Retail Banking, Al Lanning
Vice President Wealth Advisor, John Simonds
Vice President Team Lead Retail Banking Grand Rapids, Sandy Siedlecki
Commercial Banker Vice President, Mike Vanommen
Auditors: BDO USA, LLP

LOCATIONS

HQ: Macatawa Bank Corp.
10753 Macatawa Drive, Holland, MI 49424
Phone: 616 820-1444
Web: www.macatawabank.com

PRODUCTS/OPERATIONS

2014 Sales

	$ mil.	% of total
Interest		
Loans including fees	42	67
Securities	3	5
Other	0	2
Noninterest		
ATM and debit card fees	4	8
Service charges & fees	4	7
Trust fees	2	4
Gain on sales of loans	2	3
Other	2	4
Total	**63**	**100**

COMPETITORS

Comerica	Huntington Bancshares
Fifth Third	PNC Financial
Flagstar Bancorp	

HISTORICAL FINANCIALS
Company Type: Public

Income Statement
FYE: December 31

	ASSETS ($ mil.)	NET INCOME ($ mil.)	INCOME AS % OF ASSETS	EMPLOYEES
12/16	1,741	15	0.9%	374
12/15	1,729	12	0.7%	385
12/14	1,583	10	0.7%	389
12/13	1,517	9	0.6%	395
12/12	1,560	35	2.3%	404
Annual Growth	**2.8%**	**(18.1%)**	**—**	**(1.9%)**

2016 Year-End Financials

Debt ratio: 2.37%
Return on equity: 10.13%
Cash ($ mil.): 89
Current ratio: —
Long-term debt ($ mil.): —
No. of shares (mil.): 33
Dividends
  Yield: 0.0%
  Payout: 25.5%
Market value ($ mil.): 353

	STOCK PRICE ($) FY Close	P/E High/Low		PER SHARE ($) Earnings	Dividends	Book Value
12/16	10.41	22	12	0.47	0.12	4.78
12/15	6.05	16	13	0.38	0.11	4.48
12/14	5.44	18	15	0.31	0.08	4.21
12/13	5.00	—	—	(0.29)	0.00	3.92
12/12	2.89	3	2	1.31	0.00	4.80
Annual Growth	**37.8%**	**—**		**(22.6%)**	**—**	**(0.1%)**

MACK-CALI REALTY, L. P.

Auditors: PRICEWATERHOUSECOOPERS LLP NE

LOCATIONS

HQ: MACK-CALI REALTY, L. P.
4 BECKER FARM RD STE 104, ROSELAND, NJ 070681734
Phone: 973 577-2472

HISTORICAL FINANCIALS
Company Type: Private

Income Statement
FYE: December 31

	ASSETS ($ mil.)	NET INCOME ($ mil.)	INCOME AS % OF ASSETS	EMPLOYEES
12/16	4,296	130	3.0%	2
12/15	4,063	(142)		—
12/14	4,192	31	0.7%	—
12/13	4,515	(19)		—
Annual Growth	**(1.6%)**	**—**	**—**	**—**

2016 Year-End Financials

Debt ratio: ——
Return on equity: 21.20%
Cash ($ mil.): 31
Current ratio: —
Long-term debt ($ mil.): —
Dividends
  Yield: —
  Payout: —
Market value ($ mil.): —

Macy's Inc

Auditors: KPMG LLP

LOCATIONS

HQ: Macy's Inc
151 West 34th Street, New York, NY 10001
Phone: 212 494-1602   **Fax:** 212 494-1838
Web: www.macys.com

HISTORICAL FINANCIALS
Company Type: Public

Income Statement
FYE: January 28

	REVENUE ($ mil.)	NET INCOME ($ mil.)	NET PROFIT MARGIN	EMPLOYEES
01/17	25,778	619	2.4%	148,300
01/16	27,079	1,072	4.0%	157,900
01/15*	28,105	1,526	5.4%	166,900
02/14	27,931	1,486	5.3%	172,500
02/13	27,686	1,335	4.8%	175,700
Annual Growth	**(1.8%)**	**(17.5%)**	**—**	**(4.1%)**

*Fiscal year change

2017 Year-End Financials

Debt ratio: 34.61%
Return on equity: 14.48%
Cash ($ mil.): 1,297
Current ratio: 1.35
Long-term debt ($ mil.): 6,562
No. of shares (mil.): 304
Dividends
  Yield: 0.0%
  Payout: 75.0%
Market value ($ mil.): 8,851

	STOCK PRICE ($) FY Close	P/E High/Low		PER SHARE ($) Earnings	Dividends	Book Value
01/17	29.11	22	14	1.99	1.49	14.22
01/16	40.41	22	11	3.22	1.39	13.70
01/15*	63.88	16	12	4.22	1.19	15.79
02/14	53.20	14	10	3.86	0.95	17.12
02/13	39.51	13	10	3.24	0.80	15.61
Annual Growth	**(7.4%)**	**—**		**(11.5%)**	**16.9%**	**(2.3%)**

*Fiscal year change

Magellan Health Inc.

Magellan Health has charted its course to become one of the largest managed behavioral health care companies in the nation. The company manages mental health plan employee assistance and work/life programs through its nationwide third-party provider network. Magellan also provides radiology benefits management specialty pharmaceutical management and Medicaid management. Overall it serves some 68 million members through contracts with federal and local government agencies insurance companies and employers. Magellan's Pharmacy Management segment's services include administration billing claims handling technology programs and coordination of care.

Operations

Magellan operates through two primary business segments: Healthcare (which brings in some 55% of revenue) and Pharmacy Management (some 45% of revenue).

The Healthcare segment provides managed behavioral health care services and employee assistance program (EAP) services as well as managing other specialty areas including diagnostic imaging and musculoskeletal health. It also provides the integrated management of physical behavioral and pharmaceutical health care for special populations through Magellan Complete Care (MCC).

Magellan's Pharmacy Management segment offers products and services to help its clients manage pharmacy benefit programs. It provides pharmacy benefit management (PBM) services pharmacy benefit administration (PBA) for Medicaid and other government-sponsored programs medical pharmacy management and programs to integrate management of specialty drugs across medical and pharmacy benefits in complex cases.

Geographic Reach

Magellan Health operates about 60 offices in nearly 30 states and Washington DC.

Sales and Marketing

Magellan's customers include health plans and employer groups as well as government and military agencies in some 30 states and Washington DC. The company also provides services to select pharmaceutical manufacturers. It has a network of some 175000 health care providers as well as a third-party network of facilities including psychiatric and substance abuse hospitals partial hospitalization facilities rehab centers and community health centers.

Advertising expenses in 2016 totaled some $2 million. The company markets its offerings through print media event sponsorships and promotional items.

Financial Performance

Magellan's revenues have been trending upward over the past few years. In 2016 revenues increased 5% to $4.8 billion. That growth was led by the pharmacy benefit management and dispensing business but was partially offset by a decline in the managed care business. That year the company had terminated contracts of some $666 million but revenues from acquired companies and increased membership from existing customers helped boost overall sales.

Despite the higher revenues net income fell between 2012 and 2015. It rebounded in 2016 rising 148% to $77.9 million due largely to a 17% decrease in cost of care expenses.

However cash flow from operations fell 72% to $66.7 million in 2016. Changes in assets and liabilities drove that decline.

Strategy

Magellan's growth strategy includes three primary areas of focus. First it aims to expand its management programs for special populations such as individuals dealing with serious mental illness. The company is expanding Medicaid management programs for certain high-cost populations including dual-eligibility patients (those qualifying for both Medicare and Medicaid services) forming partnerships and ventures with regional health plans. According to the Centers for Medicare and Medicaid Services Medicaid enrollment is projected to increase rapidly over the next decade and Magellan intends to take advantage of that increase by marketing itself to states that need guidance navigating the public mental health system.Towards that end it agreed to buy Senior Whole Health in 2017; that purchase will provide entry into Massachusetts' Senior Care Options program and New York City's managed long-term care market.

Secondly Magellan is working to expand its pharmacy management business. It has acquired pharmacy benefit management (PBM) companies such as Veridicus Holdings (in 2016) 4D Pharmacy Management Systems (2015). The company markets these offerings to new and existing clients.

Magellan's third primary strategy is to grow its existing behavioral health care and other specialty businesses. It does this by promoting and adding new services; acquisitions and organic measures have allowed the company to enter new business segments including radiology benefits management which is showing rapid growth.

Mergers and Acquisitions

Magellan acquired Senior Whole Health for $400 million in 2017. The formerly privately held Senior Whole Health provides Medicare and Medicaid dual-eligible benefits in the states of Massachusetts and New York. With that purchase Magellan expanded into Massachusetts' Senior Care Options program as well as the managed long-term care market in New York City.

In 2016 Magellan purchased Virginia-based Armed Forces Services Corporation for $117.5 million; that deal expanded its business with military and veteran agencies. Later that year it acquired Utah-based pharmacy benefit management (PBM) firm Veridicus Holdings for some $74.5 million. Veridicus provides PBM services medication therapy management clinical care management and Medicare Part D services to employers sponsors and third-party administrators.

Also in 2016 the company purchased The Management Group for $15 million. That firm provides home and long-term care services; the deal aligned with Magellan's plans to expand in the long-term services and supports market.

EXECUTIVES

Chairman and CEO, Barry M. Smith, age 63, $1,000,000 total compensation

CFO, Jonathan N. (Jon) Rubin, age 53, $535,600 total compensation

General Counsel and Secretary, Daniel N. (Dan) Gregoire, age 62, $470,350 total compensation

CEO Magellan Healthcare, Sam K. Srivastava, age 49, $609,000 total compensation

CTO, Srinivas (Srini) Koushik

Chief Medical Officer, Karen Amstutz

CEO Magellan Rx Management, Mostafa M. Kamal, age 36, $412,000 total compensation

Vice President Business Development, Lauren Murphy

Senior Vice President Government Affairs and Communications, John Littel

Clinical Director, Omar Vega

Vice President Provider Relations, Christine Kaplan

Vice President Enterprise Account Development BSC, Julie Larson

Senior Vice President Employer Segment Leader, Adam Weliver

Auditors: Ernst & Young LLP

LOCATIONS

HQ: Magellan Health Inc.
4800 Scottsdale Rd., Suite 4400, Scottsdale, AZ 85251
Phone: 602 572-6050
Web: www.magellanhealth.com

PRODUCTS/OPERATIONS

2016 Sales

	% of total
Healthcare	54
Pharmacy management	46
Eliminations	-
Total	**100**

2016 Sales

% of total	$ mil
Managed care & other	60
PBM & dispensing	40
Total	**100**

COMPETITORS

APS Healthcare	Express Scripts
American Imaging Management	First Health Group
CIGNA Behavioral Health	Health Net
CareCore	Horizon Health
Caremark Pharmacy Services	Mental Health Network
ComPsych	OptumRx
Comprehensive Care	PharMerica
	Schaller Anderson Inc
	UBH

HISTORICAL FINANCIALS

Company Type: Public

Income Statement

FYE: December 31

	REVENUE ($ mil.)	NET INCOME ($ mil.)	NET PROFIT MARGIN	EMPLOYEES
12/16	4,836	77	1.6%	9,700
12/15	4,597	31	0.7%	6,900
12/14	3,760	79	2.1%	6,600
12/13	3,546	125	3.5%	5,949
12/12	3,207	151	4.7%	5,030
Annual Growth	**10.8%**	**(15.3%)**	**—**	**17.8%**

2016 Year-End Financials

Debt ratio: 25.31%
Return on equity: 7.17%
Cash ($ mil.): 304
Current ratio: 1.21
Long-term debt ($ mil.): 214

No. of shares (mil.): 23
Dividends
Yield: —
Payout: —
Market value ($ mil.): 1,770

	STOCK PRICE ($) FY Close	P/E High/Low		PER SHARE ($) Earnings	Dividends	Book Value
12/16	75.25	23	15	3.22	0.00	46.76
12/15	61.66	57	37	1.21	0.00	43.18
12/14	60.03	21	18	2.90	0.00	42.08
12/13	59.91	13	10	4.53	0.00	41.88
12/12	49.00	10	7	5.42	0.00	37.19
Annual Growth	**11.3%**	**—**	**—**	**(12.2%)**	**—**	**5.9%**

MAINE STATE HOUSING AUTHORITY

Auditors: BAKER NEWMAN & NOYES LLC POR

LOCATIONS

HQ: MAINE STATE HOUSING AUTHORITY
353 WATER ST, AUGUSTA, ME 043306113
Phone: 207 626-4600
Web: WWW.MAINEHOUSING.ORG

HISTORICAL FINANCIALS

Company Type: Private

Income Statement

FYE: December 31

	ASSETS ($ mil.)	NET INCOME ($ mil.)	INCOME AS % OF ASSETS	EMPLOYEES
12/13	1,604	(2)	—	123
12/09	1,920	(1)	—	—
12/07	1,954	5	0.3%	—
12/06	2,010	3	0.2%	—
Annual Growth	**(3.2%)**	**—**	**—**	**—**

2013 Year-End Financials

Debt ratio: —
Return on equity: (-1.50%)
Cash ($ mil.): 1
Current ratio: 0.10
Long-term debt ($ mil.): —

Dividends
Yield: —
Payout: —
Market value ($ mil.): —

MainSource Financial Group Inc

MainSource Financial wants to be the main source of financial services for residents and businesses in Indiana and beyond. It is the holding company of MainSource Bank which operates about 80 branches in the Hoosier State as well as neighboring portions of Ohio Illinois and Kentucky. The bank offers standard deposit and lending products in addition to trust and insurance services. Real estate loans account for the majority of MainSource Financial's lending portfolio which also includes other commercial and consumer loans. Through MainSource Insurance the company provides annuities and credit life insurance.

Operations

MainSource generated 53% of its total revenue from interest income on loans (including fees) in 2014 while another 17% of revenue came from interest income on the company's investment securities. The bank's service charges on deposit accounts contributed 14% to total revenue during the year while its mortgage banking income and trust and investment product fees made up 5% and 3% respectively.

Geographic Reach

MainSource Bank boasts around 80 branches across Iowa Ohio Illinois and Kentucky. Its branches span 31 counties in Indiana three counties in Illinois three counties in Ohio and five counties in Kentucky.

Sales and Marketing

MainSource Financial spent $3.19 million on marketing in 2014 compared to $3.66 milion and $4.40 million in 2013 and 2012 respectively.

Financial Performance

After several years of revenue declines Main-Source Financial's revenue rebounded by 1% to $146.10 million in 2014 mostly thanks to higher interest income from loan business growth but also thanks to higher service charges on deposit accounts.

Higher revenue and lower loan loss provisions from a more credit-worthy loan portfolio in 2014 drove the bank's net income higher by 10% to a record $29.00 million for the year. Longer term the bank's annual profits have trended higher over the years as the bank's loan portfolio continues to improve its credit-quality amidst the strengthening economy.

Despite higher earnings during the year Main-Source's operating cash fell by 28% to $43.36 million as the bank collected less in net proceeds from the sale of its loans-held-for-sale.

Strategy

MainSource Financial has continued to selectively expand its branch network in recent years acquiring new branches from other banks in target markets while closing under-performing branches in other regions. Its 2015 branch purchases from Old National Bank and its full acquisition of MBT Bancorp in late 2014 added more than 10 branches to MainSource's network in Indiana and Ohio and added millions in new deposits and loan assets.

Meanwhile in mid-2014 the bank closed two of its branches in Indiana (in Linton and Griffith) and an additional branch in Frankfurt Kentucky. In April 2013 MainSource closed eight of its branches — or roughly 10% of its total branch network — in seven locations in Indiana (Redkey Fortville Cambridge City Fountain City Trafalgar East Enterprise and Covington) as well as in Troy Ohio.

Mergers and Acquisitions

In 2017 MainSource acquired FCB Bancorp for $58.9 million. The acquisition comprises FCB's seven offices in Kentucky and its $520 million in assets and $385 million in deposits.

In January 2015 MainSource Financial agreed to purchase Old National Bank branches located in Union City Ohio as well as in Portland Richmond Brownstown and Batesville Indiana from Old National Bank which would add a total of $120 million in deposits and $30 million in loans to Main-Source's books.

In October 2014 the company completed its full acquisition of all shares of MBT Bancorp for a total of $13.9 million. The deal added MBT's bank subsidiary The Merchant Bank and Trust Company and extended MainSource's market presence in southeastern Indiana and the greater Cincinnati markets with six new branches.

Company Background

The company has made several acquisitions over the years including National City Corporation's Madison Bank & Trust Union Community Bancorp Peoples Ohio Financial and 1st Independence Financial Group.

EXECUTIVES

SVP CFO and Secretary, James M. (Jamie) Anderson, age 43, $262,457 total compensation
Chairman President and CEO, Archie M. Brown, age 56, $500,097 total compensation
Chief Consumer Banking Officer, Chris M. Harrison, $241,815 total compensation
Commercial Banking Regional President, Chris Bower
Auditors: Crowe Horwath LLP

LOCATIONS

HQ: MainSource Financial Group Inc
2105 North State Road 3 Bypass, Greensburg, IN 47240
Phone: 812 663-6734   **Fax:** 812 663-4812
Web: www.mainsourcebank.com

PRODUCTS/OPERATIONS

2011 Sales

	$ mil.	% of total
Interest		
Loans including fees	92	55
Investment securities	28	17
Other	0	-
Noninterest		
Service charges on deposit accounts	18	11
Net realized gains on securities	11	7
Interchange income	6	3
Mortgage banking	5	3
Other	6	4
Adjustments	(2.7)	
Total	**166**	**100**

COMPETITORS

1st Source Corporation	KeyCorp
Bank of America	Old National Bancorp
Fifth Third	U.S. Bancorp
First Merchants	
German American Bancorp	

HISTORICAL FINANCIALS

Company Type: Public

Income Statement

FYE: December 31

	ASSETS ($ mil.)	NET INCOME ($ mil.)	INCOME AS % OF ASSETS	EMPLOYEES
12/16	4,080	38	0.9%	888
12/15	3,385	35	1.0%	841
12/14	3,122	29	0.9%	801
12/13	2,859	26	0.9%	772
12/12	2,769	27	1.0%	808
Annual Growth	**10.2%**	**8.9%**	**—**	**2.4%**

2016 Year-End Financials

Debt ratio: 1.01%	No. of shares (mil.): 24
Return on equity: 9.20%	Dividends
Cash ($ mil.): 88	Yield: 0.0%
Current ratio: —	Payout: 37.2%
Long-term debt ($ mil.): —	Market value ($ mil.): 828

	STOCK PRICE ($) FY Close	P/E High/Low	PER SHARE ($) Earnings	Dividends	Book Value
12/16	34.40	21 12	1.64	0.61	18.68
12/15	22.88	15 11	1.62	0.54	17.67
12/14	20.92	15 11	1.39	0.42	16.63
12/13	18.03	14 10	1.26	0.28	14.96
12/12	12.67	10 7	1.30	0.08	15.94
Annual Growth	**28.4%**	**— —**	**6.0%**	**66.2%**	**4.0%**

ManpowerGroup

Millions of men (and women) have helped power this firm to the upper echelon of the staffing industry. ManpowerGroup is one of the world's largest providers of temporary employees connecting more than 10 million people in office industrial and professional positions every year. It offers services through different brands including ManpowerGroup Solutions Manpower Experis (accounting finance health and engineering positions) Manpower UK and Right Management which provides management consulting services focused on leadership development and assessment. Manpower-Group has some 2800 owned or franchised offices in 80 countries and territories and assists more than 400000 clients.

Operations

Supplying temporary employees to businesses on an as-needed basis accounts for the bulk of ManpowerGroup's business with most of its sales coming from office and light-industrial placements.

ManpowerGroup's operating segments are primarily aligned by geography. They include the Americas Southern Europe Northern Europe APME (Asia Pacific and the Middle East) and Right Management.

Geographic Reach

Europe is ManpowerGroup's largest market accounting for almost 65% of the company's revenue. The Americas follow (generating more than 20%) while Asia/Pacific and the Middle East contribute nearly 15%.

Sales and Marketing

ManpowerGroup's client mix of 400000 customers consists of both small and medium-sized businesses and large national multinational clients. Large businesses accounted for 57% of the company's revenues during fiscal 2016. The firm spent $24.4 million on advertising in 2016 compared to

$28.8 million and $25.7 million in fiscal 2015 and 2014 respectively.

Financial Performance

ManpowerGroup's revenue has been steady in recent fiscal years. The company reported $19.65 billion in revenue for fiscal 2016 up from $19.33 billion in fiscal 2015.

ManpowerGroup's net income also improved in fiscal 2016 compared to the prior fiscal period. The company claimed $443.70 million in net income for fiscal 2016 up from $419.20 million in fiscal 2015.

The improved revenue and net income led to increased cash from operations. ManpowerGroup ended fiscal 2016 with $600 million in cash from operations up from $511 million at the end of the previous fiscal year.

Strategy

Apart from growing its services and geographic footprint through acquisitions ManpowerGroup focuses on diversifying its revenues beyond its core staffing and employment services by building its consulting and leadership training services. However the company relies heavily on acquisitions to expand its business.

ManpowerGroup is one year into its Sustainability Plan. The plan supports four of the United Nation's Sustainable Development Goals: contributing to making progress in education decent work gender equality and inclusive growth. ManpowerGroup's Work to Change the World sustainability website showcases what companies and individuals can do to get ready for work upskill to remain employable and create inclusive workplaces.

Mergers and Acquisitions

In 2017 ManpowerGroup acquired Ciber a leading global information technology consulting services and outsourcing company. The acquisition strengthened ManpowerGroup Spain's capacity to deliver best-in-class IT staffing solutions in Spain.

In 2016 ManpowerGroup acquired global IT consulting services and outsourcing company Ciber?s business in Norway. The purchase helped ManpowerGroup build on the strength of its Experis business in Norway and to meet demand in the IT sector. Also during 2016 ManpowerGroup acquired the Dutch business of IT solutions and staffing provider Ciber Netherland for $25 million.

HISTORY

Milwaukee lawyers Elmer Winter and Aaron Scheinfeld founded Manpower in 1948. It originally concentrated on supplying temporary help to industry during the first few years of the postwar boom. In the next few years the company expanded and in 1956 it began franchising. During the 1960s Manpower opened franchises in Europe Asia and South America. Unlike many of its competitors however it continued to emphasize blue-collar placements.

EXECUTIVES

EVP Global Strategy and Talent, Mara E. Swan, age 57, $560,000 total compensation

President and COO, Darryl E. Green, age 56, $800,000 total compensation

Chairman and CEO, Jonas Prising, age 57, $1,200,000 total compensation

President ManpowerGroup North America, Becky Frankiewicz

SVP Operational Excellence and IT; President Asia/Pacific and Middle East, Sriram (Ram) Chandrashekar, age 50, $568,035 total compensation

EVP and CFO, John T. (Jack) McGinnis, age 50, $519,231 total compensation

Vice President Finance the Americas, Julie Krey

Auditors: Deloitte & Touche LLP

LOCATIONS

HQ: ManpowerGroup
100 Manpower Place, Milwaukee, WI 53212
Phone: 414 961-1000   **Fax:** 414 332-0796
Web: www.manpower.com

2016 Sales

	$ mil.	% of total
Southern Europe	7,497	38
Northern Europe	5,129	26
Americas	4,297	22
Asia Pacific & Middle East	2,471	13
Right Management	258	1
Total	**19,654**	**100**

PRODUCTS/OPERATIONS

Selected Services

Staffing
Industrial trades
Manpower Professional
  Engineering
  Finance
  Information technology
  Telecommunications
Office and clerical

COMPETITORS

Adecco	Randstad Holding
Kelly Services	Robert Half
Korn/Ferry	TrueBlue
PageGroup	Volt Information

HISTORICAL FINANCIALS

Company Type: Public

Income Statement

FYE: December 31

	REVENUE ($ mil.)	NET INCOME ($ mil.)	NET PROFIT MARGIN	EMPLOYEES
12/16	19,654	443	2.3%	28,000
12/15	19,329	419	2.2%	27,000
12/14	20,762	427	2.1%	26,000
12/13	20,250	288	1.4%	25,000
12/12	20,678	197	1.0%	28,000
Annual Growth	(1.3%)	22.4%	—	0.0%

2016 Year-End Financials

Debt ratio: 10.90%
Return on equity: 17.75%
Cash ($ mil.): 598
Current ratio: 1.40
Long-term debt ($ mil.): 785

No. of shares (mil.): 66
Dividends
  Yield: 0.0%
  Payout: 27.4%
Market value ($ mil.): 5,952

	STOCK PRICE ($) FY Close	P/E High/Low		PER SHARE ($) Earnings	Dividends	Book Value
12/16	88.87	15	9	6.27	1.72	35.27
12/15	84.29	18	12	5.40	1.60	35.94
12/14	68.17	16	11	5.30	0.98	37.68
12/13	85.86	23	12	3.62	0.92	36.72
12/12	42.44	19	13	2.47	0.86	32.63
Annual Growth	20.3%	—	—	26.2%	18.9%	2.0%

Marathon Oil Corp.

In the long-running competition for success in the oil and gas industry Marathon Oil is keeping up a steady pace. It has proved reserves of more than 2.1 billion barrels of oil equivalent including 692 million barrels of synthetic oil derived from oil sands mining. It major focus of production is the US in the Gulf of Mexico Oklahoma Texas and North Dakota. Its areas of production outside of the US include Europe (the UK); Africa (Equatorial Guinea Gabon and Libya); and Canada (the Athabasca Oil Sands Project which the company agreed to exit in 2017).

HISTORY

Marathon Oil was founded in 1887 in Lima Ohio as The Ohio Oil Company by 14 independent oil producers to compete with Standard Oil. Within two years Ohio Oil was the largest producer in the state. This success did not go unnoticed by Standard Oil which proceeded to buy Ohio Oil in 1889. In 1905 the company moved to Findlay Ohio where it remained until it relocated to Houston in 1990.

When the US Supreme Court broke up Standard Oil in 1911 Ohio Oil became independent once again and expanded its exploration activities to Kansas Louisiana Texas and Wyoming.

In a 1924 attempt to drill three wells west of the Pecos River in Texas Ohio Oil mistakenly drilled three dry holes to the east. The company was on the verge of abandoning the project until a geologist reported the error. Ohio Oil drilled in the right area and the wells flowed. That year the company bought Lincoln Oil Refining — its first venture outside crude oil production.

Ohio Oil continued its expansion into refining and marketing operations in 1927. Following WWII the company began international exploration. Through Conorada Petroleum (later Oasis) a partnership with Continental Oil (later Conoco and then ConocoPhillips) and Amerada Hess the company explored in Africa and South and Central America. Conorada's biggest overseas deal came in 1955 when it acquired concessions on more than 60 million acres in Libya.

In 1962 the company acquired Plymouth Oil and changed its name to Marathon Oil Company; it had been using the Marathon name in its marketing activities since the late 1930s. Marathon added a 200000-barrel-a-day refinery in Louisiana to its operations in 1976 when it acquired ECOL Ltd.

After a battle with Mobil U.S. Steel acquired Marathon in 1982 for $6.5 billion. U.S. Steel changed its name to USX in 1986 and acquired Texas Oil & Gas. That year the US government introduced economic sanctions against Libya putting Marathon's Libyan holdings in suspension.

USX consolidated Texas Oil and Marathon in 1990. After a protracted struggle with corporate raider Carl Icahn USX split Marathon and U.S. Steel into two separate stock classes in 1991. A third offering USX-Delhi Group (the pipeline operator division) followed the next year. (Koch Industries bought USX-Delhi in 1997.)

A consortium led by USX-Marathon signed an agreement with the Russian government in 1994 to develop oil and gas fields off Sakhalin Island (although USX-Marathon sold its stake in the project in 2000). In 1996 Marathon formed a venture ElectroGen International with East Coast utility DQE to develop power generation projects in the Asia/Pacific region.

In 1998 Marathon and Ashland merged their refining and retail operations creating Marathon Ashland Petroleum (MAP) with Marathon owning 62%. That year Marathon in a deal that boosted its reserves by 18% acquired Calgary-based Tarragon Oil and Gas.

As part of a restructuring drive in 1999 MAP sold its crude oil gathering business Scurlock Permian to Plains All American Pipeline. With oil prices rebounding Marathon ramped up its oil exploration in 2000 buying more deepwater leases in the Gulf of Mexico and acquiring an interest in an oil and gas play offshore the Republic of Congo.

Marathon Petroleum's net income dropped by 12% to $1.2 billion in 2016 mostly as higher refinery operating costs (due to significantly higher turnaround activity in 2016) outweighed the positive impact of lower sales volumes.

The company's operating cash levels fell from $4.1 billion in 2015 to $4.0 billion in 2016 decreased operating results partially offset by favorable changes in working capital of $1.2 billion compared to 2015. In 2016 changes in working capital were a net $200 million source of cash primarily due to higher accounts payable and accrued liabilities partially offset by increases in current receivables and inventories. Accounts payable increased $850 million due to higher crude oil payable prices. Current receivables grew by $690 million as the result of higher refined product and crude oil receivable prices.

Strategy

Marathon Petroleum is looking to expand its refining midstream logistics and retail businesses through acquisitions and organic growth. It continued in 2016 to grow its portfolio of midstream assets with investments in the Sandpiper pipeline project the recently finished SAX pipeline and through its new marine joint venture Crowley Ocean Partners. That year Marathon also focused on growing organically in existing markets in its legacy seven-state Midwest footprint as well as its more recently entered markets of Pennsylvania and Tennessee.

Managing its risk and its balance sheet in early 2017 Marathon Petroleum dropped down to its MPLX midstream business certain terminal pipeline and storage assets for $2 billion. The assets included 62 light-product terminals; 11 pipeline systems consisting of 604 miles of pipeline; 73 tanks; a crude oil truck unloading facility at MPC's refinery in Canton Ohio; and eight natural gas liquids storage caverns in Woodhaven Michigan. Later in the same year the company announced a further drop down of refining logistics assets and fuels distribution services for $8.1 billion expanding MPLX's balance sheet by some 50%.

One of the company's most significant achievements was the 2014 acquisition of Hess? retail operations. This transaction was truly transformative for Speedway increasing its store count to approximately 2750 and expanding its retail presence from nine Midwestern states to 22 states throughout the Midwest East Coast and Southeast. By the end of 2014 the company had converted 60 stores to the Speedway brand and converted of all Hess stores by the end of 2016.

Mergers and Acquisitions

In 2017 Enbridge and Marathon Petroleum bought a partial indirect equity interest in the Dakota Access Pipeline and Energy Transfer Crude Oil Company Pipeline projects (the Bakken Pipeline system) which transports crude from North Dakota to the eastern Gulf Coast for $2 billion. Enbridge agreed to pay $1.5 billion for its 28% share of the network while Marathon will pay $500 million for its 9% stake.

Boosting its midstream footprint in December 2015 MXLP (the midstream master limited partnership sponsored by Marathon) purchased MarkWest Energy Partners whereby MarkWest became a wholly owned subsidiary of MPLX. The acquisition (which had an enterprise value for MarkWest of $20 billion) transformed MPLX into a large-cap diversified master limited partnership.

Company Background

Growing its retail network in September 2014 Marathon Petroleum bought Hess' gasoline station network for $2.8 billion. The move expanded Speedway's retail presence to 22 US states throughout the East Coast and Southeast.

That year it also purchased a facility in Cincinnati Ohio from Felda Iffco Sdn Bhd Malaysia. The plant currently produces several products including biodiesel and glycerin.

To expand its refining capacity in 2013 Marathon Petroleum bought BP's 451000 barrels-of-oil-per-day refinery in Texas City in Galveston Bay for about $2.5 billion. (The base purchase price was $598 million plus inventories valued at $1.1 billion. The agreement also contains an earnout provision under which Marathon Petroleum might pay up to an additional $700 million over six years subject to certain conditions).

That year the company also acquired interests in three ethanol companies from Mitsui & Co. (U.S.A.) Inc. for $75 million.

Growing its retail network in 2012 Marathon Petroleum's Speedway America unit bought 87 gas stations in Indiana and Ohio from GasAmerica Services. It purchased 23 in Illinois and Indiana in 2011.

In early 2012 Marathon Petroleum formed a tax-exempt limited partnership (MPLX) to take over some of its midstream operations. MPLX has an indirect 51% stake in about 2800 miles of pipeline across nine states in the Midwest and Gulf Coast as well as a Mississippi River barge dock and tank farms. (Marathon Petroleum retains the other 49% stake.) MPLX filed a $365 million initial public offering in July 2012 and went public in October 2012. Marathon Petroleum intends for MPLX to be the primary growth vehicle for its midstream business by transferring even more assets to the tax-exempt entity.

With an improving economy in 2011 Marathon Oil Corporation spun off Marathon Petroleum to improve shareholder returns by having two publicly traded companies — an exploration and production entity and a refining and marketing company.

To free up cash and to help it meet expansion costs in 2010 the company sold its Minnesota downstream assets (including a refinery and more than 230 gas stations/convenience stores) to investment firms TPG Capital and ACON Investments for about $900 million.

The company has invested $3.3 billion in a conventional refinery expansion at its Garyville Louisiana plant (completed in 2009) and put up $2.2 billion to upgrade its heavy oil processing unit in Detroit (completed in 2012).

Marathon Petroleum traces it roots to the formation of the Ohio Oil Company in 1887.

EXECUTIVES

Chairman and CEO, Gary R. Heminger, age 63, $1,600,000 total compensation
EVP Human Resources Health and Administrative Services, Rodney P. Nichols, age 64
VP Business Development, Anthony R. (Tony) Kenney, age 64, $687,500 total compensation
Brand Marketing Division Manager, Thomas M. (Tom) Kelley, age 57
SVP CFO and Treasurer, Timothy T. Griffith, age 47, $600,000 total compensation
SVP Supply Distribution and Planning, C. Michael Palmer, age 63, $637,500 total compensation
President, Donald C. (Don) Templin, age 53, $800,000 total compensation
SVP Transportation and Logistics, John S. Swearingen, age 57
VP and CIO, Donald W. Wehrly, age 57
SVP Refining, Raymond L. Brooks, age 56
President MPLX LP, Mike Hennigan
Vice President Digital Creative Director, Sarah Fowler
Auditors: PricewaterhouseCoopers LLP

LOCATIONS

HQ: Marathon Petroleum Corp.
539 South Main Street, Findlay, OH 45840-3229
Phone: 419 422-2121
Web: www.marathonpetroleum.com

PRODUCTS/OPERATIONS

2016 Sales

	% of total
Refining & marketing	68
Speedway	29
Midstream	3
Total	**100**

2016 Sales

	% of total
Refined products	86
Merchandise	8
Crude oil & refinery feedstocks	3
Transportation & other	3
Total	**100**

Selected Products

Asphalt
Branded Distillates
Branded Gasoline
Branded Lubricants
Heavy Oil
Petroleum Coke
Specialty Products
Wholesale Light Products

COMPETITORS

BP	Koch Industries Inc.
CITGO	Motiva Enterprises
Chevron	Murphy Oil
ConocoPhillips	Shell Oil Products
Exxon Mobil	Sunoco
Hess Corporation	Tesoro
HollyFrontier	Valero Energy

HISTORICAL FINANCIALS

Company Type: Public

Income Statement

FYE: December 31

	REVENUE ($ mil.)	NET INCOME ($ mil.)	NET PROFIT MARGIN	EMPLOYEES
12/16	63,364	1,174	1.9%	44,460
12/15	72,258	2,852	3.9%	45,440
12/14	98,102	2,524	2.6%	45,340
12/13	100,254	2,112	2.1%	29,865
12/12	82,492	3,389	4.1%	25,985
Annual Growth	**(6.4%)**	**(23.3%)**	**—**	**14.4%**

2016 Year-End Financials

Debt ratio: 23.80%	No. of shares (mil.): 528
Return on equity: 8.74%	Dividends
Cash ($ mil.): 887	Yield: 0.0%
Current ratio: 1.46	Payout: 61.5%
Long-term debt ($ mil.): 10,544	Market value ($ mil.): 26,585

	STOCK PRICE ($) FY Close	P/E High/Low		PER SHARE ($) Earnings	Dividends	Book Value
12/16	50.35	23	14	2.21	1.36	25.68
12/15	51.84	20	8	5.26	1.14	24.93
12/14	90.26	22	17	4.39	1.84	19.62
12/13	91.73	27	18	3.32	1.54	18.38
12/12	63.00	13	6	4.95	1.20	17.56
Annual Growth	**(5.4%)**	**—**	**—**	**(18.2%)**	**3.2%**	**10.0%**

Markel Corp (Holding Co)

Have you ever thought about who insures the manicurist or an antique motorcycle? Specialty insurer Markel takes on the risks other insurers won't touch from amusement parks to thoroughbred horses to summer camps. Coverage is also available for one-time events such as golf tournaments and auto races. The company provides customized direct and facultative placements in the US and abroad as well as treaty reinsurance. Markel International provides specialty insurance internationally from its base in the UK and Alterra handles specialty insurance and reinsurance in the US and parts of Europe and Latin America. Meanwhile subsidiary Markel Ventures invests in non-insurance companies.

Operations

Markel operates through three primary segments: US Insurance (more than half of all sales) International Insurance and Reinsurance.

US Insurance writes commercial risks primarily excess and surplus lines which are distributed through a network of wholesale brokers. It also writes specialty coverage for niche markets. Excess insurance kicks in when a company's regular insurance fizzles out. For example a regular policy might pay up to $100000 on claims but the excess policy could then pay any amounts over $100000 and up to $10 million. Surplus insurance is coverage that no regular insurance company can offer and typically comes with a higher level of risk and higher-priced premiums.

US Insurance also provides specialty insurance to clients that engage in highly specialized activities requiring niche coverage typically not offered by standard insurers. Underwriting entities include FirstComp Insurance for workers' compensation as well as the Markel Insurance and Markel American Insurance units. Specialty reinsurance products including general casualty coverage property professional liability workers' compensation and credit and surety risks are provided by Evanston Insurance.

The International Insurance segment offers primary and excess of loss property excess liability marine and energy professional liability and other specific coverages. Its Markel International division based in London writes business worldwide. Another division Markel Assurance specializes in Fortune 1000 businesses around the world. It was established in 2017 from the combination of the former Wholesale and Global units.

The Reinsurance segment provides property casualty and specialty treaty reinsurance to other insurers around the world. Key products include property professional liability credit surety general casualty auto and workers' compensation. These are underwritten by the Global Reinsurance and Market International divisions. Reinsurance distributes its coverage through brokers.

The remainder of revenues comes from private equity unit Markel Ventures — which invests in entities ranging from food equipment makers to medical providers — and other investment income.

Geographic Reach

Markel primarily operates in the US market which accounts for more than 75% of premiums. Its UK unit Markel International writes policies for UK clients as well as on a global basis through the Lloyd's of London market. Markel has more than 25 locations in North America and about 30 in Europe.

Sales and Marketing

Markel distributes its products through independent agents and brokers. Its top three independent brokers represent nearly 30% of the group's gross premiums written.

Financial Performance

Markel's revenues have leveled off somewhat after seeing significant rises in 2013 and 2014. In 2016 revenue rose 5% to $5.6 billion. Driving that increase earned premiums net investment income and other revenues (including managing general agent operations life and annuity product sales and Markel Ventures) rose that year. Those gains were partially offset by a decline in net realized investment gains.

Net income which spiked 82% in 2015 due to favorable underwriting results and higher net realized investment gains slipped 22% to $455.7 million in 2016. Higher costs ranging from interest expense to losses on early extinguishment of debt as well as less favorable underwriting results led to that year's decline.

Cash flow from operations which has declined since 2013 fell another 18% to $534.6 million in 2016 as a result of the lower net income. Also negative adjustments to net cash provided by operating activities — including deferred income tax expenses losses on early extinguishment of debt and a decrease in other liabilities — caused operating cash flow to decline.

Strategy

Markel's strategy for growth is to leverage its expertise and specialized market knowledge of niche markets to differentiate its business from competitors. Financially the company's aim is to generate consistent underwriting and operating profits and produce superior returns on its investments to increase its value for shareholders. It is also looking to diversify into new specialty insurance markets as well as developing innovative products to reach more clients. The firm works at improving its existing policies to provide its customers with the evolving types of coverage they need. For example in 2017 it expanded the professional liability offerings it provides for law firms. Additionally Markel is strategic in selecting profitable venture capital investments through its private equity unit.

Acquisitions are another realm of interest for the group. It plans to buy insurance fronting services provider State National Companies for $919 million fresh on the heels of its 2017 purchase of commercial surety firm SureTec.

The company is also focused on expanding international operations in the UK Bermuda Europe the Middle East the Asia/Pacific region and South America. It plans to establish an insurance provider in Germany ahead of the UK's pending exit from the European Union. (It currently offers insurance in Germany from a branch office in Munich where the new company will eventually be located.) That should help the company as it seeks other opportunities to expand in Europe.

Mergers and Acquisitions

In 2017 Markel acquired surety firm SureTec Financial for $250 million. SureTec operates in all 50 states specializing in small and midsize contract bonds and commercial surety. The company joined the specialty division of Markel's US Insurance segment. Also that year the company bought State National Companies the nation's largest provider of fronting services. With that $919 million purchase Markel entered that line of business and it will begin offering collateral protection coverage for financial institutions.

In 2015 the company acquired an 80% stake in CapTech Ventures for $60.6 million. CapTech is a management consulting firm; the deal helped Markel build its technological expertise. It also bought CATCo Investment Management a fund manager and reinsurance manager based in

Bermuda. That company now markets Markel's offerings in the US.

HISTORY

In the 1920s Sam Markel formed a mutual insurance company for "jitneys" (passenger cars refurbished as public transportation buses). In 1930 he founded Markel Service to expand nationally. To keep up with industry growth the company revamped itself as a managing general agent and independent claims service organization in the late 1950s. In 1978 Markel began covering taverns restaurants and vacant buildings. It created excess and surplus lines underwriter Essex Insurance in 1980.

Markel went public in 1986. The next year it invested in Shand Morahan and Evanston Insurance (specialty coverage including architects engineers and lawyers professional liability; officers and directors insurance; errors and omissions; and medical malpractice). It bought summer camp insurer Rhulen Agency in 1989.

In the 1990s Markel began buying insurers with their own offbeat niches. In 1990 it bought the rest of Shand Morahan and Evanston Insurance. In 1995 it bought Lincoln Insurance (excess and surplus lines) from media giant Thomson (now Thomson Reuters). The next year the company bought Investors Insurance Holding (excess and surplus lines). Markel which already owned nearly 10% of Gryphon Holdings (commercial property/casualty) bought the rest in 1999.

Expanding internationally Markel bought Bermuda-based Terra Nova Holdings a reinsurer and a Lloyd's managing agency in 2000. The company experienced heavy losses in 2001 not only related to the events of September 11 but also to its slumping international business (the company took a $100 million charge).

Unlike standard insurers (whose rates are generally regulated) specialty insurers can charge the rates they consider reasonable. To that end after taking significant losses from the 2005 hurricane season (Katrina Rita Wilma) and additional hits from the 2008 season (Gustav Ike) the company decided to raise the rates on its catastrophe-exposed businesses.

EXECUTIVES

Co-CEO, Thomas S. Gayner, age 55, $807,692 total compensation

Co-CEO, Richard R. Whitt, age 53, $807,692 total compensation

Vice Chairman, F. Michael Crowley, age 65, $793,269 total compensation

Chief Administrative Officer, Britton L. (Britt) Glisson, age 60

EVP and Chief Underwriting Officer, Gerard Albanese, age 64, $615,385 total compensation

EVP and CFO, Anne G. Waleski, age 50, $578,846 total compensation

EVP and Chief Actuarial Officer, Bradley J. Kiscaden, age 54

CIO, Mike Scyphers

Associate Vice President of Claims, David Ashley

Associate Vice President, Kathleen Olear

Vice President and Chief Administrative Officer, Robert Blazer

Vice President Investor, Mike Kotlowski

Vice President Marketing, Cara Bowen

Assistant Vice President and Claims Counsel, Jeanette McDonough

VICE PRESIDENT UNDERWRITING, Ron Pardo

Associate Vice President Markel Southeast, Jeffrey Craig

VICE PRESIDENT WESTERN REGION MARINE UNDERWRITING, Philip B Nelson

Regional President, Mimi Fiske

The company bought Pennaco Energy a Colorado-based producer of coalbed methane gas for about $500 million in 2001 and it agreed to buy CMS Energy's Equatorial Guinea (West Africa) oil and gas assets in a $993 million deal that was completed in 2002. At the end of 2001 USX spun off U.S. Steel and changed the name of the remaining company to Marathon Oil Corporation. In 2002 Marathon acquired Globex Energy a privately held exploration and production company with assets in West Africa for $155 million.

In 2005 Ashland sold its 38% stake in Marathon Ashland to Marathon Oil for about $3.7 billion.

In addition to acquiring MAP Marathon Oil also obtained Ashland's maleic anhydride business a share of its Valvoline Instant Oil Change business in Michigan and Ohio and other assets.

In 2006 the company sold its oil and gas assets in the Khanty-Mansiysk autonomous region of western Siberia to LUKOIL for $787 million. That year Marathon Oil announced a plan to spend $3.2 billion to expand the crude oil refining capacity of its refinery in Garyville Louisiana.

As a way to expand its hydrocarbon asset base the company has been investing heavily in non-conventional exploration and production areas. In 2006 as part of a five-year $1.5 billion investment the company announced plans to drill as many as 225 new wells in western North Dakota in the Bakken Oil Formation (tight shale layers) over a five-year period. The following year Marathon Oil expanded into the Canadian oil sands market through the acquisition of Western Oil Sands for about $5.8 billion.

Seeking stronger financial returns in 2011 Marathon Oil (formerly a holding company with both upstream and downstream operations) spun off its downstream unit Marathon Petroleum (which had accounted for the bulk of its revenues) and became a pure-play exploration and production company.

On the acquisition side Marathon Oil has made significant investments in the South Texas Eagle Ford resource play. In 2011 it bought $3.5 billion of Eagle Ford assets from KKR and Hilcorp Energy. In 2012 it acquired 25000 net acres in the Eagle Ford shale play. The largest deals were the acquisitions of Paloma Partners II LLC for $768 million and an separate acquisition of proved and unproved properties for $232 million.

To free up cash to reinvest in core properties and pay down debt in 2014 the company sold it Norwegian assets to Det Norske Oljeselskap ASA for $2.7 billion. It also sold its non-operated 10% working interests in the Production Sharing Contracts and Joint Operating Agreements for Angola Blocks 31 and 32 for $2.1 billion.

EXECUTIVES

EVP and CFO, Dane E. Whitehead, age 55
VP Human Resources and Administrative Services, Deanna L. Jones
EVP Operations, T. Mitchell (Mitch) Little, age 53, $529,615 total compensation
President and CEO, Lee M. Tillman, age 55, $1,050,000 total compensation
VP and CIO, Bruce A. McCullough
SVP General Counsel and Secretary, Reggie Hedgebeth
VP Conventional Assets, Catherine Krajicek, $371,442 total compensation
Vice President Geophysical It, Trevor Chargois
Vice President Manager Director, Ellen Norton
Vice President of Fleet Sales, Frank W Bassetti
SENIOR VICE PRESIDENT GENERAL COUNSEL AND SECRETARY, Reginald D Hedgebeth
REGIONAL VICE PRESIDENT, Thomas Hellman
REGIONAL VICE PRESIDENT, James Crawford

Chairman, Dennis H. Reilley, age 64
Auditors: PRICEWATERHOUSECOOPERS LLP

LOCATIONS

HQ: Marathon Oil Corp.
5555 San Felipe Street, Houston, TX 77056-2723
Phone: 713 629-6600
Web: www.marathonoil.com

2016 Sales

	% of total
United States	60
Canada	21
Libya	1
Other international	18
Total	**100**

PRODUCTS/OPERATIONS

2016 Sales

	% of total
North American E&P	61
International E&P	19
Oil Sands Mining (OSM)	21
Total	**100**

2016 Sales

	% of total
Crude oil and condensate	65
Synthetic crude oil	20
Natural Gas	9
Natural Gas liquids	5
Other	1
Total	**100**

COMPETITORS

BP	Occidental Petroleum
Chevron	PEMEX
ConocoPhillips	Petr☐leos de
Exxon Mobil	Venezuela
Hess Corporation	Royal Dutch Shell
Koch Industries Inc.	

HISTORICAL FINANCIALS

Company Type: Public

Income Statement

FYE: December 31

	REVENUE ($ mil.)	NET INCOME ($ mil.)	NET PROFIT MARGIN	EMPLOYEES
12/16	4,650	(2,140)	—	2,117
12/15	5,861	(2,204)	—	2,611
12/14	11,258	3,046	27.1%	3,330
12/13	14,959	1,753	11.7%	3,359
12/12	16,221	1,582	9.8%	3,367
Annual Growth	**(26.8%)**	**—**		**(11.0%)**

2016 Year-End Financials

Debt ratio: 23.40%
Return on equity: (-11.83%)
Cash ($ mil.): 2,490
Current ratio: 1.64
Long-term debt ($ mil.): 6,589

No. of shares (mil.): 847
Dividends
  Yield: 0.0%
  Payout: —
Market value ($ mil.): 14,662

	STOCK PRICE ($) FY Close	P/E High/Low		PER SHARE ($) Earnings	Dividends	Book Value
12/16	17.31	—	—	(2.61)	0.20	20.71
12/15	12.59	—	—	(3.26)	0.68	27.40
12/14	28.29	9	6	4.46	0.80	31.14
12/13	35.30	15	12	2.47	0.72	27.75
12/12	30.66	16	10	2.23	0.68	25.86
Annual Growth	**(13.3%)**	**—**	**—**	**—**	**(26.4%)**	**(5.4%)**

Marathon Petroleum Corp.

Marathon Petroleum has a long running commitment to fuel its customers. The former refining and marketing unit of Marathon Oil Corporation operates seven refineries with the capacity to process about 1.8 million barrels of crude oil a day. Marathon Petroleum sells refined products through a nationwide network of branded gas stations. It also holds stakes in pipelines and is one of the largest asphalt and light oil product terminal operators in the US. The company distributes petroleum products wholesale to private-brand marketers and to large commercial and industrial consumers as well as to the spot market.

Operations

Marathon?s operations consist of three business segments. Its Refining & Marketing segment which makes up 68% of the company's total revenue refines crude oil and other feedstocks at seven refineries in the US Gulf Coast and Midwest regions purchases ethanol and refined products for resale and distributes refined products. It sells refined products to wholesale marketing customers buyers on the spot market its Speedway business segment and to independent entrepreneurs who operate Marathon retail outlets.

The Speedway segment (29%) sells transportation fuels and convenience products in the retail market in the Midwest primarily through Speedway convenience stores. The Midstream segment (3% of revenue) transports crude oil and other feedstocks to Marathon Petroleum's refineries and other locations delivers refined products to wholesale and retail markets and affiliated pipeline assets and investments.

Marathon holds stakes in 8400 miles of pipeline (MPLX LP) and is one of the largest asphalt and light oil product terminal operators in the US (79 terminals in 2015). In addition the company has a large US private inland product fleet that includes 19 inland towboats and more than 200 barges.

Geographic Reach

Marathon Petroleum sells refined products at some 5600 Marathon-branded gas stations in 19 US states and through retail subsidiary Speedway SuperAmerica's 2730 outlets in more than 20 states.

Sales and Marketing

Marathon Petroleum sells to wholesale suppliers of gasoline and distillates to resellers and consumers. Customers include independent retailers wholesale customers their Marathon brand jobbers and Speedway brand convenience stores airlines transportation companies and utilities. It also sells gasoline distillates and asphalt for export primarily out of their Garyville and Galveston Bay refineries.

The company sells 50% of its gasoline sales volumes and 87% of its distillates sales volumes on a wholesale or spot market basis. It also sells via retail outlets primarily in Florida Mississippi Tennessee and Alabama and branded lessee dealer marketing contract assignments primarily in Connecticut Maryland and New York.

Financial Performance

Marathon's annual revenues had long been trending higher with rising oil prices but have fallen along with prices for the fossil fuel more recently. The company's annual profits have fluctuated with volatile operating costs.

The company's revenue plunged 12% to $63.4 billion in 2016 as the Refining & Marketing segment suffered from lower refined product sales prices and volumes as the result of lower oil prices.

Assistant Vice President Excess Liability, Michael Souza
Senior Vice President, Paul Carroll
SVP Professional Liability, Tim Rowan
Vice Chairman, Anthony F. Markel, age 75
Vice Chairman, Steven A. Markel, age 68
Chairman, Alan I. Kirshner, age 81
Auditors: KPMG LLP

LOCATIONS

HQ: Markel Corp (Holding Co)
4521 Highwoods Parkway, Glen Allen, VA 23060-6148
Phone: 804 747-0136
Web: www.markelcorp.com

2016 Gross Written Premiums

	% of total
United States	77
United Kingdom	7
Canada	3
Other countries	13
Total	**100**

PRODUCTS/OPERATIONS

2016 Sales

	% of total
Earned premiums	
U.S. Insurance	39
International Insurance	15
Reinsurance	15
Net investment income	7
Net realized investment gains	1
Other Insurance	23
Other revenues (Discontinued Lines)	-
Total	**100**

Selected Products

Re-Insurance
CasualtyProperty
Public Entity
Specialty
US Insurance
FirstComp - Workers' Comp
Global Insurance
Practice Groups
Specialty Commercial
Specialty Personal
Wholesale

COMPETITORS

Assurant
CNA Financial
Great American Insurance Company
HCC Insurance
Meadowbrook Insurance
Medical Liability Mutual Insurance
National Indemnity Company
Nationwide
Penn-America
Philadelphia Insurance Companies
ProSight Specialty Insurance Group
RLI
Travelers Companies
United States Liability Insurance Group
XL Group plc

HISTORICAL FINANCIALS

Company Type: Public

Income Statement

	ASSETS ($ mil.)	NET INCOME ($ mil.)	INCOME AS % OF ASSETS	EMPLOYEES
12/16	25,875	455	1.8%	10,900
12/15	24,941	582	2.3%	10,600
12/14	25,200	321	1.3%	8,600
12/13	23,955	281	1.2%	7,200
12/12	12,556	253	2.0%	6,400
Annual Growth	**19.8%**	**15.8%**	**—**	**14.2%**

2016 Year-End Financials

Debt ratio: 9.95%
Return on equity: 5.58%
Cash ($ mil.): 1,738
Current ratio: —
Long-term debt ($ mil.): —

No. of shares (mil.): 13
Dividends
Yield: —
Payout: —
Market value ($ mil.): 12,622

	STOCK PRICE ($) FY Close	P/E High/Low	Earnings	PER SHARE ($) Dividends	Book Value
12/16	904.50	31 26	31.27	0.00	606.30
12/15	883.35	22 16	41.74	0.00	561.23
12/14	682.84	31 24	22.27	0.00	543.98
12/13	580.35	26 19	22.48	0.00	477.17
12/12	433.42	19 15	25.89	0.00	403.84
Annual Growth	**20.2%**	**— —**	**4.8%**	**—**	**10.7%**

Marquette National Corp (IL)

LOCATIONS

HQ: Marquette National Corp (IL)
10000 West 151st Street, Orland Park, IL 60462
Phone: 888 254-9500

HISTORICAL FINANCIALS

Company Type: Public

Income Statement

FYE: December 31

	ASSETS ($ mil.)	NET INCOME ($ mil.)	INCOME AS % OF ASSETS	EMPLOYEES
12/16	1,584	6	0.4%	—
12/15	1,550	5	0.3%	—
12/14	1,528	7	0.5%	—
12/98	1,139	12	1.1%	—
12/97	1,154	10	0.9%	—
Annual Growth	**1.7%**	**(2.9%)**	**—**	**—**

2016 Year-End Financials

Debt ratio: 3.58%
Return on equity: 4.57%
Cash ($ mil.): 279
Current ratio: —
Long-term debt ($ mil.): —

No. of shares (mil.): 4
Dividends
Yield: 0.0%
Payout: 27.7%
Market value ($ mil.): 425

	STOCK PRICE ($) FY Close	P/E High/Low	Earnings	PER SHARE ($) Dividends	Book Value
12/16	96.00	81 66	1.35	0.38	30.34
12/15	102.00	85 72	1.31	0.34	32.22
12/14	97.00	243 55	1.52	0.91	31.78
Annual Growth	**(0.1%)**	**— —**	**(0.6%)**	**(4.6%)**	**(0.2%)**

Marriott International, Inc.

Marriott International is one of the world's leading hoteliers. The company has some 6000 operated or franchised properties worldwide. Its hotels include such full-service brands as Renaissance Hotels and its flagship Marriott Hotels & Resorts as well as select-service and extended-stay brands Courtyard and Fairfield Inn. It also owns the Ritz-Carlton luxury chain and resort and manages about 80 golf courses. The Marriott family including J. W. Marriott Jr. owns about 30% of Marriott International. The company acquired Starwood Hotels & Resorts Worldwide in 2016.

Operations

Marriott International operates through three reportable business segments. Its North American Full-Service is the company's largest segment. It accounts for more than 60% of the company's revenue. The North American Full-Service segment includes Marriott International's Luxury and Premium brands (JW Marriott The Ritz-Carlton W Hotels The Luxury Collection St. Regis EDITION Marriott Hotels Sheraton Westin Renaissance Hotels Le M ©ridien Autograph Collection Hotels Delta Hotels Gaylord Hotels and Tribute Portfolio) located in the US and Canada.

Marriott International's North American Limited-Service segment includes brands such as Courtyard Residence Inn Fairfield Inn & Suites SpringHill Suites Four Points TownePlace Suites Aloft Hotels AC Hotels by Marriott Element Hotels and Moxy Hotels in the US and Canada.

The company's International segment includes all properties located outside the US and Canada.

Geographic Reach

Following the merger with Starwood more than 55% of Marriott International's properties are international. The company has operations in more than 120 countries in the Americas the UK and Ireland the Middle East and Africa Asia Australia and Continental Europe.

Financial Performance

Marriott International reported a little more than $17 billion in revenue for fiscal 2016. That was an increase compared to the $14.4 billion the company reported as revenue for fiscal 2015.

Marriott International's net income decreased in fiscal 2016 compared to the prior fiscal period. The company reported net income of $780 million in fiscal 2016 after netting about $860 million in fiscal 2015.

The company ended fiscal 2016 with $1.5 billion in cash flow from operations. That was a slight increase compared to fiscal 2015.

Strategy

Marriott International's business model focuses on managing and franchising hotels rather than owning them. More than 50% of its hotel rooms are operated by franchisees that pay the company fees and royalties as well as a percentage of their food and beverage revenue.

Mergers and Acquisitions

In 2016 Marriott International acquired Starwood Hotels & Resorts Worldwide in a $13.3 billion deal. The deal gave Marriott International more hotel properties in Asia Europe and Latin America. The two companies have combined their respective customer loyalty programs but most of the hotels in the portfolio will retain their current branding.

HISTORY

The company began in 1927 as a Washington DC root beer stand operated by John and Alice Marriott. Later they added hot food and named their business the Hot Shoppe. In 1929 the couple incorporated and began building a regional chain.

Hot Shoppes opened its first hotel the Twin Bridges Marriott Motor Hotel in Arlington Virginia in 1957. When the Marriotts' son Bill became president in 1964 (CEO in 1972 chairman in 1985) he focused on expanding the hotel business. The company changed its name to Marriott Corp. in 1967. With the rise in airline travel Marriott built several airport hotels during the 1970s. By 1977 sales had topped $1 billion.

Marriott became the #1 operator of airport food beverage and merchandise facilities in the US with its 1982 acquisition of Host International and it introduced moderately priced Courtyard hotels in 1983. Acquisitions in the 1980s included a time-share business foodservice companies and competitor Howard Johnson. (Marriott later sold the hotels but kept the restaurants and turnpike units.)

The company entered three new market segments in 1987: Marriott Suites (full-service suites) Residence Inn (moderately priced suites) and Fairfield Inn (economy hotels). It also began developing "life-care" communities which provide apartments meals and limited nursing care to the elderly in 1988.

Marriott split its operations into two companies in 1993: Host Marriott to own hotels and Marriott International primarily to manage them. However Marriott International still owned some of the properties and in 1995 it bought 49% of the Ritz-Carlton luxury hotel group.

In 1996 Marriott purchased the Forum Group (assisted living communities and health care services) and merged it into Marriott Senior Living Services.

Marriott introduced its Marriott Executive Residences in 1997. Also that year the firm expanded overseas operations with its purchase of the 150-unit Hong Kong-based Renaissance Hotel Group a deal that included branding rights to the Ramada chain.

In 1998 after the division of its lodging and food distribution services the new Marriott International then began trading as a separate company. That year Marriott also acquired the rest of Ritz-Carlton and established SpringHill Suites by Marriott.

Marriott entered the corporate housing business in 1999 through its acquisition of ExecuStay Corporation (renamed ExecuStay by Marriott) which provided fully furnished and accessorized apartments for stays of 30 days or more. The following year it joined Italy's Bulgari the world's #3 jeweler in a $140 million venture of luxury hotels sporting the Bulgari name.

Marriott refocused its operations on the lodging market in 2003 when it exited both the senior living and distribution services businesses. It sold Marriott Distribution Services (food and beverage distribution) to Services Group of America and sold Marriott Senior Living Services to Sunrise Assisted Living (the management business) and CNL Retirement Properties (nine communities). The following year Marriott sold the international branding rights to the Ramada and Days Inn chains to Cendant (now Avis Budget Group) for about $200 million.

In 2005 Marriott acquired about 30 properties from CTF Holdings (an affiliate of Hong Kong-based New World Development) for nearly $1.5 billion. It sold 14 properties immediately to Sunstone Hotel Investors and Walton Street Capital. The deal put an end to an ongoing legal battle between Marriott and CTF Holdings which had alleged that the hotelier had pocketed kickbacks and fees from outside vendors.

Marriott invested about $200 million in 2005 to upgrade its hotel beds with higher thread-count sheets and triple-sheeted tops and it renovated and upgraded many of its Courtyard and Residence Inn locations during 2006. A difficult 2009 called for the elimination of more than 1000 jobs. Also that year the company cut costs by modifying menus and restaurant hours adjusting room amenities and relaxing some brand standards.

In 2010 Marriott introduced two new hotel brands into the market: Edtion (a boutique luxury chain) and Autograph Collection (independent luxury properties that each have their own unique identity). The firm spun off its time-share business Marriott Vacations Worldwide in 2011.

EXECUTIVES

Group Vice President, Kevin Kimball
Executive Vice President Financial Information and Enterprise Risk Ma, Carl Berquist
President and CEO, Arne M. Sorenson, age 58, $1,236,000 total compensation
EVP Finance and Global Treasurer, Carolyn B. Handlon
Group President, David J. Grissen, age 59, $725,000 total compensation
EVP and Chief Human Resources Officer, David A. Rodriguez, age 58
SVP and Associate General Counsel, Edward A. (Ed) Ryan, age 63
President and Managing Director Europe, Amy C. McPherson, age 55
EVP and Global Chief Communications and Public Affairs Officer, Tricia Primrose Wallace
EVP and Global Chief Development Officer, Anthony G. (Tony) Capuano, age 51, $750,000 total compensation
President Caribbean and Latin America (CALA), Tim Sheldon
EVP and Chief Marketing and Commercial Officer, Stephanie C. Linnartz, age 48, $700,000 total compensation
President and COO The Ritz-Carlton Bulgari Hotels and Resorts and St. Regis Hotels and Resorts, Herve Humler
Global CIO, Bruce Hoffmeister
President and Managing Director Middle East and Africa, Alex Kyriakidis, age 64
CEO Greater China, Stephen Ho
EVP and CFO, Kathleen K. (Leeny) Oberg, age 56, $650,000 total compensation
President and Managing Director Asia Pacific, Craig S. Smith, age 54
President Marriott Hotels of Canada, Don Cleary
Senior Vice President Development Planning, Carol Wagner
Vice President Engineering and Technical Services, Terry Smith
V Pres, Joseph Ryan
Vice President Customer Knowledge at, Stephan Chase
Vice President Sales and Marketing, Bryan Moore
Executive Vice President Project Finance, Michael E Dearing
Vice President Asset Management, Sarah Facciobene
Senior Vice President, Cathy Young
Assistant Vice President, Karina Barney
Vice President and Senior Counsel, Darryl L Franklin
Vice President Information Technology, Stephanie De Celis
Vice President Benefits Delivery, Anjuman Nyman
East Coast Vice President Operations, Richard Morris
Vice President Information Technology, Jim Abramson
Vice President Estimating, Allan Smeaton
Senior Vice President, Nancy Harper
Vice President Sales and Customer Care, Drew Pinto
Vice President Finance, Jennifer Chacon
Senior Vice President Talent Acquisition, Kristy Godbold
Vice President Global eCommerce Marketing, Andy Kauffman
Vice President Finance, Kent Duffie
Vice President human Resources, Peter Schiffrin
Vice President, Cecilia Lewis
Vice President and Senior Counsel, Yasmin Mehrain
Vice President, Jeff Spilman

Vice President Sales, Dennis Edwards
Vice President and Senior Scientist, Molaine Noel
Vice President Ecommerce, Glen Harvell
Vice President Human Resources, Porter Shifflett
VP brand Marketing, Johara Haniffa
Vice President Global Human Resources Business Proces, Cheryl Amick
Vice President And Senior Counsel, Theresa Coetzee
VICE PRESIDENT DIRECTOR OF SALES, Lisa Pauley
Vice President Training Development and Entusiastic Learning, Gerry Hudson-Martin
Regional Vice President Sales And Marketing Asia Pacific, Kent Maury
Vice President And Senior Counsel, Taisha Urland
Senior Vice President Lodging Development, Christopher Rose
Senior Vice President Finance Department, Gary Rosenthal
Vice President, Jennie Benzon
Vice President And Senior Counsel, Linda Miller
Vice President Reg Finance Businesspartner, Timothy Brown
Senior Vice President Brand Strategy And Innovation, Julie Moll
Executive Vice President, David Marriott
Senior Vice President, Timothy Grisius
Vice President Global Marketing, Jennifer K Utz
Senior Vice President And General Counsel, Myron Walker
Senior Vice President Global Asset Management, Catherine Young
Vice President, William Holmes
Vice President Marketing, Daniel Vihn
Vice President, Jim O'Hern
Senior Vice President, Jasraj Singh
Senior Vice President Of Human Resources, Lynda Dubay
Vice President, Tony Reid
Vice President Research and Technology, Dawn Robertson
Vice President Operations, Christoph Roshardt
Vice President and Managing Assistant General Counsel, Ward Cooper
Vice President, Judy Fennimore
Vice President Of Human Resources, Debbie Wilson
Area Vice President Caribbean Marriott International, Andrew Houghton
Vp Sales, Michael Balderaz
Vice President Leisure Business Development, Warren Ruello
Vice President Jw Marriott Hotels And Resorts Marriott Hotels And Resorts, Michael Darne
Communications Vice President, Leigh Brummerhoff
Vice President Sales And Marketing Support, Beth Jones
Vice President, Anne Gunsteens
Executive Vice President Architecture And Construction, Susan Levenson
Vice President Administration, Patricia Exposito
Senior Vice President and Deputy General Counsel, Nancy Lee
Vice President And Senior Counsel, Stephanie Carrick
VICE PRESIDENT INTERNATIONAL BUSINESS, Howard Leigh
Senior Vice President Owner and Franchise Services, James Fisher
Senior Vice President Digital Marketing, George Corbin
Senior Vice President, Deborah Harrison
Vice President eCommerce, Devin Sung
Senior Vice President Starwood Preferred Guest and Revenue Management, David Flueck
Vice President, Scott Gold
Vice President of Training, Sjaloom Stringer

Vice President Hotel Development, Laurent de
  Kousemaeker
Vice President, Joseph Donahue
**Executive Vice President and Chief Financial
  Officer,** Leeny Oberg
**Senior Vice President and Global Compliance
  Counsel,** William Dempster
**Global Vice President Infrastructure Engineering
  and Operations,** Lenny Guardino
VICE PRESIDENT SALES AND MARKETING,
  Andrew Cymrot
Chairman, J. W. (Bill) Marriott, age 84
Board Member, Ron Couget
Vice Chairman, John W Marriott
Auditors: Ernst & Young LLP

LOCATIONS

HQ: Marriott International, Inc.
  10400 Fernwood Road, Bethesda, MD 20817
Phone: 301 380-3000
Web: www.marriott.com

PRODUCTS/OPERATIONS

2016 Sales

	$ mil.	% of total
North American Full-Service segment	10,376	61
North American Limited-Service segment	3,561	21
International	2,636	15
Other unallocated corporate	499	3
Total	**17,072**	**100**

2016 Sales

	$ mil.	% of total
Cost reimbursements	13,546	79
Owned leased and other revenue	1,307	8
Franchise fees	988	6
Base management fees	806	5
Incentive management fees	425	2
Total	**17,072**	**100**

COMPETITORS

Accor	Four Seasons Hotels
Best Western	Hilton Worldwide
Carlson Hotels	Hyatt
Choice Hotels	InterContinental
Club Med	Hotels
Extended Stay America	LXR Luxury Resorts
Inc.	Loews Hotels
FRHI Hotels and	
Resorts	

HISTORICAL FINANCIALS

Company Type: Public

Income Statement

FYE: December 31

	REVENUE ($ mil.)	NET INCOME ($ mil.)	NET PROFIT MARGIN	EMPLOYEES
12/17	22,894	1,372	6.0%	177,000
12/16	17,072	780	4.6%	226,500
12/15	14,486	859	5.9%	127,500
12/14	13,796	753	5.5%	123,500
12/13	12,784	626	4.9%	123,000
Annual Growth	**15.7%**	**21.7%**	**—**	**9.5%**

2017 Year-End Financials

Debt ratio: 34.40%	No. of shares (mil.): 359
Return on equity: 30.19%	Dividends
Cash ($ mil.): 383	Yield: 0.0%
Current ratio: 0.46	Payout: 35.7%
Long-term debt ($ mil.): 7,840	Market value ($ mil.): 48,741

	STOCK PRICE ($) FY Close	P/E High/Low	Earnings	Dividends	Book Value
12/17	135.73	37 22	3.61	1.29	10.39
12/16	82.68	32 22	2.64	1.15	13.87
12/15	67.04	26 20	3.15	0.95	(14.01)
12/14	78.03	30 18	2.54	0.77	(7.86)
12/13	49.35	24 18	2.00	0.64	(4.75)
Annual Growth	**28.8%**	**— —**	**15.9%**	**19.2%**	

Marsh & McLennan Companies Inc.

One of the world's largest insurance brokers Marsh & McLennan Companies (MMC) is a heavyweight insurance middleman. Through core subsidiary Marsh the company provides a broad array of insurance-related brokerage consulting and risk management services to clients in more than 130 countries. Customers include large and small companies government entities and not-for-profit organizations. MMC's global reinsurance brokerage business is handled by subsidiary Guy Carpenter. The company also owns Mercer which provides human resources and financial consulting services to customers in 40 nations worldwide; and Oliver Wyman which provides management consulting services.

Operations

MMC's operations are split into two groups — the Risk and Insurance Services (RIS) segment (consisting of Marsh and Guy Carpenter) and the Consulting segment (Mercer and Oliver Wyman). Both segments help clients assess risks in their businesses and ascertain whether those risks are insurable.

The RIS segment accounts for about 55% of revenue; insurance subsidiary Marsh alone accounts for about 45% of MMC's total revenues while Guy Carpenter accounts for about 10%. The Consulting segment brings in the remaining revenue; its Mercer human resources unit (MMC's second-largest subsidiary) accounts for a third of the group's total revenues. Oliver Wyman brings in another 10%.

Geographic Reach

MMC provides services in the Americas the Asia/Pacific region and the EMEA (Europe Middle East and Africa) region.

The US contributes about half of annual revenues.The UK and Continental Europe bring in about 15% of revenue each while the Asia/Pacific region and other markets each bring in about 10%.

Sales and Marketing

MMC's business customers include small mid-sized and multinational corporations. Its consulting division serves entities engaged in industries including transportation communication technology energy retail distribution and wholesale and finance.

Financial Performance

MMC has seen relatively steady revenue growth over the last few years. In 2016 revenue rose 2% to 13.2 billion: Both segments had increased sales that year. In the RIS segment Marsh rose 4% while Guy Carpenter rose 2%. The Consulting segment's Oliver Wyman rose 2% and its Mercer unit stayed flat. Geographically the US Continental Europe and the Asia/Pacific region had gains that year

while the UK and other markets had modest declines.

Net income has been steadily growing and in 2016 it increased 11% to $1.8 billion. The higher revenue that year plus a drop in non-compensation/benefits operating expenses drove that increase.

After dipping in 2015 cash flow from operations rose 6% to $2 billion. This was largely due to the increase in net income.

Strategy

Citing the rise of economic difficulties natural disasters such as tsunamis and hurricanes international terrorism and other hazards for businesses MMC has been working to expand its role as a risk consultant. Subsidiary Marsh has been steadily branching out from its straight brokerage operations expanding its offerings of risk and insurance-related services including benefits management international risk placement and consumer programs for executives employees and high-net-worth individuals.

Nonetheless like its leading US competitors Marsh's most basic strategy for growth through the years has been to buy up regional brokerages large and small. It has kept up a steady pace of acquisitions of regional commercial brokerage firms especially in the mid-sized business market.

The Mercer business has also been expanding through acquisitions in recent years especially in the growing field of data solutions. Mercer is also seeking to expand its investment consulting operations.

While continuing to pursue an aggressive acquisition strategy — the firm has acquired some 130 businesses since 2009 — MMC has also been working to de-risk its own operations by enacting some cost-cutting measures in recent years. Restructuring measures including divesting under-performing businesses aim to overcome the impact of historical regulatory and litigation issues as well as economic and competitive conditions on its bottom line.

Mergers and Acquisitions

MMC is a very acquisitive group; its Marsh subsidiary makes numerous purchases each year.

In 2015 acquisitions included Belgium-based credit insurer Trade Insurance Hong Kong-based compensation/benefits specialist HR Business Solutions (Asia) and US-based Benefit Planning Group. Also that year Oliver Wyman bought Team-SAI a US-based specialist in aviation and aerospace technical advisory services.

Expanding its small and midsized enterprise offerings in the UK Marsh acquired Jelf and Bluefin in 2015 and 2016 respectively. Those firms provide technical consulting services including claims advisory personal lines solutions and risk management.

In 2016 Marsh's middle market agency unit acquired San Francisco-based Presidio Benefits Group Atlanta-based Benefits Advisory Group and Florida-based Vero Insurance. Oliver Wyman acquired LShift Limited and Mercer acquired Pillar Administration.

Group purchases in 2017 included Insurance Partners of Texas Georgia-based J. Smith Lanier & Company and Minnesota-based Blakestad.

HISTORY

Marsh & McLennan Companies dates back to the Dan H. Bomar Company founded in 1871 after the Great Chicago Fire. In 1885 a plucky Harvard dropout named Henry Marsh joined the company then known as R.A. Waller and Company. When Robert Waller died in 1889 Marsh and fellow employee Herbert Ulmann bought a controlling stake and renamed the company Marsh Ulmann & Co.

Marsh pioneered insurance brokering and in 1901 set up U.S. Steel's self-insurance program.

In 1904 different directors at Burlington Northern Railroad promised their account to Marsh Ulmann as well as Manley-McLennan of Duluth (railroad insurance) and D.W. Burrows (a small Chicago-based railroad insurance firm). Rather than fight over it the firms joined forces to form the world's largest insurance brokerage. When Burrows retired in 1906 the firm became Marsh & McLennan.

In the early 20th century Marsh won AT&T's business and McLennan landed the account of Armour Meat Packing.

In 1923 Marsh & McLennan became a closely held corporation. Marsh sold out to McLennan in 1935. The company weathered the Depression without major layoffs by cutting pay and branching into life insurance and employee-benefits consulting after passage of the Social Security Act (1935).

The firm grew through acquisitions in the 1950s went public in 1962 and in 1969 formed a holding company that became Marsh & McLennan Companies. In the 1970s it diversified into investment management employee-benefits consulting and geographically into the UK with C.T. Bowring Reinsurance. As the insurance business slowed in the 1980s the financial and consulting fields grew through acquisitions and organic growth.

With offices in the World Trade Center the company lost some 300 employees in the September 11 terrorist attacks. Following the attacks on the World Trade Center Marsh & McLennan launched a new subsidiary (AXIS Specialty) to deal with the capacity shortage in the insurance industry.

Two major Marsh & McLennan units came under legal fire in probes of the mutual fund and insurance brokerage industries respectively in the early 2000s. In 2003 Putnam agreed to settle securities fraud charges with the SEC and reimburse investors; many of Putnam's top officers were replaced and its compliance procedures were restructured.

The following year Marsh found itself at the center of a price-fixing investigation that involved several insurance companies including AIG and Chubb Limited. At least nine employees of Marsh and AIG pled guilty to criminal charges. Jeffery Greenberg the son of outspoken AIG chairman and CEO Maurice Greenberg who had served as Marsh & McLennan's chairman and CEO since 1999 resigned in 2004 as a result of the price-fixing allegations.

EXECUTIVES

Senior Vice President and Chief Compliance Officer, E Gilbert

President and CEO Mercer, Julio A. Portalatin, age 57, $900,000 total compensation

CFO, Mark C. McGivney, age 49, $750,000 total compensation

President CEO and Director, Daniel S. (Dan) Glaser, age 56, $1,400,000 total compensation

EVP and General Counsel, Peter J. Beshar, age 56, $800,000 total compensation

SVP and CIO, E. Scott Gilbert, age 62

President Marsh, John Q. Doyle, age 53

President and CEO Oliver Wyman Group, Scott McDonald, age 51

Chief Executive Marsh Continental Europe, Flavio Piccolomini

CEO Marsh, John Doyle

Chief Executive Marsh Continental Europe, Siegmund Fahrig

Vice President Operations, Joe Curran

Senior Vice President and Chief Human Resource Officer, Laurie Ledford

Vice President, Bradley Morrow

Vice President Of Client Operations, William Walker

Senior Vice President, Lisa Kremer

Vice President Corporate Development and Investor, Michael Bischoff

Vice President Associate Client Executive (ACE), Tina Summers

Vice President Marsh USA Inc., Benjamin Laurenzi

Senior Vice President Marsh Finpro, Peter Stagias

Senior Vice President, Ellen Colasurdo

Vice President Marsh Risk Consulting, Belinda Berwick

Vice President, Robert Planos

Assistant Vice President, Charles Chen

Senior Vice President, Michelle Pingor

Vice President Risk Consultant, Edward Guzy

Assistant Vice President, Sue McCaw

Vice President Fleet Safety, Joseph Darby

Senior Vice President, John Samuels

Senior Vice President, Holden Burrow

Vice President Human Resources, Mark Allen

Vice President Networking, Tony Iorio

Vice President Operations, Jim Halkins

Senior Vice President and Western Zone Education, Bruce Bernstein

Senior Vice President, Michael Serricchio

Senior Vice President, Isabella M Stengele

Senior Vice President and Placement Specialist, Mary Naughton

Senior Vice President, Christopher Pease

Vice President, Joshua Forbes

Vice President Account Executive, Matthew Thompson

Vice President Property Practice, Sabrina Fabris

Assistant Vice President, Sebastian Aguayo

Vice President, Tarique Nageer

Vice President, Sakurako Yagi

Assistant Vice President, Kathi Cavanagh

Vice President Casualty Placement, Daniel Gibbons

Vice President Audit and Risk Management, Michelle Viotty

Senior Vice President, James Wright

Senior Vice President, Michael Rouse

Senior Vice President, Jay Simione

Senior Vice President, Ali Rizvi

Senior Vice President Information Technology, Brian Wood

Vice President Global Technology Infrastructure, Jeffrey Pustay

Senior Vice President, Ronald Reinartz

Senior Vice President Global Information Technology, Scott Francis

Senior Vice President Senior Advisory Specialist 1166 Avenue of the Americas, Marla Nicholson

Placement Specialist Assistant Vice President, Tricia Richardson

CPCU Vice President and Knowledge Manager, Karen Parker

Vice President Risk Consulting, Matthew Blair

Senior Vice President Marsh Marine Practice, Raymond Komorowski

Senior Vice President Finance, Mike Rinehart

Assistant Vice President and Manager West Zone Marketing, Patricia Ramirez

Senior Vice President, Thomas Edridge

Vice President Global Broking Specialties, Dan Carlson

Senior Vice President, Kristen Stokes

Senior Vice President, Eric Peabody

Assistant Vice President, Jim Randello

Vice President, Ralph Chiumenti

Vice President and Chief Information Officer Middl, Nixon Thomas

Assistant Vice President Client Manager, Martin Goh

Senior Vice President, Eileen Quenell

Assistant Vice President, Heather Razo

Senior Vice President, Derek Martisus

Assistant Vice President Sales And Business Development, Pepper Periquet

Senior Vice President Retail Industry Practice, Linda Brown

Senior Vice President, Mark Crites

Vice President, Joan Spiegel

Vice President, Patricia Robinson

Senior Vice President, Joseph Asmar

Vice President Finance, Michael Murphy

Senior Vice President, John McGuire

Senior Vice President, Robert Curtis

Vice President, Brian Rath

Senior Vice President, Stephanie Nagrath

Senior Vice President, Randy Dickman

Vice President Business Development, Hallie Beddes

Vice President, Michael Price

Cpcu Senior Vice President Marsh Usa Inc, Maureen Biehl

Vice President, Romaneo Adams

Vice President In Marsh Risk Consulting's Reputational Risk And Crisis Management Practice Based, Susan Morton

Vice President, Virginia Del Lago

Assistant Vice President, Felix Chung

Vice President Of Marketing, Erica Jones

Vice President, Catherine Ricia

Senior Vice President, Dawn Buelow

Vice President, Jessica Hatch

Assistant Vice President, Thadd Northam

Vice President Environmental Practice, Jack Palis

Vice President Director, Michael Rahill

Senior Vice President, Mark Alderman

Senior Vice President Global Program Manager, Lori Suske

Vice President, Raegan Buckley

Senior Vice President, Jenny Daby

Senior Vice President, Jeralyn Sorensen

Senior Vice President, Stanley Zimmerman

Senior Vice President, Eugene Charney

Assistant Vice President, Edward Mitchell

Executive Vice President Of Information Technology, Jennifer Adams

Vice President, Louise Casazza

Senior Vice President, Marcy Waterfall

Senior Vice President U S Marine And Energy, John Pallasch

Dip Fs (Gen Ins) Qpib Cipvice President Head Of Businessdevelopment Singapore, Andrew Paul

Vice President Human Resources Manager, Sarah Randall

Assistant Vice President, Kristin Will

Senior Vice President, Janis Thornton

Senior Vice President, Rita Patullo

Vice President, Michael Hargis

Senior Vice President Advanced Risk Solutions, Scott Sanderson

Senior Vice President, Ben Hetzer

Senior Vice President, James Helm

Vice President Information Technology, Gursharan Sant

Senior Vice President, Mary Berry

Vice President, Thomas Luty

Senior Vice President Global Compliance, Jean Mahon

Vice President National Brokerage Property Practice, Natalie Kenny

Vice President At Mars, Desrene Edwards

Senior Vice President, Chris Victorino

Senior Regional Premium Finance Vice President, Natasha Lee

Senior Vice President Strategic Development Officer At Marsh And McLennan, Leonard Battifarano

Senior Vice President, Brett Gillmon

Assistant Vice President, Jenny Dickson

Assistant Vice President Asia Client Services, Kathleen Schimmenti

Senior Vice President, Michaela Grasshoff

Senior Vice President Global Broking North America, Jason Monteforte

Senior Vice President Global Broking Specialties,
Jack Reid
Vice President Public Entities, Sandra McFarland
Vice President Human Resources, Vanessa Boneta
Senior Vice President, Kristi Whistle
Vice President, David Erdman
Senior Vice President, Carl Patchke
Vice President, Kristin Greenwald
Senior Vice President, Natasha Tarasova
Assistant Vice President, Michael Hourihan
Senior Vice President, Christine Williams
Senior Vice President, Greg Miller
**Senior Vice President Multinational Trade Credit
Practice,** Liam Duffy
Vice President, Melanie Dunne
Senior Vice President, Tracey Cole
Senior Vice President At Marsh, Holly Brumbelow
**Assistant Vice President Information Technology
Project Manager,** Tarek Timol
Vice President Private Client Services, Susan Ott
Auditors: Deloitte & Touche LLP

LOCATIONS

HQ: Marsh & McLennan Companies Inc.
1166 Avenue of the Americas, New York, NY 10036-2774
Phone: 212 345-5000   **Fax:** 212 345-4809
Web: www.mmc.com

2016 Sales

	$ mil.	% of total
US	6,573	50
UK	2,019	15
Continental Europe	2,022	15
Asia/Pacific	1,363	10
Other regions & countries	1,278	10
Adjustments	(44)	-
Total	**13,211**	**100**

PRODUCTS/OPERATIONS

2016 Sales

	$ mil.	% of total
Risk & insurance services		
Marsh	5,976	45
Guy Carpenter	1,141	9
Fiduciary interest income	26	-
Consulting		
Mercer	4,323	33
Oliver Wyman Group	1,789	13
Adjustments	(44)	-
Total	**13,211**	**100**

COMPETITORS

Accenture
Anthony Clark International Insurance Brokers
Aon
Bain & Company
Bollinger Inc.
Booz Allen
Brown & Brown
FTI Consulting
Fortegra Financial
Gallagher
Hub International
ING
Jardine Lloyd
McKinsey & Company
National Financial Partners
THB Group
USI
Willis Towers Watson

HISTORICAL FINANCIALS

Company Type: Public

Income Statement

FYE: December 31

	REVENUE ($ mil.)	NET INCOME ($ mil.)	NET PROFIT MARGIN	EMPLOYEES
12/16	13,211	1,768	13.4%	60,000
12/15	12,893	1,599	12.4%	60,000
12/14	12,951	1,465	11.3%	57,000
12/13	12,261	1,357	11.1%	55,000
12/12	11,924	1,176	9.9%	54,000
Annual Growth	**2.6%**	**10.7%**	**—**	**2.7%**

2016 Year-End Financials

Debt ratio: 26.43%
Return on equity: 27.76%
Cash ($ mil.): 1,026
Current ratio: 1.20
Long-term debt ($ mil.): 4,495

No. of shares (mil.): 514
Dividends
Yield: 0.0%
Payout: 38.4%
Market value ($ mil.): 34,774

	STOCK PRICE ($) FY Close	P/E High/Low	Earnings	Dividends	Book Value
12/16	67.59	20 15	3.38	1.30	12.04
12/15	55.45	20 17	2.98	1.18	12.48
12/14	57.24	22 17	2.65	1.06	13.06
12/13	48.36	20 14	2.43	0.96	14.46
12/12	34.47	17 14	2.13	0.90	11.99
Annual Growth	**18.3%**	**— —**	**12.2%**	**9.6%**	**0.1%**

Masco Corp.

Masco's ideal customer is a home improvement junkie with a thing for cabinets and plumbing fixtures. It is a leading manufacturer of a variety of home improvement and building products with cabinet and plumbing products accounting for more than 60% of its sales. Cabinet brands include KraftMaid Cardell Quality Cabinets and Merillat in the US and The Moores Group in Europe. Faucets and bath and shower accessories are sold under the Delta and Peerless brands in the US and as Hansgrohe in Europe. Masco also makes BEHR paints and stains windows doors staple guns locksets and HVAC products. It spun off its installation services business as TopBuild in 2015.

HISTORY

Masco founder Alex Manoogian moved to the US at age 19 in 1920. He wound up in Detroit and with partners Harry Adjemian and Charles Saunders he started Masco (the first letters of their last names plus "co" for "company") Screw Products Company eight days before the crash of 1929. Manoogian's partners left within the year.

Largely reliant on Detroit's auto industry Masco grew slowly during the Depression making custom parts for Chrysler Ford and others. With sales of $200000 by 1937 it went public on the Detroit Stock Exchange. During WWII Masco focused on defense and in 1942 sales passed $1 million. A new plant opened in 1948 in Dearborn Michigan as Masco resumed peacetime business mainly in the auto industry.

In 1954 Masco began selling Manoogian's one-handle kitchen faucet (Delta). Sales of faucets passed $1 million by 1958 and Masco opened a new faucet factory in Indiana.

Under Manoogian's son Richard — whose dinner was often delayed while his father used the stove to test the heat tolerance of new faucet parts —

Masco Corporation (so renamed in 1961) diversified. From 1964 to 1980 it bought more than 50 companies concentrating on tool and metal casting energy exploration and air compressors. In 1984 the firm split. Masco Corporation pursued the course set by its successful faucet sales expanding its interests in home improvement and furnishings. The industrial products business was spun off as Masco Industries a separate public corporation (later Metaldyne) in which Masco maintained a sizable stake.

Masco Corporation became the #1 US furniture maker in the late 1980s by buying Lexington Furniture (1987) and Universal Furniture (1989) both of North Carolina. In 1990 Masco acquired Kraft-Maid cabinets.

Two years later the company sold its interests in Mechanical Technology Payless Cashways and Emco Limited of Canada (Masco bought back 40% of Emco in 1997). Masco reduced its stake in Metaldyne from 47% to 35% in 1993.

Masco sought to establish itself in Europe and in 1994 it bought a German cabinetmaker and a UK producer of handheld showers. In 1996 founder Manoogian died but the company flowed on. It added a UK cabinetmaker a German shower manufacturer and a German insulation firm. That year Masco sold its troubled furniture unit to a group of investors and executives (who renamed the unit LifeStyle Furnishings International) for about $1 billion and further reduced its stake in Metaldyne to less than 20% (and later sold it all).

Acquisitions in 1997 included cabinetmakers Texwood Industries of Texas and Liberty Hardware Manufacturing of Florida. The next year it bought Vasco (heating systems and equipment Belgium) and Brugman (building and home-improvement products the Netherlands). It sold its Thermador unit (ovens and ranges) to US joint venture Bosch-Siemens Hausgerate.

Masco made 13 acquisitions from 1999 through early 2000 including Heritage Bathrooms (bathroom equipment UK) Faucet Queens (plumbing and hardware supply) GMU Group (kitchen cabinets Spain) Avocet Hardware (locks and hardware UK) BEHR Process (coatings) and Mill's Pride (cabinets). Boosting its services in 1999 it acquired The Cary Group an installer of fiberglass insulation.

To increase its geographic reach Masco bought Tvilum-Scanbirk (ready-to-assemble furniture Denmark) Masterchem Industries (specialty paint products) and Glass Idromassaggio (bathroom equipment Italy) in 2000. In late 2000 and early 2001 it acquired two US-based installation services companies Davenport Insulation Group and BSI Holdings respectively. Also in 2001 Masco acquired Milgard Manufacturing a vinyl window and patio door maker.

During 2002 Masco acquired home improvement products and service companies that included Bristan Ltd. (kitchen and bath faucets and shower and bath accessories) Brasstech Inc. (faucets plumbing specialties and bath accessories; California) Cambrian Windows Ltd. (vinyl window frames) Duraflex Ltd. (extruded vinyl frame components) Premier Manufacturing Ltd. (vinyl window and door frames) SCE Unlimited (siding shutters gutters; Illinois) IDI Group (fireplaces garage doors shower enclosures; Atlanta) Service Partners LLC (insulation and other building products Virginia) several small installation and other service companies and Diversified Cabinet Distributors (cabinets and countertops Atlanta). Masco also increased its interest in Hansgrohe AG (kitchen and bath faucets hand-held and fixed showerheads luxury shower systems and steam showers; Germany) to 64%. The company sold its StarMark Cabinetry business for about $15 million.

In 2003 Masco increased its ownership interest in Hansgrohe AG (kitchen and bath faucets handheld and fixed showerheads luxury shower systems and steam showers; Germany) to 64% from 27%. The company established Color Solutions Centers in more than 1500 Home Depot stores throughout the US. Masco sold its Baldwin Hardware and Weiser Lock businesses (builders' hardware and locksets) to Black & Decker (now Stanley Black & Decker) and The Marvel Group a provider specialty products such as office work stations and machine stands to members of Marvel's management team (led by president John Dellamore) for $289 million in total. Acquisitions in 2003 included PowerShot Tool Company Inc. (fastening products New Jersey) and several small installation service companies for a combined $63 million.

The next year Masco sold its Jung Pumpen (pumps) The Alvic Group (kitchen cabinets) Alma Kuchen (kitchen cabinets) E. Missel (acoustic insulation) and SKS Group (shutters and ventilation systems) businesses for $199 million. Masco continued its business review in 2005 selling two operating companies that made and distributed cabinets vanities medicine cabinets shower rods and bath accessories.

After reorganizing its European business operations Masco sold off several of its operating units including Gebhardt Consolidated (HVAC) The Heating Group (radiators) and GMU Group (cabinets). The company also disposed of North American businesses that were not core to its long-term growth strategy which included Computerized Security Systems (CSS) and Zenith Products (bathroom storage).

In 2008 the company merged its Mill's Price brand with KraftMaid to form the Masco Retail Cabinet Group . It also merged Merillat and Quality Cabinets to form Masco Builder Cabinet Group .

In addition to cutting costs through divestitures Masco has streamlined its operating structure to trim spending. In 2011 the company merged its wholesale and retail cabinet units to form Masco Cabinetry. It also decided to stop making ready-to-assemble cabinets a non-core offering.

Looking toward a growth market in 2012 Masco entered into the fast-growing Indian bathroom and kitchen faucet sector by launching its line of residential and commercial products in that country. The company sees India as an integral part of the global expansion plan for the Delta Faucet Company.

During 2013 Behr Process Corporation completed the rollout of its products to Home Depot stores across Mexico continued to build the foundation of its China business with dealers and expanded its retail relationships into Latin America. Hansgrohe one of the leading global bathroom specialists continued geographic expansion in its Decorative Architectural Products and Plumbing Products segments.

In 2013 Masco Cabinetry launched Arbor Creek Cabinets a stand-alone brand of ready-to-assemble cabinetry in four birch door styles and three finishes offering customers choices ranging from a sleek contemporary look to more traditional options.

EXECUTIVES

VP General Counsel and Secretary, Kenneth G. Cole, $421,058 total compensation
VP CFO and Treasurer, John G. Sznewajs, age 50, $653,353 total compensation
President and CEO, Keith J. Allman, $1,126,654 total compensation
Group President Global Plumbing, Richard O'Reagan, $481,188 total compensation

VP Strategy and Corporate Development, Amit Bhargava, $339,231 total compensation
VP Masco Operating System, Christopher K. Kastner, $366,962 total compensation
Chairman, J. Michael (Mike) Losh, age 71
Auditors: PricewaterhouseCoopers LLP

LOCATIONS

HQ: Masco Corp.
17450 College Parkway, Livonia, MI 48152
Phone: 313 274-7400
Web: www.masco.com

2016 sales

	$ mil.	% of total
North America	5,834	79
Europe & other regions	1,523	21
Total	**7,357**	**100**

PRODUCTS/OPERATIONS

2016 sales

	$ mil.	% of total
Plumbing products	3,526	48
Decorative architectural products	2,092	28
Cabinetry products	970	13
Windows and Other specialty products	769	11
Total	**7,357**	**100**

Selected Brand Names

Plumbing products
  Alsons
  American Shower & Bath
  Aqua Glass
  Axor
  BrassCraft
  Brasstech
  Breuer
  Bristan
  Brizo
  Caldera
  Damixa
  Delta
  Glass
  Hansgrohe
  Heritage
  Hot Spring
  HÜPPE
  BrassCraft
  Mirolin
  Newport Brass
  Peerless
  Pharo
  Plumb Shop
Cabinets products
  KraftMaid
  Merillat
  Moores
  Quality Cabinets
  Tvilum-Scanbirk
  Woodgate
Decorative architectural products
  BEHR
  Decor Bathware
  Expressions
  Franklin Brass
  Kilz
  Liberty
Windows and Other specialty products
  Arrow
  Brugman
  Cambrian
  Duraflex
  Griffin
  Milgard Windows
  Powershot
  Premier
  Superia
  Thermic
  Vasco

COMPETITORS

Akzo Nobel Paints	MasterBrand Cabinets
Armstrong World Industries	Moen
	Norcraft Companies

Benjamin Moore	Inc.
Columbia Pipe	PPG Industries
Elkay Manufacturing	Pfister
Gerber Plumbing Fixtures	Republic National Cabinet
Grohe	Sherwin-Williams
Jacuzzi Brands	Waxman
Kohler	

HISTORICAL FINANCIALS

Company Type: Public

Income Statement

FYE: December 31

	REVENUE ($ mil.)	NET INCOME ($ mil.)	NET PROFIT MARGIN	EMPLOYEES
12/17	7,644	533	7.0%	26,000
12/16	7,357	491	6.7%	26,000
12/15	7,142	355	5.0%	25,000
12/14	8,521	856	10.0%	32,000
12/13	8,173	272	3.3%	32,000
Annual Growth	(1.7%)	18.3%	—	(5.1%)

2017 Year-End Financials

Debt ratio: 56.21%	No. of shares (mil.): 310
Return on equity:	Dividends
Cash ($ mil.): 1,302	Yield: 0.0%
Current ratio: 1.97	Payout: 24.4%
Long-term debt ($ mil.): 2,969	Market value ($ mil.): 13,639

	STOCK PRICE ($) FY Close	P/E High/Low		PER SHARE ($) Earnings	Dividends	Book Value
12/17	43.94	26	19	1.66	0.41	(0.19)
12/16	31.62	25	16	1.47	0.39	(0.94)
12/15	28.30	30	22	1.02	0.37	(0.41)
12/14	25.20	11	8	2.38	0.33	2.68
12/13	22.77	30	22	0.76	0.30	1.53
Annual Growth	17.9%	—	—	21.6%	7.8%	—

MASSACHUSETTS HOUSING FINANCE AGENCY PROPERTY ACQUISITION AND DISPOSITION CORPORATION

LOCATIONS

HQ: MASSACHUSETTS HOUSING FINANCE AGENCY PROPERTY ACQUISITION AND DISPOSITION CORPORATION
1 BEACON ST, BOSTON, MA 021083107
Phone: 617 854-1000
Web: WWW.MYMASSMORTGAGE.ORG

Company Type: Private

Income Statement   FYE: June 30

	ASSETS ($ mil.)	NET INCOME ($ mil.)	INCOME AS % OF ASSETS	EMPLOYEES
06/07*	5,457	80	1.5%	325
12/06	1	0	0.8%	—
Annual Growth	—	—		

*Fiscal year change

2007 Year-End Financials

Debt ratio: ——
Return on equity: 22.60%
Cash ($ mil.): 578
Current ratio: 1.80
Long-term debt ($ mil.): —

Dividends
Yield: —
Payout: —
Market value ($ mil.): —

MasTec Inc. (FL)

MasTec goes the last mile ? and the first mile and the miles in between ? to bring communications and energy to homes offices factories and other places. The company digs the trenches lays the cable and builds the towers that power communications and provide cell service and high-speed internet. The contractor plans and builds pipelines that transport natural gas and oil from wells to processing plans. It provides infrastructure construction to telecom vendors wireless providers cable TV operators and energy and utility companies. MasTec also builds electrical utility transmission and distribution and power generation wind and solar farms industrial infrastructure and water and sewer systems.

Operations

MasTec has five business units: Communications; Electrical Transmission; Oil and Gas; Power Generation and Industrial; and Other.

The Communications segment performs engineering construction and maintenance of communications infrastructure primarily related to wireless and wireline communications and install to the home and infrastructure for electrical utilities. It accounts for about 45% of sales.

The Oil and Gas segment does engineering construction and maintenance on oil and natural gas pipelines and processing facilities for the energy and utilities industries. It accounts for about 40% of sales.

The Electrical Transmission segment primarily serves energy and utility industries through the engineering construction and maintenance of electrical transmission lines and substations. It accounts for less than 10% of sales.

The Power Generation and Industrial segment serves the energy and utility through the installation and construction of power plants wind farms solar farms related electrical transmission infrastructure ethanol plants and other industrial infrastructure. It accounts for less than 10% of sales.

The Other segment primarily includes small business units that perform construction services for a variety of end markets in Mexico and in other locations outside the US. It accounts for less than 1% of sales.

Geographic Reach

MasTec has more than 500 locations in the US and Canada as well as in parts of Latin America and the Caribbean. North America accounts for most of the company?s sales.

Sales and Marketing

MasTec sells directly to existing and potential customers for service agreement contracts and individual projects. AT&T including work for DirecTV accounts for about a third of MasTec?s revenue and Energy Transfer is responsible for more than a quarter of revenue. The company?s level of business with AT&T has been consistent in recent years but business with Energy Transfer grew from just 6% of revenue in 2014.

Financial Performance

After eight years of steady gains MasTec recorded a dip in revenue and a loss in 2015. The company recovered in 2016 with a 22% sales gain and a $131 million profit.

Sales were driven by a 35% sales increase in MasTec?s Oil and Gas segment which was fueled by an more large long-haul pipeline infrastructure construction projects. That was somewhat offset by a decrease in pipeline work in its Canadian operations. The Communications business posted an 18% revenue increase from install-to-the-home wireline/fiber installation and wireless services projects. Higher levels of renewable energy work helped the Power Generation and Industrial segment to a 6% increase and project timing raised Electrical Transmission revenue more than 10%.

Expenses as a percentage of revenue were lower in 2016 than in 2015 helping MasTec post a profit for the year the second highest in its history. The company recorded about $15 million in restructuring costs for 2016 that included headcount reduction and facility closure.

Cash flow from operations dropped to $206 million in 2016 from $367 million in 2015. The decrease was due to increased investment in working capital from higher revenue and project activity.

Strategy

Communications has accounted for the bulk of MasTec?s revenue but its oil and gas business has been catching up. The oil and gas pipeline business is fueled by expanded activity in natural gas and the company looks for that to continue as more large pipeline projects are built out. MasTec also sees more business in communications as telecom companies lay more fiber optic lines and as the age of 5G cellular transmission dawns. Work on the US electric grid should benefit the electrical transmission segment as old lines are replaced and renewable energy sources such as wind and solar are blended into the energy mix.

MasTec hopes to get boosts from Washington D.C. with a new administration in power. The company looks for a reduction in regulation which could speed up projects and reduced costs. It also hoped for a reduction in corporate taxes which could beef up its bottom line.

Mergers and Acquisitions

MasTec uses acquisitions to grow its service capabilities and expand its footprint into new geographic regions.

The company added to its wireless capabilities with the 2014 acquisition of WesTower Communications a subsidiary of Exchange Income Corp. for about $200 million in cash. WesTower focuses on construction and maintenance of communications infrastructure related to wireless networks throughout the US.

Also in 2014 MasTec paid $126 million for Pacer Construction a Canadian company that provides infrastructure services to the oil and gas industry there. (Pacer is one of the larger contractors in Western Canada with 1600 employees.) Previous acquisitions to its oil and gas segment are Canada-based Big Country Energy Services (2013) Texas-based Bottom Line Services (2012) and Go Green Services (2012) and Canada-based Fabcor (2011).

HISTORY

MasTec was formed by the merger of Burnup & Sims (B&S) and Church & Tower (C&T). B&S was founded in 1929 to provide construction and maintenance services to the phone and utilities industries. C&T began in 1968 building phone networks in Miami and Puerto Rico. Jorge Mas Canosa was brought on board in 1969 and given half of the company in exchange for managing it. By 1971 he had succeeded in turning C&T around and had bought the remainder.

In 1994 C&T and B&S merged; B&S became MasTec and C&T became a subsidiary. Mas was named chairman and his son who had been at C&T since 1980 was named president and CEO. The company began a program of acquisitions and started building a presence in Latin America.

MasTec doubled its size in 1996 by acquiring Sintel a telecom infrastructure construction firm operating in South America and Spain from Tel ©fonica. MasTec continued to grow through acquisitions buying 10 more companies the next year. Mas died in 1997 and his son Jorge Jr. succeeded him. It sold a near-bankrupt Sintel and began to refocus on domestic operations.

EXECUTIVES

CEO and Director, Jos © R. Mas, age 45, $980,000 total compensation

EVP and CFO, George L. Pita, age 55, $450,000 total compensation

EVP General Counsel and Secretary, Alberto de Cardenas, age 48, $385,000 total compensation

COO, Robert E. (Bob) Apple, age 67, $585,000 total compensation

CIO, Albert Iturrey

Division Vice President, John Audi

Senior Vice President, Bruce Budagher

Vice President Contract Management and Marketing, Robert Jackson

Vice President Virginia Operations, Henry Rudd

Vice President of Sales and Marketing, Jeff Mock

Vice President Business Development, Kevin Donnelly

Vice President Business Development Power, Dennis Pungitore

Vice President Operations Support, Tony Brisco

Vice President of Human Resour, Jerry Williams

Executive Vice President, Ray Zeldenthuis

Senior Vice President Business Development, Dale Clymer

Vice President, Sonya Roshek

Senior Vice President, Rick Gray

Vice President Field Service, Chris Gera

Vice President, Dee Farquhar

Vice President Of Operations, Fred Mercado

Vice President And Controller, Giovanni Lima

Vice President Southwest Region, Erik Hughes

Assistant Vice President Construction Services, Jose Tarafa

Vice President, Ron Martin

Division Vice President, Carl Basden

Vice President Business Development, Andrei Trach

Chairman, Jorge Mas, age 54

Auditors: BDO USA, LLP

LOCATIONS

HQ: MasTec Inc. (FL)
800 S. Douglas Road, 12th Floor, Coral Gables, FL 33134
Phone: 305 599-1800
Web: www.mastec.com

PRODUCTS/OPERATIONS

2016 Sales

	$ mil.	% of total
Communications	2,323	45
Oil & Gas	2,024	39
Electrical Transmission	383	8
Power Generation & Industrial	405	8
Other	15	-
Adjustments	(18.7)	
Total	**5,134**	**100**

Selected Services

Broadband networks
  Aerial and underground construction
  Bonding/grounding
  Engineering and design
  FCC testing
  Modem installation
  Optical fiber splicing activation and testing
  Warehouse and inventory management
Telecommunications
  Aerial construction
  Copper/coaxial cable systems
  Directional drilling
  Engineering
  Fiber-optic cable systems
  Fiber-to-the-premises (FTTP) deployment
  Splicing and testing
  Underground construction
Utilities
  Design and engineering
  Gas distribution construction and maintenance
  Storm restoration
  Submarine cable installation
  Substation construction
  Transmission line construction
  Trench construction

COMPETITORS

Bechtel	MDU Construction
Black & Veatch	Services
Dycom	MYR Group
General Dynamics	Pike Corporation
Goldfield	Quanta Services
Henkels & McCoy	Sirti
M. A. Mortenson	Willbros

HISTORICAL FINANCIALS

Company Type: Public

Income Statement

FYE: December 31

	REVENUE ($ mil.)	NET INCOME ($ mil.)	NET PROFIT MARGIN	EMPLOYEES
12/16	5,134	131	2.6%	15,400
12/15	4,208	(79)	—	15,900
12/14	4,611	115	2.5%	15,550
12/13	4,324	140	3.3%	13,450
12/12	3,726	107	2.9%	12,300
Annual Growth	**8.3%**	**5.1%**	**—**	**5.8%**

2016 Year-End Financials

Debt ratio: 32.23%	No. of shares (mil.): 82
Return on equity: 12.86%	Dividends
Cash ($ mil.): 38	Yield: —
Current ratio: 1.67	Payout: —
Long-term debt ($ mil.): 961	Market value ($ mil.): 3,157

	STOCK PRICE ($) FY Close	P/E High/Low		PER SHARE ($) Earnings	Dividends	Book Value
12/16	38.25	25	8	1.61	0.00	13.28
12/15	17.38	—	—	(0.98)	0.00	11.73
12/14	22.61	31	13	1.35	0.00	13.50
12/13	32.72	19	14	1.66	0.00	13.15
12/12	24.93	18	10	1.31	0.00	11.21
Annual Growth	**11.3%**		**—**	**5.3%**	**—**	**4.3%**

Mastercard Inc

Surpassing Visa in market share — now that would be priceless. Serving more than 20000 member financial institutions around the world Mastercard is the #2 payment system in the US. The company does not issue credit or its namesake cards; rather it markets the Mastercard Maestro and Cirrus brands provides a transaction authorization network establishes guidelines for use and collects fees from members. The company provides its services in more than 200 countries and territories and its branded cards are accepted at millions of locations around the globe. Mastercard also operates the Cirrus ATM network.

HISTORY

A group of bankers formed The Interbank Card Association (ICA) in 1966 to establish authorization clearing and settlement procedures for bank credit card transactions. This was particularly important to banks left out of the rapidly growing BankAmericard (later Visa) network sponsored by Bank of America.

By 1969 ICA was issuing the Master Charge card throughout the US and had formed alliances in Europe and Japan. In the mid-1970s ICA modernized its system replacing telephone transaction authorization with a computerized magnetic strip system. ICA had members in Africa Australia and Europe by 1979. That year the organization changed its name (and the card's) to MasterCard.

In 1980 Russell Hogg became president when John Reynolds resigned after disagreeing with the board over company performance and direction. Hogg made major organizational changes and consolidated data processing in St. Louis. MasterCard began offering debit cards in 1980 and traveler's checks in 1981.

MasterCard issued the first credit cards in China in 1987. The next year it bought Cirrus then the world's largest ATM network. It also secured a pact with Belgium-based card company Eurocard (which later became Europay) to supervise MasterCard's European operations and help build the brand.

Hogg resigned in 1988 after disagreements with the board and was succeeded by Alex Hart. In 1991 the Maestro debit card was unveiled.

The 1990s were marked by trouble in Europe: The pact with Europay hadn't resulted in the boom MasterCard had hoped for customer service was below par and competition was keen. Alex Hart retired in 1994 and was succeeded by Eugene Lockhart who tackled the European woes. Lockhart considered ending the relationship but eventually worked things out with Europay. By the end of the decade Europay was locked in a vicious battle to undercut Visa's market share through lower fees.

MasterCard in 1995 invested in UK-based Mondex International maker of electronic set-value refillable smart cards. But US consumer resistance to cash cards and competition in the more advanced European market delayed growth in this area.

In October 1996 a group of merchants including Wal-Mart and Sears filed class-action lawsuits against both MasterCard and Visa challenging the "honor all cards" rule. Because usage fees are higher merchants balked at accepting consumers' MasterCard- or Visa-branded off-line or signature-based debit cards and claimed the card issuers violated antitrust laws by tying acceptance of debit to that of credit. In a dramatic twist minutes before the trial was set to begin in 2003 MasterCard announced a settlement (the card issuer was required to pay $125 million in 2003 and $100 million annually from 2004 through 2012).

Just months later armed with the lawsuit's settlement which also freed merchants to pick which credit and debit card services they use Wal-Mart (along with a handful of others) stopped accepting signature debit cards issued by MasterCard.

Lockhart resigned in 1997 and was succeeded by former head of overseas operations Robert Selander. Yet another management upheaval began in 1999 as the company moved to streamline its organizational structure and shift away from geographical divisions. It also said member banks could boost visibility by putting their logos on card fronts and moving MasterCard's logo to the back.

In 2002 MasterCard merged with Europay with which it already had close ties. As part of the transaction holding company MasterCard Incorporated was formed; MasterCard International become the company's main subsidiary and MasterCard Europe (formerly Europay) became its European subsidiary.

After some 40 years as a private entity MasterCard went public in 2006 in one of the largest IPOs of its time. Following the offering the approximately 1400 financial institutions that wholly owned MasterCard before the offering retained a stake of more than 40%. Two of the top three US banks (Citigroup and JPMorgan Chase) remained among MasterCard's largest shareholders.

Some of the proceeds from the company's IPO were used to fight antitrust lawsuits from such rivals as American Express and Discover as well as other payment processors. In 2008 the company agreed to a $1.8 billion settlement with American Express which had claimed that MasterCard and others tried to stop financial institutions from issuing its AmEx cards. Later that year MasterCard settled the Discover lawsuit agreeing to pay $862.5 million.

Also in 2008 MasterCard bought Ireland-based software provider Orbiscom. The acquired company's technology was used to create MasterCard inControl a platform for making secure Internet and telephone purchases.

MasterCard promoted president and COO Ajay Banga to CEO in 2010. He succeeded Robert Selander who stepped down after more than a dozen years at the helm.

EXECUTIVES

Executive Vice President and General Manager US National Accounts North American Markets, Michael Fiore

CFO, Martina Hund-Mejean, age 57, $691,667 total compensation

President and CEO, Ajaypal S. (Ajay) Banga, age 57, $1,200,000 total compensation

EVP Global Account Management, Gary J. Flood, age 59, $650,000 total compensation

President International Markets, Ann Cairns, age 60, $609,427 total compensation

Chief Services Officer, Kevin J. Stanton

President U.S. Issuers, Raj Seshadri

President Europe, Javier Perez

General Counsel and Chief Franchise Officer, Timothy H. (Tim) Murphy, age 50

Chief Product Officer, Michael Miebach

Chief Innovation Officer, Garry Lyons

President Operations and Technology, Edward (Ed) McLaughlin

Vice Chairman and President Center for Inclusive Growth, Walt W. Macnee, age 62

President North America, Craig Vosburg, age 50

President Middle East and Africa, Raghu Malhotra

President Enterprise Security Solutions, Ajay Bhalla

Co-President Asia/Pacific, Hai Ling

Co-President Asia/Pacific, Ari Sarker
President Latin America and Caribbean Region, Gilberto Caldart
President Processing Services, Andrea Scerch
President Prepaid Management Services, Fabrizio Burlando
Senior Vice President and Group Head, Michael Robichaud
Vice President of Promotions and Interactives, Cheryl Guerin
Senior Vice President Chief Admin Officer, Joy Thoma
Vice President Business Leader, Mark Aquilina
Vice President And Business Leader, Jon Briggs
Vice President Financial Analysis, Richard Strauss
Vice President Business Leader, Ashfaq Kamal
Executive Vice President, Rennis Li
Vice President Of Program Development, Adrienne Chambers
Vice President Business Leader, Bernhard Mors
Vice President Finance, Herman Green
Vice President, Michael Moutenot
Vice President, Naya Larsson
Vice President Prepaid Product Management, Ed Wang
Vice President and Senior Counsel, Joseph Halprin
Vice President Business Leader Social Media, Gregory Weiss
Consumer Marketing Vice President, Beatriz Galloni
Vice President Product Management, Eric McIlwain
Vice President Global Marketing and Communications Strategy and Operations, Amy Fuller
Vice President Senior Business Leader, Mathias Lilja
Vice President Caribbean, Mario Perez
Vice President Systems Development Global Technology and Operations, Sheryl Andrasko
Vice President, Peter Berardino
Vice President Business Information Systems, Richard Derizans
Vice President Consulting, Alma Robles
Vice President and Senior Business Leader Worldwide Communications, Jean Altz
Vice President and Sbl Commercial Business Development, Patrick Sulston
Vice President Communications Mea, Sami Lahoud
Vice President Global Merchant Development, Rachel Bale
Vice President, Ramzy AL Amary
Vice President Account Management, Patricia Costanzo
Vice President and Business Leader, Cheryl Castro
Vice President, Patrick Dwyer
Vice President And Business Leader, Regina NG
Vice President Account Management, Tor Opedal
Senior Vice President Business Development Unit Supervisor, Hunter Woolley
Vice President Mergers and Acquisitions, Michael Luchinsky
Vice President Business Leader Senior Counsel Global Mergers and Acquisitions, Markus Lotz
Vice President Corporate Philanthropy and Citizenship, Leslie Meek-Wohl
Vice President National Merchant Sales, Nick Pifani
Vice President Performance Analysis, John Tullo
Vice President Global Product Development Markertplace, Holliday Haynes
Senior Vice President Business Development Finance, Rich Mascali
Vice President Senior Business Leader, Ingrid R Jones
Vice President Advance Payments, William Giles
Vice President New Markets, Rich Ciamillo
Senior Vice President Total Rewards, Stuart Finkelstein
Vice President Member Relations, Peter Patrissi

Senior Vice President Global Core Products Business Finance Officer, Pam Loscher
Vice President Product Management, Gowri Narayanan
Senior Executive Vice President, Trish Preston
Vice President Mobile Alliances, Jeffrey Allen
Vice President Customer Marketing, Liza Tillinghast
Vice President Global Interactive Marketing, Elena D'andrea
Vice President Retail And Luxury Markets, Vivienne Conatser
Vice President Digital Partnerships, Chris Kangas
Vice President, Melanie Gluck
Marketing Vice President, Cristina Paslar
Vice President In The Global Insights Group, Christina Sommer
Vice President and Business Leader US Regional Accounts, Sharie Hunziker
Senior Management (Senior Vice President General Manager Director), Elisa Romm
Senior Vice President Global Consumer Products, Jim Carrington
Vice President, Deb Morrison
Executive Vice President, Tim Berger
Vice President and Business Leader Worldwide Communications, Jane Khodos
Senior Vice President Integration Lead Enterprise Security Solutions, Ian Webb
Office of the Senior Executive Vice President Risk Management, Lynne Cullari
Vice President Prepaid Product Management, Jason Tymms
Vice President Business Leader Global Prepaid Solutions, Henry Gewirtz
Vice President, Carlos Rubio
Vice President, Elizabeth Brett
Vice President Corporate Security, Richard Gunthner
Vice President Senior Business Leader Mobile and Industry Alliances, Kathleen Reilly
Vice President Global Account Management, Brian Moran
Vice President Business Development, Marco Castro
Vice President Product Management and Account Support, Brandy Luetkenhaus
Senior Business Leader Vice President, Mark Mirabile
Vice President Senior Account Manager, Greg Pastorek
Vice President Network Engineering, Lisa Rief
Senior Vice President, Michael Timko
Vice President, Ellen Stibler
Vice President Product Management and Account Support, Janet Smith
Vice President Business Development, Chris Morris
Vice President Corporate Strategy, Gaurav Mittal
Vice President, Hemant Baijal
Vice President Senior Business Leader, Mark Lerner
Senior Vice President Retail and Commerce Solutions Development, Curtis Villars
Vice President Global Products, Jeff Pollard
Senior Vice President National and Local Accounts, Bob Glowasky
Senior Vice President Direct Sales, Elizabeth Wolgemuth
Vice President And Business Leader Counsel, Jessica L Hawkins
Vice President Senior Business Leader Global Digital Marketing, Adam Bell
Vice President Technology Account Management, Bruce Owens
Vice President Develop, Paulo Fernandes
Senior Vice President Investor Relations, Catherine Murchie
Vice President Develop, Jeff Feuerstein
Vice President, Victor Nordenson
Vice President, Connie Frawley

Vice President Software Engineering, Mike Prusaczyk
Vice President Technology Account Management, Andrea Soto
Vice President: Global Product Development, Natashe Barnard
Global New Product Development Senior Vice President, Diana Robino
Vice President President Direct Interactive Marketing, Jeff White
Vice President, Teik Tung
Vice President U.S. Market Development, Adam Goodman
Executive Vice President Account Management, Ed Glassman
Senior Vice President, Pilar S Ramos
Vice President, Salman Syed
Vice President Human Resources, Jason Colvin
Senior Vice President Marketing, Eslam Darwish
Vice President, Siddharth Pande
Vice President Account Management, Kashif Sohail
Vice President Mastercard Enterprise Partnerships, Will Judge
Vice President Global Marketing and Communications, Joe Khanna
Vice President Product Operations, Thomas Rempe
Vice President Global Prepaid Product, Mark Vanni
Executive Vice President North America Services, Chris Reid
Senior Vice President Head of Operations and Technology Payment Gateway Services, Luigi Zanghellini
Vice President, Patricio Hernandez
Vice President, Johan Lindstrom
Vice President Sales And Business Develo, Michael Dubin
Vice President And Business Leader, Adriana Phillips
Vice President and Business Leader Business Development, Daniel De Michele
Vice President, Sheri Branson
Vice President, Shubhra Srivastava
Vice President Systems Development Global Technology, Mike Norton
Vice President, Tory Jarvis
Vice President Information Governance Advisors Data Strategy Lead, Ori Peled
Senior Vice President and Head Global Digital Consumer Technology, Ankur Sharma
Executive Vice President, John Ainsworth
Auditors: PricewaterhouseCoopers LLP

LOCATIONS

HQ: Mastercard Inc
2000 Purchase Street, Purchase, NY 10577
Phone: 914 249-2000
Web: www.mastercard.com

2016 Revenue

	% of total
US	38
International	62
Total	**100**

PRODUCTS/OPERATIONS

2016 Sales

	$ mil.	% of total
Transaction processing fees	5,143	33
Domestic assessments	4,411	28
Cross-border volume fees	3,568	23
Other	2,431	16
Adjustments	(4777)	-
Total	**10,776**	**100**

COMPETITORS

Alibaba.com	JCB International
Amazon.com	NYCE Payments Network
American Express	PULSE Network

China UnionPay
Discover
Fifth Third
First Data

PayPal
Total System Services
Visa Inc
Visa International

HISTORICAL FINANCIALS

Company Type: Public

Income Statement

FYE: December 31

	REVENUE ($ mil.)	NET INCOME ($ mil.)	NET PROFIT MARGIN	EMPLOYEES
12/17	12,497	3,915	31.3%	13,400
12/16	10,776	4,059	37.7%	11,900
12/15	9,667	3,808	39.4%	11,300
12/14	9,473	3,617	38.2%	10,300
12/13	8,346	3,116	37.3%	8,200
Annual Growth	10.6%	5.9%	—	13.1%

2017 Year-End Financials

Debt ratio: 25.43%
Return on equity: 70.39%
Cash ($ mil.): 5,933
Current ratio: 1.57
Long-term debt ($ mil.): 5,424

No. of shares (mil.): 1,054
Dividends
Yield: 0.0%
Payout: 24.1%
Market value ($ mil.): 159,533

	STOCK PRICE ($) FY Close	P/E High/Low	PER SHARE ($) Earnings	Dividends	Book Value
12/17	151.36	42 29	3.65	0.88	5.19
12/16	103.25	29 22	3.69	0.76	5.23
12/15	97.36	30 24	3.35	0.64	5.40
12/14	86.16	271 22	3.10	0.44	5.89
12/13	835.46	324191	2.56	0.21	6.27
Annual Growth	(34.8%)		9.3%	43.1%	(4.6%)

Mattel Inc

Barbie is the platinum blonde in power at Mattel the #1 toy maker in the world. Its products include Barbie and Polly Pocket dolls Fisher-Price toys Hot Wheels and Matchbox cars American Girl dolls and books and various Disney Nickelodeon and other licensed brands. Mattel also sells action figures and toys based on Walt Disney and Warner Bros movies as well as games (UNO) arts and crafts (MEGA BLOX RoseArt) and puzzles. Mattel is trying to reduce its reliance on its biggest customers — Wal-Mart Toys "R" Us and Target— through its own catalog and internet sales.

Operations

Mattel operates three business segments: North America International and American Girl.

The North American segment which makes up around 50% of Mattel's total sales markets and sells toys in the US and Canada through the Mattel Girls & Boys Brands and Fisher-Price Brands categories. In the Mattel Girls & Boys Brands category Barbie includes brands such as Barbie fashion dolls and accessories with the Ever After High Polly Pocket Little Mommy Disney Classics and Monster High lumped into the Other Girls Brands. Wheels include Hot Wheels Matchbox and Tyco R/C vehicles and play sets. Entertainment includes CARS Disney Planes BOOMco Toy Story Max Steel WWE Wrestling Batman and Superman as well as games and puzzles. The Fisher-Price Brands category includes Fisher-Price Little People Laugh & Learn BabyGear Imaginext Dora the Explorer Shimmer and Shine Thomas & Friends Minnie Mouse Octonauts Mickey Mouse Clubhouse Dis-

ney's Jake and the Never Land Pirates and Power Wheels.

Products marketed by the International segment (some 40% of sales) are generally the same as those developed and marketed by the North America segment although some are developed or adapted for particular international markets. Mattel's products are sold directly to retailers and wholesalers in most European Latin American and Asian countries and in Australia and New Zealand and through agents and distributors in those countries where Mattel has no direct presence.

The American Girl segment (approx. 10% of sales) is a direct marketer children's publisher and retailer known for its flagship line of historical dolls books and accessories as well as the My American Girl Truly Me Girl of the Year and Bitty Baby brands. American Girl also publishes best-selling Advice & Activity books and the award-winning American Girl magazine. American Girl products are sold primarily in the US.

Looking at its brands the Mattel Girl's and Boy's brand products generate more than 50% of all sales while the Fisher-Price branded products generate some 30%. The company's American Girl brand brings in 10% of sales. The Construction and Arts & Crafts branded products bring in the remainder.

Geographic Reach

El Segundo California-based Mattel fills toy chests worldwide. The toymaker sells products in more than 150 nations across North America Europe Latin America and Asia Pacific. North America accounts for around half of total sales. Europe is the company's second-largest market generating about a quarter of Mattel's total sales. Latin America and the Asia-Pacific region both bring in around 10% each.

Sales and Marketing

Mattel sells its products through its own retailers and wholesalers in most of the world and through agents and distributors in those countries where it has no direct presence. American Girl products are sold directly to consumers. Wal-Mart Stores ($1.1 billion in sales) Toys "R" Us ($600 million) and Target ($400 million) are the company's three largest customers altogether accounting for nearly 40% of its worldwide sales each year.

Mattel capitalizes on major events such as movie releases by focusing on product tie-ins. It also promotes its toys and characters through online and broadcast media.

Financial Performance

The world's largest toy maker has seen its sales and profits decline in recent years as its markets and brands in the US and Europe have matured.

In fiscal 2016 sales fell 4% to $5.5 billion due to a sharp fall in the Other Girls product category and unfavorable currency exchange effects partially offset by increases in Barbie Wheels and Entertainment. Fisher-Price posted modest 3% growth while American Girls Brands was flat.

Net income fell 14% to $318 million due to lower gross profits partially offset by lower SGA expenses and lower advertising. Gross profits were impacted by currency effects and higher input costs. Mattel's Funding Our Future cost cutting program reduced expenses by $60 million and it reduced compensation costs by $36 million and severance and restructuring costs by $32 million.

Cash from operations fell 195 to $594.5 million due to higher working capital usage and lower net income.

Strategy

With sales declining and Hasbro and Lego threatening to seize Mattel's long-held toy crown the company launched in 2017 a strategic growth plan based on five pillars. The pillars are: 1) build its power brands into 360-degree play systems and experiences; 2) drive emerging market growth via

digital; 3) strengthen its innovation pipeline; 4) seek cost efficiencies through restructuring; and 5) shake up its culture.

The 360-degree play approach means building out its key brands into physical and digital space and creating a community of shared interest around them. Moving away from being purely a seller of toys its physical products will be supplemented by video games particularly on mobile platforms and storytelling.

Its emerging market growth strategy rests on deepening relationships with Chinese parents in particular. It struck a deal with Chinese e-commerce giant Alibaba to sell learning products based on its Fisher-Price toys. The emphasis on learning products is hoped to chime with the "Tiger Mother" archetype that pushes her child to succeed in school.

To bolster its innovation pipeline Mattel is democratizing its approach by opening up product ideas to amateur inventors who can now submit ideas via an online portal. Early successes of this new approach include Artsplash which sold out online and in Toys "R" Us in short order.

Following on from its Funding Our Future cost savings program was saved around $295 million in 2015-16 Mattel is further refining its operations with the goal of saving another $150-200 million. It also aims to drive down speed to market from 18 months to just nine.

The fifth pillar is around bringing in fresh talent in the areas of brand management commercial manufacturing connected product development e-commerce content and digital marketing.

Mergers and Acquisitions

In January 2016 Mattel bought Fuhu Inc. a developer of high-tech products for children and families that is best known for its Nabi Brand products for $21.5 million. Also that month the toy maker acquired Sproutling Inc. which makes smart tech products for parents and families. Both of the acquired companies bolstered Mattel's digital and smart technology product offerings.

HISTORY

A small California toy manufacturer began operating out of a converted garage in 1945 producing dollhouse furniture. Harold Matson and Elliot Handler named their new company Mattel using letters from their last and first names. Matson soon sold his share to Handler and his wife Ruth who incorporated the business in 1948.

The company's toy line had expanded by 1952 to include burp guns and musical toys and sales exceeded $5 million. Sponsorship of Walt Disney's Mickey Mouse Club (debuted 1955) a first in toy advertising was a shrewd marketing step for Mattel providing direct year-round access to millions of young potential customers.

In 1959 Mattel introduced the Barbie doll named after the Handlers' daughter Barbara and later introduced Ken named after their son. Barbie with her fashionable wardrobe and extensive line of accessories was an instant hit and eventually became the most successful brand-name toy ever sold.

Mattel went public in 1960 and within two years sales had jumped from $25 million to $75 million. It launched the popular Hot Wheels miniature cars line in 1968.

The Handlers were ousted from management in 1974 after an investigation by the SEC found irregularities in reports of the company's profits. The new management moved into non-toy businesses adding Western Publishing (Golden Books) and the Ringling Brothers-Barnum & Bailey Combined Shows circus in 1979.

Mattel and two former employees agreed in 2002 to pay $477000 in fines for making political donations in other people's names the third-largest fine ever imposed by the Federal Election Commission. Also that year the company closed its Kentucky manufacturing and distribution facilities and in early 2003 consolidated two of its manufacturing facilities in Mexico.

In a stinging defeat for Mattel in April 2011 a federal jury sided with MGA Entertainment in the long-running legal battle over ownership of the billion-dollar Bratz doll franchise. (MGA and Mattel started their catfight a decade ago.) The jury rejected Mattel's copyright infringement claims. Instead it found that Mattel has stolen trade secrets from MGA and said it owed the company $88.5 million. The decision reversed a 2008 ruling in which a jury sided with Mattel.

EXECUTIVES

EVP Chief Legal Officer and Secretary, Robert (Bob) Normile, age 58, $580,000 total compensation
EVP and Chief Human Resources Officer, Richard R. Gros, age 62
CFO, Joseph J. (Joe) Euteneuer, age 62
EVP and Chief Supply Chain Officer, Peter D. Gibbons, age 56, $600,000 total compensation
President and COO, Richard Dickson, age 49, $900,000 total compensation
CEO, Margaret H. (Margo) Georgiadis
EVP and Chief Strategic Technology Officer, Geoffrey H. Walker, age 51, $530,000 total compensation
CTO, Sven Gerjets
Vice President, Sejal Shah
Senior Vice President and Chief Information Officer, Paul Rasmusson
GM Senior Vice President Consumer Products, Jessica Dunne
Vice President Human Resources, Huey Wilson
Vice President Marketing, Lori Pantel
Vice President Of Barbie Product Development, Jon Marine
Vice President Global Sales Training and Global Diversity, Graciela Meibar
Vice President, Sibylle Addotta
Vice President Product Planning, Thomas Zeiler
Vice President Finance and Strategic Planning for Mattel Brands, Eric Chan
Vice President China Operations, Mike Burrows
Vice President, Michael Shore
Vice President Corporate Strategy and Investor Relations, Martin Gilkes
Vice President Product Development, Scott Goodman
Vice President And Assistant General Cou, Melinda Mehringer
Vice President of Global Product Development Design Technical Support, Steve Sucher
Vice President Litigation and Assistant General Counsel, Jill Thomas
Vice President Global Procurement At Mattel, Linda Theisen
Vice President Sales and Marketing, Theresa Chatt
Vice President Entertainment and Franchise Development, David Voss
Vice President Global Softlines Consumer Products, Aaron Duncan
Vice President Global Marketing Fisher Price Baby, Melissa Kustell
Senior Vice President Marketing and Design Girls, Tim Kilpin
Design Vice President, Evelyn Viohl
Senior Vice President and Corporate Treasurer, Mandana Sadigh
Executive Vice President Global Brands Teams Fisher Price, Geoff Walker
Vice President AGC Business and Legal Affairs, Jeff Korchek
Vice President Human Resources, Kim Giordanella
Vice President of Information Technology, Yohan Lee

Vice President, Dave Okada
Executive Vice President and Chief Brand Officer, Juliana Chugg
VP Supply Chain, Michael Gielink
VP and GM MONTOI, Jonathan Waite
VICE PRESIDENT AND ASSISTANT GENERAL COUNSEL, Donald B Aiken
Vice President Global Brand Marketing and Design, Gabe Carlson
Chairman, Christopher A. Sinclair, age 66
Assistant Treasurer, Brent Hirsh
Auditors: PricewaterhouseCoopers LLP

LOCATIONS

HQ: Mattel Inc
333 Continental Blvd., El Segundo, CA 90245-5012
Phone: 310 252-2000
Web: www.mattel.com

PRODUCTS/OPERATIONS

2016 Sales

	$ mil.	% of total
Mattel Girls & Boys Brands	3,194	53
Fisher-Price Brands	1,888	31
American Girl Brands	570	9
Construction and Arts & Crafts Brands	377	6
Other	43	1
Eliminations	(617.0)	-
Total	**5,456**	**100**

2016 Sales

	$ mil.	% of total
North America	3,036	50
International	2,447	40
American Girl	589	10
Eliminations	(617.0)	-
Total	**5,456**	**100**

Selected Brands:
Barbie
BoomCo
DC Universe
DC Superhero Girls
Dinotrux
Disney Cars
Disney Planes
Ever After High
Fast & Furious
Ghostbusters
Halo
Hot Wheels
Masters of the Universe
Matchbox
Mattel Games
Mega Construx
Minecraft
Monster High
My Mini MixieQ's
My Password Journal
nabi
Rose Art
Thundercats
Toy Story
Tyco RC
View-Master
VS Rip Spin Warriors
WWE)
Wonder Woman

COMPETITORS

Electronic Arts	Playmobil
Hasbro	Radio Flyer
JAKKS Pacific	Sanrio
LEGO	Simba Dickie Group
LeapFrog	Spin Master
MGA Entertainment	TakaraTomy
Marvel Entertainment	Toy Quest
Motorsports Authentics	Ty
Namco Bandai	VTech Holdings
Ohio Art	

HISTORICAL FINANCIALS

Company Type: Public

Income Statement

FYE: December 31

	REVENUE ($ mil.)	NET INCOME ($ mil.)	NET PROFIT MARGIN	EMPLOYEES
12/16	5,456	318	5.8%	32,000
12/15	5,702	369	6.5%	31,000
12/14	6,023	498	8.3%	31,000
12/13	6,484	903	13.9%	29,000
12/12	6,420	776	12.1%	28,000
Annual Growth	**(4.0%)**	**(20.0%)**	**—**	**3.4%**

2016 Year-End Financials

Debt ratio: 35.83%
Return on equity: 12.58%
Cash ($ mil.): 869
Current ratio: 1.95
Long-term debt ($ mil.): 2,134

No. of shares (mil.): 342
Dividends
Yield: 0.0%
Payout: 165.2%
Market value ($ mil.): 9,433

	STOCK PRICE ($) FY Close	P/E High/Low		PER SHARE ($) Earnings	Dividends	Book Value
12/16	27.55	37	27	0.92	1.52	7.03
12/15	27.17	29	18	1.08	1.52	7.75
12/14	30.95	33	20	1.45	1.52	8.72
12/13	47.58	18	14	2.58	1.44	9.58
12/12	36.62	17	12	2.22	1.24	8.96
Annual Growth	**(6.9%)**	**—**	**—**	**(19.8%)**	**5.2%**	**(5.9%)**

MB Financial Inc

The "MB" in MB Financial doesn't stand for "Midsized Businesses" though that's its target market. The $16 billion-asset holding company owns MB Financial Bank which has about 80 branches in the Chicago area and one in Philadelphia. Commercial-related credits including mortgages operating loans lease financing and construction loans make up 85% of the bank's loan portfolio. In addition to serving small and middle-market businesses MB Financial provides retail banking and lending to consumers. The company also offers wealth management and trust services through its Cedar Hill Associates subsidiary and brokerage through Vision Investment Services. LaSalle Systems leases technology-related equipment to corporations.

Operations
MB Financial operates three main business segments: Banking which counts its deposit and lending activities; Leasing which originates leases and related services through subsidiaries LaSalle Systems Leasing Celtic Leasing Corp and MB Equipment Finance; and Mortgage Banking which originates and services residential mortgage loans to hold in its portfolio or list for sale to investors via retail or third party channels.

Broadly speaking about 54% of the bank's total revenue came from loan interest during 2015 while another 10% came from interest on its investment securities. The rest of its revenue came from mortgage banking revenue (13% of revenue) lease financing (9%) commercial deposits and treasury management fees (6%) trust and asset management fees (3%) card fees (2%) capital markets and international banking fees (1%) and other miscellaneous fee sources.

Geographic Reach

Beyond its 80 branches in Chicago and one branch in Philadelphia MB Financial boasts 39 mortgage retail offices in 18 states.

Sales and Marketing

MB Financial mostly targets small and middle market businesses and individuals. The bank spent $10.07 million on advertising during 2015 up 14% from the $8.85 million it spent in 2014.

Financial Performance

The bank's annual revenues have risen more than 65% since 2011 thanks to a combination of mortgage banking revenue growth and steady loan business growth driven by bank acquisitions. Its profits have quintupled over the same time period as a result.

MB Financial's revenue jumped 37% to $816 million during 2015 mostly driven by strong loan business and mortgage banking revenue growth both stemming from the full-year results of its 2014 acquisition of Taylor Capital.

Double-digit revenue growth in 2015 drove the bank's net income up 85% to $159 million for the year. MB Financial's operating cash levels climbed 23% to $205 million as cash earnings rose in 2015.

Strategy

MB Financial mainly pursues growth by acquiring banks and other financial companies to expand its branch network across its target geographies and boost its loan and deposit business. Other strategies for growth include expanding its private banking and asset managements operations as well as its fee-based business services including treasury management and leasing.

Mergers and Acquisitions

In mid-2016 MB Financial bought American Chartered Bancorp— along with its 15 American Chartered Bank branches in the Chicago-area $2.8 billion in assets and $2.2 billion in deposits — in a deal valued at $449 million.

In December 2015 the company expanded its investment management and trust business after buying MSA along with its MainStreet and Cambium subsidiaries. MainStreet which boated $2.9 billion in assets under management (AUM) provided investment management services to the bank trust and independent trust markets while Cambium ($109 million in AUM) was a registered investment advisor that served affluent individuals and institutions.

In August 2014 MB Financial completed its $649-million acquisition of Rosemont Illinois-based Taylor Capital Group the holding company for Cole Taylor Bank (CTB). With $5.7 billion in assets and some 10 branches in the Chicago metro area CTB was merged with MB Financial Bank. Like its acquirer CTB is a commercial bank focused on the middle market.

Company Background

Taking advantage of the dozens of bank failures in 2009 MB Financial acquired Heritage Community Bank InBank Corus Bank and Benchmark Bank in separate FDIC-assisted transactions. In 2010 it acquired failed Chicago-area institutions Broadway Bank and New Century Bank in similar deals. Gains on these acquisitions helped the company's revenues (and profits) grow in 2010. Although the company didn't have the benefit of gains on acquisitions in 2011 (and revenues fell 20% to $493.7 million) profits continued to climb that year growing 89% to $38.7 million largely due to a lowered provision for loan losses. Also that year the bank got millions of dollars of non-performing loans off of its books via a sale to Colony Capital.

EXECUTIVES

President and CEO, Mitchell S. Feiger, age 58, $895,308 total compensation

Chairman MB Financial Bank, Ronald D. Santo, age 74, $321,741 total compensation

EVP Credit Management MB Financial Bank, Mark A. Heckler, age 53, $293,077 total compensation

EVP Commercial Banking Specialty, Edward F. Milefchik, age 52

EVP MB Financial Bank; President MB Business Capital, Michael D. Sharkey, age 63, $456,923 total compensation

EVP and Chief Credit Officer, Michael J. Morton, age 54

President and CEO MB Financial Bank, Mark A. Hoppe, age 63, $726,923 total compensation

EVP Wealth Management Card Services Leasing and Indirect Lending, Jill E. York, age 53, $489,461 total compensation

VP MB Financial Inc. and EVP Administration MB Financial Bank, Rosemarie Bouman, age 60, $287,846 total compensation

EVP Commercial Banking, Lawrence G. Ryan, age 58

VP and CFO MB Financial Inc. and EVP COO and CFO MB Financial Bank N.A., Randall T. Conte, age 56, $451,731 total compensation

EVP Consumer Banking and Risk Management and Chief Risk Officer MB Financial Bank N.A., Brian J. Wildman, age 54, $292,846 total compensation

Vice President, Michael Scarsella

Vice President Trust Operations Manager, Abimbola Okubanjo

First Vice President, Priscilla Rodriguez

First Vice President, Mike Markovitz

Vice President Item Processing Manager, Veronica McGowan

Vice President, Kathy Grele

Assistant Vice President Commercial Bank, Nick Cox

Vice President Financial Reporting, Debbie Petrungaro

Senior Vice President Division Manager, Matthew Robertson

First Vice President, Michael Lynch

Vice President Commercial Banking, Evelyn Berthold

Assistant Vice President Commercial Real Estate, Sarah Hunter

Vice President Business Intelligence, George Ostendorf

Assistant Vice President Banking Center Manager III, Sue Anderson

Senior Vice President, Judy Hill

Senior Vice President of Commerical Banking, Carl Anfenson

Vice President, Virginia Buschman

Senior Vice Presicfent, Christopher Foltman

Vice President Cdc, Lisa Herrera

Vice President Commercial Real Estate, Pam Farrell

Senior Vice President and Division Manager, Jerry Kallio

Senior Vice President, Christoph Schneider

Vice President, Rick J Chang

Vice President Collateral Manager, Lisette Alamo

Vice President, Anthony Gattuso

Assistant Vice President, Jessica Redman

Senior Vice President, Jennifer Brogan

Vice President Business Banking, Robert Baitler

Vice President Business Banking, Jim Marshall

Senior Vice President, Greg Urban

Vice President Treasury Management Sales, Eloy Hodges

Vice President, Sandra Biske

Vice President Business Bankin, Steve Grabavoy

Assistant Vice President Compensation, Cindy Katsikas

Vice President Business Banking, Sam Elhaj

Assistant Vice President Banking Center Manager, Galina Veksler

Assistant Vice President Branch Manager, John Crouse

Assistant Vice President, Brenda Allen

Vice President, Cindy Voda

Assistant Vice President Quality Control Manager, Margie Acevedo

Vice President, Dion Haintz

First Vice President Chief Appraiser, Mitchell Zaveduk

Assistant Vice President Bsa Aml Loss Prevention Management, Michelle Mercer

Assistant Vice President Compensation And Benefits, Catherine Nacpil

Assistant Vice President Marketing And Crm Administrator, Cari Dam

Senior Vice President Division Head, Thomas Moran

Senior Vice President Lease Banking, Dennis Roesslein

First Vice President Regional Division M, Deborah Wheeler

Senior Vice President Lease Banking, Stewart Kapnick

Vice President Senior Product Manager, Joseph Vitale

Assistant Vice President Deposit Operations, Anna Zyworonek

Senior Vice President, Melissa Bleiweis

Vice President Commercial Banking, Dawn Lauderdale

Senior Vice President, Mitch Morgenstern

Assistant Vice President Accounting Manager, Patricia Basan

First Vice President, Thomas Carmody

Senior Vice President Operations, Pete Steger

Senior Vice President Corporate Controller, David Emerson

Vice President Senior Field Credit Officer, Brian Monson

Vice President Treasury Management Solutions Group, Isela Calabrese

Senior Vice President CRA Fair Lending Program Manager, Mary Boetel

Assistant Vice President Banking Center Manager, Lesya Schrader

Vice President, Kenneth Holub

Vice President Banking Center Manager, Karen Franciere

Senior Vice President, Dawn Dieter

Assistant Vice President Treas, Luke Chesick

Senior Vice President, Eric Staczek

Banking Center Manager II Assistant Vice President, Jennifer Glocksen

Assistant Vice President Operations, Jackie Schmitz

Senior Vice President, Lisa Gibbs

Assistant Vice President Customer Solutions Specialist, Lori Rottmuller

Senior Vice President, Martha Gaskin

Senior Vice President and Division Head Commercial Lending, Arnold Brown

Senior Vice President, Mark Staunton

Senior Vice President, David Enghauser

Senior Vice President, Jack Gracheck

Assistant Vice President Banking Center Manager, Casey Weaver

Senior Vice President Commercial Real Estate, Molly Oelerich

Senior Vice President, Timothy Carstens

Senior Vice President documentation for MB Equipment Finance, Jeannie McManus

Vice President MB Community Development Corp., Ailisa Herrera

Mortgage Senior Vice President Lead Counsel, Mark Reid

Vice President Portfolio Management, William Bence

Vice President Relationship Manager, Evan Zwerman
Vice President Business Banking, Jennifer Cortese
Vice President, Susan Kruesi
Senior Vice President, William Stapel
Vice President Commercial Banking, Creighton Hartanov
Senior Vice President, Joel Regier
Senior Vice President, Matthew Sloan
Senior Vice President, Jon Spoerry
Senior Vice President, John Littrell
Senior Vice President, Bryan Orton
Senior Vice President and Division Manager, Joseph Wolsfeld
Assistant Vice President Banking Center Manager, Jane Miller
Assistant Vice President, Adam Novak
First Vice President, Thomas Cha
Senior Vice President, Chuck Gitles
Senior Vice President, Kip Read
First Vice President, Robert Thompson
Vice President Senior Underwriter, Brian Roman
Vice Presidentmanager, Maria Spanos
Senior Vice President, Steven Janson
Assistant Vice President, Charlie Nason
Senior Vice President, Steve Herseth
Vice President, Harry Petruleas
Vice President Loss Mitigation, Michael van Ede
Vice President Business Banking, Steven Grabavoy
Assistant Vice President, Andrea Calabrese
Senior Vice President Correspondent Banking, Thomas Wilson
Chairman, Thomas H. Harvey, age 56
Executive Board Member, Matt Weberling
Vice Chairman, Bruce Taylor
Treasurer, Dale Saari
Auditors: RSM US LLP

LOCATIONS

HQ: MB Financial Inc
  800 West Madison Street, Chicago, IL 60607
Phone: 888 422-6562
Web: www.mbfinancial.com

PRODUCTS/OPERATIONS

2015 Sales

	$ mil.	% of total
Interest		
Loans	413	51
Investment securities	80	10
Other	0	-
Noninterest		
Mortgage banking	117	13
Lease financing net	76	9
Commercial deposit and treasury management fees	45	6
Trust and Asset management	23	3
Card fees	15	2
Consumer and other deposit service fees	13	2
Loan service fees	6	1
Others	24	3
Total	**816**	**100**

Selected Services

Business Banking
Commercial Banking
Personal Banking
Wealth Management

Selected Subsidiaries

MB Financial Bank N.A.
  Ashland Management Agency Inc.
  Cedar Hill Associates LLC (80%)
  LaSalle Systems Leasing Inc.
  LaSalle Business Solutions LLC
  Melrose Equipment Company LLC
  MB Deferred Exchange Corporation
  MB Financial Center LLC
  MB Financial Center Land Owner LLC
  MB Financial Community Development Corporation
  Vision Investment Services Inc.
  Vision Insurance Services Inc.7

Bank of America
Citigroup
Fifth Third
Harris
JPMorgan Chase
Northern Trust
PNC Financial
PrivateBank
U.S. Bancorp
Wintrust Financial

HISTORICAL FINANCIALS

Company Type: Public

Income Statement

FYE: December 31

	ASSETS ($ mil.)	NET INCOME ($ mil.)	INCOME AS % OF ASSETS	EMPLOYEES
12/16	19,302	174	0.9%	3,486
12/15	15,585	158	1.0%	2,980
12/14	14,602	86	0.6%	2,839
12/13	9,641	98	1.0%	1,775
12/12	9,571	90	0.9%	1,758
Annual Growth	**19.2%**	**17.8%**	**—**	**18.7%**

2016 Year-End Financials

Debt ratio: 2.71%	No. of shares (mil.): 83
Return on equity: 7.45%	Dividends
Cash ($ mil.): 463	Yield: 0.0%
Current ratio: —	Payout: 34.7%
Long-term debt ($ mil.): —	Market value ($ mil.): 3,954

	STOCK PRICE ($) FY Close	P/E High/Low		PER SHARE ($) Earnings	Dividends	Book Value
12/16	47.23	22	13	2.13	0.74	30.80
12/15	32.37	18	14	2.02	0.65	28.31
12/14	32.86	25	20	1.31	0.52	27.11
12/13	32.06	18	11	1.79	0.44	24.11
12/12	19.75	14	11	1.60	0.13	23.26
Annual Growth	**24.4%**	**—**	**—**	**7.4%**	**54.5%**	**7.3%**

MBIA Inc.

MBIA will make sure that bonds get paid no matter what. The holding company's independent subsidiary National Public Finance Guarantee Corporation is a leading provider of insurance for municipal bonds and stable corporate bonds (such as utility bonds) in the US. Separately its MBIA Insurance Corporation provides global structured finance products and non-US public financial guarantees. MBIA's Cutwater business manages assets for public-sector clients. Other lines of business include tax compliance and risk management services along with buying and servicing municipal real estate tax liens.

Operations

The company conducts most of its business through three subsidiaries. Cutwater Asset Management handles asset management and has $23 billion in assets under management. MBIA Insurance Corporation issues structured finance and international insurance from six offices around the globe. National Public Finance Guarantee offers US public finance insurance. Formed after the economic collapse in 2008 National hasn't written any new business since 2009.

Geographic Reach

MBIA is headquartered in New York with several offices in the state along with operations in California and Colorado. Internationally the company has one office each in Spain France and Mexico.

Financial Performance

The company reported a 50% drop in revenue for 2013 after showing growth the previous year.

A decreased in premiums earned along with increased losses and other settlements caused the drop. Net income was affected and fell 80%. Cash from operations was the bright spot however as it rose nearly $3 billion after as it settled legal claims and saw reduced payments for some expenses.

Strategy

After years of work to stabilize its financial position and deal with the massive fallout from the subprime mortgage-backed security implosion that lead to the housing collapse and the Great Recession MBIA seems to be on more solid ground. In 2013 it settled the last of the subprime-related lawsuits with Bank of America Flagstar Bank and ResCap (it is still pursuing claims against Credit Suisse). It also resolved pending litigation and government investigations reduced its workforce saw the first dividend payment from National to the parent late in the year.

Unfortunately MBIA found itself in more trouble when certain investment vehicles it had guaranteed soured with one defaulting in late 2016. To help cover its losses the company sold its UK operations to Assured Guaranty.

Company Background

That MBIA is still standing is remarkable. As one of the largest providers of insurance to asset- and mortgage-based securities MBIA was among the most vulnerable companies when the US housing market imploded in 2007. The company posted losses of $2.3 billion the last quarter of 2007 a result of its investments in subprime mortgage-backed securities.

MBIA split apart its public structured and asset management businesses to separate the stable from the unstable in early 2009: MBIA split its municipal bond insurance business off into an independent subsidiary named National Public Finance Guarantee Corporation. It receives a credit rating separate from the rest of MBIA's riskier structured-finance businesses.

Following the split some 20 banks grew prickly and sued MBIA with one hand while steadily collecting claims with the other. However by mid-2011 banks began dropping out of the lawsuit; the company settled with the final three in 2013.

EXECUTIVES

EVP Chief Legal Officer and Secretary, Ram D. Wertheim, age 63, $500,000 total compensation
CEO, William C. (Bill) Fallon, age 57, $812,500 total compensation
EVP and CFO, Anthony McKiernan, age 47, $500,000 total compensation
Vice President, Timothy Keefe
Assistant Vice President, Jackie Perez
Assistant Vice President, Joseph Beattie
Assistant Vice President Investor Relations, Jacquelyn Cruz
Assistant Vice President, Emily Johnson
Vice President, Mark Garofalo
Vice President, Cathleen Murray
Vice President, Greg Wright
Chairman, Charles R. Rinehart, age 70
Auditors: PricewaterhouseCoopers LLP

LOCATIONS

HQ: MBIA Inc.
  1 Manhattanville Road, Suite 301, Purchase, NY 10577
Phone: 914 273-4545
Web: www.mbia.com

Selected Locations

US
  Armonk NY
  Denver
  New York
  San Francisco
International
  Madrid
  Mexico City

PRODUCTS/OPERATIONS

2016 Sales

	% of total
U.S. Public Finance Insurance	86
International and Structured Finance Insurance	-
Corporate	14
Total	**100**

COMPETITORS

Ambac	Primus Guaranty
Assured Guaranty	Radian Group
FGIC	Syncora Holdings

HISTORICAL FINANCIALS

Company Type: Public

Income Statement

FYE: December 31

	ASSETS ($ mil.)	NET INCOME ($ mil.)	INCOME AS % OF ASSETS	EMPLOYEES
12/16	11,137	(338)	—	164
12/15	14,855	180	1.2%	170
12/14	16,284	569	3.5%	252
12/13	16,953	250	1.5%	277
12/12	21,724	1,234	5.7%	352
Annual Growth	**(15.4%)**	**—**		**(17.4%)**

2016 Year-End Financials

Debt ratio: 45.99%
Return on equity: (-9.69%)
Cash ($ mil.): 187
Current ratio: —
Long-term debt ($ mil.): —

No. of shares (mil.): 135
Dividends
Yield: —
Payout: —
Market value ($ mil.): 1,447

	STOCK PRICE ($) FY Close	P/E High	P/E Low	PER SHARE ($) Earnings	PER SHARE ($) Dividends	PER SHARE ($) Book Value
12/16	10.70	—	—	(2.54)	0.00	23.87
12/15	6.48	9	5	1.06	0.00	24.61
12/14	9.54	5	3	2.76	0.00	20.47
12/13	11.94	12	6	1.29	0.00	17.05
12/12	7.85	2	1	6.33	0.00	16.22
Annual Growth	**8.1%**			**—**	**—**	**10.1%**

McCormick & Co Inc

McCormick & Company is more than just the flavor of the month. As the world's #1 spice maker the company offers a tasty assortment of herbs spices seasonings flavorings sauces and extracts. McCormick distributes and markets its products under brands including Lawry's Club House and McCormick and ethnic labels Zatarain's Thai Kitchen and Simply Asia as well as regional brands Ducros and Schwartz and private labels. Its products are sold in some 140 countries to customers spanning the entire food industry from food retailers to food service businesses and industrial food manufacturers. McCormick operates in North America and Europe and in South Africa Central America and the Asia/Pacific region.In mid-2017 McCormick agreed to acquire Reckitt Benckiser's food business for $4.2 billion.

HISTORY

McCormick & Company was founded in 1889 by 25-year-old Willoughby McCormick who crafted fruit syrups root beer and nerve and bone liniment in his Baltimore home. He employed three assis-

tants to hawk his wares door-to-door. His company soon expanded its product line to include food coloring cream of tartar and blood purifier. By 1894 McCormick was exporting and two years later it acquired the F.G. Emmett Spice Company of Philadelphia firmly committing itself to the spice industry. By the turn of the century McCormick was trading around the world.

Willoughby's nephew Charles McCormick joined the company as a part-time shipping clerk in 1912. When Willoughby died in 1932 Charles succeeded him as CEO. He increased employee wages shortened the workweek and established the Multiple Management system (still an integral part of the company's management structure) which solicited employee input. By 1933 McCormick was on a growth track that continued unabated through the 1930s. In 1938 Charles wrote a book expounding his participative management philosophy.

The company opened its first international office in 1940 and achieved coast-to-coast distribution seven years later with the acquisition of A. Schilling & Co. producers of spices and extracts. In 1959 McCormick purchased Gorman Eckert & Co. Canada's largest spice business and the precursor to Club House Foods. It acquired Gilroy Foods in 1961 and rival Baker Extract in 1962. From 1962 until its sale in 1988 McCormick ran a real estate subsidiary Maryland Properties (renamed McCormick Properties 1979).

Charles died in 1970. Though the years following his death were characterized by acquisitions and joint venture agreements in the US and abroad profits slumped until his son Charles "Buzz" McCormick took over as CEO in 1987.

In 1989 Australia's Burns Philp began challenging McCormick by buying up spice companies in the US and Europe including the Spice Islands and Durkee French brands. Buzz — succeeded twice as CEO in the mid-1990s only to return when one successor died and the other left for health reasons — responded with a bruising battle for shelf space that led to Burns Philp's near-collapse in 1997. The company also sold garlic and onion processing subsidiary Gilroy Foods Minipack Systems (UK) and several smaller noncore operations. In 1997 Buzz yielded the CEO's post — for good — to Robert Lawless.

The company's earnings were erratic in the 1990s partly because of a price war with then-rival Burns Philp but also due to the decline of home cooking in the US. McCormick countered with increased advertising and a growing emphasis on industrial sales to flavor the foods eaten outside the home. McCormick also has been expanding internationally through its Decors spice business and operations in China.

Economic woes in Venezuela caused McCormick to cease manufacturing operations there in 1998. In 1999 Lawless succeeded Buzz as chairman. That year the company announced it would cut costs by eliminating 300 jobs (mostly overseas) and closing a British plant.

McCormick's sweet victory over Burns Philp was soured by an FTC investigation into its alleged practice of offering some grocery chains low prices in exchange for up to 90% of their shelf space for spices. The investigation brought scrutiny on a common supermarket practice known as slotting fees. McCormick settled with the FTC in 2000 agreeing not to illegally discriminate against retailers in its pricing. Also that year the company bought France-based Ducros (spices herbs dessert aid products) from B ©ghin-Say for about $380 million.

In 2003 McCormick's UK subsidiary acquired condiment maker Uniqsauces adding the Beswicks and Hammonds as well as the licensed Newman's Own brands to its European product line. That year the company also acquired New Orleans-style

cuisine product maker Zatarain's. Saying that the packaging business was not a strategic part of the company McCormick also sold its packaging business (Setco and Tubed Products) to Kerr Group in 2003.

Acquisitions continued in 2004 with McCormick's purchase of C.M. van Sillevoldt and its Silvo brand of spices herbs and seasonings which is sold in the Netherlands and Belgium. In 2006 the company consolidated its North American operations with the closure of its manufacturing facility in California.

About 39% of McCormick's sales came from its international operations in 2005. The year was not the company's best however as a drop in vanilla prices and the effects of Hurricane Katrina both cut into sales.

Continuing its expansion via acquisitions the company purchased Dessert Products International (DPI) in 2006. DPI markets the Vahine brand dessert toppings in Europe. It also purchased Simply Asia Foods that year for $97.6 million in cash. Simply Asia manufactures products under the Thai Kitchen and Simply Asia brands; its products include noodle and soup bowls meal kits coconut milk and sauces and pastes.

Expanding its well-known roster of brands McCormick acquired Lawry's marinades and spice blends from Unilever for $605 million in 2008; the deal represented McCormick's largest acquisition in company history. To buy Lawry's however the company was required by the FTC to sell its Season-All business which it did — to Morton International. The company also purchased Canada's largest honey business Billy Bee Honey Products for $75 million.

EXECUTIVES

President Global Consumer Business and North America, Brendan M. Foley, age 53, $519,809 total compensation
Chairman President and CEO, Lawrence E. Kurzius, age 60, $861,374 total compensation
President Global Industrial and International Business, Malcolm Swift, age 56, $407,714 total compensation
SVP Corporate Finance, Michael R. Smith, $394,943 total compensation
Vice President Product Development Consumer Food Manufacturer's, Denise McCafferty
Vice President Distributor Sales, Ron Dallara
Auditors: Ernst & Young LLP

LOCATIONS

HQ: McCormick & Co Inc
18 Loveton Circle, P. O. Box 6000, Sparks, MD 21152-6000
Phone: 410 771-7301   **Fax:** 410 771-7462
Web: www.mccormickcorporation.com

2016 Sales

	$ mil.	% of total
US	2,565	58
Europe the Middle East & Africa	896	20
Other countries	950	22
Total	**411**	**100**

PRODUCTS/OPERATIONS

2016 Sales

	$ mil.	% of total
Consumer products	2,753	62
Industrial products	1,658	38
Total	**4,411**	**100**

Selected Brands

Billy Bee
Club House
Ducros

Kamins
Kohinoor
Lawry's
McCormick
Old Bay
Schwartz
Silvo
Simply Asia
Thai Kitchen
Vahiné;
Zatarain's

Selected Products

Consumer
  Dessert items
  Extracts
  Food colors
  Grill mates
  Herbs
  Seafood
  Seasoning mixes
  Seasonings
  Spices
Industrial
  Coating systems
  Compound flavors
  Herbs
  Seasoning blends
  Spices
  Wet flavors

COMPETITORS

A.A. Sayia	Goya
ACH Food Companies	Heinz
Adams Extract & Spice	International Flavors
Associated British	Kerry Group
Foods	La Flor
B&G Foods	M & F Worldwide
Bolner's Fiesta	Magic Seasoning Blends
Products	Main Street
D. D. Williamson	Ingredients
Danisco A/S	Newly Weds Foods
Denali Flavors	Nielsen-Massey
First Spice Mixing	Ottens Flavors
Flavormatic Industries	RFI Ingredients
Flayco Products	Sensient
Givaudan	Sterling Extract

HISTORICAL FINANCIALS

Company Type: Public

Income Statement

FYE: November 30

	REVENUE ($ mil.)	NET INCOME ($ mil.)	NET PROFIT MARGIN	EMPLOYEES
11/17	4,834	477	9.9%	11,700
11/16	4,411	472	10.7%	10,500
11/15	4,296	401	9.3%	10,000
11/14	4,243	437	10.3%	10,000
11/13	4,123	389	9.4%	10,000
Annual Growth	4.1%	5.3%	—	4.0%

2017 Year-End Financials

Debt ratio: 48.40%
Return on equity: 22.81%
Cash ($ mil.): 186
Current ratio: 0.83
Long-term debt ($ mil.): 4,443

No. of shares (mil.): 131
Dividends
  Yield: 1.8%
  Payout: 50.8%
Market value ($ mil.): 13,386

	STOCK PRICE ($) FY Close	P/E High/Low		PER SHARE ($) Earnings	Dividends	Book Value
11/17	102.18	28	24	3.72	1.88	19.54
11/16	91.20	29	21	3.69	1.72	12.98
11/15	85.92	27	23	3.11	1.60	13.12
11/14	74.33	22	19	3.34	1.48	13.96
11/13	69.00	25	21	2.91	1.36	14.74
Annual Growth	10.3%	—	—	6.3%	8.4%	7.3%

McDonald's Corp

Serving billions of hamburgers has put a shine on these arches. McDonald's has more than 36000 restaurants serving burgers and fries in about 120 countries. (There are more than 14150 Golden Arches locations in the US.) The popular chain is well-known for its Big Macs Quarter Pounders and Chicken McNuggets. Most of the outlets are freestanding units offering dine-in and drive-through service but McDonald's also has many eateries located in airports retail areas and other high-traffic locations. Almost 85% of the restaurants are run by franchisees or affiliates.

HISTORY

The first McDonald's opened in 1948 in San Bernardino California. In 1954 owners Dick and Mac McDonald signed a franchise agreement with 52-year-old Ray Kroc (a malt machine salesman) and a year later Kroc opened his first restaurant in Des Plaines Illinois. By 1957 Kroc was operating 14 McDonald's restaurants in Illinois Indiana and California. In 1961 Kroc bought out the McDonald brothers for $2.7 million.

In 1962 the now-ubiquitous Golden Arches appeared for the first time and the company sold its billionth burger. Ronald McDonald made his debut the following year and the company introduced its first new menu item — the Filet-O-Fish. Two years later McDonald's went public and ran its first TV ads. The company opened its first stores outside the US (in Canada) in 1967 and the next year it added the Big Mac to the menu and opened its 1000th restaurant.

During the 1970s McDonald's grew at the rate of about 500 restaurants per year and the first Ronald McDonald House (a temporary residence for families of hospitalized children) opened in 1974. The drive-through window appeared in 1975.

McDonald's introduced Chicken McNuggets in 1983. Kroc who had become senior chairman in the 1970s died the next year. Growing competition slowed the company's US sales growth to about 5% per year at the end of the 1980s. In response McDonald's added specially priced "value menu" items.

In 1990 the company made history and headlines when it opened the first McDonald's in Moscow. Two years later the Golden Arches expanded into China. The company stumbled with the pricey Arch Deluxe hamburger in 1996 and its Campaign 55 discount promotion the next year. However the giveaway of Teenie Beanie Babies in 1997 was its most successful promotion ever. McDonald's decentralized US operations that year to bring decision-making closer to local franchises. US division CEO Edward Rensi retired and was replaced by division chairman Jack Greenberg.

The next year Greenberg launched the Made For You food preparation system designed to reduce waste and produce a better tasting burger. He was named CEO later that year. McDonald's also made its first investment in another restaurant concept in 1998 when it bought a stake in Chipotle Mexican Grill a Denver-based chain of Mexican food restaurants. That same year saw the death of co-founder Dick McDonald who died at age 89.

During Greenberg's first year he slowed US expansion and stepped up international growth. In 1999 McDonald's added a third brand to its family when it acquired the Ohio-based Donatos Pizzeria chain. The company's biggest deal though came in 2000 when it purchased the Boston Market

chain from struggling Boston Chicken for about $175 million.

Early in 2001 McDonald's unveiled its New Tastes Menu in which local markets could feature up to four regional or seasonal foods out of a 40-item national selection. The company continued its move toward diversification and international expansion purchasing a 33% stake in the UK limited-service sandwich chain Pret A Manger for $40 million. It also spun off its Japanese unit to the public retaining a 50% ownership stake.

But even with all its size and power McDonald's found out it was not immune to economic trouble and corporate blunders. The company suffered from ill-thought product changes less-than-successful marketing plans and the growing public preference for lighter fast-food options such as sub sandwiches and salads. Following three quarters of declining profits in 2001 McDonald's announced a major restructuring of its US operations. It cut about 700 corporate jobs hired five new managers and consolidated its service regions.

Business failed to improve however and in 2002 it laid off approximately 600 corporate employees and closed about 175 underperforming units. At the end of 2002 after the company posted its first quarterly loss in history vice chairman and president Jim Cantalupo a veteran of McDonald's international operation replaced Jack Greenberg as chairman and CEO.

McDonald's business began to improve during 2003 with the introduction of healthier menu fare. Late that year the company sold Donatos Pizza back to its founder Jim Grote and closed all Boston Market locations outside the US in order to focus more attention on its core chains. The company ended a joint venture with Seed Restaurant Group that would have led to the development of new Fazoli's locations. Japan however remained a particularly rough market: McDonald's Holdings (Japan) posted losses for both 2002 and 2003. It also gave up on efforts to establish the Pret A Manger sandwich shops in Japan.

Putting its advertising dollars to work McDonald's introduced a global branding campaign in 2003 to help change its image. Called 'I'm Lovin' It" the campaign attempted to up the restaurant chain's hip factor and draw young customers. These efforts showed positive results: McDonald's posted steady sales increases through most of 2003 and into early 2004 and investors were encouraged by the progress.

Cantalupo died in 2004. Director Andrew McKenna was named chairman and president. Charlie Bell became CEO. Diagnosed with cancer and undergoing surgery a month later Bell curtailed his workload but returned to his job fulltime later that month. He underwent a second surgery procedure later that year again cancer-related and eventually stepped down near the end of 2004 in order to devote all his time to fighting cancer. (Bell died early the next year.) Vice chairman Jim Skinner assumed the mantle of CEO becoming the company's third chief executive in seven months. Mike Roberts the CEO of McDonald's USA assumed the additional titles of president and COO.

In a David and Goliath scenario the Venezuelan government ordered all 80 of the country's McDonald's restaurants closed for three days in 2005 as punishment for not following the country's tax laws. McDonald's sold a 35% stake in Chipotle through an IPO in 2006 and disposed of its remaining holdings later that year. It sold Boston Market to private equity firm Sun Capital Partners for $250 million the following year and in 2008 McDonald's cashed out its stake in Pret A Manger as part of a $670 million buyout by private equity firm Bridgepoint Capital.

In 2011 McDonald's sold its 50% stake in Hardcastle Restaurants one of two joint ventures operating McDonald's restaurants in India and converted it to a franchisee operation.

EXECUTIVES

EVP and Global Chief Marketing Officer, Silvia Lagnado, $615,000 total compensation

EVP Supply Chain and Development, Douglas M. (Doug) Goare, age 64, $648,750 total compensation

President McDonald's USA, Chris (Chris K) Kempczinski, age 48, $111,538 total compensation

EVP and Chief People Officer, David Fairhurst, age 49

Corporate EVP and CFO, Kevin M. Ozan, age 54, $683,333 total compensation

President CEO and Director, Stephen J. (Steve) Easterbrook, age 49, $1,266,667 total compensation

Corporate EVP Operations and Technology Systems, Jim Sappington, age 58

EVP Corporate Relations; Chief Communications Officer, Robert Gibbs

President High Growth Markets, Joe Erlinger

EVP General Counsel and Secretary, Jerry Krulewitch

President Foundational Markets, Ian Borden

Vice President, Gerald Newman

Vice President Of Operations, Marcy Amble

Vice President of Strategy, Greg Watson

Chairman, Enrique (Rick) Hernandez, age 62

Auditors: Ernst & Young LLP

LOCATIONS

HQ: McDonald's Corp
One McDonald's Plaza, Oak Brook, IL 60523
Phone: 630 623-3000
Web: www.mcdonalds.com

2016 Sales

	$ mil.	% of total
U.S.	8,253	34
International Lead Markets	7,223	29
High Growth Markets	6,161	25
Foundational Markets & Corporate	2,985	12
Total	**24,622**	**100**

2016 Locations

	No.
US	14,155
International Lead Markets	6,851
High Growth Markets	5,552
Foundational Markets & Corporate	10,341
Total	**36,899**

PRODUCTS/OPERATIONS

2016 Locations

	No.
Franchised	31,230
Company-owned	5,669
Total	**36,899**

2016 Sales

	$ mil.	% of total
Company-owned restaurants	15,295	62
Franchised restaurants	9,326	38
Total	**24,621**	**100**

Selected Products

Big Mac
Chicken McNuggets
Egg McMuffin
Filet-O-Fish
Happy Meal
Mac Snack Wrap
McCafe
McChicken
McDouble
McFlurry
McGriddle
McRib
Quarter Pounder

COMPETITORS

Burger King	Quiznos
CKE Restaurants	Sonic Corp.
Chick-fil-A	Starbucks
Church's Chicken	Subway
Dairy Queen	Tim Hortons
Jack in the Box	Wendy's
Panda Restaurant Group	YUM!
Popeyes	

HISTORICAL FINANCIALS

Company Type: Public

Income Statement

FYE: December 31

	REVENUE ($ mil.)	NET INCOME ($ mil.)	NET PROFIT MARGIN	EMPLOYEES
12/16	24,621	4,686	19.0%	375,000
12/15	25,413	4,529	17.8%	420,000
12/14	27,441	4,757	17.3%	420,000
12/13	28,105	5,585	19.9%	440,000
12/12	27,567	5,464	19.8%	440,000
Annual Growth	**(2.8%)**	**(3.8%)**	**—**	**(3.9%)**

2016 Year-End Financials

Debt ratio: 83.66%
Return on equity: 191.40%
Cash ($ mil.): 1,223
Current ratio: 1.40
Long-term debt ($ mil.): 25,878

No. of shares (mil.): 819
Dividends
  Yield: 0.0%
  Payout: 66.3%
Market value ($ mil.): 99,725

	STOCK PRICE ($) FY Close	P/E High/Low	PER SHARE ($)		
			Earnings	Dividends	Book Value
12/16	121.72	24 20	5.44	3.61	(2.69)
12/15	118.14	25 18	4.80	3.44	7.82
12/14	93.70	21 18	4.82	3.28	13.35
12/13	97.03	19 16	5.55	3.12	16.16
12/12	88.21	19 16	5.36	2.87	15.25
Annual Growth	**8.4%**	**— —**	**0.4%**	**5.9%**	

McKesson Corp

McKesson is one of the top pharmaceuticals distributors in North America. The company delivers prescription and generic drugs as well as health and beauty care products to more than 40000 retail and institutional pharmacies throughout the US. The company is also a major medical supplies wholesaler providing medical and surgical equipment to alternate health care sites such as doctors' offices surgery centers and long-term care facilities. In addition to distribution services McKesson offers software and technical services that help pharmacies health care providers and insurers manage supply chain clinical administrative and financial operations. The company was found in 1883.

HISTORY

John McKesson opened a Manhattan drugstore in 1833 and Daniel Robbins joined him as a partner in 1840. McKesson-Robbins soon expanded into chemical and drug production and the enterprise grew steadily. In 1926 after differences arose between the McKesson and Robbins heirs the company was sold to Donald Coster.

Coster was actually convicted felon Philip Musica who purchased McKesson-Robbins with fraudulently obtained bank loans. For more than a decade his real identity remained secret from all but one blackmailer. By 1930 McKesson-Robbins

had wholesale drug operations in 33 states. The company appeared to be growing but a treasurer discovered a Musica-orchestrated accounting scam and a cash shortfall of $3 million. Faced with exposure Musica killed himself in 1939; company bankruptcy followed. McKesson-Robbins emerged from bankruptcy in 1941.

In a hostile takeover in 1967 San Francisco-based Foremost Dairies bought McKesson-Robbins to form Foremost-McKesson. Over the next 20 years the company bought liquor chemical and software wholesalers as well as several bottled-water companies. It sold Foremost Dairies in 1983 to focus on distribution changed its name to McKesson the next year and continued to build its drug wholesaling business through acquisitions. By 1985 it was the US's largest distributor of drugs and medical equipment wine and liquor bottled water and car waxes and polishes.

In 1986 McKesson narrowed its focus to the health industry by selling its liquor and chemical distributors. It acquired Canadian drug distributor Medis by halves in 1990 and 1991 and a 23% stake in Mexican drug distributor Nadro in 1993.

McKesson sold PCS the US's #1 prescription claims processor (acquired in 1970) to Eli Lilly in 1994. In 1996 the firm bought bankrupt distributor FoxMeyer Drug and sold its stake in Armor All (auto and home cleaning products) to Clorox.

In 1997 the company purchased General Medical the US's largest distributor of medical surgical supplies for about $775 million. McKesson began to focus on health care selling its Millbrook Distribution Services unit (health and beauty products general merchandise and specialty foods).

Under new CEO Mark Pulido it agreed to buy drug wholesaler AmeriSource Health (now AmerisourceBergen) but withdrew the offer in 1998 facing FTC opposition. Instead McKesson moved into information systems paying $14 billion for health care information top dog HBO & Company and forming McKesson HBOC. HBO a high-flyer in the high-growth health information systems segment balanced its rather dowdy drug and medical distribution operations.

But just months after the deal closed accounting inconsistencies at HBO prompted McKesson to restate fourth-quarter results for fiscal 1999 twice triggering shareholder lawsuits and a housecleaning of top brass. Five ex-HBO executives including McKesson HBOC chairman Charlie McCall (who was later indicted for securities fraud) were canned for using improper accounting methods. McKesson's veteran CEO Pulido and CFO Richard Hawkins were forced to resign for not seeing the problems coming.

The company changed its name to McKesson Corporation in 2001. The National Health Services Information Authority entered into an agreement with McKesson to develop a human resources and payroll system for use at the more than 600 NHS locations throughout the UK.

To catch then #1 pharmaceutical distributor Cardinal Health McKesson built up its core areas in 2003 and 2004 while trimming away some of the dead weight (Abaton.com Amysis Managed Care Systems and ProDental Corp.). The company bought PMO a specialty mail-order prescription business. It also acquired Canadian firm A.L.I. Technologies which provided systems for managing medical images.

In 2007 McKesson acquired Oncology Therapeutics Network a specialty pharmaceuticals distributor for $519 million. McKesson launched a new Plasma and BioLogics division in 2008 to deliver plasma and plasma-related products to hospital pharmacies and it expanded its regional drug distribution network through the purchase of Midwest pharmacy distributor McQueary Brothers for $190 million.

EXECUTIVES

Chairman President and CEO, John H. Hammergren, age 58, $1,680,000 total compensation
EVP Human Resources, Jorge L. Figueredo, age 56, $708,167 total compensation
EVP and CFO, James A. Beer, age 56, $840,167 total compensation
EVP and Group President Domestic and International Distribution Solutions, Paul C. Julian, age 61, $1,148,333 total compensation
EVP CIO and CTO, Kathleen D. (Kathy) McElligott, age 61
EVP General Counsel and Chief Compliance Officer, Lori A. Schechter, age 55
EVP and Group President McKesson Technology Solutions, Patrick J. (Pat) Blake, age 53, $765,500 total compensation
EVP Corporate Strategy and Business Development, Bansi Nagji, age 52
Vice President Home Care Sales, Jeff Bowman
Senior Vice President and GM, Jeff Reinke
Vice President, Rich McKeon
Senior Vice President Dist Support, Donald Walker
Vice President of Sales, Vince Tighe
Director of Surgery Centers Northeast, Keith Slattery
Vice President E Commerce, Robert Fearing
Regional Senior Vice President, Chad Warnick
Vice President Rxownership, Tammy McDonald
Vice President Independent National Accounts, Perry L Anderson
Division Vice President Sales, Peter Emmott
Senior Vice President Operations, Eddie Miller
Senior Vice President Program and Release Management, Craig Allan
Vice President Global Sourcing Medical, James Hodges
Director of Health Systems and Corporate Accounts, Francis D'Avanza
Vice President, Kevin Ballew
Vice President Of Corporate Tax, Paul A Smith
Legal Secretary, Janis Valiao
Senior Vice President Governance Relations Associate General Counsel, Michele Lau
Vice President National Accounts, Mark Snodgrass
Vice President of Sales, Joe Bivins
Vice President General Manager Technology Solutions, Dan Lodder
Territory Vice President Revenue Management Solutions McKesson Provider Technologies, Brian Baughman
Vice President And General Manager, Andrew Moore
Vice President Manager Director, Sunitha Jois
Enterprise Vice President, Kendall Echols
Associate Vice President, Lynn Garbee
Vice President High School National Accounts McKesson HBOC, Sharon Longwell
Vice President National Accounts, Mike Ferguson
Vice President, Mike Cesarz
Vice President Sales, Andy Weissel
Regional Vice President Sales Western Region, David Clark
Vice President Data Center Operations, Barry Gilbert
Area Vice President, Keith Andelman
Assistant Vice President Software Development McKesson Corporation, Karen Erickson
Vice President of Marketing, Andy Burtis
Vice President Human Resources, Tiffany Owens
Vice President Sales, Scott Spackman
Senior Vice President Distribution Systems, Ronald Bone
Vice President Business Development, Deann Cushman
Vice President Of Strategic Development, Brian Grobbel
Assistant Vice President, Stephen Ayers
Vice President Of Sales, Deborah Smith

Vice President Of Sales And Operations, Mauricio Chavez
Vice President Strategic Solutions, Jeanine Singer
Vice President of Enterprise Architecture and Technology, Robert Franceschini
Vice President Of Sales, Casey Antonson
Specialty Vice President, Randal Sanderson
Vice President Office Product Sales, Kevin Boyle
Vice President Marketing And Sales Program, David Brown
Director of Radiology Coding, Dee Fulenwider
Vice President Laboratory Account Sales, Jerry Morrow
Vice President Software Engineering, Jason Warner
Vice President Of Customer Operations, Kathy McGrath
Executive Vice President and CIO, Zalise Edwards
Vice President Marketing, Emma Reynolds
National Vice President Of Sales, Kevin Sheilds
Senior Vice President and Chief Information Officer User Services. Pharmaceutical, Rashmi Kumar
Executive Vice President National Accounts, Jack Fragie
Vice President General Manager, Ed Escalante
Vice President Marketing, Deborah Bulger
Vice President Level, Vice president-sales Kim Diemand
Senior Vice President Chief, Robert Pocica
Vice President and General Manager HIS and Revenue Cycle Solutions McKesson Provider Technologies, Jim Morrison
Vice President and Treasurer, Nicholas Loiacono
Regional Vice President Sales, Sean Nelson
Vice President General Manager Southeast Markets, Scott Miller
Senior Vice President and GM Pharmacy Optimization, Mark Eastham
Senior Vice President Human Resources US Pharmaceutical, Tracy Faber
Regional Vice President Sales, Steven Dissing
Vice President of Sales, Lisa Vicicondi
Vice President Shared Services, Douglas Caro
Vice President Workplace Management, Sara Baldi
Vice President Sales, Noreen Browne
Senior Vice President Strategy and Business Development, Matt Yordy
Associate Vice President Project Management, Marivi Lem
Senior Vice President of Global Corporate Real Estate, Michael Huaco
Vice President GPO Services Onmark, Chris Wixson
Assistant Secretary, Karen Pineda
Secretary, Nancy Tyree
Auditors: DELOITTE & TOUCHE LLP

LOCATIONS

HQ: McKesson Corp
One Post Street, San Francisco, CA 94104
Phone: 415 983-8300
Web: www.mckesson.com

2017 Sales

	$ mil.	% of total
United States	164,428	83
Foreign	34,105	17
Total	**198,533**	**100**

PRODUCTS/OPERATIONS

2017 Sales

	$ mil.	% of total
Distribution Solutions		
North America pharmaceutical distribution & services	164,832	83
International pharmaceutical distribution & services	24,847	13
Medical-Surgical distribution & services	6,244	3
Technology Solutions - products and services	2,610	1
Total	**198,533**	**100**

Selected Operations and Services

Distribution Solutions (North America)
McKesson Canada (drug distribution pharmacy and provider services)
McKesson Medical-Surgical (includes ZEE Medical and Moore Medical supplies and equipment distribution)
McKesson Patient Relationship Solutions (consumer adherence coaching outreach discount/trial programs)
McKesson Pharmaceutical (drug health and beauty care products distribution)
Institutional pharmacy services (consulting inventory management cost control SKY Packaging)
Retail pharmacy services (Health Mart franchising consulting data and claims management cost control inventory management value brands redistribution repackaging refilling software)
McKesson Pharmacy Systems (EnterpriseRx and PharmacyRx software financial operational and clinical solutions for retail and institutional pharmacies)
McKesson Plasma and BioLogics (plasma-derivative products for hospitals)
McKesson Specialty Health (solutions for specialty drug manufacturers and specialist care providers includes iKnowMed EHR)
The US Oncology Network (cancer drug distribution)
Nadro S.A. de C.V. (49% drug distribution Mexico)
Parata Systems LLC (39% automated pharmacy and supply management systems and services)
Technology Solutions (North America Europe Israel)
McKesson Automation (hospital dispensing and inventory management InterQual claims payment)
McKesson Health Solutions (disease and case management claims management)
McKesson Provider Technologies (clinical automation and physician practice management hospital inventory management and dispensing electronic health records software enterprise imaging revenue cycle outsourcing)
RelayHealth (connectivity vendor neutral health information exchange)

Selected Acquisitions

COMPETITORS

Allscripts	Henry Schein
AmerisourceBergen	Imperial Distributors
Apothecary Products	Kinray
BioScrip	Medline Industries
Cardinal Health	Omnicare
Cerner	Owens & Minor
CuraScript	PharMerica
FFF Enterprises	Quality King
Franz Haniel	Surgical Express
Grifols	The Harvard Drug Group
H. D. Smith Wholesale Drug	athenahealth

HISTORICAL FINANCIALS

Company Type: Public

Income Statement

	REVENUE ($ mil.)	NET INCOME ($ mil.)	NET PROFIT MARGIN	EMPLOYEES
03/17	198,533	5,070	2.6%	78,000
03/16	190,884	2,258	1.2%	68,000
03/15	179,045	1,476	0.8%	70,400
03/14	137,609	1,263	0.9%	42,800
03/13	122,455	1,338	1.1%	43,500
Annual Growth	**12.8%**	**39.5%**	**—**	**15.7%**

FYE: March 31

2017 Year-End Financials

Debt ratio: 14.02%
Return on equity: 50.65%
Cash ($ mil.): 2,783
Current ratio: 1.04
Long-term debt ($ mil.): 7,305

No. of shares (mil.): 211
Dividends
  Yield: 0.7%
  Payout: 4.9%
Market value ($ mil.): 31,283

	STOCK PRICE ($)	P/E		PER SHARE ($)		
	FY Close	High/Low	Earnings	Dividends	Book Value
03/17	148.26	9 5	22.73	1.12	52.58
03/16	157.25	25 15	9.70	1.08	39.66
03/15	226.20	36 26	6.27	0.96	34.49
03/14	176.57	34 19	5.41	0.92	36.89
03/13	107.96	19 15	5.59	0.80	31.15
Annual Growth	8.3%	— —	42.0%	8.8%	14.0%

Mercantile Bank Corp.

Mercantile Bank Corporation is the holding company for Mercantile Bank of Michigan (formerly Mercantile Bank of West Michigan) which boasts assets of nearly $3 billion and operates more than 50 branches in central and western Michigan around Grand Rapids Holland and Lansing. The bank targets local consumers and businesses offering standard deposit services such as checking and savings accounts CDs IRAs and health savings accounts. Commercial loans make up more than three-fourths of the bank's loan portfolio. Outside of banking subsidiary Mercantile Insurance Center sells insurance products.

Operations

Mercantile Bank Corp. generated 82% of its total revenue from loan interest (including fees) in 2014 with securities interest contributing another 8% to total revenue. Service charges on deposit and sweep accounts and credit and debit card fees made up another 5% of Mercantile's total revenue while its mortgage banking income generated another 2%.

Sales and Marketing

Mercantile provides its banking services to businesses individuals and government organizations. Its commercial banking services mostly cater to small- to medium-sized businesses.

The company spent $1.315 million on advertising in 2014 compared to $1.113 million and $1.167 million in 2013 and 2012 respectively.

Financial Performance

Mercantile Bank Corp.'s revenues had been declining for a number of years as its loan business withered while profits have remained mostly flat.

The company had a breakout year in 2014 however after its historic acquisition of FirstBank Corp. The bank's revenue skyrocketed by 53% to $99.15 million (the highest level since 2009) mostly as the acquisition nearly doubled its loan assets and boosted its interest income on loans and securities by significant amounts. The bank's non-interest income also grew by 46% thanks to higher fee income across the board also resulting from the recent acquisition.

Higher revenue and a $3.2 million reduction in loan loss provisions with a stronger credit portfolio in 2014 also pushed the company's net income up by 2% to $17.33 million for the year. Mercantile's operating cash declined by 50% to $14.41 million due to changes in accrued interest and other liabilities during the year.

Strategy

Mercantile Bank Corporation has been growing its loan business and branch network reach through strategic acquisitions of smaller banks and bank branches. Its mid-2014 acquisition of Firstbank Corporation was perhaps the most effective to date as the purchase doubled its assets and boosted the size of its branch network nearly seven-fold from seven branches to a whopping 53.

Mergers and Acquisitions

In June 2014 Mercantile Bank Corp. purchased Firstbank Corp of Alma Michigan for a total purchase price of $173 million adding 46 branches and $1.3 billion in assets. The deal which made Mercantile the third-largest bank based in the state also expanded the bank's service offerings diversified its loan portfolio boosted its loan origination capacity and significantly extended its geographic footprint into Michigan's lower peninsula.

EXECUTIVES

SVP CFO and Treasurer Mercantile Bank Corporation and SVP and CFO Mercantile Bank of Michigan, Charles E. (Chuck) Christmas, age 51, $263,000 total compensation
President and CEO, Robert B. Kaminski, age 55, $315,000 total compensation
EVP Corporate Finance and Strategic Planning Mercantile Bank Corporation and Mercantile Bank of Michigan, Samuel G. Stone, age 72, $159,833 total compensation
Vice President Internal Auditor, Sandy Jager
Vice President Electronic Banking, Shannon Tramontin
Senior Vice President Commercial Lending, Kevin Paul
Assistant Vice President Human Resources Specialist, Tina Van Valkenburg
Vice President Treasury Management, Joe Allen
Senior Vice President Retail Banking Director, Dave Miller
Assistant Vice President, Amy Ervin
Senior Vice President Business Development Officer, Brian Talbot
Vice President Commercial Loan Officer, Jeff Hicks
Vice President, Teresa Rupert
Senior Vice President Commercial Lending, David Deboer
Vice President, Mike Siminski
Assistant Vice President Assistant Controller, Peggy Coutchie
Senior Vice President Information Systems Manager, Allen Smith
Assistant Vice President Commercial Loan Officer, Justin Horn
Senior Vice President Operations, Richard Rice
Vice President Corporate Banking, Bob Klimczak
Senior Vice President Mortgage Sales Manager, Michael Yates
Vice President, Douglas Ouellette
Vice President, Holly Williams
Senior Vice President Commercial Loan Manager, Joe Valicevic
Chairman, Michael H. Price, age 60
Auditors: BDO USA, LLP

LOCATIONS

HQ: Mercantile Bank Corp.
310 Leonard Street N.W., Grand Rapids, MI 49504
Phone: 616 406-3000
Web: www.mercbank.com

PRODUCTS/OPERATIONS

2014 Sales

	$ mil.	% of total
Interest income		
Loans and leases including fees	80	82
Securities taxable	6	6
Securities tax-exempt	1	2
Other	0	-
Noninterest income		
Service charges on accounts	2	3
Credit and debit card fees	2	2
Mortgage banking activities	1	2
Other	3	3
Total	**99**	**100**

COMPETITORS

Chemical Financial	Flagstar Bancorp
ChoiceOne Financial Services	Huntington Bancshares
Comerica	Independent Bank (MI)
Fifth Third	Macatawa Bank

HISTORICAL FINANCIALS

Company Type: Public

Income Statement

FYE: December 31

	ASSETS ($ mil.)	NET INCOME ($ mil.)	INCOME AS % OF ASSETS	EMPLOYEES
12/16	3,082	31	1.0%	682
12/15	2,903	27	0.9%	701
12/14	2,893	17	0.6%	731
12/13	1,426	17	1.2%	268
12/12	1,422	12	0.9%	264
Annual Growth	21.3%	26.3%	—	26.8%

2016 Year-End Financials

Debt ratio: 1.45%	No. of shares (mil.): 16
Return on equity: 9.44%	Dividends
Cash ($ mil.): 183	Yield: 0.0%
Current ratio: —	Payout: 59.1%
Long-term debt ($ mil.): —	Market value ($ mil.): 619

	STOCK PRICE ($)	P/E		PER SHARE ($)		
	FY Close	High/Low	Earnings	Dividends	Book Value
12/16	37.70	19 11	1.96	1.16	20.76
12/15	24.54	16 12	1.62	0.58	20.41
12/14	21.02	19 15	1.28	2.48	19.33
12/13	21.58	11 8	1.95	0.45	17.54
12/12	16.50	14 7	1.33	0.09	16.84
Annual Growth	22.9%	— —	10.2%	89.5%	5.4%

Merchants Bancorp (Indiana)

LOCATIONS

HQ: Merchants Bancorp (Indiana)
11555 North Meridian Street, Suite 400, Carmel, IN 46032
Phone: 317 569-7420
Web: www.merchantsbankofindiana.com

HISTORICAL FINANCIALS

Company Type: Public

Income Statement

FYE: December 31

	ASSETS ($ mil.)	NET INCOME ($ mil.)	INCOME AS % OF ASSETS	EMPLOYEES
12/16	2,718	33	1.2%	157
12/15	2,269	28	1.3%	—
Annual Growth	19.8%	16.7%		—

2016 Year-End Financials

Debt ratio: —	No. of shares (mil.): 21
Return on equity: 18.64%	Dividends
Cash ($ mil.): 445	Yield: —
Current ratio: —	Payout: 13.6%
Long-term debt ($ mil.): —	Market value ($ mil.): —

	STOCK PRICE ($) FY Close	P/E High/Low	PER SHARE ($) Earnings	Dividends	Book Value
12/16	0.00	— —	1.47	0.20	9.77
12/15	0.00	— —	1.35	0.20	7.02
/0.00	—	—(0.00)	0.00	(0.00)	
Annual Growth	—	— —	—	—	—

Merck & Co Inc

Merck makes medicines for a number of maladies from stuffy noses and asthma to hypertension and arthritis. The pharmaceutical giant's top prescription drugs include diabetes drugs Januvia and Janumet anti-inflammatory Remicade cholesterol combatants Vytorin and Zetia and hypertension fighters Cozaar and Hyzaar. In addition Merck makes childhood and adult vaccines for such diseases as measles mumps pneumonia and shingles as well as veterinary pharmaceuticals through Merck Animal Health.

HISTORY

Merck traces its roots to the formation of Schering-Plough in 1851 and the founding of the original Merck entity in 1887. (The two companies merged in 2009.)

Schering-Plough dates back to 1851 when Berlin chemist Ernst Schering began to sell chemicals to apothecary shops. By 1880 Schering's business (which eventually became Bayer Schering Pharma) was exporting pharmaceuticals to the US where a subsidiary (the predecessor to Schering-Plough) was established in 1928.

At the outbreak of WWII the US government seized the US Schering subsidiary severing links with its German parent. The company went on to develop such new drugs as Chlor-Trimeton one of the first antihistamines and the cold medicine Coricidin. The US government sold Schering in 1952 to Merrill Lynch which took it public. Schering bought White Labs (which made Coppertone sunscreen) in 1957. In the 1960s the company introduced Garamycin (antibiotic 1964) Tinactin (antifungal 1965) and Afrin (decongestant 1967).

Schering's 1971 merger with Memphis-based Plough expanded the product line to include such cosmetics and consumer items as Coppertone and Di-Gel. Plough's founder Abe Plough had borrowed $125 from his father to found the company in 1908. Abe remained chairman at Schering-Plough until 1976. Schering-Plough introduced many products after the merger including Lotrimin AF (antifungal 1975) antibiotic Netromycin (1980) and Drixoral (a cold remedy made nonprescription in 1982).

The company was one of the first drug giants to make significant investments in biotechnology: It bought DNAX Research Institute of Palo Alto California in 1982. Acquisitions in the late 1970s and 1980s included Scholl (foot care 1979) Key Pharmaceuticals (cardiovascular drugs 1986) and Cooper Companies (eye care 1988).

In 1993 Schering-Plough began marketing its non-sedating antihistamine Claritin in the US. (Claritin became an OTC drug in 2002.) The next year it gained FDA approval to market the first colored disposable contact lenses only to sell its contact lens business later in the year. In 1996 Schering-Plough bought Canji to strengthen its gene therapy research program. It strengthened its veterinary medicine segment in 1997 when it bought Mallinckrodt's animal health operations.

The firm bought the marketing rights to Centocor's treatment for Crohn's disease in 1998. In 1999 the FDA approved the company's Temodar a chemotherapy treatment for brain tumors and it bought the US rights to Pfizer's Bain de Soleil sun care product line. In 2000 Schering-Plough formed its first collaboration with Merck. In 2002 the company paid a $500 million fine to the FDA over manufacturing concerns.

As Schering-Plough's revenues started to decline in 2003 the company brought in several executives from Pharmacia including CEO Fred Hassan (who retired following the 2009 merger with Plough) to help streamline its operations and expand its R&D programs and product offerings. The firm gave itself a major boost by acquiring Akzo Nobel's Organon unit in 2007 growing in the areas of women's health care neurology vaccines animal health (Intervet) and third-party biologics manufacturing (through Diosynth).

The original Merck was started in 1887 when German chemist Theodore Weicker came to the US to set up a branch of German firm E. Merck AG (which was founded in 1668 and later became Merck KGaA). George Merck (grandson of the German company's founder) came in 1889 and formed a partnership with Weicker and eventually bought out Weicker's shares. At first the firm imported and sold drugs and chemicals from Germany but in 1903 it began manufacturing its own products. During WWI Merck gave the US government the 80% of the US Merck unit's stock owned by the family in Germany (George kept his shares). After the war the stock was sold to the public.

The firm acquired Powers-Weightman-Rosengarten of Philadelphia (a producer of antimalarial quinine) in 1927. Merck opened its first research lab in 1933; Merck scientists there developed the first steroid cortisone in 1944. Five Merck scientists received Nobel Prizes in the 1940s and 1950s. In 1953 Merck bought drugmaker Sharp & Dohme of Philadelphia which brought with it a strong sales force.

The 1958 introduction of Diuril (antihypertensive) and several other drugs (including the first measles vaccine) in the early 1960s was followed by a dry spell. In the 1970s an accelerated R&D organization created new products including Clinoril (antiarthritic) Flexeril (muscle relaxant) and Timoptic (for glaucoma). Merck introduced 10 major new drugs in the 1980s including Mevacor (high cholesterol) and Vasotec (high blood pressure).

In 1990 the company bought the nonprescription drug segment of ICI Americas; products from the purchase were contributed to a Consumer Pharmaceuticals joint venture with Johnson & Johnson. Merck bought pharmacy benefits manager Medco Containment Services in 1993. New drug launches in 1995 and 1996 included Cozaar (for reducing hypertension) and Pepcid AC (antacid). Also in 1996 Merck expanded its pharmacy benefit management operations with the purchase of Systemed.

In 1997 Merck and Rhône-Poulenc (now part of Sanofi-Aventis) merged their animal health units to form Merial. Merck also sold its insecticide and fungicide business to Novartis that year. In 1998 DuPont bought out Merck's 50% stake in a drug-marketing joint venture formed by the two firms in 1991. In 1999 the FDA approved Merck's preservative-free hepatitis B vaccine Recombivax HB.

In 2001 Merck acquired biotech firm Rosetta Inpharmatics. The company spun off its highly successful Medco Health Solutions drug distribution subsidiary in 2003.

In 2004 Merck pulled its blockbuster pain medication Vioxx off the market after studies linked the drug to increased risks of strokes and heart attacks. (Merck settled thousands of class-action and personal-injury lawsuits related to Vioxx in 2007 for $4.85 billion.) The Vioxx safety scandal along with the pending loss of patent protection on some of its biggest sellers like Zocor (which began facing competition in 2006) sent the company into recovery mode. Merck announced restructuring plans to make the company's operations leaner and more cost-effective in 2005 under new CEO Richard (Dick) Clark a longtime Merck executive. Between 2005 and 2008 the company eliminated more than 10000 jobs and closed a handful of manufacturing plants.

From 2006 to 2009 Merck worked aggressively to expand its biotech operations through the acquisition of companies including GlycoFi (biologic drug molecules) Abmaxis (monoclonal antibodies) Sirna Therapeutics (RNA interference or RNAi) and NovaCardia (cardiology drugs) as well as the follow-on (generic) biologic assets of Insmed. New drug launches included HIV drug Isentress and diabetes therapy Janumet in 2007 and blockbuster HPV vaccine Gardasil the world's first anti-cancer vaccine which was approved by the FDA in 2006.

In 2008 Merck sold off the assets of its Rosetta Inpharmatics subsidiary to Covance (gene expression laboratory assets) and Microsoft (expression analysis software assets). It also sold another research lab to PPD and contracted out certain lab functions to the buyer. Merck launched a new product Emend for chemotherapy side-effects that year. New drug launches in 2009 included Saphris a treatment for schizophrenia and bipolar disorder and Simponi the next-generation version of top-selling drug Remicade.

Cholesterol drug Vytorin — a combination of Schering-Plough's Zetia and Merck's Zocor — began facing controversy in 2008 when study results were released questioning the drug's effectiveness compared to Merck's older medication Zocor. Controversy over Vytorin along with some other pipeline setbacks (including the FDA's rejection of a Merck/Schering-Plough combo asthma drug and Merck's Cordaptive cholesterol candidate) led both predecessors Merck and Schering-Plough to announce layoffs and restructuring measures in 2008. Each company reduced its workforce by around 10% that year with their respective US sales teams bearing the brunt of the cuts. The companies' troubles with Vytorin came to a head in 2009 when they agreed to pay about $42 million to settle class-action lawsuits filed by consumers and health plans over Vytorin's efficacy.

Later that year Merck and Schering-Plough decided to merge taking the logical step of marriage to strengthen their defenses against future troubles (especially in light of increasing competitive challenges in the market) as well as to create cost savings opportunities and expanded avenues for revenue growth. The $41 billion transaction was conducted through a reverse-merger transaction in which the legacy Schering-Plough entity acquired the legacy Merck entity and took on the Merck name.

Following the merger Merck began simplifying its global branding under the Merck and MSD names gradually phasing out the Schering-Plough moniker. The purchase expanded Merck's offerings in areas including inflammation allergy and cancer treatment as well as biotech drugs. The acquisition also greatly expanded Merck's operations in the animal health and consumer health arenas.

However to gain Schering-Plough's animal health unit Intervet (later renamed Merck Animal Health) Merck had to sell its stake in veterinary joint venture Merial to partner Sanofi-Aventis for about $4 billion later that year to avoid anti-trust issues. (Merck and Sanofi-Aventis later explored options to strike a fresh veterinary medicine joint venture by combining Merial with Intervet; however after a year of planning the two companies called off the deal in 2011 due to concerns over further anti-trust issues.)

The company experienced a sharp gain in profits in 2009 (reporting net income of $12.9 billion) due to gains on the sale of the Merial stake and on recognized equity from assets previously owned jointly with Schering-Plough.

When the Merck/Schering-Plough merger closed the existing Merck CEO Dick Clark took the helm at the new Merck. Once the dust from the merger settled however Clark retired from the CEO post at the end of 2010 while remaining as chairman. President Kenneth Frazier stepped into the CEO role.

EXECUTIVES

Chairman and CEO, Kenneth C. (Ken) Frazier, age 62, $1,527,404 total compensation
EVP Strategic Communications Global Public Policy and Population Health and Chief Patient Officer, Julie L. Gerberding, age 62
EVP Global Services and CFO, Robert M. Davis, age 50, $991,654 total compensation
EVP; President Merck Research Laboratories, Roger M. Perlmutter, age 64, $1,052,288 total compensation
EVP; President Global Human Health, Adam H. Schechter, age 53, $1,003,094 total compensation
EVP Human Resources, Mirian M. Graddick-Weir, age 63
EVP; President Merck Animal Health, Richard R. DeLuca, age 54
EVP and General Counsel, Michael J. Holston, age 54, $761,538 total compensation
EVP and CIO, Clark Golestani, age 50
EVP; President Merck Manufacturing, Sanat Chattopadhyay
CEO Merck Foundation, Rasha Kelej, age 45
Vice President, Kevin Ravaioli
National Sales Manager, Ron McDaniel
Associate Vice President, Ben Thorner
Vice President Biotechnology Development, Stephen Farrand
Vice President Manufacturing Division Strategy And Integration, Richard Hofmann
Senior Vice President At Merck Research Labs, Madelyn Caltabiano
Vice President Global Compensation And Benefits, Jeff Geller
Vice President Finance Global Supply Chain, Joe Sukola
Vice President Global Engineering Services, Arthur Burson
Associate Medical Director, Lana Garafola
Legal Pa For Uk Director And Also Pa To The Assistant Vice President For Europe And Canada, Michele Creamer
Senior Vice President, Dorthe Mikkelsen
Vice President Discovery Chemistry, Yvette Espeleta
Assistant Vice President Global Communications, Mary Elizabeth Blake
Office Of The Vice President And Chief C, Beth Colnett
Executive Vice President Process Solutions, Andrew Bulpin
Senior Vice President Strategy And Business Development, Galeota James
Associate Vice President Sterile Operations, David Zisa
Vice President and Global Leader Atherosclerosis, Karim Mikhail
Associate Vice President Emerging Markets, Steven Cianciosi
National Sales Manager, Brett Cookman
Associate Vice President of Operations and General Manager MSD Oss, Cees Mens
Associate Vice President Merck Consumer Care Information Technology, Fran Geatens
Associate Vice President Global Clinical Safety and Pharmacovigilance, Nina Stuccio
Senior Vice President Finance, Caroline Litchfield
Vice Presidentb, Shelli Andrews
Vice President, Julie Lepin
Vice President Of Imaging, Jeffrey Evelhoch
Vice President of Sales, Dave Clark
Vice Presidents Club, George McDowell
Assistant Treasurer, Joe Promo
Auditors: PricewaterhouseCoopers LLP

LOCATIONS

HQ: Merck & Co Inc
2000 Galloping Hill Road, Keniworth, NJ 07033
Phone: 908 740-4000   **Fax:** 908 735-1500
Web: www.merck.com

2016 Sales

	$ mil.	% of total
United States	18,478	46
Europe Middle East and Africa	10,953	28
Asia Pacific	3,918	10
Japan	2,846	7
Latin America	2,155	5
Other	1,457	4
Total	**39,807**	**100**

PRODUCTS/OPERATIONS

2016 Sales

	$ mil.	% of total
Pharmaceutical segment		
Primary Care and Women's Health	11,984	30
Vaccines	10,494	26
Hospital and Specialty	7,556	19
Diversified Brands	2,883	7
Oncology	2,234	6
Other segment	3,862	10
Other	794	2
Total	**39,807**	**100**

COMPETITORS

Abbott Labs	Johnson & Johnson
Alcon	Meda Pharmaceuticals
Allergan plc	Merck KGaA
Amgen	Mylan
AstraZeneca	Novartis
Bayer AG	Perrigo
Biogen	Pfizer
Boehringer Ingelheim	Roche Holding
Bristol-Myers Squibb	Sandoz International
Eli Lilly	GmbH
Enanta	Sanofi
Gilead Sciences	Shire
GlaxoSmithKline	Teva
Heska	Virbac Corporation

HISTORICAL FINANCIALS

Company Type: Public

Income Statement

FYE: December 31

	REVENUE ($ mil.)	NET INCOME ($ mil.)	NET PROFIT MARGIN	EMPLOYEES
12/16	39,807	3,920	9.8%	68,000
12/15	39,498	4,442	11.2%	68,000
12/14	42,237	11,920	28.2%	70,000
12/13	44,033	4,404	10.0%	76,000
12/12	47,267	6,168	13.0%	83,000
Annual Growth	**(4.2%)**	**(10.7%)**	**—**	**(4.9%)**

2016 Year-End Financials

Debt ratio: 26.05%—
Return on equity: 9.22%
Cash ($ mil.): 6,515
Current ratio: 1.78
Long-term debt ($ mil.): 24,274

Dividends
Yield: 0.0%
Payout: 131.2%
Market value ($ mil.): —

	STOCK PRICE ($) FY Close	P/E High/Low		PER SHARE ($) Earnings	Dividends	Book Value
12/16	58.87	46	34	1.41	1.85	14.58
12/15	52.82	40	31	1.56	1.81	16.06
12/14	56.79	15	12	4.07	1.77	17.14
12/13	50.05	34	27	1.47	1.73	17.00
12/12	40.94	24	18	2.00	1.69	17.52
Annual Growth	**9.5%**	**—**	**—**	**(8.4%)**	**2.3%**	**(4.5%)**

Mercury General Corp.

Named after the Roman god of commerce and travel Mercury General hopes to combine the two and become the ultimate auto insurance provider. The company is the parent of a group of insurers including Mercury Casualty Company that write automobile insurance for all risk classifications in about a dozen states. Plain old private auto insurance accounts for a majority of premiums written. However Mercury General also sells commercial vehicle insurance and a bit of homeowners mechanical breakdown umbrella and fire insurance. The company is a leader in the California auto market and has significant operations in Florida.

Operations

Mercury General offers automobile insurance products including comprehensive collision property damage body injury personal injury protection underinsured/uninsured motorist and other coverage. It also provides homeowners' coverage including dwelling liability personal property fire and other products.

Geographic Reach

While Mercury General has ventured out of its California comfort zone the state still accounts for about 85% of total premiums. The company operated solely in its home state until 1990; it now underwrites auto insurance in about a dozen other states including Arizona Florida Georgia Illinois Nevada New Jersey New York Oklahoma Texas and Virginia.

Sales and Marketing

Mercury General sells policies through approximately 9700 independent agents including around 1900 in California and another 1500 in Florida.

The company uses television radio newspaper direct mail and online campaigns to market its products. It launched a national advertising campaign in 2015.

Mercury General spent $40 million on advertising in 2016 versus $44 million in 2015 and $23 million in 2014.

Financial Performance

Mercury General's net revenue has been rising for the past five years with the exception of 2015 when it fell less than 1% to $3 billion. In 2016 it rose 7% to $3.2 billion as net premiums earned increased and net realized investment losses decreased. The company had a 5% increase in net premiums written primarily due to rate increases and higher sales in California.

Net income which fell 58% to $74 million in 2015 dropped another 2% to $73 million in 2016. Higher losses loss adjustment expenses and policy acquisition costs led to that decline. Profits were impacted by losses related to automobile accidents in California and Florida as well as catastrophe losses due to severe storms and rainstorms.

Cash flow from operations has generally been rising. It grew 51% to $287.5 million in 2016. Major factors in that jump included positive adjustments to unpaid losses and loss adjustment expenses changes in current and deferred income taxes and in accounts payable and accrued expenses.

Strategy

Core to Mercury General's strategy for growth is managing rates to achieve the right balance between attracting customers through lower rates and remaining competitive. For example to counteract the overall increase in auto accidents the company implemented price hikes in 2016. It expects its returns to improve in that arena.

The company also places value in its agent relationships and underwriting processes to achieve favorable margins. To encourage policy growth and broaden its customer base Mercury General offers multi-policy discounts to those who bundle their home and car insurance together. It also employs marketing initiatives to build brand recognition and generate leads.

Additionally Mercury General is gradually widening its operations by expanding into new states while being mindful of the risks of establishing new divisions. Mercury General also maintains a conservative investment strategy by maximizing long-term performance opportunities.

EXECUTIVES

VP and Chief Underwriting Officer, Kenneth G. Kitzmiller, age 70
President and CEO, Gabriel Tirador, age 52, $948,931 total compensation
SVP and CFO, Theodore R. Stalick, age 53, $589,445 total compensation
VP and Chief Investment Officer, Christopher Graves, age 51, $381,679 total compensation
VP and Chief Actuary, Charles Toney, age 55
SVP and CIO, Allan Lubitz, age 59, $449,470 total compensation
VP and Chief Product Officer, Robert Houlihan, age 60, $404,493 total compensation
VP Marketing, Brandt N. Minnich, age 50
Vice President Information Technology Operations, Abby Hossein
Vice President Corporate Controller, David Yeager
Chairman, George Joseph, age 95
Auditors: KPMG LLP

LOCATIONS

HQ: Mercury General Corp.
4484 Wilshire Boulevard, Los Angeles, CA 90010
Phone: 323 937-1060   **Fax:** 323 857-7116
Web: www.mercuryinsurance.com

PRODUCTS/OPERATIONS

2016 Sales

	$ mil.	% of total
Net premium earned	3,131	96
Net investment income	121	4
Other	8	-
Net realized investment (losses)gains	(34.3)	-
Total	**3,227**	**100**

Selected Products

Auto
  Commercial auto
  Mechanical breakdown (extended warranty coverage)
  Niche commercial
  Personal auto
Condo
  Contents coverage
  Guest medical protection and liability

Personal liability protection
Personal property
Homeowners
  Apartments
  Condominiums
  Single-family homes
Personal umbrella
Renter
  Liability protection
  Personal property

Selected Operating Brands and Divisions

AIS Management
American Mercury Insurance
American Mercury Lloyds Insurance
American Mercury MGA
Auto Insurance Specialists
California Automobile Insurance
California General Underwriters Insurance
Concord Insurance Services
Mercury Casualty
Mercury County Mutual Insurance
Mercury Group
Mercury Indemnity
Mercury Insurance
Mercury National Insurance
Mercury Select Management
PoliSeek AIS Insurance Solutions

COMPETITORS

21st Century Insurance
Allstate
Auto Club of Southern California
Covanta Holding
Farmers Group
GEICO
State Farm
USAA

HISTORICAL FINANCIALS

Company Type: Public

Income Statement

FYE: December 31

	ASSETS ($ mil.)	NET INCOME ($ mil.)	INCOME AS % OF ASSETS	EMPLOYEES
12/17	5,101	144	2.8%	4,300
12/16	4,788	73	1.5%	4,200
12/15	4,628	74	1.6%	4,300
12/14	4,600	177	3.9%	4,400
12/13	4,315	112	2.6%	4,500
Annual Growth	**4.3%**	**6.6%**	**—**	**(1.1%)**

2017 Year-End Financials

Debt ratio: 7.28%
Return on equity: 8.25%
Cash ($ mil.): 291
Current ratio: —
Long-term debt ($ mil.): —
No. of shares (mil.): 55
Dividends
  Yield: 0.0%
  Payout: 95.1%
Market value ($ mil.): 2,957

	STOCK PRICE ($) FY Close	P/E High/Low	Earnings	Dividends	Book Value
12/17	53.44	24 20	2.62	2.49	31.83
12/16	60.21	46 33	1.32	2.48	31.70
12/15	46.57	45 34	1.35	2.47	33.01
12/14	56.67	18 13	3.23	2.46	34.02
12/13	49.71	25 18	2.04	2.45	33.15
Annual Growth	**1.8%**	**—**	**6.5%**	**0.4%**	**(1.0%)**

Meridian Bancorp Inc

EXECUTIVES

CFO and Treasurer, Mark L. Abbate, age 62
SVP Consumer and Business Banking, Keith D. Armstrong
Chairman President and CEO Meridian Interstate Bancorp and East Boston Savings Bank, Richard J. Gavegnano, age 69, $311,400 total compensation
EVP Corporate Banking, Frank Romano
EVP Lending, John Migliozzi
EVP and COO, John A. Carroll
SVP Electronic Banking, Mary Hagen
SVP Retail Banking, James Morgan
SVP Residential Lending, Joseph Nash
Vice President, Michael Raftery
Auditors: Wolf & Company, P.C.

LOCATIONS

HQ: Meridian Bancorp Inc
67 Prospect Street, Peabody, MA 01960
Phone: 617 567-1500

Selected Locations

Allpoint Locator
Allston
Belmont
Cambridge
Danvers
Dorchester
East Boston
Everett
Jamaica Plain
Lynn
Medford
Melrose
Peabody
Revere
Saugus
Somerville
South Boston
South End
Wakefield
West Roxbury
Winthrop

PRODUCTS/OPERATIONS

2015 Sales

	$ mil.	% of total
Interest & dividend income		
Interest & fees on loans	118	87
Interest on debt securities	1	1
Dividends on equity securities	1	1
Others	1	1
Non-interest income		
Customer service fees	8	6
Gain on sales of securities net	2	2
Income from bank-owned life insurance	1	1
Loan fees	1	1
Mortgage banking gains & other income	0	-
Total	**136**	**100**

Selected Products & Services

Personal
  Deposit Rates
  Investments
  Personal Checking
  Personal Lending
  Personal Online Banking
  Retirement Services
  Savings & CDs
Business
  Business Checking
  Business Lending
  Business Online Banking
  Business Retirement Services
  Business Savings
  Deposit Rates
  Institutional Banking
  Merchant Services
Commercial
  Cash Management
  Commercial Lending
  Corporate Banking
  Deposit Rates

COMPETITORS

Bank of America
Cambridge Financial
Citizens Financial Group
Eastern Bank
Middlesex Savings
Peoples Federal Bancshares Inc.
Sovereign Bank
TD Bank USA

HISTORICAL FINANCIALS

Company Type: Public

Income Statement

FYE: December 31

	ASSETS ($ mil.)	NET INCOME ($ mil.)	INCOME AS % OF ASSETS	EMPLOYEES
12/16	4,436	34	0.8%	500
12/15	3,524	24	0.7%	488
12/14	3,278	22	0.7%	466
12/13	2,682	15	0.6%	455
12/12	2,278	12	0.5%	433
Annual Growth	18.1%	28.8%	—	3.7%

2016 Year-End Financials

Debt ratio: 7.27%
Return on equity: 5.70%
Cash ($ mil.): 316
Current ratio: —
Long-term debt ($ mil.): —

No. of shares (mil.): 53
Dividends
  Yield: 0.0%
  Payout: 18.4%
Market value ($ mil.): 1,013

	STOCK PRICE ($) FY Close	P/E High/Low		PER SHARE ($) Earnings	Dividends	Book Value
12/16	18.90	29	19	0.65	0.12	11.33
12/15	14.10	31	24	0.46	0.06	10.72
12/14	11.22	27	24	0.42	0.00	10.56
Annual Growth	13.9%	—	—	11.5%	—	1.8%

MERRICK BANK CORPORATION

LOCATIONS

HQ: MERRICK BANK CORPORATION
10705 S JORDAN GTWY # 200, SOUTH JORDAN, UT 840953977
Phone: 801 545-6600
Web: WWW.MERRICKBANK.COM

HISTORICAL FINANCIALS

Company Type: Private

Income Statement

FYE: December 31

	ASSETS ($ mil.)	NET INCOME ($ mil.)	INCOME AS % OF ASSETS	EMPLOYEES
12/12	1,666	107	6.4%	135
12/11	1	0	7.4%	—
12/10	1,112	47	4.2%	—
12/09	1,118	6	0.5%	—
Annual Growth	14.2%	160.1%	—	—

2012 Year-End Financials

Debt ratio: —
Return on equity: 26.70%
Cash ($ mil.): 11
Current ratio: —
Long-term debt ($ mil.): —

Dividends
  Yield: —
  Payout: —
Market value ($ mil.): —

Merrill Lynch Life Insurance Co - Insurance Products

EXECUTIVES

Pres, Marilyn Carp
Auditors: PricewaterhouseCoopers LLP

LOCATIONS

HQ: Merrill Lynch Life Insurance Co - Insurance Products
4333 Edgewood Road, NE, Cedar Rapids, IA 52499-0001
Phone: 800 346-3677
Web: www.transamerica.com

HISTORICAL FINANCIALS

Company Type: Public

Income Statement

FYE: December 31

	ASSETS ($ mil.)	NET INCOME ($ mil.)	INCOME AS % OF ASSETS	EMPLOYEES
12/16	8,670	(20)	—	—
12/15	9,165	13	0.1%	—
12/14	10,108	33	0.3%	—
12/13	10,555	(254)	—	—
12/12	10,535	165	1.6%	—
Annual Growth	(4.8%)	—	—	—

2016 Year-End Financials

Debt ratio: 0.05%
Return on equity: (-1.71%)
Cash ($ mil.): 267
Current ratio: —
Long-term debt ($ mil.): —

No. of shares (mil.): 0
Dividends
  Yield: —
  Payout: —
Market value ($ mil.): —

Meta Financial Group Inc

Don't worry the money is real. Meta Financial Group is the holding company for MetaBank a thrift with about a dozen branches in Iowa and South Dakota. MetaBank offers standard deposit products and services including checking and savings accounts. Its lending and investment activities are weighted towards real estate and real estate-related assets; commercial and multifamily residential mortgages comprise more than half of the bank's loan portfolio. It also writes single-family residential mortgages and business loans. Meta Financial's bread and butter however is the bank's Meta Payment Systems (MPS) division which provides prepaid cards consumer credit and ATM sponsorship services nationwide.

Strategy

The company has invested in MPS' growth by marketing new products and programs such as prepaid debit cards for tax refunds eco-friendly recycled or recyclable cards and lines of credit on prepaid cards.

In 2016 Meta Financial agreed to buy most of the assets of EPS Financial for some $42.5 million.

EPS Financial provides tax-related financial transaction services including refund settlement products and merchant services.

EXECUTIVES

Chairman and CEO Meta Financial Group and MetaBank, J. Tyler Haahr, age 54, $550,000 total compensation
EVP Sales and Operations MetaBank and Director Meta Financial Group (MFG) and MetaBank, Troy Moore, age 49, $252,350 total compensation
EVP Secretary Treasurer and CFO, David W. Leedom, age 63, $215,000 total compensation
President Meta Financial Group Inc. (MFG) and MetaBank and Division President Meta Payment System, Bradley C. (Brad) Hanson, age 53, $550,000 total compensation
EVP Meta Payment Systems, Scott Galit, age 47, $235,000 total compensation
EVP and CFO Meta Financial Group (MFG) and MetaBank, Glen W. Herrick, age 54, $255,000 total compensation
Vice Chairman Meta Financial Group (MFG) and MetaBank, Frederick V. (Fred) Moore, age 61
Auditors: KPMG LLP

LOCATIONS

HQ: Meta Financial Group Inc
5501 South Broadband Lane, Sioux Falls, SD 57108
Phone: 605 782-1767
Web: www.metabank.com

COMPETITORS

Bank of America
Blackhawk Network
Citi Prepaid Services
First National of Nebraska
Great Western Bancorp
Green Dot
HF Financial
U.S. Bancorp
West Bancorporation
nFinanSe

HISTORICAL FINANCIALS

Company Type: Public

Income Statement

FYE: September 30

	ASSETS ($ mil.)	NET INCOME ($ mil.)	INCOME AS % OF ASSETS	EMPLOYEES
09/17	5,228	44	0.9%	827
09/16	4,006	33	0.8%	672
09/15	2,529	18	0.7%	638
09/14	2,054	15	0.8%	453
09/13	1,691	13	0.8%	432
Annual Growth	32.6%	35.3%	—	17.6%

2017 Year-End Financials

Debt ratio: 1.64%
Return on equity: 11.67%
Cash ($ mil.): 1,267
Current ratio: —
Long-term debt ($ mil.): —

No. of shares (mil.): 9
Dividends
  Yield: 0.0%
  Payout: 10.7%
Market value ($ mil.): 754

	STOCK PRICE ($) FY Close	P/E High/Low		PER SHARE ($) Earnings	Dividends	Book Value
09/17	78.40	22	13	4.83	0.52	45.15
09/16	60.61	16	9	3.92	0.52	39.30
09/15	41.77	20	12	2.66	0.52	33.24
09/14	35.26	18	14	2.53	0.52	28.33
09/13	38.00	16	9	2.38	0.52	23.55
Annual Growth	19.8%	—	—	19.4%	(0.0%)	17.7%

MetLife Inc

While its name evolved from "metropolitan" MetLife's policies are found in villages towns and huge cities around the world. Its Insurance Products segment includes all of its group and individual life insurance and non-medical health insurance products (dental disability illness). Its Retirement Products segment includes annuity products. MetLife's Auto & Home segment works through subsidiary Metropolitan Property and Casualty. MetLife is a big player in Japan and growing in more than 50 other countries especially in Latin America. In mid-2017 MetLife split off much of its US life business.

Operations

MetLife is organized into five primary segments: US; Latin America; Asia; and Europe the Middle East and Africa (EMEA); and MetLife Holdings. Certain results are also reported in the operations of the Corporate & Other segment including MetLife Home Loans.The US segment is MetLife's largest accounting for some 45% of total sales. Asia accounts for around 20% of revenue and Latin America and EMEA each account for some 5%. MetLife Holdings brings in some 20% of revenue.

In the US MetLife provides a range of insurance and financial services offerings including life property/casualty disability dental guaranteed interest and annuities. These are distributed through both in-house and independent retail channels and in the workplace. Internationally the company provides life accident medical dental credit and other insurance as well as annuities and other retirement and savings products to individuals and groups.

MetLife Holdings comprises businesses no longer actively promoted in the US including variable life and universal life products term and whole life products and annuities. It also includes the group's discontinued long-term care business.

Geographic Reach

MetLife operates in the Americas and Asia and in Europe the Middle East and Africa (EMEA). In Latin America it operates in Argentina Brazil Chile Colombia Ecuador and Mexico (with the bulk of regional revenues coming from Mexico and Chile).

The company operates in 10 countries in Asia with its largest operations in Japan. It also does business in Australia Bangladesh Hong Kong and Nepal and through a joint venture in China Malaysia and Vietnam.

MetLife operates in 26 countries across EMEA. The segment's biggest operations are in the UK the Persian Gulf and Turkey.

Sales and Marketing

MetLife's policies and other products are sold to some 100 million customers through a vast network of targeted marketing and sales forces financial advisors consultants agency distribution groups captive agents independent agents affiliated broker-dealers and direct marketing (including direct response television web-based lead generation telemarketing as well as through third parties and e-commerce). In addition MetLife sells some products through affinity groups and through employers.

Financial Performance

MetLife's revenue after peaking in 2014 has slipped since. In 2016 revenue fell 9% to $63.5 billion. Although premiums saw a modest rise that year the company suffered from $6.8 billion in net derivative losses reflecting changes in foreign currencies interest rates and equity markets. Because of this decline plus a $2 billion increase in claims payouts net income plummeted 85% to $800 million that year.

Cash flow from operations has remained relatively stable over the years. Despite the lower income operating cash flow rose 5% to $14.8 billion in 2016. This was driven by changes in premiums and other receivables and changes in income tax.

Strategy

In 2017 MetLife spun off much of its US retail operations into a new company named Brighthouse Financial. Its MetLife Insurance Company USA Metropolitan Tower Life Insurance Company General American Life Insurance Company (which is being merged into Metropolitan Tower Life) and several other units were included in the transaction which took the form of an initial public offering. Together those units represented about 20% of MetLife's total earnings.

MetLife's move to divest part of its core operations came in the wake of the financial crisis and subsequent changes in the regulatory landscape. US regulators had designated MetLife one of four non-bank systemically important financial institutions (meaning it would pose a risk to the economy if it should collapse) but MetLife fought the designation winning its case in a federal court in 2016. Regardless the separation of its US life insurance business should calm any unrest over the group's size. The newly created company also benefits from having a lower capital and compliance burden.

In another divestiture in mid-2016 MassMutual bought MetLife's US retail captive agency distribution channel MetLife Premier Client Group and broker dealer MetLife Securities. (US retail businesses that were not sold in the deal included the closed-block life insurance property/casualty and Metropolitan Life Insurance Company's life and annuity operations.)

These moves were not the first major shufflings of MetLife's operations in recent years. It is exiting the bulk of its banking operations to avoid the increased scrutiny of banks under Dodd-Frank financial regulations. The company is working to surrender its status as a bank holding company. It has already sold its MetLife Bank depository operations and has stopped writing new residential mortgages and reverse mortgages.

Going forward MetLife plans to focus on pension and retirement products insurance sold to employers and non-US life insurance. In a shift away from market-sensitive products it will only invest in businesses that have strong rates of return require less capital and offer a higher ratio of free cash flow to operating earnings. The company has pinned much of its growth efforts on emerging markets by increasing its already-strong presence in the Asia/Pacific region and in Latin America through acquisitions and new product introductions. To support this growth the company has organized its operations along geographic lines: US; Latin America; Asia; and Europe the Middle East and Africa (EMEA).

Other strategic areas of focus include creating a high-performance operation with competitive prices transforming distribution channels (especially through digital means) and connecting customers with the most appropriate products and services.

Some of the individual and group products MetLife sells overseas include life insurance accident and health insurance credit insurance and annuities and retirement products. It has also created a global employee benefits business to reach into new markets. To focus on core international businesses Metlife has been selling off select foreign assets.

Mergers and Acquisitions

In 2017 MetLife acquired Logan Circle Partners from Fortress Investment Group for some $250 million. Logan was the traditional fixed income asset management business of Fortress; it serves institutional investors and has more than $33 bil-lion in assets under management. The purchase helps expand MetLife's investment management business for third-party customers.

HISTORY

New York merchant Simeon Draper tried to form National Union Life and Limb Insurance to cover Union soldiers in the Civil War but investors were scared away by heavy casualties. After several reorganizations and name changes the enterprise emerged in 1868 as Metropolitan Life Insurance (MetLife) a stock company.

Sustained at first by business from mutual assistance societies for German immigrants MetLife went into industrial insurance with workers' burial policies. The firm was known for its aggressive sales methods. Agents combed working-class neighborhoods collecting small premiums. If a worker missed one payment the company could cancel the policy and keep all premiums paid a practice outlawed in 1900.

MetLife became a mutual company (owned by its policyholders) in 1915 and began offering group insurance two years later.

After a period of conservative management under the Eckers family from 1929 to 1963 MetLife began to change dropping industrial insurance in 1964. It started offering auto and homeowners insurance in 1974.

To diversify the company bought State Street Research & Management (1983) Century 21 Real Estate (1985 sold 1995) London-based Albany Life Assurance (1985) and Allstate's group life and health business (1988). In 1987 it took over the annuities segment of the failed Baldwin United Co. and expanded into Spain and Taiwan in 1988. During the early 1990s MetLife reemphasized insurance adding such new products as long-term-care insurance.

EXECUTIVES

EVP and Global Chief Marketing Officer, Esther Lee

Chairman President and CEO, Steven A. (Steve) Kandarian, age 65, $1,525,000 total compensation

EVP and CFO, John C. R. Hele, age 59, $781,250 total compensation

EVP Global Employee Benefits, Maria R. Morris, age 54, $525,000 total compensation

EVP and General Counsel, Ricardo A. Anzaldua

EVP Chief Investment Officer and Interim President MetLife Asia, Steven J. Goulart, age 58, $725,000 total compensation

President US, Michel Khalaf, $476,313 total compensation

EVP Global Technology and Operations and MetLife Holdings, Martin J. (Marty) Lippert, $756,250 total compensation

Managing Director Institutional Client Group, Thomas Metzler

CEO MetLife Hong Kong, Lee Wood

Vice President Corporate Services and Vendor Sourcing. Chief Procurement Officer, John Vazquez

Executive Vice President and Chief Human Resources Officer, Frans Hijkoop

Vice President of Enterprise Technology Solutions, Elizabeth Langone

Regional Sales Vice President, Jordan Teel

Vice President Retirement And Savings, Sherif Zakhary

Regional Vice President Northeast Region, Joe Heaney

Vice President Information Technology, Annette Fugina

Vice President Information Technology Institutiona, Bernice Beedle

Vice President Information Technology, Marcella Kelly

Vice President Sales and Global Strategies, Maximo Saravi

Vice President human Resources information Technology, David Bess

Assistant Vice President Regional Business Planning and Coordination, Flavia Miranda

Senior Vice President Employee Benefit Sales, Michael Malouf

Vice President, Stephanie Miller

Senior Vice President Chief Information Officer Te, Jeff Carlson

Assistant Vice President, Gary Glacken

Vice President Information Technology, Neil Melleky

Executive Vice President National Accounts, Glenn Petersen

Vice President, Brenda Murphy

Assistant Vice President, Anjana Sivakumar

Vice President of Sales, Lewis Robyn

Vice President Information Technology, Alvin Sheinheit

Vice President Information Technology, Tom Kelly

Vice President And Chief Privacy Officer, Joseph Trovato

Director human Resources Assistant Vice President, Adam Portnoy

Second Vice President Information Technology, Glenn Reese

Vice President, Bob Broseker

Vice President Actuary Reserve Coordination, Stewart Ashkenazy

Vice President, Ilia Castellano

Assistant Vice President, Joseph Reo

Vice President Information Technology, Roderick Pasqualicchio

Vice President Actuary, Marian Zeldin

Regional Sales Vice President, Scott Safranek

Vice President, Guy Lawrence

Vice President Of National Accounts, Scott Beck

Vice President, Randy Stram

Assistant Vice President And Actuary, Jonathan Trend

Vice President, Alan Hirschberg

Assistant Vice President, George Harrington

Vice President Enterprise Application Development Project Management Office, Dee Dee Schreitmueller

Medical Director, Charles Arnold

Assistant Vice President Sec Reporting, Lynne Liberatore

Vice President and Actuary Asset Liability Management, Scott Yan

Vice President of Operations MetLife Broker Dealer, Bob Begun

Regional Vice President MetLife Investors, Ted Feitt

Senior Vice President, Robert Wright

Vice President, Joe Perillo

Vice President of Application Development, Jack Rooney

Assistant Vice President, Gladys Rosetta

Vice President, Jan Eckert

Assistant Vice President: Business Intelligence, Florence Tsang

Vice President, Michael Nardone

Vice President, Rahul Magan

Vice President, Harry Xiao

Assistant Vice President, Ian Connor

Assistant Vice President, Tonya Richardson

Assistant Vice President, Andy Vigar

Assistant Vice President, Robert Bean

AVP International Strategic Planning, Won Yi

Asst. Vice President, Mattie Bolus

Assistant Vice President, Thomas Mulligan

Vice President Capital Markets Group, Todd Stockton

Assistant Vice President Solutions Delivery, David Trigo

Vice President Investments Information Technology Global Strategy Derivatives Collateral Mgmnt Securities Lending and CMIP, Santhosh Aravindakshan

Vice President Information Technology Infrastructu, Gail Weimer

Regional Sales Vice President, Michael Casimiro

Assistant Vice President International Benefits, Francesca Pulis

Assistant Vice President, Jeffrey Hollander

Assistant Vice President Chief of Staff to the Head of Global Operations, Richard Ross

Vice President, Steve Vnuck

Vice President Portfolio And Program Man, Ninna Roco

Vice President of Information Technology, Ron Gillmore

Assistant Vice President Shared Service, Shari A Corrigan

Assistant Vice President And Cre Relationship Manager Global Corporate Services, Betty Dubuisson

Vice President Group Life Products, Graham Cox

Vice President, Michele Zachensky

Executive Vice President U S Business MetLife Inc, Todd Katz

Executive Vice President Co CIO, Tom Wolf

Vice President, Ignazio Greco

Assistant Vice President, Cindy Pace

Assistant Vice President Advisor Teaming Field Implementation, Michael O'brien

Vice President, Kim Donica

Assistant Vice President, William Quinn

Vice President Advanced Markets and Financial Planning, Lori Epstein

Assistant Vice President, Dean Vescera

Assistant Vice President, George Tang

Vice President, Mike Paleos

Vice President Global Internal Audit, Carlos Mendez

AVP Head of Security Engineering, Joe Gatt

Regional Sales Vice President, Ed Wustefeld

Assistant Vice President, Amie Donahue

Vice President, David Waldman

Assistant Vice President Enterprise Strategy Group, Kevin Chean

Vice President, Nancy Davenport

Avp Underwriting Metlife Expatriate Benefits, Brian Prange

Vice President, Robert Klahre

Regional Sales Vice President, Stacey Waite

Vice President, Michael Evenzwig

Regional Sales Vice President, Steve Shrout

Vice President Of Retail Marketing, Matthew Quale

Regional Sales Vice President, Tony Nguyen

Vice President, Emilia Kyff

Regional Sales Vice President, Chris Bunting

Vice President, George Bell

Assistant Vice President And Actuary Financial Research, William Chirolas

Executive vice president and HeadCorporate Affairs Chief of Staff Office of the Chairman and CEO, Michael Zarcone

Regional Sales Vice President, Nancy Power

Vice President Investments Controller, David Rooney

Second Vice President, Mark Remington

Regional Sales Vice President, Lane O'Connor

Vice President, James Donnellan

Assistant Vice President, John Zelinske

Senior Vice President, Joseph Reali

Vice President, Dale King

Vice President Operations, John Abela

Assistant Vice President Individual Disability Underwriting, Rod Boggs

Assistant Vice President, Ian Clinton

Assistant Vice President Sales Force Development, Anna Lavery

Regional Sales Vice President, Jan Primmer

Assistant Vice President Information Technology, Paul Mattern

Assistant Vice President, Jennifer Kischell

Assistant Vice President Solutions Delivery, Phil Kurumunda

Regional Sales Vice President, Sarah Kim

Vice President of Reverse Mortgage Division, Craig Corn

Vice President and Actuary Information Technology, Mike Rigby

Assistant Vice President, Jeff Denault

Account Management Vice President, Annette Cunanan

Vice President Workforce Enablement Glob, Kate Day

Assistant Vice President Planning And Analytics Global Corporate Security, Dillon Twombly

Assistant Vice President, Jai Maxwell

Assisttant Vice President Growth Strategies, Tina Beckwith

Vice President of Public Relations, Jack Calanga

Vice President Workforce Enablement Global Technology Operations, Kurt Day

Vice President Information Technology, Leonard Kasendorf

Vice President, Marc Cohn

Vice President Sales and Marketing, Suzanne Andrews

Vice President Information Technology Services, Bob Levin

Vice President Global Technology, Ed Evans

Assistant Vice President, Jude Eidenberg

Vice President, Melissa Grady

Assistant Vice President Global Benefits, Mark Davis

Auditors: Deloitte & Touche LLP

LOCATIONS

HQ: MetLife Inc
200 Park Avenue, New York, NY 10166-0188
Phone: 212 578-9500
Web: www.metlife.com

2016 Sales

	$ mil.	% of total
U.S	29,263	45
Asia	11,930	19
MetLife Holding	11,547	18
Latin America	4,816	7
EMEA	3,810	6
Brighthouse Financial	3,019	5
Corporate & other	(909)	-
Total	**63,476**	**100**

PRODUCTS/OPERATIONS

2016 Sales

	$ mil.	% of total
Premiums	39,153	56
Net investment income	19,947	28
Universal life and investment-type product policy fees	9,206	13
Other revenues	1,759	3
Net investment gains (losses)	171	0
Net derivative gains (losses)	(6760)	0
Total	**63,476**	**100**

Selected Subsidiaries and Affiliates

American Life Insurance Co. (ALICO)
General American Life Insurance Company
Hyatt Legal Plans Inc. (prepaid legal plans)
MetLife Insurance Company USA
MetLife Investors Group Inc. (distribution)
Metropolitan Property and Casualty Insurance Company
New England Life Insurance Company

COMPETITORS

AEGON USA	Lincoln Financial
AIG	Group
AXA	MassMutual
Aetna	Meiji Yasuda Life
Aflac	Mutual of Omaha

Allianz
Allstate
American General
Aon
CIGNA
COUNTRY Financial
Genworth Financial
Guardian Life
ING
John Hancock Financial
  Services
Liberty Mutual

Nationwide
New York Life
Nippon Life Insurance
Northwestern Mutual
Pacific Mutual
Principal Financial
Prudential
State Farm
TIAA
The Hartford
USAA
Zurich Insurance Group

HISTORICAL FINANCIALS

Company Type: Public

Income Statement

FYE: December 31

	ASSETS ($ mil.)	NET INCOME ($ mil.)	INCOME AS % OF ASSETS	EMPLOYEES
12/16	898,764	800	0.1%	58,000
12/15	877,933	5,310	0.6%	69,000
12/14	902,337	6,309	0.7%	68,000
12/13	885,296	3,368	0.4%	65,000
12/12	836,781	1,324	0.2%	64,000
Annual Growth	1.8%	(11.8%)		(2.4%)

2016 Year-End Financials

Debt ratio: 2.64%
Return on equity: 1.18%
Cash ($ mil.): 17,877
Current ratio: —
Long-term debt ($ mil.): —

No. of shares (mil.): 1,095
Dividends
  Yield: 0.0%
  Payout: 250.0%
Market value ($ mil.): 59,038

	STOCK PRICE ($) FY Close	P/E High/Low	PER SHARE ($) Earnings	Dividends	Book Value
12/16	53.89	91 56	0.63	1.58	61.44
12/15	48.21	13 10	4.57	1.48	61.95
12/14	54.09	10 9	5.42	1.33	63.74
12/13	53.92	18 11	2.91	1.01	55.65
12/12	32.94	35 25	1.12	0.74	59.15
Annual Growth	13.1%	— —	(13.4%)	20.8%	1.0%

METROPOLITAN TRANSPORTATION AUTHORITY

The largest public transportation system in the US New York City's Metropolitan Transportation Authority (MTA) provides about 2.6 billion passenger trips and sees about 380 million vehicles travel its system annually. The MTA's largest agency the New York City Transit Authority operates about 8700 rail and subway cars that provide service across New York's five boroughs; it also runs a fleet of some 5900 buses. Other MTA units offer bus and rail service to Connecticut and Long Island and operate the Triborough system of toll bridges and tunnels.

Strategy

The government-owned MTA a public-benefit corporation chartered by the New York Legislature in 1965 operates with an annual budget of $12.6 billion. The system has been working to become more self-sufficient in recent years but it has battled persistent operating losses brought on by among other causes high operating costs and the struggling US economy. In an attempt to reduce

its expenses the company in 2010 cut payroll by 20% at its headquarters and 15% at other agencies. The MTA has also bolstered its revenue through increased fares and tolls and freed up capital by restructuring its debt at lower interest rates.

While it is making cuts in some areas the MTA is investing in capital improvements to its system including extending the Long Island Rail Road to Grand Central Station and creating a direct link between John F. Kennedy Airport and downtown Manhattan. Other key projects have included the construction of the Second Avenue Subway and renovations at the Fulton Street Transit Center. The MTA also is looking at installing wireless Internet access on its Metro-North and Long Island rail lines' trains.

EXECUTIVES

CFO, Robert E. (Bob) Foran
Executive Officer Corporate Communications Marketing and Branding, John McKay
Director Security, Raymond Diaz
COO, Phil Eng
Interim Executive Director, Veronique Hakim
President MTA Bridges and Tunnels, Cedrick Fulton
Vice President Human Resources And Diversity, Gregory Bradley
Chairman, Joseph J. Lhota, age 62
Secretary, Ashmine John

LOCATIONS

HQ: METROPOLITAN TRANSPORTATION AUTHORITY
2 BROADWAY BSMT B, NEW YORK, NY 100043354
Phone: 212 878-7000
Web: WWW.MTAHQ.ORG

PRODUCTS/OPERATIONS

Selected Operations
Bus
  Long Island Bus
  MTA Bus Company
  New York City Transit
Commuter Rail
  Long Island Rail Road
  Metro-North Railroad
  Staten Island Railway

HISTORICAL FINANCIALS

Company Type: Private

Income Statement

FYE: December 31

	REVENUE ($ mil.)	NET INCOME ($ mil.)	NET PROFIT MARGIN	EMPLOYEES
12/15	8,408	370	4.4%	67,457
12/12*	7,067	(0)	—	—
06/12	3,495	604	17.3%	—
Annual Growth	24.5%	(11.5%)		

*Fiscal year change

2015 Year-End Financials

Debt ratio: —
Return on equity: 4.40%
Cash ($ mil.): 454
Current ratio: 0.20
Long-term debt ($ mil.): —

Dividends
  Yield: —
  Payout: —
Market value ($ mil.): —

MGIC Investment Corp. (WI)

Since a pinkie-promise isn't good enough for most lenders there's MGIC Investment's mortgage insurance to protect lenders from homebuyers who don't hold up their end of the bargain. MGIC owns Mortgage Guaranty Insurance Corporation (MGIC) the largest provider of private mortgage insurance in the US. Such coverage allows otherwise-qualified buyers who aren't able to scrape up the standard 20% down payment to get mortgages. MGIC writes primary insurance on individual loans. The company's customers include banks mortgage brokers credit unions and other residential mortgage lenders. In 2014 MGIC had $159.3 billion primary insurance in force covering 1 million mortgages.

Operations

MGIC's businesses include a range of investment subsidiaries reinsurance subsidiaries and assurance corporations. The company also offers some online products: eMagic.com a web portal where mortgage providers can shop for a variety of loan origination tools and Myers Internet a web hosting provider and lead generator.

Primary insurance provides mortgage default protection on individual loans and covers unpaid loan principal delinquent interest and certain expenses associated with the default and subsequent foreclosure or sale approved by MGIC. Pool insurance is generally used as an additional credit enhancement for certain secondary market mortgage transactions. It generally covers the excess of the loss on a defaulted mortgage loan which exceeds the claim payment under the primary coverage if primary insurance is required on that mortgage loan as well as the total loss on a defaulted mortgage loan which did not require primary insurance.

Geographic Reach

MGIC operates in every US state Washington DC Puerto Rico and Guam.

Sales and Marketing

The company's customers include savings institutions commercial banks mortgage brokers credit unions mortgage bankers and other lenders.

Financial Performance

Still recovering from the US mortgage loan crisis of the late 2000s MGIC has reported a steady annual decline in its revenues since 2009. In 2013 its revenues dropped by 25% due to a decrease in net premium earned as the result of lower average insurance in force as well as an increase in premiums ceded under risk sharing arrangements and lower investment income driven by the realized gains taken in prior years. The company saw a huge decline in realized losses and other-than-temporary impairments in 2013 due to lower sales of fixed income investments.

Since inception the company has reported annual net losses. However MFIC saw a improvement in net loss in 2013 ($50 million compared to $927 million in 2012) due to a decrease in the number of new default notices received as well as a decrease in the estimated claim rate on recently reported delinquencies. Underwriting and other expenses for 2013 decreased primarily reflecting a reduction in headcount lower contract underwriting remedy costs and an increase in ceding commission related to risk sharing arrangements.

After reaching its minimum point of $1.8 billion operating cash outflow in 2011 the company recovered over next two years. In 2013 operating cash outflow decreased by $597 million to $971 million due to decline in net loss and cash generated from deferred insurance policy acquisition costs and unearned premiums.

Strategy

The company saw home price appreciation continue as well as modest improvements in the employment picture throughout 2013. These conditions allowed MGIC to see an increase in new insurance policies issued while new delinquent notices delinquent inventory and claim payments declined.

Despite the company's careful pruning MGIC Investment's capital reserves are still vulnerable and have dipped below some regional regulatory requirements. To operate in markets where it doesn't meet minimum capital requirements the company created MGIC Indemnity Corporation (MIC) in 2010 and gave it a tidy pile of capital reserves and nice fresh books with no murky liabilities.

As the entire private mortgage insurance industry nervously gauges its future government-sponsored enterprises Freddie Mac and Fannie Mae have taken over a huge share of the business during the past few years. To gain customers MGIC has lowered its rates based upon borrower's credit scores.

Company Background

Before the mortgage mess unfolded in the US MGIC had marked its entry into the global market by opening offices in Toronto and in Sydney Australia. In less than two years however MGIC closed its Canadian office stopped issuing new policies abroad and began searching for a buyer for its Australian operations (which it records as immaterial) in order to focus on its domestic operations.

EXECUTIVES

Senior Vice President Information Services and Chief Information Officer of MGIC, Michael Meade

President and COO, Patrick Sinks, age 60, $524,423 total compensation

EVP General Counsel and Secretary, Jeffrey H. Lane, age 67, $415,385 total compensation

EVP Risk Management, Lawrence J. Pierzchalski, age 64, $449,654 total compensation

Chairman and CEO, Curt S. Culver, age 64, $898,269 total compensation

EVP and CFO, Timothy Mattke

Vice President Marketing and Customer Experience, Margaret Crowley

Vice President, John Schroeder

Vice President Product Development, Geoffrey Cooper

Auditors: PricewaterhouseCoopers LLP

LOCATIONS

HQ: MGIC Investment Corp. (WI)
250 E. Kilbourn Avenue, Milwaukee, WI 53202
Phone: 414 347-6480
Web: www.mgic.com

PRODUCTS/OPERATIONS

2015 Sales

	$ mil.	% of total
Net premiums earned	896	86
Investment income	103	10
Realized investment gains	28	3
Other revenue	12	1
Total	**1,040**	**100**

Selected Direct and Indirect Subsidiaries

MGIC Assurance Corporation
MGIC Australia Pty Limited
MGIC Credit Assurance Corporation
MGIC Indemnity Corporation
MGIC Insurance Services Corporation
MGIC Investor Services Corporation
MGIC Mortgage and Consumer Asset I LLC

MGIC Mortgage and Consumer Asset II LLC
MGIC Mortgage Reinsurance Corporation
MGIC Mortgage Services LLC
MGIC Reinsurance Corporation
MGIC Reinsurance Corporation of Vermont
MGIC Reinsurance Corporation of Wisconsin
MGIC Residential Reinsurance Corporation
MGICA Pty Limited
MIC Reinsurance Corporation
MIC Reinsurance Corporation of Wisconsin
Mortgage Guaranty Insurance Corporation

COMPETITORS

Allied Home Mortgage	Radian Group
Essent Guaranty	Regions Mortgage
Freddie Mac	United Guaranty
Genworth Mortgage Insurance	VBA
	Wells Fargo Home Mortgage
National Mortgage Insurance	

HISTORICAL FINANCIALS

Company Type: Public

Income Statement

FYE: December 31

	ASSETS ($ mil.)	NET INCOME ($ mil.)	INCOME AS % OF ASSETS	EMPLOYEES
12/16	5,734	342	6.0%	823
12/15	5,879	1,172	19.9%	800
12/14	5,266	251	4.8%	800
12/13	5,601	(49)	—	819
12/12	5,574	(927)	—	877
Annual Growth	**0.7%**	**—**	**—**	**(1.6%)**

2016 Year-End Financials

Debt ratio: 20.56%
Return on equity: 14.28%
Cash ($ mil.): 155
Current ratio: —
Long-term debt ($ mil.): —

No. of shares (mil.): 340
Dividends
  Yield: —
  Payout: —
Market value ($ mil.): 3,471

	STOCK PRICE ($) FY Close	P/E High/Low		PER SHARE ($) Earnings	Dividends	Book Value
12/16	10.19	11	5	0.86	0.00	7.48
12/15	8.83	3	2	2.60	0.00	6.58
12/14	9.32	13	10	0.64	0.00	3.06
12/13	8.44	—	—	(0.16)	0.00	2.20
12/12	2.66	—	—	(4.59)	0.00	0.97
Annual Growth	**39.9%**	**—**	**—**	**—**	**—**	**66.4%**

MGM Resorts International

MGM Resorts International is one of the world's largest gaming firms. The company's properties include some of the biggest names on the Las Vegas Strip including MGM Grand The Mirage and the Monte Carlo as well as Luxor Bellagio Mandalay Bay and the new T-Mobile Arena. MGM Resorts International also owns or has a stake in other casinos in Nevada as well as in Michigan (MGM Grand Detroit) and Mississippi (Beau Rivage). Internationally it operates in China and Dubai. The company changed its name from MGM MIRAGE to MGM Resorts International back in 2010 to better reflect its family of hotel brands and its expanding global presence.

Geographic Reach

The company's two main reportable segments are based on the regions in which it operates: Domestic Resorts and MGM China. MGM Resorts International's China operations consist of the MGM Macau resort and casino. Domestic Resorts accounted for more than 75% of sales in fiscal 2016 while MGM China accounted for 20%.

Sales and Marketing

MGM Resorts International spent about $171 million on advertising during fiscal 2016. The company advertises on the radio television internet billboards and in newspapers and magazines in selected cities throughout the US and overseas. MGM Resorts International also use direct mail and social media to reach out to past guests and potential customers. The company advertises through regional marketing offices located in major cities.

Financial Performance

During fiscal 2016 the company's revenue increased compared to fiscal 2015. MGM Resorts International reported $9.46 billion in revenue for fiscal 2016 up from $9.19 billion the prior fiscal year.

MGM Resorts International suffered a net loss in fiscal 2015. However the company rebounded to report net income of $1.1 billion in fiscal 2016 largely due to decreased operating expenses.

Cash provided by operating activities was $1.5 billion in fiscal 2016 compared to $1 billion in fiscal 2015.

Strategy

MGM Resorts International continues to make significant investments in its resorts through newly remodeled hotel rooms restaurants entertainment and nightlife offerings as well as other new features and amenities. In Macau the company plans to spend approximately $2.9 billion to develop a resort and casino featuring approximately 1600 hotel rooms 500 gaming tables and up to 2500 slots. MGM Resorts International has also been actively pursuing development opportunities in markets such as Maryland and Massachusetts.

In 2016 MGM Resorts International opened the new 20000 seat T-Mobile arena in Las Vegas. The company hopes to attract a large number of high-profile concerts and sporting events. The long-term plan is to lure a NHL or NBA team to Las Vegas.

The company also spun off its MGM Growth Properties subsidiary during 2016 as a real estate investment trust.

Mergers and Acquisitions

In 2016 MGM Resorts International acquired Borgata Hotel Casino & Spa in Atlantic City New Jersey from Boyd Gaming Corporation for about $900 million. The acquisition added to the company?s growing presence in the mid-Atlantic and Northeast United States.

EXECUTIVES

COO, Corey I. Sanders, age 53, $1,119,368 total compensation

Senior Vice President Taxes, Shawn Sani

President and Chief Marketing Officer, William J. Hornbuckle, age 59, $1,269,368 total compensation

Chairman and CEO, James J. Murren, age 55, $2,000,000 total compensation

Chief Design and Construction Officer and Director, Robert H. Baldwin, age 66, $1,650,000 total compensation

EVP Special Counsel Litigation and Chief Diversity Officer, Phyllis A. James, age 64

EVP CFO and Treasurer, Daniel J. D'Arrigo, age 48, $875,000 total compensation

EVP and Chief Accounting Officer, Robert C. Selwood, age 61, $439,286 total compensation

EVP General Counsel and Secretary, John M. McManus, age 49

President and COO Borgata Hotel Casino & Spa, Marcus Glover

Representative Officer and President MGM Resorts Japan, Jason P. Hyland

President and COO Gold Strike Casino Resort, Melonie Johnson

Vice President Chief Financial Officer Corporate Benefits, Jeff Ellis

Vice President Far East MKG Aria, John Lai

Senior Vice President and Chief Sustainability Officer, Cindy Ortega

Vice President Creative Services, Christopher Hume

Executive Vice President Corporate Operations and Executive Vice President and Chief Financial Officer CityC, Christopher Nordling

Senior Vice President Design and Development, Joyen Vakil

Vice President, Vanesa Bui

Vice President of Events and Communication, Kelley Tucky

Vice President, Tom C Tuchschmidt

Vice President International Compliance, Joshua Smith

Assistant Vice President, Joyce Chester

Vice President, Randy Dearborn

Senior Vice President, Robert Zapletal

Vice President, Bob Rosati

Vice President of Strategic Operations, Christopher Oh

Vice President Marketing Latin American MGM Grand, Marilyn Portillo

Vice President Of Player Development, Pete Brascia

Vice President Gaming Operations, Todd Haushalter

Vice President and Chief Financial Officer Beau Rivage Resort, Jorge Perez

Vice President of labor Relations, Wendy Nutt

Senior Vice President Customer Development, Larry Altschul

Corporate Vice President Talent And Organizational Effec, Christopher Henry

Assistant Vice President Taxes, Michael Mcbeath

Senior Vice President of Finance, Yvette Harris

Vice President Of Arena Booking, Sid Greenfeig

Vice President Strategic Initiatives Program Management, Jeff Gebben

Vice President Of Hotel Sales, Jay Simpson

Vice President Diversity And Inclusion Development, Ondra L Berry

Vice President Environmental Compliance, Chris Brophy

Vice President Marketing Far East, Eddie Ly

Vice President Marketing International, Kimie Masumoto

Executive Vice President Corporate Strategy and Special Counsel and Senior Resident Executive for G, William Scott

Assistant Vice President Finance and Treasury, Bernard Efendi

Vice President Internal Audit, Robert Rudloff

Vice President Human Resources, Christine Higgins

Executive Vice President Marketing Hong Kong, Elisa Lau

Senior Vice President of Marketing, Kate Wik

National Sales Manager, Michelle Lizarraga

Senior Vice President Marketing Internat, Dima Howard

Corporate Vice President, Lance Evans

Vice President Far East Marketing MGM Grand, Tony Lay

Vice President, Kelly Litster

Senior Vice President Hotel Sales Marketing And, Fletch H Brunelle

Vice President Of Corp Surveillance, Ted Whiting

Vice President Hotel Operations, Micah Richins

Senior Vice President and Chief Compliance Officer, Stephen Martino

Vice President Customer Development, Jodi Myers

National Sales Manager, John Montes

Vice President of Construction, Russ Davis

National Sales Manager, Doug Wangsmo

Senior Vice President, Paul Siu

Vice President Marketing Far East, William Loh

Vice President Marketing Far East, Angela Chan

Vice President Gaming Finance, Trent Walker

Vice President, Bruce Barclay

Vice President and Chief Accounting Officer, Michele Ensign

Vice President of Brand Marketing, Nick Parks

Senior Vice President Marketing Far East, Cindy Wong

Vice President Sox Compliance, Tricia Wilton

Senior Vice President General Counsel, Thomas Reich

Vice President and Legal Counsel, Greg Riches

Vice President of Labor Analytics, Jason Ansuini

Vice President Social Portfolio Strategy, Beverly Jackson

Executive Vice President of Customer Development, Neil Lewis

Treasurer, Emily Wang

Auditors: Deloitte & Touche LLP

LOCATIONS

HQ: MGM Resorts International
3600 Las Vegas Boulevard South, Las Vegas, NV 89109
Phone: 702 693-7120
Web: www.mgmresorts.com

2016 Sales

	$ mil.	% of total
Domestic resorts	7,055	75
MGM China	1,920	20
Corporate & other	478	5
Total	**9,455**	**100**

PRODUCTS/OPERATIONS

2016 Sales

	$ mil.	% of total
Casino	4,936	48
Rooms	2,023	20
Food and beverage	1,639	16
Entertainment	517	5
Retail	200	2
Other	533	5
Reimbursed costs	397	4
Less: Promotional allowances -793.5 -		
Total	**9,455**	**100**

Selected Properties

Nevada
  Las Vegas
  Bellagio
  Circus Circus
  CityCenter (50%)
  Excalibur
  Luxor
  Mandalay Bay Resort & Casino
  MGM Grand
  The Mirage
  T-Mobile Arena
  Monte Carlo
  New York-New York
  Reno
  Circus Circus Reno
  Silver Legacy (50%; Reno NV)
  Other
  Railroad Pass (Henderson)
  Gold Strike (Jean)
Other US
  Beau Rivage (Biloxi MS)
  Gold Strike (Tunica County MS)
  MGM Grand Detroit
China
  MGM Grand Macau (51%; Macau)

COMPETITORS

Boyd Gaming
Caesars Entertainment
Galaxy Entertainment
Las Vegas Sands

Sands China
Star City
Station Casinos
Stratosphere

Pinnacle Entertainment
Rio All-Suite Hotel & Casino
Riviera Holdings
SJM

Tropicana Entertainment
Trump Resorts
Wynn Resorts

HISTORICAL FINANCIALS

Company Type: Public

Income Statement

FYE: December 31

	REVENUE ($ mil.)	NET INCOME ($ mil.)	NET PROFIT MARGIN	EMPLOYEES
12/16	9,455	1,101	11.6%	69,000
12/15	9,190	(447)	—	59,500
12/14	10,081	(149)	—	68,100
12/13	9,809	(156)	—	67,800
12/12	9,160	(1,767)	—	66,650
Annual Growth	**0.8%**	**—**		**0.9%**

2016 Year-End Financials

Debt ratio: 46.10%
Return on equity: 19.37%
Cash ($ mil.): 1,446
Current ratio: 0.97
Long-term debt ($ mil.): 12,979

No. of shares (mil.): 574
Dividends
  Yield: —
  Payout: —
Market value ($ mil.): 16,552

	STOCK PRICE ($) FY Close	P/E High/Low		PER SHARE ($) Earnings	Dividends	Book Value
12/16	28.83	15	9	1.92	0.00	10.83
12/15	22.72	—	—	(0.82)	0.00	9.06
12/14	21.38	—	—	(0.31)	0.00	8.33
12/13	23.52	—	—	(0.32)	0.00	8.63
12/12	11.64	—	—	(3.62)	0.00	8.92
Annual Growth	**25.5%**	—	—	**—**	**—**	**5.0%**

Michaels Companies Inc

Auditors: Ernst & Young LLP

LOCATIONS

HQ: Michaels Companies Inc
8000 Bent Branch Drive, Irving, TX 75063
Phone: 972 409-1300
Web: www.michaels.com

HISTORICAL FINANCIALS

Company Type: Public

Income Statement

FYE: January 28

	REVENUE ($ mil.)	NET INCOME ($ mil.)	NET PROFIT MARGIN	EMPLOYEES
01/17	5,197	378	7.3%	50,000
01/16	4,912	362	7.4%	50,000
01/15*	4,738	217	4.6%	51,000
02/14	4,570	243	5.3%	50,200
02/13	4,408	200	4.5%	—
Annual Growth	**4.2%**	**17.3%**	**—**	**—**

*Fiscal year change

2017 Year-End Financials

Debt ratio: 128.25%
Return on equity: ***,***.**%
Cash ($ mil.): 298
Current ratio: 1.51
Long-term debt ($ mil.): 2,723

No. of shares (mil.): 193
Dividends
  Yield: —
  Payout: —
Market value ($ mil.): 3,781

	STOCK PRICE ($) FY Close	P/E High/Low	PER SHARE ($) Earnings	Dividends	Book Value
01/17	19.56	17 11	1.82	0.00	(8.79)
01/16	21.80	17 12	1.72	0.00	(8.25)
01/15*	25.80	25 14	1.05	0.00	(10.25)
Annual Growth	(6.7%)	— —	—	14.7%	— —

*Fiscal year change

Micron Technology Inc.

Micron Technology is one of the largest memory chip makers in the world. It makes DRAM (Dynamic Random Access Memory) NAND Flash and NOR Flash memory and other memory technologies. The company sells to customers in networking and storage consumer electronics solid-state drives and mobile telecommunications but its largest concentration (nearly a third of sales) is the computer market. Micron's products are offered under the Micron Lexar Crucial SpecTek and Elpida brands as well as private labels. The company generates about 85% of sales internationally.

Operations

Micron operates through four segments centered on its markets. Its largest accounting for more than 40% of sales is the Compute and Networking Business Unit which sells products for the computing networking graphics and cloud server markets. The Storage Business Unit contributes more than 20% of revenue with the Mobile Business Unit memory for smartphone tablet and other mobile-device markets generating more than 20% of sales. About 15% of revenue comes from the Embedded Business Unit which makes memory products for the automotive industrial and consumer markets.

Almost two-thirds of revenue comes from DRAM products and NAND Flash memory products supply the rest. DRAM and flash are sold throughout each of Micron's segments.

The company makes its own products in fabrication plants throughout the world and most of its products are made on 300mm wafers.

Geographic Reach

Micron generates about 50% of its revenue in China with another 25% from Taiwan Japan and other Asia/Pacific region countries. The US and Europe contribute about 15% and 5% respectively.

It has fabrication and assembly facilities in China Japan Malaysia Singapore Taiwan and the US.

Sales and Marketing

Micron sells to equipment manufacturers and retailers via a direct sales force third-party sales representatives and distributors. The company sells Lexar-branded NAND Flash memory products primarily through retail channels and its Crucial-branded products through a web-based customer direct sales channel as well as through channel and distribution partners.

Intel is Micron's biggest customer generating about 15% of sales with sales to Kingston primarily DRAM amounting to a tenth of sales.

Financial Performance

Micron?s financial results over the past two years are Exhibit A in the volatility of the semiconductor business. The company rode increased demand to a 64% revenue increase to about $20 billion in 2017 (ended September) from 2016. On the bottom line the company posted about $5 billion in net income wiping about a $276 million loss in 2016. Revenue and profit were company records.

Micron reported strong conditions across its markets particularly for enterprise mobile client and SSD storage. The company recorded higher sales in all operating segments and significant sales volume increases for DRAM and Trade NAND products as well higher prices for DRAM products. Output was aided by improvements in product and process technology.

The improvements in manufacturing and revenue translated to the leap in net income. The 25% profit margin in 2017 was the highest in at least a decade.

Micron generated plenty of cash in 2017 hitting more than $8 billion in operating cash flow upo from about $3 billion in 2016. Cash came from operations and the effect of working capital adjustments.

Strategy

Changes Micron made to improve its manufacturing processes and to alter its product mix met the market at the right time. The company?s memory products are selling into growing markets such as cloud computing data centers and automotive applications. That has increased demand. At the same time Micron increased its pace of production and made it more efficient with changes to its development and fabrication processes. That enabled it to sell at higher prices for some products and gather market share from slower competitors.

Mergers and Acquisitions

In 2016 Micron acquired the two-thirds of Inotera that it did not own. Micron paid $4 billion to Nanya Technology Corp. for the DRAM maker based in Taiwan. The deal brought Inotera's DRAM production entirely in-house at Micron which already buys 100% of Inotera's output. Most of Inotera's manufacturing operations run at Micron's 20 nanometer process with the rest to convert in 2016.

EXECUTIVES

President and CEO, Sanjay Mehrotra, age 58
Vice President Operations, Jay Hawkins
VP Finance and CFO, Ernest E. (Ernie) Maddock, age 59, $550,000 total compensation
VP Information Technology and CIO, Trevor Schulze
Vice President, Matt Elzie
Vice President, Nathan Burt
Vice President Advanced Storage Solutions, Robert Peglar
National Account Manager, Mary Smith
Vice President Of Software Engineering, Steve Moyer
Vice President Japan Process Research, Hideki Gomi
Vice President Wsg Marketing, Reynette Au
Vice President WW Enterprise Sales, Mark Glasgow
VP Human Resources, Michael Zeigler
Vice President of Storage Marketing, Eric Endebrock
Vice President Director Manager, Brian Kalisek
Vice President Director Manager, Michael Knapp
Vice President Business Planning and Process Management, Karen Metz
Vice President, Gino Skulick
Vice President Enigneering, Currie Munce
Chairman, Robert E. (Bob) Switz, age 70
Assistant Treasurer, Gregory Routin
Auditors: PricewaterhouseCoopers LLP

LOCATIONS

HQ: Micron Technology Inc.
8000 S. Federal Way, Boise, ID 83716-9632
Phone: 208 368-4000
Web: www.micron.com

2017 Sales

	$ mil.	% of total
China	10,388	41
United States	2,763	13
Asia Pacific (exclusive China Taiwan and Japan)	1,808	9
Taiwan	2,544	12
Europe	1,360	7
Japan	1,025	5
Other	434	2
Total	**20,322**	**100**

PRODUCTS/OPERATIONS

2017 Sales

	$ mil.	% of total
Compute and Networking Business Unit	414	42
Storage Business Unit	4,514	22
Mobile Business unit	4,424	22
Embedded Business Unit	2,695	13
All Other	65	-
Total	**20,322**	**100**

2017 Sales

	$ mil.	% of total
DRAM	12,963	64
Trade NAND	6,228	31
Non-Trade	553	3
Other	578	3
Total	**20,322**	**100**

Semiconductor Products
Dynamic random-access memories (DRAMs)
   Direct Rambus DRAMs (RDRAMs)
   Synchronous DRAMs (SDRAMs)
   Double data rate synchronous DRAMs (DDR SDRAMs)
Flash memory devices
Memory modules
Photomasks

COMPETITORS

Atmel	SK Hynix
Cypress Semiconductor	SMART Modular
Integrated Device	Technologies
Technology	Samsung Electronics
Intel	SanDisk
Kingston Technology	Seagate Technology
Mosel Vitelic	Sharp Corp.
Nanya	Toshiba Semiconductor
PNY Technologies	& Storage Products
Quantum Corporation	Western Digital
Rambus	

HISTORICAL FINANCIALS

Company Type: Public

Income Statement

FYE: August 31

	REVENUE ($ mil.)	NET INCOME ($ mil.)	NET PROFIT MARGIN	EMPLOYEES
08/17*	20,322	5,089	25.0%	34,100
09/16	12,399	(276)	—	31,400
09/15	16,192	2,899	17.9%	31,800
08/14	16,358	3,045	18.6%	30,400
08/13	9,073	1,190	13.1%	30,900
Annual Growth	22.3%	43.8%	—	2.5%

*Fiscal year change

2017 Year-End Financials

Debt ratio: 31.51%	No. of shares (mil.): 1,112
Return on equity: 33.24%	Dividends
Cash ($ mil.): 5,109	Yield: —
Current ratio: 2.34	Payout: —
Long-term debt ($ mil.): 9,872	Market value ($ mil.): 35,551

STOCK PRICE ($)	P/E		PER SHARE ($)		
FY Close	High/Low	Earnings	Dividends		Book Value
08/17*	31.97	7	4	4.41	0.00	16.75
09/16	16.64	—	—	(0.27)	0.00	11.62
09/15	16.59	13	5	2.47	0.00	11.84
08/14	32.81	12	5	2.54	0.00	10.04
08/13	13.57	13	4	1.13	0.00	8.75
Annual Growth	23.9%	—	—	40.6%	—	17.6%

*Fiscal year change

Microsoft Corporation

Microsoft is omnipresent. Its Windows operating system and Office suite of productivity software dominate their markets. The company's cloud computing platform Azure is one of the leaders in that burgeoning market. Customers range from individuals and small businesses to the world's biggest companies and government agencies. Microsoft makes tablets (Surface) game consoles (Xbox) and even laptop computers (introduced in 2015) and it also owns Skype the video meeting service. And in 2016 Microsoft added LinkedIn the business-oriented social network to its portfolio in a $26 billion deal. Microsoft's software is included in most personal computers including those from Dell Technologies HP Inc. and Lenovo.

Operations

Microsoft operates three business segments: More Personal Computing Productivity and Business Processes and Intelligent Cloud along with a Corporate segment.

The More Personal Computing segment generates about 43% of revenue by selling products and services for end users developers and IT managers across devices. Included are Windows OS products; devices including the Surface tablet phones and PC accessories; gaming such as Xbox hardware and Xbox Live; video games; HoloLens virtual reality technology; and third-party video game royalties; and search advertising.

The Productivity and Business Processes segment about 33% of sales covers productivity communication and information products and services across devices and platforms. Among the products are Office Office 365 (the cloud version) Exchange SharePoint Skype and Skype for Business and the Dynamics ERP and CRM products. Sales ofMicrosoft Office alone comprises nearly 30% of the company's total revenue. Newly acquired LinkedIn resides in this segment.

The Intelligent Cloud segment 25% consists of its public private and hybrid server products and cloud services. Products and services include SQL Server Windows Server Visual Studio System Center and Azure.

Geographic Reach

Redmond WA-headquartered Microsoft operates in some 190 countries with international sales accounting for 52% of revenue and the balance coming from the US.

The company has regional centers around the world as well as data centers and research and development facilities.Corporate headquarters outside of Seattle WA resides on nearly 500 acres and has approximately 15 million square feet of space that houses engineering sales marketing and operations organizations. It also has significant a R&D presence in China and India and large a technical support location in Dublin Ireland.

Sales and Marketing

Microsoft sells its products and services online and through OEMs distributors and resellers. Maintaining its brand identity and keeping itself in front-of-mind for potential consumer and commercial buyers is a key strategy to ongoing sales and to that end the company spends about $15 billion annually on sales and marketing activities.

Financial Performance

Following a year of lower revenue in FY2016 the company's revenue recovered with a 5% increase to $90.0 billion in FY2017 (ended June 30). The sales upswing was due to growth in its Microsoft Office product line revenue inclusion from its LinkedIn acquisition and higher revenue from server products and cloud services.

Net income continued a multi-year upward trend rising 26% to $21.2 billion on higher revenues and lower charges against impairments and restructuring activities.

At the end of FY2017 cash on hand was $7.7 billion up $1.2 billion from the prior year end. Cash from operations was nearly $40.0 billion based in large part on net income and large adjustment concerning deferred revenue. Financing activities contributed $8.4 billion by issuing $44.3 billion in debt while returning a large amount of money to shareholders via dividends and stock buy-backs. Investing activities used $46.7 billion during the year most of it via exchanging investments purchased with the company's massive cache of $125 billion in short-term investments.

Strategy

Microsoft isn't just on the desktop anymore and its not just for PCs either.

From its Azure cloud computing operations to its Surface tablets (and now Surface Book notebook computer) the company is planting its flag in the cloud and mobile. Cloud customers are attracted by the stability of Microsoft products (and the company itself) as well as the industries — such as health care — that Microsoft's customers are in. Microsoft competes with Amazon's Amazon Web Services and Google in cloud services a fight that has seen prices drop as services increase. Microsoft keys on the capability of its public cloud to integrate with customers' hybrid and private clouds.

Microsoft also has adapted its software for other devices such as those that run on the Apple iOS and the Android OS from Google. The Office 365 is a cloud-based version of its Office productivity suite; its consumer client base now numbers 27.0 million.

The company continues to depend on PC makers such as Dell HP and Lenovo to load its software on their computers. That means not only the operating system but Office as well. Microsoft's notebook computer is a direct competitor with similar products of its customers. The hope within Microsoft is that the computer will inject energy into the slumping PC market improving the environment for other PC makers as well.

In the phone business Microsoft shifted its focus toward providing software rather than hardware. It sold its feature phone business to Hon Hai/Foxconn Technology Group and HMD Global a deal that included manufacturing facilities in Vietnam. Without the entry-level class of phones Microsoft continues with Windows 10 Mobile and the Lumia line of phones and those from OEM partners Acer Trinity and VAIO.

Mergers and Acquisitions

In June 2017 Microsoft moved to bolster the security of its enterprise software by agreeing to acquire Hexadite. The company develops tools for automatically investigating security incidents and remedying them. Microsoft expects Hexadite's products to strengthen and extend its enterprise security offerings.The price was reported to be about $100 million.

Microsoft in April 2017 bought Deis a startup software company to aid in its competition with Amazon Web Services and Google to provide cloud services. Deis provides open-source software that helps companies build applications on top of cloud services. With Deis Microsoft seeks to make it easier for developers to write applications for its Azure cloud services. Terms of the deal were not disclosed.

The 2016 acquisition of LinkedIn adds to Microsoft's services and deepens capability to compete with relationship-oriented software providers such as Salesforce.com. At $26 billion it was Microsoft's biggest acquisition. LinkedIn will operate as an independent subsidiary of Microsoft with the same management. That said Microsoft and LinkedIn intend to integrate a number of their products. For example people drafting their r ©sum ©s in Microsoft's Word can update their LinkedIn profiles and find and apply for jobs there. LinkedIn Learning will be available in Office 365 and the Windows ecosystem.

HISTORY

Bill Gates and Paul Allen founded Microsoft (originally named Micro-soft) in 1975 after Gates dropped out of Harvard at age 19 to sell a version of the programming language BASIC. While Gates was at Harvard the pair wrote the language for Altair the first commercial microcomputer. The company was born in Albuquerque New Mexico and grew by modifying BASIC for other computers.

Gates and Allen moved Microsoft to their native Seattle in 1979 and began developing software that let others write programs. The modern PC era dawned in 1980 when IBM chose Microsoft to write the operating system for its new machines. Although hesitant at first Gates bought QDOS short for "quick and dirty operating system" for $50000 from a Seattle programmer renaming it the Microsoft Disk Operating System (MS-DOS).

Allen fell ill with Hodgkin's disease and left Microsoft in 1983. In the mid-1980s Microsoft introduced Windows a graphics-based version of MS-DOS that borrowed from rival Apple's Macintosh system. The company went public in 1986 and Gates became the industry's first billionaire a year later. Microsoft introduced Windows NT in 1993 to compete with the UNIX operating system popular on mainframes and large networks.

The early 1990s brought monopoly charges from inside and outside the industry. In 1995 antitrust concerns scotched a $1.5 billion acquisition of personal finance software maker Intuit.

EXECUTIVES

Vice President of Finance and Administration and Chief Accounting Officer, Frank Brod
EVP and President Microsoft Global Sales Marketing and Operations, Jean-Philippe Courtois, age 56
CEO, Satya Nadella, age 49, $1,200,000 total compensation
VP Office Business Platform Group, Kurt DelBene, age 56, $638,333 total compensation
President and Chief Legal Officer, Bradford L. (Brad) Smith, age 58, $704,167 total compensation
EVP and Chief Marketing Officer, Christopher C. (Chris) Capossela, age 47
CEO Microsoft UK, Cindy Rose
EVP Applications and Services, Lu Qi
EVP Artificial Intelligence (AI) and Research Group, Harry Shum, $573,939 total compensation
EVP Human Resources, Kathleen T. Hogan, age 51
EVP Office Product Group, Rajesh Jha
Corporate VP and President Middle East and Africa, Ali Faramawy

EVP Microsoft Cloud and Enterprise Group, Scott Guthrie

EVP Worldwide Commercial Business, Judson Althoff

Corporate VP and President Latin America, Cesar Cernuda

EVP Windows and Devices Group, Terry Myerson

EVP and CFO, Amy E. Hood, age 45, $731,250 total compensation

CTO, J. Kevin Scott

EVP Business Development, Margaret L. (Peggy) Johnson, age 55, $704,167 total compensation

Worldwide SVP and President Asia Pacific, Ralph Haupter

President and COO Russia, Tomasz Bochenek

Acting CEO Microsoft Viet Nam, Aung San Maung

President Microsoft Indonesia, Haris Izmee

Corporate Vice President, Will Kennedy

Vice President and Deputy General Counsel, Hossein Nowbar

Vice President, Kelly Rollin

Vp WW Sales and Marketing Group Strategy Microsoft Corp, Matthew Bishop

Vice President Manufacturing, Alfred Ojukwu

Vice President, Jeff Tokar

Corporate Vice President, Brad Anderson

Corporate Vice President Dynamics CRM, Robert Stutz

MBS Emerging Solutions Vice President Sales for MSCRM, Errol Schoenfish

Vice President Worldwide Original Equipment Sales, Alvaro Celis

Vice President Finance and Human Resources, Christina Bauer

Corporate Vice President Software Development Core Operating System, Henry Sanders

Vice President, Mark Wilson

Executive Vice President Business Development, Peggy Johnson

Corporate Vice President, Joseph Sirosh

Human Resources Director Or Vice President Of Human Resources, Rupert Bader

Vice President Engineering, Ed Clark

Assistant Vice President, Patrick Dengler

Vice President, Vidhya Bala

Svp Microsoft Services And It, Richard R Devenuti, age 60

Corporate Vice President Microsoft Online, Ron Markezich

Vice President Dtag Global Account, Arnd Hungerberg

Corporate Vice President, Zig Serafin

Corporate Vice President Windows Marketing, Tony Prophet

Vice President Commercial Services, Robert Jorgenson

Corporate Vice President Small And Midmarket Solutions And Partners Microsoft Corporation, Eduardo Rosini

Senior Vice President Product Strategy (Xbox Entertainment Studios), Randy Ahn

Executive Vice President Operating, Terry Ramsey

MVP Program Strategy Lead, Danilo Bordini

CVP WW Epg, Susan Hauser

Vice President Finance And Administration, Jack Martin

Corporate Vice President, David Porter

Corporate Vice President Smsg Human Resources, Sue Bevington

Corporate Vice President, Joe Matz

Vice President International Strategic Search AD Sales, Axel Steinman

Corporate Vice President, Mark Walker

Executive Vice President, Ravi Prakash

Corporate Vice President and Deputy General Counsel Litigation Competition Law and Compliance, David Howard

CVP WDG Core Quality, Michael Fortin

Vice President North America, Rob Wilk

Assistant Vice President, Varun Desai

Vice President Corporate Controller and Chief Accounting Officer at Dynamics Research, Shaun Mccarthy Shaun Mccarthy

Senior Vice President of Marketing for Phones, Tuula Rytil

Vice President Worldwide Information Technology Volume Licensing Systems, BJ Moore

Corporate Vice President, Charlotte Yarkoni

Corporate Vice President One Commercial Partner, Ron Huddleston

Corporate Vice President Mixed Reality Marketing (Windows and Devices Group), Liz Hamren

Vice President Consumer Channels Western Europe, Simon Ainslie

Vice President Global Procurement and Production Planning, Jennifer Weitzel

Corporate Vice President Worldwide Inside Sales, Debbie Dunnam

Chairman, John W. Thompson, age 67

Board Member, Nicole Summitt

Board Member, Timothy Chen

Auditors: DELOITTE & TOUCHE LLP

LOCATIONS

HQ: Microsoft Corporation
  One Microsoft Way, Redmond, WA 98052-6399
Phone: 425 882-8080
Web: www.microsoft.com

2017 Sales

	$ mil.	% of total
US	45,248	51
Other countries	44,702	49
Total	**89,950**	**100**

PRODUCTS/OPERATIONS

2017 Sales

	% of total
More Personal Computing	40
Productivity and Business Processes	32
Intelligent Cloud	28
Corporate and Other	-
Total	**100**

2017 Sales

	% of total
Product	64
Services & other	36
Total	**100**

2017 Sales

	$ mil
% of total	
Microsoft Office system	28
Server products and tools	24
Xbox	10
Windows PC operating system	10
Advertising	8
Consulting and product support services	6
Devices	5
LinkedIn	3
Other	6
Total	**100**

Selected Products

Consumer software services and devices
  Xbox (video game console)
Desktop applications
  Access (relational database management)
  Excel (integrated spreadsheet)
  FrontPage (website publishing)
  MS Office (business productivity software suite)
  Outlook (messaging and collaboration)
  PowerPoint (presentation graphics)
  Project (project scheduling and resource allocation)
  Word (word processing)
Enterprise software
  BackOffice (server software suite)
  Content Management Server (content management)
  Exchange Server (messaging server)
  Proxy Server (Internet gateway)
  Site Server (website management)
  SQL Server (database and data analysis management)

Systems Management Server (centralized management)
Visio (visualization and diagramming suite)

COMPETITORS

Adobe Systems	Mozilla
Amazon.com	Nintendo
Apple Inc.	Nokia
BMC Software	Novell
CA Inc.	Opera Software
Cisco Systems	Oracle
Dell	Red Hat
EMC	SAP
Facebook	Sony
Google	VMware
HP	Yahoo!
IBM	salesforce.com
Logitech	

HISTORICAL FINANCIALS

Company Type: Public

Income Statement

FYE: June 30

	REVENUE ($ mil.)	NET INCOME ($ mil.)	NET PROFIT MARGIN	EMPLOYEES
06/17	89,950	21,204	23.6%	124,000
06/16	85,320	16,798	19.7%	114,000
06/15	93,580	12,193	13.0%	118,000
06/14	86,833	22,074	25.4%	128,000
06/13	77,849	21,863	28.1%	99,000
Annual Growth	3.7%	(0.8%)	—	5.8%

2017 Year-End Financials

Debt ratio: 35.75%—
Return on equity: 29.37%
Cash ($ mil.): 7,663
Current ratio: 2.48
Long-term debt ($ mil.): 76,073
Dividends
  Yield: 2.2%
  Payout: 56.4%
Market value ($ mil.): —

	STOCK PRICE ($) FY Close	P/E High/Low		PER SHARE ($) Earnings	Dividends	Book Value
06/17	68.93	26	19	2.71	1.53	9.39
06/16	51.17	27	19	2.10	1.39	9.22
06/15	44.15	33	27	1.48	1.21	9.98
06/14	41.70	16	12	2.63	1.07	10.90
06/13	34.55	14	10	2.58	0.89	9.48
Annual Growth	18.9%	—	—	1.2%	14.5%	(0.2%)

Midland States Bancorp Inc

Born in rural Illinois Midland States Bancorp is now discovering banking life in new states. It is the $3 billion-asset holding company for Midland States Bank a community bank that operates more than 35 branches in central and northern Illinois and around 15 branches in the St. Louis metropolitan area. The bank offers traditional consumer and commercial banking products and services as well as merchant card services insurance and financial planning. Subsidiary Midland Wealth Management which boasts $1.2 billion-plus in assets under administration provides wealth management services while Heartland Business Credit offers commercial equipment leasing services. Midland States Bancorp went public in 2016.

IPO

The bank holding company raised $80.1 million in its initial public offering. It plans to contribute some $25 million to Midland States Bank and use the rest for general corporate purposes including possible acquisitions.

Operations

About 57% of Midland States Bancorp's total revenue came from loan interest during 2014 while another 17% came from interest income from investment securities. The rest came from wealth management fees (8% of revenue) deposit account service charges (3%) ATM and interchange revenue (3%) mortgage banking revenue (3%) merchant services revenue (1%) and nonrecurring gains on the sales of assets (around 8%).

Subsidiary Love Funding provides multifamily and healthcare facility FHA financing.

Geographic Reach

Midland has more than 80 branches and offices across the US with around 50 in Illinois and around the St. Louis metro area and the rest in California Colorado Florida Massachusetts North Carolina Ohio Tennessee and Texas.

Financial Performance

Midland States Bancorp's revenue climbed 3% to $93 million despite a decline in loan interest income during 2014 mostly thanks to profitable asset sales and other income.

Despite modest revenue growth in 2014 the bank's net income dove 67% to $3.2 billion as acquisition and integration expenses stemming from its late 2014 acquisition of Heartland ate up any revenue gains it had made. Excluding these nonrecurring items the bank's net income grew modestly.

Strategy

Midland States Bancorp has been pursuing an acquisition and branch expansion growth strategy since 2007 after it replaced its executive management and laid out a plan to expand Midland States Bank's presence in Illinois. Midland States Bank continues to focus on moving into suburban areas and other markets in Illinois and Missouri that have growing populations. During 2015 it opened a new branches in the St. Louis region (in Jennings) downtown Joliet and downtown Effingham areas as well as a wealth management office in downtown Decatur.

The company also planned in 2016 to continue building its fast-growing wealth management business which now makes up nearly 10% of its total revenue. Thanks to Midland's efforts the business' wealth management assets under administration have skyrocketed twelve-fold since 2008 growing from $95 million then to $1.19 billion at the end of 2014.

Mergers and Acquisitions

In February 2017 CEO Leon Holschbach signed a $175 million deal with rival Centrue Bank to merge. The two banks had been treading on each others' toes in Princeton Illinois.

In February 2016 Midland States Bank agreed to purchase $400 million in wealth management assets from Sterling National Bank which would boost its assets under administration by more than 30% to $1.6 billion. Sterling Bank had originally obtained the wealth management assets — which were mostly Special Needs and Settlement Trusts — after buying Hudson Valley Bank.

In December 2014 the bank acquired Heartland Bank as well as its $900 million in assets 13 Heartland Bank branches in the St. Louis metropolitan area four branches in Colorado and single locations in Joplin Missouri and Raleigh/Durham North Carolina.

Company Background

Between 2008 and 2010 the bank's branch locations grew from just a half-dozen in central Illinois and St. Louis to nearly 30 around the state and in the St. Louis metropolitan area. During that time the bank acquired the assets of Waterloo Bancshares and WestBridge in St. Louis AMCORE in northern Illinois and Strategic Capital in central Illinois. It also opened new locations in some of its faster-growing markets. As a result of its efforts Midland States Bancorp has watched its revenue and profits trend upward significantly from 2007 levels.

EXECUTIVES

Vice Chairman President and CEO, Leon J. Holschbach, age 64, $529,389 total compensation
EVP Midland States Bancorp and President Midland States Bank, Jeffrey G. Ludwig, age 45, $367,500 total compensation
EVP Banking, Jeffrey S. Medford
CFO Midland States Bancorp and Midland States Bank, Kevin L. Thompson
Vice President and Client Relationship Manager, Linda L Perry
Senior Vice President Community Banking, Jeffrey Mefford
Vice President of Customer Service, Kylene Hoelscher
Vice President, Deanna Haught
Vice President Mortgage Banking, Mark Widdicombe
Assistant Vice President Mortgage Platform Manager, Diann West
Chairman, John M. Schultz, age 65

LOCATIONS

HQ: Midland States Bancorp Inc
1201 Network Centre Drive, Effingham, IL 62401
Phone: 217 342-7321
Web: www.midlandsb.com

PRODUCTS/OPERATIONS

2014 Sales

	% of total
Interest income	
Loans	57
Investment Securities & others	17
Noninterest income	
Wealth management revenue	8
Service charges on deposit accounts	3
Mortgage banking revenue	3
Gain on sale of other assets	3
ATM and interchange revenue	3
Impairments	
Other	6
Total	**100**

Selected Services

Bank By Phone
Bill Paying
Checking
Debit Card
Online Banking
Savings & CDs

COMPETITORS

Bank of America	Harris
Edward D. Jones	Mercantile Bancorp
Fifth Third	PNC Financial
First Mid-Illinois Bancshares	U.S. Bancorp

HISTORICAL FINANCIALS

Company Type: Public

Income Statement

FYE: December 31

	ASSETS ($ mil.)	NET INCOME ($ mil.)	INCOME AS % OF ASSETS	EMPLOYEES
12/16	3,233	31	1.0%	715
12/15	2,884	24	0.8%	700
12/14	2,676	10	0.4%	—
12/13	0	14	—	—
Annual Growth	—	29.6%	—	—

2016 Year-End Financials

Debt ratio: 2.84%	No. of shares (mil.): 15
Return on equity: 11.34%	Dividends
Cash ($ mil.): 189	Yield: 0.0%
Current ratio: —	Payout: 16.5%
Long-term debt ($ mil.): —	Market value ($ mil.): 560

	STOCK PRICE ($) FY Close	P/E High/Low		PER SHARE ($) Earnings	Dividends	Book Value
12/16	36.18	17	9	2.17	0.36	20.78
12/15	0.00	—	—	2.00	0.65	19.74
Annual Growth	—			2.8%	(17.9%)	1.7%

MidSouth Bancorp, Inc.

For banking in the Deep South try MidSouth. MidSouth Bancorp is the holding company for MidSouth Bank which boasts roughly $2 billion in assets and around 60 branches across Louisiana and Texas. Targeting individuals and local business customers the bank offers such standard retail services as checking and savings accounts savings bonds investment accounts and credit card services. About 55% of its loan portfolio is made up of real estate mortgages while commercial loans make up more than 35%. Consumer and construction loans round out the rest of its lending activities.

Operations

About 67% of MidSouth Bancorp's total revenue came from loan interest (including fees) in 2014 while another 10% came from interest on its taxable and non-taxable investment securities. The rest of its revenue came from deposit account service charges (9%) ATM and debit card income (7%) and other miscellaneous income sources. The company had a staff of nearly 550 employees at the end of 2014.

Geographic Reach

The bank's branches are in Louisiana and central and east Texas along the Interstate 10 Interstate 49 Highway 90 Interstate 45 Interstate 20 and Interstate 35 corridors.

Sales and Marketing

The bank offers commercial and consumer loan and deposit services to small and middle-market business their owners and employees and other individuals in its markets in Texas and Louisiana.

Oil and gas is the key industry in these markets though medical technology and research companies are becoming increasingly prevalent. In addition major universities in the areas from Louisiana State University to Texas A&M contribute to a substantial number of jobs as well as a highly-educated workforce in these markets.

Financial Performance

MidSouth Bancorp's revenues and profits have been rising in recent years thanks to continued loan business growth partially stemming from the bank's late 2012 acqusition of PSB Financial and also thanks to lower interest expenses with the low-interest environment.

The bank's revenue rose by 5% to $107.91 million in 2014 mostly thanks to a non-recurring $3 million-executive officer life insurance proceed and a $1.1 million gain on the sale of an ORE though its loan interest grew by 2% helping to add to the company's top-line during the year.

Higher revenue coupled with lower interest expenses on borrowings and a decline in salary and benefit costs in 2014 helped boost MidSouth's net income by 35% to $19.11 million during the year. Its operating cash levels grew by 15% to $29.8 million on higher cash earnings.

Strategy

Seeking potential expansion into new market areas MidSouth Bancorp in 2015 planned to grow its loan and deposit business organically as well as through bank acquisitions. The bank would also continue its long-term strategy of focusing on commercial and small-business customers while continuing to serve its retail customers as well.

Company Background

In late 2012 Midsouth acquired PSB Financial which operated 16 branches in Louisiana under the Peoples State Bank banner. The deal expanded its presence into central and northwest Louisiana and east Texas.

EXECUTIVES

Executive Vice President And Chief Credit Officer, John Nichols
Senior Vice President, Lorraine Miller
Vice President, Cal Guirard
Auditors: Porter Keadle Moore, LLC

LOCATIONS

HQ: MidSouth Bancorp, Inc.
102 Versailles Boulevard, Lafayette, LA 70501
Phone: 337 237-8343
Web: www.midsouthbank.com

PRODUCTS/OPERATIONS

2014 Sales

	$ mil.	% of total
Interest income		
Loans including fees	72	67
Investment securities	10	10
Others	0	-
Non-interest income		
Service charges on deposit accounts	9	9
ATM and debit card income	7	7
Others	7	7
Total	**107**	**100**

COMPETITORS

American Bancorp	Home Banc
Bank of America	IBERIABANK
Capital One	Regions Financial
Hancock Holding	Teche Holding
Henderson Citizens Bancshares	

HISTORICAL FINANCIALS

Company Type: Public

Income Statement

FYE: December 31

	ASSETS ($ mil.)	NET INCOME ($ mil.)	INCOME AS % OF ASSETS	EMPLOYEES
12/16	1,943	9	0.5%	535
12/15	1,927	11	0.6%	536
12/14	1,936	19	1.0%	549
12/13	1,851	14	0.8%	604
12/12	1,851	9	0.5%	604
Annual Growth	**1.2%**	**(0.5%)**	**—**	**(3.0%)**

2016 Year-End Financials

Debt ratio: 1.14%	No. of shares (mil.): 11
Return on equity: 4.40%	Dividends
Cash ($ mil.): 78	Yield: 0.0%
Current ratio: —	Payout: 62.0%
Long-term debt ($ mil.): —	Market value ($ mil.): 155

	STOCK PRICE ($) FY Close	P/E High/Low	PER SHARE ($) Earnings	Dividends	Book Value
12/16	13.60	25 12	0.58	0.36	18.87
12/15	9.08	19 10	0.90	0.36	18.76
12/14	17.34	12 10	1.58	0.35	18.43
12/13	17.86	16 12	1.12	0.31	16.95
12/12	16.35	22 16	0.77	0.28	16.84
Annual Growth	**(4.5%)**	**— —**	**(6.8%)**	**6.5%**	**2.9%**

MidWestOne Financial Group, Inc.

This could be the saga of How the MidWest Was One . MidWest One Financial Group is the holding company for Midwest One Bank which operates about two dozen branches throughout central and east-central Iowa. The bank offers standard deposit products such as checking and savings accounts CDs and IRAs in addition to trust services credit cards insurance and brokerage and investment services. About two-thirds of MidWest One Financial's loan portfolio consists of real estate loans including residential and commercial mortgages and farmland and construction loans. Founded in 1983 MidWest One has total assets of $1.8 billion.

Geographic Reach

Headquartered in Iowa City Midwest One Bank has branches and loan production offices in 15 counties in central and east-central Iowa.

Financial Performance

The company reported net income of $18.6 million in 2013 a 13% increase over 2012. Earnings have been rising steadily while the bank's revenue has been trending downward. Indeed 2013's $80.8 million in revenue was 10% below 2012. Assets declined slightly over the same period as did deposits. (The bank is facing stiff competition for deposits from aggressive credit unions offering above market deposit rates.) However loans increased 5% year over year and the growth in loans combined with stable net interest margins of about 3.5% resulted in a modest uptick in net interest income. Non-interest income got a boost from the bank's wealth management division which posted a 7% revenue gain in 2013 versus 2012.

EXECUTIVES

President and CEO, Charles N. Funk, age 63, $422,000 total compensation
EVP Chief Lending Officer and Commercial Banking, Kent L. Jehle, age 57, $271,000 total compensation
VP and Chief Risk Officer, James M. Cantrell, $205,000 total compensation
COO, Kevin Kramer
SVP and CFO, Katie A. Lorenson, age 37, $206,231 total compensation
Senior Regional President, Mitchell W. Cook, age 53, $204,400 total compensation
Vice President Information Technology Managing Officer, Allen Schneider
Senior Vice President Loan Sales, Jason Swestka
Vice President Commercial and Ag Lending, Paul Jones
Vice President Senior Loan Review Officer, Jeff Richards
Executive Vice President, Kurt Weise
Vice President and Program Manager, Daniel Bailey
Vice President, Janeen Benoy
Vice President, Linda Nelson
SECOND VICE PRESIDENT AND RETAIL MANAGING OFFICER, Vanessa Mauer
SECOND VICE PRESIDENT MORTGAGE BANKER, Niki Gysbers
SENIOR VICE PRESIDENT SMALL BUSINESS ADMINISTRATION, John Kimball
VICE PRESIDENT COMMERCIAL BANKING, Jeff Schebler
SECOND VICE PRESIDENT MORTGAGE BANKER, Kerri Higgins
VICE PRESIDENT COMMERCIAL LENDING, Andrew L Brust
VICE PRESIDENT HUMAN RESOURCE MANAGER, Cathi Weber
Chairman, Kevin W. Monson, age 65
Auditors: RSM US LLP

LOCATIONS

HQ: MidWestOne Financial Group, Inc.
102 South Clinton Street, Iowa City, IA 52240
Phone: 319 356-5800
Web: www.midwestone.com

PRODUCTS/OPERATIONS

2015 Sales

	% of total
Interest Income	
Interest and fees on loans	71
Interest on investment securities	11
Other	1
Non-Interest Income	
Trust investment and insurance fees	5
Other service charges commissions and fees	5
Service charges and fees on deposit accounts	3
Mortgage origination and loan servicing fees	2
Other	2
Total	**100**

Selected Subsidiaries

MidWestOne Bank
MidWestOne Insurance Services Inc.
MidWestOne Statutory Trust II

COMPETITORS

Bank of the West	U.S. Bancorp
Hills Bancorporation	Wells Fargo
QCR Holdings	West Bancorporation

Income Statement

FYE: December 31

	ASSETS ($ mil.)	NET INCOME ($ mil.)	INCOME AS % OF ASSETS	EMPLOYEES
12/16	3,079	20	0.7%	587
12/15	2,979	25	0.8%	648
12/14	1,800	18	1.0%	374
12/13	1,755	18	1.1%	376
12/12	1,792	16	0.9%	390
Annual Growth	14.5%	5.0%	—	10.8%

2016 Year-End Financials

Debt ratio: 1.34%	No. of shares (mil.): 11
Return on equity: 6.76%	Dividends
Cash ($ mil.): 43	Yield: 0.0%
Current ratio: —	Payout: 35.9%
Long-term debt ($ mil.): —	Market value ($ mil.): 430

	STOCK PRICE ($) FY Close	P/E High/Low	PER SHARE ($) Earnings	Dividends	Book Value
12/16	37.60	22 14	1.78	0.64	26.71
12/15	30.41	14 12	2.42	0.60	25.96
12/14	28.81	13 10	2.19	0.58	23.07
12/13	27.20	13 9	2.18	0.50	20.99
12/12	20.51	12 8	1.96	0.36	20.51
Annual Growth	16.4%	— —	(2.4%)	15.5%	6.8%

MISSOURI HIGHER EDUCATION LOAN AUTHORITY

EXECUTIVES

Vice President Of Information Systems, Harry Lohse
Vice President Of Human Resources, Susan Crump
Vice President Information Technology, Jeannine Maciak

LOCATIONS

HQ: MISSOURI HIGHER EDUCATION LOAN AUTHORITY
633 SPIRIT DR, CHESTERFIELD, MO 630051243
Phone: 636 733-3700
Web: WWW.MOHELALOANTRANSFER.COM

COMPETITORS

Bank of America
Brazos Higher Education Service Corp.
Great Lakes Higher Education
JPMorgan Chase
Nelnet
Pennsylvania Higher Education Assistance Agency
Sallie Mae
Texas Guaranteed

Income Statement

FYE: June 30

	ASSETS ($ mil.)	NET INCOME ($ mil.)	INCOME AS % OF ASSETS	EMPLOYEES
06/16	2,208	8	0.4%	550
06/03	3,344	24	0.7%	—
06/02	2,730	19	0.7%	—
06/00	1,821	15	0.9%	—
Annual Growth	1.2%	(3.5%)	—	—

2016 Year-End Financials

Debt ratio: —	
Return on equity: 7.90%	Dividends
Cash ($ mil.): 26	Yield: —
Current ratio: 0.10	Payout: —
Long-term debt ($ mil.): —	Market value ($ mil.): —

MODERN WOODMEN OF AMERICA

No need to pitch a tent to have Modern Woodmen in your camp. One of the largest fraternal benefit societies in the US Modern Woodmen of America provides annuities life insurance and other financial savings products to more than 770000 members through some 1600 agents. The group founded in 1883 is organized into "camps" (or chapters) that provide financial social recreational and service benefits to members. Founder Joseph Cullen Root chose the society's name to compare pioneering woodmen clearing forests to men using life insurance to remove the financial burdens their families could face upon their deaths.

Operations

The organization claims some 2400 family and summit chapters and more than 900 youth clubs nationwide. In addition to financial services the chapters also offer social activities and community service opportunities for members and their families. In addition to life insurance and annuities the company offers retirement accounts including IRAs college savings plans investment assistance and other insurance products. Modern Woodmen has more than $36 billion in life insurance in force.

Subsidiary MWA Financial Services offers securities and brokered insurance products. The MWA-Bank (dba Modern Woodmen Bank) division provides retail banking services.

Financial Performance

All told the company has more than $13 billion in assets and roughly $36 billion of life insurance in force. Its 2013 surplus totaled $1.5 billion a 14% increase over 2012.

Strategy

The company enhances its operations by adding new products as well as through marketing efforts for existing products. For instance in 2012 Modern Woodsmen's financial representatives increased promotional efforts for life insurance products leading to a 5% increase in certificates and a 12% rise new policies that year. The increase in life insurance sales was also attributed to the Planning for Life program a system introduced in 2011 to help members understand the role of life insurance in financial planning.

Mergers and Acquisitions

In 2012 Modern Woodmen grew its membership by more than 17000 through the acquisition of Equitable Reserve Association. Through the combination Modern Woodmen assumed the assets liabilities and operations of Equitable Reserve.

Company Background

Although Modern Woodmen's roots are tangled with Woodmen of the World Life Insurance Society the two fraternal benefit societies are not related.

LOCATIONS

HQ: MODERN WOODMEN OF AMERICA
1701 1ST AVE, ROCK ISLAND, IL 612018779
Phone: 309 793-5537
Web: WWW.MYMODERNWOODMENOFFICE.ORG

PRODUCTS/OPERATIONS

Selected Products

Annuities (fixed immediate and variable; through MWA Financial Services)
Banking (MWABank)
  Certificates of Deposit
  Checking and savings accounts
  Credit cards and gift cards
  First mortgage and refinancing home loans
  Home equity loans
Insurance (through MWAGIA)
  Dental and vision insurance
  Disability income insurance
  Group employee benefits
  Group voluntary benefits
  Impaired risk life insurance
  International life and health insurance
  Long-term care insurance
  Major medical insurance
  Medicare supplement insurance
Investment (through MWA Financial Services)
  Brokerage services
  College savings plans
  Mutual funds
  Retirement plans
Life Insurance
  Term life insurance
  Term life insurance for children
  Universal life insurance
  Whole life insurance

COMPETITORS

Allstate	Reliance Standard
MassMutual	Royal Neighbors Of
MetLife	America
Nationwide Financial	State Farm
New York Life	Thrivent Financial
Northwestern Mutual	Woodmen of the World
Prudential	Life Insurance

HISTORICAL FINANCIALS

Company Type: Private

Income Statement

FYE: December 31

	ASSETS ($ mil.)	NET INCOME ($ mil.)	INCOME AS % OF ASSETS	EMPLOYEES
12/07	8,318	96	1.2%	480
12/06	7,928	99	1.3%	—
Annual Growth	4.9%	(2.6%)	—	—

2007 Year-End Financials

Debt ratio: —	
Return on equity: 9.10%	Dividends
Cash ($ mil.): 40	Yield: —
Current ratio: —	Payout: —
Long-term debt ($ mil.): —	Market value ($ mil.): —

Mohawk Industries, Inc.

Mohawk Industries is one of the largest makers of commercial and residential carpets rugs and other floor coverings in the US (competing with rival Shaw Industries) and one of the largest carpet makers in the world. It produces a range of broadloom carpets and rugs under such names as Mohawk Aladdin Durkan Karastan and Lees. Mohawk's Dal-Tile International division is a giant maker of ceramic tile and stone flooring. Unilin's laminate and wood flooring and other wood products round out Mohawk's operations. The company sells its wares to carpet retailers home centers mass merchandisers department stores and dealers.

Operations

Mohawk works through three main business segments: Flooring North America (nearly 45% of total sales) Global Ceramic (35%) and Flooring Rest of World (almost 20%).

Once focused exclusively on carpets and rugs Mohawk has evolved adapting itself to changing customer tastes and spending habits. The company now offers popular alternatives to carpet such as hardwood laminate and ceramic tile. It has also reached outside of its premium-priced portfolio by rolling out a do-it-yourself flooring line that mimics the elegant look of materials like marble or limestone without the coldness chipping or costly installation of real stone.

On a product level Mohawk generates nearly 40% of its revenue from its soft surface product group. Other product categories include tile (about 35%) and laminate and wood (about 25%).

Geographic Reach

Mohawk generates around 65% of its revenues in North America. It has manufacturing facilities located in Australia Brazil Canada Europe India Malaysia Mexico New Zealand Russia and the US.

Sales and Marketing

The company's top 10 customers account for nearly 20% of its total sales. It sells its products to more than 28000 customers which include independent floor covering retailers home centers and mass merchandisers department stores commercial dealers and end users.

Financial Performance

Mohawk has experienced several straight years of unprecedented growth. Its revenues jumped 11% from $8.1 billion in 2015 to peak at almost $9 billion its highest total in history. This was attributed to growth across all its segments: Flooring North America (5%) Global Ceramic (7%) and Flooring Rest of World (32%). Most of this growth was attributed to additional revenue from previous acquisitions and a favorable impact of price and product mix.

Profits also climbed 51% from $615 million in 2015 to reach $930 million in 2016 another milestone. This was fueled by about $140 million in savings from capital investments and cost reduction initiatives lower material costs and the favorable impact of lower restructuring acquisition and integration-related costs.

Like its revenues the company's operating cash flow has surged the last few years increasing from $912 million in 2015 to $1.3 billion in 2016. This was due to the higher profits driven by additional revenue. Cash flow also increased in 2016 due to the absence of a litigation charge of $123 million it paid in 2015.

Strategy

Mohawk has posted milestone revenue and profit totals over the years through an aggressive growth strategy. This involves acquisitions that enable it to enter new product categories or markets.

It then strengthens those acquisitions through investments and upgrades which allow it to modernize its locations and infrastructure and lower costs. In 2016 the company used about $672 million for internal investments and estimates it will spend $750 million in 2017.

Through these actions Mohawk is focused on broadening its countertop business in the US and Europe enhancing its carpet tile business in Europe entering the sheet vinyl industry in Russia and strengthening its indoor/outdoor rug and utility mat businesses in the US.

Mergers and Acquisitions

Mohawk is looking to extend its international reach and augment its product portfolio through acquisitions. In 2015 the company acquired International Flooring Systems S.A. a global manufacturer distributor and marketer of vinyl flooring products for $1.1 billion. The acquisition expanded Mohawk's luxury vinyl tile category portfolio and its fiberglass sheet vinyl business.

Also that year the company extended its European footprint when it purchased Advent KAI Luxembourg Holdings an eastern European ceramic tile floor manufacturer for $195 million; and Xtratherm Limited an Ireland-based manufacturer of insulation boards in Ireland the UK and Belgium for $160 million.

HISTORY

Mohawk traces its origins to the Shuttleworth family who founded the company in Amsterdam New York in 1878 setting up their business with 14 second-hand looms imported from England. The company was incorporated as Shuttleworth Brothers in 1902. It introduced the popular Karnak carpet design in 1908.

EXECUTIVES

SVP Marketing, Karen R. Mendelsohn
Chairman and CEO, Jeffrey S. Lorberbaum, age 62, $1,142,473 total compensation
President and COO, W. Christopher (Chris) Wellborn, age 61, $987,186 total compensation
President Ceramic North America, John C. Turner, age 48
President Flooring North America, Brian M. Carson, age 52, $618,000 total compensation
VP Finance and CFO, Frank H. Boykin, age 61, $615,605 total compensation
President Flooring Rest of World, Bernard P. Thiers, age 61, $609,312 total compensation
Senior Vice President and Chief Information Officer, Jana Kanyadan
Vice President Of Brand Management, Kent Clauson
Vice President Yarn and Extrusion Manufacturing, Larry Perugini
Vice President Manufacturing, Jeff Bruggs
Vice President Quality, Ed Richardson
Vice President Sales Bigelow and Mohawk Commercial Brands, Jeff Davis
Regional Vice President Strategic and Global Customers Pacific Northwest, Lori Edwards
Vice President Internal Audit, Carley Ferguson
Vice President of Flooring Production, Willy Chandler
Senior Vice President Sales, Randy Gardner
RVP Sales Central, Greg Tant
Regional Vice President, Russell Ence
Senior Vice President Commercial Product, Mike Gallman
Senior Vice President Prod Management, Bobby Berrier
Regionalvice President. Middle Atlantic, Jeff Shine
Vice President Design and Product Development, Jackie Dettmar
Mohawk Residential Sales Flooring Residential Sales RVP MID, Kevin Reilly
Vice President and Treasurer, Shailesh Bettadapur
Vp Sales, Ken Duning
Vice President Industry Relations, Allen Parker
Vice President Finance, Christy Thomas
Vice President Sales, Tom Merriman
Vice President Research And Development, Silvano Cornia
Vice President Marketing and Sales, David Moyer
Vice President, Barry Kelley
Vice President Of Residential Carpet Product Development, Jamie Welborn
Vice President Residential Marketing, Seth Arnold
National Sales Manager Multi Family, Doug Davis
Mohawk Commercial Sales Flooring Commercial RVP Mountain West, Ralph Holland
Senior Vice President Vice President Director, Roy Shelton
Vice President Information Technology, Danny Branch
Vice President of Sales, Kelly Moore
Vice President of Design and Product Development, Neil Hegwood
Vice President of Design, Tracy Pruitt
National accounts manager, Farris Cagle
Vice President Marketing, Tom Donoghue
Vice President Human Resources, ERIKA CROY
Vice President Credit and Assistant Treasurer, Tony Patti
Vice President Business Development and International Sales, Nick Sterghos
Vice President, Kurt Hoffman
Vp, Paul Woolverton
Regional Vice President, Frank Abraham
MVP, Michelle Rhodes
Regional Vice President Sales Southeast, Tracy Lambeth
Regional Vice President, Jim Waters
MVP Coordinator, Cathy Ballew
Regional Vice President Retail and Strategic Accounts, Kurt Brooks
Region Vice President Sales OHIO Valley, Bill Sayre
Regional Vice President Mid Atlantic, Jeff Weaver
Board Member, Mark Ruppert
Auditors: KPMG LLP

LOCATIONS

HQ: Mohawk Industries, Inc.
160 S. Industrial Blvd., Calhoun, GA 30701
Phone: 706 629-7721
Web: www.mohawkind.com

2016 Sales

	$ mil.	% of total
US	5,842	65
All other countries	3,116	35
Total	**8,959**	**100**

PRODUCTS/OPERATIONS

2016 Sales

	$ mil.	% of total
Soft Surface	3,415	38
Tile	3	36
Laminate and wood	2,286	26
Total	**8,959**	**100**

2016 Sales

	$ mil.	% of total
Flooring NA	3,865	43
Global Ceramic	3,174	36
Flooring ROW	1,918	21
Total	**8,959**	**100**

Products Selected
Residential Carpet
Commercial Carpet
Bath Rugs Area Rugs and Mats
Ceramic Tile & Stone
Laminate Flooring

Hardwood Flooring
Luxury Vinyl Tile (LVT)

Selected Operations
Glazed wall tile
Hardwood flooring
Hardwood flooring
Insulation panels
Laminate flooring
Laminate flooring
Porcelain tile
Quarry tile
Resilient flooring
Roofing systems
Rugs
Stone products

Selected Brand NamesAladdinAmerican OleanBigelow CommercialCentury FlooringColumbia FlooringDal-TileDurkanHorizonKarastanLeesMeritMohawkMohawk HomeQuick-Step

COMPETITORS

Armstrong World	Interface Inc.
Industries	International Textile
Beaulieu of America	Group
Couristan	JJJ Floor Covering
Dixie Group	Mannington Mills
Formica	MasterTile
Guilford Performance	Perstorp
Textiles	Shaw Industries
Hollander Home	Tarkett Inc.
Fashions	Wilsonart
Interceramic Inc.	International

HISTORICAL FINANCIALS

Company Type: Public

Income Statement

	REVENUE ($ mil.)	NET INCOME ($ mil.)	NET PROFIT MARGIN	EMPLOYEES
12/16	8,959	930	10.4%	37,800
12/15	8,071	615	7.6%	34,100
12/14	7,803	531	6.8%	32,300
12/13	7,348	348	4.7%	32,100
12/12	5,787	250	4.3%	25,100
Annual Growth	11.5%	38.9%	—	10.8%

FYE: December 31

2016 Year-End Financials

Debt ratio: 24.55%
Return on equity: 17.46%
Cash ($ mil.): 121
Current ratio: 1.28
Long-term debt ($ mil.): 1,128

No. of shares (mil.): 74
Dividends
  Yield: —
  Payout: —
Market value ($ mil.): 14,810

	STOCK PRICE ($) FY Close	P/E High/Low	PER SHARE ($) Earnings	Dividends	Book Value
12/16	199.68	17 12	12.48	0.00	77.88
12/15	189.39	25 18	8.31	0.00	65.66
12/14	155.36	22 17	7.25	0.00	60.59
12/13	148.90	30 19	4.82	0.00	61.37
12/12	90.47	25 16	3.61	0.00	53.79
Annual Growth	21.9%	—	36.4%	—	9.7%

Molina Healthcare Inc

Molina Healthcare is dedicated to helping low-income Americans receive health and behavioral health coverage as well as primary care services. The company's Health Plan segment arranges for the delivery of health services to some 4.2 million people who receive their care through Medicaid Medicare and other government-funded programs in about a dozen states and Puerto Rico. It also operates health clinics in six states. Molina's Medicaid Solutions segment provides business process outsourcing (BPO) solutions to Medicaid agencies in five states for their Medicaid Management Information Systems (MMIS) the tool used to support administration of state health care entitlement programs. The family of founder C. David Molina controls the company through holdings and trusts.

Operations

Molina operates through two primary segments: Health Plan and Molina Medicaid Solutions. Altogether the company's operations provide plans or services to 4.2 million individuals in about a dozen states. Molina's Health Plans segment accounts for more than 95% of revenues. The company's health plans provide medical services through state networks of contracted hospitals and physicians that accept Molina health plan coverage.

The Medicaid Management segment helps state agencies administer their Medicaid programs with such offerings as IT development and business processing.

Other operations include Pathways which provides behavioral health and social services.

Geographic Reach

Molina's health plans primarily operate in Washington California South Carolina Texas Ohio and Michigan as well as in New Mexico and Florida. The direct delivery line of business consists of about 30 primary care community clinics in California Florida New Mexico Utah Virginia and Washington.

The Medicaid Solutions segment provides IT services in Idaho Louisiana Maine New Jersey West Virginia and the US Virgin Islands; it also administers a drug rebate program in Florida.

Molina's Health Plans segment leases around 90 facilities while the Medicaid solutions segment leases a dozen facilities.

Sales and Marketing

Molina's client base includes independent physicians physician groups hospitals and ancillary care providers as well as its own clinics.

Financial Performance

Molina has seen steady revenue increases over the last few years. In 2016 revenue rose 25% to $17.8 billion as all revenue streams saw growth. Leading these gains was the largest area of business premiums. These increased 24% to $16.4 billion thanks to a 27% increase in membership. Additionally services revenue more than doubled to $539 million; this was primarily due the Pathways behavioral health subsidiary which was acquired in late 2016.

Net income which had been rising rapidly took a fall in 2016 declining 25% to $52 million on higher operating expenses. Molina's medical care costs costs of services and general expenses all increased that year. As a result cash flow from operations fell 40% to $673 million.

Strategy

One of Molina's immediate initiatives is advocating for the improvement of the insurance marketplace under regulatory guidelines. The company says that it is owed more than $142 million in risk corridor payments from the federal government and it has yet to recognize revenue from these payments. (The risk corridor program established as part of the Affordable Care Act aimed to protect insurers participating in exchanges from higher-than-expected claims through 2016.) In a mid-2017 win a federal claims court ruled that the government owes Molina $52 million in risk corridor payments.That ruling followed a string of upsets from quarterly losses and company layoffs to the withdrawal from Utah's and Wisconsin's ex-

changes and the firing of the company's CEO and CFO (both sons of Molina's founder).

A key Molina strategy for growth is to expand membership especially in its existing markets by acquiring the Medicaid contracts of other businesses. It made several of these purchases in 2016 adding more than 220000 Medicaid members to its books. It has also secured a number of state contracts including deals made in 2017 to provide Medicaid coverage in Illinois and Mississippi. That year the company was also granted a contract for north-central Washington's new integrated managed care program. In addition Molina enters new markets through both organic measures and through acquisitions targeting large markets with competitive provider communities.

The company is also working on cutting costs to improve efficiency. It underwent restructuring efforts in 2017 as mentioned above but has also improved its care management systems and processes. It is increasingly utilizing hospitalists (dedicated physicians working in hospitals) and coordinating care efforts among teams of providers to both save money and improve health outcomes.

Molina's newest subsidiary Pathways (acquired in late 2016) provides behavioral health managed care which the company believes will see a growth in demand over the next few years. For example substance abuse and mental illness are expected to be the leading causes of disability within five years. Additionally Medicaid members have twice as much a chance of suffering from a mental illness than the members of the general population. As a Medicaid specialist Molina stands to benefit from the growing need for coordinated care for these individuals. In the past Molina's growth strategy also consisted of opening additional primary care clinics in existing and new territories. The addition of more clinics helped Molina diversify its operations by expanding its involvement in the direct delivery of primary care.However in what may be the beginning of a general move away from primary care the company announced the closure of a Michigan specialty clinic in mid-2017.

Mergers and Acquisitions

In 2015 Molina Healthcare of Michigan acquired certain assets of HealthPlus of Michigan for $47 million expanding its operations in that state. The deal included assets of HealthPlus' Medicaid and MIChild (for uninsured children) businesses. Later that year Molina Healthcare of Florida bought assets of Preferred Medical Plan's Medicaid business in Florida for $8 million while Molina Healthcare of Illinois entered the Chicago market with the acquisition of certain assets of Accountable Care Chicago (aka MyCare Chicago). The Illinois unit also purchased certain Cook County-based Medicaid assets of accountable care entity Better Health Network for $18 million.

Also in 2015 the company acquired Providence Human Services (which provides behavioral and mental health services in more than 20 states) and Providence Community Services from The Providence Service Corporation for some $200 million. Those companies now operate under the Pathways brand.

In 2016 Molina Healthcare bought Total Care Medicaid a plan serving some 39000 members in upstate New York from Universal American for $41.3 million. Other deals that year included the purchases of Loyola Physician Partners ($15 million adding 21000 Medicaid members in Illinois) and HAP Midwest Health Plan (adding some 81000 Medicaid and MIChild members).

EXECUTIVES

CFO and Treasurer, Joseph W. White, age 58, $538,000 total compensation

EVP Research and Development, Martha Molina Bernadett, $357,000 total compensation
President CEO and Director, Joseph M. Zubretsky, age 61
COO, Terry P. Bayer, age 66, $644,000 total compensation
SVP General Counsel and Secretary, Jeff D. Barlow, age 54, $525,000 total compensation
CIO, Rick Hopfer
Medical Director, Richard Tompkins
Vice President Office of the Chief Information Officer, Debbie Simkins
Mhi Associate Vice President Program Management, Kristine MacRae
Assistant Vice President Mhi Enrollment Accounting, Becky Gutierrez
Mhi Executive Vice President Research and Development, M Bernadett
Medical Director, Lawrence O'Brien
Associate Vice President Projects Project Management Office, Sanjay Bhat
Vice President Finance and Analytics, Richard Rosenberg
Assistant Vice President Rating, Ben Lynam
Vice President Network Management, Michelle Espinoza
Vice President of Accounting, Derek Danley
Assistant Vice President Data Analytics, Yva Szeto
Vice President of Pharmacy Services, Angelo Giambrone
Associate Vice President Enterprise Infrastructure Services, Bharani Krish
Health Services Director, Bonnie Blitz
Vice President Healthcare Services, Jeffrey King
MHU Associate Vice President Government Contracts, Douglas Springmeyer
Vice President, Mohit Ghose
Director of Pharmacy, John Vu
Vice President Of Finance, Jane D Dawson
Mhi Associate Vice President Corporate Oprs, Andrea Orleans
Associate Vice President, Andrew Ramirez
Vice President Of Call Centre, Randall Fillmore
Associate Vice President of State Affairs, Cameron Smyth
Assistant Vice President Medicare Pharmacy Services, Erin Gordon
Associate Vice President Mltss, Lisa Hayes
Assistant Vice President of Health Plan Operations, Betty Thomas
Vice President Tax, George Figueroa
Medical Director of Behavioral Health, Ayo Afejuku
Associate Vice President of Government Contracts, David Vinkler
Vice President Business Innovation, Tom Giedlin
Associate Vice President of Molina Healthcare Inc., Brian Monsen
Vice President CPS, Marianne Czapla
Executive Vice President Finance, Stephen Harris
Vice President of Finance, Jeffrey Don Barlow
Assistant Vice President Business Development, Russ Fendley
Vice President Financial Planning and Analysis, Eduardo Silva
ASSOCIATE VICE PRESIDENT, Larry Baldwin
Assoc Vice President, Anita Carter
Vice President Government Contracts, Karen Zeiler
Medical Director, David Eibling
Vice President, Eric De Garceau
Medical Director, Terry Fowler
Vice President of Operations, Elizabeth Richardson
Assistant Vice President Operations, Jaime Perikly
Medical Director, Michael Siegel
Assistant Vice President Government Contracts, Nichole Mitchell
Assistant Vice President of Community Engagement, Cynthia Young
Vice President, Dave Boim
Medical Director, Harold Gooch

Associate Vice President Business Innovation, Kimberly Katsuyama
Executive Assistant To Sudhakar Gummadi Vice President, Chandara Toler
Vice President of Centralized Operations, Beth Richardson
Associate Vice President Sales, Rick Knickerbocker
Associate Vice President Medicare Sales, Brian Shasha
Assistant Vice President Marketing and Branding, Robert Pearson
MEDICAL DIRECTOR, Ann Bay
MEDICAL DIRECTOR, Latha R Shankar
ASSOCIATE VICE PRESIDENT, Mario J Garza
VICE PRESIDENT, Lekan J Lawal
DIRECTOR OF PHARMACY, Jacqueline Jacobi
ASSISTANT VICE PRESIDENT HEALTH PLAN OPERATIONS, Kathy Lyall
MEDICAL DIRECTOR, Arik Olson
Vice President of Network and Operations, Matt Wolf
Chairman, Dale B. Wolf, age 62
Auditors: Ernst & Young LLP

LOCATIONS

HQ: Molina Healthcare Inc
200 Oceangate, Suite 100, Long Beach, CA 90802
Phone: 562 435-3666   Fax: 562 437-1335
Web: www.molinahealthcare.com

2016 Membership by Health Plan

	% of total
Washington	17
California	16
Florida	13
Michigan	9
Texas	8
Ohio	8
Puerto Rico	8
New Mexico	6
Illinois	5
Utah	3
Wisconsin	3
South Carolina	3
New York	1
Total	**100**

PRODUCTS/OPERATIONS

2016 Revenues

	$ mil.	% of total
Health Plans	17,234	97
Medicaid Solutions	195	1
Other	353	2
Total	**17,782**	**100**

2016 Sales

	$ mil.	% of total
Premiums	16,392	92
Services	539	3
Premium tax revenue	468	3
Health insurer fee	345	2
Investments	38	-
Total	**17,782**	**100**

Selected Plans

Abria Health Plan
Molina Healthcare Plans by individual state subsidiaries
Molina Medicare Options (Medicare plan with prescription drug benefit)
Molina Medicare Options Plus (Medicare plan for dual-eligible individuals)

COMPETITORS

AMERIGROUP	HCSC
Aetna	HP Enterprise Group
Anthem	Health Net
Blue Cross Blue Shield of Michigan	Humana
CIGNA	Kaiser Foundation Health Plan
CNSI	L. A. Care Health Plan
Cambia Health	Premera Blue Cross

Solutions	Priority Health
Centene	Total Health Care
Community Health Group	UnitedHealth Group
Computer Sciences Corp.	WellCare Health Plans
	Xerox
Coventry Health Care	

HISTORICAL FINANCIALS

Company Type: Public

Income Statement

FYE: December 31

	REVENUE ($ mil.)	NET INCOME ($ mil.)	NET PROFIT MARGIN	EMPLOYEES
12/16	17,782	52	0.3%	21,000
12/15	14,178	143	1.0%	21,000
12/14	9,666	62	0.6%	10,500
12/13	6,588	52	0.8%	8,200
12/12	6,028	9	0.2%	5,800
Annual Growth	31.1%	51.8%	—	37.9%

2016 Year-End Financials

Debt ratio: 22.08%
Return on equity: 3.24%
Cash ($ mil.): 2,819
Current ratio: 1.31
Long-term debt ($ mil.): 1,173
No. of shares (mil.): 57
Dividends
   Yield: —
   Payout: —
Market value ($ mil.): 3,093

	STOCK PRICE ($) FY Close	P/E High/Low	PER SHARE ($) Earnings	Dividends	Book Value
12/16	54.26	73 49	0.92	0.00	28.93
12/15	60.13	30 18	2.58	0.00	27.80
12/14	53.53	41 25	1.29	0.00	20.32
12/13	34.75	35 22	1.13	0.00	19.47
12/12	27.06	167 85	0.21	0.00	16.73
Annual Growth	19.0%	— —	44.7%	—	14.7%

Molson Coors Brewing Co.

Auditors: PricewaterhouseCoopers LLP

LOCATIONS

HQ: Molson Coors Brewing Co.
1555 Notre Dame Street East, Montreal, Quebec H2L 2R5
Phone: 514 521-1786
Web: www.molsoncoors.com

HISTORICAL FINANCIALS

Company Type: Public

Income Statement

FYE: December 31

	REVENUE ($ mil.)	NET INCOME ($ mil.)	NET PROFIT MARGIN	EMPLOYEES
12/16	4,885	1,975	40.4%	17,400
12/15	3,567	359	10.1%	17,500
12/14	4,146	514	12.4%	17,400
12/13	4,206	567	13.5%	17,650
12/12	3,916	443	11.3%	18,700
Annual Growth	5.7%	45.3%	—	(1.8%)

2016 Year-End Financials

Debt ratio: 41.14%
Return on equity: 21.35%
Cash ($ mil.): 560
Current ratio: 0.69
Long-term debt ($ mil.): 11,387

No. of shares (mil.): 214
Dividends
Yield: 0.0%
Payout: 17.7%
Market value ($ mil.): 20,912

	STOCK PRICE ($) FY Close	P/E High/Low		PER SHARE ($) Earnings	Dividends	Book Value
12/16	97.31	12	9	9.26	1.64	53.13
12/15	93.92	49	34	1.93	1.64	38.17
12/14	74.52	28	18	2.76	1.48	42.39
12/13	56.15	18	13	3.08	1.28	46.90
12/12	42.71	19	16	2.44	1.28	43.89
Annual Growth	22.9%	—	—	39.6%	6.4%	4.9%

Mondelez International Inc

One of the world's largest snack companies Mondelez International owns a pantry of billion-dollar brands such as Cadbury and Milka chocolates; LU Nabisco and Oreo biscuits; Trident gum; and Tang powdered beverages. The company's portfolio includes global national and regional brands many of which are more than 100 years old. Biscuits (cookies crackers and salted snacks) and chocolate account for most of the company?s sales. Mondelez which operates worldwide generates most of its revenue outside the US.

HISTORY

The Kraft tale began in 1903 when James L. Kraft began delivering cheese to Chicago grocers. His four brothers joined in forming the J.L. Kraft & Bros. Company in 1909. By 1914 the company had opened a cheese factory and was selling cheese across the US. Kraft developed its first blended pasteurized cheese the following year.

Kraft went public in 1924; four years later it merged with Philadelphia cream-cheese maker Phoenix and also created Velveeta cheese spread. In 1930 Kraft was bought by National Dairy but its operations were kept separate. New and notable products included Miracle Whip salad dressing (1933) macaroni and cheese dinners (1937) and Parkay margarine (1940). In the decades that followed Kraft expanded into foreign markets.

National Dairy became Kraftco in 1969 and Kraft in 1976 hoping to benefit from its internationally known trademark. To diversify Kraft merged with Dart Industries in 1980; Dart's subsidiaries (including Duracell batteries) and Kraft kept separate operations. With non-food sales sagging Dart & Kraft split up in 1986. Kraft kept its original lines and added Duracell (sold 1988); the rest became Premark International. Tobacco giant Philip Morris Companies bought Kraft in 1988 for $12.9 billion. The next year Philip Morris joined Kraft with another unit General Foods.

General Foods began when Charles Post who marketed a wheat/bran health beverage established the Postum Cereal Co. in 1896; he expanded the firm with such cereals as Grape-Nuts and Post Toasties. The company went public in 1922. Postum bought the makers of Jell-O (1925) Baker's chocolate (1927) Log Cabin syrup (1927) and Maxwell House coffee (1928) and in 1929 it acquired control of General Foods (owned by frozen vegetable pioneer Clarence Birdseye) and changed its own name to General Foods.

Its later purchases included Perkins Products (Kool-Aid 1953) and Kohner Brothers (toys 1970). Most of its non-food lines proved unsuccessful and were sold throughout the years. General Foods bought Oscar Mayer the US's #1 hot dog maker in 1981. Philip Morris bought General Foods for $5.6 billion in 1985.

The 1989 combination of Kraft and General Foods (the units still ran independently) created the largest US food maker Kraft General Foods. In the 1990s Kraft General Foods lost market share in areas such as frozen vegetables and processed meat. It introduced "light" meat products and stopped making nearly 300 food items. In 1993 it bought RJR Nabisco's cold cereal business (Shredded Wheat) and sold its Breyers ice-cream business to Unilever.

To streamline management Philip Morris integrated Kraft and General Foods in 1995. Newly named Kraft Foods sold off lower-margin businesses including its bakery unit and its North American table spreads business. Kraft bought Del Monte's shelf-stable pudding business (1995) and Taco Bell's grocery line (1996). It also sold its Lender's bagels (1996) and Log Cabin (1997) lines.

Deciding to eat healthy in early 2000 Kraft bought Boca Burger (soy products) for about $100 million and Balance Bar (meal-replacement snack bars drink mixes and beverages) for $268 million.

In 2000 parent Philip Morris (which renamed itself the Altria Group in 2003) outbid Danone and Cadbury Schweppes (later Cadbury) and agreed to buy Nabisco Holdings. It completed the deal that December for $18.9 billion (including $4 billion in debt) and began integrating those operations into Kraft Foods and Kraft Foods International. Then Philip Morris created a holding company for the newly combined food operations under the Kraft Foods Inc. name in 2001. The original Kraft Foods was renamed Kraft Foods North America.

Kraft Foods International CEO Roger Deromedi was appointed co-CEO of the new holding company along with Betsy Holden. Kraft Foods Inc. was spun off by Altria in 2001 in what was the US's second-largest IPO ever at the time (behind AT&T Wireless now AT&T Mobility).

Kraft cut 7500 jobs in 2002 as a result of the integration of Nabisco operations paying out $373 million in cash for severance and related costs. That year Kraft was also part of a $9 million settlement of a federal lawsuit regarding the use of genetically modified corn in its taco shells.

A strategy to shed brands that do not fit with the rest of the company's portfolio led Kraft to sell Farley's and Sathers in 2002 to FS Partners which renamed the company Farley's & Sathers Candy Company. Later that year Kraft sold some of its candy brands (Now and Later Intense Fruit Chews and Mity Bite) to FS Partners.

In a move to combat the population's growing obesity problem Kraft said in 2003 that it intended to reduce the fat and sugar content and cut the portion sizes of its food products as well as cease marketing in schools.

Deromedi shared the CEO slot with co-CEO Betsy Holden until 2003 at which time Deromedi was named sole CEO. (Holden was demoted to a marketing slot in the company and eventually left Kraft in 2005.) During his tenure as CEO Deromide was dogged by Kraft's looming spinoff from Altria and struggled to improve company profits by selling off underperforming and non-core brands.

The company in 2004 formed an alliance with Dr. Arthur Agatston of low-carb South Beach Diet fame to use the South Beach Diet trademark on some of its products including cereal meal replacements cereal bars refrigerated sandwich wraps and frozen entrees and pizza.

As part of Deromedi's plan to refashion Kraft's product lineup in 2005 the company sold its Altoids breath mints LifeSavers and CremeSavers candies brands whose combined sales were at the time estimated to be about $660 million a year. Wm. Wrigley Jr. Company paid about $1.4 billion for the popular brands.

Despite his best efforts to improve the bottom line Deromedi was shown the door in 2006. He was replaced by Frito-Lay's CEO Irene Rosenfeld (a former top Kraft executive who was instrumental in the company's acquisition and integration of Nabisco). She returned to Kraft after being head of Pepsico's Frito-Lay from 2004 to 2006.

Kraft extricated itself from the haze of second-hand tobacco smoke when it was spun off from Altria in 2007. Having edged toward splitting from its former parent for years the separation relieved the food maker of many headaches. It freed Kraft from any tobacco-related liability that Altria may be found guilty of post-spinoff. It also eliminated a significant layer of management which made it easier for Kraft to improve its sluggish sales.

Focusing on sharpening its brand portfolio Kraft sold off its hot cereals business in 2007. The $200 million sale to B&G Foods included two old favorites Cream of Wheat and Cream of Rice. It also sold its Fruit2O and Veryfine juice brands and operations to Sunny Delight Beverages.

As part of its plan to offer new product categories Kraft entered the lucrative and popular pre-made salad market in 2007 with the introduction of South Beach Living brand chicken-salad kits.

Adding more on the expansion front Kraft bought the Spanish and Portuguese operations of United Biscuits that year; the deal returned to Kraft the rights to Nabisco trademarks such as Oreo Ritz and Chips Ahoy! in Europe the Middle East and Africa.

Kraft further expanded its foreign operations with its 2007 purchase of the cookie/biscuit business of Groupe Danone for some $7.6 billion. The purchase gave the company brands such as LU Petit Ecolier and Cr¨me Roul©e and made biscuits (cookies to us Yanks) the company's largest global business. It also added the Tiger and Prince brands to its Egyptian portfolio.

Billionaire Warren Buffett acquired a small percentage of Kraft in 2007 (less than 5% at the time) joining the also famously rich and famous-on-Wall Street corporate raiders Nelson Peltz (whose estimated Kraft holdings are 3%) and Carl Icahn (who owns about 3%) in ownership of the Velveeta vendor. Peltz and Ichan are typically activist investors making suggestions regarding company operations. Peltz has suggested that Kraft concentrate on its core brands as well as undertake divestitures to fund overseas expansion.

Kraft acquiesced to Peltz on one front agreeing with his investment operations collectively known as Trian Partners by adding two directors (selected by the company and supported by Trian) to its board in 2007. Kraft also signed a "standstill" agreement with Trian agreeing to support the board's full list of nominees at Kraft's next two annual meetings.

Late in 2007 Kraft announced the re-rebranding of its South Beach products from South Beach Diet to South Beach Living saying that it wanted to capture a more positive image for the products. That year the company also sold its Veryfine juice and Fruit2O water brands and operations to Sunny Delight company.

Kraft's 2008 sale of its slow-growing Post (Shredded Wheat Raisin Bran Honeycomb Grape-Nuts Pebbles and others) to Ralcorp a maker of private-label cereals and other foods is part of

Kraft's strategy to pare down its brand offerings and concentrate on high-yield products. Ralcorp paid some $1.6 billion in stock for the acquisition. Post is the #3 US cereal maker by sales after General Mills and Kellogg. Post brought in more than $1 billion for Kraft in both 2006 and 2007.

In February 2010 Kraft acquired Cadbury for about $19 billion of which 60% was cash and 40% was stock. A majority of Cadbury's shareholders (almost 72% according to Kraft) accepted the offer effectively making Cadbury part of Kraft.

In October 2012 Kraft Foods split into two companies: a global snacks business Mondelez International and Kraft Foods Group (formerly Kraft Foods North America).

EXECUTIVES

EVP Human Resources, Karen J. May, age 58
EVP and CFO, Brian T. Gladden, age 52, $900,000 total compensation
CEO and Director, Dirk Van de Put, age 55
EVP and President North America, Glen Walter
EVP Integrated Supply Chain, Daniel Myers, age 62
EVP and President Europe, Hubert Weber, age 54
EVP and General Counsel, Gerhard (Gerd) Pleuhs, age 60
EVP and President Asia Middle East & Africa, Maurizio Brusadelli, age 48
EVP Research Development and Quality, Robin S. (Rob) Hargrove, age 51
EVP and President Latin America, Alejandro R. Lorenzo, age 45
Executive Vice President President North America, Roberto Marques
Senior Vice President And Corporate Controller, Kim Jones
Vice President Human Resources Grocery Bu And Kraft University Relations, Ginny Packer
Senior Vice President Corporate Finance, James Kehoe
Chairman, Irene B. Rosenfeld, age 63
Auditors: PricewaterhouseCoopers LLP

LOCATIONS

HQ: Mondelez International Inc
Three Parkway North, Deerfield, IL 60015
Phone: 847 943-4000
Web: www.mondelezinternational.com

2016 Sales

	$ mil.	% of total
Europe	9,755	38
North America	6,960	27
AMEA	5,816	22
Latin America	3,392	13
Total	**25,923**	**100**

PRODUCTS/OPERATIONS

2016 Sales

	$ mil.	% of total
Biscuits	10,590	41
Chocolate	7,739	30
Gum & candy	3,947	15
Cheese & grocery	2,202	8
Beverages	1,445	6
Total	**25,923**	**100**

Selected Products and Brands

Biscuits
  Barni
  BelVita
  Chips Ahoy
  Club Social
  Oreo
  Tuc
Chocolate
  Cadbury
  Lacta
  Milka

Toblerone
Gum & Candy
  Chicklets
  Halls
  Stride
  Trident
Other
  Philadelphia (cream cheese)

COMPETITORS

Associated British Foods	Kraft Heinz
Campbell Soup	Lindt & Sprüngli
Clif Bar	Maple Leaf Foods
Coca-Cola	Mars Incorporated
Community Coffee	Michael Foods
Dairy Crest	Mott's
Dairy Farmers of America	Mrs. Fields
	Naked Juice
Dr Pepper Snapple Group	Nestlé
	Newman's Own
Fehr Foods	Otis Spunkmeyer
Frito-Lay	Parmalat Canada
Fromageries Bel	Pepperidge Farm
Galaxy Nutritional Foods	PowerBar
	Procter & Gamble
General Mills	Russell Hobbs
Hershey	Smucker
Kellogg	Snapple
Kellogg U.S. Snacks	Snyder's-Lance
Kerry Group	Unilever PLC
Keurig Green Mountain	Voortman Cookies
	WhiteWave

HISTORICAL FINANCIALS
Company Type: Public

Income Statement
FYE: December 31

	REVENUE ($ mil.)	NET INCOME ($ mil.)	NET PROFIT MARGIN	EMPLOYEES
12/17	25,896	2,922	11.3%	90,000
12/16	25,923	1,659	6.4%	90,000
12/15	29,636	7,267	24.5%	99,000
12/14	34,244	2,184	6.4%	104,000
12/13	35,299	3,915	11.1%	107,000
Annual Growth	**(7.5%)**	**(7.1%)**		**(4.2%)**

2017 Year-End Financials

Debt ratio: 27.97%
Return on equity: 11.40%
Cash ($ mil.): 761
Current ratio: 0.48
Long-term debt ($ mil.): 12,972

No. of shares (mil.): 1,488
Dividends
  Yield: 0.0%
  Payout: 42.9%
Market value ($ mil.): 63,692

	STOCK PRICE ($) FY Close	P/E High/Low	PER SHARE ($) Earnings	Dividends	Book Value
12/17	42.80	24 20	1.91	0.82	17.55
12/16	44.33	43 34	1.05	0.72	16.46
12/15	44.84	10 8	4.49	0.64	17.73
12/14	36.33	30 25	1.28	0.58	16.68
12/13	35.30	16 12	2.19	0.54	18.98
Annual Growth	**4.9%**	— —	**(3.4%)**	**11.0%**	**(1.9%)**

MONOGRAM RESIDENTIAL TRUST, INC.

Auditors: DELOITTE & TOUCHE LLP DALLAS

LOCATIONS

HQ: MONOGRAM RESIDENTIAL TRUST, INC.
  5800 GRAN PKWY STE 1000, PLANO, TX 75024
Phone: 469 250-5500
Web: WWW.MONOGRAMRES.COM

HISTORICAL FINANCIALS
Company Type: Private

Income Statement
FYE: December 31

	ASSETS ($ mil.)	NET INCOME ($ mil.)	INCOME AS % OF ASSETS	EMPLOYEES
12/16	3,200	7	0.2%	370
12/15	3,283	66	2.0%	—
12/13	2,898	32	1.1%	—
12/12	2,744	(30)		—
Annual Growth	**3.9%**	—	—	—

2016 Year-End Financials

Debt ratio: —
Return on equity: 2.80%
Cash ($ mil.): 74
Current ratio: —
Long-term debt ($ mil.): —

Dividends
  Yield: —
  Payout: —
Market value ($ mil.): —

Monsanto Co

Monsanto is something of a growth stalk in helping farmers grow corn and other crops. The company applies its biotechnology and genomics know-how to develop seeds and herbicides to help farmers produce corn (43% of revenue) cotton oilseeds and vegetables. It produces genetically altered seeds that tolerate Roundup (its flagship product and the world's #1 herbicide) and resist bugs. The company also produces Asgrow DEKALB Deltapine and Seminis seeds. About 60% of sales are in the US. Monsanto agreed to be bought by Bayer in a landmark $66 billion deal reached in September 2016.

HISTORY

Realizing he had only a German source for saccharin and foreseeing growing US demand for the product in 1901 drug firm buyer John Queeny spent $5000 to found Monsanto Chemical Works (using his wife's maiden name) to make saccharin in St. Louis. Monsanto soon added caffeine vanillin antiseptic phenol and aspirin; it went public in 1927.

Queeny's son Edgar became president in 1928. He branched out into rubber additives and plastics through acquisitions. In 1943 Monsanto began making styrene monomer used to produce the US Army's first synthetic rubber tires.

Monsanto and American Viscose joined forces to form synthetic-fiber firm Chemstrand in 1949

(Monsanto bought it in 1961). Chemstrand also developed Acrilan fibers (1952) and the synthetic surface AstroTurf (first used commercially in Houston's Astrodome 1966). In 1954 Monsanto and Bayer formed a joint venture to develop urethane foams (sold to Bayer 1967). Monsanto debuted the herbicides Lasso (1969) and Roundup (1973) and stopped making saccharin in 1972.

Monsanto bought drugmaker G. D. Searle (founded 1868) in 1985 inheriting lawsuits relating to its Copper-7 contraceptive IUD. It also got the rights to artificial sweetener aspartame (NutraSweet). In 1993 Monsanto bought Chevron's Ortho lawn and garden business for $416 million. It launched its first biotech product (to increase milk yields) the next year.

Searle's Robert Shapiro became CEO in 1995 and set out to create genetically altered foods. That year Monsanto bought Merck's specialty chemicals unit Syntex (birth-control pills) and 50% of biotech firm Calgene (it bought the rest in 1997).

In 1996 Monsanto bought a stake in DEKALB Genetics (it bought the rest in 1998) and introduced a Roundup-tolerant soybean. It bought Holden's Foundation Seeds (corn seed) in 1997 and spun off chemicals unit Solutia. Purchases in 1998 included the seed business of Cargill and the wheat-breeding business of Unilever (UK). It also said it would buy #1 cottonseed producer Delta and Pine Land but that deal was delayed by regulators and dropped altogether in 1999.

After calling off a $35 million merger with drugmaker American Home Products in 1998 Monsanto laid off workers and sold Ortho to The Scotts Company (now Scotts Miracle-Gro).

In 1999 Monsanto launched Celebrex an arthritis drug that set new prescription records. Meanwhile concerns about genetically modified foods prompted bans in the UK and Brazil (and later in other countries). Negative public reaction led Monsanto to stop developing seeds with a terminator gene that rendered them sterile.

To pay for acquisitions Monsanto sold its pharmaceutical intermediates business to Great Lakes Chemical (now Chemtura) and its algins (derived from algae) food ingredients business to International Specialty Products. Late in 1999 activists stepped up protests over bioengineered crops and lawyers filed a class-action suit alleging inadequate testing and unfair price influence.

Monsanto merged with Pharmacia & Upjohn in 2000 and the new entity Pharmacia Corporation (with Monsanto now a wholly owned subsidiary) set about restructuring selling Monsanto's NutraSweet Equal and Canderel sweeteners (in part to a group led by Michael Dell) as well as its biogums (food texturing and processing) business. The "new" Monsanto is focused solely on using advanced technology to grow better crops — the pharmaceutical and other operations of the old Monsanto have been assumed by Pharmacia. Consumer apprehension over so-called "Frankenfoods" and the like prompted Pharmacia to spin off about 15% of Monsanto to the public in 2000; the company spun off the remainder as a dividend to shareholders in 2002.

After two disappointing years of results in December 2002 CEO Hendrik Verfaillie resigned and chairman Frank AtLee assumed the position. In late May 2003 COO Hugh Grant was named president and CEO with AtLee returning to chair the board of directors. Less than a month later Grant initiated a reorganization of Monsanto placing focus on growing the company's seed business and redefining its goals and strategies for public acceptance of biotechnology. The company elected Grant chairman at its annual meeting in October of that year with AtLee staying on the board as a director.

The company formed American Seeds Inc. in 2004 as a holding company that would acquire and build up regional seed businesses. First on its plate was Indiana seed company Channel Bio Corp. which Monsanto bought for $120 million. Channel has three main lines of seed — Crow's Hybrid Corn Company Midwest Genetics Seed Genetics Inc. and Wilson Seeds — and 2% of the US corn seed market. Monsanto already had 14% of that market. It added Nebraskan corn-seed producer NC Hybrids in 2005 at a price of $40 million.

In a more significant move Monsanto announced in the spring of 2005 that it had acquired fruit and vegetable seed maker Seminis for about $1.4 billion in cash and assumed debt. Seminis is among the world's largest fruit and vegetable seed producers with about 3500 varieties of seed sold in more than 150 countries. It continues as a wholly owned subsidiary of Monsanto with its own management remaining in place. The deal furthered the company's recent emphasis on growing its seeds business and changing its focus from agricultural chemicals.

Many analysts saw the move for Seminis as an indication Monsanto was trying to broaden its seed portfolio to give the company something to balance out its biotech business. Perhaps but Monsanto isn't content with the size of its GM seed business either. Later in 2005 the company purchased the cotton business of Emergent Genetics for $300 million. That business gives Monsanto a foothold in the cotton seed business similar to its existing corn and soybean product lines. Emergent ranked among the top three cotton seed companies with 12% of the market.

In 2010 Monsanto completed the purchase of the Chesterfield Village Research Center located in Chesterfield Missouri from Pfizer. In 2011 the company acquired Beeologics a start-up company engaged in the R&D of biological tools to provide targeted pest and disease control (with a focus on bee health).

In January 2013 Monsanto acquired select assets of privately-held Agradis a California firm focused on developing and commercializing products to improve crop production using new scientific and technology advances in genomics.

EXECUTIVES

EVP and CTO, Robert T. Fraley, age 64, $662,405 total compensation

Chairman and CEO, Hugh Grant, age 58, $1,602,156 total compensation

EVP Human Resources, Steven C. Mizell, age 57

President and COO, Brett D. Begemann, age 56, $813,600 total compensation

EVP Global Strategy, Kerry J. Preete, age 57

EVP Secretary and General Counsel, David F. Snively, age 63, $610,200 total compensation

SVP and CFO, Pierre Courduroux, age 52, $610,200 total compensation

VP and President and COO Climate Corporation, Michael K. Stern, age 55

Vice President of Global Technology transfer, Stefan Bledig

Vice President of Finance, Susie Cyr

Vice President Of Commercial Operations, Lisa Safarian

Vice President Information Technology Enterprise Services, Aldo Noseda

Executive Vice President, Michael Scallan

National Account Manager, Marty Krebs

Vice President US Technology Development, Philip Miller

Vice President and General Auditor, Nanci Daesch

Vice President, Natalie Dinicola

VP Supply Chain, Mark Deadwyler

Vice President of External Affairs, Jerry Glover

Senior Vice President Government Affairs, Steven Engeberg

Vice President Monsanto, Caroline Mulia

Vice President, Francisco Diaz

Vice President Human Resources, Nancy Wolfe

Vice President Marketing, Tom Wilson

Vice President Technology, Ganesh Kishore

Vice President, Jayme Collins

Vice President of Biotechnology, Steve Schaefer

Vice President Global Talent Management Hrit Analytics And Benefits, Ray Kleeman

GOVERNMENT RELATIONS, Gary Kajander

Vice President and Treasurer, Duraiswami Narain

Assistant Secretary, Jennifer L Woods

Secretary, Natalia Voruz

Assistant Treasurer, Pam Moench

Board Member, Ray Drachenberg

ABM, William Girten

Auditors: DELOITTE & TOUCHE LLP

LOCATIONS

HQ: Monsanto Co
800 North Lindbergh Blvd., St. Louis, MO 63167
Phone: 314 694-1000   **Fax:** 314 694-1057
Web: www.monsanto.com

2016 Sales

	$ mil.	% of total
US	8,008	59
Europe & Africa	1,536	11
Brazil	1,437	11
Argentina	856	6
Canada	619	5
Asia/Pacific	483	4
Mexico	436	3
Other	127	1
Total	**13,502**	**100**

PRODUCTS/OPERATIONS

2016 Sales

	$ mil.	% of total
Seeds & genomics		
Corn seed & traits	5,825	43
Soybean seed & traits	2,162	16
Vegetable seeds	801	6
Cotton seed & traits	440	3
Other crop seed & traits	760	6
Agricultural productivity	3,514	26
Total	**13,502**	**100**

Selected Brands

Crop protection
  Bullet
  Degree Brands
  Field Master
  Harness Brands
  INTRRO
  Landmaster II
  Lariat
  Maverick
  Micro-Tech
  PARRLAY
  Roundup PowerMAX
  Roundup WeatherMAX
  Roundup with CROPSHIELD Formulas
  RT 3
Industrial turf and ornamental
  AquaMaster
  Campaign
  Certainty Turf Herbicide
  Outrider
  QuikPRO
  Roundup Original MAX
  Roundup Pro
  Roundup ProConcentrate
  Roundup ProDry
Input traits
  Bollgard II
  Bollgard II Cotton with Roundup Ready Flex
  Roundup Ready Canola
  Roundup Ready Corn 2
  Roundup Ready Flex Cotton
  Roundup Ready Soybeans
  YieldGard Corn Borer

YieldGard Plus
YieldGard Plus with Roundup Ready Corn 2
YieldGard Rootworm
YieldGard Rootworm with Roundup Ready Corn 2
YieldGard VT
Output traits
　Processor Preferred
　High Extractable Corn
　I-85 Program
　Vistive
Seed
　Asgrow
　DEKALB
　Interstate Seed
　Deltapine
　NC Hybrid

Selected Subsidiaries

Alellyx S.A.
American Seeds LLC
Asgrow Seed Company LLC
CanaVialis S.A. (Brazil)
Corn States LLC
Seminis Vegetable Seeds Inc.
WestBred LLC

COMPETITORS

ADM	Nippon Soda
BASF SE	Origin Agritech
Bayer CropScience	Pfister Hybrid Corn
Dow AgroSciences	Pioneer Hi-Bred
DuPont Agriculture	Sakata Seed
FMC	Scotts Miracle-Gro
GROWMARK	Syngenta
NC Hybrids	Syngenta Seeds

HISTORICAL FINANCIALS

Company Type: Public

Income Statement

FYE: August 31

	REVENUE ($ mil.)	NET INCOME ($ mil.)	NET PROFIT MARGIN	EMPLOYEES
08/17	14,640	2,260	15.4%	23,300
08/16	13,502	1,336	9.9%	24,100
08/15	15,001	2,314	15.4%	25,500
08/14	15,855	2,740	17.3%	27,000
08/13	14,861	2,482	16.7%	26,200
Annual Growth	(0.4%)	(2.3%)	—	(2.9%)

2017 Year-End Financials

Debt ratio: 38.08%
Return on equity: 41.20%
Cash ($ mil.): 1,856
Current ratio: 1.35
Long-term debt ($ mil.): 7,254

No. of shares (mil.): 439
Dividends
Yield: 1.8%
Payout: 46.4%
Market value ($ mil.): 51,519

	STOCK PRICE ($) FY Close	P/E High/Low	PER SHARE ($) Earnings	Dividends	Book Value
08/17	117.20	23　19	5.09	2.16	14.65
08/16	106.50	37　28	2.99	2.16	10.36
08/15	97.65	26　18	4.81	1.96	14.94
08/14	115.65	24　19	5.22	1.72	16.23
08/13	97.89	23　18	4.60	1.50	23.74
Annual Growth	4.6%	—　—	2.6%	9.5%	(11.4%)

Morgan Stanley

One of the world's top investment banks Morgan Stanley serves up a smorgasbord of financial services. It offers everything from advising corporate clients on mergers & acquisitions to raising capital for large companies to managing real estate investments for wealthy individuals. It boasts one of the largest financial advisor networks which works with clients to pursue their investment goals. Morgan Stanley has over $400 billion of assets under management. Morgan Stanley is a global enterprise with a presence in more than 40 nations serving corporate institutional government and individual clients.

HISTORY

In 1934 the Glass-Steagall Act required the J. P. Morgan bank (now part of JPMorgan Chase & Co.) to sell its securities-related activities. The next year Henry Morgan Harold Stanley and others established Morgan Stanley as an investment bank. Capitalizing on old ties to major corporations the firm handled $1 billion in issues its first year. By 1941 when it joined the NYSE it had managed 25% of all bond issues underwritten since Glass-Steagall took effect.

In the 1950s Morgan Stanley was known for handling large issues alone. Clients included General Motors U.S. Steel General Electric and DuPont. The firm avoided the merger wave of the 1960s but in the early 1970s it formed Wall Street's first mergers and acquisitions (M&A) department. In 1974 Morgan Stanley handled its first hostile takeover International Nickel's (now Vale Inco) buy of ESB the world's #1 battery maker.

Morgan Stanley went public in 1986. It escaped the carnage of the 1987 crash but a lawsuit arising from investor dissatisfaction with its M&A and LBO activities during that period lasted well into the 1990s.

By 1994 it was talking to possible merger mates including Dean Witter and finally merged with Dean Witter Discover in 1997 creating Morgan Stanley Dean Witter & Co. The San Francisco brokerage founded by Dean Witter in 1924 had remained regional for 40 years serving wealthy customers. In 1977 the firm merged with Reynolds Securities another regional retail brokerage started by Richard Reynolds Jr. the son of the founder of Reynolds Metals (now part of Alcoa) and grandnephew of the founder of R.J. Reynolds Tobacco. The new company Dean Witter Reynolds became the #2 US brokerage after Merrill Lynch and one of the top 10 US underwriters.

Dean Witter needed capital in the early 1980s and sold itself to Sears which hoped to turn it into a financial Allstate. Sears put in a retail-oriented management team and tried to shoehorn Dean Witter into in-store brokerages. Sears' indifference to the investment side hobbled operations.

The Discover card introduced by Sears and Dean Witter in 1986 was a hit but by the late 1980s it was obvious Sears would never be a financial giant. The retailer spun off Allstate Insurance and the newly renamed Dean Witter Discover in 1993.

Amazingly all but six of Morgan Stanley's 3700 World Trade Center employees survived the September 11 2001 terrorist attack on the towers. Hoping to capitalize on deregulations and privatizations in Europe as well as the rise of the individual investor Morgan Stanley acquired UK-based private bank Quilter & Co. in 2001 (then later sold it to Citigroup in 2006). Also that year the firm dropped the public use of "Dean Witter" in 2001 for promotional purposes and then dropped it completely in 2002.

When regulatory scrutiny fell on the mutual fund industry Morgan Stanley was charged with failing to adequately disclose the incentives its brokers and managers received for selling certain funds. In 2003 the firm agreed to pay a $50 million fine and adopt a "plain English" approach to informing investors about its product fees and broker compensation.

In mid-2004 the firm agreed to pay $54 million to settle a sex discrimination lawsuit filed on behalf of more than 300 female employees who claimed they were denied promotions and salary raises.

Unhappy with the firm's performance eight former Morgan Stanley executives (dubbed the Group of Eight) publicly called for the ouster of chairman and CEO Philip Purcell in 2005; Purcell was replaced by John Mack. That year a jury ordered Morgan Stanley to pay more than $1.5 billion to Ronald Perelman now the chairman of cosmetics giant Revlon. (Morgan Stanley in 2003 rejected an offer from Perelman to settle the dispute for $20 million.) Perelman contended that Morgan Stanley withheld knowledge of massive accounting fraud at appliance maker Sunbeam when he sold his camping gear firm Coleman to that company for some $1.5 billion in cash and stock in 1998; a Florida appeals court overturned the verdict in 2007.

In 2006 the firm agreed to pay a $15 million fine to settle charges that it was uncooperative and did not produce documents during investigations performed by the Securities and Exchange Commission (SEC). In addition the company settled charges (while not pleading guilty) that it falsely claimed to arbitration claimants and regulators that it lost e-mails on September 11 2001; it agreed to pay $12.5 million in 2007.

Morgan Stanley had been one of the largest credit card issuers through Discover Financial Services. However it spun those operations off in 2007. Discover was the last remnant of the company's merger with the venerable Dean Witter at the end of the previous century.

After the company wrote down more than $9 billion in mortgage-related investments in 2007 it was compelled to sell part of itself to an investment arm of the Chinese government China Investment Corp. for some $5 billion in order to raise capital. The equity units included in the deal could be converted to a nearly 10% stake in Morgan Stanley.

As its traditional investment banking business faced hard times Morgan Stanley increasingly focused on private equity investing. In 2008 the company's Infrastructure unit teamed up with Ontario Teachers' Pension Plan to acquire electrical services provider SAESA the Chilean subsidiary of Public Service Enterprise Group. In 2007 Morgan Stanley teamed up with Apax Partners Worldwide to buy insurance brokerage Hub International. The previous year Morgan Stanley acquired TransMontaigne a Denver-based oil and gas transportation company (sold 2014) and Heidmar Group a Connecticut-based marine transportation and logistics firm (it later sold Heidmar's lightering business).

In order to shore up the big banks during the financial crisis the US government invested $250 billion in healthy banks to help them jumpstart their operations; Morgan Stanley received about $10 billion of that. The cash — part of the $700 billion taxpayer-fueled bailout in 2008 — came with several stipulations including restrictions on executive pay and the order to use the funds not hoard them. Deciding it didn't need the money that badly Morgan Stanley repaid the $10 billion in 2009. The company announced in late 2008 that it would cut its staff by 10% in an effort to reduce costs.

Also in 2008 the Federal Reserve mandated that Morgan Stanley and Goldman Sachs (the other remaining independent bulge-bracket US investment bank) convert to a bank holding company structure. The structure subjected them to tighter scrutiny but enabled them to acquire a commercial bank to shore up their balance sheets if need be. The move came after rivals Bear Stearns Merrill Lynch and Lehman Brothers were either acquired or went bankrupt.

In 2009 Morgan Stanley sold its remaining stake in investment analysis and market index firm MSCI to raise capital. The deal brought the company some $625 million.

Morgan Stanley also shook up its top leadership. John Mack stepped down as CEO in early 2010; he remained chairman but stepped down at the end of 2011. James Gorman the firm's co-president succeeded Mack at the helm of the company and as chairman. The change marked a significant shift for Morgan Stanley as it scaled back its operations in riskier proprietary trading.

Morgan Stanley's Asian operations got a boost in 2011 when regulators in China gave the go-ahead for the company to begin establishing operations there. It launched a joint securities venture with China Fortune Securities later that year; Morgan Stanley owns a third of the business the maximum stake allowed. China is a strategic market for growth for the company as are the emerging economies of Brazil and India.

The company in 2012 sold its Quilter wealth management division which serves the UK's mass-wealth market to private equity firm Bridgepoint Capital to focus on its wealthiest clients and institutional investors.

EXECUTIVES

Chairman and CEO, James P. Gorman, age 59, $1,500,000 total compensation
Head of Global Capital Markets, Franck Petitgas
President, Colm Kelleher, age 60, $1,666,041 total compensation
Co-Head Wealth Management, Andy Saperstein
Global Head Sales and Trading, Ted Pick
EVP and CFO, Jonathan Pruzan, age 49, $1,000,000 total compensation
EVP and Chief Risk Officer, Keishi Hotsuki, age 54
Global Co-Head Investment Banking, Mark Eichorn
CEO Morgan Stanley International and Head Europe Middle East and Africa, Robert Rooney
COO Institutional Securities, Clare Woodman
Head Investment Management, Daniel A. (Dan) Simkowitz, $1,000,000 total compensation
Vice President Private Wealth, Pamela Lawrence
Senior Vice President Financial Advisor, Karen Varnhagen
First Vice President, Gwen Cohen
Vice President Wealth Manageme, Timothy Ely
Vice President Capital Introdu, Anne Loughlin
Vice President Wealth Advisor, Scott Tomoda
Vice President, Markus Maier
Vice President, Tom Anderson
Vice President Financial Advisor, Michael Souza
Senior Vice President Senior Consultant, David Esham
Vice President Of Learning and Development, Theresa Dinh
Vice President Investment Bank, Aden Pavkov
Vice President, Hoi Chan
Senior Vice President Investme, Todd Forman
Vice President Of Data Centers, Christopher Mcdermott
Vice President In Senior Relat, Tiffany Fung
Vice President Financial Advisor Retirement Planni, Bruce Donaghy
Vice President, Micah Chalmer
Vice President, Desiree Ally
Senior Vice President Investments; Financial Advisor, Douglas Ruby
Vice President Morgan Stanley Operations Risk And, Michelle Cuilla
Vice President Compliance, Andrew Lipton
Senior Vice President And Senior Financial Advisor, Lee Corey
Senior Vice President Wealth, Michael Delvecchio
Vice President, Darrin Frankel
Vice President Senior Investme, Anthony David
Senior Vice President Greater, Robert Meredith
Senior Vice President Of Client Services Nationa, Richard French
Senior Vice President Portfolio Manager, Andrew Zimmerman
Senior Vice President Financial Advisor, Ralph Colo
Vice President And Financial Advisor, Charles Walz
Vice President Of Information Technology Enterpris, Peter Galea
Senior Vice President, John Grazioli
Vice President, Daniel Nito
Vice President, Amy May
First Vice President, Bryan Welbaum
Vice President Technology Risk, Marc Hersh
Vice President Investments, Sandra Moyer
Vice President, Geoffrey Burke
Vice President, Ruben Badar
Vice President, Duncan Fudge
Vice President, Andy Jaglall
National Account Manager, Rosie Bailey
Vice President, John Schlegel
Vice President Information Technology, Anne Egan
First Vice President, Thomas Niles
Senior Vice President And Financial Advisor, Anthony Brock
Vice President Information Technology Department, Francis Rial
Vice President and Financial Advisor, Roger Richard
Vice President Head Of Engineering, Philip O'Dwyer
Vice President Associate Branch Manager Financial, Lisa Kittner
Vice President, Thomas Hartl
First Vice President, Ronald Phelps
Vice President Enterprise Infrastructure And Tech And Info Risk And Qapm, Zhenqin Li
Vice President Information Technology, Richard Wong
First Vice President, John Crowley
Vice President Information Technology, Alex Raykis
Vice President, Wendy Lowe
Vice President In Charge Of European Media And Internet, Fausto Zanetton
Vice President, Andrew Mento
Vice President Risk And Margins, Manu Agarwal
Vice President Network, Nathan Alexander
Senior Vice President, Adam Schur
Certified Wealth Strategist Vice President Morgan Stanley Smith Barney, Brian Weinkle
Vice President, Donny Chia
Vice President And Certified Financial Planner, Paul Ward
Vice President, David Cohen
Vice President Finance, Philip Dur
First Vice President Morgan Stanley Smith Barney, Leo Robinson
Vice Chairman, Thomas R. (Tom) Nides, age 56
Board Member, Larry Ferdig
Auditors: Deloitte & Touche LLP

LOCATIONS

HQ: Morgan Stanley
1585 Broadway, New York, NY 10036
Phone: 212 761-4000
Web: www.morganstanley.com

2016 Sales

	% of total
Americas	74
EMEA	14
Asia-Pacific	12
Total	**100**

PRODUCTS/OPERATIONS

2016 Sales

	$ mil.	% of total
Interest income	7,016	19
Non-interest income		
Asset management distribution and administration fees	10,697	28
Trading	10,209	27
Investment banking	4,933	13
Commission and fees	4,109	11
Investments	160	0
Others	825	2
Total	**37,949**	**100**

2016 Sales

	% of total
Institutional Securities	50
Wealth Management	44
Investment Management	6
Total	**100**

COMPETITORS

Brown Brothers Harriman	MF Global
CIBC	Marsh & McLennan
Charles Schwab	Merrill Lynch
Citigroup	Nomura Securities
Citigroup Global Markets	Oppenheimer Holdings
Deutsche Bank	Raymond James Financial
FMR	State Street
Franklin Templeton	T. Rowe Price
Goldman Sachs	TD Bank
JPMorgan Chase	UBS
Lehman Brothers	Wells Fargo Securities

HISTORICAL FINANCIALS

Company Type: Public

Income Statement

FYE: December 31

	ASSETS ($ mil.)	NET INCOME ($ mil.)	INCOME AS % OF ASSETS	EMPLOYEES
12/16	814,949	5,979	0.7%	55,311
12/15	787,465	6,127	0.8%	56,218
12/14	801,510	3,467	0.4%	55,802
12/13	832,702	2,932	0.4%	55,794
12/12	780,960	68	0.0%	57,061
Annual Growth	**1.1%**	**206.2%**	**—**	**(0.8%)**

2016 Year-End Financials

Debt ratio: 20.22%
Return on equity: 7.89%
Cash ($ mil.): 43,381
Current ratio: —
Long-term debt ($ mil.): —
No. of shares (mil.): 1,852
Dividends
Yield: 0.0%
Payout: 23.9%
Market value ($ mil.): 78,267

	STOCK PRICE ($) FY Close	P/E High/Low		PER SHARE ($) Earnings	Dividends	Book Value
12/16	42.25	15	7	2.92	0.70	41.05
12/15	31.81	14	10	2.90	0.55	39.16
12/14	38.80	24	17	1.60	0.35	36.34
12/13	31.36	23	14	1.36	0.20	33.89
12/12	19.12	—	—	(0.02)	0.20	31.46
Annual Growth	**21.9%**		**—**	**—**	**36.8%**	**6.9%**

Mosaic Co (The)

Big pieces of the global agricultural chemical industry come together to form The Mosaic Company. It ranks as one of the world's largest producers of phosphate and potash both used as crop nutrition and as input to animal feed. In North America it accounts for 75% of the region?s annual phosphate production and nearly 40% of potash production. In the rest of the world it still holds a significant market share about 15% of phosphate and 12% of potash production. The raw materials of its products are mined from location in Canada and the US. Mosaic?s sales are about equally split between North America and the rest of the world.

EXECUTIVES

EVP and CFO, Richard L. (Rich) Mack, age 49, $624,000 total compensation
President and CEO, James (Joc) O'Rourke, age 56, $893,833 total compensation
SVP Phosphates, Walter F. (Walt) Precourt, age 52
SVP Potash, Bruce Bodine
Chairman, Robert L. Lumpkins, age 73
Auditors: KPMG LLP

LOCATIONS

HQ: Mosaic Co (The)
3033 Campus Drive, Suite E490, Plymouth, MN 55441
Phone: 800 918-8270   **Fax:** 763 577-2990
Web: www.mosaicco.com

2015 Sales

	% of total
United States	37
Brazil	24
Canpotex	12
Canada	8
India	4
others regions	15
Total	**100**

PRODUCTS/OPERATIONS

2015 Sales

	$ mil.	% of total
Phosphates	3,920	44
Potash	2,437	28
International distribution	2,503	28
Elimination	32	-
Total	**8,895**	**100**

Premium Crop Nutrients

Premium Crop Nutrients
MicroEssentials®; SZ;
MicroEssentials®; S15;
MicroEssentials®; S10;
K-Mag®; Granular
K-Mag®; Premium
K-Mag®; Special Standard
K-Mag®; Standard
Pegasus®; Fine
Pegasus®; Granular
Potash
White Standard 0-0-62
Red Granular 0-0-60
Red Standard 0-0-60
Crystal Granular 0-0-60
Crystal Turf 150
Phosphates
Diammonium Phosphate (DAP) 18-46-0
Monoammonium Phosphate (MAP) 11-52-0
Powdered MAP
Feed Ingredients
Biofos®;
Dyna-K®;
Dynamate®;
Dyna-K White®;
Nexfos®;
Industrial Products
FSA Products
Hydrofluorosilicic Acid (FSA or HFS)
Potash Products
White Fine 0-0-62
White Granular 0-0-62
White Industrial High Quality
White Industrial Special
Red Standard 0-0-60

COMPETITORS

Arab Potash	Potash Corp
CF Industries	Sinofert
Israel Chemicals	Uralkali
K+S	

HISTORICAL FINANCIALS

Company Type: Public

Income Statement

FYE: December 31

	REVENUE ($ mil.)	NET INCOME ($ mil.)	NET PROFIT MARGIN	EMPLOYEES
12/16	7,162	297	4.2%	8,700
12/15	8,895	1,000	11.2%	8,900
12/14	9,055	1,028	11.4%	9,100
12/13*	4,765	340	7.1%	8,200
05/13	9,974	1,888	18.9%	8,400
Annual Growth	**(7.9%)**	**(37.0%)**	**—**	**0.9%**

*Fiscal year change

2016 Year-End Financials

Debt ratio: 22.67%	No. of shares (mil.): 350
Return on equity: 3.11%	Dividends
Cash ($ mil.): 673	Yield: 0.0%
Current ratio: 2.07	Payout: 129.4%
Long-term debt ($ mil.): 3,779	Market value ($ mil.): 10,272

	STOCK PRICE ($) FY Close	P/E High/Low		PER SHARE ($) Earnings	Dividends	Book Value
12/16	29.33	37	26	0.85	1.10	27.37
12/15	27.59	19	10	2.78	1.08	27.04
12/14	45.65	19	15	2.68	1.00	29.12
12/13*	47.27	77	51	0.80	1.00	26.53
05/13	60.82	14	10	4.42	1.00	31.53
Annual Growth	**(16.7%)**		**—**	**(33.8%)**	**2.4%**	**(3.5%)**

*Fiscal year change

Motorola Solutions Inc.

"Do you copy?" and "Roger that" might be snippets of conversation heard over two-way radios and other devices made by Motorola Solutions. The company's radios and wireless broadband products are used by government public safety and first-responder agencies for communications and personnel deployment. Commercial and industrial customers use products from Motorola to stay in touch in mobile work forces. Besides two-way radios the company makes vehicle-mounted radios body cameras headsets and other devices and develops software systems to connect them. Some 60% of sales are to customers in the US. Motorola Solutions goes back to the late 1920s when the company made radios for police cars.

Operations

Motorola's Products segment offers a communications portfolio of infrastructure devices accessories software and systems and accounts for about 60% of sales. Among the company?s device offerings are two-way portable radios and vehicle-mounted radios microphones batteries earpieces headsets and software. In its Systems unit (part of Products) Motorola also offers radio network and central processing software base stations consoles and repeaters.

The Services segment which accounts for the remainder of sales is composed of several units. Integration services offers implementation and integration of systems devices software and applications. Managed & Support services includes repair

technical support and hardware maintenance. iDEN (Integrated Digital Enhanced Network) services is the company?s proprietary push-to-talk technology.

Geographic Reach

Motorola Solutions operates throughout the world but the US is its biggest market accounting for about 60% of sales. The UK the only other single geographic market reported by the company contributes about 10% of sales. Motorola runs major facilities for manufacturing and distribution in the US and Germany. The company outsources about a quarter of its manufacturing to third-parties outside the US.

Sales and Marketing

Motorola Solutions sells through an in-house sales operation that directly approaches its largest accounts and through channel partners for other accounts. Primary customers are government public safety first-responder agencies and municipalities. Other important customers are commercial and industrial companies that operate private communications networks and manage mobile work forces.

Motorola?s biggest customers are the US federal government and the Home Office of the UK which each account for just under 10% of sales.

Financial Performance

Motorola Solutions? revenue rose 6% to about $6 billion in 2016 from 2015. The company reported growth in North America Europe and the Asia/Pacific region but lower sales in Latin America. Stronger sales in Europe which boosted the region?s share of revenue to 21% in 2016 from 15% in 2015 were fueled by the 2016 acquisition of Guardian Digital Communications Holdings Limited (GDCL) in the UK. Sales in North America and Asia/Pacific grew on both Services and Products sales. Lower Latin America sales in Products and Services were blamed on the region?s general economy.

The company?s profit slid about 8% to $560 million in 2016 from the year before. It reported a higher operating profit in 2016 with help from the GDCL deal but that was undercut by higher expenses for headcount reductions and charges for reorganization including building and aircraft impairment.

Cash from operations bumped up to $1.2 billion in 2016 from $1 billion in 2015 on earnings from continuing operations but offset by higher employee incentive compensation payments.

Strategy

Motorola Solutions is moving to expand its recurring revenue stream from managed and support services and infrastructure- and software-as-a-service offerings. Recurring revenue grew to about a quarter of revenue in 2016 from about 10% several years go. The company has expanded managed services to include hosting software applications which helps customers save on buying and running their own software.

On the acquisition side the deal for Guardian Digital Communications Holdings Limited expanded Motorola?s reach in the UK. Revenue from GDCL in 2016 raised Europe?s share of Motorola?s revenue to more than 20% from about 15%.

In 2017 the company moved to strengthen its software business in North America with the agreement to acquire of Airbus DS Communications from Airbus SE. The deal is to enable Motorola to create a full suite of 911 services that include call routing call taking records management and dispatch for agencies of all sizes.

Mergers and Acquisitions

In 2017 Motorola Solutions agreed to buy Airbus DS Communications from Airbus SE which would allow Motorola to greatly expand its software for 911 services in North America. Terms were not disclosed.

The company acquired Interexport a provider of managed and support services for communications systems for government agencies public safety and enterprise customers in Chile in another 2017 transaction. The deal boosts Motorola?s Managed & Support Services business and expands operations in Latin America. Interexport was expected to add about $50 million in revenue in 2017. Terms were not disclosed.

In 2016 Motorola acquired Guardian Digital Communications Holdings Limited (GCDL) a holding company of Airwave for about $1 billion. The deal brought Motorola the largest private operator of a public safety network in the world delivering voice and data communications to more than 300 public service agencies in Great Britain. The acquisition expands Motorola's managed and support services business and its footprint in Europe.

In 2016 Motorola acquired Spillman Technologies a provider of comprehensive law enforcement and public safety software solutions for $217 million. The acquisition expands its smart public safety portfolio and provides agencies of all sizes with a full suite of solutions for the command center.

EXECUTIVES

Chairman and CEO, Gregory Q. (Greg) Brown, age 58, $1,250,000 total compensation

EVP Strategy and Innovation, Eduardo F. Conrado, age 50, $448,750 total compensation

EVP Products and Services, Bruce W. Brda, age 56, $550,769 total compensation

EVP and CFO, Gino A. Bonanotte, age 53, $645,385 total compensation

EVP General Counsel and Chief Administrative Officer, Mark S. Hacker, age 46, $526,337 total compensation

EVP Worldwide Sales, John P. (Jack) Malloy, age 46, $497,615 total compensation

Executive Vice President President Global Custo, Joseph M Guglielmi

Mssi Vice President Director of Sales, Derek Phipps

Vice President Of Environment Health And Safety, Jodi Shapiro

Vice President Of Sales, Edward Fuerst

Vice President records and evidence systems, Alam Ali

Vice President, Fernando Bonilla

Secretary To Vice President of Human Resources, Laura Davis

Auditors: KPMG LLP

LOCATIONS

HQ: Motorola Solutions Inc.
500 West Monroe Street, Chicago, IL 60661
Phone: 847 576-5000   **Fax:** 847 576-3477
Web: www.motorolasolutions.com

2016 Sales

	$ mil.	% of total
US	3,566	59
UK	528	9
Other countries	1,944	32
Total	**6,038**	**100**

PRODUCTS/OPERATIONS

2016 Sales

	$ mil.	% of total
Products	3,649	60
Services	2,389	40
Total	**6,038**	**100**

Selected Products and Services

Devices

Mobile computers
Mobile-to-mobile wireless modules
Public safety LTE infrastructure devices and services (handheld USB modem vehicle modem)
Radio-frequency identification products (RFID) and accessories
Two-way radios and pagers
Two-way radio accessories
Networks
Mobile broadband (public safety LTE)
Private broadband networks
Wireless broadband networks

Services

Enterprise
Enterprise video solutions
Integrated enterprise communications
Managed network infrastructure
Managed security and compliance
Supply chain visibility solutions
Government and Public Safety
Advanced video security systems
Complex network design and integration
Interoperability and unified communications
Next-generation command and control
Public safety managed services
Software
Application development framework
Mobility software
Network design software
Public sector applications
Support and help desk applications
Systems
Dispatch systems
Enterprise voice systems
SCADA Systems (real-time facilities monitoring and control)

COMPETITORS

Airbus Group	Honeywell
Alcatel-Lucent	International
Cisco Systems	Intermec
EF Johnson	JVC KENWOOD
Technologies	Sepura
Harris Corp.	

HISTORICAL FINANCIALS

Company Type: Public

Income Statement

FYE: December 31

	REVENUE ($ mil.)	NET INCOME ($ mil.)	NET PROFIT MARGIN	EMPLOYEES
12/17	6,380	(155)	—	15,000
12/16	6,038	560	9.3%	14,000
12/15	5,695	610	10.7%	14,000
12/14	5,881	1,299	22.1%	15,000
12/13	8,696	1,099	12.6%	21,000
Annual Growth	**(7.5%)**	**—**		**(8.1%)**

2017 Year-End Financials

Debt ratio: 54.47%
Return on equity: ***,***.**%
Cash ($ mil.): 1,268
Current ratio: 1.35
Long-term debt ($ mil.): 4,419

No. of shares (mil.): 161
Dividends
  Yield: 0.0%
  Payout: —
Market value ($ mil.): 14,563

	STOCK PRICE ($) FY Close	P/E High/Low	PER SHARE ($) Earnings	Dividends	Book Value
12/17	90.34	— —	(0.95)	1.93	(10.81)
12/16	82.89	25 18	3.24	1.70	(5.85)
12/15	68.45	24 19	3.02	1.43	(0.61)
12/14	67.08	13 11	5.29	1.30	12.44
12/13	67.50	16 13	4.06	1.14	14.38
Annual Growth	**7.6%**	**— —**	**—**	**14.1%**	

Murphy USA Inc

It may not be the biggest but Murphy USA is flexing its muscles in the US gas station market. Murphy USA (a former operating unit of Murphy Oil) markets refined products through its network of branded gasoline stations and convenience stores customers and unbranded wholesale customers in more than 25 Southern and Midwestern US states to more than 1.6 million customers. The company's more than 1400 retail gas stations (more than 1150 of which are in Wal-Mart Supercenter parking lots) sell gas under the Murphy USA brand. It also operates about 250 Murphy Express locations.

Operations

The company markets retail motor fuel products and convenience merchandise through its own chain of retail stations almost all of which are in close proximity to Wal-Mart stores. Its business also includes product supply and wholesale assets such as product distribution terminals and pipelines.

Petroleum product sales account for almost 80% of the company's total revenues.

Geographic Reach

Murphy USA has retail stations in more than 25 US states (primarily in the Southeast — Florida and Tennessee) as well as in the Southwest and the Midwest.

Texas Florida Georgia North Carolina and Tennessee together account for about 50% of its total retail outlets with Texas accounting for about 20%.

Sales and Marketing

The sells gasoline under the Murphy USA and Murphy Express brands.

Financial Performance

Murphy USA's revenues decreased by 9% in 2016 to $11.6 billion primarily due to a drop in retail fuel prices of 24 cents per gallon and lower wholesale prices. Lower wholesale volumes were partially offset by a 2% increase in retail fuel due to an increase in stores.

Net income increased by 26% to $221.5 million thanks to the company?s gain on the sale of the Camline pipeline in 2016; increased merchandise margins; and higher sales of renewable blends (volumes and prices) partially offset by higher renewable blends costs embedded in spot prices for motor fuels.

The company?s operating cash flow increased by 56% in 2016 to $337.4 million due to higher net income and the improved drawdown of working capital (up by $100.3 million).

Strategy

The company has built retail gas stations at Wal-Mart Supercenters and at other standalone locations. In 2015 it opened 56 Murphy USA stores in Walmart Supercenter parking lots (including its 1300th store) as well as 17 Murphy Express stores. It opened 67 new stores in 2016.

In 2016 Murphy USA announced an independent growth plan apart from Wal-Mart. Rather than continuing to acquire land from Wal-Mart (on which it has built 1044 stores) it is raising capital to allow it to pursue opening stores in non-Wal-Mart locations.

The company also focuses on improving its infrastructure to lower overhead costs and on long-term investment. It plans to continue to focus its product supply and wholesale efforts on activities that enhance its ability to be a low-price retail fuel leader by optimizing its fuel supply contracts to capitalize on market dynamics whenever possible and minimizing physical product supply and wholesale asset ownership.

Focusing on its core business in 2015 the company sold its Hereford ethanol plant for nearly $100 million.

Company Background

Boosting its customer offerings in 2010 the company teamed up with Western Union signing a deal to offer online money transfer services at its Murphy USA gas stations and Murphy Express convenience stores across the country.

As part of its former parent's decision to exit the refining business in 2011 MUSA sold its Superior Wisconsin refinery to Calumet Specialty Products Partners for $475 million. It also sold its refinery in Meraux Louisiana to Valero Energy for $625 million. The divestitures transformed MUSA into a pure gas station/convenience store company.

In 2013 Murphy Oil completed the spin-off of its US retail marketing business into an independent public company — Murphy USA Inc. The spin-off was achieved through the distribution to Murphy Oil's shareholders of one share of Murphy USA common stock for every four shares of Murphy Oil stock. It holds through its subsidiaries the US retail marketing business that was separated from its former parent company plus certain ethanol production facilities and other assets and liabilities of Murphy Oil that supported the activities of the US retail marketing operations.

In an effort to exit non-core businesses in the fall of 2013 the company sold underperforming subsidiary Hankinson Renewable Energy LLC (which owns and operates the Hankinson North Dakota ethanol plant) to Guardian Hankinson LLC for $173 million.

EXECUTIVES

EVP and CFO, Mindy K. West, age 48, $546,083 total compensation

SVP Retail Operations and Support, Marn K. Cheng, age 51, $382,627 total compensation

President and CEO, R. Andrew Clyde, age 53, $991,667 total compensation

SVP Marketing, Robert J. (Rob) Chumley, $116,667 total compensation

Vice President And Controller, Donnie Smith

Chairman, R. Madison Murphy, age 59

Auditors: KPMG LLP

LOCATIONS

HQ: Murphy USA Inc
200 Peach Street, El Dorado, AR 71730-5836
Phone: 870 875-7600
Web: www.murphyusa.com

2016 Stores

States	no. of stores
Texas	294
Florida	120
Georgia	94
Tennessee	92
North Carolina	86
Alabama	76
Louisiana	75
Arkansas	68
Mississippi	55
South Carolina	56
Oklahoma	53
Missouri	48
Kentucky	47
Ohio	44
Indiana	38
Illinois	37
Michigan	27
Iowa	22
Virginia	22
New Mexico	12
Colorado	12
Minnesota	9
Kansas	5
Utah	4
Nebraska	3
Nevada	2
Total	**1,401**

PRODUCTS/OPERATIONS

2016 Sales

	$ mil.	% of total
Petroleum product sales	9,070	78
Merchandise sales	2,338	20
Other operating revenue	185	2
Total	**11,594**	**100**

COMPETITORS

7-Eleven	Hess Corporation
Alon Brands	QuikTrip
Chevron	Racetrac Petroleum
ConocoPhillips	Royal Dutch Shell
Couche-Tard	Valero Energy
Exxon Mobil	

HISTORICAL FINANCIALS

Company Type: Public

Income Statement

FYE: December 31

	REVENUE ($ mil.)	NET INCOME ($ mil.)	NET PROFIT MARGIN	EMPLOYEES
12/16	11,594	221	1.9%	9,100
12/15	12,699	176	1.4%	9,800
12/14	17,209	243	1.4%	9,450
12/13	18,083	235	1.3%	8,250
12/12	19,655	83	0.4%	7,900
Annual Growth	(12.4%)	27.6%	—	3.6%

2016 Year-End Financials

Debt ratio: 32.09%
Return on equity: 29.66%
Cash ($ mil.): 153
Current ratio: 1.00
Long-term debt ($ mil.): 629

No. of shares (mil.): 36
Dividends
Yield: —
Payout: —
Market value ($ mil.): 2,270

	STOCK PRICE ($) FY Close	P/E High/Low	Earnings	PER SHARE ($) Dividends	Book Value
12/16	61.47	14 10	5.59	0.00	18.87
12/15	60.74	18 12	4.02	0.00	19.01
12/14	68.86	13 7	5.26	0.00	18.79
12/13	41.56	9 7	5.02	0.00	14.04
Annual Growth	10.3%	— —	2.7%	—	7.7%

COMPETITORS

Ameriana Bancorp	Huntington Bancshares
Fifth Third	MainSource Financial
First Financial Bancorp	Old National Bancorp
First Merchants	PNC Financial
German American Bancorp	STAR Financial Group

HISTORICAL FINANCIALS

Company Type: Public

Income Statement

FYE: December 31

	ASSETS ($ mil.)	NET INCOME ($ mil.)	INCOME AS % OF ASSETS	EMPLOYEES
12/16	1,553	13	0.9%	442
12/15	1,478	12	0.8%	445
12/14	1,424	10	0.8%	438
12/13	1,391	9	0.7%	412
12/12	1,422	7	0.5%	413
Annual Growth	2.2%	16.3%	—	1.7%

2016 Year-End Financials

Debt ratio: 0.27%
Return on equity: 9.53%
Cash ($ mil.): 27
Current ratio: —
Long-term debt ($ mil.): —

No. of shares (mil.): 7
Dividends
Yield: 0.0%
Payout: 32.9%
Market value ($ mil.): 242

	STOCK PRICE ($) FY Close	P/E High/Low	Earnings	PER SHARE ($) Dividends	Book Value
12/16	33.10	19 13	1.76	0.58	19.12
12/15	24.80	15 12	1.62	0.48	18.46
12/14	21.88	15 11	1.46	0.32	17.63
12/13	17.13	16 10	1.09	0.24	15.69
12/12	11.43	15 9	0.82	0.24	19.77
Annual Growth	30.5%	— —	21.0%	24.7%	(0.8%)

MutualFirst Financial Inc

EXECUTIVES

Vice President, Karen Harshbarger
Vice President, Scott Taylor
Vice President Mutual Federal Savings Bank, James Tinkey
Vice President, Kathy Balser
Vice President, Jenny Yarbrough
Vice President Chief Information Secur, Bonita Ramirez
Auditors: BKD, LLP

LOCATIONS

HQ: MutualFirst Financial Inc
110 E. Charles Street, Muncie, IN 47305-2419
Phone: 765 747-2800
Web: www.bankwithmutual.com

NASB Financial Inc

EXECUTIVES

Vice President, Stephen Ankle
Vice President Operations, Karen Jacobson
Executive Vice President, Bruce J Thielen
Information Technology Vice President, John Nestlerod
Vice President, Lori West
Vice President Loan Servicing, Rachel Jones
Vice President Residential Lending, Pat Cox
Vice President, Dan Morton
Executive Vice President, Rhonda Byhus
Auditors: BKD, LLP

LOCATIONS

HQ: NASB Financial Inc
12498 South 71 Highway, Grandview, MO 64030
Phone: 816 765-2200   **Fax:** 816 761-4113
Web: www.nasb.com

COMPETITORS

Bank of America	Guaranty Federal
Commerce Bancshares	U.S. Bancorp
Dickinson Financial	UMB Financial

HISTORICAL FINANCIALS

Company Type: Public

Income Statement
FYE: September 30

	ASSETS ($ mil.)	NET INCOME ($ mil.)	INCOME AS % OF ASSETS	EMPLOYEES
09/17	2,062	29	1.4%	—
09/16	1,949	22	1.1%	—
09/15	1,530	21	1.4%	—
09/14	1,168	16	1.4%	—
09/13	1,144	27	2.4%	463
Annual Growth	15.9%	1.6%	—	—

2017 Year-End Financials

Debt ratio: 1.25%
Return on equity: 13.14%
Cash ($ mil.): 43
Current ratio: —
Long-term debt ($ mil.): —

No. of shares (mil.): 7
Dividends
  Yield: 0.0%
  Payout: 30.6%
Market value ($ mil.): 267

	STOCK PRICE ($) FY Close	P/E High/Low		PER SHARE ($) Earnings	Dividends	Book Value
09/17	36.11	10	8	3.98	1.22	31.55
09/16	33.75	11	9	3.02	0.98	28.92
09/15	29.00	11	8	2.90	2.80	26.66
09/14	23.70	14	9	2.13	0.80	26.64
09/13	27.43	8	6	3.51	0.00	24.85
Annual Growth	7.1%	—	—	3.2%	—	6.1%

National Bank Holdings Corp

National Bank Holdings is the holding company for NBH Bank which operates nearly 100 branches in four south and central US states under various brands including: Bank Midwest in Kansas and Missouri Community Banks of Colorado in Colorado and Hillcrest Bank in Texas. Targeting small to medium-sized businesses and consumers the banks offer traditional checking and savings accounts as well as commercial and residential mortgages agricultural loans and commercial loans. The bank boasted $4.7 billion in assets at the end of 2015 including $2.6 billion in loans and $3.8 billion in deposits. Over 80% of its total revenue is made up of interest income.

Operations

About 63% of the bank's total revenue came from loan interest (including fees) during 2015 while another 19% came from interest on its investment securities. The rest of its revenue came from service charges (7%) bank card fees (5%) and other miscellaneous income sources.

Geographic Reach

National Bank Holdings had a network of 97 banking centers in four states at the end of 2015 with more than half of those in Colorado a third in Missouri nearly a dozen branches in Kansas and two branches in Texas.

Sales and Marketing

The bank serves small- to medium-sized businesses and consumers via its network of banking locations and through online and mobile banking products. It spent $4.3 million on advertising during 2015 down from $4.6 million and $5.3 million in 2014 and 2013 respectively.

Financial Performance

The group's annual revenues and profits have been trending downward over the past few years as it has been selling off branches and loan busi-

---

ness to concentrate on the geographic markets and loan types where it carries the most expertise.

National Bank Holdings' revenue rebounded 5% to $192.86 million during 2015 mostly as it earned $21 million in FDIC-related income related to lower indemnification amortization increased FDIC loss-share income and a $5 million gain on an FDIC loss-share agreement termination.

Despite revenue growth in 2015 the group's net income plummeted 47% to $4.9 million mostly on higher loan loss provisions which climbed more than $6.2 million during the year as it increased its specific reserves on non 310-30 loans. National Bank Holdings' operations used $37.65 million compared to just $2.76 million in cash during 2014 mostly after adjusting its earnings for non-cash items mostly related to a decrease in net amounts due to the FDIC.

Strategy

National Bank Holdings has been trimming its branch count in recent years to focus on serving clients through full-service banking centers across its four chief markets of Colorado Kansas Missouri and Texas as well as through online and mobile banking channels. Toward this end in 2013 the bank began integrating its limited-service retirement center locations into its full-service banking centers while also exiting its limited presence in California (its banks there had operated under the Community Banks of California banner).

Meanwhile the regional community bank continues to selectively acquire smaller banks and complementary financial companies that serve small- and medium-sized businesses to grow its loan and deposit business.

Mergers and Acquisitions

In August 2015 National Bank Holdings bought $142 million-asset Pine River Bank in Colorado along with its $64 million in loans and $130 million in deposits for $9.5 million in cash.

Company Background

Formed in 2009 National Bank Holdings went public in 2012. Prior to its filing National Bank Holdings was minority-owned by a number of private shareholders and corporate entities including Taconic Capital Advisors Wellington Management and Paulson & Co.

EXECUTIVES

Chairman President and CEO, G. Timothy (Tim) Laney, age 57, $500,000 total compensation
Chief of Enterprise Technology & Integration and NBH Bank N.A. Midwest/ Texas Division President, Thomas M. (Tom) Metzger, $300,000 total compensation
Chief Financial Officer, Brian F. Lilly, age 58, $295,705 total compensation
Chief Risk Officer, Richard U. Newfield, age 56, $300,000 total compensation
Auditors: KPMG LLP

LOCATIONS

HQ: National Bank Holdings Corp
  7800 East Orchard Road, Suite 300, Greenwood Village, CO 80111
Phone: 720 529-3336

PRODUCTS/OPERATIONS

2015 Sales

	% of total
Interest and dividend income:	
Interest and fees on loans	63
Interest and dividends on investment securities	18
Dividends on non-marketable securities	1
Interest on interest-bearing bank deposits	-
Total	82
Non-interest income:	
Service charges	7

Bank card fees	5
Gain on sales of mortgages net	1
Bank-owned life insurance income	1
Other non-interest income	2
Bargain purchase gain	1
Gain on previously charged-off acquired loans	1
OREO related write-ups and other income	1
FDIC indemnification asset amortization net of gain on termination	-
FDIC loss sharing income (expense)	-
Total Non-Interest Income	18
Total	**100**

COMPETITORS

BBVA Compass Bancshares	FirstBank Holding Company
Bank of America	JPMorgan Chase
Bank of the West	KeyCorp
Capitol Federal Financial	U.S. Bancorp
Central Bancompany	UMB Financial
Commerce Bancshares	Wells Fargo
Enterprise Financial Services	Zions Bancorporation

HISTORICAL FINANCIALS

Company Type: Public

Income Statement
FYE: December 31

	ASSETS ($ mil.)	NET INCOME ($ mil.)	INCOME AS % OF ASSETS	EMPLOYEES
12/16	4,573	23	0.5%	1,004
12/15	4,683	4	0.1%	1,042
12/14	4,819	9	0.2%	1,056
12/13	4,914	6	0.1%	1,108
12/12	5,410	(0)	—	1,205
Annual Growth	(4.1%)	—	—	(4.5%)

2016 Year-End Financials

Debt ratio: —
Return on equity: 3.99%
Cash ($ mil.): 152
Current ratio: —
Long-term debt ($ mil.): —

No. of shares (mil.): 26
Dividends
  Yield: 0.0%
  Payout: 27.8%
Market value ($ mil.): 841

	STOCK PRICE ($) FY Close	P/E High/Low		PER SHARE ($) Earnings	Dividends	Book Value
12/16	31.89	40	23	0.79	0.22	20.32
12/15	21.37	166	127	0.14	0.20	20.34
12/14	19.41	97	84	0.22	0.20	20.43
12/13	21.40	155	126	0.14	0.20	19.99
12/12	18.99	—	—	(0.01)	0.05	20.84
Annual Growth	13.8%	—	—	—	44.8%	(0.6%)

National Commerce Corp

Auditors: Porter Keadle Moore, LLC

LOCATIONS

HQ: National Commerce Corp
  813 Shades Creek Parkway, Suite 100, Birmingham, AL 35209
Phone: 205 313-8100
Web: www.nationalbankofcommerce.com

HISTORICAL FINANCIALS

Company Type: Public

Income Statement

FYE: December 31

	ASSETS ($ mil.)	NET INCOME ($ mil.)	INCOME AS % OF ASSETS	EMPLOYEES
12/16	1,950	17	0.9%	297
12/15	1,763	9	0.5%	289
12/14	1,138	5	0.5%	235
12/13	791	4	0.5%	—
12/12	0	2		—
Annual Growth	—	71.6%	—	—

2016 Year-End Financials

Debt ratio: 1.26%	No. of shares (mil.): 10
Return on equity: 8.11%	Dividends
Cash ($ mil.): 217	Yield: —
Current ratio: —	Payout: —
Long-term debt ($ mil.): —	Market value ($ mil.): 406

	STOCK PRICE ($) FY Close	P/E High/Low	PER SHARE ($) Earnings	Dividends	Book Value
12/16	37.15	23 13	1.61	0.00	21.01
12/15	25.05	27 20	1.02	0.00	19.33
Annual Growth	10.4%	— —	12.1%	—	2.1%

National General Holdings Corp

Auditors: Ernst & Young LLP

LOCATIONS

HQ: National General Holdings Corp
59 Maiden Lane, 38th Floor, New York, NY 10038
Phone: 212 380-9500
Web: www.nationalgeneral.com

HISTORICAL FINANCIALS

Company Type: Public

Income Statement

FYE: December 31

	ASSETS ($ mil.)	NET INCOME ($ mil.)	INCOME AS % OF ASSETS	EMPLOYEES
12/16	7,244	172	2.4%	6,930
12/15	5,563	142	2.6%	4,630
12/14	4,439	102	2.3%	2,980
12/13	2,837	42	1.5%	2,029
12/12	2,718	32	1.2%	2,101
Annual Growth	27.8%	51.5%	—	34.8%

2016 Year-End Financials

Debt ratio: 11.57%	No. of shares (mil.): 106
Return on equity: 10.08%	Dividends
Cash ($ mil.): 220	Yield: 0.0%
Current ratio: —	Payout: 10.2%
Long-term debt ($ mil.): —	Market value ($ mil.): 2,660

	STOCK PRICE ($) FY Close	P/E High/Low	PER SHARE ($) Earnings	Dividends	Book Value
12/16	24.99	18 13	1.37	0.14	17.79
12/15	21.86	18 13	1.27	0.09	14.34
12/14	18.61	18 12	1.07	0.05	11.34
Annual Growth	7.6%	— —	6.4%	29.4%	11.9%

National Oilwell Varco Inc

National Oilwell Varco provides goods and services to exploration and production companies operating in oil patches around the world as well to infrastructure clients. The company makes distributes and services oil and gas drilling equipment for land and offshore drilling rigs. Its mechanical components include drawworks mud pumps cranes jacking systems automated pipe-handling tools top drives and traveling equipment. Other products include masts derricks substructures and cranes. In good years it deploys and operates more than 3000 oil rigs worldwide. Following the 2014 crash in oil prices the company operates about half as many. Roughly 25% of revenue comes from US operations and the remaining from more than ten other countries. Land-based operations are generating an increased amount of total revenue up to 60% in 2016.

Operations

National Oilwell Varco operates four business segments: Rig Systems Wellbore Technologies Completion & Production Services and Rig Aftermarket.

Rig Systems (National Oilwell Varco's largest segment) designs makes and sells land rigs offshore drilling equipment packages and drilling rig components. Equipment and technologies include substructures derricks and masts; cranes; pipe lifting racking rotating and assembly systems; fluid transfer technologies such as mud pumps; pressure control equipment (including blowout preventers; power transmission systems including drives and generators; and rig instrumentation and control systems. The segment supports land and offshore drillers. It accounts for approximately 40% of total net sales.

National Oilwell Varco's Wellbore Technologies segment (20 of sales%) provides equipment and technologies used to perform drilling operations and offers services that optimize their performance including solids control and waste management equipment and services drilling fluids premium drill pipe wired pipe tubular inspection and coating services instrumentation downhole tools and drill bits.

The Completion & Production Solutions segment (20 of sales%) designs manufactures and sells equipment and technologies needed for hydraulic fracture stimulation (including pressure pumping trucks and pumps blenders sanders hydration units injection units flowline manifolds and wellheads); well intervention (coiled tubing units coiled tubing and wireline units and tools); onshore production (composite pipe surface transfer and progressive cavity pumps and artificial lift systems); and offshore production (floating production systems and subsea production technologies).

The company's Rig Aftermarket segment provides comprehensive aftermarket products and services to support land rigs and offshore rigs and drilling rig components manufactured by the Rig Systems segment. It provides spare parts repair and rentals as well as technical support field service and first well support field engineering and customer training through a network of aftermarket service and repair facilities strategically located in major areas of drilling operations.

The hard-hit oil market took its toll on National Oilwell as its employee count decreased from 60000 in 2014 to 37000 at the end of 2016.

Geographic Reach

National Oilwell Varco has significant non-US operations in Canada Europe the Far East the Middle East Africa Southeast Asia Latin America. It operates 835 locations on six continents including a network of 400 distribution service centers and 300 repair and manufacturing facilities to serve its oil and gas company customers. It has major facilities in Denmark France the Netherlands Norway Canada UK and US and a presence in Singapore Mexico Malaysia Brazil South Korea and the UAE. The company produces about 75% of its total revenues from operations outside of the US.

Sales and Marketing

Substantially all of Rig Systems' capital equipment and Rig Aftermarket's spare parts sales and a large portion of their smaller pumps and parts sales are made through the company's direct sales force and distribution service centers. Sales to foreign oil companies are often made with or through agent or representative arrangements.

The company's Rig Systems and Rig Aftermarket segments' customers include drilling contractors shipyards and other rig fabricators well servicing companies pressure pumpers national oil companies major and independent oil and gas companies supply stores and pipe-running service providers. Rig Systems sells directly to drilling contractors rig fabricators well servicing companies pressure pumping companies national oil companies major and independent oil and gas companies and also through distribution companies.

Products within Wellbore Technologies and Completion & Production Solutions are rented and sold worldwide through National Oilwell Varco's own sales force and through commissioned representatives.

Wellbore Technologies' customers are mainly oil and gas companies drilling contractors oilfield service companies and oilfield rental companies. Completion & Production Solutions' customers are predominantly service companies and oil and gas companies.

Financial Performance

Until the crash in oil prices in 2014 National Oilwell Varco?s revenue had been climbing and net income had been moving upwards. All that changed however when the price of oil dropped from over $110/barrel to lows around $30/barrel. Revenue crashed from $21.4 billion in 2014 to less than $7.3 billion in 2016. Net income similarly tanked from $2.5 billion in 2014 to a more than $2.0 billion loss in 2016.

For the year 2016 revenue fell more than 50% to $7.2 billion due to decreased drilling activity and lessened demand for oilfield equipment and services. Industry average worldwide rig count according to trusted entity Baker Hughes dropped 32% compare to the prior year. Rig Systems? segment revenue fell 66% from the prior year; Rig Aftermarket fell 44% Wellbore Technology dropped 41% and Completion and Production Services decreased 33%.

In 2016 the net loss more than tripled the previous year?s $770 million loss ending with a $2.4 billion deficit. No amount of cost cutting layoffs or site closures could overcome the tremendous loss of business. Typically its operating expenses represent 80% of revenues but in 2016 they ballooned to over 133% triggering the year?s significant loss

Cash on hand at the end of 2016 was $1.4 billion down nearly $700 million from the prior year. Cash from operations added $960 million due to adjustments for depreciation amortization and goodwill impairments. Investing and Financing activities combined used more than $1.5 billion of cash.

Strategy

National Oilwell?s strategy is first and foremost one of survival and once that is assured to position itself for the assumed next surge in oil prices and along with it demand for the company?s services.

The company's Rig Systems group will continue to focus on designing and manufacturing discrete drilling equipment components as well as building complete integrated drilling equipment packages for both land and offshore applications. The Completion & Production Solutions segment is focusing on improving wellbore completions while the Wellbore Technologies segment is directing its attention to enhancing drilling performance through offering a superior range of downhole tools bits premium drill pipe waste management services solids control drilling fluids instrumentation tubular inspection and tubular coating services.

In 2016 National Oilwell Varco Wellbore Technologies launched a power sections mobile application. Available through the Apple App Store and Google Play the new application is the first and only custom spec generator app in the industry.

Company Background

In 2013 it acquired Robbins & Myers a provider of services and equipment to the upstream oil and gas industry in an all-cash transaction for $2.5 billion. Robbins & Myers' complementary products include downhole tools pumps and valves. This was the company's second-largest acquisition since it bought Grant Prideco for about $7.2 billion in 2008. That year it also bought Canadian equipment distributor CE Franklin for about $240 million.

In 2012 National Oilwell Varco bought parts and supplies provider Wilson International from Schlumberger. Wilson has an extensive supply chain portfolio with which National Oilwell Varco expects to take advantage of new market opportunities. It also bought Denmark-based flexible pipe maker NKT Flexibles (a joint venture between NKT Holding and Subsea 7) for $670 million.

National Oilwell Varco bought 17 companies for $2.9 billion in 2012 and 10 companies for more than $1 billion in 2011. Significant acquisitions included that of oilfield equipment maker and services provider Ameron in a $777 million deal a move that helped to expand National Oilwell Varco's Fiberglass & Composite Tubulars business.

National Oilwell Varco took its current form when National Oilwell and Varco International merged in 2005.

EXECUTIVES

Chairman President and CEO, Clay C. Williams, age 54, $800,000 total compensation

President NOV Wellbore Technologies, Isaac A. Joseph, age 59

SVP and CFO, Jose A. Bayardo, age 45, $650,000 total compensation

President Rig Systems and Rig Aftermarket, Joseph W. (Joe) Rovig, age 56, $550,000 total compensation

President Completion and Production Solutions, Kirk Shelton

VP Corporate Controller Chief Accounting Officer, Scott K. Duff, age 49, $360,000 total compensation

CIO, Alex Philips

SVP and General Counsel, Craig L. Weinstock, age 58, $510,000 total compensation

Vice President Sales Effectiveness, Jed Niederer

Group Vice President Global Manufacturing and Sourcing Rig Solutions, Bruce Dawson

Grupo Vice President, Kevin McDonough

Vice President Floating Production Systems, Gerald Mosley

Chief Sales Officer, Michael Hart

Executive Vice President Of Information Technology, Wendy Ho-Schnell

Vice President Manufacturing, Jeff Stolasz

Vice President Sales, Bob Lepera

Vice President of Sales and Operations, Todd Lee

Senior Vice President, Jaehwa Park

Vice President Operations China, Lynn White

Senior Vice President, Sungwoo Lee

Vice President Research and Development and Quality Assurance, David W Granderson

Vice President Education Services, Grant Almond

Vice President Information Technology, Ringo Szeto

Vice President Business Development, Bobby Chance

Finance Vice President, Rosemary Al-Tayar

Vice President Finance, David Keener

Vice President Application Engineering, Randy Lucas

Vice President Sales Operations Latin America, Jim Stephen

Vice President Finance, Jim Lock

Vice President Finance, Brad Frederick

Vice President Drill Bits, Mark Tooley

Vice President Customer Service, Janis Ballow

Vice President Finance, Lisa Jones

Vice President, Dick Juelich

Corporate Vice President and Chief Technology Officer, Hege Kvernland

Vice President Internal Audit and Chief Compliance Officer, Brent A Benoit

Vice President Global Business Development and Marketing, Brad R Wood

Vice President Engineering, Robert Bloom

Vice President Global Accounts and Investor Relations, Singletary Loren

Vice President Technology Groups, Russ Gilleylen

VP Supply Chain, Marcina Guevara

VICE PRESIDENT BUISNESS DEVELOPEMENT, Frank J Torma

Auditors: Ernst & Young LLP

LOCATIONS

HQ: National Oilwell Varco Inc
7909 Parkwood Circle Drive, Houston, TX 77036-6565
Phone: 713 346-7500
Web: www.nov.com

2016 Sales

	$ mil.	% of total
US	1,961	27
China	557	8
South Korea	495	7
Singapore	340	5
Norway	339	5
United Arab Emirates	334	5
UK	299	4
Saudi Arabia	258	3
Brazil	242	3
Canada	217	3
Other countries	2,209	30
Total	**7,251**	**100**

PRODUCTS/OPERATIONS

2016 Sales

	$ mil.	% of total
Rig System	2,386	29
Completion and Production	2,241	27
Wellbore Technologies	2,199	27
Rig After market	1,416	17
Eliminations	(991)	-
Total	**7,251**	**100**

2016 Sales

	$ mil.	% of total
Sales	5,351	74
Services	1,900	26
Total	**7,251**	**100**

Selected Products and Services

Automation systems
Computer control systems
Derricks
Drawworks
Drilling motors
Electrical power systems
Masts
Mud pumps
Specialized downhole tools (including fishing tools drilling jars shock tools)
Substructures
Supply chain management
Top drives
Well drilling and servicing (drill stem technology)
Technology Solutions
Coiled Tubing Equipment
Coiled Tubing Equipment Services
Coiled Tubing Instrumentation
Coiled Tubing Pressure Control
Coiled Tubing Products and Service
Coiled Tubing Pumping Support
Coiled Tubing Software
CT Equipment Repair Center
Well Service and Completion
All Terrain Vehicles
Cementing
Completion Fluids and Services
Flowline Equipment
Fluid End Expandables
Frac Sand Handling Equipment
Multipurpose Pumps
Nitrogen Equipment
Rigs
Snubbing Equipment
Stimulation Equipment
TCP Products
Wireline
Workover
Tubular and Corrosion Control
Coiled Tubing Products and Service
Conductors and Casing
Corrosion Control
Drill Pipe Services
Drilling Tubulars
Fiber Glass Pipe
Inspection Services
Line Pipe Services
Machining Services
New Pipe Services
Specialty Inspection Services
Sucker Rod Services
Surveillance Services
Tubular Leak Detection
Used Pipe Services
Supply Chain
Artificial Lift
Electrical Products
Integrated Supply
Oilfield Supply
RigPAC
RigStore
ValveAutomation
Production
Artificial Lift
Floating Production Solutions
Fluid King Pump Expendables
Multipurpose Pumps
Process Equipment
Production Pressure Control
Lifting and Handling
AHTS Equipment Packages
Cabelay Systems
Cranes
Marine Vessel Equipment
Mooring Systems
Pipelay Systems
Winches
Industrial
Construction Supply
Fiber Glass Pipe
Fluid End Expendables
Monoflo - Mono
Multipurpose Pumps
Nitrogen Equipment
Power Systems
Protective Lining Products
Solids Control
Water Transmission
Engineering and Project Management
New Technology Development
Project Specific Solutions
Successful Project Execution
Drilling
Aftermarket Services
Control and Advisory Systems
Drill Bits

Drilling Business Solutions
Drilling Expendables Databook
Drilling Fluids
Drilling Fluid Equipment
Drilling Pressure Control
Drilling Tubulars
Flowline Equipment
Fluid End Expendables
Fluid End Modules and Accessories
Fluid Transfer Systems
Handling Tools
Hoisting
Instrumentation Data Acquisition
Iron Roughnecks
Jacking and Skidding
Mining and Minerals
Motion Compensation
Multipurpose Pumps
Pipe Handling
Power Systems
Rigs
Rotating Equipment
Specialty Inspection Services
Structures
Top Drive Systems
Waste Management
Downhole
Advanced Drilling Solutions
Borehole Enlargement
Coring Services
Directional Tools
Downhole Motors
Drill Bits
Drilling Tools
Fishing Tools
Intervention and Completion Tools
Service Equipment
Telemetry Drill Strings

Selected Brands
AmClyde
Ameron
Baylor
Bear Pumps
Best Flow Products
BlackMax - BlackStar
Bowen
Brandt
Continental Emsco
CTES
Fiber Glass Systems
Gaso
HSI
Hydrastab
IntelliServ
Quality Tubing
ReedHycalog
Rolligon
Texas Oil Tools
Wheatley
Wheatley Gaso
XL Systems

COMPETITORS

Aker Solutions	Nabors Industries
Baker Hughes	Schlumberger
Bechtel	Siemens AG
Cameron International	Stewart & Stevenson
Forum Energy	LLC
GE Oil	Superior Energy
Halliburton	Weatherford
McDermott	International

HISTORICAL FINANCIALS
Company Type: Public

Income Statement
FYE: December 31

	REVENUE ($ mil.)	NET INCOME ($ mil.)	NET PROFIT MARGIN	EMPLOYEES
12/17	7,304	(237)	—	31,889
12/16	7,251	(2,412)	—	36,627
12/15	14,757	(769)	—	50,197
12/14	21,440	2,502	11.7%	63,642
12/13	22,869	2,327	10.2%	63,779
Annual Growth	(24.8%)	—	—	(15.9%)

2017 Year-End Financials

Debt ratio: 13.42%	No. of shares (mil.): 380
Return on equity: (-1.69%)	Dividends
Cash ($ mil.): 1,437	Yield: 0.0%
Current ratio: 3.07	Payout: —
Long-term debt ($ mil.): 2,706	Market value ($ mil.): 13,691

	STOCK PRICE ($) FY Close	P/E High/Low		PER SHARE ($) Earnings	Dividends	Book Value
12/17	36.02	—	—	(0.63)	0.20	37.08
12/16	37.44	—	—	(6.41)	0.61	36.82
12/15	33.49	—	—	(1.99)	1.84	43.60
12/14	65.53	15	11	5.82	1.64	49.39
12/13	79.53	15	12	5.44	0.91	51.89
Annual Growth	(18.0%)	—	—	—	(31.5%)	(8.1%)

National Western Life Group Inc

LOCATIONS

HQ: National Western Life Group Inc
850 East Anderson Lane, Austin, TX 78752-1602
Phone: 512 836-1010
Web: www.nwlgi.com

HISTORICAL FINANCIALS
Company Type: Public

Income Statement
FYE: December 31

	ASSETS ($ mil.)	NET INCOME ($ mil.)	INCOME AS % OF ASSETS	EMPLOYEES
12/16	11,894	100	0.8%	265
12/15	11,612	98	0.8%	261
12/14	11,351	105	0.9%	—
12/13	0	96	—	—
Annual Growth	—	1.6%	—	—

2016 Year-End Financials

Debt ratio: —	No. of shares (mil.): 3
Return on equity: 6.04%	Dividends
Cash ($ mil.): 51	Yield: 0.0%
Current ratio: —	Payout: 0.8%
Long-term debt ($ mil.): —	Market value ($ mil.): 1,130

	STOCK PRICE ($) FY Close	P/E High/Low		PER SHARE ($) Earnings	Dividends	Book Value
12/16	310.80	7	4	42.80	0.36	473.53
12/15	251.94	6	5	41.73	0.36	443.32
12/14	269.25	6	5	44.78	0.00	428.01
12/13	223.55	5	4	40.80	0.00	(0.00)
/0.00	—	—	(0.00)	0.00	(0.00)	
Annual Growth	—	—	—	—	—	—

Navient Corp

Navient is a new name for an old business: namely the loan management servicing and asset recovery unit of SLM Corp. (aka Sallie Mae). Navient services a $300 billion student loan portfolio comprised of federal and private education

---

loans issued to more than 12 million customers. In addition to serving indebted former students Navient provides asset recovery services (collections) to the government higher education institutions and business clients. Navient manages the largest portfolio of Federal Family Education Loan Program (FFELP) loans as well as the largest portfolio of private education loans. Navient began life as an independent company in 2014 the outcome of a strategic divestiture from Sallie Mae which still exists and continues to provide consumer loans.

Operations

Navient operates three business segments two that own and collect interest on loans and one that services loans and provides loan processing services. The largest segment the Federal Family Education Loan Program (FFELP) makes up about 50% of total revenue. It collects interest income from its $87.7 billion portfolio of FFELP loans and adds to its holdings by opportunistically buying FFELP loans from other servicers. More than 95% of FFELP loans are government guaranteed providing Navient a significant buffer against the financial impact of loan losses. Originations of FFELP loans no longer occur replaced with new programs headed by the US Department of Education.

Navient's Private Education Loans segment (about 35% of revenue) buys finances and services Private Education loans while also collecting interest on a $23.3 billion portfolio of such loans. Legal constraints related to the spin-off from Sallie Mae prohibit Navient from originating new private education loans until early 2019.

Business Services (15% of revenue) generates revenue from loan & credit servicing collecting on delinquent loans (asset recovery) and business processing activities. The segment services the company's own FFELP loan portfolio as well as those from other institutions notably the US Department of Education which accounts for nearly $200 billion in serviced loans. It also offers asset recovery services for loans and receivables for FFELP loan guarantors higher education institutions and federal state and municipal clients.

Broadly Navient makes more than 80% of revenue from interest income on its FFELP and Private Education loan portfolios while servicing revenue combined with asset recovery and business processing revenue accounts for another 15%.

Geographic Reach

The Wilmington Delaware-based company operates throughout the US.

Most of its properties are loan servicing and collection centers in the New England and Midwestern regions with additional offices in Virginia Florida Texas and Tennessee. Its largest facility in Fishers Indiana houses 450000 square feet of space representing more than 30% of all owned and leased space.

Sales and Marketing

Navient?s sales and marketing model is composed of building relationships with the institutions that originate loans ? such as universities ? as well as bidding for government contracts most notably with the US Dept. of Education with whom Navient has an existing significant contract through 2019.

Financial Performance

Navient's annual revenues and profits have been falling in recent years due to a decline in interest income as its education loans portfolio continues to shrink. At year-end 2016 FFELP loans amounted to $87.7 billion compared to $96.4 billion in 2015 and private loans fell to $23.3 billion from $26.4 billion.

The company's revenue fell $230 million or 4% to $5.0 billion during 2016 on lower interest income on its shrinking and margin-falling portfolio of student loans as well as from a smaller contribution from gains on derivative and hedging activities.

Revenue declines and a 20% increase in interest expense contributed to a nearly 31% tumble in net income in 2016. Although the Navient?s debt decreased by about $10 billion between 2015 and 2016 the average interest rate on that debt rose from 1.71% to 2.14% enough to add more than $325 million of interest expense on the borrowings.

Cash and cash equivalents decreased by $341 million in 2016. The company generated ample cash from customers making loan payments ($15 billion) with a further $1.4 billion in cash accumulated from operating activities. Cash uses went primarily to repaying its own borrowings and to acquiring $3.7 billion of education loans from other originators.

Strategy

While Navient?s loan holdings generate a large and consistent cash flow from interest income its holdings are shrinking over time and therefore its revenue and income are declining. The company is hindered in that it is not permitted to originate new private student loans until January 2019 as part of its spin-off from Sallie Mae. Additionally the US government modified its student loan programs in 2014 which precluded issuance of new FFELP loans. All US federal government student loans now originate through the US Department of Education. The US government holds approximately $1.1 trillion of the country?s $1.4 trillion student loan debt. Of that amount Navient provides loan servicing for (but does not own) about $200 billion of the government's portfolio.

Navient?s overarching strategy includes both maintenance and growth. It seeks to maintain income streams from its $110 billion portfolio of loan holdings and from servicing more than $200 billion of others? loans the latter being heavily dependent on its contracts with the US Dept. of Education. Keeping default rates low and collecting on delinquent loans are a major focus.

The company seeks to grow its business through opportunistically acquiring existing education loans and branching into new business service markets. It acquired $3.7 billion of education loans in 2016 and agreed in early 2017 to purchase nearly $7 billion from JPMorgan Chase. Its recent acquisitions of Duncan Solutions (2017) Xtend Healthcare (2016) and Gila (2015) for example allow it to serve clients in the healthcare toll road authorities and various public-sector markets. In early 2017 the company began collecting overdue US federal tax debts on behalf of the IRS. Although non-education related revenue in its Business Processing Solutions segment represents less than 30% of total it grew 70% in 2016 from about $100 million to $170 million.

EXECUTIVES

President and CEO, John F. (Jack) Remondi, age 54, $1,000,000 total compensation

EVP and Chief Decision Management Officer, Somsak Chivavibul, age 50, $379,999 total compensation

EVP Chief Legal Officer and Secretary, Mark L. Heleen, age 55, $369,357 total compensation

EVP and Chief Risk and Compliance Officer, Timothy (Tim) Hynes, age 48, $370,000 total compensation

Group President Business Processing Solutions, John Kane, age 48, $449,999 total compensation

EVP and CIO, Pat Lawicki

Group President Asset Management and Servicing, John F. (Jeff) Whorley, age 56, $449,999 total compensation

EVP and CFO, Christian Lown, age 48

National Account Manager, Todd Newton

Vice President and Assistant Controller, Jason Wheeler

Vice President and President of Student Assistance Corp, Kevin Campbell

EXECUTIVE VICE PRESIDENT AND CHIEF LEGAL OFFICER, Mark L Heleen

Chairman, William M. Diefenderfer, age 72

Auditors: KPMG LLP

LOCATIONS

HQ: Navient Corp
123 Justison Street, Wilmington, DE 19801
Phone: 302 283-8000
Web: www.navient.com

PRODUCTS/OPERATIONS

2016 Sales

	$ mil.	% of total
Interest income:		
FFELP Loans	2,528	51
Private Education Loans	1,587	32
Other	31	1
Other income (loss):		
Servicing	304	6
Asset recovery and business processing	390	8
Gains (losses) on derivative and hedging activities net	117	2
Other	8	-
Gains (losses) on sales of loans and investments	0	-
Total	**4,965**	**100**

COMPETITORS

Bank of America
Brazos Higher Education Service Corp.
Great Lakes Higher Education
KeyCorp
Mohela
Nelnet
Pennsylvania Higher Education Assistance Agency
Texas Guaranteed

HISTORICAL FINANCIALS

Company Type: Public

Income Statement

FYE: December 31

	ASSETS ($ mil.)	NET INCOME ($ mil.)	INCOME AS % OF ASSETS	EMPLOYEES
12/16	121,136	681	0.6%	6,773
12/15	134,112	997	0.7%	7,300
12/14	146,352	1,149	0.8%	6,200
12/13	159,543	1,418	0.9%	—
12/12	0	939	—	—
Annual Growth	—	**(7.7%)**	—	—

2016 Year-End Financials

Debt ratio: 92.76%
Return on equity: 17.70%
Cash ($ mil.): 1,253
Current ratio: —
Long-term debt ($ mil.): —

No. of shares (mil.): 290
Dividends
　Yield: 0.0%
　Payout: 30.1%
Market value ($ mil.): 4,779

	STOCK PRICE ($) FY Close	P/E High/Low		PER SHARE ($) Earnings	Dividends	Book Value
12/16	16.43	8	4	2.12	0.64	12.72
12/15	11.45	8	4	2.61	0.64	11.42
12/14	21.61	8	6	2.69	0.45	10.45
Annual Growth	**(6.6%)**	—	—	**(5.8%)**	**9.2%**	**5.0%**

Navigators Group Inc (The)

The Navigators Group writes specialty lines of insurance and reinsurance to clients whom it hopes are good navigators themselves. The company's various subsidiaries write marine liability and other lines of business primarily in the US and the UK. Its Navigators Insurance and Navigators Underwriting Agency (NUA) units specialize in ocean marine insurance including hull energy and cargo insurance as well as property insurance for inland marine and onshore energy concerns. Navigators Specialty primarily provides excess and surplus (high risk) lines. The firm's subsidiaries are also involved in professional liability especially directors' and officers' coverage as well as general liability for contractors.

Operations

In early 2015 Navigators realigned its reporting structure creating four primary segments that align with the types of coverage it writes: US Insurance International Insurance Global Reinsurance and Corporate.

Navigators' global product lines are distributed through a network of retail and wholesale brokers. In addition to its specialty property/casualty insurance and reinsurance policies the company and its subsidiaries provide catastrophe risk management services.

In the International Insurance segment NUA serves as a Lloyd's of London underwriting agency managing Lloyd's Syndicate 1221. The unit primarily underwrites marine and related lines of business along with offshore energy professional liability insurance and construction coverage for onshore energy businesses.

Geographic Reach

Outside its core markets of the US and the UK Navigators has operations in several European nations such as Belgium Denmark and Sweden mainly through NUA's activity on the European Lloyd's of London insurance exchange (via Lloyd's Syndicate 1221). The firm has also established offices in emerging markets such as Brazil and China.

Financial Performance

Navigators' revenue which has largely been on the rise for the past five years rose 12% to $1 billion in 2014 on higher net written premiums and investment income. Net written premiums increased 12.6% that year due to higher retention rates in the reinsurance business as well as growth in gross written property/casualty premiums.

Net income on the other hand has been more erratic than revenue. In 2014 it grew 50% to $95 million thanks primarily to Navigator's higher revenue. Cash flow from operations has been growing every year and in 2014 it rose 63% to $222 million.

Strategy

Navigators is focused on strengthening and controlling costs within its existing operations. At the same time Navigators is looking for opportunities to expand into new niche coverage areas and regions aiming for underserved commercial markets with high-value assets and low-frequency loss levels.

Mergers and Acquisitions

In late 2017 Navigators agreed to buy Belgian insurer ASCO-BDM which specializes in marine and industrial coverage. That purchase will further strengthen its operations in Europe

EXECUTIVES

President CEO and Director and Chair Navigators Insurance and Navigators Management, Stanley A. (Stan) Galanski, age 58, $1,000,000 total compensation

Senior Vice President and General Counsel, Emily B Miner

SVP and Chief Underwriting Officer, H. Clay Bassett, age 51, $525,000 total compensation

President and CEO Navigators Management Company Inc., Vincent C. Tizzio, age 50, $570,833 total compensation

President International Insurance, Michael J. Casella, age 56

President Navigators Specialty, Jeff L. Saunders, $412,500 total compensation

EVP and CFO, Ciro M. DeFalco, age 61, $780,833 total compensation

SVP and Chief Marketing Officer, LoriAnn V. Lowery-Biggers, age 50

Managing Director Asia, Jon Doherty

President Navigators Technical Risk, Patrick J. Milner

Vice President Cargo, Tod Sklens

Vice President And Corporate Treasurer, Ellen Dion

Vice President Professional Liability, Rocco Malandrino

Assistant Vice President Environmental Practice, Brett Schoech

Vice President and Group Controller, George Iacono

East Coast Zonal Vice President Environmental Division, Paul Dastis

Assistant Vice President, Kathleen Boswell

Vice President of Application Development, Roger Horvath

Assistant Vice President, Joshua Elmore

Vice President, David Crudo

Assistant Vice President, Jaime Rodriguez

VICE PRESIDENT, SPHR VACCARO

Vice President and Associate General Counsel, Daniel Bollinger

Senior Vice President Surety, David Pesce

Vice President, Tracy Kiffer

Vice President, Chris Piazza

Vice President Eastern and Central Regional Cargo Manager, Robert Ryan

Senior Vice President, Ed Wu

Vice President E and S Primary Casualty, Jerry O'Neill

Chairman, Terence N. Deeks, age 77

Auditors: KPMG LLP

LOCATIONS

HQ: Navigators Group Inc (The)
400 Atlantic Street, Stamford, CT 06901
Phone: 203 905-6090
Web: www.navg.com

PRODUCTS/OPERATIONS

2014 Gross Written premiums

	% of total
Insurance companies	75
Lloyd's Operations	25
Total	**100**

2014 Sales

	$ mil
% of total	
Net earned premiums	91
Net investment income	7
Net realized gains	1
Others	1
Total	**100**

Selected Subsidiaries

Millennium Underwriting Ltd. (UK)
Navigators A/S (Denmark)
Navigators Corporate Underwriters Ltd. (UK)

Navigators Holdings (UK) Ltd.
Navigators Insurance Company
Navigators Management Company Inc.
Navigators Management (UK) Limited
Navigators NV (Belgium)
Navigators Specialty Insurance Company
Navigators Underwriting Agency Ltd. (UK)
Navigators Underwriting Limited (UK)
NUAL AB (Sweden)

Selected Products and Services:

Commercial Surety
Standard Transactional
Non Standard Transactional
Account
Program
Energy and Engineering
Onshore Energy
Offshore Energy
Construction
Operational Engineering
Excess Casualty
Umbrella & Excess (Wholesale Brokerage)
Umbrella & Excess (Retail Agency)
Environmental Casualty
Contractors Pollution Liability
Site Pollution Legal Liability
NP3 sm General & Environmental Liability (Mfg. & Distributors)
NP4 sm General Environmental & Professional Liability (Env'l Consultants)
Environmental Excess
Inland Marine
Commercial Output Policy
Construction
Specialty
Transportation
Management Liability
Directors & Officers Liability
Employment Practices Liability
Fiduciary Liability
Crime Liability
Nonprofit D & O Liability
Marine
Bluewater Hull
Brownwater Hull
Cargo
Specie
Transportation
Marine & Energy Liability
War
Protection & Indemnity
Primary Casualty
General Liability
NAVIGATORS RE
Accident & Health
Agriculture
Latin American & Caribbean
Professional Liability Reinsurance
Property & Casualty
Life Sciences
Global Package Solutions
Commercial Auto
Professional Liability
Lawyers Professional Liability
Accountants Professional Liability
Miscellaneous Professional Liability
Insurance Agents & Brokers E&O
Technology Media & Cyber Liability
Design Professionals Liability
Real Estate Professionals E&O

COMPETITORS

AIG
AXA Corporate Solutions
Allianz
Amica Mutual
Arch Insurance Group
Aspen Insurance
Berkshire Hathaway
CNA Financial
Global Indemnity
ProSight Specialty Insurance Group
RLI
Safeco
Specialty Underwriters' Alliance
Travelers Companies
White Mountains Insurance Group
XL Group plc
Zurich American

HISTORICAL FINANCIALS

Company Type: Public

Income Statement

FYE: December 31

	ASSETS ($ mil.)	NET INCOME ($ mil.)	INCOME AS % OF ASSETS	EMPLOYEES
12/16	4,814	82	1.7%	683
12/15	4,584	81	1.8%	675
12/14	4,464	95	2.1%	651
12/13	4,169	63	1.5%	596
12/12	4,007	63	1.6%	567
Annual Growth	**4.7%**	**6.7%**	**—**	**4.8%**

2016 Year-End Financials

Debt ratio: 5.48%
Return on equity: 7.25%
Cash ($ mil.): 64
Current ratio: —
Long-term debt ($ mil.): —
No. of shares (mil.): 29
Dividends
Yield: 0.0%
Payout: 4.9%
Market value ($ mil.): 3,429

	STOCK PRICE ($) FY Close	P/E High/Low		PER SHARE ($) Earnings	Dividends	Book Value
12/16	117.75	41	28	2.75	0.14	40.45
12/15	85.79	31	24	2.74	0.00	37.98
12/14	73.34	22	17	3.26	0.00	35.96
12/13	63.16	30	23	2.21	0.00	31.77
12/12	51.07	24	20	2.23	0.00	31.31
Annual Growth	**23.2%**	**—**	**—**	**5.4%**	**—**	**6.6%**

Navistar International Corp.

Navistar's gonna roll its truckin' convoy 'cross the USA and beyond. The company makes its products under brand names International (commercial trucks and military/defense vehicles) MaxxForce (diesel engines) and IC Bus (school and commercial buses). It makes diesel engines for the pickup truck van and SUV markets. Navistar's parts group supplies engine parts and its financial sector offers sales and lease financing for dealers and customers. Navistar which operates production plants in Argentina Brazil Canada Mexico and the US derives most of its sales from North America.

Operations

Navistar operates in four industry segments: Truck Parts Global Manufacturing Operations and Financial Services which consists of NFC and foreign finance operations. The Truck division which is the company's largest segment has manufacturing operations in Canada Mexico and the US.

Parts has manufacturing operations located in the US Brazil and Argentina and sells to OEMs in North and South America. Engine brands include MaxxForce and MWM International. The Parts segment supports large fleet and other customers with a wide selection of truck trailer and engine parts. It distributes to North America and the rest of the world through its 11 regional parts distribution centers or by direct shipment.

The Operations segment's revenue comes from outside the North America markets and primarily consists of its Brazilian subsidiary and its truck and parts export businesses under the International and IC brands. Operations also has engine manufacturing units in Argentina. The Financial Services segment provides retail wholesale and lease financing of products which are sold by the truck segment and its dealers within the US and Mexico.

Geographic Reach

Navistar's main product development and engineering facilities reside in Lisle and Melrose Park Illinois; Madison Heights Michigan; and New Carlisle Indiana. In North America the company has 8 manufacturing and assembly facilities. The US accounts for more than 75% of its revenues while other major markets include Brazil (3%) Canada (8%) and Mexico (7%).

Sales and Marketing

The company sell sits products through its independent dealer network in North America. It has about 730 distribution and service network retail outlets in the US and Canada about 95 in Mexico and 360 international locations.

Financial Performance

Navistar's revenues dropped 20% from $10.1 billion in 2015 to $8.1 billion in 2016. The decline was fueled by a 33% drop in Global Operations due to lower volumes and unfavorable foreign currency exchange rates in its South American engine operations driven by an economic downturn in Brazil. The company also experienced a 25% dip in Truck sales in 2016 attributed to a decline in sales of CAT-branded units sold to Caterpillar a decline in export truck volumes and lower used truck revenue.

The company has suffered five straight years of net losses: $3 billion $898 million $619 million $184 million and $97 million for 2012 2013 2014 2015 and 2016 respectively. Over the years the company has suffered from high income tax expenses and restructuring charges among other costs.

On the flip side Navistar's cash flow from operations skyrocketed from $46 million in 2015 to $267 million in 2016. This was mainly due to additional earnings from finance receivables.

Strategy

Looking to get out of the red Navistar is focused on improving its Truck and Parts businesses in its core markets. It is looking to divest or close underperforming and non-strategic areas and aims to realize incremental benefits from these actions in the near future. As a result of these evaluations the company sold Pure Power Technologies a components business focused on air and fuel systems and its engine and foundry facilities in Indianapolis Indiana in 2016. It also sold its Waukesha Wisconsin foundry operations and closed its Indianapolis Indiana foundry facility in 2015.

For the important China market the company has found a partner in Anhui Jianghuai Automobile (JAC) and the two have signed a joint venture agreement to manufacture diesel engines for that country's market. The company is continuing to explore South Central and North America with a primary focus on Brazil for manufacturing expansion opportunities.

HISTORY

Virginia-born inventor Cyrus McCormick perfected the reaper in 1831 and moved west to open a factory in Chicago in 1846. Before his death in 1884 McCormick had implemented such innovations as installment plans written guarantees and factory-trained repairmen. In 1902 with help from banker J. P. Morgan the company merged with Deering Harvester (agricultural machinery) and several smaller companies to form International Harvester (IH); it soon controlled 85% of US harvester production.

IH set up its first overseas plant in 1905 in Sweden. It entered the tractor industry in 1906 and in 1907 it began making the forerunner of the truck — the Auto Buggy. By 1910 IH was making 1300

trucks and 1400 tractors annually and had exceeded $100 million in sales. After several decades the company was renamed Navistar International in 1986.

EXECUTIVES

EVP and CFO, Walter G. Borst, age 56, $742,630 total compensation
SVP and General Counsel, Steven K. (Steve) Covey, age 67, $611,455 total compensation
SVP and CIO, Terry S. Kline, age 55
President Operations, Phil Christman
Chairman President and CEO, Troy A. Clarke, age 61, $950,000 total compensation
SVP and Chief Procurement Officer, Persio V. Lisboa, age 52, $544,688 total compensation
Treasurer; President Financial Services, William V. McMenamin
Vice President and Chief Procurement Officer, David McKean
VP Quality, William Osborne
Chief Sales Officer Service Readiness Manager, Beatrice Borges
Vice President Tax, Kristene Schumacher
Vice President, Jan Allman
Vice President General Manager Global Commercial Bus, Carl Webb
Vice President Tax, Carol Garnant
Vice President Representative Clients Customers, Michael Scribner
Senior Vice President And General Manager Parts Division, Phyllis Cochran
Senior Vice President Corporate Development, Eric Tech
Vice President Dealer Sales, Bob Mann
National Account Manager, Chris Cummings
National Account Manager, Gio DeVito
Assistant Treasurer, Petrina Rauzi
Auditors: KPMG LLP

LOCATIONS

HQ: Navistar International Corp.
2701 Navistar Drive, Lisle, IL 60532
Phone: 331 332-5000
Web: www.navistar.com

2014 Sales

	$ mil.	% of total
US	7,760	72
Brazil	833	8
Canada	749	7
Mexico	657	6
Other	807	7
Total	**10,806**	**100**

PRODUCTS/OPERATIONS

2016 Sales

	$ mil.	% of total
Truck	5,403	64
Parts	2,427	29
Global Operations	341	4
Financial services	235	3
Corporate and Eliminations	(295)	-
Total	**8,111**	**100**

2016 Sales

	$ mil.	% of total
United States	6,186	76
Canada	604	8
Mexico	575	7
Brazil	240	3
Other	506	6
Total	**8,111**	**100**

Selected Brands Products and Services

Engines
  MaxxForce
  MWM International

Services

Navistar Electronics
Navistar Financial
Navistar Parts
Vehicles
  IC Bus
  International Trucks
  Navistar Defense

COMPETITORS

All American Group	Hino Motors
BAE SYSTEMS	Isuzu
Blue Bird	Mercedes-Benz U.S.
Cummins	International
Daimler	Mitsubishi Motors
Deere	North America
Detroit Diesel	Oshkosh Truck
Fiat Chrysler	PACCAR
Force Protection	Scania
Ford Motor	Spartan Motors
Forest River	Thor Industries
Freightliner Custom	Tiffin Motorhomes
Chassis	Toyota
General Dynamics	UD Trucks
General Dynamics Land	Volvo
Systems	Winnebago
General Motors	

HISTORICAL FINANCIALS

Company Type: Public

Income Statement

FYE: October 31

	REVENUE ($ mil.)	NET INCOME ($ mil.)	NET PROFIT MARGIN	EMPLOYEES
10/17	8,570	30	0.4%	11,400
10/16	8,111	(97)	—	11,300
10/15	10,140	(184)	—	13,200
10/14	10,806	(619)	—	14,200
10/13	10,775	(898)	—	14,800
Annual Growth	**(5.6%)**	**—**		**(6.3%)**

2017 Year-End Financials

Debt ratio: 82.44%
Return on equity: ***,***.**%
Cash ($ mil.): 706
Current ratio: 1.14
Long-term debt ($ mil.): 3,889

No. of shares (mil.): 98
Dividends
  Yield: —
  Payout: —
Market value ($ mil.): 4,168

	STOCK PRICE ($) FY Close	P/E High/Low	Earnings	Dividends	Book Value
10/17	42.31	140 71	0.32	0.00	(46.48)
10/16	22.30	— —	(1.19)	0.00	(64.93)
10/15	12.30	— —	(2.25)	0.00	(63.40)
10/14	35.37	— —	(7.60)	0.00	(57.15)
10/13	36.16	— —	(11.17)	0.00	(45.28)
Annual Growth	**4.0%**		**—**	**—**	**—**

NBT Bancorp. Inc.

NBT Bancorp is the holding company for NBT Bank which operates about 155 branches mainly in suburban and rural areas of central and northern New York northeastern Pennsylvania western Massachusetts southern New Hampshire and northwestern Vermont. The bank offers traditional deposit accounts and trust services and specializes in making business and commercial real estate loans. NBT also holds two main financial services subsidiaries: the EPIC Advisors unit administers retirement plans while Mang Insurance Agency sells personal and commercial coverage. NBT Capital provides venture funding to growing area businesses.

Operations

Other subsidiaries include property manager Broad Street Property Associates title insurance firm NBT Realty Services real estate investment trusts CNB Realty Trust and Alliance Preferred Funding Corp and and equipment leasing services provider Alliance Leasing.

About 63% of the bank's total revenue came from loan interest (including fees) in 2015 while another 7% came from interest on investment securities. The rest of its revenue came from insurance and other financial services fees (6% of revenue) deposit account service charges (4%) ATM and debit card fees (5%) retirement plan administration fees (4%) trust fees (5%) and other miscellaneous sources.

Sales and Marketing

NBT Bancorp serves individuals businesses and municipalities. The bank spent $2.7 million on advertising during 2015 down from $2.8 million and $3.2 million in 2014 and 2013 respectively.

Financial Performance

NBT Bancorp's annual revenue has risen more than 20% since 2011 mostly as bank acquisitions have buoyed its loan business. Meanwhile its annual profit has grown by one-third.

The bank's revenue dipped 2% to $391.7 million during 2015 however mostly as the low-interest environment continued to squeeze its interest margins on its loans and investment securities. It also collected $15 million less in (non-recurring) gains from the sale of its Springtone investment compared to the prior year.

Despite modest revenue declines in 2015 NBT's net income climbed 2% to $76.43 million primarily because in 2014 it had incurred $17.9 million in non-recurring prepayment penalties as it paid down its long-term debt. The company's operating cash levels jumped 42% to $124.54 million for the year mostly as it collected more in net proceeds on the sale of its loans held for sale and sold off more of its non-loan assets.

Strategy

New York-based NBT Bancorp has expanded its financial service lines outside of traditional banking on its own and through acquisitions in recent years.

Mergers and Acquisitions

In October 2015 NBT Bancorp beefed up its Wealth Management and 401(k) recordkeeping businesses after purchasing New Hampshire-based Third Party Administrators Inc which provided administrative services for 401(k) profit sharing and defined benefit plans on behalf of 700 businesses and Section 125 administration. The $4.1 million acquisition helped complement services offered by its Wealth Management division and EPIC Advisors affiliate.

In March 2013 NBT purchased Alliance Financial for $233 million which bolstered its presence in central New York by adding 26 branches in Onondaga Cortland Madison Oneida and Oswego counties. The deal also added $1.4 billion in assets including $920 million in net loans held for investment and $1.1 billion in deposits.

Company Background

NBT Bancorp remained profitable through the recession even as real estate values fell and the number of non-performing loans in its portfolio grew. To do this the company increased its loan collection efforts and focused on selling conforming real estate mortgages. It also stopped originating auto leases.

NBT Bancorp was founded in 1986. However NBT Bank traces its roots to 1856.

EXECUTIVES

Executive Vice President and President Retail Banking; President Pennsylvania, David Raven
SEVP and CFO, Michael J. Chewens, age 55, $446,610 total compensation
EVP; President Commercial Banking, Jeffrey M. Levy, age 55, $436,000 total compensation
President and CEO, John H. Watt, age 58
EVP Operations and Retail Banking, Joseph R. Stagliano
EVP Chief Human Resources Officer and Chief Ethics Officer, Catherine M. Scarlett
EVP; President Wealth Management, Timothy L. Brenner, age 60, $331,050 total compensation
EVP General Counsel and Corporate Secretary, F. Sheldon Prentice
EVP; President New England, Matthew K. Durkee
EVP and President Commercial Banking, Sarah A. Halliday
Vice President and Retirement Plan Services Manager, Peter Kain
Senior Vice President Of Sales, Rita Demarko
Assistant Vice President, Kellyanne Truesdale
Assistant Vice President Information Technology Officer Security Officer, Heidi Fisher
Executive Vice President and Director Human Resources, Thomas Delduchetto
Regional President, Stephen Lubelczyk
Senior Vice President Southern Tier Regional Commercial Banking Manager Director of Business Banking, David Theleman
Vice President and Director of Compliance Risk Man, Patrick Gleason
Vice President Information Processing, Robert Keller
Assistant Vice President And Desktop Services Mana, Robert Hill
Assistant Vice President Systems Development, Jennifer Olds
Assistant Vice President and Audit Manager, Bryan Green
Director Media Relations, Salvator Arcidiacono
Vice President Commercial Lending, Richard Soden
Executive Vice President Marketing, Constance Bucknell
Chairman, Martin A. Dietrich, age 61
Auditors: KPMG LLP

LOCATIONS

HQ: NBT Bancorp. Inc.
52 South Broad Street, Norwich, NY 13815
Phone: 607 337-2265 **Fax:** 607 336-7538
Web: www.nbtbancorp.com

PRODUCTS/OPERATIONS

2015 Sales

	$ mil.	% of total
Interest		
Interest and fees on loans	241	63
Securities available for sale	20	5
Securities held to maturity	9	2
Other	1	-
Non-interest		
Insurance and other financial services revenue	24	6
Service charges on deposit accounts	17	4
Trust	19	5
ATM & debit card fees	18	5
Retirement plan administration fees	14	4
Bank-owned life insurance income	4	1
Gain on the sale of Springtone investment	4	1
Net securities gains	3	1
Other	14	4
Total	**391**	**100**

Selected Subsidiaries

Broad Street Property Associates Inc.
CNB Realty Trust
Colonial Finance Services Inc.
EPIC Advisors Inc.
FNB Financial Services Inc.
Hathaway Agency Inc.
LA Lease Inc.
Mang Insurance Agency LLC
NBT Bank National Association
NBT Capital Corp.
NBT Financial Services Inc.
NBT Holdings Inc.
NBT Services Inc.
Pennstar Bank Services Company
Pennstar Financial Services Inc.

COMPETITORS

Astoria Financial	M&T Bank
Community Bank System	Oneida Financial
HSBC USA	Sovereign Bank
KeyCorp	TrustCo Bank Corp NY

HISTORICAL FINANCIALS

Company Type: Public

Income Statement

FYE: December 31

	ASSETS ($ mil.)	NET INCOME ($ mil.)	INCOME AS % OF ASSETS	EMPLOYEES
12/16	8,867	78	0.9%	1,704
12/15	8,262	76	0.9%	1,721
12/14	7,797	75	1.0%	1,840
12/13	7,652	61	0.8%	1,742
12/12	6,042	54	0.9%	1,581
Annual Growth	**10.1%**	**9.5%**	**—**	**1.9%**

2016 Year-End Financials

Debt ratio: 2.32%	No. of shares (mil.): 43
Return on equity: 8.71%	Dividends
Cash ($ mil.): 149	Yield: 0.0%
Current ratio: —	Payout: 50.0%
Long-term debt ($ mil.): —	Market value ($ mil.): 1,812

	STOCK PRICE ($) FY Close	P/E High/Low	PER SHARE ($) Earnings	Dividends	Book Value
12/16	41.88	23 13	1.80	0.90	21.11
12/15	27.88	17 13	1.72	0.87	20.31
12/14	26.27	16 13	1.69	0.84	19.69
12/13	25.90	18 13	1.46	0.81	18.77
12/12	20.27	15 12	1.62	0.80	17.24
Annual Growth	**19.9%**	**— —**	**2.7%**	**3.0%**	**5.2%**

NCL CORPORATION LTD.

Auditors: PRICEWATERHOUSEC-OOPERS LLP MI

LOCATIONS

HQ: NCL CORPORATION LTD.
7665 CORPORATE CENTER DR, MIAMI, FL 331261201
Phone: 305 436-4000

HISTORICAL FINANCIALS

Company Type: Private

Income Statement

FYE: December 31

	REVENUE ($ mil.)	NET INCOME ($ mil.)	NET PROFIT MARGIN	EMPLOYEES
12/16	4,874	643	13.2%	24,900
12/15	4,345	437	10.1%	—
12/14	3,125	339	10.8%	—
12/13	2,570	119	4.7%	—
Annual Growth	**23.8%**	**75.1%**		

Debt ratio: ——
Return on equity: 13.20%
Cash ($ mil.): 126
Current ratio: 0.10
Long-term debt ($ mil.): ——

Dividends
Yield: —
Payout: —
Market value ($ mil.): —

NCR Corp

NCR?s products don?t ?ka-ching? anymore but the company still registers with people and money. Born in the 1880s as National Cash Register NCR is a leading maker of ATMs point-of-sale (POS) terminals bar code scanners and related printer consumables. Its other retail and financial systems offerings include check image processing systems and self-service kiosks for hospitality retail and travel. NCR's services segment provides maintenance and support as well as professional services such as systems integration and managed services. NCR does business in more than 180 countries. International customers generate more than half of the company?s sales. Its products enable more than 650 million transactions a day.

Operations

In 2016 NCR began reporting financial results as solutions segments rather than line-of-business reflecting the switch to a more software-oriented business model. The new segments are software services and hardware.

The company?s hardware products about 40% of revenue consist of several lines of automated teller machines (ATMs) cash dispensers cash recycling ATMs and hardware for check and image processing. Among other hardware products are point-of-sale (POS) terminals self-checkout kiosks order and payment kiosks bar code scanners printers and peripherals.

NCR?s services segment generates 35% of revenue by helping users get hardware and software up and running and in some cases managing entire systems. The company Predictive Services helps customers identify and address technology issues.

NCR?s software products accounting for the remaining revenue run the company?s hardware. Its software platforms include the Cx Banking self-service ATM software application suite for financial services the Retail ONE and Aloha Enterprise software for the retail and hospitality industries and NCR Silver a cloud-based point-of-sale (POS) system for small businesses.

Geographic Reach

The US is NCR's largest market accounting for about 45% of sales. Europe and the AMEA (Asia Middle East and Africa) region account for more than 30% of revenue. The Asia/Pacific region ? including Japan ? generates about 15% of revenue.

The company operates more than a dozen research and development and manufacturing facilities around the world.

Sales and Marketing

NCR's products and services are marketed primarily through a direct sales force although it does tap a network of distributors and resellers.

Recurring revenue and product revenue each supply more than 40% of NCR?s sales with installation services accounting for 15%.

Financial Performance

NCR rebounded with higher revenue and a profit in 2016 after a sales dip and net loss in 2015. Cash flow from operations also surged in 2016 from 2015.

Revenue rose about 3% to $6.5 billion in 2016 from $6.4 billion. The Americas drove the increase with higher sales in hardware software and services. Overall software and services increased sales in 2016 while hardware broke even as growth from ATM and self-checkout machines was offset by declines in point-of-sale and consumables because of a divestiture. Cloud revenue was up 9% from previous bookings aided by mobile banking growth.

NCR rang up a $270 million profit in 2016 a turnaround from a $180 million loss in 2015. The company reduced costs for sales general and administrative functions as well as pension-related costs. The company spent more on research and development in 2016 but the amount was consistent with past levels of R&D as a percentage of revenue.

Higher net income and improvements in working capital pushed cash flow from operations to $895 million in 2016 from $680 million in 2015.

Strategy

NCR is building software hardware and services to help businesses and customer conduct transactions however they want ? what NCR calls the omni-channel experience. That could mean conducting an ATM transaction with a live teller via video or checking out of a grocery store without putting items on the checkout conveyor belt.

Software drives the hardware and that?s what NCR emphasizes. Software can be updated more frequently to provide better experiences for stores and their customers. But NCR continues to roll out new ATM and POS hardware. In fact the company said it introduced a record number of hardware products in 2016. The costs associated with the new products reduced NCR?s hardware revenue for the year. The company?s service segment gets into the mix by helping customers make the best use of their hardware and software.

The company has also improved its business processes including investing in systems for billings and invoices that helped reduce its days sales outstanding by six days in 2016.

In 2016 NCR sold its Interactive Printer Solutions Division to Atlas Holdings. The division provided consumable products that include stock and custom color-printed paper receipt rolls pressure-sensitive labels impact inking and thermal transfer ribbons. NCR said the division no longer fit into its software-focused portfolio.

Mergers and Acquisitions

In 2016 NCR acquired CimpleBox Inc. a provider of simplified Software-as-a-Service-based back office software to small and medium-sized businesses such as restaurants and retailers. CimpleBox software helps businesses reduce the time spent on manual processes consolidates data and scheduling and gives managers more insight into the business and day-to-day operations.

EXECUTIVES

Chairman CEO and President, William R. (Bill) Nuti, age 53, $1,000,000 total compensation
President and COO, Mark D. Benjamin, age 47, $129,808 total compensation
SVP and CTO Software Solutions, Eli Rosner
EVP CFO and Chief Accounting Officer, Robert P. (Bob) Fishman, age 53, $611,539 total compensation
EVP Chief Administration Officer and Chief Human Resources Officer, Andrea L. Ledford, age 51
EVP Global Software, Paul Langenbahn, $460,193 total compensation
SVP and President Retail Solutions Division, Michael B. Bayer, age 53, $497,358 total compensation
CIO, William T. (Bill) VanCuren
EVP Services Hardware Solutions and Enterprise Quality, Frederick J. (Rick) Marquardt, age 58, $611,539 total compensation

SVP General Counsel and Secretary, Edward Gallagher
Assistant Law Vice President, Ellen Samuels
Vice President, Ken Fabian
Assistant Vice President, Carl Cirillo
Vice President Global Services, Mark Vigoroso
Executive Vice President, Jon Wulf
Vice President Hospitality North American Channel Operations, Lyn Ivester
Vice President Financial Solutions Division Manufacturing Operations Solutions Delivery, Ernest Miller
Vice President of Architecture and Engineering, Joe White
Vice President Fp And A, Adam Mallah
Vice President Travel and Entertainment, Dennis Davidson
Vice President Services, Peter Christie
Accounting Vice President, Kitty Reed
Vice President of Services Wal Mart, Phillip Pack
Vice President of Healthcare and Retail Sales, Ralph Lamphere
Vice President Sales, John Carter
Vice President Communications, Anthony Piniella
National Account Manager, Wayne Miller
Vice President, Richard Arnold
Vice President Retail Marketing Retail Solutions Group, Daniel Bogen
Global Vice President For Operational Excellence A, George Patterson
National Account Manager, Greg O'Brien
Vice President Marketing and Sales Transformation, Greta Krupetsky
Vice President, Jeffrey Davison
Vice President Of Information Technology, Sam Coursen
Vice President Operations, Dion Shelton
Vice President Global Sales and Marketing, Joao Perez
Vice President Latin America and Caribbean, Marcelo Zuccas
Vice President and General Manager, Steven Arthur
Vice President, Reza Ghorieshi
Auditors: PricewaterhouseCoopers LLP

LOCATIONS

HQ: NCR Corp
3097 Satellite Boulevard, Duluth, GA 30096
Phone: 937 445-5000
Web: www.ncr.com

2015 Sales

	$ mil.	% of total
Americas		
US	2,909	46
Other	590	9
Europe Middle East & Africa	1,964	31
Asia Pacific	910	14
Total	**6,373**	**100**

PRODUCTS/OPERATIONS

2015 Sales

	$ mil.	% of total
Product	2,711	42
Service		
Recurring revenue	2,718	43
Professional and installation services	944	15
Total	**6,373**	**100**

2015 Sales

	$ mil.	% of total
Financial services	3,319	52
Retail solutions	2,001	31
Hospitality	686	11
Emerging industries	367	6
Total	**6,373**	**100**

COMPETITORS

ACI Worldwide	IBM
Acxiom	Ingenico
BancTec	MICROS Systems
Cummins-Allison	Motorola Solutions
Datalogic Scanning	Netflix
De La Rue	Oki Electric
Dell	Optimal Group
Diebold	Oracle
Fidelity National	Outerwall
Information Services	PAR Technology
Fiserv	Retalix
Fujitsu	SANYO
Gilbarco	SITA
HP	Toshiba TEC
Honeywell	Triton Systems
International	Unisys
Hyosung	VeriFone

HISTORICAL FINANCIALS

Company Type: Public

Income Statement

FYE: December 31

	REVENUE ($ mil.)	NET INCOME ($ mil.)	NET PROFIT MARGIN	EMPLOYEES
12/16	6,543	270	4.1%	33,500
12/15	6,373	(178)	—	32,600
12/14	6,591	191	2.9%	30,200
12/13	6,123	443	7.2%	29,300
12/12	5,730	146	2.5%	25,700
Annual Growth	3.4%	16.6%	—	6.9%

2016 Year-End Financials

Debt ratio: 39.76%
Return on equity: 17.60%
Cash ($ mil.): 498
Current ratio: 1.40
Long-term debt ($ mil.): 3,001

No. of shares (mil.): 124
Dividends
  Yield: —
  Payout: —
Market value ($ mil.): 5,054

	STOCK PRICE ($) FY Close	P/E High/Low		PER SHARE ($) Earnings	Dividends	Book Value
12/16	40.56	24	11	1.71	0.00	12.38
12/15	24.46	—	—	(1.09)	0.00	11.41
12/14	29.14	33	21	1.12	0.00	11.10
12/13	34.06	16	10	2.62	0.00	10.62
12/12	25.48	28	18	0.89	0.00	7.66
Annual Growth	12.3%	—	—	17.7%	—	12.7%

Neiman Marcus Group Ltd LLC

LOCATIONS

HQ: Neiman Marcus Group Ltd LLC
1618 Main Street, Dallas, TX 75201
Phone: 214 743-7600

HISTORICAL FINANCIALS

Company Type: Public

Income Statement

FYE: July 29

	REVENUE ($ mil.)	NET INCOME ($ mil.)	NET PROFIT MARGIN	EMPLOYEES
07/17	4,766	(531)	—	13,700
07/16*	5,010	(406)	—	14,300
08/15	5,147	14	0.3%	15,100
08/14	3,750	(134)	—	
11/13	1,143	(13)	—	
Annual Growth	42.9%	—	—	—

*Fiscal year change

2017 Year-End Financials

Debt ratio: 61.08%
Return on equity:
Cash ($ mil.): 49
Current ratio: 1.72
Long-term debt ($ mil.): 4,675

No. of shares (mil.): 0
Dividends
  Yield: —
  Payout: —
Market value ($ mil.): —

Nelnet Inc

Got Ivy League tastes on a community college budget? Nelnet may be able to help. The education planning and financing company helps students and parents plan and pay for college educations. Nelnet is mostly known for servicing federal student loans. The firm manages about $76 billion in student loan assets most of which are government loans. However in light of regulatory changes to the student lending market Nelnet is increasingly expanding its fee-based education services. It serves the K-12 and higher education marketplace providing long-term payment plans college enrollment services and software and technology services. The firm is part of financial holding company Farmers & Merchants Investment.

Operations

Nelnet provides innovative educational services in loan servicing payment processing education planning and asset management for families and educational institutions. The Company's four operating segments offer a broad range of services designed to simplify education planning and financing for students and families and the administrative and financial processes for schools and financial institutions.

The largest is Asset Generation and Management which acquires and manages Nelnet's student loan holdings. The portfolio includes Nelnet's existing loans originated under the now-defunct Federal Family Education Loan Program (FFELP). However in efforts to diversify its fee-based business and lessen its dependence on student loans the company is focused on developing new products and growing in areas such as tuition payment processing and lead generation products and services such as enrollment management and test prep services.

The three fee-based segments include Student Loan and Guaranty Servicing which services FFELP and other third-party loans writes and services private student loans and provides loan servicing software. (Nelnet is one of four companies providing servicing for the Department of Education.) Tuition Payment Processing and Campus Commerce serves the K-12 market as well as higher education providing financing for families and processing services for schools. Enrollment Services works to connect students with schools by providing marketing for schools and publishing school directories and test preparation study guides for potential students.

Geographic Reach

The company has offices in the US and Canada.

Sales and Marketing

The company's customers include students and families colleges and universities specifically financial aid business and admissions offices K-12 schools lenders state agencies and government entities.

Financial Performance

Nelnet has seen steady growth in revenues in the last few years. In 2013 the company's revenue increased to $1.14 billion (compared to $923.7 million in 2012) primarily due to an increase in Student Loan and Guaranty Servicing (as the result of growth in servicing volume under the company's contract with the Department of Education) and an increase in collection revenues from defaulted FFELP loan assets on behalf of guaranty agencies. Tuition Payment Processing and Campus Commerce revenues grew due to a higher number of managed tuition payment plans as a result of providing more plans at existing schools and obtaining new school customers.

Net income increased to $302.7 million in 2013 (from $117.8 million in 2012) due to higher revenues and lower operating costs (the result of a decrease in depreciation and amortization costs).

In 2013 Nelnet's operating cash flow increased to $387.2 million (compared to $299.3 million in 2012) due to higher net income and proceeds from the termination of one of the company's cross-currency interest rate swaps. The increase in cash provided by operating activities was partially offset by the impacts of changes in non-cash fair value adjustments for derivatives.

Strategy

The company grows organically and through acquisitions.

Mergers and Acquisitions

To strengthen its student loans business Nelnet in 2014 acquired CIT's student lending business for $1.1 billion. The deal included all of CIT's government-guaranteed student loans assets and servicing rights.

In 2014 FACTS Management brand a part of Nelnet's Tuition Payment Processing and Campus Commerce segment and the leader in payment plan services for K-12 schools acquired RenWeb School Management Software one of the leading school information systems for private and faith-based schools. RenWeb currently helps over 3000 schools automate administrative processes like admissions scheduling student billing attendance and grade book management. By automating these tasks RenWeb gives teachers more time to shape the lives of students while saving money and resources. FACTS helps over 6500 schools with tuition management billing and financial aid assessment services.

Company Background

Nelnet has been through a turbulent few years as student loan reform and the financial crisis disrupted business and sent revenues down. The company's ability to adapt to the economic pressures and policy changes have helped it land face-up following the recession. Measures taken including laying off staff and tightening lending practices helped boost profits despite lower revenues. Although non-FFELP servicing income and payment processing revenues grew in 2011 FFELP servicing revenues declined as the portfolio further shrunk and school marketing sales decreased as schools cut back on spending. As a result revenues fell that year by 8% to $979 million. Net income increased 8% (to $204 million) in 2011 compared to 2010 when the company had expenses related to restructuring. Also in 2010 Nelnet paid the US government $55 million to settle a lawsuit claiming it had made false statements to receive extra subsidies.

In a blow to the student lending industry President Barack Obama eliminated the FFELP and prohibited private lenders from making federal student loans in 2010. All new federal student loans began going directly through the Department of Education's Direct Loan Program. As a result Nelnet no longer originates new FFELP loans.

But the change didn't put an end to Nelnet. The company was awarded a five-year servicing contract for federally owned student loans including existing FFELP loans. Nelnet also began servicing new loans generated directly under the Federal Direct Loan Program. The contract was a major win for the company. Nelnet expects that its fee-based revenue will increase as the servicing volume for these loans increases (while the FFELP portfolio declines). The company is also focusing on improving its customer service to increase the allotted percentage of new government loans it services.

CEO Michael Dunlap controls the company holding 68% of the voting power for Nelnet. Dunlap and his family also own Farmers & Merchants Investment.

EXECUTIVES

COO, Terry J. Heimes, age 53, $550,000 total compensation
CEO, Jeffrey R. (Jeff) Noordhoek, age 51, $550,000 total compensation
President, Timothy A. (Tim) Tewes, age 58, $375,000 total compensation
CFO, James D. (Jim) Kruger, $375,000 total compensation
Regional Vice President Of Sales K 12 Mi, Mike Spanier
Executive Chairman, Michael S. (Mike) Dunlap, age 54
Vice Chairman, Stephen F. (Steve) Butterfield, age 65
Auditors: KPMG LLP

LOCATIONS

HQ: Nelnet Inc
121 South 13th Street, Suite 100, Lincoln, NE 68508
Phone: 402 458-2370
Web: www.nelnet.com

PRODUCTS/OPERATIONS

2015 Sales

	$ mil.	% of total
Interest		
Loans	726	60
Investments	7	1
Noninterest		
Loan & guaranty servicing	239	20
Enrollment services	70	6
Tuition payment processing & campus commerce revenue	120	10
Gains on sale of loans & debt repurchases net	5	1
Other	32	2
Total	**1,202**	**100**

COMPETITORS

American Student Assistance
Bank of America
Brazos Higher Education Service Corp.
College Loan Corporation
First Marblehead
Great Lakes Higher Education
JPMorgan Chase
Pennsylvania Higher Education Assistance Agency
Sallie Mae
Texas Guaranteed
Wells Fargo

HISTORICAL FINANCIALS

Company Type: Public

Income Statement

FYE: December 31

	ASSETS ($ mil.)	NET INCOME ($ mil.)	INCOME AS % OF ASSETS	EMPLOYEES
12/16	27,180	256	0.9%	3,700
12/15	30,485	267	0.9%	3,400
12/14	30,098	307	1.0%	3,100
12/13	27,770	302	1.1%	2,800
12/12	26,607	178	0.7%	2,500
Annual Growth	0.5%	9.6%	—	10.3%

2016 Year-End Financials

Debt ratio: 90.76%
Return on equity: 12.98%
Cash ($ mil.): 69
Current ratio: —
Long-term debt ($ mil.): —

No. of shares (mil.): 42
Dividends
Yield: 0.0%
Payout: 8.3%
Market value ($ mil.): 2,137

	STOCK PRICE ($) FY Close	P/E High/Low		PER SHARE ($) Earnings	Dividends	Book Value
12/16	50.75	9	5	6.02	0.50	48.96
12/15	33.57	8	5	5.89	0.42	42.87
12/14	46.33	7	5	6.62	0.40	37.31
12/13	42.14	7	4	6.50	0.40	31.13
12/12	29.79	8	6	3.74	1.40	25.00
Annual Growth	14.2%	—	—	12.6%	(22.7%)	18.3%

NetApp, Inc.

NetApp knows storage backwards and forwards and on premise and in the cloud. The company makes hardware and software for storing managing accessing and analyzing data. Its products extend customers' IT infrastructure to the cloud environments of Amazon Google IBM and Microsoft.. The company?s Data Fabric platform is designed to simplify and automate data while its FlexPod product developed with Cisco Systems is designed to helped customers manage applications from Oracle SAP and Citrix. The company mainly sells to the energy financial services government health care and IT sectors through distributors.

Operations

NetApp gets revenue from the sale of products and providing software maintenance and hardware maintenance. Products provide about 55% of revenue while hardware maintenance accounts for nearly 30% and software maintenance about 15%.

The company sells configured systems which are bundled hardware and software products as well as add-on flash disk and hybrid storage and related operating systemS original equipment manufacturer products and add-on hardware and software.

The company?s products include flash storage systems and the software for running those systems. Hardware and software fall under the company?s Data Fabric platform designed to help customers store manage and access data. Hardware products include all-flash and hybrid flash arrays. Software systems include NetApp Cloud Sync NetApp Private Storage (NPS) for Cloud AltaVault Cloud-integrated Solutions the NetApp Software Portfolio and the ONTAP Storage Operating System. The ONTAP Cloud storage data management service runs on Amazon Web Services and the Microsoft Azure public cloud.

NetApp outsources the production of its hardware to third parties operating in the US Mexico Europe and Asia.

Geographic Reach

NetApp has customers that it reaches directly or through partners in some 140 countries. The US is the company?s largest market with 55% of sales. The Europe the Middle East and Africa region accounts for about 30% of revenue while the Asia/Pacific region generates the rest.

Sales and Marketing

NetApp has field sales offices in 45 countries. It employs a multichannel distribution strategy selling products and services to end users and service providers through a direct sales force and through channel partners including value-added resellers

system integrators OEMs and distributors. Distributors handle a significant amount of NetApp?s sales with Arrow Electronics Inc. and Avnet Inc. each accounting for some 20% of revenue.

Financial Performance

While NetApp's revenue declined for the third year in a row in 2017 (ended April) at $5.5 billion it was off less than 1% from 2016. Sales of the company?s newer products rose 17% in 2017 driven by a 15% rise in unit volume of Clustered ONTAP systems. Sales of mature products fell about 21% propelled by a 57% decrease in unit volume of 7-mode systems. Sales of add-on hardware storage and related OS products dropped 11% while OEM revenues rose 4%.

NetApp?s net income soared 122% to $509 million in 2017 from 2016 generated by lower operating expenses from cost reduction initiatives and a lower tax rate (23.5% in 2017 down from 33.6% in 2016).

The company generated cash flow from operations of $986 million in 2017 up from $974 million in 2016 from the higher net income.

Strategy

A large part of NetApp's strategy is to help its customers move their storage to the cloud computing environment and manage data between different environments such as between private and hybrid clouds. The company has concentrated on developing software that helps customers manage data over various systems as storage hardware has fallen in favor with companies.

That means that instead of competing with cloud providers like Amazon's Amazon Web Services IBM SoftLayer and Microsoft's Azure NetApp wants to make it easier for customers to use those services. NetApp is focused on products to help customers extend their IT infrastructure including data management and data protection to Azure and AWS.

To help develop new cloud and other product offerings NetApp operates a research and development lab in Research Triangle Park North Carolina. The lab provides shared-services infrastructure for testing its hardware and software against conditions found in enterprise data centers and cloud environments.

In 2017 the company restructured and reduced headcount (6%) for the second straight year. The 207 restructuring incurred charges of about $52 million that were mostly related to employee terminations. The company also reduced its R&D spending in 2017. It fell to about $780 million for the year down from $861 million in 2016 and from about $920 in 2015 and 2014.

Mergers and Acquisitions

NetApp continues to use acquisitions to add functionality to its product line to enter new markets and to adapt to evolving technology.

In 2016 the company acquired SolidFire Inc. a maker of all-flash storage systems based in Colorado for $870 million. The purchase extended NetApp's presence in the all-flash array market. SolidFire products were incorporated into NetApp's Data Fabric strategy.

EXECUTIVES

EVP, David Hitz, age 54, $322,500 total compensation
EVP Human Resources, Gwendolyn (Gwen) McDonald
CTO, Mark F. Bregman, age 60
EVP Worldwide Field and Customer Operations, Henri Richard
SVP Field Strategy and Operations, Tom Gerstenberger
President and CEO, George Kurian, age 50, $480,000 total compensation
EVP Product Operations, Joel Reich

SVP Chief Strategy Officer and General Manager Cloud Business, Jonathan (Jon) Kissane
EVP and CFO, Ron Pasek
CIO, Bill Miller
Senior Vice President, Jay Kidd
Senior Vice President Finance Corporate Controller, Nicholas Noviello
Vice President Information Technology, Dona Munsch
Vice President of Continuous Product Engineering, Deepak Visweswariah
Vice President, Maria Olson
Vice President and General Manager France, Marc Montiel
Vice President World Wide Legal Commer, Tim OLeary
Vice President Of Field Information technology, Michael Kiernan
Vice President of Human Resources Operations, Nancy Saunders
Assistant Vice President, Carole Lloyd
Vice President, Cherie Farris
Vice President Produc, Steffen Low
Vice President corporate Controller, Mark Valentine
Vice President Advanced Technology Group, Scott Dawkins
Executive Vice President Global SVS, Ed Deenihan
Vice President tax, Jeffrey Bergmann
Vice President Worldwide Sales Operations, Jane Vaillancourt
Senior Director Vice President Service Support, Larry Bump
Vice President of Engineering, Kirk Law
Vice President Of Human Resources, Sven Kinden
Vice President And General Manager, Jon Mellon
Vice President Americas Channel Sales, Todd Palmer
Vice President Corporate Development, Steve Mitzenmacher
Vice President Americas Marketing, Brian Bakstran
Vice President of Human Resources, Derek Bomar
Vice president, Brett Colbert
Vice President Quality And Customer Advocacy, Fred Pocock
Vice President Customer Experience, Steve Blaz
Vice President Of Human Resources, Jeanne Mccready
Executive Vice President Operations, Rob Salmon
NATIONAL ACCOUNT MANAGER, Scott Susi
Senior Vice President Operations, Bill Berg
Senior Vice President, John Kidd
Vice President, Thomas Kurian
VICE PRESIDENT OF QUALITY AND CUSTOMER ADVOCACY, Jim Bampos
Executive Vice President and Chief Financial Officer, Jeff Hall
VICE PRESIDENT GLOBAL CUSTOMER SUCCESS, Andrew Kahl
Vice President Software Engineering, Bob Wood
Vice President, David Mooney
Chairman, T. Michael (Mike) Nevens, age 68
Vice Chairman, Tom Mendoza
Board Of Directors, Ronald Fisher
Member Board Of Directors, Robert Wall
Treasurer Sergeant, Dan Chilton
Treasurer, Chris Afarian
Auditors: DELOITTE & TOUCHE LLP

LOCATIONS

HQ: NetApp, Inc.
1395 Crossman Avenue, Sunnyvale, CA 94089
Phone: 408 822-6000
Web: www.netapp.com

2017 Sales

	$ mil.	% of total
Americas	3,077	56
Europe Middle East & Africa	1,712	31
Asia Pacific	730	13
Total	5,546	100

PRODUCTS/OPERATIONS

2017 Sales

	$ mil.	% of total
Product	3,006	54
Hardware maintenance and other services	1,548	29
Software maintenance	965	17
Total	5,519	100

Selected Products

Object Storage Software
OnCommand Management Software
Platform OS
Protection Software
Protocols
Storage Security Systems
Storage Systems
Data OnTap storage operating system.

COMPETITORS

Dell	Microsoft
Dot Hill	Oracle
Hewlett Packard Enterprise	Quantum Corporation
Hitachi Data Systems	XIO
IBM	Xyratex

HISTORICAL FINANCIALS

Company Type: Public

Income Statement

FYE: April 28

	REVENUE ($ mil.)	NET INCOME ($ mil.)	NET PROFIT MARGIN	EMPLOYEES
04/17	5,519	509	9.2%	10,100
04/16	5,546	229	4.1%	12,030
04/15	6,122	559	9.1%	12,810
04/14	6,325	637	10.1%	12,490
04/13	6,332	505	8.0%	13,060
Annual Growth	(3.4%)	0.2%		(6.2%)

2017 Year-End Financials

Debt ratio: 15.73%
Return on equity: 18.03%
Cash ($ mil.): 2,444
Current ratio: 1.50
Long-term debt ($ mil.): 744

No. of shares (mil.): 269
Dividends
　Yield: 1.9%
　Payout: 68.4%
Market value ($ mil.): 10,720

	STOCK PRICE ($) FY Close	P/E High/Low	PER SHARE ($) Earnings	Dividends	Book Value
04/17	39.85	23 12	1.81	0.76	10.33
04/16	23.64	47 27	0.77	0.72	10.25
04/15	36.12	25 19	1.75	0.66	11.15
04/14	35.00	25 18	1.83	0.60	11.67
04/13	34.87	29 19	1.37	0.00	13.23
Annual Growth	3.4%	— —	7.2%	—	(6.0%)

Netflix Inc

Netflix and chill? More like Netflix and bill the ever more viewers who subscribe to the video streaming service and watch for more than 125 million hours a day. Besides streaming movies TV shows documentaries and original productions such as Stranger Things to more than 90 million monthly subscribers in more than 190 countries it stills sends DVDs to US customers through the mail (though it now counts for about 5% of revenue). Netflix strikes deals with movie and TV production studios independent producers and others for the rights to distribute their content. To keep viewers binging it deploys increasingly sophisti-

cated algorithms to predict viewer preferences and make recommendations on what to watch next.

Operations

Netflix allows members to view as much as they want with its streaming service and allows simultaneous streaming on multiple devices with higher-cost subscriptions.

The company has organized its business into three operating segments: domestic streaming (about 60% of revenue) international streaming (more than a third of revenue) and domestic DVD (about 5% of revenue).

Geographic Reach

Netflix's business has moved beyond the borders of the US to around the world. The company declares that it does business in more than190 countries. The four countries in which Netflix is not available are the People?s Republic of China Crimea North Korea and Syria.

Sales and Marketing

Netflix has spent increasing amounts of money on advertising hitting more than $840 million in 2016 up from $714 million in 2015 and some $530 million in 2014.

Financial Performance

Netflix has surfed video streaming to revenue increases for the past decade and had been profitable for that time.

In 2016 revenue rose 30% to $8.8 billion from 2015 as the number of subscribers in the US and internationally grew. The average revenue per paying subscriber also has increased up 8% in the US and 4% overseas. The company?s emphasis on international growth is paying off as overseas sales rose about 65% in 2016 and accounted for more than 35% of revenue (up from about 30% in 2015). The US market continued to grow with a greater than 20% revenue increase in 2016 cresting the $5 billion mark. The DVD business shrank once again in 2016 to account for just about 5% of revenue. That?s OK with Netflix since it costs more to run the DVD business than the streaming service. Besides subscriber growth Netflix mixed price increases into its formula.

Netflix posted a better than 50% increase in net income which rose to about $188 million in 2016. Higher revenue drove profit higher but the company also had higher content creation and acquisition costs as well as increased marketing and headcount costs to support international expansion. Further the company had higher interest expense and taxes in 2016.

To support its content acquisition needs Netflix spends more cash than it takes in. It's negative cash flow was about $1.5 billion in 2016 nearly double the 2015 cash outflow. Payments for streaming content assets increased to about $6.8 billion in 2016 from $4.6 billion in 2015.

Strategy

To grow overseas Netflix must contend with rivals that offer DVD rentals in Europe and online downloads of movies. Through strategic agreements Netflix has expanded its library of available selections to satisfy the growing appetites of its customers. During the past few years it has added content from CBS MTV Networks and Sony and continues to explore agreements with pay TV channels and networks such as HBO as it invests in streaming content.

Netflix has shifted to offering more original content that's developed in-house or licensed from production companies and producers. Film and TV stars have become developed Netflix-only productions. They include of Will Smith Brad Pitt Jane Fonda and Robert Redford as well as younger less well-known actors and directors. In 2017 Netflix signed TV producers like Shonda Rhimes and Jenji Kohan to exclusive development deals.

In the past two or so years the company aggressively expanded internationally launching streaming in countries from Cuba to Japan to Australia and New Zealand to Europe and more. It is now available in all but four or so countries. Netflix has created and licensed content for local markets.

The company has plenty of competition much of it coming from producers of content that it licenses. Broadcast networks such as CBS ABC and NBC stream their content. Pay TV companies such as HBO and Showtime also offer streaming services apart from their subscriber businesses. Hulu offers subscription-based TV and movie content as well. Netflix will lose Disney movies from its streaming service by the end of 2018 as Disney intends to launch its own streaming service in 2019. The losses include Disney and Pixar films. Apple Inc. also has initiated its own streaming service. Competition remains in DVD rental too. Redbox offers DVD rentals of new releases and popular movies from many locations such as grocery stores.

Netflix has a cooperative-competitive relationship with Amazon.com. It has moved all of its content to services run by Amazon Web Services even while it competes with Amazon's streaming business.

Mergers and Acquisitions

In 2017 Netflix acquired Millarworld a comic book publisher whose characters include Kick-Ass and Kingsman. With the deal Millarworld's characters will move from the page to the screen via Netflix production and streaming and theatrical release. Mark Millar formerly worked at Marvel and started Millarworld to develop his own comic book franchises. The Kick-Ass and Kingsman comics are not part of the deal but Netflix gets access to other comics in superhero science fiction and other genres. Terms of the deal were not disclosed. The acquisition was Netflix's first.

EXECUTIVES

Chairman President and CEO, Reed Hastings, age 57, $900,000 total compensation

Chief Product Officer, Neil Hunt, age 56, $1,000,000 total compensation

Chief Content Officer, Ted Sarandos, age 53, $1,000,000 total compensation

International Development Officer, Greg Peters, age 46, $1,000,000 total compensation

CFO, David Wells, age 45, $2,400,000 total compensation

Vice President of Product Engineering, Mark White

Vice President, Larry Tanz

Vice President of Product Innovation, Todd Yellin

Vice President and Associate General Counsel, Hilary Ware

Vice President Partner Product Development, Gregory Peters

Vice President Consumer Insights, Zoe Friend

Vice President, Eric Hawkins

Auditors: Ernst & Young LLP

LOCATIONS

HQ: Netflix Inc
100 Winchester Circle, Los Gatos, CA 95032
Phone: 408 540-3700
Web: www.netflix.com

PRODUCTS/OPERATIONS

2016 Sales

	% of total
Domestic Streaming	58
International Streaming	36
Domestic DVD	6
Total	**100**

Selected Netflix Streaming Devices

Apple iPhone
Apple iPad
Apple iPod touch
Apple TV
Blu-ray disc players
Digital video recorders
Google TV
Internet video players
Internet-connected TVs
Home theatre systems
Microsoft Xbox 360 console
Nintendo Wii console
Sony PS3 console

COMPETITORS

AT&T	Google
Amazon.com	HBO
Apple Inc.	Hastings Entertainment
Best Buy	Hulu
Charter Communications	Kroger
Columbia House	Redbox
Comcast	Showtime Networks
Cox Communications	Target Corporation
DIRECTV	Time Warner Cable
DISH Network	Verizon
EchoStar	Wal-Mart

HISTORICAL FINANCIALS

Company Type: Public

Income Statement

				FYE: December 31
	REVENUE ($ mil.)	NET INCOME ($ mil.)	NET PROFIT MARGIN	EMPLOYEES
12/17	11,692	558	4.8%	5,500
12/16	8,830	186	2.1%	4,700
12/15	6,779	122	1.8%	3,700
12/14	5,504	266	4.8%	2,450
12/13	4,374	112	2.6%	2,327
Annual Growth	**27.9%**	**49.3%**	**—**	**24.0%**

2017 Year-End Financials

Debt ratio: 34.18%
Return on equity: 17.85%
Cash ($ mil.): 2,822
Current ratio: 1.40
Long-term debt ($ mil.): 6,499

No. of shares (mil.): 433
Dividends
  Yield: —
  Payout: —
Market value ($ mil.): 83,194

	STOCK PRICE ($) FY Close	P/E High/Low		PER SHARE ($) Earnings	Dividends	Book Value
12/17	191.96	157	99	1.25	0.00	8.26
12/16	123.80	292	188	0.43	0.00	6.23
12/15	114.38	244	0327	0.28	0.00	5.20
12/14	341.61	764	495	0.62	0.00	4.39
12/13	368.17	1380	334	0.26	0.00	3.20
Annual Growth	**(15.0%)**	**—**	**—**	**47.5%**	**—**	**26.8%**

NEW JERSEY HOUSING AND MORTGAGE FINANCE AGENCY

Auditors: CLIFTONLARSONALLEN LLP BALTIM

LOCATIONS

HQ: NEW JERSEY HOUSING AND MORTGAGE FINANCE AGENCY
637 S CLINTON AVE, TRENTON, NJ 086111811
Phone: 609 278-7400
Web: WWW.NJ-HMFA.COM

HISTORICAL FINANCIALS

Company Type: Private

Income Statement

				FYE: December 31
	ASSETS ($ mil.)	NET INCOME ($ mil.)	INCOME AS % OF ASSETS	EMPLOYEES
12/11	4,370	(56)	—	250
12/09	4,362	(21)	—	
Annual Growth	**0.1%**			

2011 Year-End Financials

Debt ratio: ——
Return on equity: (-21.50%)
Cash ($ mil.): 21
Current ratio: 0.10
Long-term debt ($ mil.) ——

Dividends
  Yield: —
  Payout: —
Market value ($ mil.) —

New York Community Bancorp Inc.

It's big banking in the Big Apple and beyond. New York Community Bancorp is the holding company for one of the largest thrifts in the US New York Community Bank as well as New York Commercial Bank (also dba Atlantic Bank) and seven other banking divisions. In its home state New York Community Bank operates through Queens County Savings Bank Richmond County Savings Bank Roosevelt Savings Bank and Roslyn Savings Bank. It serves customers in New Jersey through its Garden State Community Bank division. New York Community Bank also does business as AmTrust Bank which operates in Arizona and Florida and Ohio Savings Bank. Altogether New York Community Bancorp has about 275 bank branches in five states.

Operations

New York Community Bancorp operates two businesses: Banking Operations and Residential Mortgage Banking.

The main banking business generates some 95% of total revenue and serves consumers and businesses with standard services such as checking and savings accounts CDs IRAs credit cards mortgages and loans. It offers life and long-term care insurance through an agreement with third-party provider LPL Financial. New York Community Bancorp typically does not open new stand-alone branches but has been increasing its presence in its market areas by adding locations inside grocery stores and extending business hours. Its commercial arm New York Commercial Bank has 30 branches in Manhattan Queens Brooklyn Westchester County and Long Island including 18 that operate under the name Atlantic Bank. New York Community Bancorp also owns investment advisory firm Peter B. Cannell & Co.

Multifamily mortgage loans (with an emphasis on rent-regulated apartment buildings) are the company's key assets making up more than 70% of its loan book. New York Community Bancorp prefers rent-regulated properties because they tend to have lower-than-average tenant turnover and can often be expected to bring in steady income during economic downturns. The company also focuses on loans secured by commercial real estate in New York and New Jersey.

Geographic Reach

Westbury New York-based New York Community Bancorp has branches in five states: New York home to about 160 community and commercial bank branches; New Jersey with about 45 locations; Ohio and Florida with more than 25 branches each; and Arizona with more than a dozen locations.

Financial Performance

New York Community Bancorp has seen a slow decline in revenue since 2010. In fiscal 2016 sales fell a further 4% to $1.8 billion due to lower returns from securities and money market investments as well as lower mortgage banking income.

Net income was $495.4 in 2016 a sharp increase on the loss of $47.2 million incurred in the previous year. The results reflect a one-off item in 2015 that saw the bank pay $773.8 million to reduce $10.4 billion in wholesale borrowings to a lower cost of debt.

Cash from operations was $755.7 million in 2016 compared to a cash usage of $420.4 million in 2015 primarily for the same reason as changes in net income.

Strategy

To strengthen its balance sheet New York Community Bancorp paid a one-off charge of $773.8 million in 2016 to amend its loan repayment rate from 3.16% to 1.58%. The reduction will save the company $100 million each year.

The company called off its merger with Astoria Bank in later 2016. The deal would have taken the bank over the $50 billion threshold that delineates a systematically important bank and brings tougher regulations and Astoria's more unwieldy footprint would have dragged New York's best-in-class efficiency ratio up.

Company Background

In 2012 it acquired some $2.2 billion in deposits mainly short-term CDs but also money market accounts from Aurora Bank.

New York Community Bank was founded in 1859. New York Community Bancorp was incorporated in 1993.

EXECUTIVES

SEVP and COO, Robert Wann, age 62, $1,100,000 total compensation
President and CEO, Joseph R. Ficalora, age 70, $1,400,000 total compensation
SEVP and CFO, Thomas R. (Tom) Cangemi, age 48, $850,000 total compensation
EVP Chief Corporate Governance Officer and Corporate Secretary, R. Patrick Quinn
SEVP and Chief Lending Officer, James J. Carpenter, age 56, $775,000 total compensation
EVP and Chief Accounting Officer, John J. Pinto, age 46, $575,000 total compensation
EVP and CIO, Robert Brown
Vice President Risk Management, Debbie Messina
Executive Vice President, Barbara Ann Tosi-Renna
Second Vice President Staff Attorney, Laura Coleman
Senior Vice President Mortgage, Charles Baker
Vice President of Advanced Engineering, Marquita Guerra
EXECUTIVE VICE PRESIDENT, William Disalvatore
Senior Vice President, Michael Frain
Vice President Loan Review Officer, Ronald Lehrer
Vice President, Luis Bermeo
Senior Vice President Human RE, Michele Reid
Second Vice President, Boris Gadol
Executive Vice President And Corporate Secretary, R Quinn

First Vice President Loan Recovery Officer, Marc Thomaes
First Senior Vice President and Branch Coordinator, Louis Riccio
Assistant Vice President Procurement, Susan Pace-Burke
Senior Vice President Director of External Reporting, Stephen Zahn
Senior Vice President, Mitchel Baffa
Vice President Sarbanes Oxley Project Manager Executive Oversight Group, Janet Shand
Vice President, Rich Bucceri
Vice President of Finance Treasury, Olga Collins
First Vice President, Debbie Schaum
Edandt Training Manager Vice President, Susan Weaver
Senior Vice President and Controller, James Speranza
First Vice President Marketing, Donna Winfield
Vice President Commercial Lending, John Adams
Senior Vice President Regional Executive, Gail Castellano
Assistant Vice President Manager Of Loan Admin Customer Service, Ken Hsiung
Senior Vice President Development And Reporting Specialist, Artie Gyftopoulos
Vice President Market Manager, Leonard Bosso
Vice President And Commercial Loan Officer, Linda Orth
Second Vice President retail product Manager, Thomas Graziano
Senior Vice President, Ed May
First Vice President, Anna Mak
Vice President, Ines Kurtov
Vice President, Jeff Lee
First Vice President, Scott Armstrong
Second Vice President, Howard Farber
Vice President Audit Manager, Adam Sullivan
Vice President Hris Manager, Nancy Librandi
Senior Vice President, Levi Richardson
Second Vice President, Jeffrey Williams
Second Vice President, Fiona Ng
FIRST VICE PRESIDENT, Sharon Murphy
SECOND VICE PRESIDENT, Sarah Salupo
First Vice President Stock Awards and Options Human Resources, Felicia Lehan
Second Vice President Senior Auditor, Vanessa Carlson
First Vice President, Christopher Beck
First Vice President, Sean Westfall
First Vice President and SOX Compliance Officer, Andrew LaRocca
Vice President Benefits Manager, Frances Kaiser
Assistant Vice President, Danielle Delgrosso
Senior Vice President Portfolio Management, Gordon Roder
Vice President Commercial Lending Relationship Manager, Crystal Quagliata
Vice President Premier Banking Business Development Officer NYCB_123 Bug.png, Dimitra DiFranco
SRPA Assistant Vice President Senior Review Appraiser Appraisal Department, Judy Dean
Vice President Loan Recovery, Laurence Gluckman
Assistant Vice President Network Engineering, Anthony Ardezzone
Executive Vice President and Chief Human Resources Officer, Eric Kracov
Assistant Vice President Commercial Lending, Antoinette Difinizio
First Vice President, Douglas Orth
Chairman, Dominick Ciampa, age 84
Auditors: KPMG LLP

LOCATIONS

HQ: New York Community Bancorp Inc.
615 Merrick Avenue, Westbury, NY 11590
Phone: 516 683-4100
Web: www.mynycb.com

2016 Locations

	No.
New York Community Bank	
New York	111
New Jersey	45
Ohio	28
Florida	27
Arizona	14
New York Commercial Bank	48
Total	**273**

PRODUCTS/OPERATIONS

2016 Sales

	$ mil.	% of total
Interest		
Mortgage & other loans	1,472	81
Securities & money market investments	202	11
Noninterest		
Fee income	32	2
Bank-owned life insurance	31	2
Mortgage banking income	27	1
Net gain on sale of loans	15	1
Net gain on sales of securities	3	.
Other	41	2
FDIC indemnification expenses	(6.2)	.
Total	**1,820**	**100**

2016 Sales

	% of total
Banking operations	
Interest	89
Non Interest	7
Residential Mortgage banking	
Interest	1
Non Interest	3
Total	**100**

Selected Operations

AmTrust Bank (Arizona Florida)
Atlantic Bank (New York commercial bank)
Garden State Community Bank (New Jersey)
Ohio Savings Bank (Ohio)
Queens County Savings Bank (Queens NY)
Richmond County Savings Bank (Staten Island NY)
Roosevelt Savings Bank (Brooklyn NY)
Roslyn Savings Bank (Long Island NY)

COMPETITORS

Apple Bank for Savings	Provident Financial
Astoria Financial	Services
Bank of America	Ridgewood Savings Bank
Citigroup	Safra Bank
Emigrant Bank	TD Bank USA
Flushing Financial	Valley National
HSBC USA	Bancorp
Investors Bancorp	Wells Fargo
JPMorgan Chase	

HISTORICAL FINANCIALS

Company Type: Public

Income Statement

FYE: December 31

	ASSETS ($ mil.)	NET INCOME ($ mil.)	INCOME AS % OF ASSETS	EMPLOYEES
12/16	48,926	495	1.0%	3,487
12/15	50,317	(47)	—	3,448
12/14	48,559	485	1.0%	3,416
12/13	46,688	475	1.0%	3,381
12/12	44,145	501	1.1%	3,458
Annual Growth	**2.6%**	**(0.3%)**	**—**	**0.2%**

2016 Year-End Financials

Debt ratio: 0.73%	No. of shares (mil.): 487
Return on equity: 8.19%	Dividends
Cash ($ mil.): 557	Yield: 0.0%
Current ratio: —	Payout: 67.3%
Long-term debt ($ mil.): —	Market value ($ mil.): 7,749

STOCK PRICE ($) FY Close	P/E High/Low	PER SHARE ($) Earnings	Dividends	Book Value
12/16 15.91	17 14	1.01	0.68	12.57
12/15 16.32	— —	(0.11)	1.00	12.24
12/14 16.00	16 14	1.09	1.00	13.06
12/13 16.85	16 12	1.08	1.00	13.01
12/12 13.10	13 10	1.13	1.00	12.88
Annual Growth 5.0%	— —	(2.8%)	(9.2%)	(0.6%)

NEW YORK COMMUNITY TRUST AND COMMUNITY FUNDS INC

Auditors: KPMG LLP NEW YORK NY

LOCATIONS

HQ: NEW YORK COMMUNITY TRUST AND
COMMUNITY FUNDS INC
909 3RD AVE FL 22, NEW YORK, NY 100224752
Phone: 212 686-0010
Web: WWW.NYCOMMUNITYTRUST.ORG

HISTORICAL FINANCIALS
Company Type: Private

Income Statement
FYE: December 31

	ASSETS ($ mil.)	NET INCOME ($ mil.)	INCOME AS % OF ASSETS	EMPLOYEES
12/14	2,570	130	5.1%	65
12/13	2,443	302	12.4%	—
12/12	2,147	239	11.1%	—
12/11	1,908	17	0.9%	—
Annual Growth	10.4%	95.4%	—	—

2014 Year-End Financials

Debt ratio: —
Return on equity: 42.80%
Cash ($ mil.): 60
Current ratio: —
Long-term debt ($ mil.): —
Dividends
Yield: —
Payout: —
Market value ($ mil.): —

NEW YORK PRESBYTERIAN HOSPITAL WEILL CORNELL UNIVERSITY MEDICAL CENTER

Auditors: ERNST & YOUNG US LLP INDIANAP

LOCATIONS

HQ: NEW YORK PRESBYTERIAN HOSPITAL WEILL
CORNELL UNIVERSITY MEDICAL CENTER
525 E 68TH ST, NEW YORK, NY 100654870
Phone: 212 746-1754
Web: WWW.MED.CORNELL.EDU

HISTORICAL FINANCIALS
Company Type: Private

Income Statement
FYE: December 31

	REVENUE ($ mil.)	NET INCOME ($ mil.)	NET PROFIT MARGIN	EMPLOYEES
12/15	4,505	265	5.9%	5
12/12	75	21	28.2%	—
Annual Growth	290.4%	131.8%	—	—

2015 Year-End Financials

Debt ratio: —
Return on equity: 5.90%
Cash ($ mil.): 227
Current ratio: 0.80
Long-term debt ($ mil.): —
Dividends
Yield: —
Payout: —
Market value ($ mil.): —

NEW YORK STATE CATHOLIC HEALTH PLAN INC

Fidelis Care hopes for always faithful health plan members. The New York State Catholic Health Plan which does business as Fidelis Care serves more than 921000 residents in some 60 counties across the state including the New York City area. The church-sponsored plan's provider network includes more than 63000 physicians hospitals and other health care professionals and facilities. Fidelis Care provides managed Medicaid Medicare and state-sponsored family and children's Health Plus plans as well as long-term care and behavioral health coverage.

Operations

The company boasts an overall statewide member retention rate of more than 78% with a s Child Health Plus retention rate of more than 85%.

Geographic Reach

Fidelis Care's regional offices are located in Rego Park Queens (Greater Metropolitan); Albany (Northeast); Syracuse (Central); and Buffalo (Western) with satellite offices in Poughkeepsie Rochester and Suffern.

Sales and Marketing

The health plan has expanded its membership by seeking new low-income patients who lack coverage. In addition to direct sales efforts Fidelis Care tries to maintain a presence at health centers frequented by its target audience partnering with neighborhood clinics to hold free health screenings and Health Plus enrollment information sessions.

Enroll NY a new website sponsored by not-for-profit organization Hudson Center for Health Equity & Quality is also connecting Fidelis Care and other Medicaid providers with potential customers. In 2013 Fidelis Care began selling through the New York State of Health insurance exchange marketplace.

To bosst membership in 2013 the company ran the "I Want Fidelis Care" campaign (which promoted Fidelis Care as a health care resource) in English and Spanish. TV was added to the media buy in the New York City and Buffalo regions. It also established a social media presence on Facebook Twitter YouTube and Google+.

Financial Performance

Fidelis Care reported gross revenues of $4.1 billion in 2013 up from $3.3 billion in 2012.

Strategy

The company is expanding its office to keep up with demand. In 2014 it opened Ridgewood Community Office; in 2013 it completed of?ce expansion projects in the Albany and Syracuse regional of?ces and the satellite of?ce in Suffern and opened new community of?ces in Flushing (Queens) the Bronx and Bath (Steuben County).

Forecasting substantial growth in 2014 with the enrollment of more than 120000 new members the company announced plans to add more than 75 new information technology jobs at its Buffalo regional office.

In 2013 Fidelis Care moved into 12 new counties with the Medicare Advantage program highlighted by the opportunity to serve residents of western New York for the ?rst time. It also made plans to expand into Seneca Yates and Jefferson counties in 2014 and served additional Managed Long Term Care members as part of the State's phased-in expansion of mandatory enrollment in counties beyond New York City.

Fidelis Care has grown by expanding rapidly into new counties in New York including a number of growth measures in the Medicare marketplace during 2012 and 2013. The health plan's recent activity includes completing construction of Fidelis Care's new operations center and offices in Getzville (Erie County) and the launch of its new provider portal (Provider Access Online). Other growth measures include a 2012 partnership with DentaQuest to promote dental checkups; it also launched a new member portal for members to access benefit information. In 2013 the company gained approval to be a qualified health plan provider on the official New York State of Health marketplace.

Fidelis Care regularly evaluates and broadens its plan offerings. Recent additions include its Fidelis Care at Home managed long-term care offering; the behavioral health and developmental disabilities coverage options; and its fully integrated dual advantage plans (for consumers with both Medicare and Medicaid coverage).

Company Background

The church-sponsored plan was founded in 1993 by the bishops of New York's Roman Catholic dioceses and the Catholic Medical Center of Brooklyn and Queens.

EXECUTIVES

Assistant Vice President Government Affairs and Compliance, Robert Fazzolari
Vice President Quality Health Care Manager, Carey Shoemaker
Vice President Finance, Dina Soroka
Executive Vice President and Chief Operating Officer, David Thomas
Vice President of Infrastructure, Duncan Ross
Vice President of Finance, Brian Baker
Vice President Strategic Planning, James Burnosky
Assistant Vice President Pharmacy Services, Erick Moncayo
Vice President of Human Resources, Claudia Shoro
Assistant Vice President Goverment Relations, Franceen Spadaccino
Auditors: LB DELOITTE TAX LLP JERICHO

LOCATIONS

HQ: NEW YORK STATE CATHOLIC HEALTH PLAN INC
9525 QUEENS BLVD, REGO PARK, NY 113744510
Phone: 888 343-3547
Web: WWW.FIDELISCARE.ORG

PRODUCTS/OPERATIONS

Selected Plans

Child Health Plus
Dual Advantage
Family Health Plus
Fidelis Care at Home (managed long-term care)
Medicaid Advantage Plus (managed long-term care)
Medicaid Managed Care
Medicare Advantage
New York State of Health

COMPETITORS

Aetna
Affinity Health
Anthem
CIGNA
Capital District Physicians' Health Plan
EmblemHealth
Health Net
HealthPlus Amerigroup
Healthfirst
Healthplex
Humana
Independent Health
Lifetime Healthcare
MVP Health Plan
UnitedHealth Group
Vytra Healthcare
healthnow new york inc

HISTORICAL FINANCIALS

Company Type: Private

Income Statement

FYE: December 31

	REVENUE ($ mil.)	NET INCOME ($ mil.)	NET PROFIT MARGIN	EMPLOYEES
12/14	5,304	271	5.1%	1,625
12/10	1,920	51	2.7%	—
12/09	1,435	27	1.9%	—
Annual Growth	29.9%	57.7%	—	—

2014 Year-End Financials

Debt ratio: ——
Return on equity: 5.10%
Cash ($ mil.): 948
Current ratio: 8.60
Long-term debt ($ mil.): —

Dividends
Yield: —
Payout: —
Market value ($ mil.): —

NEW YORK UNIVERSITY

Higher education is at the core of this Big Apple institution. The setting and heritage of New York University (NYU) make it one of the nation's most popular educational institutions. With more thanÂ 50000 students attending its 18 schools and colleges NYU is among the largest private schools in the US. Its Tisch School of the Arts is well-regarded and its law school and Leonard N. Stern School of Business are among theÂ foremost in the country. NYU occupies five major centers in Manhattan; its Washington Square campus is in the heart of Greenwich Village. The school wasÂ founded in 1831. Notable alumni include former Federal Reserve Chairman Alan Greenspan and film producer Oliver Stone.

Operations

The school confers about 12000 degrees annually. Of those roughly 4500 are bachelor's degrees nearly 5000 are master's degrees and about 400 are doctoral. Associate and professional degrees make up the rest. NYU alumni and faculty also boast several prestigious awards including more than a dozen Nobel and Crafoord prizes and another four Pulitzer prizes.

NYU is one of the largest employers in New York City with more than 16000 employees.

Geographic Reach

Along with its campuses in New YorkÂ NYU operates branch campus and research programs in other parts of theÂ US and abroad as well as study abroad programs in more than 25 countries. International students make up about 10% of the school's student body.

Financial Performance

Undergraduate tuition for the university runs more than $37000 per year.

Strategy

NYU has established itself as the first global network university with a comprehensive liberal arts campus in Abu DhabiÂ that opened in 2010.

HISTORY

New York University was founded by several prominent New Yorkers in 1831. The school held its first classes the following year in rented rooms on the corner of Beekman and Nassau streets then moved to a building in Washington Square in 1835. It established its law school that year. NYU started its school of medicine in 1841 followed by the school of engineering and science (1854). Postgraduate studies in arts and science (its first coeducational program) began in 1886.

NYU's enrollment jumped from fewer than 2000 in 1900 to 28000 in 1930. After a lull during the Depression and WWII the campus boomed again in the postwar years. During the 1950s the university began focusing on improving academics rather than on increasing enrollment. It created a school of the arts in 1965 and in the early 1970s it completed the Elmer Holmes Bobst Library. However a cash crunch during that decade almost forced the school into bankruptcy.

President Jay Oliva took the reins in 1981 and focused on transforming NYU from a largely commuter college into a global university. The school began a campaign to raise $1 billion in 1984 but earmarked the funds for campus improvements rather than swelling its endowment. During the late 1980s NYU opened several new dormitories and conference spaces. In 1994 British historian and collector Sir Harold Acton bequeathed to the school his Tuscany estate — five art-filled villas overlooking Florence Italy.

In 1996 NYU's Medical Center began talks with Mount Sinai Medical Center aimed at merging their hospitals and medical schools. The talks fell apart in early 1997 but the following year the two sides agreed to merge hospitals and keep their medical schools distinct. Also in 1998 NYU formed NYU On-Line Inc. a for-profit subsidiary to develop and sell specialized Internet courses to other schools training centers and students; the venture was subsequently folded in late 2001. During 1999 contributions to the school approached $250 million. That year however two upper-level school officials were fired following allegations of improper use of university money.

Oliva retired as president in 2002 and was replaced by John Sexton former School of Law dean. In 2004 Sexton announced that NYU would give $1 million to New York City towards renovation of Washington Square Park (the school annually gives some $200000 for the park's ongoing maintenance).

EXECUTIVES

Division President, Matthew S Santirocco
EVP Health, Robert (Bob) Berne
VP Information Technology and Chief Information Technology Officer, Marilyn A. McMillan
Provost, David W. McLaughlin
EVP Finance and Information Technology, Martin S. Dorph
Director Global Institute of Public Health; Dean of Global Public Health, Cheryl G. Healton
Dean Libraries, Carol A. Mandel
Herman Robert Fox Dean College of Dentistry, Charles N. Bertolami
EVP Operations, Alison Leary
Director Institute for the Study of the Ancient World, Roger Bagnall
Director Courant Institute of Mathematical Sciences, G ©rard Ben Arous
Saul J. Farber Dean NYU School of Medicine; CEO NYU Hospitals Center, Robert I. Grossman
Dean Gallatin School of Individualized Study, Susanne L. Wofford
Dean Polytechnic School of Engineering, Katepalli R. (Sreeni) Sreenivasan
Dean Silver School of Social Work, Lynn Videka
Dean Liberal Studies, Fred Schwarzbach
Judy and Michael Steinhardt Director Institute of Fine Arts, Patricia Lee Rubin
Dean Leonard N. Stern School of Business, Peter B. Henry, age 47
Vice Chancellor New York University Abu Dhabi, Alfred H. Bloom
VP Global Technology and Chief Global Technology Officer, Thomas A. (Tom) Delaney
Dean for Science Faculty of Arts and Science, Michael D. Purugganan
President, Andrew Hamilton
Gale and Ira Drukier Dean Steinhardt School for Culture Education and Human Development, Dominic Brewer
Anne and Joel Ehrenkranz Dean Faculty of Arts and Sciences, Thomas J. Carew
Dean for Humanities Faculty of Arts and Sciences, Joy Connolly
Harvey J. Stedman Dean School of Professional Studies, Dennis DiLorenzo
Dean Robert F. Wagner Graduate School of Public Service, Sherry A. Glied
Dean Tisch School of the Arts, Allyson Green
Dean for Social Sciences Faculty of Arts and Science, Michael Laver
Vice Chancellor NYU Shanghai, Jeffrey S. Lehman
Dean Undergraduate College Leonard N. Stern School of Business, Geeta Menon
Dean School of Law, Trevor Morrison
Director Marron Institute of Urban Management, Paul Romer
Seryl Kushner Dean College of Arts and Science, G. Gabrielle Starr
Dean College of Nursing, Eileen Sullivan-Marx
Chancellor NYU Shanghai, Yu Lizhong
Interim Dean Graduate School of Arts and Science, Anna L. Harvey
Associate Vice President Student Health, Carlo Ciotoli
Assistant Vice President, Trudy Steinfeld
Vice President for Financial Operations and Treasurer, Stephanie Pianka
Vice President finance, Harold T Read
Assistant Vice President Information Systems, Keith Whiteman
Department Chair, Christina Reuterskiold
Assistant Vice President, Dennis Clark
Senior Vice President, Lynne Brown
Associate Vice President for Stewardship and Events, Gustave Fleury
Medical Director, Marcy Ferdschneider
Chair Department Of Anthropology, Fred Myers

Vice President Commercial Real Estate, Edward Lombardo

Assistant Vice President For Public Safety and Investigations, Jerry Matthews

Assistant Vice President Global Standards and Compliance, Rebecca Holland

Assistant Vice President, Janet Alperstein

Vice President Human Resources, Robert White

Vice President, Charles Mullen

Global Finance Chief Of Staff To Executive Vice President For Finance And Information Technology, Carolyn Wood

Executive Vice President for Health, Bob Berne

VP of Marketing, Mahin Rahaman

Vice President RXR Realty Michael Aisner, Luis Rosa

Medical Director, Ryan Harper

Associate Vice President For Global Technologies, Heather Stewart

Vice President and Chief Information Officer, Leonard Peters

Senior Vice President University Development and Alumni Relations, Kenneth Manotti

Clinic Manager, Danielle Bartlett

Administrative Aide To the Associate Vice President of Alumni Relations, Danielle Ohrenberger

Director of Admissions, Katie Korhonen

Vice President Finance, Pamela Morris

Chairman Board of Trustees, William R. (Bill) Berkley, age 71

Vice President Financia Operations and Treasurer, Rosemarie Loffredo

Board Director, Christine Trump

Secretary, John Leiva

Treasurer, Peter Rajsingh

Secretary, Christine Fewell

Assistant Treasurer, Elisa Cohen

Secretary, Jennifer Neuman

MS Global Affairs Candidate Treasurer Energy Policy International Club, Jude Buenaseda

Auditors: PRICEWATERHOUSECOOPERS LLP NE

LOCATIONS

HQ: NEW YORK UNIVERSITY
70 WASHINGTON SQ S, NEW YORK, NY 100121019
Phone: 212 998-1212
Web: WWW.NYU.EDU

PRODUCTS/OPERATIONS

Selected Schools and Colleges

College of Arts and Science (founded 1832)
College of
Courant In
Gallatin S
Graduate S
Leonard N.
Robert F.
School of
School of
School of
School of
Steinhardt
Tisch Scho

HISTORICAL FINANCIALS

Company Type: Private

Income Statement

FYE: August 31

	REVENUE ($ mil.)	NET INCOME ($ mil.)	NET PROFIT MARGIN	EMPLOYEES
08/11	5,172	563	10.9%	21,000
08/06	2,148	195	9.1%	—
Annual Growth	19.2%	23.6%	—	—

2011 Year-End Financials

Debt ratio: ——
Return on equity: 10.90%
Cash ($ mil.): 1,180
Current ratio: —
Long-term debt ($ mil.): —

Dividends
  Yield: —
  Payout: —
Market value ($ mil.): —

Newell Brands Inc

Home is where Newell Brands (formerly Newell Rubbermaid) is. The go-to company for men women and children makes housewares (Rubbermaid plastic products Calphalon cookware) juvenile products (Graco) hair products (Goody) and office items (DYMO and Sharpie). Newell Brands sells its items to mass retailers (Target) and home and office supply stores (Staples). As a result of a more than $18 billion acquisition of consumer products giant Jarden in mid-2016 Newell Brands also inherited popular products such as Bicycle Playing Cards Mr. Coffee Coleman Jostens Oster Rawlings Sunbeam and Yankee Candle.

Operations

Newell Brands operates its business through several segments: Branded Consumables Outdoor Solutions Writing Consumer Solutions Home Solutions Baby and Parenting Commercial Products and Process Solutions.

Branded Consumables is its largest segment and manufactures markets and distributes a broad line of branded consumer products. Outdoor Solutions offers global consumer active lifestyle products for outdoor and outdoor-related activities.

The Writing segment makes writing instruments for use in business and at home. It markets its products directly to mass merchants warehouse clubs grocery/drug stores office superstores office supply stores contract stationers and travel retail and other retailers.

Consumer Solutions provides a diverse line of household products including kitchen appliances and home environment products. It primarily sells its products under the Crock-Pot FoodSaver Holmes Oster Rainbow and Sunbeam names.

Home Solutions makes and distributes tubs bins containers and other storage tools under multiple brand names. Its indoor/outdoor organization items and food and home storage products are primarily sold under the Rubbermaid Roughneck and TakeAlongs names.

Baby and Parenting makes infant and juvenile products such as swings highchairs car seats strollers and play yards sold under the Graco Baby Jogger Aprica and Teutonia names.

Commercial Products offers cleaning and refuse products hygiene systems and material handling equipment. Process Solutions offers a wide variety of plastic products including closures contact lens packaging medical disposables plastic cutlery and rigid packaging.

Geographic Reach

Newell Brands operates in nearly 100 countries in the Americas Europe the Middle East Africa and the Asia Pacific region. More than 70% of the company's business comes from the US while Europe Middle East and Africa (EMEA) region generates about 15% of sales. Latin America and the Asia Pacific regions split nearly 10% of revenue while Canada brings in the remainder of total sales.

Sales and Marketing

The office products maker sells its products in almost 200 countries through large mass merchandisers such as discount stores home centers warehouse clubs office superstores commercial distributors and e-commerce companies.

Newell Brands relies on the largest retailer in the world to help peddle its products. Sales to Wal-Mart and its subsidiaries generate about 10% to 15% of its net sales each year.

Financial Performance

Newell Brands enjoyed explosive growth in 2016 due to its acquisition of consumer products giant Jarden. Revenues more than doubled from $5.9 billion in 2015 to $13.3 billion in 2016 as a result of that acquisition volume growth pricing and its 2015 purchase of Elmer's Brands.

All this growth led to a 10% increase in Writing segment sales and an 8% bump in Baby and Parenting sales. These factors also fueled additional sales stemming from its newly created segments of Branded Consumables Consumer Solutions Outdoor Solutions and Process Solutions.

In conjunction with the higher sales net income surged by more than 50% from $350 million in 2015 to $528 million in 2016. In addition Newell Brands' operating cash flow skyrocketed from $566 million in 2015 to $1.8 billion in 2016 due to its Jarden acquisition.

Strategy

During 2016 Newell Brands launched its New Growth Game Plan an initiative to simplify its organization and develop resources to invest in growth initiatives to build a bigger faster-growing and more global company. The plan involves making strategic cuts to dispose of under-performing brands and business lines. Adhering to this strategy in early 2017 it sold its Tools business to Stanley Black & Decker for nearly $2 billion. Brands involved in the sale included Irwin Lenox and Hilmor.

Mergers and Acquisitions

The company has been pursuing large strategic acquisitions to expand its product lines and significantly add to its revenue stream.

In a sweeping move for the consumer goods industry Newell Brands purchased Jarden in a total transaction valued at $18.7 billion in mid-2016. The mega-deal gave the company access to popular brands such as Sunbeam and Oster appliances Coleman outdoor gear First Alert home safety products Ball canning jars Loew-Cornell art supplies K2 snowboards and Bee and Bicycle brand playing cards. It estimates that the combined company will eventually earn $16 billion in revenue.

In 2016 Newell Brands acquired New Zealand-based Sistema Plastics a leading provider of innovative food storage containers primarily under the Sistema brand for $460 million. The transaction broadened the company's international footprint of food and beverage categories and strengthened its core category of home fragrance in the US.

Newell Brands made another large deal in 2015 through the $1.5 billion acquisition of Visant Holding Corp. (Visant) the parent company of Jostens. A partner to schools and students nationwide Josten has a product portfolio that includes yearbooks class and championship rings for students and professional athletes caps and gowns diplomas and varsity jackets. Post acquisition Jostens became a part of Newell Brands' Outdoor Solutions segment.

Newell Brands inherited more famous brands in late 2015 when it purchased Elmer's Brands for $600 million. Through the purchase the company inherited popular brands Elmer's Krazy Glue and X-Acto and significantly enhanced its Writing segment.

HISTORY

Businessmen in Ogdensburg New York advanced curtain rod maker W.F. Linton Co. $1000 to relocate from Rhode Island in the early 1900s.

Local wholesaler Edgar Newell signed off on the loan; when the company went bankrupt in 1903 he was forced to take over. The company renamed Newell Manufacturing set up plants in Canada and Freeport Illinois to ease shipping costs and speed delivery.

Production expanded into towel racks ice picks and other items; Woolworth's decision to carry Newell's products turned the company into a national supplier. Edgar Newell died in 1920. The company made its first acquisition in 1938 buying window treatment specialist Drapery Hardware.

The Newell companies were consolidated in the mid-1960s into a single corporation. Daniel Ferguson was named president in 1965 and served alongside his CEO father Leonard one of Newell's original employees. During his tenure Daniel hitched the company's future to the growing dominance of large discount stores. Newell went from a $14 million family business to a global multi-line conglomerate by acquiring products that it distributed to these big buyers. The company went public in 1972.

As for Rubbermaid it was originally a balloon maker in the 1920s called Wooster Rubber. By the mid-1930s Ohio's Wooster Rubber had acquired the Rubbermaid product line of rubber housewares. It went public in 1955 and two years later changed its name to Rubbermaid. During the 1980s the company enjoyed a decade of phenomenal growth. Newell's $6 billion purchase of Rubbermaid in 1999 sealed its biggest deal yet and resulted in a name change: Newell Rubbermaid.

Decades later the company changed its name to Newell Brands in 2016 after it purchased consumer goods giant Jarden in a mega-merger valued at around $15.4 billion.

EXECUTIVES

EVP and CFO, Ralph J. Nicoletti, age 59, $493,845 total compensation
CEO, Michael B. (Mike) Polk, age 56, $1,312,500 total compensation
COO, William A. (Bill) Burke, age 56, $796,053 total compensation
Chief Development Officer, Richard Davies
Chief Customer Officer, Joseph W. Cavaliere
President, Mark S. Tarchetti, age 41, $922,212 total compensation
SVP Information Technology and CIO, Dan Gustafson
Chief Transformation Officer, Russ Torres
Chairman, Michael T. Cowhig, age 70
Auditors: PricewaterhouseCoopers LLP

LOCATIONS

HQ: Newell Brands Inc
221 River Street, Hoboken, NJ 07030
Phone: 201 610-6600
Web: www.newellrubbermaid.com

2016 Sales

	$ mil.	% of total
North America		
United States	9,518	72
Canada	720	5
Europe Middle East and Africa	1,659	13
Latin America	643	5
Asia Pacific	722	5
Total	**13,264**	**100**

PRODUCTS/OPERATIONS

2016 Sales

	$ mil.	% of total
Writing:		
Writing instruments	1,469	11
Adhesive and cutting products	243	2
Technology solutions	228	2

Home Solutions:		
Home and food storage products	1,058	8
Dé;cor	141	1
Other	367	3
Branded Consumables	2,839	21
Outdoor Solutions	2,415	18
Consumer Solutions	1,766	13
Baby and Parenting	919	7
Tools	760	6
Commercial Products	776	6
Process Solutions	275	2
Total	**13,264**	**100**

Selected Brands & Trade Names

Cleaning organization and decor
  Brute
  Roughneck
  Rubbermaid
  TakeAlongs
Office products
  Accent
  Berol
  DYMO
  Expo
  Liquid Paper
  Paper Mate
  Parker
  Rotring
  Sharpie
  Uni-Ball (under license)
  Waterman
Home and family
  Aprica
  Avex
  Calphalon
  Calphalon One
  Contigo
  Cooking with Calphalon
  Goody
  Graco
  Katana
  Kitchen Essentials
  Teutonia

COMPETITORS

ACCO Brands	Knape & Vogt
Acme United	Lancaster Colony
Alticor	Libbey
Avery Dennison	Lifetime Brands
BIC	Myers Industries
Bridgestone	Owens-Illinois
Coleman	Springs Global US
Crayola	Sterilite
Decorator Industries	Tupperware Brands
Dixon Ticonderoga	Uniek
Faber-Castell	WKI Holding
Home Products	Wilton Brands
International	ZAG Industries
Katy Industries	

HISTORICAL FINANCIALS

Company Type: Public

Income Statement

FYE: December 31

	REVENUE ($ mil.)	NET INCOME ($ mil.)	NET PROFIT MARGIN	EMPLOYEES
12/16	13,264	527	4.0%	53,400
12/15	5,915	350	5.9%	17,200
12/14	5,727	377	6.6%	17,400
12/13	5,692	474	8.3%	18,300
12/12	5,902	401	6.8%	18,300
Annual Growth	**22.4%**	**7.1%**	**—**	**30.7%**

2016 Year-End Financials

Debt ratio: 35.15%
Return on equity: 7.99%
Cash ($ mil.): 587
Current ratio: 1.74
Long-term debt ($ mil.): 11,290
No. of shares (mil.): 482
Dividends
  Yield: 0.0%
  Payout: 60.8%
Market value ($ mil.): 21,544

	STOCK PRICE ($) FY Close	P/E High/Low	PER SHARE ($) Earnings	PER SHARE ($) Dividends	PER SHARE ($) Book Value
12/16	44.65	44 27	1.25	0.76	23.52
12/15	44.08	37 28	1.29	0.76	6.82
12/14	38.09	28 21	1.35	0.66	6.88
12/13	32.41	20 13	1.63	0.60	7.44
12/12	22.27	16 12	1.37	0.43	6.96
Annual Growth	**19.0%**	**— —**	**(2.3%)**	**15.3%**	**35.6%**

Newmont Mining Corp (Holding Co)

Newmont Mining goes for the gold. Once the clear #1 gold producing company in the world Newmont now ranks #2 behind Barrick. Newmont produces about 5.2 million ounces of gold annually and has proved and probable reserves of 68.5 million ounces of gold and 5.7 million pounds of copper. Mining in Nevada since 1965 it has significant assets in the US and also has assets in Australia Canada Ghana and Peru. Newmont mines copper mostly through its Boddington project in Australia. It produces about 120 million pounds of copper annually. The company was established in 1921 and began publicly trading in 1925.

Operations

Worldwide Newmont holds mineral rights on about 23000 square miles of land.

The company's North American operations include mines in Nevada's Carlin Trend one of the largest gold-mining areas in North America. Other sites in North America reside in Phoenix Twin Creeks and Long Canyon; Nevada. Its Cripple Creek & Victor pit operations are also located in Victor Colorado.

In the Asia/Pacific Newmont owns the Boddington project one of Australia's largest gold mining properties. Other holdings include the Tanami and Kalgoorlie sites.

Newmont's South America segment operates two sites Yanacocha and Merian and manages the Conga Project.

Geographic Reach

Newmont has mineral assets in Australia Canada Ghana Peru and the US. Customers from the UK account for nearly 80% of its net sales.

Sales and Marketing

About 95% of Newmont's total revenues are attributable to gold (mainly refined gold). End uses of gold are jewelry electronics dentistry industrial and decorative uses medals medallions and official coins. Gold investors buy gold bullion official coins and jewelry. The company generally sells at the prevailing market price.

Copper sales account for 5% of Newmont's net revenues. Copper customers include the construction electric utility communications and transportation industries. Copper is also used in industrial equipment and machinery consumer products and a variety of other electrical and electronic applications and is also used to make brass.

Financial Performance

Note: Newport restated its 2015 annual report due to recent divestitures. As a result revenues increased from 2015 to 2016 mainly due to gold sales increasing 11% primarily due to the addition of new projects starting in 2016 additional revenue from a previous acquisition higher average realized

prices and higher sales volumes at its existing operations.

After posting two straight years of net income Newmont posted a net loss of $627 million in 2016. This was mainly due to a $970 impairment charge taken in 2016 related to its Yanacocha assets in Peru and a more than $130 million loss from discontinued operations.

Despite the net loss cash flow from operations jumped from $2.2 billion in 2015 to $2.8 billion in 2016 primarily due to $920 million it earned from the selling of its Batu Hijau copper and gold mine in Indonesia.

Strategy

Newport's strategy includes strengthening its portfolio (by building a longer-life lower-cost asset portfolio) and moving on promising exploration project development and inorganic opportunities.

It conducts this strategy on several projects each in different stages of development. One of these is its Tanami Expansion project in Australia. The scope for this project includes installing upgrades adding mining equipment and increasing process plant capacity and recovery. It expects the Tanami Expansion to reach commercial production by mid-2017 and will maintain production of between 425000 and 475000 gold ounces for the first five years.

Another growth initiative involves its North American Long Canyon project. As commercial production for the Long Canyon project in North America was reached in November 2016 Newport expects average estimated gold production of 100000 to 150000 ounces per year over an eight year mine life.

To raise cash in 2015 Newport sold its 60.64% ownership interest in European Gold Refinery Holdings for $119 million and its Waihi gold mine in New Zealand to OceanaGold Corporation for $102 million. In late 2016 the company sold its 48.5% economic interest in PT Newmont Nusa Tenggara (PTNNT) which operated the Batu Hijau copper and gold mine in Indonesia for $920 million.

Mergers and Acquisitions

Boosting its reserve base in 2015 Newmont bought the Cripple Creek & Victor gold mine in Colorado from AngloGold Ashanti for $820 million in cash. This acquisition added between 350000 and 400000 oz per year (of gold in 2016 and 2017 at all-in sustaining costs of between $825/oz and $875/oz.

HISTORY

The company was founded in 1921 and began publicly trading in 1925.

Colonel William Boyce Thompson a flamboyant trader founded the Newmont Co. in 1916 to trade his various oil and mining stocks. The Newmont name was a combination of New York and Montana where Thompson grew up. The company was renamed Newmont Corporation in 1921 and Newmont Mining Corporation in 1925 when it went public. Thompson died five years later. During its first 10 years Newmont focused on investing and trading stocks in promising mineral properties including US copper and gold mines.

Newmont's gold mines bolstered the company throughout the Depression. During the 1940s its focus shifted to copper and Africa. It bought Idarado Mining in 1943 and Newmont Oil in 1944 (sold 1988). The company grew during the 1950s by acquiring stakes in North American companies involved in offshore oil drilling nickel mining and uranium oxide production. It also bought stakes in copper mines in South Africa and South America.

Newmont started producing gold from the Carlin Trend in Nevada in the mid-1960s. It bought a one-third stake in Foote Mineral (iron alloys and lithium) in 1967; by 1974 it controlled 83% of the company (sold 1987). In 1969 Newmont merged with Magma Copper one of the US's largest copper companies. A Newmont-led consortium bought Peabody Coal the US's largest coal producer from Kennecott Copper in 1977 (sold 1990).

After its 1980 discovery of one of the century's most important gold stakes Gold Quarry in the Carlin Trend Newmont spent a decade fending off takeover attempts. The company began selling off noncore operations to focus on gold. Magma Copper was spun off to stockholders in 1988.

A proposed merger with American Barrick Resources a major stockholder collapsed in 1991. Former Freeport-McMoRan VP Ronald Cambre became CEO in 1993 and that year the company began mining in Peru. A 1994 action by the French government one of Newmont's partners in Peru's Yanacocha Mine kicked off a protracted battle over the property's ownership. The claim was upheld in 1998 raising Newmont's stake to more than 50%. Reflecting its increasing interest in Indonesia in 1996 Newmont and Japan's Sumitomo formed a joint venture to exploit gold reserves on Sumbawa Island. In 1997 the company increased its gold reserves and territory by acquiring Santa Fe Pacific Gold for about $2.1 billion.

For years Newmont and Barrick Gold Corporation operated interlocked mining claims in Nevada's Carlin Trend which prevented optimal exploitation by either company. In 1999 both companies agreed to a mutually advantageous land swap in the region.

In 2000 an Indonesian court ordered the closure of the Minahasa mine over a local tax dispute; the company's joint venture agreed to pay a $500000 penalty to settle the matter. Newmont was fined $500000 after a mercury spill at its Yanacocha mine. That year Newmont settled the lingering ownership dispute over the Yanacocha.

Company president Wayne Murdy became CEO early in 2001 (he replaced Cambre as chairman in 2002). Newmont acquired Battle Mountain Gold in 2001 for nearly $600 million. Late that year Newmont moved to acquire Australia's top gold producer Normandy Mining (setting off a bidding war with AngloGold) as well as Canadian gold miner France-Nevada Mining Corp. AngloGold bowed out of the "battle for Normandy" in early 2002 but later completed a three-way deal in which it acquired Normandy and Franco-Nevada.

In 2003 Newmont reduced its stake in Kinross Gold from 14% to 5% and it considered selling off the Ghanaian interests it had gained in the Normandy merger. However in 2004 Newmont literally discovered a gold mine in Ghana — a major district with some 16 million equity ounces of gold.

Murdy retired in 2007; taking the helm was former CEO Richard O'Brien. In 2007 Newmont spun off its royalty assets acquired in 2002 as Franco-Nevada Corporation. Those assets then operated as Newmont Mining Corporation of Canada now a subsidiary of Newmont.

In 2008 Newmont bought Canadian gold producer Miramar Mining which controls the Hope Bay project for about $1.5 billion. It also acquired in 2009 a 33% stake in Boddington from AngloGold Ashanti for about $1 billion giving Newmont 100% of the Boddington project.

In 2011 Newmont acquired Fronteer Gold a Canadian company with properties in the US Turkey and Peru for $2.3 billion. The deal significantly expands Newmont's holdings in Nevada.

EXECUTIVES

Executive Vice President Opera, Brian Hill
SVP South America, Trent Tempel

EVP Human Resources, William N. (Bill) MacGowan, age 57, $450,000 total compensation
VP and CIO, James (Jim) Zetwick
EVP and CFO, Nancy K. Buese, age 48, $90,865 total compensation
EVP Strategic Development, Randy Engel, age 50, $627,196 total compensation
EVP and General Counsel, Stephen P. Gottesfeld, age 49, $512,074 total compensation
SVP Exploration, Grigore Simon
EVP Technical Services, Scott P. Lawson
President and CEO, Gary J. Goldberg, age 58, $1,270,742 total compensation
EVP Sustainability and External Relations, Elaine Dorward-King, $468,297 total compensation
SVP Africa, Alwyn Pretorius, age 45
SVP Asia Pacific, Thomas (Tom) Palmer, $615,134 total compensation
Vice President, Chip Clark
Vice President Environmental Affairs And Sustainable Development, David Baker
Vice President, Mike Hubbard
Senior Vice President Operations Services Development, Bruce Hansen
Regional Vice President Human Resources, David Kern
Board Member, Joel Melgar
Auditors: Ernst & Young LLP

LOCATIONS

HQ: Newmont Mining Corp (Holding Co)
6363 South Fiddler's Green Circle, Greenwood Village, CO 80111
Phone: 303 863-7414   **Fax:** 303 837-5837
Web: www.newmont.com

2016 Sales

	$ mil.	% of total
United Kingdom	5,413	81
Korea	298	4
Philippines	283	4
Germany	191	3
Switzerland	148	2
Canada	124	2
US	70	1
Japan	59	1
Other	125	2
Total	**6,711**	**100**

PRODUCTS/OPERATIONS

2016 Sales

	$ mil.	% of total
Gold	6,461	96
Copper	250	4
Total	**6,711**	**100**

COMPETITORS

AngloGold Ashanti	Harmony Gold
Barrick Gold	Inmet Mining
Freeport-McMoRan	Kinross Gold
Gold Fields	Newcrest Mining
Goldcorp	

HISTORICAL FINANCIALS

Company Type: Public

Income Statement

				FYE: December 31
	REVENUE ($ mil.)	NET INCOME ($ mil.)	NET PROFIT MARGIN	EMPLOYEES
12/16	6,711	(627)	—	12,400
12/15	7,729	220	2.8%	15,600
12/14	7,292	508	7.0%	13,700
12/13	8,322	(2,462)	—	15,085
12/12	9,868	1,809	18.3%	16,400
Annual Growth	**(9.2%)**	**—**	**—**	**(6.8%)**

2016 Year-End Financials

Debt ratio: 21.94%
Return on equity: (-5.67%)
Cash ($ mil.): 2,756
Current ratio: 2.67
Long-term debt ($ mil.): 4,049

No. of shares (mil.): 530
Dividends
Yield: 0.0%
Payout: —
Market value ($ mil.): 18,073

	STOCK PRICE ($) FY Close	P/E High/Low	PER SHARE ($) Earnings	Dividends	Book Value
12/16	34.07	— —	(1.18)	0.13	20.21
12/15	17.99	64 36	0.43	0.10	21.43
12/14	18.90	27 17	1.02	0.23	20.60
12/13	23.03	— —	(4.94)	1.23	20.38
12/12	46.44	18 12	3.63	1.40	27.73
Annual Growth	(7.5%)			—(45.3%)	(7.6%)

News Corp (New)

News Corp. is in the news business. The company consists of iconic newspapers (The Wall Street Journal New York Post Australia's Herald Sun and The Sun and The Times in the UK) information services (Dow Jones and Factiva) and book publishing (HarperCollins). News Corp. also owns FOX SPORTS Australia a stake in Australian real estate web portal REA Group and a 50% share of Australian pay-TV provider FOXTEL. Owner Rupert Murdoch's US-based TV and film holdings are now organized into Twenty-First Century Fox which includes networks FOX and FOX News.

Operations

News Corp. divides its operations into five segments — news and information services book publishing cable network programming digital real estate services and other. (Its 50% stake in FOXTEL is treated as an equity investment.) The print and digital media publications (news and information services book publishing) account for the majority of revenues.

The news and information services segment also includes News America Marketing Group (NAMG) a publisher and distributor of coupons in newspapers and on the SmartSource.com website. NAMG's customers include many of the largest consumer packaged-goods advertisers in the US and Canada. It reaches 74 million households for its freestanding coupon inserts and about 56000 retail outlets for its in-store advertising.

Murdoch moved his Australian TV operations to News Corp. in order to allow the US TV operations to grow as a stand-alone division.

Geographic Reach

The company's subsidiaries are located in Australia the UK and the US. In addition book publisher HarperCollins has a warehouse in Scotland and Dow Jones runs an office in Hong Kong. North America accounted for 47% of sales during fiscal 2016.

Sales and Marketing

The company spent about $607 million on advertising and promotional expenses during fiscal 2016.

Financial Performance

The company's revenue was $8.29 billion for fiscal 2016 which was a decrease of $341 million (or 4%) compared to News Corporation's fiscal 2015 revenue. The decrease was largely attributed to the sale of the company's digital education business during the first quarter of fiscal 2016.

News Corporation's net income was $179 million in fiscal 2016 compared to a net loss of $147 million it suffered for the prior fiscal period. Rebounding from a net loss to a $170 million profit in fiscal 2016 was primarily attributed to a tax benefit of $54 million compared to a tax expense of $185 million during the previous fiscal year.

Strategy

Splitting the business into separate publishing and entertainment companies allowed each company to pursue uninhibited industry-specific opportunities benefit from greater financial and operational flexibility and provide investors with a more targeted investment opportunity.

Mergers and Acquisitions

During fiscal 2016 News Corporation spent around $800 million on acquisitions. The company acquired Checkout 51 Mobile Apps ULC Unruly Holdings Limited DIAKRIT International Limited iProperty Group Limited Flatmates.com.au Pty Ltd Australian Regional Media and Wireless Group plc.

EXECUTIVES

CEO Harper Collins, Brian Murray, age 50
Chairman and CEO News America Marketing, Martin (Marty) Garofalo
CEO News UK, Rebekah Brooks, age 49
CTO, Marc Frons, age 59
CEO Unruly, Sarah Wood
CEO, Robert Thomson, age 57, $2,038,462 total compensation
CFO, Susan Panuccio
General Counsel and Chief Compliance Officer, David B. Pitofsky, $968,269 total compensation
CEO The New York Post, Jesse Angelo
CEO Dow Jones & Company, William (Will) Lewis
CEO Storyful, Rahul Chopra
CEO Move Inc., Ryan OÂ'Hara
EVP and Chief Communications Officer, James E. (Jim) Kennedy
Chairman News Corp Australasia, Michael Miller
EVP and Global Head Government Affairs, Antoinette (Toni) Bush
Vice President, Linden Slaugh
Senior Vice President Treasurer, Rakesh Jobanputra
Senior Vice President and Global Chief Information Security Officer, Latha Maripuri
Vice President Telecommunications, Guy Wheaton
Vice President Strategic Sourcing Procurement, Tracey Williamson
Vice President Of Technology, Dan Gould
Vice President Marketing Services At News America Marketing, Marissa Bishop
Senior Vice President and Deputy General Counsel, James Marcovitz
Vice President Tax Operations, Scott Lindstrom
Senior Vice President, Paula Wardynski, age 60
Senior Vice President Physical Production, Thomas Imperato
Vice President Information Technology, Cindy Schwan
Senior Vice President Strategy And Corporate Development European Television, Marc Heller
Vice President Manager Director, Trista Reiser
Senior Vice President Corporate Affairs, Jim Platt
Vice President Global Transfer Pricing, Kathrin Zoeller
Vice President, Robert Ennis
Executive Vice President Office Of The Chairman, Jeremy Phillips
Senior Vice President Global Government Affairs, Joanne Dowdell
Senior Vice President of Strategic Initiatives, Ruth Altchek
Vice President, Gabrielle Haskell
Senior Vice President Global Head of Programmatic, Chris Guenther
Vice President Head of Cyber Security Technology Passionate. Principled. Purposeful, Miguel El Lakkis
Senior Vice President Corporate Development, Brandon Sokol

Co-Chairman News Corp and 21st Century Fox, Lachlan K. Murdoch, age 44
Chairman, K. Rupert Murdoch, age 86
Assistant Treasurer, Stanley Pauzer
Auditors: Ernst & Young LLP

LOCATIONS

HQ: News Corp (New)
1211 Avenue of the Americas, New York, NY 10036
Phone: 212 416-3400
Web: www.newscorp.com

2016 Sales

	$ mil.	% of total
US & Canada	3,920	47
Europe	1,873	23
Australia and others	2,499	30
Total	**8,292**	**100**

PRODUCTS/OPERATIONS

2016 Sales

	$ mil.	% of total
News & information services	5,338	64
Book publishing	1,646	20
Digital real estate services	822	10
Cable Network programming	484	6
Other	2	-
Total	**8,292**	**100**

2016 Sales

	$ mil.	% of total
Advertising	3,644	44
Circulation & subscription	2,569	31
Consumer	1,578	19
Other	501	6
Total	**8,292**	**100**

List of Items

List of Items
Newspapers
Dow Jones
Barron's (magazine)
Dow Jones Licensing Services
Dow Jones Newswires
Factiva (online news and business research)
The Wall Street Journal
The Wall Street Journal Digital Network
All Things Digital
BigCharts (stock market information)
FINS (financial services employment listings)
MarketWatch
WSJ.com
New York Post
News International Limited (UK)
The Sun
The Sunday Times
The Times
News Limited (Australia)
The Advertiser (Adelaide)
The Australian (national daily)
The Courier-Mail (Brisbane)
The Daily Telegraph (Sydney)
Herald Sun (Melbourne)
The Mercury (Hobart)
Northern Territory News (Darwin)
Sunday Herald Sun (Melbourne)
Sunday Mail (Adelaide)
The Sunday Mail (Brisbane)
Sunday Tasmanian (Hobart)
The Sunday Telegraph (Sydney)
The Sunday Times (Perth)
Book publishing
HarperCollins Publishers
Cable network programming
FOX SPORTS Australia
Digital real estate services
REA (61.6% stake)
Other
Amplify (digital education)
Foxtel (50% stake)

HISTORICAL FINANCIALS

Company Type: Public

Income Statement

FYE: June 30

	REVENUE ($ mil.)	NET INCOME ($ mil.)	NET PROFIT MARGIN	EMPLOYEES
06/17	8,139	(738)	—	26,000
06/16	8,292	179	2.2%	24,000
06/15	8,633	(147)	—	25,000
06/14	8,574	239	2.8%	22,000
06/13	8,891	506	5.7%	24,000
Annual Growth	(2.2%)	—	—	2.0%

2017 Year-End Financials

Debt ratio: 2.60%
Return on equity: (-6.59%)
Cash ($ mil.): 2,016
Current ratio: 1.56
Long-term debt ($ mil.): 276

No. of shares (mil.): 581
Dividends
Yield: 1.4%
Payout: —
Market value ($ mil.): 7,972

	STOCK PRICE ($) FY Close	P/E High/Low	PER SHARE ($) Earnings	Dividends	Book Value
06/17	13.70	— —	(1.27)	0.20	18.57
06/16	11.35	52 35	0.30	0.20	19.97
06/15	14.59	— —	(0.26)	0.00	20.57
06/14	17.94	45 36	0.41	0.00	22.91
Annual Growth	(6.5%)	— —	—	—	(5.1%)

NextEra Energy Inc

NextEra Energy is moving its power business into the future. The holding company is mainly comprised of Florida Power & Light (FPL) and NextEra Energy Resources (NEER). FPL generates more than 26000 MW of electricity and delivers it to nearly 5.0 million customers in Florida. NEER generates nearly 20000 MW of modern energy via wind and solar sources making NextEra Energy one of the world?s largest generators of renewable energy. FPL operates primarily in Florida while NEER has assets in nearly 30 US states four Canadian provinces as well as in Spain.

Operations

NextEra Energy (NEE) operates two reportable segments: Florida Power & Light (FPL) a rate-regulated electric utility and NextEra Energy Resources (NEER) a competitive energy business. FPL accounts for some 67% of total revenue NEER accounts for 30% with the rest attributed to other activities.

FPL is a rate-regulated utility that generates transmits distributes and sells electricity in Florida. It serves nearly 5.0 million customers 90% of which are residential and the rest commercial. FPL's operating revenues come from the sale of electricity to retail customers at rates established by the Florida Public Services Commission through base rates and cost recovery clause mechanisms. Its power plants have some 26000 MW of capacity which is supplemented with 800 MW of additional electricity obtained through power pur-

chase agreements. It generates about 70% of its energy with oil/gas-sourced power plants an additional roughly 20% from four nuclear plants and the rest from coal oil and solar.

NEER owns develops constructs manages and operates electric generating facilities in wholesale energy markets primarily in the US but also in Canada and Spain. NEER also provides full energy and capacity requirements services engages in power and gas marketing and trading activities and invests in natural gas natural gas liquids and oil production and pipeline infrastructure assets. It has almost 14000 MW of wind-generated capacity in 20 US states and four Canadian provinces. It also owns solar fossil-fuel and nuclear powered generation facilities which brings its total capacity to some 20000 MW. Approximately 80% of the subsidiary?s power is contracted out for sale via long-term purchase agreements.

Geographic Reach

Juno Beach FL-headquartered NextEra?s FPL serves retail customers along Florida?s Atlantic and southern Gulf Coasts. Its NEER subsidiary has wind farms throughout much of the US and in Canada. It owns a myriad of solar farms mainly in southern California and George and one in Spain. NEER sells to wholesale customers throughout the US and Canada.

Sales and Marketing

FPL provides service to its customers through an integrated transmission and distribution system that links its generation facilities to its customers. As a state-regulated utility its market is largely restricted to other entrants although niche project such as rooftop solar provide negligible competition.

NextEra Energy Resources sells products associated with its own generating facilities (energy capacity RECs and ancillary services) in competitive markets.

Financial Performance

NextEra Energy produced stable operating revenues in recent years and grew net income in an even stair-stepped fashion. Operating revenues typically fall in a range of $15 billion and $16 billion. Net income rose from $1.6 billion in 2007 to nearly $3.0 billion in 2016.

For the year 2016 operating revenue dropped 7% to $16.2 billion. The decrease resulted from much lower fuel recovery revenue in the FPL subsidiary and lower revenues from NEER?s divested natural gas generation facilities in that were sold in 2016.

In 2016 net income grew for the fourth straight year and up 6% to $2.9 billion when compared to 2015. The increase was due to earnings from new investments (mainly NEER-added wind and solar capacity) and a one-time gain on the sale of natural gas generation facilities.

Cash at the end of 2016 was $1.3 billion up $720 million from the prior year. Investments in FPL capital expenditures and investments in NEER?s generation assets contributed to an $8.1 billion depletion of cash due to investing activities. Counteracting that were a $6.3 billion contribution from operating activities and a $2.3 billion provision from financing activities (mostly from issuance of long-term debt).

Strategy

NextEra?s Florida Power and Light subsidiary has a 2017-2020 budget of some $18 billion to pursue its strategic endeavors. About half of the capital expenditures are targeted for improvements and expansion of its transmission and distribution segment. It plans to invest heavily into solar farms envisioning nearly $3.0 billion to construct new facilities the first of which is expected to open in early 2018. Capacity expansion and modernization of generation facilities will receive the remaining funds.

NextEra Energy Resources is viewed as the big growth engine of the holding company. It wants to be the leading American clean energy company and is humming along with excellent progress. It owns $45 billion in assets including 14000 MW of wind farm capacity 2000 MW of solar 3000 MW of nuclear and 1000 MW of natural gas. With the levelized cost of electricity from wind and solar declining some 70% between 2010 and 2016 the company believes the renewable power sources will be competitive into the next decade. Similar technological improvements in the ability to store energy in batteries are expected to enable even greater use of renewables. To that end in 2017 it is constructing a 100 MW solar farm (with storage) and when finished in 2019 will sell power to the Tucson Electric Power company.

Another area of anticipated growth is NEER?s natural gas pipeline business. It acquired in 2015 seven pipelines in Texas invested $1.5 billion in the Florida-based Sabal Trail pipeline which began operation in mid-2017. It expects to invest $1.1 billion to build along with partners a 300-mile pipeline in the Virginias with an in-service data in late 2018.

Mergers and Acquisitions

In mid-2017 Texas utility regulators spurned NextEra?s proposed $18 billion purchase of Oncor Electric Delivery. In 2016 Hawaiian regulator nixed NextEra?s proposed purchase of the Hawaiian Electric Company.

In January 2017 NextEra sold its fiber-optic telecommunications business (FPL FiberNet) to Crown Castle for proceeds of $1.1 billion.

In 2016 NextEra sold its Marcus Hook Energy Center natural gas fired energy facility located in Marcus Hook PA. The compensation was $760 and after costs and repayments resulted in proceeds of about $250 million.

HISTORY

During Florida's land boom of the early 1920s new homes and businesses were going up fast. But electric utilities were sparse and no transmission lines linked systems.

In 1925 American Power & Light Company (AP&L) which operated utilities throughout the Americas set up Florida Power & Light (FPL) to consolidate the state's electric assets. AP&L built transmission lines linking 58 communities from Miami to Stuart on the Atlantic Coast and from Arcadia to Punta Gorda on the Gulf.

FPL accumulated many holdings including a limestone quarry streetcars phone companies and water utilities and purchases in 1926 and 1927 nearly doubled its electric properties. In 1927 the company used an electric pump to demonstrate how swamplands could be drained and cultivated.

During the 1940s and 1950s FPL sold its nonelectric properties. The Public Utility Holding Company Act of 1935 forced AP&L to spin off FPL in 1950. The company was listed on the NYSE that year.

FPL grew with Florida's booming population. In 1972 its first nuclear plant (Turkey Point south of Miami) went on line. In the 1980s it began to diversify with the purchase of real estate firm W. Flagler Investment in 1981 and FPL Group was created in 1984 as a holding company. It subsequently acquired Telesat Cablevision (1985) Colonial Penn Group (1985 insurance) and Turner Foods (1988 citrus groves). FPL Group formed ESI Energy in 1985 to develop nonutility energy projects.

Diversification efforts didn't pan out and in 1990 the firm wrote off about $750 million. That year sticking to electricity the utility snagged its first out-of-state power plant in Georgia acquiring a 76% stake (over five years). FPL Group sold its ailing Colonial Penn unit in 1991; two years later it sold its real estate holdings and some of its cable TV businesses.

The utility gave environmentalists cause to complain in 1995. First the St. Lucie nuclear plant was fined by the Nuclear Regulatory Commission for a series of problems. FPL also wanted to burn orimulsion a cheap tar-like fuel. (Barred by the governor the utility gave up the plan in 1998.)

In 1997 FPL Group created FPL Energy an independent power producer (IPP) out of its ESI Energy and international operations; FPL Energy teamed up with Belgium-based Tractebel the next year to buy two gas-fired plants in Boston and Newark New Jersey.

FPL Energy built wind-power facilities in Iowa in 1998 and in Wisconsin and Texas in 1999; it also bought 35 generating plants in Maine in 1999. That year FPL Group sold its Turner Foods citrus unit and the rest of its cable TV holdings. By 2000 FPL Energy owned interests in plants in 12 states.

EXECUTIVES

Chairman and CEO, James L. (Jim) Robo, age 55, $1,300,000 total compensation

EVP and General Counsel, Charles E. Sieving, age 44, $689,000 total compensation

President and CEO NextEra Energy Resources, Armando Pimentel, age 55, $838,100 total compensation

President and CEO Florida Power & Light, Eric E. Silagy, $796,100 total compensation

EVP Human Resources and Corporate Sevices, Deborah H. Caplan

EVP Finance and CFO, John Ketchum, $575,000 total compensation

Vice President and Associate General Counsel, Max Guinn

Vice President E and C, Tom Broad
Auditors: DELOITTE & TOUCHE LLP

LOCATIONS

HQ: NextEra Energy Inc
700 Universe Boulevard, Juno Beach, FL 33408
Phone: 561 694-4000   **Fax:** 561 694-4620
Web: www.nexteraenergy.com

PRODUCTS/OPERATIONS

2016 sales

	$ mil.	% of total
Florida Power & Light	10,895	68
NextEra Energy Resources	4,893	30
Corporate & other	367	2
Total	**16**	**100**

Selected Subsidiaries and Divisions

Florida Power & Light Company
Energy Marketing and Trading
NextEra Energy Capital Holdings Inc.Next
Era Energy Resources LLCNext
Era Energy Partners
NextEra Energy Transmission

COMPETITORS

AES	Florida Public
Bangor Hydro-Electric	Utilities
Berkshire Hathaway	JEA
Energy	Oglethorpe Power
CMS Energy	Progress Energy
Calpine	Public Service
Chesapeake Utilities	Enterprise Group
Duke Energy	Seminole Electric
Entergy	Southern Company
Exelon	TECO Energy

HISTORICAL FINANCIALS

Company Type: Public

Income Statement

FYE: December 31

	REVENUE ($ mil.)	NET INCOME ($ mil.)	NET PROFIT MARGIN	EMPLOYEES
12/17	17,195	5,378	31.3%	13,900
12/16	16,155	2,912	18.0%	14,200
12/15	17,486	2,762	15.8%	13,800
12/14	17,021	2,469	14.5%	13,800
12/13	15,136	1,908	12.6%	13,400
Annual Growth	3.2%	29.6%	—	0.9%

2017 Year-End Financials

Debt ratio: 35.86%
Return on equity: 20.47%
Cash ($ mil.): 1,714
Current ratio: 0.64
Long-term debt ($ mil.): 31,463

No. of shares (mil.): 471
Dividends
Yield: 0.0%
Payout: 34.5%
Market value ($ mil.): 73,565

	STOCK PRICE ($) FY Close	P/E High/Low	PER SHARE ($) Earnings	Dividends	Book Value
12/17	156.19	14 10	11.38	3.93	59.89
12/16	119.46	21 16	6.25	3.48	52.01
12/15	103.89	18 15	6.06	3.08	48.97
12/14	106.29	19 15	5.60	2.90	44.96
12/13	85.62	20 15	4.47	2.64	41.47
Annual Growth	16.2%	— —	26.3%	10.5%	9.6%

NGL Energy Partners LP

NGL Energy Partners is devoted to natural gas liquids (NGL) logistics crude oil logistics water services and retail propane. Its crude oil logistics segment (its largest) buys crude oil from producers and transports it for resale at pipeline injection points storage terminals barge loading facilities rail facilities refineries and other trade hubs. It also retails wholesales and stores propane and other natural gas liquids. Wholesale operations deliver propane to third-party storage and transportation facilities. Retail operations include leasing propane tanks and other equipment and propane delivery. The retail propane segment has a propane storage capacity of 11.9 million gallons.

Operations

Its refined products and renewables segment (58% of sales) conducts gasoline diesel ethanol and biodiesel marketing operations. NGL Energy Partners' TransMontaigne Product Services LLC unit purchases refined petroleum products primarily in the US Gulf Coast East Coast and Midwest for delivery primarily on the Colonial Plantation and Magellan pipelines.

The company's crude oil logistics segment (27%) purchases crude oil from producers and transports it for resale at pipeline injection points storage terminals barge loading facilities rail facilities refineries and other trade hubs. In 2015 it owned 200 trucks 270 trailers 400 owned and 600 leased rail cars 11 towboats and 24 barges. In addition it also owned 35 pipeline injection facilities in Kansas Oklahoma North Dakota New Mexico Texas and Montana and leased three pipeline injection stations in Kansas Montana and North Dakota. Its operations are centered near areas of high crude oil production across the US.

NGL Energy Partners' water services segment revenues are derived from the gathering transportation treatment and disposal of wastewater

generated from oil and natural gas production operations from the sale of recycled water and recovered hydrocarbons and from the disposal of solids such as tank bottoms and drilling fluids. The company owns 70 water treatment and disposal facilities including 87 wells.

The Liquids segment supplies natural gas liquids to retailers wholesalers refiners and petrochemical plants throughout the US and in Canada and provides NGL terminaling and storage services through its 19 owned terminals throughout the US its salt dome storage facility in Utah and its leased storage and railcar transportation services. The company sold 2.1 billion gallons of NGLs a year.

The company's retail propane business (retail marketing and the sale and distribution of propane and distillates propane tanks equipment and supplies) serves more than 300000 residential agricultural commercial and industrial customers. It owns or leases 113 customer service locations and 98 satellite distribution locations. In addition it owns more than 400 bulk storage tanks with capacities ranging from 2000 to 90000 gallons; and has more than 300000 stationary customer storage tanks with capacities ranging from 7 to 30000 gallons. The company owns a fleet of 440 bulk delivery trucks 40 semi-tractors 30 propane transport trailers and 520 other service trucks.

NGL Energy Partners owns two major operating subsidiaries: High Sierra Energy LP; and NGL Energy Operating LLC.

Geographic Reach

The company's Crude oil logistics segment's operations are located near areas of high crude oil production such as the Bakken Shale Basin in North Dakota the DJ Basin in Colorado the Mississippi Lime shale play in Oklahoma the Permian Basin in Texas and New Mexico the Eagle Ford shale play in Texas the Anadarko Basin in Oklahoma and Texas and southern Louisiana. It Water Services' facilities are near fields with high levels of oil and natural gas production such as the Pinedale Anticline Basin in Wyoming the DJ Basin in Colorado and the Permian and Eagle Ford Basins in Texas. The natural gas liquids logistics segment's terminals are in Jefferson City Missouri East St. Louis Illinois and in St. Catherines Ontario Canada.

Headquartered in Tulsa Oklahoma the company has corporate offices in Denver and Houston.

Sales and Marketing

The company sells its refined and renewables products to commercial and industrial end users independent retailers distributors marketers government entities and other wholesalers of refined petroleum products. It also sells its products at TransMontaigne Partners L.P.'s terminals and at terminals owned by third parties.

Its liquids business serves national regional and independent retail industrial wholesale petrochemical refiner and natural gas liquids production customers.

NGL Energy Partners sells retail propane products to residential commercial and industrial and agricultural customers.

Financial Performance

The company's revenues decreased by 30% to $11.7 billion in fiscal 2016 (March year end) primarily due to the knock-on effect of lower oil and gas prices. Crude Oil Logistics revenues dropped to $3.2 billion from $6.6 million. Propane liquids sales dropped from $1.3 billion to $608.9 million.

Water Solutions revenues fared better with revenues only declining from $200 million to $185 million as higher service fees help to mitigate lower volumes of water processed at the company's existing facilities.

In fiscal 2016 NGL Energy Partners' results slumped from a net income of $29.9 million in fiscal 2015 to a net loss of $187.1 million a year later due to lower revenues higher operating expenses a rise in depreciation and amortization expenses and $381.7 million of costs on the disposal/impairment of assets (compared to $7.5 million in fiscal 2015).

That year its cash flow from operations increased from $262.4 million to $351.5 million as the result of decreases in natural gas liquids prices which lowered cash requirements to fund increases in the company's inventories.

Strategy

Take advantage of its vertical integration the company is looking enhance its ability to transport crude oil from the wellhead to refiners wastewater from the wellhead to treatment for disposal recycle or discharge and transport natural gas liquids from processing plants to end users including retail propane customers. It plans to achieve organic growth by investing in new assets that increase volumes and pursue acquisitions that add scale to its crude oil logistics platform and enhance the geographic diversity of its water services segment.

However low commodity prices over the last few years have hurt the company's bottom line and limited its access to investment capital.

To raise cash in 2016 NGL Energy Partners sold TransMontaigne GP LLC (a general management services company and general partner of Denver-based fuel-terminal owner TransMontaigne Partners L.P.) to ArcLight Capital for $350 million.

Mergers and Acquisitions

Expanding its portfolio in 2017 NGL Energy Partners LP bought assets from Murphy Energy. The assets included the Port Hudson Louisiana Terminal an NGL terminal that supports refined products blending and the Kingfisher Oklahoma Facility a natural gas liquids and condensate facility. The combined purchase price of the assets was $51 million.

In 2016 the company acquired 57% of an existing produced water pipeline company operating in the Delaware Basin portion of West Texas.

In 2015 the company acquired Sawtooth NGL Caverns which owns a natural gas liquids salt dome storage facility in Utah with rail and truck access to western US markets and entered into a construction agreement to expand the storage capacity of the facility. It also bought Magnum NGLs LLC from Magnum Development LLC enhancing it above ground services and adding customers. Magnum owns and operates a natural gas liquids storage facility with multiple existing salt caverns and a potential capacity of greater than 10 million barrels.

That year NGL Energy Partners acquired an 1.8-million-barrels-of-NGL capacity underground storage facility near Delta Utah.

Growing its water services businesses in 2014 NGL Energy Partners acquired the water disposal and hauling business of Oilfield Water Lines LP (a partnership between High Roller Wells and the Mark Cuban Companies) for $168 million. The deal added strategically located oil and gas water disposal facilities to its portfolio of water treatment and gathering infrastructure assets. The acquisition brings 90000 barrels per day of additional disposal capacity to the Eagle Ford Shale play in South Texas.

Company Background

Expanding its midstream business in 2013 NGL Energy Partners acquired diversified midstream energy company Gavilon LLC for $890 million. (The deal follows the company's 2011 purchase of SemGroup's SemStream unit for about $282 million).

That year the company continued its buying spree with the acquisition of Denver-based High Sierra Energy LP and its general partner High Sierra Energy GP LLC for about $693 million. High Sierra Energy has crude oil gathering water treatment and natural gas liquids (NGL) operations.

NGL Energy Partners is part of NGL Energy Holdings which is owned by company management and NGL Holdings. Silverthorne Operating holds the company's operating subsidiaries. The multi-layer structure is common among energy companies. NGL Holdings owned about 27% of the company pre-IPO. Brothers and co-presidents Shawn and Todd Coady together owned 38% through Hicks Oil & Hicksgas Incorporated.

Formed in 2010 by several investors NGL Energy Partners acquired and combined the assets and operations of NGL Supply a wholesale propane and terminalling business founded in 1967 and Hicksgas a retail propane business founded in 1940.

EXECUTIVES

Vice President wholesale, Stan Bugh
Are Vice President Georgia and Kansas, Aaron Reece
CEO, H. Michael Krimbill, age 63, $292,500 total compensation
EVP and CFO, Robert W. (Trey) Karlovich, age 40
President Retail Division, Shawn W. Coady, age 55, $311,250 total compensation
President Eastern Retail Operations, Vincent J. Osterman, age 60, $250,000 total compensation
President NGL and President and CEO High Sierra Energy, James J. (Jim) Burke, age 61, $381,750 total compensation
EVP NGL Crude Logistics, Don Robinson
EVP NGL Liquids, Jack Eberhardt
CIO, Jennifer Kingham
Executive Vice President Midstream Division, David Eastin
Vice President Of Business Development, Bradley Atkinson
Senior Vice President Accounting, Patrice Armbruster
Senior Vice President Refined Fuels, Donald Jensen
Vice President supply, Mark McGinty
Vice President of Tax, Joel Gustafson
Executive Vice President Operations, Greg Pound
Vice President Administration, Charles Wilkin
Vice President Eagle Ford, Tim Jurco
Vice President, Mark Henson
Vice President Legal andamp; Secretary, Kurston Mcmurray
Auditors: GRANT THORNTON LLP

LOCATIONS

HQ: NGL Energy Partners LP
6120 South Yale Avenue, Suite 805, Tulsa, OK 74136
Phone: 918 481-1119
Web: www.nglenergypartners.com

PRODUCTS/OPERATIONS

2016 Sales

	$ mil.	% of total
Refined products and renewables	6,792	58
Crude oil logistics	3,217	27
Liquids	1,194	10
Retail propane	353	3
Water solutions	185	2
Other	0	0
Total	**11,742**	**100**

COMPETITORS

AmeriGas Partners	Equistar Chemicals
Crestwood Midstream Partners LP	Exxon Mobil
	Ferrellgas Partners
Duke Energy	Huntsman International
Dynegy	Occidental Petroleum
Energy Transfer	Williams Companies
Enterprise Products	

HISTORICAL FINANCIALS

Company Type: Public

Income Statement

FYE: March 31

	REVENUE ($ mil.)	NET INCOME ($ mil.)	NET PROFIT MARGIN	EMPLOYEES
03/17	13,022	137	1.1%	2,700
03/16	11,742	(198)	—	3,200
03/15	16,802	16	0.1%	3,100
03/14	9,699	47	0.5%	2,500
03/13	4,417	47	1.1%	1,970
Annual Growth	**31.0%**	**30.0%**		**8.2%**

2017 Year-End Financials

Debt ratio: 47.36%
Return on equity: —
Cash ($ mil.): 12
Current ratio: 1.58
Long-term debt ($ mil.): 2,963

No. of shares (mil.): 120
Dividends
Yield: 6.9%
Payout: 164.2%
Market value ($ mil.): 2,719

	STOCK PRICE ($) FY Close	P/E High/Low		PER SHARE ($) Earnings	Dividends	Book Value
03/17	22.60	26	7	0.95	1.56	18.32
03/16	7.52	—	—	(2.35)	2.54	15.88
03/15	26.23	—	—	(0.29)	2.37	20.46
03/14	37.53	74	52	0.51	2.01	19.22
03/13	26.90	28	21	0.96	1.69	16.46
Annual Growth	**(4.3%)**	—	—	**(0.3%)**	**(1.9%)**	**2.7%**

Nicolet Bankshares Inc

EXECUTIVES

Pres-ceo, Robert Atwell
Auditors: Porter Keadle Moore, LLC

LOCATIONS

HQ: Nicolet Bankshares Inc
111 North Washington Street, Green Bay, WI 54301
Phone: 920 430-1400
Web: www.nicoletbank.com

HISTORICAL FINANCIALS

Company Type: Public

Income Statement

FYE: December 31

	ASSETS ($ mil.)	NET INCOME ($ mil.)	INCOME AS % OF ASSETS	EMPLOYEES
12/16	2,300	18	0.8%	480
12/15	1,214	11	0.9%	280
12/14	1,215	9	0.8%	280
12/13	1,198	16	1.3%	290
12/12	745	3	0.4%	175
Annual Growth	**32.6%**	**57.0%**	—	**28.7%**

2016 Year-End Financials

Debt ratio: 1.63%
Return on equity: 9.55%
Cash ($ mil.): 128
Current ratio: —
Long-term debt ($ mil.): —

No. of shares (mil.): 8
Dividends
Yield: —
Payout: —
Market value ($ mil.): 408

STOCK PRICE ($)		P/E		PER SHARE ($)		
	FY Close	High/Low		Earnings	Dividends	Book Value
12/16	47.69	19	12	2.37	0.00	32.26
12/15	31.79	12	9	2.57	0.00	26.36
12/14	25.00	11	7	2.25	0.00	27.35
12/13	16.54	5	4	3.80	0.00	24.73
Annual Growth	30.3%	—	—	(11.1%)	—	6.9%

NIELSEN HOLDINGS PLC

EXECUTIVES

Ceo, Mitch Barns
Senior Vice President Investor Relations, Kate Vanek

LOCATIONS

HQ: NIELSEN HOLDINGS PLC
85 BROAD ST, NEW YORK, NY 100042434
Phone: 646 654-5000

HISTORICAL FINANCIALS

Company Type: Private

Income Statement

FYE: December 31

	REVENUE ($ mil.)	NET INCOME ($ mil.)	NET PROFIT MARGIN	EMPLOYEES
12/15	6,172	575	9.3%	43,061
12/14	6,288	381	6.1%	—
12/13	5,703	736	12.9%	—
12/12	5,612	273	4.9%	—
Annual Growth	3.2%	28.2%	—	—

2015 Year-End Financials

Debt ratio: ——
Return on equity: 9.30%
Cash ($ mil.): 357
Current ratio: 0.90
Long-term debt ($ mil.): —

Dividends
Yield: —
Payout: —
Market value ($ mil.): —

NIKE Inc

Fleet-of-footwear NIKE named for the Greek goddess of victory is the world's #1 shoe and apparel company. NIKE designs develops and sells a variety of products and services to help in playing basketball and soccer (football) as well as in running men's and women's training and other action sports. Under its namesake brand NIKE also markets sports-inspired products for children and various competitive and recreational activities such as golf tennis and walking and sportswear by Converse and Hurley. NIKE sells through more than 1000-owned retail stores worldwide an e-commerce site and to thousands of retail accounts independent distributors and licensees.

Operations

NIKE operates in six geographic segments: North America Western Europe Central & Eastern Europe Greater China Japan and Emerging Markets. Almost all of the company's branded footwear and apparel is made by third-party manufacturers outside of the US mainly in Vietnam China and Indonesia. Its equipment products are made both in the US and abroad.

Each NIKE Brand geographic segment operates predominantly in one industry namely the design development marketing and selling of athletic footwear apparel and equipment. The segments include results for the NIKE Jordan and Hurley brands. The Company's NIKE Brand DTC operations are managed within each geographic operating segment. Converse is also a reportable segment and operates in one industry: the design marketing licensing and selling of casual sneakers apparel and accessories.

Converse and Hurley its affiliate brands and NIKE Golf comprise NIKE's Other Businesses. NIKE sells to thousands of US retail accounts which include a mix of footwear stores; sporting goods stores; athletic specialty stores; department stores; skate tennis and golf shops; and other retail accounts. During 2016 NIKE's three largest customers accounted for more than 25% of US sales.

NIKE sells its products to retail accounts through its own Direct-to-Consumer operations and through a mix of independent distributors licensees and sales representatives worldwide. The company sells to thousands of retail accounts and operates more than 40 distribution centers outside of the US.

Footwear accounted for 61% of the company's revenues in 2016.

Geographic Reach

NIKE is based near Beaverton Oregon; it has a 400-acre site with more than 40 buildings. In fiscal 2016 (May year end) North America accounted for 46% of sales Western Europe (18%) Greater China (12%) Emerging Markets (11%) Central & Eastern Europe (4%) and Japan (3%). Other operations account for the rest of its revenues.

In the US NIKE owns a full product line distribution center in Memphis Tennessee and four other distribution centers three of which are leased also in Memphis. NIKE Brand apparel and equipment are also shipped from its Foothill Ranch California distribution center which the company leases. The company also owns or leases distribution and customer service facilities outside the United States. The most significant are the distribution facilities located in Laakdal Belgium; Taicang China; Tomisato Japan and Incheon Korea all of which the company owns.

The company has branch offices and subsidiaries in Argentina Australia Austria Belgium Bermuda Brazil Canada Chile China Croatia Cyprus the Czech Republic Denmark Finland France Germany Greece Hong Kong Hungary India Indonesia Ireland Israel Italy Japan Korea Malaysia Mexico New Zealand the Netherlands Norway Panama the Philippines Poland Portugal Russia Singapore Slovakia Slovenia South Africa Spain Sri Lanka Sweden Switzerland Taiwan Thailand Turkey the UAE the UK the US Uruguay and Vietnam.

Sales and Marketing

Worldwide NIKE sells its products to retail accounts through NIKE-owned retail stores and Internet websites and through a mix of independent distributors and licensees. NIKE also sells its products to wholesale customers and directly to consumers through its Direct to Consumer operations. It also enters into licensing agreements that permit unaffiliated parties to make and sell certain apparel digital devices and applications and other equipment designed for sports activities.

The company sells to thousands of retail accounts and ships products from more than 40 distribution centers outside of the US.

NIKE markets its footwear and other products globally through diverse advertising and promotional programs and campaigns including print social media online advertising and endorsement contracts with celebrity athletes. Total advertising and promotion expenses were about $3.3 million $3.2 million and $3.0 million for 2016 2015 and 2014 respectively.

During fiscal 2014 NIKE's three largest customers helped to bring in 25% of US sales. During the same reporting period the company's three largest customers outside of the US accounted for 13% of total non-US sales.

The company is supplied by approximately 142 footwear factories located in 15 countries and is supplied by approximately 394 apparel factories located in 39 countries.

Financial Performance

Net sales of the company have seen an upward trend since 2012.

In fiscal 2016 net sales increased by 6% due to higher North America and Greater China revenues partially offset by decreased sales from Emerging Markets.

Excluding changes in foreign currency exchange rates North America revenues increased primarily due to growth in its Sportswear Jordan Brand and Running categories. Direct-To-Consumer revenues grew fueled by strong online sales growth the addition of new stores. and comparable store sales growth.

Currency-neutral footwear revenue growth was attributable to higher revenues in most key categories led by the Jordan Brand Sportswear Running and Women's Training. Apparel revenue growth was driven by its Sportswear and Men's Training categories.

Net income has also moved upward since 2012.

In fiscal 2016 net income increased by 15% due to higher sales.

Net cash provided by the operating activities decreased by $1.5 billion due to changes in accounts payable accrued liabilities and income tax payable.

Strategy

Sagging sales pushed NIKE's directors into kicking off an organizational restructure in 2017. The firm will cut 2% of its workforce consolidate its six segments into four and sharpen its focus on 12 key global cities including New York London Beijing and Shanghai. NIKE expects the majority of its growth into 2020 to come from these global trend-setting cities. The company will also reduce the number of trainer lines by a quarter.

In addition to brand strength NIKE has fueled momentum by launching a stream of new products including the NIKE Fuelband a digital device to track daily activity and the Flyknit a technology designed to lighten footwear weight and improve fit. In anticipation of replacing rival Reebok as the maker of NFL-branded apparel and uniforms NIKE also expanded its offerings with new high-performance uniforms for all 32 NFL teams.

The company continues to diversify one of its apparel technologies Dri-FIT which is the adaptive foundation of everything from shirts to socks. Key Dri-FIT performance products introduced in 2015 included Running Dri-FIT Knit and the NIKE Pro Bra Collection.

NIKE invests in new technologies that increase automation helps reduce waste and have long-term potential to increase both customization of its products and speed to market. Automation is also driving growth in its higher gross margin Direct-To-Consumer business led by NIKE.com as part of an integrated marketplace growth strategy across its DTC and wholesale operations.

Facing a slump in its golf division sales in 2016 the company announced that it would shift away from equipment (golf clubs balls and bags) and instead focus on expanding its golf footwear and apparel business.

HISTORY

Phil Knight a good miler and Bill Bowerman a track coach who tinkered with shoe designs met at the University of Oregon in 1957. The two men formed Blue Ribbon Sports in 1962 in an effort to make quality American running shoes. The next year they began selling Tiger shoes manufactured by Japanese shoe manufacturer Onitsuka Tiger. They sold the running shoes out of cars at track meets.

The company rebranded as NIKE in 1972 named for the Greek goddess of victory. The NIKE "Swoosh" logo was designed by a graduate student named Carolyn Davidson who was paid $35. The same year NIKE broke with Onitsuka in a dispute over distribution rights.

NIKE re-evaluated its long-term growth strategy in fiscal 2012 and as a result divested its Cole Haan and Umbro businesses in February 2013 and November 2012 respectively. NIKE sold Umbro to Iconix Brand Group for $225 million. The company sold Cole Haan to London-based private equity firm Apax Partners for $570 million.

EXECUTIVES

Vice President and Chief Information Officer, Roland Paanakker

Vice President US Brand, Ken Dice

Chairman President and CEO, Mark G. Parker, age 61, $1,550,000 total compensation

COO, Eric D. Sprunk, age 53, $990,000 total compensation

President NIKE Brand, Trevor A. Edwards, age 54, $990,000 total compensation

President Geographies and Sales, Elliott J. Hill

President Converse North American Footwear and Global Apparel, Michael Spillane, age 54

EVP Chief Administrative Officer and General Counsel, Hilary K. Krane, age 53

President and CEO Converse, Davide Grasso

EVP Global Sports Marketing, John F. Slusher, age 48

EVP Global Human Resources, David J. Ayre, age 57

President DTC, Heidi OÂ'Neill

EVP and CFO, Andrew (Andy) Campion, $822,306 total compensation

Global CIO, Jim Scholefield

Vice President of Brand Human Resources, Steve Conroy

Vice President Human Resources Business Partner Geographies, Mike Tarbell

Vice President North America Supply Chain Operations, Trish Young

Executive Vice President, Reham Habib

Vice President Creative Director Apparel, Thomas Walker

Vice President USA Footwear, Dan Jones

Senior Vice President Of Commercial Banking, Evelyn Gomez

Vice President General Manager Global Womens Training, Heidi ONeill

Vice President Creative Director Nike Sportswear, Kurt Parker

VP Manufacturing, Greg Bui

Executive Vice President of Meth Production, Jim Ford

Event Vice President, Leroy Ebanks

Vice President Young Athletes Sales, Mark Trelease

Vice President Global Apparel and Equipment Materials Nike, Susi Proudman

Vice President E Commerce, Lisa Lynham

Vice President Global Digital Commerce, Kristine Rebber

National Account Manager, Joni Kristo

Vice President Creative Director Athletic Training, Janett Nichol

Vice President Global Entertainment Marketing, Pamela McConnell

Executive Assistant Senior Vice President Government and Public Affairs, Keyanus Jacobo

Global Vice President Sports Apparel, Aaron Heiser

Vice President Treasure, Bob Woodruff

Associate Vice President of Information technology and Sales, James Johnson

Vice President Human Resources Business Partner, Karen Weisz

Vice President Direct To Consumer Technology, Steven Dee

Vice President Marketing, Todd Jacobs

Vice President Director Manager, Nick Athanasakos

Vice President Director Other, Beth Pollack

Vice President Director of Technology, Scott Marien

Vice President Global Basketball Sports Marketing, Lynn Merritt

Vice President and Chief Marketing Officer, Dirk-Jan van Hameren

Vice President Global Operations and Technology, Hans Vanalebeek

Management Vice President, Hubertus Hoyt

Vice President North America Athletic Training, Mark Riley

Vice President of International Business and Government Relations, Joseph Ha

Vice President North America Brand Marketing, David Schriber

Vice President Global Operations And Technology, Hugo Mora

Vice President Creative Director Nike Sportswear, Adrian Nyman

Inp: Vice President Human Resources Business Partner Asia Pacific, Lilly Liang

Vice President Broad Based Total Rewards, Kimberly Lupo

Vice President Sales Brand Jordan, Susan Carey

Vice President and Chief Tax Officer, Patti Johnson

VP Manufacturing, Rich Sayre

CLINIC DIRECTOR, Laura E Cooper

VICE PRESIDENT GLOBAL DIGITAL OPERATIONS AND GEO EXPANSION, Shannon Glass

VICE PRESIDENT AND GENERAL MANAGER GREATER CHINA SOUTH TERRITORY, Simon Men

VICE PRESIDENT SALES ACCOUNT, Eddie Hu

Vice President Football Baseball Apparel, Matt Park

Board Member, Nico Harrison

Board Member, Ruth Karanga

Auditors: PricewaterhouseCoopers LLP

LOCATIONS

HQ: NIKE Inc
One Bowerman Drive, Beaverton, OR 97005-6453
Phone: 503 671-6453
Web: www.nike.com

2016 Sales

	% of total
North America	46
Western Europe	18
Greater China	12
Emerging Markets	11
Converse	6
Central & Eastern Europe	4
Japan	3
Global Brand Divisions	-
Total	**100**

PRODUCTS/OPERATIONS

2016 Sales

	% of total
Footwear	61
Apparel	28
Equipment	5
Other	6
Total	**100**

Selected Products

Athletic Shoes
Aquatic
Auto racing
Baseball
Basketball
Bicycling
Cheerleading
Cross-training
Fitness
Football
Golf
Running
Soccer
Tennis
Volleyball
Wrestling
Athletic Wear and Equipment
Accessories
Athletic bags
Bats
Caps
Digital devices
Eyewear
Fitness wear
Gloves
Golf clubs
Headwear
Jackets
Pants
Protective equipment
Running clothes
Shirts
Shorts
Skirts
Snowboards and snowboard apparel
Socks
Sport balls
Timepieces
Uniforms

COMPETITORS

ASICS	Quiksilver
Acushnet Holdings	R. Griggs
Amer Sports	Ralph Lauren
Callaway Golf	Rawlings Sporting
Columbia Sportswear	Goods
Deckers Outdoor	Rollerblade
FUBU	Russell Brands
Fila Korea	Saucony
Fruit of the Loom	Skechers U.S.A.
Hanesbrands	Steven Madden
Iconix Brand Group	Timberland
Juicy Couture	Timex
K-Swiss	Tommy Hilfiger
Levi Strauss	Under Armour
Li Ning	VF Corporation
Mizuno	Victoria's Secret
New Balance	Stores
Oakley	Wolverine World Wide
PUMA SE	adidas

HISTORICAL FINANCIALS

Company Type: Public

Income Statement

FYE: May 31

	REVENUE ($ mil.)	NET INCOME ($ mil.)	NET PROFIT MARGIN	EMPLOYEES
05/17	34,350	4,240	12.3%	74,400
05/16	32,376	3,760	11.6%	70,700
05/15	30,601	3,273	10.7%	62,600
05/14	27,799	2,693	9.7%	56,500
05/13	25,313	2,485	9.8%	48,000
Annual Growth	**7.9%**	**14.3%**	**—**	**11.6%**

2017 Year-End Financials

Debt ratio: 16.35%
Return on equity: 34.38%
Cash ($ mil.): 3,808
Current ratio: 2.93
Long-term debt ($ mil.): 3,471

No. of shares (mil.): 1,643
Dividends
Yield: 1.2%
Payout: 28.3%
Market value ($ mil.): 87,063

Nordstrom, Inc.

Service with a smile is a part of Nordstrom's corporate culture. One of the nation's largest up-scale apparel and shoe retailers Nordstrom sells clothes shoes and accessories through more than 115 Nordstrom department stores and more than 215 off-price outlet stores (Nordstrom Rack) in nearly 40 states and online. It also operates a pair of Jeffrey luxury boutiques a "Last Chance" clearance store online private sale site HauteLook and personalized clothing service Trunk Club. With its easy-return policy and touches such as thank-you notes from employees Nordstrom has earned a reputation for top-notch customer service. Nordstrom family members who own about 25% of the retailer's stock closely supervise the chain.

Operations

The family-run company operates two business segments: Retail and Credit. The Retail segment accounts for the vast majority (98%) of Nordstrom's revenue and includes sales from its full-line and Nordstrom Rack stores as well as from its Nordstrom.com nordstromrack.com Hautelook.com Trunk Club.com Jeffrey and its Canadian operations.

Nordstrom's Credit segment (2% of sales) owns a federal savings bank Nordstrom fsb through which it offers a private-label credit card two co-branded Nordstrom VISA cards and a debit card for Nordstrom purchases. The cards also include a loyalty program that rewards shoppers depending on their spending levels.

Nordstrom's full-line stores generate 50% of its net sales while its Nordstrom Rack stores contributed roughly 25%. Its fast-growing Nordstrom.com channel generated 15% of net sales while its Nordstromrack.com and Hautelook channels combined made up around 5%.

By product the company generates over 30% of its net sales from women's apparel while shoe sales make up nearly 25%. The rest of its net sales came from men's apparel (15%) women's accessories (10%) cosmetics (10%) kid's apparel and other items (5% each).

Geographic Reach

Nordstrom has some 345 full-line and Nordstrom Rack stores in 40 US states as well as three Nordstrom full-line stores in Canada. California is the retailer's largest market with over 80 full-line and Rack stores. Other major markets for the chain include Florida Texas and Washington.

Financial Performance

Nordstrom shrugged off industry-wide malaise to record 2% revenue growth in fiscal 2017. Sales of $14.8 billion were a result of innovative approaches to customer service and store openings. The company re-imagined the role of the department store in the internet age driving foot traffic through a program of exclusive pop-up stores and new retail concepts. While comparable store sales still fell (by less than 1%) the figure compares fa-

vorably to its peers such as JCPenney and Macy's. Off-price sales through Nordstrom Rack increased 11% due to 21 store openings. Sales at the company's credit card business softened slightly.

Net income fell 41% to $354 million due to higher cost of sales and SGA expenses. Nordstrom ramped up marketing spend and invested in technology and supply chain to open up new digital capabilities.

Cash from operating activities fell 33% to $1.6 billion due to a particularly high fiscal 2016 after it sold its credit card receivables. When excluded cash increased due to improvements in working capital.

Strategy

Department stores across the US are having a hard time of it having found themselves somewhat outdated as consumers gravitate increasingly towards the internet and small brand-specific stores. Revenue at stalwarts such as JCPenney and Macy's are eroding but 116-year-old Nordstrom is proving more adaptable than most.

New ideas such as short-term pop-up shops and link-ups with emerging designers promote a discovery dynamic and give millennials — the most department store resistant consumer group — social media currency and thus reason to visit stores.

It has also found new ways to leverage online such as allowing customers to pre-select clothing and book a changing room to try them on in. Customers can also pay by text.

Nordstrom also continually expands and refreshes its store base. In 2016 it opened 27 new stores (and closed one) of which 21 were Nordstrom Rack discount stores. Indeed the company is pumping up Nordstrom Rack at a fast pace to entice the less affluent consumer.

In October 2015 the company sold off a substantial majority of its US Visa and private label credit card portfolio to TD Bank Group and entered into an agreement for the bank to be the exclusive issuer of Nordstrom's consumer credit cards.

HISTORY

In 1901 John Nordstrom a lumberjack and successful gold miner used his Alaska Gold Rush money to open Wallin & Nordstrom shoe store in Seattle with shoemaker Carl Wallin. Nordstrom retired in 1928 and sold half of the business which included a second store to his sons Everett and Elmer. Wallin sold his share to the brothers after retiring the following year. A third Nordstrom son Lloyd joined in 1933. The shoe chain thrived and incorporated as Nordstrom's in 1946.

By 1963 Nordstrom's was the largest independent shoe chain in the country. The company diversified by acquiring Best Apparel's stores in Seattle and Portland Oregon. Three years later Nordstrom's bought Portland's Nicholas Ungar a fashion retailer and merged it with one of its shoe stores in Portland under the name Nordstrom Best.

Renaming itself Nordstrom Best in 1966 the company went public in 1971 and changed its name again in 1973 to Nordstrom. The retailer grew steadily throughout the 1970s opening new stores boosting sales in existing stores and diversifying. In 1976 Nordstrom started Place Two featuring apparel and shoes in smaller stores than its traditional department store layouts. It moved into Southern California (Orange County) two years later. Buoyed by almost $300 million in new sales Nordstrom executives planned an aggressive expansion.

Nordstrom opened its first store on the East Coast in 1988 in Virginia. The chain continued to expand opening stores in Northern California and in the affluent Washington DC suburbs.

The 1989 San Francisco earthquake along with a national downturn hurt retail sales significantly. Nordstrom's much-touted focus on customer service had a downside: The company was investigated in 1990 for not paying employees for customer services they performed including delivery of merchandise on their own time. (Three years later Nordstrom set aside $15 million to pay back wages to employees who had performed off-the-clock services.)

The company continued to expand in the East and Midwest opening its first store in the New York City area in 1991. In 1993 the retailer opened a men's boutique in New York (Fa Șonnable). Looking for new ways to attract customers Nordstrom introduced a mail-order catalog the next year.

Following the family's business tradition six members of Nordstrom's fourth generation began running the company in 1995. Third-generation members James Nordstrom John Nordstrom Bruce Nordstrom and Jack McMillan retired as co-chairmen and were replaced by non-family members Ray Johnson and John Whitacre. (Johnson retired in 1996.)

Nordstrom created Nordstrom.com a partnership with Benchmark Capital and Madrona Investment Group in 1999 to consolidate its catalog and Internet operations.

In early 2000 amid slumping sales the company dissolved the co-presidency. Less than a year later however the Nordstroms were back in charge. Chairman and CEO Whitacre resigned and Blake Nordstrom took over running the company as president. His father Bruce came out of retirement to take the chairman's role. Later the company bought the French design company Fa Șonnable which supplies the products for its Fa Șonnable boutiques.

In May 2002 the company bought out Benchmark's and Madrona's minority stake in Nordstrom.com.

Nordstrom bought a majority interest in August 2005 in luxury specialty stores Jeffrey New York and Jeffrey Atlanta. Terms of the agreement were not disclosed. The Jeffrey stores had about $35 million in sales in 2004. Also in 2005 the company opened stores in Atlanta; Dallas; Irvine California; and San Antonio.

In late 2007 Nordstrom sold its four US Fa Șonnable boutiques and 37 European locations to Lebanon-based M1 Group for about $210 million. Overall in 2007 Nordstrom opened three full-line department stores and a single Rack store.

Nordstrom opened its first full-line department store in Hawaii in early 2008. That October amid economic gloom the retailer opened a store in Pittsburgh. Overall the retailer opened eight new Nordstrom stores and half a dozen Rack outlets in 2008. In 2009 it added three full-line Nordstrom locations and 13 Rack outlets.

Nordstrom acquired e-tailer HauteLook for $180 million in stock in March 2011. Based in Los Angeles HauteLook is a leader in online private sales.

EXECUTIVES

Co-President, Blake W. Nordstrom, age 56, $751,152 total compensation

Co-President, Peter E. (Pete) Nordstrom, age 55, $751,152 total compensation

Co-President, Erik B. Nordstrom, age 55, $751,152 total compensation

EVP General Counsel and Secretary, Robert B. Sari, age 61

EVP and Chief Innovation Officer, Geevy S.K. Thomas, age 52

EVP and CIO, Daniel F. (Dan) Little, age 56, $552,806 total compensation

EVP and President Stores, James F. (Jamie) Nordstrom, age 44

EVP and General Merchandise Manager Designer Women's Apparel, Tricia D. Smith, age 46

EVP and Chief Marketing Officer, Scott A. Meden, age 54

EVP Finance and Treasurer, James A. Howell, age 52

EVP and General Merchandise Manager MenÂ's and Kids Wear, Paige L. Thomas, age 46

EVP and President Nordstrom.com, Kenneth J. (Ken) Worzel, age 52, $657,417 total compensation

EVP Nordstrom Merchandising Group, Teri Bariquit, age 51

EVP and General Merchandise Manager Accessories At Home and Beauty, Gemma Lionello, age 52

EVP; Chairman and CEO Nordstrom fsb; President Nordstrom Credit, Steven C. Mattics, age 48

EVP Supply Chain, Michael Sato

CFO, Anne L. Bramman, age 49

EVP Online Merchandising, Kirk M. Beardsley

EVP and President Nordstromrack.com HauteLook and Trunk Club, Terence Boyle

EVP Human Resources, Christine F. Deputy, age 51, $319,206 total compensation

EVP Strategy, Lisa C. Luther

EVP and President Nordstrom Product Group, Jennifer Jackson Brown

EVP and General Merchandise Manager Shoe Division, Kristin Frossmo

EVP and President Nordstrom Rack, Karen S. McKibbin, age 57

EVP and General Merchandise Manager Nordstrom Rack, Brian Roberts

SENIOR VICE PRESIDENT HUMAN RESOURCES, Lisa V Price

SENIOR VICE PRESIDENT TECHNOLOGY, Magali Muratore

VICE PRESIDENT, Matt Skally

VICE PRESIDENT MERCHANDISE PLANNING, Angie L Caldwell

VICE PRESIDENT FINANCE, Chris Goelkel

VP Fashion Office, Red Godfrey

VICE PRESIDENT PUBLIC RELATIONS AND CORPORATE AFFAIRS, Gigi Ganatra

VICE PRESIDENT ASSISTANT GENERAL COUNSEL AND ACO NFSB, Janine M Weaver

VICE PRESIDENT NFSB SENIOR VICE PRESIDENT STRATEGIC DELIVERY AND SUPPORT, Jeanne Muenchau

VICE PRESIDENT DIVISIONAL MERCH PLANNING AND INVENTORY, Joe Brazell

EXECUTIVE VICE PRESIDENT CHIEF SUPPLY CHAIN OFFICER, Brent Beabout

VICE PRESIDENT NMG STRATEGY AND OPERATIONS, Corinne E Copello

VICE PRESIDENT COMPENSATION AND LEADERSHIP BENEFITS, Dave Anders

Auditors: Deloitte & Touche LLP

LOCATIONS

HQ: Nordstrom, Inc.
  1617 Sixth Avenue, Seattle, WA 98101
Phone: 206 628-2111
Web: www.nordstrom.com

PRODUCTS/OPERATIONS

2017 Sales

	$ mil.	% of total
Full-line stores US	7,186	48
Nordstrom.com	2,519	17
Nordstrom Rack	3,809	25
Nordstromrack.com/Hautelook	700	4
Other retail	554	4
Corporate/Other	(270)	0
Credit Card revenues net	259	2
Total	14,757	100

2017 Sales

	% of total
Retail	98
Credit	2
Corporate/Other	0
Total	100

2017 Products category

	% of total
Women's Apparel	32
Shoes	23
Men's Apparel	17
Women's Accessories	11
Beauty	11
Kids' Apparel	3
Other	3
Total	100

2017 sales

	No.
Nordstrom full-line stores - U.S.and Canada	123
Nordstrom Rack and others	226
Total	349

PRODUCTS OFFERED:

Dresses
Tops
Jeans
Sweaters
Coats
Jackets
Pants
Suits
Skirts
Swimsuits & Cover-Ups
Active Yoga & Outdoor
Bras Panties & Lingerie
Shapewear
Sleep Lounge & Robes
Hosiery Leggings & Socks
Plus-Size Clothing
Petite-Size Clothing
Maternity Clothing
Shoes
Handbags & Wallets
Watches
Jewelry
Fine Jewelry
Optical Frames & Reading Glasses
Sunglasses
Scarves & Wraps
Hats & Hair Accessories
Winter Accessories
Gloves
Belts
Luggage & Travel
Tech Accessories & Cases
Hosiery & Socks

Selected Retail Operations

HauteLook (private-sale website for apparel and home decor)
Jeffrey (boutiques)
Last Chance (clearance store)
Nordstrom (specialty stores selling apparel shoes and accessories for women men and children)
Nordstrom Direct (catalogs and online ordering)
Nordstrom Rack (outlets selling merchandise from Nordstrom specialty stores and manufacturers)

COMPETITORS

Ann Taylor	J. Crew
Astor & Black	Lands' End
Barneys	Macy's
Benetton	Neiman Marcus
Bloomingdale's	Nine West
Bluefly	Saks Fifth Avenue
Brooks Brothers	Tailored Brands
Caleres	Talbots
Dillard's	The Gap
Donna Karan	Tiffany & Co.
Eddie Bauer LLC	Von Maur
J. C. Penney	Wayfair

HISTORICAL FINANCIALS

Company Type: Public

Income Statement

FYE: January 28

	REVENUE ($ mil.)	NET INCOME ($ mil.)	NET PROFIT MARGIN	EMPLOYEES
01/17	14,757	354	2.4%	72,500
01/16	14,437	600	4.2%	72,500
01/15*	13,506	720	5.3%	67,000
02/14	12,540	734	5.9%	62,500
02/13	12,148	735	6.1%	61,000
Annual Growth	5.0%	(16.7%)	—	4.4%

*Fiscal year change

2017 Year-End Financials

Debt ratio: 35.30%
Return on equity: 40.78%
Cash ($ mil.): 1,007
Current ratio: 1.07
Long-term debt ($ mil.): 2,763

No. of shares (mil.): 170
Dividends
  Yield: 0.0%
  Payout: 73.2%
Market value ($ mil.): 7,281

	STOCK PRICE ($) FY Close	P/E High/Low	PER SHARE ($) Earnings	Dividends	Book Value
01/17	42.83	30 18	2.02	1.48	5.12
01/16	49.10	26 14	3.15	6.33	5.02
01/15*	76.20	21 15	3.72	1.32	12.84
02/14	57.45	17 14	3.71	1.20	10.88
02/13	55.12	16 13	3.56	1.08	9.71
Annual Growth	(6.1%)	—	(13.2%)	8.2%	(14.8%)

*Fiscal year change

Norfolk Southern Corp.

Transportation titan Norfolk Southern is the one big train that could. Its main subsidiary Norfolk Southern Railway transports freight over a network consisting of about 20000 route miles in 20-plus states in the eastern southeastern and Midwestern US and in Ontario and Quebec. The rail system is made up of more than 16000 route miles owned by Norfolk Southern and more than 7000 route miles of trackage rights which allow the company to use tracks owned by other railroads. Norfolk Southern transports coal and general merchandise including automotive products and chemicals.

Operations

Norfolk Southern operates more than 4250 locomotives and more than 71000 freight cars. It reports through three segments: General Merchandise (more than 60% of net sales) Intermodal (more than 20%) and Coal (15%).

General Merchandise is subdivided into five commodity groups: Agriculture/Consumer/Government (such commodities and products as soybeans wheat beverages canned goods ethanol and military items); Chemicals (sulfur petroleum products plastics among others); Metals/Construction (steel aluminum cement bricks etc); Automotive (finished vehicles from and auto parts for such auto OEMs as Ford General Motors and Toyota); and Paper/Clay/Forest (lumber and wood products pulp board and paper products wood fibers wood pulp scrap paper and clay). The General Merchandise segment maintains more than 2.5 million railroad carloads each year.

Coal is Norfolk Southern's single largest commodity group. The coal segment carried about 100 million tons of coal originating from major coal basins and destined for about 80 coal generation plants as well as export metallurgical and industrial facilities. Operating in the eastern US Intermodal carries about 4 million units for such clients as intermodal marketing companies international steamship lines and truckers.

Geographic Reach

Norfolk Southern operates in 22 US states and Washington DC and transport overseas freight via several Atlantic and Gulf Coast ports.

Sales and Marketing

Norfolk Southern mainly targets the agriculture metals construction automotive and paper sectors. Its automotive clients include BMW Honda Hyundai Mercedes-Benz Nissan and Tesla.

Financial Performance

Norfolk Southern's revenues have declined the last two years dipping 6% from $10.5 billion in 2015 to $9.9 billion in 2016 due to declines across most of its segments.

Coal segment sales in 2016 dropped by 18% due to a decline in carload volumes which were impacted by a decrease in natural gas prices which shifted the customer's preference from coal to natural gas usage. General Merchandise sales fell 2% in 2016 due to a 6% decline from Chemicals and a 4% decline from Paper/Clay/Forest. In addition Intermodal's revenue decreased by 8% due to lower fuel surcharge revenues.

The decline in Chemicals was attributed to lower traffic volume reflecting fewer shipments of crude oil originated from the Bakken oil fields. Chemicals also experienced lower chlor-alkali and rock salt traffic which was the result of market consolidations and softened demand. Paper/Clay/Forest in 2016 experienced decreases within the pulpboard and woodchip markets due to customer sourcing changes in addition to lower paper shipments as a result of decreased demand and the ongoing contraction of the paper market.

Norfolk Southern's profits on the other hand surged by 7% from $1.56 billion in 2015 to $1.67 billion in 2016. This was due to higher income from railway operations and an 11% decrease in railway operating expenses during 2016 as a result of its strategic focus on cost-cutting.

Strategy

To shield itself against economic forces that it cannot control Norfolk Southern focuses on projected expense reduction and focused cost-control initiatives. In early 2016 it announced a five-year plan to achieve annual productivity savings of more than $650 million per year by 2020. As a result it achieved $250 million in savings for 2016 after initially planning to save $130 million for the year.

Mergers and Acquisitions

In 2015 Norfolk Southern acquired 282.55 miles of rail line between Sunbury Pennsylvania and Schenectady New York from the Delaware & Hudson Railway (D&H) a subsidiary of Canadian Pacific Railway. The deal allowed the company to connect businesses in central Pennsylvania to upstate New York and New England and gave it single-line routes from Chicago and the southeastern US to Albany New York.

HISTORY

Norfolk Southern Corporation resulted from the 1982 merger of two US rail giants — Norfolk & Western Railway Company (N&W) and Southern Railway Company — which had emerged from more than 200 and 150 previous mergers respectively.

N&W dates to 1838 when one track connected Petersburg Virginia to City Point (now Hopewell). This eight-miler became part of the Atlantic Mississippi & Ohio (AM&O) which was created by consolidating three Virginia railways in 1870.

In 1881 Philadelphia banker E.W. Clark bought the AM&O and renamed it the Norfolk & Western.

N&W rolled into Ohio by purchasing two other railroads (1892 1901).

The company took over the Virginian Railway a coal carrier with track paralleling much of its own in 1959. In 1964 N&W became a key railroad in the Midwest by acquiring the New York Chicago & St. Louis Railroad and the Pennsylvania Railroad's line between Columbus and Sandusky Ohio. It also leased the Wabash Railroad with lines from Detroit and Chicago to Kansas City and St. Louis.

Southern Railway can be traced back to the South Carolina Canal & Rail Road a nine-mile line chartered in 1827 and built by Horatio Allen to win trade for Charleston's port. It began operating the US's first regularly scheduled passenger train in 1830 and became the world's longest railway when it opened a 136-mile line to Hamburg South Carolina (1833).

Soon other railroads sprang up in the South including the Richmond & Danville (Virginia 1847) and the East Tennessee Virginia & Georgia (1869) which were combined to form the Southern Railway System in 1894. Southern eventually controlled more than 100 railroads forging a system from Washington DC to St. Louis and New Orleans.

The 1982 merger of Southern and N&W created an extensive rail system throughout the East South and Midwest. Norfolk Southern (a holding company created for the two railroads) also bought North American Van Lines in 1985. Triple Crown Services the company's intermodal subsidiary was started in 1986. The company also made a failed attempt to take over Piedmont Aviation the next year.

Norfolk Southern revived North American Van Lines by selling its refrigerator truck operation Tran-star (1993) and suspending its commercial trucking line. But it later sold the rest of the motor carrier (1998) to focus on rail operations.

When CSX announced its plans to buy Conrail in 1997 Norfolk Southern's counteroffer led to a split of the former Northeastern monopoly between Norfolk Southern (58%) and CSX (42%). Problems with integrating Conrail's assets hurt Norfolk Southern's results. But by 2000 it had regained some of the traffic it had lost to service problems and its intermodal shipping business also gained speed. In 2004 Norfolk Southern and CSX reorganized Conrail to give each parent company direct ownership of the portion of Conrail's assets that it operates. Conrail still operates switching facilities and terminals used by both Norfolk Southern and CSX.

Norfolk Southern got hit in the wallet in 2001: The company agreed to pay $28 million to settle a racial discrimination lawsuit brought by black employees in 1993. Norfolk Southern began rounds of layoffs and closed redundant depots and facilities in 2001.

In 2005 nine people died in South Carolina when chlorine gas leaked from a ruptured car on a Norfolk Southern freight train. The car was breached when the train crashed into a company-owned locomotive and two train cars that were parked on a siding.

Jumping ahead ten years the company in 2015 rejected an unsolicited takeover by Canadian Pacific in a deal worth $37.8 billion.

EXECUTIVES

Vice President Government Relations, Bruno Maestri

EVP CFO and CIO, Cynthia C. (Cindy) Earhart, $600,000 total compensation

Chairman President and CEO, James A. (Jim) Squires, age 55, $900,000 total compensation

EVP and Chief Marketing Officer, Alan H. Shaw, $500,000 total compensation

EVP and COO, Michael J. Wheeler, $581,250 total compensation

Vp Business, Robert Martinez

Vice President Intermodal and Automotive Marketing, Jeffrey S Heller

National Account Manager, Rick Lentz

AVP Finance, Michael Hostutler

Vice President, Frank Macchiaverna

Vice President Industrial Products, Michael R McClellan

Assistant Vice President Benefits and Compensation, Chris Williams

Vice President Chief Engineer Design, Dave Becker

AVP Accounting Operations, Stacia Minton

Vice President Audit and Compliance, Tom Hurlbut

Government Relations, Herbert Smith

National Account Manager, Bill Flanagan

Vice President Process Engineering, Terry Evans

Vice President Labor Relations, Scott Weaver

Manager Government Relations, Derek J Sublette

Vice President Engineering, Philip Merilli

AVP MWS Secretary, Shawna Hendley

National Account Manager, John Reilly

Board Member, Thomas Bell

Treasurer, Rachael Sears

Secretary, Donna Coleman

Auditors: KPMG LLP

LOCATIONS

HQ: Norfolk Southern Corp.
Three Commercial Place, Norfolk, VA 23510-2191
Phone: 757 629-2680
Web: www.norfolksouthern.com

PRODUCTS/OPERATIONS

2016 Sales

	$ mil.	% of total
General merchandise		
Chemicals	1,648	17
Agriculture consumer government	1,548	16
Metals & construction	1,267	13
Automotive	975	10
Paper clay and forest	744	7
Intermodal	2,218	22
Coal	1,488	15
Total	**9,888**	**100**

Selected Facilities Served

Active coal-loading facilities
Auto assembly plants
Auto distribution facilities
Bulk transfer facilities
Coal and iron ore transload facilities
General warehouses/distribution centers
Intermodal terminals
Just-in-time rail auto parts center
Lumber reload centers
Metals distribution centers
Paper distribution centers
Paper mills
Power generation plants served
Steel mills and processing facilities
Triple Crown Service terminals
Vehicle mixing centers

COMPETITORS

APL Logistics	J.B. Hunt
American Commercial Lines	Kansas City Southern
Burlington Northern Santa Fe	Kirby Corporation
CSX	Landstar System
Canadian National Railway	PVH
Canadian Pacific Railway	Piedmont Natural Gas
Genesee & Wyoming	Pier 1 Imports
Hub Group	Pilgrim's Pride
Ingram Industries	Pinnacle West
	Pitney Bowes
	Schneider National
	Union Pacific
	Werner Enterprises

HISTORICAL FINANCIALS

Company Type: Public

Income Statement

FYE: December 31

	REVENUE ($ mil.)	NET INCOME ($ mil.)	NET PROFIT MARGIN	EMPLOYEES
12/17	10,551	5,404	51.2%	27,110
12/16	9,888	1,668	16.9%	28,044
12/15	10,511	1,556	14.8%	30,456
12/14	11,624	2,000	17.2%	29,482
12/13	11,245	1,910	17.0%	30,103
Annual Growth	(1.6%)	29.7%	—	(2.6%)

2017 Year-End Financials

Debt ratio: 27.54%
Return on equity: 37.57%
Cash ($ mil.): 690
Current ratio: 0.84
Long-term debt ($ mil.): 9,136

No. of shares (mil.): 284
Dividends
  Yield: 0.0%
  Payout: 13.1%
Market value ($ mil.): 41,174

	STOCK PRICE ($) FY Close	P/E High/Low		PER SHARE ($) Earnings	Dividends	Book Value
12/17	144.90	8	6	18.61	2.44	57.57
12/16	108.07	20	12	5.62	2.36	42.73
12/15	84.59	22	14	5.10	2.36	40.93
12/14	109.61	18	14	6.39	2.22	40.25
12/13	92.83	15	10	6.04	2.04	36.55
Annual Growth	11.8%	—	—	32.5%	4.6%	12.0%

Northern Trust Corp

Individuals and institutions put their confidence in the Northern Trust Corporation. Through its flagship subsidiary The Northern Trust Company the corporation provides banking and trust services brokerage asset servicing securities lending and proprietary mutual funds (the Northern Funds). The firm offers its services to institutional clients and affluent individuals through more than 90 offices in nearly 20 states and more than 20 countries. Operating two main segments ? Corporate and Institutional Services (C&IS) and Wealth Management ? Northern Trust has nearly 10 trillion in assets under custody/administration and $1.1 trillion under direct management.

Operations

The firm operates through two segments: Corporate and Institutional Services (C&IS) and Wealth Management. A third business unit Asset Management provides asset management and related services to its other segments.

The C&IS segment provides asset servicing and related services to corporate and public retirement funds foundations endowments fund managers insurance companies sovereign wealth funds and other institutional investors. Its offerings include fund administration investment operations outsourcing investment management risk and analytical services employee benefit services securities lending foreign exchange brokerage services and banking. Assets under management are roughly $700 billion and assets under custody exceed $6.0 trillion. The segment accounts for about 55% of total revenue.

The Wealth Management business focuses on high-net-worth individuals and families business owners executives and the like. It provides services such as investment management philanthropic services trust management financial consulting guardianship brokerage services and private &

business banking. This segment has some $250 billion in assets under management and $550 billion in assets under custody. This business generates roughly 40% of revenue.

Geographic Reach

Based in Chicago Northern Trust has a presence in 20 US states and more than 20 countries. About 80% of the company?s assets and revenues originate in the US.

Sales and Marketing

The firm serves corporations institutions (foundations endowments sovereign wealth funds) and affluent families and individuals. Relationship management and personalized service are keys to maintaining and growing its client base.

Financial Performance

Following the Financial Crisis of 2008/2009 Northern Trust saw steep declines in both revenue and net income. Since 2011 however it has stabilized financial performance and experienced steady consistent growth in both metrics. Revenue grew from $3.9 billion to over $5.0 billion. Net income improved from $570 million to exceeding $1.0 for the first time in 2016.

The 2016 revenue result ticked up 5% from the prior year to $5.1 billion. Trust fees the company?s largest source of revenue grew 4% and net interest income exceeded 15% growth helped in no small part to a rise in US interest rates.

Net income for the year rose 6% to $1.0 billion the highest amount in over a decade. Expenses ? operating and income ? stayed in line with the previous year enabling Norther Trust to flow the bump in revenue to its bottom line.

Cash on hand at the end of 2016 was $5.3 billion a decrease of $1.1 billion from 2015. Operating activities provided $1.5 billion to cash. Investing activities used $10.2 billion due in large part to purchasing more securities than it sold. Financing activities added $7.5 billion to the coffers mainly by attracting $6.7 billion in client deposits and selling $500 million in preferred stock.

Strategy

Northern Trust?s strategy involves riding growth waves in private wealth management and institutional asset management both of which are predicted to have (on average) 8.5% compounded annual growth. It is firmly entrenched in these markets and need only to continue what it has been doing to expand its business both by attracting additional clients in existing markets and by serving greater needs for its existing clients.

The company is also addressing the risks associated with data security and the opportunities enabled through artificial intelligence and data analytics. Of the company?s $473 million in 2016 capital expenditures $430 million went to computer software and hardware including for the build-out of its new mobile application for its wealth management clients.

Northern Trust continued to expand slowly and methodically its geographic footprint across the world. Although still a very small amount of its revenue non-US operations allow the firm to project a global presence for families firms and institutions who themselves are global in nature and seek investment management firms that can meet their international needs. In 2015 it established a team in Melbourne Australia to provide its asset management products and services to institutional investors across Australia and New Zealand. Also in 2015 to support its Asia Pacific growth strategy and its "local business" strategy to support clients as close to their local markets as possible Northern Trust opened its Seoul representative office in fast-growing South Korea.

Mergers and Acquisitions

In late 2017 Northern Trust acquired UBS Asset Management?s fund administration servicing business in Luxembourg and Switzerland for some $200 million.

Company Background

As part of its international growth plan Northern Trust expanded in Europe with the 2011 purchase of Bank of Ireland's fund administration investment operations outsourcing and custody business. The acquisition was combined with Northern Trust's existing operations in Ireland which is a European hub for cross-border fund administration. The company worked to support European fund managers by expanding its depositary services across multiple fund types asset classes fund locations and investment strategies as well as by implementing the Alternative Investment Fund Managers Directive (AIFMD).

In 2010 Northern Trust expanded its Wealth Management business with the acquisition of Los Angeles-based investment advisory Waterline Partners.

HISTORY

When banker Byron Smith took time off to handle family concerns in 1885 friends turned to him for advice on trust and estate matters. It occurred to him that there was a market for such services within a banking framework.

Smith tested new Illinois banking and trust laws by arranging for state banking authorities to reject his charter application for Northern Trust. As Smith had hoped the charter was upheld by the Illinois Supreme Court.

Northern Trust opened in 1889 in one of Chicago's new skyscrapers the Rookery. With $1 million in capital — about 40% from Smith and the rest from the likes of Marshall Field (retailing) Martin Ryerson (steel) and Philip Armour (meatpacking) — the bank attracted $138000 in deposits its first day.

By 1896 the bank was firmly established; Smith began taking a salary and the company issued its first dividend. Ten years later the firm built its solid granite edifice the "Gray Lady of LaSalle Street" where it still resides.

The bank began buying commercial paper in 1912 joined the Federal Reserve System in 1917 and became a custodian for expropriated German assets during WWI. Byron Smith died in 1914 and was succeeded by his son Solomon.

Northern Trust rejected the get-rich-quick ethos of the 1920s. It was so strong during the Depression that after the 1933 bank holiday people actually clamored to make deposits and the bank administered the Depression-era scholarship fund that helped Ronald Reagan attend college. By 1941 almost half of Northern Trust's commercial deposits originated outside the Chicago area. The bank kept growing during and after WWII.

Solomon Smith retired in 1963; his son Edward took over and launched the company's expansion overseas (Northern Trust International was formed in 1968) and out of state (Florida in 1971 Arizona in 1974). The firm's business was helped by the 1974 passage by Congress of ERISA which required company retirement plans to be overseen by an outside custodian. Edward retired in 1979.

Northern Trust expanded locally when Illinois legalized intrastate branch banking in 1981. In 1987 the company lost money due in part to defaults on loans made to developing countries. It moved into California in 1988 and Texas in 1989.

Northern Trust navigated the early 1990s recession expanded geographically in the mid-1990s and added services through acquisitions. In 1995 the company became the first foreign trust company to operate throughout Canada. That year it bought investment management service RCB International (now Northern Trust Global Advisors). It expanded in the Sun Belt with such acquisitions as Dallas' Metroplex Bancshares and was made first custodian for the Teacher Retirement System of Texas (1997).

In 1998 the company expanded into Michigan and broke into the Cleveland and Seattle markets in 1999. Northern Trust entered cyberspace as well launching a website for its mutual funds. In 2000 the company opened locations in Nevada and Missouri and bought Florida-based investment adviser Carl Domino Associates (renamed Northern Trust Value Investors). Also that year the bank bought Ireland's Ulster Bank Investment Services.

In 2004 Northern Trust bought the fund management custody and trust operations of Baring Asset Management from Amsterdam-based ING Groep.

EXECUTIVES

Executive Vice President, Peter Rossiter
Group Vice President, Kelly R Welsh
Ex Vice President, Lyle L Logan
Ex Vice President, Lee S Selander
Vice President Of Loans, Jean Sheridan
Ex Vice President, Lloyd A Wennlund
Second Vice President Trust Administration, Monique Noblett
Senior Vice President, Donald Berk
Senior Vice President and Senior Portfolio Manager for Northern Trust Global Inv, George Maris
Senior Vice President, Michael A Vardas
Ex Vice President, R H Magill
EVP and President Wealth Management, Steven L. (Steve) Fradkin, age 55, $600,000 total compensation
EVP and President Corporate and Institutional Services, Jeffery D. Cohodes, age 56
EVP and COO, Jana R. Schreuder, age 58, $693,750 total compensation
EVP and President Asset Management, Stephen N. Potter, age 60, $587,500 total compensation
EVP Northern Trust Company, Joyce St. Clair, age 57
EVP and President Corporate and Institutional Services, Peter B. Cherecwich, age 52
EVP and Chief Risk Officer, Wilson Leech, age 55
EVP and CFO, Stephen B. (Biff) Bowman, age 53, $568,750 total compensation
EVP and Chief Investment Officer, Robert P. (Bob) Browne, age 52
President CEO and Director, Michael G. O'Grady, age 51, $606,250 total compensation
EVP and General Counsel, Susan C. Levy, age 59
Executive Vice President and Head of Funds and Managed Accounts Group, Shundrawn Thomas
EVP Human Resources, S. Gillian Pembleton, age 58
Senior Vice President Information Technology Applications, Barry Bonds
Director Wealth Management Media Relations Vice President, Amy Bickers
Vice President, Ken Bell
Senior Vice President Enterprise Architect, Ravi Gundimeda
Senior Vice President, Paul D'Ouville
Senior Vice President, Barbara A O'Connell, age 67
Senior Vice President and Director, Deborah Liverett
Senior Vice Presiden, Lawrence Au
Senior Vice President, Robert Chapelle
Vice President, Tracy Nguyen
Senior Vice President and Head of Corp Strategy, Caroline Devlin
Senior Vice President Global Compliance, Ted Sausen
Vice President Human Resources, Susanne Dahl
Vice President Information Technology, James Heneghan
Senior Vice President Regional Fiduciary Director, Thomas Iskalis
Second Vice President, Tanya Griggs

Vice President Of Information Technology, Jeffrey Blust
Vice President, David Nickel
Vice President, Ken Le Breux
Vice President, James Lange
Vice President, Thomas Smith
Senior Vice President of Sales, Marie Dzanis
Vice President of Marketing Financial Advisor, Joyce Clair
Senior Vice President and Global Product Manager, Debra Clayton
Vice President, Eric Strickland
Senior Vice President Worldwide Operat, Thomas Jaeggin
Senior Vice President Enterprise Productivity, Laurel Neu
Senior Vice President, Elizabeth V White
Vice President Portfolio Manager, Chris Fronk
Vice President and Senior Director Institutional Sales, Richard Clark
Senior Vice President Treasury, Duane Rocheleau
Vice President Integrated Risk Management, Carolyn M Schiffels
Senior Vice President Relationship Manager, Stephen M Kuropas
Vice President, Rich Michaels
Senior Vice President, Ofelia Fernandez
Senior Vice President Wealth Strategies Group, Kelly Summerwill
Vice President Corporate Advertising and Creative Services, Mark Reeves
Regional President, Timothy J Geraghty
Senior Vice President Public Finance, Allan Ambrose
Vice President Division Head, James Monhart
Vice President, Michael Hunniford
Vice President for Worldwide Operations and Technology, Steven Gale
Vice President Hedge Fund Quantitative Strategist, Adam Magyar
Senior Vice President, John Freel
Senior Vice President and Managing Director, Gene Harvey
Vice President, Sheldon Woldt
Vice President Portfolio Manager, Michael Chico Michael Chico
Vice President, Vivek Kinra
Vice President Level, Mark Warner
Senior Vice President Compliance, Debra Brzoska
Vice President, Inez Micun
VP Senior Business Analyst, Peter Matteucci
Senior Vice President, Paul Fahey
Senior Vice President private Banker, Jeff White
Vice President, Greg Werra
Senior Vice President, Linda M Nolan
Vice President of Marketing, Andrew Rakowski
Vice President Finance, David Sullivan
Second Vice President, Judith Wilson
Senior Vice President, Dan Lindley
Senior Vice President, Peter Williams
Vice President Application Architecture, Nihar Karnik
Senior Vice President, Stephen Brown
Second Vice President Emea Talent Acquisition, Catherine Coltart
Vice President Human Resources, Subhashini Sriram
Vice President Global learning and Development, Brian Winchar
Senior Vice President Managing Director Private Client Services, Deb Finnegan
Senior Vice President Worldwide Technology Security, Patricia Burroughs
Senior Vice President, Julia Briggs
Vice President Investment Risk and Analytical Services, William Frieske
Vice President, Mike Yau
Vice President Technology Risk Management, Penny Hogue
Second Vice President, Yueru Gu

Vice President Human Resources, Denyse Reese
Executive Vice President, Jennifer Driscoll
Senior Vice President Chief Banking Officer PFS Central Region, Paul Theiss
Vice President, Andrew Glick
Vice President, John Burke
Vice President Technical Risk, Karen Smilie
Senior Vice President and Corporate Human Resources Manager PFS East Region, Kurt W Adler
Senior Vice President, James Ferguson
Vice President Operations and Technology, Manan Mehta
Second Vice President, Annie L Berni
Senior Vice President Information Technology, Jim Pecyna
Senior Vice President And Senior Program Manager, Mark Maly
Senior Vice President and Manager, Alex Cavallo
Vice President Product, Ellie Dumas
VICE PRESIDENT, KAREN FALK
Senior Vice President, Nina Staley
Senior Vice President Senior Investment Officer, Ann Farrall
Vice President Corporate Re Western Division, Jennifer Dryden
Vice President Worldwide Technology, Mike Morena
Vice President database administrator, Gary Sako
Vice President, Alex Latovin
Vice President, Raje Kantamneni
Vice President Global Learning and Development, Sonia Vora
Senior Vice President and Managing Director, Maria M Moreno
Senior Vice President, Jeffery L Williams
Senior Vice President, Chris Carlson
Senior Vice President, Scott Hensley
Second Vice President Manager Client Services, Richard Boland
Vice President, Raj Vora
Vice President Corporate Banking, Daniel Hintzen
Vice President, Matthew Riegel
Senior Vice President, Mary Prado
Vice President, Anita Nikolov
Senior Vice President, Tom Eichenberger
Vice President and Senior Relationship Manager Commercial Banking, Rick Eddington
Vice President and Portfolio Manager, Jason A Lawit
Vice President, Russell H Stamey
Senior Vice President, Nancy Lyon
Vice President Private Banking, Dick Resseguie
Vice President Credit Policy, Tom Bernhardt
Vice President Infrastructure Project Management O, Nita Cabuso
Second Vice President business Product Development, Serena Sparacino
Senior Vice President Client Relationship Manager, William Egan
Vice President Estate Settlement Services, George Metzler
Second Vice President, Alex Hingston
Senior Vice President Foundation and Institutional, Dave Cyganiak
Vice President Information Technology Project Manager, Angela Campbell
Senior Vice President, Michael Furey
Vice President of Human Resources, Mae Jones
Senior Vice President, Mark Hardtke
Senior Vice President, Thomas Kim
Vice President, Chris Price
Senior Management (Senior Vice President General Manager Director), Brad Biales
Vice President Applications, Evans Chang
Auditors: KPMG LLP

LOCATIONS

HQ: Northern Trust Corp
50 South LaSalle Street, Chicago, IL 60603
Phone: 312 630-6000
Web: www.northerntrust.com

Selected Operations

US
Arizona
California
Colorado
Connecticut
Delaware
Florida
Georgia
Illinois
Massachusetts
Michigan
Minnesota
Missouri
Nevada
New York
Ohio
Texas
Washington
Wisconsin
International
Africa
Australia
Canada
China
Hong Kong
India
Ireland
Japan
Luxembourg
Middle East
The Netherlands
New Zealand
Saudi Arabia
Singapore
Sweden
UK

PRODUCTS/OPERATIONS

2016 sales

	% of total
Trust Investment & Other Servicing Fees	83
Foreign Exchange Trading Income	7
Treasury Management Fees	2
Security Commissions & Trading Income	2
Other Operating Income	6
Investment Security Lossesnet	-
Total	**100**

Selected Subsidiaries

Northern Investment Corporation
Northern Investment Management Company
Northern Trust Bank FSB
The Northern Trust Company
  MFC Company Inc.
  Norlease Inc.
  The Northern Trust Company Canada
  Northern Trust Holdings Limited (UK)
  Northern Trust Global Services Limited (UK)
  The Northern Trust International Banking
  Corporation
  Northern Trust Cayman International Ltd. (Cayman
  Islands)
  The Northern Trust Company of Hong Kong Limited
  Northern Trust Fund Managers (Ireland) Limited
  Northern Trust (Ireland) Limited
  Northern Trust Custodial Services (Ireland) Limited
  Northern Trust Fund Services (Ireland) Limited
  Northern Trust Investor Services (Ireland) Limited
  Northern Trust Property Services (Ireland) Limited
  Northern Trust Management Services Limited (UK)
  Northern Trust Partners Scotland Limited (UK)
  Northern Trust Scottish Limited Partnership (99%
  UK)
  Northern Trust Luxembourg Capital S.A.R.L.
  Northern Trust Investments Inc.
  NTG Services LLC
  NT Mortgage Holdings LLC
The Northern Trust Company of Delaware
The Northern Trust Company of New York
Northern Trust Global Advisors Inc.

The Northern Trust Company of Connecticut
NT Global Advisors Inc. (Canada)
Northern Trust Global Investments Japan K.K.
Northern Trust Holdings L.L.C.
Northern Trust NA
  Northern Annuity Sales Inc.
  Realnor Properties Inc.
  Waterline Partners LLC
Northern Trust Securities Inc.
Northern Trust Services Inc.
Nortrust Holding Corporation
  Northern Trust Bank N.A.
Nortrust Realty Management Inc.

COMPETITORS

Bank of America
Bank of New York
  Mellon
Barclays
Citigroup
Deutsche Bank
Fifth Third

Goldman Sachs
Harris
JPMorgan Chase
Morgan Stanley
SEI Investments
State Street
Wells Fargo

HISTORICAL FINANCIALS

Company Type: Public

Income Statement
FYE: December 31

	ASSETS ($ mil.)	NET INCOME ($ mil.)	INCOME AS % OF ASSETS	EMPLOYEES
12/16	123,926	1,032	0.8%	17,100
12/15	116,749	973	0.8%	16,200
12/14	109,946	811	0.7%	15,400
12/13	102,947	731	0.7%	14,800
12/12	97,463	687	0.7%	14,200
Annual Growth	**6.2%**	**10.7%**	**—**	**4.8%**

2016 Year-End Financials

Debt ratio: 2.51%
Return on equity: 11.15%
Cash ($ mil.): 36,806
Current ratio: —
Long-term debt ($ mil.): —
No. of shares (mil.): 228
Dividends
  Yield: 0.0%
  Payout: 34.2%
Market value ($ mil.): 20,357

	STOCK PRICE ($) FY Close	P/E High/Low	PER SHARE ($) Earnings	Dividends	Book Value
12/16	89.05	21 13	4.32	1.48	42.74
12/15	72.09	20 15	3.99	1.41	37.97
12/14	67.40	21 17	3.32	1.30	36.20
12/13	61.89	21 17	2.99	1.23	33.34
12/12	50.16	18 14	2.81	1.18	31.50
Annual Growth	**15.4%**	**— —**	**11.4%**	**5.8%**	**7.9%**

Northfield Bancorp Inc (DE)

Auditors: KPMG LLP

LOCATIONS

HQ: Northfield Bancorp Inc (DE)
581 Main Street, Woodbridge, NJ 07095
Phone: 732 499-7200
Web: www.eNorthfield.com

HISTORICAL FINANCIALS

Company Type: Public

Income Statement
FYE: December 31

	ASSETS ($ mil.)	NET INCOME ($ mil.)	INCOME AS % OF ASSETS	EMPLOYEES
12/16	3,850	26	0.7%	366
12/15	3,202	19	0.6%	306
12/14	3,020	20	0.7%	321
12/13	2,702	19	0.7%	326
12/12	2,813	16	0.6%	330
Annual Growth	**8.2%**	**13.0%**	**—**	**2.6%**

2016 Year-End Financials

Debt ratio: 12.08%
Return on equity: 4.41%
Cash ($ mil.): 96
Current ratio: —
Long-term debt ($ mil.): —
No. of shares (mil.): 48
Dividends
  Yield: 0.0%
  Payout: 54.3%
Market value ($ mil.): 969

	STOCK PRICE ($) FY Close	P/E High/Low	PER SHARE ($) Earnings	Dividends	Book Value
12/16	19.97	35 24	0.57	0.31	12.80
12/15	15.92	36 31	0.45	0.28	12.29
12/14	14.80	36 30	0.41	0.26	12.27
12/13	13.20	45 32	0.34	0.49	12.36
12/12	15.25	55 43	0.29	0.09	10.00
Annual Growth	**7.0%**	**— —**	**18.4%**	**36.2%**	**6.4%**

Northrim BancCorp Inc

EXECUTIVES

Senior Vice President and Senior Lender, Leonard
F Horst
Svp Information Services, Suzanne Whittle
Vice President Commercial Cash Management,
Kimberly F Brewington
Auditors: Moss Adams LLP

LOCATIONS

HQ: Northrim BancCorp Inc
3111 C Street, Anchorage, AK 99503
Phone: 907 562-0062

PRODUCTS/OPERATIONS

2007 Sales

	$ mil.	% of total
Interest		
Loans including fees	66	80
Securities	4	6
Other	2	2
Noninterest		
Service charges on deposit accounts	3	4
Purchased receivable income	2	3
Other	4	5
Total	**82**	**100**

COMPETITORS

Alaska Pacific
  Bancshares
Alaska USA

First National Bank
  Alaska
KeyCorp

HISTORICAL FINANCIALS

Company Type: Public

Income Statement

FYE: December 31

	ASSETS ($ mil.)	NET INCOME ($ mil.)	INCOME AS % OF ASSETS	EMPLOYEES
12/16	1,526	14	0.9%	451
12/15	1,499	17	1.2%	441
12/14	1,449	17	1.2%	426
12/13	1,215	12	1.0%	269
12/12	1,160	12	1.1%	245
Annual Growth	7.1%	2.7%	—	16.5%

2016 Year-End Financials

Debt ratio: 1.50%
Return on equity: 7.90%
Cash ($ mil.): 50
Current ratio: —
Long-term debt ($ mil.): —

No. of shares (mil.): 6
Dividends
  Yield: 0.0%
  Payout: 37.8%
Market value ($ mil.): 218

	STOCK PRICE ($) FY Close	P/E High/Low		PER SHARE ($) Earnings	Dividends	Book Value
12/16	31.60	16	10	2.06	0.78	27.05
12/15	26.60	11	8	2.56	0.74	25.74
12/14	26.24	11	9	2.54	0.70	23.97
12/13	26.24	15	11	1.87	0.64	22.05
12/12	22.65	11	9	1.97	0.56	20.93
Annual Growth	8.7%	—	—	1.1%	8.6%	6.6%

Northrop Grumman Corp

Northrop Grumman is well equipped to defend its high place in the defense sector. As one of the world's top military contractors (behind Lockheed Martin and Boeing) the company operates through three business sectors: Aerospace Systems (aircraft spacecraft laser systems electronic subsystems); Mission Systems (radar sensors chemical detection countermeasure systems); and Technology Services (systems support training and simulation). The US government represents most of Northrop Grumman's sales.The company traces its historical roots back to 1927.

HISTORY

Huntington Ingalls Industries Jack Northrop co-founded Lockheed Aircraft in 1927 and designed its record-setting Vega monoplane. He founded two more companies — Avion Corporation (formed in 1928 and bought by United Aircraft and Transportation) and Northrop Corporation (formed in 1932 with Douglas Aircraft which absorbed it in 1938) — before founding Northrop Aircraft in California in 1939.

During WWII Northrop produced the P-61 fighter and the famous Flying Wing bomber which failed to win a production contract. In the 1950s Northrop depended heavily on F-89 fighter and Snark missile sales. When Thomas Jones succeeded Jack Northrop as president (1959) he moved the company away from risky prime contracts in favor of numerous subcontracts and bought Page Communications Engineers (telecommunications 1959) and Hallicrafters (electronics 1966) to reduce its dependence on government contracts.

In the early 1970s Northrop was hit with a bribery scandal and the disclosure of illegal payments to Richard Nixon's 1972 campaign fund; Jones was eventually fined for an illegal contribution. As a result a shareholder lawsuit forced Jones to resign as president (he was allowed to remain as chairman). In 1981 the company won the B-2 bomber contract. Jones retired as chairman in late 1990 and under the leadership of Kent Kresa (who became CEO in early 1990 and chairman when Jones retired) Northrop pleaded guilty to 34 counts related to fudging test results on some government projects; it was fined $17 million. In a related shareholders' suit Northrop paid $18 million in damages in 1991.

Northrop and The Carlyle Group bought LTV's Vought Aircraft Industries (now named Triumph Aerostructures - Vought Aircraft Division) in 1992. In 1994 it paid $2.1 billion for Grumman Corporation a premier electronic systems firm and manufacturer of fighter aircraft for the US Navy and changed its name to Northrop Grumman.

In 1929 Roy Grumman Jake Swirbul and Bill Schwendler founded Grumman; within three months it had a contract to design a Navy fighter. Grumman completed its first commercial aircraft (the Grumman Goose) in 1937 and went public in 1938. It soared during WWII on the wings of its Wildcat and Hellcat fighter planes.

Grumman built its first corporate jet (Gulfstream) in 1958 and began work on the Lunar Module for the Apollo space program in 1963. It was near bankruptcy during the 1970s due to costs related to its F-14 Tomcat fighter. Grumman rebuilt its military business in the 1980s and achieved its greatest success in electronic systems.

The UK Ministry of Defence awarded a $279 million contract to Northrop Grumman in 1995 to develop and produce a system to counter infrared missiles. In 1997 Northrop Grumman bought Logicon (information and battle-management systems). It then agreed to an $11.6 billion purchase by Lockheed Martin but the US government citing concerns about increased lack of competition in the defense industry blocked the deal in 1998. As a result Northrop Grumman began a restructuring that cut 10500 defense and aircraft jobs and added 2500 positions to its Logicon subsidiary.

In 1999 Northrop Grumman bought the information systems division of California Microwave for $93 million and Allegheny Teledyne's Ryan Aeronautical (aerial drones) for $140 million. The next year Northrop Grumman sold its underperforming commercial aerostructures business to The Carlyle Group in a $1.2 billion transaction in order to focus on its growing defense electronics and information technology segments. Later in 2000 Northrop Grumman acquired Comptek Research and bought Federal Data (information systems for the US government) from Carlyle in a transaction valued at $302 million. Pension income that year accounted for more than $500 million (about 55%) of the company's pretax profit.

In 2001 the company completed the deal to acquire Litton Industries for $3.8 billion plus $1.3 billion in debt. In the fall Northrop Grumman acquired the electronics and information unit of Aerojet-General Corp. a subsidiary of GenCorp (later renamed Aerojet Rocketdyne) for about $300 million (it became Grumman's Space Systems Division). While its wallet was open the company agreed to match the $2.6 billion that General Dynamics had agreed to pay for submarine and aircraft carrier builder Newport News— a move that the US Defense Department endorsed. In December Honeywell agreed to pay Northrop Grumman $440 million to settle an antitrust and patent infringement lawsuit that Litton had filed against Honeywell in 1990.

The deal to buy Newport News was completed in early 2002. Northrop Grumman then made a hostile $6 billion bid for conglomerate TRW when TRW's stock plunged following the sudden departure of its CEO David Cote to Honeywell. In the wake of Northrop Grumman's spurned initial bid Raytheon General Dynamics and BAE SYSTEMS made offers for TRW's aerospace and defense assets. Finally though TRW accepted a sweetened $7.8 billion offer from Northrop Grumman in July 2002.

The acquisition fortified Northrop Grumman's position in military satellites missile systems and systems integration. In fact Northrop signed a consent decree with the US Justice Department in which the company agreed (under pain of fines) that it wouldn't take unfair advantage of its exclusive position when selling certain components — such as satellite sensors — to competitors.

TRW's Systems unit became Northrop Grumman Mission Systems; TRW's Space and Electronics unit was later known as Northrop Grumman Space Technology. As for TRW's car parts business Northrop sold all but 19.6% of the unit to Blackstone Group for about $4.7 billion to pay down debt; by early 2005 Northrop reduced its stake to 9.9%.

In April 2003 Kresa stepped down as president and CEO and Ronald Sugar took over those roles; Sugar added the chairmanship to his title when Kresa retired in October.

Among Northrop's 2004 contracts were $1.04 billion for X-47B Joint Unmanned Combat Air Systems $1.2 billion (preferred bidder) for E-3D AWACS contract support and $1.4 billion for the CVN 21 generation aircraft carrier. The company also split an $8.4 billion submarine contract with General Dynamics.

Early in 2005 Northrop sold 7.2 million shares of its TRW Automotive stake raising more than $142 million and reducing its stake to 9.9%. It also acquired Integic Corporation an IT company that specialized in business process management and enterprise health applications.

In 2006 Northrop Grumman established Northrop Grumman Technical Services (NGTS) as a separate sector; it was tasked with consolidating Northrop's logistics operations across its various sectors.

Late that same year Northrop Grumman agreed to buy Essex Corporation — a provider of signal image and information processing for defense and intelligence customers in the US. The deal was valued at about $580 million including the assumption of debt. The deal was completed early in 2007 and Essex became a part of Northrop Grumman Mission Systems (now Northrop Grumman Information Systems).

In 2008 the company shed its Electro-Optical Systems business (night vision and applied optics products) to L-3 Communications for $175 million.

In 2009 Northrop Grumman sold its Advisory Services Division comprising subsidiary TASC (engineering and consulting services to the US military and state governments) to private equities General Atlantic LLC and KKR for $1.65 billion. The sale brings Northrop Grumman into compliance with a new federal law that strengthens conflict of interest rules for defense contractors that both sell to and provide consulting for the US military.

Expanding its aerospace and information capabilities the company purchased Sonoma Photonics and assets from Swift Engineering's Killer Bee Unmanned Air Systems lineup for its Aerospace Systems sector (2009). The deal followed its acquisition of 3001 International for $92 million (a nearly three times larger investment) in 2008. The Virginia-based geospatial data collection and analysis provider not only bolstered Northrop Grumman's military offerings but it also reeled in a host of new civilian customers.

Also in 2009 Northrop Grumman settled two decade-old lawsuits with the US government. It agreed to pay $325 million to resolve allegations that it provided defective military satellite parts to the National Reconnaissance Office. The second lawsuit was filed by Northrop Grumman against the US government for uncompensated costs incurred as a result of the cancellation of the Tri-Service Standoff Attack Missile program.

To concentrate more on its core areas Northrop Grumman spun off its shipbuilding business under former subsidiary Huntington Ingalls Industries in 2011. Despite modest increases in year-over-year revenues the shipbuilding sector had struggled to regain profitability after suffering a loss in 2008 attributable to absorbing most of the company's goodwill impairment charge. Also in 2011 the company reduced operations in other segments. It sold its Viper Strike laser-guided bomb operations in Alabama to European consortium MBDA for an undisclosed amount. And it lowered its participation in the National Security Technologies joint venture that manages and operates the Nevada National Security Site.

Focusing on increasing its presence in the Asia/Pacific in 2012 Northrop Grumman purchased M5 Network Security a provider of cyber security and secure mobile communications technology based in Australia.

EXECUTIVES

Chairman President and CEO, Wesley G. (Wes) Bush, age 55, $1,530,000 total compensation
VP and CTO, Patrick M. Antkowiak, age 56
VP and President Technical Services, Christopher T. Jones, age 52
President and COO, Kathy J. Warden, age 45, $772,500 total compensation
Corporate VP and President Mission Systems, Mark A. Caylor, age 52
VP and CFO, Kenneth L. Bedingfield, age 44, $756,539 total compensation
Chief Executive Northrop Grumman Japan, Stan Crow
General Manager Strategic Systems Aerospace Systems, Janis G. Pamiljans
Corporate VP and President Enterprise Services, Shawn N. Purvis
Vice President Intelligence, Scott White
Vp-em&l, Douglas Lawton
VP Supply Chain, Jaime Bohnke
Senior Vice President, Monty Frahm
Vice President Of Unmanned Systems, Gene Fraser
Vice President, Anne Szemborski
Vice President And Chief Information Officer Space Technology Sector, Brad Furukawa
Vice President Business Development Northrop Grumman Space Technology, Jeffrey Grant
Vice President corporate Lead Executive Huntsville, Kevin Campbell
Vice President of Contracts and Pricing, Diane Balderson
Vice President Engrg Space Sys and Deputy Program Manager, Carol Erikson
VP Information Security, Michael Papay
Deputy Vice President, Jessica E Lewis
Vice President, Thomas McLemore
Vice President Technology Development, Scott Stapp
Senior Vice President, Neil Jones
Assistant Treasurer, Steve Spiegel
Auditors: Deloitte & Touche LLP

LOCATIONS

HQ: Northrop Grumman Corp
2980 Fairview Park Drive, Falls Church, VA 22042
Phone: 703 280-2900
Web: www.northropgrumman.com

PRODUCTS/OPERATIONS

2016 Sales

	$ mil.	% of total
Aerospace Systems	10,828	41
Mission Systems	10,928	41
Technology Services	4,825	18
Intersegment eliminations	(2073)	-
Total	**24,508**	**100**

2016 Sales

	$ mil.	% of total
Product	14,738	60
Service	9,770	40
Total	**24,508**	**100**

2016 Sales

	$ mil.	% of total
U.S. Government	20,573	84
International	3,205	13
Other Customers	730	3
Total	**24,508**	**100**

Selected Capabilities

Unmanned Systems
C4ISR
Cyber
Logistics
Advanced Electronics
Commercial Aviation
Directed Energy
IT & Enterprise Solutions
Manned Aircraft
Military Aviation
Missile Defense
Naval Systems
Navigation Systems

COMPETITORS

BAE SYSTEMS	Leonardo
Boeing	Lockheed Martin
Booz Allen	Meggitt
General Dynamics	Raytheon
L3 Technologies	Thales
Leidos	

HISTORICAL FINANCIALS

Company Type: Public

Income Statement

FYE: December 31

	REVENUE ($ mil.)	NET INCOME ($ mil.)	NET PROFIT MARGIN	EMPLOYEES
12/17	25,803	2,015	7.8%	70,000
12/16	24,508	2,200	9.0%	67,000
12/15	23,526	1,990	8.5%	65,000
12/14	23,979	2,069	8.6%	64,300
12/13	24,661	1,952	7.9%	65,300
Annual Growth	**1.1%**	**0.8%**	**—**	**1.8%**

2017 Year-End Financials

Debt ratio: 41.24%
Return on equity: 32.75%
Cash ($ mil.): 11,225
Current ratio: 2.35
Long-term debt ($ mil.): 14,399

No. of shares (mil.): 174
Dividends
Yield: 0.0%
Payout: 34.0%
Market value ($ mil.): 53,429

	STOCK PRICE ($) FY Close	P/E High/Low		PER SHARE ($) Earnings	Dividends	Book Value
12/17	306.91	27	20	11.47	3.90	40.49
12/16	232.58	20	14	12.19	3.50	30.04
12/15	188.81	18	14	10.39	3.10	30.46
12/14	147.39	15	11	9.75	2.71	36.37
12/13	114.61	14	8	8.35	2.38	48.81
Annual Growth	**27.9%**	**—**	**—**	**8.3%**	**13.1%**	**(4.6%)**

Northwest Bancshares, Inc. (MD)

EXECUTIVES

Evp Of Banking Services Group, Steven Fisher
Chief Executive Officer, Julie McTpavish
Divisional AVP Office Manager, Mari Pravlik
Auditors: KPMG LLP

LOCATIONS

HQ: Northwest Bancshares, Inc. (MD)
100 Liberty Street, Warren, PA 16365
Phone: 814 726-2140
Web: www.northwestsavingsbank.com

HISTORICAL FINANCIALS

Company Type: Public

Income Statement

FYE: December 31

	ASSETS ($ mil.)	NET INCOME ($ mil.)	INCOME AS % OF ASSETS	EMPLOYEES
12/16	9,623	49	0.5%	2,466
12/15	8,951	60	0.7%	2,364
12/14	7,775	61	0.8%	2,220
12/13	7,881	66	0.8%	2,231
12/12	7,942	63	0.8%	2,220
Annual Growth	**4.9%**	**(6.0%)**	**—**	**2.7%**

2016 Year-End Financials

Debt ratio: 1.16%
Return on equity: 4.24%
Cash ($ mil.): 386
Current ratio: —
Long-term debt ($ mil.): —

No. of shares (mil.): 101
Dividends
Yield: 0.0%
Payout: 122.4%
Market value ($ mil.): 1,834

	STOCK PRICE ($) FY Close	P/E High/Low		PER SHARE ($) Earnings	Dividends	Book Value
12/16	18.03	38	24	0.49	0.60	11.51
12/15	13.39	22	18	0.64	0.56	11.42
12/14	12.53	22	18	0.67	1.62	11.22
12/13	14.78	20	16	0.73	0.62	12.27
12/12	12.14	19	16	0.68	0.60	12.05
Annual Growth	**10.4%**	**—**	**—**	**(7.9%)**	**(0.0%)**	**(1.1%)**

NORTHWEST FARM CREDIT SERVICES

Customer-owned financial cooperative Northwest Farm Credit Services is an agricultural lender that provides financial services to farmers ranchers agribusinesses commercial fishermen timber producers and rural home owners in Alaska Idaho Montana Oregon and Washington. The company has a network of around 45 branches and offers a broad range of flexible loan programs to meet the needs of people in the agriculture business. Northwest Farm Credit also provides leasing services appraisal services and life mortgage disability and crop insurance as well as legal advocacy and assistance to customers in need. It is part of the Farm Credit System a network of lenders serving the US agriculture industry.

Operations

The credit union provides financing and related services to farmers ranchers agribusinesses commercial fishermen timber producers rural homeowners and crop insurance customers. Northwest Farm Credit provides $10.3 billion in loans. Farm Credit System a nationwide network of borrower-owned lending institutions of which it is part provides $205 billion in loans to rural America.

Geographic Reach

Northwest Farm Credit serves customers through 45 offices located in Idaho Alaska Montana Oregon and Washington.

Sales and Marketing

Northwest Farm Credit finances farmers ranchers agribusinesses commercial fishermen timber producers and rural homeowners as well as farm-related businesses agricultural cooperatives and rural utilities.

Financial Performance

In 2015 the company's net revenue increased by 5% due to higher net interest income driven by increased loan volume.

Northwest Farm Credit's net income rose by 12% due to higher net revenues and a decrease in income tax expense.

In 2015 the company's operating cash inflow increased by 19%.

Strategy

The company plans to continue to fund lending operations primarily through its borrowing relationship with CoBank (a fellow Farm Credit System member) and from retained earnings.

Mergers and Acquisitions

In 2014 the company expanded its operations in Montana by buying Culbertson State Agency's crop insurance portfolio.

Company Background

The US Congress created the Farm Credit System in 1916 to meet the financial needs of farmers ranchers and cooperatives who invest as well as borrow from the institutions within the system. All Farm Credit System members are regulated by the Farm Credit Administration.

EXECUTIVES

EVP Financial Services, Fred (Fred) DePell
EVP and General Counsel, Thomas (Tom) Tracy
EVP Corporate Administration and Secretary, Joan E. Haynes
EVP CFO and CIO, Tom Nakano
Vice President Operations, Jessi Dressen
Senior Vice President and Chief Information Officer, David Barbieri
Chairman, Drew Eggers
Vice Chairman, Kevin Riel
Auditors: PRICEWATERHOUSECOOPERS LLP S

LOCATIONS

HQ: NORTHWEST FARM CREDIT SERVICES
2001 S FLINT RD, SPOKANE, WA 992249198
Phone: 509 838-2429
Web: WWW.NORTHWESTFCS.COM

PRODUCTS/OPERATIONS

2015 Sales

	$ mil.	% of total
Interest Income	412	82
Patronage income	52	11
Financially Related Services	19	4
loans and other fee	6	1
Other non-interest income	11	2
Total	**502**	**100**

COMPETITORS

Bank of America	U.S. Bancorp
First Interstate	Wells Fargo
Idaho Independent Bank	Zions Bancorporation
KeyCorp	
Northwest Bancorporation	

HISTORICAL FINANCIALS

Company Type: Private

Income Statement

FYE: December 31

	ASSETS ($ mil.)	NET INCOME ($ mil.)	INCOME AS % OF ASSETS	EMPLOYEES
12/14	10,252	228	2.2%	500
12/13	9,604	236	2.5%	—
12/12	9,471	187	2.0%	—
12/11	8,696	159	1.8%	—
Annual Growth	5.6%	12.7%	—	—

2014 Year-End Financials

Debt ratio: —	
Return on equity: 47.90%	Dividends
Cash ($ mil.): 51	Yield: —
Current ratio: —	Payout: —
Long-term debt ($ mil.): —	Market value ($ mil.): —

NRG Energy Inc

The name says it all — NRG Energy is all about energy. The company is a leading power producer with a generating capacity of 47216 MW (including 1825 MW of solar power assets). The vast majority of NRG's power plants are in North America but it also has one in Australia and one in Turkey. Its portfolio includes 140 generation units at 85 power plants. It also markets natural gas oil and other commodities. NRG's retail units (including Reliant Energy and Green Mountain Energy) distribute power to about 3 million customers across the US.

Operations

NRG's operating segments are Retail (50% of revenues) Generation (40%) Renewables and NRG Yield.

Retail includes commercial industrial governmental and institutional customers and other distributed and reliability products.

Generation includes generation international and Boston Energy Trading and Marketing LLC.

Renewables includes solar and wind assets excluding those in NRG Yield.

NRG Yield owns operates and acquires diversified contracted renewable and conventional generation and thermal infrastructure assets.

The company's corporate segment include residential solar and electric vehicle services.

Geographic Reach

NRG Energy has generation assets in the US Australia and Turkey. Its retail and thermal subsidiaries serve customers in 16 US states. Its NRG Thermal unit provides third-party steam to downtown heating and cooling systems in cities such as Pittsburgh San Diego San Francisco and Harrisburg Pennsylvania.

The company's generation plants are in Houston New York City Chicago Washington DC New Jersey southwestern Connecticut Pittsburgh Cleveland and the Los Angeles San Diego and San Francisco metropolitan areas.

Most of its retail sales come from Connecticut Delaware Illinois Maryland Massachusetts New Jersey New York Pennsylvania Ohio and Texas as well as Washington DC.

Sales and Marketing

NRG's retail electricity divisions serve nearly 3 million residential business commercial and industrial customers in all 50 US states and Washington DC.

The company's sales channels include direct sales call centers websites brokers and brick-and-mortar stores. It also sells directly to residential commercial and industrial customers.

Wholesale customers include utilities and other companies including Kaiser Permanente Unilever and Cisco Systems.

Financial Performance

In 2016 NRG's net revenues decreased by 16% to $12.4 billion mainly due to a decline in revenues from mark-to-market for economic hedging activities and a drop in energy revenues due to a decrease in electricity sales volume and lower economic gross margin (the result of warm winter weather conditions and plant deactivations and conversion projects).

The company posted an improved net loss of $774 million (compared to $6.4 billion in 2015) mainly due to lower impairment losses (related to various facilities as well as goodwill for its Texas and home solar reporting units) which outpaced a further drop in revenue and higher losses on investments.

In 2016 operating cash flow increased to $2.1 billion from $1.3 billion in 2015 primarily due to a change in cash collateral in support of risk management activities and lower operations and maintenance expenses

Strategy

As part of a strategy move away from coal in 2016 the company completed coal-to-gas projects at four power plants across NRG?s fleet.

To raise cash in 2016 NRG sold Seward Generation to Pennsylvania-based Robindale Energy Services for $75 million. It also sold Shelby County Energy Center to Rockland Power Partners a private equity fund for $46 million.

NRG has pulled back on international exposure looking to grow its position in the fragmented but less risky North American market. The company has reorganized its businesses and personnel on the basis of key target customer segments. It has also focused on deploying alternative energy technologies such as solar. In 2015 the company assumed the Northeast sales and operational resources of Verengo Solar a top-tier provider of residential solar one of the fastest growing areas for residential solar in the US.

However in a major strategy shift in late 2015 NRG announced plans to spin off its renewables businesses to pay down debt. In 2015 the company entered into partnership with subsidiary NRG Yield to invest in and hold operating portfolios of residential solar assets developed by NRG Home Solar. As a part of the agreement NRG will monetize its residential leases through NRG Yield?s upfront equity investment and retain a residual economic interest in the portfolio while also providing NRG Yield with additional cash available for distribution. NRG Yield committed to invest up to $150 million into the partnership.

In 2015 NRG Home expanded its US operations into North Carolina. The company is offering solar solutions in the state providing homeowners with the opportunity to install solar through financing options that require zero-money down.

Mergers and Acquisitions

In 2016 NRG acquired SunEdison's Utah-based solar and wind projects (1500 MW including 530 MW of solar assets) for $183 million.

Expanding its US generation capacity in 2015 the company acquired all of the assets of Edison Mission Energy for $3.5 billion. It also bought the competitive retail electricity business of Dominion Resources for $192 million. Dominion serves more than 600000 customer accounts in Connecticut Illinois Maryland Massachusetts New Jersey New York Ohio and Pennsylvania and through its Cirro Energy brand in Texas

Company Background

In 2014 the company acquired the remaining 50% ownership that it did not already hold of Mission Del Sol LLC (which owns the Sunrise facility a 586 MW natural gas facility in Fellows California) from Chevron Power Holdings in exchange for six cogeneration plants previously co-owned with Chevron Power Holdings.

That year NRG also acquired New Jersey-based Roof Diagnostics Solar a solar sales and installation company.

In 2014 the company acquired Pure Energies Group (a residential solar industry leader in the critical area of web-based customer acquisition) and Goal Zero (which offers personal solar devices).

In 2013 NRG launched NRG Residential Solutions a retail energy business that offers consumers choice in their energy options by allowing them to customize their electricity plans based on what is important to them.

In 2012 NRG bought GenOn Energy in a $1.7 billion stock deal. The deal created the largest competitive generator in the US with generating capacity in the East Gulf Coast and West and an enterprise value of $18 billion. The parties hoped that synergies balance sheet efficiencies increased economies of scale and geographic diversity would save the expanded company $300 million a year in free cash flow.

Responding to government demands for utilities to increase their use of renewables in 2011 it bought the 290-MW Agua Caliente solar project in Arizona from First Solar. (To secure financial support in 2012 NRG sold a 49% stake in the project to MidAmerican Energy). When completed in 2014 it will be the largest operational photovoltaic site in the world producing enough energy to power more than 225000 homes. Its electricity will be sold to Pacific Gas and Electric in California through 2039.

Expanding its retail presence in the US Northeast in 2011 the company bought Philadelphia-based electricity and natural gas provider Energy Plus Holdings for $190 million.

In 2011 it began to create the US's first privately funded network of electric vehicle charging stations. Based in Houston the chain opened its first charging station that year and plans to open about 60 more under the eVgo brand.

EXECUTIVES

President and CEO, Mauricio Gutierrez, age 47, $1,125,000 total compensation
EVP and CFO, Kirkland B. Andrews, age 50, $642,952 total compensation
SVP; President NRG Retail, Elizabeth Killinger, age 47, $504,634 total compensation
EVP National Business Development; President West Region, John Chillemi, age 50, $475,001 total compensation
EVP and General Counsel, David R. Hill, age 54, $500,000 total compensation
SVP Operations, Chris Moser
SVP Information Technology, Donna Benefield
Vice President, Gaetan Frotte
Vice President Finance, Mark Ogle
Chief Sales Officer, Regina Reitz
Senior Vice President Asset Management And Development, Howard Taylor
VP Information Technology, Muthu Govindan
VP Human Resources, Kit Ford
VP Information Security, Jennifer Wallace
Chairman, Lawrence S. Coben, age 58
Auditors: KPMG LLP

LOCATIONS

HQ: NRG Energy Inc
804 Carnegie Center, Princeton, NJ 08540
Phone: 609 524-4500
Web: www.nrgenergy.com

PRODUCTS/OPERATIONS

2016 Sales

	$ mil.	% of total
Retail revenue	6,274	47
Energy revenue	4,469	34
Capacity revenue	1,970	15
Other revenues	558	4
Mark-to-market activities	(865)	—
Contract amortization	(55)	—
Total	**12,351**	**100**

2016 Sales

% of total	$ mil
Retail	47
Generation	42
NRG Yield	7
Renewables	3
Corporate	1
Other	-
Total	**100**

2016 Sales

% of total	$ mil
Generation	51
Retail Mass	37
NRG Yield	8
Renewable	3
Corporate	1
Eliminations	-
Total	**100**

Selected Subsidiaries

Energy Plus
Green Mountain Energy Company (retail power)
NEO Corporation (distributed generation; landfill gas hydroelectric and other renewable generation)
NRG Power Marketing Inc. (power sales)
NRG Resource Recovery (waste-to-energy facilities)
NRG Texas LLC (power generation)
NRG Thermal Corporation (district heating and cooling combined heat and power facilities)
Reliant Energy Texas Retail LLC
Texas Genco LP (power generation)
West Coast Power LLC (power generation)

COMPETITORS

AEP	Entergy
AES	FirstEnergy
Accent Energy	Gexa Energy
Alliant Energy	Integrys Energy
Avista	Services
Berkshire Hathaway	Nicor Gas
Energy	PG&E Corporation
Calpine	PPL Corporation
Cogentrix Energy	PSEG Power
Community Energy	Preferred Energy
Direct Energy	Services
Duke Energy	SCANA
Dynegy	Sempra Generation
Edison International	Tenaska
Energy Future	

HISTORICAL FINANCIALS

Company Type: Public

Income Statement

FYE: December 31

	REVENUE ($ mil.)	NET INCOME ($ mil.)	NET PROFIT MARGIN	EMPLOYEES
12/16	12,351	(774)	—	8,763
12/15	14,674	(6,382)	—	10,468
12/14	15,868	134	0.8%	9,806
12/13	11,295	(386)	—	7,786
12/12	8,422	559	6.6%	8,792
Annual Growth	**10.0%**	**—**		**(0.1%)**

2016 Year-End Financials

Debt ratio: 63.34%
Return on equity: (-30.57%)
Cash ($ mil.): 1,975
Current ratio: 1.46
Long-term debt ($ mil.): 18,006

No. of shares (mil.): 315
Dividends
 Yield: 0.0%
 Payout: —
Market value ($ mil.): 3,867

	STOCK PRICE ($) FY Close	P/E High/Low	PER SHARE ($) Earnings	Dividends	Book Value
12/16	12.26	— —	(2.22)	0.24	6.47
12/15	11.77	— —	(19.46)	0.58	9.58
12/14	26.95	164 112	0.23	0.54	29.86
12/13	28.72	— —	(1.22)	0.45	30.43
12/12	22.99	10 6	2.35	0.18	31.82
Annual Growth	**(14.5%)**	**— —**	**—**	**6.9%**	**(32.8%)**

Nucor Corp.

Nucor takes a "minimillist" approach to succeeding in the steel industry. At its minimills Nucor produces hot- and cold-rolled steel steel joists and metal buildings. It has the capacity to produce more than 26 million tons of steel per year. North America's largest recycler of scrap metal it produces steel by melting scrap in electric arc furnaces. Most products are sold to steel service centers manufacturers and fabricators. Subsidiary Harris Steel fabricates rebar for highways and bridges and other construction projects. Its David J. Joseph Company unit processes and brokers metals pig iron hot briquetted iron and direct reduced iron (DRI). In 2015 Nucor recycled 16.9 million tons of scrap steel.

HISTORY

Nucor started as the second carmaking venture of Ransom Olds who built his first gasoline-powered car in 1897. Two years later Samuel Smith a Detroit copper and lumber magnate put up $199600 to finance Olds Motor Works. A fire destroyed the company's Detroit plant in 1901 so Olds moved production to Lansing Michigan where he built America's first mass-produced car — the Oldsmobile. In 1904 Olds left Olds Motor Works which was bought by General Motors (GM) in 1908 and formed Reo Car Company (renamed Reo Motor Car in 1906). In addition to cars it eventually made trucks and buses.

By the end of the Depression Ford GM and Chrysler commanded over 85% of the US passenger car market. Reo stopped making cars in 1936 and sold its truck manufacturing operations in 1957. Meanwhile it had formed Reo Holding which in 1955 merged with Nuclear Consultants to form Nuclear Corporation of America. The new company offered services such as radiation studies and made nuclear instruments and electronics.

In 1962 Nuclear bought steel joist maker Vulcraft and gained the services of Kenneth Iverson. The diverse company was unprofitable losing $2 million on $22 million in sales in 1965. That year Iverson took over as CEO moved headquarters to Charlotte North Carolina and shut down or sold about half of the company's businesses. By focusing on its profitable steel joist operations the firm ended 1966 in the black. Because the company depended on imports for 80% of its steel needs Iverson decided to move into steel production. Nuclear Corporation built its first minimill in 1969.

The company was renamed Nucor in 1972. It started making steel deck (1977) and cold-finished steel bars (1979). Production tripled and sales more than doubled between 1974 and 1979.

Nucor began to diversify adding grinding balls (used in the mining industry to process ores 1981); steel bolts steel bearings and machined steel parts (1986); and metal buildings and components (1987). Nucor and Japanese steelmaker Yamato Kogyo formed Nucor-Yamato and built a mill in 1988 to produce wide-flange beams (for heavy construction). The following year Nucor opened a state-of-the-art mill in Crawfordsville Indiana and another mill near Hickman Arkansas in 1992.

Iverson turned over his CEO duties to company veteran John Correnti in 1996. The next year Nucor began building a steel beam mill in South Carolina and added a galvanizing facility to its Hickman mill.

In 1998 Nucor announced plans to build its first steel plate mill which became operational in 2000. The company slashed prices twice in 1998 to compete against low-cost imports from Russia Japan and Brazil. Both sales and earnings declined that year due to low metal prices reduced shipments and start-up costs for new plants. The company raised its prices in 1999 and continued its expansion plans. Differences with the board prompted Correnti to resign in 1999; chairman David Aycock assumed his duties. In September 2000 Aycock resigned from the company and Daniel DiMicco formerly an EVP moved up to the rank of CEO.

Nucor along with Australia's Broken Hill Proprietary Corporation and Japan's Ishikawajima-Harima Heavy Industries began a joint venture in 2000 for its technology strip casting. The new technology allows steel production in smaller cheaper plants. In 2001 Nucor purchased a significant amount of assets of Auburn Steel a producer of merchant steel bar for $115 million.

In 2002 Nucor teamed up with Companhia Vale do Rio Doce (Vale) a Brazilian producer and exporter of iron-ore pellets to develop low-cost iron based products. That year Nucor purchased Alabama-based Trico Steel a steel sheet producer for approximately $116 million. In late 2002 Nucor bought financially troubled Birmingham Steel for $615 million in cash and debt.

Nucor Steel Kingman LLC a subsidiary of Nucor Corporation purchased the Kingman Arizona

rebar and wire rod rolling unit of North Star Steel for around $35 million in 2003.

Its Vulcraft unit saw an increase in non-residential building construction in 2004 which boosted sales of joist girders steel deck and steel joists. Nucor bought Nucor Tuscaloosa in mid-2004 a producer of coiled plate with an annual capacity of around 700000 tons. The following year saw the company purchase Ohio's Marion Steel for approximately $110 million. The mill was added to Nucor's bar products line.

Record high prices in the industry (led by high demand throughout the world) led to record high sales in 2004. As a matter of fact Nucor's first half of the year outpaced previous annual highs and the company achieved that feat again in the second half.

The company named CEO DiMicco chairman in 2006.

In the latter half of the last decade it started a program of rapid external growth. It acquired the former Connecticut Steel Verco Manufacturing and Canadian steel products maker Harris Steel which like Connecticut Steel had been a customer and partner of Nucor for years. Harris itself made an acquisition in 2008 when it bought rebar fabricator and distributor Ambassador Steel. Nucor also expanded its downstream operations with the 2007 acquisition of building systems maker MAGNA-TRAX for $280 million. Its largest acquisition was that of the David J. Joseph Company a scrap metal broker that had supplied Nucor's minimills for 40 years.

The company has always operated primarily in the US but in 2008 it moved into the international market with the formation of a European joint venture with Duferco. The JV produces steel beams and merchant bar products from manufacturing locations in Italy and serves the European and North African markets. Nucor put about $650 million into the new venture called Nucor S.r.l. Duferdofin.

That year it also expanded considerably in the US by spending $1 billion to buy ferrous and nonferrous metals group The David J. Joseph Company .

In 2010 Nucor formed a US-based joint venture with Mitsui & Co. Nucor paid $225 million for its half of the venture named Steel Technologies .

In 2012 Nucor acquired New Jersey-based Skyline Steel and its subsidiaries from ArcelorMittal for about $605 million. Skyline which has served as a distributor of Nucor's products for more than 20 years accelerated Nucor's growth in steel piling and foundation products. Steel sheet piles are long structural sections having a vertical interlocking system that creates a wall. Skyline's flagship products include hot-rolled and cold-formed sheet piles and pipe piling. A steel foundation distributor in North America Skyline serves industries that include marine construction bridge and highway construction heavy civil construction and underground commercial parking.

In 2011 Nucor sold its NuPro Steel subsidiary to Steel Technologies its joint venture with Mitsui & Co . NuPro produces flat-rolled steel at its plant in Crawfordsville Indiana. Nucor also announced that Steel Technologies would build a steel processing plant in Mexico to serve Japanese electronics and auto companies moving into the region.

In early 2011 Nucor and joint venture partners Rio Tinto Group Mitsubishi and Shougang Corp. permanently closed the high-intensity smelt (hismelt) steel plant in Kwinana Western Australia. Nucor had a 25% stake in the joint venture that was terminated.

Continuing its strategy for key acquisitions in 2013 Nucor acquired Gallatin Steel for $780 million. This addition allowed the company to better

serve customers by offering them a wider range of products and further enhancing our reliability. Nucor Steel Gallatin has an annual capacity of 1.8 million tons increasing Nucor's total flat-rolled production to 13 million tons annually. The acquisition also strengthens Nucor's position serving flat-rolled customers in the growing pipe and tube segment.

EXECUTIVES

EVP Flat-Rolled Products, Ladd R. Hall, age 60, $463,100 total compensation

VP; General Manager Sheet Mill Group (Crawfordsville IN), John J. Ferriola, age 64, $1,300,000 total compensation

EVP Merchant and Rebar Products, James R. Darsey, age 61, $463,100 total compensation

EVP Raw Materials and Chief Digital Officer, R. Joseph Stratman, age 60, $473,914 total compensation

EVP CFO and Treasurer, James D. (Jim) Frias, age 60, $490,350 total compensation

EVP Fabricated Construction Products, Raymond S. Napolitan, age 59

EVP Beam and Plate Products, D. Chad Utermark, age 49

EVP Engineered Bar Products, David A. Sumoski, age 50

Vice President, Paige Okelley

Vice President Of Tax, Elizabeth Bowers

Vice President Manufacturing, Bob McKee

Executive Vice President Beam Plate Products, Chad Utermark

Vice President and General Counsel, Gregory Murphy

Vice President General Manager Vulcraft Division Fort Payne Alabama, D Ryan

Secretary, A Rae Eagle

Auditors: PricewaterhouseCoopers LLP

LOCATIONS

HQ: Nucor Corp.
1915 Rexford Road, Charlotte, NC 28211
Phone: 704 366-7000 **Fax:** 704 362-4208
Web: www.nucor.com

PRODUCTS/OPERATIONS

2016 Sales

	$ mil.	% of total
Steel Mills	11,312	70
Steel Products	3,687	23
Raw Materials	1,208	7
Total	**16,208**	**100**

2016 Sales by Product

	$ mil.	% of total
Sheet	5,178	32
Steel products	3,687	23
Bar	2,886	18
Structural	1,982	12
Raw materials	1,208	8
Plate	1,204	7
Tubular products	60	-
Total	**16,208**	**100**

Selected Products

Alloy steel
  Cold-drawn steel bars
  Finished hex caps
  Hex-head cap screws
  Locknuts
  Structural bolts and nuts
Carbon steel
  Angles
  Beams
  Channels
  Cold-drawn steel bars
  Finished hex nuts
  Flats
  Floor plate

Galvanized sheet
Grinding balls
Hexagons
Hot-rolled sheet
Reinforcing bars
Structural bolts and nuts
Wide-range beams
Engineered products
Composite floor joists
Floor deck
Joists
Joist girders
Pre-engineered metal buildings
Roof deck
Special-profile steel trusses
Stainless steel
Cold-rolled steel
Hot-rolled steel
Pickled sheet

Selected Subsidiaries

Harris Steel Inc.
Harris Steel ULC (Canada)
The David J. Joseph Company
Magnatrax Corporation
Nucor Castrip Arkansas LLC
Nucor Energy Holdings Inc.
Nucor-Yamato Steel Company

COMPETITORS

AK Steel Holding Corporation	Gerdau Ameristeel
ArcelorMittal USA	Harsco
Arconic	Illinois Tool Works
BlueScope Steel	Renco
Commercial Metals	Schnitzer Steel
Cummins	Steel Dynamics
Dow Chemical	Tata Europe
	United States Steel

HISTORICAL FINANCIALS

Company Type: Public

Income Statement

FYE: December 31

	REVENUE ($ mil.)	NET INCOME ($ mil.)	NET PROFIT MARGIN	EMPLOYEES
12/16	16,208	796	4.9%	23,900
12/15	16,439	357	2.2%	23,700
12/14	21,105	713	3.4%	23,600
12/13	19,052	488	2.6%	22,300
12/12	19,429	504	2.6%	22,200
Annual Growth	(4.4%)	12.1%	—	1.9%

2016 Year-End Financials

Debt ratio: 28.62%
Return on equity: 10.38%
Cash ($ mil.): 2,045
Current ratio: 2.72
Long-term debt ($ mil.): 3,739

No. of shares (mil.): 318
Dividends
Yield: 0.0%
Payout: 60.5%
Market value ($ mil.): 18,971

	STOCK PRICE ($) FY Close	P/E High/Low		PER SHARE ($) Earnings	Dividends	Book Value
12/16	59.52	27	14	2.48	1.50	24.72
12/15	40.30	45	33	1.11	1.49	23.33
12/14	49.05	26	21	2.22	1.48	24.36
12/13	53.38	36	28	1.52	1.47	24.02
12/12	43.16	29	22	1.58	1.46	24.06
Annual Growth	8.4%	—	—	11.9%	0.7%	0.7%

NVIDIA Corp

NVIDIA is racking up points in computer games logging miles in driverless cars and going deep into data centers with artificial intelligence. The company?s graphics processing units (GPUs) are used to generate computer game images in many PCs and game consoles in the growing gaming market. What?s more its GPUs work well in applications for autonomous vehicles and deep learning a branch of AI. NVIDIA?s GPU brands are GeForce for games Quadro for designers and digital artists and Tesla and DGX for scientists and researchers. Its Tegra line is a family of system-on-a-chip devices for mobile gaming and entertainment as well as autonomous robots drones and cars.

Operations

NVIDIA keeps track of its operations by product and market. GPUs account for about 85% of the company?s revenue while the Tegra brand brings in another 12% with other operations accounting for the rest. In terms of markets gaming produces about 60% of revenue followed by visualization and data centers accounting for about 12% of revenue each and automotive less than 10%. Sales of intellectual property and of products to OEMs generate about 10% of revenue.

The GPU products include GeForce for PC gaming and GeForce NOW for cloud-based game-streaming services; Quadro for computer-aided design video editing and special effects; Tesla for AI using deep learning and accelerated computing; and GRID for providing NVIDIA graphics capabilities through the cloud and data centers.

The Tegra line includes DRIVE PX automotive chip systems that provide self-driving capabilities and SHIELD which includes a family of devices and services for cloud-based mobile applications for home entertainment AI and gaming.

The company also develops software and software libraries for running its chips.

NVIDIA outsources manufacturing to Taiwan Semiconductor Manufacturing Company Limited and Samsung Electronics Co. Ltd. The assembly testing and packaging work is done by independent subcontractors that include Advanced Semiconductor Engineering Inc. BYD Auto Co. Hon Hai Precision Industry Co. and JSI Logistics Ltd.

Geographic Reach

NVIDIA has design centers laboratories and offices in Australia Canada China Finland France Germany Hong Kong India Japan Russia Singapore South Korea Sweden Switzerland Taiwan the UK and the US.

Customers in Taiwan generate nearly 40% of NVIDIA?s revenue followed by customers in China at about 20% and the US customers with just under 15%.

Sales and Marketing

NVIDIA?s sales and marketing team works with end customers and through partner networks that include original equipment manufacturers original device manufacturers system builders add-in board makers and retailers and distributors. A small number of customers in the partner networks account for most of NVIDIA?s revenue. ASUSTeK Computer Inc. is the only customer to account for more than 10% of revenue.

As part of its sales and marketing efforts NVIDIA offers rebates to resellers as incentives and it provides marketing development funds to help partners in promoting NVIDIA?s products as well as their own.

Financial Performance

NVIDIA?s revenue took off in 2017 (ended January) after several years of irregular gains. It posted a company record $6.9 billion in revenue in 2017 a 38% improvement over $5 billion in 2016. With the revenue leap NVIDIA rose to No. 379 on the 2017 Fortune 500 list from ranking of 508 in 2016. Profit rocketed 171% higher to $1.7 billion in 2017 from $614 million the year before.

The GPU business accounted for most of the growth adding $1.6 billion in revenue over the year. Gains from GeForce GPUs particularly high-end processors were driven by adoption of the company?s new Pascal architecture. Data center growth of 145% to $830 million came from demand for deep learning cloud and virtualized computing as well as sales of the DGX-1 processor. Sales declined for GeForce products going to mainstream PC makers. The Tegra business rose 47% (reaching $824 million in sales) from infotainment applications in the automotive market and from gaming development platforms and services.

The billion-dollar increase in net income was driven by the strong revenue growth better operating margins and a lower income tax rate.

The big jump in net income in turn pushed cash flow from operations to $1.7 billion in 2017 from $1.2 billion in 2016.

Strategy

It takes a lot of computing power to render graphics capable of holding gamers' attention for hours at a time. In providing that power NVIDIA established itself as the dominant player in computer game graphics controlling more than 70% of the market. The company continues to turn out architectures and processors that generate realistic renderings of all kinds of games played on all kinds of platforms. The company sees potential for continued gaming growth in the rise of computer gaming as a spectator sport. The company?s GeForce GPUs run PCs used in the top esports tournaments.

From its gaming base NVIDIA has positioned its GPUs for the artificial intelligence and automotive markets. The high processing power of GPUs enables them to handle the demands of artificial intelligence applications. The biggest cloud infrastructure providers ? Amazon Web Services Microsoft and Google ? use NVIDIA processors in their operations. GPUs also are used to turn analyzed information into graphics through visualization applications.

In the automotive market NVIDIA?s DRIVE PX 2 AI car platform operates multiple functions such as auto-piloted cars driverless shuttles cloud mapping and in-car AI capabilities. NVIDIA has partnered with car and component manufacturers to develop automotive applications. The company?s processors also are used in information and entertainment applications in vehicles.

Virtual reality is another area where NVIDIA?s processors are firmly established. They run the VR headsets of top companies in the emerging business including Oculus Epic Valve and Vive.

There are plenty of challengers in these markets. AMD a long-time player in graphics has released processors recently that rival others in the market. Intel Corp. has used its deep resources to develop and buy technologies to compete in these markets including automotive with its acquisition of Mobileye.

EXECUTIVES

Svp Gpu Engineering, Brian Kelleher
Senior Vice President GPU Engineering, Jonah M Alben
Senior Vice President Advanced Technology Group, Joseph Greco
Vice President Corporate Comm, Bob Sherbin
President and CEO, Jen-Hsun Huang, age 54, $996,216 total compensation
EVP Operations, Debora C. Shoquist, age 62, $695,131 total compensation
EVP Worldwide Field Operations, Ajay K. (Jay) Puri, age 62, $889,573 total compensation
EVP and CFO, Colette M. Kress, age 49, $769,609 total compensation
Vice President Software Engineering, Dwight Diercks
Vice President Platform Software, Scott Pritchett
Vice President, Alejandro Troccoli

Vice President Hardware Engineering, John Schafer
Vice President and General Manager Tegra, Deepu Talla
Vice President of Hardware Engineering, Rajeev Jayavant
Vice President, Lin Cong
Senior Vice President and Treasurer, Nickolas Fortino
Vice President Software Engineering, Sam Azar
Senior Vice President, Ilyas Elkin
Vice President Worldwide GeForce Sales, John Milner
Vice President Automotive Software, Kevin Flory
Vice President, James van Welzen
Vice President Human Resousres, Anurag Chaudhary
Senior Vice President, Kirk Twardowski
Vice President Im, Ann Chang
Vice President Engineering, Laurent Coudrelle
Vice President of Branding, Ming-Ju Lee
Vice President Customer Program Management, Jerry Vogel
Vice President Of Operations, Arnold Suratos
Vice President, Jay Huang
Vice President of the Investment Group, Shantanu Kalchuri
Vice President, Richard Cameron
Vice President Product Engineering, David Greenlaw
Senior Vice President, Jizhi Zhang
Assistant Vice President Residential Solutions, Kenneth MacDonald
Vice President HW Engineering, Jonathan Sweedler
Vice President World Wide Sales NVIDIA Professional Solutions Group, Walter Mundt-Blum
Vice President Internal Audit, Bruce Carpenter
Senior Vice President Vlsi Engineering, Joe Grech
Vice President OEM Sales, John Leggio
Vice President And General Manager Professional Solution Group, Ashok Pandey
Vice President, Jeff Herbst
Vice President Software Security, Daniel Rohrer
Vice President of Architecture, Mike Cox
Senior Vice President MCP Engineering, Gary Hicok
Vice President of External Affairs, Ned Finkle
Vice President GPU ASIC Engineering, Arjun Prabhu
Senior Vice President Consumer Electronics Engineering, Frank Fox
Senior Vice President Operations, Debbie Shoquist
Vice President and General Counsel, Mike Polley
Vice President and Assistant General Counsel and Chief Operating Officer, Elizabeth Hansel
Vice President Systems Supply Chain, Jeff Whitmer
Board Member, Nancy Smith
Board Member, Darrell Boggs
Board Member, Luke Durant
Board Member, Keegan Brown
US Treasurer, Jay Landre
Board Member, Guru Nutheti
Vice Chairman and President, Gerald Luiz
Advisory Board Member, Barry Patel
Board Member, Hyungon Ryu
Board Member, Eric Anderson
Auditors: PricewaterhouseCoopers LLP

LOCATIONS

HQ: NVIDIA Corp
2701 San Tomas Expressway, Santa Clara, CA 95050
Phone: 408 486-2000
Web: www.nvidia.com

2017 Sales

	$ mil.	% of total
Asia/Pacific		
Taiwan	2,546	37
China	1,305	19
Other Asia/Pacific	1,010	15
Americas		
US	904	13
Other Americas	659	9
Europe	486	7
Total	6,910	100

PRODUCTS/OPERATIONS

2017 Sales

	$ mil.	% of total
GPU	5,822	84
Tegra Processor	824	12
All other	264	4
Total	6,910	100

2017 sales by Market

% of total	in mil.
Gaming	59
Professional Visualization	12
Datacenter	12
Automotive	7
OEM & IP	10
Total	100

COMPETITORS

AMD
ARM Holdings
Ambarella
Apple Inc.
Creative Technology
Epson
Fujitsu Semiconductor
Imagination Technologies
Intel
Marvell Technology
Matrox Electronic Systems
MediaTek
NEC
QUALCOMM
Renesas Electronics
STMicroelectronics
Samsung Electronics
Sigma Designs
Silicon Integrated Systems
Spreadtrum
Texas Instruments
Toshiba America Electronic Components
VIA Technologies

HISTORICAL FINANCIALS

Company Type: Public

Income Statement

FYE: January 29

	REVENUE ($ mil.)	NET INCOME ($ mil.)	NET PROFIT MARGIN	EMPLOYEES
01/17	6,910	1,666	24.1%	10,299
01/16	5,010	614	12.3%	6,566
01/15	4,681	630	13.5%	9,228
01/14	4,130	439	10.7%	8,808
01/13	4,280	562	13.1%	7,974
Annual Growth	12.7%	31.2%	—	6.6%

2017 Year-End Financials

Debt ratio: 28.30%
Return on equity: 32.28%
Cash ($ mil.): 1,766
Current ratio: 4.77
Long-term debt ($ mil.): 1,989
No. of shares (mil.): 585
Dividends
 Yield: 0.0%
 Payout: 18.8%
Market value ($ mil.): 65,385

	STOCK PRICE ($) FY Close	P/E High	P/E Low	PER SHARE ($) Earnings	Dividends	Book Value
01/17	111.77	38	8	2.57	0.49	9.90
01/16	29.29	30	17	1.08	0.40	8.45
01/15	20.71	19	14	1.12	0.34	8.11
01/14	15.56	22	16	0.74	0.31	7.85
01/13	12.41	18	13	0.90	0.08	7.83
Annual Growth	73.2%	—	—	30.0%	59.5%	6.1%

NVR Inc.

From finished lot to signed mortgage NVR offers homebuyers everything — including the kitchen sink. The company builds single-family detached homes townhomes and condominiums mainly for first-time and move-up buyers primarily in the eastern US. NVR markets its homes as Ryan Homes Fox Ridge Homes Heartland Homes and NVHomes. Its largest markets the Washington DC and Baltimore areas account for around 45% of sales. NVR's housing sizes range from 1000 sq. ft. to 9000 sq. ft. with the average price of a home selling for around $380000. Its subsidiary NVR Mortgage Finance offers mortgage and title services. NVR was founded in 1980 as NVHomes.

Operations

NVR's homebuilding divisions — Ryan Homes Fox Ridge Homes and Heartland Homes — primarily market to first-time buyers. Ryan Homes operates in some thirty metropolitan areas along the eastern seaboard and in Indiana Kentucky Ohio Pennsylvania and West Virginia. Fox Ridge Homes is dedicated to first-time and move-up buyers in the Nashville market. NVHomes and Heartland Homes cater to upscale buyers and builds primarily in the Baltimore Philadelphia and DC metro areas as well as on Maryland's eastern shore. Homes sell for between $140000 and $1.8 million.

NVR's Building Products unit supports the homebuilder's construction activities with manufacturing facilities in Maryland New Jersey New York North Carolina Pennsylvania and Tennessee. It supplies structural building components to the job sites. To support its homebuilding operations the company offers settlement and title services through NVR Settlement Services.

Homebuilding accounts for 98% of the builder's total sales while its mortgage banking business which closes some 12300 loans totaling $4.0 billion generates the other 2% of its total sales.

Geographic Reach

Virginia-based NVR's homebuilding operations serve around 30 metropolitan areas in 14 states in the eastern half of the US. Home sales in Mid-Atlantic states (Maryland Virginia West Virginia Delaware and Washington DC) bring in more than 55% of the builder's total sales while homes sales in the Mid-Eastern states (New York Ohio Western Pennsylvania Indiana and Illinois) account for another 20%. Its largest markets are in Washington DC (30% of sales) and Baltimore Maryland (13%).

Sales and Marketing

NVR markets its homes through sales representatives and through model homes that are typically converted into temporary sales offices where a salesperson can review alternative floor plans facades and designs for other house models with the client.

Its houses are aimed at move-up and upscale buyers.

Financial Performance

NVR has enjoyed healthy sales and profit growth over the years as the recovery in residential construction has picked up steam. The company is finally closing in of the peak $6.1 billion recorded before the financial crash in 2007.

In fiscal 2016 revenue grew another 13% to $5.7 billion thank to an increase in units settled on prior year. The increase was due to a 14% increase in backlog unit balance going into 2016. New order sales increased 2%.

Net income ticked up 11% to $425 million. Higher net revenue was offset by tighter margins due to higher construction and selling related costs.

Cash from operations increased 89% to $384.4 million due to favorable increases in accounts receivable and net proceeds of $50.0 million from mortgage loan activities.

Strategy

Favorable sales and pricing trends driven by historically low mortgage interest rates and rising rental costs are a boon to NVR and other homebuilders. The builder keeps its profits high by focusing on building in areas where it has a high market share finding it to be more cost-efficient to expand within its existing markets.Higher cash generation in 2016 has been put to use to fund further homebuilding inventory increases.

Company Background

NVR expanded its portfolio of home-building companies in late 2012 when it acquired Heartland Homes the second-largest homebuilder in Pittsburgh. As part of the purchase NVR planned to continue to use the Heartland Homes name and pair the company with its complementary Ryan Homes.

HISTORY

NVR got its start when Dwight Schar founded NVHomes Inc. in 1980. Schar had worked for Ryan Homes (founded 1948) since 1969. Like Ryan Homes NVHomes specialized in single-family homes around Washington DC. The strong economy of the 1980s and the deregulation of lending institutions — coupled with favorable partnership and real estate tax laws passed by the Reagan administration — resulted in rapid growth. The company was clearing income of more than $1 million a year by 1983 and soon branched into building townhomes and condominiums.

In 1986 when the company was reorganized as a limited partnership (NVH L.P.) income was up to $14 million. The new entity soon acquired a controlling interest in Ryan Homes; it completed its acquisition of that company in 1987. NVH reorganized as a holding company (NVRyan L.P.) and 1988 profits reached $33.5 million. Over the years the company formed or acquired almost 100 subsidiaries that were involved in all aspects of homebuilding — from land acquisition and construction to home finance and investment advice. It had also branched out into California Florida Indiana Kentucky North Carolina Ohio Pennsylvania and Virginia.

Following an economic recession in 1989 demand for new housing dropped off in the US. The company shortened its name to NVR L.P. and its inventory of unsold land and houses started to grow. The situation was exacerbated by changes in the tax code that made real estate less attractive as an investment; sales from development and construction projects dropped from more than $1 billion in 1988 to about $600 million in 1991. NVR posted a $260 million loss in 1990 as sales and the value of its inventory nose-dived.

NVR reorganized in 1990 and 1991. Focused on eight mid-Atlantic states it put homebuilding under one management structure consolidated its finance activities exited its land-development businesses and offered its mortgage services to customers who weren't NVR homebuyers. It also organized its business into two product lines: upscale (NVHomes) and moderately priced (Ryan Homes) homes. Despite the reorganization and introduction of innovative marketing NVR and several of its subsidiaries filed for Chapter 11 bankruptcy relief in 1992. That year the CFO of NVR's thrift (NVR Savings Bank) went on the lam to Malta after embezzling more than $750000.

The company emerged from bankruptcy as NVR Inc. in 1993 with less debt new owners and a new line of credit; it also had its IPO that year. The next year NVR sold NVR Savings Bank which had

four branches in northern Virginia. The robust mid-1990s economy aided NVR; as home sales rose the company entered new markets including the Cleveland and Nashville areas in 1995. To reduce its vulnerability to downturns in the mid-Atlantic area it continued its expansion outside that region buying Fox Ridge Homes (the #2 builder in Nashville) in 1997.

In 1999 it merged its homebuilding subsidiary NVR Homes and mortgage banking holding company NVR Financial Services into NVR. It also acquired Rockville Maryland-based First Republic Mortgage that year but closed the subsidiary's retail operations in 2000 and realigned its mortgage banking business to serve NVR customers exclusively.

From 1994 through 2003 the company benefited from increased housing activity recording steady increases in unit sales backlog and profits for nine years. During the housing downturn that began in 2008 the company performed better than its competitors reporting only one losing quarter in the period.

In late 2012 NVR expanded its portfolio of home-building companies when it acquired Heartland Homes the second-largest homebuilder in Pittsburgh. As part of the purchase NVR planned to continue to use the Heartland Homes name and pair the company with its complementary Ryan Homes.

EXECUTIVES

President CEO and Director, Paul C. Saville, age 61, $1,566,375 total compensation
President NVR Mortgage (NVRM), Robert W. Henley, age 50, $460,000 total compensation
VP CFO and Treasurer, Daniel D. Malzahn, age 47, $490,000 total compensation
VP Chief Accounting Officer and Controller, Eugene J. Bredow, $341,250 total compensation
President Homebuilding Operations, Jeffrey D. Martchek, age 52, $539,000 total compensation
Chairman, Dwight C. Schar, age 75
Auditors: KPMG LLP

LOCATIONS

HQ: NVR Inc.
11700 Plaza America Drive, Suite 500, Reston, VA 20190
Phone: 703 956-4000
Web: www.nvrinc.com

2016 Sales

	% of total
Homebuilding	
Mid-Atlantic	57
Mid-east	20
Southeast	13
Northeast	8
Mortgage banking	2
Total	**100**

PRODUCTS/OPERATIONS

Selected Brands

Fox Ridge Homes
Heartland Homes
NVHomes
Ryan Homes

COMPETITORS

Beazer Homes	KB Home
Brookfield Homes	Lennar
Champion Home Builders	M.D.C.
D.R. Horton	M/I Homes
David Weekley Homes	Orleans Homebuilders
Hovnanian Enterprises	PulteGroup
John Wieland Homes	Toll Brothers

HISTORICAL FINANCIALS
Company Type: Public

Income Statement
FYE: December 31

	REVENUE ($ mil.)	NET INCOME ($ mil.)	NET PROFIT MARGIN	EMPLOYEES
12/17	6,322	537	8.5%	5,200
12/16	5,834	425	7.3%	4,900
12/15	5,169	382	7.4%	4,300
12/14	4,453	281	6.3%	3,942
12/13	4,220	266	6.3%	3,944
Annual Growth	10.6%	19.2%		7.2%

2017 Year-End Financials

Debt ratio: 19.97%	No. of shares (mil.): 3
Return on equity: 36.94%	Dividends
Cash ($ mil.): 666	Yield: —
Current ratio: 4.35	Payout: —
Long-term debt ($ mil.): 597	Market value ($ mil.): 12,949

	STOCK PRICE ($) FY Close	P/E High/Low	PER SHARE ($) Earnings	Dividends	Book Value
12/17	3,508.22	24 11	126.77	0.00	434.97
12/16	1,669.00	17 14	103.61	0.00	353.22
12/15	1,643.00	18 13	89.99	0.00	318.47
12/14	1,275.33	19 15	63.50	0.00	277.66
12/13	1,026.01	19 15	54.81	0.00	284.49
Annual Growth	36.0%	—	23.3%	—	11.2%

O'Reilly Automotive, Inc.

O'Reilly Automotive has its foot hard on the gas. The company sells automotive aftermarket parts (both new and remanufactured) maintenance supplies professional service equipment tools and accessories through some 4800 stores across 47 US states and online. Many O'Reilly stores also offer customers a range of services including oil and battery recycling battery testing paint mixing and tool rental. The family-founded and -operated company wheels and deals with automotive professionals as well as do-it-yourself customers.

Operations

O?Reilly's stores carry about 23000 SKUs and average 7300 total square feet. The stores receive inventory five nights a week from O'Reilly's 27 regional distribution centers and 312 Hub stores.

The company gets around 60% of sales from its DIY customers and approximately 40% of sales from its professional service provider customers.

O?Reilly sells automotive products directly to independently owned parts stores (?jobber stores?) in certain markets.

As well as its vast array of products O?Reilly?s also offers an almost equally vast array of services such as used oil oil filter and battery recycling; battery wiper and bulb replacement; battery diagnostic testing; electrical and module testing; paint mixing; and much more.

Geographic Reach

Missouri-based O'Reilly has stores in 47 US states including Alaska and Hawaii. Texas and California are its largest markets with some 670 stores 530 stores in each.

Sales and Marketing

O'Reilly leverages television radio direct mail and newspaper distribution in-store and online promotions and sports and event sponsorships. The company also participates in cooperative advertising with its vendors. Its combination of brand and product/price messaging drives retail traffic and purchases which frequently coincide with key sales events. To stimulate sales among racing enthusiasts O'Reilly sponsors multiple nationally-televised races and more than 1600 grassroots local and regional motorsports events throughout 45 states.

The company has promotions through Spanish language radio print and outdoor advertising as well as sponsorships of more than 45 local and regional festivals and events. The company also awards customers with points through purchases and other special events and redeems those points for coupons and discounts.

O'Reilly maintains a full-time sales staff of 750. Targeted marketing materials such as flyers quick reference guides and catalogs are produced and distributed on a regular basis to professional service providers paint and body shops and fleet customers.

Financial Performance

O'Reilly's revenues has been on an upward trend since 2003. In fiscal 2016 (ended December) revenue increased by 8% to $8.6 billion due to higher comparable store sales 210 store openings the 48 acquired Bond stores and the additional day due to the Leap Year as well as the positive effect on inventory availability of same-day and overnight access to distribution center inventory.

Net income has likewise been on the up-and-up climbing a further 11% to $1.0 billion in 2016 due to higher net revenue and greater leverage in negotiations with suppliers to lower product acquisition costs. SGA expenses in relation to total sales fell half a point.

Cash from operating activities increased 14% to $1.5 billion.

Strategy

O'Reilly adheres to a "dual market" strategy by appealing to both do-it-yourself (DIY) and professional service providers. The company believes that its tiered distribution model provides industry-leading parts availability and store in-stock positions while lowering its inventory carrying costs and controlling inventory. To this end the auto parts chain has made significant capital investments in its distribution center network allowing it to efficiently service its aggressive 200-a-year store opening program as well as servicing its existing stores network. It opened up same-day and overnight inventory access to its distribution centers in 2016. O'Reilly is aiming for a total growth capacity of more than 800 stores in its distribution center network. The company also relies on its stores? position as ?destination stores? to pull in punters.

As part of its continuing efforts to enhance its distribution network it's implementing a voice-picking technology in additional distribution centers; rolling out enhanced routing software to enhance logistics efficiencies; launching additional labor management software to improve distribution center productivity and overall operating efficiency; developing further automated paperless-picking processes; improving proof of delivery systems to boost the accuracy of product movement to stores; continuing to define and implement best practices in all distribution centers; and making proven return-on-investment-based capital enhancements to material handling equipment in distribution centers including conveyor systems picking modules and lift equipment.

The company is expanding its nationwide presence by opening stores at a rapid rate. In 2016 it opened 210 net new stores a similar figure to the preceding few years.

Company Background

In 2012 the company expanded its capabilities by acquiring the auto-parts-related assets of VIP Parts Tires & Service a large privately-held automotive parts tires and service chain in New England. The asset purchase included 56 stores located throughout Maine New Hampshire and Massachusetts as well as a distribution center located in Lewiston Maine.

O'Reilly was founded in 1957 by Charles F. O'Reilly and his son "Chub."

EXECUTIVES

President and CEO, Gregory L. (Greg) Henslee, age 56, $1,238,461 total compensation

Co-President, Jeff M. Shaw, age 54, $396,923 total compensation

EVP Finance and CFO, Thomas G. (Tom) McFall, age 46, $713,846 total compensation

Co-President, Gregory D. (Greg) Johnson, age 51, $342,308 total compensation

SVP Information Systems, Jeff Lauro

Vice President Northern Division, Kenny Martin

Senior Vice President Merchandise And Marketing, Mike Swearengin

Vice Chairman, Lawrence P. (Larry) O'Reilly, age 70

Vice Chairman, Charles H. O'Reilly, age 78

Chairman, David E. O'Reilly, age 68

Auditors: Ernst & Young LLP

LOCATIONS

HQ: O'Reilly Automotive, Inc.
233 South Patterson Avenue, Springfield, MO 65802
Phone: 417 862-6708
Web: www.oreillyauto.com

2016 Stores

	No.
Texas	667
California	534
Missouri	195
Georgia	187
Illinois	186
Ohio	169
Florida	163
Tennessee	162
Michigan	158
North Carolina	155
Washington	155
Arizona	136
Alabama	125
Oklahoma	121
Indiana	120
Minnesota	119
Wisconsin	118
Louisiana	109
Arkansas	107
Colorado	99
South Carolina	91
Kansas	82
Kentucky	77
Mississippi	75
Iowa	73
Oregon	66
Virginia	66
Utah	61
Nevada	54
New Mexico	52
Nebraska	41
Idaho	40
New Hampshire	38
Maine	35
Massachusetts	30
Montana	27
Vermont	24
Wyoming	20
South Dakota	16
Alaska	15
North Dakota	15
Hawaii	12
Pennsylvania	12
West Virginia	12
Connecticut	5
Rhode Island	3
New York	2
Total	**4,829**

PRODUCTS/OPERATIONS

Selected Products

Accessorie
Accessorie
Air Conditioning
Battery & Accessories
Belts & Hoses
Body & Trim
Brakes
Charging & Starting
Cooling & Heating
Engine Parts & Mounts
Exhaust
Filters & PCV Valves
Fuel & Emissions
Hardware & Fasteners
Ignition & Tune-Up
Lighting & Electrical
Oil Fluids & Chemicals
Performance
Suspension & Steering
Tire & Wheel
Tools & Equipment
Transmission & Transaxle
Truck & Towing
Waxes & Washes
Wipers

COMPETITORS

Acheeve Inc.	Target Corporation
Advance Auto Parts	U.S. Auto Parts
AutoZone	VIP
CARQUEST	Wal-Mart
Genuine Parts	Whitney Automotive
Pep Boys	Group
Sears	

HISTORICAL FINANCIALS

Company Type: Public

Income Statement

FYE: December 31

	REVENUE ($ mil.)	NET INCOME ($ mil.)	NET PROFIT MARGIN	EMPLOYEES
12/16	8,593	1,037	12.1%	74,715
12/15	7,966	931	11.7%	71,943
12/14	7,216	778	10.8%	67,926
12/13	6,649	670	10.1%	62,533
12/12	6,182	585	9.5%	53,615
Annual Growth	8.6%	15.4%	—	8.7%

2016 Year-End Financials

Debt ratio: 26.19%
Return on equity: 57.68%
Cash ($ mil.): 146
Current ratio: 0.96
Long-term debt ($ mil.): 1,887
No. of shares (mil.): 92
Dividends
　Yield: —
　Payout: —
Market value ($ mil.): 25,851

	STOCK PRICE ($) FY Close	P/E High/Low	PER SHARE ($) Earnings	Dividends	Book Value
12/16	278.41	27 21	10.73	0.00	17.52
12/15	253.42	30 19	9.17	0.00	20.07
12/14	192.62	26 17	7.34	0.00	19.87
12/13	128.71	22 14	6.03	0.00	18.56
12/12	89.42	22 16	4.75	0.00	18.66
Annual Growth	32.8%	— —	22.6%	—	(1.6%)

Occidental Petroleum Corp

Harnessing its heritage of Western technical know-how Occidental Petroleum engages in oil and gas exploration and production and makes basic chemicals plastics and petrochemicals. It boasts proved reserves of 2.4 billion barrels of oil equivalent primarily from assets in the US the Middle East North Africa and Latin America. Subsidiary Occidental Chemical (OxyChem) produces acids chlorine and specialty products and owns Oxy Vinyls the #1 maker of polyvinyl chloride (PVC) resin in North America. Occidental Petroleum's midstream and marketing units gather treat process transport store trade and market crude oil natural gas NGLs condensate and CO2 and generate and market power.

HISTORY

Founded in 1920 Occidental Petroleum struggled until 1956 when billionaire industrialist Dr. Armand Hammer sank $100000 into the company then worth $34000. It drilled two wells and both came in. Hammer eventually gained control of the company.

Occidental's discovery of California's second-largest gas field (1959) was followed by a concession from Libya's King Idris (1966) and the discovery of a billion-barrel Libyan oil field. In 1968 Occidental bought Signal Oil's European refining and marketing business as an outlet for the Libyan oil. It also diversified buying Island Creek Coal and Hooker Chemical.

In 1969 Occidental sold 51% of its Libyan production to the Libyan government under duress after Idris was ousted. (It suspended operations there in 1986). It soon began oil exploration in Latin America (1971) and in the North Sea (1972-73) where it discovered the lucrative Piper field. Other projects included a 20-year fertilizer-for-ammonia deal with the USSR (1974) and a coal joint venture with China (1985).

During the 1980s Occidental sold some foreign assets and bought US natural gas pipeline firm MidCon (1986). It also bought Iowa Beef Processors (IBP) for stock worth $750 million (1981) and then spun off 49% of it in 1987 for $960 million.

In 1983 Hammer hired Ray Irani to revive Occidental's ailing chemicals business (losses that year: $38 million). Irani integrated operations to ensure higher margins during industry downturns and purchased Diamond Shamrock Chemicals (1986) Shell's vinyl chloride monomer unit (1987) a DuPont chloralkali facility (1987) and Cain Chemical (1988). OxyChem's profits reached almost $1.1 billion by 1989.

Hammer died in 1990 and Irani became CEO. In 1991 to reduce debt Occidental exited the Chinese coal business and sold the North Sea oil properties. Occidental also spun off IBP the largest US red-meat producer to its shareholders.

Occidental paid Irani $95 million in 1997 to buy out his employment contract; instead his compensation (a minimum of $1.2 million a year) was tied to the company's fortunes. That year Occidental's $3.65 billion bid won the US government's auction of its 78% stake in California's Elk Hills petroleum reserve one of the largest in the continental US.

To help pay for Elk Hills the company sold MidCon to K N Energy for $3.1 billion in 1998. Occidental traded its petrochemical operations to Equistar Chemicals a partnership between Lyondell

(now LyondellBasell) and Millennium Chemicals for $425 million and a 29.5% stake.

In a venture with The Geon Company Occidental in 1999 formed Oxy Vinyls the #1 producer of polyvinyl chloride (PVC) resin in North America. That year also brought a windfall: Chevron agreed to pay Occidental $775 million to settle a lawsuit stemming from the 1982 withdrawal by Gulf (later acquired by Chevron) of an offer to buy Cities Service (later acquired by Occidental).

In 2000 Occidental sold its 29% stake in Canadian Occidental back to the company for $828 million to help fund the purchase of oil and gas producer Altura Energy a partnership of BP and Shell Oil for $3.6 billion. Later that year the company sold some Gulf of Mexico properties to Apache for $385 million.

Occidental acquired a new exploration block in Yemen in 2001. The next year it sold its 30% of Equistar Chemicals to Lyondell in exchange for a 21% stake in Lyondell. In 2005 it acquired a stake in a gas and oil production site located in Texas' Permian Basin from ExxonMobil for a reported $972 million. Occidental closed the acquisition of Vintage Petroleum for a reported $3.8 billion in early 2006.

The government of Ecuador seized Occidental Petroleum's Ecuadorian assets in 2006 as part of a nationalization drive. That year Plains Exploration and Production sold non-core oil and gas properties to Occidental for $865 million.

Also in 2006 Occidental reduced its stake in Lyondell from 12% to 8%. The following year Occidental sold its remaining Lyondell shares on the open market.

In North America in 2008 the company bought a 15% stake in the Joslyn Oil Sands project for nearly $500 million. That project is based in Alberta Canada and is operated by Total.

The company re-entered Libya in 2008.

Beefing up its investment vehicles in 2009 the company purchased Citigroup's commodities trading unit (Philbro LLC).

To raise cash to pay down debt in 2011 the company sold its Argentina-based assets to China Petrochemical for $2.45 billion. The deal helped cover some of the costs of Occidental's $3.4 billion acquisition (in late 2010 and early 2011) of safer US-based assets — oil and gas properties in South Texas and North Dakota.

In the US in 2012 Occidental paid $2.3 billion for oil and gas properties in the Permian Basin Williston Basin South Texas and California.

That year Occidental and Magellan Midstream Partners L.P. formed BridgeTex Pipeline Company LLC (BridgeTex) to build the 450-mile-long BridgeTex Pipeline to transport 300000 barrels per day of crude oil between the Permian region and the Gulf Coast refinery markets.

In 2013 OxyChem and Mexichem formed a 50/50 joint venture Ingleside Ethylene LLC to build a 1.2-billion-pound per year capacity ethylene cracker at the OxyChem plant in Ingleside Texas along with pipelines and storage at Markham Texas. As part of a long-term strategic supply relationship between the companies essentially all of the ethylene produced from the cracker will be consumed in the manufacture of vinyl chloride monomer (VCM) utilizing existing VCM capacity. VCM will be delivered to Mexichem to produce polyvinyl chloride (PVC) and PVC piping systems.

Growing it assets in 2013 the company and Qatar Petroleum agreed on the Phase 5 Field Development Plan of the Idd El Shargi North Dome Field offshore Qatar. The project will sustain oil production levels at about 100000 barrels per day through 2019. (In 2011 Occidental also teamed up with ADNOC to develop the major Shah gas field in the UAE).

In 2013 the company paid approximately $500 million to acquire various US-based oil and gas properties.

EXECUTIVES

SVP and CFO, Cedric W. Burgher, age 57
SVP General Counsel and Chief Compliance Officer, Marcia E. Backus, age 62, $646,970 total compensation
EVP and Group Chairman - Middle East, Edward A. (Sandy) Lowe, age 65, $625,000 total compensation
SVP Marketing and Midstream Operations and Development, Cynthia L. Walker, age 41, $600,000 total compensation
President CEO and Director, Vicki A. Hollub, age 57, $1,143,314 total compensation
VP and CIO, Ioannis A. Charalambous
SVP and President Oxy Oil and Gas Domestic, Joseph C. Elliott, age 59
SVP and President Occidental Chemical Corporation, Robert L. Peterson
Vice President Marketing and Asset Optimization, Shawn McGovern
Vice President U.S. Oil Marketing Permian Basin and Hugoton, Steven Rafferty
Vice President Business Development, Kevin Pilkington
Vice President Health Environment Safety And Security, Wesley Scott
Vice President Sales and Marketing, James Clarken
Executive Vice President Business Support, James Lienert
Vice President Exploration and Geoscience, Pedro Romero
Vice President Worldwide Drilling and Completions, Brenda Harris
Chairman, Eugene L. (Gene) Batchelder, age 69
Auditors: KPMG LLP

LOCATIONS

HQ: Occidental Petroleum Corp
5 Greenway Plaza, Suite 110, Houston, TX 77046
Phone: 713 215-7000
Web: www.oxy.com

2016 Sales

	% of total
US	62
Qatar	12
Oman	11
United Arab Emirates	7
Colombia	5
Other countries	3
Total	**100**

PRODUCTS/OPERATIONS

2016 Sales

	% of total
Oil & gas	59
Chemicals	35
Midstream marketing & other	6
Adjustments	-
Total	**100**

Selected Subsidiaries

Occidental Chemical Corp. (OxyChem; chemicals polymers and plastics)
    Oxy Vinyls LP (76% polyvinyl chloride)
Occidental Energy Marketing Inc. (energy marketing)
Occidental Exploration and Production Company (exploration and production)

COMPETITORS

Apache	Huntsman International
Ashland	Imperial Oil
BP	J.M. Huber
ConocoPhillips	Koch Industries Inc.

Devon Energy	Marathon Oil
Dow Chemical	Olin
DuPont	PEMEX
Eastman Chemical	Royal Dutch Shell
Exxon Mobil	Sunoco
Hess Corporation	TOTAL

HISTORICAL FINANCIALS
Company Type: Public

Income Statement
FYE: December 31

	REVENUE ($ mil.)	NET INCOME ($ mil.)	NET PROFIT MARGIN	EMPLOYEES
12/16	10,398	(574)	—	11,000
12/15	12,699	(7,829)	—	11,100
12/14	21,947	616	2.8%	11,700
12/13	25,736	5,903	22.9%	12,900
12/12	24,253	4,598	19.0%	12,300
Annual Growth	(19.1%)	—	—	(2.8%)

2016 Year-End Financials
Debt ratio: 22.78%
Return on equity: (-2.50%)
Cash ($ mil.): 2,233
Current ratio: 1.32
Long-term debt ($ mil.): 9,819

No. of shares (mil.): 764
Dividends
Yield: 0.0%
Payout: —
Market value ($ mil.): 54,437

	STOCK PRICE ($) FY Close	P/E High/Low		PER SHARE ($) Earnings	Dividends	Book Value
12/16	71.23	—	—	(0.75)	3.02	28.13
12/15	67.61	—	—	(10.23)	2.97	31.89
12/14	80.61	133	93	0.79	2.88	39.26
12/13	95.10	14	10	7.32	2.56	48.46
12/12	76.61	19	13	5.67	2.16	49.68
Annual Growth	(1.8%)	—	—	—	8.7%	(13.3%)

OceanFirst Financial Corp

Ask the folks at OceanFirst Bank for a home loan and they might say "shore." The subsidiary of holding company OceanFirst Financial operates 25 branches in the coastal New Jersey counties of Middlesex Monmouth and Ocean. The community-oriented bank caters to individuals and small to midsized businesses in the Jersey Shore area offering standard products such as checking and savings accounts CDs and IRAs. It uses funds from deposits mainly to invest in mortgages loans and securities. One- to four-family residential mortgages make up more than half of OceanFirst Financial's loan portfolio which also includes commercial real estate (about 30%) business construction and consumer loans.

Operations

The Bank's principal business is attracting deposits from the general public in the communities surrounding its branch offices and investing those deposits primarily in single-family owner-occupied residential mortgage loans and commercial real estate loans. It active subsidiaries include Ocean-First Services LLC OceanFirst REIT Holdings Inc. and 975 Holdings LLC.

Geographic Reach

OceanFirst has operations in the New Jersey counties of Middlesex Monmouth and Ocean.

Financial Performance

OceanFirst's revenues dropped by 4% in 2012 due to decrease in loans and mortgage-backed securities partially offset by higher revenues from investment securities and other.

Net income declined by 3% in 2012 due to an increase in provision for loan losses and non-interest expenses (higher professional fees).

Strategy

OceanFirst seeks to grow commercial loans receivable by offering commercial lending services to local businesses; grow core deposits through broader product offerings andbranch expansion; and increase non-interest income by expanding its fee-based products and services.

Part of the company's strategy for growth includes expanding its fee-based offerings. The bank for example offers trust and asset management services. Company subsidiary OceanFirst Services sells mutual funds annuities and insurance products from third-party vendors. OceanFirst is also seeking opportunities to grow by opening new branch locations within its existing markets.

In 2013 the Bank opened a full service Financial Solutions Center in Red Bank New Jersey offering deposit lending and asset management services. It also opened an additional branch office in Jackson New Jersey.

Since 1995 OceanFirst has opened sixteen branch offices (twelve in Ocean County and four in Monmouth County).

Mergers and Acquisitions

In January 2016 OceanFirst Financial agreed to buy Cape Bancorp— along with its 22 branches in central and southern New Jersey counties $1.1 billion in loans and $1.3 billion in deposits — for $208.1 million. The deal would grow OceanFirst's total total assets by over 60% and nearly double the size of its branch network.

Company Background

OceanFirst Bank's employee stock option plan owns more than 10% of OceanFirst Financial's shares. The company's charitable foundation OceanFirst Foundation owns 7%.

The Bank was founded as a state-chartered building and loan association in 1902. It converted to a Federal savings and loan association in 1945 and became a Federally-chartered mutual savings bank in 1989.

EXECUTIVES
Senior Vice President, Jill Hewitt
EVP and CFO, Michael J. Fitzpatrick, age 60, $285,577 total compensation
EVP and Chief Administrative Officer, Joseph R. Iantosca, age 55, $284,808 total compensation
EVP and Chief Lending Officer, Joseph J. Lebel, age 53, $284,808 total compensation
First SVP General Counsel and Corporate Secretary, Steven J. Tsimbinos, $252,798 total compensation
Chairman President and CEO, Christopher D. Maher, age 49, $566,346 total compensation
Vice President It, Elizabeth Alexander
Assistant Vice President and Branch Manager, Rosemarie Horvath
Senior Vice President and Chief Sales Officer, Mark Tasy
Assistant Vice President and Branch Manager, Stefanie Nolan
Assistant Vice President oceanfirst Bank, Lynn Wingender
Assistant Vice President, Catherine Farley
Assistant Vice President OceanFirst Bank, Loretta Petrocco
Senior Vice President Credit Administration, Carol E Strang
Assistant Vice President OceanFirst Bank, Karen Rack
Assistant Vice President oceanfirst Bank, Andrew Martin
Assistant Vice President and Business Development Officer, Frank Scarpone
Vice President, Christine Schiess
Senior Vice President and Director of Commercial Lending, Steven Pellegrinelli
Senior Vice President and Senior Relationship Manager of OceanFirst Bank, George Destafney
Vice President, Sean Kauffman
Assistant Vice President Commercial Lending Officer, Natalie Markevich
Senior Vice President, Brad Fouss
AVP Project Manager, David Mowder
Senior Vice President Senior Operations Officer, Anthony Giordano
Assistant Vice President Collections Department, Karen Farrell
Assistant Secretary OceanFirst Bank, Laurel Fluet
Auditors: KPMG LLP

LOCATIONS
HQ: OceanFirst Financial Corp
975 Hooper Avenue, Toms River, NJ 08753
Phone: 732 240-4500
Web: www.oceanfirst.com

PRODUCTS/OPERATIONS

2016 sales

	% of total
Interest Income	
Loans	80
Mortgage-backed securities	4
Investment securities & other	2
Non-interest	
Bankcard services revenue	3
Wealth management revenue	2
Fees & service charges	7
Loan Servicing income	—
Net gains on sales of loans	1
Net loss from other real estate operations	—
Income from Bank owned Life Insurance	1
Other	—
Total	**100**

COMPETITORS

Bank of America	PNC Financial
Cape Bancorp	Sovereign Bank
Citibank	TD Bank USA
Hudson City Bancorp	Valley National
Investors Bancorp	Bancorp
JPMorgan Chase	

HISTORICAL FINANCIALS
Company Type: Public

Income Statement
FYE: December 31

	ASSETS ($ mil.)	NET INCOME ($ mil.)	INCOME AS % OF ASSETS	EMPLOYEES
12/16	5,167	23	0.4%	797
12/15	2,593	20	0.8%	393
12/14	2,356	19	0.8%	376
12/13	2,249	16	0.7%	409
12/12	2,269	20	0.9%	401
Annual Growth	22.8%	3.6%	—	18.7%

2016 Year-End Financials
Debt ratio: 1.09%
Return on equity: 5.67%
Cash ($ mil.): 301
Current ratio: —
Long-term debt ($ mil.): —

No. of shares (mil.): 32
Dividends
Yield: 0.0%
Payout: 55.1%
Market value ($ mil.): 965

	STOCK PRICE ($) FY Close	P/E High/Low	PER SHARE ($) Earnings	Dividends	Book Value
12/16	30.03	30 16	0.98	0.54	17.80
12/15	20.03	17 13	1.21	0.52	13.79
12/14	17.14	16 13	1.19	0.49	12.91
12/13	17.13	19 14	0.95	0.48	12.33
12/12	13.75	13 11	1.12	0.48	12.28
Annual Growth	21.6%	— —	(3.3%)	3.0%	9.7%

Office Depot, Inc.

Paper and paper clips add up to big money for Office Depot. The world's #2 office supply chain (behind Staples) Office Depot sells office supplies through some 1400 retail stores. The big-box retail stores sell to both consumers and small and medium-sized businesses. In addition to general office supplies its stores offer computer hardware and software furniture art and school supplies and printing and copying services. Office Depot also sells goods through catalogs and call centers the Internet and a contract sales force. Faced with declining organic sales in 2015 the company agreed to be bought by Staples but the merger was called off in 2016.

HISTORY

Pat Scher Stephen Dougherty and Jack Kopkin opened the first Office Depot one of the first office supply superstores in Lauderdale Lakes Florida in 1986. Scher was selected as chairman. By the end of the year the fledgling company had opened two more stores (both in Florida).

Office Depot opened seven more stores in 1987. When Scher died of leukemia that year the company recruited David Fuente former president of Sherwin-Williams' Paint Store Division as chairman and CEO. Office Depot continued its breakneck expansion under Fuente. In 1988 — the year the company went public — it opened 16 stores and broke into new markets in four states.

The chain stepped up its pace and by 1990 it had expanded into several other areas including the South and Midwest. Office Depot also added computers and peripherals and opened its first delivery center.

In 1991 the company became North America's #1 office products retailer and expanded its presence in the West through the acquisition of Office Club another warehouse-type office supply chain with 59 stores (most in California). Fuente remained chairman and CEO while former Office Club CEO Mark Begelman became president and COO. (Begelman who left in 1995 and eventually formed the MARS music chain had founded the first Office Club in 1987 in Concord California; he took it public in 1989.)

The company entered the international market with its 1992 purchase of Canada's H. Q. Office International and through licensing agreements in 1993 (in Colombia and Israel). Office Depot created its business services division by acquiring various contract stationers including Eastman Office Products (the West Coast's #1 contract office supplier) in the mid-1990s and added locations in Mexico and Poland; it established a joint venture in France with retailer Carrefour in 1996.

Also in 1996 Office Depot announced a $3.4 billion agreement to be acquired by Staples which would have created a company with more than 1100 stores. However the government blocked the purchase on antitrust grounds in 1997 and the agreement dissolved. Unfettered by merger distractions Office Depot resumed opening stores at a rapid pace including two in Thailand and took its catalog and delivery services online. It then established a joint venture with Japanese retailer Deo Deo.

In 1998 Office Depot acquired Viking Office Products in a $2.7 billion deal. With more than 60% of its sales coming from outside the US Viking augmented Office Depot's already strong delivery network and international expansion. Office Depot acquired the remaining 50% of its French operations from Carrefour in 1998 and the remaining 50% of its Japanese operations from Deo Deo in 1999.

Office Depot started putting Internet kiosks in its US stores in 2000 allowing customers to browse and shop company Web sites. In July 2000 Bruce Nelson CEO of Viking replaced Fuente as CEO of Office Depot. Citing weak computer sales and high warehouse prices the company closed about 70 stores and cut its workforce. In early 2002 Nelson was named chairman as well as CEO after Fuente stepped down.

Office Depot sold its Australian operations to Officeworks a unit of Coles Myer in January 2003. Office Depot used the proceeds to expand its faster-growing European operations. Also that year the company acquired the retail operations of French office supplier Guilbert from Pinault-Printemps-Redoute a move that doubled the company's business in Europe. (Staples had acquired Guilbert's mail-order business the previous year.)

In 2004 the company acquired about 125 retail locations from troubled toy seller Toys "R" Us converting 50 of those into Office Depot locations and selling off the remainder.

Nelson left the company and Neil Austrian served as interim head. Office Depot named AutoZone leader Steve Odland as CEO and chairman in 2005. That year the company shuttered its Viking Office Products brand in the US consolidating its catalog sales under the Office Depot banner. (It still markets products through Viking in international markets.) The business services division also sells technology products through Tech Depot (formerly 4SURE.com).

The company acquired privately held Allied Office Products (AOP) the largest independent dealer of office products and services in the US in 2006. AOP became part of Office Depot's North American Business Solutions Division.

Office Depot opened 70 new stores in 2007 (vs. 115 the previous year).

In mid-2008 the company acquired 13 stores in Sweden through the acquisition of AGE Kontor & Data AB a contract and retail office supply company operating there.

In 2009 the company closed about 125 stores in North America and exited the Japanese market.

CEO Steve Odland resigned in November 2010. In late 2010 Israeli department store operator New Hamashbir Lazarchan acquired Office Depot's operations in Israel for $50 million. New Hamashbir Lazarchan also agreed to pay royalties on revenues generated by Office Depot Israel which has about 45 stores.

Office Depot appointed new leadership in mid-2011 naming interim leader Neil Austrian as the company's permanent replacement for chief executive and chairman. Austrian has served as a director at Office Depot since 1998. He stepped in to lead the office products retailer on a temporary basis following the resignation of Steve Odland in late 2010. Odland's resignation came soon after Office Depot settled Securities and Exchange Commission charges that the company selectively informed analysts and institutional investors that its earnings would fall short of estimates. Office Depot agreed to pay $1 million while Odland and the firm's former CFO agreed to pay $50000.

EXECUTIVES

EVP and CFO, Joseph T. (Joe) Lower, age 50
EVP Chief Legal Officer and Corporate Secretary, N. David Bleisch, age 58
EVP and Chief Marketing Officer, Jerri L. DeVard, age 57
CEO and Director, Gerry P. Smith, age 54
EVP Chief Legal Officer Corporate Secretary and President Business Solutions Division, Steve Calkins, age 46
EVP and Chief Administrative Officer, Michael Allison, age 59, $539,423 total compensation
EVP Transformation and Strategic Sourcing, John W. Gannfors
SVP eCommerce, Kevin Moffitt
SVP Retail Division, Marko Ibrahim
Vice President Enterprise Account Management, Steve Dvorchak
Vice President Transformation Delivery, Sharon McGregor
Vice President, Alex Jaime
Executive Vice President and President International, Steven Schmidt
Vice President eCommerce, Natalie Malaszenko
Chairman, Joseph S. (Joe) Vassalluzzo, age 69
Auditors: Deloitte & Touche LLP

LOCATIONS

HQ: Office Depot, Inc.
 6600 North Military Trail, Boca Raton, FL 33496
Phone: 561 438-4800   **Fax:** 561 265-4406
Web: www.officedepot.com

PRODUCTS/OPERATIONS

2016 Sales

	$ mil.	% of total
North American Retail	5,603	51
North American Business Solutions	5,400	49
Other	18	
Total	**11,021**	**100**

COMPETITORS

Amazon.com	Lyreco
Apple Inc.	RadioShack
BJ's Wholesale Club	Ricoh USA
Best Buy	School Specialty
CDW	Staples
Costco Wholesale	Systemax
Essendant	Target Corporation
FedEx Office	The UPS Store
Fry's Electronics	Wal-Mart
Insight Enterprises	

HISTORICAL FINANCIALS

Company Type: Public

Income Statement   FYE: December 31

	REVENUE ($ mil.)	NET INCOME ($ mil.)	NET PROFIT MARGIN	EMPLOYEES
12/16	11,021	529	4.8%	38,000
12/15	14,485	8	0.1%	49,000
12/14	16,096	(354)	—	56,000
12/13	11,242	(20)	—	64,000
12/12	10,695	(77)	—	38,000
Annual **Growth**	0.8%	—	—	0.0%

Debt ratio: 6.99%
Return on equity: 30.13%
Cash ($ mil.): 763
Current ratio: 1.46
Long-term debt ($ mil.): 358

No. of shares (mil.): 515
Dividends
Yield: 0.0%
Payout: 5.2%
Market value ($ mil.): 2,328

	STOCK PRICE ($) FY Close	P/E High/Low		PER SHARE ($) Earnings	Dividends	Book Value
12/16	4.52	8	3	0.96	0.05	3.60
12/15	5.60	968	533	0.01	0.00	2.92
12/14	8.84	—	—	(0.66)	0.00	2.97
12/13	5.19	—	—	(0.29)	0.00	3.89
12/12	3.27	—	—	(0.39)	0.00	3.67
Annual Growth	8.4%	—	—	—	—	(0.5%)

Old Line Bancshares Inc

Old Line Bancshares is the holding company for Old Line Bank serving consumers businesses and wealthy individuals in the Old Line State and in the Washington DC area. With some 20 branch offices and total assets in excess of $1.2 billion the bank offers standard retail products including deposit accounts CDs and credit cards. Commercial and industrial and commercial real estate loans make up 75% of the bank's loan portfolio though it also offers consumer loans and luxury boat financing. The company also owns 50% of real estate firm Pointer Ridge Office Investment.

Operations

About 81% of its revenue came from interest income on loans in 2014 while another 7% came from interest on securities (including mortgage-backed US government agency and municipal securities). About 4% of revenue was generated from service charges on deposit accounts 4% came from fees and commissions and 2% came from gains on the sales of its loans.

Geographic Reach

Old Line Bank more than 20 branches mostly in suburban Maryland (which includes Washington DC and suburbs and Southern Maryland) in the counties of Anne Arundel Calvert Charles Prince George's and St. Mary's.

Financial Performance

Old Line Bancshares' revenues and profits have been trending higher over the past several years mostly driven by strong loan business growth obtained through acquisitions and organically.The bank's revenue dipped by 3% to $51.6 million in 2014 despite loan growth during the year mostly as its non-interest income shrank due to a decline in gains from the sale of its loans and investment securities compared to the prior year.

Lower revenue and higher loan loss provisions from a less credit-worth loan portfolio in 2014 caused Old Line's net income to fall by 8% to $7.1 million. The company's operating cash levels declined by 35% to $10.2 million on lower cash earnings.

Strategy

Old Line Bancshares in 2015 laid out its short-term plans to collect on its non-accrual and past due loans and strategically selling its acquired loans and real-estate owned loans to boost its credit quality. It also expressed its strategy of extending its core banking services growing its fee income (especially in the low-interest environment)

and embracing digital banking technologies such as online and mobile banking to reduce its spending on costly branch expansion plans.

Management also touted success in organically growing its loan and deposit business in Montgomery Prince George's Anne Arundel counties in Maryland during 2014.

The company sometimes grows its loan business and branch network by strategically acquiring banks in its primary markets. Its agreement to acquire Regal Bancorp for example would add three new banking locations to its network and $133.7 million in assets to its books — which would make it the third-largest commercial bank in Maryland by assets and the second-largest by branch network.

Mergers and Acquisitions

In August 2015 the company agreed to acquire Regal Bancorp including its Regal Bank & Trust subsidiary its three branches and assets of $133.7 million. The deal was expected to close in late 2015 or early 2016.

In May 2013 Old Line Bancshare closed on its $54.7-million purchase of WSB Holdings adding five Washington Savings Bank FSB branches and $310 million in assets.

Previously Old Line acquired Maryland Bankcorp in 2011 in a move that doubled its branch network and asset portfolio.

EXECUTIVES

Senior Vice President Old Line Bank, William Bush
Senior Vice President, David Seyler
Senior Vice President, Kevin Frere
Executive Vice President and Chief Operating Officer, Mark Semanie
Vice President, Erik W Fridley
Assistant Vice President, Salisha Khan
Vice President, Rob Bowling
Senior Vice President Information Technology, Jim Thompson
Senior Vice President Chief Risk Officer, Dannette VanCleaf
Vice President Special Assets Manager, Sammy Pulliam
Assistant Vice President Director of Information Technology, Gregory Caroots
Auditors: Dixon Hughes Goodman LLP

LOCATIONS

HQ: Old Line Bancshares Inc
1525 Pointer Ridge Place, Bowie, MD 20716
Phone: 301 430-2500
Web: www.oldlinebank.com

COMPETITORS

BB&T
Bank of America
M&T Bank

PNC Financial
Tri-County Financial

HISTORICAL FINANCIALS

Company Type: Public

Income Statement

FYE: December 31

	ASSETS ($ mil.)	NET INCOME ($ mil.)	INCOME AS % OF ASSETS	EMPLOYEES
12/16	1,709	13	0.8%	234
12/15	1,510	10	0.7%	248
12/14	1,227	7	0.6%	228
12/13	1,167	7	0.7%	254
12/12	861	7	0.9%	182
Annual Growth	18.7%	15.0%	—	6.5%

Debt ratio: 2.21%
Return on equity: 8.91%
Cash ($ mil.): 23
Current ratio: —
Long-term debt ($ mil.): —

No. of shares (mil.): 10
Dividends
Yield: 0.0%
Payout: 20.0%
Market value ($ mil.): 262

	STOCK PRICE ($) FY Close	P/E High/Low		PER SHARE ($) Earnings	Dividends	Book Value
12/16	23.98	21	14	1.20	0.24	13.81
12/15	17.57	19	15	0.97	0.21	13.31
12/14	15.82	27	21	0.65	0.18	12.51
12/13	14.50	17	13	0.86	0.16	11.71
12/12	11.29	11	7	1.09	0.16	10.94
Annual Growth	20.7%	—	—	2.4%	10.7%	6.0%

Old National Bancorp (Evansville, IN)

Old National Bank is old but it's not quite national. Founded in 1834 the main subsidiary of Old National Bancorp operates about 200 bank centers across Indiana Kentucky Michigan and Illinois. The bank serves consumers and business customers offering standard checking and savings accounts credit cards and loans. Its treasury segment manages investments for bank and commercial clients. Business loans commercial and residential mortgages and consumer loans account for most of Old National's lending activity. The company also sells insurance manages wealth for high-net-worth clients and offers investment and retirement services through third-party provider LPL Financial.

Operations

Old National Bancorp operates two main segments: Banking which generates the bulk of Old National's revenue and provides traditional loan and deposit products as well as wealth management services; and Insurance which provides commercial property and casualty surety loss control services employee benefits consulting and administration as well as personal insurance.

The bank generated 51% of its revenue from loan interest (including fees) in 2014 while another 14% came from interest on investment securities. Insurance premiums and commissions contributed 7% to the company's total revenues that year while wealth management fees made up another 5%.

Geographic Reach

The bank's nearly 200 banking centers are located across four Midwestern states and Kentucky. Most are in the central northern and southern parts of Indiana; while others are in central Illinois; Western Kentucky and Louisville; Grand Rapids Southeastern and Southwestern Michigan; and Ohio.

Sales and Marketing

Old National has identified metropolitan areas within its market including Indianapolis; Louisville Kentucky; and Lafayette Indiana for growth within its core community banking segment.

The company spent $9.59 million on marketing in 2014 up from $7.21 million and $7.45 million in 2013 and 2012 respectively.

Financial Performance

Old National Bancorp's revenues and profits have been on the uptrend for the past several years thanks to new loan business from a series of bank acquisitions and declining loan loss provisions as its loan portfolio's credit quality has improved with the strengthened economy.

The company's revenue rose by 5% to $554.86 million in 2014 mostly thanks to new loan business stemming from the bank's acquisitions of Tower Financial United Bancorp and LSB Financial during the year along with organic loan growth. Higher revenue in 2014 coupled with strong cost controls lower interest on deposits and a continued decline in loan loss provisions drove Old National's net income higher by 3% to $103.62 million for the year.

Old National's operating cash fell by 21% to $199.72 million after adjusting its earnings for non-cash items related to its net sales proceeds from the sale of its residential real estate loans held-for-sale.

Strategy

Old National continues to seek out additional branch and whole bank acquisitions to grow its loan business and expand its geographic reach. Its acquisition of United Bancorp in mid-2014 for example added nearly $1 billion in new loan business and $869 million in wealth management assets under management while doubling Old National's presence in Michigan to 36 total branches.

The company is also pursuing growth by increasing its focus on commercial banking and cross-selling its insurance and wealth management offerings. To this end Old National in 2014 bought the insurance accounts (consisting of mostly commercial property/casualty accounts) serviced by the Evansville branch office of Wells Fargo Insurance.

Meanwhile it is also selectively exiting markets that haven't been profitable. In early 2015 as part of its ongoing efficiency improvement efforts the bank announced that it would sell 17 of its banking centers including all twelve of its branches in Southern Illinois and close or consolidate another 19 branches in other states over the following months.

Mergers and Acquisitions

In December 2014 Old National agreed to acquire Founders Financial Corporation along with its Founders Bank & Trust subsidiary in Grand Rapids Michigan for $91.7 million which would add nearly $460 million in total assets and four branches in Kent County.

In November 2014 the company purchased LSB Financial and its Lafayette Savings Bank subsidiary for $51.8 million adding five branches near Lafayette Indiana.

In July 2014 the company acquired Ann Arbor-based United Bancorp along with United Bank & Trust for a total of $122 million adding 18 branches in Michigan nearly $919 million in total assets a $963 million loan servicing portfolio and $688 million in trust assets under management.

In April 2014 Old National purchased Indiana-based Tower Financial along with its Tower Bank & Trust subsidiary adding seven new branches and some $556 million in trust assets under management.

In 2013 the bank bolstered its presence in Michigan after acquiring two dozen Bank of America branches in northern Indiana and southwest Michigan. The previous year the bank purchased Indiana Community Bancorp which added 17 branches in the southeastern part of the state. The transaction was valued at nearly $80 million.

EXECUTIVES

Chairman President and CEO, Robert G. (Bob) Jones, age 60, $668,269 total compensation
SVP and Corporate Secretary, Jeffrey L. (Jeff) Knight, age 57, $321,051 total compensation

EVP and Chief Credit Officer, Daryl D. Moore, age 59, $305,040 total compensation
CEO North Central Region, Mark D. Bradford, age 59
EVP and Chief Client Services Officer, Annette W. Hudgions, age 59, $250,016 total compensation
President and CEO Wealth Management, Caroline J. Ellspermann, age 49
CEO Eastern Region, Dennis P. Heishman
SEVP and CFO, Christopher A. (Chris) Wolking, age 57, $364,730 total compensation
EVP and Chief Community Relations and Social Responsibility Officer, Kathy A. Schoettlin
Region CEO Old National Bank, Randall (Randy) Reichmann
CEO Central and Western Michigan Region, Todd C. Clark, age 47
EVP and Chief Risk Officer, Candice J. Rickard, age 53
EVP and Chief Banking Officer, James Sandgren, $357,673 total compensation
CEO Central Region, Dan L. Doan
EVP and Director Corporate Strategy, James C. Ryan, age 45
EVP and CIO, John R. Kamin
EVP Associate Engagement and Integrations, Kendra L. Vanzo
EVP Chief Auditing Executive and Chief Ethics Officer, Richard W. (Dick) Dub ©
President ONB Investment Services, Kenneth J. Ellspermann
President Old National Insurance, Scott J. Evernham
CEO Southern Region, Sara L. Miller
President and COO, Jim Sandgren
President North Central Region, Scott Shishman
Vice President Technology Services Manager, Janet Wandling
Executive Vice President And Group Executive North American Information Services, John Clayton
Assistant Vice President, Sherry Beck
Vice President, Brian Henning
Assistant Vice President Product Manager, Tim Hadley
Vice President Associate Counsel, Tom Washburne
Vice President Treasury Operations Manager Controller Old National Bancorp, Doug Schuba
Vice President and Manager Benefits, Bart Emig
Senior Vice President, Mark Gorski
Senior Vice President of Marketing, Scott Adams
Assistant Vice President Director of Procurement, Mark Preske
Assistant Vice President, Sandy Keen
Executive Vice President Chief Marketing Officer, Julie A Williams Daugherty
Vice President, Amanda Castaneda
Vice President Finance, Alan ORear
Vice President Sarbanes Oxley Analyst, Denise Rexing
Vice President, Randy Lilly
Assistant Vice President, Jenny Clark
Assistant Vice President Mortgage Loan Officer, Debra Fulkerson
Vice President, Rob Snyder
Vice President Business Banking, Glen Jacobs
Vice President of Customer Service, Clay Sills-Memorial
Vice President, Kim Bouch
Vice President, Roger Ferguson
Private Banker II Vice President, Tony Patrick
Assistant Vice President Commercial Lender, Mike Devoy
Vice President and Banking Center Manager, Helen Habib
Assistant Vice President Branch Manager, Geoff Thompson
Senior Vice President Treasurer, Jennifer Guzman
Retail Center Manager Vice President, Stacy Fuqua

Vice President Commercial Relationship Manager, Sarah Strimmenos
Vice President Commercial Banking, Shawn Brumfield
Assistant Vice President, Todd Treadway
Vice President Corporate Banking, James Tutt
Vice President of Community Banking and Office V, Tammy Hall
Assistant Vice President Corporate Benefits Director, James Schmidt
Senior Vice President, Lynell Walton
Senior Vice President Community Engagement Executive, Jamie Guise
Vice President, Jaron Hargis
Assistant Vice President and Retail Center Manager, Sheila Alexander
Vice President Mortgage Lending, Joel Epstein
Senior Human Resources Analyst Assistant Vice President, Sharon Wilson
Senior Vice President, Dan Carwile
Retail Center Manager Vice President, Cathy Stidham
Community Relations Manager AVP, Kortney Blaylock
Vice President, Rob Henson
Senior Vice President, Tommy Elliott
Vice President, Robert Ogburn
Vice President Corporate Banking, Michael McCulloch
Vice President, Rob Triplett
1st Vice President, Karl Sachtjen
Small Business Banker Vice President, Diana Brown
Vice President Cash Management, Andrea Solis
Commercial Relationship Manager Vice President, Heather Foster
Retail Center Manager AVP, Martel Vanlandingham
Vice President, Regina Levchets
Vice President, Roland Shelton
Senior Vice President, Marty Richardson
Senior Corporate Lender Vice President, Matt Merkel
Auditors: Crowe Horwath LLP

LOCATIONS

HQ: Old National Bancorp (Evansville, IN)
One Main Street, Evansville, IN 47708
Phone: 812 464-1294
Web: www.oldnational.com

PRODUCTS/OPERATIONS

2014 Sales

	$ mil.	% of total
Interest		
Loans including fees	306	51
Investment securities	83	14
Noninterest		
Service charges on deposit accounts	47	8
Insurance premiums & commissions	41	7
Wealth management fees	28	5
ATM Fees	25	4
Investment product fees	17	3
Mortgage banking revenue	6	1
Other	41	7
Adjustments	(43.3)	-
Total	**554**	**100**

COMPETITORS

Fifth Third	JPMorgan Chase
First Financial (IN)	MainSource Financial
German American Bancorp	PNC Financial
	Peoples Bancorp (IN)
Huntington Bancshares	U.S. Bancorp

HISTORICAL FINANCIALS

Company Type: Public

Income Statement

FYE: December 31

	ASSETS ($ mil.)	NET INCOME ($ mil.)	INCOME AS % OF ASSETS	EMPLOYEES
12/16	14,860	134	0.9%	2,733
12/15	11,991	116	1.0%	2,652
12/14	11,647	103	0.9%	2,938
12/13	9,581	100	1.1%	2,608
12/12	9,543	91	1.0%	2,684
Annual Growth	11.7%	10.0%	—	0.5%

2016 Year-End Financials

Debt ratio: 1.47%
Return on equity: 8.10%
Cash ($ mil.): 255
Current ratio: —
Long-term debt ($ mil.): —

No. of shares (mil.): 135
Dividends
Yield: 0.0%
Payout: 49.5%
Market value ($ mil.): 2,453

	STOCK PRICE ($) FY Close	P/E High/Low	Earnings	PER SHARE ($) Dividends	Book Value
12/16	18.15	17 10	1.05	0.52	13.42
12/15	13.56	15 13	1.00	0.48	13.05
12/14	14.88	16 13	0.95	0.44	12.54
12/13	15.37	16 12	1.00	0.40	11.64
12/12	11.87	15 11	0.95	0.36	11.81
Annual Growth	11.2%	—	2.5%	9.6%	3.3%

Old Republic International Corp.

Old Republic International keeps pace with changing financial times. With more than 100 subsidiaries across North America Old Republic International's primary operations are conducted through the Old Republic General Insurance division which offers commercial liability and property/casualty insurance (mostly commercial trucking workers' compensation and general liability policies). In addition the company's Title Insurance group specializes in naturally issuing title insurance to property owners and lenders. Its Old Republic National Title subsidiary is one of the US's oldest and largest title insurance companies with offices throughout the US.

Operations

Old Republic's subsidiaries market underwrite and offer risk management services for insurance products including general and title coverage. Commercial property/casualty policies issued by the general insurance segment account for more than half of the company's sales. Meanwhile the title insurance segment accounts for nearly 40% of revenues and the company's Republic Financial Indemnity Group (RFIG comprising mortgage guaranty and consumer credit indemnity runoff operations) brings in about 5% of sales. The company also maintains a small life and health insurance business.

More than 70% of the company's consolidated title premium and fee income comes from independent title agents and underwritten title companies. The rest stem from direct operations including branches of its title insurance businesses and wholly owned agency and service subsidiaries.

Geographic Reach

Through its subsidiaries Old Republic is licensed to do business throughout the US Puerto Rico the US Virgin Islands Guam and in all Canadian provinces.

Sales and Marketing

While Old Republic does sell some of its property/casualty and specialty products directly it relies on independent agencies brokers and financial institutions to distribute the majority. The company focuses on certain sectors especially transportation commercial construction health care education forest products energy manufacturing retail and wholesale trade and financial services.

Title insurance and related settlement products are sold through some 270 company offices and through agencies and underwritten title companies throughout the US.

Financial Performance

Old Republic's revenues have been steadily rising over the past five years. In 2016 revenue increased 2% to $5.9 billion as net premiums earned and fee income went up. General insurance title insurance and even run-off operations of RFIG all had higher revenue. That helped boost net income which rose 11% to $466.9 million.

Despite the increase in profits cash flow from operations fell 7% to $637.3 million that year. That was largely due to negative adjustments to unpaid claims and related items and premiums and other receivables.

Revenue roller coasters and net income fluctuations don't bother Old Republic as its public filings clearly state that it looks at its business in five-to-10-year intervals and therefore isn't concerned by the ups and downs in shorter cycles. The health of its general insurance business and the fact that it carries very little debt make it easier to take that view.

Strategy

In response to financial strains during the Great Recession Old Republic has chosen to focus on its general and title insurance operations while placing its RFIG mortgage guaranty and consumer credit indemnity operations in run-off. The firm targets long-term returns on its underwriting operations. As such it spreads its risk over diversified businesses and assets to reduce liability exposures.

However Old Republic has been disappointed by its results which it attributes to such factors as low interest rates and an increase in competitors entering the market. To counteract these factors it plans to carefully explore the markets in which it operates with the intent to diminish its focus on saturated geographies. It also aims to alter and to a certain degree expand its distribution channels. To improve underwriting activities Old Republic will also remediate where it is needed most avoiding riskier contracts that are unlikely to deliver strong returns

EXECUTIVES

Chairman President and CEO, Aldo C. (Al) Zucaro, age 78, $895,000 total compensation

President and COO, R. Scott Rager, age 68, $510,000 total compensation

SVP Title Insurance; President Old Republic National Title Insurance, Rande K. Yeager, age 68, $510,000 total compensation

SVP and CFO, Karl W. Mueller, age 57, $465,000 total compensation

President and COO Old Republic General Insurance Group Inc. (ORGIG), Craig R. Smiddy, age 53, $485,000 total compensation

Vice President Director Financial Reporting, Stephanie Richards

Assistant vice president And Director MIS, Jim Arends

SVP GENERAL INSURANCE PRESIDENT OLD REPUBLIC IN, James Kellogg

VICE PRESIDENT, Mandi Zollotuchen
ASSISTANT VICE PRESIDENT COMMERCIAL COUNSEL, Avi A Marcus
Vice President, Linda Johnson
Auditors: KPMG LLP

LOCATIONS

HQ: Old Republic International Corp.
307 North Michigan Avenue, Chicago, IL 60601
Phone: 312 346-8100
Web: www.oldrepublic.com

PRODUCTS/OPERATIONS

2016 Sales

	$ mil.	% of total
General insurance	3,354	57
Title insurance	2,244	38
Runoff (RFIG)	193	3
Consolidated realized investment gains	72	1
Other	35	1
Total	**5,900**	**100**

COMPETITORS

AIG	Investors Title
AXA	Kingsway
Allianz	Progressive
Berkshire Hathaway	Corporation
CNA Financial	Stewart Information
Chubb Limited	Services
Farmers Group	The Hartford
Fidelity National	Travelers Companies
Financial	Unum Group
First American	W. R. Berkley
ING	

HISTORICAL FINANCIALS

Company Type: Public

Income Statement

FYE: December 31

	ASSETS ($ mil.)	NET INCOME ($ mil.)	INCOME AS % OF ASSETS	EMPLOYEES
12/16	18,591	466	2.5%	8,500
12/15	17,110	422	2.5%	8,200
12/14	16,988	409	2.4%	8,000
12/13	16,534	447	2.7%	7,900
12/12	16,226	(68)	—	7,800
Annual Growth	3.5%	—	—	2.2%

2016 Year-End Financials

Debt ratio: 8.22%
Return on equity: 11.15%
Cash ($ mil.): 145
Current ratio: —
Long-term debt ($ mil.): —

No. of shares (mil.): 262
Dividends
Yield: 0.0%
Payout: 46.3%
Market value ($ mil.): 4,992

	STOCK PRICE ($) FY Close	P/E High/Low	Earnings	PER SHARE ($) Dividends	Book Value
12/16	19.00	11 9	1.62	0.75	17.02
12/15	18.63	12 9	1.48	0.74	14.81
12/14	14.63	11 9	1.44	0.73	15.04
12/13	17.27	10 6	1.74	0.72	14.49
12/12	10.65	—	(0.27)	0.71	13.86
Annual Growth	15.6%	—	—	1.4%	5.3%

Old Second Bancorp., Inc. (Aurora, Ill.)

Old Second won't settle for a silver finish when it comes to community banking around Chicago. Old Second Bancorp is the holding company for Old Second National Bank which serves the Chicago metropolitan area through 25 branches in Kane Kendall DeKalb DuPage LaSalle Will and Cook counties. The bank provides standard services such as checking and savings accounts credit and debit cards CDs mortgages loans and trust services to consumers and business clients. Subsidiary River Street Advisors offers investment management and advisory services. Another unit Old Second Affordable Housing Fund provides home-buying assistance to lower-income customers.

Operations

Commercial real estate loans accounted for 53% of Old Second's loan portfolio at the end of 2015 while residential mortgages made up another 31%. The rest was made up of general commercial loans (12% of loan assets) and construction lending (2%).

Roughly 70% of the bank's revenue comes from interest income. About 54% of its revenue came from loan interest (including fees) during 2015 with another 15% coming from interest on investment securities. The remainder of Old Second's revenue came from deposit account service charges (7%) trust income (6%) mortgage loan sale gains (6%) secondary mortgage fees (1%) and other sources.

Geographic Reach

The bank mostly serves customers in Aurora Illinois (which is 40 miles west of Chicago) and surrounding communities. Its 24 branches are located in the Kane Kendall DeKalb DuPage LaSalle Will and Cook counties of Illinois.

Sales and Marketing

Old Second has been ramping up its advertising spend in recent years. It spent $1.34 million on advertising in 2015 up from $1.28 million and $1.23 million in 2014 and 2013 respectively.

Financial Performance

Old Second's annual revenues have fallen 20% since 2011 as it's had to sell of many of its non-performing loan assets to de-risk its loan portfolio. The company's profits however have been on the mend as its de-risking measures have led to declining loan loss provisions.

The bank's revenue rebounded by less than 1% to $97.46 million during 2015 as its average loans including loans held for sale grew by 2% for the year.

Revenue growth in 2015 combined with lower interest and amortization costs on deposits drove Old Second Bancorp's net income up by over 50% to $15.39 million. The bank's operating cash levels jumped sharply to $21.14 million (operations had used $6.3 million in 2014) partially thanks to earnings growth but mostly thanks to positive working capital changes related to sales proceeds from loans held for sale and changes in accrued interest payable and other liabilities.

Strategy

Old Second Bancorp continued in 2016 to focus on shedding riskier loan assets that led to deep losses in 2011 while focusing on securing high-quality loans with more creditworthiness. Its efforts began to pay off in 2015 as its average loan balances and revenues began to grow again after years of being in decline.

EXECUTIVES

EVP CFO and Director, J. Douglas Cheatham, age 61, $252,000 total compensation
CEO and Director Old Second Bancorp Inc. and Old Second National Bank, James L. Eccher, age 52, $325,000 total compensation
Senior Vice President Commercial Banking, Jeff Downs
Senior Vice President and Treasurer, Stan Faries
Executive Vice President Human Resources, Robert Dicosola
Senior Vice President, Chris Barry
AVP RESIDENTIAL LENDER, Terri Hanson
Senior Vice President, Keith Gottschalk
Executive Vice President, Joel Binder
Vice President Treasury Management, John Annis
Vice President, Jocelyn Retz
Vice President, Troy Langeness
Vice President, Jeri Ott
Vice President commercial Banking, Kristin Zell
Senior Vice President Business Banking, Roger Schnorr
Senior Vice President Commercial Lending, Mark Fleming
Vice President, Michelle Almond
Assistant Vice President commercial Banking Chief Commercial Officer, Greg Faleskin
Vice President Commercial and Industrial Lending, John Gorzak
First Vice President, Chris Hainey
First Vice President Director of Treasury Management Sales, Juwana Zanayed
Vice President Treasury Management Advisor, Sherry Pass
Senior Vice President, Peter Harrison
Chairman Old Second Bancorp Inc. and Old Second National Bank, William B. Skoglund, age 67
Vice Chairman, Gary S. Collins, age 59
Auditors: Plante & Moran, PLLC

LOCATIONS

HQ: Old Second Bancorp., Inc. (Aurora, Ill.)
37 South River Street, Aurora, IL 60507
Phone: 630 892-0202
Web: www.oldsecond.com

PRODUCTS/OPERATIONS

2015 sales

	% of total
Interest and dividend income	
Loans including fees	54
Taxable	14
Tax exempt	1
Non-interest income	
Service charges on deposits	7
Trust income	6
Net gain on sales of mortgage loans	6
Debit card interchange income	4
Secondary mortgage fees	1
Increase in cash surrender value of bank-owned life insurance	1
Other income	6
Total	**100**

Products/Services
Personal Banking
Card Services
Checking
Loans
Money Services
Online and Mobile Banking
Prime Time Club
Retirement Services
Savings
Loans
Auto and Personal Loans
Home Equity Loans
Home Loans
Mortgage Lenders
Required Documents
SAFE Act
Business Banking
Commercial Banking

Online and Mobile Banking
Small Business Banking
Wealth Management
Business Plan Options
Real Estate Services
Retirement Services

COMPETITORS

Bank of America	Harris
BankFinancial	MB Financial
Fifth Third	Northern Trust
First Midwest Bancorp	West Suburban Bancorp

HISTORICAL FINANCIALS

Company Type: Public

Income Statement

FYE: December 31

	ASSETS ($ mil.)	NET INCOME ($ mil.)	INCOME AS % OF ASSETS	EMPLOYEES
12/16	2,251	15	0.7%	467
12/15	2,077	15	0.7%	450
12/14	2,061	10	0.5%	485
12/13	2,004	82	4.1%	492
12/12	2,045	(0)	—	481
Annual Growth	2.4%	—	—	(0.7%)

2016 Year-End Financials

Debt ratio: 4.51%
Return on equity: 9.45%
Cash ($ mil.): 47
Current ratio: —
Long-term debt ($ mil.): —
No. of shares (mil.): 29
Dividends
　Yield: 0.0%
　Payout: 5.6%
Market value ($ mil.): 327

	STOCK PRICE ($) FY Close	P/E High/Low	PER SHARE ($) Earnings	Dividends	Book Value
12/16	11.05	22 12	0.53	0.03	5.93
12/15	7.84	18 11	0.46	0.00	5.29
12/14	5.37	12 10	0.46	0.00	6.59
12/13	4.62	1 0	5.45	0.00	10.61
12/12	1.22	— —	(0.36)	0.00	5.15
Annual Growth	73.5%	— —	—	—	3.6%

Olin Corp.

The making of bleach and bullets is all in a day's work for Olin Corporation. The company manufactures chemicals used to make bleach water purification and swimming pool chemicals pulp and paper processing agents and PVC plastics. Olin Chlor Alkali Products is one of the top chlor-alkali producers in North America along with OxyChem. Olin also distributes caustic soda vinyls epoxies chlorinated organics hydrochloric acid and bleach. In addition in a quite divergent business the company's Winchester Ammunition unit makes branded sporting ammunition reloading components small caliber military ammunition and components and industrial cartridges. The company more than doubled in size when it completed the reverse acquisition of Dow Chemical's chlor alkali and vinyl chlorine and epoxys business.

HISTORY

Vermont-born engineer Franklin Olin founded Equitable Powder in East Alton Illinois in 1892 to make blasting powder for midwestern coal fields. By 1898 the company called Western Cartridge was also making ammunition for small arms.

When WWI increased demand for military cartridges Western Cartridge built a brass mill. After the war it began making custom brass and other copper alloys for industrial customers. The company bought Winchester Repeating Arms maker of the famous Winchester Model 1876 repeating rifles in 1931. During WWII Western Cartridge developed the US carbine and M-1 rifles.

The various businesses of Western Cartridge merged as Olin Industries in 1944. Franklin then retired handing the company to sons John and Spencer.

Enriched by the war effort Olin Industries grew. In 1949 it began making cellophane and in 1951 it acquired Frost Lumber Industries and Ecusta Paper a maker of cigarette papers. Olin Industries merged with Mathieson Chemical in 1954 to form Olin Mathieson Chemical the fifth-largest US chemical company.

The Mathieson Alkali Works was founded in Saltville Virginia in 1892 to produce alkalis using a process acquired from English chemical firm Neil Mathieson. By 1909 the company began producing liquid chlorine and in 1923 it built one of the earliest plants for producing synthetic ammonia. During WWII Mathieson manufactured chlorine for water purification and alkali chemicals for sanitation. In 1952 Mathieson acquired drugmaker Squibb.

Olin Mathieson continued to diversify in the mid-1950s buying Blockson Chemical (industrial phosphates) and Brown Paper Mill (kraft paper bags and corrugated cardboard containers). Frost Lumber and Brown Paper Mill formed the Forest Products Division later dubbed Olinkraft. In 1956 Olin Mathieson entered the aluminum business via a joint venture — just in time for a drop in aluminum demand.

In the 1960s the company began making urethane chemicals. It also created Olin-American a subsidiary that built houses and spun off Squibb. In 1969 it shortened its name to Olin Corporation and moved to Stamford Connecticut.

The 1970s saw Olin reining in its diverse businesses. It spun off Olinkraft and sold its aluminum operations. During the 1980s Olin sold its sporting-arms business (but kept Winchester ammunition) as well as its paper housing and cellophane units. John Olin died in 1982. The company acquired Rockcor which included Rocket Research Pacific Electro Dynamics and Physics International in 1985.

Olin moved its headquarters to Norwalk Connecticut in 1995 the same year Spencer Olin died. In 1996 as the earnings potential of its ordnance and aerospace operations lagged Olin spun them off as Primex Technologies. It also sold its isocyanate (used in plastics and adhesives) and other cyclical businesses. Olin bought the remaining 50% of its Niachlor chlor alkali joint venture from DuPont in 1997 after considering putting Niachlor up for sale.

Aspiring to become a leading basic-materials company Olin spun off its specialty chemical business in early 1999 under the name Arch Chemicals. Citing regulatory issues Olin cancelled plans in 2000 to form a chlor alkali chemicals joint venture with Occidental's OxyChem subsidiary. Olin acquired Monarch Brass & Copper Corp. for about $49 million in 2001. The next year it bought brass rod maker Chase Industries. Olin closed its copper and copper alloy sheet plant in Indianapolis in 2003.

In 2007 Olin grew its core chemicals business acquiring chlor-alkali producer Pioneer Companies for about $415 million. To help pay for the deal in late 2007 Olin sold its former Metals unit to investment group KPS Capital Partners for almost $400 million. The Metals unit — which had accounted for about two-thirds of sales — made copper and copper alloy sheets clad metal foil and stainless-steel strips.

In 2011 Olin acquired the balance of the SunBelt Chlor Alkali joint venture it did not own from partner PolyOne Corp. for $175 million in cash and assumed debt. It had held a 50% stake in the venture which produces chlorine and caustic soda. The SunBelt chlor alkali plant located within Olin's McIntosh Alabama facility has approximately 350000 tons of membrane technology capacity and generated some $70 million in earnings in 2010.

The company in 2012 acquired Illinois-based KA Steel for $328 million in cash. KA Steel is one of the largest caustic soda distributors in North America and its acquisition increased Olin's capacity to manufacture bleach by about 20% as well as to sell some of its other products such as hydrochloric acid and potassium hydroxide. A result the purchase Olin formed a chemical distribution segment that year.

EXECUTIVES

EVP Synergies and Systems, John L. McIntosh, age 63, $509,000 total compensation

Chairman President and CEO, John E. Fischer, age 62, $836,000 total compensation

VP and CFO, Todd A. Slater, age 54, $518,000 total compensation

EVP; President Epoxy and International, Pat D. Dawson, age 59, $636,000 total compensation

SVP Ammunition, Thomas J. OÂ'Keefe, age 58

EVP; President Chlor Alkali Vinyls and Services, James A. Varilek, age 58, $447,000 total compensation

Vice President Finance and Controller, Randee Sumner

Auditors: KPMG LLP

LOCATIONS

HQ: Olin Corp.
190 Carondelet Plaza, Suite 1530, Clayton, MO 63105
Phone: 314 480-1400
Web: www.olin.com

2016 sales

	$ mil.	% of total
US	3,356	60
Other countries	2,193	40
Total	**5,550**	**100**

PRODUCTS/OPERATIONS

2016 sales

	$ mil.	% of total
Chlor Alkali Products and Vinyls	2,999	54
Epoxy	1,822	33
Winchester	729	13
Total	**5,550**	**100**

Business Segments

Business Segments
Chlor Alkali Products
    Caustic soda
    Chlorine
    Hydrochloric acid
    Sodium hydrochlorite (Industrial and institutional cleaning products)
    Sodium hydrosulfite (bleaching)
Winchester
    Ammunition (shot-shell small-caliber and rimfire)
    Government-owned arsenal operation (maintenance for the US Army)
    Industrial cartridges (eight-gauge loads and powder-actuated tool loads for the construction industry)
Chemical Distribution
    Bleach
    Caustic soda

COMPETITORS

Axiall	Mitsubishi Chemical
Blount International	Occidental Chemical
Brenntag	Orbital ATK
FMC	PPG Industries
Formosa Plastics USA	Remington Arms
Freedom Group	Sumitomo Chemical
Herstal	Univar Inc.
Huntsman Corp	Westlake Chemical

HISTORICAL FINANCIALS

Company Type: Public

Income Statement

FYE: December 31

	REVENUE ($ mil.)	NET INCOME ($ mil.)	NET PROFIT MARGIN	EMPLOYEES
12/16	5,550	(3)	—	6,400
12/15	2,854	(1)	—	6,200
12/14	2,241	105	4.7%	3,900
12/13	2,515	178	7.1%	4,100
12/12	2,184	149	6.8%	4,100
Annual Growth	**26.3%**	**—**	**—**	**11.8%**

2016 Year-End Financials

Debt ratio: 41.28%	No. of shares (mil.): 165
Return on equity: (-0.17%)	Dividends
Cash ($ mil.): 184	Yield: 0.0%
Current ratio: 1.68	Payout: —
Long-term debt ($ mil.): 3,537	Market value ($ mil.): 4,236

	STOCK PRICE ($) FY Close	P/E High/Low		Earnings	PER SHARE ($) Dividends	Book Value
12/16	25.61	—	—	(0.02)	0.80	13.74
12/15	17.26	—	—	(0.01)	0.80	14.65
12/14	22.77	22	16	1.33	0.80	13.09
12/13	28.85	13	10	2.21	0.80	13.87
12/12	21.59	12	10	1.85	0.80	12.45
Annual Growth	**4.4%**	**—**	**—**	**—**	**(0.0%)**	**2.5%**

Omnicom Group, Inc.

It might not be omnipotent but Omnicom Group creates advertising that is omnipresent. The company ranks as the world's #1 corporate media services conglomerate with advertising marketing and public relations operations. It serves global advertising clients through its agency networks BBDO Worldwide DDB Worldwide and TBWA Worldwide while such firms as GSD&M's Idea City Merkley + Partners and Zimmerman Advertising provide services for regional and national clients. Its Diversified Agency Services division including Fleishman-Hillard Integer and Rapp provides public relations and other marketing services.

Geographic Reach

Omnicom has US offices in New York Connecticut and Florida while it has international offices in London Shanghai and Singapore. The group's network of agencies serves some 5000 clients in more than 100 countries. In fiscal 2016 more than 60% of the company's revenue came from the Americas while EMEA (Europe Middle East and Africa) contributed more than 25% and the remaining 11% came from the Asia Pacific region.

Sales and Marketing

As a leading global advertising marketing and corporate communications company Omnicom has a large and diverse client base. Its largest client accounted for 3% of fiscal 2016 revenue. Its top 100 clients accounted for a little more than 50% of fiscal 2016 revenue.

Financial Performance

The company reported $15.4 billion in revenue for fiscal 2016. That was an increase compared to the previous fiscal year's revenue of $15.1 billion. Omnicom's net income also increased slightly in fiscal 2016 compared to the prior fiscal period. Omnicom claimed a net income of $1.15 billion in fiscal 2016 up from $1 billion in fiscal 2015.

Strategy

Omnicom's fortunes have been buoyed in part by its agency networks and their consistently strong creative work (traditional media advertising accounts for almost half of its revenue) but the bulk of its growth has traditionally come from such areas as customer relationship management (CRM) and specialty communications.

Omnicom sees continued growth being tied to its ability to provide an ever-expanding menu of services to its largest clients especially in the digital and social media arenas. The company has also been focused on expanding its media planning and buying operations.

Mergers and Acquisitions

In 2016 Omnicom acquired Pennsylvania-based BioPharm Communications. BioPharm specializes in marketing programs for physicians pharmaceutical clients and biotechnology clients.

HISTORY

Omnicom Group was created in 1986 to combine three leading ad agencies into a single group capable of competing in the worldwide market. BBDO Worldwide founded in New York in 1928 as Batten Barton Durstine & Osborn had a huge PepsiCo account and developed the Pepsi Generation campaign. Doyle Dane Bernbach Group (DDB) which had created the fahrvergn gen ads for Volkswagen had strong ties in Europe. And Needham Harper Worldwide which had served up the "You Deserve a Break Today" commercials for McDonald's had connections in Asia. BBDO remained separate but DDB and Needham Harper were merged to form DDB Needham Worldwide. The business services units (public relations firms and direct marketers) of each of these companies were tucked under the Diversified Agency Services (DAS) umbrella.

Bruce Crawford a previous chairman of BBDO who had just finished a stint running New York's Metropolitan Opera became chairman and CEO in 1989. He transformed DAS from a chaotic group of shops into an integrated marketing giant and ran Omnicom as a holding company of independent operating units working together through cross-referrals. By keeping costs low especially interest expenses Omnicom survived the 1990-91 recession with little pain. The company acquired Goodby Berlin & Silverstein (now Goodby Silverstein & Partner s) in 1992. The next year TBWA Advertising (founded in Paris in 1970 by American Bill Tragos) was added to Omnicom's roster.

The merger spree continued in 1994 when Omnicom purchased WWAV Group the largest direct-marketing agency in the UK. In 1995 Omnicom fused TBWA with Chiat/Day (founded in 1968 by Jay Chiat and Guy Day) to form TBWA International Network. Omnicom also acquired Michigan-based Ross Roy Communications (later Interone Marketing Group). In 1997 DDB Needham won back its McDonald's account after a 15-year hiatus. That year Crawford stepped down as CEO (though he remained chairman) and John Wren took control of Omnicom.

In 1998 the company acquired PR firm Fleishman-Hillard adding to the PR clout it established with the acquisition of Ketchum Communications (now Ketchum) in 1996. Omnicom also acquired GGT Group of London for $235 million. (GGT's New York office Wells BDDP had lost a large Procter & Gamble account that year.) It merged GGT's BDDP Worldwide with TBWA to form TBWA Worldwide. BBDO landed a $200 million account with PepsiCo's Frito-Lay that year.

Omnicom's position in Europe was boosted in 1999 when it bought the Abbot Mead Vickers (now Abbot Mead Vickers BBDO) shares it didn't already own. That year TBWA founder William Tragos retired from the company (replaced by Lee Clow) and DDB Needham changed its moniker to DDB Worldwide Communications Group. Omnicom also bought market research firm M/A/R/C for about $95 million and invested $20 million in pharmaceutical clinical trials company SCIREX. In 2000 BBDO scored a major coup over rival FCB Worldwide (now part of Interpublic) by landing the $1.8 billion DaimlerChrysler account. The next year it formed Seneca Investments to hold its stakes in several i-services shops including Agency.com and Organic. (Omnicom acquired the interactive agencies outright in 2003.)

After years of acquisitions and fine-tuning its operating structure Omnicom encountered the effects of the global recession in late 2008. Like most players in the media communications and advertising industries Omnicom experienced declines in revenue and net income at the end of 2009. It attributed the crisis within the automotive industry and declines in the demand for its sports and event marketing services as major reasons for the drops.

In 2010 the company acquired seven companies including Sales Power an in-store promotion company catering to South China and Maslov PR a public relations firm based in Moscow. Among the twelve companies it acquired in 2011 was Nancy Bailey & Associates a corporate licensing and consulting firm.

EXECUTIVES

EVP and CFO, Philip J. Angelastro, age 53, $850,000 total compensation

Treasurer Omnicom Group and President and CEO Omnicom Capital, Dennis E. Hewitt, age 72, $395,000 total compensation

President and CEO, John D. Wren, age 65, $1,000,000 total compensation

Vice Chairman; Chairman Asia Pacific, Serge Dumont

EVP, Asit Mehra

EVP and Dean Omnicom University, Janet Riccio

EVP, Rita E. Rodriguez

EVP, Peter Sherman

CEO Omnicom Digital, Jonathan B. Nelson, age 49, $850,000 total compensation

SVP General Counsel and Secretary, Michael J. O'Brien, age 55, $700,000 total compensation

Senior Vice President of Finance and Corporate Development, Adrian Sapollnik

Vice President Health and Welfare Benefits, Mark Low

Senior Vice President Finance Contrller, Peter Swiecicki

Executive Vice President, Thomas Carey

Vice President Human Resources, Leslie Chiocco

Vice President, Robert Miller

Senior Vice President, Tiffany R Warren

Senior Vice President, Joe Ricciardi

Senior Vice President and Global Chief Information Officer, Craig Cuyar

Chairman, Bruce Crawford, age 87

Treasurer, Angie Hickman

Auditors: KPMG LLP

LOCATIONS

HQ: Omnicom Group, Inc.
437 Madison Avenue, New York, NY 10022
Phone: 212 415-3600   **Fax:** 212 415-3393
Web: www.omnicomgroup.com

2016 sales

	$ mil.	% of total
Americas		
North America	9,174	60
Latin America	424	3
EMEA		
Europe	3,904	25
Middle East and Africa	279	1
Asia Pacific	1,636	11
Total	**15,417**	**100**

PRODUCTS/OPERATIONS

2016 sales

	$ mil.	% of total
Advertising	8,195	53
Customer relationship management	4,738	31
Public relations	1,375	9
Specialty communications	1,109	7
Total	**15,417**	**100**

Selected Operations

Global advertising networks
  BBDO Worldwide
  DDB Worldwide
  TBWA Worldwide
National advertising agencies
  Goodby Silverstein & Partners (San Francisco)
  GSD&M's Idea City (Austin TX)
  Martin|Williams (Minneapolis)
  Merkley + Partners (New York City)
  Zimmerman Partners Advertising (Fort Lauderdale FL)
Direct response
  Interbrand (brand identity)
  M/A/R/C Research (market research)
  Rapp (direct marketing)
  Targetbase (direct marketing)
Promotional marketing
  The Beanstalk Group (brand licensing and consulting)
  CPM (field marketing)
  The Integer Group (retail marketing)
  Kaleidoscope (sports and event marketing)
  Millsport (sports and event marketing)
Public relations
  Clark & Weinstock
  Cone
  Fleishman-Hillard
  Gavin Anderson & Company
  GPC International
  Ketchum
  Porter Novelli International
  Smythe Dorward Lambert
Specialty communications
  Adelphi Group (health care)
  Corbett Accel Healthcare (health care)
  Dieste (multicultural marketing)
  Doremus (business-to-business advertising)
  SafirRosetti (security and intelligence)
Media services
  Icon International
  Novus Print Media
  OMD Worldwide
  PHD Network

COMPETITORS

Dentsu	Interpublic Group
Dentsu Aegis	Publicis Groupe
Hakuhodo	WPP
Havas	

HISTORICAL FINANCIALS

Company Type: Public

Income Statement

	REVENUE ($ mil.)	NET INCOME ($ mil.)	NET PROFIT MARGIN	EMPLOYEES
12/17	15,273	1,088	7.1%	77,300
12/16	15,416	1,148	7.5%	78,500
12/15	15,134	1,093	7.2%	74,900
12/14	15,317	1,104	7.2%	74,000
12/13	14,584	991	6.8%	71,800
Annual Growth	1.2%	2.4%	—	1.9%

FYE: December 31

2017 Year-End Financials

Debt ratio: 19.75%
Return on equity: 45.57%
Cash ($ mil.): 3,796
Current ratio: 0.93
Long-term debt ($ mil.): 4,912

No. of shares (mil.): 230
Dividends
  Yield: 0.0%
  Payout: 48.3%
Market value ($ mil.): 16,758

	STOCK PRICE ($) FY Close	P/E High/Low	PER SHARE ($) Earnings	Dividends	Book Value
12/17	72.83	19 14	4.65	2.25	11.37
12/16	85.11	18 14	4.78	2.15	9.21
12/15	75.66	18 15	4.41	2.00	10.23
12/14	77.47	18 15	4.24	1.90	11.55
12/13	74.37	20 13	3.71	1.60	13.91
Annual Growth	(0.5%)	— —	5.8%	8.9%	(4.9%)

ONEAMERICA FINANCIAL PARTNERS, INC.

LOCATIONS

HQ: ONEAMERICA FINANCIAL PARTNERS, INC.
  1 AMERICAN SQ, INDIANAPOLIS, IN 462820020
Phone: 317 285-1877
Web: WWW.ONEAMERICA.COM

HISTORICAL FINANCIALS

Company Type: Private

Income Statement

	ASSETS ($ mil.)	NET INCOME ($ mil.)	INCOME AS % OF ASSETS	EMPLOYEES
12/07	19,921	88	0.4%	9,875
12/06	18,491	67	0.4%	—
12/05	0	0	—	—
12/04	15,028	56	0.4%	—
Annual Growth	9.9%	16.1%	—	—

FYE: December 31

2007 Year-End Financials

Debt ratio: ——
Return on equity: 8.00%
Cash ($ mil.): 152
Current ratio: ——
Long-term debt ($ mil.): ——

Dividends
  Yield: —
  Payout: —
Market value ($ mil.): —

OneMain Holdings Inc

OneMain Holdings makes consumer loans its one main priority. Formerly known as Springleaf Holdings the consumer finance company offers auto loans and personal loans to high-risk customers who have limited access to credit from banks credit card companies and other lenders through 1800 branches in around 45 states. In addition it provides credit insurance non-credit insurance and related products through subsidiaries Merit Life Insurance AHL Triton and Yosemite Insurance. Tracing its roots back to 1920 the company renamed itself in late 2015 after acquiring OneMain Financial.

Operations

OneMain Holdings' Consumer and Insurance division mostly makes and services personal loans and auto loans (typically ranging from $1500 to $25000+). It offers credit insurance (also known as payment protection insurance) an optional add-on for borrowers to ensure repayment even if they can't repay the loan. It also offers non-credit insurance (auto membership plans). The company has $13.6 billion in personal loan assets due from more than 2.4 million customers.

Geographic Reach

The Evansville Indiana-based company serves customers across the US and has servicing facilities in Mendota Heights Minnesota; Tempe Arizona; London Kentucky; Fort Mill South Carolina; and Irving and Fort Worth Texas.

Sales and Marketing

OneMain Holdings is aggressive in targeting high-risk borrowers who might be reluctant to seek financing. It uses direct mail offers banner ads search engine optimization and telephone sales to solicit new prospects. Mail solicitations include pre-qualified offers of guaranteed personal loan credit. The company purchases lists of potential borrowers based on predetermined criteria such as credit scores.

Financial Performance

The company's revenues climbed from $2.2 billion in 2015 to $3.9 billion in 2016 mainly due to its 2015's OneMain Financial acquisition and the continued growth of its loan portfolio (primarily secured personal loans).

After suffering a net loss of $242 million in 2015 in part due to acquisition-related costs OneMain Holdings posted net income of $215 million in 2016.

Strategy

OneMain Holdings acquires consumer loan origination and servicing companies to grow its personal loan assets and overall business. The company's late 2015 acquisition of OneMain Financial which led it to change its name from Springleaf Holdings to its current name doubled its branch network and made it one of the largest sub-prime lenders in the US.

It also seeks to simplify its balance sheet and focus on its core operations. In mid-2016 it sold its SpringCastle Portfolio which held unsecured loans and loans secured by sub-prime residential mortgages consisting of 232000-plus acquired loans totaling $1.7 billion in net finance receivables.

Mergers and Acquisitions

In late 2015 the company purchased OneMain Financial from Citigroup's CitiFinancial Credit Company for $4.45 billion which more than doubled its branch network from 831 to nearly 1800 and made it one of the nation's largest sub-prime lenders.

EXECUTIVES

EVP Legal Compliance and Operational Risk, John C. Anderson, age 59, $350,000 total compensation
President and CEO, Jay N. Levine, age 55, $400,000 total compensation
EVP and CFO, Scott T. Parker, age 50, $400,000 total compensation
EVP Branch Operations, Bradford D. Borchers, age 53, $350,000 total compensation
EVP Credit and Analytics, David P. Hogan, age 48, $350,000 total compensation
EVP and COO, Robert A. Hurzeler, age 56, $350,000 total compensation
EVP and Chief Administrative Officer, Lawrence N. Skeats, age 52, $336,539 total compensation
EVP Human Resources, Angela Celestin, age 46, $26,442 total compensation
Vice President Investor Relations, Rohit Dewan
Chairman, Wesley R. (Wes) Edens, age 55
Auditors: PricewaterhouseCoopers LLP

LOCATIONS

HQ: OneMain Holdings Inc
  601 N.W. Second Street, Evansville, IN 47708
Phone: 812 424-8031
Web: www.springleaf.com

PRODUCTS/OPERATIONS

2016 Sales

	$ mil.	% of total
Consumer and Insurance	3,940	92
Acquisition and Serving	318	8
Real Estate	18	-
Others	(5)	-
Adjustments	(388)	-
Total	3,883	100

COMPETITORS

Advance America
Atlanticus
Check 'n Go
Check Into Cash
Community Choice Financial
DFC Global
EZCORP
FirstCash
NetSpend
QC Holdings
Regional Management
Security Finance Corporation of Spartanburg
World Acceptance
Xponential

HISTORICAL FINANCIALS

Company Type: Public

Income Statement

	ASSETS ($ mil.)	NET INCOME ($ mil.)	INCOME AS % OF ASSETS	EMPLOYEES
12/16	18,123	215	1.2%	10,100
12/15	21,056	(242)	—	11,400
12/14	11,057	504	4.6%	5,030
12/13	15,402	(19)	—	4,900
12/12	14,673	(218)	—	4,500
Annual Growth	5.4%	—	—	22.4%

FYE: December 31

2016 Year-End Financials

Debt ratio: 77.02%
Return on equity: 7.37%
Cash ($ mil.): 579
Current ratio: —
Long-term debt ($ mil.): —

No. of shares (mil.): 134
Dividends
  Yield: —
  Payout: —
Market value ($ mil.): 2,986

	STOCK PRICE ($)	P/E	PER SHARE ($)		
	FY Close	High/Low	Earnings	Dividends	Book Value
12/16	22.14	26 11	1.59	0.00	22.73
12/15	41.54	— —	(1.89)	0.00	20.45
12/14	36.17	9 5	4.38	0.00	17.64
12/13	25.28	— —	(0.19)	0.00	13.42
Annual Growth	(3.3%)	— —	—	—	14.1%

ONEOK Inc

ONEOK (?one oak?) is having a gas pursuing its pipeline dreams. ONEOK is an Oklahoma-based midstream natural gas corporation that plays a key role in transforming and transporting natural gas from exploration & producer (E&P) businesses to downstream customers such as refiners and petrochemical companies. Through its primary subsidiary ONEOK Partners its operations include a 38000-mile integrated network of natural gas and natural gas liquid (NGL) pipelines processing plants fractionators and storage facilities in the Mid-Continent Williston Permian and Rocky Mountain regions. In recent years ONEOK divested its commercial and residential natural gas delivery company ONE Gas and purchased all outstanding shares of its key master limited partnership ONEOK Partners and absorbed it into ONEOK.

HISTORY

In 1906 Oklahoma Natural Gas (ONG) was founded to pipe natural gas from northeastern Oklahoma to Oklahoma City. A 100-mile pipeline was completed the next year. In 1921 ONG created two oil companies to pump the oil it found as a result of its natural gas exploration.

ONG changed hands many times in the 1920s ending up with utility financier G. L. Ohrstrom and Company which milked it dry by brokering acquisitions (purchasing gas properties and then selling them to ONG) and collecting fees. Stock sales drove revenues inflating the stock's price and the inflated price triggered more stock sales. The bubble burst on October 29 1929. A series of leadership changes ensued and in 1932 the company was dissolved and reincorporated. Under president Joseph Bowes ONG recovered wooing back dissatisfied customers and upgrading its pipelines.

In the late 1930s the company pioneered a type of underground storage that injected gas into depleted gas reservoirs in the summer and withdrew it during winter's peak use times.

The 1950s and 1960s saw the company expand. In 1962 it created its first subsidiary Oklahoma Natural Gas Gathering Company selling gas out of state and therefore subject to federal regulation.

ONG was not affected in the lean 1970s by federal laws that kept wellhead prices low for gas transported across state lines because its main operations were confined to Oklahoma. Congress deregulated wellhead prices in 1978 spurring exploration but causing great price fluctuations in the 1980s. In 1980 ONG changed its name to ONEOK.

In the 1980s ONEOK signed take-or-pay contracts which forced it to pay for gas offered by its suppliers even if it had no customers. When recession in the 1980s caused demand to drop ONEOK had to pay for high-priced natural gas it couldn't sell. In 1988 the company was ordered to pay some $50 million to supplier Forest Oil of Denver.

A year later ONEOK was sued for allegedly failing to tell stockholders about the take-or-pay agreements (settled in 1993 for $5.5 million). It later sold more than half of its oil and gas reserves to Mustang Energy for $52 million to finance the Forest Oil court award. The company was still settling lawsuits over the agreements into the 1990s; it settled the last of the claims by 1998.

ONEOK began buying gas transmission and production facilities in Oklahoma and creating drilling alliances in the 1990s. In 1997 ONEOK bought the natural gas assets of Westar Energy formerly Western Resources for $660 million and ONEOK stock worth $800 million. The acquisition doubled the number of ONEOK's customers and increased its gas marketing gathering and transmission operations.

The company also acquired Southern Union's Texas natural gas distribution business (540000 customers) as well as Southern Union's stake in a Mexican gas utility and its propane distribution gas marketing and gas transmission operations in the southwestern US for $420 million.

ONEOK acquired Northern Plains Natural Gas a general partner of pipeline operator Northern Border Partners (later renamed ONEOK Partners) from CCE Holdings (a joint venture of Southern Union and GE Commercial Finance) for $175 million in 2004. The transaction followed CCE Holdings' acquisition of Enron's CrossCountry Energy unit.

Also in 2004 ONEOK changed the name of its wholesale energy unit from ONEOK Energy Marketing and Trading to ONEOK Energy Services.

The company bought Koch Industries' natural gas liquids assets in 2005 for $1.35 billion.

In 2013 the company announced plans to invest $440 million in the natural gas liquids-rich area in the Powder River Basin in Wyoming to by a 50-million cubic feet per day natural gas processing facility in Wyoming (the Sage Creek plant and related infrastructure) for $305 million. It plans to invest $135 million to upgrade and construct natural gas gathering and processing related infrastructure NGL gathering pipelines and well connections.

EXECUTIVES

EVP and Chief Administrative Officer, Robert F. (Rob) Martinovich, age 59, $500,000 total compensation

President and CEO, Terry K. Spencer, age 57, $700,000 total compensation

SVP Operations, Wesley J. Christensen, age 63, $400,000 total compensation

SVP CFO and Treasurer, Derek S. Reiners, age 46, $375,000 total compensation

SVP Natural Gas Gathering and Processing, Kevin L. Burdick, age 52

VP and CIO, Brien H. Brown

SVP Natural Gas Pipelines, J. Phillip (Phill) May

EVP Strategic Planning and Corporate Affairs, Walter S. Hulse, age 53, $500,000 total compensation

SVP Natural Gas Liquids ONEOK Partners, Sheridan C. Swords

Vice President Commercial G And P, Michael A Fitzgibbons

Vice President Manufacturing, Lane Fisher

Vice President of Procurement, Gwen Bayhylle

Vice President, Walter Allen

Vice President Project Development and Business Analysis, Michael Crisman

Vice President Financial Controller, Michael D Clark

Vice President Information Technology, Charles Andrews

Vice President Technology fixed Income, Jackie Mitchell

Vice President Sales and Marketing, Carl Holliday

Vice President Marketing Oneok Energy Resources, George Drake

Vice President and Associate General Counsel, Stephen B Allen

Senior Vice President General Counsel Assistant Secretary, Stephen Lake

Vice President Rates and Regulatory Affairs, Ron Mucci

Vice President Gas Supply, Michael Fitzgibbons

Vice President western Region, Dan Walker

Regional Vice President Kansas Region Gas Service, Teryl C Rose

Vice President Information Technology, Kevin Burbick

Senior Vice President, Dan Harrison

Senior Vice President Pipelines, Mike Nelson

VICE PRESIDENT OF INVESTOR RELATIONS AND PUBLIC AFFAIRS, Dan L Harrison

Vice President Associate General Counsel Secretary, Eric Grimshaw

Chairman ONEOK ONEOK Partners and ONE Gas, John W. Gibson, age 64

Board Member, Michael Ryan

Auditors: PricewaterhouseCoopers LLP

LOCATIONS

HQ: ONEOK Inc
100 West Fifth Street, Tulsa, OK 74103
Phone: 918 588-7000   **Fax:** 918 588-7273
Web: www.oneok.com

PRODUCTS/OPERATIONS

2016 Sales

	$ mil.	% of total
Natural Gas Liquids	7,675	76
Natural Gas Gathering and Processing	2,051	20
Natural Gas Pipeline	379	4
Reconciled Intersegment Revenues	(1185.7)	-
Total	**8,920**	**0**

COMPETITORS

BP	Exxon Mobil
DCP Midstream Partners	National Fuel Gas
EQT Corporation	SemGroup
Enable Midstream Partners	Southwest Gas
Enterprise Products	TRII
	Williams Companies

HISTORICAL FINANCIALS

Company Type: Public

Income Statement

FYE: December 31

	REVENUE ($ mil.)	NET INCOME ($ mil.)	NET PROFIT MARGIN	EMPLOYEES
12/16	8,920	352	3.9%	2,384
12/15	7,763	244	3.2%	2,364
12/14	12,195	314	2.6%	2,269
12/13	14,602	266	1.8%	1,927
12/12	12,632	360	2.9%	4,859
Annual Growth	(8.3%)	(0.6%)	—	(16.3%)

2016 Year-End Financials

Debt ratio: 58.50%	No. of shares (mil.): 210
Return on equity: 133.86%	Dividends
Cash ($ mil.): 248	Yield: 0.0%
Current ratio: 0.50	Payout: 148.1%
Long-term debt ($ mil.): 7,920	Market value ($ mil.): 12,095

STOCK PRICE ($)		P/E		PER SHARE ($)		
	FY Close	High/Low	Earnings	Dividends	Book Value
12/16	57.41	35 12	1.66	2.46	0.90
12/15	24.66	44 16	1.16	2.43	1.60
12/14	49.79	47 30	1.49	2.13	2.84
12/13	62.18	48 31	1.27	1.48	11.31
12/12	42.75	51 23	1.71	1.27	10.39
Annual Growth	7.6%	— —	(0.7%)	18.0%	(45.8%)

Opus Bank (Irvine, CA)

Auditors: KPMG LLP

LOCATIONS

HQ: Opus Bank (Irvine, CA)
19900 MacArthur Blvd., 12th Floor, Irvine, CA 92612
Phone: 949 250-9800
Web: www.opusbank.com

HISTORICAL FINANCIALS

Company Type: Public

Income Statement

FYE: December 31

	ASSETS ($ mil.)	NET INCOME ($ mil.)	INCOME AS % OF ASSETS	EMPLOYEES
12/16	7,882	11	0.1%	835
12/15	6,649	59	0.9%	661
12/14	5,084	43	0.9%	585
12/13	3,738	143	3.8%	550
12/12	2,860	22	0.8%	—
Annual Growth	28.8%	(15.9%)	—	—

2016 Year-End Financials

Debt ratio: 1.68%
Return on equity: 1.27%
Cash ($ mil.): 935
Current ratio: —
Long-term debt ($ mil.): —

No. of shares (mil.): 34
Dividends
  Yield: 0.0%
  Payout: 160.6%
Market value ($ mil.): 1,030

STOCK PRICE ($)		P/E		PER SHARE ($)		
	FY Close	High/Low	Earnings	Dividends	Book Value
12/16	30.05	112 58	0.33	0.53	27.01
12/15	36.97	21 13	1.79	0.34	26.68
12/14	28.37	22 18	1.38	0.00	28.41
Annual Growth	1.4%	— —	(30.1%)	—	(1.3%)

Oracle Corp

Oracle predicts the future of computing is in the cloud. A leader in enterprise software Oracle provides hardware and services to help companies improve their processes. Best known for its focus on databases (its RMDBS and MySQL are popular database management programs) Oracle also offers software for enterprise resource planning data management collaboration application development customer relationship management and supply chain management. In recent years the company has aggressively expanded through acquisitions. More than half its revenue comes from international customers.

Operations

Oracle?s software businesses generate 80% of its sales.

The company traditionally sold on-premise software applications that were loaded onto customers' computers at their offices. The company?s on-premise software brands are Siebel PeopleSoft and JD Edwards and the company?s Oracle E-Business Suite.

Oracle is moving its products to cloud computing environments where customers can access programs from multiple locations and devices. The company?s cloud applications are Oracle Human Capital Management (HCM) Cloud Oracle Enterprise Resource Planning (ERP) Cloud Oracle Customer Experience (CX) Cloud Oracle Supply Chain Management (SCM) Cloud Oracle Cloud Industry Solutions and Oracle Data Cloud.

Oracle also offers services that help customers operate their businesses from a cloud environment with software-as-a-service platform-as-a-service and infrastructure-as-a-service. Those businesses account for about an eighth of Oracle's revenue.

The other 20% of Oracle?s sales come from its hardware business which includes computers and related software and services and its consulting services business.

The company?s manufacturing operations are devoted to its Oracle Engineered Systems and some of its enterprise and data center servers and storage products. It relies on third-party manufacturing partners to make other hardware.

Geographic Reach

Oracle?s US customers generate just less than 50% of sales. The UK Germany and Japan account for about 5% of sales each.

Sales and Marketing

Oracle uses direct and indirect channels including independent distributors and value-added resellers to market and sell its products and services. The companies that comprise Oracle's indirect channel network are members of the Oracle Partner Network.

The company counts more than 400000 customers including each company on the Fortune 100. Its customers are in industries such as aerospace and defense automotive financial technology manufacturing oil and gas retail telecommunications and utilities. The company has scaled up its advertising spending in recent years.

Financial Performance

Oracle Corp.?s revenue rose about 2% to $37.7 billion in 2017 (ended May) from about $37 billion in 2016. The company had reported lower revenue for the preceding two years.

The company?s overall software sales increased 2% but the cloud ?as-a-service? offerings drove the company?s growth for the year adding about $1.8 billion in revenue. The cloud software as a service business grew nearly 70% and the cloud platform and infrastructure businesses increased about 60%. The NetSuite acquisition also boosted cloud revenue. Sales were lower in new software licenses (which the company expected as customers move to cloud services) hardware and services. Sales rose in the Americas and the Asia/Pacific region but declined in the Europe the Middle East and Africa region.

Oracle?s bottom line improved in 2017 rising 5% to $9.3 billion from $8.9 billion in 2016.

Net cash provided by operating activities increased to $14.1 billion for 2017 from $13.6 billion in 2016 because of higher net income in 2017.

Strategy

Oracle Corp.?s move to cloud computing began to pay off in its 2017 fiscal year ended in May. The company reported strong growth in its cloud platform and infrastructure businesses and it continues to attract customers to its cloud applications for

enterprising resource planning human capital management and financials.

Oracle scored a big win in 2017 when it signed an agreement with AT&T to move thousands of the communications company?s large scale internal databases to Oracle?s infrastructure and platform cloud services. AT&T will transfer thousands of existing Oracle databases containing petabytes of data plus associated applications workloads to Oracle Cloud. AT&T also agreed to use Oracle?s Field Service Cloud to schedule and dispatch its more than 70000 field technicians.

While Oracle?s sales have grown in the Americas and the Asia/Pacific region they have lagged in Europe. The company in 2017 began a hiring push for sales staff to generate more cloud sales in the Europe Middle East and Africa region.

Oracle quickly recognized the importance of cloud computing for its application software products. In that area the company claims to be catching and passing rival Salesforce.com in sales of software-as-a-service applications. But Oracle was late in providing cloud infrastructure and platform services. In that race it remains behind market leaders Amazon Web Services Microsoft?s Azure Alphabet?s Google and IBM. An advantage that Oracle claims is that it uses its own server and storage hardware products and can ramp up production to build out data centers only when more capacity is needed.

Mergers and Acquisitions

Oracle's recent acquisitions have deepened its cloud portfolio. In late 2017 the company agreed to buy Aconex an Australian provider of web-based collaboration tools for the construction industry for about $1.2 billion. More than 70000 organizations have used Aconex to manage more than $1 trillion in projects in 70 countries. The deal was expected to close in the first half of 2018.

In July 2016 Oracle bought NetSuite for $9.3 billion. NetSuite ($741 million revenue and $124 million loss in 2015) provides cloud-based business management products similar to Oracle's. But the product lines are complementary in that NetSuite's products are built for the medium-sized business market while Oracle's are designed for enterprise businesses. The acquisition could help Oracle in competing with Salesforce.com which also is an Oracle partner. Oracle chief Larry Ellison had a significant ownership share in NetSuite.

In November 2016 Oracle bought privately held Dyn a company that helps increase internet performance and domain name system (DNS) provider. Dyn operates a global network that drives 40 billion traffic optimization decisions a day for some 3500 customers including Netflix Twitter Pfizer and CNBC. Oracle said the addition of Dyn's DNS will extend and strengthen its cloud capabilities.

Other recent acquisitions were of MICROS Systems Textura Datalogix and Maxymiser.

EXECUTIVES

EVP, David A. (Dave) Donatelli, age 51
Executive Chairman and CTO, Lawrence J. (Larry) Ellison, age 73, $1 total compensation
EVP Oracle Customer Support Services, Charles A. (Chuck) Rozwat, age 69, $600,000 total compensation
CEO, Mark V. Hurd, age 60, $950,000 total compensation
EVP Global Business Units, Robert K. (Bob) Weiler, age 67
SVP Oracle Cloud Go-To-Market and Product Business Groups, Shawn Price
CEO, Safra A. Catz, age 55, $950,000 total compensation
SVP Human Resources, Joyce Westerdahl

President Oracle Product Development, Thomas Kurian, age 50, $800,000 total compensation

EVP Oracle Applications Development, Steve Miranda

EVP Oracle Database Server Technologies, Andrew Mendelsohn

EVP Microelectronics Group, Michael E. (Mike) Splain, age 61

SVP and CIO, Mark E. Sunday, age 62

EVP Systems, John F. Fowler, age 56, $700,000 total compensation

EVP General Counsel and Secretary, Dorian E. Daley, age 58

SVP and General Manager Financial Services Global Business Unit, Sonny Singh

EVP Chief of Staff and Head Corporate Development, Douglas Kehring

SVP North American Technology Division, Rich Geraffo

SVP Cloud Development, Peter S. Magnusson

SVP Worldwide Operations, Karl Braitberg

EVP Oracle Fusion Middleware Development, Inderjeet Singh

Senior Vice President Applications Technology, Cliff Godwin

Senior Vice President Alliances And Channels Asia Pacific, Mark Lewis

Vice President, Brian S Higgins

Senior Vice President And General Manager, Rodger Smith

Vice President Of Standards Strategy And Architect, Donald Deutsch

Vice President, Brent Grech

Vice President Global HRMS Product Development, Rob Watson

Vice President PeopleTools Development, Willie Suh

Group Vice President, Greg Calhoun

Vice President Of Software Development, Markus Flierl

Vice President Customer Loyalty, Joan Smeal

Vice President, Michael Brewer

Vice President, Terrance Wampler

Vice President Product Development Information Technology, Campbell Webb

Vice President, Buffy Ransom

Regional Vice President ??? Consulting, Vishal Singh

Vice President Channels and Solutions UK and Irel, David Callaghan

Vice President Sales Consulting, Kristen McGregor

Area Vice President Sales, Steve Sybert

Vice President Fusion Applications Development, Lewis Thompson

Regional Vice President, George Yen

Senior Vice President and Chief Customer Officer, Jeb Dasteel

Vice President Product Management, Peter Utzschneider

Senior Vice President Investor Relations, Ken Bond

Regional Vice President, Jeff Keplar

Consulting Vice President JD Edwards, Steven Reeter

Vice President Product Development, Prakash Dodeja

Senior Vice President, Ian Smith

Vice President Develop, Ilan Bensimhon

Vice President of Manufacturing and Distribution, Matthew Mayerson

Vice President Global Information Technology Risk Management, Brennan Baybeck

Vice President Strateg, Sohan Demel

Consulting Vice President, Ellen Lapriore

Vice President, John Emery

Regional Vice President, Michael Placido

Vice President Business Development, Hemanth Vedagarbha

Vice President Software Development, Meeten Bhavsar

Vice President, Paolo Juvara

Vice President CRM Sales Support, Frank Mouthaan

Vice President Sales, Prashant Lele

Vice President Global Practices, Ellen Eder

Vice President of Product Management, Linda Jackman

Group Vice President And Global Head Of Product Consulting, Kishore Kapoor

Sales Consulting Vice President, Carl Griffin

Group Vice President, Brendan Logan

Senior Vice President Of Engineering, Douglas Doedens

Vice President Sales, Paul Macura

Vice President EPM Applications, Matthew Bradley

Vice President Customer Services Marketing, Steve Pinedo

Executive Vice President, Rex Wang

Regional Vice President, Kirby Rouser

Vice President, Carol Adams

Vice President Technology Solutions And Channels, Alan Hartwell

Senior Vice President of Global Practices and Risk Management, Richard Allison

Group Vice President, Jim Standard

Vice President Data Warehouse And Language Technology, Cetin Ozbutun

Vice President of Application Strategy, Paco Aubrejuan

Vice President Product Marketing, Stephen Fioretti

Vice President of EPM and BI Marketing, Rich Clayton

Vice President Process, Gopi Tummala

Vice President, Denise Grills

Group Vice President Sales and Bus Development (saas), Mike Hogan

Regional Vice President, Scott Carlin

Vice President Professional Services, Brad Kitchin

Vice President Product Strategy, Stephen Johnston

Vice President Quality Assurance, Kyle Lucas

Vice President Worldwide Isv Oem And Java Business, David Hicks

Vice President Customer Services Emea Major Accounts, Nick Harber

VP Business Planning, Sridhar Padmanabhan

Vice President, Penelope Lie

Vice President Of Product Support, Paul Martin

Senior Vice President of Engineering Systems, Ali Alasti

Vice President Operations Tech and System Suppor, Paul Williamson

Vice President of Drug Product Operations, Rajesh Banerjee

Vice President, Chuck Jones

Sales Vice President Bi Analytics And Epm Latin America, Marvio Portela

Vice President Global Tech, Susan Zwinger

Oracle Client Advisor Vice President, Jim Mckeighan

Retail Vice President, William O'Brien

Vice President Finance Europe North, Oliver Schlemper

Vice President Consulting, Heather Graham

Senior Vice President Strategy, Gretchen Alarcon

Vice President Of Bd, Giovanna Sangiorgi

Group Vice President, Mandar Borkar

Vice President Central Europe, Pawel Piwowar

Regional Vice President, Timothy Tarkinton

Vice President Accounts, Jason Lerman

Vice President, Maha Muzumdar

Vice President Product Managment, Alex Gleyzer

Vice President Software Development, Ryan Carroll

Vice President Of Product Management And Product Development, Amit Zavery

Vice President Sales Manufacturing Industry, Junichi Iijima

Vice President and General Manager, Barry Dyer

Vice President Of Mobile Strategy Product Manageme, Suhas Uliyar

Vice President of Product Strategy, John Kelley

Vice President Of Business Operations, Mitch Codkind

New Business; Vice President Operational Risk, Peter Hill

Vice President Sales Operations, Cynthia Kuzemkan

Vice President and North America Sales Strategy Lead, Cheryl Martin

Vice President Linux And Infrastructure, Van Okamura

National Sales Manager FSGBU (India and SA), Prasad Kerkar

Senior Vice President Oracle Managed Cloud Services, Steve McMillan

Vice President CRM Project Management Office, David Williamson

Regional Vice President, Jonathan Conwell

Vice President Of Sales For The Americas, Ed Coke

Vice President Applications Specialist Team Asia Pacific, Karen Yip

Vice President Business Operations North America Infrastructure Sales, Laurie Birch

Vice President Hcm Sales, Scott Stoll

Vice President Enterprise Accounts, Bob Barrett

Ofss Employee Software Development Vice President, Manmath Kulkarni

Vice President Of Sales Smb, Brendan Caleca

Vice President Sales Operations, David Hoffman

Vice President, Juana Schurman

VICE PRESIDENT, Tania Weidick

Executive Vice President, Mike Splain

Vice President Of Strategic Programs, Patrick Mungovan

Vice President, Brian Higgins

Executive Vice President of Research and Development, Lisa Cangemi

Vice President Worldwide Customer Care, Gemma Martinez

Vice President of Sales Eastern Region Oracle Communications, Robert Hayes

Vice President Retail Sales, Katherine Rizzuto

Assistant Vice President Global Accounts, Jason Blair

Group Vice President Operations, Doug Roseborough

National Account Manager, Shaun Winter

Vice President Strategy, Brian Bradford

Regional Vice President Sales, Jim Kallio

Vice President Of Loyalty And Marketing, Melissa Boxer

VP Mso And Wireless Sales, Don Hutton

Vice President Applications Marketing, Joyce Boland

Vice President of Technology Integration, Lisa Parekh

Auditors: Ernst & Young LLP

LOCATIONS

HQ: Oracle Corp
500 Oracle Parkway, Redwood City, CA 94065
Phone: 650 506-7000
Web: www.oracle.com

2017 Sales

	$ mil.	% of total
United States	17,770	47
United Kingdom	1,999	5
Japan	1,618	4
Germany	1,417	4
Canada	1,102	3
Other countries	13,822	37
Total	**37,728**	**100**

Selected Acquisitions

FY 2017
Moat (SaaS search engine)
Wercker (cloud infrastructure software)
Apiary (API development)
FY 2016
Dyn (managed DNS and cloud infrastructure)
Palerra (cloud security)
LogFire (cloud management for retailers)

NetSuite (cloud-based applications)
Opower (SaaS energy efficiency)
Textura (online collaboration for construction)
Crosswise (cross-device ID mapping)
FY 2013
Responsys (marketing automation software)
Nimbula (private cloud infrastructure management software)
Tekelec (data management)
Acme Packet (data management)
FY 2012
Collective Intellect (social media monitoring software)
Vitrue (social media software)
Eloqua (marketing automation software)
Skire (project management software)
SelectMinds (human resources software)
Xsigo Systems (networking technology)

PRODUCTS/OPERATIONS

2017 Sales

	$ mil.	% of total
Software license updates and product support	19,229	51
New software licenses	6,418	17
Hardware revenues	4,152	11
Services revenues	4,152	9
Cloud software as a service	3,211	8
Cloud platform as a service and infrastructure as a service	1,360	4
Total	**37,728**	**100**

2017 Sales

	$ mil.	% of total
Cloud and on-premise software	30,218	80
Hardware	4,152	11
Services	3,358	9
Total	**37,728**	**100**

Selected Products
Software
  Business applications
  Business intelligence
  Customer experience
  Customer relationship
  Enterprise content
  Financial
  Governance risk & compliance
  Human capital
  Supply chain
  Databases
  Enterprise application integration
  Middleware

Services
  Consulting
  Cloud computing
  Enterprise architecture
  Systems integration
  Education/training
Hardware
  Servers (SPARC servers x86 servers)
  Solaris operating system (hardware-related software)
  Storage & tape

COMPETITORS

ADP	Intel
Accenture	JDA Software
Akana	JasperSoft
BMC Software	Manhattan Associates
CA Inc.	MicroStrategy
CDC Software	Microsoft
Ceridian	NCR
Cisco Systems	Novell
Courion	Open Text
Dell Software	Pegasystems
EMC	Progress Software
Fujitsu Technology	Red Hat
Solutions	SAP
HP	SAS Institute
HP Autonomy	Sage Group
Hewlett Packard	Software AG
Enterprise	SuccessFactors
Hitachi	TIBCO Software
IBM	Teradata
Infor Global	Workday Inc.
Informatica	salesforce.com

HISTORICAL FINANCIALS
Company Type: Public

Income Statement
FYE: May 31

	REVENUE ($ mil.)	NET INCOME ($ mil.)	NET PROFIT MARGIN	EMPLOYEES
05/17	37,728	9,335	24.7%	138,000
05/16	37,047	8,901	24.0%	136,000
05/15	38,226	9,938	26.0%	132,000
05/14	38,275	10,955	28.6%	122,000
05/13	37,180	10,925	29.4%	120,000
Annual Growth	**0.4%**	**(3.9%)**	**—**	**3.6%**

2017 Year-End Financials
Debt ratio: 42.90%—
Return on equity: 18.46%
Cash ($ mil.): 21,784
Current ratio: 3.08
Long-term debt ($ mil.): 48,112
Dividends
  Yield: 1.4%
  Payout: 28.9%
Market value ($ mil.): —

	STOCK PRICE ($) FY Close	P/E High/Low		PER SHARE ($) Earnings	Dividends	Book Value
05/17	45.39	20	17	2.21	0.64	13.02
05/16	40.20	21	16	2.07	0.60	11.45
05/15	43.49	20	17	2.21	0.51	11.20
05/14	42.02	17	12	2.38	0.48	10.50
05/13	33.78	16	11	2.26	0.42	9.61
Annual Growth	**7.7%**	**—**	**—**	**(0.6%)**	**11.1%**	**7.9%**

Oritani Financial Corp (DE)

Oritani Financial could give an oratory on local banking in New Jersey. The holding company owns Oritani Bank which offers retail and commercial deposit and loan banking services from about 25 locations inÂ severalÂ Garden StateÂ counties. OritaniÂ Financial specializes in multi-family and commercial real estate lending which make upÂ more than halfÂ of its loan portfolio. Oritani Financial also writesÂ one- to four-family and secondÂ mortgages as well as equity and construction loans. It invests in real property through its Hampshire Financial Oritani LLC and Ormon divisions; Oritani Asset is a real estate investment trust (REIT). Century-old Oritani Bank has more than $2 billion in assets.

Geographic Reach
Oritani Bank has 25 full-service branches in Bergen Essex Hudson and Passaic counties in New Jersey.

Financial Performance
The bank's 2012 (ends June) revenue increased 4% vs. the prior year and net income grew by 11% over the same period. The revenue increase was due to a 4% jump in interest income. partially offset by a nearly 1% drop in non-interest income. Fiscal 2012 markedÂ Oritani Bank'sÂ eighth consecutive year of increasing revenue although growth has slowed somewhat. The increase in net income in 2012 was primarily due to a higher net interest spread and a larger asset base.

Strategy
Oritani Bank is expanding its branch network. It recently opened new branches in Ramsey Upper Montclair and Clifton New Jersey.

EXECUTIVES

Executive Vice President and Chief Operating Officer, Michael DeBernardi
Vice President, Paul Cordero
Chairman President and CEO, Kevin J. Lynch, age 70, $705,769 total compensation
EVP and CFO, John M. Fields, age 54, $315,046 total compensation
EVP and Chief Lending Officer, Thomas G. Guinan, age 53, $305,539 total compensation
Senior Vice President Chief Credit Officer, Louis Manderino
Vice President, John Pagano
Vice President, Bing Luh
Vice President Commercial Lending, Noah Littell
Senior Vice President and Secretary, Philip Wyks
Senior Vice President and Human Resources Officer, Anne Mooradian
Auditors: Crowe Horwath LLP

LOCATIONS

HQ: Oritani Financial Corp (DE)
  370 Pascack Road, Township of Washington, NJ 07676
Phone: 201 664-5400
Web: www.oritani.com

Selected Services
Mobile Banking
Checking Accounts
Money Market Accounts
Savings Accounts
Business Accounts
Business Services
Commercial Loans

PRODUCTS/OPERATIONS

2016 Sales

	$ mil.	% of total
Interest		
Mortgage loans	125	70
Interest on securities available for sale	4	2
Interest on securities held to maturity	2	2
Dividends on FHLB stock	1	1
Non-interest		
Bank-owned life insurance	2	2
Net income from investments in real estate joint ventures	1	1
Net gain on sale of securities	1	1
Net gain loss)on sale of assets and loans	37	21
Other	1	-
Total	**178**	**100**

COMPETITORS

1st Colonial Bancorp	Sun Bancorp (NJ)
Hudson City Bancorp	Valley National
OceanFirst Financial	Bancorp
Provident Financial	
Services	

HISTORICAL FINANCIALS
Company Type: Public

Income Statement
FYE: June 30

	ASSETS ($ mil.)	NET INCOME ($ mil.)	INCOME AS % OF ASSETS	EMPLOYEES
06/17	4,137	49	1.2%	245
06/16	3,669	52	1.4%	238
06/15	3,353	46	1.4%	235
06/14	3,140	41	1.3%	233
06/13	2,831	39	1.4%	212
Annual Growth	**9.9%**	**5.6%**	**—**	**3.7%**

2017 Year-End Financials
Debt ratio: 15.52%
Return on equity: 8.98%
Cash ($ mil.): 33
Current ratio: —
Long-term debt ($ mil.): —
No. of shares (mil.): 45
Dividends
  Yield: 7.0%
  Payout: 90.2%
Market value ($ mil.): 784

STOCK PRICE ($)	P/E	PER SHARE ($)		
FY Close	High/Low	Earnings	Dividends	Book Value
06/17	17.05	17 14	1.10	1.20	12.16
06/16	15.99	14 12	1.21	1.20	11.83
06/15	16.05	14 12	1.10	0.95	11.76
06/14	15.39	17 15	0.94	0.95	11.57
06/13	15.68	17 15	0.92	1.03	11.43
Annual Growth	2.1%	— —	4.6%	4.0%	1.6%

Oshkosh Corp (New)

Oshkosh Corp. makes vehicles that carry troops lift firefighters pick up trash tow cars and handle a bevy of other heavy vehicle duties. The company?s commercial and access lines include concrete batch plants refuse vehicle bodies (McNeilus brand) tow trucks (Jerr-Dan) and aerial work platforms (JLG). Its emergency offerings range from snow blowers to aircraft rescue and firefighting vehicles (Pierce). Oshkosh makes its products in more than 30 plants in the US and around the world. Vehicles are sold via dealers to global airport institutional construction and municipal markets. Oshkosh also makes tactical vehicles for the Department of Defense. The company traces its roots back to 1917.

Operations

Oshkosh divides its operations across four segments. The access equipment segment — consisting of JLG and Jerr-Dan — generates about 45% of sales and makes aerial work platforms tow trucks and telehandlers used by rental companies construction contractors manufacturing companies home improvement stores and the military.

Commercial (roughly 15% of sales) makes rear- and front-discharge concrete mixers refuse collection vehicles portable and stationary concrete batch plants for ready-mix companies and waste haulers.

The defense segment (about 25% of sales) manufactures vehicles that perform tasks such as hauling tanks missile systems ammunition fuel troops and cargo for a broad range of missions. It supplies the US and foreign militaries as well as law-enforcement agencies with military tactical wheeled vehicles. These include the Joint Light Tactical Vehicle (JLTV) Heavy Expanded Mobility Tactical Truck (HEMTT) the Heavy Equipment Transporter (HET) and the Logistic Vehicle System Replacement (LVSR).

The fire and emergency segment (15%) supplies commercial and custom firefighting vehicles and equipment vehicles for aircraft rescue snow removal and broadcasting vehicles.

Geographic Reach

Oshkosh has more than 30 manufacturing locations in seven US states and in Australia Belgium Canada China France Mexico the UK and Romania. It also has joint ventures in Brazil and Mexico. The company sells and services products in more than 130 countries around the globe. The US accounts for about 75% of sales.

Sales and Marketing

Oshkosh?s JLG unit sells its products through 3500 locations spanning six continents. Oshkosh markets its Jerr-Dan carriers and wreckers through a network of 60 independent distributors. JLG's customers include Caterpillar and SAME Deutz-Fahr. The US government represents about 20% of the company's sales.

Financial Performance

Pushed by a military vehicle Oshkosh?s revenue grew 9% and profit surged 32% in 2017 (ended September) from 2016. It was the second straight year of revenue gain after three consecutive declines.

In 2017 revenue hit $6.8 billion drive by increased sales of Joint Light Tactical Vehicles (JLTV) as part of an eight-year program with the US Department of Defense. Another revenue boost came from higher sales of Mine Resistant Ambush Protected-All Terrain Vehicles (M-ATV) under an international contract. A 26% increase in sales in the Europe Middle East and Africa region reflects the M-ATV contract.

Oshkosh posted a profit of about $285 million in 2017 up from $216 million in 2016. Higher gross margins came with higher sales which helped drive profit as did lower start-up costs of a manufacturing facility in Mexico. Offsetting factors were charges for restructuring asset impairment and workforce reduction.

Oshkosh? cash flow from operations fell to about $246 million in 2017 from about $584 million in 2016 when access equipment inventory levels were much lower because of decreased demand. In 2017 higher demand resulted in more inventory on hand.

Strategy

Oshkosh Corp. has parlayed its Department of Defense work to higher revenue in the past two years. It expects that to continue as it fills an eight-year contract to supply Joint Light Tactical Vehicles (JLTV) to the US military. The $6.7 billion program which was in a start-up phase in the past two years calls for delivery of 18000 vehicles and services. The company believes that the program increases its profile in the DoD which could lead to more contracts.

The company continues to look for ways to streamline operations and save money. An example is the shift of warehousing for aftermarket parts in access equipment segment to a third party. In January 2017 the company?s streamlining attention turned to Europe where it planned to close a manufacturing plant in Belgium offer fewer telehandler products on the continent transfer European telehandler production to its facility in Romania and close a UK-based engineering facility. In the US Oshkosh planned to move North American telehandler production from Ohio to Pennsylvania.

Oshkosh aims to generate some 15% of revenue from new products. In 2017 and 2018 the company looked for such sales to come from the Ascendant Aerial ladder with a 107-ft. reach the Meridian Front-Load refuse collection vehicle and the JLG 1500AJP articulating boom lift (which it claims is the world?s tallest).

Other prongs in its strategy include using new technologies to expand the functions of its products and developing business in the emerging markets of Asia Eastern Europe the Middle East and Latin America. Expanding international operations and sales is a significant part of the company's growth strategy for 2018.

HISTORY

Bernhard Mosling and William Besserdich founded Oshkosh Truck in 1917 attracting investors with Old Betsy a four-wheel-drive 3000-pound truck. Over the next few decades the company developed a range of heavy-duty vehicles. Sales took off when the US Army gave truck contracts to Oshkosh during WWII. Commercial sales increased after the war the result of demand from mining and plantation companies. Oshkosh Truck went public in 1985. To reflect its more diverse operations Oshkosh changed its name from Oshkosh Truck Corporation to Oshkosh Corporation in 2008.

EXECUTIVES

EVP General Counsel and Secretary, Bryan J. Blankfield, age 55, $457,744 total compensation
VP and Managing Director Oshkosh Capital, Kevin S. Ramsburg
EVP Government Operations and Industry Relations, Joseph H. (Jay) Kimmitt, age 66, $390,886 total compensation
CEO, Wilson R. Jones, age 55, $629,232 total compensation
EVP and CFO, David M. Sagehorn, age 53, $609,237 total compensation
EVP and Chief Procurement Officer, Gregory L. (Greg) Fredericksen, age 55
EVP and President Access Equipment, Frank R. Nerenhausen, age 52, $408,770 total compensation
EVP and President Fire and Emergency, James W. (Jim) Johnson, age 52
EVP Technology, Gary W. Schmiedel, age 55
EVP and President Defense, John M. Urias, age 63, $447,348 total compensation
VP and CIO, Dave Scheckkman
SVP and President Commercial, Bradley M. (Brad) Nelson
EVP and Chief Human Resources Officer, Janet L. Hogan, age 52, $134,039 total compensation
Vice President Of Engineering, Tom Quigley
Assistant Vice President Digital Marketing, Steve Tighe
Corporate Vice President Materials And P, Robert Hathaway
Executive Vice President and Chief Human Resources Officer, Robert Sims
Vice President and Deputy General Counsel, Bradford Bauknecht
EXECUTIVE VICE PRESIDENT, Stewart Sevey
Chairman, Richard M. Donnelly, age 73
Assistant Treasurer, John Verich
Auditors: DELOITTE & TOUCHE LLP

LOCATIONS

HQ: Oshkosh Corp (New)
P.O. Box 2566, Oshkosh, WI 54903-2566
Phone: 920 235-9151
Web: www.oshkoshcorporation.com

2017 Sales

	$ mil.	% of total
North America		
US	5,094	75
Other North America	191	3
Europe Africa & the Middle East	1,146	16
Rest of the world	396	6
Total	6,829	100

PRODUCTS/OPERATIONS

2017 Sales

	$ mil.	% of total
Access equipment	3,026	44
Defense	1,820	27
Commercial	1,030	15
Fire & emergency	970	14
Adjustments	(18.1)	-
Total	6,829	100

BRANDS

BRANDS
JLG Industries
Oshkosh Defense
Pierce
McNeilus
IMT
Frontline Communications
CON-E-CO
London Machinery
Jerr-Dan
Oshkosh Airport Products

Selected Products

Access equipment
  Aerial work platforms
  Boom lifts
  Scissor lifts
  Stock pickers
  Telehandlers
  Towing & recovery equipment
  Trailers
  Vertical mast lifts
Commercial
  All-make parts
  Automated mobile & stationary compactors
  Concrete batch plants
  Container handling equipment
  Demountable containers
  Rear- & front-discharge mixers
  Rear front & side loaders
  Refuse collection vehicle bodies
  Revolution®; mixer drums
Defense
  Armored wheeled vehicles
  Heavy equipment transporters (HET)
  Heavy expanded mobility tactical trucks (HEMTT)
  High-mobility trailers
  Logistic vehicle system replacements (LVSR)
  Medium tactical trucks (MTT)
  Medium tactical vehicle replacements (MTVR)
  Off road tractor/trailers
  Palletized load system (PLS) trucks & trailers
  Urban assault vehicles
Fire & emergency
  Aircraft rescue & fire fighting (ARFF) vehicles
  Ambulances
  Custom & commercial fire apparatus
  Rescue & homeland security apparatus
  Snow blowers & plow trucks

COMPETITORS

AM General	Iveco S.p.A.
BAE Systems Land & Armaments	J C Bamford Excavators
Collins Industries	L3 Technologies
Daimler	Lockheed Martin
Daimler Trucks North America	MAN
Dover Corp.	MANITOU BF
E-ONE	Mack Trucks
Federal Signal	Miller Industries
Force Protection	Navistar
General Dynamics	Navistar International
General Dynamics Land Systems	PACCAR
Haulotte	Skyjack
Heil Environmental	Spartan Motors
Hyundai Motor	Terex
	Trinity Industries
	UD Trucks
	Volvo

HISTORICAL FINANCIALS

Company Type: Public

Income Statement

FYE: September 30

	REVENUE ($ mil.)	NET INCOME ($ mil.)	NET PROFIT MARGIN	EMPLOYEES
09/17	6,829	285	4.2%	14,000
09/16	6,279	216	3.4%	13,800
09/15	6,098	229	3.8%	13,300
09/14	6,808	309	4.5%	12,000
09/13	7,665	318	4.1%	11,900
Annual Growth	(2.8%)	(2.7%)	—	4.1%

2017 Year-End Financials

Debt ratio: 16.30%
Return on equity: 13.33%
Cash ($ mil.): 447
Current ratio: 1.81
Long-term debt ($ mil.): 807
No. of shares (mil.): 75
Dividends
  Yield: 0.0%
  Payout: 22.2%
Market value ($ mil.): 6,192

	STOCK PRICE ($) FY Close	P/E High/Low		PER SHARE ($) Earnings	Dividends	Book Value
09/17	82.54	22	14	3.77	0.84	30.76
09/16	56.00	19	10	2.91	0.74	26.74
09/15	36.33	19	12	2.90	0.68	25.33
09/14	44.15	16	12	3.61	0.15	24.86
09/13	48.98	14	7	3.55	0.00	24.36
Annual Growth	13.9%	—	—	1.5%	—	6.0%

Owens & Minor, Inc.

Owens & Minor (O&M) is a leading distributor of medical and surgical supplies. The company carries products from about 1100 manufacturers. Those products include surgical dressings endoscopic and intravenous products needles syringes sterile procedure trays gowns gloves and sutures. The firm also offers software consulting and other services to help customers manage their supplies. O&M's customers are primarily hospitals and health systems and the purchasing organizations that serve them. It delivers products to roughly 4500 health care providers across the US.

Operations

O&M operates in three segments: Domestic (more than 90% of revenue) International and Clinical and Procedural Solutions(CPS). The Domestic segment provides distribution packaging and logistics services in the US while the International segment comprises its European third-party logistics and packaging businesses.CPS gathers assembles and delivers procedure kits for surgical specialties (including robotics cardiology and orthopedics) and minor procedures.

In addition to delivering products made by its supply partners the distributor sells value products under its own MediChoice label. To support its distribution operations O&M offers training programs for health professionals on topics ranging from equipment use supply management leadership and safety.

O&M's supply chain management services include third-party logistics services for medical device and pharmaceutical firms. Such services are provided by subsidiaries OM HealthCare Logistics (in the US) and Movianto (in Europe).

Geographic Reach

O&M operates some 40 distribution centers across the US.

Though US operations account for most of O&M's sales (more than 90%) the company is working to branch out into international medical distribution markets including Europe. Its Movianto unit operates 20 logistics centers in about a dozen European countries including Belgium the Czech Republic Denmark France Germany the Netherlands Poland Slovakia Spain Switzerland and the UK.

Sales and Marketing

Most of O&M's sales are attributed to contracts with acute care hospitals which are often represented by group purchasing organizations (GPOs) or integrated healthcare networks (IHNs). GPOs Novation MedAssets Premier and HealthTrust Purchasing Group are the company's largest customers. O&M also has an ongoing exclusive supplier agreement with the US Department of Defense. Additional clients include other government agencies and alternate health care locations such as physician clinics nursing homes and surgery centers. In addition O&M provides outsourced distribution services to suppliers of surgical and medical products.

About 95% of O&M's sales come from the distribution of medical supplies. The company's major product suppliers include Covidien (acquired by Medtronic in 2015) and Johnson & Johnson.

Financial Performance

O&M's revenues have remained relatively static over the past few years. In 2016 revenue fell less than 1% to $9.7 billion. Although the Domestic segment saw a small amount of growth that year (despite the loss of a major customer) that was offset by declines in the International and CPS segments. All geographic markets with the exception of Germany had slightly lower sales in 2016.

Net income which took a dip in 2014 recovered somewhat the following year. In 2016 it rose another 5% to $108.8 million as cost of goods sold distribution and selling expenses and acquisition and realignment charges went down.

Cash flow from operations declined 31% to $186.9 million. Key factors in that decline included changes in accounts and notes receivable and in other assets and liabilities.

Strategy

As the health care industry has come under pressure so have the industries that serve it. To stay competitive in a struggling market O&M restructured its operations and realigned its leadership team in 2016. Its new strategies for growth include streamlining the distribution of medical supplies by utilizing technology productivity tools and data connectivity. The company is developing a new multi-team customer engagement center in Richmond Virginia for example. Secondly O&M is working to further expand into patient settings beyond hospitals such as surgery centers clinics and other non-acute care facilities that can benefit from its offerings.

The company also works with manufacturers for whom it strives to be the delivery mechanism of choice. Finally O&M complements its product sales services by offering resource management services to care providers including physical inventory reviews inventory tracking and purchasing software.

Mergers and Acquisitions

In 2017 O&M acquired Byram Healthcare for $380 million. Byram is a nationwide distributor of direct-to-patient medical supplies including wound care incontinence and diabetes supplies.

Later that year O&M agreed to buy the surgical and infection prevention operations of medical supplies maker Halyard Health for $710 million. The purchase will include products including sterilization wraps surgical gowns and medical exam gloves.

HISTORY

George Gilmer Minor Jr.'s great-grandfather was an apothecary and surgeon in colonial Williamsburg Virginia. His grandfather was Thomas Jefferson's personal physician. Minor himself worked as a wholesale drug salesman in Richmond after the Civil War. In 1882 he and rival wholesaler Otho Owens partnered to form the Owens & Minor Drug Company. The company was both a retail and wholesale business with a storefront that filled prescriptions and sold sundries paints oils and window glass. When Owens died in 1906 Minor became the company's president.

During the 1920s the Owens family sold their stake in the firm. George Gilmer Minor III served briefly as the company's president in the early 1940s; his son George Gilmer Minor IV (called Mr. Minor Jr. to differentiate him from his father) became president in 1947.

In 1954 Owens & Minor installed its first computerized order fulfillment system. The following year the firm became Owens Minor & Bodeker when it bought the Bodeker Drug Company which was both older and larger than Owens & Minor.

After 84 years in the drug wholesale business the company entered the medical and surgical distribution business after buying A&J Hospital Supply in 1966 and Powers & Anderson in 1968. In 1971 Owens Minor & Bodeker went public. By the end of the decade the company had operations in 10 states.

The fourth Minor to run the firm G. Gilmer Minor III (Mr. Minor Jr.'s son) was named president in 1981 (he became CEO in 1984). Under his direction Owens Minor & Bodeker would complete the transition from a drug wholesaler to a medical supplies distributor. In 1981 it purchased the Will Ross subsidiary of G.D. Searle (then the country's #2 medical and surgical supplies distributor).

The company reverted to its original name on its 100th anniversary in 1982. By 1984 medical supplies supplanted wholesale drugs as its primary source of income. In 1988 Owens & Minor listed on the NYSE.

The company passed the $1 billion revenue mark in 1990 and later sold its wholesale drug business. It extended its reach with the purchase of Lyons Physician Supply in 1993 and Stuart Medical (the #3 national distributor) in 1994.

EXECUTIVES

SVP and Chief of Staff, Erika T. Davis, age 54, $513,719 total compensation

SVP Owens & Minor Europe Operations, Charles C. Colpo, age 60, $453,466 total compensation

Vice President Technology, Charles Eismamn

EVP and CFO; President International, Richard A. (Randy) Meier, age 57, $648,260 total compensation

Chairman President and CEO, P. Cody Phipps, age 55, $915,577 total compensation

EVP North American Operations, Rony C. Kordahi, age 53, $328,846 total compensation

EVP Global Manufacturer Services, Stuart Morris-Hipkins

SVP Clinical Procedural Solutions, James S. Glasscock

SVP Manufacturer Services, Geoff T. Marlatt

SVP and CIO, Stephen R. Olive

SVP Strategic Supply Management, Javara D. Perrilliat

SVP Commercial Services, Joseph B. Zaluzney

Vice President Supply Chain Performance, Scott Watkins

Vice President Global Tax, Chris McGowan

Auditors: KPMG LLP

LOCATIONS

HQ: Owens & Minor, Inc.
9120 Lockwood Boulevard, Mechanicsville, VA 23116
Phone: 804 723-7000   **Fax:** 804 723-7100
Web: www.owens-minor.com

2016 sales

	$ mil.	% of total
US	9,338	96
UK	169	2
Ireland	41	-
France	38	-
Germany	47	-
Other European countries	87	2
Total	**9,723**	**100**

PRODUCTS/OPERATIONS

2016 sales

	$ mil.	% of total
Domestic	9,191	91
International	343	3
CPS	539	6
Inter-Segment	(351.3)	-
Total	**9,723**	**100**

Selected Products and Services

Clinical Supply Solutions (inventory and contract management service)
Implant Purchase Manager (utilization contract compliance and billing)
OMDirect (Internet order fulfillment)
OMSolutions (resource management and consulting)
PANDAC system (helps track and control operating room inventories)
QSight (clinical inventory management system)
SurgiTrack (customizable surgical supply service)
WISDOM Gold (allows customers to track inventory usage and other information to keep costs down)

COMPETITORS

AmerisourceBergen	Kerma Medical Products
Buffalo Supply	McKesson
Cardinal Health	Medline Industries
DHL	PSS World Medical
FedEx	Patterson Companies
Henry Schein	SourceOne
Invacare Supply Group	Surgical Express
Johnson and Johnson	Tri-anim
Health Care Systems	UPS

HISTORICAL FINANCIALS

Company Type: Public

Income Statement

FYE: December 31

	REVENUE ($ mil.)	NET INCOME ($ mil.)	NET PROFIT MARGIN	EMPLOYEES
12/16	9,723	108	1.1%	7,900
12/15	9,772	103	1.1%	8,100
12/14	9,440	66	0.7%	5,700
12/13	9,071	110	1.2%	6,700
12/12	8,908	109	1.2%	4,800
Annual Growth	**2.2%**	**(0.0%)**	**—**	**13.3%**

2016 Year-End Financials

Debt ratio: 20.77%
Return on equity: 11.11%
Cash ($ mil.): 185
Current ratio: 1.90
Long-term debt ($ mil.): 564

No. of shares (mil.): 61
Dividends
Yield: 0.0%
Payout: 57.9%
Market value ($ mil.): 2,154

	STOCK PRICE ($) FY Close	P/E High/Low	PER SHARE ($) Earnings	Dividends	Book Value
12/16	35.29	23 18	1.76	1.02	15.73
12/15	35.98	24 19	1.65	1.01	15.80
12/14	35.11	35 30	1.06	1.00	15.71
12/13	36.56	22 16	1.76	0.96	16.23
12/12	28.51	18 16	1.72	0.88	15.37
Annual Growth	**5.5%**	**— —**	**0.6%**	**3.8%**	**0.6%**

Owens Corning

Owens Corning (OC) operates in the PINK. Famous for its Pink Panther mascot and its trademarked PINK glass fiber insulation the company is a top global maker of building and composite material systems. The building materials company makes insulation roofing fiber-based glass reinforcements and other materials for the residential and commercial markets. Its composite products business makes glass fiber reinforcement materials for the transportation industrial infrastructure marine wind energy and consumer markets. Owens Corning traces its historical roots to 1938.In early 2018 the company acquired European stone wool insulation producer Paroc Group from CVC Capital Partners for ?900 (US$1 billion).

HISTORY

In the 1930s Corning Glass Works and Owens-Illinois Glass independently found that glass fiber has special resilience and strength. Realizing the potential market they formed joint venture Owens-Corning Fiberglas in 1938. The companies expanded rapidly in the 1940s and 1950s establishing several US plants and one in Canada. Their products included fine fibers thermal wool textiles and continuous filaments.

A US antitrust decree in 1949 denied the two founding firms any control over Owens-Corning. Each retained one-third ownership when the company went public in 1952. During the 1950s Owens-Corning developed new uses for fiberglass in automobile bodies shingles and insulation. In the 1960s the company expanded overseas. Fiberglass uses multiplied as applications developed in aerospace tires and underground tanks.

By 1980 the company had invested more than $700 million in acquisitions and made the Pink Panther its mascot. Owens-Corning introduced a rolled insulation in 1982.

The company successfully fended off a takeover attempt by Wickes Companies in 1986 but the effort left Owens-Corning with $2.6 billion in debt. It sold 10 businesses halved its research budget and laid off or lost to divestitures 46% of its workforce.

The company bought Fiberglas Canada that country's largest fiberglass-insulation maker in 1989. To expand globally Owens-Corning formed alliances in 1990 with BASF Lucky-Goldstar and Siam Cement.

Owens-Corning spent $65 million in 1991 on restructuring and took an $800 million charge to cover its liability to asbestos-exposure lawsuits (the company stopped making asbestos in 1972). That year it exchanged its commercial roofing business for the residential roofing business of Schuller International.

In 1994 Owens-Corning acquired UC Industries a maker of foam board insulation and bought Pilkington's insulation and industrial supply business. It also formed joint venture Alpha/Owens-Corning the largest producer of polyester resin in North America.

The company bought Western Fiberglass Group in 1995. That year Owens-Corning Fiberglas changed its name to Owens Corning and recouped part of its asbestos-related charge when it received a $330 million arbitration settlement from one of its insurers. Owens Corning formed a joint venture in India in 1995. Asbestos-litigation charges led to another loss in 1996.

In 1997 Owens Corning made several acquisitions including vinyl-siding maker Fibreboard and Amerimark Building Products a maker of vinyl and aluminum materials. In 1998 falling insulation prices led the company to announce layoffs and a restructuring plan that included plant closures. To pay off debt the company sold its half of Alpha/Owens-Corning to Alpha Corporation marking its exit from polyester-resin manufacturing. The company also agreed to take $550 million in a deal with France's Groupe Porcher Industries to form a joint venture for its fiberglass yarns and specialty materials businesses.

Seeking to end a liability issue that had dogged the company for a quarter of a century Owens Corning agreed in 1998 to pay out $1.2 billion to settle 176000 asbestos-related lawsuits. However the deal dissolved in 1999 when the US Supreme Court disallowed the settlement. Owens Corning then set up a $2.6 billion reserve fund to settle the claims. Also that year the company formed a joint venture (Decillion) with Geon to make fiberglass and PVC composites. In 2000 Owens Corning added to its acoustic panel business with the acquisition of Conwed Designscape. Still dogged by lawsuits that could eventually cost the company billions the company filed for bankruptcy protection late in 2000.

In 2001 Owens Corning sold its engineered pipe systems business to joint venture partner Saudi Arabian Amiantit Company. Seeking a foothold in the growing acoustic ceiling market the restructured company bought Wall Technology later that year.

Owens Corning increased its loose fill and thermacube insulation products line and capacity in 2002 in response to growing demand. It also acquired Woodbridge Virginia-based Certified Basements a basement finishing systems franchise and strengthened its position in Europe through a distribution contract with an Ashland Inc. subsidiary Ashland Finland OY to distribute its composite products through Ashland Specialty Chemical Company. Also that year Owens Corning's HOM-Experts Home Repair and Improvements business expanded its service to Los Angeles San Francisco and Sacramento by acquiring assets of California-based Home Finishes LLC. (HOMExperts also operates in Atlanta Boston Chicago Denver Indianapolis Minneapolis/St. Paul and Washington DC.)

Following a period of falling stock prices for the company the New York Stock Exchange suspended its trading in December 2002. In early 2003 the company filed a bankruptcy reorganization plan to settle asbestos litigation. Under the plan Owens Corning provided partial payments to its creditors (mainly through distributing common stock and notes of the new reorganized company) and its existing common stock was canceled.

In 2004 Owens Corning Automotive (UK) Ltd. acquired the automotive assets of long-time customer Lancaster Fibre Technology Ltd. (UK). Lancaster Fibre Technology bases its automotive solutions on Owens Corning's Silentex Noise Control automotive silencer technology. It also purchased full ownership of Vitro Fibras (Mexico) a venture it had begun with Vitro (glass products Mexico) in 1957 to make light-density fiberglass products; molded pipe; board; and composite reinforcements. Owens Corning paid $71.5 million for Vitro's 60% stake.

The company emerged from bankruptcy in 2006. As part of the bankruptcy reorganization the company's paid some $5 billion in asbestos claims along with an additional $2.4 billion earmarked for debt holders.

After shedding the ponderous weight of bankruptcy the company didn't stand still. Owens Corning strengthened its composite operations in late 2007 when it acquired the reinforcements and composite fabrics business of materials giant Saint-Gobain.

While the company focused growth on its composites business it began trimming off other operations. Saint-Gobain acquired Owens Corning's vinyl siding business Norandex in 2007. Also that year it sold its continuous filament mat business to AGY and its Fabwel composite panels business to Crane.

In June 2013 Owens Corning acquired Thermafiber Inc. a manufacturer of mineral wool commercial and industrial insulation products. The purchase included a 145000 square-foot manufacturing plant in Wabash Indiana.

EXECUTIVES

Chairman President and CEO, Michael H. (Mike) Thaman, age 53, $1,140,500 total compensation
President Roofing and Asphalt, Brian D. Chambers, age 48, $450,000 total compensation
SVP Organization and Administration, Daniel T. (Dan) Smith, age 52, $527,500 total compensation
President Composite Solutions, Arnaud P. Genis, age 52, $596,667 total compensation
SVP and CFO, Michael C. McMurray, age 52, $589,167 total compensation
President Insulation, Julian Francis
Auditors: PricewaterhouseCoopers LLP

LOCATIONS

HQ: Owens Corning
One Owens Corning Parkway, Toledo, OH 43659
Phone: 419 248-8000
Web: www.owenscorning.com

2016 Sales

	$ mil.	% of total
United States	3,963	70
Asia Pacific	666	12
Europe	550	10
Canada and other	498	8
Total	**5,677**	**100**

PRODUCTS/OPERATIONS

2016 Sales

	$ mil.	% of total
Roofing	2,194	37
Composites	1,952	33
Insulation	1,748	30
Corporate eliminations	(217)	-
Total	**5,677**	**100**

COMPETITORS

Ball Corp.	Mohawk Industries
CertainTeed	Nippon Electric Glass
China Fiberglass Co.	Owens-Illinois
Ltd.	PPG Industries
Deceuninck	SIG plc
Dow Chemical	Saint-Gobain
GAF Materials	Sherwin-Williams
Johns Manville	Stanley Black and
Knauf Insulation	Decker
Lennox	TAMKO
Louisiana-Pacific	USG
Masco	Valspar

HISTORICAL FINANCIALS

Company Type: Public

Income Statement

FYE: December 31

	REVENUE ($ mil.)	NET INCOME ($ mil.)	NET PROFIT MARGIN	EMPLOYEES
12/16	5,677	393	6.9%	16,000
12/15	5,350	330	6.2%	15,000
12/14	5,276	226	4.3%	14,000
12/13	5,295	204	3.9%	15,000
12/12	5,172	(19)	—	15,000
Annual Growth	**2.4%**	**—**	**—**	**1.6%**

2016 Year-End Financials

Debt ratio: 27.15%
Return on equity: 10.33%
Cash ($ mil.): 112
Current ratio: 1.65
Long-term debt ($ mil.): 2,099
No. of shares (mil.): 112
Dividends
  Yield: 0.0%
  Payout: 21.7%
Market value ($ mil.): 5,811

	STOCK PRICE ($) FY Close	P/E High/Low	PER SHARE ($) Earnings	Dividends	Book Value
12/16	51.56	16 12	3.41	0.74	34.15
12/15	47.03	17 12	2.79	0.68	32.26
12/14	35.81	24 15	1.91	0.64	31.34
12/13	40.72	26 21	1.71	0.00	32.20
12/12	36.99	— —	(0.16)	0.00	29.91
Annual Growth	**8.7%**		**—**	**—**	**3.4%**

Owens-Illinois, Inc.

Owens-Illinois (O-I) is one of the world's largest makers of glass containers touting a leading market presence with more than 49000 customers in 85 countries around the world. O-I offers more than 10000 types of glass containers such as bottles in a wide range of shapes sizes and colors used to hold beer wine liquor as well as soft drinks juice and other beverages. It also makes glass containers for foods such as soups salad dressings and dairy products and for pharmaceuticals. Some of its products are made using recycled glass. Major customers have included such heavy hitters as Anheuser-Busch InBev Coca-Cola Diageo H.J. Heinz and Nestle.

Operations

O-I is a major glass container manufacturer catering to many of the world's leading food and beverage brands. It produces glass containers for alcoholic beverages including beer flavored malt beverages spirits and wine. It also produces glass packaging for a variety of food items including soft drinks teas juices and pharmaceuticals.

Geographic Reach

Altogether O-I operates almost 80 manufacturing plants in 23 countries. It has joint ventures in China Malaysia Mexico the US and Vietnam. In addition the company operates machine shops that rebuild and repair its glass forming machines as well as a mold shop to make molded shapes. Engineering support sites for its glass manufacturing operations are located Australia Columbia Poland Peru and the US.

The company divides its operations across four reportable segments based on geography: Europe (34% of total sales) North America (33%) Latin America (22%) and Asia/Pacific (10%).

Sales and Marketing

O-I sells most of its glass container products directly to customers under yearly or multi-year supply agreements however some of its products are sold through distributors. Customers range from large multinationals to small local breweries and wineries.Its largest customers are leading global food and beverage manufacturers including Anheuser‑Busch InBev Carlsberg Coca-Cola Constellation Diageo Heineken MillerCoors Nestle PepsiCo and Pernod Ricard.

Financial Performance

The company's revenues have fluctuated over the years; after declining in 2015 revenues jumped 9% to $6.7 billion in 2016. The growth was attributed to about $608 million of additional sales stemming from its previous Vitro acquisition. In addition on a global basis sales volumes of beer wine spirits food and non-alcoholic beverages all grew from 2015 to 2016.

O-I was conversely affected by unfavorable foreign currency exchange rates primarily due to a weaker Brazilian real Mexican peso Colombian peso Canadian dollar and British pound in relation to the US dollar. This impacted sales by $108 million in 2016 compared to 2015.

After posting a net loss of $74 million in 2015 O-I posted positive net income of $209 million in 2016 primarily due to the additional revenue from the Vitro acquisition. In addition the company's operating cash flow jumped from $608 million in 2015 to $751 million in 2016.

Strategy

O-I is placing a priority on winning over customers that have shied away from glass packaging as well as encouraging existing ones to use more. To this end its marketing efforts piggyback on the wave toward sustainable packaging. Along with developing a variety of container features and functions the company highlights the benefits of glass recyclability.

Mergers and Acquisitions

In a historic transaction O-I in 2015 acquired the food and beverage glass container business from Vitro S.A.B. de C.V. for $2.15 billion. Vitro is the largest supplier of glass containers in Mexico. The deal included Vitro's five food and beverage glass container plants in Mexico a plant in Bolivia and the food and beverage business of Vitro Packaging its North American distribution business based in Plano Texas. The transaction cemented O-I with a competitive position in the attractive glass segment within the packaging market in Mexico.

HISTORY

The Owens Bottle Machine Corp. was incorporated in Toledo Ohio in 1907 as the successor to a four-year-old New Jersey company of the same name. It initially grew by acquiring small glass companies. In 1929 Owens bought the Illinois Glass Co. (medical and pharmaceutical glass) and became Owens-Illinois Glass.

The company bought Libbey Glass (tableware) in 1935. Three years later Owens-Illinois and Corning Glass which were both studying uses for glass fiber began Owens-Corning Fiberglas a joint venture with a virtual industry monopoly.

After WWII Owens-Illinois (O-I) started to diversify beyond glass. The company went public in 1952. In 1956 it bought National Container (cardboard boxes). It also created a semi-rigid plastic container that was adopted by bleach and detergent companies.

EXECUTIVES

SVP and Chief Strategy and Innovation Officer, John Haudrich, $334,546 total compensation

SVP and Chief Administrative Officer, Paul Jarrell, $417,000 total compensation

SVP CTO and Supply Chain Officer, Giancarlo Currarino

President Asia/Pacific, Sergio Galindo

SVP and CFO, Jan A. Bertsch, $650,000 total compensation

CEO, Andres A. Lopez, $850,000 total compensation

President O-I Europe, Vitaliano Torno, $507,305 total compensation

President O-I Latin America, Miguel I. Alvarez, $380,467 total compensation

President O-I Asia Pacific, Timothy Connors

SVP and General Counsel, James W. (Jim) Baehren, $450,000 total compensation

Vice President Internet Marketing, Benjamin Hagan

Vice President of Quality, Steve Jenkins

Vice President Finance and Corporate Controller, Juan Amezquita

VP Purchasing, David Abela

Vice President and Associate General Counsel, Joseph J O'Hara

Vice President Global Business Processes, Jim Nordmeyer

L Ki Lu Vice President Global Supply Chain, Carlos Londono

Vice President Strategy and Integration, Brett Miller

Vice President and Chief Procurement Officer, David Furr

Vice President, Randolph Burns

Vice President Global Product Management and Innovation, Asad Hamid

Chairman, Carol A. Williams

Treasurer and Vice President of Investor Relations, Dave Johnson

Auditors: Ernst & Young LLP

LOCATIONS

HQ: Owens-Illinois, Inc.
One Michael Owens Way, Perrysburg, OH 43551
Phone: 567 336-5000
Web: www.o-i.com

2016 Sales

	$ mil.	% of total
Europe	2,300	34
North America	2,220	33
Latin America	1,432	22
Asia Pacific	684	10
Other	66	1
Total	**6,702**	**100**

PRODUCTS/OPERATIONS

Selected Subsidiaries

Owens-Illinois Group Inc.
OI General Finance Inc.
OI General FTS Inc.
OI Castalia STS Inc.
OI Levis Park STS Inc.
Owens-Illinois General Inc.
Owens Insurance Ltd.
Universal Materials Inc.
OI Advisors Inc.
OI Securities Inc.
OI Transfer Inc.
Maumee Air Associates Inc.
OI Australia Inc.
Continental PET Holdings Pty. Ltd.
ACI America Holdings Inc.
ACI Ventures Inc.
Owens-Brockway Packaging Inc.
Owens-Brockway Glass Container Inc.
OI Andover Group Inc.
The Andover Group Inc.
Brockway Realty Corporation
NHW Auburn LLC
OI Auburn Inc.
SeaGate Inc.
SeaGate II Inc.

COMPETITORS

Amcor	Plastipak
Anchor Glass	Reynolds Group
AptarGroup	Holdings Limited
Arconic	Saint-Gobain
BWAY	Saint-Gobain
Ball Corp.	Containers
Bemis	Sealed Air Corp.
Berry Global	Silgan
Consolidated Container	Sonoco Products
Crown Holdings	Tetra Pak
Graham Packaging	Tupperware Brands
Newell Brands	Vidrala

HISTORICAL FINANCIALS

Company Type: Public

Income Statement

FYE: December 31

	REVENUE ($ mil.)	NET INCOME ($ mil.)	NET PROFIT MARGIN	EMPLOYEES
12/17	6,869	180	2.6%	26,500
12/16	6,702	209	3.1%	27,000
12/15	6,156	(74)	—	27,000
12/14	6,784	75	1.1%	21,100
12/13	6,967	184	2.6%	22,500
Annual Growth	**(0.4%)**	**(0.5%)**	**—**	**4.2%**

2017 Year-End Financials

Debt ratio: 54.15%
Return on equity: 33.90%
Cash ($ mil.): 492
Current ratio: 1.06
Long-term debt ($ mil.): 5,121
No. of shares (mil.): 163
Dividends
Yield: —
Payout: —
Market value ($ mil.): 3,615

	STOCK PRICE ($) FY Close	P/E High/Low	PER SHARE ($) Earnings	Dividends	Book Value
12/17	22.17	23 16	1.10	0.00	4.95
12/16	17.41	16 9	1.28	0.00	1.56
12/15	17.42	—	(0.47)	0.00	2.90
12/14	26.99	78 51	0.45	0.00	7.05
12/13	35.78	32 19	1.11	0.00	8.84
Annual Growth	**(11.3%)**	**— —**	**(0.2%)**	**—**	**(13.5%)**

PACCAR Inc.

PACCAR is one of the world's largest designers and manufacturers of big rig diesel trucks. Its lineup of light- medium- and heavy-duty trucks includes the Kenworth Peterbilt and DAF nameplates. The company also manufactures and distributes aftermarket truck parts for these brands. PACCAR's other products include Braden Carco and Gearmatic industrial winches. With the exception of a few company-owned branches PACCAR's trucks and parts are sold through independent dealers. Its PACCAR Financial Services and PacLease subsidiaries offer financing and truck leasing respectively.

Operations

PACCAR's truck segment generates roughly 75% of total sales while parts accounts for nearly 20%. The remainder comes from its financial services and other segment.

Geographic Reach

The company owns manufacturing plants in five US states four countries in Europe and a facility in each of Australia Canada South America and Mexico. PACCAR Financial Services operates through three continents spanning around 20 countries.

In the European light/medium market PACCAR competes with DAF cab-over-engine trucks assembled in the UK by Leyland. About 45% of PACCAR's revenues are generated outside the US with nearly 30% coming from Europe.

Sales and Marketing

PACCAR delivers its products and services to customers worldwide in 100 countries through its dealer network of more than 2100 locations.

Financial Performance

After PACCAR posting record-setting revenues of $19.1 billion in 2015 the company saw its revenues decline 11% to $17 billion in 2016. This was attributed to a decrease in worldwide truck net sales primarily due to lower truck deliveries in the US and Canada partially offset by higher truck deliveries in Europe. Its parts segment also decreased by 2% in 2016 primarily due to lower aftermarket demand in North America and the unfavorable effects of translating weaker foreign currencies into the US dollar.

In addition to revenues PACCAR's net income fell 67% from $1.6 billion in 2015 to $522 million in 2016. This was attributed to a non-recurring non-tax-deductible European Commission (EC) settlement charge of $833 million it paid that was related to fines for fixing truck prices over a 14-year period. (Many other major European truck makers also reached settlements.) The significant EC charge also reduced PACCAR's operating cash flow by 10% from $2.6 billion in 2015 to $2.3 billion in 2016.

Strategy

To achieve growth PACCAR regularly expands its vehicle product range invests in truck and engine technologies that enhance vehicle fuel efficiency and reliability and reinforces and upgrades its manufacturing and parts distribution facilities. It spent $403 million in 2016 on capital investments in 2016 compared to $308 million in 2015; this reflected additional investments for the construction of a new DAF cab paint facility in Belgium a Peterbilt plant expansion in Denton Texas and a new parts distribution center (PDC) in Renton Washington.

HISTORY

William Pigott founded the Seattle Car Manufacturing Company in 1905 to produce railroad cars for timber transport. Finding immediate success Pigott began to make other kinds of railcars in 1906. When the Seattle plant burned the next year the company moved near Renton Washington. In 1911 Pigott renamed the company Seattle Car & Foundry.

In 1917 Seattle Car merged with the Twohy Brothers of Portland. The new company Pacific Car & Foundry was sold to American Car & Foundry in 1924. Pacific Car then diversified into bus manufacturing structural steel fabrications and metal technology.

Pacific Car was in decline by 1934 when William's son Paul bought it; since then the company has remained under family management. Paul Pigott added Hofius Steel and Equipment and Tricoach a bus manufacturer in 1936. The company entered the truck-making business with the 1945 purchase of Seattle-based Kenworth.

In the 1950s Pacific Car became the industry leader in mechanical refrigerator car production. It began producing off-road heavy trucks and acquired Peterbilt Trucks of Oakland (1958). To augment its winch business Pacific Car bought Canada's Gearmatic in 1963.

The company moved its headquarters to Bellevue Washington in 1969 and changed its name to PACCAR in 1971.

EXECUTIVES

Vice President Human Resources, Jack Levier
President, Ronald E. (Ron) Armstrong, age 61, $1,210,000 total compensation
SVP and General Manager Peterbilt, T. Kyle Quinn, age 56, $440,000 total compensation
EVP and CFO, Harrie C.A.M. Schippers, age 55, $396,022 total compensation
SVP Financial Services, Robert A. Bengston, age 61, $449,615 total compensation
EVP, Gary L Moore, age 61, $547,693 total compensation
VP and General Manager KW, C. Michael Dozier
VP PACCAR and President DAF Trucks N.V., R. Preston Feight, age 49
VP and CIO, A. Lily Ley, age 51
Executive Vice President, Dan Sobic
Vice President, James Cardillo
Vice President And General Manager Canadian Operations, Jay Van Leeuwen
Vice President Information Technology, Tom Plimpton
National Account Manager, Ian Griffin
Executive Chairman, Mark C. Pigott, age 64
Treasurer, Ulrich Kammholz
Auditors: Ernst & Young LLP

LOCATIONS

HQ: PACCAR Inc.
777 - 106th Ave. N.E., Bellevue, WA 98004
Phone: 425 468-7400
Web: www.paccar.com

2016 Sales

	$ mil.	% of total
US	9,221	54
Europe	4,903	29
Other regions	2,908	17
Total	**17,033**	**100**

PRODUCTS/OPERATIONS

2016 Sales

	$ mil.	% of total
Truck	12,767	75
Parts	3,005	18
Financial services	1,186	7
Other	73	-
Total	**17,033**	**100**

Selected Divisions and Subsidiaries

DAF Trucks N.V. (The Netherlands)
Kenworth
Kenworth Mexicana S.A. de C.V.
Leyland Trucks Limited (UK)
PACCAR Australia Pty. Ltd.
PACCAR Engines
PACCAR Financial Corp.
PACCAR Mexico S.A. de C.V.
PACCAR of Canada Ltd.
  Canadian Kenworth Co.
  Peterbilt of Canada
PACCAR Parts
PACCAR Sales North America Inc.
PACCAR Winch
  Braden Winches & Hoists
  Carco Winches
  Gearmatic Winches

COMPETITORS

AGCO	Iveco S.p.A.
CNH Industrial	MAN
Caterpillar	Mack Trucks
Cummins	Meritor
Dana	Morris Material
Deere	Handling
Eaton	Navistar International
Fiat Chrysler	Oshkosh Truck
Ford Motor	Scania
General Motors	UD Trucks
Hino Motors	Volvo
Isuzu	

HISTORICAL FINANCIALS

Company Type: Public

Income Statement

FYE: December 31

	REVENUE ($ mil.)	NET INCOME ($ mil.)	NET PROFIT MARGIN	EMPLOYEES
12/16	17,033	521	3.1%	23,000
12/15	19,115	1,604	8.4%	23,000
12/14	18,997	1,358	7.2%	23,300
12/13	17,123	1,171	6.8%	21,800
12/12	17,050	1,111	6.5%	21,800
Annual Growth	**(0.0%)**	**(17.2%)**	**—**	**1.3%**

2016 Year-End Financials

Debt ratio: 41.06%
Return on equity: 7.59%
Cash ($ mil.): 1,915
Current ratio: 1.85
Long-term debt ($ mil.): 8,475

No. of shares (mil.): 350
Dividends
  Yield: 0.0%
  Payout: 105.4%
Market value ($ mil.): 22,410

	STOCK PRICE ($) FY Close	P/E High/Low		PER SHARE ($) Earnings	Dividends	Book Value
12/16	63.90	46	30	1.48	1.56	19.33
12/15	47.40	15	10	4.51	2.32	19.76
12/14	68.01	18	14	3.82	1.86	19.05
12/13	59.17	18	14	3.30	1.70	18.73
12/12	45.21	15	11	3.12	1.58	16.54
Annual Growth	**9.0%**	**—**	**—**	**(17.0%)**	**(0.3%)**	**4.0%**

Pacific Premier Bancorp Inc

Auditors: Crowe Horwath LLP

LOCATIONS

HQ: Pacific Premier Bancorp Inc
17901 Von Karman Avenue, Suite 1200, Irvine, CA 92614
Phone: 949 864-8000
Web: www.ppbi.com

HISTORICAL FINANCIALS

Company Type: Public

Income Statement

FYE: December 31

	ASSETS ($ mil.)	NET INCOME ($ mil.)	INCOME AS % OF ASSETS	EMPLOYEES
12/16	4,036	40	1.0%	448
12/15	2,790	25	0.9%	335
12/14	2,038	16	0.8%	285
12/13	1,714	8	0.5%	231
12/12	1,173	15	1.3%	183
Annual Growth	**36.2%**	**26.3%**	**—**	**25.1%**

2016 Year-End Financials

Debt ratio: 9.84%
Return on equity: 10.54%
Cash ($ mil.): 160
Current ratio: —
Long-term debt ($ mil.): —

No. of shares (mil.): 27
Dividends
  Yield: —
  Payout: —
Market value ($ mil.): 983

	STOCK PRICE ($) FY Close	P/E High/Low		PER SHARE ($) Earnings	Dividends	Book Value
12/16	35.35	24	13	1.46	0.00	16.54
12/15	21.25	20	12	1.19	0.00	13.86
12/14	17.33	18	14	0.96	0.00	11.81
12/13	15.74	28	18	0.54	0.00	10.52
12/12	10.24	8	4	1.44	0.00	9.85
Annual Growth	**36.3%**	**—**	**—**	**0.3%**	**—**	**13.8%**

Pacificorp

PacifiCorp has refocused on its core businesses: regulated utilities Pacific Power and Rocky Mountain Power which together provide electricity to 1.8 million customers in six western states. The subsidiaries operate 16300 miles of transmission lines and 62800 miles of distribution lines. PacifiCorp owns or has stakes in almost 75 thermal hydroelectric and renewable generation facilities that supply its utilities with about 10600 MW of net capacity. Its PacifiCorp Energy unit purchases power from other generators and it sells excess power to wholesale customers in the western US. The company is a unit of Berkshire Hathaway's MidAmerican Energy Holdings.

Operations

PacifiCorp consists of three business units: PacifiCorp Energy (electric generation commercial energy trading and coal mining) Pacific Power (electricity distribution to customers in Oregon Washington and California) and Rocky Mountain Power (power distribution to customers in Utah Wyoming and Idaho).

Geographic Reach

PacifiCorp is headquartered in Oregon and serves customers in California Idaho Oregon Utah Washington and Wyoming.

Financial Performance

PacifiCorp's 2013 revenues followed a years long trend and rose by about 5% to $5.14 billion from $4.88 billion in 2012 due to higher energy prices. Net income also increased by 27% to $682 million from $537 million the prior year due to some unusual items which lead to lower after tax charges. Exclusive of those net income rose 11%. Cash from operations on the other hand decreased about 5% from $1.62 billion to $1.55 billion as the company used cash to pay income taxes.

Strategy

As part of its plan to continuously expand it generating capacity PacifiCorp through Rocky Mountain Power began building a 9000-panel solar farm in Utah that will provide power for about 500 homes.

EXECUTIVES

Senior Vice President and Group Risk Director, Robert Klein

Chairman and CEO, Gregory E. (Greg) Abel, age 54

President and CEO Pacific Power, Stefan A. Bird, age 47

President PacifiCorp Transmission, R. Patrick (Pat) Reiten, age 56, $320,000 total compensation

SVP and CFO, Douglas K. (Doug) Stuver, age 53, $252,000 total compensation

President and CEO Rocky Mountain Power, Cindy A. Crane, age 55, $224,538 total compensation

SVP Transmission and System Operations, Natalie L. Hocken, age 47

President and CEO PacifiCorp Energy, Michael G. Dunn, age 52, $320,000 total compensation

Vice President and Assistant General Counsel, Ann Johnson

Vice President and General Counsel, Bret Reich

Vp And Chief Environmental Counsel, Cathy Woollums

Vice President Customer Service, Paula Broussard

Vice President Services, Loren Morse

Executive Vice President of Operations, Deanna Thompson

Vice President and General Counsel, Sarah Kamman

VICE PRESIDENT OF RESEARCH AND DEVELOPMENT, Blackham Bruce

EXECUTIVE VICE PRESIDENT OF PROFESSIONAL DEVELOPMENT, Jeff Howcroft

Member Board of Directors, Melissa Nottingham

Auditors: Deloitte & Touche LLP

LOCATIONS

HQ: Pacificorp
825 N.E. Multnomah Street, Portland, OR 97232
Phone: 888 221-7070
Web: www.pacificorp.com

PRODUCTS/OPERATIONS

2016 Customers

	% of total
Residential	87
Commercial	11
Industrial and irrigation	2
Total	**100**

Selected Subsidiaries

Pacific Power
Rocky Mountain Power

COMPETITORS

AES Wind Generation
Avista
Bonneville Power
Cascade Natural Gas
Chelan County PUD
Dominion Questar
Edison International
First Wind Holdings
IDACORP
Idaho Power
NV Energy
NW Natural
PG&E Corporation
PPL Montana
Pacific Gas and Electric
Pinnacle West
Portland General Electric
Public Utility District No. 1 of Clark County
Puget Energy
Questar Gas
Riverside Electric Utility
San Diego Gas & Electric
Seattle City Light
Sempra Energy
Sierra Pacific Power

HISTORICAL FINANCIALS

Company Type: Public

Income Statement

FYE: December 31

	REVENUE ($ mil.)	NET INCOME ($ mil.)	NET PROFIT MARGIN	EMPLOYEES
12/16	5,201	763	14.7%	5,600
12/15	5,232	695	13.3%	5,700
12/14	5,252	698	13.3%	5,900
12/13	5,147	682	13.3%	6,000
12/12	4,882	537	11.0%	6,300
Annual Growth	**1.6%**	**9.2%**	**—**	**(2.9%)**

2016 Year-End Financials

Debt ratio: 32.82%
Return on equity: 10.22%
Cash ($ mil.): 17
Current ratio: 1.13
Long-term debt ($ mil.): 7,021

No. of shares (mil.): 357
Dividends
  Yield: —
  Payout: 114.6%
Market value ($ mil.): 39,984

	STOCK PRICE ($) FY Close	P/E High/Low	Earnings	Dividends	Book Value
12/16	112.00	— —	(0.00)	6.00	20.70
12/15	112.00	— —	(0.00)	6.00	21.02
12/14	106.50	— —	(0.00)	6.00	21.73
12/13	105.00	— —	(0.00)	6.00	21.81
12/12	101.00	— —	(0.00)	6.00	21.41
Annual Growth	**2.6%**	**— —**	**—**	**(0.0%)**	**(0.8%)**

Packaging Corp of America

One of the largest containerboard manufacturers in the US Packaging Corporation of America (PCA) produces about 3.7 million tons of containerboard a year most of which is converted into corrugated boxes and ships about 51.3 billion square feet of corrugated products. PCA's mills also churn out about 1.1 million tons of kraft linerboard and about a million tons of semi-chemical corrugating medium. The company sells to a diverse group of industries. Its corrugated packaging includes shipping containers for manufactured goods retail boxes and displays and wax-coated boxes and meat boxes for agricultural use.

Operations

The company operates in three segments: packaging paper and corporate and other. Packaging which accounts for almost 80% of sales produces a variety of corrugated packaging products. The paper segment 20% of sales makes and sells a range of papers including communication papers and pressure sensitive papers (collectively white papers) and market pulp. PCA?s Paper segment operates under the trade name Boise Paper. Corporate and other includes support staff services and related assets and liabilities transportation assets and activity related to other ancillary support operations.

Nationwide the corrugated products industry consists of 500 companies and 1200 plants. Plants generally serve a market radius of around 150 miles. At PCA more than 80% of the containerboard produced at its plants are used by its corrugated products locations. External customers use the remaining output. Along with containerboard corrugated containers retail packaging storage supplies and heavy-duty packaging products the company provides services including graphics design technical support value improvement branding and e-commerce support.

Geographic Reach

PCA operates eight containerboard mills (five containerboard mills and three paper mills) and about 100 corrugated products plants in more than 35 US states. The company's substantial manufacturing footprint is enhanced by a technical and development hub half a dozen regional graphic design centers and several printing and distribution sites.

PCA also leases cutting rights on 75000 acres of timberland and has supply agreements on an additional 281000 acres — most neighboring its Counce Tennessee and Valdosta Georgia mills. The company operates also has some converting operations in China and Canada.

Sales and Marketing

PCA promotes its products through a direct sales and marketing force as well as independent brokers and distribution partners. It employs a sales manager and sales representatives at most of its corrugated product manufacturing locations. The company serves 17000 customers in more than 34000 locations. About three-quarters of sales of corrugated products go to local and regional accounts (located near a single PCA plant); remaining sales come from national accounts (customers who have widespread locations and are served by several PCA plants). Products are distributed by rail or truck. PCA's largest paper segment customer is Office Depot which contributes more than 40% of net sales.

Financial Performance

PCA?s revenues increased marginally by 1% from $5.74 billion in 2015 to $5.78 billion in 2016. PCA's profits jumped 3% from $437 million in 2015 to $450 million in 2016 and cash flow jumped from $763 million to $801 million during that same time period.

The light growth for 2016 was fueled by a 2% bump in packaging sales. This was driven by increased corrugated products sales volume of $177 million of which $117 million was related to its TimBar and Columbus acquisitions. Paper sales however decreased 4% in 2016 primarily due to the closing of the market pulp operations of a mill located in Washington.

Strategy

The company has been trimming its operations in order to increase its profits. In 2015 it sold its Hexacomb corrugated manufacturing operations in Mexico and Europe for $23 million. The year before PCA exited it newsprint business.

Mergers and Acquisitions

PCA uses acquisitions as a means for bolstering its manufacturing capacity and extending its geographic footprint. In 2016 it acquired Pennsylvania-based TimBar Corporation for $387 million. TimBar is a corrugated products producer with six corrugated products production facilities.

Also that year PCA picked up Indiana-based Columbus Container for $100 million. Columbus is a corrugated products producer with one corrugated products production facility and five warehousing facilities.

Company Background

PCA was formed by Madison Dearborn in 1999 in order to acquire the containerboard and corrugated product operations of Pactiv. PCA blossomed five years later when it purchased the assets of Acorn Corrugated Box Company a maker of graphics packaging and displays.

EXECUTIVES

Vice President Human Resources, Stephen T Calhoun

Chairman and CEO, Mark W. Kowlzan, age 62, $1,157,004 total compensation

EVP Corrugated Products, Thomas A. (Tom) Hassfurther, age 61, $913,002 total compensation

SVP General Counsel and Corporate Secretary, Kent A. Pflederer, age 46, $478,002 total compensation

SVP Sales and Marketing Corrugated Products, Thomas W. H. (Tom) Walton, age 57, $361,002 total compensation

SVP Mill Operations, Charles J. (Jack) Carter, age 58, $519,670 total compensation

SVP and CFO, Robert P. (Bob) Mundy, age 55, $618,000 total compensation

Vice President Tax, Darla Olivier

Vice President Engineering, Nam Shin

Vice President Containerboard Mill Operations, Jack Carter

Vice President, Cheryl Sheffield

Vice President And General Manager, Donald Haag

Vice President Engineering, Annie Kim

Vice President Technology Development, Al Forbes

Vice President Operation Services, Bryan Sorensen

Vice President Containerboard Sales, Gerald Greeter

Vice President, Kevin Hart

Senior Vice President and Chief Financial Officer, Richard West

Vice President, Bernadette Madarieta

Auditors: KPMG LLP

LOCATIONS

HQ: Packaging Corp of America
1955 West Field Court, Lake Forest, IL 60045
Phone: 847 482-3000
Web: www.packagingcorp.com

PRODUCTS/OPERATIONS

2016 Sales

	% of total
Packaging	79
Paper	19
Corporate and other	2
Total	**100**

Selected Products:
Corrugated Containers
Retail Packaging and Displays
Heavy-Duty Packaging
Produce Packaging
Hexacomb
Falconboard
Tharco Stock Boxes

Record Storage Boxes
Interior Packaging
Packaging Supplies
Printing Capabilities
Containerboard

COMPETITORS

Amcor	Kapstone Paper and
Atlas Container	Packaging
Bio Pappel	Norampac
Georgia-Pacific	Pratt Industries USA
Graphic Packaging	Sonoco Products
Holding	Southern Container
Greif	corp
International Paper	WestRock

HISTORICAL FINANCIALS
Company Type: Public

Income Statement
FYE: December 31

	REVENUE ($ mil.)	NET INCOME ($ mil.)	NET PROFIT MARGIN	EMPLOYEES
12/16	5,779	449	7.8%	14,000
12/15	5,741	436	7.6%	13,000
12/14	5,852	392	6.7%	14,000
12/13	3,665	436	11.9%	13,600
12/12	2,843	163	5.8%	8,600
Annual Growth	**19.4%**	**28.7%**	**—**	**13.0%**

2016 Year-End Financials

Debt ratio: 46.17%	No. of shares (mil.): 94
Return on equity: 26.43%	Dividends
Cash ($ mil.): 239	Yield: 0.0%
Current ratio: 2.71	Payout: 49.6%
Long-term debt ($ mil.): 2,640	Market value ($ mil.): 7,991

	STOCK PRICE ($) FY Close	P/E High/Low		PER SHARE ($) Earnings	Dividends	Book Value
12/16	84.82	18	9	4.75	2.36	18.68
12/15	63.05	19	13	4.47	2.20	16.99
12/14	78.05	20	15	3.99	1.60	15.47
12/13	63.28	14	9	4.47	1.51	13.37
12/12	38.47	23	15	1.68	1.00	9.88
Annual Growth	**21.9%**	**—**	**—**	**29.7%**	**23.9%**	**17.3%**

PacWest Bancorp

PacWest Bancorp is the holding company for Pacific Western Bank which operates about 80 branches mostly in southern and central California plus an additional branch in Durham North Carolina. The $21 billion-asset bank caters to small and midsized businesses and their owners and employees offering traditional deposit and loan products and services. Commercial real estate mortgages make up more than 30% of its loan portfolio while cash flow- and asset-based business loans make up another 40%. The bank also originates residential mortgage real estate construction and land loans venture capital equipment finance and consumer loans. PacWest offers investment services and international banking through agreements with correspondent banks.

Operations

Like other retail banks PacWest generates the bulk of its revenue from interest income. About 83% of its total revenue came from interest income on loans and leases during 2015 while another 7% came from interest income on investments. The rest of its revenue came from leased equip-

ment income (3% of revenue) deposit account service charges (1%) other commissions and fees (3%) and other miscellaneous income sources.

The bank's Square 1 Bank Division caters to entrepreneurial businesses and their venture capital and private equity investors while its CapitalSource Division provides cash flow asset-based equipment and real estate loans and leases as well as treasury management services to established middle-market businesses across the country.

Geographic Reach

PWB's branches are located across California in Los Angeles Orange Riverside San Bernardino Santa Barbara San Diego San Francisco San Luis Obispo San Mateo and Ventura Counties. It also has a branch in Durham North Carolina.

Financial Performance

PacWest's acquisitions in 2014 and 2015 boosted its interest-earning loan asset balances more than three-fold which sent its revenues and profits soaring during those years.

The bank's revenue jumped 30% to $968.3 million during 2015 mostly as newly acquired loans from its CapitalSource boosted its interest income during the year.

Strong revenue growth coupled with lower acquisition integration and reorganization costs in 2015 drove PacWest's net income up 77% to $300 million. Its operating cash levels spiked 79% to $594 million with the rise in cash-denominated earnings.

Strategy

PacWest has grown its loan and deposit business as well as its branch network through acquisitions of California community banks and specialized financial services companies. It has made 28 acquisitions since 2000 with some of its most recent being the Square 1 acquisition in 2015 and the CapitalSource Inc. acquisition in 2014.

Mergers and Acquisitions

In October 2015 PacWest purchased $4.6 billion-asset Square 1 and its Square 1 Bank subsidiary for $849 million forming the Square 1 Bank Division of the Bank. The deal boosted its core deposits expanded its national lending platform and bolstered its presence in the technology and life-sciences markets.

In April 2014 the bank bought $10.7 billion-asset CapitalSource Inc. and its CapitalSource Bank (CSB) subsidiary.

In May 2013 PacWest acquired $1.7 billion-asset First California Financial Group operator of First California Bank for $237 million. The purchase added six branches (after consolidation) in Los Angeles Orange Riverside San Bernardino San Diego San Luis Obispo and Ventura Counties.

Company Background

During the economic downturn PacWest took advantage of a rash of bank failures through FDIC-assisted transactions. The acquired institutions were merged into Pacific Western Bank. Under the loss-sharing deals the FDIC agreed to reimburse PacWest for future losses tied to the acquisitions. In a 2012 non-FDIC-assisted deal PacWest bought American Perspective Bank adding two branches and a loan office in the Central Coast area.

EXECUTIVES

EVP and Director the Company and Pacific Western Bank, Daniel B. Platt, age 70, $52,500 total compensation

EVP and Chief Risk Officer, Suzanne R. Brennan, age 66, $165,000 total compensation

CEO, Matthew P. (Matt) Wagner, age 60, $754,167 total compensation

EVP and CFO Pacific Western Bank, Patrick J. (Pat) Rusnak, age 53

EVP and Chief Accounting Officer, Lynn M. Hopkins, age 49

EVP; Director Human Resources, Christopher D. Blake, age 57, $298,958 total compensation

EVP and Chief Credit Officer, Bryan M. Corsini, age 55, $375,624 total compensation

EVP; President CapitalSource, James J. (Jim) Pieczynski, age 54, $554,539 total compensation

EVP Operations and Systems, Mark Christian

EVP General Counsel and Corporate Secretary, Kori L. Ogrosky

Chairman, John M. Eggemeyer, age 71

Auditors: KPMG LLP

LOCATIONS

HQ: PacWest Bancorp
9701 Wilshire Blvd., Suite 700, Beverly Hills, CA 90212

Phone: 310 887-8500

Web: www.pacwestbancorp.com

PRODUCTS/OPERATIONS

2015 Sales

	% of total
Interest income	
Loans and leases	87
Investment securities & other	7
Noninterest income	
Other commissions and fees	3
Leased equipment income	3
Service charges on deposit accounts	1
Other	3
FDIC loss sharing expense net	-
Total	**100**

Selected Mergers & Acquisitions

COMPETITORS

Bank of America	Rabobank America
CVB Financial	San Diego County
California Bank &	Credit Union
Trust	U.S. Bancorp
City National	Wells Fargo
JPMorgan Chase	Westamerica
MUFG Americas Holdings	

HISTORICAL FINANCIALS

Company Type: Public

Income Statement
FYE: December 31

	ASSETS ($ mil.)	NET INCOME ($ mil.)	INCOME AS % OF ASSETS	EMPLOYEES
12/16	21,869	352	1.6%	1,669
12/15	21,288	299	1.4%	1,670
12/14	16,234	168	1.0%	1,443
12/13	6,533	45	0.7%	1,110
12/12	5,463	56	1.0%	991
Annual Growth	**41.4%**	**57.8%**	**—**	**13.9%**

2016 Year-End Financials

Debt ratio: 2.20%
Return on equity: 7.91%
Cash ($ mil.): 419
Current ratio: —
Long-term debt ($ mil.): —

No. of shares (mil.): 121
Dividends
Yield: 0.0%
Payout: 68.9%
Market value ($ mil.): 6,603

	STOCK PRICE ($) FY Close	P/E High/Low	Earnings	Dividends	Book Value
12/16	54.44	19 10	2.90	2.00	36.93
12/15	43.10	17 14	2.79	2.00	36.22
12/14	45.46	25 20	1.92	1.25	34.04
12/13	42.22	40 23	1.08	1.00	17.66
12/12	24.77	16 13	1.54	0.79	15.74
Annual Growth	**21.8%**	**— —**	**17.1%**	**26.1%**	**23.8%**

Park National Corp (Newark, OH)

Customers can park their money with Park National. The holding company owns Park National Bank which operates more than 120 branches in Ohio and northern Kentucky through 11 community banking divisions. The banks provide an array of consumer and business banking services including traditional savings and checking accounts and CDs. Business loans including commercial leases and mortgages operating loans and agricultural loans account for about 35% of Park National's loan portfolio. The banks also originate consumer residential real estate and construction loans. Park National's nonbank units include consumer finance outfit Guardian Finance Scope Aircraft Finance and Park Title Agency.In 2018 it acquired Charlotte NC-based NewDominion Bank for some $75 million.

Operations

Each of Park National Corporation's bank affiliates specialize in serving specific geographic locations. It's bank divisions include: Century National Bank; Fairfield National Bank; Farmers Bank; First-Knox National Bank; Park National Bank; Richland Bank; Security National Bank; Second National Bank; Unity National Bank; and United Bank.

Geographic Reach

Park National Corporation and its subsidiaries operate in Ohio and northern Kentucky.

Financial Performance

The company's revenue decreased in fiscal 2013 compared to the previous year. It reported $336.2 million in revenue for fiscal 2013 down from $378.1 million in fiscal 2012.

The company's net income dropped slightly in fiscal 2013 compared to the prior period as well. It reported a net income of $77 million in fiscal 2013 after netting a little more than $78 million the prior year.

Park National Corporation's cash on hand increased by almost $10 million in fiscal 2013 compared to fiscal 2012 levels.

EXECUTIVES

President and CEO, David L. Trautman, age 55, $775,000 total compensation

CFO Treasurer and Secretary; SVP and CFO Park National Bank, Brady T. Burt, age 42, $325,000 total compensation

Chairman, C. Daniel (Dan) DeLawder, age 67

Auditors: Crowe Horwath LLP

LOCATIONS

HQ: Park National Corp (Newark, OH)
50 North Third Street, Newark, OH 43055

Phone: 740 349-8451

Web: www.parknationalcorp.com

PRODUCTS/OPERATIONS

2015 Sales

	$ mil.	% of total
Interest and fees on loans	228	66
Interest and dividends	37	10
Income from fiduciary activities	20	7
Service charges on deposit accounts	14	4
Checkcard fee income	14	4
Other service income	11	3
Other	16	6
Total	**342**	**100**

Selected Affiliates

Century National Bank
Fairfield National Bank
Farmers Bank
First-Knox National Bank
Guardian Finance Company
Park National Bank
Richland Bank
Scope Aircraft Finance
Second National Bank
Security National Bank
United bank
Unity National Bank

COMPETITORS

Bank of America	U.S. Bancorp
Fifth Third	Wayne Savings
Huntington Bancshares	Bancshares
JPMorgan Chase	Wells Fargo
PNC Financial	

HISTORICAL FINANCIALS

Company Type: Public

Income Statement
FYE: December 31

	ASSETS ($ mil.)	NET INCOME ($ mil.)	INCOME AS % OF ASSETS	EMPLOYEES
12/16	7,467	86	1.2%	1,726
12/15	7,311	81	1.1%	1,793
12/14	7,003	84	1.2%	1,801
12/13	6,638	77	1.2%	1,836
12/12	6,642	78	1.2%	1,826
Annual Growth	**3.0%**	**2.3%**	**—**	**(1.4%)**

2016 Year-End Financials

Debt ratio: 4.54%
Return on equity: 11.80%
Cash ($ mil.): 146
Current ratio: —
Long-term debt ($ mil.): —

No. of shares (mil.): 15
Dividends
Yield: 0.0%
Payout: 67.2%
Market value ($ mil.): 1,836

	STOCK PRICE ($) FY Close	P/E High/Low	Earnings	Dividends	Book Value
12/16	119.66	22 14	5.59	3.76	48.38
12/15	90.48	19 15	5.26	3.76	46.53
12/14	88.48	16 13	5.46	3.76	45.39
12/13	85.07	17 13	5.01	3.76	42.29
12/12	64.63	15 13	4.88	3.76	42.20
Annual Growth	**16.6%**	**— —**	**3.5%**	**(0.0%)**	**3.5%**

Parker Hannifin Corp

Parker-Hannifin is a leading global manufacturer of motion and control technologies including fluid power systems for the manufacturing and processing industries. It additionally makes hydraulic fuel pneumatic and electromechanical systems and components for the aerospace/defense industry; and motion and control systems for the heating ventilation air conditioning and refrigeration (HVACR) and transportation industries. It owns some 330 manufacturing plants and operates through the two business segments of Diversified Industrial and Aerospace. The company traces its historical roots back to 1918.

Operations

Parker-Hannifin is a worldwide diversified manufacturer of motion and control technologies and systems. It provides precision engineered technologies products and services for a wide variety of mobile industrial and aerospace markets.

Its largest division the Industrial segment is made up of the Automation Filtration Fluid Connectors Hydraulics Instrumentation and Seal groups. Sales of Industrial products in North American and international markets are made primarily to original equipment manufacturers (OEMs) and their replacement markets in various sectors within the manufacturing processing and transportation industries. They include agriculture alternative energy chemical processing construction machinery factory automation food production life sciences material handling paper robotics and water among many others.

Aerospace segment products are sold mainly to commercial and military customers in the OEM and maintenance repair and overhaul end user markets. They are used in aircraft engines missiles unmanned aerial vehicles and in power generation applications.

Geographic Reach

Parker-Hannifin operates more than 330 manufacturing plants and nearly 130 distribution centers and 160 sales and administrative offices in 40 states and in roughly 50 other countries worldwide. North America accounts for roughly 60% of its sales.

Sales and Marketing

Diversified Industrial products are made primarily to original equipment manufacturers (OEM) and their replacement markets in manufacturing packaging processing transportation mobile construction refrigeration and air conditioning agricultural and military machinery and equipment industries. This segment's sales are marketed primarily through field sales employees and approximately 13700 independent distributor locations throughout the world.

Aerospace products cater to the commercial and military aerospace markets to both OEMs and to end-users for spares maintenance repair and overhaul.

Financial Performance

After declining the previous year Parker-Hannifin' revenues spiked by 6% to reach $12 billion in 2017. The growth was primarily a result of acquisitions (contributing almost $560 million in sales) and an increase in volume in both its Diversified Industrial International and Aerospace Systems segment partially offset by the effect of currency rate changes (which decreased net sales in 2017 by almost $85 million).

Its net income also increased 22% to $983 million in 2017 largely due to additional gains made from its CLARCOR acquisition. The rise in net income and additional sales from previous acquisitions also helped Parker-Hannifin's operating cash flow climb from $1.17 billion in 2016 to $1.3 billion in 2017.

Strategy

The company seeks to enhance its operations and profitability through a strategy of identifying and acquiring businesses with complementary products and services and by divesting businesses that are not considered to be a good long-term fit. It also focuses on building up its operations around targeted regions technologies and markets through acquisitions and organic growth.

Mergers and Acquisitions

Parker-Hannifin uses acquisitions as a means of enhancing its product portfolio and growing its global footprint.

In a move that significantly expanded its filtration portfolio in early 2017 Parker Hannifin bought CLARCOR a maker of mobile industrial and environmental filtration products in a deal valued at $4.3 billion.The transaction added more than a dozen respected CLARCOR brands including CLARCOR Baldwin Fuel Manager Airguard Altair Hastings and United Air Specialists among others. In addition it gave Parker-Hannifin stronger rela-tionships with original equipment manufacturers and customers in international markets especially for recurring sales in the aftermarket.

In mid-2016 Parker Hannifin acquired J ¤ger Automobil-Technik GmbH and J ¤ger Automotive Polska Sp. z.o.o headquartered in Hannover Germany. The J ¤ger Group is a pioneer in rubber-to-plastic direct bonded sealing systems for automotive markets and a leading developer of two-component (2K) direct injection molding technology. The deal provided Parker with innovative injection molding technology and businesses with a strong reputation in the automotive industry.

HISTORY

Entrepreneurial engineer Arthur Parker founded the Parker Appliance Company in 1918 to make pneumatic brake boosters. Its products were designed to help trucks and buses stop more easily. Unfortunately Parker's own truck slid off an icy road and over a cliff in 1919 destroying the company's inventory and ending that line of business.

Undeterred Parker started a hydraulics and pneumatic components business in 1924 to serve automotive and industrial clients. In 1927 the fuel-linkage system the company developed for the Spirit of St. Louis helped Lindbergh cross the Atlantic. The company prospered during the Depression; sales reached $2 million in 1934. Two of Parker's long-term clients were Douglas Aircraft and Lockheed.

The company went public in 1938. It employed 5000 defense workers during WWII. After Parker died in 1945 his wife Helen hired new management to focus on the automation market. The firm bought cylinder maker Hannifin in 1957 and became Parker-Hannifin.

In 1960 Parker-Hannifin formed an international unit in Amsterdam and it set up a German subsidiary in 1962. Overseas acquisitions and increased demand from the space program and the aviation market spurred growth in the 1960s. Patrick Parker the founder's son became president in 1968 and chairman in 1977. Parker-Hannifin expanded its aerospace business in 1978 with the purchase of Bertea (electrohydraulic flight controls). Patrick Parker continued as CEO until 1983 and as chairman until 1999.

EXECUTIVES

VP eBusiness IoT and Services, Robert W. (Bob) Bond, age 59, $548,700 total compensation
President and COO, Lee C. Banks, age 54, $850,000 total compensation
VP and CIO, William G. (Bill) Eline, age 61
VP and President Instrumentation Group, John R. Greco, age 63
VP and Chief Technology and Innovation Officer, M. Craig Maxwell, age 59
VP and President Aerospace Group, Roger S. Sherrard, age 51
Chairman and CEO, Thomas L. (Tom) Williams, age 58, $1,000,000 total compensation
VP Global Supply Chain and Procurement, John G. Dedinsky, age 60
VP and President Automation Group, Yoon (Michael) Chung, age 54
VP and President Asia Pacific Group, Kurt A. Keller, age 59
CFO, Catherine A. (Cathy) Suever, age 59
VP and President - Fluid Connectors Group, Andrew D. Ross
VP and President Latin America Group, Candido Lima
VP and President Filtration Group, Robert W. Malone
VP and President Europe Middle East and Africa Group (EMEA), Joachim Guhe
EVP Human Resources and External Affairs, Mark J. Hart
VP and President Engineered Materials Group, Jennifer A. Parmentier
VP and President Hydraulics Group, Andrew M. Weeks, $400,956 total compensation
VP General Counsel and Secretary, Joseph R. Leonti, $410,400 total compensation
Vice President of Sales and Marketing SEAL GROUP, Bruse Balthaser
Vice President Sales and Marketing, Dan Hartnett
Vice President Human Resources, Kevin Ruffer
VP Information Technology, Mark Czaja
Vice President Business Development Au, Paul Horvac
Vice President Human Resources, Linda Smith
Vice President QHSE and Operations Services, Russell Holness
Vice President Technology and Innovation, Brian Lane
VP Operations, Skip Bowman
Vice President Of Operations, Jim Rowell
Vice President Tax, Guy Fabe
Vice President of Worldwide Business Systems, Bob McAdoo
Vice President Sales and Marketing, Robert Mitchell
National Account Manager, Deirdre Stinson
Group Vice President Supply Chain, Mark Manthey
Vice President: Corporate Strategy, Shawn Horner
Group Vice President Sales and Marketing, Dave Roberts
Vice President of Operations North America, Rob Malone
National Accounts Manager, Rachel Hoffman
Group Vice President Supply Chain, Thomas Gentile
Vice President Operations, Beth Byrd
Board Member, Glenn Crame
Board Member, Grace Monserrate
Auditors: DELOITTE & TOUCHE LLP

LOCATIONS

HQ: Parker Hannifin Corp
6035 Parkland Boulevard, Cleveland, OH 44124-4141
Phone: 216 896-3000
Web: www.parker.com

2017 Sales

	$ mil.	% of total
North America	7,585	63
International	4,443	37
Total	**12,029**	**100**

PRODUCTS/OPERATIONS

2017 Sales

	$ mil.	% of total
Diversified Industrial		
North America	5,366	45
International	4,377	36
Aerospace Systems	2,284	19
Total	**12,029**	**100**

Selected Brand Names

Atlas Cylinders
Balston
Bayside
Bellows
Cabett
Calzoni
Chelsea
Chomerics
Compumotor
croloop
CTC
Ermeto
Fluid Power
Gold Ring
Greer
Gresen
Hiross
IPS

Jet-Pipe
Lucifer
Miller
Ross
Schrader
Sempress
Skinner
Sporlan
STC
Operating Groups and Selected Products
Aerospace
  Aircraft wheels and brakes
  Flight control components
  Fuel systems
  Pneumatic pumps and valves
Climate and industrial controls
  Expansion valves
  Filter-dryers
  Hose assemblies
  Pressure regulators
  Solenoid valves
Industrial
  Automation
  Air preparation units
  Electric actuators
  Human/machine interface hardware and software
  Indexers
  Multi-axis positioning tables
  Pneumatic valves
  Stepper and servo drives
  Structural extrusions
  Vacuum products
Filtration
  Cabin air filters
  Compressed-air and gas-purification filters
  Fuel conditioning filters
  Fuel filters/water separators
  Gas generators
  Gas generators
  Hydraulic lubrication and coolant filters
  Lube oil and fuel filters
  Monitoring devices
  Nitrogen and hydrogen generators
  Process chemical and microfiltration filters
  Water desalinization and purification
Fluid Connectors
  Couplers
  Diagnostic equipment
  Hoses and hose fittings
  Tube fittings
  Valves
Hydraulics
  Accumulators
  Cylinders
  Electrohydraulic systems
  Hydrostatic steering units
  Metering pumps
  Motors and pumps
  Power units
  Rotary actuators
  Sensors
  Valves
Instrumentation
  Ball plug and needle valves
  Cylinder connections
  Fluoropolymer fittings
  Miniature solenoid valves
  Multi-solenoid manifolds
  Packless ultra-high-purity valves
  Quick connects
  Regulators
  Spray guns
  Transducers
  Tubing
  Ultra-high-purity tube fittings
Seals
  Gaskets and packings
  Metal and plastic composite seals
  Medical devices seals and instruments
  O-rings
  O-seals
  Thermal management products

COMPETITORS

Bosch Rexroth	ITT Corp.
Crane Co.	Moog
Danaher	SMC Corp.
Danfoss	Swagelok
Donaldson Company	Trelleborg

Eaton
Emerson Electric
Honeywell
  International

Woodward Governor
Zodiac Aerospace

HISTORICAL FINANCIALS

Company Type: Public

Income Statement

FYE: June 30

	REVENUE ($ mil.)	NET INCOME ($ mil.)	NET PROFIT MARGIN	EMPLOYEES
06/17	12,029	983	8.2%	56,690
06/16	11,360	806	7.1%	48,950
06/15	12,711	1,012	8.0%	54,754
06/14	13,215	1,041	7.9%	57,450
06/13	13,015	948	7.3%	58,150
Annual Growth	(2.0%)	0.9%	—	(0.6%)

2017 Year-End Financials

Debt ratio: 37.90%
Return on equity: 19.99%
Cash ($ mil.): 884
Current ratio: 1.41
Long-term debt ($ mil.): 4,861

No. of shares (mil.): 133
Dividends
  Yield: 1.6%
  Payout: 37.6%
Market value ($ mil.): 21,287

	STOCK PRICE ($) FY Close	P/E High/Low	PER SHARE ($) Earnings	Dividends	Book Value
06/17	159.82	22 15	7.25	2.58	39.50
06/16	108.05	20 15	5.89	2.52	34.14
06/15	116.33	19 15	6.97	2.37	36.84
06/14	125.73	19 14	6.87	1.86	44.72
06/13	95.40	16 11	6.26	1.70	38.44
Annual Growth	13.8%	— —	3.7%	11.0%	0.7%

PARTNERS HEALTHCARE SYSTEM, INC.

Partners HealthCare System is looking out for the health of the Bay State. Partners HealthCare includes two large acute-care medical centers — Brigham and Women's Hospital and Massachusetts General Hospital— and six community hospitals. The system also provides primary and specialty care through clinics physician offices long-term care facilities and home health and hospice agencies. Its rehabilitation facilities include the Spaulding Rehabilitation Hospital Network. Partners HealthCare also provides medical training and research through an affiliation with Harvard. Other ventures include the Dana-Farber/Partners CancerCare clinic (a collaboration with Harvard and Dana-Farber Cancer Institute).

Operations

The system's Partners Community HealthCare division is a management services organization that provides support for a physician network encompassing some 6500 practitioners. Partners HealthCare also sponsors community health outreach programs. Community hospitals owned by or affiliated with Partners include McLean Hospital Newton-Wellesley Hospital North Shore Medical Center Nantucket Cottage Hospital and the Martha's Vineyard Hospital. Partners HealthCare also operates Faulkner Hospital as a subsidiary of the Brigham and Women's facility.

Brigham and Women's (a 777-bed facility) and Massachusetts General are both teaching hospitals for the Harvard Medical School. The Harvard Clin-

ical Research Institute is a partnership between the Harvard Medical School Partners HealthCare and CareGroup (parent of Boston facilities including Beth Israel Deaconess Medical Center). Outside the US the system's Partners HealthCare International provides clinical advisory patient care research and educational programs with a number of global partners. With an annual research budget of $1.6 billion Partners HealthCare has a strong research funding base including awards of some $600 million annually from the National Institutes of Health.

The system serves 1.5 million patients annually. In 2014 it invested $210 million in community programs.

Geographic Reach

Partners HealthCare provides services to patients in the Greater Boston area as well as New England and beyond. It also partners with health care systems and health-related academic institutions in more than 40 countries.

Financial Performance

Partners HealthCare's revenues increased by 5% in 2014 due to growth in net patient service and premium revenues.

The company reported net loss of $181 million in 2014 (compared to net income in 2013) due to a change in the fair value of non-hedging interest rate swaps absence of contribution income from affiliates and achange in funded status of defined benefit plans.

Despite the net loss the company's operating cash flow increased by 23% due to higher cash generated from accrued medical claims and related expenses and change in accrued compensation and benefits unexpended funds on research grants and accrued employee benefits and other.

Strategy

Partners HealthCare strives to provide innovative yet affordable medical care to area residents. To keep its operations efficient as well as to comply with federal health reform incentive measures Partners HealthCare has put in place a health information system that requires all of its doctors to use electronic health records (EHRs). As one of the early adopters of EHR systems Partners HealthCare is upgrading its IT systems to install a new clinical information system across its facilities using new technologies from software maker Epic. The new system — which will enhance coordination of care reduce unnecessary health spending and simplify reporting and patient access features — will be implemented over ten years and will cost between $600 and $700 million.

Other programs to meet new health care standards include reducing prices on certain procedures and renegotiating contracts with insurers as well as encouraging patients to participate in preventative care wellness and generic drug programs.

In 2014 the company broke ground on its new administrative offices in Assembly Square that will bring 4500 permanent and 1500 construction jobs to the 45-acre Assembly Row development.

That year Partners HealthCare also formed a partnership known as Partners Urgent Care with MedSpring Urgent Care to open and operate multiple urgent care clinics in eastern Massachusetts. The joint venture opened its first urgent care center in Brookline Massachusetts in early. Additional locations in Newton and Watertown were under construction in 2015.

Mergers and Acquisitions

Following an expansion trend in the region Partners HealthCare has laid out plans to acquire Neighborhood Health Plan. Instead of paying cash to acquire the not-for-profit insurance provider which serves 200000 low-income and disabled residents with Medicaid policies Partners HealthCare intends to provide grants to some 50 smaller community health centers affiliated with the health plan. The deal will require approval from state regulators before it can proceed.

The organization has also agreed to acquire the 140-bed Cooley Dickinson Hospital in Northampton as well as specialty hospital Massachusetts Eye and Ear.

In 2015 the company acquired Harbor Medical Associates which has some 70 physicians and 60000 patients.

Company Background

Partners HealthCare has been recognized by the federal government and other organizations for its quality and efficiency programs. In 2012 the health network was selected by the Centers for Medicare and Medicaid Services to participate in the Pioneer ACO (accountable care organization) program which aims to slow cost growth in the Medicare market by enhancing care coordination.

Partners HealthCare was founded in 1994 through the merger of Brigham and Women's Hospital and Massachusetts General Hospital.

EXECUTIVES

EVP Administration and Finance CFO and Treasurer, Peter K. Markell, age 61
President and CEO Massachusetts General Hospital, Peter L. Slavin
CIO, James W. (Jim) Noga
President and CEO North Shore Medical Center, Robert G. (Bob) Norton, age 67
President and CEO Neighborhood Health Plan, Deborah C. Enos
President and CEO Partners Continuing Care, David E. Storto
President and CEO Brigham and Women's Hospital, Elizabeth G. (Betsy) Nabel
President and Chief Executive Officer, David F. Torchiana
President of Partners Community, Thomas H. Lee
President and CEO Spaulding Rehabilitation Network, Maureen Banks
President McLean Hospital, Scott L. Rauch
President and CEO Brigham and Women's Physicians Organization, Allen L. Smith
President and CEO Martha's Vineyard Hospital, Timothy J. Walsh
President and CEO MGH Institute of Health Professions, Janis P. Bellack
President and CEO, David Torchiana
President and CEO Nantucket Cottage Hospital, Margot Hartmann
President and CEO Partners HealthCare at Home, Rod Carnifax
Medical Director Bipolar Clinic and Research Programs, Andrew Nierenberg
Nursing Director, Karen Reilly
Nursing Director, Lauren Willard
Medical Director of The Breast and Ovarian Cancer, Paula Ryan
Nursing Director, Elizabeth McGrath
Clinic Director, Bruce Chabner
Nursing Director, Colleen West
Nursing Director, Janet Quigley
Director Of Radiology, Tina Maloney
Director of Nursing, Heidi Larkin
Nursing Director, Barbara Crawley
Medical Director Of Quality Safey And Population Management, Adrienne Allen
Medical Director, Richard Kaufman
Project Manager To Senior Vice President Research, Angela Vail
Clinical Director, Jane Evans
NURSING DIRECTOR, Michele Ohara
Clinical Director, Martha Kane
Senior Vice President Human Re, J Davison
VICE PRESIDENT OF OPERATIONS, Hofmann Erika
DIRECTOR OF MEDICAL RECORDS, Doherty Linda

NURSING DIRECTOR, Dorothy Parker
Executive Vice President and Chief Technology Officer for Strategy and Technology, Richard Goldberg
NURSING DIRECTOR, Christine Flanagan
VICE PRESIDENT, Edward Liston-kraft
Chairman, Edward P. Lawrence, age 75
Board Member, Peter Ardagna
Secretary, Maria Sanchez
Board Member, Warren Foote
Executive Board Member, Denise Goldsmith
Board Member, Jonathan Katz
Vice Chair Departrment Of Pediatrics, Peter Greenspan
Auditors: PRICEWATERHOUSECOOPERS LLP B

LOCATIONS

HQ: PARTNERS HEALTHCARE SYSTEM, INC.
800 BOYLSTON ST STE 1150, BOSTON, MA 021998123
Phone: 617 278-1000

PRODUCTS/OPERATIONS

2014 Sales

	% of total
Net patient service revenue	65
Premium revenue	15
Direct academic and research	11
Indirect academic and research	3
Other revenue	6
Total	**100**

COMPETITORS

Baystate Health	Lahey Health System
Boston Medical Center	Milford Regional Medical Center
Cambridge Health Alliance	Northeast Health System
Cape Cod Healthcare	Southcoast Hospitals Group
Cape Cod Hospital	
Care New England	
CareGroup	Steward Health Care
Children's Hospital Boston	Universal Health Services

HISTORICAL FINANCIALS

Company Type: Private

Income Statement

FYE: September 30

	REVENUE ($ mil.)	NET INCOME ($ mil.)	NET PROFIT MARGIN	EMPLOYEES
09/15	11,665	(916)	—	67,000
09/10	8	(0)	—	—
09/08	551	(44)	—	—
Annual Growth	54.7%	—	—	—

2015 Year-End Financials

Debt ratio: ——
Return on equity: (-7.90%)
Cash ($ mil.): 621
Current ratio: 0.70
Long-term debt ($ mil.): —
Dividends
Yield: —
Payout: —
Market value ($ mil.): —

Patterson Companies Inc

Patterson Companies' catalogs are like wish lists for veterinary and dental practices. The company operates through two primary segments — whole-

salers Patterson Animal Health (formerly Patterson Veterinary) and Patterson Dental. Patterson Animal Health distributes animal supplies including pharmaceuticals parasiticides and equipment in the US Canada and the UK. Patterson Dental distributes products including X-ray film and machines hand instruments sterilization products dental chairs and lights and diagnostic equipment. Additionally it sells office supplies computer equipment software and other products and services for dental offices and laboratories. Patterson Dental serves the US and Canada.

Operations

Patterson Animal Health is a leading US distributor of health products for companion animals and horses. It sells more than 100000 products including vaccines and drugs consumables and diagnostic supplies and is responsible for nearly 60% of the company's revenue. Patterson Animal Health became the larger of the two segments after the 2015 acquisition of Animal Health International which more than doubled its size.

In business since 1877 Patterson's dental unit is the second-largest dental supply wholesaler in the US and Canada (after Henry Schein); it accounts for more than 40% of the company's sales. The segment offers its customers more than 89000 different items including approximately 4000 private-label products marketed under the Patterson name. In addition to consumables and equipment Patterson Dental offers services such as technology consulting; office design; equipment installation maintenance and repair; and financing for big-ticket purchases.

Geographic Reach

The US market accounts for some 85% of Patterson's annual revenues. Patterson Dental provides dental supplies throughout the US and Canada. Patterson Animal Health distributes items throughout the UK Canada and the US.

Patterson Logistics Services operates distribution centers in Alabama California Colorado Florida Hawaii Indiana Iowa Pennsylvania South Carolina Texas and Washington.

Sales and Marketing

Patterson's products are sold through direct sales and marketing representatives in the US and Canada to over 164000 customers. Marketing is conducted through its website and through catalogs magazines and direct mail. Customers include dentists dental laboratories veterinarian offices laboratories and other health care providers and institutions.

Subsidiary Patterson Logistics Services operates seven primary distribution centers and six smaller facilities in the US that conduct distribution functions for both Patterson segments. Some of the centers stock products from multiple business units while others serve one segment.

Advertising expenses were $10128 in fiscal 2017 versus $12113 in 2016 and $16798 in 2015.

Financial Performance

Continuing on its path of rising revenues over the past five years Patterson Companies' revenue rose 4% to $5.6 billion in fiscal 2017 (ended April) due primarily to a 10% growth in animal health sales. This was partially offset by a 4% decline in Patterson Dental sales. In that segment equipment and software sales fell slightly but sales of core equipment increased.

Net income has been more volatile over recent years. It dropped 9% to $170.9 million in fiscal 2017 as cost of sales and operating expenses increased. Despite that drop cash flow from operations rose 4% to $162.7 million that year.

Strategy

Patterson Companies relies on its ability to provide a diverse platform of products and services in a total-package approach. A key strategy is to promote its value-added services such as equipment installation and maintenance financing and technology guidance.

The company has also invested in its own technology platforms. The focus on enhancing its online ordering systems has allowed Patterson to build up its client base while freeing up sales representatives to spend more time with customers. Additionally the company offers technology troubleshooting claims and electronic statements through its Patterson Technology Center.

Patterson has grown through internal expansion and via acquisitions including its $1.1 billion purchase of Animal Health International which more than doubled its veterinary operations. It seeks opportunities to take advantage of the fractured markets in which it operates. Such opportunities include buying other distributors or opening new locations to enter additional markets.

Mergers and Acquisitions

In late 2017 Patterson Dental acquired dental office design and equipment dealer Fitzpatrick Dental Design based out of California. That purchase helped build the company's equipment design and sales operations.

HISTORY

In 1877 brothers Myron and John Patterson bought a Milwaukee drugstore and later added dental supplies to the inventory. Myron bought the dental side of the business from his brother in 1891 moved to St. Paul Minnesota and started a dental supply store. His business later became a subsidiary of diversified manufacturer Esmark which sold Patterson to food giant Beatrice in 1982. Recognizing that food and dental supplies were an odd mix Patterson executives initiated a leveraged buyout in 1985.

In an industry as fragmented as some dental patients' smiles the firm used acquisitions to secure a leading position as a full-service provider. In 1987 Patterson bought D.L. Saslow then the #3 distributor. Between 1989 and 1993 it bought smaller distributors in eight states and Washington DC. In 1993 a year after it went public Patterson bought the Canadian arm of bankrupt rival Healthco International.

During the mid- and late 1990s Patterson continued to buy small local dental-supply distributors branching out across the US and Canada. In 1996 and 1997 Patterson expanded into front-office products with the purchase of Colwell Systems and EagleSoft. It took a few more bites out of the market with purchases of two more local distributors in 1998. In 2000 it bought Micheli Dental Supply a dental products distributor in California and eCheck-Up.com an online provider of payroll human resources payables processing and other services.

In 2001 Patterson expanded beyond dental products distribution when it purchased J. A. Webster a distributor of veterinary supplies. Patterson broadened its operations further in 2003 acquiring AbilityOne Products a provider of medical rehabilitation supplies. It also acquired Smith & Nephew's rehab division and with it the Rolyan and Homecraft brand names. The following year the company changed its name from Patterson Dental to Patterson Companies to reflect this expansion.

However returning its focus on its dental and veterinary businesses the firm sold its Patterson Medical unit in 2015.

EXECUTIVES

Southwest Regional Manager Patterson Dental, Paul A. Guggenheim, age 57, $384,482 total compensation

VP Strategy and Planning, Ann B. Gugino, age 45, $399,167 total compensation
VP Operations, Sean M. Muniz
VP General Counsel and Secretary, Les B. Korsh, age 47, $280,833 total compensation
President Patterson Dental U.S., Dave Misiak
CIO, Dave Lardy
Interim President Patterson Animal Health, Kevin Pohlman
President CEO and Director, Mark S. Walchirk
Chairman, John D. Buck, age 66
Tr, Norman Dagher
Auditors: Ernst & Young LLP

LOCATIONS

HQ: Patterson Companies Inc
1031 Mendota Heights Road, St. Paul, MN 55120
Phone: 651 686-1600
Web: www.pattersoncompanies.com

2017 Sales

	$ mil.	% of total
US	4,725	84
UK	548	10
Canada	319	6
Total	**5,593**	**100**

PRODUCTS/OPERATIONS

2017 Sales by Segment

	$ mil.	% of total
Animal Health	3,159	56
Dental	2,390	43
Corporate	43	1
Total	**5,593**	**100**

2017 Sales

	$ mil.	% of total
Consumable	4,400	79
Equipment & software	834	15
Other	357	6
Total	**5,593**	**100**

Selected Acquisitions

COMPETITORS

Benco Dental	IVESCO
Burkhart Dental	MWI Veterinary Supply
Cardinal Health	McKesson
Carestream Health	Medline Industries
Darby Dental	Universal Medical
Henry Schein	Systems

HISTORICAL FINANCIALS

Company Type: Public

Income Statement

FYE: April 29

	REVENUE ($ mil.)	NET INCOME ($ mil.)	NET PROFIT MARGIN	EMPLOYEES
04/17	5,593	170	3.1%	7,500
04/16	5,386	187	3.5%	7,000
04/15	4,375	223	5.1%	7,000
04/14	4,063	200	4.9%	7,000
04/13	3,637	210	5.8%	7,000
Annual Growth	**11.4%**	**(5.1%)**	**—**	**1.7%**

2017 Year-End Financials

Debt ratio: 30.56%
Return on equity: 12.08%
Cash ($ mil.): 94
Current ratio: 2.00
Long-term debt ($ mil.): 998

No. of shares (mil.): 96
Dividends
　Yield: 0.0%
　Payout: 54.7%
Market value ($ mil.): 4,295

	STOCK PRICE ($) FY Close	P/E High/Low	PER SHARE ($) Earnings	Dividends	Book Value
04/17	44.49	28 22	1.79	0.98	14.44
04/16	43.35	27 20	1.91	0.90	14.55
04/15	48.19	23 17	2.24	0.82	14.66
04/14	40.91	22 19	1.97	0.68	14.16
04/13	37.47	19 16	2.03	0.58	13.21
Annual Growth	**4.4%**	**— —**	**(3.1%)**	**14.0%**	**2.3%**

PayPal Holdings Inc

Auditors: PricewaterhouseCoopers LLP

LOCATIONS

HQ: PayPal Holdings Inc
2211 North First Street, San Jose, CA 95131
Phone: 408 967-1000
Web: www.paypal.com

HISTORICAL FINANCIALS

Company Type: Public

Income Statement

FYE: December 31

	REVENUE ($ mil.)	NET INCOME ($ mil.)	NET PROFIT MARGIN	EMPLOYEES
12/17	13,094	1,795	13.7%	18,700
12/16	10,842	1,401	12.9%	18,100
12/15	9,248	1,228	13.3%	16,800
12/14	8,025	419	5.2%	15,800
12/13	6,727	955	14.2%	—
Annual Growth	**18.1%**	**17.1%**	**—**	**—**

2017 Year-End Financials

Debt ratio: —
Return on equity: 11.69%
Cash ($ mil.): 2,883
Current ratio: 1.43
Long-term debt ($ mil.): —

No. of shares (mil.): 1,200
Dividends
　Yield: —
　Payout: —
Market value ($ mil.): 88,344

	STOCK PRICE ($) FY Close	P/E High/Low	PER SHARE ($) Earnings	Dividends	Book Value
12/17	73.62	53 26	1.47	0.00	13.33
12/16	39.47	38 27	1.15	0.00	12.19
12/15	36.20	40 31	1.00	0.00	11.24
Annual Growth	**19.4%**	**— —**	**10.1%**	**—**	**4.4%**

PBF Energy Inc

Established US oil refiners meet the new kid on the block. Formed in the first decade of 21st century PBF Energy's five oil refineries are located in California Delaware Louisiana New Jersey and Ohio and have a combined production capacity of about 900000 barrels per day making the company the fourth-largest refiner in the US. PBF's refineries produce gasoline ultra-low-sulfur diesel heating oil jet fuel lubricants petrochemicals and asphalt for the Midwestern and Northeastern US. The company indirectly owns the general partner and approximately 44.2% of the limited partnership interest of PBF Logistics LP. PBF Energy is majority-owned by investment firms The Blackstone Group and First Reserve.

Operations

PBF Energy operates two business segments: Refining which accounts for more than 95% of its sales and Logistics (through PBF Logistics) which accounts for the remaining less-than 5% of sales.;

Refineries in the East Coast (Delaware City and Paulsboro) average total throughput rates of 370000 barrels per day (bpd) and in the Mid-Continent (Toledo) 170000 bpd. Total refined product barrels sold are around 365000 at East Coast refineries; 170000 at Mid-Continent refineries; and 206000 at Gulf Coast refineries.

Gasoline and distillates account for more than 85% of PBF Energy's total sales; chemicals asphalt and blackoils lubricants and feedstocks all account for less than 5% each.

Geographic Reach

PBF Energy operates refineries in Torrance California; Delaware City Delaware; New Orleans Louisiana; Paulsboro New Jersey; and Toledo Ohio and sells its products in Canada and the US.

Sales and Marketing

PBF has product offtake agreements for a large portion of its product sales. The remainder of its refined products are sold through short-term contracts or on the spot market.

Financial Performance

The collapse in the oil price put a severe dent in PBF Energy's revenue in 2015 but in fiscal 2016 the company defied industry trends and grew revenue 21% to $15.9 billion. The increase was primarily a result of contributions from the Torrance refinery acquired from ExxonMobil mid-year. On the downside average selling prices for refined oil fell around $10 per barrel. Volume sales outstripped total throughput meaning the company dipped into inventory.

Net income increased 17% to $170.8 million as changes in the oil price triggered a positive pretax adjustment to inventory value of $521.3 million. Aside from this single large item net income was put under pressure by tighter margins relating to crude oil differentials lower refined selling prices versus raw material costs and increased interest.

Cash from operations increased 16% to $651.9 million due to deferred income taxes worth $244.8 million and changes in inventories.

Strategy

PBF's strategy is to opportunistically acquire refineries. Its latest such acquisition is of the Torrance refinery in California (following the Chalmette acquisition in 2015) which has daily refining capacity of 155000 barrels per day and was bought in 2016. The refinery can process heavy and medium crude oils and has a sophisticated logistics network of crude and products pipelines distribution terminals and refinery crude. Subsequent to its acquisitions PBF targets margin increases by installing new management and carrying out turnarounds.

PBF Logistics PBF's logistics partner acquires new storage capacity and accepts drop-down transactions from PBF. In 2016 it bought four million barrels of capacity in the Philadelphia region and bought from PBF a 50% interest in Torrance Valley Pipeline Company to look after the gathering and pipeline delivery systems hooked up to the Torrance refinery. The two deals increased PBF Logistics' revenue base by 70%. In addition the cash received by PBF accelerates turnaround activities at its acquired refineries.

Mergers and Acquisitions

Expanding to the US West Coast in 2016 PBF Energy acquired the Torrance refinery and related logistics assets from Exxon Mobil for $537.5 million. The Torrance refinery located on 750 acres in Torrance California is a high-conversion 155000

barrel per day delayed-coking refinery.It sold the logistics assets linked to the refinery to its joint venture PBF Logistics.

Company Background

PBF Energy was created in 2008 by Swiss oil refiner Petroplus to help it establish a foothold in the US. Petroplus and The Blackstone Group each invested $667 million to begin buying oil refineries at the height of the global economic recession when larger companies were looking to sell off assets to drum up cash. PBF first bought the Delaware refinery from Valero in 2010 for $220 million. (The low price tag came because the refinery had been shut down since 2009). Next came the New Jersey refinery again purchased from Valero for $358 million.

In 2011 PBF Energy bought an Ohio refinery from Sunoco for $400 million.

PBF Energy went public in 2012 with an IPO that raised $429 million. The IPO came as a quick turnaround before PBF Energy was able to recognize any significant revenue and the company used the $613 million in proceeds to pay back its principal investors Blackstone and First Reserve.

In 2013 PBF Energy signed a deal with Continental Resources for the oil company to supply PBF Energy with Bakken crude oil. The deal marks a shift for the East Coast refinery market - a market that has historically relied on imports of foreign oil.

EXECUTIVES

Chairman and CEO, Thomas J. Nimbley, age 65, $1,500,000 total compensation
SVP Commercial, Thomas L. O'Connor, age 44, $500,000 total compensation
President, Matthew C. Lucey, age 43, $600,000 total compensation
CFO, C. Erik Young, age 41, $523,958 total compensation
SVP Refining, Herman Seedorf, age 65
President Western Region, Timothy Paul Davis
Managing Vice President, Gerald Pechulis
Vice President, Clark Wrigley
Assistant Treasurer, John Rebele
Auditors: Deloitte & Touche LLP

LOCATIONS

HQ: PBF Energy Inc
One Sylvan Way, Second Floor, Parsippany, NJ 07054
Phone: 973 455-7500
Web: www.pbfenergy.com

PRODUCTS/OPERATIONS

Products
Clean Fuels
Lubes
Petrochemicals
LPG

2016 sales by segment

	% of total
Refining	99
Logistics	1
Elimination	-
Total	**100**

2016 sales

	% of total
Gasoline & distillates	88
Asphalt and blackoils	5
Chemicals	3
Feedstocks and other	2
Lubricants	2
Total	**100**

COMPETITORS

Alon USA Energy	Paramount Petroleum
CITGO Refining and Chemicals	Placid Refining
	San Joaquin Refining
Chevron	Shell Oil Products
ConocoPhillips	Sunoco
Exxon Mobil	Tauber Oil
Flint Hills	Tesoro Refining and
HollyFrontier	Marketing
Marathon Petroleum	United Refining
Motiva Enterprises	Valero Energy

HISTORICAL FINANCIALS

Company Type: Public

Income Statement

FYE: December 31

	REVENUE ($ mil.)	NET INCOME ($ mil.)	NET PROFIT MARGIN	EMPLOYEES
12/16	15,920	170	1.1%	3,165
12/15	13,123	146	1.1%	2,270
12/14	19,828	(38)	—	1,714
12/13	19,151	39	0.2%	1,735
12/12	20,138	1	0.0%	1,612
Annual Growth	**(5.7%)**	**205.7%**	**—**	**18.4%**

2016 Year-End Financials

Debt ratio: 28.18%	No. of shares (mil.): 109
Return on equity: 9.28%	Dividends
Cash ($ mil.): 746	Yield: 0.0%
Current ratio: 1.66	Payout: 68.9%
Long-term debt ($ mil.): 2,108	Market value ($ mil.): 3,045

	STOCK PRICE ($) FY Close	P/E High/Low		PER SHARE ($) Earnings	Dividends	Book Value
12/16	27.88	22	11	1.74	1.20	18.54
12/15	36.81	25	14	1.65	1.20	16.85
12/14	26.64	—	—	(0.51)	1.20	14.86
12/13	31.46	34	17	1.20	1.20	16.49
12/12	29.05	354	328	0.08	0.00	17.81
Annual Growth	**(1.0%)**	**—**	**—**	**116.0%**	**—**	**1.0%**

Peabody Energy Corp (New)

Peabody Energy has long been the king of coal. The world's largest private-sector coal producer Peabody owns stakes in 26 mines (22 majority owned) and processing facilities in the US and Australia. It sells about 190 million tons of coal annually and sits on 5.6 billion tons of proved and probable reserves. US customers primarily power companies account for most of Peabody's sales. Its operations include coal trading and brokering coalbed methane production transportation-related services and development of coal-based generating plants. Facing regulatory pressure and a down market Peabody sought Chapter 11 bankruptcy protection in 2016 from which it emerged in 2017.

Operations

Peabody divides its business into five segments based on where and what they mine (as well as a trading segment): Powder River Basin Mining; Australian Metallurgical Mining; Australian Thermal Mining; Midwestern U.S. Mining; Western U.S. Mining; and Trading and Brokerage.

Powder River Basin Mining accounts for 30% of total company sales and carries out mining in the — you guessed it — Powder River Basin in

Wyoming. It digs up low-sulfur coal through surface mining extraction processes.

Australian Metallurgical Mining brings in nearly 25% of revenue and consists of the surface and underground extraction of hard semi-hard and semi-soft coking coal as well as low-volatile pulverized coal injection coal. Its mines are mostly in Queensland.

The Australian Thermal Mining segment mines low-sulfur high Btu thermal coal in New South Wales.

The Midwestern US Mining operation digs up high sulfur and Btu coal.

Western US Mining covers operations in New Mexico Arizona and Colorado characterized by mid-range sulfur content.

The Trading & Brokerage segment brokers coal and freight-related contracts and provides transportation services.

Geographic Reach

St. Louis Missouri-based Peabody has offices in Australia China Germany India Indonesia Singapore the UK and the US. The company serves metallurgical and thermal coal customers in 25 countries on six continents.

About 55% of Peabody's revenue comes from the US.

Sales and Marketing

Coal brokering is conducted both as principal and agent in support of various coal production-related activities that may involve coal produced from their mines coal sourcing arrangements with third-party mining companies or offtake agreements with other coal producers. Peabody's five largest customers account for around 30% of total sales.

Supply agreements are mostly with electricity generators industrial facilities and steel manufacturers. Around 75% of sales by volume are to US electricity generators. Its international sales are mostly delivered under long-term contracts.

Financial Performance

Peabody's sales have been falling sharply for a few years now while the company falls further into the red. It entered Chapter 11 bankruptcy protection in 2016 before emerging in 2017. The coal industry in the US is under severe pressure from the rise of natural gas as well as solar and wind energy.

In fiscal 2016 sales dropped 16% or $894 million to $4.7 billion due to lower prices in the US and lower sales volumes.

Net loss narrowed from $2.0 billion in 2015 to $739.8 million in 2016 due to a bout of rigorous cost cutting that saved the company some $900 million in the year.

Cash from operating activities fell $38.4 million to an outflow of $52.8 million.

Strategy

The coal industry is taking a battering from natural gas which is out-competing coal on price and green credentials. A slew of Peabody's rivals — Arch Coal Alpha Natural Resources Patriot Coal and Walter Energy — all went under in 2015-16 as did Peabody itself in mid-2016. The fall in the price of coal came just after it took on significant debt to finance the $5 billion purchase of a mine in Australia. Peabody soon couldn't finance its debts and entered Chapter 11 bankruptcy protection.

Peabody exited bankruptcy just under a year later by selling off stock and cutting costs.

Company Background

Peabody was founded in 1883 as a coal supplier but began coal mining in earnest in 1926.

In 2011 Peabody joined with the world's largest steel producer ArcelorMittal to make an offer to jointly acquire Macarthur Coal and its extensive holdings in Australia's Bowen Basin (270 million tons of coal reserves and mines that produced

about 4 million metric tons in 2010). Under terms of the deal Peabody was to hold a 60% stake in Macarthur and ArcelorMittal 40%. Their joint venture was called PEAMCoal. Macarthur's largest shareholder China-based Citic Resources which owned 25% agreed to an offer of A$16 a share. Shortly after PEAMCoal took a majority stake in Macarthur ArcelorMittal backed out of the deal and sold its stake in the joint venture back to Peabody. Through its subsidiary PEAMCOAL Peabody acquired full control of Macarthur at a cost of about $5 billion.

As part of this geographic expansion in 2012 Peabody opened an office in Balikpapan Indonesia a seaport city in the East Kalimantan province (Indonesia is the fastest-growing supplier of thermal coal to both China and India).

For better returns in 2012 the company converted its Wilpinjong and Millennium mines in Australia from contract mining to owner-operated sites. To meet safety standards and cut costs that year Peabody closed its Willow Lake Mine in Illinois and its Air Quality Mine in Indiana.

In 2013 Peabody and China's Shenhua Group signed a deal to create Sino-Pacific Coal Trading Corporation Pte. Ltd. a Singapore-based joint-venture company to supply Shenhua's growing coal import demand with thermal coal from Peabody's global production and coal trading platform.

That year Peabody closed its underperforming Wilkie Creek Mine in Queensland's Surat Basin.

EXECUTIVES

Vice President Geological Services, John A Rusnak
EVP Corporate Services and Chief Commercial Officer, Charles F. Meintjes, age 54, $554,583 total compensation
President Americas, Kemal Williamson, age 57, $504,167 total compensation
Peabody Energy President Australia, George J. Schuller
EVP and CFO, Amy B. Schwetz, $479,583 total compensation
President and CEO, Glenn L. Kellow, age 49, $997,896 total compensation
EVP Chief Legal Officer Government Affairs and Corporate Secretary, A. Verona Dorch, $456,667 total compensation
Executive Vice President Chief Technical Officer, Jeane Hull
Vice President Of Information Technology, Dina Ostro
Vice President, Ian Humphris
Vice President and General Manager of Colorado Operations, Pat Sollars
Vice President, Keith Davis
Vice President Business Continuous Improvement, Jeff Maher
Vice President and Treasurer, Jim Tichenor
Senior Vice President Technical Services, Bertus de Jager
Chairman, Robert A. (Bob) Malone, age 65
Auditors: Ernst & Young LLP

LOCATIONS

HQ: Peabody Energy Corp (New)
701 Market Street, St. Louis, MO 63101-1826
Phone: 314 342-3400
Web: www.peabodyenergy.com

2016 Sales

	% of total
United States	55
Japan	7
China	5
South Korea	1
Other	32
Total	**100**

PRODUCTS/OPERATIONS

2016 Sales

	$ mil.	% of total
Powder River Basin Mining	1,473	31
Australian Metallurgical Mining	1,090	23
Midwestern U.S. Mining	792	17
Australian Thermal Mining	824	18
Western U.S. Mining	526	11
Trading and Brokerage	(10.9)	-
Corporate and Other	19	0
Total	**4,715**	**100**

Selected Mergers and Acquisitions

COMPETITORS

Alliance Resource	CONSOL Energy
Alpha Natural	China Coal Energy
Resources	Cloud Peak Energy
Anglo American	Glencore
Arch Coal	North American Coal
BHP Billiton	RAG AG

HISTORICAL FINANCIALS

Company Type: Public

Income Statement

FYE: December 31

	REVENUE ($ mil.)	NET INCOME ($ mil.)	NET PROFIT MARGIN	EMPLOYEES
12/16	4,715	(739)	—	6,700
12/15	5,609	(1,996)	—	7,600
12/14	6,792	(787)	—	8,300
12/13	7,013	(524)	—	8,300
12/12	8,077	(585)	—	8,200
Annual Growth	**(12.6%)**			**(4.9%)**

2016 Year-End Financials

Debt ratio: 0.17%	No. of shares (mil.): 19
Return on equity: (-118.32%)	Dividends
Cash ($ mil.): 926	Yield: —
Current ratio: 2.07	Payout: —
Long-term debt ($ mil.): —	Market value ($ mil.): —

Peapack-Gladstone Financial Corp.

Peapack-Gladstone Financial is the $3.4 billion-asset holding company for the near-century-old Peapack-Gladstone Bank which operates more than 20 branches in New Jersey's Hunterdon Morris Somerset Middlesex and Union counties. Founded in 1921 the bank provides traditional deposit accounts credit cards and loans to individuals and small businesses as well as trust and investment management services through its PGB Trust and Investments unit. Multifamily residential mortgages represent nearly 50% of the company's loan portfolio while commercial mortgages make up around 15%. The bank also originates construction consumer and business loans.

Operations

Peapack-Gladstone Financial operates two main divisions: Banking which offers traditional deposit and loan services merchant card services; and Wealth Management which boasts more than $3.3 billion in assets under administration (as of early 2016) and operates through PGB Trust and Investments which offers asset management services for individuals and institutions as well as personal trust services. More than 80% of the bank's total revenue came from interest income (mostly on its loans) during 2015 while 14% came from its wealth management fee income and 3% came from service charges and fees.

Multifamily residential mortgages represented nearly 50% of the company's loan portfolio at the end of 2015 while commercial mortgages made up another 15%. The rest of its portfolio was made up of construction consumer and business loans.

Geographic Reach

The bank's branches are located across New Jersey in Somerset Morris Hunterdon Middlesex and Union counties Its private banking and wealth management locations are located in Bedminster Morristown Princeton and Teaneck.

Sales and Marketing

The bank's commercial banking business serves business owners professionals retailers contractors and real estate investors. Its wealth management division serves individuals families foundations endowments trusts and estates.

Peapack-Gladstone has been ramping up its advertising spend in recent years. It spent $637000 on advertising during 2015 up from $594000 and $519000 in 2014 and 2013 respectively.

Financial Performance

Peapack-Gladstone's annual revenues and profits have swelled more than 60% since 2011 as its nearly tripled its loan assets to over $2.9 billion.

The bank's revenue jumped 27% to $122.86 million during 2015 mostly thanks to higher interest income as its loan assets grew by 30% with exceptional increases in its multifamily mortgage and commercial loan volumes. Peapack-Gladstone's wealth management division income grew 20% with increases in securities gains service charges and other non-interest income.

Strong revenue growth in 2015 drove Peapack-Gladstone's net income up 34% to $19.97 million. The bank's operating cash levels climbed 11% to $30.31 million thanks to a rise in cash-based earnings.

Strategy

Peapack-Gladstone Financial continued in 2016 to focus on: enhancing its risk management to keep its loan provisions at a minimum and its profits up; expanding its multi-family loans as well as its commercial real estate loans (to a lesser extent); growing its commercial and industrial (C&I) lending business through its private banking divisions; and expanding its wealth management business which now accounts for 15% of its annual revenue.

Mergers and Acquisitions

In May 2015 Peapack-Gladstone bolstered its wealth management division after buying Morristown-based Wealth Management Consultants LLC for $2.8 million. The deal boosted the bank's assets under advisement and administration to $3.5 billion.

EXECUTIVES

SEVP and CFO Peapack-Gladstone Financial and Peapack-Gladstone Bank, Jeffrey J. Carfora, age 59
EVP and COO, Robert A. (Bob) Plante, age 58
President and CEO Peapack-Gladstone Financial and Peapack-Gladstone Bank, Douglas L. Kennedy, age 58
EVP CIO and Head of Banking Services Peapack-Gladstone Bank, Kevin B. Runyon
SEVP Chief Strategy Officer and General Counsel, Finn M.W. Casperson, age 47
EVP and Head of Retail Banking Peapack-Gladstone Bank, Anthony V. Bilotta, age 57
EVP and Head of Commercial Real Estate Peapack-Gladstone Bank, Vincent A. Spero
SEVP and President Private Wealth Management, John P. Babcock

EVP and Chief Credit Officer Peapack-Gladstone Bank, Lisa Chalkan
EVP and Director Human Capital Peapack-Gladstone Bank, Philip Portantino
EVP and President Wealth Management Consultants Peapack-Gladstone Bank, Thomas J. Ross
EVP and Head of Commercial Banking Peapack-Gladstone Bank, Eric H. Waser
SVP and Head of Residential and Consumer Lending Peapack-Gladstone, Glenn R. Straffi
Vice President Global Online Marketing, Karen Chiarello
Vice President, Dominic Sedicino
Vice President, Glenn Carroll
Vice President Portfolio Manager, Sarah Krieger
Vice President, Timothy Doyle
Vice President, Georgette Barnes
Vice President, Amy Messler
Chairman, F. Duffield (Duff) Meyercord, age 70
Auditors: Crowe Horwath LLP

LOCATIONS

HQ: Peapack-Gladstone Financial Corp.
500 Hills Drive, Suite 300, Bedminster, NJ 07921-0700
Phone: 908 234-0700
Web: www.pgbank.com

PRODUCTS/OPERATIONS

2015 Sales

	$ mil.	% of total
Interest Income		
Loans including fees	94	77
Securities available for sale	4	4
Other	0	—
Other Income		
Wealth management fee income	17	14
Service charges and fees	3	3
Bank owned life insurance	1	1
Other income	1	1
Other	1	—
Total	**122**	**100**

COMPETITORS

Bank of America	PNC Financial
Hudson City Bancorp	TD Bank USA
JPMorgan Chase	Valley National
MSB Financial	Bancorp

HISTORICAL FINANCIALS

Company Type: Public

Income Statement

FYE: December 31

	ASSETS ($ mil.)	NET INCOME ($ mil.)	INCOME AS % OF ASSETS	EMPLOYEES
12/16	3,878	26	0.7%	338
12/15	3,364	19	0.6%	316
12/14	2,702	14	0.6%	306
12/13	1,966	9	0.5%	326
12/12	1,667	9	0.6%	292
Annual Growth	**23.5%**	**28.5%**	**—**	**3.7%**

2016 Year-End Financials

Debt ratio: 1.51%	No. of shares (mil.): 17
Return on equity: 8.80%	Dividends
Cash ($ mil.): 162	Yield: 0.0%
Current ratio: —	Payout: 12.5%
Long-term debt ($ mil.): —	Market value ($ mil.): 533

	STOCK PRICE ($) FY Close	P/E High/Low		PER SHARE ($) Earnings	Dividends	Book Value
12/16	30.88	20	10	1.60	0.20	18.79
12/15	20.62	18	14	1.29	0.20	17.16
12/14	18.56	18	14	1.22	0.20	15.99
12/13	19.10	20	14	1.01	0.20	14.48
12/12	14.08	16	10	1.05	0.20	13.69
Annual Growth	**21.7%**	**—**	**—**	**11.1%**	**(0.0%)**	**8.2%**

Penney (J.C.) Co.,Inc. (Holding Co.)

J. C. Penney Company is a holding company for department store operator J. C. Penney Corp. One of the largest department store and e-commerce retailers in the US J. C. Penney Corp. operates more than 1000 JCPenney department stores in 49 states and Puerto Rico. Its stores are mostly found in suburban shopping malls and sell clothing for men women and children as well as accessories homeware appliances and curtains and drapes. They may contain shop-in-shops like Sephora cosmetics and US Vision among others. Founded in 1902 current CEO Marvin Ellison is tasked with steadying the ship after his two predecessors were unable to do so.

Operations

J. C. Penney Corp. is one of the nation's largest apparel and home furnishing retailers. It has about 1000 stores selling mid-range clothing for women men and children as well as cosmetics furniture kitchenware home decoration appliances and luggage. It operates some 575 Sephora stores. As well as physical stores J. C. Penney operates an e-commerce website and omnichannel offering.

Apparel is the company's biggest revenue producer accounting for about half of revenue and split between women's apparel and men's apparel and accessories. Home and women's accessories including Sephora split another 25% of revenue with the rest generated by children's apparel footwear and handbags jewelry and services and other.

Geographic Reach

J. C. Penney Company's operating business J. C. Penney Corp. has a presence throughout the continental US Alaska and Puerto Rico. Its supply chain network operates about a dozen facilities in the US.

Sales and Marketing

J.C Penney sells merchandise and services to consumers through its department stores and its website (jcpenney.com). The company fulfills online customer purchases by direct shipment to the customer from its distribution facilities and stores or from its suppliers' warehouses and by in-store customer pick up.

The company markets its products via newspaper television programmatic marketing radio and other media.

Financial Performance

J. C. Penney?s revenue which has inched up for the past two years dropped slightly in 2016 to $12.5 billion from $12.6 billion in 2015. Same store sales increased by $2 million in 2016 but there were fewer stores. The company?s sales fell by $76 million in the difference between new stores (one added in 2016) and closed stores (9). The bright spots in J.C. Penney stores in 2016 were the Sephora Home and Footwear and Handbags divisions which posted higher sales from the year before. experienced sales increases. Sephora had the biggest gain helped by the addition of 60 in-store stores.

A glimpse of good news came at the J.C. Penney?s bottom line where a $1 million profit appeared following a $513 million loss in 2015 and for the first time since 2010. The company had lower expenses for selling general and administrative functions as well as lower costs for pensions and restructuring. There were higher expenses as well as the company invested in adding section for selling appliances and toys to its stores.

J.C. Penney?s cash flow from operations was $334 million in 2016 down from $440 million in 2015. The decrease was caused by higher incentive compensation and other expenses in 2016 than 2016. The company also carried more inventory and turned inventory fewer times in 2016.

Strategy

J. C. Penney is working in three areas to rebuild revenue and profit. It is turning to private brands investing in omnichannel sales and trying to increase revenue per customer.

With an emphasis on private brand the company seeks to leverage its sourcing offices around the world its manufacturing infrastructure and in-house designers to increase production of private brands for style quality and value.

J.C. Penney borrows from its catalog heritage for much of the infrastructure for omnichannel sales. Its website and mobile apps allow customers to place orders at anytime. The company has three distribution centers totaling about five million square feet to fulfill online orders. As retailers lose foot traffic the company wants to integrate its digital apps and the in-store experience with features like buy-online-pick-up-in-store (BOPIS).

The third area revenue per customer is the strategy most visible in stores. The Sephora stores in J.C. Penney stores has proven to be a revenue-producing hit and the company is adding more. With the addition of appliance departments to more than 600 stores by the end of 2017 and the testing of home installation services the company has moved into the ?Home Refresh? market as another revenue generating area.

J.C. Penney added a toy section to all its stores in 2017 prompted by what the company called an enthusiastic response to its toy offerings in the 2016 holiday. The company also significantly expanded its selection of toys online.

It?s not all about addition at J.C. Penney. The company said it would close 130 to 140 stores or about 13% of its locations that it deemed unprofitable.

EXECUTIVES

EVP Stores, Joseph M. (Joe) McFarland, age 47, $650,000 total compensation
SVP and General Merchandise Manager Fine Jewelry and Accessories, Pam Mortensen, age 62
EVP Supply Chain, Michael (Mike) Robbins, age 51
EVP Human Resources, Brynn L. Evanson, age 47, $515,937 total compensation
EVP and CIO, Therace M. Risch, age 44, $90,009 total compensation
SVP and Senior General Merchandise Manager Women's Apparel Sephora Salon Women's Specialty Footwear and Handbags, Jodie Johnson
Chairman and CEO, Marvin R. Ellison, age 52, $1,446,667 total compensation
EVP and CFO, Jeffrey (Jeff) Davis, age 54
SVP and Group President Northern Stores Division, Sean Lee
SVP and General Merchandise Manager MenÂ's Apparel Children Apparel and Jewelry, James Starke

EVP Omnichannel, Michael Amend, age 39
SVP and Group President Southern Stores Division, Jennifer Hipskind
SVP and General Merchandise Manager Sephora Salon & Intimate Apparel and Accessories, Angela Swanner
EVP and Chief Marketing Officer, Marci Grebstein
SVP and General Merchandise Manager Home, Tony Hurst
SVP and General Counsel, Brandy Treadway
Senior Vice President E Commerce, Dennis Johnson
Vice President womens design, Geoffrey Henning
Vice President Planning and Allocation Ecommerce, Jim Favors
Executive Vice President For Womens Apparel, Elizabeth Sweney
Vice President Of Store Operations, Thomas Stogner
Svp And Controller, Dennis P Miller, age 65
VP Human Resources, Larry Viands
DVP Prod Development Des, Mike Trampas
Vice President, Eric Blackwood
Divisional Vice President, Rebecca McComb
Legal Secretary, Jo Nolte
Vice President Division Merchandise Manager Juniors, Roger Taylor
Vice President Digital Experience, Josh Friedman
Vice President of Marketing, Laura Sandall
Vice President, Michael Hanson
Senior Counsel Government Relations, Arnold Grothues
Auditors: KPMG LLP

LOCATIONS

HQ: Penney (J.C.) Co.,Inc. (Holding Co.)
6501 Legacy Drive, Plano, TX 75024-3698
Phone: 972 431-1000
Web: www.jcpenney.com

PRODUCTS/OPERATIONS

BRANDS
The JCPenney
JCP
Liz Claiborne
Claiborne
Okie Dokie
Worthington
a.n.a
St. John's Bay
The Original Arizona Jean Company
Ambrielle
Decree
Stafford
J. Ferrar
Xersion

2016 Sales

	% of total
Women's apparel	24
Men's apparel and accessories	22
Home	13
Women's accessories including Sephora	13
Children's apparel	10
Family footwear	8
Fine jewelry	6
Services and other	4
Total	**100**

COMPETITORS

Amazon.com	Kohl's
Ascena Retail	Macy's
Bed Bath & Beyond	Nordstrom
Belk	Ross Stores
Bon-Ton Stores	Sears
Caleres	Stage Stores
Costco Wholesale	TJX Companies
Destination XL Group	Tailored Brands
Dillard's	Target Corporation
Eddie Bauer LLC	The Gap
Foot Locker	Wal-Mart
J. Crew	Zale
Kmart	

HISTORICAL FINANCIALS
Company Type: Public

Income Statement
FYE: January 28

	REVENUE ($ mil.)	NET INCOME ($ mil.)	NET PROFIT MARGIN	EMPLOYEES
01/17	12,547	1	0.0%	106,000
01/16	12,625	(513)	—	105,000
01/15*	12,257	(771)	—	114,000
02/14	11,859	(1,388)	—	117,000
02/13	12,985	(985)	—	116,000
Annual Growth	(0.9%)	—	—	(2.2%)

*Fiscal year change

2017 Year-End Financials

Debt ratio: 51.92%
Return on equity: 0.08%
Cash ($ mil.): 887
Current ratio: 1.69
Long-term debt ($ mil.): 4,558

No. of shares (mil.): 308
Dividends
  Yield: —
  Payout: —
Market value ($ mil.): 1,989

	STOCK PRICE ($) FY Close	P/E High/Low		PER SHARE ($) Earnings	Dividends	Book Value
01/17	6.45	—	—	(0.00)	0.00	4.39
01/16	7.26	—	—	(1.68)	0.00	4.28
01/15*	7.27	—	—	(2.53)	0.00	6.28
02/14	5.92	—	—	(5.57)	0.00	10.13
02/13	19.88	—	—	(4.49)	0.20	14.46
Annual Growth	(24.5%)	—	—	—	—	(25.8%)

*Fiscal year change

PENNSYLVANIA HOUSING FINANCE AGENCY

LOCATIONS

HQ: PENNSYLVANIA HOUSING FINANCE AGENCY
211 N FRONT ST, HARRISBURG, PA 171011406
Phone: 717 780-3800
Web: WWW.PHFA.ORG

HISTORICAL FINANCIALS
Company Type: Private

Income Statement
FYE: June 30

	ASSETS ($ mil.)	NET INCOME ($ mil.)	INCOME AS % OF ASSETS	EMPLOYEES
06/12	5,593	10	0.2%	250
06/11	6,051	39	0.7%	—
06/10	6,265	24	0.4%	—
06/09	5	0	0.1%	—
Annual Growth	909.7%	1420.8%	—	—

2012 Year-End Financials

Debt ratio: —
Return on equity: 1.40%
Cash ($ mil.): 393
Current ratio: 1.40
Long-term debt ($ mil.): —

Dividends
  Yield: —
  Payout: —
Market value ($ mil.): —

Pennymac Financial Services Inc

If you're thinking residential mortgage this company has more than a penny for your thoughts. The parent of investment management loan services and investment trust companies PennyMac Financial Services (PennyMac) focuses on the US residential mortgage market offering loans and investment management services. Through its Private National Mortgage Acceptance Company the company's PennyMac Loan Services (PLS) originates home loans in 45 states and DC and services loans in 49 states DC and the US Virgin Islands. PLS's counterpart PNMAC Capital Management acts as investment manager and advisor. The companies service and advise PennyMac Mortgage Investment Trust (PMT). PennyMac went public in 2013.

IPO

PennyMac hoped to raise $287.5 million in its IPO but investors responded with $199.9 million. The company plans to use the proceeds to fund growth of its mortgage business through Private National Mortgage Acceptance Company. It will also use the funds for general corporate purposes.

Operations

PennyMac's mortgage banking segment includes correspondent lending retail lending and loan servicing. The correspondent line includes conventional residential mortgages acquired by PMT as well as those guaranteed by FreddieMac FannieMae and other government agencies. The company has more than 140 approved sellers; in 2012 it had $13 billion in conventional loans and $8.4 billion in government-insured loans. Retail lending originates new prime residential conventional and government-backed mortgage loans for purchasing or refinancing homes. PennyMac uses the Internet and a call center rather than traditional branch locations for direct-to-consumer approach. The company's loan servicing business includes the back office work of loan administration collection and default activities. It serves PennyMac subsidiaries and other mortgage companies. The unit handles prime credit and distress loans under the prime servicing and special servicing headings respectively.

PennyMac's investment management segment operates as an investment manager through PNMAC Capital Management (PCM). PCM handles the $1.8 billion in combined assets from PMT and PennyMac's other investment funds. PMT is a publicly traded real estate investment trust (REIT).

Geographic Reach

While PennyMac serves nearly the entire US its portfolio is heavily weighted toward California (38%) Florida (5%) and Colorado (5%).

Financial Performance

The company's revenue has increased on the strength of gains in both the loan servicing and management segments. Other operating metrics include net assets under management total mortgage loans serviced and total mortgage loan production; all have increased in the last three years. PennyMac reported lower net income for 2012 due to amortization and impairment charges and higher spending on compensation. It sold and repurchased loans loans and earned interest on investments to more than double its cash flow for the same period.

Strategy

Since PennyMac was formed during the financial crisis it hasn't had to scramble and adapt like many of its competitors. As many mortgage shoppers turn away from large banks the company believes its poised to take advantage of growth and a lack of stringent regulations imposed on banks. For growth the company intends to focus on expanding its servicing business organically and through acquisitions increasing the number of loan sellers from which it purchases loans and leveraging its servicing portfolio to increase refinance and loan servicing opportunities.

EXECUTIVES

Senior Managing Director and Chief Enterprise Operations Officer, Anne D. McCallion, age 62
President and CEO, David A. Spector, age 54, $503,370 total compensation
President PennyMac Loan Services, Douglas E. (Doug) Jones, age 60, $325,000 total compensation
Senior Managing Director and Chief Risk Officer, David M. (Dave) Walker, age 61
Senior Managing Director and Chief Mortgage Operations Officer, Steve R. Bailey, age 55
Senior Managing Director and CFO, Andrew S. Chang, age 39
Senior Managing Director and Chief Capital Markets Officer, Vandad Fartaj, age 42
Senior Managing Director and Chief Administrative and Legal Officer, Jeffrey P. Grogin, age 56
Senior Managing Director and Chief Asset and Liability Management Officer, Daniel S. Perotti, age 36
Chairman and CEO PennyMac Financial Services Inc. and Private National Mortgage Acceptance Company LLC, Stanford L. Kurland, age 64
Auditors: Deloitte & Touche LLP

LOCATIONS

HQ: Pennymac Financial Services Inc
3043 Townsgate Road, Westlake Village, CA 91361
Phone: 818 224-7442
Web: www.pennymacusa.com

2016 Sales

	$ mil.	% of total
Net gains on mortgage loans held for sale	531	56
Net mortgage loan servicing fees	185	19
Loan origination fees	125	13
Fulfillment fees from PennyMac Mortgage Investment Trust	86	9
Management fees and Carried Interest	23	2
Other	4	1
Net interest expense	-25.1	-
Total	**931**	**0**

COMPETITORS

Bank of America	Quicken Loans
Citigroup	Stonegate Mortgage
JPMorgan Chase	U.S. Bancorp
Nationstar Mortgage	Wells Fargo
Ocwen Financial	

HISTORICAL FINANCIALS

Company Type: Public

Income Statement

FYE: December 31

	ASSETS ($ mil.)	NET INCOME ($ mil.)	INCOME AS % OF ASSETS	EMPLOYEES
12/16	5,133	66	1.3%	3,038
12/15	3,505	47	1.3%	2,509
12/14	2,507	36	1.5%	1,816
12/13	1,584	14	0.9%	1,373
12/12	832	118	14.2%	1,011
Annual Growth	**57.6%**	**(13.6%)**	**—**	**31.7%**

2016 Year-End Financials

Debt ratio: 3.40%	No. of shares (mil.): 22	
Return on equity: 21.32%	Dividends	
Cash ($ mil.): 99	Yield: —	
Current ratio: —	Payout: —	
Long-term debt ($ mil.): —	Market value ($ mil.): 373	

	STOCK PRICE ($) FY Close	P/E High/Low		PER SHARE ($) Earnings	Dividends	Book Value
12/16	16.65	6	4	2.94	0.00	15.49
12/15	15.36	9	7	2.17	0.00	12.32
12/14	17.30	11	8	1.73	0.00	9.92
12/13	17.55	27	19	0.82	0.00	8.04
Annual Growth	**(1.3%)**	—	—	**37.6%**	—	**17.8%**

Penske Automotive Group Inc

Penske Automotive Group has lots of lots. The US' #2 publicly traded auto dealer behind AutoNation Penske operates about 165 auto franchises from California to New York and Puerto Rico and another 190 franchises abroad mainly in the UK. It sells more than 40 car brands. Non-US brands including AUDI BMW and Honda generate more than 70% of sales. Penske also sells used vehicles provides financing and runs about 35 collision repair centers. UK subsidiary Sytner Group operates more than 145 franchises selling 20 brands of mostly high-end models. Additionally Penske holds a 28.9% stake in Penske Truck Leasing (PTL) known for commercial leasing and contract maintenance. The company is named after its Chairman Roger Penske.

Operations

Penske operates through two main segments: Retail Automotive and Retail Commercial Truck.

The Retail Automotive segment brings in the vast majority of company revenue (some 95%) and consists of its 355 retail automotive franchises in the US and abroad. It sells new and used cars under around 40 auto brands; around 70% of sales are from premium brands particularly Audi BMW and Porsche. The segment sells around 550000 cars each year.

Retail Commercial Truck accounts for most of the remaining revenue and consists of the heavy-duty truck dealerships Premier Truck Group. Premier Truck Group has 20 locations in the US and Canada that offer used trucks servicing and parts. Many dealerships are open 24/7.

Penske also has a few other interests such as its commercial vehicle business that imports and distributes Western Star heavy-duty trucks MAN heavy and medium duty trucks and buses and Dennis Eagle garbage trucks in Oceania.

Geographic Reach

Michigan-based Penske rings up some 60% of its sales in the US and Puerto Rico. The remainder comes from its overseas franchises which are predominantly found in the UK but also in Germany Canada and Italy. The company also has operations in Australia and New Zealand.

Sales and Marketing

Penske conducts its advertising and marketing at the local level. In recent years it has concentrated on the internet and other digital media including its own websites. In many markets it also taps traditional marketing formats including newspaper direct mail magazine television and radio advertising. The automobile manufacturer supplement its local and regional advertising through large advertising campaigns that promote their brands and offer attractive financing packages and other incentive programs.

By manufacturer BMW/MINI franchises brings in over 25% of Penske's total revenue while Volkswagen brand franchises (Audi/Volkswagen/Porsche/Bentley) account for over 20% of revenue. Toyota brands (Toyota and Lexus) generate some 15% of revenue and Mercedes-Benz brands (Mercedes-Benz/Sprinter/Smart) 10%.

Financial Performance

The decade following the financial crash in 2008 has seen Penske lifted by the economic recovery and the release of pent-up demand.

In fiscal 2016 sales increased a relatively modest 4% to $20.1 billion (it grew 12% and 18% the previous two years). Growth of 7% in new unit volume split between a 21.4% increase in international markets and a 0.5% fall in the US was offset by a 3% fall in retail prices. Volume growth was driven by acquisitions and was concentrated in Penske's non-US markets particularly Germany where its joint venture began and the UK. Weakness in sales volume in the US was a result of prioritizing gross profit which had a negative impact on sales.

Used car and service and parts revenue was also grown via acquisitions.

Net income was up 5% as higher revenue was offset by reduced profits from same-store sales due to lower average sales prices.

Cash from operations was down 6% to $365.5 million.

Strategy

Penske's growth strategy is based on entering new markets and growing its truck business.

It continues to grow its significant UK operation and has entered into joint ventures in Germany and Japan. In Japan Penske bought a 49% stake in Nicole Group a luxury brand dealership operating in Tokyo. It is probable that Penske will buy the remaining equity in the next few years. Penske's Japan operation will supported by its business partner Mitsui a large general trader.

The company is increasing its equity in Penske Truck Leasing its joint venture with Penske Corporation and Mitsui. In a year Penske has grown its stake in Penske Truck Leasing from 9% to 28.9%. Penske is expanding into the truck business to tap into the exceptionally good margins available in the truck parts and servicing segment.

Mergers and Acquisitions

In 2017 Penske bought CarShop a UK-based used car dealer expanding its presence in the country.

Similarly in the same year it acquired CarSense a US-based used car dealer.

Additionally it bought Jaguar and Land Rover dealerships from Prestige Family of Fine Cars a New Jersey-based dealership.

EXECUTIVES

EVP Human Resources, Claude H. (Bud) Denker, age 58, $500,000 total compensation
Chairman and CEO, Roger S. Penske, age 80, $1,200,000 total compensation
President, Robert H. Kurnick, age 55, $700,000 total compensation
Chairman Sytner Group, Gerard Nieuwenhuys, age 56
EVP Investor Relations and Corporate Development, Anthony R. (Tony) Pordon, age 53
Managing Director Sytner Group, Darren Edwards
EVP West Operations, Bernie Wolfe, age 61
EVP Strategic Development, George Brochick, age 69

EVP Central Operations, R. Whitfield Ramonat, age 56
EVP General Counsel and Secretary, Shane M. Spradlin, age 47, $500,000 total compensation
EVP East Operations, John Cragg
EVP and CFO, J.D. Carlson, age 47, $475,000 total compensation
EVP Marketing and Business Development, Terri Mulcahey
SVP and CIO, Rich Hook
Vice President Finance, Terry Speer
Vice President {, Christian Collins
Executive Vice President Marketing, Bud Denker
Executive Vice President And General Counsel, Walter P Czarnecki, age 74
Senior Vice President and Chief Information Officer, Richard Hook
Vice President Finance, James Harris
Assistant Vice President Business Process Improvement, Matt Gaor
Senior Vice President Human Resources, Tim Roop
Senior Vice President Manufacturer Relations, Robert K Wilshaw
Senior Vice President of Premium Brands, Michael Famiglietti
Vice President Manufacturer Relations, John Sullivan
Executive Vice President International Business De, Hiroshi Ishikawa
Vice President Manufacturer Relations, Jason Beidelman
EXECUTIVE VICE PRESIDENT OPERATIONS, Art Vallely
Area Vice President, John Robben
Auditors: Deloitte & Touche LLP

LOCATIONS

HQ: Penske Automotive Group Inc
2555 Telegraph Road, Bloomfield Hills, MI 48302-0954
Phone: 248 648-2500   **Fax:** 248 648-2525
Web: www.penskeautomotive.com

2016 Sales

	$ mil.	% of total
U.S	12,005	60
International	8,112	40
Total	**20,118**	**100**

2016 Stores

	No.
U.S	164
U.K	146
Germany	28
Italy	17
Total	**355**

PRODUCTS/OPERATIONS

2016 Sales

	$ mil.	% of total
Retail Automotive	18,673	93
Retail Commercial Truck	1,000	5
Commercial vehicle and Other	448	2
Elimination	(3.9)	-
Total	**20,118**	**100**

COMPETITORS

Asbury Automotive	JM Family Enterprises
AutoNation	Jordan Automotive
Autobytel	Larry H. Miller Group
Avis Budget	Lithia Motors
CarMax	Lookers
Ed Morse Auto	Microsoft
Enterprise Group	National Car Rental
Fletcher Jones	Pendragon
Group 1 Automotive	Potamkin Automotive
Hendrick Automotive	Serra Automotive
Holman Enterprises	Sonic Automotive

HISTORICAL FINANCIALS

Company Type: Public

Income Statement

FYE: December 31

	REVENUE ($ mil.)	NET INCOME ($ mil.)	NET PROFIT MARGIN	EMPLOYEES
12/16	20,118	342	1.7%	24,000
12/15	19,284	326	1.7%	22,000
12/14	17,177	286	1.7%	22,100
12/13	14,705	244	1.7%	18,000
12/12	13,163	185	1.4%	16,700
Annual Growth	**11.2%**	**16.6%**	**—**	**9.5%**

2016 Year-End Financials

Debt ratio: 58.63%
Return on equity: 19.31%
Cash ($ mil.): 24
Current ratio: 1.05
Long-term debt ($ mil.): 1,828

No. of shares (mil.): 85
Dividends
Yield: 0.0%
Payout: 27.5%
Market value ($ mil.): 4,418

	STOCK PRICE ($) FY Close	P/E High/Low		PER SHARE ($) Earnings	Dividends	Book Value
12/16	51.84	14	8	3.99	1.10	20.55
12/15	42.34	15	12	3.63	0.94	20.00
12/14	49.07	16	12	3.17	0.78	18.31
12/13	47.16	17	10	2.70	0.62	16.67
12/12	30.09	16	9	2.05	0.46	14.44
Annual Growth	**14.6%**	**—**	**—**	**18.1%**	**24.4%**	**9.2%**

People's United Financial Inc

People's United Financial is the holding company for People's United Bank (formerly People's Bank) which boasts more than 400 traditional branches supermarket branches commercial banking offices investment and brokerage offices and equipment leasing offices across New England and eastern New York. In addition to retail and commercial banking services the bank offers trust wealth management brokerage and insurance services. Its lending activities consist mainly of commercial mortgages (more than a third of its loan portfolio) commercial and industrial loans (more than a quarter) residential mortgages equipment financing and home equity loans. Founded in 1842 the bank has $36 billion in assets.

Operations

People's United operates two core business segments Retail Banking and Commercial Banking which both share duties of the bank's now-defunct Wealth Management division. The bank also has a non-core Treasury division that manages the company's securities portfolio and other investments.

Commercial Banking which makes up more than half of the company's total revenue provides business loans equipment financing (through People's Capital and Leasing Corp. or PCLC and People's United Equipment Finance Corp or PUEFC) and municipal banking as well as trust services for corporations and institutions and private banking services for wealthy individuals.

Retail Banking which makes up around 20% of total revenues provides deposit services residential mortgages and home equity loans financial advisory and investment management services as well as life insurance through People's United Insurance Agency.

Overall the bank generated 68% of its total revenue from loan interest in 2014 and 7% from interest on securities. About 10% of total revenues came from bank service charges while investment management fees commercial banking lending fees insurance revenue and brokerage commissions each made up less than 3% of overall revenue for the year.

Geographic Reach

People's United has more than 400 branches across Connecticut southeastern New York Massachusetts Vermont New Hampshire and Maine. Connecticut is its largest lending market with 27% of the bank's loan portfolio being extended to consumers and businesses in the region in 2014. New York and Massachusetts are the bank's next largest markets with a 19% and 18% share of its loan portfolio.

Sales and Marketing

The bank sells its products and services through investment and brokerage offices commercial branches online banking and investment trading and through its 24-hour telephone banking service. The company's PCLC and PUEFC affiliates have a sales presence in 16 states to support equipment financing operations throughout the US.

People's United spent $13 million on advertising in 2014 compared to $15.4 million and $17.7 million in 2013 and 2012 respectively.

Financial Performance

People's United has struggled to meaningfully grow its revenue in recent years though profits have been rising as the bank has taken fewer loan losses as its loan portfolio has become more creditworthy amidst the improving economy.

The bank's revenue inched up by less than 1% to $1.35 billion in 2014 mostly thanks to residential mortgage business growth as well as growth among the bank's other loan types. Driving higher interest income People's United grew its loan assets by $2.6 billion while interest-earning securities assets grew by $201 million for the year.

Higher revenue coupled with a decline in loan loss provisions in 2014 drove the bank's net income higher by 8% to $251.7 million. The company's operating cash slipped by 8% to $350 million for the year after adjusting its earnings for non-cash items.

Strategy

People's United emphasizes cross-selling financial products by developing client relationships and has increasingly tied employee compensation to this ability. The company is particularly focused on building its small business lending wealth management and insurance business. It also continues to open new branches and seeks acquisition targets for further growth.

One other key element of its strategy involves boosting its deposit assets through its expanded convenient store reach. In early 2015 the company boasted nearly 150 full-service branches in Stop & Shop supermarkets across Connecticut and southeastern New York which comprised 36% of the bank's total branch network and held 14% of its total deposits. Much of this is attributed to a key acquisition in 2012 when the company purchased nearly 60 branches (many within Stop & Shop supermarkets) in the New York metro area from RBS Citizens. People's United already had more than 80 Stop & Shop branches in Connecticut so the deal strengthened its relationship with the retailer and expanded its presence in the New York market.

Mergers and Acquisitions

In 2016 People's United agreed to buy Long Island-based Suffolk Bancorp holding company of Suffolk County National Bank for $402 million. That bank has some 30 branches on Long Island;

the purchase supports People's United's growth in the New York Metro area.

Company Background

One of the main goals of People's United has been to build its presence in the two largest metropolitan areas in its market New York City and Boston. One of the largest in the Boston area Danvers Bancorp added some 30 branches and carried a price tag of approximately $493 million. People's United also acquired LSB Corporation and Butler Bank the latter in an FDIC-assisted transaction that included a loss-sharing agreement with the regulator covering all acquired loans and foreclosed real estate of the failed bank bringing in another 10 branches in the Boston area. In 2010 People's United bought Bank of Smithtown which had about 30 branches primarily on Long Island in New York.

People's United Financial acquired commercial lender Financial Federal Corporation in 2010 (now People's United Equipment Finance) which provides financing and leasing to small and midsized business nationwide.

People's United Financial underwent significant transformation in past years. The company demutualized and converted to a stock holding company in 2007 and early the following year acquired multibank holding company Chittenden Corporation. The deal added some 140 branches doubling People's United Bank's branch network and expanding its reach beyond Connecticut and New York and into the rest of New England.

EXECUTIVES

Vice President, Susan D Stanley
President and CEO, John P. (Jack) Barnes, age 61, $890,384 total compensation
SEVP Corporate Development and Strategic Planning, Kirk W. Walters, age 62, $468,461 total compensation
SVP and President Merrill Bank, William P. (Bill) Lucy, age 58
Chief Financial Officer, R. David Rosato, age 55
EVP Marketing and Regional Banking People's United Bank, Robert R. (Bob) D'Amore, age 64, $429,323 total compensation
SVP and President Chittenden Bank, Michael L. Seaver
SEVP Wealth Management, Louise T. Sandberg, age 65
President Massachusetts, Timothy P. Crimmins
Market Leader New York, Sara M. Longobardi
SVP and President People's United Bank North Connecticut, Michael J. Casparino
SEVP Human Resources, David K. Norton, age 62, $411,231 total compensation
SEVP Commercial Banking, Jeffrey J. (Jeff) Tengel, age 54, $408,654 total compensation
SVP and Division President People's United Bank Southern Connecticut, Armando F. Goncalves
SEVP and General Counsel, Robert E. Trautmann, age 63
SEVP and Chief Administrative Officer, Lee C. Powlus
President New Hampshire, Dianne M. Mercier
President Southern Maine, Daniel P. (Dan) Thornton
Vice President Information Technology, Carol Anderson
Divisional Vice President, Ellen Kritemeyer
Vice President Information Technology, Albert Sanna
Vice President Financial Services Manager, Cheryl Nickerson
Senior Vice President Credit Officer, Walter Kaercher
Vice President Of Sales, Jeffrey Morrison
Vice President Market Research, Craig Noble

Executive Vice President Chief Credit Officer, David Bodor
First Vice President Wealth Management, John Lescure
Senior Vice President and Market Development Officer, Brian Shea
Assistant Vice President, Jim Gorman
Vice President, Peter Martinez
Vice President, Amy York
Vice President Loan Resolution, Matthew Carter
Divisional Vice President, Peter Brestovan
Assistant Vice President, Patrick Talcott
Senior Vice President Financial Planner, George Clough
Vice President Customer Experience Manager, Thomas Griesing
Vice President New Haven Regional Manager., James Macdonald
Vice President Information Techonlogy Control and Assurance, Sue Bascom-Erazmus
Vice President Director of Tax, Kathleen Jones
Vice President and Cra Officer, Art Casavant
Market Manager Assistant Vice President, Alice Baird
Senior Vice President And Director Marketing, Kathleen Schirling
Vice President, Fabrizio Anthony
Vice President, Robert Bursey
Vice President, Daniel Reilly
Vice President, Robert Donahue
Vice President Customer Service Manager, Magda Wachel-Florczyk
Vice President, Elaine Khu
Vice President, Patrick Lorent
Market Manager Vice President, Marjorie Downing
Assistant Vice President Customer Service, Ana Saraiva
Financials Services Manager Assistant Vice President, Andrea Kantaros
Assistant Vice President, Kasey Franzoni
Senior Vice President, Kathleen Lepak
Vice President Financial Analyst, Rita Rivers
Senior Vice President And Growth Manager, Jill Desousa
Vice President Finance, Brian Connery
Vice President Purchasing, Theresa Knies
Assistant Vice President, David Schalk
Senior Vice President Senior Portfolio, Michael Williams
Financial Services Mananger Assistant Vice President, Amy Pasquarelli
Senior Vice President, Jeffery Paz
Assistant Vice President, Tuyen LE
First Vice President, John Bundschuh
Assistant Vice President, Kurtis Denison
Senior Private Banker Senior Vice President, Bethany Dubuque
Vice President, Lisa Rollins
Senior Vice President, Jody Cole
Vice President Market Manager, David Cavanaugh
Senior Vice President, Roz Rubin
Senior Vice President Commercial Lending, Tom Wolcott
Assistant Vice President, Janet Vita
Relationship Manager Vice President, Steven Wurtz
Assistant Vice President Customer Service Manager, Shannon Galliford
Vice President, Rose Morgan
Senior Vice President Business Services And Digital Channels, Ravi Vakacherla
Vice President Commercial Lending, Debbie Boyle
Vice President Financial Services Manager, Jennifer Lynch
Vice President of Loans, Cynthia P Belak
Region Manager Senior Vice President Commercial Real Estate Finance, Kathleen Hayes
Senior Lender Vice President, Peter Lange
Executive Vice President, Henry R Mandel
Senior Vice President Consumer Deposit P, Peter Scotch

Vice President, Darrin Fodor
Vice President, James Bucko
Assistant Vice President Financial Services Manager, Angela Gallagher
Market Manager Vice President, Sheldon Berg
Vice President, Timothy B Hodges
Vice President, Michael Rispoli
Senior Vice President, Mark Leonardi
Vice President Financial Service Manager, Octaviana Volk
Financial Services Manager Assistant Vice President, Cheryl Hagmann
Financial Services Manager Assistant Vice President, Alex Slootskiy
Financial Services Manager AVP, Martin Couture
Assistant Vice President Financial Services Manager, Robert Duffus
Financial Services Manager Assistant Vice President, Jennifer Cassidy
Vice President Market Manager, Michelle Marshall
Fixed Income Strategist Senior Vice President, Karissa McDonough
Vice President Cash Manager, Melissa Babineau
Assistant Vice President Branch Manager, Kristen Lavallee
Vice President Financial Services Manager, Kristen Keil
Senior Wealth Management Officer Senior Vice President, Amy Thompson
First Vice President Loss Management and Deposit Risk, Sara Wilbur
Financial Services Manager Assistant Vice President, Cathy Ferreira-Golino
Vice President Commercial Lending, Russell Rohan
Senior Vice President Commercial Lending, Skip Poczobut
Assistant Vice President Customer Service Manager, Sylvana Chiluisa
Assistant Vice President Financial Services Manager, Kiera McCourt
Commercial Portfolio Manager Assistant Vice President, Timothy Pereira
Financial Services Manager Assistant Vice President, Christian Estevez
NA Vice President Treasury Management, Mary Lonczak
Vice President Relationship Manager, Seth Arvanites
Assistant Vice President Customer Service Manager, Jonathan Ugas
Assistant Vice President Customer Servic, Elaine Bandeira
Vice President Model Validation, Julien Lee
Assistant Vice President Customer Service Manager, Amy Tucker
Assistant Vice President Customer Service Manager, Lamia Amirouche
Growth Manager FVP, Sandra Morris
Assistant Vice President Mortgage Account Officer, Laura Kelly
Assistant Vice President Mortgage Account Officer, Richard Klein
Business Banker Vice President, Keri Denis
Senior Vice President, Stephanie Wernhoff
Financial Service Manager Assistant Vice President, Dina Lopes
First Vice President, Jack Good
Assistant Vice President and Operations Manager, Julie Lochowicz
Vice President Commercial Real Estate Finance Department, Joseph Cammilleri
Vice President, Brian Boyaji
Assistant Vice President Customer Service Manager, Krupali Doshi
Vice President Sales and Leasing, Rick Curtiss
Vice President, Tom Emery
Mortgage Account Officer Assistant Vice President, Matthew McGuckin
Assistant Vice President, Amy Maheux
Senior Vice President, Ann Swenson

Senior Vice President Commercial Lending, Edward Borden
Senior Vice President Commercial Real Estate Finance, Mark Dalton
Vice President and Sr.Market Manager Bridgeport Market, Virgilio Lopez
Vice President, Joseph Korecki
VICE PRESIDENT, Justin Jennings
Vice President Wealth Management Marketing, Sara Sparks
Assistant Vice President Branch Manager Danbury Market, Todd Clifford
Senior Market Manager Vice President, Raymond DiPresso
Assistant Vice President, Brad Thorpe
Vice President, Michael Whitman
Vice President Healthcare and Non Profit Banking, Brian Mason
VICE PRESIDENT, Kenneth Vaccaro
VICE PRESIDENT CUSTOMER SERVICE MANAGER, Lacey Bicknell
First Vice President, Maria Kastanis
Senior Vice President, Mark Danie
Senior Vice President Commercial Banking, David Estes
Business Banker Vice President, Colin Branon
Assistant Vice President Bank Manager, Andrew Matarese
Auditors: KPMG LLP

LOCATIONS

HQ: People's United Financial Inc
  850 Main Street, Bridgeport, CT 06604
Phone: 203 338-7171   Fax: 203 338-2545
Web: www.peoples.com

PRODUCTS/OPERATIONS

2014 Sales

	$ mil.	% of total
Interest & dividends		
Loans		
Commercial real estate	354	26
Commercial	351	26
Residential mortgage	153	12
Consumer	73	5
Securities	96	7
Other	1	-
Noninterest		
Bank service charges	128	10
Investment management fees	41	3
Operating lease income	41	3
Commercial banking lending fees	33	2
Insurance revenue	29	2
Other	76	4
Adjustment	(0.9)	-
Total	1,381	100

COMPETITORS

Bank of America	KeyCorp
Citibank	Liberty Bank
Citizens Financial Group	Sovereign Bank
Fairfield County Bank	TD Bank USA
	Webster Financial

HISTORICAL FINANCIALS

Company Type: Public

Income Statement

FYE: December 31

	ASSETS ($ mil.)	NET INCOME ($ mil.)	INCOME AS % OF ASSETS	EMPLOYEES
12/16	40,609	281	0.7%	5,173
12/15	38,877	260	0.7%	5,139
12/14	35,997	251	0.7%	5,397
12/13	33,213	232	0.7%	5,429
12/12	30,324	245	0.8%	5,442
Annual Growth	7.6%	3.5%	—	(1.3%)

2016 Year-End Financials

Debt ratio: 2.54%
Return on equity: 5.68%
Cash ($ mil.): 602
Current ratio: —
Long-term debt ($ mil.): —
No. of shares (mil.): 315
Dividends
  Yield: 0.0%
  Payout: 73.6%
Market value ($ mil.): 6,116

	STOCK PRICE ($) FY Close	P/E High/Low		PER SHARE ($) Earnings	Dividends	Book Value
12/16	19.36	22	15	0.92	0.68	16.28
12/15	16.15	20	16	0.86	0.67	15.26
12/14	15.18	19	16	0.84	0.66	15.05
12/13	15.12	21	16	0.74	0.65	14.88
12/12	12.09	19	16	0.72	0.64	14.84
Annual Growth	12.5%	—		6.3%	1.5%	2.3%

People's Utah Bancorp

Auditors: Tanner LLC

LOCATIONS

HQ: People's Utah Bancorp
  1 East Main Street, American Fork, UT 84003
Phone: 801 642-3998
Web: www.PeoplesUtah.com

HISTORICAL FINANCIALS

Company Type: Public

Income Statement

FYE: December 31

	ASSETS ($ mil.)	NET INCOME ($ mil.)	INCOME AS % OF ASSETS	EMPLOYEES
12/16	1,665	23	1.4%	430
12/15	1,555	19	1.3%	414
12/14	1,367	14	1.1%	367
12/13	1,299	11	0.9%	—
12/12	0	9	—	—
Annual Growth		26.4%	—	—

2016 Year-End Financials

Debt ratio: —
Return on equity: 10.75%
Cash ($ mil.): 64
Current ratio: —
Long-term debt ($ mil.): —
No. of shares (mil.): 17
Dividends
  Yield: 0.0%
  Payout: 16.9%
Market value ($ mil.): 478

	STOCK PRICE ($) FY Close	P/E High/Low		PER SHARE ($) Earnings	Dividends	Book Value
12/16	26.85	21	11	1.30	0.22	12.82
12/15	17.21	15	13	1.17	0.12	11.92
Annual Growth	11.8%	—		2.7%	16.4%	1.8%

Peoples Bancorp, Inc. (Marietta, OH)

Peoples Bancorp offers banking for the people by the people and of the people. The holding company owns Peoples Bank which has about 50 branches in rural and small urban markets in Ohio Kentucky and West Virginia. The bank offers traditional services such as checking and savings accounts CDs loans and trust services. Commercial and agricultural loans including those secured by commercial real estate account for the majority of the bank's lending activities. Its Peoples Financial Advisors division offers investment management services while Peoples Insurance sells life health and property/casualty coverage.

Operations

Credit cards and brokerage services are offered through third-party providers.

Financial Performance

The company's revenue increased from $103.7 million in fiscal 2012 up to $104.6 million for fiscal 2013. However despite the slight spike in annual revenue Peoples Bancorp's net income decreased from $29.9 million in fiscal 2012 down to $29 million for fiscal 2013.

The company's cash on hand decreased by about $1 million in fiscal 2013 compared to fiscal 2012 levels.

Strategy

Peoples Bancorp is looking to increase its revenue from service changes and other fees and commissions particularly from insurance and wealth management which are not reliant on fluctuating interest rate margins.

The company is also looking to strengthen its brand and build deeper relationships with its clients.

EXECUTIVES

EVP and Chief Administrative Officer Peoples Bancorp and EVP Chief Administrative Officer and CashierPeoples Bank N.A., Carol A. Schneeberger, age 60, $233,000 total compensation
EVP and Chief Commercial Lending Officer Peoples Bancorp and Peoples Bank N.A., Daniel K. (Dan) McGill, age 62, $250,000 total compensation
EVP and Chief Credit Officer Peoples Bancorp and Peoples Bank N.A., Timothy H. Kirtley, age 47, $221,500 total compensation
President CEO and Director Peoples Bancorp and Peoples Bank N.A., Charles W. Sulerzyski, age 59, $500,000 total compensation
EVP CFO and Treasurer Peoples Bancorp and Peoples Bank N.A., John C. Rogers, age 57, $26,136 total compensation
Executive Vice President, Richard Stafford
Senior Vice President, Matthew Evans
Vice President Sales and Marketing, Thomas E Betz
Executive Vice President Human Resources, Michael W Hager
Vice President, Keith Cropper
Vice President Commercial Banking, Kristi Beeman
Vice President Director of Risk Management, Ann Helmick
Vice President Commercial Lend, Greg Ullman
Vice President, Larry Holdren
Vice President Commerical Lender, Kevin Connors
Senior Vice President, Thomas Greathouse
Senior Vice President Credit Administration, Robyn Stevens
Vice President Huntington WV, Jack Massey
Senior Vice President, Roger Reeves
Senior Vice President Chief Financial Officer, Amanda Bryan
Senior Vice President And Corporate Counsel, Ryan Kirkham
Assistant Vice President Trust Officer, Stuart Dekker
Assistant Vice President Branch Market Manager, Julie Music
Assistant Vice President Branch Market Manager, Candace Frump
Branch Market Manager Assistant Vice President, Peggy Scott-Morgan
Vice President and Controller, Jeffrey Baran

VICE PRESIDENT, Randy Barengo
Chairman Peoples Bancorp and Peoples Bank N.A., David L. Mead, age 62
Auditors: Ernst & Young LLP

LOCATIONS

HQ: Peoples Bancorp, Inc. (Marietta, OH)
138 Putnam Street, P.O. Box 738, Marietta, OH 45750
Phone: 740 373-3155
Web: www.peoplesbancorp.com

PRODUCTS/OPERATIONS

2016 Sales

	$ mil.	% of total
Interest Income:		
Interest and fees on loans	93	56
Interest and dividends on taxable investment securities	18	11
Interest on tax-exempt investment securities	3	2
Other Income:		
Insurance income	13	8
Deposit account service charges	10	6
Trust and investment income	10	6
Electronic banking income	10	6
Bank owned life insurance income	1	1
Mortgage banking income	1	1
Commercial loan swap fee income	1	1
Net gain on investment securities	0	1
Net loss on asset disposals and other transactions (1.1) -		
Other	1	1
Total	**166**	**100**

COMPETITORS

1st West Virginia Bancorp	Huntington Bancshares
BB&T	Ohio Valley Banc
Fifth Third	U.S. Bancorp
	United Bankshares

HISTORICAL FINANCIALS

Company Type: Public

Income Statement

FYE: December 31

	ASSETS ($ mil.)	NET INCOME ($ mil.)	INCOME AS % OF ASSETS	EMPLOYEES
12/16	3,432	31	0.9%	782
12/15	3,258	10	0.3%	817
12/14	2,567	16	0.6%	699
12/13	2,059	17	0.9%	546
12/12	1,918	20	1.1%	494
Annual Growth	15.7%	11.2%	—	12.2%

2016 Year-End Financials

Debt ratio: 1.37%
Return on equity: 7.27%
Cash ($ mil.): 66
Current ratio: —
Long-term debt ($ mil.): —
No. of shares (mil.): 18
Dividends
Yield: 0.0%
Payout: 37.4%
Market value ($ mil.): 589

	STOCK PRICE ($) FY Close	P/E High/Low	PER SHARE ($) Earnings	Dividends	Book Value
12/16	32.46	19 10	1.71	0.64	23.99
12/15	18.84	42 30	0.61	0.60	22.88
12/14	25.93	20 15	1.36	0.60	22.92
12/13	22.51	15 12	1.63	0.54	20.89
12/12	20.43	12 8	1.92	0.45	21.02
Annual Growth	12.3%	— —	(2.9%)	9.2%	3.4%

Peoples Financial Services Corp

Power to the Peoples Financial Services. The firm is the holding company for Peoples Security Bank and Trust Company (formerly Peoples National Bank) which operates about 25 branches across northeastern Pennsylvania and neighboring Broome County in New York. Established in 1905 the bank offers standard retail products and services including checking and savings accounts CDs and credit cards to local businesses and individuals. Commercial loans including mortgages construction loans and operating loans make up the greatest portion (40%) of the company's loan book followed by residential mortgages (25%) and consumer loans. The company's Peoples Advisors subsidiary provides investment and brokerage services.

Operations

About 80% of Peoples Financial Services' total revenue came from interest income (mostly on loans) in 2014 while the remainder comes from non-interest income. The bank had a staff of 354 full-time employees at the end of that year.

Geographic Reach

Scranton-based Peoples Security Bank has more than 25 branches across Northeastern Pennsylvania (in the Lackawanna Lehigh Luzerne Monroe Susquehanna Wayne and Wyoming counties) and Broome County in New York state.

Sales and Marketing

The company primarily makes loans to small- and medium-sized businesses. It spent $450 on advertising in 2014 up from $350 and $287 in 2013 and 2012 respectively.

Financial Performance

Peoples has struggled to consistently grow its revenues in recent years due to shrinking interest margins on loans amidst the low-interest environment. Its profits however have been rising thanks to lower interest expenses on deposits and declining loan loss provisions as its loan portfolio's credit quality has improved with higher property valuations in the strengthened economy.

The company enjoyed a breakout year in 2014 however as its revenue jumped 60% to a record $79.21 million mostly as its interest income swelled from new loan business from its 2013 acquisition of Penseco Financial Services. Its service charge fees and commissions merchant services income and commission and fee income from fiduciary services also rose mostly as a result of the significant acquisition.

Higher revenue in 2014 allowed Peoples' net income to more than triple to a record $17.6 million while its operating cash levels more than doubled to $20.6 million on higher cash earnings for the year.

Strategy

Peoples Security Bank occasionally acquires smaller banks to extend its branch network across target markets while adding new loan and deposit business. Its late 2013 acquisition of Penseco Financial Services Corporation for example nearly doubled its loan and deposit business and more than doubled its branch network to 25 branches.

Mergers and Acquisitions

In November 2013 Peoples acquired Penseco Financial Services Corporation along with its Penn Security Bank and Trust subsidiary. The $155 million-deal doubled Peoples' branch network from 12 to 25 branches creating the largest community bank headquartered in Northeastern Pennsylvania.

EXECUTIVES

CEO and President, Alan W. Dakey, age 65
EVP and COO Peoples National Bank, Debra E. Dissinger, age 62, $110,000 total compensation
Director, Richard S. Lochen, age 53, $130,000 total compensation
Senior Vice President Chief Financial Officer, Scott Seasock
Vice President, Howard Updyke
Vice President, Jeff Drobins
Vice President Commercial Lending, Diane Effting
Chairman, William E. Aubrey, age 54
Auditors: Baker Tilly Virchow Krause, LLP

LOCATIONS

HQ: Peoples Financial Services Corp
150 North Washington Avenue, Scranton, PA 18503
Phone: 570 346-7741
Web: www.peoplesnatbank.com

PRODUCTS/OPERATIONS

2014 Sales

	$ mil.	% of total
Interest	64	81
Non-interest	15	19
Total	**79**	**100**

COMPETITORS

Citizens & Northern	HSBC USA
Citizens Financial	M&T Bank
Services	NBT Bancorp
Fidelity D & D	Penns Woods Bancorp
First Keystone	
First National	
Community Bancorp	

HISTORICAL FINANCIALS

Company Type: Public

Income Statement
FYE: December 31

	ASSETS ($ mil.)	NET INCOME ($ mil.)	INCOME AS % OF ASSETS	EMPLOYEES
12/16	1,999	19	1.0%	364
12/15	1,819	17	1.0%	348
12/14	1,741	17	1.0%	354
12/13	1,688	5	0.3%	354
12/12	918	10	1.2%	—
Annual Growth	**21.5%**	**16.6%**	**—**	**—**

2016 Year-End Financials

Debt ratio: —	No. of shares (mil.): 7
Return on equity: 7.73%	Dividends
Cash ($ mil.): 39	Yield: 0.0%
Current ratio: —	Payout: 46.7%
Long-term debt ($ mil.): —	Market value ($ mil.): 360

	STOCK PRICE ($) FY Close	P/E High/Low	PER SHARE ($) Earnings	Dividends	Book Value
12/16	48.70	19 13	2.65	1.24	34.71
12/15	38.08	21 15	2.36	1.24	33.57
12/14	49.68	23 16	2.34	1.24	32.69
12/13	38.00	33 25	1.21	0.92	31.62
12/12	30.50	13 12	2.37	0.86	29.65
Annual Growth	**12.4%**	**— —**	**2.8%**	**9.6%**	**4.0%**

PepsiCo Inc

PepsiCo butts heads with its eternal rival The Coca-Cola Company for the title of world's biggest soft drinks maker. PepsiCo's soft drink brands include Pepsi Mountain Dew Tropicana Gatorade and Aquafina water. The company also owns Frito-Lay the world's #1 snack maker with offerings such as Lay's Ruffles Doritos and Cheetos. The Quaker Foods unit makes breakfast cereals (Quaker oatmeal Life) Rice-A-Roni rice and Near East side dishes. Pepsi products are available in 200-plus countries. The company operates its own bottling plants and distribution facilities.

HISTORY

Pharmacist Caleb Bradham invented Pepsi in 1898 in New Bern North Carolina. He named his new drink Pepsi-Cola (claiming it cured dyspepsia or indigestion) and registered the trademark in 1903. Following The Coca-Cola Company's example Bradham developed a bottling franchise system. By WWI 300 bottlers had signed up. After the war Bradham stockpiled sugar to safeguard against rising costs but in 1920 sugar prices plunged forcing him into bankruptcy in 1923.

Pepsi existed on the brink of ruin under various owners until Loft Candy bought it in 1931. Its fortunes improved in 1933 when in the midst of the Depression it doubled the size of its bottles to 12 ounces without raising the five-cent price. In 1939 Pepsi introduced the world's first radio jingle. Two years later Loft Candy merged with its Pepsi subsidiary and became The Pepsi-Cola Company.

Donald Kendall who became Pepsi-Cola's president in 1963 turned the firm's attention to young people ("The Pepsi Generation"). It acquired Mountain Dew in 1964 and became PepsiCo in 1965 when it acquired Frito-Lay.

In 1972 PepsiCo agreed to distribute Stolichnaya vodka in the US in exchange for being the only Western firm allowed to bottle soft drinks in the USSR. With the purchases of Pizza Hut (1977) Taco Bell (1978) and Kentucky Fried Chicken (1986) it became a major force in the fast-food industry.

When Coca-Cola changed its formula in 1985 Pepsi had a short-lived victory in the cola wars (until the return of Coca-Cola classic the new formula having been a dismal failure). The rivalry was extended to ready-to-drink tea in 1991 when in response to Coca-Cola's Nestea venture with Nestl © PepsiCo teamed up with Lipton.

Between 1991 and 1996 PepsiCo aggressively expanded its overseas bottling operations. However its efforts contrasted markedly with Coca-Cola's well-oiled international distribution machine. The firm then shifted its attention to the organization of its overseas network. Roger Enrico became CEO in 1996.

A year later PepsiCo spun off its $10 billion fast-food unit as TRICON Global Restaurants (now known as YUM! Brands Inc.) putting itself in a better position to sell its soft drinks at other restaurants. Also in 1997 it bought Borden's Cracker Jack snack and Smith's snacks from the UK's United Biscuits.

In 1998 it bought Seagram's market-leading Tropicana juices (rival of Coca-Cola's Minute Maid) for $3.3 billion. The firm sold a 65% stake in its new Pepsi Bottling Group to the public in 1999.

Its more than $13 billion purchase of The Quaker Oats Company in 2001 added the dominant Gatorade sports drink brand to its lineup. To make room for Gatorade PepsiCo sold its competing All Sport energy drink to The Monarch Beverage Company an Atlanta-based soda company later that year.

PepsiCo began a major restructuring of its PepsiCo Beverages & Foods division in 2003. The restructuring resulted in four company divisions: PepsiCo International PepsiCo Beverages North America Frito-Lay North America and Quaker Foods North America.

In 2004 PepsiCo approached juice maker Ocean Spray about a joint venture but was turned away by the cranberry farmers who own the juice manufacturer. The company bought General Mills' stake of their joint venture Snack Ventures Europe (SVE) in 2005 for $750 million. The deal gave Pepsi control of Europe's largest snack food company.

It's also been driving its snack brands to new markets as it bolts on new and more nutritious foods categories through small acquisitions and alliances. In 2013 Muller Quaker Dairy a joint venture between PepsiCo and Theo Muller Group (a Germany-based privately held dairy holding company) opened of its new yogurt manufacturing facility in Batavia New York. It serves as the national production and distribution center for a premium lineup of M ller brand yogurts to US supermarket and club retailers.

EXECUTIVES

CEO North America, Albert P. (Al) Carey, age 65, $984,615 total compensation
Chairman and CEO, Indra K. Nooyi, age 61, $1,725,000 total compensation
EVP Human Resources and Chief Human Resources Officer, Cynthia M. Trudell, age 64
Vice Chairman EVP Global Research and Development and Chief Scientific Officer, Mehmood Khan, age 58, $756,731 total compensation
SVP and CIO, Jody R. Davids, age 61
President ESSA Category Teams Franchise and Po1 Sub-Saharan Africa, Richard D. Evans
Vice Chairman EVP and CFO, Hugh F. Johnston, age 56, $960,577 total compensation
President PepsiCo Russia, Silviu Popovici, age 49
President Global Beverages Group, Brad Jakeman
President PepsiCo Mexico, Pedro Padierna
President Latin America Beverages, Luis Montoya
President and COO Frito-Lay North America (FLNA), Vivek Sankaran, age 55
President Global Snacks Group and Global Insights, Simon Lowden
EVP Corporate Strategy and Chief Venturing Officer, Jim Andrew, age 56
Chief Operating Officer (COO) NAB and President Global Foodservice, Kirk Tanner, age 49
CEO Asia Middle East and North Africa, Sanjeev Chadha, age 57, $764,423 total compensation
President PepsiCo, Ramon Laguarta, age 53, $748,846 total compensation
EVP Global Categories and Franchise Management, Eugene Willemsen
EVP Communications, Jon Banner
CEO Latin America (LATAM) and Europe Sub-Saharan Africa (ESSA), Laxman Narasimhan, age 49
EVP Government Affairs General Counsel and Corporate Secretary, Tony West, age 51
EVP Global Operations, Brian Newman
President and CEO Greater China Region, Mike Spanos
COO PepsiCo North America Foodservice, Anne Fink
Vice President Information Technology, Thad Lents
Marketing Vice President, Haston Lewis
Vice President, Art Lawrence
Senior Vice President and Chief Design Officer, Mauro Porcini

Vice President Information Technology, Darrell Harvey

Vice President of Bottler Relations, Denis Sacks

Vice President Risk Management, Jason McDonell

Vice President Purchasing, Chris Gullucci

Vice President Worldwide Government Affairs, David Wright

Vice President China and HK Market Units, George Kovoor

Vice President Human Resources, Dave Moncur

Vice President of Organization and Management Development, Allan Church

Finance Senior Vice President Paf Controller, Kathy Nittolo

Vice President, Joseph Sim

Region Vice President Assistant, Valerie Matthews

Vice President, David Sklarew

Vice President Supplier Development and Procurement, Deepak Gupta

Vice President Marketing, Jim Foderaro

National Sales Manager, Jill Griffith

Executive Vice President Flna, David C Rader

Vice President Corporate Communications, Tiffany Novinger

Customer Management Vice President Walmart, Deanna Jurgens

Senior Vice President Sales, Mario Mercurio

Vice President of Industry Relations, Doug Allison

Sc Vice President, Tony Mattei

Vice President Engineering, Piper Thornton

Vice President Business Development, Bryan Morrow

Customer Management Senior Vice President, Jeffery Swearingen

Vice President, Sheri Mungai

Vice President Corporate and Commercial Planning Europe, Claire Stone

National Sales Manager, Joseph Huxta

Vice President Selling and Delivery, Greg Moore

Shop Insights Vice President, Scott Finlow

Vice President of Business Development, Jean Jakoby

Vice President of Public Relations, Larry Jabbonsky

Sales Vice President, Byron Brooks

SENIOR VICE PRESIDENT GRAINS, Marc Schroeder

Vice President, Kevin Davis

Channel Vice President Retail Foodservice, Brian Ripley

Finance Vice President Bus Cntrl, Joan Horgan

Assistente Do Vice Presidente De Research and Development, Alessandra Lucas

Senior Vice President Finance North America, Cynthia Swanson

Vice President, Ruchira Jain

Area Vice President, David Laurie

Vice President of Sales, Jason Richards

National Account Manager, Chris Saline

Sc Vice President, Carl Pfleger

Vice President Acquisitions and Alliances, Leonard Berry

National Account Manager, Josh Barker

Vice President of Sales Information technology, Herb Jarvis

Vice President Research and Development Strategy, Opokua Kwapong

Vice President of Customer Service, Pamela Monroe

Vice President Human Resources, Jessica Tolle

Senior Vice President Research and Development, Rene Lammers

Legal Vice President, Thomas P Schur

Marketing Fin Vice President, Christy A Jacoby

Sc Vice President, Tim Purtell

Vice President worldwide Ingredients, Chris Gallucci

Vice President Field Sales, Richard Tompkins

Sc Vice President North Bu, Craig Eberly

National Sales Manager, Jennifer Caro

Vice President Sales, Mike Herman

Sales Vice President, Craig Musgrove

EA Tessa Hilado Senior Vice President and Treasury Finance, Denise Woodard

Vice President Finance, Mark Beach

Vice President Northern California, Ron Walker

Sc Senior Vice President, Myra Franke

Executive Vice President Marketing, Craig Denney

Vice President Finance, Eric Russo

Vice President Technical Operations, Mary Good

Medical Director Cardiovascular, Maria Afonso

Vice President Human Resources, Bhavna Bhaskar

National Sales Manager Modern Trade, Ismail Sabry

Vice President of Procurement, Art Schick

Vice President Infrastructure and Engineering, Johnathan Thibodeau

Vpgm, Rose Bollman

Vice President Projects, Bhaskar Choudhury

Vice President and General Manager Delmarva Region, Michael Langley

Assistant Vice President and Exchange Coordinator, John Shumate

Vice President, Carla De Quintal

Vice President Consumer Strategy, Tekla Back

Vice President Transportation, Jim Farrell

Vice President Beverage Operations for KSA and Yemen, Ahmed ELsheikh

Vice President Multicultural Marketing Pepsi Cola North America, Frank Cooper

Vice President Foodservice Division, Kathryn Matheson

Vice President, Olga Nuti

Rvp Assistant, Linda Sullivan

Customer Management Vice President, Van Bakke

PBC Vice President Controller, Felitia Lee

Vice President, Kenneth Gordineer

Vice President Of It, Dominick Salvato

Vice President Strategic Insights, Laura Jones

Vice President Legal India Region, Paul Walton

Vice President Human Resources, Clair Niver

Vice President Marketing and Business Development, Marissa Solis

Vice President of Manufacturing and Warehouse Operations, Tyrone A Sapenter

Vice President Go To Market and Sales Capability, Michael Pavan

Vice President, Tarkan Gurkan

Vice President of Yum Brands, Mike Valdron

Vice President Of Marketing For Atlantic Business Unit, Tammy Sumpter

Vice President Of Consumer Engagement, Anne Howarth

Sales Fin Vice President, Jim Hathaway

SVP Human Resources Pepsico, Sean McDevitt

Vice President, Tom Winters

Vice President of Engineering, Rashid Mehmood

Marketing Vice President PEPSICO Europe, Cesc Bordas

Senior Vice President and General Counsel AMEA, David Flavell

Vice President, Robin Jones

Vice President Marketing National Restaurants, Tom Balte

Vice President Of Finance, Brent Bracey

Vice President Supply Chain, Rod Robinson

Vice President Of Ne Region, Jeff Wadsworth

Region Vice President of Operations, Frank Armetta

Senior Vice President Chief Compliance And Ethics Officer, Debra Torres

Vice President tax Planning, Jeff Coniaris

VP Supply Chain, Mark Brinker

Vice President, Steve Llewellyn

Regional Vice President, James Simms

Vice President Finance Revenue Management, Scott Davis

Vice President Operations Middle East and Africa, Hussein Foda

Vice President Human Resources, Jam Johnson

Vice President Domestic Taxes, Tom Salcito

National Account Manager, Terry Thaden

Ssm Agro Vice President Naf Ssm Agro, Jim Cleary

Vice President Contract Manufacturing, Karl Schraer

Vice President and General Manager of the Chesapeake Marketing Unit, Vaughn Dickinson

Vice President and Assistant Treasurer for International, Noha Topalian

Auditors: KPMG LLP

LOCATIONS

HQ: PepsiCo Inc
700 Anderson Hill Road, Purchase, NY 10577
Phone: 914 253-2000
Web: www.pepsico.com

2016 Sales

	$ mil.	% of total
United States	36,732	59
Mexico	3,431	5
Canada	2,692	4
Russia	2,648	4
United Kingdom	1,737	3
Brazil	1,305	2
All other countries	14,254	23
Total	**62,799**	**100**

PRODUCTS/OPERATIONS

2016 Sales

	$ mil.	% of total
NAB	21,312	34
FLNA	15,549	25
ESSA	10,216	16
Latin America	6,820	11
AMENA	6,338	10
QFNA	2,564	4
Total	**62,799**	**100**

COMPETITORS

American Beverage	Jones Soda
Anadolu Efes	Kellogg
Arla Foods	Lactalis
Asahi Breweries	Merisant
Big Red	Monarch Beverage
Bongrain	Monarch Beverage (GA)
Britvic	Mondelez International
Campbell Soup	Monster Beverage
Carolina Beverage	Mountain Valley
Celestial Seasonings	National Beverage
Chiquita Brands	National Grape
Clearly Canadian	Cooperative
Coca-Cola	Nestlé©
Coca-Cola FEMSA	New Leaf
ConAgra	Odwalla
Cott	Parmalat
DS Services	Polar Beverages
Danone Water	Princes Limited
Diamond Foods	Procter & Gamble
Dr Pepper Snapple	Red Bull
Group	Reed's
Energy Brands	Snapple
Fraser & Neave	Snyder's-Lance
FrieslandCampina	Sunny Delight
General Mills	Tree Top
Golden Enterprises	True Drinks
Grupo Bimbo	Weaver Popcorn Company
Hawaiian Springs	Wet Planet Beverages
Inventure foods	

Company Type: Public

Income Statement

FYE: December 30

	REVENUE ($ mil.)	NET INCOME ($ mil.)	NET PROFIT MARGIN	EMPLOYEES
12/17	63,525	4,857	7.6%	263,000
12/16	62,799	6,329	10.1%	264,000
12/15	63,056	5,452	8.6%	263,000
12/14	66,683	6,513	9.8%	271,000
12/13	66,415	6,740	10.1%	274,000
Annual Growth	(1.1%)	(7.9%)	—	(1.0%)

2017 Year-End Financials

Debt ratio: 49.22%
Return on equity: 44.31%
Cash ($ mil.): 10,610
Current ratio: 1.51
Long-term debt ($ mil.): 33,796

No. of shares (mil.): 1,420
Dividends
  Yield: 0.0%
  Payout: 93.7%
Market value ($ mil.): 170,286

	STOCK PRICE ($) FY Close	P/E High/Low		PER SHARE ($) Earnings	Dividends	Book Value
12/17	119.92	35	30	3.38	3.17	7.67
12/16	104.63	25	21	4.36	2.96	7.77
12/15	100.54	28	24	3.67	2.76	8.23
12/14	97.05	23	18	4.27	2.53	11.72
12/13	82.71	20	16	4.32	2.24	15.88
Annual Growth	9.7%	—	—	(6.0%)	9.0%	(16.6%)

Performance Food Group Co

Auditors: DELOITTE & TOUCHE LLP

LOCATIONS

HQ: Performance Food Group Co
12500 West Creek Parkway, Richmond, VA 23238
Phone: 804 484-7700
Web: www.pfgc.com

HISTORICAL FINANCIALS

Company Type: Public

Income Statement

FYE: July 1

	REVENUE ($ mil.)	NET INCOME ($ mil.)	NET PROFIT MARGIN	EMPLOYEES
07/17	16,761	96	0.6%	14,000
07/16*	16,104	68	0.4%	13,000
06/15	15,270	56	0.4%	12,000
06/14	13,685	15	0.1%	—
06/13	12,826	8	0.1%	—
Annual Growth	6.9%	84.0%	—	—

*Fiscal year change

2017 Year-End Financials

Debt ratio: 34.11%
Return on equity: 11.17%
Cash ($ mil.): 8
Current ratio: 1.51
Long-term debt ($ mil.): 1,285

No. of shares (mil.): 100
Dividends
  Yield: —
  Payout: —
Market value ($ mil.): 2,762

	STOCK PRICE ($) FY Close	P/E High/Low		PER SHARE ($) Earnings	Dividends	Book Value
07/17	27.40	30	21	0.93	0.00	9.18
07/16*	26.92	39	27	0.70	0.00	8.04
Annual Growth	0.4%	—	—	7.4%	—	3.4%

*Fiscal year change

PETER KIEWIT SONS', INC.

A heavyweight in the heavy construction industry Peter Kiewit Sons' is one of North America's largest construction and engineering firms. The company is active in building mining oil power transportation and water. It builds everything from roads and dams to high-rise office towers and power plants. Focusing on projects located throughout the US Canada and Australia the contractor makes more than half of its revenue from oil and gas electrical power and waterworks projects while another 35% comes from transportation projects such as bridges rail lines airport runways and mass transit systems. Affiliate Kiewit Mining owns coal mines in Texas Montana and Wyoming. Founded in 1884 Peter Kiewit Sons is owned by employees and Kiewit family members.

Operations

Kiewit's biggest earner is transportation projects accounting for over 35% of sales. Oil gas and chemical projects bring over 20%; power projects account for +20%; building projects 10%; wastewater 5% and mining 5%.

Kiewit's fields of transportation expertise include air bridge marine and port rail roads and tunnels. It has carried out a large number of airport runway projects and several notable highway and bridge projects. The latter includes replacing a segment of the San Francisco-Oakland Bay Bridge Skyway to upgrading the Sea-to-Sky Highway between Vancouver and Whistler British Columbia. Water supply and dam projects include the Olivenhain and East dams in California underground storage tanks for the Hollywood Hills Quality Improvement Project and an intake valve at Lake Mead in Nevada.

The Building segment's specialties are commercial data center education Government healthcare hospitality manufacturing mixed use sports and entertainment transit and services.

Mining carries out contract mining mine infrastructure ore processing and owned operations. Oil's operations include offshore oil sands gas processing compressor and pump stations pipelines and terminals LNG and refining. The Power business is active in gas air quality control systems power delivery renewables nuclear and engineering.

Water/Wastewater carries out dam water supply and wastewater projects including a pumping station in Texas a storm-surge protection facility in Louisiana and a water treatment plant in Arizona.

Kiewit operates a number of subsidiaries. Kiewit Offshore Services fabricates complex offshore oil production platforms at a facility in Texas. The company counts many of the world's largest oil companies as its clients. Another subsidiary Kiewit Energy Group focuses on the petroleum refining business. Kiewit's TIC Holdings subsidiary is a heavy industrial construction and engineering firm based in Colorado. TIC operates through divisions including TIC Industrial and Western Summit Constructors. It has more than 40 area and district offices throughout North America and provides construction services in the power mining oil/gas/chemicals renewable energy water marine food and beverage and pulp and paper industries.

Geographic Reach

Based in Nebraska Kiewit operates across the US Canada Mexico and Western Australia.

Financial Performance

While annual financials are not made public Peter Kiewit brings in around $8-9 billion each year.

Strategy

Kiewit has completed more than 4500 projects since 2006. Recent major projects have included rebuilding and modernizing the Goethals Bridge connecting Staten Island to New Jersey; and "Project Neon" a project to widen Interstate 15 going into downtown Las Vegas.

HISTORY

Born to Dutch immigrants Peter Kiewit and brother Andrew founded Kiewit Brothers a brickyard in 1884 in Omaha Nebraska. By 1912 two of Peter's sons worked at the yard which was named Peter Kiewit & Sons. When Peter Kiewit died in 1914 his son Ralph took over and the firm took the name Peter Kiewit Sons'. Another son Peter joined Ralph at the helm in 1924 after dropping out of Dartmouth and later took over.

During the Depression Kiewit managed huge federal public works projects and in the 1940s it focused on war-related emergency construction projects.

One of the firm's most difficult projects was top-secret Thule Air Force Base in Greenland above the Arctic Circle. For more than two years 5000 men worked around the clock beginning in 1951; the site was in development for 15 years. In 1952 the company won a contract to build a $1.2 billion gas diffusion plant in Portsmouth Ohio. It also became a contractor for the US interstate highway system (begun in 1956).

Peter Kiewit died in 1979 after stipulating that the largely employee-owned company should remain under employee control and that no one employee could own more than 10%. His 40% stake when returned to the company transformed many employees into millionaires. Walter Scott Jr. whose father had been the first graduate engineer to work for Kiewit took charge. Scott made his mark by parlaying money from construction into successful investments.

When the construction industry slumped Kiewit began looking for other investment opportunities and in 1984 it acquired packaging company Continental Can Co. (selling off noncore insurance energy and timber assets). Continental was saddled with a 1983 class action lawsuit alleging that it had plotted to close plants and lay off workers before they were qualified for pensions. In 1991 Kiewit agreed to pay $415 million to settle the lawsuit. In the face of a consolidating packaging industry the company sold Continental in the early 1990s.

In 1986 Kiewit loaned money to a business group to build a fiber-optic loop in Chicago; by 1987 it had launched MFS Communications to build local fiber loops in downtown districts. In 1992 Kiewit split its business into two pieces: the construction group which was strictly employee-owned; and a diversified group to which it added a controlling stake in phone and cable TV company C-TEC in 1993. That year Kiewit took MFS public; by 1995 it had sold all its shares and the next year MFS was bought by telecom giant WorldCom.

In 1996 Kiewit assisted CalEnergy (now MidAmerican Energy) in a hostile $1.3 billion takeover of the UK's Northern Electric. Kiewit got stock in CalEnergy and a 30% stake in the UK electric company all of which it sold to CalEnergy in 1998.

That year Kiewit spun off its telecom and computer services holdings into Level 3 Communications. Scott who had been hospitalized the year before for a blood clot in his lung stepped down as CEO and Ken Stinson CEO of Kiewit Construction Group took over Peter Kiewit Sons'.

In 1999 Kiewit acquired a majority interest in Pacific Rock Products a construction materials firm in Canada. Kiewit spun off its asphalt concrete and aggregates operations in 2000 as Kiewit Materials. Also that year the company created Kiewit Offshore Services to focus on construction for the offshore drilling industry. In 2001 the company acquired marine construction firm General Construction Company (GCC). The next year it expanded its offshore business further by buying a Canadian subsidiary from oil and gas equipment services company Friede Goldman Halter which was trying to emerge from bankruptcy.

Kiewit made history in 2002 for the fastest completion of a project of its type when it completed the rebuilding of Webbers Falls I-40 Bridge in Oklahoma at the end of July. (The bridge had collapsed in May after being hit by a pair of barges resulting in 14 fatalities.)

In 2004 Kiewit greatly increased its coal sales and reserves with the acquisition of the Buckskin Mine in Wyoming from Arch Coal.

Kiewit underwent a changing of the guard at the end of 2004 when 22-year veteran Bruce Grewcock took the reins as the company's fourth CEO since its founding. Stinson stayed on as the company's chairman.

In 2008 the group acquired TIC Holdings Co. a heavy industrial construction and engineering firm.

Through its Kiewit Power Engineers Co. the company was contracted by Plutonic Energy Corporation and GE Energy Financial Services to work on the 235 MW hydroelectric Toba Montrose project one of British Columbia's largest renewable energy projects (completed around 2011).

In 2013 Kiewit entered the Australian market through a joint venture agreement that involves as $247 million engineer-procure-construct contract for a wet front end and ore wash plant situated at the Cloudbreak Mine in Northwest Australia. Fortescue Metals Group is the previous owner of Cloudbreak prior to the handover in early 2013.

EXECUTIVES

SVP and CFO, Michael J. Piechoski, age 61, $236,600 total compensation
Chairman President and CEO, Bruce E. Grewcock, $750,000 total compensation
EVP Energy, Thomas S. Shelby, age 57
CIO, Kris Lappala
Treasurer, Stephen Thomas
Auditors: KPMG LLP OMAHA NEBRASKA

LOCATIONS

HQ: PETER KIEWIT SONS', INC.
3555 FARNAM ST STE 1000, OMAHA, NE 681313374
Phone: 402 342-2052
Web: WWW.KIEWIT.COM

Selected Locations
US
Alaska
Arizona
Arkansas

California
Colorado
Florida
Georgia
Hawaii
Idaho
Illinois
Iowa
Kansas
Louisiana
Maryland
Massachusetts
Minnesota
Nebraska
Nevada
New Jersey
New York
North Carolina
Oregon
Tennessee
Texas
Utah
Virginia
Washington
Wyoming
Australia
Western Australia
Canada
Alberta
British Columbia
Manitoba
Newfoundland
New Brunswick
Ontario
Quebec
Saskatchewan

PRODUCTS/OPERATIONS

2014 Market Diversity

	% of total
Oil gas & chemicals	37
Transportation	25
Power	18
Building	10
Water/Wastewater	6
Mining	4
Total	**100**

Selected Subsidiaries and Affiliates

Aero Automatic Sprinkler
Cherne Contracting Corporation
Continental Fire Sprinkler Company
Ganotec Corporation
General Construction Company
Kiewit Australia
Kiewit Bridge & Marine
Kiewit Building Group
Kiewit Constructors Inc.
Kiewit Energy Inc.
Kiewit Engineering Co.
Kiewit Infrastructure Co.
Kiewit Infrastructure South Co.
Kiewit Infrastructure West Co.
Kiewit Mining Group
　Dry Valley/No. Rassmussen Ridge Mines
　Buckskin Mining Company
　San Miguel Mine
　Walnut Creek Mining Company
Kiewit Offshore Services Ltd..
Kiewit Power Constructors
Kiewit Power Engineers
Kiewit Texas Construction L.P.
Mass. Electric Construction Co.
TIC Holdings Inc.

COMPETITORS

ABB	KBR
Ames Construction	Lane Construction
Balfour Beatty	PCL Constructors
Infrastructure	Parsons Corporation
Bechtel	Raytheon
Black & Veatch	Rio Tinto plc
CH2M HILL	Skanska USA Civil
Fluor	Turner Corporation
Granite Construction	Tutor Perini
Halliburton	Walsh Group

Hubbard Group
Jacobs Engineering
Whiting-Turner
Williams Companies

HISTORICAL FINANCIALS
Company Type: Private

Income Statement
FYE: December 29

	REVENUE ($ mil.)	NET INCOME ($ mil.)	NET PROFIT MARGIN	EMPLOYEES
12/12	11,220	515	4.6%	14,700
12/11	10,381	790	7.6%	—
Annual Growth	8.1%	(34.8%)	—	—

2012 Year-End Financials

Debt ratio: ——
Return on equity: 4.60%
Cash ($ mil.): 1,447
Current ratio: 1.20
Long-term debt ($ mil.): —

Dividends
Yield: —
Payout: —
Market value ($ mil.): —

Pfizer Inc

Pfizer is one of the world's largest research-based pharmaceuticals firms producing medicines for ailments in fields including cardiovascular health metabolism oncology and inflammation and immunology. Its top prescription products include cholesterol-lowering Lipitor pain management drugs Celebrex and Lyrica pneumonia vaccine Prevnar and erectile dysfunction treatment Viagra as well as arthritis drug Enbrel antibiotic Zyvox and high-blood-pressure therapy Norvasc. Consumer health products (which Pfizer is looking to sell) include such leading brands as Advil Centrum and Robitussin. Pfizer and Allergan called off their $160 billion mega-merger in 2016 citing tax reasons.

HISTORY

Charles Pfizer and his cousin confectioner Charles Erhart began making chemicals in Brooklyn in 1849. Products included camphor citric acid and santonin (an early antiparasitic). The company incorporated in 1900 as Chas. Pfizer & Co. was propelled into the modern drug business when it was asked to mass-produce penicillin for the war effort in 1941.

Pfizer discovered Terramycin and introduced it in 1950. Three years later it bought drugmaker Roerig its first major acquisition. In the 1950s the company opened branches in Belgium Canada Cuba Mexico and the UK and began manufacturing in Asia Europe and South America. By the mid-1960s Pfizer had worldwide sales of more than $200 million.

Beginning in the late 1950s Pfizer made Salk and Sabin polio vaccines and added new drugs such as Diabinese (antidiabetic 1958) and Vibramycin (antibiotic 1967). It moved into consumer products in the early 1960s buying BenGay Desitin and cosmetics maker Coty (sold 1992). It bought hospital products company Howmedica in 1972 (sold 1998) and heart-valve maker Shiley in 1979.

When growth slowed in the 1970s new chairman Edmund Pratt increased R&D expenditures resulting in Minipress (antihypertensive 1975) Feldene (arthritis pain reliever 1980) and Glucotrol (antidiabetic 1984). Licensing agreements with foreign companies let Pfizer sell antihypertensive Procardia XL and antibiotic Cefobid. In the 1980s

Pfizer expanded its hospital products division buying 18 product lines and companies.

Lawsuits over the failure of about 500 heart valves and the alleged falsification of records led Pfizer to divest most of Shiley's operations in 1992. Drugs released that year included antidepressant Zoloft antibiotic Zithromax and cardiovascular agent Norvasc.

In 1995 Pfizer bought SmithKline Beecham's animal health business and Procter & Gamble's Bain de Soleil skin care line (sold 1999).

In 1997 Pfizer began promoting Lipitor the cholesterol-lowering drug discovered by partner Warner-Lambert; it grabbed nearly 13% of the market in its first four months. Pfizer also launched Aricept Eisai's treatment for Alzheimer's disease.

Pfizer made headlines (and lots of men happy) when the company won FDA approval for Viagra in 1998. The little blue pill became a pop icon and made the company a household name.

When Warner-Lambert said in 1999 that it would merge with American Home Products (now Wyeth) Pfizer sued to prevent the union and eventually succeeded with its own hostile bid. The merger with Warner-Lambert was completed and CEO William Steere retired. Pfizer also sold its animal feed additive business.

Pfizer IBM and Microsoft in 2001 formed a joint venture to sell software to automate prescription writing and other administrative procedures in physicians' offices. Determined to narrow its focus on pharmaceuticals the company in 2002 sold its Tetra fish care then sold its Adams confectionery and Schick-Wilkinson Sword shaving products businesses in 2003.

That year Pfizer purchased rival Pharmacia for $54 billion making it the world's largest research-based pharmaceutical company. Following its two giant acquisitions the company trimmed some 20000 people. In 2004 Pfizer acquired the research divisions of QuoreX which develops antibacterial drugs targeting hospital infections. It also purchased Esperion Therapeutics a developer of cholesterol drugs headed by Lipitor discoverer Roger Newton for $1.2 billion. (Pfizer eventually spun Esperion back off into a private independent entity in 2008 after its development drugs didn't pan out as planned although Pfizer retained some assets and a minority stake in the spinoff.)

In the wake of revelations that Merck's Vioxx increased the risk for cardiovascular diseases in 2004 Pfizer reviewed its own COX-2 pain medication Celebrex. Preliminary studies showed Celebrex increased the risk of heart attack; Pfizer didn't pull Celebrex off the market but did add a "black box" warning of possible cardiovascular and gastrointestinal risks. (In 2008 Pfizer reached an agreement in principle to settle for $894 million most of its pending patient lawsuits alleging that Celebrex caused heart attacks and strokes.)

Acquisitions in 2005 included the purchase of Angiosyn a private biotech working on an anti-angiogenesis therapy for macular degeneration (which can lead to blindness) and Idun Pharmaceuticals which was developing apoptosis (programmed cell death) inhibitors to treat liver disease cancer and other diseases.

That year the company scooped up research partner Vicuron Pharmaceuticals which had two anti-infective (anidulafungin and dalbavancin) drugs under review by the FDA and Bioren which has developed a technology that helps drugs last longer through antibody optimization. (Pfizer divested Vicuron as part of its cost-cutting efforts in 2009.)

While acquiring new holdings on the pharmaceutical front Pfizer trimmed its non-pharmaceutical businesses between 2003 and 2005 including operations it acquired with Pharmacia and its European generics portfolio. The company's animal health division sold off its diagnostics products division (which manufactured tests for bovine tuberculosis and paratuberculosis) to Swiss firm Prionics.

On the consumer health care front the population's increased germaphobia translated into high dollars for Pfizer following the acquisition of Purell. However Pfizer later unloaded its consumer unit altogether refocusing efforts onto its core pharmaceutical business. Johnson & Johnson in 2006 acquired the whole consumer caboodle including such brands as Benadryl Listerine Nicorette Rolaids and Sudafed for $16.6 billion. To comply with regulatory requirements for the deal the companies sold Zantac marketing rights in the US to Boehringer Ingelheim for $510 million; they sold the Cortizone Kaopectate and Unisom brands to Chattem.

As part of its ongoing acquisition strategy Pfizer bought biotech firm Rinat Neuroscience which was developing drugs for pain Alzheimer's disease and other neurological disorders in 2006. Pfizer also acquired vaccine technology firm PowderMed that year and it spent $1.4 billion acquiring Sanofi's joint rights to inhaled insulin drug Exubera. (Pfizer dropped Exubera from its product list in late 2007 however due to lukewarm response from physicians and patients. The company took a $2.8 billion charge as a result.)

EXECUTIVES

EVP Corporate Affairs, Sally Susman, age 56
Senior Vice President Clinical Development and Medical Affairs of Oncology Business Unit, Mace Rothenberg
EVP Business Operations and CFO, Frank A. D'Amelio, age 59, $1,324,000 total compensation
Chairman and CEO, Ian C. Read, age 63, $1,905,250 total compensation
EVP and Chief Medical Officer, Freda C. Lewis-Hall, age 61, $800,000 total compensation
EVP and President Worldwide Research and Development, Mikael Dolsten, age 58, $1,237,500 total compensation
EVP and General Counsel, Douglas M. (Doug) Lankler, age 51
EVP and Chief Development Officer, Alexander R. (Rod) MacKenzie, age 57
EVP Worldwide Human Resources, Charles H. (Chuck) Hill, age 61
Group President Pfizer Innovative Health, John D. Young, age 52, $1,130,000 total compensation
EVP Strategy and Commercial Operations, Laurie J. Olson, age 53
COO, Albert Bourla, age 55, $1,117,500 total compensation
EVP and Chief Compliance and Risk Officer, Rady A. Johnson, age 55
VP Innovative Health Product Portfolio Management and Consumer Operations, Kirsten Lund-Jurgensen, age 57
Global President and General Manager for Pfizer Inflammation & Immunology, Angela Hwang
Vice President Information Management, Craig Barrila
Vice President WSS Specialty Care, Christopher Wohlberg
Medical Director, Michael Wajnrajch
Vice President US Trade Group, Lou Dallago
Medical Director Worldwide Safety and Regulatory Operations, Gianluca Strozzi
Senior Vice President Executive Compensation Strategy and Programs, Stephen Pennacchio
Medical Director, Jean Chow
Vice President External Affairs and Worldwide Communications, Elizabeth Golden
Pharmd, John Ostrosky
Vice President, Charles Knirsch

Vice President Finance Onc and SC, Peter S McGuigan
Vice President Finance Establ Products, Kevin Sullivan
National Account Manager, Teri Kittredge
Vice President and Assistant Treasurer, Brian McMahon
Executive Vice President Development, Shaileen English
Vice President Consumer Healthcare QO, Moira Griffiths
Commercial Vice President, Nanette Cocero
Medical Director, Charles Tressler
Vice President Global Procurement, Mike Hoffman
Clinical Director, Peter Park
Vice President and Chief Scientific Officer, Puja Sapra
Medical Director, Alejandra Nieto
National Account Manager, Mark Desantis
Vice President, John P Clark
Assistant Vice President Chem Tech, Will Somers
National Account Manager, Alan J Hemler
Senior Vice President, Salomon Azoulay
Vice President Organizational Capability and Change, Kim Stepanski
Senior Vice President Global Regulatory Affairs, Peter Honig
Vice President and ssociate General Counsel, Cara Cuenot
Senior Vice President, Kostas Giamouridis
Vice President, Lynne Handanyan
Senior Vice President, Jaume Pons
Medical Director, Seth Woodruff
Senior Vice President, Kathrin U Jansen
Medical Director, Judith Hadavi
Past President Vice President Education Instructor, Micheal Manchester
Assistant Vice President, Kevin Higgins
Vice President EMEA Logistics and Supply Operations, Danny Hendrikse
Associate Medical Director, Silvina Gallo
Vice President Leadership, Julian Thompson
Associate Medical Director, Barbara Sleight
Vice President and Assistant General Counsel, Tiffany Trunko
Vice President, Hong Lu
Senior Vice President Science and Technology, Patrick Gage
Senior Vice President, Andy Schmeltz
Senior Vice President Human Resources Gep And Compliance, Don Stewart
Vice President Research and Development Supplements Franchise, Rowena Pullan
Vice President, Mark Schneyer
Senior Vice President Wrd Development And Strategic Operations, Evan Loh
Vice President, Regina Rantz
Vice President Compliance and Quality Systems, Michael Davidson
Executive Vice President, Karine Gravel
Medical Director Psychiatry and Neurology, Brian Klee
Vice President, Chewah Lee
National Sales Manager, Gary Ellis
National Account Manager, John Bartholme
Vice President Human Resources, Karen Anderson
Vice President And Assistant General Counsel, Lindsay Havern
Executive Vice President and General Manager, Linda Blacken
National Sales Manager Immun, Simon Goodger
Vice President Of Marketing, Martina Porru
Vice President Sales America, Jim Carr
Vice President Assistant General Counsel, Stephanie Meltzer
Senior Vice President and Chief Information Officer, Jeffrey Keisling
Vice President Payer And Channel Group, David Gans
Regional President Emea Pch, Tarek Youssef

Pharmacy Manager, Dirk Potgieter
Associate Medical Director, David Witcombe
Medical Director, Jun Musa
National Sales Manager, Beatriz Sanchez
Vice President, John Hutchison
Vice President Of Research And Development, Gerry Taber
Vice President Of Pharmaceutical Sciences, Peter Green
Vice President of Clinical Project Management, Dean Gianarkis
Vice President, Kanwar Nasir Khan
Clinical Director, Raymond Cheung
Vice President Global Vac Pneumo, Raul Isturiz
Medical Director, Francesco Orlando
Medical Director, Ioana Russ
Vice President Legal Affairs And General Counsel, Darren Noseworthy
National Sales Manager, Tuncay Ekici
Vice President Bio Enhancement Develo, Michael Corbo
National Sales Manager Consumer Healthcare, Jung-tak Shin
Vice President and Chief Sales Officer Bacterial Vaccines, Annaliesa Anderson
Vice President Of Worldwide Communications, Anna Ruder
Vice President Human Resources, Kristi Reinholz
Vice President, Om Arora
Vice President Global Sales And Marketing Services, Andreas Wandelt
Vice President Endocrine Care, Jose Cara
Business Devpt And Evpert Marktg Asc, Kara Chain
Vice President, Cory Stiff
Medical Director, Thomas Jones
Vice President, Kevin Filipski
Senior Vice President Of Sales, Mike Byrne
Vice President For Translational Oncology, Chris Boshoff
Vice President Corporate Audit, Jennifer Damico
Medical Director, Judith Hey-Hadavi
Vice President and Corporate Secretary and Chief Counsel of Corporate Governance, Matthew Lepore
Medical Director, Mohamed Ben Abdallah
Vice President, Tracey Boyden
Medical Director, Jose Dias
Vice President and Assistant General Counsel, Arthur Cohn
Vice President Oncology Public Affairs, Nina Hill
NAtional Sales Manager, Leonore JAcobs
Senior Vice President Total Rewards, Steve Pennacchio
Medical Director Risk Management Lead, Vlad Bykoriz
Vice President Leadership, Craig Whitehead
National Account Manager, Ron Lorenzo
Government Relations, Ryan Bounsy
Vice President of Human Resources, Laura Larbalestier
Vice President and Chief Scien, Michael White
Vice President Vaccine Clinical Research, Dan Scott
National Sales Manager, Alem Muminovic
Medical Director, Mohamed Harti
Medical Director US Medical Affairs, Elif Silva
Vice President Finance, Edmund Huver
Medical Director, Rebecca Luk
Vice President Rare Disease Clinical Resea, Michael Binks
Executive Vice President, Ashish Shah
Clinical Director, VERA J STECHER
Administrative Lead Senior Vice President Chief Sales Officer CVMED, Michele M Dobbert
Vice President Global Medical Affairs Biosimilars, Javier Coindreau
Vice President and Assistant General Counsel, Peter Brensilver
Vice President Cons Hlthcare Quality Operations, Anabel Ocasio-Velez

Assistant Vice President Clinical Data Sciences, Jane Clarke
Vice President Investor Relations, James Gardner
Vice President of Marketing Eucrisa Brand Team Leader, Ruth Dovdavany
Senior Vice President Worldwide Safety, Patrick Caubel
Interim Vice President Senior Buyer Planner, Tamara Glover
Vice President Cim, Deborah Reynolds
Vice President International Developed Markets, Pascale Mauran
Senior Vice President, Ken Verburg
Medical Director Vaccines Medicines Development Group and Scientific Affairs, Paul Balmer
Vice President of Public Affairs Specialty Care Business Unit, Bryon Wornson
Chairman Emeritus Director, William Steere
Auditors: KPMG LLP

LOCATIONS

HQ: Pfizer Inc
235 East 42nd Street, New York, NY 10017
Phone: 212 733-2323
Web: www.pfizer.com

2016 Sales

	$ mil.	% of total
US	26,369	50
Developed Europe	9,306	17
Developed Rest of World	6,729	13
Emerging Markets	10,420	20
Total	**52,824**	**100**

PRODUCTS/OPERATIONS

2016 Sales

	% of total
Innovative Health	55
Essential Health	45
Total	**100**

Selected Products

Pharmaceuticals
Aricept (Alzheimer's disease)
Aromasin (breast cancer)
+Arthrotec (osteoarthritis and rheumatoid arthritis)
BeneFIX (hemophilia)
BMP2 (bone and cartilage development)
Caduet (high cholesterol and blood pressure dual therapy)
Camptosar (colorectal cancer)
Cardura (hypertension and enlarged prostate disease)
Celebrex (arthritis pain)
Chantix/Champix (smoking cessation)
Dalacin/Cleocin (antibiotic for bacterial infections)
Detrol/Detrol LA (overactive bladder)
Diflucan (antifungal)
Effexor (antidepressant and anxiety disorder treatment)
Enbrel (arthritis treatment)
Fragmin (anticoagulant)
Genotropin (growth hormone deficiency)
Geodon/Zeldox (schizophrenia and bipolar disorder)
Inspra (high blood pressure)
Lipitor (cholesterol)
Lyrica (nerve pain)
Medrol (inflammation)
Methotrexate (severe psoriasis)
Neurontin (epilepsy)
Norvasc (hypertension)
Premarin (hormone replacement therapy)
Prevnar (pneumococcus vaccine)
Pristiq (antidepressant)
Protonix (protein pump inhibitor)
Quillivant XR (ADHD)
Rapamune (organ rejection preventative)
Rebif (multiple sclerosis)
ReFacto AF/Xyntha (hemophilia)
Relpax (migraines)
Revatio (hypertension)
Selzentry (HIV)
Skelaxin (muscle relaxant)
Somavert (acromegaly)
Spiriva (chronic obstructive pulmonary disease)

Sulperazon (antibiotic)
Sutent (carcinoma and tumors)
Toviaz (overactive bladder)
Tygacil (anti-infective)
Unasyn (injectable antibacterial)
Vfend (fungal infections)
Viagra (impotence)
Xalatan/Xalacom (glaucoma)
Xanax XR (anti-anxiety treatment)
Zithromax/Zmax (antibiotic)
Zoloft (depression)
Zosyn/Tazocin (anti-infective)
Zyvox (antibiotic)
Animal Health
Cerenia (nausia treatment for canines)
Convenia (canine and feline antibiotics)
Draxxin (cattle antibiotic)
Excede (cattle antibiotic)
Improvac (swine vaccine for boar taint)
Palladia (dog cancer treatment)
Revolution/Stronghold (antiparasitic for dogs and cats)
Rimadyl (canine osteoarthritis treatment)
Suvaxyn (swine vaccine)
Consumer Health
Advil (analgesic)
Anbesol (oral pain relief)
Caltrate (nutritional supplement)
Centrum (vitamins)
ChapStick (lip care)
Dimetapp (cough/cold remedy)
Emergen-C (vitamin C supplement)
FiberCon (laxative)
Nexium (acid reflux)
Preparation H (hemorrhoid treatment)
Robitussin (cough/cold remedy)
ThermaCare (aches and pains)

Selected Mergers & Acquisitions

COMPETITORS

AbbVie	GlaxoSmithKline
Allergan plc	Johnson & Johnson
Amgen	Merck
Apotex	Merck KGaA
Astellas	Mylan
AstraZeneca	Novartis
Bayer AG	Novo Nordisk
Biogen	Perrigo
Boehringer Ingelheim	Prestige Brands
Bristol-Myers Squibb	Roche Holding
Carma Laboratories	Sanofi
Chattem	Sun Pharmaceutical
Eli Lilly	Teva

HISTORICAL FINANCIALS

Company Type: Public

Income Statement

FYE: December 31

	REVENUE ($ mil.)	NET INCOME ($ mil.)	NET PROFIT MARGIN	EMPLOYEES
12/16	52,824	7,215	13.7%	96,500
12/15	48,851	6,960	14.2%	97,900
12/14	49,605	9,135	18.4%	78,300
12/13	51,584	22,003	42.7%	77,700
12/12	58,986	14,570	24.7%	91,500
Annual Growth	(2.7%)	(16.1%)	—	1.3%

2016 Year-End Financials

Debt ratio: 24.52%—
Return on equity: 11.58%
Cash ($ mil.): 2,595
Current ratio: 1.25
Long-term debt ($ mil.): 31,398

Dividends
Yield: 0.0%
Payout: 102.5%
Market value ($ mil.): —

	STOCK PRICE ($) FY Close	P/E High/Low		PER SHARE ($) Earnings	Dividends	Book Value
12/16	32.48	32 24		1.17	1.20	9.81
12/15	32.28	32 27		1.11	1.12	10.48
12/14	31.15	23 19		1.42	1.04	11.33
12/13	30.63	10 8		3.19	0.96	11.92
12/12	25.08	13 11		1.94	0.88	11.17
Annual Growth	**6.7%**	— —		**(11.9%)**	**8.1%**	**(3.2%)**

PG&E Corp (Holding Co)

Pacific Gas and Electric is specific about its services. The utility distributes electricity to more than 5.5 million residential commercial and industrial customers and natural gas to approximately 4.4 million customers in Central and Northern California. Pacific Gas and Electric has interests in power plants with a total of 7700 MW of generating capacity. It is also engaged in electricity procurement and transmission and natural gas procurement transportation and storage. Pacific Gas and Electric is the major subsidiary of holding company PG&E Corporation.

Operations

Pacific Gas and Electric operates more than 100 electric generating power plants using a variety of fuel inputs such as nuclear fossil fuels hydroelectric solar and wind. It delivers more than 83000 GWh of electricity annually.

Electricity accounts for about 80% of the utility's revenue.

Financial Performance

In 2016 Pacific Gas and Electric produced $17.7 billion in revenue and $1.4 billion of net income.

Strategy

Pacific Gas and Electric is focused on safety and reliability particularly in response to the 2010 San Bruno incident for which the company is under 3rd party oversight until at least 2020. It is the process of upgrading gas pipeline infrastructure including use of in-line inspection tools that will provide more timely operational status. To meet a California state regulation that requires an aggressive push into clean renewable energy the utility is modifying its mix of power generating sources including the eventual retirement of its Diablo Canyon nuclear plant. In 2016 about one third of its delivered power came from renewable sources.

EXECUTIVES

President Electric, Geisha J. Williams, age 55, $634,183 total compensation
SVP and CIO, Karen A. Austin, age 55
SVP Human Resources, Dinyar B. Mistry, age 55, $381,433 total compensation
President Gas, Nickolas (Nick) Stavropoulos, age 58, $613,221 total compensation
EVP Corporate Services and Human Resources, John R. Simon, age 53, $424,994 total compensation
SVP Generation and Chief Nuclear Officer, Edward D. (Ed) Halpin, age 55
VP CFO and Controller, David S. Thomason, age 42
Vice President Network Services, Jeff Hernandez
Government Relations, Michele Williams
Auditors: DELOITTE & TOUCHE LLP

LOCATIONS

HQ: PG&E Corp (Holding Co)
77 Beale Street, P.O. Box 770000, San Francisco, CA 94177
Phone: 415 973-1000　　**Fax:** 415 267-7265
Web: www.pgecorp.com

PRODUCTS/OPERATIONS

2016 Sales

	% of total
Electric	78
Natural gas	22
Total	**100**

COMPETITORS

AEP	PacifiCorp
AES	Portland General
APX	Electric
Avista	Riverside Electric
Bonneville Power	Utility
Calpine	Sacramento Municipal
Constellation Energy	Utility
Group	San Diego Gas &
Duke Energy	Electric
Edison International	Sempra Energy
Entergy	SoCalGas
Exelon	Southern California
FirstEnergy	Edison
Modesto Irrigation	Southern Company
District	Tractebel Engineering
NV Energy	Turlock Irrigation
NW Natural	District
North Baja Pipeline	Western Area Power
Northern California	Administration
Power Agency	

HISTORICAL FINANCIALS

Company Type: Public

Income Statement

FYE: December 31

	REVENUE ($ mil.)	NET INCOME ($ mil.)	NET PROFIT MARGIN	EMPLOYEES
12/17	17,135	1,660	9.7%	23,000
12/16	17,666	1,407	8.0%	24,000
12/15	16,833	888	5.3%	23,000
12/14	17,090	1,450	8.5%	22,581
12/13	15,598	828	5.3%	21,166
Annual Growth	**2.4%**	**19.0%**	**—**	**2.1%**

2017 Year-End Financials

Debt ratio: 28.13%
Return on equity: 8.93%
Cash ($ mil.): 449
Current ratio: 0.88
Long-term debt ($ mil.): 17,753

No. of shares (mil.): 514
Dividends
　Yield: 0.0%
　Payout: 48.2%
Market value ($ mil.): 23,077

	STOCK PRICE ($) FY Close	P/E High/Low		PER SHARE ($) Earnings	Dividends	Book Value
12/17	44.83	22 14		3.21	1.55	37.34
12/16	60.77	23 18		2.78	1.93	35.39
12/15	53.19	33 26		1.79	1.82	33.69
12/14	53.24	18 13		3.06	1.82	33.09
12/13	40.28	26 22		1.83	1.82	31.41
Annual Growth	**2.7%**	— —		**15.1%**	**(3.9%)**	**4.4%**

Philip Morris International Inc

Philip Morris International (PMI) knows how to light up a room. The company makes six of the world's top 15 tobacco brands laying claim to more than 10% of the international cigarette market outside the US. The company's primary international brands are Marlboro (the world's #1-selling cigarette) L&M Bond Street Philip Morris Chesterfield and Parliament. (Marlboro accounts for about a third of PMI's total shipment volume.) Top local brands include Fortune Morven Gold and Dji Sam Soe. PMI's portfolio spans the price spectrum with premium mid-priced and value-priced products. Despite being ostensibly a US company PMI has no US presence: its former parent Altria spun PMI off to handle its international operations as a separate entity.

Operations

The company operates four segments according to the company's top geographic markets. PMI's European Union segment generates more than 35% of PMI's total revenue while the Eastern Europe Middle East & Africa (EMEA) and Asia-Pacific segments account for around a quarter each. Latin American and Canada bring in the remainder.

PMI's international brands make up more than 75% of its shipment volume while the Marlboro brand accounts for some 35%. PMI's other tobacco products (OTP) primarily include tobacco for roll-your-own and make-your-own cigarettes pipe tobacco cigars and cigarillos.

It has contract manufacturing relationships with more than 20 third-party manufacturers in 20-plus markets. In addition the company manufactures its hand-rolled cigarettes through 38 third-party operators in Indonesia. PMI's more than 25 facilities each manufacture more than 10 billion cigarettes each year of which six produce more than 30 billion units.

Its international brands are premium price brands Marlboro Parliament and Virginia S; mid-price brands L&M Lark Merit Muratti and Philip Morris; and low-price brands Bond Street Chesterfield Next and Red & White.

Important local brands include Dji Sam Soe Sampoerna and U Mild in Indonesia; Champion Fortune and Jackpot in the Philippines; Apollo-Soyuz and Optima in Russia; Morven Gold in Pakistan; Boston in Colombia; Belmont Canadian Classics and Number 7 in Canada; f6 in Germany; Delicados in Mexico; Assos in Greece; and Petra in the Czech Republic and Slovakia.

PMI also makes four types smokeless tobacco products that heat but don't burn tobacco. Two of the four are still undergoing clinical trials while the other two are on the market under the IQOS and TEEPS brands.

Geographic Reach

New York-based Philip Morris International's (PMI) products are sold in more than 180 markets worldwide. PMI operates nearly 50 manufacturing facilities located in Africa Asia Canada Europe Latin America and the Middle East.

PMI?s largest factories are based in St. Petersburg and Krasnodar (Russia) Sukorejo and Karawang (Indonesia) Izmir (Turkey) Marikina and Batangas (Philippines) Krakow (Poland) Berlin (Germany) Kharkiv (Ukraine) and Klaipeda (Lithuania).

Sales and Marketing

Philip Morris International's (PMI) products are marketed and promoted through channels such as: point of sale communications brand events access-restricted Web sites print and direct communication to verified adult smokers (via mail e-mail and other electronic communication tools). The Marlboro brand has a long association with motorsports particularly Formula 1 and Moto GP.

PMI distributes its products directly to retailers single independent distributors zonified distribution and national or regional wholesalers. The company also directly supplies key accounts which include gas stations retail chains and supermarkets.

Financial Performance

In fiscal 2016 Philip Morris succeeded in putting a stop to a three-year decline in net revenue. In the year revenue increased 1% or around $1 billion to $75.0 billion. It recorded strong increases in Asia and the EU while Eastern Europe the Middle East and Africa (EMEA) recorded a mild decline while Latin America and Canada fell sharply. Higher prices compensated for falls in volume sales. After accounting for excise taxes revenue fell by less than a percent to $26.7 billion.

Net income increased a modest 1% to $7.0 billion due to price increases lower marketing and research costs and $68 million asset impairment expense incurred in 2015.

Cash from operations increased by $212 million to $8.1 billion due to earnings growth and lower cash payments relating to exit costs.

Strategy

With traditional cigarette sales inversely correlating with upwards health consciousness Philip Morris International (PMI) has partnered with its former parent Altria Group to transition its product commercialization toward more reduced-risk products such as e-cigarettes. It has two types of e-cigarette on the market and two still in development. At the forefront is its IQOS brand the result of a $3 billion investment which sold 7.4 billion "units" (the insertable tobacco filament rather than the electronic device) in 2016. The product has been a huge hit in Japan where it grabbed a 10% share of the tobacco market in a matter of months and saw 72% of smokers switch to IQOS permanently. PMI has also partnered with Altria to market its e-vapor products and Altria in return markets PMI's heated tobacco products in the US.

Meanwhile PMI competes for smokers' loyalty with the international tobacco giants British American Tobacco Imperial Brands and Japan Tobacco several regional and local tobacco companies and also state-owned companies in Algeria Egypt and several Asian countries by offering a range of premium mid-price and low-price brands. Its American blend cigarettes Marlboro L&M and Chesterfield are its most popular brands with the Marlboro brand alone making up more than a third of the company's shipment volume.

Company Background

PMI is a result of a spinoff from Altria in 2008. The separation positioned PMI as an independent publicly traded company free from its US branch Philip Morris USA. Altria simultaneously avoided an entanglement in various US legal and regulatory issues.

PMI has made a number of acquisitions to enhance its brand-rich portfolio and geographic presence. In mid-2011 PMI took over a cigarette manufacturer in Jordan. The purchase followed PMI's acquisition of a cigar business comprising trademarks in Australia and New Zealand. During 2011 PMI also revised its joint venture with Vietnam National Tobacco Corp. (Vinataba) in Vietnam opening the door to licensing the Marlboro label as PMI established a local branch to build its brands.

In 2009 PMI acquired the South African tobacco branch of Swedish Match for 1.93 billion ZAR (about $256 million) giving PMI a leg up in producing smokeless tobacco products and builds

upon a joint venture between PMI and Swedish Match to market Swedish style snus and other smokeless tobacco lines outside of Scandinavia and the US. (Altria moved to dominate the rapidly rising niche by taking over UST a leader in the US market for smokeless products including the Copenhagen Husky and Skoal brands.) In the same month PMI purchased the Petter.es tobacco business for $209 million pocketing fine-cut brands popular in Sweden and Norway.

EXECUTIVES

CEO, Andr © Calantzopoulos, age 59, $1,501,552 total compensation

Managing Director China, Martin G. King, age 52, $842,239 total compensation

President External Affairs & General Counsel, Marc S. Firestone, age 58, $1,015,680 total compensation

President Science & Innovation, Miroslaw Zielinski, age 56, $943,738 total compensation

Managing Director Germany Austria Croatia and Slovenia, Stacey Kennedy

COO, Jacek Olczak, age 52, $971,563 total compensation

SVP and CIO, Patrick Brunel, age 51

President European Union Region, Frederic de Wilde, age 49

President Eastern Europe Middle East Africa Region and PMI Duty Free including North Africa, Drago Azinovic, age 54

President Latin America and Canada Region, Jeanne Poll˜s, age 52

SVP Commercial, Werner Barth, age 52

SVP Corporate Affairs, Marco Mariotti

President PMI Japan, Paul Riley

Chief Digital Officer, Jaime Suarez

Vice President Finance, Andreas Kurali

Chairman, Louis C. Camilleri, age 62

Auditors: PricewaterhouseCoopers SA

LOCATIONS

HQ: Philip Morris International Inc
120 Park Avenue, New York, NY 10017
Phone: 917 663-2000   **Fax:** 917 663-5372
Web: www.pmi.com

2016 Sales

	$ mil.	% of total
European Union	27,129	36
Eastern Europe Middle East & Africa	18,286	25
Asia	20,531	27
Latin America & Canada	9,007	12
Total	**74,953**	**100**

PRODUCTS/OPERATIONS

Selected Brands
Local brands
  Apollo-Soyuz (Russia)
  Assos (Greece)
  Belmont (Canada)
  Best (Serbia)
  Boston (Colombia)
  Canadian Classics (Canada)
  Champion (Philippines)
  Classic (Serbia)
  Delicados (Mexico)
  Diana (Italy)
  Dji Sam Soe (Indonesia)
  f6 (Germany)
  Fortune (Philippines)
  Hope (Philippines)
  Morven Gold (Pakistan)
  Number 7 (Canada)
  Optima (Russia)
  Petra (Czech Republic and Slovakia)
  Sampoema A (Indonesia)
  Sampoema Kretek (Indonesia)
Mid-price brands
  L&M

  Chesterfield
Other international brands
  Benson & Hedges
  Bond Street
  Lark
  Muratti
  Next
  Philip Morris
  Red & White
Premium-price
  Marlboro
  Merit
  Parliament
  Virginia Slims
Other tobacco products
  Interval (France)
  Petterøes (Norway and Sweden)
  Swedish Match snus smokefree tobacco

2016 Shipment Volumes

	% of total
International brands	77
Local brands	23
Total	**100**

COMPETITORS

British American Tobacco	Japan Tobacco
Gudang Garam	Reemtsma
Imperial Brands	Cigarettenfabriken

HISTORICAL FINANCIALS

Company Type: Public

Income Statement

FYE: December 31

	REVENUE ($ mil.)	NET INCOME ($ mil.)	NET PROFIT MARGIN	EMPLOYEES
12/17	78,098	6,035	7.7%	80,600
12/16	74,953	6,967	9.3%	79,500
12/15	73,908	6,873	9.3%	80,200
12/14	80,106	7,493	9.4%	82,500
12/13	80,029	8,576	10.7%	91,100
Annual Growth	(0.6%)	(8.4%)	—	(3.0%)

2017 Year-End Financials

Debt ratio: 79.92%
Return on equity: ***.***.**%
Cash ($ mil.): 8,447
Current ratio: 1.35
Long-term debt ($ mil.): 31,334

No. of shares (mil.): 1,553
Dividends
  Yield: 0.0%
  Payout: 108.7%
Market value ($ mil.): 164,097

	STOCK PRICE ($) FY Close	P/E High/Low	PER SHARE ($) Earnings	Dividends	Book Value
12/17	105.65	32 23	3.88	4.22	(7.78)
12/16	91.49	23 19	4.48	4.12	(8.18)
12/15	87.91	20 17	4.42	4.04	(8.55)
12/14	81.45	19 16	4.76	3.88	(8.16)
12/13	87.13	18 16	5.26	3.58	(4.89)
Annual Growth	4.9%	— —	(7.3%)	4.2%	—

Phillips 66

Phillips 66 is a leading marketer of gas aviation fuels and other refined petroleum products as well as specialty products such as oils waxes solvents and lubricants. It markets in the US under the Phillips 66 Conoco and 76 brands and internationally under the JET and Coop brands. One of the largest crude oil refiners the company processes transports and markets natural gas and natural gas liquids as well as liquefied petroleum gas. It produces olefins and polyolefins and other products through CPChem a joint venture with

Chevron. Phillips 66 operates primarily in the US and Europe.

Operations

Of the four segments that Phillips 66 reports Marketing and Specialties is the largest contributing about 75% of sales. It includes sales of refined petroleum products (gasoline distillates aviation fuel) through 7800 branded sites in the US and 1500 owned leased or joint venture sites in Europe. Specialty products (for example lubricants sold under Phillips 66 Kendall and Red Line brands) and power generation operations also add to this segment?s revenue.

The Refining segment which accounts for just more than 20% of total revenue has a throughput global refining capacity of 2.1 million barrels per day.

The Midstream segment of Phillips 66 — which gathers transports and markets NGL crude oil and feedstocks — makes up less than 5% of total revenue; it includes the company's interest in Phillips 66 Partners LP which has been acquiring Phillips 66's midstream assets. A very small fraction of company revenue comes from its equity in CPChem (a joint venture with Chevron) which is one of the world?s top producers of olefins and polyolefins and a major supplier of aromatics and specialty chemicals.

Geographic Reach

Phillips 66 operates primarily in the US. Its presence in Europe is largely concentrated in the UK with some assets in mainland Europe. The US accounts for more than 70% of revenue followed by the UK at about 10%.

CPChem is involved in more than 30 global manufacturing facilities in five continents but most significant assets are on the Texas Gulf Coast.

Sales and Marketing

Phillips 66 markets petroleum and specialty products through a network of nearly 8000 marketer-owned or -supplied outlets across the US under brand names 76 Conoco and Phillips 66. It also holds brand-licensing agreements with nearly 1000 sites. Its refined products are marketed on both a branded and unbranded basis.

In Europe Phillips 66 sells retail and wholesale products in Austria Germany and the UK under the JET brand and in Switzerland under the Coop brand (equity interest).

Financial Performance

Phillips 66 posted annual sales of around $86 billion in 2016 a $14 billion reduction from the year before. This marks a continuing trend for the company of steep revenue decline which has fallen more than 50% in five years.

In 2016 revenue fell due to lower average prices for petroleum products which particularly impacted the Marketing and Specialties and Refining segments (sales in those two segments fell by a combined $15 billion). Midstream revenue rose slightly and the Chemicals segment was flat.

The company posted net income of $1.5 billion a 63% reduction from the previous year. Refining profits dropped by more than $2 billion as historically high refining throughput led to significant weakening of US crack spread (refinery margins). Marketing and Specialties the firm?s most profitable segment and Chemicals both saw significant reductions in profit. Only the Midstream segment reported improvement on lower equity losses from DCP Midstream.

Along with revenue and net income Phillips 66's operating cash flow also declined shrinking 48% to about $3 billion.

Strategy

Phillips 66 is recalibrating resources from Refining to the Midstream and Chemical segments with a focus on wholesale trading (because of its lower capital requirements) and operational cost-cutting measures.

Low demands in the refining sector prompted Phillips 66 to follow a high-return quick payout strategy with investments in that business focused on increasing returns from existing assets.

Midstream Phillips 66 hopes to gain production increases from several construction completions based on its long-term growth strategy. This includes the buildout of the energy manufacturing center in Sweeney Texas and the expansion of the Beaumont Terminal in Nederland Texas. The company also sees benefit in the continued expansion of its master limited partnership (Phillips 66 Partners) with assets from Phillips 66 and third parties. In 2016 the limited partnership acquired NGL logistics assets in Louisiana (500 miles of pipelines and storage caverns) further increasing revenue potential.

CPChem also expanded operations by opening two new polyethylene units in the Texas Gulf Coast in November 2017 taking advantage of higher demands for plastics globally and cheap supply of domestic natural gas.

EXECUTIVES

Chairman and CEO, Greg C. Garland, age 60, $1,616,816 total compensation
EVP and CFO, Kevin J. Mitchell, $688,448 total compensation
EVP Refining, Lawrence M. (Larry) Ziemba, $690,312 total compensation
EVP Midstream, Robert A. (Bob) Herman, age 59, $661,608 total compensation
VP Technology, Merl R. Lindstrom
President, Tim G. Taylor, age 63, $1,071,376 total compensation
EVP Legal and Government Affairs General Counsel and Corporate Secretary, Paula A. Johnson, $698,976 total compensation
EVP Marketing and Commercial, Timothy D. (Tim) Roberts
VPP Maintenance Coordinator, Joe Garcia
VPP Maintenance Coordinator, Crystal Stewart
Vice President and Treasurer, Brian Wenzel
Vice President And Treasurer, Joseph Baj
Auditors: Ernst & Young LLP

LOCATIONS

HQ: Phillips 66
2331 CityWest Blvd., Houston, TX 77042
Phone: 281 293-6600
Web: www.Phillips66.com

2016 Sales

	% of total
US	71
UK	12
Germany	7
Other countries	10
Total	**100**

PRODUCTS/OPERATIONS

2016 Sales

	% of total
Refined products	87
Crude oil resales	9
NGL	4
Total	**100**

2016 Sales

	$ mil.	% of total
Marketing and Specialties	63,367	74
Refining	17,948	21
Midstream	2,927	3
Chemicals	5	—
Corporate and Other	32	—
Equity in earnings of affiliates	1,414	2
Net gains of dispositions	10	—
Other income	74	—
Total	**85,777**	**100**

Selected Brands
76
Conoco
Coop
Copylene
JET
Kendall
Phillips 66
Red Line

COMPETITORS

BP	Marathon Petroleum
CITGO	Motiva Enterprises
CVR	NOVA Chemicals
Chevron	National Cooperative
CrossAmerica Partners	Refinery Association
Dow Chemical	Shell Oil Products
Exxon Mobil	Sinclair Oil
Gibson Energy	Sunoco
Hess Corporation	TOTAL
HollyFrontier	Tesoro
LyondellBasell	Valero Energy

HISTORICAL FINANCIALS
Company Type: Public

Income Statement
FYE: December 31

	REVENUE ($ mil.)	NET INCOME ($ mil.)	NET PROFIT MARGIN	EMPLOYEES
12/16	85,777	1,555	1.8%	14,800
12/15	100,949	4,227	4.2%	14,000
12/14	164,093	4,762	2.9%	14,000
12/13	174,809	3,726	2.1%	13,500
12/12	182,922	4,124	2.3%	13,500
Annual Growth	**(17.2%)**	**(21.6%)**	**—**	**2.3%**

2016 Year-End Financials

Debt ratio: 19.63%	No. of shares (mil.): 518
Return on equity: 6.82%	Dividends
Cash ($ mil.): 2,711	Yield: 0.0%
Current ratio: 1.34	Payout: 83.9%
Long-term debt ($ mil.): 9,588	Market value ($ mil.): 44,827

	STOCK PRICE ($) FY Close	P/E High/Low		Earnings	PER SHARE ($) Dividends	Book Value
12/16	86.41	31	25	2.92	2.45	43.16
12/15	81.80	12	8	7.73	2.18	43.63
12/14	71.70	10	8	8.33	1.89	39.51
12/13	77.13	12	8	6.02	1.33	37.19
12/12	53.10	8	4	6.48	0.45	33.32
Annual Growth	**12.9%**		**—**	**—(18.1%)**	**52.8%**	**6.7%**

PHILLIPS EDISON - ARC SHOPPING CENTER REIT INC.

Auditors: DELOITTE & TOUCHE LLP CINCINN

LOCATIONS

HQ: PHILLIPS EDISON - ARC SHOPPING CENTER REIT INC.
11501 NORTHLAKE DR FL 1, CINCINNATI, OH 452491667
Phone: 513 554-1110
Web: WWW.GROCERYCENTERREIT1.COM

HISTORICAL FINANCIALS

Company Type: Private

Income Statement

FYE: December 31

	ASSETS ($ mil.)	NET INCOME ($ mil.)	INCOME AS % OF ASSETS	EMPLOYEES
12/14	2,150	(22)	—	18
12/13	1,721	(12)	—	—
12/12	325	(4)	—	—
12/11	85	(2)	—	—
Annual Growth	193.4%	—	—	—

2014 Year-End Financials

Debt ratio: —
Return on equity: (-12.00%)
Cash ($ mil.): 15
Current ratio: —
Long-term debt ($ mil.): —

Dividends
Yield: —
Payout: —
Market value ($ mil.): —

Pilgrims Pride Corp.

Pilgrim's Pride couldn't be blamed if it spread its tail feathers and did a barnyard strut. As one of the world's top chicken processors it boasts operations in the US Mexico and Puerto Rico in breeding hatching raising processing and distributing chicken. The company sells prepared poultry products under the Pilgrim's Pride and EatWellStayHealthy labels to retail food outlets distributors and food service operators. It sells fresh frozen value-added prepared chicken and deli products. In addition to producing 10.2 billion pounds of live chicken annually Pilgrim's Pride also produces table eggs and chicken by-products for use as animal feed. The company is majority owned by Brazil's JBS.

Operations

The company operates its business in a dozen US states Mexico and Puerto Rico. (For reporting purposes Pilgrim's Pride rolls its sales from Puerto Rico into its US business segment.) The poultry producer operates 27 fresh processing plants eight prepared foods cook plants five fresh processing plant in Puerto Rico three processing plants in Mexico and distribution centers inlcuding 13 in Mexico and one in Puerto Rico.

Pilgrim's Pride generates approximately 90% of its sales by processing 6.9 billion pounds of dressed chicken. The chicken processor operates 28 feed mills 36 hatcheries processing plants and distribution centers in more than a dozen states in the US as well as in Puerto Rico and Mexico. It also owns a small pork-raising operation acquired during the Gold Kist acquisition.

Geographic Reach

Colorado-based Pilgrim's Pride rings up about 80% of its sales in the US. Mexico is next with 13%. The company exports its products to about 100 countries worldwide; its key foreign export markets include Eastern Europe (including Russia) the Far East (including China) and Mexico. It is the #2 poultry company in Mexico (behind Bochco).

Sales and Marketing

Pilgrim's Pride which exports its products to customers in some 95countries (including Mexico) It's two biggest customers accounted for about 15% of sales. The company targets the food service industry primarily chain restaurants and food processors such as YUM! Brands Burger King Wendy's and Chick-fil-A as well as retail customers the likes of grocery store chains Wal-Mart Kroger and Publix and wholesale clubs Costco and Sam's Club.

Financial Performance

Net sales for Pilgrim's Pride rose 2% in 2014 versus 2013 to $8.58 billion while net income jumped 29% to $711 million over the same period. It was the third consecutive year of steeply increasing profits after Pilgrim's posted a loss of nearly $500 million in 2011. Cash flow from operations has soared along with growth in net income.

The rise in 2014 revenue was attributed to higher sales in the US and Mexico Pilgrim's two core markets. Higher poultry prices and continued strong demand for chicken products in combination with constrained supply boosted sales by 2% in the US. The cost of sales for US segment decreased because of lower feed costs and a decrease in wages and benefits. In Mexico sales increased by 2.8% due to favorable foreign currency translation and an increase in prices.

Strategy

In June 2014 Pilgrim's Pride lost a bidding war to acquire Hillshire Brands (the maker of Jimmy Dean Sausages) to meat giant Tyson Foods. Tyson acquired Hillshire for $63 per share topping Pilgrim's $55 bid. The battle for Hillshire emphasizes how badly large commodity meat companies want to acquire popular and more profitable brands. As a consolation prize or sorts Pilgrim's Pride in July agreed to buy Tyson's poultry business in Mexico (Tyson de M ©xico) in a deal valued at $400 million. Indeed the poultry provider is working to expand to additional international markets to reduce its reliance on the US. In Mexico for instance it is expanding distribution of dark meat chicken products. It also identifies the Commonwealth of Independent States (CIS) including Russia and Asia Pacific as regions with promising growth potential.

Additionally the company's strategy focuses on improving its product mix and reducing selling general and administrative expenses through employee layoffs and supply chain and margin improvements. It is also reviewing more drastic options for streamlining operations including restructuring selling assets consolidating operations and relocating employees.

Mergers and Acquisitions

In late 2016 Pilgrim's Pride agreed to acquire smaller rival GNP Company from The Maschhoffs LLC in a deal worth $350 million allowing Pilgrim's Pride to expand its production and customer base.

Company Background

JBS acquired its stake after Pilgrim's Pride emerged from Chapter 11 bankruptcy in 2009. Since its initial investment the beef and pork producer has increased its share in Pilgrim's Pride to about 75% gained through subsidiary JBS USA's acquisition of nearly 19 million shares from Lonnie "Bo" Pilgrim in 2012. Pilgrim's Pride has used the money from the stock sale to pay off creditors and fund its struggling operations. Taking over Pilgrim's Pride opened the door for JBS into the US poultry market. As part of the acquisition Pilgrim's Pride was integrated into JBS USA which itself is controlled by the Batista family (specifically Wesley Batista and his brother Joesley Batista). The chicken processor's longtime headquarters in East Texas and a satellite corporate office in Atlanta were shuttered and its corporate and administrative functions relocated to JBS's US headquarters in Greeley Colorado.

EXECUTIVES

EVP Operations - Technical Services and Engineering, Walter F. Shafer

CEO, Don Jackson, age 66

SVP Commodity Risk Management Feed Ingredient Purchasing and Export Sales, Charles Von Der Heyde

CFO, Fabio Sandri, age 45, $375,000 total compensation

EVP Sales and Operations, Jayson Penn

EVP Sales and Operations - Prepared Foods, Kevin Miller

Business Development Senior Vice President, Greg Tatum

Senior Vice President Human Resources, Doug Schult

Vice President Of Sales, Randy Meyers

Vice President, Roger Austin

Seniorvice President Sales and Marketing Frozen Food Service, Tom Bell

Vice President Logistics, Clay Matthews

Senior Vice President Of Research and Development, Phil Hurwitz

Vice President Operations Acctng, Mark Glover

Senior Vice President Commodity Risk Management and Feed Ingredients, Aaron Wiegand

Vice President of Foodservice Sales Prepared Foods, Alan Kahn

Vice President Further Processing, Heath Loyd

Vice President International and Head Of E, Alexander Ivannikov

Vice President Corporate Accounts, Brenda Ray

Vice President Corporate Accounts, Stacy Fiedler

Vice President Foodservice Marketing, Keith Arnold

Chairman, Wesley Mendon §a Batista

Auditors: KPMG LLP

LOCATIONS

HQ: Pilgrims Pride Corp.
1770 Promontory Circle, Greeley, CO 80634-9038
Phone: 970 506-8000
Web: www.pilgrims.com

2014 Sales

	% of total
US	89
Mexico	11
Total	100

PRODUCTS/OPERATIONS

2014 Sales

	% of total
US chicken	
Fresh chicken	55
Prepared chicken	21
Export & other chicken by-products	7
Mexico chicken	11
Other products	
US	6
Mexico —	
Total	100

Brands

Brands
Pilgrim's
Pierce Chicken
Gold Kist Farms
Country Pride
Savoro
Products
Fresh chicken
Fully cooked
Ready to cook
Individually frozen

COMPETITORS

Allen Family Foods	Hormel
American Foods	Jobbers Meat Packing
Bachoco	Keystone Foods
Cargill Meat Solutions	Perdue Incorporated
Clougherty Packing	Rose Acre Farms
Coleman Natural Foods	Sanderson Farms

Cooper Farms
Eberly Poultry
Farmer's Pride
Harvest Meat Company
Smithfield Foods
Tecumseh Poultry
Tyson Fresh Meats

HISTORICAL FINANCIALS
Company Type: Public

Income Statement
FYE: December 25

	REVENUE ($ mil.)	NET INCOME ($ mil.)	NET PROFIT MARGIN	EMPLOYEES
12/16	7,931	440	5.6%	39,600
12/15	8,180	645	7.9%	38,850
12/14	8,583	711	8.3%	35,000
12/13	8,411	549	6.5%	36,700
12/12	8,121	174	2.1%	33,000
Annual Growth	(0.6%)	26.1%	—	4.7%

2016 Year-End Financials

Debt ratio: 33.64%
Return on equity: 41.17%
Cash ($ mil.): 120
Current ratio: 1.52
Long-term debt ($ mil.): 1,011

No. of shares (mil.): 249
Dividends
Yield: 0.1%
Payout: 158.9%
Market value ($ mil.): 4,737

	STOCK PRICE ($) FY Close	P/E High/Low	PER SHARE ($) Earnings	Dividends	Book Value
12/16	19.02	16 10	1.73	2.75	3.56
12/15	22.49	15 7	2.50	5.77	4.94
12/14	34.07	14 6	2.74	0.00	8.47
12/13	16.47	9 3	2.12	0.00	5.75
12/12	7.19	12 6	0.70	0.00	3.50
Annual Growth	27.5%	— —	25.4%	—	0.5%

Pinnacle Financial Partners Inc

Pinnacle Financial Partners works to be at the top of the community banking mountain in central Tennessee. It's the holding company for Tennessee-based Pinnacle Bank which has grown to some 40 branches in the Nashville and Knoxville areas since its founding in 2000. Serving consumers and small- to mid-sized business the $9 billion financial institution provides standard services such as checking and savings accounts CDs credit cards and loans and mortgages. The company also offers investment and trust services through Pinnacle Asset Management while its insurance brokerage subsidiary Miller Loughry Beach specializes in property/casualty policies.Pinnacle agreed to merge with North Carolina-based BNC Bancorp in 2017.

Operations

Pinnacle Financial Partners' commercial and industrial loans and commercial real estate loans account for nearly 40% and 20% respectively of its total portfolio of loans.

As part of its primary services to both individual and commercial clients Tennessee-based subsidiary Pinnacle Bank provides core deposits including savings checking interest-bearing checking money market and certificate of deposit accounts.

The bank's lending products include commercial real estate and consumer loans to individuals and small- to medium-sized businesses and professional entities. Pinnacle Bank Partners also offers auto dealer finance services to certain automobile

dealers and their customers. Additionally it offers Pinnacle-branded consumer credit cards to select clients.

Its convenience-centered products and services include 24-hour telephone and Internet banking debit and credit cards direct deposit and cash management services.

Geographic Reach

Based in Tennessee Pinnacle Financial Partners has become the second-largest bank holding company in the state with nearly 35 offices in eight Middle Tennessee counties and four Knoxville offices. It boasts locations in Nashville Knoxville Murfreesboro Dickson Ashland City Mt. Juliet Lebanon Franklin Brentwood Hendersonville Goodlettsville Smyrna and Shelbyville.

Sales and Marketing

Pinnacle Bank traditionally has obtained its deposits through personal solicitation by its officers and directors although it has used media advertising more in recent years due to its advertising and banking sponsorship with the Tennessee Titans NFL Football team. While it would prefer its customers to bank in person the institution allows customers to bank remotely.

Its marketing and other business development costs have risen in recent years: $4.13 million $3.639 million and $3.636 million in 2014 2013 and 2012 respectively.

Financial Performance

Pinnacle Financial Partners has enjoyed steady revenue and profit growth for the past several years thanks to positive loan growth. Revenue in 2014 rose by 9% to a record $258.77 million mostly to thanks to 9% growth in interest income from loans as the bank's loan assets grew by double digits. Pinnacle also saw double-digit growth in its fee income from service charges on deposit accounts as deposit balances grew and double-digit growth in its investment services income and trust fees as brokerage and trust account balances grew.

Higher revenue drove net income up by 22% to a record $70.47 million. Operations provided $95.06 million or 25% less cash than in 2013 primarily because the bank collected roughly $30 million less in proceeds from its mortgage loans held for sale than it did the year before.

Strategy

Pinnacle's goal is to become the dominant bank in its home market of the Southeast. In 2016 it acquired Avenue Financial Holdings for $200 million and followed up the acquisition by agreeing to merge with regional rival BNC Bancorp of North Carolina in 2017. Once the merger completes the combined company will be the biggest in the region.

Pinnacle Financial Partners been looking to diversify its revenue streams through strategic investments in recent years. In early 2015 for example Tennessee-based subsidiary Pinnacle Bank purchased a 30% membership interest in Bankers Healthcare Group LLC which makes term loans to healthcare professionals and practices for $75 million.

Primarily serving small- to medium-sized businesses in the Nashville and Knoxville areas the company in 2013 began extending its reach in its primary markets by opening its fourth full-service banking location in the Knoxville market in the Cedar Bluff area.

Mergers and Acquisitions

In 2017 Pinnacle agreed to merge with BNC Bancorp. The combined company will have assets of some $20 billion and a presence in four states and in 12 of the largest metropolitan markets in the Southeast.

In 2016 Pinnacle acquired Avenue Financial Holdings (holding company of Avenue Bank with five banking locations in Nashville); the transaction

was valued at some $201.4 million. Avenue Bank will operate as a division of Pinnacle Bank for a few months after which the companies will combine operations.

EXECUTIVES

President and CEO, M. Terry Turner, age 61, $784,700 total compensation

EVP and Chief Administrative Officer, Hugh M. Queener, age 61, $376,700 total compensation

EVP and Senior Lending Officer; Manager Client Advisory Group Nashville, J. Edward (Ed) White, age 67, $145,000 total compensation

EVP and Director Associate and Client Experience, Joanne B. Jackson, age 60, $117,000 total compensation

CFO, Harold R. Carpenter, age 58, $376,700 total compensation

SVP and Manager Trust and Investment Advisory, Robert Newman

President Pinnacle Knoxville, Mike DiStefano

Chief Credit Officer; President Pinnacle Knoxville, J. Harvey White, $283,800 total compensation

EVP and Manager Pinnacle Asset Management, Gary Collier

SVP and Senior Credit Officer Real Estate, Mike Hendren

SVP and Senior Credit Officer, Tim Huestis

SVP and CIO, Randy Withrow

President and CEO PNFP Capital Markets, Roger Osborne

SVP and Manager Residential Mortgage Services, Ross Kinney

EVP and Area Executive Rutherford County, Bill Jones

Chief Investment Officer, Mac Johnston

SVP Small Business Banking, Chip Higgins

EVP and Financial Advisor, Jerry Hampton

President Pinnacle Memphis, Damon Bell

Senior Vice President, Bill Decamp

Senior Vice President and financial advisor in Nashville, Lynn Kendrick

Senior Vice President, Kay Mcalister

Senior Vice President, Rhonda Smith

Vice President, Tyane Powell

Senior Vice President Financial Advisor, Cynthia Oliva

Senior Vice President Mortgage Advisor, Jeff Anderson

Senior Vice President, Larry Kain

Senior Vice President Financial Advisor, Lynn Lassiter

Senior Vice President, Michael G Lindseth

Senior Vice President, David Edwards

Senior Vice President And Financial Advisor, Brande Thomas

Mortgage Advisor Senior Vice President, Jeff Mayfield

Senior Vice President And Mortgage Advisor, Jamie Lacy

Senior Vice President, Steve Uebelhor

Senior Vice President Mortgage Advisor, Chris Maultsby

Senior Vice President, Sarah Teague

Senior Vice President, Kirk Garrett

Senior Vice President, Mary Isham

Senior Vice President, Rex Jones

Senior Vice President, Ken Warren

Senior Vice President, Darin Kellett

Senior Vice President, William Diehl

Senior Vice President Financial Advisor, Kim Ciukowski

Vice President Automotive Finance, Jeff Rhodes

Vice President, Luciano Scala

Senior Vice President, Todd Carter

SRVP; Mortgage Advisor, Scott Ractliffe

Senior Vice President Mortgage Advisor, Deon Ducey

Senior Vice President And Office Leader, Sherrie Hicks
Senior Vice President Business Banking Financial Advisor, Dennis Mitchell
Senior Vice President, Kim Jenny
Senior Vice President Financial Advisor, Cindy Oliva
Executive Vice President And Chief Financial Officerand#8230, Alan Haefele
Vice President Finance, Dale Floyd
Senior Vice President, Sherry McHaffie
Senior Vice President And Financial Adviser In Commercial Real Estate, Thomas Vester
Senior Vice President Lending, Roger Leitner
Vice President, Kevin Roddey
Executive Vice President and Senior credit Officer, Edward White
Senior Vice President, Sarae J Lewis
Senior Vice President Financial Advisor, Keely Ritchie
Senior Vice President Financial Advisor, Stacey Richards
Vice President Treasury Management Advisor, Jondra Settle
Senior Vice President, Bryan Bean
Senior Vice President and Financial Advisor, Ashley Preskenis
Senior Vice President and Financial Advisor, Nancy Benskin
Senior Vice President Credit Advisor, Stacey Fantom
Senior Vice President Credit Advisor, Kendria Northcutt
Senior Vice President, Sam King
Senior Vice President, Gina Scott
Senior Vice President and Trust Officer, Scott Lindsey
Senior Vice President, Tim Bewley
Senior Vice President, Jason Reierson
Senior Vice President, Lisa Baskette
Senior Vice President, Bridget Mounger
Vice President, Bob Stimson
Senior Vice President, John Douglas
Senior Vice President, Leslie Godfrey
Executive Vice President, Phil Stevenson
Senior Vice President Financial Advisor, Cooper Samuels
Senior Vice President, Diane Jones
Senior Vice President, Steven Zimmerman
Vice President: Treasury Management Advisor, Joy Bowen
CMB Senior Vice President, Jeff Tucker
Senior Vice President, Ryan Murphy
CTFA Senior Vice President Financial Advisor, Steve Scott
Senior Vice President and Mortgage Advisor, Donathan Cassidy
Senior Vice President, Cameron Puckett
Senior Vice President, Rick Nelson
Senior Vice President, Bruce Von Almen
Senior Vice President, Jimmy Moncrief
Senior Vice Presiclent, Kate Dailey
Executive Vice President Music and Entertainment, Andy Moats
Senior Vice President, Dan Neumann
Vice Chairman, Ed C. Loughry, age 74
Chairman, Robert A. (Rob) McCabe, age 66
Auditors: Crowe Horwath LLP

LOCATIONS

HQ: Pinnacle Financial Partners Inc
150 Third Avenue South, Suite 900, Nashville, TN 37201
Phone: 615 744-3700
Web: www.pnfp.com

PRODUCTS/OPERATIONS

2014 Revenue

	% of total
Interest Income	80
Non-interest Income	20
Total	**100**

Selected Subsidiaries

Pinnacle Advisory Services Inc.
Pinnacle Credit Enhancement Holdings Inc.
Pinnacle National Bank
 Miller & Loughry Inc. (dba Miller Loughry Beach)
 PFP Title Company
Pinnacle Community Development Corporation
Pinnacle Nashville Real Estate Inc.
Pinnacle Rutherford Real Estate Inc.
Pinnacle Rutherford Towers Inc.
Pinnacle Service Company Inc.
PNFP Insurance Inc.

COMPETITORS

BB&T	Regions Financial
Bank of America	SunTrust
Fifth Third	U.S. Bancorp
First Horizon	

HISTORICAL FINANCIALS

Company Type: Public

Income Statement
FYE: December 31

	ASSETS ($ mil.)	NET INCOME ($ mil.)	INCOME AS % OF ASSETS	EMPLOYEES
12/16	11,194	127	1.1%	1,180
12/15	8,715	95	1.1%	1,065
12/14	6,018	70	1.2%	767
12/13	5,563	57	1.0%	748
12/12	5,040	41	0.8%	726
Annual Growth	**22.1%**	**32.0%**	**—**	**12.9%**

2016 Year-End Financials

Debt ratio: 3.13%
Return on equity: 9.57%
Cash ($ mil.): 183
Current ratio: —
Long-term debt ($ mil.): —
No. of shares (mil.): 46
Dividends
 Yield: 0.0%
 Payout: 19.2%
Market value ($ mil.): 3,213

	STOCK PRICE ($) FY Close	P/E High/Low	PER SHARE ($) Earnings	Dividends	Book Value
12/16	69.30	24 15	2.91	0.56	32.28
12/15	51.36	22 14	2.52	0.48	28.25
12/14	39.54	20 15	2.01	0.32	22.46
12/13	32.53	20 11	1.67	0.08	20.55
12/12	18.84	18 14	1.10	0.00	19.57
Annual Growth	**38.5%**	**— —**	**27.5%**	**—**	**13.3%**

PLACID HOLDING COMPANY

Auditors: HEIN & ASSOCIATES LLP DALLAS

LOCATIONS

HQ: PLACID HOLDING COMPANY
1601 ELM ST STE 3900, DALLAS, TX 752014708
Phone: 214 880-8479

HISTORICAL FINANCIALS

Company Type: Private

Income Statement
FYE: December 31

	REVENUE ($ mil.)	NET INCOME ($ mil.)	NET PROFIT MARGIN	EMPLOYEES
12/13	4,929	47	1.0%	2
12/02	532	3	0.6%	—
12/01	579	18	3.1%	—
12/00	564	5	1.0%	—
Annual Growth	**18.1%**	**17.5%**	**—**	**—**

2013 Year-End Financials

Debt ratio: —
Return on equity: 1.00%
Cash ($ mil.): 51
Current ratio: 1.10
Long-term debt ($ mil.): —
Dividends
 Yield: —
 Payout: —
Market value ($ mil.): —

PLACID REFINING COMPANY LLC

EXECUTIVES

V Pres, Ron Hurst
Treasurer, Barry Joffrion
Auditors: HEIN & ASSOCIATES LLP DALLAS

LOCATIONS

HQ: PLACID REFINING COMPANY LLC
2101 CEDAR SPRINGS RD # 600, DALLAS, TX 752011591
Phone: 214 880-8479
Web: WWW.PLACIDREFINING.COM

COMPETITORS

CITGO Refining and Chemicals	United Refining
NuStar Energy	Valero Energy

HISTORICAL FINANCIALS

Company Type: Private

Income Statement
FYE: December 31

	REVENUE ($ mil.)	NET INCOME ($ mil.)	NET PROFIT MARGIN	EMPLOYEES
12/13	4,929	47	1.0%	200
12/11	4,699	4	0.1%	—
12/10	3,686	39	1.1%	—
12/06	2,925	128	4.4%	—
Annual Growth	**7.7%**	**(13.1%)**	**—**	**—**

2013 Year-End Financials

Debt ratio: —
Return on equity: 1.00%
Cash ($ mil.): 42
Current ratio: 1.10
Long-term debt ($ mil.): —
Dividends
 Yield: —
 Payout: —
Market value ($ mil.): —

Plains All American Pipeline LP

The term "All American" includes Canada for Plains All American Pipeline which has pipeline operations in the US and north of the border. The limited partnership is engaged in the transportation storage terminalling and marketing of crude oil refined products natural gas liquids (NGL) and liquefied petroleum gas (LPG) and owns extensive gathering terminal and storage facilities in across the US and in Canada. At the end of 2014 Plains All American Pipeline owned 17800 miles of gathering crude oil NGL and refined product pipelines throughout the US and Canada operated a fleet of 800 trailers 150 barges and 72 transport tugs and owned 29 million barrels of storage capacity.

HISTORY

Goodyear Tire & Rubber subsidiary Celeron began designing the All American Pipeline in 1983 to bring heavy crude from California to the less-regulated refineries of Texas. It was completed in 1987 at a cost of $1.6 billion but by 1991 only a trickle of oil was dribbling through. The pipeline did not post a profit until 1994.

Prospects began to look up in the mid-1990s when Chevron Texaco and Exxon signed contracts to use the pipeline beginning in 1996. Plains Resources bought the pipeline in 1998 for $400 million; the company created Plains All American Pipeline to acquire and operate the pipeline then sold off a 43% stake in an IPO that raised $260 million. The next year Plains All American bought Scurlock Permian (2300 miles of pipeline) from Marathon Ashland Petroleum for $141 million and the West Texas Gathering System from Chevron (450 miles) for $36 million.

Shareholders sued Plains All American in 1999 after it reported that an employee's unauthorized crude-oil trading would cost the company about $160 million. (In 2000 the company agreed to pay $29.5 million plus interest to settle the cases.)

Plains All American announced plans to mothball all but the California section of the All American Pipeline in 1999. The next year El Paso Energy bought the 1088-mile section of the pipeline that was to be deactivated plus the right to run fiber-optic cable over the entire pipeline for $129 million.

Targeting Canada as part of its expansion strategy in 2001 Plains All American bought about 450 miles of oil pipeline and other midstream assets from Murphy Oil and acquired crude oil and LPG marketing firm CANPET Energy. Also that year Plains Resources reduced its stake in Plains All American from 44% to 29%.

In 2002 the company acquired the Wapella Pipeline System located in southeastern Saskatchewan and southwestern Manitoba. It also bought Shell Pipeline's West Texas crude oil pipeline assets for $315 million. Plains All American Pipeline continued its acquisition streak in 2003 with the acquisitions of the South Saskatchewan pipeline system in Canada and the ArkLaTex pipeline system originating in Sabine Texas.

In 2004 Plains All American continued its expansion with the acquisition of interests in the Capline and Capwood pipeline systems from Shell Pipeline Company for about $158 million. It also acquired the crude oil and pipeline operations of Link Energy for about $330 million and the Cal Ven pipeline system from Unocal Canada for about $19 million. Later that year the company continued its system expansion by acquiring the Schaefferstown propane storage facility from Koch Hydrocarbon for about $32 million.

In 2006 the company acquired Andrews Petroleum and Lone Star Trucking for $205 million. It also acquired stakes in a number of Gulf Coast crude oil pipeline systems from BP Oil Pipeline Company for $133.5 million. That year in a major deal the company acquired Pacific Energy Partners for $2.4 billion moving the company beyond crude oil and into the refined products and barging businesses.

In 2007 Plains All American Pipeline acquired LPG storage facilities in Arizona and South Carolina.

In 2008 Occidental Petroleum acquired 10% of the company's general partner boosting the amount of new capital available for Plains All American Pipeline to pay down debt and make further acquisitions. It also boosted its Canadian midstream assets with the acquisition of Rainbow Pipeline (crude oil gathering and pipelines).

In 2012 to boost its midstream assets the company bought BP's Canadian NGL operations for $1.7 billion.

EXECUTIVES

President and COO, Harry N. Pefanis, age 60, $300,000 total compensation
EVP, Phillip D. (Phil) Kramer, $250,000 total compensation
Chairman and CEO, Greg L. Armstrong, age 59, $375,000 total compensation
EVP Operations and Business Development, Mark J. Gorman
EVP General Counsel and Secretary, Richard K. McGee, age 56
SVP Technology Process and Risk Management, Alfred A. (Al) Lindseth
EVP and CFO, Al Swanson, age 53, $250,000 total compensation
President Plains Midstream Canada, W. David (Dave) Duckett, $276,666 total compensation
EVP Commercial Activities, John P. von Berg, $250,000 total compensation
EVP, John R. Rutherford, $62,500 total compensation
President PNGS, Dean Liollio, age 59
Executive Vice President Commercial Activities, John Berg
Vice President Director, James Capra
Vice President of Information Technology, Rebecca Mcconnell
Vice President Community Research and Development Director, Tamra Brayer
Vice President Tax, Walter van Zanten
Senior Vice President Technology Process Risk Management, Al Lindseth
Vice President, Patrick Diamond
Vice President of Operations, Phil Smith
Vice President Engineering, Daniel Nerbonne
Assistant Treasurer, Michael McLaughlin
Assistant Secretary, Ann Gullion
Auditors: PricewaterhouseCoopers LLP

LOCATIONS

HQ: Plains All American Pipeline LP
333 Clay Street, Suite 1600, Houston, TX 77002
Phone: 713 646-4100
Web: www.plainsallamerican.com

2014 Sales

	$ mil.	% of total
US	34,860	80
Canada	8,604	20
Total	**43,464**	**100**

PRODUCTS/OPERATIONS

2014 Sales

	$ mil.	% of total
Supply and logistics	42,114	97
Transportation	774	2
Facilities	576	1
Total	**43,464**	**100**

COMPETITORS

Buckeye Partners	ONEOK
Enbridge	Sunoco Logistics
Enterprise Products	TransMontaigne
NGL Energy Partners	

HISTORICAL FINANCIALS

Company Type: Public

Income Statement

FYE: December 31

	REVENUE ($ mil.)	NET INCOME ($ mil.)	NET PROFIT MARGIN	EMPLOYEES
12/16	20,182	726	3.6%	5,100
12/15	23,152	903	3.9%	5,400
12/14	43,464	1,384	3.2%	5,300
12/13	42,249	1,361	3.2%	4,900
12/12	37,797	1,094	2.9%	4,700
Annual Growth	**(14.5%)**	**(9.7%)**	**—**	**2.1%**

2016 Year-End Financials

Debt ratio: 48.90%	No. of shares (mil.): 669
Return on equity: —	Dividends
Cash ($ mil.): 47	Yield: 0.1%
Current ratio: 0.92	Payout: 616.2%
Long-term debt ($ mil.): 10,124	Market value ($ mil.): 21,608

	STOCK PRICE ($) FY Close	P/E High/Low	PER SHARE ($) Earnings	Dividends	Book Value
12/16	32.29	78 36	0.43	2.65	13.09
12/15	23.10	67 24	0.77	2.76	19.82
12/14	51.32	25 19	2.38	2.55	21.68
12/13	51.77	21 16	2.80	2.33	21.28
12/12	45.24	38 18	2.40	2.11	19.80
Annual Growth	**(8.1%)**	**—**	**— (34.9%)**	**5.9%**	**(9.8%)**

Plains GP Holdings LP

Auditors: PricewaterhouseCoopers LLP

LOCATIONS

HQ: Plains GP Holdings LP
333 Clay Street, Suite 1600, Houston, TX 77002
Phone: 713 646-4100
Web: www.plainsallamerican.com

HISTORICAL FINANCIALS

Company Type: Public

Income Statement

FYE: December 31

	REVENUE ($ mil.)	NET INCOME ($ mil.)	NET PROFIT MARGIN	EMPLOYEES
12/16	20,182	94	0.5%	5,100
12/15	23,152	118	0.5%	5,400
12/14	43,464	70	0.2%	5,300
12/13	42,249	15	0.0%	4,900
12/12	37,797	3	0.0%	—
Annual Growth	**(14.5%)**	**136.6%**	**—**	**—**

2016 Year-End Financials

Debt ratio: 45.35% No. of shares (mil.): 731
Return on equity: — Dividends
Cash ($ mil.): 50 Yield: —
Current ratio: 0.92 Payout: —
Long-term debt ($ mil.): 10,124 Market value ($ mil.): 25,357

	STOCK PRICE ($) FY Close	P/E High/Low		PER SHARE ($) Earnings	Dividends	Book Value
12/16	34.68	38	6	0.94	0.00	2.38
12/15	9.45	21	5	1.41	0.00	7.74
12/14	25.68	25	18	1.25	0.00	7.28
12/13	26.77	100	81	0.27	0.00	4.55
Annual Growth	6.7%	—	—	37.1%		—(15.0%)

PNC Financial Services Group (The)

PNC Financial Services has returned to its traditional banking roots but it also offers a wide range of other financial services. Boasting total assets of some $370 billion and total deposits nearing $260 billion its flagship PNC Bank subsidiary operates upwards of 2500 branches in almost 20 states in the mid-Atlantic the Midwest and Florida. In addition to retail and corporate banking the company offers insurance investments personal and institutional asset management and capital markets products and services. The firm also owns boutique investment bank Harris Williams and about a quarter of money management giant BlackRock.

Operations

The diversified financial services organization provides a wide range of services retail and business banking; residential mortgage banking; specialized services for corporations and government bodies (corporate banking real estate finance asset-based lending and other). It also offers wealth management and asset management services.

PNC Financial Services operates five core business segments based on these activities. It generates nearly 45% of its total revenue from its Retail Banking business while 35% of revenue comes from its Corporate & Institutional Banking business. Another nearly 10% came from its Asset Management Group and another 10% from a combination of its Residential Mortgage Banking business and its BlackRock investment (it owns a 25% stake in BlackRock the world's largest publicly traded asset management firm).

Broken down further the firm generates about 60% of its total revenue from interest income (mostly loan interest) while most of the rest came from a combination of asset management fees (10% of revenue) corporate services fees (10%) consumer services fees (over 5%) and residential mortgage fees and service charges on deposits (each about 5%).

Geographic Reach

PNC's major geographic markets are in Alabama Delaware Florida Georgia Kentucky Illinois Indiana Maryland Michigan Missouri New Jersey North Carolina Ohio Pennsylvania South Carolina Washington D.C. Wisconsin and Virginia. It's international offices are in Canada China Germany and the UK.

Financial Performance

PNC's financial performance has been more or less static for a few years now.

In fiscal 2016 total revenue increased 1% to $16.4 billion. A $329 million increase in interest income was partially offset by a $176 million fall in non-interest income. Interest income was boosted by an increase in loan and securities balances and higher loan yields. The increase in average loans was driven by $3.6 billion growth in average commercial real estate loans and $2.2 billion of average commercial loans. The fall in non-interest income related to lower earnings from BlackRock and $134 million lower net gains on sales of Visa Class B common shares.

Net income fell 4% to $4.0 billion as an increase in interest expense outweighed the increase in interest income.

Cash from operations fell a fairly sharp 34% to $3.6 billion due to net changes in accrued expenses and other liabilities.

Strategy

PNC is in the final year of its five-year $1.2 billion plan to modernize its core infrastructure and making its operations faster more stable and more secure. In 2016 PNC consolidated its datacenters and moved its systems into an internal cloud system. The new datacenter allows the company to triple its capacity. The company also has built new computing architecture that allows for simple integration of APIs (application programming interface) while bolstering its cybersecurity.

Mergers and Acquisitions

PNC acquired ECN Capital Corp's US-based commercial and vendor finance business for $1.1 billion. The acquisition includes the portfolio of construction transportation industrial franchise and technology loans and leases. It adds to PNC's existing vendor franchise and supports leading vendors in a number of growth industries.

Company Background

PNC acquired RBC Bank (USA) from Royal Bank of Canada in 2012. The nearly $3.5 billion acquisition extended PNC's retail banking franchise in the Southeast and cemented its place among the five largest banks in the US.

HISTORY

First National Bank of Pittsburgh opened in 1863. In 1913 the bank consolidated with Second National Bank of Pittsburgh and in 1921 it bought Peoples National. The company changed its name to Pittsburgh National after a long expansion following the Depression and WWII. In 1983 Pittsburgh National merged with Provident National of Philadelphia (founded by Quakers in 1865) to form PNC Corp. The union combined Pittsburgh National's corporate lending strength with Provident's money management and trust operations.

EXECUTIVES

EVP and Chief Credit Officer, Michael J. Hannon, age 60
Chairman President and CEO, William S. (Bill) Demchak, age 54, $1,100,000 total compensation
EVP Chief Investment Officer and Treasurer, E. William (Bill) Parsley, age 51, $588,462 total compensation
EVP and CFO, Robert Q. (Rob) Reilly, age 52, $500,000 total compensation
EVP and Head Corporate and Institutional Banking, Michael P. Lyons, age 46, $700,000 total compensation
EVP and Head Technology and Operations, Steven C. (Steve) Van Wyk, age 58, $500,000 total compensation
EVP and Head Asset Management Group, Orlando C. Esposito, age 58
EVP and Chief Customer Officer, Karen L. Larrimer, age 54

EVP and Chief Risk Officer, Joseph E. Rockey, age 52
EVP General Counsel and Head Regulatory and Government Affairs, Gregory B. Jordan, age 57
EVP and General Auditor, Stacy M. Juchno, age 41
EVP and Chief Human Resources Officer, Vicki C. Henn, age 48
EVP and Director Investor Relations, Bryan K. Gill
Executive Vice President and Chief Investment Strategist PNC Wealth Management, E William Stone
Executive Vice President Treasury Management Sales Manager, Lynn Aleksov
Vice President Strategic Accounts, Jim Foley
Senior Vice President Wellness and Work Life Balance, Kathleen D'Appolonia
Vice President Credit Risk Portfolio Manager, Michelle Grommesh
Senior Vice President And Senior Relationship Manager, Tracy Decock
Assistant Vice President, Barbara Jones
Vice President Senior Organizational Devel, Vicki Brown
Vice President, Roderick Hirsch
Vice President Product Development, Mark Vizza
Senior Vice President and Chief Economist, Stuart G Hoffman
Regional Manager Senior Vice President, Alisa Winslow
Vice President Community Development Banking Consultant, Maria Thompson
Senior Vice President Product Manager, Janet Hoyt
Assistant Vice President, Kregg Heenan
Vice President, Brent Ludwick
Vice President Senior Relationship Manager, Moises Almonte
Vice President, Mike Hrycenko
Senior Vice President, Mark Kiskorna
Vice President, Catherine Jones
Executive Vice President, Peter Thompson
Senior Vice President, Kurt Putkonen
Vice President, Timothy Thieneman
Vice President Sales and Marketing, Darin Fetsko
Senior Vice President Of Real Estate Finance, Bill G Lashbrook
Vice President Western PA Territory, Gavin Geraci
Assistant Vice President Mortgage Operations Manager, Carl Barbarino
Senior Vice President and Chief Procurement Officer, James Vespoli
Vice President Program Management Offi, Naimesh Patel
Assistant Vice President Senior Property Administrator, Michael Conway
Vice Chairman, Walter E Grgg
Auditors: PricewaterhouseCoopers LLP

LOCATIONS

HQ: PNC Financial Services Group (The)
The Tower at PNC Plaza, 300 Fifth Avenue, Pittsburgh, PA 15222-2401
Phone: 412 762-2000 **Fax:** 412 762-5798
Web: www.pnc.com

Selected Banking Markets
Delaware
Florida
Georgia
Illinois
Indiana
Kentucky
Maryland
Michigan
Missouri
New Jersey
Ohio
Pennsylvania
Virginia
Washington DC
West Virginia
Wisconsin

PRODUCTS/OPERATIONS

2016 Sales

	% of total
Retail Banking	44
Corporate and Institutional Banking	35
Asset Management group	8
Residential Mortgage Banking	5
BlackRock	4
Non-Strategic Asset Portfolio	2
Others	2
Total	**100**

2016 Sales

	$ mil.	% of total
Interest		
Loans	7,414	45
Investment securities	1,826	11
Other	412	3
Non-interest		
Asset management	1,521	9
Corporate services	1,504	9
Consumer services	1,388	8
Service charges on deposits	667	4
Residential mortgage	567	4
Other	1,124	7
Total	**16,423**	**100**

Selected Subsidiaries

PNC Bancorp Inc.
 PNC Bank National Association
 PNC Bank Capital Securities LLC
 PNC Capital Leasing LLC
 PNC Preferred Funding LLC
 PNC REIT Corp.
PNC Holding LLC
 PNC Funding Corp
 PNC Investment Corp.
 PNC Venture LLC

COMPETITORS

Bank of America	JPMorgan Chase
Capital One	KeyCorp
Citigroup	M&T Bank
Citizens Financial	Sovereign Bank
Group	TD Bank USA
Fifth Third	U.S. Bancorp
Harris	Wells Fargo
Huntington Bancshares	

HISTORICAL FINANCIALS

Company Type: Public

Income Statement

FYE: December 31

	ASSETS ($ mil.)	NET INCOME ($ mil.)	INCOME AS % OF ASSETS	EMPLOYEES
12/16	366,380	3,903	1.1%	52,006
12/15	358,493	4,106	1.1%	52,513
12/14	345,072	4,184	1.2%	53,587
12/13	320,296	4,220	1.3%	54,433
12/12	305,107	3,013	1.0%	56,285
Annual Growth	**4.7%**	**6.7%**	**—**	**(2.0%)**

2016 Year-End Financials

Debt ratio: 9.60%	No. of shares (mil.): 485
Return on equity: 8.61%	Dividends
Cash ($ mil.): 30,590	Yield: 0.0%
Current ratio: —	Payout: 29.0%
Long-term debt ($ mil.): —	Market value ($ mil.): 56,726

	STOCK PRICE ($) FY Close	P/E High/Low		PER SHARE ($) Earnings	Dividends	Book Value
12/16	116.96	16	10	7.30	2.12	94.22
12/15	95.31	13	11	7.39	2.01	88.71
12/14	91.23	12	10	7.30	1.88	85.18
12/13	77.58	10	8	7.39	1.72	79.56
12/12	58.31	13	10	5.30	1.55	73.87
Annual Growth	**19.0%**		**—**	**8.3%**	**8.1%**	**6.3%**

Polaris Industries Inc.

One of the world's top makers of off-road vehicles Polaris Industries makes and sells all-terrain vehicles (ATVs) and side-by-side recreational and utility RANGER-brand vehicles. It also manufactures snowmobiles on-road vehicles such as the Victory and Indian brands motorcycle and small electric vehicles (SEVs). Offerings include replacement parts accessories (covers windshields backrests) and riding gear (bags and helmets). Polaris' lineup is sold through dealers and distributors in North America Western Europe Australia and Mexico.

Operations

The company operates through three chief segments: Off-Road Vehicles (ORV)/Snowmobiles (around 75% of net sales) Motorcycles (15%) and Global Adjacent Markets (almost 10%).

Polaris? vehicle line-up includes RANGER RZR and Polaris GENERAL side-by-side off-road vehicles; Sportsman and Polaris ACE all-terrain off-road vehicles; Indian Motorcycle midsize and heavyweight motorcycles; Slingshot moto-roadsters; and Polaris RMK INDY Switchback and RUSH snowmobiles.

Geographic Reach

Polaris has about 30 manufacturing and distribution facilities in Alabama California Florida Idaho Iowa Minnesota Ohio South Dakota Texas and Wisconsin. International facilities reside in Australia Canada China France Mexico and Poland. The US represents around 80% of sales while Canada contributes about 10%; the remainder comes from international sales.

Sales and Marketing

Polaris' products are sold through a network of 1800 independent dealers in North America in addition to almost 30 subsidiaries and over 80 distributors in more than 100 countries outside of North America.

The company advertises its products directly to consumers using print advertising and on the internet social media billboards television and radio. It also provides media advertising and produces promotional films for its products which are available to dealers for use in showrooms or at special promotions. It even provides product brochures posters dealer signs and other miscellaneous promotional items for use by dealers.

Financial Performance

After posting record-setting revenues of $4.7 billion in 2015 Polaris saw its revenues decline 4% to $4.5 billion in 2016. The decline was attributed to a 5% volume decrease mainly the result of lower ORV and snowmobile shipments as well as lower retail driven by a weak powersports market and a weaker-than-usual end to the 2016 snow season. Polaris was also negatively affected by foreign currency translations and a lower retail environment driven by the oil and gas producing regions of Canada.

Polaris' profits declined sharply by 53% from $455 million in 2015 to $213 million in 2016. This was due to increased operating expenses stemming from increased legal expenses and other costs related to product recalls. After declining to $440 million in 2015 the company's operating cash flow surged to $572 million in 2016. This was fueled by a $335 million decrease in net working capital.

Strategy

A part of Polaris' strategy involves how it handles product recalls which can damage its public perception and reputation. Throughout 2016 it invoked a voluntary recall for certain off-road vehicles manufactured since model year 2013 due to

reports of thermal-related incidents including fire. When recalls occur Polaris' plan is to act quickly and communicate with its customers as clearly as possible.

Polaris also is optimizing its cost structure and shutting down underperforming products. In early 2017 it announced plans to wind down production of its Victory motorcycles brand which experienced cumulative losses exceeding $100 million. The company estimates the total costs to wind down the brand which has operated for 18 years could be in a range of $50 to $70 million throughout 2017.

Mergers and Acquisitions

Acquisitions as well as internal investments and business alliances are fundamental to Polaris' strategy for building its portfolio and market presence. In late 2016 Polaris purchased Transamerican Auto Parts a manufacturer distributor retailer and installer of off-road Jeep and truck accessories for $669 million. The deal enhanced Polaris' ecommerce platform and bolstered its ability to serve off-road enthusiasts with a variety of Jeep and truck aftermarket accessories.

Earlier in 2016 Polaris enhanced its Global Adjacent Markets segment through the purchase of California-based Taylor-Dunn Manufacturing Company a provider of industrial vehicles serving a broad range of commercial manufacturing warehouse and ground-support customers.

In 2015 Polaris acquired the electric motorcycle business of Brammo in a deal that allowed it to focus exclusively on the design development and integration of electric vehicle powertrains.

Company Background

Originally called Hetteen Hoist & Derrick Polaris Industries was founded in Roseau Minnesota in 1945 by Edgar Hetteen and David Johnson. The friends did welding and repair work and made custom machinery for local farmers.

EXECUTIVES

SVP Customer Experience and Chief Marketing Officer, Timothy M. Larson, age 44

President International, Michael D. Dougherty, age 49

Chairman and CEO, Scott W. Wine, age 49, $985,000 total compensation

EVP Operations Engineering and Lean, Kenneth J. (Ken) Pucel, age 51, $600,000 total compensation

EVP Finance and CFO, Michael T. (Mike) Speetzen, age 47, $550,000 total compensation

President Parts Garments and Accessories, Stephen L. Eastman, age 52, $391,635 total compensation

CTO, Stephen J. Kemp

VP and CIO, Matthew J. Emmerich

President Motorcycles, Steven D. Menneto

VP Snowmobiles, Christopher G. Wolf

SVP Corporate Development and Strategy; President Global Adjacent Markets, Robert P. (Bob) Mack, $295,385 total compensation

President Off-Road Vehicles, Chris Musso

Vice President, Janette Klis

Auditors: Ernst & Young LLP

LOCATIONS

HQ: Polaris Industries Inc.
2100 Highway 55, Medina, MN 55340
Phone: 763 542-0500
Web: www.polaris.com

2016 Sales

	$ mil.	% of total
United States	3,557	79
Canada	307	7
Other foreign countries	652	14
Total	**4,516**	**100**

PRODUCTS/OPERATIONS

2016 Sales

	$ mil.	% of total
ORV/Snowmobiles	3,357	74
Motorcycles	708	16
Global Adjacent Markets	341	8
Other	108	2
Total	**4,516**	**100**

PRODUCTS
Off-Road Vehicles
ACE Single-Seat ORV
General REC Utility Side x Side
RANGER Utility REC Side x Side
RZR Sport Side x Side
Sportsman ATV
Motorcycles
Indian Motorcycle
Victory Motorcycles
Snow
Snowmobiles
Timbersled
Commercial
GEM Electric
Generators
Government & Defense
Lubricants
Slingshot

COMPETITORS

Arctic Cat	Kawasaki Heavy
BMW	Industries
Deere	Kubota
E-Z-GO	Suzuki Motor
Harley-Davidson	Yamaha Motor
Honda	

HISTORICAL FINANCIALS

Company Type: Public

Income Statement

FYE: December 31

	REVENUE ($ mil.)	NET INCOME ($ mil.)	NET PROFIT MARGIN	EMPLOYEES
12/16	4,516	212	4.7%	8,600
12/15	4,719	455	9.6%	8,100
12/14	4,479	454	10.1%	7,000
12/13	3,777	377	10.0%	5,400
12/12	3,209	312	9.7%	4,500
Annual Growth	**8.9%**	**(9.1%)**	**—**	**17.6%**

2016 Year-End Financials

Debt ratio: 36.84%
Return on equity: 22.75%
Cash ($ mil.): 127
Current ratio: 1.24
Long-term debt ($ mil.): 1,138

No. of shares (mil.): 63
Dividends
Yield: 0.0%
Payout: 67.2%
Market value ($ mil.): 5,200

	STOCK PRICE ($) FY Close	P/E High/Low	PER SHARE ($) Earnings	Dividends	Book Value
12/16	82.39	31 21	3.27	2.20	13.88
12/15	85.95	23 12	6.75	2.12	15.18
12/14	151.24	23 17	6.65	1.92	13.19
12/13	145.64	26 15	5.35	1.68	8.29
12/12	84.15	19 12	4.40	1.48	10.06
Annual Growth	**(0.5%)**	**— —**	**(7.2%)**	**10.4%**	**8.4%**

Popular Inc.

Founded in 1893 Popular is the holding company for Banco Popular de Puerto Rico (BPPR) the largest bank on the island with some 170 branches (and around 10 more on the Virgin Is-

lands). In addition to commercial and retail banking services BPPR owns subsidiaries that offer vehicle financing and leasing (Popular Auto) insurance (Popular Insurance) financial advisory and brokerage services (Popular Securities) and mortgages (Popular Mortgage). Popular also owns Banco Popular North America (BPNA) which serves the US Hispanic population from about 50 Popular Community Bank branches in New York Florida and New Jersey.

Operations

Commercial real estate and business loans (mostly in Puerto Rico) make up more than 40% of Popular's loan portfolio while residential mortgage loans made up about 35% and consumer loans comprised an additional 20%. The rest of the portfolio was made up of lease financings and constructions loans.

The bank generates the bulk of its revenue from interest income. Upwards of 65% of its total revenue comes from loan interest while another 10% comes from interest on its investment securities. The remainder of its revenue came from service charges on deposit accounts (nearly 10% of revenue) a mix of credit/debit card insurance trust and other service fees (over 10%) mortgage banking income (2%) and other non-interest sources.

Popular's other financial services include the insurance agency and reinsurance businesses of Popular Insurance Popular Insurance V.I. Popular Risk Services and Popular Life Re. BPNA also owns E-LOAN Popular Equipment Finance and Popular Insurance Agency USA. E-LOAN's sole purpose is to provide an online platform to raise deposits for BPNA.

Geographic Reach

Popular operates over 230 branches and almost 50 E-Loan and other subsidiary offices including 180 Banco Popular de Puerto Rico branches in Puerto Rico 33 branches in New York and others in south Florida New Jersey and the Virgin Islands. Over 80% of the bank's loan assets are based in Puerto Rico.

Financial Performance

Popular's revenue climbed 2% to $1.6 billion in fiscal 2016 (ended December) due to higher interest income. The company's revenue has been unsteady since 2011 up one year and down the next.

Net income of $216.7 million was 76% lower than the previous year mostly due to an exceptional income tax benefit (on a valuation allowance reversal related to its US operations) recorded in 2015.

Cash from operating activities fell 12% to $589.5 million.

Strategy

Popular looks to expand its branch reach while bolstering its loan and deposit business by acquiring smaller banks in its target markets. It also continued in 2015 to restructure its US business selling its operations in California Chicago and central Florida to focus more on its business in the New York metro and Miami regions. Even with the cutbacks in the US organic commercial loan assets through Popular Community Bank swelled by 42% during 2015.

Popular has also been moving toward digital banking channels that are quickly taking the industry by storm allowing it to slow expensive branch-expansion plans and cut operating costs significantly while giving customers faster access to banking services. As a testament to this about 592000 customers in Puerto Rico used its Mi Banco online channel during 2015 with 67% of those customers using mobile devices to do so. Additionally 29% of Banco Popular de Puerto Rico deposit transactions were made through ATMs or mobile devices that year.

Mergers and Acquisitions

In February 2015 Popular purchased receivership-status Doral Bank from the FDIC including $1 billion in deposits from eight of its Puerto Rican branches its online deposit platform $848 million in performing Puerto Rico residential and commercial loans $1.3 billion in deposits from three New York branches and $931 million in performing commercial loans based primarily in the New York City metro area. The deal brought stability to Puerto Rico's banking sector.

Company Background

To broaden its target audience beyond the Hispanic community Popular rebranded itself in the US switching its name from "Banco Popular" to "Popular Community Bank". The change which was initially begun in pilot markets in 2010 was completed officially in 2012 when the company changed its name in New York City.

EXECUTIVES

Chairman, Richard L. Carri n, age 64, $1,453,846 total compensation
EVP Financial and Insurance, Juan O. Guerrero, age 57, $375,000 total compensation
EVP Administration, Eduardo J. Negr n, age 52, $385,000 total compensation
EVP and COO Popular Community Bank, Manuel Chinea, age 51
EVP Retail Banking, N ©stor O. Rivera, age 70, $375,000 total compensation
EVP and CFO, Carlos J. V zquez, age 58, $700,962 total compensation
EVP and Chief Risk Officer, Lidio V. Soriano, age 48, $519,231 total compensation
President and CEO, Ignacio lvarez, age 58, $742,500 total compensation
EVP Commercial Credit, Eli S. Sep lveda, age 54, $420,000 total compensation
EVP Individual Credit, Gilberto F. Monz n, age 57
EVP and Chief Legal Officer, Javier D. Ferrer, age 55, $571,154 total compensation
EVP CTO and Chief Digital Officer, Camille Burckhart, age 38
First Vice President, Jorge Roig
Executive Vice President Individual Credit Banco Popular de Puerto Rico, Gilberto Monzon
Assistant Vice President Loan Operations Manager, Deborah Monaco
Vice President, Andrew Boland
Senior Vice President and Division Head of the Corporate Compliance Division, Marilu Jimenez
Vice President, Pauline Pisciotta
Assistant Vice President, Laura Torres
Senior Vice President, Jose Vazquez
Senior Vice President and Division Manager, Oran Bowry
Vice President, David Shahrabani
Account Vice President and Retirement Plans Administration Supervisor, Carla Conde
Vice President International Private Banking, David Hitt
Auditors: PricewaterhouseCoopers LLP

LOCATIONS

HQ: Popular Inc.
  Popular Center Building, 209 Munoz Rivera Avenue, Hato Rey, San Juan 00918
Phone: 787 765 9800
Web: www.popular.com

PRODUCTS/OPERATIONS

Sales 2016

	$ mil.	% of total
Interest income:	1,459	67
Loans	16	1
Money market investments	152	7
Investment securities	6	0

Non-interest income:		
Service charges on deposit accounts	160	8
Other service fees	234	12
Mortgage banking activities	56	2
Net gain (loss) and valuation adjustments on investment securities	2	0
Other-than-temporary impairment losses on investment securities	(0.2)	-
Trading account (loss) profit	(0.8)	-
Net gain on sale of loans including valuation adjustments on loans held-for-sale	8	0
Adjustments (expense) to indemnity reserves on loans sold	(17.2)	-
FDIC loss-share (expense) income	(207.8)	-
Other operating income	61	3
Total	**1,923**	**100**

Selected Subsidiaries and Affiliates

Banco Popular de Puerto Rico
  BP Sirenusa International LLC (US)
  Popular Auto Inc.
  Popular Mortgage Inc.
Popular Capital Trust I (US)
Popular Insurance Inc.
Popular International Bank Inc.
  Banco Popular North America (US)
  E-LOAN Inc.
  Equity One Inc.
  Popular Insurance V.I. Inc. (US Virgin Islands)
Popular Life RE
Popular Securities Inc.

COMPETITORS

Bank of America	JPMorgan Chase
Bolivar Banco Venezuela	OFG Bancorp
	RBC Financial Group
Citigroup	Santander BanCorp
First BanCorp (Puerto Rico)	Scotiabank

HISTORICAL FINANCIALS

Company Type: Public

Income Statement

FYE: December 31

	ASSETS ($ mil.)	NET INCOME ($ mil.)	INCOME AS % OF ASSETS	EMPLOYEES
12/16	38,661	216	0.6%	7,828
12/15	35,769	895	2.5%	7,810
12/14	33,096	(313)	—	7,752
12/13	35,749	599	1.7%	8,059
12/12	36,507	245	0.7%	8,072
Annual Growth	1.4%	(3.1%)	—	(0.8%)

2016 Year-End Financials

Debt ratio: 2.33%	No. of shares (mil.): 103
Return on equity: 4.19%	Dividends
Cash ($ mil.): 11,498	Yield: 0.0%
Current ratio: —	Payout: 29.1%
Long-term debt ($ mil.): —	Market value ($ mil.): 4,548

	STOCK PRICE ($) FY Close	P/E High/Low	PER SHARE ($) Earnings	Dividends	Book Value
12/16	43.82	22 11	2.06	0.60	50.08
12/15	28.34	4 3	8.65	0.30	49.27
12/14	34.05	— —	(3.08)	0.00	41.24
12/13	28.73	6 4	5.78	0.00	44.74
12/12	20.79	9 1	2.35	0.00	39.84
Annual Growth	20.5%	— —	(3.2%)	—	5.9%

Post Holdings Inc

Breakfast food company Post Holdings has a healthy appetite. The maker of Grape-Nuts Toasties Honey Bunches of Oats Raisin Bran Shredded Wheat Bran Flakes Pebbles and Alpha-Bits Post is the third-best-selling breakfast cereal brand in the US behind Kellogg and General Mills). As well as cereal the company also makes egg products potato products and cheese pasta and other dairy-based products. More recently it has moved beyond the breakfast table by adding snacks active nutrition products and pasta through a series of major acquisitions. It also manufactures nut butters and cereals for private labels. The company has warehouses manufacturing facilities and distribution facilities located throughout the US and Canada.

Operations

Post operates four business segments: Michael Foods Post Consumer Brands Active Nutrition and Private Brands.

Michael Foods accounts for around 45% of revenue and sells refrigerated egg products; potato products; and cheese pasta and other dairy products. Egg products include Better 'N Eggs All Whites and Papetti's among others. Its potato brands are primarily Simply Potatoes and Diner's Choice; and its main cheese pasta and other dairy brand is Crystal Farms.

Post Consumer Brands generates around 35% of total company sales and makes ready-to-eat cereal products such as Honey Bunches of Oats Shreddies Pebbles Great Grains and Alpha-Bits among others.

The Active Nutrition (10% of sales) makes high-protein drinks bars and gels under the Premier Protein Dymatize Supreme Protein and PowerBar brands.

Post's Private Brand manufacturing operation (10% of sales) makes peanut and other nut butters for third-parties primarily in the US and Canada. The segment also includes the Attune Foods business which makes natural cereals and snacks such as Uncle Sam cereals Attune probiotic bars Erewhon gluten-free cereals.

Geographic Reach

Post in headquartered in Missouri. More than 90% of the company's products are sold to customers in the US. The Post Consumer Brands segment has eight owned manufacturing facilities while Michael Foods owns six egg products production facilities.

Sales and Marketing

Post Holdings deploys a variety of consumer-targeted marketing campaigns across television digital and print advertisement coupon offers co-op advertising with certain retail customers and co-marketing arrangements with complementary consumer product companies. It also utilizes traditional billboard print digital and social media advertising as well as grass-roots advertising using sampling events and business drops.

Retail giant Wal-Mart Stores is the company's largest customer accounting for around 15% of total sales. Michael Foods serves foodservice distributors restaurant chains and major retail grocery chains with its largest customers being Sysco and US Foods which accounted for 14% and 12% of sales respectively. Private Brands products are sold in natural and specialty grocery stores such as Whole Foods and Trader Joe's which together account for 25% of the segment's sales.

Financial Performance

After a game-changing fiscal 2015 that saw Post more than double its revenue the company maintained its upward trajectory in fiscal 2016 (ended September) by growing its top line 8% to $5.0 billion.

The growth came from the first full-year contributions from businesses acquired in 2015 particularly MOM Brands and from Willamette Egg Farms acquired part-way through fiscal 2016. Beyond acquisitions Post recorded organic growth in Premier Protein products and ready-to-eat cereal peanut butter and private brand granola. Egg potato cheese pasta products saw sales decline.

Post incurred a net loss of $3.3 million in fiscal 2016 an improvement on the losses of $115 million and $343 million recorded in fiscals 2015 and 2014. The narrowing loss was a result of profit contributions of the acquired businesses.

Cash from operating activities increased 11% or $50.8 million to $502.4 million. As before incremental contributions from the acquired businesses drive operating cash growth as did higher organic earnings from Post Consumer Brands Michael Food and Active Nutrition.

Strategy

Post Holdings has continued to move beyond breakfast cereal into higher-growth categories including snacks sports nutrition supplements and weight loss. The company's recent feeding frenzy of food companies included the $2.45 billion acquisition of Michael Foods its largest-ever which gave it the Simply Potatoes All Whites and Crystal Farms brands. The acquisitions demonstrate its willingness to adapt to shifts in consumer tastes such as capitalizing on the popularity of high-protein products and away-from-home snacks.

Post made a major move into the UK with the purchase of British breakfast food firm Weetabix in 2017. As well as its famous eponymous wheat bricks Weetabix owns Alpen Weetos and Oatibix.

Mergers and Acquisitions

Post has made a ton of acquisitions in recent years. In 2017 it acquired UK cereal maker Weetabix in a $1.76 billion deal. The acquisition which includes the Weetabix Alpen Barbara's Puffins and other cereal brands expands Post's international market presence and bolsters Weetabix's brand presence in the US. Also that year the company agreed to purchase Bob Evans Farms which makes refrigerated potato and veggie side dishes and convenience food items as well as pork sausage. The deal will expand Post's refrigerated offerings portfolio strengthen its presence in commercial foodservice and move it into breakfast sausage.

In 2016 it acquired National Pasteurized Eggs an Illinois-based egg producer and in 2015 another egg producer Willamette Egg Farms. Also in 2015 it acquired MOM Brands a market leader in the ready-to-eat value cereal segment.

Company Background

Prior to the spinoff Post represented Ralcorp's branded cereal segment which was in decline. (Ralcorp acquired Post from Kraft Foods in 2008 for about $2.7 billion but its success with the brand was sporadic.) In the end Ralcorp decided to launch Post on its own to focus on its own burgeoning private-label food business.The acquisition in 2014 of Michael Foods transformed the business more than doubling its revenue. It followed Michael Foods up with two other major purchases MOM Brands in 2015 and Weetabix in 2017.

EXECUTIVES

Chairman, William P. (Bill) Stiritz, age 82
EVP; President and CEO Private Brands, Richard R. Koulouris, age 61, $521,875 total compensation
SVP and CFO, Jeff A. Zadoks, age 52, $462,500 total compensation
EVP; President and CEO Michael Foods Group, James E. (Jim) Dwyer, $657,692 total compensation
President and CEO, Robert V. Vitale, $975,000 total compensation
President and CEO Post Consumer Brands, Christopher J. Neugent, $619,988 total compensation
SVP General Counsel and Chief Administrative Officer, Diedre Gray, $347,083 total compensation
Vice President Business Solutions and Application Development, Peter Hogan

Vice President of Architecture and Operations, Brian Hofmeister
Regional Vice President, Lori Brown
Vice President and General Counsel, Jill Bollettieri
Regional Vice President, Don Larson
Regional Vice President Sales, Bob Burnson
Senior Vice President and Chief Procurement Officer, Brian Palmer
Vice President of, Pete Hogan
Senior Vice President Quality and Food Safety, Dan Ludwig
Senior Vice President Human Resources and Chief Compliance Officer, Nicole Bolton
Vice President Quality and Food Safety Post Consumer Brands, John Batz
DIVISION VICE PRESIDENT OF INFORMATION TECHNOLOGY PCB, Richard E Colestock
VICE PRESIDENT SUPPLY CHAIN, Carla E Carver
VICE PRESIDENT MARKETING, David Bagozzi
VICE PRESIDENT OF TAX, Edward T Short
Auditors: PricewaterhouseCoopers LLP

LOCATIONS

HQ: Post Holdings Inc
2503 S. Hanley Road, St. Louis, MO 63144
Phone: 314 644-7600
Web: www.postholdings.com

PRODUCTS/OPERATIONS

2016 Sales

	$ mil.	% of total
Michael Foods Group	2,184	44
Post Consumer Brands	1,728	34
Active Nutrition	574	11
Private Brands	540	11
Eliminations	(1.2)	-
Total	**5,026**	**100**

Selected Products

Alpha-Bits
Attune
Bran Flakes
Fruity Pebbles
Golden Crisp
golden Temple
Grape-Nuts
Great Grains
Honey Bunches of Oats
Honeycomb
Joint Juice
Peace Cereal
Premier Protein
Raisin Bran

Selects Blueberry Morning

Shredded Wheat
Sweet Home Farm
Toasties
Uncle Sam
Waffle Crisp

COMPETITORS

Abbott Nutrition	Nature's Path
American Italian Pasta	Nestl ©
Clif Bar	New World Pasta
ConAgra	Nissin Food Products
Danone	PepsiCo
General Mills	Weetabix
Gilster-Mary Lee	Wessanen
Kellogg	granoVita
NBTY	

HISTORICAL FINANCIALS

Company Type: Public

Income Statement

FYE: September 30

	REVENUE ($ mil.)	NET INCOME ($ mil.)	NET PROFIT MARGIN	EMPLOYEES
09/17	5,225	48	0.9%	11,410
09/16	5,026	(3)	—	8,700
09/15	4,648	(115)	—	8,500
09/14	2,411	(343)	—	7,950
09/13	1,034	15	1.5%	1,600
Annual Growth	**49.9%**	**33.5%**	**—**	**63.4%**

2017 Year-End Financials

Debt ratio: 60.38%
Return on equity: 1.67%
Cash ($ mil.): 1,525
Current ratio: 3.71
Long-term debt ($ mil.): 7,149

No. of shares (mil.): 66
Dividends
　Yield: —
　Payout: —
Market value ($ mil.): 5,835

	STOCK PRICE ($) FY Close	P/E High/Low	Earnings	Dividends	Book Value
09/17	88.27	173 139	0.50	0.00	42.06
09/16	77.17	— —	(0.41)	0.00	46.36
09/15	59.10	— —	(2.33)	0.00	49.35
09/14	33.18	— —	(9.03)	0.00	53.10
09/13	40.37	164 100	0.30	0.00	48.50
Annual Growth	**21.6%**	**— —**	**13.6%**	**—**	**(3.5%)**

PowerShares DB Commodity Index Tracking Fund

Auditors: PricewaterhouseCoopers LLP

LOCATIONS

HQ: PowerShares DB Commodity Index Tracking Fund
c/o Invesco PowerShares Capital Management LLC,
3500 Lacey Road, Suite 700, Downers Grove, IL 60515
Phone: 800 983-0903
Web: www.invescopowershares.com

HISTORICAL FINANCIALS

Company Type: Public

Income Statement

FYE: December 31

	ASSETS ($ mil.)	NET INCOME ($ mil.)	INCOME AS % OF ASSETS	EMPLOYEES
12/16	2,559	(13)	—	—
12/15	2,011	(25)	—	—
12/14	4,948	(45)	—	—
12/13	6,799	(53)	—	—
12/12	6,614	(50)	—	—
Annual Growth	**(21.1%)**			

2016 Year-End Financials

Debt ratio: —
Return on equity: (-0.60%)
Cash ($ mil.): 5
Current ratio: —
Long-term debt ($ mil.): —

No. of shares (mil.): 161
Dividends
　Yield: —
　Payout: —
Market value ($ mil.): 2,560

	STOCK PRICE ($) FY Close	P/E High/Low	Earnings	Dividends	Book Value
12/16	15.84	— —	(0.09)	0.00	15.83
12/15	13.36	— —	(0.15)	0.00	13.35
12/14	18.45	— —	(0.21)	0.00	18.40
12/13	25.66	— —	(0.21)	0.00	25.61
12/12	27.78	— —	(0.22)	0.00	27.72
Annual Growth	**(13.1%)**	**— —**	**—**	**—**	**(13.1%)**

PPG Industries Inc

Thanks to its extensive range of paints coatings and other product offerings you won't catch PPG Industries painting itself into a corner. Performance and industrial coatings — such as paints (Pittsburgh Paints Comex and SIGMA) stains (Olympic) and sealants — account for most of its sales; the remainder comes from glass materials. PPG's glass offerings include fiberglass used in construction energy and transportation. The company sold its chemical commodities and flat glass businesses to focus on its core coating and glass segments.

HISTORY

After the failure of his first two plate-glass manufacturing plants John Ford persuaded former railroad superintendent John Pitcairn to invest $200000 in a third factory in 1883 in Creighton Pennsylvania. The enterprise Pittsburgh Plate Glass (PPG) became the first commercially successful US plate-glass factory.

Ford left in 1896 after Pitcairn established a company distribution system replacing glass jobbers. Ford went on to found a predecessor of competitor Libbey-Owens-Ford (now owned by glassmaker Pilkington).

Pitcairn built a soda ash plant in 1899 bought a Milwaukee paint company the following year and began producing window glass in 1908. Pitcairn died in 1916 leaving his stock to his sons.

Strong automobile and construction markets in the early 20th century increased demand for the company's products. In 1924 PPG revolutionized glass production with the introduction of a straight-line conveyor manufacturing method. In the 1930s and 1940s PPG successfully promoted structural glass for use in the commercial construction industry.

PPG was listed on the NYSE in 1945. In 1952 it started making fiberglass and in 1968 the company adopted its present name.

Vincent Sarni (CEO 1984-93) recognized that 85% of the company's sales were to the maturing construction and automobile industries. Sarni decided to move the company into growing industries such as electronics.

In 1986 PPG spent $154 million on acquisitions including the medical electronics units of Litton Industries and Honeywell. It acquired the medical technology business of Allegheny International in 1987 and bought Casco Nobel a coatings distributor and the Olympic and Lucite paint lines from Clorox in 1989.

The company which owned one-third of Dutch fiberglass producer Silenka BV acquired the rest in 1991. In 1992 PPG acquired a silica plant in the Netherlands its first in Europe. Two years later it acquired the European automotive coatings business of Netherlands-based Akzo Nobel.

In the 1990s PPG backed away from Sarni's earlier strategies for greater diversification and unloaded a number of high-tech businesses. The firm refocused on its core coatings glass and chemicals operations. PPG acquired Matthews Paints a leading maker of paints for outdoor signs and the refinish coating business of Lilly Industries in 1995.

The company bolstered its chemical operations in 1997 with the addition of France's Sipsy Chime Fine. That same year President and COO Raymond LeBoeuf took over as CEO. In 1998 PPG sold its European flat and automotive glass business to Belgium-based Glaverbel. Acquisitions that year included Australia-based Orica's technical coatings unit and the US paint operations (Porter Paints) of Akzo Nobel.

In 1999 PPG expanded its European coatings business with the purchase of Belgium-based Sigma Coatings' commercial transport coatings unit and Akzo Nobel's aircraft coatings and sealants company PRC-DeSoto International. That year PPG also bought Imperial Chemical Industries' Germany-based coatings business for large commercial vehicles and its US-based auto refinish and industrial coatings businesses. PPG's acquisition spree continued in 2000 with architectural coating maker Monarch Paint.

Early in the new decade PPG suffered from flat or declining earnings from existing operations. Amid falling sales and lower prices for chemicals and glass PPG began to cut jobs and closed some facilities. Still the company recorded its first loss in more than 10 years in 2002 and its second straight year of declining sales.

Like many manufacturers in its industry PPG has been exposed to potentially costly asbestos litigation mainly because of its 50% stake in the bankrupt Pittsburgh Corning a joint venture with Corning that made insulation with asbestos. In 2002 PPG and its insurers agreed to pay roughly $2.7 billion to settle its asbestos claims.

LeBoeuf retired in 2005. He was replaced by president and COO Charles Bunch who had joined the company in 1979 and worked up through the ranks of first the finance department and then the coatings operations.

In 2008 PPG acquired SigmaKalon for $3 billion. SigmaKalon was among the top 10 paint manufacturers in the world and did business almost entirely outside the US. The company now operates as PPG's Architectural Coatings segment. That same year PPG sold its auto glass business to private equity group Kohlberg & Company which set the unit up as a stand-alone company called Pittsburgh Glass Works. PPG received $330 million plus a 40% interest in the company.

In 2011 PPG acquired Equa-Chlor a producer of chlorine caustic soda and muriatic acid for $27 million. Equa-Chlor produces about 220 tons of chlorine per day. In addition to its products PPG also bought Equa-Chlor's distribution system which includes a railcar fleet it integrated into its own. The deal for the Washington state-based company bolsters PPG's chlor-alkali business in the Northwest US and expands its overall supply chain.

As part of its push to expand in emerging markets in 2011 PPG formed a joint venture with an India-based company Harsha Exito Engineering Private to produce fiber glass reinforcement products.

It made two foreign acquisitions to expand its international operations in 2011. First it bought the business assets of Ducol Coatings South Africa Ltd. which had served as an importer and distributor of PPG's automotive refinish products in South Africa since 2003. PPG also expanded its joint venture with India-based Asian Paints (India's largest coatings company) and created a second 50-50 JV in 2012. The deals boosts PPG's position in the Chinese and Asian packaging coatings industry part of its global strategy to expand into emerging regions.

During 2012 the company made four acquisitions related to its coatings business for a total of $288 million including US-based Spraylat Corp. Denmark based Dyrup A/S and the coatings business of Ecuador-based Colpisa Colombiana de Pinturas.

Expanding PPG's architectural coatings business in the US Canada and the Caribbean in 2013 it bought Azko Nobel's North American Decorative Paints business for $1.05 billion.

EXECUTIVES

Chairman and CEO, Michael H. McGarry, age 59, $1,100,000 total compensation

EVP, Viktoras R. Sekmakas, age 56, $646,667 total compensation

SVP Architectural Coatings; President PPG EMEA, Jean-Marie Greindl, age 54

VP Science and Technology and CTO, David S. Bem

President PPG Asia Pacific and VP Protective and Marine Coatings Asia Pacific, Michael Horton

SVP Industrial Coatings, Timothy M. Knavish, age 51, $438,333 total compensation

VP Coatings Services; President MetoKote, Jeffrey J. Oravitz

Chief Commercial Officer PPG Comex, Henrik Bergstr ¶m, age 46

SVP and CFO, Vincent J. Morales, age 52

VP Information Technology, Christopher R. Caruso

SVP Protective and Marine Coatings, Ramaparasad (Ram) Vadlamannati, age 54

Executive Vice President, Eiji Hamaoka

Auditors: PricewaterhouseCoopers LLP

LOCATIONS

HQ: PPG Industries Inc
One PPG Place, Pittsburgh, PA 15272
Phone: 412 434-3131
Web: www.ppg.com

2016 Sales

	$ mil.	% of total
United States and Canada	6,595	45
Europe Middle East and Africa	4,304	29
Asia Pacific	2,431	16
Latin America	1,421	10
Total	**14,751**	**100**

PRODUCTS/OPERATIONS

2016 Sales

	$ mil.	% of total
Performance Coatings	8,580	58
Industrial Coatings	5,690	39
Glass	481	3
Total	**14,751**	**100**

Selected Products

Performance Coatings
  Aerospace coatings
  Architectural coatings (Lucite paints Olympic stains)
  Refinish
Industrial Coatings
  Automotive coatings chemicals adhesives and sealants
  Industrial coatings
  Packaging coatings (food and beverage containers)
Commodity Chemicals
  Calcium hypochlorite
  Caustic soda
  Chlorine
  Chlorine derivatives
  Phosgene derivatives
Optical and Specialty Materials
  Optical products (Transitions variable-tint lenses)
  Silica products
Glass
  Aircraft transparencies

Coated glass
Continuous-strand fiberglass
Flat glass

COMPETITORS

3M	KANSAI PAINT CO. LTD.
Akzo Nobel	Kelly-Moore
Axalta Coating Systems	Nippon Paint
BASF Coatings AG	Nippon Sheet Glass
BEHR	Pilkington Group
Benjamin Moore	RPM International
Dow Chemical	Sherwin-Williams
Ferro	Valspar

HISTORICAL FINANCIALS

Company Type: Public

Income Statement

FYE: December 31

	REVENUE ($ mil.)	NET INCOME ($ mil.)	NET PROFIT MARGIN	EMPLOYEES
12/17	14,750	1,591	10.8%	47,200
12/16	14,751	877	5.9%	47,000
12/15	15,330	1,406	9.2%	46,600
12/14	15,360	2,102	13.7%	44,400
12/13	15,108	3,231	21.4%	41,400
Annual Growth	**(0.6%)**	**(16.2%)**	**—**	**3.3%**

2017 Year-End Financials

Debt ratio: 25.07%	No. of shares (mil.): 251
Return on equity: 30.64%	Dividends
Cash ($ mil.): 1,436	Yield: 0.0%
Current ratio: 1.66	Payout: 27.5%
Long-term debt ($ mil.): 4,134	Market value ($ mil.): 29,342

	STOCK PRICE ($) FY Close	P/E High/Low		PER SHARE ($) Earnings	Dividends	Book Value
12/17	116.82	19	15	6.17	1.70	22.13
12/16	94.76	35	27	3.28	1.56	18.75
12/15	98.82	46	16	5.14	1.42	18.67
12/14	231.15	31	23	7.52	1.31	19.05
12/13	189.66	17	12	11.14	1.21	17.79
Annual Growth	**(11.4%)**	—	—	**(13.7%)**	**8.9%**	**5.6%**

PPL Corp

PPL packs a powerful punch in Kentucky Pennsylvania Tennessee Virginia and the UK. It distributes electricity to 10 million customers through regulated subsidiaries PPL Electric Utilities two utilities in Kentucky and Western Power Distribution Holdings in the UK. The company has more than 19000 MW of generating capacity. Western Power Distribution operates four of the 15 distribution networks providing electricity service in the UK though WPD (South West) and WPD (South Wales). In 2015 PPL sold its competitive energy operations in order to focus on its regulated utility businesses.

HISTORY

PPL's wires reach back to Lehigh Coal & Navigation which was formed in 1822 to mine Pennsylvania coal and build a canal to deliver it to Philadelphia. Heavy industry and steel mills flourished in the Lehigh Valley and Thomas Edison formed small electric companies to serve the area in the early 1880s. Rivals soon followed and by 1900 there were 64 companies in what would become PPL's territory.

Lehigh formed Lehigh Navigation Electric in 1912 to provide power to its coal mines only to lose control of the company to conglomerate Electric Bond & Share in 1917. S. Z. Mitchell Electric Bond & Share's president merged the renamed Lehigh Valley Light & Power with six other utilities to form Pennsylvania Power & Light (PP&L) in Allentown in 1920. The next year PP&L became a subsidiary of National Power & Light.

PP&L bought more than 60 neighboring utilities in a decade and by 1930 industrial customers accounted for 70% of power sales. The company also built a 220000-volt transmission interconnection line with neighbors Philadelphia Electric (now PECO Energy a unit of Exelon) and Public Service Electric and Gas of New Jersey (now part of Public Service Enterprise Group). During the Depression the company offset falling industrial sales with residential sales.

The Public Utility Holding Company Act of 1935 forced large utility holding companies to streamline their businesses and by 1948 National Power & Light had unloaded PP&L.

To keep up with postwar demand PP&L built several coal-fired power plants. By 1964 industry still accounted for about a third of sales but suburbs assumed greater importance. PP&L began operating coal mines in the early 1970s and started building the Susquehanna nuclear plant.

Although its proprietary coal supply helped PP&L weather skyrocketing fuel costs in the 1970s huge construction delays endemic to nukes hit the utility for $4 billion by the time Susquehanna was completed in 1982. Flat sales in the late 1980s led to 2000 job cuts and to a reorganization by CEO William Hecht.

In 1992 the federal Energy Policy Act signaled the end of the monopoly era by promoting wholesale competition. PP&L formed Power Markets Development (now PPL Global) in 1994 to make energy investments worldwide. The next year it created holding company PP&L Resources to house both regulated and non-regulated businesses.

The Customer Choice Act was passed in Pennsylvania in 1996 ushering in competition and the utility formed its non-regulated retail power sales arm PP&L EnergyPlus. PP&L also bought 25% of Chile's Empresas Emel in 1997 (upped to 67% 1999). Fellow US utility Southern Company which bought UK utility SWEB in 1995 had turned over a 51% stake in SWEB to PP&L Resources by 1998.

PP&L Resources began buying mechanical contracting firms in 1998 to complement its electric business and it purchased natural gas and propane distributor Penn Fuel Gas.

In 1999 the company bought generating facilities with a total capacity of 1315 MW from Montana Power. Also that year PP&L Resources and Southern sold SWEB's supply business and the SWEB brand name to London Electricity a unit of Electricit © de France. PP&L Resources and Southern retained their stakes in SWEB's distribution network which was renamed Western Power Distribution (later changed to WPD Holdings UK after it acquired British utility Hyder in 2000).

PP&L Resources changed its name to PPL Corporation in 2000 and reorganized into four major operating subsidiaries: PPL Utilities PPL EnergyPlus PPL Generation and PPL Global. PPL's restructuring efforts separated its regulated distribution operations from its non-regulated generation supply and services operations.

In 2002 PPL's Brazilian utility Companhia Energ ©tica do Maranh o (Cemar) filed for bankruptcy protection and fell under the control of the Brazilian government. (PPL divested its interest in Cemar in 2004.) Also in 2002 PPL purchased the remaining 49% stake in WPD Holdings UK (now Western Power Distribution Holdings) from Mirant (now GenOn Energy) for $235 million.

In 2007 the company sold its Latin American companies as well as its domestic telecommunications and synthetic fuels businesses.

In 2008 PPL sold its US propane and gas distribution unit.

Buoyed by a rebounding economy in 2010 PPL acquired E.ON U.S. the owner of Kentucky's two major utilities Louisville Gas & Electric and Kentucky Utilities for $7.6 billion. The utilities serve 1.2 million customers primarily in Kentucky. The deal made PPL stronger (with 19000 MW of generating capacity) and more geographically diverse.

Expanding its regulated power operations in 2011 the company acquired the UK's #2 electric distribution business WPD Midlands Holdings (formerly Central Networks) for $5.7 billion. The deal gave the company greater market share in the UK and added to 2011 earnings and cash flow. In 2012 and 2013 PPL invested in several projects to upgrade the UK distribution system.

In 2011 to raise cash PPL sold its stakes in some non-core generating stations in the US to an affiliate of LS Power Equity for $381 million. The company was also pursuing further rate increases across its service areas in order to defray costs.

Growing its US power capacity in 2012 PPL acquired AES Ironwood and AES Prescott which together own and operate the 705 MW AES Ironwood natural gas-fired power plant in Lebanon Pennsylvania from a unit of AES Corporation for $302 million.

EXECUTIVES

President and COO LG&E and KU Energy, Paul W. Thompson
Chairman and CEO LG&E and KU Energy, Victor A. Staffieri, age 61, $811,220 total compensation
CHief Executive Western Power Distribution, Robert A. Symons, age 63, $741,127 total compensation
Chairman President and CEO, William H. Spence, age 59, $1,154,712 total compensation
President PPL Electric Utilities, Gregory N. Dudkin, age 59, $524,143 total compensation
SVP and CFO, Vincent (Vince) Sorgi, age 45, $524,134 total compensation
Vice President Administration and Inside Sales and Marketing Coordinator, Barb Sipe
Vice President of Marketing, Linda Miller
Vice President Sales, Daniel Persa
Vice President Operations, James Miller
Vice President Finance and Treasurer, Mark Wilten
Vice President, Michael Kroboth
Executive Vice President General Counsel and Secretary, Robert Grey
Vice President, John Barbera
Vice President and Chief Information Security Officer, Mark Brooks
Board Member, Joe Macieunas
ASSISTANT TREASURER, Tadd J Henninger
Auditors: Ernst & Young LLP

LOCATIONS

HQ: PPL Corp
Two North Ninth Street, Allentown, PA 18101-1179
Phone: 610 774-5151
Web: www.pplweb.com

2015 Sales

	$ mil.	% of total
US	5,259	68
UK	2,410	32
Total	**7,669**	**100**

PRODUCTS/OPERATIONS

2015 Sales

	$ mil.	% of total
Utility	2,410	31
Kentucky Regulated	3,115	41
Pennsylvania Regulated including corporate and others	2,144	28
Total	**7,669**	**100**

Selected Subsidiaries

PPL Development Corporation (acquisition and divestiture activities)
PPL Electric Utilities Corporation (electricity distribution)
PPL Energy Supply (nonregulated operations)
  PPL EnergyPlus LLC (wholesale and retail energy marketing)
  PPL Generation LLC (electricity generation)
  PPL Montana LLC (electricity generation)
  PPL Global LLC (international utility operations)
  Western Power Distribution Holdings Limited (formerly WPD Holdings UK electricity distribution)
PPL Services Corporation (shared services for PPL Corp. and other subsidiaries)

COMPETITORS

ABB	Green Mountain Energy
AEP	HC Energa
Avangrid	Maine & Maritimes
Canadian Utilities	Midwest Generation
Centrica	Ontario Power
Con Edison	Generation
Constellation Energy	Orange & Rockland
Group	Utilities
Covanta	Pepco Holdings
Delmarva Power	Public Service
Dominion Energy	Enterprise Group
Duke Energy	Scottish and Southern
Duquesne Light	Energy
Holdings	South Jersey
EnergySolve	Industries
Exelon	Southern Company
FirstEnergy	TransAlta

HISTORICAL FINANCIALS

Company Type: Public

Income Statement

FYE: December 31

	REVENUE ($ mil.)	NET INCOME ($ mil.)	NET PROFIT MARGIN	EMPLOYEES
12/16	7,517	1,902	25.3%	12,689
12/15	7,669	682	8.9%	12,799
12/14	11,499	1,737	15.1%	17,391
12/13	11,860	1,130	9.5%	18,108
12/12	12,286	1,526	12.4%	17,729
Annual Growth	**(11.6%)**	**5.7%**	**—**	**(8.0%)**

2016 Year-End Financials

Debt ratio: 50.24%
Return on equity: 19.14%
Cash ($ mil.): 341
Current ratio: 0.54
Long-term debt ($ mil.): 17,808

No. of shares (mil.): 679
Dividends
  Yield: 0.0%
  Payout: 54.4%
Market value ($ mil.): 23,145

	STOCK PRICE ($) FY Close	P/E High/Low	PER SHARE ($) Earnings	Dividends	Book Value
12/16	34.05	14 11	2.79	1.52	14.56
12/15	34.13	36 29	1.01	1.50	14.72
12/14	36.33	14 11	2.61	1.49	20.47
12/13	30.09	18 15	1.76	1.47	19.78
12/12	28.63	12 10	2.60	1.44	18.01
Annual Growth	**4.4%**	**— —**	**1.8%**	**1.4%**	**(5.2%)**

Praxair Inc

Praxair makes lighter-than-air and heavier-than-air gases. The largest North American industrial gas supplier it produces and sells atmospheric gases (oxygen nitrogen argon and rare gases) as well as process and specialty gases (CO2 helium and hydrogen) for the chemicals food and beverage semiconductor and healthcare industries worldwide. It serves around 10 industries across more than 50 countries. Its Praxair Surface Technologies unit supplies high-temperature and corrosion-resistant metallic ceramic and powder coatings mainly to the aircraft plastics and primary metals markets. In a long-running saga Praxair and German gases comapny Linde have agreed to merge in a deal worth $80 billion.

HISTORY

The origins of Praxair date to the work of Karl von Linde a professor of mechanical engineering at the College of Technology in Munich Germany in the late 1800s. In 1895 he created the cryogenic air liquefier. Von Linde built his first oxygen-production plant in 1902 and a nitrogen plant in 1904 and in the first decade of the 20th century he built a number of air-separation plants throughout Europe.

By 1907 von Linde had moved to the US and founded Linde Air Products in Cleveland to extract oxygen from air. Linde Air Products joined rival Union Carbide in 1911 in experimenting with the production of acetylene; it became a unit of Union Carbide in 1917. America's war effort and economic expansion in the 1920s spurred the development of new uses for industrial gases. Union Carbide's Linde unit also contributed to the development of the atomic bomb in the 1940s when its scientists perfected a process for refining uranium.

As Union Carbide expanded worldwide over the next two decades Linde became America's #1 producer of industrial gases. In the 1960s Linde expanded into oxygen-fired furnaces for steel production and the use of nitrogen in refrigerators. By the early 1980s Linde accounted for 11% of Union Carbide's annual sales.

The disastrous 1984 chemical accident at Union Carbide's plant in Bhopal India coupled with heavy debt and falling sales forced Union Carbide to reorganize. In 1992 Linde was spun off as Praxair. William Lichtenberger former president of Union Carbide headed the new company and pushed global expansion. Two years later Praxair set up China's first helium transfill plants for medical magnetic resonance imaging. In 1995 the company began operations in India and Peru.

In 1996 Praxair Surface Technologies bought Miller Thermal (thermal spray coatings) and Maxima Air Separation Center (industrial and specialty gases Israel). Also that year the company picked up $60 million when it sold the Linde name and trademark to Linde a German engineering and industrial gas company. Praxair purchased and then spun off Chicago Bridge & Iron. The company kept only its Liquid Carbonic division the world's leading supplier of carbon dioxide for processing. The move opened up a new market in carbonated beverages for Praxair.

In 1997 and 1998 Praxair constructed plants and to control its own delivery systems acquired 20 packaged-gases distributors in the US and one in Germany. The company also formed a joint venture in China to produce high-purity nitrogen and other specialty gases for electronics and then teamed up with rival L'Air Liquide in a production joint venture.

Praxair supplied an argon-based protection system for the Shroud of Turin's public display in Italy in 1998. It also installed the industry's first small on-site hydrogen-generating system at an Indiana powdered-metals plant. In 1999 the company formed a global alliance with German pharmaceutical and chemicals company Merck KGaA to provide gases and chemicals to the semiconductor industry. The same year Praxair acquired Materials Research Corporation a maker of thin-film deposition materials for semiconductors and the TAFA Group which makes thermal-spray equipment and related products.

In 2001 Praxair underwent a restructuring that included layoffs in its surface technologies unit (hurt by the decline in jet orders) and Brazilian operations. The next year the company started work on a new plant to serve Singapore's high-tech industry. Praxair boosted its health care segment with the acquisition of Alpine Medicine.

In 2004 Praxair Healthcare Services bought Home Care Supply for $245 million. With Home Care Supply joining the company's existing operations the combined Healthcare Services unit grew its sales to $750 million worldwide slightly more than 10% of Praxair's total annual sales. The home care market became more important for Praxair as the company saw high growth potential in it (and high margins) and wanted to be able to compete with rivals L'Air Liquide and Air Products and Chemicals.

The company bought some of L'Air Liquide's German assets for about $650 million later that year. Due to antitrust requirements the French company needed to dispose of the businesses after buying much of Messer Group earlier in the year. The acquisition put Praxair's European sales over $1 billion annually.

In 2006 Praxair sold the aviation repair business of the Surface Technologies unit to Gridiron Capital and Skyview Capital. The firms created a new company called PAS Technologies to house operations that serve both the commercial and military sectors with the repair of aviation engine and airframe parts and the application of protective coatings to those parts. Also that year Praxair's distribution unit acquired Medical Gas of Illinois and Withrow Oxygen Service of California.

Praxair expanded its presence in the Middle East in 2010 by acquiring a 49% stake in the ROC Group's operations in Kuwait United Arab Emirates and Qatar.

In 2011 Praxair sold its US homecare business to Apria Healthcare. The former Praxair segment provided home respiratory services home medical equipment and nutrition therapies through a network of more than 80 branches across the country. The transaction allowed Praxair to focus on expanding its institutional healthcare business worldwide although it maintains some of its homecare units outside of the US.

In 2011 the company spent $294 million on acquisitions primarily for industrial and specialty packaged gas distributors in the US. It also invested in a joint venture in the Middle East and gained a larger ownership stake in its Scandinavian joint venture (Yara Praxair).

That year Praxair also agreed to develop and market a new process technology with Midrex Technologies (a subsidiary of Kobe Steel) to produce direct reduced iron (DRI) using a variety of fuels including coke oven gas. The company hopes to find new markets for the production of DRI which is usually made from a gas produced from natural gas or coal.

Subsidiary Praxair Distribution also expanded in 2011 acquiring Houston-based National Alloy and Equipment which supplies technical support to makers of high-pressure control packages and drilling risers for oil and energy companies and

American Gas Group one of the largest independent specialty gas producers in North America.

Building on its presence in Russia Praxair agreed to acquire the industrial and packaged gases operations of Russian tire company SIBUR - Russian Tyres in 2012. With four major projects in Russia having a total production capacity of more than 3500 tons of gases per day under its belt the company hopes to become the leading industrial gas manufacturer throughout southern Russia.

In 2012 it signed a 15-year agreement with Honeywell Resins & Chemicals to buy carbon dioxide for Praxair's new plant at the Honeywell site.

That year the company's Shanghai-based Praxair China unit started up a new air separation plant in Nanjing for Meishan Iron and Steel Co. a subsidiary of giant steel manufacturer Baosteel Group.

In 2012 Praxair Canada acquired Canadian Cylinder & Gases Inc. an independent distributor of industrial and specialty gases and welding equipment. It also acquired five Airgas branch locations in western Canada including Calgary Red Deer and Edmonton Alberta and Regina and Saskatoon Saskatchewan. This acquisition supports its growth strategy in western Canada to better serve existing customers and home oxygen clients in Alberta and Saskatchewan.

In 2012 Praxair Distribution acquired Harlingen Texas-based Acetylene Oxygen Company a distributor of Praxair industrial gases. Praxair Distribution also acquired Welders Industrial Supply LLC an independent distributor of industrial and specialty gases welding equipment supplies and related services to customers in the greater Houston area.

In 2013 company opened its first air separation plant in Bahrain to produce liquid nitrogen oxygen and argon to supply a diverse group of customers in the regional merchant market including hospitals metal fabricators and aluminum manufacturers. That year Praxair China signed a new contract to expand supply with its existing customer Jinlong Copper Co Ltd. the largest copper smelting joint venture in China.

In 2013 Praxair India Private Limited signed a long-term contract with its existing customer JSW Steel Ltd. to expand the supply of gaseous oxygen nitrogen and argon to JSW's steel mill located in Tornagallu in Karnataka.

EXECUTIVES

Chairman President and CEO, Stephen F. (Steve) Angel, $1,318,750 total compensation
SVP; President White Martins Gases Industriais and President Praxair South America, Domingos H. G. Bulus
EVP, Eduardo F. Menezes, $611,250 total compensation
President Praxair Europe, Daniel H. (Dan) Yankowski
VP and CIO, Earl Newsome
President Praxair Asia, John M. Panikar
Managing Director Germany and Benelux, Eduardo Gil
SVP, Anne K. Roby, $471,250 total compensation
President US Industrial Gases, Kevin C. Foti
President Praxair Distribution Inc., Dick Marini
EVP, Scott E. Telesz, $615,000 total compensation
SVP and CFO, Matthew J. (Matt) White, $587,500 total compensation
CTO, Todd A. Skare
President Praxair Canada, Sean Durbin
President Praxair Mexico, Benjamin (Ben) Glazer
President Praxair Surface Technologies, Pierre L thi
Vice President And General Manager Us Praxair Distribution, Randall Brittingham
Vice President Sales, Ed Haversang
Auditors: PricewaterhouseCoopers LLP

LOCATIONS

HQ: Praxair Inc
10 Riverview Drive, Danbury, CT 06810-6268
Phone: 203 837-2000
Web: www.praxair.com

2016 Sales

	% of total
North America	53
Asia	15
South America	13
Europe	13
Surface technologies	6
Total	**100**

PRODUCTS/OPERATIONS

2016 Sales by End Market

	% of total
Manufacturing	21
Metals	16
Chemicals	14
Food & Beverage	12
Healthcare	11
Electronics	7
Energy	5
Aerospace	1
Other	13
Total	**100**

2016 Sales by Distribution Method

	% of total
Merchant(delivered liquids)	38
On-site (includes noncryogenics)	28
Packaged gases (cylinders)	31
Other	3
Total	**100**

Selected Mergers and Acquisitions

COMPETITORS

Air Products	GKN Aerospace
Airgas	Chem-tronics
Balchem	L'Air Liquide
Chromalloy Gas Turbine	The Linde Group

HISTORICAL FINANCIALS

Company Type: Public

Income Statement

FYE: December 31

	REVENUE ($ mil.)	NET INCOME ($ mil.)	NET PROFIT MARGIN	EMPLOYEES
12/16	10,534	1,500	14.2%	26,498
12/15	10,776	1,547	14.4%	26,657
12/14	12,273	1,694	13.8%	27,780
12/13	11,925	1,755	14.7%	27,560
12/12	11,224	1,692	15.1%	26,539
Annual Growth	(1.6%)	(3.0%)	—	(0.0%)

2016 Year-End Financials

Debt ratio: 49.22%
Return on equity: 31.79%
Cash ($ mil.): 524
Current ratio: 1.16
Long-term debt ($ mil.): 8,917

No. of shares (mil.): 284
Dividends
  Yield: 0.0%
  Payout: 57.5%
Market value ($ mil.): 33,388

	STOCK PRICE ($) FY Close	P/E High/Low		PER SHARE ($) Earnings	Dividends	Book Value
12/16	117.19	24	18	5.21	3.00	17.62
12/15	102.40	24	18	5.35	2.86	15.41
12/14	129.56	23	21	5.73	2.60	19.44
12/13	130.03	22	18	5.87	2.40	22.47
12/12	109.45	21	18	5.61	2.20	20.47
Annual Growth	1.7%	—	—	(1.8%)	8.1%	(3.7%)

Preferred Bank (Los Angeles, CA)

Preferred Bank wants to be the bank of choice of Chinese-Americans in Southern California. Employing a multilingual staff the bank provides international banking services to companies doing business in the Asia/Pacific region. It targets middle-market businesses typically manufacturing service distribution and real estate firms as well as entrepreneurs professionals and high-net-worth individuals through about a dozen branches in Los Angeles Orange and San Francisco Counties. Preferred Bank offers standard deposit products such as checking accounts savings money market and NOW accounts. Specialized services include private banking and international trade finance.

Geographic Reach

Preferred Bank markets its services in half a dozen Southern Californian counties: Los Angeles Orange Riverside San Bernardino San Francisco and Ventura.

Financial Performance

In 2013 Preferred Bank reported about $72 million in revenue up just more than 10% from the prior year. The increase was solely from interest income as non-interest income (a very small part of overall revenue anyway) fell more than 40%. The company saw growth in its loan portfolio that year as well as overall deposit growth. Net income fell 20% to $19 million; the decline was primarily related to a boost in net income for 2012 because of a $20 million income tax benefit (compared to income tax expense of $12 million in 2013).

Strategy

Historically the company was focused on the Chinese-American market and although it continues to cater to that clientele most of its current customer base is from the diversified mainstream market.

EXECUTIVES

EVP and CFO, Edward J. Czajka
President and COO, Wellington Chen, age 57
Chairman and CEO, Li Yu, age 76
Senior Vice President, Ted Hsu
Vice President Commercial Real ESATE LOAN Officer, Sally Chang
Senior Vice President, Jim Belanic
Senior Vice President, John C Stipanov
Vice President, Craig Miller
First Vice President, Nancy Pepper
Assistant Vice President Compliance Officer, Kristie Yang
Vice President, Elsa Chen
First Vice President, Johnny Hsu
Vice President Lending, Luey Couto
Senior Vice President, Ann Cheung
Vice President, Wayne Chow
Vice President Human Resources Manager, Karen Cangey
Senior Vice President, Pam Lau
Vice President, Isabella LI
First Vice President, Philip Wong
Vice President Product Manager, John Wong
Vice President Relationship Manager, Erin Johnsen
Senior Vice President, Bill Oberholzer
Board Member, Clark Hsu
Auditors: Crowe Horwath LLP

LOCATIONS

HQ: Preferred Bank (Los Angeles, CA)
601 S. Figueroa Street, 29th Floor, Los Angeles, CA 90017
Phone: 213 891-1188
Web: www.preferredbank.com

PRODUCTS/OPERATIONS

2015 Sales

	% of total
Interest income	
Loans and leases	90
Investment securities available for sale	6
Federal funds sold	-
Non-interest income	
Fees and service charges on deposit accounts	1
Trade finance income	2
BOLI income	-
Other income	1
Total	**100**

COMPETITORS

Bank of America	City National
Bank of the West	East West Bancorp
Broadway Financial	Far East National Bank
Cathay General Bancorp	Hanmi Financial
Citigroup	MUFG Americas Holdings

HISTORICAL FINANCIALS

Company Type: Public

Income Statement

FYE: December 31

	ASSETS ($ mil.)	NET INCOME ($ mil.)	INCOME AS % OF ASSETS	EMPLOYEES
12/16	3,221	36	1.1%	218
12/15	2,598	29	1.1%	205
12/14	2,054	24	1.2%	163
12/13	1,768	19	1.1%	148
12/12	1,554	23	1.5%	133
Annual Growth	20.0%	11.1%	—	13.1%

2016 Year-End Financials

Debt ratio: 3.07%
Return on equity: 12.90%
Cash ($ mil.): 306
Current ratio: —
Long-term debt ($ mil.): —

No. of shares (mil.): 14
Dividends
  Yield: 0.0%
  Payout: 23.4%
Market value ($ mil.): 746

	STOCK PRICE ($) FY Close	P/E High/Low		PER SHARE ($) Earnings	Dividends	Book Value
12/16	52.42	20	10	2.56	0.60	20.94
12/15	33.02	17	12	2.14	0.46	19.02
12/14	27.89	15	11	1.78	0.10	17.40
12/13	20.05	15	10	1.42	0.00	15.58
12/12	14.20	8	4	1.78	0.00	14.19
Annual Growth	38.6%	—	—	9.5%	—	10.2%

Priceline Group Inc (The)

The Priceline Group is the princeling of online travel. It made its name through flights hotels and car rental website priceline.com but ascended to travel royalty after the purchase of booking.com in 2006 which now brings in billions of dollars each year. With Agoda KAYAK RentalCars and OpenTable filling out its portfolio the travel company offers an array of booking options for travelers worldwide. Priceline.com also employs its famous Name Your Own Price booking system that allows customers to haggle on prices for hotels and cars. In the case of airline tickets and hotel reservations it generates sales on the margin keeping the difference between the price paid by the individual and what it shelled out for the ticket or hotel room. Priceline was founded in 1997 .

Operations

Priceline operates an online global travel services network. It works to connect customers looking to make travel reservations with providers of travel services worldwide including more than 1.12 million hotels and accommodations. Hotel reservation services are conducted primarily under the Booking.com priceline.com and Agoda.com brands.

In the US the company offers reservations via its namesake priceline.com brand for rental cars airline tickets vacations packages destination services and cruises. Internationally the company offers a retail price-disclosed hotel and accommodation reservation service through global brands Booking.com (the world's largest online hotel and accommodation website) and Agoda.com (an online hotel reservation service with operations primarily in Asia). Priceline Group's OpenTable allows consumers to set up restaurant reservations online and provide reservation management services for restaurants.

About 75% of Priceline Group's total revenue comes from Agency revenue while Merchant revenue and Advertising revenue make up 20% and 5% of its total revenue respectively.

Geographic Reach

The Connecticut-based global online travel giant serves more than 220 countries. Its ownership of Amsterdam-based Booking.com means the company generates around 70% of its total revenue from the Netherlands. The US and other international markets generate around 15% each.

Priceline Group's Agoda.com is based in Bangkok; KAYAK is headquartered in Stamford Connecticut; OpenTable is based in San Francisco; and Rentalcars.com is located in Manchester UK. Additional offices and data centers are located in the US UK Switzerland the Netherlands and Hong Kong.

Sales and Marketing

Priceline Group aggressively promotes its brands online relying on internet search engine (mostly Google) keyword purchases referrals from meta-search sites and travel research websites affiliate programs banner and pop-up advertisements and email campaigns to boost its business. The company is one of Google's biggest search marketing customers. The Priceline Group spent $3.5 billion on online advertising during 2016.

Financial Performance

Priceline Group's annual revenue has more than doubled since 2012 thanks to the rising popularity of the online travel booking business.The company is also immensely profitable consistently posting profit margins of around 20%.

In fiscal 2016 sales crested the $10-billion mark for the first time climbing a further 16% to $10.7 billion. Growth was concentrated in Agency revenue — travel reservation commissions mostly as well as travel insurance and global distribution system reservation booking fees — which grew $1.45 billion. Advertising revenue grew by $100 million while Merchant revenue slipped 2% due to lower "Name Your Own Price" reservations on Priceline.com.

Net income however fell for the first time in over a decade declining 16% to $2.1 billion due almost entirely to an impairment charge of $940.7 million relating to OpenTable after the business suffered a sharp write-down. OpenTable has not proved

the revenue driver that was hoped for following its costly acquisition in 2014. Excluding this one significant item the company otherwise performed well succeeding in growing sales while reducing cost of revenue and only small increases in higher expenses in headcount and marketing as the company expands.

Cash from operations increased x% to $3.9 billion due to adjustments made to reconcile the asset impairment. Priceline also recorded favorable changes to working capital.

Strategy

Priceline Group reiterated in 2016 its long-term strategy for growth is to expand its service offerings and markets and become the market leader in online travel and travel-related services by "providing consumers better service partnering with travel service providers and restaurants to its mutual benefit and operating entrepreneurial independent brands that share best practices."In 2017 it added a flights section to Booking.com while the KAYAK business acquired two flight meta-search companies — Momondo Group and Mundi — in the same year.

Priceline is scaling backits renowned and sometimes controversial opaque bookings system Name Your Own Price (NYOP). The company's (successful) push to drive more mobile traffic brought about the demise of Priceline's original product — NYOP flights booking — as the bid system proved too cumbersome to port over to the smaller-screened smartphones and tablets. The NYOP flights service was brought to an end in fall 2016.

Mergers and Acquisitions

The Priceline Group strengthened its presence in Europe with the 2017 acquisition of Momondo Group for about $550 million. Momondo operates momondo a meta travel site and Cheapflight. They were folded into Priceline's Kayak brand. In the same year subsidiary KAYAK bought Brazilian meta-search company Mundi which ended its relationship with KAYAK rival Skyscanner.

Company Background

In April 2014 the company changed its name from Priceline.com to The Priceline Group to better reflect the growth of its business and all of its subsidiaries and brands including Booking.com priceline.com KAYAK OpenTable and others.

HISTORY

Priceline founder Jay Walker launched a string of ventures before making the leap into e-commerce. In 1994 he founded Walker Digital an entrepreneurial think tank formed to develop business models that could germinate into new companies.

In 1996 Walker Digital found the impetus that would drive Priceline: Each day major airlines have more than 500000 empty seats. Walker's team reasoned that if the airlines were offered even a discounted price for these empty seats they'd jump at the chance to cut their losses. Based on that premise Walker Digital developed a "name your price" system and founded Priceline in 1997.

The company launched its airfare service in 1998 and obtained financing from General Atlantic Partners and Paul Allen's Vulcan Ventures (now called Vulcan Northwest). That year it expanded into hotel reservations and added a car-buying service. Richard Braddock became chairman and CEO in 1998.

Priceline added home financing services to its offerings in 1999. The company went public with a chart-busting IPO later that year. Priceline also launched a rental car service. Branching into the retail arena it licensed its technology to WebHouse Club for use in selling grocery products. The company sued Microsoft in 1999 claiming that com-

pany's Expedia unit's name-your-own-price hotel reservation service violated Priceline's patent.

In 2000 the company licensed its business model to several international ventures including General Atlantic Partners' Priceline.com Europe (headed by Dennis Malamatinas former Burger King CEO) SOFTBANK's Priceline.com Japan (a deal that was later cancelled) MyPrice in Australia and New Zealand (also cancelled) and Asian conglomerate Hutchinson Whampoa. In collaboration with Alliance Capital (now AllianceBernstein) Priceline created subsidiary pricelinemortgage to act as mortgage broker.

Daniel Schulman became CEO later that year. Jay Walker resigned as vice chairman at the end of 2000 after taking on the role of CEO at Walker Digital. After deciding it would probably never be profitable WebHouse Club shut down ending Priceline's foray into grocery sales. Known for its splashy ads Priceline dumped pop icon William Shatner as its TV spokesperson in favor of Sex and the City star Sarah Jessica Parker. (Shatner returned in 2002.) Later that year the company fired Schulman and reappointed Braddock as CEO.

In 2002 the company joined with National Leisure Group to offer cruises from its website. Later that year Priceline purchased the assets of discount travel site Lowestfare.com. It also announced plans to sell cars under a marketing agreement with Autobytel. In late 2002 Braddock passed his CEO responsibilities to president Jeffery Boyd. (Braddock remained as chairman.)

A handful of new international destinations (Australia Japan Indonesia Malaysia South Korea Taiwan) was added in 2003 to Priceline's hotel reservation service. In April 2004 chairman Richard Braddock (former president of Citicorp and one of the last remaining high-profile board members) resigned from the company. Director Ralph Bahna was then named chairman. The following month Priceline acquired most of Travelweb.com. That September it bought Active Hotels of Britain for about $161 million in cash. In December 2004 Priceline acquired the remaining stake in Travelweb for about $4 million.

EXECUTIVES

CEO priceline.com, Brett Keller, age 49
SVP and General Counsel, Peter J. Millones, age 47, $330,000 total compensation
SVP International; Senior Manager
  Priceline.co.uk, Glenn D. Fogel, age 55, $315,000 total compensation
SVP CFO and Chief Accounting Officer, Daniel J. Finnegan, age 54, $315,000 total compensation
CEO agoda.com, Robert Rosenstein, age 50
CEO KAYAK, Steve Hafner
President and CEO Booking.com, Gillian Tans, age 46, $498,356 total compensation
CEO rentalcars.com, Ian Brown
CEO OpenTable Inc., Christa Quarles
Senior Vice President Global Infrastructure, Glen Dalgleish
Chairman, Jeffery H. (Jeff) Boyd, age 60
Auditors: Deloitte & Touche LLP

LOCATIONS

HQ: Priceline Group Inc (The)
  800 Connecticut Avenue, Norwalk, CT 06854
Phone: 203 299-8000   **Fax:** 203 595-0160
Web: www.pricelinegroup.com

2016 Sales

	$ mil.	% of total
The Netherlands	7,783	72
US	1,680	16
Other	1,279	12
Total	**10,743**	**100**

PRODUCTS/OPERATIONS

2016 Sales

	$ mil.	% of total
Agency	7,982	74
Merchant	2,048	19
Advertising and other	712	7
Total	**10,743**	**100**

Selected Products

Airline tickets
Cruises
Hotel rooms
Rental cars
Restaurant reservations
Vacation packages

Selected Brands

agoda.com
Booking.com
KAYAK
OpenTable
priceline.com
rentalcars.com

COMPETITORS

Alibaba Group	Hotwire Inc.
Amazon.com	Internet Brands
American Express	Intuit
Apple Inc.	Microsoft
AutoNation	Orbitz Worldwide
AutoTrader	Prestige Travel
Autobytel	Restaurant.com
BCD Travel	SavvyDiner.com
Carlson Wagonlit	Travelocity
Expedia	Travelport
Facebook	Travelzoo
GetThere	TripAdvisor
Google	Yahoo!
Groupon	Yelp

HISTORICAL FINANCIALS

Company Type: Public

Income Statement

FYE: December 31

	REVENUE ($ mil.)	NET INCOME ($ mil.)	NET PROFIT MARGIN	EMPLOYEES
12/16	10,743	2,134	19.9%	18,500
12/15	9,223	2,551	27.7%	15,500
12/14	8,441	2,421	28.7%	12,700
12/13	6,793	1,892	27.9%	9,500
12/12	5,260	1,419	27.0%	7,000
Annual Growth	**19.5%**	**10.7%**	**—**	**27.5%**

2016 Year-End Financials

Debt ratio: 35.98%
Return on equity: 22.87%
Cash ($ mil.): 2,081
Current ratio: 1.89
Long-term debt ($ mil.): 6,170

No. of shares (mil.): 49
Dividends
  Yield: —
  Payout: —
Market value ($ mil.): 72,113

	STOCK PRICE ($) FY Close	P/E High/Low	PER SHARE ($) Earnings	Dividends	Book Value
12/16	1,466.06	37 23	42.65	0.00	199.64
12/15	1,274.95	29 20	49.45	0.00	177.29
12/14	1,140.21	30 22	45.67	0.00	164.96
12/13	1,162.40	32 17	36.11	0.00	132.86
12/12	620.39	27 17	27.66	0.00	78.14
Annual Growth	**24.0%**	**— —**	**11.4%**	**—**	**26.4%**

Primerica Inc

Auditors: KPMG LLP

LOCATIONS

HQ: Primerica Inc
  1 Primerica Parkway, Duluth, GA 30099
Phone: 770 381-1000
Web: www.primerica.com

HISTORICAL FINANCIALS

Company Type: Public

Income Statement

FYE: December 31

	ASSETS ($ mil.)	NET INCOME ($ mil.)	INCOME AS % OF ASSETS	EMPLOYEES
12/16	11,438	219	1.9%	2,662
12/15	10,612	189	1.8%	2,626
12/14	10,738	181	1.7%	2,579
12/13	10,329	162	1.6%	2,605
12/12	10,337	173	1.7%	2,547
Annual Growth	**2.6%**	**6.0%**	**—**	**1.1%**

2016 Year-End Financials

Debt ratio: 7.65%
Return on equity: 18.49%
Cash ($ mil.): 211
Current ratio: —
Long-term debt ($ mil.): —

No. of shares (mil.): 45
Dividends
  Yield: 0.0%
  Payout: 15.2%
Market value ($ mil.): 3,162

	STOCK PRICE ($) FY Close	P/E High/Low	PER SHARE ($) Earnings	Dividends	Book Value
12/16	69.15	16 9	4.59	0.70	26.71
12/15	47.23	15 11	3.70	0.64	23.72
12/14	54.26	17 12	3.29	0.48	23.87
12/13	42.91	15 10	2.83	0.44	22.29
12/12	30.01	11 8	2.71	0.24	22.62
Annual Growth	**23.2%**	**— —**	**14.1%**	**30.7%**	**4.2%**

Principal Financial Group Inc

Seeking out The Principal may bring future financial windfalls. Founded in 1879 Principal Financial Group (or The Principal) is a top administrator of employer-sponsored retirement plans offering pension products and services as well as mutual funds annuities asset management trust services and investment advice. Its insurance segment provides group and individual life and disability insurance and group dental and vision coverage. PFG serves 22 million customers and has more than $650 billion in assets under management.

Operations

Principal offers its financial products and services through four main segments: Retirement and Income Solutions US Insurance Solutions Principal International and Principal Global Investors.

The Retirement and Investor Services segment generates about 50% of annual revenue. It provides retirement and other financial products and services such as 401(k) plans Individual Retirement Accounts (IRAs) personal trusts and annuities to individuals and businesses.

The U.S. Insurance Solutions segment (around 30% of revenue) provides individual life insurance and specialty benefits insurance which includes group dental and vision individual and group disability insurance and group life insurance along with non-medical fee-for-service claims administration services.

The Principal International segment (10% of revenue) serves retirement and insurance needs to clients in countries with large middle classes and growing long-term savings. The company typically enters a new market through acquisitions joint ventures and sometimes its own start-up operations.

The Principal Global Investors segment (less than 10% of revenue) offers asset management services to the company's internal asset accumulation business insurance operations and the Corporate segment along with third-party clients.

Geographic Reach

Principal Financial Group operates out of offices in nearly 20 countries and serves clients in more than 75 countries. It is headquartered in Des Moines IA.

PFG?s International segment has operations in Brazil Chile Mexico China Hong Kong India Singapore Thailand Malaysia and Indonesia.

The Principal Global Investors segment has offices in about a dozen countries including Australia China Japan Singapore Germany Malaysia Hong Kong the United Arab Emirates the Netherlands.

Sales and Marketing

Principal distributes its products and services through institutional and retail sales representatives relationship management and client service professionals who work with consultants and directly with investors to acquire and retain institutional clients retail clients and other investors. The company maintains relationships with independent broker-dealers to distribute its products and services maintaining relationships with over 61000 independent brokers consultants and agents.

PFG?s International segment focuses on regions with a growing middle class and demographics that are aligned with PFG?s target customer criteria as well as where it is common for workers to contribute to defined contribution retirement plans (similar to 401(k) and IRA plans).

Financial Performance

PFG?s financial results in 2016 continued a long-term upward trend. Its annual revenues have risen more than 30% since 2011 mostly thanks to growing premium income from annuity and life insurance sales. The firm's assets under management have swelled by more than 60% since 2011 which has led to higher fee-based income. The company's profits have doubled thanks to strong cost controls.

In 2016 revenue moved up 4% to $12.4 billion its growth slowing a bit compared to the prior two years. Net investment income was the primary driver of growth rising nearly $200 million as a result of higher average invested assets in PFG?s US operations. Premiums for the US Insurance segment increased in the year but not enough to offset the reduction in premiums for the Retirement and Income Solutions segment. The Principal International segment performed well in Latin America increasing sales by $28 million.

Net income rose 9% in 2016 on the back of higher revenue tighter expense controls and the positive effect of not distributing dividends for its preferred stock which was retired in 2015.

Cash at the end of the year was $2.7 billion up roughly $150 million from 2015. Cash from operations added $3.9 billion to the coffers and financing activities contributed $1.4 billion. Investing activities used $5.2 billion.

Strategy

PFG aims to become a global player in retirement services targeting countries in Asia and Latin America that rely on private-sector defined-contribution pension plans to accommodate their growing number of retirees. The company typically builds its international business through startups acquisitions and joint ventures.

PFG has exited underperforming businesses such as medical insurance to focus on asset management at home and abroad. It aims to grow its assets under management (AUM) at a 6% compound annual clip with the goal of surpassing $100 trillion AUM in 2020 and $400 trillion by 2050.

In the US PFG courts firms with fewer than 1000 employees for its insurance and pension products; that market is primed for growth as a relatively low percentage of small to midsized businesses currently offer these products. Its strategy for growth also includes targeting large institutional clients for its asset management operations which include Principal Global Investors. The company serves approximately 650 institutional investors.

HISTORY

Principal Financial was founded as the Bankers Life Association in 1879 by Edward Temple a Civil War veteran and banker. Life insurance became popular after the war but some dishonest insurers canceled customers' policies before they had to pay out benefits. Bankers Life an assessable association (members shared the cost of death benefits as the claims arose) was intended to provide low-cost protection to bankers and their families. The company soon began offering life insurance to nonbankers but it refused to insure women because of the high mortality rate among mothers during childbirth.

In October 2012 PFG scooped up First Dental Health a California-based preferred provider organization (PPO) with more than 11000 dentists operating in Arizona California and Nevada. The acquisition bolstered PFG's specialty benefits insurance business.

EXECUTIVES

Evp And Cfo, Terrance Lillis
Chairman President and CEO, Daniel J. (Dan) Houston, age 56, $795,192 total compensation
EVP General Counsel and Secretary, Karen E. Shaff, age 63
President Global Asset Management; CEO Principal Global Investors, James P. (Jim) McCaughan, age 64, $663,500 total compensation
EVP CIO and Chief Digital Officer, Gary P. Scholten, age 60
SVP Retirement and Investor Services; President and CEO Principal Funds, Nora M. Everett, age 57
CEO Principal Real Estate Investors, Patrick G. (Pat) Halter
Senior Executive Director and COO Strategy and Boutique Operations, Barbara A. (Barb) McKenzie
SVP and Controller, Gregory B. (Greg) Elming, age 56
President Principal International, Luis Vald ©s, age 59, $589,288 total compensation
Chairman Principal Financial Group Asia, Rex Auyeung
EVP Principal Financial Group Inc. and Principal Life and Chief Investment Officer, Timothy M. (Tim) Dunbar, age 59, $483,577 total compensation
SVP; President Principal Financial Group Latin America, Roberto Walker
SVP and Chief Marketing Officer, Elizabeth S. (Beth) Brady
SVP and Chief Investment Officer Principal Life Insurance Company, Dennis Menken

Senior Executive Director and Head Global Fixed Income, David M. Blake
EVP and CFO, Deanna D. Strable-Soethout, age 48, $488,846 total compensation
President United States Insurance Solutions, Amy C. Friedrich, age 46
National Vice President Individual Life Sales, Warren May
Vice President Network Development, Lance Marshall
Regional Vice President Life, Mark Householder
Vice President Sales, Joseph Martin
Vice President Sales, Rob Elwood
Vice President, Robert Annexstad
Second Vice President, Rajesh Chalamalasetti
Vice President Tax, Rich Wireman
Senior Vice President, Cindy Dicks
Second Vice President, Shelly Meighan
Senior Vice President Risk Management, Lou Flori
Regional Vice President, Peter Seltz
Vice President Sales, David Sandstead
Assistant Vice President, Diane Howe
Regional Vice President Life, Jeff Warkenthien
Vice President, Jill Szambelan
Life Regional Vice President, Dave House
Senior Vice President Retirement Distrib, Timothy Minard
Regional Vice President Nonqualified Plans, Daniel Barry
Disability Income Regional Vice President (DI RVP) covering the states of Indiana, Dianne Crouse
Vice President of Annuity Distribution, Steven Becker
Regional Vice President Nonqualified Plans, Jack Leavy
Second Vice President, Lynda Markwardt
Assistant Vice President, Laricke Blanchard
Auditors: Ernst & Young LLP

LOCATIONS

HQ: Principal Financial Group Inc
711 High Street, Des Moines, IA 50392
Phone: 515 247-5111
Web: www.principal.com

Selected Geographic Locations
Australia
Brazil
Chile
China
Hong Kong
India
Indonesia
Japan
Malaysia
Mexico
Singapore
Thailand
UK
US

PRODUCTS/OPERATIONS

2016 Sales by Segment

	$ mil.	% of total
Retirement & Investor Services	6,150	49
US Insurance Solutions	3,637	29
Principal International	1,252	10
Principal Global Investors	1,387	11
Corporate	(46.3)	-
Net realized capital gains	80	1
Adjustments	(67.6)	-
Total	**12,394**	**100**

2016 Sales

	% of total
Premiums & other considerations	43
Fees and other revenues	29
Net investment income	27
Net realized capital gains	1
Total	**100**

COMPETITORS

AIG
AXA
Aetna
Allianz
BlackRock
FMR
JPMorgan Chase
John Hancock Financial Services
Lincoln Financial Group
MassMutual
MetLife
Morgan Stanley Investment Management
PIMCO
T. Rowe Price
The Vanguard Group
Unum Group
Voya Financial

HISTORICAL FINANCIALS

Company Type: Public

Income Statement

FYE: December 31

	ASSETS ($ mil.)	NET INCOME ($ mil.)	INCOME AS % OF ASSETS	EMPLOYEES
12/17	253,941	2,310	0.9%	15,378
12/16	228,014	1,316	0.6%	14,854
12/15	218,685	1,234	0.6%	14,895
12/14	219,087	1,144	0.5%	14,873
12/13	208,191	912	0.4%	14,792
Annual Growth	**5.1%**	**26.1%**	**—**	**1.0%**

2017 Year-End Financials

Debt ratio: 1.25%
Return on equity: 20.02%
Cash ($ mil.): 2,470
Current ratio: —
Long-term debt ($ mil.): —
No. of shares (mil.): 289
Dividends
  Yield: 0.0%
  Payout: 23.7%
Market value ($ mil.): 20,392

	STOCK PRICE ($) FY Close	P/E High/Low		PER SHARE ($) Earnings	Dividends	Book Value
12/17	70.56	9	7	7.88	1.87	44.46
12/16	57.86	13	8	4.50	1.61	35.55
12/15	44.98	14	11	4.06	1.50	31.95
12/14	51.94	15	11	3.65	1.28	34.65
12/13	49.31	17	10	2.95	0.98	32.81
Annual Growth	**9.4%**			**27.8%**	**17.5%**	**7.9%**

ProAssurance Corp

ProAssurance protects professional health associates — the doctors dentists and nurses of the US. One of the largest medical liability insurance providers in the nation ProAssurance is the holding company for ProAssurance Indemnity ProAssurance Casualty and other subsidiaries that sell liability coverage for health care providers primarily in the South and Midwest. Its customers include individual doctors in private practice as well as large physician groups clinics and hospitals. Its ProAssurance Specialty Insurance subsidiary writes excess and surplus (higher risk) lines of medical professional liability insurance. ProAssurance Casualty also provides some coverage for legal professionals.

Operations

ProAssurance operates through four primary segments: Specialty Property and Casualty (more than half of all sales) Workers' Compensation (about a quarter of sales) Lloyd's Syndicate and Corporate.

Physician policies make up ProAssurance's largest business accounting for about 80% of annual insurance premiums. Other key product groups include policies covering other health professionals medical facilities and legal professionals. Medmarc Casualty Insurance and Noetic Specialty Insurance write products liability coverage for medical technology and life sciences while Eastern Alliance Insurance provides workers' compensation. ProAssurance is also the majority capital provider to Lloyd's of London Syndicate 1729 which began writing business in 2014.

Geographic Reach

Although the company is licensed throughout the US its operations are concentrated in select states in the southern and midwestern US. Its largest markets — Alabama Pennsylvania and Texas — together account for about a third of the company's premiums.

The company owns office facilities in Alabama Michigan Nevada Tennessee and Wisconsin.

Sales and Marketing

ProAssurance employs an internal sales force to write its health care professional liability policies. It also utilizes independent agencies and brokerages.

Customers include physicians dentists specialists (including podiatrists) allied health care professionals medical facilities lawyers life science and medical technology entities.

Financial Performance

ProAssurance is able to sustain financial stability during turbulent market conditions through disciplined underwriting prudent pricing and loss reserve practices and conservative investment strategies. Revenue rose 15% to $852 million in 2014 largely due to the recent addition of workers' compensation business acquired with Eastern Alliance Insurance. The group's participation in the new Lloyd's Syndicate 1729 also drove up earnings. These increases were partially offset by a decline in net premiums for the Specialty Property and Casualty segment.

Net income has been somewhat turbulent over the past five years. It dropped 34% to $196 million in 2014 largely as a result of higher expenses related to the acquisition of Eastern Alliance Insurance and the investment in Lloyd's Syndicate 1729.

Cash flow from operations was on the decline until 2014 when it rebounded by 149% to $96 million. That turnaround was attributed to an increase in cash generated by receivables from reinsurers and a change in unearned premiums.

Strategy

ProAssurance's plans for long-term growth are based on the controlled expansion of its existing operations and by acquiring other specialty insurance companies or books of business. The company looks to expand in both existing and new territories and product lines. For instance the firm is working to grow in fields outside of the medical professional customer base partly due to increasing competition in the physician coverage market.

The company's aggressive acquisitions are part of its strategy to better compete against larger property/casualty insurance firms as well as smaller niche providers. ProAssurance works to provide local services that cater to the liability climates of its core geographies; it also focuses on targeted customer segments (medical and legal) to allow for a deep understanding of the industries' needs. In addition to acquisitions ProAssurance expands through organic growth efforts including new product launches as well as by forming partnerships with professional associations. As part of its strategy to expand geographically its Eastern Alliance Insurance unit opened a new office in Michigan in 2014.

In late 2013 the company became a corporate member of Lloyd's of London becoming the majority capital provider to the new Syndicate 1729. The move provided ProAssurance and its subsidiaries with more direct access to international professional liability opportunities in the health care sector.

Mergers and Acquisitions

In 2013 the company expanded through the purchase of Medmarc Insurance Group a liability underwriter for medical technology and life science policies in a $154 million transaction. The purchase also added some legal professional coverage operations.

EXECUTIVES

Vice President, Clay Shaw

Chairman President and CEO, W. Stancil (Stan) Starnes, age 68, $854,100 total compensation

President Healthcare Professional Liability Group Chief Underwriting Officer and Chief Actuary, Howard H. Friedman, age 58, $476,325 total compensation

EVP and CFO, Edward L. (Ned) Rand, age 50, $443,475 total compensation

SVP and Chief Marketing Officer Professional Liability Group, Jeffrey L. Bowlby

President Eastern Insurance, Michael L. Boguski, age 54

EVP Corporate Secretary and General Counsel, Jeffrey P. Lisenby, age 48

SVP and Chief Medical Officer, Hayes V. Whiteside

Group Technology Officer Information Systems, Michael Stoeckert

President and Chief Medical Officer Podiatric Insurance Company of America (PICA), Ross E. Taubman

Vice President And General Manager, Charles Francis

Assistant Vice President External Reporting, Dianne Baldwin

Regional Vice President Claims, Richard Walter

Vice President Actuarial Services, Randy Chaffinch

Regional Vice President Claims, Scott Hunsberger

Vice President Operations, Duncan Manley

Vice President and Chief of Internal Audit, Kim Lawter

Vice President of Corporate Investments, Larry Cochran

Regional Assistant Vice President Underwriting, Ross Hess

Assistant Vice President Corporate Controller, Rhett Plugge

Regional Vice President Claims, Hal Mcclelland

Assistant Vice President Information Technology, Brent Wells

Vice President, Brady Chris

Vice President of Operations, Sally Gilmore

Assistant Vice President, Sandy Cook

Board Member, Julie Kus

Auditors: Ernst & Young LLP

LOCATIONS

HQ: ProAssurance Corp
100 Brookwood Place, Birmingham, AL 35209
Phone: 205 877-4400   **Fax:** 205 802-4799
Web: www.proassurance.com

PRODUCTS/OPERATIONS

2014 Sales by Segment

	% of total
Specialty Property and Casualty	58
Workers' Compensation	23
Corporate	17
Lloyd's Syndicate	2
Eliminations	-
Total	100

2014 Sales

	$ mil
% of total	
Net premium earned	82
Net investment	15
Net realized investment gains	2
Other income	1
Total	**100**

COMPETITORS

Berkshire Hathaway	NCMIC
CNA Financial	Physicians' Reciprocal
COPIC	Insurers
Coverys	Princeton Insurance
Dentists Insurance	Company
Company	State Volunteer Mutual
EDIC	Insurance
Markel	The Doctors Company
Medical Liability	Travelers Companies
Mutual Insurance	White Mountains
Monitor Liability	Insurance Group
Managers Inc.	

HISTORICAL FINANCIALS

Company Type: Public

Income Statement

FYE: December 31

	ASSETS ($ mil.)	NET INCOME ($ mil.)	INCOME AS % OF ASSETS	EMPLOYEES
12/16	5,065	151	3.0%	965
12/15	4,908	116	2.4%	938
12/14	5,169	196	3.8%	967
12/13	5,150	297	5.8%	962
12/12	4,876	275	5.6%	690
Annual Growth	1.0%	(13.9%)	—	8.7%

2016 Year-End Financials

Debt ratio: 8.85%
Return on equity: 8.02%
Cash ($ mil.): 117
Current ratio: —
Long-term debt ($ mil.): —

No. of shares (mil.): 53
Dividends
  Yield: 0.1%
  Payout: 209.5%
Market value ($ mil.): 2,993

	STOCK PRICE ($) FY Close	P/E High/Low		PER SHARE ($) Earnings	Dividends	Book Value
12/16	56.20	22	16	2.83	5.93	33.78
12/15	48.53	25	21	2.11	2.24	36.88
12/14	45.15	15	13	3.30	3.86	38.17
12/13	48.48	11	9	4.80	1.05	39.13
12/12	42.19	21	9	4.46	3.13	36.85
Annual Growth	7.4%	—	—	(10.7%)	17.4%	(2.2%)

Procter & Gamble Company (The)

The Procter & Gamble Company (P&G) boasts dozens of billion-dollar brands for home and health. The world's largest maker of consumer packaged goods divides its business into five global segments that comprise its vast portfolio of hair skin and personal oral family feminine and baby care product lines. About two dozen of P&G's brands are billion-dollar sellers including Always Braun Crest Fusion Gillette Head & Shoulders Mach3 Olay Oral-B and Pantene as well as Bounty Charmin Dawn Downy Gain Pampers and Tide. Other major brands include Febreze Mr. Clean Old Spice and Swiffer. In 2016 P&G sold a significant portion of its Beauty segment's products to beauty products company Coty for $11.4 billion.

HISTORY

Candle maker William Procter and soap maker James Gamble merged their small Cincinnati businesses in 1837 creating The Procter & Gamble Company (P&G) which incorporated in 1890. By 1859 P&G had become one of the largest companies in Cincinnati with sales of $1 million. It introduced Ivory a floating soap in 1879 and Crisco shortening in 1911.

The Ivory campaign was one of the first to advertise directly to the consumer. Other advertising innovations included sponsorship of daytime radio dramas in 1932. P&G's first TV commercial for Ivory aired in 1939.

Family members headed the company until 1930 when William Deupree became president. In the 29 years that Deupree served as president and then chairman P&G became the largest US seller of packaged goods.

After years of researching cleansers for use in hard water P&G introduced Tide detergent in 1947. It began a string of acquisitions when it picked up Spic and Span (1945; sold 2001) Duncan Hines (1956; sold 1998) Charmin Paper Mills (1957) and Folgers Coffee (1963 sold 2008). P&G launched Crest toothpaste in 1955 and Head & Shoulders shampoo and Pampers disposable diapers in 1961.

Rely tampons were pulled from shelves in 1980 when investigators linked them to toxic shock syndrome. In 1985 P&G moved into health care when it purchased Richardson-Vicks (NyQuil Vicks) and G.D. Searle's nonprescription drug division (Metamucil). The acquisitions of Noxell (1989; CoverGirl Noxzema) and Max Factor (1991) made it a top cosmetics company in the US. (It sold Noxzema in 2008.)

P&G began a major restructuring in 1993 cutting 13000 jobs and closing 30 plants. The firm acquired Eagle Snacks from Anheuser-Busch in 1996 and sued rival Amway over rumors connecting P&G and its moon-and-stars logo to Satanism. (The suit was dismissed in 1999.) Also in 1996 the FDA approved the use of olestra a controversial fat substitute developed by P&G.

In 1997 it acquired Tambrands (Tampax tampons) making P&G #1 in feminine sanitary protection. Impatient with progress on its sales goals in 1998 P&G began restructuring to focus on global business units rather than geographic regions. Chairman John Pepper handed over his chairman and CEO title in 1999 to president Durk Jager who promised five new products a year and a shakeup of the corporate culture.

In 1999 the company announced further reorganization plans including 15000 job cuts worldwide by 2005. That same year P&G bought The Iams Company (maker of Eukanuba- and Iams-brand dog and cat foods).

With earnings flat Jager resigned in 2000. P&G insider Alan G. Lafley immediately assumed the president and CEO duties and Pepper returned to succeed Jager as chairman.

In 2001 P&G announced job cuts for 9600 employees to further reduce costs. It also sold its Comet cleaner business. That year P&G completed its purchase of the Clairol hair care company from Bristol-Myers Squibb for nearly $5 billion.

In 2002 P&G closed three Clairol plants one warehouse and one distribution center — eliminating about 750 jobs. Production of Clairol products was moved to existing P&G plants. It also sold its olestra plant in Cincinnati to Twin Rivers Technologies but retained ownership of the Olean brand and technology. Additionally it sold its Jif peanut butter and Crisco shortening brands to J.M. Smucker and several personal care brands (including Sea Breeze and Vitalis) to Helen of Troy.

In 2002 P&G branched out in a joint venture with Clorox to help it improve the Glad-brand plastic bags and wraps. P&G held a 10% stake in the Glad venture until late 2004 when the company invested another $133 million to boost its stake to 20% the limit allowed by the agreement.

Also that year Lafley announced that P&G had completed its multiyear restructuring and would stop reporting two sets of results (one with restructuring charges and one without).

Further expanding its hair care segment and building on its successes with Clairol P&G purchased the first of several stakes in Wella in 2003 (it now owns the entire company). That year P&G also entered the premium pet food market with its purchase of The Iams Company for $2.3 billion. And to secure its foothold in China P&G bought the remaining 20% stake in its joint venture with partner Hutchison Whampoa China Ltd. in 2004 for $1.8 billion.

P&G bought four brands to sell in Southeast Asia in its effort to erode market share from Unilever. In 2005 P&G purchased Fab Trojan Dynamo and Paic laundry brands sold in Hong Kong Singapore Thailand and Malaysia from Colgate-Palmolive.

The company reached its lofty spot as the world's largest consumer products company in 2005 through one of its boldest moves — buying Boston-based The Gillette Company for about $57 billion. Overnight the ambitious deal gave P&G the golden ticket to leapfrog over former #1 supplier Unilever. P&G's purchase of Gillette added well-known complementary brands to its already vast portfolio such as Gillette razors and blades Duracell batteries Oral-B oral care items and Braun appliances.

In 2006 P&G paired up with ARYx Therapeutics to develop that company's gastrointestinal disorder treatment.

In 2007 P&G paired its marketing savvy with the diagnostics expertise of Inverness Medical Innovations to form a joint venture company called SPD Swiss Precision Diagnostics. The joint venture makes and markets in-home diagnostic products including pregnancy tests and ovulation/fertility monitoring products under the Clearblue PERSONA Accu-Clear and other names. P&G paid $325 million for its 50% stake in the venture.

EXECUTIVES

Group President Global Grooming, Charles E. Pierce, age 61

Chairman President and CEO, David S. Taylor, age 59, $1,393,333 total compensation

Group President North America Selling and Market Operations, Carolyn Tastad, age 54

Group President Global Health Care, Steven D. (Steve) Bishop, age 53, $796,667 total compensation

VP UK and Ireland, Giovanni Ciserani, age 55, $845,833 total compensation

VP North America Family Care, Mary L. Ferguson-McHugh, age 58

VP North America Pharmaceuticals and VP Worldwide Strategic Planning and New Business Development Global Pharmaceuticals, Thomas M. Finn, age 55

Vice Chairman and CFO, Jon R. Moeller, age 53, $950,000 total compensation

Global Design Officer, Philip J Duncan, age 52

CIO, Linda W. Clement-Holmes, age 55

Global Product Supply Officer, Yannis Skoufalos, age 59

President Beauty Specialty Businesses, Colleen E. Jay, age 55

President Europe Selling & Market Operations, Gary Coombe

CTO, Kathleen B. (Kathy) Fish

President India Middle East and Africa Selling and Market Operations, Mohamed Samir

President Global Home Care and P&G Professional, George Tsourapas, age 57

President Global Fabric Care and Brand Building Organization Global Fabric and Home Care, Shailesh G. Jejurikar

President Global Skin and Personal Care, R. Alexandra Keith

President Global Business Services, Julio Nemeth

President Latin America Selling and Market Operations, Juan F. Posada

President Greater China Selling and Market Operations, Matthew S. Price

President Asia/Pacific Selling and Market Operations, Magesvaran Suranjan

Vice President Management Systems, Frank Caccamo

Vice President and General Manager, Jeff Davis

Vice President, Charlene Patten

Vice President North American Oral Care, Doreen Bayliff

Vice President, Jerry Vikara

Vice President Sales, Matthew Zirkle

Chief Sales Officer Reinvention Training Developer, Ryan P Siereveld

Vice President Of Communications, Lisa Bartz

Chief Sales Officer Team Operations Leader, Kelly Horton

Vice President Sales, Frank Craft

Vice President, Patrick Conklin

Vice President, Gale Beckett

Vice President, Jason Witko

Vice President Operations, Dawn Seiler

Director Managed Care, Debbie Burge

Vice President New Business Creation, J Brad Lang

Vice President And General Manager Research And Development, Petra Hanke-baier

Chief Sales Officer Manager Romania, Georgeta Parchisanu

Vice President Corporate Development and Strategic Planning, Becky Frayer

Vice President Of Sales, Ingrid Jones

National Account Manager, Shelagh Clark

Vice President Female Beauty Latin America, Gerardo Rios

Vice President Finance and Accounting Gillette, Samy Zekhout

Vice President Of Facilities Planning, Jalal Zarhoun

National Sales Manager, Lisa Richards

Vice President and Brand Franchise Leader (Baby Care), Stefano Volpetti

Vice President (Retired), Peter Schmid

Board Member, Lou Cedrone

SHS Band Booster Treasurer, Lisa Hennessy

Board Member, Bob Kruthaupt

Board Member, BO Passey

Secretary, Jenny Tan

Abm, Christina Morazzani

Russia And Ccar Treasurer, Alisa Latypova

Assistant Treasurer, Douglas Gerstle

Secretary, Julie Taylor

Auditors: DELOITTE & TOUCHE LLP

LOCATIONS

HQ: Procter & Gamble Company (The)
One Procter & Gamble Plaza, Cincinnati, OH 45202
Phone: 513 983-1100
Web: www.pg.com

2016 Sales

	% of total
North America	44
Europe	23
Asia Pacific	9
China	8
India Middle East and Africa (IMEA)	8
Latin America	8
Total	**100**

PRODUCTS/OPERATIONS

2016 Sales

	% of total
Fabric Care and Home Care	32
Baby Care and Family Care	28
Beauty	18
Health Care	11
Grooming	10
Corporate	1
Total	**100**

Selected Segments and Brands

Fabric Care & Home Care
  Ariel
  Dawn
  Downy
  Febreze
  Gain
  Tide
Beauty
  Head & Shoulders
  Olay
  Old Spice
  Pantene
  SK-II
Baby Feminine & Family Care
  Always
  Bounty
  Charmin
  Luvs
  Pampers
  Tampax
Health Care
  Crest
  Oral-B
  Vicks
Grooming
  Braun
  Fusion
  Gillette
  Mach3
  Venus

COMPETITORS

Alticor	Mary Kay
Amway	Meda Pharmaceuticals
Avon	Nestl©e
BIC	Pfizer
Bath & Body Works	Philips Electronics
Baxter of California	Revlon
Body Shop	Russell Hobbs
Bristol-Myers Squibb	S.C. Johnson
Church & Dwight	SANYO
Clorox	SEB
Colgate-Palmolive	Sanofi
Discus Dental	Scott's Liquid Gold
Dr. Bronner's	Shiseido
Edgewell Personal Care	Spectrum Brands
Est©e Lauder	Tom's of Maine
Henkel	Turtle Wax
Johnson & Johnson	Unilever PLC
Kimberly-Clark	VIVUS
L'Or©al	

HISTORICAL FINANCIALS

Company Type: Public

Income Statement

	REVENUE ($ mil.)	NET INCOME ($ mil.)	NET PROFIT MARGIN	EMPLOYEES
06/17	65,058	15,326	23.6%	95,000
06/16	65,299	10,508	16.1%	105,000
06/15	76,279	7,036	9.2%	110,000
06/14	83,062	11,643	14.0%	118,000
06/13	84,167	11,312	13.4%	121,000
Annual Growth	(6.2%)	7.9%	—	(5.9%)

FYE: June 30

2017 Year-End Financials

Debt ratio: 26.24%—
Return on equity: 27.24%
Cash ($ mil.): 5,569
Current ratio: 0.88
Long-term debt ($ mil.): 18,038

Dividends
Yield: 3.1%
Payout: 49.4%
Market value ($ mil.): —

	STOCK PRICE ($) FY Close	P/E High/Low		PER SHARE ($) Earnings	Dividends	Book Value
06/17	87.15	16	14	5.59	2.70	21.61
06/16	84.67	22	18	3.69	2.66	21.49
06/15	78.24	37	31	2.44	2.59	22.99
06/14	78.59	20	18	4.01	2.45	25.53
06/13	76.99	20	15	3.86	2.29	24.82
Annual Growth	3.1%	—	—	9.7%	4.2%	(3.4%)

Progressive Corp. (OH)

Progressive Corporation long a leader in non-standard high-risk personal auto insurance has motored beyond its traditional business into standard-risk and preferred auto insurance as well as other personal-use vehicle coverage (motorcycles RVs and snowmobiles). Its insurance carriers include majority-owned American Strategic Insurance. Progressive also offers commercial policies for heavy trucks vans and lighter trucks. It writes a bit of professional liability insurance for directors and officers as well. The company markets directly to consumers online and by phone and through more than 35000 independent agents who account for the majority of its business.

Operations

Personal insurance accounted for 83% of the company's 2015 revenues while commercial auto represented 12%. Other indemnity and service business accounts for less than 1% of the company's revenues while fees and other revenues account for 1%. Progressive offers coverage to auto insurance customers underwritten by third-party insurance carriers. Progressive also offers personal umbrella insurance that provides coverage for the extras in life such as personal injury and legal defense. Majority-owned subsidiary American Strategic Insurance provides home insurance. Progressive had 14.3 million policies in force at the end of 2015.

Progressive has more than 50 subsidiaries one mutual insurance affiliate and a limited partnership investment affiliate.

Geographic Reach

Progressive operates more than 450 offices throughout the US and sells personal auto insurance on via Internet in Australia.

In addition to its headquarters additional offices and call center operations in Mayfield Village Ohio the company owns locations in Colorado Springs Colorado; Tampa and St. Petersburg Florida; and Tempe Arizona.

Sales and Marketing

Its US customer service group (which support policy servicing agency distribution claims and direct sales operations) are located at call centers in Mayfield Village Ohio; Tampa and St. Petersburg Florida; Sacramento California; Tempe Arizona; and Colorado Springs Colorado.

Progressive sells its personal lines through more than 35000 independent agencies and through partnerships with other insurance companies and financial institutions. It also sells directly to customers online and by telephone.

Commercial lines are distributed directly and through independent agencies.

Total advertising costs in 2015 were $748.3 million up from $681.8 million in 2014 and $619.8 million in 2013.

Financial Performance

Organic growth has lifted the company's revenues every year since 2008. Revenue grew 8% in 2015 on growth in the personal lines of business as rates increased and customers bought higher premium policies. Policy growth and higher average premium policies also led to an overall 15% increase on commercial lines premiums. The company has been working on providing its customers with new insurance options (as well as increasingly investing in marketing efforts) which has paid off in higher revenues. For example higher media spend helped the company secure more than 400000 new policies during 2015.

Net income which had risen in 2013 and 2014 remained relatively flat at some $1.3 billion in 2015 (a 1% decline from 2014). The higher revenues that year were partially offset by higher losses and loss adjustment expenses cutting into the firm's bottom line. Cash flow from operations has been rising for the past few years (with the exception of a dip in 2014) and in 2015 it rose 33% to $2.3 billion. That increase was largely driven by an increase in unearned premiums and loss adjustment expense reserves.

Strategy

Unlike some insurers who in fat markets earn more from their investments than their premiums more than 90% of Progressive's revenues have historically come from policy premiums.

The company's actual insurance operations have remained profitable and grown as it has entered into new geographic markets and expanded distribution of its personal auto products online. Already among the leading US auto insurers based on premiums (just behind State Farm and Allstate) Progressive is aiming to be on top.

Because it is fairly easy for customers to switch auto insurers Progressive competes on price and accessibility. To attract new customers the company's television ads featuring its perky spokesperson "Flo" have shot up the company's brand recognition. Operating on the premise that a few drivers are responsible for the majority of claims and that previous risk models were incomplete Progressive is now also offering rates that are tied to actual usage.

To retain customers Progressive is promoting its non-auto personal products through bundled packages with lower auto rates. Once a customer has bought a bundled package of home/auto/umbrella coverage they are also much less likely to switch insurance providers.

Progressive expanded its product line in 2015 by launching travel insurance and wedding/event insurance. Also that year it introduced its Snapshot mobile application program which monitors drivers' habits for potential discounts on coverage.

In 2014 the company introduced its agency auto product in Massachusetts; with this launch Progressive now offers Agency and Direct auto insurance in every US state.

Mergers and Acquisitions

In 2015 Progressive acquired a majority stake (67%) of ARX Holding a homeowners' insurance carrier for $875 million. That deal expanded its product portfolio; Progressive intends to acquire the rest of the firm it doesn't already own by the year 2021.

HISTORY

Attorneys Jack Green and Joseph Lewis founded Progressive Mutual Insurance in Cleveland in 1937. Initially offering standard auto insurance the company attracted customers through such innovations as installment plans for premiums (a payment method popularized during the Depression) and drive-in claims services (the company was headquartered in a garage). Progressive's early years were uncertain — at one point the founders were even advised to go out of business — but the advent of WWII bolstered business: Car and insurance purchases were up but accidents were down as gas rationing limited driving.

Then came the suburbs and cars of the 1950s. While most competitors sought low-risk drivers Progressive exploited the high-risk niche through careful underwriting and statistical analysis. Subsidiary Progressive Casualty was founded in 1956 (the year after Joseph Lewis died) to insure the best of the worst. Lewis' son Peter joined the company in 1955 and helped engineer its early-1960s expansion outside Ohio. After Green retired in 1965 Peter gained control of the company through a leveraged buyout and renamed it The Progressive Corporation. Six years later Lewis took it public and formed subsidiary Progressive American in Florida.

In the mid-1970s the industry went into a funk as it was hit by a wave of consolidations and rising interest rates. Lewis set a goal for the company to always earn an underwriting profit instead of depending on investments to make a profit. Progressive achieved stellar results during the 1970s especially after states began requiring drivers to be insured and other insurers began weeding out higher risks.

Competition in nonstandard insurance grew in the 1980s as major insurers such as Allstate and State Farm joined the fray with their larger sales forces and deeper pockets. In 1988 California's Proposition 103 retroactively reduced rates; Progressive fought California's demand for refunds but set aside reserves to pay them.

That year Lewis hired Cleveland financier Alfred Lerner to guide company investments. Lerner invested $75 million in Progressive via a convertible debenture; five years later he converted it to stock half of which he sold for $122 million. Soon after he was asked to resign. In 1993 Progressive settled with California for $51 million and applied to earnings the remaining $100 million in refund reserves. (Company soul-searching related to Proposition 103 led to the launch of Progressive's now-famous "Immediate Response" vehicles which provide 24-hour claims service at accident sites.)

In 1995 Progressive's practice of using consumer credit information to make underwriting decisions drew the attention of Arkansas and Vermont insurance regulators who said the company might be discriminating against people who didn't have the credit cards Progressive used to evaluate creditworthiness. In 1996 insurance regulators in Alaska Maryland and Texas also began probing Progressive's credit information practices.

In 1997 Progressive bought nonstandard auto insurer Midland Financial Group. As competition grew in 1999 the company cut rates and said it would write no new policies in Canada. In 2000 — with underwriting margins dropping industrywide — the company continued advertising aggressively. Progressive stopped writing new homeowners insurance in 2002 instead concentrating on its core operations. In 2006 the company began offering personal umbrella coverage.

The company took a bold international expansion measure in 2009: Launching personal auto insurance online in Australia. International expansion has not been a key strategy for Progressive but apparently the time was right for such growth. And apparently the company is prepared to give the new operation time to grow which is good considering that it has not yet made significant contributions to overall revenues.

EXECUTIVES

Chief Investment Officer, William M. (Bill) Cody, age 55, $463,269 total compensation
President of Customer Operations, S. Patricia (Tricia) Griffith, age 53, $616,346 total compensation
President Commercial Lines Group, John A. Barbagallo, age 58, $463,269 total compensation
CFO, John P. Sauerland, age 53, $546,538 total compensation
Chief Legal Officer, Dan Mascaro
President Personal Lines, Patrick K. (Pat) Callahan, age 46
President Claims, Michael D. (Mike) Sieger, age 55
CIO, Steven A. (Steve) Broz, age 46
Customer Relationship Management President, John Murphy, age 47
Medical Director, Crystal Kastberg
Assistant Vice President Human Resources Director Business, Patricia Bemer
Vice President Information Technology, Edward Fowler
Vice President of Human Resour, Kathy Cramer
Chairman, Glenn M. Renwick, age 62
Auditors: PricewaterhouseCoopers LLP

LOCATIONS

HQ: Progressive Corp. (OH)
6300 Wilson Mills Road, Mayfield Village, OH 44143
Phone: 440 461-5000   **Fax:** 440 446-7168
Web: www.progressive.com

PRODUCTS/OPERATIONS

2016 Sales

	% of total
Personal Lines	82
Commercial Auto	14
Investments	2
Fees & other revenues	1
Services	1
Gains (losses) on extinguishment of debt	—
Total	**100**

Selected Insurance Options

Auto Insurance
Local Car Insurance
Motorcycle Insurance
Boat Insurance
RV Insurance
Commercial Insurance
Snowmobile Insurance
PWC Insurance
Homeowners Insurance
Renters Insurance
ATV Insurance
Life Insurance
Health Insurance
Umbrella Insurance

COMPETITORS

21st Century Insurance	Nationwide
Allstate	Ohio Casualty
American Family Insurance	Old Republic
	State Auto Financial
Cincinnati Financial	State Farm
Farmers Group	Travelers Companies
GEICO	USAA
Infinity Property & Casualty	White Mountains Insurance Group
Liberty Mutual	

HISTORICAL FINANCIALS

Company Type: Public

Income Statement

FYE: December 31

	ASSETS ($ mil.)	NET INCOME ($ mil.)	INCOME AS % OF ASSETS	EMPLOYEES
12/16	33,427	1,031	3.1%	31,721
12/15	29,819	1,267	4.3%	28,580
12/14	25,787	1,281	5.0%	26,501
12/13	24,408	1,165	4.8%	26,145
12/12	22,694	902	4.0%	25,889
Annual Growth	**10.2%**	**3.4%**	**—**	**5.2%**

2016 Year-End Financials

Debt ratio: 9.42%	No. of shares (mil.): 579
Return on equity: 13.49%	Dividends
Cash ($ mil.): 211	Yield: 0.0%
Current ratio: —	Payout: 50.4%
Long-term debt ($ mil.): —	Market value ($ mil.): 20,586

	STOCK PRICE ($) FY Close	P/E High/Low		PER SHARE ($) Earnings	Dividends	Book Value
12/16	35.50	20	17	1.76	0.89	13.72
12/15	31.80	16	12	2.15	0.69	12.49
12/14	26.99	13	10	2.15	1.49	11.79
12/13	27.27	14	11	1.93	1.28	10.39
12/12	21.10	16	13	1.48	1.41	9.94
Annual Growth	**13.9%**	—	—	**4.4%**	**(10.9%)**	**8.4%**

Prospect Capital Corporation

Prospect Capital is a closed-end investment fund with holdings in the consumer food health care and manufacturing sectors among others. The company targets privately held middle-market firms with annual revenues of less than $750 million; it also considers thinly traded public companies or turnaround situations. Prospect's portfolio includes interests in more than 100 companies mainly through senior loans and mezzanine debt. The company also makes equity and secured debt investments. Typically investing from $5 million to $250 million per transaction Prospect is a long-term investor that maintains regular contact with its portfolio company's management and participates in their board meetings.

Operations

Prospect has elected to be regulated as a business development company (BDC) a status which affords the firm certain tax benefits. Although it initially targeted on industrial and energy investments the company has broadened its focus in the past few years and minimized its holdings in the energy sector.

Geographic Reach

New York-based Prospect Capital invests primarily in US companies but also in Canada the Cayman Islands and Ireland. About 80% of the firm's investment portfolio is in the US.

Financial Performance

Prospect Capital reported revenue of $576.3 million in fiscal 2013 (ended June) an 80% increase over the year earlier period. Net income rose 16% over the same period to nearly $221 million. Prospect's financial prospects have brightened considerably in recent years with revenue up more than 500% since fiscal 2009 and steeply rising profits. The 80% increase in fiscal 2013 revenue was primarily due to 98% increase in interest income as a result of interest earned on the mezzanine loan. Dividend income rose as well.

Strategy

Prospect Capital pursues a diversified investment strategy investing in 124 long-term portfolio investments and CLOs (collateralized loan obligations) and to a lesser extent money market funds. In fiscal 2013 (ended June) the firm originated $3.1 million of new investments. Prospect's origination efforts are focused primarily on secured lending to reduce portfolio risk investing primarily in first lien loans and subordinated notes in CLOs though it also engages in select junior debt and equity investments. First lien loans represent about 55% of its investment portfolio with second lien loans representing about 25%. Diversified financial services is the firm's single largest industry sector for investment followed by consumer finance durable consumer products consumer services and software and computer services. Together these five industries constitute more than half of Prospect's investment portfolio.

In 2013 the firm invested $144.5 million in four new transactions encompassing 19 rent-producing multifamily residential properties totaling 5652 rental units. Combined with its prior investments Prospect has a invested a total of $288.3 million in 10 separate transactions encompassing 25 multifamily residential properties with more than 9100 rental units.

Mergers and Acquisitions

In 2013 Prospect acquired A 94% stake in Nationwide Acceptance LLC a Chicago based consumer finance company.

EXECUTIVES

Board Member, Andrew C Cooper
Auditors: BDO USA, LLP

LOCATIONS

HQ: Prospect Capital Corporation
10 East 40th Street, 42nd Floor, New York, NY 10016
Phone: 212 448-0702
Web: www.prospectstreet.com

PRODUCTS/OPERATIONS

Selected Current Investments
AIRMALL USA Inc. (property management)
Ajax Rolled Ring & Machine Inc. (manufacturing)
AWCNC (machinery)
Blue Coat Systems Inc. (software computer service)
Borga Inc. (manufacturing)
Boxercraft (textiles and leather)
Broder Bros. Co. (Textiles)
Crossman Corp. (manufacturing)
Focus Products (consumer products)
Grocery Outlet (supermarkets)
Harley Marine Services (transportation)
Injured Workers Pharmacy (health care)
Nationwide Acceptance Holdings LLC (consumer finance)
National Bankruptcy Services (financial services)
NMMB (advertising media buying)
NRG Manufacturing Inc. (drilling rig components)
R-V Industries Inc. (metal fabrication)
Wind River Resources (oil and gas production)

COMPETITORS

ACI Capital	OHA Investment
Apollo Investment	Stephens Group
First Reserve	TPG
GFI Energy Ventures	Venrock
Katalyst	

HISTORICAL FINANCIALS

Company Type: Public

Income Statement

FYE: June 30

	ASSETS ($ mil.)	NET INCOME ($ mil.)	INCOME AS % OF ASSETS	EMPLOYEES
06/17	6,172	306	5.0%	—
06/16	6,276	371	5.9%	—
06/15	6,798	362	5.3%	—
06/14	6,477	357	5.5%	—
06/13	4,448	324	7.3%	—
Annual Growth	8.5%	(1.5%)	—	—

2017 Year-End Financials

Debt ratio: 42.80%
Return on equity: 9.01%
Cash ($ mil.): 318
Current ratio: —
Long-term debt ($ mil.): —

No. of shares (mil.): 360
Dividends
Yield: 12.3%
Payout: 109.8%
Market value ($ mil.): 2,924

	STOCK PRICE ($) FY Close	P/E High/Low		PER SHARE ($) Earnings	Dividends	Book Value
06/17	8.12	11	9	0.85	1.00	9.32
06/16	7.82	8	5	1.04	1.00	9.62
06/15	7.37	11	7	1.03	1.19	10.31
06/14	10.63	10	8	1.19	1.32	10.56
06/13	10.80	8	6	1.57	1.28	10.72
Annual Growth	(6.9%)	—	—	(14.2%)	(6.0%)	(3.4%)

Prosperity Bancshares Inc.

Prosperity Bancshares reaches banking customers across the Lone Star State. The holding company for Prosperity Bank operates about 230 branches across Texas and about 15 more in Oklahoma. Serving consumers and small to midsized businesses the bank offers traditional deposit and loan services in addition to wealth management retail brokerage and mortgage banking investment services. Prosperity Bank focuses on real estate lending: Commercial mortgages make up the largest segment of the company's loan portfolio (33%) followed by residential mortgages (24%). Credit cards business auto consumer home equity loans round out its lending activities.

Operations

About 63% of Prosperity's total revenue came from loan interest (including fees) in 2014 while another 22% came from interest on its investment securities. The rest of its revenue came from non-sufficient fund fees (4%) credit and debit card income (3%) deposit account service charges (2%) trust income (1%) mortgage income (1%) and brokerage income (1%).

Geographic Reach

Prosperity Bancshares operates 230 Texas banking locations across Houston South Texas the Dallas/Fort Worth metroplex East Texas Bryan/College Station Central Texas and West Texas. It also has 15 branch locations in Oklahoma (including Tulsa).

Sales and Marketing

The bank mainly targets consumers and small and medium-sized businesses and tailors its products to the specific needs of a given market.

Financial Performance

Prosperity's revenues and profits have been prospering thanks to loan and deposit business growth from acquisitions and declining loan loss provisions as its loan portfolio's credit quality has improved with higher property valuations in a strengthened economy.

The company's revenue jumped by 32% to $837.7 million in 2014 mostly as its loan interest income swelled by 40% on loan asset growth from its F&M acquisition. The bank's non-interest income rose by 29% as well from new deposit account service fees from the acquisition and additional income from its newly added brokerage and trust business.

Higher revenue and strong operating cost controls in 2014 drove Prosperity's net income higher by 34% to $297.4 million while its operating cash levels rose by 13% to $348.3 million on higher cash earnings.

Strategy

Prosperity Bancshares bases its growth strategy on three key elements: Internal loan and deposit business growth through "individualized customer service" and service line expansion opportunities; cost controls to maximize profitability; and acquisitions.

Toward its internal business growth initiatives Prosperity spent 2012 and 2013 launching its new trust brokerage mortgage lending and credit card products and services to customers for the first time.

With cost-controls in mind the bank tracks its branches "as separate profit centers" noting each branch's interest income efficiency ratio deposit growth loan growth and overall profitability. That way it can reward individual branch managers and presidents accordingly by merit rather than giving higher compensation across the board.

The acquisitive Prosperity Bancshares has been buying up small banks in Texas — and now Oklahoma — as it hopes to hit a sweet spot in the market between the national giants that dominate the Texas banking scene and smaller community banks.

Mergers and Acquisitions

In January 2016 furthering its presence in the Houston market Prosperity Bancshares purchased Tradition Bancshares along with its seven branches in the Houston Area (Bellaire Katy and the Woodlands) $540 million in assets $239 million in loans and $483.8 million in deposits.

In April 2014 toward expansion in the Oklahoma and Dallas markets Prosperity purchased Tulsa-based F&M Bancorporation and its subsidiary The F&M Bank & Trust Company. The deal added 13 branches including nine in Tulsa and surrounding areas three in Dallas and a loan production office in Oklahoma City.

In April 2013 it acquired Coppermark Bank one of Oklahoma City's largest banks with six branches in Oklahoma City and three locations in North Dallas for $194 million. The deal also added the credit card and agent bank merchant processing business from its subsidiary Bankers Credit Card Services.

In January 2013 the company boosted its market share in East Texas after buying East Texas Financial Services and its four First Federal Bank Texas branch locations including three branches in Tyler and one in Gilmer.

Company Background

In early 2012 Prosperity acquired Texas Bankers a three-branch Austin bank with some $72 million in assets. The merger increased Prosperity's number of Central Texas branches to 34 banking locations. It followed that deal with the purchase of The Bank Arlington a single-branch bank operating in the Dallas/Ft. Worth area. It acquired single-branch Community National Bank of Bellaire Texas in late 2012.

Also in 2012 Prosperity expanded into West Texas after it merged American State Financial Corporation and its American State Bank subsidiary into its operations. The deal added $3 billion in assets and 37 West Texas banking offices in Lubbock Midland/Odessa and Abilene.

EXECUTIVES

EVP Cashier Prosperity Bank, Mike Harris
Senior Chairman and CEO, David Zalman, age 60, $851,567 total compensation
CFO; EVP and CFO Prosperity Bank, David Hollaway, age 61, $425,000 total compensation
Vice Chairman; Chairman and COO Prosperity Bank, H. E. (Tim) Timanus, age 73, $452,400 total compensation
Vice Chairman and Area Chairman Central Texas, Edward Z. (Eddie) Safady
EVP Regulatory and Compliance Prosperity Bank, Rhonda L. Carroll
Chief Lending Officer Prosperity Bank, Randy D. Hester, $325,000 total compensation
SEVP Financial Operations and Administration Prosperity Bank, Mike Epps, $327,625 total compensation
EVP and CIO Prosperity Bank, Gisela Riggan
Chief Risk Oficer, Jennifer Willcoxon
Chief Credit Officer Prosperity Bank, Merle Karnes
President Prosperity Bank, Bob Benter
EVP Prosperity Bancshares and Prosperity Bank, Robert (Bob) Dowdell
Chairman Wealth Management, Russell Marshall
Senior Vice President Facilities, Tom Allen
Vice President and Lobby ManagerLakeway Banking Center, Dala Campbell
Senior Vice President SBA Lending, Beverly Layne
Assistant Vice President of Technology Procurement, Lausanne Barrett
Assistant Vice President and Lobby Manager, Laura Arroyo
Assistant Vice President, Jill Kruger
Assistant Vice President, Jack Biffle
Executive Vice President, Sam Sicola
Regional President, Jim Habern
Auditors: Deloitte & Touche LLP

LOCATIONS

HQ: Prosperity Bancshares Inc.
Prosperity Bank Plaza, 4295 San Felipe, Houston, TX 77027
Phone: 281 269-7199
Web: www.prosperitybankusa.com

PRODUCTS/OPERATIONS

2014 Sales

	$ mil.	% of total
Interest		
Loans including fees	525	63
Securities	188	22
Federal funds sold	0	—
Noninterest		
Non-sufficient funds fees	37	4
Debit card and ATM card income	22	3
Service charges on deposit accounts	16	2
Trust income	8	1
Brokerage income	5	1
Mortgage income	4	1
Other	28	3
Total	**837**	**100**

COMPETITORS

Amegy	JPMorgan Chase
BBVA Compass	North Dallas Bank
Bancshares	Texas Capital
Bank of America	Bancshares
Citibank	Wells Fargo
Comerica	Woodforest Financial
Cullen/Frost Bankers	

HISTORICAL FINANCIALS

Company Type: Public

Income Statement

FYE: December 31

	ASSETS ($ mil.)	NET INCOME ($ mil.)	INCOME AS % OF ASSETS	EMPLOYEES
12/16	22,331	274	1.2%	3,035
12/15	22,037	286	1.3%	3,037
12/14	21,507	297	1.4%	3,096
12/13	18,642	221	1.2%	2,995
12/12	14,583	167	1.2%	2,266
Annual Growth	**11.2%**	**13.1%**		**7.6%**

2016 Year-End Financials

Debt ratio: 4.44%
Return on equity: 7.70%
Cash ($ mil.): 436
Current ratio: —
Long-term debt ($ mil.): —
No. of shares (mil.): 69
Dividends
Yield: 0.0%
Payout: 31.4%
Market value ($ mil.): 4,988

	STOCK PRICE ($) FY Close	P/E High/Low		PER SHARE ($) Earnings	Dividends	Book Value
12/16	71.78	19	9	3.94	1.24	52.41
12/15	47.86	14	11	4.09	1.12	49.45
12/14	55.36	16	12	4.32	0.99	46.50
12/13	63.39	18	11	3.65	0.89	42.19
12/12	42.00	15	12	3.23	0.80	37.01
Annual Growth	**14.3%**	—	—	**5.1%**	**11.6%**	**9.1%**

Protective Life Insurance Co

Protective Life & Annuity markets and sells financial security in the form of term and universal life insurance policies and fixed and variable annuity products. Although the company is based in Alabama and licensed to sell insurance throughout the US it exclusively serves clients in New York. Sister companies include West Coast Life Insurance (life insurance and annuities) MONY Life Insurance (ditto) and Lyndon Insurance (specialty coverage). Protective Life & Annuity is a unit of Protective Life Insurance which is part of Dai-Ichi Life Holdings subsidiary Protective Life Corporation.

Operations
Every state has unique requirements that insurance companies must meet in order to gain permission to operate there. New York's insurance code has the stiffest requirements and many small companies simply choose not to operate in that market. However the market is so large and tempting that other companies opt to maintain separate subsidiaries that exclusively serve New York. In this instance parent company Protective Life Insurance Company serves the rest of the US while Protective Life & Annuity is strictly focused on New York.

Protective Life Corporation was acquired by Japanese insurer Dai-ichi Life in early 2015.

Sales and Marketing
Protective Life & Annuity sells coverage through independent agents broker-dealers and financial institutions as well as through partnerships with employer groups and through its own sales division.

EXECUTIVES

EVP Chief Legal Officer Secretary and General Counsel, Deborah J. Long, age 63
Chairman and CEO, John D. Johns, age 64
EVP and Chief Investment Officer, Carl S. Thigpen, age 60
EVP and Chief Administrative Officer, D. Scott Adams, age 52
President and COO, Richard J. Bielen
EVP Finance and Risk; Chief Risk Officer, Michael G. (Mike) Temple, age 54
SVP Chief Information and Operations Officer, Mark J. Cyphert
EVP CFO and Controller, Steven G. Walker
Vice President of Marketing, Teri Schultz
III CCIM Vice President Investments, Steve Clikas
Second Vice President Reinsurance Field Accounting, Richard Ostrowski
Auditors: PricewaterhouseCoopers LLP

LOCATIONS

HQ: Protective Life Insurance Co
2801 Highway 280 South, Birmingham, AL 35223
Phone: 205 268-1000
Web: www.protective.com

COMPETITORS

Guardian Insurance and Annuity	Penn Mutual
	Prudential
MetLife	The Hartford
New York Life	

HISTORICAL FINANCIALS

Company Type: Public

Income Statement

FYE: December 31

	ASSETS ($ mil.)	NET INCOME ($ mil.)	INCOME AS % OF ASSETS	EMPLOYEES
12/16	74,465	352	0.5%	2,719
12/15*	68,031	179	0.3%	2,541
01/15	0	88	—	—
12/14	69,992	491	0.7%	2,457
12/13	68,296	291	0.4%	2,415
Annual Growth	**2.9%**	**6.5%**		**4.0%**

*Fiscal year change

2016 Year-End Financials

Debt ratio: 5.07%
Return on equity: 5.90%
Cash ($ mil.): 214
Current ratio: —
Long-term debt ($ mil.): —
No. of shares (mil.): 5
Dividends
Yield: —
Payout: 153.1%
Market value ($ mil.): —

Provident Financial Services Inc

Provident wants to be a prominent force in the New Jersey banking scene. Provident Financial Services owns The Provident Bank which serves individuals businesses and families from 85 branches across more than 10 northern and central New Jersey counties. Founded in 1839 the $8.5 billion-bank offers traditional deposit and lending products as well as wealth management and trust services. About 50% of its revenue comes from real estate loan interest while another 25% comes from interest on commercial and consumer loans. Construction loans round out its lending activities. The company's Provident Investment Services subsidiary sells life and health insurance and investment products.

Operations

Provident which staffed more than 1020 employees boasted some $8.5 billion in total assets loans of $6.1 billion and deposits of $5.8 billion at the end of 2014. Mortgages loans made up 70% of its total loan portfolio that year.

Geographic Reach

The bank's 86 branches are located in northern and central New Jersey as well as in Pennsylvania (in the Bucks Lehigh and Northampton counties). Its administrative offices are in Iselin New Jersey while its satellite loan production offices are in Covent Station Flemington Paramus Princeton and West Orange in New Jersey; and in Bethleham and Newtown Pennsylvania.

Sales and Marketing

Provident targets individuals families and businesses in its primary market areas in New Jersey (which covered a population of 6.9 million or 78% of the state's population) and Pennsylvania (where the bank's primary market covered 10% of that state's population.

Provident's primary markets include a mix of urban and suburban communities. It serves companies in a variety of industries including pharmaceutical and other manufacturing companies network communications insurance and financial services healthcare and retail businesses.

Financial Performance

Provident has struggled to consistently grow its revenues in recent years due to shrinking interest margins on loans amidst the low-interest environment. Its profits however have been rising thanks to declining loan loss provisions as its loan portfolio's credit quality has improved with higher property valuations in a strengthened economy.

The bank's revenue rose by 8% to $320.5 million in 2014 mostly thanks to added interest income from loan asset growth — including a 9% rise in real estate secured loan business and a 24% rise in commercial loan business — stemming from its acquisition of Team Capital Bank.

Higher revenue and a continued decline in loan loss provisions in 2014 drove Provident's net income higher by 4% to $73.6 million. Its operating cash levels dipped by 3% to $96.4 million after adjusting its earnings for non-cash items mostly related to an increase in other assets.

Strategy

Provident Financial continues to look for strategic acquisition opportunities of banks and other financial services providers to grow its loan and deposit business and extend its branch network into more of its primary market areas.

The company also remains focused on its conservative lending practices and is seeking to diversify its portfolio and reduce risk by placing more emphasis on commercial real estate multifamily residential and business loans.

Mergers and Acquisitions

In May 2014 Provident Financial Services purchased Team Capital Bank for $115.1 million effectively extending its reach into Eastern Pennsylvania and the affluent counties of Hunterdon and Somerset. The deal also added $964 million in total assets $631 million in loan assets and $770 million in deposits.

Company Background

In 2011 the company acquired Beacon Trust Company an asset manager for individuals municipalities corporations pension funds and not-for-profit organizations. The deal significantly expanded its wealth management business and boosted its assets under management to some $1.5 billion.

EXECUTIVES

Chairman President and CEO, Christopher P. Martin, age 61, $608,846 total compensation

EVP and CFO, Thomas M. Lyons, age 53, $349,308 total compensation

EVP and Director Retail Banking The Provident Bank, Michael A. Raimonde, age 65, $238,370 total compensation

EVP General Counsel and Corporate Secretary The Provident Bank, John F. Kuntz, age 62, $312,700 total compensation

EVP and Chief Lending Officer The Provident Bank, Donald W. Blum, age 61, $314,562 total compensation

First VP Delivery and Distribution Division The Provident Bank, Jack Novielli, age 58

EVP and and Chief Human Resources Officer The Provident Bank, Janet D. Krasowski, age 64

EVP and Chief Credit Officer The Provident Bank, Brian Giovinazzi, age 63, $161,138 total compensation

EVP and Chief Wealth Officer The Provident Bank, James D. Nesci, age 45, $274,423 total compensation

SVP and Chief Risk Officer The Provident Bank, James Christy

Vice President, Colleen Hanley

Executive Vice President Human Resources, John Falco

First Vice President Marketing Director, Robert Capozzoli

Relationship Manager Vice President, John Oliver

Vice President, Charles Pocsi

Assistant Vice President Branch Manager, Carlos Martin

Banking Center Manager Assistant Vice President, Rebecca Peraza

Assistant Vice President, Joseph Labib

Assistant Vice President Branch Center Manager, Carol Viola

Auditors: KPMG LLP

LOCATIONS

HQ: Provident Financial Services Inc
239 Washington Street, Jersey City, NJ 07302
Phone: 732 590-9200
Web: www.providentnj.com

PRODUCTS/OPERATIONS

2014 Sales

	$ mil.	% of total
Interest		
Real estate secured loans	166	52
Commercial loans	50	16
Consumer loans	23	7
Securities & other	38	12
Non-interest		
Fees	31	10
Other	9	3
Total	**320**	**100**

COMPETITORS

Bank of America	PNC Financial
Capital One	TD Bank USA
Citibank	Valley National
Hudson City Bancorp	Bancorp
JPMorgan Chase	
New York Community Bancorp	

HISTORICAL FINANCIALS

Company Type: Public

Income Statement

FYE: December 31

	ASSETS ($ mil.)	NET INCOME ($ mil.)	INCOME AS % OF ASSETS	EMPLOYEES
12/16	9,500	87	0.9%	1,057
12/15	8,911	83	0.9%	1,064
12/14	8,523	73	0.9%	1,021
12/13	7,487	70	0.9%	942
12/12	7,283	67	0.9%	941
Annual Growth	6.9%	6.9%	—	2.9%

2016 Year-End Financials

Debt ratio: 3.34%
Return on equity: 7.15%
Cash ($ mil.): 144
Current ratio: —
Long-term debt ($ mil.): —

No. of shares (mil.): 66
Dividends
  Yield: 0.0%
  Payout: 51.4%
Market value ($ mil.): 1,870

	STOCK PRICE ($) FY Close	P/E High/Low	Earnings	Dividends	Book Value
12/16	28.30	21 13	1.38	0.71	18.94
12/15	20.15	16 13	1.33	0.65	18.26
12/14	18.06	16 13	1.22	0.60	17.63
12/13	19.32	16 12	1.23	0.76	16.87
12/12	14.92	14 11	1.18	0.71	16.37
Annual Growth	17.4%	— —	—	4.0% (0.0%)	3.7%

Prudential Annuities Life Assurance Corp

Auditors: PricewaterhouseCoopers LLP

LOCATIONS

HQ: Prudential Annuities Life Assurance Corp
One Corporate Drive, Shelton, CT 06484
Phone: 203 926-1888
Web: www.investor.prudential.com

COMPETITORS

American Equity Investment Life Holding Company
Genworth Financial
Great American Financial Resources
John Hancock Financial Services
Kansas City Life
Lincoln Financial Group
MassMutual
MetLife
National Western
Northwestern Mutual
Presidential Life

HISTORICAL FINANCIALS

Company Type: Public

Income Statement

FYE: December 31

	ASSETS ($ mil.)	NET INCOME ($ mil.)	INCOME AS % OF ASSETS	EMPLOYEES
12/16	59,822	(1,090)	—	—
12/15	47,254	173	0.4%	—
12/14	52,472	250	0.5%	—
12/13	53,521	848	1.6%	—
12/12	52,855	634	1.2%	—
Annual Growth	3.1%	—	—	—

2016 Year-End Financials

Debt ratio: 1.62%
Return on equity: (-25.77%)
Cash ($ mil.): 2,945
Current ratio: —
Long-term debt ($ mil.): —

No. of shares (mil.): 0
Dividends
　Yield: —
　Payout: —
Market value ($ mil.): —

Prudential Financial, Inc.

Prudential Financial wants to make sure its position near the top of the life insurance summit is set in stone. Prudential known for its Rock of Gibraltar logo is one of the top US life insurers and one of the largest life insurance companies worldwide. The firm is perhaps best known for its individual life insurance though it also sells group life and disability insurance as well as annuities. Prudential also offers investment products and services including asset management services mutual funds and retirement planning. In Asia the company operates through its Gibraltar Life Insurance unit. Prudential has some $1.2 trillion in assets under management.

HISTORY

In 1873 John Dryden founded the Widows and Orphans Friendly Society in New Jersey to sell workers industrial insurance (low-face-value weekly premium life insurance). In 1875 it became The Prudential Friendly Society taking the name from England's Prudential Assurance Co. The next year Dryden visited the English company and copied some of its methods such as recruiting agents from its targeted neighborhoods.

Prudential added ordinary whole life insurance in 1886. By 1900 the firm was selling more than 2000 such policies annually and had 3000 agents in eight states. In 1896 the J. Walter Thompson advertising agency (now the WPP Group) designed Prudential's Rock of Gibraltar logo.

The firm issued its first group life policy in 1916 (Prudential became a major group life insurer in the 1940s). In 1928 it introduced an Accidental Death Benefit which cost it an extra $3 million in benefits the next year alone (death claims rose drastically early in the Depression).

In 1943 Prudential mutualized. The company began decentralizing operations in the 1940s. Later it introduced a Property Investment Separate Account (PRISA) which gave pension plans a real estate investment option. By 1974 the firm was the US's group pension leader.

The insurer bought securities brokerage The Bache Group to form Pru Bache (now Prudential Securities) in 1981. Bache's forte was retail invest-ments an area expected to blend well with Prudential's insurance business. Under George Ball Pru Bache tried to become a major investment banker — but failed. In 1991 Ball resigned leaving losses of almost $260 million and numerous law-suits involving real estate limited partnerships.

Despite the 1992 settlement of the real estate partnership suits Prudential remained under scrutiny by several states because of "churning" a process in which agents generated commissions by inducing policyholders to trade up to more expensive policies. In 1995 new management led by former Chase Manhattanite Arthur Ryan brought sales under control sold such units as reinsurance and mortgage servicing and put its $6 billion real estate portfolio on the block. (In 1997 it sold its property management unit and Canadian commercial real estate unit; in 1998 it sold its landmark Prudential Center complex in Boston.)

In 1996 regulators from 30 states found that Prudential knew about the churning earlier than it had admitted had not stopped the perpetrators and had even promoted them. A 1997 settlement called for the company to pay restitution but the more than $2 billion estimated cost was thought to be less than the losses customers had suffered.

As the financial services industry continued to restructure Prudential in 1998 announced plans to demutualize. To focus on life insurance the company sold its health care unit to Aetna in 1999. The same year Prudential paid $62 million to resolve more churning claims revamped itself into international institutional and retail divisions and trimmed jobs. Ending its attempts to originate business the company cut 75% of its investment banking staff in 2000.

Demutualized Prudential Financial's 2001 IPO — one of the largest ever in the insurance industry — raised more than $3 billion. Prudential Financial became the holding company name for all operations making Prudential Insurance (the company's former name) a subsidiary and pure life insurer.

EXECUTIVES

Senior Vice President, Susan Blount
Chairman and CEO, John R. Strangfeld, age 63, $1,400,000 total compensation
Executive Vice President Prudential Financial and Prudential Institution, Jean Hamilton
SVP Corporate Human Resources and Chair The Prudential Foundation, Sharon C. Taylor, age 63
EVP and COO International, Charles F. (Charlie) Lowrey, age 59, $770,000 total compensation
SVP and CIO, Barbara G. Koster, age 62
Chairman and CEO International Investments, Stephen (Steve) Pelletier, age 63, $770,000 total compensation
Managing Director and CEO European Business; Head of Global Merchant Banking Group, Robert M. Falzon, age 57, $759,231 total compensation
SVP and Chief Investment Officer, Scott G. Sleyster, age 57
SVP and Chief Risk Officer, Nicholas C. (Nick) Silitch, age 55
SVP and Chief Actuary, Richard F. Lambert, age 60
President and CEO Prudential Retirement, Phil Waldeck
EVP and General Counsel, Timothy P. Harris, age 56
Vice President of Information Technology, Kelly Nicholson
Vice President Information Technology, Robert Bastian
Vice President Information Technology, Jim Tonno
Vice President Information Technology, Diana D'Amore
Senior Vice President Treasurer, Bernard Jacob
Vice President Human Resources, Dawn Gammon

Vice President Global Business and Technology Solutions, Ed Martinez
Vice President Information Systems, Scott Neely
Vice President Information Technology Shared Services, Chris Donahue
Medical Director, Myrtho Montes
Vice President Information Technology, Elaine Forsyth
Vice President, Robert Davis
Vice President, Peter Freitag
Vice President Investor Relations, Ruth Hiatt
Senior Vice President Human Resources, Sue Taylor
Vice President Information Technology, Robert Piascik
Vice President Client Services, Nicole Olivieri
Vice President and Corporate Counsel, Phillip Yang
Senior Vice President Investments, Moya Chew-Lai
Vice President Institutional Client Services, Lynn Myers
Vice President of International Operations and Systems, Ryugo Toh
Vice President Enterprise Information Security, Carol Haeberle
Vice President Information Technology, Joel Neice
Vice President and Corporate Counsel, Bianca Butler
Vice President and Corporate Counsel, Kelley H Butler
Vice President Information Systems, Matt Schuette
Vice President, Peter Cody
Vice President Information Systems, Dele Oladapo
Vice President, Marla Jackson
Investment Vice President, Richard Toner
Vice President Financial Systems, John Toner
Vice President, Jack Lerner
Vice President and Chief Information Security Officer, Thomas Doughty
Vice President Corporate Counsel (1998), Todd Moffett
Vice President Issues Management, Greg Loder
Investment Vice President, Scott Swanson
Vice President, Anthony Coletta
Vice President and Actuary, Dennis C Dressel
Vice President marketing Management, Eric Philip
Vice President, Noah Krieger
Vice President Financial Analysis, Wei Jin
Divisional Vice President Pacific Northwest, Randy Cox
Vice President Process Management, Greg Steffe
Vice President, Juzer Mohammedshah
Vice President Institutional Investment Products Group, John Bradley
Vice President Information Sys, Allison Shilling
Vice President Project Management, Mary Mathern
Vice President of Annuities Information Technology, Dawn Davis
Vice President, Richard Miller
M Sales Vice President, Doug Peterson
Vice President Information Systems, Venkata Natarajan
Vice President Voluntary Benefits, Bob Patience
Vice President Financial Reporting, Rita Lombardi
Vice President Corporate Counsel and Chief Tax Officer (2007), James Joseph Shea
Regional Vice President, Chad Faucett
Vice President Marketing Metrics, Bob Conover
Vice President Planning and Strategy, Chris Huydic
Vice President Corporate Counsel (1997), William H Bulmer
Vice President Information Technology, Nicholas Defeis
Vice President Program Management Office, Annemarie Bowman
Vice President and Corporate Counsel, Judith Jaffess
Vice President In The San Francisco Corporate Finance Office, David Nguyen
Vice President Learning, Mary McCabe

Vice President Finance (Chief Financial Officer) Prudential Group Insurance, Christine Knight

Vice President Accounting Policy, Karen Kaempffer

Vice President, Paula Olenskyj

Vice President, Kelly Williams

Vice President of Operations and Service Management, Christopher Flanagan

Regional Sales Vice President, Kolina Vortman

Vice President Head of Infrastructure PIM Public Equity, Timothy Cahill

Assistant Vice President Banki, Marylene Melim

Vice President, Guy Principe

Vice President Information Technology, Ray Slider

Vice President and Actuary, Hank Ramsey

Vice President of Financial Reporting, Stanley Lezon

Vice President, Anne Thibeault

Vice President Advanced Planning, Jill Perlin

Vice President of Project Management, Aimara Toledo

Senior Vice President strategic Relationships, Harry Dalessio

Senior Vice President, Stephen Collins

Vice President And Corporate Counsel, Christine Parsadaian

Vice President, Marcus Berry

Vice President, Usha Archer

Senior Vice President, Lourenco de Matos

Regional Vice President, Sean Kath

Vice President Information Technology, Ann Delmedico

Vice President Corporate Development, Everett Miles

Vice President Business Finance, Stephen Durocher

Vice President Field Technology, Anthony Melchione

Vice President, Susanna Horng

Vice President, Richard Parke

Vice President Life Financial Strategy, Caroline Zhang

Vice President of Recruiting, Jim Viris

Vice President Operational Risk Management, Robert Tyndall

Senior Vice President and Actuary, Jason Tokuda

Vice President, Catherine Marcus

Vice President, Frank Papasavas

Vice President and Chief Operating Officer Prudential Bank and Trust, Heather Corrado

Vice President Annuities Compliance And Chief Compliance Officer Prudential Annuities Distributors, Michael Mccauley

Vice President and Chief Diversity Officer, Michele C Meyer-Shipp

Executive Vice President Retail and Client Service Fixed Income, Shaun Byrnes

Senior Vice President Strategic Relationships, Harry Delassio

Vice President, John Hom

Vice President Asset Liability Management Finance, Thomas Brennan

Functional Vice President Human Resources, Louise Sheppard

Vice President Information Systems, Susan Alfano

Vice President and Corporate Counsel, Robert Fishbein

Vice President Head TRS B2C MktgStrategy Prudential Reti, Jennifer Putney

Vice President and Actuary, Lisa Tokuda

Vice President Human Resources, Annmarie Jackiewicz

Regional Vice President Michigan, Greg Talpey

Vice President National Accounts, Trish Dedolce

Executive Vice President Marketing, John Doscher

Investment Senior Vice President, Anne Fifick

Vice President, Paul McLean

Vice President, Gerson Levin

Vice President Global Security, Michael Didomizio

Vice President And Corporate Counsel, Lisa Price

Vice President, James Mcclure

Vice President and Assistant Secretary, Brian J Morris

Vice President Financial Reporting, Warren Hoffman

Vice President Of Sales, John Bigelow

Vice President and Actuary, Sarah J Hamid

Senior Vice President Product Management, James McInnes

Vice President and Actuary, Marc Buzzelli

Vice President, Teri Sullivan-Yelko

Vice President, Keith Kehlbeck

Vice President Strategic Sourcing, Mark Vogt

Senior Vice President Business Development, Marc Pester

Vice President, Alan Brubaker

Vice President of Product Development, Kelly Rome

Regional Sales Vice President, Wai Miks

Vice President of Information Technology, Rob Lowther

Vice President Human Resources, Peter Capizzi

Vice President And Assistant Treasurer, Kathleen Hoffman

Vice President, Kalyan Ramanathan

Regional Sales Vice President, Tom O'Neill

Vice President of Voluntary Benefits, Cathleen Paugh

Auditors: PricewaterhouseCoopers LLP

LOCATIONS

HQ: Prudential Financial, Inc.
751 Broad Street, Newark, NJ 07102
Phone: 973 802-6000
Web: www.investor.prudential.com

2016 Sales

	$ mil.	% of total
US	36,079	61
Other countries	22,700	39
Total	**58,779**	**100**

PRODUCTS/OPERATIONS

2016 Revenues

	$ mil.	% of total
International insurance	21,009	36
US Retirement solutions & investment management	20,503	35
US Individual Life & group insurance	10,698	18
Closed block business	6,271	11
Corporate & adjustments	298	0
Total	**58,779**	**100**

2016 Revenues

	$ mil.	% of total
Premiums	30,964	53
Policy charges and fee income	5,906	10
Net investment income	15,520	26
Asset management and service fees	3,752	6
Other income	443	1
Realized investment gains (losses) net	2,194	4
Total	**58,779**	**100**

COMPETITORS

AEGON	Great-West Lifeco
AIG	ING
AXA	John Hancock Financial
Aetna	Services
Aflac	MassMutual
Allianz	Meiji Yasuda Life
American Financial	Merrill Lynch
Group	MetLife
American Life	Nationwide Life
Insurance	Insurance
Aviva	Nippon Life Insurance
Berkshire Hathaway	Northwestern Mutual
COUNTRY Financial	Principal Financial
Charles Schwab	Prudential plc
Citigroup	The Hartford
Dai-ichi Life	The Vanguard Group
FMR	Zurich Insurance Group

Company Type: Public

Income Statement
FYE: December 31

	ASSETS ($ mil.)	NET INCOME ($ mil.)	INCOME AS % OF ASSETS	EMPLOYEES
12/17	831,921	7,863	0.9%	49,705
12/16	783,962	4,368	0.6%	49,739
12/15	757,388	5,642	0.7%	49,384
12/14	766,655	1,381	0.2%	48,331
12/13	731,781	(667)	—	47,355
Annual Growth	**3.3%**	**—**	**—**	**1.2%**

2017 Year-End Financials

Debt ratio: 2.35%
Return on equity: 15.74%
Cash ($ mil.): 14,490
Current ratio: —
Long-term debt ($ mil.): —
No. of shares (mil.): 422
Dividends
Yield: 0.0%
Payout: 16.8%
Market value ($ mil.): 48,585

	STOCK PRICE ($) FY Close	P/E High/Low		PER SHARE ($) Earnings	Dividends	Book Value
12/17	114.98	6	5	17.86	3.00	127.96
12/16	104.06	11	6	9.71	2.80	106.76
12/15	81.41	7	6	12.17	2.44	93.69
12/14	90.46	29	24	3.23	2.17	91.84
12/13	92.22	—	—	(1.55)	1.73	76.19
Annual Growth	**5.7%**			**—**	**14.8%**	**13.8%**

Public Service Enterprise Group Inc

In the Garden State Public Service Enterprise Group's (PSEG) diversified business model has it smelling like a rose. Regulated subsidiary Public Service Electric and Gas (PSE&G) transmits and distributes electricity to 2.2 million customers and natural gas to 1.8 million customers in New Jersey. Subsidiary PSEG Power operates power generating plants and sells its energy wholesale to PSE&G and others. PSEG Power's 11800-MW generating capacity comes mostly from nuclear and fossil-fuel plants in the US Northeast and Mid-Atlantic regions.

HISTORY

Tragedy struck Newark New Jersey in 1903 when a trolley slid down an icy hill and collided with a train killing more than 30 people. While investigating the accident state attorney general Thomas McCarter discovered the mismanagement of the trolley company and many of New Jersey's other transportation gas and electric companies. Planning to buy and consolidate these companies McCarter resigned and established the Public Service Corporation in 1903 with several colleagues.

The company formed divisions for gas utilities electric utilities and transportation companies. The trolley company generated almost half of Public Service's sales during its first year.

In 1924 the gas and electric companies consolidated as Public Service Electric and Gas (PSE&G). A new company was formed that year to operate buses and in 1928 it merged with the trolley company to form Public Service Coordinated Transport (later Transport of New Jersey). PSE&G signed interconnection agreements with two Pennsylvania electric companies in 1928 to form the first integrated power pool — later known as the Pennsylvania-New Jersey-Maryland Interconnection. The Public Utility Holding Company Act of 1935 ushered in the era of regulated regional monopolies ensuring PSE&G a captive market.

During the 1960s PSE&G joined Philadelphia Electric to build its first nuclear plant at Peach Bottom Pennsylvania. The company completed a second plant in 1977 at Salem New Jersey. Its third one went on line at Hope Creek New Jersey. However plant mismanagement earned PSE&G a slew of fines in the 1980s and 1990s.

The company sold its transportation system to the State of New Jersey in 1980. Five years later PSE&G formed holding company Public Service Enterprise Group (PSEG) to move into nonutility enterprises and created Community Energy Alternatives (CEA now PSEG Global) to invest in independent power projects. In 1989 Enterprise Diversified Holdings (now PSEG Energy Holdings) was formed to handle activities ranging from real estate to oil and gas production.

CEA and three partners acquired a Buenos Aires power plant in 1993. Taking advantage of overseas privatization in the late 1990s it expanded into Asia and with AES purchased two Argentine electric companies.

PSE&G's nuclear problems resurfaced when the Salem plant was shut down in 1995 to rectify equipment breakdowns. In 1997 PSEG paid Salem partners Delmarva Power & Light and PECO Energy $82 million to settle their lawsuits charging mismanagement of Salem; both units were back on line by 1998.

Continuing to diversify in the late 1990s PSEG formed PSEG Energy Technologies in 1997 to market power and acquired five mechanical services companies in 1998 and 1999.

In 1999 PSEG Global teamed up with Panda Energy International to build three merchant plants in Texas (to be completed by 2001). It also planned plants in India and Venezuela and joined Sempra Energy to buy 90% of Chilquinta Energ - a an energy distributor in Chile and Peru. In 2000 it bought 90% of a distributor serving Argentina and Brazil.

New Jersey's electricity markets were deregulated in 1999; a year later the company transferred PSE&G's generation assets to nonregulated unit PSEG Power. PSEG Power also took charge of PSEG Global's plants under development in Illinois Indiana and Ohio; announced plans for new plants in New Jersey; and acquired an Albany New York plant from Niagara Mohawk.

PSEG Global completed a power plant in Texas in 2001. It also bought 94% of generator and distributor Saesa from Chile's largest conglomerate Copec for $460 million; it later acquired the rest of Saesa through a tender offer. It also purchased a Peruvian generation firm ElectroAndes for $227 million.

In 2002 PSEG Power acquired two Connecticut plants from WEC Energy for approximately $270 million.

PSEG had agreed to be acquired by Exelon but both New Jersey and Pennsylvania opposed the merger and the deal fell through in 2006.

In 2006 PSEG Global sold its 32% stake in RGE a Brazilian electric distribution company with approximately 1.1 million customers to Companhia Paulista de For §a e Luz. In 2008 it sold the SAESA Group of Companies (a power distribution group) in southern Chile to a consortium formed by Morgan Stanley Infrastructure and the Ontario Teachers' Pension Plan for $887 million.

In 2013 PSEG Solar Source announced that it purchased two utility-scale solar power plants totaling 4.4 MW from Canadian Solar Inc. The solar installations are the largest in Shasta county California built at more than 3300 feet in elevation.

EXECUTIVES

VP Electric Delivery PSE&G, Ralph A. LaRossa, age 54, $684,308 total compensation
Chairman President and CEO, Ralph Izzo, age 59, $1,298,269 total compensation
EVP and CFO, Daniel J. (Dan) Cregg, age 53, $520,000 total compensation
EVP and General Counsel, Tamara L. Linde, age 52, $533,789 total compensation
VP Asset Management and Centralized Services PSE&G, David M. Daly, age 55
President PSEG Services Corporation, Derek M. Di Risio, age 52
Vice President Supply Chain Management, David Frank
Vice President Construction and Engineering, Kevin Cellars
Vice President Manager Director, Donald Staudt
Vice President of Customer Information technology, Thomas Flaherty
Vice President of Tax, Norman Chadwick
Vice President Corporate And Commercial, Shawn Leyden
Vice President of Tax, Jose M Perez
LEGAL SECRETARY, Sandra Mayer
Assistant Treasurer, Lynn Manganaro
Treasurer, Bradford Huntington
Board Member, Michael F Percarpio
Assistant Treasurer, Benjamin Zoe
Auditors: Deloitte & Touche LLP

LOCATIONS

HQ: Public Service Enterprise Group Inc
80 Park Plaza, Newark, NJ 07102
Phone: 973 430-7000
Web: www.pseg.com

PRODUCTS/OPERATIONS

2016 Sales

	$ mil.	% of total
PSE&G	6,221	59
Power	4,023	38
Others	370	3
Adjustments	(1553)	-
Total	**9,061**	**100**

Selected Subsidiaries

PSEG Energy Holdings Inc. (nonutility companies)
  PSEG Global Inc. (solar plants and other alternative energy investments)
  PSEG Resources Inc. (energy infrastructure investments)
PSEG Power LLC
  PSEG Fossil LLC (operator of PSEG's fossil fuel plants)
  PSEG Nuclear LLC (operator of PSEG's nuclear plants)
  PSEG Energy Resources and Trade LLC (energy marketing)
PSEG Services Corporation (management and administrative services for PSEG)
Public Service Electric and Gas Company (PSE&G distribution of electricity and gas)

COMPETITORS

AEP	FirstEnergy
CenterPoint Energy	NRG Energy
Con Edison	National Grid USA
Constellation Energy Group	New Jersey Resources
Delmarva Power	NextEra Energy
Eversource Energy	PPL Corporation
Exelon	South Jersey Industries

HISTORICAL FINANCIALS

Company Type: Public

Income Statement

FYE: December 31

	REVENUE ($ mil.)	NET INCOME ($ mil.)	NET PROFIT MARGIN	EMPLOYEES
12/16	9,061	887	9.8%	13,065
12/15	10,415	1,679	16.1%	13,025
12/14	10,886	1,518	13.9%	12,689
12/13	9,968	1,243	12.5%	9,887
12/12	9,781	1,275	13.0%	9,798
Annual Growth	**(1.9%)**	**(8.7%)**	**—**	**7.5%**

2016 Year-End Financials

Debt ratio: 29.41%
Return on equity: 6.75%
Cash ($ mil.): 423
Current ratio: 0.99
Long-term debt ($ mil.): 10,895
No. of shares (mil.): 504
Dividends
  Yield: 0.0%
  Payout: 93.7%
Market value ($ mil.): 22,154

	STOCK PRICE ($) FY Close	P/E High/Low		PER SHARE ($) Earnings	Dividends	Book Value
12/16	43.88	27	22	1.75	1.64	26.01
12/15	38.69	13	11	3.30	1.56	25.86
12/14	41.41	15	10	2.99	1.48	24.09
12/13	32.04	15	12	2.45	1.44	22.95
12/12	30.60	13	12	2.51	1.42	21.31
Annual Growth	**9.4%**	**—**	**—**	**(8.6%)**	**3.7%**	**5.1%**

Publix Super Markets, Inc.

Publix Super Markets tops the list of privately owned grocery operators in the US. By emphasizing service and a family-friendly image over price Publix has outgrown and outperformed its regional rivals. More than two-thirds of its 1136 stores are in Florida but it also operates in Alabama Georgia South Carolina Tennessee and North Carolina (a new market for the company). Publix makes some of its own bakery deli dairy goods and fresh prepared foods at its own manufacturing plants in Florida and Georgia. Also many stores house pharmacies and banks. Founder George Jenkins began offering stock to Publix employees in 1930. Employees own about 31% of Publix which is still run by the Jenkins family.

Operations

Publix stores sell grocery products (dairy produce deli baker meat and seafood) health and beauty care products general merchandise pharmacy products flowers and other products and services. Grocery activities account for 85% of sales.

In addition to more than 1124 supermarkets Publix operates seven distribution centers in Florida and one in Georgia. The company also has ten manufacturing facilities including three dairies two bakeries and a deli plant. Publix's private label items are produced at its facilities and by suppliers.

Geographic Reach

Publix has supermarkets located in Florida Georgia Alabama South Carolina Tennessee and North Carolina.

It restocks store shelves from eight distribution centers — seven in Florida and one in Georgia.

Sales and Marketing

Supermarkets are often in strip shopping centers where Publix is the anchor tennant.

Financial Performance

In fiscal 2016 Publix recorded a further consecutive year of growth. Total revenue of $34.0 billion was up 5.1% on the previous year. Growth was a result of an extra trading week (accounting for 1.9 points of growth) and a 1.9 point increase in comparable store sales. New stores openings contributed as well.

Net income ticked up 3% to $2.0 billion due to higher revenue although as a percentage of sales net income fell a notch to 6.0%. This was due to an increase in promotional activity.

Cash from operating activities climbed 11% to $3.3 billion largely as a timing quirk relating to fiscal year end and the Christmas holidays.

Strategy

Publix's growth strategy is based on net store openings.

In fiscal 2016 it opened 32 stores and closed ten. Seven of the openings were replacement supermarkets while 156 supermarkets were remodeled. The openings added 1.3 million square feet or 2.4% of total square footage. Publix has 29 supermarkets under construction — twelve in Florida seven in North Carolina four in Virginia two in Alabama two in Tennessee one in Georgia and one in South Carolina.

The company opened 28 supermarkets in 2015 including five in North Carolina three in South Carolina three in Alabama and two in Georgia. The company closed nine under-performing stores during the year.

To drive more foot traffic to stores Publix partnered with Starbucks to open franchise outlets in its supermarkets. The first such in-store coffee shop opened in late 2016 with five more scheduled to open in 2017.

EXECUTIVES

EVP and CFO, David P. Phillips, age 57, $1,051,090 total compensation

SVP General Counsel and Secretary, John A. Attaway, age 58, $690,310 total compensation

SVP, David E. Bornmann, age 59, $488,300 total compensation

President CEO and Director, Randall T. (Todd) Jones, age 54, $1,688,750 total compensation

SVP and CIO, Laurie Z. Douglas, age 53, $890,255 total compensation

Manager Government Relations, Shane Kunze

Vice Chairman, Hoyt R. (Barney) Barnett, age 74

President and Director, William E. (Ed) Crenshaw, age 66

Auditors: KPMG LLP

LOCATIONS

HQ: Publix Super Markets, Inc.
3300 Publix Corporate Parkway, Lakeland, FL 33811
Phone: 863 688-1188
Web: www.publix.com

2016 Supermarkets

	No.
Florida	774
Georgia	184
Alabama	63
South Carolina	57
Tennessee	39
North Carolina	19
Total	**1,136**

PRODUCTS/OPERATIONS

2016 Sales

	% of total
Grocery	84
Other	16
Total	**100**

Selected Supermarket Departments

Bakery
Dairy
Deli
Floral
Groceries
Health and beauty care
Meat
Pharmacy
Produce
Seafood
Foods Processed
Baked goods
Dairy products
Deli items

COMPETITORS

ALDI	Kroger
ALDI	Rite Aid
CVS	Rite Aid
CVS	Sedano's
Costco Wholesale	Sedano's
Costco Wholesale	Southeastern Grocers
Food Lion	Southeastern Grocers
Food Lion	The Pantry
IGA	The Pantry
IGA	Wal-Mart
Ingles Markets	Wal-Mart
Ingles Markets	Walgreen
Kmart	Walgreen
Kmart	Whole Foods
Kroger	Whole Foods

HISTORICAL FINANCIALS

Company Type: Public

Income Statement

FYE: December 31

	REVENUE ($ mil.)	NET INCOME ($ mil.)	NET PROFIT MARGIN	EMPLOYEES
12/16	34,274	2,025	5.9%	191,000
12/15	32,618	1,965	6.0%	180,000
12/14	30,802	1,735	5.6%	175,000
12/13	29,147	1,653	5.7%	166,000
12/12	27,706	1,552	5.6%	158,000
Annual Growth	**5.5%**	**6.9%**	**—**	**4.9%**

2016 Year-End Financials

Debt ratio: 1.43%
Return on equity: 20.08%
Cash ($ mil.): 438
Current ratio: 1.56
Long-term debt ($ mil.): 136

No. of shares (mil.): 763
Dividends
 Yield: —
 Payout: 32.9%
Market value ($ mil.): —

	STOCK PRICE ($) FY Close	P/E High/Low		PER SHARE ($) Earnings	Dividends	Book Value
12/16	0.00	—	—	2.63	0.87	13.63
12/15	0.00	7	7	2.54	0.79	12.26
12/14	14.75	7	7	2.23	0.74	11.13
Annual Growth	**—**	—	—	**4.2%**	**4.1%**	**5.2%**

PUBLIX SUPER MARKETS, INC.

Publix Super Markets tops the list of privately owned grocery operators in the US. By emphasizing service and a family-friendly image over price Publix has outgrown and outperformed its regional rivals. More than two-thirds of its 1136 stores are in Florida but it also operates in Alabama Georgia South Carolina Tennessee and North Carolina (a

new market for the company). Publix makes some of its own bakery deli dairy goods and fresh prepared foods at its own manufacturing plants in Florida and Georgia. Also many stores house pharmacies and banks. Founder George Jenkins began offering stock to Publix employees in 1930. Employees own about 31% of Publix which is still run by the Jenkins family.

Operations

Publix stores sell grocery products (dairy produce deli baker meat and seafood) health and beauty care products general merchandise pharmacy products flowers and other products and services. Grocery activities account for 85% of sales.

In addition to more than 1124 supermarkets Publix operates seven distribution centers in Florida and one in Georgia. The company also has ten manufacturing facilities including three dairies two bakeries and a deli plant. Publix's private label items are produced at its facilities and by suppliers.

Geographic Reach

Publix has supermarkets located in Florida Georgia Alabama South Carolina Tennessee and North Carolina.

It restocks store shelves from eight distribution centers — seven in Florida and one in Georgia.

Sales and Marketing

Supermarkets are often in strip shopping centers where Publix is the anchor tennant.

Financial Performance

In fiscal 2016 Publix recorded a further consecutive year of growth. Total revenue of $34.0 billion was up 5.1% on the previous year. Growth was a result of an extra trading week (accounting for 1.9 points of growth) and a 1.9 point increase in comparable store sales. New stores openings contributed as well.

Net income ticked up 3% to $2.0 billion due to higher revenue although as a percentage of sales net income fell a notch to 6.0%. This was due to an increase in promotional activity.

Cash from operating activities climbed 11% to $3.3 billion largely as a timing quirk relating to fiscal year end and the Christmas holidays.

Strategy

Publix's growth strategy is based on net store openings.

In fiscal 2016 it opened 32 stores and closed ten. Seven of the openings were replacement supermarkets while 156 supermarkets were remodeled. The openings added 1.3 million square feet or 2.4% of total square footage. Publix has 29 supermarkets under construction — twelve in Florida seven in North Carolina four in Virginia two in Alabama two in Tennessee one in Georgia and one in South Carolina.

The company opened 28 supermarkets in 2015 including five in North Carolina three in South Carolina three in Alabama and two in Georgia. The company closed nine under-performing stores during the year.

To drive more foot traffic to stores Publix partnered with Starbucks to open franchise outlets in its supermarkets. The first such in-store coffee shop opened in late 2016 with five more scheduled to open in 2017.

EXECUTIVES

EVP and CFO, David P. Phillips, age 57, $1,051,090 total compensation

SVP General Counsel and Secretary, John A. Attaway, age 58, $690,310 total compensation

SVP, David E. Bornmann, age 59, $488,300 total compensation

President CEO and Director, Randall T. (Todd) Jones, age 54, $1,688,750 total compensation

SVP and CIO, Laurie Z. Douglas, age 53, $890,255
total compensation
Manager Government Relations, Shane Kunze
Vice Chairman, Hoyt R. (Barney) Barnett, age 74
President and Director, William E. (Ed) Crenshaw,
age 66
Auditors: KPMG LLP TAMPA FLORIDA

LOCATIONS

HQ: PUBLIX SUPER MARKETS, INC.
3300 PUBLIX CORP PKWY, LAKELAND, FL
338113311
Phone: 863 688-1188
Web: WWW.PUBLIX.COM

2016 Supermarkets

	No.
Florida	774
Georgia	184
Alabama	63
South Carolina	57
Tennessee	39
North Carolina	19
Total	**1,136**

PRODUCTS/OPERATIONS

2016 Sales

	% of total
Grocery	84
Other	16
Total	**100**

Selected Supermarket Departments

Bakery
Dairy
Deli
Floral
Groceries
Health and beauty care
Meat
Pharmacy
Produce
Seafood
Foods Processed
Baked goods
Dairy products
Deli items

COMPETITORS

ALDI	Kroger
ALDI	Rite Aid
CVS	Rite Aid
CVS	Sedano's
Costco Wholesale	Sedano's
Costco Wholesale	Southeastern Grocers
Food Lion	Southeastern Grocers
Food Lion	The Pantry
IGA	The Pantry
IGA	Wal-Mart
Ingles Markets	Wal-Mart
Ingles Markets	Walgreen
Kmart	Walgreen
Kmart	Whole Foods
Kroger	Whole Foods

HISTORICAL FINANCIALS

Company Type: Private

Income Statement

FYE: December 31

	REVENUE ($ mil.)	NET INCOME ($ mil.)	NET PROFIT MARGIN	EMPLOYEES
12/16	34,274	2,025	5.9%	191,000
12/15	32,618	1,965	6.0%	—
12/14	30,802	1,735	5.6%	—
12/12	27,706	1,552	5.6%	—
Annual Growth	**5.5%**	**6.9%**	**—**	**—**

2016 Year-End Financials

Debt ratio: —
Return on equity: 5.90%
Cash ($ mil.): 438
Current ratio: 0.40
Long-term debt ($ mil.): —

Dividends
Yield: —
Payout: —
Market value ($ mil.): —

PulteGroup Inc

PulteGroup pulls its weight in providing homes for American families. PulteGroup targets a cross-section of home buyers nationwide by buying land to build single-family houses duplexes townhouses and condominiums. Its Centex brand is marketed to entry-level buyers while Pulte Homes aims to capture customers looking to trade up. PulteGroup also builds Del Webb retiree communities mostly in Sun Belt locales for the growing number of buyers in the 55-plus age range. The company sells its homes in some 50 markets across 25 states. Its homes go for an average price of $370000. PulteGroup became one of the top homebuilders in the US by buying rivals John Wieland Homes and Centex Homes.

HISTORY

William Pulte built his first home in Detroit in 1950 and incorporated his business in 1956 as William J. Pulte Inc.

In 1961 the company built its first subdivision in Detroit. During that decade Pulte moved into Washington DC (1964) Chicago (1966) and Atlanta (1968). In 1969 Pulte merged with Colorado's American Builders to form the Pulte Home Corporation a publicly traded company.

Originally a builder of high-priced single-family homes Pulte began expanding into affordable and midrange housing markets. To lower costs it pioneered modular designs and prebuilt components. Pulte architects designed the Quadrominium a large structure with four separate two-bedroom units each with its own entrance and garage (priced at a mere $20000 per unit in the 1970s).

Pulte formed Intercontinental Mortgage (later renamed ICM Mortgage) and began making home loans in 1972. The company ran into trouble in 1988 when it was accused of forcing Pulte homebuyers in Baltimore to use ICM financing instead of cheaper loans from the county. Pulte settled by repaying the difference in loan costs.

By the mid-1980s Pulte was one of the US's largest on-site homebuilders. PHM Corporation was created in 1987 as a holding company for the Pulte group of companies. That year PHM entered the thrift business by assisting the Federal Savings and Loan Insurance Corp.'s S&L bailout. It acquired five Texas S&Ls (with assets of $1.3 billion) for $45 million and eventually combined them to form First Heights (finally discontinuing the business in 1994).

Pulte Homes' Quality Leadership customer satisfaction program introduced in the early 1990s paid off in 1991 as Pulte enjoyed record sales despite a depressed home market. Renamed Pulte Corporation in 1993 the company soon faced rising interest rates which dampened the US housing market and affected the Mexican peso. Pulte recorded a $2 million foreign-currency loss on an affordable-housing venture in Mexico in 1994. Nonetheless it began a second joint venture in that country in 1995 and helped form mortgage bank Su Casita with nine Mexican homebuilders to finance home construction on its border. That year it also started developing retirement communities when it bought the Ponds at Clearbrook in New Jersey.

In 1996 its Mexican joint venture Condake-Pulte began building thousands of affordable homes for General Motors and Sony employees in maquiladora residential areas near the US-Mexico border. The company also bought Rhode Island's top homebuilder LeBlanc.

Pulte restructured in 1997 and a year later shed its manufactured housing and building supply business. It also acquired DiVosta one of Florida's largest homebuilders and Tennessee-based Radnor Homes.

The company's 1988 foray into S&Ls came back to haunt it in 1998: The Federal Deposit Insurance Corp. won a lawsuit that accused the builder of abusing tax benefits associated with the S&Ls. (Pulte settled the case in 2001 by paying $41.5 million.) In 1999 Pulte bought the interest held by investment firm Blackstone Group its partner in active-adult homebuilding.

The next year Pulte joined other builders in an Internet-based building materials cooperative. Also in 2000 the company began dealings to expand its homebuilding operations into Argentina.

The company changed its name to Pulte Homes in 2001. That year Mark O'Brien became the company's CEO. He directed Pulte through the major acquisition of retirement community developer Del Webb for about $800 million in stock and $950 million in assumed debt. The combined company became the largest US homebuilder. In 2002 Pulte reorganized the structure of its operations in Mexico and created Pulte Mexico S. de R.L. de C.V. one of the largest builders in that country.

Adding to its portfolio of accolades Pulte was named 2002 "Builder of the Year" by Professional Builder magazine and in 2003 Pulte ranked 19th among the "Top 50 Best-Performing Companies" in Business Week' s performance rankings of the Standard & Poor's 500-stock index.

Pulte expanded its operations in the fast-growing San Diego area in 2003 by purchasing assets of ColRich Communities which included about 500 entitled lots in five communities in the South Bay and Coastal North areas of San Diego. It boosted its presence in the Albuquerque Phoenix and Tucson markets by acquiring Sivage-Thomas Homes (Albuquerque) with about 7000 lots in the region and Del Webb entered the Reno Nevada market with its Sierra Canyon active adult community. O'Brien left the company in June 2003 after having served in senior management positions for six years (and 21 total years) within the company. EVP and COO Richard Dugas stepped up to become the company's president and CEO at that time.

In September 2003 the US Court of Federal Claims awarded Pulte and related parties $48.7 million as a result of a breach of contract by the US government related to Pulte's acquisition of five savings and loans in 1988.

J.D. Power and Associates recognized Pulte as a top performer for its fifth consecutive year in its "2004 New Home Builder Customer Satisfaction Study." Out of the 25 markets it surveyed Pulte ranked highest in 14 markets #2 in nine markets and #3 in six markets.

At the close of 2004 Pulte sold some operations in Argentina to real estate developer Grupo Farallon. The next year it sold its Mexican and remaining Argentine homebuilding enterprises to focus exclusively on US operations.

The downturn in the US housing market — due to a toxic cocktail of higher home prices increased foreclosures high unemployment and constraints on mortgage lending — led to weakened demand for new homes and higher cancellation rates. For Pulte this trend meant decreased profitability and a decline in homebuilding activity. Pulte responded to the downturn and adjusted its operations by cutting jobs and shuttering plants to meet lower demand levels.

The company bought rival Centex in 2009. The acquisition made Pulte the largest homebuilder in the US and also strengthened Pulte's offerings in the lower-priced home segment.

A year following the Centex merger founder William Pulte retired from the company and from its board of directors. He was named chairman emeritus.

EXECUTIVES

President Divosta Homes, Harmon D. Smith, age 53, $688,462 total compensation
VP and CIO, Joseph L. Drouin
EVP Human Resources, James R. (Jim) Ellinghausen, age 59, $546,154 total compensation
EVP and CFO, Robert T. (Bob) O'Shaughnessy, age 51, $742,307 total compensation
President CEO and Director, Ryan R. Marshall, age 42, $738,462 total compensation
EVP General Counsel and Corporate Secretary, Todd N. Sheldon
VP and Chief Marketing Officer, Manish M. Shrivastava
Sales Vice President, Sean Clancy
Area Vice President of Human Resources for the East Area, Michelle Hairston
Vice President Finance and Controller, James Ossowski
Vice President Of Finance Illinois St. Louis Division, Andrew Bodary
Vice President of Finance, Michael Hyland
Vice President Land, Cisco Garcia
Division Vice President of Land Acquisition, Matt Callahan
Vice President of Construction Operations Mid Atlantic Division, Brad Nicholas
Auditors: Ernst & Young LLP

LOCATIONS

HQ: PulteGroup Inc
3350 Peachtree Road NE, Suite 150, Atlanta, GA 30326
Phone: 404 978-6400
Web: www.pultegroupinc.com

Selected Homebuilding Regions
Florida
North (IL IN MI MN MO Northern CA OH OR WA)
Northeast (CT DE MD MA NJ NY PA RI VA)
Southeast (GA NC SC TN)
Southwest (AZ CO HI NV NM Southern CA)
Texas

PRODUCTS/OPERATIONS

2016 Sales

	% of total
Northeast	9
Southeast	19
Florida	17
Midwest	16
Texas	14
West	23
Financial Services	2
Total	**100**

2016 Sales

	$ mil.	% of total
Home building		
Home Sales	7451.3	97
Land Sales	36.1	1
Financial Serivces	181	2
Total	**7,668**	**100**

Selected Brands

Centex (entry-level buyers)
Del Webb (active-adult buyers)
DiVosta (Florida)
Pulte Homes (move-up buyers)

COMPETITORS

Beazer Homes	M.D.C.
CalAtlantic	Meritage Homes
D.R. Horton	NVR
Hovnanian Enterprises	Pardee Homes
KB Home	Toll Brothers
Lennar	

HISTORICAL FINANCIALS

Company Type: Public

Income Statement

FYE: December 31

	REVENUE ($ mil.)	NET INCOME ($ mil.)	NET PROFIT MARGIN	EMPLOYEES
12/17	8,573	447	5.2%	4,810
12/16	7,668	602	7.9%	4,623
12/15	5,981	494	8.3%	4,542
12/14	5,822	474	8.1%	4,149
12/13	5,679	2,620	46.1%	3,843
Annual Growth	**10.8%**	**(35.7%)**	**—**	**5.8%**

2017 Year-End Financials

Debt ratio: 35.56%
Return on equity: 10.15%
Cash ($ mil.): 272
Current ratio: 8.81
Long-term debt ($ mil.): 3,444

No. of shares (mil.): 286
Dividends
  Yield: 0.0%
  Payout: 25.0%
Market value ($ mil.): 9,535

	STOCK PRICE ($) FY Close	P/E High/Low		PER SHARE ($) Earnings	Dividends	Book Value
12/17	33.25	24	13	1.44	0.36	14.49
12/16	18.38	13	9	1.75	0.36	14.60
12/15	17.82	17	12	1.36	0.33	13.63
12/14	21.46	17	13	1.26	0.23	13.01
12/13	20.37	4	2	6.72	0.15	12.19
Annual Growth	**13.0%**		**—**	**(32.0%)24.5%**		**4.4%**

PVH Corp

PVH has the buttoned-up look down. A top global apparel player PVH is the world's largest dress shirt and neckwear company. The company owns three titans of the apparel industry: Calvin Klein Tommy Hilfiger and Heritage Brands. The former two are multi-billion dollar global lifestyle brands while Heritage Brands is a luxury apparel wholesaler that owns the brands Van Heusen IZOD ARROW Warner's Olga and True&Co. PVH is also has licenses for third-party brands such as DKNY Speedo Kenneth Cole Reaction Michael Kors Collection and others. The company generates sales from multiple channels including about 1600 company-operated retail stores as well as retailers and licensees. It also charges royalty and advertising fees.

Operations
PVH organizes its business into three main areas: Calvin Klein Tommy Hilfiger and Heritage Brands.

Calvin Klein accounts for over 35% of revenue and runs a number of sub-brands alongside its Calvin Klein "master" brand: Calvin Klein By Appointment Calvin Klein Jeans CK Calvin Klein Calvin Klein Jeans and Calvin Klein 205 W39 NYC (the unusual name relates to its New York address). Together they fill various product niches categories and price points.

Tommy Hilfiger split into Tommy Hilfiger North America and Tommy Hilfiger International contributes some 45% to PVH's revenue. The brand

makes everyday and formalwear for the upper-middle class characterized by its classic American preppy stylings. As with Calvin Klein it runs a number of sub-brands: Hilfiger Collection Tommy Hilfiger Tailored Tommy Hilfiger and Hilfiger Denim. It sells its products wholesale to third party retailers and at retail via a network of owned outlets and has around 25 license agreements with third parties in Australia Brazil India and Mexico among other countries.

Heritage Brands accounts for around 20% of revenue and makes shirts neckwear sportswear swimwear intimates underwear and accessories through a range of owned brands and licensed brands. Its licensed brands are Speedo Geoffrey Beene Kenneth Cole New York Kenneth Cole Reaction Sean John MICHAEL Michael Kors Michael Kors Collection and Chaps. It sells wholesale and through Heritage Brands retail outlets across the United States and Canada. Some of its stores stock IZOD Golf Warner's and Speedo products. Heritage Brands also licenses its products to 35 US and 40 international companies.

PVH also completes e-commerce sales through its various brand websites.

The company's products are made in more 1600 factories in more than 50 countries worldwide. In addition to the more than 1900 retail stores that it operates PVH maintains wholesale and retail warehousing and distribution centers in the US Canada Japan and the Netherlands. The centers inspect sort pack and ship goods to customers.

Geographic Reach
The company sells products in the US Canada Europe Asia Mexico and Brazil. Its US business accounts for over 50% of sales.

Sales and Marketing
Macy's is PVH's largest Calvin Klein and Tommy Hilfiger wholesale customer. Heritage Brands sells wholesale to department stores such as Bon-Ton Stores J. C. Penney Kohl's and Sears. Each of the Calvin Klein Tommy Hilfiger and Heritage Brands businesses have a number of licensing partners domestically and abroad who have the right to manufacture and wholesale specified products under one or more brands or are granted the right to open retail stores under the licensed brand name.

PVH targets the marketing of its brands at distinct consumer demographics. The company advertises its brands through digital media (including its e-commerce and social media sites) national print media television outdoor signage special events promotions and store locations. It also advertises through product tie-ins and sport sponsorships (Calvin Klein/basketball Van Heusen/football and IZOD/golf). The Tommy Hilfiger marketing team also coordinates appearances by the designer himself Tommy Hilfiger at runway shows special events and flagship store openings.

PVH's five largest customers account for more than a fifth of total revenues.

Financial Performance
After several years of steady revenue growth sales dipped in 2015 before bouncing back in fiscal 2016: sales climbed 2% to $8.2 billion.

PVH's revenue growth in fiscal 2016 was uneven with solid gains in Calvin Klein (International and North America) and Tommy Hilfiger International offset by falls in Tommy Hilfiger North America and Heritage Brands. Growth came from the Calvin Klein domestic wholesale business and the Tommy Hilfiger International business in Europe. The business was impacted across the board by the strong US dollar.

Net income slid 4% to $549 million as selling general and administrative expenses were pushed up by acquisition costs and higher marketing costs.

Cash from operating activities increased by $55 million to $955 million due to changes in working capital relating to inventory and accrued expenses.

Strategy

PVH is unifying Calvin Klein under one creative vision. The process began when it took back full control of its jeans and underwear businesses in 2013 and continued in 2016 with the sacking of Francisco Costa and Italo Zucchelli the women's and men's creative directors to clear the way for a unified global creative director role. Raf Simons was given the position.

The company focuses on reinvesting in businesses and pursuing strategic acquisitions.PVH's strength lies in the fact that it maintains a strong diversified brand portfolio. Its portfolio is growing through acquisitions and it is supported by a model that offers multiple brands and product types globally at different price points and across a range of distribution channels. The variety in products and distribution channels allows the company to reach a broad range of consumers in various geographic regions. The move in 2016 to buy full control of TH Asia signaled the start of direct involvement in the Chinese market

Mergers and Acquisitions

In 2017 PVH acquired True&Co an online retailer specializing in bras.

In 2016 the company bought the remaining 55% of TH Asia Ltd. its joint venture for Tommy Hilfiger in China. With the closing of this transaction Tommy Hilfiger business now operates directly in its fastest growing market while leveraging its well-established infrastructure in Asia.

HISTORY

Moses Phillips came to America from Poland in 1881. While living in a one-room apartment in Pottsville Pennsylvania he sold flannel shirts (which his wife sewed) to coal miners from a pushcart. He soon brought the rest of his family to the US and upgraded the pushcart to a horse and buggy. Business continued to grow and the Phillips-Jones Corporation was formed in 1907.

The company moved to New York in 1914 and control passed from father to son for four generations. Isaac followed Moses then Seymour took over in 1941 until he handed the reins to Lawrence who joined the company in 1948 and became president and CEO in 1969. Ads in the 1950s featured such actors as Anthony Quinn Burt Lancaster and Ronald Reagan in Van Heusen shirts. In 1957 the company received its new name Phillips-Van Heusen (PVH). It grew via acquisitions throughout the 1970s and began selling its merchandise at its own outlet stores in 1979 but it didn't want its products sold at the off-price outlets that became popular in the early 1980s. The company stopped doing business with stores and distributors that allowed PVH merchandise to reach cut-price vendors.

In 1987 PVH bought back more than 5 million shares of stock in order to fend off an acquisition bid by the Hunt family of Texas. Lawrence stepped down in 1993 ending the unbroken chain of Phillipses at the helm. In 1995 the Phillips family sold its stake in the business. In June 2011 the company renamed itself PVH Corp. officially dropping the Phillips-Van Heusen moniker to emphasize its diversified portfolio of brands.

EXECUTIVES

President Van Heusen Retail, Margaret P. (Meg) Lachance

Chairman and CEO, Emanuel (Manny) Chirico, age 60, $1,350,000 total compensation

EVP Chief Operating and Financial Officer, Michael A. (Mike) Shaffer, age 55, $891,667 total compensation

CEO Heritage Brands and North America Wholesale, Francis K. (Ken) Duane, age 61, $1,091,667 total compensation

President Licensing, Kenneth L. (Ken) Wyse

CEO Tommy Hilfiger and PVH Europe, Daniel Grieder, age 55, $937,209 total compensation

EVP The Marketing Group, Michael (Mike) Kelly

CEO Tommy Hilfiger Americas, Gary Sheinbaum

CEO Calvin Klein, Steven B. (Steve) Shiffman, age 59, $908,333 total compensation

President Branded Sportswear PVH Sportswear Group, Geoffrey (Geoff) Barrett

EVP Logistics Services, Kevin J. Urban

President Calvin Klein Retail, Barrie Scardina, age 53

President Calvin Klein 205W39NYC and Calvin Klein by Appointment, Michelle Kessler-Sanders

President Calvin Klein North America Design and Product Development, Alexander (Alex) Cannon

SVP and Chief Risk Officer, Melanie Steiner

President The Dress Furnishings Group, David Sirkin

President Core Intimates, Leslie (Les) Hall

President The Underwear Group, Cheryl Abel-Hodges

President Calvin Klein Retail, Nicholas (Nick) Strange

Regional President PVH Asia Pacific, Frank Cancelloni

EVP General Counsel and Secretary, Mark D. Fischer, age 55

EVP and Chief Human Resources Officer, David F. (Dave) Kozel, age 61

EVP and CIO, Eileen Mahoney

Chief Supply Chain Officer, William (Bill) McRaith

EVP Wholesale Canada, Richard Deck

President Calvin Klein Europe Brand Management, Marcela Wartenbergh

Country Manager Calvin Klein Brazil, Fábio Vasconcellos

SVP Sales Speedo, John Graham

President PVH Japan, Tom Chu

Managing Director Calvin Klein Asia Pacific Korea, You Hyun-Ko

Managing Director Calvin Klein Asia Pacific China, Hanson Gu

Managing Director Calvin Klein Asia Pacific Commercial, Annie Wong

Managing Director France, Laurent Albouy

Managing Director Turkey, Hakan Atalay

Managing Director Russia, Georg Faisst

Managing Director Middle East Africa and The Netherlands, Maela Mandelli

Managing Director UK and Ireland, David Pyne

Managing Director Nordic, Jesper Waerum

Senior Vice President Sales and Marketing, Joel Friedman

Senior Vice President of Planning, Becky Quinn

Senior Vice President and Controller, James Holmes

Vice President, Tom Whitmer

Vice President National Sales Manager, Lex Israel

Group Vice President Womens Sourcing, Susan Parson

VP Purchasing, Jason Zuckerman

Group Vice President Human Resources, Danielle Korins

Executive Vice President Global Tax, Matt O'Laughlin

Vice President of Mens Design Van Heusen Retail, Jeanne Clarke

Vice President Regional Sales Manager, John Karwacki

Vice President Purchasing, Lisa Barbosa

Vice President Talent Management, Lori Bradley

Executive Vice President North America Wholesale Finance Heritage Brands, John Hayes

Global Vice President Design and Product Development Technology, Paula Scarpellini

Vice President of Planning and Allocation, Robert Yavorsky

VP Human Resources, Danielle Bernier

Vice President Distribution, Richard Vuich

Senior Vice President Strategic Accounts, Milena Schaefer

Vice President Human Rights, Roopa Nair

Vice President Of Design, Kevin Michales

Senior Vice President, Jillian Zino

Vice President Of Design For Timberland Apparel, Michael Flynn

Vice President Finance Global Supply Chain, John Benz

Senior Vice President Sales and Planning, Becky Vogel

Vice President Finance And Operations, Guilford Robinson

Vice President Retail Operations, Lenore Dunn

Vice President Real Estate, Lauren Kinder

Senior Vice President Tax, Elizabeth Maguire

Vice President Dmm Vh Men's Sportswear Dress, Donna Williams

Senior Vice President of Communications, Tiffin Jernstedt

Vice President Of Finance And Administration, Harry MA

Vice President Construction X 6306, Susan Pierce

Vice President Associate General Counsel Employmena, Lauren Tanen

Vice President And Director of Advertising, Henry Justus

Senior Vice President Sales and Marketing the Underwear group, Larry Meltzer

Executive Vice President, Franck Belochi

National Sales Manager, Ray Hennessy

Vice President of Technical, Jin Chung

Vice President, Paul Callahan

Vice President DMM Sportswear and Accessories, Judith Colaiacovo

Vice President Distribution and CS, Douglas Christian

Senior Vice President of Retail Planning and Analysis, Thomas Whitmer

Vice President eCommerce (Tommy Hilfiger), Sean Reynolds

Executive Vice President eCommerce (Calvin Klein), Mike Dupuis

Senior Vice President Europe Calvin Klein Underwear PVH, Melanie Gallop

Senior Vice President Gmm Mens and Childrenswear, Danielle Lafleur

Vice President Payroll, Gillian Kerollis

Vice President eCommerce (DMM Calvin Klein), Jimmy Carter

Vice President, Jennifer Underwood

Senior Vice President Technical Design and Quality Assurance, Michael Collinson

Vice President of Communications, Timothy Robertson

VICE CHAIRMAN, Ken Duane

Assistant Secretary, Michelle Odonnell

Auditors: Ernst & Young LLP

LOCATIONS

HQ: PVH Corp
200 Madison Avenue, New York, NY 10016
Phone: 212 381-3500
Web: www.pvh.com

2016 Sales

	$ mil.	% of total
U.S.	4,226	51
Canada	484	6
Europe	2,372	29
Asia	910	11
Other	208	3
Total	**8,203**	**100**

PRODUCTS/OPERATIONS

2016 Sales

	$ mil.	% of total
Calvin Klein North America	1,689	20
Calvin Klein International	1,445	18
Tommy Hilfiger North America	1,563	19
Tommy Hilfiger International	1,947	24
Heritage Brands Wholesale	1,295	16
Heritage Brands Retail	261	3
Total	**8,203**	**100**

2016 Sales

	$ mil.	% of total
Net sales	7,791	95
Royalty	320	4
Advertising and other	91	1
Total	**8,203**	**100**

Selected Brands

Owned
  ARROW
  Bass
  Calvin Klein
  Eagle
  IZOD
  Tommy Hilfiger
  Van Heusen
Licensed
  Chaps
  Claiborne
  DKNY
  Geoffrey Beene
  Kenneth Cole New York
  Kenneth Cole Reaction
  MICHAEL Michael Kors
  Michael Kors Collection
  Robert Graham
  Sean John

COMPETITORS

Allen-Edmonds	Kellwood
Armani	Kenneth Cole
Caleres	Levi Strauss
Capital Mercury	Nine West
Apparel	Oxford Industries
Donna Karan	Perry Ellis
Eddie Bauer LLC	International
Genesco	Prada
Gucci	Ralph Lauren
Haggar	Reebok
Hugo Boss	The Gap
J. Crew	Timberland
Kate Spade	VF Corporation

HISTORICAL FINANCIALS

Company Type: Public

Income Statement

FYE: January 29

	REVENUE ($ mil.)	NET INCOME ($ mil.)	NET PROFIT MARGIN	EMPLOYEES
01/17	8,203	549	6.7%	44,500
01/16*	8,020	572	7.1%	34,200
02/15	8,241	439	5.3%	34,100
02/14	8,186	143	1.8%	33,200
02/13	6,043	433	7.2%	28,700
Annual Growth	**7.9%**	**6.1%**	**—**	**11.6%**

*Fiscal year change

2017 Year-End Financials

Debt ratio: 29.06%	No. of shares (mil.): 78
Return on equity: 11.77%	Dividends
Cash ($ mil.): 730	Yield: 0.0%
Current ratio: 1.84	Payout: 2.2%
Long-term debt ($ mil.): 3,197	Market value ($ mil.): 7,093

	STOCK PRICE ($) FY Close	P/E High/Low	PER SHARE ($) Earnings	Dividends	Book Value
01/17	90.30	17 10	6.79	0.15	61.16
01/16*	73.38	17 10	6.89	0.15	55.86
02/15	110.26	25 20	5.27	0.15	52.89
02/14	120.87	78 59	1.74	0.15	52.76
02/13	116.26	20 12	5.87	0.15	44.61
Annual Growth	**(6.1%)**	**— —**	**3.7%**	**(0.0%)**	**8.2%**

*Fiscal year change

QCR Holdings Inc

Quad City is muscling in on the community banking scene in the Midwest. QCR Holdings is the holding company for Quad City Bank & Trust Cedar Rapids Bank & Trust Rockford Bank & Trust and Community State Bank. Together the banks have about 20 offices serving the Quad City area of Illinois and Iowa as well as the communities of Cedar Rapids Iowa; Rockford Illinois; and Milwaukee. The banks offer traditional deposit products and services and concentrate their lending activities on local businesses: Commercial real estate loans make up about half of the loan portfolio; commercial loans and leases make up another third.

Operations

QCR Holdings' Bancard subsidiary provides credit card processing services; its majority-owned M2 Lease Funds leases machinery and equipment to commercial and industrial businesses.

Strategy

QCR Holdings has grown by launching operations in new geographic markets and then building upon them. It also expands through acquisitions. In mid-2016 the company acquired Iowa-based Community State Bank which operates some 10 branches in the Des Moines area.

EXECUTIVES

President and CEO, Douglas M. (Doug) Hultquist, age 62, $290,000 total compensation
Director; President and CEO Cedar Rapids Bank and Trust, Larry J. Helling, age 61, $251,899 total compensation
EVP and Chief Credit Officer, Dana L. Nichols
EVP COO and CFO, Todd A. Gipple, age 54, $251,899 total compensation
EVP Corporate Strategy Human Resources and Branding, Cathie Whiteside, $162,000 total compensation
President and CEO Rockford Bank and Trust, Thomas D. Budd, $172,000 total compensation
President and CEO Quad City Bank and Trust, John H. Anderson, $200,000 total compensation
EVP Deposit Operations and Information Services, John A. Rodriguez
SVP and CIO, Michael J. Wyffels
EVP and Chief Operations Officer, John R. McEvoy
President and CEO Community Bank and Trust, Stacey Bentley
President m2 Lease Funds, Richard W. Couch
Chairman and CEO m2 Lease Funds, John R. Engelbrecht
EVP and Chief Investment Officer, M. Randolph (Rand) Westlund
Senior Vice President Director Of Hum, Jill Dekeyser
Vice President Controller, Jeri Vandervinne
Vice President And Controller, Nick Anderson

Assistant Vice President Compliance, Thomas King
ASSISTANT VICE PRESIDENT MARKETING AND PUBLIC RELATIONS OFFICER, Stacey L Keller
Chairman, Patrick S. (Pat) Baird, age 64
Auditors: RSM US LLP

LOCATIONS

HQ: QCR Holdings Inc
3551 7th Street, Moline, IL 61265
Phone: 309 736-3580
Web: www.qcbt.com

PRODUCTS/OPERATIONS

2015 Sales

	$ mil.	% of total
Quad City Bank & Trust	52	46
Cedar Rapids Bank & Trust	37	32
Rockford Bank & Trust	14	13
Wealth Management	9	8
All other	0	1
Inter-company Eliminations	(0.4)	
Total	**114**	**100**

COMPETITORS

Bank of America	First National of
Blackhawk Bancorp	Nebraska
First Business	MidWestOne
Financial	U.S. Bancorp
First Midwest Bancorp	

HISTORICAL FINANCIALS

Company Type: Public

Income Statement

FYE: December 31

	ASSETS ($ mil.)	NET INCOME ($ mil.)	INCOME AS % OF ASSETS	EMPLOYEES
12/16	3,301	27	0.8%	572
12/15	2,593	16	0.7%	406
12/14	2,524	14	0.6%	409
12/13	2,394	14	0.6%	400
12/12	2,093	12	0.6%	356
Annual Growth	**12.1%**	**21.7%**	**—**	**12.6%**

2016 Year-End Financials

Debt ratio: 3.44%	No. of shares (mil.): 13
Return on equity: 10.79%	Dividends
Cash ($ mil.): 134	Yield: 0.0%
Current ratio: —	Payout: 7.3%
Long-term debt ($ mil.): —	Market value ($ mil.): 568

	STOCK PRICE ($) FY Close	P/E High/Low	PER SHARE ($) Earnings	Dividends	Book Value
12/16	43.30	20 10	2.17	0.16	21.82
12/15	24.29	15 11	1.61	0.08	19.21
12/14	17.86	10 10	1.72	0.08	18.12
12/13	17.03	8 6	2.08	0.08	18.72
12/12	13.22	8 5	1.85	0.08	28.55
Annual Growth	**34.5%**	**— —**	**4.1%**	**18.9%**	**(6.5%)**

Qualcomm Inc

Cell phone makers wireless carriers and governments worldwide call on QUALCOMM to engineer a quality conversation. The company pioneered the commercialization of the code-division multiple access (CDMA) technology used in digital wireless communications equipment and satellite ground stations mainly in North America. It generates most of its sales through the development and marketing of semiconductor chips such as its Snapdragon line and system software based on CDMA and other technologies. Its biggest customers have been suppliers to mobile phone makers Samsung and Apple. QUALCOMM has offered $47 billion to buy NXP Semiconductors. Meanwhile QUALCOMM is trying to fend off a $103 billion takeover by Broadcom.

Operations

While CDMA is QUALCOMM?s flagship technology it has makes products based on Orthogonal Frequency Division Multiple Access (OFDMA) which allows multiple access on the same channel and Wideband Code Division Multiple Access (WCDMA) designed to ease the transmission of multimedia content.

QUALCOMM CDMA Technologies (QCT) is the company's biggest business generating 75% of revenue. Its QUALCOMM Technology Licensing (QTL) unit brings in the rest.

The company outsources manufacturing to contractors.

Geographic Reach

QUALCOMM dials in 65% of its revenue from customers based in China (including Hong Kong) while customers based in South Korea supply about 15% of revenue.

Sales and Marketing

A good portion of QUALCOMM?s products have gone into phones made by Apple Inc. (and its supplier Hon Hai Precision) and Samsung Electronics making them the company?s biggest customers. Other significant customers are GuangDong OPPO Mobile Telecommunications Corp. Ltd. and Vivo Communication Technology Co.

Financial Performance

QUALCOMM?s financials have stumbled since their peak in 2014 when the company earned nearly $8 billion on about $25 billion in sales. In 2017 (ended September) revenue hit about $22 billion down 1% from 2016 and profit plummeted 57% to $2.5 billion in 2017 from 2016.

Revenue for the QCT segment rose in 2017 from 2016 from sales of Mobile Station Modem chips and RF power management and wireless connectivity circuits. Sales to Apple declined in 2017 as the iPhone maker shifted some of its chip business to Intel. A dispute with Apple and another licensee of QUALCOMM technology reduced revenue from the QTL segment in 2017.

Fines QUALCOMM paid to regulators in South Korea and Taiwan for violating trade rules helped more than halve the company?s net income to $2.5 million in 2017 from about $5.7 in 2016.

Cash provided by operations fell to $4.7 billion in 2017 from $7.4 billion in 2016 because of cash used to settle fines levied by regulators in South Korea and Taiwan as well as changes in working capital related to an increase in accounts receivable and inventories.

Strategy

It seems QUALCOMM spent more time in the courtroom and boardroom in 2017 than in the lab and factory. The company?s proposed acquisition of NXP has dragged on more than a year slowed by regulatory review and tepid response from NXP shareholders. While that deal has simmered QUALCOMM was the target of a takeover bid by rival Broadcom. QUALCOMM turned the $103 billion offer down flat. But instead of going away Broadcom put up a board of directors slate that shareholders are to vote on at QUALCOMM?s annual meeting in March 2018.

That?s the boardroom. In the courtroom QUALCOMM and Apple have traded suits and countersuits over licensing deals. Apple shifted some of the business for communications chips in its iPhones to Intel and a dispute arose over who

owns what inside the phone. Those arguments look to continue indefinitely.

Those activities somewhat obscure what could be a lucrative future for QUALCOMM with the advent of 5G wireless networks. The company has worked to develop 5G technology for about a decade and the toil is nearing payoff. The next generation of wireless networking has promise of providing faster communication with less latency unleashing a host of new and powerful applications. On the list is car-to-car communication involved in self-driving cars. NXP and its strong automotive business is a key building block for QUALCOMM in that area.

The first 5G networks could launch in 2018 with more rolling out over the next several years. If it plays out like previous wireless generations it means big business for QUALCOMM.

Mergers and Acquisitions

QUALCOMM moved to buy NXP Semiconductors with a $47 billion offer in October 2016. NXP accepted the offer but the deal has taken time to wend its way through regulatory bodies around the world that must confer their approval. QUALCOMM is interested in NXP's line of chips for automotive internet of things and networking and security. The deal continued a wave of consolidation that's intended overall to create what companies hope are bulwarks against increasing competition and decreasing price points.

QUALCOMM and TDK formed a joint venture in 2017 to provide chips for mobile devices and internet of things applications. The entity called RF360 Holdings combines QUALCOMM?s chip expertise with that of TDK in filters. Application areas are mobile devices automotive and drones. The ownership of the joint venture is split 51% by QUALCOMM and 49% by TDK.

In August 2015 QUALCOMM completed the acquisition of CSR a UK-based maker of multifunction computer chips for about $2.5 billion. CSR makes semiconductors for the auto consumer voice and music market segments. The acquisition provides QUALCOMM with CSR's products channels and customers in burgeoning markets of the internet of things (the idea that billions of devices can be connected to the internet) and automotive infotainment.

EXECUTIVES

Senior Vice President, Greg Rose
EVP and CFO, George S. Davis, age 60, $760,011 total compensation
SVP and Chief Marketing Officer, Penny Baldwin
EVP General Counsel and Corporate Secretary, Donald J. Rosenberg, age 66, $675,002 total compensation
CEO and Director, Steven M. (Steve) Mollenkopf, age 48, $1,138,694 total compensation
EVP Technology, Matthew S. (Matt) Grob, age 50
EVP Engineering Qualcomm Technologies Inc. and CTO, James H. (Jim) Thompson, age 53
President, Cristiano R. Amon, age 47, $523,090 total compensation
EVP Human Resources, Michelle Sterling, age 50
EVP Strategy and M&A, Brian T. Modoff, age 57, $542,324 total compensation
EVP and President Qualcomm Technology Licensing (QTL), Alexander H. (Alex) Rogers, age 60
Vice President Finance, Will Wyatt
Vice President Sales Americas, Vishal Gupta
Executive Vice President and Chief Financial Officer, William E Keitel
VP Engineering, Charles Bergan
Vice President and General Manager nPhase, Steve Pazol
Vice President Regulatory Engineering, Paul Guckian

VICE PRESIDENT, BETH WAPNER
Vice President and Division Counsel of Government Technologies Division, Brian DeWitt
Vice President Engineering, Sudeepto Roy
Senior Vice President Chief Ip Strategist, Roger Martin
VP Supply Chain, Jim Seto
Vice President Learning and Development, Tamar Elkeles
Senior Vice President Engineering, Frank Quick
Vice President of Product Marketing and Business Development, Roberto Di Pietro
Vice President of Product Management for CDMA Technologies, Sayeed Choudhury
Senior Vice President Engineering, Nick Yu
Senior Vice President, Magnus Felke
Vice President Finance and Assistant General Manager, Steve Dhanens
Vice President Engineering, Scott Runner
Vice President Engineering, Chienchung Chang
Vice President of Operations, Roawen Chen
Vice President and Legal Counsel, Adam Schwenker
Senior Vice President Engineering, Steve Sprigg
Vice President Engineering, Manvinder Singh
Vice President, Annie Romano
Senior Vice President Ventures and Innovation North America and Head Qualcomm Ventures, Nagraj Kashyap
National Account Manager, Leslie Perretti
VICE PRESIDENT, ANDREW CHIU
Senior Vice President of Distributions and eMarketing, Rana Birouty
VICE PRESIDENT, SUSIE ARMSTRONG
Senior Management (Senior Vice President General Manager Director), Kerri Graham
Senior Vice President Technology, Peter Black
Vice President of Engineering, Brian Banister
Vice President Engineering, Jack Steenstra
Vice President Of Corporate Security, Steve Davis
Vice President Of Technology, Sherman Gregory
Executive Vice President Asia Pacific and Middle East and Africa, Jing Wang
VP of Engineering, Vladimir Aparin
Vice President, Mark Jerger
Vice President of Business Development, Chris Talbot
Vice President of Business Development, Jim Cathey
Senior Vice President and General Manager, Neville Meijers
Senior Vice President President Qualcomm Mems Technologies, John Batey
Vice President Marketing, Khalid Sidiqi
Senior Vice President Strategy And Corporate Development, Matt Eichenberger
Senior Vice President and General Manager, Eric Reifschneider
VP Technology, Ahmad Jalali
Vice President Engineering, Gene McAllister
Executive Vice President of the Americas and India, Peggy L Johnson
Vice President and President, John Stefanac
Vice President of Technology, Rob Gilmore
Vice President Technology, John Hong
Vice President of Sales, Andrew Gilbert
Vice President, Akash Palkhiwala
Vice President Engineering, Daniel Waldburger
Senior Vice President Engineering, Ed Tiedemann
Vice President of Government Affairs, Alice Tornquist
Executive Vice President And Group President, Derek Aberle
Vice President, Sandra Sisco
Vice President Business Development Latin America, Carlos Rivera
Vice President Of Technology, Geoffrey Yeap
Executive Vice President And General Manager Qualc, James Lederer
Vice President Techonology, Benny Katibian

Vice President Engineering and Operations, Mark Halfman
Vice President Information Technology, Brian Baker
VICE PRESIDENT, JEFFERY TORRANCE
Vice President Engineering QCT Software, Tony Schwarz
Executive Vice President Learning and Development, John Parks
Vice President, Alex Rogers
Vice President Contracts, Samimi Abbaseh
Vice President, Sanjay Mehta
VP Engineering Operations, Chuck Albers
Vice President, Mike Lapadula
VICE PRESIDENT, J KYRILLOS
Vice President of Technology, Roger Olmstead
VP Finance, Daniel Welch
Executive Chairman, Paul E. Jacobs, age 55
Secretary, Maria Terris
Treasurer, Scott C Rusnak
Secretary Executive, Laurie Mee
Treasurer, David Vargas
Vice President and Treasurer, Dick Grannis
Vice Chairman Qualcomm, Steven Altman
Secretary Senior, Katy Martin
Secretary Executive, Robin Frampton
Auditors: PricewaterhouseCoopers LLP

LOCATIONS

HQ: Qualcomm Inc
  5775 Morehouse Dr., San Diego, CA 92121-1714
Phone: 858 587-1121
Web: www.qualcomm.com

2017 Sales

	$ mil.	% of total
China (including Hong Kong)	14,579	65
South Korea	3,538	16
United States	513	2
Other foreign	3,661	16
Total	**22,291**	**100**

PRODUCTS/OPERATIONS

2017 Sales

	$ mil.	% of total
QCT (Qualcomm CDMA Technologies)	16,479	74
QTL (Qualcomm Technology Licensing)	6,445	29
QSI (Qualcomm Strategic Initiatives)	113	1
Adjustments	746	4
Total	**22,291**	**100**

2017 Sales

	$ mil.	% of total
Equipment & services	16,647	75
Licensing	5,644	25
Total	**22,291**	**100**

Selected Operations and Products

Code-Division Multiple Access (CDMA) Technologies
  Group
  Integrated circuits
  Baseband
  Intermediate-frequency
  Power management
  Radio-frequency
  Systems software
Engineering Services Group
Enterprise Services
Firethorn Holdings
Flarion Technologies
Government Technologies
Innovation Center
Internet Services
MediaFLO Technologies
MEMS Technologies
Qualcomm Ventures
Strategic Initiatives
Technology Licensing Group
  CDMA technologies and patents (cdmaOne CDMA2000 WCDMA TD-SCDMA)
  Royalties from products incorporating CDMA technology

Wireless and Internet Group
  Digital Media
  Digital motion picture delivery systems (under development)
  Government systems (development and analysis services; wireless base stations and phones)
  Internet Services
  Applications development software for wireless devices (BREW)
  Wireless Systems
  Low-Earth-orbit satellite-based telecommunications system (Globalstar)

COMPETITORS

Apple Inc.	Motorola Mobility
Broadcom	NEC
Cirrus Logic	NVIDIA
Ericsson	NXP Semiconductors
Fujitsu	Nokia
Infineon Technologies	Panasonic Corp
Intel	Renesas Electronics
InterDigital	STMicroelectronics
Marvell Technology	Samsung Electronics
Maxim Integrated Products	Spreadtrum
	Texas Instruments
MediaTek	Trimble
Microchip Technology	

HISTORICAL FINANCIALS

Company Type: Public

Income Statement

FYE: September 24

	REVENUE ($ mil.)	NET INCOME ($ mil.)	NET PROFIT MARGIN	EMPLOYEES
09/17	22,291	2,466	11.1%	33,800
09/16	23,554	5,705	24.2%	30,500
09/15	25,281	5,271	20.8%	33,000
09/14	26,487	7,967	30.1%	31,300
09/13	24,866	6,853	27.6%	31,000
Annual Growth	(2.7%)	(22.5%)	—	2.2%

2017 Year-End Financials

Debt ratio: 33.43%
Return on equity: 7.91%
Cash ($ mil.): 35,029
Current ratio: 4.00
Long-term debt ($ mil.): 19,398

No. of shares (mil.): 1,474
Dividends
  Yield: 0.0%
  Payout: 133.3%
Market value ($ mil.): 76,781

	STOCK PRICE ($) FY Close	P/E High/Low	Earnings	Dividends	Book Value
09/17	52.09	42 30	1.65	2.20	20.86
09/16	62.75	17 11	3.81	2.02	21.53
09/15	53.22	24 16	3.22	1.80	20.62
09/14	75.06	17 14	4.65	1.54	23.47
09/13	67.38	18 14	3.91	1.20	21.42
Annual Growth	(6.2%)	— —	(19.4%)	16.4%	(0.7%)

Quanta Services, Inc.

Quanta Services is a specialty contractor that designs installs repairs and maintains network infrastructure across North America and abroad. The company serves the electric power and oil and natural gas pipeline industries mainly in the US Canada and Australia. Capabilities include pylon construction distribution infrastructure and emergency response among much more. Its oil and gas business offers onshore and offshore services. Quanta's other services include outsource management and other specialty work such as installing traffic and light rail control systems directional drilling and constructing wind and solar power facilities. The company was founded in 1997.

Operations

Quanta operates through two primary segments: Electric Power Infrastructure which makes up 65% of revenue; and Oil and Gas Infrastructure (35% of revenue).

The Electric Power segment offers a vast array of physical infrastructure construction and maintenance. Services include transmission construction distribution construction substations power generation emergency response EPC (engineering procurement and construction) services helicopter services and more.

Oil and Gas onshore includes pipeline construction gas distribution horizontal drilling trenching and facilities construction.

Oil and Gas offshore activities include fabrication of structural skids heliports and new and refurbished decks and jackets; derrick barge services; heavy lift; diving; pipelay; and more.

Geographic Reach

Houston-based Quanta Services generates around 80% of its revenue in the US. Its next largest market is Canada which makes up about 15% of its business followed by Australia. Other international offices are in South Africa India and Latin America (Chile Colombia Costa Rica Ecuador Guatemala Mexico Panama and Peru).

Sales and Marketing

The company mostly serves companies in the electric power and oil & gas markets though it also serves commercial industrial and governmental organizations.

Quanta's 10 largest customers account for more than 30% of revenue and its largest customer about 5%. Clients include American Electric Power Duke Energy PG&E Corp. and TransCanada Corp ITC Holdings and Exelon Corp. among others.

Financial Performance

After a revenue dip in 2015 Quanta finished 2016 back on an upward trajectory.

In fiscal 2016 (ended December) sales grew 1% to $7.7 billion as 6% growth in Oil and Gas was offset by a 2% fall in Electric Power. The increase in Oil and Gas is attributable to higher capital spending among Quanta's customers particularly in H2 2016 as well as higher natural gas distribution spending. Acquired businesses also contributed $125 million to sales mostly in the Electric Power segment.

Net income fell by a third to $198.4 million due mostly to a gain of $190 million on the sale of its fiber optic leasing business in the previous year. However business performance as a whole improved with gains on operating profit outweighing higher selling general and administrative expenses.

Cash provided by operations fell 38% to $381.2 million due to an increase in working capital requirements relating to larger oil and gas infrastructure projects and billing delays on two electric transmission projects in remote Canada.

Strategy

Quanta maintains a strategy growing by acquiring companies that complement its business broaden its portfolio of service offerings and extend its geographic footprint in its three main markets of the US Canada and Australia. A larger service portfolio also allows the company to boost sales with existing customers through cross-selling. The company made several acquisitions in those markets in 2016 and 2015.

In 2016 Quanta acquired five companies across the US Canada and Australia mostly working in electric infrastructure.

Several trends in the market place present Quanta with opportunities to grow. As demand for electricity in North America continues to increase and the electric power grid system is aging

Quanta is well positioned to take advantage of increased demand for its services. Renewable energy such as wind and solar also present opportunities for Quanta to provide transmission line installation and project management services. Indeed some recent notable projects it's secured include the 1100 km-Labrador Island Link HVdc Transmission Project in Newfoundland and the 500 kV Transmission Project in Alberta (both awarded in 2014) — two of the largest electric transmission projects ever undertaken in North America.

Quanta also sees potential for growth in the natural gas segment as development of gas shale formations in North America have provided more supply of natural gas — and thus expectations of more demand for natural gas-fired power plants and pipelines over the next two decades. Recent project procurements have include Maurepas Pipeline and the ort McMurray West 500 kV Transmission Project.

The company has retreated from a few business lines over the past few years to free up resources and better focus on its main energy infrastructure operations. In 2015 for example it sold its Fiber Optic Leasing business to Crown Castle International for $1 billion.

Mergers and Acquisitions

During 2016 we completed five acquisitions including an Australian electrical infrastructure services company a Canadian utility contracting company an American medium- and high-voltage powerline contracting company and a telecommunications company located in Canada.

In the first half of 2016 Quanta acquired three companies which followed five purchases in the second half of 2015. The acquired companies fell into the electric power and oil and gas segments and were mainly in the US and Canada as well as Australia.

These companies included a foundation services company an electrical contracting company and a powerline construction company all in the US. Quanta also bought an electrical engineering company in Australia.

EXECUTIVES

CFO, Derrick A. Jensen, age 46, $600,000 total compensation
President CEO and COO, Earl C. (Duke) Austin, age 47, $979,924 total compensation
EVP Corporate Development and President Infrastructure Solutions, Jesse E. Morris, age 49, $466,900 total compensation
EVP Operations and Health/Safety and Environmental, Randall C. Wisenbaker, age 52, $475,625 total compensation
President Electric Power, Dale L. Querrey, age 53, $595,880 total compensation
President Oil and Gas Division and Chief Strategy Officer, Paul C. Gregory, age 53
Chairman, Bruce E. Ranck
Auditors: PricewaterhouseCoopers LLP

LOCATIONS

HQ: Quanta Services, Inc.
2800 Post Oak Boulevard, Suite 2600, Houston, TX 77056
Phone: 713 629-7600
Web: www.quantaservices.com

PRODUCTS/OPERATIONS

2016 sales

	$ mil.	% of total
Electric power infrastructure	4,850	63
Oil and gas infrastructure	2,800	37
Total	**7,651**	**100**

COMPETITORS

Cable Com	MDU Construction
Comm-Works	Services
Dycom	MYR Group
EMCOR	MasTec
Goldfield	Mass Electric
Henkels & McCoy	Pike Corporation
IES Holdings	Tetra Tech

HISTORICAL FINANCIALS

Company Type: Public

Income Statement

FYE: December 31

	REVENUE ($ mil.)	NET INCOME ($ mil.)	NET PROFIT MARGIN	EMPLOYEES
12/16	7,651	198	2.6%	28,100
12/15	7,572	310	4.1%	24,500
12/14	7,851	296	3.8%	24,600
12/13	6,522	401	6.2%	20,900
12/12	5,920	306	5.2%	17,800
Annual Growth	**6.6%**	**(10.3%)**	**—**	**12.1%**

2016 Year-End Financials

Debt ratio: 6.60%	No. of shares (mil.): 151
Return on equity: 6.16%	Dividends
Cash ($ mil.): 112	Yield: —
Current ratio: 1.90	Payout: —
Long-term debt ($ mil.): 353	Market value ($ mil.): 5,270

	STOCK PRICE ($) FY Close	P/E High/Low	PER SHARE ($) Earnings	Dividends	Book Value
12/16	34.85	28 14	1.26	0.00	22.08
12/15	20.25	19 12	1.59	0.00	19.31
12/14	28.39	28 19	1.35	0.00	20.69
12/13	31.56	17 14	1.87	0.00	19.56
12/12	27.29	19 14	1.44	0.00	17.67
Annual Growth	**6.3%**	**— —**	**(3.3%)**	**—**	**5.7%**

Quest Diagnostics, Inc.

Quest Diagnostics is testing its ability to be the world's leading clinical lab. The company performs diagnostics on some 160 million specimens each year including routine clinical tests such as cholesterol checks Pap smears and HIV screenings. Quest Diagnostics also performs esoteric testing (such as genetic screening) and anatomic pathology testing (such as tissue biopsies for cancer testing). Its Quest Diagnostic Nichols Institute develops new diagnostics. In all the company serves half of the physicians and hospitals in the US as well as government agencies and other clinical labs. Quest Diagnostics has more than 2200 patient service centers where samples are collected.

HISTORY

Quest Diagnostics began as one man's quest to make clinical tests more affordable. Pathologist Paul Brown started Metropolitan Pathological Laboratory (MetPath) in his Manhattan apartment in 1967. To help his business take off in 1969 he bought two $55000 blood analyzers that could automatically perform a dozen common tests; the machines allowed him to charge patients $5.50 while hospitals and other labs were charging upwards of $40. Investments in emerging lab technology helped MetPath continue to beat competitors' prices and grow its business. It made its first profit in 1971 and eventually attracted the atten-

tion of Corning Glass Works which bought 10% of the company in 1973.

MetPath's growth was due in part to investments in technology. The company built a state-of-the-art central lab in New Jersey in 1978 that could process some 30000 specimens daily; it also went on an acquisition spree to expand across the US. These investments left the firm swamped with debt and Corning bought the company in 1982.

An autonomous unit of Corning MetPath continued to grow as Medicare reimbursement for lab tests went up and more doctors ordered more tests to catch and prevent disease before it happened. To cut costs in the mid-1980s the company reorganized its facilities to create a regional lab network. A reorganization in 1990 at its parent placed MetPath in the Corning Lab Services subsidiary.

Corning Lab Services strengthened its operations in the early 1990s by buying labs from regional operators. In 1994 MetPath became Corning Clinical Laboratories. Around the same time the company found itself besieged with demands from HMOs and other managed care providers to lower its costs. Also during this time the company settled a handful of federal suits accusing it of fraudulent Medicare billing. In the face of increasing pressure parent Corning spun off its lab testing business to the public as Quest Diagnostics in 1996.

On its own Quest aimed to grow through acquisitions. In 1999 it bought rival SmithKline Beecham Clinical Laboratories from GlaxoSmithKline. (GSK gained a minority stake in Quest through the deal; it gradually sold off all shares in Quest by 2011.) Continuing its growth strategy in the 21st century it bought American Medical Laboratories to expand its esoteric testing operations in 2002. The company was finally able to close its acquisition of Unilab in early 2003 after the deal ran into delays with the FTC. Quest sold some labs and service contracts in northern California to LabCorp to appease FTC regulators.

To expand internationally the company began providing testing services in India in 2008 including esoteric testing for hospitals tests for the life insurance industry and diagnostics for global clinical trials.

EXECUTIVES

Chairman President and CEO, Stephen H. (Steve) Rusckowski, age 59, $1,100,000 total compensation
Vice President Tax, Stephen Calamari
SVP and Group Executive Diagnostic Solutions, Jon R. Cohen, age 62, $575,000 total compensation
SVP and Group Executive Clinical Franchise Solutions and Marketing, Catherine T. Doherty, age 54, $575,000 total compensation
SVP Commercial, Everett V. Cunningham, age 50
VP Global Markets and Chairman Q2 Solutions, John B. Haydon
EVP and CFO, Mark J. Guinan, age 55, $586,538 total compensation
EVP General Diagnostics, James E. Davis, age 54, $586,538 total compensation
SVP Research and Development and Medical and Chief Medical Officer, Jay G. Wohlgemuth
SVP and CIO, Lidia Fonseca
Vice President and Treasurer, Tracy Cinco-Abela
Medical Director, Harvey Kaufman
Vice President Clinical Trials, Christopher Fikry
Corporate Vice President Human Resources Strategic, Kathi Geter
Vice President Operations, James Garczynski
Medical Director Neurology, Joseph J Higgins
Vice President and General Manager North Region, Denis Gallagher
Senior Vice President Strategy Mergers and Acquisitions and Ventures, Dermot Shorten
Vice President R and D, Rick Pesano

Regional Vice President Commercial, Geoffrey Albrecht
Treasurer, Garrett H Hansen
Board Member, Maya Patel
Auditors: PricewaterhouseCoopers LLP

LOCATIONS

HQ: Quest Diagnostics, Inc.
Three Giralda Farms, Madison, NJ 07940
Phone: 973 520-2700
Web: www.QuestDiagnostics.com

PRODUCTS/OPERATIONS

2016 Sales

	$ mil.	% of total
Diagnostic information services		
Routine clinical testing services	4,179	56
Gene-based and esoteric (including advanced diagnostics)		
testing services	2,335	31
Anatomic pathology testing services	624	8
All Other	377	5
Total	**7,515**	**100**

Selected Acquisitions

COMPETITORS

Alere	Oncolab
Arup Laboratories	Pathology Associates
Bio-Reference Labs	Medical Laboratories
Genomic Health	Psychemedics
LabCorp	Solstas
Medtox Scientific	Sonic Healthcare

HISTORICAL FINANCIALS

Company Type: Public

Income Statement

FYE: December 31

	REVENUE ($ mil.)	NET INCOME ($ mil.)	NET PROFIT MARGIN	EMPLOYEES
12/16	7,515	645	8.6%	43,000
12/15	7,493	709	9.5%	44,000
12/14	7,435	556	7.5%	45,000
12/13	7,146	849	11.9%	41,000
12/12	7,382	555	7.5%	41,000
Annual Growth	0.4%	3.8%	—	1.2%

2016 Year-End Financials

Debt ratio: 36.97%
Return on equity: 13.82%
Cash ($ mil.): 359
Current ratio: 1.56
Long-term debt ($ mil.): 3,728
No. of shares (mil.): 137
Dividends
Yield: 0.0%
Payout: 35.0%
Market value ($ mil.): 12,590

	STOCK PRICE ($) FY Close	P/E High/Low		PER SHARE ($) Earnings	Dividends	Book Value
12/16	91.90	20	13	4.51	1.58	33.78
12/15	71.14	16	12	4.87	1.47	32.76
12/14	67.06	18	13	3.81	1.29	29.87
12/13	53.54	11	9	5.54	1.20	27.42
12/12	58.27	19	16	3.46	0.68	26.29
Annual Growth	12.1%	—		6.9%	23.5%	6.5%

QVC, INC.

The phones are ringing off the hook at television home shopping company QVC. QVC (its name stands for "quality value and convenience") offers about 1000 items each week to TV-tied consumer shoppers. Merchandise includes apparel cosmetics electronics housewares jewelry and toys. It broadcasts 24 hours a day; viewers call in their orders to one of its three US call centers. If you can't find what you're shopping for on the tube it also sells online at QVC.com through mobile apps and some half dozen outlet stores in four states. The company has shopping channels in Germany Japan Italy and the UK. QVC is a subsidiary of shopping and travel site operator Liberty Interactive.

Operations

The video and e-commerce retailer has operations in the US the UK Germany Italy and Japan. Recognizing growth potential in China QVC established a joint venture there in 2012 with China's government-owned radio division China National Radio (CNR).

Geographic Reach

The US is QVC's largest market contributing two-thirds of its total sales followed by Japan (15%) and Germany (11%). The UK and the company's newest market Italy make up the rest. QVC operates eight distribution centers and eight call centers worldwide.

Sales and Marketing

QVC distributes its programming through affiliation agreements with many television providers including Comcast Time Warner Cable DIRECTV and DISH Network in the US; JCN Jupiter Telecommunications in Japan; Kabel Deutschland in Germany; Sky plc and Virgin Media in the UK; and Telecom Italia Media Broadcasting in Italy.

While the phones are still ringing at QVC call centers business is booming on its QVC.com website. In 2012 the company's global e-commerce sales totaled $2.9 billion or 34% of its consolidated sales.

Financial Performance

After a couple of tough years during the global recession QVC is solidly back in sales growth mode. In 2012 global sales topped $8.5 billion up 3% versus 2011 after increasing by 6% in the prior annual comparison. Sales increased in all of the retailer's markets with the exception of Germany where sales fell by 10%. Japan posted an 11% gain in sales while the US and UK saw more modest sales gains. The company credited its revenue growth to an 3% increase in average selling price and an increase in shipping and handling revenue.

QVC's profitability is also on the rise with operating income up 11% in 2012 versus 2011 to nearly $1.3 billion.

Strategy

From its roots in television shopping QVC's goal is to entice buyers across all forms of media including TV the Internet and mobile devices. With about 90% of its business coming from repeat customers the company is looking to international markets for additional customers. China is one such place. QVC entered China in 2012 through a Beijing-based joint venture called CNR Home Shopping Co. Ltd. (CNRS). QVC holds a 49% stake while partner China National Radio owns the remaining 51%. The JV operates a multimedia retailing business in China through the CNR Mall TV shopping channel and its e-commerce site. The CNR Mall channel reaches about 48 million homes in China.

Mergers and Acquisitions

QVC's parent company Liberty Interactive agreed to buy the 62% of HSN Inc. it didn't own for about $2.1 billion in an all-stock deal in 2017.The deal is a bet that bigger is better in battling Amazon.com and other online retailers. The companies said larger scale will help them develop ecommerce mobile and over-the-top platforms optimize content across five networks and cross market among the networks. The HSN assets are to be packaged with QVC and Zulily an ecommerce company owned by Liberty in an asset-backed spin off from Liberty late in 2017. The HSN acquisition was expected to close by the end of 2017.

In mid-2015 QVC purchased Zulily in a $2.4 billion deal to gain access to millennial moms.

EXECUTIVES

President and CEO, Michael (Mike) George, age 55
Svp Quality Assurance And Inbound Supply Chain, Mike Appleby
Vice President Broadcast Technology, Todd Sprinkle
Senior Vice President and Controller, John John Misko
Vice President Distribution Operations, Jim Reid
Vice President Procurement, Jeff Nord
Vice President of Sales, Julie Batenburg
Vice President Digital Media, Courtney Cason
Vice President, Patti Reilly
Vice President Customer Servic, Lisa Norden
Senior Vice President And General Counsel, Larry Hayes
Area Vice President, Kristi Hanifin
Secretary, Joan Ruffenach
Auditors: KPMG LLP PHILADELPHIA PENNSY

LOCATIONS

HQ: QVC, INC.
1200 WILSON DR, WEST CHESTER, PA 193804262
Phone: 484 701-1000
Web: WWW.QVC.COM

2016 Sales

	$ mil.	% of total
QVC-U.S.	6,120	70
QVC-International	2,562	30
Total	**8,682**	**100**

COMPETITORS

Access TV	Macy's
Alticor	Modern Times Group AB
Amazon.com	Overstock.com
Blue Nile Inc.	Priceline
Bluestem Brands	Provell
EVINE Live	Sears
HSN	Walmart.com
J. C. Penney	

HISTORICAL FINANCIALS

Company Type: Private

Income Statement

FYE: December 31

	REVENUE ($ mil.)	NET INCOME ($ mil.)	NET PROFIT MARGIN	EMPLOYEES
12/16	8,682	642	7.4%	17,700
12/15	8,743	662	7.6%	—
12/14	8,801	633	7.2%	—
12/13	8,623	633	7.3%	—
Annual Growth	0.2%	0.5%	—	—

2016 Year-End Financials

Debt ratio: ——
Return on equity: 7.40%
Cash ($ mil.): 284
Current ratio: 1.00
Long-term debt ($ mil.): —
Dividends
Yield: —
Payout: —
Market value ($ mil.): —

Qwest Corp

EXECUTIVES

Exec V Pres-cao-contrl, David D Cole
Auditors: KPMG LLP

LOCATIONS

HQ: Qwest Corp
100 CenturyLink Drive, Monroe, LA 71203
Phone: 318 388-9000
Web: www.centurylink.com

HISTORICAL FINANCIALS

Company Type: Public

Income Statement

	REVENUE ($ mil.)	NET INCOME ($ mil.)	NET PROFIT MARGIN	EMPLOYEES
12/16	8,910	1,085	12.2%	22,000
12/15	8,964	1,074	12.0%	22,000
12/14	8,838	970	11.0%	23,000
12/13	8,753	964	11.0%	22,800
12/12	8,848	849	9.6%	21,400
Annual Growth	0.2%	6.3%	—	0.7%

FYE: December 31

2016 Year-End Financials

Debt ratio: 38.65%	No. of shares (mil.): 0
Return on equity: 12.30%	Dividends
Cash ($ mil.): 5	Yield: —
Current ratio: 0.61	Payout: 119.8%
Long-term debt ($ mil.): 6,747	Market value ($ mil.): —

R. DIRECTIONAL DRILLING & UNDERGROUND TECHNOLOGY, INC.

Auditors: KEN DUSSEAU PC

LOCATIONS

HQ: R. DIRECTIONAL DRILLING & UNDERGROUND TECHNOLOGY, INC.
8560 N 77TH DR, PEORIA, AZ 853457969
Phone: 602 374-3173
Web: WWW.RDIRECTIONALDRILLING.COM

HISTORICAL FINANCIALS

Company Type: Private

Income Statement

	REVENUE ($ mil.)	NET INCOME ($ mil.)	NET PROFIT MARGIN	EMPLOYEES
12/12	7,667	(1,040)	—	61
12/11	7	2	29.9%	—
Annual Growth	99380.2%	—	—	—

FYE: December 31

2012 Year-End Financials

Debt ratio: —	
Return on equity: (-13.60%)	Dividends
Cash ($ mil.): 416	Yield: —
Current ratio: 1.10	Payout: —
Long-term debt ($ mil.): —	Market value ($ mil.): —

RACETRAC PETROLEUM, INC.

RaceTrac Petroleum hopes it's a popular pit stop for gasoline and snacks in the South. The company operates more than 600 gas stations and convenience stores in 10 southern US states under the RaceTrac and RaceWay names. (RaceWay stores are operated by independent contractors.) The chain plans to grow by expanding its store count by about 10% a year. Carl Bolch founded RaceTrac in Missouri in 1934. His son chairman Carl Bolch Jr. moved the company into high-volume gas stations with long self-service islands that can serve as many as two dozen vehicles at one time. Race-Trac's convenience stores sell fresh deli food and offer some fast-food fare. The Bolch family owns and runs the company.

Geographic Reach

Atlanta-based RaceTrac Petroleum operates stores in Alabama Florida Georgia Louisiana Kentucky Mississippi North Carolina South Carolina Tennessee and Texas.

Financial Performance

One of the largest private companies in the US Racetrac Petroleum's stores rang up more than $9 billion in sales in 2012.

Strategy

RaceTrac prefers to build its own stores from the ground up rather than grow through acquisitions. Indeed in the past 16 years the company has only bought one store. Recently RaceTrac has been increasing the number of independently-operated RaceWay stores in its portfolio. (While the RaceWay stores are operated by independent contractors RaceTrac stills owns and controls the gasoline business and real estate.) It has also consolidated its company-operated stores into four key markets: Atlanta Dallas Florida and Louisiana. In 2014 the chain is building new stores in key markets such as Florida and adding services. In 2013 it partnered with Fifth Third Bancorp to install ATMs at 225 RaceTrac convenience stores in Georgia and Florida.

RaceTrac Petroleum got a new leader Allison Moran in 2013. Moran who led the RaceTrac company-operated stores division before her promotion to CEO succeeded Carl Bloch Jr. (who retained the chairman's title). Moran is Bloch's eldest daughter.

In 2015 RaceTrac sold five retail operations in Florida to Town Star Holdings an affiliate of Junonia Capital LLC. Four of the convenience stores are in the Orlando area with the other in Jacksonville.

EXECUTIVES

President, Billy Milam
VP Information Systems, Will Alexander
Chief Supply Officer, Max McBrayer
Chairman and CEO, Carl E. Bolch
Auditors: GRANT THORNTON LLP ATLANTA G

LOCATIONS

HQ: RACETRAC PETROLEUM, INC.
3225 CUMBERLAND BLVD SE # 100, ATLANTA, GA 303396407
Phone: 770 850-3491
Web: WWW.RACETRAC.COM

COMPETITORS

7-Eleven	Love's Country Stores
Chevron	Motiva Enterprises
Couche-Tard	Pilot Corporation
Cumberland Farms	Pilot Flying J
E-Z Mart Stores	QuikTrip
Exxon Mobil	The Pantry
Gate Petroleum	

HISTORICAL FINANCIALS

Company Type: Private

Income Statement

	REVENUE ($ mil.)	NET INCOME ($ mil.)	NET PROFIT MARGIN	EMPLOYEES
12/15	7,501	107	1.4%	3,479
12/14	9,101	161	1.8%	—
12/13	8,843	122	1.4%	—
12/12	0	55	—	—
Annual Growth	—	24.3%	—	—

FYE: December 31

2015 Year-End Financials

Debt ratio: —	
Return on equity: 1.40%	Dividends
Cash ($ mil.): 193	Yield: —
Current ratio: 0.70	Payout: —
Long-term debt ($ mil.): —	Market value ($ mil.): —

Radian Group, Inc.

Radian Group is glowing from a conflagration of private mortgage insurance claims. Through subsidiaries Radian Guaranty Radian Mortgage Assurance and Radian Insurance Radian Group provides traditional private mortgage insurance coverage to protect lenders from defaults by borrowers who put down a deposit of less than 20% when buying a home. Such coverage provides protection on individual loans and covers unpaid loan principal and delinquent interest. Its pool insurance covers limited exposure on groups of loans. Radian still insures municipal bonds written before 2008 through its financial guaranty business. Radian Group's customers include mortgage bankers commercial banks and savings institutions.

Operations

Radian operates in two segments: The mortgage insurance division offers credit-related insurance coverage primarily private mortgage insurance as well as risk services for lending agencies. These operations are primarily conducted through the Radian Guaranty subsidiary. The company also provides mortgage and real estate services through its principal services subsidiary Clayton as well as Green River Capital Red Bell Real Estate and ValuAmerica.

Meanwhile the financial guaranty segment — handled by the Radian Asset Assurance unit — insures a runoff portfolio of public finance and structured finance credits. The unit which no longer actively markets policies historically offered direct insurance or reinsurance for credit based risks as well as credit protection through default swaps and financial guaranty transactions.

During headier days the government encouraged lenders to turn more Americans into homeowners and Radian made a steady diet of insuring subprime mortgages. However that strategy meant that it was among the first to be hit and hit hard when the housing market imploded and mortgage defaults piled up.

Geographic Reach

Headquartered in Philadelphia Radian has offices across the US as well as in Hong Kong and in Bristol UK.

Sales and Marketing

The principal customers of its mortgage insurance business are mortgage originators such as mortgage bankers mortgage brokers commercial banks savings institutions credit unions and community banks.

Financial Performance

In fiscal 2015 revenue climbed 11% to $1.2 billion due mainly to a 101% increase in revenue from the Services segment. It also recorded higher net premiums in the year. Net income dropped however by 70% to $286.9 million due to a large income tax benefit in the prior fiscal year. The company's cash position strengthened with cash from operating activities climbing to $15.5 million from a loss of $153.2 million in 2014.

Strategy

Radian is looking expand the depth and breadth of its mortgage offering as the housing market in the US continues to strengthen.

Mergers and Acquisitions

In 2015 real estate consulting subsidiary Clayton Holdings acquired Pittsburgh-based title agency ValuAmerica. Through that purchase Clayton gained ValuAmerica's technology platform which streamlines supply chains and workflows for mortgage lenders. The company also acquired Red Bell a real estate brokerage valuation and technology company to expand its mortgage and real estate services offerings.

Clayton followed up those deals with the 2017 acquisition of California-based ValuEscrow which continues to operate under its own brand name.

HISTORY

Radian Group was born from the ashes of the 1987 stock crash and the rubble of the natural disasters of the early 1990s. Parent insurance company Reliance Group was deep in debt and desperately in need of cash. To raise money Reliance separated CMAC Investment (and operating subsidiary Commonwealth Mortgage Assurance) from subsidiary Commonwealth Land Title and took the company public in 1992.

In 1994 after two years of lackluster stock performance the board promoted CFO Frank Filipps (an American International Group veteran) to CEO. Filipps limited commissions to new policies rather than retained business. The pokey stock nosed up with some help from low interest rates and high numbers of new mortgage loans. Despite a raise in interest rates in 1995 the company continued to expand its market share.

In 1996 the company launched Prophet Score a new risk-assessment model that allowed CMAC to expand its coverage to include subprime loans. These measures jump-started sales to new highs in 1997 and 1998. Nevertheless CMAC (and its competitors) suffered in the market because of negative publicity: private mortgage (PMI) insurers were slammed for keeping quiet when borrowers' equity rose to 20% the point when PMI is usually considered unnecessary. In 1999 CMAC bought former rival Amerin and changed the name of the combined company to Radian Group.

Radian diversified its operations through the 2001 acquisition of credit-based insurance and financial services provider Enhance Financial (renamed Radian Reinsurance and later merged into Radian Asset Assurance Inc.) In 2002 Radian sold off the Enhance Consumer Services subsidiary.

In 2005 Filipps departed to join Clayton Holdings. Sanford Ibrahim was then named CEO.

The company expanded into Asia in 2005 through a partnership with Standard Chartered Bank (Hong Kong) with Radian as the exclusive provider of residential mortgage insurance to the lender. However the deal did not take root and Standard Chartered Bank yanked their contract in early 2008.

As the credit markets went into meltdown that year the company began pulling back on the riskiest of bonds (such as second-liens) by mid-2007 but by early 2008 its ratings had been lowered.

In response to the market troubles Radian stopped insuring certain types of higher-risk home loans and began working with existing mortgage services to help distressed borrowers modify their loan terms. The company's Radian Asset Assurance operations in the US and UK also stopped accepting new business as part of its general hunkering down to ride out the storm and in 2010 it put the UK unit into liquidation.

EXECUTIVES

CEO, Richard G. (Rick) Thornberry
President Radian Guaranty, Teresa A. Bryce Bazemore, age 57, $550,000 total compensation
EVP and CFO, J. Franklin (Frank) Hall, age 49, $400,000 total compensation
EVP and CIO, Richard I. (Rick) Altman, age 50
EVP and Chief Risk Officer, Derek V. Brummer, $415,000 total compensation
President Clayton Holdings, Jeff Tennyson
Vice President, Maria Mast
Vice President, Nina Zotter
Vice President Underwriting, Bob Mullins
Senior Vice President and Deputy General Counsel, Glenn Davis
Assistant Vice President Corporate Accounting, Abigail Rodriguez
Vice President Strategic Services, Susan King
Chairman, Herbert Wender, age 80
Auditors: PricewaterhouseCoopers LLP

LOCATIONS

HQ: Radian Group, Inc.
1500 Market Street, Philadelphia, PA 19102
Phone: 215 231-1000
Web: www.radian.biz

PRODUCTS/OPERATIONS

2016 Revenues

	$ mil.	% of total
Net premiums earned;insurance	921	74
Services revenue	168	14
Net investment income	113	9
Net gains (losses) on investments and other financial instruments	30	3
Other income	3	-
Total	**1,238**	**100**

COMPETITORS

Assured Guaranty	Old Republic
Essent Guaranty	Triad Guaranty
Genworth Financial	US Department of
MGIC Investment	Veterans Affairs
National Mortgage	United Guaranty
Insurance	

HISTORICAL FINANCIALS

Company Type: Public

Income Statement
FYE: December 31

	ASSETS ($ mil.)	NET INCOME ($ mil.)	INCOME AS % OF ASSETS	EMPLOYEES
12/16	5,863	308	5.3%	1,971
12/15	5,642	286	5.1%	1,881
12/14	6,859	959	14.0%	1,702
12/13	5,621	(196)	—	782
12/12	5,903	(451)	—	696
Annual Growth	(0.2%)	—	—	29.7%

2016 Year-End Financials

Debt ratio: 18.24%
Return on equity: 11.45%
Cash ($ mil.): 52
Current ratio: —
Long-term debt ($ mil.): —

No. of shares (mil.): 214
Dividends
　Yield: 0.0%
　Payout: 0.7%
Market value ($ mil.): 3,857

	STOCK PRICE ($) FY Close	P/E High/Low		Earnings	Dividends	Book Value
12/16	17.98	13	6	1.37	0.01	13.39
12/15	13.39	13	9	1.22	0.01	12.07
12/14	16.72	3	2	4.16	0.01	11.37
12/13	14.12	—	—	(1.18)	0.01	5.43
12/12	6.11	—	—	(3.41)	0.01	5.51
Annual Growth	31.0%	—	—	—	(0.0%)	24.9%

Ralph Lauren Corp

Ralph Lauren Corporation is galloping at a faster clip than when its namesake founder first entered the arena over 45 years ago. With golden mallet brands such as Polo by Ralph Lauren Chaps RRL Club Monaco and RLX Ralph Lauren the company designs and markets apparel and accessories home furnishings and fragrances. Its collections are available at more than 13000 retail locations worldwide including many upscale and mid-tier department stores (Macy's contributes 25% to RL's wholesale revenue). It operates 465-plus Ralph Lauren and Club Monaco retail stores worldwide as well as 615-plus concession-based shops-within-shops and 10 e-commerce sites.

HISTORY

Ralph Lauren a suave Manhattanite was actually born Ralph Lifschitz in the Bronx New York. It is said that his father Frank an immigrant Russian housepainter and muralist informally changed the family's name to Lauren and inspired his son to recreate himself in the image of a mythic upper class.

After high school Ralph who formally changed his name to Lauren became a salesman at Brooks Brothers and then a sales representative for Rivetz a Boston tie maker. In 1967 he landed a job as a tie designer for Beau Brummel of New York. The company gave him his own style division which he named Polo because of the sport's refined image. The next year Lauren started Polo Fashions to make tailored menswear. Partner Peter Strom teamed up with Lauren in the early 1970s. Although its designs received critical acclaim Polo Fashions had a bumpy start as Lauren adjusted to the business aspect of his fashion label.

Lauren's profile rose in the 1970s when he won three Coty Awards for design and produced costumes for the movie The Great Gatsby. In 1971

Lauren adopted his polo-player-on-a-horse logo and introduced a line for women. That year the first licensed Polo store opened (on Rodeo Drive in Beverly Hills) along with his first in-store boutique (at Bloomingdale's in New York City). He added shoes to the lineup in 1972 licensed his womenswear line the next year and launched a licensed fragrance line in 1978.

By 1980 Polo Fashions had become Polo Ralph Lauren. Encouraged by the success of the licensed products Lauren led the designer charge into home furnishings introducing his Home Collection in 1983. He opened his flagship store in New York City three years later. The company expanded upmarket with its Purple Label and downmarket with Polo Jeans denims and a line of paints in 1996.

Following the stampede of fashion-house IPOs Polo went public in 1997. The next year moving to reduce expenses the company restructured its divisions. In 1999 Polo paid $85 million for hip Canadian retailer Club Monaco to compete in the burgeoning youth market. It also opened RL a fine-dining restaurant adjacent to its retail outlet in Chicago's famed shopping district.

In early 2000 Polo purchased its European licensee Poloco for $230 million giving the company greater control of its brand. Then in a 50-50 joint venture with NBC and its affiliates Polo formed Ralph Lauren Media Company to sell its products via the Internet as well as broadcast cable and print media. Also that year the company closed 11 underperforming Club Monaco locations and announced plans to shut down all of its jeans stores. To extend its European reach even further Polo bought its Italian licensee PRL Fashions of Europe in 2001.

Polo Ralph Lauren inked one of the most significant licensing deals in company history — and what it considers to be a great match to boot — in 2005. The firm paired with the United States Tennis Association (USTA) to form a four-year global partnership and was designated the official apparel sponsor of the US Open through 2008. The agreement involved among other things an official shirt designed by Lauren for on-court officials co-branded US Open/Polo Ralph Lauren merchandise and joint marketing programs. In 2006 the company entered a licensing agreement with Luxottica valued at more than $1.75 billion over a 10-year period.

The company's agreement with the USTA gave it the momentum to seal a deal with The All England Club and Wimbledon in 2006 that extends through 2010. Polo Ralph Lauren as part of the agreement became the exclusive outfitter of Wimbledon — the first official designer in the 129-history of the games. Polo Ralph Lauren creates and outfits on-court officials and sells its Wimbledon collection at its freestanding stores as well as through select retailers and Polo.com.

Initiatives for 2007 included the launch of a new group named Global Brand Concepts formed to develop lifestyle brands for specialty and department stores including J.C. Penney's American Living Collection. The group designs and markets new products including accessories home decor and women's men's and children's apparel.

That year Polo Ralph Lauren purchased the remaining 50% stake in Polo.com from both Ralph Lauren Media a unit of NBCUniversal and ValueVisions Media for about $175 million. The move gave Polo full control over its plans to develop its online presence domestically and abroad.

The company brought its East Coast lifestyle brand to Asia when it opened its first freestanding flagship store in Tokyo in 2006. The next year Polo Ralph Lauren secured a foothold in the Japanese apparel and accessories market by purchasing the 50% balance of Polo Ralph Lauren Japan for some $23 million and making it a wholly

owned subsidiary. The company also increased its stake in Impact 21 Co. a Japanese sub-licensee from 20% to 97% in. Impact 21 operates the company's men's women's and jeans apparel and accessories business in Japan.

Founder Ralph Lauren stepped down as CEO in November 2015 but remained involved with the company as chairman and chief creative officer.

During 2013 RLC brought several licensing arrangements in-house. In April 2013 it acquired the Chaps Menswear Business from PVH for about $18 million. In July it bought the Australia and New Zealand licensed operations from its licensee for about $15 million.

EXECUTIVES

President CEO and Director, Patrice J. L. Louvet, age 53

President Global Brands, Val ©rie Hermann, age 54, $917,308 total compensation

CFO, Jane H. Nielsen, age 53

Brand President Men's Polo Purple Label and Double RL, Tom Mendenhall

Vice President Design, Nancy Beck

Executive Vice President and Creative Director Mens Design, John Wrazej

Business Operations Vice President Director Manager, Miriah Page

Vice President of Manufacturing and Operations, Janet Monaco

Vice President Of Merchandising Blue Label, Brooke Allinson

Vice President GMM RalphLauren com, Flo Dessen

Vice President, Michel Botbol

Vice President Planning And Allocation Factory Store Concept, Bradley Eckhart

Vice President Business Development Retail and Merchandising for Emerging Markets Latin America, Kim Babka

Vice President, Maureen Whitaker

Vice President Information Technology, Elizabeth Block

Vice President Production, Paul Haffner

Vice President Information Technology Infrastructure, Jonathan Zwang

Vice President Sales Uk, Aldo Fleri

Vice President Sales and Marketing, Ken Zavala

Vice President Knit Design and Development, Julie Mastrarrigo

Vice President Global Brand Planning Lauren, Anna Pasquini

Vice President, Jay Kimpton

Vice President Mens Production, Cindy Tse

Senior Management (Senior Vice President General Manager Director), Avery Fischer

Vice President, Vince Dellosa

Senior Vice President polo Store Development, John Heist

Vice President Visual Presentation, Jamey Mangum

Senior Vice President, Wendy Berloe-Buch

Vice President Merchandise Planning And, Dana Levy

Vice President Of Design, Callery McGee

Senior Vice President Sales for Polo brands, Olin Lancaster

Vice President Design And Development, Peter Sjonell

Vice President of Production, Michael Marafioti

Vice President Finance and Supply Chain, David Clarke

Vice President Global Brand Planning, Jane Cho

Executive Vice President Manufacturing, Richard Bangs

Vice President Corporate Business Development, Andrew Nkongho

Vice President Product Management, Mike Cottell

Vice President Finance, Paul Wickman

Vice President, Patricia Faz

Vice President Merchandising, Janet Scholder

Vice President Women 's Marketing, Amy Fisher

Vice President of Woven Production, Patgun Chen

Marketing Vice President, Liz Paley

Vice President Of Design Women's Footwear, Nancy Boas

Senior Vice President Mens Specialty Store Division, Tom Cush

Vice President Platform Engineering, Atif Khan

Vice President Sales Polo Ralph Lauren Tailored Clothing, Phil Faust

Vice President Of Photography And Video, Kristen Bowman

Vice President Of Licensed Business, Meegan Colgan

Vice President, Elise Schneider

Senior Vice President Of Merchandising Lauren Collection And Women's Licensed Businesses, Sandy Aronson

Vice President, Christine Imundi

Senior Vice President Of Luxury Strategy, Frederic Dechnik

Vice President Merchandising, Hus Mozaffar

Vice President Global Marketing, Tom Jarrold

Vice President Sales and Marketing, Mary Randolph Carter

Executive Assistant To The Senior Vice President Of Interactive Technology, Erika Keller

Assistant Vice President of MIS, Peggy Love

Vice President Home Design, Stavros Garger

Senior Vice President Footwear Design, John Ascher

Vice President Production and Sourcing, Hannah Bradford

Vice President Denim Design, Spencer Barksdale

Vice President Real Estate Counsel, Smita Butala

Vice President of creativeservice, Salvatore Disanto

Vice President of Operations, Ralph Wear

Vice President Human Resources, Andrea Carter

Vice President Business Development, Vladimir Martynenko

Vice President of Marketing, Nancy Vignola

Vice President of Asset Protection, Patti Felz

Senior Vice President, Maura Manning

Vice President, David G Rush

Executive Vice President, Jerry Lauren

Senior Vice President, Read Worth

Executive Vice President for Sales, Pesaro Roberto

Vice President, Frances Middleman

Executive Vice President Chief Creative Officer, Alfredo Paredes

Vice President Product Development, Rebecca Handler

Senior Vice President, Gilbert Rucas

Senior Vice President Accessories Merchandising, Louise Mimicopoulos

Division President Womenswear For American Living And Chaps, Gail Ornato

Vice President Finance, Daniel Thorson

Divisional Senior Vice President Of Business Process Integration, Robbin Mitchell

VP Human Resources, Katie Murphy

Vice President Creative Services, Sarah O'reilly

Vice President Creative Services, Quinn Pofahl

Vice President Sales, Cameron Lambert

Senior Vice President Product Innovation, Jason Berns

Vice President Design Sweaters, Susann Epperlein

Vice President Purple Label Merchandising, Nicholas Picchione

Vice President Finance and Operations, Jennifer Tsigaras

Vice President Global Manufacturing, Lance Baran

Executive Vice President, Jacki Nemerov

Executive Vice President, Birrittella Buffy

Divisional Svp Supply Chain Operations, Howard Formichellac

Vice President Information Technology Infrastructure, Alex Santillana

Vice President Vintage Buyer, Douglas Bihlmaier

LOCATIONS

HQ: Ralph Lauren Corp
650 Madison Avenue, New York, NY 10022
Phone: 212 318-7000
Web: www.RalphLauren.com

2016 Sales

	% of total
Americas	67
Europe	21
Asia	12
Total	**100**

PRODUCTS/OPERATIONS

2016 Sales

	% of total
Retail	53
Wholesale	45
Licensing	2
Total	**100**

Selected Brand Names & Licenses
Wholesale

Lauren by Ralph Lauren
Pink Pony
Polo Ralph Lauren
Ralph by Ralph Lauren
Ralph Lauren Black Label
Ralph Lauren Blue Label
Ralph Lauren Purple Label
Ralph Lauren Polo Sport
Retail
Club Monaco
Ralph Lauren
Polo Ralph Lauren
Polo Sport
Licensing Partners
Fitz and Floyd Inc.
Hanesbrands
Kohl's Department Stores Inc.
L'Oré;al S.A.
Luxottica Group
Peerless Inc.
The Warnaco Group
WestPoint Home Inc.

COMPETITORS

Abercrombie & Fitch	Jos. A. Bank
American Eagle	Kate Spade
Outfitters	Kenneth Cole
Ann Taylor	Kering
Armani	L.L. Bean
Benetton	LVMH
Brand Matter	Lands' End
Burberry	Laura Ashley
Calvin Klein	Levi Strauss
Christian Dior	Martha Stewart Living
Coach Inc.	Michael Kors Holdings
Donna Karan	Nautica Apparel
Ermenegildo Zegna	Nine West
Escada	PVH
Est©e Lauder	Perry Ellis
Gianni Versace	International
Gucci	Richemont
Guess?	St. John Knits
H&M	The Gap
Haggar	Tiffany & Co.
Herm□'s	Tommy Bahama
Hugo Boss	Tommy Hilfiger
J. Crew	VF Corporation

HISTORICAL FINANCIALS

Company Type: Public

Income Statement

	REVENUE ($ mil.)	NET INCOME ($ mil.)	NET PROFIT MARGIN	FYE: April 1 EMPLOYEES
04/17	6,652	(99)	—	23,300
04/16*	7,405	396	5.3%	26,000
03/15	7,620	702	9.2%	25,000
03/14	7,450	776	10.4%	23,000
03/13	6,944	750	10.8%	23,000
Annual Growth	**(1.1%)**	**—**	**—**	**0.3%**

*Fiscal year change

2017 Year-End Financials

Debt ratio: 15.25%
Return on equity: (-2.83%)
Cash ($ mil.): 668
Current ratio: 2.55
Long-term debt ($ mil.): 839

No. of shares (mil.): 81
Dividends
  Yield: 0.0%
  Payout: —
Market value ($ mil.): 6,611

	STOCK PRICE ($) FY Close	P/E High/Low		Earnings	Dividends	Book Value
04/17	81.62	—	—	(1.20)	2.00	40.74
04/16*	97.26	30	18	4.62	2.00	45.16
03/15	131.22	23	16	7.88	1.85	45.09
03/14	158.24	22	17	8.43	1.70	45.48
03/13	169.31	22	17	8.00	1.60	41.63
Annual Growth	**(16.7%)**	—	—	**—**	**5.7%**	**(0.5%)**

*Fiscal year change

Raymond James Financial, Inc.

Diversified financial services company Raymond James offers financial advice to retail clients and corporations alike. With over $600 billion in total client assets held in nearly 3 million client accounts and more than 7000 advisors Raymond James is a substantial retail brokerage house. Its non-retail business provides M&A guidance equity research reports IPO underwriting and private corporate debt placements. It has an extended geographic reach with operations in the US Canada and Europe.

HISTORY

Robert James often called the "founder of financial planning" first started a construction business in Ohio after his WWII service in the US Navy and then began a Florida home-building company. He got into the financial services business in 1954 with Florida Mutual Fund a company he and Gerard Jobin formed that eventually became American National Growth Fund. But when most companies were selling just stocks or mutual funds James saw a need for a more comprehensive approach to investing. He decided to focus on helping individual clients learning about their financial needs and goals and then working with them on everything from investments to taxes. To that end he began offering seminars for retirees.

In 1960 those seminars had turned into a new company James and Associates which two years later became Robert A. James Investments. In 1964 James acquired Raymond and Associates a firm started by Edward Raymond in 1962; the

newly merged firm was renamed Raymond James & Associates (RJA).

James' son Thomas joined the firm in 1966 the year the company's revenues first surpassed $1 million. Over the next several years the company expanded its investment offerings and set up new divisions. It added Investment Management & Research as an affiliate broker/dealer in 1967 and Planning Corporation of America as a general insurance agency in 1968.

Raymond James Financial incorporated as a holding company in 1969 and Thomas James became CEO the next year. RJA formed Eagle Asset Management in 1975 RJ Oil & Gas (subsidiary for oil and gas limited partnerships) in 1977 securities and real estate subsidiaries in 1980 (Robert Thomas Securities and RJ Properties respectively) and an equipment leasing subsidiary (RJ Leasing) in 1982.

Raymond James Financial went public in 1983 the year Robert James died. Two years later the company organized its Heritage Family of Funds. RJA became an international company in the late 1980s opening an office in Paris in 1987 and in Geneva the next year. It also began offering a cash management program in 1988 and began its Stock Loan Department. Trust and banking subsidiaries were begun in 1992 and 1994 respectively followed by the creation of Equity Capital Markets Group in 1996.

In 2000 Raymond James Financial crossed the billion-dollar-mark hitting $1.7 billion in sales. That year it acquired Canadian investment firm Goepel McDermid (renamed Raymond James Ltd.) to offer individual and institutional investment services to the Canadian market and it launched Raymond James Killik a UK joint venture that became Raymond James Investment Services in 2002.

In 2006 Raymond James Financial reduced front-end commissions with variations of variable annuity products; the next year it kicked off its Wealth Solutions department a unit designed to help high-net-worth clients and their advisors. Also that year Raymond James Financial extended its deal to attach its name to the home stadium of the NFL's Tampa Bay Buccaneers through 2015.

In 2012 to build its capital markets business in one of its largest purchases to date the company bought the investment banking and brokerage business of Morgan Keegan from Regions Financial for $1.2 billion and integrated the Morgan Keegan platform into its RJ&A platform. Raymond James Financial previously purchased boutique investment bank Lane Berry & Co. International in Boston in 2009 and Chicago-based investment bank and brokerage Howe Barnes Hoefer & Arnett in 2011.

To boost its large-cap investments the firm in 2012 acquired a 45% interest in ClariVest Asset Management.

RJ Bank acquired the Canadian operations of Allied Irish Banks in 2012 adding a portfolio of approximately $430 million in loan commitments. In conjunction with the deal RJ Bank launched a new finance company in Canada which will help the company grow its corporate and real estate banking business. It's part of Raymond James Financial's strategy of expanding its corporate lending business to additional markets.

EXECUTIVES

EVP Finance CFO and Treasurer, Jeffrey P. (Jeff) Julien, age 60, $280,000 total compensation

COO Raymond James Financial and CEO Raymond James & Associates, Dennis W. Zank, age 62, $330,000 total compensation

President Raymond James Financial and Fixed Income Capital Markets, John C. Carson, age 60, $300,000 total compensation

President Raymond James Financial Services, Scott A. Curtis, age 54

Chairman and CEO, Paul C. Reilly, age 62, $445,000 total compensation

President and CEO Raymond James Bank, Steven M. (Steve) Raney, age 51

Chairman and CEO Raymond James Ltd., Paul D. Allison, age 60

President Raymond James & Associates Private Client Group, Tashtego S. (Tash) Elwyn, age 45

EVP Technology and Operations, Bella Loykhter Allaire, age 63

EVP and President Asset Management Group, Jeffrey A. (Jeff) Dowdle, age 52

EVP General Counsel and Secretary, Jonathan N. Santelli, age 45

Vice President, Steven Ballard

Vice President of Financial Services, Howard Sachs

Senior Vice President Fixed income sales, Gerard Buquicchio

Vice President Managing Direct, Kevin Kilbane

Vice President Information Technology, Genie Blanton

Executive Vice President, William H Dietz

Vice President Sales, Jay Natkow

Senior Vice President Investments, Kevin Byrne

Senior Vice President Chief Architect, Sateesh Prabakaran

Executive Vice President, Ed Cashman

Vice President Public Finance, Tim Wranovix

Vice President Deposit Operations, Barbara Shore

Associate Vice President, Peter H Delaney

Vice President, Steve Romanoff

Vice President Investments, Scott Thompson

Senior Vice President of Investments, Stephen Crabtree

Senior Vice President, David Schaffer

Senior Vice President and Chief Compliance Officer, Sandy Martin

Vice President Consulting Services, Nicholas Lacy

First Vice President Investments, Lance Powers

First Vice President, Beth Smith

Senior Vice President, Bob Blain

Senior Vice President, Bill Specht

Vice President, Scott Brinner

Vice President Investments, Sandy Russell

Senior Vice President Investments, John Reuter

Assistant Vice President Personal Banker, Valerie Pratt

Senior Vice President, Jeff Factor

Vice President Information Technology, Frank Bugh

Vice President Director of Acquisitions, James Dunton

Senior Vice President and Chief Information Technology Security Officer, Andy Zolper

Senior Vice President, Chris Choate

Vice President, Terry McCormick

Vice President, Bill McMurray

Associate Vice President Support Center Analyst, Lisa Kuhl

Assistant Vice President Of Information Technology, Brian Miller

Vice President, Ann M Hensler

Senior Vice President Wealth Management Technology, Juergen Dittgen

Senior Vice President of Operations, Denise Samson

First Vice President Investments, Robert Hodgson

Vice President Investments, Sonya Choeff

Senior Vice President Investments, J Weissert

Vice President, Vasanta Pundarika

Vice President, Jake Shumacker

Senior Vice President Office Services, Raymond Lacour

Senior Vice President Investments, Dave Barber

Vice President structured Credit Trading, Brian Linde

Vice President, John Peters

Senior Vice President, Sharon Ioannidis

Vice President for Investments, Brian Rimel

Senior Vice President Equity Research Infrastruct, Michael Turits

Senior Vice President of Investments and Branch Manager, Mark K Mekler

Vice President, Daniel Fairweather

Associate Vice President, Nick Roederer

Vice President, Kevin Tierney

Associate Vice President Investments, Elizabeth Aulick Robertson

Vice President of Customer Service, Ryan Downing

Vice President, Stacy W Houston

Vice President Investments, Mark Mazman

Senior Vice President, Fred Coble

Senior Vice President, Tom Donegan

Senior Vice President Investments, Doug Cooper

Associate Vice President, Daniel Allen

Vice President, Christine Pedrick

Assistant Vice President, Ruth Quinlan

First Vice President, Kenny Mcclain

Vice President International Financial Consultant, Vita Barrio

First Vice President Investments, John Chesney

Senior Vice President, Jeanna Bryan

Branch Director Vice President Investments Patrick Dowden, Patrick Dowden

FVP Fi Sales, Bill Nowlin

Senior Vice President Operations, Joe Barkley

Senior Vice President, Jennifer Mills

Vice President Senior Manager Corporate Loan Administration, Rose Flores

Vice President Trading And Project Management, AL Caudullo

Senior Vice President Chief Lending Officer, Tom Macina

Vice President, Scott Englehardt

Vice President, Lee Morthland

Senior Vice President financial advisor, Chip Lee

Vice President Investments, Neil Lauro

Senior Vice President, Rick Hadrava

Senior Vice President Controller, Ken Ginel

First Vice President, Tom Owens

Senior Vice President Investments, Tom Ross

Vice President, Chris Cowing

Assistant Vice President Application Development, John D'Agostino

Senior Vice President Investments, John Fagan

Senior Vice President Investments, Bob Taylor

First Vice President of Investments, Douglas Clark

Senior Vice President, Christine Spencer

Vice President, Stephen Christenson

Vice President, Rob Arnold

Senior Vice President, Mark Ranney

Vice President, Garrett DeNinno

Vice President, Bob Jones

Assistant Vice President, Roberta Green

Senior Vice President Investments, Todd Evans

Assistant Vice President Asset Management Services, Robert Lyublanovits

Vice President Investments, Matt McCurry

Senior Vice President Of Investments, Todd Tindall

Vice President Public Finance, Ogden Kniffin

Vice President, Matt Stemmler

Vice President, Jozsi Popper

Vice President, Holly Hayes

First Vice President Investments, Charles Robinton

Vice President National Sales Manager, Dan Mallard

Certified Financial Planner??? Senior Vice President Investments, Frank Maurno

Senior Vice President Investments, Jamey Sullivan

Senior Vice President, Brian Nestor

First Vice President, Eduardo Bonilla

Senior Vice President Senior Credit Risk Executive, Mark Moody

Vice President Finance, Rupert Guy

Vice President Investments, Jeffrey Wahl

Vice President Mortgage Backed Trading, Nick Petrarca

Senior Vice President Investments, Mary Brooks

First Vice President Brokered CDS, Joseph Evans

Vice President, Landon Myers

Vice President National Director Of Sales Administ, Jamie Kosharek

Senior Vice President Of The Millstone Evans Group, Sacha Millstone

Wms Senior Vice President Investments, James McLean

Senior Vice President, Chris Fienup

Assistant Vice President Product Specialist, Kristen Read

Vice President Equity Derivative Sales, Alec Levine

Vice President, Carla Hargett

Vice President, Neil Tagaras

Senior Vice President, Gene Marx

Vice President Head Of Procurement, Larry Martiny

Vice President, Bobby Wolfe

Vice President, Tim Hansen

Senior Vice President Investments and Branch Manager, Doug Adler

First Vice President Investments, Keith Dubauskas

Senior Vice President Government Guaranteed Desk, Michelle Shadix

First Vice President Investments, Dwayne Peltier

Vice President of Investments, Mark Palios

Senior Vice President Investments, Travis McAfee

Assistant Vice President Credit Risk Officer, Sloan Yadley

Senior Vice President, Ted Fellman

Auditors: KPMG LLP

LOCATIONS

HQ: Raymond James Financial, Inc.
880 Carillon Parkway, St. Petersburg, FL 33716
Phone: 727 567-1000
Web: www.raymondjames.com

2015 Sales

	$ mil.	% of total
US	4,911	92
Canada	279	5
Europe	85	2
Other	32	1
Total	5,308	100

PRODUCTS/OPERATIONS

FY2017 Sales By Segment

	$ mil.	% of total
Private Client Group	4,437	68
Capital Markets	1,034	16
RJ Bank	627	9
Asset Management	487	7
Other	65	1
Eliminations	(128.0)	-1
Total	5,520	100

FY2016 Sales by Revenue Type

	$ mil.	% of total
Securities commissions & fees	4,020	62
Interest	802	12
Account & service fees	667	10
Investment advisory fees	462	7
Investment banking	398	6
Net trading profits	81	1
Other	91	2
Total	5,403	100

Selected Subsidiaries

Alex. Brown
Eagle Asset Management Inc.
Eagle Boston Investment Management Inc.
Eagle Fund Distributors Inc.

Howe Barnes Hoefer & Arnett Inc.
Lane Berry & Co. International
Planning Corporation of America
Raymond James & Associates
Raymond James Asset Management International S.A.
 (France)
Raymond James Bank FSB (dba RJ Bank)
Raymond James Canada LLC
Raymond James Capital Partners L.P.
Raymond James European Holdings Inc.
Raymond James Financial Services Inc.
Raymond James Financial Services Advisors
Raymond James Investment Services Limited (UK 75%)
Raymond James Ltd. (Canada)
Raymond James Tax Credit Funds Inc.
Raymond James Trust N.A.
Reams Asset Management
Scout Investments

COMPETITORS

Charles Schwab	Merrill Lynch
E*TRADE Financial	National Financial
Edward Jones	Partners
FMR	Piper Jaffray
LPL Financial	TD Ameritrade
Legg Mason	Wells Fargo Advisors

HISTORICAL FINANCIALS

Company Type: Public

Income Statement

FYE: September 30

	REVENUE ($ mil.)	NET INCOME ($ mil.)	NET PROFIT MARGIN	EMPLOYEES
09/17	6,524	636	9.8%	17,000
09/16	5,520	529	9.6%	15,900
09/15	5,308	502	9.5%	14,850
09/14	4,965	480	9.7%	13,900
09/13	4,595	367	8.0%	13,650
Annual Growth	9.2%	14.7%	—	5.6%

2017 Year-End Financials

Debt ratio: 8.78%
Return on equity: 12.12%
Cash ($ mil.): 7,284
Current ratio: 0.46
Long-term debt ($ mil.): 2,452

No. of shares (mil.): 144
Dividends
 Yield: 0.0%
 Payout: 20.3%
Market value ($ mil.): 12,152

	STOCK PRICE ($) FY Close	P/E High/Low	PER SHARE ($) Earnings	Dividends	Book Value
09/17	84.33	19 13	4.33	0.88	38.74
09/16	58.21	16 11	3.65	0.80	34.72
09/15	49.63	17 14	3.43	0.72	31.64
09/14	53.58	16 12	3.32	0.64	29.33
09/13	41.67	18 14	2.58	0.56	26.25
Annual Growth	19.3%	— —	13.8%	12.0%	10.2%

Raytheon Co.

Raytheon ("light of the gods") shines in the upper pantheon of US military contractors; the company regularly places among the Pentagon's top 10 prime contractors. Its air/land/sea/space/cyber defense offerings include reconnaissance targeting and navigation systems as well as missile systems (Patriot Sidewinder and Tomahawk) unmanned ground and aerial systems sensing technologies and radars. Additionally Raytheon makes systems for communications (satellite) and intelligence radios cybersecurity and air traffic control. It also offers commercial electronics products and services as well as food safety

processing technologies. The US government accounts for a large portion of sales.

Operations

To support its customers worldwide Raytheon serves defense and intelligence markets via five business segments: Integrated Defense Systems (IDS) Intelligence Information and Services (ISS) Missile Systems (MS) Space and Airborne Systems (SAS) and Forcepoint (joint venture launched in 2015).

Having patented the first microwave more than 65 years ago Raytheon is still developing and designing futuristic realities. The product that stands out most in the company's portfolio is the missile however. As the world's #1 missile maker Raytheon is a key player in US efforts to construct a comprehensive missile defense system.

Such systems need intercept vehicles sensors command and control systems and systems integration expertise. Raytheon's precision engagement offerings include the company's missiles as well as radars data links targeting and warning systems and lasers. In recent years the company has released an air and missile defense systems product line which includes the Standard Missile-3 the Exoatmospheric Kill Vehicle (EKV) and branded development programs.

Geographic Reach

Raytheon maintains offices in nearly 20 countries and has established global companies to serve customers Australia Canada Germany the US and the UK. The company sells products and services to customers in 80 nations although the US accounts for about 70% of net sales.

Sales and Marketing

The US government accounts for about 70% of Raytheon's sales. While it consistently counts among its customers the US Department of Defense (DoD) the Federal Bureau of Investigation (FBI) and NASA as well as members of the US military and US intelligence communities Raytheon also has some key international customers.

The company has contracts with South Korea to provide air and missile defense systems with Japan for training Saudi Arabia for surveillance systems and Australia for joint standoff weapons. Other main global clients include Finland Germany Taiwan and the United Arab Emirates.

Financial Performance

Raytheon's revenues have increased the last two years climbing 4% from $23.3 billion in 2015 to $24.1 billion in 2016. The growth was fueled by increases in its MS and SAS segments and strong gains from Forcepoint.

MS sales climbed in 2016 due to higher net sales on its Paveway program (portfolio of laser and GPS precision guided munitions) that was principally driven by international requirements and SAS experienced higher net sales on classified programs. In addition Forcepoint sales surged by more than 70% due to two previous acquisitions and the growing global demand for cybersecurity products.

Raytheon's profits also jumped 7% from $2.1 billion in 2015 to $2.2 billion in 2016 mainly due to the increase in total revenues. In addition Raytheon's operating cash flow jumped 7% from $2.4 billion in 2015 to almost $2.9 billion in 2016 primarily due to lower net tax payments and favorable changes in inventory.

Strategy

Raytheon's diverse product lineup puts it in a better position to weather budget cuts than some of its competitors that handle a limited number of defense products and services. Its business is also contingent to a great extent on the federal defense budget. With the US budget deficit fluctuating with each president's administration Raytheon has focused on growing its international business by

treating key foreign countries as individual markets with multiple customers.

Raytheon's internal investments including capital expenditures and spending on software increased 37% from 2015 to 2016 and enabled it to support future growth and productivity initiatives across the company. One key investment is the expansion of its main Arizona operations to meet the growth demands at its MS segment.

Mergers and Acquisitions

The company's cybersecurity business has been a point of focus of late primarily through multiple acquisitions which reflect Raytheon's general strategy for building its operations and growing its customer base.

In 2015 Raytheon created Forcepoint a new cybersecurity joint venture company (with Vista Equity Partners) in order to extend its cyber capabilities into the commercial markets. At the time Forcepoint purchased Websense a provider of advanced threat protection and data theft prevention services across web email cloud and endpoint infrastructure for $1.9 billion. Raytheon combined Websense with Raytheon Cyber Products formerly part of its IIS segment.

Also in 2015 Raytheon augmented its MS segment through the purchase of Sensintel a privately held provider of unmanned aircraft systems products to the intelligence and special operations markets.

HISTORY

In 1922 Laurence Marshall and several others founded American Appliance Company to produce home refrigerators. When their invention failed Marshall began making Raytheon (meaning "light of/from the gods") radio tubes. Raytheon was adopted as the company's name in 1925. It bought the radio division of Chicago's Q. R. S. Company in 1928 and formed Raytheon Production Company with National Carbon Company (makers of the Eveready battery) to market Eveready Raytheon tubes in 1929.

EXECUTIVES

VP; President Intelligence Information and Services, David C. Wajsgras, age 58, $971,943 total compensation

VP; President Global Business Services, Rebecca B. Rhoads, age 59

VP Business Development and CEO Raytheon International, John D. Harris, age 55

VP; President Space and Airborne Systems, Richard R. (Rick) Yuse, age 66, $792,506 total compensation

Chairman and CEO, Thomas A. (Tom) Kennedy, age 62, $1,299,979 total compensation

VP; President Missile Systems, Taylor W. Lawrence, age 54, $728,151 total compensation

VP General Counsel and Corporate Secretary, Frank R. Jimenez, age 52, $627,706 total compensation

CIO, Kevin T. Neifert

VP and CFO, Anthony F. OÁ'Brien, $608,510 total compensation

VP; President Integrated Defense Systems, Wesley D. Kremer, age 52

Chief Executive Raytheon Arabia, Kurt Amend

Vice President, Roger W Anderson

Vp Legal, Mark D Nielsen

Vice President Of Information Technology, Jeffrey Brown

Vice President Internal Controls and Accounting, Kathy Slate

Vice President Global Security Services, Dan Schlehr

Assistant Vice President Risk, Diane Murphy

Vice President, Michael Ellison

Vice President Account Services, Glenn D Henseler
Technology Division Vice President, Mike Brennan
Vice President Cao Contrl, Michael Wood
Vice President Emerging Technologies, Chris Bencal
Vice President of International Strategy and Business Development, Jim Hvizd
Vice President, Jon Sastri
Vice President; Program Management Excellence, Larry Briggs
Vice President and Chief Accounting Officer, Abbott Woods
RTSC Vice President, John Balaguer
Vice President of Integrated Communications Systems, David Farnsworth
Vice President Subcontracts Espx, John Norton
Vice President, Roger Luong
Vice President, James Wade
EXECUTIVE VICE PRESIDENT, Brad Herndon
Vice President, Scott Henderson
Vice President of Human Resources, Cathy Murphy
Vice President, Mitch Kugler
Vice President, Kevin Brown
Vice President Business Development, Jessica K Wyles
Vice President and Chief Learning Officer, Karen D Omobono
Vice President General Sales Manager, Richard D Neckorcuk
Assistant Vice President, Luis A Cabrera
Vice President of Human Resources, Karen Clark
Senior Vice President Information Technology, Thomas Madison
Regional Vice President, Larry Wasielewski
Vice President Technology Innovation and Strategic Pursuits, Neil Kacena
Vice President, Dan Darnell
Vice President product Engineering and Technology, Pamela Donaldson
Deputy Vice President And General Manage, Roy Azevedo
Vice President, Jim Dunne
Vice President Missile Defense Programs, Marvin McNamara
Vice President, Mitch Stevison
Vice President, Richard Hunt
Vice President Space and Intelligence, Gil Klinger
Secretary, Maria Gaglio
Auditors: PricewaterhouseCoopers LLP

LOCATIONS

HQ: Raytheon Co.
870 Winter Street, Waltham, MA 02451
Phone: 781 522-3000
Web: www.raytheon.com

2016 Sales

	$ mil.	% of total
US	16,517	69
Asia/Pacific	2,531	10
Middle East & North Africa	3,772	16
Europe & other regions	1,249	5
Total	**24,069**	**100**

PRODUCTS/OPERATIONS

2016 Sales

	$ mil.	% of total
Products	20,166	84
Services	3,903	16
Total	**24,069**	**100**

2016 Sales

	$ mil.	% of total
Missile Systems	7,071	28
Space & Airborne Systems	6,199	24
Intelligence & Information Systems	6,194	24
Integrated Defense Systems	5,476	22
Force point	566	2
Adjustments	(1437)	—
Total	**24,069**	**100**

Selected Products

Integrated Defense Systems (IDS)
Aegis Weapon Systems radar equipment
AN/AQS Minehunting Sonar System
Joint Land Attack Cruise Missile Defense Elevated Netted Sensor (JLENS)
Landing Platform Dock Amphibious Ship LPD-17
Patriot Air and Missile Defense System
Sea-Based X-Band Radar (SBX)
Ship Self-Defense System (SSDS)
Surface-Launched AMRAAM (SLAMRAAM)
Terminal High Altitude Area Defense (THAAD) Radar
Intelligence and Information Systems (IIS)
Army Research Lab
Communications systems
Department of Education programs
Distributed Common Ground System
Emergency Patient Tracking System
Global Broadcast Service
Global Hawk Ground Segment
Information solutions programs
Managed data storage solutions
Mobile Very Small Aperture Satellite Terminal
National Polar-Orbiting Operational Environmental Satellite System Program
RedWolf telecommunications surveillance
Signal and imagery intelligence programs
Supercomputing
U-2 (field support)
UAV systems and ground stations
Missile Systems (MS)
Advanced Medium-Range Air-to-Air missile (AMRAAM)
AIM-9X Sidewinder
Evolved SeaSparrow (ESSM)
Excalibur long-range artillery system
Exoatmospheric Kill Vehicle
Extended Range Guided Munition (ERGM)
High-Speed Anti-Radiation Missile Targeting System
Paveway laser-guided bombs
Maverick AGM-65 missiles
Tomahawk and Tactical Tomahawk cruise missiles
TOW Javelin Phalanx Standard and SeaRAM missiles
Network Centric Systems (NCS)
Airspace management and homeland security
Command and control systems
Combat systems
Integrated communications systems
Precision technologies and components
Space and Airborne Systems (SAS)
Active electronically scanned array radars
Airborne radars and processors
Electronic warfare systems
Electro-optic/infrared sensors
Intelligence surveillance and reconnaissance systems
Space and missile defense technology
Technical Services (TS)
Base operations
Logistics support
Maintenance support
Professional services
Treaty compliance monitoring
Weapons security and destruction

Selected Markets

Command Control Communication and Intelligence (C3I)
Systems provide integrated real-time support for on- and off-battlefield and transform raw data into actionable intelligence
Cybersecurity
Provides cyber capabilities to the Intelligence DoD and DHS markets as well as embedding cybersecurity in Raytheon's products and IT infrastructure
Effects
Achieves specific military actions or outcomes from force protection to theater/national missile defense
Homeland Security
Domestic and international homeland security markets especially transportation security immigration control/identity management critical infrastructure protection maritime security energy security intelligence program support law enforcement solutions a
Mission Support
Provides total life-cycle and training system engineering logistics and maintenance support to customer
Sensing

Acquires precise situational data across air space ground and underwater domains and generates information needed for effective battlespace decisions

COMPETITORS

BAE Systems Inc.	Honeywell Aerospace
Boeing	Interstate Electronics
Crane Aerospace & Electronics	L-3 Avionics
DRS Technologies	Lockheed Martin
Emerson Electric	MBDA
Exelis	Meggitt-USA
Fluor	Northrop Grumman
GE	Rockwell Collins
Harris Corp.	Saab AB
	Sierra Nevada Corp

HISTORICAL FINANCIALS

Company Type: Public

Income Statement

FYE: December 31

	REVENUE ($ mil.)	NET INCOME ($ mil.)	NET PROFIT MARGIN	EMPLOYEES
12/17	25,348	2,024	8.0%	64,000
12/16	24,069	2,211	9.2%	63,000
12/15	23,247	2,074	8.9%	61,000
12/14	22,826	2,244	9.8%	61,000
12/13	23,706	1,996	8.4%	63,000
Annual Growth	**1.7%**	**0.3%**	**—**	**0.4%**

2017 Year-End Financials

Debt ratio: 16.36%	No. of shares (mil.): 288
Return on equity: 20.21%	Dividends
Cash ($ mil.): 3,103	Yield: 0.0%
Current ratio: 1.54	Payout: 34.4%
Long-term debt ($ mil.): 4,750	Market value ($ mil.): 54,101

	STOCK PRICE ($) FY Close	P/E High/Low	PER SHARE ($) Earnings	Dividends	Book Value
12/17	187.85	27 21	6.95	2.39	34.59
12/16	142.00	20 16	7.44	3.60	34.35
12/15	124.53	19 14	6.80	2.62	33.87
12/14	108.17	15 12	7.18	2.37	31.03
12/13	90.70	15 9	6.16	2.20	35.03
Annual Growth	**20.0%**	**— —**	**3.1%**	**2.1%**	**(0.3%)**

Realogy Group LLC

Auditors: PRICEWATERHOUSEC-OOPERS LLP

LOCATIONS

HQ: Realogy Group LLC
175 Park Avenue, Madison, NJ 07940
Phone: 973 407-2000
Web: www.realogy.com

HISTORICAL FINANCIALS

Company Type: Public

Income Statement

FYE: December 31

	REVENUE ($ mil.)	NET INCOME ($ mil.)	NET PROFIT MARGIN	EMPLOYEES
12/16	5,810	213	3.7%	11,800
12/15	5,706	184	3.2%	11,400
12/14	5,328	143	2.7%	10,700
12/13	5,289	438	8.3%	10,800
12/12	4,672	(543)	—	10,800
Annual Growth	**5.6%**	**—**		**2.2%**

Realogy Holdings Corp

Realogy Holdings is one of the largest franchisors of residential real estate offices in the world with about 14100 offices in more than 110 countries. Its brands include Century 21 Coldwell Banker ERA Better Homes and Gardens Real Estate and Sotheby's. In addition to franchising the company owns and operates about 790 offices under the already mentioned brands along with the Corcoran Group and Citi Habitats labels. It also provides relocation title and settlement services and mortgages.

Operations

Realogy operates through the four business segments of Company Owned Real Estate Brokerage Services (known as NRT) Real Estate Franchise Services (known as Realogy Franchise Group or RFG) Title and Settlement Services (known as Title Resource Group or TRG) and Relocation Services (known as Cartus).

NRT (around 70% of net sales) operates a full-service real estate brokerage business under the Coldwell Banker Corcoran Sotheby's International Realty Citi Habitats and ZipRealty brand names in more than 50 of the 100 largest metropolitan areas in the US.

RFG (almost 15%) franchises the Century 21 Coldwell Banker Coldwell Banker Commercial ERA Sotheby's International Realty and Better Homes and Gardens Real Estate brand names.

TRG (nearly 10%) provides full-service title and settlement services to real estate companies affinity groups corporations and financial institutions with many of these services provided in conjunction with the company's real estate brokerage and relocation services business.

Cartus (more than 5%) offers clients employee relocation services such as homesale assistance providing home equity advances to transferees (generally guaranteed by the client) home finding and other destination services and intercultural and language training and group move management services among other services.

Geographic Reach

Realogy conducts its business through 14100 offices in more than 110 countries. The US accounts for 98% of its net revenue.

Sales and Marketing

Realogy's franchise system operates through 14100 franchised and company owned offices and approximately 273200 independent sales associates operating under its franchise and proprietary brands in the US and 111 other countries and territories around the world.

Financial Performance

Realogy's business has been steadily growing in tandem with the strengthening US housing market for the past several years. Revenue in 2016 climbed 2% to peak at $5.8 billion a company milestone. The historic growth for 2016 was primarily due to a spike in revenue at TRG as a result of acquisitions as well as an increase in revenue at RFG driven by higher average homesale price and number of homesale transactions.

Like revenues net income jumped 16% to $213 million in 2016. This was attributed to the absence in 2016 of $6 million related to certain transaction costs associated with the acquisition of Coldwell Banker United and the settlement of a legal matter in 2015.

Realogy's cash flow from operations has also risen the last few years jumping from $544 million in 2015 to $587 million in 2016. This was attributed to $55 million of additional cash provided by operating results and $31 million more cash provided by the net change in relocation and trade receivables.

Strategy

Realogy's strategy for growth includes the launching of new software platforms that improve the productivity of its independent sales associates. Its ZapLabs subsidiary (which changed its name from ZipRealty in 2016) is the developer of its proprietary technology platform used by its real estate brokerages and independent sales associates across its franchise system. During 2016 Realogy launched ZapLabs' comprehensive integrated Zap technology platform to approximately 1110 franchisees bringing the total enrolled to 1500 of its approximately 2600 franchisees. It aims to roll out this platform to the majority of its remaining franchisees throughout 2017 and beyond.

Beyond large company acquisitions Realogy likes to purchase local real estate brokerages to expand its reach into communities. In 2016 the company acquired 11 real estate brokerage and property management operations through its NRT segment for around $80 million.

Mergers and Acquisitions

One of the ways Realogy has achieved record-setting revenue growth over the years is through the use of acquisitions. In 2015 Realogy acquired Coldwell Banker United realtors in the active markets of Texas Florida North Carolina and South Carolina. Coldwell brought 60 offices staffed by 2000 affiliated sales associates to Realogy. It continues to operate under the Coldwell Banker brand.

Company Background

Realogy in October 2012 raised $1 billion in its IPO a vote of confidence of sorts in the recovery of the residential real estate market in the US. Realogy used the IPO proceeds to reduce its more than $7 billion in debt. Despite losing $540 million in the two years prior to its IPO the firm believed the real estate market was poised for recovery. Its strategy included growing all segments of its business though it offered no specifics on that front. The company's name changed from Domus to Realogy in 2012.

EXECUTIVES

EVP General Counsel and Corporate Secretary, Marilyn J. Wasser, age 61
Chairman President and CEO, Richard A. Smith, age 63, $1,000,000 total compensation
President and CEO NRT, Bruce G. Zipf, age 60, $625,000 total compensation
President and CEO Cartus, Kevin J. Kelleher, age 62, $475,000 total compensation
EVP and Chief Human Resources Officer, Sunita Holzer
EVP CFO and Treasurer, Anthony E. (Tony) Hull, age 58, $675,000 total compensation
President and CEO Title Resource Group, Donald J. (Don) Casey, age 55, $450,000 total compensation
SVP and CIO, Stephen Fraser
President and CEO Realogy Franchise Group, John Peyton
Senior Vice President Technology, Jeff Krupp
National Vice President, Henry Weber
Auditors: PricewaterhouseCoopers LLP

LOCATIONS

HQ: Realogy Holdings Corp
  175 Park Avenue, Madison, NJ 07940
Phone: 973 407-2000
Web: www.realogy.com

2016 Sales

	$ mil.	% of total
US	5,683	98
All other countries	127	2
Total	**5,810**	**100**

PRODUCTS/OPERATIONS

2016 Sales

	$ mil.	% of total
Company-owned real estate brokerage services	4,344	71
Real estate franchise services	781	13
Title and settlement services	573	9
Relocation services	405	7
Corporate and other	(293)	-
Total	**5,810**	**100**

Selected Brands

Better Homes and Gardens Real Estate
Century 21
Coldwell Banker
Coldwell Banker Commercial
ERA
Sotheby's International Realty
Corcoran
Citi Habitats
ZipRealty

COMPETITORS

Brookfield Global Relocation	Keller Williams
Ebby Halliday Realtors	Move Inc.
HomeServices	NRT LLC
HomeVestors of America	RE/MAX
Jones Lang LaSalle	SIRVA
	Weichert Realtors

HISTORICAL FINANCIALS

Company Type: Public

Income Statement

FYE: December 31

	REVENUE ($ mil.)	NET INCOME ($ mil.)	NET PROFIT MARGIN	EMPLOYEES
12/16	5,810	213	3.7%	11,800
12/15	5,706	184	3.2%	11,400
12/14	5,328	143	2.7%	10,700
12/13	5,289	438	8.3%	10,800
12/12	4,672	(543)	—	10,800
Annual Growth	**5.6%**	**—**	**—**	**2.2%**

2016 Year-End Financials

Debt ratio: 50.02%
Return on equity: 8.70%
Cash ($ mil.): 274
Current ratio: 0.78
Long-term debt ($ mil.): 3,265
No. of shares (mil.): 140
Dividends
  Yield: 0.0%
  Payout: 12.3%
Market value ($ mil.): 3,608

	STOCK PRICE ($) FY Close	P/E High/Low		PER SHARE ($) Earnings	Dividends	Book Value
12/16	25.73	25	15	1.46	0.18	17.57
12/15	36.67	39	29	1.24	0.00	16.48
12/14	44.49	51	35	0.97	0.00	14.89
12/13	49.47	18	14	2.99	0.00	13.76
12/12	41.96	—	—	(14.41)	0.00	10.43
Annual Growth	**(11.5%)**	**—**	**—**	**—**	**—**	**13.9%**

REDWOOD CREDIT UNION

Auditors: CLIFTONLARSONALLEN LLP PHOENI

LOCATIONS

HQ: REDWOOD CREDIT UNION
3033 CLEVELAND AVE # 100, SANTA ROSA, CA
954032126
Phone: 707 545-4000
Web: WWW.REDWOODCU.ORG

HISTORICAL FINANCIALS

Company Type: Private

Income Statement

FYE: December 31

	ASSETS ($ mil.)	NET INCOME ($ mil.)	INCOME AS % OF ASSETS	EMPLOYEES
12/14	2,468	47	1.9%	390
12/13	2,271	48	2.1%	—
12/05	1,323	14	1.1%	—
Annual Growth	7.2%	14.5%	—	—

2014 Year-End Financials

Debt ratio: ——
Return on equity: 41.90%
Cash ($ mil.): 530
Current ratio: 29.70
Long-term debt ($ mil.): —

Dividends
Yield: —
Payout: —
Market value ($ mil.): —

Regeneron Pharmaceuticals, Inc.

Regeneron is fighting some serious enemies. Regeneron Pharmaceuticals develops protein-based drugs used to battle a variety of diseases and conditions including cancer high cholesterol inflammatory ailments and eye diseases. The biotechnology company's first commercialized product is ARCALYST a treatment for rare inflammatory diseases including Muckle-Wells Syndrome. Regeneron collaborates with Sanofi to develop candidate aflibercept (VEGF Trap) as a possible treatment for cancerous tumors. It is also developing aflibercept with Bayer HealthCare to treat eye diseases using intraocular delivery with EYLEA approved in the US and Australia as a treatment of neovascular age-related macular degeneration (wet AMD).

Operations

The company operates in one business segment which includes all activities from discovery and development through commercialization of its pharmaceutical products. It has development candidates in areas including hypercholesterolemia oncology rheumatoid arthritis asthma and atopic dermatitis.

The company and Sanofi globally collaborate on the development and commercialization of ZALTRAP (to treat patients with metastatic colorectal cancer) and share profits and losses from commercialization of ZALTRAP except for Japan.

Sanofi has committed to pay up to $160 million per year or a total of $1.28 billion between 2010 and 2017 to fund its efforts to identify and validate drug discovery targets and preclinically develop fully human monoclonal antibodies against such targets. Antibody-based clinical programs in collaboration with Sanofi include PRALUENT Antibody to PCSK9; Sarilumab (REGN88); Dupilumab (REGN668); REGN1033; and REGN2222.

Regeneron has a non-exclusive license to certain patents relating to VEGF receptor proteins.

In addition in 2014 the FDA European Commission and Japanese Ministry of Health Labour and Welfare approved EYLEA for the treatment of diabetic macular edema (DME).

Geographic ReachRegeneron has its corporate and research & development headquarters in New York and a satellite office in New Jersey. It manufactures bulk drug materials in Rensselaer New York. Internationally it is headquartered in Dublin Ireland and has a manufacturing facility (under construction) in Limerick.

Sales and Marketing

Research and development expenses accounted for some 40% of Regeneron's revenues in 2015.

Financial Performance

Regeneron has reported strong revenue growth trend over the last few years. In 2015 its revenues increased 46% to $4.1 billion due to higher product sales (particularly EYLEA net sales) and Sanofi collaboration reimbursements.

Net income which has been fluctuating rose 88% to $636.1 million in 2015 primarily as a result of Regeneron's increased revenue that year. Decreases in interest expenses and losses on extinguishment of debt also helped boost profits.

Cash flow from operations also rose that year gaining 77% to reach $1.3 billion.

Strategy

The company has expanded the applications of its protein-based technology to include the creation of human monoclonal antibodies (laboratory-produced cloned proteins). It has a pipeline of a dozen clinical-stage antibodies with programs in eye disease infectious disease cancer pain management cardiovascular disease and inflammation.

Outside of their partnership on aflibercept Regeneron has an antibody development agreement with Sanofi that includes $475 million in potential milestone payments and covers potential treatments for ailments including cancer rheumatoid arthritis pain cholesterol and allergic conditions.

As its largest partner Sanofi (which also owns a 20% stake in Regeneron) accounts for about 20% of sales. The company's other collaborations account for more than 15% of sales; firms are working together to treat ophthalmic diseases including diabetic macular edema and wet age-related macular degeneration.

The company also licenses its human antibody technology out to drug developers who then use Regeneron's technology in researching their own antibody drugs. Licensing partners include AstraZeneca and Astellas Pharma.

In 2015 the EYLEA injection was approved by the European Commission for the treatment of visual impairment due to macular edema secondary to retinal vein occlusion.

In 2014 Regeneron entered into an agreement with Bayer HealthCare governing the joint development and commercialization outside the US of an antibody product candidate to PDGFR-beta including in combination with EYLEA for the treatment of ocular diseases or disorders. That year it signed a similar deal with Adverum Biotechnologies to discover develop and commercialize novel gene therapy products for the treatment of ophthalmologic diseases.

The company launched a new human genetics initiative in 2014 via a wholly owned subsidiary Regeneron Genetics Center.

In 2015 Regeneron spent $1.6 billion on R&D expenses up from $1.3 billion spent in 2014.

Company Background

In 2012 Regeneron and Bayer HealthCare converted their 50-50 global profit-share agreement for marketing EYLEA (aflibercept) Injection as a treatment for wet AMD outside the US into a royalty arrangement in Japan where approval for the treatment is pending authorization. Applications for marketing EYLEA have been submitted by Bayer HealthCare in Europe and other countries. The treatment is also in Phase 3 clinical studies for other indications including diabetic macular edema myopic choroidal neovascularization and branch retinal vein occlusion.

ARCALYST (rilonacept) was approved by the FDA in 2008 and subsequently became the company's first market-stage product. Regeneron has built up a small marketing force to promote the product in the US; ARCALYST is manufactured at the company's plant in New York and is distributed through third parties. ARCALYST targets Cryopyrin-Associated Periodic Syndromes (CAPS) a series of diseases caused by genetic mutations including Muckle-Wells Syndrome and Familial Cold Auto-inflammatory Syndrome. The drug is also being tested for the treatment of gout.

The company was founded in New York City in 1988.

EXECUTIVES

EVP Research and Development, Neil Stahl, age 60, $619,300 total compensation
Chief Scientific Officer; President Regeneron Laboratories, George D. Yancopoulos, age 57, $1,055,700 total compensation
President and CEO, Leonard S. Schleifer, age 64, $1,242,000 total compensation
EVP Commercial, Robert J. Terifay, age 57, $550,700 total compensation
SVP Finance and CFO, Robert E. Landry, $585,600 total compensation
EVP; General Manager Industrial Operations and Product Supply, Daniel P. Van Plew, age 44, $349,200 total compensation
Medical Director, Mark Ballard
Medical Director Immunology and Inflammation, Gregory St John
Chairman, P. Roy Vagelos, age 87
Auditors: PricewaterhouseCoopers LLP

LOCATIONS

HQ: Regeneron Pharmaceuticals, Inc.
777 Old Saw Mill River Road, Tarrytown, NY 10591-6707
Phone: 914 847-7000
Web: www.regeneron.com

PRODUCTS/OPERATIONS

2016 sales

	$ mil.	% of total
Net product sales	3,338	69
Sanofi collaboration	658	14
Bayer collaboration	744	15
other	119	2
Total	**4,860**	**100**

COMPETITORS

Abbott Labs	Merck
Amgen	Novartis
AstraZeneca	Onyx Pharmaceuticals
Bayer AG	Pfizer
Bristol-Myers Squibb	Roche Holding
Eli Lilly	Sanofi
GlaxoSmithKline	XOMA
Johnson & Johnson	

Company Type: Public

Income Statement

FYE: December 31

	REVENUE ($ mil.)	NET INCOME ($ mil.)	NET PROFIT MARGIN	EMPLOYEES
12/17	5,872	1,198	20.4%	6,200
12/16	4,860	895	18.4%	5,400
12/15	4,103	636	15.5%	4,300
12/14	2,819	348	12.3%	2,925
12/13	2,104	424	20.2%	2,340
Annual Growth	29.2%	29.6%	—	27.6%

2017 Year-End Financials

Debt ratio: 8.03%
Return on equity: 22.63%
Cash ($ mil.): 812
Current ratio: 3.82
Long-term debt ($ mil.): 703

No. of shares (mil.): 107
Dividends
  Yield: —
  Payout: —
Market value ($ mil.): 40,463

	STOCK PRICE ($) FY Close	P/E High/Low	PER SHARE ($) Earnings	Dividends	Book Value
12/17	375.96	47 30	10.34	0.00	57.09
12/16	367.09	63 39	7.70	0.00	41.97
12/15	542.87	96 64	5.52	0.00	34.92
12/14	410.25	126 77	3.07	0.00	24.82
12/13	275.24	73 37	3.81	0.00	19.58
Annual Growth	8.1%	— —	28.4%	—	30.7%

REGENTS OF THE UNIVERSITY OF MICHIGAN

Michigan — it's shaped like a mitten and higher education fits the state like a glove. With nearly 60000 students and about 7000 faculty members scattered across three campuses in Ann Arbor Dearborn and Flint the university's diverse academic units span such areas of study as architecture education law medicine music and social work. Notable alumni include the late President Gerald Ford (the university is home to the Gerald R. Ford Library and the Ford School of Public Policy) actor James Earl Jones Google cofounder Larry Page and seven Nobel laureates. In addition to state funding the university is supported by a $6.6 billion endowment.

Operations

The university operates some 20 schools offering education in everything from dentistry and medicine to music theater and dance. About 70% of the students are enrolled in undergraduate programs while the rest are graduate students.

There are seven museums on campus — including the Museum of Art the Exhibit Museum of Natural History (with a planetarium) and the Kelsey Museum of Archaeology — as well as the Nichols Arboretum and the Matthaei Botanical Gardens.

Through its Health System the university maintains one of the largest health care complexes in the world. It is made up of more than 50 health centers and 120 outpatient clinics around the state and is responsible for more than 40% of The University of Michigan's revenue.

Along with its various health centers and clinics the university operates the C.S. Mott Children's Hospital. The children's hospital is noted for its heart surgery neonatal care and respiratory disorders and ranks among the nation's best for all other pediatric specialties — cancer digestive disorders general pediatrics and neurology.

Geographic Reach

The University of Michigan was founded in Detroit in 1817 but moved to Ann Arbor in 1837.

Financial Performance

The university has enjoyed an upward trend in revenue during recent fiscal years as a result of increases in tuition rates and undergraduate enrollment. It claimed more than $5 billion in revenue for fiscal 2012 up more than 5% compared to the $4.77 billion the university reported in revenue for fiscal 2011. The school brought in about $453 billion during fiscal 2010.

EXECUTIVES

VP Government Relations, Cynthia H. Wilbanks
VP Development, Jerry A. May
Chancellor University of Michigan-Dearborn, Daniel Little
EVP and CFO, Kevin P. Hegarty, age 61
Chairman Victors for Michigan, Stephen M. Ross
President, Mark S. Schlissel
Dean School of Public Health, Martin Philbert
VP Information Technology and CIO, Kelli Trosvig
Dean Stamps School of Art and Design, Gunalan Nadarajan
Dean School of Dentistry, Laurie McCauley
Dean Law School, Mark D. West
Chancellor University of Michigan-Flint, Susan E. Borrego
Interim Provost and EVP Academic Affairs, Paul N. Courant
EVP Medical Affairs; Dean Medical School; CEO Michigan Medicine, Marschall S. Runge
VP and General Counsel, Timothy G. Lynch
VP Research, S. Jack Hu
Interim Dean Taubman College of Architecture and Urban Planning, Robert Fishman
Edward J. Frey Dean Ross School of Business, Scott DeRue
Dean School of Education, Elizabeth Birr Moje
Dean School of Engineering, Alec D. Gallimore
Dean School of Information, Thomas A. Finholt
Dean School of Kinesiology, Lori Ploutz-Snyder
Dean College of Literature Science and the Arts, Andrew D. Martin
Dean College of Music Theatre and Dance, Aaron Dworkin
Interim Dean School of Natural Resources and Environment, Dan Brown
Dean School of Nursing, Patricia D. Hurn
Dean College of Pharmacy, James T. Dalton
Dean School of Social Work, Lynn Videka
Dean Rackham Graduate School; Vice Provost Academic Affairs Graduate Studies, Carol A. Fierke
Vice President Sec Of University, Sally Churchill
Assoc Vice President For Human RSCS, Laurita Thomas
Associate Vice President Development, Julie Sparkman
Vice President, David John Hiemstra
Medical Director Employee Health Service, Susan Blitz
Vice President Marketing, Rachelle Caoagas
Senior Executive SECRETARY Office of Vice President for Research Department, BettyL Cook
Provost And Executive Vice President For Academic Affairs, Teresa Sullivan
Vice President Research, Stephen Forrest
Associate Vice President for Human Resources, Catherine Lilly
Vice President, Rachel Goldman

Vice President, Dan Salinas
Vice President Research and Development, Bruce Nourse
Vice President of Industry Relations, Matthew Singelyn
Vice President Finance technology, William Hausman
Associate Vice President and Deputy General Counsel, Kara Morgenstern
Vice Chairman, Michael J. Behm
Chairman, Mark J. Bernstein
Treasurer, Kevin Morrison
Secretary, Alfreda Onimo
Secretary IV Office Of The General Counsel Department, Linda Meakes
Board Member, Margie Perrett
Treasurer, Seema Kedia
Secretary II Unions Administration Department, Samantha Hallman
Secretary III Umh Mworks Employ Assistant Program Department, Angela Hurlbut
Secretary IV Lsa Dean Deans Office Department, Sandra Petee
Secretary III Academic Affairs Dentistry Department, Diane Pasma
Secretary III Occupational Safety And Environ Department, Patricia Bostain
Secretary IV Umh Administration Department, Melody Bond
Secretary III Vice President And Secretary Of Univ Department, Cary Varney
Secretary Intermediate, Marie Bien
Executive Board Member, Garrett Stephens
Board Member, Lisong NI
Board Member, Jason Townsend
Secretary, Jessica Mims
Treasurer, Nahiyan Bakr
Secretary, Salam Smidi
Board Member Family and Youth Chair, Fatima Salman
Secretary Commercial Players Community Assistant South Quadrangle Residential College Class of 2017, Kyle Stefek
Secretary II Flint School Partnerships Department, Pamela Zemore
Auditors: PRICEWATERHOUSECOOPERS LLP DE

LOCATIONS

HQ: REGENTS OF THE UNIVERSITY OF MICHIGAN
503 THOMPSON ST, ANN ARBOR, MI 481091340
Phone: 734 764-1817
Web: WWW.UMICH.EDU

PRODUCTS/OPERATIONS

Selected Academic Units
Architecture and urban planning
Art and design
Business administration
Dentistry
Education
Engineering
Kinesiology
Law
Literature science and the arts
Medicine
Music
Natural resources and environment
Nursing
Pharmacy
Public health
Public policy
Social work

HISTORICAL FINANCIALS

Company Type: Private

Income Statement

FYE: June 30

	REVENUE ($ mil.)	NET INCOME ($ mil.)	NET PROFIT MARGIN	EMPLOYEES
06/16	6,278	(294)	—	34,624
06/14	5,534	1,574	28.5%	—
06/13	5,317	729	13.7%	—
06/12	5,038	(171)	—	—
Annual Growth	5.7%	—	—	—

2016 Year-End Financials

Debt ratio: ——
Return on equity: (-4.70%)
Cash ($ mil.): 349
Current ratio: 0.50
Long-term debt ($ mil.): —

Dividends
Yield: —
Payout: —
Market value ($ mil.): —

Regions Financial Corp

Regions Financial Corporation sprouted in the US South and has spread its roots across the region by acquiring other financial services firms. The holding company for Regions Bank Regions Financial boasts nearly $125 billion in total assets and has around 1500 branches and about 1900 ATMs across 15 states stretching from the Southeast and Texas northward through the Mississippi River Valley. In addition to providing standard banking services such as deposit accounts loans and mortgages and credit cards to retail customers and small businesses Regions Financial also serves larger corporations and boasts wealth management division for affluent individuals.

Operations

Regions Financial operates three main segments: Corporate Bank Consumer Bank and Wealth Management.

The Consumer Bank accounts for some 55% of sales and serves mainly retail and small business customers. The Corporate Bank (35% of sales) serves middle-market and large commercial clients. Region's Wealth Management division (10% of sales) provides trust and investment services to affluent individuals.

Typically slightly more than half of Regions Financial's total revenue comes from loan interest (including fees) while more than 10% comes from deposit account service charges and another approximately 10% comes from interest on taxable securities. Card and ATM fees and mortgage banking income make up around 5% of total revenue each. About 30% of the bank's total loan portfolio is made up of consumer residential real estate loans.

Regions Insurance Group a subsidiary of Regions Financial provides insurance products to bank customers.

Geographic Reach

Alabama-based Regions Financial boasts some 1500 banking offices and about 1900 ATMs across 15 Southern and Central US states. More than 50% of its branches are in Florida Tennessee and Alabama around 25% are in Mississippi Georgia and Louisiana. The rest are in Arkansas Illinois Indiana Iowa Kentucky Missouri North Carolina South Carolina Texas and Virginia.

Sales and Marketing

Regions Financial serves some four million households throughout the South Midwest and Texas. It sells and markets its products directly through its branches and through other channels such as the internet and mobile banking. Its Wealth Management customers are affluent individuals while its business customers include corporate middle market small business and commercial real estate developers and investors.

Financial Performance

Regions Financial has reversed four years of declining revenue by posting consecutive gains in fiscals 2015 and 2016. In 2016 sales grew 5% to $6.0 billion with gains concentrated in loans and fees and an increase in operating lease assets.

Interest income was boosted by higher interest rates average loan growth and higher securities balances. Noninterest income increased due to higher capital markets fee income ATM fees and bank-owned life insurance income.

Net income increased 10% to $1.0 billion as the company was able to increase its revenue without a comparable increase in expenses.

Cash from operating activities increased 24% to $2.0 billion due to a reduction in liabilities payments.

Strategy

In 2016 Regions Bank partnered with online lending platform Avant to offer a online consumer loan application and underwriting service. The agreement brings together Regions Financial's banking experience with Avant's technology platform.

Regions is looking for ways to fight back against lower cost online lenders that are eating into its customer base. In 2015 the company partnered with funding startup Fundation to provide online loans to small businesses.

Mergers and Acquisitions

In October 2016 Regions acquired two businesses from First Sterling Financial to build on its real estate and capital markets capabilities. It acquired First Sterling's Low Income Housing Tax Credit (LIHTC) corporate fund syndication and asset management businesses.

HISTORY

Regions Financial was created out of three venerable Alabama banks. The oldest First National Bank of Huntsville was founded in 1855. When 10 years later the bank was besieged by Union troops a loyal cashier hid securities in the chimney and refused to tell the soldiers where they were. A few years later it was robbed by Jesse James (for years the bank kept in its vaults a gun purported to belong to a James gang member). First National Bank of Montgomery was founded in 1871 and Exchange Security Bank in 1928.

Banking veteran Frank Plummer consolidated the three banks to form Alabama's first multibank holding company First Alabama Bancshares in 1971. The combined firm then became the bank that ate Alabama. But even as it gobbled up other banks its diet remained bland: Its lending programs were modest and focused on a narrow range of business.

The bank's growth in the 1980s was solid if unexciting as it picked up community banks in Alabama (Anniston National Bank and South Baldwin Bank among others) and Georgia (Georgia Co. a mortgage subsidiary of Columbus Bank and Trust). Before he died in 1987 Plummer brought in Willard Hurley as chairman. Hurley put the brakes on acquisitions when they overloaded the bank's data-processing systems. He also put the company up for sale igniting its stock price for a while but there were no serious suitors.

When Hurley passed the baton to Stanley Mackin in 1990 the bank was still rumored to be for sale. But Mackin had other ideas. He put the bank back on its acquisition track and raised the bar on profitability expectations for each department. In 1993 Mackin orchestrated First Alabama's purchase of Secor a failed New Orleans thrift outbidding rival AmSouth Bancorporation. The Secor purchase raised eyebrows but First Alabama sold some branches and folded other operations into its organization.

In 1994 First Alabama changed its name to Regions Financial in order to reflect its out-of-state operations. The next year Regions rolled into Georgia in a big way leaping from a few banks to holdings with approximately $4 billion in assets. Rumors of a merger with either Wachovia or SunTrust Banks popped up in 1996 but the bank continued on its independent course. The next year the company's tank-like progress was halted when it was outbid for Mississippi's Deposit Guaranty Corp. by First American.

By way of consolation Regions in 1998 bought First Commercial Corp. of Little Rock paying a premium price for its 26 banks mortgage company and investment company. Regions also acquired 13 other companies that year and began a major overhaul of its systems concurrently with the assimilation of these operations. This effort included the consolidation of the back-office aspects of its retail and indirect lending operations.

Mackin retired in 1998 and banking veteran Carl Jones Jr. became CEO. Under his direction the bank continued its geographic infill strategy with acquisitions of banks and branches in Arkansas Florida Louisiana Tennessee and Texas in 1999 and 2000. The company also sold its credit card portfolio to MBNA (since acquired by Bank of America) and in 2001 acquired Memphis-based investment bank Morgan Keegan.

Regions Financial has looked for acquisitions in order to grow geographically and diversify its product and services mix. It fortified its foothold in the South and expanded into the Midwest with its blockbuster merger with Union Planters in 2004. Roughly two years later the company acquired fellow Birmingham-based bank AmSouth for nearly $10 billion in stock. The latter deal created one of the 10 largest banks in the US and helped Regions Financial keep pace with other megabanks in its markets such as Bank of America and SunTrust. The deals also helped entrench the company in states such as Alabama Arkansas Mississippi and Tennessee where it is a market leader.

EXECUTIVES

Chairman President and CEO, O. B. Grayson Hall, $1,000,000 total compensation

SEVP; Head Corporate Banking, John M. Turner, age 57

SEVP; Head General Banking, John B. Owen, $659,816 total compensation

SEVP General Counsel and Corporate Secretary, Fournier J. (Boots) Gale, $570,554 total compensation

SEVP; President Mid-America Region, Ronald G. (Ronnie) Smith

SEVP; Head Commercial Banking, William E. (Bill) Horton

SEVP Strategic Planning and Execution, C. Keith Herron

SEVP; President East Region, Brett D. Couch

SEVP; Head Consumer Services, Scott M. Peters

SEVP; Head Wealth Management, William D. (Bill) Ritter

SEVP and CFO, David J. Turner, $644,062 total compensation

SEVP; Head Human Resources, David R. (Dave) Keenan

SEVP and Chief Credit Officer, Barbara (Barb) Godin

SEVP and Chief Risk Officer, C. Matthew Lusco, $566,308 total compensation

SEVP; Head Strategic Performance and Alignment, Ellen Jones

Senior Executive Vice President Human Resources systems and Administration, Christine Germanson

Senior Vice President of Data Center, James Pryor

Vice President, Glena Dameron

Vice President, William Tracy

Senior Vice President Regional Community Affairs Manager, Mike Scott

Senior Vice President Credit Risk Management, Tommy Tynes

Vice President, Evin Lumsden

Vice President Operational Risk Management, Justin Wygal

Senior Vice President and Assistant Corporate Secretary, Lachelle Koon

Senior Vice President, Aubrey Earnheart

Vice President Operations, Jane Sebeck

Vice President, John Eubank

Vice President Business Banking, Jan Conrad

Senior Vice President, Kim Bradley

Treasury Management Sales Executive Senior Vice President, David Luke David Luke

Assistant Vice President, Santosh Singh

Vice President Business Banking Sales Support, Ginger Blake

Senior Vice President, Houston Cook

AVP Corporate Marketing Strategist, Shana Fail

Senior Vice President and Director Market and Liquidity Risk, Jason Ross

Vice President Mortgage Lending, David Moon

Vice President and Technology Contract Manager, Mike Ritchie

Senior Vice President, Kerri Raines

Assistant Vice President Mortgage Loan Officer, Elizabeth Hickman

Vice President, Greg Smith

Vice President Mortgage Loan Originator, Scott Wells

Senior Vice President, David Neely

Vice President of Estates, Kevin Collins

Senior Vice President Strategic Planning, Hinton Taylor

Vice President Business Banking Relationship Manager, John Marshall

Vice President, Paul Carruthers

Senior Vice President, Donald Hinds

Vice President, Johnny Lynaugh

Vice President, Alan Christian

Vice President Senior Review Appraiser, Denise Newsome

Financial Sales Director Vice President, Theresa Zeringue

Vice President Senior Talent Acquisition Partner Audit Compliance Finance and Risk, Sharon Chandler

Senior Vice President Regional Community Affairs Manager, Latrisha Jemison

Executive Vice President, Markel Wyatt

Senior Vice President, Bryan Grantham

Vice President Issues Management, Chris Scribner

Senior Vice President, Susan Voss

Vice President, Brad Bradford

Senior Vice President, Gaynor Scogin

Vice President Information Technology, Joe Massery

Vice President Commercial Real Estate, Todd Harris

Senior Vice President Consumer Sales Manager, Ken Knapp Ken Knapp

Senior Vice President Director of Enterprise Risk, Chad Webb

Vice President, Brad Morris

Senior Vice President, Keith Harrah

Senior Vice President, Shelby Mackey

Vice President Client Services Officer, Stuart White

Assistant Vice President Application Development, Jeffrey Tennessen

Vice President and Manager Benefits Communications and Wellness, Jonna Wallace

Senior Vice President Risk Management Audit, Chad Fooshee

Senior Vice President, Donald Sinclair

Senior Vice President, Dave Hackney

Senior Vice President, John Gerety

Vice President, Stephanie Hughson

Vice President and Trust Officer, Michelle Wieneke

Vice President, Harold Putnam

Assistant Vice President SAS Programmer, Jesse Smedley

Senior Vice President Database Marketing, Gene Hurst

Senior Vice President Risk Special Assets, Lynn Johnston

Vice President Customer Communications, Bret Pippen

Senior Vice President of Mortgage Systems, Ginger Ricchetti

Senior Vice President, Harry Waugh

Vice President Business Intelligence Analys, Robert Butterfield

Senior Vice President, Dale Johnson

Assistant Vice President, Terrence Cannon

Assistant Vice President Business Systems Analyst, Tim Boles

Vice President, Darlene Beanblossom

Vice President, Pierre Fox

Vice President, Valerie Ramsbacher

Senior Vice President Consumer Lending, Mike Wood

Vice President Secondary Marketing, Jonathan Loukotka

Vice President, Valia Rich

Senior Vice President, Teresa Vick

Vice President, Rob Keith

Vice President, Thomas Helvaty

Vice President, Paula Smith

Vice President Audit Manager, Lisa Bickerton

Vice President, Scott Underberg

Vice President Mortgage Loan Originator, Ellie Teed

Vice President Branch Sales Manager, Cathy Cosey

Assistant Vice President Project Manager, Brian Osborn

Vice President, John Collier

Vice President, Jeremy Jenkins

Senior Vice President, Tammy Harris

Senior Vice President Human RE, Stacia Fagan

Vice President, Greg Hoerbelt

Senior Vice President Procurement, John McGowan

Senior Vice President, Clarissa Keeney

Executive Vice President Head of Investor Relations, Dana Nolan

Senior Vice President Leadership and Management Development, Susan Hengel

Vice President, William Laenger

Assistant Vice President, Mary Robinson

Executive Vice President, Scott Hartwig

Vice President, Nerissa Bright

Vice President Relationship Manager, Cory Guillory

Senior Vice President Corporate Marketing, Ben McLeod

Vice President Finance, John Parker

Senior Vice President Capital Markets, David Coody

Vice President Payments, Robert Brown

Executive Vice President Of Commercial Banking, Tammi Sanchez

Assistant Vice President And Manager O, Gary White

Vice President, Jimmy Walker

Assistant Vice President, Beth Stagner

Vice President, Colleen Atkinson

Senior Vice president Real Estate, Emilio Cerice

Assistant Vice President and Branch Manager and Small Business Lender, Bryan Furlong

Assistant Vice President Branch Manager Hunters Creek Branch, Rossy Santos

Assistant Vice President Branch Manager, Linda Barton

Assistant Vice President Branch Manager III, Pamela Weaver

Vice President Business Banking Relationship Manager, Kendra Metcalf

Vice President, Jon Kral

Senior Vice President Birmingham, Dorothy Yellock

Senior Vice President Senior Real Estate Credit Portfolio Manager, Danny Roberson

Vice President, Sharon Scott

Vice President, Jerron Hall

Senior Vice President Texas Market Manager, Wendel Pardue

Senior Vice President, Bryan Harper

Vice President Midwest Area Community Affairs Manager, Eric Madkins

Vice President, Paul Schuster

Vice President, Wayne Humphreys

Senior Vice President of Financial Planning and Analysis, Jay Baxter

Vice President Environmental Program Manager, Michelle Long

Vice President, Kimberly McDonald

Executive Vice President Marketing, Alice Elliott

Senior Vice President and Trust Officer, Carla Gale

Senior Vice President Commercial Real, Roger Fox

Vice President Branch Sales Manager, Rosie Garcia

Senior Vice President Program Development Manager, David Fron

Senior Vice President middle Market Commercial And, Dennis Wright

Senior Vice President Information Security, John Ballew

Vice President of Information Technology, Adrian Castanon

Auditors: Ernst & Young LLP

LOCATIONS

HQ: Regions Financial Corp
1900 Fifth Avenue North, Birmingham, AL 35203
Phone: 205 581-7890
Web: www.regions.com

2016 Branch Locations

	No.
Florida	326
Tennessee	230
Alabama	226
Missippi	132
Georgia	124
Louisiana	104
Arkansas	88
Texas	76
Missouri	57
Indiana	55
Illinois	55
South Carolina	26
Kentucky	12
Iowa	10
North Carolina	6
Total	**1,527**

PRODUCTS/OPERATIONS

2016 Sales

	$ mil.	% of total
Interest income		
Loansincluding fees	3,066	51
Securities - taxable	566	9
Operating lease assets	125	2
Loans held for sale	16	-
Trading account securities	5	-
Other earning assets	36	1
Non-interest income		
Service charges on deposits	664	11
Card and ATM fees	402	7
Investment management and trust fee income	213	4
Mortgage income	173	3
Securities gains (losses) net	6	0
Others	695	12
Total	**5,967**	**100**

2016 Sales

	% of total
Consumer Bank	55
Corporate Bank	35
Wealth Management	10
Total	**100**

Selected Products

Banking
 Checking
 Money Market
 Savings
 CDs
 Regions Visa CheckCard
 Business Checking
 Business Savings
 Merchant Services
 Treasury Management
 Payroll
 Audit Confirmations
Commercial Banking
 Deposit Services
 Treasury Management
 Online Services
 Merchant Services
 Global Trade Finance
 Corporate Trust
Private Wealth Management
 Solutions for Individuals
 Credit and Risk Management
 Wealth Management
 Solutions for Professionals

COMPETITORS

Arvest Bank	First Horizon
BB&T	Investar
BBVA Compass	JPMorgan Chase
Bancshares	SunTrust
Bank of America	Synovus
Capital One	Trustmark
Citigroup	Wells Fargo
First Citizens	Woodforest Financial
BancShares	

HISTORICAL FINANCIALS

Company Type: Public

Income Statement

FYE: December 31

	ASSETS ($ mil.)	NET INCOME ($ mil.)	INCOME AS % OF ASSETS	EMPLOYEES
12/16	125,968	1,163	0.9%	22,166
12/15	126,050	1,062	0.8%	23,916
12/14	119,679	1,155	1.0%	23,723
12/13	117,396	1,122	1.0%	24,255
12/12	121,347	1,120	0.9%	23,427
Annual Growth	**0.9%**	**0.9%**	**—**	**(1.4%)**

2016 Year-End Financials

Debt ratio: 2.79%
Return on equity: 6.92%
Cash ($ mil.): 5,436
Current ratio: —
Long-term debt ($ mil.): —

No. of shares (mil.): 1,214
Dividends
 Yield: 0.0%
 Payout: 29.3%
Market value ($ mil.): 17,441

	STOCK PRICE ($) FY Close	P/E High/Low		PER SHARE ($) Earnings	Dividends	Book Value
12/16	14.36	17	8	0.87	0.26	13.72
12/15	9.60	14	12	0.75	0.23	12.98
12/14	10.56	14	11	0.80	0.18	12.55
12/13	9.89	13	9	0.77	0.10	11.44
12/12	7.13	11	6	0.71	0.04	10.97
Annual Growth	**19.1%**	**—**	**—**	**5.2%**	**58.9%**	**5.8%**

Reinsurance Group of America, Inc.

Just what is reinsurance? Here hold this pile of insurance risk while we explain that holding company Reinsurance Group of America (RGA) is one of the largest life reinsurers in the US. RGA provides insurance companies with reinsurance on the risks they've taken on allowing them to reduce their liability and increase their business volume. Its operations are organized into two large groups: Traditional and Financial Solutions. Traditional reinsurance includes individual and group life and health disability and critical illness coverage while Financial Solutions includes longevity financial and asset-intensive products. RGA operates in about 30 countries in the Americas the Asia/Pacific region Europe and South Africa.

Operations

RGA's US operating unit RGA Reinsurance provides both traditional life reinsurance and reinsurance on investment assets such as annuities and corporate-owned life insurance policies. Its customers are generally large US-based life insurance companies. In addition to its traditional mortality-risk and asset reinsurance the US operations also offer financial reinsurance to help its customers meet regulatory requirements. Its Global Financial Solutions unit consists of three businesses: asset-intensive reinsurance (full-risk coinsurance of annuities or reinsurance with a large investment component) financial reinsurance (involving ceding companies) and longevity risk transfer (employee retirement benefits).

The company also provides e-underwriting solutions to help customers write policies better and more quickly.

At the close of 2016 RGA had life reinsurance in force valued at about $3.1 trillion and about $53.1 billion in consolidated assets.

Geographic Reach

RGA organizes its operating segments by geographic region: US and Latin America; Canada; Europe Middle East and Africa; and Asia Pacific. The US and Latin America segment accounts for around 60% of total sales.

The company is expanding internationally particularly in such emerging markets as China India Mexico and the Middle East. It has offices in Australia Barbados Bermuda Canada China France Germany Hong Kong India Ireland Italy Japan Malaysia Mexico the Netherlands New Zealand Poland Singapore South Africa South Korea Spain Taiwan the United Arab Emirates the UK and the US.

Sales and Marketing

RGA's top five customers generate some $2.1 billion representing about one-fifth of its gross premiums.

Financial Performance

RGA's revenue which has been relatively static over the past few years rose 11% to $11.5 billion in 2016. That increase was led by growth in net premiums (which rose 8%) investment income and net investment-related gains. All geographic segments showed gains in premiums.

Net income increased 40% to $701.4 million that year. Although buoyed by the higher revenue net income was partially offset by an increase in benefits and other expenses. Cash flow from operations has fallen since 2014; it declined 30% to $1.5 billion in 2016. This was primarily driven by changes in operating assets and liabilities.

Strategy

RGA's strategy for growth has positioned the company well for harsh economic times and industry challenges. To achieve profitable results the company relies on its strong underwriting capabilities and disciplined pricing as well as geographic expansion and diversification in the products and services it offers. It is especially widening its mortality offerings in North America including facultative automatic and in-force block reinsurance. It also looks to leverage existing client relationships. In addition the company is looking to profit from the aging US population of baby boomers which is concerned with retirement income and estate planning.

As part of its efforts to diversify RGA has been seeking new longevity risk contracts. (Longevity risk refers to the risk of having to make payments to a retiree for a longer period than planned for if the person lives longer than expected.) For example in late 2016 the company entered into a longevity transaction with AXA France; the swap covered more than 150000 annuitants and related commitment.

In recent years RGA has opened new offices in Singapore and China to expand its global presence. It is also constructing a new US headquarters building to meet future growth needs.

Mergers and Acquisitions

In 2015 RGA acquired Aurora National Life Assurance from Swiss Re for $191.5 million; that business includes some 82000 policies in force (roughly two-thirds annuities and one-third life products). Later that year the company bought some $22 billion in term life reinsurance policies (approximately 290000 policies) from Ireland-based XL Group.

RGA also purchased Netherlands-based cooperative PGGM Levensverzekeringen in a move to provide closed-block solutions in Europe.

EXECUTIVES

EVP General Counsel and Secretary, William L. Hutton
SEVP and CFO, Todd C. Larson, age 54, $472,428 total compensation
EVP and Chief of Staff, Robert M. Musen
EVP Global Financial Solutions; President RGA Financial Group, John P. Laughlin
EVP and CIO, Mark E. Showers
EVP and Chief Human Resources Officer, Gay Burns
President and CEO, Anna Manning, $750,000 total compensation
EVP Global Acquisitions, Scott D. Cochran
SEVP and COO, Alain P. N ©emeh, $563,750 total compensation
EVP and Chief Investment Officer, Timothy (Tim) Matson
EVP and CIO, Suzy Scanlon
EVP and Global Chief Risk Officer, Jonathan Porter
Senior Vice President U S Sales, Wayne Adams
Vice President Information Security, Chris Cooper
Senior Vice President and Chief Actuary, Doug Knowling
Vice President Credit Research and Risk Management, Scott Stone
Vice President Deputy Compliance Counsel, Robert Jett
Vice President Information Management And Analytics Services, Mike Foster
Vice President and Actuary Financial M, Christopher Clark
Senior Vice President Public Relations, Yuko Oshima
Vice President Business Development, Andr Dreyer
Executive Vice President and Chief Corporate Officer, Allan O'Bryant
Senior Executive Vice President and Head of EMEA Markets, Paul Schuster

Senior Vice President, Brian Haynes

Vice President Finance, John Hayden

Vice President, James Kellett

Executive Vice President and Chief of Staff, Bob Musen

VP Technical Architecture Solutions, Mike Corum

Vice President Architecture Solutions, Shawn Crain

Vice President Life Product Services, David Burgoon

Senior Vice President and Global Tax Director, Kent Zimmerman

Vice President, Wendy Swanson

Senior Vice President Of The Latin American Division, Jaime Correa

Vice President and Actuary, Thomas Dlouhy

Vice President Underwriting Operations, David Wheeler

Vice President, Jeffrey Schuh

Vice President, Donna Megregian

Vice President, Susan Willeat

Vice President Valuation and Financial Analysis, Chris Murphy

Vice President for Financial Markets, Mark M Hopfinger

Vice President, Jeff Hopson

Vice President, David Vnenchak

Vice President Business Development, Lisa Renetzky

Vice President Research And Development And Actuary, Rodney Brown

Vice President and Actuary, Dustin Hetzler

Vice President of Operations, Anne Riley

Senior Vice President Heathcare, Steven Abood

Senior Vice President, Dave Fischer

Vice President Global Financial Solutions, Keith Politte

Vice President, Curt Zepeda

Senior Vice President and Associate Gc, Dana Wiele

Vice President Business Development, Mike Choate

Vice President Director of Investment Strategy and Research, Amy Gibson

Vice President Innovation Studio Lead, Farron Blanc

Vice President Aura Product Management, Brad Butler

SVP and Chief Medical Director of U.S. Mortality Markets, Holowaty Carl

Chairman, J. Cliff Eason

Assistant Treasurer, Jeffrey Boyer

Auditors: Deloitte & Touche LLP

LOCATIONS

HQ: Reinsurance Group of America, Inc.
16600 Swingley Ridge Road, Chesterfield, MO 63017
Phone: 636 736-7000
Web: www.rgare.com

2015 Revenues

	$ mil.	% of total
US and Latin America	6,108	59
Asia/Pacific	1,694	16
Europe Middle East and Africa	1,477	14
Canada	1,068	10
Corporate & other	68	1
Total	**10,418**	**100**

Selected Countries of Operation

Australia
Barbados
Bermuda
Canada
China
France
Germany
Hong Kong
India
Ireland
Italy
Japan
Malaysia
Mexico
Netherlands
New Zealand
Poland
Singapore
South Africa
South Korea
Spain
Taiwan
Turkey
United Arab Emirates
UK
US

PRODUCTS/OPERATIONS

2016 Revenues

	$ mil.	% of total
U.S. and Latin America	6,805	59
Canada	1,164	10
Europe Middle East and Africa	1,535	13
Asia Pacific	1,834	16
Corporate and Other	180	2
Total	**11,521**	**100**

Selected Products and Services

e-Underwriting solutions
Facultative and underwriting expertise
Financial solutions
Group reinsurance
Individual life reinsurance
Individual living benefits reinsurance
Product development

Selected Subsidiaries

Reinsurance Company of Missouri Incorporated (RCM)
RGA Americas Reinsurance Company Ltd. (RGA Americas)
RGA Atlantic Reinsurance Company Ltd. (RGA Atlantic)
RGA International Reinsurance Company (RGA International)
RGA Life Reinsurance Company of Canada (RGA Canada)
RGA Reinsurance Company (Barbados) Ltd. (RGA Barbados)
RGA Reinsurance Company (RGA Reinsurance)
RGA Reinsurance Company of Australia Limited (RGA Australia)

COMPETITORS

AEGON USA	Munich Re Group
Berkshire Hathaway	Pacific Life
General Re	Prudential
Generali	SCOR Reinsurance
Hannover Re	Swiss Re
Munich Re America	XL Group plc

HISTORICAL FINANCIALS

Company Type: Public

Income Statement

FYE: December 31

	ASSETS ($ mil.)	NET INCOME ($ mil.)	INCOME AS % OF ASSETS	EMPLOYEES
12/16	53,097	701	1.3%	2,482
12/15	50,383	502	1.0%	2,201
12/14	44,679	684	1.5%	2,070
12/13	39,674	418	1.1%	1,890
12/12	40,360	631	1.6%	1,766
Annual Growth	**7.1%**	**2.6%**	**—**	**8.9%**

2016 Year-End Financials

Debt ratio: 7.40%
Return on equity: 10.58%
Cash ($ mil.): 1,200
Current ratio: —
Long-term debt ($ mil.): —
No. of shares (mil.): 64
Dividends
  Yield: 0.0%
  Payout: 14.4%
Market value ($ mil.): 8,091

	STOCK PRICE ($) FY Close	P/E High/Low		Earnings	PER SHARE ($) Dividends	Book Value
12/16	125.83	12	7	10.79	1.56	110.31
12/15	85.55	13	11	7.46	1.40	94.09
12/14	87.62	9	7	9.78	1.26	102.13
12/13	77.41	13	9	5.78	1.08	83.87
12/12	53.52	7	6	8.52	0.84	93.47
Annual Growth	**23.8%**	**—**	**—**	**6.1%**	**16.7%**	**4.2%**

Reliance Steel & Aluminum Co.

Reliance Steel & Aluminum shows its mettle as North America's largest metals service center company. Through a network of 300-plus service and distribution centers (many dealing only in specialty metals) in 39 US states it processes and distributes more than 100000 metal products worldwide to more than 125000 customers in a broad range of industries. Reliance markets carbon alloy stainless steel and specialty steel products as well as aluminum brass copper and titanium products. Markets include the aerospace energy construction manufacturing semiconductor and electronics and transportation industries.

Operations

The company purchases a variety of metals from primary producers and sell these products in small quantities based on its customers' needs. It performed metals processing services or first-stage processing (47% of sales orders in 2015) before delivering the products to customers through a network of metals service centers. Carbon steel accounted for 52% of Reliance's revenues in 2015.

Geographic Reach

Reliance operates in 39 US states and about a dozen other countries including Australia Belgium Canada China France Malaysia Mexico Singapore South Korea Turkey the UAE and the UK.

Sales and Marketing

Reliance has 2080 sales personnel in 44 US states and 13 other countries that provide marketing services. It also operates a fleet of 1750 trucks to service its smaller customers. It serves 125000 customers in a broad range of industries.

It is estimated that there are approximately 10100 metal wholesale locations in the US operated by approximately 7400 companies. The four largest US metals service center companies represented less than 10% of the estimated $202.2 billion industry total in 2015. Based on this estimate the company's US revenues of $8.62 billion accounted for approximately 4.3% of the entire US market. In 2015 approximately 97% of its orders were from repeat customers.

Financial Performance

In 2015 Reliance's net revenue decreased by 11% due to lower metals pricing as the result of continued high levels of imported metal products because of the strength of the US dollar coupled with weak global economies and a decline in volume sold to the depressed oil and gas market. This decline was partially offset by growth in automotive (primarily through the toll processing businesses in the US and Mexico reflecting increased traffic) and aerospace.

Net income decreased by 16% due to lower revenues and the impairment of long-lived assets related to certain energy-related businesses as a result of continued low crude oil prices and the resulting decline in the demand for the products the company sells to the energy market.

In 2015 Reliance's operating cash flow increased by 188% due to a change in inventories and accounts receivable as the result of continued declines in metal prices throughout the year coupled with internal inventory management efforts.

Strategy

The company seeks to improve its operating results through organic growth activities and strategic acquisitions to enhance products add customers and increase its geographic diversification. Reliance believes that this strategy makes the company less vulnerable to regional or industry-specific economic volatility. Its internal growth activities includes opening new plants and adding to its processing capabilities or relocating centers to new facilities. It also continues to expand the types of metals it sells and the processing services it offers.

Reliance focuses on improving the operating performance at acquired locations by integrating them into its operational model and providing it access to capital and other resources to promote growth and efficiencies. It also believes that its focus on servicing customers with small order sizes and quick turnaround along with its growth and diversification strategy have been instrumental in the company's ability to produce industry-leading operating results among publicly traded metals service center companies in North America.

The company continues to pursue internal growth by opening new facilities building or expanding existing facilities and adding processing equipment.

Since its IPO in 1994 Reliance has been on something of a spending binge buying up a number of smaller rivals. The company has grown significantly over the years through a series of acquisitions both large and small. It has successfully purchased 60 businesses.

Mergers and Acquisitions

In 2016 Reliance acquired Missouri-based Tubular Steel (a distributor and processor of carbon alloy and stainless steel pipe tubing and bar products); and Best Manufacturing headquartered in Jonesboro Arkansas a custom sheet metal fabricator of steel and aluminum products on both a direct and toll basis.

In 2014 Reliance acquired Aluminium Services UK Limited the holding company parent of All Metal Services the world's largest independent raw material service provider to the aerospace and defense industries supporting customers in more than 40 countries worldwide.

That year it also bought Fox Metals and Alloys (a Houston Texas-based steel distributor specializing in alloy carbon and stainless steel bar and plate products primarily servicing OEMs and machine shops that serve the oil gas and petrochemical industries) and Northern Illinois Steel Supply (a value-added distributor and fabricator of a variety of steel and non-ferrous metal products primarily structural steel components and parts for the energy and petrochemical sectors).

The company bought Metals USA in 2013 for $786 million. Metals USA makes a wide range of products and services in the heavy carbon steel flat-rolled steel non-ferrous metals and building products markets. The acquisition adds 48 service centers across the US to Reliance's existing operations and complements its existing customer base product mix and geographic footprint.

That year it also acquired Travel Main Holdings LLC a real estate holding company with a portfolio of 18 real estate properties all of which are leased by certain of its subsidiaries. The $78.9 million deal included the assumption of $43.8 million of debt.

Company Background

In 2012 the company acquired through subsidiary Feralloy Corporation Alabama-based GH Metal Solutions for an undisclosed price. GH Metal is a carbon steel products processor and fabricator with about $44 million in annual sales.

That year it moved to expand its operations in Tennessee again when subsidiary Precision Strip acquired the Worthington Steel Vonore plant part of Worthington Industries for an undisclosed price. The plant processes and distributes carbon steel aluminum and stainless steel products on a toll basis (processing the metal for a fee without taking ownership of it).

A key addition for serving energy companies came in 2011 when Reliance acquired Houston-based Continental Alloys & Services for about $200 million. Continental is a materials management company that supplies steel and alloy pipe tube and bar products and manufactures various tools designed for energy service companies. It has 12 locations in seven countries.

The company was founded in 1939.

EXECUTIVES

President CCC Steel, Brian M. Tenenbaum
SEVP and CFO, Karla R. Lewis, age 52, $604,250 total compensation
Executive SVP Operations, William K. Sales, age 60, $550,000 total compensation
President and CEO, Gregg J. Mollins, age 62, $1,025,000 total compensation
Managing Director All Metal Services, David L. Potts
President AMI Metals, Scott A. Smith
Executive SVP Operations, James D. Hoffman, age 58, $577,500 total compensation
President Allegheny Steel Distributors, Bernie J. Herrmann
President Aluminum and Stainless, Joseph B. Wolf
President Pacific Metal, John S. Nosler
President Infra-Metals, Mark A Haight, age 58
President Earle M. Jorgensen Co., James Desmond
SVP Operations, Stephen P. (Steve) Koch, age 50, $486,250 total compensation
President Siskin Steel & Supply, Paul J. Loftin
President Yarde Metals, Matthew L. (Matt) Smith
President Sugar Steel, Robert J. Sugar
President Chapel Steel, Stanley J. (Stan) Altman
President Clayton Metals, Brian K. Cleveland
CIO, Susan C. Borchers, age 56
President Feralloy, Carlos Rodriguez-Borjas
President American Metals, Nicole Heater
President Crest Steel, Kristofer M. Farris
President Delta Steel, Eric J. Offenberger
President Diamond Manufacturing, David L. Simpson
President National Specialty Alloys, Mark Russ
President Service Steel Aerospace, Douglas Nesbitt
President Viking Materials, Michael E. Allen
President Chatham Steel, Jerome Rooney
President Precision Strip, Joseph P. Wolf
President Continental Alloys & Services, Randall C. (Randy) Zajicek
President Liebovich Bros., David Corirossi
President Northern Illinois Steel Supply, Michael J. Ruth
President PDM Steel Service Centers, Sean Mollins
President Phoenix Metals, Barry L. Epps
President Best Manufacturing, James Best
President Precision Flamecutting and Steel, Susan McKay
President Valex, Steve Simon
Managing Director Metalweb Limited, Karl Weston
Vice President, Kay Rustand
Vice President Finance, Judy Bennett
Chairman, Mark V. Kaminski, age 62
Auditors: KPMG LLP

LOCATIONS

HQ: Reliance Steel & Aluminum Co.
350 South Grand Avenue, Suite 5100, Los Angeles, CA 90071
Phone: 213 687-7700
Web: www.rsac.com

2016 Sales

	$ mil.	% of total
United States	7,867	91
Foreign Countries	746	9
Total	**8,613**	**100**

2016 Sales

	% of total
Midwest	32
Southeast	17
West/Southwest	12
California	10
International	9
Mid-Atlantic	7
Northeast	6
Pacific Northwest	4
Mountain	3
Total	**100**

PRODUCTS/OPERATIONS

2016 Sales

	% of total
Carbon steel	52
Aluminum	20
Stainless steel	14
Alloy	5
Toll processing	3
Other	6
Total	**100**

PRODUCTS

Alloy Steel
Aluminum
Brass & Copper
Carbon Steel
Stainless Steel
Titanium

COMPETITORS

A. M. Castle	Ryerson
O'Neal Steel	Steel Technologies
Olympic Steel	Ternium Mexico
Russel Metals	Worthington Industries

HISTORICAL FINANCIALS

Company Type: Public

Income Statement

FYE: December 31

	REVENUE ($ mil.)	NET INCOME ($ mil.)	NET PROFIT MARGIN	EMPLOYEES
12/16	8,613	304	3.5%	14,500
12/15	9,350	311	3.3%	14,000
12/14	10,451	371	3.6%	14,900
12/13	9,223	321	3.5%	14,000
12/12	8,442	403	4.8%	11,600
Annual Growth	**0.5%**	**(6.8%)**	**—**	**5.7%**

2016 Year-End Financials

Debt ratio: 26.03%
Return on equity: 7.53%
Cash ($ mil.): 122
Current ratio: 4.10
Long-term debt ($ mil.): 1,846

No. of shares (mil.): 72
Dividends
　Yield: 0.0%
　Payout: 39.6%
Market value ($ mil.): 5,781

STOCK PRICE ($)		P/E		PER SHARE ($)		
	FY Close	High/Low		Earnings	Dividends	Book Value
12/16	79.54	21	12	4.16	1.65	57.08
12/15	57.91	16	12	4.16	1.60	54.56
12/14	61.27	16	12	4.73	1.40	53.00
12/13	75.84	18	15	4.14	1.26	50.00
12/12	62.10	12	8	5.33	0.80	46.79
Annual Growth	6.4%	—	—	(6.0%)	19.8%	5.1%

Renasant Corp

Those who are cognizant of their finances may want to do business with Renasant Corporation. The holding company owns Renasant Bank which serves consumers and local business through about 80 locations in Alabama Georgia Mississippi and Tennessee. The bank offers standard products such as checking and savings accounts CDs credit cards and loans and mortgages as well as trust retail brokerage and retirement plan services. Its loan portfolio is dominated by residential and commercial real estate loans. The bank also offers agricultural business construction and consumer loans and lease financing. Subsidiary Renasant Insurance sells personal and business coverage. Shareholders approved a merger with Metropolitan Bank in mid-2017.

Financial Performance

The company's revenue increased in fiscal 2013 compared to the prior year. It reported revenue of $252.6 million for fiscal 2013 up from $228 million in revenue for fiscal 2012.

Renasant's net income also went up in fiscal 2013 compared to the previous fiscal period. It reported net income of about $33.5 million for fiscal 2013 up from net income of $26.6 million in fiscal 2012.

The company's cash on hand decreased by about $24 million in fiscal 2013 compared to fiscal 2012 levels.

Strategy

Renasant has looked to diversify its loan portfolio. The bank has reduced its amount of loans for construction and land development — a sector that has been hit particularly hard — by tightening its underwriting standards.

It's also been growing through acquistions. In late 2014 for example Renasant purchased Heritage Financial Group in an all stock merger deal that amounted to $258 million. The move added $1.9 billion in assets $1.2 billion in loan assets and $1.3 billion in deposit assets to Renasant's collection. In addition the move significantly expanded the bank's geographic reach adding 48 banking mortgage and investment offices in Alabama Florida and Georgia. All told the deal made Renasant one of the largest community banks in the Southeast region of the United States.

Mergers and Acquisitions

In 2017 Renasant agreed to a $190 million merger with Metropolitan Bank.

EXECUTIVES

EVP, Stuart R. Johnson, age 64, $250,000 total compensation

Chairman President and CEO, E. Robinson (Robin) McGraw, age 70, $750,000 total compensation

EVP, James W. Gray, age 61, $230,000 total compensation

President and COO, C. Mitchell (Mitch) Waycaster, age 59, $450,000 total compensation

EVP, Mary J. Witt, age 58

First VP and Community Bank Performance and Lending Support The Peoples Bank & Trust, W. Mark Williams, age 54

EVP, R. Rick Hart, age 69, $496,000 total compensation

EVP and General Counsel, Stephen M. Corban, age 62, $75,000 total compensation

EVP; President Eastern Region Renasant Bank, O. Leonard (Len) Dorminey, age 64, $213,285 total compensation

EVP and CFO, Kevin D. Chapman, age 42, $375,000 total compensation

EVP; President Western Region Renasant Bank, J. Scott Cochran, age 54

CFP Senior Vice President and Director of Asset Management, Terry Bullard

Assistant Vice President Branch Manager, Cathy Jarvis

Assistant Vice President Account Executive, Brian Gagel

Branch President, Heath Stribling

Senior Vice President, Ryan New

Senior Vice President, Donna Wade

Senior Vice President, Robert Hankins

Senior Vice President, Bobby Harper

Senior Vice President, John Willis

Senior Vice President, Shay Barkley

Executive Vice President Credit Administration, Stuart Weise

Senior Vice President, Scott Rossman

Vice President, Jack Stuart

Senior Vice President Commercial Banking, David Harwell

Senior Vice President, Jason McClimans

Division President, Lucius Brock

Southern Division President, Jeff Lacey

Senior Vice President Small Business Advisor Lending, Melanie Brown

Senior Vice President Pinnacle Banking, Scott Parrish

Workout Officer Vice President, Joey Shiver

Vice President Client Portfolio Manager Asset Manage Ement Renasant Asset Management, Matt Legg

Vice President, Randy Harris

First Vice President Associate Counsel, Jared Carrubba

Auditors: Horne LLP

LOCATIONS

HQ: Renasant Corp
209 Troy Street, Tupelo, MS 38804-4827
Phone: 662 680-1001
Web: www.renasant.com

PRODUCTS/OPERATIONS

2015 Sales

	$ mil.	% of total
Interest income		
Loans	236	64
Securities	26	7
Other	0	-
Non-interest income		
Mortgage banking income	35	10
Service charges on deposit accounts	29	8
Fees and commissions	16	4
Wealth management	9	3
Other	17	4
Total	**371**	**100**

COMPETITORS

BBVA Compass Bancshares	First Horizon
BancorpSouth	Hancock Holding
Citizens Holding	Regions Financial
Citizens National Bank of Meridian	Trustmark

HISTORICAL FINANCIALS

Company Type: Public

Income Statement

FYE: December 31

	ASSETS ($ mil.)	NET INCOME ($ mil.)	INCOME AS % OF ASSETS	EMPLOYEES
12/16	8,699	90	1.0%	1,965
12/15	7,926	68	0.9%	1,996
12/14	5,805	59	1.0%	1,471
12/13	5,746	33	0.6%	1,483
12/12	4,178	26	0.6%	1,096
Annual Growth	20.1%	35.9%	—	15.7%

2016 Year-End Financials

Debt ratio: 2.23%
Return on equity: 7.99%
Cash ($ mil.): 306
Current ratio: —
Long-term debt ($ mil.): —

No. of shares (mil.): 44
Dividends
  Yield: 0.0%
  Payout: 32.7%
Market value ($ mil.): 1,872

STOCK PRICE ($)		P/E		PER SHARE ($)		
	FY Close	High/Low		Earnings	Dividends	Book Value
12/16	42.22	20	14	2.17	0.71	27.81
12/15	34.41	20	14	1.88	0.68	25.73
12/14	28.93	17	14	1.88	0.68	22.56
12/13	31.46	26	15	1.22	0.68	21.21
12/12	19.14	19	14	1.06	0.68	19.80
Annual Growth	21.9%	—	—	19.6%	1.1%	8.9%

Republic Bancorp, Inc. (KY)

As one of the top five bank holding companies based in Kentucky $4 billion-asset Republic Bancorp is the parent of Republic Bank & Trust (formerly First Commercial Bank) which offers deposit accounts loans and mortgages credit cards private banking and trust services through more than 30 branches in across Kentucky and around 10 more in southern Indiana Nashville Tampa and Cincinnati Ohio. About one-third of the bank's $3 billion-loan portfolio is tied to residential real estate while another 25% is made up of commercial real estate loans. Warehouse lines of credit home equity loans and commercial and industrial loans make up most of the rest. The company also offers short-term consumer loans and tax refund loans.

Operations

Republic Bancorp operates three "core banking" segments: Traditional Banking which generated more than 80% of the company's total profit during 2015; Warehouse (almost 20% of profit) and Mortgage Banking (less than 1%). Its Warehouse lending business offers short-term credit facilities secured by single-family residences to mortgage bankers nationwide. Its Republic Processing Group segment offers short-term consumer loans prepaid debit cards and tax refund loans.

The bank made 75% of its total revenue from interest income almost entirely from loans during 2015 though a small percentage came from taxed investments and Federal Home Loan Bank stock. The rest of its revenue came from net refund transfer fees from its Republic Processing Group segment (9% of revenue) deposit account service charges (7%) interchange fee income (4%) mortgage banking income (2%) and other miscellaneous income sources.

Subsidiary Republic Insurance Services (also known as the Captive) provides property and casualty insurance coverage to the company and eight other third-party insurance captives for which insurance may not be available or cost effective.

Geographic Reach

The company had 40 RB&T branches at the end of 2015 including 32 in Kentucky mostly in the Louisville Metro area and others in the Central Western and Northern parts of the state. It had 3 branches in southern Indiana (in Floyds Knobs Jeffersonville and New Albany); two branches in the Tampa Florida metro area; two branches in the Nashville Tennessee metro area; and one more in the Cincinnati Ohio metro area.

Sales and Marketing

Republic spent $3.16 million on marketing and development expenses during 2015 compared to $3.26 million and $3.11 million in 2014 and 2013 respectively.

Financial Performance

Republic Bancorp's revenues and profits have been trending higher since 2013 as its loan assets have risen more than 30% over the period.

The company's revenue climbed 9% to $190 million during 2015 mostly thanks to higher interest income as its loan assets grew by 9% to $3.33 billion with commercial loans (real estate and business loans) and residential mortgage loans and lines of credit driving most of the growth.

Strong revenue growth in 2015 drove Republic's net income up 22% to $35 million for the year. The company's operating cash levels nearly doubled to $50 million after adjusting its earnings for non-cash items related to mortgage loan sales and thanks to favorable working capital changes related to changes in other liabilities.

Strategy

Republic Bancorp is moving toward building its commercial loans business launching a Corporate Banking division in 2015 to originate commercial loans with amounts ranging from $2.5 million to $25 million to borrowers with the highest credit ratings in its existing geographic markets. It also acquires smaller community banks to expand into new geographic markets while building its loan and deposit business.

Additionally Republic Bancorp has been moving into other revolving credit lines while also looking to take advantage of the rapidly growing prepaid card market. During 2015 for example it partnered with netSpend to become a pilot issuer of netSpend-branded prepaid cards; and partnered with ClearBalance to originate revolving lines of credit nationally for hospital receivables.

Mergers and Acquisitions

In October 2015 Republic Bancorp expanded its presence in Florida and grew its loan business after agreeing to buy $250 million-asset Cornerstone Bancorp along its four Cornerstone Community Bank branches in the Tampa Florida metro area $190 million in loans and $200 million in deposits. The deal was expected to be completed in the first half of 2016.

Company Background

In 2012 Republic Bancorp entered the Nashville and Minneapolis market through the FDIC-assisted acquisitions of the failed Tennessee Commerce Bank and First Commercial Bank respectively.

EXECUTIVES

Vice Chairman; President Republic Bank & Trust, A. Scott Trager, age 64, $350,000 total compensation
President and CEO; CEO Republic Bank & Trust, Steven E. (Steve) Trager, age 56, $353,000 total compensation

EVP CFO and Chief Accounting Officer Republic Bancorp and Republic Bank & Trust, Kevin Sipes, age 45, $281,500 total compensation
Vice President and Risk Manager, Bryan Hendrick
Senior Vice President, Steve Pieragowski
Assistant Vice President, Mike Long
Vice President Banking Center Manager Georgetown Republic Bank And Trust, Susan Smith
Executive Vice President Marketing, Darryl Witten
Senior Vice President CRA Compliance Republic Bankand#8230, Nancy Presnell
Senior Vice President, Lisa Butcher
Assistant Vice President Technology Services Managerand#8230, Scott Estes
Assistant Vice President Finance Project Manager, Tim Wheatley
Vice President Project Services Manager, Michelle Cunningham
Assistant Vice President Assistant Fin, Lara Recktenwald
Assistant Vice President Card Operations and Development Manager, Chris Braun
Vice President Bank Administration, Denise Brown
Assistant Vice President Senior Business Development Officer, Kevin Herthel
Senior Vice President Private Banking, Sarah Johnson
Senior Vice President, David Buchanon
Vice President Finance, Jack Horn
Vice President Commercial Lending Officer, Jim Dusil
Senior Vice President, Doug Burgess
Vice President, Karen McGee
Assistant Vice President Managing Director, Brad Savko
Assistant Vice President, Amy Quinn
Assistant Vice President, Megan Scheps
Chairman, Bernard M. Trager, age 88
Auditors: Crowe Horwath LLP

LOCATIONS

HQ: Republic Bancorp, Inc. (KY)
601 West Market Street, Louisville, KY 40202
Phone: 502 584-3600
Web: www.republicbank.com

PRODUCTS/OPERATIONS

2015 Sales

	$ mil.	% of total
Interest		
Loans including fees	134	70
Taxable investment securities	7	4
Other	1	1
Noninterest		
Net refund transfer fees	17	9
Service charges on deposit accounts	13	7
Interchange fee income	8	4
Mortgage banking	4	2
Other	5	3
Adjustments	(0.3)	-
Total	**190**	**100**

Selected Services

Checking
Credit & Debit Cards
Internet & Mobile Banking
Lending
Private Banking & Wealth Management
Savings & Investing

COMPETITORS

BB&T	Home Federal
Bank of America	KeyCorp
Citizens First	PNC Financial
Community Trust	Stock Yards Bancorp
Farmers Capital Bank	U.S. Bancorp
Fifth Third	

Income Statement
FYE: December 31

	ASSETS ($ mil.)	NET INCOME ($ mil.)	INCOME AS % OF ASSETS	EMPLOYEES
12/16	4,816	45	1.0%	954
12/15	4,230	35	0.8%	799
12/14	3,747	28	0.8%	735
12/13	3,371	25	0.8%	750
12/12	3,394	119	3.5%	820
Annual Growth	9.1%	(21.2%)	—	3.9%

2016 Year-End Financials

Debt ratio: 0.86%
Return on equity: 7.75%
Cash ($ mil.): 289
Current ratio: —
Long-term debt ($ mil.): —

No. of shares (mil.): 20
Dividends
  Yield: 0.0%
  Payout: 37.1%
Market value ($ mil.): 825

	STOCK PRICE ($) FY Close	P/E High/Low	PER SHARE ($) Earnings	Dividends	Book Value
12/16	39.54	18 11	2.22	0.83	28.97
12/15	26.41	16 13	1.70	0.78	27.59
12/14	24.72	18 16	1.38	0.74	26.80
12/13	24.54	23 17	1.22	0.69	26.09
12/12	21.13	5 3	5.69	1.75	25.60
Annual Growth	17.0%	— —	(21.0%)	(17.1%)	3.1%

Republic First Bancorp, Inc.

Republic First Bancorp is the holding company for Republic Bank which serves the Greater Philadelphia area and southern New Jersey from more than 15 branches. Boasting over $1 billion in assets the bank targets individuals and small to midsized businesses offering standard deposit products including checking and savings accounts money market accounts IRAs and CDs. Commercial mortgages account for more than 70% of the company's loan portfolio which also includes consumer loans business loans and residential mortgages. Republic has been transitioning from a commercial bank into a major regional retail and commercial bank.

Operations

The bank's loan portfolio is made up of mostly commercial loans including commercial real estate loans construction and land development loans commercial and industrial loans as well as owner occupied real estate loans consumer-related loans and residential mortgages. As of 2015 each its commercial loans typically ranged from $250000 to $5 million though it sometimes lent up to its legal limit of $19.9 million.

About 72% of Republic First Bancorp's total revenue came from loan interest (including fees) in 2014 while another 11% came from interest and dividends on its taxable and tax-exempt investment securities. The rest of its revenue came from gains on sales of SBA loans (10%) loan advisory and servicing fees (3%) service fees on deposit accounts (3%) and other miscellaneous income sources. The bank had a staff of 235 full-time employees at the end of 2014.

Geographic Reach

Republic First boasts more than 15 branch offices in Pennsylvania (in Abington Ardmore Bala Cynwyd Plymouth Meeting Media and Philadelphia) and New Jersey (in Berlin Cherry Hill Glassboro Haddonfield Marlton and Voorhees).

Sales and Marketing

The bank's commercial loans are mostly made to small and medium-sized businesses as well as professionals who need working capital financing for asset acquisitions or other financial services.

Republic First has been ramping up its advertising spend in recent years. It spent $597 thousand on advertising in 2014 compared to $447 thousand and $307 thousand in 2013 and 2012 respectively.

Financial Performance

The company has struggled to consistently grow its revenues in recent years due to shrinking interest margins on loans amidst the low-interest environment. Republic First has been steadily climbing out from prior years of losses (2013 2011 2010) however thanks to declining interest expenses and lower loan loss provisions as its loan portfolio's credit quality has improved with higher property valuations in the strengthened economy.

Republic First's revenue rose by 4% to $48.4 million in 2014 mostly thanks to an 8% jump in interest income as loan balances increased during the year. The bank's non-interest income fell on lower sales of SBA loans with fewer SBA loan originations which offset some of its top-line growth.

The company shot back into the black with a $2.4 million profit in 2014 (compared to a net loss of $3.5 million in 2013) mostly because in 2013 it had suffered a non-recurring $3.6 million loan loss on a bad loan as well as a non-recurring $1.9 million charge related to a legal settlement. Republic First's operating cash levels also skyrocketed to $9.7 million mostly on higher cash earnings.

Strategy

Republic Bank which had historically been known for its business and commercial lending has been focused on retail banking in the past few years and is working to become a major regional retail and commercial bank. As part of this strategy the bank has restructured its loan portfolio to reduce its emphasis on commercial real estate loans and has pursued a "retail-focused" strategy by offering customers "extended store hours absolutely free checking and coin counting more than 55000 surcharge ATMs and free VISA gift cards" according to the company's CEO letter included in the 2014 annual report.

The company has been expanding organically through new branch openings in recent years. In 2015 for example Republic Bank opened three new branches in South New Jersey in Berlin Marlton and Glassboro. In April of that year the company also sold $45 million in common stock through a private placement offering to cover its "aggressive expansion plans in 2015 and beyond."

EXECUTIVES

Vice President of Commercial Lending for South Jersey, John Lavin
Assistant Vice President Network Engineer, John Rudolph
Vice President Commercial Lender South Jersey Market, Don Colligan
Vice President Commercial Lender, Tom Waller
Executive Vice President and Chief Retail Officer of the Bank, Rhonda Costello
Vice President and Store Manager, Michael Mikstas
Senior Vice President, Jay Neilon
Executive Vice President of the Bank, Andrew Logue
Senior Vice President Of Sales, Katie Michaleski

Senior Vice President, Patricia Binck
Vice President and Commercial Lending, Frederick A Marcell
Vice President Senior Business Development Officer, Judy Rosner
Vice President And Cash Management Product And Operations, Matthew Mcgonigal
Auditors: BDO USA, LLP

LOCATIONS

HQ: Republic First Bancorp, Inc.
50 South 16th Street, Philadelphia, PA 19102
Phone: 215 735-4422
Web: www.myrepublicbank.com

PRODUCTS/OPERATIONS

2014 Sales

	$ mil.	% of total
Interest income		
Interest and fees on taxable loans	34	71
Interest and dividends on taxable investment securities	5	10
Interest and fees on tax-exempt loans	0	1
Interest and dividends on tax-exempt investment securities	0	1
Interest on federal funds sold and other interest-earning assets	0	0
Non interest		
Gain on sales of SBA loans	4	10
Loan advisory and servicing fees	1	3
Service fees on deposit accounts	1	3
Gain on sale of investment securities	0	1
Legal settlements	0	0
Other-than-temporary impairment	0	0
Portion recognized in other comprehensive income (before taxes) 0		(0.03)
Net impairment loss on investment securities	0	0
Bank owned life insurance income	0	0
Other non-interest income	0	0
Total	**48**	**100**

COMPETITORS

Bank of America	Sovereign Bank
Citizens Financial Group	Sun Bancorp (NJ)
PNC Financial	TD Bank USA
Prudential Bancorp	TF Financial
Royal Bancshares	Wells Fargo

HISTORICAL FINANCIALS

Company Type: Public

Income Statement

FYE: December 31

	ASSETS ($ mil.)	NET INCOME ($ mil.)	INCOME AS % OF ASSETS	EMPLOYEES
12/16	1,923	4	0.3%	306
12/15	1,439	2	0.2%	277
12/14	1,214	2	0.2%	235
12/13	961	(3)	—	226
12/12	988	3	0.4%	205
Annual Growth	**18.1%**	**8.2%**		**10.5%**

2016 Year-End Financials

Debt ratio: 1.14%
Return on equity: 3.00%
Cash ($ mil.): 34
Current ratio: —
Long-term debt ($ mil.): —

No. of shares (mil.): 56
Dividends
  Yield: —
  Payout: —
Market value ($ mil.): 474

	STOCK PRICE ($) FY Close	P/E High/Low	PER SHARE ($) Earnings	Dividends	Book Value
12/16	8.35	69 29	0.12	0.00	3.79
12/15	4.33	77 55	0.06	0.00	3.00
12/14	3.75	76 43	0.07	0.00	2.98
12/13	2.98	— —	(0.13)	0.00	2.41
12/12	2.07	17 10	0.14	0.00	2.68
Annual Growth	**41.7%**	**— —**	**(3.8%)**	**—**	**9.0%**

Republic Services Inc

Republic Services is the second-largest nonhazardous waste management provider in the US behind leader Waste Management in terms of revenue and geographic coverage. Republic provides waste disposal services for commercial industrial municipal and residential customers through its network of 340 collection firms. It owns or operates some 190 solid waste landfills more than 200 transfer stations and about 65 recycling centers eight treatment recovery and disposal facilities and 10 salt water disposal wells. It also has about 70 landfill-to-gas and a handful of other renewable energy projects.

Operations

Republic Services divides its operations into two broad geographic categories. Group 1 covers the western US and parts of the Midwest. Group 2 covers other parts of the Midwest as well as Texas and the Southeast. Group 2 furnishes more than 50% of revenue while Group 1 provides about 45%.

Geographic Reach

Republic Services' operations span the US. It has collection businesses transfer stations active solid waste landfills and recycling centers in about 40 US states and Puerto Rico. Its active solid waste landfills total 106000 acres including 37100 permitted acres.

Sales and Marketing

Republic has municipal marketing representatives who are responsible for working with municipalities or communities to which it provides residential service. It also employs a National Accounts selling organization.

The company can?t pick up trash online but it can interact with customers through its My Resource customer portal and mobile app. About 2 million customers use the service to sign up for residential small container and temporary large container services.

Financial Performance

Republic Services posted its fourth straight year of revenue growth in 2016 hitting about $9.4 billion up about 3% from 2015. The company reported increases in average yield of about 2% volume of 1% acquisitions (subtracting divestitures) of less than 1% and recycled commodities of half a percentage point.

In 2016 Republic Services? net income dropped 18% to $612 million from 2015. The company had higher costs in 2016 including for employee expenses and restructuring.

The company's operating cash flow increased to $1.8 billion in 2016 from $1.7 billion in 2015.

Strategy

Perhaps the most visible reminder of a waste company is the truck making its rounds. For Republic Services the truck and the entire fleet is where it can save money through automation and standardization. About three-quarters of the company?s fleet is automated which means a truck needs just a driver while an mechanical hoists the trash receptacle to and from the truck. The company has used its national footprint to make sure that its operations throughout the country used the same preventive maintenance procedures which helps reduce costs. Further Republic Services has shifted much its fleet to compressed natural gas which burns cleaner and is usually cheaper than gasoline.

The company has rolled out and improves its digital platform for interacting with customers. Twice as many customers used the MyResource digital service in 2016 as did the previous year.

Besides lowering costs the service helps improve customer service and satisfaction.

Republic Services snaps up local and regional waste services through acquisitions. Its acquisition spending fell to just more than $70 million in 2016 about half of its five-year average of about $140 million. The company?s goal is to put about $100 million a year toward acquisitions.

The company is adding more sustainable resources to its mix. It plans to add about 150000 tons a year of recycling capability through 2018 develop two landfill-gas-to-energy projects a year through 2018 and reduce its fleet emission by 3% by 2018.

Mergers and Acquisitions

Expanding into the E&P sector in 2015 Republic acquired Tervita LLC for $485 million. Tervita is an environmental solutions provider serving US oil and natural gas producers.

In 2014 Republic acquired Rainbow Disposal for $112 million. The transaction enhances its recycling and waste diversion capabilities which will allow it to better serve California's growing sustainability initiatives.

HISTORY

Republic Services began in 1980 as Republic Resources an oil exploration and production company. In 1989 after a stockholder group tried to force Republic into liquidation Browning-Ferris (BFI) founder Thomas Fatjo stepped in gained control of Republic Resources and refocused it on a field he knew well — solid waste. Renamed Republic Waste the company began making acquisitions.

In 1990 Michael DeGroote founder of BFI competitor Laidlaw bought into Republic Waste. In 1995 Wayne Huizenga — who co-founded Waste Management in 1971 and was beginning to develop a national auto sales organization in the mid-1990s after his tenure as chairman and CEO of Blockbuster Entertainment — approached DeGroote about a deal. They rejected an immediate merger of the waste and auto businesses because the latter was not well-enough developed and would drag down Republic's numbers. Instead they agreed to merge Republic and the Hudson Companies (a trash business owned by Huizenga's brother-in-law Harris Hudson) to sell Huizenga a large interest in Republic through a private offering and to give him control of the board (in 1995). The company became Republic Industries.

Huizenga's investment brought a flood of new investors. With new resources Republic Industries became a driving force in the garbage industry's consolidation binge and the company bought more than 100 smaller waste haulers between 1995 and 1998. Republic Industries spun off about 30% of its waste business as Republic Services in 1998; the IPO raised $1.3 billion. Republic's acquisition trend continued as it agreed to buy 16 landfills 136 commercial collection routes and 11 transfer stations from Waste Management for $500 million. Later that year Waste Management veteran James O'Connor succeeded Huizenga as CEO although Huizenga continued as chairman.

Investors filed class-action lawsuits against Republic in 1999 claiming the Waste Management purchases held far more integration problems than the company admitted. In 2000 Republic swapped nine of its solid-waste operations for eight Allied Waste businesses which Allied needed to divest in order to gain federal approval for its merger with BFI.

While many firms in the industry were selling off assets in 2001 Republic was expanding its operations in the Northern California market by acquiring Richmond Sanitary Services. Huizenga retired as chairman at the end of 2002 and was once

again succeeded by O'Connor. Huizenga stayed on the board as a director until May 2004.

In 2007 the company sold Living Earth Technology Company (a noncore stand-alone business in Texas) for about $37 million. In 2008 prior to its megadeal with Allied Waste Republic rebuffed a takeover bid by industry leader Waste Management.

In late 2008 Republic Services the once #3 industry player acquired #2 company Allied Waste for $6 billion to place it closer to industry leader Waste Management in terms of revenues and geographic coverage. Following the acquisition Republic divested assets in seven markets (six municipal solid waste landfills six collection businesses and three transfer stations) in order to meet US antitrust regulations.

During 2012 the company invested $76 million on five recycling centers and plans to continue to look for opportunities to expand its recycling capabilities.

In 2013 the company dedicated a 2037 acre state-of-the-art landfill and transfer station in Texas to meet the Rio Grande Valley's waste needs for the next 100 years. The new La Gloria landfill replaced Republic's Rio Grande Valley Landfill in Donna Texas that had reached full capacity.

EXECUTIVES

President and CEO, Donald W. (Don) Slager, age 55, $1,100,000 total compensation
EVP and Chief Development Officer, Brian A. Bales
EVP Chief Legal Officer Chief Ethics and Compliance Officer and Corporate Secretary, Catharine D. Ellingsen, age 53, $395,107 total compensation
EVP and Chief Administrative Officer, Jeffrey A. (Jeff) Hughes, age 61, $482,061 total compensation
EVP Operations, Jon Vander Ark
Region President East Region, Tim Stuart
SVP and CIO, Bill Halnon
SVP and Chief Accounting Officer, Charles F. (Chuck) Serianni, age 55, $511,779 total compensation
EVP Operations Support, Nathan Cabbil
EVP and Chief Transformation Officer, Stuart Levy
EVP and Chief Customer Officer, Tom Lynch
EVP and Chief Marketing Officer, Sue Klug
Senior Vice President Treasurer, Edward A Lang
Sales Vice President, Bob Pickens
Vice President Purchasing, Nick Stefkovich
Vice President Safety and Environmental Compliance, Jim Olson
Vice President Talent Acquisition, Randy Goldberg
National Account Manager, Nicole Brunick
Vice President Mkt Planning and Development, Andy Shipe
Executive Vice President, Michael Rissman
District Vice President, Michael Summers
Senior Vice President, Jim Vanweelden
Vice President Accounting Services, Mike Guilleaume
Vice President Chief Accounting Officer, Brian Goebel
Area President, Jeff Kintzle
Area President, Heath Eddleblute
National Account Manager, Eileen Wargo
District Vice President, Andrew White
Region Vice President, William Meade
Vice President Customer Resource Centers, Jeffrey Morley
Senior Vice President Training and Talent Development, Douglas Borro
Area President, John Lamanna
Chairman, Manuel Kadre, age 51
Auditors: Ernst & Young LLP

LOCATIONS

HQ: Republic Services Inc
18500 North Allied Way, Phoenix, AZ 85054
Phone: 480 627-2700
Web: www.republicservices.com

2016 sales

	$ mil.	% of total
Group1	4,185	45
Group2	5,014	53
Corporate entities	189	2
Total	**9,388**	**100**

PRODUCTS/OPERATIONS

2016 sales

	$ mil.	% of total
Residential	2,240	24
Small-container commercial	2,878	31
Large-container industrial	1,976	21
Other	38	0
Transfer	464	5
Landfill	1,121	12
Energy services	76	1
Other	595	6
Total	**9,388**	**100**

COMPETITORS

Casella Waste Systems	Waste Connections
Recology	Waste Connections US
Rumpke	Waste Industries USA
Safety-Kleen	Waste Management
WCA Waste	

HISTORICAL FINANCIALS

Company Type: Public

Income Statement

FYE: December 31

	REVENUE ($ mil.)	NET INCOME ($ mil.)	NET PROFIT MARGIN	EMPLOYEES
12/16	9,387	612	6.5%	33,000
12/15	9,115	749	8.2%	33,000
12/14	8,788	547	6.2%	31,000
12/13	8,417	588	7.0%	31,000
12/12	8,118	571	7.0%	30,000
Annual Growth	**3.7%**	**1.7%**	**—**	**2.4%**

2016 Year-End Financials

Debt ratio: 37.13%
Return on equity: 7.90%
Cash ($ mil.): 67
Current ratio: 0.71
Long-term debt ($ mil.): 7,653
No. of shares (mil.): 339
Dividends
  Yield: 0.0%
  Payout: 69.6%
Market value ($ mil.): 19,363

	STOCK PRICE ($) FY Close	P/E High/Low	PER SHARE ($) Earnings	Dividends	Book Value
12/16	57.05	32 24	1.78	1.24	22.66
12/15	43.99	21 18	2.13	1.16	22.49
12/14	40.25	27 20	1.53	1.08	21.96
12/13	33.20	22 18	1.62	0.99	21.93
12/12	29.33	20 16	1.55	0.91	21.33
Annual Growth	**18.1%**	**— —**	**3.5%**	**8.0%**	**1.5%**

REXFORD INDUSTRIAL REALTY, INC.

Rexford Industrial Realty knows that there's more to business in Southern California than moviemaking and fashion. A real estate investment trust or REIT Rexford Industrial owns and manages a portfolio of nearly 70 industrial properties in Los Angeles County and surrounding areas. Its portfolio comprises about 7.6 million sq. ft. of warehouse distribution and light manufacturing space that's leased to small and midsized businesses. It manages 20 more properties — altogether comprising 1.2 million sq. ft. of rentable space. A self-administered and self-managed REIT Rexford Industrial was formed in 2013 from the assets of its predecessor. In mid-2013 the company went public.

IPO

Rexford Industrial intends to use a portion of the $224 million in proceeds to repay debt much of which is secured by various properties.

Operations

Rexford Industrial's portfolio spans several California counties including Los Angeles Orange Ventura San Bernadino Riverside and San Diego.

Financial Performance

Revenue rose for Rexford Industrial by 27% in fiscal 2012 to $34 million from 2011's $28 million thanks to increases in rental revenue and tenant reimbursements from rising occupancy rates and a boost in revenues from properties it acquired during both 2012 and 2011. Rexford Industrial logged 64% increases in revenue from management leasing and development services due to the additional third-party management fees.

Strategy

Rexford Industrial is seeking to acquire equity stakes and debt in stable and distressed industrial properties in infill markets (i.e. highly developed urban centers) in Los Angeles Orange San Diego and Ventura counties and the West Inland Empire to the east. The REIT is also looking to manage properties located in these same areas that are owned by third parties.

The REIT has been buying properties throughout Southern California particularly in the cities of Van Nuys and Tarzana as well as in Glenview Illinois. It looks to purchase both newer and older vintage properties as well as single (40% of its portfolio) and multi-tenant (60%) projects. The REIT invests in every category of industrial property. Tenants are typically small and medium-sized businesses that are tied to the Southern California economy. Rexford Industrial boasts an average tenant size of about 9000 sq. ft. Nearly 70% of its tenants occupy fewer than 50000 sq. ft. apiece.

EXECUTIVES

Co-CEO and Director, Howard Schwimmer, $495,000 total compensation
Co-CEO and Director, Michael S. Frankel, age 54, $495,000 total compensation
CFO, Adeel Khan, $315,000 total compensation
Chairman, Richard S. Ziman, age 74
Auditors: ERNST & YOUNG LLP LOS ANGELES

LOCATIONS

HQ: REXFORD INDUSTRIAL REALTY, INC.
11620 WILSHIRE BLVD # 1000, LOS ANGELES, CA 900256821
Phone: 310 966-1680
Web: WWW.REXFORDINDUSTRIAL.COM

PRODUCTS/OPERATIONS

2015 Revenue

	$ mil.	% of total
Rental		
Rental Revenues	81	86
Tenant Reimbursements	10	11
Management Leasing & Development Services	0	1
Other Income	1	1
Interest Income	0	1
Total	**93**	**100**

Selected Property Categories

Core
Core Plus
First Mortgages Tied to Target Industrial Property
Value Add

COMPETITORS

Brandywine Realty	Prologis
Brandywine Realty	Prologis
PS Business Parks	Terreno Realty
PS Business Parks	Terreno Realty

HISTORICAL FINANCIALS

Company Type: Private

Income Statement

FYE: December 31

	ASSETS ($ mil.)	NET INCOME ($ mil.)	INCOME AS % OF ASSETS	EMPLOYEES
12/16	1,515	25	1.7%	40
12/15	1,153	1	0.2%	—
12/14	932	0	0.1%	—
12/13	554	(0)	—	—
Annual Growth	39.8%	—	—	—

2016 Year-End Financials

Debt ratio: ——
Return on equity: 20.50%
Cash ($ mil.): 15
Current ratio: ——
Long-term debt ($ mil.): —

Dividends
Yield: —
Payout: —
Market value ($ mil.): —

Rite Aid Corp

Rite Aid ranks a distant third (behind Walgreen and CVS) in the US retail drugstore business with more than 4600 drugstores in more than 30 states and the District of Columbia. Rite Aid stores generate roughly 70% of their sales from filling prescriptions while the rest comes from selling health and beauty aids convenience foods greeting cards and more including some 3500 Rite Aid brand private-label products. More than 60% of all Rite Aid stores are freestanding and over half have drive-through pharmacies. The company was founded in 1962. A deal to be acquired by Walgreens Boots Alliance was dropped in mid-2017; instead Rite Aid will sell about half of its retail stores to the pharmacy leader.

HISTORY

Wholesale grocer Alex Grass founded Rack Rite Distributors in Harrisburg Pennsylvania in 1958 to provide health and beauty aids and other sundries to grocery stores. He offered the same products at his first discount drugstore Thrif D Discount Center opened in 1962 in Scranton Pennsylvania. Four years later the company began placing pharmacies in its 36 stores. Rite Aid went public and adopted its current name in 1968 and the next year it made the first of many diverse acquisitions: Daw Drug Blue Ridge Nursing Homes and plasma suppliers Immuno Serums and Sero Genics.

Purchases in the 1970s included Sera-Tec Biologicals of New Jersey (blood plasma) and nearly 300 stores. By 1981 Rite Aid was the #3 drugstore chain and sales exceeded $1 billion. In 1984 it bought the American Discount Auto Parts chain and Encore Books discount chain and spun off its wholesale grocery operation in 1984 as Super Rite retaining a 47% stake (sold 1989).

Acquisitions added almost 900 stores during the 1980s. Expansion costs eroded Rite Aid's profit margins and the company focused on integrating its buys in 1990.

As part of a major restructuring in 1994 the company began selling its non-drugstore assets. Also in 1994 Rite Aid acquired Pharmacy Card and Intell-Rx and merged the two to form Eagle Managed Care.

Martin Grass took Rite Aid's reins from his dad in 1995. That year the company agreed to buy Revco at the time the #2 drugstore operator but the deal was derailed by FTC and Department of Justice objections in 1996. Rite Aid bounced back and acquired Thrifty PayLess (with more than 1000 stores) for about $2.3 billion in 1996. The deal gave the company more than 3600 stores and a presence in the western US. Also in 1996 Rite Aid exited several markets. In 1998 it closed many smaller stores and bought PCS Health Systems (the #1 US pharmacy benefits manager) from drug maker Eli Lilly and merged its Eagle Managed Care division into PCS.

In 1999 after a Wall Street Journal investigation Rite Aid revealed that Martin Grass Alex Grass and other family members held stakes in several suppliers and real estate interests doing business with the company. That year Rite Aid partnered with General Nutrition Companies Inc. (GNC) and took a 25% stake in the Internet retailer drugstore.com. Later in 1999 Rite Aid began slashing its $5.1 billion debt by cutting corporate staff and selling off some stores in California and the Pacific Northwest. CEO Martin Grass resigned and a team of former Fred Meyer officers — led by Robert Miller — took over.

In 2000 the company secured $1 billion from Citibank to reduce debt and provide capital. In July 2000 the company announced it would restate profits that over the past two years had been inflated in excess of $1 billion. Later that year Rite Aid sold PCS Health Systems to pharmacy benefits manager Advance Paradigm for more than $1 billion (about $500 million less than what Rite Aid originally paid for it). Rite Aid announced plans in 2001 to expand GNC concessions to additional stores.

To raise cash Rite Aid sold large blocks of its drugstore.com stock trimming its original 25% stake to less than 10% by April 2002. Former chairman and CEO Martin Grass former general counsel and vice chairman Franklin Brown and former CFO Frank Bergonzi among others were indicted in June 2002 for allegedly falsifying Rite Aid's books.

In April 2003 former chairman and CEO Martin Grass agreed to pay nearly $1.5 million to settle a lawsuit in which shareholders alleged that Rite Aid's books were falsified inflating the stock's value. In June Grass and former CFO Franklyn Bergonzi both pleaded guilty to conspiracy to defraud shareholders. Eric Sorkin Rite Aid's former VP of pharmacy services pleaded guilty to conspiring to obstruct justice. The following month Rite Aid began mailing checks totaling nearly $140 million to thousands of its current and former shareholders damaged by the accounting scandal at the company. In October former chief counsel Franklin Brown was convicted of conspiracy and lying to the Securities and Exchange Commission among other charges.

Despite its high debt load Rite Aid reportedly made a $4 billion cash-and-stock offer for struggling rival Eckerd but lost out to CVS and Canada's Jean Coutu Group who divvied up Eckerd in mid-2004.

In May 2004 Grass whose father founded Rite Aid struck a plea deal with prosecutors under which he was sentenced to eight years in prison. Also in May several other former company executives including Sorkin and ex-CFO Frank Bergonzi were sentenced in the accounting scandal. In June Rite Aid agreed to pay the US government $5.6 million (plus another $1.4 million to more than 20 states) to settle a federal lawsuit alleging the drugstore chain submitted false prescription claims to government insurance programs. In October former vice chairman Brown was sentenced to 10 years in prison the longest sentence of six Rite Aid officials charged in the accounting scandal.

CFO John Standley resigned in 2005 to join supermarket operator Pathmark Stores as its CEO. Standley joined Rite Aid as its CFO in 1999.

In April 2007 the company agreed to a store swap with California-based Longs Drug Stores. Under the terms of the agreement Rite Aid acquired six Longs stores in Northern California Oregon and Washington in exchange for giving Longs six of its stores in Nevada.

In its first major deal since its brush with bankruptcy in 1999 Rite Aid acquired more than 1850 Brooks and Eckerd drugstores and six distribution centers from Canada's Jean Coutu Group in a cash-and-stock deal valued at about $4 billion in June 2007.

Rite Aid exited the Las Vegas market in 2008 saying it was not a core market and had not contributed to overall results. It sold 27 of its Las Vegas stores to Walgreens. It March 2009 Rite Aid made a similar disposal of all seven of its stores in San Francisco and five locations in eastern Idaho when it sold them to Walgreen. Rite Aid said the stores were in areas with too light a store presence to operate efficiently. In July Rite Aid agreed to pay $500000 in consumer refunds to settle charges by the FTC that the company falsely advertised its Germ Defense line of cold-and-flu remedies as preventing illness or reducing the severity and duration of symptoms. The FTC said Rite Aid did not have evidence to support its Germ Defense product claims. Rite Aid founder Alex Grass died in August 2009 at the age of 82.

President and CEO John Standley added the title of chairman in mid-2012.

EXECUTIVES

Chairman and CEO, John T. Standley, age 54, $1,184,500 total compensation
SVP NY Metro Division, Mark Kramer, age 67
SEVP CFO and Chief Administrative Officer, Darren W. Karst, age 57, $809,751 total compensation
EVP Merchandising and Distribution, Enio A. (Tony) Montini, age 65, $471,500 total compensation
President and COO, Kermit R. Crawford, age 58
COO Rite Aid Stores, Bryan Everett, age 44, $461,250 total compensation
EVP Marketing, David Abelman, age 58
SVP Mid-Atlantic Division, Scott Bernard
SVP Western Division, Bill Romine
SVP Northeast Division, Derek Griffith
SVP and CIO, Steve Rempel
EVP Pharmacy, Jocelyn Konrad, age 47
SVP Southern Division, Bill Jackson
SVP General Counsel and Secretary, Jim Comitale
SVP and Chief Human Resources Officer, Ken Black
Pharmacy Manager, John Stanbrough
Rph, Rajesh Kumar
Pharmacy Manager, Shannon Casta
Pharmacy Manager, Malou Solomon
Pharmacy Manager, Sherri Wiswell
Pharmacy Manager, Kari McCabe
Pharmacy Manager, Ngozi Onumonu
Regional Vice President, Sri Pinninti
Regional Vice President Rx, Jenny Bui
Vice President of Operations, Scott Jacobson
Vice President Information Technology Applications Delivery Services, Sarah Taylor

Pharmacy Manager, Wael Wassef
Pharmacy Manager, Wafik Bichay
Director of Pharmacy Acquisitions, Todd Rossi
Regional Vice President, Dave Ricketts
Pharmacy Manager, Fiona Richardson
Vice President Pharmacy Operations, Dennis Yoney
Pharmacy Manager, Maged Salama
Group Vice President Loss Prevention, Bob Oberosler
Pharmacy Manager, Donald Brensinger
Pharmacy Manager, Robert West
Pharmacy Manager, Melanie C Weitz
RPH, Fady Soliman
Pharmacy Manager, Brett Sherwood
Pharmacy Manager, Diane Brown
Pharmacy Manager, Paula Ogilvie
Regional Vice President Administration, Nancy Wight-Tally
Pharmacy Manager, Joshua Maher
Regional Vice President, Kirt Patel
Secretary And Clerk, Cindy Kelley
Auditors: DELOITTE & TOUCHE LLP

LOCATIONS

HQ: Rite Aid Corp
30 Hunter Lane, Camp Hill, PA 17011
Phone: 717 761-2633   **Fax:** 717 975-5905
Web: www.riteaid.com

2016 Stores

	No.
New York	604
California	580
Pennsylvania	537
Michigan	275
New Jersey	257
North Carolina	225
Ohio	224
Virginia	190
Georgia	179
Massachusetts	146
Maryland	140
Washington	139
Kentucky	116
West Virginia	104
Alabama	93
South Carolina	91
Tennessee	81
Maine	79
Connecticut	77
Oregon	72
New Hampshire	68
Louisiana	62
Rhode Island	44
Delaware	42
Vermont	37
Mississippi	26
Utah	22
Colorado	20
Idaho	13
Indiana	10
District of Columbia	7
Nevada	1
Total	**4,561**

PRODUCTS/OPERATIONS

2016 Sales

	$ mil.	% of total
Retail Pharmacy	26,865	88
Pharmacy Services	4,103	12
Inter-segment elimination	(232.8)	-
Total	**30,736**	**100**

2016 Sales

	% of total
Prescription drugs	69
General merchandise & other	16
Over-the-counter medications & personal care	10
Health & beauty aids	5
Total	**100**

Selected Merchandise and Services

Beverages
Convenience foods

Cosmetics
Designer fragrances
Greeting cards
Health and personal care products
Household items
Over-the-counter drugs
Photo processing
Prescription drugs
Private-label products
Seasonal merchandise
Vitamins and minerals

COMPETITORS

A&P	Kroger
BJ's Wholesale Club	Marc Glassman
CVS	Medicine Shoppe
Costco Wholesale	Publix
Dollar General	Safeway
Family Dollar Stores	Target Corporation
Kinney Drugs Inc.	Wal-Mart
Kmart	Walgreens

HISTORICAL FINANCIALS

Company Type: Public

Income Statement

FYE: March 4

	REVENUE ($ mil.)	NET INCOME ($ mil.)	NET PROFIT MARGIN	EMPLOYEES
03/17*	32,845	4	0.0%	87,000
02/16	30,736	165	0.5%	88,000
02/15	26,528	2,109	8.0%	89,000
03/14	25,526	249	1.0%	89,000
03/13	25,392	118	0.5%	89,000
Annual Growth	**6.6%**	**(57.0%)**	**—**	**(0.6%)**

*Fiscal year change

2017 Year-End Financials

Debt ratio: 63.21%
Return on equity: 0.67%
Cash ($ mil.): 245
Current ratio: 1.69
Long-term debt ($ mil.): 7,307

No. of shares (mil.): 1,053
Dividends
  Yield: —
  Payout: —
Market value ($ mil.): 5,743

	STOCK PRICE ($) FY Close	P/E High/Low	PER SHARE ($) Earnings	Dividends	Book Value
03/17*	5.45	— —	(0.00)	0.00	0.58
02/16	7.96	58 38	0.16	0.00	0.55
02/15	7.98	4 2	2.08	0.00	0.06
03/14	6.59	29 7	0.23	0.00	(2.18)
03/13	1.68	17 8	0.12	0.00	(2.72)
Annual Growth	**34.2%**	**— —**	**—**	**—**	**—**

*Fiscal year change

RiverSource Life Insurance Co

EXECUTIVES

Executive Vice President, Brian J McGrane
Chb-pres, John R Worner
RVP Insurance, Michele Turner
Senior Regional Vice President, Matthew D Hartigan
Executive Vice President Human Resources, Kelli Hunter
Auditors: PricewaterhouseCoopers LLP

LOCATIONS

HQ: RiverSource Life Insurance Co
1099 Ameriprise Financial Center, Minneapolis, MN
55474
Phone: 612 671-3131

HISTORICAL FINANCIALS

Company Type: Public

Income Statement

FYE: December 31

	ASSETS ($ mil.)	NET INCOME ($ mil.)	INCOME AS % OF ASSETS	EMPLOYEES
12/16	114,053	686	0.6%	—
12/15	113,356	895	0.8%	—
12/14	118,136	965	0.8%	—
12/13	117,004	842	0.7%	—
12/12	109,748	650	0.6%	—
Annual Growth	1.0%	1.4%	—	—

2016 Year-End Financials

Debt ratio: —
Return on equity: 17.42%
Cash ($ mil.): 323
Current ratio: —
Long-term debt ($ mil.): —

No. of shares (mil.): 0
Dividends
　Yield: —
　Payout: 145.7%
Market value ($ mil.): —

RLI Corp.

You might wonder what folks in Illinois know about earthquake insurance but as a specialty property/casualty insurer Peoria-based RLI knows how to write such policies. Through its subsidiaries the company mainly offers coverage for US niche markets — risks that are hard to place in the standard market and are otherwise underserved. It focuses on public and private companies as well as non-profit organizations. RLI's commercial property/casualty lines include products liability property damage marine cargo directors and officers liability medical malpractice and general liability. It also writes commercial surety bonds and a smattering of specialty personal insurance.

Operations

RLI's specialty commercial property/casualty operations are conducted through its RLI Insurance Mt. Hawley Insurance Contractors Bonding and Insurance Company and RLI Indemnity subsidiaries. Personal offerings account for small portion of RLI's revenues and include homeowners insurance in Hawaii home business coverage pet insurance and personal umbrella (supplemental property/casualty) policies.

Geographic Reach

While the company operates in all 50 US states the District of Columbia and Puerto Rico California is RLI's largest market accounting for about 20% of the company's premiums.

Sales and Marketing

RLI markets its products to brokers and independent agents through branch offices scattered across the US.

Financial Performance

Like many insurers RLI's finances took a negative hit from the economic turmoil of 2008 and 2009. The company improved its returns as of 2010 and hasn't looked back. In 2013 it reported a 7% increase in revenue from $661 million to $706 million due to increased net premiums especially in the casualty segment. New products also made strong contributions. Net income grew 33% from $103 million to $126 million on increased revenue and decline in losses. Cash from opera-

tions a category that has fluctuated for RLI improved by $99 million due to investments.

Strategy

The company has gradually expanded its range of products with an emphasis on property insurance. In 2012 RLI entered the recreational vehicle (RV) insurance market by forming an underwriting partnership with Recreation Insurance Specialists. In 2013 it saw growth in its casualty business in transportation professional liability umbrella and admitted package businesses.

Mergers and Acquisitions

In 2014 the company purchased 20% of Prime Holdings Insurance Services for $5.3 million. The Utah-based company sells excess and surplus lines insurance in 49 states through a network of brokers; it specializes in hard-to-place risks (underwater hotels English Channel swims bungee jumps from helicopters).

In 2012 RLI moved into the field of medical malpractice coverage through the acquisition of Rockbridge Underwriting Agency. Two years later it launched RLI Healthcare a healthcare liability division serving hospital systems long-term and outpatient care facilities and clinical research providers with surplus lines in all 50 states.

Company Background

Gerald Stephens founded the company in 1961 and served as its chairman from 2001 until his retirement in 2011.

EXECUTIVES

Assistant Vice President Ets Entrprise Technical Support, Bill Pearce
Chairman and CEO, Jonathan E. Michael, age 63, $775,000 total compensation
President and COO, Craig W. Kliethermes, age 52, $473,269 total compensation
VP and Chief Investment Officer, Aaron P. Diefenthaler, age 43
SVP and CFO, Thomas L. Brown, age 60, $417,308 total compensation
President RLI Transportation Division, Dan Meyer
SVP Operations RLI Product Divisions, Jennifer L. Klobnak, age 45, $298,462 total compensation
Vice President Information Technology, Murali Natarajan
Vice President, Chad Berberich
Assistant Vice President Specialty Markets, Paul V Harris
Assistant Vice President, Carol Rawls Smith
Assistant Vice President, Betsy McLaughlin
Assistant Vice President fidelity Group, Thomas Huber
Vice President, Marty Marion
Assistant Vice President Communications, Lisa Gates
Vice President Risk Services, Chris Randall
Vice President, Bart Davis
Assistant Vice President, Terry Driggs
Assistant Vice President Executive Products Group, Kerrick Porter
Vice President Human Resources, Jeffrey Fick
Vice President Operations, Richard W Quehl
Assistant Vice President Commercial Surety, Bob Kirk
Vice President, Donald Driscoll
Assistant Vice President Risk Services, Tim Obryan
Assistant Vice President Claims, Ted McGrath
Vice President General Counsel, Mary Beth Nebel
Auditors: KPMG LLP

LOCATIONS

HQ: RLI Corp.
9025 North Lindbergh Drive, Peoria, IL 61615
Phone: 309 692-1000　Fax: 309 692-1068
Web: www.rlicorp.com

PRODUCTS/OPERATIONS

2016 Revenues

	$ mil.	% of total
Net premiums earned		
Casualty	454	56
Property	152	19
Surety	121	15
Net investment income	53	6
Net realized gains	34	4
Total	816	100

Selected Products

Commercial
　Casualty
　Contractors bonding and insurance
　Executive products liability
　Marine
　Professional services
　Property
　Reinsurance
　Specialty programs
　Transportation
Personal
　Homeowners (Hawaii)
　Home business owners
　Personal umbrella
Surety Bonds

COMPETITORS

Arch Insurance Group
Baldwin & Lyons
CNA Financial
Chubb Limited
Crum & Forster
Great American Insurance Company
Great West Casualty
HCC Insurance
James River Group
Lancer Insurance
Lexington Insurance
Markel
Meadowbrook Insurance
Navigators
Philadelphia Insurance Companies
Safeco
Sompo International
The Hartford
Travelers Companies
United States Liability Insurance Group

HISTORICAL FINANCIALS

Company Type: Public

Income Statement

FYE: December 31

	ASSETS ($ mil.)	NET INCOME ($ mil.)	INCOME AS % OF ASSETS	EMPLOYEES
12/16	2,777	114	4.1%	943
12/15	2,736	137	5.0%	902
12/14	2,775	135	4.9%	882
12/13	2,740	126	4.6%	870
12/12	2,644	103	3.9%	897
Annual Growth	1.2%	2.7%	—	1.3%

2016 Year-End Financials

Debt ratio: 5.35%
Return on equity: 13.92%
Cash ($ mil.): 18
Current ratio: —
Long-term debt ($ mil.): —

No. of shares (mil.): 43
Dividends
　Yield: 0.0%
　Payout: 107.7%
Market value ($ mil.): 2,774

	STOCK PRICE ($) FY Close	P/E High/Low		PER SHARE ($) Earnings	Dividends	Book Value
12/16	63.13	27	21	2.59	2.79	18.74
12/15	61.75	20	15	3.12	2.75	18.91
12/14	49.40	31	13	3.09	3.71	19.61
12/13	97.38	35	22	2.90	4.34	19.29
12/12	64.66	31	13	2.40	6.26	18.73
Annual Growth	(0.6%)	—	—	2.0%	(18.3%)	0.0%

ROBERT BOSCH LLC

Robert Bosch LLC is your one-stop shop for German-engineered auto parts appliances and power tools. The North American subsidiary of German giant Robert Bosch GmbH Bosch LLC divides its operations among three divisions. Automotive Technology produces gasoline/diesel systems (and electrical drives); chassis and steering systems; and auto electronics for OEMs and the aftermarket. The Consumer Goods and Building Technology division builds various power tools security systems home appliances and HVAC equipment. Automation drive controls solar/wind power and packaging systems are the focus of its Industrial Technology division. Operating since 1906 Bosch LLC has grown to more than 100 North American locations.

Operations

The Automotive Technology business segment is Bosch LLC's largest generating about 65% of annual revenues. With the rebound of the automotive industry in 2010 — vehicle production increased almost 40% — the company's Automotive Technology unit realized a 13% increase in sales over 2010. The improvement was attributed to a better economy but also to the increased demand for the company's advanced vehicle technology offerings that are touted as safer cleaner and more economical.

The company's Consumer Goods and Building Technology division — portable power tools security systems thermotechnology and home appliances units — generated 20% of its total sales for 2011. This division also has expertise in making home appliances such as refrigerators and freezers washers and dryers dishwashers and ovens and cooktops.

Bosch LLC's Industrial Technology division generated 15% of total sales in 2011. Along with an aptitude in factory automation and engineering this segment is on an accelerated path to discovering newer better sources and uses of renewable energy. Subsidiaries Bosch Rexroth and Bosch Solar Energy are in the business of manufacturing wind turbine gearboxes hydraulics-based solar tracking systems solar cell making equipment and other photovoltaic (PV) products. Also part of Industrial Technology is the Bosch Packaging Technology unit that designs and makes packaging machinery and aftermarket parts as well as provides service.

Strategy

The Bosch Automotive Aftermarket division in 2011 acquired Taiwan-based UniPoint Group one of the world's largest manufacturers of starters alternators temperature control units and wiper blades. Unipoint manufactures products in Asia which is distributed throughout North America South America and Europe. The dell augmented Bosch's position as the leading supplier of starters and alternators and added another Asian production facility to its wiper blade business unit.

EXECUTIVES

President Bosch Security Systems, Christopher P. Gerace

CFO; EVP Controlling Finance and Administration, Maximiliane Straub

Regional President Bosch Rexroth Americas, Berend Bracht

Regional President Gasoline Systems, Sujit Jain

Regional President Chassis Systems Control, D. Scott Winchip

Regional President Car Multimedia North America, Juergen Peters

EVP Original Equipment Sales Ford, Manfred Mueller, age 61

President and CEO BSH Home Appliances, Michael Traub

Regional President Automotive Electronics North America, Timothy (Tim) Frasier

Regional President Diesel Systems North America, Bernd Boisten

President, Mike Mansuetti

Regional President Robert Bosch Automotive Aftermarket Division, Odd Joergenrud

EVP Original Equipment Sales General Motors, Clesio Honma

Regional President Electrical Drives, Peter Denk

Regional President Starter Motors and Generators North America, Pres Lawhon

Regional President Bosch Engineering Group North America, Wayne (Keith) Andrews

President Robert Bosch Healthcare Systems Inc., Micha Kirchhoff

VP Original Equipment Sales Chrysler, Paul Thomas

Vice President and Deputy General Counsel, Jerry L Johnson

Vice President Business Development, Michael Barhaug

President And Executive Vice President Automotive Aftermarket, David Coolidge

Vice President, Tim Williams

Vice President, Christine Zimmerman

Vice President Finance, Nancy Gustitus

Chairman, Werner Struth

LOCATIONS

HQ: ROBERT BOSCH LLC
2800 S 25TH AVE, BROADVIEW, IL 601554532
Phone: 248 876-1000
Web: WWW.BOSCHTECHINFO.COM

PRODUCTS/OPERATIONS

2011 Sales

	$ mil.	% of total
Automotive Technology	6	65
Consumer Goods & Building Technology	2	20
Industrial Technology	1	15
Total	**9**	**100**

Selected Products

Automotive Technology
  Aftermarket
  Alternators
  Brake pads
  Car audio products
  Diesel parts
  Filters
  Fuel pumps
  Ignition products
  Oxygen sensors
  Spark plugs
  Spark plug wire sets
  Starters
  Wiper blades
  Original equipment
  Actuators
  Braking and chassis systems
  Car multimedia
  Electrical systems
  Electronic systems
  Powertrain systems - diesel
  Powertrain systems - gasoline
Consumer Goods and Building Technology
  Household appliances
  Cooktops
  Dishwashers
  Ovens
  Washers and dryers
  Power tools
  Angle grinders
  Belt sanders
  Circular saws

Drill bits
Drills
Drywall drivers
Impact wrenches
Jigsaws
Orbit sanders/polishers
Planers
Reciprocating saws
Rotary hammers
Routers
Screwdriver bits and accessories
Wet/dry vacuums
Security Systems
  Access control
  Communications
  Fire detection
  Security management
  Video surveillance
  Thermotechnology
  Indoor climate control (heating and cooling and hot water production)
Industrial Technology
  Drive and control
  Assembly
  Electric drives and controls
  Gears
  Hydraulics
  Linear motion
  Pneumatics
  Packaging
  Confectionary cosmetics and chemicals
  Packaging machines
  Packaging services
  Pharmaceuticals
  Production tools
  Air assembly tools
  Cordless assembly tools
  DC electric assembly tools
  Electric assembly tools
  Solar Energy
  Crystalline PV modules
  Solar cells
  Thin-film modules
  Wafers

COMPETITORS

AISIN World Corp.	LG Electronics
Advanced Security & Controls	Makita
	Molins
DENSO America	Motorcar Parts
Dana	NGK Spark Plugs
Delphi Automotive Systems	Neaton Auto Products
	Stanley Black and Decker
GE	Visteon
Hitachi Automotive Systems Americas	Whirlpool

HISTORICAL FINANCIALS

Company Type: Private

Income Statement

FYE: December 31

	REVENUE ($ mil.)	NET INCOME ($ mil.)	NET PROFIT MARGIN	EMPLOYEES
12/15	10,868	457	4.2%	12,986
12/14	10,474	181	1.7%	—
12/10	6,810	326	4.8%	—
12/09	5,464	59	1.1%	—
Annual Growth	**12.1%**	**40.7%**	**—**	**—**

2015 Year-End Financials

Debt ratio: ——
Return on equity: 4.20%
Cash ($ mil.): 760
Current ratio: 1.10
Long-term debt ($ mil.): ——

Dividends
  Yield: —
  Payout: —
Market value ($ mil.): ——

Robert Half International Inc.

Robert Half International carries the full load of personnel services. The company places temporary and permanent staff through eight divisions: Accountemps Robert Half Finance and Accounting Robert Half Legal OfficeTeam (general administrative) Robert Half Technology (information technology) Robert Half Management Resources (senior level professionals) and The Creative Group (advertising marketing and Web design). The firm also publishes job reports and surveys on the latest employment trends and annual salary guides to track pay trends and has an internal audit and risk consulting division in Protiviti.

Operations

Robert Half operates in three business segments: temporary and consultant staffing permanent placement staffing and risk consulting and internal audit services. Temporary and consulting accounts for the largest portion of business (more than 75% of sales in fiscal 2016).

Geographic Reach

Robert Half's temporary and permanent staffing services business has some 320 offices in more than 40 states Washington DC and 17 foreign countries. Protiviti has more than 55 offices in 20 states and 10 foreign countries. The firm's domestic segment accounts for about 80% of total sales.

Sales and Marketing

Robert Half recruits via direct marketing and print radio and Internet advertising. Robert Half also has joint marketing agreements with many tech-related companies to coordinate joint mailings cooperative advertising and other promotions. The firm spent around $47 million in fiscal 2016 on advertising.

Financial Performance

Robert Half has achieved significant growth over the years with revenues consistently climbing year-over-year.

Revenue went from $5 billion in fiscal 2015 up to $5.25 billion in fiscal 2016. All three of the firm's reportable segments experienced revenue growth led by Protiviti which increased 9% in 2016 compared to 2015.

However Robert Half's net income dipped slightly in fiscal 2016 compared to the prior fiscal period. The firm claimed a net income of $343 million in fiscal 2016 after reporting net income of $357 million in fiscal 2015.

Cash flow has remained stable and has mirrored the firm's growth in revenue during recent fiscal years. Cash provided by operating activities less cash used for investing activities in fiscal 2016 was $330 million up slightly from $320 million a year earlier.

Strategy

Robert Half prefers to grow organically rather than by making material acquisitions. The majority of Robert Half's capital spending in fiscal 2016 was for technological infrastructure and software. The firm continued installation of its updated cloud-based customer relationship management (CRM) platform. It expects to complete the installation of the platform during 2017 after which capital spending should slow down. Robert Half has also been installing a new client accounting system for Protiviti. The firm still plans to direct much of its capital outlay to creating and strengthening its technology.

The company's clients are predominantly small and midsize businesses but Robert Half sees an opportunity to grow by serving larger accounts.

HISTORY

Robert Half founded Robert Half Inc. in 1948 as an employment agency for accountants. He developed Accountemps on the side to supply firms with accountants and other finance professionals on a temporary basis. His concept was a hit and Half became known as a pioneer in the specialized employment services industry. He started franchising his business nationwide. The temp industry grew slowly in the 1960s and 1970s until the 1980s brought a rapid expansion. By 1985 there were 150 independent Accountemps and Robert Half franchises.

Harold "Max" Messmer joined the company in 1985 for what would prove to be a tumultuous first couple of years. In 1986 Boothe Financial Corporation bought all of Robert Half's outstanding stock and Messmer launched a program to buy all the Robert Half franchises. A year later Boothe sold Robert Half which then went public as Robert Half International placing Messmer at the helm as CEO and president.

EXECUTIVES

EVP Corporate Development, Robert W. Glass, age 58, $245,000 total compensation
Vice Chairman President and CFO, M. Keith Waddell, age 60, $265,000 total compensation
Chairman and CEO, Harold M. Messmer, age 71, $525,000 total compensation
President and COO Staffing Services, Paul F. Gentzkow, age 61, $265,000 total compensation
EVP Chief Administration Officer and Treasurer, Michael R. Buckley, age 51, $265,000 total compensation
SVP and CIO, Sean Perry
Senior Regional Vice President, Phil Willingham
Assistant Vice President, Rachel Van Fossen
Vice President Division Director, Tony Hablian
Vice President Director of Permanent Placement Services, James Setteducato
Auditors: PricewaterhouseCoopers LLP

LOCATIONS

HQ: Robert Half International Inc.
2884 Sand Hill Road, Suite 200, Menlo Park, CA 94025
Phone: 650 234-6000
Web: www.rhi.com

2016 sales

	$ mil.	% of total
Domestic	4,220	80
Foreign	1,029	20
Total	**5,250**	**100**

PRODUCTS/OPERATIONS

2016 sales

	$ mil.	% of total
Temporary & consultant staffing	4,026	77
Risk consulting & internal audit services	804	8
Permanent placement staffing	419	15
Total	**5,250**	**100**

Selected Operating Units

Accountemps (temporary accounting and finance personnel)
The Creative Group (advertising marketing and Web design)
OfficeTeam (temporary administrative and office personnel)
Protiviti (internal audit and risk consulting)
Robert Half Finance and Accounting (temporary accounting and finance personnel)
Robert Half Legal (temporary and full-time legal support personnel)
Robert Half Management Resources (senior-level accounting and finance personnel)
Robert Half Technology (temporary and contract IT personnel)

COMPETITORS

Adecco	Kelly Services
Deloitte Consulting	Kforce
Ernst & Young Global	ManpowerGroup
General Employment	PricewaterhouseCoopers
Enterprises	Randstad Holding
Headway Corporate	Solomon Page
Resources	Winston Resources
KPMG	

HISTORICAL FINANCIALS

Company Type: Public

Income Statement

FYE: December 31

	REVENUE ($ mil.)	NET INCOME ($ mil.)	NET PROFIT MARGIN	EMPLOYEES
12/16	5,250	343	6.5%	231,400
12/15	5,094	357	7.0%	236,000
12/14	4,695	305	6.5%	225,000
12/13	4,245	252	5.9%	210,000
12/12	4,111	209	5.1%	203,000
Annual Growth	**6.3%**	**13.1%**	**—**	**3.3%**

2016 Year-End Financials

Debt ratio: 0.06%
Return on equity: 32.76%
Cash ($ mil.): 260
Current ratio: 1.89
Long-term debt ($ mil.): 0
No. of shares (mil.): 127
Dividends
  Yield: 0.0%
  Payout: 32.9%
Market value ($ mil.): 6,234

	STOCK PRICE ($) FY Close	P/E High/Low	PER SHARE ($) Earnings	Dividends	Book Value
12/16	48.78	18 13	2.67	0.88	8.50
12/15	47.14	23 17	2.69	0.80	7.65
12/14	58.38	26 17	2.26	0.72	7.25
12/13	41.99	23 17	1.83	0.64	6.69
12/12	31.82	21 17	1.50	0.60	6.04
Annual Growth	**11.3%**	**— —**	**15.5%**	**10.0%**	**8.9%**

ROBERT W. BAIRD & CO. INCORPORATED

Employee-owned Robert W. Baird & Co. bringsÂ midwestern sensibility to the high-flying world of investment banking. The company offers brokerage asset management and investment banking services to middle-market corporations institutional clients and wealthy individuals and families.Â Its investment banking activities include underwriting and distributing corporate securities mergers and acquisition advisory and institutional sales and trading. The company also conducts equity research on more than 600 US firms.Â Baird manages more than $97 billion in client assets.

Operations

The companyÂ manages aboutÂ 10 bond and equity mutual funds: Baird Advisors manages fixed income investments while Baird Investment Management handles the equities side. Baird also invests in private equity and venture capital.

Geographic Reach

The firm has more than 100Â officesÂ in North America Asia and Europe where it ownsÂ 48% of Baird UK. More than half of Baird's locations areÂ wealth management offices in the US.

Sales and Marketing

Baird is the marketing name for Robert W. Baird & Co. Incorporated and its subsidiaries and affiliates worldwide.

Financial Performance

The company's revenues increased by 9% in 2011 and net incomeÂ grew by 2%.

Strategy

The driving forces for the company's growth have been its wealth management and investment banking operations. Unlike many financial services firms Baird has been adding staff and opening new offices in the US.

The company has also turned to the East for its fortunes. Its private equity group recently has an office in Shanghai hoping to capitalize on China's increasingly business-friendly environment.Â The outpost focuses on small high-growth businesses that have been overlooked by other venture capitalists.Â Baird hasÂ also expanded its investment banking operations in the region.

In 2012 Baird formed a strategic alliance with Axis Capital the investment banking subsidiary of Axis Bank with an initial focus on cross-border mergers and acquisitions between India and Europe and India and the US.

Company Background

Founded in 1919 Baird had been majority-owned by Northwestern Mutual since 1982. However employees bought back the company's stock in a series of purchases that culminated in 2004.

EXECUTIVES

COO, Russell P. (Russ) Schwei
Chief Investment Officer, Mary Ellen Stanek
CFO, Terrance P. (Terry) Maxwell
President Private Wealth Management, Michael J. (Mike) Schroeder
Director Fixed Income Capital Markets, Patrick S. (Pat) Lawton, age 60
Chairman Equity Capital Markets, William W. (Bill) Mahler
Co-Head Global Investment Banking, Brian S. Doyal
President and COO, Steven G. (Steve) Booth
Co-Head Global Investment Banking, Brian McDonagh
Director Risk Management, Mark A. Roble
Managing Partner Baird Capital, Gordon G. Pan
Head Global Equities and Director Equity Research, Jon A. Langenfeld
CIO, Timothy (Tim) Byrne
Vice President Vice President Administration, Thomas Swift
Senior Vice President Senior Portfolio Manager, Jay Schwister
Vice President, Mark Zalewski
Vice President Vice President Administration, Thomas Seidcheck
Senior Vice President, Randall North
Vice President, Tyler Pace
Senior Vice President and Senior Investment Consultant, Terry Monroe
Senior Vice President, Steve Satchell
Vice President, John B Lipe
Vice President Associate Investment Strategist, William Delwiche
Vice President, Joseph G Verdi
Assistant Vice President Facilities, Marty Young
Vice President, Terry Sommerdyke
Senior Vice President, Dustin Hutter
Senior Vice President, Drew Perryman
Senior Vice President Branch Manager, Karen Heintz
Vice President, Michael Bellisario
Vice President Technology Product Manager, Lesley Augustine
Vice President, Tom Coburn
Senior Vice President of Wealth Management Office, Paul McWane

First Vice President Client Services, Richard Whittow
Assistant Vice President Corporate Recruiter Human Resources, Carla Nelson
Vice President Information Technology Architect, Jim Cornelius
VICE PRESIDENT, Charles Galarza
Vice President, Robert Ferriman
Senior Vice President, Peter Hammond
Vice President, Tim Duchow
Vice President, John W Diemer
First Vice President Investments, Owen Wrassman
Vice President, Juanita Nayeri
Senior Vice President Investments, Cory Davis
Senior Vice President, Jayson C Bales
Senior Vice President and Senior Portfolio Manager, Daniel Tranchita
Senior Vice President, Michael Chorley
Vice President, Janet Holsclaw
Vice President, Marla Regan
Vice President, Dalena Welkomer
Vice President, Trea Floyd
Vice President Financial, David Beck
Vice President, Adrianne Limjoco
Vice President, Randy Pfingsten
Vice President, Ryan Unthank
Vice President Public Finance, Dale Jacques
Vice President and Financial Advisor, Matthew Fields
Senior Vice President Of Investments, Randy Stary
Assistant Vice President, Delana Sass
Assistant Vice President Compliance Officer, Heidi M McLemore
Vice President, Denise Ingersoll
Vice President, Mike Monfeli
Vice President Financial Advisor, Dan Koth
Vice President, Doralyn Retzlaff
First Vice President, Jeff Prager
Assistant Vice President Assistant Manager Fee Based Account Administration, Kelly Witt
Senior Vice President, Shawn B Smith
Senior Vice President Public Relations, Angela Pittman Taylor
FVP, Clarence Draughon
ASSISTANT VICE PRESIDENT, Dominic Burrescia
Assistant Vice President And Pam Administrative Supervisor, Nona Hocking
Vice President, Abhishek Pulakanti
Vice President, Kurt Myszewski
Senior Vice President, Douglas Stencel
First Vice President Tech and Systems, Dennis Weishan
Vice President Financial Advisor, Jeff Pedersen
First Vice President, Guy Sawyer
Vice President and Art Director, Virginia Sunu
Vice President Platform Manager, Casey Foltz
Vice President Institutional Equity Sales, Mike Malone
Vice President Wealth Management, Theresa Rynaski
Vice President Transition Process Manager, Denise Renner
Vice President Information Technology Project Services, Jim Whittet
Vice President Institutional Services, Ryan Conner
Senior Vice President, Chuck Cairns
Vice President, Frank Downey
Senior Vice President, Jack Robinson
Vice President Financial Advisor, Blaine Gibson
Assistant Vice President and Marketing Specialist, Karen Sweeney
Vice President, Mike Kopischkie
First Vice President, Bryan Fiene
Vice President, Mary E Levar
Private Equity Finance Manager Vice President, Erin Jelenchick
Senior Vice President, Rob Zwiebel
Vice President and Fixed Income Compliance Officer, Heather C Melzer
SENIOR VICE PRESIDENT, Howard Yasgur

Vice President, Jennifer Mitchell
Vice President Cash Management, Stephanie Raykuczynski
Senior Vice President Private Wealth Management, Bryan Sampson
Vice President Private Wealth Management, Joseph R Maye
Vice President, Jay Scheller
Assistant Vice President, Dan Myhre
Senior Vice President Internal Audit Director, David Cook
Vice President Investments, Thomas Olson
Senior Vice President, Alison Rowe
Vice President Investment Banking, Christopher Hildreth
Vice President, Alex Ballantine
Investment Banking Vice President (Industrial), Eric Stetler
Vice President Portfolio Analyst, Aaron Benson
Vice President Finance Systems Manager, Patricia Hoerig
Vice President and Project Services Manager, Talal Butt
Vice President, John P Campbell
Vice President, Thomas M Boh
Cima?? Senior Vice President Private Wealth Management, Matthew Schmitt
First Vice President, Terry Lineberger
Vice President and Financial Advisor, Jon Bolton
Senior Vice President, Rosa Ebling
Vice President, Rich Nigro
Senior Vice President Private Wealth Management, Conrad Zimmerman
Senior Vice President Investments, Ronald Christian
Vice President, Marcy Finley
Vice President, Patrick Montani
Senior Vice President, Mike Parrott
Senior Vice President, Kristin M Lindblom
Vice President Equity Research, Mircea Dobre
First Vice President Institutional Fixed Income Sales, Stephen Akos
Senior Vice President, David Schwarz
Vice President Senior Research Associate, Luke Junk
First Vice President, Randal Leonard
First Vice President Manager, Yolanda Carmona
Senior Vice President, Mark Falci
Vice President, Chase Hinderstein
Assistant Vice President, Kim Henke
First Vice President, James Derdzinski
Vice President, Jim Lothary
Vice President And Associate General Counsel, Matt Deering
Vice President, Brian Ellenbecker
Vice President Institutional Municipal Trading, Erik Irish
Assistant Vice President, Stacey Leigh
Vice President, Coley Hoffman
Assistant Vice President, Deanne Soetenga
Vice President, Sally Marrs
Vice President Private Wealth Management, Robert King
Vice President, Ryan Cox
Senior Vice President, Douglas Crandall
Senior Vice President, Timothy Butler
Vice President Senior Compliance Officer, Pat Nowak
Vice President, Randall McLaughlin
Vice President, Richard Roesch
Senior Vice President, Brian Penn
Senior Vice President, Orlando C Montesino

LOCATIONS

HQ: ROBERT W. BAIRD & CO. INCORPORATED
777 E WISCONSIN AVE FL 29, MILWAUKEE, WI 532025391
Phone: 414 765-3500
Web: WWW.RWBAIRD.COM

PRODUCTS/OPERATIONS

Business Groups
Asset Management
Equity Capital Markets
Fixed Income Capital Markets
Private Equity
Private Wealth Management

COMPETITORS

Citigroup Global   Piper Jaffray
  Markets   Raymond James
Cowen Group   Financial
Goldman Sachs   Stephens
Greenhill   Stifel Financial
Jefferies Group   Thomas Weisel Partners
Morgan Stanley   William Blair

HISTORICAL FINANCIALS
Company Type: Private

Income Statement

	ASSETS ($ mil.)	NET INCOME ($ mil.)	INCOME AS % OF ASSETS	EMPLOYEES
12/09	2,063	41	2.0%	3,238
12/08	1,080	36	3.4%	
Annual Growth	91.0%	14.5%	—	—

2009 Year-End Financials

Debt ratio: —
Return on equity: 6.00%   Dividends
Cash ($ mil.): 78   Yield: —
Current ratio: —   Payout: —
Long-term debt ($ mil.): —   Market value ($ mil.): —

Robinson (C.H.) Worldwide, Inc.

C.H. Robinson Worldwide (CHRW) keeps merchandise moving. A third-party logistics (3PL) provider the company arranges freight transportation using trucks trains ships and airplanes belonging to other companies. It contracts with more than 71000 carriers. CHRW handles about 18 million shipments per year for its 113000-plus customers that include companies in the food and beverage manufacturing and retail industries. Besides transportation the company also offers logistics for supply chain management services through some 280 offices. In addition CHRW buys sells and transports fresh produce throughout the US.

HISTORY

In the early 1900s Charles H. Robinson began a produce brokerage in Grand Forks North Dakota. Robinson entered a partnership in 1905 with Nash Brothers the leading wholesaler in North Dakota and the company C.H. Robinson was born. Robinson became president but soon relinquished control under mysterious circumstances (rumor had it he ran off with Annie Oakley). H. B. Finch took charge and by 1913 a new company Nash Finch became C.H. Robinson's sole owner.

As a subsidiary C.H. Robinson primarily procured produce for Nash Finch which helped it expand into Illinois Minnesota Texas and Wisconsin. To avoid FTC scrutiny over preferential treatment Nash Finch split CHR in two: C.H. Robinson Co. owned by C.H. Robinson employees which sold produce to Nash Finch warehouses; and C.H. Robinson Inc. owned by Nash Finch.

After WWII the interstate highway system and refrigerated trucks changed the industry. No longer dependent on railroads C.H. Robinson began charging for truck brokerage of perishables. The two companies formed by the 1940s split reunited under the C.H. Robinson name in the mid-1960s; Nash Finch kept a 25% stake in the company and sold the rest to employees. Not surprisingly Nash Finch wanted to divert C.H. Robinson profits to its other businesses so in 1976 C.H. Robinson employees bought out Nash Finch.

The next year D. R. "Sid" Verdoorn was named president and Looe Baker became chairman. They focused on increasing C.H. Robinson's data-processing capability and adding branch offices. In 1980 the Motor Carrier Act deregulated the transportation industry and C.H. Robinson entered the freight-contracting business acting as a middleman for all types of goods. The company grew rapidly from about 30 offices in 1980 to more than 60 in 1990.

As part of its overall effort to become a full-service provider C.H. Robinson formed its Intermodal Division (more than one mode of transport) in 1988. It also established an information services division (1991) and bought fruit juice concentrate distributor Daystar International (1993). By this time the company was working with more than 14000 shippers and moving more than 500000 shipments a year.

Meanwhile C.H. Robinson had ventured overseas with the launch of its international division in 1989. It entered Mexico in 1990 and added airfreight operations and international freight forwarding through the 1992 purchase of C.S. Green International. In 1993 C.H. Robinson picked up a 30% stake in French motor carrier Transeco (acquiring the rest later) and opened offices in Mexico Chile and Venezuela.

The company went public in 1997 and became C.H. Robinson Worldwide (CHRW). The next year Verdoorn who was CEO assumed the additional role of chairman. The following year the company acquired Argentina's Comexter transportation group to gain market share in South America and it expanded its European operation in 1999 through the purchase of Norminter a French third-party logistics provider. Much closer to home CHRW bought Eden Prairie-based Preferred Translocation Systems a logistics provider to LTL carriers and Chicago-based transportation provider American Backhaulers.

In 2000 CHRW partnered with PaperExchange.com Inc. the global e-business marketplace for the pulp and paper industry to provide an exclusive logistics service to PaperExchange.com members. CHRW continued to expand in 2002 with the purchase of Miami-based Smith Terminal Transportation Services. Verdoorn stepped down as CEO that year and company president John Wiehoff was promoted to replace him. Verdoorn retired at the end of 2006 and Wiehoff succeeded him as chairman.

The company acquired three US-based produce sourcing and marketing companies — FoodSource Inc. FoodSource Procurement and Epic Roots — in 2004 for a reported $270 million. That year CHRW added seven offices in China by acquiring a Dalian-based freight forwarder and in 2005 it gained operations in Germany Italy and the US by buying two freight forwarding companies Hirdes Group Worldwide and Bussini Transport. Also in 2005 CHRW bought US-based freight broker Payne Lynch & Associates as well as an India-based freight forwarder Triune. The following year (2006) the company acquired US-based LXSI Services a specialist in domestic airfreight and expedited ground transportation management that had gross revenue of about $25 million.

In mid-2008 CHRW acquired Transera International Holdings a project forwarding business based in Canada. Transera has office locations in Canada Dubai Singapore and the US and has annual revenues of about $125 million.

In 2009 the company purchased London-based Walker Logistics Overseas an international freight forwarder serving primarily the electronics telecommunications medical sporting goods and military industries. The acquisition expanded its capabilities in Asia-to-Europe trade and brought two key distribution gateways — London and Amsterdam. CHRW then expanded its produce distribution business even further in 2009 by opening a European-based produce sourcing company in France which will focus on bringing fresh produce from France Italy and Spain to North and South America Europe Asia and Middle Eastern countries. That same year CHRW acquired certain assets of International Trade & Commerce (ITC) a US customs brokerage company that specializes in warehousing distribution and services between the US and Mexico. Also in 2009 the company bought Rosemont Farms as well as Quality Logistics which provides logistics for produce transportation; both companies are based in Florida.

In 2010 CHRW expanded its transportation management services to India by building a new facility and control tower operations. The India-based facility was established to serve customers in South and Southeast Asia as well as in Pakistan and the Middle East.

CHRW divested its former payment services segment T-Chek (only 1% of total sales in 2012) in October 2012 to Electronic Funds Source LLC for $303 million in cash. The T-Chek unit provided such services as funds transfer and fuel purchasing management and CHRW made the deal to focus on its core transportation and logistics services.

In late 2012 CHRW acquired Phoenix International a provider of international ocean air and customs brokerage freight forwarding services. CHRW bought Phoenix for nearly $572 million in cash and roughly $63.5 million in newly-issued CHRW stock in a deal that sizably enhanced its international freight forwarding capabilities.

During that same time period CHRW swallowed up Apreo Logistics S.A. a freight forwarding firm based in Poland. The acquisition strengthened the company's toehold in Europe and further diversified its modal offering.

EXECUTIVES

CIO, Chad M. Lindbloom, age 53, $590,000 total compensation
Chairman President and CEO, John P. Wiehoff, age 55, $1,167,000 total compensation
CFO, Andrew C. Clarke, age 46, $525,000 total compensation
President Robinson Fresh, James P. (Jim) Lemke, age 50, $210,000 total compensation
Chief Commercial Officer, Christopher J. (Chris) O'Brien, age 49, $500,000 total compensation
President Asia, Andy Wang
VP Global Forwarding North America, Michael J. (Mike) Short, age 46, $500,000 total compensation
VP Management Services, Jordan T. Kass, age 44
President North American Surface Transportation, Robert C. Biesterfeld, age 41
President Europe, Jeroen Eijsink, age 44
VP Human Resources, Angela Freeman
Vice President, Scott Shannon
Vice President Transportation, Dan Ryan
National Account Manager, Zach DeLoache
National Sales Manager, Jason Williams
National Account Manager, Andy Hutson

National Account Manager, Jen Theisen
National Account Manager, Kayla Simons
National Accounts Manager, Jose Molina
Vice President Information Technology, Steve Enberg
National Account Manager, Matt Lapolice
Vice President, Pat Nolan
Executive Vice President Sales and Marketing, Alec Getschow
National Account Manager, Michelle Clayton
Vice President, Thomas Mahlke
Vice President Global Operations, Kevin Mitchell
Treasurer, Troy A Renner, age 52
Board Member, Kevin Grossi
Board Member, Brian Short
Board Member, James Stake
Auditors: Deloitte & Touche LLP

LOCATIONS

HQ: Robinson (C.H.) Worldwide, Inc.
14701 Charlson Road, Eden Prairie, MN 55347-5088
Phone: 952 937-8500   **Fax:** 952 937-6714
Web: www.chrobinson.com

2016 Sales

	$ mil.	% of total
United States	11,749	89
Other locations	1,394	11
Total	**13,144**	**100**

PRODUCTS/OPERATIONS

2016 Sales

	$ mil.	% of total
NAST	9,036	66
Global Forwarding	1,605	12
Robinson Fresh	2,463	18
All Other and Corporate	490	4
Eliminations	(450.4)	-
Total	**13,144**	**100**

2016 Sales

	$ mil.	% of total
Transportation	11,704	89
Sourcing	1,439	11
Total	**13,144**	**100**

Selected Services
Air
Intermodal
Less-than-truckload
Logistics
  Customs brokerage
  Transportation management services
  Warehousing services
Ocean
Truckload

COMPETITORS

ALC	Hub Group
APL Logistics	J.B. Hunt
BNSF Logistics	Kuehne + Nagel
CEVA Logistics	International
Cass Information	Landstar Inway
Systems	MIQ Logistics
Chiquita Brands	Panalpina
Comdata	Penske Truck Leasing
CorTrans Logistics	Ryder System
DHL	Schneider Logistics
Dole Food	TLC
Exel	Transplace
Expeditors	UPS Supply Chain
FedEx Trade Networks	Solutions
Fresh Del Monte	
Produce	

HISTORICAL FINANCIALS

Company Type: Public

Income Statement

FYE: December 31

	REVENUE ($ mil.)	NET INCOME ($ mil.)	NET PROFIT MARGIN	EMPLOYEES
12/16	13,144	513	3.9%	14,125
12/15	13,476	509	3.8%	13,159
12/14	13,470	449	3.3%	11,521
12/13	12,752	415	3.3%	11,676
12/12	11,359	593	5.2%	10,929
Annual Growth	**3.7%**	**(3.6%)**	**—**	**6.6%**

2016 Year-End Financials

Debt ratio: 33.62%
Return on equity: 42.52%
Cash ($ mil.): 247
Current ratio: 1.09
Long-term debt ($ mil.): 500
No. of shares (mil.): 141
Dividends
  Yield: 0.0%
  Payout: 48.4%
Market value ($ mil.): 10,349

	STOCK PRICE ($) FY Close	P/E High/Low	PER SHARE ($) Earnings	Dividends	Book Value
12/16	73.26	22 17	3.59	1.74	8.90
12/15	62.02	22 17	3.51	1.57	8.02
12/14	74.89	25 17	3.05	1.43	7.15
12/13	58.35	26 21	2.65	1.40	6.26
12/12	63.22	19 14	3.67	1.34	9.32
Annual Growth	**3.8%**	**— —**	**(0.5%)**	**6.7%**	**(1.1%)**

Rockwell Automation, Inc.

Rockwell Automation traces its roots back to the Allen Bradley Company founded in the US in 1903 and still sells products under the Allen-Bradley and A-B trademarks among others. The company makes industrial automation products and controls including industrial sensors motion control systems safety components machine protection modules and more. It also provides industrial software and training services. Rockwell serves a broad range of global industries including transportation oil and gas life sciences and food and beverage although the US still accounts for more than half of revenue.

Operations

The company organizes its operations in two segments: Architecture & Software (45% of sales) and Control Products & Solutions (55%).

Products in the Architecture & Software segment include hardware and software that help control clients' industrial processes such as controllers interface devices communication and networking products and industrial computers. Rockwell's flagship Logix controllers provide modular and scalable industrial controls. Software products in this segment relate to configuration and visualization process control manufacturing execution systems (MES) and productivity.

The Control Products & Solutions segment provides intelligent motor control and industrial control products as well as project management services. Products in these areas are motor starters circuit protection devices signaling devices and relays and timers to name a few. Services include life-cycle support asset management maintenance services and safety and network consulting.

Geographic Reach

Rockwell does business globally with operations in more than 80 countries. Customers in the US account for about 55% of total sales.

Its global headquarters and Control Products segment operations are located in Milwaukee Wisconsin; the Architecture & Software segment is based in Mayfield Heights Ohio.

The company's regional headquarters are in Cambridge Ontario (Canada) Belgium and The Netherlands (EMEA) Hong Kong (Asia Pacific) and Weston Florida (Latin America). Principle manufacturing locations include the US Canada Mexico Switzerland China Singapore Poland and Brazil.

Sales and Marketing

Rockwell Automation serves manufacturers across a range of markets including those in heavy industries (oil and gas mining metals) consumer industries (food and beverage home and personal care) and transportation.

Approximately 75% of global sales are through independent distributors. The company's largest distributor consistently represents about 10% of revenue.

Financial Performance

Overall sales for Rockwell Automation have been stagnant for the past five years. Sales in 2017 (ended September 30) were $6.3 billion a 7% increase from 2016 but flat compared to previous years. Growth in 2017 was broad-based across regions and was led by strength in the automotive semiconductor and food and beverage industries in the US and increased sales in emerging markets especially Asia Pacific (a more than 13% increase).

Net income has experienced the same trend as revenue with a similar increase of about 7% in 2017 primarily due to revenue growth as well as the sale of a product distribution business within its Control Products & Solutions segment for $94 million.

Cash from operations was more than $1 billion for 2017 compared to about $950 million for 2016. The increase in cash provided by operating activities was attributed to lower incentive compensation and income tax payments.

Strategy

Rockwell is focused on developing new products and services as well as expanding its global footprint.

The Connected Enterprise is Rockwell's initiative to provide solutions for its customers' digital transformations. The company released several new technologies in 2018 — Project Scio an analytics platform for Industrial Internet of Things (IIoT) applications which organizes structured and unstructured data; FactoryTalk Cloud industrial data center servers; and network and cybersecurity services such as remote monitoring assessments and design and pre-engineered network solutions. Its Project Sherlock uses artificial intelligence (AI) to create and diagnose analytics solutions in industrial operations.

With about 45 % of sales outside the US the company also continues to expand in emerging markets (China and India Latin America Central and Eastern Europe and Africa) and has made significant investments to globalize its operations in these regions. Rockwell is in the midst of a multi-year re-footprinting of its manufacturing operations to put resources closer to its customers in the fastest growing areas.

Internally ongoing productivity initiatives are aimed at cost reduction and improved asset utilization throughout the enterprise; a program to implement common global processes and an enterprise-wide business system is nearing completion in 2018.

Mergers and Acquisitions

The December 2017 acquisition of Odos Imaging a Scottish technology company that provides three-dimensional time-of-flight sensing systems for industrial imaging applications will enable Rockwell Automation to build on its portfolio of smart sensing and safety products for The Connected Enterprise.

Rockwell acquired systems integrator Maverick Technologies in September 2016 significantly enhancing its expertise in key process and batch applications. In the same month it acquired Automation Control Products a provider of centralized thin client remote desktop and server management software. This acquisition strengthens the company?s ability to provide customers with visual display and software solutions to manage information and streamline workflows for a more connected manufacturing environment.

The acquisition of MagneMotion Inc. (intelligent conveying systems) in 2016 helped with Rockwell?s strategy to build a portfolio of smart manufacturing technologies by expanding existing capabilities in independent cart technology.

HISTORY

Rockwell Automation is the legacy of two early-20th-century entrepreneurs: Willard Rockwell and Clement Melville Keys. Rockwell gained control in 1919 of Wisconsin Parts Company an Oshkosh Wisconsin maker of automotive axles. He went on to buy a number of industrial manufacturers merging them in 1953 to create Rockwell Spring & Axle. Renamed Rockwell-Standard in 1958 it led the world in the production of mechanical automotive parts by 1967.

In 1928 Keys founded North American Aviation (NAA) as a holding company for his aviation interests. General Motors bought NAA in 1934 and named James Kindelberger as its president. The company moved in 1935 from Maryland to Inglewood California where it built military training planes. NAA merged with Rockwell-Standard creating North American Rockwell in 1967. The company adopted the Rockwell International name in 1973. It wasn't until the beginning of the new century when the company changed its name to Rockwell Automation.

EXECUTIVES

SVP General Counsel and Secretary, Douglas M. (Doug) Hagerman, age 56, $590,785 total compensation
SVP Global Sales and Marketing, John P. McDermott, age 59, $436,699 total compensation
SVP Control Products and Solutions, Theodore D. (Ted) Crandall, age 62, $635,431 total compensation
SVP Advanced Technology and CTO, Sujeet Chand, age 59
SVP Operations and Engineering Services, Martin (Marty) Thomas, age 59
Chairman President and CEO, Blake D. Moret, age 54, $594,923 total compensation
SVP Architecture and Software, Frank C. Kulaszewicz, age 53, $594,923 total compensation
President Latin America, Alejandro Capparelli
Regional VP. Canada, Thomas Donato
President Asia/Pacific, Joseph (Joe) Sousa
VP Investor Relations and Finance Architecture and Software, Patrick Goris
SVP IT and CIO, Chris Nardecchia
Vice President Logistics, David Kenney
Regional Vice President Sales Services and Solutions (North America), Rachael Conrad
Vice President Global Finance Shared Services, Terry Riesterer
Vice President and Auditor, Sue Von Heimburg
Senior Vice President, Michelle Love
Vice President Information Technology Rockwell Automation Inc., Jerome Fox

Vice President Professional Services (RA Incuity), Andrew Ellis
Vice President WW Sales, Naveen Vashist
Senior Vice President, BOB RUFF
SVP CHIEF TECHNOLOGY OFFICER, Carol Rose
Auditors: DELOITTE & TOUCHE LLP

LOCATIONS

HQ: Rockwell Automation, Inc.
  1201 South Second Street, Milwaukee, WI 53204
Phone: 414 382-2000
Web: www.rockwellautomation.com

2017 Sales

	% of total
US	55
Europe Middle East & Africa	19
Asia Pacific	14
Latin America	7
Canada	5
Total	**100**

PRODUCTS/OPERATIONS

2017 Sales

	$ mil.	% of total
Control Products & Solutions	3,412	54
Architecture & Software	2,899	46
Total	**6,311**	**100**

2017 Sales

	$ mil.	% of total
Products and solutions	5,628	89
Services	682	11
Total	**6,311**	**100**

PRODUCT CATEGORIES

PRODUCT CATEGORIES
Advanced Process Control
Condition Monitoring & I/O
Design & Operations Software
Distributed Control Systems
Drive Systems
Drives
Human Machine Interface
Industrial Control Products
Industrial Network Products
Industrial Sensors
Manufacturing Execution System
Motion Control
Motor Control Centers
Programmable Controllers
Safety Components
Safety Instrumented Systems
Training

COMPETITORS

ABB	OMRON
Danaher	Rexnord
Dematic SARL	Schneider Electric
Eaton	Select Business
Emerson Electric	Solutions
Hitachi	Siemens AG
Honeywell	Toshiba
International	Weiss Instrument
Leonardo	Wonderware
Metso	Yokogawa Electric
Mitsubishi Corp.	

HISTORICAL FINANCIALS
Company Type: Public

Income Statement

FYE: September 30

	REVENUE ($ mil.)	NET INCOME ($ mil.)	NET PROFIT MARGIN	EMPLOYEES
09/17	6,311	825	13.1%	22,000
09/16	5,879	729	12.4%	22,000
09/15	6,307	827	13.1%	22,500
09/14	6,623	826	12.5%	22,500
09/13	6,351	756	11.9%	22,000
Annual Growth	(0.2%)	2.2%	—	0.0%

2017 Year-End Financials

Debt ratio: 25.75%
Return on equity: 35.49%
Cash ($ mil.): 1,410
Current ratio: 2.06
Long-term debt ($ mil.): 1,243
No. of shares (mil.): 128
Dividends
  Yield: 0.0%
  Payout: 47.8%
Market value ($ mil.): 22,882

	STOCK PRICE ($) FY Close	P/E High/Low	PER SHARE ($) Earnings	Dividends	Book Value
09/17	178.21	28 18	6.35	3.04	20.74
09/16	122.34	22 16	5.56	2.90	15.49
09/15	101.47	21 16	6.09	2.60	17.05
09/14	109.88	21 17	5.91	2.32	19.44
09/13	106.94	20 13	5.36	1.98	18.61
Annual Growth	13.6%	— —	4.3%	11.3%	2.7%

Rockwell Collins Inc

Rockwell Collins makes aviation electronics and communication equipment for commercial and military aircraft. The company also provides flight simulation and training MRO services navigation and surveillance systems. It has three primary segments: commercial systems (avionics and in-flight entertainment systems for commercial aircraft); government systems (airborne/ground/shipboard communication systems with military applications and overhaul services); and information management services business (communications systems integration and security solutions). In 2017 Rockwell Collins agreed to be acquired by diversified manufacturing giant United Technologies for $23 billion.

Change in Company Type
In the biggest aerospace deal in history Rockwell Collins agreed to be purchased by United Technologies Corporation (UTC) for $23 billion in September 2017. When the deal is completed Rockwell Collins will become a new UTC division named Collins Aerospace Systems. UTC projects the new division will generate more than $23 billion in revenue per year and will make aviation electronics and communication equipment for commercial and military aircraft. Rockwell Collins will also work in tandem with UTC's reputable Pratt & Whitney subsidiary which makes commercial military and business jet engines.
Operations
Rockwell Collins operates in four segments: Interior systems government systems commercial systems and information management systems.

The commercial systems segment (about 35% of revenue) provides systems and products for the original manufacturing retrofitting and upgrading of aircraft. Products include the Pro Line Fusion integrated avionics system cabin management systems head-up guidance systems primary actuation systems and simulators for crew training. The segment serves a range of customers from the biggest aircraft makers in the world to owners of individual aircraft. Aftermarket products are sold through distributors and to regional airline operators.

Rockwell Collins' government systems segment (about a third of sales) provides products for a variety of uses but they all have the common theme of design for use under rugged conditions constrained by challenges in relation to size weight and power. These products include satellite communications systems handheld navigation devices flight controls helmet-mounted displays and training systems.

The interior systems segment about 20% of revenue joined the lineup when Rockwell Collins bought B/E Aerospace in 2017. The unit make cabin interior products that include aircraft seats aircraft food and beverage preparation and storage equipment modular lavatory systems wastewater management systems and galley systems chemical and gaseous aircraft oxygen storage distribution and delivery systems protective breathing equipment and lighting products.

The information management services segment (almost 10%) provides communications services systems integration and security services across the aviation airport rail transit and nuclear security markets to customers located around the world. Its customer base includes commercial airlines business aircraft operators the US Federal Aviation Administration (FAA) airport and critical infrastructure operators and major passenger and freight railroads.

Geographic Reach

Rockwell Collins operates in countries including France Canada Germany Japan Australia China India Ireland Italy Spain Singapore Brazil South Korea the United Arab Emirates Saudi Arabia South Korea the UK and the US. The company makes about 65% of its sales in the US.

Sales and Marketing

Rockwell Collins markets its systems products and services directly to government systems and commercial systems customers through an internal marketing and sales force. The company also works through a worldwide dealer network to distribute its products and international sales representatives to assist with international sales and marketing.

The US government accounts for almost 35% of sales. Customers include the Department of Defense US Coast Guard civil agencies defense contractors foreign ministries commercial air support manufacturers and airlines.

Financial Performance

Rockwell Collins posted a 30% sales increase to $6.8 billion in 2017 (ended September) from 2016. About 90% of the increase came from revenue provided by the B/E Aerospace in April 2017. Organic sales rose 3 percent from higher sales in government systems information management services and commercial systems. The acquisition also drove an 18% jump in US sales. Other factors behind rising sales were higher Airbus A350 production rates higher customer-funded development program revenue in commercial systems and increased international use of connectivity services.

Despite the revenue jump Rockwell Collins? profit slipped 3% to $705 million in 2017 from 2016 as because of expenses associated with the B/E Aerospace acquisition.

Operating cash flow rose to about $1.3 billion 2017 from $723 million in 2016. Much of the cash flow increase came with the B/E deal as well as higher cash collections from customers in the company's other segments.

Strategy

The B/E Aerospace acquisition opened aircraft interiors to Rockwell Collins. The company seeks to capitalize on that market from trends in seating lighting systems food preparation and storage. It also sees opportunity in aftermarket retrofit and parts from the large installed base.

Joint ventures are an important element of the company's strategy for growth. It maintains 50-50 JVs with BAE Systems for Data Link Solutions (serving the worldwide data link market); Elbit Systems for Vision Systems International (helmet-mounted cueing systems for the military fixed-wing market); Honeywell International for Integrated Guidance Systems (weapons guidance and navigation products); and Quadrant Group for Quest Flight Training (aircrew training for the UK Ministry of Defense).

Mergers and Acquisitions

Over the years Rockwell Collins has achieved revenue milestones with the aid of key acquisitions.In its largest acquisition to date Rockwell Collins in 2017 acquired B/E Aerospace in a transaction valued at $8.6 billion including the assumption of debt. The major deal largely expanded the range of products that Rockwell Collins supplies to major commercial and business aircraft and broadened its customer base internationally. It specifically added seating food and beverage preparation and storage equipment lighting and oxygen systems and modular galley and lavatory systems to its product portfolio.

In 2015 the company acquired International Communications Group (ICG) which provides satellite-based global voice and data communication products and services for the aviation industry for $50 million. The deal broadened the company's flight deck and connectivity portfolio. Previously in 2015 Rockwell Collins acquired Pacific Avionics Pty. Limited which provides technologies used for wireless information distribution. It made the purchase for $24 million as the acquisition further enhanced its cabin products and information management services portfolios.

EXECUTIVES

EVP and COO Commercial Systems, Kent L. Statler, age 52, $630,932 total compensation
SVP and CFO, Patrick E. Allen, age 53, $633,491 total compensation
SVP Operations, Bruce M. King, age 56
SVP Engineering and Information Technology, Nan Mattai, age 65
EVP and COO Interior Systems, Werner Lieberherr, age 57
SVP International and Service Solutions, Colin Mahoney, age 52
VP Commercial Sales Marketing and Customer Support, Scott R. Gunnufson
SVP Information Management Services (IMS), David J. (Dave) Nieuwsma, age 53
VP and Managing Director Europe Middle East and Africa International and Service Solutions, Claude Alber
EVP and COO Government Systems, Philip J. (Phil) Jasper, age 49, $528,995 total compensation
Chairman President and CEO, Robert K. (Kelly) Ortberg, age 57, $997,348 total compensation
VP and Managing Director Asia Pac, Jim Walker
SVP Washington Operations, Robert A. (Bobby) Sturgell, age 58
Vice President, Glen Dodson
Executive Vice President, Kelly Ortberg
Vice President Information Technology, Greg Arundale
Senior Vice President and Electrical Engineer, Nathan Adams
Senior Vice President, Jeffrey MacLauchlan
Vice President Strategy M and A and Busdev Acting, Shawn Shiley
Vice President, John Chapin
Vice President, Tom Lemke

Vice President of Customer Care, Tim Kane
Vice President Strategy Development, Bryan Vester
Vice President Global Total Rewards and Labor Relations Human Resources, Laura Patterson
SENIOR VICE PRESIDENT HUMAN RESOURCES, Ronald W Kirchenbauer
VICE PRESIDENT TAX, Thomas J Stanczyk
Treasurer, Heather Stansberry
Treasurer, Stefanie Wiese
Board Member, Craig Goudie
Secretary, Tippett Cindi
Auditors: DELOITTE & TOUCHE LLP

LOCATIONS

HQ: Rockwell Collins Inc
  400 Collins Road N.E., Cedar Rapids, IA 52498
Phone: 319 295-1000
Web: www.rockwellcollins.com

2017 Sales

	$ mil.	% of total
US	3,873	57
Europe / Africa / Middle East	1,607	24
Asia-Pacific	787	11
Americas excluding US	555	8
Total	**5,259**	**100**

PRODUCTS/OPERATIONS

2017 Sales

	$ mil.	% of total
Commercial Systems	2,418	35
Government Systems	2,280	33
Interior Systems	1	21
Information Management Services	718	11
Total	**6,822**	**100**

Selected Products and Services

Government/Defense (airborne and surface)
  Cockpit display
  Communications
  Engineering services
  Flight deck subsystems
  Maintenance repair parts and after-sales support
  Military data link
  Navigation (including radio navigation)
  Simulation and training
Commercial (air transport aviation electronics and business and regional aviation electronics)
  Communications
  Electro-mechanical
  Information management
  Integrated avionics (Pro Line Fusion)
  Integrated cabin electronics
  Maintenance repair parts and after-sales support services
  Navigation
  Simulation and training
  Surveillance

COMPETITORS

BAE SYSTEMS	Honeywell Aerospace
Ball Corp.	L3 Technologies
Boeing	Meggitt
CAE Inc.	Northrop Grumman
Chemring	Panasonic Avionics
DRS Technologies	Radiall
Esterline	Raytheon
Exelis	Smiths Group
FlightSafety	Thales
General Dynamics	Trimble
Harris Corp.	ViaSat

Company Type: Public

Income Statement

FYE: September 30

	REVENUE ($ mil.)	NET INCOME ($ mil.)	NET PROFIT MARGIN	EMPLOYEES
09/17	6,822	705	10.3%	29,000
09/16	5,259	728	13.8%	19,000
09/15	5,244	686	13.1%	19,500
09/14	4,979	604	12.1%	20,000
09/13	4,610	632	13.7%	18,300
Annual Growth	10.3%	2.8%	—	12.2%

2017 Year-End Financials

Debt ratio: 39.76%	No. of shares (mil.): 162
Return on equity: 17.36%	Dividends
Cash ($ mil.): 703	Yield: 0.0%
Current ratio: 1.55	Payout: 27.5%
Long-term debt ($ mil.): 6,676	Market value ($ mil.): 21,293

	STOCK PRICE ($) FY Close	P/E High/Low	PER SHARE ($) Earnings	PER SHARE ($) Dividends	PER SHARE ($) Book Value
09/17	130.71	27 16	4.79	1.32	37.10
09/16	84.34	17 14	5.51	1.32	15.96
09/15	81.84	19 14	5.13	1.26	14.22
09/14	78.50	19 15	4.42	1.20	14.06
09/13	67.86	16 11	4.58	1.20	11.98
Annual Growth	17.8%	— —	1.1%	2.4%	32.7%

Ross Stores, Inc.

Ross wants you to dress for less. A leading off-price apparel retailer (behind TJX Cos. and Kohl's) Ross operates some 1340 Ross Dress for Less and more than 190y 200 dd's Discounts stores that sell closeout merchandise including men's women's and children's clothing at prices well below those of department and specialty stores. While apparel accounts for more than half of sales it also sells small furnishings toys and games luggage and jewelry. Featuring the Ross "Dress for Less" trademark the chain targets 18- to 54-year-old white-collar shoppers from primarily middle-income households. Ross and dd's stores are located in strip malls in over 35 states and mostly in the western US and Guam.

Operations

Ross Stores operates two brands of off-price retail apparel and home fashion stores: Ross Dress for Less and dd's DISCOUNTS. Ross does a roaring trade in off-price apparel and home fashion chain offering first-quality in-season name-brand and designer apparel as well as accessories footwear and home decor at between 20%-60% off department and specialty store regular prices.

Launched in 2004 dd's DISCOUNTS serves one of the fastest-growing demographic markets in the US. The ultra-low-price spinoff which offers brand-name apparel at a 20%-70% discount has grown to almost 200 locations in about 15 states including big ones such as California Florida and Texas. The stores which average 23200 square feet are located in strip shopping centers in urban and suburban neighborhoods.

The retailer operates six distribution processing facilities: three in California two in South Carolina and one in Pennsylvania. These distribution centers are the sole source of its stores merchandise. Additionally the discounter owns four and leases three other warehouse facilities for packaway storage. To distribute merchandise to stores on a regular basis Ross Stores enlists the help of third-party cross docks. Shipments are made by contract carriers to stores between three and six times per week depending on the location.

Geographic Reach

Half of California-based Ross' stores are located in the states of California Texas and Florida. The company's distribution centers and warehouses are in Pennsylvania South Carolina and California.Aside from the territory of Guam Ross does not have an international presence.

Sales and Marketing

Ross Stores relies primarily on television as a medium to share the Ross Dress for Less value proposition with its current and potential customers. The company believes that television advertising is the most efficient and cost-effective medium while it continues to use additional channels to build brand awareness. However advertising for its dd's DISCOUNTS stores is focused on new store grand openings and local grass roots initiatives.It also employs social media to communicate its brand position.

Financial Performance

Ross Stores' annual sales have risen more than 40% since 2011 thanks to rapid store expansion and steady same-store sale growth of between 3% and 7% per year. Its annual profits have kept pace with top line growth over the period as the chain has managed to slow its overhead cost growth.

The fast-growing chain's sales jumped 8% to $12.9 billion — a $1 billion gain — during fiscal 2017 (ended January) mostly thanks to continued store growth. Comparable store sales also increased a solid 4%.

Net income was up 10% to $1.1 billion due to lower cost of goods sold partially offset by higher selling general and administrative expenses. Cash from operating activities grew 14% to $1.6 billion due to higher net income.

Strategy

Ross Stores continues its aggressive retail expansion strategy opening additional stores based on market penetration local demographic characteristics competition expected store profitability and the ability to leverage overhead expenses. The company anticipates room in the US to support at least 2000 Ross locations and 500 dd's DISCOUNTS locations.

Indeed the chain has expanded its store count by 40% to 1533 at the end of 2016 from 1125 at the end of 2011. During 2016 alone the retailer added 87 net new stores (including 71 Ross stores) in established regions and in the less-tapped Midwest markets (including its first stores in the Dakotas). It plans to open a further 90 stores in 2017.

Other objectives the discount chain emphasized in 2016 included: maintaining a sufficient library of well-known brands labels and fashions sold with strong discounts; meeting customer needs on a local basis; delivering an "off-price customer" suited shopping experience; and managing effective and competitive store growth in all of its markets.

To boost its relationships with suppliers Ross does not require them to provide markdown/promotional allowances or return privileges. This combined with opportunistic purchases (closeouts such as manufacturer overruns and canceled orders) allows the company to obtain large discounts on merchandise. As a result Ross Stores' customers typically pay 20% to 60% less than department and specialty store prices. Ross holds down costs by offering minimal service and few frills inside its stores.

HISTORY

In 1957 the Ross family founded Ross Stores and opened its first junior department store; by 1982 there were six of the stores in the San Francisco area. That year two retailing veterans Stuart Moldaw (founder of Country Casuals and The Athletic Shoe Factory) and Donald Rowlett (creator of Woolworth's off-price subsidiary J. Brannam) led the acquisition of the company. Moldaw (chairman) and Rowlett (president) wanted to create an off-price chain in California where — despite the success such endeavors were having in the rest of the country — such stores were largely absent. The duo intended to establish a foothold by saturating California markets before competitors muddied the waters.

They restocked the stores with brand-name men's women's and children's apparel shoes accessories and domestics merchandise at reduced prices. Before the end of 1982 they opened two more Ross "Dress for Less" stores; the next year 18 more were added including the chain's first non-California store in Reno Nevada (much of the chain's expansion came through the acquisition of existing strip mall stores). Another 40 stores were added in 1984.

The company went public in 1985 to help fund its expansion and extended its reach to include Colorado Florida Georgia New Mexico and Oregon; that year it opened 41 stores.

In August 2004 Ross opened its first three dd's DISCOUNTS stores in Vallejo San Leandro and Fresno California. The retailer moved its headquarters from Newark California to Pleasanton in mid-2004 and then sold the Newark property for about $17 million.

EXECUTIVES

CEO, Barbara Rentler, age 59, $1,301,875 total compensation
President and COO, Michael B. O'Sullivan, age 53, $1,147,250 total compensation
President and Chief Merchandising Officer ddÂ's DISCOUNTS, Brian R. Morrow, age 57
President Merchandising Ross Dress for Less, Bernard (Bernie) Brautigan, age 52, $1,070,750 total compensation
Group SVP and CFO, Michael J. Hartshorn, age 49, $651,375 total compensation
Vice President Property Management, John Fox
Senior Vice President and General Merchandise Manager Ross Stores Inc., Pamela Smith
Group Vice President Human Resources, Anjali Vichare
Chairman, Michael A. Balmuth, age 67
Auditors: Deloitte & Touche LLP

LOCATIONS

HQ: Ross Stores, Inc.
5130 Hacienda Drive, Dublin, CA 94568-7579
Phone: 925 965-4400
Web: www.rossstores.com

2017 Stores

	No.
California	364
Texas	222
Florida	185
Arizona	74
Illinois	62
Georgia	56
North Carolina	45
Pennsylvania	44
Washington	42
Virginia	38
Colorado	33
Nevada	33
Tennessee	31
Oregon	30
Maryland	24

Oklahoma	23
South Carolina	23
Alabama	23
Missouri	21
Louisiana	18
Hawaii	17
Utah	17
New Jersey	13
Wisconsin	13
New Mexico	12
Idaho	11
Kansas	10
Kentucky	9
Indiana	9
Mississippi	8
Arkansas	8
Montana	6
Wyoming	3
Delaware	2
District of Columbia	1
Guam	1
North Dakota	1
South Dakota	1
Total	**1,533**

PRODUCTS/OPERATIONS

2017 Sales

	% of total
Women's apparel	28
Home accents bed & bath	25
Accessories lingerie fine jewelry & fragrances	13
Men's apparel	13
Shoes	13
Children's apparel	8
Total	**100**

2017 Stores

	No.
Ross Dress for Less	1,340
dd's DISCOUNTS	193
Total	**1,533**

Selected Merchandise

Bed and bath
Children's apparel
Cookware
Educational toys
Fine jewelry
Fragrances
Gourmet foods
Home accents
Ladies' apparel
  Accessories
  Dresses
  Junior
  Lingerie
  Maternity
  Misses sportswear
  Petites
  Women's World
Luggage
Men's apparel
  Traditional men's
  Young men's
Shoes
Small electronics
Small furnishings
Sporting goods and exercise equipment

COMPETITORS

Ascena Retail	J. C. Penney
Big Lots	Kmart
Burlington Coat	Kohl's
Factory	Sears
Cato	TJX Companies
Charming Shoppes	Tailored Brands
Family Dollar Stores	Target Corporation
Fred's	Wal-Mart

HISTORICAL FINANCIALS

Company Type: Public

Income Statement

FYE: January 28

	REVENUE ($ mil.)	NET INCOME ($ mil.)	NET PROFIT MARGIN	EMPLOYEES
01/17	12,866	1,117	8.7%	78,600
01/16	11,940	1,020	8.5%	77,800
01/15*	11,041	924	8.4%	71,400
02/14	10,230	837	8.2%	66,300
02/13	9,721	786	8.1%	57,500
Annual Growth	**7.3%**	**9.2%**	**—**	**8.1%**

*Fiscal year change

2017 Year-End Financials

Debt ratio: 7.47%	No. of shares (mil.): 391
Return on equity: 42.94%	Dividends
Cash ($ mil.): 1,111	Yield: 0.0%
Current ratio: 1.61	Payout: 19.0%
Long-term debt ($ mil.): 396	Market value ($ mil.): 25,602

	STOCK PRICE ($) FY Close	P/E High/Low		PER SHARE ($) Earnings	Dividends	Book Value
01/17	65.33	24	18	2.83	0.54	7.01
01/16	56.26	42	18	2.51	0.47	6.14
01/15*	91.71	43	28	2.21	0.40	5.49
02/14	67.91	42	28	1.94	0.34	4.70
02/13	59.43	39	29	1.77	0.28	4.00
Annual Growth	**2.4%**	**—**	**—**	**12.5%**	**17.8%**	**15.0%**

*Fiscal year change

RPM International Inc (DE)

Maker of home repair favorites like Rust-Oleum Zinsser and DAP RPM International is divided into three units: Industrial Consumer and Specialty products. Industrial offerings (which account for half of total sales) include products for waterproofing corrosion resistance floor maintenance and wall finishing. RPM's Consumer do-it-yourself items include caulks and sealants rust preventatives and general-purpose paints repair products personal care items and hobby paints. The Specialty segment offers industrial cleaners restoration services equipment and colorants.RPM operates through about 140 locations around the globe.

HISTORY

Frank Sullivan founded Republic Powdered Metals in 1947 to make an industrial aluminum paint. The company went public in 1963 and three years later it bought Reardon Co. (household coatings) the first of more than 50 acquisitions. After his father's death in 1971 Thomas Sullivan took over and reorganized RPM as a holding company.

By 1979 RPM though successful was taken to task by its board for lack of formal planning. In 1985 it bought Sun Oil's Carboline coating and tank-lining subsidiary. This purchase forced RPM to lay off employees for the first time.

RPM bought Rust-Oleum in 1994. In its largest acquisition at that time the company bought roofing-product expert Tremco in 1996 for $236 million. The purchase amassed debt and to compensate RPM sold its Craft House hobby activity subsidiary and Swiggle Insulating Glass in 1997.

The company resumed acquisitions and overseas expansion in 1998 by purchasing Flecto (wood finish) the UK's Nullifire (fireproof coatings) and Germany's Alteco Technik (floors); it also established joint ventures in Russia and China. In 1999 RPM paid $290 million for UK-based Wassall's DAP adhesives division. Softer sales in the Americas and Asia plus increased distribution expenses that fiscal year prompted the company to begin restructuring its operations.

RPM sold its Alox metalworking additive business to Lubrizol in 2000. The next year the company finished its restructuring — which had resulted in 17 plant closures and a 10% workforce reduction — and set its sights on reducing debt.

Thomas C. Sullivan's son — and grandson of the company's founder — Frank Sullivan took the chief executive reins in 2002; Thomas Sullivan remained with the company as chairman.

The company went through a spate of acquisitions in the middle of the decade. Its flooring services division has acquired National Building Facilities Services and Harsco's fiberglass-reinforced plastics business and its corrosion control division has acquired AD Fire Protection Systems. Tremco has acquired German sealant manufacturer Illbruck Sealant Systems. In early 2007 Rust-Oleum acquired the UK's Tor Coatings in an effort to grow the unit's European coatings operations. Later that year the company sold its auto restoration products subsidiary Bondo to 3M.

In 2010 two RPM subsidiaries Bondex International and its holding company Specialty Products Holding Corp. filed for Chapter 11 reorganization in a move to resolve asbestos claims against Bondex. The process allowed the companies to establish a trust fund and a court order directing all present and future claims to the fund for compensation.

The company also went on an international shopping trip in 2010. RPM acquired Hummervoll Industribelegg AS a Norway-based supplier and installer of industrial flooring systems; UK-based Pipeline & Drainage Systems a supplier of curb bridge and channel drainage products; and Turkish company Park Dis Ticaret AS a provider of sealant tapes and membranes.

RPM subsidiary Euclid Chemical acquired PSI Packaging in 2011. PSI is a producer of micro- and macro-fibers for the ready-mixed and pre-cast concrete market. The PSI deal will expand both Euclid and RPM's manufacturing and sales capacity for concrete reinforcement fibers particularly in the international market.

In 2011 the company expanded further internationally when its Performance Coatings Group acquired API an Italian flooring and deck coatings company. The buy also complemented RPM's Flowcrete and Stonhard commercial flooring businesses. That year the company's Performance Coatings Group acquired Spanish company Grupo P&V a top European supplier of fire protection and insulation products. Grupo P&V manufactures sells and installs expanded perlite and vermiculite used in passive fire protection soundproofing and heat insulation. The acquisition fits in with RPM's Carboline product line and expands the company's fire protection market in Europe.

In 2012 the company purchased nail care enamel and related products maker Kirker Enterprises for an undisclosed amount. Kirker became part of the consumer segment. Earlier in the year RPM's Rust-Oleum Group acquired Australia-based HiChem Paint Technologies which makes automotive aftermarket coatings and specialty coatings for both industrial applications and home use.

That year it also acquired Brazilian building materials and construction products company Viapol for an undisclosed amount. Viapol has brand-leading products in Brazil including its rolled asphalt roofing materials waterproofing products concrete admixtures and retail paints and varnishes. The buy broadens RPM's global footprint by moving the company into the Brazilian market South America's largest economy.

In 2013 RPM's Performance Coatings Group acquired Expanko a producer of FritzTile brand terrazzo tile (as well as cork rubber and rubber/cork floor tiles) for the education health-care hospitality and sports/entertainment markets.

EXECUTIVES

Vice President Investor Relations and Planning, Barry Slifstein

President and COO, Ronald A. Rice, age 54, $720,000 total compensation

Chairman and CEO, Frank C. Sullivan, age 56, $960,000 total compensation

President Tremco Incorporated, Paul G. P. Hoogenboom, age 56, $425,000 total compensation

President and CEO DAP, John J. McLaughlin

President RPM Industrial Segment, David P. Reif

Director Information Technology, Lonny R. DiRusso

President and CEO DAP, Terry Horan

SVP General Counsel and Chief Compliance Officer, Edward W. Moore, age 60, $360,000 total compensation

VP and CFO, Russell L. Gordon, age 51, $465,000 total compensation

VP Corporate Benefits and Risk Management, Janeen B. Kastner, age 50, $295,000 total compensation

Vice President Public Affairs, Randy McShepard

Auditors: DELOITTE & TOUCHE LLP

LOCATIONS

HQ: RPM International Inc (DE)
P.O. Box 777, 2628 Pearl Road, Medina, OH 44258
Phone: 330 273-5090   **Fax:** 330 225-8743
Web: www.rpminc.com

2017 Sales

	$ mil.	% of total
US	3,269	66
Europe	908	18
Canada	321	7
Other regions	458	9
Total	**4,958**	**100**

PRODUCTS/OPERATIONS

2017 Sales

	$ mil.	% of total
Industrial	2,564	52
Consumer	1,680	34
Specialty	713	14
Total	**4,958**	**100**

Selected Products

Industrial
  Carboline (industrial coatings)
  Chemspec (commercial carpet cleaning chemicals)
  Day-Glo (fluorescent colorants and pigments)
  Dryvit (exterior finishing systems)
  Dymeric (sealants)
  Fibergrate (reinforced plastic grating)
  Flowcrete (polymer flooring system)
  Nullifire (fireproofing coatings)
  Republic (roofing products)
  Stonhard (flooring products)
  Tremco (industrial and commercial sealants)
  Woolsey/Z-Spar (marine coatings)
Consumer
  DAP (sealants caulks and patch and repair products)
  OKON (sealants and stains)
  Painter's Touch (general purpose coatings)
  Rust-Oleum (rust preventative coatings)
  Testors (hobby and leisure products)
  Tremclad (coatings)

Varathane (wood finishes)
Watco (wood finishes)
Zinsser (primer-sealers and wallcovering removers)

COMPETITORS

3M	H.B. Fuller
Akzo Nobel	Henkel
Ameron	Masco
Axalta Coating Systems	PPG Industries
Benjamin Moore	Sherwin-Williams
Ferro	Valspar

HISTORICAL FINANCIALS

Company Type: Public

Income Statement   FYE: May 31

	REVENUE ($ mil.)	NET INCOME ($ mil.)	NET PROFIT MARGIN	EMPLOYEES
05/17	4,958	181	3.7%	14,318
05/16	4,813	354	7.4%	13,394
05/15	4,594	239	5.2%	12,864
05/14	4,376	291	6.7%	10,848
05/13	4,078	98	2.4%	10,553
Annual Growth	**5.0%**	**16.5%**	**—**	**7.9%**

2017 Year-End Financials

Debt ratio: 41.06%
Return on equity: 12.95%
Cash ($ mil.): 350
Current ratio: 1.94
Long-term debt ($ mil.): 1,836

No. of shares (mil.): 133
Dividends
  Yield: 2.1%
  Payout: 77.8%
Market value ($ mil.): 7,243

	STOCK PRICE ($) FY Close	P/E High/Low	PER SHARE ($) Earnings	Dividends	Book Value
05/17	54.23	41 34	1.36	1.18	10.75
05/16	50.19	19 14	2.63	1.09	10.32
05/15	50.03	29 22	1.78	1.02	9.69
05/14	43.07	20 14	2.18	0.95	10.38
05/13	33.13	45 33	0.74	0.89	9.06
Annual Growth	**13.1%**	**— —**	**16.4%**	**7.2%**	**4.4%**

Ryder System, Inc.

When it comes to commercial vehicles and distribution Ryder System wants to be the designated driver. The company's Fleet Management Solutions (FMS) segment acquires manages maintains and disposes of fleet vehicles for commercial customers. Similarly the Supply Chain Solutions (SCS) segment provides logistics and supply chain services from industrial start (raw material supply) to finish (product distribution). SCS also offers dedicated contract carriage service by supplying trucks drivers and management and administrative services to customers on a contract basis. Ryder's worldwide fleet of more than 222000 vehicles ranges from tractor-trailers to light-duty trucks.

Operations
Ryder operates through three main divisions: Fleet Management Solutions (FMS — full service leasing contract maintenance contract-related maintenance and commercial rental of trucks tractors and trailers in North America and the UK); Dedicated Transportation Solutions (DTS — provides vehicles and drivers as part of a dedicated transportation solution in the US) and Supply Chain Solutions (SCS — supply chain solutions including distribution and transportation services in North America and Asia).

FMS generates almost 65% of its total sales while SCS and DTS bring in about 25% and 15% respectively.

Geographic Reach
Ryder operates in North America (Canada Mexico and the US) Europe (Germany and the UK) and Asia (China and Singapore). The US accounts for around 85% of its total revenues.

Sales and Marketing
Ryder's FMS customers in the US range from small businesses to large national enterprises operating in a wide variety of industries the most significant of which are food and beverage transportation and warehousing housing business and personal services and industrial. The company's customers have included Associated Grocers Bendix Cisco Clark and Reid and CVS/Caremark.

Financial Performance
Ryder's revenues increased 3% in 2016 to peak at $6.8 billion its highest total in at least 10 years. This was attributed to growth in its full service lease fleet and higher prices on full service lease replacement vehicles. It also grew from new business and increased volumes and higher pricing within its SCS and DTS segments.

The company's profits however fell 14% from $305 million in 2015 to $262 million in 2016 mainly due to lower used vehicle sales. In addition Ryder's operating cash flow has trended upward for five straight years jumping from $1.44 billion in 2015 to $1.6 billion in 2016.

Strategy
One way Ryder remains competitive is being prepared for the unpredictability of supply chain logistics due in part to higher fuel prices and increased regional labor costs. To achieve this the company creates partnerships with third-party logistics (3PL) providers. Such alliances enable the company to keep its networks flexible and efficient.

Ryder is also aiming to capitalize on trends that make it more difficult for companies to manage commercial transportation and logistics on their own. These include higher truck purchase prices and operating costs new government regulations growing technology complexity talent shortages for drivers and increased demand for faster delivery options.

To meet these trends in 2016 Ryder launched a new suite of commercial vehicle lease products. Ryder ChoiceLease gives customers a more flexible set of maintenance choices: full service preventive or on-demand. The more scalable model allows customers to decide the terms of their lease in conjunction with the level of maintenance they prefer. In the past Ryder only offered a traditional full-services maintenance lease.

HISTORY

Ryder Truck Rental founded in Miami by Jim Ryder in 1933 was the first truck leasing company in the US. It rented trucks in four southern states until 1952 when it bought Great Southern Trucking (renamed Ryder Truck Lines) doubling its size. In 1955 it went public as Ryder System Ryder bought Carolina Fleets (a South Carolina trucking company) and Yellow Rental (a northeastern leasing service). More purchases over the next decade extended its truck rental business across the US and into Canada. Ryder Truck Lines was sold to International Utilities in 1965.

EXECUTIVES

EVP and CFO, Art A. Garcia, age 55, $479,783 total compensation

Chairman and CEO, Robert E. Sanchez, age 51, $785,225 total compensation

EVP and Chief Marketing Officer, Karen M. Jones, age 54

EVP Chief Legal Officer and Secretary, Robert D. Fatovic, age 51, $392,650 total compensation

President Global Fleet Management Solutions, Dennis C. Cooke, age 52, $543,750 total compensation

EVP and Chief Sales Officer, John J. Gleason, age 61

President Dedicated Transport Solutions, John J. Diez, $411,000 total compensation

President Global Supply Chain Solutions, J. Steven (Steve) Sensing

SVP and CIO, Melvin (Mel) Kirk

Senior Vice President and Deputy General Counsel, Sanford Hodes

Vice President Information Technology, Greg Knott

Vice President And General Manager, Richard Jennings

Senior Vice President And Treasurer, Daniel Susik

Vice President Finance, Chuck Hurst

Vice President Integrated Marketing Strategy and Planning, Natalie Putnam

Vice President and Deputy General Counsel, Alena Brenner

Vice President Supply Management FMS, Scott Perry

Vice President, Mike Thompson

Vice President and Group Manager, Norm Brouillette

First Vice President, Tammy Megowan

Vice President Business Development, Jason Sonnbichler

Vice President Asset Management, Eugene Tangney

Vice President Logistics, Steve Sensing

Vice President Information Technology, Mike Parvor

Vice President Business Development, Tim Sweeney

Vice President Manager Director, Tom Knutilla

Vice President Information Technology, Stephen Hitchings

Vice President Automotive, Dick Jennings

Vice President Technology Services and Operations, Mike Pivowar

Vice President Global Supply Chain Solutions Sales, Todd Skiles

National Sales Manager, Sean Mollenauer

Senior Vice President and General Manager, Tom Pettit

Vice President, Eugenio Sevilla-Sacasa

Vice President Information Technology, Mel Kirk

Vice President Of Operations, Bryce Kinsley

Vice President Of Business Development, Dave Walby

Senior Vice President and General Manager Supply Chains Solutions, Tom Jones

Vice President andamp; Global Product Manager Rental Operations, Rick Mohr

VICE PRESIDENT AND GENERAL MANAGER, Gerald Brown

Vice President and Controller, Frank Mullen

VICE PRESIDENT, Leonard Mall

Executive Board Member, Scott Marie

Auditors: PricewaterhouseCoopers LLP

LOCATIONS

HQ: Ryder System, Inc.
11690 N.W. 105th Street, Miami, FL 33178
Phone: 305 500-3726
Web: www.ryder.com

2016 Sales

	$ mil.	% of total
US	5,892	87
Canada	387	6
Europe	339	5
Mexico	139	2
Asia	28	-
Total	**6,787**	**100**

PRODUCTS/OPERATIONS

2016 Sales

	$ mil.	% of total
Lease and rental revenues	3,170	47
Services revenue	3,152	46
Fuel services revenue	463	7
Total	**6,787**	**100**

2016 Sales

	$ mil.	% of total
Fleet Management Solutions	4,556	63
Supply Chain Solutions	1,020	14
Dedicated Transportation Solutions	1,637	23
Eliminations	(427.9)	-
Total	**6,787**	**100**

Selected Services

Fleet Management Solutions
  Commercial rental
  Contract maintenance
  Full service leasing
  Used vehicles
Supply Chain Solutions
  Distribution management
  Transportation management
Dedicated Contract Carriage

COMPETITORS

ArcBest	Penske Truck Leasing
Barloworld Handling	Schenker Inc.
C.H. Robinson	Schneider National
Worldwide	UPS
FedEx	UniGroup
J.B. Hunt	YRC Worldwide
Landstar System	

HISTORICAL FINANCIALS

Company Type: Public

Income Statement

FYE: December 31

	REVENUE ($ mil.)	NET INCOME ($ mil.)	NET PROFIT MARGIN	EMPLOYEES
12/16	6,786	262	3.9%	34,500
12/15	6,571	304	4.6%	33,100
12/14	6,638	218	3.3%	30,600
12/13	6,419	237	3.7%	28,900
12/12	6,256	209	3.4%	27,700
Annual Growth	**2.1%**	**5.7%**	**—**	**5.6%**

2016 Year-End Financials

Debt ratio: 49.45%	No. of shares (mil.): 53
Return on equity: 12.96%	Dividends
Cash ($ mil.): 58	Yield: 0.0%
Current ratio: 0.63	Payout: 34.6%
Long-term debt ($ mil.): 4,599	Market value ($ mil.): 3,980

	STOCK PRICE ($) FY Close	P/E High/Low		PER SHARE ($) Earnings	Dividends	Book Value
12/16	74.44	17	10	4.90	1.70	38.39
12/15	56.83	17	9	5.71	1.56	37.15
12/14	92.85	23	17	4.11	1.42	34.30
12/13	73.78	16	11	4.53	1.30	35.56
12/12	49.93	14	8	4.09	1.20	28.57
Annual Growth	**10.5%**	**—**	**—**	**4.6%**	**9.1%**	**7.7%**

RYMAN HOSPITALITY PROPERTIES, INC.

Ryman Hospitality Properties (formerly Gaylord Entertainment) may be hollerin' for attention in the hospitality game but it's no corporate hayseed. Its properties consist of resort hotels tethered closely to attractions that appeal to the meetings and conventions market. They include the Gaylord Opryland Resort & Convention Center in Nashville the Gaylord Palms Resort in Florida (close to Disney World) the Gaylord Texan Resort near Dallas and the Gaylord National Resort and Convention Center in the Washington DC area. Ryman's hotels are managed by hotel giant Marriott. In 2012 the company changed its name convered to a REIT and sold its hotel brand and management business to Marriott.

HISTORY

The origins of Gaylord Entertainment can be traced back to the Oklahoma Publishing Co. a newspaper publishing company founded by Edward K. Gaylord Ray Dickinson and Roy McClintock in 1903. The publisher of The Daily Oklahoman Oklahoma Publishing branched into radio in 1928 with the purchase of Oklahoma City radio station WKY. With its 1949 creation of Oklahoma City television station WKY-TV Oklahoma Publishing made the leap into television.

Edward K. Gaylord died in 1974 at the age of 101 and his son Edward L. Gaylord was appointed CEO. Under his leadership the company purchased Opryland USA in 1983 — an acquisition that netted it the Grand Ole Opry Opryland Themepark and the Opryland Hotel. Opryland USA also launched country music cable network The Nashville Network that year.

In 1991 the increasingly diverse Oklahoma Publishing spun off its entertainment and broadcast holdings in the form of public company Gaylord Entertainment which established its headquarters in Nashville Tennessee. Gaylord Entertainment acquired a majority interest in cable music network Country Music Television (CMT) the same year. It later expanded CMT into Latin America Asia and the Pacific Rim. CMT also made a brief foray into Europe but that initiative was ended in 1998.

Facing a consolidating entertainment and media landscape Gaylord sold The Nashville Network and the US operations of CMT to Westinghouse (now CBS) in 1997. It also sold television station KSTW that year. The company expanded its reach into Christian music with the purchase of Word Entertainment and its 1997 acquisition of Blanton Harrell Entertainment gave Gaylord a presence in artist management. Terry London was appointed CEO in 1997.

The company closed its Opryland theme park in 1998 in the face of declining attendance and broke ground at the same site for the Opry Mills entertainment shopping and restaurant complex (opened 2000). Gaylord also purchased a Nashville Ramada Inn in 1998 (later renaming it Radisson Hotel at Opryland). With its 1998 acquisition of Paris-based Pandora Investment Gaylord branched into film distribution.

In 1999 the company formed Opryland Hospitality Group to oversee expansion of the Opryland hotel concept across the US. It also sold its last television station KTVT in Dallas/Fort Worth to CBS. Edward K. Gaylord II succeeded his father as chairman in 1999. That year the company launched its Internet division GETdigitalmedia (later renamed

Gaylord Digital) and moved online with the purchase of Christian Web sites Musicforce.com and Lightsource.com. Later the same year the company expanded its Internet presence with the purchase of Songs.com a music Web site focused on independent artists. But in late 2000 the company announced it would close its Internet unit. Also in 2000 the company bought Corporate Magic a firm focused on producing entertainment events for corporate audiences.

At the end of 2000 Gaylord sold Musicforce.com to Christian Book Distributors. Following that sale it sold Lightsource.com to LifeAudio.com in early 2001. That year the company sold its film and television production units and announced a restructuring in order to cut costs. It also renamed Opryland Hotels to Gaylord Opryland while expanding into Texas and Florida. Colin Reed was appointed CEO in 2001.

Between 2001 and 2003 Gaylord Entertainment sold Word Entertainment to Warner Music Group the Opry Mills shopping and restaurant complex to The Mills Corporation the Acuff-Rose Music Publishing business to Sony/ATV two of its Nashville radio stations to Cumulus Media and its majority interest in the Oklahoma City Redhawks minor league baseball team.

Edward L. Gaylord officially retired from the company in 2003 at age 83. Also that year the company significantly expanded its hospitality business with the purchase of ResortQuest a vacation and condominium property management firm. In 2004 the Gaylord family sold more than half its shares in the company making Gabelli Funds the majority owner.

In 2005 Gaylord acquired 50% of Corporate Magic a Dallas-based provider of production support for corporate meetings and events. It did so to support its meeting and convention facilities.

The company unloaded its minority interest in minor league hockey team the Nashville Predators in 2005. Two years later it sold ResortQuest to a subsidiary of Leucadia National Corp. for $35 million. Also in 2007 it sold its interest in sporting goods store operator Bass Pro Group. In 2008 the company opened the Gaylord National Resort and Convention Center in the Washington DC area. The property has some 2000 rooms and approximately 450000 square feet of meeting space.

Also in 2008 Gaylord terminated plans to acquire the Westin La Cantera Resort in San Antonio for about $253 million citing a tough economic environment. In addition the 2008 sale of its ResortQuest subsidiary an online booking service in vacation rentals property management and resort real estate sales fit the company's strategy of selling off assets that aren't related to its Grand Ole Opry or its operations in the meetings and convention market.

In 2009 the company responded to weak earnings by cutting approximately 500 jobs across all areas of the business. Gaylord reported steep dip in profits in 2010 primarily due to harsh flooding in Nashville when the Cumberland River rose to historic levels flowing over protective levees. The flood resulted in property damage and temporary closures at its properties in Nashville causing lost revenues and an increase in expenses. Also in 2010 Gaylord sold its 50% stake in Corporate Magic back to that company's CEO.

The company changed its name to Ryman Hospitality Properties in 2012. It also converted to an REIT and sold the Gaylord brand to Marriott which now manages Ryman's hotel properties and certain other entertainment holdings.

EXECUTIVES

EVP Ryman Hospitality Properties; President OPRY Entertainment Group, Stephen G. (Steve) Buchanan
Chairman and CEO, Colin V. Reed, age 69, $782,830 total compensation
SVP Investments Design and Construction, Bennett D. Westbrook, age 50, $318,447 total compensation
President and CFO, Mark Fioravanti, age 55, $469,407 total compensation
SVP Asset Management, Patrick Chaffin, age 43, $274,975 total compensation
SVP General Counsel and Secretary, Scott J. Lynn, age 43, $364,876 total compensation
Senior Vice President and Corporate Controller, Jennifer Hutcheson
Vice President Human Resources, Shawn Smith
Auditors: ERNST & YOUNG LLP NASHVILLE

LOCATIONS

HQ: RYMAN HOSPITALITY PROPERTIES, INC.
1 GAYLORD DR, NASHVILLE, TN 372141207
Phone: 615 316-6000
Web: WWW.RYMANHP.COM

PRODUCTS/OPERATIONS

2015 Sales

	$ mil.	% of total
Hospitality	994	91
Entertainment (previously Opry and Attractions)	97	9
Total	**1,092**	**100**

2015 Sales

	$ mil.	% of total
Food and beverage	461	42
Rooms	404	37
Other hotel revenue	129	12
Entertainment (previously Opry and Attractions)	97	9
Total	**1,092**	**100**

Select Operations

Hospitality
Gaylord Opryland Resort & Convention Center (Tennessee)
Gaylord Palms Resort & Convention Center (Florida)
Gaylord Texan Resort & Convention Center
Radisson Hotel at Opryland (Tennessee)
Attractions
Gaylord Springs Golf Links (golf club Tennessee)
General Jackson Showboat
Grand Ole Opry
Ryman Auditorium
Wildhorse Saloon
WSM-AM

COMPETITORS

CKX
CKX
Caesars Entertainment
Caesars Entertainment
Disney Parks & Resorts
Disney Parks & Resorts
Elvis Presley Enterprises
Elvis Presley Enterprises
Herschend Entertainment
Herschend Entertainment
Hershey Entertainment
Hershey Entertainment
Hilton Worldwide
Hilton Worldwide
Kennywood
Kennywood
Las Vegas Sands
Las Vegas Sands
Live Nation Entertainment
Live Nation Entertainment
MGM Resorts
MGM Resorts
Marriott

Marriott
New York Convention Center Operating Corporation
New York Convention Center Operating Corporation
SeaWorld
SeaWorld
Welk Group
Welk Group

HISTORICAL FINANCIALS
Company Type: Private

Income Statement

	ASSETS ($ mil.)	NET INCOME ($ mil.)	INCOME AS % OF ASSETS	EMPLOYEES
12/16	2,405	159	6.6%	682
12/15	2,331	111	4.8%	—
12/14	2,413	126	5.2%	—
12/13	2,424	113	4.7%	—
Annual Growth	**(0.3%)**	**12.0%**	**—**	**—**

FYE: December 31

2016 Year-End Financials

Debt ratio: ——
Return on equity: 13.90%
Cash ($ mil.): 59
Current ratio: —
Long-term debt ($ mil.): —
Dividends
Yield: —
Payout: —
Market value ($ mil.): —

S & T Bancorp Inc (Indiana, PA)

S&T Bancorp is the bank holding company for S&T Bank which boasts nearly $5 billion in assets and serves customers from some 60 branch offices in western Pennsylvania. Targeting individuals and local businesses the bank offers such standard retail products as checking savings and money market accounts CDs and credit cards. Business loans including commercial mortgages make up more than 80% of the company's loan portfolio. The bank also originates residential mortgages construction loans and consumer loans. Through subsidiaries S&T Bank sells life disability and commercial property/casualty insurance provides investment management services and advises the Stewart Capital Mid Cap Fund.

Operations
S&T Bancorp operates through three main business segments: Community Banking which offers traditional banking services and commercial and consumer loans; Wealth Management which boasts $2 billion in assets under management and administration and provides brokerage services trust and custodial services and investment advisory for affluent individuals and institutions; and Insurance which offers commercial property and casualty insurance group life and health coverage employee benefit services and personal insurance products through S&T Insurance Group LLC.

Its S&T Bancholding subsidiary provides investment services in the Wealth Management segment while its Stewart Capital Advisors subsidiary provides investment advisory services in the segment.

Overall S&T Bancorp generated 72% of its total revenue from loan interest (including fees) in 2014 plus another 6% from interest on its investment securities. About 10% of its total revenue came from debit and credit card fees and deposit account service charges while wealth management fees and insurance fees made up 6% and 3% of total revenue that year respectively.

Geographic Reach

Headquartered in Indiana Pennsylvania S&T Bancorp boasts branches in a dozen counties in the state including: Allegheny Armstrong Blair Butler Cambria Centre Clarion Clearfield Indiana Jefferson Washington and Westmoreland counties. It also has loan production offices in northeast and central Ohio and in western New York.

Sales and Marketing

Targeting both individuals and local businesses S&T Bancorp spent $3.32 million on marketing in 2014 up from the $2.93 million and $3.21 million it spent in 2013 and 2012 respectively.

Financial Performance

S&T Bancorp's revenue has slowly declined in recent years due to shrinking interest margins on loans amidst the low-interest environment. The firm's profits however have been rising thanks to declining loan loss provisions as its loan portfolio's credit quality has improved with the strengthened economy.

Following several years of top-line declines the bank's revenue inched up by nearly 1% to $206.86 million in 2014. The rise was mostly thanks to higher interest income as overall earning-asset balances grew by nearly 7% during the year reflecting the bank's growing loan business and increased investment securities assets. Wealth Management fees also continued to grow rising by 6% during the year.

Higher revenue coupled with lower interest expenses on deposits and a $6.6 million reduction in loan loss provisions in 2014 drove S&T Bancorp's net income higher by 15% to $57.91 million. S&T's operating cash levels fell by 9% to $78.1 million for the year after adjusting its earnings for non-cash items mostly related to its net proceeds from sales of its mortgage loans originated-for-sale.

Strategy

S&T Bancorp reiterated in 2015 that its growth strategy is centered around organic growth in existing and new markets and growth through strategic acquisitions that introduce new lines of business. Its 2015 acquisition of Integrity Bancshares for example expanded S&T's footprint eastward across four counties in Pennsylvania and added millions of dollars worth of new loan business. Also that year the bank entered the western part of New York for the first time with the opening of a new loan production office in the region.

In late 2012 the bank extended its operations into its neighbor Ohio when it opened a handful of branches in Akron. That same year the bank acquired Mainline Bancorp and Gateway Bank of Pennsylvania bolstering its presence in its core western Pennsylvania market.

Mergers and Acquisitions

In March 2015 S&T Bancorp purchased Camp Hill-based Integrity Bancshares for $155 million adding $860 million in assets and eight branches expanding S&T's geographic footprint eastward into Cumberland Dauphin Lancaster and York counties in Pennsylvania. S&T added that the acquisition positioned the bank in high-growth markets within the state and added experienced members to the bank's loan team.

In 2012 the bank acquired Mainline Bancorp and Gateway Bank of Pennsylvania. Both transactions served to expand S&T's presence in western Pennsylvania.

EXECUTIVES

SVP Operations and Technology, David P. Ruddock, age 55, $265,000 total compensation
Executive Vice President, Tony E Kallsen
President and CEO S&T and S&T Bank, Todd D. Brice, age 54, $525,000 total compensation

EVP and Retail Banking Division Manager, Richard A. (Rich) Fiscus
SEVP and CFO, Mark Kochvar, age 56, $278,000 total compensation
SEVP and Chief Lending Officer, David G. Antolik, age 50, $302,000 total compensation
EVP and Chief Investment Officer Wealth Management, Malcolm E. Polley, age 54
SEVP Chief Risk Officer and Secretary, Ernest J. Draganza
EVP and Deputy Chief Credit Officer, William (Bill) Kametz
SEVP and Chief Credit Officer, Patrick Haberfield
SEVP and Chief Banking Officer, Rebecca Stapleton
EVP and Commercial Loan Officer, Steve Drahnak
EVP and Chief Audit Executive, LaDawn D. Yesho
EVP, David Richards
EVP Marketing Division Manager, Rob Jorgenson
EVP and CIO, Jim Mill
EVP and Manager, Robert Jogrenson
SEVP and Market Executive, Thomas J. Sposito
Market President Central Pennsylvania, Jordan Space
Market President Northeast Ohio, Steve Hendricks
Assistant Vice President Finance Analyst, Stephanie Kline
Vice President Credit Analysis Operation Manager, Dennis Scott
Vice President Marketing, Kelly Corrinne
Vice President Network Operations Manager, Ron Todd
Vice President Community Banking, Tammy Czyz
Vice President Regional Manager, Megan White
Chairman S&T and S&T Bank, Charles G. Urtin
Vice Chairman S&T and S&T Bank, Christine J. Toretti, age 60
Auditors: KPMG LLP

LOCATIONS

HQ: S & T Bancorp Inc (Indiana, PA)
800 Philadelphia Street, Indiana, PA 15701
Phone: 800 325-2265
Web: www.stbancorp.com

PRODUCTS/OPERATIONS

2014 Sales

	% of total
Interest	
Loans including fees	72
Investment securities & other	6
Noninterest	
Wealth management fees	6
Debit and credit card fees	5
Service charges on deposit accounts	5
Insurance fees	3
Others	3
Total	**100**

Selected Subsidiaries

9th Street Holdings Inc.
Commonwealth Trust Credit Life Insurance Company (50%)
S&T Bank
  S&T Insurance Group LLC
  S&T-Evergreen Insurance LLC
  S&T Bancholdings Inc.
  S&T Professional Resources Group LLC
  S&T Settlement Services LLC
  Stewart Capital Advisors LLC

COMPETITORS

AmeriServ Financial
Citizens Financial Group
F.N.B. (PA)
Fidelity Bancorp (PA)
First Commonwealth Financial
Northwest Bancshares
PNC Financial

HISTORICAL FINANCIALS

Company Type: Public

Income Statement

FYE: December 31

	ASSETS ($ mil.)	NET INCOME ($ mil.)	INCOME AS % OF ASSETS	EMPLOYEES
12/16	6,943	71	1.0%	1,080
12/15	6,318	67	1.1%	1,067
12/14	4,964	57	1.2%	945
12/13	4,533	50	1.1%	948
12/12	4,526	34	0.8%	1,027
Annual Growth	**11.3%**	**20.2%**	**—**	**1.3%**

2016 Year-End Financials

Debt ratio: 0.87%
Return on equity: 8.71%
Cash ($ mil.): 139
Current ratio: —
Long-term debt ($ mil.): —

No. of shares (mil.): 34
Dividends
  Yield: 0.0%
  Payout: 37.5%
Market value ($ mil.): 1,363

	STOCK PRICE ($) FY Close	P/E High/Low	PER SHARE ($) Earnings	Dividends	Book Value
12/16	39.04	19 11	2.05	0.77	24.12
12/15	30.82	17 13	1.98	0.73	22.76
12/14	29.81	16 11	1.95	0.68	20.42
12/13	25.31	15 10	1.70	0.61	19.21
12/12	18.07	20 13	1.18	0.60	18.08
Annual Growth	**21.2%**	**—**	**14.8%**	**6.4%**	**7.5%**

S&P Global Inc

S&P Global (formerly McGraw-Hill Financial) is a provider of credit ratings benchmarks and analytics for the global capital and commodity markets. The company was a leading publisher of textbooks tests and related materials serving the elementary secondary and higher education markets through McGraw-Hill Education (MHE) before it spun that business off in 2013. Its products include businesses include S&P Ratings (indexes and credit ratings) and S&P Indices (financial and business information).

Operations

S&P Global has three reportable segments: Ratings Market and Commodities Intelligence and S&P Dow Jones Indices.

Market and Commodities Intelligence is the largest segment. It contributed for 45% of the company's total revenue in fiscal 2016. The segment helps the financial community track performance generate better investment returns identify new trading and investment ideas perform risk analysis develop mitigation strategies and provide high-value information. It includes the following business lines: Financial Data & Analytics Risk Services and S&P Global Platts.

The Ratings segment (44% of revenue in fiscal 2016) provides credit ratings research and analytics to investors issuers and other market participants.

S&P Dow Jones Indices (11% of revenue in fiscal 2016) maintains a wide variety of indices for investors. It makes its money from investment vehicles exchange listed derivatives index-related licensing fees and data and customized index subscription fees.

Geographic Reach

S&P Global operates in 95 countries around the world. The company has more than 100 office locations with about 30 in the US. The US is the company's largest market accounting for more than 60% of the company's revenue while Europe is responsible for roughly 25% of total revenue and Asia 10%.

Sales and Marketing

S&P Global's Ratings segment serves investors corporations governments municipalities commercial and investment banks insurance companies asset managers and other debt issuers.

The company's Market and Commodities Intelligence segment serves asset managers investment banks investors brokers financial advisors and insurance companies among others.

S&P Global spends millions per year on advertising and promotional costs. It spent $35 million on advertising in fiscal 2016.

Financial Performance

S&P Global's revenue has been growing year-over-year.

In fiscal 2016 revenue climbed $5.6 billion (up from $5.3 billion the prior fiscal year) as increases in average contract values for each new customer relationships drove growth in the Capital IQ and SNL segment. Points of strength were S&P Capital IQ Desktop RatingsXpress and RatingsDirect.

S&P Global's net income nearly doubled in fiscal 2016 compared to the previous fiscal period. It claimed a net income of $2.1 billion in fiscal 2016 up from $1.2 billion for 2015. This was a result of higher net revenue combined with a decrease in selling and general expenses.

Net cash from operations was $1.4 billion in fiscal 2016 up from $195 million for 2015.

Strategy

S&P Global spun off its education business (and changed its name) in response to decreased spending on elementary and high school textbooks. Its financial business which provides global financial information research and analytics tools to investment advisors wealth managers and institutional investors has fared better.

Mergers and Acquisitions

In 2016 S&P Global acquired RigData a provider of daily information on rig activity for the natural gas and oil markets across North America. The acquisition strengthened S&P Global's position in natural gas and enhanced its oil offering.

S&P Global also acquired PIRA Energy Group a leader in global energy market analysis in 2016. The acquisition extended S&P Global's energy analytical capabilities.

EXECUTIVES

Vice President Technology, Rosalin Danner
President and CEO, Douglas L. (Doug) Peterson, age 58, $1,000,000 total compensation
President S&P Global Platts, Martin Fraenkel
Chief Global Economist and Head of Global Economics and Research, Paul Sheard, age 63
President S&P Global Ratings, John L. Berisford, age 53, $600,000 total compensation
EVP and General Counsel, Steven J. (Steve) Kemps, age 53, $204,167 total compensation
Managing Director and CEO CRISIL, Ashu Suyash, age 50
EVP and CFO, Ewout L. Steenbergen, age 48, $99,432 total compensation
CEO S&P Dow Jones Indices, Alexander J. (Alex) Matturri, age 58, $493,750 total compensation
EVP Public Affairs, Courtney Geduldig
President S&P Global Market Intelligence, Michael A. (Mike) Chinn, $152,308 total compensation
SVP Human Resources, France M. Gingras, age 52
CIO, Swamy Kocherlakota
Vice President Of Marketing, Connie Howard
Vice President International Affairs, Cynthia Baraddon
Vice President Investor Relations, Chip Merritt
Vice President, Maryann Johnston

Senior Vice President and Publisher North America BusinessWeek, Geoffrey A Dodge
Senior Vice President, Peter Scheschuk
Senior Vice President and Treasurer, Edward Haran
Vice President Global Channel Sales and Alliances, Dominic Camillo
Vice President Head of Innovation, Dmitri Sedov
Vice President Senior Sales Manager, Bill Eggers
Vice President Index Services, Roby Muntoni
National Accounts Manager, Nicole Nicdao
Chairman, Charles E. (Ed) Haldeman, age 68
Auditors: Ernst & Young LLP

LOCATIONS

HQ: S&P Global Inc
  55 Water Street, New York, NY 10041
Phone: 212 438-1000
Web: www.spglobal.com

2016 Sales

	$ mil.	% of total
US	3,461	61
Europe	1,330	24
Asia	575	10
Other regions	295	5
Total	**5,661**	**100**

PRODUCTS/OPERATIONS

2016 Sales

	$ mil.	% of total
Market and Commodities Intelligence	2,585	45
Ratings	2,535	44
Indices	639	11
Adjustments	(98)	-
Total	**5,661**	**100**

COMPETITORS

A.M. Best	Interactive Data
Bloomberg L.P.	MSCI
D&B	Moody's
DBRS	Morningstar
Fair Isaac	Thomson Reuters
Fitch Ratings Inc.	

HISTORICAL FINANCIALS

Company Type: Public

Income Statement

FYE: December 31

	REVENUE ($ mil.)	NET INCOME ($ mil.)	NET PROFIT MARGIN	EMPLOYEES
12/17	6,063	1,496	24.7%	20,400
12/16	5,661	2,106	37.2%	20,000
12/15	5,313	1,156	21.8%	20,400
12/14	5,051	(115)	—	17,000
12/13	4,875	1,376	28.2%	17,000
Annual Growth	**5.6%**	**2.1%**	**—**	**4.7%**

2017 Year-End Financials

Debt ratio: 37.87%	No. of shares (mil.): 253
Return on equity: 219.84%	Dividends
Cash ($ mil.): 2,779	Yield: 0.0%
Current ratio: 1.35	Payout: 28.3%
Long-term debt ($ mil.): 3,170	Market value ($ mil.): 42,977

	STOCK PRICE ($) FY Close	P/E High/Low		PER SHARE ($) Earnings	Dividends	Book Value
12/17	169.40	30	19	5.78	1.64	2.80
12/16	107.54	16	10	7.94	1.44	2.52
12/15	98.58	25	20	4.21	1.32	0.73
12/14	88.98	—	—	(0.42)	1.20	1.79
12/13	78.20	15	9	4.91	3.62	4.80
Annual Growth	**21.3% (12.6%)**			**4.2% (18.0%)**		

Safety Insurance Group, Inc.

Buckle up Bostonians car safety first! Safety Insurance Group through subsidiaries Safety Insurance Safety Indemnity Insurance and Safety Property and Casualty sells property/casualty insurance exclusively in Massachusetts Maine and New Hampshire. It is one of the top private passenger automobile and commercial automobile insurers in the region controlling more than 10% of the markets in its home state. Safety Insurance also provides homeowners dwelling fire personal umbrella and business-owner policies; it cross-sells its non-auto property/casualty products to increase its share of the market. The firm sells its products through more than 920 independent agents and more than 1100 offices.

Geographic Reach

Safety Insurance operates in Massachusetts Maine and New Hampshire.

Sales and Marketing

The company distributes its policies through more than 920 independent agents in some 1102 offices.

Auto insurance makes up the lion's share of the group's written premiums with private passenger auto insurance contributing 60% of its direct written premiums Homeowners insurance accounts for about 20% of written premiums while commercial automobile insurance accounts for about 15%.

In 2015 Safety Insurance spent $1.9 million on advertising down from $2.1 million in each of 2014 and 2013.

Financial Performance

Revenue has been rising for the past five years. It grew 2% to $798 million in 2015 thanks to growth in its commercial automobile and homeowners insurance businesses which was largely attributed to the company's efforts to cross-sell those products to existing personal automobile coverage customers. However Safety Insurance saw a decline in investment income that year.

The company also saw its first net loss that year. It lost a net $14 million due to higher loss and loss adjustment expenses brought about by record snowfall in Massachusetts (which resulted in higher catastrophe and non-catastrophe claims). Following suit cash flow from operations fell 77% to $23 million.

Strategy

Safety Insurance's strategy for growth includes the possibility of reaching out beyond its core market and entering new territories although this has been done on a limited basis. Another measure the company takes to build business is to lower costs by bundling policies (homeowners and auto for instance) to attract and retain customers. Additionally Safety Insurance has been investing in technology to improve the way independent agents serve its customers.

EXECUTIVES

VP CFO and Secretary, William J. Begley, age 62, $400,000 total compensation
VP Property Claims, David E. Krupa, age 56, $210,796 total compensation
VP Underwriting, James D. Berry, age 57, $263,682 total compensation
President and CEO, George M. Murphy, age 50, $350,000 total compensation
VP Insurance Operations, Ann M. McKeown
VP Casualty Claims, Paul J. Narciso, age 53

VP Management Information Systems, Stephen A. Varga, age 49
VP Marketing, John P. Drago
Auditors: PricewaterhouseCoopers LLP

LOCATIONS

HQ: Safety Insurance Group, Inc.
20 Custom House Street, Boston, MA 02110
Phone: 617 951-0600   **Fax:** 617 603-4837
Web: www.safetyinsurance.com

PRODUCTS/OPERATIONS

2015 Sales

	% of total
Net earned premiums	92
Net investment income	5
Finance & other service income	2
Earnings from partnership investments	1
Adjustments	-
Total	**100**

COMPETITORS

AIG	Plymouth Rock
Allstate	Assurance
Ameriprise	Preferred Mutual
Arbella Insurance	Progressive
Electric Insurance	Corporation
Foremost Insurance	Quincy Mutual
GEICO	Travelers of
Liberty Mutual	Massachusetts
MAPFRE USA	Vermont Mutual
OneBeacon	

HISTORICAL FINANCIALS

Company Type: Public

Income Statement

FYE: December 31

	ASSETS ($ mil.)	NET INCOME ($ mil.)	INCOME AS % OF ASSETS	EMPLOYEES
12/16	1,758	64	3.7%	643
12/15	1,703	(13)	—	622
12/14	1,675	59	3.5%	610
12/13	1,625	61	3.8%	605
12/12	1,574	58	3.7%	599
Annual Growth	**2.8%**	**2.7%**	**—**	**1.8%**

2016 Year-End Financials

Debt ratio: —
Return on equity: 9.79%
Cash ($ mil.): 20
Current ratio: —
Long-term debt ($ mil.): —

No. of shares (mil.): 15
Dividends
  Yield: 0.0%
  Payout: 65.5%
Market value ($ mil.): 1,117

	STOCK PRICE ($) FY Close	P/E High/Low	PER SHARE ($) Earnings	Dividends	Book Value
12/16	73.70	17 12	4.27	2.80	44.27
12/15	56.38	— —	(0.93)	2.80	42.70
12/14	64.01	17 13	3.91	2.60	47.19
12/13	56.30	14 12	3.98	2.40	45.18
12/12	46.17	13 10	3.80	2.20	45.31
Annual Growth	**12.4%**	**— —**	**3.0%**	**6.2%**	**(0.6%)**

SAINT THOMAS HEALTH SERVICES, INC.

Auditors: DELOITTE TAX LP CINCINNATI O

LOCATIONS

HQ: SAINT THOMAS HEALTH SERVICES, INC.
4220 HARDING PIKE, NASHVILLE, TN 372052005
Phone: 615 222-2111
Web: WWW.STTHOMAS.ORG

HISTORICAL FINANCIALS

Company Type: Private

Income Statement

FYE: June 30

	ASSETS ($ mil.)	NET INCOME ($ mil.)	INCOME AS % OF ASSETS	EMPLOYEES
06/13	1,967	(28)	—	4,650
06/10	79	(20)	—	—
06/09	95	(25)	—	—
06/08	8	0	0.2%	—
Annual Growth	**200.7%**	**—**	**—**	**—**

2013 Year-End Financials

Debt ratio: —
Return on equity: (-12.80%)
Cash ($ mil.): 0
Current ratio: 0.30
Long-term debt ($ mil.): —

Dividends
  Yield: —
  Payout: —
Market value ($ mil.): —

Salesforce.Com Inc

Salesforce.com could fill the sky with its clouds. The company offers cloud-based applications that manage employee collaboration as well as customer information for sales (Salesforce Sales Cloud) marketing (Salesforce Marketing Cloud) and customer support (Salesforce Service Cloud). Other products offer e-commerce analytics and social media tools through cloud-based applications. Salesforce counts more than 150000 users of its customer relationship management (CRM) software and its customers come from a variety of industries including financial services telecommunications manufacturing and entertainment. It generates most of its revenue in the US.

Operations

Besides its big three cloud products ? Sales Cloud Service Cloud and Marketing Cloud Salesforce.com offers several others that help companies manage their relationships with customers.

They include: Commerce Cloud which provides e-commerce experience tools for web mobile social and store environments; Community Cloud which helps companies create and manage branded digital destinations for customers partners and employees; IoT (Internet of Things) Cloud which helps companies collect information from connected devices products sensors and apps; Analytics Cloud which helps an employee across explore business data and uncover from any device; and Salesforce Quip a productivity tool designed for teams.

Salesforce also offers consulting services for deployment training and design and integration.

The company runs many of its cloud services on Amazon Web Services.

Geographic Reach

About three-quarters of Salesforce.com?s sales comes from customers in the Americas. The US accounts for about 96% of the Americas revenue. Customers in Europe account for about 15% of revenue and those in the Asia/Pacific region generate about 10%.

Sales and Marketing

Salesforce.com counts more than 150000 users from small businesses with one subscription to large enterprises with thousands. With such a large customer base no one customer counts for more than 5% of sales.

The company uses a direct sales force made up of telephone sales reps based in regional hubs and field sales reps in territories close to their customers. It also works with consulting firms systems integrators and others to find customers. For successful sales Salesforce pays a fee based on the first-year subscription revenue generated by the referred customers.

Salesforce spends about 45% of revenue on sales and marketing a level the company expects to maintain as it seeks more customers and build awareness. The company continues to ramp up advertising spending which has increased more than 40% in recent years.

Financial Performance

Salesforce has reported robust revenue increases over its history but it lost money from 2012-2016. That streak ended in 2017 (ended January).

Revenue reached about $8.4 billion in 2017 a 26% increase from $6.7 billion in 2016. Subscription and support revenue jumped about 25% to $7.8 billion (more than 90 percent of total revenue) in 2017. The increase was driven by new business which includes new customers and existing customers buying upgrades and additional subscriptions. Demandware acquired during the fiscal year contributed about $120 million in revenue. Revenue from professional services (8% of revenue) increased 38% in 2017.

Salesforce recorded net income of about $180 million in 2017 compared to a $4.7 million loss in 2016. The jump in revenue more than covered expenses that were higher across the board in 2017. A 34% increase in headcount (about 5000 workers) was responsible for much of the higher expense.

Cash generated by operating activities rose to $2.2 billion in 2017 from $1.7 billion in 2016. Among the factors affecting cash flow from operations were acquisition-related transaction fees.

Strategy

In 2017 Salesforce.com?s record highs in sales and profit put the company on Cloud 9. Its biggest business Sales Cloud accounted for $3 billion in revenue by itself making it bigger than some independent cloud software companies. The company?s other strong performer Service Cloud brought in another $2.5 billion. While those are the big moneymakers Salesforce?s customers generally buy more than one of the company?s clouds. In the fourth quarter of its 2017 year 80% of customers bought multiple cloud services.

To strengthen those clouds Salesforce injected artificial intelligence into them in 2017. Called Einstein the AI helps Salesforce?s customers more effectively analyze data and draw meaningful conclusions that help them understand their customers better. Salesforce sees Einstein as an advantage in attracting new customers as well as tempting current customers to upgrade their services.

Another key move in 2017 was the acquisition of Demandware. At a price of $2.8 billion it was Salesforce?s biggest purchase in its history. The deal added e-commerce capabilities to Salesforce?s offerings in addition to its customer relationship management products. Demandware was renamed Commerce Cloud in Salesforce and accounted for $120 million in revenue in less than a year. The acquisition gives Salesforce another product to offers its customers and it exposes Salesforce to another set of customers.

Mergers and Acquisitions

Salesforce.com added to its cloud products with its 2016 acquisition of Demandware for $2.8 billion. As a part of Salesforce Demandware became Commerce Cloud an integration of its e-commerce capabilities with Salesforce's customer relationship management offerings.

Other acquisitions in the company 2017 fiscal year (ended January) were SteelBrick Inc. which automates the quote-to-cash process; MetaMind Inc. natural language processing and image recognition across the Salesforce clouds; BeyondCore Inc. smart data discovery technology for structured data sources; Quip Inc. productivity software; and Krux Digital Inc. a data management platform.

EXECUTIVES

Chairman and CEO, Marc Benioff, age 52, $1,550,000 total compensation
President and Chief Strategy Officer, Alexandre (Alex) Dayon, age 49, $900,000 total compensation
Vice Chairman President and COO, Keith G. Block, age 55, $1,150,000 total compensation
President Global Customer Success and Salesforce Latin America, Maria Martinez, age 59
President and CFO, Mark J. Hawkins, age 57, $750,000 total compensation
EVP Global Real Estate, Elizabeth Pinkham
President and Chief Product Officer, Bret Taylor
President Legal and General Counsel, Amy E. Weaver, age 49
EVP Corporate Relations and Chief Philanthropy Officer, Suzanne DiBianca
President and Chief People Officer, Cindy Robbins, age 44
Vice President Technology and Alliance, Ryuji Enoki
Regional Vice President, Adam Gilberd
Vice President Customer Success Strategy and Operations, Neeracha Taychakhoonavudh
Vice President Custom Cloud and Sales Strategy, Allyson Fryhoff
Area Vice President, Robert Zimmermann
Vice President Corporate Sales, Phil Bradley
Regional Vice President Sales Salesforce. experience success, Julie Hall
Vice President Sale, Paul Seminara
Executive Vice President Operations And Mobility, Todd Pierce
Vice President Global Operations Salesforce University, Shane Anastasi
Vice President, Sherie Berger
Regional Vice President Corporate Sales Silicon Valley, Tony Rodoni
Executive Vice President, Nasi Jazayeri
Vice President Customer Success, Greg Tate
VP Admin Marketing, Sarah Franklin
Area Vice President, Philip Klebba
Vice President Strategic Events Dreamforce, Catherine Simmons
Sr. Vice President, Jon Sigler
Senior Vice President and UKI Managing Director, Andrew Lawson
Assistant Vice President Enterprise Sales, Olivier Derrien
SVP and Global Head of Tax, Darryl Yee
Vice President of Engineering for Data com, Alex Hu
SVP Communities Engineering, Stephen Ayers
Regional Vice President, Jeffrey Pope
Regional Vice President West Area Enterprise Key Accounts, Grant Wood
Vice President, Mary Heston

Regional Vice President, Craig Lashmet
Regional Vice President, Sheldon Buytenhuys
Vice President Customer Intelligence, Ashfaq Mohiuddin
Regional Vice President, David Rubinstein
Regional Vice President, Joe Haney
Regional Vice President Success Services, Jon Lokay
Regional Vice President, Tim Murdoch
Area Vice President Financial Services, Shane Trigg
Regional Vice President Commercial Sales, David Jeffrey
Vice President Product Management, Ketan Karkhanis
Vice President Technical Strategy, Philip Richardson
Vice President Commercial Sales, Colin Lau
RVP Central Region, Jean Bright
Regional Vice President Healthcare and Life Sciences, Sonia Xavier
Regional Vice President Public Sector, Marie Hannigan
Regional Vice President Sales, Bob Vanstraelen
Area Vice President, Samuel Bonamigo
Regional Vice President Sales for French Market, Julien Bucaille
Area Vice President Commercial Sales, Michael Hartman
Vice President of Developer Relations EMEA, Guillaume Roques
Vice President Industry ISVs, Ross Eberhart
Vice President Global Recruiting Futureforce, Suzana Dellisanti
EVP Global Corporate Services, Lisa Edwards
Area Vice President Retail and Consumer Goods, Brian Weinberger
Regional Vice President, Andrew Boehm
Area Vice President Enterprise Sales, Laurent Peron
Regional Vice President, Jerry Haywood
Vice President of Sales, Eduardo Merino
RVP N Europe, Luc Schamhart
Area Vice President, Greg Barton
Vice President Enterprise Sales, Greg Janaczek
Senior Vice President, Eric Eyken-Sluyters
Regional Vice President, Carie Buchanan
Senior Vice President, Adam Caplan
Regional Vice President, Norman Gallagher
Vice President, Jason Lorber
Area Vice President, Jerry Schorn
Senior Vice President and General Counsel, Shanti Ariker
Senior Vice President and General Manager Service Cloud, Michael Milburn
Vice President Admin Marketing, Kris Lande
Vice President Partner Account Management, Amy Kodl
Regional Vice President Healthcare and Life Sciences, Darran Newman
Regional Vice President Alliances and Channels Southern Europe, Pascal Voirand
Senior Vice President Ipdo, Casey Cerretani
Regional Vice President Enterprise Sales Service Cloud, Brian Remmel
Vice President North American Sales Consumer Goods Commerce Cloud, Janet Megdadi
Regional Vice President Commerce Cloud Northeast, Charles Ellis
Vice President Enterprise Sales Quip, Lenore Lang
Regional Vice President Retail Solutions, Dan Powers
Assistant Vice President Sales Commerce Cloud, Genna Gwynn
Area Vice President Partner Sales Enterprise AMER, Nicole Gallant
Regional Vice President Alliances Strategic West, Kristine Marlborough
Regional Vice President, Stephanie Glenn
Auditors: Ernst & Young LLP

LOCATIONS

HQ: Salesforce.Com Inc
The Landmark @ One Market, Suite 300, San Francisco, CA 94105
Phone: 415 901-7000
Web: www.salesforce.com

2016 Sales

	$ mil.	% of total
Americas	4,910	74
Europe	1,162	17
Asia/Pacific	593	9
Total	**6,667**	**100**

Selected Mergers and Acquisitions

FY2017
Demandware ($2.8 billion e-commerce software)
SteelBrick Inc. (quote-to-cash automation software)
Quip Inc. (productivity software)
Krux Digital Inc. (data management platform)
FY2013
ExactTarget ($2.5 billion email marketing software)
FY2012
Buddy Media ($690 million social media marketing software)
GoInstant ($50 million collaboration software)
Jigsaw ($140 million business contact data provider)
FY2011
Assistly ($58 million customer service software)
Dimdim (collaboration software)
Heroku ($210 million app development platform)
Manymoon ($13 million social productivity app)
Radian6 ($320 million social networking software)
Model Metrics ($66 million consultancy)
Rypple (social performance management software)

PRODUCTS/OPERATIONS

2016 Sales

	$ mil.	% of total
Subscription & support	6,205	93
Professional services & other	461	7
Total	**6,667**	**100**

COMPETITORS

CDC Software	NetSuite
Google	Oracle
IBM	SAP
Infor Global	Sage Software
KANA	ServiceNow
Microsoft Dynamics	SugarCRM

HISTORICAL FINANCIALS

Company Type: Public

Income Statement

FYE: January 31

	REVENUE ($ mil.)	NET INCOME ($ mil.)	NET PROFIT MARGIN	EMPLOYEES
01/17	8,391	179	2.1%	25,000
01/16	6,667	(47)	—	19,000
01/15	5,373	(262)	—	16,000
01/14	4,071	(232)	—	13,300
01/13	3,050	(270)	—	9,800
Annual Growth	28.8%	—		26.4%

2017 Year-End Financials

Debt ratio: 11.42%	No. of shares (mil.): 707
Return on equity: 2.87%	Dividends
Cash ($ mil.): 1,606	Yield: —
Current ratio: 0.83	Payout: —
Long-term debt ($ mil.): 2,008	Market value ($ mil.): 55,960

	STOCK PRICE ($) FY Close	P/E High/Low	PER SHARE ($) Earnings	Dividends	Book Value
01/17	79.10	322208	0.26	0.00	10.60
01/16	68.06	— —	(0.07)	0.00	7.46
01/15	56.45	— —	(0.42)	0.00	6.11
01/14	60.53	— —	(0.39)	0.00	5.02
01/13	172.13	— —	(0.48)	0.00	4.05
Annual Growth	(17.7%)	— —	—	—	27.2%

Sandy Spring Bancorp Inc

Sandy Spring Bancorp is the holding company for Sandy Spring Bank which operates around 50 branches in the Baltimore and Washington DC metropolitan areas. Founded in 1868 the bank is one of the largest and oldest headquartered in Maryland. It provides standard deposit services including checking and savings accounts money market accounts and CDs. Commercial and residential real estate loans account for nearly three-quarters of the company's loan portfolio; the remainder is a mix of consumer loans business loans and equipment leases. The company also offers personal investing services wealth management trust services insurance and retirement planning.

Operations

Sandy Spring Bancorp's nonbank subsidiaries include money manager West Financial Services and Sandy Spring Insurance which sells annuities and operates insurance agencies Chesapeake Insurance Group and Neff & Associates.

Financial Performance

The company's revenue increased in fiscal 2013 compared to the previous year. It reported $196.9 million in revenue for fiscal 2013 after bringing in revenue of $190.8 million in fiscal 2012.

The company's net income also went up in fiscal 2013 compared to the prior period. It claimed a profit of about $44 million in fiscal 2013 after netting a little more than $36 million in fiscal 2012.

Sandy Spring Bancorp's cash on hand increased by about $43 million in fiscal 2013 compared to fiscal 2012 levels.

Mergers and Acquisitions

In 2012 Sandy Spring Bancorp acquired CommerceFirst Bancorp a small Maryland bank with a strong Small Business Administration lending practice. The $25.4 million transaction added five branches to Sandy Spring Bank's network.

EXECUTIVES

EVP General Counsel and Secretary, Ronald E. Kuykendall, age 64, $279,039 total compensation
EVP Wealth Management Insurance Mortgage, R. Louis (Lou) Caceres, age 54, $333,865 total compensation
President and CEO Bancorp and Bank, Daniel J. (Dan) Schrider, age 52, $600,692 total compensation
EVP and CFO Bancorp and Bank, Philip J. Mantua, age 58, $333,192 total compensation
EVP and CIO, John D. Sadowski, age 53
EVP Commercial and Retail Banking, Joseph O'Brien, $355,038 total compensation
EVP and Chief Credit Officer, Ronda M. McDowell
Senior Vice President, Brian Schott
Assistant Vice President Information Technology, Steve Hyde

Vice President, Christopher Huang
Senior Vice President, Todd Ellis
Senior Business Analyst Assistant Vice President, Stephen Marsico
Vice President Marketing Communications Manager, Jennifer Schell
Vice President Commercial Portfolio, Michael Irwin
Assistant Vice President Branch Manager, Bachi Baldeh
Vice President, Denise Kratz
Vice President HRIS Project Administrator, Patti Boyle
Vice President, Bill Howland
Vice President Commercial Real Estate, Douglas Greene
Vice President, Jeff Richards
Vice President, Isaac Sterbenz
Vice President Commercial Lending, Heather Burke
Assistant Vice President Public Relations Specialist, Amanda Walsh
Vice President Mortgage Division, Bradley Preisinger
VP, Tim Keogh
Assistant Vice President, Chrissy Niper
Senior Vice President, Scott Sims
Assistant Vice President Bsa Aml Administrator, Susan Booth
Assistant Vice President Trust Administrator, Mardelle Channon
Senior Vice President, Mark Slatin
Vice President Manager Of Personal, Larry Arch
Vice President eCommerce, Lisa Johnson
Assistant Vice President, Mark Aswall
Assistant Vice President Branch Manager, Phil Hicks
Vice President of Marketing, Marc Meoli
Vice President, Jessica Butler
Vice President and Fiduciary Officer, Barbara Mulitz
Senior Vice President, Don Haasen
Vice Presidente, Eba Elorza
Vice President, Paul Macdonald
Vice President and Senior Investment Advisor, Jennifer Owen
Vice President Debit and Credit Card Product Manager, Ron Waters
Vice President, Donna Coursey
Vice President Commercial Lending, Tina Dasler
Transaction Services Vice President, Anne Clements
Vice President, John Walker
Executive Vice President, Lou Caceres
Vice President, Christine Wilson
Assistant Vice President Market Relationship Manager, Bud Martin
Vice President Private Banking Division, Ann Conger
VICE PRESIDENT, Cave Katie
SENIOR VICE PRESIDENT DIRECTOR OF REGULATORY MANAGEMENT, Diane Slack
Vice President, Alexis Vining
Vice President Relationship Manager Commercial Banking, Tim Kelley
Vice President Market Relationship Manager, Todd Levine
Chairman, Robert L. Orndorff, age 61
Auditors: Ernst & Young LLP

LOCATIONS

HQ: Sandy Spring Bancorp Inc
17801 Georgia Avenue, Olney, MD 20832
Phone: 301 774-6400
Web: www.sandyspringbank.com

PRODUCTS/OPERATIONS

2015 Sales

	$ mil.	% of total
Interest Income:		
Interest and fees on loans and leases	135	65
Interest and dividends on investment securities	22	11
Other	0	-
Non-interest Income:		
Wealth management income	19	10
Service charges on deposit accounts	7	4
Insurance agency commissions	5	2
Bank card fees	4	2
Mortgage banking activities	3	2
Other Income	9	4
Total	208	100

COMPETITORS

BB&T	Fulton Financial
Bank of America	OBA Financial Services
Bay Bancorp	PNC Financial
Capital One	SunTrust

HISTORICAL FINANCIALS

Company Type: Public

Income Statement

FYE: December 31

	ASSETS ($ mil.)	NET INCOME ($ mil.)	INCOME AS % OF ASSETS	EMPLOYEES
12/16	5,091	48	0.9%	752
12/15	4,655	45	1.0%	737
12/14	4,397	38	0.9%	727
12/13	4,106	44	1.1%	725
12/12	3,955	36	0.9%	707
Annual Growth	6.5%	7.2%	—	1.6%

2016 Year-End Financials

Debt ratio: 0.59%	No. of shares (mil.): 23
Return on equity: 9.10%	Dividends
Cash ($ mil.): 132	Yield: 0.0%
Current ratio: —	Payout: 49.0%
Long-term debt ($ mil.): —	Market value ($ mil.): 956

	STOCK PRICE ($) FY Close	P/E High/Low	PER SHARE ($) Earnings	Dividends	Book Value
12/16	39.99	20 12	2.00	0.98	22.32
12/15	26.96	16 13	1.84	0.90	21.58
12/14	26.08	18 15	1.52	0.76	20.83
12/13	28.19	16 11	1.77	0.64	19.98
12/12	19.42	13 11	1.48	0.48	19.41
Annual Growth	19.8%	— —	7.8%	19.5%	3.6%

Sanmina Corp

Sanmina means to be a top contract manufacturer of sophisticated electronic components. It designs and makes printed circuit boards and board assemblies backplanes and backplane assemblies enclosures cable assemblies optical components and modules and memory modules. In addition the company increasingly provides more value-added services such as design and engineering materials management order fulfillment and in-circuit testing. It serves OEMs in the health care defense medical aerospace telecommunications and technology industries among others. Sanmina puts its manufacturing facilities close to its customers in lower-cost regions. More than 80% of its sales come from operations outside the US.

Operations

Sanmina's Integrated Manufacturing Solutions unit (about 80% of sales) makes printed circuit boards optical and radio frequency modules and conducts assembly and testing. The Components Products and Services unit (about 20% of sales) makes interconnect systems and mechanical systems components in addition to memory and storage products.

Geographic Reach

Sanmina based in San Jose California operates nearly 80 facilities in more than 20 countries. Mexico is the company's largest geographic segment producing 30% of revenue. China accounts for 20% of revenue with US customers generating about 15%.

Sales and Marketing

The company supplies OEMs primarily in the communications networks defense and aerospace industrial and semiconductor systems medical multimedia computing and storage automotive and clean technology sectors. Two markets — Industrial Medical and Defense and Communications Networks — each account for about 40% of revenue. Sanmina's top 10 customers together generate half of sales. Nokia and Motorola Solutions each account for more than 10% of Sanmina's revenue.

Sanmina sells through its direct sales force as well as representative sales firms.

Financial Performance

Sanmina recorded higher revenue for the fourth year in a row with a 6% rise to $6.8 billion n 2017 (ended September). Sales to industrial medical and defense customers rose about 10% driven by a customer program acquisition in February 2016. Communications network sales increased about 10% from program ramps with current customers. Sales to embedded computing and storage customers dropped about 11% due to lower demand for customers' point-of-sale equipment and set-top boxes.

Sanmina?s profit tumbled 25% to about $139 million in 2017 from 2016. The company blamed an unfavorable change in customer mix and reduced overhead efficiency caused by supply constraints design changes and low yields related to new projects in 2017. Several new programs took longer to reach efficienet production levels because of design and manufacturing problems that reduced yields.

In 2017 cash flow from operations slid to $251 million from $390 million in 2016. Despite higher revenue in 2017 several factors combined to reduce cash flow. They included higher inventory fewer inventory turns and an increase in days sales outstanding.

Over the past four years Sanmina has allocated about 43% of cash flow to stock buybacks 35% to capital expenditures 13% to acquisitions and 9% to debt reduction.

Strategy

Part of Sanmina's strategy is to do as much work for its clients as possible. In an increasing number of cases that means working with a customer to design a product practically from the ground up. Additional services provide higher margins to Sanmina than its basic contract manufacturing work. In 2016 Sanmina teamed up with Nokia to make and sell a series of data center products. Sanmina's worldwide network of facilities provide quick delivery of the Nokia data center products to customers in nearby markets. In another situation Sanmina provided hardware elements for products from software provider SAS. While SAS concentrated on the software Sanmina designed and made high speed PCBs enclosures and backplanes for the products.

This feeds into another element of Sanmina's strategy the pursuit of diversification. With half of its revenue coming from just 10 customers the company is seeking new customers in various markets. In the past several years Sanmina's industrial segment has overtaken its communications segments as its biggest revenue producer. Business from the automotive sector has increased as the electronics content of vehicles increases. The company aims to maintain or even increase its rate of customer diversification.

Mergers and Acquisitions

Sanmina supplemented its storage hardware offerings with a software component through an acquisition. The $40 million deal for a privately held company adds data storage software for OEM's and systems integrators to Sanmina's portfolio. With another acquisition Sanmina expanded in manufacturing capabilities in Malaysia. The company bought the factory from a customer for more than $50 million.

In 2015 Sanmina bought a privately-held company that designs and manufactures equipment for the oil and gas industry.

EXECUTIVES

CEO, Robert K. (Bob) Eulau, age 55, $510,000 total compensation

EVP Europe and Asia Sales, Dennis R. Young, age 66, $350,000 total compensation

SVP and CIO, Manesh Patel

EVP Global Human Resources, Alan M. Reid, age 54, $290,000 total compensation

EVP and CFO, David Anderson, age 57

Vice President Business Development, Randy Thomas

Senior Vice President EMS Manufacturing Systems and Services, Bob Swift

Vice President of Sales, Darryl Smith

Vice President, Joseph Mello

Vice President Business Development, Carter Smith

Vice President And General Manager, Joe Wong

Executive Vice President, Bob Cusick

Vice President Finance and Controller, Amy Jones

Vice President and General Manager Assistant, Ingrid Naggiar

Senior Vice President Strategy, Mark Carlton

Vice President Global Supply Management, Troy Hiner

Senior Vice President For Operational Excellence And Quality, Ryan Mehdizadeh

Senior Vice President Marketing, Gelston Howell

Vice President Corporate Sales Services, Richard Laponzina

Vice President Environmental Affairs, Khalid Ruhullah

Vice President Manufacturing Engineering, John Jamieson

Senior Vice President of Mexico Operations, Marco Hagelsieb

Vice President, Tim S Trandai

Vice President Finance, Kevin Collins

Senior Vice President of Global Manufacturing Medical Operations, Gary Switzer

Vice President Corporate Development, George Chen

Vice President Quality Assurance And Ra, Tim McGinnis

Vice President Sales Operations NEMEA, Trevor Black

Senior Vice President Finance And Corporate Controller, Todd Schull

Vice President of Marketing, Frank Guerrero

Vice President, Carl Boklund

Vice President Corporate Finance, Lynne Sullivan

Vice President of Marketing, Daniel Liddle

Vice President General Manager, Alejandro Avila

Vice Presedent GTS Europe, Robert L Hallenbeck

Vice President Finance Tcg, Ted Wilson

Vice President Finance, James Moylan

Senior Vice President Operations, Sushil Dhiman

Vice President Internal Audit, Wendy Phillips

Vice President Business Development, Henrik Oja

Vice President Strategy And Innovation, Geoff Gagne

Executive Vice President, Robert Alberico

Senior Vice President Sales And Marketing Optical And Micro Electronics, Nat Mani

Vice President Internal Audit, Aroon Gudibande

Vice President Operations, Alasdair Waugh

Senior Vice President of New Technologies and Ventures, Naresh Nigam

Vice President Global Business Services, Jean-Marc Orozco

Vice President Quality Assurance Ra, Daniel Marinsik

Vice President, James Griffin

Vice President of Marketing, Michael Sparcino

Senior Vice President PCB Operations, Steve Bruton

Senior Vice President, Robert Swift

EVP Global Human Resources, Dave Pulatie

Senior Vice President East Coast Operations, Jose Carrasquillo

Vice President Finance Controller, Rodger Dunfield

Senior Vice President, Joe Rauschmayer

Senior Vice President Of Operations, Michael Doty

Senior Vice President, Bob Moffat

Vice President Quality Assurance and RA, Kok-kheong Chan

Vice President General Manager, Doug Scrimes

Vice President And General Manager, K?roly Hoffmann

Vice President, Frank O'Reilly

Vice President of Marketing and Recruiting, Deeney Graham

Senior Vice President Quality and Operational Excell, Susaan Hughes

Senior Vice President, Kevin Walkup

Vice President Global Automotive, Bernd Enser

Vice President Business Development EMEA, Doede Douma

Vice President Business Development, David Roeloffs

Chairman, Jure Sola, age 66

Treasurer, Nick Ravlich

Auditors: PricewaterhouseCoopers LLP

LOCATIONS

HQ: Sanmina Corp
2700 N. First Street, San Jose, CA 95134
Phone: 408 964-3500
Web: www.sanmina.com

2017 Sales

	$ mil.	% of total
Mexico	1,935	28
China	1,336	19
US	1,234	16
Malaysia	743	11
Other countries	1,618	25
Total	**6,868**	**100**

PRODUCTS/OPERATIONS

2017 Sales

	$ mil.	% of total
Industrial Medical and Defense	3,064	45
Communications Networks	2,650	39
Embedded Computing and Storage	1,153	17
Total	**6,868**	**100**

2016 Sales

	$ mil.	% of total
IMS	5,645	82
CPS	1,422	18
Inter segment Revenue	(199.1)	-
Total	**6,868**	**100**

Selected Services

Backplane assembly
Cable assembly
Circuit assembly

Circuit fabrication
Configuration
Distribution
Enclosures
Engineering
Forward logistics
In-circuit testing
Inventory management
Materials management
Order fulfillment
Printed circuit board design
Reverse engineering
Sustaining engineering
System assembly and testing

COMPETITORS

Benchmark Electronics	NCR
CTS Corp.	Nam Tai
Celestica	Plexus
Flextronics	SMTC Corp.
Hon Hai	SYNNEX
Inventec	Seagate Technology
Jabil	TTM Technologies
Lexmark	Universal Scientific
Molex	Venture Corp.
Multi-Fineline	Western Digital
Electronix	Wistron

HISTORICAL FINANCIALS

Company Type: Public

Income Statement

FYE: September 30

	REVENUE ($ mil.)	NET INCOME ($ mil.)	NET PROFIT MARGIN	EMPLOYEES
09/17*	6,868	138	2.0%	47,000
10/16	6,481	187	2.9%	45,397
10/15	6,374	377	5.9%	43,854
09/14	6,215	197	3.2%	43,101
09/13	5,917	79	1.3%	40,909
Annual Growth	3.8%	15.0%	—	3.5%

*Fiscal year change

2017 Year-End Financials

Debt ratio: 12.47%
Return on equity: 8.55%
Cash ($ mil.): 406
Current ratio: 1.62
Long-term debt ($ mil.): 391
No. of shares (mil.): 71
Dividends
  Yield: —
  Payout: —
Market value ($ mil.): 2,662

	STOCK PRICE ($) FY Close	P/E High/Low		PER SHARE ($) Earnings	Dividends	Book Value
09/17*	37.15	23	15	1.78	0.00	22.99
10/16	28.47	12	7	2.38	0.00	22.04
10/15	21.37	6	4	4.41	0.00	19.48
09/14	21.60	10	6	2.27	0.00	15.18
09/13	17.54	19	8	0.93	0.00	12.97
Annual Growth	20.6%	—	—	17.6%	—	15.4%

*Fiscal year change

Santander Consumer USA Holdings Inc

This auto finance company aims to put credit-impaired car buyers in the driver's seat. Santander Consumer USA (SCUSA) makes subprime new and used vehicle loans to buyers at more than 14000 Chrysler Ford GM and Toyota dealerships throughout the US. The technology-driven company also originates loans through independent dealers such as CarMax banks and its direct-to-consumer website Roadloans.com. SCUSA also provides refinancing and cash-back refinancing services. While subprime loans make up more than 80% of its loan portfolio the company is looking to increase its prime loan business. Founded in 1995 SCUSA is owned by Spanish banking giant Banco Santander SA. The company went public in 2014.

IPO

Santander Consumer USA (SCUSA) went public in January 2014 with an offering valued at $1.5 billion. The IPO capitalizes on the rebound in auto sales as credit-impaired borrowers return to the car market. Post IPO Banco Santander owns 61% of SCUSA.

Financial Performance

The auto lender reported more than $2.9 billion in finance and other interest income in 2012 a 14% increase versus 2011.

Strategy

SCUSA is looking to expand its portfolio of prime loans through partnerships with automakers. To that end in February 2013 SCUSA entered into a 10-year agreement with Chrysler whereby it originates private-label loans and leases under the Chrysler Capital brand. The company relies on third-party banks and parent company Banco Santander for approximately $12 billion and $5 billion respectively in committed financing. It also has agreements with Bank of America and Sovereign to fund the Chrysler Capital business.

Company Background

In 2006 Banco Santander acquired a 90% stake in Drive Financial from HBOS and the company's founding partners for $651 million. Drive changed its name to Santander Consumer USA in 2008.

Auditors: PricewaterhouseCoopers LLP

LOCATIONS

HQ: Santander Consumer USA Holdings Inc
1601 Elm Street, Suite 800, Dallas, TX 75201
Phone: 214 634-1110
Web: www.santanderconsumerusa.com

COMPETITORS

Ally Bank	Credit Acceptance
Bank of America	Ford Motor Credit
Capital One Auto Finance	GM Financial
	Toyota Motor Credit

HISTORICAL FINANCIALS

Company Type: Public

Income Statement

FYE: December 31

	ASSETS ($ mil.)	NET INCOME ($ mil.)	INCOME AS % OF ASSETS	EMPLOYEES
12/16	38,539	766	2.0%	5,100
12/15	36,570	827	2.3%	5,100
12/14	32,342	766	2.4%	4,400
12/13	26,401	697	2.6%	4,100
12/12	18,741	715	3.8%	3,900
Annual Growth	19.7%	1.8%	—	6.9%

2016 Year-End Financials

Debt ratio: 81.28%
Return on equity: 15.82%
Cash ($ mil.): 160
Current ratio: —
Long-term debt ($ mil.): —
No. of shares (mil.): 358
Dividends
  Yield: —
  Payout: —
Market value ($ mil.): 4,845

	STOCK PRICE ($) FY Close	P/E High/Low		PER SHARE ($) Earnings	Dividends	Book Value
12/16	13.50	7	4	2.13	0.00	14.60
12/15	15.85	11	7	2.31	0.00	12.36
12/14	19.61	12	8	2.15	0.15	10.20
Annual Growth	(8.9%)	—	—	(0.2%)	—	9.4%

Santander Holdings USA Inc.

Santander Holdings USA is the parent company of Sovereign Bank which reigns in the Northeast with more than 700 branch locations. TheÂ bankÂ caters to individuals and small to midsized businesses offeringÂ deposits creditÂ cards insurance and investmentsÂ as well as commercial loans and mortgages (which together account for nearlyÂ half of its total portfolio) and residential mortgages and home equity loansÂ (more than a quarter).Â Santander Holdings also owns a majority of Santander Consumer USA which purchases and services subprime car loans made byÂ auto dealerships and other companies.Â Spain-based banking giant Banco Santander acquired the rest of Sovereign BancorpÂ it didn't already own in 2009.

EXECUTIVES

Vice President, Michael Jones
Vice President Community Development Inv, George Demoulias
Vice President Strategic Marketing, Ayse Mccarthy
Vice President and Manager Commercial Real Estate Department, Frank Picone
Senior Vice President RM, Jerami A Marshal
Auditors: PricewaterhouseCoopers LLP

LOCATIONS

HQ: Santander Holdings USA Inc.
75 State Street, Boston, MA 02109
Phone: 617 346-7200
Web: www.santanderbank.com

Selected Locations
Connecticut
Delaware
Maryland
Massachusetts
New Hampshire
New Jersey
New York
Pennsylvania
Rhode Island

PRODUCTS/OPERATIONS

2013 Sales

	$ mil.	% of total
Interest		
Loans	1,958	58
Investment securities	330	10
Deposits	6	.
Noninterest		
Equity method investment	426	12
Consumer banking fees	228	7
Commercial banking fees	199	6
Mortgage bankin revenue	122	4
Bank owned life insurance	57	3
Others	54	
Total	3,384	100

Bank of America
Citibank
Citizens Financial
  Group
Fulton Financial
HSBC USA
JPMorgan Chase
KeyCorp
M&T Bank
PNC Financial
People's United
  Financial
TD Bank USA
Webster Financial
Wells Fargo

HISTORICAL FINANCIALS

Company Type: Public

Income Statement

FYE: December 31

	REVENUE ($ mil.)	NET INCOME ($ mil.)	NET PROFIT MARGIN	EMPLOYEES
12/16	10,745	362	3.4%	16,500
12/15	10,473	(1,454)	—	15,150
12/14	11,919	2,335	19.6%	14,000
12/13	3,383	628	18.6%	9,100
12/12	3,687	561	15.2%	8,920
Annual Growth	30.7%	(10.3%)		16.6%

2016 Year-End Financials

Debt ratio: 31.68%
Return on equity: 1.97%
Cash ($ mil.): 10,035
Current ratio: 0.20
Long-term debt ($ mil.): 43,524

No. of shares (mil.): 530
Dividends
  Yield: 0.0%
  Payout: —
Market value ($ mil.): 13,647

	STOCK PRICE ($) FY Close	P/E High/Low	PER SHARE ($) Earnings	Dividends	Book Value
12/16	25.73	— —	(0.00)	1.83	37.00
12/15	25.85	— —	(0.00)	1.83	32.32
12/14	25.53	— —	(0.00)	1.83	34.96
12/13	25.39	— —	(0.00)	1.83	26.03
12/12	25.17	— —	(0.00)	1.83	25.45
Annual Growth	0.6%		—	(0.0%)	9.8%

Schein (Henry) Inc

From Poughkeepsie to Prague Henry Schein outfits dental offices around the world with everything they need. The company is a leading global distributor of dental supplies equipment and pharmaceuticals. Henry Schein provides everything from delicate hand-held tools up to X-ray equipment and patient chairs as well as office supplies and anesthetics. But the company isn't only interested in teeth: It also supplies doctors' offices veterinarians and other office-based health care providers with diagnostic kits surgical tools drugs vaccines and animal health products. Other offerings include practice management software repair services and financing.

HISTORY

For more than 50 years Henry Schein distributed drugs made by Schein Pharmaceuticals. In 1992 management spun off the drug business and led by former accountant Stanley Bergman began acquiring other dental supply companies at a terrific rate: 34 between 1994 and 1996 alone.

The company went public in 1995 and bought more than a dozen businesses. These purchases which included product marketer Vertex Corporation's distribution unit moved Henry Schein into the medical and veterinary supply fields. The purchase of Schein Dental Equipment (founded by Marvin Schein) boosted per-customer sales by adding big-ticket merchandise to the product mix.

Acquisitions continued hot and heavy as the company boosted operations abroad. The purchases hit the bottom line; Schein avoided bloat by restructuring operations closing facilities and developing new systems. The company consolidated 13 distribution centers into five in 1997. The following year the firm expanded into Canada and bought a controlling stake in UK direct marketer Porter Nash.

To boost profits the company announced in 2000 that it would cut 5% of its workforce. It also shut down some facilities and sold its software development business as part of its overall restructuring plan. In 2001 the firm resumed its acquisitions when it bought the dental supply business of drug maker Zila. Over the next few years it expanded internationally when it bought up firms in the Czech Republic Germany Italy New Zealand and the UK.

Choosing to focus on supplying office-based health care practitioners in 2006 it sold its hospital supply business for $36.5 million. Other dispositions have included the sale of its oncology and specialty pharmaceutical businesses (2007) and a dental products wholesaler (2009). In 2009 Henry Schein acquired a majority stake in Butler Animal Health tripling the size of its domestic animal health operations; the unit was renamed Butler Schein Animal Health following the deal. (The company increased its stake in Butler Schein Animal Health to about 72% in 2012.)

Henry Schein expanded its health care technology segment in 2010 through the acquisition of majority ownership of ImproMed and McAllister Software Systems both developers of veterinary practice management systems in the US. In 2011 the company entered the veterinary market in Australia and New Zealand with the $92 million buy of Provet Holdings. The purchase helped Henry Schein cement its strategy to expand its international health care distribution unit which grew from some $2.5 billion in sales in 2010 to some $3 billion in sales in 2011.

EXECUTIVES

Vice President and General Man, Brad Connett
EVP and Chief Strategic Officer, Mark E. Mlotek, age 61, $555,962 total compensation
EVP and Chief Administrative Officer, Gerald A. Benjamin, age 64, $551,308 total compensation
President; CEO Global Dental Group, James P. Breslawski, age 63, $698,769 total compensation
EVP and CFO, Steven Paladino, age 60, $551,308 total compensation
Chairman and CEO, Stanley M. Bergman, age 68, $1,342,385 total compensation
SVP and Chief Merchandising Officer, Michael Racioppi, age 62, $340,275 total compensation
President International Dental Group, Robert (Bob) Minowitz, age 58
Chief Commercial Officer; President Corporate Commercial Development Group, David C. (Dave) McKinley, age 64
SVP and CTO, James A. (Jim) Harding, age 61
EVP; CEO Global Animal Health Medical and Dental Surgical Group, Karen Prange, age 53, $410,000 total compensation
President Global Animal Health Group, Peter McCarthy
President Global Medical Group, Bridget A. Ross, age 52
Vice President Global E Commerce, Robert Lamb
Vice President Global Human Resources and Financial Operations, Lorelei McGlynn
Vice President Corporate Finance, Ronald South
Vice President Corporate Inventory Management, Paul Rose
Vice President Finance, Charles Crawford
Vice President, Patrick Allen
Vice President Product Merchandising, Marguerite Walsh
Senior Vice President General Counsel, Walter Siegel
Vice President Finance, Eileen Rosenbaum
Vice President, Marie Woods
Vice President, Keith Drayer
Vice President North American Distribution, Michael Richardson
Vice President and General Manager Repair Business Group, Ron Appel
Vice President, Lynne McHugh
Executive Vice President Of Sales, Cy Elborne
Vice President Business Development And Strategic Relationships, David Chen
Vice President Sales Operations, Charlie Crawford
Vice President, Peter Dellacroce
Vice President And Chief Information Securiity Officer, Mark Viola
Vice President National Telesales Operations, Jim Loiacono
Vice President and Treasurer, Graham Stanley
Vice President Global IS Infrastructure, Joseph Buckshaw
Vice President Claims Information Technology, Pat Gunning
Vice President, Jesse Garringer
Vice President, Don Cohen
Global Security Vice President, Chris Berry
Vice President, Gene Heller
Vice President and General Manager, David Steck
Vice President Technology Global Prosthetic Solutions, Patrick Thurm
VP Safety, Shirley Taylor
Vice President Inventory Management, John Donigian
Vice President Sales, David Vann
Vice President and Chief Compliance Officer, Nancy Lanis
Senior Vice President Corporate and Legal Affairs Secretary, Michael Ettinger
Auditors: BDO USA, LLP

LOCATIONS

HQ: Schein (Henry) Inc
135 Duryea Road, Melville, NY 11747
Phone: 631 843-5500
Web: www.henryschein.com

2016 Sales

	$ mil.	% of total
US	7,536	65
Other countries	4,034	35
Total	11,571	100

PRODUCTS/OPERATIONS

2016 Sales

	$ mil.	% of total
Health care distribution		
Dental	5,555	48
Animal health	3,253	28
Medical	2,337	20
Technology & value-added services	425	4
Total	11,571	100

Selected Acquisitions

COMPETITORS

Allscripts
Benco Dental
Burkhart Dental
Cardinal Health
Carestream Health
Darby Dental
IDEXX Labs
MWI Veterinary Supply
McKesson
Medline Industries
NextGen
Omega Pharma
PSS World Medical
Patterson Companies
Sybron Dental
athenahealth
eClinicalWorks

Income Statement

FYE: December 31

	REVENUE ($ mil.)	NET INCOME ($ mil.)	NET PROFIT MARGIN	EMPLOYEES
12/16	11,571	506	4.4%	21,000
12/15	10,629	479	4.5%	19,000
12/14	10,371	466	4.5%	17,500
12/13	9,560	431	4.5%	16,000
12/12	8,939	388	4.3%	15,000
Annual Growth	6.7%	6.9%	—	8.8%

2016 Year-End Financials

Debt ratio: 18.11%	No. of shares (mil.): 158
Return on equity: 17.56%	Dividends
Cash ($ mil.): 62	Yield: —
Current ratio: 1.45	Payout: —
Long-term debt ($ mil.): 715	Market value ($ mil.): 24,092

	STOCK PRICE ($) FY Close	P/E High/Low	PER SHARE ($) Earnings	Dividends	Book Value
12/16	151.71	58 46	3.10	0.00	17.59
12/15	157.09	55 44	2.85	0.00	17.50
12/14	137.39	50 40	2.72	0.00	16.75
12/13	114.43	46 32	2.47	0.00	16.26
12/12	79.96	37 29	2.16	0.00	14.88
Annual Growth	17.4%	— —	9.4%	—	4.3%

Schwab (Charles) Corp (The)

The once-rebellious Charles Schwab is all grown up: the discount broker now offers the same traditional brokerage services it shunned over three decades ago. Schwab manages more than $2.9 trillion in assets for nearly 12.8 million individual investors and institutional clients. Traders can access its services via telephone wireless device the internet and through more than 335 offices in 45-plus states as well as London and Hong Kong. Besides discount brokerage the firm offers financial research advice and planning investment management and retirement and employee compensation plans.

Operations

The financial services and brokerage firm operates through two business segments. Its Investor Services segment generates some 70% of company revenue and offers retail brokerage and banking services to individual investors as well as retirement plan and corporate brokerage services. Its Advisor Services segment generating nearly 30% of revenue provides custodial trading and support services to institutional investors.

About 45% of its revenue is generated by interest income on cash investment securities brokerage-related receivables and loans to banking clients. More than 40% of the company's revenue comes from asset management and administration fees which are made up of mostly mutual fund service fees advice solutions fees and other fees. Trading revenue makes up 10% of its total revenue and consists of commission and principal transaction income.

The company's OneSource service offers investors access to more than 2000 no-load funds. Schwab also provides access to nearly 28000

bonds bond funds and other fixed income investment products from more than 300 dealers. Additional services include futures and commodities trading access to IPOs and educational investment materials including ratings of more than 3000 stocks. Schwab provides trading and support services to independent investment advisors as well.

Geographic Reach

San Francisco-based Schwab has more than 335 branch offices in over 45 US states as well as offices in London Hong Kong and Puerto Rico.

Sales and Marketing

The company provides financial services to both individuals and institutional clients. Its Advisor Services segment provides custodial trading and support services to independent investment advisors and retirement business services to independent retirement plan advisors and record keepers with assets plans held at Schwab Bank.

Charles Schwab has $2.9 trillion in client assets across 10.3 million active brokerage accounts more than 1.1 million banking accounts and 1.5 million corporate retirement plan participants.

Financial Performance

Thanks to a rising stock market and a growing investor base Charles Schwab has boosted its average client assets by nearly 40% since 2013 from $2.1 trillion to almost $2.9 trillion at the end of 2016. The resulting rise in asset-based fees and related trading revenue and interest income from receivables has led the firm to strong revenue and profit growth over the past few years.

Schwab's revenue climbed 17% to $7.5 billion in 2016 on the back of 1.1 million new brokerage accounts $125.5 billion in net new assets (from new and existing customers) and a 12% increase in clients assigned to a retail advisory solution.

Net income increased 28% to $1.7 billion as revenue and profit margins increased. Cash from operating activities jumped 113% to $2.7 billion due to higher net income and higher payables to brokerage clients.

Strategy

Like other banks and financial firms Charles Schwab continued in 2016 to focus on streamlining its operations to boost efficiency and productivity. The company also looks to leverage its wide array of financial services to cross-sell to its large customer base.

Charles Schwab increased its capital expenditure 23% to $353 million in 2016 to fund land purchases and investment in internal software. The company is building a new $100 million corporate campus in the Dallas-Fort Worth area of north Texas creating 1200 jobs.

HISTORY

During the 1960s Stanford graduate Charles Schwab founded First Commander Corp. which managed investments and published a newsletter. But he failed to properly register with the SEC and after a hiatus he returned to the business under the name Charles Schwab & Co. in 1971. Initially a full-service broker Schwab moved into discount brokerage after the SEC outlawed fixed commissions in 1975. While most brokers defiantly raised commissions Schwab cut its rates steeply.

From 1977 to 1983 Schwab's client list increased thirtyfold and revenues grew from $4.6 million to $126.5 million enabling the firm to automate its operations and develop cash-management account systems. To gain capital Charles sold the company to BankAmerica (now Bank of America) in 1983. Schwab grew but federal regulations prevented expansion into such services as mutual funds and telephone trading. Charles bought his company back in 1987 and took it public. When the stock market crashed later that year trading

volume fell by nearly half from 17900 per day. Stung Schwab diversified further offering new fee-based services. Commission revenues fell from 64% of sales in 1987 to 39% in 1990 but by 1995 the long bull market had pushed commissions to more than 50%.

In 1989 Schwab introduced TeleBroker a 24-hour Touch-Tone telephone trading service available in English Spanish Mandarin or Cantonese.

Schwab continued to diversify courting independent financial advisors. Other buys included Mayer & Schweitzer (1991 now Schwab Capital Markets) an OTC market maker that accounted for about 7% of all NASDAQ trades. In 1993 the firm opened its first overseas office in London but traded only in dollar-denominated stocks until it bought Share-Link (later Charles Schwab Europe) the UK's largest discount brokerage in 1995. It subsequently sold the British pound sterling brokerage business to Barclays PLC although it has maintained its US dollar business in the UK.

During the next year Schwab made a concerted effort to build its retirement services by creating a 401(k) administration and investment services unit. In 1997 Schwab allied with J.P. Morgan Hambrecht & Quist and Credit Suisse First Boston (CSFB) to give its customers access to IPOs; the next year the relationship with CSFB deepened to give Schwab access to debt offerings. In late 1997 and early 1998 Schwab reorganized to reflect its new business lines. The firm also began recruiting talent rather than promoting from within.

Expansion was key at the turn of the century. In 1999 Schwab moved toward more broker-advised investing: It inked a deal (geared towards its retirement products customers) with online financial advice firm Financial Engines and introduced Velocity a desktop system designed to make trading easier for fiscally endowed investors. In 2000 Schwab bought online broker CyBerCorp (later CyberTrader) as well as U.S. Trust which markets to affluent clients.

While Schwab's World Trade Center offices were destroyed by the September 11 terrorist attacks the company did not lose any of its New York staff.

To pare expenses Schwab reduced its workforce by about 35% between 2000 and 2003. Founder and chairman Charles Schwab relinquished his role of co-CEO in early 2003 only to move back into the driver's seat in mid-2004 when former CEO David Pottruck was asked to step down by the company's board.

One of Schwab's first orders of business was to reexamine the company's 2004 acquisition of SoundView Technology Group which was combined with its Capital Markets operations to form Schwab SoundView Capital Markets. While the purchase was intended to help the company beef up its services for institutional investors Schwab said that SoundView lacked "synergy" with the company's tradition of supporting the individual investor and sold the business to Swiss bank UBS.

Schwab acquired The 401(k) Companies from Nationwide Financial Services in 2007. The addition became part of the company's existing Charles Schwab Trust subsidiary which serves as a trustee for employee benefit plans. Also that year Schwab sold U.S. Trust to Bank of America for some $3.3 billion in cash and shut down its CyberTrader day trading arm merging the direct-access brokerage's business with its own.

In 2011 Charles Schwab acquired retail brokerage optionsXpress. The $1 billion deal expanded its client base and online equity options and futures trading business and it has already boosted the company's trading revenues.

In another 2011 transaction Charles Schwab acquired Compliance11 which allowed the company to offer compliance monitoring and reporting services.

In December 2012 the firm purchased Massachusetts-based ThomasPartners a dividend income-focused asset management firm with some $2.3 billion in assets under management for $85 million in cash.

EXECUTIVES

CFO, Peter Crawford, age 49
President and CEO, Walter W. (Walt) Bettinger, age 56, $1,041,667 total compensation
President and CEO Charles Schwab Bank, Paul V. Woolway
EVP Client Solutions, G. Andrew (Andy) Gill, age 54
EVP Corporate Initiatives, James D. McCool, age 58, $550,000 total compensation
President and CEO Charles Schwab Investment Management, Marie A. Chandoha, age 56, $572,500 total compensation
EVP International Services and Special Business Development, Lisa Kidd Hunt
SVP Advisor Services, Bernard J. Clark, age 58, $525,000 total compensation
EVP Operational Services, Ron Carter
EVP and Chief Marketing Officer, Jonathan M. Craig
EVP Corporate Risk, Nigel J. Murtagh, age 54
EVP Retirement Plan Services, Steven H. (Steve) Anderson
EVP Technology Services, Jim McGuire
EVP General Counsel and Corporate Secretary, David R. Garfield, age 61
EVP Investor Services, Terri R. Kallsen, age 49, $450,000 total compensation
EVP Investor Services Strategy Segments and Platforms, Neesha Hathi
EVP and CTO, Timothy C. Heier
EVP and CIO, Dennis Howard
EVP Internal Audit, Mitch Mantua
Vice President Financial Consultant, Dean Martines
Vice President Financial Consultant, Brian Trentsch
Vice President Financial Consultant, Rich Munneke
Vice President Financial Consultant, Tim McDonald
Vice President Financial Consultant, Mark Bergdorf
Vice President Financial Consultant, Greg Czarnecky
Vice President Financial Consultant, Michael Stolp
Vice President Global Compliance, Janet Epstein
Vice President Retirement Plan Sales, Luis R Arellano
Vice President Financial Consultant, Levent Durmus
Vice President Information Technology, Ed Fulkerson
Vice President Senior Financial Consultant, Brian Rogers
Vice President Financial Consultant, Brandon Setlock
Vice President, William Colin
Vice President Financial Consultant, David Mattox
Vice President Financial Consultant, Chad Vidovich
RVP, Don Bakhaus
Vice President Financial Consultant, Martin Dunn
Vice President Regulatory Affairs, Irene Gilbert
Vice President Financial Consultant, Brian Sanchez
Vice President Senior Financial Consultant, Mario Giannetta
Vice President, Andrew Mason
Vice President, Brian Burke
Vice President Financial Consultant, Paul Kidder
Vice President, William Matthews
Vice President Treasury, John Mason
Vice President Financial Consultant, Andrew Lindell
Vice President Financial Consultant, Robert Kay

Vice President and Branch Manager, Gregory Matthews
Vice President Financial Consultant, Tatum Schuler
Vice President Model Risk Management, Marc Bourzutschky
Vice President, James Westbay
Vice President Financial Consultant, David Burchfield
Vice President, William Parrott
Vice President Financial Consultant, Selene Argao
Vice President, Brian Openshaw
Vice President, Jason Fay
Vice President Financial Consultant, Gary Cronk
Vice President Financial Consultant, Timothy Harker
Vice President Financial Consultant, Stuart Evans
Vice President Financial Consultant, Brett Woodward
Vice President, Matthew Heck
Vice President, Steven Brakman
Vice President Financial Consultant, Danny Jones
Vice President, Michael Solomon
Vice President Of Sales, Aline Eliecagary
Vice President of Corporate Public Relations, Susan Forman
Vice President Finance, Peter Pavlakis
Vice President Financial Consultant, Michael Viselli
Vice President, Stephan Spangenberg
Vice President Financial Consultant Charles Schwab and Co. Inc., Greg Murray
Regional Vice President, Scot Kobashigawa
Vice President Financial Consultant, Nicolas Robatel
Vice President, Dennis Mojares
Vice President Financial Consultant, Tristyn Eames
Vice President Financial Consultant, Jason Burke
Vice President and Branch Manager International Schwab International Orlando, Cynthia Paul
Vice President Financial Consultant Charles Schwab and Co. Inc., George Dmowski
Vice President Financial Consultant, Shawn Jennings
Vice President Financial Consultant, Viola Ashmawee
Vice President Financial Consultant, Brian Lell
Vice President of Participant Services, Catherine Golladay
Vice President Financial Consultant, James Titus
Senior Vice President and Corporate Controller, James Egan
Vice President Financial Consultant, German Ramirez
Vice President, Erick Ibarra
Vice President, Jake King
Vice President Financial Consultant, Jeff Peterson
Vice President Financial Consultant, Kelly Senkyr
Vice President Financial Consultant Ca Insurance License #0B27845, Cynthia Leal
Vice President Financial Consultant, Denise Patridge
Vice President Legislative and Regulatory Affairs, Scott Eckel
Vice President Financial Consultant, Zubin Hodiwalla
Vice President Financial Consultant, Chris Veale
Vice President, Kevin Maas
Vice President Financial Consultant, Scott Newell
Vice President Financial Consultant, Bruce Gruenberg
Vice President Financial Consultant, Kim Bryant
Vice President Financial Consultant, Greg Kopp
Vice President Futures Optionsxpress, Daniel O'Neil
Vice President Financial Consultant, Carter Taylor
Vice President Financial Consultant, David Raymon
Vice President, J Rainey
Vice President Financial Consultant, Garrett Sloan
Vice President IBS Compliance, Gary Wachs

Vice President Financial Consultant, Gregory Kaiser
Vice President Financial Consultant, Garland Sharp
Vp Financial Consultant, Kristin Hayes
Vice President Financial Consultant, Brian Valenti
Vice President Financial Consultant, Galina Sapozhnikov
Vice President Financial Consultant, Renee Hardman
Vice President Financial Consultant, Dawn Stoffel
Vice President Financial Consultant, Abel Oonnoonny
Vice President Financial Consultant, Stefan Borso
Vice President Financial Consultant, Ken Williams
Vice President Financial Consultant, Andrew Seward
Vice President Financial Consultant, Greg Jordan
Vice President, Dan Masteller
Vice President and Branch Manager, Francisco J Vivas
Vice President, Lisa Quartarone
Vice President, Brian Balogh
Vice President, Michael Forte
Vice President, Trent Fifield
Vice President Financial Consultant, James Koenn
Vice President Financial Consultant, Tj Farrell
Vice President Financial Consultant, PAUL LIFFENGREN
Vice President Associate General Counsel, Steve Johnson
Vice President Financial Consultant, Aaron Olson
Vice President Financial Consultant, Linda Tarbet
Vice President Financial Consultant, Tiffany Dugas
Information Technology Vice President, Manoj Achrekar
Vice President Financial Consultant, Porter Ginn
Vice President Senior Financial Consultant, Scott Martinez
Vice President Financial Consultant, James McGill
Vice President Financial Consultant, Scott Miller
Vice President Financial Consultant, Madeline Alvarez
Vice President Financial Consultant, Christopher Hager
Vice President Financial Consultant, David Bubb
Vice President Financial Consultant La, Anthony Khavarani
Vice President Financial Consultant, David Spiess
Vice President Financial Consultant, Michael Messler
Vice President Senior Financial Consultant, Ryan Kaplan
Vice President Information Technology, Brian Jensen
Senior Vice President Financial Consultant, Nicholas Caruso
Vice President Financial Consultant, Angela Cochran
Vice President Senior Financial Consultant, Paul Dunk
Vice President Financial Consultant, William Lang
Vice President Financial Consultant, Brian Aguilar
Auditors: Deloitte & Touche LLP

LOCATIONS

HQ: Schwab (Charles) Corp (The)
211 Main Street, San Francisco, CA 94105
Phone: 415 667-7000 **Fax:** 415 627-8894
Web: www.aboutschwab.com

PRODUCTS/OPERATIONS

2016 Sales

	$ mil.	% of total
Investor Services	5,411	72
Advisor Services	2,067	28
Total	**7,478**	**100**

2016 Sales

	$ mil.	% of total
Interest	3,322	44
Asset management & administration fees	3,055	41
Trading	825	11
Provision for loan losses	5	-
Other	271	4
Total	**7,478**	**100**

Selected Subsidiaries

Charles Schwab Bank
Charles Schwab Investment Management Inc. (mutual fund investment adviser)
Schwab Holdings Inc.
Charles Schwab & Co. Inc. (securities broker-dealer)

COMPETITORS

Ameriprise	Morgan Stanley
Bank of America	Principal Financial
E*TRADE Financial	Raymond James
Edward Jones	Financial
FMR	Scottrade
Franklin Templeton	ShareBuilder
John Hancock Financial	T. Rowe Price
Services	TD Ameritrade
Legg Mason	The Vanguard Group

HISTORICAL FINANCIALS

Company Type: Public

Income Statement

FYE: December 31

	REVENUE ($ mil.)	NET INCOME ($ mil.)	NET PROFIT MARGIN	EMPLOYEES
12/16	7,649	1,889	24.7%	16,200
12/15	6,512	1,447	22.2%	15,300
12/14	6,160	1,321	21.4%	14,600
12/13	5,540	1,071	19.3%	13,800
12/12	5,033	928	18.4%	13,800
Annual Growth	**11.0%**	**19.4%**	**—**	**4.1%**

2016 Year-End Financials

Debt ratio: 1.29%
Return on equity: 12.63%
Cash ($ mil.): 10,828
Current ratio: 0.25
Long-term debt ($ mil.): 2,876

No. of shares (mil.): 1,332
Dividends
  Yield: 0.0%
  Payout: 20.6%
Market value ($ mil.): 52,604

	STOCK PRICE ($) FY Close	P/E High/Low	PER SHARE ($) Earnings	Dividends	Book Value
12/16	39.47	31 17	1.31	0.27	12.32
12/15	32.93	34 25	1.03	0.24	10.15
12/14	30.19	32 25	0.95	0.24	9.00
12/13	26.00	33 18	0.78	0.24	8.00
12/12	14.36	22 17	0.69	0.24	7.51
Annual Growth	**28.8%**	**— —**	**17.4%**	**3.0%**	**13.2%**

Seaboard Corp.

With pork and turkey from the US flour from Haiti and sugar from Argentina Seaboard has a lot on its plate. The diversified agribusiness and transportation firm has operations in some 45 countries in the Americas the Caribbean and Africa. Seaboard sells its pork and poultry in the US and abroad. Overseas it trades grain (wheat soya) operates power plants and feed and flour mills and grows and refines sugar cane. Seaboard owns a shipping service for containerized cargo between the US the Caribbean and South America; it has shipping terminals in Miami and Houston and a fleet of about 20 vessels (two owned the rest chartered) and ships to ports worldwide. Seaboard is run by descendants of founder Otto Bresky.

Operations

Seaboard operates in five segments.

The company?s Pork Division about a quarter of revenue is a vertically integrated pork producer and one of the largest producers and processors in the US. The unit works through the lifecycle of a hog from research in nutrition and genetics and extending to production of meat products.

The Commodity Trading and Milling (CT&M) Division about 50% of revenue trades processes and moves agricultural commodities such as wheat corn soybeans soybean meal and others. The primary destinations for the ag products are Africa South America the Caribbean and Asia.

Seaboard?s Marine Division some 15% of revenue provides cargo shipping services between the US the Caribbean and Central and South America. The company has major facilities at Port Miami and the Port of Houston.

The rest of Seaboard?s revenue comes from its operations in sugar which are mostly in Argentina power generation in the Dominican Republic and its 50% non-controlling interest in Butterball LLC the largest producer of turkeys and turkey products in the US.

Geographic Reach

Kansas-based Seaboard is a global company that serves several segments such as agribusiness and ocean cargo transportation in about 45 countries specifically in the Americas the Caribbean and Africa. Its largest market is Central and South America and the Caribbean representing about 35% of annual sales. Africa and the US are other big markets for the company.

Financial Performance

After several years of consistent growth Seaboard?s sales have stumbled in the past three years. Revenue dipped 4% in 2016 to $5.4 billion from 2015 with lower sales in five of its six segments and all but one of its geographic areas. Sales were down 8% in the Commodity Trading & Milling unit which is responsible for half the company?s revenue) on lower commodity prices and the mix of products. Sales rose 8% for the Pork unit as acquisitions increased the sales volume of market hogs and the acquisition of a second biodiesel plant produced higher biodiesel volumes.

Seaboard?s net income jumped to $312 million in 2016 an 82% increase from 2015. The company reduced the cost of sales 6% in 2016 from the year before boosting net income.

Higher net income helped pushed cash flow from operations to $427 million in 2016 from $416 million in 2015.

Strategy

Seaboard seeks growth by expanding operations in several areas.

The company continues to beef up its pork division. With its partner Triumph Seaboard opened a new Daily?s bacon plant in St. Joseph Missouri that has a production capacity of 60 million pounds a year. Seaboard and Triumph followed in 2017 with another new pork processing plant in Sioux City Iowa. But pork is more than bacon and Seaboard rehabilitated a closed biodiesel plant in St Joseph Missouri. That plant along with the one on Guymon Oklahoma gives Seaboard capacity to produce 64 million gallons of biodiesel fuel per year.

In 2016 Seaboard gain took over day-to-day work of the Brazilian flour milling operations by restructuring and consolidation. The company expects to reduce the operation?s costs by focusing on single site production.

Seaboard could face challenges if US trade agreements are renegotiated or abrogated. If the US charges higher tariffs on foreign goods entering the country other nations could retaliate by putting higher tariffs on US goods. Agricultural products are some of the US?s biggest goods for export and would be likely targets for retaliation which could increase prices reduce exports or both.

Mergers and Acquisitions

In September 2014 Seaboard's processed meats division sold a 50% stake in Daily's Premium Meats to its processing partner Triumph Foods for $72.5 million making Seaboard and Triumph co-owners of the business. The sale provided additional capital to expand production and geographic reach of the Daily's brand.

In July 2013 Seaboard acquired a 50% stake in a flour milling business in Gambia for about $9.1 million.

HISTORY

Otto Bresky founded his company as a flour broker in 1916. He acquired his first flour mill in Atchison Kansas in 1918 and the following year purchased the Imperial Brewery Co. in Kansas City and converted it to a flour mill. Over the next four decades Bresky ground out a series of acquisitions of milling companies. In 1928 he purchased Rodney Milling Co. and retained the name as the identity for the family business. The company then purchased Ismert-Hincke Milling Co. (1938) and the Consolidated Flour Mills Co. (1950). In 1959 Rodney Milling merged with publicly traded Hathaway Industries and changed its name to Seaboard Allied Milling Corp.

In the 1960s Seaboard Allied became one of the first millers to shift flour milling from the source of the raw materials (the wheat fields of the Great Plains) to the population centers in the Southeast and on the East Coast. In 1962 Seaboard Allied built a flour mill in Chattanooga Tennessee. It then purchased George Urban Milling Company in Buffalo New York (1965) and built a flour mill in Jacksonville Florida (1966). But Bresky's expansionist strategy did not stop at the Atlantic Seaboard. The company acquired a flour mill in Guayaquil Ecuador in 1966 (a joint venture with Continental Grain Co.) then constructed flour mills in Freetown Sierra Leone (1968) and Georgetown Guyana (1969).

Bresky retired in 1973 and was succeeded by his son Harry. A chip off the old block Harry acquired a flour mill in Cleveland Tennessee and built flour mills in Buchanan Liberia and in Sapele Nigeria that year. In 1978 Seaboard Allied acquired Mochasa Ecuador's leading producer of animal feed and launched Top Feeds a mixed-feed plant in Sapele.

Facing stiff competition in the mill business from agribusiness giants in 1982 Seaboard Allied sold all its US flour mills to Cargill. The company changed its name to Seaboard that year and began expanding outside the US. In 1983 the company formed Seaboard Marine a shipping business in Florida to serve its increasingly far-flung enterprises.

In addition to geographic diversification the company expanded into new agribusiness areas. Seaboard acquired Central Soya's poultry unit in 1984 and it bought the Elberton Poultry Company the next year. Seaboard commenced shrimp farming operations in Ecuador in 1986 and in Honduras in 1987. Two years later Transcontinental Capital Corporation (Bermuda) a subsidiary began supplying power from a floating power barge to the Dominican Republic.

Seaboard entered the hog business in 1990 by acquiring a pork-processing plant in Albert Lea Minnesota. It opened a hog-processing facility in Guymon Oklahoma in 1996 and closed the Minnesota plant. That year the company bought a stake in Ingenio y Refinerio San Martin del Tabacal an Argentina-based sugar cane and citrus company. It then acquired flour-mill pasta-plant and cookie operations in Beira Mozambique.

After serving as CEO for more than 30 years in 2006 Harry Bresky stepped down as CEO (but remained as chairman) and turned over the company's reins to his son Steven. Harry Bresky died in 2007.

In 2010 Seaboard acquired a 50% stake in Butterball LLC.

EXECUTIVES

Senior Vice President, Duke Sand
Vice President Taxation and Business Development, David Oswalt
SVP Engineering, James L. (Jim) Gutsch, age 63
EVP and CFO, Robert L. Steer, age 58, $763,000 total compensation
Chairman President and CEO, Steven J. Bresky, age 64, $942,000 total compensation
CEO Pork, Terry J. Holton, age 57, $552,000 total compensation
CEO Marine, Edward A. (Eddie) Gonzalez, age 52, $472,000 total compensation
CEO Commodity Trading and Milling, David M. Dannov, age 56, $472,000 total compensation
CEO Sugar, Hugo Rossi
CEO Power, Armando G. Rodriguez
Vice President, Claudio Dabelic
Vice President Internet Marketing, Doug Ewing
Vice President Business Development, David Rankin
Assistant Vice President Information Technology, Brad Rein
Assistant Vice President Information Technology, Brian Bybee
Vice President, Kenneth Brooks
VICE PRESIDENT OF MARKETING AND PROD. INNOV., Scott Webb
Assistant Secretary, David Becker
Assistant Secretary and Senior Attorney, William Croutch
Auditors: KPMG LLP

LOCATIONS

HQ: Seaboard Corp.
9000 West 67th Street, Merriam, KS 66202
Phone: 913 676-8800
Web: www.seaboardcorp.com

2016 Sales

	$ mil.	% of total
Caribbean Central & South America	1,990	37
Africa	1,572	29
US	1,161	22
Pacific Basin & Far East	309	6
Canada/Mexico	236	4
Europe	40	1
All other	71	1
Total	**5,379**	**100**

PRODUCTS/OPERATIONS

2016 Sales

	$ mil.	% of total
Products	4,334	80
Services	961	18
Other	84	2
Total	**5,379**	**100**

2016 Sales

	$ mil.	% of total
Commodity Trading & Milling	2,778	52
Pork	1,443	27
Marine	916	17
Sugar	147	3
Power	79	1
All other	16	-
Total	**5,379**	**100**

Selected Operations

Cargo shipping
Citrus production and processing
Commodity merchandising (wheat corn and soybean meal)
Domestic trucking transportation
Electric power generation
Flour maize and feed milling
Jalape?o pepper processing
Pork production and processing
Sugar production and refining

COMPETITORS

ADM	Hormel
APL	Imperial Sugar
American Crystal Sugar	Jennie-O
Bay State Milling	Johnsonville Sausage
Bunge Limited	Louis Dreyfus Group
CGC	M. A. Patout
CHS	Makino
CSX	Mondelez International
Cargill	NYK Line
Carr's Milling	Neptune Orient
Chelsea Milling	Nicor Gas
Chiquita Brands	Nutreco
Colonial Group	Organic Milling
Crowley Maritime	Overseas Shipholding
Della Natura	Group
Commodities	Smithfield Foods
Dole Food	Southern States
Evergreen Marine	Star of the West
Evergreen Mills	Sunkist
Farmers Rice Milling	S dzucker
Fresh Del Monte	Tate & Lyle
Produce	Tyson Foods
Genco Shipping and	U.S. Sugar
Trading	Western Sugar
Horizon Milling	Cooperative

HISTORICAL FINANCIALS

Company Type: Public

Income Statement

FYE: December 31

	REVENUE ($ mil.)	NET INCOME ($ mil.)	NET PROFIT MARGIN	EMPLOYEES
12/16	5,379	312	5.8%	12,000
12/15	5,594	171	3.1%	10,772
12/14	6,473	365	5.6%	10,778
12/13	6,670	205	3.1%	11,397
12/12	6,189	282	4.6%	11,295
Annual Growth	**(3.4%)**	**2.5%**		**1.5%**

2016 Year-End Financials

Debt ratio: 13.40%
Return on equity: 10.31%
Cash ($ mil.): 77
Current ratio: 3.63
Long-term debt ($ mil.): 499
No. of shares (mil.): 1
Dividends
　Yield: —
　Payout: —
Market value ($ mil.): 4,626

	STOCK PRICE ($) FY Close	P/E High/Low		PER SHARE ($) Earnings	Dividends	Book Value
12/16	3,951.99	17	9	266.50	0.00	2,701
12/15	2,894.74	32	20	146.44	0.00	2,456
12/14	4,197.95	13	8	309.96	0.00	2,320
12/13	2,794.97	17	15	171.92	0.00	2,081
12/12	2,529.88	11	8	234.54	12.00	1,924
Annual Growth	**11.8%**	—	—	**3.2%**	—	**8.9%**

Seacoast Banking Corp. of Florida

Seacoast Banking Corporation is the holding company for Seacoast National Bank which has about 35 branches in Florida with a concentration on the state's southeastern coast. Serving individuals and areas businesses the bank offers a range of financial products and services including deposit accounts credit cards trust services and private banking. Commercial and residential real estate loans account for most of the bank's lending activities; to a lesser extent it also originates business and consumer loans. The bank also provides financial planning services as well as mutual funds and other investments.

Operations

A division of the bank Seacoast Marine Finance specializes in boat loans of $200000 and greater which it typically sells into the secondary market. It has an office in Florida and two in California.

Geographic Reach

Seacoast National Bank has 34 branches in 12 counties across Florida stretching from Broward County north through the Treasure Coast and into Orlando and west to Okeechobee and surrounding counties.

Financial Performance

Seacoast Banking has been a victim of the economic turmoil and a weak housing market in Florida posting declining revenues since 2008. In 2013 sales fell 6% to $95.5 million. However the bank recorded $51.9 million in profits due to a one-time income tax benefit. The downward trend in its profits have been fueled by significant losses on loan provisions and compounded by a lack of revenue growth. The bank has in recent years been consolidating and closing branches to cut its operating costs.

Strategy

During 2013 Seacoast National Bank significantly expanded its banking technology platform by introducing digital deposit capture on smartphones new mobile platforms for consumer and business customers a rebranding of its website and enhancing its ATM capabilities. About 40% of its online customers also use the mobile application.

Mergers and Acquisitions

In 2014 the bank announced plans for its first acquisition in years. Seacoast National agreed to buy The BANKshares Inc. a Winter Park Florida-based bank that operates 12 branches under the BankFIRST name. The BankFIRST branches will be rebranded as Seacoast National creating the sixth-largest Florida bank by total assets. Previous acquisitions were completed in 2002 and 2006.

EXECUTIVES

Chairman and CEO, Dennis S. (Denny) Hudson, age 61, $537,852 total compensation
EVP and Residential Lending Executive, Michael J. (Mike) Sonego
EVP and Commercial Banking Executive, Charles K. Cross, age 59, $273,333 total compensation
EVP and Chief Risk and Credit Officer, David D. Houdeshell, age 56, $262,500 total compensation
EVP Enterprise Services and Initiatives, Kathleen (Kathy) Cavicchioli
EVP and Chief Marketing Officer, Jeffery (Jeff) Lee
EVP Service and Operations, Jeffery (Jeff) Bray
EVP and Chief Human Resources Officer, Daniel G. (Dan) Chappell

CFO and Head of Strategy, Charles M. (Chuck) Shaffer, age 43, $248,333 total compensation
EVP Community Banking, Julie Kleffel
Vice President Cre, Debra Mairs
Assistant Vice President Relationship Manager, Frances Portalatin
Vice President, Jenny Yingling
Vice President Financial Advisor, Carl Newton
Executive Vice President, Fred Roxas
Senior Vice President Loan Operations Manager, Gayle Anderson
Executive Vice President Wealth Management and The Private Bank at Seacoast, Tom Hall
Senior Vice President Risk Officer, Peter Lowery
Assistant Vice President, Patty McAuley
AVP Banking Center Manager, Amber Shirk
Executive Vice President, Mike Sonego
Senior Vice President, Tom Popieski
Vice President, Travis Engebretsen
Senior Market Manager Vice President, Monika Krumbock
Assistant Vice President Relationship Manager II, Chary Gonzalez
Vice President Relationship Manager III and Lending Officer, Cathy Roberts
AVP Relationship Manager, Jacquie Parris
Vice President Small Business Banker, Amy St Hart
AVP Banking Center Manager, Aaron Prida
Vice President Collections and Recovery Manager, Gary Albert
Board Member, Tim Huval
Auditors: Crowe Horwath LLP

LOCATIONS

HQ: Seacoast Banking Corp. of Florida
815 Colorado Avenue, Stuart, FL 34994
Phone: 772 287-4000
Web: www.seacoastbanking.com

PRODUCTS/OPERATIONS

2015 Revenue

	% of total
Interest Income	
Interest and fees on loans	63
Interest on securities and others	15
Non-interest Income	22
Total	**100**

Selected Services
Commercial and retail banking
Mortgage services
Wealth management

COMPETITORS

Atlantic Coast Financial	CenterState Banks
BB&T	EverBank Financial
BBX Capital	PNC Financial
Bank of America	Regions Financial
BankUnited	SunTrust
	Wells Fargo

HISTORICAL FINANCIALS

Company Type: Public

Income Statement

FYE: December 31

	ASSETS ($ mil.)	NET INCOME ($ mil.)	INCOME AS % OF ASSETS	EMPLOYEES
12/16	4,680	29	0.6%	725
12/15	3,534	22	0.6%	665
12/14	3,093	5	0.2%	579
12/13	2,268	51	2.3%	519
12/12	2,173	(0)	—	508
Annual Growth	**21.1%**	**—**	**—**	**9.3%**

2016 Year-End Financials

Debt ratio: 10.37%	No. of shares (mil.): 38
Return on equity: 7.38%	Dividends
Cash ($ mil.): 109	Yield: —
Current ratio: —	Payout: —
Long-term debt ($ mil.): —	Market value ($ mil.): 839

	STOCK PRICE ($) FY Close	P/E High/Low	PER SHARE ($) Earnings	Dividends	Book Value
12/16	22.06	29 17	0.78	0.00	11.45
12/15	14.98	25 18	0.66	0.00	10.29
12/14	13.75	68 48	0.21	0.00	9.44
12/13	12.20	5 1	2.44	0.00	8.40
12/12	1.61	— —	(0.25)	0.00	8.73
Annual Growth	**92.4%**		**—**	**—**	**7.0%**

Sealed Air Corp

Pop-Pop-Pop sounds like money for Sealed Air. Best known as the company that created Bubble Wrap Sealed Air also makes Instapak foam Jiffy mailers and Shanklin FloWrap shrink packaging systems through its Product Care segment. Its largest segment Food Care makes Cryovac bags for use by food processors and supermarkets to protect meat and poultry. In late 2017 Sealed Air sold its former Diversey Care division (cleaning systems chemicals and robots) and the food hygiene and cleaning business within its Food Care division to Bain Capital Private Equity for $3.2 billion. The company was founded in 1960.

Operations
Sealed Air is organized into two global business segments: Food Care (protective packaging shrink packaging and specialty materials) and Product Care (food and drink packaging).

In late 2017 Sealed Air sold its former Diversey segment (cleaning chemicals floor care machines cleaning equipment) to Bain Capital Private Equity for $3.2 billion.

Geographic Reach
Geographically the company's subsidiaries own roughly 100 manufacturing facilities worldwide with each facility tailoring the products it makes to the demands of the local market. Its largest markets include North America (about 40% of net sales) EMEA (35%) APAC (15%) and Latin America (10%).

Sales and Marketing
Sealed Air sells its products through over 6900 sales marketing and customer service personnel throughout the world who sell and market products and to through a large number of distributors fabricators converters e-commerce and mail order fulfillment firms and contract packaging firms as well as directly to customers.

It targets food and beverage processors business supply distributors consumer products manufacturers hotel operators retailers building contractors educational institutions and health care providers as customers.

Financial Performance
Sealed Air's revenues have fallen the last two years declining 4% from $7.03 billion in 2015 to $6.78 billion in 2016. The decline was fueled by revenue drops across its segments: Food Care (5%) Diversey Care (2%) and Product Care (2%).(Note: the Diversey segment was divested in late 2017.)

The segments in 2016 were negatively affected by the divestiture of its North American foam trays and absorbent pads and European food trays busi-

nesses in addition to the impact of negative foreign currency translations. They also suffered from the continued economic uncertainty and political instability in Latin America in addition to lower demand in Asia Pacific driven by historically low slaughter rates in Australia.

Sealed Air's profits however surged by 45% $335 million in 2015 to $486 million in 2016 due to lower restructuring and other related charges. In addition the company's operating cash flow declined from $955 million in 2015 to $906 million in 2016 mainly due to the absence of additional cash received from a settlement agreement the previous year.

Strategy
Sealed Air completed one of the biggest strategic moves in its history in late 2017 when it sold its former Diversey Care division (cleaning systems chemicals and robots) and the food hygiene and cleaning business within its Food Care division to Bain Capital Private Equity for $3.2 billion. The Diversey Care operations had previously been weighed down by a strong US dollar and a slowdown in several of its end-markets. The divestiture allows Sealed Air to focus on its food product and medical packaging businesses. It is using the $3.2 billion to repay debt and fund its key growth initiatives.

Mergers and Acquisitions
Sealed Air is augmenting its two core segment through the use of acquisitions. To enhance its position in Latin America Sealed Air in 2017 announced it was acquiring Brazilian flexible packaging maker Deltaplam Embalagens Ind stria e Com ©rcio Ltda.

To strengthen its position in Asia it also announced in 2017 it was purchasing Fagerdala Singapore Pte Ltd. a manufacturer and fabricator of polyethylene foam for $100 million. Fagerdala has 14 manufacturing facilities in China Thailand Singapore Malaysia Mexico and the US.

HISTORY

In the late 1950s after US engineer Al Fielding and Swiss inventor Marc Chavannes found no takers for their plastic air-bubble-embossed wallpaper they looked for another use for the material. They came up with Bubble Wrap the first product of Sealed Air which they founded in 1960 and took public soon after. AirCap as the material was first known didn't just protect products from damage; it also reduced storage and shipping costs.

EXECUTIVES

President CEO and Director, Edward L. (Ted) Doheny, age 54
Chief Accounting Officer Controller and Acting CFO, William G. Stiehl
President Food Care, Karl R. Deily, age 59, $521,350 total compensation
SVP and Chief Supply Chain Officer, Emile Z. Chammas, age 48, $518,832 total compensation
President Diversey Care, Ilham Kadri, age 48, $490,356 total compensation
CIO, Marc A. Hamer
President Product Care, Kenneth P. (Ken) Chrisman, age 52
Vice President Global Engineering, Ram Ramesh
Vice President Digital, Fano Bekker
Vice President Sales West, Bill Ihlendorf
Chairman, William J. (Bill) Marino, age 74
Auditors: Ernst & Young LLP

HQ: Sealed Air Corp
2415 Cascade Pointe Boulevard, Charlotte, NC 28208
Phone: 980 221-3235   **Fax:** 201 703-4205
Web: www.sealedair.com

2016 Sales

	$ mil.	% of total
North America	2,852	42
EMEA	2,302	34
Latin America	641	9
APAC	981	15
Total	**6,778**	**100**

PRODUCTS/OPERATIONS

2016 Sales

	$ mil.	% of total
Food Care	3,222	48
Diversey care	1,963	29
Product care	1,523	22
Other	69	1
Total	**6,778**	**100**

Selected Brands

Bubble Wrap
CRYOVAC
Ethafoam
Fill-Air
Instapak
Jiffy Mailer
Korrvu
Shanklin

Selected Products

Food Packaging
  Bulk packaging
  Laminates
  Lidstock
  Pouches
  Rollstock
  Vacuum bags
Medical Packaging
  Cleanroom blisters
  Films (Nexcel and Nelipak brands)
  Lidding material
  Medical device packaging
  Sealing machines
Protective Packaging
  Air cushioning (Bubble Wrap)
  Cushioned mailing bags (Jiffy Mailer)
  Foam packaging (Instapak)
  Inflatable packaging and cushioning (Fill-Air and FillTeck)
  Paper cushioning (PackTiger)
  Paper packaging (Kushion Kraft and Custom Wrap)
  Polyethylene fabrication foam (Cellu-Cushion CelluPlank Stratocell)
  Polyethylene foam (Cell-Aire)
  Suspension and retention packaging (Korrvu)
Shrink Packaging
  Equipment
  Films
Specialty Materials
  Foams
  Solar pool heating
  TurboTag RF Temperature Monitoring system
  Vacuum insulated panels

COMPETITORS

Ashland	Packaging Dynamics
Avery Dennison	Pactiv
Ball Corp.	Polyair Inter Pack
Bemis	Praxair
Crown Holding Company	Reynolds Food
Huntsman Corp	Packaging
Intertape Polymer	Sonoco Products
Monsanto Company	Tekni-Plex
Mosaic Company	Winpak

HISTORICAL FINANCIALS

Company Type: Public

Income Statement

FYE: December 31

	REVENUE ($ mil.)	NET INCOME ($ mil.)	NET PROFIT MARGIN	EMPLOYEES
12/16	6,778	486	7.2%	23,000
12/15	7,031	335	4.8%	23,000
12/14	7,750	258	3.3%	24,000
12/13	7,690	124	1.6%	25,000
12/12	7,648	(1,410)	—	25,000
Annual Growth	**(3.0%)**	**—**		**(2.1%)**

2016 Year-End Financials

Debt ratio: 58.99%
Return on equity: 85.34%
Cash ($ mil.): 363
Current ratio: 1.05
Long-term debt ($ mil.): 3,938

No. of shares (mil.): 193
Dividends
  Yield: 0.0%
  Payout: 24.8%
Market value ($ mil.): 8,772

	STOCK PRICE ($) FY Close	P/E High/Low		PER SHARE ($)		
		High	Low	Earnings	Dividends	Book Value
12/16	45.34	21	15	2.46	0.61	3.15
12/15	44.60	34	24	1.62	0.52	2.69
12/14	42.43	36	24	1.20	0.52	5.52
12/13	34.05	53	27	0.58	0.52	7.08
12/12	17.51	—	—	(7.31)	0.52	7.42
Annual Growth	**26.9%**	**—**	**—**	**—**	**4.1%**	**(19.3%)**

Sears Holdings Corp

Once a retail giant Sears Holdings is growing smaller and leaner these days. The company is a leading retailer of appliances and tools as well as lawn and garden fitness and automotive repair equipment. With about 1200 retail stores across the US Sears Holdings operates through subsidiaries Sears Roebuck and Co. and Kmart offering proprietary Sears brands including Kenmore and DieHard. Beyond retail Sears Holdings is the largest provider of home installation and product repair services in the US. In response to plummeting sales in a tough retail climate Sears Holdings has been forced to sell off assets and close or spin off hundreds of stores in recent years. In 2017 the company sold its Craftsman tool brand to Stanley Black & Decker for $900 million.

Operations

Sears Holdings operates two segments: Sears Domestic which boasts 670 full-line stores that generated about 60% of Sears Holdings' total sales in fiscal 2016 (ended January 30 2016); and Kmart which had 735 Kmart stores that contributed another 40% to Sears Holdings' total sales.

By product the retailer generated 43% of its total sales from hardline merchandise (electronics appliances tools etc.) and another 25% from apparel and soft home items. About 15% of sales came from food and drug sales while service (installation and repair) made up another 9% of total sales during the year.

Outside of retail Sears Holdings has a real estate business unit called Sears Holdings Real Estate one of the largest corporate real estate organizations in the world. It offers for sale or lease closed Kmart and Sears stores. It also leases empty space inside and outside of the stores.

Geographic Reach

Sears Holdings subsidiary Sears Roebuck and Co. has Sears-branded and affiliated stores in all

50 US states and Puerto Rico. Subsidiary Kmart boasts Kmart-branded stores in 49 states Guam Puerto Rico and the US Virgin Islands.

Sales and Marketing

The retailer has been decreasing its advertising spend over the past few years as sales have declined. It spent $850 million on advertising in fiscal 2016 down from $1.1 billion and $1.5 billion for 2015 and 2014 respectively.

Financial Performance

Declining store sales and mounting losses have plagued Sears Holdings for the past several years as the popularity of e-commerce and fierce competition from other big box retailers has been growing.

In fiscal 2016 Sears Holdings' net revenues decreased by 19% due to a drop in revenues from all segments (and a drop of $2.1 billion associated with Sears Canada which was de-consolidated in October 2014).

Kmart's revenues declined due to having fewer stores in operation which accounted for approximately $1.1 billion of the decline and a drop e in comparable store sales driven by declines in the consumer electronics apparel grocery and household and drugstore categories.

The revenues from Sears Domestic segment decreased due to a drop in comparable store sales of 11.1% which accounted for $1.2 billion of the decline and the effect of having fewer full-line stores in operation which accounted for $433 million of the decline.

The company's net loss decreased by 33% in fiscal 2016 mainly due to a decline in selling and administrative expenses related to decreases in payroll and advertising expenses and the absence of expenses of $603 million from Sears Canada and $77 million from the Lands' End business which Sears Holding spun off in 2014. Other factors included an income tax benefit in 2015 related to indefinite-life assets associated with the property sold in the transaction with Seritage.

In fiscal 2016 Sears Holdings' operating cash inflows increased by 56% due to changes in working capital as a result of an increase in inventory balances compared to the significant decrease in inventory balances a year earlier.

Strategy

Sears Holdings outlined three main objectives in 2015 to ensure its long-term success: restoring profitability; focusing on its best members (most loyal customers) best stores and best categories (home appliances home services and fitness equipment); and enhance its financial flexibility through sales of store assets and investor fundraising.

The retailer has been trying to adapt to the rapid consumer change from brick-and-mortar stores toward e-commerce in recent years. The likes of Amazon and Wal-Mart have ruthlessly eaten into Sears' market share as internet shopping expands. In 2015 the company continued shifting from being product-centric to becoming "member-centric" catering to members' needs "wherever whenever and however they want to shop" as stated in the February 2015 Chairman's letter. The member-centric model is built on two platforms: Shop Your Way the loyalty membership platform; and Integrated Retail the technology platform that connects its "ecosystem" of retail channels to member "touchpoints" (i.e. online and through mobile apps).

The plans also include significant cost-saving efforts: it is aiming for $1.25 billion in savings each year. Facing years of losses Sears Holdings has been forced to close hundreds of stores (from 2000 in 2013 to 1200 in 2017) cut thousands of jobs and sell assets to turn its business around. In 2017 the company sold its iconic Craftsman tool brand which it had owned since 1927 to Stanley Black & Decker for $900 million. The deal generated much-needed cash for the company and helps Sears continue to operate through 2017.

In another move to extract value from one of its name brands Sears in 2017 agreed to sell Kenmore appliances on Amazon.com. At the same time Sears said it would integrate its smart appliances with Alexa Amazon's artificial intelligence digital assistant. Owners of integrated Kenmore-Alexa appliances could operate them with voice commands. The deal exposes Kenmore appliances to a wider range of shoppers by displaying them on Amazon's popular digital showroom.

In recent years the company has cuts costs through store closings and employee reductions. In 2017 Sears announced 400 jobs would be cut from its corporate headquarters. In 2015 it sold 235 properties to Seritage Growth Properties (REIT properties) along with Sears Holdings' 50% interest in a number of joint venture properties. Sears Holdings received aggregate gross proceeds from the Seritage transaction of $2.7 billion. The previous year the company sold off most of its stake in its struggling Sears Canada business spun off its Lands' End retail business and considered doing the same for its Sears Auto Center business.

The pairing of Sears and Kmart was intended to leverage the strengths of both chains by making their products brands (Kenmore Craftsman DieHard) and services (including auto and appliance repair) available through more locations and distribution channels. That strategy failed to increase in sales for either retailer.

The company is focused on two core strategies Shop Your Way membership and Integrated Retail. Shop Your Way evolved from being store-based in 2009 to being a desktop and Mobile experience. All this is part of the company's effort to transform into a member-centric retailer. The company has increased the number of brands and expanded its network to include more partners.

Through its integrated retail strategy the company is using it existing brick-and-mortar infrastructure while integrating it with mobile experiences. The company introduced Meet with an Expert a service that helps online shoppers considering larger item purchases in Home Appliances Mattresses or Lawn & Garden connect with in-store experts.

Company Background

Sears Holdings was created in 2005 as a result of the $11.9 billion mega-merger of Sears and struggling Kmart masterminded by chairman and CEO Edward Lampert.

EXECUTIVES

Chairman and CEO, Edward S. (Eddie) Lampert, age 54, $1 total compensation
CFO, Robert A. Riecker, age 52
President Fulfillment Supply Chain and Sourcing, Girish Lakshman, age 52, $794,444 total compensation
SVP Customer Experience and Integrated Retail, Leena Munjal, age 40, $568,750 total compensation
SVP Shop Your Way, Eric D. Jaffe, age 29
President Apparel, David Pastrana Benito, age 40
President Home Services, Sean Skelley, age 50, $794,444 total compensation
President Home and Footwear, Kurt C. Staelens
Vice President Of National Sales, Mac Mcilvried
Divisional Vice President, Carlos Fojo
Divisional Vice President Chief Marketing Officer Grocery And Drug, R Whitton
Dvp Kenmore Product Development, Tom Desalvo
Divisional Vice President Home Services Online, Sandeep Patil
Chief Marketing Officer Of Home Appliances And Vice President Of, Kevin Brown

Div Vice President Ny Technical Design, Vanessa Allen
Vice President Space Management And Analytics, Amy Higgins
Vice President Ecommerce Program And Product Management, Christopher Kraft
Vice President Chief Financial Officer Grocery Drug And Rx, Jonathan Carpenter
Dvp Human Resources Retail Services, Megan Van Pelt
Divisional Vice President Head Of Sears Retail Human Resources, Colleen Kozak
Vice President Media Services, Perianne Grignon
Vice President Mobile Commerce, Mario Prizio
Auditors: Deloitte & Touche LLP

LOCATIONS

HQ: Sears Holdings Corp
3333 Beverly Road, Hoffman Estates, IL 60179
Phone: 847 286-2500
Web: www.sears.com

PRODUCTS/OPERATIONS

Sales by Segment

	$ mil.	% of total
Sears Domestic	13,488	61
Kmart	8,650	39
Total	**22,138**	**100**

Sales by Products

	$ mil.	% of total
Hardlines	9,571	43
Apparel and Soft Home	5,566	25
Food and Drug	3,099	14
Service	2,110	10
Other	1,792	8
Total	**22,138**	**100**

Selected Subsidiaries

Kmart Corporation
Kmart Holding Corporation
Sears Home Improvement Products Inc.
Sears Roebuck Acceptance Corp.
Sears Roebuck and Co.
Sears Roebuck de Puerto Rico Inc.
SRC Real Estate Holdings (TX) LLC

COMPETITORS

Ace Hardware	Macy's
Amazon.com	Menard
AutoZone	Office Depot
Bed Bath & Beyond	Pep Boys
Best Buy	ServiceMaster
Dillard's	Target Corporation
Home Depot	The Gap
Hudson's Bay	Wal-Mart
J. C. Penney	Whirlpool
Kohl's	Zale
Lowe's	

HISTORICAL FINANCIALS

Company Type: Public

Income Statement

FYE: January 28

	REVENUE ($ mil.)	NET INCOME ($ mil.)	NET PROFIT MARGIN	EMPLOYEES
01/17	22,138	(2,221)	—	140,000
01/16	25,146	(1,129)	—	178,000
01/15*	31,198	(1,682)	—	196,000
02/14	36,188	(1,365)	—	249,000
02/13	39,854	(930)	—	246,000
Annual Growth	**(13.7%)**	**—**		**(13.1%)**

*Fiscal year change

2017 Year-End Financials

Debt ratio: 44.47%	No. of shares (mil.): 107
Return on equity:	Dividends
Cash ($ mil.): 286	Yield: —
Current ratio: 1.07	Payout: —
Long-term debt ($ mil.): 3,573	Market value ($ mil.): 794

	STOCK PRICE ($) FY Close	P/E High/Low	Earnings	Dividends	Book Value
01/17	7.42	— —	(20.78)	0.00	(35.74)
01/16	16.95	— —	(10.59)	0.00	(18.35)
01/15*	31.84	— —	(15.82)	0.00	(8.89)
02/14	36.37	— —	(12.87)	0.00	16.41
02/13	47.55	— —	(8.78)	0.00	25.99
Annual Growth	**(37.1%)**	**—**	**—**	**—**	**—**

*Fiscal year change

SECURITIES INVESTOR PROTECTION CORPORATION

EXECUTIVES

President and CEO, Stephen P. Harbeck
Chairman, Orlan M. Johnson
Director, William H. Heyman, age 67
Vice Chairman, Todd S. Farha, age 46
Director, David J. Stockton
Director, William S. (Bill) Jasien
Director, Mark S. Shelton
Director, David G. Mason
Auditors: GRANT THORNTON MCLEAN VA

LOCATIONS

HQ: SECURITIES INVESTOR PROTECTION CORPORATION
1667 K ST NW STE 1000, WASHINGTON, DC 200061620
Phone: 202 371-8300
Web: WWW.SIPC.ORG

HISTORICAL FINANCIALS

Company Type: Private

Income Statement

FYE: December 31

	ASSETS ($ mil.)	NET INCOME ($ mil.)	INCOME AS % OF ASSETS	EMPLOYEES
12/15	2,652	169	6.4%	39
12/14	2,362	307	13.0%	
12/11	1,606	131	8.2%	
12/10	1,382	(271)	—	
Annual Growth	**13.9%**	**—**	**—**	

2015 Year-End Financials

Debt ratio: —	
Return on equity: 35.40%	Dividends
Cash ($ mil.): 1	Yield: —
Current ratio: —	Payout: —
Long-term debt ($ mil.): —	Market value ($ mil.): —

Selective Insurance Group Inc

Property/casualty insurance holding company Selective Insurance Group's reach primarily covers the entire eastern US seaboard and much of the Midwest. Commercial policies sold by its nine subsidiaries include workers' compensation and commercial automobile property and liability insurance. Personal lines include homeowners and automobile insurance. The company also offers federal flood insurance administration services throughout the US and some excess and surplus (E&S nonstandard) insurance. Selective Insurance Group operates through four reportable segment: Standard Commercial Lines Standard Personal Lines E&S Lines and Investments.

Operations

Selective's Standard Commercial Lines segment which serves business not-for-profit organizations and government agencies accounts for about three-fourths of Selective's net premiums written. Standard Personal Lines— including flood insurance coverage — follows representing more than 10% of net premiums written. Finally E&S Lines which covers more unusual risks than standard insurance accounts for nearly 10% of net premiums written.

The company's flood insurance is sold to businesses and individuals through the National Flood Insurance Program.

Geographic Reach

Selective primarily writes commercial policies in 22 eastern and midwestern states plus Washington DC. It also offers flood and E&S insurance policies in all 50 states plus Washington DC.

While its native New Jersey market still accounts for more than 20% of Selective's net written premiums the company worked for many years to become a "super-regional" insurer. By doing business in a wider geographic range Selective is better able to spread out its catastrophic risk exposure. It maintains its headquarters in New Jersey and regional branch offices in New Jersey Indiana Maryland North Carolina Pennsylvania and Arizona.

Sales and Marketing

Approximately 1200 independent retail agents sell Selective's Standard Commercial Lines products with a focus on providing policies to small and midsized businesses and government entities. The company's nationwide flood protection products are sold by a network of some 5600 retail agents while E&S policies are sold through about 80 wholesale agencies and brokers.

Target clients include manufacturing and wholesale contractor community and public services and mercantile and services customers.

Promotional efforts are conducted through radio television billboard and other advertising venues including sporting events.

Financial Performance

Selective's revenue which has been rising since 2010 grew another 7% to $2.3 billion in 2016. This was driven by increases in net premiums earned by the Standard Commercial Lines segment which gained 9% that year and the E&S Lines segment which gained 18%. However those gains were partially offset by the Standard Personal Lines segment which had a 3% drop in net premiums earned. Additionally the group reported $4.9 million in total net realized losses.

Profits which had also been on the rise fell 4% to $158.5 million in 2016 as operating expenses including policy acquisition costs increased. Cash flow from operations has been fairly turbulent over the past few years. In 2016 it fell 21% to $301.8 million primarily due to changes in accrued salaries and benefits and other assets and liabilities.

Strategy

Selective's three primary areas of interest are improving its overall customer experience refining its underwriting tools and enhancing its technological capabilities. The group focuses on organic business growth and activities to become more customer-centric. It has primarily been building up its portfolio of personal and commercial E&S insurance products. The company has established regional business teams with full underwriting authority in order to build up its presence in local markets.

Additionally Selective has invested in technology that speeds up the process of writing new commercial business policies to improve customer and agency services. In 2015 it rolled out customer self-servicing capabilities and launched an improved streamlined website.

EXECUTIVES

Vice President Information Management, Eric Thiessen
Assistant Vice President and Actuary, Brian Krick
Chairman and CEO, Gregory E. Murphy, age 62, $946,923 total compensation
EVP and Chief Actuary, Ronald J. Zaleski, age 63, $437,692 total compensation
EVP General Counsel and Chief Compliance Officer, Michael H. Lanza, age 56, $536,923 total compensation
President and COO, John J. Marchioni, age 47, $793,846 total compensation
EVP and CFO, Mark A. Wilcox, age 49
EVP and Chief Claims Officer, George A. Neale
EVP and Chief Human Resources Officer, Angelique Carbo
EVP and CIO, Gordon J. Gaudet
SVP and Chief Marketing Officer, Rohit Mull
Vice President, Dennis L Barger
Assistant Vice President, Robert Mitchell
Vice President underwriting and Operations, Michelle Aromando
Assistant Vice President IT Selective Insurance Company of America, Cynthia Sanchez
Vice President Field Marketing Sales, Darrell Frantz
Commercial Auto Underwriting Assistant Vice President, Stan Willey
Vice President Strategic Application Development, Richard Agresta
Senior Vice President Southwest Region, Shadi Albert
Vice President, Eva Gonzalez
Assistant Vice President Bond Claims, Gerald Carozza
Vice President OFFICE AUTOMATION, Kathy Koval
Assistant Vice President Enterprise Infrastructure and Security Architecture, Robert England
Assistant Vice President Business Case Manger, Sue Insalaco
Vice President, Jim Klotz
Assistant Vice President, Deborah Dickens-hunter
Vice President, Andria Thames
Assistant Vice President Application Architecture, Kevin Vieten
Assistant Vice President Property Line, Scott Crump
Assistant Vice President Workers Compensation, Joe Greco
Vice President Government Affairs and Compliance, Jeff Beck
Vice President Budgeting And Planning, Maurice Cueva
Senior Vice President Claims And General Counsel, Thomas M Clark
Assistant Vice President Bond Underwriting Manager, Debra Paziora
Assistant Vice President, Haide Krygoski
Vice President Specialty Programs, Lorraine Miller
Assistant Vice President, Robert L Redden
Vice President Tax and Treasury, Sarita Chakravarthi
Assistant Vice President Claims Service Center, Susan L Brown
Assistant Vice President and Compensation Manager, Cyndi Bennett
Vice President Of Flood Operations, Cassie Masone
Vice President Commercial Lines Underwriting Line of business and Product Development., Vere Bryan
Assistant Vice President And Field Operations Manager Of Northeast Region, Michael Mazzarella
Vice President, Vincent Senia
Senior Vice President Chief Investment Officer, Joseph Eppers
Assistant Vice President Corporate Systems Applica, Gary Beumee
Vice President Information Technology, Harikrishna Raghumandala
Vice President, Wesley Riley
Auditors: KPMG LLP

LOCATIONS

HQ: Selective Insurance Group Inc
40 Wantage Avenue, Branchville, NJ 07890
Phone: 973 948-3000 **Fax:** 973 948-0282
Web: www.selective.com

PRODUCTS/OPERATIONS

2016 Sales

	$ mil.	% of total
Standard Commercial Lines	1,673	73
Standard Personal lines	281	12
E&S Lines	203	9
Investments	125	6
Total	**2,284**	**100**

2016 Sales

	$ mil.	% of total
Net premiums earned	2,149	94
Net investment income earned	130	6
Other income	8	-
Net realized (losses) gains	(5.0)	-
Total	**2,284**	**100**

Selected Acquisitions

COMPETITORS

Cincinnati Financial	Progressive
GEICO	Corporation
Hanover Insurance	State Farm
Company	The Hartford
Liberty Mutual	Travelers Companies
Markel	Zurich Insurance Group
NJM Insurance	

HISTORICAL FINANCIALS

Company Type: Public

Income Statement

FYE: December 31

	ASSETS ($ mil.)	NET INCOME ($ mil.)	INCOME AS % OF ASSETS	EMPLOYEES
12/16	7,355	158	2.2%	2,250
12/15	6,904	165	2.4%	2,200
12/14	6,581	141	2.2%	2,200
12/13	6,270	106	1.7%	2,100
12/12	6,794	37	0.6%	2,100
Annual Growth	2.0%	42.9%	—	1.7%

2016 Year-End Financials

Debt ratio: 5.96%
Return on equity: 10.79%
Cash ($ mil.): 0
Current ratio: —
Long-term debt ($ mil.): —

No. of shares (mil.): 57
Dividends
Yield: 0.0%
Payout: 22.5%
Market value ($ mil.): 2,495

	STOCK PRICE ($) FY Close	P/E High/Low	PER SHARE ($) Earnings	Dividends	Book Value
12/16	43.05	16 11	2.70	0.61	26.42
12/15	33.58	13 9	2.85	0.57	24.37
12/14	27.17	11 9	2.47	0.53	22.54
12/13	27.06	15 10	1.87	0.52	20.63
12/12	19.27	29 24	0.68	0.52	19.77
Annual Growth	22.3%	— —	41.2%	4.1%	7.5%

Sempra Energy

Sempra Energy makes sure the lights are always on. In the US Sempra distributes natural gas to about 7 million customer meters and electricity to more than 3.5 million customer meters through its Southern California Gas (SoCalGas) and San Diego Gas & Electric (SDG&E) utilities. Other reporting segments include Sempra US Gas & Power (natural gas and renewables) and Sempra International (Sempra Mexico and Sempra South American Utilities) which were formerly known as Sempra Global. Sempra Energy companies serve more than 32 million consumers worldwide. In a play to acquire Oncor Electric from bankrupt parent Energy Future Holdings (EFH) Sempra agreed in 2017 to purchase a majority stake in EFH.

HISTORY

Sempra Energy is the latest incarnation of some of California's leading lights. Formed by the $6.2 billion merger between Enova and Pacific Enterprises the company traces its roots back to the 1880s.

Enova began as San Diego Gas which lit its first gaslights in 1881 and added electricity in 1887 (when it became San Diego Gas & Electric Light). Massive utility holding company Standard Gas & Electric bought the company in 1905 and renamed it San Diego Consolidated Gas & Electric. Over the next few decades San Diego Consolidated expanded through acquisitions and even stayed profitable during the Depression. But the 1935 Public Utilities Holding Company Act forced Standard to divest many of its widespread utilities and in 1940 San Diego Consolidated went public as San Diego Gas & Electric (SDG&E).

SDG&E grew quickly until the 1970s when new environmental laws slowed plans to build more power plants and rates soared because the company had to purchase power. The company finally added more generating capacity in the 1980s and the state of California allowed SDG&E to diversify into real estate software and oil and gas distribution. In 1995 it created Enova to serve as its holding company.

Meanwhile up the coast in San Francisco Pacific Enterprises began as gas lamp rental firm Pacific Lighting in 1886; it quickly moved into gas distribution to defend its market against electricity. The firm bought three Los Angeles gas and electric utilities in 1889 and continued to grow through acquisitions; it consolidated all of its utilities in the 1920s. Pacific Lighting sold its electric properties to the city of Los Angeles in 1937 in exchange for a long-term gas franchise.

The company entered oil and gas exploration in 1960. A decade later it merged its gas utility operations into Southern California Gas (SoCalGas). Pacific Lighting continued to diversify in the 1980s buying two oil and gas companies and three drugstore chains. Renamed Pacific Enterprises in 1988 the company launched an unsuccessful diversification effort that cost it $88 million in 1991. Over the next two years it sold off noncore businesses to focus on SoCalGas and in the mid-1990s it began moving into South and Central America. This included a joint venture with Enova and Mexico's Proxima SA to build and operate Mexico's first private utility.

Pacific Enterprises and Enova agreed in 1997 to a $6.2 billion merger; Sempra Energy was born in 1998. That year California began deregulating its retail power market. In response Sempra sold SDG&E's non-nuclear power plants (1900 MW) in 1999. It used the proceeds to eliminate its competitive transition charge and in turn lowered its electric rates.

But under deregulation rates tripled by mid-2000; that summer the California Public Utilities Commission (CPUC) implemented a rate freeze for electric customers. Wholesale power prices soared and rolling blackouts occurred in 2000 and 2001 as a result of the state's inadequate energy supply. In 2001 the CPUC began allowing utilities to increase their rates and SDG&E agreed to sell its transmission assets to the state for about $1 billion.

Sempra sold its 72.5% share in power marketing firm Energy America to British energy company Centrica in 2001. In 2002 the company purchased bankrupt utility Enron's London-based metals trading unit for about $145 million; later that year it purchased Enron's metals concentrates and metals warehousing businesses.

The company restructured its competitive energy business units in 2005 renaming several divisions and dividing the former Sempra Energy Solutions operations (retail energy marketing and services for commercial and industrial customers) under the Commodities and Generation divisions. That year Sempra sold one of its gas storage units to Vulcan's investment company for a reported $250 million; Vulcan is headed up by Microsoft co-founder Paul Allen

In 2006 the company settled class-action litigation that claimed that two of its subsidiaries Southern California Gas and San Diego Gas & Electric had helped to create the 2000-2001 energy crises in California by restricting the supply of natural gas to the state.

In 2007 Sempra was awarded a $172 million settlement arising from a 2002 dispute over the company's minority stakes in two Argentine natural gas holding companies.

In 2008 Sempra Energy formed a commodities marketing joint venture with The Royal Bank of Scotland RBS Sempra Commodities.

In a move to expand its midstream and distribution assets in the southeastern US in 2008 the company acquired EnergySouth for $510 million.

The company reported a jump in its revenues in 2010 thanks to a recovering global economy that drove up energy demand along with higher oil and gas prices and increased rates. Losses related to winding down its commodities unit trimmed Sempra Energy's net income for the year.

In 2013 Sempra U.S. Gas & Power acquired the Broken Bow 2 wind project in Nebraska. When Broken Bow 2 is completed Sempra U.S. Gas & Power will have joint-venture projects totaling more than 1000 MW of wind generating capacity. Sempra U.S. Gas & Power also agreed to purchase 43 1.7-MW General Electric wind turbines to power the 75-MW wind farm. Located in Custer County the wind farm will generate enough renewable power for 30000 Nebraska homes.

Building its midstream portfolio in 2010 the company acquired El Paso's Mexico-based pipeline and compression assets for $300 million.

In 2010 and 2011 Sempra Energy exited the commodities trading business. (In 2008 Sempra Energy had formed a partnership with The Royal Bank of Scotland to operate RBS Sempra Commodities including Sempra Energy Trading which traded and markets wholesale energy commodities in Asia Europe and North America. However to refocus its operations around its more financially reliable North American businesses to pay down debt and to meet EU antitrust requirements in 2010 the company sold the European and Asian segments of this partnership to JP Morgan Chase for about $1.6 billion. It also sold that unit's retail commodity operations to Noble Group for $318 million and eventually wound down its joint venture with The Royal Bank of Scotland).

In early 2012 the company consolidated Sempra Generation Sempra Pipelines & Storage and Sempra LNG (together formerly Sempra Global) into Sempra International and Sempra US Gas & Power to improve its management and pursue strategic initiatives. Sempra US Gas & Power includes natural gas and renewables while Sempra International includes subsidiaries Sempra Mexico and Sempra South American Utilities.

Taking advantage of abundant natural gas supply from US shale plays In 2013 Sempra Energy teamed up with GDF SUEZ Mitsubishi and Mitsui & Co. to design and build an LNG export facility at the Cameron LNG receipt terminal in Hackberry Louisiana capable of processing 13.5 million tons per year.

To raise cash to fund its growth initiative the company sold one 625-MW block of Sempra U.S. Gas & Power's 1250-MW Mesquite Power natural gas-fired power plant to Salt River Project Agricultural Improvement and Power District for $371 million.

In 2012 BP Wind Energy and Sempra U.S. Gas & Power expand their strategic relationship by agreeing to jointly develop the Mehoopany Wind Farm in Pennsylvania and the Flat Ridge 2 Wind Farm in Kansas (a combined investment of more than $1 billion).

Growing its natural gas footprint in the Southeast US in 2012 Sempra U.S. Gas & Power agreed to buy Hattiesburg Mississippi-based Willmut Gas & Oil Company a natural gas utility which provides service to about 20000 customers in Hattiesburg and the surrounding area.

EXECUTIVES

Vice President, Kevin Sagara

EVP and General Counsel, Martha B. Wyrsch, age 59, $577,900 total compensation

President San Diego Gas and Electric, Debra L. (Debbie) Reed, age 60, $1,391,900 total compensation

Chairman President and CEO Southern California Gas, Dennis V. Arriola, age 56

Corporate Group President Infrastructure, Joseph A. (Joe) Householder, age 61, $700,000 total compensation

Chairman and CEO Infraestructura Energ Ⓔtica Nova (IEnova), Carlos Ruiz Sacristín, age 67

President COO and Director SoCalGas, J. Bret Lane, age 58

CEO Southern California Gas Company (SoCalGas), Patricia K. (Patti) Wagner, age 55

SVP Human Resources, G. Joyce Rowland, age 62, $405,000 total compensation

Corporate Group President of Utilities, Steven D. Davis, age 61, $541,400 total compensation

EVP and CFO, Jeffrey W. Martin, age 55

President San Diego Gas & Electric (SDG&E),
Scott D. Drury, age 51
CIO, P. Kevin Chase, age 48
Vice President, Clay Faber
Senior Vice President Regulatory And Finance,
Schavrien Lee
Vice President and Chief Information Technology
Officer, Chris Baker
Senior Vice President Regulatory Affairs, Lee
Schavrien
Auditors: Deloitte & Touche LLP

LOCATIONS

HQ: Sempra Energy
488 8th Avenue, San Diego, CA 92101
Phone: 619 696-2000
Web: www.sempra.com

2016 Sales

	$ mil.	% of total
US	8,004	79
South America	1,556	15
Mexico	623	6
Total	**10,183**	**100**

PRODUCTS/OPERATIONS

2016 Sales

	$ mil.	% of total
SDG&E	4,253	40
SoCalGas	3,471	33
Sempra South American Utilities	1,556	15
Sempra Mexico	725	7
Sempra LNG & Midstream	508	5
Sempra Renewables	34	0
Adjustments and eliminations	(364)	-
Total	**10,183**	**100**

2016 Sales

	$ mil.	% of total
Utilities:		
Electric	5,211	51
Natural gas	4,050	40
Energy-related businesses	922	9
Total	**10,183**	**100**

COMPETITORS

AEP	IBERDROLA
AES	Los Angeles Water and
AT&T	Power
Avista	NRG Energy
CMS Energy	NV Energy
Calpine	PG&E Corporation
CenterPoint Energy	PacifiCorp
Constellation Energy	Public Service
Group	Enterprise Group
Dominion Energy	Sacramento Municipal
Duke Energy	Utility
Edison International	Southern Company
Endesa S.A.	Southwest Gas
Entergy	Tenaska
Exelon Energy	Williams Companies
FirstEnergy	

HISTORICAL FINANCIALS

Company Type: Public

Income Statement

FYE: December 31

	REVENUE ($ mil.)	NET INCOME ($ mil.)	NET PROFIT MARGIN	EMPLOYEES
12/16	10,183	1,371	13.5%	16,575
12/15	10,231	1,350	13.2%	17,387
12/14	11,035	1,162	10.5%	17,046
12/13	10,557	1,009	9.6%	17,122
12/12	9,647	865	9.0%	16,893
Annual Growth	**1.4%**	**12.2%**	**—**	**(0.5%)**

SENTARA HEALTHCARE

Sentara Healthcare is not-for-profit organization that operates a network of hospitals and other health facilities primarily in the coastal Hampton Roads area of southeastern Virginia. The system includes a dozen acute care hospitals housing a total of more than 2000 beds. One of its hospitals Sentara Norfolk includes a dedicated cardiac hospital with more than 100 beds. In addition to its acute care facilities Sentara Healthcare operates several outpatient care facilities as well as nursing homes rehab centers medical practices imaging centers and home health agencies. Its Optima Health unit provides HMO PPO and other health insurance products to about 450000 Virginians.

Operations

Across the Sentara Healthcare system the organization boasts a medical staff of about 3800. The medical system's multi-specialty physicians group the Sentara Medical Group has more than 380 primary care and specialty physicians. Its Sentara Senior Services unit operates about 10 nursing and assisted living centers.

The health care group also runs the 160-bed Sentara Princess Anne Hospital an acute care facility located on the Princess Anne outpatient campus in Virginia Beach. Opened in mid-2011 it operates through a 70%-owned joint venture with Bon Secours Health System. The $145 million facility encompasses five stories and offers comprehensive surgical procedures intensive care advanced cardiac care and a maternity center.

Geographic Reach

Sentara Healthcare is the region's largest integrated health care provider serving more than 2 million residents. Its facilities serve customers throughout southeastern and northern Virginia as well as in northeastern North Carolina. It operates in the Virginia cities of Alleghany Charlottesville Hampton Roads Harrisonburg Richmond and Roanoke. In North Carolina Sentara has a presence in Currituck and Elizabeth City.

Financial Performance

The system's revenues increased 9% to $4.7 billion in 2014 due to an increase in net patient services revenues and other operating revenues. Net income fell 82% to $156 million though as salaries and wages increased medical claims and other operating expenses rose and investment gains declined. Cash flow from operations decreased 25% that year to $318 million as a result of the lower net income plus an increase in cash used in receivables and changes in employee compensation and benefits.

Strategy

While it is already one of the largest health care organizations in the state Sentara Healthcare continues to grow through acquisitions construction (both expansions and new buildings) and mergers. In 2014 it acquired the assets and operations of Albemarle Hospital Albemarle Physician Services and Regional Medical Services through a 30-year capital lease agreement with Pasquotank County and Albemarle Hospital Authority. The businesses were combined into newly formed subsidiary SAMC. In 2015 Sentara Leigh Hospital opened a new tower as part of a larger renovation project.

Also in 2015 the system launched a new retail website shopsentara.com which offers over-the-counter health care products including medications vitamins exercise equipment diabetic care supplies and educational books.

Company Background

Sentara Healthcare was founded in 1888 as Norfolk's 25-bed Retreat for the Sick.

EXECUTIVES

CEO, Howard P. Kern
SVP and CIO, Bertram S. (Bert) Reese
SVP and CFO, Robert A. (Rob) Broerman
SVP; President Sentara Health Plans and Optima Health, Michael M. Dudley
President Sentara Leigh Hospital, Teresa L. (Terrie) Edwards
President Sentara CarePlex Hospital, Debra A. Flores
Corporate VP Sentara Norfolk General Hospital Sentara CarePlex Hospital and Sentara Williamsburg Regional Medical Center, Mary L. Blunt
President Sentara Martha Jefferson Hospital, Jonathan S. Davis
President Sentara Virginia Beach General Hospital, Elwood B. (Bernie) Boone
Chief Nursing Officer, Genemarie McGee
SVP and Chief Medical Officer, Terry Gilliland
President Sentara Williamsburg Regional Medical Center, David J. (Dave) Masterson
President Sentara Norfolk General Hospital, Kurt Hofelich
President Sentara Life Care Corporation, Bruce Robertson
President Sentara Princess Anne Hospital, Thomas B. Thames
Corporate VP; President Sentara RMH Medical Center, Jim Krauss
Corporate VP; President Sentara Medical Group, Robert (Doug) Culling
Corporate VP, Michael Gentry
President Sentara Enterprises, Linda R. Huffer
President Sentara Obici Hospital, Steve Julian
President Sentara Halifax Regional Hospital, Chris A. Lumsden
Corporate VP; President Sentara Northern Virgnia Medical Center, Stephen D. Porter
President Sentara Albemarle Medical Center, Coleen Santa Ana
Vice President Business Development, Katherine Harrison
Vice President Of Operations, Chet Hart
Director Of Pharmacy, Betsy Early
Vice President, Ken Krakaur
Director of HIM, Marsha Rooks
Vice President and Chief Information Security Officer, Daniel Bowden
Director of Pharmacy, Jon Horton
Vice President of Medical Affairs, David Schwartz
Vice President Government Relations and Health Policy, Paul Speidell
Vice President For Clinical Informatics and Transformation, David Mohr
Chairman, Bob Fort
Vice Chairman, Henry (Sandy) Harris

Secretary, Karen Riley
Auditors: KPMG LLP NORFOLK VA

LOCATIONS

HQ: SENTARA HEALTHCARE
6015 POPLAR HALL DR, NORFOLK, VA 235023819
Phone: 800 736-8272

PRODUCTS/OPERATIONS

Selected Hospitals
Charlottesville
  Martha Jefferson Hospital
  MJH Outpatient Care Center
  Health Services at Proffit Road
  Health Services at Spring Creek
  Sentara Home Care Services
  Optima Health
Hampton Roads
  Sentara CarePlex Hospital
  Sentara Heart Hospital
  Sentara Leigh Hospital
  Sentara Norfolk General Hospital
  Sentara Obici Hospital
  Sentara Princess Anne Hospital
  Sentara Virginia Beach General Hospital
  Sentara Williamsburg Regional Medical Center
  Orthopaedic Hospital at Sentara CarePlex
  Sentara Northern Virginia Medical Center
  Martha Jefferson Hospital
  RMH Healthcare
Harrisonburg
  RMH Healthcare
  Optima Health
Northern Virginia
  Sentara Northern Virginia Medical Center
  Sentara Lake Ridge
  Sentara Medical Group physicians
  Sentara Home Care Services
  Sentara Heart and Vascular Center
  Optima Health

Selected Services
Cancer
Cardiac (Heart)
Digestive (Colorectal)
Home Care
Imaging
Maternity
Neurosciences
Rehabilitation
Seniors
Thoracic
Transplant
Trauma/Emergency Services
Urology
Vascular
Weight Loss Surgery
Women's

COMPETITORS

Aetna
Anthem Health Plans of Virginia
Bon Secours Health
CIGNA
Carilion Clinic
Centra Health Inc.
Children's Hospital of The King's Daughters
Franklin Hospital Corp.
HCA Capital Division
Humana
Inova
Kaiser Foundation Health Plan of the Mid-Atlantic
Norton Community Hospital
Novant Health
Riverside Health System (Virginia)
Twin County Regional Healthcare
UnitedHealth Group
Wake Forest University Baptist Medical Center

HISTORICAL FINANCIALS
Company Type: Private

Income Statement FYE: December 31

	REVENUE ($ mil.)	NET INCOME ($ mil.)	NET PROFIT MARGIN	EMPLOYEES
12/15	4,833	139	2.9%	28,000
12/14	4,694	359	7.7%	—
12/13	4,298	861	20.0%	—
12/12	4,068	307	7.6%	—
Annual Growth	5.9%	(23.2%)	—	—

2015 Year-End Financials
Debt ratio: ——
Return on equity: 2.90%
Cash ($ mil.): 741
Current ratio: 1.40
Long-term debt ($ mil.): —
Dividends
  Yield: —
  Payout: —
Market value ($ mil.): —

ServisFirst Bancshares Inc

ServisFirst Bancshares is a bank holding company for ServisFirst Bank a regional commercial bank with about a dozen branches located in Alabama and the Florida panhandle. The bank also has a loan office in Nashville. ServisFirst Bank targets privately-held businesses with $2 million to $250 million in annual sales as well as professionals and affluent customers. The bank focuses on traditional commercial banking services including loan origination deposits and electronic banking services such as online and mobile banking. Founded in 2005 by its chairman and CEO Thomas Broughton III the bank went public in 2014 with an offering valued at nearly $57 million.

IPO
ServisFirst Bancshares sold 625000 shares priced at $91 per share. Proceeds from the May 2014 IPO will be used to support the bank's growth plans both in Alabama and in other states.

Geographic Reach
Birmingham-based ServisFirst Bank has branches in Birmingham Huntsville Montgomery Mobile Dothan Pensacola and Nashville.

Financial Performance
The bank reported net income of $41.2 million in 2013 compared with $34 million in 2012. The increase was primarily due to an increase in net interest income which rose nearly 20% to $112.5 million. Noninterest income increased 4% to $10 million in 2013.

As of March 2014 the bank had total assets of approximately $3.6 billion total loans of $2.9 billion and total deposits of about $3.0 billion.

EXECUTIVES

President and CEO ServisFirst Bancshares and ServisFirst Bank, Thomas A. (Tom) Broughton, age 61, $350,000 total compensation
EVP and COO ServisFirst Bancshares and ServisFirst Bank, Clarence C. Pouncey, age 60, $263,000 total compensation
EVP CFO Treasurer and Secretary ServisFirst Bancshares and ServisFirst Bank, William M. Foshee, age 62, $230,000 total compensation

EVP ServisFirst Bancshares and President and CEO ServisFirst Bank of Huntsville, Andrew N. (Andy) Kattos, age 47
President and CEO ServisFirst Bank of Mobile, William (Bibb) Lamar, age 73
EVP ServisFirst Bancshares and President and CEO ServisFirst Bank of Montgomery, G. Carlton (Carl) Barker, age 62
EVP ServisFirst Bancshares and President and CEO ServisFirst Bank of Pensacola, Rex D. McKinney, age 54
EVP Correspondent Banking ServisFirst Bancshares and ServisFirst Bank, Rodney E. Rushing, age 59, $245,000 total compensation
SVP and Chief Credit Officer ServisFirst Bancshares and ServisFirst Bank, Don G. Owens, age 65, $187,200 total compensation
President and CEO ServisFirst Bank of Atlanta, Ken Barber
EVP and Chief Lending Officer, Doug Rehm
CEO ServisFirst Bank Dothan, B. Harrison Morris, age 40
Vice President of ServisFirst Bank and Manager of ServisFirst Bank, Crystal Tennyson
First Vice President, Lee McKinnon
Senior Vice President Commercial Lending, Chad Thomason
Senior Vice President Of Commerical Banking, David Hearne
Vice President Commercial Banking, Jamie Osteen
Senior Vice President, Michael Wood
Senior Vice President of Commercial Banking, Walter Brand
Senior Vice President Private Banking, Patricia Griner
Senior Vice President Business Development, Deann Grayson
Vice President Commercial Banking Officer, Chris Blaze
Vice President Portfolio Manager, Gary Allen
FVP Commercial Banking, Cheryl Dunn
Vice President, Meredith McLaughlin
Vice President and Commercial Lender, Max Coblentz
SENIOR VICE PRESIDENT, Samantha S Curd
Senior Vice President, Hill Womble
Chairman ServisFirst Bancshares and ServisFirst Bank, Stanley M. (Skip) Brock, age 66
Auditors: Dixon Hughes Goodman LLP

LOCATIONS

HQ: ServisFirst Bancshares Inc
2500 Woodcrest Place, Birmingham, AL 35209
Phone: 205 949-0302
Web: www.servisfirstbank.com

2013 Branches

	No.
Alabama	10
Florida	2
Total	12

COMPETITORS

Bank of America
Bank of the Ozarks
Wells Fargo

HISTORICAL FINANCIALS
Company Type: Public

Income Statement FYE: December 31

	ASSETS ($ mil.)	NET INCOME ($ mil.)	INCOME AS % OF ASSETS	EMPLOYEES
12/16	6,370	81	1.3%	420
12/15	5,095	63	1.2%	371
12/14	4,098	52	1.3%	298
12/13	3,520	41	1.2%	262
12/12	2,906	34	1.2%	—
Annual Growth	21.7%	24.0%	—	—

Debt ratio: 0.87%
Return on equity: 16.73%
Cash ($ mil.): 623
Current ratio: —
Long-term debt ($ mil.): —

No. of shares (mil.): 52
Dividends
Yield: 0.0%
Payout: 12.5%
Market value ($ mil.): 1,971

	STOCK PRICE ($) FY Close	P/E High/Low	PER SHARE ($) Earnings	Dividends	Book Value
12/16	37.44	48 23	1.52	0.19	9.93
12/15	47.53	40 24	1.20	0.12	8.64
12/14	32.95	83 26	1.05	0.16	8.20
Annual Growth	3.2%	— —	9.8%	4.7%	4.9%

Sherwin-Williams Co (The)

You won?t catch Sherwin-Williams watching the paint dry. It keeps rolling on as it has for its roughly 150 year history maintaining its position as one of the world?s top paint manufacturers (along with Akzo-Nobel PPG Industries and Henkel). Sherwin-Williams' products include a variety of paints finishes coatings applicators and varnishes sold under brands such as Dutch Boy Krylon Sherwin-Williams Valspar Thompson's WaterSeal Ronseal and Minwax. The company operates throughout the world about 4100 paint stores and sells automotive finishing and refinishing products through wholesale branches. Other outlets include mass merchandisers home centers independent dealers and automotive retailers. Sherwin-Williams completed an $8.9 billion acquisition of rival Valspar in 2017.

HISTORY

In 1870 Henry Sherwin bought out paint materials distributor Truman Dunham and joined Edward Williams and A. T. Osborn to form Sherwin Williams & Company in Cleveland. The business began making paints in 1871 and became the industry leader after improving the paint-grinding mill in the mid-1870s patenting a reclosable can in 1877 and improving liquid paint in 1880.

In 1874 Sherwin-Williams introduced a special paint for carriages beginning the concept of specific-purpose paint. (By 1900 the company had paints for floors roofs barns metal bridges railroad cars and automobiles.) Sherwin-Williams incorporated in 1884 and opened a dealership in Massachusetts in 1891 that was the forerunner of its company-run retail stores. The company obtained its "Cover the Earth" trademark in 1895.

Before the Depression Sherwin-Williams bought a number of smaller paint makers: Detroit White Lead (1910) Martin-Senour (1917) Acme Quality Paints (1920) and The Lowe Brothers (1929). Responding to wartime restrictions the company developed a fast-drying and water-reducible paint called Kem-Tone and the forerunner of the paint roller the Roller-Koater.

Sales doubled during the 1960s as the company made acquisitions including Sprayon (aerosol paint 1966) but rising expenses kept earnings flat. In 1972 the company expanded its stores to include carpeting draperies and other decorating items. But long-term debt ballooned from $80 million in 1974 to $196 million by 1977 when the company

lost $8.2 million and suspended dividends for the first time since 1885.

John Breen became CEO in 1979 reinstated the dividend purged over half of the top management positions and closed inefficient plants. He also focused stores on paint and wallpaper merchandise and purchased Dutch Boy (1980).

In 1990 Sherwin-Williams began selling Dutch Boy in Sears stores and Kem-Tone in Wal-Marts. Acquisitions that year included Borden's Krylon and Illinois Bronze aerosol operations and DeSoto's architectural coatings segment which made private-label paints for Sears and Home Depot. In 1991 Sherwin-Williams bought two coatings business units from Cook Paint and Varnish and the Cuprinol brand of coatings.

Sherwin-Williams purchased paint manufacturer Pratt & Lambert in 1996. That year it introduced several new products including Low Temp 35 a paint for low temperatures; Healthspec a low-odor paint; and Ralph Lauren designer paints. Prep-Rite do-it-yourself interior primers debuted in 1997. Also that year Sherwin-Williams bought Thompson Minwax (Thompson's Water Seal Minwax Wood Products) from Forstmann Little and Chile-based Marson Chilena a spray paint maker.

The company streamlined some of its business segments and trimmed jobs in 1998. Christopher Connor president of the Paint Stores group replaced Breen as CEO in 1999 and chairman in 2000. Also in 2000 Sherwin-Williams moved into the European automotive coatings market by acquiring Italy-based ScottWarren.

In late 2001 the company acquired Wisconsin-based Mautz Paint Company.

After a rough but still profitable 2001 the company grew revenues and profits for its consumer units (consumer paints and paint stores) in 2002 thanks largely to a healthy do-it-yourself market. Sales for its automotive finishes and international units however were down because of a slow collision-repair market and currency-exchange effects.

In 2010 Sherwin-Williams bought Arch Chemicals' Sayerlack a leading Italian wood care coating company and acquired Becker Acroma Industrial Wood Coatings a Swedish manufacturer of industrial wood coatings. It also acquired all shares of AlSher Titania (a joint venture with Altair Nanotechnologies) it did not already own giving it a 100% stake in the technology company. AlSher Titania is developing a promising titanium dioxide technology that Sherwin-Williams plans to commercialize.

That same year the company also acquired Pinturas C ndor an Ecuadorian diversified coatings supplier with $60 million in annual sales bolstering its market share in architectural paint in Latin America.

Among its acquisitions in 2011 was UK-based Leighs Paints a leader in fire-protectant (intumescent) coatings. (Because the intumescent technology prolongs the structural integrity of steel and concrete in a catastrophic fire more people are able to evacuate.)

In 2012 Sherwin-Williams made a significant purchase in the buyout of Jiangsu Pulanna Coating Co. headquartered in Changzhou China. Pulanna is an automotive refinishes coatings manufacturer and the deal improved Sherwin-Williams' presence in the most populous country in the world.

Also in 2012 Sherwin-Williams picked up Geocel Holdings a maker of caulks sealants and adhesives serving construction and repair applications. Geocel has locations in the US and the UK and the deal strengthened Sherwin-Williams' Consumer Group segment.

In a major geographic expansion in late 2012 the company agreed to acquire Grupo Comex a leader in the paint and coatings market in Mexico for $2.34 billion. However Mexico's antitrust reg-

ulator blocked the deal in mid-2013 stating the new company could artificially set higher prices at its discretion. Sherwin-Williams subsequently terminated the proposed deal.

However in 2013 the company acquired the US/Canada business of Comex. Sherwin-Williams paid $90 million in cash and assumed liabilities in the range of $75 million. Comex operations in the US and Canada consist of 314 company operated stores (234 in the US and 80 in Canada) and 8 manufacturing sites (5 in the US and 3 in Canada). In addition Comex supplies paint and coatings products to 1500 external retail locations.

2013 product launches included Sherwin-Williams Protective & Marine Coatings' Magnalux 404 FF the first styrene-free vinyl ester for use with steel and concrete substrates in the oil and gas market; Fast Clad 105ER a 100% solids tank lining for crude oil and ethanol storage; and Nova-Plate 325 an extended lifecycle 100% solids tank lining for high-temperature crude oil produced water and frac tank applications.

In 2013 Sherwin-Williams teamed up with Williams-Sonoma to create seasonal palettes of Sherwin-Williams paint colors that coordinate with the Pottery Barn Pottery Barn Kids PBteen and West Elm collections.

EXECUTIVES

Chairman President and CEO, John G. Morikis, age 54, $1,095,795 total compensation
Senior Vice President Human RE, Thomas Hopkins
President and General Manager Latin America Division The Americas Group, Paul R. Clifford
CIO, Thomas J. (Tom) Lucas
President The Americas Group, Robert J. Davisson, age 57, $611,936 total compensation
President and General Manager South Western Division The Americas Group, Monty J. Griffin, age 57
President and General Manager Diversified Brands Division Consumer Group, Cheri M. Phyfer, age 46
President and General Manager Automotive Division Global Finishes Group, Thomas C. Hablitzel, age 55
President and General Manager Global Supply Chain Division Consumer Group, Joel D. Baxter, age 57
President and General Manager Mid Western Division The Americas Group, Peter J. Ippolito, age 53
President and General Manager Protective and Marine Coatings Division Global Finishes Group, Ronald B. Rossetto
President Global Finishes Group, David B. Sewell, age 49
President Southeastern Division Paint Stores Group, Todd V. Wipf
President and General Manager Product Finishes Division Global Finishes Group, Bruce G. Irussi
SVP Finance and CFO, Allen J. Mistysyn, age 48
President and General Manager Eastern Division The Americas Group, Justin T. Binns
Senior Vice President General Counsel An, Catherine Kilbane
Vice President Sales, Brian Padden
National Account Manager, Vincent Barone
Vice President of Sales, Jim Sinko
National Accounts Manager, Harvey Kulkin
Vice President of Sales and Marketing, Nate Shinsky
Vice President of Human Resources, Kerri Rodgers
Vice President and Treasurer, Jeffrey Miklich
Vice President of Sales and Business Development, Jennie S Gerardot
Vice President Engineering, Beth Egan
Vice President of Sales, Brian Laguardia

Vice President and General Manager EMEA, Thomas Bergdahl
Vice President Taxes And Assistant Secretary Sherwin Williams Company, Michael Cummins
Vice President, Bill Desantis
Vice President, Mark Mazanec
National Account Manager, Joe Di Bianca
Vice President Sales, Gary Campbell
Vice President Human Resources Canada, Patrick Keene
National Account Manager, John Hackett
Vice President, Brett White
National Accounts Manager, Kyle Davisson
Vice President Sales, Richard Gilmore
National Sales Manager, Kurt Hostetler
Vice President of Research and Development, Victoria Varley
National Account Manager, Randy Scott
Board Member, Joseph Banks
Treasurer, Scott McVeigh
Board Member, Joseph D Banks
Board Member, Vicki Deckard
Auditors: Ernst & Young LLP

LOCATIONS

HQ: Sherwin-Williams Co (The)
101 West Prospect Avenue, Cleveland, OH 44115-1075
Phone: 216 566-2000   **Fax:** 216 566-3310
Web: www.sherwin.com

PRODUCTS/OPERATIONS

2016 sales

	$ mil.	% of total
Paint Stores Group	7,790	66
Global Finishes Group	1,889	16
Consumer Group	1,584	13
Latin America Coatings Group	586	5
Administrative	5	-
Total	**11,855**	**100**

Operations

Paint Stores
  Products
  Architectural coatings
  Industrial maintenance
  Marine products
  Brands
  ArmorSeal
  Brod-Dugan
  Con-Lux
  FlexBon Paints
  Hi-Temp
  Kem
  Mautz
  Mercury
  Old Quaker
  Powdura
  Pro-Line
  SeaGuard
  Sherwin-Williams
Consumer
  Products
  Architectural paints
  Industrial maintenance
  Paints
  Private-label coatings
  Stains
  Wood finishings
  Varnishes
  Brands
  Cabot
  Cuprinol
  Dupli-color
  Dura Clad
  Dutch Boy
  EverLast
  Formby's
  H&C
  Krylon
  Martin Senour
  Maxwood Latex Stains
  Minwax
  Plastic Kote
  Pratt & Lambert

Red Devil
Rubberset
Signature Select
Thompson's WaterSeal
Valspar
White Lightning
Automotive Finishes
  Products
  Finishing refinishing and touch-up products for motor vehicles
  Brands
  Baco
  Excelo
  Lazzuril
  Martin Senour
  ScottWarren
  Sherwin-Williams
  Western
International Coatings
  Products
  Architectural paints
  Industrial maintenance products
  Stains
  Varnishes
  Wood finishing products
  Brands
  Andina
  Colorgin
  Dutch Boy
  Globo
  Kem-Tone
  Krylon
  Marson
  Martin Senour
  Minwax
  Pratt & Lambert
  Pulverlack
  Ronseal
  Sherwin-Williams
  Sumare

COMPETITORS

Akzo Nobel	Dunn-Edwards
BASF SE	Ferro
Benjamin Moore	H.B. Fuller
California Products	Kelly-Moore
Comex Group	Masco
Coronado Paint	PPG Industries
Diamond Vogel Paint	RPM International
DuPont	

HISTORICAL FINANCIALS

Company Type: Public

Income Statement

FYE: December 31

	REVENUE ($ mil.)	NET INCOME ($ mil.)	NET PROFIT MARGIN	EMPLOYEES
12/16	11,855	1,132	9.6%	42,550
12/15	11,339	1,053	9.3%	40,706
12/14	11,129	865	7.8%	39,674
12/13	10,185	752	7.4%	37,633
12/12	9,534	631	6.6%	34,154
Annual Growth	**5.6%**	**15.7%**	**—**	**5.6%**

2016 Year-End Financials

Debt ratio: 28.92%	No. of shares (mil.): 93
Return on equity: 82.26%	Dividends
Cash ($ mil.): 889	Yield: 0.0%
Current ratio: 1.28	Payout: 28.0%
Long-term debt ($ mil.): 1,211	Market value ($ mil.): 24,996

	STOCK PRICE ($) FY Close	P/E High/Low	PER SHARE ($) Earnings	Dividends	Book Value
12/16	268.74	25 19	11.99	3.36	20.20
12/15	259.60	26 19	11.16	2.68	9.41
12/14	263.04	30 20	8.78	2.20	10.52
12/13	183.50	26 21	7.26	2.00	17.72
12/12	153.82	26 15	6.02	1.56	17.35
Annual Growth	**15.0%**	**— —**	**18.8%**	**21.1%**	**3.9%**

SHI INTERNATIONAL CORP.

Businesses that need more than boxes of hardware and software can call SHI International. The company distributes scores of computer hardware and software products from suppliers such as Adobe Cisco Microsoft VMware Symantec and Lenovo. It resells PCs networking products data storage systems printers software and keyboards among other items. SHI offers a range of professional services including software licensing asset management managed desktop services systems integration and vocational training. The company serves corporate government and health care customers from more than 30 offices across the US Canada the UK Germany France and Hong Kong. SHI was founded in 1989 by Chairman Koguan Leo.

Operations

SHI serves several sectors and verticals. The company specializes in software and hardware procurement deployment planning configuration data center optimization IT asset management and cloud computing as well as custom IT solutions.

Geographic Reach

Based in Somerset New Jersey SHI has a global reach through its 30-plus offices located across the US Canada the UK Germany France and Hong Kong. In the US the company operates primarily in Texas and California but also in Arizona Colorado Florida Georgia Illinois Indiana Kansas Massachusetts Michigan Minnesota Missouri New Jersey New York Pennsylvania Virginia and Washington. Specifically its cloud briefing center is housed in New York City and its corporate call center runs from Austin Texas. The company's 420000-sq.-ft. headquarters operates beside its 305000-sq.-ft. Integration Center in Somerset New Jersey.

Financial Performance

SHI International rang up $6.8 billion in sales in 2015 a 14% increase versus the prior year. SHI's Strategic Enterprise Commercial Enterprise Corporate and Public Sector divisions contributed nearly equally to the revenue total for the year and growth outside the U.S. was steady with SHI's Canada U.K. and France divisions each posting double-digit growth. In addition SHI recognized over $1 billion in revenue from cloud products and solutions.

The seller of IT products and services boasts a 99% annual customer retention rate.

Strategy

The company has transformed itself from a $1 million regional reseller of software to a $5 billion global provider of information technology products and services.To this end SHI has invested some $20 million in a new data center that provides cloud services specifically what the company terms infrastructure-as-a-service (IaaS). The data center is one of six in the US that houses virtual machines for IT professionals to provide services such as application deployment disaster recovery software-as-a-service (SaaS). It also offers on-demand burst computing services where customers use the additional bandwidth to handle peaks in demand.

SHI's professional services unit already provides some cloud services and data center consulting. SHI sees IaaS as a logical extension of the software asset management (SAM) service it already provides. Under the SAM program SHI handles software deployment licensing compliance and inventories across a business.

SHI partners with Omaha Nebraska-based information security software specialist Solutionary to manage data security services using its Active-Guard software product to block computer network security breaches as data center security is one of the biggest concerns for businesses in a cloud computing environment. Awards and Recognition

SHI is the largest minority and women-owned Business Enterprise (MWBE) in the US. The company's ranked 13th on CRN's 2015 Solution Provider 500 list of the largest IT solution providers in North America.

EXECUTIVES

President and Co-CEO, Thai Lee, age 60
VP and General Manager, Hal Jagger
Vice President Internal Audit and Finance Operations, Kevin Boyles
National Sales Manager, Steven Hays
Chairman, Koguan Leo
Auditors: COHN & REZNICK ACCOUNTING TAX

LOCATIONS

HQ: SHI INTERNATIONAL CORP.
290 DAVIDSON AVE, SOMERSET, NJ 088734145
Phone: 732 764-8888

PRODUCTS/OPERATIONS

Selected Products
Accessories
Peripherals
Hardware
Memory
Software

Selected Services
Cloud services
Computer vocational training services
Data center services
Events
Hardware services
Networking
POLARIS Software asset management
Storage
Strategic consulting
Webinars

COMPETITORS

ASI Computer Technologies	Computacenter
Agilysys	Ingram Micro
Arrow Electronics	Insight Enterprises
Avnet	PC Mall
CDW	Softchoice
CompuCom	Tech Data

HISTORICAL FINANCIALS

Company Type: Private

Income Statement

FYE: December 31

	REVENUE ($ mil.)	NET INCOME ($ mil.)	NET PROFIT MARGIN	EMPLOYEES
12/16	7,268	104	1.4%	3,800
12/15	6,540	69	1.1%	—
12/14	5,797	89	1.5%	—
12/13	5,003	74	1.5%	—
Annual Growth	13.3%	11.8%	—	—

2016 Year-End Financials

Debt ratio: —
Return on equity: 1.40%
Cash ($ mil.): 131
Current ratio: 1.20
Long-term debt ($ mil.): —
Dividends
Yield: —
Payout: —
Market value ($ mil.): —

SI Financial Group Inc (MD)

EXECUTIVES

President CEO and Director SI Financial SI Bancorp and Savings Institute Bank and Trust, Rheo A. Brouillard, age 61, $294,831 total compensation
Auditors: Wolf & Company, P.C.

LOCATIONS

HQ: SI Financial Group Inc (MD)
803 Main Street, Willimantic, CT 06226
Phone: 860 423-4581
Web: www.mysifi.com

COMPETITORS

Bank of America	People's United Financial
Citizens Financial Group	Sovereign Bank
Liberty Bank	TD Bank USA
PSB Holdings Inc.	Webster Financial

HISTORICAL FINANCIALS

Company Type: Public

Income Statement

FYE: December 31

	ASSETS ($ mil.)	NET INCOME ($ mil.)	INCOME AS % OF ASSETS	EMPLOYEES
12/16	1,550	11	0.7%	297
12/15	1,481	4	0.3%	292
12/14	1,350	4	0.3%	299
12/13	1,346	(0)	—	315
12/12	953	1	0.1%	265
Annual Growth	12.9%	78.3%	—	2.9%

2016 Year-End Financials

Debt ratio: 0.81%
Return on equity: 7.07%
Cash ($ mil.): 73
Current ratio: —
Long-term debt ($ mil.): —
No. of shares (mil.): 12
Dividends
Yield: 0.0%
Payout: 16.8%
Market value ($ mil.): 188

	STOCK PRICE ($) FY Close	P/E High/Low		PER SHARE ($) Earnings	Dividends	Book Value
12/16	15.40	17	13	0.95	0.16	13.49
12/15	13.65	38	30	0.36	0.15	12.63
12/14	11.33	34	30	0.36	0.12	12.35
12/13	12.05	—	—	(0.08)	0.12	11.94
12/12	11.50	107	90	0.11	0.12	12.44
Annual Growth	7.6%	—	—	71.4%	7.5%	2.1%

Sierra Bancorp

Sierra Bancorp is the holding company for the nearly $2 billion-asset Bank of the Sierra which operates approximately 30 branches in Central California's San Joaquin Valley between (and including) Bakersfield and Fresno. The bank offers traditional deposit products and loans to individuals and small and mid-size businesses. About 70% of its loan portfolio is made up of real estate loans while another 15% is made up of mortgage warehouse loans and a further 10% is tied to commer-

cial and industrial loans (including SBA loans and direct finance leases). The bank also issues agricultural loans and consumer loans.

Operations
Bank of the Sierra makes almost 80% of its revenue from interest income. About 64% of its total revenue came from interest income on loans and leases (including fees) during 2015 while another 14% came from interest income on taxed and tax-exempt securities. The rest of its revenue came from deposit account service charges (12% of revenue) checkcard fees (5%) and other non-interest income sources.

Geographic Reach
The Porterville California-based bank operates branches and offices mostly in the San Joaquin Valley in Porterville Arroyo Grande Atascadero Bakersfield California City Clovis Delano Dinuba Exeter Farmersville Fillmore Fresno Hanford Lindsay Oxnard Paso Robles Reedley San Luis Obispo Santa Clarita Santa Paula Selma Tehachapi Three Rivers Visalia and Tulare.

Sales and Marketing
Bank of the Sierra has been gradually increasing its advertising spend in recent years. It spent $2.3 million on advertising and promotion in 2015 up from $2.2 million and $1.9 million in 2014 and 2013 respectively.

Financial Performance
The bank's revenue has been steadily rising over the past few years mostly as bank acquisitions and organic loan business growth has spurred higher interest income. Meanwhile its profits have more than doubled since 2011 thanks to declining loan loss provisions as its loan portfolio's credit quality has improved with higher property valuations in the strengthened economy.

Sierra Bancorp's revenue jumped 13% to $80.4 million during 2015 thanks to higher interest income from continued double-digit loan asset growth led by a jump in mortgage warehouse lines from increased line utilization a first-quarter purchase of residential mortgage loans and strong organic growth in non-farm real estate and agricultural production loans. Deposit account service fees also grew thanks to organic deposit client growth.

Strong revenue growth and lower acquisition costs in 2015 drove the bank's net income up 19% to $18 million. Sierra's operating cash levels rose 4% to $29.78 million during the year as its cash-based earnings increased.

Strategy
While the Bank of Sierra has traditionally grown organically by opening around one new branch per year in the Central Valley it has more recently acquired small area banks and individual branches to bolster its deposit and loan business while expanding into untapped markets such as further south into the Santa Clara Valley.

Mergers and Acquisitions
In July 2016 the bank bought $145 million-asset Coast Bancorp and its Coast National Bank branches in San Luis Obispo Paso Robles Arroyo Grande and Atascadero California.

In November 2014 Sierra Bancorp bought $129 million-asset Santa Clara Valley Bank N.A. and its branches in Santa Paula Santa Clarita and Fillmore in California for $15 million. the deal expanded Sierra's reach outside of its traditional market for the first time more south into the Santa Clara Valley of California.

EXECUTIVES

EVP and CFO, Kenneth R. (Ken) Taylor, age 57, $242,500 total compensation
EVP and Chief Credit Officer, James F. (Jim) Gardunio, age 66, $197,600 total compensation

President and CEO, Kevin J. McPhaill, age 44, $185,000 total compensation
Vice President And Branch Loan Officer, Amy Ott
Chairman, Morris A. Tharp, age 77
Auditors: Vavrinek, Trine, Day & Co., LLP

LOCATIONS

HQ: Sierra Bancorp
86 North Main Street, Porterville, CA 93257
Phone: 559 782-4900
Web: www.bankofthesierra.com

COMPETITORS

Bank of America	MUFG Americas Holdings
Bank of the West	United Security
Central Valley	Bancshares
Community Bancorp	Wells Fargo
Citibank	Westamerica
Comerica	Zions Bancorporation
JPMorgan Chase	

HISTORICAL FINANCIALS

Company Type: Public

Income Statement

FYE: December 31

	ASSETS ($ mil.)	NET INCOME ($ mil.)	INCOME AS % OF ASSETS	EMPLOYEES
12/16	2,032	17	0.9%	497
12/15	1,796	18	1.0%	431
12/14	1,637	15	0.9%	437
12/13	1,410	13	0.9%	406
12/12	1,437	8	0.6%	418
Annual Growth	9.0%	21.0%	—	4.4%

2016 Year-End Financials

Debt ratio: 1.69%
Return on equity: 8.84%
Cash ($ mil.): 120
Current ratio: —
Long-term debt ($ mil.): —

No. of shares (mil.): 13
Dividends
  Yield: 0.0%
  Payout: 37.2%
Market value ($ mil.): 366

	STOCK PRICE ($) FY Close	P/E High/Low	PER SHARE ($) Earnings	Dividends	Book Value
12/16	26.59	20 12	1.29	0.48	14.94
12/15	17.65	14 11	1.33	0.42	14.36
12/14	17.56	16 14	1.08	0.34	13.67
12/13	16.09	21 12	0.94	0.26	12.78
12/12	11.43	22 15	0.58	0.24	12.33
Annual Growth	23.5%	— —	22.1%	18.9%	4.9%

Signature Bank (New York, NY)

Signature Bank marks the spot where some professional New Yorkers bank. The institution provides customized banking and financial services to smaller private businesses their owners and their top executives through 30 branches across the New York metropolitan area including all five boroughs Long Island and affluent Westchester County. The bank's lending activities mainly entail real estate and business loans. Subsidiary Signature Securities offers wealth management financial planning brokerage services asset management and insurance while its Signature Financial subsidiary offers equipment financing and leasing.

Founded in 2001 the bank now boasts assets of roughly $29 billion.

Operations

Mortgage loans including commercial real estate loans multifamily residential mortgages home loans and lines of credit and construction and land loans comprise the bulk of Signature Bank's loan portfolio (and much of its asset base as well).

The bank which staffed some 1010 employees at the end of 2014 generated 68% of its revenue from interest on loans and leases that year while 20% came from interest on its securities available-for-sale and 7% came from securities held-to-maturity. The remainder of its revenue came from fees and service charges (2%) and various other miscellaneous sources.

Geographic Reach

The bank's nearly 30 branch offices are mostly in the New York metropolitan area which includes Manhattan Brooklyn Westchester Long Island Queens the Bronx Staten Island and Connecticut.

Sales and Marketing

Signature Bank mostly serves privately-owned businesses their owners and senior managers (typically with a net worth between $500000 and $20 million).

Financial Performance

The company's revenues and profits have risen in recent years thanks to strong organic loan business growth and declining loan loss provisions as its loan portfolio's credit quality has improved with higher property valuations in the strengthened economy.

Signature's revenue jumped by 22% to a record $959.3 million in 2014 mostly as loan interest (on commercial loans mortgages and leases) and security interest income continued to grow as the bank built up its interest-earning assets during the year.

Higher revenue and a continued decline and loan loss provisions in 2014 boosted the bank's net income by 30% to a record $296.7 million. Signature's operating cash levels more than doubled to $421 million on higher cash earnings.

Strategy

Signature Bank has long targeted privately-held businesses that have fewer than 1000 employees and revenues of less than $200 million. Some of its target clients include real estate owners/companies law firms accounting firms entertainment business managers medical professionals retail establishments money management firms and non-profit foundations.

The bank continues to expand its service lines particularly focusing on specialty financing to grow its business organically. In 2015 it planned to offer direct commercial vehicle financing through a network of approved commercial vehicle dealerships in New York's Tri-State area with loans targeting small and mid-size business borrowers looking to acquire commercial vehicles and fleets. Also that year it formed its Maryland-based Signature Public Funding Corp subsidiary to provide municipal finance and tax-exempt lending and leasing products to local state and federal government agencies nationwide.

Company Background

The bank's emphasis on personal service helped it to grow its deposit base and loan portfolio in 2011. During a time when many other banks struggled under the weight of bad loans in a bad economy Signature Bank achieved record earnings for the fourth consecutive year.

Founded in 2001 as an alternative to megabanks Signature Bank was spun off from Bank Hapoalim in 2004.

EXECUTIVES

Executive Vice President and Chief Credit Officer, Michael Merlo
President CEO and Director, Joseph J. DePaolo, $577,500 total compensation
SVP and CFO, Vito Susca
President CEO and Director, Michael G. O'Rourke
EVP, Kevin P. Bastuga
EVP, Bryan D. Duncan
VP Retail Operations Manager, Ella Riordan-Pacheco
Senior Vice President, Michael Doti
Vice President, John C Spagnuolo
Group Director Senior Vice President, Joseph Alexander
Senior Vice President Group Director, Gary Shulevich
Senior Vice President Melville NY, Drew S Crowley
Vice President, Phyllis Rosenfeld
SVP, James Raggi
Executive Vice President, Eric Howell
Senior Vice President, Janice Ashley
Senior Vice President Group Director, Matthew Weltman
Senior Lender Vice President, Eugene Cartin
Group Director Senior Vice President, Tamara Gavrielof
Senior Vice President Group Director, James Buck
Senior Vice President Group Director, Edwin Sirlin
Group Director Senior Vice President, David Artis
Senior Vice President Funding Officer, Brant Ward
Vice President, John Ricchezza
Vice President, Sue Frick
Senior Vice President Group Director, Nicole Rospond
Group Director Senior Vice President, Keti Dervishi
Senior Vice President, Gary Sarro
Vice President Senior Lender, George Greene
Senior Lender Vice President, Maria Vetrano
Senior Vpres, Mohammed O Kamil
Senior Vice President, George Maroulis
Senior Vice President, Anthony Daperis
Executive Vice President, Joseph Fantauzzi
SVP, Ken Bartho
Vice President Director Of Operations, Richard Pelcher
Senior Vice President, David Saunders
Compliance Vice President, Jeffrey Barrington
Vice President Senior Lender; Commercial Real Estate, Jay Byrne
Vice President, John Paglia
Vice President, John Spagnuolo
Vice President and Associate Group Director, Matthew Cohen
Vice President, Barbara Von Borstel
Senior Vice President Group Director, Stephen Reinhardt
Group Director Senior Vice President, Michael Vasami
Senior Vice President, Thomas Grippa
Senior Vice President, Peter Marra
Senior Vice President, Randi Schneer
Senior Vice President, Ron Larsen
Senior Vice President, Rosemary McLaughlin
Senior Vice President, Steven Kocoris
Senior Vice President, Joann Rossano
Senior Vice President, Judy Stern
Vice President, Joseph Fingerman
Senior Vice President Group Director, Larry Goldberg
Vice President and Associate Group Director, Marilyn Gessner
Vice President Commercial Banking, Ross Thomson
Senior Vice President and Group Director, Roseann Manos
Vice President of Real Estate, Aaron Greene
Vice President, Howard Green

Senior Vice President Underwriting and Portfolio Manager, Wendy Nelson
Group Director Senior Vice President, Jason Birnbaum
Senior Vice President Group Director, Brian Mazzotta
Group Director Senior Vice President, Bill McCarthy
Vice President, John Barfuss
Vice President, Sonya Morlock
Vice President Portfolio Manager, Leslie Roberts
Vice President, Thomas Messemer
Vice President, Henry Lee
VP Executive Sales Officer, Stephanie Paysse
Group Director Senior Vice President, Vincent Lopreto
Group Director Senior Vice President, Todd Flamenbaum
SVP, Maria Hegi
Vice President Associate Group Director, Rich Demartino
Group Director Senior Vice President, Marie Moreno
Group Director Senior Vice President, Avi Azuolay
Vice President Capital Markets, Rob Campbell
Group Director Senior Vice President, Nellie Teplinsky
Chairman and Director, Leonard S. Caronia
Auditors: KPMG LLP

LOCATIONS

HQ: Signature Bank (New York, NY)
565 Fifth Avenue, New York, NY 10017
Phone: 646 822-1500
Web: www.signatureny.com

PRODUCTS/OPERATIONS

2014 Sales

	$ mil.	% of total
Interest		
Loans net	655	68
Securities available for sale	193	20
Securities held to maturity	69	7
Other	5	1
Noninterest		
Fees & service charges	19	2
Commissions	10	1
Net gains on sales of loans	5	1
Net gains on sales of securities	5	-
Other	2	-
Adjustments	(7.8)	-
Total	**959**	**100**

COMPETITORS

Apple Bank for Savings	Herald National Bank
Astoria Financial	JPMorgan Chase
Bank Leumi USA	New York Community
Capital One	Bancorp
Citigroup	Safra Bank
HSBC USA	TD Bank USA

HISTORICAL FINANCIALS

Company Type: Public

Income Statement

FYE: December 31

	ASSETS ($ mil.)	NET INCOME ($ mil.)	INCOME AS % OF ASSETS	EMPLOYEES
12/16	39,047	396	1.0%	1,218
12/15	33,450	373	1.1%	1,122
12/14	27,318	296	1.1%	1,010
12/13	22,376	228	1.0%	945
12/12	17,456	185	1.1%	844
Annual Growth	**22.3%**	**20.9%**	**—**	**9.6%**

2016 Year-End Financials

Debt ratio: 0.66%	No. of shares (mil.): 54
Return on equity: 12.15%	Dividends
Cash ($ mil.): 538	Yield: —
Current ratio: —	Payout: —
Long-term debt ($ mil.): —	Market value ($ mil.): 8,203

	STOCK PRICE ($) FY Close	P/E High/Low		PER SHARE ($) Earnings	Dividends	Book Value
12/16	150.20	21	15	7.37	0.00	66.15
12/15	153.37	22	16	7.27	0.00	56.81
12/14	125.96	22	17	5.95	0.00	49.61
12/13	107.42	22	15	4.76	0.00	38.06
12/12	71.34	18	15	3.91	0.00	34.94
Annual Growth	**20.5%**	**—**	**—**	**17.2%**	**—**	**17.3%**

Simmons First National Corp

Simmons First National thinks it's only natural it should be one of the largest financial institutions in The Natural State. The $8.1 billion-asset holding company owns Simmons First National Bank and seven other community banks that bear the Simmons First Bank name and maintain local identities; together they operate around 150 branches throughout Arkansas and in Kansas Tennessee and Missouri. Serving consumers and area businesses the banks offer standard deposit products like checking and savings accounts IRAs and CDs. Lending activities mainly consist of commercial real estate loans single-family mortgages and consumer loans such as credit card and student loans.

Operations

In addition to Simmons First National Bank the company owns Simmons First Bank of Jonesboro Simmons First Bank of South Arkansas Simmons First Bank of Northwest Arkansas Simmons First Bank of Russellville Simmons First Bank of Searcy Simmons First Bank of El Dorado and Simmons First Bank of Hot Springs. Simmons First Trust Company a subsidiary of Simmons First National Bank provides trust and fiduciary services; Simmons First Investment Group offers broker-dealer services.

Like other retail banks Simmons makes the bulk of its money from interest income. About 65% of its total revenue came from loan interest during 2015 while another 8% came from interest on investment securities. The rest of its revenue came from service charges on deposit accounts (8% of revenue) debit and credit card fees (6%) mortgage lending income (3%) trust income (2%) investment banking income (1%) and other non-interest income sources.

Geographic Reach

The bank has around 150 branches mostly in Arkansas but also in Kansas Missouri and Tennessee.

Financial Performance

Simmons First National Bank's annual revenues and profits have been rising mostly thanks to new loan business from rapid bank expansion (mostly stemming from acquisitions).

The bank's revenue jumped 60% to $396.8 million during 2015 mostly thanks to 58% growth in legacy loans and growth in acquired loan business from the acquisitions of Liberty and Community First. Non-interest income grew 54% thanks to rising trust service charges deposit fees mortgage

lending income all also tied to its recent acquisitions.

Revenue growth in 2015 more than doubled Simmons' net income to $74.36 million. The bank's operating cash levels spiked eight-fold to $88.7 million for the year thanks to a rise in cash-based earnings and favorable changes in working capital.

Strategy

Simmons tries to differentiate itself from smaller competitors by offering a wider array of products while striving to provide more personalized service than larger regional banks. The company also likes to acquire banks to grow its loan and deposit business while expanding into new geographic markets. Between 1990 and 2015 Simmons made 11 whole bank acquisitions and a handful of branch deals with other banks adding some 125 branches to its total branch network.

Mergers and Acquisitions

In September 2016 Simmons acquired Citizens National Bank a Tennessee-based bank with about 10 branch locations.

In October 2015 the company purchased Ozark Trust & Investment Corporation and its Trust Company of the Ozarks subsidiary adding $1 billion in new assets under management and 1300 clients to its wealth management business.

In February 2015 Simmons First National acquired $1.1 billion-asset Liberty Bancshares as well as Liberty Bank branches in southwest Missouri St. Louis and Kansas City. It also added Liberty's expertise in small business lending.

Also in February 2015 the bank bought $1.9 billion-asset Community First Bancshares and its First State Bank branches in Tennessee. Community First also added expertise in small business and consumer lending.

EXECUTIVES

EVP Organizational Development, Stephen C. Massanelli, age 61
Chairman and CEO, George A. Makris, age 60, $502,500 total compensation
SEVP CFO and Treasurer, Robert A. Fehlman, age 52, $306,614 total compensation
EVP and Central and Northeast Arkansas Regional Chairman Simmons First National Bank, Barry K. Ledbetter
President and Chief Credit Officer Simmons First National Bank, N. Craig Hunt
EVP and South Arkansas Regional Chairman Simmons First National Bank, Freddie G. Black
EVP Corporate Strategy and Performance and Secretary, Susan F. Smith, age 55
President Chief Banking Officer and Director, David L. Bartlett, age 65, $376,142 total compensation
EVP, Marty D. Casteel, age 65, $304,180 total compensation
SVP and Investor Relations Officer, David W. Garner, age 47
EVP of Marketing, Robert C. Dill, age 74, $179,393 total compensation
EVP and Chief Risk Officer, Tina M. Groves, age 47
EVP Technology and Operations Simmons First National Bank, Lisa W. Hunter
SVP and Marketing Director Simmons First National Bank, Amy W. Johnson
President El Dorado Community Bank, Robert L. Robinson
Chairman Russellville Community Chairman, Ronald B. (Ron) Jackson
President Hot Springs Community Bank, Steven W. (Steve) Trusty
President Conway Community Bank, Jason Culpepper
EVP and General Counsel, Patrick A. Burrow, age 63

EVP Specialty Lending Simmons First National
Bank, Larry L. Bates
EVP and Tennessee Regional Chairman Simmons
First National Bank, John C. Clark
EVP and Kansas and Missouri Regional Chairman
Simmons First National Bank, Gary E. Metsger
Senior Vice President and Director Human
Resources, Sharon Burdine
Vice President and Personnel Manager, Leigh
Cockrum
Vice President, Pam Lawshe
Vice President of Mortgage, Deana Powell
Vice President, Angie Haynes
Vice President Benefits and Special Projects, John
Brower
Assistant Vice President Loans, Esther Chapman
Assistant Vice President Business Development,
Anastasia Blaylock
Vice President, Chad Pittillo
Vice President and Controller Rf
Communications, Clifton White
Executive Vice President Operations, Glenda
Tolson
Senior Vice President, Adam Mitchell
Vice President And Commercial Loan Officer, John
Craig
Vice President and Trust Officer, Robin Thornton
Vice President Equipment Finance, Michael
Childers
Vice President and Trust Officer, Joyce Green
Executive Vice President Regulatory Affairs and
Risk Strategy, Chris Dunn
Vice President Commercial Banking Relationship
Manager, Dave Ruby
Vice President, Ed Stahlman
Vice President Commercial Lending, Wayne Wilson
Senior Branch Manager Assistant Vice President,
Aaron Cooper
Vice President Commercial Lending, Brad Thresher
Senior Vice President Commercial Lending,
Melissa Henshaw
Senior Vice President, Steve Landry
Vice President Mortgage Manager, Darnessa Taylor
Vice President Commercial Lending, Vernon Scott
Assistant Vice President Atm Operations, Karla
Dial
Auditors: BKD, LLP

LOCATIONS

HQ: Simmons First National Corp
501 Main Street, Pine Bluff, AR 71601
Phone: 870 541-1000
Web: www.simmonsfirst.com

PRODUCTS/OPERATIONS

2015 Sales

	% of total
Interest Income	
Loans	65
Investment securities	8
Others	-
Non-interest income	
Service charges on deposit accounts	8
Debit and credit card fees	6
Mortgage lending income	3
Trust income	2
Other service charges and fees	2
others	6
Net (loss) gain on assets covered by FDIC loss share agreements	-
Total	**100**

COMPETITORS

Arvest Bank	Bear State Financial
BOK Financial	Home BancShares
BancorpSouth	IBERIABANK
Bank of America	Regions Financial
Bank of the Ozarks	U.S. Bancorp

HISTORICAL FINANCIALS

Company Type: Public

Income Statement

FYE: December 31

	ASSETS ($ mil.)	NET INCOME ($ mil.)	INCOME AS % OF ASSETS	EMPLOYEES
12/16	8,400	96	1.2%	1,875
12/15	7,559	74	1.0%	1,946
12/14	4,643	35	0.8%	1,331
12/13	4,383	23	0.5%	1,306
12/12	3,527	27	0.8%	1,052
Annual Growth	**24.2%**	**36.8%**	**—**	**15.5%**

2016 Year-End Financials

Debt ratio: 1.29%
Return on equity: 8.67%
Cash ($ mil.): 285
Current ratio: —
Long-term debt ($ mil.): —

No. of shares (mil.): 62
Dividends
Yield: 0.0%
Payout: 30.6%
Market value ($ mil.): 3,888

	STOCK PRICE ($) FY Close	P/E High/Low	PER SHARE ($) Earnings	Dividends	Book Value
12/16	62.15	42 25	1.57	0.48	18.40
12/15	51.36	44 27	1.32	0.46	17.78
12/14	40.65	41 31	1.06	0.44	13.69
12/13	37.15	52 33	0.71	0.42	12.44
12/12	25.36	35 27	0.82	0.40	12.27
Annual Growth	**25.1%**	**— —**	**17.5%**	**4.7%**	**10.7%**

Simon Property Group, Inc.

Simon Property Group is the largest shopping mall and retail center owner in the US. The self-managed self-administered real estate investment trust (REIT) owns develops and manages regional shopping malls outlet malls (under the Premium Outlet and The Mills brands) boutique malls and shopping centers. Its roughly $25 billion real estate portfolio is composed of some 200 retail properties totaling approximately 180 million sq. ft. of leasable space. Its portfolio covers 35 states and Puerto Rico though much is concentrated in the US Southeast Midwest and Northeast. The REIT also has stakes in outlet centers in Canada Mexico Europe and Asia. CEO and chairman David E. Simon is the son of Melvin Simon who founded the firm with his brother Herbert.

Operations

Simon Property?s primary operations are the ownership development leasing and management of its retail real estate portfolio. The extend of its involvement and revenue generation varies by its degree of ownership. In addition to owning some 150 properties in the US it is a joint-venture partner in about 80 mostly international properties. It also uses joint ventures to hold equity investments in several European real estate holding companies.

The extent of Simon Property?s involvement in managing the properties is also influenced by its ownership stake. It manages the day-to-day operations of its owned properties as well as about 60 of its joint-venture properties. The remaining properties all of which are located outside the US are managed through joint ventures in which Simon shares but does not have majority control.

The company makes about 60% of its revenue from rental income just less than 30% from tenant recoveries (reimbursements to Simon Properties for common area maintenance real estate taxes etc.) and the rest from overage rents management fees and other corporate revenue.

Geographic Reach

Indianapolis Indiana-based Simon Property Group owns and operates ? wholly or as part of joint ventures ? retail real estate properties in the Americas Europe and Asia.

By far its largest market is the United States where it generates over 95% of its revenue and holds nearly 95% of its long-lived assets.

Sales and Marketing

Simon Property enters long-term tenancy contracts with retailers to fill its properties. Its lease terms must be competitive to attract desirable tenants and its management services provide post-sale customer care to its lessees and also strive to pull consumer traffic into its properties with local advertising and special events (Santa Claus at the Mall for example).

Although internet-based retail presents challenges to many of Simon?s typical tenants the REIT maintains the relevance of a brick-and-mortar presence. Still it is modifying its store mix within its properties to include more entertainment and residency offerings while still working with its long-standing clients to fill space in its retail properties.

Many of its properties are anchored by major tenants such as JCPenney Macy?s Dillard?s Neiman Marcus and Bloomingdale?s and supplemented with smaller stores like Dick?s Sporting Goods Sears Nordstrom Kohl?s and AMC Theatres. Its Premium Outlets are home to a variety of popular retailers including Adidas American Eagle Outfitters Ann Taylor Columbia Sportswear Michael Kors Tommy Hilfiger and The North Face.

Occupancy for its US malls Premium Outlets and Mills-branded properties remain above 96%. No one tenant accounts for more than 5% of its consolidated revenue.

Financial Performance

The long-term trend in revenue and net income has been positive over recent years. Net income swooned a bit in 2012 ? 2014 but remained above $1 billion annually. Revenue climbed steadily since 2012 growing from $2.3 billion in that year to just more than $5.4 billion in 2016.

Simon Property?s 2016 revenue of $5.4 billion grew about 3% from 2015?s $5.3 billion as a result of a higher rents overcoming a slightly lower dollar-per-square-foot sales number from its tenants. Occupancy rates of over 96% remained near historically peak levels.

In 2016 net income from continuing operations was $2.1 billion matching 2015?s result. Depreciation and amortization along with a write-off of costs related to an abandoned project prevented the revenue increase from flowing to the bottom line.

Simon?s cash balance at the end of 2016 was $560 million a decrease of $141 million when compared to the prior year. The change arose from $3.4 billion generated by operating activities offset by just under $1 billion used by investing activities (mainly from capital expenditures acquisitions and joint-venture investments) and $2.5 billion used by financing activities (primarily for higher than usual debt repayments).

Strategy

The retail industry is encountering both cyclical and structural changes including aging US demographics (and therefore less retail spending) and internet-based e-commerce. Simon Property is changing with the times by reformulating the tenant mix in its properties and addressing new and redevelopment needs in growth markets.

Acknowledging the changing retail dynamic Simon is diversifying its properties away from apparel-heavy approaches by transitioning its tenant base to include residential space hotels entertainment options restaurants and wellness centers. The idea is to entice consumers to its property not only to shop but to be entertained and possibly even spend the weekend. Centers such as The Domain in Austin TX and the jointly-developed Brickell City Centre in Miami FL exemplify this new approach.

Simon is averaging $1 billion in annual investments to build new or redevelop existing properties. In 2016 Simon redeveloped the Stanford Shopping Center in Palo Alto CA and the East Coast?s largest shopping center King of Prussia. At the end of 2016 Simon had $1.1 billion of redevelopment and expansion projects at nearly 30 sites including at Woodbury Common Premium Outlet in New York City and La Plaza Mall in McAllen TX. The company?s approach is to start with the aesthetic and functional appeal and then to add on-site customer service and technology to make the shopping experience easier and more efficient for shoppers and retailers.

Mergers and Acquisitions

In 2016 Simon acquired with a partner a non-controlling 75% interest in an outlet center in Ochtrup Germany and later that year purchased with a joint venture partner a luxury shopping center on the Las Vegas Strip for $1.1 billion. In that same year it divested two multi-family residential investments and several retail properties for about $82 million.

EXECUTIVES

EVP and CFO, Andrew A. (Andy) Juster, age 65, $500,000 total compensation
President and COO, Richard S. (Rick) Sokolov, age 67, $800,000 total compensation
Chief Administrative Officer; President Malls, John Rulli, $463,500 total compensation
Chairman and CEO, David Simon, age 55, $1,250,000 total compensation
SVP and CIO, David Schacht
President The Mills, Gregg M. Goodman
CEO Premium Outlets, Stephen J. Yalof
Chief Marketing Officer; President Simon Brand Ventures, Mikael Thygesen
SEVP; President Simon Malls, David J. Contis, age 58, $750,000 total compensation
Chief Investment Officer, Stanley Shashoua
Vice President Information Technology Infrastructure and Operations, Scott Barnes
Regional Vice President Financial Reporting, Deanna Nelson
Assistant Vice President Retailer Development, Matt Mahar
Vice President of Acquisitions and Asset Intensification, Patrick Peterman
Executive Vice President Specialty Leasing, Marla Parr
Regional Vice President of Marketing, Jennifer Harris
Vice President Tax, Stephen Stouffer
Senior Vice President Leasing, Jay Buckey
Vice President of Business Development, Paul G Fiore
Vice President Property Tax, Michael Larson
Assistant Vice President Business Development, Kelly Mikesell
Senior Vice President Lease Services, Norman Finbloom
Senior Vice President Local Leasing, Shannon Spahr
Senior Vice President Global Creative Director, Chidi Achara
VicePresident, Donna Vosper
Group Vice President Leasing, Lisa Snead

Regional Vice President Financial Reporting, Brenda Keefe
Senior Vice President of Operations and Procuremen, Stephen Kingsley
Regional Vice President Financial Reporting, Julie Leer
Vice President, Joellyn Fellmeth
Vice President of Management and Marketing, Kelly Hartsell
Senior Vice President For Development At Investment In The Project, Kathleen M Shields
Vice President Tax Planning and Research, John Gumerson
Vice President Construction, Bob Ufland
Vice President Specialty Leasing, Ralph Higley
Regional Vice President, Teresa Tom
Vice President Of Business Development, Jim Martin
Regional Vice President Financial Reporting, Mike Ginty
Assistant Vice President of Corporate Special Events, Jacque Ellis
Executive Vice President, Barney Quinn
Senior Vice President Risk Management, Michael Horvath
Regional Vice President Financial Reporting, Jodi Calisto
Senior Vice President Leasing, Mark Hunter
Senior Vice President Chief Security Officer, Russ Tuttle
Director of Pharmacy, Kathy Burnett
Senior Vice President of Business Development SBV, Daniel Segal
Vice President Of Advertising, Cathy Iunghuhn
Vice President of Business Development, Christine Dubin
Portfolio Vice President, Michael Romstad
Senior Vice President Management, Leslie Swanson
Senior Vice President, Ronald Hanson
Vice President of Leasing, Dennis Carafiol
Senior Vice President Corporate Marketing, Shari Simon
Senior Executive Vice President, Gary Lewis
Vice President Construction Project Management, Joe Easley
Regional Vice President, Melissa Palencia
Vice President, Greg Bradbury
Vice President of Operations, Paul Sagun
Associate Vice President Consumer Branding, Lauren Lombardo
National Account Manager, Angela Motamedi
Assistant Vice President Leasing, Carolyn Preston
Vice President Leasing, Stacey Lewis
Senior Vice President, Deborah Simon
Vice President General Manager, Gene Condon
Associate Vice President Brand Strategy, Shannon Marino
REGIONAL VICE PRESIDENT, Denise Ipsen
Portfolio VP Of Marketing, Lynette Lauria
Vice President and Senior Counsel, Thomas Di Iaconi
Assistant Vice President of Business Development, Aaron Casteel
Vice President, Kevin Compton
Executive Vice President Leasing, Eric Sadi
Treasurer, Robert Demchak
Chairman Emeritus, Herbert Simon
Auditors: Ernst & Young LLP

LOCATIONS

HQ: Simon Property Group, Inc.
225 West Washington Street, Indianapolis, IN 46204
Phone: 317 636-1600   **Fax:** 317 685-7336
Web: www.simon.com

PRODUCTS/OPERATIONS

2016 Sales

	$ mil.	% of total
Minimum rent	3,358	62
Tenant reimbursements	1,494	28
Overage rent	161	3
Management fees & other revenues	143	2
Other income	276	5
Total	**5,435**	**100**

2016 US Properties

	No.
Malls	108
Premium outlets	67
Mills	14
Lifestyle centers	4
Other shopping centers	13
Total	**206**

Selected Properties

Aventura Mall Miami
Burlington Mall Boston
Copley Place Boston
Dadeland Mall Miami
Desert Hills Premium Outlets Cabazon CA
Fashion Centre at Pentagon City Washington DC
Fashion Valley San Diego
The Florida Mall Orlando
The Forum Shops at Caesars Las Vegas
The Galleria Houston
Gotemba Premium Outlets Gotemba (Tokyo) Japan
King of Prussia Mall Philadelphia
Las Vegas Premium Outlets(2) Las Vegas
Lenox Square and Phipps Plaza Atlanta
Orlando Premium Outlets(2) Orlando
Roosevelt Field New York
Sawgrass Mills Ft. Lauderdale
SouthPark Charlotte
Stanford Shopping Center Palo Alto
Town Center at Boca Raton Boca Raton
Walt Whitman Shops New York
The Westchester New York
Woodbury Common Premium Outlets New York
Woodfield Mall Chicago

COMPETITORS

Belz	Kimco Realty
CBL & Associates Properties	Macerich
Cadillac Fairview	Taubman Centers
GGP	Vornado Realty
Horizon Group Properties	Westfield Corporation

HISTORICAL FINANCIALS

Company Type: Public

Income Statement

FYE: December 31

	REVENUE ($ mil.)	NET INCOME ($ mil.)	NET PROFIT MARGIN	EMPLOYEES
12/16	5,435	1,838	33.8%	5,000
12/15	5,266	1,827	34.7%	5,000
12/14	4,870	1,408	28.9%	5,250
12/13	5,170	1,319	25.5%	5,700
12/12	4,880	1,434	29.4%	5,500
Annual Growth	**2.7%**	**6.4%**	**—**	**(2.4%)**

2016 Year-End Financials

Debt ratio: 73.87%
Return on equity: 41.00%
Cash ($ mil.): 560
Current ratio: 0.48
Long-term debt ($ mil.): 22,977

No. of shares (mil.): 313
Dividends
  Yield: 0.0%
  Payout: 110.7%
Market value ($ mil.): 55,624

	STOCK PRICE ($) FY Close	P/E High/Low	PER SHARE ($) Earnings	Dividends	Book Value
12/16	177.67	39 30	5.87	6.50	14.21
12/15	194.44	35 29	5.88	6.05	14.53
12/14	182.11	41 33	4.52	5.15	16.47
12/13	152.16	43 34	4.24	4.65	19.45
12/12	158.09	35 27	4.72	4.30	19.65
Annual Growth	3.0%	— —	5.6%	10.9%	(7.8%)

Sirius XM Holdings Inc

You might say radio programming from this company comes from a higher plane. SIRIUS XM Holdings operating through SIRIUS XM Radio manages satellite radio systems under the SIRIUS and XM brands that together boast more than 25 million subscribers. Each service offers more than 150 channels of CD-quality music news and talk shows. Programming includes National Football League Major League Baseball and college games as well as talk shows featuring hosts Howard Stern Martha Stewart and Oprah Winfrey. The company has equipment alliances with several automakers; it also sells satellite radio equipment through its website and through such retail outlets as Best Buy and Wal-Mart.

Operations

In addition to its domestic radio services SIRIUS XM has interests in the Canadian market. It owns 50% of SIRIUS Canada a joint venture with the Canadian Broadcasting Corporation (CBC). SIRIUS Canada merged with Canadian Satellite Radio (XM Canada) in 2011 giving SIRIUS a solid foundation in the Canadian market.

Sales and Marketing

Subscription satellite radio has proven to be quite popular thanks to the wealth of programming options available beyond the limited content offered by advertising-supported terrestrial radio broadcasters.

With its large subscriber base SIRIUS XM has stolen away many listeners from traditional broadcast stations operated by major radio companies such as Clear Channel and Cumulus Media. Providing all that content though is quite expensive due to rights fees for sports and exclusive talk shows as well as the satellite equipment needed to reach listeners across the country.

During fiscal 2013 the company spent about $180000 on advertising after spending roughly $140000 on advertising during fiscal 2012.

Financial Performance

SIRIUS XM has been experiencing a positive trend in its revenue since 2008. The company's fiscal 2013 revenues increased by 12% compared to fiscal 2012 primarily due to increases in its subscriber revenues advertising revenues agency fees and equipment revenues.

SIRIUS XM saw its net income nosedive in 2013. Net income decreased 98% from $3.47 billion in fiscal 2012 to only $377.2 million in fiscal 2013. The huge drop was largely due to drastically increased expenses for things such as royalties and taxes.

Even with its net income dropping so dramatically during fiscal 2013 the company's cash from operations increased due to improved operating performance lower interest payments and higher collections from subscribers and distributors.

Strategy

SIRIUS XM is dependent on automobile makers. The company works hard to convert customers who received a promotional subscription as part of the purchase or lease of a new vehicle to a self-paying subscription.

Mergers and Acquisitions

In 2013 SIRIUS XM purchased connected vehicle business Agero Inc. Agero's connected vehicle business provides services to several automakers including Acura BMW Honda Hyundai Infiniti Lexus Nissan and Toyota.

EXECUTIVES

EVP and CFO, David J. Frear, age 61, $850,000 total compensation

EVP and General Counsel, Patrick L. Donnelly, age 55, $575,000 total compensation

EVP Sales and Automotive, Stephen R. (Steve) Cook, age 61, $518,583 total compensation

SVP and CIO, William C. (Bill) Pratt

CEO, James E. (Jim) Meyer, age 63, $1,468,590 total compensation

President and Chief Content Officer, Scott A. Greenstein, age 58, $1,224,520 total compensation

EVP and Chief Administrative Officer, Dara F. Altman, age 59, $500,000 total compensation

EVP Operations and Products, Enrique Rodriguez, $531,827 total compensation

Vice President Purchasing and Procurement, Larry Simon

Vice President Business Development, Greg Corley

Senior Vice President Comedy Programming, Jack Vaughn

Chairman, Gregory B. (Greg) Maffei, age 56

Auditors: KPMG LLP

LOCATIONS

HQ: Sirius XM Holdings Inc
1290 Avenue of the Americas, 11th Floor, New York, NY 10104
Phone: 212 584-5100
Web: www.siriusxm.com

COMPETITORS

CBS Radio	Saga Communications
Cox Radio	Spanish Broadcasting
Cumulus Media	Townsquare Media
Emmis Communications	Univision Radio
Entercom	WestwoodOne
Entravision	iHeartCommunications
Radio One Inc.	

HISTORICAL FINANCIALS

Company Type: Public

Income Statement				FYE: December 31
	REVENUE ($ mil.)	NET INCOME ($ mil.)	NET PROFIT MARGIN	EMPLOYEES
12/17	5,425	647	11.9%	2,575
12/16	5,017	745	14.9%	2,402
12/15	4,570	509	11.2%	2,323
12/14	4,181	493	11.8%	2,327
12/13	3,799	377	9.9%	2,195
Annual Growth	9.3%	14.5%	—	4.1%

2017 Year-End Financials

Debt ratio: 80.99%—
Return on equity: ***,***.**%
Cash ($ mil.): 69
Current ratio: 0.17
Long-term debt ($ mil.): 6,741

Dividends
Yield: 0.0%
Payout: 29.2%
Market value ($ mil.): —

	STOCK PRICE ($) FY Close	P/E High/Low	PER SHARE ($) Earnings	Dividends	Book Value
12/17	5.36	42 32	0.14	0.04	(0.34)
12/16	4.45	31 22	0.15	0.01	(0.17)
12/15	4.07	47 37	0.09	0.00	(0.03)
12/14	3.50	43 34	0.08	0.00	0.23
12/13	3.49	69 48	0.06	0.00	0.45
Annual Growth	11.3%	— —	23.6%	—	—

SL GREEN OPERATING PARTNERSHIP, L.P.

LOCATIONS

HQ: SL GREEN OPERATING PARTNERSHIP, L.P.
420 LEXINGTON AVE RM 1800, NEW YORK, NY 101701899
Phone: 212 594-2700
Web: WWW.SLGREEN.COM

HISTORICAL FINANCIALS

Company Type: Private

Income Statement				FYE: December 31
	ASSETS ($ mil.)	NET INCOME ($ mil.)	INCOME AS % OF ASSETS	EMPLOYEES
12/16	15,857	278	1.8%	1,060
12/15	19,857	317	1.6%	—
12/14	17,096	545	3.2%	—
12/13	14,959	151	1.0%	—
Annual Growth	2.0%	22.6%	—	—

2016 Year-End Financials

Debt ratio: ——
Return on equity: 15.00%
Cash ($ mil.): 279
Current ratio: —
Long-term debt ($ mil.): —

Dividends
Yield: —
Payout: —
Market value ($ mil.): —

SLM Corp.

If SLM doesn?t seem familiar perhaps you know it by its more common moniker Sallie Mae. Holding more than $8 billion in student loans SLM's main subsidiary Sallie Mae Bank is one of the nation's largest education loan providers and specializes in originating acquiring financing and servicing private student loans which are not guaranteed by the government. The company also earns fees for its processing and administrative offerings through various subsidiaries.

HISTORY

The Student Loan Marketing Association was chartered in 1972 as a response to problems in the Guaranteed Student Loan Program of 1965. For years the GSL program had tinkered with rates to induce banks to make loans but servicing the small loans was expensive and troublesome. Sallie Mae began operations in 1973 buying loans from their originators; its size provided economies of scale in loan servicing.

Originally only institutions making educational or student loans were allowed to own stock in Sallie Mae. This was later changed so that anyone could buy nonvoting stock. In 1993 voting stock was listed on the NYSE.

Sallie Mae was always a political football altered again and again to reflect the education policies of the party in power. When it was founded during the Nixon administration its loans were restricted by a needs test which was repealed during the Carter years. The Reagan administration reimposed the needs test and at the same time sped up the schedule under which the company was to become self-supporting which it did by late 1981.

Forced to rely on its own resources Sallie Mae turned to creative financing. One of its traditional advantages was that its loan interest rates were linked to Treasury bills traditionally about 3% above the T-bill rate. The company became a master at riding the spread between its cost of funds and the interest rates it charged.

Between 1983 and 1992 Sallie Mae's assets swelled by more than 400% and its income rose by almost 500%. As the firm grew management became more visible with high pay and extravagant perks. Although salaries were not inconsistent with those of executives at comparable private corporations the remuneration level and perks irked Congress. But Sallie Mae kept growing — in 1992 it expanded its facilities and added 900 new staff members.

The 1993 Omnibus Budget Reconciliation Act with its transfer of the student loan program directly to the government and its surcharge on Sallie Mae began to adversely affect earnings in 1994. While awaiting permission to alter its charter the company stepped up its marketing efforts especially to school loan officers who advised students on loan options.

In 1995 then-COO Albert Lord led a group of stockholders in a push to cut operating expenses and repackage student loans as securities   la Freddie Mac and Fannie Mae. Lord and some of his supporters won seats on the board (as well as the enmity of Lawrence Hough who resigned as CEO in the midst of the melee). That year Sallie Mae bought HICA Holding one of two private insurers of education loans. In 1996 Congress passed legislation forcing Sallie Mae's privatization.

Despite SLM's rising stock shareholders were unhappy with chairman William Arceneaux's status quo business plan. Lord gained control in 1997.

In 1998 the organization became SLM Holding. Assets and earnings were muted that year when unfavorable market conditions prevented Sallie Mae from securitizing its loans.

The firm the next year expanded its lending operations by buying Nellie Mae. Also in 1999 Sallie Mae teamed with Answer Financial to sell insurance. Growth continued in 2000 when the company bought loan servicer Student Loan Funding Resources as well as the marketing student loan servicing and administrative operations of USA Group; the company changed its name to USA Education following the acquisition. The company also cut some 1700 jobs approximately 25% of its workforce.

The following year Sallie Mae teamed with Intuit allowing the financial software company access to Sallie Mae's 7 million customers. It also launched online recruiting service TrueCareers that year.

In 2002 it bought Pioneer Credit Recovery and General Revenue Corporation two of the nation's largest student loan collection agencies. It also reverted to the SLM moniker to reconnect with the name by which it has so long been known.

The privatization plan put into place in the mid-'90s (orchestrated in large part by then-CEO Lord) came to fruition nearly four years ahead of schedule when SLM transitioned to a private organization in December 2004.

In 2007 SLM saw its stock values plummet to their lowest levels in about a decade. A number of industry-wide factors figured into the losses not the least of which was the downturn in the credit market. Also affecting the company was the signing into law of the College Cost Reduction and Access Act (CCRAA). Intended to reform student lending and cut costs for borrowers the act slashed subsidies for lenders participating in the Federal Family Education Loan Program (FFELP). The reform cut into the company's interest-earning operations. As a result SLM increased its focus on higher-yielding private education loans which carry a lower risk.

Additionally SLM that year became ensnared in a student-lending industry probe led by New York attorney general Andrew Cuomo. The company agreed to a $2 million settlement and to abide by a code of conduct regarding its dealings with college employees.

One of the most dramatic results of the troubles was the collapse of a planned acquisition by a consortium of investment firms. The planned $8.8 billion deal included buyers J.C. Flowers (which was to own about a half of SLM) Bank of America and JPMorgan Chase. In the midst of the industry probe J.C. Flowers sought a change in SLM's leadership in an effort to secure regulatory approval for the acquisition; Thomas J. (Tim) Fitzpatrick was ousted as CEO. Ultimately the buyers canceled the deal citing the reduced potential value of SLM. The student lender filed a lawsuit to challenge the termination but eventually dropped the suit. It later cut more than 10% of its workforce.

EXECUTIVES

Vice President Of Finance And Information Research, Brian Burgess
Chairman and CEO, Raymond J. Quinlan, $600,000 total compensation
EVP and General Counsel, Laurent C. Lutz, $525,000 total compensation
EVP and CFO, Steven J. McGarry, $375,000 total compensation
SVP and Chief Risk Officer, Jeffery F. Dale, age 55, $400,000 total compensation
EVP and Chief Marketing Officer, Charles P. Rocha, $375,000 total compensation
Senior Vice President and Chief Compliance Officer, Jim Truitt
Vice President Sales, Jay Sirmans
Assistant Vice President Network Services, Peter Tropf
Vice President, Jonathan Boyles
Vice President Finance Other Credit, Doug Maurer
Senior Vice President Operations Administration, Sheila Ryan-Macie
Vice President And Associate General Counsel, Anne Milem
Vice President Asset Protection, Cornelius Tate
Vice President, Lynn M Langdon
Vice President of Operations, Michael Bandy
Vice President of Information Technology, Mike Brannon
Senior Vice President Chief Security Officer, Jerry Archer
Treasurer, Rosanne Gatta
Auditors: KPMG LLP

LOCATIONS

HQ: SLM Corp.
300 Continental Drive, Newark, DE 19713
Phone: 302 451-0200
Web: www.salliemae.com

PRODUCTS/OPERATIONS

2016 Sales

	$ mil.	% of total
Interest		
Loans	1,060	79
Investments	9	1
Cash & cash equivalents	7	1
Non-Interest income		
Gain on sale of loans	0	14
(Losses) gains on derivatives and hedging activities net	(0.9)	5
Other income	69	-
Total	**1,146**	**100**

Selected Subsidiaries

HICA Holding
Sallie Mae Bank
Sallie Mae Inc.
SLM Education Credit Finance Corporation
  Bull Run I LLC
  SLM Education Credit Funding LLC
SLM Investment Corporation
Southwest Student Services Corporation

COMPETITORS

Bank of America
Brazos Higher Education Service Corp.
Citizens Financial Group
Discover
Educational Funding of The South
First Marblehead
FirstCity Financial
Great Lakes Higher Education
KeyCorp
Mohela
Nelnet
PNC Financial
Pennsylvania Higher Education Assistance Agency
SunTrust
Texas Guaranteed

HISTORICAL FINANCIALS
Company Type: Public

Income Statement
FYE: December 31

	ASSETS ($ mil.)	NET INCOME ($ mil.)	INCOME AS % OF ASSETS	EMPLOYEES
12/16	18,533	250	1.4%	1,300
12/15	15,214	274	1.8%	1,200
12/14	12,972	194	1.5%	1,000
12/13	159,543	1,418	0.9%	7,200
12/12	181,260	939	0.5%	6,800
Annual Growth	**(43.5%)**	**(28.1%)**	**—**	**(33.9%)**

2016 Year-End Financials

Debt ratio: 11.70%	No. of shares (mil.): 428
Return on equity: 11.24%	Dividends
Cash ($ mil.): 1,918	Yield: —
Current ratio: —	Payout: —
Long-term debt ($ mil.): —	Market value ($ mil.): 4,727

	STOCK PRICE ($) FY Close	P/E High/Low		PER SHARE ($) Earnings	Dividends	Book Value
12/16	11.02	21	10	0.53	0.00	5.47
12/15	6.52	18	11	0.59	0.00	4.92
12/14	10.19	63	19	0.42	0.60	4.32
12/13	26.28	8	5	3.12	0.60	13.14
12/12	17.13	9	7	1.90	0.50	11.18
Annual Growth	**(10.4%)**	**—**	**—**	**(27.3%)**	**—**	**(16.4%)**

Smucker (J.M.) Co.

The J. M. Smucker Company gets its bread and butter from more than just making and marketing jelly. The company known for manufacturing its namesake Smucker's fruit spread and for selling the Jif peanut butter brand has expanded its product portfolio to include Folgers the #1-coffee brand in the US as well as market leaders in espresso (Caf © Bustelo) and premium java (Dunkin' Donuts licensed). Other top-shelf lines are Hungry Jack and Pillsbury baking mixes and frostings Eagle canned milk and Crisco shortening and oils among others. Smucker's brands are sold to consumers through retail outlets in the US and Canada with some products exported.

HISTORY

Jerome Smucker began operating a steam-powered cider mill in 1897 for farmers in Orrville Ohio but he found that his biggest business was selling apple butter made using a secret Smucker family recipe. By the 1920s The J. M. Smucker Company had begun producing a full line of preserves and jellies and in 1935 it acquired its first fruit-processing operations.

Under Jerome's grandson Paul Smucker the company gained widespread national distribution by the mid-1960s. Tim Smucker succeeded his father Paul as president in 1981 then as chairman in 1987 when his brother Richard became president.

The company's growth has been enhanced through the development of its industrial fruit fillings business and acquisitions of domestic natural juice and peanut butter companies including Knudsen & Sons (1984) After the Fall (1994) and Laura Scudder's (from National Grape Co-op 1994). It has gradually expanded internationally through acquisitions. In 1993 it acquired the jam preserves and pie-filling unit of Canada's Culinar. In a 1998 deal Smucker purchased Australia's Allowrie jam and Lackersteens marmalade lines.

Smucker sold its flagging Mrs. Smith's frozen pie business to Flowers in 1997 less than two years after buying the unit from Kellogg. It bought Kraft's domestic fruit spread unit in 1997 and in 1999 purchased the northwestern Adams peanut butter business from Pro-Fac Cooperative. Smucker kept the Adams name but shifted packaging to its Pennsylvania peanut butter plant.

Spreading into retail the company opened a store in 1999 in its hometown of Orrville and then launched online and catalog sales. Also that year Smucker bought a fruit filling plant in Brazil from Groupe Danone a major customer. During 2000 the company's Henry Jones Foods subsidiary (Australia) purchased Taylor Foods (sauces marinades).

Smucker acquired International Flavors & Fragrances' formulated fruit and vegetable preparation businesses in 2001. Moving beyond its stronghold in natural peanut butter brands the next year Smucker purchased the Jif peanut butter and Crisco cooking oil and shortening brands from Procter & Gamble. The $670 million purchase price for Jif and Crisco included shifting 53% of Smucker stock into the hands of P&G shareholders.

A decision to concentrate on North America led to the $37 million sale of Australian subsidiary Henry Jones Foods in 2004. Also that year Smucker sold its operations in Brazil to Cargill and closed down two fruit processing plants in California and Oregon. Its purchase of International Multifoods that year added an array of US brands to the Smucker family including Pillsbury flour baking mixes and ready-to-spread frostings; Hungry Jack pancake mixes syrup and potato side dishes; Martha White baking mixes and ingredients; and PET evaporated milk brands. Canadian brands included Robin Hood flour and baking mixes Bick's pickles and condiments and Golden Temple flour and rice.

To further its strategy of concentrating on its core retail brands in 2005 Smucker sold its US foodservice and bakery business and the Canadian operations of Gourmet Baker (all part of its International Multifoods acquisition) to Value Creation Partners. The following year the company sold its Canadian grain-based foodservice operations and industrial businesses to Cargill and CHS Inc. The operations were integrated into leading US flour miller Horizon Milling (which is jointly owned by Cargill and CHS). Adding to its name-brand offerings in 2006 Smucker acquired the White Lily brand of flours baking mixes and frozen biscuits from C.H. Guenther.

The company extended its baking offerings with the 2007 acquisition of sweetened condensed and evaporated milk producer Eagle Family Foods Holdings. Smucker paid $133 million in cash and $115 million in assumed debt for it. Eagle is a good fit with Smucker's PET milk products. Given Smucker's size and subsequent bargaining power with food retailers (including Wal-Mart the giant in US food retailing) and Eagle's domination of the North American canned-milk sector (it is the largest producer of evaporated and sweetened condensed milk in the US and Canada) the pairing of the two companies was a sensible move for both.

EXECUTIVES

Treasurer, Mark R. Belgya, age 56, $545,962 total compensation
Vp Of Sales-grocery Market, John Mayer
Vice Chairman; President U.S. Food and Beverage, Steven T. Oakland, age 56, $623,077 total compensation
President Pet Food and Pet Snacks, Barry C. Dunaway, age 54, $330,000 total compensation
President and CEO, Mark T. Smucker, age 48, $355,000 total compensation
President Canada and International, David J. Lemmon
VP Marketing Services, Tamara J. Fynan
SVP Operations, J. Randal Day
Vice President, Sonal Robinson
Vice President Sales and Trade Marketing, Stephen Kouri
Vice President Finance, Mark Draa
National Sales Manager, Mike Workman
Vice President, Bill Cortner
Vice President Corporate Communications, Maribeth Burns
Vice President Customer Logistics, Rob Fox
Vice President Sales And Marketing, John Hall
Vice President Marketing Consumer, Vince Byrd
Vice President U.S. Grocery Sales, Jim Brown
Vice President of Supply Chain and Operations, Todd Campbell
National Account Manager, Scott Dacus
National Account Manager, Matt Skordinski
National Account Manager, Mike Freitas
Chairman, Richard K. Smucker, age 69
Assistant Treasurer, Gary Misch
Auditors: Ernst & Young LLP

LOCATIONS

HQ: Smucker (J.M.) Co.
One Strawberry Lane, Orrville, OH 44667-0280
Phone: 330 682-3000
Web: www.jmsmucker.com

2017 Sales

	$ mil.	% of total
Domestic	6,865	93
International		
Canada	414	5
Other countries	112	2
Total	**7,392**	**100**

PRODUCTS/OPERATIONS

2017 Sales

	$ mil.	% of total
US Retail Pet Foods	2,135	29
US retail coffee	2,108	29
US retail consumer foods	2,085	28
International and food service	1,062	14
Total	**7,392**	**100**

Selected Products

Baking mixes and ready-to-spread frostings
Canned milk
Coffee
Flour and baking ingredients
Frozen sandwiches
Fruit spreads
Juices and beverages
Peanut butter
Pickles and condiments
Shortening and oils
Syrups
Toppings

Selected Brands by Segment

International foodservice and natural foods
  Bick's
  Café; Bustelo
  Café; Pilon
  Carnation (under license)
  Crisco
  Crosse & Blackwell
  Double Fruit
  Five Roses
  Folgers
  Golden Temple
  Jif
  Plate Scapers
  R.W. Knudsen
  Recharge
  Red River
  Robin Hood
  Santa Cruz Organic
  Smucker's
US retail coffee
  Café; Bustelo
  Café; Pilon
  Folgers
  Dunkin' Donuts (under license)
  Millstone
US retail consumer foods
  Adams
  Borden and Elsie design (under license)
  Crisco
  Dickinson's
  Eagle Brand
  Fungetti
  Goober
  Hungry Jack
  Jif
  Laura Scudder's
  Magic Shell
  Magnolia
  Martha White
  Pillsbury (under license)
  Smucker's
  Uncrustables
  White Lily

COMPETITORS

B&G Foods	Hershey
Boyd Coffee	Hormel
Caribou Coffee	Keurig Green Mountain
Chiquita Brands	Mondelez International
Coca-Cola	Monster Beverage
Coca-Cola North America	National Grape Cooperative
Community Coffee	Nestl©

ConAgra
Cranberries Limited
Darigold Inc.
Dean Foods
Diamond Foods
Diedrich Coffee
Dole Food
E.D. Smith
General Mills
Goya
H. J. Heinz Limited

Ocean Spray
PepsiCo
Pinnacle Foods
Spectrum Organic
  Products
Starbucks
Tata Global Beverages
Tree Top
Tropicana
Welch's

HISTORICAL FINANCIALS

Company Type: Public

Income Statement

FYE: April 30

	REVENUE ($ mil.)	NET INCOME ($ mil.)	NET PROFIT MARGIN	EMPLOYEES
04/17	7,392	592	8.0%	7,140
04/16	7,811	688	8.8%	6,910
04/15	5,692	344	6.1%	7,370
04/14	5,610	565	10.1%	4,775
04/13	5,897	544	9.2%	4,875
Annual Growth	5.8%	2.1%	—	10.0%

2017 Year-End Financials

Debt ratio: 34.52%
Return on equity: 8.55%
Cash ($ mil.): 166
Current ratio: 0.90
Long-term debt ($ mil.): 4,445

No. of shares (mil.): 113
Dividends
  Yield: 0.0%
  Payout: 57.2%
Market value ($ mil.): 14,375

	STOCK PRICE ($) FY Close	P/E High/Low	PER SHARE ($) Earnings	Dividends	Book Value
04/17	126.72	31 24	5.10	2.92	60.39
04/16	126.98	23 18	5.76	2.65	60.26
04/15	115.92	35 29	3.33	2.50	59.27
04/14	96.68	21 17	5.42	2.26	49.46
04/13	103.23	21 15	5.00	2.04	48.35
Annual Growth	5.3%	—	0.5%	9.4%	5.7%

SOLSTICE HOLDINGS INC.

LOCATIONS

HQ: SOLSTICE HOLDINGS INC.
7575 FULTON ST E, ADA, MI 493550001
Phone: 616 787-1000

HISTORICAL FINANCIALS

Company Type: Private

Income Statement

FYE: December 31

	REVENUE ($ mil.)	NET INCOME ($ mil.)	NET PROFIT MARGIN	EMPLOYEES
12/08	8,235	0	—	14,000
12/07	7,168	0	—	—
Annual Growth	14.9%	—	—	—

2008 Year-End Financials

Debt ratio: —
Return on equity: —
Cash ($ mil.): 1,072
Current ratio: 0.50
Long-term debt ($ mil.): —

Dividends
  Yield: —
  Payout: —
Market value ($ mil.): —

Sonic Automotive, Inc.

No stranger to speed O. Bruton Smith has raced Sonic Automotive into the leading pack of US auto dealers just behind rivals like AutoNation and Penske Automotive. Sonic has gone from five dealerships in 1997 to having today more than 100 new and used vehicle dealerships more than 115 franchised dealerships and about 20 collision repair centers in major markets in more than a dozen states including California Texas the Carolinas Alabama and Tennessee. The company sells some 25 brands of cars and light trucks and offers extended aftermarket services. Chairman Smith is also the majority owner of Speedway Motorsports which operates more than half a dozen NASCAR auto racetracks.

Operations

The company sells new vehicles including luxury cars (BMW Lexus Land Rover and Volvo) midline imports (Honda Nissan and Toyota) and domestic brands (Ford and General Motors). Luxury brands account for around more than 55% of new vehicle sales the company's mid-line brands bring in more than 30% and domestic brands nearly 15%.

Sonic also offers a range of aftermarket services including vehicle financing replacement parts performance of vehicle maintenance paint and collision repair services and arrangement of extended warranty contracts and insurance.

Sonic divides its business into Franchised Dealerships which brings in virtually all the company's revenue at 99% and EchoPark which is its stand-alone used car business.

Geographic Reach

California is Sonic's #1 market accounting for around 30% of sales followed closely by Texas at around a quarter of total sales. EchoPark's retail units are clustered in Denver.

Sales and Marketing

Sonic's website allows customers to view cars and prices schedule test drives and book trade-in appraisals.

Financial Performance

Sonic has reported consistently strong revenue growth for the past seven years. However in fiscal 2016 growth slowed with revenue up an incremental 1% to $9.7 billion. New vehicle sales were flat at $5.2 billion as a decrease in unit volumes was compensated for by an increase in selling prices. The price increases were concentrated in Sonic's Honda dealerships. Used vehicle sales were also essentially flat growing less than 1% to $2.5 billion.

Net income climbed 8% to $93.2 million. Revenue gains were offset by poor results from the Houston area as a knock-on effect of weakness in the oil & gas markets; as an oil town consumer spending in the city was down. Sonic was also negatively affected by car recalls from certain manufacturers leaving the company stuck with around 600 cars it wasn't allowed to sell until work had been completed.

Cash from operations increased from $69.7 million to $216.4 million in fiscal 2016 due to higher net income and a decrease in inventory and other assets.

Strategy

As part of the company's strategic plans Sonic is primarily focused in growing its operations in metropolitan markets in the Southeast Southwest Midwest and the West (California). The company's long-term growth strategy is to target luxury or mid-line import brands in regions where it already operates.

Sonic is continuing the rollout of its One Sonic-One Experience store strategy. The modernization program targets the shop-floor sales process with the aim one sales associate armed with a tablet computer completing a sale in under one hour. The program also removes haggling from the buying process puts its sales reps on salaries rather than commission packages and centralizes back end processes and pricing.

Sonic's EchoPark used car business expansion is based around making each EchoPark dealership a "neighborhood store" supported by specialty retail stores that can open in areas normally blocked to car dealers.

Mergers and Acquisitions

In 2016 Sonic acquired three stand-alone used vehicle businesses for $15.9 million.

Company Background

O. Bruton Smith and his son Scott control the company through their ownership of about 40% of Sonic Automotive's voting stock.

EXECUTIVES

President and CEO, B. Scott Smith, age 49, $1,085,438 total compensation
VP Eastern Division, Frank J. (Jeff) Dyke, age 50, $969,179 total compensation
VP and Chief Marketing Officer, Rachel M. Richards
EVP and CFO, Heath R. Byrd, age 50, $677,327 total compensation
VP Information Technology, Christopher (Chris) Maritato
Vice President Manufacturer Relations Facilities CSI, Raymond Valentine
Vice President Financial Planning and Analysis, Donald Harris
Regional Vice President Tn Dc, Kevin Gaither
Vice President Facilities Development, Martin Walsh
Regional Vice President, Tasos Theodorou
Chairman, O. Bruton Smith, age 89
Vice Chairman, David B. Smith, age 42
Assistant Treasurer, Melanie Stewart
Assistant Treasurer, Chris Cellini
Auditors: KPMG LLP

LOCATIONS

HQ: Sonic Automotive, Inc.
4401 Colwick Road, Charlotte, NC 28211
Phone: 704 566-2400   Fax: 704 536-5116
Web: www.sonicautomotive.com

PRODUCTS/OPERATIONS

2016 sales

	$ mil.	% of total
Franchised Dealerships	9,602	99
EchoPark	129	1
Total	9,731	100

2016 sales

	$ mil.	% of total
New vehicles	5,234	54
Used vehicles	2,533	26
Wholesale vehicles	211	2
Parts service and collision repair	1,409	14
Finance insurance and other	343	4
Total	9,731	100

Services Center List-Selected:
Acura of Serramonte Service Center
Audi West Houston Service Center
BMW of Birmingham Service Center
Cadillac of Las Vegas Service Center
Capitol Chevrolet of Columbia Service Center
Fort Mill Ford Service Center
Honda of Santa Monica Service Center
Momentum Volkswagen Service Center
North Central Ford Service Center
Toyota of Fort Worth Service Center
Volkswagen of Fort Myers Service Center

Brands

BMW
Mercedes
Lexus
Audi
Land Rover
Cadillac
Porsche
Honda
Toyota
Volkswagen
Hyundai
Ford
General Motors

COMPETITORS

Asbury Automotive	Enterprise Rent-A-Car
AutoNation	Group 1 Automotive
AutoTrader	Gunn Automotive
Autobytel	Internet Brands
CarMax	JM Family Enterprises
Darcars	Penske Automotive
David McDavid Auto	Group
Group	Sewell Automotive
DriveTime Automotive	

HISTORICAL FINANCIALS

Company Type: Public

Income Statement

FYE: December 31

	REVENUE ($ mil.)	NET INCOME ($ mil.)	NET PROFIT MARGIN	EMPLOYEES
12/16	9,731	93	1.0%	9,800
12/15	9,624	86	0.9%	9,800
12/14	9,197	97	1.1%	9,300
12/13	8,843	81	0.9%	9,100
12/12	8,365	89	1.1%	9,300
Annual Growth	3.9%	1.1%	—	1.3%

2016 Year-End Financials

Debt ratio: 66.18%
Return on equity: 12.78%
Cash ($ mil.): 3
Current ratio: 1.05
Long-term debt ($ mil.): 839

No. of shares (mil.): 44
Dividends
Yield: 0.0%
Payout: 9.8%
Market value ($ mil.): 1,024

	STOCK PRICE ($) FY Close	P/E High/Low		PER SHARE ($) Earnings	Dividends	Book Value
12/16	22.90	12	8	2.04	0.20	16.21
12/15	22.76	16	12	1.70	0.11	14.60
12/14	27.04	15	11	1.84	0.10	13.09
12/13	24.48	16	13	1.53	0.10	11.64
12/12	20.89	13	7	1.53	0.10	9.89
Annual Growth	2.3%			7.5%	18.9%	13.1%

Sonoco Products Co.

Sonoco Products believes you can judge a container by its packaging. The company is one of the world's largest makers of industrial and consumer packaging used by the food consumer goods construction and automotive industries. Its Consumer Packaging segment produces round and shaped composite cans for snack foods powdered beverages pet food and more. Sonoco makes flexible and rigid packaging (paper and plastic) for food personal care items and chemicals and it produces paperboard tubes and cores too for industrial protective packaging. The company's end-to-end packaging services include co-packing and fulfillment supply chain management and point-of-purchase display design/assembly.

Operations

The company divides its business structure into four chief business segments. Consumer Packaging is its largest segment accounting for roughly 45% of its net sales. Other segments include Paper and Industrial Converted Products (35%) Display and Packaging (more than 10%) and Protective Solutions (10%).

Geographic Reach

Sonoco operates about 320 locations around the world in nearly 35 countries concentrated in Canada Europe and the US. Around 65% of its total sales are generated from the US each year. Sonoco's international sales are concentrated in Europe (20%) followed by Canada (around 5%).

Financial Performance

Sonoco's revenues have declined the last two years dropping 4% from $4.96 billion in 2015 to $4.78 billion in 2016. Total domestic sales declined 3% from 2015 levels and international sales declined 5% compared to 2015 as most of the decreases were driven by unfavorable impacts of foreign currency translations. Additionally sales in Mexico declined in 2016 due to the loss of contract packaging business in Irapuato Mexico.

Profits however jumped 15% from $250 million in 2015 to peak at a record-setting $286 million in 2016 due to an after-tax benefit of $9 million consisting of the gain from the disposal of its rigid plastics blow molding operations.

Strategy

The company's goal is to reach $5.5 billion to $6 billion in sales over the next three or four years. (It came close in 2015 posting $4.96 billion.) It plans to achieve this by growing its existing products and services portfolio by $300 million and new product sales by $350 million. It also expects future acquisitions to contribute an additional $500 million in annual sales.

Inherit to its strategy are the company's ongoing efforts to improve its operating structure improve manufacturing capacity and keep a lid on costs. Two major projects planned for 2017 are the commercial launch of its new TruVueTM clear plastic can and development of a new contract packaging services center to support the expansion of a key North American customer.

Mergers and Acquisitions

Sonoco also looks to acquisitions as a means for growth. In 2017 the company acquired Peninsula Packaging Company a manufacturer of thermoformed packaging for fresh fruit and vegetables for $230 million from Odyssey Investment Partners. Peninsula has annual revenue of around $190 million and Sonoco hopes the acquisition will help capture new growth in the fresh fruit and vegetable market segment.

In 2016 Sonoco completed four acquisitions at a total cost of $89 million. These included Laminar Medica a privately held specialty medical products company based in the UK it purchased for $17 million. It also picked up Plastic Packaging Inc. (PPI) a privately held North Carolina-based flexible packaging firm for $68 million. The PPI transaction grew Sonoco's flexible packaging assets in the southeast US and allowed it to offer additional specialty and customization capabilities to its customers.

HISTORY

Sonoco Products originated during the South's industrial renewal after the Civil War. Major James Coker and son James Jr. (who had been badly wounded at the Battle of Chickamauga) founded the Carolina Fiber company in Hartsville South Carolina to make pulp and paper from pine trees. The business was based on a thesis James Jr. wrote in 1884 at Stevens Institute of Technology in Hoboken New Jersey. The essay explained how to make paper pulp using the sulfite process.

After failing to sell the pulp commercially the Cokers decided to use it to make paper cones for the textile industry which was seeing rapid growth in the southern US. In 1899 Major Coker and investor W. F. Smith formed the Southern Novelty Company. Major Coker's son Charles became president in 1918. As sales neared $1 million in 1923 the company changed its name to Sonoco.

EXECUTIVES

President CEO and Director, M. Jack Sanders, age 63, $1,039,817 total compensation
SVP Plastic Packaging and Protective Solutions, Vicki B. Arthur, age 58
SVP Paper/Engineered Carriers U.S./Canada and Display and Packaging, Rodger D. Fuller, age 55, $473,319 total compensation
VP Global Flexibles, Robert L. Puechl, age 61
SVP and CFO, Barry L. Saunders, age 57, $548,759 total compensation
VP Tubes and Cores U.S. and Canada, James A. Harrell, age 55
SVP Rigid Paper Containers and Paper/Engineered Carriers International, R. Howard Coker, age 54, $471,695 total compensation
EVP COO and CEO-elect, Robert C. (Rob) Tiede, age 58, $567,741 total compensation
VP Marketing and Innovation, Marcy J. Thompson, age 55
VP Human Resources, Allan H. McLeland, age 50
VP Paper and Industrial Converted Products EMEA Asia Australia and New Zealand, Adam Wood, age 48
Chairman, Harris E. DeLoach, age 71
Secretary IV, Connee Grantham
Auditors: PricewaterhouseCoopers, LLP

LOCATIONS

HQ: Sonoco Products Co.
1 N. Second St., Hartsville, SC 29550
Phone: 843 383-7000   **Fax:** 843 383-7008
Web: www.sonoco.com

2016 Sales

	$ mil.	% of total
US	3,112	65
Europe	951	20
Canada	268	6
Other	450	9
Total	4,782	100

PRODUCTS/OPERATIONS

2016 Sales

	$ mil.	% of total
Consumer Packaging	2,043	43
Paper & Industrial Converted Products	520	11
Display & Packaging	1,693	35
Protective Solutions	525	11
Total	4,782	100

Selected Products and Services

Paper and Industrial Converted Products
  Tubes and cores
  Concrete forms
  Molded plugs
  Pallets
  Pallet components
  Paperboard tubes cores
  Roll packaging
  Rotary die boards
  Void forms
  Paper
  Boxboard
  Chipboard
  Corrugating medium
  Lightweight corestock
  Linerboard

Recovered paper
Recycled paperboard
Specialty grades
Tubeboard
Sonoco Recycling
Collection processing and recycling of old corrugated containers paper plastic metal glass other recyclable materials
Consumer Packaging
Ends and closures
Aluminum steel and peelable membrane easy-open closures for composite metal and plastic containers
Printed flexible packaging
Thin-gauge rotogravure flexographic and combination printed film (laminations and rotogravure cylinder engraving brand artwork management)
Thin-gauge packaging
Rigid packaging - blow molded plastics
Monolayer and multilayer bottles and jars
Rigid packaging - paper
Composite paperboard cans (round and shaped)
Fiber cartridges
Single-wrap paperboard packages
Rigid packaging - thermoformed plastic
Mono coated and barrier and non-barrier laminated tubs cups spools consumer and institutional trays
Packaging Services
Paperboard specialties
Rixie coasters
Stancap glass covers
Other paper amenities
Point-of-purchase (P-O-P)
Contract packaging co-packing and fulfillment services
Designing manufacturing assembling packing and distributing temporary semi permanent and permanent P-O-P displays
Service centers
Packaging supply chain management (custom packing fulfillment primary package filling scalable service centers)
Protective Packaging
Molded and extruded plastics (product design tool design and fabrication; manufacturing in both injection molding and extrusion technologies)
Protective packaging
Contract package testing
Sonopost technology
Sonobase carriers
Sonopop systems

COMPETITORS

Amcor	Greif
AptarGroup	International Paper
Avery Dennison	Owens-Illinois
Ball Corp.	Pactiv
Bemis	Sealed Air Corp.
Caraustar	Silgan
Crown Holdings	The Newark Group
Graphic Packaging	WestRock
Holding	

HISTORICAL FINANCIALS

Company Type: Public

Income Statement

FYE: December 31

	REVENUE ($ mil.)	NET INCOME ($ mil.)	NET PROFIT MARGIN	EMPLOYEES
12/16	4,782	286	6.0%	20,000
12/15	4,964	250	5.0%	21,000
12/14	5,014	239	4.8%	20,800
12/13	4,848	219	4.5%	19,900
12/12	4,786	196	4.1%	19,900
Annual Growth	(0.0%)	9.9%	—	0.1%

2016 Year-End Financials

Debt ratio: 26.83%	No. of shares (mil.): 99
Return on equity: 18.76%	Dividends
Cash ($ mil.): 257	Yield: 0.0%
Current ratio: 1.68	Payout: 51.9%
Long-term debt ($ mil.): 1,020	Market value ($ mil.): 5,227

	STOCK PRICE ($) FY Close	P/E High/Low	PER SHARE ($) Earnings	Dividends	Book Value
12/16	52.70	20 13	2.81	1.46	15.45
12/15	40.87	19 15	2.44	1.37	14.99
12/14	43.70	19 16	2.32	1.27	14.98
12/13	41.72	19 14	2.12	1.23	16.75
12/12	29.73	18 15	1.91	1.19	14.76
Annual Growth	15.4%	— —	10.1%	5.2%	1.1%

South State Corp

South State Corporation (formerly First Financial Holdings) is the holding company for South State Bank (formerly South Carolina Bank and Trust and South Carolina Bank and Trust of the Piedmont both known as SCBT). The bank operates branches throughout the Palmetto state as well as in select counties in Georgia and North Carolina. Serving retail and business customers the banks provide deposit accounts loans and mortgages as well as trust and investment planning services. More than half of the firm's loan portfolio is devoted to commercial mortgages while consumer real estate loans make up more than a quarter. South State plans to merge with Southeastern Bank Financial parent of Georgia Bank & Trust.

Operations

Beyond its retail and commercial banking mortgage lending consumer finance and trust and investment businesses the bank operates registered investment advisors Minis & Co. and First Southeast 401K Fiduciaries as well as limited-purpose broker-dealer First Southeast Investor Services.

South State Corporation generated 70% of its total revenue from loan interest (including fees) in 2014 while another 4% came from interest income on investment securities. Service charges and Bankcard services income made up another 14% of total revenue while trust and investment services income and mortgage banking income each contributed roughly 4% during the year.

Geographic Reach

South State Corporation boasts nearly 130 branches across nearly 20 counties in South Carolina a handful of counties in North Carolina and about a dozen counties in the northeast and coastal regions of Georgia.

Financial Performance

South State Corporation's revenues and profits have been on the rise over the past few years mostly thanks to continued growth of its loan business and declining loan loss provisions as its loan portfolio's credit quality has improved with the strengthened economy.

The company's revenue jumped by 28% to $436.72 million in 2014 which was mostly driven by 20% growth in its loan interest income as its average loan asset balances swelled by a similar percentage. South State's non-interest income also swelled by 76% thanks to higher deposit account service charge bankcard service trust and investment service and mortgage banking fees from overall growth in the business through acquisitions and organic initiatives.

Higher revenue and controlled operating costs in 2014 drove the bank's net income higher by 53% to $75.44 million. South State's operating cash levels declined by 51% to $118.65 million for the year after adjusting its earnings for non-cash net sales proceeds from its mortgage loans held-

for-sale and as the bank spent more cash toward its accrued income taxes.

Strategy

Though it does sometimes expand or relocate its existing branches to better position its locations for more growth South State Corporation has been mostly growing its loan business and branch network through strategic bank and branch acquisitions. Its 2015 acquisition of 13 branch locations from Bank of America for example extended South State's reach into six new markets and three existing markets while adding millions of dollars worth of new loan business. Then in mid-2016 South State Corporation agreed to buy Southeastern Bank Financial the holding company of Georgia Bank & Trust (which also operates in South Carolina as Southern Bank & Trust). The combined company will operate more than 130 branches in Georgia and the Carolinas.

Mergers and Acquisitions

In 2015 South State Corporation agreed to purchase 12 South Carolina branches and one Georgia branch from Bank of America expanding its reach into six new markets. The acquired branches were located in Hartwell Georgia; as well as Florence Greenwood Orangeburg Sumter Newberry Batesburg-Leesville Abbeville and Hartsville in South Carolina.

Company Background

South State Corporation and South State Bank changed their names from First Financial Holdings and South Carolina Bank and Trust respectively in 2014. The change was designed to better promote the South State brand with customers.

EXECUTIVES

CEO, Robert R. Hill, age 50, $645,000 total compensation
Vice President of Public Relations, Donna Pullen
CFO and COO, John C. Pollok, age 51, $442,000 total compensation
Chief Banking Officer, John F. Windley, age 65, $315,000 total compensation
Chief Credit Officer and Chief Risk Officer, Joseph Burns, $295,000 total compensation
President, R. Wayne Hall, $203,405 total compensation
EVP and Corporate Secretary, William C. Bochette
Vice President, Reid Davis
Senior Vice President Technology, Ross Bagley
Senior Executive Vice President, Dane H Murray
Vice President, Stacy Cannon
Executive Vice President Chief Financial Officer, Donald Pickett
Chairman, Robert R. Horger, age 66
Vice Chairman, Paula Harper Bethea
Auditors: Dixon Hughes Goodman LLP

LOCATIONS

HQ: South State Corp
520 Gervais Street, Columbia, SC 29201
Phone: 800 277-2175
Web: www.southstatebank.com

PRODUCTS/OPERATIONS

2011 Sales

	$ mil.	% of total
Interest		
Loans including fees	319	70
Investment securities	20	4
Other	1	-
Noninterest		
Service charges on deposit accounts	36	10
Bankcard services income	29	6
Trust and investment services income	18	4
Mortgage banking	16	4
Securities gains net -	0	
Amortization of FDIC indemnification asset	(21.9)	0
Other	16	4
Total	**436**	**100**

COMPETITORS

BB&T	Regions Financial
Bank of America	Security Federal
Bank of South Carolina	
First Citizens	
Bancorporation	

HISTORICAL FINANCIALS

Company Type: Public

Income Statement

FYE: December 31

	ASSETS ($ mil.)	NET INCOME ($ mil.)	INCOME AS % OF ASSETS	EMPLOYEES
12/16	8,900	101	1.1%	2,055
12/15	8,557	99	1.2%	2,058
12/14	7,826	75	1.0%	2,081
12/13	7,931	49	0.6%	2,106
12/12	5,136	30	0.6%	1,324
Annual Growth	14.7%	35.5%	—	11.6%

2016 Year-End Financials

Debt ratio: 0.62%	No. of shares (mil.): 24
Return on equity: 9.21%	Dividends
Cash ($ mil.): 238	Yield: 0.0%
Current ratio: —	Payout: 28.9%
Long-term debt ($ mil.): —	Market value ($ mil.): 2,118

	STOCK PRICE ($) FY Close	P/E High/Low	PER SHARE ($) Earnings	Dividends	Book Value
12/16	87.40	22 14	4.18	1.21	46.83
12/15	71.95	19 14	4.11	0.98	43.84
12/14	67.08	22 18	3.08	0.82	40.78
12/13	66.51	28 17	2.38	0.74	40.72
12/12	40.18	20 14	2.03	0.69	29.97
Annual Growth	21.4%	— —	19.8%	15.1%	11.8%

Southern California Edison Co.

One of the Golden State's largest utilities Southern California Edison (SCE) distributes power to a population of more than 14 million people (4.9 million customer accounts) in central coastal and southern California (excluding Los Angeles and some other cities). SCE has 6287 MW of net generating capacity from stakes in nuclear hydroelectric and fossil-fueled power plants (although it has sold a number of its fossil-fueled facilities in response to the state's deregulation legislation). The utility sells excess power to wholesale customers. SCE is a unit of utility and competitive power holding company Edison International.

Operations

The utility's system consists of about 12782 circuit miles of transmission lines and more than 91000 circuit miles of overhead and underground distribution lines and more than 800 distribution substations.

Geographic Reach

SCE supplies and delivers electricity to a 50000 square-mile area of southern California. This service area contains a population of nearly 14 million people and SCE serves the population via about 4.9 million customer accounts.

Financial Performance

SCE's net revenues decreased by 14% in 2015 due to lower sales from utility cost-recovery activities including a drop in CPUC-related (California Public Utilities Commission) revenues.

The company's net income decreased by 29% due to lower revenues and higher expenses related to depreciation decommissioning and amortization.

Operating cash flows for 2015 increased by 26% due to changes in working capital as a result of changes in regulatory assets and liabilities including the collections of balancing accounts.

Strategy

Parent Edison International has been addressing the changing industry environment by focusing SCE on investing in and strengthening its electric grid and driving operational and service excellence to improve system safety reliability and service while controlling costs and rates. At the same time Edison International is investing in competitive businesses to meet the electricity needs of commercial and industrial customers both inside and beyond SCE's service area.

In recent years the utility has been ramping up its green energy options in order to comply with the state of California's aggressive long term renewable energy goal .In 2014 the company signed contracts with solar and geothermal energy producers representing more than 1500 MW of clean renewable power and the re-contracting of 225 MW with an existing California geothermal energy project.

As part of its strategy to reduce its fossil-fuel power plant holdings in 2013 SCE sold its ownership interest in Units 4 and 5 of the Four Corners Generating Station a coal-fired electric generating facility in New Mexico to the operator of the facility Arizona Public Service Company for $181 million.

SCE also offers power contract options designed to help smaller biomass generators and is installing up to 150 solar photovoltaic installations on Southern California commercial rooftops. The utility is also installing smart electric meters — digital two-way communication devices which allow customers and the utility to better manage energy use than the older mechanical meters can.

EXECUTIVES

Executive Vice President And General Counsel Edison International, Robert L Adler
Vice President Information Technology, John Kelly
SVP and CIO, Todd L. Inlander
CEO, Kevin M. Payne, age 56
SVP Customer and Operational Services, Stuart R. Hemphill
VP Operational Services and Chief Procurement Officer, Douglas R. Bauder
SVP Transmission and Distribution, Peter T. Dietrich
VP Distribution, Gregory M. Ferree
VP Transmission Substations and Operations, Paul J. Grigaux
President, Ronald O. (R.O.) Nichols, age 63
VP Decommissioning and Chief Nuclear Officer San Onofre Nuclear Generating Station, Thomas J. (Tom) Palmisano
VP and Treasurer, William (Tres) Petmecky, age 48
Vice President, Russell Swartz
Vice President Technology Business Development, Pedro J Pizarro
Vice President, Tim Boucher
Vice President and Chief Nuclear Officer, Tom Palmisano
Vice President Investor Relations Edison International, Scott Cunningham
Vice President, Caroline Choi
Vice President, Dan Tunnicliff
Vice President, Anthony Blakemore
Vice President Culture and Inclusion, Jorge Martinez
Vice President, Dawn Anaiscourt

Executive Vice President Generation, Harold Ray
Assistant Secretary, Bonita Smith
Assistant Treasurer, Mary Simpson
Auditors: PricewaterhouseCoopers LLP

LOCATIONS

HQ: Southern California Edison Co.
2244 Walnut Grove Avenue, P.O. Box 800, Rosemead, CA 91770
Phone: 626 302-1212
Web: www.sce.com

PRODUCTS/OPERATIONS

2015 Sales

	% of total
Commercial customers	43
Residential customers	38
Industrial customers	5
Public authorities	5
Agriculture & other operating revenue	9
Total	**100**

2015 Sales

	$ mil.	% of total
Utility Earning Activities	6,305	55
Utility Cost- Recovery Activities	5,180	45
Total	**11,485**	**100**

COMPETITORS

American States Water	Portland General
Avista	Electric
Bonneville Power	Sacramento Municipal
Calpine	Utility
Imperial Irrigation	San Diego Gas &
District	Electric
NV Energy	SoCalGas
PacifiCorp	
Pacific Gas and	
Electric	

HISTORICAL FINANCIALS

Company Type: Public

Income Statement

FYE: December 31

	REVENUE ($ mil.)	NET INCOME ($ mil.)	NET PROFIT MARGIN	EMPLOYEES
12/16	11,830	1,499	12.7%	11,947
12/15	11,485	1,111	9.7%	12,678
12/14	13,380	1,565	11.7%	13,600
12/13	12,562	1,000	8.0%	13,599
12/12	11,851	1,660	14.0%	16,515
Annual Growth	(0.0%)	(2.5%)	—	(7.8%)

2016 Year-End Financials

Debt ratio: 21.82%	No. of shares (mil.): 434
Return on equity: 10.62%	Dividends
Cash ($ mil.): 39	Yield: 0.0%
Current ratio: 0.43	Payout: 50.9%
Long-term debt ($ mil.): 9,754	Market value ($ mil.): 10,577

	STOCK PRICE ($) FY Close	P/E High/Low	PER SHARE ($) Earnings	Dividends	Book Value
12/16	24.32	— —	(0.00)	1.08	33.30
12/15	23.92	— —	(0.00)	1.20	31.44
12/14	22.50	— —	(0.00)	1.08	30.54
12/13	20.58	— —	(0.00)	1.20	27.91
12/12	22.20	— —	(0.00)	1.20	27.00
Annual Growth	2.3%	— —	—	(2.5%)	5.4%

Southern Company (The)

Southern Power provides power for the burgeoning population in the South. The company owns builds acquires and markets energy in the competitive wholesale supply business. It develops and operates independent power plants in the southeastern US. The company which is part of Southern Company's generation and energy marketing operations has more than 10500 MW of primarily fossil-fueled facilities generating capacity operating or under construction in Alabama California Florida Georgia Nevada North Carolina Texas and New Mexico. Southern Power's electricity output is marketed to wholesale customers in the region. It is growing by acquiring and developing solar power facilities.

Operations

The company is a wholesale energy provider serving electricity needs of municipalities electric cooperatives and investor-owned utilities. Southern Power and its subsidiaries owns and/or operates 35 facilities in nine states. Its renewable assets include biomass and solar.

Thanks to solar facilities under construction and the acquisitions of Calipatria Solar and Grant Wind as well as other capacity and energy contracts the Southern Power has an average of 75% of its available demonstrated capacity covered through 2020 and an average of 70% of its available demonstrated capacity covered through 2025.

Geographic Reach

Southern Power has operations Alabama California Florida Georgia Nevada New Mexico North Carolina Oklahoma and Texas.

Financial Performance

In fiscal 2015 Southern Power's net sales decreased by $111 million compared to 2014. Power purchase agreements (PPA) energy revenues declined due to lower energy prices driven by a drop in natural gas prices which was passed through in fuel revenues.

Wholesale revenues and non-affiliates revenues declined due to lower energy and capacity revenues.

In 2015 net income increased by 25% due to lower fuel expenses and purchased power partially offset by decreased sales.

Fuel expense decreased due to lower natural gas generation costs.

Purchased power expenses decreased primarily due to a drop in volume of KWhs purchased as well as a decrease associated with the average cost of purchased power.

Net cash provided by the operating activities increased by 66% due to higher income tax benefits received and higher revenues from new PPAs including solar PPAs.

Strategy

The company is expanding its regional generation portfolio (primarily with solar power plants) in order to boost its overall generating capacity to almost 10000 MW.

Mergers and Acquisitions

Growing its solar power assets in 2016 Southern Power acquired the 120-MW East Pecos solar facility (Southern Power's second solar project in Texas).

That year Southern Power and Turner Renewable Energy jointly bought the 20-MW Calipatria solar facility from Solar Frontier Americas. (Southern Power's 10th solar facility in California).

In 2015 Southern Power acquired a controlling interest in the 200-MW Garland solar facility under construction in California from Recurrent Energy a subsidiary of Canadian Solar Inc.

In 2014 Southern Power and Turner Renewable Energy acquired the largest solar facility in New Mexico the 50-MW Macho Springs Solar Facility. The Southern Power-Turner Renewable Energy partnership's seventh solar project and its second-largest overall the plant is expected to generate enough electricity to power more than 18000 homes.

EXECUTIVES

Vice President and Associate General Counsel, Patricia Roberts
SVP Commercial Operations and Planning Southern Company Services, John G. Trawick
Vice President Fleet Operations, Bradley Adams
Executive Vice President Customer Services Georgia Power, Mickey A Brown
Vice President External Affairs Gc And Corporate Secretary, Moanica Caston
Vice President Operations and Government Relations Chief Administrative Officer, Charlie Freeman
Vice President of Construction, Keith Russell
Executive Vice President General Counsel, Edison Holland
National Accounts Manager, Norman Collins
Site Vice President of Joseph M Farley Nuclear Plant, Thomas Lynch
Vice President of Corporate Services, Michael Anderson
Vice President Of Chain Supply, Jacki Lowe
VICE PRESIDENT AND ASSISTANT TREASURER, Rick L Patterson
Auditors: DELOITTE & TOUCHE LLP

LOCATIONS

HQ: Southern Company (The)
30 Ivan Allen Jr. Boulevard, N.W., Atlanta, GA 30308
Phone: 404 506-5000   **Fax:** 404 506-0455
Web: www.southerncompany.com

PRODUCTS/OPERATIONS

2015 Sales

	$ mil.	% of total
Wholesale revenues non-affiliates	964	69
Wholesale revenues affiliates	417	30
Other revenues	9	1
Total	**1,390**	**100**

COMPETITORS

AEP	Duke Energy
AEP	Duke Energy
AES	Entergy
AES	Entergy
Calpine	NextEra Energy
Calpine	NextEra Energy

HISTORICAL FINANCIALS

Company Type: Public

Income Statement

FYE: December 31

	REVENUE ($ mil.)	NET INCOME ($ mil.)	NET PROFIT MARGIN	EMPLOYEES
12/16	19,896	2,493	12.5%	32,020
12/15	17,489	2,421	13.8%	26,703
12/14	18,467	2,031	11.0%	26,369
12/13	17,087	1,710	10.0%	26,300
12/12	16,537	2,415	14.6%	26,439
Annual Growth	4.7%	0.8%	—	4.9%

2016 Year-End Financials

Debt ratio: 41.22%
Return on equity: 10.62%
Cash ($ mil.): 1,975
Current ratio: 0.75
Long-term debt ($ mil.): 42,629

No. of shares (mil.): 990
Dividends
 Yield: 0.0%
 Payout: 87.1%
Market value ($ mil.): 48,717

	STOCK PRICE ($) FY Close	P/E High/Low		PER SHARE ($) Earnings	Dividends	Book Value
12/16	49.19	21	18	2.55	2.22	25.73
12/15	46.79	20	16	2.59	2.15	23.38
12/14	49.11	23	18	2.18	2.08	23.47
12/13	41.11	26	21	1.87	2.01	22.70
12/12	42.81	18	16	2.67	1.94	22.33
Annual Growth	3.5%	—	—	(1.1%)	3.4%	3.6%

Southern Copper Corp

Auditors: Galaz, Yamazaki, Ruiz Urquiza, S.C.

LOCATIONS

HQ: Southern Copper Corp
1440 East Missouri Avenue, Suite 160, Phoenix, AZ 85014
Phone: 602 264-1375   **Fax:** 602 264-1397
Web: www.southerncoppercorp.com

HISTORICAL FINANCIALS

Company Type: Public

Income Statement

FYE: December 31

	REVENUE ($ mil.)	NET INCOME ($ mil.)	NET PROFIT MARGIN	EMPLOYEES
12/16	5,379	776	14.4%	13,414
12/15	5,045	736	14.6%	13,024
12/14	5,787	1,332	23.0%	12,735
12/13	5,952	1,618	27.2%	12,665
12/12	6,669	1,934	29.0%	12,085
Annual Growth	(5.2%)	(20.4%)	—	2.6%

2016 Year-End Financials

Debt ratio: 44.99%
Return on equity: 13.96%
Cash ($ mil.): 546
Current ratio: 2.57
Long-term debt ($ mil.): 5,954

No. of shares (mil.): 773
Dividends
 Yield: 0.0%
 Payout: 18.0%
Market value ($ mil.): 24,690

	STOCK PRICE ($) FY Close	P/E High/Low		PER SHARE ($) Earnings	Dividends	Book Value
12/16	31.94	35	22	1.00	0.18	7.54
12/15	26.12	36	26	0.93	0.34	6.80
12/14	28.20	21	16	1.61	0.46	7.20
12/13	28.71	22	13	1.92	0.68	6.26
12/12	37.86	17	12	2.28	3.71	5.39
Annual Growth	(4.2%)	—	—	(18.6%)	(53.1%)	8.8%

Southern Missouri Bancorp, Inc.

EXECUTIVES

Vice President, Mel Jackson
Vice President of Deposit Operations, Tiffany Beaton
Vice President, Kevin Alpe
Vice President Senior Commercial Loan Officer, Brock Fletcher
Auditors: BKD, LLP

LOCATIONS

HQ: Southern Missouri Bancorp, Inc.
  2991 Oak Groove Road, Poplar Bluff, MO 63901
Phone: 573 778-1800
Web: www.bankwithsouthern.com

COMPETITORS

Bank of America   Regions Financial
Commerce Bancshares   U.S. Bancorp
IBERIABANK   UMB Financial

HISTORICAL FINANCIALS

Company Type: Public

Income Statement

FYE: June 30

	ASSETS ($ mil.)	NET INCOME ($ mil.)	INCOME AS % OF ASSETS	EMPLOYEES
06/17	1,707	15	0.9%	390
06/16	1,403	14	1.1%	342
06/15	1,300	13	1.1%	327
06/14	1,021	10	1.0%	247
06/13	796	10	1.3%	181
Annual Growth	21.0%	11.5%	—	21.2%

2017 Year-End Financials

Debt ratio: 0.87%
Return on equity: 10.40%
Cash ($ mil.): 31
Current ratio: —
Long-term debt ($ mil.): —

No. of shares (mil.): 8
Dividends
  Yield: 1.2%
  Payout: 19.2%
Market value ($ mil.): 277

	STOCK PRICE ($) FY Close	P/E High/Low	PER SHARE ($) Earnings	Dividends	Book Value
06/17	32.26	18 11	2.07	0.40	20.15
06/16	23.53	12 9	1.98	0.36	16.94
06/15	18.85	22 10	1.79	0.34	17.88
06/14	35.69	25 17	1.46	0.64	16.63
06/13	25.67	18 15	1.44	0.30	15.46
Annual Growth	5.9%	— —	9.5%	7.5%	6.8%

Southside Bancshares, Inc.

Southside Bancshares is the holding company for Southside Bank which boasts nearly 65 branches across East North and Central Texas with many around the cities of Tyler and Longview. About one-third of its branches are located in su-permarkets (including Albertsons and Brookshire stores) and 40% are motor bank facilities. The bank provides traditional services such as savings money market and checking accounts CDs and other deposit products as well as trust and wealth management services. Real estate loans primarily residential mortgages make up about half of the company's loan portfolio which also includes business consumer and municipal loans. The bank has total assets exceeding $4.8 billion.

Operations

Southside generated 48% of its total revenue from loan interest in 2014 while interest income on taxable investment securities and mortgage-backed securities made up 16% and 19% respectively. About 9% of its revenue came from deposit service fees and another 2% came from trust income.

Geographic Reach

The bank's branches are located in East North and Central Texas. Its main markets are in East Texas the greater Fort Worth area and the greater Austin area. It is also an affiliate with more than 55000 foreign ATMs worldwide.

Sales and Marketing

Southside which staffed 813 employees at 2014's end serves individuals businesses municipal entities and non-profit organizations in local communities.

Financial Performance

Southside Bancshares' revenues and profits have been falling over the past several years despite consistent growth in loan and investment interest income mostly because the bank's gains on securities held-for-sale have declined.

The company's revenue dipped by 4% to $148.3 million in 2014 mostly due to a $5.6 million decline in gains on the sale of its AFS securities and a $2.8 million impairment of equity related to its investment in SFG Finance stemming from the sale of loans purchased by SFG and the repossessed assets.

Lower revenue and an uptick in loan loss provisions in 2014 caused Southside's net income to tumble 49% to $20.8 million for the year while its operating cash levels dipped by 6% to $56 million on lower cash earnings.

Strategy

Southside looks to acquire financial institutions to grow its loan business and expand its geographic reach outside of its existing markets. Its 2014 acquisition of OmniAmerican Bank alone helped boost its loan assets by more than 60% to $2.17 billion while adding 14 branches in a new market (Dallas/Fort Worth).

To grow its deposits and deepen its presence in the markets it serves the company has also been expanding its network of banking locations — both in-store and full-service branches.

Mergers and Acquisitions

In December 2014 the company acquired OmniAmerican Bank to boost its loan business and expand its footprint to the Dallas area. The deal added 14 full-service branches in the 12-county Dallas/Fort Worth metroplex and more than $763 million in new loan business.

EXECUTIVES

Senior Executive Vice President, Jeryl Story
President and CEO Southside Bancshares and Southside Bank, Lee R. Gibson, age 60, $493,325 total compensation
Regional President North Texas Southside Bank, Tim Carter, age 62
Regional President Central Texas Southside Bank, Peter M. Boyd, age 61, $435,510 total compensation
EVP and Chief Credit Officer Southside Bank, Earl W. (Bill) Clawater, age 63, $265,000 total compensation
EVP and Chief Analytics Officer Southside Bank and Company Secretary, Brian K. McCabe, age 56, $228,385 total compensation
Regional President East Texas Southside Bank, Tim Alexander, age 60
EVP and CFO, Julie N. Shamburger, age 54
Executive Vice President Chief Information Officer, Brian Foster
Assistant Vice President, Julie A Brown
Vice President, Jeff Quesenberry
Vice President, Cindy Davis
Executive Vice President of Marketing, Lonny Uzzell
Senior Vice President, Doug Cassidy
Vice President, Julie Hunter
Vice Chairman, John R. (Bob) Garrett, age 64
Chairman, W.D. (Joe) Norton, age 80
Auditors: Ernst & Young LLP

LOCATIONS

HQ: Southside Bancshares, Inc.
  1201 S. Beckham Avenue, Tyler, TX 75701
Phone: 903 531-7111
Web: www.southside.com

PRODUCTS/OPERATIONS

2014 Sales

	$ mil.	% of total
Interest		
Loans	70	48
Mortgage-backed & related securities	28	19
Investment securities	24	16
Other	0	-
Non-interest		
Deposit services	15	9
Gain on sale of securities	2	2
Trust income	3	2
Back owned life insurance income	1	1
Gain on sale of loans	0	-
Other	4	3
Adjustments	(2.8)	
Total	148	100

COMPETITORS

Bank of America   Jacksonville Bancorp
Capital One   of Illinois
East Texas Financial   Regions Financial

HISTORICAL FINANCIALS

Company Type: Public

Income Statement

FYE: December 31

	ASSETS ($ mil.)	NET INCOME ($ mil.)	INCOME AS % OF ASSETS	EMPLOYEES
12/16	5,563	49	0.9%	679
12/15	5,162	44	0.9%	683
12/14	4,807	20	0.4%	813
12/13	3,445	41	1.2%	640
12/12	3,237	34	1.1%	574
Annual Growth	14.5%	9.2%	—	4.3%

2016 Year-End Financials

Debt ratio: 2.85%
Return on equity: 10.23%
Cash ($ mil.): 161
Current ratio: —
Long-term debt ($ mil.): —

No. of shares (mil.): 29
Dividends
  Yield: 0.0%
  Payout: 53.1%
Market value ($ mil.): 1,102

STOCK PRICE ($)		P/E		PER SHARE ($)		
	FY Close	High/Low		Earnings	Dividends	Book Value
12/16	37.67	21	11	1.81	0.96	17.71
12/15	24.02	19	15	1.61	0.94	16.25
12/14	28.91	36	26	0.96	0.86	15.61
12/13	27.34	15	10	1.94	0.78	12.21
12/12	21.06	14	12	1.61	0.91	12.12
Annual Growth	15.6%	—	—	3.1%	1.5%	9.9%

Southwest Airlines Co

Southwest Airlines will fly any plane (as long as it's a Boeing) and let passengers sit anywhere they like (as long as they get there first). Sticking with what has worked Southwest has expanded its low-cost no-frills no-reserved-seats approach to air travel throughout the US to serve nearly 100 destinations across North America. Now the largest carrier of US domestic passengers Southwest still stands as an inspiration for scrappy low-fare upstarts the world over. The carrier has enjoyed 44 straight profitable years amid the airline industry's ups and downs. Southwest's fleet numbers about 720 Boeing 737s.

Operations

Simplicity has been key to Southwest's success. Most of the carrier's flights are less than two hours and it usually lands at small airports to avoid congestion at competitors' larger hubs; in Dallas it's the big dog at little Love Field its birthplace and in Chicago it accounts for most of the traffic at Midway Airport. Southwest's (and AirTran's) fleet consists primarily of one type of aircraft — the Boeing 737 — to minimize training and maintenance costs.

Geographic Reach

Southwest serves more than 100 destinations in some 40 US states in addition to the District of Columbia Puerto Rico Mexico Jamaica Costa Rica Belize Cuba The Bahamas Aruba and the Dominican Republic.

Financial Performance

Southwest has achieved unprecedented growth over the last six years. Its revenues grew 3% from $19.8 billion in 2015 to $20.4 billion in 2016 a historic milestone. The historic growth was driven by a bump in passenger revenues fueled by increased passenger yield driven by strong demand for low-fare air travel. On the flip side freight revenues declined 5% due to sluggish demand throughout 2016.

Profits jumped 3% from $2.18 billion in 2015 to a record-setting $2.24 billion in 2016 due to the higher revenue coupled with a significant decline in fuel and oil prices. Southwest's operating cash flow increased from $3.2 billion in 2015 to $4.29 billion in 2016 due to the higher profits in addition to cash generated from fuel derivative instruments.

Strategy

Protective of its low-cost image Southwest has staunchly resisted charging passengers baggage fees. However it has seen the value of this strategy and has rolled out new fees that have included allowing passengers to bring small dogs or cats into the cabin for a one-way charge of $75 and charging a one-way $50 fee for unaccompanied minors.

A large part of the carrier's strategy to stay profitable includes fleet modernization. Southwest is replacing older Boeing 737 planes with the larger and more fuel-efficient Boeing 737-800 for expansion to locations of greater distance.

During 2016 Southwest grew by adding a scheduled service to Long Beach California and the three Cuban cities of Havana Varadero and Santa Clara.

Another prong of the carrier's growth strategy involves technology. To tap into potential Latin American passengers wanting to travel to the US Southwest is investing in technology that features foreign-currency exchanges and point-of-sale programs. Southwest?s new reservations platform launched in late 2016 will also give the carrier more revenue management capabilities and functions to sell to international customers. The carrier has spent more than $500?million on the system.

HISTORY

Texas businessman Rollin King and lawyer Herb Kelleher founded Air Southwest in 1967 as an intrastate airline linking Dallas Houston and San Antonio. The now-defunct Braniff and Texas International sued questioning whether the region needed another airline but the Texas Supreme Court ruled in Southwest's favor. In 1971 the company renamed Southwest Airlines made its first scheduled flight.

Operating from Love Field in Dallas Southwest adopted "love" as the theme of its early ad campaigns serving love potions (drinks) and love bites (peanuts). When other airlines moved to the new Dallas/Fort Worth International Airport (DFW) in 1974 Kelleher insisted on staying at Love Field gaining a virtual monopoly there.

EXECUTIVES

EVP Corporate Services, Robert E. (Bob) Jordan, age 57, $470,000 total compensation
Chairman and CEO, Gary C. Kelly, age 61, $10,084 total compensation
EVP Daily Operations, Gregory D. (Greg) Wells, age 58
EVP and CFO, Tammy Romo, age 54, $460,000 total compensation
VP and Chief Technology Architect, Stan Alexander
COO, Michael G. (Mike) Van de Ven, age 55, $474,373 total compensation
VP and Chief Communications Officer, Linda B. Rutherford
VP Corporate Delivery Operations and Reservations, Kathleen Wayton
EVP and Chief Revenue Officer, Andrew Watterson
VP and Chief Marketing Officer, Ryan Green
President, Thomas M. (Tom) Nealon, age 55
Vp Operations Coordination Center, Jeff Martin
Vice Chairman, Ron Ricks, age 68
Auditors: Ernst & Young LLP

LOCATIONS

HQ: Southwest Airlines Co
P.O. Box 36611, Dallas, TX 75235-1611
Phone: 214 792-4000   **Fax:** 214 792-5015
Web: www.southwest.com

PRODUCTS/OPERATIONS

2016 Sales

	$ mil.	% of total
Passenger	18,594	91
Freight	171	1
Other	1,660	8
Total	**20,425**	**100**

COMPETITORS

Alaska Air	Frontier Airlines
American Airlines Group	JetBlue
Delta Air Lines	United Continental

HISTORICAL FINANCIALS

Company Type: Public

Income Statement

FYE: December 31

	REVENUE ($ mil.)	NET INCOME ($ mil.)	NET PROFIT MARGIN	EMPLOYEES
12/17	21,171	3,488	16.5%	56,100
12/16	20,425	2,244	11.0%	53,500
12/15	19,820	2,181	11.0%	49,583
12/14	18,605	1,136	6.1%	46,278
12/13	17,699	754	4.3%	44,831
Annual Growth	4.6%	46.7%	—	5.8%

2017 Year-End Financials

Debt ratio: 14.61%
Return on equity: 36.97%
Cash ($ mil.): 1,495
Current ratio: 0.70
Long-term debt ($ mil.): 3,320
No. of shares (mil.): 588
Dividends
  Yield: 0.0%
  Payout: 8.2%
Market value ($ mil.): 38,521

	STOCK PRICE ($)	P/E		PER SHARE ($)		
	FY Close	High/Low		Earnings	Dividends	Book Value
12/17	65.45	11	9	5.79	0.48	17.72
12/16	49.84	14	10	3.55	0.38	13.72
12/15	43.06	15	10	3.27	0.29	11.36
12/14	42.32	26	11	1.64	0.20	10.03
12/13	18.84	18	10	1.05	0.13	10.47
Annual Growth	36.5%	—	—	53.2%	38.3%	14.1%

SpartanNash Co.

In the grocery and distribution wars Spartan-Nash is up for the fight. The grocery retailer and wholesaler operates 157 supermarkets under the Family Fare Supermarkets D&W Fresh Market VG's Food and Pharmacy Sun Mart and more than a dozen other banners. Besides selling national brand-goods stores offer private-label items under the Spartan TopCare Valu Time and Full Circle names. SpartanNash is also a leading grocery wholesaler distributing over 7100 private brand items to 2100 independent supermarkets in Michigan Indiana and Ohio. It is also a leading grocery distributor for the US military. Founded in 1917 as a cooperative grocery distributor Spartan Stores came into its current being after it acquired Nash-Finch in 2013.

Operations

SpartanNash operates three main business segments: Food Military and Retail.

Food Distribution which makes up some 45% of the company's total revenue comprises 11 distribution centers that ship 60000 stock-keeping units of food general merchandise floral pharmacy and health and beauty care products.

Living up to its namesake warrior city Spartan-Nash's Military segment (nearly 30% of revenue) contracts with manufacturers to distribute grocery products to US military commissaries and exchanges. The company is the largest distributor to such US military properties.

Its Retail division (nearly 30% of revenue) sells items from its some 160 company-owned retail stores operating under more than 15 banners (including Family Fare Supermarkets No Frills Bag 'N Save Family Fresh Markets D&W Fresh Markets Sun Mart and Econo Foods). It also runs 30 gas stations and 90 in-store pharmacies.

By product SpartanNash generates over 60% of its revenue from non-perishable items while around 30% comes from the sale and distribution of perishable items. About 6% of revenue comes from fuel and pharmacy sales.

Geographic Reach

Grand Rapids Michigan-based SpartanNash owns more than 160 stores in 10 states and distributes to 2100 independent grocers across 47 US states. Its military operations serve commissaries and exchanges in 37 US states the District of Columbia Europe Cuba Puerto Rico Bahrain and Egypt.

Sales and Marketing

SpartanNash's largest Food Distribution customer is Dollar General. The company sells to more than 13000 Dollar General retail locations yearly accounting for about 11% of SpartanNash's consolidated net sales.

Financial Performance

In 2016 SpartanNash's revenue recovered by 1% to $7.7 billion following a 3% fall the previous year. Gains came from new and existing customers in the Food Distribution (4.5% growth) and Military (0.5% growth) segments. Food and Military growth offset the negative impact of food deflation across the board as well as lower comparable retail store sales and the closure of retail stores. Retail revenue fell 3%.

Net income fell 10% to $56.8 million as food price deflation ate into margins. Cash from operating activities also fell by 30% to $154.5 million.

Strategy

Through SpartanNash's neighborhood market strategy the company endeavors to distinguish itself from other food retailers such as supercenters and limited-assortment stores by emphasizing convenient locations and offering demographically targeted merchandise high-quality fresh foods and value pricing. It's been expanding its product offerings in its stores adding more than 1000 new items (and 300 unique items) during 2016 and 2017. The acquisition of Caito Foods Service expanded its presence in prepared fruits vegetables and proteins categories.

To drive sales and foster customer loyalty SpartanNash has been renovating its stores completing seventeen remodels across 2015-16. It also opened a new fuel center. The company expects to close or sell ten stores during 2017.

Another part of SpartanNash's growth strategy includes select acquisitions of retail grocery stores grocery store chains or distribution facilities. Other initiatives outlined in early 2016 included driving a "lean and efficient" operating cost structure to remain competitive in the Retail segment streamlining and obtaining better scale for its supply chain and leverage the size and scale of its Food Distribution and Retail segments to drive new customer business for its Military segment.

Mergers and Acquisitions

In early 2017 SpartanNash acquired Caito Foods Service's produce distribution business as well as its fresh produce and prepared foods businesses. The deal which included two processing facilities and temperature-controlled distribution and logistics company Blue Ribbon Transport expanded the company's presence in the prepared fruits vegetables and proteins grocery categories. SpartanNash paid $217.5 million in cash for Caito's assets.

SpartanNash acquired Dan's Super Market and its six retail locations in 2015 expanding SpartanNash's presence in North Dakota.

HISTORY

Making dinner in the early 1900s often required several shopping stops: the grocer for canned goods a butcher for meat and yet another place for produce. Eventually the big grocery chains began offering one-stop shopping not to mention better prices due to greater buying power. Worrying about how to compete in 1917 approximately 100 small grocers met in Grand Rapids Michigan to discuss organizing a cooperative; almost half of those formed the Grand Rapids Wholesale Grocery Co. The stores remained independent operating under different names but achieving economies of scale and volume buying through the co-op. They also began developing a variety of services for member stores. Sales topped $1 million in 1934.

Over the years the company expanded beyond its Grand Rapids origins. In 1950 it formed subsidiary United Wholesale which served independent grocers on a cash-and-carry basis. It acquired the Grand Rapids Coffee Company in 1953. The next year the co-op launched its first private-label item Spartan Coffee with a green Spartan logo reminiscent of the Michigan State University mascot. The company changed its name to Spartan Stores in 1957.

Spartan Stores entered retailing in the early 1970s when it bought 19 Harding's stores. It became a for-profit company in 1973 but continued to provide rebates to customers based on their purchases. Spartan Stores began offering insurance to its customers in 1979.

Concerned about the direction of the company customers named Patrick Quinn formerly a VP at a small chain of grocery stores as president and CEO in 1985. To focus on the wholesale business and to avoid any appearance of conflict of interest in both supplying member stores and operating competing stores Spartan Stores sold its 23 retail stores between 1987 and 1994 giving customer stores the first option on them. It entered the convenience store wholesale business with its 1987 acquisition of L&L/Jiroch. Two years later the co-op acquired Associated Grocers of Michigan (later known as Capistar closed in 1996).

Sales topped $2 billion in 1991. Spartan Stores expanded its convenience store operations in 1993 by buying wholesaler J.F. Walker. Despite record sales in 1996 a $46 million restructuring charge that included extensive technological improvements led to a $21.7 million loss the largest in the company's history. The following year Jim Meyer who had joined Spartan Stores in 1973 replaced the retiring Quinn as president and CEO. Also in 1997 the company stopped giving its customers rebates finally doing away with the last remnants of its co-op years.

To keep Michigan customers out of the clutches of its wholesaling rivals Spartan Stores re-entered retailing in 1999 by acquiring eight Ashcraft's Markets. It bought 13 Family Fare stores and 23 Glen's grocery stores that year. In early 2000 the company sold off its insurance business. Later that year Spartan Stores acquired food and drug chain Seaway Food Town (Michigan and Ohio) for about $180 million and began publicly trading.

In 2001 the company purchased longtime customer Prevo's Family Markets a supermarket chain with 10 stores in western Michigan. In an effort to reduce debt and improve profitability in mid-2002 the company announced plans to close its Food Town stores which suffered from competitors such as Meier Kroger and Farmer Jack's. (By mid-2003 Spartan had sold the last of its 26 Food Town stores. Spartan Stores' retail operations had accounted for about 40% of the company's sales.)

In 2003 Spartan Stores sold seven shopping centers in Michigan for $46 million as part of its strategy to sell noncore properties and focus on its retail and distributions businesses. That year James Meyer retired as president and CEO of Spartan Stores and was succeeded by Craig Sturken a former executive of the Great Atlantic & Pacific Tea Company. Later the company sold convenience store suppliers L&L/Jiroch and J.F. Walker to Knoxville Tennessee-based distributor H.T. Hackney Co.

Spartan Stores sold the assets of United Wholesale Grocery Co. a privately held firm in Michigan for about $10 million in 2004. The sale marked Spartan's exit from the convenience store distribution business. The company also closed or sold all of its Food Town stores for $42.1 million.

In 2005 the company opened three fuel centers in Michigan under the Family Fare Quick Stops and Glen's Quick Stop banners. The company acquired D&W Food Centers the following year and purchased about 20 stores from G&R Felpausch in 2007. Spartan Stores' retail expansion continued in 2008 when it acquired more than 15 stores from V.G.'s Food Center. Sturken stepped down as CEO that year and was replaced by Dennis Eidson. In early 2011 Sturken took a less responsible role as chairman and advisor as he looked to transition out of the business.

EXECUTIVES

VP Information Technology and CIO, David deS. (Dave) Couch, age 66, $205,920 total compensation
President and CEO, David M. (Dave) Staples, age 54, $600,000 total compensation
EVP Retail Operations, Theodore C. (Ted) Adornato, age 63, $369,308 total compensation
EVP and CFO, Mark E. Shamber, age 49
EVP Merchandising and Marketing, Larry Pierce, age 62
EVP Chief Legal Officer and President MDV, Kathleen M. (Kathy) Mahoney, age 62, $415,000 total compensation
EVP; CEO Caito Foods, Bob Kirch
Vice President, Mark Lamberies
Vice President of Real Estate, Dave Belock
Vice President Corporate Affairs, Jeanne Norcross
Executive Vice President SpartanNash and President MDV, Ed Brunot
Vice President Operations Finance, Francis Wong
Division Vice President, Bruce Emery
Vice President and Assistant General Counsel, Caren Fitzgerald
Vice President Private Brands, John Paul
Vice President, Peter Odonnell
Chairman, Dennis Eidson, age 63
Auditors: Deloitte & Touche LLP

LOCATIONS

HQ: SpartanNash Co.
850 76th Street S.W., P.O. Box 8700, Grand Rapids, MI 49518
Phone: 616 878-2000
Web: www.spartannash.com

PRODUCTS/OPERATIONS

2016 Sales

	$ mil.	% of total
Food Distribution	3,454	45
Military	2,197	28
Retail	2,083	27
Total	**7,734**	**100**

2016 Sales

	$ mil.	% of total
Non-perishables	4,908	63
Perishables	2,359	31
Pharmacy	356	.5
Fuel	110	1
Total	**7,734**	**100**

2016 Stores

	No.
Family Fare Supermarkets	82
VG's Food and Pharmacy	11
D&W Fresh Markets	11
Sun Mart	10
Econofoods	8
Dan's Super Market	6
Family Fresh Market	6
Valu Land	5
Family Thrift Center	4
Supermercado Nuestra Familia	3
No Frills	3
Forest Hills Foods	1
Pick ‘n Save	1
Germantown Fresh Market	1
Prairie Market	1
Dillonvale IGA	1
Madison Fresh Market	1
Purdue Fresh Market	1
Wholesale Food Outlet	1
Total	**157**

Selected Retail Brands

Full Circle
Spartan
Spartan Fresh Selections
Top Care
Valu Time

COMPETITORS

Alex Lee	IGA
Associated Wholesale	Kroger
Grocers	McLane
C&S Wholesale	Meijer
Coastal Pacific Food	Miner's
Distributors Inc.	S. Abraham & Sons
Core-Mark	SUPERVALU
Costco Wholesale	Wal-Mart

HISTORICAL FINANCIALS

Company Type: Public

Income Statement

FYE: December 31

	REVENUE ($ mil.)	NET INCOME ($ mil.)	NET PROFIT MARGIN	EMPLOYEES
12/16*	7,734	56	0.7%	14,700
01/16	7,651	62	0.8%	15,200
01/15	7,916	58	0.7%	16,100
12/13	2,597	0	0.0%	15,900
03/13	2,608	27	1.1%	8,650
Annual Growth	**31.2%**	**20.0%**	**—**	**14.2%**

*Fiscal year change

2016 Year-End Financials

Debt ratio: 22.33%	No. of shares (mil.): 37
Return on equity: 7.05%	Dividends
Cash ($ mil.): 24	Yield: 0.0%
Current ratio: 1.77	Payout: 39.7%
Long-term debt ($ mil.): 413	Market value ($ mil.): 1,484

	STOCK PRICE ($) FY Close	P/E High/Low		PER SHARE ($) Earnings	Dividends	Book Value
12/16*	39.54	26	12	1.51	0.60	21.99
01/16	21.64	20	13	1.66	0.54	21.03
01/15	25.82	17	12	1.55	0.48	19.91
12/13	23.73	810537		0.03	0.27	18.92
03/13	17.55	15	11	1.25	0.32	15.43
Annual Growth	**22.5%**	**—**	**—**	**4.8%**	**17.0%**	**9.3%**

*Fiscal year change

Spectrum Brands Holdings Inc

And you will know them by their trail of brands. Spectrum Brands makes and markets products sold under some of the most recognizable names in the world. They include batteries (Rayovac and VARTA) pet foods and supplies (Tetra Marineland Dingo) personal care (Remington) and garden care (Spectracide Cutter Hot Shot). Its small appliances unit includes such notable brands as Stanley Black & Decker George Foreman Toastmaster and Farberware. A leader in the sale of rechargeable batteries and hearing aid batteries to manufacturers Spectrum Brands markets its products in more than 1 million stores spanning 160 countries.The company is 60% owned by HRG Group and 40% by publicly traded stock.

Operations

Spectrum manages its businesses across five product lines: Global Batteries & Appliances Hardware & Home Improvement Global Pet Supplies Home and Garden and Global Auto Care. Spectrum benefits from strong product name recognition including: Kwikset Stanley Black+Decker Farberware Amor All STP HotShot and Cutter among many others.

While best known for its general-purpose alkaline batteries Spectrum Brands also makes hearing aid batteries (Beltone Miracle Ear and Starkey brands) as well as zinc carbon nickel metal hydride lithium silver oxide and coin cell (used in cameras and computer clocks) batteries. The company sells its VARTA consumer brand batteries primarily in European markets.

Spectrum owns the IAMS and Eukanuba brands of premium pet food in Europe.

Geographic Reach

The majority of Spectrum's rechargeable batteries and chargers personal care products and lighting products are manufactured in Asia. It also has manufacturing and product development operations located in Canada Europe Latin America and the US. About 35% of its total sales were from customers outside of the US mainly in Europe.

Sales and Marketing

Products are sold through retailers wholesalers and distributors including Canadian Tire Wal-Mart The Home Depot Target Lowe's Carrefour Gigante PETCO and PetSmart.

A significant percentage of Spectrum?s sales are attributable to a limited group of retailers including Amazon Autozone Dollar General Lidl Lowe?s PetSmart O?Reilly Target The Home Depot and Wal-Mart. Sales to its largest customer Wal-Mart represent about 15% of total revenue (in FY2017).

Financial Performance

In FY2017 (ended September 30) revenue was in line with the prior year at $5.0 billion. The company experienced marginal slips in sales from its Pet Supplies Home & Garden and Auto Care segments which were partially offset by increases in Hardware & Home Improvement and in Consumer Batteries.

Spectrum Brands saw net income drop 17% to $295 million due in large part to employee severance costs and increases to general and administrative expenses.

Cash on hand at FY2017 year-end was $168 million down $107 million from the previous year. Cash from operations was $665 million about half of that coming from net income and the rest mostly from an adjustment for depreciation and amortization. The company put out $305 million of cash on business acquisitions and more than $100 mil-

lion on property plant and equipment. Spectrum also put $252 million towards repurchasing shares of its own stock.

Strategy

The company bases its business strategy on consumer marketing trends product mix distribution network technology promotions and pricing and geographic foothold. It makes acquisitions that bolster its product lines and expand its global presence.It frequently looks for cost-cutting opportunities and has several programs underway to reduce staff and decrease manufacturing and other operating expenses.

Mergers and Acquisitions

In 2017 it purchased PetMatrix (rawhide-free dog chews) for $255 million GloFish (fluorescent fish) for $50 million and the remaining 44% of Shaser (skin care) that it didn?t already own for roughly $13 million.

EXECUTIVES

SVP General Counsel and Secretary, Nathan E. Fagre, age 61, $375,016 total compensation
EVP and CFO, Douglas L. (Doug) Martin, age 54, $550,688 total compensation
CEO and Director, Andreas Rouv ©, age 55, $571,339 total compensation
SVP and General Manager Global Auto Care Division, Guy J. Andrysick, age 54
SVP and General Manager Global Batteries and Appliances Division, Steven M. (Steve) Fraundorfer, age 49
SVP and General Manager Pet Home and Garden Division, Randal D. Lewis
SVP and General Manager Hardware and Home Improvement Division, Philip S. (Phil) Szuba, age 48
SVP Human Resources, Stacey L. Neu, age 50, $250,000 total compensation
Vice President of Marketing, Dann Provolo
DVP Global Purchasing, Mark Codde
Executive Vice President Human Resources, Rebeckah Long
Division Vice President Tax, Tim Lardinois
Vice President Operations, Ken Burns
Division Vice President Home and Garden Marketing, Eric Kenney
Vice President, Andy Van Wie
National Account Manager, Krista Weigand
Chairman, David M. Maura, age 44
Auditors: KPMG LLP

LOCATIONS

HQ: Spectrum Brands Holdings Inc
3001 Deming Way, Middleton, WI 53562
Phone: 608 275-3340
Web: www.spectrumbrands.com

2016 Sales

	% of total
US	64
Europe/MEA	22
Latin America	7
North America - Other	4
Asia Pacific	3
Total	**100**

PRODUCTS/OPERATIONS

FY2017 Sales

	% of total
Global Batteries & Appliances	40
Hardware & Home Improvement	25
Global Pet Supplies	16
Home & Garden	10
Global Auto Care	9
Total	**100**

Selected Divisions and Brands

Global Batteries and Appliances
Rayovac
VARTA
Remington
Black & Decker
George Foreman
Russell Hobbs
Farberware
Toastmaster
Breadman
Juiceman

Hardware & Home Improvement
Kwikset
Weiser
Baldwin
National Hardware
Stanley
Fanal
Pfister
Tell

Global Pet Supplies
Tetra
8-in-1
Dingo
Nature's Miracle
Wild Harvest
Marineland
Furminator
Littermaid
Birdola
Healthy Hide
Digest-eeze
Iams
Eukanuba
SmartBone
DreamBones
GloFish

Home & Garden
Spectracide
Cutter
Hot Shot
Real Kill
Ultra Kill
Black Flag
Liquid Fence
Rid-a-bug
TAT
Garden Safe
Repel

Global Auto Care
Armor All
STP
A/C PRO

Selected Products by Product Line

Consumer batteries (alkaline zinc carbon rechargeable hearing aid and specialty)
Electric personal care and styling devices
Electric shaving and grooming
Home and garden (insecticides insect repellants herbicides)
Pet supplies (aquatic dog and cat treats small animal food training aids health and grooming bedding)
Portable lighting
Small appliances

COMPETITORS

American Vanguard	Henkel
BYD	NACCO Industries
Bayer AG	Panasonic Corp
Central Garden & Pet	Philips Electronics
Conair	Procter & Gamble
De'Longhi	S.C. Johnson
Edgewell Personal Care	SEB
EnerSys	Scotts Miracle-Gro
GP Batteries	Ultralife
Helen of Troy	

HISTORICAL FINANCIALS

Company Type: Public

Income Statement

FYE: September 30

	REVENUE ($ mil.)	NET INCOME ($ mil.)	NET PROFIT MARGIN	EMPLOYEES
09/17	5,007	295	5.9%	16,800
09/16	5,039	357	7.1%	15,700
09/15	4,690	148	3.2%	15,500
09/14	4,429	214	4.8%	13,400
09/13	4,085	(55)	—	13,500
Annual Growth	5.2%	—	—	5.6%

2017 Year-End Financials

Debt ratio: 51.76%
Return on equity: 16.26%
Cash ($ mil.): 168
Current ratio: 1.44
Long-term debt ($ mil.): 3,804

No. of shares (mil.): 57
Dividends
 Yield: 0.0%
 Payout: 32.6%
Market value ($ mil.): 6,101

	STOCK PRICE ($) FY Close	P/E High/Low	PER SHARE ($) Earnings	Dividends	Book Value
09/17	105.92	29 20	5.02	1.64	31.91
09/16	137.69	23 15	5.99	1.47	30.30
09/15	91.51	40 31	2.66	1.29	26.31
09/14	90.53	22 15	4.02	1.15	19.79
09/13	65.84	— —	(1.06)	0.75	17.18
Annual Growth	12.6%	— —	—	21.6%	16.7%

SPECTRUM HEALTH SYSTEMS, INC.

Auditors: ERNST & YOUNG LLP

LOCATIONS

HQ: SPECTRUM HEALTH SYSTEMS, INC.
10 MECHANIC ST STE 302, WORCESTER, MA 016082419
Phone: 508 792-1508
Web: WWW.SPECTRUMHEALTHSYSTEMS.ORG

HISTORICAL FINANCIALS

Company Type: Private

Income Statement

FYE: June 30

	REVENUE ($ mil.)	NET INCOME ($ mil.)	NET PROFIT MARGIN	EMPLOYEES
06/15	4,625	352	7.6%	1,000
06/14	56	2	3.9%	—
06/13	51	1	3.1%	—
06/12	47	1	3.5%	—
Annual Growth	358.8%	495.0%	—	—

2015 Year-End Financials

Debt ratio: —
Return on equity: 7.60%
Cash ($ mil.): 296
Current ratio: 0.70
Long-term debt ($ mil.): —

Dividends
 Yield: —
 Payout: —
Market value ($ mil.): —

Spirit AeroSystems Holdings Inc

Spirit AeroSystems Holdings makes commercial and military airplane components such as fuselages propulsion systems wings and wing components. It designs and builds aerostructures for every Boeing aircraft currently in production and provides components to Boeing's chief rival Airbus. Spirit AeroSystems claims to be the largest supplier of wing parts for Airbus' A320 aircraft and produces the majority of aerostructures for Boeing's 737. Spirit AeroSystems maintains operations in the US the UK and Asia; however the US is its largest market.

Operations

Spirit AeroSystems' operations are divided among three segments. Fuselage Systems is its most lucrative generating almost 50% of total sales each year. Propulsion Systems and Wing Systems each earn around 25% of sales. The Fuselage Systems segment develops produces and markets forward mid and rear fuselage sections and systems primarily to aircraft makers.

The Propulsion Systems segment develops produces and markets struts/pylons nacelles (including thrust reversers) and related engine structural components primarily to aircraft or engine OEMs. Wing Systems develops produces and markets wings and wing components (including flight control surfaces) and other miscellaneous structural parts primarily to aircraft OEMs.

Geographic Reach

The company has its headquarters in Wichita Kansas and other operations in France Malaysia and the UK. The US accounts for more than 80% of its total sales while the UK generates 10%.

Sales and Marketing

About 80% of Spirit AeroSystems' revenues comes from Boeing while Airbus accounts for 15%. This customer concentration risk gets offset by the fact that it's the only source for most of its products and its contracts give it supplier rights for the life of the aircraft program for most models. (Spirit AeroSystems began as an internal supplier for Boeing aircraft.) Other customers include Southwest Airlines and Sikorsky the US government and major defense contractors.

Spirit AeroSystems is a key supplier for the Airbus A380 and the Airbus A350 XWB. Sales related to the commercial aircraft market represent approximately 99% of its net revenues.

Financial Performance

Spirit AeroSystems' revenues increased 2% from $6.6 billion in 2015 to $6.8 billion in 2016. The growth was attributed to higher production deliveries on the A350 XWB and B767 and higher revenues recorded on certain nonrecurring Boeing programs and one-time claim settlements with customers.

The company in 2016 experienced increased sales from all its segments: Wing Systems (5%) Fuselage Systems (2%) and Propulsion Systems (2%). In addition sales from the UK surged by 21% in 2016.

Spirit AeroSystems' profits however declined 40% from $789 million in 2015 to $470 million in 2016 mainly due to income tax payments during 2016 compared to income tax refunds in 2015. After experiencing a massive increase in operating cash flow peaking at $1.3 billion in 2015 Spirit AeroSystems saw its cash flow drop to $717 million in 2016. This was the result of lower cash receipts in 2016 coupled with the income tax payments.

Strategy

The company's strategic plan includes improving performance and productivity reducing costs leveraging its investments in support of future aircraft rate increases and continuing its progress on the Airbus A350 airliner. It is reducing cost through cost-saving initiatives and improving operational efficiency through centralization of functions and is investing in new technology to bring the most advanced techniques manufacturing and automation to Spirit AeroSystems' customers.

Company Background

The company was founded in 2005 when Boeing spun off its Wichita Division and Oklahoma operations as a new entity Spirit AeroSystems.

EXECUTIVES

SVP and CTO, John Pilla, age 57, $334,618 total compensation

SVP Corporate Administration and Human Resources, Samantha (Sam) Marnick, $460,465 total compensation

SVP and General Manager Boeing Defense and Regional Jet Programs, Duane F. Hawkins, $497,684 total compensation

SVP and CFO, Sanjay Kapoor, $624,229 total compensation

President and CEO, Thomas C. (Tom) Gentile, $770,773 total compensation

SVP and General Manager Airbus Programs, Michelle J. Lohmeier, $472,125 total compensation

SVP Business Development, Krisstie Kondrotis, $424,840 total compensation

SVP Operations, Ron Rabe

Auditors: Ernst & Young LLP

LOCATIONS

HQ: Spirit AeroSystems Holdings Inc
3801 South Oliver, Wichita, KS 67210
Phone: 316 526-9000
Web: www.spiritaero.com

2016 Sales

	$ mil.	% of total
US	5,650	83
UK	690	10
Other	452	7
Total	**6,792**	**100**

PRODUCTS/OPERATIONS

2016 Sales by Customers

	$ mil.	% of total
Boeing	5,502	81
Airbus	992	15
Other	297	4
Total	**6,792**	**100**

2016 Sales

	$ mil.	% of total
Fuselage Systems	3,498	52
Propulsion Systems	1,777	26
Wing Systems	1,508	22
All Other	8	-
Total	**6,792**	**100**

COMPETITORS

Airbus
Boeing
Bombardier
Dassault Aviation
Embraer
GKN
Gulfstream Aerospace
Kawasaki Heavy Industries
Leonardo
Lockheed Martin
Mitsubishi Heavy Industries
Northrop Grumman

Saab AB
Subaru
Textron
Triumph Aerostructures - Vought Aircraft Division
Triumph Group
United Technologies

HISTORICAL FINANCIALS

Company Type: Public

Income Statement

FYE: December 31

	REVENUE ($ mil.)	NET INCOME ($ mil.)	NET PROFIT MARGIN	EMPLOYEES
12/17	6,983	354	5.1%	15,500
12/16	6,792	469	6.9%	14,400
12/15	6,643	788	11.9%	15,200
12/14	6,799	358	5.3%	15,402
12/13	5,961	(621)	—	14,177
Annual Growth	**4.0%**	**—**		**2.3%**

2017 Year-End Financials

Debt ratio: 21.85%
Return on equity: 19.03%
Cash ($ mil.): 423
Current ratio: 1.64
Long-term debt ($ mil.): 1,119

No. of shares (mil.): 114
Dividends
 Yield: 0.0%
 Payout: 13.2%
Market value ($ mil.): 9,986

	STOCK PRICE ($) FY Close	P/E High/Low	Earnings	PER SHARE ($) Dividends	Book Value
12/17	87.25	29 17	3.01	0.40	15.74
12/16	58.35	16 11	3.70	0.10	15.85
12/15	50.07	10 7	5.66	0.00	15.63
12/14	43.04	18 10	2.53	0.00	11.49
12/13	34.08	— —	(4.40)	0.00	10.22
Annual Growth	**26.5%**	**— —**	**—**	**—**	**11.4%**

SPRINGLEAF FINANCE CORPORATION

EXECUTIVES

Pres-ceo, Jay N Levine
Director of Government Relations, Phil Hitz
Vice President Application Systems, David Smith
Executive Vice President Operations, Brad Borchers
Vice President Software Engineering, Erik Peterson
Senior Vice President Of Operations, George Roach
Vice President Tax, Marianne Ford
Vice President Risk Management, Mathew Roe
Senior Vice President Corporate Strategy Springleaf Financial Services, Joseph Tomei
Secretary, Jack R Erkilla
Auditors: PRICEWATERHOUSECOOPERS LLP CH

LOCATIONS

HQ: SPRINGLEAF FINANCE CORPORATION
601 NW 2ND ST, EVANSVILLE, IN 477081013
Phone: 812 424-8031
Web: WWW.SPRINGLEAF.COM

HISTORICAL FINANCIALS

Company Type: Private

Income Statement

FYE: December 31

	ASSETS ($ mil.)	NET INCOME ($ mil.)	INCOME AS % OF ASSETS	EMPLOYEES
12/16	9,719	233	2.4%	3,239
12/15	12,055	129	1.1%	—
12/14	11,126	492	4.4%	—
12/13	12,732	(82)	—	—
Annual Growth	**(8.6%)**	**—**		**—**

2016 Year-End Financials

Debt ratio: ——
Return on equity: 12.10%
Cash ($ mil.): 240
Current ratio: ——
Long-term debt ($ mil.): —

Dividends
 Yield: —
 Payout: —
Market value ($ mil.): —

Sprint Corp (New)

Auditors: DELOITTE & TOUCHE LLP

LOCATIONS

HQ: Sprint Corp (New)
6200 Sprint Parkway, Overland Park, KS 66251
Phone: 855 848-3280
Web: www.sprint.com

HISTORICAL FINANCIALS

Company Type: Public

Income Statement

FYE: March 31

	REVENUE ($ mil.)	NET INCOME ($ mil.)	NET PROFIT MARGIN	EMPLOYEES
03/17	33,347	(1,206)	—	28,000
03/16	32,180	(1,995)	—	30,000
03/15	34,532	(3,345)	—	31,000
03/14*	8,875	(151)	—	36,000
12/13	16,891	(1,860)	—	38,000
Annual Growth	**25.4%**	**—**		**(9.7%)**

*Fiscal year change

2017 Year-End Financials

Debt ratio: 48.06%——
Return on equity: (-6.25%)
Cash ($ mil.): 2,870
Current ratio: 1.13
Long-term debt ($ mil.): 35,878

Dividends
 Yield: —
 Payout: —
Market value ($ mil.): —

	STOCK PRICE ($) FY Close	P/E High/Low	Earnings	PER SHARE ($) Dividends	Book Value
03/17	8.68	— —	(0.30)	0.00	4.71
03/16	3.48	— —	(0.50)	0.00	4.98
03/15	4.74	— —	(0.85)	0.00	5.47
03/14*	9.19	— —	(0.04)	0.00	6.42
12/13	10.75	— —	(0.54)	0.00	6.50
Annual Growth	**(6.9%)**	**— —**	**—**	**—**	**(10.2%)**

*Fiscal year change

ST. JOSEPH HEALTH SYSTEM

EXECUTIVES

Senior Vice President General Counsel, Shannon Dwyer
President CEO, Joe Mark
Auditors: ERNST & YOUNG LLP IRVINE CA

LOCATIONS

HQ: ST. JOSEPH HEALTH SYSTEM
3345 MICHELSON DR STE 100, IRVINE, CA
926120693
Phone: 949 381-4000
Web: WWW.STJHS.ORG

COMPETITORS

Adventist Health	Loma Linda University
Arrowhead Medical	Medical Center
Center	Los Angeles County
Banner Health	Health Department
Catholic Health	Memorial Health
Initiatives	Services
Cedars-Sinai Medical	Pasadena Hospital
Center	Association
Citrus Valley Health	Prospect Medical
Partners	Scripps health
City of Hope	Sutter Health
Dignity Health	Tenet Healthcare
HCA	Western Medical Center
Kaiser Permanente	- Santa Ana

HISTORICAL FINANCIALS

Company Type: Private

Income Statement

FYE: June 30

	REVENUE ($ mil.)	NET INCOME ($ mil.)	NET PROFIT MARGIN	EMPLOYEES
06/13	4,955	2,082	42.0%	13
06/10	4,268	268	6.3%	—
Annual Growth	5.1%	98.1%	—	—

2013 Year-End Financials

Debt ratio: ——
Return on equity: 42.00%
Cash ($ mil.): 329
Current ratio: 0.80
Long-term debt ($ mil.): —

Dividends
Yield: —
Payout: —
Market value ($ mil.): —

Stanley Black & Decker Inc

Stanley Black & Decker has all the tools of the trade. One of the leading US toolmakers the company markets hand tools mechanics' tools power tools pneumatic tools and hydraulic tools. Besides the Stanley and Black & Decker brands it sells such brands as Bostitch Mac Tools and DEWALT. Stanley Black & Decker peddles its products through home centers and mass-merchant distributors as well as through third-party distributors and a direct sales force. Founded in 1843 Stanley changed its name after merging with Black & Decker in 2010.

Operations

Stanley Black & Decker operates its business through three segments: Tools & Storage (which generated 66% of 2016 sales) Security (18%) and Industrial (16%).

The company combined the Construction & Do-It-Yourself business with certain complementary elements of the Industrial and Automotive Repair and Healthcare businesses (formerly part of the Industrial and Security segments respectively) to form the Tools & Storage business.

The Tools & Storage segment is comprised of the Power Tools and Hand Tools Accessories & Storage ("HTAS") businesses. The Power Tools business includes professional products consumer products and power tool accessories. The HTAS business sells measuring leveling and layout tools planes hammers demolition tools knives saws chisels and industrial and automotive tools. Storage products include tool boxes sawhorses medical cabinets and engineered storage solution products. Power tool accessories include drill bits router bits abrasives and saw blades.

The Security segment houses the Convergent Security Solutions (CSS) and Mechanical Access Solutions (MAS) businesses. The Industrial segment consists of its Engineered Fastening and Infrastructure businesses. The Infrastructure operation consists of the Oil & Gas and the Hydraulics businesses.

Geographic Reach

Stanley Black & Decker boasts operations in the US Canada Europe and Asia. The US accounted for 54% of 2016 revenues followed by Europe (22%) Asia (9%) Other Americas (6%) Canada (4%) and France (5%). The company has major facilities for manufacturing distribution and sales in 19 US states and 17 other countries.

Sales and Marketing

The Tools & Storage segment sells its products to professional end users industrial users distributors and retail consumers. The majority of sales are distributed through retailers including home centers mass merchants hardware stores and retail lumber yards.

In the Security segment the CSS business sells to consumers retailers educational financial and healthcare institutions as well as commercial governmental and industrial customers. Products are sold predominantly on a direct sales basis. The MAS business sells and installs automatic doors commercial hardware locking mechanisms electronic keyless entry systems keying systems tubular and mortise door locksets. MAS sell to commercial customers primarily through direct and independent distribution channels.

In the Industrial segment the Engineered Fastening business primarily sells engineered fasteners designed for specific industrial applications. The Infrastructure businesses sells to the oil and natural gas pipeline industry and other industrial customers. The products and services are primarily distributed through a direct sales force and to a lesser extent third-party distributors.

Advertising cost was $124.1 million in 2016 $101.7 million in 2015 and $121.5 million in 2014. In 2016 sales to US home centers and mass merchants accounted for approximately 28% of revenues.

Financial Performance

Stanley Black & Decker's revenue was $11.407 billion in 2016 up 2% compared to $11.172 billion in 2015. The company's Tools & Storage segment saw its net sales increase 5% compared to 2015 due to strong organic growth of 7% driven by solid growth across all regions. Net sales in the Security segment were relatively flat compared to 2015. Industrial net sales declined 5% relative to 2015 primarily due to a 4% decrease in organic sales volume. The company's Industrial segment's organic growth was relatively flat in 2016.

Stanley Black & Decker's net income increased to $965 million in fiscal 2016 up from $883 million in fiscal 2015.

Cash flows from operations were $1.4 billion in 2016 compared to $1.1 billion in 2015 representing a $303 million increase. The year-over-year increase was primarily the result of higher earnings and cash flows from working capital (accounts receivable inventory accounts payable and deferred revenue).

Strategy

Beyond tools Stanley Black & Decker has been diversifying into higher growth and higher profit businesses such as security and health care to lessen its reliance on big-box retailers.

The company believes revenue growth can be achieved through a combination of: fostering growth in its newer engineered fastening infrastructure and security businesses; strengthening its presence in emerging markets; selectively choosing markets were its brand and value proposition is valuable and have room for growth; strategically acquiring companies that bolster or complement its services (mostly in the tool industry).

To cut costs and drive efficiency throughout its supply chain Stanley Black & Decker has continued to employ its Stanley Fulfillment System (SFS). The SFS uses continuous improvement strategies that work in unison and include: sales and operations planning (S&OP) operational lean complexity reduction global supply management and order-to-cash excellence techniques.

The company is continuing to pursue a growth and acquisition strategy that involves industry geographic and customer diversification to foster sustainable revenues earnings and cash flow growth.

It is also focused on growing organically including increasing its presence in emerging markets with a goal of generating greater than 20% of annual revenues from those markets.

Mergers and Acquisitions

In 2017 Stanley Black & Decker acquired Sears Holdings Corp.'s iconic Craftsman tool brand for $900 million. The acquisition will expand Black & Decker's product line up and allow the company to increase sales by expanding distribution of Craftsman tools into more international markets. Also in 2017 Stanley Black & Decker acquired the tools business from consumer products company Newell Brands for $1.95 billion.

Company Background

In 2013 the company expanded its Engineered Fastening business and extended its reach into emerging markets with its $826-million acquisition of Hong Kong's Infastech a leading global manufacturer and distributor of specialty engineered fastening technologies. Stanley Black & Decker funded the acquisition by selling off its home and hardware improvement group to Spectrum Brands Holdings for $1.4 billion in cash.

To grow its international CDIY business in 2013 Stanley Black & Decker acquired a 60% controlling share in Jiangsu Guoqiang Tools Co. Ltd. (GQ) for a total purchase price of $49 million. GQ is a manufacturer and seller of power tools armatures and stators.

In 2012 the company expanded its business segments by purchasing Tong Lung Metal Industry for nearly $103 million. The company makes and sells commercial and residential locksets. Stanley Black & Decker also acquired AeroScout for $238.8 million (to integrate into the Security and Industrial segments) Powers Fasteners for $220.5 million and Lista North America for $89.7 million.

Stanley Black & Decker is the result of a $4.5 billion merger between Stanley Works and rival Black & Decker in 2010.

The company traces its roots back to 1843 when Frederick Stanley opened a bolt shop in a converted early-19th-century armory in New Britain Connecticut. In 1852 he teamed with his brother and five friends to form The Stanley Works to cast form and manufacture various types of metal.

EXECUTIVES

President and CEO, James M. (Jim) Loree, age 58, $992,500 total compensation

VP and CIO, Rhonda O. Gass, age 53

SVP and Group Executive Global Tools and Storage, Jeffery D. (Jeff) Ansell, age 50, $660,833 total compensation

SVP and CFO, Donald (Don) Allan, age 52, $671,667 total compensation

SVP and President Global Emerging Markets, Jaime A. Ramirez, age 49, $425,000 total compensation

President Sales and Marketing Global Tools and Storage, John H. A. Wyatt, age 58, $541,667 total compensation

President Hand Tools Accessories and Storage, Lee B. McChesney, age 45

CTO, Mark T Maybury

President Stanley Security Europe, Aru Bala

President Stanley Oil and Gas, Pete Morris

President Asia, Yingli (Christine) Yan

President Power Tools and Equipment Global Tools and Storage, Frank A. Mannarino

President Emerging Markets Group, Bart Muller

President Sales and Marketing Global Tools and Storage, James P. OÂ'Sullivan

President Hydraulics, J. Douglas Redpath

Vice President industrial Design, Bob Welsh

National Account Manager, Allison Lawrence

Vice President, Debi Geyer

Vice President Comp and Benefits, Michele Webster

Regional Vice President of Sales Northeast, Brad McMullen

Vice President Global Engineering, William Harman

National Sales Manager, Maria Ford

Vice President Corporate Business Development, Tamara Bross

Vice President Sales, Bill Conn

Vice President Treasurer, Craig Douglas

VICE PRESIDENT MARKETING, Tony Nicolaidis

Vice President of National Accounts, Tom Burnside

National Account Manager, Joe Schuyler

National Account Manager, Clark Bell

Senior Vice President, Don Allan

Vice President Of Commercialization, Kevin Flatt

National Account Manager, Darren Furtney

Vice President of North American Sales, Martin Guay

VICE PRESIDENT OF FINANCE, Matthew Sibole

Vice President of Corporate Taxes, Michael Bartone

National Account Manager, Daniel Wegrzyn

National Account Manager, David Kay

National Account Manager, Dan Costanzo

Vice President and General Manager, Jim Gillis

National Sales Manager, Dan Miller

National Account Manager, Kelly Bhavsar

National Account Manager, Nikita Gordon

Vice President Field Operations, Derrick Hamilton

National Account Manager, Brian Rooke

National Account Manager, Joshua Herting

National Account Manager, Brad Anderson

Regional Vice President, Benjamin Creery

Vice President of Innovation, Zhian Hedayati

National Account Manager, Joe Durante

National Account Manager, Dean Wickwar

Regional Vice President National Accounts, Sam Fedewa

Vice President of Sales and Operations Southeast Region, Mark Hart

VP Human Resources, Maureen Carter

VICE PRESIDENT OF HUMAN RESOURCES, Rodney Hobbs

VICE PRESIDENT PRODUCTIVITY, Stan St John

VICE PRESIDENT, Paul White

NATIONAL ACCOUNT MANAGER, Brenda Holland

National Account Manager, Phil Harman

National Account Manager, Jason Viergutz

Chairman, George W. Buckley, age 70

Auditors: Ernst & Young LLP

LOCATIONS

HQ: Stanley Black & Decker Inc
1000 Stanley Drive, New Britain, CT 06053
Phone: 860 225-5111   **Fax:** 860 827-3895
Web: www.stanleyblackanddecker.com

2016 Sales

	$ mil.	% of total
North America		
US	6,135	54
Canada	515	4
Other Americas	635	6
Europe		
France	582	5
Other Europe	2,468	22
Asia	1,069	9
Total	**11,406**	**100**

PRODUCTS/OPERATIONS

2016 Sales

	$ mil.	% of total
Tools & Storage	7,469	66
Security	2,097	18
Industrial	1,840	16
Total	**11,406**	**100**

Product and Services
Commercial Security
Fastening Solutions
Hospital & Healthcare Services
Infrastructure Products
Pipeline Services
Tools & Storage

Selected Brand Names
Black & Decker
Blackhawk
Bostitch
DEWALT
Facom
FatMax
LaBounty
Mac Tools
Powerlock
Pfister
Proto
Stanley
Vidmar

COMPETITORS

ASSA ABLOY	Klein Tools
Atlas Copco	Kohler
Beam Suntory	Makita
Bosch	Masco
Danaher	Panasonic Corp
Eastern Company	Robert Bosch
Edgewell Personal Care	Robert Bosch LLC
Electrolux	Royal Appliance
Emerson Electric	Sandvik
Hitachi	Snap-on
Illinois Tool Works	Textron
Ingersoll-Rand	Toro Company
Jacuzzi Brands	Trane Inc.

HISTORICAL FINANCIALS
Company Type: Public

Income Statement
FYE: December 31

	REVENUE ($ mil.)	NET INCOME ($ mil.)	NET PROFIT MARGIN	EMPLOYEES
12/16*	11,406	965	8.5%	54,023
01/16	11,171	883	7.9%	51,250
01/15	11,338	760	6.7%	50,400
12/13	11,001	490	4.5%	50,700
12/12	10,190	883	8.7%	45,327
Annual Growth	**2.9%**	**2.2%**	**—**	**4.5%**

*Fiscal year change

2016 Year-End Financials

Debt ratio: 24.48%
Return on equity: 15.90%
Cash ($ mil.): 1,131
Current ratio: 1.71
Long-term debt ($ mil.): 3,815

No. of shares (mil.): 152
Dividends
Yield: 0.0%
Payout: 34.7%
Market value ($ mil.): 17,497

	STOCK PRICE ($) FY Close	P/E High/Low		PER SHARE ($) Earnings	Dividends	Book Value
12/16*	114.69	19	14	6.51	2.26	41.73
01/16	106.73	18	15	5.79	2.14	37.75
01/15	96.02	20	16	4.76	2.04	40.92
12/13	81.01	29	23	3.09	1.98	43.73
12/12	72.06	15	11	5.30	1.80	41.68
Annual Growth	**12.3%**	**—**	**—**	**5.3%**	**5.9%**	**0.0%**

*Fiscal year change

Starbucks Corp.

Wake up and smell the coffee — Starbucks is everywhere. The world's #1 specialty coffee retailer Starbucks has more than 25000 coffee shops in 75 countries. The outlets offer coffee drinks and food items as well as roasted beans coffee accessories and teas. Starbucks operates more than 12700 of its own shops which are located mostly in the US while licensees and franchisees operate roughly 12375 units worldwide (including many locations in shopping centers and airports). In addition Starbucks markets its coffee through grocery stores food service customers and licenses its brand for other food and beverage products.

HISTORY

Starbucks was founded in 1971 in Seattle by coffee aficionados Gordon Bowker Jerry Baldwin and Ziv Siegl who named the company for the coffee-loving first mate in Moby Dick and created its famous two-tailed siren logo. They aimed to sell the finest-quality whole bean and ground coffees. By 1982 Starbucks had five retail stores and was selling coffee to restaurants and espresso stands in Seattle. That year Howard Schultz joined Starbucks to manage retail sales and marketing. In 1983 Schultz traveled to Italy and was struck by the popularity of coffee bars. He convinced Starbucks' owners to open a downtown Seattle coffee bar in 1984. It was a success; Schultz left the company the following year to open his own coffee bar Il Giornale which served Starbucks coffee.

Frustrated by its inability to control quality Starbucks sold off its wholesale business in 1987. Later that year Il Giornale acquired Starbucks' retail operations for $4 million. (Starbucks' founders held on to their other coffee business Peet's Coffee & Tea.) Il Giornale changed its name to Starbucks

Corporation prepared to expand nationally and opened locations in Chicago and Vancouver. In 1988 the company published its first mail-order catalog.

Starbucks lost money in the late 1980s as it focused on expansion (it tripled its number of stores to 55 between 1987 and 1989). Schultz brought in experienced managers to run Starbucks' stores. In 1991 it became the nation's first privately owned company to offer stock options to all employees.

In 1992 Starbucks went public and set up shops in Nordstrom's department stores. The following year it began operating cafes in Barnes & Noble bookstores. The company had nearly 275 locations by the end of 1993. Starbucks inked a deal in 1994 to provide coffee to ITT/Sheraton hotels (later acquired by Starwood Hotels & Resorts). The next year it capitalized on its popular in-house music selections by selling compact discs. Also in 1995 Starbucks joined with PepsiCo to develop a bottled coffee drink and agreed to produce a line of premium coffee ice cream with Dreyer's.

Starbucks expanded into Japan and Singapore in 1996. Also that year the company created Caffe Starbucks an online store located on AOL's marketplace. In 1997 Starbucks began testing sales of whole-bean and ground coffees in Chicago supermarkets.

In 1998 Starbucks expanded into the UK when it acquired that country's Seattle Coffee Company chain (founded in 1995) for about $86 million and converted its stores into Starbucks locations. It also announced plans to sell coffee in supermarkets nationwide through an agreement with Kraft Foods. In 1999 Starbucks bought Tazo an Oregon-based tea company as well as music retailer Hear Music and opened its first store in China. Schultz toned down his Internet plans in late 1999 after investors and analysts voiced skepticism.

In 2000 Schultz ceded the CEO post to president Orin Smith remaining chairman but focusing primarily on the company's global strategy. Starbucks jumpstarted its worldwide expansion the next year opening about 1100 stores worldwide including locations in a handful of new European countries such as Austria and Switzerland. It also spun off its Japanese operations as a public company. The following year the company opened its first shop in Spain and went on to open Starbucks locations in Greece and Germany. Later in 2002 it announced large-scale expansion plans in Mexico and Latin America.

The next year Starbucks acquired Seattle Coffee Company (and its Seattle's Best Coffee brand) from Popeyes for $72 million. The deal gave Starbucks an additional 150 coffee shops (as if it needed them) but more importantly it gave the coffee giant the Seattle's Best Coffee brand and wholesale coffee business. It also got something new out of the deal: franchised locations.

Starbucks was one of the first national retailers to jump on the Wi-Fi bandwagon teaming with Hewlett-Packard and Deutsche Telekom's T-Mobile unit to offer high-speed wireless Internet access at 1200 of its locations in the US London and Berlin. In 2004 Starbucks and Hewlett-Packard unveiled their Hear Music service which allows Starbucks customers to create custom music CDs in some locations. It later premiered the Hear Music channel on XM Satellite Radio (later SIRIUS XM Radio) and launched a new Hear Music CD-burning media bar (co-developed with HP) in selected stores.

In 2005 the company began offering a hot chocolate in its US and Canada markets and in conjunction with Jim Beam Brands (now Beam) it introduced Starbucks Coffee Liqueur and Starbucks Cream Liqueur. That year Starbucks signed agreements with Suntory in Japan and Uni-President in Taiwan to sell its ready-to-drink coffees in those countries. Additionally Smith retired as president and CEO in 2005; he was replaced by Starbucks' North American president Jim Donald.

The company acquired full ownership of joint ventures Coffee Partners Hawaii and Cafe del Caribe (Puerto Rican outlets) in 2006. While Starbucks continued to dominate the coffee business traffic at its stores began to decline in 2007. The company brought Schultz back as CEO in 2008 replacing Donald.

Starbucks acquired fruit and vegetable juice maker Evolution Fresh in 2011 for $30 million in cash. In December 2012 the company purchased Teavana Holdings Inc. for $620 million in cash. Teavana operates some 300 Heaven of Tea retail stores.

In 2012 Starbucks agreed to acquire San Francisco-based Bay Bread LLC and its La Boulange bakery brand. It made the purchase to try its hand in the French bakery market. The previous year Starbucks acquired fruit and vegetable juice maker Evolution Fresh for $30 million as part of an effort to push itself as a healthy lifestyle brand.

EXECUTIVES

Senior Vice President Finance Global Business Operations, Troy Alstead
EVP and CTO, Gerri Martin-Flickinger
President and COO, Kevin R. Johnson, age 56, $576,923 total compensation
Group President US and Americas, Clifford (Cliff) Burrows, age 58, $796,300 total compensation
Group President China and Asia/Pacific Channel Development and Emerging Brands, John Culver, age 56, $633,300 total compensation
SVP and President Europe Middle East and Africa (EMEA), Martin Brok
EVP US Retail Store Operations, Cosimo LaPorta
EVP and Global Chief Marketing Officer, Sharon Rothstein
SVP; President Teavana, Bernard Acoca
Chief Creative Officer; President Global Innovation, Arthur Rubinfeld, age 63, $484,058 total compensation
EVP Licensed Stores US and Americas, Chris Carr
EVP Law and Corporate Affairs General Counsel and Secretary, Lucy Lee Helm, $493,172 total compensation
EVP Public Affairs, Vivek Varma
EVP and Chief Partner Resources Officer, Scott Pitasky
EVP and CFO, Scott H. Maw, $632,500 total compensation
SVP Store Services, Craig Russell
SVP; President Starbucks Canada, Rossann Williams
President Starbucks Global Channel Development, Michael Conway
EVP and Chief Digital Officer, Adam Brotman
EVP and Global Chief Strategy Officer, Matthew Ryan
Global EVP, Kris Engskov
President Starbucks China, Belinda Wong
Executive Vice President, Eduardo Garcia
Vice President Assistant General Counsel, Mark Fordham
Vice President Of Engineering And Technology, Fred Sadeghi
Vice President Partner Resources N Division US Retail, Adrienne Gemperle
Regional Vice President Of Operations, Tom Ferguson
Vice President Human Resources, Angel Yu
Vice President Technology Services, Magali Muratore
Regional Vice President, Denise Nelsen
Vice President Information Management Services, Elizabeth King
regional vice president, Anthony Pisa
Vice President Sales, Kristi Brooks
Vice President Information Technology, Kristy Cameron
Vice President Web And Mobile Engineering, Matt Fitch
VICE PRESIDENT REGIONAL OPERATIONS, Jon Liechty
Vice President Manager Director, Lesley Blyth
REGIONAL VICE PRESIDENT, Frances Ericson
National Sales Manager, Sharon Meehan
Vice President Labor and Deployment, Stephanie Traut
Vice President Global Technology Business Systems Development, Raman Bukkapatnam
Vice President Coffee Quality and Engagement, Andrew Linnemann
VICE PRESIDENT, Sandra Stark
Vice President, Jeff Ryu
Senior Vice President Gbl Design And Construction Execution, Bill Transue
Vice President Corporate Facilities, Eric Jensen
Vice President of Information Technology Supply Chain and Finance Technology, Chris Fallon
Regional Vice President, Nancy Bennett
Vice President Zone Licensed Stores East, Lisa Compton
Senior Vice President Finance, David Chichester
Regional Vice President Operations, Traci York
Regional Vice President, Suzanne Dechant
Vice President Supply Chain Operations, Nishad Alani
Vice President Field Information Technology, Lisa Orchard
Vice President of Information Systems, John Shepard
Vice President US Business, Mark Cromett
Vice President Marketing and Category, Ian Cranna
Senior Vice President Partner Resources Us Retail, James Koster
Vice President Global Learning, Stephen Krempl
National Sales Manager Foodservice, Jason Carter
Vice President of IT Support, Doug Wayles
Regional Vice President, Ross Shadix
Senior Vice President Southeast Plains, Paul Twohig
Vice President, Sophie Hume
Vice President Information Technology, Nicole Carr
Vice President design americas Global Development, Bill Smith
Vice President of Information Technology, Lori Kittle
NATIONAL ACCOUNT MANAGER, Todd Faubus
Vice President North America Talent Acquisition, Dija Fraser
Executive Vice President US Retail Store Operations, Cos LaPorta
Vice President of Operations, Jeffrey Fields
Vice President eCommerce, Marc Farrell
Vice President Compensation, Julie Ann Overcash
Senior Vice President Starbucks China, Shelli Taylor
SENIOR VICE PRESIDENT PRO AMERICAS, Valerie Danna
Vice President Distribution, Jim Wells
Vp Global Engineering, Jeff Juneau
Vice President Global Secunty, Garrett Petraia
Vice President Global Strategy, Leslie Hampel
VP Operations, Marie Fennel
VICE PRESIDENT REGIONAL OPERATIONS, Frank Sica
Vice President Information Technology, George Ballis
SENIOR VICE PRESIDENT GLOBAL COMMUNICATIONS, Maurice Van Dam
VICE PRESIDENT INTERNAL AUDIT, Randa Saleh
VICE PRESIDENT STORE DEVELOPMENT SUPPORT SERVICES, Ray Silverstein

VICE PRESIDENT FOOD SAFETY AND QUALITY, Stephen P Graham
Vice President, Chuck Little
Vice President Global Digital Commerce, Karl Hebert
Vice President Planning and Commercialization, Michael O'Brien
Vice President Concepts Studio Global Store Development, Jonas Damon
Chairman and CEO, Howard D. Schultz, age 64
Board Member, Patrick K Coe
Vice President Treasurer, Drew Wolff
Auditors: Deloitte & Touche LLP

LOCATIONS

HQ: Starbucks Corp.
2401 Utah Avenue South, Seattle, WA 98134
Phone: 206 447-1575
Web: www.starbucks.com

2016 Sales

	$ mil.	% of total
United States	15,774	74
Other Countries	5,541	26
Total	**21,315**	**100**

2016 Sales

	$ mil.	% of total
Americas	14,795	69
China /Asia Pacific	2,938	14
EMEA (Europe Middle East and Africa)	1,124	5
Channel Development	1,932	9
All Other Segments	524	3
Total	**21,315**	**100**

PRODUCTS/OPERATIONS

2016 Sales

	$ mil.	% of total
Company-operated stores	16,844	79
Licensed Stores	2,154	10
CPGfood-service & other	2,317	11
Total	**21,315**	**100**

2016 Sales

	$ mil.	% of total
Beverages	12,383	58
Food	3,495	16
Packaged and single serve coffees and teas	2,866	14
Other	2,571	12
Total	**21,315**	**100**

2016 Locations

	No.
Company-owned	12,711
Licensed	12,374
Total	**25,085**

Brand Portfolio

Brand Portfolio
Starbucks Coffee
Seattle's Best Coffee
Teavana
Tazo
Evolution Fresh
La Boulange
Ethos Water
Torrefazione Italia Coffee.

Selected Products

Coffee
Handcrafted Beverages
Merchandise
Fresh Food

COMPETITORS

Caffè Nero	Keurig Green Mountain
Caribou Coffee	Lavazza
Celestial Seasonings	McDonald's
Cinnabon	Nestlé ©
Community Coffee	Panera Bread
Dunkin	Republic of Tea
Einstein Noah	The Coffee Bean

Restaurant Group	Tim Hortons
Farmer Bros.	Whitbread
Greggs	Whole Foods
Jamba	illy

HISTORICAL FINANCIALS

Company Type: Public

Income Statement

FYE: October 1

	REVENUE ($ mil.)	NET INCOME ($ mil.)	NET PROFIT MARGIN	EMPLOYEES
10/17	22,386	2,884	12.9%	277,000
10/16*	21,315	2,817	13.2%	254,000
09/15	19,162	2,757	14.4%	238,000
09/14	16,447	2,068	12.6%	191,000
09/13	14,892	8	0.1%	182,000
Annual Growth	**10.7%**	**331.8%**	**—**	**11.1%**

*Fiscal year change

2017 Year-End Financials

Debt ratio: 27.38%
Return on equity: 51.04%
Cash ($ mil.): 2,462
Current ratio: 1.25
Long-term debt ($ mil.): 3,932
No. of shares (mil.): 1,431
Dividends
Yield: 0.0%
Payout: 50.7%
Market value ($ mil.): 76,891

	STOCK PRICE ($) FY Close	P/E High/Low	PER SHARE ($) Earnings	Dividends	Book Value
10/17	53.71	32 26	1.97	1.00	3.81
10/16*	54.14	33 28	1.90	0.80	4.03
09/15	57.99	53 26	1.82	0.64	3.92
09/14	75.17	60 50	1.36	0.52	3.52
09/13	77.33	154668994	0.01	0.42	2.97
Annual Growth	**(8.7%)**	**—**	**—345.5%**	**24.2%**	**6.4%**

*Fiscal year change

State Auto Financial Corp.

Thanks to State Auto Financial the state of auto insurance is healthy in the Midwest. The company sells property/casualty policies through several subsidiaries writing personal commercial and specialty coverage including automobile homeowners multi-peril and workers' compensation insurance. It also participates in an insurance pool through its parent company State Auto Mutual Insurance which owns more than 60% of State Auto Financial and provides the offices for its headquarters. Subsidiary Stateco Financial Services manages the company's invested assets. State Auto Financial is the only part of State Auto Mutual that is publicly traded.

Operations

The company has four reportable segments: personal insurance business insurance specialty insurance and investment operations. The personal insurance segment provides primarily personal automobile and homeowners to the personal insurance market. The business insurance segment provides commercial automobile commercial multi-peril property data compromise and risk control insurance covering small-to-medium sized commercial exposures in the business insurance market. The specialty insurance segment provides commercial coverages including workers' compensation that require specialized product underwriting claims handling or risk management services

through a distribution channel of retail agents and wholesale brokers which may include program administrators and other specialty sources. The investment operations segment managed by subsidiary Stateco provides investment services.

Geographic Reach

Through the mutual pool State Auto Financial and its sister companies known collectively as State Auto Group market products through independent insurance agencies in about 35 states. Ohio Kentucky and Texas are State Auto Financial's biggest markets accounting for almost 30% of its annual premiums. The company focuses its business insurance sales on small-to-medium-sized companies.

Financial Performance

State Auto Financial's personal insurance products account for more than half of the company's revenues.

The company saw its revenues drop by 26% in 2012 thanks to an decrease in premiums earned driven changes to the way the company accounts for personal auto and homeowner lines of business. The changes were partially based on State Auto Financial's plan to focus less on the wind-damage prone Midwest and Southeast while expanding in other geographic regions. On the plus side net income rose to $10.7 million due to fewer catastrophic losses. Cash flow took a hit as the company used more funds for operating expenses.

Strategy

While its revenues have grown steadily with just personal and standard commercial products State Auto Financial has made moves to diversify its products. The company has begun offering data protection and other more modern coverage. It has also decided to move its geographic focus away from the tornado-prone Midwest and Southeast.

EXECUTIVES

VP and Comptroller, Cynthia A. Powell, age 56
President and CEO, Michael E. (Mike) LaRocco, age 60
SVP and CFO, Steven E. English, age 56, $447,231 total compensation
SVP and Director Operations, Lyle D. Rhodebeck, age 59
SVP Secretary and General Counsel, James A. (Jay) Yano, age 66, $357,692 total compensation
SVP Standard Lines, Joel E. Brown, age 59
SVP and Director Specialty Lines, Jessica E. Buss, age 45, $372,692 total compensation
SVP and Chief Claims Officer, Stephen P. Hunckler, age 58
Vice President Public Relations, Terrence Bowshier
Senior Vice President Sec General Counsel, Melissa Centers
Assistant Vice President Marketing Shared Services, John Heffernan
Senior Vice President Standard Lines and Director of Senior Associate Labs, Kim Garland
Vice President Specialty Claims, Jay Carleton
Assistant Vice President Product Mangement, Rudy Palenik
Assistant Vice President Actuarial Department, Alp Can
Vice President and Director Sales, John M Petrucci
Vice President Sales And Business Development, Jack Abney
Vice President Specialty Programs, Greg Scullans
Assistant Vice President Reinsurance, Cpcu Olmstead
Chairman, Robert P. (Bob) Restrepo, age 66
Auditors: Ernst & Young LLP

LOCATIONS

HQ: State Auto Financial Corp.
518 East Broad Street, Columbus, OH 43215-3976
Phone: 614 464-5000

2016 Direct Written Premiums

	% of total
Ohio	9
Texas	8
Kentucky	6
California	5
Florida	5
Minnesota	4
Tennessee	4
Georgia	4
Indiana	4
Connecticut	4
Illinois	3
Maryland	3
Pennsylvania	3
North Carolina	3
South Carolina	3
All others (1)	32
Total	**100**

PRODUCTS/OPERATIONS

2016 Sales

	$ mil.	% of total
Insurance premiums		
Personal insurance	582	42
Business insurance	468	33
Specialty insurance	240	17
Investment income & other	113	8
Total	**1,405**	**100**

COMPETITORS

AIG	National General
Allstate	Holdings
American Family	Nationwide
Insurance	Progressive
American Southern	Corporation
COUNTRY Financial	State Farm
GEICO	The Hartford
Kentucky Employers'	Travelers Companies
Mutual	

HISTORICAL FINANCIALS

Company Type: Public

Income Statement

FYE: December 31

	ASSETS ($ mil.)	NET INCOME ($ mil.)	INCOME AS % OF ASSETS	EMPLOYEES
12/16	2,959	21	0.7%	2,020
12/15	2,828	51	1.8%	2,065
12/14	2,766	107	3.9%	2,274
12/13	2,496	60	2.4%	2,384
12/12	2,477	10	0.4%	2,423
Annual Growth	**4.5%**	**18.4%**	**—**	**(4.4%)**

2016 Year-End Financials

Debt ratio: 4.13%	No. of shares (mil.): 41
Return on equity: 2.36%	Dividends
Cash ($ mil.): 51	Yield: 0.0%
Current ratio: —	Payout: 80.0%
Long-term debt ($ mil.): —	Market value ($ mil.): 1,121

	STOCK PRICE ($) FY Close	P/E High/Low	PER SHARE ($) Earnings	Dividends	Book Value
12/16	26.81	54 37	0.50	0.40	21.32
12/15	20.59	22 16	1.23	0.40	21.42
12/14	22.22	9 7	2.60	0.40	21.34
12/13	21.24	15 9	1.49	0.40	19.29
12/12	14.94	64 48	0.27	0.55	18.20
Annual Growth	**15.7%**	**—**	**16.7%**	**(7.7%)**	**4.0%**

State Bank Financial Corp

State Bank Financial Corp. aspires to one day live in the center of central Georgia's banking world. The $3.5 billion-asset holding company operates through subsidiary State Bank and Trust Company a state-chartered commercial bank that serves individuals and businesses through more than 25 branches and more than half a dozen mortgage origination offices in central Georgia and in the Atlanta metropolitan area. The bank offers traditional checking and savings accounts as well as commercial and residential real estate mortgages construction and commercial loans and consumer loans.

Operations

Like other retail banks State Bank Financial makes the bulk of its money from interest income. About 47% of its total revenue came from loan interest in 2015 while another 26% came from interest on loan accretion and 8% came from interest on securities. The rest of its revenue was made up of mortgage banking income (5% of revenue) service charges on deposits (3%) SBA income (3%) payroll fee income (2%) ATM income (2%) prepayment fees (2%) and other non-interest income sources.

Geographic Reach

The Atlanta-based bank operates 26 branches and seven mortgage origination offices in Metro Atlanta Middle Georgia and Augusta Georgia.

Sales and Marketing

State Bank targets individuals small and medium-sized businesses and agribusinesses. It's been ramping up its marketing spend in recent years spending $2.3 million in 2015 up from $1.8 million and $1.5 million in 2014 and 2013 respectively.

Financial Performance

The bank's annual revenues and profits have rebounded since recent lows in 2013 as it's made healthier loans while shedding non-performing loan assets.

State Bank's revenue jumped 17% to $178.7 million during 2015 mostly as its First Bank acquisition led to a 50% jump in interest-earning loan assets and a 10-fold increase in mortgage banking originations and sales.

Despite strong revenue growth in 2015 the bank's net income fell 8% to $28.42 million as it incurred higher salary and employee benefits stemming from integration costs from the First Bank acquisition. State Bank used $45.6 million in cash or significantly more than in 2014 mostly after adjusting its earnings for non-cash proceeds for mortgage loan sales.

Strategy

State Bank Financial Corporation likes to acquire specialty financial firms to expand its non-banking service lines as was the case with its early 2015 acquisition of insurance business Boyett Agency LLC. The company also buys smaller community banks to bolster its loan and deposit business while expanding into new markets mostly in Georgia.

Aside from acquisitions State Bank Financial also looks to organically grow its loan business and add additional clients to its cash management and payments business (which include its payroll processing services). To streamline its operations and boost efficiency and profits the bank started implementing its efficiency initiatives in the second quarter of 2015 with the consolidation of its First Bank of Georgia into State Bank in July.

Mergers and Acquisitions

In April 2016 State Bank Financial Corporation entered the Athens and Gainesville markets after agreeing to buy $375 million-asset NBG Bancorp — along with its two National Bank of Georgia branches $331 million in loan assets and $304 million in deposits — for $68 million.

In October 2015 the bank bought Patriot Capital Corporation's equipment financing origination platform. Patriot Capital mostly served the retail petroleum industry.

In February 2015 State Bank began offering insurance products and services after buying Dalton Georgia-based insurance agency Boyett Agency LLC.

In January 2015 the company acquired $525 million-asset Georgia-Carolina Bancshares and its Georgia-state-chartered First Bank subsidiary for $88.9 million.

Company Background

The holding company was formed in 2010 to acquire the assets of distressed banks many of which fell victim to the 2008 credit crisis and ensuing recession. With the assistance of the FDIC and proceeds raised in a private offering of common stock State Bank Financial acquired seven community banks between 2009 and 2011 and re-branded them as State Bank and Trust Co. The acquisitions expanded the bank's presence in its core central Georgia and metro Atlanta markets. State Bank Financial intends to continue leveraging such acquisitions to strengthen its presence in these markets.

EXECUTIVES

Chairman CEO State Bank Financial Corporation and Chairman State Bank, Joseph W. (Joe) Evans, age 67, $415,000 total compensation

General Counsel Secretary SBFC and Vice Chairman and Secretary State Bank, J. Daniel (Dan) Speight, age 60, $365,000 total compensation

Vice Chairman COO SBFC and CEO State Bank, J. Thomas Wiley, age 63, $365,000 total compensation

EVP SBFC and State Bank and Chief Credit Officer State Bank, David F. Black, age 41

EVP and CIO SBFC and State Bank, David W. Cline, age 56

EVP and Enterprise Risk Officer SBFC abd State Bank, Steven G. Deaton, age 54

EVP Chief Revenue and Chief Deposit Officer State Bank, Michael R. Fitzgerald, age 58

EVP and Senior Banking Officer State Bank, Michael S. Sims, age 53

EVP and Director Real Estate Banking State Bank, Bradford L. Watkins, age 50

EVP Corporate Development, David Brown

EVP and CFO, Sheila E. Ray, age 58

Vice Chairman and Executive Risk Officer SBFC and Chief Risk Officer State Bank, Kim M. Childers, age 57

Auditors: Dixon Hughes Goodman LLP

LOCATIONS

HQ: State Bank Financial Corp
3399 Peachtree Road N.E., Suite 1900, Atlanta, GA 30326
Phone: 404 475-6599

PRODUCTS/OPERATIONS

2015 Sales

	% of total
Interest income	
Loans	47
Loan accretion	26
Investment securities	8
Deposits with other financial institutions	0

Non-interest income

Amortization of FDIC receivable for loss share agreements	
Service charges on deposits	3
Mortgage banking income	5
SBA income	3
Payroll fee income	2
ATM income	2
Bank-owned life insurance income	1
Prepayment fees	2
Gain on sale of investment securities	0
Other	1
Total	**100**

COMPETITORS

BB&T	SunTrust
Bank of America	Synovus
Citizens Bancshares	Wells Fargo
Regions Financial	

HISTORICAL FINANCIALS

Company Type: Public

Income Statement

FYE: December 31

	ASSETS ($ mil.)	NET INCOME ($ mil.)	INCOME AS % OF ASSETS	EMPLOYEES
12/16	4,224	47	1.1%	731
12/15	3,470	28	0.8%	664
12/14	2,882	30	1.1%	566
12/13	2,600	12	0.5%	577
12/12	2,662	22	0.9%	605
Annual Growth	**12.2%**	**20.3%**	**—**	**4.8%**

2016 Year-End Financials

Debt ratio: 0.01%	No. of shares (mil.): 38
Return on equity: 8.25%	Dividends
Cash ($ mil.): 146	Yield: 0.0%
Current ratio: —	Payout: 43.7%
Long-term debt ($ mil.): —	Market value ($ mil.): 1,043

	STOCK PRICE ($) FY Close	P/E High/Low		PER SHARE ($) Earnings	Dividends	Book Value
12/16	26.86	21	14	1.28	0.56	15.80
12/15	21.03	30	23	0.77	0.32	14.47
12/14	19.98	21	16	0.92	0.15	14.38
12/13	18.19	46	36	0.38	0.12	13.62
12/12	15.88	25	20	0.69	0.06	13.48
Annual Growth	**14.0%**	**—**	**—**	**16.7%**	**74.8%**	**4.0%**

STATE OF CALIFORNIA

Auditors: JOHN F COLLINS II CPA DEPUTY

LOCATIONS

HQ: STATE OF CALIFORNIA
STATE CAPITAL, SACRAMENTO, CA 95814
Phone: 916 445-2864
Web: WWW.CA.GOV

HISTORICAL FINANCIALS

Company Type: Private

Income Statement

FYE: June 30

	REVENUE ($ mil.)	NET INCOME ($ mil.)	NET PROFIT MARGIN	EMPLOYEES
06/15	249,923	6,252	2.5%	208,580
06/14	219,871	8,082	3.7%	—
06/13	204	8	3.9%	—
Annual Growth	**3392.4%**	**2690.3%**	**—**	**—**

STATE OF NEW YORK MORTGAGE AGENCY

EXECUTIVES

Assistant Vice President, Robert Rosado
Vice President Special Projects, Mark Flescher
Assistant Vice President Senior Underwriter, Maria Lasorsa
Vice President Internal Audit, Stephen Chopey
Senior Vice President, Michael Friedman
Auditors: DELOITTE & TOUCHE LLP NEW YOR

LOCATIONS

HQ: STATE OF NEW YORK MORTGAGE AGENCY
641 LEXINGTON AVE FL 4, NEW YORK, NY
100224503
Phone: 212 688-4000
Web: WWW.NYHOMES.ORG

HISTORICAL FINANCIALS

Company Type: Private

Income Statement

FYE: October 31

	ASSETS ($ mil.)	NET INCOME ($ mil.)	INCOME AS % OF ASSETS	EMPLOYEES
10/09	5,225	162	3.1%	221
10/08	5,224	30	0.6%	—
10/07	4,875	224	4.6%	—
10/04	4,212	(112)	—	—
Annual Growth	**4.4%**	**—**	**—**	**—**

STATE OF OKLAHOMA

Auditors: GARY A JONES CPA CFE OKLAH

LOCATIONS

HQ: STATE OF OKLAHOMA
421 NW 13TH ST STE 220, OKLAHOMA CITY, OK
731033784
Phone: 405 521-2342
Web: WWW.OK.GOV

HISTORICAL FINANCIALS

Company Type: Private

Income Statement

FYE: June 30

	REVENUE ($ mil.)	NET INCOME ($ mil.)	NET PROFIT MARGIN	EMPLOYEES
06/16	16,789	(1,025)	—	37,613
06/15	17,331	314	1.8%	—
06/14	17,465	303	1.7%	—
06/13	0	336	—	—
Annual Growth				

STATE OF RHODE ISLAND

LOCATIONS

HQ: STATE OF RHODE ISLAND
114 ENFIELD AVE, PROVIDENCE, RI 029081241
Phone: 401 351-8448

HISTORICAL FINANCIALS

Company Type: Private

Income Statement

FYE: June 30

	REVENUE ($ mil.)	NET INCOME ($ mil.)	NET PROFIT MARGIN	EMPLOYEES
06/14	6,282	(46)	—	3
06/13	5,965	67	1.1%	—
Annual Growth	**5.3%**	**—**	**—**	

2014 Year-End Financials

Debt ratio: —	
Return on equity: (-0.70%)	Dividends
Cash ($ mil.): 1,245	Yield: —
Current ratio: 1.20	Payout: —
Long-term debt ($ mil.): —	Market value ($ mil.): —

STATE OF RHODE ISLAND AND PROVIDENCE PLANTATIONS

Auditors: DENNIS E HOYLE CPA- OFFICE OF

LOCATIONS

HQ: STATE OF RHODE ISLAND AND PROVIDENCE
PLANTATIONS
82 SMITH ST STE 102, PROVIDENCE, RI 029031121
Phone: 401 222-2080
Web: WWW.GOPROVIDENCE.COM

HISTORICAL FINANCIALS

Company Type: Private

Income Statement

FYE: June 30

	REVENUE ($ mil.)	NET INCOME ($ mil.)	NET PROFIT MARGIN	EMPLOYEES
06/16	6,860	(10)	—	13,535
06/15	6,787	160	2.4%	—
06/14	6,282	(46)	—	—
06/13	5,965	67	1.1%	—
Annual Growth	**4.8%**	**—**	**—**	**—**

2015 Year-End Financials

Debt ratio: —	
Return on equity: 2.50%	Dividends
Cash ($ mil.): 11	Yield: —
Current ratio: 0.40	Payout: —
Long-term debt ($ mil.): —	Market value ($ mil.): —

2016 Year-End Financials

Debt ratio: —	
Return on equity: (-6.10%)	Dividends
Cash ($ mil.): 5,786	Yield: —
Current ratio: 1.60	Payout: —
Long-term debt ($ mil.): —	Market value ($ mil.): —

2016 Year-End Financials
Debt ratio: —
Return on equity: (-0.10%)
Cash ($ mil.): 1,707
Current ratio: 1.50
Long-term debt ($ mil.): —
Dividends
Yield: —
Payout: —
Market value ($ mil.): —

STATE OF TEXAS

Auditors: JOHN KENT CPA AUSTIN TEXAS

LOCATIONS

HQ: STATE OF TEXAS
CAPI BLDG 1100 N CONG AVE, AUSTIN, TX 78701
Phone: 512 463-2000

HISTORICAL FINANCIALS

Company Type: Private

Income Statement

	REVENUE ($ mil.)	NET INCOME ($ mil.)	NET PROFIT MARGIN	EMPLOYEES
08/15	107,350	1,993	1.9%	144,175
08/14	109,860	8,184	7.4%	—
08/13	0	0	—	
08/05	0	0	—	
Annual Growth	—	—	—	—

FYE: August 31

2015 Year-End Financials

Debt ratio: —
Return on equity: 1.90%
Cash ($ mil.): 36,275
Current ratio: 1.50
Long-term debt ($ mil.): —
Dividends
Yield: —
Payout: —
Market value ($ mil.): —

State Street Corp.

Ol' Blue Eyes sang about the State Street in Chicago but investors may find Boston's State Street more melodious. Through its flagship State Street Bank and other subsidiaries the bank holding company provides investment management and servicing trading and research services. Its activities include trust and custody fund accounting foreign exchange shareholder services and other administrative services for institutional clients such as mutual and other investment funds pension plans insurance companies foundations endowments and investment managers. Founded in 1792 State Street has more than $28 trillion of assets under custody and administration in addition to more than $2 trillion in assets under management.

HISTORY

The US's chaotic post-revolutionary era gave birth to the first ancestor of State Street Corporation. Union Bank was founded in 1792 by Boston businessmen breaking the eight-year monopoly held on Boston banking by Massachusetts Bank (a forerunner of FleetBoston which was acquired by Bank of America in 2004). Governor John Hancock's distinctive signature graced Union's charter; the bank set up shop at 40 State Street near the port and enjoyed the glory days of New England's shipping trade.

In the mid-19th century Boston's financial eminence faded as New York flexed its economic muscle. In 1865 the bank was nationally chartered and changed its name to National Union Bank of Boston. It got a new neighbor in 1891: Directors of Third National Bank set up State Street Deposit & Trust to engage in the newfangled business of trusts.

In 1925 National Union Bank merged with State Street and inherited its custodial business. The bank grew through the 1950s; acquisitions included the Second National Bank and the Rockland-Atlas National Bank.

In 1970 State Street converted to a holding company — the State Street Boston Financial Corp. (State Street Boston Corp. as of 1977). The company also went international that decade opening an office in Munich Germany.

Soaring inflation and the recession of the 1970s forced the company to radically rethink its mission. The 1974 passage of the Employee Retirement Income Security Act changed the laws governing the management of pension funds and created an opportunity. State Street was one of the first banks to move aggressively into high-tech information processing and affiliate Boston Financial Data Services began servicing pension assets in 1974.

Encouraged by that success in 1975 new CEO William Edgerly (who served until 1992) steered State Street away from branch banking and into investments trusts and securities processing. An early achievement was designing PepsiCo's retirement plan. Fee-based sales approached 50% of revenues; the company could now quit focusing on lending. In the 1980s and 1990s the company built its administration and investment management businesses overseas and moved into software.

Evolving in the late 1990s State Street left non-core businesses but expanded globally. In 1997 it formed European Direct Capital Management to invest in eastern and central Europe. State Street Global Advisors opened a London office in 1998 to serve wealthy individuals outside the US.

The company sold its commercial banking business to Royal Bank of Scotland in 1999 signaling an exit from that business and narrowing State Street's scope to the asset and investment management businesses. The company also bought Wachovia's custody and institutional trust business and teamed with Citigroup to sell 401(k) retirement products.

In 2000 State Street created FX Connect an electronic foreign exchange trading system. Also that year David Spina took over as CEO from the retiring Marshall Carter.

The firm bought Bel Air Investment Advisors and its broker/dealer affiliate Bel Air Securities in 2001 to cater to the ultrawealthy. In 2003 State Street sold its corporate trust business to U.S. Bancorp and its private asset management business to Charles Schwab's U.S. Trust. Spina retired in 2004; his prot©g © Ron Logue stepped in as chairman and CEO.

In 2007 State Street added bulk by acquiring another Boston-based fund accounting and servicing provider Investors Financial Services. The company boosted its foreign exchange offerings with the acquisition of Currenex. The following year State Street and Citigroup sold their CitiStreet retirement and pension plan management joint venture to ING Groep for some $900 million.

The US Treasury invested some $2 billion in the company in 2008 as part of a broader bailout plan to restore confidence and increase liquidity. State Street was among eight other top banks that received a combined $250 billion; the company repaid the full amount within months.

In the distressed economic climate State Street's servicing and management revenues declined due to lower equity market valuations and lending volumes and an increase in bankruptcies. The company hit its nadir in 2009 when it reported more than $2 billion in losses.

EXECUTIVES

President and COO, Ronald P. (Ron) O'Hanley, age 60, $784,615 total compensation
EVP and Global Head State Street Alternative Investment Solutions, George E. Sullivan
Chairman and CEO, Joseph L. (Jay) Hooley, age 60, $980,769 total compensation
EVP and Head of Regulatory Industry and Government Affairs, Stefan M. Gavell
EVP and Head Global Markets and Global Services Asia Pacific, Wai Kwong Seck, age 61
EVP and Chief Legal Officer, Jeffrey N. Carp, age 60, $675,000 total compensation
EVP, Maria F. Dwyer
EVP and Global Head State Street Portfolio Solutions, Nicholas T. (Nick) Bonn
EVP and Global CIO, Antoine Shagoury
EVP and Chief Administrative Officer State Street Global Advisors, Marc P. Brown
EVP Corporate Advisory Services, James C. Caccivio
EVP, Jeffrey D. Conway, age 51
EVP and CTO, Albert J. (Jerry) Cristoforo
EVP, Sharon E. Donovan Hart
President and CEO State Street Global Advisors, Cyrus Taraporevala
EVP and Head State Street Global Exchange, Lou Maiuri
EVP and Head Global Operations, Robert Kaplan
EVP and Head Sector Solutions Sales EMEA, Stefan Gmuer
EVP and Head Tax and Tax Advantaged Investments, Dennis E. Ross
EVP Chief Human Resources and Corporate Citizenship Officer, Kathryn M. (Kathy) Horgan
EVP, Richard G. Taggart, age 57
EVP and General Counsel, David C. Phelan
EVP Trading and Clearing, Martine Bond
EVP, Tracy Atkinson
EVP and Chief Investment Officer, Paul J. Selian
EVP and Chief Marketing Officer, Hannah Grove
EVP and General Counsel, Phillip S. Gillespie
EVP and Chief Risk Officer, Andrew Kuritzkes, age 56
EVP Alternative Asset Managers Solutions, Maria Cantillon
EVP and COO State Street Global Services EMEA, Anthony Carey
Global Chief Investment Officer, Rick Lacaille
EVP and Chief Compliance Officer, Cuan Coulter
EVP, David Crawford
EVP and Head Application Development and Maintenance, Ali El Abboud
EVP and Chief Data Officer, James Hardy
EVP and Head Specialized Products Group State Street Global Services Investment Services Americas, Brenda Lyons
EVP Head of Institutional Investor Services, Stephen F. (Steve) Nazzaro
EVP and International Chief Risk Officer, David Suetens
EVP and CFO, Eric Aboaf, age 52
EVP and Managing Director State Street Bank GmbH, Jorg Ambrosius
EVP Global Markets Sales and Trading and Research, Anthony C. Bisegna
EVP State Street Global Advisors and CIO Global Equity Beta Solutions, Lynn S. Blake
EVP and Head State Street Global Services Ireland, Susan Dargan
EVP Chief Innovation Officer and Head Advisory and Information Solutions, Jessica Donohue

EVP and Head of Global Services, Andrew Erickson

EVP and Head Sector Solutions Americas and Global Alternatives, Scott R. FitzGerald

EVP and Head Global Total Rewards and Human Resources, Todd Gershkowitz

EVP and Head Derivatives Securities Valuation and Internal Recon Centers of Excellence, John Griffin

EVP and Head EMEA State Street Global Advisors, Mike Karpik

EVP International Finance and Treasury, Mark R. Keating

EVP State Street Global Markets, Karen D. Keenan

EVP State Street Global Markets, Ian Martin

EVP, Ivan Matviak

EVP and General Auditor, Michael Richards

EVP SSGA and Global Head SPDR Exchange Traded Funds Business and Head Intermediary Distribution United States; Chairman SSgA Funds Management Inc., James E. (Jim) Ross

EVP and Head Global Markets EMEA, Rajen Shah

EVP State Street Global Advisors and CIO Investment Solutions Group, Dan Farley

EVP and Global Head of State Street Securities Finance, Paul Fleming

EVP State Street Global Services Investment Services Americas, Michael Fontaine

EVP Legal State Street Global Markets State Street Global Exchange State Street Global Operations and Credit Service, R. Bryan Woodard

EVP, Aunoy Banerjee

EVP and Head Asia Pacific SSGA, Lochiel Crafter

EVP, Pinar Kip

EVP, Jon Lehner

EVP and Head State Street Global Exchange, John Plansky

EVP, Liz Roaldsen

EVP and Treasurer, John Slyconish

EVP and Co-Head State Street Global Services EMEA, Elizabeth Nolan

Information Technology Management Executive Vice President Senior Vice President, Peter Hiotelis

Vice President of Information Technology, Phil Pengeroth

Vice President Information Technology, Chandra Busannagari

Vice President, John M White

Assistant Vice President, Simon Davies

Vice President, Carlton Hood

Executive Vice President, Gunjan Kedia

Executive Vice President, Michael Williams

Vice President Global Markets Technology, Steve Lin

Assistant Vice President Operations, Matthew Adams

Vice President Energy Tax Credit Investments, Francine Lyons

Vice President, Michelle Loranger

Vice President Equipment Leasing, Evelyn Orourke

Vice President, Kevin McCormick

Global Derivatives Metrics Assistant Vice President, Dennis Shea

Assistant Vice President Balance Sheet Strategy, Kevin Miley

Vice President, Paul Ananth

Senior Vice President, Susan Luo

Assistant Vice President Compensation and Benefits Global Human Resources, Grace Liu

Assistant Vice President, Pengbo Tang

Backup and Storage Administrator Assistant Vice President, Munawar Rangoonwala

Senior Vice President Corporate Audit, John Todd Roof

Vice President, Kishore Kottapalli

Senior Vice President, Robert Bagdasarian

Vice President Information Technology, Srihari Valiveti

Vice President Product Strategy and Commercialization, Jim Collins

Vice President OTC Derivatives and Collateral Management, Ed Matuga

Assistant Vice President Mutual Fund Tax, Adriana Grossi

Assistant Vice President, Ed Alter

Vice President, Chris Mccarthy

Assistant Vice President, Alistair Roberts

Vice President State Street Investment Analytics, Scott Verrill

Senior Vice President Information Technology Architect, Maura Evans

Assistant Vice President GCS, Andrew Cammorata

Vice President, Vikas Goel

Assistant Vice President FX Research, Michael Guidi

Assistant Vice President, Winnie W Lam

Vice President, Joanne Estabrook

Assistant Vice President, Yingying Chen

Vice President, Michael Cogliano

Vice President, Eric Larson

Vice President ADM Testing, Irina Reznikova

Vice President Wholesale Sales, Amy Johnston

Vice President, Rick Federico

Senior Vice President, Paul Connolly

Vice President Technical Project Services, Linda Schwalje

Vice President Human Resources Business Partner, Tammy Chojnowski

Senior Vice President, M Caroline Carmichael

Assistant Vice President, Sean Farren

Vice President State Street Global Services, Jay Fulchino

Vice President And Senior Portfolio Manager, Todd Bean

Assistant Vice President, Raquel Ellis

Vice President, Diane Webber

Vice President And Counsel, Matthew Kelly

Assistant Vice President, Lofgren Jennifer

Assistant Vice President, Joe Costa

Vice President Senior Application Development, Harish Babbar

Senior Vice President Global Business Reporting, Marcy Barker

Vice President Securities Finance, Brian McLoone

Vice President, Jeff Durkee

Vice President Accounting Operations, Brian Benkart

Assistant Vice President, Uma Gorantla

Vice President, Brian O'Sullivan

Vice President Enterprise Information Security Architecture, Brian Watts

Vice President Information Technology Architecture, Dushyant Ralhan

Assistant Vice President Transaction Management Investment Manager Services, Anna Zabinska

Vice President, David Chin

Vice President Strategy Consultant, JONATHAN NESBIT

Senior Vice President, Richard Young

Assistant Vice President Network Architecture, Lokesh Aggarwal

Assistant Vice President, Gregory J Mullen

Assistant Vice President Global Fixed Income, Daniel J Mazza

Assistant Vice President, Yeng Butler

Senior Vice President Privacy Officer, Gerald Spada

Vice President Marketing Support, Laurence Bardsley

Vice President, Siva Yerneni

Assistant Vice President, Kham Thirakoune

Assistant Vice President, Dennis Spaulding

Assistant Vice President Project Manager, Karen Rodeo

Assistant Vice President, Elaine Twitchell

Vice President, Jeffrey Sardinha

Vice President and Counsel, Peter Lee

Assistant Vice President Marketing Communications, John Ward

Auditors: Ernst & Young LLP

LOCATIONS

HQ: State Street Corp.
One Lincoln Street, Boston, MA 02111
Phone: 617 786-3000
Web: www.statestreet.com

2016 Assets Mix

	% of total
North America	75
Europe/Middle East/Africa	20
Asia/Pacific	5
Total	**100**

PRODUCTS/OPERATIONS

2016 Revenues

	% of total
Fees:	
Servicing fees	48
Management fees	12
Trading services	10
Securities finance	5
Processing fees & other	1
Interest revenue	24
Gains (losses) related to investment securities net	-
Total	**100**

2016 Sales

	% of total
U.S.	57
Other countries	43
Total	**100**

Selected Capabilities

Data and Analytic
Investment Management
Investment Research and Trading
Investment Servicing

COMPETITORS

Bank of New York Mellon	JPMorgan Chase
Citigroup	Morgan Stanley
Credit Suisse (USA)	Northern Trust
Deutsche Bank	Principal Financial
First Data	SEI Investments
Fiserv	UBS Financial Services

HISTORICAL FINANCIALS

Company Type: Public

Income Statement

FYE: December 31

	ASSETS ($ mil.)	NET INCOME ($ mil.)	INCOME AS % OF ASSETS	EMPLOYEES
12/16	242,698	2,143	0.9%	33,783
12/15	245,192	1,980	0.8%	32,356
12/14	274,119	2,037	0.7%	29,970
12/13	243,291	2,136	0.9%	29,430
12/12	222,582	2,061	0.9%	29,660
Annual Growth	**2.2%**	**1.0%**	**—**	**3.3%**

2016 Year-End Financials

Debt ratio: 4.71%
Return on equity: 10.10%
Cash ($ mil.): 73,273
Current ratio: —
Long-term debt ($ mil.): —

No. of shares (mil.): 381
Dividends
  Yield: 0.0%
  Payout: 28.9%
Market value ($ mil.): 29,684

	STOCK PRICE ($) FY Close	P/E High/Low		PER SHARE ($) Earnings	Dividends	Book Value
12/16	77.72	16	10	4.97	1.44	55.56
12/15	66.36	18	14	4.47	1.32	52.80
12/14	78.50	17	14	4.57	1.16	51.72
12/13	73.39	15	10	4.62	1.04	46.94
12/12	47.01	11	9	4.20	0.96	45.50
Annual Growth	**13.4%**			**4.3%**	**10.7%**	**5.1%**

STATE UNIVERSITY OF NEW YORK

SUNY days are ahead for many New Yorkers seeking higher education. With an enrollment of more than 460000 students The State University of New York (SUNY) is vying with California State University System for the title of largest university system in the US. Most students are residents of New York State. Students come from all 50 states as well as 160 countries. SUNY maintains 64 campuses around the state including four university centers about two dozen university colleges 30 community colleges and a handful of technical colleges as well as medical centers. The system has a student-teacher ratio of about 16:1.

Operations

The school offers more than 7500 undergraduate programs of study — including engineering business literature medicine agriculture performing arts and human services. SUNY also offers about 400 study abroad programs.

EXECUTIVES

Vice President for Student and Campus Life, Robert Bonfiglio
Vice President, Mike Metzgar
Interim Vice President for Finance and Administration, Kevin Seitz
Secretary 1, Diane VanDenburgh
Secretary 1, Cheri Burnham
Auditors: KPMG LLP ALBANY NY

LOCATIONS

HQ: STATE UNIVERSITY OF NEW YORK
353 BROADWAY, ALBANY, NY 122462915
Phone: 518 320-1100
Web: WWW.SUNY.EDU

HISTORICAL FINANCIALS

Company Type: Private

Income Statement

	REVENUE ($ mil.)	NET INCOME ($ mil.)	NET PROFIT MARGIN	EMPLOYEES
06/12	5,961	(374)	—	88,024
06/06	4	(2)	—	—
Annual Growth	232.9%	—	—	—

FYE: June 30

2012 Year-End Financials

Debt ratio: ——
Return on equity: (-6.30%)
Cash ($ mil.): 1,642
Current ratio: 0.70
Long-term debt ($ mil.): —
Dividends
Yield: —
Payout: —
Market value ($ mil.): —

STATOIL MARKETING & TRADING (US) INC.

EXECUTIVES

Vice President of Administration, Geir Bjornstad
Senior Vice President, Jens Okland
Vice President Of Finance, Jane Nagy
Vice President Human Resources, Shild Larsen
Vice President Operations, Gunnar Breivik
SENIOR VICE PRESIDENT FOR CORPORATE STRATEGY, Paal Eitrheim
Vice President Operations Subsea, Rune Aase
Vice President Business Development, Ase Staupe
Vice President Project Management, Erik Westad
Vice President Project Management, Johnny Wollberg
Vice President Internal Communication, Kjell Hugvik
Managing Director, Gareth Burns
Senior Vice President, Carri Lockhart
Vice President Strategy, Anders Marvik
Vice President Head of Procurement and Supplier Relations US and Mexico, Fredrik Rydin
Executive Vice President, Arne Nylund
Vice President Strategy and Policy, Charlotte Wolff-Bye
VICE PRESIDENT OPERATIONS, Bernt Tysseland
VP TAX, Tom Geczik
Auditors: KPMG LLP STAMFORD CONNECTICU

LOCATIONS

HQ: STATOIL MARKETING & TRADING (US) INC.
120 LONG RIDGE RD 3EO1, STAMFORD, CT 069021839
Phone: 203 978-6900
Web: WWW.STATOIL.COM

COMPETITORS

Global Partners	Irving Oil Limited
Gulf Oil	Shell Oil
Hess Corporation	Tauber Oil

HISTORICAL FINANCIALS

Company Type: Private

Income Statement

FYE: December 31

	REVENUE ($ mil.)	NET INCOME ($ mil.)	NET PROFIT MARGIN	EMPLOYEES
12/14	12,075	(140)	—	85
12/13	13,512	(56)	—	—
12/09	5,608	(20)	—	—
12/07	8,098	25	0.3%	—
Annual Growth	5.9%	—	—	—

2014 Year-End Financials

Debt ratio: ——
Return on equity: (-1.20%)
Cash ($ mil.): 37
Current ratio: ——
Long-term debt ($ mil.): —
Dividends
Yield: —
Payout: —
Market value ($ mil.): —

Steel Dynamics Inc.

Steel Dynamics may operate mini-mills but it produces steel on a large scale. Steel Dynamics operates electric arc furnace mini-mills steel scrap processing and metals recycling centers and steel fabrication facilities. The company sells to companies in the automotive construction and manufacturing industries as well as to steel processors and service centers primarily in the Midwestern and eastern US. Among its mini-mill output are beams rails and other products used in the construction industrial machinery and transportation industries. Steel Dynamics' annual steel shipping capacity is 11 million tons.

Operations

Steel Dynamics has three reporting segments: Steel Metals Recycling and Steel Fabrication.

Its Steel operations have six electric-arc furnace mini-mills producing steel from steel scrap using continuous casting automated rolling mills and some 10 downstream steel coating lines and Iron Dynamics (IDI). Its Flat Roll Division sheet steel products such as hot rolled cold rolled and coated steel products are used by automakers and other industries. The Long Products Division sells structural steel beams and pilings for the construction industry and industrial quality grade rail for the railroad industry. The Steel operations account for about three-quarters of sales.

The Metals Recycling operations (about 15% of revenue) consist solely of OmniSource which includes ferrous and nonferrous scrap metal processing transportation marketing brokerage and consulting services. In addition OmniSource designs installs and manages customized scrap management programs for industrial manufacturing companies.

The company's Steel Fabrication operations (about 10% of revenue) include eight New Millennium Building Systems plants which fabricate steel joists trusses girders and decking used by the non-residential construction industry.

All told Steel Dynamics operates six electric-arc-furnace steel mills 10 steel coating lines a down-stream engineered bar (SBQ) processing facility an iron production facility multiple metals recycling operations and eight steel fabrication plants.

Geographic Reach

Steel Dynamics has operations in Indiana (Butler Columbia City Jeffersonville and Pittsboro) Mississippi (Columbus) Pennsylvania (Pittsburgh) Virginia (Roanoke) and West Virginia (Huntington). It also serves the Southern US Canada and Mexico.

Sales and Marketing

Steel Dynamics' primary customers for structural steel products are steel service centers steel fabricators and a range of other manufacturers including metal building firms general construction contractors developers brokers agriculture consumer goods and governmental entities. The company's steel operation's biggest customers are construction about 35% manufacturing nearly 30% and automotive about 15%.

Financial Performance

Steel Dynamics reported revenue of about $7.8 billion in 2016 a 2% improvement over 2015 driven by record shipments in the Steel and Steel Fabrication segments. Trade duties on foreign steel reduced imported supply and lower customer inventories helped boost steel shipments in 2016. The automotive and construction industries were active customers during the year while the heavy equipment agriculture and energy markets were less active. Steel utilization rates improved in 2016 to 87% from 79% for steel mills and 99% from 86% for sheet metal. The Steel Fabrication segment's sales rose 4% while Materials Recycling sales fell 7% in 2016 from 2015.

Steel Dynamics bounced back from a $130 million loss in 2015 to post a $382 million profit in 2016. The company's bigger top line and an improved metal spread in steel operations combined to boost the bottom line to black.

The company's cash flow from operations was $853 million in 2016 down from more than $1 billion in 2015. The 2016 cash flow was affected by higher inventories and receivables that resulted from the year's record steel shipments and higher profit.

Strategy

Steel Dynamics is seeking to maintain and enhance one of the lowest operating cost structures in the North American steel industry by optimizing the use of its equipment enhancing productivity and exploring new technologies to lower production costs. It is looking to enter new markets in strategic geographic locations that offer attractive growth opportunities by acquiring new businesses or by entering joint ventures or alliances.

The company has improved at several plants to bring on more capacity and make operations more efficient. The company is investing millions of dollars in improvements at the Butler Flat Roll division and the Gavalume line at the Columbus Flat Roll division which serve the automotive market.

The company collaborates with customers to expand its range of products as illustrated by expansions at its Engineered Bar Products Division (high-quality smaller-diameter SBQ bars) and at its Structural and Rail Division (premium grade rails).

Mergers and Acquisitions

In 2016 Steel Dynamics acquired Vulcan Threaded Products for $114 million. The Birmingham Alabama-based company makes and supplies threaded rod products and also cold draws and heat-treated steel bar. The deal is an example of Steel Dynamics pursuing higher-margin downstream business opportunities that use its steel products in manufacturing processes.

In 2015 the company acquired steel decking facilities from Consolidated Systems for $45 million.

In a major move in 2014 Steel Dynamics acquired Mississippi-based Severstal Columbus LLC one of the newest and most technologically advanced mini-mills in North America for $1.6 billion. The acquisition expanded and diversified the company's steel operating base increasing Steel Dynamics' annual steel shipping capacity to 11 million tons a 40% increase.

Company Background

Growing its share of the rail market in 2012 Steel Dynamics announced plans to install a heat-treating system (capable of producing up to 350000 tons of standard strength and head hardened plain carbon steel rails for North America's railroad industry) at its Columbia City Indiana Structural and Rail Division.

Steel Dynamics entered a joint venture in 2011 with Spain's Lafarga Group to construct a $39 million facility which will produce copper wire rod from recycled copper.

Steel Dynamics was incorporated in 1993.

EXECUTIVES

Vice President Human Resources, Benjamin Eisbart
President and CEO, Mark D. Millett, age 58, $1,010,000 total compensation
EVP Metals Recycling and President and COO OmniSource, Russell B. (Russ) Rinn, age 60, $510,000 total compensation
SVP Long Products Steel Group, Glenn A. Pushis, age 51, $393,750 total compensation
VP and CIO, Robert E. (Bob) Francis
Controller, Theresa E. Wagler, age 47, $580,000 total compensation
VP and General Manager Engineered Bar Products Division, Barry T. Schneider, age 48, $363,750 total compensation
VP and President Steel of West Virginia, Timothy R. (Tim) Duke
SVP Downstream Manufacturing Group, Christopher A. (Chris) Graham, age 54, $322,500 total compensation
Vice President and Treasurer, Richard Poinsatte
Vice President Structural Products, Rob Simon
Vice President and Corporate Controller, Brent Ritenour
Vice President Finance, John Morris
VP Human Resources, Jeff Hansen
VICE PRESIDENT, Boudler Noelle
Chairman, Keith E. Busse, age 75
Auditors: Ernst & Young LLP

LOCATIONS

HQ: Steel Dynamics Inc.
7575 West Jefferson Blvd., Fort Wayne, IN 46804
Phone: 260 969-3500
Web: www.steeldynamics.com

PRODUCTS/OPERATIONS

2016 sales

	$ mil.	% of total
Steel	5,870	65
Metals Recycling	2,171	24
Steel Fabrication	703	8
Other	276	3
Eliminations	(1246.1)	-
Total	**7,777**	**100**

Selected Products

Cold-rolled galvannealed
Cold-rolled hot-dipped galvanized
Direct reduced iron
Fully processed cold-rolled sheet
Hot-rolled galvannealed
Hot-rolled hot-dipped galvanized
Hot-rolled pickled and oiled
Liquid pig iron
Structural products (steel joists trusses)
Steel Operations
Sheet Products
  Hot rolled Products
  Cold Rolled Products
Long Products
  Structural
  Wide flange American Standard and miscellaneous beams
  H piling
  Channel sections
Rail Products
  Engineered Bar Products
  Merchant Bar Products
  Specialty Shapes
Metals Recycling   No. 2 shredded
  No. 1 bundles
  Plate and structural
  No. 1 busheling
  Turnings
  Heavy melt
  Briquettes
  Copper granules
  Stainless steel bundles
Steel Fabrication Operations   Joists
  Decking
  Castellated beams
  Cambered beams

COMPETITORS

AK Steel Holding Corporation	Evraz
ArcelorMittal USA	Gerdau Ameristeel
Canam Steel Corporation	Nucor
Commercial Metals	Timken
	United States Steel
	Wheeling Corrugating

HISTORICAL FINANCIALS

Company Type: Public

Income Statement

FYE: December 31

	REVENUE ($ mil.)	NET INCOME ($ mil.)	NET PROFIT MARGIN	EMPLOYEES
12/16	7,777	382	4.9%	7,695
12/15	7,594	(130)	—	7,500
12/14	8,755	157	1.8%	7,780
12/13	7,372	189	2.6%	6,870
12/12	7,290	163	2.2%	6,670
Annual Growth	**1.6%**	**23.6%**		**3.6%**

2016 Year-End Financials

Debt ratio: 36.69%
Return on equity: 13.59%
Cash ($ mil.): 841
Current ratio: 4.11
Long-term debt ($ mil.): 2,353
No. of shares (mil.): 243
Dividends
  Yield: 0.0%
  Payout: 35.9%
Market value ($ mil.): 8,674

	STOCK PRICE ($) FY Close	P/E High/Low	PER SHARE ($) Earnings	Dividends	Book Value
12/16	35.58	25 10	1.56	0.56	12.01
12/15	17.87	—	(0.54)	0.55	11.02
12/14	19.74	37 23	0.67	0.46	12.06
12/13	19.54	23 16	0.83	0.44	11.43
12/12	13.73	22 14	0.73	0.40	10.96
Annual Growth	**26.9%**	**— —**	**20.9%**	**8.8%**	**2.3%**

Sterling Bancorp (DE)

EXECUTIVES

Senior Executive Vice President, Rodney C Whitwell
Vice President, Rita Kokkoris
Assistant Vice President Research And Database Marketing Manager, David Gerbino
Vice President, John Willis
Executive Board Member, ROBERT KRAUSE
Auditors: Crowe Horwath LLP

LOCATIONS

HQ: Sterling Bancorp (DE)
400 Rella Boulevard, Montebello, NY 10901
Phone: 845 369-8040
Web: www.sterlingbancorp.com

COMPETITORS

Capital One	JPMorgan Chase
Citibank	KeyCorp
HSBC USA	M&T Bank

HISTORICAL FINANCIALS

Company Type: Public

Income Statement

FYE: December 31

	ASSETS ($ mil.)	NET INCOME ($ mil.)	INCOME AS % OF ASSETS	EMPLOYEES
12/16	14,178	139	1.0%	970
12/15	11,955	66	0.6%	1,089
12/14*	7,424	17	0.2%	829
09/14	7,337	27	0.4%	836
09/13	4,049	25	0.6%	543
Annual Growth	**51.9%**	**77.0%**	**—**	**21.3%**

*Fiscal year change

2016 Year-End Financials

Debt ratio: 1.87%
Return on equity: 7.93%
Cash ($ mil.): 293
Current ratio: —
Long-term debt ($ mil.): —
No. of shares (mil.): 135
Dividends
  Yield: 0.0%
  Payout: 26.1%
Market value ($ mil.): 3,165

	STOCK PRICE ($) FY Close	P/E High/Low	PER SHARE ($) Earnings	Dividends	Book Value
12/16	23.40	23 13	1.07	0.28	13.72
12/15	16.22	29 22	0.60	0.28	12.81
12/14*	14.38	72 63	0.20	0.28	11.62
09/14	12.79	40 32	0.34	0.27	11.49
09/13	10.89	20 15	0.58	0.24	10.89
Annual Growth	**29.0%**	**— —**	**22.6%**	**5.3%**	**8.0%**

*Fiscal year change

Stifel Financial Corp

Through subsidiaries Stifel Nicolaus (founded 1890) Thomas Weisel Century Securities Associates Stifel Bank & Trust and others Stifel Financial provides asset management financial advice and banking services for private individuals corporations municipal and institutional clients in the US. Stifel also offers brokerage and mergers and acquisitions advisory services for corporate clients underwrites debt and equity and provides research on more than 1000 US and European equities. The firm boasts nearly 360 US offices with a concentration in the Midwest and mid-Atlantic regions and additional offices in the UK and the rest of Europe.

Operations

Stifel Financial operates two main business segments.

The Global Wealth Management segment which generates more than 60% of the firm's total revenue consists of two businesses: Stifel Bank which provides traditional banking products and services and the Private Client Group which is made up of offices across the US that provide securities brokerage services and insurance products.

The Institutional Group segment (almost 40% of revenue) provides securities brokerage trading and research services to institutions and specializes in the sale of equity and fixed-income products.

Geographic Reach

The company is headquartered in Missouri with about 360 private client offices and more than 35 Institutional Group offices mostly across the US as well as in certain foreign locations in the UK and the rest of Europe. About 95% of its revenue stems from the US.

Sales and Marketing

With its 2280-plus financial advisors and 125 independent contractors Stifel serves individuals corporations municipalities and institutions. Its broker-dealer subsidiaries boast more than 1.5 million accounts from customers based in the US and Europe.

Financial Performance

Stifel's revenues have been growing at a healthy clip in recent years thanks to business-boosting acquisitions combined with growth across all business lines as the financial markets have appreciated and demand for investor capital has strengthened.

The firm's revenues climbed 11% to peak at a record-setting $2.6 billion during 2016. This historic growth was driven by a 64% surge from interest revenue generated from the growth in interest-earning assets of Stifel Bank. In addition principal transactions revenues spiked 22% in 2016 due to higher institutional fixed income brokerage revenues as a result of increased volumes. The firm also generated additional revenue from several previous acquisitions.

Despite revenue growth in 2016 Stifel's net income dipped 12% to $82 million as the company spent more on compensation benefits and office space to support future revenue growth. In addition Stifel experienced negative cash flow of $349 million in 2016 as the firm used more cash to purchase operating assets.

Strategy

Stifel has fortified its operations and extended its national footprint mainly through strategic acquisitions as well as through organic growth. It plans to further expand its domestic private client footprint by recruiting experienced financial advisors and continuing to selectively consider acquisitions as they arise.

Mergers and Acquisitions

Stifel has achieved historic revenue growth over the years by using acquisitions primarily to fortify its wealth management business.

In late 2017 it agreed to acquire the wealth management business belonging to B.C. Ziegler & Company. The business Ziegler Wealth Management was established in 1902 and has nearly 60 private client advisors in 12 branches across five. It manages approximately $4.8 billion in client assets.

In 2017 Stifel picked up investment bank City Financial Corporation and its City Securities subsidiary. City Financial primarily operates in Indiana and the Midwest specializing in wealth management and public finance.

In early 2016 the firm bought global fund placement and advisory firm Eaton Partners. The deal enhanced Stifel's investment banking and high net worth private client business with new private equity firms hedge funds affluent family offices and institutional investor client relationships.

In another large deal Stifel in 2015 purchased Barclays' Wealth and Investment Management Americas franchise in the US along with its 180 financial advisors managing some $56 billion in total client assets.

EXECUTIVES

Vice Chairman SVP and Director Stifel Financial Corp. and EVP Investment Banking Stifel Nicolaus & Co., Richard J. Himelfarb, age 76, $250,000 total compensation

Chairman President and CEO, Ronald J. (Ron) Kruszewski, age 58, $200,000 total compensation

President CFO and Director, James M. Zemlyak, age 57, $250,000 total compensation

EVP; President and Co-Director Institutional Group, Thomas P. Mulroy, age 55, $250,000 total compensation

SVP and Director Stifel Financial Corp. and President and CEO Keefe Bruyette and Woods, Thomas B. (Tom) Michaud, age 52, $250,000 total compensation

EVP; President and Co-Director Institutional Group, Victor J. Nesi, age 57, $250,000 total compensation

Vice Chairman; EVP Stifel Nicolaus & Co., Ben A. Plotkin, age 61

Co-Chairman, Thomas W. (Thom) Weisel, age 75

Auditors: Ernst & Young LLP

LOCATIONS

HQ: Stifel Financial Corp
501 North Broadway, St. Louis, MO 63102-2188
Phone: 314 342-2000
Web: www.stifel.com

2016 Sales

	% of total
US	94
UK	5
Other European countries	1
Total	**100**

PRODUCTS/OPERATIONS

2016 Sales

	$ mil.	% of total
Commissions	730	28
Asset management and service fees	582	22
Investment banking	513	19
Principal transactions	475	18
Interest	294	11
Others	46	2
Total	**2,642**	**100**

Selected Services

Individual
Bonds

Corporate Executive Services
Estate Planning
Exchange Traded Funds
Financial And Wealth Planning
Insurance
Investment Advisory Services
Market News
Mutual Funds
Options
Portfolio Tracker
Prospectus
Retirement Plans
Stifel Bank & Trust
Stifel Cash Management Accounts
Stifel Mobile Announcement
Stifel Trust
Institutions
Asset Management
Conferences & Events
Equity Capital Markets
Equity Sales & Trading
Fixed Income Sales & Trading
Investment Banking
Public Finance
Research
Senior Management

Selected Subsidiaries

Broadway Air Corp.
CSA Insurance Agency Incorporated
Choice Financial Partners Inc.
Stifel Bank & Trust
Stifel Nicolaus Limited (UK)
Stifel Nicolaus & Company Incorporated
Ryan Beck Holdings LLC
Thomas Weisel Partners Group Inc.

COMPETITORS

Edward Jones	Oppenheimer Holdings
FBR	Piper Jaffray
Goldman Sachs	Raymond James
JMP Group	Financial
Lazard	Wells Fargo Advisors
Morgan Stanley	

HISTORICAL FINANCIALS

Company Type: Public

Income Statement

FYE: December 31

	ASSETS ($ mil.)	NET INCOME ($ mil.)	INCOME AS % OF ASSETS	EMPLOYEES
12/16	19,129	81	0.4%	7,100
12/15	13,335	92	0.7%	7,100
12/14	9,518	176	1.8%	6,200
12/13	9,008	162	1.8%	5,862
12/12	6,966	138	2.0%	5,343
Annual Growth	28.7%	(12.4%)	—	7.4%

2016 Year-End Financials

Debt ratio: 6.48%
Return on equity: 3.11%
Cash ($ mil.): 986
Current ratio: —
Long-term debt ($ mil.): —

No. of shares (mil.): 66
Dividends
Yield: —
Payout: —
Market value ($ mil.): 3,329

	STOCK PRICE ($) FY Close	P/E High/Low		PER SHARE ($) Earnings	Dividends	Book Value
12/16	49.95	45	23	1.00	0.00	41.09
12/15	42.36	44	30	1.18	0.00	37.19
12/14	51.02	20	16	2.31	0.00	35.00
12/13	47.92	19	12	2.20	0.00	32.30
12/12	31.97	15	11	2.20	0.00	27.23
Annual Growth	11.8%		—	—(17.9%)	—	10.8%

Stock Yards Bancorp Inc

Stock Yards Bancorp is the holding company of Stock Yards Bank & Trust which operates about 35 branches mostly in Louisville Kentucky but also in Indianapolis and Cincinnati. Founded in 1904 the $3 billion-asset bank targets individuals and regional business customers offering standard retail services such as checking and savings accounts credit cards certificates of deposit and IRAs. It also provides trust services while brokerage and credit card services are offered through agreements with other banks. Commercial real estate mortgages make up 40% of the bank's loan portfolio which also includes commercial and industrial loans (30%) residential mortgages (15%) construction loans and consumer loans.

Operations

Stock Yards Bank & Trust operates two main business lines: Commercial Banking which provides loans and deposits to individual consumers and businesses as well as mortgage origination and company brokerage activity; and Investment Management and Trust which provides wealth management services such as investment management trust estate administration and retirement plan services.

About 63% of the company's total revenue came from loan interest during 2015 while another 7% came from interest income on its securities. The rest came from its investment management and trust services (13% of revenue) deposit account service charges (7%) bankcard transaction revenue (4%) mortgage banking revenue (3%) brokerage commissions and fees (1%) and other non-interest sources.

Geographic Reach

Kentucky-based Stock Yards Bancorp had 37 branches at the end of 2015 including 28 branches in the Louisville Kentucky metro area and the rest in the Indianapolis Indiana and Cincinnati Ohio metro areas.

Financial Performance

Stock Yards' annual revenues have risen 11% since 2011 thanks to a combination of mostly organic loan growth and investment management and trust services fee growth. Meanwhile its annual profits have grown more than 55% on declining loan loss provisions as its loan portfolio's credit quality has improved with higher property valuations in the strengthened economy.

The bank's revenue climbed 4% to a record $133.12 million during 2015 on higher interest income mostly as its loan assets grew 9% to $2 billion with record loan production.

Revenue growth and a decline in interest expense on deposits in 2015 drove Stock Yard's net income up 7% to a record $34.82 million. The bank's operating cash levels jumped 8% to $43.17 million mostly thanks to the increase in cash-based earnings.

Strategy

Stock Yards outlined its plans for 2016 and beyond to maintain stable net interest margins achieve near-double digit loan growth manage credit quality to keep loan loss provisions down and increasing its regulatory readiness.

Mergers and Acquisitions

In 2013 the bank extended the reach of its operations into Oldham County through its purchase of $146 million-asset The BANcorp Inc. and its five THE BANK branches in the region for $19.9 million.

EXECUTIVES

SEVP, Kathy C. Thompson, age 55, $345,000 total compensation
Chairman and CEO, David P. Heintzman, age 57, $535,000 total compensation
EVP Secretary Treasurer and CFO, Nancy B. Davis, age 61, $232,000 total compensation
EVP and Chief Lending Officer, Philip S. Poindexter, age 51, $270,000 total compensation
President, James A. (Ja) Hillebrand, age 48, $375,000 total compensation
EVP and Chief Risk Officer, William M. Dishman, age 55
EVP and Chief Strategic Officer, Clay Stinnett
EVP Retail Banking Brokerage and Business Banking, Michael J. Croce
Assistant Vice President Deposit Operations, Marcia Sweat
Vice President Private Banking, Dan Thacker
Vice President Commercial Lending, Kevin Mccullough
Vice President Cre Lending, Jimmy Evans
Assistant Vice President, Crystal Fryer
Electronic Banking Services Division Manager
Assistant Vice President, Linda Moore
Vice President Equipment Finance, Rick Waddle
Assistant Vice President, June Schenk
Vice President, Joe Morrison
Vice President Financial Advisor, Sandy Willen
Vice President Area Manager, Dan Bachman
Vice President Commerical Lending, Jason Morgan
Assistant Vice President Commercial Lending, Joseph Shuff
Auditors: KPMG LLP

LOCATIONS

HQ: Stock Yards Bancorp Inc
1040 East Main Street, Louisville, KY 40206
Phone: 502 582-2571

PRODUCTS/OPERATIONS

2015 Revenues by Category

	$ mil.	% of total
Interest income	93	70
Non-interest income	40	30
Total	**133**	**100**

Selected Products & Services
Personal Banking
  Banking
  Personal Lending
  Personal Investing & Wealth Management Services
Business Banking
  Credit Loans & Leasing
  Deposit Services
  Treasury Management
  Business Retirement Plans
Wealth Management Services
  Investment Management
  Financial Planning
  Trust & Estate Services
  Brokerage Service

COMPETITORS

Fifth Third	Porter Bancorp
First Capital	Republic Bancorp
Home Federal	U.S. Bancorp
PNC Financial	

HISTORICAL FINANCIALS
Company Type: Public

Income Statement
FYE: December 31

	ASSETS ($ mil.)	NET INCOME ($ mil.)	INCOME AS % OF ASSETS	EMPLOYEES
12/16	3,039	41	1.3%	578
12/15	2,816	37	1.3%	555
12/14	2,563	34	1.4%	524
12/13	2,389	27	1.1%	519
12/12	2,148	25	1.2%	495
Annual Growth	9.1%	12.3%	—	4.0%

2016 Year-End Financials

Debt ratio: —
Return on equity: 13.63%
Cash ($ mil.): 47
Current ratio: —
Long-term debt ($ mil.): —
No. of shares (mil.): 22
Dividends
  Yield: 0.0%
  Payout: 39.8%
Market value ($ mil.): 1,062

	STOCK PRICE ($) FY Close	P/E High/Low	PER SHARE ($) Earnings	Dividends	Book Value
12/16	46.95	26 15	1.80	0.72	13.88
12/15	37.79	24 18	1.65	0.96	12.80
12/14	33.34	21 17	1.57	0.88	11.75
12/13	31.92	27 17	1.26	0.81	10.47
12/12	22.42	20 17	1.23	0.77	9.82
Annual Growth	20.3%	— —	9.9%	(1.8%)	9.0%

Stryker Corp

Is this an operating room or Dad's workshop? Stryker's surgical products include such instruments as drills saws and even cement mixers. The company's Orthopaedic segment makes artificial hip and knee joints trauma implants bone cement and other orthopedic supplies. The MedSurg equipment segment houses microsurgery instruments endoscopy equipment and communications and patient handling tools. Stryker's Neurotechnology and Spine unit provides rods screws and artificial discs for spinal surgeries as well as coils and stents for cerebral vascular procedures. The firm's products are marketed globally to doctors hospitals and other health care facilities via direct sales personnel and distributors.

Operations

Stryker operates through three primary segments — MedSurg Orthopaedic and Neurotechnology & Spine.

MedSurg is the largest segment bringing in about 45% of total revenues. Its MedSurg Equipment division provides surgical navigation systems endoscopic systems emergency medical equipment and other medical devices. Its biggest customers are hospitals and other care providers who have to invest a decent chunk of cash in order to upgrade their surgical equipment.

Stryker's Orthopaedic segment is nearly as large accounting for about 40% of annual revenues. The division's leading products include the Triathlon and Scorpio knee implant systems Simplex bone cement the VariAx and Hoffman systems and the Oasys spinal implant.

The company's smallest segment — Neurotechnology & Spine — accounts for some 20% of sales. It provides both neurosurgical and neurovascular devices for minimally invasive surgical procedures. Spinal implant products include cervical thoracolumbar and interbody systems used in various therapies.

Geographic Reach

Stryker operates more than 30 manufacturing distribution and R&D facilities in the Americas; Europe the Middle East and Africa (EMEA); and the Asia/Pacific region. While it markets its products in more than 100 countries and is looking to grow in international markets sales in the US continue to make up the majority (about 75%) of annual revenues.

Sales and Marketing

In the US Stryker uses its own sales and marketing force maintaining separate dedicated sales teams for each of its core product lines to doctors hospitals and other care providers. By allowing for specialization each team can provide expertise and guidance directed specifically to customers in each of the medical specialties Stryker serves. In markets outside the US Stryker's products are sold through company-owned subsidiaries and branch locations as well as through third-party distributors and medical device dealers.

Financial Performance

Stryker's revenues have increased steadily over the last five years. In 2016 revenue grew 14% to a record $11.3 billion due to growth across all segments especially the MedSurg division. That unit saw 26% growth through increased sales volume.Its medical division which makes patient handling emergency medical equipment and intensive care disposable products doubled its sales that year.

Despite the rising revenues net income slipped in 2013 and 2014. Net income has since rebounded and in 2016 it grew 14% to $1.6 billion. That increase was largely driven by the higher revenue but was partially offset by higher operating expenses.

Cash flow from operations which dipped in 2015 recovered the following year when it rose 101% to $1.8 billion. A decrease in recall payments that year boosted operating cash flow.

Strategy

Stryker expands its operations through a balance of internal R&D programs partnerships and a steady stream of acquisitions. Focus areas of growth including widening its presence geographically and expanding its product offerings in core and complementary fields of medicine. Geographically the company targets emerging markets including China through both its standard line of products and its lower-cost Trauson brand.

Overall the company follows the strategy of staying on top of the latest technology by consistently upgrading and introducing new versions of its popular brands. Within the past couple of years it has launched such products as the robotic-arm assisted Mako Total Knee the Neptune 3 Waste Management System and the Tritanium interbody spinal device.

Acquisitions are another important strategy for growth. In 2016 the company spent more than $4 billion to acquire firms including Sage Products and Physio-Control International (which both joined MedSurg's fast-growing medical division).

In the area of partnerships in 2017 the company formed an alliance with GE unit GE Additive to expand Stryker's additive manufacturing (or industrial 3D printing) capabilities. The companies will work together to develop new additive products and materials including metal.

Cost-cutting initiatives include rationalizing product lines implementing a global enterprise resource planning system and consolidating manufacturing sites as possible.

The company spends between 5% and 7% of annual revenues on R&D programs each year.

Mergers and Acquisitions

Purchases in recent years have brought Stryker new software and manufacturing technologies and entered it into new lines of business such as surgical imaging and minimally invasive devices for treatment of stroke and brain conditions.

In 2015 the company acquired private Canadian firm CHG Hospital Beds which markets beds across Canada the US and the UK.

The following year Stryker bought personal products maker Sage Products for $2.8 billion. Sage which specializes in items that prevent hospital-acquired conditions is now part of Stryker's MedSurg segment.The firm also purchased UK company Stanmore Implants Worldwide which makes orthopedic devices to help treat bone cancer.

Also in 2016 the company purchased Physio-Control for almost $1.3 billion and Instratek for an undisclosed amount. Physio-Control develops and manufactures monitors/defibrillators and CPR-assist devices which serve as fitting add-ons to Stryker's Emergency Medical Services (EMS) business. Instratek is a Texas-based maker of orthopedic implants and endoscopic instruments for use in hand and foot procedures.

In 2017 Stryker bought Canadian medical imaging products firm Novadaq Technologies for $701 million. Novadaq makes fluorescence imaging technology that shows blood flow during surgeries. The purchase expanded Stryker's reach into the open and plastic reconstructive surgery market.

Later that year the company acquired control of French spinal implant manufacturer Vexim for some $216 million. It plans to buy the rest of Vexim which is looking to launching its SpineJack device in the US by 2018.

In late 2017 the company agreed to buy ear nose and throat products specialist Entellus Medical in a $662 million transaction.

Company Background

Stryker was founded in 1941 by Dr. Homer Stryker.

HISTORY

Stryker was founded in 1941 by Dr. Homer Stryker an orthopedic surgeon who had invented several orthopedic devices. It was incorporated in 1946 as a Michigan company. The company expanded through organic measures and occasional acquisitions over the following decades while the Stryker family kept a hand in its operations.

Beginning in 2009 Stryker set out to further diversify its operations through acquisitions. In 2010 Stryker purchased supportive surface maker (think: beds and tables) Gaymar Industries for approximately $150 million in cash. The two companies were already well-acquainted through a long-standing supply and sales agreement in the US.

Its $1.5 billion acquisition of Boston Scientific's neurovascular division in 2011 added minimally invasive devices (such as coils stents and balloon catheters) for the treatment of cerebral conditions such as brain aneurysms and hemorrhagic and ischemic strokes.

Stryker further boosted its neurovascular operations later that year when it acquired Concentric Medical a maker of clot removal products for use in ischemic stroke procedures for some $135 million. Following these acquisitions Stryker rearranged its operating structure from two divisions into three: Reconstructive MedSurg Equipment and Neurotechnology and Spine.

The company's OP-1 bone growth product was so successful that in 2011 the company sold the product franchise to Olympus for $60 million. During 2011 Stryker acquired synthetic bone graft material maker Orthovita for some $304 million in cash. It also spent $150 million to purchase

France's Memometal Technologies for its in hand and foot device products.

EXECUTIVES

Group President Orthopaedics, David K. Floyd, $575,000 total compensation

Chairman President and CEO, Kevin A. Lobo, $1,129,167 total compensation

Group President Global Quality and Operations, Lonny J. Carpenter, $497,500 total compensation

Group President MedSurg and Neurotechnology, Timothy J. Scannell, $610,333 total compensation

VP and CIO, Bijoy Sagar

VP Communications Public Affairs and Strategic Marketing, Yin C. Becker

Group CFO MedSurg & Neurotechnology (MSNT), Glenn Boehnlein, $517,333 total compensation

President Asia Pacific, Graham A. McLean

Vice President Human Resources, Art Hartman

Vice President Global Business Development, David Fabricant

National Account Manager, Mike Mulligan

Auditors: Ernst & Young LLP

LOCATIONS

HQ: Stryker Corp
2825 Airview Boulevard, Kalamazoo, MI 49002
Phone: 269 385-2600   **Fax:** 269 385-1062
Web: www.stryker.com

2016 Sales

	$ mil.	% of total
United States	8,247	73
EMEA (Europe Middle East & Africa)	1,442	13
Asia Pacific	1,314	11
Other countries	322	3
Total	**11,325**	**100**

PRODUCTS/OPERATIONS

2016 Sales

	$ mil.	% of total
MedSurg Equipment:		
Instruments	1,553	14
Medical	1,633	14
Endoscopy	1,470	13
Sustainability	238	2
Orthopaedics:		
Knees	1,490	13
Hips	1,283	11
Trauma and Extremities	1,364	12
Other	285	3
Neurotechnology & Spine:		
Neurotechnology	1,255	11
Spine	754	7
Total	**11,325**	**100**

Selected Acquisitions

COMPETITORS

Arthrex	Medtronic Sofamor
B. Braun Melsungen	Danek
CONMED Corporation	Midmark Corporation
Corin Group	Olympus
DJO Global	Orthofix
DePuy	RTI Surgical
DePuy Spine	STERIS
Genzyme Biosurgery	Smith & Nephew
Hill-Rom Holdings	Synthes
Kinetic Concepts	Zimmer Biomet
Medtronic	

HISTORICAL FINANCIALS

Company Type: Public

Income Statement

FYE: December 31

	REVENUE ($ mil.)	NET INCOME ($ mil.)	NET PROFIT MARGIN	EMPLOYEES
12/17	12,444	1,020	8.2%	33,000
12/16	11,325	1,647	14.5%	33,000
12/15	9,946	1,439	14.5%	27,000
12/14	9,675	515	5.3%	26,000
12/13	9,021	1,006	11.2%	25,000
Annual Growth	8.4%	0.3%	—	7.2%

2017 Year-End Financials

Debt ratio: 32.54%
Return on equity: 10.45%
Cash ($ mil.): 2,542
Current ratio: 2.29
Long-term debt ($ mil.): 6,590

No. of shares (mil.): 374
Dividends
　Yield: 0.0%
　Payout: 65.1%
Market value ($ mil.): 57,972

	STOCK PRICE ($) FY Close	P/E High/Low		PER SHARE ($) Earnings	Dividends	Book Value
12/17	154.84	59	43	2.68	1.75	26.62
12/16	119.81	28	20	4.35	1.57	25.47
12/15	92.94	27	24	3.78	1.42	22.82
12/14	94.33	71	55	1.34	1.26	22.74
12/13	75.14	28	21	2.63	1.10	23.93
Annual Growth	19.8%	—	—	0.5%	12.2%	2.7%

Summit Financial Group Inc

EXECUTIVES

Senior Vice President And Chief Banking, Doug Mitchell
Senior Vice President Chief Banking Offi, Patty Owens
Executive Vice President of Business Development, Jack Rossi
SENIOR VICE PRESIDENT AND TRUST OFFICER, Julie H Johnson
VICE PRESIDENT COMMERICAL LOANS, Anna B Abbey
Auditors: Yount, Hyde & Barbour, P.C.

LOCATIONS

HQ: Summit Financial Group Inc
　300 North Main Street, Moorefield, WV 26836
Phone: 304 530-1000
Web: www.summitfgi.com

COMPETITORS

Allegheny Bancshares
BB&T
F & M Bank
Fauquier Bankshares
Highlands Bankshares Inc.
SunTrust

HISTORICAL FINANCIALS

Company Type: Public

Income Statement

FYE: December 31

	ASSETS ($ mil.)	NET INCOME ($ mil.)	INCOME AS % OF ASSETS	EMPLOYEES
12/16	1,758	17	1.0%	251
12/15	1,492	16	1.1%	231
12/14	1,443	11	0.8%	222
12/13	1,386	8	0.6%	224
12/12	1,387	5	0.4%	229
Annual Growth	6.1%	31.9%	—	2.3%

2016 Year-End Financials

Debt ratio: 3.72%
Return on equity: 11.53%
Cash ($ mil.): 46
Current ratio: —
Long-term debt ($ mil.): —

No. of shares (mil.): 10
Dividends
　Yield: 0.0%
　Payout: 24.8%
Market value ($ mil.): 296

	STOCK PRICE ($) FY Close	P/E High/Low		PER SHARE ($) Earnings	Dividends	Book Value
12/16	27.53	18	7	1.61	0.40	14.47
12/15	11.88	8	7	1.50	0.32	13.47
12/14	11.90	9	7	1.17	0.00	15.86
12/13	9.91	10	5	0.84	0.00	14.91
12/12	4.84	9	4	0.60	0.00	14.62
Annual Growth	54.4%	—	—	28.0%	—	(0.3%)

Sunoco LP

EXECUTIVES

Vice President of Sunoco Energy Services LLC, Wes Scott
Auditors: Grant Thornton LLP

LOCATIONS

HQ: Sunoco LP
　8020 Park Lane, Suite 200, Dallas, TX 75231
Phone: 832 234-3600
Web: www.sunocolp.com

COMPETITORS

CITGO	Shell Oil Products
Chevron	Sinclair Oil
ConocoPhillips	Sunoco
Exxon Mobil	TOTAL
Hess Corporation	Valero Energy
Royal Dutch Shell	

HISTORICAL FINANCIALS

Company Type: Public

Income Statement

FYE: December 31

	REVENUE ($ mil.)	NET INCOME ($ mil.)	NET PROFIT MARGIN	EMPLOYEES
12/16	15,698	(406)	—	—
12/15	16,935	237	1.4%	—
12/14*	1,889	35	1.9%	—
08/14	3,492	22	0.6%	—
12/13	4,492	37	0.8%	—
Annual Growth	51.7%	—	—	—

*Fiscal year change

2016 Year-End Financials

Debt ratio: 51.88%
Return on equity: (-15.37%)
Cash ($ mil.): 119
Current ratio: 1.17
Long-term debt ($ mil.): 4,509

No. of shares (mil.): 114
Dividends
　Yield: 0.1%
　Payout: —
Market value ($ mil.): 3,081

	STOCK PRICE ($) FY Close	P/E High/Low		PER SHARE ($) Earnings	Dividends	Book Value
12/16	26.89	—	—	(5.26)	3.27	19.16
12/15	39.61	48	28	1.11	2.68	31.25
12/14*	49.77	70	38	0.85	2.05	32.60
08/14	57.08	58	29	1.02	1.98	(0.00)
12/13	33.10	20	15	1.69	1.80	3.63
Annual Growth	(6.7%)	—	—	—	22.1%	74.1%

*Fiscal year change

SunTrust Banks Inc

Through its flagship SunTrust Bank subsidiary this company operates some 1400 branches in about a dozen southeastern and mid-Atlantic states. With total assets of about $199 billion and total deposits of over $150 billion the bank offers standard retail and commercial services such as credit deposit and investment services. SunTrust also operates subsidiaries that offer mortgage wealth and investment management insurance investment banking equipment leasing and brokerage services. The official bank of Grand American Road Racing SunTrust was also behind the original "Coke float" when it underwrote the public flotation of Coca-Cola in the 1920s and was one of the soda company's largest shareholders.

HISTORY

SunTrust was born from the union of old-money Georgia and new-money Florida. Founded in 1891 the Trust Company of Georgia (originally Commercial Traveler's Savings Bank) served Atlanta's oldest and richest institutions. It helped underwrite Coca-Cola's IPO in 1919; the bank's ownership stake in Coke stemmed from its early involvement with the beverage maker.

Beginning in 1933 Trust acquired controlling interests in five other Georgia banks. As regulation of multibank ownership relaxed in the 1970s Trust acquired the remaining interests in its original banks and bought 25 more. At the height of the Sun Belt boom in 1984 Trust was the most profitable bank in the nation. The next year it united with Sun Banks.

Sun Banks was formed in 1934 as the First National Bank at Orlando. It grew into a holding company in 1967 and in the early 1970s helped assemble the land for Walt Disney World. The Sun name was adopted in 1973.

Under president and CEO Joel Wells Sun Banks began an acquisition-fueled expansion within Florida. Between 1976 and 1984 Sun Banks' approximate asset growth was an astronomical 500% and branch count grew fivefold (51 to 274).

After a lingering courtship Sun and Trust formed a super holding company over the two organizations. When the marriage was consummated in 1985 Sun brought a dowry of $9.4 billion in assets and Trust contributed $6.2 billion. Trust's chairman Bob Strickland became chairman and CEO for the new Atlanta-based SunTrust and Wells became president.

In 1986 SunTrust bought Nashville Tennessee-based Third National Bank the #2 banking company in the Volunteer State. But problems with Tennessee real estate loans plagued SunTrust. In 1990 it increased the amount of loans it wrote off; the bank's ratings suffered because of nonperforming loans on properties in overbuilt Florida. While nonperforming assets decreased in Tennessee in 1991 they climbed in Florida and Georgia.

Strickland stepped down as chairman and CEO in 1990. Wells died in 1991 and James Williams a conservative banker who instilled strict fiscal management in the Trust banks became chairman and CEO. Under his direction the company reduced its nonperforming assets and began diversifying its business lines.

In 1993 the bank adopted accounting rules that caused it to revalue its Coca-Cola stock from its historic value of $110000 to almost $1.1 billion. The dividends from these holdings contributed substantially to revenues.

SunTrust continued developing its nonbanking financial services: It expanded its investment services outside its traditional southern US market and bought Equitable Securities (now SunTrust Equitable Securities) in 1998. That year president Phillip Humann succeeded Williams as chairman and CEO. SunTrust also nearly doubled its branch count when it bought Crestar Financial a banking powerhouse in the mid-Atlantic and Southeast.

In 1999 the company created a new trust business to serve high-net-worth clients and it consolidated its 27 banking charters in six states into one based in Georgia the following year. In 2001 SunTrust made an unsolicited offer for Wachovia which was on track to be acquired by First Union. After a heated proxy campaign Wachovia's board of directors and shareholders voted down SunTrust's bid. Also that year the company bought the institutional business of investment bank Robinson-Humphrey a unit of Citigroup's Salomon Smith Barney .

SunTrust bought National Commerce Financial in 2004 for some $7 billion. The deal helped the bank expand in existing territories as well as provide entry into the growing North Carolina market where SunTrust had been conspicuously absent. The company divested its 49% stake in First Market Bank (Ukrop's Super Markets owns the rest) which it acquired in the National Commerce deal. SunTrust unloaded the unit in part because it has branches in Kroger Publix Safeway and Wal-Mart stores.

The company placed on administrative leave or dismissed several financial officers after it had to restate its earnings for the first two quarters of 2004 due to miscalculations of its loan loss reserves. (The SEC concluded an investigation into the matter in 2006 without recommending penalties.)

Former president and COO Jim Wells became CEO in 2007; Humann remained as chairman but stepped down the following year.

SunTrust bought GB&T Bancshares in 2008 adding about 20 branches in north and central Georgia.

To raise money and streamline operations SunTrust spun off several noncore operations in 2008. Like many of its peers SunTrust took part in the Federal Reserve's bailout in 2008 selling the government about $4.9 billion in preferred shares. The company repaid the government in 2011. That helped contribute to better earnings that year. SunTrust also reported higher net interest income and lower provision for credit losses.

The nationwide economic crisis impacted many of SunTrust's core markets in the Southeast particularly hard as credit markets froze and unemployment levels increased. The bank suffered some $1.6 billion in losses in 2009 alone mainly related to bad loans both on the consumer and commercial levels. By 2010 the company began to see improvements in charge-offs delinquencies and nonperforming loans but loan demand remained soft. In 2011 Sun Trust's financial performance improved and its loan portfolio grew by 6%. However the economic recovery was slow and spotty interest rates remained low and new federal regulations hit SunTrust's fee revenue streams.

EXECUTIVES

Evp And Chief Human Resources Officer, Kenneth J Carrig

Corporate EVP General Counsel and Corporate Secretary, Raymond D. Fortin, age 64

Corporate EVP and Chief Risk Officer, Jerome T. Lienhard, age 60, $516,667 total compensation

Chairman and CEO, William H. (Bill) Rogers, age 59, $1,000,000 total compensation

Corporate EVP and Chief Human Resources Officer, Margaret L. Callihan, age 61

Vice Chairman and Consumer Segment Executive, Mark A. Chancy, age 53, $658,333 total compensation

EVP and CFO, Aleem Gillani, age 55, $611,667 total compensation

Corporate EVP and Efficiency and Strategic Partnerships Executive, Thomas E. (Tom) Freeman, age 66, $600,000 total compensation

Wholesale Segment Executive, Hugh S. (Beau) Cummins, age 54

EVP and CIO, Anil Cheriyan, age 59, $500,000 total compensation

EVP and Chief Marketing Officer, Susan S. Johnson, age 51

Senior Vice President And Corporate Director Tax, Terry Vacheron

Senior Vice President, Mark Flynn

Vice President Consumer Deposit Pricing Analyst, Brian Raack

Vice President and Group Manager Business and Professional Treasury Management Services, Steve Jenkins

Assistant Vice President Customer Care Manager, Michelle Mathews

First Vice President, Greg Greer

First Vice President BSA and AML Risk Manager 2, Charlie M Hettler

Vice President CRE Risk Officer Professional Development, Robin Dyer

First Vice President, Jennifer Sexton

Senior Vice President Commercial Banking, Reuben Clarson

Vice President, Dave Hevner

Vice President, Richard Qka

First Vice President Sales and Marketing, Julie Cooper

Vice President Wholesale Marketing Manager, Melanie Mitchell

Vice President marketing Information Analyst, Baker Belle

First Vice President, Robert Mayo

First Vice President, Ruthie B Cook Cherry

Vice President Information Technology Infrastructure, Richard Willman

Vice President Risk Review, Kathy Gearing

Vice President and Manager Profic Systems and Product Management, Nancy Peck

First Vice President, Edana Hough

First Vice President and Senior Counsel, Alan McNabb

Vice President Information Technology, Anit Patel

Assistant Vice President, Nadia Mahmoud

Assistant Vice President Business Relationship Manager, Greg Poznanski

Vice President Finance Systems Operations, Gladu Andrew

Vice President Eis Workstream Manager, Josh Takis

Assistant Vice President Executive Recruiter, John Mastro

Vice President, Lory Liberty

First Vice President And Senior Counsel, Adam Humphreys

Assistant Vice President Corporate Security, Debbie Liguori

Assistant Vice President and Legal Administrator, Marc Bearden

Senior Vice President Institutional Real Estate, Ward Ebbert

Vice President, Laura Fedor

Senior Vice President Group Portfolio Manager, Deborah Armstrong

Vice President, Calvin Daley

Group Vice President Stoli Integration Manager, Janet Solomon

Loan Closing Specialist Vice President, Jennifer Parrott

Assistant Vice President, Jennifer Fessia

GVP, Celia Mackenzie

Assistant Vice President, John Logan

Branch Manager Assistant Vice President, Laurie Tyree

Assistant Vice President, Joshua Mccann

Assistant Vice President Portfolio Manager, Alfred Newsome

Assistant Vice President, David Massey

Vice President Diversified Commercial Division, Peter Lee

Senior Vice President, K Clore

Vice President, Michael Almeda

Lead Project Manager Assistant Vice President, Allison Roddie-Crews

First Vice President, Julie Hwang

First Vice President And Senior Counsel, Ned Kuntz

First Vice President, Jasmine Grant

Assistant Vice President Talent Acquisition, Doug Ledford

Assistant Vice President, Monique Lapierre

First Vice President, Stefanie Cannella

Vice President Client Advisor, Earle Simmons

Assistant Vice President Relationship Manager Commercial Banking, Hilliary Jones

Branch Manager Assistantvice President, Stephen Ryan

Senior Vice President, Mark Kawa

Vice President President and Trust Advisor Florida Advisory Center, Thomas Vrecenak

First Vice President, Shefali Patel

Executive Vice President, Mark Smith

Vice President, Ben Cumming

Assistant Vice President, Keith Kline

Vice President Capital Management, Crosby Mulwee

FVP, Tracey Nickolson

First Vice President, John Mullins

First Vice President, Leigh Saxon

First Vice President Mass Market Segment and Deposit Marketing Manager, William Freeman

Assistant Vice President Branch Manager, Sabrina Williams

Senior Statistician Assistant Vice President, Naveen Manivannan

Assistant Vice President, Becky Pennington

Senior Vice President Commercial Division, Parker Harrington

Vice President, Michael Peden

First Vice President, Kim Krause

First Vice President Business Banking, Karen Chevalier

Fsr4 Assistant Vice President, Kim Lovell

Senior Vice President Strategic Finance, Heather Henry

Assistant Vice President Enterprise Information Systems, Chris Navo

First Vice President, Siba Noble

Vice President Business Project Manager, Jean Castleberry

Vice President, Sutton Fannon

Senior Vice President, Doris Saad
First Vice President, Stephanie White
First Vice President, Mary Werner
Executive Vice President, James Gaffney
Vice President Marketing Manager Tampa Bay, Jan Berger
Senior Vice President Private Client Advisory Services, Lori Caumeil
Vice President Audit Services, Kelley Slappey
Vice President, Michael Nocero
First Vice President, Diana Pollidore
Assistant Vice President, Jane B Blythe
First Vice President, Ashley Miller
Senior Vice President Re Finance, Patricia Levy
First Vice President, Mary Finn
Vice President And Manager, Linda Rotsztein
Senior Vice President Senior Credit Officer, H Blalock
Senior Vice President, Clay Jacob
Senior Vice President, Loretta Mervis
RE Special Assets And First Vice President, Matthew Hammond
Vice President, Chris Hodgin
First Vice President, Pamela Fleming
Assistant Vice President GA Human Resources Operations Manager, Mary James
Assistant Vice President Commercial Banking, Jeffrey Charron
Assistant Vice President, Cynthia Iwashchenko
Vice President Asset Based Lending, Chris Jensen
First Vice President And Senior Counsel, Mike Andersen
Assistant Vice President Mortgage Banker, Alia Ahmadi
Group Vice President Event Marketing and Activation, Christie Slaton
First Vice President, Neil Newberry
Assistant Vice President Loss Mitigation, James Mcnaughton
Vice President, Peter Coley
First Vice President Credit Training Manager, Scott Clemmons
Senior Vice President In the Consumer Lending Operations Area, Mike Hafdelin
Vice President Consumer Portfolio Program Management, Michael Caston
Vice President and Manager Intelligence and Risk Management, Alvin C Mitcham
Vice President, Allison Cook
Senior Vice President and Fiduciary Executive, Gary Hodges
Vice President Dealer Development Representative, Carolyn Dudley
Vice President Leasing Sales Representative, Bill Koss
Senior Vice President Regional Sales Director Of S, Mike Ohare
Vice President, Lanette Davis
Vice President, Lance Longwater
Senior Vice President, Chad Brown
Group Vice President, Greg Boyd
Senior Vice President Human Relations, Melinda Schwartz
Senior Vice President and Marketing Director for Tampa Bay Region, Kathy James
First Vice President, Marc Carpentier
Group Vice President and Manager Database Marketing, Mike Register
Group Vice President, Kim Karamarkovich
Assistant Vice President, Terri Harlow
Group Vice President, Debra Tuthill
Group Vice President Audit Services, Roberto Nieves
Vice President, Haynes Gentry
Vice President Product Management, Chelisa Boyd-smith
Vice President Process Design Manager, Andy Woltman
Vice President, William Dauska
Senior Vice President, Mark Hughes

Senior Vice President, Chandler Burns
Senior Vice President Special Assets Division, Lawrence Perry
Auditors: Ernst & Young LLP

LOCATIONS

HQ: SunTrust Banks Inc
303 Peachtree Street, N.E., Atlanta, GA 30308
Phone: 800 786-8787
Web: www.suntrust.com

PRODUCTS/OPERATIONS

Selected ServicesAuto & Home InsuranceCommercial InsuranceCommercial Investment BankingCredit CardsMobile BankingMoney ServicesOnline BankingPersonal CheckingPersonal Credit CardsPrivate Wealth ManagementSavings Money Markets & CDs2016 Sales

	$ mil.	% of total
Interest Income	5,778	63
Non-Interest Income	3,383	37
Total	9,161	100

COMPETITORS

BB&T	First Horizon
BBVA Compass Bancshares	First Republic (CA)
BBX Capital	JPMorgan Chase
BancorpSouth	KeyCorp
Bank of America	M&T Bank
Citigroup	PNC Financial
Citizens Financial Group	Regions Financial
Fifth Third	Synovus
First Citizens BancShares	U.S. Bancorp
	Wells Fargo

HISTORICAL FINANCIALS

Company Type: Public

Income Statement
FYE: December 31

	ASSETS ($ mil.)	NET INCOME ($ mil.)	INCOME AS % OF ASSETS	EMPLOYEES
12/16	204,875	1,878	0.9%	24,375
12/15	190,817	1,933	1.0%	24,043
12/14	190,328	1,774	0.9%	24,638
12/13	175,335	1,344	0.8%	26,281
12/12	173,442	1,958	1.1%	26,778
Annual Growth	4.3%	(1.0%)		(2.3%)

2016 Year-End Financials

Debt ratio: 5.97%
Return on equity: 7.96%
Cash ($ mil.): 5,116
Current ratio: —
Long-term debt ($ mil.): —

No. of shares (mil.): 491
Dividends
Yield: 0.0%
Payout: 27.7%
Market value ($ mil.): 26,942

	STOCK PRICE ($) FY Close	P/E High/Low		PER SHARE ($)		
				Earnings	Dividends	Book Value
12/16	54.85	16	9	3.60	1.00	48.08
12/15	42.84	13	10	3.58	0.92	46.07
12/14	41.90	13	11	3.23	0.70	43.86
12/13	36.81	15	11	2.41	0.35	39.96
12/12	28.35	8	5	3.59	0.20	38.94
Annual Growth	17.9%	—	—	0.1%	49.5%	5.4%

SUNY COLLEGE AT CORTLAND

Auditors: KPMG LLP ALBANY NEW YORK

LOCATIONS

HQ: SUNY COLLEGE AT CORTLAND
38 CHENEY HALL, CORTLAND, NY 130452452
Phone: 607 753-2011
Web: WWW.SUNYCORTLAND.NET

HISTORICAL FINANCIALS

Company Type: Private

Income Statement
FYE: June 30

	REVENUE ($ mil.)	NET INCOME ($ mil.)	NET PROFIT MARGIN	EMPLOYEES
06/14	6,049	(0)	—	750
06/13	6	(0)	—	
Annual Growth	100504.2%		—	—

2014 Year-End Financials

Debt ratio: —
Return on equity: —
Cash ($ mil.): 1,334
Current ratio: 1.00
Long-term debt ($ mil.): —

Dividends
Yield: —
Payout: —
Market value ($ mil.): —

Supervalu Inc

SUPERVALU understands the lure of a good deal. The company offers wholesale grocery distribution and logistics services to about 1900 independent retailers and more than 180 military commissaries in the US and overseas. It supplies brand-name and private-label goods in every price range. SUPERVALU's retail operations include more than 200 regional grocery stores under the Cub Foods Shoppers Food & Pharmacy Shop 'n Save Farm Fresh Hornbachers and Rainbow banners. All told the company covers about 40 US states from nearly 20 distribution centers. In 2016 the company sold its Save-A-Lot grocery stores to investment firm Onex Corp. for $1.36 billion in cash.

Operations

SUPERVALU generates more than 60% of its revenue from its wholesale business which involves distribution and logistics operations. It serves 1800 retail customers in 40 states from about distribution centers. SUPERVALU's wholesale customers include conventional and upscale supermarkets combination food and drugstores supercenters convenience stores limited assortment stores and e-tailers. SUPERVALU offers its retailers private labels in every price range and in virtually every store category from the value-priced Shoppers Value brand to the premium Preferred Selection and organic Wild Harvest lines. SUPERVALU also offers retailers support services such as information technology store design and construction.

Retail food or all the regional grocery stores includes more than 200 stores and contributes more than 30% of revenue.

In 2016 the company sold Save-A-Lot to private equity firm Onex Corp. for $1.36 billion. Under

SUPERVALU's ownership the 1330 owned and licensed Save-A-Lot grocery stores held the #1 spot by revenues in the extreme-value grocery category and operated in nearly 40 states.

Geographic Reach

SUPERVALU's headquarters is in Minnesota and its distribution business serves most of the nation and military commissaries in the US Puerto Rico the Azores Cuba Guam Korea Japan and in Europe.

Financial Performance

After five years of revenue in the $17 billion range SUPERVALU?s revenue fell to $12.5 billion in 2017 (ended February). The 28% drop from 2015 reflected the company?s sale of its Save-A-Lot operations. SUPERVALU also had lower sales in its wholesale and retail operations which did not previously include the Save-A-Lot business. The reduced revenue included loss of some categories supplied to some stores lower sales to existing stores and lower military sales. SUPERVALU picked up revenue from new customers and new stores opened by existing customers. In retail same store sales fell on lower customer counts lower average basket size and the impact of closed stores.

The sale of Save-A-Lot boosted SUPERVALU?s earnings to about $650 million in 2016 a 265% jump from 2015.

Cash flow from operations rose to $308 million in 2017 from $245 million in 2016 because of lower levels of cash used in operating assets and liabilities.

Strategy

After selling its Save-A-Lot chain to Onex Corp. for $1.36 billion SUPERVALU looks to build its wholesale business while shoring up its retail business. The company is working on retaining existing customers and expanding its business with them as well as finding new customers. The company said it kept about 99% of its customers in 2017 (ended February) and cited Fresh Market as a new customer of its wholesale operations.

Two acquisitions also strengthened the wholesale business geographically. SUPERVALU acquired Unified Grocers on the West Coast and Associated Grocers of Florida.

In retail SUPERVALU is building its stock to meet customers? preferences and offer more customization. The company also will emphasize its private Culinary Circle and Wild Harvest.

Mergers and Acquisitions

In October 2017 SUPERVALU agreed to acquire Associated Grocers of Florida for about $180 million. The deal opens Associated Grocers? customers in South Florida the Caribbean and international markets to SUPERVALU. The company also reached a long-term supply agreement with Associated Grocers' largest customer. The transaction was expected to close by the end of 2017.

Earlier in 2017 SUPERVALU acquired wholesale grocery distributor Unified Grocers in a deal valued at about $390 million including outstanding stock and debt. Acquiring Unified Grocers bolsters SUPERVALU's distribution network in the western US where the wholesale distributor operated prior to the acquisition.

SUPERVALU also expanded its wholesale business in 2016 by acquiring 22 Food Lion grocery stores that were sold in connection with the merger between Ahold and Delhaize. The 22 Food Lion stores are in northern West Virginia western Maryland south central Pennsylvania and northwestern Virginia. The acquired stores were converted to SUPERVALU's Shop 'N Save format.

HISTORY

SUPERVALU's predecessor was formed in Minneapolis in the 1870s — and again in 1926. In 1871 wholesalers Hugh Harrison George Newell and W. D. Washburn joined forces to create Newell and Harrison. Newell bought out his partners in 1874 and renamed the firm George R. Newell Co. Five years later Harrison formed his own operation H. G. Harrison Co. In 1926 the companies merged creating Winston & Newell Co. the largest grocery distributor to independent grocers in the Midwest.

The company was part of the Independent Grocers Alliance from 1928-1942 before adopting the name Super Valu Stores in 1954. It expanded by acquiring chains such as Piggly-Wiggly Midland (1958 Wisconsin) and a number of wholesale operations across the US.

Super Valu entered nonfood retailing in 1971 by acquiring ShopKo a discount department store chain. Two years later it founded clothing chain County Seat (sold 1983). Super Valu added a new format to its food operations by purchasing Cub Stores (warehouse-style groceries) in 1980; it later combined its Cub Stores and ShopKo formats. More acquisitions followed including Atlanta's Food Giant chain. Super Valu named Michael Wright CEO in 1981 and chairman in 1982.

Super Valu acquired Scott's an Indiana food store chain in 1991 and sold a 54% interest in ShopKo to the public. The company changed its name to SUPERVALU in 1992 and bought food wholesaler Wetterau making it the #1 independent food distributor in the US and giving it the Save-A-Lot franchise (launched in 1978).

Experiencing sluggish distribution growth SUPERVALU continued to expand its retail holdings. Acquisitions in 1994 included Sweet Life Foods (280 stores) and 30 Texas T Stores. In 1996 it acquired six St. Louis Price Chopper warehouse stores and Fleming's Sav-U-Foods converting the 21 stores to Save-A-Lots and establishing a presence in California. SUPERVALU sold its remaining 46% stake in ShopKo the next year. In 1999 the company signed a deal to supply 1350 Kmart stores. SUPERVALU also acquired distributor and food retailer Richfood Holdings.

The company completed its acquisition of 1124 stores from Albertsons in June 2006. The new stores included Acme Markets Bristol Farms Jewel Shaw's Supermarkets Star Markets and Albertsons stores. Looking to take back sales lost to natural and organic grocery chains SUPERVALU launched its own natural foods division called Sunflower Market in 2006. (SUPERVALU originally had planned to open as many as 50 Sunflower Markets but in early 2008 announced it would close its five Sunflower Markets as they did not deliver expected results.)

Throughout 2009 as recession gripped the country SUPERVALU closed or sold more than 100 stores nationwide including about 40 Albertsons stores in Utah to grocery wholesaler Associated Food Stores. The closings were part of an effort by the company to scale back spending.

In 2010 SUPERVALU made several divestments. Early in the year it sold off its Payson Store Fixtures division which made fixtures millwork and decor items to DGS Retail. It sold its Bristol Farms chain of more than a dozen upscale supermarkets in California to local management and the West Coast investment firm Endeavour Capital for an undisclosed amount in October.

In September 2011 the company sold more than 100 fuel centers associated with its Albertsons Cub Foods Hornbacher's and Jewel-Osco banners to four different buyers. The sale was part of SUPERVALU's effort to raise cash by selling non-core assets.

In 2013 the company completed the sale of five retail banners — Albertsons Jewel Acme and Shaw's/Star Market — to an affiliate of a Cerberus Capital Management-led investor consortium for $3.3 billion.

EXECUTIVES

President and CEO, Mark Gross, age 53, $1,000,000 total compensation
EVP and CIO, Randy G. Burdick, age 59, $550,385 total compensation
EVP Corporate Development and Chief Innovation Officer, James Weidenheimer, age 58, $486,538 total compensation
President Cub Foods, Michael C. (Mike) Stigers, age 58, $475,000 total compensation
EVP Chief Strategy Officer and Interim CFO, Rob N. Woseth, age 46, $414,615 total compensation
EVP Retail Marketing and Private Brands, Anne Dament
Vice President Marketing Systems Retail Systems and Retail Field, Rick Collison
Vice President Logistics, Micheal Lech
Vice President, Tom Yeager
Chairman, Gerald L. Storch, age 60
Auditors: KPMG LLP

LOCATIONS

HQ: Supervalu Inc
    11840 Valley View Road, Eden Prairie, MN 55344
Phone: 952 828-4000
Web: www.supervalu.com

PRODUCTS/OPERATIONS

2017 sales

	% of total
Wholesale	62
Retail	37
Corporate	1
Total	**100**

Selected Banners

Cub
Farm Fresh
Hornbacher's
Save-A-Lot (discount retail)
Shop 'N Save
Shoppers

Selected Services

Accounting
Category management
Consumer and market research
Financial assistance
Insurance
Merchandising assistance
Personnel training
Private-label program
Retail operations counseling
Site selection and purchasing or leasing assistance
Store design and construction
Store equipment
Store management assistance
Store planning
Strategic and business planning

Selected Private-Label Brands

Culinary Circle
essensia
equaline
Flavorite
HomeLife
Richfood
Shopper's Value
Wild Harvest

COMPETITORS

A&P	Kroger
ALDI	Marsh Supermarkets
Alex Lee	McLane
Arden Group	Meijer
Associated Wholesale Grocers	Piggly Wiggly Midwest
BJ's Wholesale Club	Rite Aid
Big Y Foods	Roundy's
Bozzuto's	Safeway
C&S Wholesale	Schnuck Markets
	Sherwood Food

CVS
Costco Wholesale
Dierbergs Markets
Dollar General
Dollar Tree
Family Dollar Stores
Giant Eagle
Hannaford Bros.
Jetro Cash & Carry
Krasdale Foods

SpartanNash
Stater Bros.
Stop & Shop
Target Corporation
Wakefern Food
Wal-Mart
Walgreen
Whole Foods
Winn-Dixie

HISTORICAL FINANCIALS

Company Type: Public

Income Statement

FYE: February 25

	REVENUE ($ mil.)	NET INCOME ($ mil.)	NET PROFIT MARGIN	EMPLOYEES
02/17	12,480	650	5.2%	29,000
02/16	17,529	178	1.0%	38,000
02/15	17,820	192	1.1%	38,500
02/14	17,155	182	1.1%	35,800
02/13	17,097	(1,466)	—	35,000
Annual Growth	(7.6%)	—	—	(4.6%)

2017 Year-End Financials

Debt ratio: 41.20%
Return on equity: ***,***.**%
Cash ($ mil.): 332
Current ratio: 1.25
Long-term debt ($ mil.): 1,449

No. of shares (mil.): 38
Dividends
  Yield: —
  Payout: —
Market value ($ mil.): 150

	STOCK PRICE ($) FY Close	P/E High/Low		PER SHARE ($) Earnings	Dividends	Book Value
02/17	3.92	0	0	17.01	0.00	9.82
02/16	4.93	3	1	4.62	0.00	(11.65)
02/15	9.88	2	1	5.11	0.00	(17.39)
02/14	6.10	2	1	4.90	0.00	(20.18)
02/13	3.85	—	—	(48.37)	0.61	(46.50)
Annual Growth	0.5%			—	—	—

SUTTER HEALTH

Whether you drink too much in Wine Country hit some rough waters off the Marin Headlands or trip during a hike through the redwood forest it's likely Sutter Health is just a stone's throw away. The Northern California not-for-profit health care system is one of the nation's largest with more than 4300 acute care beds. After being formed through the merger of Sutter Health and California Healthcare System Sutter Health now caters to residents of more than 100 communities from the California Bay Area to the beaches of Hawaii. Its services are provided through affiliated doctors from a host of health care facilities including acute care hospitals home health networks and skilled nursing facilities.

Operations

Sutter Health affiliates provide acute care services health education home health care hospice care adult day care prenatal clinics immunization services and other specialized health care services.

The system's health plan network includes 25 hospitals and campuses and dozens of other facilities with more than 5000 providers serving some 40000 members throughout Northern California.

In 2015 the system reported more than 11 million outpatient visits; 190054 discharges; and 797057 emergency room visits.

Geographic Reach

Sutter Health structures its governance into two geographic regions across Northern California: the Bay Area (which also includes Hawaii) and the Valley. Each area has its own board that oversees affiliates within the region.

Financial Performance

In 2015 Sutter Health reported $11 billion in total operating revenue up from $10.2 billion in 2014. Net income from operations totaled $287 million in 2015 a 10% decline from 2014; the drop in income was driven by higher operating expenses and a decline in investment income.

Strategy

In 2016 Sutter Health announced plans to open dialysis and chemotherapy infusion centers at its Sutter Coast Hospital facility in Crescent City.

However the system made waves that year when it said it would shutter its Alta Bates Summit Medical Center in Berkeley by 2030. Community members responded by calling for Sutter Health to keep the hospital open; Sutter plans to consolidate the facility's services with those of its sister campus Summit Medical Center which is three miles away. The move to close a hospital which has seen decreased patient stays is not unusual as many health systems are pushing to broaden their service offerings on an outpatient basis.

Like most other health care organizations across the country Sutter Health is using technology to keep its patients informed about their medical care. The company is part of a national group participating in a program called Care Everywhere a technology that enables medical teams from separate hospitals and clinics to share a patient's medical records at the time he or she receives care. Through this technology Sutter Health is linked with UC Davis Health System Stanford Health Care and Santa Cruz County Health Services to share vital patient information.

EXECUTIVES

CEO Sutter Health Sacramento-Sierra Region, Sarah Krevans, age 58
SVP and CFO, Robert D. (Bob) Reed, age 65
President Sutter Health Central Valley Region, David P. Benn
President Sutter Health East Bay Region, David Bradley
SVP and CIO, Jonathan (Jon) Manis
SVP; Executive Officer Sutter Medical Network, Jeffrey Burnich
President Sutter Health West Bay Region, Mike Cohill
President Sutter Health Sacramento Sierra Region, James E. Conforti
President Sutter Health Peninsula Coastal Region, Jeff Gerard
CEO Sutter Solano Medical Center, Abhishek Dosi
Revenue Cycle Vice President, Suzy Cliff
Vice President Strategic Marketing, Tracy Murphy
Vice President Philanthropy And Executive Director, Jennifer Svihus
Regional Vice President West Bay Region Facility Development, Jenifer Turnbull
Nursing Director Maternal Newborn Unit, Aneen Heller
Chair, Geraldine R. Brinton
Vice President Finance and Treasurer, Svend Ryge

LOCATIONS

HQ: SUTTER HEALTH
2200 RIVER PLAZA DR, SACRAMENTO, CA 958334134
Phone: 916 733-8800

Selected Hospitals
Alta Bates Summit Medical Center (Berkeley Oakland)
California Pacific Medical Center (San Francisco)
Eden Medical Center (Castro Valley)

Kahi Mohala (Ewa HI)
Marin General Hospital (Greenbrae)
Memorial Hospital Los Banos (Los Banos)
Memorial Medical Center (Modesto)
Menlo Park Surgical Hospital
Mills-Peninsula Health Services (Burlingame)
Novato Community Hospital (Novato)
Sutter Amador Hospital (Jackson)
Sutter Auburn Faith Hospital (Auburn)
Sutter Coast Hospital (Crescent City)
Sutter Davis Hospital (Davis)
Sutter Delta Medical Center (Antioch)
Sutter Lakeside Hospital (Lakeport)
Sutter Maternity & Surgery Center of Santa Cruz
Sutter Medical Center (Sacramento)
Sutter Medical Center of Santa Rosa
Sutter Roseville Medical Center
Sutter Solano Medical Center (Vallejo)
Sutter Tracy Community Hospital (Tracy)

PRODUCTS/OPERATIONS

Selected Operations (Northern California Southern Oregon and Hawaii)
Acute Care Hospitals
Neonatal Intensive Care Units
Cancer Centers
Cardiac Centers
Acute Rehabilitation Centers
Medical Foundations
Trauma Centers
Behavioral Health Services
Education Centers and Physician Training Programs
Express Medical Clinics
Home Health and Hospice Services
Long-term Care Centers
Medical Research Centers
Occupational Health Services
Long-Term Care Centers
Irene Swindells Alzheimer's Residential Care Center San Francisco
Sutter Oaks Nursing Center Sacramento
Sutter Senior Care PACE Program Sacramento
Cancer Centers
Alta Bates Summit Comprehensive Cancer Center Berkeley and Oakland
California Pacific Medical Center San Francisco
Dorothy E. Schneider Cancer Center at Mills-Peninsula Health Services Burlingame
Eden Medical Center Castro Valley
Memorial Regional Cancer Center Modesto
Sutter Auburn Faith Hospital Auburn
Sutter Cancer Center Sutter Medical Center Sacramento
Sutter Cancer Center Sutter Roseville Medical Center Roseville
Sutter Solano Cancer Center Vallejo
Programs listed above are approved by the American College of Surgeons' Commission on Cancer.
Research Institutes
California Pacific Medical Center San Francisco
Palo Alto Medical Foundation Research Institute Palo Alto
Sutter Health Institute for Research and Education San Francisco
Sutter Institute for Medical Research Sacramento
Home Health and Hospice Services
Coming Home Hospice
Cohen Cormier Home Attendant & Care Management
Sutter Auburn Faith VNA & Hospice
Sutter Care at Home
Sutter Coast Home Care
Sutter Infusion & Pharmacy Services / Emeryville and Sacramento
Sutter Lakeside Home Medical Services
Sutter Lif
Sutter North Home Health Agency
VNA of the Central Valley
VNA of Santa Cruz County
Express Medical Clinics
Sutter Express Care (Three locations in Sacramento & Placer counties)

COMPETITORS

Adventist Health System West
Alta Bates Summit Medical Center
Ascension Health
California Pacific Medical Center
Children's Hospital & Research Center at Oakland

Dignity Health
HCA
Hawai'i Pacific Health
Kuakini Health System
Memorial Health Services
Providence St. Joseph Health
Rehabilitation Hospital of the Pacific
Stanford Health Care
Tenet Healthcare
UCSF Medical

HISTORICAL FINANCIALS
Company Type: Private

Income Statement
FYE: December 31

	REVENUE ($ mil.)	NET INCOME ($ mil.)	NET PROFIT MARGIN	EMPLOYEES
12/16	11,873	422	3.6%	48,000
12/15	10,998	84	0.8%	—
12/14	9,715	(405)	—	—
12/13	9,649	961	10.0%	—
Annual Growth	7.2%	(24.0%)	—	—

2016 Year-End Financials

Debt ratio: —
Return on equity: 3.60%
Cash ($ mil.): 426
Current ratio: 0.90
Long-term debt ($ mil.): —

Dividends
Yield: —
Payout: —
Market value ($ mil.): —

SVB Financial Group

SVB Financial Group is the holding company for Silicon Valley Bank which serves emerging and established companies involved in technology life sciences and private equity and provides customized financing to entrepreneurs executives and investors in such industries. It also offers deposit accounts loans and international banking and plays matchmaker for young firms and private investors. SVB Financial also provides investment advisory brokerage and asset management services; and provides credit and banking services to wealthy individuals.

Operations

The company operates in three segments: Global Commercial Bank SVB Private Bank and SVB Capital.

Global Commercial Bank segment is comprised of Commercial Bank SVB Specialty Lending SVB Analytics and Debt Fund Investments. Commercial Bank serves commercial clients in the technology venture capital/private equity life science and cleantech industries. SVB Analytics provides equity valuation services to private companies and venture capital/private equity firms while Debt Fund Investments has investments in debt funds.

SVB Private Bank provides personal financial solutions for consumers while its capital arm SVB Capital focuses primarily on funds management.

As part of its lending activities Silicon Valley Bank sometimes pursues warrants to purchase equity stakes in its clients. About 80% of the bank's loan portfolio is dedicated to commercial loans with about half of those going to software and internet companies and another 25% of commercial loans going toward private equity or venture capital firms. Traditionally focused on up-and-coming firms the bank has implemented a strategy of courting larger later-stage clients.

Geographic Reach

SVB Financial has 28 offices in the US as well as seven branches in China India Israel and the UK.

Sales and Marketing

SVB Financial's clients are primarily venture capital and private equity professionals. Its customers include Active Power Coskata EnerNOC Joule and Solexant.

Financial Performance

SVB's revenue grew for its fifth straight year with revenue rising by 4% to $1.46 billion in 2014. Though nearly all income streams grew the main drivers of growth came from higher interest income from investment securities and loans as average deposit and loan balances grew respectively. A 130% boost in net gains on derivative instruments also contributed significantly to the company's top line.

Despite higher revenue net income reversed course in 2014 and fell by 12% to $478.72 million. The drop was mostly because SVB paid higher compensation and benefits as it gave its employees market-adjusted raises and hired 146 new staff members to support its product development operational sales advisory and commercial banking operations and initiatives.

Operations provided $255.52 million or 33% more cash than in 2013 mostly because more of its earnings were cash payments as opposed to 2013 when non-cash gains on investment securities made up a larger share of earnings. The company also enjoyed higher cash generation from foreign exchange spot contracts.

Strategy

SVB Financial Group has been focused on growing its loan business and assets to drive growth in recent years. Indeed in 2014 the company's loan assets grew by 32% to $14.4 billion while deposits grew 52% to $34.3 billion — both factors that led the company to record-high revenue by the end of the year.

It's also been selectively expanding and divesting its overseas operations to focus resources on profitable segments. In early 2015 subsidiary SVB Bank agreed to sell all of its outstanding stock in its non-banking financial subsidiary SVP India Finance Private Limited to Singapore-based investment firm Temasek. In 2012 the company opened a banking branch in the UK and started a joint venture bank in China.

Company Background

Greg Becker who joined SVB Financial in 1993 was named the company's CEO in 2011. He succeeded Ken Wilcox who became chairman and is focused on the company's efforts to expand in China including a joint venture with Shanghai Pudong Development Bank.

HISTORY

Silicon Valley Bank was founded in 1983 by Roger Smith to provide banking services to tech startups in San Jose. The bank boomed along with tech companies during the 1980s lending to the likes of Cisco Systems.

In 1990 the bank spread east to Boston's burgeoning technology alley. It also expanded into residential and commercial real estate lending. The recession of 1989 to 1991 found Silicon Valley Bancshares with an overextended loan portfolio and in 1992 the bank booked a loss due to nonperforming loans; the next year it was put under federal supervision.

To rally stockholder confidence the company brought in new management and demoted Smith from chairman to vice chairman; he left the in 1995. The bank reduced its real estate lending and diversified into factoring foreign exchange and executive banking for venture capitalists and clients' upper management.

The 1995 IPO frenzy aided the company's turnaround. Silicon Valley cashed in on warrants it had taken as collateral from young companies. Regulatory supervision was lifted in 1996 and the bank soon opened offices in the Atlanta; Austin Texas; Boulder Colorado; Phoenix; and Seattle areas.

In 1999 Silicon Valley Bancshares created a website targeted at technology firms in need of financing employees office space and equipment. However nonperforming loans began to dog the bank once again affecting profits and bringing a regulatory request to boost capital reserves.

In 2000 despite being hammered by the high-tech stock selloff the company continued to expand opening offices in West Palm Beach Florida and North Carolina's Research Triangle and successfully capitalizing its first venture fund. The following year it bought tech-focused investment bank Alliant Partners (later renamed SVB Alliant) to broaden its service offerings.

Still licking its wounds from the tech bust the company ceased lending to the entertainment industry and to churches in 2002. Silicon Valley Bancshares changed its name to SVB Financial Services in 2005.

SVB Alliant struggled with losses for years and SVB Financial explored its options including spinning the unit off to management. It ultimately decided to shut down the division which ceased operations in 2008.

EXECUTIVES

COO, Michael L. Dreyer, age 53
COO, Bruce E. Wallace, age 52, $398,113 total compensation
President and CEO SVB Financial Group and Silicon Valley Bank, Gregory W. (Greg) Becker, age 50, $925,904 total compensation
Managing Director Accounting and Financial Reporting, Michael R. (Mike) Descheneaux, age 50, $602,308 total compensation
Head of Technology Banking, John D. China, $498,385 total compensation
Head of Europe Middle East and Africa (EMEA) and President UK Branch, Philip C. Cox, age 50
Chief Credit Officer Silicon Valley Bank, Marc C. Cadieux, age 50, $447,308 total compensation
CFO, Daniel Beck
Chief Risk Officer, Laura Izurieta, age 56
CIO, Roger E. Leone, age 63
Vice President, Jennifer Zamudio
Vice President, Jenny Moody
Senior Vice President, Dave Bhagat
Vice President, Mark Harris
Vice President, Lindsay Gallion
Vice President Relationship Manager, Don Chandler
Vice President, Jocelyn Hartmann
Vice President Relationship Manager, Anthony R Raley
Vice President, Suzann Russell
Vice President, Joe Werner
Vice President, Damarie Rodriguez
Vice President, Sam Subilia
Vice President and Foreign Exchange Trader, Patrick Chin
Vice President, Mickey Swift
Vice President Regional Market Manager, John Atanasoff
Vice President, Lauren Cole
Vice President, Dan Hardman
Vice President Corporate Finance, Andrea Jones
Vice President, Ann Kim
Vice President Product Management, Susan Merrill
Senior Vice President, Laura Scott
Vice President, Patrick Haggerty
Vice President, Austin Badger
Vice President, Jigar Patel
Vice President, Jimmy Gan

Senior Vice President, Andy Tsao
Vice President Relationship Manager, John Peck
Vice President, Benjermin Colombo
Vice President, Patrick Scheper
Senior Vice President, Michael Tramack
Senior Vice President, Chris Stoecker
Vice President, Josh Dorsey
Vice President Sponsor Finance, Jesse Meyer
Vice President, Rob Walker
Vice President, Mark Rosshirt
Vice President, Sarah Kwan
Vice President, Max Lautmann
Vice President, Tamir Efraty
Vice President, Kyle Swan
Vice President, Dennis He
Vice President, Marina Bobrovich
Vice President Structured Finance, James Caron
Vice President Relationship Manager, Glenn
  Marasigan
Vice President, Jennie Bartlett
Vice President, Sarah Peluso
Vice President, Chase Little
Vice President, Marc Neri
Vice President, Sean Thompson
Vice President Life Science and Healthcare, Kaitlin
  Berube
Vice President, Erin Angerer
Vice President, Tyler Dietrich
Vice President Early Stage Banking, Navid
  Shahrestani
Vice President Global Fund Banking, Robert Pyke
Vice President, Jordan Parcell
Vice President Wine Division, Dave Morrison
Vice President, Carly Kiser
Vice President, Aerin Lim
Vice President, AJ Fang
Vice President Early Stage Practice, Joe Kopnisky
Chairman SVB Financial Group and Silicon Valley
  Bank, Roger F. Dunbar, age 71
Board Member, Eric A Benhamou
Assistant Secretary And Treasurer, Lori De Leon
Auditors: KPMG LLP

LOCATIONS

HQ: SVB Financial Group
  3003 Tasman Drive, Santa Clara, CA 95054-1191
Phone: 408 654-7400
Web: www.svb.com

Selected Offices
US
  Atlanta
  Austin TX
  Broomfield CO
  Chicago
  Dallas
  Irvine CA
  Menlo Park CA
  Minnetonka MN
  New York
  Newton MA
  Palo Alto CA
  Philadelphia
  Phoenix
  Pleasanton CA
  Portland OR
  Raleigh NC
  Salt Lake City
  San Diego
  San Francisco
  Santa Rosa CA
  Seattle
  St. Helena CA
  Tysons Corner VA
International
  Bangalore India
  Beijing
  Herzliya Pituach Israel
  London
  Mumbai India
  Shanghai

PRODUCTS/OPERATIONS

2016 Sales

	$ mil.	% of total
Interest		
Loans	834	51
Investment securities	359	22
Noninterest		
Net gains on investment securities	51	3
Net gains on derivative instruments	48	3
Foreign exchange fees	104	6
Credit card fees	68	4
Deposit service charges	52	3
Lending related fees	33	2
Letters of credit	25	2
Client investment fees	32	2
Other	40	2
Total	**1,649**	**100**

Selected Subsidiaries and Affiliates
Silicon Valley Bank
SVB Analytics Inc.
SVB Asset Management
SVB Business Partners (Beijing) Co. Ltd.
SVB Business Partners (Shanghai) Co. Ltd.
SVB Global Financial Inc.
SVB Global Investors LLC
SVB Growth Investors LLC
SVB India Advisors Pvt. Ltd.
SVB Israel Advisors Ltd.
SVB Qualified Investors Fund LLC
SVB Real Estate Investment Trust
SVB Securities
SVB Strategic Investors LLC
SVB Strategic Investors Fund L.P.
Venture Investment Managers L.P.

COMPETITORS

Bank of America	Heritage Commerce
Citigroup	MUFG Americas Holdings
City National	U.S. Bancorp
Comerica	

HISTORICAL FINANCIALS
Company Type: Public

Income Statement
FYE: December 31

	ASSETS ($ mil.)	NET INCOME ($ mil.)	INCOME AS % OF ASSETS	EMPLOYEES
12/16	44,683	382	0.9%	2,311
12/15	44,686	343	0.8%	2,089
12/14	39,344	263	0.7%	1,914
12/13	26,417	215	0.8%	1,704
12/12	22,766	175	0.8%	1,615
Annual Growth	**18.4%**	**21.6%**	**—**	**9.4%**

2016 Year-End Financials
Debt ratio: 1.78%
Return on equity: 11.16%
Cash ($ mil.): 2,481
Current ratio: —
Long-term debt ($ mil.): —
No. of shares (mil.): 52
Dividends
  Yield: —
  Payout: —
Market value ($ mil.): 8,970

	STOCK PRICE ($) FY Close	P/E High/Low		PER SHARE ($) Earnings	Dividends	Book Value
12/16	171.66	24	11	7.31	0.00	69.71
12/15	118.90	22	15	6.62	0.00	61.97
12/14	116.07	25	18	5.31	0.00	55.33
12/13	104.86	22	12	4.70	0.00	42.93
12/12	55.97	17	12	3.91	0.00	41.02
Annual Growth	**32.3%**	**—**	**—**	**16.9%**	**—**	**14.2%**

Synchrony Financial

Auditors: KPMG LLP

LOCATIONS

HQ: Synchrony Financial
  777 Long Ridge Road, Stamford, CT 06902
Phone: 203 585-2400
Web: www.synchronyfinancial.com

HISTORICAL FINANCIALS
Company Type: Public

Income Statement
FYE: December 31

	ASSETS ($ mil.)	NET INCOME ($ mil.)	INCOME AS % OF ASSETS	EMPLOYEES
12/16	90,207	2,251	2.5%	15,000
12/15	84,135	2,214	2.6%	12,000
12/14	75,707	2,109	2.8%	11,000
12/13	59,085	1,979	3.3%	9,333
12/12	53,462	2,119	4.0%	
Annual Growth	**14.0%**	**1.5%**	**—**	**—**

2016 Year-End Financials
Debt ratio: 22.33%
Return on equity: 16.75%
Cash ($ mil.): 9,321
Current ratio: —
Long-term debt ($ mil.): —
No. of shares (mil.): 817
Dividends
  Yield: 0.0%
  Payout: 9.5%
Market value ($ mil.): 29,645

	STOCK PRICE ($) FY Close	P/E High/Low		PER SHARE ($) Earnings	Dividends	Book Value
12/16	36.27	14	9	2.71	0.26	17.37
12/15	30.41	14	11	2.65	0.00	15.12
12/14	29.75	11	8	2.78	0.00	12.57
Annual Growth	**5.1%**	**—**	**—**	**(0.6%)**	**—**	**8.4%**

Synnex Corp

SYNNEX connects technology sellers with buyers and helps with customer service after the sale. The company distributes PCs peripherals software and consumer electronics from manufacturers that include Dell Hewlett-Packard Panasonic Lenovo Seagate and Microsoft. SYNNEX also provides design and support services. Its Concentrix segment offers customer support services using phone chat web e-mail and digital print. The company's online services include parts catalogs configuration and ordering. In addition the company offers contract design and assembly build-to-order and configure-to-order services for manufacturers and systems integrators.

Operations

SYNNEX operates through two segments: Technology Solutions (TS) and Concentrix. The TS segment which accounts for about 90% of the company's revenue distributes IT systems peripherals system components software networking equipment CE and complementary products. It also offers data center server and storage solutions.

Concentrix accounting for the remaining sales offers a range of business process outsourcing (BPO) services to customers such as those in technical support renewals management lead management direct sales customer service back office processing and information technology outsourcing.

Geographic Reach

Based in California SYNNEX has operations in Canada China Costa Rica India Japan Mexico Nicaragua the Philippines the UK and the US. The US is the company's largest market contributing more than 70% of sales.

The company has about 40 distribution and administrative facilities in the US Canada Japan and Mexico. It has warehouses in California Georgia Virginia Illinois Texas New Jersey Ohio Florida Mississippi and Oregon. Concentrix operates about 120 delivery centers and administrative facilities in numerous countries throughout North America Europe and Asia Pacific.

Sales and Marketing

SYNNEX maintains a sales headquarters in Greenville South Carolina. A dedicated sales staff serves its large commercial government reseller and retail customers. SYNNEX also markets its products and services to smaller resellers and OEMs through dedicated regional sales teams. The company also employs dedicated product management and business development specialists who focus on selling and promoting the products and services of selected suppliers or for specific end-market verticals.

Hewlett-Packard ranks as SYNNEX's biggest OEM supplier providing nearly 20% of revenue.

Financial Performance

SYNNEX has achieved unprecedented growth over the years with revenues reaching a record-setting $14.1 billion in 2016. Profits hit $235 million in 2016 another company milestone. The historic growth was fueled by increased sales from both its Technology Solutions and Concentrix segments.

Technology Solutions sales climbed in 2016 due to strong demand for its system design and integration services partially offset by lower sales in Japan. Concentrix sales spiked due to its acquisition of Minacs in August 2016 and the expansion of services to existing customers in addition to new customer contract signings.

The rise in profits for 2016 was attributed to the surge in revenue coupled with additional income associated with investments. In addition SYNNEX's cash flow has fluctuated wildly over the years; after rising sharply to $644 million in 2015 cash flow dropped to $327 million in 2016 mainly due to unfavorable changes in inventories.

Strategy

The tech products distributor pursues a decentralized regional strategy placing its distribution facilities near reseller customers and their end-users to benefit from lower shipping costs and shorter delivery times. SYNNEX looks to expand its business into areas primarily related to its core distribution business as well as other support logistics business process outsourcing and related value-added services. While the lion's share of the company's sales are rung up in North America and Japan the company is looking to grow in India. In 2015 the company opened a second Concentrix facility in Visakhapatnam.

SYNNEX also opened a service delivery center in Bogota Colombia to provide service to a banking clients. The center is the fifth Concentrix location in Latin America. A new delivery center in Porto Portugal is to help the company increase business from existing accounts and develop new accounts in Europe.

Mergers and Acquisitions

In 2017 SYNNEX acquired the Westcon-Comstor operations in North America and South America from Datatec Ltd. for about $800 million. SYNNEX also bought a a 10% stake in Datatec's Westcon International operations in Europe and the Asia/Pacific regions for about $30 million. The deal adds Westcon-Comstor?s products and services in security unified communications and collaboration and networking to SYNNEX's operations.

In late 2016 the company acquired Canada-based The Minacs Group Pte for $420 million which is being integrated into its Concentrix business segment. The additional revenue from Minacs helped SYNNEX to achieve record revenue growth for its fiscal 2016.

EXECUTIVES

President and CEO, Kevin M. Murai, age 54, $633,794 total compensation
Senior Vice President, David Dennis
President Hyve Solutions, Stephen Ichinaga, age 56
President North American Technology Solutions, Peter Larocque, age 56, $459,499 total compensation
President Broadline Division SYNNEX Canada, Mitchell P. Martin, age 54
SVP and CIO, Gary Gulmon, age 56
SVP Marketing North America, Robert L. (Bob) Stegner
COO, Dennis Polk, age 51, $459,499 total compensation
CFO, Marshall Witt, $437,986 total compensation
President New Age Electronics, Fred Towns
SVP and General Manager Global Business Services, Christopher (Chris) Caldwell, $441,670 total compensation
Associate Vice President Information Systems, Kirt Minor
Associate Vice President of Information Systems, Bo Li
Vice President Sales, Lisa Schroeder
Vice President of Sales, Bruce Holappa
Senior Vice President Partner Advocacy, Michael R Thomson
Vice President Sales, John Jandoc
Senior Vice President Information technology, Robert Sturycz
Vice President of Marketing, Mike Gazdic
Associate Vice President Accounting Controls, Marty Zanganeh
Vice President Sales, Nick Paul
Associate Vice President Sales, Willa Flemate
Assistant Vice President product management, Sarah Lin
Vice President Human Resources, Debra Torette
Vice President Internal Audit, Dana Aghai-Yazdy
Vice President Sales, Melanie Brown
Vice President TSD Design and Support Services, Kirk Nesbit
Vice President Microsoft GBU and Cloud Services, Rob Moyer
Vice President HP Enterprise Sales, Peter Montana
National Account Manager, Keith Cox
Senior Vice President, Gary Palenbaum
Assistant Vice President Commercial Sales Smb, John Phillips
Vice President of Product Management, Emily Chen
Vice President of retail Sales, Eric Kirkendall
Vice President of Human Resour, Deborah Laturette
Senior Vice President Systems Integration, Steve Ichinaga
Vice President Of Enterprise Products, Doug Bone
Senior Vice President Operations, Tim Rush
Vice President Credit and Collections, Ray Poulos
Senior Vice President of Product Marketing, Bob Stegner
Vice President Services, Joe Pittillo
Vice President And Senior Counsel, Jane Fogarty
National Account Manager, Chris Heim
Vice President HP Enterprise Sales, Synnex Hpenterprise
Chairman, Dwight Steffensen, age 74
Vice Chairman, Calvin Currie
Auditors: KPMG LLP

LOCATIONS

HQ: Synnex Corp
44201 Nobel Drive, Fremont, CA 94538
Phone: 510 656-3333
Web: www.synnex.com

2016 Sales

	$ mil.	% of total
United States	10,316	73
Canada	1,522	11
Other	2,223	16
Total	**14,061**	**100**

PRODUCTS/OPERATIONS

2016 Sales

	$ mil.	% of total
Technology solutions	12,490	89
Concentrix	1,587	11
Inter-segment	(16.6)	-
Total	**14,061**	**100**

Selected Subsidiaries

Concentrix Technologies Limited
ComputerLand Corporation
Concentrix Technologies (India) Private Limited
Concentrix Corporation
Concentrix Costa Rica S.A.
Concentrix Free Trade Zone S.A.
Concentrix HK Limited
Concentrix Nicaragua S.A
License Online Inc.
Sennex Enterprises Limited
SIT Funding Corporation
SYNNEX Canada Limited
SYNNEX GBS Limited
SYNNEX GBS Inc.
SYNNEX Information Technologies (Beijing) Ltd
SYNNEX Information Technologies (Chengdu) Ltd
SYNNEX Information Technologies (China) Ltd
SYNNEX Information Technologies (UK) Ltd
SYNNEX Infotec Corporation
SYNNEX Investment Holdings Corporation
SYNNEX Logistics Corporation
SYNNEX de Mé;xico S.A. de C.V
SYNNEX New (BVI) Corporation
SYNNEX NewHK Limited
SYNNEX Software Technologies (HK) Limited
SYNNEX-Concentrix Corporation
SYNNEX-Concentrix UK Limited
Concentrix Europe Limited
Intelligent Outsourcing of Central America S.A
VisionMAX Limited

Selected Services

Distribution
    Contract assembly
    Distribution services
    Logistics services
Global Business Services
    Automated service renewals software
    Customer services
    Hosted renewals services software in Europe (RenewalsManager)
    Financing services
    Marketing services
    Outsourced back-office services
    Technical support services

COMPETITORS

Arrow Electronics	Premier Farnell
Avnet	Sanmina
Benchmark Electronics	ScanSource
Celestica	ServiceSource
Convergys	Tech Data
D & H Distributing	TeleTech
Flextronics	Teleperformance
Hon Hai	Westcon
Ingram Micro	Wistron
Jabil	Yosun
Plexus	

HISTORICAL FINANCIALS

Company Type: Public

Income Statement

FYE: November 30

	REVENUE ($ mil.)	NET INCOME ($ mil.)	NET PROFIT MARGIN	EMPLOYEES
11/17	17,045	301	1.8%	113,600
11/16	14,061	234	1.7%	110,000
11/15	13,338	208	1.6%	72,500
11/14	13,839	180	1.3%	64,000
11/13	10,845	152	1.4%	14,500
Annual Growth	12.0%	18.6%	—	67.3%

2017 Year-End Financials

Debt ratio: 25.22%
Return on equity: 14.14%
Cash ($ mil.): 550
Current ratio: 1.42
Long-term debt ($ mil.): 1,136

No. of shares (mil.): 39
Dividends
Yield: 0.7%
Payout: 14.2%
Market value ($ mil.): 5,403

	STOCK PRICE ($) FY Close	P/E High/Low		PER SHARE ($) Earnings	Dividends	Book Value
11/17	136.20	18	14	7.51	1.05	57.56
11/16	116.91	20	13	5.88	0.85	50.05
11/15	94.27	18	13	5.24	0.58	45.92
11/14	71.44	17	11	4.57	0.13	42.48
11/13	66.16	16	8	3.06	0.00	37.93
Annual Growth	19.8%	—	—	25.2%	—	11.0%

Synovus Financial Corp.

Synovus Financial has a nose for community banking. The holding company owns flagship subsidiary Synovus Bank and more than 25 locally branded banking divisions that offer deposit accounts and consumer and business loans in Alabama Florida Georgia South Carolina and Tennessee. Through more than 280 branches the bank provides checking and savings accounts loans and mortgages and credit cards. Other divisions offer insurance private banking wealth and asset management and other financial services. Nonbank subsidiaries include Synovus Mortgage Synovus Trust investment bank and brokerage Synovus Securities and GLOBALT which provides asset management and financial planning services.

Geographic Reach

Georgia-based Synovus Financial has about 130 bank branches in Georgia. Florida is the bank's second largest market with nearly 50 branches while Alabama and South Carolina are home to more than 40 each.

Financial Performance

While the bank reported a 10% decline in revenue in 2013 versus 2012 to $1.18 billion and an 81% plunge in net income (to $159.4 million) it did make some progress on the long road to recovery. Significantly the bank redeemed its obligations under TARP (troubled asset relief program) in July 2013 funding more than two-thirds of the TARP redemption with internally available funds. The firm redeemed the remainder with proceeds from offerings of its common and preferred stock. Its loan portfolio grew by about $516 million up nearly 3% versus 2012. Credit quality also continued to improve while the bank lowered expenses.

Synovus blamed its continuing revenue slide on lower interest and non-interest income in 2013 versus 2012. Interest income fell on lower income on loans and investment securities. Non-interest income suffered relative to 2012 when the bank experienced higher levels of investment securities gains and gains on private equity investments as well as a decline in income from mortgage banking.

Strategy

Synovus has been cutting costs raising capital and improving efficiency in the aftermath of the residential and commercial real estate bust that hit the southeastern US particularly hard. During the dark days of the banking crisis (2008 to 2009) the company slashed about 10% of its workforce and it cut approximately 10% more in 2010 and 2011. It also closed nearly 40 branches and consolidated others.

Also Synovus which has traditionally maintained separate charters and local boards of directors for its subsidiary banks consolidated all of its charters into one in 2010 in order to reduce complexity and improve efficiency. Synovus also consolidated by merging some of its banks in Georgia and Florida; two of its Florida banking subsidiaries (one de novo and the other formed in the merger of three subsidiaries' banking charters) have taken the Synovus Bank brand a new strategy for the company.

The company returned to profitability in 2012 and remained profitable (although considerably less so) in 2013. To right itself Synovus has deemphasized commercial real estate lending and increased its focus on commercial and industrial banking including specialized services such as asset-based lending international banking and treasury management in an effort to increase revenue. The company is courting large corporate clients in the health care manufacturing distribution financial services natural resources and transportation sectors. Among smaller enterprises it targets professional practices such as physicians attorneys and accountants particularly for its private banking business.

Mergers and Acquisitions

In May 2013 Synovus assumed $56.8 million in deposits that belonged to failed Sunrise Bank from its receiver the FDIC. As part of the deal the bank acquired $492000 in loans.

The company bought specialty finance firm Entaire Global in October 2016. Entaire a private life insurance premium finance lender primarily serves small businesses. Synovus which is aiming to diversify its loan portfolio with the purchase paid an initial $30 million; it will pay extra earnings-based payments over a period of up to five years.

EXECUTIVES

EVP and COO, Allen J. Gula, age 62, $434,192 total compensation
Executive Vice President Information Technology, Andrew Klepchick
EVP and Chief Risk Officer, Mark G. Holladay, age 61, $428,454 total compensation
EVP and Chief Retail Banking Officer, D. Wayne Akins, age 54
Chairman and CEO, Kessel D. Stelling, age 61, $962,269 total compensation
EVP Financial Management Services, J. Barton Singleton, age 53, $390,606 total compensation
EVP and Chief Credit Officer, Kevin J. Howard, age 52
EVP and Chief Community Banking Officer, R. Dallis (Roy) Copeland, age 48, $412,336 total compensation
EVP and Chief Corporate Banking Officer, Curtis J. Perry, age 54
EVP and CFO, Kevin S. Blair

CIO, Renee S. Roth
CTO, Santosh Kokate
EVP General Counsel and Secretary, Allan E. Kamensky, age 56, $417,229 total compensation
Chief Information Security Officer, Kevin P. Gowen
Vice President Regional Sales, Ron Ward
Vice President Senior Credit Analyst, Lisa McCurdy
Commercial Banker Vice President, Mario Bringas
Vice President; Senior Family Office Advisor, Robert Persons
Senior Vice President Diversity and Career Resources, Audrey Hollingsworth
Assistant Vice President Project Management Synovus Financial Corp., Theresa Radney
Senior Vice President Private Wealth Advisor, Michelle McClellan
Vice President Human Resources, Amy Goins
Vice President Product Management, Lynn White
Executive Vice President Retail Branches Columbus Band And Trust, Carolynn Obleton
Vice President Senior Manager Compliance, Angela Isaac
Senior Vice President And Chief Audit Executive, Stephen Sawyer
Vice President Accounting Manager, Liz Gobbel
Assistant Vice President Senior Business Analyst, Milton Hodges
Vice President and Manager Audit, Keith Greene
Vice President And Portfolio Manager, Daniel Morgan
Vice President Information Systems, Cathy Reilly
Senior Vice President, Brick F Luke
Vice President Information Technology Audit Manager, Laurette Smith
Vice President Information Systems, Catherine OReilly
Assistant Vice President Chief Compliance Officer, Gene Gunderson
Assistant Vice President and Technology Division ATM Program Manager, Vicki Kimbro-Moore
Senior Vice President, Rob Burts
Vice President Finance Account Manager, Richard Pettit
Vice President Senior Business Analyst Lender, Alvena Pareja
Senior Vice President, Dan Summers
Senior Vice President Director of Correspondent Banking, Richard Lane
Senior Vice President and Director LCBG East, Michael Sawicki
Treasurer, Sherri Morgan
Auditors: KPMG LLP

LOCATIONS

HQ: Synovus Financial Corp.
1111 Bay Avenue, Suite 500, Columbus, GA 31901
Phone: 706 649-2311
Web: www.synovus.com

Bank Branch Locations

	No.
Georgia	114
Florida	48
South Carolina	38
Alabama	37
Tennessee	11
Total	**248**

PRODUCTS/OPERATIONS

2016 Sales

	$ mil.	% of total
Interest income:		
Loans including fees	944	73
Investment securities available for sale	67	5
Trading account assets	0	-
Mortgage loans held for sale	2	-
Federal Reserve Bank balances	4	-
Other earning assets	4	-
Non-interest income:		
Service charges on deposit accounts	81	6

Fiduciary and asset management fees	46	4
Bankcard fees	33	3
Other non-interest income	34	3
Brokerage revenue	27	2
Mortgage banking income	24	2
Other fee income	20	2
Investment securities gains net	6	-
Total	**1,296**	**100**

COMPETITORS

BB&T	First Citizens
BBVA Compass	BancShares
Bancshares	First Horizon
BBX Capital	Regions Financial
BancorpSouth	SunTrust
Bank of America	Trustmark
Citigroup	Wells Fargo
Fidelity Southern	

HISTORICAL FINANCIALS

Company Type: Public

Income Statement

FYE: December 31

	ASSETS ($ mil.)	NET INCOME ($ mil.)	INCOME AS % OF ASSETS	EMPLOYEES
12/16	30,104	246	0.8%	4,436
12/15	28,792	226	0.8%	4,452
12/14	27,051	195	0.7%	4,511
12/13	26,201	159	0.6%	4,696
12/12	26,760	830	3.1%	4,963
Annual Growth	**3.0%**	**(26.2%)**	**—**	**(2.8%)**

2016 Year-End Financials

Debt ratio: 2.78%	No. of shares (mil.): 122
Return on equity: 8.30%	Dividends
Cash ($ mil.): 423	Yield: 0.0%
Current ratio: —	Payout: 25.4%
Long-term debt ($ mil.): —	Market value ($ mil.): 5,023

	STOCK PRICE ($) FY Close	P/E High/Low		PER SHARE ($) Earnings	Dividends	Book Value
12/16	41.08	22	14	1.89	0.48	23.95
12/15	32.38	21	15	1.62	0.42	23.16
12/14	27.09	21	2	1.33	0.24	22.34
12/13	3.60	4	3	0.91	0.28	21.23
12/12	2.45	0	0	5.95	0.28	31.77
Annual Growth	**102.4%**	**—**	**—**	**(24.9%)**	**14.4%**	**(6.8%)**

Sysco Corp

From New York to San Francisco Sysco is the #1 food distributor in the US. The company serves 500000 customers in the US and internationally in the restaurant (standalone and chain) healthcare and education and hotel industries. Its 324 distribution centers and 13400 delivery vehicles deliver branded and private-label food including fresh frozen and canned foods and specialty and meat products as well as non-food items such as silverware and utensils. The SYGMA Network focuses on supplying chain restaurants. Sysco also offers management consultancy services such as menu analysis and inventory management as well as technology solutions.

Operations

Sysco operates four segments: US Food Service; International Foodservice; Sygma; and its Other operations (consisting of its hotel supply and technology solutions).

The US Foodservice business generates some 75% of total sales and consists of its food and non-food delivery operations in the US including its custom-cut meat and seafood companies Freshpoint (the specialty produce business) and European Imports (the specialty import business). The International Food Service generates 12% of sales delivers similar product lines to its customers in Canada Europe the Bahamas Mexico Costa Rica and Panama. Both segments sell a full line of frozen foods (including meats seafood fruits and vegetables and desserts) canned and dry foods fresh meats and seafood dairy products beverages and fresh produce; as well as non-food items such as disposable napkins plates and cups tableware cookware kitchen supplies and cleaning supplies.

The SYGMA segment accounts for nearly 15% of sales and consists of Sysco's customized distribution to around 3700 customers across 15000 restaurants.

The Other segment accounts for around 2% of sales.

Geographic Reach

Houston-based Sysco operates more than 160 US distribution facilities half its total; the country accounts for around 80% of total sales. Its other facilities are found in 10 other countries notably the UK (65 sites and 5% of sales) Canada (more than 35 sites and more than 5% of sales) and France (nearly 40 sites and 3% of sales).

Sales and Marketing

At over 60% sales to restaurants account for the majority of Syco's sales. The healthcare industry accounts for around 10% of sales as do sales to education and government institutions and indeed to travel leisure and retail customers. Bakeries caterers churches and other such assorted places that sell food account for the remaining more than 10% of sales.

On a national scale Sysco jockeys for customers with rivals U.S. Foods and Performance Food Group. The company claims to serve more than 15% of the estimated $280 billion foodservice market.

Financial Performance

The company has seen an increasing trend in its net revenues over the last five years.

In fiscal 2017 (ended July 1) revenue grew a healthy 10% to $55.4 billion due almost entirely to the Brakes acquisition which helped the International Foodservice segment almost double in size. The US Foodservice segment recorded a less than 1% decline which the company attributes to the extra sales week in 2016 while SYGMA grew by 1%. Excluding the Brakes acquisition International Foodservice revenue also recorded a minor decline due also to the extra trading week in 2016.

Net income grew by 20% to $1.1 billion due to the contribution from Brakes Group cost management in Canada and lower corporate expenses.

Cash from operations increased 13% to $2.2 billion due mostly to higher net income.

Strategy

To accelerate growth Sysco has outlined two strategic priorities: enhancing customer experience and tightening operations. On the former the company believes that deeper customer partnerships will result in profitable growth in the long term. It is extending its value-added services including its menu analysis and business reviews and developing its customer-facing technology. On the latter in fiscal 2017 the company improved its Canada operations and made $20 million in compensation-related savings.

The company is also expanding internationally including in 2016 the acquisition of Brakes Group a UK-based food distributor with operations in Ireland France Sweden Spain Belgium and Luxembourg.

Mergers and Acquisitions

In 2016 Sysco completed the acquisition of UK-based Brakes Group for $3.1 billion. The acquisition substantially expanded its European operations. Brakes supplies fresh refrigerated and frozen food products as well as non-food products and supplies to foodservice customers ranging from large customers including leisure pub restaurant hotel and contract catering groups to smaller customers including independent restaurants hotels fast food outlets schools and hospitals.

HISTORY

Sysco was founded in 1969 when John Baugh a Houston wholesale food distributor formed a national distribution company with the owners of eight other US wholesalers. Joining Baugh's Zero Foods of Houston to form Sysco were Frost-Pack Distributing (Grand Rapids Michigan) Louisville Grocery (Louisville Kentucky) Plantation Foods (Miami) Thomas Foods and its Justrite subsidiary (Cincinnati) Wicker (Dallas) Food Service Company (Houston) Global Frozen Foods (New York) and Texas Wholesale Grocery (Dallas). The company went public in 1970. Sysco which derives its name from Systems and Services Company benefited from Baugh's recognition of the trend toward dining out. Until Sysco was formed small independent operators almost exclusively provided food distribution to restaurants hotels and other non-grocers.

In the 2000s Sysco acquired smaller competitors who hadn't fared quite as well during the downturn. In 2013 the company acquired foodservice operations in Nassau Bahamas; San Francisco California; San Jose California; Stockton California; Ontario Canada; Quebec Canada; Orlando Florida; Dublin Ireland; St. Cloud Minnesota; Co. Down Northern Ireland; Greenville Ohio; and Houston Texas.

Its 2012 acquisition of European Imports Ltd. helped it expand into the specialty import products segment. Purchasing Crossgar a leading privately owned foodservice supplier in Northern Ireland strengthened Sysco's presence on the island and complemented its 2009 acquisition of Pallas Foods. Other 2012 conquests include Appert's Foodservice Buchy Food Service Central Seafood Company and Metro Richelieu's Distagro. Their combined annual revenues were about $520 million.

In a sweeping move for the foodservice industry Sysco in late 2013 attempted to acquire its rival U.S. Foods for $3.5 billion. The deal would have boosted its share of the US market to about 25% from about 18%. By combining Sysco and US Foods the company expected to achieve annual synergies of at least $600 million and estimated annual sales of approximately $65 billion. The deal was pushed back due to delays in talks with antitrust regulators and the parties terminated to planned transaction in 2015 after failing to obtain regulator approvals.

EXECUTIVES

Vice President, William Tubb
Vice President Human Resources, Susan Billiot
SVP Marketing, William W. (Bill) Goetz
Vice President Information Technology, Kirk Drummond
Vice President, Mark Palmer
VP Supply Chain, Robert Howell
Vice President Warehouse and Delivery Services, Gary M Mills
Assistant Controller, William B. (Bill) Day, age 60, $508,333 total compensation
EVP Supply Chain, R. Scott Charlton, age 58

SVP International Foodservice Operations Americas, Scott A. Sonnemaker

CEO, William J. (Bill) DeLaney, age 61, $1,245,833 total compensation

President and COO, Thomas L. (Tom) Ben ©, age 55, $770,833 total compensation

EVP Human Resources, Paul T. Moskowitz, age 53

SVP U.S. Foodservice Operations, Greg D. Bertrand, age 53

EVP Administration and Corporate Secretary, Russell T. Libby, age 51, $590,125 total compensation

SVP Market Segment Strategy and President Sysco Ventures (CAKE), Brian C. Beach

EVP and CFO, Joel T. Grade, age 47, $605,833 total compensation

EVP and CTO, Wayne Shurts, age 58, $621,602 total compensation

Vice President, Loren Gausman

Vice President Human Resources Search, Mark Wisnoski

VP Operations, Matthew Firlit

Vice President of Operations, John Cash

Vice President, Dick Abbey

Vice President Information Technology, Russell Hines

Regional Vice President, Justin Hiraki

Vice President Operations and Supply Chain Technology, Shannan Horner

Vice President of Human Resour, Tony Watson

Vice President, Bryan Allred

Senior Vice President Foodservice Operations (southwest Region), James Graham

Assistant Vice President, Barry Robinson

Vice President Merchandising Services, Robert Thurber

VICE PRESIDENT OF OPERATIONS, Mike Turner

Vice President Systems, Kristin Lindsay

Vice President Corporate Business Development, Gregory S Keller

Vice President Business Development, Alan Sachs

Vice President of Merchandising, Lisa Shiveley

Director of Utilization Review and Risk Management, Mark Kleiman

Vice President of Real Estate Construction, Mike Downs

Executive Vice President of Information Technology, Kathy Joachim

Vice President sales, Robbie Horton

Vice President Of Merchandising, Jeff Hartley

Vice President Human Resources and Labor Relations, Lynn Keays

Vice President Corporate Business Development, Greg Keller

Vice President, Mitchell Elmer

Vice President Enterprise Asset Management, Dan Bennett

Assistant Vice President Merchandising Center of the Plate, Jeff A Kimmich

Vice President Information Technology, Jesse Gonzales

Vice President, Thomas Randt

Vice President Merchandising, Bill Tubb

Senior Vice President Foodservice Operations South Region, Michael Headrick

Vice President Of Marketing, Sharon Armentrout

Vice President Finance, John Roderigue

Vice President, Andrew Malcolm

Vice President Of Finance, Alma Vega

Senior Vice President, Robin Mitra

National Account Manager, Jennifer Vance

Vice President of Merchandising, Kurt Chapin

RVP New Business Development, Nancy Schwartz Brooks

Vice President, Elizabeth Miles

Senior Vice President Sales and Marketing, Jim Hope

Assistant Vice President Of Marketing, Tracey Mills

Vice President Sourcing, Christopher Shepardson

Vice President human Resources, Janice Miller

Vice President Call Center, Alena Galsnte

Executive Vice President, Lisa Gough

National Account Manager, Cindy Rankin

Vice President Finance, Kristin Kotler

Vice President Supply Chain Management, Masao Nishi

VP Operations, Robert Davis

Vice President of Operations, Steven Burns

Vice President of Information Technology, Melvin Fine

Vice President Sales, John Counts

Vice President Finance, Mark Daubert

Vice President Finance, Jim Amos

Vice President Channel Marketing, Britt Dayton

Vice President of Merchandising and Marketing, Kristine Bowen

Vice President Information Systems, Matt Riddleberger

Senior Vice President Marketing, Bill Goetz

Vice President Merchandising, Brian R Todd

Assistant Vice President Information Technology, John Holzen

Vice President, Robert Kinz

Vice President of Sales, Steve Otis

Vice President, Phil Davis

Group Senior Vice President, Phillip Bryant

Vice President Industry Relations and Diversity, Albert Gaylor

VICE PRESIDENT MERCHANDISING, John Riczo

Senior Vice President Corporate Finance, Ajoy Karna

Executive Vice President and Group President, Michael W Green

Vice President Infrastructure Services, Frank Merli

Vice President Merchandising, David Passaro

NATIONAL ACCOUNT MANAGER, Kristin Smith

Vice President of Merchandising, Dena Wise

Vice President of Labor Relations, Chuck Munn

VICE PRESIDENT, Heike Gillman

NATIONAL ACCOUNT MANAGER, Martin Escatel

Vice President Purchasing, Warren Cho

Vice President Merchandising, Jerry Simons

Vice President Of Finance, Carlos Reyes

Vice President, Matt Whitney

Vice President of Sales, Amy Snook

Vice President Sales, Jonathan Turner

National Account Manager, Tracy Jones

Senior Vice President, Don Staley

Vice President of Operations, Michael Caldwell

Vice President Foodservice Operations Florida, Tim Brown

VP Logistics, Raina Valon

Vice President Government Relations, Gerald Kunde

Vice President Government Relations, Chip Kunde

Vice President Multi Unit, Ken Vaughan

Executive Vice President Marketing, Richard Doggett

VP Supply Chain, Viktoryia Aksionava

Vice President of Operations, Larry Dees

Executive Vice President Merchandising and Sysco Business Services, William Biddy

Vice President of Finance CFO, Jim Harlan

Vice President Operations, John Petrossian

VP Human Resources, Dana Morrey

VP Operations, Tony Brooks

VICE PRESIDENT INFORMATION TECHNOLOGY, Bob Brown

VP Operations, Kevin Proulx

REGIONAL VICE PRESIDENT HEALTHCARE, Greg Mcculloch

NATIONAL SALES MANAGER, Hugh G Morgan

VICE PRESIDENT OF PROCESSING, Adrian Seguin

VICE PRESIDENT AND HUMAN RESOURCES BUSINESS PARTNER, Terri L Clark

VICE PRESIDENT OF PURCHASING, Robert C Thurber

NATIONAL ACCOUNT MANAGER, Kelly P Garcia

VICE PRESIDENT OF HUMAN RESOURCES, John J Fraser

VICE PRESIDENT AND GENERAL MANAGER, Joe Napoli

VICE PRESIDENT AND TREASURER, Gregory S Keyes

VICE PRESIDENT FINANCE, Enrique X Becerra

NATIONAL ACCOUNT MANAGER, Sonnie Broxton

MARKET VICE PRESIDENT MERCHANDISING, Ruth Warthen

MERCHANDISING VICE PRESIDENT SUPER COLOSSAL, Julie Kramer

MARKET VICE PRESIDENT OPERATIONS, Michael Oller

Regional Vice President Business Development, Karl Kramer

Vice President Operations, Bill Omara

Assistant Vice President Merchandising, Jonathon R Gottfied

Chairman, Jacquelyn M. (Jackie) Ward, age 79

Secretary, Tim Davis

Board Member, Richard G Tilghman

Secretary, Carrie Tindal

Vice President Finance and Treasurer, Gregory Keyes

Auditors: Ernst & Young LLP

LOCATIONS

HQ: Sysco Corp
1390 Enclave Parkway, Houston, TX 77077-2099
Phone: 281 584-1390   Fax: 281 584-2880
Web: www.sysco.com

2015 sales

	% of total
US	88
Canada	10
Other	2
Total	**100**

PRODUCTS/OPERATIONS

2015 sales

	% of total
Broadline	77
SYGMA	12
Other	11
Total	**100**

2015 sales

	% of total
Fresh & frozen meats	21
Canned & dry food	16
Frozen fruits vegetables bakery & other	13
Dairy products	11
Poultry	11
Fresh produce	8
Paper & disposables	7
Seafood	5
Beverage products	4
Janitorial products	2
Equipment & smallware	1
Medical supplies	1
Total	**100**

COMPETITORS

Ben E. Keith
Bunzl
Edward Don
Foodbuy
Golden State Foods
Gordon Food Service
MAINES
McLane Foodservice

Meadowbrook Meat Company
Performance Food Group
Reinhart FoodService
Shamrock Foods
US Foods
UniPro Foodservice

HISTORICAL FINANCIALS
Company Type: Public

Income Statement
FYE: July 1

	REVENUE ($ mil.)	NET INCOME ($ mil.)	NET PROFIT MARGIN	EMPLOYEES
07/17	55,371	1,142	2.1%	66,500
07/16*	50,366	949	1.9%	51,900
06/15	48,680	686	1.4%	51,700
06/14	46,516	931	2.0%	50,300
06/13	44,411	992	2.2%	48,100
Annual Growth	5.7%	3.6%	—	8.4%

*Fiscal year change

2017 Year-End Financials

Debt ratio: 46.13%	No. of shares (mil.): 530
Return on equity: 39.09%	Dividends
Cash ($ mil.): 869	Yield: 0.0%
Current ratio: 1.32	Payout: 46.6%
Long-term debt ($ mil.): 7,660	Market value ($ mil.): 26,677

	STOCK PRICE ($) FY Close	P/E High/Low		PER SHARE ($) Earnings	Dividends	Book Value
07/17	50.33	27	23	2.08	0.97	4.49
07/16*	50.73	31	21	1.64	1.23	6.22
06/15	38.37	36	31	1.15	1.18	8.85
06/14	37.85	24	20	1.58	1.14	8.99
06/13	34.16	21	17	1.67	1.10	8.86
Annual Growth	10.2% (15.6%)	—	—	5.6%	(3.1%)	

*Fiscal year change

T Rowe Price Group Inc.

T. Rowe Price Group administers a family of about 100 mutual funds in a variety of investment styles. Traditionally oriented toward growth investing the funds offer products in many risk and taxation profiles including small- mid- and large-cap stock funds; money market funds; and bond funds both taxable and nontaxable. Other services include asset management advisory services (including retirement plan advice for individuals) corporate retirement plan management separately managed accounts variable annuity life insurance plans discount brokerage and transfer agency and shareholder services. Founded in 1937 T. Rowe Price has some $810 billion in assets under management.

Operations

Investment Advisory services (and the fees generated by them) are the company's cash cow accounting for more than 85% of its annual revenue. Administrative fees accounted for about 10% and distribution and servicing fees for less than 5%.

About half of T. Rowe Price's assets under management are sourced from its third-party financial intermediary distribution channel with the remaining three distribution channels accounting for the balance.

Geographic Reach

The Baltimore-based global investment management group serves clients in about 45 countries around the world from offices in 15-plus countries including London Australia Japan Hong Kong and Singapore. The firm's international clients account for nearly 5% of its total assets under management.

Sales and Marketing

T. Rowe Price's clients include individual and institutional investors and financial intermediaries.

The company distributes its products through third-party financial intermediaries defined-contribution retirement plans and directly to individual and institutional investors.

Financial Performance

T. Rowe Price has enjoyed healthy revenue and profit growth over the past few years thanks to a bullish stock market and new client inflows.

However in 2016 revenue growth flattened out: total sales of $4.2 billion represented only 0.5% growth as assets under management grew only slightly. The strongest growth segment was in investment advisory revenues in the US up 1.4%.

Net income was essentially flat at $1.2 billion. Cash from operating activities fell from $1.5 billion to just $170.5 million due to a net change in trading securities.

Strategy

T. Rowe Price regularly adds to its funds and strategies offerings to attract new investors and their capital. To this end the firm in 2017 added T. Rowe Price US High Yield Fund and in 2016 expanded its quantitative management-style series of strategic funds with three new equity funds: T. Rowe Price QM US Value Equity Fund T. Rowe 2015 Price QM US Small & Mid-Cap Core Equity Fund and T. Rowe Price QM Global Equity Fund.

HISTORY

Thomas Rowe Price Jr. left a brokerage job at Mackubin Goodrich & Co. to found his own investment advisory firm in 1937. He pushed investing for the long haul choosing stocks of promising young companies (the firm invested in IBM in 1950). Price's company was incorporated in 1947 and was employee-owned until it went public in 1986.

The firm moved into international investments in 1979. T. Rowe Price was primarily an institutional pension fund manager until the 1980s. Creativity lagged as fund managers made investments from a list selected by the research department and the Growth Stock Fund underperformed the S&P 500. In 1987 the firm opened its funds to individual investors.

Thereafter it introduced a slew of new funds slicing and dicing the market to appeal to the broadest possible industry and risk investment profiles including offerings in emerging market stocks and health and science stocks. In 1996 longtime president and CEO George Collins retired and was succeeded by then-president-CFO George Roche who eventually became the company's chairman.

In the late 1990s however the company's value investing strategy brought lagging fund results and a stagnant corporate stock price. Nevertheless cash continued to pour into the company's funds until the collapse of Russian and Asian markets in 1998. US investors got the willies slowing asset flows to T. Rowe Price and other mutual fund managers.

In response Roche began moving the company into overseas asset management markets. In 1999 the firm joined with Sumitomo Bank (now part of Sumitomo Mitsui Financial Group) and Daiwa Securities to form asset manager Daiwa SB Investments in Japan. It also targeted Europe where the growth of private retirement plans opened up new opportunities. Nevertheless the company missed out on many of the explosive returns of the high-tech boom.

In 2000 however the high-tech bubble burst seeming to vindicate T. Rowe Price's conservative approach. That year the company bought out the remaining 50% of its Rowe Price-Fleming International asset management joint venture with Robert Fleming (which is now part of JPMorgan Chase). Also that year the company reorganized itself into holding company T. Rowe Price Group. The company's UK subsidiary received regulatory approval to expand to the European continent in 2001.

EXECUTIVES

Vice Chairman VP and CEO T. Rowe Price International Ltd, Edward C. Bernard, age 60, $350,000 total compensation

President and CEO, William J. (Bil) Stromberg, age 56, $350,000 total compensation

VP CFO and Treasurer, Kenneth V. Moreland, age 61, $350,000 total compensation

Head International Equity, Christopher D. Alderson, age 55, $305,057 total compensation

Head US Investment Services, Scott B. David

Head Global Technology, Nigel Faulkner

Head Global Investment Services, Robert Higginbotham

Head Equity, Eric L. Veiel, $350,000 total compensation

Head Fixed Income, Edward A. Wiese

VP CFO and Treasurer, C ©line Duf ©tel

Data Architect Assistant Vice President, Janet Schaller

Assistant Vice President Systems Consultant, Charles Popeck

Vice President Enterprise Architecture, Paul Macek

Vice President and Human Resources Manager, Shannon Dolan

Vice President, Antonio Luna

Assistant Vice President USIS Individual Investor; Lead Manager, Jason Hammond

Vice President, Steve Hartzell

Vice President National Account Manager, Rob Seidel

Assistant Vice President, Courtney Murphy

Solutions Strategist Vice President, Justin Harvey

Vice President, Leigh Woodworth

Vice President T Rowe Price Associates, Renee Christoff

Assistant Vice President Global Client and Investment Reporting, Melissa Kinak

Vice President Trpa Trpg, Doug Talley

Assistant Vice President, Don Phillips

Vice President, Greg Franzoni

Vice President Applications Management, Jennifer Perricone

Vice President And Research Analyst, Steven Boothe

Vice President, Mark Weigman

Vice President And Crm Manager, Steve Larson

Vice President, Laura Chasney

Vice President, Steve Sullivan

Vice President Information Security Manager, Brian Porter

Vice President, Kimberly Oconnor

Vice President, Heather McPherson

Assistant Vice President Customer Sales And Services Channel Manager, Sean Rentch

Vice President, Tom McGuire

Vice President, Paul Wojcik

Vice President And Regional Relationship Manager, David Orlando

Vice President, Chris Dyer

Vice President Director Of Retail Operations, Chris Hufman

Vice President, Michael Krawczyk

Vice President Us Investment Services Financial Institutions, Cima Gordon

Vice President, Jeff Zoller

Vice President Regional Sales Consultant, Alan Valenca

Vice President And Quantitative Analyst, Kim Dedominicis

Vice President, Andy Brooks

Assistant Vice President, Craig Sauerwalt

Vice President, Brian Brennan

Assistant Vice President, Chris Clingenpeel

Assistant Vice President Project Leader, Stacy Wright
Vice President International Tax, Rebecca English
Vice President, Joe Vogelpohl
Vice President Of Real Estate, Mark Ruhe
Vice President Credit Research, Ted Robson
Vice President Production Services, Tom Tydings
Vice President Senior Retirement Sales Executive, Terence Howard
Vice President, Ng Jan
Assistant Vice President Equity Trader, Susan Klein
Assistant Vice President Lead Marketing Manager, Lauren Inskeep
Vice President; Global Head Of Corporate Actions, Larry Robinson
Vice President, Jim Ouartarone
Assistant Vice President Crm Marketing Analytics, Beverly Wisbar
Business Systems Consultantavp, Mark Story
Assistant Vice President Institutional Client Service Associate, Michelle Porter-Ward
Vice President, Matthew Johnson
Vice President, Jean Fisher
Vice President, Jason Rundell
Assistant Vice President Global Technology Services, Ronnie Kurlander
Assistant Vice President, Melissa Shank
Vice President, Eric Bolisay
Vice President Quantitative Analyst, Vinit Agrawal
Vice President Territory Sales, Mike Shamburger
Vice President, David Crotty
Vice President, Anna Dreyer
Assistant Vice President Client Experience and Digital Marketing, David Malone
Vice President Market Structure Analyst, Alexander Sedgwick
Vice President Midwest Retirement Sales Executive, Mike Palace
Vice President, Darshini Reddivari
Vice President and Group Manager; Real Estate and Workplace Strategy, Chris Calhoun
Vice President and Global Head of Enterprise Service Desk, LaShaunda Allums
Vice President National Accounts Manager Broker Dealer Distribution, Jeff Talbott
Chairman, Brian C. Rogers, age 62
Auditors: KPMG LLP

LOCATIONS

HQ: T Rowe Price Group Inc.
100 East Pratt Street, Baltimore, MD 21202
Phone: 410 345-2000   **Fax:** 410 752-3477
Web: www.troweprice.com

US Offices
Baltimore
Colorado Springs CO
Owings Mills MD
Tampa
International Offices
Amsterdam
Buenos Aires
Copenhagen
Dubai
Hong Kong
London
Luxembourg
Singapore
Sydney
Tokyo
Toronto
Zurich

PRODUCTS/OPERATIONS

2016 Sales

	$ mil.	% of total
Investment advisory fees	3,728	88
Administrative fees	352	8
Distribution & servicing fees	141	4
Total	**4,222**	**100**

Selected Subsidiaries
T. Rowe Price Advisory Services Inc.
T. Rowe Price Associates Inc.
 T. Rowe Price (Canada) Inc. (US)
 T. Rowe Price Investment Services Inc.
 T. Rowe Price Retirement Plan Services Inc.
 T. Rowe Price Services Inc.
T. Rowe Price International Ltd. (UK)
 T. Rowe Price Hong Kong Limited
 T. Rowe Price Singapore Private Ltd.

COMPETITORS

AllianceBernstein	Invesco
American Century	Legg Mason
Ameriprise	MFS
Capital Group	Northwestern Mutual
FMR	Putnam
Franklin Templeton	The Vanguard Group

HISTORICAL FINANCIALS

Company Type: Public

Income Statement
FYE: December 31

	REVENUE ($ mil.)	NET INCOME ($ mil.)	NET PROFIT MARGIN	EMPLOYEES
12/17	4,793	1,497	31.2%	6,881
12/16	4,222	1,215	28.8%	6,329
12/15	4,200	1,223	29.1%	5,999
12/14	3,982	1,229	30.9%	5,870
12/13	3,484	1,047	30.1%	5,668
Annual Growth	**8.3%**	**9.3%**	**—**	**5.0%**

2017 Year-End Financials

Debt ratio: —	No. of shares (mil.): 245
Return on equity: 27.65%	Dividends
Cash ($ mil.): 1,902	Yield: 0.0%
Current ratio: 3.43	Payout: 38.1%
Long-term debt ($ mil.): —	Market value ($ mil.): 25,719

	STOCK PRICE ($) FY Close	P/E High/Low	PER SHARE ($) Earnings	Dividends	Book Value
12/17	104.93	17 11	5.97	2.28	23.76
12/16	75.26	16 13	4.75	2.16	20.46
12/15	71.49	18 14	4.63	4.08	19.01
12/14	85.86	19 16	4.55	1.76	20.66
12/13	83.77	21 16	3.90	1.52	18.38
Annual Growth	**5.8%**	**— —**	**11.2%**	**10.7%**	**6.6%**

T-Mobile US Inc

T-Mobile US is one of the largest providers of wireless voice and data communications services in the US. The company's 61 million T-Mobile and MetroPCS contract and prepaid consumer customers use its networks domestically and are able to connect to the compatible network of Deutsche Telekom when in Europe. It also offers low-cost no-contract mobile services through the GoSmart brand. In addition T-Mobile sells phones tablets PDAs and accessories from such vendors as Apple Nokia and Samsung. It has about 8000 T-Mobile and MetroPCS branded retail sites. In 2013 Deutsche Telekom acquired smaller rival MetroPCS via a reverse merger and combined it with T-Mobile; Deutsche Telekom owns about two-thirds of the combined company.

Sales and Marketing

T-Mobile markets its services and products via its own network of retail locations as well as through more than 60000 third-party retail loca-

tions and online. Its largest customer segment (about 70% of revenue) is postpaid subscribers. Prepaid customers account for about a quarter of revenue and wholesale clients roaming charges and other services generate the rest.

Financial Performance

In 2014 T-Mobile reported about $29 billion in revenue up 21% from the prior year. The growth was powered by a $2 billion increase in prepaid service revenues a $1 billion rise in postpaid service revenues and a $1.5 billion increase in equipment sales. The contributions of the Metro PCS network also contributed to revenue growth.

T-Mobile's profit zoomed more than 600% higher in 2014 to $247 million on the higher revenue. Cash flow from operations also rose in 2014 from 2013 to $4.15 billion from $3.5 billion.

Strategy

The company has crafted a "Un-carrier" strategy to compete with the big boys such as Verizon Wireless and AT&T Mobility. It has offered a line of Simple Choice plans that eliminate annual contracts as well as caps and overage charges. T-Mobile has also introduced a simpler handset upgrade program and reduced some international calling rates and roaming fees when traveling outside the US. The company pays early termination fees for customers who leave another carrier for T-Mobile. Other carriers have followed the company's lead and done away with contracts.

Another key initiative of T-Mobile's strategy is heavy investment in network modernization to support its nationwide 4G LTE (long-term evolution) technology. Wideband LTE is available in 245 markets and is expected to be available in more than 260 markets by the end of 2015. Extended Range LTE covers nearly 175 million people and is on track to cover more than 350 markets by year-end 2015.

EXECUTIVES

Senior Vice President, Robert Strickland
Senior Vice President of Segment Marke, John Clelland
EVP and CIO, Gary A. King, age 59, $488,462 total compensation
President and CEO, John J. Legere, age 59, $1,250,000 total compensation
COO, G. Michael (Mike) Sievert, age 48, $550,000 total compensation
EVP and CFO, J. Braxton Carter, age 58, $650,000 total compensation
EVP Corporate Services, David R. (Dave) Carey, age 63
EVP General Counsel and Secretary, David A. (Dave) Miller, age 56
President T-Mobile Indirect Channels, Thomas C. Keys, age 59
SVP and Chief People Officer, Larry L. Myers, age 62
EVP Corporate Strategy, Peter A. Ewens, age 54
EVP and CTO, Neville R. Ray, age 54
EVP T-Mobile Retail and Direct Channels, Jon A. Freier
EVP and Chief Marketing Officer, J. Andrew Sherrard
Executive Vice President, Peter Ewens
Senior Vice President Corporate Development and Wholesale Roaming, Dirk Mosa
Vice President Business Sales, Ty Trenary
Senior Inside Sales Vice President, Jim Gowan
Vice President And General Manager, Marty Pisciotti
Vice President Of Enterprise Information Technology, Mike Ross
Vice President Risk Management and Assurance, Michael Morgan
Vice President Operations Sales Operations, John Whittington

Vice President Technical Quality Manager, Stefan Heinze
Vice President Engineering, David Gallacher
Vice President Real Estate Design Visual Merchandising, Robert Hill
Vice President Business Sales, Amber Powers
Vice President Systems Support Sales, Ian Blomeen
Senior Vice President Financial Planning And Analysis, Susan Loosmore
Vice President Business Sales, Amanda Owens
Vice President and Chief Litigation Counsel T Mobile USA, Laura Buckland
Vice President Local Channel Management And Reporting, Savinay Dangi
Vice President Sales, Marcus Almeida
Vice President Information Systems, Leanne Prince
Vice President Sales, Renee Williams
Vp-new York Area, Terry Hayes
Senior Vice President of Brand Communications, Peter DeLuca
Vice President Business Sales, Mike Thompson
Senior Inside Sales Vice President, Mike Davison
Vice President Business Sales, Jamie Rayeski
Vice President Risk Management, Michael Rimkus
National Account Manager, Mark Rosalsky
Vice President Business Sales, Shelley Davis
Vice President Digital Growth and Acquisition, Peter Francis
Vice President of Customer Care, Karen Sullivan
Vice President Iot and M2m, Balaji Sridharan
Vice President Product Development, Warren McNeel
Sales Vice President, Brad Treese
Vice President Sales, Cynthia Mcclarnon
Vice President IR and Head of Investor Relations, Nils Paellmann
Assistant To Senior Vice President Engineering And Operations, Kelly Digregorio
Vice President Product Management, Andrew Morrison
Vice President Business Development, Jim Porter
Vice President Marketing Strategy, Shanna Killian
Vice President Business Sales, Andrew Rainone
Vice President Sales Operations, Sara Nicholson
Vice President, Nancy Port
Vice President, Ron Avery
Senior Vice President of Sales Operations, Ami Silverman
Vice President Wireless Procurement and Planning, Tim Kohler
Vice President Customer Loyalty, Matt Staneff
Vice President Network Operations, Greg Trant
Vice President Federal Government Relations, Tony Russo
Vice President of Communications, Catherine Captain
Vice President Engineering and Operations, Mike Lord
Senior Vice President Marketing, Doug Chartier
Vice President and Chief Compliance Officer, Steve Cochran
Senior Vice President, Sam Sindha
Executive Assistant to Michael Cote Vice President of Business Sales, Carolyn Glosenger
Vice President Of Information Technology Development, Jeff Wiggin
Vice President Corp Strategy and Analysis, Joseph Mallahan
Vice President Customer Experience Transformation, Robert Gary
Regional VP Sales and Distribution, Andrew Rucker
Chairman, Timotheus (Tim) H ¶ttges, age 55
TR, Jesse Sheppard
Auditors: PricewaterhouseCoopers LLP

LOCATIONS

HQ: T-Mobile US Inc
12920 S.E. 38th Street, Bellevue, WA 98006-1350
Phone: 425 378-4000
Web: www.T-Mobile.com

PRODUCTS/OPERATIONS

2014 Sales

	$ mil.	% of total
Branded postpaid	14,392	48
Branded Prepaid	6,986	23
Equipment Sales	6,789	23
Wholesale	731	2
Roaming and other services	266	1
Other	319	1
Total	**29,564**	**100**

2014 Customers

	No. mil
Branded postpaid	27
Branded prepaid	16
Wholesale	11
Total	**55**

COMPETITORS

AT&T Mobility	TracFone
Boost Mobile	U.S. Cellular
CenturyLink	Verizon Wireless Inc.
Cricket	Virgin Mobile USA
Sprint Communications	

HISTORICAL FINANCIALS

Company Type: Public

Income Statement
FYE: December 31

	REVENUE ($ mil.)	NET INCOME ($ mil.)	NET PROFIT MARGIN	EMPLOYEES
12/17	40,604	4,536	11.2%	51,000
12/16	37,242	1,460	3.9%	50,000
12/15	32,053	733	2.3%	50,000
12/14	29,564	247	0.8%	45,000
12/13	24,420	35	0.1%	40,000
Annual Growth	**13.6%**	**237.4%**	**—**	**6.3%**

2017 Year-End Financials

Debt ratio: 43.80%	No. of shares (mil.): 859
Return on equity: 22.24%	Dividends
Cash ($ mil.): 1,219	Yield: —
Current ratio: 0.77	Payout: —
Long-term debt ($ mil.): 29,297	Market value ($ mil.): 54,581

	STOCK PRICE ($) FY Close	P/E High/Low	PER SHARE ($) Earnings	Dividends	Book Value
12/17	63.51	13 10	5.20	0.00	26.25
12/16	57.51	34 20	1.69	0.00	22.07
12/15	39.12	52 32	0.82	0.00	20.23
12/14	26.94	112 79	0.30	0.00	19.40
12/13	33.64	666330	0.05	0.00	17.76
Annual Growth	**17.2%**	**—**	**—219.3%**	**—**	**10.3%**

Targa Resources Corp

Targa Resources Corp. has the energy to deliver natural gas throughout its service territory of Texas Oklahoma and neighboring states. Through its Targa Resources Partners entity it gathers processes transports and sells natural gas natural gas liquids (NGLs) crude oil and refined petroleum products. It owns or operates about 27000 miles of natural gas gathering pipelines and more than 35 processing plants. It has a presence in many shale basins including the Permian Eagle Ford Barnett Anadarko Arkoma and Williston. In early 2016 Targa Resources Corp purchased all un-owned shares of Targa Resources Partners securing complete control of its previously majority-owned subsidiary.

Operations

Targa Resources operates two segments: Gathering and Processing and Logistics and Marketing. Two-thirds of revenue generated by Gathering and Processing comes from intersegment sales to the Logistics and Marketing segment. Putting that aside Logistics and Marketing generates about 65% of total revenue with the rest from Gathering and Processing.

The Logistics and Marketing segment is Targa?s downstream business. It converts mixed NGLs into NGL products and provides certain value-added services such as storing terminaling distributing and marketing NGLs; storing and terminaling refined petroleum products and crude oil. It performs marketing activities in support of Targa?s other businesses including services to LPG exporters. Assets owned by this segment are generally connected to and supplied in part by the Gathering and Processing segment. It also owns and leases out some 700 railcars to move product.

The Gathering and Processing segment gathers natural gas produced from oil and gas wells and processes this raw natural gas into sellable natural gas by extracting NGLs and removing impurities. It also gathers and terminals crude oil. The segment owns some 27000 miles of gathering pipeline and has a gross processing capacity of 8100 million cubic feet of natural gas per day.

Geographic Reach

Targa Resources is headquartered in Houston TX. The assets owned by the Logistics and Marketing segment are predominantly located in Mont Belvieu and Galena Park Texas in Lake Charles Louisiana in Tacoma Washington and in Baltimore Maryland.

The Gathering and Processing segment's assets are located in the Permian Basin of West Texas and Southeast New Mexico; the Eagle Ford Shale in South Texas; the Barnett Shale in North Texas; the Anadarko Ardmore and Arkoma Basins in Oklahoma and South Central Kansas; the Williston Basin in North Dakota and in the onshore and near offshore regions of the Louisiana Gulf Coast and the Gulf of Mexico.

Sales and Marketing

Targa sells its products to petrochemical companies refineries export companies large commercial and industrial customers as well as to natural gas and electric utilities that serve individual consumers. Targa also earns revenue by purchasing and reselling NGL products in the spot and forward physical markets.

Targa Resources' wholesale propane marketing operations primarily sell propane and related logistics services to major multi-state retailers independent retailers and other end-users.

Financial Performance

In recent years Targa Resources? revenue has been steady with a single positive aberration in 2014. Generally revenue comes in around $6.6 billion. Net income delivered positive though minimal results between 2011 and 2015 (averaging $50 million) before plunging in 2016.

For the year 2016 revenue rose about $30 million to $6.7 billion. Sales of commodities ticked up 3% in the year which overcame an 11% drop in fees collected from its midstream services.

In 2016 net income swing to a sizable loss of $278 million compared to a $58 million profit in 2015. Higher cost of purchased products (natural gas crude oil etc.) and higher depreciation and amortization compressed the year?s operating margin. An unfavorable comparison with the prior year?s income attributable to noncontrolling interests along with dividends paid on preferred stock (issued in 2016) hit earnings as well.

Cash held at the end of 2016 was $74 million $67 million less than at the end of 2015. Cash from operations was $837 million mostly adjustments for depreciation and amortization as well as goodwill impairment. Investing activities used $562 million for capital expenditures to improve expand and maintain the company?s assets. Financing activities were robust with issuances of common and preferred stock redemption of debt and borrowings under its credit facility all of which summed to a $345 million use of cash.

Strategy

Targa Resources is focused on production from US shale plays and by the deployment of shale exploration and production technologies in both liquids-rich natural gas and crude oil resource plays for driving its growth. It is actively pursuing natural gas gathering and processing and NGL fractionation opportunities associated with liquids-rich natural gas from shale and other resource plays such as portions of the Barnett Eagle Ford Utica and Marcellus Shales and with even richer casinghead gas opportunities from active crude oil resource plays such as the Wolfberry and the Bone Springs Avalon and Bakken Shale plays. Production growth in the major shale plays (overall not just Targa?s) is expected to be about 40% between 2016 and 2020 and 30% between 2020 and 2025. Part of Targa?s strategy is to merely ensure it has the right assets and operations in place to grow its business along with the increased production (and demand) of these shale plays.

For example in the Permian Basin Targa gathers product from a diverse set of producers spanning 2 million dedicated acres of land. With expansion projects it expects that by the end of 2018 it will have capacity to process 2.5 billion cubic/ft per day of natural gas. It connected its recently acquired Delaware and Midland Basin assets to its existing systems to more efficiently move natural gas among its pipelines and processing plants.

Of its $1.3 billion of 2017 capital expenditures 80% is focused on the Permian Basin including nearly $300 million for its joint-venture project Grand Prix NGL pipeline. The pipeline will transport volumes from the Permian Basin and from Targa's North Texas system to Targa's fractionation and storage complex in the NGL market hub at Mont Belvieu Texas. Grand Prix will be supported by Targa's volumes and other third party customer commitments and is expected to be in service in early 2019. The capacity of the pipeline from the Permian Basin will be approximately 300 thousand barrels per day expandable to 550 thousand barrels per day.

The Permian work not only allows greater acquisition of natural gas but the connection to Mont Belvieu aids its downstream operations by lowering transportation costs and increasing predictability of supply. The Downstream business segment also expects to benefit from higher demand from new petrochemical facilities in the Houston area as well as higher demand from non-US customers wanting to export Targa?s excess propane and butanes.

Mergers and Acquisitions

In 2016 Targa Resources completed the acquisition of all of the outstanding common units of Targa Resources Partners LP. As a result of the acquisition Targa improved its credit and coverage profile lowered its cost of capital and simplified its structure thereby improving its access to capital.

EXECUTIVES

CEO, Joe Bob Perkins, age 56
President Administration, Jeffrey J. (Jeff) McParland, age 62, $500,000 total compensation
EVP Southern Field Gathering and Processing, Patrick J. (Pat) McDonie, age 57
EVP General Counsel and Secretary, Paul W. Chung, age 56, $490,000 total compensation
SVP CFO and Treasurer, Mattthew J. (Matt) Meloy, age 39, $450,000 total compensation
EVP Logistics and Marketing, D. Scott Pryor, age 55
EVP Northern Field Gathering and Processing, Dan C. Middlebrooks, age 61
EVP Engineering and Operations, Clark White, age 58
EVP Commercial, Robert Muraro, age 41
Vice President Business Development, Brad D Reese
Vice President Finance, Howard M Tate
Chairman, James W. Whalen, age 76
Vice Chairman, Michael A. Heim, age 69
Auditors: PricewaterhouseCoopers LLP

LOCATIONS

HQ: Targa Resources Corp
1000 Louisiana St., Suite 4300, Houston, TX 77002
Phone: 713 584-1000   **Fax:** 713 584-1100
Web: www.targaresources.com

PRODUCTS/OPERATIONS

2016 sales

	$ mil.	% of total
Logistics and Marketing	5,519	82
Gathering and Processing	1,108	17
Other	62	1
Total	**6,690**	**100**

COMPETITORS

DCP Midstream Partners	Enterprise Products
Devon Energy	Kinder Morgan
EnLink Midstream Partners	Magellan Midstream
Enbridge	ONEOK Partners
Energy Transfer	Summit Midstream Partners LP

HISTORICAL FINANCIALS

Company Type: Public

Income Statement

FYE: December 31

	REVENUE ($ mil.)	NET INCOME ($ mil.)	NET PROFIT MARGIN	EMPLOYEES
12/16	6,690	(187)	—	1,970
12/15	6,658	58	0.9%	1,870
12/14	8,616	102	1.2%	1,350
12/13	6,556	65	1.0%	1,277
12/12	5,885	38	0.6%	1,192
Annual Growth	**3.3%**	**—**	**—**	**13.4%**

2016 Year-End Financials

Debt ratio: 37.92%
Return on equity: (-5.41%)
Cash ($ mil.): 73
Current ratio: 0.86
Long-term debt ($ mil.): 4,606

No. of shares (mil.): 184
Dividends
  Yield: 0.0%
  Payout: —
Market value ($ mil.): 10,357

	STOCK PRICE ($) FY Close	P/E High/Low		PER SHARE ($) Earnings	Dividends	Book Value
12/16	56.07	—	—	(1.80)	3.64	29.45
12/15	27.06	98	24	1.09	3.39	26.09
12/14	106.05	62	35	2.43	2.68	4.03
12/13	88.17	57	34	1.55	2.06	3.53
12/12	52.84	56	43	0.91	1.52	3.41
Annual Growth	**1.5%**	**—**	**—**	**—**	**24.4%**	**71.5%**

Target Corp

Cheap-but-chic Target is the US's #2 discount chain (behind Wal-Mart). The fashion-forward discounter operates 1800-plus Target and SuperTarget stores across North America as well as an online business at Target.com. Target and its larger grocery-carrying incarnation SuperTarget have carved out a niche by offering more upscale trend-driven merchandise than rivals Wal-Mart and Kmart. Target also issues its proprietary Target credit card good only at Target. Target sold its pharmacy and clinics business to CVS in late 2015 in a $1.9 billion deal.

HISTORY

The panic of 1873 left Joseph Hudson bankrupt. After he paid his debts at 60 cents on the dollar he saved enough to open a men's clothing store in Detroit in 1881. Among his innovations were merchandise-return privileges and price marking in place of bargaining. By 1891 Hudson's was the largest retailer of men's clothing in the US. Hudson repaid his creditors from 1873 in full with interest. When Hudson died in 1912 four nephews expanded the business.

Former banker George Dayton established a dry-goods store in 1902 in Minneapolis. Like Hudson he offered return privileges and liberal credit. His store grew to a 12-story full-line department store.

After WWII both companies saw that the future lay in the suburbs. In 1954 Hudson's built Northland in Detroit then the largest US shopping center. Dayton's built the world's first fully enclosed shopping mall in Edina a Minneapolis suburb in 1956. In 1962 Dayton's opened its first discount store in Roseville (naming the store Target to distinguish the discounter from its higher-end department stores).

Dayton's went public in 1966 the same year it began the B. Dalton bookstore chain. Three years later it merged with the family-owned Hudson's forming Dayton Hudson. Dayton Hudson purchased more malls and invested in such specialty areas as consumer electronics and hard goods. Target had 24 stores by 1970.

The Target chain became the company's top moneymaker in 1977. The next year Dayton Hudson bought California-based Mervyn's (later Mervyns). In the late 1970s and 1980s it sold nine regional malls and several other businesses including the 800-store B. Dalton chain to Barnes & Noble. The Target stores division purchased Indianapolis-based Ayr-Way (1980) and Southern California-based Fedmart stores (1983). In the late 1980s Dayton Hudson took Target to Los Angeles and the Northwest. Robert Ulrich who began with the company as a merchandise trainee in 1967 became president and CEO of the Target stores division in 1987 and chairman and CEO of Dayton Hudson in 1994.

Dayton Hudson opened the first Target Greatland store in 1990. By this time it had 420 Target stores. Also that year Dayton Hudson bought the Marshall Field's chain of 24 department stores from B.A.T Industries. Marshall Field's began as a dry-goods business that Marshall Field bought in 1865 and subsequently built into Chicago's premier upscale retailer.

SuperTarget stores were introduced in 1995. The Target stores division opened stores in the Mid-Atlantic and Northeast the next year while the department store division began selling off its Marshall Field's locations in Texas.

In 1998 Dayton Hudson boosted its Internet presence by purchasing direct-marketing company Rivertown Trading; it also bought apparel supplier Associated Merchandising that year. In 2000 Dayton Hudson renamed itself Target Corporation. In early 2001 the company renamed its Dayton's and Hudson's chains Marshall Field's. Also that year Target acquired the rights to 35 former Montgomery Wards stores from the bankrupt retailer.

The nation's #2 discounter was #1 when it came to corporate giving in 2001. Target topped the Forbes list of America's Most Philanthropic Companies that year donating 2.5% of its 2000 income (nearly $86 million). By comparison Wal-Mart gave away $116.5 million in 2001 less than 1% of its income in 2000.

In 2002 the company reopened 30 of the former Montgomery Ward stores as Target outlets. Net of closings 94 Target stores opened in 2002 while neither Mervyns nor Marshall Field's added to their store counts. In March 2003 three new SuperTarget stores opened in the Dallas/Fort Worth area.

2004 was a year of divestments for Target. In January the discounter announced it was exiting the catalog business. To that end in April Target sold its Signals and Wireless gifts catalogs to Universal Screen Arts for an undisclosed sum. In July Target sold its Marshall Field's business to The May Department Stores Co. for about $3.2 billion in cash. In September Target completed the sale of 257 Mervyns stores in 13 states to an investment group that includes Cerberus Capital Management Lubert-Adler/Klaff and Partners and Sun Capital Partners as well as its Mervyns credit card receivables to GE Consumer Finance for a combined sum of approximately $1.65 billion in cash. (Later Mervyns filed for bankruptcy and closed the last of its stores by the end of 2008.)

In October 2005 vice chairman Gerald Storch resigned unexpectedly after more than a dozen years with the company. No reason was given for his departure. In the largest mass opening in Target's history the retailer opened 60 new stores on October 9.

In July 2006 Target.com extended its partnership with Amazon Enterprise Solutions a unit of online retailer Amazon.com through August 2010. Amazon provides e-commerce technology to the discount chain.

In May 2008 Ulrich who served as chairman and CEO since 1994 handed his CEO title to president Gregg Steinhafel. (Steinhafel joined the retailer in 1979 and worked his way up the executive ranks.) Also in May Target closed on the sale of a 47% stake in its credit-card receivable to JPMorgan Chase for $3.6 billion. The five-year deal allows Target to buy back the stake at the end of the term. In October the company opened a pair of stores in Alaska thereby expanding its retail presence to 48 states. In November Target said no thanks to a plan Ackman had proposed for Target to spin off its real estate holdings in a bid to increase shareholder value citing uncertainty about valuation assumptions and the potential reduction in financial flexibility as a result of spin off.

Ulrich retired from the board in January 2009 and Steinhafel added the chairman's title to his job description.

In April 2010 Target stopped offering new credit card applicants its co-branded Visa credit card.

Chairman president and CEO Steinhafel resigned in May 2014 five months after a massive data breach at the company. In July 2014 the company named retail veteran Brian Cornell as chairman and CEO. Cornell 55 joined Target from PepsiCo Americas Foods where he served as CEO and oversaw the global food business. Before joining PepsiCo Cornell served as president and CEO of Sam's Club a division of Wal-Mart Stores.

EXECUTIVES

Senior Vice President Of Real Estate, Scott Nelson
EVP Chief Legal Officer and Corporate Secretary, Don H. Liu, age 56, $275,000 total compensation
EVP Merchandising Product Group, Patricia (Trish) Adams
Director Community Relations, Laysha L. Ward, age 49
Chairman and CEO, Brian C. Cornell, age 58, $1,300,000 total compensation
EVP and COO, John J. Mulligan, age 51, $1,000,000 total compensation
EVP and Chief Merchandising Officer, Mark J. Tritton, age 53, $396,635 total compensation
EVP and Chief Stores Officer, Janna A. Potts, age 49
EVP and CIO, Michael E. (Mike) McNamara, age 52, $468,462 total compensation
EVP and CFO, Catherine R. (Cathy) Smith, age 53, $798,558 total compensation
President Target Sourcing Services, Kelly Caruso
EVP and Chief Human Resources Officer, Stephanie A. Lundquist, age 41
EVP and Chief Risk and Compliance Officer, Jacqueline Hourigan Rice, age 45
EVP and Chief Marketing Officer, Rick H. Gomez, age 47
SVP Grocery Fresh Food and Beverage, Jeff Burt
President Target Financial and Retail Services, Scott Kennedy
President Target India, Tammy Redpath
Pharmacy Manager, Kenne Currie
Vice President Administrative Assistant, Elizabeth Carson
Vice President Technology Services, Tim Milne
Pharmacy Manager, Joseph Legrand
Pharmacy Manager, Will Peck
Pharmacy Manager, Casey Rhea
VPMM Domestics, Andrea Kellick
Senior Vice President Assistant, Katie Bensen
Pharmacy Manager, Bernard Brown
Vice President Target com Mobile and Digital Marketing, Seemantini Godbole
Executive Vice President Executive Assistant, Bridget Hicks
Senior Vice President, Stephen Brinkley
Vice President Administrative Assistant, Heather Bean
Vice President Assistant, Melissa Loth
Vice President Administrative Assistant, Cara Thrane
Senior Vice President Administ, Sommer Roux
Vice President Marketing, William White
Senior Vice President Administration Human Resour, Kate Boegemann
Pharmacy Manager, Kristopher Tidwell
Pharmacy Manager, Jacqueline Jansen
Pharmacist Manager, Kristin Hillman
Senior Vice President Talent and Organizational Effectiveness, Tim Curoe
Vice President Administrative Assistant, Michelle Halverson
Vice President of Communications, Dustee T Jenkins
Vice President Administrative Assistant, Vonnie Zuehlke
Senior Vice President Executive Assistant, Tracy Rockholt
Pharmacy Manager, David Navarro
Vice President Finance Operations, Patti Johnson
Vice President Assistant Corporate Financial Planning, Bethany Borucki
Senior Vice President Administrative Assistant Marketing, Jaime Samson
Pharmacy Manager, Carrie Kennett
Pharmacy Manager, Lisa Reilly
Vice President Administrative Assistant TTS, Amanda Clausen
Senior Vice President, Jim Hogan

Pharmacy Manager, Martine Sav
Pharmacy Manager, David Cathcart
Senior Vice President Assistant, Amanda Dale
Senior Vice President Of Sales, Desi Bellamy
Senior Vice President and Manager Financial Institutions, Addison Averett
Senior Vice President Marketing, Kristi Argyilan
Senior Vice President New Business, Tina M Tyler
Group 297 Vice President Assistant, Trina Kennedy
Senior Vice President Assistant, Milagros Hanson
Pharmacy Manager, Philip Agee
Pharmacy Manager, Mulu Gizaw
Vice President Healthcare Operations, John Holcomb
Vice President, Sarah Malik
Vice President Of Distribution Operations, Diane Closs
Executive Vice President Merchandising Apparel and Home, Trish Adams
Vice President Assistant, Rhonda Broyles
Senior Vice President GC Sec'y, TimothyR Baer
Senior Vice President, Bill Hall
Vice President Target, Nancy Whitesell
Vice President Assistant, Christina Hayes
Vice President Administration, Tara Kadow
Group Vice President Administrator, Laverne White
Vice President Assistant Style Marketing, Martie Weiske
Senior Vice President Target Sourcing Services, Annette Miller
National Sales Manager, Michael Wahlig
Vice President Business Technology, Lori Riley
Executive Vice President, Jeff Jones
Pharmacy Manager, Kari Ratkevich
Pharmacy Manager, Manish Patel
VP Operations, Preston Mosier
VP Operations, Shekar Natarajan
Pharmacy Manager, Jordan Lippmann
Vice President, Ray Fischer
Group Vice President Stores, Nikki Seitz
Senior Vice President Strategic Planning, Jeremy Miller
National Account Manager, Sherita Jackson
Pharmacy Manager, Amy Reedyk
VP Process Engineering, Tom Brewer
VICE PRESIDENT AND CO FOUNDER, Steve Worthy
Vice President Assistant, Laura Lindboe
Assistant Treasurer, Sara Ross
Board Member, Rakesh Mishra
Vice Chairman, Mollie McCarty
Auditors: Ernst & Young LLP

LOCATIONS

HQ: Target Corp
1000 Nicollet Mall, Minneapolis, MN 55403
Phone: 612 304-6073
Web: www.target.com

2017 US Locations

	No of stores
California	273
Texas	147
Florida	122
Illinois	92
Minnesota	75
New York	75
Pennsylvania	69
Ohio	61
Virginia	58
Michigan	55
Georgia	51
North Carolina	49
Arizona	46
New Jersey	46
Colorado	41
Maryland Massachusetts	40
Maryland	39
Washington	37
Wisconsin	37
Missouri	35
Indiana	31

Tennessee	31
Alabama	22
Connecticut	20
Iowa	20
Oregon	19
South Carolina	19
Kansas	18
Nevada	17
Louisiana	16
Oklahoma	15
Nebraska	14
Kentucky	13
Utah	13
New Mexico	10
Arkansas	9
New Hampshire	9
Montana	7
Hawaii	6
Idaho	6
Mississippi	6
West Virginia	6
Maine	5
South Dakota	5
North Dakota	4
Rhode Island	4
Alaska	3
Delaware	3
Wyoming	2
District of Columbia	1
Vermont	-
Total	**1,802**

PRODUCTS/OPERATIONS

2017 Sales

	% of total
Household essentials	22
Food beverage and pet supplies	22
Apparel & accessories	20
Home furnishings & dé;cor	19
Hardlines	17
Total	**100**

Selected Designer Private Labels

Amy Coe (children's bedding and accessories)
Liz Lange (maternity)
Michael Graves Design (housewares)
Mossimo (junior fashions)
Sonia Kashuk (cosmetics and fragrances)
Todd Oldham (bedding and furniture)

Selected Private Labels

Archer Farms (food)
Cherokee (apparel)
Choxie (candy)
Furio (housewares)
Honors (apparel)
In Due Time (maternity wear)
Market Pantry
Merona (apparel)
Nick & Nora (apparel)
Playwonder (toys)
Utility (apparel)
Xhilaration (apparel)

Selected Other Operations

Rivertown Trading (catalogs and e-commerce)
 Britannia (British video and gifts)
 I Love A Deal (apparel housewares and jewelry)
 Seasons (traditional)
Target Receivables Corp.

COMPETITORS

Amazon.com	L Brands
BJ's Wholesale Club	Loblaw
Bed Bath & Beyond	Lowe's
Best Buy	Macy's
CVS	PETCO
Container Store	Ross Stores
Costco Wholesale	SUPERVALU
Dillard's	Safeway
Dollar General	Sears Holdings
Euromarket Designs	TJX Companies
Foot Locker	The Gap
Hart Stores	Toys "R" Us
Home Depot	Wal-Mart
J. C. Penney Company	Walgreen
Kohl's	Williams-Sonoma
Kroger	eBay

HISTORICAL FINANCIALS

Company Type: Public

Income Statement

FYE: January 28

	REVENUE ($ mil.)	NET INCOME ($ mil.)	NET PROFIT MARGIN	EMPLOYEES
01/17	69,495	2,737	3.9%	323,000
01/16	73,785	3,363	4.6%	341,000
01/15*	72,618	(1,636)	—	347,000
02/14	72,596	1,971	2.7%	366,000
02/13	73,301	2,999	4.1%	361,000
Annual Growth	**(1.3%)**	**(2.3%)**	**—**	**(2.7%)**

*Fiscal year change

2017 Year-End Financials

Debt ratio: 34.06%
Return on equity: 22.96%
Cash ($ mil.): 2,512
Current ratio: 0.94
Long-term debt ($ mil.): 11,031

No. of shares (mil.): 556
Dividends
 Yield: 0.0%
 Payout: 49.3%
Market value ($ mil.): 35,427

	STOCK PRICE ($) FY Close	P/E High/Low		PER SHARE ($) Earnings	Dividends	Book Value
01/17	63.70	18	13	4.70	2.32	19.69
01/16	72.42	16	13	5.31	2.16	21.52
01/15*	73.61	—	—	(2.56)	1.90	21.86
02/14	56.64	24	18	3.07	1.58	25.64
02/13	61.15	14	11	4.52	1.32	25.66
Annual Growth	**1.0%**	**—**	**—**	**1.0%**	**15.1%**	**(6.4%)**

*Fiscal year change

TCF Financial Corp

TCF Financial is the holding company for TCF National Bank which offers retail and small-business services through more than 430 locations. TCF provides standard services such as checking and savings accounts CDs consumer and business loans mortgages and insurance and is a leading issuer of Visa debit cards. Residential mortgages account for nearly half of the company's loan and lease portfolio. TCF also offers specialized lending services such as commercial leasing equipment finance inventory finance and indirect auto loans across the US.

Operations

TCF operates through three primary segments: lending (71% of total revenues) funding (28%) and support services (1%).

Campus banking is also an important part of the company's operations. TCF has exclusive marketing alliances with several colleges including the University of Illinois and University of Michigan and is a leading provider of campus cards that serve as ID library security and stored-value cards in addition to ATM cards. Also as a part of its effort to build brand recognition on college campuses the company paid $35 million for the naming rights to the University of Minnesota's football stadium which opened in 2009 for 25 years.

Geographic Reach

TCF has nearly 430 locations in Arizona (seven branches) Indiana (four) Illinois (194) Michigan (53) Minnesota (108) South Dakota (one) and Wisconsin (25).

Financial Performance

TCF saw its revenues hover around the $1.4 billion mark in 2011 and 2012. However it suffered a net loss of $213 million in 2012 due to a 78% spike in noninterest expenses and provision for credit losses. Over the years the company has suffered from declines in interest income and revenues from its funding segment also declined by 13% during 2012.

Strategy

TCF aims to attract customers through convenience. To that end more than half its branches are inside supermarkets and many of its locations are open seven days a week. While many of the company's peers attempt to grow their branch networks through acquisitions TCF has expanded by opening up new branches — more than 100 since 2003.

In order to reduce its reliance on interest-based income such as loans and leases which are subject to interest rate fluctuations and other outside factors TCF is focusing on growing its income from fees and service charges from products like checking accounts and credit cards.

The company has also experienced growth in its specialty finance operations including TCF Equipment Finance TCF Inventory Finance and Winthrop Resources which leases computers servers and other technology equipment. TCF continued to grow the business in 2011 when it bought California-based Gateway One a provider of consumer loans mainly for used cars.

EXECUTIVES

Executive Vice President of Corporate Human Resources of TCF Bank, Barbara Shaw
Chairman President and CEO, Craig R. Dahl, age 62, $846,923 total compensation
Vice Chairman and COO, Thomas F. (Tom) Jasper, age 49, $550,000 total compensation
EVP Consumer Banking, Michael S. Jones, age 49, $549,231 total compensation
EVP Wholesale Banking, William S. Henak, age 60, $472,082 total compensation
Chief Risk Officer and Chief Credit Officer, James M. Costa, age 48
CIO, Tom Butterfield
Treasurer, Brian W. Maass, age 44, $328,678 total compensation
Senior Vice President Relationship Lending, Bjorn Peterson
Vice President, Dan Delgadillo
Vice President Product Management And Retail Functional, Jan Patterson
Executive Vice President, Joseph Doyle
Assistant Vice President Manager of Customer Information Systems, Mary Swindlehurst
Assistant Vice President Field Communications and Marketing, Ulises Silva
Vice President TCF Commercial Real Estate, Bryan Downie
Senior Vice President Product Development Director, Brad Barthels
Vice President and Risk Officer, Karen Knoller
Assistant Vice President and Manager Quality Assurance, Paul Bellward
VICE PRESIDENT OF HUMAN RESOURCES, Judy Gauvin
VICE PRESIDENT HUMAN RESOURCES, Barbara Drago
Auditors: KPMG LLP

LOCATIONS

HQ: TCF Financial Corp
200 Lake Street East, Wayzata, MN 55391-1693
Phone: 952 745-2760
Web: www.tcfbank.com

PRODUCTS/OPERATIONS

2016 Sales

	$ mil.	% of total
Consumer Banking	780	56
Wholesale Banking	581	42
Enterprise Services	33	2
Total	**1,396**	**100**

2016 Sales

	$ mil.	% of total
Interest	930	67
Non-interest	465	33
Total	**1,396**	**100**

Selected Subsidiaries

Fidelity National Capital Inc. (also dba Winthrop Capital)
TCF Agency Inc.
TCF Agency Insurance Services Inc.
TCF Bank International Inc.
TCF Commercial Finance Canada Inc. (also dba
   Financement Commercial TCF Canada Inc.)
TCF Equipment Finance Inc. (also dba TCF Leasing Inc.)
TCF Insurance Agency Inc.
TCF Inventory Finance Inc.
TCF Investments Management Inc.
TCF National Bank
TCF Portfolio Services Inc.
Winthrop Resources Corporation (also dba TCF Small
   Business Lending)

COMPETITORS

Associated Banc-Corp	Northern Trust
Bank Mutual	U.S. Bancorp
Bank of America	Wells Fargo
Bremer Financial	

HISTORICAL FINANCIALS

Company Type: Public

Income Statement

FYE: December 31

	ASSETS ($ mil.)	NET INCOME ($ mil.)	INCOME AS % OF ASSETS	EMPLOYEES
12/16	21,441	212	1.0%	6,427
12/15	20,691	197	1.0%	6,755
12/14	19,394	174	0.9%	7,023
12/13	18,379	151	0.8%	7,449
12/12	18,225	(212)	—	7,328
Annual Growth	**4.1%**	—	—	**(3.2%)**

2016 Year-End Financials

Debt ratio: 1.86%
Return on equity: 8.97%
Cash ($ mil.): 609
Current ratio: —
Long-term debt ($ mil.): —

No. of shares (mil.): 170
Dividends
   Yield: 0.0%
   Payout: 26.0%
Market value ($ mil.): 3,350

	STOCK PRICE ($) FY Close	P/E High/Low	PER SHARE ($) Earnings	Dividends	Book Value
12/16	19.59	17 9	1.15	0.30	14.20
12/15	14.12	16 13	1.07	0.23	13.49
12/14	15.89	18 15	0.94	0.20	12.67
12/13	16.25	20 15	0.82	0.20	11.83
12/12	12.15	— —	(1.37)	0.20	11.40
Annual Growth	**12.7%**	— —	—	**10.7%**	**5.6%**

Tech Data Corp.

Tech Data is 100% committed to IT products distribution. One of the world's largest wholesale distributors of technology products Tech Data provides thousands of different items to more than 105000 resellers in 100-plus countries. Its catalog of products includes computer components (disk drives keyboards and video cards) networking equipment (routers and bridges) peripherals (printers modems and monitors) systems (PCs and servers) and software. Tech Data also provides technical support configuration integration financing and logistics and product fulfillment services. More than 60% of Tech Data's revenues are generated outside the US. The company agreed to buy Avnet's Technology Solutions unit for $2.6 billion in 2016.

Operations

Tech Data operates as a distributor of technology products logistics management and other value-added services in the Americas (including North America and South America) and Europe.

The company sells products and services in five categories.

The Broadline unit (46% of revenue) sells notebooks tablets desktops printers printer supplies and components. Its Data Center unit (22%) has industry standard servers proprietary servers networking and storage. The Software category (18%) has virtualization cloud security desktop applications operating systems and utilities software. Mobility (11%) sells mobile phones and accessories. Finally Consumer Electronics (3%) purveys TV's digital displays consumer audio-visual devices and network-attached consumer devices

Geographic Reach

Florida-based Tech Data sells to customers in more than 100 countries throughout North America South America Europe the Middle East and Africa. Europe is the company's largest market accounting for 61% of sales with the rest coming from the Americas.

Sales and Marketing

Tech Data is one of the world's largest technology distributors. It helps companies like Apple Cisco Microsoft and hundreds of others bring their products to market and it offers a wide range of technical and business support services. Its products are purchased directly from vendors in significant quantities.

Products purchased from Apple accounted for 20% of Tech Data's net sales while HP products represented 19% in 2016 (ended January).

The company's customers include approximately 105000 value-added resellers direct marketers retailers and corporate resellers who support the diverse technology needs of end users.

Its sales team consists of field sales and inside telemarketing sales representatives. Customers typically call its inside sales teams on dedicated telephone numbers or contact it through various electronic methods to place orders. If the product is in stock and the customer has available credit customer orders are generally shipped the same day from the logistics center nearest the customer or the intended end-user.

Financial Performance

In 2016 (ended January) Tech Data's revenue slipped while net income skyrocketed.

The company 2016 revenue dropped about 5% to $26.4 billion compared to 2015. Much of the hit came from the impact of foreign currency exchange rates in Europe and Americas. Not counting the currency impact revenue in Americas rose from data center and consumer electronics product sales. In Europe growth came from the broadline mobility and data center product categories. Tech Data's exit from Chile and Peru reduced revenue in 2015.

The company's net income of about $266 million in 2016 was a 52% increase from 2015. This boost came from lower selling general and administrative expenses and a decrease in legal accounting and third party consulting fees.

Cash flow from operations rose to $189 million in 2016 from $118 million in 2015 on higher earnings and changes in accounts payable.

Strategy

With its acquisition of Avnet's Technology Solutions unit for $2.6 billion arms Tech Data in two areas. One is that it now has a broader higher-value added range of products to offer customers who might want someone else to take over tasks like data center management. The deal brings products and services from Hewlett-Packard Enterprise and IBM into Tech Data's arsenal. The purchase also gives Tech Data a big boost in Asia where it's presence has been nominal. Europe and the America's account for virtually all of Tech Data's revenue. The deal with Avnet is expected to close in 2017.

The addition of more complex products and services should bolster Tech Data's role as a middleman in the distributor business.

Tech Data sold its its operations in Chile and Peru in 2015 and started the process to exited Uruguay citing unacceptable returns in their markets. The company plans to expand its export business from Miami to Latin America and its operations in the more mature IT market of Mexico.

Mergers and Acquisitions

In 2015 Tech Data acquired certain assets of Signature Technology Group (STG a leading North American provider of data center and professional services). STG's services are offered through Tech Data's Advanced Infrastructure Solutions division the company's data center business in the Americas. The addition of STG strengthened the data center offerings further diversified the company's services portfolio and provided added value for its customers.

HISTORY

Tech Data grew out of an electronics distribution business founded by Edward Raymund a University of Southern California graduate who started out as a representative for electronics manufacturers. By the early 1960s he had established an industrial electronics distribution business in Florida. In 1974 he incorporated that business as Tech Data.

In 1981 Raymund's 25-year-old son Steven who had earned master's degrees in economics and international politics from Georgetown University's School of Foreign Service joined Tech Data on a temporary basis to work on the company's catalog. At that time Tech Data sold diskettes and other computer supplies to local companies and had about $2 million in sales.

Steven Raymund's favored status at the company angered a group of managers. Shortly after he arrived at Tech Data they copied the company's client list and walked out. The defection nearly sank Tech Data but Steven Raymund stayed on when his father handed him two-thirds of the company.

With the PC industry beginning to take off Steven Raymund positioned Tech Data as a middleman between computer and peripheral manufacturers and resellers. Steven was named COO in 1984. He became CEO in 1986 the year the company went public.

Tech Data began to distribute software in 1992 and a year later the company signed up Microsoft and inked a distribution deal for IBM computer systems. In 1994 Tech Data purchased U.S. Software Resource a California-based distributor of more than 500 business and entertainment software titles thereby increasing its software list and gaining high-profile publishers such as Borland International (now Borland Software) and Corel as suppliers.

Also in 1994 Tech Data began a global expansion when it bought France's largest distributor of wholesale computer products Softmart International.

To further build its business in Europe Tech Data in late 2012 acquired several distribution companies owned by UK-based Specialist Distribution Group (SDG) in the UK France and the Netherlands. Combined the acquired businesses generate sales of about ?1.4 billion ($1.75 billion). Previously Tech Data bought Triade Holding a Netherlands-based distributor of consumer electronics and IT products in 2010. The purchase strengthened Tech Data's IT business and accelerated its diversification into consumer electronics in the Netherlands Denmark and the Benelux region; it also supported operations across Europe by adding new specialty products vendors and customers. As part of the transaction Tech Data's joint venture with Brightstar Brightstar Europe (formed in 2007) acquired Triade subsidiary Mobile Communication Company (MCC) a mobility products distributor in Benelux. Total value of both deals was ?83 million (about $123 million). (Later Tech Data in 2012 bought its joint venture partner Brightstar's 50% ownership in Brightstar Europe for more than $165 million as well as several distribution companies in the UK from the distribution arm of IT services company Specialist Computer Holdings.)

EXECUTIVES

EVP and Chief Legal Officer, David R. (Dave) Vetter, age 57, $490,522 total compensation

Chairman and CEO, Robert M. Dutkowsky, age 62, $1,122,124 total compensation

President Americas, Joseph H. Quaglia, age 52, $526,885 total compensation

President Europe, Patrick Zammit, age 50

EVP and CIO, John Tonnison, age 48, $433,495 total compensation

EVP and CFO, Charles V. (Chuck) Dannewitz, age 63, $579,863 total compensation

EVP and COO, Richard T. (Rich) Hume, age 58, $547,500 total compensation

VP Product Marketing Client and Mobile Solutions, Linda Rendleman

EVP and Chief Human Resources Officer, Beth E. Simonetti

Vice President Of Information Technology, Scott Moore

Vice President Sales Eastern U.S, Marc McClure

Vice President Product Marketing, Ken Griffin

Vice President CyberSecurity and Global Architecture and Information Technology, Daniel Lasher

Vice President, John O'Shea

Vice President Streamone, Bob Kruger

Vice President of Credit the Americas, Jay Snyder

Auditors: Ernst & Young LLP

LOCATIONS

HQ: Tech Data Corp.
5350 Tech Data Drive, Clearwater, FL 33760
Phone: 727 539-7429
Web: www.techdata.com

Sales by Geographic Segment

	$ mil.	% of total
Europe	15,850	60
Americas	10,384	40
Total	**26,234**	**100**

PRODUCTS/OPERATIONS

Product Categories 2017

	% of total
Broadline	48
Data center	21
Software	17
Mobility	11
Consumer electronics	3
Total	**100**

Solutions

Solutions
Credit Services
Marketing Services
Education & Training
Technical Services
Products and services
Logistics & Warehousing
Supply Chain Services
Technical Services
Marketing Services
Solutions Center

COMPETITORS

ASI Computer Technologies	MA Laboratories
	MicroAge
Agilysys	NTT Com Security
Arrow Electronics	New Age Electronics
Avnet	Ricoh USA
Black Box	SED International
Communications Supply	SHI International
CompuCom	SYNNEX
D & H Distributing	ScanSource
Dell	Softmart
Gigaset	UNICOM Government
IBM	Westcon
Ingram Micro	ZT Group

HISTORICAL FINANCIALS

Company Type: Public

Income Statement

FYE: January 31

	REVENUE ($ mil.)	NET INCOME ($ mil.)	NET PROFIT MARGIN	EMPLOYEES
01/17	26,234	195	0.7%	9,500
01/16	26,379	265	1.0%	9,000
01/15	27,670	175	0.6%	8,900
01/14	26,821	179	0.7%	9,100
01/13	25,358	176	0.7%	9,100
Annual Growth	**0.9%**	**2.6%**	**—**	**1.1%**

2017 Year-End Financials

Debt ratio: 17.18%
Return on equity: 9.32%
Cash ($ mil.): 2,125
Current ratio: 1.57
Long-term debt ($ mil.): 989

No. of shares (mil.): 35
Dividends
  Yield: —
  Payout: —
Market value ($ mil.): 3,014

	STOCK PRICE ($) FY Close	P/E High/Low		PER SHARE ($) Earnings	Dividends	Book Value
01/17	85.56	16	11	5.51	0.00	61.60
01/16	62.40	11	7	7.36	0.00	57.17
01/15	57.10	15	11	4.57	0.00	52.44
01/14	53.92	12	9	4.71	0.00	55.14
01/13	50.91	13	9	4.50	0.00	50.75
Annual Growth	**13.9%**	**—**	**—**	**5.2%**	**—**	**5.0%**

TELCO INTERCONTINENTAL CORP

LOCATIONS

HQ: TELCO INTERCONTINENTAL CORP
9812 WHITHORN DR, HOUSTON, TX 770955001
Phone: 281 500-8270
Web: WWW.TELCOINTERCON.COM

HISTORICAL FINANCIALS

Company Type: Private

Income Statement

FYE: December 31

	REVENUE ($ mil.)	NET INCOME ($ mil.)	NET PROFIT MARGIN	EMPLOYEES
12/15	19,067	1,371	7.2%	24
12/14*	16	1	7.9%	—
04/10	2	0	7.5%	—
Annual Growth	**340.9%**	**337.7%**	**—**	**—**

*Fiscal year change

2015 Year-End Financials

Debt ratio: ——
Return on equity: 7.20%
Cash ($ mil.): 2,421
Current ratio: 19.20
Long-term debt ($ mil.): —

Dividends
  Yield: —
  Payout: —
Market value ($ mil.): —

Telephone & Data Systems Inc

Telephone and Data Systems (TDS) is one of the largest US phone companies that's not descended from Ma Bell. The company has about 6.1 million local phone and wireless customers in about 35 states. The company's core business unit U.S. Cellular serves about 5 million customers in about 25 states with key markets the central US and the mid-Atlantic region. The company also offers fixed-line and broadband internet services in rural and suburban markets in some 35 states through its TDS Telecom subsidiary which provides local service to 1.2 million access lines through more than 110 incumbent local-exchange carriers (ILEC). Data networking and hosted telecom services are provided to business clients through the TDS Business unit.

Operations

TDS is more telephone than data systems with more than 75% of revenue generated by wireless services sold by US Cellular. TDS owns 84% of US Cellular's stock. Another 15% of revenue comes from the company's wireline services which provides voice broadband and video.

The rest of the company's revenue is supplied by its cable operations and its hosted management services which includes the OneNeck IT Solutions brand a provider of a range of IT services including full management and hosting of a customer?s IT infrastructure and applications.

Sales and Marketing

U.S. Cellular sells its services through distribution channels that include retail sales and service centers direct sales third-party national retailers independent agents and its website and telesales.

Financial Performance

TDS posted a 1% revenue decline in 2016 to $5.1 billion from 2015. The company's service sales fell on a continued decrease in retail service revenues driven by industry-wide price competition and discounts. U.S. Cellular recognized a $58 million charge from expired rewards points in 2015 which reduced the unit's revenue 1%.

Net income tumbled 80% to $43 million in 2016 from 2015 on lower revenue smaller gains from sales and exchanges of businesses and licenses and higher interest expense in 2016.

Cash flow from operations fell to $782 million in 2016 from $790 million in 2015 because of lower net income and changes in working capital items which reduced cash by $245 million. The working capital decrease stemmed from an increase in equipment installment plan receivables.

Strategy

TDS is protective of its customer base in rural and suburban areas. The company invests in its network to deliver up-to-date services in its areas and tries to make sure its customers don't lose touch when they go out of area. It signed 4G LTE roaming agreements with other telecoms to provide a better experience for customers when they go outside of the TDS footprint. Operationally those agreements reduced the company's roaming expenses despite increased use of roaming by its customers.

While protective TDS won't beg for customers. The company has not offered calling plan promotions that it deems too costly. That said the company has focused on increasing customer engagement with employees throughout the company from network engineers to retail sales people. TDS has modified its retail stores to be more appealing to customers which led a phone purveyor to set up a store within a store.

TDS continues to invest in its network expanding 4G service to more customers. It rolled out Voice over LTE (VoLTE) starting in Iowa (working in conjunction with the roaming agreements). The company also had extended broadband to more markets and has conducted tests with 5G wireless technology.

Mergers and Acquisitions

In September 2017 Telephone and Data Systems agreed to acquire K2 Communications a provider of broadband video and voice products to residential customers. The deal would add more than 1200 service addresses to nearby TDS services areas in Colorado. Earlier in 2017 TDS bought Crestview Communications Sun Prairie Utilities and InterLinx Communications to bolster its fiber-based broadband networks.

HISTORY

LeRoy Carlson Sr. learned the ins and outs of rural phone operators when he owned a small firm that supplied equipment and forms to independent phone companies. In the mid-1950s he began buying some of these small phone companies which he consolidated with a phone book publisher and his equipment company to form Telephones Inc. Carlson sold the company to Contel in 1966.

Carlson continued to buy and sell rural carriers allowing them to retain local management while he provided centralized purchasing and system upgrades. In 1969 he bought 10 rural providers in Wisconsin and consolidated all of his companies into Telephone and Data Systems (TDS).

Between 1970 and 1975 TDS acquired 32 rural phone companies. When smaller companies in its established regions became scarce TDS bought

rural phone providers from large independents. As TDS diversified the wireline subsidiary became TDS Telecommunications.

The company began offering paging services in Wisconsin in 1972 and later created subsidiary American Paging (1981). In 1975 TDS moved into cable TV service eventually creating TDS Cable Communications (1984) but it sold the holdings in 1986.

Getting a head start on the big Bells in the cellular race TDS began seeking licenses in the early 1980s eventually winning a 5% stake in the Los Angeles market. Although buffeted by larger independents it placed a high priority on cellular operations and formed subsidiary United States Cellular Corporation in 1983. Two years later US Cellular launched services in Tennessee and Oklahoma.

EXECUTIVES

SVP Acquisitions and Corporate Development, Scott H. Williamson, age 66, $663,000 total compensation

SVP Finance and Treasurer, Peter L. Sereda, age 55

Vice President and Assistant Treasurer, John Toomey

President and CEO, LeRoy T. (Ted) Carlson, age 71, $1,352,700 total compensation

SVP and CIO, Kurt B. Thaus, age 59

SVP Technology Services and Strategy, Joseph R. Hanley, age 51

SVP Finance and Chief Accounting Officer, Douglas D. Shuma, age 55, $432,500 total compensation

VP Information Technology Operational Services and Chief Information Security Officer, Theodore E. Wiessing

Vice President Information Technology, Laurie Ruchti

Vice President Internal Audit, Frieda Ireland

Vice President Corporate Devel, Kenneth Kotylo

Vice President of Financial Analysis and Strategic Planning, Michelle Brukwicki

Chairman, Walter C. D. Carlson, age 64

Auditors: PricewaterhouseCoopers LLP

LOCATIONS

HQ: Telephone & Data Systems Inc
30 North LaSalle Street, Suite 4000, Chicago, IL 60602
Phone: 312 630-1900   **Fax:** 312 630-1908
Web: www.teldta.com

PRODUCTS/OPERATIONS

2016 Sales

	$ mil.	% of total
U.S. Cellular	3,939	77
Wireline	698	14
HMS	273	5
Cable	185	4
TDS Telecom Eliminations	(5)	-
Corporate Eliminations and Other	14	-
Total	**5,104**	**100**

2016 Sales

	$ mil.	% of total
Service	3,999	78
Equipment and product sales	1,105	22
Total	**5,104**	**100**

COMPETITORS

AT&T	HC2 Holdings
ATN International	Horry Telephone
Cavalier Telephone	NII Holdings
CenturyLink	Sprint Communications
Cincinnati Bell	Suddenlink
Cricket	Communications
FairPoint	T-Mobile USA

Communications Inc.   Verizon
Farmers   Verizon Wireless Inc.
Telecommunications   XO Holdings

HISTORICAL FINANCIALS

Company Type: Public

Income Statement

FYE: December 31

	REVENUE ($ mil.)	NET INCOME ($ mil.)	NET PROFIT MARGIN	EMPLOYEES
12/16	5,104	43	0.8%	10,300
12/15	5,176	219	4.2%	10,400
12/14	5,009	(136)	—	10,600
12/13	4,901	141	2.9%	10,500
12/12	5,345	81	1.5%	12,100
Annual Growth	(1.1%)	(14.9%)		(3.9%)

2016 Year-End Financials

Debt ratio: 25.88%   No. of shares (mil.): 110
Return on equity: 1.04%   Dividends
Cash ($ mil.): 900   Yield: 0.0%
Current ratio: 2.32   Payout: 151.7%
Long-term debt ($ mil.): 2,433   Market value ($ mil.): 3,176

	STOCK PRICE ($) FY Close	P/E High/Low		PER SHARE ($) Earnings	Dividends	Book Value
12/16	28.87	81	54	0.39	0.59	37.68
12/15	25.89	15	12	1.98	0.56	37.87
12/14	25.25	—	—	(1.26)	0.54	36.40
12/13	25.78	24	16	1.29	0.51	37.87
12/12	22.14	38	26	0.75	0.49	37.14
Annual Growth	6.9%	—	—	(15.1%)	4.8%	0.4%

TENASKA MARKETING VENTURES

LOCATIONS

HQ: TENASKA MARKETING VENTURES
14302 FNB PKWY, OMAHA, NE 681544446
Phone: 402 758-6100

HISTORICAL FINANCIALS

Company Type: Private

Income Statement

FYE: December 31

	REVENUE ($ mil.)	NET INCOME ($ mil.)	NET PROFIT MARGIN	EMPLOYEES
12/07	10,309	0	—	91
12/05	9,470	0	—	—
12/04	0	0	—	—
12/03	4,940	0	—	—
Annual Growth	20.2%	—	—	—

Tenet Healthcare Corp.

Tenet Healthcare is a for-profit company operating about 80 acute care hospitals with more than 20350 beds in 12 US states including California Florida and Texas. Its operations range from small community facilities offering basic care to major hospitals such as the 607-bed Brookwood Medical Center in Birmingham Alabama. In addition to its acute care holdings Tenet operates specialty hospitals skilled nursing facilities physician practices outpatient centers imaging centers health plans and other health care units that form regional networks around its main hospitals. It also operates Conifer Health Solutions a patient billing and communications company.

HISTORY

Hospital attorney Richard Eamer along with attorneys Leonard Cohen and John Bedrosian founded National Medical Enterprises (NME) in 1969. After its IPO NME bought 10 hospitals nursing homes an office building and land in California. Within six years the company owned operated and managed 23 hospitals and a home health care business. It sold medical equipment and bottled oxygen and provided vocational training for nurses.

In the 1970s NME expanded into hospital construction and bought five Florida hospitals. By 1981 NME was the #3 health care concern in the US owning or managing 193 hospitals and nursing homes. In the 1980s NME diversified further buying nursing homes and mental health centers. By the end of the decade the company's Specialty Hospital Group brought in more than 50% of revenues. NME was the second-largest publicly owned health care company in the US (after HCA) by 1985.

In 1990 NME reversed course spinning off most of its long-term-care businesses but kept 19 UK nursing facilities operated by its Westminster Health Care subsidiary (sold 1996). In 1992 the company acquired an Australian hospital management firm.

That year several insurance companies sued NME alleging fraudulent psychiatric claims; NME settled the suits in 1993. Federal agents later raided company headquarters seizing papers related to the suspected fraud. That year investment banker Jeff Barbakow took over as CEO forcing out Eamer and Cohen.

In 1993 and 1994 NME dumped most of its psychiatric and rehabilitation facilities using the proceeds to help pay penalties stemming from the federal investigation into alleged insurance fraud kickbacks and patient abuse at its psychiatric units. NME paid another $16 million in related state fines. (Related civil lawsuits were settled in 1997.)

The company's name change to Tenet Healthcare coincided with new purchases throughout the South in 1995 and 1996.

The next few years were mixed for Tenet. On the upside it bought OrNda HealthCorp which complemented Tenet's existing networks. Tenet and MedPartners (now Caremark Rx) then the #1 practice management firm formed a Southern California hospital-doctor network in 1997 that gave both companies heft in dealing with HMOs (the partnership crumbled in 1999 when MedPartners exited practice management to focus on pharmacy benefits management and ceased operations in California). Merger discussions began with embattled market leader Columbia/HCA (now HCA) but fizzled.

In 1998 Tenet bought eight Philadelphia hospitals owned by the bankrupt Allegheny Health Education & Research Foundation. The company was dogged by another investigation this time by the Health and Human Services Inspector General's office over allegations the company paid more than fair market value for a physician practice in return for kickbacks. Tenet in 2004 agreed to pay about $31 million to settle two lawsuits stemming from these allegations.

Like many companies in the industry in 1999 Tenet began feeling the effects of the Balanced Budget Act of 1997 which mandated more scrutiny of Medicare expenditures to health care providers. In response the company began divesting some of its hospitals; it also shed its practice management business and reorganized its corporate structure.

Tenet rebounded and acquired hospitals in 2001 and 2002 but the next year proved not so kind. Federal investigations into the company's billing practices particularly those related to Medicare began late in 2002. In 2003 the company settled claims brought by the Department of Justice that doctors performed unnecessary cardiac surgeries at its Redding Medical Center (now Shasta Regional Medical Center) in California; the settlement cost Tenet $54 million (plus millions more to settle patients' claims). Tenet sold the facility in 2004 and also disposed of more than a dozen other facilities cutting its holdings from 115 to 100.

An even larger sell-off began in 2004 and included nearly 20 hospitals in California and others in Louisiana Massachusetts (all three were sold to Vanguard Health Systems in early 2005) Missouri and Texas. The company also exited the Nevada market when it sold Lake Mead Hospital Medical Center in Las Vegas in early 2004. Additionally the company ended some operating leases and joint ventures primarily in California; sold its Barcelona Spain hospital; and sold about a dozen home health agencies and hospice providers to Amedisys.

Tenet Healthcare moved its headquarters from Santa Barbara California to Dallas in 2005. The move was intended to streamline operations and save money.

Tenet saw some hard times in 2005 and spent years struggling to emerge from several subsequent years of investigations lawsuits and bad publicity. Its New Orleans and Mississippi facilities were hit hard by Hurricane Katrina in 2005 and its Memorial Medical Hospital in New Orleans became a symbol of the city's devastation after several dozen bodies were found there in the aftermath of the storm. The company has since sold both locations.

In 2006 it resolved multiple federal investigations regarding its billing practices by agreeing to a $900 million deal with the Justice Department. Its sale of hospitals post-Katrina was part of a larger plan announced in 2006 to sell off about a dozen facilities ridding itself of some low-performing operations partly to pay its $900 million bill to government investigators and partly so it could invest in equipment upgrades at its remaining hospitals. (The sales followed a larger-scale divestiture of about 25 facilities begun earlier.) In 2009 Tenet sold the USC University Hospital and Kenneth Norris Jr. Cancer Hospital to the University of Southern California for $275 million.

In 2010 Tenet sold its stake in supply chain and clinical workforce management firm Broadlane to MedAssets for some $159 million.

In late 2010 fellow hospital operator and rival Community Health Systems (CHS) made an unsolicited bid to acquire Tenet in a deal worth some $7.3 billion ($3.3 billion in cash and stock plus the assumption of $4 billion in debt). Tenet responded with a resounding "thanks but no thanks" saying the bid undervalued the company. CHS remained persistent despite a "poison pill" plan Tenet adopted and a volley of lawsuits. After Tenet's board rejected a plumped up offer of $4.1 billion in cash CHS formally withdrew all offers in 2011.

EXECUTIVES

Vice President Information Systems, Ricky Johnston

Chairman and CEO, Ronald A. (Ron) Rittenmeyer, age 70
CEO Doctors Medical Center, Warren J. Kirk
CEO San Antonio Market, Trip Pilgrim
CEO Western Region, Jeffrey (Jeff) Koury
VP Patient Financial Services, Stephen M. (Steve) Mooney
SVP and Chief Managed Care Officer, Clint Hailey
CFO, Daniel J. (Dan) Cancelmi, age 54, $618,000 total compensation
CEO Desert Market, Michele Finney
CEO Eastern Region Â– Central Division, Garry Gause
CEO Philadelphia Market, Michael P. (Mike) Halter
CEO Texas Region, Tim Adams
CEO Eastern Region Â– Coastal Division, Marsha Powers
CEO Texas Region, J. Eric Evans, age 39, $626,538 total compensation
SVP Applied Informatics and CIO, Paul T. Browne
CEO South Texas Market, Manuel R. (Manny) Vela
CEO Memphis Market, Audrey Gregory
CEO United Surgical Partners International, William H. (Bill) Wilcox
CEO El Paso Market, Sally Deitch
CEO Detroit Market, Anthony Tedeschi
SVP and Chief Compliance Officer, Howard Hacker
VP Patient Care Services and Chief Nursing Officer, Dian Adams
Chief Medical Officer, Octavio J. (Tavi) Diaz
CEO Phoenix Market, Frank Molinaro
CEO Birmingham Market, Keith Parrott
Vice President Audit Services, Dennis McGuffie
Vice President Operations Finance, Kristy Waters
Vice President Construction and Design, Kenneth Sutherland
Senior Vice President and General Counsel, Audrey T Andrews
Assistant Vice President Med Econ Mgd Care, Amy Thomason
Regional Vice President Chief Financial Officer, Bill Durham
Assistant Vice President National Contracting and Strategic Planning, Adele Paulett
Director of Radiology, Robert Mckewen
Vice President Consumer Applications, Brian Barnes
Assistant Vice President Managed Care, John Widdel
Vice President of Medical Affairs, George Amrom
Director of Pharmacy, Alfred Ochlak
Vice President Chief Financial Officer Central Region At Tenet Healthcare, Kathryn Engstrom
Blood Bank Director, Melanie Orourke
Vice President of Physician Recruitment, Todd Wiltsie
Vice President Finance, Rod Reasoner
Director of Radiology, Jim Morrell
Vice President Case Management, Linda Vanallen
Vice President And Assistant General Counsel, Bill Morrison
Vice President Sales, David Ricker
Director of Nursing, Terraca Holmes
Assistant Vice President, Conley Cervantes
Vice President of Sales, Bruce Ballard
Assistant Vice President Managed Care, Wes Chick
Director of Him, Melissa Spayde
Auditors: Deloitte & Touche LLP

LOCATIONS

HQ: Tenet Healthcare Corp.
1445 Ross Avenue, Suite 1400, Dallas, TX 75202
Phone: 469 893-2200
Web: www.tenethealth.com

Selected Hospitals
Alabama
  Brookwood Medical Center (Birmingham)
California
  Desert Regional Medical Center (Palm Springs)
  Doctors Hospital of Manteca

818

Doctors Medical Center (Modesto)
Emanuel Medical Center (Turlock)
Fountain Valley Regional Hospital and Medical Center
John F. Kennedy Memorial Hospital (Indio)
Lakewood Regional Medical Center
Los Alamitos Medical Center
Placentia Linda Hospital
San Ramon Regional Medical Center
Sierra Vista Regional Medical Center (San Luis
Obispo)
Twin Cities Community Hospital (Templeton)
Florida
Coral Gables Hospital
Delray Medical Center (Delray Beach)
Good Samaritan Medical Center (West Palm Beach)
Hialeah Hospital
North Shore Medical Center (Miami)
Palm Beach Gardens Medical Center
Palmetto General Hospital (Hialeah)
St. Mary's Medical Center (West Palm Beach)
West Boca Medical Center (Boca Raton)
Missouri
Des Peres Hospital (St. Louis)
South Carolina
Coastal Carolina Hospital (Hardeeville)
East Cooper Regional Medical Center (Mt. Pleasant)
Hilton Head Hospital
Piedmont Medical Center (Rock Hill)
Tennessee
Saint Francis Hospital (Memphis)
Saint Francis Hospital-Bartlett
Texas
Centennial Medical Center (Frisco)
Cypress Fairbanks Medical Center (Houston)
Doctors Hospital at White Rock Lake (Dallas)
Houston Northwest Medical Center
Lake Pointe Medical Center (Rowlett)
Nacogdoches Medical Center
Park Plaza Hospital (Houston)
The Hospitals of Providence Memorial Campus (El
Paso)
Texas Regional Medical Center (Sunnyvale)

PRODUCTS/OPERATIONS

2016 Sales

	$ mil.	% of total
Hospital Operations and other	16,904	83
Ambulatory Care	1,797	9
Conifer		
Tenet	651	3
Other customers	920	5
Intercompany eliminations	(651)	—
Total	19,621	100

2016 Sales

	% of total
Managed care	61
Medicare	21
Indemnity self-pay and other	10
Medicaid	8
Total	100

COMPETITORS

Adventist Health System Sunbelt Healthcare
Ascension Health
Banner Health
CHRISTUS Health
Carolinas HealthCare System
Catholic Health Initiatives
Community Health Systems
Dignity Health
HCA
HealthSouth
LifePoint Health
Memorial Health Services
Mercy Health
SSM Health Care
Sutter Health
Texas Health Resources
Universal Health Services
University Health Services
WellStar Health System

HISTORICAL FINANCIALS

Company Type: Public

Income Statement

FYE: December 31

	REVENUE ($ mil.)	NET INCOME ($ mil.)	NET PROFIT MARGIN	EMPLOYEES
12/16	19,621	(192)	—	130,000
12/15	18,634	(140)	—	134,630
12/14	16,615	12	0.1%	108,989
12/13	11,102	(134)	—	103,711
12/12	9,119	152	1.7%	59,164
Annual Growth	21.1%			21.8%

2016 Year-End Financials

Debt ratio: 61.76%
Return on equity: (-34.56%)
Cash ($ mil.): 716
Current ratio: 1.30
Long-term debt ($ mil.): 15,064

No. of shares (mil.): 99
Dividends
  Yield: —
  Payout: —
Market value ($ mil.): 1,479

	STOCK PRICE ($) FY Close	P/E High/Low		PER SHARE ($) Earnings	Dividends	Book Value
12/16	14.84	—	—	(1.93)	0.00	4.18
12/15	30.30	—	—	(1.41)	0.00	7.02
12/14	50.67	527	323	0.12	0.00	6.62
12/13	42.12	—	—	(1.32)	0.00	7.79
12/12	32.47	25	3	1.30	0.00	10.92
Annual Growth	(17.8%)	—	—	—	—	(21.3%)

Tenneco Inc

Tenneco ensures vehicles are riding steady without exhausting a lot of smoke. The auto parts maker designs and distributes ride-control equipment (including shock absorbers struts and suspensions) under the Monroe brand and emissions-control systems (catalytic converters exhaust pipes and mufflers) under the Walker brand. It also makes Clevite elastomer products (bushings mounts and springs) for vibration control in cars and heavy trucks. It supplies both OEMs and aftermarket wholesalers and retailers. Major customers include GM Ford Advance Auto Parts and Uni-Select. Tenneco operates on six continents and is growing its presence in key Asia/Pacific markets.

Operations

Tenneco divides its operations across six segments. These are structured geographically and are managed along its two major product lines of emission control and ride control. These segments are: North America Clean Air North America Ride Performance Europe South and India Clean Air Europe South and India Ride Performance Asia Pacific Clean Air and Asia Pacific Ride Performance. Emission control accounted for about 65% of the company's revenue in 2016.

As stricter environmental standards are enacted Tenneco finds itself well positioned as a supplier of emission control systems. The company has developed diesel particulate filters (DPFs) for passenger cars and medium-duty trucks both in Europe and North America. The filters when used with converters can reduce emissions of particulates by as much as 90% and nitrogen oxide by up to 95%. Tenneco also produces selective catalytic reduction (SCR) systems.

Another trend in the automotive industry that is building Tenneco's business is OEMs endeavoring to simplify their assembly process thus reduc-

ing costs and development times. To achieve this the OEMs are outsourcing more of the design and manufacturing of vehicle parts as well as fully-integrated systems that support emission control anti-lock braking roll-control and powertrains. This trend has given rise to Tier 1 systems integrators in addition to Tier 1 suppliers — Tenneco fits the bill for both roles. To boost its position even further the company offers just-in-time (JIT) systems for its emission control operations and has built JIT facilities close to a customer's plant for quick delivery of product components.

Geographic Reach

In addition to key alliances and joint ventures Tenneco operates 90 manufacturing facilities on six continents throughout the world. Most recently the company has opened manufacturing facilities in India China and Thailand. The US represented almost 40% of its total sales in 2016; China accounted for roughly 15%.

Sales and Marketing

Tenneco has separate sales and marketing efforts underway for its OE and aftermarket businesses. For OE sales the company's sales and marketing team is an integrated group of professionals including engineers and program managers who are organized by customer and product type (ride control and emission control). In 2016 the company served more than 75 different OEMs and commercial truck and off-highway engine manufacturers worldwide.

For aftermarket sales however the sale force covers multiple product lines and sells aftermarket products through four primary channels of distribution: The traditional three-step distribution system of full-line warehouse distributors jobbers and installers; the two-step distribution system of full-line warehouse distributors that carry only specified automotive product groups and installers; direct sales to retailers; and direct sales to installer chains. The company also serves locomotive agricultural construction and commercial truck and off-highway markets.

Its customers have included National Auto Parts Association Advance Auto Parts Uni-Select O'Reilly Automotive Aftermarket Auto Parts Alliance and AutoZone in North America Temot Autoteile GmbH Autodistribution International Group Auto Union Auto Teile Ring and AP United in Europe and Rede Presidente in South America. GM accounted for 17% of 2016 revenues; Ford 13%.

Financial Performance

Tenneco enjoyed unprecedented growth in 2016 with revenues peaking at a record-setting $8.6 billion. The revenue growth for 2016 was fueled by increased sales from its ride performance and clean air division product lines. It also experienced increased aftermarket ride performance sales in Europe and South America and recognized a 14% bump in sales from China.

The company's profits surged by 47% to reach $363 million in 2016 another company milestone. This was the result of positive impacts from a US tax benefit during the year. In addition cash flow from operations declined from $517 million in 2015 to $489 million in 2016 primarily due to the timing of revenue growth at the end of the year and the resulting impact on accounts receivable.

Strategy

The company focuses on growth through increasing production volumes launching new technology and geographic expansion both organically and via strategic acquisitions and alliances. Tenneco is also eying adjacent markets to expand its portfolio of products and systems. Not limiting itself to passenger cars or medium-size trucks the company is positioning its emissions and ride control systems for heavy-duty trucks buses and agricultural and construction equipment.

In 2016 Tennoco opened new facilities in Spring Hill Tennessee; and Lansing Michigan. It also expanded its manufacturing operations in Puebla Mexico; and Birmingham UK and built out additional testing capabilities in Zwickau Germany.

HISTORY

Tennessee Gas and Transmission began in 1943 as a division of the Chicago Corporation headed by Gardiner Symonds and authorized to build a pipeline from West Virginia to the Gulf of Mexico. With the US facing WWII fuel shortages the group finished the project in 11 months.

After WWII Tennessee Gas went public with Symonds as president. It merged its oil and gas exploration interests into Tennessee Production Company (1954) which with Bay Petroleum (bought 1955) became Tenneco Oil in 1961. Symonds acquired complementary firms and entered the chemical industry by buying 50% of Petro-Tex Chemical in 1955.

Tenneco Oil moved its headquarters to Houston in 1963 to better ship natural gas from the Texas Gulf Coast. Symonds bought Packaging Corporation of America a maker of shipping containers pulp and paperboard products in 1965. A year later the company which had become a conglomerate adopted the Tenneco name.

EXECUTIVES

Vice President Human Resources, Mike Schneider
Senior Vice President Global Administration, Richard P Schneider
EVP and CFO, Kenneth R. (Ken) Trammell, age 56, $625,000 total compensation
VP and CIO, H. William Haser, age 56
CEO, Brian Kesseler, age 51, $895,000 total compensation
EVP and President Asia/Pacific, Peng (Patrick) Guo, age 51
SVP and General Manager Global Aftermarket, Joseph A. (Joe) Pomaranski, age 61
VP and General Manager North America Aftermarket, Jeff Koviak
VP and General Manager North America Clean Air, Michael Seurynck
VP and General Manager North America Ride Performance, Jack Hall
VP and General Manager Europe Aftermarket, Bruce Ronning
VP and General Manager China Clean Air, Yih Sng
VP and General Manager China Aftermarket, Edward Hang
VP and General Manager Global Elastomers, Steve Pohlman
Managing Director India, Sagar Hemade
General Manager Japan, Yasuhara Shimonishi
VP Clean Air global Research and Development and Systems Integration, Ben Patel
EVP and President Ride Performance, Martin Hendricks, age 54
VP and General Manager Europe Ride Performance, Jean-Luc Desire
VP and General Manager Europe Clean Air, Traci Melville
VP and General Manager China Ride Performance, Yi Ren
Vice President General Manager, Alex Gelbcke
Vice President, Richard Wambold
Vice President Finance, Leo Waner
Chairman, Gregg M. Sherrill, age 64
Auditors: PricewaterhouseCoopers LLP

LOCATIONS

HQ: Tenneco Inc
500 North Field Drive, Lake Forest, IL 60045
Phone: 847 482-5000
Web: www.tenneco.com

2016 Sales

	$ mil.	% of total
US	3,512	41
China	1,186	14
Germany	764	8
Canada	387	5
United Kingdom	387	5
Other Foreign	2,363	27
Total	**8,599**	**100**

PRODUCTS/OPERATIONS

2016 Sales

	$ mil.	% of total
Clean Air Products & Systems		
Aftermarket	305	4
Original Equipment		
OE Value-add	3,736	43
OE Substrate	2,028	24
Ride Performance Products & Systems		
Aftermarket	937	10
Original Equipment	1,593	19
Total	**8,599**	**100**

Selected Brands and Products

Emission control systems (DNX DynoMax Fonos Gillet Thrush and Walker)
  Aftertreatment control units
  Burner systems
  Catalytic converters and diesel oxidation catalysts
  Diesel particulate filters (DPFs)
  Exhaust manifolds
  Hangers and isolators
  High-frequency turbo decoupler
  Hydrocarbon vaporizers and injectors
  Lean NOx traps
  Mufflers
  Pipes
  Resonators
  Selective catalytic reduction (SCR)
Ride control systems (DNX Fric-Rot Kinetic Monroe and Rancho)
  Coil and leaf springs
  Computerized electronic suspension (CES)
  Corner and full axle modules
  Heavy duty truck and train shocks
  Kinetic suspension technology
  Shock absorbers and struts
  Suspension systems
  Top mounts
  Vibration control components (Clevite Elastomers)
  Engine and body mounts
  Exhaust isolators
  Leaf and coil springs
  Spring seats
  Suspension control arm link and stabilizer bar bushings

COMPETITORS

Benteler Automotive	Kolbenschmidt Pierburg
Cooper-Standard Automotive	Letts Industries
Edelbrock	Meritor
Faurecia Exhaust Systems	Wescast Industries
	ZF Group NAO

HISTORICAL FINANCIALS

Company Type: Public

Income Statement

FYE: December 31

	REVENUE ($ mil.)	NET INCOME ($ mil.)	NET PROFIT MARGIN	EMPLOYEES
12/16	8,599	363	4.2%	31,000
12/15	8,209	247	3.0%	30,000
12/14	8,420	226	2.7%	29,000
12/13	7,964	183	2.3%	26,000
12/12	7,363	275	3.7%	25,000
Annual Growth	**4.0%**	**7.2%**	**—**	**5.5%**

2016 Year-End Financials

Debt ratio: 31.87%
Return on equity: 70.91%
Cash ($ mil.): 347
Current ratio: 1.32
Long-term debt ($ mil.): 1,294

No. of shares (mil.): 54
Dividends
  Yield: —
  Payout: —
Market value ($ mil.): 3,388

	STOCK PRICE ($) FY Close	P/E High/Low		PER SHARE ($) Earnings	Dividends	Book Value
12/16	62.47	10	5	6.44	0.00	10.84
12/15	45.91	15	10	4.11	0.00	7.52
12/14	56.61	18	13	3.66	0.00	8.12
12/13	56.57	19	11	2.97	0.00	7.11
12/12	35.11	9	5	4.50	0.00	4.07
Annual Growth	**15.5%**			**9.4%**	**—**	**27.8%**

Tennessee Valley Authority

Tennessee Valley Authority (TVA) may not be an expert on state attractions like Dollywood and the Grand Ole Opry but it is an authority on power generation. A US government-owned corporation TVA is the largest public power producer in the country. It sells wholesale electricity to more than 150 municipal and cooperative power distributors which serve some 9 million people in Tennessee and parts of Alabama Georgia Kentucky Mississippi North Carolina and Virginia. It also sells power directly to large industrial customers and federal agencies. In addition TVA provides flood control and land management for the Tennessee River system and assists utilities and state and local governments with economic development.

Operations
Tennessee Valley Authority operates seven fossil plants three nuclear plants and 29 hydro plants. TVA provides electric power through a network of about 16000 miles of transmission line. While most of its power comes from traditional generation sources it operates 15 solar energy sites and one wind energy site.

TVA?s power generation mix nuclear about 40%; coal about 25%; natural gas about 20%; hydro about 10%; and the rest from wind solar and energy efficiency measures. Total generation capacity stands at nearly 170000 gigawatt-hours.

TVA has an agreement to produce tritium a radioactive gas that boosts the power of nuclear weapons for the US Department of Energy at its Watts Bar nuclear plant.

Geographic Reach
The Tennessee Valley Authority serves 170 counties in Alabama Georgia Kentucky Mississippi

North Carolina Tennessee and Virginia. Tennessee accounts for 65% of the entity's revenues.

Sales and Marketing

Tennessee Valley Authority provides electricity to more than 50 large industrial customers a handful of federal agencies and more than 150 local power company (LPC) customers that serve more than nine million people in parts of seven southeastern states. The United States Enrichment Corporation a subsidiary of USEC is TVA's largest directly served industrial customer. Two of the largest LPCs served by TVA are the Memphis Light Gas and Water Division and Nashville Electric Service.

Financial Performance

In fiscal 2017 Tennessee Valley Authority's revenue inched up about 1% although power sales fell 2% due to mild weather than reduced energy demand. The TVA made an extra $500 million contribution to its pension fund in 2017 which drove net income to $685 million in 2017 about 50% less than 2016. Fuel costs were 2% higher.

Strategy

TVA is changing its power generation mix to become a cleaner producer of energy. It has closed or is closing several older less efficient coal generated power units while putting more natural gas-fired units on line as well as increasing nuclear generation capabilities. The authority is working toward obtaining 50% of its power supply from low- or zero-carbon-emitting or renewable sources by 2020.

HISTORY

TVA was established by Congress in 1933 primarily to reduce flood damage improve navigation on the Tennessee River and promote agricultural and industrial development in the region. In 1999 government appropriations for the authority ceased.

In 1924 the Army Corps of Engineers finished building the Wilson Dam on the Tennessee River in Alabama to provide power for two WWI-era nitrate plants. With the war over the question of what to do with the plants became a political football.

An act of Congress created the Tennessee Valley Authority (TVA) in 1933 to manage the plants and Tennessee Valley waterways. New Dealers saw TVA as a way to revitalize the local economy through improved navigation and power generation. Power companies claimed the agency was unconstitutional but by 1939 when a federal court ruled against them TVA had five operating hydroelectric plants and five under construction.

During the 1940s TVA supplied power for the war effort including the Manhattan Project in Tennessee. During the postwar boom between 1945 and 1950 power usage in the Tennessee Valley nearly doubled. Despite adding dams TVA couldn't keep up with demand so in 1949 it began building a coal-fired unit. Because coal-fired plants weren't part of TVA's original mission in 1955 a Congressional panel recommended the authority be dissolved.

Though TVA survived its funding was cut. In 1959 it was allowed to sell bonds but it no longer received direct government appropriations for power operations. In addition it had to pay back the government for past appropriations.

TVA began to build the first unit of an ambitious 17-plant nuclear power program in Alabama in 1967. However skyrocketing costs forced it to raise rates and cut maintenance on its coal-fired plants which led to breakdowns. In 1985 five reactors had to be shut down because of safety concerns.

In 1988 former auto industry executive Marvin Runyon was appointed chairman of the agency. "Carvin' Marvin" cut management sold three airplanes and got rid of peripheral businesses saving $400 million a year. In 1992 Runyon left to go to the postal service and was replaced by Craven Crowell who began preparing TVA for competition in the retail power market.

TVA ended its nuclear construction program in 1996 after bringing two nuclear units on line within three months a first for a US utility. The next year it raised rates for the first time in 10 years planning to reduce its debt. In response to a lawsuit filed by neighboring utilities it agreed to stop "laundering" power by using third parties to sell outside the agency's legally authorized area.

In 1999 the authority finished installing almost $2 billion in scrubbers and other equipment at its coal-fired plants so that it could buy Kentucky coal along with cleaner Wyoming coal. That year however the EPA charged TVA with violating the Clean Air Act by making major overhauls on some of its older coal-fired plants without getting permits or installing updated pollution-control equipment. It ordered TVA to bring most of its coal-fired plants into compliance with more current pollution standards. The next year TVA contested the order in court stating compliance would jack up electricity rates.

TVA was fined by the US Nuclear Regulatory Commission in 2000 for laying off a nuclear plant whistleblower.

In 2008 a holding pond at TVA's coal-burning Kingston Fossil Plant failed and dumped some 5.4 million cu. yd. of fly ash over 400 acres in eastern Tennessee's Roane County. The slide knocked down utility poles and trees and damaged at least a dozen homes (some beyond repair). Although no one was hurt some residents were cut off by the spill prompting officials to build a new road. The flooding was the pond's third reported incident in six years. The cleanup will likely cost more than $1 billion. Some 14 lawsuits were filed against the TVA as a result of the incident.

William D. Johnson former chairman president and CEO of Progress Energy was named president and CEO of TVA in 2013.

EXECUTIVES

Vice President, Tom D Kilgore
Senior Vice President Fossil Operations, John McCormick
General Manager Operations Business Services, John M. Thomas, age 54, $577,212 total compensation
EVP and Chief Nuclear Officer, Joseph P. (Joe) Grimes, age 60, $557,135 total compensation
SVP Distributed Energy Resources, Jay C. Stowe
EVP and COO, Charles G. (Chip) Pardee, age 57, $647,481 total compensation
EVP External Relations, Van M. Wardlaw, age 57
SVP Watts Bar Operations and Construction, Michael D. (Mike) Skaggs, $446,712 total compensation
President CEO and Director, William D. (Bill) Johnson, age 62, $998,827 total compensation
SVP Chief Communications and Marketing Officer, Janet J. Brewer
EVP and General Counsel, Sherry A. Quirk, age 62
Vice President and Controller, Diane Wear
Vice President Supply Chain, Russ Steward
Vice President Risk Management, Randy Petty
Executive Vice President and Chief Nuclear Officer, Joe Grimes
Vice President, Kenneth Mullinax
Chair, V. Lynn Evans
Board Member, William Jenkins
Board Member, Robert Campbell
Vice Chairman, Allen Stokes
Auditors: Ernst & Young LLP

LOCATIONS

HQ: Tennessee Valley Authority
400 W. Summit Hill Drive, Knoxville, TN 37902
Phone: 865 632-2101
Web: www.tva.gov

2016 Sales

	$ mil.	% of total
Tennessee	6,968	66
Alabama	1,504	14
Mississippi	999	9
Kentucky	640	6
Georgia	255	2
North Carolina	155	1
Virginia	58	1
Other revenues	48	1
Off-system sales	7	—
Revenue capitalized during pre-commercial plant operations	(18)	—
Total	**10,616**	**100**

PRODUCTS/OPERATIONS

2016 Sales

	$ mil.	% of total
Electricity sales:		
Local power companies	9,696	91
Industries directly served	649	6
Other revenues	155	2
Federal agencies & other	134	1
Revenue capitalized during per-commercial plant operations	(18)	—
Total	**10,616**	**100**

HISTORICAL FINANCIALS

Company Type: Public

Income Statement

FYE: September 30

	REVENUE ($ mil.)	NET INCOME ($ mil.)	NET PROFIT MARGIN	EMPLOYEES
09/17	10,739	685	6.4%	10,092
09/16	10,616	1,233	11.6%	10,691
09/15	11,003	1,111	10.1%	10,918
09/14	11,137	469	4.2%	11,542
09/13	10,956	271	2.5%	12,612
Annual Growth	(0.5%)	26.1%	—	(5.4%)

2017 Year-End Financials

Debt ratio: 50.49%—
Return on equity: 7.80%
Cash ($ mil.): 300
Current ratio: 0.54
Long-term debt ($ mil.): 21,438
Dividends
Yield: 0.0%
Payout: —
Market value ($ mil.): —

	STOCK PRICE ($) FY Close	P/E High/Low		Earnings	PER SHARE ($) Dividends	Book Value
09/17	25.18	—	—	(0.00)	0.84	(0.00)
09/16	25.91	—	—	(0.00)	0.89	(0.00)
09/15	24.39	—	—	(0.00)	0.94	(0.00)
09/14	23.99	—	—	(0.00)	0.96	(0.00)
09/13	22.27	—	—	(0.00)	1.04	(0.00)
Annual Growth	3.1%				(5.3%)	

Territorial Bancorp Inc

Territorial Bancorp serves its customers island-style. It is the financial holding company for Territorial Savings Bank which provides standard products and services such as checking and savings accounts money market accounts CDs IRAs and loans from its nearly 30 branch locations across Hawaii. Its Territorial Financial Services subsidiary sells insurance while LPL Financial offers Mutual funds and annuities. Territorial Savings

Bank targets the territorial nature of its customers — one- to four-family residential mortgages account for 95% of its loan portfolio. Multifamily and commercial mortgages and construction and home equity loans round out its lending activities.

Operations

Territorial Bancorp generated 61% of its total revenue from loan interest in 2014 with another 31% coming from interest on its investment securities. About 3% of its revenue came from service fees on loan and deposit accounts while 2% came from gains on its investment security sales.

Sales and Marketing

The bank provides financial services to individuals families and small- to medium-sized businesses from its 28 branches spread across the state of Hawaii.

Financial Performance

Territorial's revenues and profits have been slowly declining in recent years mostly as its margins have been squeezed in the low-interest environment and as its gains on its held-for-sale loans have been shrinking.

The company's revenue ended mostly flat around $64.8 million in 2014 with mixed results. The bank's loan and investment security interest grew by 7% thanks to asset growth though these improvements were offset by lower gains on investment securities and loans compared to the year before.

Lower revenue in 2014 coupled with a slight uptick in loan loss provisions and equipment investment costs caused Territorial Bancorp's net income to tumble by 4% to $14.1 million. Its operating cash levels also fell by 19% to $14.1 million after adjusting its earnings for non-cash items mostly related to its net proceeds on its held-for-sale loans.

Strategy

Territorial Bancorp relies on its competitive rates and pricing to grow its loan and deposit business. During 2014 its deposit business grew organically by nearly 6% mostly as the bank promoted its higher-than-market rates for its passbook and statement savings accounts.

Company Background

Founded in 1921 Territorial Savings was mutually owned until 2009 when its former parent Territorial Mutual Holding Company converted to a stock form of ownership and sold shares in itself to the public. The move allowed the company to offer other financial services in addition to banking.

EXECUTIVES

Chairman President and CEO Territorial Bancorp Inc. and Territorial Savings Bank, Allan S. Kitagawa, age 71, $766,080 total compensation
Vice Chairman Co-COO General Counsel and Corporate Secretary Territorial Bancorp Inc. and Territorial Savings Bank, Vernon Hirata, age 64, $269,100 total compensation
SVP Business Development and Marketing, Denise Takashima
SVP Branch Administration, Robert Costa
Vice Chairman and Co-COO Territorial Bancorp Inc. and Territorial Savings Bank, Ralph Y. Nakatsuka, age 61, $269,100 total compensation
Svp Administration Territorial Bancorp Inc And Territorial Savings Bank, Karen Cox
Auditors: Moss Adams LLP

LOCATIONS

HQ: Territorial Bancorp Inc
1132 Bishop Street, Suite 2200, Honolulu, HI 96813
Phone: 808 946-1400
Web: www.territorialsavings.net

PRODUCTS/OPERATIONS

2014 Sales

	$ mil.	% of total
Interest and dividend income		
Loans	39	61
Investment securities	19	31
Others	0	-
Non-interest income		
Service fees on loan and deposits	2	3
Income on bank owned life insurance	1	2
Others	2	3
Total	**64**	**100**

COMPETITORS

American Savings Bank	Central Pacific
Bank of Hawaii	Financial

HISTORICAL FINANCIALS

Company Type: Public

Income Statement
FYE: December 31

	ASSETS ($ mil.)	NET INCOME ($ mil.)	INCOME AS % OF ASSETS	EMPLOYEES
12/16	1,877	16	0.9%	276
12/15	1,821	14	0.8%	280
12/14	1,691	14	0.8%	272
12/13	1,616	14	0.9%	279
12/12	1,574	14	0.9%	277
Annual Growth	4.5%	2.5%		(0.1%)

2016 Year-End Financials

Debt ratio: —
Return on equity: 7.25%
Cash ($ mil.): 61
Current ratio: —
Long-term debt ($ mil.): —
No. of shares (mil.): 9
Dividends
Yield: 0.0%
Payout: 52.2%
Market value ($ mil.): 321

	STOCK PRICE ($) FY Close	P/E High/Low		PER SHARE ($) Earnings	Dividends	Book Value
12/16	32.84	18	14	1.76	0.92	23.50
12/15	27.74	18	13	1.59	0.76	22.74
12/14	21.55	15	13	1.51	0.70	21.81
12/13	23.20	16	14	1.49	0.62	21.11
12/12	22.85	17	14	1.45	0.54	20.26
Annual Growth	9.5%	—	—	5.0%	14.2%	3.8%

Tesla Inc

Tesla intends to supercharge the public's passion for electric vehicles. Founded in 2003 the company designs manufactures and markets high-performance technologically advanced electric cars and powertrain components. Tesla sells two models: the Model S a saloon (sedan); and the Model X a SUV which are among the world's top-selling electric cars. The fuel-efficient fully electric vehicles recharge their lithium-ion batteries from an outlet and depending on a driver's speed are capable of approaching 300 miles per charge. Tesla is also gearing up for the launch of the Model 3 an affordable family saloon in 2018. Tesla CEO Elon Musk founded PayPal and also runs SpaceX and is the Chairman of SolarCity.

Operations

Tesla is primarily occupied with the design production and sale of its electric vehicles and offers two models the Model S and Model X. In support of its vehicles Tesla maintains a network of upwards of around 7110 charging ports in over 790 stations worldwide. This automotove segment is its largest accounting for more than 95% of its total revenue.

Through its acquisition of SolarCity in 2016 Tesla created its new energy generation and storage segment which makes and sells stationary energy storage products and solar energy systems to residential and commercial customers. Its Powerwall products integrate with solar panels and can store enough energy to power a two-bed home for a day. Tesla's commercial and utility offering Powerpack is an energy storage system that offers features like peak shaving load shifting emergency backup self-consumption of solar generation and demand response.

Geographic Reach

Tesla operates through 265 stores and service locations. The US accounts for 60% of sales. Other major markets include China (15%) and Norway (5%).

Sales and Marketing

The company markets and sells cars directly to consumers through an international network of company-owned stores and galleries. Tesla is notable in that it does not use dealerships and this approach means the price of its vehicles are non-negotiable.

Financial Performance

Tesla has achieved rapid revenue growth in recent years while pumping everything it earns and more into R&D. Net revenue surged by 73% from $4 billion in 2015 to $7 billion in 2016. Automotive revenue increased 63% in 2016 as its Model X and Model S cars gain in popularity and become more widely available.

In addition to these factors Tesla's automotive leasing revenue skyrocketed by more than 140% due to a surge in cumulative vehicle deliveries under leasing programs. Its service and other revenue jumped 61% during 2016 due to a spike in pre-owned vehicle sales as Tesla received more trade-ins and experienced a surge in maintenance service revenue.

Tesla however post a net loss of $675 million in 2016 as it invested further in R&D and employee compensation relating to the development of upcoming models and the expansion of its power storage and regulation products. Tesla also experienced negative operating cash flow of $124 million in 2016 due to an increase in inventory to support growth and the continued rapid expansion of its supercharger network.

Strategy

Tesla's business model is based on using profits from its high-end vehicles to fund development of more affordable vehicles; the Model 3 will retail for around $35000 and is due for release in 2018. The company is working hard to increase acceptance of electric vehicles in general the perception of which has long been hampered by low range low speed and poor styling. The company led with high-performance and stylish autos and has been investing heavily in its charging network as well as home-charging facilities.

Mergers and Acquisitions

In late 2016 Tesla made its most important acquisition to date when it purchased SolarCity in a deal valued at $2.6 billion. Both companies are led by Elon Musk and expect to achieve cost synergies of $150 million in the first full year after closing. By combining Tesla's new electric vehicles with SolarCity's newest solar products the companies expect to lower hardware costs reduce installation costs and improve their manufacturing efficiency. The acquisition also created generation and storage a new segment that designs manufactures installs and sells stationary energy storage products and solar energy systems to residential and commercial customers.

Company Background

Tesla Motors is named for Nikola Tesla (1856-1943) the renowned Serbian-American engineer and inventor. Tesla Motors was incorporated in July 2003.

EXECUTIVES

Chairman and Product Architect, Elon Musk, age 46, $45,936 total compensation

CFO, Deepak Ahuja, age 54, $338,000 total compensation

CTO, Jeffrey B. (JB) Straubel, age 41, $250,560 total compensation

President Global Sales and Service, Jon McNeill, age 49, $501,923 total compensation

VP Engineering, Doug Field, age 51, $301,153 total compensation

CIO, Gary Clark

Vice President, Jerome Guillen

Vice President Of Regulatory Affairs And Associate General Counsel, James Chen

VP Supply Chain, Paolo Cerruti

National Sales Manager, Christine Moore

Vice President Recruiting, Max Brown

Vice President Human Resources, Mark Lipscomb

VICE PRESIDENT IR AND STRATEGY, Jeff K Evanson

Vice President R and D Director of Engineering, Ed Pearce

CORPORATE TREASURER AND VICE PRESIDENT GLOBAL TAX TRADE TREASURY AND NEW VENTURES AT TESLA MOTORS, Susan J Repo

Auditors: PricewaterhouseCoopers LLP

LOCATIONS

HQ: Tesla Inc
3500 Deer Creek Road, Palo Alto, CA 94304
Phone: 650 681-5000
Web: www.teslamotors.com

2016 Sales

	$ mil.	% of total
US	4,200	60
China	1,065	15
Norway	335	5
Other	1,398	20
Total	**7,000**	**100**

PRODUCTS/OPERATIONS

2016 Sales

	$ mil.	% of total
Automotive	6,818	97
Energy generation & storage	181	3
Total	**7,000**	**100**

COMPETITORS

BMW	Kia Motors
BYD	Mitsubishi Motors
Daimler	Nissan
FCA US	Subaru of America
Ford Motor	Suzuki Motor
General Motors	Toyota
Honda	Volkswagen
Hyundai Motor	VydroTech
Isuzu	ZAP

HISTORICAL FINANCIALS

Company Type: Public

Income Statement

FYE: December 31

	REVENUE ($ mil.)	NET INCOME ($ mil.)	NET PROFIT MARGIN	EMPLOYEES
12/16	7,000	(674)	—	30,025
12/15	4,046	(888)	—	13,058
12/14	3,198	(294)	—	10,161
12/13	2,013	(74)	—	5,859
12/12	413	(396)	—	2,964
Annual Growth	**102.9%**	**—**		**78.4%**

2016 Year-End Financials

Debt ratio: 31.41%
Return on equity: (-23.04%)
Cash ($ mil.): 3,393
Current ratio: 1.07
Long-term debt ($ mil.): 5,969

No. of shares (mil.): 161
Dividends
  Yield: —
  Payout: —
Market value ($ mil.): 34,524

	STOCK PRICE ($) FY Close	P/E High/Low	PER SHARE ($) Earnings	Dividends	Book Value
12/16	213.69	— —	(4.68)	0.00	29.42
12/15	240.01	— —	(6.93)	0.00	8.29
12/14	222.41	— —	(2.36)	0.00	7.25
12/13	150.43	— —	(0.62)	0.00	5.42
12/12	33.87	— —	(3.69)	0.00	1.09
Annual Growth	**58.5%**	**— —**	**— —**		**—127.8%**

TEXAS A&M FOUNDATION

Auditors: BKD LLP HOUSTON TX

LOCATIONS

HQ: TEXAS A&M FOUNDATION
401 GEORGE BUSH DR, COLLEGE STATION, TX 778402811
Phone: 979 845-8161
Web: WWW.TAMUGIFT.ORG

HISTORICAL FINANCIALS

Company Type: Private

Income Statement

FYE: June 30

	ASSETS ($ mil.)	NET INCOME ($ mil.)	INCOME AS % OF ASSETS	EMPLOYEES
06/13	1,505	97	6.5%	95
06/12	1,313	66	5.0%	—
Annual Growth	**14.6%**	**47.2%**	**—**	**—**

2013 Year-End Financials

Debt ratio: —
Return on equity: 52.30%
Cash ($ mil.): 43
Current ratio: 21.30
Long-term debt ($ mil.): —

Dividends
  Yield: —
  Payout: —
Market value ($ mil.): —

Texas Capital Bancshares Inc

Texas Capital Bancshares is the parent company of Texas Capital Bank with more than 10 branches in Austin Dallas Fort Worth Houston and San Antonio. The bank targets high-net-worth individuals and Texas-based businesses with more than $5 million in annual revenue with a focus on the real estate financial services transportation communications petrochemicals and mining sectors. Striving for personalized services for its clients the bank offers deposit accounts Visa credit cards commercial loans and mortgages equipment leasing wealth management and trust services. Its BankDirect division provides online banking services. Founded in 1998 Texas Capital Bancshares has about $11.7 billion in assets.

Financial Performance
The bank reported $488.6 million in revenue in 2013 an nearly 11% increase versus 2012. Net income was flat at about $121 million after posting three consecutive years of gains. Cash flow from operations continued its steep three year decline. The bank's total assets increased 11% from about $10.5 billion in 2012 to $11.7 billion in 2013. Total deposits increased 24% year over year to about $9.3 billion.

Strategy
Headquartered in Dallas Texas Capital Bank (TCB) believes that its Texas roots give it a competitive advantage over larger competitors that are headquartered out of state. Indeed TCB is gaining market share and is expanding by hiring experienced bankers and support staff. The bank is looking to grow within its main metropolitan markets but has also branched out beyond the borders of its home state. The bank has an Cayman Islands branch to offer offshore cash management and deposit products to it core clientele.

EXECUTIVES

President and CEO Texas Capital Bancshares Inc. President and CEO Texas Capital Bank, C. Keith Cargill, age 64, $825,000 total compensation

President Texas and Chief Lending Officer Texas Capital Bank, Vince A. Ackerson, age 60, $454,166 total compensation

Managing Director Regional and Specialty Banking Texas Capital Bank Austin Fort Worth and San Antonio and Commercial Real Estate and Builder Finance, Mark M. Johnson

Regional President Texas Capital Bank Austin, Kerry L. Hall

Regional President Texas Capital Bank Dallas, Russell Hartsfield

Chief Risk Officer Texas Capital Bancshares Inc. and Texas Capital Bank, John D. Hudgens, age 61, $455,833 total compensation

Managing Director Specialty and Regional Banking Texas Capital Bank Dallas and Syndicated Finance Lender Finance Leasing and Financial Institutions, James D. (Jim) Recer

Regional Chairman Texas Capital Bank Houston, Bill Wilson

Regional President Texas Capital Bank San Antonio, David Pope

Managing Director Regional and Specialty Banking Texas Capital Bank Houston, John C. Sarvadi

CFO, Julie L. Anderson, age 48, $355,000 total compensation

Regional Chairman Texas Capital Bank San Antonio, Shaun Kennedy

Regional Chairman Texas Capital Bank Fort
  Worth, Robin Hamilton
Regional President Texas Capital Bank Fort
  Worth, David Williams
EVP Builder Finance, Melissa Abel
EVP Asset Based Lending, Chris Capriotti
EVP Commercial Real Estate, Rob Delph
EVP Lender Finance, David Fricke
EVP Energy/Oil and Gas Syndicated Finance and
  Financial Institutions, Lester Keliher
EVP Financial Institutions, Peter Stringer
President Mortgage Finance, Gary Ort
EVP Technology Operations Enterprise Planning
  and Information Security Texas Capital Bank,
  Kirk Coleman
EVP SBA Lending, John Gannon
EVP Public Finance, Paul Howell
EVP Strategic Sales and Marketing, Greg Lewis
President Private Wealth Advisors, Alan L. Miller
Senior Vice President Compensation Director,
  Chris Gullo
Vice President, Tricia Linderman
Vice President, Lela Naggar
Vice President Deposit Operations, Leslie Marsh
Vice President of Information Technology
  Infrastructure, Randy Tiegs
Vice President Project Management, Allen
  Baumbach
Senior Vice President and Deposit Operation,
  Connie Couch
Senior Vice President Wealth Management and
  Trust Services, Chip Glispin
Vice President Corp Security and Investigations,
  Cary Wicker
Senior Vice President Risk Management Officer,
  Terry King
Vice President Fraud Investigator, Jamie Burud
Vice President Security, Neal Baker
Senior Vice President, Don Rosics
Executive Vice President, Brent Johnston
Senior Vice President, Charlotte Lowe
Executive Vice President, Ronald Baker
Vice President Planning, Prasad Varma
Senior Vice President Energy Banking Texas
  Capital Bank, Jonathan Gregory
Senior Vice President and CRA Manager, Phil Aslin
Chairman, Larry L. Helm, age 69
Auditors: Ernst & Young LLP

LOCATIONS

HQ: Texas Capital Bancshares Inc
  2000 McKinney Avenue, Suite 700, Dallas, TX 75201
Phone: 214 932-6600
Web: www.texascapitalbank.com

PRODUCTS/OPERATIONS

2015 Sales

	% of total
Interest income	
Interest and fees on loans	92
Other	1
Non-interest income	
Brokered loan fees	3
Service charges on deposit accounts	1
Trust fee income	1
Swap fees	1
Other	1
Total	**100**

Selected Services

Association capital bank
Bankdirect
Business services
Mortgage business finance
Online services
Personal banking
Private wealth advisors
Treasury and liquidity

COMPETITORS

Amegy	Comerica
BBVA Compass	Cullen/Frost Bankers
Bancshares	JPMorgan Chase
BOK Financial	Prosperity Bancshares
Bank of America	Wells Fargo

HISTORICAL FINANCIALS

Company Type: Public

Income Statement
FYE: December 31

	ASSETS ($ mil.)	NET INCOME ($ mil.)	INCOME AS % OF ASSETS	EMPLOYEES
12/16	21,697	155	0.7%	1,442
12/15	18,909	144	0.8%	1,329
12/14	15,899	136	0.9%	1,142
12/13	11,714	121	1.0%	1,016
12/12	10,540	120	1.1%	881
Annual Growth	**19.8%**	**6.5%**	**—**	**13.1%**

2016 Year-End Financials

Debt ratio: 11.04%	No. of shares (mil.): 49
Return on equity: 8.52%	Dividends
Cash ($ mil.): 2,814	Yield: —
Current ratio: —	Payout: —
Long-term debt ($ mil.): —	Market value ($ mil.): 3,881

	STOCK PRICE ($) FY Close	P/E High/Low	PER SHARE ($) Earnings	Dividends	Book Value
12/16	78.40	26 10	3.11	0.00	40.59
12/15	49.42	21 14	2.91	0.00	35.39
12/14	54.33	23 17	2.88	0.00	32.45
12/13	62.20	22 14	2.72	0.00	26.72
12/12	44.82	17 10	3.00	0.00	20.53
Annual Growth	**15.0%**	**— —**	**0.9%**	**—**	**18.6%**

Texas Instruments Inc.

Texas Instruments sticks to basics — producing
analog and embedded processors the workhorses
of the industry. The company?s analog chips manage power in electronic equipment and its embedded processors handle specific tasks in electronic
devices. TI?s customers which number about
100000 use the company's chips for applications
that include autos industrial machinery consumer
electronics communications devices and calculators. The company also sticks to basics in production operating its own manufacturing plants which
is places around the world. Another TI basic: TI
engineer Jack Kilby was credited as co-inventor of
the integrated circuit in the late 1950s.

Operations

Texas Instruments operates through three segments: Analog Embedded Processing and Other
products.

The Analog business which accounts for about
two-thirds of sales includes high-volume analog
and logic products power management semiconductors and amplifiers and data converters. The
company?s analog products are used in the personal electronics automotive and industrial markets as well as others.

The Embedded Processing segment which generates more than a fifth of sales makes application
specific integrated circuits (ASICs) digital signal
processors (DSPs) and microcontrollers. TI?s embedded processors range from low-cost microcontrollers used in products such as electric toothbrushes to complex devices used in automotive

applications such as infotainment and advanced
driver assistance systems.

The remaining revenue comes from the Other
segment which includes digital light processors
(DLP) used in projectors to create high-definition
images and calculators custom semiconductors
and royalties received from licensing of the company?s patent portfolio.

In terms of markets TI gets about a third of revenue from industrial about 25% from personal
electronics about a fifth from automotive about
10% each from communications and enterprise.

TI operates 15 manufacturing sites in nine countries.

Geographic Reach

China is the biggest single market for Texas Instruments accounting for about 45% of revenue
with other Asia/Pacific countries (including Japan)
accounting for more than 20% of revenue. The
US generates about 12% of TI?s sales. The company has facilities for service sales and other functions in the US Europe and Asia.

Sales and Marketing

Texas Instruments markets its products through
a direct sales force as well as via distributors and
third-party sales representatives. Distributors generate about 60% of sales. About two-thirds of revenue comes from some 100 customers.

Financial Performance

Texas Instruments has had a decade of up-and-
down revenue as well as four straight years of rising profits. In 2016 revenue rose 3% to $13.4 bil-
lion from 2015 and profit jumped 20% to $3.6
billion. TI's 27% net profit margin was second only
to Linear Technology?s 33% among its competitors.

The Embedded Processing unit paced the company?s revenue increase adding more than $235
million (8% higher). The bigger Analog unit's sales
rose nearly $200 million (a 2% increase). Auto-
motive was a key market for TI in 2016 with sales
rising 22%. The company ships products from the
analog and embedded units for automotive applications. In TI?s Other segment DLPs were the only
products with higher year-over-year revenue.

Higher revenue and lower cost of revenue and
restructuring charges helped drive net income to
$3.6 billion a 20% increase.

Cash flow from operations rose to $4.6 billion
in 2016 from $4.3 billion in 2015 on higher net
income and lower costs in several areas including
depreciation and stock compensation.

TI highlights free cash flow as a financial measure. It rose to about $4 billion in 2016 from $3.8
billion in 2015. Free cash flow is cash flow from
operations minus capital expenditures. It is money
than can be invested back into the business or returned to shareholders through dividends and
stock buybacks. TI returned about $3.8 billion to
stockholders through stock buybacks and dividends in 2016.

Strategy

Texas Instruments focus on its Analog and Embedded Processing units is paying off. They combined to product 86% of the company's revenue
almost double since 2004. The company believes
that analog and embedded processors offer diversity of applications long product life cycles and
lower-cost manufacturing processes.

TI has identified two markets where analog and
embedded processes can generate growing sales
over time: industrial and automotive. More and
more functions are handled by semiconductors in
industrial machinery and vehicles. In 2016 automotive and industrial combined to provide just
more than half of TI?s revenue up from 42% in
2013. TI is investing heavily in processors for those
markets shifting resources from products for other
markets. It reduced overall R&D in products for

the personal electronics market but is making selective investments in it.

On the manufacturing end TI is moving to produce more chips on 300-millimeter wafers which hold more chips than the standard 200-millimeter wafers. Making chips on the bigger wafer reduces costs 40%. The company has 300-millimeter capacity in its Dallas and Richardson fabrication facilities and is adding more.

Unlike its rapidly consolidating competitors TI has not made recent acquisitions nor has it been a serious target for acquisition. Its last major deal was to buy National Semiconductor in 2011. Other semiconductor companies have spent billions on mergers and acquisitions in recent years to amass market share and diversify product lines.

EXECUTIVES

Chairman President and CEO, Richard K. (Rich) Templeton, age 58, $1,164,083 total compensation
SVP High-Volume Analog and Logic Central Analog Services DLPÂ® Products and Education Technology, Stephen A. (Steve) Anderson, age 55, $616,500 total compensation
SVP Analog Power Products, Niels Anderskouv, age 47
SVP Technology and Manufacturing, Kevin J. Ritchie, age 61, $688,333 total compensation
SVP Embedded Processing, R. Gregory (Greg) Delagi, age 54, $622,917 total compensation
EVP and COO, Brian T. Crutcher, age 44, $822,917 total compensation
SVP Information Technology Services and CIO, Ellen L. Barker, age 54
SVP Worldwide Sales and Applications, Bing Xie, age 49
SVP CFO and Chief Accounting Officer Finance and Operations, Rafael R. Lizardi, age 44
SVP Analog Signal Chain, Haviv Ilan, age 48
SENIOR VICE PRESIDENT MGR, Terri West
Vice President, Tim G Williams
Vice President Worldwide ASIC, Greg Hantak
Vice President Americas, Mark Roberts
National Sales Manager, Dennis Smith
Government Relations, Rosie Saucedo
Vice President, Hubie Payne
Auditors: Ernst & Young LLP

LOCATIONS

HQ: Texas Instruments Inc.
12500 TI Boulevard, Dallas, TX 75243
Phone: 214 479-3773
Web: www.ti.com

2016 Sales

	$ mil.	% of total
Asia/Pacific		
Japan	1,040	8
Other countries	8,024	60
Europe	2,393	18
US	1,682	12
Other regions	231	2
Total	**13,370**	**100**

PRODUCTS/OPERATIONS

2016 Sales

	$ mil.	% of total
Analog	8,536	64
Embedded processing	3,023	23
Other	1,811	13
Total	**13,370**	**100**

2016 Sales by Market

	% of total
Industrial	33
Personal electronics	26
Automotive	18
Communications equipment	13
Enterprise sytems	6
Calculators	4
Total	**100**

Selected Products

Semiconductors
  Analog and mixed-signal
  Amplifiers and comparators
  Clocks and timers
  Data converters
  Power management chips
  Radio-frequency (RF) chips
  Application-specific integrated circuits (ASICs)
  Digital light processors (DLPs micro-mirror-based devices for video displays)
  Digital signal processors (DSPs)
  Microcontrollers
  Microprocessors
  Standard logic
Educational Technology
  Calculators (including graphing handheld and printing models)

COMPETITORS

AMD	Marvell Technology
ARM Holdings	Maxim Integrated
Analog Devices	Products
Atmel	Microchip Technology
CASIO COMPUTER	Microsemi
CSR plc	NVIDIA
Canon	NXP Semiconductors
Fairchild	ON Semiconductor
Semiconductor	QUALCOMM
HP	Renesas Electronics
Infineon Technologies	Richtek Technology
Intel	Corp.
Intersil	STMicroelectronics
Linear Technology	Samsung Electronics

HISTORICAL FINANCIALS

Company Type: Public

Income Statement

FYE: December 31

	REVENUE ($ mil.)	NET INCOME ($ mil.)	NET PROFIT MARGIN	EMPLOYEES
12/16	13,370	3,595	26.9%	29,865
12/15	13,000	2,986	23.0%	29,977
12/14	13,045	2,821	21.6%	31,003
12/13	12,205	2,162	17.7%	32,209
12/12	12,825	1,759	13.7%	34,151
Annual Growth	**1.0%**	**19.6%**	**—**	**(3.3%)**

2016 Year-End Financials

Debt ratio: 21.96%
Return on equity: 35.12%
Cash ($ mil.): 1,154
Current ratio: 3.29
Long-term debt ($ mil.): 2,978
No. of shares (mil.): 995
Dividends
  Yield: 0.0%
  Payout: 47.1%
Market value ($ mil.): 72,677

	STOCK PRICE ($) FY Close	P/E High/Low		PER SHARE ($) Earnings	Dividends	Book Value
12/16	72.97	21	14	3.48	1.64	10.52
12/15	54.81	21	15	2.82	1.40	9.84
12/14	53.47	21	16	2.57	1.24	9.93
12/13	43.91	23	16	1.91	1.07	9.98
12/12	30.89	22	17	1.51	0.72	9.89
Annual Growth	**24.0%**	**—**		**23.2%**	**22.9%**	**1.5%**

Textron Inc

Officers corporate and military really take to Textron's vehicles. The company's E-Z-GO golf carts enrich their golfing jaunts while its Cessna and Beechcraft airplanes and Bell helicopters whisk them around the world. In addition its auto parts keep their cars running and its Financial sub-

sidiary provides loans. Besides golf carts and car parts Textron's Industrial segment makes power tools electrical and fiber optic assemblies and turf maintenance equipment. The Textron Systems segment sells land and marine systems sensors and unmanned aerial vehicles to the Defense Department. Various US government entities account for almost 25% of Textron's sales.

Operations

Textron Aviation makes Beechcraft and Cessna aircraft and it services the Hawker brand of business jets. Its product lines include aircraft sales and aftermarket. This segment generated 36% of net sales in 2016 and produces the Citation jet Caravan single-engine utility turboprop T-6 AT-6 military and CitationAir single-engine piston aircraft which are distributed through a direct sales force and independent sales representatives.

Bell Helicopter supplies the US military with the V-22 tilt rotor aircraft which can operate with the features of both a fixed-wing craft and a helicopter and the H-1 helicopter. Through service sites co-located with Textron Aviation and some 100 independent dealers Bell Helicopter provides repair and overhaul and customizing services for an installed base of 13000 helicopters. The segment represents 23% of sales.

Textron Systems 13% of sales serves markets that include aerospace defense general aviation and homeland security. Besides the US military the segment sells to foreign militaries approved by the US government. Textron systems' Overwatch business supplies intelligence software for the defense intelligence and law enforcement markets.

Industrial 28% of sales operates through subsidiaries Kautex (blow-molded plastic fuel systems for cars light trucks all-terrain vehicles); Greenlee (powered equipment electrical test and measurement instruments and other products under the Greenlee Klauke Paladin Tools and Tempo brand names); E-Z-GO (golf carts and off-road utility vehicles under the E-Z-Go and Cushman brands); and Jacobsen (professional turf-maintenance equipment and specialized turf-care vehicles).

Finance 1% of sales includes Textron Financial Corporation and offers financing for new Textron Aviation aircraft Bell helicopters E-Z-GO golf carts and Jacobsen turf-care equipment.

Geographic Reach

The company operates about 60 plants in the US and about 50 outside the US. The US accounted for 62% of its total sales in 2016. Other major markets include Europe (14%) and Asia and Australia (7%).

Sales and Marketing

Textron Aviation sells through its own sales force as well as through a network of authorized independent sales representatives. It sells to US government customers and to customers outside the US through foreign military sales sponsored by the US government and directly through commercial sales channels. The Industrial segment sells through a global network of sales representatives and distributors and also directly to home improvement retailers and OEMs.

Financial Performance

Textron's revenues have fluctuated recently; after declining in 2015 revenues jumped 3% to $13.8 billion in 2016. Textron's profits surged by 38% to peak at $962 million its highest total in at least 10 years. This was mostly the result of almost $120 million it earned from the settlement of a US federal income tax audit.

The revenue growth was fueled by increased sales from its Textron Systems (16%) Industrial (7%) and Textron Aviation (2%) segments. It also notably experienced a 45% surge in sales from the Middle East and Africa for 2016. The segment growth for 2016 was fueled by additional revenue from acquisitions plus increased volumes from its fuel systems and functional components; marine and land systems; and unmanned systems product lines.

In addition operating cash flow has declined the last few years dipping 7% from $1.09 billion in 2015 to $1.01 billion in 2016. This decrease was primarily the result of changes in working capital which included lower customer deposits of $257 million largely related to performance-based payments on certain military contracts of its Bell segment.

Strategy

In addition to acquisitions Textron is focused on launching new products to expand its customer base. The company in 2015 introduced the delivery of the new Citation Latitude a midsize jet. In addition Textron is developing the Citation Longitude a super-midsize jet which achieved first flight in late 2016 and is expected to enter into service in 2017. It also recently announced the Citation Hemisphere a large-cabin jet for which the first flight is targeted for 2019.

Mergers and Acquisitions

The company occasionally beefs up its segments through acquisitions. In 2017 Textron acquired Arctic Cat a maker of about 30 types of all-terrain vehicles (ATVs) and 60 snowmobile models. The $247 million acquisition added to its Textron Specialized Vehicles business and gave it a deeper product line. It also introduced new sales opportunities for its combined worldwide dealer network.

Textron also in 2017 picked up Canada-based TKVGPS a provider of GPS-based fleet management technologies. The acquisition enhanced the on-course experience for its golf customers and provided fleet-management products to different industries.

In 2016 the company acquired Able Engineering & Component Services and Able Aerospace an industry-leading repair and overhaul company. This acquisition enhanced its aircraft parts and maintenance operations.

HISTORY

Pioneer conglomerate builder Royal Little founded Special Yarns Corporation a Boston textile business in 1923 and merged it with the Franklin Rayon Dyeing Company in 1928. The result Franklin Rayon Corporation moved its headquarters to Providence Rhode Island in 1930 and changed its name to Atlantic Rayon in 1938.

The company expanded during WWII to make parachutes and in 1944 adopted the name Textron to reflect the use of synthetics in its textiles. Between 1953 and 1960 Textron bought more than 40 businesses including Bell Helicopter before banker Rupe Thompson took over in 1960.

Thompson sold weak businesses such as Amerotron Textron's last textile business (1963) but also bought 20 companies between 1960 and 1965. By 1968 when former Wall Street attorney William Miller replaced Thompson as CEO Textron made products ranging from chain saws to watchbands. Miller sold several companies and bought Jacobsen Manufacturers (lawn care equipment 1978) before leaving Textron in 1978 to head the Federal Reserve and become treasury secretary under President Jimmy Carter.

EXECUTIVES

VP and CIO, Diane K. Schwarz

Chairman President and CEO, Scott C. Donnelly, age 55, $1,146,500 total compensation

EVP General Counsel Secretary and Chief Compliance Officer, E. Robert Lupone, age 57, $695,192 total compensation

President and CEO Textron Aviation, Scott A. Ernest

EVP Human Resources, Cheryl H. Johnson, age 56, $445,192 total compensation

President and CEO Textron Specialized Vehicles, Kevin P. Holleran

President and CEO Textron Systems, Ellen Lord

EVP and CFO, Frank T. Connor, age 57, $940,385 total compensation

President and CEO TRU Simulation + Training, Ian K. Walsh

President and CEO Textron Airborne Solutions, Russ Bartlett

President and CEO Textron Financial, R. Danny Maldonado

President and CEO Bell Helicopter, Mitch Snyder

President and CEO Greenlee Textron Inc. Sherman + Reilly Inc. and HD Electric Company, Jason Butchko

President and CEO Kautex, J¶rg Rautenstrauch

VPGlobal Sales, Brad Compton

National Account Manager, Ben Minnick

Vice President of Government Relations, Rocky Zhang

Auditors: Ernst & Young LLP

LOCATIONS

HQ: Textron Inc
40 Westminster Street, Providence, RI 02903
Phone: 401 421-2800
Web: www.textron.com

2016 Sales

	$ mil.	% of total
United States	8,574	62
Europe	1,954	14
Asia and Australia	998	7
Latin and South America	977	7
Canada	652	5
Middle East and Africa	633	5
Total	**13,788**	**100**

PRODUCTS/OPERATIONS

2016 Sales

	$ mil.	% of total
Textron Aviation	4,921	36
Industrial	3,794	27
Bell	3,239	23
Textron Systems	1,756	13
Finance	78	1
Total	**13,788**	**100**

2016 Sales

	$ mil.	% of total
Fixed-wing aircraft	4,921	36
Rotor aircraft	3,239	23
Fuel systems and functional components	2,273	16
Unmanned aircraft systems armored vehicles precision weapons and other	1,756	13
Specialized vehicles and equipment	1,080	8
Tools and test equipment	441	3
Finance	78	1
Total	**13,788**	**100**

Selected Products

Cessna
  Business jets
  Overnight express package carrier aircraft
  Single engine piston aircraft
  Single engine turboprops
Bell
  Commercial helicopters
  Military helicopters
  Tiltrotor aircraft
Industrial
  Kautex
  Blow-molded fuel tank systems
  Headlamp washer systems
  Engine camshafts
  Plastic bottles and containers
  Windshield washer systems
  E-Z-GO
  Golf carts

Multipurpose utility vehicles
Off-road utility vehicles
Greenlee
Electrical connectors
Electrical test instruments
Fiber optic assemblies
Hydraulic power tools
Measurement instruments
Powered equipment
Jacobsen
Turf-maintenance equipment
Specialized turf-care vehicles
Textron Systems
  Advanced marine craft
  Airborne surveillance
  Armored security vehicles
  Ground-based surveillance
  Intelligence software
  Precision weapons
  Situational awareness software
  Simulation systems
  Training systems
  Unmanned aircraft systems
Finance (captive commercial finance for new aircraft helicopter golf and turf-care equipment)

COMPETITORS

AgustaWestland	Lockheed Martin
Airbus Group	Magna International
Boeing	Moog
Bombardier	Northrop Grumman
Deere	Northstar Aerospace
Embraer	Piper Aircraft
GE	Raytheon
General Dynamics	Rolls-Royce
Honda	Spirit AeroSystems
Honeywell	Sun Hydraulics
International	Terex
Illinois Tool Works	Toro Company
Ingersoll-Rand	United Technologies
Kaman	

HISTORICAL FINANCIALS

Company Type: Public

Income Statement

FYE: December 31

	REVENUE ($ mil.)	NET INCOME ($ mil.)	NET PROFIT MARGIN	EMPLOYEES
12/16*	13,788	962	7.0%	36,000
01/16	13,423	697	5.2%	35,000
01/15	13,878	600	4.3%	34,000
12/13	12,104	498	4.1%	32,000
12/12	12,237	589	4.8%	33,000
Annual Growth	**3.0%**	**13.0%**	**—**	**2.2%**

*Fiscal year change

2016 Year-End Financials

Debt ratio: 23.96%
Return on equity: 18.31%
Cash ($ mil.): 1,137
Current ratio: 1.81
Long-term debt ($ mil.): 3,317

No. of shares (mil.): 270
Dividends
  Yield: 0.0%
  Payout: 2.2%
Market value ($ mil.): 13,125

	STOCK PRICE ($) FY Close	P/E High/Low		PER SHARE ($) Earnings	Dividends	Book Value
12/16*	48.56	14	9	3.53	0.08	20.62
01/16	42.01	19	15	2.50	0.08	18.10
01/15	42.17	21	15	2.13	0.08	15.45
12/13	36.61	21	14	1.75	0.08	15.54
12/12	24.12	14	9	2.00	0.08	11.03
Annual Growth	**19.1%**	**—**	**—**	**15.3%**	**(0.0%)**	**16.9%**

*Fiscal year change

TFS Financial Corp

EXECUTIVES

Vice President, Marianne Piterans
V Pres, Meredith S Weil
Vice President of Call Centre, Jim French
Auditors: DELOITTE & TOUCHE LLP

LOCATIONS

HQ: TFS Financial Corp
7007 Broadway Avenue, Cleveland, OH 44105
Phone: 216 441-6000
Web: www.thirdfederal.com

COMPETITORS

Bank of America	KeyCorp
Citigroup	PNC Financial
Fifth Third	U.S. Bancorp
Huntington Bancshares	Wells Fargo
JPMorgan Chase	

HISTORICAL FINANCIALS

Company Type: Public

Income Statement

FYE: September 30

	ASSETS ($ mil.)	NET INCOME ($ mil.)	INCOME AS % OF ASSETS	EMPLOYEES
09/17	13,692	88	0.6%	—
09/16	12,906	80	0.6%	—
09/15	12,368	72	0.6%	—
09/14	11,803	65	0.6%	—
09/13	11,269	55	0.5%	—
Annual Growth	5.0%	12.3%	—	—

2017 Year-End Financials

Debt ratio: —	No. of shares (mil.): 281
Return on equity: 5.31%	Dividends
Cash ($ mil.): 268	Yield: 0.0%
Current ratio: —	Payout: 170.3%
Long-term debt ($ mil.): —	Market value ($ mil.): 4,537

	STOCK PRICE ($) FY Close	P/E High/Low	PER SHARE ($) Earnings	Dividends	Book Value
09/17	16.13	62 46	0.32	0.55	6.01
09/16	17.81	69 56	0.28	0.43	5.84
09/15	17.25	71 55	0.25	0.31	5.95
09/14	14.32	66 52	0.22	0.07	6.10
09/13	11.97	68 45	0.18	0.00	6.05
Annual Growth	7.7%	—	15.5%	—	(0.2%)

The Bancorp Inc

The Bancorp is — what else? — the holding company for The Bancorp Bank which provides financial services in the virtual world. Targeting non-bank financial service companies across the US and Europe from start-ups to small and midsized businesses underserved by larger banks in the market The Bancorp Bank provides private-label online banking to 200 affinity groups; offers specialty lending; issues prepaid debit cards; and processes ACH and merchant credit card transactions. Its specialty lending products include securities backed lines of credit (SBLOC) auto fleet and equipment leasing SBA loans and commercial mortgage loans for sale in capital markets.

Operations

The Bancorp and The Bancorp Bank operate three business segments: Payments which made up 45% of the bank's total revenue in 2015 and provides prepaid cards card payments and ACH processing services; Specialty Finance (31% of revenue) which consists of commercial mortgage loan sales small business administration (SBA) loans leasing and security backed lines of credit and related deposit business; and Corporate (24% of revenue) which includes the company's investment portfolio.

Unlike other banks which rely on interest income The Bancorp makes more than 60% of its revenue from fee-based income. About 38% of its total revenue came from loan interest (including fees) during 2015 while another 14% came from interest income on investment securities. The rest of its revenue came from prepaid card fees (22% of revenue) service fees on deposit accounts (3%) card payment and ACH processing fees (3%) leasing income (1%) debit card income (1%) affinity fees (2%) and non-recurring gains from the sale of its loans investment securities and health savings portfolio (27%).

Geographic Reach

Wilmington Delaware-based The Bancorp serves customers in the US and Europe from 16 offices in the two regions and Southeast Asia.

Sales and Marketing

The company targets non-bank financial services companies including start-ups small and medium businesses underserved by large banks and Fortune 500 companies. It spent $387000 on advertising during 2015 down from $621000 and $706000 in 2014 and 2013 respectively.

Financial Performance

The Bancorp's annual revenues and profits have nearly doubled since 2011 mostly as its Payments business income has nearly quadrupled over the period. Its loan assets have also near nearly tripled spurring additional interest income growth.

The company's revenue jumped 39% to $216.5 million during 2015 thanks largely to a $33.5 million gain on the sale of the majority of its health savings business and a $14.4 million gain on the sale of its tax-exempt municipal bonds portfolio. The Bancorp's loan interest revenue was also up 37% as its specialty lending balances continued to grow with new SBLOC SBA leasing and loans-for-sale business.

Despite strong revenue growth in 2015 The Bancorp's net income plunged more than 75% to $13.43 million mostly as its discontinued operations (its discontinued Philadelphia commercial loan business) generated $27 million less in revenue than the year before and because in 2014 it had collected a $14.5 million income tax benefit from a reversal of valuation allowances. The company's operations used $234.8 million or more than four times more cash than in 2014 mainly on a steep decline cash-based earnings especially after accounting for net proceeds from sales of its loans-originated-for-resale.

Strategy

The Bancorp and The Bancorp Bank has been winding down its non-core operations in recent years to concentrate more in its national specialty lending business. In October 2015 the bank sold its $400 million-HSA portfolio to HealthEquity for $34..4 million after selling its regional Commercial Lending business in 2014. As a result the bank noted that its discontinued operations were reduced by 50% at the end of 2015 and expected its discontinued loan portfolio to shrink from there through loan repayments and opportunistic loan sales.

On the growth side The Bancorp continues to buy specialty financing assets from other financial companies to bolster its loan assets and extend its geographic reach. In December 2015 it expanded its commercial fleet leasing presence in the West Coast with a new California office after buying the commercial leasing assets of Ellis Brooks Leasing Inc.

EXECUTIVES

EVP Strategy CFO and Secretary, Paul Frenkiel, age 65, $312,200 total compensation
President and CEO, Damian Kozlowski, age 50
EVP and Chief Credit Officer, Donald F. (Don) McGraw, age 60, $317,500 total compensation
EVP Commercial Fleet Leasing and Chief Lending Officer, Scott R. Megargee, age 65, $202,541 total compensation
EVP and CIO, Peter (Pete) Chiccino
SVP; Managing Director Payment Solutions, Jeremy L. Kuiper, $458,060 total compensation
SVP and General Counsel, Thomas G. Pareigat, $347,500 total compensation
EVP and COO, Gail S. Ball
EVP and Chief Risk Officer, Steven Turowski
EVP Commercial Mortgage Securitization, Ron Wechsler
Vice President Information Security Officer, Joe Curcio
Senior Vice President and General Counsel, Tom Pareigat
Vice President Business Relationship Officer, Robert Edwards
SBA Business Relationship Officer and Vice President, John Sullivan
First Vice President Business Relationship Officer, Tim Collins
Executive Vice President Head of Small Business Lending, Jeff Nager
Vice President Business Development Officer II, Thomas Turnbach
VICE PRESIDENT DATABASE ADMINISTRATION MANAGER, David Heisel
Chairman The Bancorp Inc. and The Bancorp Bank, Daniel G. Cohen, age 47
Auditors: GRANT THORNTON LLP

LOCATIONS

HQ: The Bancorp Inc
409 Silverside Road, Wilmington, DE 19809
Phone: 302 385-5000
Web: www.thebancorp.com

PRODUCTS/OPERATIONS

2015 sales

	$ mil.	% of total
Payments	98	45
Specialty finance	67	31
Corporate	51	24
Total	216	100

2015 Sales

	$ mil.	% of total
Interest income		
Loans including fees	49	23
Interest on investment securities:	30	14
Federal funds sold/securities purchased under agreements to resell	0	-
Interest earning deposits	2	1
Non-interest income		
Prepaid card fees	47	22
Gain on sale of health savings portfolio	33	15
Gain on sale of investment securities	14	7
Gain on sale of loans	10	5
Service fees on deposit accounts	7	3
Card payment and ACH processing fees	5	3
Affinity fees	3	2
Other	5	2
Change in value of investment in unconsolidated entity	1	1
Leasing income	2	1
Debit card income	1	1
Total	216	100

COMPETITORS

Citizens Financial Group	Royal Bancshares
E*TRADE Bank	Sovereign Bank
M&T Bank	Sun Bancorp (NJ)
PNC Financial	TD Bank USA
Republic First Bank	WSFS Financial

HISTORICAL FINANCIALS
Company Type: Public

Income Statement
FYE: December 31

	ASSETS ($ mil.)	NET INCOME ($ mil.)	INCOME AS % OF ASSETS	EMPLOYEES
12/16	4,858	(96)	—	589
12/15	4,765	13	0.3%	762
12/14	4,986	57	1.1%	684
12/13	4,706	25	0.5%	624
12/12	3,699	16	0.4%	532
Annual Growth	7.0%	—	—	2.6%

2016 Year-End Financials
Debt ratio: 5.69%
Return on equity: (-31.09%)
Cash ($ mil.): 959
Current ratio: —
Long-term debt ($ mil.): —
No. of shares (mil.): 55
Dividends
  Yield: —
  Payout: —
Market value ($ mil.): 435

	STOCK PRICE ($) FY Close	P/E High/Low		PER SHARE ($) Earnings	Dividends	Book Value
12/16	7.86	—	—	(2.17)	0.00	5.40
12/15	6.37	31	18	0.35	0.00	8.47
12/14	10.89	13	5	1.49	0.00	8.46
12/13	17.91	28	16	0.66	0.00	9.56
12/12	10.97	24	15	0.50	0.00	9.06
Annual Growth	(8.0%)	—	—	—	—	(12.1%)

THE CHARLOTTE-MECKLENBURG HOSPITAL AUTHORITY

TheÂ medical facilities under the watchful eye of theÂ Charlotte-Mecklenburg Hospital AuthorityÂ care for the injured and infirmed.Â As the largest health care system in the Carolinas the organizationÂ operating asÂ Carolinas HealthCare System (CHS)Â ownsÂ or managesÂ more thanÂ 30Â affiliated hospitals.Â It also operates long-term care facilities research centers rehabilitation facilitiesÂ surgery centersÂ home health agencies radiation therapy facilities and other health care operations.Â Collectively CHSÂ facilities have more than 6400 beds and affiliated physician practices employ more than 1700 doctors. The network's flagship facility is the 875-bedÂ Carolinas Medical Center in Charlotte North Carolina.

Auditors: KPMG LLP CHARLOTTE NC

LOCATIONS
HQ: THE CHARLOTTE-MECKLENBURG HOSPITAL AUTHORITY
  1000 BLYTHE BLVD, CHARLOTTE, NC 282035812
Phone: 704 355-2000

PRODUCTS/OPERATIONS

2010 Revenue

	% of total
Tertiary & acute care services	72
Physicians' services	16
Post-acute care services	3
Specialty services	2
Other services & non-operating activities	7
Total	100

Selected Hospitals and Health Care Pavilions
AnMed Health Medical Center
AnMed Health Rehabilitation Hospital
AnMed Health Women's and Children's Hospital
Anson Community Hospital
Bon Secours/St. Francis Hospital
Cannon Memorial Hospital
Carolinas Medical Center
Carolinas Medical Center - Kannapolis (health care pavilion)
Carolinas Medical Center - Lincoln
Carolinas Medical Center - Mercy
Carolinas Medical Center - NorthEast
Carolinas Medical Center - Pineville
Carolinas Medical Center - Steele Creek (health care pavilion)
Carolinas Medical Center - Union
Carolinas Medical Center - University
Carolinas Medical Center - Waxhaw (health care pavilion)
Carolinas Rehabilitation
Carolinas Rehabilitation - Mount Holly
Cleveland Regional Medical Center
CMC - Randolph
Columbus Regional Healthcare System
Crawley Memorial Hospital
Grace Hospital
Kings Mountain Hospital
Levine Children's Hospital
MedWest - Harris
MedWest - Haywood
MedWest - Swain
Roper Hospital
Roper St. Francis - Mount Pleasant Hospital
Scotland Memorial Hospital
Stanly Regional Medical Center
St. Luke's Hospital
Valdese Hospital
Wallace Thomson Hospital
Wilkes Regional Medical Center

COMPETITORS
Alamance Regional Medical Center
CaroMont
Community Health Systems
Cone Health
Conway Medical Center
Cumberland County Hospital System
Davis Regional Medical Center
Duke University Health System
FirstHealth of the Carolinas
Georgetown Hospital System
Grand Strand Regional Medical Center
Greenville Hospital System
HCA
Haywood Regional
High Point Regional Health System
McLeod Health
Mission Hospitals
Morehead Memorial Hospital
New Hanover Regional Medical Center
Novant Health
Palmetto Health
Presbyterian Healthcare
Rex Healthcare
Soliant Health
Tenet Healthcare
UNC Hospitals
Vidant Health
Wake Forest University Baptist Medical Center
WakeMed

HISTORICAL FINANCIALS
Company Type: Private

Income Statement
FYE: December 31

	REVENUE ($ mil.)	NET INCOME ($ mil.)	NET PROFIT MARGIN	EMPLOYEES
12/15	5,478	(247)	—	62,000
12/12	4,501	249	5.5%	—
12/11	4,183	147	3.5%	—
12/10	3,855	353	9.2%	—
Annual Growth	7.3%	—	—	—

2015 Year-End Financials
Debt ratio: —
Return on equity: (-4.50%)
Cash ($ mil.): 178
Current ratio: 0.90
Long-term debt ($ mil.): —
Dividends
  Yield: —
  Payout: —
Market value ($ mil.): —

THE CLEVELAND FOUNDATION

Auditors: LB ERNST & YOUNG US LLP INDIA

LOCATIONS
HQ: THE CLEVELAND FOUNDATION
  1422 EUCLID AVE STE 1300, CLEVELAND, OH 441152063
Phone: 216 861-3810
Web: WWW.CLEVELANDFOUNDATION.ORG

HISTORICAL FINANCIALS
Company Type: Private

Income Statement
FYE: December 31

	ASSETS ($ mil.)	NET INCOME ($ mil.)	INCOME AS % OF ASSETS	EMPLOYEES
12/13	1,813	(8)	—	75
12/09	1,445	(18)	—	—
Annual Growth	5.8%	—	—	—

2013 Year-End Financials
Debt ratio: —
Return on equity: (-8.90%)
Cash ($ mil.): 155
Current ratio: 72.80
Long-term debt ($ mil.): —
Dividends
  Yield: —
  Payout: —
Market value ($ mil.): —

THE FORD FOUNDATION

As one of the nation's largest philanthropic organizations the Ford Foundation can afford to be generous. The foundation offers grants to individuals and institutions worldwide that work to meet its goals of strengthening democratic values reducing poverty and injustice promoting international cooperation and advancing human achievement. The Ford Foundation's charitable giving has run the gamut from A (Association for Asian Studies) to Z (Zanzibar International Film Festival). The foundation has an endowment of about $10 billion.

Established in 1936 by Edsel Ford whose father founded the Ford Motor Company the foundation no longer owns stock in the automaker or has ties to the founding family.

Operations

The foundation which is governed by an international board of trustees makes grants in all 50 US states and supports programs in more than 50 countries.

It boasts about 10 regional offices in Latin America Africa the Middle East and Asia.

Geographic Reach

Based in New York the Ford Foundation is a grantmaking foundation that primarily serves the US but also global programs.

Strategy

The Ford Foundation's programs address several social justice issues including democratic and accountable government freedom of expression access to education economic fairness and opportunity sexuality and reproductive rights sustainable development social justice metropolitan opportunity and human rights.

A small portion of its endowment is set aside for social investing. The foundation's funds typically finance critical projects set new business models and develop sustainable organizations. By investing $1 million or more in initiatives the Ford Foundation's investment strategy aims to make a noteworthy impact and encourage other investors to also fund projects.

EXECUTIVES

Vice President and Chief Investment Officer, Eric Doppstadt
Vice President Secretary, Ken Monteiro
Program Vice President, Martin Abregu
Vice President Talent Human Resources, Samantha Gilbert

LOCATIONS

HQ: THE FORD FOUNDATION
320 E 43RD ST FL 4, NEW YORK, NY 100174890
Phone: 212 573-5370
Web: WWW.FORDFOUNDATION.ORG

PRODUCTS/OPERATIONS

Selected Core Issues
Democratic and accountable government
Economic fairness
Education opportunity and scholarship
Freedom of expression
Human rights
Metropolitan opportunity
Sexuality and reproductive health rights
Social justice philanthropy
Sustainable development

HISTORICAL FINANCIALS

Company Type: Private

Income Statement

FYE: December 31

	ASSETS ($ mil.)	NET INCOME ($ mil.)	INCOME AS % OF ASSETS	EMPLOYEES
12/14*	12,400	(7)	—	556
09/11	10,344	(5)	—	—
09/09	10,234	0	—	—
09/06	12,207	0	—	—
Annual Growth	0.2%	—	—	—

*Fiscal year change

2014 Year-End Financials
Debt ratio: ——
Return on equity: (-1.10%)
Cash ($ mil.): 302
Current ratio: 1.10
Long-term debt ($ mil.): —
Dividends
Yield: —
Payout: —
Market value ($ mil.): —

The Gap Inc

The ubiquitous clothing retailer Gap has been filling closets with jeans and khakis T-shirts button-downs and poplin since the Woodstock era. The firm which operates about 3200 stores worldwide built its iconic casual brand on basics for men women and children but over the years has expanded through the urban chic chain Banana Republic family budgeteer Old Navy and Athleta a purveyor of activewear. Other brand extensions include GapBody GapKids GapFit GapMaternity and babyGap; each also has its own online incarnation. All Gap clothing is private-label merchandise made exclusively for the company. From the design board to store displays Gap controls all aspects of its trademark casual look.

HISTORY

Donald Fisher and his wife Doris opened a small store in 1969 near what is now San Francisco State University. The couple named their store The Gap (after "the generation gap") and concentrated on selling Levi's jeans. The couple opened a second store in San Jose California eight months later and by the end of 1970 there were six Gap stores. The Gap went public six years later.

In the beginning the Fishers catered almost exclusively to teenagers but in the 1970s they expanded into activewear that would appeal to a larger spectrum of customers. Nevertheless by the early 1980s The Gap — which had grown to about 500 stores — was still dependent upon its largely teenage customer base. However it was less dependent on Levi's (about 35% of sales) thanks to its growing stable of private labels.

In a 1983 effort to revamp the company's image Donald hired Mickey Drexler a former president of AnnTaylor with a spotless apparel industry track record as The Gap's new president. Drexler immediately overhauled the motley clothing lines to concentrate on sturdy brightly colored cotton clothing. He also consolidated the stores' many private clothing labels into the Gap brand. As a final touch Drexler replaced circular clothing racks with white shelving so clothes could be neatly stacked and displayed.

Also in 1983 The Gap bought Banana Republic a unique chain of jungle-themed stores that sold safari clothing. The company expanded the chain which enjoyed tremendous success in the mid-1980s but slumped after the novelty of the stores wore off late in the decade. In response Drexler introduced a broader range of clothes (including higher-priced leather items) and dumped the safari lines in 1988. By 1990 Banana Republic was again profitable.

The first GapKids opened in 1985 after Drexler couldn't find clothing that he liked for his son. During the late 1980s and early 1990s the company grew rapidly opening its first stores in Canada and the UK. In 1990 it introduced babyGap in 25 GapKids stores featuring miniature versions of its GapKids line. The Gap announced in 1991 it would no longer sell Levi's (which had fallen to less than

2% of total sales) and would sell nothing but private-label items.

Earnings fell in fiscal 1993 because of Gap division losses brought on by low margins and high rents. The company shuffled management positions and titles as part of a streamlining effort. It rebounded in 1994 by concentrating on improving profit margins rather than sales and by launching Old Navy Clothing Co. named after a bar Drexler saw in Paris. Banana Republic opened its first two stores outside the US both in Canada in 1995.

Robert Fisher (the founders' son) became the new president of the Gap division (including baby-Gap and GapKids) in 1997 and was charged with reversing the segment's sales decline. The company refocused its Gap chain on basics (jeans T-shirts and khakis) and helped boost its performance with a high-profile advertising campaign focusing on those wares. Later in 1997 the Gap opened an online Gap store. In 1998 it began opening Torpedo Joe submarine-themed shops in select Old Navy flagships.

Also in 1998 the retailer opened its first Gap-Body stores and introduced its only catalog (for Banana Republic). In late 1999 amid sluggish Gap division sales Robert Fisher resigned and Drexler took over his duties. Gap misjudged fashion trends in 2000 which resulted in two years of disappointing earnings. After a 10% reduction in its workforce the company returned to a more conservative fashion approach.

The company split Gap and Gap International into two separate units in early 2002 to improve performance in the flagship brand. In September Drexler retired and was replaced by Paul Pressler a veteran of The Walt Disney Company.

Gap sold its 10 stores in Germany to Swedish retailer H&M in 2004 taking a $14 million writedown related to the sale.

The next year the retailer launched Forth & Towne its first new chain in a decade with the new stores catering to women over the age of 35. Also Gap dipped its toes into personal care products by signing an agreement with Inter Parfums in mid-2005. As part of the deal Inter Parfums develops formulates manufactures and packages the products which are branded under the Gap and Banana Republic names. The Gap markets and sells them in its GapBody stores.

In January 2006 Gap entered into a 10-year non-exclusive services agreement with International Business Machines valued at $1.1 billion. As a result IBM took over certain information technology functions from the retailer; up to 400 Gap employees joined IBM as a result of the deal. Gap Direct launched an online footwear business called Piperlime in November.

CEO Pressler left the company and the board in January 2007 after four years in the top job. He was succeeded as CEO on an interim basis by Robert Fisher previously the non-executive chairman of the retailer. In June the company shut down its Forth & Towne retail format after less than two years in business. In July Gap named a new chairman and CEO Glenn Murphy. Murphy joined the company from Canadian drugstore chain Shoppers Drug Mart where he had retired as chairman and CEO in March. Stung by allegations in the British press of forced child labor in India being used in the manufacture of apparel for its Gap Kids chain Gap in November announced a package of measures intended to strengthen its commitment to eradicating the exploitation of children in the garment industry. Actions include a $200000 grant to improve working conditions and an upcoming conference dedicated to finding solutions to issues related to child labor.

In October 2008 Gap acquired Athleta a direct-marketer of women's active wear for about $150 million. Gap purchased Athleta as part of its strategy to diversify its brand offerings. The company also opened its first Banana Republic and Gap brand factory stores in Canada in late October extending its outlet busuiness launched in 1994 to Canada. The retailer opened 101 new stores and shuttered 119 locations in 2008.

Don Fisher Gap co-founder died in September 2009 at the age of 81. Also in 2009 Gap began opening stores inside Mexico's leading department store chain Distribuidora Liverpool via a franchise agreement.

EXECUTIVES

President and General Manager Athleta, Nancy Green, age 55
President Growth Innovation and Digital, Arthur (Art) Peck, age 61, $1,330,288 total compensation
President and General Manager Intermix, Jyothi Rao
Global President Old Navy, Sonia Syngal, age 47, $850,000 total compensation
Head of Gap China, Jeff Kirwan, age 51, $893,269 total compensation
EVP and CFO, Teri L. List-Stoll, $30,288 total compensation
EVP; General Manager Greater China, Abinta Malik
EVP Global General Counsel Corporate Secretary and Chief Compliance Officer, Julie Gruber
EVP Strategy and Chief Customer Officer, Sebastian DiGrande, $505,385 total compensation
EVP and CIO, Paul Chapman
EVP Global Supply Chain Sourcing and Production, Michael Yee
EVP Global Supply Chain Logistics and Product Operations, Shawn Curran
Vice President Ocm, Rita Martell
Senior Vice President and General Manager, Jodi Bricker
Senior Vice President Global Sourcing and Production, Roussel Christophe
Chairman, Robert J. (Bob) Fisher, age 62
Auditors: Deloitte & Touche LLP

LOCATIONS

HQ: The Gap Inc
Two Folsom Street, San Francisco, CA 94105
Phone: 415 427-0100
Web: www.gapinc.com

2017 Sales

	$ mil.	% of total
US	11,989	77
Asia	1,544	10
Canada	1,084	7
Europe	689	5
Other regions	210	1
Total	**15,516**	**100**

PRODUCTS/OPERATIONS

2017 Sales

	$ mil.	% of total
Old Navy global	6,814	44
Gap	5,455	35
Banana Republic global	2,471	16
Other	776	5
Total	**15,516**	**100**

2017 Stores

	No.
Company-operated	
Gap	1,319
Old Navy	1,056
Banana Republic	650
Athleta	132
Intermix	43
Franchise	459
Total	**3,659**

Selected Stores and Brands

Athleta (women's activewear)
babyGap (clothing for infants and toddlers)
Banana Republic (upscale clothing and accessories)
Gap (casual and active clothing and body care products)
GapBody (intimate apparel)
GapKids (clothing for children)
Old Navy (lower-priced family clothing)

COMPETITORS

Abercrombie & Fitch	J. Crew
Amazon.com	Juicy Couture
American Eagle Outfitters	Kohl's
	L.L. Bean
Ann Taylor	Lands' End
Arcadia	Levi Strauss
A□©ropostale	Macy's
Babies "R" Us	Marks & Spencer
Benetton	NIKE
Bleach Group	Nautica Apparel
Calvin Klein	Nordstrom
Children's Place	OshKosh B'Gosh
Dillard's	PVH
Express	REI
Fast Retailing	Ralph Lauren
Foot Locker	Reebok
Fruit of the Loom	Ross Stores
Guess?	Sears
Gymboree	TJX Companies
H&M	Talbots
HSN	Target Corporation
Inditex	VF Corporation
J. C. Penney	Wal-Mart

HISTORICAL FINANCIALS

Company Type: Public

Income Statement

FYE: January 28

	REVENUE ($ mil.)	NET INCOME ($ mil.)	NET PROFIT MARGIN	EMPLOYEES
01/17	15,516	676	4.4%	135,000
01/16	15,797	920	5.8%	141,000
01/15*	16,435	1,262	7.7%	141,000
02/14	16,148	1,280	7.9%	137,000
02/13	15,651	1,135	7.3%	136,000
Annual Growth	**(0.2%)**	**(12.2%)**	**—**	**(0.2%)**

*Fiscal year change

2017 Year-End Financials

Debt ratio: 17.25%
Return on equity: 24.88%
Cash ($ mil.): 1,783
Current ratio: 1.76
Long-term debt ($ mil.): 1,248
No. of shares (mil.): 399
Dividends
 Yield: 0.0%
 Payout: 54.4%
Market value ($ mil.): 9,009

	STOCK PRICE ($) FY Close	P/E High/Low	PER SHARE ($) Earnings	Dividends	Book Value
01/17	22.58	18 10	1.69	0.92	7.28
01/16	24.72	19 10	2.23	0.92	6.41
01/15*	41.19	16 12	2.87	0.88	7.09
02/14	38.08	17 11	2.74	0.70	6.87
02/13	32.97	16 9	2.33	0.50	6.25
Annual Growth	**(9.0%)**	**— —**	**(7.7%)**	**16.5%**	**3.9%**

*Fiscal year change

THE IRVINE JAMES FOUNDATION

LOCATIONS

HQ: THE IRVINE JAMES FOUNDATION
 1 BUSH ST FL 8, SAN FRANCISCO, CA 941044414
Phone: 415 777-2244
Web: WWW.222SECOND.COM

HISTORICAL FINANCIALS

Company Type: Private

Income Statement

FYE: December 31

	ASSETS ($ mil.)	NET INCOME ($ mil.)	INCOME AS % OF ASSETS	EMPLOYEES
12/14	1,611	44	2.7%	36
12/09	1,507	(57)	—	—
12/08	1,379	0	—	—
12/06	1,772	141	8.0%	—
Annual Growth	**(1.2%)**	**(13.6%)**	**—**	**—**

2014 Year-End Financials

Debt ratio: ——
Return on equity: 28.30%
Cash ($ mil.): 60
Current ratio: 1.00
Long-term debt ($ mil.): —
Dividends
 Yield: —
 Payout: —
Market value ($ mil.): —

THE PENNSYLVANIA STATE UNIVERSITY

The Pennsylvania State University system is one of the largest state university systems in the US. Penn State has an enrollment of almost 96000 students; 13600 of them are graduate students. It offers 160 undergraduate and 150 graduate programs at about 20 campuses. The school's oldest and largest campus with about half of the system's undergraduate students is at University Park in central Pennsylvania. Other sites include the College of Medicine in Hershey Pennsylvania and the Dickinson School of Law in Carlisle Pennsylvania. It generates about $8.5 billion in annual direct and indirect economic impacts within Pennsylvania.

Operations

The university is known for its academic medical center and biomedical research. Its health-related programs include the Schools of Nursing Medicine Dental Medicine and Veterinary Medicine. The school's biomedical research ranks in the top 5 of National Institutes of Health funding.

The school offers a broad range of disciplines including medicine humanities engineering cyberscience and social science.

Financial Performance

Penn State had an annual operating budget in 2014-15 of $4.6 billion and an annual endowment of more than $2 billion. Its annual research funding is roughly $813 million of which $492 million comes from federal sources.

Strategy

In 2015 the university announced a new $30 million investment in economic development and student career success. This investment includes a one-time start-up and capital investment as well as annual funding of more than $5 million.

In 2014 the fundraising campaign For the Future: The Campaign for Penn State Students surpassed its goal raising about $2.2 billion in private support.

Company Background

Chartered in 1855 to apply scientific principles to farming Penn State has conferred almost 800000 degrees since its founding.

The university's storied football program was hit in 2012 with a four year postseason ban the significant reduction of scholarships the vacating of 112 wins and a $60 million fine all stemming from the school's handling of the child molestation scandal involving former coach Jerry Sandusky. However in 2015 the NCAA reversed its decision on the vacating of wins restoring the late head coach Joe Paterno as the winningest coach in major college football history.

EXECUTIVES

Vice President Student Affairs, Damon Sims
SVP Finance and Business and Treasurer, David J. Gray
Dean University Libraries and Scholarly Communications, Barbara I. Dewey
Dean Undergraduate Education, Robert N. Pangborn
Dean College of Medicine, A. Craig Hillemeier
Dean College of Arts and Architecture, Barbara O. Korner
Dean College of Earth and Mineral Sciences, William E. Easterling
Dean College of Education, David H. Monk
Dean College of Health and Human Development, Ann C. (Nan) Crouter
Dean College of the Liberal Arts, Susan Welch
Dean College of Nursing, Paula Milone-Nuzzo
Dean Schreyer Honors College, Christian M. M. Brady
President, Eric J. Barron, age 66
Dean Smeal College of Business, Charles H. Whiteman
EVP and Provost, Nicholas P. Jones
Chief Investment Officer, John Pomeroy
Dean Graduate School, Regina Vasilatos-Younken
Dean College of Agricultural Sciences, Richard Roush
Dean College of Communications, Marie Hardin
Dean College of Engineering, Amr S. Elnashai
Assistant Vice President For Physical Plant, Steve Maruszewski
Senior Vice President For Finance And Business Treasurer, Cynthia Hall
Vice President, Djelal Kadir
Vice President Student Affairs Interim, Gail Hurley
Vice President For Scientific Affairs, Walter Severs
Department Head Learning and Performance Systems, Roy Clariana
Student Affairs Vice President Financial Officer, Rachael Diamond
Senior Vice President for Development and Alumni Relations, Tresa Ciprich
Vice President, Sandy Rothrock
Vice President Finance, Dulin Clark
Associate Vice President For Human Resources, Blannie Bowen
Vice President Of Corporate Relations, Jessica Hunter
Department Head and Professor of Health Policy and Administration, Dennis Shea
Department Head, Scott Wing
Assistant Vice President For Principal Gifts, Glen Jack
Associate Vice President and Chief Executive Officer of the Penn State Alumni Association, Paul Clifford
Department Head and Professor, Karen Thole

Assistant Vice President and Assistant Dean For Undergraduate Education, Alan Rieck
Vice Chairman, Ira M. Lubert, age 67
Chairman, Keith E. Masser
Board Member, Jim Kustenbauter
Treasurer, Sandy Dymond
Board Member, Malcolm Taylor
Treasurer, Timothy Chiang
Board Member, Helen Sheehy
Board Member, Ann Kusnadi
Board Member, Ken Fohringer
Buck Company Treasurer, Mark Broich
Secretary, Annie Klodd
Auditors: DELOITTE & TOUCHE LLP PHILADE

LOCATIONS

HQ: THE PENNSYLVANIA STATE UNIVERSITY
201 OLD MAIN, UNIVERSITY PARK, PA 168021503
Phone: 814 865-4700
Web: WWW.PSU.EDU

PRODUCTS/OPERATIONS

Selected Colleges
College of Agricultural Sciences
College of Arts and Architecture
Smeal College of Business
College of Communications
College of Earth and Mineral Sciences
College of Education
College of Engineering
College of Health and Human Development
College of Information Sciences and Technology
School of International Affairs
School of Law
College of the Liberal Arts
College of Medicine
School of Nursing
Eberly College of Science
Graduate School
Schreyer Honors College

Selected Campuses
Penn State Abington Penn State Altoona
Penn State Beaver
Penn State Berks
Penn State Brandywine
Penn State DuBois
Penn State Erie The Behrend College
Penn State Fayette The Eberly Campus
Penn State Greater Allegheny
Penn State Harrisburg
Penn State Hazleton
Penn State Lehigh Valley
Penn State Mont Alto
Penn State New Kensington
Penn State Schuylkill
Penn State Shenango
Penn State Wilkes-Barre
Penn State Worthington Scranton
Penn State York

HISTORICAL FINANCIALS
Company Type: Private

Income Statement
FYE: June 30

	REVENUE ($ mil.)	NET INCOME ($ mil.)	NET PROFIT MARGIN	EMPLOYEES
06/16	5,764	233	4.0%	44,000
06/15	5,293	289	5.5%	—
06/14	5,148	974	18.9%	—
06/13	4,873	842	17.3%	—
Annual Growth	5.8%	(34.8%)	—	—

2016 Year-End Financials
Debt ratio: ——
Return on equity: 4.00%
Cash ($ mil.): 1,395
Current ratio: 1.90
Long-term debt ($ mil.): —
Dividends
Yield: —
Payout: —
Market value ($ mil.): —

THE PRIDDY FOUNDATION

LOCATIONS
HQ: THE PRIDDY FOUNDATION
807 8TH ST STE 1010, WICHITA FALLS, TX
763013310
Phone: 940 723-8720
Web: WWW.PRIDDYFDN.ORG

HISTORICAL FINANCIALS
Company Type: Private

Income Statement
FYE: December 31

	REVENUE ($ mil.)	NET INCOME ($ mil.)	NET PROFIT MARGIN	EMPLOYEES
12/13	8,791	3	0.0%	4
12/12	3	(4)	—	—
12/10	32	27	86.7%	—
12/09	0	0	—	—
Annual Growth	—	—	—	—

2013 Year-End Financials
Debt ratio: ——
Return on equity: —
Cash ($ mil.): 14
Current ratio: —
Long-term debt ($ mil.): —
Dividends
Yield: —
Payout: —
Market value ($ mil.): —

THE SCOULAR COMPANY

The Scoular Company doesn't move food from farm to table but it does handle a good portion of the trip. The company buys sells stores handles and transports agricultural products (mainly grains) worldwide. It gets the mainstays of farming — corn hay millet rice sorghum soybeans and wheat — where they need to go. The company transports these products via rail truck barge and seagoing container vessels. Scoular's other divisions offer fishmeal products for farm-animal pet and aquaculture feeds; ingredients for food manufacturers; renewable fuels; and truck freight brokering. It has customers in Asia Africa the Americas and Europe. George Scoular founded the business in Nebraska in 1892.

Operations

The company operates 130 independent units that together make up a grain marketing network that handles 420 million bushels of grain annually and includes facilities in 18 states Canada and Mexico. In addition to buying selling handling and transporting grain Scoular offers risk management services.

Geographic Reach

Omaha-based Scoular and it affiliates have operations in 18 US states as well as in Calgary and Montreal Canada Mexico Argentina Brazil Uruguay China and Singapore. The company has nearly 30 merchandising offices and some 93 grain-handling facilities in North America with a storage capacity topping 130 million bushels.

Sales and Marketing

Scoular serves customers in the aquaculture flour milling food processing and manufacturing grain production industrial ag processing livestock feeding and manufacturing pet food manufacturing and renewable fuels sectors. Its services include bagging blending cleaning containerizing organic certifying packaging sorting sourcing and storage.

Financial Performance

Scoular's sales totaled $5.9 billion in 2015 compared with about $6 billion in 2014.

Strategy

The company has built itself out piece by piece scouring the landscape for businesses that fit into its portfolio through acquisition or partnership. In 2015 Scoular formed a joint venture with Nova del Mar in Mexico in which Scoular will market fishmeal that Nova makes from fish from the Sea of Cortez.

Mergers and Acquisitions

Scoular capped off two years of smaller acquisitions with the purchase of the Specialty Crops Division of Legumex Walker Inc. a global merchandiser and processor of special crops for some (Canadian) $94 million. The business processes special crops at 14 facilities in Canada the US and China. Some of the special crops are lentils whole and split peas edible beans chickpeas canaryseed flaxseed and sunflower seed.

In August 2013 Scouler acquired the assets of Kansas-based Tribune Grain which include a grain elevator in Tribune Kansas that's located on the Kansas and Oklahoma Railroad as well as two seasonally-operated rural truck facilities. (In addition to the Tribune area facilities Scoular operates 10 other grain elevators in Kansas and eastern Colorado.)

EXECUTIVES

Vice President, John Heck
Senior Vice President Producer Markets Div, George Schieber
Chairman and President, David M. Faith
SVP and Division General Manager, Todd McQueen
SVP and Division General Manager, John Messerich
CFO, Richard A. (Rick) Cogdill
CEO, Paul T. Maass
CIO, Jeff Schreiner
SVP and Division General Manager, Bob Ludington
Vice President Finance, Omer Sagheer
Senior Vice President, Curt Engel
Vice President Information Technology, Jim Konz
Vice President Manager Directo, Tim Dingman

LOCATIONS

HQ: THE SCOULAR COMPANY
2027 DODGE ST STE 200, OMAHA, NE 681021229
Phone: 402 342-3500
Web: WWW.SCOULARBALLROOM.COM

PRODUCTS/OPERATIONS

Selected Customer Industries Products and Services
Aquaculture (feed ingredients)
 Animal fats
 Animal proteins
 Fish oil
 Fishmeal
 Grain byproducts
 Vegetable fats
 Vegetable proteins
Flour milling (buying selling storing and shipping)
 Durum
 Hard red spring
 Hard red winter
 Soft red winter
Food manufacturing and processing (conventional organic and functional ingredients blending packaging co-packing)
 Ingredients
 Proteins
 Dairy
 Pea
 Potato

Rice
Soy
Specialty flours
Soy
Starches
Pea
Potato
Rice
Tapioca
Textured proteins
Soy
Grain production (marketing buying storing handling and shipping programs)
 Corn
 Hay
 Millet
 Rice
 Sorghum
 Soybeans
 Wheat
Industrial ag processing (feedstock supply byproduct marketing and crush risk management)
 Products
 Citrus pulp
 Distillers grains
 Hominy feed
 Wheat mill feeds
 Whole cottonseed
Identity-preserved grain
 Corn
 Soybeans
 Wheat
 White corn
Livestock feeding and feed manufacturing (grain and feed ingredient sourcing risk management)
 Grains and oilseeds
 Barley
 Canola
 Corn
 Field peas
 Flax
 Lentils
 Rye
 Soybeans
 Wheat
 Other
 Canola meal
 Citrus pulp
 Distillers grains
 Hominy feed
 Wheat mill feed
 Whole cottonseed
Pet food manufacturing (ingredients)
 Products
 Fats
 Flours
 Gravy dust mix
 Proteins
 Starches
 Yellow corn
 Sourcing and solutions
 Animal oils
 Animal proteins
 Fish oil
 Fishmeal
 Frozen fish
 Fruits
 Grain products
 Pea protein fiber flour and starch
 Pomaces
 Specialty starches flours
 Variety meats
 Vegetable oils
 Vegetable proteins
 Vegetables
Transportation
 Container and vessel (freight forwarding logistics and documentation in more than 50 countries)
 Rail truck and barge (logistics for shipping agricultural products in North America)

COMPETITORS

ADM	Excel Maritime
Andersons	Carriers
Bartlett and Company	Louis Dreyfus Group
Bunge Limited	Syntroleum
CHS	TBS International
Cargill	TORM
DeBruce Grain	

HISTORICAL FINANCIALS

Company Type: Private

Income Statement FYE: May 31

	REVENUE ($ mil.)	NET INCOME ($ mil.)	NET PROFIT MARGIN	EMPLOYEES
05/16	4,667	(10)	—	801
05/15	234	14	6.0%	
05/14	228	29	13.0%	
05/13	211	27	12.9%	
Annual Growth	180.6%	—	—	—

2016 Year-End Financials

Debt ratio: —
Return on equity: (-0.20%)
Cash ($ mil.): 20
Current ratio: 0.40
Long-term debt ($ mil.): —
Dividends
 Yield: —
 Payout: —
Market value ($ mil.): —

THE TURNER CORPORATION

The Turner Corporation a subsidiary of German construction giant HOCHTIEF is the leading general building and construction management firm in the US (as ranked by Engineering News-Record) ahead of rivals Bechtel and Fluor. The firm operates primarily through subsidiary Turner Construction and has worked on notable projects such as Madison Square Garden the UN headquarters Yankee Stadium the Taipei 101 Tower and the 68000-seat open-air stadium for the San Francisco 49ers. Known for its large projects also offers services for midsized and smaller projects and provides interior construction and renovation services.

Operations

Turner works on more than 1500 projects in a year totaling $8 billion in volume. The group has divisions dedicated to serving the aviation health care biotechnology public assembly sports education justice and industrial sectors. Its homeland security group was established in order handle a growing demand for security systems and protection. The unit installed detection equipment in some 450 airports throughout the US. Turner Corporation also has an arm specializing in green building with a focus on Leadership in Energy and Environmental Design (LEED) -certified projects. Turner Green Building has more than 400 LEED projects and green projects either completed or in progress.

Turner Corporation has subsidiaries providing auxiliary operations. Turner's risk management department offers contract review project safety and claims handling. Turner Logistics handles procurement and supply chain management for projects and Turner Facilities Management Solutions offers ongoing operations services. Also the Turner School of Construction Management provides training for local subcontractors.

Geographic Reach

Dallas-based Turner Corporation boasts a network of offices across the US (with most in California and Ohio) and Canada (Vancouver and Toronto) with an global presence in 20 countries in Europe Africa East Asia India Latin America and the Caribbean.

Sales and Marketing

Turner works on variety of projects from several sectors. It's known for its work in the categories of healthcare education offices commercial properties cultural facilities sports facilities and hotels. The company is also a leader in the green building category.

Strategy

With the construction market rebounding from the economic downturn Turner is looking to high-growth markets in the US and overseas. As of early 2015 it was working on more than 1900 projects 80% of which were Education Commercial or Interior project-related. Some of these projects included the 17000 sq. ft- interior remodel for Salesforce's Vancouver office; the 325000 sq. ft- construction of the LEED-Certified RAND Corporation Headquarters in Santa Monica California; and the 25000-seat Charlotte Coliseum event arena for the City of Charlotte North Carolina.

The company has also been making moves to expand its business abroad in recent years. In 2012 for example Turner partnered with one of India's largest real estate developers Sahara Prime City Ltd. to form Sahara Turner which would lead the development and construction of multiple townships across the country with an approximate value of $2.5 billion by 2017. It also purchased a majority stake in Clark Builders Canada to capitalize on the country's growing construction market.

Turner often partners with fellow US-based HOCHTIEF subsidiary Flatiron which specializes in civil engineering. Examples of the teamwork are the expansions of airports in San Diego and Sacramento.

HISTORY

At the turn of the century an engineer and devout Quaker named Henry Chandlee Turner was convinced that a new type of steel-reinforced concrete (called the Ransome system) would change the construction industry. With this conviction and with the help of his partner D. H. Dixon Turner bought the rights to the technology for $25000 and in 1902 founded Turner Construction Company.

One of the company's early projects was building the stairways for New York's first subway stations. As the Ransome method proved to be successful Turner's reputation grew. Defense contracts during WWI raised Turner's take to $35 million in 1918.

Before the Depression Turner was building high-rises hotels and stadiums. During the economic crash that started in 1929 the company survived by building retail stores churches and public buildings a strategy it would employ successfully in later recessions.

Henry Turner retired in 1941. His brother Archer Turner managed the company during most of the war effort. As WWII raged more than 80% of the company's work was defense-related. Projects included building and managing a submarine base in Oak Ridge Tennessee during the development of the atomic bomb.

In 1947 Henry C. Turner Jr. the founder's son became president and within four years he had led the company to more than $100 million in sales. By the time he stepped down as chairman in 1970 the firm had built skyscrapers futuristic airports and such landmarks as Madison Square Garden and the United Nations Secretariat and Plaza in New York City. Turner went public in 1969.

Howard S. Turner (the final family member to head the business) led the company during the 1970s. The company extended its global presence opening offices in more countries including Iran Pakistan and the United Arab Emirates. Turner also developed construction management services.

In 1984 The Turner Corporation was formed as a holding company for the construction company and the subsidiaries created or acquired as a result of diversification. Property development was one

of these activities but by 1987 Turner had begun to dispose of its real estate holdings. It did not move quickly enough however and when the real estate market crashed Turner was caught with a large portfolio.

As commercial projects slowed Turner sought work in more sectors including public works and amusement projects (aquariums arenas hospitals and universities). By 1994 these areas accounted for 70% of business. In 1993 as the building slump continued Turner began a cost-cutting plan which included laying off workers and closing offices. That year the company set up an $8.5 million restructuring reserve and as the real estate market eased into recovery Turner sold more of its real estate holdings.

In 1996 Turner won a contract to build a 10000-seat arena in Salt Lake City to be used for the 2002 Winter Olympics. In 1997 Turner contracted to renovate 811 schools and build two campuses in California's San Fernando Valley and in 1998 it was chosen to manage the construction of the Kansas City Motor Speedway.

Profits were recovering quickly. Nonetheless in 1999 the company agreed to be acquired by German construction giant HOCHTIEF in a $370 million deal that ended Turner's joint venture with Switzerland's Karl Steiner. The company also relocated its corporate headquarters to Dallas that year to take advantage of the construction boom in the US Southwest.

In 2000 Turner created three new business groups to serve the aviation pharmaceutical and sports sectors. By the next year Turner's sports group was working on 17 projects. In 2001 the company was a member of the construction team that responded to the September 11 devastation at Ground Zero in New York City. The next year the company celebrated its 100th anniversary with an exhibit at the National Building Museum in Washington DC; the exhibit featured drawings and photos of some of Turner's notable projects during the past century. In 2003 Turner Construction acquired the assets of Tompkins Builders the third-largest construction company in the Washington DC area from former rival J.A. Jones Construction Co.

Turner Construction which celebrated its 100th anniversary in 2002 has ranked among the leading general builders in the US since WWI. For 80 of the 100 years the group had a Turner among its senior executives. Howard S. Turner was the last member of the family to serve in the company's senior ranks. The company's appointment of Peter Davoren in 2003 as president of Turner Construction reflected the rise of a new generation of leaders for the unit. Davoren was additionally appointed chairman and CEO in 2007.

Turner Construction announced in 2008 that it had signed the contract on its 15000th major project.

Auditors: DELOITTE & TOUCHE LLP DALLAS

LOCATIONS

HQ: THE TURNER CORPORATION
375 HUDSON ST RM 700, NEW YORK, NY 100143667
Phone: 212 229-6000
Web: WWW.TURNERCONSTRUCTION.COM

PRODUCTS/OPERATIONS

Selected Related Companies
E. E. Cruz (infrastructure)
Flatiron Construction Corp. (transportation construction civil engineering)
Clark Builders (51% Canada)

Selected Markets Served
Aviation
Commercial
Cultural and entertainment
Data center
Education
Government
Green building
Health care
Infrastructure
Industrial
Interiors
Pharmaceutical
Public Assembly
Religious
Research and development
Residential/hotel
Sports

Selected Services
Building information modeling
Building maintenance
Construction management
Design-build
Design-build/finance
Facilities management
General construction
Lean construction
Logistics
Medical planning and procurement
Preconstruction consulting
Program management
Project management

COMPETITORS

Balfour Beatty Construction	Hunt Construction
Bechtel	Imperial Construction Group
Clark Construction Group	Jacobs Engineering
Fluor	Parsons Corporation
Gilbane Building Company	Peter Kiewit Sons'
	Skanska
	Structure Tone

HISTORICAL FINANCIALS
Company Type: Private

Income Statement
FYE: December 31

	REVENUE ($ mil.)	NET INCOME ($ mil.)	NET PROFIT MARGIN	EMPLOYEES
12/15	10,523	107	1.0%	5,000
12/14	10,560	95	0.9%	—
12/13	9,522	80	0.8%	—
12/12	8,575	74	0.9%	—
Annual Growth	7.1%	12.9%	—	—

2015 Year-End Financials

Debt ratio: ——
Return on equity: 1.00%
Cash ($ mil.): 880
Current ratio: 1.00
Long-term debt ($ mil.): —

Dividends
Yield: —
Payout: —
Market value ($ mil.): —

THE WHITING-TURNER CONTRACTING COMPANY

Whiting-Turner Contracting provides construction management general contracting and design/build services primarily for large commercial institutional and infrastructure projects conducted across the US. A key player in retail construction the employee-owned company also undertakes such projects as biotech cleanrooms theme parks historical restorations senior living residences educational facilities stadiums and corporate headquarters. Clients past and present include the US military AT&T General Motors and Texas A&M University. Whiting-Turner Contracting operates from more than 30 offices across the US.

Geographic Reach

The Baltimore-based company has offices in Arizona California Colorado Connecticut Delaware Florida Georgia Maryland Massachusetts Missouri Nevada New Jersey New York North Carolina Ohio Pennsylvania Texas Virginia and Washington DC.

Sales and Marketing

The contractor works on projects across a wide range of industries related to arts and entertainment education federal and military healthcare industrial office retail multi-family residential sports and fitness transportation and utilities among other fields.

Strategy

Whiting-Turner prefers to grow organically instead of making acquisitions. It has been steadily expanding by opening new offices in places such as California Texas and Virginia. The company in 2016 continued to rank among the Engineering News Record (ENR) top domestic general building contractors in the nation.

Some of the firm's recently awarded projects (as of mid-2016) include the Tropicana Pedestrian Bridge the Jacksonville Lung Bio Facility the Westowne Elementary School the Lexington Market the Costco Meat Production Plant the Sentara Norfolk General Hospital and the CoolSprings Galleria among others.

Whiting-Turner Contracting's past projects include the Joseph B. Whitehead Building at Emory University Vanderbilt Hall at Yale University projects at Universal Studios theme park and a vaccine facility at Chesapeake Biological Laboratories. Projects in the firm's hometown of Baltimore have included the city's convention center and the football stadium for the Baltimore Ravens. More recent projects include the Horseshoe Casino Cleveland University of Maryland Baltimore County (UMBC) Performing Arts & Humanities Naval Facilities Engineering Command (NAVFAC) Jacksonville Sentara Princess Anne Hospital Norwalk Community College Texas A&M University at Galveston Mary Moody Northen Student Center renovation Opry Mills the College of Business & Economics Vinson Hall Parking Garage a Coastal Studies Institute facility a Blue Diamond Growers building and a USPS Call Center.

Company Background

G.W.C. Whiting and LeBaron Turner classmates at MIT founded the company in 1909 to build sewer lines.

EXECUTIVES

VP Richmond, Dani Niccolucci
SVP Allentown, Jack DaSilva
Division VP Fort Lauderdale, Robert (Rob) Mitchell
Division VP Delaware and Maryland, James (Jim) Martini
SVP District of Columbia, Richard L. Vogel
Division VP Pleasanton, Troy Caldwell
SVP Irvine, Len Cannatelli
SVP Baltimore, Gino J. Gemignani
Division VP Dallas, Espen S. Brooks
VP Bridgewater, Chris Martinson
SVP Atlanta, Keith Douglas
VP, Daniel (Dan) Bauer
VP Boston, Kevin Shields
Regional Manager Las Vegas, Paul Schmitt
Division VP Chantilly, Kempton C. Haile

VP Tampa, Brent A. Voyles
Senior Project Manager (Denver), Mark Faul
VP San Diego, Steven Likins
VP Orlando, Robert Minutoli
Division VP Raleigh, Chris Carlson
VP White Plains, David Brickley
VP San Antonio, Daryl Steinbeck
VP Norfolk, John Berotti
Senior Project Manager Sacramento, Jack Stackalis
VP Cleveland, Jeff Maeder
Regional Manager Kansas City, Adam Eshelbrenner
Regional Manager Charlotte, Chris Woods
Regional Manager Houston, Michael Browning
President and CEO, Timothy J. Regan, age 61
Sr V Pres, Frank Palmer
Vice President, Scott McMahon
Vice President, Susan Castellan
Vice President, Nancy Beavers
Vice President, Donald Hanky
Senior Vice President, Arch Jamieson
Senior Vice President, Kevin Higgins
ASHE CHC Vice President, Bob Moore
Vice President, Jesse Beam
Leed AP Banking Division C Vice President, Patricia Carper
Division Vice President, Ed Schlotterback
Vice President, Terry Spencer
Vice President, Jim Groff
Vice President, Irene Knott
Vice President, David McGinnis
Vice President Field Operations, Phil Knight
Vice President, Jeff Jenkins
Vice President, Bruce Delawder
Vice President, J Scott Breig
Division Vice President, David Mallik
Vice President San Diego, Miguel Huerta
Vice President, Tony Moag
Leed AP Business Development C Vice President, Patrick Duffy
Division Vice President, David Meyers
Executive Vice President and Chief Executive Officer, Tim Regan
Vice President, Craig Rayner
Executive Vice President, Steve Duffy
Vice President, Charles Konkolics
Division Vice President, Jeffrey Dodds
Vice President, Bernard LaHatte
Vice President, Andrew Linden
Division Vice President, Maynard Grizzard
Vice President, Terry Powell
Senior Vice President, Stephen Lambertson
Vice President, Kit Fawthrop
Vice President, Robert Tomlinson
Vice President, Ray MacKeen
Secretary, Willie Mcfarlin
Vice Chairman, Nick Bloch
Auditors: CLIFONLARSONALLEN TIMONIUM M

LOCATIONS

HQ: THE WHITING-TURNER CONTRACTING COMPANY
300 E JOPPA RD STE 800, BALTIMORE, MD 212863047
Phone: 410 821-1100
Web: WWW.WHITING-TURNER.COM

Selected Locations
Maryland - Baltimore (Headquarters)
California
California - Los Angeles
California
California
California - San Diego
Colorado -
Connecticut - New Haven
Delaware -
District of Columbia
Florida - Ft. Lauderdale
Florida -
Florida -
Georgia -
Maryland -

Massachuse
Missouri - Kansas City
Nevada - Las Vegas
New Jersey
New York - White Plains
North Caro
North Caro
Ohio - Cle
Pennsylvan
Texas - Da
Texas - Ho
Texas - San Antonio
Virginia -
Virginia -
Virginia -

PRODUCTS/OPERATIONS

Selected Services
Construction management
  Agency
  At-risk
Design/build
General contracting
Preconstruction

Selected Markets
Biotechnology and pharmaceutical
Cleanroom and high-technology
Education
Entertainment
Federal/military
Food/beverage distribution
Health care
Historical restoration
Industrial and manufacturing
Interiors
Life sciences
Lodging and hospitality
Mission critical facilities
Mixed use
Offices and headquarters
Parking garages
Restaurants
Retail
Senior living
Sports
Sustainable
Technology
  Microelectronics
  Nano
Theme parks
Utilities
Warehouse and distribution

COMPETITORS

Barton Malow	J.E. Dunn Construction
Bechtel	Group
Choate Construction	Jacobs Engineering
Clark Construction	Kitchell
Group	McCarthy Building
DPR Construction	Peter Kiewit Sons'
Fisher Development	Skanska
Fluor	Suffolk Construction
Gilbane	Swinerton
Hensel Phelps	Turner Corporation
Construction	Tutor Perini
Hoffman Corporation	Weitz

HISTORICAL FINANCIALS

Company Type: Private

Income Statement   FYE: December 31

	REVENUE ($ mil.)	NET INCOME ($ mil.)	NET PROFIT MARGIN	EMPLOYEES
12/15	5,729	80	1.4%	2,707
12/14	6,347	75	1.2%	—
12/12	3,781	56	1.5%	—
12/11	3,897	57	1.5%	—
Annual Growth	10.1%	8.6%	—	—

Debt ratio: —
Return on equity: 1.40%
Cash ($ mil.): 13
Current ratio: 0.60
Long-term debt ($ mil.): —

Dividends
Yield: —
Payout: —
Market value ($ mil.): —

THE WILLIAM PENN FOUNDATION

Auditors: KPMG LLP

LOCATIONS

HQ: THE WILLIAM PENN FOUNDATION
2 LOGAN SQ FL 11, PHILADELPHIA, PA 191032763
Phone: 215 988-1830
Web: WWW.WILLIAMPENNFOUNDATION.ORG

HISTORICAL FINANCIALS
Company Type: Private

Income Statement
FYE: December 31

	ASSETS ($ mil.)	NET INCOME ($ mil.)	INCOME AS % OF ASSETS	EMPLOYEES
12/13	2,283	40	1.8%	27
12/00	1,170	(21)	—	—
12/99	1,202	129	10.7%	—
12/98	904	77	8.6%	—
Annual Growth	6.4%	(4.3%)	—	—

2013 Year-End Financials

Debt ratio: —
Return on equity: 26.60%
Cash ($ mil.): 82
Current ratio: —
Long-term debt ($ mil.): —

Dividends
Yield: —
Payout: —
Market value ($ mil.): —

Thermo Fisher Scientific Inc

Thermo Fisher Scientific preps the laboratory for research analysis discovery or diagnostics. The company makes and distributes analytical instruments scientific equipment consumables and other laboratory supplies. Products range from chromatographs and spectrometers to Erlenmeyer flasks and fume hoods to gene-sequencers. Moving into other areas it offers testing and manufacturing of drugs including biologicals. Thermo Fisher also provides specialty diagnostic testing products as well as clinical analytical tools. The company tallies more than 400000 customers worldwide. Its key markets are pharmaceutical and biotech diagnostics and health care academic and government and industrial and applied research.

Operations

Thermo Fisher Scientific operates in four segments:

The Laboratory Product and Services unit which generates about 40% of revenue provides basics for the lab. It sells equipment (refrigerators ovens filtration systems) consumables (slides dishes flasks) and chemicals (solvents and reagents). It also includes the Research and Safety Market Channel (catalogs and access to more than 650000 products) and BioPharma Services (clinical trials).

Life Sciences Solutions about 25% of revenue provides reagents instruments and consumables used in biological and medical research drug discovery and drug production. The unit?s businesses are Biosciences Genetic Sciences Clinical Next-Generation Sequencing and BioProduction.

Analytical Instruments about 20% of revenue supplies instruments consumables software and services. Its businesses are Chromatography and Mass Spectrometry Chemical Analysis and Materials and Structural Analysis.

Specialty Diagnostics about 20% of revenue offers diagnostic test kits reagents culture media and instruments. Its businesses are Clinical Diagnostics ImmunoDiagnostics Anatomical Pathology Microbiology Transplant Diagnostics and the Healthcare Market Channel.

Products from those operational units are sold under Thermo Fisher?s five main brands: Thermo Scientific Applied Biosystems Invitrogen Fisher Scientific and Unity Lab Services.

Thermo Fisher makes many of its products and it also works with third-party contractors for manufacturing.

Geographic Reach

Half of Thermo Fisher?s revenue comes from its US customers. China is the second biggest single-country market accounting for 10% of revenue. Other key countries for Thermo Fisher are Japan the UK and Germany.

The company operates manufacturing research and development administrative and logistics facilities in about 50 countries outside the US.

Sales and Marketing

Thermo Fisher?s sales channels include direct sales electronic commerce distributors and catalogs. Its sales staff numbers about 11000. The company also offers supply chain management services.

Financial Performance

Thermo Fisher?s revenue has risen for seven straight years and profit has increased for four years in a row.

The company?s sales rose 8% in 2016 to $18.3 billion from just under $17 billion in 2015. About half of the gain came from acquisitions while currency effects sliced off about $145 million. The company reported strong demand from pharmaceutical and biotech customers and strong growth in Asia. Life Sciences Solutions sales surged 14% on increased sales of biosciences and bioprocess production. Analytical Instruments sales rose 12% from higher sales of chromatography and mass spectrometry equipment.

Thermo Fisher?s profit ticked 2% higher to about $2 billion in 2016 from 2015. Higher sales and productivity improvements combined to boost profit which might have been greater but for higher restructuring and acquisition-related charges in 2016.

Cash flow from operations reached about $3.2 billion in 2016 an increase from $2.8 billion in 2016. Lower investments in working capital and higher income before amortization and depreciation accounted for most of the increase.

Strategy

Thermo Fisher has been a deal-making machine spending more than $12 billion on acquisitions in 2016 and 2017. The company has expanded beyond supplying research labs with standard items like graduated cylinders and Bunsen burners to sophisticated equipment such as gene-sequencing and gene-editing tools. It also has added drug testing including running clinical trials and drug manufacturing to its portfolio. Thermo Fisher has become something of a one-stop shop for pharmaceutical companies that concentrate on developing drugs but outsource their production.

In 2017 Thermo Fisher acquired Patheon NV and Affymetrix and FEI both in 2016 in multi-billion deals. The company also had made several smaller deals.

Thermo Fisher hasn?t let its M&A department carry the entire load for stocking the product pipeline. The company has kept its research and development cycle going investing more than $750 million in 2016 up from about $690 million in 2015.

The company in 2016 offered new versions of products like its flagship Orbitrap platform which helps customers in drug discovery and food safety forensics and environmental testing. It released the Scientific Integrion HPIC system for ion chromatography as well as the latest generation of its Ion Torrent sequencing instruments. Two of the company?s CRISPR genome editing tools were recognized as Top 10 innovative products for 2016.

Besides tools to conduct research Thermo Fisher offers its cloud computing platform for storing results. The platform supports the company?s gene sequencing and proteomics systems.

Thermo Fisher has its sights set on expanding international sales particularly in China. Sales in China grew more than 25% in 2016 to account for 10% of the company?s revenue. Overall about 20% of the company?s 2016 revenue came from emerging markets which included stronger sales in India and South Korea. Thermo Fisher has built customer momentum in Asia with new facilities. It opened a BioPharma Services facility in South Korea to help meet increasing demand for clinical trials and a bioproduction development lab at its China Innovation Center in Shanghai.

In 2016 Thermo Fisher took $395 million in charges for restructuring that included headcount reductions and facilities consolidation. It also took $164 million in acquisition-related charges for severance and facilities closures. The company planned another $85 million in restructuring in 2017 that included facilities consolidation.

Mergers and Acquisitions

In 2017 Thermo Fisher acquired Patheon NV which offers services from regulatory consulting to making drug ingredients and finished medicines including biological therapies for $7.2 billion. Patheon had about $1.9 billion in revenue in 2016.

In two major deals in 2016 Thermo Fisher bought FEI and Affymetrix. FEI acquired for $4.2 billion added a complementary product mix of electron microscopes to Thermo Fisher's mass spectrometry products. The $1.3 billion deal for Affymetrix brought instruments used to analyze specimens at the cellular and genetic levels to the Thermo Fisher portfolio.

Other 2017 deals included Finesse Solutions Inc. a developer of scalable control automation systems and software for bioproduction and Core Informatics a provider of a cloud-based platform for scientific data management.

While it was transacted in 2014 the purchase of Life Technologies for more than $15 billion was major for Thermo Fisher. The deal moved the company to the head of the pack in life sciences tools particularly the growing field of genetic testing.

HISTORY

Predating the acquiring company Thermo Electron Fisher Scientific dates back to 1902 when 20-year-old Chester Fisher bought the stockroom of Pittsburgh Testing Laboratories (established 1884) and formed Scientific Materials Co. The company's earliest products supplied from Europe included simple tools such as microscopes balances and calorimeters. It published its first catalog in 1904.

When the outbreak of WWI disrupted supplies from Europe Scientific Materials established its own R&D and manufacturing facilities. It acquired Montreal-based Scientific Supplies in 1925 and the following year changed its name to Fisher Scientific Company. By 1935 Fisher had doubled its size adding glass-blowing operations and an instrument shop.

During the German occupation of Greece in WWII George Hatsopoulos part of a well-to-do family packed with politicians and engineering professors made radios for the Greek resistance. After the war he came to the US and became a professor of mechanical engineering at MIT. With a $50000 loan Hatsopoulos founded Thermo Electron in 1956 to identify emerging technology needs and create solutions for them.

In 2006 Thermo Electron merged with Fisher Scientific International in a stock-swap transaction valued at nearly $11 billion.

EXECUTIVES

President and CEO, Marc N. Casper, age 49, $1,407,471 total compensation
EVP and President Life Sciences Solutions, Mark P. Stevenson, age 54, $850,301 total compensation
VP Financial Operations, Stephen Williamson, age 51, $597,031 total compensation
SVP and Chief Commercial Officer, Thomas W. (Tom) Loewald, age 53, $610,115 total compensation
SVP and President Europe the Middle East and Africa (EMEA), Andrew J. (Andy) Thomson, age 52
SVP and President Asia-Pacific and Emerging Markets, Syed A. Jafry
SVP and President Customer Channels, Gregory J. (Greg) Herrema
SVP; President Laboratory Products, Frederick M. (Fred) Lowery
SVP and CIO, Joseph C. (Joe) Beery
SVP and President Specialty Diagnostics, Patrick M. Durbin, age 51
SVP; President Analytical Instruments, Daniel P. (Dan) Shine, age 49
Vice President Global Sourcing Indirect, Antonio Morani
Vice President, John Vernasco
Vice President Pricing, Dave Rusnak
Vice President Corporate Counsel, Peter Brennan
Vice President and General Manager, Michael Shafer
Vice President Sales National Accounts, Kim Baltier
Vice President Corporate Marketing and Social Media, Keith Bisogno
Vice President Corporate Accounts, Elizabeth Woo
Vice President, Neeraja Putta
Vice President Strategic Marketing and Planning, Liz Suter
Regional Vice President Central Region, Gary Galluzzi
Vice President of Engineering, Jerry Welch
Vice President, Clifford Farrell
Vice President Information Technology, Jeff Wilks
Vice President, Richard Dirocco
Vice President Finance, Matt Richards
Vice President World Wide Finance, Andy Long
Executive Vice President Worldwide Sales and Marketing, Michael Belford
Vice President Operations Speciality Gla, Wes Lollar
Vice President of Global Operations, Tom Grover
Vice President General Counsel Europe Middle East Africa, Alasdair Moodie
Vice President Finance EID, Kam Unninayar
Vice President of Sales, Tammy Starr

Vice President Information Technology, Liberino Martino
Vice President Finance, Jeff Besio
Executive Vice President and Chief Information Officer Wachovia Operations, Lori A Daniels
National Account Manager, Paul Scottberg
Vice President and General Council, John Sabo
Vice President and General Manager, William Geist
Vice President Information Technology, Ryan Snyder
Vice President and General Counsel, Genoffir MacLeod
Vice President and General Manager Latin America, Roberto Mendes
Vice President Finance Asia Pacific and Emerging Markets, Bob Faber
Vice President Information Technologies Life Sciences Solutions, John Stevens
Treasurer, Tony Smith
Auditors: PricewaterhouseCoopers LLP

LOCATIONS

HQ: Thermo Fisher Scientific Inc
  168 Third Avenue, Waltham, MA 02451
Phone: 781 622-1000   **Fax:** 781 933-4476
Web: www.thermofisher.com

2016 Sales

	$ mil.	% of total
US	9,085	50
China	1,729	10
Germany	995	5
UK	742	4
Japan	737	4
Other countries	4,983	27
Total	**18,274**	**100**

PRODUCTS/OPERATIONS

2016 Sales

	$ mil.	% of total
Laboratory Products & Services	7,030	37
Life Sciences Solutions	4,978	26
Analytical Instruments	3,668	19
Specialty Diagnostics	3,339	18
Adjustments	(741.4)	-
Total	**18,274**	**100**

2016 Sales

	$ mil.	% of total
Products	15,712	86
Services	2,561	14
Total	**18,274**	**100**

Selected Services
Custom Services
Instrument & Qualification Services
Out-Licensing and OEM Sales
Most Popular Products
TaqMan Real-Time PCR Assays
Oligos Primers Probes & Nucleotides
Lipofectamine Reagents
TRIzol Reagents
SuperScript Reverse Transcriptase
eSolutions
eProcurement
Supply Center
Instrument Management

Selected Products
Analytical Instruments
Automation and Robotics
Life Science Research consumables
Chemicals
Consumables
Custom Products
Diagnostics
Equipment
Furniture
Software

Selected Brands
ABgene
Barnant
Barnstead

BioImage
Cellomics
Dharmacon
Dionex
Electrothermal Engineering
Erie Scientific
Fisher Diagnostics
Gerhard Menzel
HyClone
Lab Vision/NeoMarkers
Matrix
Microgenics
Milwaukee Nucleic Acid Technologies
NERL
Owl Separation Systems Inc.
Pierce
Richard-Allan Scientific
Seradyn
TC Tech
Unity Lab Services

COMPETITORS

Abbott Labs	Life Technologies
Agilent Technologies	Corporation
Beckman Coulter	Mettler-Toledo
Becton Dickinson	Newport Corp.
Bio-Rad Labs	Nordion
Bruker	PerkinElmer
Corning	QIAGEN
Danaher	Roche Diagnostics
Emerson Electric	Roper Technologies
Halma	Shimadzu
Harvard Bioscience	Sigma-Aldrich
Hitachi	Tektronix
Honeywell	VWR
International	Waters Corp.
IDEXX Labs	Yokogawa Electric
Johnson & Johnson	

HISTORICAL FINANCIALS

Company Type: Public

Income Statement

FYE: December 31

	REVENUE ($ mil.)	NET INCOME ($ mil.)	NET PROFIT MARGIN	EMPLOYEES
12/16	18,274	2,021	11.1%	55,000
12/15	16,965	1,975	11.6%	52,000
12/14	16,889	1,894	11.2%	51,000
12/13	13,090	1,273	9.7%	50,000
12/12	12,509	1,177	9.4%	38,900
Annual Growth	9.9%	14.5%	—	9.0%

2016 Year-End Financials

Debt ratio: 36.22%
Return on equity: 9.40%
Cash ($ mil.): 786
Current ratio: 1.44
Long-term debt ($ mil.): 15,372
No. of shares (mil.): 393
Dividends
  Yield: 0.0%
  Payout: 11.7%
Market value ($ mil.): 55,515

	STOCK PRICE ($) FY Close	P/E High/Low		Earnings	PER SHARE ($) Dividends	Book Value
12/16	141.10	31	24	5.09	0.60	54.74
12/15	141.85	29	24	4.92	0.60	53.42
12/14	125.29	27	23	4.71	0.60	51.31
12/13	111.35	31	18	3.48	0.60	46.57
12/12	63.78	20	14	3.21	0.54	43.26
Annual Growth	22.0%	—	—	12.2%	2.7%	6.1%

Thor Industries, Inc.

Thor Industries is a recreation vehicle builder that makes and sells a range of RVs from motor homes to travel trailers as well as related parts.

Brands include Airstream and Dutchmen. RV manufacturing plants generally produce vehicles to dealer order; Thor's independent dealers dot the US and Canada catering to private purchasers and municipalities. The company has domestic facilities in Idaho Indiana Michigan Ohio and Oregon. The US is its largest market accounting for roughly 90% of total sales. Thor rolled out in 1980 when Wade Thompson and Peter Orthwein purchased Airstream's business.

Operations

Thor has two reportable segments: towable recreation vehicles (about three-quarters of revenue; travel trailers fifth wheels and motor homes) and motorized recreation vehicles (almost 30%).

Geographic Reach

Thor has facilities in the US (Idaho Indiana Michigan Ohio and Oregon) and Canada; the US accounts for nearly 90% of sales.

Sales and Marketing

Thor sells its products through a limited amount of consumer-oriented advertising for its recreation vehicles primarily in industry magazines product brochures direct mail advertising campaigns and on the Internet. The company markets its products through some 2200 independent dealerships carrying its products in the US and Canada. The company's dealer FreedomRoads accounts for 20% of its revenue.

Financial Performance

Thor has achieved unprecedented growth over the last few years. Revenues surged by 58% from $4.58 billion in 2016 to a record-smashing $7.2 billion in 2017. The historic growth was largely fueled by more than $1.8 billion in additional revenues from its Jayco acquisition. This acquisition helped spark sizable growth within its towable segments product lines including travel trailers and other (64%) and fifth wheels (40%).

The historic revenues for 2017 also caused Thor's profits to jump 46% from $257 million to $374 million and its operating cash flow to climb from $341 million to $419 million from 2016 to 2017.

Strategy

Thor's strategy is governed by strategic acquisitions and product introductions. RVs continue to be its mainstay line in terms of revenue as the RV industry enters its six year of recovery after the US recession according to the RV Industry Association.

In late 2016 Thor launched its Airstream Basecamp a sleek silver RV of aluminum that can be towed behind a truck. It contains one massive panoramic window solar power Italian cabinetry and a Bose Bluetooth speaker system.

Mergers and Acquisitions

Thor has achieved record-setting revenue growth over the years mainly through the use of acquisitions.

In the summer of 2016 Thor acquired Jayco for approximately $576 million. The transaction enhanced Thor's main portfolio as Jayco manufactures camping trailers light-weight trailers park and travel trailers fifth-wheels toy haulers and motor homes through a network of more than 300 authorized dealers in the US and Canada. The deal also helped Thor achieve milestone revenues of $7.2 billion for 2017.

The company also achieved success with a couple of acquisitions in 2015 including the purchases of towable RV maker Cruiser RV and luxury fifth wheel RV maker DRV for $47.5 million. It also bought Postle Aluminum an RV components supplier for $144 million.

HISTORY

Mergers and acquisitions specialist Wade Thompson and investment banker Peter Orthwein

saw the potential of the RV market after buying Hi-Lo Trailer in 1977. Thor Industries was formed when they bought the troubled Airstream Trailers unit (founded in 1931) from Beatrice Foods in 1980. Named after the mythical Norse god of thunder and containing the first two letters of the founders' last names Thor Industries went public in 1984.

EXECUTIVES

President Thor Motor Coach, Jeffery L. (Jeff) Kime
CFO, Colleen A. Zuhl, age 50, $500,000 total compensation
President Airstream, Robert H. Wheeler
President and CEO, Robert W. Martin, age 47, $750,000 total compensation
VP Administration and Human Resources, Kenneth D. Julian, age 49, $500,000 total compensation
Director Information Technology, John Stukenborg
President Heartland, Christopher J. Hermon
CEO Keystone, Matthew T. Zimmerman
SVP General Counsel and Corporate Secretary, W. Todd Woelfer, age 49, $600,000 total compensation
President K-Z Inc., Aram Koltookian
President CrossRoads RV, Ryan Juday
Vice President of Operational Improvement, John Rhymer
Executive Chairman, Peter B. Orthwein, age 71
Auditors: DELOITTE & TOUCHE LLP

LOCATIONS

HQ: Thor Industries, Inc.
601 East Beardsley Ave., Elkhart, IN 46514-3305
Phone: 574 970-7460
Web: www.thorindustries.com

PRODUCTS/OPERATIONS

2017 Sales

	% of total
Recreation vehicles	
Towables	71
Motorized	27
Other	2
Intercompany elimination	-
Total	**100**

COMPETITORS

All American Group	Prevost Car
Collins Industries	Rexhall Industries
Featherlite	Skyline
Forest River	Supreme Industries
Motor Coach Industries	Winnebago

HISTORICAL FINANCIALS

Company Type: Public

Income Statement

FYE: July 31

	REVENUE ($ mil.)	NET INCOME ($ mil.)	NET PROFIT MARGIN	EMPLOYEES
07/17	7,246	374	5.2%	17,800
07/16	4,582	256	5.6%	14,900
07/15	4,006	199	5.0%	10,450
07/14	3,525	179	5.1%	9,400
07/13	3,241	152	4.7%	8,300
Annual Growth	**22.3%**	**25.1%**	**—**	**21.0%**

2017 Year-End Financials

Debt ratio: 5.67%	No. of shares (mil.): 52
Return on equity: 26.34%	Dividends
Cash ($ mil.): 223	Yield: 1.2%
Current ratio: 1.51	Payout: 20.6%
Long-term debt ($ mil.): 145	Market value ($ mil.): 5,540

	STOCK PRICE ($) FY Close	P/E High/Low		PER SHARE ($) Earnings	Dividends	Book Value
07/17	105.35	16	10	7.09	1.32	29.98
07/16	76.54	16	10	4.88	1.20	24.11
07/15	55.88	17	13	3.74	1.08	20.33
07/14	52.97	19	15	3.35	1.92	18.33
07/13	54.05	19	9	2.88	2.22	16.78
Annual Growth	**18.2%**		**— —**	**25.3%**	**(12.2%)**	**15.6%**

Time Warner Inc

Even among media titans this company is a giant. Time Warner is one of the world's largest media conglomerates behind Walt Disney and News Corporation with operations spanning television and film. Through subsidiary Turner Broadcasting the company runs a portfolio of cable TV networks including CNN TBS and TNT. Time Warner also operates pay-TV channels HBO and Cinemax. Its Warner Bros. Entertainment meanwhile includes film studios (Warner Bros. Pictures New Line Cinema) TV production units (Warner Bros. Television Group) and comic book publisher DC Entertainment. In 2016 Time Warner agreed to be bought by AT&T Inc. for $85 billion.

HISTORY

Though formed in 2001 AOL Time Warner was the result of decades of advancement in the media industry. An elder statesman compared to relative newcomer America Online Time Warner's roots extend back to 1922 — the year that Henry Luce and Briton Hadden founded publisher Time Inc. and brothers Harry Abe Jack and Sam Warner established the origins of Warner Bros. which later became Warner Communications.

America Online's ancestry stretches back to the early 1980s when Stephen Case joined the management of a company called Control Video. Later renamed Quantum Computer Services the company created the online service that would become America Online in 1985. Quantum Computer Services changed its name to America Online in 1991. It went public the next year.

As America Online was germinating Time Inc. and Warner Communications were eyeing each other. The two companies merged in 1990 to form Time Warner. Gerald Levin was appointed CEO in 1992. To shave off debt Time Warner grouped several of its properties into Time Warner Entertainment in 1992 in which U S West (which later became MediaOne Group) bought a 25% interest.

Time Warner's 1996 acquisition of Ted Turner's Turner Broadcasting System further elevated Time Warner's profile on the media stage. For America Online 1996 marked the first year the company began charging its subscribers a flat rate vastly increasing the amount of time they spent online.

America Online grew through acquisitions of CompuServe in 1998 and Netscape Communications in 1999. Meanwhile Time Warner had created Time Warner Telecom and taken it public. After AT&T's announcement that it would acquire MediaOne MediaOne gave up its 50% management control of Time Warner Entertainment but retained its 25% ownership interest. AT&T's acquisition of MediaOne was completed in 2000 thus giving AT&T 25% of Time Warner Entertainment. (AT&T later boosted its stake to 27%.)

America Online announced that it would acquire Time Warner in early 2000. To please European regulators Time Warner subsequently abandoned its plans to combine the Warner Music Group with EMI Group's music operations. After a lengthy review by regulatory bodies America Online acquired Time Warner for $106 billion and formed AOL Time Warner in 2001. Case became chairman and Levin was appointed CEO. The newly formed company soon began streamlining cutting more than 2400 jobs in the process. (It cut another 1700 jobs at America Online later that year.) Also that year America Online invested about $100 million in Amazon.com.

Levin retired from the company in 2002 and was replaced by co-COO Richard Parsons. The following year AOL Time Warner finally succeeded in buying Comcast's stake in Time Warner Entertainment (Comcast gained its share of TWE when it bought the cable assets of AT&T in 2002). The following year Case and Turner both resigned their executive positions with the company but remained on the board of directors. (Case left the board in 2005.) And in a move to distance itself from the struggling online unit the company dropped AOL from its moniker and returned to being known as Time Warner Inc.

Time Warner started off 2004 by ridding itself of Warner Music Group which it sold for $2.6 billion to a group led by former Seagram executive Edgar Bronfman Jr. and investment firm Thomas H. Lee Partners. It also sold the NBA's Atlanta Hawks and the NHL's Atlanta Thrashers for $250 million to a private investment group called Atlanta Spirit.

The company's flagship Internet service officially shortened its name to simply AOL in early 2006. Also that year Time Warner sold its book publishing unit Time Warner Book Group to French media firm Lagard¨re. Time Warner Cable joined with Comcast to acquire Adelphia Communications for $17.6 billion in cash and stock; as part of the deal Adelphia shareholders sold part of their newly acquired stake in TWC through an IPO in 2007. Later that year Time Warner sold its Atlanta Braves baseball team (once owned by former vice chairman Ted Turner) to Liberty Media in a deal that valued the team at $460 million.

Parsons retired as CEO at the beginning of 2008 and was replaced by Jeffrey Bewkes who previously oversaw the company's entertainment divisions. Bewkes replaced Parsons as Time Warner chairman as well at the end of that year.

Never able to achieve significant synergies between the online media and traditional film and TV content arms despite several restructuring attempts Time Warner was burdened with debt and suffering losses. This ultimately led the company to spin off AOL as a separate publicly traded company in 2009. The separation valued AOL at less than $3 billion far less than the $124 billion valuation of the original AOL-Time Warner merger. In another high-profile disposal during 2009 Time Warner spun off its remaining stake in Time Warner Cable.

In 2011 the company's Filmed Entertainment unit released the final film in the immensely popular Harry Potter series. Harry Potter and the Deathly Hallows: Part 2 was the year's top film in terms of ticket sales pulling in a colossal $1.3 billion in 2011.

In 2014 Time Warner spun off its print publishing operations. In 2016 the company agreed to be acquired by AT&T.

EXECUTIVES

EVP Global Public Policy, Carol A. Melton, age 62

Senior Vice President and Chief Security Officer, Larry Cockell

EVP Corporate Marketing and Communications, Gary L. Ginsberg, age 55, $875,000 total compensation

Chairman and CEO, Jeffrey L. (Jeff) Bewkes, age 65, $2,000,000 total compensation

EVP and General Counsel, Paul T. Cappuccio, age 55, $1,400,000 total compensation

CEO Warner Bros. Entertainment, Kevin Tsujihara

President Warner Bros. Unscripted and Alternative Television, Mike Darnell

EVP International and Corporate Strategy, Olaf J. Olafsson, age 54, $925,000 total compensation

Chairman and CEO Home Box Office, Richard L. Plepler

President and Chief Content Officer Warner Bros. Pictures, Toby Emmerich, age 54

President and Chief Content Officer Warner Bros. Television Group, Peter Roth

Chairman and CEO Turner Broadcasting System Inc., John Martin, age 49, $1,600,000 total compensation

President DC Entertainment and President Warner Bros. Consumer Products, Diane Nelson

President Warner Bros. Studio Facilities, Jon Gilbert

President Worldwide Marketing and International Distribution Warner Bros. Pictures, Sue Kroll

President International Distribution and Growth Initiatives Warner Bros. Pictures, Veronika Kwan Vandenberg

President Warner Bros. Worldwide Television Distribution, Jeffrey R. Schlesinger

President HBO Documentary Films, Sheila Nevins, age 78

President Warner Bros. Worldwide Home Entertainment Distribution, Ronald J. Sanders

President Turner Broadcasting System International, Gerhard Zeiler, age 60

President The CW Television Network, Mark Pedowitz

President Business and Strategy Warner Bros. Television Group and President Warner Bros. Digital Networks, Craig Hunegs

President HBO Global Distribution, Simon Sutton

EVP and CFO, Howard M. Averill, age 53, $1,400,000 total compensation

President HBO Miniseries, Kary Antholis

EVP and Chief Human Resources Officer, Karen Magee, age 55

President International Marketing and Worldwide Planning and Operations Warner Bros. Pictures, Lynne Frank

President and Chief Marketing Officer Warner Bros. Television Group, Lisa Gregorian

President Warner Bros. Domestic Television Distribution, Kenneth (Ken) Werner, age 63

President Worldwide Business Affairs Warner Bros. Pictures, Steven S. Spira

CIO, Mitchell (Mitch) Klaif

President HBO Programming Sales, Charles Schreger

President HBO Films, Len Amato

President The Americas and Global Strategy Warner Bros. Home Entertainment, Jim Wuthrich

President HBO Programming, Casey Bloys

President CNN Worldwide, Jeff Zucker

President Music Warner Bros. Pictures, Paul Broucek

EVP and General Manager Warner Bros. Interactive Entertainment, David Haddad

President Turner Broadcasting System Inc., David Levy

President Warner Bros. Animation and Warner Digital Series, Sam Register

President Worldwide Physical Production Warner Bros. Pictures, Bill Draper

President Domestic Distribution Warner Bros. Pictures, Jeff Goldstein

President Warner Bros. Consumer Products, Pam Lifford

President Worldwide Marketing Warner Bros. Pictures, Blair Rich

Vice President Risk Management, John Carter

Vice President Project Management, Joel Brenner

Vice President Global Facilities Management, Steve Lefkowitz

Vice President and Assistant Controller, Richard Stein

Senior Vice President And Deputy General Counsel, Brenda C Karickhoff

Vice President International Tax, John Petito

Vice President Finance, Amos Smith

Vice President Finance, Saroosh Ahmed

Vice President Finance, Ken Shelton

Vice President And Assistant Controller, David Depinho

Senior Vice President Marketing, Russel Arons

Vice President and Assistant Controller, John Talamo

Vice President and Managing Director, Allison Goldberg

Vice President Corporate Responsibility, Lisa Quiroz

Executive Vice President and Chief Financial Officer Warner Bros. Entertainment, Kim Williams

Vice President Assistant Controller External Financial Reporting, Dan Happer

Senior Vice President and Chief Security Officer, Joe Petro

Group Vice President and General Manager Digital Phone, Jeff Lindsay

Auditors: Ernst & Young LLP

LOCATIONS

HQ: Time Warner Inc
   One Time Warner Center, New York, NY 10019-8016
Phone: 212 484-8000   Fax: 212 489-6183
Web: www.timewarner.com

2016 Sales

	$ mil.	% of total
United States and Canada	20,970	72
Europe	4,557	15
Asia/Pacific Rim	1,992	7
Latin America	1,413	5
All Other	386	1
Total	**29,318**	**100**

PRODUCTS/OPERATIONS

2016 Sales

	$ mil.	% of total
Warner Bros.	13,037	43
Turner	11,364	38
Home Box Office	5,890	19
Intersegment eliminations	(973)	-
Total	**29,318**	**100**

2016 Sales

	$ mil.	% of total
Content	12,935	44
Subscription	11,014	38
Advertising	4,696	16
Other	673	2
Total	**29,318**	**100**

COMPETITORS

21st Century Fox	Lagard¨re Active
Bertelsmann	Liberty Interactive
CBS Corp	Meredith Corporation
Discovery	NBCUniversal
Communications	Sony Pictures
Disney	Entertainment
Hearst Corporation	Viacom

Income Statement

FYE: December 31

	REVENUE ($ mil.)	NET INCOME ($ mil.)	NET PROFIT MARGIN	EMPLOYEES
12/16	29,318	3,926	13.4%	25,000
12/15	28,118	3,833	13.6%	24,800
12/14	27,359	3,827	14.0%	25,600
12/13	29,795	3,691	12.4%	34,000
12/12	28,729	3,019	10.5%	34,000
Annual Growth	0.5%	6.8%	—	(7.4%)

2016 Year-End Financials

Debt ratio: 36.90%
Return on equity: 16.33%
Cash ($ mil.): 1,539
Current ratio: 1.39
Long-term debt ($ mil.): 22,392

No. of shares (mil.): 772
Dividends
　Yield: 0.0%
　Payout: 32.4%
Market value ($ mil.): 74,521

	STOCK PRICE ($) FY Close	P/E High/Low	PER SHARE ($) Earnings	Dividends	Book Value
12/16	96.53	19　12	4.96	1.61	31.52
12/15	64.67	19　14	4.62	1.40	29.71
12/14	85.42	20　14	4.34	1.27	29.42
12/13	69.72	18　12	3.92	1.15	33.41
12/12	47.83	15　11	3.09	1.04	32.06
Annual Growth	19.2%	—　—	12.6%	11.5%	(0.4%)

TJX Companies, Inc.

The TJX Companies operates more than 3860 stores worldwide under half a dozen retail brand names including the two largest off-price clothing retailers in the US: T.J. Maxx and Marshalls which operate 2220-plus stores nationwide. T.J. Maxx sells brand-name family apparel accessories shoes domestics giftware and jewelry at discount prices while Marshalls offers similar items plus a broader selection of shoes and menswear through more than 1000 stores. Its HomeGoods chain of 580-plus US stores focuses exclusively on home furnishings. T.K. Maxx is the company's European retail arm with 500-plus stores in the UK Ireland Austria Germany Poland and the Netherlands.

HISTORY

Cousins Stanley and Sumner Feldberg opened the first Zayre (Yiddish for "very good") store in Hyannis Massachusetts in 1956. During the next 15 years the number of stores grew to nearly 200.

Zayre purchased the Hit or Miss chain which sold upscale women's clothing at discounted prices in 1969. When the recession of the early 1970s hit superb results at Hit or Miss prompted Zayre to look for further opportunities in the off-price apparel marketplace. Zayre hired Ben Cammarata to create a new store concept and in March 1977 he opened the first T.J. Maxx in Auburn Massachusetts to market discounted upscale family clothing. Six years later Zayre formed the catalog retailer Chadwick's of Boston to sell Hit or Miss apparel by mail.

The company came to rely increasingly on its specialty operations to provide consistent sales and income as its flagship general merchandise stores often struggled. By 1983 the specialty chains were producing almost half of Zayre's sales.

In the second half of the 1980s Zayre's upscale (yet still off-priced) retailers' sales rose while its general merchandise stores (targeting lower-income customers) dropped. To keep its specialty stores unhindered by its flagging Zayre stores it established The TJX Companies as a public company in 1987. Zayre sold about 17% of its new subsidiary to the public with Cammarata as CEO.

Zayre sold its 400 general merchandise stores in 1988 to Ames for about $430 million in cash $140 million in Ames stock and a receivable note. The next year the company spun off its warehouse club operations as Waban (the warehouse component eventually became BJ's Wholesale) and merged with its subsidiary The TJX Companies taking that name.

TJX acquired Winners Apparel a Toronto-based five-store apparel chain in 1990. That year in the same month that Ames declared bankruptcy TJX established a $185 million reserve against losses it might suffer through its ownership of Ames' stock. Ames emerged from bankruptcy two years later and TJX was left with 4% of Ames' voting shares and over 100 empty Ames stores. TJX sold or leased most of them.

Also in 1992 TJX opened HomeGoods gift and houseware outlets in three of its remaining Ames stores and closed about 70 Hit or Miss stores. That year the company paid off about $128 million of its long-term debt. Encouraged by the success of its off-price operations in Canada in 1994 TJX opened five T.K. Maxx stores (similar to T.J. Maxx and Winners Apparel) in the UK.

A year later TJX paid $550 million for Melville's ailing chain of 450 Marshalls clothing stores. In addition the company sold its Hit or Miss apparel chain.

To help pay for Marshalls TJX sold the Chadwick's of Boston catalog in 1996 to retailer Brylane for about $325 million. Two years later the company opened two T.K. Maxx stores in the Netherlands and said it planned to have 75 stores in Europe in three years. It also debuted the A.J. Wright discount chain in New England in 1998.

In 1999 TJX elected Cammarata to the additional post of chairman and elevated Ted English to president and COO. In 2000 Cammarata relinquished his CEO post to English but remained chairman. Citing the successes of its new stores the company announced in early 2001 it expected to increase its total number of stores 12% annually for the next several years. Also that year the company shuttered its T.K. Maxx stores in the Netherlands. Seven TJX employees perished on September 11 2001 when their flight bound for Los Angeles crashed into the World Trade Center during the worst terrorist attack in US history.

In 2002 the company opened HomeSense a new Canadian home furnishings chain fashioned after its US counterpart HomeGoods. In December 2003 TJX finalized its acquisition of Bob's Stores a Connecticut-based discount retail chain with 31 stores in the Northeast.

In September 2005 English resigned abruptly after five years as the company's CEO. In October the company closed down its tjmaxx.com and homegoods.com Web sites citing poor sales.

In March 2006 TJX cut about 250 jobs in its corporate and divisional offices and reduced the salaries of a dozen senior executives including its chairman and acting CEO and its president by 10% in an effort to increase profits.

A year after the abrupt resignation of CEO Edmond English in September 2005 TJX named company president Carol Meyrowitz to the post effective January 2007. (Cammarata had been acting CEO of the company in the interim.) Also in January 34 A.J. Wright stores were closed.

In November 2007 TJX reached a settlement with Visa and Fifth Third Bancorp stemming from a breach of its computer systems in which customer data was stolen. Under the terms of the agreement TJX will fund up to $40.9 million for recovery payments for US Visa issuers. Also in the fall of 2007 the retailer's European arm T.K. Maxx entered the German market with five stores there.

In 2008 TJX sold money-losing Bob's Stores which has about 35 locations in the Northeast to the private equity firms Versa Capital Management and Crystal Capital for an undisclosed amount.

EXECUTIVES

Vice President And Director Application Development TJX Companies, David Spooner
President CEO and Director, Ernie Herrman, age 56, $1,525,001 total compensation
SEVP and Group President, Richard Sherr, age 59, $921,232 total compensation
SEVP Finance and CFO, Scott Goldenberg, age 63, $813,462 total compensation
SEVP and Group President, Ken Canestrari, age 56
SEVP and Group President, Michael MacMillan, age 60, $1,052,309 total compensation
Assistant Vice President, John Forbes
Executive Vice President Merchandising and Quality, Louis Luciano
Vice President Merchandising, Joseph Domenick
SENIOR VICE PRESIDENT AND GENERAL COUNSEL, Beverly Kennedy
Vice President Real Estate Research Director, Sean Anderson
DIVISIONAL VP, Mark Azar
Assistant Vice President Merchandise Manager, David Macdonald
Vice President Merchandise Manager Bath towles Basic Bedding and Throws, Simantha Macleod
Assistant Vice President Finance and General Accounting, Kevin Foley
Assistant Vice President Merchandise Planning, Debra Duprez
VICE PRESIDENT, Caron Mcdonald
Assistant Vice President Merchandise Planning, Rose Riggieri
Vice President Merchandising, Brian Francione
Assistant Vice President Merchandise Planning, Josten Swiader
Vice President, Richard McDonald
Senior Vice President eCommerce, Elaine Boltz
Assistant Vice President Merchandising Business Solutions, Matt Martin
Assistant Vice President Store Planning Design and Fixture Director, Cindy Buffi
DVP Merchandise Manager, Paul Bibbo
Vice President Finance, Peter Daniels
Assistant Vice President Corporate Benefits Director, Lauren Mullin
Divisional Vice President Market Manager, Liz Dixon
Assistant Vice President General Manager, Tim Linton
Assistant Vice President Loss Prevention, Kate Hughes
Assistant Vice President Manager of Planning and Allocation, Nancy Atchue
Assistant Vice President Loss Prevention, Kevin Taparausky
Divisional Vice President Merchandise Manager, Beth Winkler
Assistant Vice President Store Planning, Jon Nelson
Assistant Vice President, Lisa Pratico
Assistant Vice President Director Loss Prevention, Frederick L Mullen
Regional Vice President, Guy Reda
Assistant Vice President of Application Development, Joe Walsh
Senior Vice President General Merchandise Manager, Joanne Wolfe
Vice President The Marmaxx Group, Claudia Winkle

Vice President Office Services Director, Mike Brogan

Vice President Finance, John Klinger

Assistant Vice President International Tax, Barbara House

Divisional Vice President furniture and Lamps merchandise Manager, Greg Iacono

DVP DMM E Commerce, Inna Leipzig

Divisional Vice President Merchandise Manager Ecommerce, Lisa Pena

Vice President, David Federico

Vice President Store Systems Director, Martin Whitmore

Assistant Vice President Director of Engineering, Tom Sgammato

Assistant Vice President Corporate Communications, Colleen Beauregard

Senior Vice President GMM, Pam Pretzer

Divisional Vice President Merchandise Manager, Amy Howard

Senior Vice President Store Operations A J Wright, Mike McGrath

Assistant Vice President Human Resources Business Partner, Sandi Anderson

Vice President Loss Prevention Director, Richard Peck

Vice President Real Estate And Property Development, George Drummey

DVP Merchandise Manager, Pat Kelly

Associate Vice President Compliance and Privacy Director, Matthew Garvey

Vice President, Cheryl Oldfield

Vice President, Marc Boesch

Vice President Logistics Planning and Strategy, Scott Trahan

Vice President The Marmaxx Group, Charlotte Arnold

Vice President of Planning and Allocation, Nancy Mendis

Assistant Vice President Senior Attorney Labor and E, Jennifer Brady

Assistant Vice President Store Operations Home Goods, Mike Farrell

Vice President logistics, John Beando

Assistant Vice President Loss Prevention, Kevin Kurtz

Vice President Of Global Talent Development, Carolyn Fischer

Assistant Vice President Supply Chain Business Services, Richard Oppenheimer

Assistant Vice President Senior Real Estate Director, Keith Schantz

Assistant Vice President Merchandise Manager, Sally Reilly

Assistant Vice President Compensation, April Fontaine

Assistant Vice President Product Development, Kathy Batson

Senior Vice President, David Kaplan

Vice President, Bob Cooke

Assistant Vice President Planning Marshalls, Jacqui Hebden

Assistant Vice President Merchandise Planning, Susan Arapoff

Assistant Vice President and Director Marketing, Andy Maercklein

Vice President, Beverly Edgehill

Executive Vice President and Chief Information Officer, Mark Beyerly

Vice President Human Resources Operations, Daniel Finacchio

Assistant Vice President Property Tax Director, Bradford Dunn

Assistant Vice President Consumer Insights, Rachel Cook

Divisional Vice President Market Manager, Guido Galli

Divisional Vice President Market Manager, Jeannie Seo

Vice President Data Architecture and Business Intelligence Director, Antoinette Wallace

Senior Vice President Transportation and Logistics, Jeff Tawney

Assistant Vice President and Director Corporate Communications, Erika Tower

Senior Vice President Divisional Chief Financial O, Chris Mieszczanski

Assistant Vice President Director of Human Resources, Michael Doto

Assistant Vice President Vendor Management, Mark Dolat

Assistant Vice President, Alice Wu

Assistant Vice President. Director, Mark Day

ASSISTANT VICE PRESIDENT, Glen Brenner

AVP Network Operations, Tim Kearney

Chairman, Carol M. Meyrowitz, age 63

Assistant Treasurer, Nancy Hendrickson

Auditors: PricewaterhouseCoopers LLP

LOCATIONS

HQ: TJX Companies, Inc.
770 Cochituate Road, Framingham, MA 01701
Phone: 508 390-1000   Fax: 508 390-2091
Web: www.tjx.com

2017 Stores

	No.
US	
T.J. Maxx	1,191
Marshalls	1,039
HomeGoods	596
Sierra Trading Post	12
Canada	
Winners	258
HomeSense	109
Marshalls	61
Europe	
T.K. Maxx	515
HomeSense	46
Australia	
T.K. Maxx	35
Total	**3,862**

2017 Sales

	$ mil.	% of total
US		
Marmaxx	21,246	64
HomeGoods	4,404	13
TJX Canada	3,171	10
TJX International	4,362	13
Total	**33,183**	**100**

PRODUCTS/OPERATIONS

Selected Stores

HomeGoods (off-price home fashion chain)

HomeSense (off-price home fashion chain Canada and UK)

Marshalls (off-price retailer of apparel shoes home fashions)

Marshalls Mega-Stores (combination Marshalls and HomeGoods stores)

Sierra Trading Post (off-price online retailer of outdoor gear and apparel)

T.J. Maxx (off-price retailer of apparel shoes home fashions)

T.J. Maxx 'N More (combination T.J. Maxx and HomeGoods stores)

T.K. Maxx (off-price retailer of apparel shoes home fashions Europe)

Winners Apparel (off-price family apparel chain Canada)

2017 Sales

	% of total
Clothing & footwear	55
Home fashions	30
Jewelry & accessories	15
Total	**100**

COMPETITORS

ASDA	Kmart
Amazon.com	Kohl's
Bed Bath & Beyond	Liberty Interactive
Belk	Macy's
Big Lots	Primark
Burlington Coat Factory	Ross Stores
	Sears
Caleres	Shopko Stores
Cato	Sports Authority
Charming Shoppes	Stage Stores
Children's Place	Stein Mart
Claire's Stores	Tailored Brands
Dillard's	Target Corporation
Dollar General	Tesco
Eddie Bauer LLC	The Gap
Foot Locker	Tuesday Morning
Inditex	Corporation
J. C. Penney	Wal-Mart

HISTORICAL FINANCIALS

Company Type: Public

Income Statement

FYE: January 28

	REVENUE ($ mil.)	NET INCOME ($ mil.)	NET PROFIT MARGIN	EMPLOYEES
01/17	33,183	2,298	6.9%	235,000
01/16	30,944	2,277	7.4%	216,000
01/15*	29,078	2,215	7.6%	198,000
02/14	27,422	2,137	7.8%	191,000
02/13	25,878	1,906	7.4%	179,000
Annual Growth	**6.4%**	**4.8%**	**—**	**7.0%**

*Fiscal year change

2017 Year-End Financials

Debt ratio: 18.66%
Return on equity: 52.27%
Cash ($ mil.): 2,929
Current ratio: 1.63
Long-term debt ($ mil.): 2,403

No. of shares (mil.): 646
Dividends
  Yield: 0.0%
  Payout: 28.6%
Market value ($ mil.): 47,996

	STOCK PRICE ($) FY Close	P/E High/Low	PER SHARE ($) Earnings	Dividends	Book Value
01/17	74.26	24 19	3.46	0.99	6.98
01/16	71.24	23 19	3.33	0.81	6.49
01/15*	65.94	21 16	3.15	0.67	6.23
02/14	57.36	21 15	2.94	0.55	6.00
02/13	45.30	26 13	2.55	0.44	5.06
Annual Growth	**13.2%**	**—**	**7.9%**	**22.5%**	**8.3%**

*Fiscal year change

Toll Brothers Inc.

Ask not for whom the Tolls build because if you have to ask you probably can't afford it. Toll Brothers builds luxury homes in the US targeting move-up second-home and retired buyers. Its single-family detached houses and condominium apartments sell for an average price of over $700000. The company also develops communities for active adults and operates country club communities. Subsidiaries offer related services and products including insurance coverage title and mortgage services and landscaping. Toll Brothers has operations in some 50 markets in nearly 20 states. Traditionally a suburban developer Toll Brothers has branched out to high-rise condominiums in urban markets.

Operations

Toll Brothers' two segments are Traditional Home Building and City Living. The former accounts for almost all company revenue at around 95% of sales.

The company's traditional homes sell at prices ranging from $225000 to $2.0 million. Its City Living homes sold in more expensive urban areas are priced between $420000 and $6.5 million.

In addition to home building the firm operates a slew of subsidiaries active in: architecture engineering mortgage title land development land sale golf course development and management home security and landscaping.

Geographic Reach

Pennsylvania-based Toll Brother's largest market is California which generates around 30% of sales. The company also builds houses in the North (Connecticut Illinois Massachusetts Michigan Minnesota New Jersey New York) South (Florida North Carolina Texas) West (Arizona Colorado Nevada Washington) and Mid-Atlantic (Delaware Maryland Pennsylvania Virginia) regions of the US.

Its City Living division builds luxury properties in urban markets including Manhattan and Brooklyn New York; Hoboken and Jersey City New Jersey; Philadelphia; and Washington DC.

Sales and Marketing

The builder markets its homes online and via its own sales personnel. It also advertises through newspapers in local or regional publications and on billboards. It also markets its communities through color brochures.

Financial Performance

After the housing and financial crisis tanked Toll Brothers' revenue by 75% between between 2006 to 2011 the company is once again scaling the money mountain at a relentless pace — revenue is now some 85% of its pre-crisis peak.

Toll Brothers' sales rose for a fifth straight year in fiscal 2016 (ended October) jumping a nice round $1 billion or 24% to $5.2 billion. Volumes and prices were both up during 2016. The company sold 6098 homes at an average price of $721000 per home during the year. While sales growth was strong in all regions except the South (which declined 5%) California in particular recorded a spike of over 90% to $1.4 billion with unit delivered up 50% to 1006. In the City Living segment revenue fell 19% to $257.9 million as a near-100% increase in average price (to $2.8 million) was offset by a 58% fall in units delivered (91).

Net income climbed 5% to $382 million higher income from operations was partially offset by a higher income tax expense. Cash from operating activities recovered after taking a hit in 2015 coming in at $148.8 million versus $60 million the previous year. The increase was mostly down to higher net income and a $524.6 million increase in accounts payable offset by a net purchase of $391.2 million of inventory.

Strategy

Positioning itself as a luxury home builder that provides superior quality and high-end features in its homes Toll Brothers continues to enjoy a broad recovery in the housing industry as pent-up consumer demand releases and as consumers regain confidence.

The company's City Living business which sells homes in more expensive urban markets has continued to grow as well as the US population continues to move toward urban areas. With more affluent Americans making the trek back to cities from the suburbs Toll Brothers has also stepped up is activities in select urban markets such as Washington D.C. and New York City where it has been buying properties.

Mergers and Acquisitions

In late 2016 Toll Brothers completed a $85.2 million acquisition of Coleman Real Estate Holdings an Idaho-based builder of single-family homes

ranging from first-time to luxury. The acquisition expands Toll Brothers' presence in Idaho and opens it up to a slightly lower price point niche in the luxury market.

Company Background

In November 2011 Toll Brothers acquired CamWest Development LLC for about $144.7 million. Toll Brothers was attracted to the Seattle market due to its high barriers to entry high employment rate and concentration of wealthy people who are ideal luxury home buyers. The deal included more than 1240 home sites and more than 250 sites under option.

HISTORY

Homebuilder Albert Toll's two sons Robert and Bruce Toll founded their own business in 1967. The duo began by building starter homes in the Philadelphia suburbs of Elkins Park and Yardley. As Philadelphia's population began to sprawl beyond these older suburban areas the company grew and in 1982 it moved beyond Pennsylvania to build houses in New Jersey. The young firm also began to distinguish itself by catering to up-market customers.

Toll Brothers Inc. went public in 1986 and later expanded around New York City north to the Boston area and south to the suburbs of Washington DC. The firm survived the late 1980s real estate recession in the Northeast because unlike many builders it did not overextend itself.

Until the 1990s Toll Brothers operated primarily in the northeastern US but it expanded as the housing market began an upward cycle. It entered California and North Carolina in 1994 and Arizona Florida and Texas in 1995. Toll Brothers began work in Nashville Tennessee and Las Vegas in 1997. The next year the company entered the active adult market building its first two age-qualified communities in New Jersey. Also in 1998 the company joined other investors including the Pennsylvania State Employees Retirement System and formed the Toll Brothers Realty Trust to acquire and develop commercial property.

In 1999 Toll Brothers acquired Silverman Companies a leading homebuilder and developer of luxury apartments with more than 80 years of experience in Detroit. The company also began building homes in the Chicago San Diego and San Francisco markets that year and it teamed with Marriott International to begin developing an assisted-living community in Reston Virginia.

It also set up its cable and broadband subsidiary Advanced Broadband that year to provide its communities with Internet connectivity. Toll Brothers sold those operations to Comcast in 2007.

The company began operating in Rhode Island and New Hampshire in 2000 and the next year entered Colorado. In 2002 the company entered South Carolina in the Hilton Head area to develop Hampton Hall a luxury country club community with a master-planned golf course.

In 2003 Toll Brothers acquired Jacksonville Florida-based homebuilder Richard R. Dostie Inc. for an undisclosed cash amount. The company also expanded its luxury urban in-fill market operations by acquiring The Manhattan Building Company a developer of luxury mid- and high-rise condos on northern New Jersey's waterfront. The next year Toll Brothers and Pinnacle Ltd. jointly began development of an 832-home luxury condominium community (Maxwell Place on the Hudson) on the waterfront of Hoboken New Jersey overlooking Manhattan.

For its 12th consecutive year Toll Brothers produced record fiscal-year-end results for earnings revenues contracts and backlog in 2004. The company's net income grew 57% over the previous year's earnings and it operated in more communi-

ties and offered more product lines than it had in previous years. Another record was set in 2005; revenue from home sales increased 50% and net income increased 97%. That year Toll Brothers began operations in West Virginia but stopped selling homes in Ohio.

Toll correctly predicted an industry slowdown in 2006 and for both 2006 and 2007 the number of homes it built dropped from 8600 to around 6700. As numbers continued to sink it sold land holdings reduced its backlog and divested its cable Internet and home security businesses.

CEO and co-founder Robert Toll stepped down as CEO in 2010. He was succeeded by Douglas Yearley

EXECUTIVES

President and COO, Richard T. (Rick) Hartman, age 59, $1,000,000 total compensation
CEO and Director, Douglas C. (Doug) Yearley, age 56, $1,000,000 total compensation
CFO, Martin P. (Marty) Connor, age 52, $970,833 total compensation
SVP and Chief Marketing Officer, Kira Sterling
Assistant Vice President and Director, Neil Baxter
Division Vice President, Brian Emmons
Vice President Finance, Andy Lawhorn
Vice President of Land Acquistions, David Hutcheson
Vice President Finance, Gregg Ziegler
Division Assistant Vice President, Isaac Boyd
Assistant Vice President, Jeff Brainard
Vice President of Sales Training, Suzanne Barletto
Assistant Vice President Land Development, Greg Leygraaf
Regional LD Vice President, Terry Hodge
Senior Division Vice President, Vince Rossi
Regional President, Rob Parahus
Chairman, Robert I. Toll, age 75
Auditors: Ernst & Young LLP

LOCATIONS

HQ: Toll Brothers Inc.
250 Gibraltar Road, Horsham, PA 19044
Phone: 215 938-8000   **Fax:** 215 938-8023
Web: www.tollbrothers.com

2016 Locations

	No.
Traditional home building	
Mid-Atlantic	1,432
West	1,304
North	1,172
South	1,093
California	1,006
City Living	91
Total	**6,098**

2016 Sales

	$ mil.	% of total
Traditional home building		
California	1,448	28
West	903	18
Mid-Atlantic	895	17
South	849	16
North	814	16
City Living	257	5
Total	**5,169**	**100**

PRODUCTS/OPERATIONS

Selected Operations

Architectural design services
Golf course development and operation
Engineering services
House component assembly
Land development
Landscape services
Lumber distribution
Mortgage lending
Title insurance

COMPETITORS

CalAtlantic	KB Home
D.R. Horton	Lennar
David Weekley Homes	Orleans Homebuilders
Hovnanian Enterprises	PulteGroup
John Wieland Homes	William Lyon Homes

HISTORICAL FINANCIALS

Company Type: Public

Income Statement

FYE: October 31

	REVENUE ($ mil.)	NET INCOME ($ mil.)	NET PROFIT MARGIN	EMPLOYEES
10/17	5,815	535	9.2%	4,500
10/16	5,169	382	7.4%	4,200
10/15	4,171	363	8.7%	3,900
10/14	3,911	340	8.7%	3,500
10/13	2,674	170	6.4%	3,019
Annual Growth	21.4%	33.1%	—	10.5%

2017 Year-End Financials

Debt ratio: 34.09%
Return on equity: 12.23%
Cash ($ mil.): 712
Current ratio: 4.74
Long-term debt ($ mil.): 3,220
No. of shares (mil.): 157
Dividends
Yield: 0.5%
Payout: 8.9%
Market value ($ mil.): 7,238

	STOCK PRICE ($) FY Close	P/E High/Low		PER SHARE ($) Earnings	Dividends	Book Value
10/17	46.04	14	8	3.17	0.24	28.82
10/16	27.44	17	11	2.18	0.00	26.14
10/15	35.97	20	15	1.97	0.00	24.15
10/14	31.95	21	15	1.84	0.00	22.02
10/13	32.88	38	29	0.97	0.00	19.68
Annual Growth	8.8%	—	—	34.5%	—	10.0%

Tompkins Financial Corp

Tompkins Financial is the holding company for Tompkins Trust Company The Bank of Castile and Mahopac Bank which offer traditional banking services through some 45 offices in upstate New York. It also owns the 20-branch Pennsylvania-based VIST Bank. Funds from deposit products such as checking savings and money market accounts are mainly used to originate real estate loans and mortgages as well as commercial and consumer loans. Tompkins also offers trust and estate financial and tax planning and investment management services through Tompkins Financial Advisors. Tompkins Insurance Agencies sells property/casualty coverage in central and western New York and Pennsylvania.

Operations

Tompkins Financial operates in three segments: banking insurance and wealth management. Banking represents most of its revenue — more than 80%. About 70% of the banks' loan portfolios is made up of commercial and commercial real estate loans.

Tompkins' Insurance and Wealth Management divisions operate through subsidiaries and make up roughly 10% and 5% of sales respectively. Its subsidiary Tompkins Insurance Agencies Inc. offers property and casualty insurance services and employee benefit consulting services. The firm's trust company Tompkins Financial Advisors offers trust financial planning and wealth management services.

Geographic Reach

Between its four bank subsidiaries the Tompkins operates 66 branches in the US with more than two thirds of the branches in New York and around 20 branches in Pennsylvania.

Sales and Marketing

The company's banks target individual and small business customers for its financial services. Tompkins spent $4.94 million on its marketing expenses in 2014 or slightly less than the $4.96 million spent in 2013 but 22% more than what it spent in 2012.

Financial Performance

Tompkin's revenue rose for a second straight year growing by less than 1% to $255.26 million in 2014 most thanks to growth in the company's non-interest fee income from an increase in deposit account service charges card services income and growth in personal health and benefit insurance sales.

The company's net income ended higher for a second year as well thanks to higher revenue lower interest expense on deposits and lower provisions for loan losses as its loan portfolio's credit improved. Operations provided $77.36 million or 8% less cash than in 2013 mostly because in 2013 the company was able to use more funds from its prepaid accounts to pay for FDIC insurance.

Strategy

The company's strategy for growth includes making inroads into new markets and new business areas through acquisitions. It entered the southeastern Pennsylvania market with its 2012 acquisition of VIST Financial parent of VIST Bank (which continues to operate under a separate charter under existing management) VIST Insurance and VIST Capital Management. The deal added about 20 branches to Tompkins' network along with $889 million in new loan business and $1.2 billion in new deposits.

Mergers and Acquisitions

In August 2012 Tompkins Financial purchased VIST Financial Corp in an all stock transaction valued at $86 million. The deal added all 20 VIST Bank branches (and VIST Bank's assets) in Pennsylvania the VIST Capital Management business and the VIST Insurance business which doubled Tompkin's annual insurance revenue; all of which were folded into Tompkins' banking operations Tompkins Financial Advisors and Tompkins Insurance Agencies operations respectively.

EXECUTIVES

EVP President and CEO VIST Bank, Robert D. (Bob) Davis, age 69
Director; Vice Chairman Tompkins Insurance Agencies, James R. Hardie, age 73
Executive Vice President Chief Operations Officer Chief Financial Officer & Treasurer, Francis M. Fetsko, age 52, $281,877 total compensation
President CEO and Director, Stephen S. Romaine, age 53, $474,898 total compensation
Executive Vice President, David S. Boyce, age 50, $185,000 total compensation
Executive Vice-President, Gregory J. Hartz, age 56, $237,107 total compensation
Executive Vice-President, Gerald J. Klein, age 58, $238,369 total compensation
Executive Vice President; President & COO of VIST Bank, Scott L. Gruber, age 61
EVP Corporate Marketing, Susan M. Valenti
SVP - Chief Technology Officer, Bradley G. James
Vice President Operations, Sharon Beebe
Senior Vice President Senior Commercial Loan Officer, John Kraus
Vice President Information Technology Services, Bill Steinmetz

Executive Vice President Director of Human Resources, Rosemary Hyland
Assistant Vice President Residential Lending, Timothy Thomas
Vice President of Financial Reporting, Shelly Fetterly-Bush
Senior Vice President Corporate Risk Manager, Greg Smith
Assistant Vice President Officer Branch Manager, Deborah Hoover
Vice President, Christine Allen
Vice President Telecommunications, Chuck Brown
Vice President, Nancy Phayre
Assistant Vice President Telecommunicati, Charles Brown
Vice President Architecture, Tracy Vanderzee
Assistant Vice President Commercial Banking, Jason Moore
Assistant Vice President Residential Mortgage Lending, Judy Malys
Assistant Vice President and Treasury Manager, Lisa Zazo
Senior Vice President, Brian Bisaccio
Assistant Vice President, Rebecca Polanco
Senior Vice President, Joseph Butto
Vice President Commercial Lending, Heather Moore
Senior Vice President Commercial Banking RM, Robert Mazzei
Senior Vice President Regional Lending Manager, James Whitton
Assistant Vice President Commercial Services Officer, Bob Massino
Vice President, Greg May
Vice President Finance, Michael Bozuhoski
Chairman Tompkins Financial Corporation and Tompkins Trust Company, James J. Byrnes, age 74
Vice Chairman, James W. (Jim) Fulmer, age 65
Auditors: KPMG LLP

LOCATIONS

HQ: Tompkins Financial Corp
The Commons, P.O. Box 460, Ithaca, NY 14851
Phone: 888 503-5753
Web: www.tompkinsfinancial.com

PRODUCTS/OPERATIONS

2016 Sales

	$ mil.	% of total
Interest		
Loans	169	63
Available-for-sale securities	27	10
Held-to-maturity securities	3	1
Federal Home Loan Bank stock and Federal Reserve Bank stock	1	1
Trading securities	0	-
Due from banks		
Non-interest		
Insurance commissions & fees	29	11
Investment services	15	6
Service charges on deposit accounts	8	3
Card services income	8	3
Mark-to-market gain on liabilities held at fair value	0	-
Net gain on securities transactions	0	-
Other	6	2
Mark-to-market loss on trading securities	(0.2)	-
Total	271	100

2016 Sales

% of total	$mil.
Banking	84
Insurance	11
Wealth Management	5
Others	-
Total	100

COMPETITORS

Bank of America	Community Bank System
Chemung Financial	Elmira Savings Bank
Citigroup	HSBC USA
Citizens Financial Group	JPMorgan Chase
	M&T Bank

Income Statement

FYE: December 31

	ASSETS ($ mil.)	NET INCOME ($ mil.)	INCOME AS % OF ASSETS	EMPLOYEES
12/16	6,236	59	1.0%	1,046
12/15	5,690	58	1.0%	1,038
12/14	5,269	52	1.0%	1,037
12/13	5,003	50	1.0%	989
12/12	4,837	31	0.6%	939
Annual Growth	6.6%	17.4%	—	2.7%

2016 Year-End Financials

Debt ratio: 0.86%	No. of shares (mil.): 15
Return on equity: 11.13%	Dividends
Cash ($ mil.): 63	Yield: 0.0%
Current ratio: —	Payout: 45.2%
Long-term debt ($ mil.): —	Market value ($ mil.): 1,423

	STOCK PRICE ($) FY Close	P/E High/Low		PER SHARE ($) Earnings	Dividends	Book Value
12/16	94.54	24	13	3.91	1.77	36.40
12/15	56.16	16	13	3.87	1.70	34.57
12/14	55.30	16	13	3.48	1.62	32.94
12/13	51.39	15	11	3.46	1.54	31.10
12/12	39.64	17	15	2.43	1.46	30.71
Annual Growth	24.3%	—	—	12.6%	4.9%	4.3%

Torchmark Corp

Torchmark aims to be a beacon in the world of insurance. The holding company for a family of financial firms its member companies specialize in lower-end individual life insurance and supplemental health insurance. Torchmark subsidiaries which include flagship Liberty National Life offer whole and term life insurance supplemental health insurance accidental death insurance Medicare supplements and long-term care health policies for the elderly. Its American Income Life subsidiary sells life insurance policies to labor union and credit union members in the US Canada and New Zealand. Torchmark sells its products through direct marketing as well as through a network of exclusive and independent agents.

Operations

Torchmark operates in four segments — Life Health Annuity and Investment. The Life segment offers products including traditional and interest-sensitive whole life coverage as well as term life insurance. The Health segment's offerings include Medicare Supplement cancer accident long-term care and limited-benefit hospital and surgery coverage. The Annuity segment has provided fixed-benefit contracts but Torchmark is increasingly focused on protection-oriented life and health policies so it no longer markets annuities. Finally the Investment segment manages the group's capital resources.

Targeting middle-income citizens Torchmark's Liberty National Life provides life and supplemental health policies primarily in the southeastern US. Torchmark's United American Insurance subsidiary writes supplemental health coverage and Medicare supplemental insurance. A smaller subsidiary Globe Life and Accident offers life insurance and supplemental health products directly to consumers through print online and television ads.

The Life business is the company's largest segment and delivers more than 50% of revenue; it has more than $175 million dollars of life insurance in force. The second-largest segment is Health which delivers about 25% of revenue.

Geographic Reach

Torchmark's operations are based in Oklahoma Ohio and Texas although its services extend to customers across the US and in New Zealand and Canada.

Sales and Marketing

Torchmark markets its products through a variety of channels including direct mail insert media inbound calls television magazines and the internet.Through Family Heritage Life the group even has agents that go door-to-door in non-urban markets.

The company's main Liberty National Life subsidiary uses a direct sales force to sell its products. The subsidiary has about 1750 producing agents and about 65 branch offices across the US. It also utilizes captive and independent agents.

Direct response advertising costs charged to earnings totaled $9 million in 2016 down from $10 million in 2015. Capitalized advertising costs totaled $1.25 billion in 2016 versus $1.21 billion in 2015.

Financial Performance

Torchmark's revenue and net income have remained relatively flat over the past several years. In 2016 revenue rose 4% to $3.9 billion thanks to increases in both life and health insurance premiums as well as in net investment income. These gains were partially offset by a drop in other income and higher realized investment losses.

Net income also rose 4% that year reaching $549.8 million. Although operating expenses increased overall the higher revenue made up the difference.

Cash flow has risen for the past couple of years; in 2016 it rose 25% to $1.4 billion. This was largely due to net cash provided from discontinued operations.

Strategy

Torchmark's insurance strategy is centered on selling life and health products to middle-income households which it sees as an underserved market. In recent years the company has especially been focused on young families with children. It has also been focused on expanding its distribution channels. For example American Income Life has expanded its reach beyond unions (which have declined in membership) to offer products and services to new customers through referrals and other sources; it hopes to expand its team of agents (currently at some 6900) to 10000 within five years.

Additionally the firm has invested in technology updates boosting its underwriting capabilities with analytics and modernizing its back-office infrastructure.

In early 2016 the company sold its Medicare Part D segment due to several factors including declining margins increased risks higher drug costs and growing compliance expenses. That sale has helped Torchmark focus on its core life and health insurance operations as well as providing the company with capital to invest.

Torchmark's investment segment invests almost exclusively in long-range fixed maturities that meet certain quality and yield objectives. Unlike many other life insurers Torchmark makes the bulk of its revenues from its premiums and relatively little (about 20%) from its investments. This allows it to ride out the economic downturns more smoothly while other life insurers take significant revenue hits when their investments fizzle.

HISTORY

It began as a scam plain and simple. In 1900 the Heralds of Liberty was founded as a fraternal organization — but its real reason for existence was to funnel money to its founders according to Frank Samford Torchmark's CEO from 1967 to 1985; Samford was also the great-grandson of the governor who signed the group's charter and the son of the state insurance commissioner who oversaw the Heralds of Liberty's rehabilitation into a real insurance company.

The Heralds offered a joint life distribution plan under which policyholders were divided by age; when a person died his or her beneficiary was paid along with the holder of the lowest-numbered insurance certificate in the class (if they were paid at all; the Heralds were not scrupulous about that). Postal authorities called this plan a lottery and it was illegal in many states. But the Heralds' fraternal order status allowed it to circumvent Alabama insurance laws until 1921 when its infractions could no longer be ignored.

The organization operated under state supervision until 1929 when it was recapitalized as stock company Liberty National. By 1934 despite the Depression the company was financially sound.

In 1944 Liberty National merged with funeral insurance company Brown-Service whose large sales force began selling Liberty National's policies. The added sales helped the company grow and make acquisitions from the 1950s through the 1970s. Even after it discontinued funeral insurance the company still paid out benefits. (As late as 1985 half of all Alabamans who died had the policies.)

Liberty National reorganized itself as a holding company in 1980 to accommodate the purchase of Globe Life And Accident. In 1981 it acquired Continental Investment Corp. which owned United Investors Life Insurance Waddell & Reed (financial services) and United American Insurance. In 1982 the holding company became Torchmark. Throughout its growth spurt it refrained from offering high-yield financial products and thus escaped the worst effects of the economic disruptions of the late 1980s. Its 1990 acquisition of Family Service Life Insurance put it back in the funeral insurance business (it exited again in 1995 and sold the unit in 1998).

Sales in the 1990s were affected by a decline in cash-value life insurance and Medicare supplements. Slack sales forced the company to stop having agents collect premiums personally and by 1996 all accounts were handled by mail.

In 1998 the company sought to sell its 28% stake in property insurer Vesta Insurance Group after that company became the target of numerous lawsuits. Torchmark was only able to reduce its stake to 24% on the open market but in 2000 Vesta bought out Torchmark's holdings.

Torchmark was haunted in 2000 by its own version of the undead — burial policies. An investigation by Alabama regulators was sparked by a Florida court order forcing the company to stop collecting premiums on old burial policies for which African-Americans had been charged higher premiums. In 2001 and 2002 Torchmark was hit by another dozen lawsuits including allegations of overcharging.

EXECUTIVES

Co-Chairman and Co-CEO, Larry M. Hutchison, age 63, $870,865 total compensation

Co-Chairman and Co-CEO, Gary L. Coleman, age 64, $870,865 total compensation

CEO American Income Life and Liberty National Life, Roger C. Smith, age 64, $594,846 total compensation

EVP and Chief Administrative Officer, Vern D. Herbel, age 59, $519,846 total compensation

EVP and CFO, Frank M. Svoboda, age 55, $499,692 total compensation

EVP and Chief Investment Officer, W. Michael Pressley, age 65, $499,692 total compensation

EVP and Chief Actuary, Ben W. Lutek, age 58

President LNL Agency Division, Steven J. (Steve) DiChiaro, age 50

SVP and General Counsel, R. Brian Mitchell, age 53

President and CEO Globe Life Direct Response, Bill E. Leavell, age 54

President and CEO FHL Agency Division, Kenneth J. (Ken) Matson, age 50

President United American Insurance and First United American Insurance, Michael C. Majors, age 55

EVP and CIO, James E. (Bo) McPartland, age 50

EVP and Chief Strategy Officer, J. Matthew Darden, age 46

President AIL Agency Division American Income, Steven K. Greer, age 44

Senior Vice President Facilities, Douglas Gockel

Auditors: Deloitte & Touche LLP

LOCATIONS

HQ: Torchmark Corp
3700 South Stonebridge Drive, McKinney, TX 75070
Phone: 972 569-4000
Web: www.torchmarkcorp.com

PRODUCTS/OPERATIONS

2016 Revenues

	$ mil.	% of total
Insurance		
Life	2,189	56
Health	947	24
Investment income	806	20
Other income	1	—
Realized investment loss	(10.6)	-
Total	**3,934**	**100**

Selected Subsidiaries

American Income Life Insurance Company
Family Heritage Life Insurance Company of America
First United American Life Insurance Company
Globe Life And Accident Insurance Company
Liberty National Life Insurance Company
United American Insurance Company

COMPETITORS

Aflac	Monumental Life
Allstate	Northwestern Mutual
Amalgamated Life	Penn Treaty
Gerber Life	Prudential
Guardian Life	State Farm
Lincoln Financial	Texas Life
Group	USAA
MassMutual	Unum Group
MetLife	

HISTORICAL FINANCIALS

Company Type: Public

Income Statement
FYE: December 31

	ASSETS ($ mil.)	NET INCOME ($ mil.)	INCOME AS % OF ASSETS	EMPLOYEES
12/16	21,436	549	2.6%	3,128
12/15	19,853	527	2.7%	3,115
12/14	20,214	542	2.7%	2,980
12/13	18,191	528	2.9%	2,890
12/12	18,776	529	2.8%	3,042
Annual Growth	**3.4%**	**1.0%**	**—**	**0.7%**

2016 Year-End Financials

Debt ratio: 5.30%
Return on equity: 12.72%
Cash ($ mil.): 76
Current ratio: —
Long-term debt ($ mil.): —

No. of shares (mil.): 118
Dividends
  Yield: 0.0%
  Payout: 12.3%
Market value ($ mil.): 8,706

	STOCK PRICE ($) FY Close	P/E High/Low	PER SHARE ($) Earnings	Dividends	Book Value
12/16	73.76	16 11	4.49	0.56	38.69
12/15	57.16	15 12	4.16	0.53	33.14
12/14	54.17	20 12	4.09	0.51	36.72
12/13	78.15	20 13	3.79	0.45	28.13
12/12	51.67	14 12	3.61	0.38	30.86
Annual Growth	**9.3%**	**— —**	**5.6%**	**9.9%**	**5.8%**

TowneBank

Auditors: Dixon Hughes Goodman LLP

LOCATIONS

HQ: TowneBank
5716 High Street, Portsmouth, VA 23703
Phone: 757 638-7500
Web: www.townebank.com

HISTORICAL FINANCIALS

Company Type: Public

Income Statement
FYE: December 31

	ASSETS ($ mil.)	NET INCOME ($ mil.)	INCOME AS % OF ASSETS	EMPLOYEES
12/16	7,973	67	0.8%	2,529
12/15	6,296	62	1.0%	1,903
12/14	4,982	42	0.8%	1,737
12/13	4,673	41	0.9%	1,741
12/12	4,405	37	0.9%	1,599
Annual Growth	**16.0%**	**15.4%**	**—**	**12.1%**

2016 Year-End Financials

Debt ratio: 0.40%
Return on equity: 7.11%
Cash ($ mil.): 136
Current ratio: —
Long-term debt ($ mil.): —

No. of shares (mil.): 62
Dividends
  Yield: 0.0%
  Payout: 43.2%
Market value ($ mil.): 2,078

	STOCK PRICE ($) FY Close	P/E High/Low	PER SHARE ($) Earnings	Dividends	Book Value
12/16	33.25	29 14	1.18	0.51	17.20
12/15	20.87	18 12	1.22	0.47	15.71
12/14	15.12	14 11	1.18	0.43	17.02
12/13	15.39	15 12	1.14	0.38	16.32
12/12	15.49	15 12	1.03	0.41	17.57
Annual Growth	**21.0%**	**— —**	**3.5%**	**5.9%**	**(0.5%)**

Toyota Motor Credit Corp.

Toyota Motor Credit (TMCC) is the US financing arm of Toyota Financial Services which is a subsidiary of Toyota Motor Corporation the world's largest carmaker. TMCC provides retail leasing retail and wholesale sales financing and other financial services to Toyota and Lexus dealers and their customers for the purchase of new and used cars and trucks. It offers similar services to Toyota industrial equipment dealers. TMCC which underwrites and services the finance contracts operates three regional customer service centers and some 30 dealer sales and service branches across the US and Puerto Rico.

Operations

TMCC organizes its business around two product categories: Finance and Insurance.

Its Finance segment which generates more than 90% of the company's total sales acquires a variety of retail finance products such as consumer and commercial installment sales contracts in the US and Puerto Rico as well as leasing contracts — either direct finance leases or operating leases from US vehicle or industrial equipment dealers. The segment also provides dealer financing (including wholesale financing revolving credit lines and working capital loans) and real estate financing for vehicle and industrial equipment dealers in the US and Puerto Rico.

The Insurance division operates through subsidiary Toyota Motor Insurance Services which underwrites and sells insurance products such as extended service coverage total loss protection and prepaid maintenance protection. It also provides marketing and claims administration services related to covering select risks of vehicle dealers and their customers in the US.

Broken down TMCC generated 67% of its total revenue from operating leases in fiscal 2015 (ended March) and another 20% from retail financing income. Its Insurance premium and contract revenue brought in 7% of total revenue while dealer financing revenue (4%) and investment income (2%) brought in the rest.

Geographic Reach

The California-based company serves dealers and their customers across the US. About 21% of TMCC's vehicle retail and lease contracts were based in California in fiscal 2015 while 10% were from Texas 8% were from New York and 6% came from New Jersey.

Financial Performance

TMCC has seen its revenues and profits trend downward for most of the past several years. However the company's revenue has been recovering since 2014.

TMCC's revenue inched up by more than 1% to $8.10 billion in fiscal 2015 (ended March) mostly as its Operating Lease business grew by 21% thanks to higher average outstanding earning asset balances as Toyota Motor Sales USA (the primary US distributor of Toyota Lexus and Scion vehicles) focused more on pushing lease subvention during the year. The company's Insurance business also grew thanks to higher premiums and contract revenues resulting from an increase in the average number of agreements in force during the year.

Higher revenue in fiscal 2015 allowed TMCC's profit to rebound sharply with net income jumping by 40% to $1.20 billion. Cash from operations declined by 23% to $3.77 billion as the company collected less in cash earnings after foreign exchange currency adjustments.

EXECUTIVES

Vice President Human Resources, Julia Wada
President and CEO; CFO, Michael R. (Mike) Groff, age 62
Auditors: PricewaterhouseCoopers LLP

LOCATIONS

HQ: Toyota Motor Credit Corp.
6565 Headquarters Drive, Plano, TX 75024
Phone: 469 486-9300
Web: www.toyotafinancial.com

PRODUCTS/OPERATIONS

2016 Sales

	$ mil.	% of total
Financing		
Operating leases	7,141	68
Retail	1,859	18
Dealer	403	4
Insurance premiums earned & contract revenues	719	7
Investment & other	164	1
Gain on sale of commercial finance business	197	2
Total	**10,483**	**100**

2016 Sales

	$ mil.	% of total
Financing revenues	9,403	90
Insurance earned premiums and contract revenues	719	7
Investment and other income net	164	1
Gain on sale of commercial finance business	197	2
Total	**10,483**	**100**

COMPETITORS

Ally Financial	Ford Motor Credit
American Honda Finance	GM Financial
AutoNation	Mercedes-Benz Credit
Capital One Auto Finance	Volkswagen Financial Services
Daimler Financial Services	Volvo Car Finance

HISTORICAL FINANCIALS

Company Type: Public

Income Statement

FYE: March 31

	REVENUE ($ mil.)	NET INCOME ($ mil.)	NET PROFIT MARGIN	EMPLOYEES
03/17	11,020	267	2.4%	3,185
03/16	10,483	932	8.9%	3,140
03/15	9,142	1,197	13.1%	3,251
03/14	8,099	857	10.6%	3,210
03/13	7,988	1,331	16.7%	3,210
Annual Growth	**8.4%**	**(33.1%)**	**—**	**(0.2%)**

2017 Year-End Financials

Debt ratio: 82.11%
Return on equity: 2.82%
Cash ($ mil.): 4,198
Current ratio: 0.14
Long-term debt ($ mil.): 71,601

No. of shares (mil.): 0
Dividends
Yield: —
Payout: —
Market value ($ mil.): —

TPG Specialty Lending Inc

Auditors: KPMG LLP

LOCATIONS

HQ: TPG Specialty Lending Inc
301 Commerce Street, Suite 3300, Fort Worth, TX 76102
Phone: 817 871-4000   **Fax:** 817 871-4001
Web: www.tpgspecialtylending.com

HISTORICAL FINANCIALS

Company Type: Public

Income Statement

FYE: December 31

	ASSETS ($ mil.)	NET INCOME ($ mil.)	INCOME AS % OF ASSETS	EMPLOYEES
12/16	1,675	107	6.4%	—
12/15	1,516	95	6.3%	—
12/14	1,303	104	8.0%	—
12/13	1,039	57	5.5%	—
12/12	833	28	3.4%	—
Annual Growth	**19.1%**	**39.9%**	**—**	**—**

2016 Year-End Financials

Debt ratio: 40.63%
Return on equity: 12.07%
Cash ($ mil.): 4
Current ratio: —
Long-term debt ($ mil.): —

No. of shares (mil.): 59
Dividends
Yield: 0.0%
Payout: 85.2%
Market value ($ mil.): 1,115

	STOCK PRICE ($) FY Close	P/E High/Low		PER SHARE ($) Earnings	Dividends	Book Value
12/16	18.68	10	8	1.83	1.56	15.95
12/15	16.22	16	14	1.18	1.56	15.15
12/14	16.82	14	9	1.68	1.53	15.53
Annual Growth	**2.7%**	**—**	**—**	**2.2%**	**0.5%**	**0.7%**

Tractor Supply Co.

Tractor Supply Company (TSC) does a whole lot more than its name might suggest. Besides providing agricultural machine parts TSC offers animal feed fencing power tools riding mowers work clothing and pet supplies as well as tools for gardening irrigation welding and towing. TSC offers both name-brand merchandise and its own crop of private-label goods. It operates about 1750 stores in some 49 US states under the Tractor Supply Company Del's Farm Supply and Hometown Pet banners. Stores are concentrated in rural areas and near large cities to cater to full- and part-time farmers ranchers and contractors. TSC also sells online.

Operations

The farm and ranch supplies retailer operates Tractor Supply Del's Feed & Farm Supply and Petsense stores. It also sells products online. Livestock and pet products account for more than 45% of sales.

Geographic Reach

TSC operates stores in 49 US states. Its largest market is Texas home to about 195 stores followed by Pennsylvania and North Carolina (about 90 each) Ohio and Tennessee (more than 85 each) Michigan (over 80) and Georgia and New York (upwards of 75 each). The company has distribution facilities in Arizona Georgia Indiana Kentucky Maryland Nebraska Texas and Washington.

Of its nearly 1750 stores some 1600 are Tractor Supply or Del's stores.

Sales and Marketing

TSC's products are sourced through both US and international vendors. It purchases its products from a group of roughly 850 vendors 300 of which supply 90% of TSC's products.

TSC's customers are home and landowners and pet and livestock owners located in rural areas and on the outskirts of major metropolitan areas. Its customers are often recreational farmers i.e. those that enjoy the outdoor lifestyle but are non-professionals but it also serves tradesmen and small businesses.

The company's advertising strategy is based on merchandise its website newspaper circulars direct mail and email and digital and social media.

Financial Performance

Tractor Supply Co.'s revenue has grown since 2010.

In FY2016 (ended December 2016) sales climbed 9% to $6.8 billion due to 107 net store openings the Petsense acquisition and a 1.6% increase in comparable store sales. Comparable sales were boosted by higher traffic and increased uptake in animal- and pet-related merchandise. The extra week in the financial year contributed 1.6 percentage points to growth. Sales were hampered by unpredictable weather and unseasonably warm conditions during the cold month.

Net income has broadly tracked revenue in recent years and in FY2016 ticked up 7% to $437 million. Lower margins and an increase in domestic transportation costs decreased profitability offset by lower fuel and import container costs.

Net cash provided by the operating activities increased to $639 million in FY2016 from $429 million the previous year.

Strategy

Having identified some 900 potential sites for Tractor Supply stores TSC is pumping up its store base at a rapid rate. The company opens about 100 net Tractor Supply stores a year: it opened 107 in FY2016 and has plans for another 100 in FY2017. In FY2016 TSC added a further 130-plus stores via the acquisition of Petsense take its total store count to nearly 1750; the company aims to open another 25-30 Petsense stores in 2017.

In addition TSC opened a new distribution center in Casa Grande Arizona in 2015 which supports the company's expansion in western US states.

Meanwhile TSC has stemmed the growth of Del's Farm Supply while working to refine its retail concept. With only about 25 Del's stores in the Pacific Northwest and Hawaii TSC opted not to add any new locations in recent years.

In 2015 the company announced the expansion of its Purina feed offering and its position as the first nationally authorized Purina feed retailer in the US. It began offering an extended assortment of select Purina brand feeds including Ultium horse feed Wind and Rain minerals and Honor Show Chow show feed in its stores nationwide.

The company has taken steps to improve its omni-channel capabilities relating to fulfillment options product information and site research. TSC has improved the site response time and added additional product offerings for vendor direct to customer drop shipments and optimized its site for mobile and tablet. It also opened two HomeTown Pet stores that year.

Mergers and Acquisitions

In 2016 Tractor Supply Company acquired Petsense and its 136 retail outlets for $116 million. Petsense is a small-box specialty pet supply retailer. TSC's two HomeTown Pet stores serving a similar market were rebranded as Petsense subsequently.

Company Background

TSC was founded in 1938.

EXECUTIVES

EVP Real Estate and Construction General Counsel and Corporate Secretary, Benjamin F. (Ben) Parrish, age 61, $522,615 total compensation
Senior Vice President Marketing, John Wendler
CEO, Gregory A. (Greg) Sandfort, age 62, $1,033,846 total compensation
President and Chief Merchandising Officer, Steve K. Barbarick, age 49, $607,885 total compensation

SVP and CIO, Robert D. Mills, age 44, $397,692 total compensation
SVP CFO and Treasurer, Kurt Barton
VP Logistics, Rich Wallace
Vice President Information Technology, George Argodale
Chairman, Cynthia T. Jamison, age 57
Auditors: Ernst & Young LLP

LOCATIONS

HQ: Tractor Supply Co.
5401 Virginia Way, Brentwood, TN 37027
Phone: 615 440-4000
Web: www.tractorsupply.com

2016 Stores

	No.
Texas	196
Pennsylvania	89
North Carolina	89
Ohio	87
Tennessee	87
Michigan	81
Georgia	79
New York	76
Kentucky	63
Florida	58
Virginia	54
Indiana	54
Alabama	52
Oklahoma	51
California	50
South Carolina	42
Louisiana	36
Arkansas	35
Mississippi	34
Arizona	32
West Virginia	27
New Mexico	27
Missouri	25
Washington	24
Maryland	21
New Hampshire	21
Kansas	20
Maine	19
Colorado	19
Massachusetts	19
Wisconsin	17
Connecticut	17
Nebraska	15
Utah	15
Illinois	14
New Jersey	13
North Dakota	13
Minnesota	10
Iowa	9
South Dakota	7
Vermont	7
Wyoming	7
Montana	6
Delaware	5
Idaho	4
Oregon	4
Rhode Island	4
Hawaii	2
Nevada	2
Total	**1,738**

PRODUCTS/OPERATIONS

2016 Sales

	% of total
Livestock and Pet	46
Hardware Tools Truck and Towing	22
Seasonal Gift and Toy Products	19
Clothing and Footwear	8
Agriculture	5
Total	**100**

PRODUCT CATEGORY
PRODUCT CATEGORY
Farm & Ranch
Poultry
Pets & Livestock
Lawn & Garden
Truck & Trailer
Hardware & Tools

Heating & Cooling
Outdoors
Home & Decor
Footwear
Clothing
Big & Tall
Plus Sizes
Gift Cards
BRANDS
4health (pet foods and supplies)
Bit & Bridle (apparel and footwear)
Blue Mountain (apparel)
C.E. Schmidt (apparel and footwear)
Countyline (livestock farm and ranch equipment)
Dumor (livestock and horse feed and supplies)
Equistages (horse feed)
Groundwork (lawn and garden supplies)
Huskee (outdoor power equipment)
JobSmart (tools)
Paws & Claws (pet foods and supplies)
Producer's Pride (livestock and horse feed and supplies)
Red Shed (gifts collectibles and outdoor furniture)
Redstone (heating products)
Retriever (pet foods and supplies)
Royal Wing (bird feed and supplies)
Traveller (truck and automotive products)
TSC Tractor Supply Co (trailers truck tool boxes and animal bedding)

COMPETITORS

Ace Hardware	Sears
Farm King	Southern States
Home Depot	Tennessee Farmers
Lowe's	Co-op
Menard	True Value
Miles Enterprises	Wal-Mart
Northern Tool	Wilbur-Ellis

HISTORICAL FINANCIALS

Company Type: Public

Income Statement

FYE: December 31

	REVENUE ($ mil.)	NET INCOME ($ mil.)	NET PROFIT MARGIN	EMPLOYEES
12/16	6,779	437	6.4%	26,000
12/15	6,226	410	6.6%	23,000
12/14	5,711	370	6.5%	21,100
12/13	5,164	328	6.4%	19,200
12/12	4,664	276	5.9%	17,300
Annual Growth	9.8%	12.1%	—	10.7%

2016 Year-End Financials

Debt ratio: 11.25%
Return on equity: 30.22%
Cash ($ mil.): 53
Current ratio: 1.95
Long-term debt ($ mil.): 289

No. of shares (mil.): 130
Dividends
  Yield: 0.0%
  Payout: 28.1%
Market value ($ mil.): 9,916

	STOCK PRICE ($) FY Close	P/E High/Low		PER SHARE ($) Earnings	Dividends	Book Value
12/16	75.81	29	19	3.27	0.92	11.11
12/15	85.67	32	25	3.00	0.76	10.38
12/14	77.92	29	21	2.66	0.61	9.48
12/13	75.54	56	28	2.32	0.49	8.93
12/12	87.47	53	36	1.90	0.36	7.37
Annual Growth	(3.5%)	—	—	14.5%	26.4%	10.8%

TRAMMO, INC.

Stockpiles of fertilizers liquefied petroleum gas (LPG) and petrochemicals are the "ammo" which international trader Trammo (formerly Transammonia) uses in its battle with competitors. The

company trades distributes and transports these commodities around the world. Trammo's fertilizer business includes ammonia phosphates and urea. Its Sea-3 subsidiary imports and distributes propane to residential commercial and industrial customers in the northeastern US and Florida. The Trammochem unit trades in petrochemicals specializing in aromatics and olefins. Its Trammo Gas trades LPG and propane as well as ethane butane and natural gas in the US.

Operations

The company operates three divisions: Chemicals Commodities and Gas. The Chemicals Division's annual sales volumes is about 5.6 million metric tons. It key products include aromatics olefins and oxygenates. The Commodities Division accounts for two thirds of the Trammo's sales volumes and more than half of its revenues; it's worldwide traded volume is 29.2 million metric tons a year. The Gas Division's business areas include LPG business Trammo Gas and Petrochemicals Ltd and Sea-3 Inc. Trammo's international traded ammonia volume is 3 million metric tons annually.

Sea-3 is the largest importer and distributor of liquefied propane in the Northeastern US. It also supplies propane to the western and central portions of Florida. It moves 200000 metric tons of product per year.

Trammochem merchandises and trades in petrochemicals around the world.

Trammo Gas markets and trades LPG (primarily propane) in the US. Trammo Gas International Inc. operates two gas carriers which transport LPG worldwide for third parties.

Geographic Reach

Trammo has expanded its reach into the global market establishing merchandising and trading offices in Singapore China and the United Arab Emirates. Those offices complement its other global operations in Africa Asia Europe the Middle East and North and South America (Argentina Brazil and Chile). It has major representative offices in Beijing Cairo Dubai and Shanghai.

Its Fertilizers and Commodities Division's regional hubs are in Zurich Tampa Dubai Shanghai and Singapore; the Ammonia Division has hubs in Tampa and Dubai. The Chemicals Division maintains regional hubs in Zurich Dubai Shanghai and Singapore; while the Gas Division maintains hubs in Houston Tampa and Newington (New Hampshire).

Trammo has about 30 offices worldwide.

Sales and Marketing

To bridge the gap between the production locations and consumers sites Trammo owns and operates a fleet of railcars dedicated to transporting of molten sulfur in across the US. The Commodities Division about 650 railcars to ship dry and liquid fertilizers sulfur sulfuric acid and ammonia.

Strategy

In late 2016 it was reported that Trammo would exit the petrochemicals trading market following a reorganization.

In 2015 the company's Ammonia Division and Fertilizers and Commodities Division merged into a new division — Commodities. The merger allows Trammo to increase operational synergies use its global infrastructure to provide a larger portfolio of products and to more clearly present itself as a single company with different products.

Trammo opened offices in Ivory Coast and Dar Es Salaam in 2014 to strengthens its presence in the emerging African market.

Company Background

In 2013 Transammonia changed its name to Trammo to more accurately represent the broad spectrum of products and services it provides.

In 2010 the company's bulk carriers division entered the commodity shipping business. TA Bulk

Carriers operates a fleet of 15 to 20 vessels which trade worldwide but focus on the handysize market (25000-35000 metric tons deadweight) in the Atlantic basin. In 2010 it transported about 2.9 million metric tons of cargo primarily fertilizers and grains.

Ronald Stanton founded the company in 1965 as an international ammonia trader. It branched into fertilizer merchandising and trading in 1967 LPG trading in 1978 and petrochemicals trading in 1987.

EXECUTIVES

EVP COO and CFO, Edward G. Weiner
CEO Chemicals Division, Ashok Kishore
President CEO Director and CEO Commodities Division, Brent Hart
SVP Global Risk Management, Oliver K. Stanton
Senior Vice President, Dudley Cox
Senior Vice President Finance and Treasury, James Benfield
Vice President And Controller, Robert Lovett
Vice President, David Herr
Senior Vice President And General Counsel, Louis Epstein
Vice President Of Human Resources, Pat Berry
Senior Vice President Ammonia Division, Bernard Rock
Vice President Finance and Treasury, Donald Madden
Vice President, Todd Matthes
Auditors: DELOITTE & TOUCHE LLP NEW YOR

LOCATIONS

HQ: TRAMMO, INC.
1 ROCKEFELLER PLZ FL 9, NEW YORK, NY 100202078
Phone: 212 223-3200
Web: WWW.TRAMMO.COM

PRODUCTS/OPERATIONS

Major SubsidiariesSea-3 (liquefied propane)Trammo Gas (LPG)Trammo Gas International Inc. (LPG transportation for third parties.Trammo Petroleum (crude oil and oil products)Trammochem (petrochemicals)Fertilizers and CommoditiesNitrogen BasedAnhydrous Ammo

COMPETITORS

BASF SE	HELM
CF Industries	Koch Industries Inc.
Cargill	Magellan Midstream
ConAgra	Yara
Dynegy	

HISTORICAL FINANCIALS

Company Type: Private

Income Statement

FYE: December 31

	REVENUE ($ mil.)	NET INCOME ($ mil.)	NET PROFIT MARGIN	EMPLOYEES
12/15	8,922	32	0.4%	350
12/14	11,266	31	0.3%	—
12/13	11,315	(11)	—	—
12/12	12,152	35	0.3%	—
Annual Growth	(9.8%)	(2.4%)	—	—

2015 Year-End Financials

Debt ratio: —
Return on equity: 0.40%
Cash ($ mil.): 215
Current ratio: 1.00
Long-term debt ($ mil.): —
Dividends
Yield: —
Payout: —
Market value ($ mil.): —

TravelCenters of America LLC

TravelCenters of America (TCA) is in the fuel food and relaxation business for the long haul. The company's network of more than 250 interstate highway travel centers in more than 43 US states and Ontario Canada is one of the largest of its kind in North America. Its TCA and Petro locations provide fuel fast-food and sit-down restaurants (Country Pride Buckhorn Family) convenience stores and lodging. With professional truck drivers as its main customers some outlets also offer "trucker-only" services such as laundry and shower facilities TV rooms and truck repair. TCA leases about 160 of its locations from Hospitality Properties Trust (HPT) its largest shareholder.

Operations

As part of its business TCA operates and franchises travel centers under two brands: TravelCenters of America with about 180 locations and Petro Stopping Centers (acquired in 2007) with more than 75 locations about 30 of which are company-operated. TCA also operates "RoadSquad" the largest nationwide emergency roadside service network with approximately 600 heavy-duty emergency vehicles.

While TCA offers food to fuel truck drivers and motorists about 65% of the company's revenue comes from the sale of fuel for vehicles. The rest comes from human food and other items sold in it stores.

The Travel Centers segment contributes about 85% of TCA's revenue. The Convenience Stores segment (about 15% of revenue) operates convenience stores with retail gasoline stations primarily under the Minit Mart brand name are not located at a travel center.

Geographic Reach

The company operates and franchises a total of 540 travel center standalone convenience store and standalone restaurant locations in the US and Canada.

Sales and Marketing

TCA caters to professional truck drivers and travelers who rely on gas stations and convenience stores while on the road. Customers include trucking fleets and their drivers independent truck drivers and motorists.

Financial Performance

TCA revenue has been decreasing over the past several years except for an increase in fiscal 2012. In fiscal 2016 TCA's revenues dropped by 5.8% compared to the prior fiscal period largely due to a decrease in fuel revenue. Nonfuel revenues for 2016 increased by 10.2% compared to 2015 primarily as a result of acquired locations.

The drop in revenue during fiscal 2016 led to TCA suffering a net loss of $2 million. TCA reported $27 million in net income for fiscal 2015.

In fiscal 2016 TCA's operating cash decreased by $25 million compared to the previous fiscal period.

Strategy

TCA is building its cross-country network of travel centers through acquisitions (by opportunistically buying up smaller competitors) and by opening new locations.In the past five years he company has acquired and developed 318 travel centers convenience stores and standalone restaurants. It has invested roughly $855 million to develop purchase and improve locations.

In 2016 the company opened a new travel center in Wilmington Illinois. In 2015 TCA opened a new TA Truck Service facility in Columbia South

Carolina and a Popeyes Louisiana Kitchens restaurant in Lincoln and Tuscaloosa Alabama and Coachella California.

With fuel accounting for such a large portion of its total sales TCA is vulnerable to wild swings in prices. (About 90% of TCA's historical fuel sales are diesel while 10% are gasoline. The company sells biodiesel at some locations.

Mergers and Acquisitions

In 2016 TCA acquired seventeen convenience stores located in Wisconsin. The company expects the convenience stores formerly known as Quality State Oil to be rebranded as Minit Mart convenience stores.

TCA acquired Quaker Steak & Lube casual dining restaurants and other assets in 2015 including existing restaurant operations restaurant franchise program and bottled sauces for retail sale business for $25 million. Quaker Steak & Lube had more than 50 locations most of them franchised in 16 states mostly in Pennsylvania and Ohio. TCA will convert some of its full service restaurants to the Quaker Steak & Lube brand and expand the number of franchises and the number of stand-alone company restaurants.

In 2015 the company also acquired five convenience stores in Illinois four in Kansas and Missouri 10 in Ohio and additional convenience stores in Kentucky.

EXECUTIVES

Marketing Vice President Director, Tom Liutkus
SVP Truck Service Marketing and Operations, Skip McGary
SVP Food Marketing and Operations, John Ponczoch
EVP Sales, Michael J. Lombardi, age 66, $339,000 total compensation
CEO, Andrew J. Rebholz, age 53, $300,000 total compensation
EVP and General Counsel, Mark R. Young, age 54, $300,000 total compensation
President and COO, Barry A. Richards, age 64, $300,000 total compensation
SVP Construction Maintenance and Environmental, Peter P. Ward
SVP Retail Marketing and Operations, Rodney Bresnahan
SVP and Chief Accounting Officer, William E. Myers
Vice President Of Marketing, Rick Pavia
Executive Vice President Marketing, Joseph Szima
Managing Director Board of Directors, Barry M. Portnoy, age 72
Auditors: RSM US LLP

LOCATIONS

HQ: TravelCenters of America LLC
24601 Center Ridge Road, Suite 200, Westlake, OH 44145-5639
Phone: 440 808-9100
Web: www.tatravelcenters.com

PRODUCTS/OPERATIONS

2016 Location

	No.
TravelCenters of America	178
Petro Stopping Centers	77
Total	**255**

2016 Sales

	$ mil.	% of total
Fuel	3,530	64
Non-fuel	1,963	36
Rent & royalties from franchisees	17	-
Total	**5,511**	**100**

2016 Sales

	$ mil.	% of total
Travel Centers	4,694	85
Convenience Stores	715	13
Corporate and Other	100	2
Total	**5,511**	**100**

COMPETITORS

Bowlin Travel Centers	Pilot Flying J
Chevron	Royal Dutch Shell
Exxon Mobil	Sapp Bros Travel
Love's Country Stores	Centers
Marathon Petroleum	Stuckey's

HISTORICAL FINANCIALS

Company Type: Public

Income Statement

FYE: December 31

	REVENUE ($ mil.)	NET INCOME ($ mil.)	NET PROFIT MARGIN	EMPLOYEES
12/16	5,511	(2)	—	25,204
12/15	5,850	27	0.5%	24,250
12/14	7,778	60	0.8%	22,330
12/13	7,944	31	0.4%	20,670
12/12	7,995	32	0.4%	17,750
Annual Growth	**(8.9%)**	—	—	**9.2%**

2016 Year-End Financials

Debt ratio: 42.21%
Return on equity: (-0.37%)
Cash ($ mil.): 61
Current ratio: 1.22
Long-term debt ($ mil.): 700

No. of shares (mil.): 39
Dividends
  Yield: —
  Payout: —
Market value ($ mil.): 281

	STOCK PRICE ($) FY Close	P/E High/Low		Earnings	PER SHARE ($) Dividends	Book Value
12/16	7.10	—	—	(0.05)	0.00	13.96
12/15	9.40	25	13	0.72	0.00	14.15
12/14	12.62	8	4	1.62	0.00	13.53
12/13	9.74	12	4	1.06	0.00	12.06
12/12	4.70	6	4	1.12	0.00	11.97
Annual Growth	**10.9%**			—	—	**3.9%**

Travelers Companies Inc (The)

Running a business is a risk The Travelers Companies will insure. While it does offer personal auto and homeowners insurance the company's largest segment is commercial property/casualty insurance to businesses big and small. It is one of the largest business insurers in the US providing commercial auto property workers' compensation marine and general and financial liability coverage to companies in North America (the largest percentage of business) and the UK. The company also offers surety and fidelity bonds as well as professional and management liability coverage for commercial operations.

Operations

Travelers operates in three segments — Business and International Insurance Personal Insurance and Bond & Specialty Insurance.

The Business and International segment (which accounts for more than 60% of net earned premiums) offers property/casualty insurance and related services to clients — primarily in the US as well as in Canada the UK Ireland and throughout other parts of the world as a corporate member of Lloyd's.

The Personal Insurance segment offers homeowners auto flood and umbrella policies. That segment which is growing by geographic expansion accounts for some 30% of the group's premiums.

The Bond & Specialty Insurance segment writes fidelity and surety general liability and property workers' compensation commercial automobile and commercial multi-peril lines. It accounts for about 10% of net earned premiums.

Travelers also offers reinsurance.

Geographic Reach

While the vast majority (about 95%) of Travelers' business is in the US the company does have a presence in the UK where it operates through two arms: Travelers Insurance Company and Travelers Syndicate Management within Lloyd's of London. The two businesses offer commercial property/casualty and risk management services. Travelers also has modest operations in Canada Brazil India China and Ireland. It's looking to expand in Latin America.

The company employs field claim management teams in 21 centers and 53 satellite and specialty-only offices in 45 states.

Sales and Marketing

Travelers' customers include commercial businesses government agencies associations and individuals.

The company's offerings are distributed through independent agents and brokers across the US. In business and international some 11000 agents are supported by three customer service centers and about 120 field offices. International also writes business abroad where its products are distributed through Lloyd's wholesale and retail brokers.

Personal products are distributed through some 10900 independent agents employee and affinity groups and direct marketing. Meanwhile the Bond & Specialty Insurance segment distributes products through some 5800 independent agents and brokers.

Financial Performance

Travelers' revenues have maintained a slow-but-steady growth rate in recent years — a sign that the company has spread itself smoothly across industries and took no significant hits to its premiums. In 2016 revenue rose 3% to $27.6 billion as premiums net realized investment gains and other revenues grew.

Net income rose sharply in 2013 but has been slipping since then. It dropped 12% to $3 billion in 2016 primarily due to an increase in catastrophe losses and claim adjustment expenses. Cash flow from operations increased 22% to $4.2 billion that year as a result of positive adjustments to such items as deferred acquisition costs and reinsurance recoverables.

Strategy

Travelers targets growth in operating return on equity over time in the mid-teens with the notion that economic cycles weather patterns and other factors can impact its business from year to year. The company follows disciplined underwriting and investment strategies to help it stay immune to market fluctuations and lingering depressed interest rates.

The firm also follows a disciplined acquisition strategy seeking opportunities that will help it expand into new geographic markets or build on its existing product portfolio. Although Travelers is first and foremost a US-based insurer it has recently made purchases that have expanded its operations in Canada the UK and Brazil as well as providing it with entry into Colombia's market.

Another key strategy for Travelers is to innovate to introduce new types of coverage and improve the way it conducts business. It has its eye on technology from data and analytics to digital sales (as evidenced by its 2017 acquisition of UK-based Simply Business). In 2017 the firm introduced ZoneCheck an online tool to help contractors identify job site areas that could be affected by the vibrations caused by heavy equipment. This first-of-its-kind offering follows a long thread of new types of coverage the company has introduced. Also that year Travelers released the IntelliDrive smartphone app a consumer-oriented tool to promote safe driving and potentially lower premiums.

Mergers and Acquisitions

Travelers Companies acquired Simply Business a UK-based online business insurance broker for $490 million in 2017. Simply Business offers small business coverage; the acquisition helps Travelers expand its digital channels in the UK and beyond.

In 2015 the company acquired a majority of the property/casualty business of its J. Malucelli joint venture in Brazil. That unit focuses on property construction general liability and financial insurance.

HISTORY

St. Paul Minnesota was a boomtown in 1852 thanks to traffic on the Mississippi. Settlers knew fire insurance was a must in their wooden town but there were no local insurers. Buying policies from eastern companies and getting claims processed was difficult — especially in the winter when river traffic stopped.

In 1853 a group of local investors led by George and John Farrington and Alexander Wilkin formed St. Paul Mutual Insurance a mixed stock and mutual company (mutual members shared in the firm's profits and losses while stockholders could benefit by selling if the company's value rose). St. Paul Mutual sold its first policy the following year.

The company changed its name in 1865 to St. Paul Fire and Marine Insurance stopped offering mutual policies and expanded throughout the Midwest. Claims from the Chicago Fire in 1871 nearly sank the company which assessed its shareholders $15 for each share of stock but prompt and full payment of claims resulted in more business. By the turn of the century St. Paul Fire and Marine was operating nationwide.

Although the company was hard hit by shipping losses in WWI it continued expanding joining other US insurers in the American Foreign Insurance Association to market insurance in Europe.

In 1926 St. Paul Fire and Marine organized its first subsidiary St. Paul Mercury Indemnity to write liability insurance policies. Other additions included coverage for automobiles aircraft burglary and robbery and in 1940 turkey farming.

During WWII St. Paul Fire and Marine joined the War Damage Corp. a government-financed consortium that paid claims for war damage. The St. Paul Companies was formed in 1968 as the umbrella organization for the various subsidiaries and the firm grew through purchases.

Lines of business blossomed during the 1970s including life and title insurance leasing a mail-order consumer finance company oil and gas and real estate. Many of these were sold during the 1980s but one The John Nuveen Co. (1974) became the nucleus of St. Paul's financial services operations.

EXECUTIVES

EVP and Chief Administrative Officer, Andy F. Bessette, age 64
President and COO, Brian W. MacLean, age 64, $962,548 total compensation
Vice Chairman and CFO, Jay S. Benet, age 65, $1,000,000 total compensation

EVP and Chief Human Resources Officer, John P. Clifford, age 61

EVP Strategic Development and Corporate Treasurer, Maria Olivo, age 52

EVP and General Counsel, Kenneth F. (Ken) Spence, age 62

EVP Marketing and Communications, Lisa M. Caputo, age 53

EVP Enterprise Risk Management, Fred R. Donner, age 60

Vice Chairman Chief Legal Officer and EVP Financial Professional and International Insurance, Alan D. Schnitzer, age 52, $1,000,000 total compensation

EVP Field Management and Distribution, Patrick J. Kinney

EVP Middle Market, Michael F. Klein

EVP Public Policy; President The Travelers Institute, Joan Kois Woodward

EVP; President Bond and Specialty Insurance, Thomas M. (Tom) Kunkel

EVP; President Business Insurance, Greg C Toczydlowski

EVP; President International, Kevin C. Smith

EVP and CIO, Madelyn Lankton

EVP Claim Services and Specialty Liability, Robert C. (Bob) Brody

EVP and Chief Underwriting Officer, Marlyss J. Gage

EVP and Chief Risk Officer, Bruce R. Jones

EVP President National Accounts and First Party, William C Malugen

EVP and President Small Commercial, Behram M. Dinshaw

EVP and President Middle Market, Scott F. Higgins

EVP Management Liability, Jeffrey P. (Jeff) Klenk

Agribusiness Regional Vice President, Kevin Gilronan

Second Vice President of Human Resources, Donna Grici

Claim Center Vice President, Claude Howard

Vice President Platform Office, William Devine

Second Vice President Strategic Sourcing, Sarah Pascual

Regional Vice President, Mark Boragno

Assistant Vice President Financial Controls Accounting Operations, Paul Munson

Vice President, Kevin Cahill

Vice President Select Product Management, Jaclyn Gulbrandsen

Vice President, Robert Carroll

Second Vice President Corporate Audit, Debra Barlow

Vice President, Richard Smith

Vice President and Lead Actuary Ocean Marine, Steve Finkelstein

Regional Vice President, Steven Ringler

Vice President Direct, Teri Deehan

Agribusiness Regional Vice Presidentthe Travelers Companies, Carl Miller

Second Vice President Information Systems, Edward Finkle

2VP Complex Claim Specialist, Milena Ivanis

Regional Vice President Select Group, Sean Ramalho

2Vp And Actuary, Christina Rosenzweig

Regional Vice President, Doug Dooren

Vice President, John Komidar

Vice President Finance, Jeffrey Longo

Executive Vice President Sales and Marketing, Gary Ross

2Vp Of Underwriting, Yllon Herron

Vice President Pm1 Central Southeast Region, Joseph Meisinger

Second Vice President, Richard Prior

2Vp Information Technology Operations, Bryant H Lewis

Underwriting Vice President, Rebecca Glenn

2VP Human Resources, Lorrie Higgins

Vice President, Ken Chapman

Vice President Strategy, Stewart Murchie

Vice President Operations and Systems, Steve Howard

Division President, Maureen Bass

Second Vice President Bond And Financial Products, Jan Betor

Vice President Chief Corporate Actuary, Renee Davis

Regional Vice President, Michael Verdin

Vice President Chief Underwriting Office, Robin Udhwan

Rvp Select Accounts, Lisa Pechan

Second Vice President, Mary Minor

Vice President of Technical Services, Mike Johnson

2Vp Personal Insurance Research, Keith Holler

Second Vice President, Rick Gross

Vice President, Brien Bialaski

Second Vice President Claim General Liability Prod, Rebecca Bowers

Vice President Enterprise Digital Marketing, John Bell

Regional President Southern Region, Furtick Henry

Regional Vice President National Property, Ben Leyland

Regional Vice President, Terry Dinnigan

Vice President Government Relations, Michele Balady

Vice President Finance and Investment, Robert Nelson

Second Vice President General Liability, Donald Nichols

Senior Vice President, Scott Belden

ARM Northwest Region Vice President, Ed Griffiths

Senior Vice President And General Counsel, Rene Hernandez

Rvp, Peggy Chang

Field Product Line Manager 2VP Auto Claims, Trevor Engels

Vice President, Elizabeth Napoli

2VP of Digital Marketing, Rick Heffernan

Vice President Marketing International, Mark Wright

2Vp, Carla Schirm

2Vp And Actuary, Dan Carr

Vice President Human Resources, Greg Landmark

Second Vice President, Jamie Hill

Vice President, Jennifer Lee

Vice President, Kim Kennedy-Gillette

Regional Vice President, Linda Petrillo

Second Vice President, Neeraj Juneja

Central Zone Vice President Travelers Excess Casualty, John Tsourmas

Vice President Claim Finance, John Laverty

Assistant Vice President Regional Manager Alberta Region, Jan Rasilainen

Vice President and CUO Residential Surety, Howard Friedman

Senior Vice President and Chief Financial Officer Personal Insurance, Dan Frey

Vice President, Subramaniam Kumar

2nd Vice President Corporate Procurement Strategic Sourcing Team Infrastructure, Brett Severson

2nd Vice President, Steve Piper

Regional Vice President, Toby Tiffany

Second Vice President Global Services, Shawn Lichacz

Regional President, Carrie Cheshier

Regional Vice President, Tad Cluff

Vice President and Group General Counsel Legal Shared Services, Jeff Slack

Regional Vice President Southern Region Select Accounts, Colleen Perlmutter

2VP Renewable Energy Practice, Eileen Kauffman

2VP Enterprise Customer Experience, Jason Galvin

Vice Chairman and Chief Investment Officer, William H. (Bill) Heyman, age 69

Vice Chairman and Chief Legal Officer, Avrohom J. Kess

Executive Board Member, Sue McKinney

Board Member, Alexis Cruz

Auditors: KPMG LLP

LOCATIONS

HQ: Travelers Companies Inc (The)
   485 Lexington Avenue, New York, NY 10017
Phone: 917 778-6000
Web: www.travelers.com

2016 Revenues

	$ mil.	% of total
US	25,904	94
Canada	1,154	4
Other countries	567	2
Total	**27,625**	**100**

PRODUCTS/OPERATIONS

2016 Revenues

	$ mil.	% of total
Premiums	24,534	89
Net investment income	2,302	8
Fee income	458	2
Investment gains	68	0
Other revenues	263	1
Total	**27,625**	**100**

2016 revenue

	$ mil.	% of total
Business and International Insurance	17,001	62
Bond & Specialty Insurance	2,318	8
Personal Insurance	8,227	30
Other	79	-
Total	**27,625**	**100**

List of Items

List of Items
Business
Commercial Automobile
Commercial Multi-Peril
Commercial Property
General Liability
Workers' Compensation
Individual
Affinity Auto and Home Program
Auto Insurance
Boat and Yacht Insurance
Condo Insurance
Flood Insurance
Homeowners Insurance
Identity Fraud Protection
Renters Insurance
Umbrella Insurance
Valuable Items Coverage
Wedding and Private Events Insurance

Selected Subsidiaries and Divisions

J. Malucelli Participacoes em Seguros e Resseguros S.A. (49.5% Brazil)
St. Paul Fire and Marine Insurance Company
Travelers Property Casualty Corp.
   The Standard Fire Insurance Company
   Travelers Casualty and Surety Company
   Travelers Casualty and Surety Company of America
   The Travelers Indemnity Company
   First Floridian Auto and Home Insurance Company
   First Trenton Indemnity Company (Travelers of New Jersey)
   The Premier Insurance Co. of Massachusetts
Travelers Insurance Company Limited (UK)
Travelers Syndicate Management Limited (UK)

COMPETITORS

AIG	Chubb Limited
AXA	Liberty Mutual Agency
Allianz	Markel
Allstate	Nationwide
American Financial Group	The Hartford
	W. R. Berkley
CNA Financial	Zurich Insurance Group

Company Type: Public

Income Statement

FYE: December 31

	ASSETS ($ mil.)	NET INCOME ($ mil.)	INCOME AS % OF ASSETS	EMPLOYEES
12/17	103,483	2,056	2.0%	30,800
12/16	100,245	3,014	3.0%	30,900
12/15	100,184	3,439	3.4%	30,900
12/14	103,078	3,692	3.6%	30,200
12/13	103,812	3,673	3.5%	30,800
Annual Growth	(0.1%)	(13.5%)	—	0.0%

2017 Year-End Financials

Debt ratio: 6.25%	No. of shares (mil.): 271
Return on equity: 8.76%	Dividends
Cash ($ mil.): 344	Yield: 0.0%
Current ratio: —	Payout: 38.6%
Long-term debt ($ mil.): —	Market value ($ mil.): 36,813

	STOCK PRICE ($) FY Close	P/E High/Low		PER SHARE ($) Earnings	Dividends	Book Value
12/17	135.64	18	16	7.33	2.83	87.44
12/16	122.42	12	10	10.28	2.62	83.05
12/15	112.86	11	9	10.88	2.38	79.75
12/14	105.85	10	7	10.70	2.15	77.08
12/13	90.54	9	7	9.74	1.96	70.14
Annual Growth	10.6%	—	—	(6.9%)	9.6%	5.7%

TreeHouse Foods Inc

TreeHouse Foods is the nation's #1 manufacturer of non-dairy powdered creamer sold under the Cremora brand and pickles (Farman's Nalley's Peter Piper and Steinfeld). The company also makes private-label soups salad dressings and Mexican sauces drink mixes hot cereals macaroni and cheese skillet dinners and jams. TreeHouse makes private-label products for foodservice distributors and restaurant chains as well as for supermarkets and mass merchandisers — the company's largest market that also buys its own brands. TreeHouse also boasts co-pack business and industrial customers. In a strong move to expand its product portfolio TreeHouse in early 2016 paid $2.7 billion to acquire ConAgra Foods' private brands operations.

Operations

TreeHouse's product categories include beverages salad dressings snacks beverage enhancers pickles sauces soup and infant feeding cereals dry dinners jams and other products. It also offers natural organic and preservative-free ingredients in many categories.

The North American Retail Grocery segment accounts for more than 80% of the company's sales. Food Away From Home and Industrial and Export each represent almost 10%. The snacks nuts category is TreeHouse's biggest product line generating more than 20% of revenue.

Geographic Reach

Headquartered in Oak Brook Illinois TreeHouse has offices in Green Bay Wisconsin; Omaha Nebraska; Downers Grove Illinois; St. Louis Missouri; Pittsburgh Pennsylvania; St. Paul Minnesota; and Winona Ontario Canada. TreeHouse rings up more than 85% of its sales in the US and Canada.

Sales and Marketing

TreeHouse markets its products to retailers such as supermarkets mass merchandisers and specialty retailers and also to the foodservice industry including foodservice distributors and national restaurant operators.

Retail giant Wal-Mart Stores is TreeHouse's largest customer accounting for about 20% of its sales each year.

Financial Performance

Due to its recent milestone acquisition of ConAgra Foods' private brands operations TreeHouse saw its revenues almost double from $3.2 billion in 2015 to $6.2 billion in 2016. The historic growth was partially offset by an unfavorable pricing mix and unfavorable foreign exchange translations.

TreeHouse suffered a net loss of $128 million in 2016 largely due to a 120% surge in selling and distribution expenses associated with its private brands acquisition. On the other hand operating cash flow surged from $285 million in 2015 to $489 million in 2016 mainly due to an influx in cash stemming from the acquisition.

Strategy

The company focuses on expanding partnerships with retailers; driving growth and profitability from its existing product portfolio; leveraging cross-selling opportunities across customers sales channels and geographies; and growing through acquisitions.

TreeHouse has also grown by strengthening ties with retail grocers who are demanding private-label food products as cash-strapped consumers seek goods with equivalent quality at a lower price. To maintain momentum the food maker focuses on the most-purchased categories of private-label products typically canned soup salad dressings powdered creamer and pickles.

Taking this strategy even further TreeHouse in early 2016 paid $2.7 billion to acquire ConAgra Foods' private brands operations. The milestone deal created TreeHouse Private Brands and expanded TreeHouse's presence in the private label dry and refrigerated grocery market specifically refrigerated and shelf stable products in the bars bakery cereal condiments pasta and snacks categories.

HISTORY

Dean Foods combined the businesses of its specialty foods group and its foodservice salad-dressing business in 2005 in order to create publicly traded TreeHouse Foods.

In 2006 the company it purchased pickle-maker Oxford Foods. It paid $275 million for the private-label soup and baby food (Nature's Goodness) businesses of Del Monte Foods. The following year it acquired San Antonio Farms a private-label Mexican sauce maker for about $89 million in cash. That year it also purchased DeGraffenreid a processor and distributor of pickles and related products for the foodservice industry from Bell-Carter Foods for $10.8 million. Strengthening its Canadian footprint in 2007 the company acquired Ontario-based E.D. Smith & Sons a manufacturer of branded sauces jellies jams and pie fillings for $220 million in cash plus the assumption of $100 million in debt.

TreeHouse also bought Sturm Foods a maker of private-label hot cereal and powdered soft drink mixes from HM Capital Partners for $660 million in 2010. The move strengthened TreeHouse's private-label operations as well as its packaging mixing and flavoring capabilities. Extending its reach in shelf-stable foods TreeHouse bought out S.T. Specialty Foods from Windjammer Capital Investors in an all-cash deal valued at about $180 million. S.T. Specialty Foods primarily makes private-label macaroni and cheese and skillet dinners mainstream staples of the dine-at-home

The company bought Naturally Fresh a privately-owned maker of refrigerated dressings sauces dips and marinades in 2012 for $25 million. The deal took TreeHouse from the shelf-stable grocery aisle to the refrigerated produce section providing a premium presence. In 2012 TreeHouse acquired the assets of the Aseptic Cheese and Pudding business from Associated Milk Producers Inc. The business sells products to foodservice and retail customers and strengthened the TreeHouse's existing Bay Valley Foods aseptic operation.

EXECUTIVES

Chairman President and CEO, Sam K. Reed, age 71, $1,056,250 total compensation
EVP General Counsel and Chief Administrative Officer, Thomas E. O'Neill, age 62, $533,167 total compensation
EVP and CFO, Matthew J. Foulston, age 53, $45,672 total compensation
SVP and Chief Strategy Officer, Rachel R. Bishop, age 43, $439,333 total compensation
Vice President and Assistant General Counsel, Jo Osborn
Vice President Human Resources, Lori Roberts
Auditors: Deloitte & Touche LLP

LOCATIONS

HQ: TreeHouse Foods Inc
2021 Spring Road, Suite 600, Oak Brook, IL 60523
Phone: 708 483-1300
Web: www.treehousefoods.com

2016 Sales

	% of total
North America	91
Outside North America	9
Total	**100**

PRODUCTS/OPERATIONS

2016 Sales

	$ mil.	% of total
North American Retail Grocery	5,092	76
Food Away From Home	546	12
Industrial & Export	545	12
Unallocated	(9.9)	-
Total	**6,175**	**100**

2016 Sales

	$ mil.	% of total
Snacks	1,334	22
Retail bakery	662	11
Cookies and crackers	607	10
Cereals	551	9
Pasta and dry dinners	543	9
Beverages	492	8
Salad dressings	376	6
Soup and infant feeding	372	6
Sauces	336	5
Pickles	318	5
Beverage enhancers	313	5
Jams	107	2
Aseptic products	101	1
Other products	56	1
Total	**6,175**	**100**

Selected Products & Brands

Food Away From Home (foodservice)
  Saucemaker
  Schwartz
Jams & jellies
  E.D. Smith
  Habitant
Liquid egg substitute
  Second Nature
Non-dairy creamer
  Cremora
Pickles
  Farman's
  Nalley's
  Peter Piper
  Steinfeld
Refrigerated
  Mocha Mix

Salad dressings sauces & marinades
  Private label
Sauces & syrups
  Bennett's
  Hoffman House
  Roddenberry's Northwoods
  San Antonio Farms
Soups broths & gravies
  Private label

COMPETITORS

B&G Foods	Kellogg
Campbell Soup	Lancaster Colony
ConAgra	Marzetti
Cott	McCormick & Company
Dean Foods	Mondelez International
Farmer Bros.	Newman's Own
Flowers Foods	Pinnacle Foods Inc
General Mills	Post Holdings
Goya	Reser's Fine Foods
Hain Celestial	Smucker
Heinz	Snyder's-Lance
J & J Snack Foods	

HISTORICAL FINANCIALS
Company Type: Public

Income Statement
FYE: December 31

	REVENUE ($ mil.)	NET INCOME ($ mil.)	NET PROFIT MARGIN	EMPLOYEES
12/16	6,175	(228)	—	16,027
12/15	3,206	114	3.6%	5,880
12/14	2,946	89	3.1%	6,181
12/13	2,293	86	3.8%	4,786
12/12	2,182	88	4.0%	4,300
Annual Growth	29.7%	—	—	38.9%

2016 Year-End Financials

Debt ratio: 42.64%
Return on equity: (-10.46%)
Cash ($ mil.): 62
Current ratio: 2.25
Long-term debt ($ mil.): 2,724

No. of shares (mil.): 56
Dividends
  Yield: —
  Payout: —
Market value ($ mil.): 4,097

	STOCK PRICE ($) FY Close	P/E High/Low	PER SHARE ($) Earnings	Dividends	Book Value
12/16	72.19	— —	(4.10)	0.00	44.10
12/15	78.46	35 26	2.63	0.00	43.01
12/14	85.53	39 28	2.23	0.00	41.24
12/13	68.92	31 22	2.33	0.00	34.89
12/12	52.13	27 20	2.38	0.00	32.58
Annual Growth	8.5%	— —	—	—	7.9%

TriCo Bancshares (Chico, CA)

People looking for a community bank in California's Sacramento Valley can try TriCo. TriCo Bancshares is the holding company for Tri Counties Bank which serves customers through some 65 traditional and in-store branches in 23 counties in Northern and Central California. Founded in 1974 Tri Counties Bank provides a variety of deposit services including checking and savings accounts money market accounts and CDs. Most patrons are retail customers and small to midsized businesses. The bank primarily originates real estate mortgages which account for about 65% of its loan portfolio; consumer loans contribute about

25%. TriCo has agreed to acquire rival North Valley Bancorp.

Operations

In addition to its retail banking products and services the company provides wholesale banking and investment services; TriCo offers brokerage services through an arrangement with Raymond James Financial. The company does not provide trust or international banking services.

Geographic Reach

Based in Chico California Tri Counties Bank operates 66 branches (41 traditional branches and 25 in-store branches) in 23 counties in Northern and central California including Fresno Kern Mendocino Napa Sacramento and Yuba counties.

Financial Performance

In 2013 net interest income the company's primary source of revenue rose 0.6% compared with 2012 to $102.2 million. The slight increase in net interest income was mainly due to a decrease in average balance of other borrowings a shift in deposit balances from relatively high interest rate earning time deposits to noninterest-earning demand and savings deposits an increase in the average balance of investments securities and an increase in the average balance of loans; all of which were substantially offset by a decrease in the average yield on loans.

Strategy

The bank's growth has been fueled by acquisitions and the opening of new branches; it frequently opens branches within grocery stores or other retailers including Wal-Mart. TriCo in 2010 acquired the three branches of Granite Community Bank which had been seized by regulators. The transaction which also included most of the failed bank's assets and deposits was facilitated by the FDIC and includes a loss-sharing agreement with the agency. The following year TriCo acquired Citizens Bank of Northern California. The FDIC-assisted deal included seven branches. The acquisitions are part of TriCo's strategy of adding new customers.

Mergers and Acquisitions

TriCo in January 2014 announced plans to buy its rival in Northern California North Valley Bancorp (NVB) for about $178.4 million. NVB is the parent company of North Valley Bank which had about $918 million in assets and 22 commercial banking offices across eight Northern California counties at the end of 2013. At closing which is expected in the second or third quarter of 2014 NVB will be merged into Tri Counties Bank. The combined bank would have about $3.6 billion in assets.

EXECUTIVES

EVP and CFO TriCo Bancshares and Tri Counties Bank, Thomas J. (Tom) Reddish, age 57, $309,601 total compensation
EVP and Chief Credit Officer, Craig B. Carney, age 58, $274,932 total compensation
EVP Wholesale Banking, Richard B. O'Sullivan, age 60, $260,890 total compensation
President and CEO, Richard P. Smith, age 59, $549,846 total compensation
EVP and COO, John S. Fleshood, age 55
EVP and Chief Retail Banking Officer, Daniel K. (Dan) Bailey, age 48, $268,335 total compensation
Vice President Facilities Expansion MA, Chimene Sonsteng
Senior Vice President, Raymond Rios
Executive Vice President and Chief Retail Banking Officer, Dan Bailey
Vice President Commercial Loan Supervisor, Bret Funde
Vice President Technology, Bruce Barnet
Chairman, William J. Casey, age 72

Vice Chairman, Michael W. Koehnen, age 56
Auditors: Crowe Horwath LLP

LOCATIONS

HQ: TriCo Bancshares (Chico, CA)
  63 Constitution Drive, Chico, CA 95973
Phone: 530 898-0300   **Fax:** 530 898-0310
Web: www.tcbk.com

PRODUCTS/OPERATIONS

2015 Sales

	$ mil.	% of total
Interest		
Loans including fees	131	64
Debt securities	26	13
Dividends	2	1
Other	0	-
Noninterest		
Service charges & fees	31	16
Commissions	3	2
Gain on sale of loans	3	1
Other	7	3
Total	**206**	**100**

Selected Services

Business debit cards
Business online banking
Business workshops
Cash management
Education savings and CDs
Loans and credits
Merchant services
Order checks
Overdraft services
Pension and retirement
Personal certificates of deposit
Personal checking
Personal savings and money market
Retirement savings and CDs

COMPETITORS

Bank of America	MUFG Americas Holdings
Bank of the West	PremierWest
Central Valley	Wells Fargo
Community Bancorp	Westamerica

HISTORICAL FINANCIALS
Company Type: Public

Income Statement
FYE: December 31

	ASSETS ($ mil.)	NET INCOME ($ mil.)	INCOME AS % OF ASSETS	EMPLOYEES
12/16	4,517	44	1.0%	1,063
12/15	4,220	43	1.0%	1,011
12/14	3,916	26	0.7%	1,009
12/13	2,744	27	1.0%	794
12/12	2,609	18	0.7%	831
Annual Growth	14.7%	23.9%	—	6.3%

2016 Year-End Financials

Debt ratio: 1.64%
Return on equity: 9.62%
Cash ($ mil.): 305
Current ratio: —
Long-term debt ($ mil.): —

No. of shares (mil.): 22
Dividends
  Yield: 0.0%
  Payout: 30.9%
Market value ($ mil.): 782

	STOCK PRICE ($) FY Close	P/E High/Low	PER SHARE ($) Earnings	Dividends	Book Value
12/16	34.18	18 12	1.94	0.60	20.87
12/15	27.44	15 12	1.91	0.52	19.85
12/14	24.70	19 15	1.46	0.44	18.41
12/13	28.37	17 9	1.69	0.42	15.61
12/12	16.75	15 12	1.18	0.36	14.33
Annual Growth	19.5%	— —	13.2%	13.6%	9.9%

Trinity Industries, Inc.

Trinity Industries manufactures auto carriers box cars gondola cars hopper cars intermodal cars and tank cars — in short railcars for hauling everything from coal to corn syrup. Trinity also leases and manages railcar fleets. Its Inland Barge unit builds barges used to transport coal grain and other commodities. In addition to transportation other Trinity businesses provide products and services to the industrial energy (structural towers for wind turbines metal containers for liquefied petroleum gas and fertilizer) and construction (concrete aggregates highway guardrails) sectors.

Operations

Trinity Rail Group in 2016 shipped about 27240 railcars — 42% market share (by shipment) — of the North American railcar industry. The division manufactures freight railcars that transport liquids gases and dry cargo.

The company's Construction Products Group produces concrete aggregates and asphalt; it manufactures highway products which include beams and girders used in highway bridge construction. Other highway products include guardrails cable barrier systems and crash cushions which are sold in the US and over 60 countries worldwide.

Trinity's Railcar and Leasing Management Services Group operates primarily through Trinity Industries Leasing Company (TILC) as well as other subsidiaries and markets its services under the TrinityRail brand name. It provides leasing options to companies involved in petroleum chemical agricultural and energy industries among others.

Inland Barge Group makes dry cargo barges (flat-deck and hopper) which transport products such as grain coal and aggregates. Tank barges carry petroleum fertilizer chemicals and other liquid cargoes. This business makes fiberglass barge covers and deck hardware (brand name Nabrico) including hatches castings and winches for other watercraft and dock facilities. Primary customers are commercial marine transportation companies.

Trinity's Energy Equipment Group makes tank containers and tank heads for pressure vessels propane tanks and structural wind towers. Trinity Industries de Mexico (brand name TATSA) manufactures containers for liquefied petroleum gas. It also manufactures containers for fertilizers comestibles and ammonia.

Geographic Reach

About 90% of the company's business is US-generated. The rest of the company's business is generated in Mexico where company tanks are manufactured under the brand name TATSA.

Sales and Marketing

Trinity sells its products and services through its own sales personnel operating in Canada Mexico Singapore Sweden Peru the UK and the US. Its customers include railroads leasing companies and industrial shippers of products such as utilities petrochemical companies grain shippers agricultural product companies and major construction and industrial companies.

Financial Performance

After achieving several years of growth Trinity saw its revenues decline 28% from $6.4 billion in 2015 to $4.6 billion in 2016. This was attributed to sales declines across all of its segments including Inland Barge (38%) Rail (31%) Railcar and Leasing Management Services (25%) and Energy Equipment (9%).

Lower prices for oil and other commodities the strong US dollar and an overall surplus of railcars and barges in North America were key drivers influencing demand for Trinity's products in 2016.

Trinity's profits also nosedived by 57% from $797 million in 2015 to $344 million in 2016. This was due to the revenue decline coupled with a decrease in the net gains on railcar lease fleet sales compared to the previous year.

Trinity's cash flow on the other hand has steadily increased the last five years jumping from $940 million in 2015 to $1.1 billion in 2016. This was attributed to a higher decrease in inventories a lower decrease in accrued liabilities and a higher provision for deferred taxes during 2016.

Strategy

After posting record-setting sales of $6.9 billion in 2015 Trinity experienced revenue and profit declines in 2016 as the company continues to experience weak demand levels for many of its products and services. Trinity is vulnerable to an ongoing level of uncertainty in the industrial economy that continues to impact its customers? long-term capital planning processes. The oversupply of railcars and barges in the North American market has also limited new order levels for these businesses.

As such it is focused on measuring demand for its products and services and taking steps to align its manufacturing capacity appropriately. It is also seeking acquisition opportunities that have the potential to enhance and diversify its operations so that the company is not as vulnerable to cyclical downturn. It also aims to make investments to improve our businesses so they can perform better when demand increases.

HISTORY

Trinity Industries was established through the 1958 merger of Trinity Steel a maker of metal products for the petroleum industry and Dallas Tank Co. The enterprise was headed by Ray Wallace a Trinity Steel veteran since the 1940s. The company took the name Trinity Industries in 1966.

EXECUTIVES

Vice President Information Technology, Madhuri Andrews

Chairman President and CEO, Timothy R. Wallace, age 63, $1,050,000 total compensation

SVP; Group President Construction Products and Inland Barge, William A. (Bill) McWhirter, age 52, $618,000 total compensation

SVP; Group President TrinityRail, D. Stephen (Steve) Menzies, age 61, $682,500 total compensation

SVP and CFO, James E. Perry, age 45, $556,000 total compensation

VP and CTO, Stephen W. Smith, age 67

SVP and Chief Administrative Officer, Melendy E. Lovett, age 58

VP Information Technology, W. Relle Howard, age 47

President Trinity Industries Leasing, Brian D. Madison

Vice President and Chief Audit Executive, Steve McDowell

Senior Vice President and Group President, Mark W Stiles

Senior Vice President Business Development, Bob Hulick

Vice President Business Development, Jay Tulimieri

Vice President, Eric Marchetto

Vice President Leasing Trinity Industries Leasing, Robert Wright

Vice President, Bob Pennington

Senior Vice President Supply Chain Management, John Guarino

Vice President Finance, Edgar Shaadi

Vice President sales, Joe Kvech

Vice President Org Development, Ginny Gray

Vice President Research and Development, Shaun Richmond

Vice President TANK Car Engineer, Tom Dalrymple

Vice President and Controller Trinityrail, Mark Howell

Vice President of Product Development, Keith Hall

Vice President, Georgia Rokas

Vice President Supply Chain Management, Mike Hegedus

VICE PRESIDENT, Jeffrey A Kocim

Auditors: Ernst & Young LLP

LOCATIONS

HQ: Trinity Industries, Inc.
2525 N. Stemmons Freeway, Dallas, TX 75207-2401
Phone: 214 631-4420   Fax: 214 589-8501
Web: www.trin.net

PRODUCTS/OPERATIONS

2016 Sales

	$ mil.	% of total
Rail Group	3,077	52
Energy Equipment Group	1,012	17
Railcar Leasing & Management Services Group	827	14
Construction Products Group	523	9
Inland Barge Group	403	7
Other	92	1
Eliminations	(1347.2)	-
Total	**4,588**	**100**

2016 Sales

	$ mil.	% of total
Manufacturing	3,763	82
Leasing	824	18
Total	**4,588**	**100**

Selected Products and Services

Construction products
  Aggregates
  Anti-icing systems for bridges
  Beams
  Flexible post delineators
  Girders
  Highway crash cushions
  Highway guardrails
  Highway safety devices
  Ready-mix concrete
  Truck-mounted attenuators
Energy equipment
  Container heads
  Fertilizer containers
  Liquefied petroleum gas containers
  Wind towers
Inland barge
  Deck barges
  Fiberglass barge covers
  Hopper barges
  Tank barges
Rail
  Box cars
  Freight cars
  Gondola cars
  Hopper cars
  Intermodal cars
  Tank cars
Railcar leasing and management services
  Railcar leasing repair and management

COMPETITORS

ALSTOM	GATX
American Railcar Industries	GE Rail Services
Amsted Industries	Greenbrier Companies
Blue Tee	Kawasaki Rail Car
CEMEX	Lafarge North America
Clipper Windpower	LafargeHolcim
Conrad Industries	Nippon Sharyo
FreightCar America	Union Tank Car
	Vulcan Materials

HISTORICAL FINANCIALS
Company Type: Public

Income Statement
FYE: December 31

	REVENUE ($ mil.)	NET INCOME ($ mil.)	NET PROFIT MARGIN	EMPLOYEES
12/16	4,588	343	7.5%	17,680
12/15	6,392	796	12.5%	22,030
12/14	6,170	678	11.0%	21,950
12/13	4,365	375	8.6%	18,460
12/12	3,811	255	6.7%	15,490
Annual Growth	4.7%	7.7%	—	3.4%

2016 Year-End Financials

Debt ratio: 33.50%
Return on equity: 9.05%
Cash ($ mil.): 563
Current ratio: 3.34
Long-term debt ($ mil.): 3,056

No. of shares (mil.): 152
Dividends
Yield: 0.0%
Payout: 19.5%
Market value ($ mil.): 4,225

	STOCK PRICE ($) FY Close	P/E High/Low		Earnings	PER SHARE ($) Dividends	Book Value
12/16	27.76	13	7	2.25	0.44	25.75
12/15	24.02	7	4	5.08	0.42	23.90
12/14	28.01	20	6	4.19	0.35	19.25
12/13	54.52	24	15	2.38	0.50	15.52
12/12	35.82	23	14	1.60	0.40	12.98
Annual Growth	(6.2%)			9.0%	2.4%	18.7%

TriState Capital Holdings, Inc.

TriState Capital Holdings has found its niche right in the middle of the banking industry. The holding company owns TriState Capital Bank a regional business bank that caters to midsized businesses or those annually earning between $5 million and $300 million. TriState Capital also offers private banking services nationally to high-net-worth individuals. Its loan portfolio consists of about 50% commercial loans 30% commercial real estate loans and 20% private banking-personal loans. The bank serves clients from branches in Cleveland; New Jersey; New York City Philadelphia and Pittsburgh. Altogether it has some $2 billion in assets. TriState Capital went public in mid-2013.

IPO

The company does not have any specific plans outlined for its proceeds but will likely use it for general corporate purposes which might include maintaining liquidity at the holding company providing equity capital to the bank to fund balance sheet growth and possibly investing in or acquiring wealth management businesses.

Strategy

The company's founders saw an opportunity in serving what they perceived was an underserved market — midsized businesses. Consolidation had left major national banks catering to individuals and large businesses while community banks served individuals and small businesses.

Company Background

TriState Capital was founded in 2007 by two banking industry executives — chairman and CEO James Getz who spent 20 years at Federated Investors and vice chairman William Schenck the former secretary of banking for Pennsylvania.

EXECUTIVES

Chairman President and CEO, James F. (Jim) Getz, $1,500,000 total compensation
President Commercial Banking, David A. Molnar
Vice Chairman and CFO, Mark L. Sullivan, $425,000 total compensation
Regional President New Jersey, Kenneth R. Orchard
Regional President New York, Thomas N. Gilmartin
Regional President Ohio, John D. Barrett
Regional President Eastern Pennsylvania, Joseph M. Finley
Regional President Western Pennsylvania, Vince Locher
President Private Bank Team, Charles C. Fawcett
President and CEO TriState Capital Bank, Brian S. Fetterolf
Senior Vice President Relationship Manager, Michael Blasko
Senior Vice President, David Hurtuk
Vice Chairman, A. William (Bill) Schenck
Auditors: KPMG LLP

LOCATIONS

HQ: TriState Capital Holdings, Inc.
One Oxford Centre, 301 Grant Street, Suite 2700, Pittsburgh, PA 15219
Phone: 412 304-0304

PRODUCTS/OPERATIONS

2015 Sales

	% of total
Interest income	
Loans	67
Investments	3
Interest-earning deposits	-
Noninterest income	
Investment management fees	25
Commitment and other fees	2
Other income	3
Total	**100**

COMPETITORS

Bank of America
Bank of New York Mellon
Boston Private
Brown Brothers Harriman
Citigroup
Citigroup Private Bank
First Republic (CA)

HSBC Private Bank
Herald National Bank
JPMorgan Private Bank
Julius Baer
Lakeland Bancorp
M&T Bank
Safra Bank
U.S. Trust

HISTORICAL FINANCIALS
Company Type: Public

Income Statement
FYE: December 31

	ASSETS ($ mil.)	NET INCOME ($ mil.)	INCOME AS % OF ASSETS	EMPLOYEES
12/16	3,930	28	0.7%	224
12/15	3,302	22	0.7%	192
12/14	2,846	15	0.6%	182
12/13	2,290	12	0.6%	129
12/12	2,073	10	0.5%	119
Annual Growth	17.3%	28.0%	—	17.1%

2016 Year-End Financials

Debt ratio: 6.09%
Return on equity: 8.43%
Cash ($ mil.): 96
Current ratio: —
Long-term debt ($ mil.): —

No. of shares (mil.): 28
Dividends
Yield: —
Payout: —
Market value ($ mil.): 628

	STOCK PRICE ($) FY Close	P/E High/Low		Earnings	PER SHARE ($) Dividends	Book Value
12/16	22.10	22	11	1.01	0.00	12.38
12/15	13.99	18	12	0.80	0.00	11.62
12/14	10.24	26	16	0.55	0.00	10.88
12/13	11.86	29	24	0.49	0.00	10.25
Annual Growth	16.8%			19.8%	—	4.8%

Triumph Bancorp Inc

Auditors: Crowe Horwath LLP

LOCATIONS

HQ: Triumph Bancorp Inc
12700 Park Central Drive, Suite 1700, Dallas, TX 75251
Phone: 214 365-6900
Web: www.triumphbancorp.com

HISTORICAL FINANCIALS
Company Type: Public

Income Statement
FYE: December 31

	ASSETS ($ mil.)	NET INCOME ($ mil.)	INCOME AS % OF ASSETS	EMPLOYEES
12/16	2,641	20	0.8%	705
12/15	1,691	29	1.7%	500
12/14	1,447	17	1.2%	466
12/13	1,288	11	0.9%	463
12/12	301	10	3.3%	
Annual Growth	72.0%	19.7%	—	—

2016 Year-End Financials

Debt ratio: 3.08%
Return on equity: 7.41%
Cash ($ mil.): 114
Current ratio: —
Long-term debt ($ mil.): —

No. of shares (mil.): 18
Dividends
Yield: —
Payout: —
Market value ($ mil.): 473

	STOCK PRICE ($) FY Close	P/E High/Low		Earnings	PER SHARE ($) Dividends	Book Value
12/16	26.15	24	12	1.10	0.00	16.01
12/15	16.50	11	8	1.57	0.00	14.88
12/14	13.55	10	8	1.52	0.00	13.22
Annual Growth	17.9%			(7.8%)	—	4.9%

Trustco Bank Corp. (N.Y.)

In Banking They Trust. TrustCo Bank Corp is the holding company for Trustco Bank which boasts more than 140 branches across eastern New York central and western Florida and parts of Vermont Massachusetts and New Jersey. The bank offers personal and business customers a variety of deposit products loans and mortgages and trust and investment services. It primarily originates residential and commercial mortgages which account for more than three-quarters of its loan portfolio. It also writes business construction and installment loans and home equity lines of credit.

Operations

TrustCo Bank Corp generated 77% of its total revenue from interest and fees on loans in 2014 while interest on its securities available for sale (which were mostly residential mortgage-backed securities and collateralized mortgage obligations but also its GSE SBA-backed securities) made up another 16% of the bank's revenue. Customer service fees and Trustco Financial Services income made up 6% and 3% of total revenue in 2014 respectively.

Sales and Marketing

Trustco provides personal and business banking services to individuals partnerships and corporations among other kinds of business and organizations. It spent $2.49 million on advertising in 2014 compared to $2.83 million and $3.84 million in 2013 and 2012 respectively.

Financial Performance

Trustco has struggled to grow its revenue in recent years though its profits have been rising at a healthy clip mostly because its loan loss provisions have dissipated with an improving credit portfolio amidst the strengthening economy.

TrustCo's revenue rose by nearly 4% to $176.85 million in 2014 mostly as new branch openings during the year added nearly double-digit loan business growth. The bank also collected more interest income from its securities as it invested more and made a gain on the sale of its Florida regional headquarters property.

Higher revenue and a decline in interest expense on deposits in the low-interest environment also drove the bank's net income up by 11% to $4.38 million. A continuing decline in loan loss provisions buoyed by improving economic conditions (especially in Florida) also helped boost the bank's bottom line.

Despite higher earnings in 2014 TrustCo's operating cash fell by 21% to $49.54 million during the year as it spent more toward acquiring additional assets.

Strategy

TrustCo has focused on building its loan business through new branch additions as well as through growth from its existing offices in recent years. Using this strategy in 2014 the bank added five new branches and successfully boosted its deposit business by 2.7% to $4.03 billion while loan balances swelled by 8.6% to $3.16 billion as the bank aggressively pushed its loan business during the year.

The bank underwent a major branch expansion from 2002 through 2009 and more than doubled its branch network in New York and Florida by opening new locations (more than 75 of them). It continues to open new branches albeit not as rapidly.

EXECUTIVES

President and CEO, Robert J. McCormick, age 54, $880,000 total compensation

EVP and Chief Banking Officer Trustco Bank Corp and Trustco Bank, Scot R. Salvador, age 51, $510,000 total compensation

EVP, Robert M. Leonard, age 55, $260,000 total compensation

Treasurer TrustCo and SVP Trustco Bank, Eric W. Schreck, age 50, $255,000 total compensation

SVP and CFO TrustCo Bank Corp NY and Trustco Bank, Michael M. Ozimek, age 42, $142,500 total compensation

Executive Vice President, Robert T Cushing

Vice President Mortgage Loans Trustco, Michael Lofrumento

Chairman, Thomas O. Maggs, age 73

Auditors: Crowe Horwath LLP

LOCATIONS

HQ: Trustco Bank Corp. (N.Y.)
5 Sarnowski Drive, Glenville, NY 12302
Phone: 518 377-3311   **Fax:** 518 381-3668
Web: www.trustcobank.com

PRODUCTS/OPERATIONS

2011 Sales

	$ mil.	% of total
Interest		
Loans including fees	129	73
Securities	30	17
Other	1	1
Noninterest		
Fees for services to customers	8	5
Trustco Financial Services	5	3
Other	2	1
Total	**177**	**100**

COMPETITORS

Arrow Financial	HSBC USA
Ballston Spa Bancorp	Hudson Valley FCU
Bank of America	KeyCorp
Citizens Financial	M&T Bank
Group	NBT Bancorp

HISTORICAL FINANCIALS

Company Type: Public

Income Statement

FYE: December 31

	ASSETS ($ mil.)	NET INCOME ($ mil.)	INCOME AS % OF ASSETS	EMPLOYEES
12/16	4,868	42	0.9%	808
12/15	4,734	42	0.9%	787
12/14	4,644	44	1.0%	737
12/13	4,521	39	0.9%	708
12/12	4,346	37	0.9%	759
Annual Growth	**2.9%**	**3.2%**	—	**1.6%**

2016 Year-End Financials

Debt ratio: —	No. of shares (mil.): 95
Return on equity: 10.04%	Dividends
Cash ($ mil.): 707	Yield: 0.0%
Current ratio: —	Payout: 58.9%
Long-term debt ($ mil.): —	Market value ($ mil.): 838

	STOCK PRICE ($) FY Close	P/E High/Low	PER SHARE ($) Earnings	Dividends	Book Value
12/16	8.75	20 12	0.45	0.26	4.52
12/15	6.14	16 13	0.44	0.26	4.34
12/14	7.26	16 13	0.47	0.26	4.15
12/13	7.18	18 12	0.42	0.26	3.83
12/12	5.28	15 13	0.40	0.26	3.82
Annual Growth	**13.5%**	— —	**2.7%**	**(0.0%)**	**4.3%**

Trustmark Corp

Trustmark Corporation is the holding company for Trustmark National Bank which has 208 locations mainly in Mississippi but also in East Texas the Florida panhandle and Tennessee where it also operates its Somerville Bank & Trust subsidiary in the Memphis area. Focusing on individuals and small businesses Trustmark offers a range of financial products and services such as checking and savings accounts certificates of deposit credit cards insurance investments and trust services. The diversified financial services firm has about $11.7 billion in assets.

Operations

Trustmark operates through three operating segments: General Banking Insurance and Wealth Management.

The General Banking Division is responsible for all traditional banking products and services including a full range of commercial and consumer banking services such as checking accounts savings programs overdraft facilities commercial installment and real estate loans home equity loans and lines of credit drive-in and night deposit services and safe deposit facilities offered through 208 offices in Alabama Florida Mississippi Tennessee and Texas.

The Wealth Management Division serve Trustmark's customers as a financial partner providing reliable guidance and sound practical advice for accumulating preserving and transferring wealth.

Trustmark's Insurance Division provides a full range of retail insurance products including commercial risk management products bonding group benefits and personal lines coverage through Trustmark National Bank subsidiary FBBI a Mississippi corporation.

Subsidiary Fisher Brown Bottrell sells insurance while Trustmark Investment Advisors provides wealth management products and services including the proprietary Performance Fund family of mutual funds. The latter unit has approximately $9 billion of assets under management.

Geographic Reach

Mississippi by far is Trustmark's largest market accounting for 63% of 2013 revenues. Tennessee Texas and Florida contributed about 9% 7% and 10% respectively.

Financial Performance

After experiencing a revenue dip in 2012 due to decrease in interest income in 2013 Trustmark's revenues increased by 8% thanks to an increase in the net interest income due to a significant increase in interest and fees on acquired loans related to the BancTrust acquisition as well as modest declines in the cost of interest-bearing deposits. These gains were partially offset by downward repricing of loans and securities. After experiencing sizable growth over the last few years in 2013 Trustmark's net income decreased to $117.1 million (from $117.2 million in 2012) due to an increase in the noninterest expenses as a result of BancTrust non-routine merger expenses and increases in salaries and employee benefits services and fees and ORE/foreclosure expenses.

In 2013 the company's operating cash inflow increased to $155.4 million (compared to $92.1 million in 2012) was due to a major increase in net assets and liabilities and a decline in purchases and originations of loans held for sale.

Strategy

Trustmark is growing its branch network by opening or acquiring new offices with a focus on the Houston and Memphis markets.

In 2013 Trustmark opened a new 12000-sq.-ft. office location on the first and second floors of the Nexen Building in Bunker Hill. Trustmark operates 15 locations in the Houston market with loans outstanding of approximately $835 million and deposits of approximately $425 million.

Mergers and Acquisitions

In 2013 the company purchased two branches in Oxford Mississippi from SOUTHBank F.S.B. That year it also bought Mobile Alabama-based BancTrust Financial Group for $55 million providing Trustmark entry into more than 15 markets in Alabama and enhancing the Trustmark franchise in the Florida Panhandle.

Company Background

Trustmark grew in 2011 with the FDIC-assisted acquisition of Heritage Banking Group. It took over the failed bank's assets and deposits after the institution was closed by regulators. The transaction added four bank branches in Mississippi (four other locations were consolidated due to their proximity to existing Trustmark branches).

BlackRock Inc. owns more than 11% of Trustmark Corp's. shares.

Trustmark National Bank traces its roots to 1889 when it was first chartered in Mississippi.

EXECUTIVES

President CEO and Director Trustmark Corporation and Trustmark National Bank, Gerard R. (Jerry) Host, age 62, $730,000 total compensation

President Corporate Banking Trustmark National Bank, Duane A. Dewey, age 58, $348,840 total compensation

Treasurer and Principal Financial OfficerTrustmark Corporation and EVP and CFO Trustmark National Bank, Louis E. Greer, age 62, $360,000 total compensation

President Mortgage Services Trustmark National Bank, Breck W. Tyler, age 59, $306,000 total compensation

President Wealth Management Trustmark National Bank, W. Arthur Stevens, age 52, $333,540 total compensation

Vice President RECOVERY Department, Terry Collins

First Vice President And Trust Officer, Todd Wimberly

Vice President And Trust Officer In The Trust Department, Agnes Tribble

Assistant Vice President, Marian Alderman

Senior Vice President and SCO, Tommy Lyle

VICE PRESIDENT, DEBBIE MCCRAW

Senior Vice President, Monica Day

Vice President Advertising, Kristine Jacobs

Vice President, Vincent Powell

Senior Vice President and Employee Services Manager and of Human Resources, Janice Brown

Senior Vice President, Ben Hendrix

Assistant Vice President and Trust Officer, Crystal Thompson

Vice President and Trust Officer, Kathryn Merrell

Vice President Commercial Relationship Manager, Gary Doss

Executive Vice President, Kirk Whitehouse

Vice President Mortgage Compliance Risk Manager, Melissa West

Senior Vice President and Corporate Private Banking Manager, Mark Lewis

ASSISTANT VICE PRESIDENT, Laura Ryan

SENIOR VICE PRESIDENT, Mitchell Campbell

FIRST VICE PRESIDENT, Tracy Patterson

FIRST VICE PRESIDENT, Bethany L Smith

ASSISTANT VICE PRESIDENT AND STRATEGIC SOURCING, Matt Noland

Senior Vice President, David Hagan

Vice President Sugar Land Commercial Banking, John Martinez

Vice President Mortgage Loan Originator, Jason Hebert

Chairman, R. Michael Summerford, age 68

Auditors: Crowe Horwath LLP

LOCATIONS

HQ: Trustmark Corp
248 East Capitol Street, Jackson, MS 39201
Phone: 601 208-5111   **Fax:** 601 354-5053
Web: www.trustmark.com

2016 Sales

	% of total
Mississippi	65
Alabama	12
Florida	8
Texas	8
Tennessee	7
Total	**100**

PRODUCTS/OPERATIONS

2016 Sales

	% of total
General Banking	91
Insurance	5
Wealth Management	4
Total	**100**

2016 Sales

	$ mil.	% of total
Interest Income:		
Interest and fees on LHFS & LHFI	299	51
Interest on securities	81	14
Interest and fees on acquired loans	30	5
Other interest income	1	-
Noninterest Income:		
Service charges on deposit accounts	45	8
Insurance commissions	36	6
Bank card and other fees	27	5
Mortgage banking net	28	5
Wealth management	30	5
Other net	5	1
Securities (losses) gains net	(0.3)	-
Total	**586**	**100**

COMPETITORS

BancorpSouth	Hancock Holding
Capital One	Regions Financial
Citizens Holding	Renasant
First Horizon	Wells Fargo
Great Southern Bancorp	

HISTORICAL FINANCIALS

Company Type: Public

Income Statement

FYE: December 31

	ASSETS ($ mil.)	NET INCOME ($ mil.)	INCOME AS % OF ASSETS	EMPLOYEES
12/16	13,352	108	0.8%	2,788
12/15	12,678	116	0.9%	2,941
12/14	12,250	123	1.0%	3,060
12/13	11,790	117	1.0%	3,110
12/12	9,828	117	1.2%	2,666
Annual Growth	**8.0%**	**(1.9%)**	**—**	**1.1%**

2016 Year-End Financials

Debt ratio: 0.46%	No. of shares (mil.): 67
Return on equity: 7.22%	Dividends
Cash ($ mil.): 327	Yield: 0.0%
Current ratio: —	Payout: 57.5%
Long-term debt ($ mil.): —	Market value ($ mil.): 2,411

	STOCK PRICE ($) FY Close	P/E High/Low	PER SHARE ($) Earnings	Dividends	Book Value
12/16	35.65	23 12	1.60	0.92	22.48
12/15	23.04	15 12	1.71	0.92	21.80
12/14	24.54	15 12	1.83	0.92	21.04
12/13	26.84	16 13	1.75	0.92	20.11
12/12	22.46	14 12	1.81	0.92	19.86
Annual Growth	**12.2%**	**— —**	**(3.0%)**	**(0.0%)**	**3.1%**

TURNER CONSTRUCTION COMPANY INC

Turner Construction has been the mastermind for scores of head-turning projects for more than a century. The company that built Madison Square Garden has ranked among the leading general builders in the US since the early 1900s. Turner provides construction and project management services for commercial and multifamily buildings airports and stadiums as well as correctional educational entertainment and manufacturing facilities. The company is also a leader in sustainable or green building practices. Founded in 1902 by Henry Turner the company is the main operating unit of The Turner Corporation which is a subsidiary of German construction group HOCHTIEF.

Operations

Turner works on more than 1500 projects each year (as of mid-2016). For decades Turner has kept tabs on construction prices with its quarterly Building Cost Index which forecasts construction costs by taking into account labor rates productivity and material prices. The index is used by federal and state governments to track building costs and pricing trends.

As part of HOCHTIEF's Americas division Turner works alongside other contractors in the US and Canada such as Flatiron E.E. Crus and Clark Builders. HOCHTIEF reiterated in 2016 that the America subsidiaries are closely related and work together to exchange information and experience. The Americas division generated around 50% of HOCHTIEF's total revenue during 2015.

Geographic Reach

The company has offices across North America as well as in 20 countries in Southeast Asia Europe India Latin America the Caribbean and the Middle East (as of mid-2016).

Sales and Marketing

The contractor works on projects in the aviation/transportation commercial cultural and entertainment data center education government and green building markets (as of mid-2016).

Strategy

Turner's ties to HOCHTIEF have helped strengthen the company's services and extend its international reach. Turner often teams with sister company Flatiron to complete projects. By collaborating and marketing their services jointly the two companies combine strengths in refurbishment and construction services.

Some of Turner's more recent projects (as of mid-2016) have included the Cobo Center and Quicken Loans Technology Center in Detroit as well as the NASA Computational Research Center in Hampton Virginia.

Turner has also worked to meet growing demand for green and sustainable construction. More than 425 of its projects have earned Leadership in Energy and Environmental Design (LEED) certification. A few of its green projects include the Seattle office of Perkins+Will the Yale University Health Services Center and RAND corporate headquarters.

As the residential markets slowed in past years Turner pivoted toward securing commercial projects in the public health care and science and technology sectors. Sports projects also provided the company with a solid pipeline; the company's dedicated sports division had completed some $5 billion in work since 2000.

Company Background

Other notable projects in Turner's history include the World War II Memorial in Washington DC the John F. Kennedy Memorial Library in Boston and the Rock and Roll Hall of Fame. Turner also built the new Yankee Stadium in New York. The company reached a milestone in 2008 by inking its 15000th major contract.

To expand its operations in Canada Turner in late 2011 agreed to partner with Clark Builders in a deal that gives Turner a 51% stake in the Edmonton-based company. For the effort Clark Builders gains access to Turner's financial and management resources. The alliance strengthens Turner's Toronto and Vancouver foothold and helps to extend the reach of the company's business into other Canadian markets.

EXECUTIVES

President, Peter J. Davoren, age 62
VP, Stephen W. Fort
EVP (New York New Jersey Maryland Pennsylvania Connecticut and New England), Pasquale A. (Pat) Di Filippo
EVP Global Sales and Market Segment (Southwest Northern Calfornia and Northwest Regions), Michael J. (Mike) Kuntz
SVP, Mark A. Boyle
EVP (Ohio Nashville Huntsville Atlanta Florida and the Carolinas), Richard P. Homan
SVP Turner Industrial Group and Chairman The Lathrop Company, Thomas J. (Tom) Manahan
VP, Abrar Sheriff
SVP and CFO, Karen O. Gould, age 52
SVP (Mid-Atlantic and Southeast), Tom Reilly
President The Lathrop Company, Steve Johnson
Vice President and Construction Executive, Robert Hubner
Vice President And Senior Operations Manager, Tomasz Stachowiak
Vice President and General Manager, Kris Barnard
Senior Vice President, Rory C Dejohn
Vice President and General Manager, Tom Stachowiak
Vice President and Financial Manager, Sarah Garner
Executive Assistant To Thomas B. Gerlach Senior Vice President Human Resources, Cheryl Halvorsen
Vice President and Construction Executive, Curt Zegler
Vice President and Operations Manager, Carlo DiSilvestro
Auditors: DELOITTE & TOUCHE LLP DALLAS

LOCATIONS

HQ: TURNER CONSTRUCTION COMPANY INC
375 HUDSON ST FL 6, NEW YORK, NY 100143667
Phone: 212 229-6000
Web: WWW.TCCO.COM

PRODUCTS/OPERATIONS

Selected Services
Building maintenance
Construction management
Design-build
General construction
Multiple building program
Preconstruction consulting
Program management
Project management

COMPETITORS

Bechtel	Hunt Construction
C. G. Schmidt	Jacobs Engineering
Catamount Constructors	PCL Employees Holdings
Dimeo Construction	Parsons Corporation
DooleyMack	Peter Kiewit Sons'
English Construction Company	Shook National
F.A. Wilhelm	Skanska USA Building
Fluor	Structure Tone
Gilbane Building Company	Tully Construction
Hensel Phelps Construction	Tutor Perini
	Winter Construction

HISTORICAL FINANCIALS

Company Type: Private

Income Statement

FYE: December 31

	REVENUE ($ mil.)	NET INCOME ($ mil.)	NET PROFIT MARGIN	EMPLOYEES
12/15	10,484	101	1.0%	5,000
12/14	10,516	96	0.9%	—
12/13	9,488	76	0.8%	—
12/12	8,552	70	0.8%	—
Annual Growth	7.0%	13.0%	—	—

2015 Year-End Financials

Debt ratio: —
Return on equity: 1.00%
Cash ($ mil.): 188
Current ratio: 0.80
Long-term debt ($ mil.): —

Dividends
  Yield: —
  Payout: —
Market value ($ mil.): —

Tutor Perini Corp

Tutor Perini could teach it peers a thing or two about construction. One of the largest hotel and casino builders in the US Tutor Perini also builds schools health care facilities airports and industrial buildings. The company and its subsidiaries provide pre-construction and design-build services general contracting equipment materials subcontracting and other services. Its Civil arm which includes subsidiaries Tutor-Saliba Cherry Hill Construction Lunda Construction and Black Construction builds and maintains highways bridges and mass transit. Tutor Perini's Specialty contracting division builds electrical and mechanical systems while its Buildings segment constructs buildings in the hospitality gaming and other industries.

Operations

Tutor Perini operates through three business segments. The Civil segment accounts for more than 40% of revenue while the firm's Building and Specialty Contractors segments account for about a third and a quarter of revenue respectively.

The Buildings group includes subsidiaries Tutor Perini Building Corp. James A. Cummings Inc. Rudolph and Sletten Inc. Keating Building and Roy Anderson Corp. (formerly known as Anderson Companies). The segment focuses on large and complex projects for public and private clients. Major projects include parts of the Hudson Yards project in New York City work on McCarran International Airport in Las Vegas and the San Diego California courthouse.

The Civil group includes subsidiaries Cherry Hill Construction Frontier-Kemper Construction and Becho. The segment specializes in repairing and improving highways bridges tunnels mass-transit systems and water management and wastewater treatment facilities in US.

Specialty Contractors includes subsidiaries Desert Mechanical Superior Gunite WDF and GreenStar Services. The segment specializes in electrical mechanical plumbing HVAC and fire protection systems.

Geographic Reach

About 95% of Tutor Perini?s revenue comes from the US where the firm performs work across most major geographic areas. The company also is active in parts of Canada. Overseas Tutor Pirini has completed projects for the US military in Guam Iraq Haiti and Afghanistan.

Sales and Marketing

Tutor Perini works on more than 1500 construction projects a year for federal state and local government agencies and authorities and private clients. Private clients include major hospitality and gaming resort owners Native American sovereign nations public corporations private developers healthcare companies and private universities. Its state and local clients include state transportation departments metropolitan authorities cities schools and municipalities.

The company derives about 50% of its revenue from state and local governments about 45% from the private sector and 5% from federal agencies
Financial Performance

Tutor Perini posted stronger financial results in 2016 from 2015 when it took charges that weakened its bottom line. Revenue rose a slight 1% to just less than $5 billion on the strength of a 15% increase in the Buildings segment?s revenue driven by commercial office technology health care hospitality and gaming and retail building projects in California. In the Civil segment revenue slumped 12% in 2016 from 2015 because some major New York contracts have ended or are winding down.

The company?s net income jumped more than 100% to about $96 million in 2016 from 2015 and more in line with previous profits. In 2015 the company?s net income plunged to about $45 million mostly due to "significant" project charges recorded for the Specialty Contractors segments' various Five Star Electric projects in New York lower activity on higher-margin civil projects unfavorable cost estimate adjustments to complete an office building in New York and litigation charges related to its Brightwater matters.

Cash generated by operations also rebounded in 2016 to more than $113 million from about $14 million in 2015. In 2016 Tutor Perini focused on improving billings collecting cash and reducing its unbilled costs which paid off in higher cash generation.

Strategy

Tutor Perini is banking on a wave of infrastructure spending to boost revenue. In 2016 voters around the US approved about $200 billion of state and local transportation funding (including more than $50 billion in California) that will be spent in the coming years. On the federal level the company expects the release of funding from the $305 billion Fixing America?s Surface Transportation Act (FAST Act) which aimed at road improvements nationwide. The company also anticipates a federal infrastructure program to emerge from Washington D.C. that could add billions more in construction activity around the country. Tutor Perini has a project backlog with a value of about $7.5 billion.

Company Background

In prior years the company pursued strategic acquisition of companies that showed success in their markets to grow both vertically and geographically. In 2011 Tutor Perini strengthened its building business (especially in the Southeast) when it acquired Anderson Companies the privately held parent of Roy Anderson Corporation Harrell Contracting and Brice Building. It then acquired Midwest heavy civil builder Lunda Construction. The company initially boosted its civil segment with the 2008 merger of Tutor-Saliba. It has continued to build its civil business. In 2011 it acquired Frontier-Kemper an Indiana-based builder of highways roads and rapid transit systems. That year Tutor Perini also bought Lunda Construction a Wisconsin-based heavy civil contractor.

Tutor Perini traces its roots to 1894 when Italian stonemason Bonfiglio Perini created a small family-owned civil works contracting business in Boston. The company went public in 1961. CEO Ronald Tutor owns about 22% of Tutor Perini.

EXECUTIVES

Executive Vice President Chief Operations Officer, Jack Frost
President and CEO Perini Management Services, Robert Band, age 69, $600,024 total compensation
Chairman and CEO, Ronald N. (Ron) Tutor, age 76, $1,750,000 total compensation
President and CEO Rudolph and Sletten, Martin B. Sisemore
EVP, Craig W. Shaw, age 62, $650,024 total compensation
President and CEO Roy Anderson Corp., Roy Anderson, age 59
President Fisk Electric, Darrell W. Harwood
President and CEO Lunda Construction, Dennis L. Behnke
EVP and CFO, Gary G. Smalley, age 59, $700,000 total compensation
President and COO; CEO Civil Group, James A. (Jack) Frost, age 64, $1,000,000 total compensation
President and CEO Frontier-Kemper Constructors, W. David Rogstad
President Tutor Perini Civil East, Ali M. Catik
President and CEO WDF, Lawrence (Larry) Roman
President and COO Nagelbush Mechanical, Peter McCann
President Desert Mechanical, Joseph Guglielmo
President and CEO Superior Gunite, Anthony J. Federico
President and CEO Five Star Electric, Robert Saville
EVP and President and CEO Building Group, Leonard J. Rejcek
Vice President Business Development, Stephen Buschmeyer
Senior Vice President, Danny Hoisman
Senior Vice President Business Development, Joe Perini
Vice President Of Operations, Vince Pizzi
Vice President, Scott Christensen
Vice President Of Business Development, Buschmeyer Stephen
Senior Vice President Tax Counsel and Corporate Affairs Tutor Saliba, John Barrett
Vice President Special Projects, Steve Lewis
Vice President Personnel, David Randall
Vice President of Operations, Alan Paskoff
Vice President Estimating, Tim Sarre
Assistant Treasurer, Kevin Cvengros
Auditors: Deloitte & Touche LLP

LOCATIONS

HQ: Tutor Perini Corp
15901 Olden Street, Sylmar, CA 91342-1093
Phone: 818 362-8391
Web: www.tutorperini.com

2016 Sales

	% of total
United States	97
Foreign and US territories	3
Total	**100**

PRODUCTS/OPERATIONS

2016 sales

	$ mil.	% of total
Civil	1,668	33
Building	2,069	42
Specialty contractors	1,234	25
Total	**4,973**	**100**

2016 -Customer Type

Customers	% of total
State and Local Agencies	49
Private Owners	45
Federal Agencies	6
Total	**100**

Selected Subsidiaries

Building Group
  Anderson Companies
  James A. Cummings Inc.
  Keating Building Corporation
  Rudolph and Sletten Inc.
  Tutor-Saliba Corporation
  Tutor Perini Building Corp.
Civil Group
  Cherry Hill Construction Inc.
  Frontier-Kemper Constructors
  Lunda Construction Company
  Tutor Perini Corporation
  Tutor-Saliba Corporation
Becho Inc.
  Black Construction Corporation
  Specialty Contractors Group
  Desert Mechanical Inc.
  Fisk Electric Corporation
  Five Star Electric
  Nagelbush
  GreenStar Services Corporation
  Superior Gunite
  WDF Inc.

COMPETITORS

AECOM	KBR
American Infrastructure	Kiewit Power Constructors
Balfour Beatty Construction	M. A. Mortenson
Barton Malow	Marnell Corrao
CH2M HILL	McCarthy Building
Clark Enterprises	PCL Constructors
DPR Construction	PCL Employees Holdings
Dragados	Skanska USA Civil
Flatiron Construction	Suffolk Construction
Fluor	Swinerton
Gilbane	Traylor Bros.
Granite Construction	Tully Construction
Hardin Construction	Turner Corporation
Hensel Phelps Construction	Walsh Group
Hunt Construction	Webcor Builders
J.E. Dunn Construction Group	Weitz
	Whiting-Turner
	Yates Companies
	dck worldwide

HISTORICAL FINANCIALS

Company Type: Public

Income Statement

FYE: December 31

	REVENUE ($ mil.)	NET INCOME ($ mil.)	NET PROFIT MARGIN	EMPLOYEES
12/16	4,973	95	1.9%	11,603
12/15	4,920	45	0.9%	10,626
12/14	4,492	107	2.4%	10,939
12/13	4,175	87	2.1%	10,206
12/12	4,111	(265)	—	11,016
Annual Growth	**4.9%**			**1.3%**

2016 Year-End Financials

Debt ratio: 18.81%
Return on equity: 6.43%
Cash ($ mil.): 146
Current ratio: 1.87
Long-term debt ($ mil.): 673
No. of shares (mil.): 49
Dividends
  Yield: —
  Payout: —
Market value ($ mil.): 1,378

	STOCK PRICE ($) FY Close	P/E High/Low		PER SHARE ($) Earnings	Dividends	Book Value
12/16	28.00	15	5	1.92	0.00	31.56
12/15	16.74	29	17	0.91	0.00	28.94
12/14	24.07	14	9	2.20	0.00	28.06
12/13	26.30	14	8	1.80	0.00	25.76
12/12	13.70	—	—	(5.59)	0.00	24.05
Annual Growth	**19.6%**			**—**	**—**	**7.0%**

Twenty-First Century Fox Inc

Twenty-First Century Fox (formerly known as News Corporation) owns and operates a portfolio of cable broadcast film pay television and satellite assets spanning the globe. The company's massive portfolio of cable and broadcasting networks and properties includes FOX FX FXX FXM FS1 Fox News Fox Business Network Fox Sports National Geographic Channels MundoFox STAR India and nearly 30 local television stations in the US and more than 300 international channels;; film studio Twentieth Century Fox Film ; and television production studios Twentieth Century Fox Television and 50% ownership in Endemol Shine Group. In 2017 the company agreed to sell much of itself to the Walt Disney Company for $52.4 billion in stock.

HISTORY

In 1952 Rupert Murdoch inherited two Adelaide Australia newspapers from his father. After launching the Australian the country's first national daily in 1964 Murdoch moved into the UK market. He bought tabloid News of the World a London Sunday paper in 1968 and London's Sun the next year. In 1973 Murdoch hit the US buying the San Antonio Express-News and founding the Star tabloid. He followed this up in 1976 by buying the New York Post. Murdoch formed News Corporation in Australia in 1979.

Moving upmarket in 1981 Murdoch bought the London Times and 40% of Collins Publishers a London book publisher. After buying the Chicago Sun-Times in 1983 (sold 1986) Murdoch bought 13 US travel hotel and aviation trade magazines from Ziff-Davis as well as film studio Twentieth Century Fox in 1985. In 1986 Murdoch bought six Metromedia stations and launched FOX Broadcasting the first new US TV network since 1948.

Print was not forgotten however and in the late 1980s News Corp. picked up US book publisher Harper & Row as well as Triangle Publications (TV Guide and other magazines). It also bought textbook publisher Scott Foresman and the rest of Collins Publishers. (Harper & Row was later merged with Collins to form HarperCollins.)

In 1996 Murdoch launched the FOX News Channel an all-news cable channel. The next year News Corp.'s FOX Kids joint venture bought Pat Robertson's International Family Entertainment.

In 1998 the company bought the Los Angeles Dodgers and stakes in the new Los Angeles-area Staples Center sports arena. (It sold its stake in the Staples Center in 2004.) Also that year News Corp. spun off part of Fox Entertainment in one of America's largest IPOs raising $2.7 billion.

That year News Corp. sold TV Guide to Tele-Communications Inc.'s United Video Satellite Group (now Gemstar-TV Guide International) for $800 million in cash and a 21% stake. The company also bought the 50% of FOX/Liberty Networks (now FOX Sports Net) it didn't own and transferred ownership to Fox Entertainment. The deal gave John Malone's Liberty Media holding company an 8% stake (later 19%) in News Corp.

In 1999 News Corp. purchased a 10% stake of wireless ISP OmniSky. The following year Sky acquired nearly 25% of Kirch PayTV the German pay-TV operation of KirchGruppe. Murdoch placed all of the company's satellite holdings into a new entity Sky Global Networks. (News Corp. folded Sky Global back into its operations in 2002 when it failed in its initial bid to buy DIRECTV.) Also that year News Corp. bought a stake in China's state-owned telecom operator Netcom.

In 2001 along with partner Haim Saban News Corp. sold the Fox Family Channel to Disney for about $5.2 billion. That year the FCC approved the company's $4.8 billion purchase of TV station group Chris-Craft. The deal gave News Corp. an additional 10 TV stations.

News Corp. in 2003 finally realized its dream of owning a chunk of DIRECTV when it bought 34% of Hughes Electronics the satellite television company's parent from General Motors. News Corp. transferred its interest in Hughes (which changed its name to The DIRECTV Group) to its Fox Entertainment subsidiary. The following year in an effort to make its stock more attractive to US investors News Corp. shifted its incorporation from Australia to the US. It also purchased the rest of Fox Entertainment that it didn't already own for $6.2 billion.

In 2005 News Corp. made its push into online and digital entertainment. Anchoring the new operations it acquired MySpace.com operator Intermix Media for about $580 million. (Other assets owned by Intermix were later sold to Demand Media.) The deal was an about-face for a company that eschewed the World Wide Web during the dotcom boom of the 1990s.

The company made another splash in the television industry when it launched MyNetworkTV in 2006. The startup network was established in response to rivals WB and UPN merging to form The CW Television Network.

The following year News Corp. expanded its holdings significantly when it acquired newspaper giant Dow Jones along with its flagship paper The Wall Street Journal for $5.6 billion. A newspaper man at heart Murdoch doggedly pursued Dow Jones and its controlling Bancroft family through a lengthy — and at times contested — negotiation process primarily to get his hands on the flagship title.

In 2008 the company exchanged its 40% stake in DIRECTV along with some regional sports networks and $625 million in cash for Liberty Media's 19% stake in News Corp.

Looking to still expand its interests in television broadcasting in 2011 News Corp acquired UK TV production company Shine Group in a stock swap deal valued at $670 million. Shine which was founded and is managed by Elisabeth Murdoch the daughter of Rupert has operations in 10 territories. The deal gave News Corp. a stronger presence in the increasingly crucial international TV production market.

In 2011 the company finally decided that its Myspace investment failed to pay off as growth in online ad revenue significantly slowed and the social network site decisively lost the battle to attract users against the reigning social media champion Facebook. As a result News Corp. sold Myspace to digital advertising network provider Specific Media for a paltry $35 million. (It also obtained a minority equity stake in Specific Media.)

Also during this time News Corp. was faced with troubles at its News International UK newspaper unit when it became embroiled in scandal. In the summer of 2011 its News of the World was accused of hiring private investigators to hack into citizens' and public officials' voice mails. The paper was eventually shut down after 168 years of publication. In addition several senior executives resigned and the company dropped plans to acquire the remaining 61% of Sky that it didn't already own for about Â 7.8 billion ($12.5 billion).

In 2013 News Corp. split itself into two companies. Entertainment assets like Fox News formed a new company called Twenty-First Century Fox while publishing units including The Wall Street Journal The New York Post and HarperCollins formed a company called News Corporation.

EXECUTIVES

CEO, James R. Murdoch, age 44, $3,000,000 total compensation
Chairman and CEO, Stacey Snider
Vice Chairman, Chase Carey, age 63, $4,050,000 total compensation
EVP Investor Relations, Reed Nolte
SEVP and CFO, John P. Nallen, age 61, $2,000,000 total compensation
Chairman and CEO Fox Television Group, Gary Newman
Chairman and CEO Fox Television Group, Dana Walden
Chairman and CEO Fox Networks Group, Peter Rice, age 51
President and COO Fox Networks Group, Randy Freer
CEO Fox Television Stations Group, Jack Abernethy
EVP and Chief Communications Officer, Julie Henderson
CEO National Geographic Global Networks, Courteney Monroe
CEO FX Networks and FX Productions, John Landgraf, age 54
President COO and Executive Producer FOX Sports, Eric Shanks, age 45
EVP and Deputy Group General Counsel, Janet Nova
SEVP Group General Counsel and Chief Compliance Officer, Gerson A. Zweifach, age 64, $3,000,000 total compensation
CEO Star India, Uday Shankar
CEO National Geographic Partners, Declan Moore
EVP Public Affairs, Chip Smith
Vice President Government Relations, Kristopher Jones
Vice President Government Relations, Christopher Wilson
Vice President Fox One Integrated Global Sales And Marketing, Karolina Cuprys
Senior Vice President Global Sourcing, Joseph Burke
Executive Vice President Government Affairs, Michael Regan
Senior Vice President Government Affairs, Rick Lane
Senior Vice President Treasurer, Rakesh Jobanputra
Senior Vice President Human RE, Ted Exarhakos
Vice President Corporate Security, Bobby Butler
Executive Vice President Finance Tax and Benefits, Paul Haggerty
Executive Vice President Sales Research Insights and Strategy, Audrey Steele
Executive Vice President Marketing (Fox Broadcasting Company), Darren Schillace
Senior Vice President Corporate Security, Karl Solterer
Vice President and Assistant Treasurer, Stan Pauzer
Co-Chairman, Lachlan K. Murdoch, age 44
Co-Chairman, K. Rupert Murdoch, age 86
Auditors: Ernst & Young LLP

LOCATIONS

HQ: Twenty-First Century Fox Inc
1211 Avenue of the Americas, New York, NY 10036
Phone: 212 852-7000
Web: www.21cf.com

sales 2017

	$ mil.	% of total
U.S. and Canada	20,643	72
Europe	3,122	11
Other	4,735	17
Total	**28,500**	**100**

PRODUCTS/OPERATIONS

Sales 2017

	$ mil.	% of total
Cable Network Programming	16,130	54
Filmed Entertainment	8,235	27
Television	5,649	19
Other Corporate and Eliminations (-1514) -		
Total	**28,500**	**100**

Sales 2017

	$ mil.	% of total
Affiliate fees	12,172	43
Content	8,039	28
Advertising	7,707	27
Other	582	2
Total	**28,500**	**100**

Selected Operations

Filmed entertainment
  Feature film production and distribution
  Fox Filmed Entertainment
  Fox 2000
  Fox Atomic
  Fox Searchlight Pictures
  Twentieth Century Fox
  Twentieth Century Fox Animation
  Twentieth Century Fox Home Entertainment
  Television production and distribution
  Fox Television Studios
  Twentieth Century Fox Television
  Twentieth Television
Cable network programming
  Big Ten Network (49%)
  Fox Business Network
  Fox College Sports
  Fox International Channels
  LAPTV (32% Latin American pay television)
  Fox Movie Channel
  Fox News Channel
  Fox Pan American Sports (33%)
  Fox Sports en Espa?ol
  Fox Sports Latin America
  Fox Reality
  Fox Soccer Channel
  Fox Sports Net
  FUEL TV
  FX
  National Geographic Channel (67% cable channel)
  NGC Network Latin America (67% National Geographic Channel)
  NGC Network International (75% National Geographic Channel International)
  SPEED
Television
  FOX Broadcasting
  Fox Television Stations
  KCOP (MyNetworkTV Los Angeles)
  KDFI (MyNetworkTV Dallas)
  KDFW (FOX Dallas)
  KMSP (FOX Minneapolis)
  KRIV (FOX Houston)
  KSAZ (FOX Phoenix)
  KTBC (FOX; Austin TX)
  KTTV (FOX Los Angeles)
  KTXH (MyNetworkTV Houston)
  KUTP (MyNetworkTV Phoenix)
  WAGA (FOX Atlanta)
  WDCA (MyNetworkTV; Washington DC)
  WFLD (FOX Chicago)
  WFTC (MyNetworkTV Minneapolis)
  WFXT (FOX Boston)
  WHBQ (FOX Memphis)
  WJBK (FOX Detroit)
  WNYW (FOX New York City)
  WOFL (FOX; Orlando FL)
  WOGX (FOX; Gainesville FL)
  WPWR (MyNetworkTV Chicago)
  WTTG (FOX; Washington DC)
  WTVT (FOX Tampa)
  WTXF (FOX Philadelphia)
  WUTB (MyNetworkTV Baltimore)
  WWOR (MyNetworkTV New York City)
  MyNetworkTV
  Shine Ltd. (television production UK)
  Star Group (international television broadcasting Asia)
Direct broadcast satellite
  British Sky Broadcasting (39% UK)
  Sky Deutschland (45% Germany)
  SKY Italia

COMPETITORS

CBS Corp	Sony Pictures
Disney	Entertainment
MGM	Time Warner
NBCUniversal	Viacom

HISTORICAL FINANCIALS

Company Type: Public

Income Statement

FYE: June 30

	REVENUE ($ mil.)	NET INCOME ($ mil.)	NET PROFIT MARGIN	EMPLOYEES
06/17	28,500	2,952	10.4%	21,700
06/16	27,326	2,755	10.1%	21,500
06/15	28,987	8,306	28.7%	20,500
06/14	31,867	4,514	14.2%	27,000
06/13	27,675	7,097	25.6%	25,600
Annual Growth	0.7%	(19.7%)	—	(4.0%)

2017 Year-End Financials

Debt ratio: 39.26%	No. of shares (mil.): 1,851
Return on equity: 20.09%	Dividends
Cash ($ mil.): 6,163	Yield: 1.2%
Current ratio: 2.25	Payout: 22.6%
Long-term debt ($ mil.): 19,456	Market value ($ mil.): 52,459

	STOCK PRICE ($) FY Close	P/E High/Low	PER SHARE ($) Earnings	Dividends	Book Value
06/17	28.34	20 15	1.59	0.36	8.49
06/16	27.05	24 17	1.42	0.30	7.31
06/15	32.55	10 8	3.90	0.28	8.45
06/14	35.15	18 15	1.99	0.25	7.89
06/13	32.58	11 7	3.03	0.17	7.34
Annual Growth	(3.4%)	— —	(14.9%)	20.6%	3.7%

Tyson Foods Inc

Tyson Foods spreads its wings beyond the chicken coop. While it?s one of the largest US chicken producers (processing some 40 million a week) Tyson's Fresh Meats division makes it a giant in the beef and pork sectors. The company also offers value-added processed and pre-cooked meats and refrigerated and frozen prepared foods. Its chicken operations are vertically integrated — the company hatches the eggs supplies contract growers with the chicks and feed and brings them back for processing when ready. Tyson's brands include Tyson Jimmy Dean Hillshire Farm Ball Park Wright Aidells and State Fair. Its customers include retail wholesale and food service companies worldwide.

HISTORY

During the Great Depression Arkansas poultry farmer John Tyson supported his family by selling vegetables and poultry. In 1935 after developing a method for transporting live poultry (he installed a food-and-water trough and nailed small feed cups on a trailer) he bought 500 chickens in Arkansas and sold them in Chicago.

For the next decade Tyson bought sold and transported chickens. By 1947 the year he incorporated the company as Tyson Feed & Hatchery he was raising the chickens himself. He emphasized chicken production opening his first processing plant in 1958 in Springdale where he implemented an ice-packing system that allowed the company to send its products greater distances.

John's son Don took over as manager in 1960 and in 1963 it went public as Tyson Foods. Tyson Country Fresh Chicken (packaged chicken that would become the company's mainstay) was introduced in 1967.

Rapid expansion included a new egg-processing building (1970) a new plant and computerized feed mill (1971) and the acquisitions of Prospect Farms (1969 precooked chicken) and the Ocoma Foods Division (1972 poultry) as well as hog operations.

Health-conscious consumers increasingly turned from red meats to poultry during the 1980s. Tyson became the industry leader with several key acquisitions of poultry operations including the Tastybird division of Valmac (1985) Lane Processing (1986) and Heritage Valley (1986). Its 1989 purchase of Holly Farms added beef and pork processing.

Don Tyson relinquished the CEO position to Leland Tollett in 1991. The company increased its presence in Mexico the next year through a joint venture with poultry producer Trasgo. Also in 1992 the firm plunged into seafood with the purchase of Arctic Alaska Fisheries and Louis Kemp Seafood.

Tyson bought Culinary Foods (frozen foods) and Trasgo in 1994 and the seafood division of International Multifoods in 1995. High feed costs and an oversupply of chickens brought down company earnings the next year. In 1997 the company pleaded guilty to charges that it illegally gave former Agriculture Secretary Mike Espy thousands of dollars' worth of gifts; the settlement included $6 million in fines and fees.

Tyson bought embattled Hudson Foods' poultry operations in 1998. The company said it would take a charge that year of $196 million to restructure. It also sold turkey processor Willow Brook Foods (now part of Cargill Meat Solutions) to Willow Brook management in 1998. That year John H. Tyson grandson of the founder was elected chairman.

In 1999 Tyson sold its seafood business for about $180 million in a two-part transaction to International Home Foods and Trident Seafoods. John Tyson became CEO in 2000.

As the winner in a bidding war with Smithfield Foods in 2001 Tyson agreed to buy IBP Inc. the #1 beef processor and #2 pork processor in the US for nearly $3.2 billion. Tyson tried to back away from the table after accounting irregularities were discovered at an IBP subsidiary but a Delaware judge ordered Tyson to sit down and finish dinner. The deal was made final in September and Tyson changed the beef processor's name to IBP Fresh Meats.

In late 2001 Tyson Foods and six managers were indicted for conspiring to smuggle illegal immigrants from Mexico and Central America to work for lower than legal wages in 15 of its US poultry processing plants. Two managers made plea bargains and testified for the government; another manager committed suicide. Tyson and the remaining three managers were acquitted of the conspiracy charges in 2003.

Suffering from mild indigestion after the merger in 2002 Tyson announced a restructuring to trim some fat from its fresh pork operations and agreed to sell its Specialty Brands (frozen foods) subsidiary. In early 2003 sold off its frozen appetizer business DFG Foods.

Following the discovery of bird flu on a Texas chicken farm in 2004 and the subsequent banning of the importation of US chicken products by other countries Tyson consolidated and automated its poultry operations resulting in hundreds of layoffs at the company.

Tyson announced in 2004 it was being formally investigated by the SEC regarding perquisites

given to executives including retired senior chairman Don Tyson and then-current chairman and CEO John Tyson. By August the SEC recommended civil action against the company for its failure to disclose $1.7 million in corporate perks given to Don Tyson without authorization from Tyson's compensation committee. Although Don Tyson had already reimbursed the company $1.53 million for then-unspecified benefits the SEC also announced plans to recommend civil action be taken against him. With neither the company nor Tyson admitting any guilt the case was settled in 2005 with Tyson paying the SEC $700000 in fines and the company $1.5 million. Many of the perks were not disclosed because Don Tyson did not fill out SEC-required questionnaires; however disclosed perks included having the company pay for his housekeeping and lawn maintenance and routine non-business use of the corporate jet by his family and friends.

In 2005 the company opened its largest case-ready meat plant in Sherman Texas. However that January and February it suspended operations at four of its other beef plants and cut back at a fifth due to a shortage of cattle and the loss of beef exports due to the US's 2003 case of BSE (Bovine spongiform encephalopathy or "mad cow" disease).

Growing concern over the role of trans-fatty acids (from hydrogenated vegetable oils) in diet and health led Tyson to begin removing them from its processed foods such as breaded chicken nuggets and chicken tenders. The company announced the removal of trans-fats from all its retail poultry and school foodservice products in 2005.

Recognizing the growing market for alternative and renewable fuels and recognizing its unending supply of meat by-products (in this case such lovelies as fat tallow lard and grease) Tyson decided to get into the alternative fuel market in 2007 with the formation of a 50-50 joint venture with fuel refiner Syntroleum called Dynamic Fuels. The joint venture was set up to explore the possibility of producing synthetic fuel from Tyson's waste products for the diesel- jet- and military-fuel markets. In conjunction with this joint venture Tyson created a new business unit Tyson Renewable Products.

EXECUTIVES

EVP and General Counsel, David L. Van Bebber, age 61

EVP and Chief Human Resources Officer, Mary A. Oleksiuk, age 55

COO, Noel White, age 59, $777,716 total compensation

CFO, Stewart F. Glendinning, age 51

President North American Foodservice and International, Andrew P. (Andy) Callahan, age 50

President North American Retail, Sally Grimes, age 45

EVP Operations Services, Howell P. (Hal) Carper, age 62

President CEO and Director, Thomas P. (Tom) Hayes, age 51, $712,954 total compensation

Chief Growth Officer, Monica McGurk, age 46

President Poultry Operations, Doug Ramsey

CTO, Scott Spradley

Senior Vice President Corporate International Human Resources, Russell Tooley

Vice President of Food Safety and Quality Assurance, Dean Danilson

Vice President of Operations, Joel Sappenfield

Vice President Sales, Lyle Nicholson

Vice President Of Direct Materials, Lindsay Piepho

Vice President Generate Demand, Sue Quillin

Assistant Vice President Credit Finance, Larry Alsip

Vice President of Operations, Rob Tanksley

Vice President Customer Development East, Bill Creighton
Senior Vice President of Operations, Steve Taylor
Vice President of Business Development, Lori Simco
Vice President Customer Services, Cary Wiese
National Account Manager, Charles Adams
Division Vice President Case ready Meats Poultry, Bernie Adcock
Vice President Marketing, Bill Welsh
Assistant Vice President Credit Finance, Todd Walker
Vice President of Marketing, Michael Rogers
National Accounts Manager, Peter Chesna
Vice President General Manager Greater China, James Rice
VICE PRESIDENT SALES NATIONAL ACCOUNTS, Brad Johnston
Vice President Division, John Halter
Vice President, Russell Nugent
Vice Presidentof Sales, Mike Brown
Vice President Of Human Resources Operations, Hector Gonzalez
Tyson CVP, Todd McCool
Vice President, Chad Vacha
Division Vice President, David Mantooth
VP Operations, Michael Roetzel
Vice President of Foodservice Marketing, Kim M Cupelli
RSM West Coast CVP, Kristopher Duckworth
Vice President Government Relations, Chuck Penry
Vice President Diversity, Cathy Clark
Senior Vice President Consumer Products, Gary Sheneman
Vice President Fresh Meats Foodservice, Glenn Strickholm
Sls Deli Vice President, Brent Schmiegelow
Vice President Food Service Sales East, Mike Curtin
Senior Vice President Corporate Marketing and Communications, Charlie Young
Vice President Internal Audit, April Gage
Vice President Engineering, Scott Henkes
Executive Vice President and General Counsel, David Vanbebber
Vice President, James Lochner
Senior Vice President Chief Accounting Officer And Controller, Craig Hart
Vice President, Davis L Van Bebber
Vice President Information Technology, Robert Zimmerman
Vice President Of Pork Procurement, Gary Machan
National Account Manager, Steve Maher
National Account Manager, Kevin Gaffney
Vice President F, Hubert Mendonca
Executive Vice President, Steven Hankins
Vice President Customer Marketing, Christopher Haller
Senior Vice President Insights and Innovation, Jennifer Bentz
National Account Manager, Dave Collins
Vice President Shared Accounting Services, Alan Shanks
Vice President of Information Systems, Carla T Woods
Vice President Engineering, Kent Bearson
Senior Vice President, Nick Tyler
Vice President Marketing Services, Christopher Miles
VP Supply Chain, Gregory Schweitzer
VICE PRESIDENT NATIONAL ACCOUNTS, Brian Roberts
VICE PRESIDENT SALES, Geordie Shaw
VICE PRESIDENT SS FINANCIAL ACCOUNTING, Virgil Rehkemper
SENIOR VICE PRESIDENT AND GENERAL MANAGER BEEF ENTERPRISE, Dan Brooks
Vice President, Daniel Heffernan
Chairman, John H. Tyson, age 64
Board Of Directors, Lloyd Hackley

Treasurer, Michelle Brown
Secretary Interim Vice, Sarah Wharry
Auditors: PricewaterhouseCoopers LLP

LOCATIONS

HQ: Tyson Foods Inc
2200 West Don Tyson Parkway, Springdale, AR 72762-6999
Phone: 479 290-4000   **Fax:** 479 290-7984
Web: www.tyson.com

PRODUCTS/OPERATIONS

2017 Sales

	% of total
Beef	38
Chicken	29
Prepared foods	20
Pork	13
Other	1
Inter segment Sales	
Total	**100**

COMPETITORS

Big Heart Pet Brands	Koch Foods
Buckhead Beef	Laura's Lean Beef Co.
CGC	Mars Incorporated
Cargill	Mondelez International
Casa de Oro Foods	National Beef Packing
Clougherty Packing	New Market Poultry
Coleman Natural Foods	Perdue Incorporated
ConAgra	Petaluma Poultry
Cooper Farms	Pilgrim's Pride
Eberly Poultry	Plainville Farms
Empire Kosher Poultry	Raeford Farms
Foster Farms	Rosen's Diversified
Freedman Meats	Sanderson Farms
Gruma	Shelton's
H. J. Heinz Limited	Smithfield Foods
Hormel	Tecumseh Poultry
JBS	U.S. Premium Beef

HISTORICAL FINANCIALS

Company Type: Public

Income Statement

FYE: September 30

	REVENUE ($ mil.)	NET INCOME ($ mil.)	NET PROFIT MARGIN	EMPLOYEES
09/17*	38,260	1,774	4.6%	122,000
10/16	36,881	1,768	4.8%	114,000
10/15	41,373	1,220	2.9%	113,000
09/14	37,580	864	2.3%	124,000
09/13	34,374	778	2.3%	115,000
Annual Growth	**2.7%**	**22.9%**	**—**	**1.5%**

*Fiscal year change

2017 Year-End Financials

Debt ratio: 36.35%
Return on equity: 17.66%
Cash ($ mil.): 318
Current ratio: 1.55
Long-term debt ($ mil.): 9,297

No. of shares (mil.): 368
Dividends
  Yield: 0.0%
  Payout: 18.7%
Market value ($ mil.): 25,926

	STOCK PRICE ($) FY Close	P/E High/Low		PER SHARE ($) Earnings	Dividends	Book Value
09/17*	70.45	15	11	4.79	0.90	28.64
10/16	74.67	16	9	4.53	0.60	26.61
10/15	44.39	15	12	2.95	0.40	26.26
09/14	37.74	18	11	2.37	0.30	23.64
09/13	28.60	14	7	2.12	0.30	18.03
Annual Growth	**25.3%**	—	—	**22.6%**	**31.6%**	**12.3%**

*Fiscal year change

U.S. VENTURE, INC.

Smitten with the love of oil distribution the founding Schmidt family owns and operates U.S. Venture (formerly U.S. Oil). The company's U.S. Oil division (formerly U.S. Petroleum Operations) supplies refined oil products to residents in the Midwest and does a lot more. In addition to the wholesale distribution of oil products (its largest revenue generator) the company operates gas stations and installs gas pumps tanks and other petroleum-related equipment. U.S. Venture also provides plumbing and HVAC services (Design Air) collects used waste oil to be processed into burner fuel and has a metal custom manufacturing unit.

Operations

U.S. Venture's operating divisions are:

Design Air (serving commercial and residential HVAC contractors throughout Wisconsin and Upper Michigan);

Express Convenience Centers (gas stations and convenience stores throughout Wisconsin);

U.S. AutoForce (tires automotive parts and lubricants);

U.S. Custom Manufacturing (forming and supplying metal tubing for the automotive furniture and lawn and garden and other industries; it also makes frame components handles and rails);

U.S. Lubricants (lubricants for trucking industrial and commercial customers in the Upper Midwest);

U.S. Oil (bulk storage terminals wholesale and branded distribution of petroleum products multiple-brand C-store Jobbership and gas station-related real estate activities); and

U.S. Petroleum Equipment (tanks pumps and related equipment for petroleum-based products and vehicle lift equipment; it also offers installation and lighting services throughout Wisconsin and Upper Michigan).

Geographic Reach

Under its U.S. AutoForce brand U.S. Oil also operates about a dozen warehouses in Illinois Minnesota Missouri Nebraska Iowa South Dakota and Wisconsin offering auto parts (for brakes exhausts and suspensions) and tires. U.S. Venture operates 12 refined products terminals across the Midwest (with a total storage capacity of about 127 million gallons at its bulk fuel storage tanks) including the Cheboygan 164000 barrels facility.

Strategy

The company has grown its geographic presence through complementary acquisitions.

Mergers and Acquisitions

Expanding its green fuel options in 2013 U.S. Oil bought six compressed natural gas fueling stations from We Energies (two in Milwaukee and one each in Appleton Franklin Racine and Waukesha) bring U.S. Oil's total to nine in Wisconsin. U.S. Oil plans to add a minimum of 50 additional GAIN Clean Fueling sites by 2018.

Growing is presence in North Central Wisconsin and the Upper Peninsula of Michigan in 2012 the bought Draeger Oil Company's branded dealer division. Under the terms of the deal U.S. Oil provides fuel supply to more than 50 retail gas stations while Draeger retained the transportation portion.

U.S. Ventures (U.S. Oil) also expanded its petroleum products distribution presence in Indiana in 2012 through the purchase of Farmersburg-based Trueblood Oil's branded wholesale fuel supply business.

Company Background

U.S. Oil was established in the 1950s as Schmidt Oil by the sons of local fuel distributor Albert Schmidt who landed his first job in the oil business in 1923. The company changed its name to U.S.

Venture in 2010 to reflect the company's increasingly diverse portfolio of entrepreneurial businesses.

EXECUTIVES

President and CEO, John Schmidt
VP Marketing and Strategy, Jeff Van Brunt
President U.S. Gain, Mike Koel
Vice President and Chief Financial Officer, Jay Walters
VP Human Resources, Lori Hoersch
Vice President Purchasing and Product Management, Joe Gretz
TREASURER, Judy Engen-pazdera
Auditors: DELOITTE & TOUCHE LLP MILWAU

LOCATIONS

HQ: U.S. VENTURE, INC.
425 BETTER WAY, APPLETON, WI 549156192
Phone: 920 739-6101
Web: WWW.USVENTURE.COM

PRODUCTS/OPERATIONS

Selected Operations

Design Air (heating and air conditioning equipment)
Express Convenience Centers (gas stations and car washes)
U.S. AutoForce (exhaust pipe manufacturing and autoparts distribution)
U.S. Custom Manufacturing (tube bending and fabrication)
U.S. Lubricants (motor oil and related products)
U.S. Oil (gasoline fuel oil and natural gas)
U.S. Petroleum Equipment (petroleum-related equipment installation)

COMPETITORS

7-Eleven	Quality State Oil
Apex Oil	Company
Marathon Oil	QuikTrip
Motiva Enterprises	Sunoco

HISTORICAL FINANCIALS

Company Type: Private

Income Statement				FYE: July 31
	REVENUE ($ mil.)	NET INCOME ($ mil.)	NET PROFIT MARGIN	EMPLOYEES
07/16	6,413	97	1.5%	1,182
07/15	8,076	173	2.1%	—
07/14	9,088	49	0.5%	—
07/13	7,346	47	0.6%	—
Annual Growth	(4.4%)	27.4%		

2016 Year-End Financials

Debt ratio: ——
Return on equity: 1.50%
Cash ($ mil.): 4
Current ratio: 0.70
Long-term debt ($ mil.): —

Dividends
Yield: —
Payout: —
Market value ($ mil.): —

UGI Corp.

UGI (derived from its original name United Gas Improvement) is a leading energy services marketing and distribution company and distributes propane across the US and internationally. The company is led by its 26%-owned propane distributor AmeriGas Partners the largest source of the holding company's sales and a leading US propane marketer. It also has utility operations: Its UGI Utilities subsidiary distributes electricity to 62000 customers and gas to about 626000 customers in Pennsylvania. The company's other operations include energy marketing in the mid-Atlantic region propane distribution in Asia and Europe and electricity generation and energy services.

HISTORY

United Gas Improvement was set up in 1882 by Philadelphia industrialist Thomas Dolan and other investors to acquire a gasworks and a new coal-gas manufacturing process. The firm also bought electric utilities and street railways across the US and moved into construction. The 1935 Public Utility Holding Company Act led to United Gas Improvement's restructuring when the SEC ordered the divestiture of many of its operations in 1941. The company converted to natural gas in the 1950s and entered the liquefied petroleum gas (LPG) business in 1959. It became UGI Corporation in 1968.

UGI shifted its emphasis to propane in the late 1980s buying Petrolane in 1995 and combining it with AmeriGas Propane to create AmeriGas Partners which then went public. Overseas UGI launched a joint venture in 1996 to build an LPG import project in Romania. The next year it signed a deal to distribute propane in China.

In 1999 UGI moved into consumer products by opening its first Hearth USA retail store in Rockville Maryland which offered hearth items spas grills and patio accessories. It ventured into a growing European market by purchasing FLAGA GmbH a leading gas distributor in Austria and the Czech Republic.

That year a 1997 Pennsylvania law kicked in restructuring the state's electricity industry and enabling customers to choose their electricity provider. In response UGI separated its distribution and power generation operations and in 2000 contributed the bulk of its generation assets to a partnership with Allegheny Energy that sells power to UGI Utilities and other distributors.

In 2001 UGI Enterprises purchased a 20% interest in French propane distributor Antargaz. Also that year the company closed its Hearth USA retail stores. Through its UGI Energy Services subsidiary UGI completed the acquisition of TXU Energy in 2003.

UGI acquired the remaining 80% interest in Antargaz in 2004 expanding its operations in France. Later that year the company continued its European expansion through the acquisition of BP's retail propane distribution business in the Czech Republic.

In 2006 the company acquired the natural gas utility assets of PG Energy for about $580 million. During the next year its Gas Utility unit purchased approximately 79 billion cu. ft. of natural gas for sale to retail core market and off-system sales customers.

To expand its base of gas customers in Pennsylvania in 2008 UGI Utilities acquired PPL Gas Utilities for $32 million. It soon changed that company's name to UGI Central Penn Gas.

In 2010 UGI took advantage of BP's need to raise cash due to its oil spill problems and acquired the liquefied petroleum gas distribution business of BP in Denmark. It also picked up Shell's LPG operations in Poland. Both deals expanded UGI's footprint in the European LPG market.

In fiscal year 2012 the company acquired some of Shell's LPG distribution operations in Europe. The terms of the deal were not disclosed but included the businesses in Belgium Denmark Finland Luxembourg the Netherlands Norway Sweden and the UK adding to the UGI's European market growth with an estimated 300 million gallons of LPG.

That year AmeriGas Partners acquired Energy Transfer Partners' propane distribution business (Heritage Propane). The acquired business conducted propane operations in 41 US states through HOLP and Titan Propane LLC.

In 2013 UGI subsidiary Flaga acquired BP's LPG distribution business in Poland. BP's Polish LPG business distributes more than 150 million gallons of LPG a year.

EXECUTIVES

Chief Risk Officer and Vice President and Chief Financial Officer UGI International, Davinder Athwal
VP New Business Development; President UGI Enterprises and UGI Energy Services, Bradley C. Hall, age 64, $390,723 total compensation
President and CEO, John L. Walsh, age 62, $1,078,342 total compensation
CFO, Kirk R. Oliver, age 59, $532,902 total compensation
VP General Counsel and Secretary, Monica M. Gaudiosi, age 55, $434,611 total compensation
President and CEO UGI Utilities, Robert F. (Bob) Beard, age 51
CEO Antargaz, Eric Naddeo
President and CEO AmeriGas, Jerry E. Sheridan, age 51, $526,474 total compensation
Managing Director AvantiGas, Neil Murphy
President UGI International, Roger Perreault
Vice President Engineering, Chuck Hurchalla
Regional Vice President, Steve Quagliana
Vice President Of Human Resources, Carole Hagy
Senior Vice President Finance And Chief Financial Officer, Anthony Mendicino
Senior Vice President, Brett Hart
Vice President of Human Resources, Jim Budd
Vice President Finance and Administration, David Pataki
Vice President and Chief Accounting Officer, Marie-Dominique Ortiz-Landazabal
Vice Presidenr and General Counsel, Bob Knauss
Treasurer, Robert Knauss
Chairman, Marvin O. Schlanger, age 69
Assistant Secretary, Jessica Milner
Auditors: Ernst & Young LLP

LOCATIONS

HQ: UGI Corp.
460 North Gulph Road, King of Prussia, PA 19406
Phone: 610 337-1000
Web: www.ugicorp.com

PRODUCTS/OPERATIONS

2016 sales

	$ mil.	% of total
AmeriGas propane	2,311	40
UGI International		
UGI France	1,344	23
Flaga & other	524	9
Midstream & marketing		
Energy Services	813	14
Electric generation	62	1
UGI utility	768	13
Corporate	3	-
Adjustments	(143.9)	-
Total	**5,685**	**100**

Selected Subsidiaries and Affiliates

AmeriGas Inc.
AmeriGas Propane Inc.
AmeriGas Partners L.P. (26%)
AmeriGas Propane L.P.
AmeriGas Technology Group Inc.
Petrolane Incorporated
Four Flags Drilling Company Inc.
Ashtola Production Company

UGI Ethanol Development Corporation
Newbury Holding Company
UGI Enterprises Inc. (energy marketing and services)
  CFN Enterprises Inc.
  Eastfield International Holdings Inc.
  FLAGA GmbH (propane distribution; Austria the
    Czech Republic and Slovakia)
  Eurogas Holdings Inc.
  McHugh Service Company
  UGI Energy Services Inc.
  GASMARK (gas marketing)
  POWERMARK (electricity marketing)
  UGI International Enterprises Inc.
  UGI Europe Inc.
  Antargaz (propane distribution France)
  FLAGA GmbH (propane distribution Austria)
UGI Properties Inc.
UGI Utilities Inc. (natural gas and electric utility)
United Valley Insurance Company

COMPETITORS

Chesapeake Utilities	Ferrellgas Partners
Dominion Energy	National Fuel Gas
Duquesne Light	NorthWestern
Holdings	PPL Corporation
Energy Transfer	Suburban Propane
Exelon	

HISTORICAL FINANCIALS

Company Type: Public

Income Statement

FYE: September 30

	REVENUE ($ mil.)	NET INCOME ($ mil.)	NET PROFIT MARGIN	EMPLOYEES
09/17	6,120	436	7.1%	13,000
09/16	5,685	364	6.4%	13,320
09/15	6,691	281	4.2%	13,570
09/14	8,277	337	4.1%	12,800
09/13	7,194	278	3.9%	12,800
Annual Growth	(4.0%)	11.9%	—	0.4%

2017 Year-End Financials

Debt ratio: 39.19%	No. of shares (mil.): 173
Return on equity: 14.52%	Dividends
Cash ($ mil.): 558	Yield: 0.0%
Current ratio: 1.00	Payout: 39.6%
Long-term debt ($ mil.): 3,994	Market value ($ mil.): 8,114

	STOCK PRICE ($) FY Close	P/E High/Low	PER SHARE ($) Earnings	Dividends	Book Value
09/17	46.86	21 17	2.46	0.98	18.27
09/16	45.24	23 15	2.08	0.93	16.48
09/15	34.82	24 20	1.60	0.89	15.62
09/14	34.09	28 17	1.92	1.08	15.44
09/13	39.13	26 19	1.61	1.11	14.52
Annual Growth	4.6%	— —	11.2%	(3.1%)	5.9%

Ulta Beauty Inc

EXECUTIVES

SVP General Counsel and Secretary, Robert S. Guttman, age 62, $290,285 total compensation
CEO and Director, Mary N. Dillon, age 55
Senior Vice President Marketing, Jeffrey Severts
CFO and Assistant Secretary, Scott Settersten
SVP Store Operations, Cynthia Payne
SVP Merchandising, Janet Taake
Director, Robert F. DiRomualdo, age 71
Director, Charles J. Philippin, age 64
Director, Charles Heilbronn, age 61
Director, Lorna E. Nagler, age 58

President CEO and Director, Carl (Chuck) Rubin, age 55
Independent Director, Catherine Halligan
Independent Director, Kenneth Stevens
Independent Director, Michael MacDonald
Auditors: Ernst & Young LLP

LOCATIONS

HQ: Ulta Beauty Inc
  1000 Remington Blvd., Suite 120, Bolingbrook, IL
  60440
Phone: 630 410-4800
Web: www.ulta.com

COMPETITORS

Bath & Body Works	Nordstrom
Bed Bath & Beyond	Premier Salons
Body Shop	Regis Corporation
CVS Caremark	Sally Beauty
Dillard's	Sephora USA
J. C. Penney	Supercuts
L'Oreal USA	Target Corporation
Lush Ltd.	Wal-Mart
Macy's	Walgreen
Merle Norman	

HISTORICAL FINANCIALS

Company Type: Public

Income Statement

FYE: January 28

	REVENUE ($ mil.)	NET INCOME ($ mil.)	NET PROFIT MARGIN	EMPLOYEES
01/17	4,854	409	8.4%	31,800
01/16	3,924	320	8.2%	26,500
01/15*	3,241	257	7.9%	22,400
02/14	2,670	202	7.6%	19,600
02/13	2,220	172	7.8%	16,100
Annual Growth	21.6%	24.1%	—	18.5%

*Fiscal year change

2017 Year-End Financials

Debt ratio: —	No. of shares (mil.): 62
Return on equity: 27.46%	Dividends
Cash ($ mil.): 385	Yield: —
Current ratio: 2.90	Payout: —
Long-term debt ($ mil.): —	Market value ($ mil.): 16,864

	STOCK PRICE ($) FY Close	P/E High/Low	PER SHARE ($) Earnings	Dividends	Book Value
01/17	271.44	42 23	6.52	0.00	24.95
01/16	181.17	37 26	4.98	0.00	22.71
01/15*	131.94	34 21	3.98	0.00	19.44
02/14	85.71	41 23	3.15	0.00	15.62
02/13	97.54	37 28	2.68	0.00	12.29
Annual Growth	29.2%	— —	24.9%	—	19.4%

*Fiscal year change

UMB Financial Corp

UMB Financial is the holding company for four UMB-branded commercial banks serving Arizona Colorado Illinois Kansas Nebraska Oklahoma and Missouri. Through some 110 branches the banks offer standard services such as checking and savings accounts credit and debit cards and trust and investment services. Commercial loans account for more than 50% of UMB's loan portfolio. Beyond its banking business it offers insurance brokerage services leasing treasury management health sav-ings accounts and proprietary mutual funds through its more than 20 subsidiaries. Founded in 1913 the bank ranks first in the Kansas City market (based on deposits).

Operations

It operates through four business segments: Bank Payment Solutions Institutional Investment Management and Asset Servicing.

Its Bank segment focuses on traditional commercial and consumer banking treasury management leasing foreign exchange merchant bankcards wealth management brokerage insurance capital markets investment banking corporate trust and correspondent banking.

The Payment Solutions segment offers consumer and commercial credit and debit cards prepaid debit card solutions healthcare services and institutional cash management.

UMB Financial's Institutional Investment Management segment serves the intermediary and institutional markets through mutual funds traditional separate accounts and sub-advisory relationships using private equity and fixed income investment strategies.

The Asset Servicing segment caters to the asset management industry and supports investment products such as mutual funds alternative investments and managed accounts.

Geographic Reach

UMB Financial's four commercial banks are located in Arizona Colorado Kansas and Missouri. Its principal subsidiary bank Missouri-based UMB Bank n.a. also has branches in Illinois Kansas Nebraska and Oklahoma. In Texas the firm operates a loan production office.

Sales and Marketing

UMB Financial serves commercial retail government and correspondent bank customers through its branch locations call center Internet banking and network of ATMs.

The company spent $24.15 million toward marketing and business development expenses in 2014; up from $22.7 million in 2013 but down from the $24.6 million it spent in 2012.

Financial Performance

UMB Financial has enjoyed rising revenue and profit in recent years thanks to loan asset growth and . Revenue in 2014 grew by more than 2% to $862.56 million thanks to 8% growth in trust and securities processing fee income and thanks to higher loan interest income from another year of double-digit growth in average loan balances.

Following several years of profit growth net income in 2014 fell by 10% to $120.66 million mostly because the bank spent more toward salary raises and incurred higher benefit costs but also because it spent more on equipment and a contingency reserve it established in 2014 related to a settlement agreement involving the sellers and employees of PCM.

Cash from operations fell by 21% to $243.78 million partially from lower cash earnings but also because it adjusted for fewer non-cash items such as accrued expenses and taxes than it did in 2013.

The company's loan assets grew by 14% to $7.47 billion in 2014 while its total deposits increased slightly to $13.62 billion.

Strategy

UMB Financial is focused on four main strategies for growth. The first is to grow its fee-based business through acquisitions or organically as fee-based services are typically non-credit related and are not generally affected by fluctuations in interest rates. Accordingly the bank has boosted its non-interest income by 20% over the past three years from $414 million in 2011 to $498.7 million in 2014. In mid-2014 to add fuel to this growth UMB Bank purchased the Oklahoma Corporate Trust Business from RCB Bank to be incorporated into its own business in the region expanding the company's reach into the Oklahoma Corporate Trust Market.

The second strategy is to focus on net interest income through loan and deposit growth. In 2014 for example the bank grew its loan assets by a whopping 14% adding $16.8 million in net interest income (5% more than in 2013) to the bank's top line.

Thirdly UMB Financial aims to improve operating efficiencies by offering more services through its existing branch network which helped it grow its loan and deposit business greatly in 2014.

Fourth the firm is focused on managing its capital to promote investor confidence and acquisition opportunities.

Mergers and Acquisitions

In late 2014 UMB agreed to buy commercial finance firm Marquette Financial from longtime owners the Pohlad family for $182 million. The acquisition would increase UMB's presence in key growth markets Arizona and Texas — where Marquette operated Meridian Bank. As part of the deal the Pohlad family gained a 7% stake in UMB (the second-largest stake behind chairman Mariner Kemper who holds 12%).

Company Background

To grow its fee-based business and diversify its business model UMB has made several acquisitions in its past. The company built up its investment advisory and corporate trust business through several 2009 purchases. In 2010 UMB made 10 acquisitions including Prairie Capital Management and Indiana-based Reams Asset Management. The deals more than doubled UMB's Scout Investment Advisors' assets under management to more than $27 billion.

EXECUTIVES

Senior Vice President and Director Purchasing, Nancy Grasse

Senior Vice President and Corporate Controller, Bryan Walker

Chairman President and CEO, J. Mariner Kemper, age 44, $862,110 total compensation

Vice Chairman UMB Financial Corporation and President and CEO UMB Bank, Michael D. (Mike) Hagedorn, age 51, $444,986 total compensation

CEO Scout Investments, Andrew J. (Andy) Iseman, age 53, $6,047 total compensation

President UMB Fund Services Inc., Anthony J. (Tony) Fischer, age 58, $281,154 total compensation

EVP and Chief Credit Officer, Christian R. (Chris) Swett, age 61

EVP and Chief Lending Officer, Thomas S. (Tom) Terry, age 53

CFO, Ram Shankar, age 44

EVP and Chief Human Resources Officer, Shannon A. Johnson, age 37

EVP and Director of Operations Bank, Kevin M. Macke, age 44

EVP and Chief Risk Officer, Jennifer M. Payne, age 40

Executive Vice President of Subsidiary, Stephen Kitts

Vice President of Commercial Underwriting, Rebecca A Lang

Vice President Marketing, Kelli Christman

Senior Vice President Investment Division, Raleigh Trovillion

Vice President Banking Services Compliance Directo, Stephanie Boryla

Vice President Information Technology, Kris Loveless

Assistant Vice President Information Security, Scott Bennett

Vice President of Commercial Banking, Mark Winker

Senior Vice President Management Information Syste, John Switzer

Vice President private Banking Client Manager, Chad Roberts

Vice President Commercial Banking, Jess Adams

Vice President Commercial Bankcard Sales Manager, Tom Carignan

Senior Vice President Loan Operations, Linda Gallagher

Vice President, Douglas Hare

Vice President Correspondent Banking, Jackie Wise

Vice President Financial Consultant, Tony Beach

Senior Vice President Credit Risk Director, Jim Caniglia

Vice President and Manager Applications Development, Bart Klein

Vice President New Business Development, Scott Reeves Scott Reeves

Vice President And Assistant Treasurer, Jean Evans

Executive Vice President, Christine Pierson

Vice President, Michael Nash

Vice President Channel Product Manager, Mark Courtney

Vice President Director Of Interactiv, Terry Kincheloe

Senior Vice President Director of Compliance And Oversight, Warren Green

Vice President, Cory Miller

Vice President Payroll Manager, John Morris

Vice President Regional Operation Manager, Kimberly Romero

Senior Vice President, Gordon Gendler

Vice President, Sandy Battas

Assistant Vice President Branch Manager, Teresa Shuffield

Assistant Vice President Business Banking, Edin Salkic

Small Business Credit Officer Assistant Vice President, Claude Einstein

Vice President, Mark Volkmer

Vice President Business Development Manager Card Services, Jennifer M Russell

Assistant Vice President, Lori Kohler

Executive Vice President; Director Payment and Technology Solutions Division of UMB Bank, Terry D'Amore

Vice President Corporate Trust, Brian Krippner

Senior Vice President, Ann Porter

Senior Vice President Retail Banking, Eric Craine

Vice President And Program Operations Management Lssbb, Renee Taylor

Vice President Product Development and Marketing, Bruce Parker

Assistant Vice President and B, Sean Renfro

Vice President Senior Loan Review, James Engelhart

Vice President Senior Loan Review Officer, Chris Landry

Assistant Vice President Financial Center Manager, James Davis

Vice President Of Commercial Underwriting, Rebecca Lang

Executive Vice President Trust Investments, James Moffett

Senior Vice President Chief Lending Officer Arizona, Robert Faver

Assistant Vice President and Commercial Banking Officer, Josh Fink

Assistant Vice President, Josh Hahn

Vice President Finance, Debbie Johnson

Assistant Vice President, Steve Collins

Executive Vice President, Thomas Hof

Vice President Commercial Banking, William Thomasjr

Finance: Vice President, Benjamin Black

Senior Vice President, Randall Tharp

Senior Vice President, Rick Bennett

Senior Vice President Treasury Management, David Pucci

Assistant Vice President Commercial Banking, Michael Laplant

Assistant Vice President Financial Center Manager, Eric Putnam

Assistant Vice President Financial Center Manager, Keva Whitley

Senior Vice President Director of Investor Relations, Kay Gregory

Assistant Vice President Consumer Loan Officer, Patrick Johnson

Senior Vice President Commercial Real Estate, Cydney Gurgens

Vice President, Laurie Box

Vice President, Rick Beaver

Vice President, Robin Waters

Assistant Vice President and Financial Center Manager, Douglas Empson

Executive Vice President, Peter Mennihan

Vice President Product Manager, Uma Wilson

Senior Vice President, Janet Clements

Senior Vice President and Counsel, Paul Scheuerman

Assistant Vice President Marketing Activation, Jeff Bowers

Senior Vice President Corporate Communication, Barry Brakeville

Vice President Commercial Relationship Manager, Shawn Harbour

Vice President Treasury Management, Lanie Sedlacek

Vice President Implementation Manager, Lori Lamanno

Executive Vice President and Senior Credit Officer, Bruce McGrath

Senior Vice President, Malcolm Evans

Vice President Private Wealth Marketing, Leigh Adams

Vice President Relationship Manager Business Banki, Sean Scibienski

Senior Vice President Commercial Lending, Aaron Emel

Senior Vice President Commercial Banking, David Walters

Vice President, Ryan Lynch

Assistant Vice President Treasury Analyst, Mike Groff

Vice President Relationship Manager, Jan Dunham

Vice President And Corporate Legal Couns, Megan Mercer

VICE PRESIDENT, CHIP SCHULTZ

Vice President and Director of Financial Markets and Fiduciary Compliance, Cathy Clark

Vice President, Karen Hanson

Vice President Commercial Relationship Manager, Bryson Bowden

Vice President, Robert Gladu

Senior Vice President Commercial Lending, Richard Trease

Vice President, Clay Phillips

Vice President Business Banking, Gerry Smith

Senior Vice President Commercial Lending, Valerie Kroiss

Senior Vice President, Dennis Wright

Senior Vice President Public Finance, Todd Holder

Vice President Senior Trust Advisor, James Gilmour

Vice President, Marcia Matthews

Vice President Legal Counsel, Terri Munsell

Senior Vice President Private Wealth Management, Clinton Patterson

Assistant Vice President Business Banking, Steve Shumate

Assistant Vice President Small Business Banking, Michelle Mountjoy

Vice President Corporate Trust and Escrow Services, Madelyn Wallace

Senior Vice President, Reginald Johnson

Fund Accounting Manager Assistant Vice President, Brian Schmidt

Assistant Vice President Information Technology Help Desk and Olbs Manager, Michael Meredith

Auditors: KPMG LLP

LOCATIONS

HQ: UMB Financial Corp
1010 Grand Boulevard, Kansas City, MO 64106
Phone: 816 860-7000 **Fax:** 816 860-7143
Web: www.umb.com

PRODUCTS/OPERATIONS

2016 Sales

	$ mil.	% of total
Interest income		
Loans	386	29
Securities	131	13
Federal funds and resell agreements	2	-
Interest-bearing due from banks	2.4	
Trading securities	0.6	
Non-interest income		
Trust and securities processing	239	24
Trading and investment banking	21	2
Service charges on deposit accounts	86	9
Insurance fees and commissions	4	
Brokerage fees	17	2
Bankcard fees	68	7
Gains on sales of securities available for sale net	8	1
Equity earnings (losses) on alternative investments	2	-
Other	26	3
Total	**999**	**100**

Selected Subsidiaries & Affiliates

Grand Distribution Services LLC
J.D. Clark & Company
Kansas City Financial Corporation
Kansas City Realty Company
Prairie Capital Management LLC
Scout Distributors LLC
Scout Investment Advisors Inc.
UMB Banc Leasing Corp.
UMB Bank and Trust n.a.
UMB Bank Arizona n.a.
UMB Bank Colorado n.a.
UMB Capital Corporation
UMB Community Development Corporation
UMB Distribution Services LLC
UMB Financial Services Inc.
UMB Fund Services Inc.
UMB Insurance Inc.
UMB National Bank of America
UMB Realty Company LLC
UMB Redevelopment Corporation
UMB Trust Company of South Dakota
United Missouri Insurance Company

COMPETITORS

BOK Financial	Great Southern Bancorp
Bank of America	Guaranty Bancorp
Capitol Federal	TCF Financial
Financial	U.S. Bancorp
Commerce Bancshares	Zions Bancorporation
Dickinson Financial	
First National of	
Nebraska	

HISTORICAL FINANCIALS

Company Type: Public

Income Statement

FYE: December 31

	ASSETS ($ mil.)	NET INCOME ($ mil.)	INCOME AS % OF ASSETS	EMPLOYEES
12/16	20,682	158	0.8%	3,688
12/15	19,094	116	0.6%	3,830
12/14	17,500	120	0.7%	3,592
12/13	16,911	133	0.8%	3,498
12/12	14,927	122	0.8%	3,448
Annual Growth	**8.5%**	**6.7%**	**—**	**1.7%**

2016 Year-End Financials

Debt ratio: 0.37%	No. of shares (mil.): 49
Return on equity: 8.21%	Dividends
Cash ($ mil.): 1,177	Yield: 0.0%
Current ratio: —	Payout: 30.7%
Long-term debt ($ mil.): —	Market value ($ mil.): 3,831

	STOCK PRICE ($) FY Close	P/E High/Low		PER SHARE ($) Earnings	Dividends	Book Value
12/16	77.12	25	13	3.22	0.99	39.51
12/15	46.55	24	19	2.44	0.95	38.34
12/14	56.89	25	20	2.65	0.91	36.10
12/13	64.28	20	13	3.20	0.87	33.30
12/12	43.82	17	12	3.04	0.83	31.71
Annual Growth	**15.2%**	**—**	**—**	**1.4%**	**4.5%**	**5.6%**

Umpqua Holdings Corp

Umpqua Holdings thinks of itself not so much as a bank but rather a retailer that sells financial products. Consequently many of the company's 380-plus Umpqua Bank "stores" in northern California northern Nevada Idaho Oregon and Washington feature coffee bars and computer cafes. While customers sip Umpqua-branded coffee pay bills online attend a financial seminar catch a poetry reading or check out wares from local merchants staff members pitch deposit accounts mortgages loans life insurance investments and more. Subsidiary Umpqua Investments (formerly Strand Atkinson Williams & York) provides retail brokerage services through more than a dozen locations mostly inside Umpqua Bank branches.

Operations

Umpqua operates two business segments: Community Banking which made up 79% of the company's total revenue during 2015 and provides traditional banking services as well as wealth management and private banking services for wealthier individuals; and Home Lending (21% of revenue) which originates and sells residential mortgage loans.

The company makes more than 75% of its revenue from interest income. About 72% of its revenue came from loan interest (including fees) during 2015 with another 5% coming from interest on investment securities. The rest of its revenue came from residential mortgage banking revenue (9% of revenue) deposit account service charges (5%) brokerage revenue (2%) and other miscellaneous income streams.

Geographic Reach

Oregon-based Umpqua Bank has branches in Idaho Washington Oregon California and Northern Nevada. Umpqua Investments has offices in Portland Lake Oswego and Medford Oregon as well as Santa Rosa California.

Sales and Marketing

Umpqua Holdings promotes its brand through customer-facing channels public relations social media and community-based events. It spent $11.4 million on marketing to promote its brand during 2015 up from $9.5 million and $6.1 million in 2014 and 2013 respectively.

Financial Performance

The bank's annual revenues have doubled since 2011 as its loan and lease assets have tripled to $16.85 billion which has resulted in strong interest income growth. Exceptional revenue growth and effective cost controls have helped the bank's net income triple over the same period.

Umpqua Holdings' revenue jumped 20% to $1.21 billion during 2015 mostly as its earning assets (including loans investments and loans held for sale) swelled by 20% which led to higher interest income. The bank's non-interest income also rose 52% for the year mostly thanks to the 2014 acquisition of Sterling Financial with residential

mortgage banking revenue brokerage commissions and deposit service charges all growing during the year.

Strong revenue growth in 2015 drove the bank's net income up 51% to $222.54 million for the year. Umpqua's operating cash levels climbed 5% to $376.74 million as earnings rose.

Strategy

Umpqua Bank's primary mission is to become the top community-oriented financial services firm in the Western US by strategically acquiring banks in new markets and building its brand by offering unique personal experience for customers entering its "store" branches. Its mid-2014 acquisition of Sterling Financial — the largest ever acquisition in Umpqua's history — successfully extended the bank's presence in Southern California Eastern Washington Eastern Oregon and Idaho.

The bank differentiates itself by encouraging clients to come into its stores instead of using impersonal interfaces like ATMs and electronic banking more cost-effective methods preferred by many of its competitors. The bank's "Next Generation" stores feature interactive touch-screen walls fresh fruit and cold drinks. It hopes the comfortable environment will inspire customers to use more of the bank's financial services.

Hoping to build upon its one-of-a-kind branch experiences Umpqua Bank in 2015 launched its Silicon Valley-based Pivotus Ventures Inc subsidiary to explore disruptive new bank technologies.

In 2016 Umpqua launched its corporate banking division which is dedicated to providing companies with access to such offerings as treasury management international banking debt capital markets and others.

Mergers and Acquisitions

In April 2014 Umpqua Bank acquired $10-billion-in-assets Sterling Financial Corp. headquartered in Spokane Washington. The largest merger in Umpqua's history created the West Coast's largest community bank with some $22 billion in assets and 394 stores across five states. The Sterling branches were rebranded as part of the $1.9 billion deal.

Company Background

Traditionally consumer focused Umpqua Bank established a business banking division in 2011 to court small and mid-sized business clients. That year it pursued deposit growth assembled new lending teams and added new stores in key metropolitan areas like Portland Oregon; Seattle; San Francisco; and California's Silicon Valley.

Umpqua Holdings established a wealth management division in 2009 and launched a trust services group the following year. It provided asset management services through an agreement with independent firm Ferguson Wellman Capital Management.

EXECUTIVES

Evp Wealth Management Umpqua Holdings And Umpqua Bank, Kelly Johnson
EVP Creative Strategies Group Umpqua Bank, Lani Hayward, age 50
EVP and Chief Lending Officer Umpqua Holdings Corp and Umpqua Bank, David F. (Dave) Shotwell, age 58
EVP CFO and Principal Financial Officer Umpqua Holdings and Umpqua Bank, Ronald L. (Ron) Farnsworth, age 47, $425,000 total compensation
EVP Treasurer and Principal Accounting Officer Umpqua Holdings and Umpqua Bank, Neal T. McLaughlin, age 49
EVP Corporate Communications Umpqua Bank, Eve Callahan, age 43
President CEO and Director, Cort O'Haver, age 54, $565,000 total compensation

EVP and Chief Auditor Umpqua Bank, Joel Brandenburg, age 54

EVP Enterprise Risk Management Umpqua Holdings Corp and Umpqua Bank, Gary F. Neal, age 62

EVP Associate Relations Umpqua Holdings Corp and Umpqua Bank, Sheri T. Burns, age 49

EVP Cultural Enhancement and Government Relations Umpqua Bank, Marty J. Dickinson, age 47

EVP General Counsel and Corporate Secretary Umpqua Holdings Corp and Umpqua Bank, Andrew H. Ognall, age 45, $300,000 total compensation

Executive Vice President and Chief Credit Officer of the Company and the Bank, Mark Wardlow

Senior Vice President Data Processing, Bo Harrison

Vice President Rewards and Recognition, Sandy Hunt

Vice President eBanking Product Manager, Jim Averna

Vice President, Patrice Mabie

Vice President Manager, Laurie Vohs

Vice President Retail Operations, Dana Murdock

AVP Store Manager, Patricia Choquette

Senior Vice President International Banking Manager, Anthony Oriti

Chairman, Raymond P. (Ray) Davis, age 68

Vice Chairman, Bryan L. Timm, age 53

Auditors: Moss Adams LLP

LOCATIONS

HQ: Umpqua Holdings Corp
One S.W. Columbia Street, Suite 1200, Portland, OR 97258
Phone: 503 727-4100
Web: www.umpquaholdingscorp.com

PRODUCTS/OPERATIONS

2015 Sales

	$ mil.	% of total
Interest		
Interest and fees on loans and leases	869	72
TaxableInterest and dividends investment securities	58	5
Other	2	-
Non-interest		
Mortgage banking	124	9
Service charges on deposit accounts	59	5
Brokerage	18	2
Gain on loan sales net	22	2
BOLI income	8	1
Gain on investment securities net	2	-
Other	46	4
Adjustments	(7.2)	-
Total	**1,205**	**100**

2015 Sales

	$ mil.	% of total
Community Banking	954	79
Home Lending	250	21
Total	**1,205**	**100**

COMPETITORS

Bank of America	KeyCorp
Bank of the West	U.S. Bancorp
Banner Corp	Washington Federal
Cascade Bancorp	Wells Fargo
Columbia Banking	

HISTORICAL FINANCIALS

Company Type: Public

Income Statement

FYE: December 31

	ASSETS ($ mil.)	NET INCOME ($ mil.)	INCOME AS % OF ASSETS	EMPLOYEES
12/16	24,813	232	0.9%	4,295
12/15	23,387	222	1.0%	4,491
12/14	22,613	147	0.7%	4,569
12/13	11,636	98	0.8%	2,490
12/12	11,795	101	0.9%	2,376
Annual Growth	**20.4%**	**23.0%**	**—**	**16.0%**

2016 Year-End Financials

Debt ratio: 4.90%	No. of shares (mil.): 220
Return on equity: 5.98%	Dividends
Cash ($ mil.): 1,449	Yield: 0.0%
Current ratio: —	Payout: 60.9%
Long-term debt ($ mil.): —	Market value ($ mil.): 4,135

	STOCK PRICE ($) FY Close	P/E High/Low	PER SHARE ($) Earnings	Dividends	Book Value
12/16	18.78	18 13	1.05	0.64	17.79
12/15	15.90	19 15	1.01	0.62	17.48
12/14	17.01	24 20	0.78	0.60	17.17
12/13	19.14	22 14	0.87	0.60	15.43
12/12	11.79	15 13	0.90	0.34	15.41
Annual Growth	**12.3%**	**—**	**3.9%**	**17.1%**	**3.7%**

Under Armour Inc

Chainmail might be out of style but Under Armour makes performance clothes for doing battle on the sports field and in the gym. The maker of performance athletic clothing and technology has risen to the top tier of the industry. Under Armour is the official footwear supplier of the NFL and MLB and partners with the NBA. Its locker room of athlete endorsers include top performers in football basketball soccer and baseball. Products made from its moisture-wicking and heat-dispersing fabrics keep athletes dry and comfortable during workouts. The company is also adding technology to apparel to help customers track their fitness. Under Armour sells online by catalog and through its more than 25000 retail and outlet stores worldwide.

Operations

Apparel designed for winter (COLDGEAR) summer (HEATGEAR) and year-round (ALLSEASONGEAR) wear accounts for over 65% of sales. Footwear runs in about 20% with accessories such as hats bags and gloves contributing under 10%.

Under Armour also has a small but growing Connected Fitness business which comprises fitness-related apps such as MapMyFitness MyFitnessPal Endonondo and UA Record. The free-to-use apps generate revenue from advertising. The segment accounts for about 2% of revenue.

Almost all of Under Armour's products are made by third party manufacturers in 18 countries. Some 60% of the company's products are made in China Jordan Vietnam and Malaysia.

Geographic Reach

Headquartered in Baltimore Under Armour operates its business globally. It has European and Asian subsidiaries and sources from suppliers worldwide. Besides North America where it generates about 85% of sales Under Armour's products are sold primarily in France Germany and the UK.

It sells in Japan and Korea as well through a third-party licensee.

The company?s distribution facilities are located in Glen Burnie Maryland; Mount Juliet Tennessee; and Rialto California.

Sales and Marketing

Under Armour generates about two-thirds of its sales through its wholesale business. Its customers include the likes of Cabela's the Army and Air Force Exchange and Dick's Sporting Goods; the latter is its largest customer and accounts for over 10% of Under Armour's annual revenue.

The company's direct-to-consumer business is also growing rapidly — Under Armour operates over 150 of its own factory outlet and specialty stores primarily located in outlet centers in the US. Many of the company stores are going in Class A malls throughout the US. Some international locations are being targeted as well.

Financial Performance

Under Armour has shown strong growth in revenue and net income over the past decade. In fiscal 2016 sales surged to $4.8 billion up 22%. The company attributes its impressive growth since 2012 to growing interest in performance apparel and its strong brand.

In fiscal 2016 Under Armour's wholesale and direct-to-consumer businesses grew revenue by 19% and 27%. By product type apparel grew 15% footwear 49% and accessories 17%. The company's geographic picture looks good too with US revenue up 16% Asia-Pacific region revenue up 85% EMEA (Europe Middle East and Africa) up 63% and Latin America 34%.

Net income grew 10% to $257.0 million as a result of the higher revenue although a relatively higher cost of goods sold and the negative impact of the strong US dollar on the growing international business meant bottom line growth lagged behind top-line growth.

Cash from operations in fiscal 2016 was $304 million up from an outflow of $44 million the previous year. The increase was due to a $323.1 million increase in cash from operating assets and liabilities as well as a $24.4 million increase in net income.

Strategy

Under Armour is working to increase revenue outside North America. The company has been opening direct sales channels in several South American companies expanding in China and partnering with football (soccer) teams in Europe and South America. The US as a percentage of total sales has fallen from 90% in 2014 to 83% in 2016; the company is growing in Europe and the Asia-Pacific region at roughly the same rate.

The company sees a longer term play in its Connected Fitness category which provides fitness-related apps such as the famous MyFitnessPal nutrition tracker which it acquired in 2015. The segment's revenue increased 320% from 2014 to 2016 and now occupies nearly 2% of total company sales.

Under Armour sees potential in the wearables market going beyond wristwear to embedding sensors into clothing that track fitness metrics for anyone from world-class athletes to people out for a walk. The company's digital fitness center in Austin Texas is expected to play a key role in those developments.

Despite its strong revenue growth internationally in the first half of 2017 near-zero growth in the US in the same period triggered job cuts amounting to 2% of its total workforce. The Connected Fitness segment absorbed around 25 of the 280 layoffs.

Mergers and Acquisitions

In 2015 Under Armour continued its connected fitness investment with the acquisition of MyFitnessPal a digital nutrition and connected fitness firm for $474 million. Another 2015 deal was the acquisition of Endomondo a Denmark-based fitness tracking and social fitness network for about $85 million.

EXECUTIVES

Vice President, Raphael Peck
Chairman and CEO, Kevin A. Plank, age 44, $26,000 total compensation
President and COO, Patrik Frisk, age 54
CTO, Paul Fipps
Chief Supply Chain Officer, Colin Browne, $169,231 total compensation
Chief Digital Officer, Michael Lee, $434,423 total compensation
President North America, Jason LaRose
Acting CFO, David E. Bergman, age 44
Senior Vice President Global Retail, Susie McCabe
Senior Vice President Strategic Partnerships and Entertainment, Todd Montesano
National Sales Manager, Jeff Schwaninger
Senior Vice President Corporate Real Estate, Neil Jurgens
Vice President and Chief Global Security Officer, Frederick Bealefeld
Vice President Global Communications and Entertainment, Diane Pelkey
Senior Vice President Talent, Melissa Wallace
Vice President and Managing Director Europe, Chris Bate
Vice President, Amy Larkin
Senior Vice President Global Operations, Dagmar Chlosta
Senior Vice President Sales, David Heath
Vice President eCommerce North America, George Hanson
Executive Vice President of Business Development, J S Plank
Vice President Supply Chain, Sanjeev Mathur
VP Human Resources, Michele Campion
Vice President Outdoor Apparel, Jordan Wand
VP Running, Fritz Taylor
Auditors: PricewaterhouseCoopers LLP

LOCATIONS

HQ: Under Armour Inc
1020 Hull Street, Baltimore, MD 21230
Phone: 410 454-6428
Web: www.underarmour.com

2016 Sales

	$ mil.	% of total
North America	4,005	83
EMEA	330	7
Asia-Pacific	268	5
Latin America	141	3
Connected Fitness	80	2
Eliminations	(1.4)	—
Total	**4,825**	**100**

PRODUCTS/OPERATIONS

2016 Sales

	$ mil.	% of total
Apparel	3,229	67
Footwear	1,010	21
Accessories	406	8
Licensing	99	2
Connected Fitness	80	2
Eliminations	(1.4)	-
Total	**4,825**	**100**

COMPETITORS

Calvin Klein	North Face
Columbia Sportswear	Patagonia Inc.
Fruit of the Loom	Skechers U.S.A.
Hanesbrands	Victoria's Secret
Jockey International	Stores
L.L. Bean	Warnaco Swimwear
NIKE	adidas

HISTORICAL FINANCIALS

Company Type: Public

Income Statement

FYE: December 31

	REVENUE ($ mil.)	NET INCOME ($ mil.)	NET PROFIT MARGIN	EMPLOYEES
12/16	4,825	256	5.3%	9,400
12/15	3,963	232	5.9%	13,400
12/14	3,084	208	6.7%	10,700
12/13	2,332	162	7.0%	7,800
12/12	1,834	128	7.0%	5,900
Annual Growth	**27.3%**	**18.9%**	**—**	**12.3%**

2016 Year-End Financials

Debt ratio: 22.43%
Return on equity: 13.86%
Cash ($ mil.): 250
Current ratio: 2.87
Long-term debt ($ mil.): 790

No. of shares (mil.): 438
Dividends
Yield: —
Payout: 29.8%
Market value ($ mil.): 12,737

	STOCK PRICE ($) FY Close	P/E High/Low	PER SHARE ($) Earnings	Dividends	Book Value
12/16	29.05	191 65	0.45	0.00	4.63
12/15	80.61	193119	0.53	0.00	3.86
12/14	67.90	254 94	0.48	0.00	3.16
12/13	87.30	226119	0.38	0.00	2.49
12/12	48.53	346148	0.30	0.00	1.95
Annual Growth	**(12.0%)**	**— —**	**10.4%**	**—**	**24.2%**

UNION BANK AND TRUST COMPANY

Union Bank & Trust a subsidiary of financial services holding company Farmers & Merchants Investment operates more than 35 branches throughout Nebraska and in Kansas. As Nebraska's third-largest privately-owned bank it offers traditional deposit and trust services as well as insurance equipment finance and investment management services. Consumer loans account for the largest portion of the bank's portfolio followed by commercial real estate and farmland loans. Union Bank also originates business loans and residential mortgages. Affiliate company Union Investment Advisors manages the Stratus family of mutual funds. Another Farmers & Merchants unit Nelnet Capital offers brokerage services.

Operations
Union Bank has grown to become one of Nebraska's largest privately-owned banks. As of mid-2013 it boasted bank assets of $2.6 billion and trust assets of $11.8 billion.

Aside from its branches in Nebraska and Kansas Union Bank offers banking products and services through its online mobile and electronic banking services.

Geographic Reach
Union Bank operates mostly in Nebraska but also in Kansas.

Sales and Marketing
The bank primarily serves customers in Lincoln and Omaha as well as the Kansas City metropolitan area.

Strategy
Union Bank continues to expand its footprint in existing markets. The financial institution will have added three new Nebraska branches to its portfolio by 2014.

Company Background
The bank was originally founded in 1917 as Farmer's State Bank. It took on the Union Bank name in 1935 and became Union Bank & Trust in 1959.

EXECUTIVES

Vice President Small Business Banking, Stephanie Dinger
First Vice President Manager Commercial Real Estate, Tom Weinandt

LOCATIONS

HQ: UNION BANK AND TRUST COMPANY
3643 S 48TH ST, LINCOLN, NE 685064390
Phone: 402 488-0941
Web: WWW.UBT.COM

PRODUCTS/OPERATIONS

Selected Services
Business banking
Investment & retirement
Personal banking
Wealth management

Selected Affiliates
InfoVisa
Nelnet Capital LLC
Nelnet Inc.
Union Agency Inc.
Union Equipment Finance LLC
Union Investment Advisors
Union Title Company LLC
Zelle

COMPETITORS

Bank of America	Great Western Bancorp
Bank of the West	JPMorgan Chase
Citigroup	Pinnacle Bancorp
First National of Nebraska	U.S. Bancorp
	Wells Fargo

HISTORICAL FINANCIALS

Company Type: Private

Income Statement

FYE: December 31

	ASSETS ($ mil.)	NET INCOME ($ mil.)	INCOME AS % OF ASSETS	EMPLOYEES
12/15	3,351	32	1.0%	800
12/14	3,040	29	1.0%	—
12/13	2,862	35	1.3%	—
12/08	2,437	16	0.7%	—
Annual Growth	**4.7%**	**9.7%**	**—**	**—**

2015 Year-End Financials

Debt ratio: ——
Return on equity: 19.10%
Cash ($ mil.): 47
Current ratio: —
Long-term debt ($ mil.): —

Dividends
Yield: —
Payout: —
Market value ($ mil.): —

Union Bankshares Corp (New)

Union Bankshares (formerly Union First Market Bankshares) is the holding company for Union Bank & Trust which operates approximately 100 branches in central northern and coastal portions of Virginia. The bank offers standard services such as checking and savings accounts credit cards and certificates of deposit. Union Bank & Trust maintains a loan portfolio heavily weighted towards real estate: Commercial real estate loans make up more than 30% while one- to four-family residential mortgages and construction loans account for approximately 15% and 20% respectively. The bank also originates personal and business loans.

EXECUTIVES

EVP and Director of Mortgage and Wealth Management, Jeffrey W. Farrar, age 56
EVP Union Bankshares and Chief Retail Officer Union Bank & Trust, Elizabeth M. Bentley, age 56, $268,491 total compensation
EVP and Chief Risk Officer, David G. (Dave) Bilko, age 57
President and CEO Union Bankshares Corporation and CEO Union Bank & Trust, John C. Asbury, age 52
EVP and CFO, Robert M. (Rob) Gorman, age 58, $351,167 total compensation
EVP Union Bankshares and Chief Banking Officer Union Bank & Trust, D. Anthony (Tony) Peay, age 57, $348,997 total compensation
EVP and CIO, M. Dean Brown, age 52, $259,625 total compensation
SVP and Chief Marketing Officer, L. Duane Smith, age 50
EVP and Chief Human Resource Officer, Loreen A. LaGatta, age 48
EVP and President Union Bank & Trust, John G. Stallings, age 50
Vice President Commercial Banking, Adam Hill
Senior Vice President, Tom Dillon
Assistant Vice President Commercial Real Estate, Diana Allen
Vice President and Senior Branch Manager, Sherry Cillo
Assistant Vice President Branch Manager, Jody Hardy
Assistant Vice President Branch Manager, Diane Collier
Senior Vice President and Director of Bank Operations, Barbara Fischer
Senior Vice President and Commercial Banker, Debbie Morfit
Vice President Commercial Lender, Sherry Gravatt
Senior Vice President and Trust Advisor, John Catlett
Senior Vice President, Charlie Vaughters
Vice Chairman Union Bankshares Corporation and Union Bank & Trust, G. William (Billy) Beale, age 67
Chairman, Raymond D. (Ray) Smoot, age 70
Auditors: Ernst & Young LLP

LOCATIONS

HQ: Union Bankshares Corp (New)
1051 East Cary Street, Suite 1200, Richmond, VA 23219
Phone: 804 633-5031
Web: www.bankatunion.com

PRODUCTS/OPERATIONS

2015 Sales

	$ mil.	% of total
Interest		
Loans including fees	247	72
Other	29	9
Noninterest		
Other service charges commission and fees	15	5
Service charges on deposit accounts	18	5
others	30	9
Adjustments	(0.3)	-
Total	**341**	**100**

Selected Subsidiaries
Union First Market Bank
Union Insurance Group LLC
Union Investment Services Inc.
Union Mortgage Group Inc.

COMPETITORS

BB&T	PNC Financial
Bank of America	Regions Financial
C&F Financial	SunTrust
Eastern Virginia Bankshares	TowneBank
JPMorgan Chase	Wells Fargo

HISTORICAL FINANCIALS

Company Type: Public

Income Statement
FYE: December 31

	ASSETS ($ mil.)	NET INCOME ($ mil.)	INCOME AS % OF ASSETS	EMPLOYEES
12/16	8,426	77	0.9%	1,416
12/15	7,693	67	0.9%	1,422
12/14	7,359	52	0.7%	1,471
12/13	4,176	34	0.8%	1,025
12/12	4,095	35	0.9%	1,044
Annual Growth	**19.8%**	**21.6%**	**—**	**7.9%**

2016 Year-End Financials

Debt ratio: 4.90%	No. of shares (mil.): 43
Return on equity: 7.74%	Dividends
Cash ($ mil.): 178	Yield: 0.0%
Current ratio: —	Payout: 43.5%
Long-term debt ($ mil.): —	Market value ($ mil.): 1,559

	STOCK PRICE ($) FY Close	P/E High/Low	PER SHARE ($) Earnings	Dividends	Book Value
12/16	35.74	21 12	1.77	0.77	22.95
12/15	25.24	18 13	1.49	0.68	22.23
12/14	24.08	23 19	1.14	0.58	21.66
12/13	24.81	19 11	1.38	0.54	17.55
12/12	15.77	12 10	1.37	0.37	17.25
Annual Growth	**22.7%**	**— —**	**6.6%**	**20.1%**	**7.4%**

Union Pacific Corp

Venerable Union Pacific Railroad (UP) has been chugging down the track since the 19th century. Owned by Union Pacific Corporation (UPC) UP is one of the nation's leading rail carriers operating about 66000 freight cars and more than 8500 locomotives. UP transports automobiles; chemicals; energy; and industrial agricultural and other bulk freight over a system of some 32000 rail miles in 23 states in the western two-thirds of the US. UPC owns more than 26000 route miles of its rail network; leases and trackage rights which allow it to use other railroads' tracks account for the rest. UP's customers have included such big names as automakers General Motors and Toyota.

HISTORY

In 1862 the US Congress chartered the Union Pacific Railroad (UP) to build part of the first transcontinental railway. The driving of the Golden Spike at Promontory Utah in 1869 marked the linking of the East and West coasts as UP's rails met those of Central Pacific Railroad (predecessor of Southern Pacific or SP) which had been built east from Sacramento California.

In 1872 the New York Sun revealed the Credit Mobilier scandal: UP officials had pocketed excess profits during the railroad's construction. Debt and lingering effects of the scandal forced UP into bankruptcy in 1893.

A syndicate headed by E. H. Harriman bought UP in 1897. After reacquiring the Oregon branches it lost in the bankruptcy UP gained control of SP (1901) and Chicago & Alton (1904). The Supreme Court ordered UP to sell its SP holdings in 1913 on antitrust grounds. In the 1930s UP diversified into trucking and in the 1970s and 1980s it moved into oil and gas production.

UP bought trucking firm Overnite Transportation in 1986. During the 1980s UP also built up its rail operations acquiring the Missouri Pacific and Western Pacific railroads in 1982 and the Missouri-Kansas-Texas Railroad in 1988. It joined Chicago and North Western (CNW) Railway managers in an investment group led by Blackstone Capital Partners that bought CNW in 1989.

CNW traced its roots to the Galena & Chicago Union Railroad which was founded by Chicago's first mayor W. B. Ogden in 1836 and merged with CNW in 1864. By 1925 the North Western (as it was then known) had tracks throughout the Midwest. In 1995 UP completed its purchase of CNW and made a bid for SP.

SP was founded in 1865 but its history dates to 1861 when four Sacramento merchants founded Central Pacific. By building new track and buying other railroads (including SP in 1868) Central Pacific had expanded throughout California Texas and Oregon by 1887. The two railroads merged in 1885 under the SP name. In 1983 SP was sold to a holding company controlled by Philip Anschutz which in 1995 agreed to sell the company to UP.

UP completed its SP acquisition in 1996 but assimilation of the purchase led to widespread rail traffic jams. UP also sold its remaining interest in Union Pacific Resources an oil company it had spun off the year before. In 1997 UP moved from Bethlehem Pennsylvania to Dallas and joined a consortium led by mining company Grupo México that won a bid to run two major Mexican rail lines. In the US however fatal collisions led to a federal review of UP which found a breakdown in rail safety such as overworked employees and widespread train defects. Meanwhile regulators seeking to resolve UP's massive freight backlog ordered the railroad to open its Houston lines to competitors.

The company decentralized its management into three regions (north south and west) in 1998 to improve traffic flow. It also hired more workers added new trains and realigned routes while selling Skyway Freight Systems its logistics services unit.

In 1999 UP moved its headquarters from Dallas to Omaha Nebraska where Union Pacific Railroad offices already were located. In 2000 it formed Fenix a holding company charged with developing and expanding the company's telecommunications and technology assets. (By 2003 however UP had reabsorbed Fenix and scaled back its support for its remaining technology subsidiaries.)

The company expanded its less-than-truckload operations into the western US in 2001 by buying Motor Cargo Industries. Also that year it completed the integration of Southern Pacific's operations.

UP sold its trucking unit Overnite Corporation (a holding company for Overnite Transportation and Motor Cargo Industries) in an IPO in 2003. (Overnite Corporation was acquired by United Parcel Service in 2005 and renamed UPS Freight the next year.) UP sold its Timera subsidiary (workforce management software) in 2004.

Traffic congestion in the UP system brought on by a shortage of train crews caused some freight from UPS and other customers to be rerouted onto trucks in 2004. The crew shortage was attributed in part to a greater-than-expected number of retirements in 2003. UP accelerated its hiring and training efforts but the company still had to restrict freight volume in an effort to minimize bottlenecks.

In 2006 Union Pacific Railroad reorganized its operating structure going from four regions to three: northern southern and western. Service units of the company's central region were reassigned to the northern and southern regions. The company added 45 miles of double track to its Sunset Corridor in 2008.

In the midst of the Great Recession UPC's 2009 freight volumes decreased 16% from 2008's numbers. The company was forced to raise its rates by about 6%; it also parked approximately 26% of its locomotives 18% of its freight car stock and furloughed about 3000 employees.

As the nation slowly recovered economically UPC realized a 13% increase in volume in 2010 over 2009 with automotive intermodal and industrial product shipments showing the strongest growth. Even with 2010 fuel prices more than 30% higher than 2009 the company's freight revenues increased 20% in 2010. UPC cited economic improvement across the majority of its market sectors as the reason for the recovery.

In mid-2012 UPC subsidiary PS Technology (PST) acquired the Yard Control Systems division of Ansaldo STS USA. The acquisition boosted PST's enterprise management capabilities by adding rail yard process control and automation technology.

EXECUTIVES

EVP and CFO, Robert M. Knight, age 60, $575,000 total compensation

SVP and CIO, Lynden L. Tennison

Chairman President and CEO, Lance M. Fritz, age 54, $1,000,000 total compensation

EVP and Chief Administration Officer, Eric L. Butler, age 56, $485,000 total compensation

EVP and Chief Legal Officer, Rhonda S. Ferguson, age 48, $200,000 total compensation

EVP and Chief Marketing Officer, Elizabeth F. (Beth) Whited, age 52

EVP and COO, Cameron A. Scott, age 54, $457,500 total compensation

President ShipCarsNow Inc., Peter Decher

VP; General Manager Chemicals, Kari Kirchhoefer

Vice President, Bernardo Ayala

Assistant Vice President Network and Capital Planning, Haley Cowan

Assistant Vice President Information Technology, Ashok Fichadia

Assistant Vice President Intermodal Operator, Greg Garrison

Vice President Public Affairs, Brenda Smainwaring

SENIOR ASSISTANT VICE PRESIDENT CHEMICALS, Robert G Worrell

Auditors: DELOITTE & TOUCHE LLP

LOCATIONS

HQ: Union Pacific Corp
1400 Douglas Street, Omaha, NE 68179
Phone: 402 544-5000
Web: www.up.com

PRODUCTS/OPERATIONS

2016 Sales

	$ mil.	% of total
Freight	18,601	93
Other	1,340	7
Total	**19,941**	**100**

2016 Sales

	$ mil.	% of total
Freight revenues		
Intermodal	3,714	19
Agricultural Products	3,625	18
Chemicals	3,474	17
Industrial Products	3,348	17
Coal	2,440	12
Automotive	2,000	10
Other revenues	1,340	7
Total	**19,941**	**100**

COMPETITORS

American Commercial Lines	Ingram Industries
Burlington Northern Santa Fe	J.B. Hunt
CSX	Kansas City Southern
Canadian National Railway	Kirby Corporation
Canadian Pacific Railway	Landstar System
	Norfolk Southern
	Schneider National
	Werner Enterprises

HISTORICAL FINANCIALS

Company Type: Public

Income Statement

FYE: December 31

	REVENUE ($ mil.)	NET INCOME ($ mil.)	NET PROFIT MARGIN	EMPLOYEES
12/17	21,240	10,712	50.4%	41,992
12/16	19,941	4,233	21.2%	42,919
12/15	21,813	4,772	21.9%	47,457
12/14	23,988	5,180	21.6%	47,201
12/13	21,963	4,388	20.0%	46,445
Annual Growth	**(0.8%)**	**25.0%**	**—**	**(2.5%)**

2017 Year-End Financials

Debt ratio: 29.31%
Return on equity: 47.83%
Cash ($ mil.): 1,275
Current ratio: 1.02
Long-term debt ($ mil.): 16,144

No. of shares (mil.): 780
Dividends
Yield: 0.0%
Payout: 18.5%
Market value ($ mil.): 104,721

	STOCK PRICE ($) FY Close	P/E High/Low		Earnings	PER SHARE ($) Dividends	Book Value
12/17	134.10	10	8	13.36	2.48	31.83
12/16	103.68	21	14	5.07	2.26	24.43
12/15	78.20	22	14	5.49	2.20	24.38
12/14	119.13	35	17	5.75	1.91	23.99
12/13	168.00	35	27	4.71	1.48	23.27
Annual Growth	**(5.5%)**			**29.8%**	**13.8%**	**8.1%**

United Bankshares Inc

United Bankshares (no relation to Ohio's United Bancshares) keeps it together as the holding company for two subsidiaries doing business as United Bank (WV) and United Bank (VA). Combined the banks boast some $12 billion in assets and operate roughly 130 branches that serve West Virginia Virginia and Washington DC as well as nearby portions of Maryland Pennsylvania and Ohio. The branches offer traditional deposit trust and lending services with a focus on residential mortgages and commercial loans. United Bankshares also owns United Brokerage Services which provides investments asset management and financial planning in addition to brokerage services.

Operations

The company's loan portfolio is made up of commercial and construction commercial and residential real estate and consumer loans (including credit card and home equity loans).

United Bankshares generated 75% of its total revenue from interest and fees on loans in 2014 plus an additional 7% from interest and dividends on its investment securities. The company generated about 9% of its total revenue from deposit services fees and another 4% from trust and brokerage services fees.

Geographic Reach

United Bankshares boasts some 130 full-service branches including more than 55 across the state of West Virginia nearly 70 in the Shenendoah Valley region of Virginia and the Northern Virginia Maryland and Washington DC metro area and a handful of branches split between southwestern Pennsylvania and southeastern Ohio.

Sales and Marketing

The company spent $4.76 million on advertising in 2014 up from $3.78 million and $4.27 million spent in 2013 and 2012 respectively.

Financial Performance

United Bankshares' revenues and profits have trended higher over the past few years thanks to growth in its loan business from acquisitions increased trust and brokerage services fee income and declining interest expense on deposits amidst the low-interest environment.

The company's revenue jumped by nearly 34% to a record $499.50 million in 2014 mostly as its interest income spiked by 37% after its Virginia Commerce acquisition added new interest-earning assets and increased the average yields on its loans investments and security assets. United Bankshare's non-interest income also swelled by 22% thanks to higher income from fees from trust and brokerage services bankcard fees and merchant discounts and net gains on investment securities.

Higher revenue in 2014 boosted the company's profits by 52% to a record $129.89 million while the company's operating cash grew by 2% thanks to higher cash earnings.

Strategy

United Bankshares has historically expanded through small bank and branch acquisitions closing nearly 30 bank purchases in the past quarter-century. Its growth strategy has mainly been focused in on the Washington DC/suburban Maryland/northern Virginia market though its also expanded into Pennsylvania in recent years as well. In 2014 for example the company extended its reach into Washington DC while boosting its loan business by $2 billion after completing its largest-ever acquisition of Virginia Commerce Bancorp.

In 2016 the company agreed to buy Cardinal Financial which has some $4.2 billion in assets and operates 30 branches in Virginia Maryland and Washington DC.

Mergers and Acquisitions

In January 2014 United Bankshares acquired Arlington-based Virginia Commerce Bancorp for a total cost of $585.53 million. The deal expanded United's reach into the Washington DC metropolitan area and added $2.07 billion in new loan business and $2.02 billion in deposits.

Company Background

The 2011 acquisition of West Virginia-based Centra Financial Holdings gave United Bankshares its first branches in Pennsylvania and entry into the Pittsburgh market.

EXECUTIVES

EVP the Company and United Bank and WV, James B. Hayhurst, age 71, $225,000 total compensation

President, Richard M. Adams, age 49, $328,846 total compensation

COO, James J. Consagra, age 57, $334,462 total compensation
EVP and COO United Bank (VA), Craige L. Smith, age 65, $243,750 total compensation
EVP and CFO, W. Mark Tatterson, age 42
EVP, Darren K. Williams
Vice President Director Of Institutional Sales, Bill Vyskocil
Assistant Vice President Information Technology Audit Manager, Jason Moore
Assistant Vice President and Corporate Security Officer, Erica Fowler
Auditors: Ernst & Young LLP

LOCATIONS

HQ: United Bankshares Inc
300 United Center, 500 Virginia Street, East, Charleston, WV 25301
Phone: 304 424-8716
Web: www.ubsi-inc.com

PRODUCTS/OPERATIONS

2014 Sales

	$ mil.	% of total
Interest		
Loans including fees	383	75
Interest and dividends on securities	33	7
Other	0	-
Noninterest		
Fees from deposit services	42	9
Fees from trust & brokerage services	18	4
Other	28	5
Adjustment (losses)	(8.4)	-
Total	**499**	**100**

COMPETITORS

BB&T	JPMorgan Chase
Bank of America	M&T Bank
Burke & Herbert Bank	PNC Financial
Cardinal Financial	SunTrust
City Holding	United Bancorp
Fifth Third	Virginia Commerce
Fulton Financial	Bancorp
Huntington Bancshares	WesBanco

HISTORICAL FINANCIALS

Company Type: Public

Income Statement
FYE: December 31

	ASSETS ($ mil.)	NET INCOME ($ mil.)	INCOME AS % OF ASSETS	EMPLOYEES
12/16	14,508	147	1.0%	1,701
12/15	12,577	137	1.1%	1,701
12/14	12,328	129	1.1%	1,703
12/13	8,735	85	1.0%	1,528
12/12	8,420	82	1.0%	1,529
Annual Growth	**14.6%**	**15.5%**	**—**	**2.7%**

2016 Year-End Financials

Debt ratio: 1.55%	No. of shares (mil.): 81
Return on equity: 7.43%	Dividends
Cash ($ mil.): 1,433	Yield: 0.0%
Current ratio: —	Payout: 66.3%
Long-term debt ($ mil.): —	Market value ($ mil.): 3,748

	STOCK PRICE ($) FY Close	P/E High/Low	PER SHARE ($) Earnings	Dividends	Book Value
12/16	46.25	25 16	1.99	1.32	27.59
12/15	36.99	22 17	1.98	1.29	24.61
12/14	37.45	20 15	1.92	1.28	23.90
12/13	31.45	19 14	1.70	1.25	20.66
12/12	24.34	19 14	1.64	1.24	19.74
Annual Growth	**17.4%**	**— —**	**5.0%**	**1.6%**	**8.7%**

United Community Banks Inc (Blairsville, GA)

United Community Banks is the holding company for United Community Bank (UCB). UCB provides consumer and business banking products and services through nearly 150 branches across Georgia North Carolina Tennessee and South Carolina. Commercial loans including construction loans and mortgages account for the largest portion of UCB's loan portfolio (more than 50%); residential mortgages make up 30%. The company which boasts roughly $10 billion in assets also has a mortgage lending division and provides insurance through its United Community Insurance Services subsidiary (aka United Community Advisory Services).

Operations

The bank's retail mortgage lending division United Community Mortgage Services (UCMS) sells and services mortgages for Fannie Mae and Freddie Mac and provides fixed and adjustable-rate home mortgages. It also offers retail brokerage services through an affiliation with a third-party broker/dealer.

About 65% of UCB's total revenue came from loan interest (including fees) in 2014 while another 16% came from taxable investments. The rest of its revenue came from service charges and fees (10%) mortgage loan fees (2%) and brokerage fees (2%) among other sources.

Geographic Reach

UCB's nearly 105 branches are located in Georgia (in the north the Atlanta-Sandy Springs-Roswell metro area Gainsville metro area and coastal areas); western North Carolina; eastern and central Tennessee; and South Carolina (in the Greenville-Anderson-Mauldin metro area).

Sales and Marketing

The bank provides community banking services for individuals small businesses and corporations.

Financial Performance

UCB has struggled to consistently grow its revenues in recent years due to shrinking interest margins on loans amidst the low-interest environment. Its profits however have been rising thanks to declining loan loss provisions as its loan portfolio's credit quality has improved with higher property valuations in the strengthened economy.

The bank's revenue inched higher by 1% to $304 million in 2014 thanks to an increase in interest income stemming from strategic business growth initiatives designed to add new business lines and expand into new markets as well as balance sheet management and restructuring actions taken in the second quarter of the year.

Despite higher revenue in 2014 UCB's net income dove 75% to $67.6 million mostly because in 2013 it had received a non-recurring income tax benefit of $238 million stemming from reversal of a deferred tax valuation allowance. Not counting this item however the bank's profit before taxes nearly tripled during the year. UCB's operating cash levels dropped by 47% to $101.9 million in 2014 due to lower cash earnings.

Strategy

UCB has been concentrating on growing its small business lending business in recent years. In 2014 it made "significant investments" in its SBA business after acquiring Business Carolina which specialized in SBA and USDA lending.

It also continues to pursue bank acquisitions to expand its reach in its existing core markets and boost its loan and deposit business. Its acquisitions in 2015 and 2014 alone have added over $1 billion in new loan business and $1.3 billion in new deposits.

Mergers and Acquisitions

In 2016 United Community Banks expanded into key markets in coastal South Carolina after buying Mt. Pleasant-based Tidelands and its seven Tidelands Bank branches in the Charleston Myrtle Beach and Hilton Head areas.

In 2015 UCB bought Tennessee-based MoneyTree Corporation and its 10 First National Bank branches in east Tennessee. The deal added $425 million in assets $354 million in deposits and $253 million in new loan business to UCB's books.

In 2014 the company purchased Palmetto Bancshares and its Palmetto Bank branches expanding its footprint into "major" southeastern metro markets in Greenville and the Upstate South Carolina area. The deal also added $1.2 billion in assets $832 million in loans and $967 million in deposits.

Also in 2014 UCB purchased Columbia-based Business Carolina a commercial lender that specialized in SBA and USDA loans for $31.3 million in cash. The deal included $25 million in loans $6 million in other assets and substantially all of the company's employees.

EXECUTIVES

Senior Vice President and Legal Counsel, Brad Miller
President of Specialized Lending, Richard W. Bradshaw, age 55
Chairman and CEO, Jimmy C. Tallent, age 64, $750,000 total compensation
SVP Retail Banking; Chairman United Community Bank Adairsville and Summerville, William M. (Bill) Gilbert, age 64, $308,334 total compensation
President and Director United Community Banks Inc. and President CEO and Director United Community Bank, H. Lynn Harton, age 55, $575,000 total compensation
EVP General Counsel and Chief Risk Officer, Bradley J. (Brad) Miller, age 46
EVP and Chief Credit Officer, Robert A. (Rob) Edwards, age 52, $305,000 total compensation
EVP and CFO United Community Banks Inc. and United Community Bank, Jefferson L. Harralson
Senior Vice President, Debbie Williams
Vice President Special Assets, Marla Kephart
Senior Vice President Commercial Banking, Jay Roper
Executive Vice President, Rick Rowland
Assistant Vice President Branch Manager, Kathy Christiansen
Executive Vice President, Deepika Paul
Vice President, RONNEY DIXON
Senior Vice President Retail Credit Administration, Chuck Valerio
Vice President and Financial Systems Manager, Betsy Mull
Assistant Vice President, Ginger Kilman
Senior Vice President, Rebecca Munteanu
Assistant Vice President, Wendy Cawthon
Senior Vice President, Alan Kumler
Vice President Of Business Development And Marketing, Elaine Bell
Vice President Business Services, James Magness
Senior Vice President, Ron King
Senior Vice President, Donald Harris
Assistant Vice President, Deborah Wright
Senior Vice President, Skip Swain
Vice President and Branch Manager, Vicky Helton
Assis Vice President Branch Manager, David Sherrod
Vice President, Jane Callihan

Assistant Vice President Business Banking Underwriting, Eric Rivenbark
Senior Vice President Commercial Banking, Ben Walker
Vice President, Judy Levine
Senior Vice President, Phil Beaudette
Assistant Vice President, Rob Andrews
Vice President and Director Bank Security, Dennis Tarnowski
Senior Vice President Builder Finance, Scott Ernest
Vice President, Darryl Meadows
Vice President and ORE Manager, Angela Burnette
Vice President Treasury Management, Will Ward
Senior Vice President, Carol A Chastain
Vice President Portfolio Specialist, Justin Rutledge
Vice President, Anne Wade
Vice President Business Development, Micha Meyer
Assistant Vice President Mortgage Lending Covering SC NC GA TN Alabama and Florida, Todd Coleman
Senior Vice President, Jessie Marolis
Senior Vice President, William Ferguson
Vice President, Wendy Martin
Vice President Regional Sales Manager, Mikell Richards
Regional President, Anastasia Katapodis
Vice President Relationship Manager, Tim Ash
Vice President Business Development Officer Senior Analyst Lending, David Brindley
Regional President, Dixon Woodward
Vice President Retail Sales Manager, Sandra Page
Vice President Franchise Lending, Mike Stone
Vice President, Jimmy Rambo
Senior Vice President United Community Bank, Dennis McBride
Assistant Treasurer, Mitchell Bleske
Auditors: PricewaterhouseCoopers LLP

LOCATIONS

HQ: United Community Banks Inc (Blairsville, GA)
125 Highway 515 East, Blairsville, GA 30512
Phone: 706 781-2265
Web: www.ucbi.com

PRODUCTS/OPERATIONS

2011 Sales

	$ mil.	% of total
Interest		
Loans including fees	239	69
Taxable investment securities	55	16
Other	3	1
Noninterest		
Service charges & fees	29	8
Mortgage loans & related fees	5	2
Brokerage fees	3	1
Net securities gains	0	-
Other	12	3
Adjustment	(0.7)	-
Total	**347**	**100**

COMPETITORS

Atlantic Coast Financial	Peoples Bancorp (NC)
BB&T	Regions Financial
Bank of America	Southeastern Bank Financial
Bank of Oak Ridge	Southeastern Banking
Fidelity Southern	SunTrust
First Citizens BancShares	Synovus
Georgia Bancshares	WGNB
Georgia-Carolina Bancshares	

HISTORICAL FINANCIALS

Company Type: Public

Income Statement

FYE: December 31

	ASSETS ($ mil.)	NET INCOME ($ mil.)	INCOME AS % OF ASSETS	EMPLOYEES
12/16	10,708	100	0.9%	1,916
12/15	9,626	71	0.7%	1,883
12/14	7,566	67	0.9%	1,506
12/13	7,425	273	3.7%	1,472
12/12	6,802	33	0.5%	1,553
Annual Growth	**12.0%**	**31.3%**	**—**	**5.4%**

2016 Year-End Financials

Debt ratio: 1.63%	No. of shares (mil.): 70	
Return on equity: 9.59%	Dividends	
Cash ($ mil.): 217	Yield: 0.0%	
Current ratio: —	Payout: 21.4%	
Long-term debt ($ mil.): —	Market value ($ mil.): 2,100	

	STOCK PRICE ($) FY Close	P/E High/Low	PER SHARE ($) Earnings	Dividends	Book Value
12/16	29.62	21 11	1.40	0.30	15.17
12/15	19.49	20 15	1.09	0.22	14.24
12/14	18.94	18 14	1.11	0.11	12.27
12/13	17.75	4 2	4.44	0.00	13.39
12/12	9.44	27 17	0.38	0.00	10.07
Annual Growth	**33.1%**	**— —**	**38.5%**	**—**	**10.8%**

United Community Financial Corp. (OH)

This thrift wants to keep your savings and your loans united. United Community Financial is the holding company for The Home Savings and Loan Company of Youngstown Ohio a community bank with more than 30 full-service branches and about 10 loan production offices in Ohio and western Pennsylvania. Boasting nearly $2 billion in assets the bank offers traditional checking and savings accounts CDs retirement accounts investments and credit cards as well as a variety of loans. Residential mortgages account for over 60% of the company's loan portfolio while commercial and consumer loans split the remainder.

Operations

About 62% of United Community's total revenue came from loan interest (including fees) in 2014 while another 16% came from interest on its securities held for sale. The rest of its revenue came from fees on deposit accounts (6%) mortgage servicing fees (3%) non-deposit investment income 2%) and other miscellaneous income sources. The bank had a staff of 428 full-time employees at the end of 2014.

Geographic Reach

Youngstown Ohio-based United Community Financial boasts more than 30 branches across Ohio and western Pennsylvania. Its primary markets include Allegheny and Beaver counties in Pennsylvania and Ashland Columbiana Cuyahoga Erie Franklin Geauga Huron Lake Mahoning Portage Richland Stark Summit and Trumbull Counties in Ohio.

Sales and Marketing

The company spent $838 thousand on advertising in 2014 compared to $893 thousand and $778 thousand in 2013 and 2012 respectively.

Financial Performance

United Community Financial has struggled to grow its revenue in recent years as its interest income has fallen with lower interest rates and because it's had to sell of many of its non-performing loan assets to de-risk its loan portfolio. The group's profits however are on the mend as its de-risking measures have led to declining loan loss provisions.

The company's revenue fell by 9% to $77 million in 2014 mostly due to a combination of lower interest income after it sold off some of its investment securities a $2.1 million decline in gains from security sales and a $3.2 million drop in mortgage banking income due to a reduction in mortgage origination sales.

Despite revenue declines in 2014 United's net income grew five-fold to a record $50.2 million for the year mostly thanks to a $39.7 million income tax benefit related to a reversal of a previous year's bad loan allowance and thanks to continued declines in loan loss provisions. The company's operating cash levels fell sharply with operations using $2.8 million in 2014 after its earnings were adjusted for non-cash items related to its net proceeds from its loans held for sale.

Strategy

Home Savings mainly focuses on originating residential real estate loans by real estate in its primary market area. United Community Financial has been working to build its capital and shed its riskier assets to get its business back on solid footing. Indeed while the bank suffered several years of heavy losses between 2008 and 2012 its de-risking measures made 2014 the company's most profitable year in its history.

Mergers and Acquisitions

United Community agreed to buy Ohio Legacy Corp holding company of the four-branch Premier Bank & Trust for $40.3 million. Ohio Legacy also operates a wealth management and trust division.

Company Background

In 2012 federal and state regulators lifted a cease-and-desist order that the bank had been operating under since 2008. In its place the company began operating under a consent order under which United Community Financial would need to submit a formal capital plan to the regulators. To satisfy targets under the consent order the bank sold about $115 million worth of bad assets in late 2012.

EXECUTIVES

CFO United Community Financial Corp. and EVP and CFO Home Savings and Loan, Timothy W. Esson, age 67, $216,577 total compensation
VP General Counsel and Corporate Secretary, Jude J. Nohra, age 48, $248,871 total compensation
President CEO and Director United Community Financial Corp. and Home Savings and Loan, Gary M. Small, age 57, $412,885 total compensation
EVP and Head of Commercial Lending and Credit Administration Home Savings and Loan, Matthew T. Garrity, age 50, $251,007 total compensation
EVP Retail Banking Home Savings and Loan, Barbara J. Radis, age 48
SVP and CIO, Douglas Young
Assistant Vice President Education Center, Patti Hanna
Vice President, Anthony Dantuono
Chairman United Community Financial and Home Savings and Loan, Richard J. Schiraldi, age 62
Auditors: Crowe Horwath LLP

LOCATIONS

HQ: United Community Financial Corp. (OH)
275 West Federal Street, Youngstown, OH 44503-1203
Phone: 330 742-0500
Web: www.ucfconline.com

PRODUCTS/OPERATIONS

2014 Sales

	$ mil.	% of total
Interest	63	80
Non-interest	13	20
Total	**77**	**100**

COMPETITORS

Central Federal	PNC Financial
F.N.B. (PA)	PVF Capital
Farmers National	U.S. Bancorp
KeyCorp	

HISTORICAL FINANCIALS

Company Type: Public

Income Statement
FYE: December 31

	ASSETS ($ mil.)	NET INCOME ($ mil.)	INCOME AS % OF ASSETS	EMPLOYEES
12/16	2,191	18	0.9%	442
12/15	1,987	16	0.8%	428
12/14	1,833	50	2.7%	428
12/13	1,737	10	0.6%	514
12/12	1,808	(20)	—	490
Annual Growth	**4.9%**	**—**	**—**	**(2.5%)**

2016 Year-End Financials

Debt ratio: 0.02%	No. of shares (mil.): 46
Return on equity: 7.60%	Dividends
Cash ($ mil.): 27	Yield: 0.0%
Current ratio: —	Payout: 27.5%
Long-term debt ($ mil.): —	Market value ($ mil.): 416

	STOCK PRICE ($) FY Close	P/E High/Low	PER SHARE ($) Earnings	Dividends	Book Value
12/16	8.94	24 13	0.40	0.11	5.36
12/15	5.90	18 14	0.34	0.07	5.14
12/14	5.37	5 3	1.00	0.02	4.88
12/13	3.57	71 41	0.07	0.00	3.48
12/12	2.89	— —	(0.62)	0.00	5.17
Annual Growth	**32.6%**	**—**	**—**	**—**	**0.9%**

United Continental Holdings Inc

United Continental Holdings (UAL) unites cities around the globe through its primary United Air Lines subsidiary. While United Air Lines is its main line the company also has regional operations which are operated under contract by United Express. Combined the company handles an average of roughly 4500 flights a day to more than 335 domestic and international destinations from hubs that include Chicago Denver Houston Los Angeles San Francisco New York (Newark) and Washington DC. Like most airlines the company sells the majority of its seat inventory through travel agencies and global distribution systems in addition to its main website.

Operations

UAL operates more than 1220 aircraft including aircraft operated by regional carriers on its behalf. It generates its revenues across four segments: passenger mainline (70% of total sales) passenger regional (more than 15%) cargo (less than 5%) and other (more than 10%).

The company is a member of the Star Alliance network which offers more than 18450 daily flights to 190 countries worldwide and includes 28 member airlines.

Geographic Reach

Headquartered in Chicago UAL operates across five continents from its hubs at Newark Liberty International Airport Chicago O'Hare International Airpor Denver International Airport George Bush Intercontinental Airport Los Angeles International Airport A.B. Won Pat International Airport San Francisco International Airport and Washington Dulles International Airport.

US and Canada collectively account for 60% of its total net sales. Other major markets include the Atlantic (more than 15%) and Pacific (more than 10%) regions in addition to Latin America (almost 10%).

Financial Performance

UAL's revenues have declined the last two years dipping 3% from $37.9 billion in 2015 to $36.6 billion in 2016. Its passenger revenue for 2016 decreased due to a competitive domestic fare environment unfavorable foreign currency results due to the strengthening of the US dollar international surcharge declines travel reductions from corporate customers in the energy sector and increased industry capacity in certain regions.

Profits nosedived by nearly 70% from 2015 to 2016. This was due to about $413 million in impairment charges coupled with increases in ground handling costs food and technology costs restructuring costs and income tax expenses (compared to tax benefits its received the prior year).

After experiencing an influx of operating cash flow in 2015 UAL saw its cash flow decline in 2016 due to a decrease in frequent flyer and advanced purchases of miles and unfavorable timing of payments in accounts payable.

Strategy

UAL has ordered a number of fuel-efficient Airbus and Boeing aircraft to replace the older fleet. It has 50 Dreamliners scheduled for delivery between 2013 and 2020. The 787 anticipated to be "a game changer" for the company and for the airline industry will allow both United Air Lines and Continental to enter new long-haul markets and to replace older less-efficient widebody aircraft.

In 2016 UAL took delivery of five new Boeing 787-9 Dreamliners eight new Boeing 737-900ERs seven new Boeing 737-800s two new Boeing 777-300ERs and six used Airbus A319s.

HISTORY

In 1929 aircraft designer Bill Boeing and engine designer Fred Rentschler of Pratt & Whitney joined forces to form United Aircraft and Transport. Renamed United Air Lines in 1931 the New York-based company offered one of the first coast-to-coast airline services. In 1934 United's manufacturing and transportation divisions split. Former banker Bill Patterson became president of the latter United Air Lines and moved it to the Chicago area. In 1969 UAL Corp. was formed as a holding company.

A subsidiary of UAL Corporation merged with and into Continental in October 2010 with Continental surviving as a wholly-owned subsidiary of UAL. Upon closing of the merger UAL became the parent company of both Continental and United Air Lines and UAL Corporation's name was changed to United Continental Holdings. The transaction created the world's largest airline. In

2013 United Air Lines Inc. was merged into Continental to form one legal entity and Continental's name and brand was changed to United Airlines Inc.

EXECUTIVES

SVP Finance and Procurement and Treasurer, Gerald (Gerry) Laderman, age 59, $500,000 total compensation
President, J. Scott Kirby, age 49, $301,763 total compensation
EVP and Chief Revenue Officer, Andrew P. Nocella
CEO, Oscar Munoz, age 59, $1,193,909 total compensation
EVP and CIO, Linda P. Jojo, age 51
SVP Technical Operations, Kris B. Bauer, age 53
EVP and CFO, Andrew C. Levy, age 47, $243,750 total compensation
EVP and General Counsel, Brett J. Hart, age 47, $715,000 total compensation
EVP and COO, Gregory L. (Greg) Hart, age 51, $850,000 total compensation
EVP Human Resources and Labor Relations, Michael P. (Mike) Bonds, age 55, $650,000 total compensation
Chairman, Robert A. Milton, age 57
Auditors: Ernst & Young LLP

LOCATIONS

HQ: United Continental Holdings Inc
233 South Wacker Drive, Chicago, IL 60606
Phone: 872 825-4000
Web: www.unitedcontinentalholdings.com

2016 Sales

	$ mil.	% of total
Domestic (US & Canada)	22,202	61
Atlantic	6,167	17
Pacific	4,959	13
Latin America	3,238	9
Total	**36,556**	**100**

PRODUCTS/OPERATIONS

2016 Sales

	$ mil.	% of total
Passenger		
Main line	25,414	70
Regional	6,043	16
Cargo	876	2
Other	4,223	12
Total	**36,556**	**100**

COMPETITORS

Air France-KLM	Japan Airlines
AirTran Airways	JetBlue
Alaska Air	Mesa Air
Alitalia	Qantas
American Airlines Group	SkyWest
	Southwest Airlines
British Airways	UPS
Delta Air Lines	Virgin Atlantic
FedEx	Airways
Frontier Airlines	

HISTORICAL FINANCIALS

Company Type: Public

Income Statement

FYE: December 31

	REVENUE ($ mil.)	NET INCOME ($ mil.)	NET PROFIT MARGIN	EMPLOYEES
12/16	36,556	2,263	6.2%	88,000
12/15	37,864	7,340	19.4%	84,000
12/14	38,901	1,132	2.9%	84,000
12/13	38,279	571	1.5%	87,000
12/12	37,152	(723)	—	88,000
Annual Growth	(0.4%)	—	—	0.0%

2016 Year-End Financials

Debt ratio: 29.16%
Return on equity: 25.61%
Cash ($ mil.): 4,428
Current ratio: 0.59
Long-term debt ($ mil.): 10,740

No. of shares (mil.): 314
Dividends
  Yield: —
  Payout: —
Market value ($ mil.): 22,929

	STOCK PRICE ($) FY Close	P/E High/Low		PER SHARE ($) Earnings	Dividends	Book Value
12/16	72.88	11	6	6.85	0.00	27.52
12/15	57.30	4	3	19.47	0.00	24.59
12/14	66.89	22	12	2.93	0.00	6.40
12/13	37.83	24	14	1.53	0.00	8.24
12/12	23.38	—	—	(2.18)	0.00	1.45
Annual Growth	32.9%			—	—	—108.8%

United Financial Bancorp Inc (New)

EXECUTIVES

Secretary Rockville Financial and Rockville Bank, Judy L. Keppner, age 57
SVP Human Resources and Organizational Development Rockville Bank, Richard J. Trachimowicz, age 61, $138,531 total compensation
SVP and CFO Rockville Financial SVP and CFO Rockville Bank, John T. Lund, age 45
President and CEO; President and CEO Rockville Bank, William H. W. Crawford IV
Senior Vice President Investor Relations, Marliese Shaw
Director, William J. (Bill) McGurk, age 74
Director, Michael A. Bars, age 60
Director, C. Perry Chilberg, age 67
Director, David A. Engelson, age 72
Director, Raymond H. Lefurge Jr., age 66
Director, Stuart E. Magdefrau, age 61
Director, Rosemarie Novello Papa, age 71
Director, Richard M. Tkacz, age 63
Auditors: Wolf & Company, P.C.

LOCATIONS

HQ: United Financial Bancorp Inc (New)
  225 Asylum Street, Hartford, CT 06103
Phone: 860 291-3600
Web: www.bankatunited.com

COMPETITORS

Bank of America
Citibank
Liberty Bank
Naugatuck Valley
  Financial
New England Bancshares

RBS Citizens Financial
  Group
SI Financial
Sovereign Bank
TD Bank USA
United Financial

PSB Holdings Inc.
People's United
  Financial

Bancorp
Webster Financial
Westfield Financial

HISTORICAL FINANCIALS

Company Type: Public

Income Statement

FYE: December 31

	ASSETS ($ mil.)	NET INCOME ($ mil.)	INCOME AS % OF ASSETS	EMPLOYEES
12/16	6,599	49	0.8%	768
12/15	6,228	49	0.8%	732
12/14	5,476	6	0.1%	725
12/13	2,301	14	0.6%	358
12/12	1,998	15	0.8%	346
Annual Growth	34.8%	33.2%	—	22.1%

2016 Year-End Financials

Debt ratio: 2.06%
Return on equity: 7.73%
Cash ($ mil.): 90
Current ratio: —
Long-term debt ($ mil.): —

No. of shares (mil.): 50
Dividends
  Yield: 0.0%
  Payout: 48.4%
Market value ($ mil.): 922

	STOCK PRICE ($) FY Close	P/E High/Low		PER SHARE ($) Earnings	Dividends	Book Value
12/16	18.16	18	11	0.99	0.48	12.91
12/15	12.88	14	12	1.00	0.46	12.53
12/14	14.36	91	76	0.16	0.40	12.16
12/13	14.21	28	23	0.54	0.40	11.53
12/12	12.90	24	18	0.56	0.52	11.39
Annual Growth	8.9%			—	—	15.3% (2.0%) 3.2%

United Fire Group, Inc.

The United Fire Group companies join together to offer a unified range of property/casualty and life insurance products. The group operates through its United Fire & Casualty subsidiary which in turn holds entities that carry a variety of property/casualty offerings including fidelity and surety bonds and fire auto employee liability homeowners and workers' compensation lines. More than 1300 independent agencies in some 45 states sell its property/casualty products to businesses and individuals. The United Life division of United Fire & Casualty sells life annuity and credit life products to individuals and groups through some 950 independent agents in more than 30 states.

Operations

United Fire's property/casualty insurance offerings account for more than 90% of its annual insurance premiums with a majority of those policies being written to commercial group customers. The company also offers certain personal policies to individual customers.

Geographic Reach

The company markets its products from its headquarters in Iowa and from four regional offices in California Colorado New Jersey and Texas and it operates primarily in adjacent areas of the midwestern southern and western US.

Sales and Marketing

In order to increase policy placement in its existing markets United Fire offers profit-sharing and commission programs to its independent agents. It also seeks to provide modern technological tools to best serve both its agents and its policyholders.

Financial Performance

The company's revenue has been growing year-over-year. It reported revenue of $877 million in fiscal 2013 up from $813.2 million in revenue for fiscal 2012.

Net income also increased in fiscal 2013 compared to the prior year. The company netted $76 million in fiscal 2013 after reporting net income of $40 million in fiscal 2012.

United Fire's cash flow decreased by about $11 million in fiscal 2013 compared to the previous fiscal period.

Strategy

United Fire looks to expand into new markets to reduce the risk potential in its concentrated areas of operation.

EXECUTIVES

VP General Counsel and Secretary, Neal R. Scharmer, age 61, $250,000 total compensation
COO, Michael T. Wilkins, age 54, $388,600 total compensation
VP and Chief Investment Officer, Barrie W. Ernst, age 63, $305,000 total compensation
President and CEO, Randy A. Ramlo, age 56, $595,000 total compensation
VP and Chief Claims Officer, David E. Conner, age 59
CFO, Dawn M. Jaffray, age 52
VP Information Services, Scott A. Minkel, age 56
VP Corporate Marketing, Colleen R. Sova, age 64
Assistant Vice President Midwest Regional Office, Corey J. Ruehle
VP and COO United Life Insurance Company, Michael J. Sheeley
CTO, Brian Frese
Assistant Vice President and Midwest Regional Claims Manager, Dean Walstrom
Assistant Vice President Personal Lines, Victoria Hefel
Vice President Of Accounting, Sue Haupert
Vice President, Douglas Penn
Vice President Human Resources, Timothy Spain
Assistant Vice President and Senior Human Resources Admin., Debbie Johnstone
Assistant Vice President West Coast Regional Claims Manager, Mary Bianco
Assistant Vice President and Great Lakes Reg. Marketing Manager, Patrick P Kane
Assistant Vice President and Marketing Manager, Miguel Diaz
Vice Chairman, John A. Rife, age 75
Chairman, Jack B. Evans, age 69
Auditors: Ernst & Young LLP

LOCATIONS

HQ: United Fire Group, Inc.
  118 Second Avenue S.E., Cedar Rapids, IA 52401
Phone: 319 399-5700
Web: www.unitedfiregroup.com

PRODUCTS/OPERATIONS

2016 Sale

	% of total
Property and casualty insurance	88
Life insurance	12
Total	**100**

2016 Sale

	% of total
Life insurance	90
Investment income	9
Net realized investment gains	1
Other income	-
Total	**100**

Selected Subsidiaries

United Fire & Casualty Company
  Addison Insurance Company

American Indemnity Financial Corporation
Texas General Indemnity Company
Lafayette Insurance Company
Mercer Insurance Group Inc.
Financial Pacific Insurance Company
Mercer Insurance Company
Franklin Insurance Company
Mercer Insurance Company of New Jersey Inc.
United Fire & Indemnity Company
United Fire Lloyds
United Life Insurance Company

COMPETITORS

AIG	Hanover Insurance
Allstate	John Hancock Financial
American Family	Services
Insurance	Liberty Mutual
American Financial	MassMutual
Group	Progressive
Arrowpoint Capital	Corporation
Corp.	Prudential
CNA Surety	State Farm
Chubb Limited	The Hartford
Erie Indemnity	Travelers Companies
Farmers Group	White Mountains
GEICO	Insurance Group

HISTORICAL FINANCIALS

Company Type: Public

Income Statement

FYE: December 31

	ASSETS ($ mil.)	NET INCOME ($ mil.)	INCOME AS % OF ASSETS	EMPLOYEES
12/16	4,054	49	1.2%	1,112
12/15	3,890	89	2.3%	1,070
12/14	3,856	59	1.5%	981
12/13	3,720	76	2.0%	943
12/12	3,694	40	1.1%	909
Annual Growth	2.4%	5.5%	—	5.2%

2016 Year-End Financials

Debt ratio: —	No. of shares (mil.): 25
Return on equity: 5.47%	Dividends
Cash ($ mil.): 110	Yield: 0.0%
Current ratio: —	Payout: 50.2%
Long-term debt ($ mil.): —	Market value ($ mil.): 1,250

	STOCK PRICE ($) FY Close	P/E High/Low	PER SHARE ($) Earnings	Dividends	Book Value
12/16	49.17	26 18	1.93	0.97	37.04
12/15	38.31	11 8	3.53	0.86	34.94
12/14	29.73	14 10	2.32	0.78	32.67
12/13	28.66	11 7	2.98	0.69	30.87
12/12	21.84	17 10	1.58	0.60	28.90
Annual Growth	22.5%	— —	5.1%	12.8%	6.4%

United Natural Foods Inc.

Distribution comes naturally to United Natural Foods Inc. (UNFI). The company is one of the top wholesale distributors of natural organic and specialty foods in the US and Canada. It owns around 35 distribution centers that supply more than 100000 items to 43000 customers including independently-owned retailers supernatural chain Whole Foods (its #1 customer) and conventional supermarkets. The company offers groceries supplements produce frozen foods and ethnic and kosher food products. UNFI also operates about a dozen natural-products retail stores under the Earth Origins banner and it produces roasted nuts dried fruits and other snack items through subsidiary Woodstock Farms.

Operations

The company's operations are comprised of three principal divisions: Wholesale Retail and Manufacturing and Branded products.

UNFI's wholesale division generates around 95% of sales and consists of its US natural organic and specialty distribution business. Its operations cover major subsidiaries such as Tony's and Albert's as well as newly acquired businesses like Haddon and Gourmet Guru. The segment supplies more than 5000 customers with fruits vegetables and other perishable items. The division also distributes vitamins through Select Nutrition and ethnic food items and related products through its UNFI Specialty business. The company has built up its own food brands through subsidiary Blue Marble Brands. The unit offers more than 650 products marketed under 15 brand names directly to retailers as well as third party distributors.

UNFI's retail arm Earth Origins operates a dozen natural products stores primarily in Florida but also in Maryland and Massachusetts. The company also has a retail store in Vancouver British Columbia that does business as Drive Organics.

The Manufacturing and Branded products division consists of Woodstock Farms Manufacturing which specializes in importing roasting packaging and the distribution of nuts dried fruit seeds trail mixes granola natural and organic snack items and confections; and the Blue Marble Brands product lines.

Geographic Reach

Through UNFI's acquisition of SunOpta Distribution Group the company's wholly-owned subsidiary UNFI Canada became the largest distributor of natural organic and specialty foods including kosher fare in Canada. UNFI has four distribution centers in Canada. UNFI Canada contributes about 5% of UNFI's sales.

The company has 33 distribution centers in US and Canada.

Sales and Marketing

Amazon subsidiary Whole Foods Market is UNFI's largest wholesale customer representing about 35% of its net sales. It's the only customer that accounts for more than 10% of sales. Conventional supermarkets including Kroger Publix and Wegman's and mass market chains account for about 27% of sales.

UNFI's marketing includes multiple monthly region-specific consumer circular programs; coupon programs truck advertising programs wholesale biannual catalogs; and certain supply chain marketing programs.

Financial Performance

UNFI has seen strong growth over the past decade. In fiscal 2017 (July 30 year end) revenue increased 9% to $9.3 billion on the back of higher sales in the Wholesale division. Major factors included the acquisitions of Haddon and Gourmet Guru higher sales to Whole Foods Market thanks to new store openings and higher online sales. Revenue gains were partially offset by broad-based food retail softness margin enhancement initiatives and low inflation.

Net income increased by 3% to $130.2 million as revenue gains were partially offset by higher operating expenses. The acquired businesses have higher costs and required $6.9 million in restructuring expense.

In fiscal 2017 cash from operations fell 5% to $280.8 million due to changes in accounts receivable.

Strategy

UNFI has succeeded at taking market share away from its competition thanks to demand for its slate of premium services coupled with its expanding distribution capacity and targeted acquisitions. It has grown its business organically and through the acquisition of a number of distributors and suppliers which has expanded its distribution network product selection and customer base.

To implement its growth strategy it intends to continue increasing market share of the growing natural and organic products industry by expanding its customer base increasing the company's share of existing customers' business and continuing to expand and further penetrate new distribution territories.

A key element of the company's current growth strategy is to increase the amount of fresh perishable products that it distributes. Its acquisitions of Haddon Gourmet Guru Nor-Cal and Global Organic continue this current strategy with the addition of gourmet ethnic products and conventional produce. Its strategic plan also includes the rollout of new technology including a national warehouse management and procurement system and transportation management system upgrade.

Indeed the company continually invests in its distribution network and infrastructure. In 2016 it opened a new 40000 sq. ft. distribution center in Gilroy California and in 2015 a 300000 sq. ft. center in Prescott Wisconsin.

Mergers and Acquisitions

In 2016 the company acquired certain assets of Global Organic/Specialty Source Inc. and related affiliates through Albert's Organics for $20.6 million. Global Organic is a premier distributor of organic fruits vegetables juices milk eggs nuts and coffee and serves customers across the Southeastern US.

UNFI also spent $68.6 million to purchase Nor-Cal Produce and an affiliated entity as well as certain real estate. Nor-Cal is a family-owned and - operated distributor of conventional and organic produce and other fresh products in Northern California.

That year it also bought Haddon House Food Products and Gourmet Guru.

HISTORY

Rhode Island retailer Norman Cloutier founded Cornucopia Natural Foods in 1978 and soon focused on distribution. During the 1980s Cornucopia grew by acquiring other natural foods distributors. It bought suppliers Natural Food Systems (seafood) and BGS Distributing (vitamins) in 1987 and 1990 respectively. Cornucopia expanded into the Southeast in 1991 when it opened a distribution center in Georgia.

Reviving its interest in retailing Cornucopia formed Natural Retail Group in 1993 to buy and run natural foods stores. During the next two years it acquired several retailers. The company expanded its distribution operations in the West in 1995 adding Denver-based Rainbow Distributors.

In 1996 Cornucopia merged with the leading natural foods distributor in the western US Sacramento-based Mountain People's which Michael Funk had founded 20 years earlier. The combined company became United Natural Foods with Cloutier as chairman and CEO and Funk as president and vice chairman; it went public later that year.

United Natural Foods became the largest natural foods distributor when it bought New Hampshire-based Stow Mills in 1997. The next year it added Hershey Imports an importer and processor of nuts seeds and snacks and Albert's a distributor of organic produce. With the purchase of Mother Earth Markets in 1998 the company's retailing operations had grown to 16 stores but by mid-1999 it had sold four stores. That year United Natural Foods' East Coast consolidation problems became so profound that top customer Whole Foods announced it was finding backup distribution sources.

Funk replaced Cloutier as CEO and the company handed the chairman's post to board member Thomas Simone in 1999. In 2000 after the resignation of Cloutier from the board of directors United Natural Foods adopted a poison-pill plan to block potential takeovers. The company leased a distribution center in the Los Angeles area in 2001 to increase market share in the Southwest. It also acquired Florida's Palm Harbor Natural Foods.

In mid-2002 United Natural Foods lost one of its two largest customers — Wild Oats Markets—when that company defected to rival specialty foods distributor Tree of Life. However United Natural Foods soon won that business back. In October the company completed the acquisition of privately held Blooming Prairie Cooperative for approximately $31 million. In late 2002 the company merged with Northeast Cooperatives a natural foods distributor in the Midwest and Northeast.

That year United Natural Foods discontinued the management sales and support operations at its Hershey Imports subsidiary but continued to manufacture and distribute products from the Edison New Jersey plant.

In 2004 the company renewed its distribution agreement with Wild Oats with a five-year pact. United Natural Foods later announced a new three-year distribution agreement with Whole Foods which it renewed in 2006. Whole Foods later acquired Wild Oats in 2007. That year United Natural Foods acquired ethnic and specialty food distributor Millbrook Distribution Services for about $85 million.

EXECUTIVES

Chairman President and CEO, Steven L. (Steve) Spinner, age 58, $872,300 total compensation
COO, Sean F. Griffin, age 57, $440,300 total compensation
SVP General Counsel Chief Compliance Officer and Corporate Secretary, Joseph J. (Joe) Traficanti, age 66, $367,150 total compensation
SVP Chief Administrative and Information Officer, Eric A. Dorne, age 55
President Atlantic Region, Christopher P. Testa, age 46
SVP CFO and Treasurer, Michael P. Zechmeister
President Pacific Region, Paul S. Green
President Central Region, John M. Hummel
National Vice President Technology Operations, Michael Buchetto
Vice President Of Field Sales, Jack Murphy
Auditors: KPMG LLP

LOCATIONS

HQ: United Natural Foods Inc.
313 Iron Horse Way, Providence, RI 02908
Phone: 401 528-8634
Web: www.unfi.com

PRODUCTS/OPERATIONS

2015 Sales by Customer Type

	$ mil.	% of total
Supernatural chains	2,822	35
Independently-owned natural products retailers	2,650	32
Conventional supermarkets	2,132	26
Other	581	7
Total	**8,185**	**100**

2015 Sales

	$ mil.	% of total
Wholesale	8,099	97
Other	225	3
Adjustments	(140.4)	-
Total	**8,185**	**100**

Selected Acquisitions

Fiscal 2012
B.K. Sethi Distribution Ltd. ($3 million; Ontario Canada; specialty food distribution)
Fiscal 2011
SunOpta Distribution Group ($66 million; Ontario Canada; specialty food distribution)

Selected Operations

Manufacturing division
Woodstock Farms (import roasting packaging and distribution of nuts dried fruit seeds trail mixes granola natural and organic snack items and confections and Blue Marble Brands products)
Retail division
Earth Origins (natural products retail stores in Florida Maryland Massachusetts)
Wholesale division
Albert's Organics (distributor of organically grown produce and perishable items)
Select Nutrition (distributor of vitamins minerals and supplements)
UNIFI Canada (natural organic and specialty business in Canada)
UNFI Specialty (specialty distributor in the Eastern and Midwestern portions of the US)

COMPETITORS

Associated Wholesale Grocers	KeHE Distributors
C&S Wholesale	SUPERVALU
DPI Specialty Foods	SpartanNash
	Wal-Mart

HISTORICAL FINANCIALS

Company Type: Public

Income Statement

FYE: July 29

	REVENUE ($ mil.)	NET INCOME ($ mil.)	NET PROFIT MARGIN	EMPLOYEES
07/17	9,274	130	1.4%	9,700
07/16*	8,470	125	1.5%	9,554
08/15	8,184	138	1.7%	8,700
08/14	6,794	125	1.8%	8,700
08/13	6,064	107	1.8%	7,300
Annual Growth	**11.2%**	**4.8%**	**—**	**7.4%**

*Fiscal year change

2017 Year-End Financials

Debt ratio: 13.36%
Return on equity: 8.15%
Cash ($ mil.): 15
Current ratio: 2.36
Long-term debt ($ mil.): 373

No. of shares (mil.): 50
Dividends
Yield: —
Payout: —
Market value ($ mil.): 1,918

	STOCK PRICE ($) FY Close	P/E High/Low		PER SHARE ($) Earnings	Dividends	Book Value
07/17	37.88	19	13	2.56	0.00	33.23
07/16*	49.98	22	12	2.50	0.00	30.16
08/15	45.53	30	16	2.76	0.00	27.66
08/14	58.71	30	23	2.52	0.00	24.98
08/13	60.31	28	22	2.18	0.00	22.28
Annual Growth	**(11.0%)**	**—**	**—**	**4.1%**	**—**	**10.5%**

*Fiscal year change

United Parcel Service Inc

United Parcel Service (UPS) with its ubiquitous brown is the world's largest package delivery company transporting more than 19 million packages and documents per business day throughout the US and to 220-plus countries. Its delivery operations use a fleet of 114000 motor vehicles and 655-plus aircraft. In addition to package delivery the company offers services such as logistics and freight forwarding through UPS Supply Chain Solutions and less-than-truckload (LTL) and truckload (TL) freight transportation through UPS Ground Freight. The company traces its historical roots back to 1907.

Operations

Domestic package delivery is the company's largest business segment accounting for about 65% of sales. International package delivery is its second largest segment representing roughly 20% of UPS' total sales. The company also offers UPS SurePost an economy residential ground service for customers with non-urgent lightweight residential shipments. It acts as a contractual residential ground service that partners its UPS Ground network with final delivery often provided by the US Postal Service.

Along with logistics and trucking the company's supply chain and freight segment which generates the remainder of sales includes mail expediting (UPS Expedited Mail Services) and financial services (UPS Capital) businesses as well as postal and business services store franchiser Mail Boxes Etc. which maintains UPS Store and Mail Boxes Etc. locations in the US and overseas.

Geographic Reach

The company's international scope is immense; it serves customers in more than 220 countries worldwide. However the US generates roughly 80% of its total revenue while other countries account for the remainder. It has more than 2300 operating facilities.

Sales and Marketing

UPS delivers packages each business day for 1.6 million shipping customers to 8.7 million receivers (consignees). It targets industries such as health care government retail automotive industrial manufacturing and aerospace.

Financial Performance

UPS has enjoyed six years of steady revenue growth with revenues peaking at a record-setting $61 billion in 2016. The historic growth for 2016 was fueled by increases from its domestic (4%) international (2%) and supply chain and freight (8%) package segments.

Business-to-consumer shipments grew nearly 9% for 2016 which drove increases in both air and ground shipments. Business-to-business volume however remained flat in 2016 due to the company's revenue management initiatives and the overall slowing of the industrial manufacturing sector.

The rise in ground volume in 2016 was driven by growth in residential ground and SurePost volume while business-to-business shipments remained flat. Accelerating growth in e-commerce drove demand for its SurePost service with volume increasing 19% in 2016.Next Day Air volume spiked by 5% in 2016 due to strong growth in e-commerce. UPS also experienced increased volume for its deferred air services in 2016 particularly for products most aligned with business-to-consumer shipping.

Unlike its revenues UPS's profits have fluctuated over the years. After climbing sharply in 2015 profits declined 29% to $3.4 billion in 2016 mainly due to an increase in operating expenses particularly compensation and benefits.

Strategy

UPS's extensive global reach is a selling point for its supply chain management offerings which are tailored to customers in industries such as consumer goods and retail health care and technology. The company is seeing a growing trend in how businesses are outsourcing supply chain management with businesses viewing it as a strategic advantage to have effective management of their supply chains.

Package delivery revenue is increasing overseas where UPS continues to expand through infrastructure investments and selected acquisitions. The company has completed a $200 million 70% expansion of its European air hub in Cologne Germany.

UPS is also experimenting with the newest innovative form of transportation: drones. With about 66000 delivery drivers on the road each day UPS is looking for ways to bolster efficiency in its network while also reducing carbon emissions. Throughout 2017 and beyond it is experimenting with methods of using a drone as a supplement to its drivers docking on a vehicle and delivering packages at the discretion of the driver.

Mergers and Acquisitions

Over the years UPS has enhanced its operations through the use of acquisitions. In early 2017 it obtained UK-based Freightex an asset-light provider of truckload less-than-truckload specialized and refrigerated over-the-road services. The acquisition established UPS? presence in the growing UK and European third-party logistics 3PL over-the-road brokerage transportation market

In 2016 the company previously enhanced its UK healthcare logistics services portfolio through the purchase of London-based Marken a global provider of supply chain services to the life sciences industry and expert in clinical trials material storage and distribution.

The company in mid-2015 made the $1.8 billion purchase of Coyote Logistics a Chicago-based third party logistics (3PL) company that offers truckload less-than-truckload (LTL) and intermodal air land and ocean transportation services in North America and Europe. Through the deal UPS expects to benefit from synergies in purchased transportation backhaul utilization and cross-selling to customers in addition to technology systems and industry best practices.

HISTORY

Seattle teens Jim Casey and Claude Ryan started American Messenger Company a delivery and errand service in 1907. They were soon making small-parcel deliveries for local department stores and in 1913 changed the company's name to Merchants Parcel Delivery. Casey who led the company for 50 years established a policy of manager ownership best service and lowest rates. In 1916 new employee Charlie Soderstrom chose the brown paint still used on the company's vehicles. Service expanded outside Seattle in 1919 when Merchants Parcel bought Oakland California-based Motor Parcel Delivery later changing its name to United Parcel Service (UPS).

EXECUTIVES

Vice President Cargo, Don Herbert
SVP and President UPS International, James J. (Jim) Barber, age 56, $500,706 total compensation

Chief Sales Marketing and Strategy Officer, Alan Gershenhorn, age 59, $565,956 total compensation
Chairman and CEO, David P. Abney, age 62, $1,082,421 total compensation
President US Operations, Myron A. Gray, age 60, $514,509 total compensation
SVP CFO and Treasurer, Richard N. Peretz, age 55, $485,070 total compensation
SVP Global Engineering and Sustainability, Mark R. Wallace, age 54
SVP Chief Marketing and Business Services Officer, Teresa M. Finley, age 56
SVP and CIO, Juan R. Perez
President Operations UPS Latin America, Jose Maria (Chema) Odriozola
President Latin America Operations, Jose Maria Odriozola
President UPS China, Harld Peters
Vice President West Los Angeles District, Timothy Robinson
Vice President Technology and Architecture, Mark Hilbush
Vice President Information Services, John Nallin
VP Safety, Alexi Carli
Vice President Rocky Mountain District, George Brooks
Vice President Finance Corporate Strategy Group, Andy Dolny
Global Vice President CRM Technology, Tina Latuga
Vice President Customer Solutions, Charlie Covert
Vice President Of Global Forwarding Logistics Engineering, Bruce Kidwell
Vice President of Sales and Marketing, Norm Brothers
Vice President, Rick Rufolo
Corporate Vice President Global Accounts, Jim Darcy
Vice President, Angela Jack
Vice President; Sales And Marketing, Joe Racanelli
Vice President, Kelly Taylor
Vice President International Marketing, John Miltenis
Vice President Global Accounts, Bill Fitzpatrick
National Account Manager, Theresa Saltarelli
Senior Vice President Marketing and Sales, James Thome
Vice President of E Commerce, Jane Harmon
Vice President, Carlos Cubias
Vice President Global Sales, Mike Mulholland
Vice President, Paul White
Vice President Of Marketing, Alan Hall
Vice President, Ken Torok
Vice President of Cach, Bob Latchford
Vice President Global Accounts Sales Johnson and Johnson, Jeffrey Carney
VICE PRESIDENT CORPORATE STRATEGY, Vern Higberg
Vice President of Sales, Richard Behrendt
Vice President Customer Care Americas, Patty Cheek
Vice President, Stuart Marcus
Vice President, Mark Aaron
Vice President Marketing, Ross Mccullough
VP Operations Global Business Services, Elias Hakim
Vice President, Bill Kruger
Vice President East Central Region, Joseph Zito
National Account Manager, Robert Musca
Vice President Sales Global Accounts, Jerry Felton
Vice President, William Smith
Vice President SAG and Program Management, Ron Jordan
Vice President Enterprise Sales, Bill Washington
Vice President Air District, Steve Mockus
Vice President of Enterprise Sales, Gary Carleton
Vice President Corporate Public Affairs, Nicole Clifton
Vice President Finance US Domestic Operations, Chris Langan

Vice President, Susan Ward
Senior Vice President Strategy Ups Freight, Kevin Hartman
Vice Prespident Of Sales Americas, Pedro Anaya
Vice President of Healthcare Strategic Accounts, Angela Watson
Vice President Enterprise Sales, Sheila Dunn
Vice President, Tom Cox
Senior Vice President Blue Water Hull, Anita Moran
Vice President of Sales, Jon Reitz
Vice President Marketing, Charles Strain
VP Finance, Jay Bowers
National Accounts Manager, Brian F mcQuade
Vice President Strategy, Joe Reuter
Vice President, Allen Hill
SENIOR VICE PRESIDENT WORLDWIDE SALES, John Bystehner
Vice President of Human Resources, David Cole
VICE PRESIDENT INFORMATION SYSTEMS ATLANTA GA, Jerry Aurillio
Vice President Information Systems, Roger Dingus
National Account Manager, Lynn Caldwell-Denny
Vice President Of Human Resources, Juliana Atieno
Vice President Labor Relations, Chuck Martorana
Vice President; Global Head of Mergers and Acquisitions, Jeff Firestone
Vice President, Derrick Johnson
Vice President US Engineering, Mark Susor
National Account Manager, Mike Buffon
VICE PRESIDENT OF HUMAN RESOURCES, Debra Harding
Vice President Plant Engineering, Steve Carter
Vice President Of Logistics, Steve Tesker
Vice President Flight Operations, Matt Capozzoli
Vice President Finance Services, Todd St John
Vice President Worldwide Operations, Phil Thomison
Senior Vice President, Deryl Hill
Vice President, David Lee
Vice President, David Birkmeyer
Vice President Operations, Byron Ballard
Senior Vice President Global Trade Finance, Mike Bryant
VICE PRESIDENT SALES HEALTHCARE SECTOR, Peter Tostevin
VICE PRESIDENT, Arnold Wellman
VICE PRESIDENT OF HUMAN RESOURCES, Yvonne Mchenry
VICE PRESIDENT FINANCE, Joseph Tillman
Vice President Of Human Resources, Stephan Tremblay
Vice President Of Human Resources, Gary Carraway
Vp Of Hr, Dave Lovely
Vice President And General Manager, David LaBonte
Vice President State Gov Affairs, Bruce Mac
Vice President of Transportation, Mark Mehler
National Account Manager, Tom Loranger
Senior Vice President, Jim Bruce
Secretary, John Galuski
Vice Chairman Of The Board, John Alden
Board Member, Wayne Powell
Assistant Treas, Winifer Tong
secretary, Melisa Villa
Auditors: Deloitte & Touche LLP

LOCATIONS

HQ: United Parcel Service Inc
55 Glenlake Parkway N.E., Atlanta, GA 30328
Phone: 404 828-6000
Web: www.ups.com

2015 Sales

	$ mil.	% of total
US	45,309	78
International	13,054	22
Total	**58,363**	**100**

PRODUCTS/OPERATIONS

2015 Sales

	$ mil.	% of total
US domestic package		
Ground	26,274	45
Next day air	6,570	11
Deferred	3,903	7
International package		
Export	9,092	16
Domestic	2,425	4
Cargo	632	1
Supply chain & freight		
Forwarding & logistics	5,900	10
Freight	2,881	5
Other	686	1
Total	**58,363**	**100**

2015 Sales

	$ mil.	% of total
U.S. Domestic Package	36,747	63
International Package	12,149	21
Supply Chain & Freight	9,467	16
Total	**58,363**	**100**

COMPETITORS

American Airlines Group	Nippon Express
Canada Post	Panalpina
Deutsche Post	Royal Mail
FedEx	Ryder System
Japan Post	TNT Express
La Poste	US Postal Service
Lufthansa	United Continental
	YRC Worldwide

HISTORICAL FINANCIALS

Company Type: Public

Income Statement
FYE: December 31

	REVENUE ($ mil.)	NET INCOME ($ mil.)	NET PROFIT MARGIN	EMPLOYEES
12/16	60,906	3,431	5.6%	434,000
12/15	58,363	4,844	8.3%	444,000
12/14	58,232	3,032	5.2%	435,000
12/13	55,438	4,372	7.9%	395,000
12/12	54,127	807	1.5%	399,000
Annual Growth	**3.0%**	**43.6%**	—	**2.1%**

2016 Year-End Financials

Debt ratio: 39.81%
Return on equity: 238.03%
Cash ($ mil.): 3,476
Current ratio: 1.18
Long-term debt ($ mil.): 12,394

No. of shares (mil.): 868
Dividends
Yield: 0.0%
Payout: 80.6%
Market value ($ mil.): 99,508

	STOCK PRICE ($) FY Close	P/E High/Low	PER SHARE ($) Earnings	PER SHARE ($) Dividends	PER SHARE ($) Book Value
12/16	114.64	31 23	3.87	3.12	0.47
12/15	96.23	21 18	5.35	2.92	2.79
12/14	111.17	34 28	3.28	2.68	2.37
12/13	105.08	23 16	4.61	2.48	7.01
12/12	73.73	97 83	0.83	2.28	4.88
Annual Growth	**11.7%**	— —	**46.9%**	**8.2%**	**(44.4%)**

United Rentals Inc

No cash to buy a bulldozer? Just lease one from United Rentals. The company considers itself the #1 commercial and construction equipment renter in the world serving customers in the commercial infrastructure industrial and residential sectors. It operates through a network of more than 885 locations in the US and Canada and provides about 3200 equipment items — everything from general to heavy construction and industrial equipment to hand tools special-event items (such as aerial towers) power (diesel generators) and HVAC equipment and trench-safety equipment. It also sells new and used equipment as well as rental-related and contractor supplies and parts.

Operations

United Rentals' general rentals segment typically accounts for 85% of net sales; trench safety power and HVAC equipment rentals 15%.

Geographic Reach

The largest equipment rental company in the world operates about 770 rental locations in the US and nearly 120 in Canada. The US is its largest market accounting for more than 90% of net sales.

Sales and Marketing

The company markets its products and services through its Sales Force (sales staff at the company's branches and customer care centers); National Account Program (managers dedicated to large customer accounts); E-Rentals portal (online e-commerce site) and advertising (trade publications yellow pages the Internet radio and direct mail).

Financial Performance

After posting record-setting revenues of $5.82 billion in 2015 United Rentals saw its revenues dip slightly by 1% to $5.76 billion in 2016. This was driven by an 8% decrease in sales of rental equipment due to a decrease in the volume of equipment sold through wholesale channels. Rental revenue also dipped in 2016 primarily due to a 2% percent rental rate decrease.

The company's profits fell 3% from $585 million in 2015 to $566 million in 2016 mainly due to the addition of restructuring charges. United Rentals' operating cash flow remained consistent for 2015 and 2016 hovering around the $1.95 billion to $2 billion mark for both years.

Strategy

Because of its size United Rentals rallies more resources over smaller businesses. Competitive advantages include more purchasing leverage a wider range of equipment and services and the more convenient movement of assets between locations. United Rentals enhances its operating efficiencies by ramping up through consolidation of functions including payroll and accounts payable.

In order to manage the age composition and size of its fleet the company routinely sells used rental equipment and invests in new equipment. United Rentals acts as a dealer of new equipment for many leading equipment makers such as Genie Industries Skyjack (aerial lifts) Sullair (compressors) and Terex (telehandlers). At most branches United Rentals sells various supplies and merchandise and offers repair and maintenance services.

Mergers and Acquisitions

In mid-2017 United Rentals acquired NES Rentals a provider of aerial rental equipment (from scissor and boom lifts to rough terrain and truck-mounted cranes) for $965 million. NES serves about 18000 customers across the industrial and non-residential construction sectors. The deal will enhance the company's density in strategically important markets including the East Coast Gulf States and the Midwest.

HISTORY

Bradley Jacobs had made a fortune in the garbage business having used United Waste Systems as a roll-up company to buy small trash-hauling firms in that fragmented industry. Flush with cash after he sold United Waste Systems in 1997 to USA Waste Services (now Waste Management) Jacobs launched the same roll-up strategy to consolidate the equipment-rental industry. He and his management team bought six leasing companies and started United Rentals. The company which went public in 1997 had acquired 38 rental companies in 20 states by mid-1998.

EXECUTIVES

Vice President Business Development, Ned Graham
Senior Vice President Strategy and Planning, Kenneth Mettel
Regional Vice President, Robert Krause
Vice President, Jonathan M Gottsegen
EVP and CFO, William B. Plummer, age 58, $595,504 total compensation
President and CEO, Michael J. Kneeland, age 63, $950,000 total compensation
EVP and COO, Matthew J. Flannery, age 52, $595,504 total compensation
SVP Business Services and CIO, Dale A. Asplund, age 49, $519,807 total compensation
EVP Chief Administrative and Legal Officer, Craig A. Pintoff, age 47, $473,046 total compensation
VP Midwest Region, Chris Burlog
VP Mid-Central Region, Kevin M. OBrien
SVP and Chief Marketing Officer, Chris Hummel
VP Pacific West Region, Robert C. Bower
VP Southeast Region, Michael G. Cloer
VP Western Canada Region, John (Scott) Fisher
Region VP Tools and Industrial Solutions, Joshuah P. Flores
VP Trench Safety Region, Todd M. Hayes
VP Mid-Atlantic Region, John J. Humphrey
VP Pump Solutions, William A. (Bill) Kiker
VP Industrial Region, Donald (Chad) Matter
VP South Region, Jeffrey S. (Jeff) McGinnis
VP Northeast Region, Craig Schmidt
VP Power and HVAC Region, David C. Scott
VP Gulf South Region, Larry (Don) Irwin
Senior Vice President Business Development, Jeffrey Fenton
Executive Vice President, Anthony Leopold
Region Vice President, Chad Matter
National Account Manager, Frank Branca
Vice President Environmental Health and Safety, James Dorris
Vice President of Corporate Communications, Fred Bratman
Executive Vice President Corporate Services, Kurtis Barker
National Account Manager, Bill Kenyon
National Account Manager, SHAWNA ERMOLD
National Account Manager, Sidney Six
Senior Vice President Operations, David A Hobbs
Vice President Customer Service Operations, Kenneth Perkins
Vice President Operations Finance, Joe Pledger
National Account Manager, Jeremy Epps
Vice President, Scott Gorton
National Account Manager, Brian Knauer
National Accounts Manager, Chad Edwards
National Account Manager, Chad Cedotal
National Account Manager, Bobby Bennett
National Account Manager Oil and Gas, Brian Nagel
National Account Manager, Greg Littler
National Account Manager, Ray Cruz
National Account Manager, Rick Clinaz
Region Vice President, Bill Kiker
Chairman, Jenne K. Britell, age 74
Board of Directors, Don Roof
Auditors: Ernst & Young LLP

LOCATIONS

HQ: United Rentals Inc
100 First Stamford Place, Suite 700, Stamford, CT 06902
Phone: 203 622-3131
Web: www.unitedrentals.com

2016 Sales

	$ mil.	% of total
Domestic	5,252	91
Foreign	510	9
Total	**5,762**	**100**

PRODUCTS/OPERATIONS

2016 Sales

	$ mil.	% of total
General Rental	4,908	85
Trench power and pump	854	15
Total	**5,762**	**100**

2016 Sales

	$ mil.	% of total
Equipment rentals	4,941	86
Sales of rental equipment	496	9
Sales of new equipment	144	2
Contractor supplies sales	79	1
Service & other revenues	102	2
Total	**5,762**	**100**

Selected Products

Aerial lifts
Backhoes
Barricades
Compressors
Concrete & Masonry
Cones
Contractor supplies
Ditching equipment
Earth-moving equipment
Forklifts
Generators
Hand tools
Heaters
HVAC
Lawn & Landscape
Light towers
Material-handling equipment
Message boards
Pavement-marking systems
Portable power units
Power washers
Pumps
Skid-steer loaders
Trench shields
Trucks & Trailers
Warning lights
Water pumps
Welders & Accessories

COMPETITORS

AMECO	Maxim Crane Works
Atlas Lift Truck	Neff
Rentals	RDO Equipment
Case Power & Equipment	Sunbelt Rentals
Herc Holdings	Ziegler inc

HISTORICAL FINANCIALS

Company Type: Public

Income Statement

FYE: December 31

	REVENUE ($ mil.)	NET INCOME ($ mil.)	NET PROFIT MARGIN	EMPLOYEES
12/17	6,641	1,346	20.3%	14,800
12/16	5,762	566	9.8%	12,500
12/15	5,817	585	10.1%	12,700
12/14	5,685	540	9.5%	12,500
12/13	4,955	387	7.8%	11,850
Annual Growth	**7.6%**	**36.6%**	**—**	**5.7%**

2017 Year-End Financials

Debt ratio: 62.81%	No. of shares (mil.): 84
Return on equity: 56.63%	Dividends
Cash ($ mil.): 352	Yield: —
Current ratio: 1.06	Payout: —
Long-term debt ($ mil.): 8,717	Market value ($ mil.): 14,520

	STOCK PRICE ($) FY Close	P/E High/Low		PER SHARE ($) Earnings	Dividends	Book Value
12/17	171.91	11	6	15.73	0.00	36.77
12/16	105.58	17	7	6.45	0.00	19.57
12/15	72.54	17	10	6.07	0.00	16.08
12/14	102.01	21	13	5.15	0.00	18.37
12/13	77.95	19	11	3.64	0.00	19.81
Annual Growth	**21.9%**	**—**	**—**	**44.2%**	**—**	**16.7%**

United States Steel Corp.

Steel crazy after all these years United States Steel (U.S. Steel) is North America's largest integrated steelmaker. The company operates mills throughout the US Midwest and in Slovakia. U.S. Steel makes a wide range of flat-rolled and tubular steel products and its annual production capacity is 22 million net tons of raw steel. Its customers are primarily in the automotive appliance construction oil and gas and petrochemical industries. In addition U.S. Steel mines iron ore and procures coke which provide the primary raw materials used in steel making. It is also engaged in railroad and barge operations and real estate.

HISTORY

U.S. Steel was conceived through a 1901 merger of 10 steel companies that combined their furnaces ore deposits railroad companies and shipping lines. The deal involved industrial pioneers Andrew Carnegie Charles Schwab Elbert Gary and J. P. Morgan.

Morgan had helped organize the Federal Steel Company in 1898 and he then wanted to create a centralized trust to dominate the soaring steel market. Carnegie owned the largest US steel company at the time Carnegie Steel but wanted to retire.

In 1900 Schwab Carnegie Steel's president outlined the idea of the steel trust based on a merger of the Carnegie and Federal steel companies. Morgan asked Schwab to persuade Carnegie to sell his steel mills and name his price. Morgan didn't haggle when Carnegie responded that he would sell for almost half a billion dollars.

The Carnegie-Morgan combination created the world's first billion-dollar company. It produced 67% of the country's steel in its first year (its steel complex and the Indiana town where it was located were named after Gary who was CEO until 1927).

The company boomed during WWI and WWII. But its market share fell to about 30% by the 1950s although it set new profit records in 1955. During the 1970s prospects for long-term growth in steel became dismal in light of rising costs foreign competition and competitive pricing.

In 1982 U.S. Steel doubled its size when it bought Marathon Oil a major integrated energy company with huge oil and gas reserves in the US and abroad. It continued to cut back its steelmaking capacity laying off 100000 employees closing steel mills and selling off assets.

The company bought Texas Oil & Gas in 1986 and renamed itself USX Corporation to reflect the decreasing role of steel in its business. Also that year corporate raider Carl Icahn USX's largest single shareholder unsuccessfully tried to get the company to sell its steel operations. In 1988 USX bought 49% of Transtar a group of rail and water transport providers. (It purchased the remaining stake in 2001 making Transtar a wholly owned subsidiary.)

Stockholders in 1991 approved splitting the company into two separate entities under the USX umbrella: U.S. Steel and Marathon. During the 1990s U.S. Steel continued to close steelmaking facilities. In 1992 USX joined five other leading US steel producers in a suit against subsidized foreign steelmakers. The next year the company formed two joint ventures with Japan's Kobe Steel.

In 1994 U.S. Steel teamed up with rival Nucor to explore a new technology that would reduce much of the cost and pollution of the steelmaking process. The company agreed to pay $106 million in fines and improvements in 1996 to settle charges of air pollution violations involving its Indiana plant. That year blast furnace outages at two U.S. Steel plants cost the company more than $100 million.

U.S. Steel began upgrading several of its facilities in 1997 and 1998 and entered into a number of domestic and foreign joint ventures including one in Slovakia and another in Mexico. Seeing prices drop in 1998 and 1999 the company cut production and joined other US steelmakers in charging rivals in Brazil Japan and Russia with unlawfully dumping low-priced steel in the US.

In 2000 U.S. Steel acquired the core activities of leading central European steelmaker VSZ. The $495 million (excluding investments) deal — U.S. Steel's first major foray into Europe — included an agreement to invest some $700 million in VSZ's facilities.

Early in 2001 USX spun off its steel operations as United States Steel Corporation; the remaining energy businesses began operating as Marathon Oil Corporation. Also that year USX-U.S. Steel and Bethlehem Steel announced they were in talks about possibly merging the two companies. Subsequently USX-U.S. Steel and National Steel (U.S. subsidiary of NKK) began talks of merging its businesses. In order for the deal to close National Steel would have to restructure its debt and the Bush administration would have to implement its plan to curtail steel imports. At the end of 2001 due to shareholder pressure USX-U.S. Steel split apart from its holding company USX Corporation and the steel operations unit went back to trading under its original name United States Steel Corporation. The breakup left the company with over $1.3 billion in debt (Marathon Oil assumed $900 million of the company's debt).

U.S. Steel signed an option agreement to purchase the remaining 53% of National Steel in 2002. That year U.S. Steel sold its stake in VSZ.

In its pursuit to consolidate U.S. Steel along with other US steelmakers received concessions (40% import tariffs and assistance with its huge retiree health-care costs) from the Bush administration. In March 2002 the Bush administration on recommendations of the International Trade Commission imposed tariffs of 8%-30% providing temporary relief to U.S. Steel and the US steel industry. The administration rejected any retiree bailout plan and in December 2003 ended the tariffs 16 months ahead of schedule.

In 2003 U.S. Steel made the monumental move to purchase National Steel for roughly $1.1 billion in cash including liabilities. AK Steel which had an offer of roughly $1.1 billion vehemently challenged U.S. Steel but the deal fell through after labor negotiations with United Steelworkers of America proved unsuccessful. With the combined manufacturing capabilities of National Steel and U.S. Steel the company's raw steel production came in at around 20 million tons of steel annually both domestically and internationally which made it the nation's largest steel producer until the formation of Mittal Steel USA in 2005. The year 2003 also saw the expansion of U.S. Steel's European businesses with the acquisition of Sartid.

U.S. Steel again jumped into the industrywide consolidation game in 2007 when it spent a combined $3.3 billion to buy tubular goods maker Lone Star Technologies and the former Stelco in separate deals. Lone Star Technologies was among the nation's largest makers of welded steel tubes for use in the oilfield. The acquired business complemented U.S. Steel's own product line for the energy industry which consisted largely of seamless tubes. The Stelco deal on the other hand added to the company's core business. Focusing on slab products used in the flat-rolled market Stelco raised U.S. Steel's production capacity to more than 30 million tons a year. Upon closing of the deal U.S. Steel changed Stelco's name to U.S. Steel Canada.

Although U.S. Steel agreed to maintain certain production and employment levels at the plants in Canada it stopped operations in 2009 when demand weakened in response to the global economic slump. The Canadian government responded by taking the company to court in 2009 and a later settlement of the dispute led U.S. Steel to agree to invest $50 million in its two Canadian plants by 2015.

U.S. Steel Canada sold its Bar Mill and Bloom and Billet Mill at its Ontario operations to Max Aicher (North America) in 2010. Also in 2010 U.S. Steel sold the assets of its Mobile River Terminal Company and of Warrior and Gulf Navigation.

In 2011 the company sold Oklahoma-based subsidiary Steel Coil Services to Macsteel Service Centers USA.

In 2012 it exited its Serbia business (U.S. Steel Serbia) after the European economy slid significantly and weak demand caused the company to lose more than $200 million from its Serbian operations in 2011. U.S. Steel sold the segment to the Serbian government for only $1. U.S. Steel Serbia was part of the company's U.S. Steel Europe business.

In 2012 U.S. Steel also sold the non-core assets of Birmingham Southern Railroad Company and the Port Birmingham Terminal and recognized a pretax gain of $89 million.

In 2013 U. S. Steel permanently shut down its iron and steel making facilities at Hamilton Works reducing U. S. Steel's North American annual raw steel capability by 2.3 million tons.

EXECUTIVES

President CEO and Director, David B. (Dave) Burritt, age 61, $800,000 total compensation
SVP Consumer Solutions, Sara A. Greenstein, age 42
SVP Industrial Service Center and Mining Solutions, Douglas R. Matthews, age 52, $541,000 total compensation
SVP Tubular Business, David J. Rintoul, age 60
VP European Solutions and President US Steel Ko Ašice, Scott D. Buckiso, age 50
VP and CIO, Charles G. Balawajder, age 61
SVP Government Affairs General Counsel and Chief Compliance Officer, Suzanne R. Folsom, age 55, $700,000 total compensation
SVP Automotive Solutions, James E. Bruno, age 51, $403,500 total compensation
VP and Chief Supply Chain Officer, Christine S. Breves
EVP and CFO, Kevin P. Bradley

Senior Vice President Of Development, Emmett Beever
Executive Vice President And Chief Financial Officer, Joseph Stinnett
Vice President, Pat Mullarkey
Senior Vice President and Treasurer, Albert Ferrara
Senior Vice President Automotive Solutions, Jim Bruno
Chairman, David S. (Dave) Sutherland, age 67
Assistant Treasurer Credit and Banking, Gregg Schmidt
Auditors: PricewaterhouseCoopers LLP

LOCATIONS

HQ: United States Steel Corp.
600 Grant Street, Pittsburgh, PA 15219-2800
Phone: 412 433-1121   **Fax:** 412 433-4818
Web: www.ussteel.com

2016 Sales

	$ mil.	% of total
North America	8,018	78
Europe	2,243	22
Total	**10,261**	**100**

PRODUCTS/OPERATIONS

2016 Sales

	$ mil.	% of total
Flat-rolled	7,507	73
US Steel Europe	2,243	22
Tubular products	449	4
Other	62	1
Total	**10,261**	**100**

Selected Products
Steel
Tin
Tubular

Selected Subsidiaries
Acero Prime S. R. L de CV (44% steel processing and warehousing)
Delray Connecting Railroad Company (transportation)
Double Eagle Steel Coating Company (50% with Severstal; steel processing)
PRO-TEC Coating Co. (50% with Kobe Steel; steel processing)
Transtar Inc. (transportation)
U. S. Steel Kosice sro (steelmaking Slovakia)
USS-POSCO Industries (50% with Pohang Iron & Steel; steel processing)
Worthington Specialty Processing (50% with Worthington Industries; steel processing)

COMPETITORS

AK Steel Holding Corporation
Allegheny Technologies
ArcelorMittal
Baosteel
BlueScope Steel
BÖHLER-UDDEHOLM
Carpenter Technology
Gerdau Ameristeel
JFE Holdings
Kobe Steel
Nippon Steel & Sumitomo Metal Corporation
Nucor
POSCO
SSAB North America
SSAB Svenskt
Salzgitter
Simec
Steel Dynamics
Tata Steel
Ternium
ThyssenKrupp Steel
Wuhan Iron & Steel

HISTORICAL FINANCIALS
Company Type: Public

Income Statement

FYE: December 31

	REVENUE ($ mil.)	NET INCOME ($ mil.)	NET PROFIT MARGIN	EMPLOYEES
12/16	10,261	(440)	—	29,800
12/15	11,574	(1,642)	—	33,200
12/14	17,507	102	0.6%	23,000
12/13	17,424	(1,672)	—	38,500
12/12	19,328	(124)	—	39,000
Annual Growth	**(14.6%)**	**—**	**—**	**(6.5%)**

2016 Year-End Financials
Debt ratio: 33.09%
Return on equity: (-18.63%)
Cash ($ mil.): 1,515
Current ratio: 1.87
Long-term debt ($ mil.): 2,981
No. of shares (mil.): 173
Dividends
  Yield: 0.0%
  Payout: —
Market value ($ mil.): 5,737

	STOCK PRICE ($) FY Close	P/E High/Low		PER SHARE ($) Earnings	Dividends	Book Value
12/16	33.01	—	—	(2.81)	0.20	13.08
12/15	7.98	—	—	(11.24)	0.20	16.65
12/14	26.74	65	32	0.69	0.20	26.08
12/13	29.50	—	—	(11.56)	0.20	23.14
12/12	23.85	—	—	(0.86)	0.20	24.10
Annual Growth (14.2%)	**8.5%**	**—**	**—**	**—**	**(0.0%)**	

United Technologies Corp

United Technologies (UTC) has the worldwide industrial expertise to lift you up and cool you down. Its Otis UTC Climate Controls & Security and Pratt & Whitney segments develop technologies systems and services for the aerospace construction and security industries. Climate Controls & Security makes alarms monitoring equipment surveillance and access control systems and fire and hazard detection products. Otis is the world's largest elevator and escalator manufacturing company while Pratt & Whitney makes commercial and military engines. UTC Aerospace Systems produces engine controls and flight systems for military and commercial clients. In a major move to bolster its aerospace operations UTC in 2017 agreed to purchase aircraft parts manufacturer Rockwell Collins for $23 billion.

Operations

UTC's Climate Controls & Security segment (30% of net sales) makes security products and firefighting equipment for the commercial governmental and residential sectors.

Pratt & Whitney (some 25%) makes and sells aircraft engines for the commercial military business jet and general aviation markets. It also provides fleet management services and aftermarket maintenance services.

UTC Aerospace Systems (25%) provides aerospace products and aftermarket services for aircraft manufacturers airlines and the general aviation markets. (This division will soon be transformed into Collins Aerospace Systems following UTC's pending acquisition of Rockwell Collins that was announced in late 2017.)

In addition UTC owns Otis (20%) one of the world?s largest elevator and escalator manufacturing installation and servicing companies.

Geographic Reach

UTC operates through 4000 locations in more than 70 countries. The US generates around 55% of its total sales; Europe and the Asia/Pacific follow contributing about 20% and 15% respectively.

Sales and Marketing

The company serves customers residing in the commercial and industrial (contributing 50% revenue) commercial aerospace (almost 40%) and military aerospace and space (10%) sectors. The US government contributes roughly 20%.

Financial Performance

UTC's revenues increased 2% from $56.1 billion in 2015 to $57.2 billion in 2016. This growth was attributed to higher commercial aftermarket sales from Pratt & Whitney and increased commercial OEM and aftermarket sales from UTC Aerospace Systems. In addition UTC experienced higher service sales in the Americas and Asia and increased new equipment sales in North America partially offset by lower new equipment sales in China from Otis in 2016.

UTC's profits however declined 34% from $7.6 billion in 2015 to $5.1 billion in 2016. This was attributed to a 3% rise in selling general and administrative expenses driven by a pension settlement charge and increased expenses at Otis that reflected higher labor and information technology costs.

Strategy

UTC strives to maintain a balance between its private and military sectors its commercial and aerospace operations and its original equipment (OE) and aftermarket products and services. It also juggles fluctuations in the market that may impact one or more of its businesses. These fluctuations include changing fuel costs and contracts from the US Department of Defense (DoD) which are subject to policies set by the White House and Congress.

This strategy of product balance is combined with geographic balance which has the company investing in emerging markets that show great growth potential such as Argentina Brazil China Mexico the Middle East Russia and South Africa. UTC is champing at the bit to acquire aerospace and commercial companies with operations in India. Adhering to this strategy in late 2017 it announced it was acquiring aircraft parts maker Rockwell Collins for $23 billion.

Mergers and Acquisitions

In the biggest aerospace deal in history UTC agreed to purchase aircraft parts manufacturer Rockwell Collins for $23 billion in September 2017. When the deal is completed Rockwell will become a new UTC division named Collins Aerospace Systems. UTC projects the new division will generate more than $23 billion in revenue per year and will make aviation electronics and communication equipment for commercial and military aircraft. UTC is making the deal to boost its aerospace business and position it as a key springboard for growth in the years ahead.

HISTORY

In 1925 Frederick Rentschler and George Mead founded Pratt & Whitney Aircraft (P&W) to develop aircraft engines. P&W merged with Seattle-based Boeing Airplane Company and Chance Vought Corporation in 1929 to form United Aircraft & Transport. United Aircraft soon bought aviation companies Hamilton Aero Standard Steel Propeller and Sikorsky.

After congressional investigations led to new antitrust laws United Aircraft split in 1934 into three independent entities: United Airlines Boeing Airplane Company and United Aircraft. United Air-

craft retained P&W and several other manufacturing interests.

A design flaw in engines produced for Boeing 747s sent P&W on an expensive trip back to the drawing board in the late 1960s. A concerned board of directors appointed Harry Gray a 17-year veteran of Litton Industries as president in 1971. Gray transformed the company into a conglomerate; it adopted its present name in 1975.

The company entered into a new stage of development with the milestone 2012 acquisitions of Goodrich and Rolls-Royce's share in the International Aero Engines (IAE) joint venture. The $16.5 billion acquisition of Goodrich an aircraft components manufacturer was one of UTC's largest. Through the transaction UTC absorbed $1.9 billion in assumed debt but it also sizably boosted its services to the commercial aerospace/defense industry and increased its revenues. Goodrich was combined with the former Hamilton Sundstrand operations and now form its UTC Aerospace Systems segment.

UTC in early 2013 sold its UTC Power unit to Oregon-based ClearEdge Power. In late 2015 it also sold its former Sikorsky helicopter subsidiary to Lockheed Martin for $9 billion.

EXECUTIVES

President Pratt & Whitney, Robert F. Leduc, age 61, $665,057 total compensation
President UTC Climate Controls and Security (CCS), Robert J. (Bob) McDonough, age 57, $806,250 total compensation
Chairman President and CEO, Gregory J. Hayes, age 56, $1,450,000 total compensation
President Otis Elevator, Judy F. Marks
EVP and General Counsel, Charles D. Gill, age 53, $715,000 total compensation
EVP Operations and Strategy, Michael R. (Mike) Dumais, age 50
President UTC Aerospace Systems, David L. Gitlin, age 47
EVP and Chief Human Resources Officer, Elizabeth B. Amato, age 60
SVP and CFO, Akhil Johri, age 56, $766,667 total compensation
SVP Digital and CIO, Vince Campisi
SVP and CTO, Paul Eremenko
Vice President, Greg Deldicque
Vice President Engineering And Technology Hamilton Sundstrand, Dave Carter
Vice President, Richard Pierpont
Auditors: PricewaterhouseCoopers LLP

LOCATIONS

HQ: United Technologies Corp
  10 Farm Springs Road, Farmington, CT 06032
Phone: 860 728-7000   **Fax:** 860 728-7028
Web: www.utc.com

2016 Sales

	$ mil.	% of total
US	32,335	56
Europe	11,151	20
Asia/Pacific	8,260	14
Other	5,479	10
Eliminations and other	19	-
Total	**57,244**	**100**

PRODUCTS/OPERATIONS

2016 Sales

	$ mil.	% of total
UTC Climate Controls & Security	16,851	29
Pratt & Whitney	14,894	26
UTC Aerospace Systems	14,465	25
Otis	11,893	20
Eliminations	(859)	-
Total	**57,244**	**100**

2016 Sales by Market

	% of total
Commercial & industrial	50
Commercial aerospace	38
Military aerospace & space	12
Total	**100**

2016 Sales

	$ mil.	% of total
Product sales	40,735	71
Service sales	16,509	29
Total	**57,244**	**100**

Products & Brands Selected

Actuation & Propeller Systems
Air Management Systems
Carrier
Carrier Transicold
Chubb
Chubb eConnect Monitoring Solution
Delta Security Solutions

Selected Operations

Otis (elevators escalators moving walkways and service)
Pratt & Whitney (commercial military business jet and general aviation aircraft engines auxiliary power units and parts and services)
UTC Aerospace Systems (aerospace products and aftermarket services)
UTC Climate Controls & Security (heating ventilating air conditioning and refrigeration systems and security systems)

COMPETITORS

Aerojet Rocketdyne	L3 Technologies
CFM International SA	Lockheed Martin
GE Aviation	Mitsubishi Electric
General Dynamics	Parker-Hannifin
Hitachi	Precision Castparts
Honeywell	Raytheon
International	Siemens AG
IDEX	ThyssenKrupp
Kaman	Trane Inc.

HISTORICAL FINANCIALS

Company Type: Public

Income Statement

FYE: December 31

	REVENUE ($ mil.)	NET INCOME ($ mil.)	NET PROFIT MARGIN	EMPLOYEES
12/17	59,837	4,552	7.6%	205,000
12/16	57,244	5,055	8.8%	201,600
12/15	56,098	7,608	13.6%	197,200
12/14	65,100	6,220	9.6%	211,500
12/13	62,626	5,721	9.1%	212,400
Annual Growth	**(1.1%)**	**(5.6%)**	**—**	**(0.9%)**

2017 Year-End Financials

Debt ratio: 28.36%
Return on equity: 15.92%
Cash ($ mil.): 8,985
Current ratio: 1.35
Long-term debt ($ mil.): 24,989

No. of shares (mil.): 799
Dividends
  Yield: 0.0%
  Payout: 47.7%
Market value ($ mil.): 101,945

	STOCK PRICE ($) FY Close	P/E High/Low		PER SHARE ($) Earnings	Dividends	Book Value
12/17	127.57	22	19	5.70	2.72	37.05
12/16	109.62	18	14	6.12	2.62	34.10
12/15	96.07	14	10	8.61	2.56	32.63
12/14	115.00	17	14	6.82	2.36	34.32
12/13	113.80	18	13	6.25	2.20	34.76
Annual Growth	**2.9%**	—	—	**(2.3%)**	**5.5%**	**1.6%**

UnitedHealth Group Inc

UnitedHealth unites its health plans with consumers across the US. As a leading health insurer it offers a variety of plans and services to group and individual customers nationwide. Its UnitedHealthcare health benefits segment manages health maintenance organization (HMO) preferred provider organization (PPO) and point-of-service (POS) plans as well as Medicare Medicaid state-funded and supplemental vision and dental options. In addition UnitedHealth's Optum health services units — OptumHealth OptumInsight and OptumRx— provide wellness and care management programs financial services information technology solutions and pharmacy benefit management (PBM) services to individuals and the health care industry.

HISTORY

Dr. Paul Ellwood became known as the "Father of the HMO" for his role as an early champion of the health care concept. As a neurology student in the 1950s Ellwood recognized that applying business principles to medicine could minimize costs and make health care more affordable. Although the HMO was considered a radical approach to health care reform Ellwood got Congress and the Nixon administration to approve his HMO model in 1970; the next year he hired Richard Burke to put the model into action. Burke established United HealthCare (UHC) in 1974 to manage the not-for-profit Physicians Health Plan of Minnesota (PHP). UHC incorporated in 1977.

The company bought HMOs and began managing others operating 11 HMOs in 10 states by 1984 the year it went public. Its expansion continued with the purchases of HMOs Share Development (1985) and Peak Health Care (1986). Unfortunately acquisitions and startups began to eat away at UHC's financial health. Meanwhile Burke CEO of both UHC and PHP was accused by PHP doctors of having a conflict of interest after a change in the HMO's Medicare policy threatened to cut off patients from some member hospitals. Burke resigned in 1987 and was replaced by Kennett Simmons formerly president of Peak.

That year investment firm Warburg Pincus bought nearly 40% of UHC providing it with much-needed cash. UHC lost nearly $16 million in 1987 largely from a restructuring that axed the company's Phoenix HMO as well as startups in six other markets. The next year UHC sold its share of Peak Health Care.

In the late 1980s UHC adopted a new strategy of acquiring specialty companies that provided fee income. It also continued building its HMO network through acquisitions hoping to gain critical mass in such varied markets as the Midwest and New England.

Physician William (Bill) McGuire another former Peak president was named UHC's chairman and CEO in 1991. That year PHP and Share merged into Medica. Warburg Pincus distributed its UHC shares to several pension funds and financial institutions.

The company's expansion accelerated in the 1990s with a string of purchases in the Midwest but there were also divestitures. In 1994 UHC sold subsidiary Diversified Pharmaceutical Services providing cash for still more purchases including Gen-Care (St. Louis) Group Sales and Service of Puerto Rico and MetraHealth a former joint venture of Travelers Group and Metropolitan Life. UHC's interest in fee-based businesses continued with the

1997 purchase of Medicode a major provider of health care information products.

In 1998 the firm planned to buy rival Humana. However bloated UHC decided it should slim down to prepare to consummate the agreement; when UHC announced that it would charge $900 million in costs against earnings its plummeting stock price devalued the primary currency of the deal which quickly collapsed. That year it began offering MediGap and other supplements to AARP members.

The company changed its name to UnitedHealth Group in 2000. It also added UK-based contract research organization ClinPharm International to Ingenix that year and it announced it would let doctors — not administrators — choose what treatment patients would get partially because it was spending more on care scrutiny than the practice saved. Nevertheless many doctors claimed the process was still restrictive.

In 2000 the American Medical Association (AMA) and other parties sued the company claiming it used faulty Ingenix data to reduce payments to member doctors. (UnitedHealth settled the AMA lawsuit in 2009 for $350 million without admitting any wrongdoing as well as some state lawsuits related to the database.)

UnitedHealth's strategy for expansion in the early 21st century concentrated on acquisitions and joint ventures. To expand its Medicaid services business the firm bought AmeriChoice in 2002. The company also bought Mid Atlantic Medical Services because its HMOs and specialty health care operations complemented UnitedHealth's core operations. Golden Rule was acquired in late 2003 so UnitedHealth could enter the individual health insurance market by providing medical savings accounts. UnitedHealth also bought individual health care reimbursement account provider Definity Health in late 2004 for the same purpose. To increase its market share in the northeastern US the company bought Oxford Health Plans that year.

UnitedHealth spent $8.8 billion to acquire and integrate PacifiCare in 2005. Adding 3 million customers the acquisition gave UnitedHealth a leading position in the California and West Coast markets but it also prompted a landslide of complaints from customers alleging mishandled claims. The California Insurance Commissioner and other state agencies sought fines of more than $1 billion. While PacifiCare continued to exist as a health plan brand of UnitedHealth the PacifiCare administrative operations were integrated into other UnitedHealth units including UnitedHealthcare. The PacifiCare Prescription Benefits unit became separate operating division of UnitedHealth.

Chairman and CEO McGuire became the focus of inquiry in 2006 over a scandal involving the back-dating of stock options awarded to him and other company executives. Following a board inquiry McGuire was shown the door and was replaced by Stephen Hemsley formerly the company's president and COO. The back-dating brouhaha continued to be a distraction for UnitedHealth and in 2008 it opted to settle several related shareholder lawsuits by agreeing to pay more than $900 million.

Continuing the acquisitive strategy it laid out after the turn of the millennium the company in 2006 bought Deere & Company's employee health plan as well as Student Resources the student insurance division of HealthMarkets' MEGA Life subsidiary.

The company changed the name of its supplemental health division from Specialized Care Service to OptumHealth in 2007. As part of the restructuring a number of other UnitedHealth businesses were merged into OptumHealth including ACN Group United Resources Networks United

Behavioral Health PacifiCare Behavioral Health Exante Bank and Exante Financial Services.

UnitedHealth completed several large acquisitions in 2008 spending $730 million to purchase Fiserv's health-related businesses including Fiserv Health (benefits administration for 2 million members) Avidyn Health (care facilitation) Fiserv Health Specialty Solutions (administration) and Innoviant Pharmacy Benefits Management. UnitedHealth also paid $980 million to acquire Unison Health Plans and used it to expand its AmeriChoice unit.

UnitedHealth completed its controversial purchase of Nevada insurance provider Sierra Health Services for approximately $2.6 billion in 2008 gaining some 600000 health plan members in the state and boosting its position in the growing Southwest market. The acquisition took nearly a year to receive approval from the Department of Justice due to competition concerns. Approval was finally gained on the contingency that UnitedHealth sell its Las Vegas Medicare Advantage program representing some 27000 customers to Humana for $185 million. Sierra Health's operating units including Health Plan of Nevada and Sierra Health and Life became part the UnitedHealthcare Nevada division following the acquisition.

EXECUTIVES

Senior Vice President Capital Markets Communications Strategy, John Penshorn

Executive Vice President, Simon Stevens

EVP, Jeannine M. Rivet, $465,000 total compensation

Vice Chairman and CEO Optum, Larry C. Renfro, age 63, $1,100,000 total compensation

EVP Medical Affairs and Chief Medical Officer, Richard Migliori

CEO, David S. Wichmann, age 55, $1,100,000 total compensation

CEO Community Plan of Kansas, Kevin P. Sparks

EVP Human Capital, D. Ellen Wilson, age 59, $701,923 total compensation

EVP and Chief Legal Officer, Marianne D. Short, age 65, $800,000 total compensation

EVP External Affairs, Cory B. Alexander

CEO Employer and Individual Iowa-Kansas-Nebraska, Robert Broomfield

EVP and CFO, John Rex, $721,923 total compensation

SVP and Chief Marketing Officer, Terry M. Clark

Vice President, Mark Dicello

National Vice President Sales and Field Marketing, Lenys Alcoreza

Regional Sales Vice President, Shawn Mobley

Senior Vice President Client Development, Bruce Mead

Vice President Brand and Marketing Services United Healthcare Medicare and Retirement, Bart Reed

VICE PRESIDENT PROD, Joe Altman

Vice President New Product Strategy, Patsy Piazza

Vice President Marketing Ovations, Ellen Sexton

Senior Vice President, Anne Gavel

Regional Vice President of Human Resources, Cheryl Lippert

Vice President and Chief Information Security Officer, Robert Booker

Vice President, Gayle Adams

Vice President Sales, Philip Brun

Senior Vice President Human Capital, Chris Coleman

Senior Vice President Software Innovation and Technical Product Services, Karsten Flagstad

Vice President of Enterprise Quality, Todd Masser

Vice President market medical director co nm wy mt, Jacqueline Stiff

Vice President Research and Development, James Little

VICE PRESIDENT ACCOUNT MANAGEMENT, Caitlin Clipp

Senior Vice President Center for Nursing Advancement, Dawn Bazarko
Executive Vice President Of Sales, Nancy Goldberg
Medical Director, May Jung
Vice President Product Marketing, Julia Ducayet
Vice President Business Development, Matthew AAefedt
Vice President Software Engineering, Milla Hautman
Senior Vice President Business Development, Lisa Pierre
Vice President Of Key Account Sales, Robert Benkert
Vice President Data Analytics and Marketing Operations, Tom Allenburg
Vice President Center For Health Reform, Deborah Sundal
Vice President of Claims, Robert Carreiro
Vice President Of Sales, Bryan Palmer
Vice President Product And Innovation, Denise Mount
Vice President, Steven Burdick
Vice President Innovation and RandD, Robert Plourde
Vice President Product Management, Monty Page
Vice President Digital Product, Cara Sjodin
VICE PRESIDENT INNOVATION DIRECTOR HUMAN CENTERED DESIGN STUDIO, Ryan Armbruster
Benefits Regional Vice President, Mark Stecklein
Vice President, Ipyana Spencer
Health Services Director, Marguerite Mauradian
Vice President Information Technology, Donna McCart
Vice President Office Of Provider Data, Regan Ristich
Vice President Product Management, Todd Spaulding
Senior Vice President Development Management, Dave Pelner
Vice President Accounting Policy, Amy Shaw
Executive Vice President, Chris Ritchie
REGIONAL VICE PRESIDENT PROVIDER RELATIONS, Tom Wicklund
Vice President Oxford, Randall Weinstock
Vice President Client Management, Matthew MacEwen
Vice President, Christine DuBord
Senior Vice President, Molly Knorr
VICE PRESIDENT, Cheryl Popeck
Vice President, Rita Tolbert
Regional Vice President, Matt Guisinger
Vice President Global Health, David Powell
Regional Vice President Account Manager, Kelli Lowery
Vice President of Sales Shared Services, Cecilia Harbison
Vice President, Mark Young
Vice President, Cris Dubord
Vice President Sales and Account Management, Paul Marden
Vice President Operations, Wayne White
NATIONAL ACCOUNT MANAGER, Beth Beamer
Vice President Client Relations, Kelly McDevitt
Vice President Information Technology, Kevin Kantola
Vice President Clinical Product Development, Michael Weitzner
Vice President Sales, Danielle Peacock
Executive Vice President, Jeffery Verney
Vice President Finance, Troy Borca
Vice President Sales and Account Management, Mary Goodwin
Vice President Talent Acquisition, Heather Lemke
Vice President Public Sector Sales, Ray Devault
Vice President Information Technology, Oren Hermel
Vice President Application Development, Guy Grindberg
Vice President Small Business, Doug Metzger

Vice President Information Technology, Deb McQuade
Vice President Business Development, Neal Heyman
Vice President Information Technology, John R Turnbull
Vice President Finance, Paul Runice
Director of Pharmacy Management, Susan Maddux
National Vice President Consulting Relations, Michael Finn
Vice President Sales and Marketing at Ingenix, David Schultz
Vice President Clinical Strategy, Karen Keown
Vice President Sales, Kim Lewis
Vice President and Actuary, Dewayne Ullsperger
Vice President Sales, Geoff Buro
Vice President National Alliances, Randy Spicer
Vice President Quality Solutions, Peter Naumann
Vice President, Robert Oberrender
Vice President, Erin Carnish
VICE PRESIDENT CUSTOMER SERVICE, Scott Naasz
Senior Vice President Application Development, John Doddy
Senior Vice President Sales, Craig Lafiandra
Vice President Continuous Improvement, Michael Fogarty
Vice President External Affairs Communic, L Platt
Vice President Account Management UnitedHealth Networks, M-Laurie Wasserstein
HEALTH SERVICES DIRECTOR, Joanne Sullivan
VICE PRESIDENT, Brian Dean
SENIOR VICE PRESIDENT PROV SERVICE, Michelle Ferensic
VICE PRESIDENT OF QUALITY, Kie Kawano
SENIOR APPS DEVPR, Daniel Hackney
MEDICAL DIRECTOR, Gale Browning
VICE PRESIDENT, Jim Gates
APPS DEVPR II, Karolina Laso
VICE PRESIDENT FINANCE, Joseph Gaudio
Chairman, Stephen J. Hemsley, age 54
Treasurer, Janis Verruso
Secretary General Counsel, Thomas McGuire
Auditors: DELOITTE & TOUCHE LLP

LOCATIONS

HQ: UnitedHealth Group Inc
UnitedHealth Group Center, 9900 Bren Road East, Minnetonka, MN 55343
Phone: 952 936-1300
Web: www.unitedhealthgroup.com

PRODUCTS/OPERATIONS

2016 Sales

	$ mil.	% of total
UnitedHealthcare	148,581	64
Optum		
OptumRx	60,440	26
OptumHealth	16,908	7
OptumInsight	7,333	3
Adjustments	(48422)	-
Total	**184,840**	**100**

2016 Sales

	$ mil.	% of total
Premiums	144,118	78
Products	26,658	14
Services	13,236	7
Investment and other income	828	1
Total	**184,840**	**100**

Selected Operations

Optum (Health Services division)
OptumHealth (specialty benefits)
OptumInsight (formerly Ingenix information technology and consulting services)
OptumRx (formerly Prescription Solutions pharmacy benefit management)
UnitedHealthcare (Health Plans division)
UnitedHealthcare Community & State (former operations of AmeriChoice public-sector programs)

UnitedHealthcare Employer & Individual (health plans for individuals businesses employers)
UnitedHealthcare International (expatriate coverage for global accounts)
UnitedHealthcare Medicare & Retirement (former operations of Ovations benefits for people age 50 and older)
UnitedHealthcare Military & Veterans (TRICARE West Region contract)

COMPETITORS

AMERIGROUP	HCSC
APS Healthcare	Health Net
ActiveHealth	Humana
Management	IMS Health
Aetna	Kaiser Foundation
Anthem	Health Plan
CIGNA	Magellan Health
CVS	MetLife
Centene	Molina Healthcare
Coventry Health Care	Prudential
Delta Dental Plans	Qmedtrix Systems
Dental Health Alliance	Tivity Health
Express Scripts	WellCare Health Plans

HISTORICAL FINANCIALS

Company Type: Public

Income Statement

FYE: December 31

	REVENUE ($ mil.)	NET INCOME ($ mil.)	NET PROFIT MARGIN	EMPLOYEES
12/17	201,159	10,558	5.2%	260,800
12/16	184,840	7,017	3.8%	230,000
12/15	157,107	5,813	3.7%	200,000
12/14	130,474	5,619	4.3%	170,000
12/13	122,489	5,625	4.6%	156,000
Annual Growth	**13.2%**	**17.0%**	**—**	**13.7%**

2017 Year-End Financials

Debt ratio: 22.79%
Return on equity: 24.54%
Cash ($ mil.): 11,981
Current ratio: 0.73
Long-term debt ($ mil.): 28,835
No. of shares (mil.): 969
Dividends
  Yield: 0.0%
  Payout: 26.8%
Market value ($ mil.): 213,626

	STOCK PRICE ($) FY Close	P/E High/Low		PER SHARE ($) Earnings	Dividends	Book Value
12/17	220.46	21	14	10.72	2.88	49.30
12/16	160.04	22	15	7.25	2.38	40.20
12/15	117.64	21	16	6.01	1.88	35.50
12/14	101.09	18	12	5.70	1.41	34.02
12/13	75.30	13	9	5.50	1.05	32.54
Annual Growth	**30.8%**	**—**	**—**	**18.2%**	**28.6%**	**10.9%**

Univar Inc

Auditors: Ernst & Young LLP

LOCATIONS

HQ: Univar Inc
3075 Highland Parkway, Suite 200, Downers Grove, IL 60515
Phone: 331 777-6000
Web: www.univar.com

Company Type: Public

Income Statement

FYE: December 31

	REVENUE ($ mil.)	NET INCOME ($ mil.)	NET PROFIT MARGIN	EMPLOYEES
12/16	8,073	(68)		8,700
12/15	8,981	16	0.2%	9,200
12/14	10,373	(20)	—	8,900
12/13	10,324	(82)	—	—
12/12	9,747	(197)	—	—
Annual Growth	(4.6%)	—	—	—

2016 Year-End Financials

Debt ratio: 55.03%
Return on equity: (-8.39%)
Cash ($ mil.): 336
Current ratio: 1.63
Long-term debt ($ mil.): 2,845

No. of shares (mil.): 138
Dividends
Yield: —
Payout: —
Market value ($ mil.): 3,938

	STOCK PRICE ($) FY Close	P/E High/Low	PER SHARE ($) Earnings	Dividends	Book Value
12/16	28.37	— —	(0.50)	0.00	5.84
12/15	17.01	195 116	0.14	0.00	5.92
Annual Growth	13.6%	— —	—	—	(0.4%)

Universal Health Services, Inc.

With dozens of health care facilities in nearly every state Universal Health Services (UHS) isn't quite ubiquitous but it's working on it. One of the nation's largest for-profit hospital operators UHS owns or leases about 25 acute care hospitals with a total of some 5900 beds primarily in rural and suburban communities. It also operates outpatient surgery centers and radiation treatment facilities most located near its acute care hospitals. In addition UHS' behavioral health division operates some 440 psychiatric and substance abuse hospitals with a combined capacity of more than 21000 beds; its UK-based Cygnet unit operates another 21 facilities. UHS is controlled by founder and CEO Alan Miller.

Operations

UHS receives more than half of its annual revenues from its acute care segment which includes medical hospitals surgical outpatient facilities and radiation oncology centers. The remainder of the company's revenue comes from its portfolio of behavioral health hospitals which includes residential facilities for teens adult psychiatric hospitals substance abuse facilities and special education schools for students with emotional problems.

The company's behavioral health business accounts for nearly half of total revenues.

UHS provides central resources to its network of facilities including purchasing information services finance facilities planning administrative personnel marketing public relations and physician recruitment.

Geographic Reach

UHS' acute care facilities are located in more than half a dozen states and are situated mostly in smaller towns and cities with limited competition though the division does have facilities in a few larger markets (such as Las Vegas and Washington DC). UHS' behavioral health hospitals are scat-

tered across about 40 US states as well as Puerto Rico the US Virgin Islands and the UK. The company's biggest markets for both segments are California Nevada and Texas.

Headquartered in King of Prussia Pennsylvania UHS also has offices in Wayne Pennsylvania; Brentwood Tennessee; Denton Texas; and Reno Nevada.

Sales and Marketing

Both of UHS' operating segments (acute care hospitals and behavioral health hospitals) earn more than half of revenues from managed care providers (HMOs PPOs) with the remainder of sales coming from traditional Medicare and Medicaid plans and other sources.

Financial Performance

UHS' growth strategies have helped it to steadily increase sales over the past decade with the exception of 2012. In fiscal 2016 revenue increased 8% to $9.8 billion. That growth occurred as income from both acute care and behavioral health care increased. In terms of existing facilities acute care services revenue increased 9% that year while behavioral health care services increased 3%. Acquisitions made in 2015 (UK hospitals addiction treatment firm Foundations Recovery Network) also boosted revenue in 2016.

Net income has also been rising and in 2016 it increased 3% to $702.4 million. This was primarily due to the higher revenue that year but was partially offset by higher operating expenses as well as a reduction in incentives paid for transitioning to electronic health records. Cash flow from operations rose 26% to $1.3 billion due to positive adjustments to reconcile net income to net cash provided by operating activities including accrued interest accrued and deferred income taxes and other working capital accounts.

Strategy

UHS has a focused strategy for growth: Add more facilities to its network improve the services and operations at its facilities and increase the efficiency of its services (including shifting to outpatient care when preferable).

By focusing its operations on high-growth regions UHS also works towards its goal of increasing hospital utilization rates (which is often a key indicator of the financial health of a hospital). To further draw more patients and high-quality physicians to its existing facilities the company invests in new technology makes capital improvements and increases the breadth of services it offers. Initiatives include upgrades to surgical equipment and billing systems as well as the installation of operating room light fixtures that continuously disinfect the environment. UHS is especially expanding its outpatient service capabilities as payers put pressure on hospitals to control inpatient care costs.

While the company's growth strategy is to build or purchase new facilities in rapidly growing areas — it has grown both of its units through selective acquisitions and construction efforts over the years — UHS also has no qualms about ridding itself of operations that just don't quite fit anymore.

Mergers and Acquisitions

UHS is focused on acquiring hospitals and other facilities to expand operations. In 2015 it purchased the 46-bed Orchard Portman House Hospital (now named Cygnet Hospital-Taunton) and the four-hospital system Alpha Hospitals both in the UK. Then in late 2016 it acquired the adult services division of Cambian Group another UK operation for some $464 million; that purchase added 81 behavioral facilities housing some 1200 beds bringing UHS' UK holdings to more than 100 facilities.

In the US UHS purchased addiction treatment system Foundations Recovery Network for $350 million in 2015. That deal added four inpatient

and eight outpatient facilities. The following year the company acquired Desert View Hospital a 25-bed acute care facility in Nevada.

EXECUTIVES

Vp And Controller, Charles F Boyle
Vice President and General Counsel, Matthew Klein
EVP and CFO, Steve G. Filton, age 59, $584,606 total compensation
Chairman and CEO, Alan B. Miller, age 79, $1,600,061 total compensation
EVP; President Behavioral Health, Debra K. Osteen, age 61, $638,025 total compensation
EVP; President Acute Care, Marvin G. Pember, age 63, $618,502 total compensation
President, Marc D. Miller, age 46, $720,861 total compensation
SVP Information Services and Business Solutions, Michael S. Nelson
Vice President Market Development, Angela Rayson
Executive Vice President General Counsel and Secretary, Kim Lederer
Senior Vice President General Counsel and Secretary, Melissa Alvarado
Vice President And Director, Brenda Simons
Vice President, Cheryl Livesay
Vice President Center Applications, Lorraine Castro
Vice President and Director of Environmental Laboratory, Pat Tyrrell
Executive Vice President of Finance, Debbie Onofrey
Vice President and Associate General Counsel, Connie Ulibarri
Senior Vice President ARC Information Systems, Cathy Terlescki
Vice President and Director, Russann Jeantet
Vice President and Director, Stephen Carlson
Executive Vice President of Finance, Eileen Vido
Vice President E Health Financial Advisor, Andrew Ganti
Vice President of Hawaii Division, Donna Murray
Senior Vice President Business Development, Brad Balon
Vice President and Director, Timothy Powell
Senior Vice President, James Antosy
Senior Vice President President Acute Care, Michael Marquez
Vice President, Thomas Marchozzi
Vice President And Director, Jerilin Cummings
Vice President and Director, Brandy Albright
Director Of Radiology Services, Jeff Otto
Vice President Human Resources, Gerry Geckle
Vice President And Director, Frank Pizzuto
Executive Vice President of Finance, Andy Belen
Senior Vice President Marketing and Sales, Stephanie Stephenson
Vice President and Director, Douglas Coffey
Vice President and Director, Shawna Edmundson
Division Vice President, Roz Hudson
Executive Vice President of Finance, Stephanie Hill
First Vice President, Fred Mchugh
Vice President, Karla Perez
Director of Utilization Review, Cari Pelc
Vice President Behavioral Health Services, Philip J Moraci
Vice President, Tom Marchozzi
Director of Clinical Services, Eric Levinson
Medical Director, Michael Vines
Director of Clinical Services, Bill Snyder
Director of Radiology, Mark Lerner
Vice President Hospital Finance Bh, Lawrence Harrod
Secretary Treasurer, Martha Syms
Auditors: PRICEWATERHOUSECOOPERS LLP

LOCATIONS

HQ: Universal Health Services, Inc.
Universal Corporate Center, 367 South Gulph Road,
King of Prussia, PA 19406
Phone: 610 768-3300
Web: www.uhsinc.com

Selected Acute Care Hospitals and Specialty Centers

California
Corona Regional Medical Center (Corona)
Palmdale Regional Medical Center (Palmdale)
Southwest Healthcare System — Inland Valley
Campus (Wildomar)
Southwest Healthcare System — Rancho Springs
Campus (Murrieta)
Temecula Valley Day Surgery and Pain Therapy Center
(Murrieta)

Florida
Lakewood Ranch Medical Center (Bradenton)
Manatee Memorial Hospital (Bradenton)
Palms Westside Clinic ASC (50% Royal Palm Beach)
Wellington Regional Medical Center (West Palm
Beach)

Nevada
Centennial Hills Hospital Medical Center (Las Vegas)
Desert Springs Hospital (72% Las Vegas)
Northern Nevada Medical Center (Sparks)
Spring Valley Hospital Medical Center (72% Las Vegas)
Summerlin Hospital Medical Center (72% Las Vegas)
Valley Hospital Medical Center (72% Las Vegas)

South Carolina
Aiken Regional Medical Centers (Aiken)
Aurora Pavilion (Aiken)
Cancer Care Institute of Carolina (Aiken)

Oklahoma
St. Mary's Regional Medical Center (Enid)

Puerto Rico
OJOS/Eye Surgery Specialists of Puerto Rico
(Santurce)

Texas
Cornerstone Regional Hospital (50% Edinburg)
Doctors' Hospital of Laredo (Laredo)
Fort Duncan Regional Medical Center (Eagle Pass)
Northwest Texas Healthcare System (Amarillo)
Northwest Texas Surgery Center (majority owned
Amarillo)
The Pavilion at Northwest Texas Healthcare System
(Amarillo)
South Texas Health System (Edinburg)
Edinburg Regional Medical Center (Edinburg)
Edinburg Children's Hospital (Edinburg)
McAllen Medical Center (McAllen)
McAllen Heart Hospital (McAllen)
South Texas Behavioral Health System (Edinburg)
Texoma Medical Center (Denison)
TMC Behavioral Health Center (Denison)

Washington D.C.
The George Washington University Hospital (80%)

PRODUCTS/OPERATIONS

2016 Sales

	$ mil.	% of total
Acute care hospital services	5,112	52
Behavioral health services	4,645	48
Other	8	—
Total	**9,766**	**100**

COMPETITORS

Adventist Health System Sunbelt Healthcare
Adventist Health System West
Ascension Health
Banner Health
CHRISTUS Health
CRC Health
Community Health Systems
Devereux Foundation
HCA
Hazelden Betty Ford
LifePoint Health
Mercy Health
Northwestern Human Services
Sutter Health
Tenet Healthcare
Texas Health Resources
UBH
United Surgical Partners

HISTORICAL FINANCIALS

Company Type: Public

Income Statement

FYE: December 31

	REVENUE ($ mil.)	NET INCOME ($ mil.)	NET PROFIT MARGIN	EMPLOYEES
12/16	9,766	702	7.2%	75,325
12/15	9,043	680	7.5%	74,600
12/14	8,065	545	6.8%	68,700
12/13	7,283	510	7.0%	66,100
12/12	6,961	443	6.4%	65,100
Annual Growth	**8.8%**	**12.2%**	**—**	**3.7%**

2016 Year-End Financials

Debt ratio: 40.09%
Return on equity: 15.95%
Cash ($ mil.): 33
Current ratio: 1.28
Long-term debt ($ mil.): 4,030

No. of shares (mil.): 96
Dividends
Yield: 0.0%
Payout: 5.6%
Market value ($ mil.): 10,280

	STOCK PRICE ($) FY Close	P/E High/Low		Earnings	Dividends	Book Value
12/16	106.38	19	14	7.14	0.40	46.91
12/15	119.49	21	15	6.76	0.40	43.23
12/14	111.26	21	13	5.42	0.30	37.85
12/13	81.26	16	9	5.14	0.20	33.06
12/12	48.35	11	8	4.53	0.60	27.80
Annual Growth	**21.8%**	**—**	**—**	**12.0%**	**(9.6%)**	**14.0%**

UNIVERSITY OF TEXAS AT TYLER

LOCATIONS

HQ: UNIVERSITY OF TEXAS AT TYLER
3900 UNIVERSITY BLVD, TYLER, TX 757996600
Phone: 903 566-7000
Web: WWW.UTTYLER.EDU

HISTORICAL FINANCIALS

Company Type: Private

Income Statement

FYE: August 31

	REVENUE ($ mil.)	NET INCOME ($ mil.)	NET PROFIT MARGIN	EMPLOYEES
08/15	12,635	(2,780)	—	425
08/14	58	42	73.2%	—
08/13	51	(4)	—	—
08/12	49	(7)	—	—
Annual Growth	**535.7%**	**—**	**—**	**—**

2015 Year-End Financials

Debt ratio: —
Return on equity: (-22.00%)
Cash ($ mil.): 2,633
Current ratio: 0.60
Long-term debt ($ mil.): —

Dividends
Yield: —
Payout: —
Market value ($ mil.): —

UNIVERSITY OF TEXAS SYSTEM

These students are hooked on higher education. The University of Texas System runs 14 universities throughout the Lone Star State with a total enrollment of more than 228000 students making it one of the nation's largest university systems. Its flagship UT Austin campus with some 51000 students and a Longhorn mascot has of the largest student populations in the US. UT System also runs half a dozen health institutions including four medical schools. Fields of science technology engineering and math also account for a good number of the undergraduate and graduate degrees conferred by the system. Established in 1876 UT Austin opened in 1883. The UT System was formally organized in 1950.

Operations

The primary purpose of the system is to provide administrative services for all of its campuses and institutions including fundraising endowment management performance benchmarking construction planning and legal and real estate services. With more than 20000 faculty and more than 80000 health care professionals researchers student advisors and support staff the UT System is one of the largest employers in Texas. UT System is governed by a nine-member board of regents that is appointed by the Texas governor and confirmed by the Texas Senate.

Geographic Reach

The UT System's primary central administration office is located on the UT Austin campus. Besides Austin the system boasts eight additional academic campuses in the Texas cities of Arlington Brownsville Dallas Edinburg El Paso Odessa San Antonio and Tyler. The system also has a land management office in West Texas and a federal relations center in Washington DC.

Financial Performance

UT System has an annual budget of $16.9 billion.

The UT System's revenue rose in fiscal 2016 to $13.3 billion from $12.6 billion a year earlier. Increases in net tuition and fees net sales and services of hospitals net professional fees as a result of increases in patient volumes and rates all helped the system's revenue increase as well as net auxiliary enterprises attributable to increased gate receipts for athletic events.

Operating loss increased from $3.4 billion to $4 billion in 2016 thanks to rising operating expenses due to growing student enrollment research and patient care activities.

Strategy

The UT System's administration has continued to work toward the overall goals of maintaining quality and affordability at the campuses increasing graduation rates and enhancing the system's standing in research and medical education. The organization has also been working to reduce its student-teacher ratios by increasing the number of faculty members.

In addition the UT System has launched a $3 billion renovation and construction program at its campuses.

A large portion of the UT System's student population comprises students pursuing degrees in health-related fields. UT health institutions include the UT Medical Branch (UTMB) in Galveston which includes medical schools and hospital locations and the M. D. Anderson Cancer Center in Austin.

The UT Systems also expanded in South Texas opening of The University of Texas Rio Grande

Valley in 2015. In 2016 it opened two new medical schools at The University of Texas at Austin and UT Rio Grande Valley.

The UT System is also heavily focused on research. The system's institutions have about $2.6 billion annually in research expenditures more than half of which is funded through federal grants.

EXECUTIVES

Executive Vice Chancellor Business Affairs, Scott C. Kelley

Executive Vice Chancellor Academic Affairs, Pedro Reyes

President UT Health Science Center at San Antonio, Francisco G. Cigarroa

Executive Vice Chancellor Health Affairs, Raymond S. Greenberg

Vice Chancellor Strategic Initiatives, Stephanie Bond Huie

Associate Vice President, David Gabler

Vice Chairman, R. Steven (Steve) Hicks, age 67

Chairman, Paul L. Foster, age 59

Vice Chairman, Wm. Eugene (Gene) Powell

Secretary Historian, Ann Quaid

LOCATIONS

HQ: UNIVERSITY OF TEXAS SYSTEM
210 W 6TH ST, AUSTIN, TX 787012901
Phone: 512 499-4587
Web: WWW.UTSYSTEM.EDU

PRODUCTS/OPERATIONS

Selected Institutions
Academic Institutions
The University of Texas at Arlington (established 1895)
The University of Texas-Pan American (Edinburg; 1927)
The University of Texas of the Permian Basin (Odessa; 1969)
Health Institutions
The University of Texas Health Science Center at Houston (established 1972)
The University of Texas M.D. Anderson Cancer Center (Houston 1941)

HISTORICAL FINANCIALS

Company Type: Private

Income Statement

FYE: August 31

	REVENUE ($ mil.)	NET INCOME ($ mil.)	NET PROFIT MARGIN	EMPLOYEES
08/16	13,282	1,589	12.0%	81,260
08/09	8,564	(3,592)	—	—
08/08	46	1	2.3%	—
08/06	0	0	—	—
Annual Growth	—	—	—	—

2016 Year-End Financials

Debt ratio: ——
Return on equity: 12.00%
Cash ($ mil.): 2,545
Current ratio: 0.70
Long-term debt ($ mil.): —
Dividends
Yield: —
Payout: —
Market value ($ mil.): —

Univest Corp. of Pennsylvania (Souderton)

Univest Corporation of Pennsylvania will keep your money close to its vest. The holding company owns $3 billion-asset Univest Bank and Trust which serves the southeastern part of the Keystone State and the broader Mid-Atlantic region online and though 30 branches and provides standard retail and commercial banking services such as checking and savings accounts CDs IRAs and credit cards. Subsidiary Univest Capital provides small-ticket commercial financing while Univest Insurance offers personal and commercial coverage. Univest Investments which boasts some $3 billion in assets under management offers brokerage and investment advisory services.

Operations

Univest operates three main business segments: Banking which accounted for 79% of the company's total revenue during 2015 and provides traditional banking services to consumers businesses and government entities through Univest Bank and Trust; Wealth Management (12% of revenue) which offers investment advisory retirement plan trust municipal pension and broker/dealer services through Univest Investments; and Insurance (9% of revenue) which offers commercial and personal insurance lines as well as benefits and human resources consulting through Univest Insurance.

Broadly speaking Univest Corporation gets more than 60% of its revenue from interest income. About 61% of its total revenue came from loan interest (including fees on loans and leases) during 2015 while another 5% came from interest on its investment securities. The rest of its revenue came from insurance commissions and fees (8% of revenue) investment advisory commission and fee income (7%) trust fee income (5%) deposit account service charges (3%) mortgage banking sales (3%) and other miscellaneous income sources.

More than 40% of the company's loan portfolio was made up of commercial real estate loans at the end of 2015 while another 23% of loan assets were made up of commercial loans that were financial or agricultural-related. The remainder of the portfolio was made up of loans tied to residential properties secured for business purposes (10% of loan assets) residential properties for personal purposes (8%) lease financings (7%) construction real estate loans (4%) and loans to individuals (less than 2%).

Geographic Reach

Souderton Pennsylvania-based Univest Corporation and its subsidiaries serve clients across the Mid-Atlantic region. The company has around 30 bank branches and nearly 20 offices in the Montgomery Bucks Philadelphia Chester Berks Lehigh and Delaware counties of Pennsylvania as well as in Calvert County in Maryland Camden County in New Jersey and Lee County in Florida.

Sales and Marketing

Univest Corporation serves individuals businesses municipalities and non-profit organizations. It spent $2.25 million on marketing and advertising during 2015 to reach these clients up from $1.88 million and $1.95 million in 2014 and 2013 respectively.

Financial Performance

The bank's revenues and profits have been trending higher over the past several years thanks to 50% loan asset growth and 50% non-interest

revenue growth since 2011 along with a continued reduction in loan loss provisions as its loan portfolio's credit quality has improved with higher property valuations in the strengthened economy.

Univest Corporation's revenue jumped 24% to a record $154.41 million during 2015 mostly as 35% loan asset growth (loan balances swelled to $2.16 billion) stemming from its Valley Green Bank acquisition helped boost interest income. The company's non-interest income also rose 9% as its mortgage banking gains doubled during the year on higher volumes and as its insurance commissions and fee income rose 20% after acquiring Sterner Insurance in mid-2014.

Strong revenue growth in 2015 drove the company's net income up 23% to $27.27 million for the year. Univest Corporation's operating cash levels climbed 12% to $35.63 thanks to the rise in earnings.

Strategy

Univest Corporation has been expanding its service lines and building its loan and deposit businesses by strategically acquiring other banks and investment or insurance-related financial firms.

Mergers and Acquisitions

In December 2015 Univest Corporation agreed to buy Fox Chase Bancorp along with its $1.1 billion in assets $768 million in loans $765 million in deposits and several Fox Chase Bank branches in Pennsylvania and New Jersey for a price exceeding $240 million. The deal would also expand Univest's presence in Bucks Chester Philadelphia and Montgomery counties in Pennsylvania as well as into Atlantic and Cape May counties in New Jersey.

In January 2015 the company purchased Valley Green Bank as well as its three branches and two loan production offices in the greater Philadelphia market for $77 million.

In July 2014 Univest bolstered its Univest Insurance subsidiary after acquiring Sterner Insurance Associates a full-service insurance and consultative risk management firm that served individuals and businesses across the Lehigh Valley Berks Bucks and Montgomery counties.

In January 2014 flagship subsidiary Univest Bank and Trust Co. bought registered investment advisory firm Girard Partners Ltd. as well as its $500 million in assets under management. The deal boosted Univest's assets under management by 20% to a total of $3 billion after the acquisition.

EXECUTIVES

Senior Vice President and Director of Technology, Richard Boaman

President Corporate Banking, Philip C. (Phil) Jackson, $250,000 total compensation

SEVP and Chief Risk Officer, Duane J. Brobst, $200,000 total compensation

President and CEO, Jeffrey M Schweitzer, $450,000 total compensation

SEVP and CFO, Michael S Keim, $270,000 total compensation

Executive Vice President, John Duerksen

Assistant Vice President of Information Technology, Sara Natali

Senior Vice President Marketing Underwriting Manager, Maria Di Marco

Vice President of Finance and Accounting, Kim Koch

Vice President Corporate Communication, Kimberly Detwiler

Senior Vice President Credit Administration, Tami Garber

Vice President, Michael G Davisson

Vice President, Lisa Hartley

Vice President Finance and Accounting, Kimberly Koch

Senior Vice President of is, Richard Swartley

Unum Group

Through injury or illness Unum works to keep employees employed. A top disability insurer in the US and the UK it offers short-term and long-term disability insurance as well as life and accidental death and dismemberment insurance to individuals and groups in a workplace benefits setting. Specialty coverage offerings include cancer and dental insurance. US subsidiaries include Unum Life Insurance Company of America Provident Life and Accident First Unum Life Colonial Life & Accident and Paul Revere Life Insurance. It operates as Unum Limited in the UK. Unum's products are sold through field sales agents and independent brokers.

Operations

More than 60% of Unum's annual premiums come from the Unum US segment which offers group disability life and accident policies as well as supplemental and voluntary policies under the Unum America and Provident Brands.

The group's Colonial Life segment — which offers accident sickness disability and life products — accounts for nearly 20% of sales while the Unum UK segment represents more than 5% of sales.

Unum also generates revenue from its Closed Block segment (about 15% of sales) which services policies in the runoff segments (long-term care non-workplace individual disability) where the company no longer issues new policies.

The company covers 33 million people worldwide and counts 181000 businesses in the US among its customers (including a third of the Fortune 500).

Geographic Reach

The US market contributes more than 60% of Unum's annual revenues. Unum runs four primary operating centers (in Tennessee Maine Louisiana South Carolina) and more than 35 sales offices scattered across the US market. Its Unum Limited office is the headquarters for the smaller Unum UK operations which include Ireland.

Sales and Marketing

Unumy uses its own sales force as well as with independent agents consultants and brokers to market its products to employers.

Financial Performance

Unum's revenues have remained fairly stable for the past five years. In 2016 revenue rose 3% to $11 billion. Premium income rose 3% but that increase was partially offset by declines in investment income net realized investment gains and other income.

Net income which more than doubled to $867.1 million in 2015 increased another 7% to $931.4 million in 2016. Higher revenue drove that increase.

Cash flow from operations declined 13% to $1.1 billion that year due primarily to changes in receivables.

Strategy

Unum seeks to achieve a competitive edge by providing group individual and voluntary workplace products that can be combined with other coverage to better integrate benefits for customers. The insurer has stayed ahead of the game in the disability market by sticking to conservative investment and growth strategies primarily seeking to expand its group product offerings and its geographic presence through organic measures.

Specific goals include securing new customers investing in growth that meets new demands of the market and expanding into new geographic areas and distribution channels. Acquisitions play an important part of reaching these goals. For example it acquired the UK-based National Dental

Plan in 2015 to enter the employee dental benefits market there.Unum now plans to expand its presence in Europe by acquiring Polish insurer Pramerica ?ycie.

The company has especially seen growth in its voluntary benefits products which allow employees to purchase individual coverage products on a supplemental basis. Such options are increasingly important as economic difficulties put pressure on low and middle-income workers. Unum has also expanded its offering of services to help employers and government agencies manage costs such as its leave management program flexible corporate contribution programs and wellness initiatives.

While expanding in areas where the greatest market needs are seen the firm also occasionally exits (or places into run-off) certain businesses where demand has slowed.

Mergers and Acquisitions

In 2016 Unum bought Louisiana-based H&J Capital which owns Starmount Life Insurance and third-party administrator AlwaysCare Benefits for $127 million. Starmount operates in 49 states plus the District of Columbia offering individual products for dental vision life and accident coverage. It also offers group and voluntary benefits including dental vision life accident disability and critical illness under the AlwaysCare Benefits brand.

In 2018 the company agreed to buy Pramerica ?ycie a Polish life insurer from Prudential Financial for an undisclosed amount. That deal will allow Unum to expand its European operations beyond the UK.

HISTORY

Coal was discovered in eastern Tennessee in the 1870s; in 1887 several Chattanooga professional men formed the Provident Life & Accident Insurance Co. to provide medical insurance to miners. But it was a case of the inexperienced serving the uninsurable and by 1892 the company was on the brink of ruin. The founders sold half the company for $1000 to Thomas Maclellan and John McMaster two Scotsmen who had failed at banking in Canada.

While Maclellan handled the business end McMaster scoured the coalfields for customers. He even went into the mines pitching to individual miners and bringing along someone to dig coal for them so they wouldn't lose money by stopping work to listen.

The partners bought the rest of the company in 1895. Provident grew thanks to the cooperation of mining companies which deducted premiums from miners' pay. Provident added sickness and industrial insurance (low-benefit life policies). In 1900 after a period of strained relations Maclellan bought out McMaster.

After 1905 northern insurers began moving into the industrializing South. To meet the competition Provident reorganized and added capital and its stepped-up sales efforts brought in such lucrative business as railroad accounts. Provident added life insurance in 1917. The first policy was bought by Robert Maclellan who became president when his father died in 1916.

Provident acquired the Southern Surety Co. in 1931. During and after WWII group sales exploded as employee benefit packages proliferated. Provident which by then operated nationally entered Canada in 1948. Four years later R. L. Maclellan succeeded his father as president (R. L. stepped down in 1971). Provident's growth in the 1970s stemmed from its life units but it also developed a large health insurance operation.

The health care operations were hammered by rising medical costs in the 1980s so the company moved into managed care. But the combination of increased health care costs and a real estate crash gave the company a one-two punch in the late 1980s and early 1990s. An accounting change in 1993 further hit profits. In 1994 new president Harold Chandler initiated a reevaluation of Provident's operations and future which resulted in Provident's exit from the health care business beginning in 1995.

Provident began a major move into disability insurance in 1997. It bought 83% of rival disability insurer The Paul Revere Corporation from Textron. About 10000 Paul Revere insurance brokers later filed suit alleging they were denied millions of dollars in commissions. In exchange for its $300 million aid in the purchase Switzerland's Zurich Insurance (now Zurich Financial Services) received about 15% of Provident. The company also acquired GENEX Services (vocational rehabilitation and related services) and sold its dental insurance business to Ameritas Life Insurance. In 1998 Provident sold its annuity business to American General (now a subsidiary of AIG).

In 1998 with both Provident and Unum Corporation looking for ways to enhance business the companies commenced merger negotiations and completed the transaction the next year. But the merger was more expensive than anticipated and problems in integrating the companies' sales forces slowed policy sales.

Company operations began melding more smoothly and UnumProvident began addressing the problems with its sales force as well as adding customer service staff in 2000. It pulled money out of reserves by reinsuring several blocks of acquisition-related businesses and sold an inactive shell subsidiary licensed to sell annuities in most states to Allstate. In 2001 the company sold its Provident National Assurance subsidiary to Allstate. UnumProvident faced accusations that the company denied valid disability claims in 2002. These accusations resulted in legal actions in a number of states.

UnumProvident acquired Sun Life Financial's UK life insurance group in 2003 in a move designed to expand the company's operations in the UK. UnumProvident sold its Unum Japan Accident Insurance subsidiary to Hitachi Capital Corporation (Hitachi) in 2004.

As part of a rebranding effort following years of corporate restructuring to focus on core operations the company changed its name from UnumProvident to Unum Group in 2007.

In 2007 the company divested its GENEX Services unit a provider of disability management and workers' compensation services. GENEX's specialty services no longer fit into Unum's strategy to focus on its primary disability insurance operations. In 2009 it stopped offering new individual long-term care policies as part of its strategy to focus on core offerings in the workplace setting. In 2011 the company decided to exit the group long-term care insurance business as well after deeming the product line as non-core.

EXECUTIVES

EVP and General Counsel, Lisa G. Iglesias, age 51, $492,692 total compensation
Vice President The Benefits Center, Rob Hecker
SVP Corporate Marketing and Public Relations, Joseph R. (Joe) Foley
President CEO and Director, Richard P. (Rick) McKenney, age 49, $994,231 total compensation
President and CEO Unum US, Michael Q. Simonds, age 43, $594,231 total compensation
EVP and CFO, John F. (Jack) McGarry, age 59, $588,461 total compensation
EVP Global Services, Christopher J. (Chris) Jerome, age 55

EVP and Chief Investment Officer, Breege A. Farrell, age 57, $451,500 total compensation
President and CEO Colonial Life, Timothy G. (Tim) Arnold, age 54
President and CEO Unum UK, Peter G. O'Donnell, age 50
SVP and Global CIO, Katherine M. (Kate) Miller
Assistant Vice President and Special Counsel at Unum, Michael Parker
Assistant Vice President and Chief Information Security Officer, Lynda Fleury
Assistant Vice President and Senior Counsel, David Layden
Assistant Vice President Contact Center, Charlene Jackson
National Account Manager, Melana C Kipp
Assistant Vice President, Stephen Reed
Vice President Internal Controls, Rick Patton
Vice President Uk Fixed Income, Bob Brant
Assistant Vice President, Tony Bombassi
Assistant Vice President, Ken Barber
AVP Broker Compensation and Contact Center OPS, Wes Hilliard
Assistant Vice President And Senior Counsel, Wendy Harlan
Assistant Vice President And Senior Counsel, Mike Hill
Assistant Vice President Actuary, Paul Lavallee
Assistant Vice President, Jay Barriss
Assistant Vice President, Glenda Wilson
Vice President, Greg Breter
Assistant Vice President and Senior Counsel (1996), Stephen William Walker
Assistant Vice President, Chris Castleberry
Assistant Vice President Digital Marketing, Bethany Branon
Assistant Vice President LTD Benefit Operations, Bob Berry
Assistant Vice President Learning And Performance Development, Debra Chaloux
Assistant Vice President Corporate Treasury, Tyler Siira
Assistant Vice President Business Strategy and Transformation, Matthew Murrell
Assistant Vice President Consumerism, Jocelyn Grega
National Account Manager, Douglas Burnip
Assistant Vice President Health And Insurance Prog, Benjamin Kahn
Assistant Vice President and Counsel, Oliver Murray
Assistant Vice President, Denise Houser
Vice President, Stephanie Dyhrberg
Assistant Vice President Human Resources Senior Business Partner, Debbie Plager
Assistant Vice President Senior Human Re, Laura Coleman
Vice President Distribution Channel Expansion, Christopher Quinn
Assistant Vice President And Senior Counsel Employment Law, Ellen Mccann
Assistant Vice President Corporate Development, Andrew Sharp
Assistant Vice President, Anna Stein
Assistant Vice President IDI Benefits, Adele Mucera
Assistant Vice President, Debra VandeVenter
Assistant Vice President IDI Benefits, Laura Chillo
AVP Sales Enablement, Pierre Meahl
Assistant Vice President Health and Productivity, Michelle Jackson
Executive Vice President, Jacquelyn Warrington
Executive Vice President, Andrew Sayers
Vice President, William Stutts
Executive Vice President and General Counsel, Steven Johnson
Assistant Vice President Global Health And Insurance Programs, Joanne Abate
National Account Manager, Kathy McCarter
AVP and Senior Counsel, Ann Courtney

Assistant Vice President and Senior Counsel, Matthew Bell
Assistant Vice President Senior Human Resources Business Partner, Kristen B Prophater
Assistant Vice President Long Term Care Benefits, Donald St Cyr
Assistant Vice President LTD Benefits, Joseph Pratico
Assistant Vice President, Matthew Purington
National Account Manager, Jennifer Vonderhaar
Assistant Vice President Tax, Glenn Black
Assistant Vice President Customer Experience, Susan Hoffman
Chairman, Kevin T. Kabat, age 60
Auditors: Ernst & Young LLP

LOCATIONS

HQ: Unum Group
1 Fountain Square, Chattanooga, TN 37402
Phone: 423 294-1011
Web: www.unum.com

2016 Sales

	% of total
Premium Income	76
Net Investment Income	22
Net Realized Investment Gain Loss	-
Other Income	2
Total	**100**

2016 Sales

	% of total
Unum US	63
Unum UK	6
Colonial Life	17
Closed Block	14
Total	**100**

PRODUCTS/OPERATIONS

Selected Products and Services
Accidental death and dismemberment
Dental insurance
Disability (long-term and short-term)
Life insurance
Supplemental health
Voluntary benefits

Selected Subsidiaries and Brands
Colonial Life & Accident Insurance
Duncanson & Holt (US and UK)
 Trafalgar Underwriting Agencies (UK)
First Unum Life Insurance
Provident Investment Management
Provident Life and Accident Insurance
Provident Life and Casualty Insurance
The Paul Revere Life Insurance
The Paul Revere Variable Annuity Insurance
Unum Life Insurance Company of America
Unum Limited (UK)
UnumProvident International (Bermuda)

COMPETITORS

AEGON	Liberty Mutual
AXA Financial	Lincoln Financial
Aflac	Group
Allianz	MassMutual
American General	MetLife
Assurant	Mutual of Omaha
CIGNA	Northwestern Mutual
CNA Financial	Principal Financial
Guardian Life	Prudential
John Hancock Financial	Torchmark
Services	

HISTORICAL FINANCIALS

Company Type: Public

Income Statement

FYE: December 31

	ASSETS ($ mil.)	NET INCOME ($ mil.)	INCOME AS % OF ASSETS	EMPLOYEES
12/16	61,941	931	1.5%	9,400
12/15	60,589	867	1.4%	9,400
12/14	62,497	413	0.7%	9,500
12/13	59,403	858	1.4%	9,200
12/12	62,236	894	1.4%	9,100
Annual Growth	(0.1%)	1.0%	—	0.8%

2016 Year-End Financials

Debt ratio: 4.84%
Return on equity: 10.54%
Cash ($ mil.): 100
Current ratio: —
Long-term debt ($ mil.): —

No. of shares (mil.): 229
Dividends
  Yield: 0.0%
  Payout: 19.4%
Market value ($ mil.): 10,096

	STOCK PRICE ($) FY Close	P/E High/Low		PER SHARE ($) Earnings	Dividends	Book Value
12/16	43.93	11	6	3.95	0.77	39.02
12/15	33.29	11	9	3.50	0.70	35.96
12/14	34.88	23	19	1.61	0.62	33.90
12/13	35.08	11	6	3.23	0.55	33.30
12/12	20.82	8	6	3.17	0.47	31.87
Annual Growth	20.5%	—	—	5.7%	13.1%	5.2%

UPMC PRESBYTERIAN SHADYSIDE

Auditors: ERNST & YOUNG LLP PITTSBURGH

LOCATIONS

HQ: UPMC PRESBYTERIAN SHADYSIDE
200 LOTHROP ST, PITTSBURGH, PA 152132536
Phone: 412 647-2345
Web: WWW.UPMC.COM

HISTORICAL FINANCIALS

Company Type: Private

Income Statement

FYE: June 30

	REVENUE ($ mil.)	NET INCOME ($ mil.)	NET PROFIT MARGIN	EMPLOYEES
06/10	8,046	276	3.4%	8,200
06/09	1,723	83	4.8%	—
Annual Growth	366.9%	231.0%	—	—

2010 Year-End Financials

Debt ratio: —
Return on equity: 3.40%
Cash ($ mil.): 158
Current ratio: 0.50
Long-term debt ($ mil.): —

Dividends
  Yield: —
  Payout: —
Market value ($ mil.): —

US Bancorp (DE)

As one of the largest bank holding companies in the US U.S. Bancorp does a pretty good job of living up to its name. The bank has $450 billion in assets and owns U.S. Bank (the US's 5th largest commercial bank) and other subsidiaries that provide consumer and commercial loans deposits and credit cards as well as merchant processing mortgage banking trust and investment management brokerage services insurance and corporate payments. The bank has around 3100 branches and some 4850 ATMs in 25 states in the Midwest and West including one of the most extensive networks of branches inside grocery stores. Commercial loans account for nearly 35% of its total loan portfolio and commercial real estate loans 15%.

Operations

The bank holding company's major lines of business are: wholesale banking and commercial real estate; consumer and small business banking; wealth management and securities services; payment services; and treasury and corporate support. The company is also one of the largest providers of corporate credit cards and payment services to the US government. Its largest fee-gathering subsidiary is Elavon a leading processor of merchant credit card transactions in the US Canada Latin America and Europe.

Consumer and Small Business Bank is the company's largest earner raking in some 35% of sales annually. Payment Services which does consumer and business credit cards among other card-related services is responsible for over 25% of sales. Wholesale Banking & Commercial Real Estate and Treasury and Corporate Support both bring in around 15% of sales. Wealth Management & Securities Services brings in the remainder.

Interest income accounts for nearly 60% of total revenue.

Geographic Reach

U.S. Bancorp provide services through a network of around 3100 banking offices in 25 US states. Its ATMs are principally located in the Midwest and West. California is its largest market. It is also active in Canada Mexico Brazil and Europe.

Sales and Marketing

U. S. Bancorp has some 18.7 million customers including individuals businesses institutions government entities and other financial institutions.

Financial Performance

In fiscal 2016 U.S. Bancorp's revenue climbed 6% to $22.7 billion amid a 6% increase or $765 million in interest income and a 5% increase or $485 million in noninterest income.

Interest income was buoyed by growth in new and existing customers particularly in commercial real estate residential mortgages and credit card loans.

Net income was unchanged at $5.9 billion as an increase in net interest income (interest income less interest expense) was counterbalanced by a $192 million increase for provision for credit losses amid higher commercial loan net charge-offs and lower commercial real estate recoveries.

Cash from operations fell 39% to $5.3 billion due to changes in net proceeds from sales of loans held for sale.

Strategy

U.S. Bancorp has been growing its business through acquisitions sometimes expanding its operations internationally. Since the 2008 recession the bank has found success in purchasing troubled banks for cheap but generally pursues acquisitions to expand service offerings add branches and extend its reach pad its interest-earning loan assets

and add customer deposits to fuel future loan business.

U.S. Bancorp moved into the premium credit card space in 2017 with the launch of the Altitude Reserve Visa Infinite. The card's target demographic is the young and wealthy and as such the offering extends to digital wallets such as Apple Pay.

The bank has also been dabbling in technology to retain and grow its customer base. It launched VantagePoint a receivables management tool for multiple payment types Liquidity Advantage and AP Optimizer.

In 2017 U.S Bank partnered with travel technology company Amadeus to offer a B2B wallet to facilitate payments between entities in the travel industry. The partnership has the aim of improving crash flow reducing fraud risk and boosting revenue per transaction.

HISTORY

When Farmers and Millers Bank was founded in 1853 it operated out of a strongbox in a rented storefront. After surviving a panic in the 1850s the bank became part of the national banking system in 1863 as First National Bank of Milwaukee. The bank grew and in 1894 it merged with Merchants Exchange Bank (founded 1870).

In 1919 the bank merged again with Wisconsin National Bank (founded 1892) to form First Wisconsin National Bank of Milwaukee a leading financial institution in the area from the 1920s on.

First Wisconsin grew through purchases over the next decade though the number of banks fell after the 1929 stock market crash; by the end of WWII it had 11 banks. State and federal legislation particularly the 1956 Bank Holding Company Act (which proscribed acquisitions and branching) constrained postwar growth. In the 1970s Wisconsin eased restrictions on intrastate branching and the bank began to grow again.

Growth accelerated in the late 1980s after Wisconsin and surrounding states legalized interstate banking in adjoining states in 1987. That year First Wisconsin bought seven Minnesota banks and then moved into Illinois. The company focused on strong well-run institutions. Also that year it sold its headquarters and used the proceeds to fund more buys. In 1988 in its first foray outside the Midwest the company bought Metro Bancorp in Phoenix targeting midwestern retirees moving to Arizona.

In 1989 First Wisconsin changed its name to Firstar. The early 1990s saw the company move into Iowa (Banks of Iowa 1990) buy in-state rivals (Federated Bank Geneva Capital Corporation 1992) and roll into Illinois (DSB Corporation 1993). The next year it bought First Southeast Banking Corp. (of Wisconsin) and merged it along with Firstar Bank Racine and Firstar Bank Milwaukee into one bank.

To strengthen its position against larger competitors Firstar continued its buying spree in 1995 (Chicago bank First Colonial Bankshares and Investors Bank Corp. of Minneapolis/St. Paul) and 1996 (Jacob Schmidt Company). The acquisitions left the company bloated: In 1996 Firstar began a restructuring designed to cut costs and increase margins. The restructuring project ended in 1997 but by then its performance lagged behind other midwestern banks considerably. In an effort to diversify it allied with EVEREN Securities to offer debt underwriting and sales fixed income products and public finance advisory services. But it was too little too late; under pressure from major stockholders to seek a partner Firstar began looking for a buyer.

It found Star Banc. Established in 1863 as The First National Bank of Cincinnati under a bank charter signed by Abraham Lincoln Star Banc over the years added branches and bought other banks. The company renamed all of its subsidiary banks Star Bank in 1988 and took the name Star Banc in 1989.

In 1998 Star Banc chairman Jerry Grundhofer approached Firstar about a combination. Negotiations proceeded quickly and a new Firstar was born.

The next year Firstar bought Mercantile Bancorporation. The purchase enabled the bank to expand its international banking services into such markets as Kansas Nebraska and Missouri. In 2000 the company made arrangements to buy U.S. Bancorp a Minneapolis-based bank with roots dating back to 1929. Under the terms of the acquisition Firstar would shed its own name in favor of the more appropriate U.S. Bancorp moniker. U.S. Bancorp completed the conversion of Firstar Bank branches to the U.S. Bank moniker during 2002.

EXECUTIVES

Vice Chairman Wholesale Banking, Leslie V. Godridge, age 61

Vice Chairman and CFO, Terrance R. (Terry) Dolan, age 55, $545,833 total compensation

EVP Human Resources, Jennie P. Carlson, age 56

Regional President, Ward Wilson

President CEO and Director, Andrew Cecere, age 56, $800,000 total compensation

EVP and General Counsel, James L. Chosy, age 53

Vice Chairman Wealth Management and Securities Services, Gunjan Kedia, age 46

EVP, John R. Elmore, age 61

Vice Chairman and Chief Risk Officer, P. William (Bill) Parker, age 60, $625,000 total compensation

Vice Chairman Technology and Operations Services, Jeffry H. (Jeff) von Gillern, age 51, $575,000 total compensation

Vice Chairman Consumer Banking Sales and Support, Kent V. Stone, age 59

EVP and Chief Credit Officer, Mark G. Runkel, age 41

Vice Chairman Payment Services, Shailesh M. Kotwal, age 52

EVP and Chief Strategy and Reputation Officer, Katherine B. Quinn, age 52

Vice Chairman Wholesale Banking, James B. Kelligrew, age 51

Vice President and Managing Director, Terri L Dowell

Assistant Vice President Communications, Bill Brady

Senior Vice President, Derek Hansen

Senior Vice President, Patricia Gnetz

Private Banking Vice President, Scott Brophy

Vice President of Information Technology Security, Coni Pasch

Senior Vice President Dealer Services Regional Manager North Central Region, Dave Donarski

Assistant Vice President Application Consultant Commercial Leasing, Krishna Devarajulu

Senior Vice President Customer Solutions, Mary Ellen Carney

Vice President US Bancorp Investments and Insurance, John Falk

Vice President, Scott Miller

Vice President, Scott Olson

Senior Vice President Risk Analytics, Jacob Seljan

Vice President And Area Sales Manager, Frank Annello

Assistant Vice President Database Development, Melissa Schoenecker

Senior Vice President, Michael Dorn

Senior Vice President Credit Administration, David Silander

Vice President Real Estate Transactions And Risk Management, Barbara Cochran

Vice President Treasury Management Consultant, Paul Kozar Paul Kozar

Vice President, Scott Farrell

Vice President corporate Credit Risk Manager, Brian Richter

Vice President Business Banking Sales Manager, Javier Iglesias Javier Iglesias

Vice President of Market Information and Research, Jill Enabnit

Vice President, Brad Hounsel

Vice President, Stephen Truso

Vice President, Mark Sowinski

Vice President Information Technology Service Managmt, Jim Berghs

Assistant Vice President Marketing Research, Molly McMahon

Vice President Technology Finance Group, Gregory Giannone

Vice President Senior Property Manager, Andrew McGlenon

Assistant Vice President Marketing, Jeff Pick

Vice President, Kelly Matsuoka

Vice President, Zenaida Maniates

Vice President, Michael Lamarche Michael Lamarche

Vice President Commercial Operations Manager, Victor Kapusinski

Assistant Vice President, Dhiren Patel Dhiren Patel

Senior Vice President National Community Outreach Manager, Melissa Borino Melissa Borino

Senior Vice President, Marcia Palmer

Senior Vice President, Terry Neher

Vice President, Louis Caresani

Vice President Corporate Banking Portfolio Manager, Daniel Yu

Assistant Vice President Associate Client Manager, Nick Kapki Nick Kapki

Vice President Relationship Manager, Patricia Bonnemere

Vice President, Wally Jones

Vice President, Alice Warren

Vice President of Operation, Sean Skaggs

Vice President, Jeff Sutherland

Vice President AZ Sales Manager, Ryan Summers

Senior Vice President National Corporate Banking, Barry Litwin

Vice President Wealth Management Advisor, Todd Nichols

Vice President Corporate Trust, Linda Mcconkey

Assistant Vice President Senior Recruiter, Corey Hoen

Vice President, Roger Gross

Vice President Network Security Engineering, Jonathan Rogness

Senior Vice President, Christopher Schaaf

Assistant Vice President, Kalyan Gangeyula

Vice President Technology Services, Paul Ylonen

Vice President Commercial Real Estate Lender, Howard Goldberg

Senior Vice President Enterprise Risk Services, Bob Kellner

Senior Vice President and Market Credit Manager, Rick Shamberger

Vice President of Marketing, Becky Hill

Assistant Vice President Finance Manager, Wendy Brock

Vice President And Site Manager, Elizabeth Thuning

Vice President Relationship Manager Commercial Lending, Dana Jergenson

Assistant Vice President Data Center Design and Planning, David Fortuna

Vice President, Suzanne Bedros

EXECUTIVE VICE PRESIDENT KANSAS CITY, Tim Petty

Vice President, Kevin Penders

Vice President and Credit Manager, Melanie Rossetta

Senior Vice President, Carol Gilstrap

Vice President Loan Administration, Cheryl Dingess

Vice President, Rudy Fors

Vice President and Senior Corporate Counsel, Kyle Bakken

Vice President eCRM Business Capabilities Team, Diane Morse

Vice President, John Pearson

Senior Vice President Of Asset Management, Steve Brigger

Vice President Consumer Lending Project Management Office, John Gemrich

Vice President of Credit Administration, Scott Kohls

Senior Vice President, Andrew Hyde

Vice President Quality Management, Richard McCarthy

Senior Vice President, Douglas Boe

Assistant Vice President Real Estate Asset Manager, Karen Thomas

Vice President, Dorothy Smaglick

Vice President and Senior Corporate Counsel, Benjamin Carpenter

Vice President and Relationship Manager, Bryan Carow

Vice President, Joseph Bree

Assistant Vice President, Rita Halbur

Vice President, Philip Koski

Assistant Vice President Voice Implementation Projects, Joy Abts

Vice President Information Technology, Alfonso Gonzalez

Vice President and Assistant General Counsel, Ilyse Goldsmith

Vice President Area Manager, John Cronen

Vice President; Credit Manager, Jared Baysinger

Senior Vice President Senior Credit Of, Lanigan Steven

Vice President National Sales Manager, Richard Struck

Senior Vice President and Industry Manager, Matthew Sargent

Assistant Vice President Information Technology, David Brus

Vice President Regional Manager, Chad Laipple

Senior Vice President, Brian Reisenauer

Senior Vice President Regional Credit Officer, Randall Borchardt

Vice President Derivative Products Group, Nick Geeza

Vice President, Rod Swenson

Vice President Portfolio Manager, Matt Scullin

Vice President Comercial Team Lead, Corey Hansen

Vice President Business Banking, Brent Blume

Senior Vice President commercial Real Estate relationship Manager, Curt Steiner

Senior Manager Assistant Vice President, Ryan Smith

Assistant Vice President, Becky Burton

Senior Vice President Sales, Doug Ichiuji

Vice President, Monique Green

Vice President and Commercial Relationship Manager, Margaret Sato

Community Banking Relationship Manager Assistant Vice President, Chester Anonson

Vice President, Ryan Perrault

Vice President PRM, Robert Hickman

Vice President Community Relations Manager Northwest Region Portland Main Complex, Karen Kervin

Business Banking Senior Vice President Region Manager, Joey Nix

Vice President Pricing and Analysis User Services. Bank Credit and Debit Cards, Charles Gorsuch

Senior Corporate Counsel And Vice President, Daniel Sundell

Assistant Vice President, Jackie Cole

Assistant Vice President Alternative Investments, Tatiana Kadyrova

Asst.Vice President Technology Services, Laura Rumrey

Assistant Vice President And Assistant, Stacey Dennehy

Assistant Vice President, Cregg Rogers

Assistant Vice President, Ryan Frank

Vice President Credit Risk Management, Olivier Haise

Vice President and Oregon Manager Community Affairs and Development, Michael Montgomery

Senior Vice President, Kevin Miller

Vice President, Peter LaMontagna

Assistant Vice President, Chrissy Kolakowski

Vice President Chicago West District Manager, Michael Fasshauer

Senior Vice President of Consumer Products and Services, Steve Saloutos

Vice President, Jason Fry

Vice President Credit Risk Assessment, Trina Johnson

Vice President Customer Care, Scott Tostengard

Vice President Special Assets Group, John Phillipi

Vice President, Randy Grau

Auditors: Ernst & Young LLP

LOCATIONS

HQ: US Bancorp (DE)
800 Nicollet Mall, Minneapolis, MN 55402
Phone: 651 466-3000
Web: www.usbank.com

Selected Locations

Arizona
Arkansas
California
Colorado
Idaho
Illinois
Indiana
Iowa
Kansas
Kentucky
Minnesota
Missouri
Montana
Nebraska
Nevada
New Mexico
North Dakota
Ohio
Oregon
South Dakota
Tennessee
Utah
Washington
Wisconsin
Wyoming

PRODUCTS/OPERATIONS

2016 Sales

	$ mil.	% of total
Interest		
Loans	10,810	48
Investment securities	2,078	9
Loans held for sale	154	1
Other	125	1
Non-interest		
Merchant processing services	1,592	7
Trust & investment management fees	1,427	6
Credit & debit card revenue	1,177	5
Mortgage banking	979	4
Commercial products	871	4
Corporate payment products	712	3
Deposit service charges	725	3
Treasury management fees	583	3
ATM processing services	338	1
Investment products fees	158	1
Other	1,015	4
Total	**22,744**	**100**

2016 sales

	% of total
Consumer and Small Business Banking	34
Payment Services	27
Wholesale Banking and Commercial Real Estate	15
Treasury and Corporate Support	14
Wealth Management and Securities Services	10
Total	**100**

Selected Subsidiaries

111 Tower Investors Inc. (Minnesota)
Access Mortgage Solutions LLC (Delaware)
AIS Europe Limited (UK)
AIS Fund Administration Ltd. (Cayman Islands)
CF Title Co. (Delaware)
Daimler Title Co. (Delaware)
DSL Service Company (California)
Eclipse Funding LLC (Delaware)
Elan Life Insurance Company Inc. (Arizona)

COMPETITORS

Bank of America
Capital One
Citigroup
Fifth Third
First National of Nebraska
Great Western Bancorp
Huntington Bancshares
JPMorgan Chase
KeyCorp
MUFG Americas Holdings
TCF Financial
Wells Fargo
Zions Bancorporation

HISTORICAL FINANCIALS

Company Type: Public

Income Statement

FYE: December 31

	ASSETS ($ mil.)	NET INCOME ($ mil.)	INCOME AS % OF ASSETS	EMPLOYEES
12/16	445,964	5,888	1.3%	71,191
12/15	421,853	5,879	1.4%	65,433
12/14	402,529	5,851	1.5%	66,750
12/13	364,021	5,836	1.6%	65,565
12/12	353,855	5,647	1.6%	64,486
Annual Growth	**6.0%**	**1.1%**		**2.5%**

2016 Year-End Financials

Debt ratio: 5.55%
Return on equity: 12.57%
Cash ($ mil.): 15,705
Current ratio: —
Long-term debt ($ mil.): —

No. of shares (mil.): 1,696
Dividends
  Yield: 0.0%
  Payout: 33.0%
Market value ($ mil.): 87,170

	STOCK PRICE ($) FY Close	P/E High/Low		PER SHARE ($) Earnings	Dividends	Book Value
12/16	51.37	16	12	3.24	1.07	27.87
12/15	42.67	14	13	3.16	1.01	26.43
12/14	44.95	15	13	3.08	0.97	24.35
12/13	40.40	13	11	3.00	0.89	22.53
12/12	31.94	12	10	2.84	0.78	20.86
Annual Growth	**12.6%**	—	—	**3.3%**	**8.2%**	**7.5%**

US Foods Holding Corp

LOCATIONS

HQ: US Foods Holding Corp
9399 W. Higgins Road, Suite 500, Rosemont, IL 60018
Phone: 847 720-8000
Web: www.usfoods.com

HISTORICAL FINANCIALS

Company Type: Public

Income Statement

FYE: December 31

	REVENUE ($ mil.)	NET INCOME ($ mil.)	NET PROFIT MARGIN	EMPLOYEES
12/16*	22,918	209	0.9%	25,000
01/16	23,127	167	0.7%	25,000
12/14	23,019	(72)	—	—
12/13	22,297	(57)	—	—
Annual Growth	**0.9%**			

*Fiscal year change

2016 Year-End Financials

Debt ratio: 43.88%
Return on equity: 9.46%
Cash ($ mil.): 131
Current ratio: 1.42
Long-term debt ($ mil.): 3,705

No. of shares (mil.): 220
Dividends
  Yield: —
  Payout: —
Market value ($ mil.): 6,071

	STOCK PRICE ($) FY Close	P/E High/Low		PER SHARE ($) Earnings	Dividends	Book Value
12/16*	27.48	26	21	1.03	0.00	11.49
01/16	0.00	—	—	0.98	0.00	11.47
Annual Growth	—	—	—	**1.7%**	—	**0.0%**

*Fiscal year change

UTAH HOUSING CORPORATION

Auditors: DELOITTE & TOUCHE LLP SALT L

LOCATIONS

HQ: UTAH HOUSING CORPORATION
2479 S LAKE PARK BLVD, WEST VALLEY CITY, UT 841208217
Phone: 801 902-8200
Web: WWW.UTAHHOUSINGCORP.ORG

HISTORICAL FINANCIALS

Company Type: Private

Income Statement

FYE: June 30

	ASSETS ($ mil.)	NET INCOME ($ mil.)	INCOME AS % OF ASSETS	EMPLOYEES
06/16	1,830	23	1.3%	90
06/15	1,885	20	1.1%	—
06/14	1,659	14	0.9%	—
06/13	1,596	7	0.5%	—
Annual Growth	**4.7%**	**45.5%**		

2016 Year-End Financials

Debt ratio: ——
Return on equity: 20.40%
Cash ($ mil.): 108
Current ratio: 0.40
Long-term debt ($ mil.): —

Dividends
  Yield: —
  Payout: —
Market value ($ mil.): —

Valero Energy Corp

Valero Energy was not only named after a mission (the Mission San Antonio de Valero) it is on a mission to be the largest independent refiner in the US. Valero churns out about 3 million barrels per day refining low-cost residual oil and heavy crude into cleaner-burning higher-margin products including low-sulfur diesels. It operates 15 refineries in the US Canada and the UK. It also has 11 ethanol plants with a combined production capacity of about 1.4 billion gallons per year. Once a more diversified company Valero has exited the retail business in order to focus on its oil refining and ethanol operations.

HISTORY

Valero Energy was created as a result of the sins of its father Houston-based Coastal States Gas Corporation. Led by flamboyant entrepreneur Oscar Wyatt energy giant Coastal had established Lo-Vaca Gathering Company as a gas marketing subsidiary. Bound by long-term contracts to several Texas cities Coastal was not able to meet its contractual obligations when gas prices rose in the early 1970s and major litigation against the company resulted. The Texas Railroad Commission (the energy-regulating authority) ordered Coastal to refund customers $1.6 billion.

To meet the requirements 55% of Lo-Vaca was spun off to disgruntled former customers as Valero Energy at the end of 1979. The new company was born fully grown — as the largest intrastate pipeline in Texas — with accountant-cum-CEO Bill Greehey the court-appointed chief of Lo-Vaca at its head. Greehey relocated the company to San Antonio where it took its Valero name (from the Alamo or Mission San Antonio de Valero) and put some distance between itself and its discredited former parent. Under Greehey's direction Valero developed a squeaky-clean image by giving to charities stressing a dress code and keeping facilities clean.

Greehey diversified the company into refining unleaded gasoline. Valero bought residual fuel oil from Saudi Arabian refiners and in 1981 built a refinery in Corpus Christi Texas which went on line two years later. But in 1984 a glut of unleaded gasoline on the US market from European refiners undercut Valero's profits. To stay afloat Valero sold pipeline assets including 50% of its West Texas Pipeline in 1985 and 51% of its major pipeline operations in 1987. Refining margins finally began to improve in 1988. With one of the most modern refineries in the US Valero did not have to spend a bundle to upgrade its refining processes to meet the tougher EPA requirements of the 1990s.

In 1992 Valero expanded its refinery's production capacity and acquired two gas processing plants and several hundred miles of gas pipelines from struggling oil firm Oryx Energy (acquired by Kerr-McGee in 1999). That year Valero became the first non-Mexican business engaged in Mexican gasoline production when it signed a deal with state oil company Petr leos Mexicanos S.A. to build a gasoline additive plant there.

To expand its natural gas business substantially in 1994 Valero bought back the 51% of Valero Natural Gas Partners it didn't own. Valero also teamed up with regional oil company Swift Energy in a transportation marketing and processing agreement. As part of that arrangement Valero agreed to build a pipeline linking Swift's Texas gas field with a Valero plant.

In 1997 the company sold Valero Natural Gas to California electric utility PG&E gaining $1.5 billion for expansion. It then purchased Salomon's oil refining unit Basis Petroleum (two refineries in Texas and one in Louisiana) and the next year picked up Mobil's refinery in Paulsboro New Jersey.

With low crude oil prices hurting its bottom line in 1999 Valero explored partnerships with other refiners as a way to cut operating costs. In 2000 the company bought Exxon Mobil's 130000-barrel-per-day Benicia California refinery along with 340 retail outlets for about $1 billion.

In 2001 Valero gained two small refineries when it bought Huntway Refining a leading supplier of asphalt in California. Dwarfing that deal Valero also bought Ultramar Diamond Shamrock for $4 billion in cash and stock (it assumed about $2.1 billion of debt in the deal). As part of the deal and to comply with the demands of regulators in 2002 Valero sold the Golden Eagle (San Francisco-area)

refinery and 70 retail service stations in Northern California to Tesoro for $945 million.

In 2003 the company acquired Orion Refining's Louisiana refinery for about $530 million and the next year it acquired an Aruba refinery from asset-shedding El Paso Corp. for $640 million. Suncor Energy bought a Colorado-based refinery from Valero for a reported $30 million in 2005.

The 2005 acquisition of Premcor made Valero the largest independent refiner on the Gulf Coast a major national player.

Greehey turned over the leadership reins to another company veteran Bill Klesse in early 2006. The following year the company sold its Lima Ohio refinery to Husky Energy.

In 2008 the company sold its Krotz Springs Louisiana refinery to Alon USA Energy for $333 million.

In 2009 Valero had an opportunity for international refinery expansion and a foothold in Europe when it agreed to acquire Dow Chemical's 45% interest in Dutch refinery Total Raffinaderij Nederland N.V. However the deal fell through and the stake was sold to LUKOIL.

That year it bought seven ethanol production facilities from VeraSun Energy for $475 million.

To cut costs in 2010 it sold its Delaware City refinery. It also sold its Paulsboro New Jersey refinery that year to PBF Holding for $340 million. It also sold its 50% stake in a pipeline that brings deepwater crude oil from the Gulf of Mexico to the US to Genesis Energy for $330 million.

Expanding its global footprint in 2011 Valero bought Chevron's Pembroke refinery and marketing and logistics assets across the UK for $1.7 billion. It also boosted its US assets that year buying Murphy Oil's refinery outside New Orleans for $585 million to complement its St. Charles facility. Valero also bought Chevron USA Inc.'s Louisville and Lexington Kentucky product terminals expanding its wholesale marketing presence in eastern Kentucky with product supplied primarily from the Valero Memphis Refinery.

It made its first foray into ethanol production in 2009 buying seven ethanol production facilities from VeraSun Energy which was operating under Chapter 11 bankruptcy protection. Valero paid about $475 million for the facilities.

In 2013 the new hydrocracker unit at the Valero St. Charles Refinery began operations.

To better control costs in 2014 the company abandoned our Aruba Refinery except for the associated crude oil and refined products terminal assets that it continues to operate. It also sold its Texas Crude Systems Business to VLP for $154 million.

To get better shareholder returns in 2013 the company spun off its retail business as an independent public company CST Brands. This unit held Valero's company-operated convenience stores in the US and Canada; and filling stations cardlock facilities and heating oil operations in Canada. Valero continues to supply fuel to CST Brands' retail sites through long-term supply agreements. (Valero subsequently sold its remaining 20% stake in the company.)

In 2013 the company's Valero Terminaling and Distribution unit formed a joint venture with TGS Development to start construction on a new marine terminal on the lower Sabine-Neches Waterway near Port Arthur Texas to support the expansion of oil receipts and the marine movements of other commodities at that strategic port.

Growing its foothold in the petrochemical segment that year Valero also announced plans to build a major methanol plant at its 270000 barrel per day St. Charles refinery near New Orleans. Scheduled to commence operating in 2016 the $700 million plant will yield 1.6 million tons of methanol per year.

LOCATIONS

HQ: Valero Energy Corp
One Valero Way, San Antonio, TX 78249
Phone: 210 345-2000 **Fax:** 210 246-2646
Web: www.valero.com

2015 Sales

	$ mil.	% of total
US	60,319	68
UK and Ireland	11,232	13
Canada	6,841	8
Other countries	9,412	11
Total	**87,804**	**100**

PRODUCTS/OPERATIONS

2015 Sales

	$ mil.	% of total
Refining	84,521	96
Ethanol	3	4
Elimination	(151)	-
Total	**87,804**	**100**

Selected Products

Asphalt
Bunker oils
CARB Phase II gasoline
Clean-burning oxygenates
Conventional gasoline
Crude mineral spirits
Customized clean-burning gasoline blends for export
  markets
Ethanol
Gasoline blendstocks
Home heating oil
Jet fuel
Kerosene
Low-sulfur diesel
Lube oils
Petrochemical feedstocks
Petroleum coke
Premium reformulated and conventional gasolines
Reformulated gasoline
Sulfur

COMPETITORS

ADM	Motiva Enterprises
BP	National Cooperative
CITGO	Refinery Association
CVR	Phillips 66
Chevron	Sinclair Oil
Exxon Mobil	Sunoco
Green Brick Partners	TOTAL
HollyFrontier	TPC Group
Marathon Petroleum	Tesoro

HISTORICAL FINANCIALS

Company Type: Public

Income Statement

FYE: December 31

	REVENUE ($ mil.)	NET INCOME ($ mil.)	NET PROFIT MARGIN	EMPLOYEES
12/16	75,659	2,289	3.0%	9,996
12/15	87,804	3,990	4.5%	10,103
12/14	130,844	3,630	2.8%	10,065
12/13	138,074	2,720	2.0%	10,007
12/12	139,250	2,083	1.5%	21,671
Annual Growth	**(14.1%)**	**2.4%**	**—**	**(17.6%)**

2016 Year-End Financials

Debt ratio: 17.33%	No. of shares (mil.): 451
Return on equity: 11.26%	Dividends
Cash ($ mil.): 4,816	Yield: 0.0%
Current ratio: 2.02	Payout: 48.5%
Long-term debt ($ mil.): 7,886	Market value ($ mil.): 30,847

	STOCK PRICE ($) FY Close	P/E High/Low		PER SHARE ($) Earnings	Dividends	Book Value
12/16	68.32	15	10	4.94	2.40	44.35
12/15	70.71	9	6	7.99	1.70	43.39
12/14	49.50	9	6	6.85	1.05	40.20
12/13	50.40	10	7	4.97	0.85	36.34
12/12	34.12	9	5	3.75	0.65	32.66
Annual Growth	**19.0%**	**—**	**—**	**7.1%**	**38.6%**	**7.9%**

Valley National Bancorp (NJ)

Valley National Bancorp is high on New Jersey and New York. The holding company owns Valley National Bank which serves commercial and retail clients through more than 200 branches in northern and central New Jersey and in the New York City boroughs of Manhattan Brooklyn and Queens as well as on Long Island. The bank provides standard services like checking and savings accounts loans and mortgages credit cards and trust services. Subsidiaries offer asset management mortgage and auto loan servicing title insurance asset-based lending and property/casualty life and health insurance. Founded as The Passaic Park Trust Company in 1927 Valley National is looking to expand in Florida.

Operations

In addition to its commercial and retail banking operations Valley National Bancorp through its subsidiaries operates: an all-line insurance agency that offers property and casualty life and health insurance; a wealth management advisory business; title insurance agencies in New York and New Jersey. It also specializes in general aviation financing commercial equipment leasing and custom financing for health care professionals and law firms.

Financial Performance

Valley National reported revenue of $744.7 million in 2013 a decline of 6% versus 2012 on lower interest income caused by lower yields on average interest earning assets as a result of low long-term market interest rates. Net income fell 8% over the same period to about $132 million on lower revenue and an increase in non-interest expenses.

Strategy

One of the leading commercial banks in the New York and New Jersey metro areas Valley National has set its sights on Florida with its proposed acquisition of Boca Raton-based 1st United Bankcorp the largest commercial bank in Palm Beach County. The deal which is valued at $312 million would add a 21 branch network covering urban banking markets in Florida and approximately $1.7 billion in assets. Combined the two companies will have about $18.1 billion in assets nearly $13 billion in loans and $12.7 billion in deposits. The deal is expected to close in late 2014.

Commercial real estate and construction loans account for the largest portion of Valley's loan portfolio (47%). However the bank has ramped up its residential lending and has been actively marketing its home loan refinancing products amid continued low interest rates.

Mergers and Acquisitions

Valley National completed its approximately $222 million acquisition of New York-based bank holding company State Bancorp at the beginning of 2012. The deal which brought in 17 branches is part of Valley's overall strategy to expand its presence throughout New York City metropolitan area. It marked the company's first foray in Long Island and added locations in Manhattan and Queens as well. It also provides an opportunity to build retail relationships in new markets as State Bancorp focused more on commercial clients. Valley typically targets consumers disillusioned with larger banks.

In 2010 the company acquired the branches and most of the assets and deposits of failed Manhattan-based financial institutions LibertyPointe Bank and Park Avenue Bank in FDIC-assisted transactions. It also opened a loan production office in Bethlehem Pennsylvania to offer residential mortgages and title insurance. Valley continues to look for additional expansion opportunities.

EXECUTIVES

President and Chief Banking Officer Valley National Bank, Rudy E. Schupp, age 66, $425,000 total compensation
SEVP and CFO, Alan D. Eskow, age 69, $545,750 total compensation
Chairman President and CEO, Gerald H. Lipkin, age 77, $1,123,500 total compensation
EVP and Chief Retail Lending Officer, Albert L. Engel, age 69, $440,000 total compensation
EVP and Director Sales Retail Banking Marketing and Customer Service, Dianne M. Grenz
EVP and Senior Community Reinvestment Act Officer, Bernadette M. Mueller, age 58
SEVP and Treasurer, Ira Robbins, age 42, $425,000 total compensation
EVP and Chief Administrative Officer, Andrea Onorato
EVP and CIO, Robert J. Bardusch
EVP and Chief Risk Officer, Melissa Scofield
Assistant Vice President Commercial Loans, John Kenny
Vice President, Peter Alvarez
Assistant Vice President, Tony Dibenedetto
Vice President Of Commercial Lending, Mark Gomberg
Vice President, Dave Denoya
Vice President, Timothy Tierney
Assistant Vice President Branch Sales Manager, Marie Castro
Vice President, Claudia Orourke
Assistant Vice President Business Development Commercial Loans, Kristen Upadek
Vice President Sales Manager, Veronica Valentine
Senior Vice President Commercial Lending, John Murphy
Vice President Retail Training, Mary Black
Senior Vice President, Chip Woodbury
Vice President, Karen Conway
Assistant Vice President, Paul Cronen
First Vice President, Gary Michael
Senior Corporate Management Vice President GM, Ralph Passafiume
Vice President Business Development, Floyd Wilmoth
Vice President and Branch Sales Manager, Tina Brand
Vice President, Claudia O'Rourke
Vice President, Tony Zeleszko
Senior Vice President; Regional Manager, Steven Vitale
Vice President, Luba Gelman
Vice President of Sales, John Siberio
Executive Vice President Chief Financial Officer and Chief Operating Officer, Stan Pinkham
Vice President Commercial Lender, Linda Parsons-Danisovszky
Vice President and Credit Officer, Peter Tomasi
Vice President Commercial Middle Market Banking, Dan Smith

Vice President Commercial Banking, Jordan Simler
Vice President, Joanne Serros
Vice President Commercial Lending, James Blasdel
Senior Vice President Corporate Bnkg, Kenneth Nickel
Senior Vice President Director of Association Banking and Treasury Management, Marc Nuzzolo
Vice President Healthcare Financial Services, Adam Nendza
Vice President, Joe Gargiulo
Vice President, John Meyer
Vice President Commercial Relationship Manager, Cindy Dunlop
Vice President, Thomas Russo
Regional President, Jeff Klink
Vice President, Jaime Zamudio
Executive Vice President, Ted Sheppe
Vice President, Mikel Sharpe
Vice President, James Devaney
Vice President, Yulia Murphy
Vice President, Oscar Hernandez
Vice President Property Management Specialist, Charissa Eller
Assistant Vice President Risk Analytics Officer, Stacey Greaves
Assistant Vice President Assistant Banking Office Manager One North Federal Highway Boca Raton, Ann Longworth
Vice President Branch Manager Residential Mortgage, Robert Nardone
Vice President Commercial Lending Valley National Bank Florida Division, Gus Treichel
Assistant Vice President Loan Services Officer Florida Division, Dawn Keogh
First Vice President, Martha Soper
Assistant Vice President, Timika Muhammad
Vice President Territory Sales Manager, Matthew Coppola
Assistant Vice President and CRE LOAN Officer, Frank Canova
Auditors: KPMG LLP

LOCATIONS

HQ: Valley National Bancorp (NJ)
  1455 Valley Road, Wayne, NJ 07470
Phone: 973 305-8800
Web: www.valleynationalbank.com

PRODUCTS/OPERATIONS

2016 Sales

	$ mil.	% of total
Interest Income		
Interest and fees on loans	685	79
Interest and dividends on investment securities	79	9
Interest on federal funds sold and other short-term investments	1	0
Non-Interest Income		
Gains on sales of loans net	22	3
Service charges on deposit accounts	20	2
Insurance commissions	19	2
Trust and investment services	10	1
Bank owned life insurance	6	1
Fees from loan servicing	6	1
Gains on sales of assets net	1	0
Gains on securities transactions net	0	0
Change in FDIC loss-share receivable	(1.3)	0
Other	16	2
Total	**870**	**100**

COMPETITORS

Bank of America	JPMorgan Chase
Capital One	New York Community
Citigroup	Bancorp
Dime Community	PNC Financial
Bancshares	TD Bank USA
Hudson City Bancorp	Wells Fargo

HISTORICAL FINANCIALS
Company Type: Public

Income Statement
FYE: December 31

	ASSETS ($ mil.)	NET INCOME ($ mil.)	INCOME AS % OF ASSETS	EMPLOYEES
12/16	22,864	168	0.7%	2,828
12/15	21,612	102	0.5%	2,929
12/14	18,793	116	0.6%	2,907
12/13	16,156	131	0.8%	2,908
12/12	16,012	143	0.9%	2,910
Annual Growth	9.3%	4.0%	—	(0.7%)

2016 Year-End Financials

Debt ratio: 1.94%
Return on equity: 7.32%
Cash ($ mil.): 392
Current ratio: —
Long-term debt ($ mil.): —

No. of shares (mil.): 263
Dividends
Yield: 0.0%
Payout: 69.8%
Market value ($ mil.): 3,069

	STOCK PRICE ($) FY Close	P/E High/Low	Earnings	PER SHARE ($) Dividends	Book Value
12/16	11.64	19 13	0.63	0.44	9.02
12/15	9.85	27 22	0.42	0.44	8.70
12/14	9.71	19 16	0.56	0.44	8.03
12/13	10.12	16 13	0.66	0.60	7.72
12/12	9.30	18 12	0.73	0.65	7.57
Annual Growth	5.8%	—	(3.6%)	(9.4%)	4.5%

Veritiv Corp

Auditors: Deloitte & Touche LLP

LOCATIONS

HQ: Veritiv Corp
  1000 Abernathy Road N.E., Building 400, Suite 1700, Atlanta, GA 30328
Phone: 770 391-8200
Web: www.veritivcorp.com

HISTORICAL FINANCIALS
Company Type: Public

Income Statement
FYE: December 31

	REVENUE ($ mil.)	NET INCOME ($ mil.)	NET PROFIT MARGIN	EMPLOYEES
12/16	8,326	21	0.3%	8,700
12/15	8,717	26	0.3%	8,800
12/14	7,406	(19)	—	8,900
12/13	4,089	242	5.9%	
12/12	4,123	5	0.1%	
Annual Growth	19.2%	42.4%	—	

2016 Year-End Financials

Debt ratio: 37.97%
Return on equity: 3.91%
Cash ($ mil.): 69
Current ratio: 2.25
Long-term debt ($ mil.): 925

No. of shares (mil.): 15
Dividends
Yield: —
Payout: —
Market value ($ mil.): 844

	STOCK PRICE ($) FY Close	P/E High/Low	Earnings	PER SHARE ($) Dividends	Book Value
12/16	53.75	43 21	1.30	0.00	34.51
12/15	36.22	32 20	1.67	0.00	33.13
12/14	51.87	—	(1.62)	0.00	32.03
Annual Growth	0.9%	—	—	—	1.9%

Verizon Communications Inc

Verizon Communications is the #1 wireless phone service in the US (ahead of rival AT&T Mobility) and the #2 US telecom services provider overall (after AT&T). The company's core mobile business Verizon Wireless serves more than 146 million connections. Verizon's wireline unit with more than 18 million voice connections provides local telephone long-distance internet access and digital TV services to residential and wholesale customers. In addition Verizon offers a wide range of telecom managed network and IT services to commercial and government clients in more than 150 countries. Verizon has expanded its video and advertising capabilities with the acquisitions of AOL and Yahoo assets.

Operations

Verizon Communications? Verizon Wireless segment accounts for 70% of revenue. It operates one of the most extensive wireless networks in the US and the largest 4G LTE and third-generation Evolution-Data Optimized (EV-DO) networks. The 4G LTE network is available to more than 98% of the US population.

The wireline segment which provides about a quarter of revenue provides voice data and video communications products and enhanced services including broadband video and data corporate networking services data center and cloud services security and managed network services and local and long distance voice services. AOL and Verizon?s telematics business are included in the wireline segment. The segment also includes Verizon?s Fios service which offers high-speed internet and TV. The company reported nearly 6 million Fios internet and close to 5 million Fios video subscribers at the end of 2016.

A corporate category supplies about 5% of revenue.

Geographic Reach

Verizon is all over the horizon with a network that stretches across the US and offices in more than 150 countries. The company conducts research in San Francisco and Waltham Massachusetts.

Sales and Marketing

Verizon sells its prepaid and postpaid wireless phone services through its website its own stores and national retailers such as Best Buy Target and Wal-Mart. It also has a dedicated telemarketing sales force. The average retail customer account pays about $144 a month.

The company is a major advertiser with a coordinated program of TV print radio outdoor signage internet and point-of-sale media promotions. Those Verizon ads commercials and other promotional vehicles cost the company about $2.7 billion a year which is about two-thirds of what AT&T spends on advertising.

Financial Performance

After several years of riding the wireless wave Verizon?s 2016 financial performance stumbled in the wake of changes in pricing plans. Revenue dropped 4% to about $126 billion in 2016 from about $132 billion in 2015. Service revenue fell about $4 billion in 2016 because of lower retail postpaid service revenue as customers flocked to unsubsidized service pricing. Equipment revenue rose about $600 million in 2016 from better sales of smartphones under the company?s device payment program. Revenue from the wireline business decreased about 2% in 2016 from declines in Global Enterprise and Global Wholesale as well as a reduction in Fios marketing activities during a month-and-a-half long union work stoppage.

Verizon?s net income slumped 27% to about $13 billion in 2016 from about $18 billion in 2015. The lower profit resulted mainly from the revenue decrease as the company?s operating expenses increased just $361 million in 2016 from 2015.

Cash flow from operations was $23 billion in 2016 down from about $39 billion in 2015. Some of the difference came from a change in how Verizon monetizes device payments. It changed them from receivables to asset-backed securitizations. That switches the proceeds from operating activities to financing activities. It means Verizon reports lower cash flow from operations but does not reduce the cash available to run the business.

Strategy

When its rivals slash prices on wireless service Verizon Communications touts the coverage speed and reliability of its network. Maybe it costs a bit more Verizon tells customers but the network is worth it. Verizon is investing to expand and strengthen the network to develop new streams of revenue.

The company has committed to spend about $1.4 billion over the next three years to extend its fiber optic cable network to improve 4G service and get ready for higher-speed 5G service in a few years. It has contracted with Corning and the Italian fiber cable maker Prysmian to supply more than 20 million fiber miles over the next several years. In 2017 Verizon shelled out another $1.8 billion to buy the fiber network business of XO Communications. The deal included metro rings in 45 of the top 50 US markets.

In Boston Verizon is installing a fiber network to deliver high-speed service to businesses and consumers. It plans to build similar networks in several other markets. In another network bolstering move Verizon is installing small cell antennas on utility poles and the like to improve network density and relieve network congestion.

While wireless telephone service remains Verizon?s main business the company is moving into markets that leverage its network. With its telematics and Smart City initiatives Verizon looks to monetize data traffic through Internet of Things applications.

Verizon wants to use its network to deliver its own content. Its acquisitions of AOL and Yahoo (which closed in June 2017) provide it with advertising technology and a range of content that could open new revenue streams. Verizon maintains its go90 video platform with content aimed millennials; daily use was about 30 minutes per view in 2016. It also plans to launch a streaming service in 2017.

The company has assembled a digital rights portfolio that includes the NFL and NBA and provides enhanced viewing options for Verizon wireless customers. In 2017 Verizon agreed to pay about $20 million to stream over the internet an NFL game from London. Verizon can stream the game on any of its properties including AOL and Yahoo.

Mergers and Acquisitions

Verizon Communications agreed to buy Straight Path Communications for more than $3 billion gaining a trove of 28 GHz and 39 GHz millimeter wave spectrum used in mobile communications. The spectrum could give Verizon a boost in developing 5G technology. Verizon outbid AT&T for Straight Path.

In 2016 Verizon bought Fleetmatics a telematics company for about $2.4 billion. Verizon made Fleetmatics a part of its telematics unit that focuses on fleet management mobile workforce services and the Internet of Things.

Verizon acquired XO Holdings? wireline business which owns and operates one of the largest

fiber-based IP and Ethernet networks for about $1.8 billion in February 2017. The purchase extends Verizon?s fiber tracks in the US.

Verizon's acquisition of AOL provides the carrier with boosts in traffic for mobile and video as well as a strong presence in programmatic advertising. AOL's ad technologies are to enable Verizon to more precisely place ads in front of willing buyers. AOL also brought several high-profile content sites including the Huffington Post TechCrunch and Engadget.

The Yahoo purchase which concluded in 2017 brings some one billion users including 600 million on mobile devices (according to Yahoo figures) to Verizon. The deal includes Yahoos news finance and sports websites as well as Flickr and Tumblr. Also important are the advertising assets that Brightroll a programmatic ad platform; Flurry a mobile apps analytics service; and Gemini a native and search advertising service. Verizon was the winning bidder in a process that took several months to work through. In early 2017 Verizon lowered the amount it would for Yahoo by $350 million bringing the deal?s value to $4.48 billion. The move came after several hacking episodes exposed Yahoo to liabilities. As part of the rejiggered deal the companies will split certain legal and financial liabilities.

In 2016 Verizon agreed to acquire Volicon a provider of video capture archival compliance monitoring and clip creation workflow. The acquisition expands Verizon Digital Media Services as a provider of technology and media services for broadcast and online video.

EXECUTIVES

EVP and Chief Strategy Officer, Roy H. Chestnutt, age 58

Chairman and CEO, Lowell C. McAdam, age 63, $1,600,000 total compensation

EVP Wireless Network Operations, David Small

EVP and Chief Information and Technology Architect, Roger Gurnani, age 56

EVP and Chief Administrative Officer, Marc C. Reed, age 58, $792,307 total compensation

EVP and President Network and Technology, Hans Vestberg, age 52

EVP and President Customer and Product Operations, John G. Stratton, age 56, $896,154 total compensation

EVP and President Product Innovation and New Businesses, Marni M. Walden, age 49, $896,154 total compensation

SVP and Group President Verizon Enterprise Solutions, George J. Fischer, age 54

SVP and Group President Consumer Sales and Service, Kenneth (Ken) Dixon

EVP and Group President Verizon Wireless, Ronan Dunne

EVP Public Policy and General Counsel, Craig L. Silliman, age 49

SVP and Group President Verizon Business Markets (VBM), Martin Burvill

EVP Wireless Operations, Tami Erwin

SVP and CFO Operations Finance, Matthew D. (Matt) Ellis, age 45, $488,462 total compensation

President Verizon Partner Solutions, Eric Cevis

EVP Solutions and Sales Channels, Joe Chuisano

Vice President, Christopher Kimm

National Account Manager, Fran Morris

Vice President hrbp, Lisa Damask

Vice President Of Operations, Kwame Trotman

Vice President Wireless Policy Development, Charla Rath

Vice President Associate General Counsel, David Wheeler

Vice President Digital Meda Services, Kurt Smith

Vice President, Michele Dupre

Executive Director Network Operations Vps, Sam Luxton

Vice President, Roland Hicks

Vice President Of Marketing And Sales For Middle Atlantic Region, Mary Yarbrough

Regional Vice President, Jim Tinson

National Account Manager, Rob Parker

Vice President of Video Solutions, Shawn Strickland

Vice President Of Sales, Philip Burroughs

Vice President of Product Development, Michael Palmer

Senior Vice President Global Real Estate, John Vazquez

National Account Manager, Shirley Bily

Manager Vps Marketing And Sales, Janice Crandall

Vice President Marketing, Bob Smith

Senior Vice President Netwrokservices Group, Chris Creager

Secretary Manager Network Operations, Paul Mcguire

Board Member, Beryl Thompson

Auditors: Ernst & Young LLP

LOCATIONS

HQ: Verizon Communications Inc
1095 Avenue of the Americas, New York, NY 10036
Phone: 212 395-1000
Web: www.verizon.com

PRODUCTS/OPERATIONS

2016 Sales

	$ mil.	% of total
Wireless	89,186	70
Wireline	31,345	25
Corporate and Other	6,943	5
Eliminations	(1494)	0
Total	**125,980**	**100**

2016 Sales

	$ mil.	% of total
Service revenues and other	108,468	86
Wireless equipment revenues	17,512	14
Total	**125,980**	**100**

COMPETITORS

360networks	Level 3
AT&T	Sprint Communications
CenturyLink	T-Mobile USA
Charter Communications	Time Warner Cable
Comcast	U.S. Cellular
Cox Communications	XO Holdings
Cricket	Yellowbook

HISTORICAL FINANCIALS

Company Type: Public

Income Statement

FYE: December 31

	REVENUE ($ mil.)	NET INCOME ($ mil.)	NET PROFIT MARGIN	EMPLOYEES
12/16	125,980	13,127	10.4%	160,900
12/15	131,620	17,879	13.6%	177,700
12/14	127,079	9,625	7.6%	177,300
12/13	120,550	11,497	9.5%	176,800
12/12	115,846	875	0.8%	183,400
Annual Growth	**2.1%**	**96.8%**	**—**	**(3.2%)**

2016 Year-End Financials

Debt ratio: 44.26%—
Return on equity: 67.22%
Cash ($ mil.): 2,880
Current ratio: 0.87
Long-term debt ($ mil.): 105,433

Dividends
Yield: 0.0%
Payout: 70.7%
Market value ($ mil.): —

	STOCK PRICE ($)	P/E	PER SHARE ($)		
	FY Close	High/Low	Earnings	Dividends	Book Value
12/16	53.38	18 14	3.21	2.27	5.53
12/15	46.22	12 10	4.37	2.22	4.03
12/14	46.78	21 19	2.42	2.14	2.96
12/13	49.14	13 10	4.00	2.08	13.57
12/12	43.27	152119	0.31	2.02	11.60
Annual Growth	5.4%	— —	79.4%	3.1%	(16.9%)

VF Corp.

When the outdoor action gets tough the tough head to V.F. Corporation. The company is a leading retailer in the outdoor & action sports industry owning a number of brands in specialist product categories: Timberland The North Face and Napapijri (outdoor footwear and apparel); JanSport Eastpak Eagle Creek and Kipling (backpacks); and Reef and Vans (surf and skateboarding inspired footwear). V.F. also does a roaring trade in jeans owning the brands Lee Riders Wrangler and Rock & Republic. Its Majestic label offers licensed MLB NFL and NBA apparel. The company sells directly to consumers online and through more than 1500 V.F.-operated retail stores worldwide. V.F. also sells wholesale to department and specialty stores mass merchants and discounters.

Operations

V.F. operates four main business segments: Outdoor & Action Sports is the largest at over 60% of total sales followed by Jeanswear (nearly 15%) Imagewear (9%) and Sportswear (under 5%).

V.F.'s Outdoor & Action Sports segment has a stable of 11 popular outdoor brands across the apparel footwear equipment backpacks luggage and accessories categories. Vans a youth counterculture brand is the segment's biggest earner and sells shoes and clothing through 600 V.F.-owned retail units online and through distributors. The North Face the next biggest brand sells tents sleeping bags backpacks and other such outdoor accessories alongside its rugged apparel and footwear lines. The segment also sells handbags luggage backpacks women's activewear and surf-inspired footwear across its various other brands.

The Jeanswear segment sells jeans and related clothing and accessories through 7 brands. In the US the Lee brand is sold through mid-tier department stores and the Rustler and Rider by Lee brands are sold through regional discount stores. Outside the US Wrangler and Lee are sold as high-end brands.

The Imagewear business is divided into occupational workwear and uniforms and the Licensed Sports Group (LSG) businesses; each makes about 50% of segment revenue. Imagewear has three workwear brands: Red Kap (premium workwear) Bulwark (protective workwear for the petrochemical utility and mining industries) and Horace Small (law enforcement). The LSG business owns the Majestic brand the official uniform supplier for all 30 Major League Baseball teams until the license expires in 2019. LSG also has licenses for NFL NBA and NHL as well as motorcycle firm Harley-Davidson.

Sportswear consists of the Nautica and Kipling brands.

Geographic Reach

V.F. Corp. rings up over 60% of its sales in the US while the remainder mostly comes from Europe. It also sells in Asia Canada Mexico and Latin America. The apparel maker has more than 25 manufacturing plants in the US Mexico Central and South America the Caribbean Europe and the Middle East.

The company operates more than 30 distribution centers primarily in the U.S. Argentina Belgium Canada Chile China Mexico the Netherlands Turkey and the UK.

Sales and Marketing

V.F. makes sales through specialty stores department stores national chains mass merchants and its direct-to-consumer (DTC) operations. V.F. makes direct-to-customer sales through owned-operated stores concession retail stores and online and accounts for nearly 30% of total sales. VF generates a significant chunk of its sales through third-party retail chains. V.F.'s 10 largest customers account for more than 20% of total sales.

The apparel maker advertises in trade publications and on radio and television. Its digital initiatives include social media mobile platforms and the internet.

Financial Performance

V.F. Corporation has enjoyed revenue and profit growth for the past several years as it continues its worldwide expansion.

However in fiscal 2016 sales flattened out falling a negligible $13.6 million. Growth of 2% in the Outdoor & Action Sports and Imagewear segments was offset entirely by falls in Jeanswear (-$54.5 million) and Sportswear (-$99 million). Growth came mainly from International sales which grew 4% despite unfavorable currency movements. Direct-to-consumer sales increased 8%.

Net income fell 11% or $143 million to $1.2 billion as the company incurred restructuring costs without adding to the top line. V.F. also took a writedown of is lucy business which it is merging into The North Face. Restructuring costs aside bottom line performance was good aided by lower product costs better pricing and a shift towards higher margin business.

Cash from operating activities increased 23% to $1.5 billion due to the absence of a discretionary contribution to a pension plan undertaken in 2015 as well as higher collections of accounts receivable.

Strategy

V.F. is reshaping its business as intensifying higher competition meant the company fell short its lofty revenue goals. It is selling off underperforming units to place greater focus on its main growth drivers Vans The North Face and Timberland. The lucy brand trounced by activewear rivals such as Athleta Lululemon and Fabletics is being merged into the stronger North Face brand. V.F. is also shipping off its entire Licensed Sports Group business to online licensed sports merchandiser Fanatics.

On the flipside V.F. expanded its workwear business by acquiring Dickies hospital scrubs and Kodiak boots maker Williamson-Dickie. W-D is viewed as having strong potential to break the $1 billion annual sales milestone and will double V.F.'s workwear business.

Mergers and Acquisitions

In 2017 V.F. Corp. agreed to acquire family-owned Williamson-Dickie Manufacturing Co. a maker of work wear for $820 million in cash. The deal adds Williamson-Dickie's Workrite Kodiak Terra Walls and Dickies brands to V.F.'s closet. V.F. expects that it will gain about $200 million in revenue from the deal in 2017 and as much as $1 billion by 2021. The transaction is expected to close in the 2017 fourth quarter. Also that year it announced plans to purchase New Zealand outdoor and sports apparel brand Icebreaker which focuses on natural fibers and is available in nearly 50 countries.

Company Background

The gear-and-apparel maker has invested heavily in acquisitions to further build its outdoor and action sports business which has grown to account for more than 50% of sales. V.F. in September 2011 acquired global footwear maker Timberland for $2 billion. Marking the biggest acquisition in the company's history V.F. was enticed by Timberland's overseas presence and its strong growth during the past decade.

In 2010 on the wholesaling side V.F. took control of its Vans-branded products marketing venture in Mexico. The roughly $30 million purchase also put V.F. in charge of Vans retail stores.

V.F. founded in 1899 is controlled in part by trusts established by its late founder John Barbey.

HISTORY

In 1899 six partners including banker John Barbey started the Reading Glove and Mitten Manufacturing Company. Barbey bought out his five partners in 1911 and changed the name of the Reading Pennsylvania company to Schuylkill Silk Mills in 1913. Barbey expanded the mills' production to include underwear and changed the mills' name to Vanity Fair Silk Mills (after a contest with a $25 prize in 1919).

Barbey (who banned the word "underwear") and his son J. E. led their lingerie company to national prominence. The mills made only silk garments until the 1920s when synthetics were developed. In response to the US embargo on silk in 1941 Vanity Fair changed to rayon finally converting to the new wonder fabric nylon tricot in 1948. Vanity Fair was then manufacturing all stages of its nylon products from filament to finished garment. It won awards for its innovative advertising with photographs of live models in Vanity Fair lingerie.

J. E. owned all of Vanity Fair's stock until 1951 when he sold one-third of his holdings to the public. In 1966 the stock previously traded over the counter was listed on the NYSE. V.F. Corp. is not afraid to cut brands that aren't profitable to free up resources. In 2012 for example it sold its majority stake in upscale men's designer brand John Varvatos to private equity Lion Capital.

In 2013 V.F. Corp. was hoping to boost its outdoor business and its bottom line further through its 2013 bid to take over Australia's boardwear maker Billabong but the Aussie company wanted more than the 526.8 million Australian dollars (US $556 million) V.F. was willing to pay.

EXECUTIVES

Vice President Americas Sourcing, John Strasburger

Vice President, Susan Williams

Vice President Mergers And Acquisitions, Franklin Terkelsen

VP and Group President International, Karl Heinz Salzburger, age 59, $798,324 total compensation

President Asia/Pacific Region, Kevin D. Bailey

VP; Group President Outdoor and Action Sports Americas, Scott H. Baxter, age 52, $659,200 total compensation

President Workwear Jeans and Sportswear Brands, Curt Holtz

VP and CFO, Scott A. Roe, age 52, $675,000 total compensation

VP Global Business Technology, Sandra Harris

VP; Group President VF International, Aidan O'Meara, age 68

VP and CIO, Martin Schneider

President Europe Middle East and Africa, Martino Scabbia Guerrini, age 53

Brand President Smartwool, Travis Campbell

VP; President Supply Chain, Thomas A. Glaser

Chairman President and CEO, Steven E. (Steve) Rendle, age 57, $945,000 total compensation
President Sportswear, Brendan Sullivan
Vice President Business Systems, Chris Hobson
Vice President, Joan Stogner
Human Resources Vice President, Ronald Lawrence
Vice President, Kishore Patwa
Senior Vice President, Terri J Miller
Vice President Sourcing Lee Jeans, Steve Miller
Vice President of Retail, Kurt Kleespies
Vice President of Marketing Nautica U, Nina FloodCampo
Vice President Product Stewardship and Sustainability, Sean Cady
Vice President General Manager, Doug Mathison
Vice President, Sudhakar Puvvada
Vice President, Ryan Smith
Vice President, Jim Sinor
Vice President Sales, Steve Morton
Vice President Operations, Jackie Sullivan
Vice President, Sam Tucker
Vice President General Manager, Richard Blaya
Vice President Sales, Ken Wood
Vice President Human Resources Supply Chain, Rod Hewitt
Vice President, Jimmy Shafer
Vice President Gmm, Bill Lynch
Vice President Design Research And Development, Paul Herron
Vice President of Product Merchandising Design Product Development, Peggi Jones
Vice President of Merchandising and Marketing Lucys Activewear, Kira Karmazin
Vice President Retail Marketing, Jeff Sharp
Vice President Customer Service, Linda P Cullum
Vice President Strategy and Innovation, Stephen F Dull
Vice President, Mark Dimuro
Vice President Marketing, Aaron Carpenter
Vice President Finance, Chastity Black
Vice President of Merchandising, Dave Theiss
Vice President Human Resources, Cheryl Van Doren
Vice President Information Technology, Raymond Harris
Vice President Sales and Marketing, Todd Spaletto
Vice President GM, Hector Torres
Vice President, Joe Karns
Vice President of Marketing, Kim Yates
Vice President, Joseph Giles
Vice President Sourcing, Randy Fortenberry
Vice President and General Cou, Lisa Whitney
National Accounts Manager, Sam Leslie
Vice President, Steven Guy
Vice President Human Resources, Monica Valseschini
Vice President and General Counsel, Kristine Marvin
Vice President and General Counsel, Vincent Castiglione
National Accounts Manager, Harry Holbrook
Board Member, Garrett Chapman
Auditors: PricewaterhouseCoopers LLP

LOCATIONS

HQ: VF Corp.
105 Corporate Center Boulevard, Greensboro, NC 27408
Phone: 336 424-6000
Web: www.vfc.com

2016 Sales

	$ mil.	% of total
US	7,444	62
Foreign primarily Europe	4,574	38
Total	12	100

PRODUCTS/OPERATIONS

2016 Sales

	$ mil.	% of total
Net sales	11,902	99
Royalty income	116	1
Total	12,019	100

2016 Sales

	$ mil.	% of total
Outdoor & action sports	7,533	63
Jeanswear	2,737	23
Imagewear	1,103	9
Sportswear	536	5
Other	108	-
Total	12,019	100

Selected Brands

Imagewear
  Bulwark
  Horace Small
  Majestic
  Red Kap
  MLB (licensed)
  NFL (licensed)
  Harley-Davidson (licensed)
Jeanswear
  Lee
  Riders
  Rock & Republic
  Rustler
  Timber Creek by Wrangler
  Wrangler
Sportswear
  Kipling
  Nautica
Outdoor and action sports
  Eagle Creek
  Eastpak
  JanSport
  Kipling
  lucy
  Napapijri
  Reef
  SmartWool
  The North Face
  Timberland
  Vans

Selected Licenses

Harley-Davidson Motor Company
Major League Baseball
MLB Players Association
National Basketball Association
National Football League
National Hockey League

Selected major colleges and universities

COMPETITORS

Abercrombie & Fitch	L.L. Bean
American Eagle Outfitters	Levi Strauss
Calvin Klein	OshKosh B'Gosh
Columbia Sportswear	Patagonia Inc.
Diesel SpA	REI
Guess?	Reebok
J. C. Penney	Rocky Brands
Joe's Jeans	Russell Brands
Johnson Outdoors	Sears Holdings
Kate Spade	The Gap
Kellwood	Tommy Hilfiger
Koos Manufacturing	True Religion Apparel
L Brands	Williamson-Dickie Manufacturing

HISTORICAL FINANCIALS

Company Type: Public

Income Statement

FYE: December 31

	REVENUE ($ mil.)	NET INCOME ($ mil.)	NET PROFIT MARGIN	EMPLOYEES
12/16*	12,019	1,074	8.9%	69,000
01/16	12,376	1,231	10.0%	64,000
01/15	12,282	1,047	8.5%	59,000
12/13	11,419	1,210	10.6%	59,000
12/12	10,879	1,086	10.0%	57,000
Annual Growth	2.5%	(0.3%)	—	4.9%

*Fiscal year change

2016 Year-End Financials

Debt ratio: 23.81%	No. of shares (mil.): 414
Return on equity: 20.86%	Dividends
Cash ($ mil.): 1,227	Yield: 0.0%
Current ratio: 2.40	Payout: 60.2%
Long-term debt ($ mil.): 2,039	Market value ($ mil.): 22,088

	STOCK PRICE ($) FY Close	P/E High/Low	Earnings	PER SHARE ($) Dividends	Book Value
12/16*	53.35	26 21	2.54	1.53	11.93
01/16	62.25	27 21	2.85	1.33	12.62
01/15	73.76	31 23	2.38	1.11	13.01
12/13	61.58	89 22	2.71	0.92	13.80
12/12	148.29	68 51	2.43	0.76	11.63
Annual Growth	(22.6%)	— —	1.2%	19.2%	0.7%

*Fiscal year change

Viacom Inc

Viacom is a leading media conglomerate with an extensive portfolio of cable TV and film production assets. Its MTV Networks unit runs such cable networks as Comedy Central Nickelodeon and the family of MTV channels (MTV MTV2 VH1). Viacom also owns Black Entertainment Television which airs programming on BET BET Gospel and BET Hip Hop. In the film business Viacom operates through Paramount Pictures which includes imprints Paramount Pictures and Paramount Vantage. Viacom has a presence in more than 180 countries and territories primarily in North America Europe and Asia.

Operations

Viacom operates through two reporting segments: Media Networks and Filmed Entertainment. Media Networks provides entertainment content and related branded products for consumers in demographics attractive to advertisers content distributors and retailers through three brand groups: the Global Entertainment Group the Nickelodeon Group and BET Networks. The largest segment which accounts for about 80% of company?s total revenue.

Filmed Entertainment produces finances acquires and distributes motion pictures television programming and other entertainment content under the Paramount Pictures Paramount Animation Nickelodeon Movies MTV Films and Paramount Television brands.

Viacom's media networks including Nickelodeon Comedy Central MTV VH1 Spike BET CMT TV Land Nick at Nite Nick Jr. Logo Nicktoons TeenNick Channel 5 (UK) Telefe (Argentina) and Paramount Channel reach more than 3.9 billion cumulative television subscribers worldwide.

Geographic Reach

The US contributes about 75% of the company's revenue and International markets account for about 25%.

Sales and Marketing

The company's Music & Entertainment group (including Comedy Central MTV VH1 and Classic Spike and Logo) focuses on music-lovers youth and young adults. The Kids & Family group (Nickelodeon and Nick at Nite Nick Jr TeenNick Nicktoons CMT and TV Land) targets kids ages 2-17 and their families while BET dominates the important urban demographic with entertainment music and special interest programming.

Viacom does not have the broad complement of media assets that characterize integrated conglomerates such as Time Warner and Walt Disney but the company still realizes some potential by integrating its TV and film businesses such as through DVD sales and cross-promotion. Viacom itself incurred total advertising expenses of $748 million in fiscal 2015.

Financial Performance

The company's revenue was $12.49 billion in fiscal 2016. That was a decrease compared to its fiscal 2015 revenue of almost $13.3 billion. The drop was mainly due to decreased sales from the Filmed Entertainment unit partially offset by an increase in media network revenue.

Viacom's net income was $1.4 billion in fiscal 2016 which was a decrease compared to the prior fiscal period when the company claimed a net income of more than $1.9 billion. The decrease was largely caused by the combination of decreased revenue and increased operating expenses.

However even with decreased revenue and net income the company ended fiscal 2016 with $1.3 billion in cash on hand from operations.

Strategy

Viacom's strategy includes expanding its relationships with advertising cable satellite digital mobile and licensing partners to develop new ways to deepen its connection with audiences through insightful research and the development of content that resonates with targeted audiences.

What particularly drives Viacom's business is its success in building entertainment brands. The company is notable for creating and promoting such names as MTV and Nickelodeon into easily recognizable banners that stand for a particular form of entertainment.

Viacom has been looking to expand its reach into digital media in an effort to reach its young and increasingly online target audience.

Mergers and Acquisitions

In 2017 Viacom planned to acquire Scripps Networks Interactive. The agreement is pending between the two companies. In 2016 Viacom acquired Spain-based Telefonica S.A. one of the main free-to-air channels in Argentina for $345 million. The acquisition improved the company's growth in Argentina one of the most advanced and valuable media markets in Latin America.

EXECUTIVES

EVP Human Resources and Administration, Scott M. Mills, $1,750,000 total compensation
Senior Vice President Communications VH1, Laura Nelson
Svp Creative Grp/creative Vh1, Carole Robinson
Chairman and CEO BET Networks, Debra L. Lee, age 62
Chairman and CEO Paramount Pictures, James N. (Jim) Gianopulos
President Nickelodeon, Cyma Zarghami
President CEO and Director, Robert M. (Bob) Bakish, age 53, $931,731 total compensation
EVP Government Affairs, Doretha F. (DeDe) Lea, age 53, $843,365 total compensation

EVP Distribution Partnerships, Samantha Cooper
EVP and CFO, Wade C. Davis, age 45, $1,750,000 total compensation
EVP and CTO, David Kline
President and CEO Viacom International Media Networks (VIMN), David Lynn
EVP General Counsel and Secretary, Christa A. D'Alimonte
EVP and Chief Data Officer, Kern Schireson
EVP Distribution Marketing, Deena Demasi
Senior Vice President, Henry Moniz
Vice President Facilities, Byron Cotton
Senior Vice President Treasurer New Vi, George Nelson
Vice President Communications, David Bittler
Vice President Information Technology Audit, Anthony Noble
Senior Vice President Mtv Networks, Pauline Wen
Vice President of Corporate Communications, Jeremy Zweig
EVP Marketing and Creative Content Solutions, Niels Schuurmans
Vice President Information Technology, Woody Eversz
Vice President of LAN and Messaging Services, Lee Lee Larchevesque Larchevesque
Senior Vice President Content MTV Entertainment Group, Eddie Dalva
Executive Vice President Digital Advertising Sales and Marketing, Nada Stirratt
Senior Vice President BROADCAST TECHNOLOGIES, Paul Sartain
Vice President Production Finance, Brian Martin
Vice President Ad Sales Planning and Market Intelligence, Mike Dunn
Vice President Business and Legal Affairs, Marlo Lyons
Vice President of Engineering Production Technologies, Michael Bivona
Senior Vice President, Daniel Mandil
Vice President Vh1 And Logo Digital, Dan Sacher
Vice President of Production Special Events, Stephen Kipp
VP SEO Content Discovery Viacom, LiLi Cunningham
Vice President, Pier Borra
VP Ad Sales, Jennifer Choromanski
Vice President, Ron Meglio
Vice President Talent Acquisition, John Bongiorno
Vice President Mobile Strategy and Advertising, Peter Chelala
Research MTV Networks VH1 Executive Vice President, Colleen Fahey-Rush
Vice President of Network Services, Lee L'archenesque
Senior Vice President Digital Content, Claire Curley
EVP Integrated Marketing, Dario Spina
Vice President, Sue King
VP International Programming Operations, Tomas Rodriguez
Vice President Digital Mag, Jennifer Tracy
Senior Vice President Product Architect, Chaki Ng
Vice President, Adam Tucker
Senior Vice President Integrated Marketing, Chris Ficarra
Vice President Business Development, Amy Singer
Senior Vice President Associate General Counsel Law and Business Affairs (2000), William Keyes Hill-Edgar
Executive Vice President, Jim Perry
Vice President Network Operations, Malik Zegdi
Vice President Core Services, Bill Hutten
Vice President Operations, Eric Squires
Vice President Digital, Don Steele
Vice President Digital Marketing Nickelodeon, Jim Malaga
Vice President Integrated Marketing, Lisa Saffian
Vice President Of Strategic Business Development, Daniel Reich

Vice President Digital, Shannon Burke
Vice President, Sean Wylie
Vice President Federal Tax Audits, Victor Rappa
Vice President Operations Online, Pier Chapman
Senior Vice President Internal Audit, Norman Tsacalis
Vice President Counsel Corporate, Sarah Harp
Vice President New Business Development, Rick Beispel
Vice President and Associate General Counsel Real Estate (2000), Jack S Cohen
Vice President Assistant Treasurer, Lou Converse
Vice President Level, Vice president Tim Stevenson
Vice President of Information Technology, Luke Murphy
Vice President of Application Development, Stephen Flatt
Executive Vice President Human Resources, Joanne Griffith
Executive Vice President Human Resources, Catherine Houser
Executive Vice President for Distribution, Don Harris
Senior Vice President Tax and International Finance, Jay Kushner
Executive Vice President General Counsel and Secretary, Michael Fricklas
Vice President, Allan Infeld
Senior Vice President Development and Production, Jim Ackerman
Executive Vice President corporate Communications, Carl Folta
Vice President of Security, Johnathan Honovic
Vice President Audience Research, Beth Coleman
Senior Vice Presidentmusicandamp;Ent Digital Ad Sales, Sarah Iooss
Vice President Public Affairs the Americas, Mario Cader-Frech
Senior Vice President Media Engineering and Global Distribution, Stuart Baillie
Vice President Business and Legal Affairs, Susannah Verity
Vice President, Lee Sears
Vice President ON Air Creative, Amy Campbell
Senior Vice President Integrated Marketing CMT, Adam Steingart
Vice President and Associate General Counsel for Intellectual Property and Content Protection, Stanley Pierre-Louis
Vice President Integrated Marketing, Lesley Kantor
Senior Vice President Executive Compensation and Deputy General Tax Counsel, Andrew Greenberg
Vice President Insights Innovation, Alison Hillhouse
Executive Vice President Global Inculsion Strategy, Marva Smalls
VP Design and Construction, Yetta Banks
Senior Vice President, Monica Harris
VP Advertising Sales, Gary Merrifield
Senior Vice President Applications Development, Joseph S Leggio
Vice President Information Security and Compliance, Lee L'archevesque
Senior Vice President production, Drana Prekelezaj
Vice President Tax Accounting and Analysis, James Krebs
Vice President Benefits and Benefits Administ, Priscilla Lecator
Vice President IT, Tom Melina
Vice President Operations, Noreen Rafferty
SVP VMN Ad Sales Strategy, Kalina Nikolova
Senior Vice President Strategy and Business Development, Bryan Schiller
Senior Vice President Network standards and practices, Janet Borelli
Vice President, Carlos Martinez
Vice President Finance, Tony Augi
Web Site Content Vice President, Ezra Greene

EVP Strategy and Operations Music Group, Richard Gay
Vice President of Security, Jonny Honovic
Vice President International Media and Publishing, Gavin Metcalfe
Vice President, Leigh Wit
Senior Vice President Talent Acquisition, Daisy Auger-Dominguez
Manager Government Relations, Sarah Hudson
Executive Vice President of Security, John Honovic
Sr VP Marketing, Free Spirit
SVP Advertising Sales, Peter Graseck
Senior Vice President Research, David Giles
Vice President, Sarah Landy
Senior Vice President Engineering, John Pavley
Vice President Direct Response, Jennifer Karlson
Vice President, Evelyn Sias
Senior Vice President Human Resources, Patrick Bynum
Vice President, Andrea Rice
Senior Vice President Dep General Counsel MTV, Michael Minden
Vice President Lead and Professor Development, Nicole Kahny
Vice President Global Process Owner OTC, Victoria Tragianopoulos
Vice President Ent Ad Sales, Ted Spriggs
Vice President Strategic Account Management, Rebecca Blumberg
Executive Vice President Gmbet Intl and Prmt Pic Chnls, Michael Armstrong
Senior Vice President Operation Technical Support, Steven Kaufman
Chairman, Thomas J. (Tom) May, age 70
Vice Chairman, Shari E. Redstone, age 63
Board Of Directors, Alan Greenberg
Auditors: PricewaterhouseCoopers LLP

LOCATIONS

HQ: Viacom Inc
1515 Broadway, New York, NY 10036
Phone: 212 258-6000
Web: www.viacom.com

2016 Sales

	$ mil.	% of total
US	9,308	75
EMEA	2,182	17
All other regions	998	8
Total	**12,488**	**100**

PRODUCTS/OPERATIONS

2016 Sales

	$ mil.	% of total
Advertising	4,809	38
Affiliated Fees	4,556	36
Feature Film	2,488	20
Ancillary	751	6
(Eliminations)	(116)	—
Total	**12,488**	**100**

2016 Segment sale

	$ in mils
% of total	
Media Networks	79
Filmed Entertainment	21
Eliminations	-
Total	**100**

Selected Brands:BET NetworksBET Centric Entertainment GroupComedy CentralSpike TV Land Music GroupCMTLogoMTV VH1 Nickelodeon GroupNickelodeon

COMPETITORS

Discovery Communications	NBCUniversal Sony Pictures
Disney	Entertainment
Lionsgate	Time Warner
MGM	

HISTORICAL FINANCIALS

Company Type: Public

Income Statement

FYE: September 30

	REVENUE ($ mil.)	NET INCOME ($ mil.)	NET PROFIT MARGIN	EMPLOYEES
09/17	13,263	1,874	14.1%	11,650
09/16	12,488	1,438	11.5%	9,300
09/15	13,268	1,922	14.5%	9,200
09/14	13,783	2,391	17.3%	9,900
09/13	13,794	2,395	17.4%	10,350
Annual Growth	(1.0%)	(5.9%)	—	3.0%

2017 Year-End Financials

Debt ratio: 46.92%	No. of shares (mil.): 402
Return on equity: 36.35%	Dividends
Cash ($ mil.): 1,389	Yield: 0.0%
Current ratio: 1.55	Payout: 17.0%
Long-term debt ($ mil.): 11,100	Market value ($ mil.): 11,203

	STOCK PRICE ($) FY Close	P/E High/Low		PER SHARE ($) Earnings	Dividends	Book Value
09/17	27.84	10	6	4.68	0.80	15.00
09/16	38.10	15	9	3.61	1.40	10.77
09/15	43.15	16	8	4.73	1.46	8.89
09/14	76.94	16	14	5.43	1.26	8.98
09/13	83.58	17	10	4.84	1.15	11.56
Annual Growth	(24.0%)	—	—	(0.8%)	(8.7%)	6.7%

Virginia Electric & Power Co.

Virginia Electric and Power Company (Virginia Power) operates under the Dominion Virginia Power and Dominion North Carolina Power brands and provides regulated electric delivery services to about 2.4 million homes and businesses. Power generation is derived by means of coal gas oil hydro and nuclear plants. The utility's power plants (with 24300 MW of generating capacity) are managed by the Dominion Generation unit of parent Dominion Energy. Control of Virginia Power's transmission facilities is maintained by PJM Interconnection. Dominion Virginia Power also sells wholesale power to other users.

Geographic Reach

Virginia Power generates transmits and distributes electricity for sale in Virginia and North Carolina.

Sales and Marketing

Virginia Power primarily serves retail customers. It sells electricity at wholesale prices to rural electric cooperatives municipalities and wholesale electricity markets.

Strategy

Virginia Power is trying to beef up its green energy profile. In addition to exploring wind farm options to help produce alternative energy the company is pushing energy conservation programs with the aim of cutting peak demand by electric consumers in Virginia by 650 MW.

In 2016 the company announced plans to invest nearly $2 billion per year through 2020 to add cleaner generation to its infrastructure including solar energy. It also plans to expand secure and upgrade its electric grid in Virginia and northeastern North Carolina.

EXECUTIVES

President Dominion Virginia Power, Robert M. Blue
Auditors: Deloitte & Touche LLP

LOCATIONS

HQ: Virginia Electric & Power Co.
120 Tredegar Street, Richmond, VA 23219
Phone: 804 819-2000

COMPETITORS

Appalachian Power	Pepco Holdings
Columbia Gas of Virginia	Rappahannock Electric Cooperative
Duke Energy Carolinas	SCANA
Duke Energy Progress Inc.	South Carolina Electric & Gas

HISTORICAL FINANCIALS

Company Type: Public

Income Statement

FYE: December 31

	REVENUE ($ mil.)	NET INCOME ($ mil.)	NET PROFIT MARGIN	EMPLOYEES
12/16	7,588	1,218	16.1%	6,800
12/15	7,622	1,087	14.3%	6,800
12/14	7,579	858	11.3%	6,800
12/13	7,295	1,138	15.6%	6,700
12/12	7,226	1,050	14.5%	6,800
Annual Growth	1.2%	3.8%	—	0.0%

2016 Year-End Financials

Debt ratio: 31.81%	No. of shares (mil.): 0
Return on equity: 10.79%	Dividends
Cash ($ mil.): 11	Yield: —
Current ratio: 0.89	Payout: —
Long-term debt ($ mil.): 9,852	Market value ($ mil.): —

	STOCK PRICE ($) FY Close	P/E High/Low		PER SHARE ($) Earnings	Dividends	Book Value
12/16	0.00	—	—	(0.00)	0.00	
43,188.96						
12/15	0.00	—	—	(0.00)	0.00	
38,733.56						
Annual Growth	—	—	—	—	—	2.8%

VIRGINIA HOUSING DEVELOPMENT AUTHORITY

Though Virginia is famous for its Civil War-era plantations these historic estates represent a lifestyle out of reach for most. For Virginians seeking a more modest homestead there's the Virginia Housing Development Authority (VHDA). The not-for-profit quasi-government agency founded by the Virginia General Assembly in 1972 provides developers of rentalÂ propertiesÂ and low- to moderate-income borrowers with low interest rate loans to renovate or purchase houses and apartments across the state. Its loan products are offered by more than 140 authorized lenders throughout Virginia. The VHDA is self-supporting issuing bonds to raise capital.

EXECUTIVES

Executive Director, Susan F. Dewey
Managing Director Rental Housing, Arthur N. (Art) Bowen
Managing Director Community Outreach, J. Michael Hawkins
Managing Director Executive Services, Llewellyn C. Anderson
Managing Director Homeownership, Janet Wiglesworth
Managing Director Internal Audit and Risk Management, Julie Camus
Managing Director Finance, Pat Carey
Acting Managing Director Information Technology Services, J. Kyle Howard
Vice President of Operation, Jackie Gibbs
Chairman, Timothy M. Chapman
Vice Chairman, Sarah B. Stedfast
Auditors: KPMG LLP RICHMOND VA

LOCATIONS

HQ: VIRGINIA HOUSING DEVELOPMENT AUTHORITY
601 S BELVIDERE ST, RICHMOND, VA 232206504
Phone: 804 780-0789
Web: WWW.VHDA.COM

HISTORICAL FINANCIALS

Company Type: Private

Income Statement

FYE: June 30

	ASSETS ($ mil.)	NET INCOME ($ mil.)	INCOME AS % OF ASSETS	EMPLOYEES
06/16	8,024	171	2.1%	300
06/15	8,070	176	2.2%	—
06/14	8,014	132	1.7%	—
06/13	8,722	111	1.3%	—
Annual Growth	(2.7%)	15.6%	—	—

2016 Year-End Financials

Debt ratio: —
Return on equity: 31.00%
Cash ($ mil.): 1,027
Current ratio: 1.00
Long-term debt ($ mil.): —
Dividends
Yield: —
Payout: —
Market value ($ mil.): —

VIRTU FINANCIAL LLC

Auditors: DELOITTE & TOUCHE LLP NEW YOR

LOCATIONS

HQ: VIRTU FINANCIAL LLC
900 3RD AVE FL 29, NEW YORK, NY 100224777
Phone: 212 418-0100
Web: WWW.VIRTUFINANCIAL.COM

HISTORICAL FINANCIALS

Company Type: Private

Income Statement

FYE: December 31

	ASSETS ($ mil.)	NET INCOME ($ mil.)	INCOME AS % OF ASSETS	EMPLOYEES
12/14	3,324	190	5.7%	158
12/13	3,963	182	4.6%	—
Annual Growth	(16.1%)	4.3%	—	—

2014 Year-End Financials

Debt ratio: —
Return on equity: 26.30%
Cash ($ mil.): 75
Current ratio: —
Long-term debt ($ mil.): —
Dividends
Yield: —
Payout: —
Market value ($ mil.): —

Visa Inc

Paper or plastic? Visa hopes you choose the latter. Visa operates the world's largest global consumer payment system (ahead of rivals MasterCard and American Express) and boasts more than 3 billion credit and other payment cards in circulation across more than 200 countries. As part of its business the company licenses the Visa name to member institutions which issue and market their own Visa products and participate in the VisaNet payment system that provides authorization processing and settlement services. The company also offers debit cards Internet payment systems value-storing smart cards and traveler's checks. Visa's network connects thousands of financial institutions worldwide.

HISTORY

Although the first charge card was issued by Western Union in 1914 it wasn't until 1958 that Bank of America (BofA) issued its BankAmericard which combined the convenience of a charge account with credit privileges. When BofA extended its customer base outside California the interchange system controlling payments began to falter because of design problems and fraud.

In 1968 Dee Hock manager of the BankAmericard operations of the National Bank of Commerce in Seattle convinced member banks that a more reliable system was needed. Two years later National BankAmericard Inc. (NBI) was created as an independent corporation (owned by 243 banks) to buy the BankAmericard system from BofA.

With its initial ad slogan "Think of it as Money" the Hock-led NBI developed BankAmericard into a widely used form of payment in the US. A multinational corporation IBANCO was formed in 1974 to carry the operations into other countries. People outside the US resisted BankAmericard's nominal association with BofA and in 1977 Hock changed the card's name to Visa. NBI became Visa USA and IBANCO became Visa International.

By 1980 Visa had debuted debit cards begun issuing traveler's checks and created an electromagnetic point-of-sale authorization system. Visa developed a global network of ATMs in 1983; it was expanded in 1987 by the purchase of a 33% stake in the Plus System of ATMs then the US's second-largest system. Hock retired in 1984 with the company well on its way to realizing his vision of a universal payment system.

The company built the Visa brand image with aggressive advertising such as sponsorship of the 1988 and 1992 Olympics and by co-branding (issuing cards through other organizations with strong brand names such as Blockbuster and Ford).

In 1994 Visa teamed up with Microsoft and others to develop home banking services and software. Visa Cash was introduced during the 1996 Olympics. Visa pushed its debit cards in 1996 and 1997 with humorous ads featuring presidential also-ran Bob Dole and showbiz success story Daffy Duck.

Visa expanded its smart card infrastructure in 1997. It published with MasterCard encryption and security software for online transactions. The gloves came off the next year as the companies vied to convince the world to rally around their respective e-purse technology standards.

During the 1990s Visa fought American Express' attempts to introduce a bank credit card of its own by forbidding Visa members in the US from issuing the product; the Justice Department responded with an antitrust suit against Visa and MasterCard. The case went to trial in 2000 with the government claiming that Visa and MasterCard stifle competition and enjoy an exclusive cross-ownership structure. Visa eventually agreed to pay American Express $2.25 billion to settle the case.

Also in 2000 the company made a deal with Gemplus the French smart card company to enable payments over wireless networks. Visa then inked e-commerce agreements with telecommunications companies Nokia and Ericsson. The company continued its technology push with a deal with Financial Services Technology Consortium to test biometrics — the use of fingerprints irises and voice recognition to identify cardholders. The company also launched a prepaid card Visa Buxx targeted at teenagers.

The European Union in 2000 launched an investigation into the firm's transaction fees alleging that the fees could restrict competition. The following year Visa International agreed to drop its fee to 0.7% of the transaction value over five years.

Led by retail giant Wal-Mart some 4 million merchants claimed Visa and MasterCard violated antitrust laws and attempted to monopolize a legally defined market for debit cards. The plaintiffs sought up to $200 billion in damages in their class-action suit. Just as the 1996 lawsuit was to go to trial in early 2003 Visa settled agreeing to pay $2 billion (twice that of co-defendant MasterCard) over the next decade. Both agreed to pay $25 million immediately as well as reduce the fee merchants pay for signature-based debit cards.

Visa settled a similar case with Discover Financial in 2008. Visa's net share of the deal totaled some $1.8 billion; MasterCard which was also named agreed to pay $862.5 million.

The group restructured in 2007 in order to offer a more seamless international payments processing platform and to take itself public. Visa International Visa Canada Visa U.S.A. and several other regional organizations merged to create Visa Inc. which became the new parent of the group. It raised about $17 billion in a 2008 IPO.

Visa dedicated some of the funds raised to exploring new payment-related technologies and expanding into more regions. It established joint ventures with payment processors and banks to strengthen its global payment network. Other funds were set aside to cover costs resulting from legal settlements with American Express and Discover Financial totaling more than $4 billion.

EXECUTIVES

CEO, Alfred F. (Al) Kelly, age 59
Vice Chairman Risk and Public Policy, Ellen Richey, age 68, $600,023 total compensation
EVP and CFO, Vasant M. Prabhu, age 56, $547,616 total compensation
EVP and CEO European Operations, Charlotte M. Hogg, age 46
EVP Strategy Mergers and Acquisitions and Government Relations, William M. (Bill) Sheedy, age 50, $525,020 total compensation
EVP and General Counsel, Kelly M. Tullier, age 51
EVP Technology, Rajat Taneja, age 52, $750,029 total compensation

President, Ryan McInerney, age 42, $750,029 total compensation
Vice President, Brian Wood
Senior Vice President, Elizabeth Hurvitz
Vice President Head of Payment Services Marketing Visa Europe, Neil Horseman
Vice President Processing Solutions, Manny Fernandez
Vice President, Daysi Rojas
Gcas VPS Clients Inquiries North America LAC And Europe, Abdallah Saoud
Vice President Enterprise Risk, Joanne Charlick
First Vice President Value Added Services Latin America, Javier Vazquez
Senior Vice President, Phillip Kumnick
Assistant Vice President Marketing, Michelle Pasos
Vice President, Seth Friedman
Senior Vice President Global Financial I, Stephen Kehoe
Vice President Visa Uk, Rob Walter
Vice President, Mario Rivero
Vice Presidente, Sergio Botelho
Vice President, Jeff Allison
Senior Vice President Switching Systems, Manny Trillo
Vice President, Andrew Carpenter
Vice President, Odalys Ruiz
Vice President, Julie Miller
Vice President Global Head of Customer Experience, Diego J Todeschini
Senior Vice President, Mark Nelsen
Vice President, Guillermo Antnez
Senior Vice President Innovation and Strategic Partnerships, Shiv Singh
Vice President Technology Strategy and Governance, David Worth
Vice President Pricing And Costing, Philip Joseph
Vice President Marketing, Sergio De Anda
Vice President Strategy, Brian Weiner
Vice President, Laura Nadler
Vice President, Manoj Marathe
Assistant Vice President Business Development, Robert Gonzalez
Vice President of Human Resources, Puja Jaspal
Senior Vice President Visa Research Labs, Min Wang
Senior Vice President and Chief Procurement Officer, Rob Falivene
Vice President, Margaret Fitzpatrick
Vice President, Sang Lee
Senior Vice President Product Digital Solutions, Ansar Ansari
Vice President, Vanesa Meyer
Chairman, Robert W. Matschullat, age 70
Auditors: KPMG LLP

LOCATIONS

HQ: Visa Inc
P.O. Box 8999, San Francisco, CA 94128-8999
Phone: 650 432-3200
Web: www.corporate.visa.com

FY2017 Sales by Geography

	$ mil.	% of total
United States	8	47
International	9,654	53
Total	**18,358**	**100**

PRODUCTS/OPERATIONS

FY2017 Sales by Type

	$ mil.	% of total
Service Revenues	7,975	34
Data Processing Revenues	7,786	33
International Transaction Revenues	6,321	28
Other Revenues	841	4
Client Incentives	-4565 -	
Total	**18,358**	**100**

Selected Products and Services

Commercial and government
  Visa Business Credit Card (small business)
  Visa Business Debit Card (small business)
  Visa Business Electron (international)
  Visa Business Line of Credit
  Visa Commercial One Card
  Visa Corporate Card (travel and entertainment)
  Visa Gift Card
  Visa Incentive Card
  Visa Purchasing Card
  Visa Signature Business Card
Consumer credit
  Visa Classic
  Visa Gold
  Visa Infinite
  Visa Platinum
Consumer deposit
  Interlink Debit (POS debit network)
  Prepaid
  Visa Debit
  Visa Classic
  Visa Gold
  Visa Infinite
  Visa Platinum
  Visa Electron Debit

COMPETITORS

American Express	JCB International
Apple Inc.	MasterCard
China UnionPay	PayPal
Citigroup	Rewards Network
Discover	

HISTORICAL FINANCIALS

Company Type: Public

Income Statement

FYE: September 30

	REVENUE ($ mil.)	NET INCOME ($ mil.)	NET PROFIT MARGIN	EMPLOYEES
09/17	18,358	6,699	36.5%	15,000
09/16	15,082	5,991	39.7%	—
09/15	13,880	6,328	45.6%	11,300
09/14	12,702	5,438	42.8%	9,500
09/13	11,778	4,980	42.3%	9,500
Annual Growth	**11.7%**	**7.7%**		**12.1%**

2017 Year-End Financials

Debt ratio: 27.02%
Return on equity: 20.40%
Cash ($ mil.): 9,874
Current ratio: 1.90
Long-term debt ($ mil.): 16,618
No. of shares (mil.): 2,076
Dividends
  Yield: 0.0%
  Payout: 23.5%
Market value ($ mil.): 218,478

	STOCK PRICE ($) FY Close	P/E High/Low		PER SHARE ($) Earnings	Dividends	Book Value
09/17	105.24	38	27	2.80	0.66	15.78
09/16	82.70	33	27	2.48	0.56	15.43
09/15	69.66	108	25	2.58	0.48	13.47
09/14	213.37	108	84	2.16	0.40	8.99
09/13	191.10	105	71	1.90	0.33	8.61
Annual Growth	**(13.9%)**	**—**	**—**	**10.2%**	**18.9%**	**16.3%**

Voya Financial Inc

Auditors: Ernst & Young LLP

LOCATIONS

HQ: Voya Financial Inc
230 Park Avenue, New York, NY 10169
Phone: 212 309-8200
Web: www.ing.us

HISTORICAL FINANCIALS

Company Type: Public

Income Statement

FYE: December 31

	ASSETS ($ mil.)	NET INCOME ($ mil.)	INCOME AS % OF ASSETS	EMPLOYEES
12/16	214,235	(428)	—	6,700
12/15	218,249	408	0.2%	7,000
12/14	226,951	2,299	1.0%	6,500
12/13	221,023	600	0.3%	7,000
12/12	216,394	473	0.2%	7,000
Annual Growth	**(0.3%)**	**—**	**—**	**(1.1%)**

2016 Year-End Financials

Debt ratio: 1.66%
Return on equity: (-3.23%)
Cash ($ mil.): 2,910
Current ratio: —
Long-term debt ($ mil.): —
No. of shares (mil.): 194
Dividends
  Yield: 0.0%
  Payout: —
Market value ($ mil.): 7,634

	STOCK PRICE ($) FY Close	P/E High/Low		PER SHARE ($) Earnings	Dividends	Book Value
12/16	39.22	—	—	(2.13)	0.04	66.76
12/15	36.91	27	20	1.80	0.04	64.26
12/14	42.38	5	4	9.02	0.04	66.60
12/13	35.15	15	9	2.38	0.02	50.72
Annual Growth	**2.8%**	**—**	**—**	**—**	**18.9%**	**7.1%**

WAKEFERN FOOD CORP.

Grocery stores getting supplies from this co-op may be on the "Rite" track. Wakefern Food is the largest member-owned wholesale distribution co-operative in the US supplying groceries and other merchandise to more than 250 supermarkets under the ShopRite and The Fresh Grocer banners in New Jersey New York Connecticut Delaware Maryland Pennsylvania and Virginia. It also operates more than 50 PriceRite stores in these states plus Rhode Island and Massachusetts. Beyond supplying its member-owned stores Wakerfern distributes products to other supermarkets across the northeastern US and Bermuda. Founded by seven grocers in 1946 the coop now boasts 50 members 70000-plus employees and over $15 billion in annual sales.

Operations

Wakefern Food supplies retail and wholesale members mostly in the Northeast US. PriceRite a subsidiary of Wakefern Food and its nearly 50 supermarkets offer over 500 grocery items at discounted prices such as fresh fruits and vegetables breads prepackaged meat and seafood kosher products and national brands. Stores average about 35000 square feet in size which are smaller than traditional supermarkets. While the vast majority of ShopRite brand stores are member owned subsidiary ShopRite Supermarkets Inc operates nearly 35 company-owned stores.

Sales and Marketing

The coop added its 50th member The Fresh Grocer in July 2013. Outside of its members the company also supplies grocery stores like Saker ShopRite (New Jersey) Village Super Market (New Jersey and Pennsylvania) and Inserra Supermarkets (New York and New Jersey).

Financial Performance

Wakern Food's revenues have been rising over the past several years thanks to new member additions and their store openings.

The company's retail sales rose 4% to a record $14.7 billion in fiscal 2014 (ended September 27) thanks to the addition of six new ShopRite stores five new PriceRite discount supermarkets and six new The Fresh Grocer stores over the course of the year. The company also continued to expand its ShopRite from Home services store reach which would be provided from a total of 214 of its stores.

Strategy

Like other grocery wholesalers Wakefern Food's success depends on its ability to distribute goods at the lowest possible cost to its customers meaning the company focuses on keeping expenses low and improving efficiencies throughout its supply operation. But as a member-owned cooperative the company differs from other wholesalers such as Nash-Finch in that its primary focus is on its member stores. Wakefern Food also has the added responsibility of promoting its ShopRite retail chain and helping its member retailers expand the chain's footprint.

The ShopRite chain boasts a loyal following in its core markets but the supermarkets have been feeling the pinch from rivals in the price-competitive grocery business. The company is especially feeling pressure from non-supermarket chains such as Wal-Mart CVS Health and Wawa. To help boost customer loyalty Wakefern has turned to new technology in the form of mobile applications (developed in partnership with technology firm MyWebGrocer) for the Apple iPhone that allow users to get alerts about weekly store specials in their area. The company also rolled out an online pharmacy where customers can place orders through the Internet.

Company Background

Wakefern Food announced in 2012 it was supplying New York-based Food Bazaar stores which had supermarkets in New York New Jersey and Connecticut. Wakefern will supply ShopRite private label brands along with non-private labels such as dairy frozen food grocery nonfoods and specialty products.

HISTORY

Wakefern Food was founded in 1946 by seven New York- and New Jersey-based grocers: Louis Weiss Sam and Al Aidekman Abe Kesselman Dave Fern Sam Garb and Albert Goldberg. The company got its name by taking the first letters of the last names of five of the original founders (Weiss Sam and Al Aidekman Kesselman and Fern). Like many cooperatives the association sought to lower costs by increasing its buying power as a group.

They each put in $1000 and began operating a 5000-sq.-ft. warehouse often putting in double time to keep both their stores and the warehouse running. The shopkeepers' collective buying power proved valuable enabling the grocers to stock many items at the same prices as their larger competitors.

In 1951 Wakefern members began pooling their resources to buy advertising space. A common store name — ShopRite — was chosen and each week co-op members met to decide which items would be sale priced. Within a year membership had grown to over 50. Expansion became a priority and in the mid-1950s co-op members united in small groups to take over failed supermarkets. One such group called the Supermarkets Operating Co. (SOC) was formed in 1956. Within 10 years it had acquired a number of failed stores remodeled them and given them the ShopRite name.

During the late 1950s sales at ShopRite stores slumped after Wakefern decided to buck the supermarket trend of offering trading stamps (which could then be exchanged for gifts) figuring that offering the stamps would ultimately lead to higher food prices. The move initially drove away customers but Wakefern cut grocery prices across the board and sales returned. The company did embrace another supermarket trend: stocking stores with nonfood items.

The co-op was severely shaken in 1966 when SOC merged with General Supermarkets a similar small group within Wakefern becoming Supermarkets General Corp. (SGC). SGC was a powerful entity with 71 supermarkets 10 drugstores six gas stations a wholesale bakery and a discount department store. Many Wakefern members opposed the merger and attempted to block the action with a court order. By 1968 SGC had beefed up its operations to include department store chains as well as its grocery stores. In a move that threatened to break Wakefern SGC broke away from the co-op and its stores were renamed Pathmark.

Wakefern not only weathered the storm it grew under the direction of chairman and CEO Thomas Infusino elected shortly after the split. The co-op focused on asserting its position as a seller of low-priced products. Wakefern developed private-label brands including the ShopRite brand. In the 1980s members began operating larger stores and adding more nonfood items to the ShopRite product mix. With its number of superstores on the rise and facing increased competition from club stores in 1992 Wakefern opened a centralized nonfood distribution center in New Jersey.

In 1995 30-year Wakefern veteran Dean Janeway was elected president of the co-op. The company debuted its ShopRite MasterCard cobranded with New Jersey's Valley National Bank in 1996. The following year the co-op purchased two of its customers' stores in Pennsylvania then threatened to close them when contract talks with the local union deteriorated. In 1998 Wakefern settled the dispute then sold the stores.

The company partnered with Internet bidding site Priceline in 1999 offering customers an opportunity to bid on groceries and then pick them up at ShopRite stores. Big V Wakefern's biggest customer filed for Chapter 11 bankruptcy protection in 2000 and said it was ending its distribution agreement with the co-op. In July 2002 however Wakefern's ShopRite Supermarkets subsidiary acquired all of Big V's assets for approximately $185 million in cash and assumed liabilities.

Infusino retired in May 2005 after 35 years with Wakefern Food. He was succeeded by former vice chairman Joseph Colalillo. The cooperative added to its footprint in 2007 when it acquired about 10 underperforming retail locations from Stop & Shop. The stores located mostly in South Jersey were rebranded under the ShopRite banner.

EXECUTIVES

Vice President, Robert Rohlander
Vice President Deli And Seafood, Terry Sharkey
Vice President Of Finance, Steven Savas
Vice President Quality Assurance Food Safety, Michael Ambrosio
Vice President Finance, Neil Falcone
Vice President Dairy Deli and Frozen Food Division, Jeff Reagan
Vice President of Administration, Shawn Ravitz
Auditors: KPMG LLP SHORT HILLS NJ

LOCATIONS

HQ: WAKEFERN FOOD CORP.
5000 RIVERSIDE DR, KEASBEY, NJ 088321209
Phone: 908 527-3300
Web: WWW.PRICERITESUPERMARKETS.COM

PRODUCTS/OPERATIONS

2012 Corporate Stores

	No.
PriceRite	48
ShopRite	40
Total	**88**

COMPETITORS

A&P	IGA
Acme Markets	Krasdale Foods
Bozzuto's	SUPERVALU
C&S Wholesale	Stop & Shop
CVS	Wal-Mart
Hannaford Bros.	Wawa Inc.

HISTORICAL FINANCIALS

Company Type: Private

Income Statement

FYE: October 3

	REVENUE ($ mil.)	NET INCOME ($ mil.)	NET PROFIT MARGIN	EMPLOYEES
10/15*	12,573	5	0.0%	3,500
09/14	11,871	5	0.0%	—
09/13	11,455	0	—	—
09/12	11,010	5	0.0%	—
Annual Growth	**4.5%**	**(0.0%)**	—	—

*Fiscal year change

2015 Year-End Financials

Debt ratio: ——
Return on equity: —
Cash ($ mil.): 138
Current ratio: 0.30
Long-term debt ($ mil.): —

Dividends
Yield: —
Payout: —
Market value ($ mil.): —

Walgreens Boots Alliance Inc

Whether you get your drugs from the pharmacist or the chemist Walgreens Boots Alliance has you covered. The company formed when US-based Walgreen Co. bought its European counterpart Alliance Boots includes more than 13200 retail pharmacies (or chemists in some parts of the world) in 11 countries mostly the US and its territories and the UK selling prescription and OTC drugs along with health and beauty products and general merchandise. The Alliance Boots part of the company also includes wholesale operations serving more than 230000 pharmacies hospitals and clinics in upwards of 20 countries. Walgreens Alliance Boots was formed in 2014.

Operations

Walgreens Boots Alliance operates three core segments: Retail Pharmacy USA Retail Pharmacy International and Pharmaceutical Wholesale.

The Retail Pharmacy USA segment generates around 75% of revenue and sells pharmacy and beauty and other items through 8100 retail stores under the Walgreens and Duane Reade banners. It sells third party and own-brand products in store and online. It also has a prescription management app for customers. The pharmacy arm accounts for around 70% of sales and its retail arm (beauty products toiletries and general merchandise) the remainder.

Retail Pharmacy International generates more than 10% of revenue and consists mainly of the

Boots pharmacy network across the UK Norway Ireland the Netherlands and Thailand. The segment operates more than 4700 stores across the Boots brand as well as Benavides in Mexico and Ahumada in Chile. Boots stocks over 35000 products and offers around 640 in-store and standalone optician services alongside its retail and pharmacy operations.

The Pharmaceutical Wholesale segment (more than 10% of revenue) flies the Alliance Healthcare banner and delivers drugs and other healthcare products and services from around 290 distribution centers to about 110000 customers primarily in Europe; its the continents largest pharmaceutical distributor. It delivers to pharmacies hospitals clinics and doctor's offices and helps pharmacists develop their businesses. Its Alphega Pharmacy is a membership group for independent pharmacies.

Geographic Reach

Walgreens Boots Alliance is headquartered in the US and has stores in all fifty US states the District of Columbia Puerto Rico the US Virgin Islands Mexico Chile the UK Thailand Norway Ireland the Netherlands and Lithuania. The Walgreen part of the business is headquartered in the US while the Alliance Boots retail and wholesale operations are headquartered in Switzerland.

Altogether the company generates around 75% of its sales in the US while 15% comes from Europe (excluding the UK) and 10% of revenues were tied to business in the UK.

Sales and Marketing

Walgreens Boots Alliance sells in physical stores and online. It offers various loyalty programs such as Balance Rewards and the Boots Advantage Card.

Financial Performance

After posting explosive acquisition-driven growth between 2014 and 2016 in fiscal 2017 Walgreens Boots Alliance's sales grew by a relatively minor $1 billion or less than 1%. The company's USA segment grew 4% on the back of higher Medicare Part D prescriptions and the contribution from the newly formed AllianceRx Walgreens Prime specialty and mail services business. The balance of sales shifted further towards pharmacy sales which grew 7% and away from retail sales which fell 2%. Meanwhile the company recorded a 10% fall to $11.8 billion with the drop concentrated in comparable store sales mostly down to the weakness of the British pound against the dollar. The Wholesale business was likewise impacted by currency effects.

Net income fell 1% to $4.2 billion due to fluctuations in fair value adjustments of the company's AmerisourceBergen warrants and a gain in the previous year on equity interest in Alliance Boots.

Cash from operations fell 8% to $7.3 billion due to lower cash from changes in accrued expenses offset by higher cash inflows from changes in inventories.

Strategy

After years of using acquisitions to fuel growth at both Walgreen and Alliance Boots Walgreens Boots Alliance is looking to leverage its massive size as the world's largest purchaser of prescription drugs to lower costs. The company's presence in growing and untapped markets in South America and Asia give it great potential to continue expanding its footprint while its sheer size give it bargaining power with wholesalers of everything from prescription drugs to toothpaste to potato chips.

While it continues its store expansion the company's Retail Pharmacy USA division has been slowing its net new store openings in recent years and has been concentrating on emphasizing its exclusive private brand offerings to grow comparable store sales through technological innovations. It shed around 200 stores in 2016 while

driving usage of its digital channels. The company believes customers that engage in-store and online are 3.5 times more valuable than in-store only and those that engage in in-store and mobile are 6 times more valuable. In 2016 Walgreens launched an app that allows users to refill or transfer prescriptions live chat with a pharmacy technician and create a shopping list. It also flips to "in-store mode" when a user enters a store pointing them to relevant needs.

Mergers and Acquisitions

In a long-running saga Walgreens' attempt to acquire Rite Aid ended after two years of back-and-forth in September 2017 with the retailer acquiring 1932 of Rite Aid's around 5500 stores. Regulators objected strongly to the move as it would have left with the US with just two major pharmacist chains: Walgreens and CVS. The deal closed for around $4.4 billion; Rite Aid's stores will slowly be rebranded as Walgreens.

Company Background

Walgreen the largest drugstore company in the US bought 45% of Alliance Boots Europe's largest pharmacy retailer and wholesaler in 2012. The two got along well enough that in 2014 Walgreen exercised its option to purchase the rest of Alliance Boots. It formed Walgreens Boots Alliance and became a subsidiary of the parent along with Alliance Boots.

EXECUTIVES

Co-COO, Ornella Barra, age 63, $946,897 total compensation
Executive Vice Chairman and CEO, Stefano Pessina, age 76
EVP and Global CFO, George R. Fairweather, age 60, $977,118 total compensation
Co-COO, Alexander W. (Alex) Gourlay, age 56, $937,076 total compensation
EVP Global Chief Administrative Officer and General Counsel, Marco Pagni, age 54
EVP and Global Chief Human Resources Officer, Kathleen Wilson-Thompson, age 59, $627,000 total compensation
EVP and Chief Commercial Officer and President Global Brands, Ken Murphy, age 51
President Operations, Richard M. Ashworth
CIO, Steve Turner
Pharmacy Manager, Kinnari Gandhi
Pharmacy Manager, Eric Cwengros
Pharmacy Manager, John Love
Pharmacy Manager, Franklyn Osakwe
Pharmacy Manager, Denise Rhone
Pharmacy Manager, Anthony Silva
Pharmacy Manager, Maria Troia
Pharmacy Manager, Kurt Ratliff
Pharmacy Manager, Malcolm Humphries
Pharmacy Manager, Mohamed Elsheikh
Pharmacy Manager, Evangelia Katsamanis
Pharmacy Manager, Merykokeb Beyene
Pharmacy Manager, Hugh Zuengler
Pharmacy Manager, Jerry Huff
Pharmacy Manager, Alan Sobery
Pharmacy Manager, Joseph Rancour
Pharmacy Manager, Adel Shamseddine
Pharmacist Manager, Bianca Caraballo
Pharmacy Manager, Candice Reed
Pharmacy Manager, Mike Wiener
Pharmacy Manager, Ken Emelonye
Pharmacy Manager, Phuong Luc
Pharmacy Manager, Nicole Salata
Pharmacy Manager, Tamara Cisneros
Pharmacy Manager, Heather Rosenblum
Pharmacy Manager, Parnaz Najimi
Pharmacy Manager, Shenjin Orr
Pharmacy Manager, Benjamin Koenig
Pharmacy Manager, Dustin Hutmacher
Pharmacy Manager, Christina Bruce

Divisional Vice President Human Resources Mergers and Acquisitions, Mark Wattley
Group Vice President Supply Chain Global Inventory And Transportation, Dov Shenkman
Pharmacy Manager, Joel Neal
Pharmacy Manager, Hung Tran
Pharmacy Manager, Eleni Mastromihalis
Pharmacy Manager, Brooke Bailey
Pharmacy Manager, Hugh Tobias
Vice President Digital Engineering Walgreens, Chintan Mehta
Pharmacy Manager, Jigna Solanki
Pharmacy Manager, Mike Corvino
Pharmacy Manager, Jennifer Iwegbue
Pharmacy Manager, Bonnie Vu
Pharmacy Manager, Amina Saad
Pharmacy Manager, Veronica Zavala
Director of Pharmacy and Retail Operations, Vince Wilkinson
Pharmacy Manager, Gopal Pillai
Pharmacy Manager, Sofia Betancourt
Pharmacy Manager, Alejandra Russo
Group Vice President Walgreens Retail Brands, Helayna Minsk
Chairman, James A. (Jim) Skinner, age 72
Assistant Treasurer, Dan Morrell
Auditors: Deloitte & Touche LLP

LOCATIONS

HQ: Walgreens Boots Alliance Inc
108 Wilmot Road, Deerfield, IL 60015
Phone: 847 315-2500
Web: www.walgreensbootsalliance.com

PRODUCTS/OPERATIONS

2016 Sales

	$ mil.	% of total
Retail Pharmacy USA	83,802	72
Pharmaceutical Wholesale	20,293	17
Retail Pharmacy International	13,256	11
Total	**117,351**	**100**

2016 Sales

	$ mil.	% of total
United States	83,802	72
Europe (excluding the United Kingdom)	16,793	14
United Kingdom	14,081	12
Other	2,675	2
Total	**117,351**	**100**

COMPETITORS

BioScrip	OptumRx
Body Shop	Rite Aid
CVS	Sigma Pharmaceuticals
Costco Wholesale	Superdrug
H-E-B	Target Corporation
Kroger	UDG Healthcare
McKesson	Wal-Mart
Medicine Shoppe	

HISTORICAL FINANCIALS

Company Type: Public

Income Statement

FYE: August 30

	REVENUE ($ mil.)	NET INCOME ($ mil.)	NET PROFIT MARGIN	EMPLOYEES
08/17	118,214	4,078	3.4%	345,000
08/16	117,351	4,173	3.6%	360,000
08/15	103,444	4,220	4.1%	360,000
08/14	76,392	1,932	2.5%	—
08/13	72,217	2,548	3.5%	—
Annual Growth	**13.1%**	**12.5%**	**—**	**—**

Debt ratio: 19.60%
Return on equity: 14.26%
Cash ($ mil.): 3,301
Current ratio: 1.07
Long-term debt ($ mil.): 12,684

No. of shares (mil.): 1,023
Dividends
Yield: 1.8%
Payout: 38.5%
Market value ($ mil.): 83,730

	STOCK PRICE ($) FY Close	P/E High/Low	PER SHARE ($) Earnings	Dividends	Book Value
08/17	81.78	23 20	3.78	1.53	26.83
08/16	80.71	25 19	3.82	1.46	27.59
08/15	86.55	24 15	4.00	1.04	28.32
08/14	60.52	37 24	2.00	0.00	21.58
08/13	48.07	19 12	2.67	0.00	(0.00)
Annual Growth	14.2%	— —	9.1%	—	—

Walmart Inc

Wal-Mart Stores is an irresistible (or at least unavoidable) retail force that has yet to meet any immovable objects. It is the world's #1 retailer as well as the world's largest company by revenue (and largest employer with 2.3 million associates). The company sells groceries and general merchandise operating more than 5300 stores in the US including about 4600 Walmart stores and 660 Sam's Club membership-only warehouse clubs. Walmart's international division numbers more than 6500 locations; it's the #1 retailer in Canada and Mexico and has operations in Asia Africa Europe and Latin America. Some 260 million customers visit Walmart's stores and websites each week.

HISTORY

Sam Walton began his retail career as a J. C. Penney management trainee and later leased a Ben Franklin-franchised dime store in Newport Arkansas in 1945. In 1950 he relocated to Bentonville Arkansas and opened a Walton 5 & 10. By 1962 Walton owned 15 Ben Franklin stores under the Walton 5 & 10 name.

After Ben Franklin management rejected his suggestion to open discount stores in small towns Walton with his brother James "Bud" Walton opened the first Wal-Mart Discount City in Rogers Arkansas in 1962. Wal-Mart Stores went public in 1970 with 18 stores and sales of $44 million.

Avoiding regional retailers Walton opened stores in small and midsized towns in the 1970s. The company sold its Ben Franklin stores in 1976. By 1980 Wal-Mart's 276 stores had sales of $1.2 billion.

In 1983 Wal-Mart opened SAM'S Wholesale Club a concept based on the successful cash-and-carry membership-only warehouse format pioneered by the Price Company of California (now Costco Wholesale Corp.).

The company started Hypermart*USA in 1987 as a joint venture with Dallas-based supermarket chain Cullum Companies (now Randall's Food Markets). The 200000-sq.-ft. discount store/supermarket hybrid was later retooled as Wal-Mart Supercenters. Sam stepped down as CEO in 1988 and president David Glass was appointed CEO. Wal-Mart bought out Cullum the next year.

Wal-Mart acquired wholesale distributor McLane Company in 1990. In 1992 the year Sam died the company expanded into Mexico through a joint venture to open SAM'S CLUBS with Mexico's largest retailer Cifra (renamed Wal-Mart de

Mexico in 2000). Wal-Mart acquired 122 former Woolco stores in Canada in 1994. Co-founder Bud died a year later.

More international expansion included entering China in 1996; the acquisition of German hypermarket chain Wertkauf in 1997; the purchase of Brazilian retailer Lojas Americanas' 40% interest in a joint venture (1998); and the addition of four stores and other sites in South Korea. Also in 1998 the company began testing the Neighborhood Market format a 40000-sq.-ft. grocery and drug combination store. In 1999 Wal-Mart bought 74 German-based Interspar hypermarkets and acquired ASDA Group the UK's third-largest supermarket chain.

COO Lee Scott succeeded Glass as CEO in 2000; Glass stayed on as chairman of the executive committee. Wal-Mart later began testing its customers' demand for appliances by selling household appliances in selected stores.

Following the bankruptcy and closure of the Montgomery Ward department store chain in 2001 Wal-Mart offered to replace Ward's customers' credit cards with Wal-Mart branded cards. Wal-Mart also formed an alliance with America Online to offer Internet access and later launched its No Boundaries private-label cosmetics for pre-teens and teenagers. In June 2001 a group of six current and former female Wal-Mart employees filed a sex-discrimination lawsuit (seeking to represent up to 500000 current and former Wal-Mart workers) against the company. The next month Wal-Mart said it would acquire all the minority interests in Walmart.com and integrate its online operations with its store operations. It also laid off 100 employees at its corporate headquarters and eliminated 300 unfilled positions. In August it said it was testing the sale of Sealy and private-label mattresses in some of its superstores and it began offering college textbooks discounted up to 30% at its online College Bookstore.

2002 was a huge year for Wal-Mart both at home and abroad. In April the company was crowned America's largest corporation by FORTUNE magazine. In March Wal-Mart gained a foothold in Japan taking a 6% stake in one of Japan's top retailers SEIYU. That December it increased its SEIYU stake to 36% and retains the option to up that to nearly 67% by 2007. In a rare defeat Wal-Mart in July closed its first store in Germany and 2000 workers there went on a two-day strike over wages. (In 2001 Wal-Mart scrapped plans to open 50 more Supercenters there by 2003.) Also in 2002 Wal-Mart Puerto Rico acquired Supermercados Amigo the #1 supermarket chain on the island. (Wal-Mart opened its first Supercenter there in April 2001.)

Overall in 2002 Wal-Mart opened 178 supercenters 33 discount stores and 25 SAM'S CLUB stores. It opened 107 international units with two in Brazil 22 in Canada eight in China two in Germany three in South Korea 59 in Mexico two in Puerto Rico and nine in the UK. The company's attempt to open a state industrial bank in California in 2002 failed however after legislators barred retailers.

In May 2003 Wal-Mart sold its McLane grocery distribution business to Berkshire Hathaway; a rare divestment for the world's largest retailer. In July it opened its first store in Beijing.

In February 2004 a federal judge ruled that Wal-Mart should pay workers for overtime hours. The complaint which was brought by plaintiffs who said they were forced to work unpaid overtime between 1994 and 1999 came at a time when working conditions at the company were being scrutinized. Also that month Wal-Mart acquired the 118-store Bompre So chain of Brazilian supermarkets and hypermarkets from troubled Dutch retailer Royal Ahold for $300 million advancing the

world's largest retailer from fifth to third place in the Brazilian market. In March Wal-Mart opened its online music store which sells digital downloads for 11 cents less than major competitors (including Apple's iTunes and Napster). In April voters in Inglewood California overwhelmingly rejected Wal-Mart's proposal to build a supercenter there over the objections of local officials. Wal-Mart had sought to bypass local development and environmental regulations by spending more than $1 million to take its case directly to the voters. Also in April Wal-Mart's Japanese partner Seiyu opened its first Wal-Mart-style supercenter in Numazu.

In May 2004 Wal-Mart agreed to pay $3.1 million in fines for violating the Clean Water Act at 24 sites in nine states. (The retailer was fined $1 million in 2001 for similar violations involving its failure to manage storm-water runoff.)

Vice chairman Tom Coughlin retired in January 2005 after 25 years with Wal-Mart. Coughlin remained on the company's board until March 25 2005 when he resigned prematurely following an internal investigation related to "the alleged unauthorized use of corporate-owned gift cards and personal reimbursements." He was due to retire from the board on June 3 2005. In June the company rescinded Coughlin's retirement agreement including stock awards and incentive payments which may total as much as $12 million.

Also in January Wal-Mart agreed to pay $135540 to settle federal charges that it violated child labor laws. The 24 violations which the retailer denied involved teenage workers in three states using hazardous equipment such as chain saws paper balers and fork lifts. Soon after Wal-Mart was ordered to pay $7.5 million in damages to a disabled former employee who claimed the retailer unfairly reassigned him. In March the retailer settled a high-profile lawsuit by agreeing to pay $11 million to the US government to close an investigation into the use of illegal immigrants by Wal-Mart contractors to clean its stores. In May Wal-Mart increased its stake in SEIYU to 42% (up from 37%).

In August 2005 Wal-Mart signed Garth Brooks to a multiyear exclusive contract under which the country star's music will only be sold in Wal-Mart-owned stores. The deal marks the first time an artist has contracted himself and his entire catalog of music with a single chain. In October the company launched its Metro 7 line of urban women's apparel in 500 stores in and around urban areas. In December Wal-Mart opened its third superstore in the downtown Xuanwu District of Beijing. Also in December Wal-Mart acquired some 140 stores in Brazil from Portuguese retailer Sonae for about $757 million increasing the number of outlets it operates in Brazil to nearly 300.

In January 2006 Wal-Mart opened a supercenter in Santa Clarita California its second in Los Angeles County. In February the company acquired an additional 17.7% interest in CARHCO from Royal Ahold increasing its stake in the Central America supermarket operator to 51%. Wal-Mart's former vice chairman Thomas Coughlin who was accused of misusing more than $500000 in company funds pleaded guilty to fraud and tax charges in January 2006. In August he was sentenced to 27 months of house arrest and ordered to pay $400000 in restitution to his former employer. Wal-Mart itself was ordered by a Pennsylvania jury to pay more than $78 million in damages in a class-action suit brought by employees alleging that they were forced to work during breaks and off the clock. In October Wal-Mart disposed of its retail operations in Germany and South Korea. It sold the last of its 85 stores in Germany to rival METRO AG and sold 16 stores in South Korea to Shinsegae Co. for about $882 million.

In early 2007 Wal-Mart agreed to pay $33.5 million in back wages and interest to settle a federal lawsuit that accused the company of violating overtime laws involving more than 86000 employees. In February the company announced an agreement with all six major Hollywood studios to sell digital movies and TV shows on walmart.com becoming the first traditional retail chain to do so. In April Helen Robson Walton wife of Wal-Mart founder Sam Walton died at the age of 87. Wal-Mart and Bharti Enterprises formed a 50:50 joint venture in August to jointly build wholesale outlets that will buy goods from farmers and small manufacturers and sell to retailers through a nationwide supply chain. True to form Wal-Mart again cut prices of toys and some 15000 more items such as apparel home and food products for the 2007 holiday selling season.

In May 2008 the retailer revised its $4 prescription program launched in 2006 to cover 90-day prescriptions for $10. In November Mike Duke was named to Wal-Mart's board of directors in preparation for his elevation to president and CEO of the company in February 2009. Also in November Eduardo Castro-Wright president and CEO of Wal-mart US was promoted to vice chairman of Wal-Mart Stores. He assumed responsibility for the firm's global procurement operation.

The management shuffle continued in 2009 with Lee Scott retiring as CEO in February. Scott was succeeded by Duke who had headed the international arm of the company. In January Wal-Mart acquired a majority stake in Chile's largest food retailer Distribuci n y Servicio through a tender offer. In May of that year it opened its first location in India vis a joint venture with Bharti Enterprises.

In February 2010 the company opened its new Latin America regional headquarters in Miami Florida.

In June 2011 Walmart International acquired a 51% stake in South African retailer Massmart which operates 288 stores in 13 countries in sub-Saharan Africa in a deal valued at about $2.4 billion. Massmart operates stores under the Makro Game Dion Wired Builders Warehouse Builders Express Builders Trade Depot CBW Jumbo Cash and Carry and the Shield buying group. On the day of the Massmart closing the company scored a huge win when the US Supreme Court threw out a massive employment discrimination class-action lawsuit (Dukes vs. Wal-Mart) brought filed back in 2001. While the court did not rule on whether or not Wal-Mart discriminated against women it said they could not proceed as a class.

EXECUTIVES

Executive Vice President and President Walmart South, Rosalind Brewer

Executive Vice President Membership Marketing and E Commerce Sam's Club, Cindy Davis

President and CEO Walmart U.S., Gregory S. (Greg) Foran, age 55, $1,006,424 total compensation

President and CEO, C. Douglas (Doug) McMillon, age 51, $1,278,989 total compensation

Chief Merchandising Officer Walmart U.S., Steve Bratspies

EVP and President and CEO International, David Cheesewright, age 54, $1,071,743 total compensation

EVP and CFO Walmart U.S., Michael P. Dastugue, age 53

EVP and Chief Administrative Officer Walmart International, Scott Price, age 56

EVP and President and CEO Walmart eCommerce U.S., Marc Lore, age 45, $346,154 total compensation

EVP Softlines and General Merchandise Walmart U.S., James A. (Andy) Barron

EVP Supply Chain Walmart U.S., Gregory L. (Greg) Smith, age 54

EVP Food Walmart U.S., Charles Redfield

EVP and CFO Walmart International, Richard Mayfield

EVP Global Governance and Corporate Secretary, Jeffrey J. (Jeff) Gearhart, age 52

EVP Corporate Affairs, Daniel J. (Dan) Bartlett, age 45

EVP Consumables and Health and Wellness, Scott Huff

EVP and President Supercenters Walmart U.S., Michael S. (Mike) Moore

EVP and CFO, M. Brett Biggs, age 48, $854,670 total compensation

EVP Membership and Technology and CEO SamsClub.com, Jamie Iannone, age 44

EVP Operations Sam's Club, Gisel Ruiz, age 46

EVP and General Counsel, Karen Roberts

EVP and President and CEO Walmart Latin America India and Africa and Chairman Walmart Mexico and Central America, Enrique Ostal ©

EVP and COO Walmart U.S., Judith McKenna

SVP and President Jet.com, Liza K. Landsman

SVP New England Division Walmart U.S., Julie Murphy

EVP and Global Chief Ethics and Compliance Officer, Jay T. Jorgensen

SVP and Chief Marketing Officer Walmart U.S., Tony Rogers

EVP Global People Division, Jacqueline P. (Jacqui) Canney, age 49

EVP and President and CEO Sam's Club, John Furner, age 43

EVP Central Operations Walmart U.S., Mark Ibbotson

EVP and CTO, Jeremy King

EVP and Enterprise Chief Information Officer, Clay Johnson

EVP and Chief Merchandising Officer Sam's Club, Ashley Buchanan

SVP Chief Sustainability Officer and President Walmart Foundation, Kathleen McLaughlin

EVP Walmart Realty, JP Suarez

Vice President and Assistant Treasurer, Mike Cook

Executive Vice President and Chief Administrative Officer, Rollin Lee Ford

Vice President and Chief Legal Compliance Officer, Tom Gean

Vice President Isd Architecture Chief Technology A, John Collier

Senior Vice President, Anthony Fuller

Vice President Corporate Affairs, Lee Culpepper

Executive Vice President Sales Innovation Walmart U.S., John Aden

Vice President of Large Systems, Rita D Carney

Vice President of Ecommerce, Todd Harbaugh

Vice President Intl Merchandise Development, Ronald F Virta

Pharmacy Manager, Steve Goldblatt

Pharmacy Manager, Lydia Orr

Pharmacy Manager, Joby Young

Pharmacy Manager, John Cox

Pharmacy Manager, Gary Durfey

Pharmacy Manager, Tram Romero

Vice President E Commerce, Fred Quandt

Vice President Supply Chain, Lesley Smith

Vice President and Regional General Manager, Todd Libbra

Vice President International, Ashley Taylor

Vice President Human Resources Central America, Ana Concepcion Rodriguez

Senior Vice President and Chief Data Officer, Suja Chandrasekaran

Exec Vp-sams Club Operations, Greg Johnston

Vice President, Carol Schumacher

Vice President Compliance, Phyllis Harris

Vice President, Mehrdad Akbar

Vice President Desarrollo Comercial, Jesus Lopez

Pharmacy Manager, Terry Bennett

Vice President Manager Director, Shelli Stevens

Senior Vice President Innovation, Rick Webb

Vice President Global Sourcing, Ashish Bharara

Vice President Compensation Walmart International and Global Leverage, Marty Autrey

Vice President Public Affairs and Government Relat, Maggie Sans

Pharmacy Manager, Tara Green

Vice President Merchandising, Jody Pinson

Pharmacy Manager, Kimberly Baublitz

Senior Vice President International Development, Daniel Mallory

Vice President Home Management, Stephanie Reibling

Vice President, Pat Waynick

Executive Vice President Marketing and Membership, Mark Goodman

Pharmacy Manager, Angie Davis

Vice President of Information Technology and Creative Services, Ben-Saba Hasan

Assistant Vice President of People, Jennifer Baggett

Vice President Sales, Janet Walls

Vice President, Thomas Colella

Vice President Marketing, Catherine Corely

Vice President Private Brands, Marty Esarte

Vice President Marketing Assistant, Rosalyn Harris

Senior Vice President Assistant, Teri Davis

Vice President And Regional General Manager, David Reitnauer

Vice President Indirect Sourcing, Caroline Clarke

Vice President Corporate Recruiting, Anne Thomas

Vice President and Controller Wal Mart International, Olga Aragon-Hernandez

Vice President Human Resources, Clark Bill

Vice President Finance and Strategy Services, Jonathan Hall

Vice President of International, Mike Duke

Vice President Inbound Transportation, Kevin Jones

Vice President Financial Services, Max Pedro

Vice President Assistant, Angelisa Henry

VPDMM Assistant, Kelly Adams

VICE PRESIDENT LOGISTICS, Kenneth Woodlin

Vice President Assistant To Manolo Reyes Produce and Floral, Philip Bentley

Vice President Assistant, Sandra Harper

Senior Vice President Logistics, Laura Wilkin

Vice President, Mark Henneberger

Executive Vice President, Ed Kolodzieski

Vice President Information Technology, Dave Frizzell

Assistant To Kerry Kilker Vice President Information Systems, Eileen Smith

Vice President, Hans Holmer

Senior Vice President Central Plains Division Walmart Usa, Dacona Smith

PHARMACY Manager, Lee Fallon

Pharmacy Manager, Teresa Compton

Rph, Susan Long

Vice President Administration, Albert Lowe

Pharmacy Manager, Victor Hernandez

Vice President Produce, Ron McCormick

Pharmacy Manager, Dan Rafferty

Vice President, Eddie Tutt

Vice President of Corporate Affairs, James Lee

Senior Vice President Contrl, David M Chojnowski

Senior Vice President General Merchandise Manager Hardli, Gary Severson

Vice President of Global Talent Managerment, Stephanie Wong

Vice President Supplier Diversity, Theresa Barrera

Vice President External Distribution, Kathy Schroeder

Vice President Dmm Deli, Karla Mcbride

Senior Vice President Finance, Pedro Farah

Vice President, David Badeen

Vice President, Daniel Williams

Human Resources Director And Vice President, Erica Henson

Senior Vice President and GMM Sam's Club, Dawn vonBechmann

Vice President Risk Management, William Newberg

Vice President Regional General Manager, Ben Hassing

Vice President Of Financial, Tom Heffron

Rvp 16, Ken Reese

Vice President Of Corporate Communications, Dan Toporek

Vice President Assistant, Cheryl Creighton

Vice President Finance, Kathy Kress

Vice President of Operations, Henry Jordan

Vice President Assistant, Nancy Towe

Vice President Merchandise Planning and Category Management, David Scogin

Vice President Strategic Real Estate Finance, Scott Carroll

Vice President of Sales and Marketing, Lee Hill

Vice President Finance Strategy General Merchandise, Galagher Jeff

Vice President Marketing, Demetrio Moysen

Vice President Jewelry, Chris Callahan

Vice President Brand Merchandising Active Classics And Shoes, Jimmy Olsson

Vice President Warehouse Administration, Joel Marpe

Ex Vp, Johnnie Dobbs

Vice President Finance, Brent Seay

Vice President of Isd Infrastructure Engineering, James Martin

Senior Vice President and GMM Boys Mens Apparel and Housewares, Jacqueline Sazekas

Vice President Finance, Scott Draper

Vice President and General Counsel Corporate, Gordon Y Allison

Senior Vice President Proprietary Brands, John Boswell

Vice President Human Resources, Don Swann

Vice President Intl Merchandise Development, Ron Virta

Auditors: Ernst & Young LLP

LOCATIONS

HQ: Walmart Inc
  702 S.W. 8th Street, Bentonville, AR 72716
Phone: 479 273-4000
Web: www.stock.walmart.com

2017 sales

	$ mil.	% of total
U.S.	367,784	76
Non-U.S.	118,089	24
Total	485,873	100

2017 Stores

	No.
North America	
US	5,332
Canada	410
Latin America	
Mexico	2,411
Brazil	498
Chile	363
Costa Rica	234
Guatemala	220
El Salvador	90
Argentina	107
Nicaragua	92
Honduras	95
Asia	
Japan	341
China	439
India	20
UK	631
Africa	412
Total	11,695

PRODUCTS/OPERATIONS

2017 Sales

	$ mil.	% of total
Net sales	481,317	99
Membership and other income	4,556	1
Total	485,873	100

2017 Sales

	% of total
Wal-Mart US	64
International	24
SAM'S CLUB	12
Total	100

Selected Private Labels and Licensed Brands

Athletic Works
Better Homes & Gardens (licensed)
Black & Decker (licensed)
Canopy
Danskin Now (licensed)
Disney (licensed)
Equate (health and beauty aids)
Everstart
Faded Glory (jeans licensed)
General Electric (licensed)
George
Great Value (dairy dry grocery meat and produce)
Home Trends
Just My Size (licensed)
Mainstays
Marketside
No Boundaries
Oak Leaf
Ol' Roy (dog food)
OP (licensed)
Ozark Trail
Parent's Choice
Prima Della
Puritan
Rival (licensed)
Sam's Choice (grocery items)
Secret Treasures
Spring Valley
Starter
White Stag

COMPETITORS

99 Cents Only	J Sainsbury
AEON	J. C. Penney
ALDI	Katz Group
Ace Hardware	King Kullen Grocery
Albertsons	Kmart
Amazon.com	Kohl's
Army and Air Force	Kroger
Exchange	Lianhua Supermarket
AutoZone	Loblaw
BJ's Wholesale Club	Lowe's
Bed Bath & Beyond	METRO AG
Best Buy	Maruetsu
Big Lots	Meijer
Bridgestone Retail	Office Depot
Operations	PETCO
CVS	Pep Boys
Carrefour	Publix
Chedraui	Rite Aid
Comerci	SUPERVALU
Costco Wholesale	Safeway
Dollar General	Sears
El Puerto de Liverpool	Soriana
Family Dollar Stores	Staples
Farmacias Benavides	TJX Companies
Gigante	Target Corporation
Grupo Carso	Tesco
Grupo Elektra	Toys "R" Us
H-E-B	True Value
Home Depot	Walgreen
Hudson's Bay	

HISTORICAL FINANCIALS

Company Type: Public

Income Statement

FYE: January 31

	REVENUE ($ mil.)	NET INCOME ($ mil.)	NET PROFIT MARGIN	EMPLOYEES
01/17	485,873	13,643	2.8%	2,300,000
01/16	482,130	14,694	3.0%	2,200,000
01/15	485,651	16,363	3.4%	2,200,000
01/14	476,294	16,022	3.4%	2,200,000
01/13	469,162	16,999	3.6%	2,200,000
Annual Growth	0.9%	(5.3%)	—	1.1%

2017 Year-End Financials

Debt ratio: 23.10%—
Return on equity: 17.19%
Cash ($ mil.): 6,867
Current ratio: 0.86
Long-term debt ($ mil.): 42,018
Dividends
  Yield: 3.0%
  Payout: 44.1%
  Market value ($ mil.): —

	STOCK PRICE ($) FY Close	P/E High/Low	PER SHARE ($) Earnings	Dividends	Book Value
01/17	66.74	17 14	4.38	2.00	25.52
01/16	66.36	19 12	4.57	1.96	25.47
01/15	84.98	18 14	5.05	1.92	25.21
01/14	74.68	17 14	4.88	1.88	23.59
01/13	69.95	15 11	5.02	1.59	23.04
Annual Growth	(1.2%)	— —	(3.4%)	5.9%	2.6%

Washington Federal Inc.

Washington Federal is the holding company for Washington Federal Savings which operates about 190 branches in eight western states. The thrift which was founded in 1917 collects deposits from consumers and business by offering standard products such as CDs IRAs and checking savings and money market accounts. With these funds the bank mainly originates single-family residential mortgages which account for nearly three-quarters of its loan portfolio. The bank also writes business consumer construction land and multifamily residential loans. Washington Federal sells life home and auto coverage to individuals and businesses through its First Insurance Agency subsidiary.

Operations

In addition to its consumer and commercial banking operations Washington Federal has four wholly-owned subsidiaries: First Insurance Agency which offers a full line of individual and business insurance products to its customers and others; Statewide Mortgage Services Co. which holds about $18.6 million of real estate held for investment (REHI); Washington Services which also holds and markets REHI; and First Mutual Sales Finance a servicer of consumer loans.

Geographic Reach

As its name suggests Washington State is Washington Federal's largest market. Oregon and Arizona are other major markets for the bank.

Financial Performance

Washington Federal's fiscal 2012 (ends September) revenue fell by about 9.5% vs. the previous year due to a decrease both interest and non-interest income. Total interest income which accounts for about 97% of WF's total revenue declined 8% on fewer loans mortgage-backed securities and investment securities and cash equivalents. Other income fell 36%. With the exception of fiscal 2010 which saw a slight gain in revenue WF's revenue has been declining for several years. Net income increased 24% in fiscal 2012 vs. the prior year due to overall lower credit costs.

Strategy

Small relative to its national bank competitors Washington Federal has been building its business through acquisitions adding new markets and growing in established ones. Acquisitions have included both healthy smaller rivals and failed banks seized by regulators. In a bid to unify its brand and increase its name recognition WF rebrands acquired banks under its own moniker.

The bank is also working through its portfolio of nonperforming loans which peaked during the height of the recession in 2009 but now are on the decline.

Mergers and Acquisitions

In 2017 Washington Federal agreed to acquire Anchor Bancorp for $63.9 million. The combined company will have 248 offices in eight states in the Western US and total assets of $15.3 billion.

EXECUTIVES

Chairman President and CEO, Roy M. Whitehead, age 64, $765,179 total compensation
President and CEO, Brent J. Beardall, age 45, $390,925 total compensation
SVP and CFO, Vincent L. Beatty, age 58
EVP and Chief Credit Officer, Mark A. Schoonover, age 58, $335,259 total compensation
Utah and Nevada Regional President, Marlise G. Fisher
Southern Oregon Regional President, Peggy L. Hobin
EVP and CIO, Angela D. Veksler, age 55
Northern Washington Regional President, Tom Kenney
Western Idaho Regional President, Tom Van Hemelryck
Northern Oregon Regional President, Gary Haines
Arizona Regional President, Mike Brown
New Mexico Regional President, Bill Synnamon
Southern Washington Regional President, Greg Toso
Texas Regional President, Tony Barnard
Vice President Credit Administration, Marc A Rasmussen
Executive Vice President, Jack Jacobson
Vice President, John Iasonides
Vice President, Jeff Birkelo
Assistant Vice President Branch Manager, Gail Vitale
Assistant Vice President Senior Credit Analyst, Jocelyn Stockton
Assistant Vice President Human Resources Administrator, Lori Szallar
Vice President, Delbert Hague
Assistant Vice President Manager, Sheila DeGuise
AVP Branch Manager, Eric Madsen
Vice President Compliance Manager, Monsy Crcm
Auditors: DELOITTE & TOUCHE LLP

LOCATIONS

HQ: Washington Federal Inc.
425 Pike Street, Seattle, WA 98101
Phone: 206 624-7930
Web: www.washingtonfederal.com

Selected Markets
Arizona
Idaho
Nevada
New Mexico
Oregon
Texas
Utah
Washington

PRODUCTS/OPERATIONS

2013 Sales

	$ mil.	% of total
Interest		
Loans	430	73
Mortgage-backed securities	80	14
Investment securities	22	4
Other income		
Deposit fee income	14	3
Loan fee income	7	1
Others	8	2
Total	**564**	**100**

COMPETITORS

Bank of America	Washington Banking
Banner Corp	Wells Fargo
KeyCorp	Zions Bancorporation
U.S. Bancorp	

HISTORICAL FINANCIALS

Company Type: Public

Income Statement

FYE: September 30

	ASSETS ($ mil.)	NET INCOME ($ mil.)	INCOME AS % OF ASSETS	EMPLOYEES
09/17	15,253	173	1.1%	1,818
09/16	14,888	164	1.1%	1,806
09/15	14,568	160	1.1%	1,838
09/14	14,756	157	1.1%	1,909
09/13	13,082	151	1.2%	1,457
Annual Growth	**3.9%**	**3.5%**	**—**	**5.7%**

2017 Year-End Financials

Debt ratio: —	No. of shares (mil.): 87
Return on equity: 8.72%	Dividends
Cash ($ mil.): 313	Yield: 0.0%
Current ratio: —	Payout: 43.3%
Long-term debt ($ mil.): —	Market value ($ mil.): 2,934

	STOCK PRICE ($) FY Close	P/E High/Low	Earnings	PER SHARE ($) Dividends	Book Value
09/17	33.65	18 14	1.94	0.84	23.00
09/16	26.68	15 11	1.78	0.55	22.03
09/15	22.75	14 12	1.67	0.54	21.04
09/14	20.36	15 13	1.55	0.41	20.05
09/13	20.68	16 11	1.45	0.34	18.91
Annual Growth	**12.9%**	**— —**	**7.5%**	**25.4%**	**5.0%**

Washington Trust Bancorp, Inc.

Without seeming naive Washington Trust Bancorp can utter Washington and trust in the same breath. The holding company owns The Washington Trust Company one of the oldest and largest banks in Rhode Island and one of the oldest banks in the entire US. Chartered in 1800 the bank boasts over $3.5 billion in assets and operates nearly 20 branches in the state and one in southeastern Connecticut. Washington Trust offers standard services such as deposit accounts CDs and credit cards. The company's commercial mortgages and loans account for more than half of its loan portfolio while residential mortgages and consumer loans make up most of the rest. The bank also offers wealth management services.

Operations

Around one-third of the bank's loan portfolio was made up of commercial real estate loans in 2014 while business loans made up another 21%.

About 60% of Washington Trust's total revenue came from loan interest (including fees) in 2014 while another 7% came from interest on its taxable and tax-exempt investment securities. The rest of its revenue came from wealth management income (18%) deposit account charges (2%) card interchange fees (2%) merchant processing fees (1%) and other miscellaneous income sources. The bank had a staff of 590 employees at the end of 2014.

Washington Trust's wealth management division includes Washington Trust Investors Weston Financial and 1800 Asset Management. The division offers financial planning investment management and trust services and has more than $4 billion of assets under administration.

Geographic Reach

Of its nearly 20 branches 10 of its branches are located in Southern Rhode Island (Washington County) nearly 10 branches are in the greater Providence area and one branch is in southeastern Connecticut. The company's commercial lending office in Providence and six residential mortgage lending offices in eastern Massachusetts (Sharon Burlington and Braintree); Glastonbury and Darien Connecticut; and Warwick Rhode Island.

Financial Performance

Washington Trust has struggled to consistently grow its revenues in recent years due to shrinking interest margins on loans amidst the low-interest environment. Its profits however have been rising thanks to declining interest expenses and falling loan loss provisions as its loan portfolio's credit quality has improved with higher property valuations in the strengthened economy.

The bank's revenue inched higher by 1% to $180 million in 2014 mostly as its interest income grew with higher average loan balances.

Higher revenue in 2014 combined with lower interest expenses on deposits lower loan loss provisions and lower non-interest expenses boosted Washington Trust's net income higher by 13% to $40.8 million for the year. The company's operating cash levels fell to half the levels of the prior year to $2.7 million after adjusting its earnings for non-cash items mostly related to its mortgage banking net loan proceeds.

Strategy

Washington Trust Bank has been growing its loan and deposit business organically by opening new branches and loan production offices in its target markets. In early 2015 it opened a new branch in Rumford making it the bank's second location in East Providence. In 2014 it opened a branch in Johnston Rhode Island and furthered its expansion into Connecticut with the opening of a new mortgage office in Glastonbury Connecticut.

The company also pursues acquisitions to expand its service offerings extend its reach into new geographic markets and bolster its existing business lines.

Mergers and Acquisitions

In 2015 Washington Trust purchased SEC-registered investment advisory firm Halsey Associates which added more than $850 million in assets under management to its Wealth Management business' books. Acquiring the New Haven Connecticut-based firm also expanded its reach in the Connecticut and metropolitan New York region.

EXECUTIVES

Vice President and Retail Lending Officer The Washington Trust Company, Linda S Smith
Vice Chair Secretary and CFO, David V. Devault, age 63, $299,731 total compensation

Chairman and CEO, Joseph J. (Joe) MarcAurele, $514,596 total compensation
EVP and Chief Lending Officer of the Bank, James Hagerty
President and COO, Edward O. (Ned) Handy, $385,000 total compensation
EVP Wealth Management and Treasurer, Mark K. W. Gim, $239,462 total compensation
Assistant Vice President Mortgage Lending, John Mohan
Executive Vice President of Retail Lending of the Bank, Stephen Bessette
Auditors: KPMG LLP

LOCATIONS

HQ: Washington Trust Bancorp, Inc.
23 Broad Street, Westerly, RI 02891
Phone: 401 348-1200
Web: www.washtrust.com

PRODUCTS/OPERATIONS

2014 Sales

	$ mil.	% of total
Interest		
Loans including fees	107	60
Securities	12	7
Other	0	-
Non-interest		
Wealth management services	33	18
Loan sales & commissions	6.8	4
Gain on sale of business line	6	3
Service charges on deposit accounts	3	2
Other	9	6
Total	**180**	**100**

COMPETITORS

Bank of America	People's United
Citizens Financial	Financial
Group	Sovereign Bank
Liberty Bank	Webster Financial

HISTORICAL FINANCIALS

Company Type: Public

Income Statement

FYE: December 31

	ASSETS ($ mil.)	NET INCOME ($ mil.)	INCOME AS % OF ASSETS	EMPLOYEES
12/16	4,381	46	1.1%	596
12/15	3,771	43	1.2%	582
12/14	3,586	40	1.1%	590
12/13	3,188	36	1.1%	570
12/12	3,071	35	1.1%	592
Annual Growth	**9.3%**	**7.3%**	**—**	**0.2%**

2016 Year-End Financials

Debt ratio: 0.52%	No. of shares (mil.): 17
Return on equity: 12.10%	Dividends
Cash ($ mil.): 106	Yield: 0.0%
Current ratio: —	Payout: 54.0%
Long-term debt ($ mil.): —	Market value ($ mil.): 962

	STOCK PRICE ($) FY Close	P/E High/Low	PER SHARE ($) Earnings	Dividends	Book Value
12/16	56.05	21 13	2.70	1.46	22.76
12/15	39.52	16 14	2.54	1.36	22.06
12/14	40.18	17 13	2.41	1.22	20.68
12/13	37.22	17 12	2.16	1.03	19.84
12/12	26.31	13 11	2.13	0.94	18.05
Annual Growth	**20.8%**	**— —**	**6.1%**	**11.6%**	**6.0%**

Waste Management, Inc. (DE)

Holding company Waste Management tops the heap in the US solid-waste industry. Through subsidiaries the company serves more than 20 million residential industrial municipal and commercial customers in the US and Canada. Waste Management provides waste collection transfer recycling and resource recovery and disposal services. Its sites include more than 250 owned or operated landfills (the industry's largest network) 310 transfer stations and around 95 material recovery facilities. Collection services account for more than half of sales.

HISTORY

In 1956 Dean Buntrock joined his in-laws' business Ace Scavenger Service an Illinois company that Buntrock expanded into Wisconsin.

Waste Management Inc. was formed in 1971 when Buntrock joined forces with his cousin Wayne Huizenga who had purchased two waste routes in Florida in 1962. In the 1970s Waste Management bought companies in Michigan New York Ohio Pennsylvania and Canada. By 1975 it had an international subsidiary.

The company divided into specialty areas by forming Chemical Waste Management (1975) and offering site-cleanup services (ENRAC 1980) and low-level nuclear-waste disposal (Chem-Nuclear Systems 1982).

USA Waste was founded in 1987 to run disposal and collection operations in Oklahoma. It went public in 1988 and in 1990 Don Moorehead a founder and former CEO of Mid-American Waste Systems bought a controlling interest (most of which he later sold). Moorehead moved the business to Dallas and began buying companies in the fragmented industry. John Drury a former president of Browning-Ferris joined USA Waste in 1994 as CEO.

As USA Waste gathered steam Waste Management got off track. It diversified and Buntrock renamed the company WMX Technologies in 1993 to de-emphasize its waste operations. In 1997 however the company reverted to the Waste Management name and pressured by disappointed investor George Soros CEO Phillip Rooney resigned. After more management changes turnaround specialist Steve Miller became CEO the fourth one in eight months and Buntrock retired.

USA Waste picked up market share with large acquisitions including Envirofill (1994) Chambers Development Corporation (1995) and Western Waste Industries and Sanifill (1996). In 1996 the company moved to Houston. During the next two years it bought United Waste Systems Mid-American Waste the Canadian operations of Allied Waste and Waste Management and TransAmerican Waste Industries .

1998 saw the $20 billion merger between USA Waste and Waste Management. The new company bearing the Waste Management name and led by Drury and other former USA Waste executives controlled nearly a quarter of North America's waste business. The company finished the year by agreeing to pay shareholders $220 million in a suit over overstated earnings.

The new Waste Management bought Eastern Environmental Services for $1.3 billion in 1999. (A legal battle over negotiations between Eastern and Waste Management executives was settled out of court in 2000.) Drury took leave in 1999 because of an illness that would claim his life and director Ralph Whitworth known as a shareholder activist stepped in as acting chairman.

The company faced shareholder lawsuits after it was reported that executives had sold shares before a second-quarter earnings shortfall was announced. Waste Management said it would investigate the sales; later so did the SEC. (By 2001 the company had settled with both the SEC and shareholders.) In the fallout president and COO Rodney Proto who had sold shares before the earnings announcement was fired. Later that year the company tapped Maury Myers CEO of trucking company Yellow Corp. to take over as chairman and CEO.

In 2000 to concentrate on its core business in North America Waste Management sold operations in Europe Asia and South America in a series of transactions that raised about $2.5 billion. The next year the company established a pulp and paper trading group.

Waste Management announced plans in early 2002 to restructure the company by reorganizing its operating areas and cutting its workforce of 57000 by about 3.5%. Also that year the SEC sued six former Waste Management executives charging that they had enriched themselves through accounting fraud between 1992 and 1997.

The company formed a new recycling unit Recycle America Alliance in 2003 after acquiring Milwaukee-based The Peltz Group the largest privately held recycler in the US. The company also acquired 75 complementary collection businesses for about $337 million and divested some operations for about $18 million. That year two former executives of Waste Management Proto and CFO Earl DeFrates agreed to a settlement with the SEC on allegations that they had profited from insider trading in 1999.

In a bid to consolidate its leadership position in the US waste market in 2008 the company made a bid to acquire Republic Services but was rebuffed.

In 2009 the company acquired PharmEcology Associates a national pharmaceutical waste management consulting services firm and Mountain High Medical Disposal Services. In 2010 it added some medical waste assets from MedServe following that company's acquisition by Stericycle. It also acquired a medical waste processing facility and other assets from Milum Textile Services in Phoenix.

In 2010 it invested in Canadian waste-to-biofuels company Enerkem. Further expanding its "green" businesses the company acquired control of Garick LLC a leading maker and distributor of organic lawn and garden products. The deal helped grow Waste Management's organics recycling services business.

In 2011 it bought Access Computer Products a leading provider of cell phone ink and toner cartridge and consumer electronics reverse logistics remarketing and recycling services and acquired three recycling facilities in Maryland and Virginia in a separate deal.

Also that year Waste Management picked up Connecticut-based Oakleaf Global Holdings and its operations for $425 million. The unit manages a North American network of some 2500 operators who provide hauling disposal waste diversion and recycling services.

In 2012 the company removed a management layer in its four geographic groups consolidated and reduced its geographic areas from 22 to 17 and eliminated some 700 positions.

Expanding its recycling portfolio and supporting its efforts to manage 20 million tons of recyclable material in 2013 Waste Management acquired Greenstar LLC from NTR plc for $170 million.

Greenstar manages some 1.5 million tons of material through a dozen material recovery facilities.

That year the company acquired Summit Energy Services and Liquid Logistics two Williston North Dakota-based energy services companies. The acquisitions enhance Waste Management's environmental service offerings to oil and gas industry customers working in the Bakken Shale.

EXECUTIVES

EVP and COO, James E. Trevathan, age 64, $676,885 total compensation
SVP Field Operations, Jeff M. Harris, age 63, $608,846 total compensation
EVP Corporate Operations; President Recycling, Puneet Bhasin, age 54
President and CEO, James C. (Jim) Fish, age 55, $705,996 total compensation
SVP Field Operations, John J. Morris, age 47, $593,462 total compensation
SVP CFO and Treasurer, Devina A. Rankin
Vice President Finance, Brent Bell
Vice President Information Technology, Mark Madsen
Senior Vice President, Don Carpenter
Vice President Innovation And Business Optimization, David Murphy
Vice President Business Development and Sports Marketing, Steve Ness
Vice President Strategic Business Solutions, Paul Foody
Senior Vice President of operations, John Donahue
Vice President Tax, Mark Lockett
Senior Vice President of Operations for Waste Management, Charles Williams
Vice President Information Technology Solutions OCIO, David Lewis
Vice President, Surya Sahoo
National Account Manager, Brian Bierman
Vice President Commercial Lines Underwriting, Mary Fisher
Vice President and Assistant General Counsel, Steven Morgan
Vice President Customer Service, Katy Lydon
Vice President Pricing, Nikolaj Sjoqvist
Vice President, Everett A Bass
Vice President Information technology, Michele Newell
Vice President Market Area, Pittman Alec
Vice President Area, Tim Wells
Assistant Vice President, Don Smith
Vice President Customer Experience, Dianne McSweeney
National Account Manager, Timothy Fraumann
Vice President and Chief Accounting Officer Waste Management, Darren Shade
Vice President Business Development, Dan Grosshauser
Area Vice President, Steve Batchelor
Vice President Commodity Sales, Don Majka
Vice President Business Development, Tom Carroll
Chairman, Bradbury H. (Brad) Anderson, age 66
Assistant Treasurer and Director Investor Relations, Ed Egl
Treasurer, Josh Allen
Auditors: Ernst & Young LLP

LOCATIONS

HQ: Waste Management, Inc. (DE)
1001 Fannin Street, Houston, TX 77002
Phone: 713 512-6200   **Fax:** 713 512-6299
Web: www.wm.com

2016 Sales

	$ mil.	% of total
US & Puerto Rico	12,915	95
Canada	694	5
Total	**13,609**	**100**

PRODUCTS/OPERATIONS

2016 sales

	$ mil.	% of total
Collection	8,802	54
Landfill	3,110	19
Transfer	1,512	9
Recycling	1,221	8
Other	1,601	10
Adjustments	(2637)	-
Total	**13,609**	**100**

Selected Services

Collection
Disposal
Hazardous waste management
Landfill management
Portable sanitation services
Recycling
Transfer stations
Treatment

Selected Mergers and Acquisitions

COMPETITORS

Casella Waste Systems	WCA Waste
Republic Services	Waste Connections
Rumpke	Waste Connections US
Safety-Kleen	

HISTORICAL FINANCIALS
Company Type: Public

Income Statement
FYE: December 31

	REVENUE ($ mil.)	NET INCOME ($ mil.)	NET PROFIT MARGIN	EMPLOYEES
12/17	14,485	1,949	13.5%	42,300
12/16	13,609	1,182	8.7%	41,200
12/15	12,961	753	5.8%	40,600
12/14	13,996	1,298	9.3%	39,800
12/13	13,983	98	0.7%	42,700
Annual Growth	**0.9%**	**111.2%**	**—**	**(0.2%)**

2017 Year-End Financials

Debt ratio: 43.48%
Return on equity: 34.45%
Cash ($ mil.): 22
Current ratio: 0.80
Long-term debt ($ mil.): 8,752

No. of shares (mil.): 433
Dividends
Yield: 0.0%
Payout: 38.5%
Market value ($ mil.): 37,395

	STOCK PRICE ($) FY Close	P/E High/Low	PER SHARE ($) Earnings	Dividends	Book Value
12/17	86.30	19 16	4.41	1.70	13.89
12/16	70.91	27 19	2.65	1.64	12.06
12/15	53.37	33 28	1.65	1.54	11.95
12/14	51.32	18 14	2.79	1.50	12.79
12/13	44.87	220 161	0.21	1.46	12.29
Annual Growth	**17.8%**	**— —**	**114.1%**	**3.9%**	**3.1%**

Waterstone Financial Inc (MD)

Auditors: RSM US LLP

LOCATIONS

HQ: Waterstone Financial Inc (MD)
11200 W. Plank Court, Wauwatosa, WI 53226
Phone: 414 761-1000
Web: www.wsbonline.com

HISTORICAL FINANCIALS
Company Type: Public

Income Statement
FYE: December 31

	ASSETS ($ mil.)	NET INCOME ($ mil.)	INCOME AS % OF ASSETS	EMPLOYEES
12/16	1,790	25	1.4%	895
12/15	1,762	16	0.9%	770
12/14	1,783	12	0.7%	731
12/13	1,947	14	0.8%	849
12/12	1,661	34	2.1%	782
Annual Growth	**1.9%**	**(7.5%)**	**—**	**3.4%**

2016 Year-End Financials

Debt ratio: 4.69%
Return on equity: 6.34%
Cash ($ mil.): 20
Current ratio: —
Long-term debt ($ mil.): —

No. of shares (mil.): 29
Dividends
Yield: 0.0%
Payout: 27.9%
Market value ($ mil.): 542

	STOCK PRICE ($) FY Close	P/E High/Low	PER SHARE ($) Earnings	Dividends	Book Value
12/16	18.40	20 14	0.93	0.26	13.95
12/15	14.10	25 22	0.56	0.20	13.33
12/14	13.15	34 27	0.38	0.15	13.08
12/13	11.10	27 15	0.43	0.00	6.84
12/12	7.80	7 2	1.12	0.00	6.46
Annual Growth	**23.9%**	**— —**	**(4.5%)**	**—**	**21.2%**

Webster Financial Corp (Waterbury, Conn)

Webster Financial is the holding company for Webster Bank which operates about 170 branches in southern New England primarily in Connecticut but also in Massachusetts New York and Rhode Island. The bank provides commercial and retail services such as deposit accounts loans and mortgages and consumer finance as well as government and institutional banking services. It performs asset-based lending through its Webster Business Credit subsidiary and equipment financing through Webster Capital Finance. The company's HSA Bank division offers health savings accounts nationwide. Webster Bank provides brokerage and investment services through an agreement with UVEST a division of LPL Financial.

Geographic Reach

The regional bank's largest market is Connecticut with about 125 branches. Massachusetts has about 20 branches; Rhode Island about 15; and New York about 10. It also operates more than 300 ATMs across New England.

Financial Performance

Overall sales were up 1% in 2012 to $886 million. While interest income and fees for loans and deposit services decreased the bank saw gains in wealth and investment services and mortgage banking activities. In 2012 Webster implemented a strategy of selling a higher percentage of conforming fixed-rate loans with favorable pricing in the secondary markets. Profits also increased 15% in 2012 after the bank was able to reduce both interest and non-interest expenses across the board.

Strategy

As a regional bank Webster has tried to keep up with technological advances and services offered by its larger competitors. In 2012 it finally began offering mobile banking through a smartphone app. That year it also upgraded its ATMs with customized settings touchscreens and speech capabilities.

In 2015 Webster acquired JPMorgan Chase Bank's health savings account (HSA) business. The move involved the migration of about 785000 accounts including an estimated $1.3 billion in deposits and $185 million in other assets under administration. It nearly doubled Webster's HSA Bank division which now has some 1.6 million accounts including more than $4 billion in assets under administration.

EXECUTIVES

Chairman and CEO Webster Financial Corporation and Webster Bank N.A., James C. (Jim) Smith, age 67, $882,435 total compensation
EVP General Counsel and Corporate Secretary Webster Financial Corporation and Webster Bank N.A., Harriet M. Wolfe, age 63
President and COO Webster Business Credit Corporation (WBCC), Warren K. Mino
Regional President Boston Webster Bank N.A., Paul F. Mollica
EVP and Chief Human Resources Officer Webster Financial Corporation and Webster Bank N.A., Bernard M. Garrigues, age 58
EVP and Chief Marketing Officer Webster Financial Corporation and Webster Bank N.A., Dawn C. Morris, age 49
Regional President New Haven Conn. Webster Bank N.A., Jeffrey A. (Jeff) Klaus
President Webster Financial Corporation and Webster Bank N.A., John R. Ciulla, age 51, $363,479 total compensation
EVP and Head of Community Banking, Nitin J. Mhatre, age 46, $358,521 total compensation
EVP and CFO Webster Financial Corporation and Webster Bank N.A., Glenn I. MacInnes, age 55, $453,310 total compensation
EVP and CIO Webster Financial Corporation and Webster Bank N.A., Colin D. Eccles, age 58
EVP Consumer Deposits Investments and Network Management Webster Bank N.A., David D. Miree
EVP and Chief Risk Officer Webster Financial Corporation and Webster Bank N.A., Daniel H. Bley, age 48
EVP and Head of Private Banking Webster Financial Corporation and Webster Bank N.A., Daniel M. (Dan) FitzPatrick, age 58, $300,000 total compensation
EVP Commercial Real Estate, William E. Wrang
EVP Webster Financial Corporation and Webster Bank N.A. and Head of HSA Bank, Charles L. (Chad) Wilkins, age 55
Regional President Metro New York, Abby Parsonnet
Regional President Southern Massachusetts and Rhode Island Webster Bank N.A., Douglas E. (Doug) Scala
Regional President Waterbury Conn. Webster Bank N.A., Michael L. (Mike) O'Connor
Regional President for Pennsylvania Webster Bank N.A., Scott C. Meves
Regional President Hartford Conn. Webster Bank N.A., Timothy D. Bergstrom
EVP Middle Market Banking Webster Bank N.A., Christopher J. (Chris) Motl
Senior Vice President, Sue Murray
Vice President Information Technology, Tom Clark
Vice President Human Resources Technology, Chris Muller
Vice President Small Business Banking, Larry Levitts
Vice President Information Technology Applications, Jay Clark
Vice President Corporate Facilities Operations, Mark Nisbett
Vice President Procurement, Jeff Brownlee
Senior Vice President, Denise Hall
Vice President eBanking, Chris Barlow
Vice President External Communications, Sarah Barr
Vice President Database, Jennifer Zbell
Vice President Finance, Shelly Abdella
Senior Vice President Middle Market Commercial Banking Webster Bank, Stephen Corcoran
Executive Vice President Human Resources Marketing and Communications, Jeffrey Brown
Vice President Commercial Banking, Joe Pelliccia
Vice President Organization Effectiveness, Denise Thomas
Vice President Accounting, Lynn Ryan
Vice President Information Security, Thomas Woodbury
Vice President Human Resources, Laura Chandler
Senior Vice President, Kevin Collins
Executive Vice President Human Resources, Lynn Faraca-Bond
Vice President Continuity Planning, Larry Lovering
Vice Chairman Webster Financial Corporation and Webster Bank N.A., Joseph J. (Joe) Savage, age 64
Auditors: KPMG LLP

LOCATIONS

HQ: Webster Financial Corp (Waterbury, Conn)
145 Bank Street, Waterbury, CT 06702
Phone: 203 578-2202
Web: www.websterbank.com

2016 Bank Branches

	No.
Connecticut	117
Massachusetts	37
Rhode Island	13
New York	8
Total	**175**

PRODUCTS/OPERATIONS

2016 Sales

	$ mil.	% of total
Interest		
Interest and fees on loans and leases	621	57
Taxable interest and dividends on securities	180	17
Non-taxable interest on securities	19	2
Loans held for sale	1	-
Non-interest		
Deposit service fees	140	13
Loan and lease related fees	30	3
Wealth and investment services	29	3
Mortgage banking activities	11	1
Increase in cash surrender value of life insurance policies	14	1
Gain on sale of investment securities net	0	-
Impairment loss on securities recognized in earnings	(0.1)	-
Other income	38	3
Total	**1,086**	**100**

2016 Sales

	% of total
Community Banking	48
Commercial Banking	33
HSA Bank	16
Private Banking	2
Corporate and Reconciling	1
Total	**100**

COMPETITORS

Bank of America	New England Bancshares
Citibank	Patriot National
Citizens Financial	Bancorp
Group	People's United
Fairfield County Bank	Financial
First Connecticut	SBT Bancorp Inc.
Bancorp	SI Financial
JPMorgan Chase	TD Bank USA
KeyCorp	Washington Trust
Liberty Bank	Bancorp

HISTORICAL FINANCIALS

Company Type: Public

Income Statement
FYE: December 31

	ASSETS ($ mil.)	NET INCOME ($ mil.)	INCOME AS % OF ASSETS	EMPLOYEES
12/16	26,072	207	0.8%	3,168
12/15	24,677	206	0.8%	2,946
12/14	22,533	199	0.9%	2,764
12/13	20,853	179	0.9%	2,744
12/12	20,146	173	0.9%	2,826
Annual Growth	**6.7%**	**4.5%**	**—**	**2.9%**

2016 Year-End Financials

Debt ratio: 0.86%	No. of shares (mil.): 91
Return on equity: 8.36%	Dividends
Cash ($ mil.): 220	Yield: 0.0%
Current ratio: —	Payout: 45.3%
Long-term debt ($ mil.): —	Market value ($ mil.): 4,980

	STOCK PRICE ($) FY Close	P/E High/Low	PER SHARE ($) Earnings	Dividends	Book Value
12/16	54.28	25 14	2.16	0.98	27.54
12/15	37.19	19 13	2.15	0.89	26.38
12/14	32.53	16 13	2.08	0.75	25.70
12/13	31.18	16 11	1.86	0.55	24.56
12/12	20.55	13 10	1.86	0.35	24.64
Annual Growth	**27.5%**	**— —**	**3.8%**	**29.4%**	**2.8%**

WEC Energy Group Inc

WEC Energy Group keeps the lights illuminated and the gas fires burning for 4.4 million customers in four upper Midwest states. The utility holding company serves energy through its seven regulated utilities. It is one of the largest natural gas distributors in the US and even provides steam (for heating) to a few hundred customers in Milwaukee WI. It owns 8600 MW of electric generation capacity and thousands of miles of natural gas distribution and electrical transmission lines. The former Wisconsin Energy acquired for $9 billion Integrys Energy in mid-2015 and renamed the combined entity WEC Energy Group.

Operations

WEC Energy Group operates four reportable segments: Wisconsin Illinois Other States and Electric Transmission. Embedded within the segments WEC records the operations and results of its regulated utility companies.

The Wisconsin segment accounts for about 80% of total revenue and includes the electric and natural gas utility operations of Wisconsin Electric (WE) Wisconsin Gas and Wisconsin Public Service Corporation (WPS). The segment also included WE's and WPS's electric and natural gas operations in Michigan until it spun them into the separate Upper Michigan Energy Resources utility in early 2017. The segment generates and transmits electric energy and distributes natural gas to some 3 million customers.

The Illinois segment produces about 15% of WEC revenue and includes the natural gas utility and non-utility operations of The Peoples Gas Light and Coke Company (PGL) and North Shore Gas Company (NSG). PGL and NSG provide energy to Chicago and its northern suburbs. PGL also owns and operates a 38 Bcf natural gas storage facility in central Illinois.

The Other States segment includes the natural gas utility and non-utility operations of Minnesota Energy Resources Corporation (MERC) and Michigan Gas Utilities Corporation (MGU).

WEC holds approximately 60% of the in American Transmission Company LLC which owns maintains monitors and operates electric transmission systems throughout WEC?s service territory. These operations are recorded in WEC?s Electric Transmission segment and contribute between $60 million and $140 million in annual equity earnings.

WEC serves Wisconsin Illinois Michigan and Minnesota with roughly 69000 miles of electric distribution lines and more than 45000 miles of natural gas distribution and transmission lines. The company generates two thirds of its energy needs and purchases the rest through power purchase agreements. Of its owned plants about 50% of energy is sourced from coal 20% from natural gas and 4% from renewables. Most of the purchased power is nuclear sourced.

Geographic Reach

WEC Energy Group has customers throughout Wisconsin though most are in the eastern portion of the state. It serves customers in southern Michigan and in that state?s Upper Peninsula. It also provides energy in and around Chicago and in various portions of Minnesota.

Its power generation plants are located throughout Wisconsin.

Sales and Marketing

The company serves retail customers through its regulated utility operations. It also serves wholesale customers through unregulated sales of electricity. Most of its sales are to retail customers which include residential farming commercial business and industrial clients.

Financial Performance

WEC Energy produced steady financial results in recent years with revenue ranging between $4.1 billion and $5.0 billion and net income gradually climbing. The acquisition of Integrys in 2015 spiked both revenue and net income for that year and the next.

In 2016 revenue reached $7.5 billion up 26% from the prior year. The increase was largely due to the inclusion of Integrys revenue though warmer summer weather triggered additional cooling needs by retail customers.

The 2016 the company achieved $940 million in net income a 47% jump from 2015. The increase was the result of higher revenue (from Integrys) a favorable comparison against 2015?s acquisition costs (about $100 million) and a $50 million boost from WEC?s equity interest in American Transmission Company. Lower fuel costs helped as well but was almost completely offset by a rise in operating expenses.

Cash at the end of 2016 was $37 million $12 million lower than the prior year?s amount. Operating activities provided $2.1 billion mainly from net income and deferred taxes. Investing activities used $1.2 billion mostly for capital improvement projects. Financing activities used $845 million to retire debt repurchase company stock shares and payout shareholder dividends.

Strategy

WEC?s strategy is two-fold with the first tweaking its business mix following the 2015 acquisition of Integrys and the second tending to typical utility company developments such as modernizing its electric grid extending gas operations and addressing the push towards renewable energy sources.

In early 2016 WEC divested components that were either acquired via Integrys or no longer fit into the company?s business mix. It sold the ITF business a provider of compressed natural gas (CNG) fueling services as well as a provider of CNG facility design construction operation and mainte-

nance. It also sold its Milwaukee County (steam) Power Plant and its chilled water generation and distribution assets in early 2016. In 2017 it acquired a natural gas storage facility in Michigan and formed the Upper Michigan Energy Resources utility into which WEC placed its utility operations serving the state?s Upper Peninsula.

WEC?s more typical strategic endeavors stem from its capital expenditure plan. Between 2018 and 2022 the firm plans to invest $11.8 billion across its operations. $2.7 billion is earmarked for its generation assets including buildout of new gas and renewable power plants. A similar amount is targeted for electric distribution operations to expand its transmissions reach and to modernize its grid. Gas delivery will get the largest investment at $5.5 billion including funding to replace 2000 miles of aging natural gas pipeline in and around Chicago.

WEC plans on retiring 1800 MW of coal-sourced generation by 2020 including its Pulliam Power Plant Edgewater 4 facility and Presque Isle Power Plant. It will replace some of that lost power with natural gas-fueled plants in Michigan and Wisconsin and with solar facilities.

Mergers and Acquisitions

In a major move in 2015 Wisconsin Energy acquired rival Integrys Energy in a transaction valued at $9.1 billion. The deal established WEC Energy Group as the energy leader serving the Midwestern US.

EXECUTIVES

Chairman WEC Energy Group Inc. and Wisconsin Electric Power Company, Gale E. Klappa, age 67, $589,043 total compensation

President CEO and Director, Allen L. Leverett, age 51, $941,667 total compensation

EVP General Counsel and Corporate Secretary Wisconsin Energy Corp and We Energies, Susan H. Martin, age 64, $515,000 total compensation

EVP External Affairs, Robert M. (Bert) Garvin, age 50, $416,120 total compensation

EVP and President Michigan Gas Utilities Minnesota Energy Resources Corp. WEC Business Services LLC, J. Patrick Keyes, age 51, $546,400 total compensation

EVP and CFO, Scott J. Lauber, age 51, $351,784 total compensation

President Â– We Energies and Wisconsin Public Service, J. Kevin Fletcher, age 58, $411,345 total compensation

President and CEO Peoples Gas and North Shore Gas, Charles R. Matthews, age 60

President Wispark LLC, Jerold P. Franke

EVP Human Resources and Organizational Effectiveness and Compliance Officer, Joan M. Shafer, age 63

VP and CIO, Molly Mulroy

EVP We Energies and Wisconsin Public Service, Tom Metcalfe, age 49

Vice President, Bill Mastoris

Vice President Chief Administrative Officer, Kristine Rappe

Treasurer, David Hughes

Auditors: Deloitte & Touche LLP

LOCATIONS

HQ: WEC Energy Group Inc
231 West Michigan Street, P.O. Box 1331, Milwaukee, WI 53201
Phone: 414 221-2345 **Fax:** 414 221-2172
Web: www.wisconsinenergy.com

PRODUCTS/OPERATIONS

2016 sales

	$ mil.	% of total
Wisconsin	5,805	78
Illinois	1,242	17
other States	376	5
We Power	24	-
Corporate and others	23	-
Total	**7,472**	**100**

Selected Subsidiaries

American Transmission Company LLC (partial ownership)
Michigan Gas utilities Corporation
Minnesota Energy Resources Corporation
North Shore Gas Company
The Peoples Gas Light and Coke Company
Upper Michigan Energy Resources
W.E. Power LLC (We Power regulated power plant construction)
Wisconsin Electric Power Company (operates as We Energies electric gas and steam utility)
Wisconsin Gas LLC (operates as We Energies gas and water utility)
Wisconsin Public Service Corporation
Wispark LLC (real estate development)

COMPETITORS

AEP	MGE Energy
ALLETE	Minnesota Power
Alliant Energy	SEMCO ENERGY
CMS Energy	Wisconsin Power &
Commonwealth Edison	Light
DTE	Xcel Energy
Dairyland Power	

HISTORICAL FINANCIALS

Company Type: Public

Income Statement

FYE: December 31

	REVENUE ($ mil.)	NET INCOME ($ mil.)	NET PROFIT MARGIN	EMPLOYEES
12/16	7,472	940	12.6%	8,164
12/15	5,926	640	10.8%	8,443
12/14	4,997	588	11.8%	4,248
12/13	4,519	577	12.8%	4,303
12/12	4,246	546	12.9%	4,504
Annual Growth	**15.2%**	**14.5%**	**—**	**16.0%**

2016 Year-End Financials

Debt ratio: 33.78%
Return on equity: 10.63%
Cash ($ mil.): 37
Current ratio: 0.89
Long-term debt ($ mil.): 9,158
No. of shares (mil.): 315
Dividends
Yield: 0.0%
Payout: 66.8%
Market value ($ mil.): 18,511

	STOCK PRICE ($) FY Close	P/E High/Low	PER SHARE ($) Earnings	Dividends	Book Value
12/16	58.65	22 17	2.96	1.98	28.39
12/15	51.31	24 19	2.34	1.74	27.51
12/14	52.74	21 15	2.59	1.56	19.73
12/13	41.34	18 15	2.51	1.45	18.87
12/12	36.85	17 14	2.35	1.20	18.19
Annual Growth	**12.3%**	**— —**	**5.9%**	**13.3%**	**11.8%**

WEGMANS FOOD MARKETS, INC.

One name strikes fear in the hearts of supermarket owners in New York New Jersey Pennsylvania Virginia Maryland and Massachusetts: Wegmans Food Markets. The regional grocery chain owns almost 90 stores but they are hardly typical. Much larger than most supermarkets (up to 140000 sq. ft.) each store offers up to 70000 products and house huge in-store cafes cheese shops with some 300 different varieties sub shops and French-style pastry shops. The company is known for its gourmet cooking classes and an extensive employee-training program. Founded in 1916 Wegmans now boasts revenues of nearly $8 billion and is one of the largest private companies in the US. The grocery chain is owned and run by the family of founder John Wegman.

Geographic Reach

Rochester New York-based Wegmans Food Markets operates more than half (46) of its 88 stores in its home state. Pennsylvania is next with about 17 stores. The rest of its stores are in New Jersey Virginia Maryland and Massachusetts.

Financial Performance

Wegman's addition of new stores in new markets has spurred several consecutive years of sales growth. Indeed Wegman's sales have jumped more than 27% since 2011 from $6.2 billion to $7.9 billion during 2015.

Strategy

Wegmans has been entering new markets in recent years to boost sales. In late 2015 the chain planned to open a new store in Lancaster Pennsylvania as well as two more Wegmans stores out of a handful of existing stores in Massachusetts in Natick and Westwood. During 2014 it entered the Richmond Virginia market with two new stores and opened two more stores in Massachusetts (which it first entered in 2011) in Cherry Hill and Burlington.

The upscale regional grocery chain which aims to deliver a shopping experience more akin to a European open-air market than a traditional supermarket has also benefited from the recovering US economy. Key to Wegmans' success is its competitive pricing mostly on its popular private-label products. The retailer's aggressive private-label strategy includes frequent product updates and innovation. Wegmans recently introduced a line of gluten-free private-label items including pasta and cake mixes.

Wegmans ranked 33rd on the 2015 Supermarket News list of Top 75 Supermarkets based on sales volume. The chain is not only popular with shoppers but also with employees. The company has landed on FORTUNE magazine's list of the "100 Best Companies to Work For" in each of the past 18 years and captured the #7 spot in 2015. It was ranked #1 in 2005.

EXECUTIVES

SVP Store Operations, Jack DePeters
SVP CFO and Treasurer, James (Jim) Leo
President and CEO, Colleen Wegman, age 43
SVP Wine, Nicole Wegman
VP Seafood Sustainability, Carl Salamone
SVP Syracuse Division, Shari Constantine
CIO, David DeLaus
Vice President, Robert Maybee
Vice President Corporate Promotions, Tom Di Nardo

Senior Vice President Merchandising, Marty Gardner
Senior Vice President Division, Mike Keating
Senior Vice President, John A Depeters
Vice President of Dairy Frozen, Ken Cassara
Senior Vice President of Pharmacy, John Carlo
Vice President Asset Protection, Brian Scanlon
Director of Pharmacy Operations, Dan Ferrara
Vice President store Operations Human Resources, Kevin Stickles
Vice President of Finance, Sue Pietropaolo
Vice President of WegmansBrand, Mike Decoly
Vice President of Design Services and Maintenance, Carol Duquette
Vice President, Jim Schaeffer
Director Media Relations, Joe Natale
Senior Vice President, Jim Leo
Vice President, Richard Vanderhorst
VP Human Resources, Gerald Pierce
Pharmacy Manager, Mike Zambuto
Director of Pharmacy and Healthcare, Sherrie Diamond
Director of Pharmacy and Healthcare, Kevin Frantzen
Chairman, Daniel R. (Danny) Wegman
Executive Board Member, Art Pires

LOCATIONS

HQ: WEGMANS FOOD MARKETS, INC.
1500 BROOKS AVE, ROCHESTER, NY 146243589
Phone: 585 328-2550
Web: WWW.ROCWIKI.ORG

2014 Stores

	No.
New York	46
Pennsylvania	17
New Jersey	7
Maryland	7
Virginia	7
Massachusetts	4
Total	**88**

PRODUCTS/OPERATIONS

Selected Products and Operations

Asian foods
Bath and body
Bulk foods
Cheeses
Coffee/cappuccino bar
Cooking classes
Deli
Dry cleaning
European bread bakery
Floral department
Food from around the world
Gift and fruit baskets
Kosher deli
Market café;
Meat service
Nature's Marketplace (organic health and food items)
Organic produce
Pasta Station
Pharmacy
Photo processing and photo enlarging
Photocopies
Pizza Primo
Ready-to-cook meat and seafood
Rotisserie
Rug Doctor carpet cleaner rental
Seafood
Sub sandwiches
Sushi bar
UPS parcel service
Video player and game system rentals
Videos and DVDs
WKids Fun Center
Wokery

COMPETITORS

A&P	Safeway
Albertsons	Saker ShopRites
BJ's Wholesale Club	Stop & Shop
CVS	TOPS Markets
Giant Eagle	Target Corporation
Giant Food Stores	Wal-Mart
Golub	Walgreen
IGA	Wawa Inc.
Rite Aid	Weis Markets

HISTORICAL FINANCIALS

Company Type: Private

Income Statement
FYE: December 26

	REVENUE ($ mil.)	NET INCOME ($ mil.)	NET PROFIT MARGIN	EMPLOYEES
12/15	8,005	0	—	45,000
12/14	7,560	114	1.5%	—
12/10	5,687	93	1.6%	—
12/09	5,193	85	1.6%	—
Annual Growth	7.5%	—	—	—

2015 Year-End Financials

Debt ratio: —
Return on equity: —
Cash ($ mil.): 331   Dividends
Current ratio: 0.40   Yield: —
Long-term debt ($ mil.): —   Payout: —
Market value ($ mil.): —

WellCare Health Plans Inc

WellCare Health Plans provides managed-care administrative services to government-funded health care programs that provide benefits via Medicaid Medicare and various State Children's Health Insurance Programs (SCHIPs). Services include benefits management and claims processing. WellCare Health Plans administers its Medicaid plans under various brands such as Care1st in Arizona Staywell in Florida; WellCare in Georgia Kentucky New York New Jersey and South Carolina; Harmony in Illinois; Missouri Care in Missouri; and 'Ohana in Hawaii. The company's Medicare prescription-drug and Medicare Advantage plans operate primarily under the WellCare brand.Altogether WellCare serves some 3.9 million customers throughout the US.

Operations

WellCare offers a range of health plans for families children and the aged blind and disabled. It also offers prescription drug plans.The company operates through three segments: Medicaid Health Plans Medicare Health Plans and Medicare PDPs.

Medicaid Health Plans is the largest segment bringing in some 65% of total revenue. Its offerings include plans for beneficiaries of Temporary Assistance for Needy Families (TANF) Aged Blind and Disabled (ABD) Supplemental Security Income (SSI) Managed Long-Term Care (MLTC) and other state programs that are not a part of Medicaid. The segment generates revenues primarily from state-paid premiums.

The Medicare Health Plans segment accounts for about 25% of revenues. It offers hospital medical and prescription coverage to eligible customers aged 65 or older or with disabilities. The company contracts with the Centers for Medicare & Medicaid Services (CMS) under the Medicare program to provide a comprehensive array of Part C and Part D benefits to eligible persons. WellCare offers Medicare Advantage plans in about 400 counties across 16 states.

The smallest segment Medicare PDPs (about 5% of revenue) offers standalone Part D coverage. It works with a network of approximately 69000 pharmacies.

WellCare serves some 3.9 million members nationwide. About 2.5 million customers are Medicaid members in six states (including State Children's Health Insurance Programs — SCHIP members) and some 2.1 million of those are recipients of TANF benefits. The company also serves more than 345000 Medicare Advantage members who are largely enrolled in HMO coordinated care plans (CCPs) in 16 states. WellCare also serves about 1 million Medicare prescription members throughout the US.

Geographic Reach

WellCare operates throughout the US. Its largest markets are Florida and Georgia which account for about 25% and 20% of annual membership respectively followed by Kentucky (about 15%).

The company operates Medicaid health plans in Arizona Florida Georgia Hawaii Illinois Kentucky Missouri New Jersey New York and South Carolina. It also offers MA coordinated care plans (CCPs) in certain areas of Arizona Arkansas California Connecticut Florida Georgia Hawaii Illinois Kentucky Louisiana Mississippi New Jersey New York South Carolina Tennessee and Texas.

Sales and Marketing

WellCare contracts with state Medicaid agencies to expand its operations; it also enters new Medicare markets through both organic growth and acquisition efforts.

The company contracts with medical providers to provide services to its members. It also promotes services to consumers through minimal advertising campaigns. WellCare contracts with approximately 407000 health care providers and 69000 pharmacies to provide members with access to necessary services.

Financial Performance

WellCare's revenue has risen over the past five years due to membership growth decreased legal expenses and successfully implemented cost-control efforts. In 2016 revenue rose 3% to $14.2 billion largely because Medicaid Health Plan premiums increased that year. Organic membership growth in New York and Missouri helped boost the company's revenue.

Net income fell in 2013 and 2014 but has been rising since. With the higher revenue net income more than doubled to $242.1 million in 2016. Improvements in operating margins and pharmacy benefit management also contributed to the higher profits. Like revenue operating cash flow has been increasing for the past few years. It rose 5% to $748.3 million in 2016 thanks to the higher net income.

Strategy

WellCare focuses on serving lower income individuals and those who are dually eligible for Medicaid and Medicare. The company also aims to add more members to its Part D prescription plans. Among its key strategies are providing integrated care management (bringing together medical behavioral social and pharmacy programs) and connecting members to community-based resources such as food banks and child care. For example its Georgia subsidiary partnered with behavioral health provider Georgia HOPE to open a behavioral health home in 2017. The company also strives to build regulatory and provider partnerships in each of its local markets.

To maintain growth WellCare works to diversify its sources of revenue through its "bid build and buy" initiatives. Growth through "bidding" and "building" is focused on creation of the marketing network community support and other capabilities required to expand organically into new service areas. In one example of a recent win WellCare began offering Medicaid management services under Nebraska's Medicaid Managed Care program Heritage Health in 2017. Also that year the company expanded its Medicaid value-added benefits in Georgia. Acquiring businesses with important market and/or product positions — the "buy" element — has supplemented its organic growth. The company's "bid build and buy" efforts have resulted in a significant increase in the company's revenues since 2010.

On the tech side WellCare is developing two artificial intelligence platforms to help deliver medical data to providers and patients. They will use company records and user data to determine when patients might be at risk for certain conditions. Its Care Plan customer-facing system should be rolled out nationwide by 2018.

Mergers and Acquisitions

At the beginning of 2017 WellCare acquired Care1st Health Plan Arizona and its One Care unit adding some 115000 Medicaid and Medicare members in Arizona. That deal marked the firm's entrance into another Medicaid state. Later that year the company bought smaller rival Universal American which specializes in providing Medicare Advantage coverage for $600 million. That deal added some 114000 Medicare Advantage members primarily in Texas and New York.

In 2016 WellCare bought certain assets of managed care organization Advicare which serves Medicaid members in South Carolina. That purchase aligned with the firm's strategy of deepening its presence in existing markets.

EXECUTIVES

CEO and Director, Kenneth A. (Ken) Burdick, age 58, $1,000,000 total compensation
SVP and Division President Connecticut Hawaii Illinois Kentucky Missouri New Jersey New York and Nebraska, Dave Reynolds
SVP Medicare and Operations, Michael R. (Mike) Polen, age 37, $440,385 total compensation
SVP and Division President, Gregg MacDonald
EVP and CFO, Andrew L. (Drew) Asher, age 48, $590,385 total compensation
EVP Medicaid, Kelly A. Munson, age 45, $440,385 total compensation
SVP and CIO, Darren Ghanayem, age 47
SVP and Chief Compliance Officer, Michael C. Yount, age 41
SVP and Division President, Stephanie Davis
EVP Clinical Operations and Business Development, Michael R. (Mike) Radu, age 49, $430,000 total compensation
Vice President, Jason Hamilton
Vice President Quality, Bill Hinsdale
Medical Director, Howard Shaps
Market Vice President, Nancy Laux
Vice President Information Technology, Kathleen Bennett
Vice President Human Resources, Michael Wellman
Medical Director, David Sandh
Vice President of Infrastructure, Paul Kohler
Vice President of Finance, Michael Lisman
Medical Director, Brett Darwin
Vice President National Provider Contracting And Relations, Mark Fehring
Vice President and Chief Litigation Counsel, John Richter
Vice President and Chief Audit Executive, David Cure
Senior Vice President and Chief Public Affairs Officer, Rhonda Mims
Senior Vice President Chief human resources officer, Timothy Trodden

Vice President Government Affairs, Craig Hansen
Medical Director, Robert Wilson
Medical Director, Stephen Lazoritz
Medical Director, Amy Tunanidas
Vice President Business Development, Scott Henderson
Chairman, Christian P. Michalik, age 49
Board Member, Paul Weaver
Auditors: DELOITTE & TOUCHE LLP

LOCATIONS

HQ: WellCare Health Plans Inc
8735 Henderson Road, Renaissance One, Tampa, FL 33634
Phone: 813 290-6200
Web: www.wellcare.com

2016 Membership

	% of total
Florida	23
Georgia	16
Kentucky	12
New York	6
Illinois	6
Other states	37
Total	**100**

PRODUCTS/OPERATIONS

2016 Sales

	$ mil.	% of total
Medicaid Health Plans	9,499	67
Medicare Health Plans	3,876	27
Medicare PDPs	845	6
Investments & other	16	-
Total	**14,237**	**100**

COMPETITORS

AMERIGROUP	Health Net
Aetna	HealthSpring
Anthem	Humana
CIGNA	Kaiser Foundation
Centene	Health Plan
Coventry Health Care	Molina Healthcare
Florida Blue	UnitedHealth Group
Health First Health	Universal American
Plans	

HISTORICAL FINANCIALS
Company Type: Public

Income Statement
FYE: December 31

	REVENUE ($ mil.)	NET INCOME ($ mil.)	NET PROFIT MARGIN	EMPLOYEES
12/16	14,237	242	1.7%	7,400
12/15	13,890	118	0.9%	6,900
12/14	12,959	63	0.5%	6,700
12/13	9,527	175	1.8%	5,200
12/12	7,409	184	2.5%	4,460
Annual Growth	**17.7%**	**7.0%**	**—**	**13.5%**

2016 Year-End Financials

Debt ratio: 16.21%	No. of shares (mil.): 44
Return on equity: 12.95%	Dividends
Cash ($ mil.): 3,961	Yield: —
Current ratio: 1.68	Payout: —
Long-term debt ($ mil.): 997	Market value ($ mil.): 6,072

	STOCK PRICE ($) FY Close	P/E High/Low	PER SHARE ($) Earnings	Dividends	Book Value
12/16	137.08	26 13	5.43	0.00	45.16
12/15	78.21	37 27	2.67	0.00	39.18
12/14	82.06	58 39	1.44	0.00	36.34
12/13	70.42	19 11	3.98	0.00	34.68
12/12	48.69	17 11	4.22	0.00	30.62
Annual Growth	**29.5%**	**— —**	**6.5%**	**—**	**10.2%**

Wells Fargo & Co.

Auditors: KPMG LLP

LOCATIONS

HQ: Wells Fargo & Co.
420 Montgomery Street, San Francisco, CA 94163
Phone: 866 878-5865
Web: www.wellsfargo.com

HISTORICAL FINANCIALS

Company Type: Public

Income Statement

	ASSETS ($ mil.)	NET INCOME ($ mil.)	INCOME AS % OF ASSETS	EMPLOYEES
12/16	1,930,115	21,938	1.1%	269,100
12/15	1,787,632	22,894	1.3%	264,700
12/14	1,687,155	23,057	1.4%	264,500
12/13	1,527,015	21,878	1.4%	264,900
12/12	1,422,968	18,897	1.3%	269,200
Annual Growth	7.9%	3.8%	—	(0.0%)

FYE: December 31

2016 Year-End Financials

Debt ratio: 13.22%
Return on equity: 11.15%
Cash ($ mil.): 228,552
Current ratio: —
Long-term debt ($ mil.): —

Dividends
Yield: 0.0%
Payout: 37.9%
Market value ($ mil.): —

	STOCK PRICE ($) FY Close	P/E High/Low	PER SHARE ($) Earnings	Dividends	Book Value
12/16	55.11	14 11	3.99	1.52	39.79
12/15	54.36	14 12	4.12	1.48	37.90
12/14	54.82	13 11	4.10	1.35	35.66
12/13	45.40	12 9	3.89	1.15	32.36
12/12	34.18	11 8	3.36	0.88	29.92
Annual Growth	12.7%	— —	4.4%	14.5%	7.4%

WesBanco Inc

WesBanco wants to be the "BesBanco" for its customers. The holding company owns WesBanco Bank which has about 120 branches in West Virginia Ohio and western Pennsylvania. In addition to providing traditional services such as deposits and loans the bank operates a wealth management department with ten offices in West Virginia and Ohio and some $3 billion of assets under management and custody including the company's proprietary WesMark mutual funds. Other units include brokerage firm WesBanco Securities and multiline insurance provider WesBanco Insurance Services.

Operations

Commercial loans including real estate and operating loans account for more than half of of WesBanco's loan portfolio. Its retail portfolio mainly consists of home equity loans and deposit overdraft limits. The bank usually sells new residential mortgages that it originates into the secondary market. It plans to continue to grow its portfolio of commercial and industrial loans.

Financial Performance

The company's revenue increased in fiscal 2013 compared to the prior fiscal period. WesBanco reported $287.2 million in revenue for fiscal 2013 up from $276.5 in fiscal 2012.

The company's net income also increased in fiscal 2013 compared to the previous year. It reported net income of $63.9 million in fiscal 2013 up from net income of $49.5 million for fiscal 2012.

As another sign of the company's health WesBanco's cash on hand spiked by about $65 million during fiscal 2013 compared to fiscal 2012 levels.

Strategy

WesBanco likes to purchase smaller banks to expand its reach into new geographic markets while bolstering its loan and deposit business. It's acquired more than 50 banks and financial services firms in the past 25 years.

Mergers and Acquisitions

In May 2016 WesBanco Inc. expanded its branch network into "attractive" markets in Kentucky and Southern Indiana after agreeing to buy $1 billion-asset Your Community Bank. WesBanco planned to shrink its asset size to remain below the $10 billion-asset line a point where banks face much higher regulatory scrutiny.

In 2012 the company announced plans to expand in the Pittsburgh area through the acquisition of Fidelity Bancorp. Valued at more than $70 million the deal will bring in about a dozen branches in the city and its northern suburbs.

EXECUTIVES

EVP Treasury and Strategic Planning, Brent E. Richmond, age 54
EVP and Chief Credit Officer, Peter W. Jaworski, age 62, $212,101 total compensation
EVP and CFO, Robert H. Young, age 61, $269,363 total compensation
President and CEO, Todd F. Clossin, age 55, $466,923 total compensation
EVP and Chief Risk & Administrative Officer, Michael L. Perkins
President East Region Wesbanco Bank, Lynn D. Asensio
EVP and Senior Operations Officer, Gregory A. Dugan
EVP Wealth Management, Jonathan D. Dargusch, age 59, $230,270 total compensation
EVP Human Resources Management, Anthony F. Pietranton
EVP and Chief Lending Officer, Jayson M. Zatta
Market President Kanawha Region, David L. Sayre
Vice President, George Spanos
Vice President District Sales Manager, Nick Taylor
Senior Vice President And Cco, David Kaczmarek
Senior Vice President human Resources, Lee Blundon
Vice President, Thomas Phillips
Senior Vice President and Senior Credit Officer, Michael Schwarz
Vice President and Manager Human Resources, Sheri Clarke
Senior Vice President, Howard Bertram
Senior Vice President Chief Compliance Officer, Dave Kaczmarek
Senior Vice President Special Assets, Jodi Pagnanelli
Vice President Of Enterprise Services And Business Services Support, Jan Kees
Senior Vice President, Timothy Grady
Vice President Credit Risk Management, Ann Vucelik
Vice President Community Banker, Tom Timmons
Vice President Commercial Real Estate, Traci Boeing
Vice President, Matt Reed
Assistant Vice President, Bruce Bandi
Vice President, Allen Retton
Vice President, Tom Medovic
Senior Vice President, Anthony Costantino
Assistant Vice President And Manager Payroll And Benefits, Kimberly Griffith

Executive Vice President Human Resources, Tony Pietranton
Assistant Vice President Branch Operations, Beth Bussard
Assistant Vice President Business Development Manager, Lycia Maurits
Assistant Vice President Information Technology Services, W Terrance Naughton
Vice President Of Information Technology, Mike Robbins
Vice President Compliance, Ryan Leszun
Senior Vice President Human Resources, Patricia Lowe
Senior Vice President, Gregory Agresta
Senior Vice President Human Resources, Patty Lowe
Senior Vice President Branch Operation, Roanne Burech
Vice President, Mark Whitt
Vice President Private Banking, Laura Weeks
Banking Center Manager Assistant Vice President, Jodi McKnight
Senior Vice President Senior Lender, Bob Friend
Vice President Business Development Officer, Neal Jackson
VICE PRESIDENT ALM AND PROFITABILITY, Gregory Shirak
Assistant Vice President Information Technology Services, Terry Naughton
Vice President of Commercial Banking, Michael Mistovich
Senior Vice President, Mike Lander
Senior Vice President and Business Banking, Eric Babbert
Banking Center Manager Assistant Vice President, Nicholas Beresh
Senior Vice President Corporate Banking, Charles Wharton
Assistant Vice President Commercial Banking, Scott Rothenbush
Assistant Vice President and Private Banker, Beth Fuller
Assistant Vice President Information Technology, John Busack
Assistant Vice President BCM Business Development, Jason Lucarelli
Vice President Consumer Lending Product Manager, Jeffrey Rice
Assistant Vice President, Dan Baxter
Senior Vice President, Dave Mendenhall
Vice President, Brent Dapper
Assistant Vice President Banking Center Manager, Linda Yon
Vice President District Sales Manager, David Dunn
Vice President Commercial Banking Officer, Craig Kinslow
Vice President and Service Design Manager, Christopher Crossley
VICE PRESIDENT AND COMMERCIAL BANKER, Michael Epperley
SENIOR VICE PRESIDENT AND SENIOR COMMERCIAL BANKER, Michael T Misich
VICE PRESIDENT COMMERCIAL LENDER, Robert E Krzeminski
VICE PRESIDENT SENIOR TRUST OFFICER, Thomas D Barsody
VICE PRESIDENT, Thomas Nigon
VICE PRESIDENT COMMERCIAL LENDING, Kurt C Bevan
ASSISTANT VICE PRESIDENT AND COMMERCIAL BANKER, Benjamin Curtis
SENIOR VICE PRESIDENT, Ed Hensley
VICE PRESIDENT AND TECHNOLOGY SERVICES COORDINATOR, Stephanie Skivington
Vice President, Dave Klick
AVP and BCMBusiness Development WeSBanCO, Michelle Donaldson
AVP Bcm Business Development, Lenee Landry
Chairman, James C. (Jim) Gardill, age 71
Auditors: Ernst & Young LLP

LOCATIONS

HQ: WesBanco Inc
1 Bank Plaza, Wheeling, WV 26003
Phone: 304 234-9000
Web: www.wesbanco.com

PRODUCTS/OPERATIONS

2016 Sales

	$ mil.	% of total
Interest and Dividend Income		
Loans including fees	227	61
Interest and dividends on securities	56	15
Other interest income	2	1
Non-Interest Income		
Trust fees	21	6
Service charges on deposits	18	5
Electronic banking fees	15	4
Net securities brokerage	6	2
Bank-owned life insurance	4	1
Net gains on sales of mortgage loans	2	1
Net securities gains	2	1
Net gain / (loss) on other real estate owned and other assets	0	-
others	9	3
Total	**367**	**100**

Selected Products and Services

Personal Banking
Internet Banking
Checking
Savings
Time Deposits
Debit Cards
Credit Cards
Loans
Mortgage Lending
Other Services
Business
Internet Banking
Checking
Savings
Time Deposits
Credit Cards
Loans
Treasury Management
Insurance Services
Wealth Management

COMPETITORS

1st West Virginia Bancorp	Huntington Bancshares
BB&T	Ohio Valley Banc
Bank of America	PNC Financial
Cheviot Financial	United Bancorp
City Holding	United Bankshares
First Community Bancshares	

HISTORICAL FINANCIALS

Company Type: Public

Income Statement
FYE: December 31

	ASSETS ($ mil.)	NET INCOME ($ mil.)	INCOME AS % OF ASSETS	EMPLOYEES
12/16	9,790	86	0.9%	1,928
12/15	8,470	80	1.0%	1,633
12/14	6,296	69	1.1%	1,448
12/13	6,144	63	1.0%	1,469
12/12	6,078	49	0.8%	1,507
Annual Growth	**12.7%**	**15.0%**	**—**	**6.4%**

2016 Year-End Financials

Debt ratio: 1.67%	No. of shares (mil.): 43
Return on equity: 7.01%	Dividends
Cash ($ mil.): 128	Yield: 0.0%
Current ratio: —	Payout: 44.4%
Long-term debt ($ mil.): —	Market value ($ mil.): 1,892

	STOCK PRICE ($) FY Close	P/E High/Low		PER SHARE ($) Earnings	Dividends	Book Value
12/16	43.06	20	13	2.16	0.96	30.53
12/15	30.02	17	14	2.15	0.92	29.18
12/14	34.80	15	11	2.39	0.88	26.90
12/13	32.00	15	10	2.18	0.78	25.59
12/12	22.22	12	10	1.84	0.70	24.45
Annual Growth	**18.0%**	**—**	**—**	**4.1%**	**8.2%**	**5.7%**

Wesco International, Inc.

When contractors and manufacturers need parts it's WESCO to the rescue. The company distributes electrical products (fuses terminals connectors enclosures circuit breakers transformers switchboards) industrial supplies (tools abrasives filters safety equipment) lighting (lamps fixtures ballasts) wire and conduit materials automation equipment (motors drives logic controllers) and data communication gear (patch panels terminals connectors). WESCO offers more than a million products from some 25000 suppliers with about 75000 customers worldwide. It operates through a dozen subsidiaries. The company generates nearly all of its sales in North America predominantly the US.

Operations

WESCO divides its operations among several businesses. Automation comprises Cascade Controls EESCO RECO and W.R. Controls. Its Data Communications segment is made up of Communications Supply Corporation and TVC Communications while Industrial/Construction operates through Avon Electrical Supplies Brown Wholesale Electric Calvert Wire & Cable Liberty Electrical Supply and Whitehill Lighting and Supplies.

Integrated Supply is composed of Bruckner Supply Company and WESCO Sourcing and Procurement Services; its Industrial/Electrical OEM operations are helped by Carlton-Bates Company Fastec Industrial and J-Mark. Finally its International Operations are run through its main WESCO distribution subsidiary while its Utility segment is made up of Allied Utility Products Hamby Young Herning Enterprises Industrial Electric Supply and KVA Supply.

Geographic Reach

The company operates more than 500 branches across North America and in international markets serviced by its nine distribution centers located in the US Canada and Mexico. It boasts offices in about 15 additional countries. The US accounts for more than 75% of sales while Canada brings in roughly 20%.

Sales and Marketing

WESCO caters to 75000 customers. Sales to electrical contractors range from major industrial commercial and data communication projects to small residential contractors. Utilities and specialty utility contractors include large and rural electric cooperatives and municipal power authorities which maintain transmission distribution lines and power plants.

Commercial institutional and governmental customers include schools hospitals property management firms retailers and government agencies of all types. WESCO sells integrated lighting control and distribution equipment in a single package for multisite specialty retailers restaurant chains and department stores.

Financial Performance

WESCO's revenues have declined the last two years dipping by 2% from $7.52 billion in 2015 to $7.34 billion in 2016. Net income has also experienced a downward trend the last two years falling 51% from $211 million to $102 million during that same time period.

The declines were fueled by a 11% drop in sales from Mexico and a 9% decline in sales from Canada. This was attributed to a decrease in normalized organic sales and a negative impact of foreign exchange rates.

Strategy

WESCO has been building its business through acquisitions and organic growth. As part of this effort the company's working to develop new end markets broaden its product and service offerings expand its geographic footprint and enhance its sales and customer service.

The company is focused on its global account and integrated supply programs to boost its customer base and extend its use of supply services to customers. It targets customers in the fields of construction contracting; education; engineering procurement and construction firms; government; healthcare; and utilities. Among product growth areas WESCO looks to data communications and security systems and to clean tech lighting systems.

Mergers and Acquisitions

In recent years WESCO has been buying up distributors and other firms to extend its reach and capabilities. In 2016 it obtained Atlanta Electrical Distributors an expert in the construction and maintenance repair and operating (MRO) markets operating from five locations in Georgia. With the addition WESCO expanded its presence in this growing Southeastern end market.

In 2015 WESCO acquired Needham an electrical distributor focused on commercial construction and lighting national account markets owning 24 locations in Massachusetts New Hampshire and Vermont. Also in 2015 WESCO picked up Hill Country an electrical distributor focused on the commercial construction market operating from nine locations in Central and South Texas.

HISTORY

WESCO International got its start as a subsidiary of electrical power pioneer Westinghouse Electric Company. George Westinghouse founded the company bearing his name in Pittsburgh in 1886. The company installed the nation's first alternating current power system in Telluride Colorado in 1891. Two years later Westinghouse built the generating system that powered the Chicago World's Fair. The company also was chosen to provide generators for the hydroelectric power station at Niagara Falls.

George Westinghouse was ousted in 1910 after the company was unable to meet its debt obligations. He died four years later at the age of 67. During the next decade the company added the burgeoning radio and appliance markets to its portfolio of electrical distribution and production operations.

In 1922 the firm established Westinghouse Electric Supply Company (WESCO) to distribute power products and appliances. Westinghouse had its share of troubles over the years many of which were caused by ill-advised diversification attempts. These included forays into uranium supply financial services and real estate.

By the 1990s Westinghouse was buried under nearly $10 billion in debt and too busy putting out fires to tend to day-to-day operations properly. Not surprisingly WESCO was caught up in Westinghouse's problems: Sales declined four years in a row and employee turnover was around 25% a year.

Westinghouse embarked on a divestiture program and sold WESCO to investment firm Clayton Dubilier & Rice (CD&R) in 1994 for about $340 million. At the time WESCO had about 250 branch locations. The new owners brought in Roy Haley a veteran insurance and finance executive to turn the ailing business around. Haley tied pay and bonuses to performance and emphasized multisite customers such as contractors and companies with multiple retail industrial or administrative locations. WESCO grew through acquisitions and in 1995 sales reached $2 billion.

By 1996 the company had added 1000 employees; it operated about 300 distribution branches throughout the world. Sales reached $2.6 billion in 1997 as WESCO continued acquiring complementary companies and formed an alliance with Australian mining and steel company BHP (now BHP Billiton). Managers led a $1.1 billion buyout of the company in 1998 increasing their stake in WESCO from 15% to 33%. Costs related to acquisitions and the buyout caused WESCO to post a loss even though 1998 sales passed the $3 billion mark. The company opened sales offices in the UK Singapore and Mexico.

As it geared up for its IPO in 1999 WESCO bought distributors Industrial Electric Supply Company and Statewide Electrical Supply. The company continued to shop during 2000 adding electrical distributors Orton Utility Supply (Tennessee) Control Corporation of America (Virginia) and KVA Supply Company (Colorado and California).

In 2001 WESCO acquired two distributors (Herning Underground Supply and Alliance Utility Products) that supplied contractors who install gas lighting and communication utility infrastructure in Arizona California Utah and Washington.

The Cypress Group the private-equity firm that helped lead the $1.1 billion management buyout in 1998 sold most of its shares in WESCO in 2004 and 2005. Cypress owned nearly half of WESCO prior to those sales.

WESCO acquired fastener distributor Fastec Industrial and electronics distributor Carlton-Bates in 2005. The following year it bought Communications Supply Corporation (CSC) a distributor of low-voltage network infrastructure and industrial wire and cable products for about $525 million in cash.

In 2007 WESCO acquired J-Mark a supplier of building products which strengthened the company's position in the manufactured housing industry. It also acquired the assets of Monti Electric Supply which provides electricity and furnishes lighting. The purchase gave WESCO a broader market position in the reconstruction of the Gulf Coast region. The company sold a 60% stake in LADD which is a distributor of industrial electrical connectors and accessories to Deutsch Engineered Connecting Devices for approximately $75 million. Proceeds were earmarked to purchase shares of WESCO's common stock.

In 2008 WESCO offered to purchase Industrial Distribution Group (IDG) for about $130 million in cash topping a bid for IDG by Platinum Equity.

Roy Haley stepped aside as CEO in 2009 becoming WESCO's executive chairman. SVP/COO John Engel was promoted to president and CEO as a result.

WESCO acquired TVC Communications for about $246 million in late 2010. The deal expanded WESCO's broadband and telecom distribution network in the Americas and its ties to manufacturers.

EXECUTIVES

Vice President, Andrew Bergdoll
Chairman President and CEO, John J. Engel, age 55, $974,519 total compensation
SVP and Chief Human Resources Officer, Kimberly G. Windrow, age 59, $399,615 total compensation
SVP and CFO, David S (Dave) Schulz, age 51, $109,375 total compensation
SVP and General Counsel, Diane E. Lazzaris, age 50, $435,096 total compensation
Vice President Global Sales and Marketing, Kevin Kerby
Vice President Human Resources, Ruth Boyd
Vice President Of Evening Operations, Joseph Astroth
Group Vice President and General Manager, Les Kebler
Vice President Compensation Benefits HRIS, Clarence Dodge
Vice President Of Operations And Supply Chains, Edward Jankowski
Sales Vice President, James Blumhardt
Vice President eCommerce, Dale Kendall
Vice President and Global Chief Information Officer, Rob Minicozzi
Regional Vice President, Mark Giessing
Treasurer, Brian Begg
Auditors: PricewaterhouseCoopers LLP

LOCATIONS

HQ: Wesco International, Inc.
225 West Station Square Drive, Suite 700, Pittsburgh, PA 15219
Phone: 412 454-2200
Web: www.wesco.com

2016 Sales

	$ mil.	% of total
US	5,635	77
Canada	1,394	19
Mexico	62	1
Other countries	243	3
Total	**7,336**	**100**

PRODUCTS/OPERATIONS

2016 Sales

	% of total
Industrial customers	36
Construction	34
Utility	16
Commercial institutional & governmental customers	14
Total	**100**

Selected Services

Collaborative cross-functional cost savings teams;
Consultation on energy-efficient product upgrades
Dedicated on-site support personnel;
Inventory optimization programs including just-in-time delivery and vendor managed inventory;
Safety and product training for customer employee
Technical support for operational and transactional process improvements;

Selected Products

Automation equipment
Ballasts
Boxes
Busways
Cable
Circuit breakers
Connectors
Data communications products
Drives
Electrical products
Fittings
Fixtures
Fuses
Industrial supplies
Light bulbs
Lighting
Lugs
Metallic and nonmetallic conduits
Motor control devices
MRO supplies
Operator interfaces
Panelboards
Patch panels
Premise wiring
Programmable logic controllers
Pushbuttons
Switchboards
Tape
Terminals
Tools
Transformers
Wire
Wire and conduit products

COMPETITORS

Anixter International	HWC
Bearing Distributors	McNaughton-McKay
Border States Electric	Premier Farnell
Consolidated	Rexel Inc.
Electrical	Richardson Electronics
Electro-Wire	SUMMIT Electric Supply
Electrocomponents	Sonepar USA
Graybar Electric	W.W. Grainger

HISTORICAL FINANCIALS

Company Type: Public

Income Statement

FYE: December 31

	REVENUE ($ mil.)	NET INCOME ($ mil.)	NET PROFIT MARGIN	EMPLOYEES
12/16	7,336	101	1.4%	9,000
12/15	7,518	210	2.8%	9,300
12/14	7,889	275	3.5%	9,400
12/13	7,513	276	3.7%	9,200
12/12	6,579	201	3.1%	9,000
Annual Growth	2.8%	(15.8%)	—	0.0%

2016 Year-End Financials

Debt ratio: 30.85%
Return on equity: 5.35%
Cash ($ mil.): 110
Current ratio: 2.42
Long-term debt ($ mil.): 1,363
No. of shares (mil.): 48
Dividends
Yield: —
Payout: —
Market value ($ mil.): 3,235

	STOCK PRICE ($) FY Close	P/E High/Low	PER SHARE ($) Earnings	Dividends	Book Value
12/16	66.55	31 16	2.10	0.00	41.42
12/15	43.68	16 8	4.18	0.00	42.13
12/14	76.21	15 11	5.18	0.00	43.35
12/13	91.07	15 10	5.25	0.00	39.87
12/12	67.43	15 11	3.95	0.00	35.26
Annual Growth	(0.3%)	— —	(14.6%)	—	4.1%

West Bancorporation, Inc.

West Bancorporation is the holding company for West Bank which serves individuals and small to midsized businesses through about a dozen branches mainly in the Des Moines and Iowa City Iowa areas. Founded in 1893 the bank offers checking savings and money market accounts CDs Visa credit cards and trust services. The bank's lending activities primarily consist of commercial mortgages; construction land and land development loans; and business loans such as revolving lines of credit inventory and accounts receivable financing equipment financing and capital expenditure loans to borrowers in Iowa.

Sales and Marketing

West Bank focuses on small to medium-sized businesses in its local markets. The thinking is that smaller local firms want to develop an exclusive relationship with a single bank.

Financial Performance

The company's revenue has been remarkably consistent year-over-year. It reported $61.2 million in annual revenue for fiscal 2013 after claiming $61.7 million in fiscal 2012 and $64.1 million in fiscal 2011.

Net income has also remained very consistent in recent years. The bank reported net income of $16.8 million for fiscal 2013 after clearing $16 million in fiscal 2012 and $15.27 million in fiscal 2011.

The company's net cash on hand has decreased dramatically in recent fiscal years however mostly as a result of property investments.

Strategy

West Bank has slowly but surely been expanding its territory. The company is working on building a new headquarters building and expanding into Minnesota.

EXECUTIVES

EVP; President West Bank, Brad L. Winterbottom, age 61, $275,000 total compensation

EVP CFO and Treasurer, Douglas R. (Doug) Gulling, age 64, $275,000 total compensation

President and CEO, David D. (Dave) Nelson, age 57, $400,000 total compensation

EVP and Chief Risk Officer, Harlee N. Olafson, age 60, $275,000 total compensation

Vice President, Donavon Paulson

Vice President, Nancy Behmer

Senior Vice President, Keith Kurth

Chairman, David R. Milligan

Auditors: RSM US LLP

LOCATIONS

HQ: West Bancorporation, Inc.
1601 22nd Street, West Des Moines, IA 50266
Phone: 515 222-2300
Web: www.westbankstrong.com

PRODUCTS/OPERATIONS

2015 Sales

	$ mil.	% of total
Interest		
Loans including fees	52	77
Taxable investment Securities	4	6
Tax-exempt investment Securities	3	5
Federal funds sold	0	.
Noninterest		
Service charges on deposit accounts	2	4
Debit card usage fees	1	3
Trust services	1	2
Revenue from residential mortgage banking	0	1
Increase in cash value of bank-owned life insurance	0	1
Realized investment securities gains net	0	.
Other income	1	2
Total	**68**	**100**

COMPETITORS

BTC Financial	Regions Financial
Bank of America	U.S. Bancorp
Bank of the West	Wells Fargo
MidWestOne	

HISTORICAL FINANCIALS

Company Type: Public

Income Statement

FYE: December 31

	ASSETS ($ mil.)	NET INCOME ($ mil.)	INCOME AS % OF ASSETS	EMPLOYEES
12/16	1,854	23	1.2%	165
12/15	1,748	21	1.2%	174
12/14	1,615	20	1.2%	178
12/13	1,442	16	1.2%	187
12/12	1,448	16	1.1%	180
Annual Growth	6.4%	9.5%		(2.2%)

2016 Year-End Financials

Debt ratio: 1.38%
Return on equity: 14.45%
Cash ($ mil.): 40
Current ratio: —
Long-term debt ($ mil.): —

No. of shares (mil.): 16
Dividends
Yield: 0.0%
Payout: 47.1%
Market value ($ mil.): 399

	STOCK PRICE ($) FY Close	P/E High/Low	PER SHARE ($) Earnings	Dividends	Book Value
12/16	24.70	17 11	1.42	0.67	10.25
12/15	19.75	15 12	1.35	0.62	9.49
12/14	17.02	14 11	1.25	0.49	8.75
12/13	15.82	16 10	1.02	0.42	7.74
12/12	10.78	13 10	0.92	0.36	7.73
Annual Growth	23.0%	— —	11.5%	16.8%	7.3%

WestAmerica Bancorporation

Annie get your checkbook? Maybe not as wild as Buffalo Bill's West but Westamerica Bancorporation still shoots high with its subsidiary Westamerica Bank. The bank operates almost 100 branches in Northern and Central California. It offers individuals and businesses such standard fare as checking and savings accounts as well as electronic banking trust services and credit cards. It focuses on the banking needs of small businesses; business loans and commercial mortgages together account for more than half of the company's loan portfolio. Westamerica Bank chartered in 1884 also originates construction residential mortgage and consumer loans.

Operations

Westamerica Bancorporation provides a full range of banking services to individual and corporate customers through its subsidiary bank Westamerica Bank.

Westamerica Bank subsidiary Community Banker Services Corporation provides the company and its other subsidiaries with data processing and various support services.

Geographic Reach

The bank has 95 branches and 2 trust offices in 21 Northern and Central California counties. Westamerica owns 33 branch office locations and one administrative facility and leases 70 facilities.

Financial Performance

In 2012 the company had assets of $5 billion deposits of $4.2 billion and shareholders' equity of $560.1 million

Revenues declined by 10% in 2012 due to a drop in loan revenues a decrease in ATM processing fees (due to lower transaction volumes) and loss on sale of securities.

Net income dropped by 8% in 2012 due to lower revenues partially offset by a decline in expenses.

Strategy

Westamerica's conservative lending practices (it avoided the clamor around subprime lending) and operating principles helped it weather the economic recession better than some of its banking peers.

Company Background

However the company's revenues and profits have fallen since 2009 when Westamerica netted a record $125 million. In 2011 net income fell 7% to $88 million (versus the $95 million it made in 2010) partly due to higher expenses as the company absorbed the operations of the recently acquired Sonoma Valley Bank. Revenues also fell 5% to $268 million. The declines were attributed to interest and fee earnings which fell as the company's lending activities slowed down and regulatory changes limited the amount of service charges banks can charge. (However both merchant processing fees and trust fees increased as those businesses grew.)

Over the years Westamerica had grown through acquisitions of other banks. In 2010 it added three branches in northern California when it acquired most of the assets and deposits of the failed Sonoma Valley Bank; the deal included loss-sharing agreements with the FDIC. That deal followed a similar transaction when the bank acquired County Bank after it was seized by regulators. That deal added nearly 40 branches to Westamerica Bank's network most of them in California's Central Valley.

EXECUTIVES

SVP and Controller; SVP Controller and Cashier Westamerica Bank, Dennis R. Hansen, $130,008 total compensation

Chairman President and CEO, David L. Payne, $371,000 total compensation

SVP and CFO, Robert A. Thorson, $149,000 total compensation

SVP Banking Division, David L. Robinson, $150,000 total compensation

SVP Credit Administrator, Russell Rizzardi, $120,960 total compensation

Vice President Risk Management, Marcie Lewis

Vice President Training and Development Manager, Gary Lepiane

Vice President, Jane Jones

Auditors: Crowe Horwath LLP

LOCATIONS

HQ: WestAmerica Bancorporation
1108 Fifth Avenue, San Rafael, CA 94901
Phone: 707 863-6000
Web: www.westamerica.com

PRODUCTS/OPERATIONS

2016 Sales

	$ mil.	% of total
Interest and Fee Income:		
Loans	69	38
Investment securities available for sale	34	19
Investment securities held to maturity	30	17
Noninterest Income:		
Service charges on deposit accounts	20	12
Merchant processing services	6	4
Debit card fees	6	4
Other service fees	2	1
Trust fees	2	1
ATM processing fees	2	1
Financial services commissions	0	.
Other	4	3
Total	**180**	**100**

COMPETITORS

Bank of America	MUFG Americas Holdings
Citigroup	Mechanics Bank
Comerica	U.S. Bancorp
First Republic (CA)	Wells Fargo
JPMorgan Chase	Western Alliance

HISTORICAL FINANCIALS
Company Type: Public

Income Statement
FYE: December 31

	ASSETS ($ mil.)	NET INCOME ($ mil.)	INCOME AS % OF ASSETS	EMPLOYEES
12/16	5,366	58	1.1%	783
12/15	5,168	58	1.1%	813
12/14	5,035	60	1.2%	858
12/13	4,847	67	1.4%	914
12/12	4,952	81	1.6%	935
Annual Growth	2.0%	(7.7%)	—	(4.3%)

2016 Year-End Financials

Debt ratio: —
Return on equity: 10.73%
Cash ($ mil.): 462
Current ratio: —
Long-term debt ($ mil.): —
No. of shares (mil.): 25
Dividends
Yield: 0.0%
Payout: 68.1%
Market value ($ mil.): 1,630

	STOCK PRICE ($) FY Close	P/E High/Low		PER SHARE ($) Earnings	Dividends	Book Value
12/16	62.93	28	18	2.29	1.56	21.67
12/15	46.75	23	18	2.30	1.53	20.85
12/14	49.02	24	19	2.32	1.52	20.45
12/13	56.46	23	17	2.50	1.49	20.48
12/12	42.59	17	14	2.93	1.48	20.58
Annual Growth	10.3%	—	—	(6.0%)	1.3%	1.3%

Western Alliance Bancorporation

Western Alliance Bancorporation and its flagship Western Alliance Bank (WAB) have an alliance with several bank brands in the West operating as the Alliance Bank of Arizona; Bank of Nevada; First Independent Bank (Nevada); as well as Bridge Bank and Torrey Pines Bank which are both located across California. Combined the banks operate nearly 50 branches that provide standard consumer and business deposit and loan products. About half of the Western Alliance's loan portfolio is made up of commercial and industrial loans while another 40% is made up of commercial real estate loans. It also makes land development loans and consumer residential mortgages and other lines of credit.

Operations

Western Alliance focuses on commercial lending. About 46% of the bank's loan portfolio consisted of commercial and industrial loans at the end of 2015 while another 39% was made up of commercial real estate loans. The bank also had construction and land development loans (10% of loan assets) residential mortgages (3%) commercial leases (1%) and consumer loans (less than 1%).

More than 90% of the bank's revenue comes from interest income. About 86% of its total revenue came from loan interest during 2015 while another 9% came from interest or dividends on investment securities. The remainder of its revenue came from service charges and fees (2% of revenue) card income (1%) and other miscellaneous sources.

Geographic Reach

Western Alliance's 40 branches and seven loan offices are spread across Arizona Nevada and California as well as Boston Dallas and Reston Virginia. At the end of 2015 its loan business was concentrated in the Los Angeles San Francisco San Jose Phoenix Tuscon Reno and Las Vegas metropolitan areas.

Sales and Marketing

The bank serves local businesses real estate developers and investors not-for-profit organizations and consumers. It specializes in lending to such customers operating in the healthcare professional services manufacturing and distribution resorts and timeshares technology and startups municipalities and local governments non-profit and renewable energy markets. Some of its clients (as of early 2016) include Cutter Aviation FNF Construction Hollenbeck Palms New American Funding and Signature Healthcare Services.

Western Alliance spent $2.89 million on marketing in 2015 up from $2.30 million and $2.58 million in 2014 and 2013 respectively.

Financial Performance

Western Alliance's annual revenues have risen nearly 70% since 2011 as its loan business has swelled. Meanwhile the bank's annual profits have ballooned more than five-fold as its credit portfolio's credit quality has improved with higher property valuations in the strengthened economy.

The group's revenue jumped 26% to $555 million during 2015 mostly thanks to new loan business more than half of which was obtained from the Bridge Bank acquisition which spurred more interest income for the year. Non-interest income especially service charges and lending-related fees grew by double digits during the year also thanks to the acquisition as well as from more organic deposit business growth.

Strong revenue growth and a continued decline in credit loss provisions in 2015 drove Western Alliance's net income up by 31% to $194 million for the year. The company's operating cash levels climbed 30% to $213 million mostly thanks to the rise in cash earnings.

Strategy

Western Alliance Bancorporation looks to expand its branch network and selectively acquire other banks to boost its loan and deposit business and extend its geographic reach. The bank may also buy other financial services businesses to bolster its line of service offerings.

Mergers and Acquisitions

In June 2015 Western Alliance bought $13 billion-asset Bridge Capital Holdings along with its 48 Bridge Bank branches in California Arizona and Nevada in a deal worth about $425 million. The purchase brought expertise in technology and international banking among other areas and expands Western Alliance's market into Northern California.

EXECUTIVES

EVP and Chief Credit Officer, Robert R. (Bob) McAuslan, age 64
Chairman and CEO, Robert G. Sarver, age 56, $830,000 total compensation
EVP and CFO, Dale M. Gibbons, age 56, $400,000 total compensation
EVP Northern California Administration and President and CEO Bridge Bank division, Daniel P. (Dan) Myers, age 56, $212,885 total compensation
EVP Southern Nevada Administration and CEO Bank of Nevada Division, John Guedry
EVP and CIO, John P. Peckham
EVP California Administration and President Torrey Pines Bank, Gerald A. (Gary) Cady, age 62, $360,000 total compensation
EVP and Chief Risk Officer, Patricia A. Taylor
EVP and General Counsel, Randall S. Theisen
EVP and COO, Jim Haught
EVP Arizona Administration and CEO Alliance Bank of Arizona, Don Garner
Auditors: RSM US LLP

LOCATIONS

HQ: Western Alliance Bancorporation
One E. Washington Street, Suite 1400, Phoenix, AZ 85004
Phone: 602 389-3500
Web: www.westernalliancebancorp.com

PRODUCTS/OPERATIONS

2015 Sales

	% of total
Interest income	
Loans including fees	86
Investment securities	7
Dividends	2
Other	—
Non-interest income	
Service charges and fees	2
Income from bank owned life insurance	1
Card income	1
Other	1
Total	**100**

Selected Services

Business Checking & Savings
Business Loans & Credit
Card Services
International Banking
Personal Banking
Treasury Management

COMPETITORS

Bank of America	PacWest Bancorp
Bank of the West	U.S. Bancorp
Desert Schools FCU	Wells Fargo
First Banks	Westamerica
MUFG Americas Holdings	Zions Bancorporation

HISTORICAL FINANCIALS
Company Type: Public

Income Statement
FYE: December 31

	ASSETS ($ mil.)	NET INCOME ($ mil.)	INCOME AS % OF ASSETS	EMPLOYEES
12/16	17,200	259	1.5%	1,557
12/15	14,275	194	1.4%	1,446
12/14	10,600	147	1.4%	1,131
12/13	9,307	114	1.2%	1,051
12/12	7,622	72	1.0%	982
Annual Growth	22.6%	37.4%	—	12.2%

2016 Year-End Financials

Debt ratio: 2.14%
Return on equity: 14.88%
Cash ($ mil.): 284
Current ratio: —
Long-term debt ($ mil.): —
No. of shares (mil.): 105
Dividends
Yield: —
Payout: —
Market value ($ mil.): 5,118

	STOCK PRICE ($) FY Close	P/E High/Low		PER SHARE ($) Earnings	Dividends	Book Value
12/16	48.71	20	11	2.50	0.00	18.00
12/15	35.86	19	12	2.03	0.00	15.44
12/14	27.80	17	12	1.67	0.00	11.29
12/13	23.86	19	8	1.31	0.00	9.81
12/12	10.53	13	8	0.83	0.00	8.79
Annual Growth	46.7%	—	—	31.7%	—	19.6%

Western Digital Corp

When it comes to data storage Western Digital has drive and more than a splash of flash. The company is one of the largest independent makers of hard-disk drives (HDDs) which record store and recall volumes of data. It is also active in the fast-growing area of solid-state drives (SSDs) which are faster than HDDs. Drives for PCs account for a major portion of Western Digital's sales although the company also makes devices used in servers cloud computing data centers and home entertainment products such as set-top boxes and video game consoles. The company sells to manufacturers and through retailers and distributors. It generates more than half its sales from the Asia/Pacific region.

Operations

Western Digital has combined its subsidiaries WD Technologies and Hitachi Global Storage Technologies (HGST) and 2015 acquisition San-Disk into one reportable segment. The company reports its sales in terms of end markets. The company?s biggest market is for client devices such as PCs smartphone gaming devices and security equipment; they account for about half of its sales. Data center devices account for about 30% of sales and client solutions which are external memory such as USB flash drives and wireless drives generate about 20% of sales.

Geographic Reach

Western Digital?s largest market is Asia (which represents more than half of sales including more than 20% in China). The US is Western Digital's second biggest market accounting for about 20% of revenue. The EMEA region accounts for less 20%.

Western Digital has manufacturing facilities in the US as well as in China Japan Malaysia the Philippines Singapore and Thailand; it has sales offices worldwide.

Sales and Marketing

Western Digital sells to OEMs as well as through distributors and retailers. The OEM customer segment is its largest (two-thirds of revenue) with Hewlett-Packard as a major buyer of storage devices for PCs and servers. Distributors and retailers account for about 20% and 14% of sales respectively.

Financial Performance

Western Digital arrested three years of declining revenue with a big sales boost in 2017 (ended June). The company reported $19 billion in revenue for the year a 47% increase from 2016. The bulk of the added $6.1 billion in revenue came from the sales of NAND-flash products from the SanDisk acquisition of 2015. At the same time Wester Digital had lower revenue from PC and enterprise HDD products.

Along with revenue profit rose at Western Digital in 2017 jumping about 65% from 2016 to $397 million. The revenue gain helped the company weather amortization expense on acquired intangible assets charges related to cost-saving initiatives stock-based compensation and acquisition-related charges.

Cash flow from operating activities rose to $3.4 billion in 2017 from $1.98 billion in 2016 boosted by the rise in net income adjusted for non-cash charges.

Strategy

Buying SanDisk and its flash drive products proved to be a boon for Western Digital. SanDisk products helped drive Western Digital?s revenue and profit higher in 2017 (ended June) and Western Digital looks for increasing returns in the years ahead. SanDisk provided Western Digital with key flash storage technology beefing up Western?s offerings as the market transitions from the traditional hard disk drives to flash.

In a deal that Western Digital could not complete it lost out on buying Toshiba?s chip business after a long-running fight concluded in late 2017. Suffering from a host of financial problems Toshiba put it chip unit up for sale to raise cash. Western Digital of course made a bid but Toshiba sold the unit to a group led by Bain Capital. Western Digital reached a deal with the new owners to continue joint ventures in research and development and manufacturing with the chip unit.

Western Digital continues to develop and release new NAND flash products including the next generation of its 3D NAND technology called BiCS3. The company claimed that it?s the smallest 256 gigabit chip available. The company is devoting more of its 3D NAND manufacturing capacity conversion to BiCS3 allowing it to move more quickly with the newer product. That?s not to say Western Digital is deep-sixing its 2D NAND technology. The company expects to produce for certain markets for some time.

In HDD Western Digital is heeding the market which has driven down prices for part of the HDD market. The company had moderated its production of products at the low end of the 2.5-inch HDD market and the 8TB capacity drive for enterprise market.

Mergers and Acquisitions

Western Digital has long used acquisitions to add new product lines and extend its geographic reach.

In 2017 Western Digital made two deals in short order acquiring UpThere a developer of cloud storage systems and Tegile Systems a maker of flash storage announcing the deals of the same day. UpThere makes apps for storing and accessing date in the cloud and making it available from multiple devices and operating systems. With Tegile Western Digital extends its reach into enterprise data storage. Tegile's IntelliFlash products offer quick access to match Western Digital's dig data programs. Western Digital also gains 1700 new customers from the deal.

In 2015 Western Digital bought SanDisk for $19 billion in cash and stock. SanDisk which had $6.6 billion in annual revenues was a leader in non-volatile memory and helped Western Digital offer a more comprehensive product line. Western Digital also gains a long-term source of NAND products and technology. NAND is a type of flash memory that is used for high-capacity data storage a market growing with the rise of cloud computing big data and analytics.

In another 2015 deal Western Digital acquired Amplidata a developer of object storage software for public and private cloud data centers for about $267 million The acquisition is expected to help the HGST subsidiary to expand into higher value data storage platforms and systems in cloud data centers.

EXECUTIVES

EVP Memory Technology, Siva Sivaram
CTO, Martin Fink, age 52
President and CEO, Stephen D. (Steve) Milligan, age 54, $1,050,000 total compensation
EVP Silicon Operations, Manish Bhatia
President and COO, Michael D. Cordano, age 53, $725,000 total compensation
EVP and CFO, Mark P. Long, age 50, $500,000 total compensation
EVP and Chief Human Resources Officer, Jacqueline M. DeMaria, age 55
EVP Chief Legal Officer and Secretary, Michael C. Ray, age 50, $500,000 total compensation

Senior Vice President Materials, Rubik Babakanian
Vice President Facilities Asia, Shahzad Mahmud
Vice President, Vince Mastropietro
Vice President Gm Of Manufacturing Head Operations, Norm Armour
Vice President of Asia Human Resources, Michael Meston
Executive Vice President Andchief Technology Officer, Steven Campbell
Assisant To Vice President, Carmen Jardon
Vice President Engineering Director Engineering, Gerardo Bertero
Vice President Operations, Dennis Brown
SVP Devices, Mark Grace
SVP and CTO (FIO) VP and Senior Fellow (SNDK)(WDC), Pankaj Mehra
Chairman, Matthew E. (Matt) Massengill, age 56
Auditors: KPMG LLP

LOCATIONS

HQ: Western Digital Corp
5601 Great Oaks Parkway, San Jose, CA 95119
Phone: 408 717-6000
Web: www.westerndigital.com

2017 Sales

	$ mil.	% of total
Asia		
China	4,271	22
Rest of Asia	6,437	34
US	3,882	20
Europe Middle East & Africa	3,276	17
Other	1,277	7
Total	**19,093**	**100**

PRODUCTS/OPERATIONS

2017 Sales by Market

	% of total
Client Devices	50
Data Center Devices and Solutions	29
Client Solutions	21
Total	**100**

COMPETITORS

Apple Inc.	SK Hynix
EMC	SMART Modular
Fujitsu	Technologies
Intel	Samsung Electronics
LaCie	Seagate Technology
Micron Technology	TEAC
Roku	Toshiba

HISTORICAL FINANCIALS

Company Type: Public

Income Statement

FYE: June 30

	REVENUE ($ mil.)	NET INCOME ($ mil.)	NET PROFIT MARGIN	EMPLOYEES
06/17*	19,093	397	2.1%	68,000
07/16	12,994	242	1.9%	72,878
07/15	14,572	1,465	10.1%	76,449
06/14	15,130	1,617	10.7%	84,072
06/13	15,351	980	6.4%	85,777
Annual Growth	**5.6%**	**(20.2%)**	**—**	**(5.6%)**

*Fiscal year change

2017 Year-End Financials

Debt ratio: 44.04%	No. of shares (mil.): 294
Return on equity: 3.53%	Dividends
Cash ($ mil.): 6,354	Yield: 2.2%
Current ratio: 2.55	Payout: 149.2%
Long-term debt ($ mil.): 12,918	Market value ($ mil.): 26,048

STOCK PRICE ($) FY Close	P/E High/Low	PER SHARE ($) Earnings	Dividends	Book Value
06/17* 88.60	68 31	1.34	2.00	38.84
07/16 46.47	86 35	1.00	2.00	39.24
07/15 80.87	18 12	6.18	1.80	40.08
06/14 92.90	14 9	6.68	1.25	37.79
06/13 62.09	16 7	3.98	1.00	33.30
Annual Growth 9.3%	— —	(23.8%)	18.9%	3.9%

*Fiscal year change

Western New England Bancorp Inc

EXECUTIVES

Vice President; Residential Loan Officer, Deborah McCarthy
AVP Residential Lending, Michael Laga
Auditors: Wolf & Company, P.C

LOCATIONS

HQ: Western New England Bancorp Inc
141 Elm Street, Westfield, MA 01086
Phone: 413 568-1911
Web: www.westfieldbank.com

COMPETITORS

Bank of America
Citizens Financial Group
Sovereign Bank
TD Bank USA

HISTORICAL FINANCIALS

Company Type: Public

Income Statement

FYE: December 31

	ASSETS ($ mil.)	NET INCOME ($ mil.)	INCOME AS % OF ASSETS	EMPLOYEES
12/16	2,076	4	0.2%	310
12/15	1,339	5	0.4%	195
12/14	1,320	6	0.5%	200
12/13	1,276	6	0.5%	201
12/12	1,301	6	0.5%	207
Annual Growth	12.4%	(6.2%)	—	10.6%

2016 Year-End Financials

Debt ratio: 6.01%
Return on equity: 2.55%
Cash ($ mil.): 65
Current ratio: —
Long-term debt ($ mil.): —
No. of shares (mil.): 30
Dividends
  Yield: 0.0%
  Payout: 12.5%
Market value ($ mil.): 284

STOCK PRICE ($) FY Close	P/E High/Low	PER SHARE ($) Earnings	Dividends	Book Value
12/16 9.35	38 30	0.24	0.03	7.85
12/15 8.40	25 22	0.33	0.12	7.63
12/14 7.34	23 20	0.34	0.21	7.61
12/13 7.46	23 19	0.34	0.29	7.65
12/12 7.23	33 25	0.26	0.44	8.28
Annual Growth 6.6%	— —	(2.0%)	(48.9%)	(1.3%)

Western Union Co

Though the joy of receiving a singing telegram is mired in the dusty past of yesteryear you may still jump for joy at the receipt of a Western Union money transfer. The company provides in-person and electronic means to swiftly send remittances within and across country borders managing currency exchanges as needed. It achieves this with a global network of some 550000 agent locations in more than 200 countries. While the US is its largest single market most of its revenue originates elsewhere. Western Union agents work out of kiosks located in a variety of businesses including post offices banks and grocery stores.

Operations

Western Union operates three main segments: Consumer-to-Consumer (C2C) Consumer-to-Business (C2B) and Business Solutions.

The C2C provides money transfer services around the world through a network of third-party agents who fulfill transactions in nearly 130 currencies. Roughly 90% of agent locations are outside the US. In 2016 the segment completed nearly 270 million transactions (valued at $80 billion) and accounted for nearly 80% of the company?s revenue. C2C?s top 40 agents generated some 60% of the segment?s revenue in 2016. The segment is experiencing growth in its online money transfers offered through mobile applications and the westernunion.com website.

The C2B segment enables consumers to make recurring or one-time payments to everyday businesses such as utility providers auto finance companies and mortgage servicers. The segment generates 10% of revenue. C2B supports both in-person cash payments as well as online and electronic payments. Much of the revenue comes from the US and the rest is generated primarily through Pago Fácil-branded payments in Argentina.

The Business Solutions segment facilitates payment and foreign exchange solutions typically across borders and between currencies mainly for small and medium businesses. A significant portion of this segment?s revenue is generated outside the US.

Geographic Reach

Colorado-based Western Union has offices in approximately 50 countries with four company-owned and over 400 leased. Its reach is amplified by hundreds of thousands of worldwide agent locations. It?s customers ? primarily consumers ? use the company?s services around the globe.

Western Union?s biggest single market is the US which generates about 30% of revenue.

Sales and Marketing

Payment volumes in the money transfer business correlate with immigration trends general economic conditions and employment levels. The ease of relocation particularly to other countries has given Western Union a consistent and eager customer base of immigrants looking to send money back home.

To ensure its potential customers know from where to initiate a transfer the company markets a global consistent brand. The Western Union name is ubiquitous in the world of consumer remittances having achieved this envied position with an unwavering allegiance to a worldwide branding approach. It markets services to consumers through its vast agent network using promotions advertising and loyalty programs. Call campaigns and trade show presence augment marketing efforts for its C2B services. True for all services is the company?s online branding presence found in its mobile applications and westernunion.com website.

Financial Performance

In 2016 Western Union?s revenue declined 1% to $5.4 billion. The small variance is due primarily to currency exchange fluctuations which if removed from revenue calculations indicate low single-digit upticks in 2016 revenue generation versus the previous two years. Western Union's revenues have remained consistent around the $5.5 billion mark since 2011.

While 2016?s gross profit was in line with previous years an extraordinary charge of $600 million due to regulatory compliance failures pulled net income down to just over $250 million a reduction of 70% against 2015?s $838 million.

In 2016 net cash slipped by nearly $440 million a nearly similar reduction as in 2015. Although several factors contributed to the cash flow swings the company has had a years-long effort of share buybacks and continued dividend issuance to common shareholders which it partially offset by issuing debt but also partly funded through cash from operations.

Strategy

Western Union?s corporate strategy is focused on protecting existing business growing through advancements in digital payment markets and technologies and improving regulatory compliance.

The lifeblood of Western Union?s business is revenue generated from C2C transaction fees and foreign exchange activities. Protecting this segment from new financial technology (FinTech) competitive pressures is a considerable corporate focus. To stay relevant and compete Western Union continues to invest in a digital channels strategy by forming alliances with third parties and offering services via social and mobile networks such as Viber and WeChat. In addition to providing smartphone applications it promotes worldwide use of its westernunion.com website as a transfer payment platform a strategy that has seen transaction growth of over 25% in each of 2015 and 2016.

Given the recent hefty settlements with US government agencies over aiding and abetting wire fraud and failing to implement an effective anti-money laundering program the company is upping its regulatory compliance vigilance. Funding for compliance has increased 200% since 2012. In 2016 the company spent $200 million to address the need and allocated 20% of its workforce to compliance functions. Although financial penalties of $600 million were paid to the government in 2016 for the 2004 ? 2012 activities the settlement agreement includes a government mandate for continued oversight of the company?s compliance in coming years.

EXECUTIVES

Chief Strategy and Product Officer, Elizabeth G. (Libby) Chambers, $535,000 total compensation
EVP Global Operations and Technology and CIO, John D. (David) Thompson, age 50, $540,000 total compensation
President and CEO, Hikmet Ersek, age 56, $1,000,000 total compensation
SVP; President Business Solutions, Kerry Agiasotis
EVP General Counsel and Secretary, John R. Dye, age 57, $500,000 total compensation
EVP and CFO, Rajesh K. (Raj) Agrawal, age 52, $566,500 total compensation
President Global Money Transfer, Odilon Almeida, age 55, $612,000 total compensation
EVP; President Middle East Africa Asia/Pacific Eastern Europe and CIS, Jean Claude Farah, age 46
SVP; General Manager Digital, Khalid Fellahi
EVP and Chief Human Resources Officer, Richard L. Williams, age 51

SVP; **General Manager Digital,** Molly Shea
SVP and Chief Compliance Officer, Jacqueline
  Molnar
Chief Transformation Officer, Scott Coad
Senior Vice President of Investor Relations,
  Michael A Salop
**Executive Vice President and Chief Product and
  Marketing Officer,** Diane Scott
Executive Vice President, David Barnes
Vice President Information Technology, Samba
  Diallo
Vice President, Alfred Nader
Vice President of Marketing, Paul Jost
Vice President, Nicole Zimmermann
Finance Vice President, Brooke Vass
Vice President Digital, Antonio Alvarez
Vice President Aml Compliance, Fabrice Borsello
Vice President Finance, Steve Cornell
Vice President Global Public Affairs, Barbara Span
Vice President of Finance, Andy Barich
Vice President, Michael Hafer
**Vice President Information Technology
  Governance,** Tim Langley-Hawthorne
Vice President of Finance, Ed Trofino
Vice President and Assistant Res, Joel Campbell
**Vice President Records And Information
  Management,** Jim Keyes
**Senior Management (Senior Vice President
  General Manager Director),** Srinivas Surapaneni
National Account Manager Sales, Paul Colombe
**Vice President Global Operations AML
  Compliance,** Kristine Diehl
Vice President Sales, Jeff Zallaps
Vice President Global Compensation, Terry Lodes
Vice President Consumer Segments Usmt, Daniel
  Canning
Vice President Risk And Asset Management, Doug
  Groetken
**Senior Vice President Global Business
  Development,** Marcus Cudina
Vice President Global Social Media, Karen O'Brien
Vice President, Greg Bishop
Vice President, Guy Bhattista
Vice President, Julie Sullivan
Vice President; Controller, Wendi Boykin
Vice President Operations and Site Leader, Daphne
  Brookens
Regional Vice President, Rocco Pilla
Vice President Risk Assessment and Systems,
  Noel Brandt
VICE PRESIDENT, MIKE BROWN
NATIONAL ACCOUNT MANAGER, Matthew
  Kurlapski
Chairman, Jeffrey A. Joerres, age 57
Treasurer, Laston Charriez
Auditors: Ernst & Young LLP

LOCATIONS

HQ: Western Union Co
  12500 East Belford Avenue, Englewood, CO 80112
Phone: 866 405-5012
Web: www.westernunion.com

2016 Sales

	$ mil.	% of total
US	1,672	31
International	3,750	69
Total	**5,422**	**100**

PRODUCTS/OPERATIONS

2016 Sales

	$ mil.	% of total
Transaction fees	3,795	70
Foreign exchange revenue	1,490	27
Commissions & other	137	3
Total	**5,422**	**100**

2016 Sales by Segment

	$ mil.	% of total
Consumer-to-consumer		
Transaction fees	3,123	57
Foreign exchange	1,116	21
Other	64	1
Consumer-to-business		
Transaction fees	596	11
Foreign exchange & other	24	1
Business solutions		
Foreign exchange	352	7
Transaction fees & other	43	0
Other	101	2
Total	**5,422**	**100**

COMPETITORS

American Express	PayPal
Citigroup	Santander Mexico
First Data	Sigue
Global Payments	US Postal Service
MasterCard	Visa Inc
MoneyGram	
International	

HISTORICAL FINANCIALS

Company Type: Public

Income Statement

FYE: December 31

	REVENUE ($ mil.)	NET INCOME ($ mil.)	NET PROFIT MARGIN	EMPLOYEES
12/16	5,422	253	4.7%	10,700
12/15	5,483	837	15.3%	10,000
12/14	5,607	852	15.2%	10,000
12/13	5,542	798	14.4%	10,000
12/12	5,664	1,025	18.1%	9,000
Annual Growth	(1.1%)	(29.5%)	—	4.4%

2016 Year-End Financials

Debt ratio: 29.58%	No. of shares (mil.): 481
Return on equity: 21.89%	Dividends
Cash ($ mil.): 877	Yield: 0.0%
Current ratio: 0.62	Payout: 125.4%
Long-term debt ($ mil.): 2,786	Market value ($ mil.): 10,458

	STOCK PRICE ($) FY Close	P/E High/Low		PER SHARE ($) Earnings	Dividends	Book Value
12/16	21.72	43	32	0.51	0.64	1.87
12/15	17.91	14	10	1.62	0.62	2.80
12/14	17.91	12	9	1.59	0.50	2.49
12/13	17.25	14	9	1.43	0.50	2.01
12/12	13.61	12	7	1.69	0.43	1.64
Annual Growth	12.4%	—	—	(25.9%)	10.8%	3.3%

Westlake Chemical Corp

Money matters and vertically integrated Westlake Chemical turns matter into money. The company produces petrochemicals and plastics such as PVC. Its petrochemicals include ethylene ethyl benzene and styrene which are building blocks in plastics. Its plastics offerings include PVC and polyethylene both of which are common in packaging products and grocery bags. Westlake also produces the chlorine used in PVC as well as caustic soda. Other Westlake operations make PVC products such as pipe (North American Pipe) fencing (Westech Fence) and windows. All in Westlake produces about 40 billion pounds of product each

year and is the third largest producer of both PVC and chlor-alkali in the world. In 2016 Westlake acquired rival Axiall in a $3.8 billion deal. The Chao Group owns more than 70% of Westlake.
Operations
The company operates in two business segments: Olefins and Vinyls.

Westlake's Vinyls segment produces PVC (polyvinyl chloride) VCM (vinyl chlorida monomer) EDC (ethylene dichloride) chlor-alkali (chlorine and caustic soda) and ethylene. The company is the third-largest chlor-alkali producer in the world and can produce 2.3 billion pounds of chlorinated derivative products and 7 billion pounds of VCM each year. Its PVC products are fabricated into automotive sealants cable sheathing pipe window and door profiles fencing and decking and film and sheet products. Caustic soda is used in pup and paper manufacturing organic/inorganic chemicals and neutralization. The segment accounts for around 65% of sales.

The Olefins segment makes and markets polyethylene styrene monomer and various ethylene co-products used in the company's polyethylene styrene and vinyl chloride monomer (VCM) operations. The company's primary ethylene co-products are chemical grade propylene crude butadiene pyrolysis gasoline and hydrogen. Olefins generate around 35% of total sales.
Geographic Reach
Houston-Texas based Westlake has more than 40 manufacturing facilities: 27 are in the US 6 in Canada 5 in Germany and one each in China Taiwan the UK and India. The US accounts for around 70% of total sales while Germany generates around 10% Canada 5% and other countries the remaining 15% or so.

Its olefin activity is clustered around Lake Charles in Louisiana. Westlake's sites in Lake Charles include two OpCo-owned ethylene plants two polyethylene plants and a styrene monomer plant. Lake Charles also has a port terminal for worldwide shipping and is located near rail transport links.

Westlake owns 26 building products plants consisting of 15 PVC pipe plants eight siding trim and mouldings plants two profile plants producing PVC fence decking windows and door profiles and one film and sheet plant. The company's plants are mostly located close to major markets and serve customers throughout the United States Canada and Asia

Sales and Marketing
Westlake's products are sold directly to polyethylene customers (some of the largest producers of film and flexible packaging in the US). It also sells ethylene and ethylene co-products to external customers. The majority of olefins sales are made under long-term agreements.

The company has the capacity to use all of their chlorine internally to produce VCM and EDC most of which in turn is used to produce PVC. It sells substantially all of its caustic soda production to external customers. The majority of its North American-produced PVC is used internally in the production of building products. The remainder of its PVC including the PVC produced at their European facilities is sold to downstream fabricators and the international markets.

No single customer accounts for more than 10% of sales.
Financial Performance
Westlakes's revenue has been trending upwards in recent years. In fiscal 2016 sales increased a further 14% to $5.1 billion largely as a result of the contribution of the acquired Axiall business from August 31. Higher sales volume of PVC resin was partially offset by lower prices for all major products and lower sales volumes for the major

olefins products. Prices fell on average 6.4% due to low crude oil prices.

Net income fell 38% to $398.9 million due to acquisition costs totaling $103.7 million turn-around costs of $155.1 million at the Lake Charles Petro 1 ethylene unit and lost sales due to outages partially offset by a $49.1 million gain on previously held Axiall stock and a lower effective tax rate.

Cash from operations fell 23% to $833.9 million a result of lower income from operations an increase in working capital requirements and an increase in deferred turnaround costs associated with the Lake Charles facility.

Strategy

Westlake's growth strategy focuses on acquisitions new plant construction and internal expansion.

In 2016 the company continued work on its ethylene investments. In its Lake Charles ethylene facility Westlake added 250 million pounds of production capacity and in 2017 began work on increasing ethylene capacity in its Calvert City facility. Additionally Westlake has a 10% stake in a 2.2 billion pound per year ethylene plant in Lake Charles expected to complete in 2019; it will increase its ownership to 50% in the first three years of operations.

Mergers and Acquisitions

In 2016 Westlake acquired Atlanta-based Axiall Corporation a major manufacturer of caustic soda chlorine VCM EDC and PVC resins for $3.8 billion. The acquisition made Westlake the world's third-largest chlor-alkali producer in the world and the second largest PVC producer in the US.

HISTORY

Westlake came into being in 1986 when T.T. Chao bought a polyethylene plant near Lake Charles Louisiana from Occidental Petroleum. Over the years the company has acquired or constructed about 20 more. The founding Chao family took Westlake Chemical public in 2004 with the hope of paying down some of the debt accumulated from those acquisitions

In 2008 a joint venture between Westlake and Chinese chemical company INEOS began producing some 33 million pounds of PVC film each year. Westlake owns 59% of the Suzhou Huasu Plastics.

Westlake made several changes to its PVC production in 2009. Early in the year the company acquired a PVC pipe plant in Janesville Wisconsin and opened its new PVC plant in Yucca Arizona to expand its operations. However to reduce costs Westlake closed its facilities in Bristol Indiana later that year and moved that production to its other PVC operations.

In 2010 Westlake purchased a 50% stake in Cypress Interstate Pipeline LLC from Kinder Morgan Energy Partners. The 104-mile pipeline supplies natural gas liquid feedstocks to Westlake's Lake Charles Louisiana petrochemical complex. The pipeline will continue to be operated by Kinder Morgan under a contract.

Westlake also made a move in 2012 to strengthen its presence in Asia by opening a Singapore office. Its operations there will focus on serving its existing customers and seeking new opportunities for growth in the region.

In early 2012 the company made an all cash offer for Atlanta-based Georgia Gulf one of North America's largest manufacturers of vinyl construction products. However Georgia Gulf rejected the $1.03 billion takeover bid as being financially inadequate and adopted a stockholder rights plan also called a poison pill that allows existing shareholders to buy stock at a discount when a suitor acquires more than 10% of outstanding shares.

Westlake wanted to combine its resin and pipe production with Georgia Gulf's chemicals and vinyl products but later that year withdrew its proposal to buy the company.

The company has expanded capacity to meet growing demand. In 2013 it opened a new chlor-alkali plant in Greismar Louisiana that doubles Westlake's chlor-alkali production capacity. It also beefed up the ethylene capacity at its Lake Charles facility in 2013 (increasing the ethane-based ethylene capacity of the unit and its conversion to 100% ethane feedstock capability). It is also upgrading ethylene production facilities at Calvert City Kentucky.

In 2013 Westlake bought CertainTeed's Pipe and Foundation Group a leading producer of PVC pipe and fittings for municipal water well mining agriculture and irrigation applications for $175 million. It also acquired technologies and intellectual property for the production of a number of specialized products including Certa-Lok restrained joint pipe and Yelomine branded products.

EXECUTIVES

President and CEO, Albert Chao, age 67, $979,667 total compensation

SVP CFO and Treasurer, M. Steven (Steve) Bender, age 60, $520,833 total compensation

VP Manufacturing, Andrew Kenner, age 52, $377,167 total compensation

SVP Vinyls, Robert F. Buesinger, age 60, $406,333 total compensation

SVP Olefins, Lawrence E. (Skip) Teel, age 59

Svp Polyethylene, Mike Mattina

Vice President, Benjamin Ederington

Vice President, David Hubler

Chairman, James Y. Chao, age 69

Auditors: PricewaterhouseCoopers LLP

LOCATIONS

HQ: Westlake Chemical Corp
2801 Post Oak Boulevard, Suite 600, Houston, TX 77056
Phone: 713 960-9111
Web: www.westlake.com

2016 Sales

	$ mil.	% of total
US	3,525	69
Germany	402	8
Canada	317	6
Switzerland	101	2
China	87	2
Italy	84	2
Belgium	50	1
France	50	1
Other countries	457	9
Total	**5,075**	**100**

PRODUCTS/OPERATIONS

2016 Sales

	$ mil.	% of total
Olefins		
Polyethylene	1,462	29
feedstock styrene & other	431	8
Vinyls		
PVC caustic soda & other	2,492	49
Building products	689	14
Total	**5,075**	**100**

Selected Products

Olefins
Ethylene
Polyethylene
Styrene
Vinyls
Caustic soda
Chlorine
PVC

VCM

COMPETITORS

BASF SE	J-M Manufacturing
Chevron Phillips Chemical	LyondellBasell
	Mexichem
Diamond Plastics	NOVA Chemicals
Dow Chemical	Occidental Chemical
ExxonMobil Chemical	Oxy Vinyls
Formosa Plastics	Shell Chemicals
Formosa Plastics USA	Shintech

HISTORICAL FINANCIALS
Company Type: Public

Income Statement

	REVENUE ($ mil.)	NET INCOME ($ mil.)	NET PROFIT MARGIN	EMPLOYEES
12/16	5,075	398	7.9%	8,870
12/15	4,463	646	14.5%	4,225
12/14	4,415	678	15.4%	3,550
12/13	3,759	610	16.2%	2,200
12/12	3,571	385	10.8%	1,895
Annual Growth	**9.2%**	**0.9%**		**47.1%**

FYE: December 31

2016 Year-End Financials

Debt ratio: 35.15%	No. of shares (mil.): 128
Return on equity: 11.72%	Dividends
Cash ($ mil.): 459	Yield: 0.0%
Current ratio: 2.04	Payout: 24.3%
Long-term debt ($ mil.): 3,678	Market value ($ mil.): 7,219

	STOCK PRICE ($) FY Close	P/E High/Low		PER SHARE ($)		
			Earnings	Dividends	Book Value
12/16	55.99	19 13	3.06	0.74	27.33
12/15	54.32	16 10	4.86	0.69	25.08
12/14	61.09	27 11	5.07	0.58	21.91
12/13	122.07	27 17	4.55	0.41	18.14
12/12	79.30	28 14	2.88	2.14	13.99
Annual Growth	**(8.3%)**	— —		**1.6%(23.2%)**	**18.2%**

WestRock Co

Auditors: Ernst & Young LLP

LOCATIONS

HQ: WestRock Co
501 South 5th Street, Richmond, VA 23219-0501
Phone: 804 444-1000
Web: www.westrock.com

HISTORICAL FINANCIALS
Company Type: Public

Income Statement

FYE: September 30

	REVENUE ($ mil.)	NET INCOME ($ mil.)	NET PROFIT MARGIN	EMPLOYEES
09/17	14,859	708	4.8%	44,800
09/16	14,171	(396)	—	39,000
09/15	11,381	507	4.5%	41,400
09/14	9,895	479	4.8%	—
09/13	9,545	727	7.6%	—
Annual Growth	**11.7%**	**(0.7%)**	—	—

Debt ratio: 26.13%	No. of shares (mil.): 254	
Return on equity: 7.06%	Dividends	
Cash ($ mil.): 298	Yield: 0.0%	
Current ratio: 1.49	Payout: 57.7%	
Long-term debt ($ mil.): 5,946	Market value ($ mil.): 14,438	

	STOCK PRICE ($) FY Close	P/E High/Low		PER SHARE ($)		
			Earnings	Dividends	Book Value	
09/17	56.73	21 16	2.77	1.60	40.64
09/16	48.48	— —	(1.54)	1.50	38.76
09/15	51.44	22 17	2.93	0.38	45.34
Annual Growth	2.5%	— —	(1.4%)	43.7%	(2.7%)

Weyerhaeuser Co

Forest products company Weyerhaeuser produces a variety of softwood lumber and other building materials in North America. The company harvests trees for its products through its timberlands division which owns or controls more than 13 million acres of forest in the US and Canada. Exports account for more than 30% of the company's sales. Incorporated in 1900 as Weyerhaeuser Timber Co. the company is classified as a real estate investment trust (REIT). More than 85% of its sales come from the US. The company merged with rival Plum Creek in a deal worth $8.4 billion bringing together the two biggest owners of timberland in the US; shortly after it spun off its cellulose fibers business for $2.2 billion.

HISTORY

Frederick Weyerhaeuser a 24-year-old German immigrant bought his first lumberyard in 1858 in Illinois. He also participated in joint logging ventures in Illinois Minnesota and Wisconsin. In 1900 he and 15 partners bought 900000 timbered acres from the Northern Pacific Railway. The venture was named Weyerhaeuser Timber Company.

During the Depression the business recouped losses in the deflated lumber market by selling wood pulp. Frederick's grandson J. P. "Phil" Weyerhaeuser Jr. took over as CEO in 1933.

Diversification into the production of containerboard (1949) particleboard (1955) paper (1956) and other products led the company to drop "Timber" from its name in 1959. In 1963 Weyerhaeuser went public and opened its first overseas office in Tokyo.

In the 1970s George Weyerhaeuser (Phil's son) diversified further to insulate the company from the forest-product industry's cyclical nature and ended up with a mishmash of businesses and products from private-label disposable diapers to pet supplies.

The eruption of Mount St. Helens in 1980 destroyed 68000 acres of Weyerhaeuser timber. That disaster and the soft US lumber market depressed the company's earnings through 1982. Weyerhaeuser reduced its workforce by 25% during this period.

Under John Creighton (president since 1988 and CEO from 1991 until 1998) Weyerhaeuser refocused on forest products and organized along product lines rather than by geographic region. Less-successful ventures were put up for sale including milk carton hardwood and gypsum board plants. The company took a $497 million pretax charge in 1989 related to the decision to close unprofitable operations. Earnings improved in 1990

but dropped again in 1991 reflecting the recession in the US and plant closures.

In 1992 the company outbid Georgia-Pacific paying $600 million for two pulp mills three sawmills and more than 200000 acres of forest land to boost its market-pulp capacity by 40%. The following year the company sold its disposable-diaper business through a public offering in a new company Paragon Trade Brands. It also sold GNA Corporation to General Electric subsidiary GE Capital.

The federal government in 1995 allowed the company to harvest trees in an area inhabited by the endangered northern spotted owl. The move angered environmental groups. In 1997 Weyerhaeuser began to reorganize its recycling business by selling or closing noncore units. It also purchased a stake in 193000 acres on New Zealand's South Island the company's first overseas investment in more than a decade. In 1998 the company restructured its joint venture with Nippon Paper with Weyerhaeuser decreasing its stake in North Pacific Paper Company from 80% to 50% and closed a lumber mill in Canada. Also that year Steve Rogel a veteran from competitor Willamette succeeded Creighton as CEO and became the first outsider to head Weyerhaeuser.

In 1999 Weyerhaeuser paid $2.5 billion for Canada's MacMillan Bloedel and early in 2000 it acquired TJ International 51% owner of leading engineered lumber products company Trus Joist MacMillan (Weyerhaeuser already owned the other 49%). Also in 2000 Weyerhaeuser purchased two sawmills and a 70% stake in lumber distributor Pine Solutions from Australia-based CSR Limited. Weyerhaeuser sold its Marshfield Door architectural wood door business and closed some of its manufacturing operations to consolidate its business.

After a protracted courtship in March 2002 Weyerhaeuser acquired Oregon-based Willamette Industries in a $6.1 billion cash deal. The company closed three North American plants (in Colorado Louisiana and Oregon) later that year. In October the company closed a Canadian containerboard mill cutting 140 jobs in the process. At the close of the year Weyerhaeuser sold approximately 115000 acres of timberlands in western Washington to Boston-based Hancock Timber Resource Group (international timber investment and management) for about $211 million to aid in paying down its debt associated with the Willamette acquisition.

On the heels of the deals for MacMillan Bloedel Trus Joist MacMillan and Willamette Weyerhaeuser moved to pay down debt. It sold more than 320000 acres of the timberland (in the Carolinas and Tennessee) that it acquired with the Willamette purchase. Before the end of 2003 Fountain Investments had acquired about 168000 acres of the west-central Tennessee acreage and Forest Investment Associates purchased about 160000 acres of western North Carolina and South Carolina timberlands. Weyerhaeuser gained about $140 million in after-tax proceeds from the latter sale.

Also in 2003 Weyerhaeuser sold its Nipigon Multiply hardwood plywood underlayment operation in Ontario Canada to Columbia Forest Products. Late in the year the company closed its fine-paper operations in Longview Washington (eliminating 119 jobs there). Altogether Weyerhaeuser closed 12 facilities and sold about 444000 acres of non-strategic timberlands in 2003 in keeping with its plan to reduce company debt and increase productivity.

The company closed its Grande Cache Alberta sawmill in 2004 (affecting more than 150 jobs there) and sold its oriented strand board (OSB) mill in Slave Lake Alberta to Tolko Industries for

about $43 million. Also in 2004 Weyerhaeuser sold roughly 270000 acres of timberlands in central Georgia for about $400 million to investment and property firms in Georgia and South Carolina.

Also in 2004 subsidiary Weyerhaeuser Brasil Participa § μes acquired two-thirds ownership in Brazil-based Aracruz Produtos de Madeira (APM) a subsidiary of Aracruz Cellulose to produce lumber made from a eucalyptus hybrid for use in furniture flooring cabinetry and other applications. Aracruz Cellulose holds the remaining third ownership in the joint venture. Also that year Weyerhaeuser changed the name of its pulp business to Weyerhaeuser Cellulose Fibers to reinforce its focus on developing unique or specialized applications for cellulose fibers.

Weyerhaeuser agreed early in 2005 to sell five Canadian sawmills two finishing plants 635000 acres of timber and some government land-cutting rights to Brascan for $970 million. It had acquired the timber and sawmill assets when it bought MacMillan Bloedel in 1999.

The company's debt reduction strategy continued in 2004. Weyerhaeuser sold roughly 270000 acres of its timberlands in Georgia and several mills in the US and Canada. The sale of the assets helped the company more than quadruple net earnings for 2004: $1.3 billion its best result of the decade. It used the proceeds to reduce debt by some $730 million. In the meantime Weyerhaeuser reported that it wrung out the $300 million in expected Willamette-related synergies in half the time predicted.

Weyerhaeuser continued to streamline and focus on its softwood lumber business in 2005 selling $970 million in assets (five sawmills two finishing plants 635000 acres and timber rights) to Brascan. Weyerhaeuser also closed a Saskatchewan pulp and paper mill in 2006 cutting 690 jobs; not long afterward amid weak profits it announced multiple plant closures and sales including another pulp mill another sawmill several corrugated plants and a paper bag plant.

In 2007 Weyerhaeuser merged its fine paper business with Domtar. According to the terms of the $3.3 billion deal Weyerhaeuser shareholders got a 55% stake in the renamed company Domtar Corporation. Weyerhaeuser controls the board and several Weyerhaeuser executives manage the company.

The company sold its Trus Joist commercial business including four manufacturing plants to Atlas Holdings in 2009. Also that year Weyerhaeuser announced it was closing its noncore trucking division. Other divestitures in 2009 included non-strategic timberland in Oregon (representing about 10% of its holdings in the Pacific Northwest) in an effort to focus on Douglas fir production in that region.

Weyerhaeuser converted to a real estate investment trust (REIT) in 2010. The status allows the company to pay less in taxes and pay its shareholders larger dividends. Weyerhaeuser folded its timberland operations into the REIT while its real estate wood products and cellulose fibers units operate under a taxable REIT subsidiary.

EXECUTIVES

President CEO and Director, Doyle R. Simons, age 53, $1,000,000 total compensation
SVP Real Estate Energy and Natural Resources, James A. (Jim) Kilberg, age 60, $428,778 total compensation
SVP Timberlands, Rhonda C. Hunter, age 54, $560,000 total compensation
SVP Wood Products, Adrian M. Blocker, age 60, $560,000 total compensation

SVP and CFO, Russell S. Hagen, age 51, $434,201 total compensation
SVP Human Resources and Information Technology, Denise M. Merle, age 53
Chairman, Rick R. Holley, age 65
Auditors: KPMG LLP

LOCATIONS

HQ: Weyerhaeuser Co
220 Occidental Avenue South, Seattle, WA 98104-7800
Phone: 206 539-3000
Web: www.weyerhaeuser.com

2016 Sales

	% of total
US	86
Japan	6
Canada	5
China	2
Korea	0
South America	0
Europe	0
Other foreign countries	1
Total	**100**

PRODUCTS/OPERATIONS

2016 Sales

	$ mil.	% of total
Wood Products	4,334	68
Timberlands	1,805	28
Real Estate & ENR	226	4
Total	**6,365**	**100**

Selected Products and Services

Wood and Building Products
　Engineered lumber products
　Flooring
　Lumber (softwood)
　Oriented Strand Board
　Plywood
　Structural panels
　Veneer
Real Estate and Related Assets
　Master-planned communities
　Multifamily homes
　Residential lots
　Single-family homes
Timberlands
　Chips
　Logs
　Mineral resources
　Seedlings
　Weyerhaeser Select Douglas Fir seed
Other
　Recycling
　Transportation

COMPETITORS

Canfor	Potlatch
Cascades Boxboard	Pratt Industries USA
ENCE Energia y	Rayonier
Celulosa SA	Resolute Forest
Georgia-Pacific	Products
Indiana Veneers	Sierra Pacific
Louisiana-Pacific	Industries
McFarland Cascade	Smurfit Kappa
Mendocino Redwood	Stora Enso
Company	Tembec
Norbord	Tenon
Packaging Corp. of	UPM-Kymmene
America	West Fraser Timber

Income Statement
FYE: December 31

	REVENUE ($ mil.)	NET INCOME ($ mil.)	NET PROFIT MARGIN	EMPLOYEES
12/17	7,196	582	8.1%	9,300
12/16	6,365	1,027	16.1%	10,400
12/15	7,082	506	7.1%	12,600
12/14	7,403	1,826	24.7%	12,800
12/13	8,529	563	6.6%	13,700
Annual Growth	**(4.2%)**	**0.8%**	**—**	**(9.2%)**

2017 Year-End Financials

Debt ratio: 36.01%
Return on equity: 6.44%
Cash ($ mil.): 824
Current ratio: 1.47
Long-term debt ($ mil.): 6,232

No. of shares (mil.): 755
Dividends
　Yield: 0.0%
　Payout: 162.3%
Market value ($ mil.): 26,629

	STOCK PRICE ($) FY Close	P/E High/Low		PER SHARE ($) Earnings	Dividends	Book Value
12/17	35.26	47	39	0.77	1.25	11.78
12/16	30.09	24	16	1.39	1.24	12.26
12/15	29.98	41	30	0.89	1.20	9.54
12/14	35.89	11	9	3.18	1.02	10.11
12/13	31.57	34	28	0.95	0.81	11.64
Annual Growth	**2.8%**		**—**	**— (5.1%)**	**11.5%**	**0.3%**

Whirlpool Corp

With brand names recognized by just about anyone who has ever separated dark colors from light Whirlpool is one of the world's top home appliance makers. It specializes in laundry appliances refrigerators and freezers cooking appliances dishwashers and compressors. They're sold under a bevy of brand names including Whirlpool Amana KitchenAid Maytag Jenn-Air and Roper. The company markets and distributes these major home appliances in North America Latin America EMEA (Europe the Middle East and Africa) and Asia. It has manufacturing operations in more than a dozen countries. Major customers include retailers Lowe's Home Depot Sears and Best Buy.

HISTORY

Brothers Fred and Lou Upton and their uncle Emory Upton founded the Upton Machine Company manufacturer of electric motor-driven washing machines in 1911 in St. Joseph Michigan. Sears Roebuck and Co. began buying their products five years later and by 1925 the company was supplying all of Sears' washers. The Uptons combined their company with the Nineteen Hundred Washer Company in 1929 to form the Nineteen Hundred Corporation the world's largest washing machine company.

Sears and Nineteen Hundred prospered during the Great Depression and during WWII Nineteen Hundred's factories produced war materials. In 1948 it began selling its first automatic washing machine (introduced a year earlier) under the Whirlpool brand. In 1950 the company changed its name to Whirlpool following the success of the product and introduced its first automatic dryer.

During the 1950s and 1960s Whirlpool became a full-line appliance manufacturer while continuing as Sears' principal Kenmore appliance supplier. In 1955 the company bought Seeger Refrigerator

Company and the stove and air-conditioning interests of RCA. Three years later it made its first investment in Multibras Eletrodom ©sticos an appliance maker in Brazil. (It has increased that investment over the years.) Other purchases included the gas refrigeration and ice-maker manufacturing facilities of Servel (1958); a majority interest in Heil-Quaker makers of central heaters and space heaters (1964); Sears' major television set supplier Warwick Electronics (1966); and 33% of Canadian appliance maker John Inglis Company (1969). It made a deal with Sony in 1973 for the distribution of Whirlpool-brand products in Japan. Whirlpool sold its TV manufacturing business to SANYO of Japan three years later.

Between 1981 and 1991 despite a static US market Whirlpool's sales tripled to almost $6.6 billion. In 1986 the firm bought top-end appliance manufacturer KitchenAid (from Dart and Kraft) and 65% of Italian cooling compressor manufacturer Aspera. Also that year it sold its Heil-Quaker central heating business. David Whitwam was appointed CEO in 1987. Whirlpool took over total ownership of Inglis in 1990.

The company formed Whirlpool Europe a joint venture with Philips Electronics in 1989; in 1991 it bought out Philips. Two years later Whirlpool took control of appliance marketer SAGAD of Argentina and entered a joint venture with Slovakia's Tatramat (which it bought out in 1994).

Whirlpool acquired control of Kelvinator of India in 1994 and formed a joint venture in China with Shenzhen Petrochemical Holdings in 1995 to produce air conditioners. The following year Whirlpool merged its Whirlpool Washing Machines and Kelvinator of India companies to form Whirlpool of India. The company's European division plunged into the red when competition and a recession kept consumers away from its higher-priced appliances.

In 1997 Whirlpool initiated a restructuring (due to losses from its foreign operations) that included plant closures and substantial layoffs (as much as 10% of its workforce). The next year Whirlpool sold its appliance financing subsidiary to Transamerica. The company also began using a new more efficient product development model in 1998 similar to one used in the auto industry. In 2000 Whirlpool launched the Cielo Bath line of jetted tubs and in 2001 it introduced the Calypso dishwasher and the Duet washer and dryer.

Another global restructuring plan swept through the company in 2000 resulting in significant pretax charges ($373 million incurred in 2001 and 2002) and the elimination of about 6000 employees by October 2003.

In February 2002 Whirlpool bought the remaining 51% of Vitromatic it didn't already own. (Vitromatic — the second-largest appliance manufacturer in Mexico — is now called Whirlpool Mexico.) In March the company purchased 95% of Polar Poland's second-largest appliance maker.

Whirlpool introduced Gladiator GarageWorks (modular storage systems for the garage) and Polara (the first electric range with cooking and refrigeration capabilities) in 2002.

Whirlpool acquired Maytag in early 2006 for about $1.9 billion. The deal added several top brands to its already bulging portfolio including Admiral Amana Jenn-Air Magic Chef and of course the eponymous Maytag. Once the dust settled Whirlpool sold several businesses including Dixie-Narco the Amana commercial business its Hoover unit to Techtronic Industries and its Jade unit to Middleby Corporation. Buying Maytag also spurred Whirlpool to streamline operations and purge staff. In 2006 it laid off some 4500 employees consolidated duplicate functions related to administration and manufacturing and shuttered some offices including a Maytag research and development center based in Newton Illinois. Whirlpool shuttered May-tag's Iowa-based administrative offices and moved them to Michigan and other locations. The company cut 700 jobs at several Tennessee plants the following year.

In 2007 Whirlpool acquired a minority stake in Elica Group in its effort to extend its reach into the global air ventilation market.

The company formed a 50-50 joint venture in 2008 with China's Hisense-Kelon Electrical Holdings to make and sell home appliances there.

In June 2010 Whirlpool closed its refrigerator factory in Evansville Indiana; some 1100 US jobs were lost as a result of the move.

EXECUTIVES

Executive Vice President and CFO, Roy W Templin
Vice President, David Binkley
Vice President of Corporate Counsel, Daniel Hopp
Vice President and General Manager, John Alexander
Vice President, Henry Marcy
Vice President Supply Chain North American Region, Brian Hancock
Executive Vice President and President of Whirlpool Europe Middle East and Africa, Esther Galindo
CEO and Director, Marc R. Bitzer, age 52, $1,000,000 total compensation
EVP Global Product Organization, David T. (Dave) Szczupak, age 61, $746,667 total compensation
EVP and President of Whirlpool Europe Middle East and Africa (EMEA), Esther Berrozpe Galindo, age 47, $659,041 total compensation
EVP and President Latin America, Jo o Carlos Brega, age 53, $498,901 total compensation
President Whirlpool U.S. Operations, Joseph T. Liotine, age 44
EVP and CFO, James W. (Jim) Peters, age 47, $456,667 total compensation
President Whirlpool Asia, Shengpo (Samuel) Wu
Vice President Operations, Tom Egan
Corporate Vice President and Treasurer, Blair Clark
Senior Vice President Risk Management Stephens Insurance Advisors, Andrew Batson
Vice President Global Consumer Design, Patrick Schiavone
National Sales Manager, Michele Garrett
Assistant Vice President Networking Security, Carrick Jay
Vice President of Human Resources, Michael Reusswig
Vice President Manager Director, Melissa Little
Senior Manager Government Relations, Luke Harms
Vice President of Marketing, Gary Power
Senior Vice President of Development, Marek Kaszuba
Vice President Product Marketing North America, Ludovic Beaufils
National Account Manager, Chris Ridout
Vice President of Human Resour, Sarthak Raychaudhuri
Vice President of Sales and Marketing, Vipul Sabharwal
Vice President Finance Pricing And Promotions, Thomas Drews
Vice President and of General Manager of Emerging Categories, Timothy Kee
Vice President Human Resources Global Pr, Tomas Linden
Vice President Of Finance, Tom Fowler
Vice President Information Services, Nancy Berendsen
Vice President Taxes, Matthew Nochowitz
VICE PRESIDENT WHIRLPOOL BRAND GROUP, Roberto Ronchi
National Sales Manager, Robert Schneider
National Sales Manager, Erin Brown

National Sales Manager RV MH Marine, Drew Radtke
Vice President, Aaron Spira
Vice President Product Development, David Klein
National Sales Manager, Jonathan Hodges
Vice President of Operations, Tim White
Corporate Vice President Strategic Competency Creation, Nancy Tennant
VP Innovation and Whirlpool University, Nancy Tennet
Information Technology Management: Executive Vice President Senior Vice President, Mrutyunjaya Rao
National Sales Manager, Brittany Birdsall
Vice President and President of North Asia, Ian Lee
Corporate Vice President and Chief Information Officer, Michael Heim
Vice President Human Resources, Tiffany Voglewede
Division Vice President, Kenny D Thompson
Vice President Global Application Development, James Shrimp
Vice President Global Engineering, Inara Shields
Vice President Quality, J D Rapp
Vice President Global Product Development Food Stream Solutions, Hank Marcy
Vice President Sales, Tamal Saha
Vice President Human Resources, Adriano Mureddu
Vice President, Robert Thompson
Vice President Quality, Jd Rapp
Corporate Vice President Finance Project Management Office, Ted A Dosch
Vice President Director of Facilities, Bryan Babel
Vice President Supply Chain, Al Holiday
Vice President of Public Relations, Douglas Horstman
Vice President Marketing, Reuben Slone
Vice President and General Manager, Carel Czanderna
VICE PRESIDENT, ALEJANDRO QUIROZ
Operations Vice President, Tom Wright
Government Relations, Sean Southard
National Sales Manager, Allen Prough
Chairman, Jeff M. Fettig, age 60
Treasurer Emea, Peter Davidsson
Board of Directors, John Liu
Auditors: Ernst & Young LLP

LOCATIONS

HQ: Whirlpool Corp
2000 North M-63, Benton Harbor, MI 49022-2692
Phone: 269 923-5000
Web: www.whirlpoolcorp.com

2016 Sales

	$ mil.	% of total
North America	11,147	53
Europe the Middle East & Africa	5,148	25
Latin America	3,191	15
Asia	1,424	7
Other/eliminations (192) —		
Total	**20,718**	**100**

2016 Sales

	$ mil.	% of total
U.S	9,901	48
Brazil	1,895	9
China	945	5
All other countries	7,977	38
Total	**20,718**	**100**

PRODUCTS/OPERATIONS

2016 Sales

	% of total
Laundry Appliances	28
Refrigerators & Freezers	28
Cooking Appliances	18
Other	26
Total	**100**

COMPETITORS

BSH Bosch und Siemens Hausger␣te	Haier Group
Candy Group	Hitachi
Daewoo Electronics	LG Electronics
Electrolux	Panasonic Corp
Electrolux Home Appliances China	SANYO Samsung Electronics America
Fisher & Paykel Appliances Holdings	Sears Holdings Sharp Corp.
Gree Electrical Appliances	Sub-Zero Viking Range
GuangDong Midea	

HISTORICAL FINANCIALS

Company Type: Public

Income Statement

FYE: December 31

	REVENUE ($ mil.)	NET INCOME ($ mil.)	NET PROFIT MARGIN	EMPLOYEES
12/17	21,253	350	1.6%	92,000
12/16	20,718	888	4.3%	93,000
12/15	20,891	783	3.7%	97,000
12/14	19,872	650	3.3%	100,000
12/13	18,769	827	4.4%	69,000
Annual Growth	**3.2%**	**(19.3%)**	**—**	**7.5%**

2017 Year-End Financials

Debt ratio: 26.04%	No. of shares (mil.): 71
Return on equity: 7.80%	Dividends
Cash ($ mil.): 1,196	Yield: 0.0%
Current ratio: 0.93	Payout: 91.4%
Long-term debt ($ mil.): 4,392	Market value ($ mil.): 11,973

	STOCK PRICE ($) FY Close	P/E High/Low		PER SHARE ($) Earnings	Dividends	Book Value
12/17	168.64	41	34	4.70	4.30	59.13
12/16	181.77	16	11	11.50	3.90	64.10
12/15	146.87	22	14	9.83	3.45	61.42
12/14	193.74	23	15	8.17	2.88	62.66
12/13	156.86	15	10	10.24	2.38	63.60
Annual Growth	**1.8%**	**—**	**—**	**(17.7%)**	**16.0%**	**(1.8%)**

Williams Cos Inc (The)

Auditors: Ernst & Young LLP

LOCATIONS

HQ: Williams Cos Inc (The)
One Williams Center, Tulsa, OK 74172-0172
Phone: 918 573-2000
Web: www.williams.com

HISTORICAL FINANCIALS

Company Type: Public

Income Statement

FYE: December 31

	REVENUE ($ mil.)	NET INCOME ($ mil.)	NET PROFIT MARGIN	EMPLOYEES
12/16	7,499	(424)	—	5,604
12/15	7,360	(571)	—	6,578
12/14	7,637	2,114	27.7%	6,742
12/13	6,860	430	6.3%	4,909
12/12	7,486	859	11.5%	4,639
Annual Growth	**0.0%**	**—**	**—**	**4.8%**

Debt ratio: 49.98%   No. of shares (mil.): 750
Return on equity: (-7.84%)   Dividends
Cash ($ mil.): 170   Yield: 0.0%
Current ratio: 0.50   Payout: —
Long-term debt ($ mil.): 22,624   Market value ($ mil.): 23,355

	STOCK PRICE ($) FY Close	P/E High/Low	PER SHARE ($) Earnings	Dividends	Book Value
12/16	31.14	— —	(0.57)	1.68	6.19
12/15	25.70	— —	(0.76)	2.45	8.21
12/14	44.94	20 13	2.92	1.96	11.75
12/13	38.57	61 50	0.62	1.44	7.12
12/12	32.74	26 19	1.37	1.20	6.98
Annual Growth	(1.2%)	— —	—	8.9%	(2.9%)

Williams Partners LP (New)

Williams Partners (formerly Access Midstream Partners) is a midstream gathering company that owns operates develops and acquires natural gas natural gas liquids (NGLs) and oil gathering assets in the US. It gathers about 3.9 billion cu. ft. of natural gas per day via some 5800 miles of gathering and transmission lines. The company also has processing facilities that provide services to thousands of wells. Its assets are located in a dozen states with operations in the Barnett Eagle Ford Haynesville Marcellus Niobrara and Utica shales and several unconventional plays in the Mid-Continent region.

Change in Company Type

In 2015 The Williams Companies bought the 50% general partner interest and 55.1 million limited partner units in Access Midstream Partners held by Global Infrastructure Partners II for about $6 billion. It was then merged into Williams Partners and changed its name to Williams Partners.

Geographic Reach

The company's pipelines are located in Arkansas Kansas Louisiana Maryland New York Ohio Oklahoma Pennsylvania Texas Virginia West Virginia and Wyoming.

Sales and Marketing

Through long-term fixed-fee contracts Williams Partners provides its midstream services to Chesapeake Energy Total Mitsui Anadarko Petroleum Statoil and other major producers.

Financial Performance

The company's revenues grew by 8% in 2012 as a result of higher throughput in its Barnett Shale segment and an increase in rates in its Mid-Continent segment. This was partially offset by lower revenues from its Springridge gathering system in the Haynesville Shale due to lower drilling activities and natural declines in production. The Chesapeake Midstream Operating acquisition also contributed to revenue growth.

Williams Partners' net income decreased by 8% in 2012 due to the higher interest operating expenses partially offset by increased other income from unconsolidated affiliates. Increased throughput in the Barnett Shale region also led to higher operating expenses that year.

Strategy

The company grows through acquisitions of its former parent Chesapeake Energy's midstream assets and by organically expanding its midstream infrastructure.

Mergers and Acquisitions

In 2012 Williams Partners acquired Chesapeake Midstream Operating from a Chesapeake Energy unit for $2.2 billion. The deal gave the partnership certain midstream assets in the Eagle Ford Utica and Niobrara shale plays and expanded the company's assets and operations in the Haynesville Marcellus and Mid-Continent regions by adding 1675 miles of pipeline and 4.3 million acres of land. It also allowed the company to move into a new business — processing gas to produce NGLs.

As part of the acquisition the company also acquired a 49% of Utica East Ohio Midstream LLC with M3 Midstream L.L.C. and EV Energy Partners L.P. to develop infrastructure for the gathering processing and fractionation of natural gas and NGLs in the Utica Shale play in Eastern Ohio and 33% of Ranch Westex JV LLC (with Regency Energy Partners LP and Anadarko Pecos Midstream LLC) to build a processing plant in Ward County Texas.

EXECUTIVES

COO and Director, Robert S. (Bob) Purgason, age 60, $448,269 total compensation
CEO and Director, J. Mike Stice, age 57, $747,115 total compensation
CFO, David C. Shiels, age 51, $398,462 total compensation
SVP Eastern Operations, John D. Seldenrust, age 52, $371,077 total compensation
Vice President - Western Operations, Walter L. Bennett, age 47, $311,385 total compensation
CIO and Corporate Services, Deanna Farmer
Chairman, David A. Daberko, age 72
Secretary Treasurer, Keri Cooper
Auditors: Ernst & Young LLP

LOCATIONS

HQ: Williams Partners LP (New)
One Williams Center, Tulsa, OK 74172-0172
Phone: 918 573-2000
Web: www.williamslp.com

2012 Sales

	% of total
Barnett Shale	65
Mid-Continent	22
Haynesville Shale	11
Chesapeake Midstream Operating	2
Total	**100**

COMPETITORS

Atlas Pipeline Partners	Magellan Midstream
Crestwood Midstream Partners LP	MarkWest Energy Partners
DCP Midstream Partners	Martin Midstream Partners
EOG	Regency Energy
EnLink Midstream LLC	SandRidge Energy
Enable Oklahoma	Tristream Energy
Energy Transfer	XTO Energy
Enterprise Products	

HISTORICAL FINANCIALS

Company Type: Public

Income Statement

FYE: December 31

	REVENUE ($ mil.)	NET INCOME ($ mil.)	NET PROFIT MARGIN	EMPLOYEES
12/16	7,491	431	5.8%	5,604
12/15	7,331	(1,449)	—	6,578
12/14	1,378	398	28.9%	6,742
12/13	1,073	336	31.3%	1,411
12/12	608	178	29.3%	1,255
Annual Growth	87.3%	24.7%	—	45.4%

Debt ratio: 39.92%   No. of shares (mil.): 623
Return on equity: —   Dividends
Cash ($ mil.): 145   Yield: 0.1%
Current ratio: 0.52   Payout: —
Long-term debt ($ mil.): 17,685   Market value ($ mil.): 23,721

	STOCK PRICE ($) FY Close	P/E High/Low	PER SHARE ($) Earnings	Dividends	Book Value
12/16	38.03	— —	(0.17)	3.40	34.39
12/15	27.85	— —	(3.27)	3.40	37.92
12/14	54.20	66 50	1.01	2.20	18.28
12/13	56.58	60 35	0.95	1.83	18.79
12/12	33.54	36 22	1.05	1.55	17.96
Annual Growth	3.2%	— —	—	21.6%	17.6%

Williams Sonoma Inc

Epicureans are at home at Williams-Sonoma a leading multichannel retailer of high-end goods for well-appointed kitchens bedrooms and baths. Home products include bath and storage bedding cookware furniture lighting and tableware. The company's retail chains Williams-Sonoma (upscale cookware) West Elm (modern housewares) Rejuvenation (lighting and hardware) Mark and Graham (monogrammed gifts) and Pottery Barn and Pottery Barn Kids (housewares furniture) sell wares through 630 stores in 43 US states and in Canada Australia the UK and Puerto Rico. Williams-Sonoma also distributes half a dozen catalogs and sells merchandise at eight corresponding websites and online bridal and baby registries.

Operations

Williams-Sonoma operates retail stores and a direct-to-consumer business including online destinations and catalogs for all of its retail brands. The company's 630 stores account for 48% of sales although the direct-to-consumer business is growing at a faster pace. Indeed e-commerce which amounted to 52% of direct-to-consumer revenues in fiscal 2017 (January year end) is the company's fastest growing and most profitable sales channel.

The company's seven brands include Williams-Sonoma (almost 235 stores) Pottery Barn (200) Pottery Barn Kids (90) PBteen West Elm (almost 100) Rejuvenation (7) and Mark and Graham; PBteen and Mark and Graham products are only available via catalogs and online.

Geographic Reach

Beyond the US Williams-Sonoma operates 26 stores across Canada representing all of the company's retail brands except Rejuvenation. About 65 Pottery Barn and Pottery Barn Kids stores operate in the Middle East (Dubai and Kuwait) through a multi-year franchise agreement with M.H. Alshaya Co. It also has a presence in the Philippines and Mexico. The company's global e-commerce business serves customers in 100 countries.

Financial Performance

The company has seen an increasing trend in net revenues over the last five years with revenues peaking at more than $5 billion in 2017 the first time in its history. The historic growth was fueled by a 4% spike in e-commerce net revenues (primarily driven by West Elm Williams Sonoma and Rejuvenation) with a particular strength in furniture.

Williams-Sonoma's net income however dipped 2% from $310 million in 2016 to $305 million in 2017 mainly due to foreign currency translations.

In addition cash flow from operations declined from $544 million in 2016 to $524 million in 2017 mainly due to the lower net income and an increase in income taxes paid.

Strategy

E-commerce is Williams-Sonoma's growth engine. Strong online sales growth has made Williams-Sonoma less reliant on retail store expansion which can be risky and expensive to drive its business. To support growth of its online business Williams-Sonoma is investing in back-end technology and leveraging multi-channel customer data to improve the online shopping experience. It is investing in high-growth newer brands (particularly West Elm) and is continuing to rapidly expand its global reach through existing and new franchise relationships and other opportunities.

Williams-Sonoma sees the greatest opportunity in global expansion. It is partnering with Mexican department store chain Distribuidora Liverpool through a franchise agreement to expand its operations into Mexico. Its first store opened in 2015. In 2014 it opened new stores in the UK and in Australia and partnered with franchisers in the Philippines and the Middle East.In addition during 2016 it entered into a franchise agreement with an unaffiliated franchisee to operate stores and e-commerce websites in South Korea beginning in fiscal 2017.

HISTORY

Food lover and hardware store owner Charles Williams founded a cookware store in 1956 in Sonoma California moving it to San Francisco in 1958.

Edward Marcus (of Neiman Marcus) acquired a third of the company in 1972 which then began adding new stores and started its first catalog A Catalog for Cooks. Marcus died in 1976 and Williams unable to manage the burgeoning enterprise sold it to Howard Lester owner of several computer service firms.

Lester acquired Gardeners Eden a mail-order merchandiser of home gardening and related products in 1982. The next year he bought the rights to a new catalog Hold Everything (expanded into retailing later). Williams-Sonoma went public that year. In 1986 it acquired Pottery Barn from The Gap and soon added a catalog business. The company moved into bed and bath goods three years later when it introduced its Chambers catalog.

EXECUTIVES

President and CEO, Laura J. Alber, age 48, $1,400,000 total compensation
EVP and COO, Dean A. Miller
EVP and General Merchandise Manager, Marta H. Benson, age 54
EVP Retail and Business Sales, Vicki D. McWilliams
EVP and CIO, John F. Strain
EVP and CFO, Julie P. Whalen, age 46, $750,000 total compensation
President Williams-Sonoma Brand, Janet M. Hayes, age 49, $925,000 total compensation
EVP and Chief Talent Officer, Linda Lewis
EVP and Chief Real Estate and Development Officer, Bud Cope
President West Elm Brand, Alex Bellos
Chairman, Adrian D. P. Bellamy, age 75
Auditors: DELOITTE & TOUCHE LLP

LOCATIONS

HQ: Williams Sonoma Inc
3250 Van Ness Avenue, San Francisco, CA 94109
Phone: 415 421-7900   **Fax:** 415 434-0881
Web: www.williams-sonomainc.com

PRODUCTS/OPERATIONS

2017 Stores

	No.
Williams-Sonoma	234
Pottery Barn	201
Pottery Barn Kids	98
West Elm	89
Rejuvenation	7
Total	**629**

2017 Sales

	$ mil.	% of total
E-Commerce	2,633	52
Retail	2,450	48
Total	**5,083**	**100**

2017 Sales

	$ mil.	% of total
Pottery Barn	2,024	40
Williams-Sonoma	1,002	20
West Elm	971	19
Pottery Barn kids	635	12
PBteen	237	5
Other	212	4
Total	**5,083**	**100**

Retail

Retail
PBteen (teen home furnishings)
Pottery Barn (home furnishings flatware and table accessories)
Pottery Barn Kids (children's home furnishings)
Rejuvenation (classic American lighting and house parts)
West Elm (home furnishings decorative accessories tabletop items and textile collection)
Williams-Sonoma (cookware cookbooks cutlery dinnerware glassware and table linens)

Selected Catalogs

PBteen (home furnishings for teenage market)
Pottery Barn (home furnishings and housewares)
Pottery Barn Bed + Bath (bed and bath products)
Pottery Barn Kids (children's linens and furniture)
Rejuvenation (classic American lighting and house parts)
West Elm (home furnishings and housewares)
Williams-Sonoma (kitchen products)

COMPETITORS

Ashley Furniture	King Arthur Flour
Bed Bath & Beyond	Lands' End
Brookstone	Levenger
Container Store	Longaberger
Cornerstone Brands	Macy's
Cost Plus	Neiman Marcus
Dean & DeLuca	Pampered Chef
Decorize	Pier 1 Imports
Eddie Bauer LLC	RH
Ethan Allen	Room & Board
Euromarket Designs	Target Corporation
Garden Ridge	Tuesday Morning
Hanover Direct	Corporation
IKEA	Z Gallerie

HISTORICAL FINANCIALS

Company Type: Public

Income Statement

FYE: January 29

	REVENUE ($ mil.)	NET INCOME ($ mil.)	NET PROFIT MARGIN	EMPLOYEES
01/17	5,083	305	6.0%	28,300
01/16*	4,976	310	6.2%	28,100
02/15	4,698	308	6.6%	26,800
02/14	4,387	278	6.4%	37,200
02/13	4,042	256	6.4%	26,800
Annual Growth	**5.9%**	**4.4%**	**—**	**1.4%**

*Fiscal year change

2017 Year-End Financials

Debt ratio: —	No. of shares (mil.): 87
Return on equity: 25.03%	Dividends
Cash ($ mil.): 213	Yield: 0.0%
Current ratio: 1.42	Payout: 43.4%
Long-term debt ($ mil.): —	Market value ($ mil.): 4,148

	STOCK PRICE ($) FY Close	P/E High/Low		PER SHARE ($) Earnings	Dividends	Book Value
01/17	47.50	18	13	3.41	1.48	14.29
01/16*	51.66	26	14	3.37	1.40	13.38
02/15	78.25	25	16	3.24	1.32	13.33
02/14	54.52	21	15	2.82	1.24	13.35
02/13	45.02	19	13	2.54	0.88	13.39
Annual Growth	**1.3%**	**—**	**—**	**7.6%**	**13.9%**	**1.6%**

*Fiscal year change

Wilson Bank Holding Co.

EXECUTIVES

Chairman; Chairman Of The Board, John Freeman
Senior Vice Presiden, Michael Flanagan
Auditors: Maggart & Associates, P.C.

LOCATIONS

HQ: Wilson Bank Holding Co.
623 West Main Street, Lebanon, TN 37087
Phone: 615 444-2265
Web: www.wilsonbank.com

HISTORICAL FINANCIALS

Company Type: Public

Income Statement

FYE: December 31

	ASSETS ($ mil.)	NET INCOME ($ mil.)	INCOME AS % OF ASSETS	EMPLOYEES
12/16	2,198	25	1.2%	444
12/15	2,021	23	1.2%	446
12/14	1,873	20	1.1%	406
12/13	1,748	15	0.9%	419
12/12	1,680	12	0.7%	396
Annual Growth	**6.9%**	**20.5%**	**—**	**2.9%**

2016 Year-End Financials

Debt ratio: —	No. of shares (mil.): 10
Return on equity: 10.92%	Dividends
Cash ($ mil.): 47	Yield: —
Current ratio: —	Payout: 22.4%
Long-term debt ($ mil.): —	Market value ($ mil.): —

Windstream Holdings Inc

Windstream Holdings offers a range of telecommunications services to consumers carriers and businesses. The company?s business services include multi-site networking internet access cloud computing colocation online backup and other managed services. For residential customers Windstream offers high-speed internet (including gigabit speed in several markets) and voice services as well as video and bundles of several services. The company provides infrastructure services such as call connection and backhaul connections to wireless carriers. Windstream operates a fiber optic network that measures nearly 150000 route miles mostly in the Eastern and Midwest US.

Operations

Windstream Holdings? operating segments are Enterprise ILEC (Incumbent Local Exchange Carrier) Consumer and Small Business Wholesale and CLEC (Competitive Local Exchange Carrier) Small Business.

The Enterprise business which generates about 40% of revenue provides integrated voice and data services multi-site networking services cloud computing and colocation and managed services. Windstream classifies enterprise customers as those that generate at least $1500 a month in recurring revenue.

The ILEC Consumer and Small Business segment about 30% of revenue consists of incumbent local exchange carriers that offer traditional local and long-distance voice services and high-speed internet services. It also offers consumer video services through Dish Network LLC and owns own and operates cable TV franchises in some of service areas. The segment offers Windstream?s Kinetic video entertainment service in Lincoln Nebraska Lexington Kentucky and Sugar Land Texas.

Wholesale operations about 12% of revenue sell Windstream?s infrastructure and related services to other telecom companies. Leveraging Windstream?s fiber network the segment provides wave transport services carrier Ethernet services fiber-to-tower connections to support backhaul services to wireless carriers and high speed internet access.

The Small Business CLEC segment about 10% of revenue is composed of the company?s competitive local exchange carriers. Their services include integrated voice and data services advanced data and traditional voice and long-distance services as well as value added services including online backup managed web design and web hosting and e-mail services.

Geographic Reach

Windstream Holdings is headquartered in Little Rock Arkansas. It manages more than 10 data centers and it has operating authority in 48 states and the District of Columbia. The company maintains more than 60 offices throughout the US.

Sales and Marketing

Windstream Holdings sells its products and services through several channels. It has a direct sales force; an account management team; an indirect sales channel in which the company partners with third-party dealers who sell directly to customers; and third-party agents who refer sales leads to the company.

Financial Performance

Windstream has posted declining revenue for the past four years and has lost money for two of the past four years.

In 2016 Windstream?s revenue fell about 7% to $5.4 billion from about $5.8 billion in 2015. The company had lower sales in all segments led by a 13% drop in the Small Business CLEC segment. Customers continue to abandon voice services in favor of voice and data services through high speed internet. But Windstream customers aren?t necessarily switching to its internet offerings. While voice-only service dropped in the Consumer and Small business ILEC and Small Business CLEC in 2016 the growth in high-speed internet bundles didn?t keep pace. The company cited competition as a road block to growth. The Enterprise segment

has fared better in the service transition. Revenue from voice and long distance service fell more than 30% in 2016 from 2015 but revenue from data and integrated services rose about 46%.

Windstream?s bottom line veered to a loss of $380 million after posting $27 million in net income 2015. The company reduced expenses in most areas in 2016 but it suffered a loss on its investment in CS&L had higher interest expenses and paid taxes instead of receiving a tax benefit in 2015.

The company?s cash flow from operations dropped to $924 million in 2016 from about $1.3 billion in 2015. The decrease started with Windstream?s net loss and was compounded by additional interest expense and changes in working capital attributed to timing differences in the collection of trade receivables and the payment of trade accounts payable.

Strategy

Windstream believes has the pieces of services and products in place and now it needs to connect them to customers. In the ILEC Consumer and Small Business segment the company is rolling out its premium high-speed internet service to more markets including its gigabit service. The Enterprise business is expanding its fixed wireless service to dozens of new markets and it is moving its networks to software-defined networking which is to improve design and management of the networks. The technology was to be available for network management in more than 50 locations in 2017.

The Wholesale segment is expanding its longhaul network in the western US which increases access to established technology companies and startups. The CLEC Consumer and Small Business segment is working to keep its most profitable customers get new customers in select markets and managing customer-level profit margins. The unit is using the Enterprise infrastructure to improve costs.

The acquisition of EarthLink enabled Windstream to open five new fiber routes in 2017 which can offer cloud connectivity between major interconnection points in Tier 1 Tier 2 and Tier 3 markets in the US. At the same time Windstream is working to integrate EarthLink?s operations into its own. The company expects to save more than $150 million over three years.

With its Project Excel the company has upgraded its broadband network to offer faster speeds Most of the physical plant work was completed by the end of 2016 with testing going into 2017. That means Windstream should have improved internet speeds to sell to consumer and small business customers in 2017.

To take advantage of high-speed internet into the home Windstream started a video entertainment service. The service called Kinetic is available in several Windstream markets.

Before embarking on the EarthLink deal Windstream divested some of its real estate holdings. It sold 14 of its 27 data centers to TierPoint for $575 million. As part of the deal Windstream and TierPoint can sell their respective products and services to each other's prospective customers through referrals.

Windstream also spun off its fiber and copper networks and other real estate in an independent publicly traded real estate investment trust. The spin-off also included almost all of Windstream's consumer wireline business.

Mergers and Acquisitions

Windstream Holdings acquired Broadview Networks Holdings for nearly $230 million in 2017. Broadview provides cloud-based unified communications services for small and medium-sized businesses. Windstream plans to aggressively push Broadview's cloud operations and deploy its sales-

force to compete across the country with companies like Vonage and RingCentral as well as cable companies. The deal was expected to close in the third quarter of 2017.

In 2017 Windstream completed its acquisition of EarthLink Holdings for $1.1 billion. The deal added EarthLink's networks around the country to Windstream's operations and filled in gaps of Windstream's map of service areas across the country.

EXECUTIVES

President Enterprise, Layne L. Levine
EVP Chief Human Resources and Legal Officer, John P. Fletcher, age 51, $515,000 total compensation
President and CEO, Anthony W. (Tony) Thomas, age 45, $1,000,000 total compensation
CFO and Treasurer, Robert E. (Bob) Gunderman, age 44, $450,000 total compensation
President Carrier, Mike Shippey
Head of Engineering, Jeff Small
EVP and CIO, Lewis Langston
EVP and Enterprise Chief Marketing Officer, Joe Harding
President Consumer Small and Medium Sized Businesses, Sarah Day, $298,615 total compensation
CLEC Consumer Small and Medium-Sized Business, Drew Smith
EVP Access, John Dobbins
Executive Vice President Senior Vice President Vice President, Rodney Hawkins
Vice President of Sales Great Lakes Region, Kristin King
Division Vice President, Phillip McAbee
Vice President Enterprise Business Unit, Jeff Mote
Chairman, Jeffrey T. Hinson, age 60
Auditors: PricewaterhouseCoopers LLP

LOCATIONS

HQ: Windstream Holdings Inc
4001 Rodney Parham Road, Little Rock, AR 72212
Phone: 501 748-7000
Web: www.windstream.com

PRODUCTS/OPERATIONS

2016 Sales

	$ mil.	% of total
Enterprise	2,031	38
Consumer and Small Business - ILEC	1,579	29
Wholesale	631	12
Small Business - CLEC	483	9
Regulatory and other operating revenues and sales	661	12
Total	**5,387**	**100**

2016 Sales

	$ mil.	% of total
Service revenues	5,279	98
Product sales	107	2
Total	**5,387**	**100**

COMPETITORS

AT&T	Equinix
CenturyLink	FullNet Communications
Cox Communications	Momentum Telecom
Crown Castle International	Sprint Communications
	Verizon

HISTORICAL FINANCIALS

Company Type: Public

Income Statement

FYE: December 31

	REVENUE ($ mil.)	NET INCOME ($ mil.)	NET PROFIT MARGIN	EMPLOYEES
12/16	5,387	(383)	—	11,870
12/15	5,765	27	0.5%	12,326
12/14	5,829	(39)	—	12,626
12/13	5,988	241	4.0%	13,434
12/12	6,156	168	2.7%	13,787
Annual Growth	(3.3%)	—	—	(3.7%)

2016 Year-End Financials

Debt ratio: 83.81%	No. of shares (mil.): 96
Return on equity: (-160.56%)	Dividends
Cash ($ mil.): 59	Yield: 0.0%
Current ratio: 0.69	Payout: —
Long-term debt ($ mil.): 9,680	Market value ($ mil.): 706

	STOCK PRICE ($) FY Close	P/E High/Low		PER SHARE ($) Earnings	Dividends	Book Value
12/16	7.33	—	—	(4.11)	0.60	1.77
12/15	6.44	50	19	0.24	0.41	3.17
12/14	8.24	—	—	(0.42)	6.00	2.24
12/13	7.98	4	3	2.40	6.00	8.46
12/12	8.28	7	5	1.68	6.00	11.27
Annual Growth (37.1%)	(3.0%)	—	—	—	—(43.8%)	

Wintrust Financial Corp (IL)

Wintrust Financial is a holding company for 15 subsidiary banks (mostly named after the individual communities they serve) with more than 150 branches primarily in the metropolitan Chicago and southern Wisconsin (including Milwaukee) markets. Boasting assets of more than $23 billion the banks offer personal and commercial banking wealth management and specialty lending services with business and commercial real estate loans making up 60% of the company's loan portfolio. Wintrust's banks target small business customers though some of Wintrust's banks also provide niche lending for homeowners associations medical practices franchisees and municipalities.

Operations

Wintrust operates three business segments: Community Banking which accounted for 77% of total revenue in 2015 and serves individuals and small businesses; Specialty Finance (13% of revenue) operating through First Insurance Funding and First Insurance Funding of Canada which provide financing for commercial insurance and life insurance premiums in the US and Canada respectively; and Wealth Management (10% of revenue) which offers financial planning and brokerage services through The Chicago Trust Company N.A. Wayne Hummer Investments LLC and Great Lakes Advisors LLC.

Wintrust makes more than 70% of its revenue from interest income. About 66% of its total revenue came from loan interest (including fees) during 2015 while another 6% came from interest on investment securities. The rest of its revenue came from mortgage banking (12%) wealth management services (7%) deposit account service charges (3%) and other miscellaneous income sources.

Geographic Reach

Wintrust's banks operate more than 150 branches and 220-plus automatic teller machines mostly located in communities throughout the Chicago metropolitan area and southern Wisconsin. Its wealth management offices are in Chicago; Appleton Wisconsin; and Safety Harbor Florida. Its Wintrust Mortgage subsidiary has 55 locations in a dozen states while its insurance subsidiaries have locations in Northbrook Illinois; Jersey City; Long Island New York; Toronto; Mississauga Ontario; and Vancouver.

Sales and Marketing

The bank's customers include individuals small to mid-sized businesses local governmental units and institutional clients residing primarily in the banks' local service areas.

Wintrust has been ramping up its advertising spend in recent years. It spent $21.9 million on advertising during 2015 up from $13.6 million and $11.1 million in 2014 and 2013 respectively.

Financial Performance

Wintrust Financial's annual revenues have risen more than 40% since 2011 as its loan assets have swelled by nearly 70% with rapid branch expansion. Its annual profits have doubled over the same period.

The banking group's revenue jumped 12% to $990.1 million during 2015 mostly as its average loan balances grew by 15% for the year. Mortgage banking revenue increased 26% for the year thanks to higher origination volumes and purchases on a more favorable mortgage banking environment also helping buoy the company's topline growth.

Strong revenue growth in 2015 drove Wintrust's net income up 4% to $156.75 million despite a rise in acquisition-related professional and legal fees. The group's operating cash levels fell 82% to $37.95 million due to unfavorable working capital changes mainly tied to an increase in accrued interest receivable and other assets.

Strategy

Wintrust has developed its community-based banking franchise through rapid branch expansion stemming from either through new openings or small bank acquisitions. Indeed the bank's branch count has flourished by more than 50% since 2011 from 99 back then to 152 branches at the end of 2015.

Beyond branch expansion the company remains focused on making new loans especially of the commercial and commercial real estate type where opportunities that meet its underwriting standards exist.

Mergers and Acquisitions

In January 2016 Wintrust Financial expanded into Pewaukee Wisconsin after agreeing to buy Generations Bancorp and its Foundations Bank subsidiary. Later that year the company finalized the $33.5 million purchase of First Community Financial Corporation the holding company of First Community Bank (which operates two branches in Elgin Illinois).

In July 2015 the company purchased Community Financial Shares Inc. and its four Community Bank of Wheaton/Glen Ellyn bank branches in the respective communities they serve in Illinois for a total of $42.4 million.

Also in July 2015 the company bought $118 million-asset North Bank and its two branches in Chicago.

In April 2015 Wintrust acquired Suburban Illinois Bancorp and its 10 Suburban Bank & Trust Company (SBT) branches in Chicago and surrounding suburbs for $12.5 million. The SBT locations would operate under Wintrust's Hinsdale Bank & Trust Company subsidiary.

In January 2015 the bank group purchased $224 million-asset Delavan Bancshares Inc. and its Community Bank CBD subsidiary.

Company Background

In 2012 Wintrust expanded its premium funding business into Canada with the acquisition of Macquarie Premium Funding Inc which was a subsidiary of Macquarie Group. The deal marked Wintrust's first international venture.

EXECUTIVES

Assistant Vice President E marketing, Michael Limjoco

EVP Technology; President Wintrust Information Technology Services, Lloyd M. Bowden, age 64, $167,333 total compensation

SEVP COO and Treasurer, David A. Dykstra, age 57, $759,167 total compensation

President CEO and Director, Edward J. Wehmer, age 62, $1,100,000 total compensation

EVP and Regional Market Head, Frank J. Burke

EVP and Chief Credit Officer, Richard B. Murphy, age 58, $509,167 total compensation

EVP and Chief Administration Officer, Leona A. Gleason

SVP Finance, David L. Stoehr, age 58, $419,167 total compensation

EVP and Regional Market Head, Timothy S. (Tim) Crane, age 55

EVP Wealth Management, Thomas P. (Tom) Zidar

EVP General Counsel and Secretary, Lisa J. Pattis, $446,167 total compensation

EVP and Regional Market Head, David L. Larson

EVP and COO Wintrust Commercial Finance (WCF), Joseph F. Thompson

Vice President Compliance, Kellie Oostendorp

Senior Vice President, Earl Goldman

Executive Vice President, Paul Carlisle

Vice President, Tim Edwards

Executive Vice President, Ursula Moncau

Vice President Loan Operations, Sharon Hiller

Vice President Managed Assets Division, Irene Calzadilla

Vice President, Philip Sheridan

Senior Vice President commercial Lender, Gregory Pinter

Vice President Managed Assets Division, Will Knapik

Assistant Vice President Treasury Management, Judy Majon

Assistant Vice President Financial System Management, Marty Lavin

Vice President, Mary Koehler

Senior Vice President, Rhonda Pokoj

Vice President, Diane Gorka

Assistant Vice President Tax, Michelle Serna

Assistant Vice President, Robert Murphy

Assistant Vice President, Brett Davis

Vice President Real Estate Services, Trey Meers

Vice President, Jason Girardin

Vice President, Jaime Hung

Senior Vice President, Darragh Griffin

Assistant Vice President, Kimberly Okoye

Vice President Wintrust Commercial Banking, John Hills

Executive Vice President Commercial Banking, Jeffrey Steigelman

Vice President and Assistant General Counsel, Daniel Stolarsky

Senior Vice President Commercial Banking, Sean Dunn

Senior Vice President, Ryan Witte

Senior Vice President and Chief Human Resources Officer, Jennifer Campe

Vice President Tax, Mike Masterson

Vice President, Jon Swanson

Assistant Vice President President Financial Systems Management, Michal Latawiec

Vice President, Teresa Handley

Vice President Professional Practice Group, Jan Eriksen

Vice President, Kam Kniss

Assistant Vice President BSA Officer Support Manager, Karin Jacobson

Vice President, Caroline Gonos

Senior Vice President Purchased Assets Division, Deann Kovalan

Vice President, Zornitsa Titova

Assistant Vice President, Julie Janssen

Vice President Credit Administration, Tim Rasmussen

Senior Vice President market Risk, Mark Bedigian

Assistant Vice President, Todd Shifrin

Vice President, Kyle Furry

Vice President Managed Assets Division, Hany Morsy

Vice President, Maria Colangelo

Vice President Human Resources, Janet Huffman

Vice President Marketing, Wendy Schenker

Senior Vice President Division Head, Jeffrey Eversden

Executive Vice President, Matthew Doucet

Assistant Vice President, Kristina Adomaviciute

Senior Vice President, Michael O'Malley

Vice President, Nick Koricanac

Vice President, Susan Puraleski

Senior Vice President Sales, Steve Cusick

Vice President Information Technology Audit Manager, Tushar Mathur

Vice President of Business Banking, Miguel Gomez

Assistant Vice President Commercial Product Manager, Karon Gater

Assistant Vice President Retail Digital Product Manager, Natalie Fedus

Senior Vice President Comm Banking Manager, Jolie A Horen

Assistant Vice President Commercial Banking, Mark Skubak

Senior Vice President, David Feldser

Assistant Vice President, Katie Cagney

Assistant Vice President Branch Manager, Anthony Scott

Executive Vice President Commercial Banking, John Dvorak

Senior Vice President Sales, Tom Forbes

Vice President, Kim Endsley

Vice President Risk, Tim Doran

Senior Vice President, Brian de la Houssaye

Vice President, Liz Deboni

Senior Vice President Commercial Real Estate, Daniel Lawlor

Vice President of Infrastructure, Bill Eisenstot

Senior Vice President, Kendra Castelloni

Executive Vice President, Chris Newton

Vice President, Tara Fedorko

Vice President, Rafiq Harris

Senior Vice President, Dawn Mase

AVP Learning and Development, Nancy Dome

Senior Vice President, Frank Gruber

Vice President Business Lending, Katie Moore

Assistant Vice President Commercial Real Estate, Lauren Barnard

Senior Vice President, Tom Carlson

Senior Vice President Risk Strategy and Analytics, Venkat Veeramani

Chairman, Peter D. Crist, age 66

Board Member, Larry Wright

Auditors: Ernst & Young LLP

LOCATIONS

HQ: Wintrust Financial Corp (IL)
9700 W. Higgins Road, Suite 800, Rosemont, IL 60018
Phone: 847 939-9000   Fax: 847 615-4091
Web: www.wintrust.com

PRODUCTS/OPERATIONS

2015 Sales

	$ mil.	% of total
Interest		
Loans including fees	651	66
Securities	61	6
Other	5	-
Non-interest		
Mortgage banking	115	12
Wealth management	73	7
Service charges on deposit accounts	27	3
Fees from covered call options	15	2
Other	40	4
Trading (losses) gains net	(0.2)	-
Total	**990**	**100**

Selected Subsidiaries and Affiliates

Banking
Barrington Bank & Trust Company N.A.
Beverly Bank & Trust Company N.A.
Crystal Lake Bank & Trust Company N.A.
Hinsdale Bank & Trust Company
Lake Forest Bank & Trust Company
Libertyville Bank & Trust Company
North Shore Community Bank & Trust Company
Northbrook Bank & Trust Company
Old Plank Trail Community Bank N.A.
Schaumburg Bank & Trust Company N.A.
St. Charles Bank & Trust
State Bank of The Lakes
Town Bank
Village Bank & Trust
Wheaton Bank and Trust Company
Non-banking
Chicago Trust Company N.A.
First Insurance Funding Corporation
Great Lakes Advisors LLC
Tricom Inc. of Milwaukee
Wayne Hummer Asset Management Company
Wayne Hummer Investments LLC
Wayne Hummer Trust Company N.A.
Wintrust Information Technology Services Company
Wintrust Mortgage Corporation (formerly WestAmerica Mortgage Company)

COMPETITORS

Associated Banc-Corp	Harris
Bank of America	JPMorgan Chase
Citigroup	MB Financial
Citizens Financial Group	Northern Trust
Fifth Third	PrivateBank
First Midwest Bancorp	U.S. Bancorp

HISTORICAL FINANCIALS

Company Type: Public

Income Statement

FYE: December 31

	ASSETS ($ mil.)	NET INCOME ($ mil.)	INCOME AS % OF ASSETS	EMPLOYEES
12/16	25,668	206	0.8%	3,878
12/15	22,917	156	0.7%	3,770
12/14	20,010	151	0.8%	3,491
12/13	18,097	137	0.8%	3,413
12/12	17,519	111	0.6%	3,269
Annual Growth	**10.0%**	**16.8%**	**—**	**4.4%**

2016 Year-End Financials

Debt ratio: 2.31%		No. of shares (mil.): 51	
Return on equity: 8.17%		Dividends	
Cash ($ mil.): 1,247		Yield: 0.0%	
Current ratio: —		Payout: 13.1%	
Long-term debt ($ mil.): —		Market value ($ mil.): 3,765	

	STOCK PRICE ($) FY Close	P/E High/Low		PER SHARE ($) Earnings	Dividends	Book Value
12/16	72.57	19	10	3.66	0.48	51.96
12/15	48.52	18	14	2.93	0.44	48.62
12/14	46.76	16	14	2.98	0.40	44.22
12/13	46.12	14	10	2.75	0.18	41.21
12/12	36.70	14	10	2.31	0.18	48.96
Annual Growth	**18.6%**	**—**	**—**	**12.2%**	**27.8%**	**1.5%**

World Fuel Services Corp.

World Fuel Services can't yet affect the earth's spin but it plays a part in moving mostly everything else across its surface. The company sells fuel and fuel handling services to small-to-midsized air carriers cargo and charter carriers and private aircraft. as well as support activities such as flight planning weather reports and card payment services. It is also a marine fuel reseller on hand to deliver marine fuel to the shipping industry and commercial vessels and supplies land transport markets via hundreds of terminals in the US and Watson Fuels in the UK. It has almost 50 offices around the world and does business or virtually every country. The company was founded in 1985 as a marine fuel brokerage firm.

HISTORY

Neighbors Ralph Weiser and Jerrold Blair founded International Oil Recovery an oil recycling company in Florida in 1984. The company moved into aviation fueling by acquiring Advance Petroleum in 1986. Two years later International Oil Recovery diversified further entering the hazardous waste market by buying Resource Recovery of America a soil remediation company. In 1989 the firm acquired JCo Energy Partners an aviation fuel company and subsequently renamed its aviation fueling division World Fuel Services. The company set up International Petroleum in 1993 to operate a Delaware used-oil and water-recycling plant.

The company changed its name to World Fuel Services Corporation in 1995 to reflect its expanded range of operations. Also that year it nearly doubled its revenue base with the purchase of Trans-Tec the world's #1 independent marine fuel services company. World Fuel also exited the environmental services business in 1995 to focus on its fuel services and oil recycling businesses.

The following year the company formed World Fuel International a subsidiary based in Costa Rica that serves World Fuel's aviation customers in South and Central America Canada and the Caribbean. In 1998 it acquired corporate jet fuel provider Baseops International which has offices in the UK and Texas.

In 1999 the company expanded its share of the marine fuel market with the acquisition of the Bunkerfuels group of companies one of the world's top marine fuel brokerages.

To focus on its marine and aviation fueling businesses World Fuel exited the oil recycling segment in 2000 when it sold its International Petroleum unit to waste services company EarthCare for about $33 million.

The company expanded into the United Arab Emirates with its 2001 acquisition of fuel services provider Marine Energy of Dubai. World Fuel acquired Rotterdam-based marine fuel reseller Oil Shipping Group in 2002.

In 2004 World Fuel Services acquired UK-based marine fuel reseller Tramp Holdings for $83 million.

The company diversified further in 2007 acquiring AVCARD a leading provider of contract fuel sales and charge card services to the aviation industry for $55 million.

In 2009 it bought wholesale motor fuel distributor TGS Petroleum. The company combined TGS with Texor to expand World Fuel Services' presence as the largest independent wholesale motor fuel distributor in Illinois.

Expanding its UK market share in 2009 the company acquired the Henty Oil Group of Companies a leading independent provider of marine and land fuels in the UK.

In 2010 it beefed up its position in the branded onshore wholesale market to 1 billion gallons a year by acquiring Lakeside Oil Company based in Milwaukee. It also boosted its market position through the acquisition of leading independent petroleum marketing company Western Petroleum for $95 million.

Boosting its aviation fuel segment in 2011 (for an undisclosed amount) World Fuel Services acquired The Hiller Group an aviation fuel supplier to more than 600 fixed base operators. It also bought Ascent Aviation a national branded reseller of aviation fuel for ConocoPhillips and deicing fluid for Dow Chemical and which supplies more than 450 airports and fixed base operators and NATO aviation fuel and logistics supplier Nordic Camp Supply (for $68.5 million.)

In 2012 the company acquired CarterEnergy's wholesale motor fuel distribution business. Kansas-based CarterEnergy with an annual volume of more than of 500 million gallons distributes branded fuel to more than 700 retail operators and is a supplier to industrial commercial and government customers in more than a dozen states. The deal boosted World Fuel Services' land fuel volume to more than 3.5 billion gallons.

In 2013 to improve its payment processing operations it also bought certain assets from Multi Service Corporation (which specializes in fleet government and commercial payment programs) for $137 million. The Multi Service acquisition expands World Fuel Services' presence in the payment processing industry.

EXECUTIVES

Chairman President and CEO, Michael J. Kasbar, age 61, $875,100 total compensation
VP Finance, Carlos Rego
EVP and CFO, Ira M. Birns, age 55, $583,400 total compensation
EVP; Regional Managing Director Asia, Francis L Boon Meng
EVP and COO, Jeff S. Smith
EVP; Regional Managing Director EMEA, Wade N. DeClaris
SVP and CIO, Massoud Sedigh, age 62
EVP Global Aviation and Marine, John P. Rau, $475,100 total compensation
EVP Global Land, Michael J. Crosby, $487,550 total compensation
Vice President People And Performance Development, Marcia Morales-jaffe
Senior Vice President Finance, Carlos Velazquez
Vice President Commercial Services, Charles Davies
Senior Vice President, Carlos Cuervo
Vice President Advanced Logistics, Piers Gorman
Vice President Credit and Risk Management, Kauleen Kershisnik
Vice President and Treasurer, Adrienne Urban

Vice President Credit and Risk, Tim Bohall
Vice President Global Information Technology Operations, Jeff White
Vice President Credit and Risk Management, Greg Zemaitis
Vice President Domestic Supply, Brad Hurwitz
Senior Vice President Risk, Prasad Venkata
Vice President Finance, Monesh Sakhrani
Vice President Application Development, Scott Deloach
Vice President Associate General Counsel, Ruth Giansante
Senior Vice President Land North America, Kerry Oliver
Senior Vice President Of Global Tax, Peter Tonyan
Vice President, Jos Heijmen
Vice President Human Resources, Derek Scott
Vice President Of Supply Emeaa, Michael Ranger
Senior Vice President and Chief Marketing Officer, Amy Abraham
Executive Vice President, Martin Miller
Vice President, Rebecca Hing
Vice President Corporate Controller, Will Billings
Senior Vice President Global Energy Management, Todd Overgard
Vice President Enterprise Transformation, Wayde Hauptmeier
Vice President Retail Channel Development, Ken Wootton
Senior Vice President and Treasurer, Adrienne Bolan
Vice President Business Development, Michael Brown
VICE PRESIDENT SALES AND MARKETING, Randall Fairbank
VICE PRESIDENT SALES, Robert Loyd
Senior Vice President, Michele Wills
Vice President, Gene McDougald
Executive Vice President And Chief Financial Officer, Guru Acharya
Auditors: PricewaterhouseCoopers LLP

LOCATIONS

HQ: World Fuel Services Corp.
9800 Northwest 41st Street, Miami, FL 33178
Phone: 305 428-8000   **Fax:** 305 392-5621
Web: www.wfscorp.com

2016 sales

	$ mil.	% of total
Americas	16,726	62
Asia/Pacific	6,018	22
Europe & Middle East & Africa	4,271	16
Total	**27,015**	**100**

PRODUCTS/OPERATIONS

2016 sales

	$ mil.	% of total
Aviation	10,914	40
Marine Land 8918.8		33
Marine	7,182	27
Total	**27,015**	**100**

Selected Subsidiaries

Ascent Aviation Group Inc.
Baseops Europe Ltd. (UK)
Baseops International Inc.
Casa Petro S.R.L. (Costa Rica)
Henty Oil Limited (UK)
Marine Energy Arabia Co. (L.L.C.) (United Arab Emirates)
Nordic Camp Supply ApS (Denmark)
PetroServicios de Costa Rica S.R.L.
TGS Petroleum
The Hiller Group Incorporated
Tramp Holdings Limited (UK)
Trans-Tec International S.R.L. (Costa Rica)
Western Petroleum Company
World Fuel International S.R.L. (Costa Rica)
World Fuel Services Inc.
World Fuel Services Ltd. (UK)
World Fuel Services (Singapore) Pte. Ltd.

Selected Products and Services

Aviation
Business and General Aviation
Request an Authorization
Validate a Card
Report a Lost Card
Commercial Aviation
Deicing Services
Export Supply
Fuel Management
Risk Management
Tax Information
Marine
Marine Fuels
Lubricants
Operations
Consulting
Yacht Services
Quality Assurance
Physical Supply
Risk Management

COMPETITORS

BBA Aviation	Mercury Air Group
BP Marine	Shell Aviation
Exxon Mobil	Sun Coast Resources
Fuchs Lubricants	

HISTORICAL FINANCIALS

Company Type: Public

Income Statement

FYE: December 31

	REVENUE ($ mil.)	NET INCOME ($ mil.)	NET PROFIT MARGIN	EMPLOYEES
12/16	27,015	126	0.5%	5,000
12/15	30,379	186	0.6%	4,700
12/14	43,386	221	0.5%	4,041
12/13	41,561	203	0.5%	2,758
12/12	38,945	189	0.5%	2,490
Annual Growth	**(8.7%)**	**(9.6%)**	**—**	**19.0%**

2016 Year-End Financials

Debt ratio: 21.92%	No. of shares (mil.): 69
Return on equity: 6.58%	Dividends
Cash ($ mil.): 698	Yield: 0.0%
Current ratio: 1.76	Payout: 13.2%
Long-term debt ($ mil.): 1,170	Market value ($ mil.): 3,209

	STOCK PRICE ($) FY Close	P/E High/Low		PER SHARE ($) Earnings	Dividends	Book Value
12/16	45.91	28	20	1.81	0.24	27.54
12/15	38.46	22	13	2.64	0.24	27.00
12/14	46.93	16	12	3.11	0.15	25.74
12/13	43.16	16	12	2.83	0.15	23.29
12/12	41.17	18	13	2.64	0.15	21.03
Annual Growth	**2.8%**	**—**	**—**	**(9.0%)**	**12.5%**	**7.0%**

WORLD WIDE TECHNOLOGY HOLDING CO., INC.

Auditors: ERNST & YOUNG LLP ST LOUIS

LOCATIONS

HQ: WORLD WIDE TECHNOLOGY HOLDING CO., INC.
60 WELDON PKWY, SAINT LOUIS, MO 63101
Phone: 314 919-1400
Web: WWW.2.WWT.COM

HISTORICAL FINANCIALS

Company Type: Private

Income Statement

FYE: December 31

	REVENUE ($ mil.)	NET INCOME ($ mil.)	NET PROFIT MARGIN	EMPLOYEES
12/15	7,437	83	1.1%	1,052
12/14	6,702	88	1.3%	—
12/13	6,392	77	1.2%	—
12/12	5,041	68	1.3%	—
Annual Growth	13.8%	7.1%	—	—

2015 Year-End Financials

Debt ratio: ——
Return on equity: 1.10%
Cash ($ mil.): 62
Current ratio: 0.80
Long-term debt ($ mil.): —

Dividends
Yield: —
Payout: —
Market value ($ mil.): —

WORLD WIDE TECHNOLOGY, INC.

World Wide Technology (WWT) has a broad view of its business. The company primarily provides such IT services as network design and installation systems and application integration and procurement. It also offers a range of Web-based products and services including e-commerce systems development order tracking and catalog management. WWT serves businesses in the automotive retail and telecommunications industries as well as government agencies. Top clients have included Dell the State of Missouri and the State of Alaska. WWT was founded in 1990.

Geographic Reach

WWT has more than 25 facilities throughout the world and about 2 million-sq.-ft of warehouse and distribution space in the US. It also has three distribution outlets in Brazil Mexico and Singapore as well as facilities in London; Amsterdam; Hong Kong; and Chengdu China.

Mergers and Acquisitions

In 2015 WWT purchased St. Louis-based software development firm Asynchrony. The strategic acquisition will allow WWT to deliver complete custom user-facing software and the systems and infrastructure that support it.

EXECUTIVES

CEO, James P. (Jim) Kavanaugh
President Commercial Sales, Mark J. Catalano
CFO, Thomas W. (Tom) Strunk
VP Corporate Properties, Dan B. Svoboda
President, Joseph G. (Joe) Koenig
VP Professional Services, Matt Horner
VP Supply Chain Operations, Kurt Grimminger
VP Global Supply Chain, Mark Franke
Vice President of Information Technology, Mike P. Taylor
Vice President Sales Operations, Tim Loughman
Vice President Advanced Technology, Brian Ortbals
Vice President Professional Services, Tom Gain
Vice President of Information Technology, Michael Taylor
Vice President Global Accounts, Leo Makhlin
Area Vice President Global Service Provider, Kraig Ecker
Associate Vice President Production, Tonya Miller

Vice President of Security Solutions, Mike McGlynn
Chairman, David L. Steward

LOCATIONS

HQ: WORLD WIDE TECHNOLOGY, INC.
60 WELDON PKWY, MARYLAND HEIGHTS, MO 630433202
Phone: 314 569-7000
Web: WWW.WWT.COM

PRODUCTS/OPERATIONS

Selected Services

IT Products and Solutions
  Facilities Infrastructure
  Integration and Staging
  Leasing
  Managed Services
  Order Management and Reporting

  Pre-Sales Support
  Value Added Reseller
Professional Services
  Configuration
  Implementation
  Planning and Design
  Training
Supply Chain Services
  Business Process Outsourcing
  Logistics/Warehousing
  Material Planning and Scheduling
  Outsourced Procurement
  Supplier Management

COMPETITORS

Accenture
Black Box
Computer Sciences Corp.
DataSpan
Dynamics Research
En Pointe

HP Enterprise Services
IBM Global Services
PC Mall
Rose International
Unisys
WebLinc

HISTORICAL FINANCIALS

Company Type: Private

Income Statement

FYE: December 31

	REVENUE ($ mil.)	NET INCOME ($ mil.)	NET PROFIT MARGIN	EMPLOYEES
12/15	5,927	95	1.6%	1,052
12/14	5,057	95	1.9%	—
12/13	4,545	77	1.7%	—
12/12	3,396	57	1.7%	—
Annual Growth	20.4%	18.3%	—	—

2015 Year-End Financials

Debt ratio: ——
Return on equity: 1.60%
Cash ($ mil.): 46
Current ratio: 1.00
Long-term debt ($ mil.): —

Dividends
Yield: —
Payout: —
Market value ($ mil.): —

WSFS Financial Corp

WSFS isn't a radio station but it is tuned to the banking needs of Delaware. WSFS Financial is the holding company for Wilmington Savings Fund Society (WSFS Bank) a thrift with nearly $5 billion in assets and more than 75 branches mostly in Delaware and Pennsylvania. Founded in 1832 WSFS Bank attracts deposits from individuals and local businesses by offering standard products like checking and savings accounts CDs and IRAs. The bank uses funds primarily to lend to businesses: Commercial loans and mortgages account for about 85% of its loan portfolio. Bank subsidiaries Christiana Trust Cypress Capital Management and WSFS Wealth Investment provide trust and investment advisory services to wealthy clients and institutional investors.

Operations

Its Christiana Trust division boasts nearly $9 billion in assets under administration and provides investment fiduciary agency bankruptcy and commercial domicile services from offices in Delaware and Nevada.

The company's Cash Connect division operates more than 450 ATMs for WSFS Bank which boasts the largest branded ATM network in Delaware. The division also manages some $490 million of vault cash in approximately 15000 ATMs nationwide and provides online reporting and ATM cash management predictive cash ordering armored carrier management and ATM processing and equipment sales.

Overall the bank generated roughly 57% of its total revenue from interest and fees on loans in 2014 plus an additional 10% from interest on its mortgage-back and other investment securities. About 7% of its total revenue came from wealth management income while mortgage banking income contributed another 2%. The majority of the remaining revenue came from credit/debit card and ATM income and deposit service charges.

Geographic Reach

WSFS Bank has 45 branches throughout Delaware nearly 10 branches in Pennsylvania one branch in Nevada and one in Virginia.

Financial Performance

WSFS Financial's revenues and profits have been trending higher in recent years thanks to sustained growth in its lending business organically and through acquisitions and thanks to declining loan loss provisions as its loan portfolio's credit quality has improved with the strengthened economy.

The company's revenue rose by 5% to $238.62 million in 2014 thanks to interest income growth mostly driven by increased loan business and higher securities interest; which stemmed from a combination of the bank's First Wyoming Financial Corporation acquisition improvements in its balance sheet mix and additional income from its reverse mortgage-related assets.

Higher revenue and a continued decline in loan loss provisions in 2014 pushed WSFS Financial's net income up by 15% to $53.73 million during the year while the company's operating cash levels jumped by 17% to $67.06 million thanks to higher cash earnings.

Strategy

WSFS Financial reiterated its long-term growth strategy in 2015 which included growing the bank's lending business boosting its Trust and Wealth Management group's assets under administration and expanding Cash Connect's ATM customer base and customer cross-sell.

Beyond utilizing its community-oriented and local commercial lending teams the company has been growing its loan business and its branch reach through strategic acquisitions of banks and bank branches in target markets with preference toward markets in southeastern Pennsylvania. Its 2014 acquisition of First Wyoming Financial Corp for example bolstered WSFS' presence in Kent county while strengthening its position as the one of Delaware's top independent community banks.

Mergers and Acquisitions

In 2014 WSFS Financial acquired First Wyoming Financial Corporation along with its main subsidiary The First National Bank of Wyoming which would be folded into WSFS Bank.

In 2016 the company acquired Penn Liberty Financial a community bank with 10 branches in Pennsylvania's Montgomery and Chester counties.

Later in 2016 the company bought Philadelphia-based wealth management firm West Capital Management which targets institutions and wealthy individuals.

EXECUTIVES

Chairman President and CEO, Mark A. Turner, age 54, $639,336 total compensation

EVP and Chief Risk Officer, Thomas W. Kearney

EVP and Chief Retail Banking Officer, Richard M. (Rick) Wright, age 64, $337,173 total compensation

EVP and COO, Rodger Levenson, age 55, $348,721 total compensation

EVP and Chief Human Capital Officer, Peggy H. Eddens, age 61

EVP and Chief Wealth Officer, Paul D. Geraghty, $310,671 total compensation

EVP and CTO, S. James (Jim) Mazarakis, $337,173 total compensation

President Cash Connect, Tom Stevenson

CFO, Dominic Canuso

Vice President, John Olsen

Executive Vice President Human Resources, Robert Silwa

Assistant Vice President Network Services Director, Jason Berkowitz

Vice President Retail Office Manager, Patricia Frechette

Vice President Small Business Relationship Manager, Mike Ciavarelli

Executive Vice President, Cynthia Cole

Executive Vice President and Chief Technology Officer, James Mazarakis

Assistant Vice President Small business Lender Retail Office Manager, Carol Brindle

Senior Vice President, Cheryl Hughes

Vice President, John A Molster

Vice President and Retail Office Manager, CJ Murphy

Vice President of Technology, Albert Roop

Assistant Vice President Commercial Banking, Don Lee

Vice President Retail Administration, Vernita Dorsey

AVP Facilities Manager, Bill Hornung

Vice Chairman, Charles G. Cheleden, age 73

Auditors: KPMG LLP

LOCATIONS

HQ: WSFS Financial Corp
WSFS Bank Center, 500 Delaware Avenue, Wilmington, DE 19801
Phone: 302 792-6000
Web: www.wsfsbank.com

2012 Branches

	No.
Delaware	42
Pennsylvania	7
Nevada	1
Virginia	1
Total	**51**

PRODUCTS/OPERATIONS

2014 Sales

	$ mil.	% of total
Interest		
Loans including fees	137	57
Mortgage-backed securities	13	6
Investment securities	9	4
Noninterest		
Credit/debit card & ATM income	24	11
Deposit service charges	17	7
Wealth management income	17	7
Mortgage baning activities	4	2
Other	15	6
Total	**238**	**100**

COMPETITORS

Bank of America	M&T Bank
Citizens Financial	PNC Financial
Group	Sovereign Bank
Fulton Financial	TD Bank USA
JPMorgan Chase	The Bancorp

HISTORICAL FINANCIALS

Company Type: Public

Income Statement

FYE: December 31

	ASSETS ($ mil.)	NET INCOME ($ mil.)	INCOME AS % OF ASSETS	EMPLOYEES
12/16	6,765	64	0.9%	1,116
12/15	5,585	53	1.0%	947
12/14	4,853	53	1.1%	841
12/13	4,515	46	1.0%	762
12/12	4,375	31	0.7%	763
Annual Growth	11.5%	19.6%	—	10.0%

2016 Year-End Financials

Debt ratio: 3.24%
Return on equity: 10.08%
Cash ($ mil.): 821
Current ratio: —
Long-term debt ($ mil.): —

No. of shares (mil.): 31
Dividends
 Yield: 0.0%
 Payout: 12.1%
Market value ($ mil.): 1,455

	STOCK PRICE ($) FY Close	P/E High/Low	PER SHARE ($) Earnings	Dividends	Book Value
12/16	46.35	22 13	2.06	0.25	21.90
12/15	32.36	42 13	1.85	0.31	19.50
12/14	76.89	40 33	1.93	0.17	17.34
12/13	77.53	46 25	1.69	0.16	14.35
12/12	42.25	40 33	1.08	0.16	16.00
Annual Growth	2.3%	— —	17.4%	11.8%	8.2%

Wyndham Worldwide Corp

Wyndham Worldwide is one of the world's largest hospitality firms. Its portfolio includes some 8000 franchised hotels worldwide. Wyndham operates about 20 familiar hotel brands such as Days Inn Howard Johnson Ramada and Super 8. Wyndham also has a relationship with some 121000 vacation exchange and rental properties in about 110 countries. In addition its Wyndham Vacation Ownership operates vacation ownership resorts in North America Europe Latin America the Caribbean the Middle East Asia Pacific and the South Pacific. The company's revenues primarily come from franchise and hotel management fees membership dues and timeshare sales.

Operations

Wyndham operates in the following business segments: Hotel Group Destination Network and Vacation Ownership. The Vacation Ownership segment is the largest segment accounting for about 50% of the company's total sales. The Vacation Ownership segment develops markets and sells vacation ownership interests to individual consumers. It also provides consumer financing and provides property management services at resorts. The Destination Network segment provides vacation exchange services and products to owners of intervals of vacation ownership interests. It also manages and markets vacation rental properties on behalf of independent owners. The Hotel Group

segment franchises hotels and provides hotel management services for full-service and select limited-service hotels.

Geographic Reach

All of Wyndham's businesses have both domestic and international operations. However more than 75% of the company's revenues come from the US.

Sales and Marketing

While the hospitality industry targets both business and leisure travelers most of Wyndham's customers come from the leisure market. Wyndham markets its properties through several marketing channels including direct mail email telemarketing online distribution channels brochures magazines and travel agencies. Additionally it promotes its offerings to owners of resorts and vacation homes through trade shows. Wyndham spent $167 million on advertising and promotions in fiscal 2016.

Financial Performance

During fiscal 2016 Wyndham's revenue increased slightly to $5.6 billion compared to $5.54 billion in fiscal 2015. The company's net income decreased from $612 million in fiscal 2015 to $611 million in fiscal 2016.

Wyndham's net cash provided by operating activities decreased $18 million compared to the prior fiscal year. The decline reflected a $206 million increase in cash utilized for working capital (net change in assets and liabilities) primarily due to an increase in vacation ownership contract receivables and a reduction in accrued expenses.

Strategy

Wyndham is strategically focused on two objectives that it believes are essential to its business: increasing system size and strengthening customer value proposition. To increase its system size the company intends to acquire more properties add new rooms to existing properties and spur new construction by developing new and existing properties.

Mergers and Acquisitions

In 2016 the company acquired Latin America's leading F «n Hotels adding 26 management contracts across Argentina Peru Costa Rica Uruguay Paraguay Bolivia and the US including two new F «n-built Wyndham Grand hotels opening in Montevideo Uruguay and Asunci n Paraguay.

Also during 2016 the company acquired Blue Chip Holidays cottage and luxury lodge agency. The acquisition helped Wyndham expand its growing national portfolio.

Wyndham completed the acquisition of Dolce Hotels and Resorts for $57 million in 2015. Also that year the company acquired ResortQuest Whistler. The ResortQuest Whistler acquisition gave Wyndham its first property in Canada and added nearly 600 condominium units to the company's portfolio of vacation rental properties.

EXECUTIVES

Chairman and CEO, Stephen P. Holmes, age 61, $1,571,150 total compensation

EVP and CFO, Thomas G. (Tom) Conforti, age 58, $740,384 total compensation

President and CEO Wyndham Hotel Group, Geoffrey A. (Geoff) Ballotti, age 56, $740,384 total compensation

EVP and Chief Human Resources Officer, Mary R. Falvey, age 57

EVP and General Counsel, Scott G. McLester, age 55

SVP and Global CIO, Walter A. Yosafat, age 57

President and CEO Wyndham Destination Network, Gail Mandel, $565,391 total compensation

Senior Vice President Internal Audit, Glenn Robertson

Vice President International Tax, Scott Seiler

Vice President Business Development Strategic Sourcing Department, Terrence Gilligan
Executive Vice President Human Resources, Sara Salvatore
Vice President, Andrea Mattei
Vice President of Design, George L Scammell
RVP Ne, Joe Daly
Vice President Construction Services, Frank Campana
Vice President of Finance, Christiane Ciombor
Vice President of Finance Financial Reporting, Don Huber
Senior Vice President, Steve Meetre
Vice President Sales Administration, Scott Cavanaugh
Vice President of Human Resources, Suzanne Gregory
Vice President, Jasmine Chay
Vice President of Network Planning, Clement Bence
Senior Vice President Revenue Management, Kathy Maher
Vice President Global Sales Emea, Marc Stanley
Vice President Information Technology, Gus Bahamondes
Group Vice President Legal, Susan Crane
Vice President Sales and Marke, Tim Rector
Vice President Securitization and Risk Management, Jeffrey Leuenberger
Vice President, Carolyn Bonifacemesce
Senior Vice President Sales And Mrktg Regional, Terry Godfrey
Vice President, Tom Sharpin
Vice President of Human Resources, Lisa Maher
Executive Vice President Global Human Resources Wyndham Hotel Group, Faye Tylee
Vice President, David Unger
Vice President Finance Systems and Reporting, David Gutt
Vice President Sales, Steve Forsberg
Senior Vice President Marketing, Mark Young
Vice President and Treasurer, Jeff Leuenberger
Group Vice President, Mike Jablon
Area Vice President Human Resources, Amy B Krallman
Senior Vice President Government Affairs and Commercial Contracts, Richard Constable
Vice President Project Management, Nick Muir
National Sales Manager, Elizabeth Dexter
Regional Vice President, Kirk Hart
Senior Vice President Operations, Richard Maxfield
Vice President Sales and Marketing, Michael O'Dwyer
Vice President Global Sales, Eliot Hamlisch
Assistant To Global Chief Technology Officer and Senior Vice President, Suzanne Shortman
Vice President Global Learning and Development, Annmarie Fairweather
Vice President, Travis Miller
Vice President Lifestyle Brands, Glenn Moon
Treasurer, Michael Mueller
Auditors: Deloitte & Touche LLP

LOCATIONS

HQ: Wyndham Worldwide Corp
22 Sylvan Way, Parsippany, NJ 07054
Phone: 973 753-6000   Fax: 973 496-8906
Web: www.wyndhamworldwide.com

2016 Sales

	$ mil.	% of total
US	4,238	76
UK	253	5
Netherlands	243	4
Other regions	865	15
Total	5,599	100

PRODUCTS/OPERATIONS

2016 Sales

	% of total
Service and membership fees	45
Vacation ownership interest sales	29
Franchise fees	12
Consumer financing	8
Other	6
Total	100

2016 Sales

	$ mil.	% of total
Vacation Ownership	2,794	49
Destination Network	1,571	28
Hotel Group	1,309	23
Adjustments	(75)	-
Total	5,599	100

Selected Brands

Wyndham Vacation Ownership
  WorldMark by Wyndham
  Wyndham Vacation Resorts
Vacation Exchange & Rentals
  Canvas Holidays
  Cottages4you.com
  Cuendet
  Endless Vacation Rentals
  Landal GreenParks
  Novasol
Wyndham Hotel Group
  AmeriHost Inn
  Baymont Inn & Suites
  Days Inn
  Hawthorn Suites
  Howard Johnson
  Knights Inn
  Microtel Inns & Suites
  Ramada
  Super 8
  Travelodge
  Wingate by Windham
  Wyndham Hotels and Resorts

COMPETITORS

Accor North America	Hilton Worldwide
Best Western	Hyatt
Carlson Hotels	InterContinental
Disney Parks & Resorts	Hotels
FRHI Hotels and	Marriott
Resorts	Starwood Hotels &
Four Seasons Hotels	Resorts

HISTORICAL FINANCIALS

Company Type: Public

Income Statement

FYE: December 31

	REVENUE ($ mil.)	NET INCOME ($ mil.)	NET PROFIT MARGIN	EMPLOYEES
12/16	5,599	611	10.9%	37,800
12/15	5,536	612	11.1%	37,700
12/14	5,281	529	10.0%	34,400
12/13	5,009	432	8.6%	32,800
12/12	4,534	400	8.8%	32,500
Annual Growth	5.4%	11.2%		3.8%

2016 Year-End Financials

Debt ratio: 56.14%
Return on equity: 73.24%
Cash ($ mil.): 185
Current ratio: 0.89
Long-term debt ($ mil.): 5,283

No. of shares (mil.): 105
Dividends
  Yield: 0.0%
  Payout: 36.1%
Market value ($ mil.): 8,063

	STOCK PRICE ($) FY Close	P/E High/Low		PER SHARE ($) Earnings	Dividends	Book Value
12/16	76.37	15	11	5.53	2.00	6.76
12/15	72.65	18	14	5.14	1.68	8.35
12/14	85.76	21	16	4.18	1.40	10.37
12/13	73.69	23	16	3.21	1.16	12.64
12/12	53.21	20	13	2.75	0.92	14.06
Annual Growth	9.5%	—	—	19.1%	21.4%	(16.7%)

Xcel Energy Inc

Xcel Energy has accelerated its energy engine in utility markets across the US. The utility holding company distributes electricity to 3.6 million customers and natural gas to 2 million in eight states through its four regulated utilities. Colorado and Minnesota account for most of the company's customers. Xcel owns power plants that have combined capacity of more than 17500 MW of electricity. It also owns transmission and distribution lines as well as natural gas assets. It is investing in wind power with wind farms in Colorado Minnesota and Texas and more planned.

Operations

Xcel's reportable segments are Regulated Electric Utility Regulated Gas Utility and Other. Regulated Electric is the largest segment and produces about 85% of total revenue through the generation purchase transmission and distribution of electricity. Regulated Natural Gas transports stores and distributes natural gas to generate most of the remaining revenue.

The two power segments achieve their objectives through several subsidiaries: Northern States Power Minnesota (NSP-M) Northern States Power Wisconsin (NSP-W) the Public Service Company of Colorado (PSCo) and Southwestern Public Service (SPS).

Xcel owns and operates roughly 17500 MW of electric generating capacity and purchases additional power from third parties through long-term power purchase agreements. Generally Xcel?s power plants produce about two-thirds of its needs and the company purchases the other third. Of its generated electricity 40% comes from coal 40% from natural gas just less than 10% from nuclear and the rest from wind hydroelectric and other sources. Electricity flows to its customers over more than 20000 miles of Xcel?s transmission lines and through more than 1200 substations.

The Regulated Natural Gas segment purchases the natural gas from producers and contracts with transmission pipeline companies to move it to Xcel?s distributions facilities from there the company sends it on to its gas customers.

Geographic Reach

Minneapolis MN-based Xcel serves a number of US states. It?s Northern States Power Minnesota serves 2 million customers in North and South Dakota and in Minnesota. Northern States Power Wisconsin delivers energy to about 370000 customers in Wisconsin and Michigan. Public Service Company of Colorado provides energy to 2.8 million customers throughout the state while Southwestern Public Service Company serves nearly 400000 in New Mexico and Texas.

Xcel?s supply of natural gas comes from basins in Colorado Montana Wyoming Texas Kansas New Mexico and Canada.

Sales and Marketing

Xcel Energy's major commercial and industrial electric sales are to customers in the petroleum coal and food products industries. It also serves small commercial and industrial customers and produces significant electric retail sales from residential customers.

Financial Performance

In recent years the company?s financial performance produced steady revenue and slowly rising net income results. Revenue generally stayed between $10 billion and $11 billion while net income rose from about $600 million back in 2007 to more recent results near $1 billion.

For the year 2016 revenue rose marginally to $11.1 billion with electricity sales gaining a bit more than $200 million and natural gas sales tick-ing down. The amount of delivered electricity (kilowatt hours) dipped slightly but the dollar amount charged to customers rose. Natural gas experienced the opposite as prices charged to customers decreased while the amount of delivered natural gas rose about 1%.

Net income in 2016 rose 14% to a ten-year high of $1.1 billion. The year-over-year increase was primarily due to a favorable comparison to 2015 which saw a $130 million loss on Xcel?s Monticello power generation project.

Cash at year end was $84 million a negligible change from 2015. Cash activities were largely in line with previous years as operating activities provided $3.0 billion investing activities (mostly capital expenditures) used $3.3 billion and financing activities delivered $210 million largely through issuance of additional debt.

Strategy

Like many electricity companies Xcel Energy is pursuing a long-term shift towards carbon-neutral and renewable energy sources. It also invests in its infrastructure modernizing its grid for safety security and reliability. In the coming five years it anticipates spending $18.3 billion on such projects.

Infrastructure will receive the lion?s share of the $18.3 billion in capital expenditures. Electric transmission & gas distribution systems are targeted to receive $8.2 billion electric generation (such as maintenance of power facilities and refueling nuclear plants) is earmarked for $2.9 billion. Input fuel ? mainly natural gas ? is expected to collect $2.0 billion while the build out of its wind and solar energy sources are expected to receive $3.5 billion.

Of the $3.5 billion for renewables Xcel expects to allocate it to several projects including its 600 MW Rush Creek wind project in Colorado a proposed 750 MW wind generation facility for its NSP-Minnesota utility its 300 MW Dakota Range wind project and even an outreach endeavor to gain regulatory support for 1000 MW of self-build (i.e. customer-built) wind energy. With the exception of Rush Creek which receive approval in 2016 these projects are in various stages of regulatory approval.

HISTORY

The Minnesota Electric Light & Electric Motive Power Company was founded in 1881 and changed its name to Minnesota Brush Electric the next year. In the 1890s it provided street lighting and power for trolleys and became Minneapolis General Electric.

In 1909 Henry Byllesby formed rival firm Washington County Light and Power Co. (soon renamed Consumers Power Company) then created holding company Northern States Power Company of Delaware (NSPD). In 1910 he founded Standard Gas and Electric a holding company overseeing NSPD and many other US utilities.

NSPD bought Minneapolis General Electric in 1912 and Consumers Power was renamed the Northern States Power Company (NSP) in 1916. During the 1920s NSPD connected its subsidiaries via transmission lines. Byllesby died in 1924.

In 1931 NSP was placed under NSPD but the Public Utility Holding Company Act of 1935 dissolved Standard and NSPD. NSP became independent in the 1940s and spent $335 million on new facilities after WWII.

During the 1960s NSP moved into Michigan South Dakota and Wisconsin and brought its first nuclear power plant on line in 1964 (converted to natural gas in 1968). It began operating the Monticello and Prairie Island nukes in the early 1970s.

Company sales nearly doubled in the 1980s. In 1989 NSP created NRG Energy (incorporated 1992) to invest in independent power projects. The

Federal Energy Policy Act allowed wholesale power competition in 1992 and NSP lost nine of its 19 municipal customers.

NSP acquired Viking Gas Transmission which owned an interstate pipeline in 1993. It also began developing affordable housing. In 1995 NSP and Wisconsin Electric planned to merge but dropped the deal amid antitrust concerns. NSP continued to diversify forming telecommunications provider Seren Innovations in 1996 and starting its cable-testing business in 1997. The next year NSP formed a power marketing unit.

NRG Energy began a shopping spree abroad in 1994 buying interests in plants in Germany and Australia. In 1996 it bought a 48% stake in Bolivia's COBEE (increased to 99% in 2001). Also that year it acquired PacifiCorp's Pacific Generating unit which owned stakes in a dozen geographically scattered plants.

In 1999 NRG Energy gained nearly 7600 MW of capacity through power plant acquisitions in California Connecticut Massachusetts and New York. The next year NRG Energy picked up another 1700 MW in Louisiana and it agreed to buy fossil-fueled plants (1875 MW) from Delaware's Conectiv for $800 million (half of the deal was completed in 2001 the other half was canceled the following year). NSP spun off part of NRG in 2000 in an IPO.

Meanwhile as the utility-merger trend gathered steam in 1999 NSP agreed to acquire Denver-based New Century Engines in a $4.9 billion deal. The acquisition was completed in 2000 and the expanded company changed its name to Xcel Energy.

The next year Xcel sold nearly all of its stake in UK-based Yorkshire Power Group which had been held by New Century Energies to Innogy (now RWE npower). It sold its remaining 5% stake in Yorkshire Power in 2002. NRG purchased several Latin American projects from Swedish utility Vattenfall in 2001. NRG also agreed to purchase four coal-fired plants (2500 MW) in Ohio from FirstEnergy for $1.5 billion; however the deal was later canceled.

In 2002 Xcel repurchased the 26% stake in NRG that it sold to the public in 2000-01.

EXECUTIVES

EVP and Group President Operations, Kent T. Larson, age 57, $550,000 total compensation
Chairman President and CEO, Benjamin G. S. (Ben) Fowke, age 59, $1,200,000 total compensation
President Xcel Energy - Colorado, David L. Eves, age 59
SVP and CIO, David C. Harkness
EVP and Group President Utilities and Chief Administrative Officer, Marvin E. McDaniel, age 57, $550,000 total compensation
President Xcel Energy Michigan Wisconsin, Mark E. Stoering, age 56
SVP and Chief Nuclear Officer, Timothy (Tim) O'Connor, age 57
President Xcel Energy New Mexico Texas, David T. Hudson, age 56
President Xcel Energy Minnesota South Dakota North Dakota, Christopher B. (Chris) Clark, age 50
EVP and General Counsel, Scott M. Willensky, age 60, $505,000 total compensation
EVP and CFO, Robert C. (Bob) Frenzel, age 46, $397,500 total compensation
Vice President, Megan Scheller
Legal Secretary, Sara Parmenter
Vice President of Corporate Tax, James Duevel
Senior Vice President, Roy Palmer
Vice President Construction Operations and Maintenance, Tim Brossart
Treasurer Assistant, Brian Van Abel
Auditors: Deloitte & Touche LLP

LOCATIONS

HQ: Xcel Energy Inc
 414 Nicollet Mall, Minneapolis, MN 55401
Phone: 612 330-5500
Web: www.xcelenergy.com

PRODUCTS/OPERATIONS

2016 Sales

	$ mil.	% of total
Electric	9,501	85
Natural gas	1,532	14
Other	75	1
Eliminations	(2.4)	-
Total	**11,106**	**100**

COMPETITORS

AEP	Dynegy
ALLETE	FirstEnergy
Alliant Energy	NextEra Energy
Ameren	OGE Energy
Atmos Energy	PPL Corporation
Basin Electric Power	Public Service
Black Hills Power	Enterprise Group
CMS Energy	SCANA
CenterPoint Energy	WEC Energy
DTE	

HISTORICAL FINANCIALS

Company Type: Public

Income Statement

FYE: December 31

	REVENUE ($ mil.)	NET INCOME ($ mil.)	NET PROFIT MARGIN	EMPLOYEES
12/16	11,106	1,123	10.1%	11,512
12/15	11,024	984	8.9%	11,687
12/14	11,686	1,021	8.7%	11,691
12/13	10,914	948	8.7%	11,581
12/12	10,128	905	8.9%	11,198
Annual Growth	2.3%	5.5%	—	0.7%

2016 Year-End Financials

Debt ratio: 36.06%	No. of shares (mil.): 507
Return on equity: 10.36%	Dividends
Cash ($ mil.): 84	Yield: 0.0%
Current ratio: 0.88	Payout: 61.5%
Long-term debt ($ mil.): 14,194	Market value ($ mil.): 20,644

	STOCK PRICE ($) FY Close	P/E High/Low	Earnings	PER SHARE ($) Dividends	Book Value
12/16	40.70	21 16	2.21	1.36	21.73
12/15	35.91	20 16	1.94	1.28	20.89
12/14	35.92	18 13	2.03	1.20	20.20
12/13	27.94	17 14	1.91	1.11	19.21
12/12	26.71	16 14	1.85	1.07	18.19
Annual Growth	11.1%	— —	4.5%	6.2%	4.5%

Xerox Corp

Today?s Xerox Corp. is not a copy of its former self. With some 1.5 million devices under its management Xerox remains a leading seller of printers and copiers as well as technology for managing documents and other information services. The company aims to sell its extended portfolio of digital cloud-based automated and security-conscious products and services to its installed base of customers and new ones. But Xerox has been changed significantly through one split and one union. The company cleaved itself in two at the end of 2016. Xerox claimed document technology and related services while spinning off business process outsourcing to a new company Conduent. In 2018 Xerox agreed to become a part of Fujifilm through a combination of a joint venture the companies operate.

Change in Company Type

Xerox agreed to become majority owned by Fujifilm through a joint venture between the companies. When the deal is concluded Fujifilm would own 50.1% and Xerox 49.9%. The cost of the deal would be about $6.1 billion. As part of the agreement Xerox shareholders got a cash dividend totaling $2.5 billion ($9.80 a share). The companies plan to achieve about $1.7 billion in savings following the combination. The savings would include cutting about 10000 jobs. The companies have operated the Fuji Xerox joint venture which has sold office equipment in the Asia-Pacific region for decades.

The companies said the combination will enable them to exploit areas such as high-speed inkjet industrial print and workplace tools while pivoting off Fujifilm's stable of technologies. The company will have joint headquarters in Norwalk Connecticut and Tokyo. The deal has been approved the boards of directors of the companies and it is expected to close in the second half of 2018.

That deal came about a year after Xerox split its business process outsourcing business into a separate company Conduent. After the split Xerox began to streamline operations intensify focus on its products and markets and make better use of resources. It had expected to save $1.5 billion over three years in efficiency improvements and reduced costs.

Operations

Xerox Corp. operates in two segments Document Technology and Services.

Document Technology accounting for more than 60% of revenue sells Xerox's mid-range products (about 60% of segment revenue) small and mid-sized business offerings (about 20%) and high-end products for graphic communications and large clients (about 25%).

The Services segment generating about a third of revenue includes its legacy Document Outsourcing business as well as a set of communications and marketing products and services that had been part of the business process outsourcing (BPO) business and were transferred to Xerox upon the company breakup.

Geographic Reach

Xerox Corp. operates in more than 160 countries with about 60% of sales coming from the US and about 30% from Europe. The company has primary facilities in Canada France India Ireland Jamaica Guatemala Mexico the Netherlands Philippines Romania the UK and the US.

The company outsources a significant amount of its manufacturing to third parties while maintaining its own production facilities in the US Ireland France and the Netherlands.

Sales and Marketing

Xerox Corp. markets its products and services by geography sales channel type and line of business. It complements its global sales team and sales website with a network of third-party sales channels such as independent agents dealers value-added resellers and systems integrators. Xerox customers are in a wide range of businesses that include banking education government healthcare manufacturing and retail.

Financial Performance

Xerox Corp.?s revenue in 2015 was $18 billion (counting revenue from operations that became part of Conduent) and $10.8 billion (not counting Conduent operations) in 2016. Net income was $474 million in 2015 and a net loss of $477 million

in 2016. Cash flow from operations was $1.7 billion in 2015 and $1.1 billion in 2016.

In reporting its financials for 2016 and 2015 Xerox Corp. took into account only its post-separation operations which did not include contributions from Conduent. It backtracked and eliminated Conduent operations from 2015 results to show a like-to-like comparison.

Xerox reported revenue of $10.8 billion in 2016 down 6% from 2015. Equipment sales dropped 9% in 2016 because of lower sales of entry and mid-range products stemming from the timing of product launches as well as lower OEM sales. The decline was also partially driven by lower sales in the developing markets along with lower revenue from the company?s high-end products and lower sales to partner Fuji Xerox. The company also saw a decline in annuity/post-sale revenue because of lower sales for maintenance services supplies and financing.

Xerox reported a $477 million net loss in 2016 a reversal from its $474 million profit in 2015. An increase in restructuring and related costs in 2016 helped drive the company to a loss.

Cash flow from operations dropped to $1.02 billion in 2016 from $1.08 million in 2015 because of lower earnings.

Strategy

If Xerox were a start-up company its strategy might be called a pivot — turning away from a defining but fading business to a different business that has more perceived upside. While documents remain a key Xerox component it is shifting to services in a big way. About 75% of Xerox?s revenue comes from what it calls post-sales which is revenue that follows the sale of equipment. Post-sale sources of revenue include document services equipment maintenance services consumable supplies and financing and other elements.

As a large well-established company Xerox has challenges in trying to change. Sometimes large organizations are unable to adapt quickly enough to changing markets and customer preferences? But it also has a big advantage: a large base of customers and more than 1.5 million Xerox-managed devices serving businesses throughout the world. The company seeks to exploit that resource to sell new products and expanded services.

With new products Xerox is targeting what it believes are growth areas which include document outsourcing and the subcategory of managed print services in the small and medium business market. The company emphasizes the medium-business sector with a range of products.

In 2016 Xerox added two new inkjet presses to its portfolio the cut-sheet Brenva HD and the continuous-speed Trivor 2400 as well at ConnectKey-enabled i-Series multifunction printers which are equipped with ready-to-use apps which are available from the Xerox App Gallery. Xerox has what it called the biggest product launch in its history in 2017 rolling out nearly 30 ConnectKey-enabled printers and multifunction devices with cloud connectivity and access to more features and apps.

Xerox is targeting costs as well as developing and introducing new products. In 2016 Xerox started a three-year Strategic Transformation program to accelerate cost productivity. The company expects to increase productivity and reduce costs by $500 million a year over the three years compared to $300 million to $350 million for each of the previous three years. The program targets efficiency gains in delivery remote connectivity sales productivity pricing design and supply chain.

Mergers and Acquisitions

Following the breakup Xerox Corp. remains on the prowl for acquisitions. Its recent purchases included:

— Global Imaging Systems a multiple-brand dealer in Iowa and MT Business Technologies a

multi-brand dealer in Ohio in 2017. The deals expand Xerox?s distribution in those states.

— Intellinex formerly Intrepid Learning Solutions a Seattle-based provider of outsourced learning services.

— RSA Medical a provider of health assessment and risk management for members interacting with health and life insurance companies.

— Healthy Communities Institute a California-based company with a cloud platform for health analytics.

— inVentiv Patient Access Solutions a patient access and reimbursement services hub.

EXECUTIVES

EVP and Chief Commercial Officer, Kevin M. Warren, age 54

CEO, Jeffrey (Jeff) Jacobson, age 57, $812,500 total compensation

President Xerox Canada, John Corley

EVP; President International Operations, Herv © Tessler, age 53

SVP and Chief Strategy and Marketing Officer, Farooq Muzaffar, age 42

EVP; President North America Operations, Michael (Mike) Feldman, age 50

EVP and Chief Human Resources Officer, Darrell L. Ford, age 52

SVP and Chief Delivery Officer, Yehia Maaty

EVP and CFO, William F. (Bill) Osbourn, age 52

SVP and CTO, Stephen (Steve) Hoover, age 56

President Northern Southern and Central European Operations, Al Varney

EVP General Counsel and Corporate Secretary, Sarah Hlavinka McConnell, age 52

Senior Vice President and Group President of Healthcare Provider Solutions, Chad Harris

Assistant Vice President Information Technology Vendor Management, James Burnell

Legal Secretary, Joni Woo

National Account Manager, Jerry de Frates

Senior Vice President and Senior Counsel, Michelle Marlett

Vice President, Dino Ventresca

Senior Vice President Of Technology, Stephen Garner

Executive Vice President Of Cause Branding And Nonprofit Marketing, Christina Paliouras

Vice President of Environmental Policy, Daniel Renkas

Vice President Sales Operations US Solutions Group Xerox, Charles Alexander

Senior Vice President Major Account O, Patricia Elizondo

Senior Vice President and Managing Director Xerox Healthcare Provider Solutions, Justin Lanning

Vice President Of Sales, Michael Hartman

Senior Vice President United States Client Operations, Kelly Jenson

Svp Sales - It Outsourcing, George Love

Vice President Information Technology, Karin Gleissle

Vice President, Ajay Dhingra

Vice President, Ivy McKinney

Vice President, Sharon Haight

Vice President And Corporate Counsel, Stephanie F Grossman

Regional Vice President, Gary Sentiff

Senior Vice President Homeland Security, Martin Gunter

Vice President Technology, Jack Devos

Senior Vice President Head of Financial Services Sales, Alex Hillman

Vice President, David J Tritschler

Vice President And Corporate Counsel, Hope Shimabuku

Division Vice President, Todd Crouse

Vice President Sales, Lynn Macdougall

Vice President And Client Executive, Andrew Hunkin

Vice President Service Delivery, Robert Scarry

Vice President Offering Development Xerox Print Services, Mike Heacock

Vice President Information Technology Program Management, Lisa Withers

Corporate Vice President and Chief Financial Officer Xerox Technology Business, Grant Fitz

Senior Vice President and Chief Accountant Commercial, Cara Shore

Senior Vice President And Senior Corporate Counsel, Robert H Strasser

Vice President Fare Collection Solutions, Steve Frazzini

Vice President of Strategy and Alliances, Tom Kavassalis

Senior Vice President and Managing Director State Enterprise Solutions Customer Care, Michael Langenohl

Assistant Vice President Systems Development, Russ Klein

Senior Vice President And Group Counsela, Clay Scheitzach

Vice President Global Advertising, Barbara Basney

Vice President, Paul Smith

Senior Vice President, Trent Thrash

Vice President Client Support Services, Linda Harrison

Senior Vice President Of Transaction Services, Scott Bashrum

Executive Vice President XBS, Mike Peffer

Vice President, Richard David

Vice President and General Manager, Steve Simpson

Vice President Sales, Michael Murphy

Senior Vice President, Brian Helmey

Vice President Information Technology, Helena Murrin

Vice President Client Services, Michael Sheridan

Vice President, Karen Moore

Division Vice President, Bob Nash

Vice President Market, Dale Sedgwick

Vice President Information Technology Program Services, Tracy Johnson

Vice President, Michael Weldon

Vice President Operations North Dakota, Greg Bryant

National Sales Manager, David Stahler

Vice President and Country Director, Aman Mustafa

Vice President Strategy And Workplace Services, David Nappi

Vice President Global Delivery Im Group, Robert Lyubomirsky

Sbu Division Vice President, Jim Selwood

Vice President, Charles Poynter

Vice President and Partner, Jan Mccarty

Vice President Information Services, Jake Oner

Vice President National Field Controller, Nate Loomis

Vice President, Shreve Bill

Vice President, Dick Jennings

Vice President Of Business Development, Matt Bologna

Xsbg Vice President Of Finance, Enos Steve

Vice President, Terence Oi

National Account Manager, Friedman Karen

Vice President Of Operations, Jeff Dalrymple

Vice President Service, Betty Mitchell

Vice President Finance Us Solutions Group, Dave Aquilla

Regional Vice President, Jim Forrest

Vpse, Jules Roche

Vice President Mps Business Operations, Robert Coward

National Account Manager, Amanda Carmichael

Vice President Sales, Kendall Brown

Vice President, Eric West

Vice President, Carl R Bothner

Senior Vice President, Joe Valenti

Division Vice President, Rebecca Taylor

Vice President Recruitment, James Siena

Senior Vice President, Nicola Posa

Vice President, Gavin Jordan-smith

Senior Vice President And Managing Director Of Mmis East, Dan Dwyer

Vice President and Chief Innovation Officer For GHS, Lydie Quebe

Vice President Of Operations Travel And Retail, Patrick White

Vice President Supply Chain Strategy, Alan Gamble

Senior Vice President Supplies Business Group, Franklin Edmonds

Vice President, Bob Tisone

Vice President And Operations, Kathy Mangan

Vice President Operations, Tom Hinds

Executive Vice President Operations, Chris Weadick

Vice President, Victor Lee

Assistant Vice President Recruiting Operations, Craig Deaton

Vice President Human Resources And Administration, George Dourlias

Assistant Vice President Talent Acquisition And Staffing, Darrin Johnson

Assistant Vice President Talent Leader Executive And Corporate Talent, James Munson

Vice President Business Development, Gloria D'Arezzo

Vice President Human Resources, Jamie Son

Vice President Us Operations, Karen Jacques

Vice President Of Sales Commercial Health Plans, Robert Levy

Vice President Of Sales, Tami Angelo

Vice President People Information Technology, Michael Macduff

Vice President And Group Controller, Sarra Kell

Vice President Applications And Project Management Office, Kim Ringold

Sbu Director And Vice President, Tom Boyle

Vice President and Senior Corporate Counsel Legal, Don Delorenz

Senior Vice President Southwest Operations, Mary Nelson

Vice President Midrange Hosting, Martin Webb

Senior Vice President Global Service Operations An, Jimmy Brown

Senior Vice President Managing Director Hro Services, Esther Laspisa

Vice President Human Resources Latin America, Cristian Parada

Medical Director, Guillermo Delatorre

Assistant Vice President, Daneen Muto

Executive Vice President, Debbie Redman

Vice President Service Delivery, Ellen Amarose

National Sales Manager, Erika Albuquerque

Vice President, Debra Early

Vice President Global Sales, Ed Jakubik

Vice President Of Process Excellence Healthcare Paye, Oxana Dantchenko

Vice President Strategy and Entry Products OSBG, Tracey Koziol

Executive Vice President And President Corporate O, James Firestone

Vice President and Chief Accounting Officer, Joseph Mancini

Vice President Of Operations, Gayle Cambre

Vice President, David Moreland

Corporate Vice President and President Project Management Office, James Lesko

Vice President, Jeffrey Dalrymple

Assistant Vice President, Michael Normandin

Senior Vice President, Sherry Jones

Vice President of Sales, Fernando Perez-coira

Vice President Business Development, Brian Vann

Vice President And Corporate Counsel, Jonathon Melton

Vice President Account Executive, Jeffrey Cutts

Auditors: PricewaterhouseCoopers LLP

LOCATIONS

HQ: Xerox Corp
P.O. Box 4505, 201 Merritt 7, Norwalk, CT 06851-1056
Phone: 203 968-3000
Web: www.xerox.com

2016 Sales

	$ mil.	% of total
US	6,403	59
Europe	2,861	27
Other regions	1,507	14
Total	**10,771**	**100**

PRODUCTS/OPERATIONS

2016 Sales

	$ mil.	% of total
Annuity revenue	8,246	77
Equipment sales	2,525	23
Total	**10,771**	**100**

2016 Sales

	$ mil.	% of total
Document Technology	6,709	62
Services	3,505	33
Other	557	5
Total	**10,771**	**100**

Selected Services

Banking Industry Solutions
Communication & Marketing
Document Management Landing
Document Transaction Processing Services
Education Solutions
Enterprise Content Management
Government Solutions
Healthcare Industry Solutions
Managed Print Services
Manufacturing Industry Solutions
Retail Industry Solutions
Workflow Automation

Selected Products

Office (commercial government and education sectors)
  Copiers
  Displays
  Multifunction devices (copy fax print scan)
  Printers
  Projectors
  Scanners
Production (graphics communications industry and large corporations)
  Digital presses
  High-volume printers
  Software
Other
  Services
  Wide-format printers

COMPETITORS

Accenture	IBM
Agfa	Infosys
Aon	Konica Minolta
Brother Industries	Kyocera Document
Canon	Solutions
Capgemini	Lexmark
Computer Sciences	NEC
Corp.	Oc:©
Convergys	Oki Data
Dell	Olivetti
Eastman Kodak	Panasonic Corp
Epson	Pitney Bowes
FUJIFILM	Sharp Corp.
Fujitsu	Tata Consultancy
Genpact	TeleTech
HP	Toshiba
Heidelberger	Unisys
Druckmaschinen	Wipro
Hitachi	

Company Type: Public

Income Statement

FYE: December 31

	REVENUE ($ mil.)	NET INCOME ($ mil.)	NET PROFIT MARGIN	EMPLOYEES
12/16	10,771	(477)	—	37,600
12/15	18,045	474	2.6%	143,600
12/14	19,540	969	5.0%	147,500
12/13	21,435	1,159	5.4%	143,100
12/12	22,390	1,195	5.3%	147,600
Annual Growth	(16.7%)	—	—	(29.0%)

2016 Year-End Financials

Debt ratio: 34.81%	No. of shares (mil.): 253
Return on equity: (-6.59%)	Dividends
Cash ($ mil.): 2,223	Yield: 0.1%
Current ratio: 1.50	Payout: —
Long-term debt ($ mil.): 5,305	Market value ($ mil.): 2,214

	STOCK PRICE ($) FY Close	P/E High/Low		PER SHARE ($) Earnings	Dividends	Book Value
12/16	8.73	—	—	(1.96)	1.24	19.78
12/15	10.63	8	6	1.68	1.12	37.21
12/14	13.86	4	3	3.24	1.00	39.34
12/13	12.17	3	2	3.64	0.92	42.58
12/12	6.82	2	2	3.52	0.68	38.80
Annual Growth	6.4%	—	—	—	16.2%	(15.5%)

XPO Logistics, Inc.

XPO Logistics is a leading provider of third-party logistics and one of the largest less-than-truckload (LTL) carriers in North America. (LTL carriers consolidate freight from multiple shippers into a single truckload.) XPO owns the largest natural gas truck fleet in Europe and it offers domestic and international freight forwarding services as well as truckload freight brokerage service to more than 50000 customers across North America Asia and Europe. It operates through more than 1400 locations. The company was founded in 1989 as Express-1 Expedited Solutions.

Operations

XPO's primary segments include transportation (around 65% of total sales) and logistics (35%).Transportation provides freight brokerage last mile LTL full truckload and global forwarding services. Logistics provides a range of contract logistics services.

Geographic Reach

XPO is stationed in Greenwich Connecticut and its European headquarters is in Lyon France. It operates through more than 1400 locations across the US and in some three dozen countries. The US is its largest market accounting for 60% of its total revenue.

Sales and Marketing

XPO has more than 10000 independent owner-operators under contract to provide drayage expedite last mile and LTL services to customers. It also has 50000 independent brokered carriers representing approximately 1 million trucks on the road.

More than 50000 customers are served in a wide range of industries including high-tech retail e-commerce manufacturing telecommunications aerospace and defense life sciences healthcare medical equipment agriculture and food and beverage. The retail and e-commerce sector accounts for the largest portion of the company?s revenue at roughly 25% followed by food and beverage at 15%.

Financial Performance

XPO has experienced monumental growth over the years due to a flurry of acquisitions. Revenues almost doubled from $7.6 billion in 2015 to $14.6 billion in 2016. The record-shattering growth was driven by a massive 92% increase in sales from each of its logistics and transportation segments largely fueled by its Norbert Dentressangle and Con-way acquisitions.

After suffering through several straight years of net losses XPO posted net income of $69 million in 2016 mainly due to the surge in revenue and gains made on foreign currency translations. In addition XPO's cash flow from operations skyrocketed from $91 million in 2015 to $625 million in 2016 mainly due to its milestone revenue and net income totals.

Strategy

XPO's strategy for growth revolves around making strategic acquisitions and maintaining synergies from these transactions. As a result of purchasing a 67% stake in European logistics provider Norbert Dentressangle and US-based trucking provider Con-way in 2015 XPO has experienced record-setting revenues. The Norbert Dentressangle acquisition significantly extended XPO's geographical reach into Europe while the Con-way purchase quickly made XPO one of the leaders in the LTL and trucking market.

XPO also focuses on developing strong synergies with newly acquired companies to maximize efficiency and save on costs. For example sales general and administrative expense (SGA) as percentage of revenue decreased to 11% in 2016 compared to 15% in 2015. The decrease was attributed to a reduction in acquisition-related costs a favorable change in the company's business operations mix stemming from the Con-way acquisition and the cost-saving measures implemented as part of the integration of acquired businesses particularly within its LTL service operations.

Mergers and Acquisitions

XPO's strategy for growth involves making significant acquisitions that extend its global reach or add new product and service offerings.

In a sweeping move for the logistics industry XPO in 2015 acquired a 67% stake in Norbert Dentressangle a large transportation and logistics provider in Europe. XPO bought Norbert for $3.53 billion in order to significantly up-size its global reach. The deal created the world's second-largest freight brokerage firm by revenue.

In late 2015 XPO also obtained Con-way one of the largest trucking providers in the US. XPO purchased Con-way for $2.3 billion in a milestone deal that made XPO one of the largest freight transportation and logistics providers in the US transforming it from a logistics middleman into a company generating one-third of its revenue from its own truck fleet.

Also that year the company picked up UX Specialized Logistics (UX) a North American provider of last mile logistics services for major retail chains and e-commerce companies for $59 million. The acquisition expanded the company?s network for heavy goods home delivery and added more density to its growing e-commerce logistics footprint.

EXECUTIVES

Chairman and CEO, Bradley S. Jacobs, age 60, $607,000 total compensation
Managing Director LogisticsÂ–Europe, Malcolm Wilson
President Less-Than-Truckload (LTL), Tony Brooks
CIO, Mario A. Harik, age 36
President of Transportation North America, Christopher R. Synek
President Intermodal, Paul V. Smith
CFO, John J. Hardig, age 52, $498,385 total compensation
Chief Strategy Officer, Scott B. Malat, age 40, $472,308 total compensation
COO and CEO Europe, Troy A. Cooper, age 47, $511,539 total compensation
Chief Human Resources Officer, Meghan A. Henson
Managing Director TransportÂ–Europe, Luis-Angel Gomez Izaguirre
President Supply Chain Americas and Asia Pacific, Ashfaque Chowdhury
President Last Mile, Charles Hitt
Vice President Human Resources, Angela F Gibbons
Senior Vice President Strategic Accounts, Lyndon Cron
Senior Vice President Strategic Accounts, Greg Russo
Vice President Strategic Accounts, Brent Stark
Vice President of Transportation, Don Ingersoll
Senior Vice President of Acquisitions, Thomas Connolly
Vice President Information Technology, Eric Christian
National Account Manager, Jeremy Watkins
National Account Manager, Blake Ugron
Vice President Strategic Accounts, Michael Doumas
Vice President Strategic Accounts, Keith Weaver
Vice President Controller Bus Unit, Brenda Shepherd
Vice President of Strategic Accounts, Andy Sommers
Branch President, Ken Howard
Vice President Strategic Accounts, Bob Giarratano
Assistant Vice President Operations, Tim Donnelly
Auditors: KPMG LLP

LOCATIONS

HQ: XPO Logistics, Inc.
Five American Lane, Greenwich, CT 06831
Phone: 855 976-6951
Web: www.xpologistics.com

2016 Sales

	$ mil.	% of total
United States	8,758	60
North America (excluding United States)	322	2
France	1,902	13
United Kingdom	1,700	12
Europe (excluding France and United Kingdom)	1,644	11
Asia	264	2
Other	27	.
Total	**14,619**	**100**

PRODUCTS/OPERATIONS

2016 Sales

	$ mil.	% of total
Transportation	9,457	64
Logistics	5,323	36
Eliminations	(161.8)	.
Total	**14,619**	**100**

Service

Service
Last Mile
Intermodal
Global Forwarding
Supply Chain
Expedite
Freight Brokerage

COMPETITORS

Alliance Air	New Penn Motor Express
C.H. Robinson	Panther Expedited
Worldwide	Services

DHL
Daylight Transport
Expeditors
FedEx
Forward Air
J.B. Hunt

Ryder System
Schneider National
Towne Air Freight
UPS
YRC Worldwide

HISTORICAL FINANCIALS

Company Type: Public

Income Statement

	REVENUE ($ mil.)	NET INCOME ($ mil.)	NET PROFIT MARGIN	EMPLOYEES
12/17	15,380	340	2.2%	95,000
12/16	14,619	69	0.5%	87,000
12/15	7,623	(191)	—	89,000
12/14	2,356	(63)	—	10,000
12/13	702	(48)	—	2,259
Annual Growth	116.3%	—	—	154.7%

2017 Year-End Financials

Debt ratio: 35.88%
Return on equity: 10.79%
Cash ($ mil.): 396
Current ratio: 1.20
Long-term debt ($ mil.): 4,417

No. of shares (mil.): 119
Dividends
 Yield: —
 Payout: —
Market value ($ mil.): 10,983

	STOCK PRICE ($) FY Close	P/E High/Low		PER SHARE ($) Earnings	Dividends	Book Value
12/17	91.59	34	16	2.45	0.00	30.06
12/16	43.16	87	34	0.53	0.00	24.31
12/15	27.25	—	—	(2.65)	0.00	24.81
12/14	40.88	—	—	(2.00)	0.00	21.38
12/13	26.29	—	—	(2.26)	0.00	14.93
Annual Growth	36.6%	—	—	—	—	19.1%

YOSEMITE FARM CREDIT, ACA

LOCATIONS

HQ: YOSEMITE FARM CREDIT, ACA
 806 W MONTE VISTA AVE, TURLOCK, CA 953827242
Phone: 209 667-2366
Web: WWW.YOSEMITEFARMCREDIT.COM

HISTORICAL FINANCIALS

Company Type: Private

Income Statement

FYE: December 31

	ASSETS ($ mil.)	NET INCOME ($ mil.)	INCOME AS % OF ASSETS	EMPLOYEES
12/15	2,368	41	1.7%	100
12/14	2,154	38	1.8%	—
12/13	1,993	37	1.9%	—
12/12	1,879	37	2.0%	—
Annual Growth	8.0%	3.3%	—	—

2015 Year-End Financials

Debt ratio: —
Return on equity: 46.70%
Cash ($ mil.): 2
Current ratio: —
Long-term debt ($ mil.): —

Dividends
 Yield: —
 Payout: —
Market value ($ mil.): —

YRC Worldwide Inc

YRC Worldwide stands for more than Your Regional Carrier. The company has one of the largest less-than-truckload (LTL) networks in North America with local regional national and international capabilities. YRC Worldwide is a holding company that operates through such subsidiaries as YRC Freight and YRC Reimer which transport goods for manufacturing wholesale retail and government customers in the US Canada and certain international markets as well as YRC Regional Transportation which provides regional next-day ground services in the US Canada Mexico and Puerto Rico through subsidiaries New Penn USF Holland and USF Reddaway.

HISTORY

In 1924 A. J. Harrell established a trucking company in conjunction with his Oklahoma City bus line and Yellow Cab franchise. Harrell's Yellow Transit trucking operation hauled less-than-truckload (LTL) shipments between Oklahoma City and Tulsa. By 1944 Yellow had more than 50 independent subsidiaries in Illinois Indiana Kansas Kentucky Missouri and Texas. That year the company was sold to an investment firm and renamed Yellow Transit Freight Lines. But Yellow's policy of paying high dividends stunted its growth and by 1951 it faced bankruptcy.

George Powell Sr. took over in 1952 and turned Yellow around. His son George Powell Jr. became CEO in 1957 and the company went public two years later. George Jr. focused the company on long-haul interstate shipments and started buying up other trucking companies.

In 1965 Yellow expanded to the West Coast and the Southeast by purchasing Watson-Wilson Transportation System. Changing its name to Yellow Freight System (1968) the company acquired part of Norwalk Truck Lines and its routes in the Northeast (1970) and Adley Express (1972) providing new East Coast routes. Yellow extended routes into the Pacific Northwest by buying Republic Freight Systems in 1975. Its 1978 purchase of Braswell Motor Freight Lines consolidated its routes in California Texas and the Southeast. Yellow's only deviation from route acquisitions was its $4 million investment in oil firm Overland Energy in 1976 which it dissolved in the early 1980s.

The company was unprepared however when Congress deregulated trucking routes and shipping rates in 1980. Yellow upgraded its aging depots and terminals but profits still declined by 1983. In 1982 Yellow Freight formed a holding corporation (renamed Yellow Corporation in 1992). George Powell III took over from his father as CEO in 1990. Yellow purchased Preston Trucking an overnight freight hauler in 1992.

In 1994 Yellow Freight was hit by a 24-day Teamsters' strike that allowed nonunion carriers to gain a chunk of its market. The next year struggling during industry price wars it reported a $30 million loss. Yellow laid off about 250 employees mostly from Yellow Freight. George III resigned in 1996 and Maurice "Mr. Fix-it" Myers became CEO. Myers began moving the firm from a one-size-fits-all LTL trucker to a more flexible customer-responsive trucking and logistics firm.

Yellow Freight was restructured in 1997 into decentralized business units to improve customer service and hundreds of workers were laid off. The misfortunes of other companies also created good fortune for Yellow: UPS went on strike and rail traffic was still snarled from the 1996 Union Pacific-Southern Pacific merger.

To expand international operations Yellow created YCS International in 1998 (renamed Yellow Global in 2000). It also secured a five-year labor contract with its unions ending the danger of a strike. Loss-making Preston was sold to three company executives and Yellow acquired regional carriers Action Express (1998) and Jevic Transportation (1999).

Myers drove off into the sunset in 1999 to take over another troubled giant Waste Management and Yellow Freight president William Zollars became CEO of Yellow Corp. In 2000 Yellow and two venture capital firms set up online transportation marketplace transportation.com to provide freight-forwarding and multimodal brokerage services.

Yellow integrated Action Express and WestEx into Saia Motor Freight Line in 2001. The next year Yellow renamed its Yellow Freight subsidiary Yellow Transportation. The company created SCS Transportation to act as a holding company for its regional nonunion carriers Saia and Jevic. Also in 2002 Yellow combined transportation.com with its other logistics services to form Meridian IQ. That same year Yellow spun off SCS Transportation (later Saia Inc.). The next year Yellow and other leading LTL carriers negotiated a new contract with the Teamsters union.

Also in 2003 Yellow bought rival Roadway and became Yellow Roadway Corporation. The company expanded in 2005 with the acquisition of USF. The following year Yellow Roadway changed its name to YRC Worldwide and in 2007 it also changed the name of its Meridian IQ unit to YRC Logistics.

In order to reduce costs and improve its operating efficiency YRC Worldwide restructrued its operations and integrated its Roadway and Yellow Transportation units in March 2009. In mid-2011 the company appointed James Welch as its new CEO. Welch served at Yellow Transportation as CEO and later on as president and CEO of Dynamex. He succeeds William Zollars who retired as CEO of YRC.

YRC Worldwide formerly reported a Truckload segment which included the operations of USF Glen Moore a provider of US truckload services. Glen Moore concluded operations in December 2011 when some of its fleet was sold to a third-party and the rest was redeployed to YRC Freight and Regional Transportation companies. Truckload had accounted for only about 1% to 2% of sales over its last few years.

As part of its focus on North America YRC Worldwide sold its 65% interest in its China-based joint venture Shanghai Jiayu Logistics Co. Ltd. to its Chinese JV partner for an undisclosed amount in 2012.

EXECUTIVES

CEO and Director, James L. Welch, age 63, $850,000 total compensation
President YRC Freight, Thomas J. (T.J.) O'Connor, age 56, $280,257 total compensation
President Holland, Scott D. Ware, age 56, $395,000 total compensation
President and COO, Darren D. Hawkins, age 47, $481,000 total compensation
President New Penn, Donald R. (Don) Foust, age 59
VP General Counsel and Corporate Secretary, James A. Fry, age 55, $259,474 total compensation
VP and Controller, Stephanie D. Fisher, age 40
CIO, Jason T. Ringgenberg
Chief Customer Officer, Justin M. Hall, age 37, $239,167 total compensation
President Reddaway, Bob Stone
Vice President And Treasurer, Mark D Boehmer
Vice President Of Pricing, Brian Thompson

Vice President Human Resources and Benefits, Sandra Stocke
Vice President Cash Management, Joe Whitsel
Vice President of Quality, Melissa Tomlen
Senior Vice President of Marketing, Bill Crowe
Vice President Controller, Tom Ventura
Vice President Corporate Account Sales, Chad Clark
Division Vice President, Dan Gatta
VP Legal and Regulatory Compliance, Andrean Horton
Vp Ir, Anthony Carreno
Chairman, James E. (Jim) Hoffman, age 64
Auditors: KPMG LLP

LOCATIONS

HQ: YRC Worldwide Inc
10990 Roe Avenue, Overland Park, KS 66211
Phone: 913 696-6100
Web: www.yrcw.com

PRODUCTS/OPERATIONS

2016 Sales

	$ mil.	% of total
YRC Freight	2,958	63
Regional Transportation	1,739	37
Elimination	(0.7)	-
Total	**4,697**	**100**

2016 Sales

	$ mil.	% of total
United States	4,596	98
Foreign	101	2
Total	**4,697**	**100**

COMPETITORS

ABF Freight System	Landstar System
ArcBest	Mullen Group
C.H. Robinson Worldwide	Old Dominion Freight
Central Freight Lines	Saia
Estes Express	Schneider National
FedEx Freight	UPS Freight
J.B. Hunt	UPS Supply Chain Solutions

HISTORICAL FINANCIALS

Company Type: Public

Income Statement

FYE: December 31

	REVENUE ($ mil.)	NET INCOME ($ mil.)	NET PROFIT MARGIN	EMPLOYEES
12/16	4,697	21	0.5%	32,000
12/15	4,832	0	0.0%	32,000
12/14	5,068	(67)	—	33,000
12/13	4,865	(83)	—	32,000
12/12	4,850	(140)	—	32,000
Annual Growth	**(0.8%)**	**—**		**0.0%**

2016 Year-End Financials

Debt ratio: 56.33%
Return on equity: ***.***.**%
Cash ($ mil.): 136
Current ratio: 1.39
Long-term debt ($ mil.): 980

No. of shares (mil.): 32
Dividends
  Yield: —
  Payout: —
Market value ($ mil.): 431

	STOCK PRICE ($) FY Close	P/E High/Low	PER SHARE ($) Earnings	Dividends	Book Value
12/16	13.28	25 10	0.65	0.00	(12.82)
12/15	14.18	1125614	0.02	0.00	(11.80)
12/14	22.49	— —	(3.00)	0.00	(15.47)
12/13	17.37	— —	(8.96)	0.00	(58.73)
12/12	6.75	— —	(19.20)	0.00	(78.88)
Annual Growth	**18.4%**		**—**	**—**	**—**

Yum China Holdings Inc

LOCATIONS

HQ: Yum China Holdings Inc
7100 Corporate Drive, Plano, TX 75024
Phone: 469 980-2898
Web: www.yumchina.com

HISTORICAL FINANCIALS

Company Type: Public

Income Statement

FYE: December 31

	REVENUE ($ mil.)	NET INCOME ($ mil.)	NET PROFIT MARGIN	EMPLOYEES
12/16	6,752	502	7.4%	420,000
12/15	6,909	323	4.7%	400,000
12/14	6,934	(7)	—	
12/13	6,905	126	1.8%	
Annual Growth	**(0.7%)**	**58.5%**		

2016 Year-End Financials

Debt ratio: 0.75%
Return on equity: —
Cash ($ mil.): 885
Current ratio: 1.42
Long-term debt ($ mil.): 28

No. of shares (mil.): 382
Dividends
  Yield: —
  Payout: —
Market value ($ mil.): 9,992

	STOCK PRICE ($) FY Close	P/E High/Low	PER SHARE ($) Earnings	Dividends	Book Value
12/16	26.12	22 19	1.36	0.00	6.21
12/15	0.00	— —	(0.00)	0.00	(0.00)
Annual Growth	**—**	**—**	**—**	**—**	**—**

Yum! Brands Inc

YUM! Brands is the largest fast-food operator in the world in terms of number of locations with more than 43500 outlets in some 135 countries. (It trails only hamburger giant McDonald's in sales.) The company's flagship chains include #1 chicken fryer KFC (with more than 20600 units) top pizza joint Pizza Hut (more than 16400) and quick-service Mexican leader Taco Bell (more than 6600). In 2016 YUM! Brands spun off its Chinese operations into a separately traded public company.

HISTORY

Yum! Brands took its original name TRICON from the three brand icons — KFC Pizza Hut and Taco Bell— it inherited from former parent PepsiCo. The soft drink company entered the fast-food business with its acquisition of Pizza Hut in 1977. The pizza chain had begun in 1958 when brothers Dan and Frank Carney borrowed $600 from their mother and opened the first Pizza Hut in Wichita Kansas with partner John Bender. Their first franchise opened the next year in Topeka Kansas. By 1971 the company had become the world's largest pizza chain with more than 1000 restaurants. Pizza Hut went public the following year. The chain had grown to 3000 locations by the time it was acquired.

In 1978 PepsiCo acquired Taco Bell. After trying other fast-food formats Glen Bell settled on the Mexican-style market. He bought and sold several chains before beginning Taco Bell in Downey Cal-

ifornia in 1962. The first franchise was sold two years later and by 1967 — the year after it went public — Taco Bell had more than 335 restaurants most of them franchised.

KFC was acquired in 1986. It had been founded by Harland Sanders — that's Colonel Sanders to you — who developed his secret 11-herbs-and-spices recipe and method of pressure-frying chicken during the 1930s. The Colonel began franchising the secret in 1952 and founded Kentucky Fried Chicken in 1955. More than 600 outlets in the US and Canada were open by 1963. It went public in 1969 and was operating some 6600 units in 55 countries when it was acquired by PepsiCo.

Through these acquisitions PepsiCo hoped to diversify and build sales channels for its beverages but the company had also incurred a huge debt load and fast-food competition had intensified. As same-store sales faltered shareholders clamored for PepsiCo to spin off the restaurants. Restaurant officials grumbled that PepsiCo put more effort into marketing blitzes than into building restaurants (its 1991 renaming of Kentucky Fried Chicken as KFC didn't fool many health-conscious consumers).

In 1997 PepsiCo created a new restaurant subsidiary which it spun off in the fall as TRICON Global Restaurants. To improve cash flow it stepped up efforts to close or franchise underperforming Pizza Huts and KFCs. TRICON also began opening "three-in-one" restaurants featuring all its brands under one roof. In 1998 it launched a Taco Bell advertising campaign featuring a bilingual Chihuahua; the sassy pooch quickly became a cultural icon.

The KFC Taco Bell and Pizza Hut cooperatives joined in 1999 to form Unified FoodService Purchasing the largest purchasing cooperative for fast-food restaurants in the US. Also that year TRICON spent some $2 billion on a massive Star Wars: Episode I — The Phantom Menace promotion that failed to increase traffic at its restaurants. Vice chairman David Novak took over as CEO in 2000. Additionally in 1999 the company joined Burger King in lending $150 million to its distributor AmeriServe (now McLane Foodservice) which had filed for bankruptcy. The following year TRICON began experimenting with debit and credit cards at Pizza Huts and KFCs. It also opened more than 300 multi-branded sites.

In 2002 TRICON acquired Yorkshire Global Restaurants for $320 million which brought Long John Silver's and A&W All-American Food Restaurants into the fold. Now a five-pack of well-known brands rather than a trio TRICON changed its name to YUM! Brands. Later that year it formed a joint venture with Favorite Restaurants Group (a leading franchisee of KFC and Pizza Hut in Indonesia and Hong Kong) to open a chain of Yan Can Asian restaurants based around popular international chef Martin Yan. (YUM! Brands dissolved its partnership in Yan Can and liquidated the business in 2004.)

Being market leaders did not save YUM!'s chains from the overall downturn in the economy however nor from the effects of changing eating habits as Americans sought healthier meal alternatives. KFC was hit particularly hard prompting the company to appoint veteran Gregg Dedrick the chain's new president in 2003. Both KFC and Pizza Hut saw same-store sales and the number of transactions decline in the US during 2003.

In 2004 KFC opened its 1000th restaurant in China where the chain had been operating since 1987. As YUM! Brands' China operations continued to grow it formed a separate division in 2005 to oversee its expansion. The company acquired the 50% stake it didn't already own in Pizza Hut (UK) from joint venture partner Whitbread in 2006 for almost $185 million plus the assumption of about $25 million in debt.

The following year YUM! was stung by an E. coli outbreak at some of its Taco Bell outlets. The source of the outbreak was traced to a lettuce supplier; the company announced new steps to test its food supply. YUM! also sold its 31% stake in KFC Japan to Mitsubishi that same year.

YUM! Brands sold its Long John Silver's chain and A&W All-American Food locations in 2011. The divestitures were made to allow the company to focus on growing its international business particularly in China.

In 2012 the company upped its stake in Chinese restaurant operator Little Sheep Group to 93%.

In 2015 YUM! Brands announced plans to spin off its Chinese operations which it did in 2016.

EXECUTIVES

CEO, Greg Creed, age 59, $1,188,942 total compensation

General Counsel Corporate Secretary and Chief Government Affairs Officer, Marc L. Kesselman, $530,769 total compensation

President and CFO, David W. Gibbs, $792,115 total compensation

CEO Taco Bell, Brian R. Niccol, age 44, $803,846 total compensation

CEO KFC Division, Roger G. Eaton, age 56, $812,500 total compensation

SVP Corporate Finance and Controller, David E. Russell, $476,867 total compensation

Chief Transformation and People Officer, Tracy Skeans

Chief People Officer (indian Subcontinent), Sanchita Singh

Vice President of Human Resour, Mary Yamanaka

Vice President and Global Chief Information Security Officer, Marc Varner

Chairman, Robert D. (Bob) Walter, age 71

Auditors: KPMG LLP

LOCATIONS

HQ: Yum! Brands Inc
1441 Gardiner Lane, Louisville, KY 40213
Phone: 502 874-8300
Web: www.yum.com

PRODUCTS/OPERATIONS

2016 Sales

	$ mil.	% of total
Company sales	4,200	66
Franchising and License fees	2,166	34
Total	**6,366**	**100**

2016 sales

	$ mil.	% of total
KFC Division	3,232	51
Taco Bell Division	2,025	32
Pizza Hut Division	1,111	17
Unallocated	(2)	0
Total	**6,366**	**100**

COMPETITORS

A&W Restaurants	Jack in the Box
American Dairy Queen	Little Caesar's
Arby's	Long John Silver's
Burger King	McDonald's
CKE Restaurants	Papa John's
Chick-fil-A	Popeyes
Chipotle	Quiznos
Church's Chicken	Sonic Corp.
Dairy Queen	Subway
Del Taco	Wendy's
Domino's	

HISTORICAL FINANCIALS

Company Type: Public

Income Statement

FYE: December 31

	REVENUE ($ mil.)	NET INCOME ($ mil.)	NET PROFIT MARGIN	EMPLOYEES
12/16	6,366	1,619	25.4%	90,000
12/15	13,105	1,293	9.9%	505,000
12/14	13,279	1,051	7.9%	537,000
12/13	13,084	1,091	8.3%	539,000
12/12	13,633	1,597	11.7%	523,000
Annual Growth	**(17.3%)**	**0.3%**	**—**	**(35.6%)**

2016 Year-End Financials

Debt ratio: 166.61%
Return on equity: ***,***.**%
Cash ($ mil.): 704
Current ratio: 1.08
Long-term debt ($ mil.): 9,061

No. of shares (mil.): 355
Dividends
  Yield: 0.0%
  Payout: 46.7%
Market value ($ mil.): 22,482

	STOCK PRICE ($) FY Close	P/E High/Low		PER SHARE ($) Earnings	Dividends	Book Value
12/16	63.33	22	15	4.04	1.89	(15.93)
12/15	74.00	32	23	2.92	1.69	2.17
12/14	73.14	35	28	2.32	1.52	3.56
12/13	73.87	32	26	2.36	1.38	4.89
12/12	64.72	22	17	3.38	1.19	4.78
Annual Growth	**(0.5%)**		**—**	**4.6%**	**12.3%**	**—**

ZEN-NOH GRAIN CORPORATION

Auditors: KPMG LLP HOUSTON TX

LOCATIONS

HQ: ZEN-NOH GRAIN CORPORATION
1127 HWY 190 E SERVICE RD, COVINGTON, LA 704334929
Phone: 985 867-3500

HISTORICAL FINANCIALS

Company Type: Private

Income Statement

FYE: May 31

	REVENUE ($ mil.)	NET INCOME ($ mil.)	NET PROFIT MARGIN	EMPLOYEES
05/16	5,722	37	0.7%	213
05/15	6,000	86	1.4%	—
05/14	7,550	56	0.7%	—
05/13	7,704	51	0.7%	—
Annual Growth	**(9.4%)**	**(10.4%)**	**—**	**—**

2016 Year-End Financials

Debt ratio: ——
Return on equity: 0.70%
Cash ($ mil.): 6
Current ratio: 0.10
Long-term debt ($ mil.): —

Dividends
  Yield: —
  Payout: —
Market value ($ mil.): —

Zimmer Biomet Holdings Inc

Zimmer Biomet can put the spring back in your step or the zing back in your swing. The company designs and markets orthopedic products including reconstructive implants used in knee or hip replacement surgery shoulder implants that restore function in arthritic joints bone and tissue grafting materials and sports medicine products. It also makes dental implant systems spinal implants to fix aching or injured backs and trauma products (such as plates screws and pins) that help broken bones to heal. Additionally Zimmer Biomet makes surgical products used in orthopedic surgeries including tourniquets and devices for wound cleansing. The firm's products are sold around the globe.

Operations

Zimmer Biomet's four primary operating segments are: Americas Spine Office Based Technologies Craniomaxillofacial and Thoracic (CMF) and Dental. Its operations are managed through three major geographic segments: Americas Asia/Pacific and Europe Middle East and Africa (EMEA).

The company makes most of its money from sales of knee and hip replacement products (around 60% of revenues). Some of its lead products are the Alloclassic hip system Zimmer M/L taper hip prosthesis and NexGen knee product line. In addition to knee and hip replacements the company makes reconstructive systems for extremities including the Bigliani/Flatow line for shoulder procedures.

In its smaller segments top products include the Tapered Screw-Vent dental implant system the PathFinder minimally invasive pedicle spine screw system and the Zimmer locking plate systems for bone fractures. Surgical supplies and other operations make up a fraction of sales and include the Palacos and Hi-Fatigue bone cement surgical products as well as the Accelero Health Partners unit (surgeon consulting).

Geographic Reach

Zimmer Biomet?s operations are managed through three major geographic segments: Americas Asia/Pacific and Europe Middle East and Africa (EMEA).

The Americas segment (largely consisting of US operations) accounts for more than 60% of the company's annual revenues though sales in international markets (especially in the Asia/Pacific region which includes such markets as Australia China India and Hong Kong) are rising. EMEA including sales in France Germany and the UK accounts for about a quarter of all revenues. Zimmer Biomet's products are sold in more than 100 countries worldwide and the company has direct operations in more than 40 countries.

Zimmer Biomet's primary manufacturing facilities are located in the US (Warsaw Indiana; Dover Ohio; Austin Texas; Jacksonville and Palm Beach Gardens Florida; and Parsippany New Jersey) Puerto Rico (Ponce) Ireland (Shannon Galway) China (Beijing Changzhou and Jinhua) France (Valence) Germany (Berlin) Spain (Valencia) South Wales (Bridgend) and Switzerland (Winterthur).

Sales and Marketing

Zimmer Biomet sells its orthopedic products directly to health care providers (such as hospitals surgery centers and surgeons themselves) as well as to purchasing organizations distributors and health care dealers. Its dental products are sold directly to dental practices and laboratories. Zimmer Biomet markets biologic bone and tissue allografts for dental spinal and trauma procedures through a partnership with RTI Surgical.

The US sales force is made up of direct employees and contracted exclusive agents. European sales are handled by direct associates support employees commissioned agents and independent distributors while Asia/Pacific sales are handled through a network of dealers and associates. Direct channels account for around 80% of the company's net sales.

Financial Performance

After remaining flat for years Zimmer Biomet?s net sales increased 28% to $5.9 billion in 2015 and another 28% to $7.7 billion in 2016. This growth can primarily be attributed to the 2015 merger with Biomet and the numerous follow-up acquisitions made in 2016. Sales rose in all three geographic regions (Americas EMEA and Asia/Pacific) and demand for knee hip and upper extremity products rose in 2016. However this was partially offset by the negative impact of foreign exchange rates and product pricing pressures.

Expenses related to the Biomet merger caused net income to drop 80% to $147 million in 2015. With most of those expenses out of the way net income began rebounding in 2016 more than doubling to $305.9 million that year.

Cash flow from operations rose 92% to $1.6 billion in 2016 thanks to the higher net income and factors including changes in inventory receivables and accounts payable.

Strategy

Zimmer Biomet works to keep its sales figures on the rise through new product development efforts as well as by introducing next-generation versions of existing best-sellers that add functionality or ease of use. New products include its X-PSI Knee System a pre-operative instrument that allows surgeons to use X-Ray images to develop 3D customized plans to improve the fit of surgical implants; it was launched in Europe in 2017. Other recent launches include the PrimaGen Advanced Allograft and the Comprehensive Vault Reconstruction System.

The firm also conducts substantial R&D work in the field of orthobiologics or the implantation of biological materials to help repair and regenerate damaged tissue. In 2015 the company added new musculoskeletal offerings; the following year it launched three new hip offerings.

Along with increasing its sales through product growth Zimmer Biomet expands through acquisitions partnerships and international expansion efforts. The company expects overall industry trends to help keep its sales in the black: The aging US population chronic obesity and advances in surgical techniques are all expected to contribute to increased demand for its products. However the company could continue to see depressed prices in some segments due to economic conditions (causing patients to decrease non-essential expenses) and government and hospital cost-control programs.

Mergers and Acquisitions

In mid-2015 Zimmer acquired fellow implant maker Biomet for $14 billion. The deal made the combined company the #2 orthopedics seller worldwide behind Johnson & Johnson. It also doubled Zimmer's knee and dental lines and gave it entry into the lucrative sports medicine business. Upon completion of the transaction Zimmer took on the Biomet name.

In 2016 the combined company completed a number of acquisitions to expand its product portfolio. It bought Texas-based LDR Holding Corporation for $1 billion; that deal furthered its presence in the spine disorder business. Zimmer Biomet also acquired Arizona-based Cayenne Medical in a move that strengthened its sports medicine operations including its portfolio of soft tissue re-

construction solutions. It purchased the Netherlands-based imaging firm Clinical Graphics which specializes in 3D range-of-motion simulation technology; that deal boosted the company?s hip preservation portfolio.

Also that year Zimmer Biomet acquired Colorado-based Ortho Transmission for an undisclosed price. Ortho Transmission develops skeletal implant technology for limb amputee patients; Zimmer Biomet is utilizing the unit's technology as part of its ongoing collaboration with the US Department of Defense which aims to restore mobility for amputee patients.

Company Background

Formerly part of Bristol Myers Squibb Zimmer Holdings was spun off into an independent operation in 2001.

EXECUTIVES

Executive Vice President Finance and Chief Financial Officer, James T Crines
Vice President Global Operations and Logistics, Richard Stair
Group President Joint Reconstruction, Daniel E. (Dan) Williamson, age 51, $224,329 total compensation
Group President Biologics Extremities Sports Medicine Surgical Trauma Foot Ankle and Bone Healing, David A. Nolan
SVP General Counsel and Secretary, Chad F. Phipps, age 46, $470,615 total compensation
SVP CFO and Interim CEO and Director, Daniel P. (Dan) Florin, age 53, $562,692 total compensation
President Europe Middle East and Africa, Katarzyna Mazur-Hofsaess, age 53, $612,644 total compensation
Group President Spine Dental CMF and Thoracic, Adam R. Johnson, age 40
President Asia/Pacific, Sang Yi, $459,156 total compensation
VP U.S. Sales, Robert D. (Rob) Delp
SVP Global Operations and Logistics, Adrian Furey
Vice President Manager Director, Amy Feldman
Vice President Information Technology Americas, Michael Barnett
Chairman, Larry C. Glasscock, age 68
Auditors: PricewaterhouseCoopers LLP

LOCATIONS

HQ: Zimmer Biomet Holdings Inc
345 East Main Street, Warsaw, IN 46580
Phone: 574 267-6131
Web: www.zimmer.com

2016 Sales

	$ mil.	% of total
Americas	4,802	62
EMEA	1,730	23
Asia/Pacific	1,151	15
Total	**7,683**	**100**

PRODUCTS/OPERATIONS

2016 Sales

	$ mil.	% of total
Reconstructive		
Knees	2,751	36
Hips	1,867	24
S.E.T.	1,645	21
Dental	427	6
Spine and CMF	662	9
Other	328	4
Total	**7,683**	**100**

Selected Products

Reconstructive implants
 Alloclassic hip system
 Anatomical shoulder implants
 Bigliani/Flatow shoulder implants
 MIS 2-Incision Total Hip Replacement
 MIS Mini-Incision Total Knee Procedure
 NexGen knee replacement
 Trabecular Metal Primary Hip Prosthesis
 VerSys Hip System
 Zimmer Collagen Repair Patch (rotator cuff repair)
Trauma products
 I.T.S.T. Nail System (hip and proximal femur fractures)
 M/DN Intramedullary Fixation (for long bone fractures)
 NCB Locking Plate System (complex long bone fractures)
 Sirus Intramedullary Nail System (for long bone fractures)
Dental products
 AdVent dental implant system
 Tapered screw-vent implant system
Spine products
 CopiOs Bone Void Filler
 Dynesys Dynamic Stabilization System
 Optima ZD Spinal Fixation System
 Puros allografts
 ST360 Spinal Fixation System
Surgical products
 A.T.S. Tourniquet Systems
 Brasseler USA surgical power tools (for long bones)
 Pneumicro surgical power tools (for small bones)
 Pulsavac Plus (wound cleaning)
 Zimmer Ambulatory Pump (pain management)

COMPETITORS

B. Braun Melsungen	MAKO Surgical
Corin Group	Medtronic
DJO Global	Nobel Biocare
DePuy	NuVasive
Dentsply Sirona	Orthofix
Exactech	ReGen Biologics
Genzyme Biosurgery	Smith & Nephew
Globus Medical	Straumann
JRI Orthopaedics	Stryker
Johnson & Johnson	Synthes
Lifecore Biomedical	

HISTORICAL FINANCIALS

Company Type: Public

Income Statement

FYE: December 31

	REVENUE ($ mil.)	NET INCOME ($ mil.)	NET PROFIT MARGIN	EMPLOYEES
12/16	7,683	305	4.0%	18,500
12/15	5,997	147	2.5%	17,500
12/14	4,673	720	15.4%	10,000
12/13	4,623	761	16.5%	9,500
12/12	4,471	755	16.9%	9,300
Annual Growth	**14.5%**	**(20.2%)**	**—**	**18.8%**

2016 Year-End Financials

Debt ratio: 42.13%
Return on equity: 3.12%
Cash ($ mil.): 634
Current ratio: 1.96
Long-term debt ($ mil.): 10,665

No. of shares (mil.): 200
Dividends
 Yield: 0.0%
 Payout: 63.5%
Market value ($ mil.): 20,702

	STOCK PRICE ($) FY Close	P/E High/Low		PER SHARE ($) Earnings	Dividends	Book Value
12/16	103.20	87	60	1.51	0.96	48.20
12/15	102.59	156	118	0.77	0.88	48.78
12/14	113.42	27	21	4.19	0.88	38.43
12/13	93.19	21	15	4.43	0.80	37.09
12/12	66.66	16	12	4.29	0.72	34.15
Annual Growth	**11.5%**	**—**	**—**	**(23.0%)**	**7.5%**	**9.0%**

Zions Bancorporation

Multibank holding company Zions Bancorporation operates some 440 bank branches in 11 states through a number of subsidiary banks. These include Zions First National Bank Nevada State Bank National Bank of Arizona Vectra Bank Colorado The Commerce Bank of Washington California Bank & Trust The Commerce Bank of Oregon and Texas-based Amegy Bank. The Zion banks focus on commercial and retail banking as well as mortgage and construction lending deposit accounts home mortgages and home equity lines of credit residential and commercial development loans small business administration loans credit cards and trust and wealth management services.

Operations

Alongside its core banking services Zions offers wealth management services. It also offers online and traditional brokerage services via Zions Direct and Amegy Investments. In addition the company controls a handful of venture capital funds working with startups in the West.

Like any other bank Zions generates the majority of its revenue through interest payments on the loans it issues. Interest income generated by loans money marketing investments and other securities account for around 80% of Zion's revenue with the remainder coming from fees for deposit accounts and other service-related charges.

Geographic Reach

Based in Utah the holding company operates banks in Utah Idaho California Texas Arizona Wyoming Nevada Colorado New Mexico Oregon and Washington.

Sales and Marketing

Of its network of approximately 445 branch locations Zions owns more than 270 and leases 165.

Financial Performance

In fiscal 2016 (ended December) Zions' revenue picked up after a few years of underwhelming results. Total revenue for the year came in at $2.4 billion a 15% increase. Interest income was up $152.1 million as Zions pivoted towards higher-yielding loans and investment securities while reducing interest expense related to long-term debt.

Net income jumped 52% to $469 million due to an increase in net interest margin. Zions also improved its efficiency ratio to 65% from 69% meaning it spend less on operations as a proportion of revenue. Net income growth also related to a pre-tax loss of $136.8 million recorded in 2015.

Cash from operating activities increased 28% to $569.1 million due to higher net revenue.

Strategy

Zions Bancorporation has set a target of an efficiency ratio in the low 60s by 2017. The company was able to surpass its 2016 target of 66% by developing a more profitable asset mix while exerting better control over operating expenses including paying off more of its long-term debt. In December 2015 Zions consolidated its seven subsidiary banks and other financial affiliates into the Zions Bank operations (while keeping their localized brands as-is) to streamline its operations.

In response to the struggles of the oil and gas industry Zions reduced its exposure to the sector by $900 million during 2016 taking its oil and gas portfolio to $3.9 billion.

With such distinct and localized bank subsidiaries Zions strives to maintain a local community and regional bank approach as opposed to a larger bank that doesn't have a local management team. It does centralize many non-customer facing operations such as risk and capital management technology and back-office operations making for a more cost-effective endeavor.

Company Background

Zions which built its business through acquisitions strategically managed to extend its reach during the economic downturn in part by helping the FDIC clean up failed banks and it continues to search for acquisition opportunities. It is also building its business by growing its wealth management and advisory services organically.

HISTORY

Zions' history is entwined with that of the Mormon Church. Founded by the church in 1873 to take over the savings department of the Bank of Deseret when it obtained a national charter the new bank was headed by Brigham Young and other church leaders. The church kept control of the bank until 1960 when it sold its interest to a group of investors led by Roy Simmons who moved it into the holding company that became Zions Bancorporation. It went public in 1966.

It has grown over the years by picking up struggling or failing banks during various financial crises. It almost bought fellow Utah bank First Security in 2000 and would have dropped the Zions name to further distance itself from the Mormon Church. But the deal fell through and the name remains.

EXECUTIVES

Executive Vice President Marketing and Communications, Rob Brough
Vice President, Jennifer R Jolley
EVP; President and CEO Zions First National Bank, A. Scott (Scott) Anderson, age 70, $548,000 total compensation
Chairman and CEO, Harris H. Simmons, age 62, $940,000 total compensation
EVP; President and CEO Vectra Bank Colorado, Bruce K. Alexander, age 64
EVP; President and CEO The Commerce Bank of Washington, Stanley D. Savage, age 71, $312,000 total compensation
EVP; President and CEO California Bank & Trust, David E. Blackford, age 68, $510,000 total compensation
EVP Texas Administration, Scott J. McLean, age 60, $644,000 total compensation
EVP and Chief Banking Officer, Keith D. Maio, age 59
EVP Retail Banking, LeeAnne B. Linderman, age 62
EVP and General Counsel, Thomas E. Laursen, age 66
EVP and Chief Risk Officer, Edward P. (Ed) Schreiber, age 59, $518,000 total compensation
EVP and Chief Human Resources Officer, Dianne R. James, age 64
SVP Internal Audit, Jennifer A. Smith, age 45
EVP; CEO Amegy Bank of Texas, Steven D. Stephens, age 58
EVP and Chief Technology Strategist, Joe Reilly, age 64
EVP and Chief Credit Officer, Michael J. Morris, age 59
EVP; President and CEO National Bank of Arizona, Mark R. Young, age 58
CFO, Paul E. Burdiss, age 52, $550,000 total compensation
EVP and Director Wealth Management, Rebecca K. Robinson, age 43
Executive Vice President Retail Banking, S Swaby
Assistant Vice President, Don L Milne
Vice President, Allen Jensen
Senior Vice President Manager, Steve Campbell
Vice President Information Technology Financial Systems, Ryan Greene
Executive Vice President, David Gill
Assistant Vice President International Operations, Anne Lane

Vice President Senior Risk Officer, Stephen Willden
Senior Vice President Managing Legal Counsel, David McGrath
Vice President Sag Intermountain, Rhett Anderson
Senior Analyst Assistant Vice President Business Intelligence, Donna Gillaspy
Senior Vice President, Melisse Grey
Vice President Enterprise Fraud Risk Management, Michael Barnes
Vice President, Doug Howard
Vice President, Matt Millis
Senior Vice President Bankcard Operations and Technology, Olga Hoff
Vice President Information Systems Manager, Jonathan Feinauer
Senior Vice President Item Processing Group Manager, Donald Barry
Vice President of Sales, Jacob Heugly
Vice President, Bret Passey
Vice President Regional Security Officer, Mary Courtney
Vice President, Jeff Hedstrom
Vice President, Brandy Deherrera
Assistant Vice President, Michael Dale
Vice President And Relationship Manager, Adam Whitefield
Regional Credit Manager Vice President, Dereck Jacobs
Senior Vice President Compliance, Norman Merritt
Vice President at zions bank, Carol Walker
Vice President, Charles Loughridge
Vice President, Alex Buxton
Vice President Commercial Banking, Jim Stanchfield
Vice President and Legal Counsel, Virginia Smith
Vice President, Nathan Tervort
Assistant Vice President Compliance, Carson Boss
Vice President Business Banking, Ryan Shelley
Vice President Womens Financial Group, Tabitha Perkins
Vice President, Cary Coombs
Vice President, Thomas Anderson
Vice President, Chad Call
Vice President, Ryan Speirs
Vice President, Ralph Matson
Senior Vice President Of Staffing Director, Prince Edwin
Vice President, Kaye Raby
Vice President Director, Karen Appelgren
Vice President of Private Banking, Todd Parker
Vice President Of Information Technology, Karl Ward
Vice President And Relationship Manager, Cheryl Ginn
Executive Vice President Capital Markets and Investments, W David Hemingway
Assistant Vice President, Willie Koosmann
Vice President, Steve Earley
Senior Vice President retail Product Division, Dave Fuhriman
Senior Vice President And Chief Credit Administrator C And I Lending, Dennis Spencer
Senior Vice President, Scott Bramhall
Vice President Finance, David Russell
Senior Vice President, Chad Peck
Assistant Vice President Call Center Tech, Jeff Newman
Vice President Real Estate Banking, Ryan Stevenson
Vice President And Manager, Dan Dixon
Vice President Financial Reporting Manager, Jeremy Johnson
Assistant Vice President Capital Markets, Karen Keeley
Vice President Corporate Purchasing, Garth Slater
Vice President Information Technology Services Management Itil, David Stirling
Senior Vice President Banking and Vice President of Compensation, Scott Law

Vice President, Shannon Israr
Vice President, Jennifer Jolley
Vice President Technology, Deva Annamalai
Vice President Employee Relations Manager
  Human Resources, Deborah Bell
Assistant Vice President, Leslie Nuon
Vice President Commercial Loans, David Kohler
Vice President, David Bata
Vice President Corporate Credit Controller, Brian
  Stringham
Senior Vice President Managing Legal Counsel,
  Rena Miller
Senior Vice President Corporate Procuremen And
  Vendor Management, Kelly Foreman
Vice President Manager Oa Core, Amy Vernon
Vice President of Public Finance, Brian Baker
Vice President corporate Compliance Manager,
  Nancy Hodge
Vice President Web Applicatio, Dennis Page
First Vice President, James Grether
Vice President, Steven Carlson
Vice President of Marketing, David Fuhriman
Executive Vice President, David Hinds
Vice President, Vicki Friece
Executive Vice President, Robert Boyd
Vice President Quantitative Financial Analyst,
  Ryan Warner
Vice President Business Development Officer,
  Mark Petrasso
Vice President Financial Analyst, Ian Spencer
Vice President Commercial Relationship Manager,
  Levi Judd
Vice President and Manager, Greg Cross
Vice President, Scott Blair
Vice President, Cordon Robbins
Assistant Vice President, Ron Dinsmoor
Vice President Commercial Relationship Manager
  Broadway Financial Center, Dane Margetts
Assistant Vice President Relationship Manager
  Executive Banking, Matt Reynolds
Vice President Treasury Relationship Manager,
  Kyle Bellnap
Vice President Relationship Manager, Russ Taylor
Vice President and Regional Director, Douglas
  Tuttle
Vice President, Richard Reed
Senior Vice President, Cecilia Mitchell
Vice President Business Analyst, John Weiland
Vice President, Kathryn Dabell
Vice President and Treasury Relationship
  Manager, James J Divver James J Divver
Assistant Vice President Information Technology
  Quality Assurance, Deana Lundin
Senior Vice President, David Mathis
Vice President, Marie Mackenzie
Senior Vice President Information Technology
  Support Services, Lorilee Stoddard
Vice President and Relationship Manager, Jeff
  Agenbroad
Vice President Learning and Organizational
  Development Instructional Design Manager,
  Nicole Boswell
Vice President Group Manager Direct Consumer
  Loan Center, Laura Larson
Vice President, Robert Oldroyd
Vice President of Operations, Barry Currah
Executive Vice President, John D'Arcy
Assistant Vice President Credit Systems Manager,
  Jedd Van Meeteren
Assistant Vice President Lead Business Systems
  Analyst, Noah Norton
Vice President Training Delivery Manager, Todd
  Hadley
Vice President Training Lead Core
  Transformation, Allison Riley
Executive Vice President Zions Bank, Richard
  Stevenson thumbnail
Vice President, Ryan Theriault
Enterprise Loan Operations Manager III Vice
  President, Lori Harding

Vice President Lending, Jim King
Vice President Regional Director, Burnett Facer
Assistant Vice President, Brian Goodwin
Assistant Vice President, Christopher Burton
Assistant Vice President, Jennifer Fillion-Hood
Assistant Vice President, Michael Miller
Vice President, Scott Sluis
Senior Vice President, Elliot Jensen
Senior Vice President, Todd Harris
Vice President, Susan Becker
Vice President, Eric Pehrson
Vice President Small Business Group, Mark
  Wilkinson
SVP Credit Risk Management, Mark Medina
Auditors: Ernst & Young LLP

LOCATIONS

HQ: Zions Bancorporation
  One South Main, 15th Floor, Salt Lake City, UT 84133
Phone: 801 844-7637
Web: www.zionsbancorporation.com

PRODUCTS/OPERATIONS

Selected Subsidiaries
Amegy Corporation
California Bank & Trust
Great Western Financial Corporation
National Bank of Arizona
Nevada State Bank
The Commerce Bank of Oregon
The Commerce Bank of Washington
Vectra Bank Colorado
Zions First National Bank
Zions Insurance Agency Inc.
Zions Management Services Company

2016 Sales

	$ mil.	% of total
Interest income		
Interest and fees on loans	1,728	70
Interest on securities	203	8
Interest on money market investment	21	1
Non-interest income		
Other service charges commission and fees	207	8
Service charges and fees on deposit accounts	171	7
Wealth management income	37	2
Loan sales and servicing income	35.5	2
Dividends and other investment income	24	1
Capital markets and foreign Exchange	21	1
Equity securities gains net	7	-
Fair value and non-hedge derivative income (loss)	2	-
Fixed income securities loss	0	-
Others	8	-
Total	2,469	100

COMPETITORS

BOK Financial	Great Western Bancorp
Bank of America	JPMorgan Chase
Bank of the West	MUFG Americas Holdings
Capital One	Prosperity Bancshares
Citigroup	U.S. Bancorp
Cullen/Frost Bankers	Washington Federal
First National of	Wells Fargo
Nebraska	

HISTORICAL FINANCIALS

Company Type: Public

Income Statement

FYE: December 31

	ASSETS ($ mil.)	NET INCOME ($ mil.)	INCOME AS % OF ASSETS	EMPLOYEES
12/16	63,239	469	0.7%	10,057
12/15	59,669	309	0.5%	10,200
12/14	57,208	398	0.7%	10,462
12/13	56,031	263	0.5%	10,452
12/12	55,511	349	0.6%	10,368
Annual Growth	3.3%	7.6%	—	(0.8%)

2016 Year-End Financials

Debt ratio: 0.85%
Return on equity: 6.18%
Cash ($ mil.): 2,148
Current ratio: —
Long-term debt ($ mil.): —

No. of shares (mil.): 203
Dividends
  Yield: 0.0%
  Payout: 14.0%
Market value ($ mil.): 8,741

	STOCK PRICE ($) FY Close	P/E High/Low		PER SHARE ($) Earnings	Dividends	Book Value
12/16	43.04	22	10	1.99	0.28	37.59
12/15	27.30	27	20	1.20	0.22	36.73
12/14	28.51	20	15	1.68	0.16	36.30
12/13	29.96	20	14	1.58	0.13	35.00
12/12	21.40	23	17	0.97	0.04	32.86
Annual Growth	19.1%	—	—	19.7%	62.7%	3.4%

Zoetis Inc

Whether you have cats or cattle Zoetis has something to keep them healthy and happy. The company manufactures and sells veterinary medicines such as parasiticides (to protect against fleas ticks and worms) anti-infectives medicated feed additives vaccines and other pharmaceuticals. Zoetis boasts more than 300 product lines sold in more than 100 countries around the world making it one of the world's largest animal health businesses. In addition to medications and vaccines Zoetis offers diagnostics genetics devices and services such as dairy data management and consulting.

Operations

Zoetis makes about 60% of its sales from medicines and vaccines for livestock (including cattle swine poultry and fish) which assist in the global food supply chain. Products for companion animals such as house pets and horses bring in some 40% of sales. The company's product sales are diverse — with 300 different lines no single product accounts for more than 10% of sales. Its top seller the antibiotic ceftiofur (sold under the brands Excede Excenel Spectramast and Naxcel) makes up more than 5% of overall revenues. Other top sellers are Revolution Draxxin and Apoquel.

Anti-infective sales provide more than a quarter of total revenues followed by vaccines (25%) parasiticides (about 15%) and other pharmaceuticals (about 20%). The remaining earnings come from medicated feed additives non-pharmaceuticals and contract manufacturing.

Geographic Reach

The US is Zoetis' largest single market accounting for about half of all sales. Internationally the company operates in Europe the Middle East Africa the Asia/Pacific region Canada and Latin America.

Zoetis has a direct sales presence in 45 countries (the Americas Europe the Asia/Pacific region and Africa) where it sells directly to livestock producers and veterinarians. In the nearly 60 other countries where it does not have a direct sales presence the company uses distributors.

Zoetis' manufacturing capabilities encompass some 25 plants in a dozen countries. But it also relies on about 200 contract manufacturers (including former parent Pfizer) to produce about 40% of its products.

The company also has a 1.5 million-sq.-ft. research and development facility in Kalamazoo Michigan.

Sales and Marketing

Zoetis uses distributors for most of its products which are available by prescription from veterinarians. It also sells directly to retail outlets including farming supply and pet stores and pharmacies.

Some livestock products are sold directly to ranchers.

Marketing efforts target veterinarians livestock producers and pet owners. Advertising and promotional expenses in 2016 totaled some $119 million compared to $106 million in 2015 and $132 million in 2014.

Financial Performance

Zoetis' sales have been slowly trending upward. Revenue rose 3% to $4.9 billion in 2016 as sales of vaccines increased but this was offset by a decline in anti-infectives sales. Other product categories remained relatively stable that year although sales of dog allergy medication Apoquel and new product launches contributed 5% of revenue growth. Geographically sales in the US rose 5% while international sales rose less than 1%.

Net income which had fallen in 2015 due to restructuring charges and acquisition-related expenses recovered the following year. With most of those expenses out of the way as well as lower overall operating costs net income rose 142% to $821 million in 2016.

Cash flow from operations has also been rising. The higher net income offset by employee termination payments and higher inventory levels led operating cash flow to increase 7% to $713 million in 2016.

Strategy

With a focus on animals Zoetis enjoys certain benefits over most pharmaceuticals. Veterinary medications don't have the same rigorous regulatory processes that human medicines do and research and development time is faster (about three years) less expensive and more predictable. In addition pet owners and ranchers pay out-of-pocket for products; Zoetis doesn't have to wait to be reimbursed by private or government-owned insurance companies. Additionally as animals will always need to be cared for the company is somewhat recession-proof.

Zoetis' plan for sustained growth includes such efforts as expanding in emerging markets (where economic development is raising demand for both livestock and companion animals) developing new products to address unmet needs pursuing mergers and acquisitions improving its manufacturing production margins and growing its complementary businesses in diagnostics genetics devices consulting and other areas.

In terms of geographic expansion the company plans to pursue emerging markets in Brazil China and India where protein consumption is up by introducing more expensive products. These include new vaccines and single-injection anti-infectives such as Draxxin for livestock and Convenia for pets. It is also exploring acquisitions to deepen its penetration in these markets.

To broaden its portfolio the company works to develop new products and expand existing products lines to new species (such as taking an antibiotic for cattle and reformulating it for swine and poultry.) New products launched in 2017 include parasiticide therapy for cats Stronghold Plus and in Europe dermatitis therapy for dogs Cytopoint. Another new drug Apoquel an allergic itch treatment has rapidly become a top seller in the atopic dermatitis space for dogs. In 2016 Zoetis spent some $376 million on research and development compared to $364 million in 2015 and $396 million in 2014.Furthermore it gained more than 170 product approvals during the year.

However Zoetis has also undertaken major restructuring moves to cut costs and increase production. In 2015 it announced plans to exit 10 manufacturing sites over time; the following year it sold facilities in Colorado and North Carolina. Also in 2016 it divested its majority stake in a Taiwan joint venture selling that holding for some $13 million and it sold a manufacturing site in India. With those initiatives in place it is now investing $70 million on its Lincoln Nebraska manufacturing site and is expanding capacity at its manufacturing facility in Kalamazoo Michigan.

Mergers and Acquisitions

Zoetis has made a number of key acquisitions recently. In mid-2017 it purchased biologic therapeutics firm Nexvet Biopharma for some $85 million. Nexvet is developing a pipeline of monoclonal antibody therapies to ease pain in pets. Also that year the company acquired Norwegian firm Nordland Sett Vaks which makes vaccination machinery for the aquaculture industry.

Zoetis acquired Scandinavian company Micro Bio-devices a specialist in diagnostics for veterinary point-of-care services for $80 million in 2016.

In 2015 Zoetis acquired Pharmaq which specializes in making vaccines for farmed fish for $765 million. It also bought KL Products a Canadian firm that makes automated systems for the poultry industry complementing its existing Embrex in egg vaccine delivery systems.

That same year the company bought certain assets of Abbott Animal Health which makes products for companion animals for $229 million. That deal added veterinarian solutions for anesthesia pain management and the diagnosis of diabetes.

Company Background

Formerly named Pfizer Animal Health Zoetis was separated from former parent Pfizer in an initial public offering worth some $2.2 billion.

EXECUTIVES

EVP and CIO, Andrew Fenton
CEO, Juan R. Alaix, age 66, $1,150,000 total compensation
EVP; President US Operations, Kristin C. Peck, age 46, $636,375 total compensation
EVP; President US Operations, Clinton A. (Clint) Lewis, age 51, $630,054 total compensation
EVP; President Europe Africa and Middle East Region, Alejandro Bernal, age 45
EVP and General Counsel, Heidi C. Chen, age 51
EVP; President Research and Development, Catherine A. (Cathy) Knupp, age 57, $499,625 total compensation
EVP and Chief Human Resources Officer, Roxanne Lagano, age 53
EVP and CFO, Glenn C. David, $483,030 total compensation
EVP; President Global Manufacturing and Supply, Roman Trawicki, age 54
Chairman, Michael B. McCallister, age 65
Auditors: KPMG LLP

LOCATIONS

HQ: Zoetis Inc
10 Sylvan Way, Parsippany, NJ 07054
Phone: 973 822-7000
Web: www.zoetis.com

2016 Sales

	$ mil.	% of total
International	2,390	49
U.S.	2,447	50
Contract manufacturing	51	1
Total	**4,888**	**100**

PRODUCTS/OPERATIONS

2016 Sales

	$ mil.	% of total
Livestock	2,881	59
Companion animal	1,956	40
Contract manufacturing	51	1
Total	**4,888**	**100**

2016 product by Sales

	$ mil.	% of total
Anti-infectives	1,255	26
Vaccines	1,245	25
Parasiticides	659	14
Medicated feed additives	500	10
Other pharmaceuticals	988	20
Other non-pharmaceuticals	190	4
Contract manufacturing	51	1
Total	**4,888**	**100**

Selected Species

Beef Cattle
Cats
Dairy Cattle
Dogs
Fish
Horses
Pigs
Poultry
Sheep
Product line / ProductAnti-infectivesCeftiofur injectable lineDraxxin®;Spectramast®;Terramycin®; lineVaccinesBovi-Shield lineRispoval lineSuvaxyn PCV / Fostera PCVParasiticidesCydectinDectomaxMedicated Feed AdditivesAureomycinBMDLasalocid lin

COMPETITORS

American Animal Health	Merck Animal Health
Bayer Animal Health	Merial
Dechra Pharmaceuticals	Novartis
ECO Animal Health	Phibro Animal Health
Eli Lilly	Skystar
Heska	Virbac
IDEXX Labs	V☐©toquinol
Kindred Biosciences	

HISTORICAL FINANCIALS

Company Type: Public

Income Statement

FYE: December 31

	REVENUE ($ mil.)	NET INCOME ($ mil.)	NET PROFIT MARGIN	EMPLOYEES
12/17	5,307	864	16.3%	9,200
12/16	4,888	821	16.8%	9,000
12/15	4,765	339	7.1%	9,000
12/14	4,785	583	12.2%	10,000
12/13	4,561	504	11.1%	9,800
Annual Growth	**3.9%**	**14.4%**	**—**	**(1.6%)**

2017 Year-End Financials

Debt ratio: 57.69%	No. of shares (mil.): 486
Return on equity: 53.05%	Dividends
Cash ($ mil.): 1,564	Yield: 0.0%
Current ratio: 3.85	Payout: 24.0%
Long-term debt ($ mil.): 4,953	Market value ($ mil.): 35,021

	STOCK PRICE ($) FY Close	P/E High/Low		PER SHARE ($) Earnings	Dividends	Book Value
12/17	72.04	41	30	1.75	0.42	3.64
12/16	53.53	32	24	1.65	0.38	3.02
12/15	47.92	81	58	0.68	0.33	2.15
12/14	43.03	39	24	1.16	0.29	2.62
12/13	32.69	34	29	1.01	0.20	1.88
Annual Growth	**21.8%**	**—**	**—**	**14.7%**	**21.1%**	**18.0%**

Hoover's Handbook of

American Business

The Indexes

Index by Headquarters

AK

Anchorage
First National Bank Alaska 357
Northrim BancCorp Inc 621
CHUGACH GOVERNMENT
SOLUTIONS, LLC 194

JUNEAU
ALASKA PERMANENT FUND
CORPORATION 26

AL

Birmingham
Regions Financial Corp 721
Alabama Power Co 24
Protective Life Insurance Co 697
Infinity Property & Casualty Corp 460
ProAssurance Corp 691
ServisFirst Bancshares Inc 763
National Commerce Corp 591

AR

Bentonville
Walmart Inc 902

Conway
Home BancShares Inc 429

El Dorado
Murphy USA Inc 589

Little Rock
Dillard's Inc. 266
Windstream Holdings Inc 925
Bank of the Ozarks Inc (New) 106
Bear State Financial Inc 118

Lowell
Hunt (J.B.) Transport Services, Inc.
447

Pine Bluff
Simmons First National Corp 768

Springdale
Tyson Foods Inc 859

AZ

PEORIA
R. DIRECTIONAL DRILLING &
UNDERGROUND TECHNOLOGY,
INC. 711

Phoenix
Avnet Inc 93
Freeport-McMoRan Inc 374
Republic Services Inc 728
Southern Copper Corp 778

Western Alliance Bancorporation 916
BANNER HEALTH 111

Scottsdale
Magellan Health Inc. 540

Tempe
Insight Enterprises Inc. 462

CA

Beverly Hills
Live Nation Entertainment Inc 532
PacWest Bancorp 652

Burbank
Disney (Walt) Co. (The) 272

Chico
TriCo Bancshares (Chico, CA) 851

Cupertino
Apple Inc 69

Dublin
Ross Stores, Inc. 740

El Segundo
A-Mark Precious Metals, Inc 3
Mattel Inc 556

Foster City
Gilead Sciences Inc 390

Fremont
Synnex Corp 804
Lam Research Corp 512

Glendale
Avery Dennison Corp 91

Irvine
Opus Bank (Irvine, CA) 642
Pacific Premier Bancorp Inc 650
First Foundation Inc 351
ST. JOSEPH HEALTH SYSTEM 785

Lodi
Farmers & Merchants Bancorp (Lodi,
CA) 323

Long Beach
Molina Healthcare Inc 581
Farmers & Merchants Bank of Long
Beach (CA) 324

Los Angeles
AECOM 14
CBRE Group Inc 169
Reliance Steel & Aluminum Co. 724
Mercury General Corp. 566
Cathay General Bancorp 166
Hope Bancorp Inc 435
Hanmi Financial Corp. 407
Preferred Bank (Los Angeles, CA) 688
KILROY REALTY, L.P. 498

REXFORD INDUSTRIAL REALTY, INC.
729

Los Gatos
Netflix Inc 602

Menlo Park
Facebook Inc 321
Robert Half International Inc. 734

Mountain View
Alphabet Inc 33
Intuit Inc 475

Novato
Bank of Marin Bancorp 104

Oakland
Clorox Co (The) 208
KAISER FOUNDATION HOSPITALS
INC 491

Ontario
CVB Financial Corp. 249

Palo Alto
HP Inc 441
Hewlett Packard Enterprise Co 424
Tesla Inc 822
ESSEX PORTFOLIO, L.P. 312

Pasadena
East West Bancorp, Inc 289

Porterville
Sierra Bancorp 766

Redwood City
Oracle Corp 642
Electronic Arts, Inc. 296

ROCKLIN
FARM CREDIT WEST 323

Rosemead
Edison International 295
Southern California Edison Co. 777

SACRAMENTO
STATE OF CALIFORNIA 790
SUTTER HEALTH 802

San Diego
Qualcomm Inc 706
Sempra Energy 761
Bofl Holding, Inc. 136

San Francisco
McKesson Corp 562
Wells Fargo & Co. 912
Visa Inc 898
PG&E Corp (Holding Co) 673
The Gap Inc 829
Salesforce.Com Inc 747
Schwab (Charles) Corp (The) 753
Williams Sonoma Inc 924
Levi Strauss & Co. 520
First Republic Bank (San Francisco,
CA) 358

Federal Home Loan Bank Of San
Francisco 329
LendingClub Corp 517
DIGNITY HEALTH 265
LEVI STRAUSS & CO. 520
AMERICAN BALANCED FUND, INC.
41
THE IRVINE JAMES FOUNDATION
830

San Jose
Cisco Systems Inc 198
Western Digital Corp 917
PayPal Holdings Inc 657
eBay Inc. 292
Adobe Systems Inc 10
Sanmina Corp 749
Heritage Commerce Corp 420

San Mateo
Franklin Resources, Inc. 372

San Rafael
WestAmerica Bancorporation 915

San Ramon
Chevron Corporation 189

Santa Ana
First American Financial Corp 338
Banc Of California Inc 97

Santa Clara
Intel Corp 464
Applied Materials, Inc. 70
NVIDIA Corp 627
SVB Financial Group 803

Santa Monica
Activision Blizzard, Inc. 9

Santa Rosa
Exchange Bank (Santa Rosa, CA) 313
REDWOOD CREDIT UNION 719

South San Francisco
Core Mark Holding Co Inc 238

Sunnyvale
NetApp, Inc. 601
Juniper Networks Inc 489

Sylmar
Tutor Perini Corp 856

Thousand Oaks
Amgen Inc 56

TURLOCK
YOSEMITE FARM CREDIT, ACA 937

Westlake Village
Pennymac Financial Services Inc 662

CO

Broomfield
Ball Corp 96

Centennial
Arrow Electronics, Inc. 76

Denver
DaVita Inc 257
CoBiz Financial Inc 214
Guaranty Bancorp (DE) 403
AIMCO PROPERTIES, L.P. 21
COLORADO HOUSING AND FINANCE
    AUTHORITY 220
DIVIDEND CAPITAL DIVERSIFIED
    PROPERTY FUND INC. 274

Englewood
Dish Network Corp 271
Liberty Interactive Corp 523
Liberty Interactive Corp 523
Liberty Interactive Corp 523
Western Union Co 918
CH2M Hill Companies Ltd 184
Liberty Media Corp (DE) 525
Liberty Media Corp (DE) 525
Liberty Media Corp (DE) 525
Liberty Media Corp (DE) 525
CATHOLIC HEALTH INITIATIVES
    167
CH2M HILL COMPANIES, LTD. 184

Greeley
Pilgrims Pride Corp. 676

Greenwood Village
Newmont Mining Corp (Holding Co)
    608
Great West Life & Annuity Insurance
    Co - Insurance Products 400
National Bank Holdings Corp 591
COBANK ACB 213

CT

Bloomfield
Cigna Corp 194

Bridgeport
People's United Financial Inc 663

Danbury
Praxair Inc 687

Farmington
United Technologies Corp 878
First Connecticut Bancorp Inc. (MD)
    347

Greenwich
XPO Logistics, Inc. 936
Berkley (WR) Corp 121

Hartford
Aetna Inc. 17
Hartford Financial Services Group Inc.
    412
Hartford Life Insurance Co 414
United Financial Bancorp Inc (New)
    872

New Britain
Stanley Black & Decker Inc 785

New Canaan
Bankwell Financial Group Inc 110

NEW HAVEN
KNIGHTS OF COLUMBUS 502

Norwalk
Xerox Corp 933
Priceline Group Inc (The) 688
Frontier Communications Corp 375

EMCOR Group, Inc. 298

Orange
Avangrid Inc 91

Shelton
Prudential Annuities Life Assurance
    Corp 698

Stamford
Charter Communications Inc (New)
    186
Synchrony Financial 804
United Rentals Inc 876
Navigators Group Inc (The) 595
STATOIL MARKETING & TRADING
    (US) INC. 793

Wallingford
Amphenol Corp. 58

Waterbury
Webster Financial Corp (Waterbury,
    Conn) 907

Willimantic
SI Financial Group Inc (MD) 766

DC

Washington
Fannie Mae 321
Danaher Corp 255
Federal Agricultural Mortgage Corp
    326
SECURITIES INVESTOR
    PROTECTION CORPORATION 759

DE

Newark
SLM Corp. 771

Wilmington
Chemours Co (The) 188
Navient Corp 594
WSFS Financial Corp 930
The Bancorp Inc 827
COMENITY BANK 223

FL

Boca Raton
Office Depot, Inc. 633

Clearwater
Tech Data Corp. 815

Coral Gables
MasTec Inc. (FL) 553

Estero
Hertz Global Holdings Inc (New) 422

Fort Lauderdale
AutoNation, Inc. 88

Jacksonville
CSX Corp 245
Fidelity National Financial Inc 331
Fidelity National Information Services
    Inc 333

Juno Beach
NextEra Energy Inc 611
Florida Power & Light Co. 363

Lakeland
Publix Super Markets, Inc. 701
PUBLIX SUPER MARKETS, INC. 701

Melbourne
Harris Corp. 411

Miami
World Fuel Services Corp. 928
Lennar Corp 518
Ryder System, Inc. 742
NCL CORPORATION LTD. 598

Miami Lakes
BankUnited Inc. 109

Orlando
Darden Restaurants, Inc. 256

St. Petersburg
Jabil Inc 480
Raymond James Financial, Inc. 714
Florida Power Corp. 363

Stuart
Seacoast Banking Corp. of Florida
    756

Tallahassee
Capital City Bank Group, Inc. 156

Tampa
WellCare Health Plans Inc 910

Weston
FCB Financial Holdings Inc 326

Winter Haven
CenterState Bank Corp 178

GA

Atlanta
Home Depot Inc 430
United Parcel Service Inc 874
Coca-Cola Co (The) 215
Delta Air Lines Inc (DE) 262
Southern Company (The) 778
Genuine Parts Co. 387
SunTrust Banks Inc 798
PulteGroup Inc 703
Georgia Power Co 389
Veritiv Corp 892
HD Supply Holdings Inc 417
Intercontinental Exchange Inc 466
Fidelity Southern Corp 334
State Bank Financial Corp 789
Atlantic Capital Bancshares Inc 85
RACETRAC PETROLEUM, INC. 711
FEDERAL HOME LOAN BANK OF
    ATLANTA 328

Blairsville
United Community Banks Inc
    (Blairsville, GA) 869

Calhoun
Mohawk Industries, Inc. 580

Columbus
AFLAC Inc 19
Synovus Financial Corp. 806

Duluth
AGCO Corp. 20
NCR Corp 599
Asbury Automotive Group Inc 77
Primerica Inc 690

Moultrie
Ameris Bancorp 53

STATESBORO
AGSOUTH FARM CREDIT ACA 21

West Point
Charter Financial Corp (MD) 187

HI

Honolulu
First Hawaiian Inc 352

Bank of Hawaii Corp 102
Central Pacific Financial Corp 179
Territorial Bancorp Inc 821

IA

Ankeny
Casey's General Stores, Inc. 163

Cedar Rapids
Rockwell Collins Inc 738
United Fire Group, Inc. 872
Merrill Lynch Life Insurance Co -
    Insurance Products 568

Des Moines
Principal Financial Group Inc 690
Federal Home Loan Bank Of Des
    Moines 329
EMC Insurance Group Inc. 297
IOWA FINANCE AUTHORITY 477

Dubuque
Heartland Financial USA, Inc.
    (Dubuque, IA) 419

Hills
Hills Bancorporation 425

Iowa City
MidWestOne Financial Group, Inc.
    578

West Des Moines
American Equity Investment Life
    Holding Co 43
FBL Financial Group Inc 325
West Bancorporation, Inc. 914
HY-VEE, INC. 452
IOWA STUDENT LOAN LIQUIDITY
    CORPORATION 477

ID

Boise
Micron Technology Inc. 574

IL

Abbott Park
Abbott Laboratories 4

Arlington Heights
HSBC Finance Corp 444

Aurora
Old Second Bancorp., Inc. (Aurora,
    Ill.) 637

BLOOMINGTON
GROWMARK, INC. 402

Bolingbrook
Ulta Beauty Inc 862

BROADVIEW
ROBERT BOSCH LLC 733

Burr Ridge
BankFinancial Corp 108

Champaign
First Busey Corp 342

Chicago
Boeing Co. (The) 134
Archer Daniels Midland Co. 73
United Continental Holdings Inc 871
Exelon Corp 314
CNA Financial Corp 210
LKQ Corp 533
Conagra Brands Inc 231
Donnelley (RR) & Sons Company 279

Jones Lang LaSalle Inc 485
Motorola Solutions Inc. 588
Old Republic International Corp. 636
Northern Trust Corp 619
Telephone & Data Systems Inc 816
Kemper Corp (DE) 495
MB Financial Inc 557
Byline Bancorp Inc 152
BOARD OF EDUCATION OF CITY OF
  CHICAGO 134
FEDERAL HOME LOAN BANK OF
  CHICAGO 328
HOMETOWN AMERICA
  MANAGEMENT CORP. 433
CHRISTIAN BROTHERS
  INVESTMENT SERVICES, INC. 192

Deerfield
Walgreens Boots Alliance Inc 900
Caterpillar Inc. 165
Mondelez International Inc 583
Baxter International Inc 114
Essendant Inc 310
Fortune Brands Home & Security, Inc.
  371

Downers Grove
Univar Inc 881
Dover Corp 280
PowerShares DB Commodity Index
  Tracking Fund 684
ADVOCATE HEALTH CARE
  NETWORK 13

Effingham
Midland States Bancorp Inc 576

FRANKLIN PARK
HILL/AHERN FIRE PROTECTION,
  LLC 425

Glenview
Illinois Tool Works, Inc. 457
Anixter International Inc 64

Hoffman Estates
Sears Holdings Corp 758

Itasca
First Midwest Bancorp, Inc.
  (Naperville, IL) 356

Lake Forest
Grainger (W.W.) Inc. 397
Tenneco Inc 819
Packaging Corp of America 651

Lincolnshire
CDW Corp 173

Lisle
Navistar International Corp. 596

MAHOMET
FARM CREDIT ILLINOIS, ACA 323

Mattoon
First Mid-Illinois Bancshares Inc 355

Moline
Deere & Co. 260
QCR Holdings Inc 706

North Chicago
AbbVie Inc 5

Northbrook
Allstate Corp. 30

Oak Brook
McDonald's Corp 561
TreeHouse Foods Inc 850
ACE HARDWARE CORPORATION 8
IRC RETAIL CENTERS LLC 479

Orland Park
Marquette National Corp (IL) 547

Peoria
RLI Corp. 732

Riverwoods
Discover Financial Services 269

ROCK ISLAND
MODERN WOODMEN OF AMERICA
  579

Rolling Meadows
Gallagher (Arthur J.) & Co. 377

Rosemont
US Foods Holding Corp 889
Wintrust Financial Corp (IL) 927

Springfield
Horace Mann Educators Corp. 435

Westchester
Ingredion Inc 461

IN

Carmel
CNO Financial Group Inc 212
Merchants Bancorp (Indiana) 564

Columbus
Cummins, Inc. 247

Elkhart
Thor Industries, Inc. 836

Evansville
Berry Global Group Inc 125
OneMain Holdings Inc 640
Old National Bancorp (Evansville, IN)
  634
SPRINGLEAF FINANCE
  CORPORATION 784

Fishers
First Internet Bancorp 353

Fort Wayne
Steel Dynamics Inc. 793

Greensburg
MainSource Financial Group Inc 542

Indianapolis
Anthem Inc 65
Lilly (Eli) & Co 527
Simon Property Group, Inc. 769
ONEAMERICA FINANCIAL
  PARTNERS, INC. 640

Jasper
German American Bancorp Inc 390

Michigan City
Horizon Bancorp (Michigan City, IN)
  436

Muncie
First Merchants Corp 354
MutualFirst Financial Inc 590

South Bend
1st Source Corp 1

Terre Haute
First Financial Corp. (IN) 351

Warsaw
Zimmer Biomet Holdings Inc 939
Lakeland Financial Corp 511

KS

KANSAS CITY
DAIRY FARMERS OF AMERICA, INC.
  253

ASSOCIATED WHOLESALE
  GROCERS, INC. 81

Merriam
Seaboard Corp. 755

Overland Park
Sprint Corp (New) 784
YRC Worldwide Inc 937

Topeka
Capitol Federal Financial Inc 159

Wichita
Spirit AeroSystems Holdings Inc 783
Equity Bancshares Inc 309

KY

BOWLING GREEN
HOUCHENS INDUSTRIES, INC. 441

Frankfort
Farmers Capital Bank Corp. 324

Louisville
Humana Inc. 445
Kindred Healthcare Inc 501
Yum! Brands Inc 938
Republic Bancorp, Inc. (KY) 726
Stock Yards Bancorp Inc 796

Pikeville
Community Trust Bancorp, Inc. 230

LA

CHALMETTE
CHALMETTE REFINING, L.L.C. 186

COVINGTON
CGB ENTERPRISES, INC. 183
CONSOLIDATED GRAIN & BARGE
  COMPANY 236
ZEN-NOH GRAIN CORPORATION
  939

DeRidder
Amerisafe Inc 54

Hammond
First Guaranty Bancshares, Inc. 352

Lafayette
IBERIABANK Corp 453
MidSouth Bancorp, Inc. 577
Home Bancorp Inc 429

Monroe
CenturyLink Inc 181
Qwest Corp 711

New Orleans
Entergy Corp 303

MA

Belmont
BSB Bancorp Inc. (MD) 148

Boston
General Electric Co 381
Santander Holdings USA Inc. 751
State Street Corp. 791
American Tower Corp (New) 50
Safety Insurance Group, Inc. 746
Boston Private Financial Holdings,
  Inc. 141
Brookline Bancorp Inc (DE) 147
PARTNERS HEALTHCARE SYSTEM,
  INC. 655

MASSACHUSETTS HOUSING
  FINANCE AGENCY PROPERTY
  ACQUISITION AND DISPOSITION
  CORPORATION 552
EAST BOSTON SAVING BANK 289

Brockton
HarborOne Bancorp Inc 410

Cambridge
Biogen Inc 128
Cambridge Bancorp 153

Framingham
TJX Companies, Inc. 839

Hanover
Independent Bank Corp (MA) 458

Hingham
Hingham Institution for Savings 427

Lowell
Enterprise Bancorp, Inc. (MA) 305

Marlborough
Boston Scientific Corp. 142

Medford
Century Bancorp, Inc. 180

Norwood
Analog Devices Inc 62
Blue Hills Bancorp Inc 134

Peabody
Meridian Bancorp Inc 567

Pittsfield
Berkshire Hills Bancorp Inc 124

Springfield
Eversource Energy 312

Waltham
Raytheon Co. 716
Thermo Fisher Scientific Inc 835
Global Partners LP 393

Westfield
Western New England Bancorp Inc
  918

Worcester
Hanover Insurance Group Inc 408
SPECTRUM HEALTH SYSTEMS, INC.
  783

MD

Baltimore
Under Armour Inc 865
T Rowe Price Group Inc. 809
THE WHITING-TURNER
  CONTRACTING COMPANY 833
JOHNS HOPKINS UNIVERSITY 483
LORD BALTIMORE CAPITAL
  CORPORATION 536

Bethesda
Lockheed Martin Corp 534
Marriott International, Inc. 547
Host Hotels & Resorts Inc 439
Eagle Bancorp Inc (MD) 288

Bowie
Old Line Bancshares Inc 634

HANOVER
ALLEGIS GROUP, INC. 28
AEROTEK, INC. 15

Olney
Sandy Spring Bancorp Inc 749

Silver Spring
Discovery Communications Inc 270

Sparks
McCormick & Co Inc 560

ME

AUGUSTA
MAINE STATE HOUSING AUTHORITY 541

Bar Harbor
Bar Harbor Bankshares 112

Camden
Camden National Corp. (ME) 154

Damariscotta
First Bancorp Inc (ME) 341

MI

ADA
ALTICOR INC. 34
SOLSTICE HOLDINGS INC. 774

ANN ARBOR
REGENTS OF THE UNIVERSITY OF MICHIGAN 720

Auburn Hills
BorgWarner Inc 139

Battle Creek
Kellogg Co 492

Benton Harbor
Whirlpool Corp 922

Bloomfield Hills
Penske Automotive Group Inc 662

Dearborn
Ford Motor Co. (DE) 369

Detroit
General Motors Co 384
DTE Energy Co 283
Ally Financial Inc 32
DTE Electric Company 283

Grand Rapids
SpartanNash Co. 780
Mercantile Bank Corp. 564
Independent Bank Corporation (Ionia, MI) 459

Holland
Macatawa Bank Corp. 539

Jackson
CMS Energy Corp 209
Consumers Energy Co. 237

Kalamazoo
Stryker Corp 796

Livonia
Masco Corp. 551

Midland
DowDuPont Inc 281
Chemical Financial Corp 187

Mt. Pleasant
Isabella Bank Corp 479

Southfield
Lear Corp. 514
FEDERAL-MOGUL HOLDINGS LLC 329

Troy
Kelly Services, Inc. 494
Flagstar Bancorp, Inc. 362

MN

Austin
Hormel Foods Corp. 436

BLOOMINGTON
HEALTHPARTNERS, INC. 419

Eden Prairie
Robinson (C.H.) Worldwide, Inc. 736
Supervalu Inc 800

Inver Grove Heights
CHS Inc 192

Medina
Polaris Industries Inc. 681

Minneapolis
Target Corp 812
US Bancorp (DE) 887
General Mills, Inc. 382
Ameriprise Financial Inc 52
Xcel Energy Inc 932
RiverSource Life Insurance Co 731

Minnetonka
UnitedHealth Group Inc 880

Plymouth
Mosaic Co (The) 587

Richfield
Best Buy Inc 126

St. Paul
3M Co 1
Ecolab Inc 293
Patterson Companies Inc 656

Wayzata
TCF Financial Corp 814

MO

Chesterfield
Reinsurance Group of America, Inc. 723
MISSOURI HIGHER EDUCATION LOAN AUTHORITY 579

Clayton
Olin Corp. 637
Enterprise Financial Services Corp 305

Des Peres
Jones Financial Companies LLLLP 485

Grandview
NASB Financial Inc 590

Kansas City
Commerce Bancshares Inc 225
UMB Financial Corp 862
Kansas City Life Insurance Co (Kansas City, MO) 491

MARYLAND HEIGHTS
WORLD WIDE TECHNOLOGY, INC. 930

North Kansas City
Cerner Corp. 182

Poplar Bluff
Southern Missouri Bancorp, Inc. 779

SAINT LOUIS
ASCENSION HEALTH ALLIANCE 79
WORLD WIDE TECHNOLOGY HOLDING CO., INC. 929
APPLE HOSPITALITY REIT, INC. 68

Springfield
O'Reilly Automotive, Inc. 629
Great Southern Bancorp, Inc. 399

St. Louis
Express Scripts Holding Co 318
Centene Corp 175
Emerson Electric Co. 299
Monsanto Co 584
Graybar Electric Co., Inc. 398
Ameren Corp 39
Post Holdings Inc 683
Peabody Energy Corp (New) 658
Stifel Financial Corp 795
Cass Information Systems Inc. 164

MS

Gulfport
Hancock Holding Co. 406

Jackson
Trustmark Corp 854

Tupelo
BancorpSouth Bank (Tupelo, MS) 99
Renasant Corp 726

MT

Billings
First Interstate BancSystem Inc 354

Kalispell
Glacier Bancorp, Inc. 392

NC

Asheville
HomeTrust Bancshares Inc. 433

Burlington
Laboratory Corporation of America Holdings 509

Charlotte
Bank of America Corp. 100
Duke Energy Corp 285
Nucor Corp. 625
Sonic Automotive, Inc. 774
Duke Energy Carolinas LLC 284
Sealed Air Corp 757
Brighthouse Financial Inc 143
Brighthouse Life Insurance Co - Insurance Products 143
THE CHARLOTTE-MECKLENBURG HOSPITAL AUTHORITY 828

Durham
IQVIA Holdings Inc 477
DUKE UNIVERSITY 286

Greensboro
VF Corp. 894

Hickory
CommScope Holding Co., Inc. 227

HUNTERSVILLE
AMERICAN TIRE DISTRIBUTORS HOLDINGS, INC. 50

Mooresville
Lowe's Companies Inc 536

Raleigh
First Citizens BancShares Inc (NC) 344
COASTAL FEDERAL CREDIT UNION 213

Southern Pines
First Bancorp (NC) 341

Wilmington
Live Oak Bancshares Inc 533

ND

Grand Forks
Alerus Financial Corp 27

NE

Lincoln
Nelnet Inc 600
UNION BANK AND TRUST COMPANY 866

Omaha
Berkshire Hathaway Inc 122
Union Pacific Corp 867
KIEWIT CORPORATION 498
PETER KIEWIT SONS', INC. 669
TENASKA MARKETING VENTURES 817
THE SCOULAR COMPANY 831
FARM CREDIT SERVICES OF AMERICA, PCA 323

NJ

Bayonne
BCB Bancorp Inc 118

Bedminster
Peapack-Gladstone Financial Corp. 659

Branchville
Selective Insurance Group Inc 760

Burlington
Burlington Stores Inc 151

Camden
Campbell Soup Co. 155

Englewood Cliffs
ConnectOne Bancorp Inc (New) 233

Fairfield
Kearny Financial Corp (MD) 492

Florham Park
Conduent Inc 233

Franklin Lakes
Becton, Dickinson & Co 119

Hoboken
Newell Brands Inc 607

Jersey City
Provident Financial Services Inc 697

KEASBEY
WAKEFERN FOOD CORP. 899

Keniworth
Merck & Co Inc 565

Madison
Quest Diagnostics, Inc. 709
Realogy Group LLC 717
Realogy Holdings Corp 718

Mahwah
Ascena Retail Group Inc 78

Morris Plains
Honeywell International Inc 433

New Brunswick
Johnson & Johnson 484

Newark
Prudential Financial, Inc. 699

ND

Grand Forks
Alerus Financial Corp 27

Winston-Salem
BB&T Corp. 116
HanesBrands Inc 406

Public Service Enterprise Group Inc 700

Oak Ridge
Lakeland Bancorp, Inc. 510

Parsippany
PBF Energy Inc 657
Avis Budget Group Inc 92
Wyndham Worldwide Corp 931
Zoetis Inc 942

Princeton
NRG Energy Inc 624

Roseland
Automatic Data Processing Inc. 87
MACK-CALI REALTY, L. P. 540

Short Hills
Investors Bancorp Inc (New) 476

SOMERSET
SHI INTERNATIONAL CORP. 765

Summit
Celgene Corp 174

Teaneck
Cognizant Technology Solutions Corp. 217

Toms River
OceanFirst Financial Corp 632

Township of Washington
Oritani Financial Corp (DE) 644

TRENTON
NEW JERSEY HOUSING AND MORTGAGE FINANCE AGENCY 603

Union
Bed, Bath & Beyond, Inc. 120

Wayne
Valley National Bancorp (NJ) 891

Woodbridge
Northfield Bancorp Inc (DE) 621

NV

Las Vegas
Las Vegas Sands Corp 513
MGM Resorts International 572

Reno
Employers Holdings Inc 300

NY

ALBANY
STATE UNIVERSITY OF NEW YORK 793

Armonk
International Business Machines Corp 469

Bridgehampton
Bridge Bancorp, Inc. (Bridgehampton, NY) 143

Brooklyn
Dime Community Bancshares, Inc 268

Buffalo
M & T Bank Corp 538

Corning
Corning Inc 239

CORTLAND
SUNY COLLEGE AT CORTLAND 800

DeWitt
Community Bank System Inc 228

Elmira
Chemung Financial Corp. 188

Glen Head
First of Long Island Corp 357

Glens Falls
Arrow Financial Corp. 77

Glenville
Trustco Bank Corp. (N.Y.) 853

Ithaca
Tompkins Financial Corp 842

Long Island City
JetBlue Airways Corp 482

Melville
Schein (Henry) Inc 752

Montebello
Sterling Bancorp (DE) 794

New York
Verizon Communications Inc 892
JPMorgan Chase & Co 487
Citigroup Inc 202
Philip Morris International Inc 673
MetLife Inc 569
Pfizer Inc 670
American International Group Inc 47
Morgan Stanley 586
Goldman Sachs Group Inc 394
American Express Co. 44
INTL FCStone Inc. 473
Time Warner Inc 837
Travelers Companies Inc (The) 848
Twenty-First Century Fox Inc 857
Macy's Inc 540
Bristol-Myers Squibb Co. 143
Icahn Enterprises LP 455
Bank of New York Mellon Corp 104
Colgate-Palmolive Co. 219
Omnicom Group, Inc. 638
Loews Corp. 535
Viacom Inc 895
Marsh & McLennan Companies Inc. 549
CBS Corp 171
Arconic Inc 75
Consolidated Edison Inc 235
Lauder (Estee) Cos., Inc. (The) 514
First Data Corp (New) 347
BlackRock Inc 130
Voya Financial Inc 899
L3 Technologies Inc 509
Consolidated Edison Co. of New York, Inc. 234
Leucadia National Corp. 519
PVH Corp 704
News Corp (New) 610
Interpublic Group of Companies Inc. 473
Foot Locker, Inc. 368
Coty, Inc. 241
Assurant Inc 82
Ralph Lauren Corp 712
Alleghany Corp. 27
S&P Global Inc 745
ABM Industries, Inc. 7
AmTrust Financial Services Inc 59
Sirius XM Holdings Inc 771
HSBC USA, Inc. 444
Altaba Inc 34
Blackstone Group LP (The) 132
HRG Group Inc 443
Hess Corp 423
National General Holdings Corp 592
CIT Group Inc 200
Annaly Capital Management Inc 65
E*TRADE Financial Corp. 287

Federal Home Loan Bank New York 327
Signature Bank (New York, NY) 767
Prospect Capital Corporation 695
Ambac Financial Group, Inc. 38
THE TURNER CORPORATION 832
TURNER CONSTRUCTION COMPANY INC 855
TRAMMO, INC. 846
METROPOLITAN TRANSPORTATION AUTHORITY 571
NIELSEN HOLDINGS PLC 614
NEW YORK UNIVERSITY 606
LUKOIL PAN AMERICAS, LLC 538
NEW YORK PRESBYTERIAN HOSPITAL WEILL CORNELL UNIVERSITY MEDICAL CENTER 605
SL GREEN OPERATING PARTNERSHIP, L.P. 771
VIRTU FINANCIAL LLC 898
THE FORD FOUNDATION 828
BRIXMOR LLC 145
NEW YORK COMMUNITY TRUST AND COMMUNITY FUNDS INC 605
STATE OF NEW YORK MORTGAGE AGENCY 790
ALFRED P. SLOAN FOUNDATION 27

Norwich
NBT Bancorp. Inc. 597

Purchase
PepsiCo Inc 667
Mastercard Inc 554
MBIA Inc. 559

REGO PARK
NEW YORK STATE CATHOLIC HEALTH PLAN INC 605

ROCHESTER
WEGMANS FOOD MARKETS, INC. 910
HOME PROPERTIES, LIMITED PARTNERSHIP 432

Tarrytown
Regeneron Pharmaceuticals, Inc. 719

Uniondale
Flushing Financial Corp. 366

Victor
Constellation Brands Inc 236

Warsaw
Financial Institutions Inc. 338

Westbury
New York Community Bancorp Inc. 603

OH

Akron
Goodyear Tire & Rubber Co. 396
FirstEnergy Corp 359

Canfield
Farmers National Banc Corp. (Canfield, OH) 324

Cincinnati
Kroger Co (The) 506
Procter & Gamble Company (The) 692
Fifth Third Bancorp (Cincinnati, OH) 335
American Financial Group Inc 46
Cintas Corporation 197
Federal Home Loan Bank Of Cincinnati 328
First Financial Bancorp (OH) 349

PHILLIPS EDISON - ARC SHOPPING CENTER REIT INC. 675

Cleveland
Parker Hannifin Corp 653
Sherwin-Williams Co (The) 764
KeyCorp 496
TFS Financial Corp 827
THE CLEVELAND FOUNDATION 828

Columbus
American Electric Power Company, Inc. 42
L Brands, Inc 508
Big Lots, Inc. 127
Huntington Bancshares Inc 448
State Auto Financial Corp. 788
BATTELLE MEMORIAL INSTITUTE INC 113
BATTELLE MEMORIAL INSTITUTE 113

Defiance
First Defiance Financial Corp 348

Dublin
Cardinal Health, Inc. 160

Fairfield
Cincinnati Financial Corp. 196

Findlay
Marathon Petroleum Corp. 546

Marietta
Peoples Bancorp, Inc. (Marietta, OH) 665

Maumee
Dana Inc 254

Mayfield Village
Progressive Corp. (OH) 694

Medina
RPM International Inc (DE) 741

Newark
Park National Corp (Newark, OH) 653

Orrville
Smucker (J.M.) Co. 773

Perrysburg
Owens-Illinois, Inc. 648

Toledo
Owens Corning 647

West Chester
AK Steel Holding Corp. 23

Westlake
TravelCenters of America LLC 847

Youngstown
United Community Financial Corp. (OH) 870

OK

Oklahoma City
Devon Energy Corp. 263
Chesapeake Energy Corp. 188
BancFirst Corp. (Oklahoma City, Okla) 98
CANDID COLOR SYSTEMS, INC. 156
STATE OF OKLAHOMA 790

Tulsa
NGL Energy Partners LP 612
ONEOK Inc 641
Williams Cos Inc (The) 923
Williams Partners LP (New) 924
BOK Financial Corp 137

CHARLES AND LYNN
SCHUSTERMAN FAMILY
FOUNDATION 186

OR

Beaverton
NIKE Inc 614

Medford
Lithia Motors Inc 531

Portland
Pacificorp 650
Umpqua Holdings Corp 864

PA

Allentown
Air Products & Chemicals Inc 21
PPL Corp 685

Bryn Mawr
Bryn Mawr Bank Corp 147

Camp Hill
Rite Aid Corp 730

Chesterbrook
AmerisourceBergen Corp. 55

Clearfield
CNB Financial Corp. (Clearfield, PA)
211

Coraopolis
Dick's Sporting Goods, Inc 264

Erie
Erie Indemnity Co. 309

HARRISBURG
PENNSYLVANIA HOUSING FINANCE
AGENCY 661

Hershey
Hershey Company (The) 421

Horsham
Toll Brothers Inc. 840

Indiana
S & T Bancorp Inc (Indiana, PA) 744
First Commonwealth Financial Corp
(Indiana, PA) 345

Kennett Square
Exelon Generation Co LLC 315
Genesis Healthcare Inc 386

King of Prussia
Universal Health Services, Inc. 882
UGI Corp. 861

Lancaster
Fulton Financial Corp. (PA) 376

Marietta
Donegal Group Inc. 279

Philadelphia
Comcast Corp 221
Aramark 71
Crown Holdings Inc 243
Radian Group, Inc. 711
Beneficial Bancorp Inc 121
Republic First Bancorp, Inc. 727
THE WILLIAM PENN FOUNDATION
835

Pittsburgh
Kraft Heinz Co (The) 505
PNC Financial Services Group (The)
680
PPG Industries Inc 684
United States Steel Corp. 877

Alcoa Corporation 27
Wesco International, Inc. 913
FNB Corp 367
TriState Capital Holdings, Inc. 853
UPMC PRESBYTERIAN SHADYSIDE
887

Radnor
Lincoln National Corp. 529

Scranton
Peoples Financial Services Corp 666

Souderton
Univest Corp. of Pennsylvania
(Souderton) 884

Stroudsburg
ESSA Bancorp Inc 310

UNIVERSITY PARK
THE PENNSYLVANIA STATE
UNIVERSITY 830

Warren
Northwest Bancshares, Inc. (MD) 623

WEST CHESTER
QVC, INC. 710
ACCESS GROUP, INC. 8

Wyomissing
Customers Bancorp Inc 248

York
Codorus Valley Bancorp, Inc. 217

QUEBEC

Montreal
Molson Coors Brewing Co. 582

RI

Pawtucket
Hasbro, Inc. 414

Providence
Textron Inc 825
United Natural Foods Inc. 873
Citizens Financial Group Inc (New)
205
STATE OF RHODE ISLAND AND
PROVIDENCE PLANTATIONS 790
STATE OF RHODE ISLAND 790

Westerly
Washington Trust Bancorp, Inc. 905

Woonsocket
CVS Health Corporation 251

SC

Charleston
Carolina Financial Corp (New) 163

Columbia
South State Corp 776

Fort Mill
Domtar Corp 278

GREENVILLE
ATHENE ANNUITY & LIFE
ASSURANCE COMPANY 85

Hartsville
Sonoco Products Co. 775

SD

Sioux Falls
Great Western Bancorp Inc 401
Meta Financial Group Inc 568

TN

Brentwood
Tractor Supply Co. 845
LifePoint Health Inc 526
Brookdale Senior Living Inc 145

Chattanooga
Unum Group 885

Dyersburg
First Citizens Bancshares, Inc.
(Dyersburg, TN) 345

Franklin
Community Health Systems, Inc. 229
Franklin Financial Network Inc 372

Goodlettsville
Dollar General Corp 275

Kingsport
Eastman Chemical Co 290

Knoxville
Tennessee Valley Authority 820
CFJ PROPERTIES LLC 183
EDUCATIONAL FUNDING OF THE
SOUTH, INC. 296

Lebanon
Wilson Bank Holding Co. 925

Memphis
FedEx Corp 329
International Paper Co 471
AutoZone, Inc. 89
First Horizon National Corp 352

Nashville
HCA Healthcare Inc 415
Pinnacle Financial Partners Inc 677
FB Financial Corp 325
RYMAN HOSPITALITY PROPERTIES,
INC. 743
SAINT THOMAS HEALTH SERVICES,
INC. 747

TX

Abilene
First Financial Bankshares, Inc. 350

Arlington
Horton (DR) Inc 438

Austin
National Western Life Group Inc 594
Citizens, Inc. (Austin, TX) 206
STATE OF TEXAS 791
UNIVERSITY OF TEXAS SYSTEM 883

Beaumont
CBTX Inc 172
COMMUNITYBANK OF TEXAS
NATIONAL ASSOCIATION 231

COLLEGE STATION
TEXAS A&M FOUNDATION 823

Dallas
AT&T Inc 83
Energy Transfer Equity LP 301
Southwest Airlines Co 780
Tenet Healthcare Corp. 817
Kimberly-Clark Corp. 498
Sunoco LP 798
Texas Instruments Inc. 824

HollyFrontier Corp 428
Jacobs Engineering Group, Inc. 481
Energy Transfer Partners LP (New)
302
Dean Foods Co. 259
Santander Consumer USA Holdings
Inc 751
Builders FirstSource Inc. 149
Neiman Marcus Group Ltd LLC 600
Trinity Industries, Inc. 852
Comerica, Inc. 223
Texas Capital Bancshares Inc 823
CIM Commercial Trust Corp 195
Triumph Bancorp Inc 853
PLACID REFINING COMPANY LLC
678
PLACID HOLDING COMPANY 678

Fort Worth
American Airlines Group Inc 41
Burlington Northern & Santa Fe
Railway Co. (The) 150
TPG Specialty Lending Inc 845

Galveston
American National Insurance Co.
(Galveston, TX) 48

Grapevine
GameStop Corp 378

Houston
Phillips 66 674
Sysco Corp 807
ConocoPhillips 234
Enterprise Products Partners L.P. 306
Halliburton Company 404
Plains GP Holdings LP 679
Plains All American Pipeline LP 679
Waste Management, Inc. (DE) 906
Kinder Morgan Inc. 499
Baker Hughes, A GE Company 95
Group 1 Automotive, Inc. 401
Occidental Petroleum Corp 631
National Oilwell Varco Inc 592
Quanta Services, Inc. 708
EOG Resources, Inc. 308
CenterPoint Energy, Inc 177
Calpine Corp 152
Targa Resources Corp 811
Apache Corp 67
Westlake Chemical Corp 919
Marathon Oil Corp. 543
Prosperity Bancshares Inc. 696
Cadence Bancorporation 152
Green Bancorp Inc 401
Allegiance Bancshares Inc 28
TELCO INTERCONTINENTAL CORP
816
BIOURJA TRADING, LLC 130

Irving
Exxon Mobil Corp 319
Fluor Corp. 364
Celanese Corp (DE) 173
Michaels Companies Inc 573
Commercial Metals Co. 227
Federal Home Loan Bank Of Dallas
328

Laredo
International Bancshares Corp. 468

McKinney
Torchmark Corp 843
Independent Bank Group Inc. 460

Mount Pleasant
Guaranty Bancshares Inc 404

Plano
Penney (J.C.) Co.,Inc. (Holding Co.)
660
Toyota Motor Credit Corp. 844
Alliance Data Systems Corp. 29

Dr Pepper Snapple Group Inc 281
Yum China Holdings Inc 938
LegacyTexas Financial Group Inc 515
MONOGRAM RESIDENTIAL TRUST, INC. 584

Round Rock
Dell Technologies Inc 261

San Antonio
Valero Energy Corp 889
Andeavor 63
iHeartMedia Inc 456
Cullen/Frost Bankers, Inc. 246

Sugar Land
CVR Energy Inc 250

The Woodlands
Anadarko Petroleum Corp 60
Huntsman Corp 451
CHEVRON PHILLIPS CHEMICAL COMPANY LLC 191
CHEVRON PHILLIPS CHEMICAL COMPANY LP 192

Tyler
Southside Bancshares, Inc. 779
UNIVERSITY OF TEXAS AT TYLER 883

WICHITA FALLS
THE PRIDDY FOUNDATION 831

UT

American Fork
People's Utah Bancorp 665

Salt Lake City
Zions Bancorporation 941
INTERMOUNTAIN HEALTH CARE INC 467

SOUTH JORDAN
MERRICK BANK CORPORATION 568

WEST VALLEY CITY
UTAH HOUSING CORPORATION 889

VA

Arlington
AES Corp. 16

Bluefield
First Community Bancshares, Inc. (NV) 346

Chesapeake
Dollar Tree Inc 276

Danville
American National Bankshares, Inc. (Danville, VA) 47

Falls Church
General Dynamics Corp 379
Northrop Grumman Corp 622
CSRA Inc 244

Glen Allen
Markel Corp (Holding Co) 545

Martinsville
Carter Bank & Trust (Martinsville, VA) 163

McLean
Freddie Mac 373
Capital One Financial Corp 157
Hilton Worldwide Holdings Inc 426
Booz Allen Hamilton Holding Corp. 138

Mechanicsville
Owens & Minor, Inc. 646

Newport News
Huntington Ingalls Industries, Inc. 450

Norfolk
Norfolk Southern Corp. 617
SENTARA HEALTHCARE 762

Portsmouth
TowneBank 844

Reston
Leidos Holdings Inc 516
NVR Inc. 628
Leidos, Inc. 517

Richmond
Altria Group Inc 35
Performance Food Group Co 669
Carmax Inc. 162
WestRock Co 920
Dominion Energy Inc (New) 277
Genworth Financial, Inc. (Holding Co) 388
Virginia Electric & Power Co. 897
Union Bankshares Corp (New) 866
VIRGINIA HOUSING DEVELOPMENT AUTHORITY 897

Roanoke
Advance Auto Parts Inc 11

STAUNTON
FARM CREDIT OF THE VIRGINIAS ACA 323

Tysons, Virginia
DXC Technology Co 287

VI

CHRISTIANSTED
LIMETREE BAY TERMINALS LLC 529

WA

Bellevue
T-Mobile US Inc 810
PACCAR Inc. 649
Expedia Inc 316

Everett
Fortive Corp 370

Issaquah
Costco Wholesale Corp 240

Olympia
Heritage Financial Corp. (WA) 420

Redmond
Microsoft Corporation 575

Seattle
Amazon.com Inc 36
Starbucks Corp. 786
Nordstrom, Inc. 616
Alaska Air Group, Inc. 25
Weyerhaeuser Co 921
Expeditors International of Washington, Inc. 317
Washington Federal Inc. 904
HomeStreet Inc 432

SPOKANE
NORTHWEST FARM CREDIT SERVICES 624

Tacoma
Columbia Banking System Inc 220

Walla Walla
Banner Corp. 110

WI

APPLETON
U.S. VENTURE, INC. 860

Brookfield
Fiserv Inc 360

Green Bay
Associated Banc-Corp 80
Nicolet Bankshares Inc 613

Madison
First Business Financial Services, Inc. 343

Menomonee Falls
Kohl's Corp. 503

Middleton
Spectrum Brands Holdings Inc 782

Milwaukee
ManpowerGroup 542
WEC Energy Group Inc 908
Rockwell Automation, Inc. 737
Harley-Davidson Inc 410
MGIC Investment Corp. (WI) 571
ROBERT W. BAIRD & CO. INCORPORATED 734

Oshkosh
Oshkosh Corp (New) 645

Wauwatosa
Waterstone Financial Inc (MD) 907

WV

Charleston
United Bankshares Inc 868
City Holding Co. 207

Moorefield
Summit Financial Group Inc 798

Wheeling
WesBanco Inc 912

Index of Executives

A

AAefedt, Matthew 881
Aaholm, Sherry A. 248
Aanur, Praveen 144
Aaron, Thomas J. (Tom) 230
Aaron, Wayne 262
Aaron, Mark 875
Aaronian, Ray 332
Aase, Rune 793
Abad, Leah 476
Abadir, Jeffrey 241
Abajian, Scott 493
Abate, Victor (Vic) 382
Abate, Jeff 507
Abate, Joanne 886
Abbaseh, Samimi 708
Abbate, Mark L. 567
Abbey, Anna B 798
Abbey, Dick 808
Abblett, Fred 336
Abbott, Edward 374
Abbott, David 431
Abbott, Justin 467
Abboud, Andrew 513
Abboud, Ali El 791
Abdallah, Mohamed Ben 672
Abdella, Shelly 908
Abdoellah, Rachmat 191
Abdoo, Elizabeth A. 440
Abdool, Jeffrey 87
Abdulmalek, Idora 320
Abel, Greg 123
Abel, Donna 249
Abel, Gregory E. (Greg) 651
Abel, Melissa 824
Abel, Brian Van 933
Abel-Hodges, Cheryl 705
Abela, John 570
Abela, David 649
Abell, Paul 117
Abelli, Donna L. 459
Abello, Marc P 224
Abelman, David 731
Abend, Marc 533
Aberle, Derek 707
Abernethy, Jack 858
Abhishek, Shukla 261
Abiera, Henry 185
Abji, Minaz B. 440
Ables, Grady L. 68
Ableson, Michael 385
Abney, Jack 788
Abney, David P. 875
Aboaf, Eric 791
Abood, Steven 724
Aboulafia, Joseph 105
Abraham, Sandra 117
Abraham, JJ 519
Abraham, Frank 580
Abraham, Amy 929
Abrahamson, Joel 435
Abramczyk, Andrew 310
Abramowicz, Daniel A. 244
Abramowitz, Scott 449
Abrams, Murray 158
Abrams, Michael 196
Abrams, Michael 273
Abrams, Jared 395
Abrams, David 457
Abrams, Ed 470
Abramson, Scott 109
Abramson, Jim 548
Abregu, Martin 829
Abreu, Robert 395
Abreu, Christopher 413
Abshire, Brian 454
Abts, Joy 888

Abws, Bassem 57
Accogli, Giuseppe 115
Acevedo, Margie 558
Ach, J. Wickliffe 350
Achara, Chidi 770
Achary, Michael M. 406
Acharya, Guru 929
Achenbach, Mark 516
Achenbach, Mark 517
Achorn, Tina 409
Achrekar, Manoj 754
Acito, Paul 3
Acito, Paiul 3
Acito, Joe 337
Ackerman, Michelle 32
Ackerman, Joel 258
Ackerman, Melana 449
Ackerman, Dean M 514
Ackerman, Jim 896
Ackermann, Peter 101
Ackerson, Vince A. 823
Ackroyd, Jim 9
Acoca, Bernard 787
Acosta, Fernando J. 95
Adair, Bryan 470
Adam, Tim 273
Adamczyk, Darius 434
Adamo, Terri 332
Adamos, Tara 456
Adams, Michael 14
Adams, Mark 60
Adams, Jimmy 87
Adams, Doug 94
Adams, Gregg T. 108
Adams, Richard 113
Adams, Ann 117
Adams, Tom 149
Adams, Kevin D. 184
Adams, Tom 186
Adams, Thomas E. 186
Adams, Harold L. 227
Adams, Melissa 246
Adams, Craig L. 314
Adams, Gregory 470
Adams, Gregory A. 491
Adams, Beth 497
Adams, Annette 504
Adams, Calvin 537
Adams, Romaneo 550
Adams, Jennifer 550
Adams, John 604
Adams, Scott 635
Adams, Carol 643
Adams, D. Scott 697
Adams, Wayne 723
Adams, Nathan 739
Adams, Bradley 778
Adams, Matthew 792
Adams, Patricia (Trish) 813
Adams, Trish 813
Adams, Tim 818
Adams, Dian 818
Adams, Charles 860
Adams, Jess 863
Adams, Leigh 863
Adams, Richard M. 868
Adams, Gayle 880
Adams, Kelly 903
Adamski, Dan 486
Adamson, Wallace 67
Adamson, Adam 129
Adamson, Shawn 222
Adamson, Ermil L. 279
Adcock, Robert H. 430
Adcock, Mary E 507
Adcock, Bernie 860
Adderley, Terence E. (Terry) 494
Addiego, Gino 71
Addison, Ann M. 516

Addotta, Sibylle 557
Adelberger, Marc 103
Adelson, Sheldon G. 513
Aden, John 903
Adjei, Latanza 389
Adkerson, Richard C. 375
Adkison, Jeff 486
Adkison, Jeffrey 487
Adler, Kate 172
Adler, Paul F. 198
Adler, Kurt W 620
Adler, Doug 715
Adler, Robert L 777
Adomaviciute, Kristina 928
Adornato, Theodore C. (Ted) 781
Afarian, Chris 602
Afejuku, Ayo 582
Afonso, Maria 668
Agarwal, Anu 162
Agarwal, Pankaj 204
Agarwal, Sahil 489
Agarwal, Achal 499
Agarwal, Manu 587
Agee, Philip 813
Agenbroad, Jeff 942
Aggarwal, Nimit 13
Aggarwal, Rohit 452
Aggarwal, Lokesh 792
Aghai-Yazdy, Dana 805
Aghdami, Amanda N 158
Aghili, Aziz S. 254
Agiasotis, Kerry 918
Agnich, Sarah 246
Agochiya, Mihir 489
Agrawal, Vinit 810
Agrawal, Rajesh K. (Raj) 918
Agresta, Richard 760
Agresta, Gregory 912
Aguayo, Sebastian 550
Aguila, Percy R 109
Aguilar, Brian 754
Aguilera, Ivan 539
Aguirre, Edward 496
Agyen, George 409
Ahearn, Chris 537
Ahearn, Tracey 537
Ahee, Joseph 449
Ahern, Stephanie 45
Aherne, Sean 142
Aherne, Andrew 273
Ahl, Jason 202
Ahmad, Rosidah 465
Ahmadi, Alia 800
Ahmed, Nadim 175
Ahmed, Amir 272
Ahmed, Sohail U. 465
Ahmed, Abdurahman 507
Ahmed, Saroosh 838
Ahn, Randy 576
Ahrendts, Angela 69
Ahuja, Deepak 823
Ai, Chen 131
Aichele, William S. 885
Aiken, Jason W. 380
Aiken, Donald B 557
Ailshie, Troy 365
Ainslie, Simon 576
Ainsworth, William P. (Billy) 166
Ainsworth, John 555
Aitken, Paul 18
Aitken, Murray L. 478
Aitkin, Stuart 507
Aiyathurai, Sashi 413
Akalski, Frank J. 366
Akasala, Jim 204
Akbar, Mehrdad 903
Akbarzadeh, Hosai 158
Akins, Nicholas K. (Nick) 42
Akins, D. Wayne 806

Akintola, Jana 159
Akos, Stephen 735
Aksdal, Roy 158
Aksionava, Viktoryia 808
Al-Tayar, Rosemary 593
Alaix, Juan R. 943
Alajajian, George 71
Alamo, Lisette 558
Alani, Nishad 787
Alarcon, Gretchen 643
Alarcon-Cabrera, Ela 176
Alasti, Ali 643
Alban, Carlos 6
Albanese, Gerard 545
Albarian, Caren 96
Alben, Jonah M 627
Alber, Claude 739
Alber, Laura J. 925
Alberico, Matt 195
Alberico, Robert 750
Albers, Lisa 137
Albers, Chuck 708
Albert, Don 293
Albert, Gary 757
Albert, Shadi 760
Alberti, Sue 263
Albertini, Jamie 110
Albi, Chris 507
Albouy, Laurent 705
Albrecht, Steve 502
Albrecht, Geoffrey 710
Albright, Dana 181
Albright, Brandy 882
Albuquerque, Erika 935
Alburg, Kenneth 80
Alcoreza, Lenys 880
Alcorn, Dawn 197
Alday, Truitt 486
Alden, John 875
Alderman, John 207
Alderman, Mark 550
Alderman, Marian 855
Alderoty, Stuart 201
Alderson, Christopher D. 809
Aldrich, Chris 457
Aleardi, Keith P 377
Alec, Pittman 907
Alegre, Erlinda D 102
Aleksov, Lynn 680
Aleman-Bermudez, Aurelio 340
Alemany, Ellen R. 201
Alesci, Megan 454
Alexander, William 12
Alexander, Ed 98
Alexander, Susan H. 129
Alexander, Mark R. 156
Alexander, Robert M. 158
Alexander, Rebecca 196
Alexander, Patricia 224
Alexander, Aaron 226
Alexander, Rosalind 289
Alexander, Brian 382
Alexander, Paul 415
Alexander, Tenzin 449
Alexander, Matthew 450
Alexander, Greg 457
Alexander, Forbes I. J. 480
Alexander, Victor 497
Alexander, Juliet 539
Alexander, Nathan 587
Alexander, Elizabeth 632
Alexander, Sheila 635
Alexander, Will 711
Alexander, Joseph 767
Alexander, Tim 779
Alexander, Stan 780
Alexander, Cory B. 880
Alexander, John 923
Alexander, Charles 934

Alexander, Bruce K. 941
Alfano, Nicholas (Nick) 294
Alfano, Susan 700
Alfonso, Diana 204
Alger, Eugene K. 317
Ali, Farah 115
Ali, Alam 589
Aliabadi, Paymon 314
Aliberto, Michael 201
Alim, Seema 185
Allaire, Bella Loykhter 715
Allalouf, Jason 158
Allan, Craig 563
Allan, Donald (Don) 786
Allan, Don 786
Allbee, Brad 282
Allbright, Justin 109
Alleman, James (Jim) 227
Allen, Hubert L. 4
Allen, John 60
Allen, Blane 99
Allen, Kim 117
Allen, Lisa 117
Allen, Andrew 129
Allen, Bertrand-Marc (Marc) 135
Allen, Lee 137
Allen, Thad W. 139
Allen, Tom 157
Allen, Lawren 158
Allen, David 161
Allen, Julianne 201
Allen, Kenneth 214
Allen, Jeremy 226
Allen, Jaime 257
Allen, Douglas 258
Allen, Samuel R. (Sam) 260
Allen, Jerry 262
Allen, Cindy 330
Allen, Gregory R. 349
Allen, Christopher 355
Allen, Jim 397
Allen, Chuck 407
Allen, George 457
Allen, David 465
Allen, Robert 467
Allen, John 483
Allen, John 511
Allen, Albert 528
Allen, Mark 550
Allen, Jeffrey 555
Allen, Brenda 558
Allen, Joe 564
Allen, Walter 641
Allen, Stephen B 641
Allen, Adrienne 656
Allen, Tom 697
Allen, Daniel 715
Allen, Michael E. 725
Allen, Patrick E. 739
Allen, Patrick 752
Allen, Vanessa 759
Allen, Gary 763
Allen, Christine 842
Allen, Diana 867
Allen, Josh 907
Allenburg, Tom 881
Allensworth, Tami 447
Allery, Lesley 274
Alles, Mark J. 175
Alley, Alex 334
Alley, Sherri 390
Alligood, Joel 60
Allinson, Brooke 713
Allison, John W. 430
Allison, Linn 503
Allison, Michael 633
Allison, Richard 643
Allison, Doug 668
Allison, Paul D. 715
Allison, Jeff 899
Allison, Gordon Y 904
Allman, Joan 39
Allman, Keith J. 552
Allman, Jan 597
Allred, Paula 454
Allred, Bryan 808
Allums, LaShaunda 810

Ally, Desiree 587
Almario, Miyuki 180
Almeda, Michael 799
Almeida, Jos© E. (Joe) 115
Almeida, Marcus 811
Almeida, Odilon 918
Almen, Bruce Von 678
Almond, Grant 593
Almond, Michelle 637
Almonte, Moises 680
Almquist, David C. (Dave) 386
Almy, Scott A. 515
Aloia, Sal 133
Alonso, German 243
Alonso, Steve 337
Alonso, Sergio 477
Alonso, Henry 497
Alpe, Kevin 779
Alperstein, Janet 607
Alpert-Romm, Adria 270
Alsip, Larry 859
Alsman, Floyd 390
Alspaugh, James 146
Alspaugh, Rick 178
Alstead, Troy 787
Alt, Jaxie 282
Altana, Jill 88
Altchek, Ruth 610
Alter, Ed 792
Althaus, Steve 437
Althauser, Chris 399
Althoff, Judson 576
Altman, William M. 501
Altman, Steven 708
Altman, Richard I. (Rick) 712
Altman, Stanley J. (Stan) 725
Altman, Dara F. 771
Altman, Joe 880
Altobelli, Tony 34
Alton, Gregg H. 391
Altre-Kerber, Alison 497
Altschul, Larry 573
Altstadt, Dale 390
Altz, Jean 555
Alvarado, Rosa 16
Alvarado, Joseph (Joe) 227
Alvarado, Melissa 882
Alvarez, Miguel I. 649
Alvarez, Madeline 754
Alvarez, Peter 891
Alvarez, Antonio 919
Alvaro, Jay 286
Alvero, Gumer 52
Alves, Richard C 18
Alves, Sandra 175
Alves, Simon 470
Alvior, Rudy Alvior Rudy 103
Alviti, Paulette R. 368
Alziari, Lucien 95
Amaba, Jane 330
Amaro, Christine 332
Amarose, Ellen 935
Amary, Ramzy AL 555
Amat, Leonardo 187
Amato, Lisa 107
Amato, Jill 141
Amato, Len 838
Amato, Elizabeth B. 879
Amaya, Tanya 106
Amaya, Rosa 141
Amberson, Susan 300
Amble, Mike 334
Amble, Marcy 562
Ambrose, Steve 283
Ambrose, Steve 284
Ambrose, Steven 338
Ambrose, Curtis L 395
Ambrose, Allan 620
Ambrosio, Anthony G. 171
Ambrosio, Michael 900
Ambrosius, Jorg 791
Amelio, William J. (Bill) 94
Amen, Darrell S. van 432
Amend, Michael 661
Amend, Kurt 716
Ames, Jacqueline 289
Amezquita, Juan 649

Amick, W. Michael 472
Amick, Cheryl 548
Amirouche, Lamia 665
Ammann, Daniel (Dan) 385
Amon, Cristiano R. 707
Amoroso, Alfred J. (Fred) 34
Amos, Daniel P. (Dan) 19
Amos, Paul S. 19
Amos, Jim 808
Amrom, George 818
Amstutz, Karen 541
Ana, Coleen Santa 762
Anaiscourt, Dawn 777
Anand, Niraj 465
Ananth, Paul 792
Anastasi, Shane 748
Anaya, Pedro 875
Anbinder, Natalie 28
Anda, Sergio De 899
Andel, Steve Van 35
Andelman, Keith 563
Anderman, Craig 12
Anders, Jeff 117
Anders, Mark 370
Anders, Dave 617
Andersen, Bryan 148
Andersen, Jesper 199
Andersen, Steve 365
Andersen, Mike 800
Anderskouv, Niels 825
Anderson, Lanesha T 7
Anderson, Greg 12
Anderson, Bryan 31
Anderson, Peter 45
Anderson, Tracy 52
Anderson, Jonie 57
Anderson, Phillip M. 63
Anderson, Bradley 80
Anderson, Neil 96
Anderson, Gaylin D. 97
Anderson, John 98
Anderson, Wes 107
Anderson, Terri 110
Anderson, Daniel 135
Anderson, Charlie D 137
Anderson, Kristine Martin 139
Anderson, Carol 158
Anderson, David 170
Anderson, Alison 201
Anderson, William 224
Anderson, Christopher 259
Anderson, Jim 261
Anderson, Robert 262
Anderson, Nina 273
Anderson, Jeri 274
Anderson, Carrie 281
Anderson, Gerard M. 284
Anderson, Melissa H. 286
Anderson, Phyllis 319
Anderson, Lars C. 336
Anderson, Megan 337
Anderson, A. Scott 468
Anderson, William 479
Anderson, Miles 486
Anderson, Zach 487
Anderson, Brian 489
Anderson, Ian D. 500
Anderson, Carl A. 502
Anderson, Kate 504
Anderson, James M. (Jamie) 542
Anderson, Sue 558
Anderson, Perry L 563
Anderson, Brad 576
Anderson, Tom 587
Anderson, Eric 628
Anderson, John C. 640
Anderson, Carol 664
Anderson, Karen 671
Anderson, Annaliesa 672
Anderson, Jeff 677
Anderson, John H. 706
Anderson, Nick 706
Anderson, Roger W 716
Anderson, David 750
Anderson, Steven H. (Steve) 754
Anderson, Gayle 757
Anderson, Michael 778

Anderson, Brad 786
Anderson, Julie L. 823
Anderson, Stephen A. (Steve) 825
Anderson, Sean 839
Anderson, Sandi 840
Anderson, Roy 857
Anderson, Tira 890
Anderson, Llewellyn C. 898
Anderson, Bradbury H. (Brad) 907
Anderson, A. Scott (Scott) 941
Anderson, Rhett 941
Anderson, Thomas 941
Anderton, Amanda 230
Andino, Peter 470
Andrade, Alex 13
Andrade, Servando 224
Andrasko, Sheryl 555
Andreadakis, Elena 329
Andrekus, Brad 495
Andrekus, Bradley 495
Andreth, David 251
Andrew, Cooley 350
Andrew, Jim 667
Andrew, Gladu 799
Andrews, Nancy C. 287
Andrews, Nathan J. 308
Andrews, John 335
Andrews, Elton 395
Andrews, Shelli 566
Andrews, Suzanne 570
Andrews, Kirkland B. 625
Andrews, Charles 641
Andrews, Wayne (Keith) 733
Andrews, Audrey T 818
Andrews, Madhuri 852
Andrews, Rob 870
Andrich, Lyne B. 215
Andrysick, Guy J. 782
Anfenson, Carl 558
Angel, Stephen F. (Steve) 687
Angelastro, Philip J. 639
Angelini, Michael P. 409
Angelis, Yamynn De 250
Angell, Diana 313
Angelo, Jesse 610
Angelo, Tami 935
Angelotti, James 170
Angerer, Erin 804
Angevine, Sandy 88
Angotta, Paul 105
Angus, Thomas 202
Ankle, Stephen 590
Ann, Peggy 69
Annamalai, Deva 942
Annand, Davi 446
Annello, Frank 888
Annese, Gretchen 147
Annett, Timothy 289
Annexstad, Robert 691
Annis, John 637
Anonson, Chester 888
Ansari, Ansar 899
Ansay, Brian 56
Anschell, Jonathan H. 171
Anschuetz, Ryan 87
Ansell, Jeffery D. (Jeff) 786
Anstice, Martin B. 512
Ansuini, Jason 573
Ant, Tracey 413
Antal, James J. 178
Antholis, Kary 838
Anthony, Christopher 224
Anthony, Nicholas 233
Anthony, Fabrizio 664
Antilley, James 405
Antkowiak, Patrick M. 623
Antnez, Guillermo 899
Antolik, David G. 745
Antonace, William 173
Antonson, Casey 563
Antos, John 87
Antosy, James 882
Antoun, Georges 199
Antrobus, Mike 530
Antunes, Lionel 358
Anvar, Saba 131
Anzaldua, Ricardo A. 569

Aparin, Vladimir 707
Apatoff, Robert 31
Apodaca, Rod 170
Appel, Ron 752
Appelbaum, P. Stephen (Steve) 164
Appelbaum, Kristin 201
Appelgren, Karen 941
Appich, Jimmy 486
Apple, Robert E. (Bob) 553
Applebee, Tim 431
Appleby, Mike 710
Applegate, Beth 322
Aquilina, Mark 555
Aquilla, Dave 935
Aquino, Rosemarie 103
Arabia, Carmine 37
Aragon, Charles 161
Aragon, Jackie 266
Aragon-Hernandez, Olga 903
Arapoff, Susan 840
Arata, Foster 135
Arata, Todd 222
Aravindakshan, Santhosh 570
Arbesfeld, Lex 383
Arbogast, Rebecca 222
Arcalgud, Anil 294
Arch, Larry 749
Archer, Pmp 10
Archer, Timothy M. (Tim) 512
Archer, Usha 700
Archer, Jerry 772
Archibald, Nolan D. 452
Arcidiacono, Salvator 598
Arcuri, Jp 153
Ardagna, Peter 656
Arden, Gale 176
Ardezzone, Anthony 604
Ardisonne, Ron 89
Ardizone, Shawn 213
Ardoin, Elizabeth A. (Beth) 454
Ardoin, Beth 454
Arduini, Peter 115
Arduini, Andy 449
Arebalos, Ish 216
Areddy, Joe 337
Arellano, Luis R 754
Arends, Jim 636
Arendt, Michael 313
Arenivas, Jesse 500
Argao, Selene 754
Argodale, George 846
Argyilan, Kristi 813
Ariker, Shanti 748
Arinelli, Wilmar 244
Ark, Jon Vander 729
Arkin, Charles 337
Arlin, Wendy 508
Armbruster, Patrice 613
Armbruster, Ryan 881
Armendariz, Irene 176
Armenti, Jeff 152
Armentrout, Sharon 808
Armetta, Frank 668
Armine-Klein, Cynthia (Cindy) 348
Armitage, Susan 885
Armour, Norm 917
Armstrong, Glenn 35
Armstrong, Duff 84
Armstrong, Dale 135
Armstrong, Steven 370
Armstrong, Kim 447
Armstrong, Bill 456
Armstrong, Melani 476
Armstrong, Steven S. (Steve) 494
Armstrong, Keith D. 567
Armstrong, Scott 604
Armstrong, Ronald E. (Ron) 650
Armstrong, Greg L. 679
ARMSTRONG, SUSIE 707
Armstrong, Deborah 799
Armstrong, Michael 897
Arnaud, Stacia 228
Arndt, Joann 274
Arndt, Kenneth A. 376
Arnett, Haynes 135
Arnett, Rhonda 221
Arnold, Steve 81

Arnold, Scott 89
Arnold, Connie 328
Arnold, Eldric 370
Arnold, Michael J. 375
Arnold, Colleen F 470
Arnold, Jeffrey 493
Arnold, Charles 570
Arnold, Seth 580
Arnold, Richard 599
Arnold, Keith 676
Arnold, Rob 715
Arnold, Charlotte 840
Arnold, Timothy G. (Tim) 886
Arnone, Charlie 304
Aromando, Ada 131
Aromando, Michelle 760
Aron, Daniel 133
Aronowitz, Scott 332
Aronowitz, Alan 411
Arons, Russel 838
Aronson, Sandy 713
Arora, Sumeet 199
Arora, Om 672
Arous, G©rard Ben 606
Arrell, Lori 52
Arrico, Libby 155
Arriola, Dennis V. 761
Arrowsmith, Andrea 121
Arroyo, F. Thaddeus 84
Arroyo, Laura 697
Arsenault, Helen 224
Arseneault, Jason 336
Artalejo, Henry 462
Arters, Doug 472
Arthur, Sarbah 39
Arthur, Randy 50
Arthur, Steven 599
Arthur, Vicki B. 775
Arthur, Gary 890
Artis, David 767
Arundale, Greg 739
Arvanites, Seth 665
Arvesen, Michael 195
Asai, Eriko 382
Asbury, Stephanie 101
Asbury, John C. 867
Ascher, John 713
Asensio, Lynn D. 912
Ash, Bruce 275
Ash, Tim 870
Ashbrook, Bradley 114
Ashburn, Kevin 328
Ashby, Valerie S. 287
Ashe, Anthony 75
Asher, Michelle 222
Asher, Andrew L. (Drew) 911
Ashkenazy, Stewart 570
Ashley, Richard W 4
Ashley, Anthony 500
Ashley, David 545
Ashley, Janice 767
Ashlyn, Sowell 483
Ashmawee, Viola 754
Ashton, Martin 465
Ashworth, Richard M. 901
Ask, Carrie 521
Ask, Carrie 523
Aska, Amina 383
Asleson, Brett 437
Aslin, Phil 824
Asmar, Joseph 550
Asplund, Dale A. 876
Aspray, Tristan 320
Assapimonwait, Betty 18
Astroth, Joseph 914
Aswall, Mark 749
Atalay, Hakan 705
Atanasoff, John 803
Atchue, Nancy 839
Athanasakos, Nick 615
Athanasia, Dean C. 101
Athias, Franklyn 222
Athreya, Anand (Andy) 490
Athwal, Davinder 861
Atieno, Juliana 875
Atkin, James 18
Atkins, Meera 18

Atkins, Mike 107
Atkins, Bruce 394
Atkinson, David 122
Atkinson, Bradley 613
Atkinson, Colleen 722
Atkinson, Tracy 791
Attaway, John A. 702
Attaway, John A. 702
Attili, Srinivas 470
Atwell, Joe 96
Atwell, Robert 613
Au, Jason 87
Au, Reynette 574
Au, Lawrence 620
Aubrejuan, Paco 643
Aubrey, William E. 667
Aubuchon, Michael 246
Audi, John 553
Auger-Dominguez, Daisy 897
Augi, Tony 896
Augsten, Eddy 53
August-deWilde, Katherine 359
Augustin, Christopher (Chris) 348
Augustine, Luke 161
Augustine, Glenn 383
Augustine, Mike 492
Augustine, Lesley 735
Augustsson, Tommy 380
Auld, David V. 439
Aulph, Karen 342
Aunan, Erik 3
Aurillio, Jerry 875
Ausberry, Sheila 224
Austin, Lucinda 117
Austin, Jeff 162
Austin, Karen A. 673
Austin, Roger 676
Austin, Earl C. (Duke) 709
Autenried, Paul von 144
Autrey, Marty 903
Auyang, Yvonne 224
Auyeung, Rex 691
Avelenda, Saily 511
Averett, Addison 813
Averill, Howard M. 838
Averna, Jim 865
Avery, Tyson 170
Avery, Linda 395
Avery, Ron 811
Avila, Arian 102
Avila, Alejandro 750
Avrutis, Ellen 489
Awada, Hassan 241
Awada, Tayssir 330
Awadallah, Ehab 158
Awasthi, Sanjiv 195
Awasthi, Puneet 395
Ayala, John C. 87
Ayala, Jodi 333
Ayala, Bernardo 868
Aycock, Angela W 224
Ayers, Stephen 563
Ayers, Stephen 748
Ayre, David J. 615
Ayres, Maria 12
Azar, Sam 628
Azar, Mark 839
Azevedo, Roy 717
Azinovic, Drago 674
Azizi, Benjamin 507
Azmon, Dan 509
Azoulay, Salomon 671
Azuara, Katherine 115
Azuolay, Avi 768
Azzinaro, James 94

B

Babakanian, Rubik 917
Babb, Ralph W. 223
Babb, Ovid 334
Babbar, Harish 792
Babbert, Eric 912
Babcock, John P. 660
Babel, Bryan 923
Babik, Amber 450

Babikian, Jeffrey C 170
Babineau, Thomas 140
Babineau, Melissa 665
Babka, Kim 713
Bach, Paul D. 386
Bachaalani, Issam 219
Bachman, Andy 14
Bachman, Dan 796
Bachmann, Lisa M. 128
Bachmann, Steve 135
Bacigalupo, George F. 124
Back, Tekla 668
Backman, Mats 86
Backs, Tim 299
Backus, Marcia E. 631
Bacon, Shawn 273
Bacon, Graham W. 307
Bacon, Ashley 488
Bacus, Lisa R. 194
Badar, Ruben 587
Badawy, Christina 87
Badders, Matt 246
Badeen, David 903
Bader, Rupert 576
Badger, William 185
Badger, Austin 803
Baehren, James W. (Jim) 649
Baer, Linda 376
Baer, Nick 486
Baer, Richard N. (Rich) 524
Baer, TimothyR 813
Baerlocher, Shawn 411
Bafaty, Jermon 516
Baffa, Mitchel 604
Bagarozza, Vincent 233
Bagattini, Roy 521
Bagattini, Roy 523
Bagdasarian, Robert 792
Bagger, Richard 175
Baggett, Jennifer 903
Bagley, Chris A. 99
Bagley, Ross 776
Bagnall, Roger 606
Bagnara, Alessandro 489
Bagnoli, Mark P. 109
Bagozzi, David 684
Bagwell, Norman P. 137
Bahamondes, Gus 932
Bahl, Tracy L. 252
Bahner, Craig 493
Bahorich, Michaels 68
Bahr, Antony M. 214
Bahr, John 498
Bahra, Paul 337
Baier, Lucinda M. (Cindy) 146
Baijal, Hemant 555
Bailey, Clay 181
Bailey, Robert 185
Bailey, James 201
Bailey, Richard 442
Bailey, Brett 449
Bailey, Todd 449
Bailey, Erin 453
Bailey, Marjorie 516
Bailey, Daniel 578
Bailey, Rosie 587
Bailey, Steve R. 662
Bailey, Daniel K. (Dan) 851
Bailey, Dan 851
Bailey, Kevin D. 894
Bailey, Brooke 901
Baillie, Andrew 16
Baillie, Stuart 896
Bailon, Monique 97
Baine, Diane 102
Bains, Amarjit 486
Baio, Richard M. 122
Baird, Lisa 470
Baird, Will 507
Baird, Alice 664
Baird, Patrick S. (Pat) 706
Baitler, Robert 558
Baj, Joseph 675
Bajpay, Pari 84
Bajraktari, Leta 204
Baker, Charles E. 96
Baker, Richard 101

Baker, Charles 105
Baker, Lloyd W. 110
Baker, Scott 112
Baker, Cassi 161
Baker, Rodney 162
Baker, David 177
Baker, Roger 193
Baker, David 204
Baker, Mary Ellen 205
Baker, Vickie 211
Baker, Diane E 217
Baker, Timothy 228
Baker, Wayne 246
Baker, Linda 246
Baker, Scott 252
Baker, Douglas M. (Doug) 294
Baker, Peter 298
Baker, Sally W 374
Baker, Jeffrey R. 437
Baker, Tim 460
Baker, Paula 470
Baker, Deborah 483
Baker, Dan 484
Baker, Charles 604
Baker, Brian 605
Baker, David 609
Baker, Brian 708
Baker, Chris 762
Baker, Neal 824
Baker, Ronald 824
Baker, Brian 942
Baker-Coy, Susie 248
Bakes, Jason 332
Bakhaus, Don 754
Bakish, Robert M. (Bob) 896
Bakke, Van 668
Bakken, A. Christopher (Chris) 304
Bakken, Kyle 888
Bakr, Nahiyan 720
Bakstran, Brian 602
Bala, Vidhya 576
Bala, Aru 786
Balaban, David 57
Balachander, Neeraja 57
Balachandran, Madhu 57
Balady, Michele 849
Balaguer, John 717
Balawajder, Charles G. 878
Balchak, Tom 276
Baldeh, Bachi 749
Balderaz, Michael 548
Balderson, Diane 623
Baldi, Sara 563
Baldwin, James L. (Jim) 282
Baldwin, Christopher 423
Baldwin, Robert H. 572
Baldwin, Larry 582
Baldwin, Dianne 692
Baldwin, Penny 707
Bale, Rachel 555
Bales, Brian A. 729
Bales, Jayson C 735
Ball, John 1
Ball, Martin 107
Ball, Vicki 246
Ball, Susan M. 251
Ball, Tracey 488
Ball, Gail S. 827
Ballance, Robert 118
Ballantine, Alex 735
Ballard, Eugene G. 122
Ballard, Shari L. 126
Ballard, Joe 377
Ballard, Daniel 457
Ballard, Janet 507
Ballard, Steven 715
Ballard, Mark 719
Ballard, Bruce 818
Ballard, Byron 875
Ballew, Kevin 563
Ballew, Cathy 580
Ballew, John 722
Ballif, Spencer 170
Ballinger, Kevin J. 142
Ballis, George 787
Ballotti, Geoffrey A. (Geoff) 931
Ballow, Janis 593

Ballweg, Sallyanne K. 357
Balmer, Paul 672
Balmuth, Michael A. 740
Balogh, Brian 754
Balogun, Kelvin 216
Balon, Brad 882
Balousek, Jon 208
Balseiro, Liana 202
Balser, Kathy 590
Balsera, Manuel 53
Balte, Tom 668
Baltes, Kevin 385
Balthaser, Bruse 654
Baltier, Kim 836
Balzo, Kristin Del 222
Bampos, Jim 602
Banati, Amit 493
Bancroft, Charles A. 144
Band, Robert 857
Bandeira, Elaine 665
Bander, Halit 115
Bandi, Bruce 912
Bandinelli, James 539
Bandy, Michael 772
Banerjea, Atish 321
Banerjee, Rajesh 643
Banerjee, Aunoy 792
Banga, Ajaypal S. (Ajay) 554
Bangalore, Ganesh 484
Bangert, Steven 215
Bangs, Richard 713
Banis, R. Daniel 250
Banister, Brian 707
Bank, Belmont 149
Banker, Anish 324
Banker, J. Barry 324
Banks, Dave 162
Banks, Mia 513
Banks, Lee C. 654
Banks, Maureen 656
Banks, Joseph 765
Banks, Joseph D 765
Banks, Yetta 896
Banner, Jon 667
Bansch, Jan L 300
Banse, Amy L. 222
Banskota, Nabin 204
Banta, Walter J 377
Banting, Anne 103
Bao, David 395
Baptist, Kevin 102
Bar-Adon, Eshel 136
Baraddon, Cynthia 746
Barambani, Mark 191
Baran, Jeffrey 666
Baran, Lance 713
Baranovsky, Leon 200
Barash, Andrew 185
Baratta, Joseph P. 133
Barba, Peter (Pete) 529
Barbagallo, John A. 695
Barbar, Kari 470
Barbari, Michael 356
Barbarick, Steve K. 845
Barbarino, Carl 680
Barbella, AL 474
Barber, Avi 135
Barber, Scott 185
Barber, Timothy C. 317
Barber, Tim 449
Barber, Walter 481
Barber, Dave 715
Barber, Ken 763
Barber, James J. (Jim) 875
Barber, Ken 886
Barbera, John 686
Barbercheck, Richard S. 349
Barberi, Carlos 272
Barbieri, David 624
Barbone, Ray 109
Barbosa, Fernando 274
Barbosa, Lisa 705
Barclay, Bruce 573
Barditch, Larry 457
Bardsley, Laurence 792
Bardusch, Robert J. 891
Bardwil, Steven 273

Barengo, Randy 666
Baresich, Michael 33
Barfuss, Ken 397
Barfuss, John 768
Barger, Dennis L 760
Barhaug, Michael 733
Barich, Andy 919
Barinka, Tim 437
Bariquit, Teri 617
Barker, Greg 25
Barker, James 161
Barker, Joanilla 355
Barker, Phyllis 416
Barker, Josh 668
Barker, G. Carlton (Carl) 763
Barker, Marcy 792
Barker, Ellen L. 825
Barker, Kurtis 876
Barkinge, Michele 487
Barkley, Chris 96
Barkley, Joe 715
Barkley, Shay 726
Barksdale, Spencer 713
Barletto, Suzanne 841
Barley, Kimberly 205
Barlow, Jeff D. 582
Barlow, Jeffrey Don 582
Barlow, Debra 849
Barlow, Chris 908
Barnaby, Rod 113
Barnard, Ray F. 365
Barnard, Natashe 555
Barnard, Kris 856
Barnard, Tony 905
Barnard, Lauren 928
Barnes, Earl 13
Barnes, Joseph 105
Barnes, Steve 454
Barnes, Robert B. (Bob) 468
Barnes, Melissa Stapleton 528
Barnes, Georgette 660
Barnes, John P. (Jack) 664
Barnes, Scott 770
Barnes, Brian 818
Barnes, David 919
Barnes, Michael 941
Barnet, Bruce 851
Barnett, Hoyt R. (Barney) 702
Barnett, Hoyt R. (Barney) 703
Barnett, Michael 940
Barnette, Mary K 228
Barney, Karina 548
Barns, Mitch 614
Barone, Vincent 764
Barquin, John 286
Barr, Scott 139
Barr, Sarah 908
Barra, Mary T. 385
Barra, Ornella 901
Barranco, David 39
Barratt, Gregg 376
Barreda, Hector de la 422
Barrentine, Curt 489
Barrera, Theresa 903
Barreto, Sue 356
Barrett, George S. 161
Barrett, Lee 286
Barrett, Clay 390
Barrett, Vanessa 392
Barrett, Kelly 431
Barrett, Bob 643
Barrett, Lausanne 697
Barrett, Geoffrey (Geoff) 705
Barrett, John D. 853
Barrett, John 857
Barrick, David 117
Barrila, Craig 671
Barrington, Martin J. (Marty) 36
Barrington, Jeffrey 767
Barrio, Vita 715
Barriss, Jay 886
Barron, Michael 196
Barron, Kathleen 314
Barron, Cheryl 333
Barron, Eric J. 831
Barron, James A. (Andy) 903
Barroso, Carlos J. 156

Barrow, David 500
Barrows, John 93
Barry, Lynda 60
Barry, Corie S. 126
Barry, Ellen 158
Barry, George 423
Barry, Chris 637
Barry, Daniel 691
Barry, Donald 941
Bars, Michael A. 872
Barselou, Mei 382
Barski, Michael 18
Barsody, Thomas D 912
Barsotti, James 324
Barta, Greggory 504
Bartee, Chris 162
Bartek, David 536
Bartel, Tony D. 379
Bartel, Gregg 504
Barth, Kevin 172
Barth, Kevin G. 226
Barth, Werner 674
Barthels, Brad 814
Bartho, Ken 767
Bartholme, John 671
Bartholomew, Ron 172
Bartlett, Julian 47
Bartlett, Thomas A. (Tom) 51
Bartlett, Danielle 607
Bartlett, David L. 768
Bartlett, Jennie 804
Bartlett, Russ 826
Bartlett, Daniel J. (Dan) 903
Bartman, Teresa 512
Bartolucci, Tony 15
Barton, Lisa M. 42
Barton, Richard B. 110
Barton, Patricia 449
Barton, Nina 505
Barton, Linda 722
Barton, Greg 748
Barton, Kurt 846
Bartone, Michael 786
Bartoshesky, Mandy 378
Bartscht, Ben 204
Bartz, Ebba 220
Bartz, Lisa 693
Baruffi, Kumi Yamamoto 221
Baruffi, Christopher 465
Barwinski, Joe 518
Basan, Patricia 558
Bascom-Erazmus, Sue 664
Basden, Carl 553
Baseler, Theodor P. (Ted) 36
Basey, Ian 94
Basey, Jim 419
Basher, Linda 204
Bashrum, Scott 935
Basilio, Karin 71
Basilio, Paulo 505
Baskette, Lisa 678
Basney, Barbara 935
Bass, Bill 276
Bass, Freda 320
Bass, Maureen 849
Bass, Everett A 907
Bassanello, Judy 203
Bassett, Lawton E. 54
Bassett, Glenn 94
Bassett, H. Clay 596
Bassetti, Frank W 546
Basson, Steve 413
Bast, Albert 15
Bastian, Edward H. (Ed) 262
Bastian, Robert 699
Bastings, Arthur 270
Bastuga, Kevin P. 767
Basu, Devjit 131
Bata, David 942
Batchelder, Eugene L. (Gene) 631
Batcheler, Colleen 232
Batchelor, Steve 907
Bate, Chris 866
Bateh, Tarik 487
Bateman, Robert H. 461
Batenburg, Julie 710
Bates, Christopher 170

Bates, Larry L. 769
Batey, Alan S. 385
Batey, John 707
Bath, Margaret 493
Batista, Juan 69
Batista, Christine 172
Batista, Wesley Mendonça 676
Batra, Radhika 140
Batson, Carol 101
Batson, Charles H. (Chuck) 343
Batson, Joni 517
Batson, Kathy 840
Batson, Andrew 923
Battaglia, Alex 483
Battas, Sandy 863
Battifarano, Leonard 550
Battiste, Margaret 215
Batts, Sherry 282
Baty, Darren 453
Batz, John 684
Baublis, Dan 185
Baublitz, Kimberly 903
Bauche, Douglas N. 306
Baude, Bruce K. 213
Bauder, Douglas R. 777
Baudo, Richard 222
Bauer, Brett C. 125
Bauer, Karen 158
Bauer, Judy 176
Bauer, Paul 261
Bauer, Michael P. (Mike) 371
Bauer, Christina 576
Bauer, Daniel (Dan) 834
Bauer, Kris B. 871
Baughman, Michael 115
Baughman, Brian 563
Baughn, Mike 504
Bauhofer, Scott 12
Bauknecht, Bradford 645
Baum, James 32
Bauman, James L. (Jim) 2
Baumann, Art 87
Baumbach, Denise 376
Baumbach, Allen 824
Baumgardner, Terri 245
Baumli, Heather 457
Bavouset, Jim 519
Bawol, Jeff 94
Baxter, Warner L. 40
Baxter, James 516
Baxter, Jay 722
Baxter, Joel D. 764
Baxter, Neil 841
Baxter, Scott H. 894
Baxter, Dan 912
Bay, Ann 582
Bayardo, Jose A. 593
Baybeck, Brennan 643
Bayer, Terry P. 582
Bayer, Michael B. 599
Bayhylle, Gwen 641
Bayles, Autumn 72
Bayliff, Doreen 693
Bays, Claudia 457
Baysinger, Jared 888
Bazan, Dora 890
Bazante, Jennifer 446
Bazarko, Dawn 881
Bazemore, Teresa A. Bryce 712
Beabout, Brent 617
Beach, Mary 246
Beach, Joan 266
Beach, Mark 668
Beach, Brian C. 808
Beach, Tony 863
Beacham, Renee 101
Beacham, Michael 257
Beacom, Sean 282
Beal, Michael W. 502
Beale, Susan M. 283
Beale, G. William (Billy) 867
Bealefeld, Frederick 866
Bealke, David 342
Beall, Brian 187
Beam, Chris T. 42
Beam, Diane 349
Beam, Jesse 834

Beamer, Beth 881
Bean, Robert 570
Bean, Bryan 678
Bean, Todd 792
Bean, Heather 813
Beanblossom, Darlene 722
Beando, John 840
Beard, Lucinda 117
Beard, Deanne 355
Beard, Robert F. (Bob) 861
Beardall, Brent J. 905
Bearden, Bryan 67
Bearden, Marc 799
Beardsley, Kimberly 261
Beardsley, Bruce 378
Beardsley, Kirk M. 617
Bearson, Kent 860
Beaton, Tiffany 779
Beattie, Joseph 559
Beatty, Mark 129
Beatty, Vincent L. 905
Beaty, Brian 170
Beaudet, Victor 95
Beaudette, Phil 870
Beaufils, Ludovic 923
Beaulieu, Pam 60
Beauregard, Colleen 840
Beaver, David A 244
Beaver, Rick 863
Beavers, Nancy 834
Bebber, David L. Van 859
Bebber, Davis L Van 860
Beberus, John 133
Beccaccio, Peter 350
Becerra, Maria 335
Becerra, Enrique X 808
Becht, Lambertus J. H. (Bart) 242
Beck, Neil 13
Beck, Andrew H. (Andy) 20
Beck, Gary L. 26
Beck, Gregory 184
Beck, Dan 201
Beck, Christophe 294
Beck, Lita 357
Beck, Constance 376
Beck, Steven 378
Beck, Joe 422
Beck, Amy 449
Beck, Elisabeth 478
Beck, Kate 503
Beck, Scott 570
Beck, Christopher 604
Beck, Sherry 635
Beck, Nancy 713
Beck, David 735
Beck, Jeff 760
Beck, Daniel 803
Becker, Jared 133
Becker, Cathleen 133
Becker, Charles 172
Becker, Merritt 248
Becker, Christopher 357
Becker, Scott 454
Becker, Scott 486
Becker, Dave 618
Becker, Steven 691
Becker, David 756
Becker, Yin C. 797
Becker, Gregory W. (Greg) 803
Becker, Susan 942
Beckett, Gale 693
Beckman, Amber 37
Beckman, James 337
Beckmann, Barbara 366
Beckner, Brad 494
Becks, Tom 237
Beckwith, Pete 161
Beckwith, Patricia 320
Beckwith, Tina 570
Beckwitt, Richard (Rick) 518
Beddes, Hallie 550
Beddow, Bill 185
Bedeau, Theresa 158
Bedigian, Mark 928
Bedingfield, Kenneth L. 623
Bedros, Suzanne 888
Beebe, Sharon 842

Beede, Byron 10
Beedle, Bernice 569
Beeman, Kristi 666
Beer, Lori A. 488
Beer, James A. 563
Beery, Joseph C. (Joe) 836
Beeson, James 195
Beever, Emmett 878
Begam, Thomas 337
Begemann, Brett D. 585
Begg, Brian 914
Beggs, Jamie 173
Begle, Curt L. 125
Begley, Jody L. 36
Begley, William J. 746
Begun, Bob 570
Behm, Michael J. 720
Behmer, Nancy 915
Behnke, Dennis L. 857
Behrendt, Richard 875
Behrens, David A. 49
Behrens, Jennifer 287
Behring, Alexandre (Alex) 505
Behringer, Brad 196
Beidelman, Jason 663
Beine, Alice Beine Alice 99
Beinhacker, Avi 45
Beirne, Nazli 489
Beirnes, Kathy 282
Beispel, Rick 896
Bejarano, Brian 161
Bekker, Fano 757
Belak, Cynthia P 664
Belanic, Jim 688
Belasco, Kent S. 356
Belaski, Stephanie 179
Belcher, Patricia 131
Belcher, Samuel L. 360
Belcourt, Tracey 371
Belden, Scott 849
Belekewicz, William D. 362
Belen, Andy 882
Beletti, Chris 237
Belford, Michael 836
Belgya, Mark R. 773
Belitsky, Lee J. 264
Bell, Patricia A 19
Bell, Chris 25
Bell, Ron 34
Bell, James 60
Bell, William 98
Bell, Casey 98
Bell, James 135
Bell, Jeffrey 170
Bell, Brad 224
Bell, John 300
Bell, Greg 370
Bell, Doug 390
Bell, Christie 454
Bell, Teri 487
Bell, Adam 555
Bell, George 570
Bell, Thomas 618
Bell, Ken 620
Bell, Tom 676
Bell, Damon 677
Bell, Clark 786
Bell, John 849
Bell, Elaine 869
Bell, Matthew 886
Bell, Brent 907
Bell, Deborah 942
Bellack, Janis P. 656
Bellamy, Desi 813
Bellamy, Adrian D. P. 925
Bellanti, Tim 81
Bellanti, Robert 497
Belle, Baker 799
Belleville, Mark R 507
Bellinger, Delaney R. 452
Bellini, Manuela 521
Bellini, Manuela 523
Bellisario, Michael 735
Belliveau, Kathrin 415
Bellnap, Kyle 942
Belloma, Kevin 226
Bellos, Alex 925

Bellward, Paul 814
Belmonte, Lawrence 45
Belmonte, Larry 45
Belochi, Franck 705
Belock, Dave 781
Below, Ellen 413
Belsito, Paul A 409
Belt, Tom 12
Beltre, Milca 133
Bem, David S. 685
Bemer, Patricia 695
Bemis, Mark A. 74
Bena, Steve 297
Benard, Laurie 539
Benattia, Isma 57
Bencal, Chris 717
Bence, William 558
Bence, Clement 932
Benchoff, Nancy 395
Bender, Jeffrey 68
Bender, Jim 89
Bender, Kevin 170
Bender, Jason C. 358
Bender, M. Steven (Steve) 920
Bene, Judi 243
Benedetto, Richard di 17
Benedict, Michael 289
Benedum, Mary 504
Benefield, Donna 625
Benet, Jay S. 848
Benetto, Michael 117
Benfield, James 847
Bengston, Robert A. 650
Benhamou, Eric A 804
Benioff, Marc 748
Benito, Michael E. 420
Benito, David Pastrana 759
Benjamin, Jeff 95
Benjamin, Rachel 201
Benjamin, David 355
Benjamin, Mark D. 599
Benjamin, Gerald A. 752
Benkart, Brian 792
Benkert, Robert 881
Benn, Markham 468
Benn, David P. 802
Bennett, Shayne 71
Bennett, Douglas M. 110
Bennett, Emily 117
Bennett, Bruce 173
Bennett, Lance J. 268
Bennett, R. Terry 324
Bennett, Chuck 345
Bennett, Jonathan R. 413
Bennett, Robyn 470
Bennett, Judy 725
Bennett, Cyndi 760
Bennett, Nancy 787
Bennett, Dan 808
Bennett, Scott 863
Bennett, Rick 863
Bennett, Bobby 876
Bennett, Terry 903
Bennett, Kathleen 911
Bennett, Walter L. 924
Bennion, Richard W. H. (Rich) 432
Bennion, Kim 468
Benoit, Brent A 593
Benoy, Rick 486
Benoy, Janeen 578
Bense, Allan 390
Bensen, Katie 813
Benshetler, Peter 378
Bensignor, Laurence E. 289
Bensimhon, Ilan 643
Bension, Ronald (Ron) 532
Benskin, Nancy 678
Benson, Norm 61
Benson, Don 129
Benson, Nigel 131
Benson, Mike 246
Benson, Mark 262
Benson, David C. 322
Benson, Jason 487
Benson, Aaron 735
Benson, Marta H. 925
Benter, Bob 697

Bentley, Stacey 706
Bentley, Elizabeth M. 867
Bentley, Philip 903
Bentz, Jennifer 860
Benz, John 705
Benzon, Jennie 548
Ben☉, Thomas L. (Tom) 808
Berain, Eduardo 247
Berardino, Peter 555
Berberian, Lance V. 510
Berberich, Chad 732
Berce, Daniel E. (Dan) 385
Berchtold, Joe 532
Berendsen, Nancy 923
Beresh, Nicholas 912
Berg, John 53
Berg, Charles G. (Chuck) 258
Berg, Tracey L. 301
Berg, Bill 602
Berg, Sheldon 665
Berg, John P. von 679
Berg, John 679
Bergan, Charles 707
Bergdahl, Thomas 765
Bergdoll, Andrew 914
Bergdorf, Mark 754
Bergeon, Christopher 338
Berger, David 52
Berger, Larry L. 294
Berger, Lou 425
Berger, Joe 427
Berger, Gary 465
Berger, Tim 555
Berger, Sherie 748
Berger, Jan 800
Berges-Gonzalez, Orlando 340
Bergh, Charles V. (Chip) 442
Bergh, Charles V. (Chip) 521
Bergh, Charles V. (Chip) 523
Berghs, Jim 888
Bergman, Terri 204
Bergman, Stanley M. 752
Bergman, David E. 866
Bergmann, Dave 256
Bergmann, Jeffrey 602
Bergrud, Gerad 403
Bergstrom, Timothy D. 908
Bergstr¶m, Henrik 685
Beri, Rajive 84
Berisford, John L. 746
Berk, Donald 620
Berkley, W. Robert (Rob) 122
Berkley, William R. (Bill) 122
Berkley, William R. (Bill) 607
Berkowitz, Paul 14
Berkowitz, Jonathan 415
Berkowitz, Jason 931
Berlin, Barry N. 195
Berloe-Buch, Wendy 713
Berman, Walter S. 52
Berman, Stuart 204
Berman, Robert 246
Bermeo, Luis 604
Bermudez, Sabrina 49
Bernacki, Jerry 93
Bernadett, Martha Molina 582
Bernadett, M 582
Bernal, Alejandro 943
Bernard, Debbie 200
Bernard, Andrea 220
Bernard, Loraine 530
Bernard, Scott 731
Bernard, Edward C. 809
Bernardo, Gary 507
Berne, Robert (Bob) 606
Berne, Bob 607
Bernet, Brant 170
Bernhardt, Tom 620
Berni, Annie L 620
Bernier, Danielle 705
Bernitt, Elisabeth 15
Bernon, Alan J. 254
Berns, Jason 713
Bernstein, Daniel 201
Bernstein, Barbara 489
Bernstein, Bruce 550
Bernstein, Mark J. 720

Bernsten, James R. 214
Berotti, John 834
Berquist, Lori 376
Berquist, Carl 548
Berres, Matthew 486
Berretta, Joseph V 419
Berrier, Bobby 580
Berry, Eric 94
Berry, Mark 184
Berry, Dottie 330
Berry, Kay 350
Berry, Liz 409
Berry, Mary 550
Berry, Ondra L 573
Berry, Leonard 668
Berry, Marcus 700
Berry, James D. 746
Berry, Chris 752
Berry, Pat 847
Berry, Bob 886
Berryhill, Evette 356
Berryman, Kevin C. 481
Bersaglini, David 299
Bershad, Stephen W. 298
Bert, Dave 189
Bertero, Gerardo 917
Berthiaume, Mark L. 409
Berthold, Evelyn 558
Bertholf, Leigh 168
Bertolami, Charles N. 606
Bertolini, Mark T. 17
Bertoni, Diana 378
Bertram, Shana 330
Bertram, Howard 912
Bertrand, Greg D. 808
Bertsch, Jan 140
Bertsch, Jan A. 649
Berube, Kaitlin 804
Berus, Robert 161
Berwick, Belinda 550
Besanko, Bruce H. 503
Besendorfer, Christopher 45
Beshah, Guenet 158
Beshar, Peter J. 550
Beshears, Kristi 96
Besio, Jeff 836
Bess, David 570
Bessant, Catherine P. (Cathy) 101
Bessel, Polly 84
Bessette, Diane J 518
Bessette, Andy F. 848
Bessette, Stephen 906
Best, Rhys J. 227
Best, James 725
Betancourt, Sofia 901
Beth, Scott 476
Bethea, Elizabeth 456
Bethea, Paula Harper 776
BETLESKY, SCOTT 409
Betor, Jan 849
Bettadapur, Shailesh 580
Bettinger, Douglas R. (Doug) 512
Bettinger, Walter W. (Walt) 754
Betz, Thomas E 666
Beumee, Gary 760
Beutin, Brian 112
Bevan, Jermey 200
Bevan, Jeremy 200
Bevan, Frank 472
Bevan, Kurt C 912
Beveridge, Roy A. 446
Bevington, Sue 576
Bewkes, Jeffrey L. (Jeff) 838
Bewley, Tim 678
Beyene, Merykokeb 901
Beyer, Gary J 224
Beyerly, Mark 840
Bezjak, Rob 399
Bezos, Jeffrey P. (Jeff) 37
Bhagat, Dave 803
Bhagwat, Abhay 248
Bhagwati, Vishal 425
Bhakhri, Sandeep 308
Bhakta, Parthiv 452
Bhalla, Ajay 554
Bharara, Ashish 903
Bhardwaj, Sunil S 504

Bhargava, Gautam 37
Bhargava, Amit 552
Bhashetty, Mahesh 102
Bhasin, Puneet 907
Bhaskar, Bhavna 668
Bhat, Sanjay 582
Bhathena, Firdaus 18
Bhatia, Qamar S 434
Bhatia, Avi 507
Bhatia, Manish 917
Bhatnagar, Manoj 259
Bhatt, Prat 199
Bhattarai, Nishant 367
Bhattista, Guy 919
Bhavsar, Meeten 643
Bhavsar, Kelly 786
Bhojwani, Gary C. 213
Bhumbla, Ravinder 191
Bhutani, Aman 316
Bialaski, Brien 849
Biales, Brad 620
Bialosky, David L. (Dave) 397
Bianca, Joe Di 765
Bianco, Mary 872
Bibbo, Paul 839
Bible, Daryl N. 116
Bichay, Wafik 731
Bickel, Michael 137
Bicker, Mark 350
Bickers, Amy 620
Bickerstaff, Robert 202
Bickerton, Lisa 722
Bickett, Brent B. 332
Bickham, Bill 182
Bickham, John R. 186
Bickings, Duane 107
Bicknell, Lacey 665
Biddy, William 808
Biegen, Gregory 103
Biegen, Arm Gregory 103
Biegger, Dave 232
Biehl, Maureen 550
Bielan, Judith Q. 118
Bielar, James 84
Bielen, Richard J. 697
Bielss, Chris 460
Bien, Marie 720
Bienert, Philip 84
Bienhoff, Bruce 226
Bienstock, Steven 151
Bierl, Andreas 57
Bierman, Brian 907
Biesterfeld, Robert C. 736
Bietsch, Julie 266
Biffle, Jack 697
Bigelow, John 700
Bigger, Jim 178
Biggers, Brant 87
Biggs, Morgan 121
Biggs, M. Brett 903
Bigler, Barbara 13
Bihlmaier, Douglas 713
Bike, Brent 247
Bilak, Gina 60
Bilanchone, Jill 89
Bilbrey, John P. (J.P.) 422
Bilko, David G. (Dave) 867
Bill, Buckner 374
Bill, Clark 903
Bill, Shreve 935
Billak, Ann 488
Billelo, Julie 158
Billing, Duncan J. 415
Billings, Sherri R. 119
Billings, Will 929
Billingsley, Mark 213
Billiot, Susan 807
Bills, Mark 299
Bilmes, Robyn 144
Bilney, Jody L. 446
Bilotta, Anthony V. 660
Bilotti-Peterson, Christine 409
Bilse, Gregory 133
Bily, Shirley 893
Binaco, Juli 14
Binck, Patricia 728
Binder, Steven G. 437

Binder, Joel 637
Binetti, Frank 18
Bing, Alden 109
Bingaman, Jonathan 172
Bingaman, Peter 470
Bingham, James 105
Bingham, Kim R. 167
Bingham, Paul 447
Bingol, Selim 286
Bingold, Michael 366
Binick, Emily Goodman 45
Binkley, David 923
Binks, Michael 672
Binnie, Lisa 409
Binns, Justin T. 764
Binzer, Ann 197
Bion, Joel 199
Biondo, Joseph 93
Biondo, Joe 93
Biossat, William 454
Birch, Robert F. 430
Birch, Laurie 643
Bird, Roger M. 4
Bird, Dean 101
Bird, Stephen 203
Bird, Andy 273
Bird, Edwin 327
Bird, Stefan A. 651
Birdsall, Brittany 923
Birdsong, Melissa 537
Birk, Mariann 3
Birk, Mark 40
Birkelo, Jeff 905
Birkmeyer, David 875
Birmingham, Martin K. 338
Birmingham-Byrd, Melody 285
Birnbaum, Jack 222
Birnbaum, Jason 768
Birns, Ira M. 929
Birouty, Rana 707
Birrer, John A. 186
Bisaccia, Lisa 252
Bisaccio, Brian 842
Bisang, Claude 72
Bischmann, Joanne M. 410
Bischmann, Ben 487
Bischofberger, Norbert W. 391
Bischoff, Michael 550
Bisegna, Anthony C. 791
Bishop, Mari 220
Bishop, Mark 330
Bishop, John 519
Bishop, Matthew 576
Bishop, Marissa 610
Bishop, Steven D. (Steve) 693
Bishop, Rachel R. 850
Bishop, Greg 919
Bisienere, Maribeth 274
Bisignano, Frank J. 348
Biske, Sandra 558
Bisno, Edward 244
Bisogno, Keith 836
Bittler, David 896
Bitzer, Marc R. 923
Bivins, Joe 563
Bivona, Stephen 516
Bivona, Michael 896
Bixby, R. Philip 492
Bixby, Walter E. (Web) 492
Bjornstad, Geir 793
Black, Barbara 53
Black, Maria 87
Black, Steve 194
Black, Vonda 502
Black, Peter 707
Black, Ken 731
Black, Trevor 750
Black, Freddie G. 768
Black, David F. 789
Black, Benjamin 863
Black, Glenn 886
Black, Mary 891
Black, Chastity 895
Blackburn, Jeffrey 37
Blackburn, Fred K. 139
Blackburn, Andy 200
Blackburn, David 228

Blackburn, Howard W 230
Blackburn, Stella 478
Blackburn, Randy 504
Blacken, Linda 671
Blackford, David E. 941
Blackler, Ellen 273
Blackley, R. Scott 158
Blackley, James A. (Jim) 186
Blackley, Jim 186
Blackman, Rob 14
Blackman, Horace 517
Blackwell, Steve 507
Blackwood, Eric 661
Blagg, Richard 15
Blain, Robert (Rob) 169
Blain, Bob 715
Blaine, Christopher A 244
Blair, Marcy 200
Blair, Rainer M. 256
Blair, Matthew 550
Blair, Jason 643
Blair, Kevin S. 806
Blair, Scott 942
Blaise, Tim 257
Blaise, Michelle 314
Blaising, Angela C 479
Blake, Sarah 16
Blake, Chris 25
Blake, James 87
Blake, Robert 119
Blake, Nancy 224
Blake, Francis S. (Frank) 262
Blake, Patrick J. (Pat) 563
Blake, Mary Elizabeth 566
Blake, Christopher D. 653
Blake, David M. 691
Blake, Ginger 722
Blake, Lynn S. 791
Blakemore, Anthony 777
Blalock, Jana 99
Blalock, Clare 390
Blalock, H 800
Blanc, Farron 724
Blancett, Cary S 330
Blanchard, Laricke 691
Blanchet, Pamela 454
Blanchette, Robert 503
Blanco, Alex 294
Blanco, Jenny 489
Bland, Christine 353
Bland, Trabue 467
Blane, September 472
Blankenburg, Susan 378
Blankenship, Charles P. (Chip) 75
Blankenship, Justin 117
Blankfein, Lloyd C. 395
Blankfield, Bryan J. 645
Blanton, Genie 715
Blasdel, James 892
Blase, William A. (Bill) 84
Blase, Marta 497
Blaser, Brian J. 4
Blasi, Kristopher 463
Blasini, David P 158
Blaske, Stephen 52
Blasko, Michael 853
Blaug, Suzanne 57
Blauser, Caryn 498
Blawn, Aaron 465
Blaya, Richard 895
Blaylock, Kortney 635
Blaylock, Anastasia 769
Blaz, Steve 602
Blaze, Chris 763
Blazejewski, Steve 161
Blazer, Robert 545
Bledig, Stefan 585
Bledsoe, Stacey 528
Bleisch, N. David 633
Bleiweis, Melissa 558
Bleske, Mitchell 870
Blessing, Russell A 197
Blevins, P. Rodney 278
Blevins, Rodney 278
Blew, Clinton J. (C.J.) 193
Bley, Daniel H. 908
Blinn, Richard P. (Dick) 386

Blittschau, Edward 299
Blitz, Bonnie 582
Blitz, Susan 720
Blitzer, David S. 133
Blivice, Marni 133
Bloch, Sandra 6
Bloch, Nick 834
Block, Robert 31
Block, Stephen 158
Block, Velinda J 168
Block, Arthur R. 222
Block, Elizabeth 713
Block, Keith G. 748
Blocker, Jeffrey 537
Blocker, Adrian M. 921
Bloemer, Steven 226
Blomeen, Ian 811
Bloom, Brent 71
Bloom, Adam 171
Bloom, William A. (Bill) 413
Bloom, Robert 593
Bloom, Alfred H. 606
Blossom, Patrick 460
Blount, Susan 699
Bloxam, Richard 486
Bloys, Casey 838
Bludau, Laurence 230
Blue, Betsy 99
Blue, Dave 135
Blue, Robert M. (Bob) 278
Blue, Robert M. 897
Blum, Donald W. 698
Blumberg, Rebecca 897
Blume, Brent 888
Blumenfeld, Stephen 395
Blumer, David J. 131
Blumhardt, James 914
Blundell, Sandra 68
Blundon, Lee 912
Blunt, Chris 133
Blunt, Mary L. 762
Blust, Jeffrey 620
Bluth, Thomas J. (Tom) 166
Blyth, Lesley 787
Blythe, Jane B 800
Boaman, Richard 884
Boas, William 128
Boas, Nancy 713
Boatright, Nancy 104
Bobb, Stevan B. 150
Bobitz, Ward E. 389
Bobker, Adam 131
Bobrovich, Marina 804
Bochenek, Tomasz 576
Bochette, William C. 776
Bocian, Jim 168
Bock, Barbara 45
Bockhorst, Daniel E. 178
Bodapati, Ramesh 200
Bodary, Andrew 704
Bodin, Elizabeth 454
Bodine, Bruce 588
Bodisch, Laurie 377
Bodor, David 664
Boe, Douglas 888
Boedeker, Kenneth W. 308
Boegemann, Kate 813
Boehm, Andrew 748
Boehmer, Mark D 937
Boehnlein, Glenn 797
Boeing, Traci 912
Boelstler, Doreen 224
Boersma, Brad 337
Boesch, Marc 840
Boetel, Mary 558
Boettcher, Frances H 15
Boettcher, Bill 109
Bogen, Daniel 599
Bogenberger, Vicki 185
Boggess, Michael 101
Boggs, Rod 570
Boggs, Darrell 628
Bogler, John A. 97
Boguski, Michael L. 692
Boh, Thomas M 735
Bohaboy, Scott 115
Bohall, Tim 929

Bohan, Julie 489
Bohanan, Yvette 37
Bohannon, Jason 447
Bohaty, Brian R. 31
Bohbrink, Marshall 402
Bohigian, Catherine 186
Bohl, Nicki 168
Bohlinger, Thomas 170
Bohman, Tom 170
Bohn, William M. 80
Bohnke, Jaime 623
Bohnsack, Gary 500
Bohuny, Bruce G 511
Boike, Brian D.J. 362
Boim, Dave 582
Boisier, Pierre 119
Boisten, Bernd 733
Boitano, Robert 334
Bojalad, Ronald 257
Bojalad, Ron 257
Bojdak, Robert J. 538
Boklund, Carl 750
Bol, Alexander A. 233
Bolan, Adrienne 929
Boland, Brandt 261
Boland, Richard 620
Boland, Joyce 643
Boland, Andrew 682
Bolander, Larry Bolander Larry 365
Bolch, Carl E. 711
Boldt, Rick 470
Bolerdavis, Alicia 385
Boles, Tim 722
Boleware, Warren 383
Boley, Joey 537
Bolgar, Paulo 115
Boli, Scott 539
Bolick, Patrick 487
Boline, Chad 226
Bolisay, Eric 810
Bolleia, Raymond 53
Bollettieri, Jill 684
Bollinger, Kathy 111
Bollinger, Daniel 596
Bollman, Rose 668
Bologna, Matt 935
Bols, Ivo 22
Bolton, John R 18
Bolton, Scott 135
Bolton, C. Anderson (Andy) 244
Bolton, Nicole 684
Bolton, Jon 735
Boltz, Elaine 839
Bolus, Mattie 570
Bolwerk, Dave 81
Bolze, Steve 382
Bomar, Derek 602
Bombara, Beth A. 413
Bombassi, Tony 886
Bonamigo, Samuel 748
Bonanni, Jim 161
Bonanno, Kelly 378
Bonanotte, Gino A. 589
Bond, Matt 222
BOND, RUTH 274
Bond, Josh 449
Bond, Ken 643
Bond, Robert W. (Bob) 654
Bond, Melody 720
Bond, Martine 791
Bonds, Barry 620
Bonds, Michael P. (Mike) 871
Bone, Danny 378
Bone, Ronald 563
Bone, Doug 805
Bonefas, Joseph 269
Boneta, Vanessa 551
Bonfiglio, Robert 793
Bonforte, Jeff 34
Bongiorno, John 896
Bonick, Martin J. 230
Bonifacemesce, Carolyn 932
Bonilla, Ruth 224
Bonilla, Fernando 589
Bonilla, Eduardo 715
Bonn, Nicholas T. (Nick) 791
Bonnemere, Patricia 888

Bonney, Paul R 314
Bonning, Kenneth 503
Bonning, Ken 504
Bontcheva, Milena 272
Bonzani, Andrew 473
Boocock, Richard 22
Booker, Martin W. 59
Booker, Robert 880
Booles, Angela 31
Boomer, Stephen L. 349
Boone, Michael 176
Boone, Elsie 246
Boone, Elwood B. (Bernie) 762
Boor, Wayne 370
Boortz, Kevin 447
Booth, Steven G. (Steve) 735
Booth, Susan 749
Boothe, Cebert 106
Boothe, Dorrett 109
Boothe, Steven 809
Boots, James 449
Boragno, Mark 849
Boras, Stephen 337
Boratto, Eva 252
Borba, George A. 250
Borca, Troy 881
Borchardt, Randall 888
Borchers, Bradford D. 640
Borchers, Susan C. 725
Borchers, Brad 784
Borcke, Wulff-Erik von 6
Bordas, Cesc 668
Borden, Ian 562
Borden, Edward 665
Border, Dave 31
Bordes, Michael P. (Mike) 298
Bordini, Danilo 576
Borelli, Cheryl 99
Borelli, Janet 896
Borges, Steven D. (Steve) 480
Borges, Beatrice 597
Borgmann, Kevin S. 158
Borino, Melissa Borino Melissa 888
Borja, Paul D. 362
Borkar, Mandar 643
Bornhorst, Donald 262
Bornhurst, Don 262
Bornmann, David E. 702
Bornmann, David E. 702
Boronat, Brian 332
Borra, Pier 896
Borrego, Susan E. 720
Borro, Douglas 729
Borsello, Fabrice 919
Borso, Stefan 754
Borst, Walter G. 597
Borstel, Barbara Von 767
Bortolazzi, Simona 175
Borton, Chad M. 336
Borucki, Bethany 813
Borup, Steve 487
Boryla, Stephanie 863
Boschelli, John M. 495
Bosco, Paul 199
Bose, Robert 39
Bose, Supratim 142
Boshoff, Chris 672
Boss, Carson 941
Bosso, Leonard 604
Bost, Melton C 465
Bostain, Patricia 720
Boster, Barry 446
Boston, Steve 24
Boston, Michelle 102
Bostrom, Brent 402
Bosway, William T. 281
Boswell, William 117
Boswell, Kathleen 596
Boswell, John 904
Boswell, Nicole 942
Botbol, Michel 713
Botelho, Sergio 899
Bothner, Carl R 935
Botifoll, Jordi 199
Botsford, Tom 52
Botsford, Bob 252
Bottcher, Benjamin 142

Bottle, Lisa 365
Bottoms, Derek W 431
Bouboulis, Panagiota 105
Bouch, Kim 635
Boucher, Harold 221
Boucher, Tim 777
Bouchereau, Sabine SE 109
Bouchereau, Valerie 382
Boudreau, Brian 101
Boudreau, Michael 413
Boudreaux, Trish 49
Boudreaux, Gail K. 66
Boudreaux, Chad N 451
Boudreaux, Brandon 454
Boughton, Bryon 237
Boughton, Judy 383
Boulding, William F. 286
Bouley, Ray 486
Bouman, Rosemarie 558
Bounsy, Ryan 672
Bourazak, Beverly 80
Bourdier, Maryanne 195
Bourke, Michael 488
Bourla, Albert 671
Bourque, Pat 243
Bourque, Robert H. 244
Bourzutschky, Marc 754
Bousbib, Ari 478
Bouseman, Andy 84
Boustouler, Stephen 131
Bovender, Jack O. 287
Bowden, Matthew 25
Bowden, James 373
Bowden, Daniel 762
Bowden, Bryson 863
Bowden, Lloyd M. 927
Bowen, Doug 112
Bowen, Russell 185
Bowen, Richard 320
Bowen, Michelle 334
Bowen, Andy 355
Bowen, Andrew 497
Bowen, Cara 545
Bowen, Joy 678
Bowen, Kristine 808
Bowen, Blannie 831
Bowen, Arthur N. (Art) 898
Bower, Joseph B. 211
Bower, Chris 542
Bower, Robert C. 876
Bowerman, Giles 431
Bowers, William 25
Bowers, Ann 69
Bowers, Douglas H. (Doug) 97
Bowers, Jon 98
Bowers, Christopher D. 176
Bowers, Paul 389
Bowers, Eric 488
Bowers, David 534
Bowers, Elizabeth 626
Bowers, Rebecca 849
Bowers, Jeff 863
Bowers, Jay 875
Bowersox, Dennis 394
Bowersox, Jim 518
Bowie, Paul J. 29
Bowlby, Jeffrey L. 692
Bowles, Crandall 261
Bowling, Rob 634
Bowman, Arthur 161
Bowman, Gina 251
Bowman, Richard 414
Bowman, Kathy 446
Bowman, Christopher 489
Bowman, Jeff 563
Bowman, Stephen B. (Biff) 620
Bowman, Skip 654
Bowman, Annemarie 699
Bowman, Kristen 713
Bowry, Oran 682
Bowshier, Terrence 788
Box, Laurie 863
Boxer, Mark L. 194
Boxer, Melissa 643
Boyaji, Brian 665
Boyce, Cari 286
Boyce, David S. 842

Boyd, Norman 20
Boyd, Thomas 170
Boyd, John J. 308
Boyd, Debby 332
Boyd, Jeff 395
Boyd, Jeffery H. (Jeff) 689
Boyd, Peter M. 779
Boyd, Greg 800
Boyd, Isaac 841
Boyd, Ruth 914
Boyd, Robert 942
Boyd-smith, Chelsa 800
Boyden, Tracey 672
Boyer, Gregg 115
Boyer, Jason 226
Boyer, Jonathan 497
Boyer, Jeffrey 724
Boyken, James W 470
Boykin, Frank H. 580
Boykin, Wendi 919
Boykins, Lamont 52
Boylan, William J. 233
Boyle, Mike 32
Boyle, Amy 53
Boyle, Hugh F. 97
Boyle, Thomas P 122
Boyle, Jim 270
Boyle, Michael T 457
Boyle, Jack 503
Boyle, Kevin 563
Boyle, Terence 617
Boyle, Debbie 664
Boyle, Patti 749
Boyle, Mark A. 856
Boyle, Charles F 882
Boyle, Dennis 885
Boyle, Tom 935
Boyles, Andrew 102
Boyles, Kathryn 395
Boyles, Kevin 766
Boyles, Jonathan 772
Boynton, Nina 202
Boysen, Harry 252
Boystak, Patrice 262
Bozuhoski, Michael 842
Bozzolo, Albert 366
Brabant, Steven 170
Brabson, Charles 307
Brace, George 432
Bracey, Brent 668
Bracher, Paul H. 246
Bracht, Berend 733
Bracken, Andrew 468
Brad, Dahlgren 244
Bradberry, Martha 530
Bradbury, Bob 191
Bradbury, Greg 770
Bradford, Douglas 96
Bradford, Mark D. 635
Bradford, Brian 643
Bradford, Hannah 713
Bradford, Brad 722
Bradley, Michael 115
Bradley, W. Bennett 116
Bradley, Leigh 117
Bradley, Michael 175
Bradley, William E. (Bill) 181
Bradley, Kevin 201
Bradley, Arthur 337
Bradley, John 488
Bradley, James H. 494
Bradley, Joe 507
Bradley, Gregory 571
Bradley, Matthew 643
Bradley, John 699
Bradley, Lori 705
Bradley, Kim 722
Bradley, Phil 748
Bradley, David 802
Bradley, Kevin P. 878
Bradshaw, Steven G. (Steve) 137
Bradshaw, Jami 355
Bradshaw, Richard W. 869
Bradway, Robert A. (Bob) 57
Brady, Bryan 94
Brady, Mariel 171
Brady, John 413

Brady, Gavin T 429
Brady, Deanna T. 437
Brady, Amy G. 497
Brady, Deborah 497
Brady, Robert T. (Bob) 539
Brady, Elizabeth S. (Beth) 691
Brady, Christian M. M. 831
Brady, Jennifer 840
Brady, Jim 885
Brady, Bill 888
Brager, David A. 250
Bragg, Chris 107
Bragg, Dorry 332
Brainard, Jeff 841
Braitberg, Karl 643
Brakeville, Barry 863
Brakman, Steven 754
Bram, Greg 890
Bramhall, Scott 941
Bramlage, Stephen P. (Steve) 72
Bramman, Anne L. 617
Branca, Frank 876
Branch, Danny 580
Brand, Meir 34
Brand, Dennis L. 98
Brand, Walter 763
Brand, Tina 891
Brandenburg, Ben 246
Brandenburg, Mark 486
Brandenburg, Joel 865
Brandom, Jessica 80
Brandon, Joseph P. 28
Brandon, John 327
Brandon, Rush 374
Brandt, Stephen W 60
Brandt, Kathleen 245
Brandt, James A. 537
Brandt, Noel 919
Brannen, James P. (Jim) 325
Brannigan, Casey 12
Brannon, Mike 772
Branon, Colin 665
Branon, Bethany 886
Branson, Sheri 555
Brant, Bob 886
Brantley, Todd 358
Brascia, Pete 573
Brashier, Randy 286
Bratley, Paul 462
Bratman, Fred 876
Bratspies, Steve 903
Bratt, Mikael 86
Brauer, Rod 185
Braun, Bill 96
Braun, Dennis 161
Braun, Randall L. 390
Braun, Chris 727
Braunschweig, Donna 377
Brause, Ken 201
Brautigan, Bernard (Bernie) 740
Braverman, Alan N. 273
Bravo, Diana 350
Bray, Natalie 332
Bray, Jeffery (Jeff) 756
Brayer, Frank 533
Brayer, Tamra 679
Brayman, Alan 377
Brazell, Joe 617
Brazier, Nigel D 322
Brda, Bruce W. 589
Bready, Bruce 511
Breakey, Mark D. 211
Breaux, Holly 500
Breber, Pierre R. 190
Brecker, Nicholas L. 66
Breckon, Steve 302
Bredow, Eugene J. 629
Bree, Joseph 888
Breeman, Steven 511
Breen, Kristi 273
Breen, Timothy P. (Tim) 387
Brega, João Carlos 923
Bregman, Mark F. 601
Breier, Benjamin A. 502
Breig, Geralyn R. 95
Breig, J Scott 834
Breight, Matthew 224

Breitfelder, John 116
Breivik, Gunnar 793
Brekke, Scott 400
Brell, Mark 246
Bremser, Brett 453
Brendis, Janet 378
Brennaman, Mandy 507
Brennan, James J. 108
Brennan, Thomas 135
Brennan, Daniel J. (Dan) 142
Brennan, Peter 161
Brennan, Norah 218
Brennan, Troyen A. 252
Brennan, Thomas 356
Brennan, Suzanne R. 652
Brennan, Thomas 700
Brennan, Mike 717
Brennan, Brian 809
Brennan, Peter 836
Brenner, Timothy L. 598
Brenner, Alena 743
Brenner, Joel 838
Brenner, Glen 840
Brensilver, Peter 672
Brensinger, Donald 731
Brent, Jacques 370
Brenton, Flint 199
Bresky, Steven J. 756
Breslawski, James P. 752
Breslin, David 358
Bresnahan, Rodney 847
Bress, Tracy 536
Bressette, Doug 175
Bressler, Trina 168
Bressler, Richard J. 456
Brestovan, Peter 664
Breter, Greg 886
Brett, Elizabeth 555
Breux, Ken Le 620
Breves, Christine S. 878
Brewer, John 170
Brewer, Allen M. 366
Brewer, Dominic 606
Brewer, Michael 643
Brewer, Tom 813
Brewer, Janet J. 821
Brewer, Rosalind 903
Brewington, Kimberly F 621
Brewster, Gregg 161
Brian, Bowser 345
Brice, Todd D. 745
Brick, Samuel 45
Bricker, Jodi 830
Brickley, David 834
Brickman, David M. 374
Bridarolli, Shelley 140
Briddon, Bob 95
Bridelli, Guido 131
Bridenbaugh, Carl 360
Bridge, Tracy B. 177
Bridger, Diana 487
Bridger, Chet 539
Bridges, Tim 395
Bridges, Terri 454
Brien, Don 96
Brier, Jeff 14
Briese, Terrence 356
Brigden, John 199
Brigger, Steve 888
Briggs, Ashlea 98
Briggs, Daniel 513
Briggs, Jon 555
Briggs, Julia 620
Briggs, Larry 717
Bright, Christopher 47
Bright, Tobias 135
Bright, Nerissa 722
Bright, Jean 748
Brigman, Vince 512
Brilli, Richard 272
Brinch, Brian 327
Brindle, Carol 931
Brindley, David 870
Bringardner, Jennifer 168
Bringas, Mario 806
Bringhurst, Scott 507
Brinker, Laura 243

Brinker, Mark 668
Brinkley, Ruth W. 168
Brinkley, Cynthia J. (Cindy) 176
Brinkley, Stephen 813
Brinner, Scott 715
Brinton, Geraldine R. 802
Brisco, Tony 553
Briscoe, Debi 137
Brisson, Zane 117
Brissot, Vincent 442
Bristow, Peter M. 344
Britell, Jenne K. 876
Brito, Michael 252
Brittain, Jim 365
Brittingham, Randall 687
Britton, Paula 257
Britton, Carl 351
Broad, Tom 612
Broadhurst, Vanessa 57
Brobst, Duane J. 884
Brocato, Melissa 182
Brochick, George 663
Brock, Pat 161
Brock, Charisse 232
Brock, Troy 330
Brock, Cindy 502
Brock, Anthony 587
Brock, Lucius 726
Brock, Stanley M. (Skip) 763
Brock, Wendy 888
Brod, Frank 575
Broderick, Craig W. 395
Broderick, Denise 453
Broderick, Kathryn E 528
Brodeur, Elaine 97
Brodhead, Richard H. (Dick) 286
Brody, Dean 486
Brody, Robert C. (Bob) 849
Broerman, Robert A. (Rob) 762
Brogan, Joseph 118
Brogan, Jennifer 558
Brogan, Mike 840
Broich, Mark 831
Brok, Martin 787
Brokaw, David 536
Brolly, Stephen H. 335
Bronchetti, Jayson 530
Bronczek, David J. 330
Bronner, James P. 122
Brons-Poulsen, Peter 219
Brooke, Gayle 459
Brookens, Daphne 919
Brookes, Andy 4
Brookfield, David 81
Brooks, Howard 117
Brooks, Christine 131
Brooks, Mark J. 176
Broxton, Brian P. 322
Brooks, Jessica 447
Brooks, Josh 457
Brooks, David R. 460
Brooks, Daniel W. 460
Brooks, Wendell M. 465
Brooks, Charles T. 495
Brooks, Ashley T. 534
Brooks, Raymond L. 544
Brooks, Kurt 580
Brooks, Rebekah 610
Brooks, Byron 668
Brooks, Mark 686
Brooks, Mary 715
Brooks, Kenneth 756
Brooks, Kristi 787
Brooks, Nancy Schwartz 808
Brooks, Tony 808
Brooks, Andy 809
Brooks, Espen S. 834
Brooks, Dan 860
Brooks, George 875
Brooks, Tony 936
Broome, Marion E. 287
Broomfield, Robert 880
Brophy, Joseph 409
Brophy, Chris 573
Brophy, Scott 888
Broseker, Bob 570
Brosnahan, Maria 158

Brosnan, David J. (Dave) 210
Bross, Julia 222
Bross, Richard A 437
Bross, Tamara 786
Brossart, Tim 933
Brossoit, Jean-Francois 210
Brothers, Robert 80
Brothers, Grace 213
Brothers, Ken 327
Brothers, Lisa 355
Brothers, Michael 447
Brothers, Norm 875
Brotman, Adam 787
Broucek, Paul 838
Brough, Rob 941
Broughton, Thomas A. (Tom) 763
Brouillard, Rheo A. 766
Brouillette, Norm 743
Broussard, Bruce D. 446
Broussard, Paula 651
Brower, Jason 88
Brower, Chris 246
Brower, John 769
Brown, Ken 3
Brown, Johnie 15
Brown, Greg 15
Brown, Jeffrey J. (JB) 33
Brown, Bradley 33
Brown, Shona 34
Brown, Marc 45
Brown, Daniel 61
Brown, Jim 77
Brown, Jennifer 101
Brown, Emily 117
Brown, Jeff 131
Brown, Gregory 135
Brown, Michael 137
Brown, James C. 141
Brown, Micheal 161
Brown, Bette 178
Brown, Michael 185
Brown, Debra 201
Brown, Kenneth 201
Brown, Ken 201
Brown, Pam 205
Brown, Adriane 240
Brown, Alison 245
Brown, William E. 268
Brown, Darrell 294
Brown, Robert 299
Brown, Marcus V. 304
Brown, Carrie 313
Brown, Julia 328
Brown, Jill 330
Brown, Marianne C. 334
Brown, Douglas 334
Brown, Rod 337
Brown, Trish 339
Brown, David D. 346
Brown, Brad 356
Brown, Jennifer 376
Brown, James S. (Jim) 405
Brown, William M. (Bill) 411
Brown, Angie 416
Brown, Doug 439
Brown, Kimberly 446
Brown, Nick 450
Brown, Michael J. (Mike) 454
Brown, Ken 454
Brown, Holly 454
Brown, Mike 468
Brown, Michael 483
Brown, Dan 489
Brown, Michelle 494
Brown, David 498
Brown, Michele 517
Brown, Karoom 517
Brown, Archie M. 542
Brown, Timothy 548
Brown, Linda 550
Brown, Arnold 558
Brown, David 563
Brown, Gregory Q. (Greg) 589
Brown, Robert 604
Brown, Lynne 606
Brown, Jennifer Jackson 617
Brown, Stephen 620

Brown, Keegan 628
Brown, Diana 635
Brown, Brien H. 641
Brown, Vicki 680
Brown, Lori 684
Brown, Ian 689
Brown, Jeffrey 716
Brown, Kevin 717
Brown, Dan 720
Brown, Robert 722
Brown, Rodney 724
Brown, Melanie 726
Brown, Denise 727
Brown, Diane 731
Brown, Thomas L. 732
Brown, Gerald 743
Brown, Kevin 759
Brown, Susan L 760
Brown, Jim 773
Brown, Mickey A 778
Brown, Julie A 779
Brown, Joel E. 788
Brown, David 789
Brown, Marc P. 791
Brown, Chad 800
Brown, Melanie 805
Brown, Tim 808
Brown, Bob 808
Brown, Bernard 813
Brown, Max 823
Brown, Chuck 842
Brown, Charles 842
Brown, Janice 855
Brown, Mike 860
Brown, Michelle 860
Brown, M. Dean 867
Brown, Mike 905
Brown, Jeffrey 908
Brown, Dennis 917
BROWN, MIKE 919
Brown, Erin 923
Brown, Michael 929
Brown, Kendall 935
Brown, Jimmy 935
Brownawell, Neil 217
Browne, Noreen 563
Browne, Robert P. (Bob) 620
Browne, Paul T. 818
Browne, Colin 866
Brownell, Kelly D. 287
Browning, Stephen 185
Browning, Nicholas 449
Browning, Bill 492
Browning, Michael 834
Browning, Gale 881
Browning, Jay D. 890
Brownlee, Jeff 908
Broxton, Sonnie 808
Broyles, Rhonda 813
Broz, Steven A. (Steve) 695
Brozyna, Roman 201
Brtalik, Joe 87
Brubaker, Lisa 176
Brubaker, Alan 700
Bruce, Blackham 651
Bruce, Jim 875
Bruce, Christina 901
Bruch, Lisa 181
Bruder, Ann J. 227
Bruder, David 411
Brudzynski, Daniel 284
Brueggman, Eric 101
Bruggeman, Kim 437
Bruggeman, Todd 489
Bruggs, Jeff 580
Bruhin, Joseph D. (Joe) 237
Brukwicki, Michelle 817
Brum, Cristina 158
Brumbelow, Holly 551
Brumfield, Shawn 635
Brummer, Derek V. 712
Brummerhoff, Leigh 548
Brummit, John 453
Brun, Scott 6
Brun, Philip 880
Brundage, Barry 224
Brundage, Adam 504

Brunel, Patrick 674
Brunelle, Fletch H 573
Brunick, Nicole 729
Bruning, Jill 15
Brunner, Steve 457
Brunngraber, Eric H. 164
Bruno, Marc 72
Bruno, John John 200
Bruno, Paul 365
Bruno, Gabriella 370
Bruno, Christopher J 465
Bruno, James E. 878
Bruno, Jim 878
Brunot, Ed 781
Bruns, Timothy D. 495
Bruns, Curtis 507
Brunson, Amos 158
Brunson, Curtis 509
Brunswick, Dan 79
Brunt, Jeff Van 861
Brus, David 888
Brusadelli, Maurizio 584
Bruss, John 13
Brust, Andrew L 578
Bruton, Steve 750
Bruzzichesi, Gina 93
Bryan, Sandy 178
Bryan, J. Randolph 454
Bryan, Glynis A. 463
Bryan, Amanda 666
Bryan, Jeanna 715
Bryan, Vere 760
Bryant, Jennifer 43
Bryant, Christian 80
Bryant, Joy 135
Bryant, Sterling 157
Bryant, Elizabeth 185
Bryant, Tom 244
Bryant, Matt 246
Bryant, Steve 299
Bryant, Mary 330
Bryant, Diane M. 465
Bryant, Andy D. 465
Bryant, John A. 493
Bryant, Lauren 507
Bryant, Kim 754
Bryant, Phillip 808
Bryant, Mike 875
Bryant, Greg 935
Bryant-Ellis, Paula 137
Bryce, Maria 353
Bryson, Helen 176
Brzezinski, Robert 497
Brzoska, Debra 620
Bubb, David 754
Bucaille, Julien 748
Bucceri, Rich 604
Buchanan, John D. 224
Buchanan, Travis 246
Buchanan, David 335
Buchanan, Stephen G. (Steve) 744
Buchanan, Carie 748
Buchanan, Ashley 903
Buchanon, Kent 411
Buchanon, David 727
Buchbauer, Paul 242
Buchen, Amy 34
Buchert, Mark 343
Buchetto, Michael 874
Buchholz, Brian 261
Buchmeier, Peter 200
Buchsbaum, Marc 14
Buck, Libby 107
Buck, Michele G. 422
Buck, John D. 657
Buck, James 767
Buckalew, Steve 402
Buckalew, John 409
Buckbee, Kevin 6
Buckey, Jay 770
Buckheit, Scott 155
Buckingham, Lisa M. 529
Buckiso, David 345
Buckiso, Scott D. 878
Buckland, Laura 811
Buckler, Bryan 286
Buckley, Guy 286

Buckley, Alicia 332
Buckley, David 440
Buckley, John 457
Buckley, Andrew 468
Buckley, Raegan 550
Buckley, Michael C. 734
Buckley, George W. 786
Buckminster, Douglas E. 44
Bucknell, Constance 598
Buckner, Phillip 52
Bucko, James 665
Buckshaw, Joseph 752
Buczko, Brian 454
Buda, David 18
Budagher, Bruce 553
Budd, Thomas D. 706
Budd, Jim 861
Budny, Kamil 200
Budraitis, Alyssa A. 22
Budzinski, Jeff 298
Buechse, Oliver 80
Buelow, Dawn 550
Buenaseda, Jude 607
Bueno, Juan 431
Buerkle, Thomas 321
Buese, Nancy K. 609
Buesinger, Robert F. 920
Buettner, Anne 274
Buff, Kathy 272
Buffa, Damiano 133
Buffett, Warren E. 123
Buffi, Cindy 839
Buffie, Craig A. 497
Buffon, Mike 875
Buffoni, Chris 516
Buffy, Birrittella 713
Bugatto, David J. 28
Bugh, Stan 613
Bugh, Frank 715
Buhay, Rene 382
Buhler, Marlene 54
Buhr, Jeffrey L. 1
Buhs, Lori 454
Bui, Vanesa 573
Bui, Greg 615
Bui, Jenny 731
Buit, Ron 540
Buitrago, Gus 366
Bukkapatnam, Raman 787
Bulanda, Mark J. 299
Bulawa, Bryan F. 307
Bulger, Deborah 563
Bullard, Terry 726
Buller, Katja 129
Bullock, Shawn 81
Bullock, Brian H. 305
Bulmer, William H 699
Bulpin, Andrew 566
Bultman, Gary 512
Bulus, Domingos H. G. 687
Bumgarner, David L. 207
Bump, Larry 602
Bumpus, Bruce 459
Bumpus, John P. 526
Bundschuh, John 664
Bundy, Jeff 515
Bunk, Craig 468
Bunnell, Ronald R. (Ron) 111
Bunte, Brent 474
Bunting, Theodore H. (Theo) 304
Bunting, Chris 570
Bunyard, Heather 382
Buonforte, Jeffrey J. 511
Buquicchio, Gerard 715
Buran, John R. 366
Burbick, Kevin 641
Burchfield, Carol 177
Burchfield, David 754
Burckhart, Camille 682
Burdic, Charles 201
Burdick, Kevin L. 641
Burdick, Randy G. 801
Burdick, Steven 881
Burdick, Kenneth A. (Ken) 911
Burdine, Sharon 769
Burdiss, Paul E. 941
Burech, Roanne 912

Burgdoerfer, Stuart B. 508
Burge, Mark 201
Burge, Debbie 693
Burger, Mark 55
Burger, Martha 189
Burgess, Matthew B 349
Burgess, Doug 727
Burgess, Brian 772
BurgessJr, Robert 187
Burgher, Cedric W. 631
Burgis, David 32
Burgoon, David 724
Burgoyne, Amy 18
Burik, Jeff 226
Burille, Linda 313
Burkard, Scott 389
Burke, Michael S. (Mike) 14
Burke, Sheryl 18
Burke, Scott 34
Burke, Kristine 80
Burke, Joseph 94
Burke, James T. 104
Burke, Sean 141
Burke, Rosaleen 142
Burke, Zane M. 183
Burke, Stephen B. (Steve) 222
Burke, George J 228
Burke, Kevin 234
Burke, Karey 274
Burke, Kevin G. 279
Burke, Joan A. 343
Burke, Brian 356
Burke, David 368
Burke, Patrick J. (Pat) 445
Burke, Sean 477
Burke, Edward J. (E.J.) 497
Burke, Ej 497
Burke, Geoffrey 587
Burke, William A. (Bill) 608
Burke, James J. (Jim) 613
Burke, John 620
Burke, Heather 749
Burke, Brian 754
Burke, Jason 754
Burke, Joseph 858
Burke, Shannon 896
Burke, Frank J. 927
Burkett, Steve 487
Burkhalter, Brandy 176
Burkhart, Megan D. 224
Burlage, David P. 214
Burlando, Fabrizio 555
Burleigh, Clarence 106
Burley, Shane 185
Burlingame, Nathan 158
Burlog, Chris 876
Burman, Darryl M. 402
Burnell, James 934
Burnett, Bonnie 168
Burnett, Matt 170
Burnett, Graeme 262
Burnett, David 441
Burnett, Kathy 770
Burnette, Angela 870
Burnham, Ken 117
Burnham, Jerry 457
Burnham, Cheri 793
Burnich, Jeffrey 802
Burnip, Douglas 886
Burnosky, James 605
Burns, Sean 88
Burns, Ned 170
Burns, Haydon 170
Burns, Austin 246
Burns, Kenneth F. 347
Burns, Mark L. 380
Burns, Nellson D. 429
Burns, Nelson 429
Burns, James 503
Burns, Randolph 649
Burns, Gay 723
Burns, Maribeth 773
Burns, Joseph 776
Burns, Ken 782
Burns, Gareth 793
Burns, Chandler 800
Burns, Steven 808

Burns, Sheri T. 865
Burnside, Tom 786
Burnson, Bob 684
Buro, Geoff 881
Burrafato, Angela 18
Burrescia, Dominic 735
Burridge, Graham 273
Burris, Alex 519
Burritt, David B. (Dave) 878
Burroughs, Phil 411
Burroughs, Patricia 620
Burroughs, Philip 893
Burrow, Lynne M. 154
Burrow, Holden 550
Burrow, Patrick A. 768
Burrowes, Todd 257
Burrowes, Astrid 366
Burrows, Mike 557
Burrows, Clifford (Cliff) 787
Burrus, Peter 245
Bursey, Robert 664
Burson, Arthur 566
Burt, Lesley 450
Burt, Nathan 574
Burt, Brady T. 653
Burt, Jeff 813

Burtis, Andy 563
Burton, Brian 105
Burton, Lynn 198
Burton, Becky 888
Burton, Christopher 942
Burts, Rob 806
Burud, Jamie 824
Burvill, Martin 893
Busack, John 912
Busannagari, Chandra 792
Buschman, Virginia 558
Buschmeyer, Stephen 857
Buschur, Diane 489
Buseman, Michael D. (Mike) 94
Bush, Ken 12
Bush, James P. 44
Bush, Jim 44
Bush, Julie 45
Bush, Carl 246
Bush, Stephanie 413
Bush, Antoinette (Toni) 610
Bush, Wesley G. (Wes) 623
Bush, William 634
Bushman, Julie L. 2
Buskey, Michael T. (Mike) 379
Buskirk, Kim 12
Buss, Jessica E. 788
Bussard, Beth 912
Busse, Keith E. 794
Bussell, Layne 269
Busso, Anthony Del 106
Busson, Donald 139
Bustamante, Jose L. M. 365
Bustamante, Jolito 514
Butala, Smita 713
Butcher, Art 142
Butcher, Lisa 727
Butchko, Jason 826
Butera, Mike 337
Butier, Mitchell R. 91
Butkus, Sean 395
Butler, Julia 135
Butler, AL 155
Butler, Pete 185
Butler, Mark 194
Butler, John 210
Butler, John M. 238
Butler, Keith G. 285
Butler, Doug 299
Butler, Bill 300
Butler, Gregory B. 312
Butler, Calvin G. 314
Butler, Ronald D. (Ron) 350
Butler, Maurice 454
Butler, Richard 459
Butler, Mark 480
Butler, Bianca 699
Butler, Kelley H 699
Butler, Brad 724
Butler, Timothy 735

Butler, Jessica 749
Butler, Yeng 792
Butler, Bobby 858
Butler, Eric L. 868
Butt, Talal 735
Butterfield, Stephen F. (Steve) 601
Butterfield, Robert 722
Butterfield, Tom 814
Butters, Stephen 272
Butto, Joseph 842
Buttrick, Tony 362
Butz, Greg R. 222
Buxton, Alex 941
Buytenhuys, Sheldon 748
Buzbee, Terry 299
Buzby, Timothy L. (Tim) 327
Buzzell, Mark 370
Buzzelli, Marc 700
Bybee, Brian 756
Byers, Jay 191
Byhus, Rhonda 590
Bykoriz, Vlad 672
Bynum, Patrick 897
Byrd, Mike 12
Byrd, Stacy 178
Byrd, Denise 201
Byrd, Laurie 341
Byrd, Daryl G. 454
Byrd, Beth 654
Byrd, Vince 773
Byrd, Heath R. 774
Byrne, Alice 31
Byrne, Rita 45
Byrne, Kevin 204
Byrne, Mike 672
Byrne, Kevin 715
Byrne, Timothy (Tim) 735
Byrne, Jay 767
Byrnes, Larry 256
Byrnes, Shaun 700
Byrnes, James J. 842
Bystehner, John 875
Bytner, Mark 470
Byun, Jimmy 507
Byunn, Jay 135
Byus, Fred 114

C

Caamano, John 173
Cab, Sandy 191
Caballero, Maximino 115
Cabbil, Nathan 729
Cable, Carol 137
Cabrera, Ramon 204
Cabrera, Luis A 717
Cabuso, Nita 620
Caccamo, Frank 693
Cacciatore, Gary 161
Caccivio, James C. 791
Caceres, R. Louis (Lou) 749
Caceres, Lou 749
Cader-Frech, Mario 896
Cadieux, Marc C. 803
Cadiz, Bruce J 135
Cady, Sean 895
Cady, Gerald A. (Gary) 916
Cafazza, Charles 80
Caffrey, Robert 84
Caforio, Giovanni 144
Cage, Jeff 456
Cagle, Lorita 101
Cagle, David P 224
Cagle, Kevin 454
Cagle, Farris 580
Cagney, Katie 928
Cahaly, Scott D 487
Cahan, Adam 34
Cahill, Dennis 106
Cahill, Denny 300
Cahill, John T. 505
Cahill, Timothy 700
Cahill, Kevin 849
Cahillane, Steven A. (Steve) 493
Cahlstadt, Timothy 539
Cai, Xiangrong 413

Cai-Lee, Wendy 290
Cain, James 57
Cain, Scott 220
Cain, Michael S 246
Cain, Charlie 273
Cain, Christopher 457
Cairns, Ann 554
Cairns, Chuck 735
Caius, J 300
Cajigas, Veronica 270
Calabrese, Kevin 99
Calabrese, Kevin J 99
Calabrese, Vincent J. 367
Calabrese, John 385
Calabrese, Isela 558
Calabrese, Andrea 559
Calabretta, Chris 156
Calabria, David T 93
Calamari, Stephen 709
Calanga, Jack 570
Calantzopoulos, Andr© 674
Calbert, Michael M. 276
Calcagni, Mark 447
Caldart, Gilberto 555
Calderon, Vanessa 88
Calderon, Enrique 365
Caldwell, Bruce 60
Caldwell, David 157
Caldwell, Ken 273
Caldwell, William J. 435
Caldwell, Melody 457
Caldwell, Angie L 617
Caldwell, Christopher (Chris) 805
Caldwell, Michael 808
Caldwell, Troy 834
Caldwell-Denny, Lynn 875
Caleca, Brendan 643
Calentino, Jeffrey 170
Calhoun, David L. (Dave) 133
Calhoun, David L. (Dave) 166
Calhoun, Matt 539
Calhoun, Greg 643
Calhoun, Stephen T 652
Calhoun, Chris 810
Cali, Jim 493
Calihan, Kevin 170
Calisto, Jodi 770
Calkins, Steve 633
Call, Barbara 228
Call, Chad 941
Callaghan, David 643
Callahan, William 53
Callahan, Don 203
Callahan, Samantha 222
Callahan, Daniel D. 226
Callahan, Patrick K. (Pat) 695
Callahan, Matt 704
Callahan, Paul 705
Callahan, Andrew P. (Andy) 859
Callahan, Eve 864
Callahan, Chris 904
Callegari, Peter 175
Callender, Scott 339
Caller, Nick 425
Callera, Stefano 69
Callicott, Bevan 161
Callihan, Margaret L. 799
Callihan, Jane 869
Callinicos, Sean 161
Callum, Sean 358
Calmes, Mark E 74
Colombo, Antonio 191
Caltabiano, Madelyn 566
Calzadilla, Irene 927
Cama, Domenick A. 477
Camardo, Joe 175
Cambern, Morgan 149
Cambre, Gayle 935
Cambria, Ian 109
Cameron, Richard 628
Cameron, Kristy 787
Camilleri, Louis C. 674
Camillo, Dominic 746
Camitta, David 266
Cammaker, Shelly 298
Cammarata, Chris 378
Cammaroto, Gerilyn 45

Cammilleri, Joseph 665
Cammorata, Andrew 792
Campana, Vincent 44
Campana, Mark 532
Campana, Frank 932
Campanella, Edward J. 77
Campanini, Marcello 170
Campany, Daniel 413
Campbell, Jeffrey C. (Jeff) 44
CAMPBELL, DIANNE 45
Campbell, Michael P. 82
Campbell, Nanci 117
Campbell, Mary 137
Campbell, Joanne T. 155
Campbell, Mark A. 164
Campbell, Jed 185
Campbell, Lee 195
Campbell, Roger A. 241
Campbell, Ryan 261
Campbell, Michael 262
Campbell, Bruce L. 270
Campbell, Rebecca 273
Campbell, Kevin 332
Campbell, Tabitha 332
Campbell, Jeff 333
Campbell, Shelley 355
Campbell, Jimmy 406
Campbell, Thomas A 413
Campbell, Kristin A. 427
Campbell, Ann-Marie 431
Campbell, Ann 431
Campbell, Jessica Barnett 517
Campbell, Claude 530
Campbell, Del 530
Campbell, Kevin 595
Campbell, Angela 620
Campbell, Kevin 623
Campbell, Dala 697
Campbell, John P 735
Campbell, Gary 765
Campbell, Rob 768
Campbell, Todd 773
Campbell, Robert 821
Campbell, Mitchell 855
Campbell, Travis 894
Campbell, Amy 896
Campbell, Steven 917
Campbell, Joel 919
Campbell, Steve 941
Campe, Jennifer 927
Campion, Andrew (Andy) 615
Campion, Michele 866
Campisi, David J. (Dave) 128
Campisi, Vince 879
Campos, Deb 159
Camus, Julie 898
Can, Alp 788
Canaday, Charles T. 48
Canavan, Mark 274
Cancelloni, Frank 705
Cancelmi, Daniel J. (Dan) 818
Candanoza, Emilio 185
Candee, Chris 504
Candels, Eileen 494
Canepa, Steven 470
Canestrari, Ken 839
Canfield, Mark 409
Cangemi, Thomas R. (Tom) 604
Cangemi, Lisa 643
Cangey, Karen 688
Caniglia, Jim 863
Canimore, Brett 14
Canizares, Claude R. 509
Cankat, Burc 219
Cannariato, Lawrence 158
Cannatelli, Len 834
Cannella, Stefanie 799
Canney, Jacqueline P. (Jacqui) 903
Canning, Daniel 919
Cannon, Mary 2
Cannon, Marc 89
Cannon, Ed 131
Cannon, Maria 200
Cannon, Thomasine 286
Cannon, Alexander (Alex) 705
Cannon, Terrence 722
Cannon, Stacy 776

Canova, Frank 892
Cantarutti, Perry 262
Canterino, Tom 415
Cantillon, Maria 791
Cantor, Nancy 468
Cantrell, Gary L. 480
Cantrell, James M. 578
Cantu, Gladys 97
Cantu, Dave 162
Cantu, Ernesto Torres 203
Cantwell, Jim 87
Cantwell, Richard 199
Canup, Steven C. (Steve) 97
Canup, Ed 157
Canup, Scott 224
Canuso, Dominic 931
Caoagas, Rachelle 720
Capek, John M. 4
Capek, Thomas 240
Capello, Jeffrey D. (Jeff) 129
Capers, Jacquelyn 101
Capizzi, Peter 700
Caplan, Deborah H. 612
Caplan, Adam 748
Capone, Jeff 431
Capossela, Christopher C. (Chris) 575
Capozzola, Peter 77
Capozzoli, Robert 698
Capozzoli, Matt 875
Capparelli, Alejandro 738
Capps, Richard 468
Cappuccio, Paul T. 838
Capra, James 679
Capriotti, Chris 824
Captain, Keith 279
Captain, Catherine 811
Capuano, Anthony G. (Tony) 548
Caputo, Marco 140
Caputo, Melissa 226
Caputo, Lisa M. 849
Cara, Jose 672
Caraballo, Darwin 18
Caraballo, Barbara 456
Caraballo, Bianca 901
Carabillas, Phillip 94
Carafiol, Dennis 770
Caram, Meredith 84
Carapella, Victor 356
Carballo, Tyson 109
Carbary, Sherry 135
Carbo, Angelique 760
Carbonari, Dominic 487
Carbone, David 297
Carboni, Michael 53
Carcy, David 449
Cardamon, Ana 199
Cardenas, Ricardo (Rick) 256
Cardenas, Javier 391
Cardenas, Alberto de 553
Cardillo, James 650
Cardinal, Greg 390
Cardone, Mark S. 233
Cardosa, Neal 266
Caresani, Louis 888
Caret, Leanne G. 135
Carew, Thomas J. 606
Carey, Nate 96
Carey, Karen E 232
Carey, K Kristann 237
Carey, Brian 413
Carey, Matthew A. (Matt) 431
Carey, Matt 431
Carey, Susan 615
Carey, Thomas 639
Carey, Albert P. (Al) 667
Carey, Anthony 791
Carey, David R. (Dave) 810
Carey, Chase 858
Carey, Pat 898
Carfora, Jeffrey J. 660
Cargill, Robyn 539
Cargill, C. Keith 823
Carhill, Norm 507
Carignan, Tom 863
Carik, Curtis 18
Carkin, Mark 103
Carkner, Alan 195

Carl, David 81
Carl, Holowaty 724
Carle, Judy 266
Carleton, Mark D. 524
Carleton, Jay 788
Carleton, Gary 875
Carli, Alexi 875
Carlin, Scott 643
Carling, Timothy 413
Carlino, Rosario 220
Carlisle, Lee 276
Carlisle, Paul 927
Carlo, Anibal 144
Carlo, John 910
Carlson, Jan 86
Carlson, Carl M. 147
Carlson, Chante 178
Carlson, W. Erik 271
Carlson, Brenda 342
Carlson, Johnathan 365
Carlson, Dan 550
Carlson, Gabe 557
Carlson, Jeff 570
Carlson, Vanessa 604
Carlson, Chris 620
Carlson, J.D. 663
Carlson, LeRoy T. (Ted) 817
Carlson, Walter C. D. 817
Carlson, Chris 834
Carlson, Stephen 882
Carlson, Jennie P. 888
Carlson, Tom 928
Carlson, Steven 942
Carlton, Mark 750
Carmack, Aaron 431
Carmel, Stephanie 470
Carmichael, James 175
Carmichael, Steve 269
Carmichael, Greg D. 336
Carmichael, M Caroline 792
Carmichael, Amanda 935
Carminati, Catherine 56
Carmody, Christine M. (Chris) 312
Carmody, Kevin 395
Carmody, Cora L. 481
Carmody, Thomas 558
Carmona, Yolanda 735
Carnaghi, Sharon 356
Carnahan, John 463
Carnahan, John 533
Carney, Wendy 80
Carney, Jack 146
Carney, Valerie 274
Carney, James 470
Carney, Craig B. 851
Carney, Jeffrey 875
Carney, Mary Ellen 888
Carney, Rita D 903
Carnifax, Rod 656
Carnish, Erin 881
Caro, Antonio 219
Caro, Douglas 563
Caro, Jennifer 668
Carolan, Edward L. (Ed) 156
Caron, James 804
Caronia, Leonard S. 768
Caroots, Gregory 634
Carotenuto, Michael 154
Carow, Bryan 888
Carozza, Gerald 760
Carp, Marilyn 568
Carp, Jeffrey N. 791
Carpenter, Wesley 84
Carpenter, Willie 178
Carpenter, Kaye 247
Carpenter, C. Douglas 324
Carpenter, William F. (Bill) 526
Carpenter, James J. 604
Carpenter, Bruce 628
Carpenter, Harold R. 677
Carpenter, Jonathan 759
Carpenter, Lonny J. 797
Carpenter, Benjamin 888
Carpenter, Aaron 895
Carpenter, Andrew 899
Carpenter, Don 907
Carpentier, Marc 800

Carper, Patricia 834
Carper, Howell P. (Hal) 859
Carpinone, Jean 367
Carr, Muneera S. 224
CARR, TONY 262
Carr, Bryan 446
Carr, Jim 671
Carr, Chris 787
Carr, Nicole 787
Carr, Dan 849
Carrasquillo, Jose 750
Carraway, Gary 875
Carre, Eric 405
Carreiro, Robert 881
Carreno, Anthony 938
Carrero, Franklin 158
Carrick, Stephanie 548
Carrier, William 135
Carrig, Kenneth J 799
Carrington, Jim 555
Carrin, Richard L. 682
Carroll, Milton 177
Carroll, Thomas M. 280
Carroll, Ray 330
Carroll, Kevin 402
Carroll, Jim 434
Carroll, Christopher F. 473
Carroll, Pamela 484
Carroll, Teresa S. 494
Carroll, Darren 528
Carroll, Paul 547
Carroll, John A. 567
Carroll, Ryan 643
Carroll, Glenn 660
Carroll, Rhonda L. 697
Carroll, Robert 849
Carroll, Scott 904
Carroll, Tom 907
Carrothers, Troy 504
Carrubba, Jared 726
Carruth, Mary 530
Carruthers, Susan 246
Carruthers, Paul 722
Carson, Joe 490
Carson, Brian M. 580
Carson, John C. 715
Carson, Elizabeth 813
Carstenbrock, Tom 380
Carstens, Timothy 558
Carswell, Scott 266
Carswell, Demario 539
Carter, Ann 115
Carter, Laurent 144
Carter, Cyndi 161
Carter, Van C 247
Carter, Peter W. 262
Carter, Robert B. (Rob) 330
Carter, Betty 332
Carter, Briggett 342
Carter, Racheal 350
Carter, Ian R. 427
Carter, Anita 582
Carter, John 599
Carter, Charles J. (Jack) 652
Carter, Jack 652
Carter, Matthew 664
Carter, Todd 677
Carter, Jimmy 705
Carter, Mary Randolph 713
Carter, Andrea 713
Carter, Ron 754
Carter, Tim 779
Carter, Maureen 786
Carter, Jason 787
Carter, J. Braxton 810
Carter, John 838
Carter, Steve 875
Carter, Dave 879
Cartin, Eugene 767
Caruso, Robert 121
Caruso, Dominic J. 484
Caruso, Christopher R. 685
Caruso, Nicholas 754
Caruso, Kelly 813
Carusona, Tom 72
Carvajal, Taylor 133
Carver, Bruce 248

Carver, Bill 447
Carver, Carla E 684
Carwile, Dan 635
Casabene, Sam 370
Casalino, Denise 15
Casas, Noe 68
Casavant, Art 664
Casazza, William 18
Casazza, Louise 550
Case, Richard 395
Case, Michael 486
Casella, Michael J. 596
Casey, Keith M. 63
Casey, Donald M. (Don) 160
Casey, Sharon 176
Casey, John P. 380
Casey, Pauline 415
Casey, Kelly M 454
Casey, Donald J. (Don) 718
Casey, William J. 851
Cash, W. Larry 230
Cash, William 240
Cash, Linda 370
Cash, John 808
Cashaw, Brad 259
Cashill, Robert M. 477
Cashman, George D. 201
Cashman, Rory 370
Cashman, Ed 715
Cashon, Craig 890
Casimiro, Michael 570
Caskran, Ronald 105
Caslin, Cindy 378
Cason, Courtney 710
Casparino, Michael J. 664
Casper, Krista 81
Casper, John 409
Casper, Marc N. 836
Casperson, Finn M.W. 660
Cassara, Ken 910
Cassidy, Frank 153
Cassidy, Jennifer 665
Cassidy, Donathan 678
Cassidy, Doug 779
Casta, Shannon 731
Castagna, Eugene A. (Gene) 121
Castaneda, German 115
Castaneda, Rodrigo 131
Castaneda, Amanda 635
Castanon, Adrian 722
Casteel, Beth 320
Casteel, Marty D. 768
Casteel, Aaron 770
Castellan, Susan 834
Castellano, Ilia 570
Castellano, Gail 604
Castello, Sam 49
Castelloni, Kendra 928
Castelvi, Christine 195
Castell, Juan L. Pier 537
Castiglione, Vincent 895
Castillo, Leandro 6
Castillo, Luis 99
Castillo, Eloise 423
Castillo, Ben 454
Castillo, Claudia 489
Castine, Cindy 537
Castle, Mark 106
Castleberry, Jean 799
Castleberry, Chris 886
Castman, Rich 106
Caston, Moanica 389
Caston, Moanica 778
Caston, Michael 800
Castonguay, Lyne 431
Castor, Richard L. (Rich) 386
Castro, Henrique De 34
Castro, Cheryl 555
Castro, Marco 555
Castro, Lorraine 882
Castro, Robert 885
Castro, Marie 891
Caswell, Laura 119
Caswell, Angie 484
Catalano, Mark J. 930
Catalfo, R O 456
Catani, Steven 484

Cates, Sonya 447
Cathcart, David 813
Cathey, Jim 707
Catik, Ali M. 857
Catino, David 416
Catlett, John 867
Cato, Cindy 200
Catton, Jack 135
Catz, Safra A. 642
Caubel, Patrick 672
Caudill, Larry 402
Caudullo, AL 715
Caumeil, Lori 800
Causby, David A. 502
Cavaliere, Joseph W. 608
Cavalline, Chris 504
Cavallo, Alex 620
Cavallucci, Eugene 411
Cavanagh, Lisa 121
Cavanagh, Michael J. (Mike) 222
Cavanagh, Kathi 550
Cavanaugh, David 664
Cavanaugh, Scott 932
Cavaness, Joel D. 378
Cave, Michael J. (Mike) 410
Cavender, Jack 207
Cavicchioli, Kathleen (Kathy) 756
Caviet, Max G. 60
Cawley, Timothy P. 235
Cawley, Joseph 241
Cawley, Kevin 279
Cawley, Christopher 536
Cawthon, Wendy 869
Caylor, Mark A. 623
Cazer, David 135
Cecere, Andrew 888
Cecil, Desmond 191
Cecil, Mark 213
Cecil, Gregory 286
Cedotal, Chad 876
Cedrone, Lou 693
Celestin, Angela 640
Celis, Stephanie De 548
Celis, Alvaro 576
Cellars, Kevin 701
Celliers, Gordon 60
Cellini, Chris 774
Cely, Monte 84
Centeno, Miguel 18
Centers, Melissa 788
Cere, Don 161
Cerepak, Brad M. 281
Cerice, Emilio 722
Cerna, Hector J. 468
Cerniglia, Gregg 334
Cernuda, Cesar 576
Cerone, Luciano 382
Cerretani, Casey 748
Cerrito, Debbie 456
Cerruti, Paolo 823
Cervantes, Conley 818
Cesarz, Mike 563
Cevis, Eric 893
Cfp, Richard 53
Cha, Thomas 559
Chabner, Bruce 656
Chack, Dennis M. 360
Chacon, Jennifer 549
Chadbourne, Jean 194
Chadha, Sanjeev 667
Chadwick, Norman 701
Chae, Michael S. 133
Chae, Sharlene 179
Chaffin, Paul B. 294
Chaffin, Patrick 744
Chaffinch, Randy 692
Chaffins, Sean 97
Chaffins, Randall 244
Chagnon, Michael L. 516
Chahal, Courtney I 415
Chai, David 199
Chaiken, Andrew 131
Chaimengyew, David 423
Chain, Kara 672
Chairoongrojsakul, Yasikaan 494
Chakrabarti, Atanu 472
Chakravarthi, Sarita 760

Chalamalasetti, Rajesh 691
Chalkan, Lisa 660
Challenger, Dave 150
Chalmer, Micah 587
Chalmers, John R 489
Chaloux, Debra 886
Chalson, David 303
Chambas, Corey A. 343
Chamberlain, Barry 172
Chamberlain, Gail 185
Chamberlain, Doug 200
Chambers, Margaret W. (Megan) 141
Chambers, Doreen 201
Chambers, Adrienne 555
Chambers, Brian D. 648
Chambers, Elizabeth G. (Libby) 918
Chami, Tori 45
Chamlee, Steve 530
Chammas, Emile Z. 757
Champlin, Byron 530
Chan, Mei 45
Chan, Jerry 105
Chan, Bryan 105
Chan, Wai Man (Raymond) 166
Chan, Owen 199
Chan, Choylin 204
Chan, Donna 204
Chan, Stephen 395
Chan, Jenny 489
Chan, Garrett 519
Chan, Eric 557
Chan, Angela 573
Chan, Hoi 589
Chan, Kok-kheong 750
Chana, Surjit 470
Chance, Diane 507
Chance, Bobby 593
Chancy, Mark A. 799
Chand, Sujeet 738
Chandler, Mark 50
Chandler, Tina 107
Chandler, Dean 170
Chandler, Mark 200
Chandler, John 207
Chandler, Willis 252
Chandler, Lenn H 390
Chandler, Willy 580
Chandler, Sharon 722
Chandler, Don 803
Chandler, Laura 908
Chandoha, Marie A. 754
Chandra, Sumeer 442
Chandramowleeswaran, Chandrashekar 248
Chandraraj, Girisha 311
Chandrasekaran, Ramakrishnan 218
Chandrasekaran, Suja 903
Chandrasekhar, Arun 465
Chandrasena, Anita 266
Chandrashekar, Sriram (Ram) 543
Chang, Tim 103
Chang, Derek 103
Chang, Daniel 133
Chang, Steve 204
Chang, Diane 224
Chang, Chris 257
Chang, Renee 290
Chang, Peter 358
Chang, Andrew 423
Chang, Rick J 558
Chang, Evans 620
Chang, Ann 628
Chang, Andrew S. 662
Chang, Sally 688
Chang, Chienchung 707
Chang, Peggy 849
Channon, Mardelle 749
Chanter, Keith 298
Chantos, Donna 494
Chao, Sue 290
Chao, Albert 920
Chao, James Y. 920
Chapanar, Marilyn 397
Chaparro, Vicky 220
Chapek, Robert (Bob) 273
Chapelle, Robert 620
Chapin, Libby 337

Chapin, John 739
Chapin, Kurt 808
Chapman, Ryan 133
Chapman, Steven M. (Steve) 248
Chapman, Rhonda 344
Chapman, Kevin D. 726
Chapman, Esther 769
Chapman, Paul 830
Chapman, Ken 849
Chapman, Garrett 895
Chapman, Pier 896
Chapman, Timothy M. 898
Chappell, Daniel G. (Dan) 756
Charalambous, Ioannis A. 631
Chardo, Toni 180
Charest, Laurie 205
Charette, Michael 484
Chargois, Trevor 546
Charles, Ronald 176
Charlick, Joanne 899
Charlie, Iovino 18
Charlton, Andrew 205
Charlton, R. Scott 807
Charmatz, Jeff 106
Charneski, Brian S. 421
Charney, Eugene 550
Charre, Christian 170
Charriez, Laston 919
Charron, Daniel J. (Dan) 348
Charron, Jeffrey 800
Charter, Robert B. (Rob) 166
Chartier, Doug 811
Chase, William J. 6
Chase, Stephan 548
Chase, P. Kevin 762
Chasney, Laura 809
Chastain, Carol A 870
Chastian, Randy 96
Chastulik, Cindy 146
Chatfield, Chris 355
Chatt, Theresa 557
Chattopadhyay, Sanat 566
Chau, Celia 131
Chau, Dennis 273
Chaubal, Prasad 489
Chaudhary, Anurag 628
Chaudhry, Jawad 477
Chavan, Pratap 299
Chavez, Veronica 204
Chavez, Joann 284
Chavez, R. Martin 395
Chavez, Jesse 425
Chavez, Mauricio 563
Chavis, Eva 332
Chawla, Sona 503
Chay, Jasmine 932
Chazin, Steve 199
Chean, Kevin 570
Cheap, Richard A. 449
Cheatham, J. Douglas 637
Checkett, Donna 18
Cheda, Edie 313
Cheek, Bruce D. 43
Cheek, Patty 875
Cheeseman, Michael 405
Cheesewright, David 903
Chelala, Peter 896
Cheleden, Charles G. 931
Chelewski, Tom 454
Chelko, Carrie 530
Chen, Lucy 69
Chen, Donald 74
Chen, Jingnong 117
Chen, Qihua 166
Chen, Heng W. 167
Chen, Min 191
Chen, Natasha 219
Chen, Larry 357
Chen, Carol 457
Chen, Tze-Chiang 470
Chen, Charles 550
Chen, Timothy 576
Chen, Wellington 688
Chen, Elsa 688
Chen, Roawen 707
Chen, Patgun 713
Chen, George 750

Chen, David 752
Chen, Yingying 792
Chen, Emily 805
Chen, James 823
Chen, Heidi C. 943
Cheney, Andrew B. (Andy) 54
Cheng, Tonya 57
Cheng, Andrew 391
Cheng, Marn K. 590
Chenna, Vijay 507
Cherbow, Jill 3
Cherecwich, Peter B. 620
Cherence, Danielle 395
Cheriyan, Anil 799
Chernett, Kevin 533
Cherry, Kimberley C. (Kim) 353
Cherry, Pedro 389
Cherry, Don J. 392
Cherry, Ruthie B Cook 799
Chery, Sulexan 39
Chery, Don 392
Cheshier, Carrie 849
Chesick, Luke 558
Chesler, Randall M. (Randy) 392
Chesley, Yonnie 416
Chesna, Peter 860
Chesney, John 715
Chesnut, Jeff 30
Chesson, Fred 101
Chester, Joyce 573
Chestnutt, Roy H. 893
Cheung, Jasper 37
Cheung, Annie 470
Cheung, Raymond 672
Cheung, Ann 688
Chevalier, Karen 799
Chew-Lai, Moya 699
Chewens, Michael J. 598
Chhabra, Harleen 320
Chho, Sara 379
Chi, David 68
Chi, Cindy 435
Chia, Donny 587
Chiang, Hwai Hai (HH) 480
Chiang, Timothy 831
Chiappone, Charles 489
Chiarello, Guy 348
Chiarello, Karen 660
Chiaromonte, Jeannie 102
Chiasson, Becky 178
Chiccino, Peter (Pete) 827
Chichester, David 787
Chick, Wes 818
Chico, Michael Chico Michael 620
Chicoine, Gerry 84
Chicoine, Jerry L. 325
Chidiac, Edward 80
Chierico, Salvatore 158
Chilberg, C. Perry 872
Chilcott, Haydn 431
Childers, Terry 207
Childers, Michael 769
Childers, Kim M. 789
Childs, Torrance 141
Chillemi, John 625
Chillo, Laura 886
Chilson, Scott 484
Chilton, Jim 135
Chilton, Dan 602
Chiluisa, Sylvana 665
Chin, Marc 131
Chin, Norene 204
Chin, Michael 356
Chin, David 792
Chin, Patrick 803
China, John D. 803
Chinea, Manuel 682
Ching, K.C. (Glenn) 179
Chinigo, Michael 446
Chinn, Michael A. (Mike) 746
Chintamaneni, Ramakrishna Prasad 218
Chiocco, Leslie 639
Chiolan, Robert 131
Chionchio, Mike 486
Chirico, Emanuel (Manny) 705
Chirolas, William 570
Chisholm, Cheryl 342

Chisholm, Craig 378
Chisholm, Timothy 423
Chisholm, Moody L. 467
Chiu, Mabel 483
CHIU, ANDREW 707
Chiumenti, Ralph 550
Chivavibul, Somsak 595
Chivinski, Beth Ann L. 376
Chlebicki, Marilee 370
Chlosta, Dagmar 866
Chlupsa, Steve 94
Cho, Ho 175
Cho, Brandie 332
Cho, Chris 408
Cho, SungHwan 455
Cho, Jane 713
Cho, Warren 808
Choate, Elizabeth 237
Choate, Chris 715
Choate, Mike 724
Chock, Lindsay 395
Chodak, Paul 42
Choeff, Sonya 715
Choi, Justin C. 64
Choi, Byung U 133
Choi, Caroline 777
Chojnowski, Tammy 792
Chojnowski, David M 903
Chokron, Jeni 107
Chomienne, Kathleen 382
Chong, Jack 19
Chong, James 435
Chopey, Stephen 790
Chopra, Rahul 610
Choquette, Patricia 865
Chorley, Michael 735
Choromanski, Jennifer 896
Choroszucha, Lech 88
Chosy, James L. 888
Chotiner, Karen 17
Choto, Miguel 489
Chou, John G. 56
Chou, Minnie 57
Chou, Ken 358
Choudhary, Ken R. 365
Choudhury, Bhaskar 668
Choudhury, Sayeed 707
Choulochas, Jason 107
Chovanec, Tony 307
Chow, Donald S. 167
Chow, Jonathan 533
Chow, Jean 671
Chow, Wayne 688
Chowdhury, Ashfaque 936
Chris, Wigger 261
Chris, Brady 692
Chrisbacher, Scott 96
Chrisman, Kenneth P. (Ken) 757
Christakes, Jennifer 487
Christakos, Bretta 178
Christensen, Michelle 128
Christensen, William 337
Christensen, Wesley J. 641
Christensen, Scott 857
Christenson, Stephen 715
Christian, David A. 278
Christian, Korey 447
Christian, Mark 653
Christian, Douglas 705
Christian, Alan 722
Christian, Ronald 735
Christian, Eric 936
Christiansen, Kathy 869
Christie, Peter 599
Christina, Rassi 18
Christman, Phil 597
Christman, Kelli 863
Christmann, John J. 68
Christmas, Charles E. (Chuck) 564
Christoff, Renee 809
Christoffersen, Gregg 487
Christofferson, Carla J. 14
Christophe, Roussel 830
Christopher, John Y 423
Christy, Lisa R 349
Christy, James 698
Chrystal, Curtis 419

Chrystie, Dale 330
Chrzan, Barbara 204
Chu, William 94
Chu, Roberta 103
Chu, Dorcus 191
Chu, Gary 383
Chu, Joshua 435
Chu, Melvin 487
Chu, Benjamin K. 491
Chu, Tom 705
Chudzinski, Marta 69
Chugg, Juliana 557
Chugh, Madhavi 131
Chugh, Harsh 470
Chui, Bennett 290
Chuisano, Joe 893
Chulos, Nicholas J. 356
Chum, Muni 109
Chumley, Robert J. (Rob) 590
Chung, Michael H. K. 291
Chung, Annie 408
Chung, Felix 550
Chung, Yoon (Michael) 654
Chung, Jin 705
Chung, Paul W. 812
Church, Brian 342
Church, John R. 383
Church, Allan 668
Churchill, Sally 720
Ciamillo, Rich 555
Ciampa, Dominick 604
Cianciosi, Steven 566
Ciani, Juliette 287
Ciavarelli, Mike 931
Cichon, Monica 497
Ciesemier, Barbara 213
Cietek, Phyllis 106
Cigarroa, Francisco G. 884
Cilento, Robert 513
Cillo, Sherry 867
Cinco-Abela, Tracy 709
Cincotta, Tiffany 5
Cindi, Tippett 739
Cindric, Michael 222
Cintron, Joanette 81
Ciombor, Christiane 932
Ciongoli, Adam G. 156
Ciotoli, Carlo 606
Cipra, Andy 272
Ciprich, Tresa 831
Cirillo, Mary 200
Cirillo, Carl 599
Cirincione, Thomas 449
Ciriscioli, Peter 504
Ciro, Tony 470
Ciroli, James K. 362
Ciserani, Giovanni 693
Ciskowski, Michael S. (Mike) 890
Cisneros, Zada 246
Cisneros, Tamara 901
Cisrik, James 307
Citrano, John A. 149
Cituk, Jacquelyn 266
Ciukowski, Kim 677
Ciulla, John R. 908
Cius, Steve 378
Civello, Stephen 237
Civetta, Vincent Vincent Civetta 87
Civgin, Don 31
Clacko, Phil 459
Claffy, Christian 328
Claggett, Kevin 367
Clair, Joyce St. 367
Clair, Joyce 620
Clamp, Len 101
Clancy, John P. (Jack) 305
Clancy, Sean 704
Clanton, Lori 15
Clanton, Mike 179
Clapham, Scott 500
Clapp, Clinton 18
Clapp, Dale 355
Clappin, James P. 240
Clara, Daniel 78
Clariana, Roy 831
Clark, Dan 18
Clark, James B 42

Clark, Gina K. 56
Clark, Colleen 101
Clark, Stacey 101
Clark, Jennifer 176
Clark, Rodney L. 184
Clark, Scott 289
Clark, Mark 360
Clark, David 383
Clark, Jeff 440
Clark, Neil S 449
Clark, Scott 456
Clark, Nelson 465
Clark, Ed 468
Clark, Michael 470
Clark, Michael S 534
Clark, David 563
Clark, Dave 566
Clark, Ed 576
Clark, Dennis 606
Clark, Chip 609
Clark, Richard 620
Clark, Todd C. 635
Clark, Jenny 635
Clark, Michael D 641
Clark, John P 671
Clark, Shelagh 693
Clark, Douglas 715
Clark, Karen 717
Clark, Christopher 723
Clark, Bernard J. 754
Clark, Thomas M 760
Clark, John C. 769
Clark, Terri L 808
Clark, Gary 823
Clark, Dulin 831
Clark, Cathy 860
Clark, Cathy 863
Clark, Terry M. 880
Clark, Tom 908
Clark, Jay 908
Clark, Blair 923
Clark, Christopher B. (Chris) 933
Clark, Chad 938
Clarke, Scott 261
Clarke, Cathy 289
Clarke, Sandra 449
Clarke, Troy A. 597
Clarke, Jane 672
Clarke, Jeanne 705
Clarke, David 713
Clarke, Andrew C. 736
Clarke, Caroline 903
Clarke, Sheri 912
Clarken, James 631
Clarkson, Thomas F. 31
Clarson, Reuben 799
Clason, Norman 3
Clatterbuck, Michelle 476
Claure, Ed 84
Clausen, Trent 181
Clausen, Cathy 256
Clausen, Amanda 813
Clauson, Kent 580
Clawater, Earl W. (Bill) 779
Claybrook, Robert 121
Clayton, Chris 214
Clayton, Janet 295
Clayton, Staci 332
Clayton, Debra 620
Clayton, John 635
Clayton, Rich 643
Clayton, Michelle 737
Cleary, James F. (Jim) 56
Cleary, Michael 135
Cleary, Mike 201
Cleary, Don 548
Cleary, Jim 668
Cleek, Don 291
Clegg, Catherine 385
Cleghorn, Jayme 52
Clelland, John 810
Clemens, John 237
Clemens, Chris 339
Clemens, Paul F. 356
Clemens, Lance 378
Clemens, Steven 449
Clement, Michele 332

Clement-Holmes, Linda W. 693
Clementi, Erich 470
Clements, Bryan 257
Clements, John 287
Clements, Anne 749
Clements, Janet 863
Clemmons, Scott 800
Clemson, Conrad 200
Cleveland, Peter 465
Cleveland, Brian K. 725
Cleymaet, James 301
Cliff, Suzy 802
Clifford, Bill 294
Clifford, Scott S. 399
Clifford, David 528
Clifford, Todd 665
Clifford, Paul R. 764
Clifford, Paul 831
Clifford, John P. 849
Clifton, Nicole 875
Clikas, Steve 697
Clinaz, Rick 876
Cline, David W. 789
Clingan, John E 345
Clingen, Stephen 356
Clingenpeel, Chris 809
Clingerman, Diane 449
Clinton, Tim 47
Clinton, Angeline 286
Clinton, Ian 570
Clipp, Caitlin 880
Cloake, Catherine 201
Cloer, Michael G. 876
Cloninger, Kriss 19
Clontz, Jerry L. 506
Clore, K 799
Closs, Diane 813
Clossin, Todd F. 912
Clothier, Kevin 244
Clough, George 664
Cloutier, Paul A. 108
Cloyd, Rhetta 457
Cluff, Tad 849
Clyde, R. Andrew 590
Clymer, Dale 553
Coad, Scott 919
Coady, Shawn W. 613
Coates, Steve 106
Coates, Spencer A. 441
Coats, Brian 488
Coaxum, Ryan 404
Cobb, Branson 18
Cobble, Angela 530
Coben, Lawrence S. 625
Coble, Fred 715
Coblentz, Max 763
Coburn, Howard 498
Coburn, Tom 735
Cocero, Nanette 671
Cochran, Jason 379
Cochran, Phyllis 597
Cochran, Larry 692
Cochran, Scott D. 723
Cochran, J. Scott 726
Cochran, Angela 754
Cochran, Steve 811
Cochran, Barbara 888
Cochrane, David 320
Cochrane, Marie 530
Cockcroft, Adrian 37
Cockell, Larry 838
Cockrum, Leigh 769
Cocks, Chris 415
Coco, Cedric T. 146
Cocq, Alex 470
Codde, Mark 782
Coder, Forrest David 151
Codkind, Mitch 643
Codsi, Jean-marc 293
Cody, Gen. Richard A. 509
Cody, William M. (Bill) 695
Cody, Peter 699
Coe, Leann 181
Coe, Nicholas P.M. (Nick) 508
Coe, Patrick K 788
Coelho, Jovita 205
Coetzee, Theresa 548

Coffey, Timothy P. 65
Coffey, Douglas 882
Coffin, Judy 266
Coffman, Brian 63
Coffman, Rhonda 98
Coffman, Thomas 287
Cogdill, Richard A. (Rick) 832
Coggans, Chris 185
Coggin, Michael S. (Mike) 526
Coggins, John 161
Cogliano, Michael 792
Cohen, Sharon 3
Cohen, Barry 78
Cohen, Gary M. 119
Cohen, Eric S 135
Cohen, Art 135
Cohen, Nathan G. 195
Cohen, David L. 222
Cohen, Jed 273
Cohen, Bob 441
Cohen, Moshe 470
Cohen, Harvey 533
Cohen, Gwen 587
Cohen, David 587
Cohen, Elisa 607
Cohen, Jon R. 709
Cohen, Don 752
Cohen, Matthew 767
Cohen, Daniel G. 827
Cohen, Jack S 896
Cohen-hillel, Avi 71
Cohill, Mike 802
Cohn, Robert 186
Cohn, Marc 570
Cohn, Arthur 672
Cohodes, Jeffery D. 620
Coindreau, Javier 672
Coke, Ed 643
Coker, Connie 99
Coker, Mike 320
Coker, R. Howard 775
Colaiacovo, Judith 705
Colaluca, Mark 425
Colangelo, Maria 928
Colasurdo, Ellen 550
Colberg, Alan B. 82
Colbert, Theodore (Ted) 135
Colbert, Brett 602
Cole, Russell G. 147
Cole, David D. 181
Cole, John 214
Cole, Michael 336
Cole, Tracey 551
Cole, Kenneth G. 552
Cole, Jody 664
Cole, David D 711
Cole, Lauren 803
Cole, David 875
Cole, Jackie 888
Cole, Cynthia 931
Colella, Domenic 203
Colella, Thomas 903
Coleman, Kenneth 25
Coleman, Christopher 34
Coleman, Johnathan 87
Coleman, Michael 117
Coleman, Rob 170
Coleman, Russell F. 259
Coleman, Caretha 266
Coleman, Gregory 273
Coleman, Eric 273
Coleman, Kenny 389
Coleman, Scott 447
Coleman, Brian 457
Coleman, Jay 497
Coleman, Heather 507
Coleman, Laura 604
Coleman, Donna 618
Coleman, Kirk 824
Coleman, Gary L. 843
Coleman, Todd 870
Coleman, Chris 880
Coleman, Laura 886
Coleman, Beth 896
Colestock, Richard E 684
Coletta, Anthony 699
Coletti, Janet M. 538

Coley, Peter 800
Colgan, Gary 185
Colgan, Meegan 713
Colin, Mark 3
Colin, William 754
Colistra, David 470
Collar, Gary L. 20
Collett, Kelly 528
Colli, Alison 413
Collier, Dirk 484
Collier, Gary 677
Collier, John 722
Collier, Diane 867
Collier, Daniel 890
Collier, John 903
Colligan, Don 728
Collignon, Dan 390
Collins, Barbara 104
Collins, James E. 118
Collins, James E. 118
Collins, Bill 135
Collins, Whitley 170
Collins, William C. 187
Collins, Martin 219
Collins, Darryl 226
Collins, Daniel 240
Collins, Jim 249
Collins, Jonathan M. 254
Collins, Rodger L. 282
Collins, Greg 282
Collins, Jodi 295
Collins, Martha 301
Collins, Scott 370
Collins, Barclay 423
Collins, Mark 425
Collins, Anitra 472
Collins, Chris 489
Collins, Vance 502
Collins, Daniel W 528
Collins, Jayme 585
Collins, Olga 604
Collins, Gary S. 637
Collins, Christian 663
Collins, Stephen 700
Collins, Kevin 722
Collins, Kevin 750
Collins, Norman 778
Collins, Jim 792
Collins, Tim 827
Collins, Terry 855
Collins, Dave 860
Collins, Steve 863
Collins, Kevin 908
Collinson, Michael 705
Collinsworth, Paul 449
Collis, Steven H. 56
Collison, Rick 801
Colman, Robin 293
Colnett, Beth 566
Colo, Ralph 587
Colombe, Paul 919
Colombo, Russell A. (Russ) 104
Colombo, William J. (Bill) 264
Colombo, Benjermin 804
Colon, Evelyn 69
Colon, Tara 84
Colon, Bill 116
Colon, Rebecc 446
Colpo, Charles C. 647
Colsman, Peggy 192
Coltart, Catherine 620
Colvin, Jeff 15
Colvin, Jason 555
Colwill, Karen 279
Colzi, Alberto 6
Comaianni, Sherri 266
Comas, Daniel L. 256
Comay, Josh 172
Combest, Debbie 276
Comer, Ruth 453
Comitale, Jim 731
Commerford, Jack 135
Compton, Brian 131
Compton, Kevin 770
Compton, Lisa 787
Compton, Brad 826
Compton, Teresa 903

Conant, Douglas R. (Doug) 95
Conant, Scott 504
Conatser, Vivienne 555
Conaway, Mary Ann 211
Concannon, William F. (Bill) 169
Concannon, Michael (Mike) 413
Conde, Cesar 222
Conde, Carla 682
Condina, Jim 201
Condon, Ashley 142
Condon, Gene 770
Condong, Carlo 489
Condrin, Mark 367
Condry, Sterling Kirk 137
Conetta, Tony 429
Conetto, Dominic 332
Coney, Bill 128
Coney, Jason 540
Conforti, James E. 802
Conforti, Thomas G. (Tom) 931
Confrey, Meg 204
Cong, Lin 628
Conger, Harry M. (Red) 375
Conger, Ann 749
Congleton, Brian 85
Coniaris, Jeff 668
Conklin, Patrick 693
Conn, W. Lance 186
Conn, Bill 786
Connatser, Gayle 516
Conneely, Todd 69
Connell, Terry 222
Connell, Jesse 297
Connell, Hope Holding 344
Connelly, Anthony 273
Conner, Peter J. 110
Conner, Raymond L. (Ray) 135
Conner, Brad L. 205
Conner, Wayne 370
Conner, Jack W. 420
Conner, Ryan 735
Conner, David E. 872
Connery, Raymond 105
Connery, Brian 664
Connett, Brad 752
Connolly, Thomas 56
Connolly, Keith 84
Connolly, Tatiana 122
Connolly, Sean M. 232
Connolly, Michael 470
Connolly, Joy 606
Connolly, Paul 792
Connolly, Thomas 936
Connor, Mitch 200
Connor, Patrick 437
Connor, Kevin 489
Connor, Ian 570
Connor, Frank T. 826
Connor, Martin P. (Marty) 841
Connors, Bill 222
Connors, Denise 489
Connors, Timothy 649
Connors, Kevin 666
Conophy, Thomas M. (Tom) 89
Conover, Bob 699
Conrad, Tim 528
Conrad, William 530
Conrad, Jan 722
Conrad, Rachael 738
Conrado, Eduardo F. 589
Conroy, Alexandre 119
Conroy, Courtney 172
Conroy, Steve 615
Consagra, James J. 869
Consolino, Joseph E. (Jeff) 47
Constable, Richard 932
Constantine, Thomas 136
Constantine, Tim 185
Constantine, Shari 910
Constantino, Tawnya 467
Contat, Kevin 450
Conte, Michael 530
Conte, Randall T. 558
Conterno, Enrique A. 528
Contis, David J. 770
Contreras, Jaime 4
Contreras, Ronaldo 39

Converse, Lou 896
Conway, John W. 244
Conway, Scott T. 324
Conway, Michael 680
Conway, Michael 787
Conway, Jeffrey D. 791
Conway, Karen 891
Conwell, Jonathan 643
Coody, David 722
Coogan, Maureen 103
Coogan, Tim 200
Cook, Timothy D. (Tim) 69
Cook, Barb 69
Cook, Fletcher 84
Cook, David 105
Cook, Derek 131
Cook, Ian M. 219
Cook, Jeff 306
Cook, Tracey 365
Cook, Brian 425
Cook, Jay 470
Cook, Bill 489
Cook, Charles 502
Cook, Brent 503
Cook, Mitchell W. 578
Cook, Sandy 692
Cook, BettyL 720
Cook, Houston 722
Cook, David 735
Cook, Stephen R. (Steve) 771
Cook, Allison 800
Cook, Rachel 840
Cook, Mike 903
Cooke, Trisha 94
Cooke, Dennis C. 743
Cooke, Bob 840
Cookman, Brett 566
Coolidge, David 733
Coombe, Gary 693
Coombs, Cary 941
Coomer, Anirvan 385
Coonan, Kevin 104
Cooney, Tom 205
Cooper, Michael 12
Cooper, Mark 15
Cooper, Mark 149
Cooper, Debra 176
Cooper, Gary 199
Cooper, Jeff 257
Cooper, Robert 330
Cooper, Michael 379
Cooper, Edith W. 395
Cooper, James 454
Cooper, Ellen 529
Cooper, Ward 548
Cooper, Geoffrey 572
Cooper, Laura E 615
Cooper, Frank 668
Cooper, Andrew C 696
Cooper, Doug 715
Cooper, Chris 723
Cooper, Aaron 769
Cooper, Julie 799
Cooper, Samantha 896
Cooper, Keri 924
Cooper, Troy A. 936
Cooperstein, Marci 172
Copa, Gail 178
Cope, Bud 925
Copeland, Scott 98
Copeland, John G. 99
Copeland, Reed 251
Copeland, Rex A. 400
Copeland, R. Dallis (Roy) 806
Copelin, Bill 447
Copello, Corinne E 617
Copenhaver, Michelle 18
Copher, Ron J. 392
Copier, Judy 457
Copley, David 200
Copper, Donna 13
Coppock, Alisa 446
Coppola, Matthew 892
Copses, Paul 385
Coray, Joe 413
Corban, Stephen M. 726
Corbat, Michael L. 203

Corbett, Kevin 31
Corbett, John 178
Corbin, Glen 330
Corbin, John 449
Corbin, George 548
Corbo, Michael A. (Mike) 219
Corbo, Michael 672
Corbridge, Michael 262
Corbusier, Drue 267
Corcoran, Mary 409
Corcoran, Thomas A. (Tom) 509
Corcoran, Stephen 908
Cordani, David M. 194
Cordano, Michael D. 917
Cordero, Paul 644
Cordes, Edward B. 403
Cordova, Ron 18
Corely, Catherine 903
Corey, Allen 338
Corey, Lee 587
Corirossi, David 725
Corker, Regina 335
Corlett, David 258
Corley, Kelly McNamara 269
Corley, Greg 771
Corley, John 934
Cormier, Joanne 93
Cormier, Deborah 101
Corn, R. E. (Ron) 192
Corn, Craig 570
Cornejo, Rene 328
Cornelious, Derrick 105
Cornelius, Jim 735
Cornell, Daniel C. 36
Cornell, Catherine 224
Cornell, Kevin 224
Cornell, Brian C. 813
Cornell, Steve 919
Cornett, Jane 289
Cornew, Kenneth W. (Ken) 314
Cornia, Kelly 101
Cornia, Silvano 580
Cornish, Kevin 14
Cornish, Thomas M. 109
Cornum, Curt 463
Cornwall, Kevin 249
Cornwell, W. Don 95
Corona, George S. 494
Corr, Patrick 172
Corrado, Heather 700
Corrales, Ana 199
Correa, Jaime 724
Corrigan, Shari A 570
Corrinne, Kelly 745
Corsini, Bryan M. 653
Corson, B. W. 320
Cortes, Fernando 282
Cortese, Jennifer 559
Cortez, Juan 356
Cortner, Bill 773
Corum, Bethany H. (Beth) 157
Corum, Mike 724
Corvino, Mike 901
Corwin, Glenda Welsh 330
Cosby, Bill 449
Cosentino, Margaret 75
Cosenza, Mark 394
Cosenza, Joe 479
Cosey, Cathy 722
Cosgrove, William 477
Cosman, James M. 147
Cosolito, James 60
Cosset, Yael 506
Costa, Rui 222
Costa, Mark J. 291
Costa, Joe 792
Costa, James M. 814
Costa, Robert 822
Costantino, Danielle 131
Costantino, Anthony 912
Costanzo, Patricia 555
Costanzo, Dan 786
Costello, Michael 208
Costello, Christopher 230
Costello, Thomas 382
Costello, Richard 413
Costello, Kevin 470

Costello, Rhonda 728
Cote, David M. (Dave) 434
Cothran, April 337
Cottell, Mike 713
Cotter, Martin 62
Cotton, Anita 300
Cotton, Charles 457
Cotton, Byron 896
Couch, Drew 96
Couch, Rick 175
Couch, Richard W. 706
Couch, Brett D. 721
Couch, David deS. (Dave) 781
Couch, Connie 824
Coudrelle, Laurent 628
Couger, Scott 409
Couget, Ron 549
Coughlin, Thomas M. 118
Coughlin, Thomas M. 118
Coughlin, Christa 204
Coughlin, Jason 378
Coughlin, Ron 442
Coulomb, Michel 69
Coulston, Lauren 489
Coulter, Ryan 131
Coulter, Sam 416
Coulter, Cuan 791
Counihan, Kevin J. 176
Counsell, Jeffrey 170
Counts, John 808
Courant, Paul N. 720
Courduroux, Pierre 585
Coursen, Sam 599
Coursey, Donna 749
Courtney, Tom 415
Courtney, Mark 863
Courtney, Ann 886
Courtney, Mary 941
Courtois, Jean-Philippe 575
Couse, Anthony 486
Cousino, Mark 284
Cousins, James 261
Coutchie, Peggy 564
Couto, Luey 688
Couture, Martin 665
Coveny, Erin 158
Covert, Michael H. 168
Covert, Brad 248
Covert, Charlie 875
Covey, Steven K. (Steve) 597
Covington, J. Curtis 327
Covington, Curt 327
Covino, Greg 129
Cowan, Mike 470
Cowan, Haley 868
Coward, Robert 935
Cowee, Terrence 164
Cowell, Chuck 404
Cowhig, Michael T. 608
Cowing, Chris 715
Cowles, James C. 203
Cowles, Brad 418
Cowley, Daron 467
Cowman, Craig 161
Cox, Matt 117
Cox, Ryan 161
Cox, Brian 272
Cox, Shawn 289
Cox, Mark K. 291
Cox, Steven 299
Cox, Christopher K. (Chris) 321
Cox, Richard 332
Cox, B. Guille 351
Cox, James W. 361
Cox, Neil C 378
Cox, Rhydian H. 445
Cox, Clay 447
Cox, Ray 470
Cox, Nick 558
Cox, Graham 570
Cox, Pat 590
Cox, Mike 628
Cox, Randy 699
Cox, Ryan 735
Cox, Philip C. 803
Cox, Keith 805

Cox, Karen 822
Cox, Dudley 847
Cox, Tom 875
Cox, John 903
Coyle, Michael J. 419
Coyner, Sheri 67
Cozza, Keith 455
Cozzone, Robert D. 459
Crabtree, Jennifer 246
Crabtree, Grant 273
Crabtree, Stephen 715
Cracchiolo, James M. (Jim) 52
Craft, Frank 693
Crafter, Lochiel 792
Cragg, John 663
Cragin, Maureen 135
Craig, Sean 245
Craig, Zac 367
Craig, Kim 402
Craig, Marian 537
Craig, Jeffrey 545
Craig, Jonathan M. 754
Craig, John 769
Crain, Robert B. 20
Crain, Shawn 724
Craine, Eric 863
Cralle, Chris 204
Crame, Glenn 654
Cramer, Errol 31
Cramer, Kathy 695
Crandall, Brett 133
Crandall, Catherine B 188
Crandall, Douglas 735
Crandall, Theodore D. (Ted) 738
Crandall, Janice 893
Crandus, Oi Eng 311
Crane, Barbara 117
Crane, Stephen A. 297
Crane, Christopher M. (Chris) 314
Crane, Cindy A. 651
Crane, Timothy S. (Tim) 927
Crane, Susan 932
Cranmer, Jonathan 34
Cranna, Ian 787
Cranston, Susie 358
Crater, Ann 201
Craven, Matthew 60
Craven, Juile 437
Cravey, Lynn 334
Crawford, Frederick J. (Fred) 19
Crawford, Christina 45
Crawford, Victor L. 72
Crawford, Michael 101
Crawford, Bill 135
Crawford, Claudia 146
Crawford, Stephen S. (Steve) 158
Crawford, Rhonda 262
Crawford, Carolyn 272
Crawford, Stephen G. (Steve) 291
Crawford, Mark 313
Crawford, James C. 341
Crawford, Michael 449
Crawford, Kelly 497
Crawford, James 546
Crawford, Bruce 639
Crawford, Kermit R. 731
Crawford, Charles 752
Crawford, Charlie 752
Crawford, Peter 754
Crawford, David 791
Crawley, Barbara 656
Craycroft, Tim 37
Crcm, Monsy 905
Creager, Dick 252
Creager, Chris 893
Creamer, Aimee 117
Creamer, Michele 566
Creamons, Joe 356
Creatura, Nick 210
Credle, Eric P. 341
Creech, Dennis 423
Creed, Cindy 295
Creed, Greg 939
Creedon, Michael 12
Creery, Thomas G. 429
Creery, Benjamin 786
Cregg, Daniel J. (Dan) 701

Creighton, Bill 860
Creighton, Cheryl 904
Crenshaw, William E. (Ed) 702
Crenshaw, William E. (Ed) 703
Crescenzo, Giovanni De 175
Crespo, Frank J. 166
Creticos, Peter 483
Cretu, Angela 95
Crews, Mark 25
Crews, Charles C 238
Criddle, John 252
Crigler, Forest 376
Crimmins, Timothy P. 664
Criner, Amy 119
Crines, James T 940
Crisman, Michael 641
Crist, Peter D. 928
Cristoforo, Albert J. (Jerry) 791
Crites, Mark 550
Croall, Gail 18
Crocco, M. Scott 22
Croce, Thomas 57
Croce, Michael J. 796
Crocitto, Linda 39
Crofts, Sharon M. 102
Croll, Terry 99
Cromett, Mark 787
Cron, Lyndon 936
Crone, Seth 106
Cronen, John 888
Cronen, Paul 891
Cronin, Dave 45
Cronin, Douglas J 142
Cronk, Gary 754
Cronyn, Kristen 539
Crooke, Robert B. 465
Crookston, Jesse 86
Croom, Marshall A. 537
Crop, Danielle 45
Cropper, Keith 666
Crosby, Carolyn 155
Crosby, Michael J. 929
Crosley, Brad 487
Cross, Jeffrey 42
Cross, Charles K. 756
Cross, Greg 942
Crossley, Christopher 912
Crosswhite, Mark 25
Crotty, Marty 16
Crotty, David 810
Crouch, M. Andrew (Drew) 96
Crouch, Andrew 96
Crouch, Tami 342
Crouchley, G. Eric 279
Crougthers, Troy 503
Crouse, John 558
Crouse, Dianne 691
Crouse, Todd 934
Croutch, William 756
Crouter, Ann C. (Nan) 831
Crovesi, Marco 529
Crovitz, Charles K. 311
Crow, M. Chad 149
Crow, Timothy M. (Tim) 431
Crow, Adam 536
Crow, Stan 623
Crowder, Charles 93
Crowder, Elizabeth 330
Crowe, Dale E 107
Crowe, Tim 155
Crowe, Mike 219
Crowe, Maria 528
Crowe, Bill 938
Crowell, Wyatt E 445
Crowley, John 142
Crowley, JD 172
Crowley, Jack 204
Crowley, F. Michael 545
Crowley, Margaret 572
Crowley, John 587
Crowley, Drew S 767
Crown, Timothy A. (Tim) 463
Crown, Marc 516
Crown, Marc 517
Crowther, David 93
Croxford, Brian 528
CROY, ERIKA 580

Cruce, Andrea 176
Crudo, David 596
Cruikshank, J. David 105
Crum, Scott A. 95
Crump, Darin 226
Crump, Susan 579
Crump, Scott 760
Cruse, Mark 184
Crutcher, Brian T. 825
Cruthers, Thomas 171
Cruz, Alexander 87
Cruz, Almedilia 159
Cruz, Sergio 499
Cruz, Jacquelyn 559
Cruz, Alexis 849
Cruz, Ray 876
Csatlos, Ferenc 310
Csuhran, Renee 498
Cubbage, Gary C. 139
Cubias, Carlos 875
Cuccias, Brian 451
Cucco, Wayne J 49
Cuddeback, Brian 194
Cuddy, Christopher M. (Chris) 74
Cude, Roger 446
Cudina, Marcus 919
Cue, Eduardo H. (Eddy) 69
Cuenot, Cara 671
Cuervo, Larry 406
Cuervo, Carlos 929
Cueva, Maurice 760
Cuevas, Mildred 101
Cuevas, Disnalda 158
Cuevas, Jason 389
Cuffe, Michael S. 416
Cugini, Dominic 497
Cuilla, Michelle 587
Culbertson, Debbie 403
Culbreth, John 276
Culhane, Michael 374
Cullari, Lynne 555
Cullen, Thomas A. (Tom) 271
Cullen, Susan 366
Cullen, William 411
Culling, Robert (Doug) 762
Cullotta, Kimberly 328
Cullum, Linda P 895
Culp, Patricia 512
Culpepper, Jason 768
Culpepper, Lee 903
Culver, Curt S. 572
Culver, John 787
Cumming, Ben 799
Cummings, Melissa 18
Cummings, Sean J. 410
Cummings, Kevin 477
Cummings, Sean 488
Cummings, Bob 489
Cummings, Chris 597
Cummings, Jerilin 882
Cummins, Jennifer 117
Cummins, Michael 765
Cummins, Hugh S. (Beau) 799
Cummiskey, Chris 389
Cunanan, Stephen R. 502
Cunanan, Annette 570
Cune, Bill 240
Cunfer, Todd 422
Cunningham, Don 60
Cunningham, Lisa 80
Cunningham, Benjamin 131
Cunningham, Shirley 193
Cunningham, Kenn 313
Cunningham, David L. 330
Cunningham, Mark 429
Cunningham, William H. 530
Cunningham, Everett V. 709
Cunningham, Michelle 727
Cunningham, Scott 777
Cunningham, LiLi 896
Cuomo, Adriana 178
Cupelli, Kim M 860
Cuprys, Rich 220
Cuprys, Karolina 858
Curcio, Michael J. 288
Curcio, Joe 827
Curd, Samantha S 763

Cure, David 911
Curleigh, James 521
Curleigh, James 523
Curley, Charles 334
Curley, Michael 358
Curley, Shannon 487
Curley, Jeffrey 530
Curley, Claire 896
Curnutte, Douglas 502
Curoe, Tim 813
Curphy, Rona 111
Currah, Barry 942
Curran, Terrie 175
Curran, Martin J. (Marty) 240
Curran, Joe 550
Curran, Shawn 830
Currarino, Giancarlo 649
Currie, Calvin 805
Currie, Kenne 813
Currin, Martin 116
Currington, Karen 182
Curry, Eric 215
Curry, Marie 385
Curry, Julie 470
Curtin, Jim 96
Curtin, David 131
Curtin, Thomas 491
Curtin, Mike 860
Curtis, Elizabeth 45
Curtis, Barbara 97
Curtis, Mark D. 357
Curtis, Robert 550
Curtis, Scott A. 715
Curtis, Benjamin 912
Curtiss, Rick 665
Curto, David 87
Curwin, Ronald 121
Cush, Tom 713
Cushing, Robert B. (Bob) 12
Cushing, Giselle 446
Cushing, Robert T 854
Cushman, Bob 304
Cushman, Deann 563
Cusick, Bob 750
Cusick, Steve 928
Custer, Timothy R. 68
Custer, Max 511
Cutler, Scott 293
Cutts, Jeffrey 935
Cuyar, Craig 639
Cvengros, Kevin 857
Cwengros, Eric 901
Cyganiak, Dave 620
Cymbola, Julie 507
Cymrot, Andrew 549
Cynthia, Tsang 374
Cyphert, Mark J. 697
Cyr, Susie 585
Cyr, Donald St 886
Czack, Karen 45
Czaja, Mark 654
Czajka, Edward J. 688
Czanderna, Carel 923
Czapla, Marianne 582
Czarnecki, Kevin 382
Czarnecki, Walter P 663
Czarnecky, Greg 754
Czartoski, Timothy 484
Czechowski, Katharine 432
Czick, Steve 115
Czuczman, Myron 175
Czyz, Tammy 745

D

Dabagia, Robert C. 436
Dabelic, Claudio 756
Dabell, Kathryn 942
Daberko, David A. 924
Daboval, Wendy 191
Dabundo, Chuck 135
Daby, Jenny 550
Daco, Katherine 133
Dacosta, Dee 87
Dacosta, Anthony 885
Dacunha, Kathleen 259

Dacus, Scott 773
Dadey, Mike 15
Dadouche, Salvatore 115
Daesch, Nanci 585
Daffey, Michael D. 395
Daga, Shobna 151
Daghe, Noelle 214
Dagher, Norman 657
Daglio, Robert 170
Dagostino, Nick 241
Dahl, Susanne 620
Dahl, Craig R. 814
Dahlgren, Bradley 244
Dahlmann, David S. (Dave) 345
Dahlweid, Michael 382
Dahut, Karen M. 139
Dailey, Jack 93
Dailey, Kate 678
Dailly, Donna 378
Dainas, Jay 356
Dakey, Alan W. 667
Dalal, Nandita 530
Dale, Jeffery F. 772
Dale, Amanda 813
Dalecki, Cristin 395
Daleiden, Pete 121
Dalessio, Harry 700
Daley, Kelli 7
Daley, Elvia 247
Daley, Paul 358
Daley, Dorian E. 643
Daley, Calvin 799
Dalgleish, Glen 243
Dalgleish, Glen 689
Dalia, Randall 470
Dall, Trisha 456
Dallabattista, Mauro 517
Dallago, Lou 671
Dallaire, Seth 37
Dallara, Ron 560
Dally, Troy 537
Dalrymple, Christopher K. 28
Dalrymple, Tom 852
Dalrymple, Jeff 935
Dalrymple, Jeffrey 935
Dalton, Gregory W. 112
Dalton, Michelle 161
Dalton, Richard J. 215
Dalton, Jill 497
Dalton, Mark 665
Dalton, James T. 720
Dalva, Eddie 896
Daly, James 15
Daly, Jim 116
Daly, Michael P. 124
Daly, Marty 172
Daly, Marilyn 218
Daly, Andrew 413
Daly, Bill 463
Daly, Tom 539
Daly, David M. 701
Daly, Joe 932
Dam, Cari 558
Dam, Maurice Van 787
Damask, Lisa 893
Dambach, Michael 129
Dambrosio, Nancy 131
DAmbrosio, Ralph 509
Dament, Anne 801
Dameron, Glena 722
Damico, Jennifer 672
Damiris, George J. 429
Damon, Jonas 788
Dan, Nick 2
Dan, James R. 13
Dan, Chad 456
Dana, Terry 259
Danes, Mike 81
Danford-Klein, Henrik 311
Dang, Harish 53
Dang, Kimberly A. (Kim) 500
Dangi, Savinay 811
Dangremond, Mark 311
Danie, Mark 665
Daniel, Jim 14
Daniel, James R. 99

Daniel, William K. (Dan) 256
Daniel, Kareem 274
Daniel, Jane 313
Daniel, Annie 336
Daniel, John M. 353
Daniel, Jill 492
Daniels, J. Todd 19
Daniels, Amy 87
Daniels, Ed 161
Daniels, Jon G. 162
Daniels, Bill 178
Daniels, Nancy 270
Daniels, Ronald J. (Ron) 483
Daniels, Lori A 836
Daniels, Peter 839
Danilenko, Anna 101
Danilewitz, Dale 56
Danilson, Dean 859
Dankanich, Ron 148
Dankner, Evan 53
Danley, Derek 582
Danmeter, Debbie 246
Danna, Valerie 787
Dannaher, Michelle 456
Danner, Rosalin 746
Dannewitz, Charles V. (Chuck) 816
Dannov, David M. 756
Dantchenko, Oxana 935
Dantuono, Anthony 870
Daperis, Anthony 767
Daponte, Ken 131
Dapper, Brent 912
Darby, Maria 139
Darby, Joseph 550
Darcy, Jim 875
Darden, J. Matthew 844
Darendinger, Steve 200
Dargan, Susan 791
Dargusch, Jonathan D. 912
Darne, Michael 548
Darnell, Dan 717
Darnell, Mike 838
Darnley, Patricia 176
Darrington, Mark 170
Darrington, Jim 467
Darsey, James R. 626
Darwin, Brett 911
Darwish, Eslam 555
Das, Sushanto 442
Das, Roshni 465
Dasari, Srinivas 45
Dasbach, Angie 251
Dasilva, Marilyn 330
DaSilva, Jack 834
Dasler, Tina 749
Dasteel, Jeb 643
Dastis, Paul 596
Dastugue, Michael P. 903
Dato, Sandra 158
Daubert, Jon 247
Daubert, Mark 808
Daugherty, Alicia 222
Daugherty, Michael 355
Daugherty, John 379
Daugherty, John 512
Daugherty, Alan 526
Daugherty, Julie A Williams 635
Daurio, Jennifer 214
Dauska, William 800
Davenport, J. Mays 515
Davenport, Nancy 570
Daverio, Mike 269
Davey, James E. (Jim) 413
Davi, Philip 158
David, Dustin 61
David, Hulsey R 84
David, Harmon 411
David, Rose Marie 432
David, Anthony 587
David, Scott B. 809
David, Richard 935
David, Glenn C. 943
Davids, Jody R. 667
Davidson, Bruce 179
Davidson, Keith 259
Davidson, Deanna 330
Davidson, William 393

Davidson, Jay 447
Davidson, Jonathan 490
Davidson, Wendy 493
Davidson, Dennis 599
Davidson, Michael 671
Davidsson, Peter 923
Davies, Debra 45
Davies, Todd 261
Davies, Bridget 293
Davies, Colin 423
Davies, Julian 528
Davies, Richard 608
Davies, Simon 792
Davies, Charles 929
Davila, Sue 332
Davine, Howard 274
Davis, Lori 10
Davis, Julia K. 19
Davis, James C. (Jim) 29
Davis, Vernessa 31
Davis, Ken 35
Davis, Steven 45
Davis, Matthew 84
Davis, Susan 101
Davis, Timothy 115
Davis, Chevol 117
Davis, Darryl W. 135
Davis, Kathy 137
Davis, Erica 146
Davis, J. Kimbrough (Kim) 157
Davis, Kurt 172
Davis, Tony 182
Davis, Patricia 207
Davis, Rhiannon 215
Davis, Shantel 245
Davis, Betty 246
Davis, Mike 246
Davis, Rod 266
Davis, Cathy 269
Davis, Ellen F. 287
Davis, Dale 330
Davis, Kevin 332
Davis, Donald 332
Davis, Chad 334
Davis, Lou J. 344
Davis, Sharon L. 349
Davis, Claude E. 349
Davis, Marion T 380
Davis, Alicia Boler 385
Davis, Stephen J. 415
Davis, Jana J. 416
Davis, Theresa FR 449
Davis, John R. 454
Davis, Douglas L. (Doug) 465
Davis, John 487
Davis, Reggie 504
Davis, Hattie 507
Davis, Robert M. 566
Davis, Mark 570
Davis, Russ 573
Davis, Jeff 580
Davis, Doug 580
Davis, Laura 589
Davis, Erika T. 647
Davis, Timothy Paul 658
Davis, Keith 659
Davis, Jeffrey (Jeff) 661
Davis, Kevin 668
Davis, Scott 668
Davis, Jeff 693
Davis, Robert 699
Davis, Dawn 699
Davis, George S. 707
Davis, Steve 707
Davis, James E. 709
Davis, Glenn 712
Davis, Bart 732
Davis, Cory 735
Davis, Steven D. 761
Davis, Jonathan S. 762
Davis, Reid 776
Davis, Cindy 779
Davis, Nancy B. 796
Davis, Lanette 800
Davis, Robert 808
Davis, Phil 808
Davis, Tim 808

Davis, Shelley 811
Davis, Robert D. (Bob) 842
Davis, Renee 849
Davis, James 863
Davis, Raymond P. (Ray) 865
Davis, Wade C. 896
Davis, Cindy 903
Davis, Angie 903
Davis, Teri 903
Davis, Stephanie 911
Davis, Brett 927
Davison, Jeffrey 599
Davison, J 656
Davison, Mike 811
Davisson, Robert J. 764
Davisson, Kyle 765
Davisson, Michael G 884
Davlin, Jim 385
Davoren, Peter J. 856
Dawidowski, Jonathan 383
Dawkins, Scott 602
Dawson, Suzanne 503
Dawson, Jane D 582
Dawson, Bruce 593
Dawson, Pat D. 638
Day, Craig 155
Day, Thomas R. 437
Day, Zane 506
Day, Kate 570
Day, Kurt 570
Day, J. Randal 773
Day, William B. (Bill) 807
Day, Mark 840
Day, Monica 855
Day, Sarah 926
Day-Salo, Ann 224
Dayon, Alexandre (Alex) 748
Dayton, Britt 808
Deacon, Mary Ann 511
Deadwyler, Mark 585
Deal, Stanley A. (Stan) 135
Deal, Helena 423
Dean, Aaron 94
Dean, Kim 158
Dean, John C. 179
Dean, Lloyd H. 266
Dean, Chad A 332
Dean, Judy 604
Dean, Brian 881
Dean-Hammel, Bridget 131
Deane, Catherine 502
DeAngelis, Michael 465
DeAngelo, Joseph J. (Joe) 418
Dear, Tina 294
Dearborn, Randy 573
Deardorff, Kevin L. 511
Dearing, Michael E 548
Dearman, Paul 131
Dearmond, Carolyn 337
Deason, Richard 516
Deaton, Marianne 11
Deaton, John 431
Deaton, Steven G. 789
Deaton, Craig 935
Deaver, W. Scott 93
Deaver, Scott 93
Deaver, Jeffrey 332
DeBatty, Jill 512
DeBenedetti, Maria 104
DeBernardi, Michael 644
Debertin, Jay D. 193
DeBlock, Andrew 447
Debnam, Henry 411
Deboer, Mieke 116
DeBoer, Bryan B. 531
DeBoer, Sidney B. (Sid) 531
Deboer, David 564
Deboni, Liz 928
Debord, Cris 276
Debuke, Robin 507
Decamp, Bill 677
Dech, Dave 245
Dechant, Suzanne 787
Decher, Peter 868
Dechnik, Frederic 713
Dechristofaro, Robert 191
Deck, Richard 705

Deckard, Steven 276
Deckard, Vicki 765
Decker, Daniel A. 146
Decker, Stephen 191
Decker, Casey 325
Decker, Edward P. (Ted) 431
DeClaris, Wade N. 929
Decock, Tracy 680
Decolli, Chris 3
Decoly, Mike 910
Decosta, Lori 313
Decraene, Dave 355
Decrane, Susanne 168
Dedicoat, Chris 199
Dedinsky, John G. 654
Dedolce, Trish 700
Dedominicis, Kim 809
Dee, Steven 615
Deegan, Matt 237
Deehan, Teri 849
Deeks, Terence N. 596
Deenihan, Ed 602
Deering, Matt 735
Dees, Larry 808
DeFalco, Ciro M. 596
DeFeciani, Patrick 204
Defeis, Nicholas 699
DeFranco, James (Jim) 271
DeFranco, Jim 272
DeFreese, Susan 454
DeFreitas, Shannie 109
DeGiorgio, Kenneth D. 339
Degnon, Laura 530
Degregorio, Nick 294
DeGregorio, Ronald J. (Ron) 314
DeGuise, Sheila 905
Deherrera, Brandy 941
Dehio, Peter 311
Deily, Karl R. 757
Deis, Ron 462
Deisinger, Jennifer 101
Deitch, Sally 818
Dejohn, Rory C 856
Dejong, Frank 299
Dejonge, Michelle 484
Dejurnett, Mikki 513
Dekay, Sam 105
Dekeyser, Jill 706
Dekker, Karen 52
Dekker, Hans 365
Dekker, Stuart 666
Delacruz, Cedric 413
Delagi, R. Gregory (Greg) 825
Delaney, Scott 94
DeLaney, Brad 197
Delaney, Chris 397
Delaney, Stephen 449
Delaney, Kristen 457
Delaney, Donald 484
Delaney, Thomas A. (Tom) 606
Delaney, Peter H 715
DeLaney, William J. (Bill) 808
Delassio, Harry 700
Delatorre, Guillermo 935
DeLaus, David 910
DeLawder, C. Daniel (Dan) 653
Delawder, Bruce 834
DelBene, Kurt 575
Deldicque, Greg 879
Delduchetto, Thomas 598
Delfino, Lisandro 45
Delgadillo, Dan 814
Delgado, Joaquin 2
Delgado, Jorge 254
DELGENIO, JULIE 248
Delgrosso, Danielle 604
Delie, Vincent J. (Vince) 367
Delimitros, Nicole 530
Delio, Anthony P. (Tony) 462
Delisio, Anthony 425
Delisser, Denise 487
Delker, Jed 361
Dell, Joseph E. 211
Dellacroce, Peter 752
Dellaglio, Vincent 131
Dellaquila, Frank J. 299
Dellisanti, Suzana 748

Dellosa, Vince 713
Dell'Osso, Domenic J. (Nick) 189
Delmedico, Ann 700
DeLoach, Thomas C. 78
DeLoach, Harris E. 775
Deloach, Scott 929
DeLoache, Zach 736
DeLongchamps, Peter C. 401
Delorenz, Don 935
DeLorenzo, Michael 53
Delorenzo, Rhonda 366
Delorenzo, Terry 477
Delorimier, John 446
Delozier, John 182
Delp, Robert D. (Rob) 940
Delph, Chuck 94
Delph, Rob 824
DeLuca, Richard R. 566
DeLuca, Peter 811
Delucia, Cathy 128
DeLuise, James 204
Delvalle, Mauricio 153
Delvecchio, Michael 587
Delwiche, William 735
Delzotto, Paul 77
DeMarco, David S. (Dave) 77
DeMaria, Jacqueline M. 917
Demarko, Rita 598
DeMarse, Fred 191
Demartino, Rich 768
Demas, Sandra 72
Demasi, Deena 896
Demastus, Jerry 279
DeMatteo, Daniel A. 379
Demchak, William S. (Bill) 680
Demchak, Robert 770
Demel, Sohan 643
Dement, Jason 337
Demeter, Chris 109
Demetriou, Steven J. 481
Demita, Tab 336
Demmerle, Stefan 140
Demmings, Keith W. 82
Demont, Adam 80
Demoulias, George 751
Dempsey, Joan A. 139
Dempsey, Jerry 241
Dempsey, Pam 284
Dempster, William 549
Demski, Renee 483
Demuro, Gerard 380
Denaro, Dona 345
Denault, Leo P. 304
Denault, Jeff 570
Denby, Kristy 224
Denehy, William 450
Dengler, Patrick 576
Denholm, David J. 493
DeNinno, Michael 395
DeNinno, Garrett 715
Denis, Keri 665
Denison, Kurtis 664
Denk, Peter 733
Denker, Claude H. (Bud) 663
Denker, Bud 663
Dennedy, Michelle 200
Dennehy, Stacey 889
Dennemann, Kelly 342
Denney, Craig 668
Dennis, Bob 53
Dennis, Bruce 135
Dennis, Rhonda 159
Dennis, Brian 503
Dennis, Staci 537
Dennis, David 805
DeNonno, Jeremiah 395
Denoya, Dave 891
Denoyel, Eric 382
Densford, Willia 446
Denson, Gerald 294
Dent, John 304
Dent, Joe 385
Denton, David M. (Dave) 252
Denult, Leo 304
Depalma, Elisa 158
DePaolo, Joseph J. 767
dePasquale, Caterina 366

DePell, Fred (Fred) 624
DePeters, Jack 910
Depeters, John A 910
Depinho, David 838
DePinto, Joseph I. 160
Depre, Christopher 57
Deprey, Matthew 270
Deputy, Christine F. 617
Derdzinski, James 735
Derick, Cynthia 273
DeRito, John A. 207
Derizans, Richard 555
Dermanuelian, Nareg 204
Dermody, Michael 106
DeRosa, Mike 367
Derpinghaus, Patrick J. 80
Derrien, Olivier 748
DeRue, Scott 720
Dervishi, Keti 767
Desai, Khyati 201
Desai, Bobby 378
Desai, Swetal 425
Desai, Varun 576
Desalvo, Pete 135
Desalvo, Tom 759
DeSanctis, Anthony 103
DeSantis, Michael 395
Desantis, Paul 517
Desantis, Mark 671
Desantis, Bill 765
Desautels, Mark 117
Descheneaux, Michael R. (Mike) 803
Deserio, Stacy 175
Deshon, Michelle 498
Deshpande, Sameer 71
DeSilva, Joe 87
Desire, Jean-Luc 820
Desmarais, Brian 249
Desmarais, Matthew 328
Desmond, Marcia 168
Desmond, Jim 337
Desmond, James 725
Desoer, Barbara J. 203
Desorbo, Louis 176
DeSousa, Dennis E. 399
Desousa, Jill 664
Despain, Michael 261
Despeaux, Kimberly 304
DeSpirt, Christa 539
Dessen, Flo 713
Destafney, George 632
DeStefano, Joseph (Joe) 393
DeStefano, Lisa 431
Detampel, Donald F. (Don) 186
Dettmar, Jackie 580
Detwiler, Kimberly 884
Deuel, Jeffrey J. (Jeff) 421
Deuprey, Charleen 103
Deutsch, William J. 108
Deutsch, Clayton G. (Clay) 141
Deutsch, Emilie 171
Deutsch, Donald 643
Deutschendorf, Alan 161
Deutscher, Dwayne 15
Devane, Anthony 45
Devaney, James 892
Devarajulu, Krishna 888
DeVard, Jerri L. 633
Devault, Ray 881
Devault, David V. 905
Develasco, Janice 251
Develder, Lucas 201
Devenuti, Richard R 576
Devereaux, Patrick 487
Devienne, Frederic 20
Devine, Jeff 199
Devine, Marty 259
Devine, Michael P. 268
Devine, Tod 273
Devine, Dan 423
Devine, Dennis A. 497
Devine, William 849
DeVito, Gio 597
DeVizio, William (Bill) 219
Devlin, Jason 131
Devlin, Caroline 620
Devoe, Clint 159

DeVos, Doug 35
Devos, Jack 934
Devoy, Mike 635
Devries, Douglas 261
Devries, Doug 261
Dewan, Rohit 640
Dewey, Brooke 486
Dewey, Barbara I. 831
Dewey, Duane A. 855
Dewey, Susan F. 898
Dewhurst, Kim 32
Dewhurst, Moray F. 363
DeWilde, Brandy 224
Dewit, Erik 242
Dewitt, H 189
DeWitt, Brian 707
Dexter, Debbie 18
Dexter, Elizabeth 932
Dhamotharan, Siva 15
Dhandapani, Chandra 170
Dhanens, Steve 707
Dhillon, Janet L. 151
Dhiman, Sushil 750
Dhingra, Ajay 934
Dial, Karla 769
Diallo, Samba 919
Diamond, Patrick 679
Diamond, Rachael 831
Diamond, Sherrie 910
Diana, Denise 413
Dias, Jose 672
Diaz, Maria 18
Diaz, Fernando 96
Diaz, Guillermo 199
Diaz, Marcos 204
Diaz, Amy J 214
Diaz, Carlos 385
Diaz, Pedro 454
Diaz, Amaris 454
Diaz, Michael 487
Diaz, Raymond 571
Diaz, Francisco 585
Diaz, Octavio J. (Tavi) 818
Diaz, Miguel 872
Diaz-Gonzalez, Marcos 15
Dibble, David E. 34
Dibenedetto, Tony 891
DiBianca, Suzanne 748
DiCarlo, Debra 437
Dice, Ken 615
Dicello, Mark 880
Dicerchio, Richard 241
DiChiaro, Steven J. (Steve) 844
DiCicco, Aimee 330
Dick, Ashley 350
Dickamore, Tony 502
Dickel, Ronald 465
Dickens-hunter, Deborah 760
Dickenson, Bill 378
Dickerman, Jonathan 42
Dickerman, Sam 274
Dickerson, Gary E. 71
Dickerson, Therese M 103
Dickey, Bill 286
Dickie, James 53
Dickinson, Laurie 497
Dickinson, Paul 516
Dickinson, Vaughn 668
Dickinson, Marty J. 865
Dickman, Randy 550
Dicks, Cindy 691
Dickseski, Jerri Fuller 451
Dickson, David 32
Dickson, James 99
Dickson, Tom 111
Dickson, Joe 390
Dickson, Jenny 550
Dickson, Richard 557
Dicosola, Robert 637
Dicus, John B. 159
Didascalou, Dirk 37
Didion, Erin 266
Didomizio, Michael 700
Dieckhoner, Craig 84
Diedrich, Robert 356
Diefenderfer, William M. 595
Diefenthaler, Aaron P. 732

Diehl, William 677
Diehl, Kristine 919
Diehl-boyle, Constance 84
Diemer, Brent 185
Diemer, John W 735
Diercks, Dwight 627
Dieringer, Brian 447
Dieter, Dawn 558
Dietrich, Martin A. 598
Dietrich, Peter T. 777
Dietrich, Tyler 804
Dietz, Chris 497
Dietz, William H 715
Diez, John J. 743
Difinizio, Antoinette 604
DiFranco, Dimitra 604
DiGeronimo, Rich 186
DiGrande, Sebastian 830
Digregorio, Kelly 811
Dikovics, Stephanie 511
Dilger, Jason 457
Dill, Kevin 15
Dill, David M. 526
Dill, Robert C. 768
Dillahunt, Sandra 287
Dillard, James E. (Jim) 36
Dillard, Maria 84
Dillard, Mike 267
Dillard, Alex 267
Dillard, William (Bill) 267
Diller, Barry 317
Dillon, Michael A. (Mike) 11
Dillon, Bob 114
Dillon, Carl 117
Dillon, Julie 219
Dillon, Mary N. 862
Dillon, Tom 867
Dillon-Falk, Shawn 213
DiLorenzo, Dennis 606
DiMartino, Chris 413
Dimino, Sal 121
Dimon, James (Jamie) 488
Dimuro, Mark 895
Dinda, Kelly 102
DiNello, Alessandro P. 362
Dines, Dauna 99
Dinger, Stephanie 866
Dingess, Cheryl 888
Dingman, Tim 832
Dingus, Roger 875
Dinh, Trang 45
Dinh, Theresa 587
Diniaco, Pete 18
Dinicola, Natalie 585
Dinius, Kent 213
Dinnage, Susanna 270
Dinnigan, Terry 849
Dinshaw, Behram M. 849
Dinsmoor, Ron 942
Dinsmore, Walter 133
Dinwiddie, Lucy 232
Dion, Ellen 596
Dionisio, Mike 263
Diorio, Philip 224
DiPaola, Steve 890
Dipetrio, Kenneth 129
DiPietro, Kenneth A. (Ken) 129
Dippold, Matthew 79
Dippolito, Tom 268
DiPresso, Raymond 665
Diprofio, Karen 45
Dircks, Bill 101
Dirks, Douglas D. 301
Dirocco, Richard 836
DiRomualdo, Robert F. 862
Dirrim, Tim 450
DiRusso, Lonny R. 742
Disalvatore, William 604
Disanti, Joseph 109
DiSanto, Edmund (Ed) 51
Disanto, Salvatore 713
DiSanza, Susan 449
Dishman, William M. 796
DiSilvestro, Anthony P. 156
DiSilvestro, Carlo 856
Dismukes, Teresa 314
Dissing, Steven 563

Dissinger, Debra E. 667
Distefano, Michael 133
DiStefano, Jim 538
DiStefano, Mike 677
Distelbrink, Ivo M. 348
DiTirro, Frank 18
Ditmars, John 355
Dittgen, Juergen 715
DiVittorio, Thomas (Tom) 386
Divver, James J Divver James J 942
Dix, Dennis 301
Dixon, Lee 12
Dixon, Gordon 49
Dixon, Gregory 211
Dixon, Kim 330
Dixon, T 528
Dixon, Liz 839
DIXON, RONNEY 869
Dixon, Kenneth (Ken) 893
Dixon, Dan 941
Djukic, Dusko 497
Djuric, Steven 6
Dlouhy, Thomas 724
Dmowski, George 754
Do, Beth 295
Doan, Dan L. 635
Dobbe, Steven 49
Dobbert, Michele M 672
Dobbins, R. Helm 48
Dobbins, Kedrick 107
Dobbins, Donald 454
Dobbins, John 926
Dobbs, Johnnie 904
Dobias, Debbie 146
Dobler, Stephen 502
Dobranski, Edward J. 358
Dobre, Mircea 735
Dobrec, Lee 218
Dobrinski, Everett M. 214
Dobzyn, Andrew 80
Dochelli, Harry A. 311
Dockendorff, Charles 142
Dockerty, Karen 176
Dockett, Bryan 533
Docter, Judith M. 80
Docter, Judy 80
Dodd, Alida 176
Dodd, Lynn 454
Dodds, Jeffrey 834
Doddy, John 881
Dodeja, Prakash 643
Dodenhoff, Steven W. 463
Dodge, R. Stanton 272
Dodge, Paul 519
Dodge, Geoffrey A 746
Dodge, Clarence 914
Dodson, LaRae 182
Dodson, Jerry 200
Dodson, Marti 391
Dodson, Glen 739
Doebele, Luke 32
Doedens, Douglas 643
Doering, Karen 146
Doessel, Johnathan 298
Doggett, Richard 808
Doheny, Edward L. (Ted) 757
Doherty, William J. 59
Doherty, Scott 88
Doherty, Michael 248
Doherty, Jon 596
Doherty, Catherine T. 709
Dolan, Michael 320
Dolan, Paula D. 338
Dolan, Joseph P 511
Dolan, Shannon 809
Dolan, Terrance R. (Terry) 888
Dolanski, Ed 135
Dolat, Mark 840
Dolbec, Brad 158
Dolce, Jeff 425
Dolfin, John 45
Dolinski, Maria 106
Dolly, Lisa 105
Dolph, Stephen J 72
Dolsten, Mikael 671
Domas, Ronald D 370

Dombowsky, Shawn 214
Dome, Nancy 928
Domenick, Joseph 839
Domick, Donna 454
Dominach, Sandy 237
Dominguez, Letty 246
Dominguez, Joseph 314
Dominiak, Christophe 254
Dominioni, Henry 413
Don, David 222
Donaghy, Bruce 587
Donahoe, John 293
Donahue, Laura 162
Donahue, Brian D. 228
Donahue, Timothy J. 244
Donahue, Patrick 256
Donahue, Hugh O 375
Donahue, Paul D. 387
Donahue, Joseph 549
Donahue, Amie 570
Donahue, Robert 664
Donahue, Chris 699
Donahue, John 907
Donald, Heald 484
Donaldson, Melinda 135
Donaldson, Michael P. 308
Donaldson, Pamela 717
Donaldson, Michelle 912
Donarski, Dave 888
Donas, Paul 53
Donatelli, David A. (Dave) 642
Donato, Thomas 738
Dondanville, Ted J. 250
Donegan, Tom 715
Donham, Julie 390
Donica, Kim 570
Donigian, John 752
Donlon, Martin 115
Donne, France 233
Donnellan, James 570
Donnelly, Christopher 60
Donnelly, C J 88
Donnelly, Michael J. (Mike) 506
Donnelly, Kevin 553
Donnelly, Richard M. 645
Donnelly, Patrick L. 771
Donnelly, Scott C. 826
Donnelly, Tim 936
Donner, Fred R. 849
Donofrio, Paul M. 101
Donoghue, Tom 580
Donoho, Wendy 84
Donohue, Sarah 84
Donohue, Martin 191
Donohue, Bill 470
Donohue, Jessica 791
Donovan, Will 3
Donovan, John M. 84
Donovan, Patrick 190
Donovan, Elizabeth 204
Donovan, Jim 457
Donovan, Gerald 487
Donovan, Michael 517
Doolan, Elizabeth A 108
Doolan, Pat 320
Dooley, Wendy 131
Dooren, Doug 849
Doornink, Barbara 517
Doot, Martin 13
Doppstadt, Eric 829
Doran, Tim 928
Dorch, A. Verona 659
Doren, Stacy 521
Doren, Stacy 523
Doren, Cheryl Van 895
Dorer, Benno 208
Dorico, Gino 241
Dority, Matt 226
Dorman, David W. (Dave) 253
Dorminey, O. Leonard (Len) 726
Dorn, Michael 888
Dornbirer, Dave 214
Dorne, Eric A. 874
Dorph, Martin S. 606
Dorr, Kent 185
Dorris, James 876
Dorsey, Josh 804

Dorsey, Vernita 931
Dorward-King, Elaine 609
Dosch, Theodore A. (Ted) 64
Dosch, Terri L 320
Dosch, Ted A 923
Doscher, John 700
Doshi, Gunjan 103
Doshi, Krupali 665
Dosi, Abhishek 802
Doss, Gary 855
Dost, Nancy 454
Dostal, Drew 112
Doti, Michael 767
Doto, Michael 840
Dotson, Judith H. (Judi) 139
Dotson, Judy 139
Dotto, John 45
Doty, Michael 750
Doucet, Matthew 928
Doucette, Lindsy 332
Doud, Art 379
Douds, Haley 159
Dougherty, Edward 105
Dougherty, Maureen 135
Dougherty, Brian 300
Dougherty, Michael 437
Dougherty, Kevin 506
Dougherty, Michael D. 681
Doughty, Thomas 699
Douglas, Dianne 101
Douglas, Jana 133
Douglas, J. Alexander M. (Sandy) 216
Douglas, Sean 452
Douglas, William A 507
Douglas, John 678
Douglas, Laurie Z. 702
Douglas, Laurie Z. 703
Douglas, Craig 786
Douglas, Keith 834
Douglass, Erin 3
Douma, Doede 750
Doumas, Michael 936
Doupe, Tom 487
Dourdis, John 422
Dourlias, George 935
Dours, Gene 195
Dovdavany, Ruth 672
Dovey, Stephen 530
Dow, Sandy 332
Dow, Charle 446
Dowd, James 250
Dowd, Michael 528
Dowdell, Joanne 610
Dowdell, Robert (Bob) 697
Dowden, Patrick 715
Dowdle, Jeffrey A. (Jeff) 715
Dowell, Tom 403
Dowell, Terri L 888
Dowler, Lynette 284
Downey, Frank 735
Downie, Mark 300
Downie, Bryan 814
Downing, Troy 12
Downing, Forrest 47
Downing, Randy 282
Downing, Marjorie 664
Downing, Ryan 715
Downs, Christopher Y. (Chris) 149
Downs, Troy 162
Downs, Ryan 293
Downs, Jeff 637
Downs, Mike 808
Doxey, William 178
Doxzon, Emily 217
Doyal, Brian S. 735
Doyle, Steve 18
Doyle, Fred 96
Doyle, Scott E. 177
Doyle, Donald 196
Doyle, Dorothy 413
Doyle, John Q. 550
Doyle, John 550
Doyle, Timothy 660
Doyle, Joseph 814
Dozier, C. Michael 650
Draa, Mark 773
Drachenberg, Ray 585

Draganza, Ernest J. 745
Drago, John P. 747
Drago, Barbara 814
Drahnak, Steve 745
Drake, Jim 101
Drake, Shelley 538
Drake, George 641
Drapac, Tom 12
Drapeau, Teri 45
Draper, David 200
Draper, Suzie 467
Draper, Bill 838
Draper, Scott 904
Draughn, James B. (Jim) 230
Draughon, Clarence 735
Draut, Eric 495
Dravenstott, Rob 272
Dravenstott, John 497
Dray, Jim 14
Drayer, Keith 752
Dreelin, Angela 117
Dreier, Gregory 246
Dressel, Dennis C 699
Dressen, Jessi 624
Drevets, Wayne 484
Drew, Brian 72
Drew, John 494
Drewel, Michael 237
Drews, Thomas 923
Drexel, William Bill 84
Dreyer, Ed 135
Dreyer, Andr 723
Dreyer, Michael L. 803
Dreyer, Anna 810
Driessen, Jack 3
Driggers, Timothy K. 308
Driggs, Terry 732
Driml, Heather 266
Driscoll, Tony 84
Driscoll, Dan 337
Driscoll, Cameron 487
Driscoll, Jennifer 620
Driscoll, Donald 732
Droal, Luc 489
Drobins, Jeff 667
Droge, Connie 276
Drop, Jeffrey S. 168
Drouin, Joseph L. 704
Drummey, George 840
Drummond, Bryan 6
Drummond, Brad C. 72
Drummond, Jim 406
Drummond, Kirk 807
Drury, Scott D. 762
Druzbik, James R. 402
Dryden, Kristi 84
Dryden, Gregory 337
Dryden, Del 537
Dryden, Jennifer 620
Duane, Mandy 189
Duane, Francis K. (Ken) 705
Duane, Ken 705
Duarte, Gianni 267
Duato, Joaquin 484
Duban, Heike 168
Dubauskas, Keith 715
Dubay, Lynda 548
Dubbins, Robert 170
Dube, Sandeep 262
Duberstein, Kenneth 322
Dubin, Michael 555
Dubin, Christine 770
Dubinsky, Andrew 395
Dubner, A 3
Dubois, Carey J. 227
Dubois, Heather 294
DuBord, Christine 881
Dubord, Cris 881
DuBose, Michael 398
Dubuc, Manuel P ©rez 16
Dubuisson, Betty 570
Dubuque, Bethany 664
Dub ©, Richard W. (Dick) 635
Duca, Michael A. 154
Ducayet, Julia 881
Ducey, Deon 677
DuCharme, L. D. 320

Duchnowski, Dan 335
Duchow, Tim 735
Duck, Barbara F. 116
Ducker, Michael L. 330
Duckett, W. David (Dave) 679
Duckworth, David 530
Duckworth, Kristopher 860
Ducommun, David 332
Dudick, Dave 383
Dudkin, Gregory N. 686
Dudleson, Jaime 117
Dudley, Paul 191
Dudley, Thomas 258
Dudley, Michael M. 762
Dudley, Carolyn 800
Dudonis, Chris 39
Due, Steve 107
Duerkop, Scott 487
Duerksen, Craig 226
Duerksen, John 884
Dueser, F. Scott 350
Duevel, James 933
Dufala, George D. (Chip) 495
Duff, Scott K. 593
Duffany, Dennis 382
Duffell, Brian 456
Duffie, Kent 548
Duffin, N. W. 320
Duffle, Denise 99
Duffus, Robert 665
Duffy, Karen 31
Duffy, Steve 72
Duffy, Jack 84
Duffy, James J. (Jim) 201
Duffy, Brian 222
Duffy, Mark 232
Duffy, Robert L. 411
Duffy, Julie 415
Duffy, Liam 551
Duffy, Patrick 834
Duffy, Steve 834
Dufour, Gregory A. (Greg) 155
Duf ©tel, C ©line 809
Dugan, Gregory A. 912
Dugar, Pankaj 442
Dugarte, Colleen 497
Dugas, Tiffany 754
Dugenske, John 31
Duijnhoven, Henk Van 256
Duke, Timothy R. (Tim) 794
Duke, Mike 903
Dukeman, Van A. 342
Dukes, Trice 335
Dull, Ken 279
Dull, Stephen F 895
Dullnig, Tammy 890
Dumais, Michael R. (Mike) 879
Dumas, Jason 332
Dumas, Ellie 620
Dumesich, Gordon 219
Dumont, Patrick 513
Dumont, Serge 639
Dumonteil, Jacques 2
Dunaway, William J. (Bill) 474
Dunaway, Barry C. 773
Dunbar, Timothy M. (Tim) 691
Dunbar, Roger F. 804
Duncan, Christopher 262
Duncan, George L. 305
Duncan, James H 332
Duncan, Ashley 337
Duncan, Aaron 557
Duncan, Philip J 693
Duncan, Bryan D. 767
Dundrea, Matthew W 68
Dunfield, Rodger 750
Dunham, Steve 124
Dunham, Jan 863
Dunigan, Debra 146
Dunigan-wernke, Jennifer 337
Duning, Ken 580
Dunk, Paul 754
Dunlap, James E. (Jim) 449
Dunlap, Michael S. (Mike) 601
Dunleavy, Michael F 244
Dunlop, Cindy 892
Dunn, Ann 54

Dunn, Gary S. 97
Dunn, David 158
Dunn, Mary 170
Dunn, Stacey A 178
Dunn, Kenneth 181
Dunn, Allison 214
Dunn, Dan 224
Dunn, Kenneth E. 308
Dunn, Jordan 339
Dunn, Marc 378
Dunn, Cind M 446
Dunn, James W. 509
Dunn, Russell 511
Dunn, Michael G. 651
Dunn, Lenore 705
Dunn, Martin 754
Dunn, Cheryl 763
Dunn, Chris 769
Dunn, Bradford 840
Dunn, Sheila 875
Dunn, Mike 896
Dunn, David 912
Dunn, Sean 927
Dunnam, Debbie 576
Dunne, Viola 131
Dunne, Brian 162
Dunne, Melanie 551
Dunne, Jessica 557
Dunne, Jim 717
Dunne, Ronan 893
Dunnigan, Lauren 60
Dunning, Joe 240
Dunsford, Robert 512
Dunson, Tom 355
Dunton, James 715
Duong, Michael 35
Duong, Julie 97
Duong, Melissa 195
Duong, John 456
Duos, Jenny 536
Dupler, Scott 449
Duprat, Pierre-Christophe 74
Dupre, Michele 893
Dupree, David 195
Dupree, Chuck 261
Duprey, David E. 223
Duprez, Debra 839
Dupuis, Mike 705
Duquette, Carol 910
Dur, Philip 587
Duran, George 533
Durand, Bob 81
Durand, Josh 530
Durant, Luke 628
Durante, Joe 786
Durbin, Sean 687
Durbin, Patrick M. 836
Durburg, Jack 170
Durchschlag, Erich 57
Durfey, Gary 903
Durham, George 135
Durham, Bill 818
Durkee, Matthew K. 598
Durkee, Jeff 792
Durkin, Dennis 10
Durkin, James W. (Jim) 378
Durmus, Levent 754
Durn, Daniel (Dan) 71
Durocher, Philip 219
Durocher, Stephen 700
Durrans, Jan 136
Dusek, Rick 202
Dusil, Jim 727
Duss, Julianne 72
Dust, Stacey 507
Dutertre, Jey 536
Dutkowsky, Robert M. 816
Dutta, Rahul 45
Dutton, Rob 263
Duvall, Gary 378
Duvvur, Amarendra 6
Duym, Tom 88
Dvorak, John 928
Dvorchak, Steve 633
Dwarka, Swaran 266
Dwight, Craig M. 436
Dworkin, Aaron 720

Dwyer, Susannah 146
Dwyer, Tim 395
Dwyer, Veronica 470
Dwyer, Patrick 555
Dwyer, James E. (Jim) 683
Dwyer, Shannon 785
Dwyer, Maria F. 791
Dwyer, Dan 935
Dyckes, Jason 102
Dye, Robert J 68
Dye, Jere 502
Dye, John R. 918
Dyer, Jeremy 88
Dyer, Jay 161
Dyer, Barry 643
Dyer, Robin 799
Dyer, Chris 809
Dyhrberg, Stephanie 886
Dyk, Nick Van 273
Dyke, Concetta Van 121
Dyke, Frank J. (Jeff) 774
Dykhouse, Richard R. 186
Dykstra, Scott 313
Dykstra, David A. 927
Dymond, Sandy 831
Dyslin, Bradley E. 19
Dzaluk, Joseph 470
Dzanis, Marie 620
Dziadzio, Richard S. 82
Dzielak, Robert 316
D'Agostino, John 715
D'Alessandro, Carl 411
D'Alimonte, Christa A. 896
D'Amato, Tim 80
D'Ambrose, Michael 74
D'Ambrosio, Ralph G. 509
D'Amelio, Frank A. 671
D'Amore, Robert R. (Bob) 664
D'Amore, Diana 699
D'Amore, Terry 863
D'andrea, Elena 555
D'Appolonia, Kathleen 680
d'Archirafi, Francesco Vanni 203
D'Arcy, John 942
D'Arezzo, Gloria 935
D'Arrigo, Daniel J. 572
D'Auria, Jay 202
D'Avanza, Francis 563
D'Elia, Robyn 121
D'Lugos, Steve 84
D'Ouville, Paul 620
D'Souza, Francisco 218

E

Eagle, A Rae 626
Eagles, Michael 222
Eagleson, Delores 342
Ealet, Isabelle 395
Eames, Tristyn 754
Earhart, Cynthia C. (Cindy) 618
Earley, Randy 102
Earley, Jean McNicholas 106
Earley, Anthony F. 283
Earley, Steve 941
Early, Betsy 762
Early, Debra 935
Earnheart, Aubrey 722
Earp, Sandra 80
Earp, Ty 80
Easley, Ed 518
Easley, Joe 770
Eason, J. Cliff 724
Easterbrook, Stephen J. (Steve) 562
Easterling, Lynn 199
Easterling, William E. 831
Easterly, Richard 189
Eastham, Mark 563
Eastin, David 613
Eastman, Laura 335
Eastman, Stephen L. 681
Eastwood, Kathy 425
Eater, Douglas 101
Eaton, Mary Jo 170
Eaton, Roger G. 939
Eatroff, Bob 222

Eaves, Davelyn 18
Eaves, Jennifer 332
Ebanks, Leroy 615
Ebbert, Ward 799
Ebbs, William 451
Eberhard, Michael 88
Eberhard, Ed 195
Eberhardt, Jack 613
Eberhart, Ross 748
Eberly, Craig 668
Ebermann, Wolfgang 463
Eberts, F. Samuel 510
Eberwein, Elise R. 41
Ebling, Rosa 735
Ebner, R. M. 320
Ebrahim, Linda 39
Eccher, James L. 637
Eccles, Colin D. 908
Eccleshare, C. William 456
Echaniz, Matthew 530
Echelson, Steven 487
Echols, Kendall 563
Eck, Robert J. (Bob) 64
Eckardt, David 328
Eckart, Cat 242
Eckel, Scott 754
Ecker, Kraig 930
Eckerle, Wayne 248
Eckert, David 121
Eckert, Jan 570
Eckhardt, Laura 247
Eckhart, Bradley 713
Eckler, Tanner 99
Eckman, Alan R 14
Eddens, Peggy H. 931
Eddington, Rick 620
Eddleblute, Heath 729
Eddy, Brenda 332
Eddy, Helen 453
Ede, Michael van 559
Edeker, Randy 453
Edel, Karsten 140
Edel, John 201
Edelman, Deane 139
Edelson, Claude 328
Edelson, David B. 536
Edens, Wesley R. (Wes) 640
Eder, Noelle 159
Eder, Ellen 643
Ederington, Benjamin 920
Edge, Judy 330
Edgehill, Beverly 840
Edgerton, Mark 484
Edgett, Paul W. 168
Edginton, Emilee 185
Edgmond, Wanda 226
Edicola, Mike 115
Edlund, Monte G. 452
Edmonds, Franklin 935
Edmondson, Emanuel 180
Edmunds, Coleman 89
Edmundson, Shawna 882
Edney, Jerry 81
Edridge, Thomas 550
Edson, David 131
Edwards, Jon S. 54
Edwards, Nate 85
Edwards, Jeff 93
Edwards, Rob 101
Edwards, Peter G. 173
Edwards, Gary 195
Edwards, Patricia L. 308
Edwards, Jennifer 332
Edwards, Rick 386
Edwards, Thomas H. 436
Edwards, Dougla 446
Edwards, Bill 454
Edwards, Wesley 487
Edwards, Dennis 548
Edwards, Desrene 550
Edwards, Zalise 563
Edwards, Lori 580
Edwards, Trevor A. 615
Edwards, Darren 663
Edwards, David 677
Edwards, Lisa 748
Edwards, Teresa L. (Terrie) 762

Edwards, Robert 827
Edwards, Robert A. (Rob) 869
Edwards, Chad 876
Edwards, Tim 927
Edwin, Prince 941
Efendi, Bernard 573
Effendi, Beverly 45
Effting, Diane 667
Efird, Derek 117
Efird, Nina 335
Efraty, Tamir 804
Egan, Lornax 465
Egan, Anne 587
Egan, William 620
Egan, James 754
Egan, Beth 764
Egan, Tom 923
Eggar, Justin 32
Eggemeyer, John M. 653
Eggers, Drew 624
Eggers, Bill 746
Eggert, Mark 176
Eggli, Doug 422
Egl, Ed 907
Eglen, Richard 240
Eglinton, Mia 486
Egloff, Tim 337
Egrican, Korkud 185
Eguiluz, Mario 323
Ehele, Stephen 52
Ehlers, Michael D. (Mike) 129
Ehret, Carmela 106
Ehret, Michael 484
Ehrhardt, Michael 60
Ehrlich, Derinda 94
Ehrlich, Hartmut 115
Ehrlich, Whitney 131
Ehst, Richard A. 249
Eibling, David 582
Eichenberger, Tom 620
Eichenberger, Matt 707
Eichenhorn, Josh 449
Eichorn, Mark 587
Eickenhorst, Thorsten 129
Eide, Kirk 395
Eidenberg, Jude 570
Eidson, Dennis 781
Eijsink, Jeroen 736
Eikenberg, Charles D. 515
Einstein, Seth 117
Einstein, Claude 863
Eippert, Debbie 246
Eisbart, Benjamin 794
Eisen, Robert 358
Eisenbarth, Jeff 93
Eisenbeis, Tara 52
Eisenberg, Paul R. 57
Eisenberg, Warren 121
Eisenberg, Sam 131
Eisenberg, Steven D. 295
Eisenberg, Stacey 457
Eisenberg, Glenn A. 510
Eisenhardt, Michael 84
Eisenhardt, Craig 487
Eisenstot, Bill 928
Eisler, Barry 87
Eismamn, Charles 647
Eisman, Robert B. 39
Eisner, Paul 411
Eitrheim, Paal 793
Ekarius, Michele 101
Ekici, Tuncay 672
Ekman, Tobias 533
Ekvall, Susan 176
Elad, Ronen 316
Elborne, Cy 752
Elcan, Clint 447
Elder, Richard M. 341
Elder, Kenneth 530
Eldon, Jack 273
Eldridge, Greg 185
Elefther, George 121
Elegant, Victoria 115
Eleser, Karen 158
Elgar, Tal 465
Elgart, Natalie 243
Elghanayan, Shahram 158

Elgohary, Nivin 214
Elhaj, Sam 558
Elia, Lois 13
Eliecagary, Aline 754
Eline, William G. (Bill) 654
Eling, Greg 198
Elisseou, Evan 204
Elizondo, Patricia 934
Elkeles, Tamar 707
Elkin, Ilyas 628
Elkind, Albert 395
Elkins, Tom 33
Ellard, Craig 157
Ellen, Martin M. (Marty) 282
Ellenbecker, Brian 735
Ellenbogen, Marc 34
Eller, Charissa 892
Ellinghausen, James R. (Jim) 704
Ellingsen, Catharine D. 729
Ellington, Kim A 355
Ellington, Debbie 472
Elliot, Douglas G. (Doug) 413
Elliott, Jeff 117
Elliott, Jeff 276
Elliott, Robin N. 342
Elliott, Mike 483
Elliott, Gerri 490
Elliott, Joseph C. 631
Elliott, Tommy 635
Elliott, Alice 722
Ellis, Mike 57
Ellis, Chris 139
Ellis, Brian 161
Ellis, Harold 199
Ellis, Brian 256
Ellis, Brain 256
Ellis, Alisa 269
Ellis, Chester 487
Ellis, Jeff 573
Ellis, Gary 671
Ellis, Andrew 738
Ellis, Charles 748
Ellis, Todd 749
Ellis, Jacque 770
Ellis, Raquel 792
Ellis, Matthew D. (Matt) 893
Ellison, P K 207
Ellison, Brian 476
Ellison, Aaron 486
Ellison, Edward 491
Ellison, Seth M. 521
Ellison, Seth M. 523
Ellison, Lawrence J. (Larry) 642
Ellison, Marvin R. 661
Ellison, Michael 716
Ells, Debbie 241
Ells, Tom 484
Ellspermann, Caroline J. 635
Ellspermann, Kenneth J. 635
Ellwood, Michelle 162
Elmer, Mitchell 808
Elming, Gregory B. (Greg) 691
Elmore, Steven 6
Elmore, John C. 227
Elmore, Joshua 596
Elmore, John R. 888
Elmquist, David 488
Elnashai, Amr S. 831
Elorza, Eba 749
Elser, Jeffrey 360
Elser, Chrisanna 420
ELsheikh, Ahmed 668
Elsheikh, Mohamed 901
Elsner, Deanie 493
Elwell, William 413
Elwood, Rob 691
Elwyn, Tashtego S. (Tash) 715
Ely, Timothy 587
Elzie, Matt 574
Embree, Tracy A. 248
Emel, Lisa 240
Emel, Aaron 863
Emelonye, Ken 901
Emerick, Mark 170
Emerson, Frances 261
Emerson, Michael 497
Emerson, David 558

Emery, Angela 274
Emery, Jean 390
Emery, John 643
Emery, Tom 665
Emery, Bruce 781
Emig, Bart 635
Emison, David 161
Emmerich, I. Robert (Bob) 345
Emmerich, Matthew J. 681
Emmerich, Toby 838
Emmick, Jeff 528
Emmons, Bill 224
Emmons, Kristi 330
Emmons, George 497
Emmons, Brian 841
Emmott, Peter 563
Empson, Douglas 863
Emptage, William 52
Enabnit, Jill 888
Enberg, Steve 737
Ence, Russell 580
Endebrock, Eric 574
Endo, Melanie 133
Endres, Helmut 21
Endres, Jeff 449
Endresen, Heather 97
Endresen, William D. 432
Endsley, Kim 928
Eng, Chester 47
Eng, Sharon 204
Eng, Phil 571
Engblom, Stephen 14
Engeberg, Steven 585
Engebretsen, Travis 757
Engel, Gretchen 185
Engel, Robert B. 214
Engel, Jody 382
Engel, Danielle 533
Engel, Randy 609
Engel, Curt 832
Engel, Albert L. 891
Engel, John J. 914
Engelbrecht, John R. 706
Engelhardt, Mark 437
Engelhart, James 863
Engels, Leeanne 195
Engels, Trevor 849
Engelson, David A. 872
Engen-pazdera, Judy 861
Enghauser, David 558
England, Robert 760
Engle, Bridget E. 105
Engle, Pam 146
Engle, Pamela 146
Engle, Barry 385
Englebright, Jane D. 416
Englehardt, Scott 715
Englert, Mitch 157
Englert, Brian 349
Englesmith, Jaason 185
English, Shaileen 671
English, Steven E. 788
English, Rebecca 810
Engskov, Kris 787
Engstrom, Gary 328
Engstrom, Kathryn 818
Enkler, Mary 60
Ennis, Ed 55
Ennis, Daniel G. 483
Ennis, Robert 610
Enoki, Ryuji 748
Enos, Deborah C. 656
Enser, Bernd 750
Ensign, Michele 573
Enters, Menno 7
Epler, Alan 264
Epperlein, Susann 713
Epperley, Michael 912
Eppers, Joseph 760
Epps, Mike 697
Epps, Barry L. 725
Epps, Jeremy 876
Epstein, Howard 395
Epstein, Lori 570
Epstein, Joel 635
Epstein, Janet 754
Epstein, Louis 847

Erb, William 57
Erb, David B. 454
Ercan, Nihat 486
Erdman, Seth 248
Erdman, David 551
Erdoes, Mary Callahan 488
Eremenko, Paul 879
Ergastolo, John 378
Ergen, Charles W. (Charlie) 271
Erhardt, Kent 214
Erickson, Gerry 3
Erickson, Randall J. 80
Erickson, Theresa 176
Erickson, Jon 193
Erickson, Wendy 246
Erickson, Vicki 301
Erickson, Mona 337
Erickson, Peter C. 383
Erickson, Chris 403
Erickson, Werner 454
Erickson, Karen 563
Erickson, Andrew 792
Ericson, Brady D. 140
Ericson, Brent 402
Ericson, Frances 787
Erika, Hofmann 656
Eriksen, Jan 928
Erikson, Carol 623
Erkan, Hafize Gaye (Gaye) 358
Erkilla, Jack R 784
Erlandson, Daniel 449
Erlinger, James H. (Jim) 478
Erlinger, Joe 562
Ermatinger, William R. (Bill) 451
ERMOLD, SHAWNA 876
Ernest, Scott A. 826
Ernest, Scott 870
Ernst, Joe 131
Ernst, Mark A. 361
Ernst, Barrie W. 872
Erny, Michelle 489
Errichetti, Ann 13
Errigo, Glenn 374
Ersek, Hikmet 918
Ervin, Michael 228
Ervin, Chuck 405
Ervin, Amy 564
Erwin, Tami 893
Erzen, Rob 378
Esamann, Douglas F. (Doug) 285
Esarte, Marty 903
Escalante, Ed 563
Escaravage, Jason 139
Escarraman, Luz 489
Escatel, Martin 808
Eschenburg, Marc 309
Eschmann, Michael 170
Escudero, Lucimar 188
Esham, David 587
Eshelbrenner, Adam 834
Eskow, Alan D. 891
Eslick, Rob 453
Espegren, William 320
Espeland, Curtis E. (Curt) 291
Espeleta, Yvette 566
Espinosa, Jonathan 194
Espinosa, Alejandro 389
Espinoza, Michelle 582
Esplin, J. Kimo 452
Esplin, J Kimo 452
ESPLIN, DEBRA 468
Esposito, Tony 15
Esposito, Donna 18
Esposito, Mike 395
Esposito, Orlando C. 680
Esselman, Tom 52
Essig, Marshall 214
Esson, Timothy W. 870
Estabrook, David 358
Estabrook, James B. 406
Estabrook, Joanne 792
Estampes, Jerome 242
Esteban, Javier 122
Esteban, Carmen 432
Esterman, Gary 474
Estes, Kim 146
Estes, Teri 204

Estes, Barbara 266
Estes, David 665
Estes, Scott 727
Estevez, Christian 665
Esther, Chet 403
Estrada, Roberto 517
Etchison, Ted 191
Etes, Tim 457
Ettinger, Michael 752
Ettore, Joseph 84
Eubank, Eliza 204
Eubank, John 722
Eubanks, Alan 54
Eulau, Robert K. (Bob) 750
Eulich, John S. 306
Eusden, Alan 240
Euteneuer, Joseph J. (Joe) 557
Evangel, Lori M. 389
Evangelista, Paul A. 180
Evangelista, W. Scott 478
Evans, Dave 113
Evans, David 114
Evans, Nicholas 115
Evans, Carol 170
Evans, Dan 224
Evans, Ginny 276
Evans, Rhonda 332
Evans, Morris 332
Evans, Eric 350
Evans, Christopher 386
Evans, Patti 390
Evans, Gerald W. 407
Evans, Godfrey B. 432
Evans, Aicha S. 465
Evans, C Thomas 496
Evans, Katrina M. (Trina) 497
Evans, Regina 502
Evans, Ed 570
Evans, Lance 573
Evans, Terry 618
Evans, Jane 656
Evans, Matthew 666
Evans, Richard D. 667
Evans, Todd 715
Evans, Joseph 715
Evans, Stuart 754
Evans, Joseph W. (Joe) 789
Evans, Maura 792
Evans, Jimmy 796
Evans, J. Eric 818
Evans, V. Lynn 821
Evans, Jean 863
Evans, Malcolm 863
Evans, Jack B. 872
Evanson, Brynn L. 661
Evanson, Jeff K 823
Evelhoch, Jeffrey 566
Evenden, Chris 297
Evenzwig, Michael 570
Everett, Teri 222
Everett, Jim 517
Everett, Nora M. 691
Everett, Bryan 731
Everling, Jeffrey 507
Evernham, Scott J. 635
Evers, Susan 45
Evers, Joseph 374
Eversden, Jeffrey 928
Eversz, Woody 896
Eves, David L. 933
Evola, Peter J 72
Ewald, Thaddeus 248
Ewans, Peter 810
Ewens, Peter A. 810
Ewig, Randall G. 408
Ewing, Clay W. 390
Ewing, Doug 756
Exarhakos, Ted 858
Exnicios, Joseph S. 406
Exposito, Patricia 548
Exton, Martha 176
Ey, Nick 367
Eyken-Sluyters, Eric 748
Eyre, Brik V. 115

F

Fabara, Paul D. 44
Fabe, Guy 654
Faber, Tracy 563
Faber, Clay 762
Faber, Bob 836
Fabian, Francia 131
Fabian, Ken 599
Fabricant, David 797
Fabris, Sabrina 550
Facciobene, Sarah 548
Facer, Burnett 942
Fackler, Jim 483
Factor, Jeff 715
Fadool, Joseph F. 140
Fafoglia, Nick 226
Fagan, Jarrod 45
Fagan, John 715
Fagan, Stacia 722
Fager, Jack 15
Faggard, Steve 191
Fagre, Nathan E. 782
Faherty, Sean 413
Fahey, Paul 620
Fahey-Rush, Colleen 896
Fahrig, Siegmund 550
Fail, Shana 722
Fain, Eric S. 4
FAIN, DANIEL 293
Faintuch, Amir 465
Fair, Jeffrey 30
Fairbairn, Robert W. (Rob) 131
Fairbank, Richard D. (Rich) 158
Fairbank, Randall 929
Fairbanks, Linda 530
Faircloth, Michael E. 407
Faircloth, David 470
Fairhurst, David 562
Fairweather, Daniel 715
Fairweather, George R. 901
Fairweather, Annmarie 932
Faisst, Georg 705
Faith, David M. 832
Faktorow, Rob 170
Fakult, James V. 360
Falaguerra, Robb 131
Falb, Mark C. 420
Falci, Mark 735
Falco, John 698
Falcone, Bryan 243
Falcone, Neil 900
Faleskin, Greg 637
Falini, Michael 185
Falivene, Rob 899
Falk, Thomas J. (Tom) 499
Falk, Christian 519
FALK, KAREN 620
Falk, John 888
Falkenrath, Rand 446
Falkin, Bruce 105
Falkowski, Peter 131
Fallin, Jonathan 395
Fallon, Sean 213
Fallon, James 226
Fallon, William C. (Bill) 559
Fallon, Chris 787
Fallon, Lee 903
Falotico, Joy 370
Faltys, Jeremy 170
Falvey, Mary R. 931
Falzon, Robert M. 699
Famiglietti, Michael 663
Fancher, Jeff 84
Fanelli, Robert 159
Fanelli, Arcangelo 199
Faneuil, Edward J. 393
Fang, Greg 440
Fang, AJ 804
Fannon, Sutton 799
Fant, Greg 293
Fantauzzi, Joseph 767
Fantom, Stacey 678
Farabaugh, Mark 470
Faraca-Bond, Lynn 908
Farache, Sergio 94

Farah, Pedro 903
Farah, Jean Claude 918
Faramawy, Ali 575
Farber, Michael 139
Farber, Jeffrey M. (Jeff) 409
Farber, Stephen D. 501
Farber, Howard 604
Fargo, Thomas B. 451
Farha, Todd S. 759
Faries, Stan 637
Farineau, Don 322
Farkas, David 187
Farley, Brian 222
Farley, Jack 286
Farley, James D. (Jim) 370
Farley, Jim 370
Farley, Thomas W. (Tom) 466
Farley, Catherine 632
Farley, Dan 792
Farmer, Jim 33
Farmer, Scott 125
Farmer, Bill 185
Farmer, Scott D. 198
Farmer, Curtis C. 224
Farmer, Carla 332
Farmer, Dennis 402
Farmer, Deanna 924
Farnan, Patrick 337
Farnsworth, Bryan D. 437
Farnsworth, David 717
Farnsworth, Ronald L. (Ron) 864
Farquhar, Dee 553
Farr, Jeremy 224
Farr, David N. 299
Farrah, Kaye 330
Farrall, Ann 620
Farrand, Stephen 566
Farrant, M. A. 320
Farrar, Marc 222
Farrar, Jeffrey W. 867
Farrel, Miles 45
Farrell, Peter 105
Farrell, Ashley 117
Farrell, Warren 149
Farrell, Dan 161
Farrell, Thomas F. 278
Farrell, Todd 518
Farrell, William J. (Bill) 538
Farrell, Pam 558
Farrell, Karen 632
Farrell, Jim 668
Farrell, Tj 754
Farrell, Marc 787
Farrell, Clifford 836
Farrell, Mike 840
Farrell, Breege A. 886
Farrell, Scott 888
Farrelly, Paul 343
Farren, Larry 241
Farren, Sean 792
Farris, Mic 182
Farris, J. Matt 439
Farris, Cherie 602
Farris, Kristofer M. 725
Fartaj, Vandad 662
Farver, Harry 449
Fasano, Mario 133
Fasano, Rebecca 135
Fasano, Gerard A. (Gerry) 516
Fasoldt, Lisa 415
Fasolo, Peter M. 484
Fasshauer, Michael 889
Fatovic, Robert D. 743
Fattore, Charles 280
Faubus, Todd 787
Faucett, Chad 699
Fauconneau, Janie 176
Faujour, Olivier 383
Faul, Mark 834
Faulk, Brent 190
Faulkner, Nigel 809
Faulmann, Maud 191
Faust, Wendy 176
Faust, Helen 273
Faust, Phil 713
Faver, Robert 863
Favorite, Annette 470

Favors, Jim 661
Fawaz, Hussein 71
Fawcett, John J. 201
Fawcett, Charles C. 853
Fawthrop, Kit 834
Fay, Gerald W. (Gerry) 94
Fay, Jason 754
Fayad, Walid 139
Faz, Patricia 713
Fazio, Carl 53
Fazio, Mark 425
Fazzolari, Robert 605
Feagin, Amy 460
Fearing, Robert 563
Feathers, Eric 351
Federico, Rick 792
Federico, David 840
Federico, Anthony J. 857
Federighi, Craig 69
Federle, Louis A. 227
Fedewa, Sam 786
Fedor, Laura 799
Fedorchak, Bill 447
Fedorko, Tara 928
Fedus, Natalie 928
Fedyszyn, Karen 9
Feehan, William 456
Feeney, Brian J. 180
Feenstra, Gregory 84
Feghali, Imad 185
Feher, William 298
Fehling, Bradley 94
Fehlman, Robert A. 768
Fehring, Mark 911
Feick, James 457
Feigelson, Sharon 224
Feiger, Mitchell S. 558
Feight, R. Preston 650
Feil, Thomas A 158
Feiler, Leonard B 330
Feille, Robert 15
Feinauer, Jonathan 941
Feinberg, David M. 42
Feinstein, Leonard (Lenny) 121
Feinstein, Fariah 489
Feitt, Ted 570
Feivelson, Neal 87
Felberg, Bret 487
Feldman, Nancy 504
Feldman, Michael (Mike) 934
Feldman, Amy 940
Feldmeyer, Kristopher 355
Feldser, David 928
Feleccia, Annie 342
Felenstein, Craig 270
Felix, Natalie 345
Felke, Magnus 707
Felkins, Jay 173
Fell, Robin 13
Fellahi, Khalid 918
Fellman, Ted 715
Fellmeth, Joellyn 770
Fellows, Melissa 81
Fellows, Talisha 159
Fellure, Diana 84
Felman, David 395
Felton, Jerry 875
Feltz, Lorianne 310
Felz, Patti 713
Femiano, Vince 170
Fendley, Russ 582
Fendrich, Amy 446
Fenech, Josie 224
Fenger, Mike 69
Fenlon, Erin A 409
Fennel, Marie 787
Fennell, Klayton 222
Fennell, Simon 395
Fennell, Laura A. 476
Fenner, Patrick 13
Fennessey, Mike 529
Fennimore, Judy 548
Fenstermaker, William H. 454
Fenton, Jeffrey 876
Fenton, Andrew 943
Ferando, Jim 111
Ferber, Dan 465

Ferber, Scott 470
Ferdig, Larry 587
Ferdschneider, Marcy 606
Ferensic, Michelle 881
Fergan, Tim 337
Fergenbaum, David 415
Ferguson, Roy C. 98
Ferguson, T. Ritson 169
Ferguson, Walter 177
Ferguson, Greg 415
Ferguson, Mike 563
Ferguson, Carley 580
Ferguson, James 620
Ferguson, Roger 635
Ferguson, Tom 787
Ferguson, Rhonda S. 868
Ferguson, William 870
Ferguson-McHugh, Mary L. 693
Fermo, Anthony 158
Fernandes, Savio 204
Fernandes, Paulo 555
Fernandez, Miguel 94
Fernandez, Martha 204
Fernandez, Carlos 204
Fernandez, Jeff 446
Fernandez, Connie 454
Fernandez, Luis 470
Fernandez, Ruben 507
Fernandez, Ofelia 620
Fernandez, Manny 899
Ferns, Peter 395
Fern□ndez, Jos◎ Luis 478
Ferracone, Robin A. 287
Ferradas, Jorge 533
Ferrando, Jonathan 89
Ferrara, Diana 449
Ferrara, Albert 878
Ferrara, Dan 910
Ferraro, Joseph A. (Joe) 93
Ferraro, Laura 511
Ferraro, Carl 511
Ferree, Gregory M. 777
Ferreira, Kathleen 122
Ferreira, Lucia P 204
Ferreira, Victor 425
Ferreira-Golino, Cathy 665
Ferrenz, Elizabeth 289
Ferrer, Javier D. 682
Ferrigno, Bob 119
Ferriman, Robert 735
Ferrin, Ed 49
Ferriola, John J. 626
FERRIS, STEPHEN 45
Fessia, Jennifer 799
Fessler, Paul 283
Festa, Stephen V. 301
Festervand, Terry 206
Fetsko, Darin 680
Fetsko, Francis M. 842
Fetterly-Bush, Shelly 842
Fetterolf, Brian S. 853
Fettig, Jeff M. 923
Fetzner, Carl 425
Feuerstein, Randy 201
Feuerstein, Jeff 555
Fewell, Christine 607
Ffolkes, Marie 22
Ficalora, Joseph R. 604
Ficarra, Chris 896
Fichadia, Ashok 868
Fick, Jeffrey 732
Fiedler, Richard 402
Fiedler, Stacy 676
Field, Doug 69
Field, James M. 260
Field, David 405
Field, Catherine 446
Field, Darren 447
Field, Doug 823
Fielder, Jessie 335
Fielding, William 178
Fielding, Ronald W 437
Fields, Felicia J 369
Fields, John M. 644
Fields, Matthew 735
Fields, Jeffrey 787
Fiene, Bryan 735

Fienup, Chris 715
Fierke, Carol A. 720
Fifick, Anne 700
Fifield, Trent 754
Figliuolo, Steve 362
Figueredo, Jorge L. 563
Figueroa, George 582
Figura, Scott 216
Fikaris, George 201
Fike, Sherri 96
Fike, Don 330
Fikry, Christopher 709
Filas, Melanie 161
Filippo, Pasquale A. (Pat) Di 856
Filipski, Kevin 672
Filley, David 60
Fillion-Hood, Jennifer 942
Fillmore, Randall 582
Filo, David 34
Filosa, Kirsten 131
Filthaut, Rich 413
Filton, Steve G. 882
Fimiani, Jaime 109
Finacchio, Daniel 840
Finan, Irial 216
Finan, Pat 330
Finard, Jeri B. 95
Finbloom, Norman 770
Finch, Mary E. 14
Fincher, C. Anderson 281
Findlay, D. Cameron 74
Findlay, Thomas 117
Findlay, David M. 511
Fine, Peter S. 111
Fine, Melvin 808
Finestone, Mark A. 90
Fingerman, Joseph 767
Finholt, Thomas A. 720
Finigan, Barbara 415
Fink, Laura 45
Fink, Laurence D. (Larry) 131
Fink, Charles 304
Fink, Chris 336
Fink, Nicholas I. 371
Fink, Mary 484
Fink, Anne 667
Fink, Josh 863
Fink, Martin 917
Finkelstein, David L. 65
Finkelstein, Stuart 555
Finkelstein, Steve 849
Finkle, Ned 628
Finkle, Edward 849
Finley, Tammy M. 12
Finley, John G. 133
Finley, Brett 371
Finley, Marcy 735
Finley, Joseph M. 853
Finley, Teresa M. 875
Finlow, Scott 668
Finn, Bradley 358
Finn, Tim 454
Finn, Gerardine 483
Finn, Thomas M. 693
Finn, Mary 800
Finn, Michael 881
Finnegan, John 84
Finnegan, Deb 620
Finnegan, Daniel J. 689
Finneran, John G. 158
Finneran, John 295
Finnerty, Shaun 474
Finney, Michele 818
Finniss, Matthew 332
Fioravanti, Mark 744
Fiore, Michael 554
Fiore, Paul G 770
Fioretti, Stephen 643
Fiorilli, Matthew 121
Fiorilli, Len 413
Fipps, Paul 866
Firestone, Marc S. 674
Firestone, Jeff 875
Firestone, James 935
Firlit, Matthew 808
Fisackerly, Haley R. 304
Fischer, Bradley 18

Fischer, Alexander 114
Fischer, James 115
Fischer, Jean-Luc 219
Fischer, Ted 415
Fischer, Jason 511
Fischer, Thomas J. (Tom) 518
Fischer, John E. 638
Fischer, Mark D. 705
Fischer, Avery 713
Fischer, Dave 724
Fischer, Ray 813
Fischer, Carolyn 840
Fischer, Anthony J. (Tony) 863
Fischer, Barbara 867
Fischer, George J. 893
Fiscus, Richard A. (Rich) 745
Fish, Brant 191
Fish, Frederick 233
Fish, Patrick 497
Fish, Kathleen B. (Kathy) 693
Fish, James C. (Jim) 907
Fishbein, Robert 700
Fisher, Kristine 87
Fisher, Daniel W. 96
Fisher, Richard 105
Fisher, Sam 117
Fisher, Tom 244
Fisher, Stephen (Steve) 293
Fisher, Douglas W. (Doug) 465
Fisher, John 472
Fisher, Lynn 491
Fisher, Rob 492
Fisher, Debby 504
Fisher, James 548
Fisher, Heidi 598
Fisher, Ronald 602
Fisher, Steven 623
Fisher, Lane 641
Fisher, Amy 713
Fisher, Jean 810
Fisher, Robert J. (Bob) 830
Fisher, John (Scott) 876
Fisher, Eric 890
Fisher, Marlise G. 905
Fisher, Mary 907
Fisher, Stephanie D. 937
Fishkin, Andrew L 101
Fishman, Robert P. (Bob) 599
Fishman, Robert 720
Fisk, George 515
Fiske, Mimi 545
Fitch, Deborah 228
Fitch, Matt 787
Fitton, Peter 274
Fitts, Tina 320
Fitz, Grant 935
Fitzgerald, Rich 94
Fitzgerald, Timothy 106
Fitzgerald, Joseph M. (Joe) 142
Fitzgerald, Paula 237
Fitzgerald, Cynthia 334
Fitzgerald, Bill 416
Fitzgerald, Caren 781
Fitzgerald, Michael R. 789
FitzGerald, Scott R. 792
Fitzgibbons, Michael A 641
Fitzgibbons, Michael 641
Fitzmaurice, Gerry 269
Fitzpatrick, Brian 131
Fitzpatrick, Peter 224
Fitzpatrick, Tim 304
Fitzpatrick, Sandy 494
Fitzpatrick, Michael J. 632
Fitzpatrick, Bill 875
Fitzpatrick, Margaret 899
FitzPatrick, Daniel M. (Dan) 908
Fitzsimmons, Brooks 85
Fixer, Mike 413
Flach, Greg 88
Flack, Kerry 31
Flagstad, Karsten 880
Flaherty, Gerard 191
Flaherty, Janice 423
Flaherty, Thomas 701
Flamenbaum, Todd 768
Flanagan, Joseph G 71
Flanagan, Michael 84

Flanagan, Bill 618
Flanagan, Christine 656
Flanagan, Christopher 700
Flanagan, Michael 925
Flanigan, John 15
Flanigan, John 276
Flanigan, Dan 336
Flannery, John L. 382
Flannery, Mark 408
Flannery, Matthew J. 876
Flappan, Bob 84
Flasz, Jerry 242
Flatt, Kevin 786
Flatt, Stephen 896
Flavell, David 668
Flavin, Laura 219
Flaxman, Jon E. 442
Fleckenstein, Michele 122
Fleet, Clifford B. (Cliff) 36
Fleet, Peter 370
Flemate, Willa 805
Fleming, Hans 45
Fleming, Paul 98
Fleming, Keith 198
Fleming, Ryan 226
Fleming, Alton 320
Fleming, Mark 637
Fleming, Paul 792
Fleming, Pamela 800
Fleri, Aldo 713
Flescher, Mark 790
Fleshood, John S. 851
Fletcher, Verna 246
Fletcher, Carl 365
Fletcher, Brock 779
Fletcher, J. Kevin 909
Fletcher, John P. 926
Fleury, Gustave 606
Fleury, Lynda 886
Flierl, Markus 643
Flinn, Tim 299
Flint, Joanna 34
Flis, Mike 449
Flood, Jim K 320
Flood, Tom 534
Flood, Gary J. 554
FloodCampo, Nina 895
Flor, Ted 117
Flores, Debbie 111
Flores, Gabriel 175
Flores, Doug 521
Flores, Doug 523
Flores, Rose 715
Flores, Debra A. 762
Flores, Joshuah P. 876
Flori, Lou 691
Florin, Daniel P. (Dan) 940
Flory, Brett 470
Flory, Bill 530
Flory, Kevin 628
Flowe, Aaron 431
Flowers, Tim 241
Flowers, Garry W. 365
Flowers, Todd 502
Floyd, Dale 678
Floyd, Trea 735
Floyd, David K. 797
Flueck, David 548
Flueckiger, Joe 207
Fluet, Laurel 632
Fluhler, Stephan H. 355
Flum, Joshua (Josh) 252
Flynn, Philip B. (Phil) 80
Flynn, Edward B. (Ed) 87
Flynn, Paul G. 307
Flynn, Thomas L. 420
Flynn, Michael 705
Flynn, Mark 799
Fochtman, Sarah 507
Foda, Hussein 668
Foderaro, Jim 668
Fodor, Darrin 665
Foehr, Matthew 191
Fogarty, Jim 186
Fogarty, Steve 220
Fogarty, Tim 237
Fogarty, Jane 805

Fogarty, Michael 881
Fogel, Arthur 532
Fogel, Glenn D. 689
Fogg, David H 380
Fogle, Natalie 103
Foglio, Neil 252
Fogt, Andrew 226
Fohringer, Ken 831
Fojo, Carlos 759
Fojut, Jack 504
Foley, Michael E. 288
Foley, Shannon 447
Foley, Peter A 530
Foley, Brendan M. 560
Foley, Jim 680
Foley, Kevin 839
Foley, Joseph R. (Joe) 886
Folger, Todd 170
Folks, Lawrence 304
Folliard, Thomas J. (Tom) 162
Folmar, William 279
Folsom, Suzanne R. 878
Folster, Brent 155
Folta, Carl 896
Foltman, Christopher 558
Foltz, Casey 735
Fong, Candace 266
Fong, Sylvia 499
Fonseca, Lidia 709
Fontaine, Michael 792
Fontaine, April 840
Fonte, Joaquin 328
Foo, Seehack 71
Foody, Paul 907
Foong, Chee Wai 199
Fooshee, Chad 722
Foot, Jim 104
Foote, James M. 245
Foote, Warren 656
Forake, Randy 99
Foraker, Randy P. 98
Foraker, John M. 383
Foran, Robert E. (Bob) 571
Foran, Gregory S. (Greg) 903
Forbes, Joshua 550
Forbes, Al 652
Forbes, John 839
Forbes, Tom 928
Ford, Robert B. 4
Ford, Mary 47
Ford, Thomas V 106
Ford, Nicole 115
Ford, Bob 242
Ford, Jody 293
Ford, William C. (Bill) 370
Ford, Gerald J. 375
Ford, Jonathan 425
Ford, Kevin 488
Ford, Jim 615
Ford, Kit 625
Ford, Marianne 784
Ford, Maria 786
Ford, Rollin Lee 903
Ford, Darrell L. 934
Fordham, Mark 787
Fore, Delbert 307
Foreman, Julie 224
Foreman, Kelly 942
Forese, James A. (Jim) 203
Forkel, Gary 333
Forkovitch, James K. 227
Forlenza, Vincent A. (Vince) 119
Forman, Dan 395
Forman, Todd 587
Forman, Susan 754
Formichellac, Howard 713
Forrest, Frank R. 336
Forrest, John 486
Forrest, Stephen 720
Forrest, Jim 935
Forrester, Craig 196
Fors, Rudy 888
Forsberg, Steve 932
Forslev, William 13
Forsyth, Elaine 699
Forsythe, Bill 306
Fort, Bob 762

Fort, Stephen W. 856
Forte, Jeffrey 454
Forte, Michael 754
Fortenberry, Randy 895
Fortier, Ray 530
Fortin, Mary Jane B. 31
Fortin, Michael 576
Fortin, Raymond D. 799
Fortino, Nickolas 628
Fortnum, Debbie 244
Fortuna, David 888
Fortunato, Kim Fremont 156
Fortunato-diaz, Annette 178
Forziati, Gina 131
Foshee, William M. 763
Foskett, Christopher M. 348
Foss, Eric J. 72
Fossen, Cymbre Van 343
Fossen, Rachel Van 734
Fossum, Jeff 139
Foster, Kelly 98
Foster, Sarah 106
Foster, Mireya 109
Foster, Jesse G. 110
Foster, Mark 124
Foster, Brian 137
Foster, Phil 168
Foster, Kimberly 175
Foster, Nancy 201
Foster, James 208
Foster, Sara E. 226
Foster, Michael 330
Foster, Greg 332
Foster, Holly M. 349
Foster, Daphne H. 393
Foster, Jon M. 416
Foster, Laurie 457
Foster, Mark 470
Foster, Robert 516
Foster, Heather 635
Foster, Mike 723
Foster, Brian 779
Foster, Paul L. 884
Foti, Kevin C. 687
Fougere, Richard 149
Fouhy, Sylvia 484
Foulkes, Helena B. 252
Foulston, Matthew J. 850
Fountain, David B. 285
Fourmas, Tom 497
Fournier, Martha 129
Fouss, Brad 632
Foust, Donald R. (Don) 937
Fowinkle, Ron 84
Fowke, Benjamin G. S. (Ben) 933
Fowle, John 409
Fowler, Pam 155
Fowler, Ross 199
Fowler, W. Randall (Randy) 307
Fowler, Jenny 446
Fowler, Sarah 544
Fowler, Terry 582
Fowler, John F. 643
Fowler, Edward 695
Fowler, Erica 869
Fowler, Tom 923
Fox, Joseph 67
Fox, Gregory C. 150
Fox, Joe 173
Fox, Joseph 173
Fox, Matthew 299
Fox, Vicki 345
Fox, John 353
Fox, John 406
Fox, Sheldon J. 411
Fox, Debra 413
Fox, Brian J. 419
Fox, Tom 487
Fox, Frank 628
Fox, Pierre 722
Fox, Roger 722
Fox, Jerome 738
Fox, John 740
Fox, Rob 773
Foye, Brian 256
Foyles, Kirsten 341
Fradin, Jackie 415

Fradkin, Steven L. (Steve) 620
Fraenkel, Martin 746
Fraga, Francisco 156
Fragie, Jack 563
Frahm, Monty 623
Frail, Mollie 133
Frain, Michael 604
Frake, Thomas G. (Tom) 166
Fraley, Robert T. 585
Fralix, Jason 54
Frame, Randall A. 360
Frampton, Michael 60
Frampton, Robin 708
Francavilla, Tony 385
Franceschini, Robert 563
Francey, Carrie 425
Francher, Joe 103
Francica, Angelo 105
Franciere, Karen 558
Francione, Brian 839
Francis, Bill 7
Francis, Victor 105
Francis, Tom 109
Francis, Roger 252
Francis, Charles P. 266
Francis, John 334
Francis, Shaun J. 363
Francis, Philip L 449
Francis, Scott 550
Francis, Julian 648
Francis, Charles 692
Francis, Robert E. (Bob) 794
Francis, Peter 811
Francis, John 890
Franco, Juan 101
Franco, Joseph 481
Franco, Ivette 484
Franco, Valerie 537
Franey, Bill 101
Frank, Janet D. (Jan) 28
Frank, Penny 45
Frank, Malcolm 218
Frank, Chris 222
Frank, Karen 272
Frank, Kaylin 273
Frank, Stacie 314
Frank, Billy 353
Frank, Jeffrey 395
Frank, Jeff 437
Frank, Matthew 513
Frank, David 701
Frank, Lynne 838
Frank, Ryan 889
Franke, Myra 668
Franke, Jerold P. 909
Franke, Mark 930
Frankel, Kenneth 121
Frankel, Darrin 587
Frankel, Michael S. 730
Frankiewicz, Becky 543
Franklin, Ken 53
Franklin, Ed 101
Franklin, Mark 390
Franklin, Darryl L 548
Franklin, Sarah 748
Franks, Brent J. 72
Frantz, Thom 351
Frantz, Darrell 760
Frantzen, Kevin 910
Franzino, Bob 423
Franzoni, Kasey 664
Franzoni, Greg 809
Frascella, Matthew 409
Frascotti, Johnathan A. (John) 415
Fraser, Jim 97
Fraser, Jane 203
Fraser, John 320
Fraser, Gene 623
Fraser, Stephen 718
Fraser, Dija 787
Fraser, John J 808
Fraser, Jason 890
Frasier, Edie 157
Frasier, Larry 248
Frasier, Timothy (Tim) 733
Fratamico, John J. 516
Frates, Caton 241

Frates, Jerry de 934
Fraumann, Timothy 907
Fraundorfer, Steven M. (Steve) 782
Frawley, Connie 555
Frayer, Becky 693
Frazier, Spencer 447
Frazier, Kenneth C. (Ken) 566
Frazzini, Steve 935
Frear, David J. 771
Frearson, Guy 14
Frease, Gina 80
Frechette, Patricia 931
Frederick, Brad 593
Fredericks, David 96
Fredericksen, Gregory L. (Greg) 645
Fredette, Larry 306
Fredin, Steven (Steve) 86
FREEBORN, TIM 531
Freed, Brian W. 68
Freel, John 620
Freeland, Richard J. (Rich) 248
Freeley, Katherine 220
Freeman, Cathy S. 99
Freeman, Mark 125
Freeman, Anthony 157
Freeman, Roger 300
Freeman, Bruce 316
Freeman, Mark 498
Freeman, Angela 736
Freeman, Charlie 778
Freeman, Thomas E. (Tom) 799
Freeman, William 799
Freeman, John 925
Freer, Randy 858
Fregelette, Don 299
Frehse, Todd 467
Freidig, Janice 104
Freier, Jon A. 810
Freilich, Josh 266
Freimuth, Stacia 215
Freitag, Randal J. 529
Freitag, Peter 699
Freitas, Mike 773
French, Sandra 168
French, Beth 185
French, Jim 330
French, Doug 334

French, Tracy M. 430
French, Richard 587
French, Jim 827
Frenkiel, Paul 827
Frent, Marty 151
Frenzel, Robert C. (Bob) 933
Frere, Kevin 634
Frese, Calvin W. (Cal) 169
Frese, Brian 872
Fresher, Brian 413
Frey, Charles 302
Frey, Dan 849
Freyling, Sylvia 332
Frias, Cristina 109
Frias, James D. (Jim) 626
Frick, Sue 767
Fricke, David 824
Fricklas, Michael 896
Fricks, William 380
Fridley, Erik W 634
Friece, Vicki 942
Fried, Asher 332
Friedery, John 96
Friedland, Eric 80
Friedlander, Benjamin 131
Friedman, Richard A. 395
Friedman, John 489
Friedman, Howard 505
Friedman, Brian P. 520
Friedman, Josh 661
Friedman, Howard H. 692
Friedman, Joel 705
Friedman, Michael 790
Friedman, Howard 849
Friedman, Seth 899
Friedrich, Amy C. 691
Friemel, Jake 224
Friend, Sean 454
Friend, Zoe 603

Friend, Bob 912
Fries, Chuck 94
Friesen, Ernie 400
Friesenhahn, Lisa 94
Frieske, William 620
Friess, Robert 71
Frisk, Patrik 866
Frisone, Jamie 53
Fritsche, R. Thomas (Tom) 119
Fritz, Robert 218
Fritz, Lance M. 868
Frizzell, Dave 903
Froehn, Ulli 140
Froio, Frank P 370
Fromknecht, Greg 299
Fron, David 722
Fronheiser, Jason 337
Fronk, Chris 620
Frons, Marc 610
Frooman, Thomas E. 198
Frossmo, Kristin 617
Frost, G. Janelle 55
Frost, Christopher 103
Frost, Robert 228
Frost, Patrick B. (Pat) 246
Frost, Jack 394
Frost, Jack 857
Frost, James A. (Jack) 857
Frotte, Gaetan 625
Fruhwirth, Paul 194
Fruin, John 403
Frump, Candace 666
Fry, Jason 889
Fry, James A. 937
Frye, Craig 116
Frye, Sue 247
Frye, Dawn 334
Fryer, Crystal 796
Fryhoff, Allyson 748
FSA, Robert 414
Fu, Frederick 94
Fuchs, Rainer 129
Fuchs, Mary Ann 286
Fudge, Kathryn 486
Fudge, Duncan 587
Fuerst, Edward 589
Fuetterer, Ken 115
Fugina, Annette 569
Fuhr, Karrie 261
Fuhriman, Dave 941
Fuhriman, David 942
Fujisaki, Catherine 103
Fulchino, Jay 792
Fulenwider, Dee 563
Fulk, Sue 459
Fulkerson, Debra 635
Fulkerson, Ed 754
Fuller, Sherrika 131
Fuller, Jeff 246
Fuller, Jeremy 350
Fuller, Lynn B. 419
Fuller, Wilford H. (Will) 529
Fuller, Amy 555
Fuller, Rodger D. 775
Fuller, Anthony 903
Fuller, Beth 912
Fullerton, Brian 60
Fullerton, Bruce 182
Fulmer, James W. (Jim) 842
Fulton, Howard 45
Fulton, Marshall 109
Fulton, Cedrick 571
Fund, Steven L. 465
Funde, Bret 851
Fung, Tiffany 587
Funk, Dan 81
Funk, Charles N. 578
Fuqua, Stacy 635
Furer, Dmitriy 395
Furey, Michael 620
Furey, Adrian 940
Furlong, Bryan 722
Furman, Dave 530
Furner, Chris 116
Furner, John 903
Furr, David 649
Furry, Kyle 928

Furtney, Darren 786
Furukawa, Brad 623
Fusaro, Michael 18
Fusco, Robert 327
Fussell, Stephen R. (Steve) 4
Futhey, Tracy 286
Futhey, John 504
Fynan, Tamara J. 773

G

Gabbard, Brian 72
Gabel, Dale 185
Gaber, Kerry 440
Gable, Steve 376
Gabler, Sean 345
Gabler, David 884
Gabriel, Jim 395
Gabrielson, Rick 537
Gack, Bruce 507
Gaddes, Kathy H. 56
Gadol, Boris 604
Gaffney, Dan 106
Gaffney, Paul J. 264
Gaffney, James 800
Gaffney, Kevin 860
Gage, E. Dean 206
Gage, Douglas 261
Gage, Patrick 671
Gage, Marlyss J. 849
Gage, April 860
Gagel, Brian 726
Gagliano, Joe 45
Gagliano, Vincent J. 55
Gagliano, Naomi 274
Gagliardotto, David 131
Gaglio, Maria 717
Gagne, Sherry 431
Gagne, Geoff 750
Gagnet, Spencer 158
Gagnon, William 194
Gahan, Johnathan 244
Gaherty, John B. 241
Gain, Tom 930
Gaines, Bennett L. 360
Gaines, Teresa 380
Gaines, Michael 385
Gaines, Andy 454
Gaither, J. Michael (Mike) 50
Gaither, Kevin 774
Gajdos, Ludovit 227
Galanski, Stanley A. (Stan) 596
Galant, Pascal 299
Galanti, Richard A. 241
Galarza, Charles 735
Galbraith, Kent 226
Gale, Steven 620
Gale, Fournier J. (Boots) 721
Gale, Carla 722
Galea, Peter 587
Gales, Amy H. 214
Galhotra, A. Kumar 370
Galin, Tomi 230
Galindo, Sergio 649
Galindo, Esther 923
Galindo, Esther Berrozpe 923
Galit, Scott 568
Gall, David 528
Gallacher, David 811
Gallagher, Patricia 105
Gallagher, Lorraine 159
Gallagher, William 244
Gallagher, Francis 325
Gallagher, J. Patrick (Pat) 378
Gallagher, Thomas J. (Tom) 378
Gallagher, Brendan 378
Gallagher, Thomas C. (Tom) 387
Gallagher, Edward 599
Gallagher, Angela 665
Gallagher, Denis 709
Gallagher, Norman 748
Gallagher, Linda 863
Gallant, Gary 242
Gallant, Nicole 748
Galler, Jennifer 131
Gallett, Scott D. 140

Galli, Guido 840
Galliford, Shannon 664
Galligan, Matthew E. (Matt) 201
Gallimore, Alec D. 720
Gallina, John E. 66
Gallinat, Jeff 199
Gallion, Lindsay 803
Gallman, Mike 580
Gallo, Mark 122
Gallo, Laurene (Laurie) 139
Gallo, Jim 203
Gallo, Joseph 530
Gallo, Silvina 671
Galloni, Beatriz 555
Gallop, Melanie 705
Gallopoulos, Gregory 380
Gallucci, Chris 668
Galluzzi, Gary 836
Galo, Diane 252
Galsnte, Alena 808
Galson, Steven K 57
Galuppi, Barb 378
Galuppo, Gail A. 19
Galura, Brett 16
Galuski, John 875
Galvez, Jean-Marc 125
Galvez, Michelle 131
Galvin, William A. (Bill) 64
Galvin, Jason 849
Gambhir, Gulu 517
Gamble, Alan 935
Gamby, Jon 105
Gamewell, William 226
Gamez, Yenisel 159
Gamez, Juan 468
Gammon, Dawn 699
Gan, Tao 248
Gan, Jimmy 803
Ganatra, Manish 52
Ganatra, Gigi 617
Gandhi, Mihir 101
Gandhi, Kumar 204
Gandhi, Kinnari 901
Gandy, Barbara 299
Gangemi, Joseph D. 233
Gangestad, Nicholas C. 2
Gangeyula, Kalyan 888
Gann, JW 429
Gannfors, John W. 633
Gannon, Michael 18
Gannon, Stephen T. (Steve) 205
Gannon, Carrie 395
Gannon, John 824
Gans, David 671
Ganser, Michael 200
Ganti, Andrew 882
Gantner, Diane 80
Gaor, Matt 663
Garafola, Lana 566
Garantiva, Fabian 107
Garavito, Patricio 161
Garbee, Lynn 563
Garber, David 336
Garber, Tami 884
Garceau, Eric De 582
Garcia, Andres 15
Garcia, Charles 80
Garcia, James P 103
Garcia, Honey 104
Garcia, Patty 117
Garcia, Luis 131
Garcia, Juan 191
Garcia, David 204
Garcia, Ignacio 248
Garcia, David 274
Garcia, Grace 423
Garcia, Nicholas 457
Garcia, Joan C 465
Garcia, Arlene 470
Garcia, Joe 675
Garcia, Cisco 704
Garcia, Rosie 722
Garcia, Art A. 742
Garcia, Eduardo 787
Garcia, Kelly P 808
Garcia-Barbon, Jennifer 109
Garcia-McCutcheon, Lynda 332

Garcia-Velez, Calixto 340
Garczynski, James 709
Garde, Sameer 199
Gardill, James C. (Jim) 912
Gardiner, Robert 103
Gardiner, Roger 395
Gardner, Karen 32
Gardner, Claudy 117
Gardner, Jenny 252
Gardner, Shannon 449
Gardner, Julie 503
Gardner, Randy 580
Gardner, James 672
Gardner, Marty 910
Gardunio, James F. (Jim) 766
Garfield, David R. 754
Garfinkel, David 87
Garfinkle, Andrew 141
Garg, Rahul 142
Gargano, Laura 18
Garger, Stavros 713
Gargiulo, Joe 892
Garison, Cathy 246
Garland, Katherine 370
Garland, Greg C. 675
Garland, Kim 788
Garnant, Carol 597
Garner, Sharon 49
Garner, Megan 104
Garner, James 178
Garner, Denise 208
Garner, Ed 356
Garner, David W. 768
Garner, Sarah 856
Garner, Don 916
Garner, Stephen 934
Garnett, Timothy 528
Garnett, Tim 528
Garofalo, Mark 559
Garofalo, Martin (Marty) 610
Garrabrants, Gregory 136
Garratt, John W. 276
Garrett, Mark S. 11
Garrett, Sheri 146
Garrett, Dave 355
Garrett, Cavarly 489
Garrett, Paula 528
Garrett, Kirk 677
Garrett, John R. (Bob) 779
Garrett, Richard 890
Garrett, Michele 923
Garrette, Brian 413
Garrigan, Allison 382
Garrigues, Bernard M. 908
Garringer, Jesse 752
Garriott, Richard 297
Garrison, Dave 261
Garrison, Cheryl 332
Garrison, Linda 370
Garrison, Greg 868
Garrity, Matthew T. 870
Garske, Rick 96
Gartmond, Simone 131
Gartner, Bruce 185
Gartner, Bill 200
Gartner, James J. (Jim) 230
Garvey, Matthew 840
Garvin, Robert M. (Bert) 909
Gary, Robert 811
Garza, Fernando 468
Garza, Mario J 582
Gasaway, Bill 447
Gasior, F. Morgan 108
Gaskill, Jeremy 446
Gaskin, Martha 558
Gaspar, Todd 158
Gasparotto, James M 530
Gasparovic, John J. 140
Gass, Michelle 503
Gass, Rhonda O. 786
Gast, James 14
Gatchalian, Ryan 519
Gater, Karon 928
Gates, David 81
Gates, Charles M. (Charlie) 153
Gates, Charlie 153
Gates, Lisa 732

Gates, Jim 881
Gatewood, Colin 328
Gatien, Philip 80
Gatling, James 115
Gatt, Joe 570
Gatta, Rosanne 772
Gatta, Dan 938
Cattle, William H. (Bill) 411
Gattuso, Anthony 558
Gauba, Gary 181
Gaudet, Gordon J. 760
Gaudio, Joseph 881
Gaudiosi, Debi 32
Gaudiosi, Monica M. 861
Gaudioso, Gary 539
Gauger, George 339
Gaughan, Patrick 168
Gaughen, Robert H. 427
Gault, James S. (Jim) 378
Gause, Garry 818
Gausman, Loren 808
Gautam, Rajeev 434
Gauthier, Eugene 395
Gauvin, Tim 101
Gauvin, Judy 814
Gavegnano, Richard J. 567
Gavel, Anne 880
Gavell, Stefan M. 791
Gavelle, Jean-Luc 59
Gavigan, John 349
Gavin, Michael E. 511
Gavrielof, Tamara 767
Gaw, Turner 109
Gawron, Mark 411
Gay, Richard 897
Gaylor, Albert 808
Gaylord, Steve 101
Gayner, Thomas S. 545
Gazdic, Mike 805
Gazitua, John 330
Geagea, Joseph C. (Joe) 190
Gean, Tom 903
Gearhart, Jeffrey J. (Jeff) 903
Gearing, Kathy 799
Geary, William C. 64
Geatens, Fran 566
Gebben, Jeff 573
Geckle, Gerry 882
Geczik, Tom 793
Geduldig, Courtney 746
Gee, Kevin 133
Gee, Jessica 382
Geekie, Matthew W. 399
Geer, Kelly 515
Geeza, Nick 888
Geffre, Kyle 354
Gegerson, Kelly 454
Gehring, John F. 232
Geier, Lori 337
Geier, Ross 457
Geier, Kristina 493
Geiersbach, Rik 135
Geiger, Jeffrey S. 380
Geir, Bill 196
Geis, Matt 530
Geist, William 836
Gelb, Andrew 348
Gelbcke, Alex 820
Gelber, Nick 395
Geldart, Scott 219
Geldzahler, Seth 121
Gelement, Kathy 336
Gelione, Joe 357
Geller, Jeff 566
Gelman, Jack 484
Gelman, Luba 891
Gelsomin, Lynn 82
Gelston, Kevin 272
Gelwix, Steve 267
Gemelos, George 486
Gemignani, Gino J. 834
Gemperle, Adrienne 787
Gemrich, John 888
Gendler, Gordon 863
Gendron, Alison 440
Gendron, Teresa S. 520
Gener, Greg 104

Genis, Arnaud P. 648
Genius, Just 6
Genovese, Marc 489
Genovesi, Diane 489
Gensler, Melanie 457
Gentile, Richard 148
Gentile, Thomas 654
Gentile, Thomas C. (Tom) 784
Gentry, Art 228
Gentry, Michael 762
Gentry, Haynes 800
Gentzkow, Paul F. 734
George, David C. (Dave) 256
George, Marlon 457
George, Martin (Marty) St. 483
George, Martin St 483
George, Stacie 533
George, Michael (Mike) 710
Georgiadis, Margaret H. (Margo) 557
Gera, Chris 553
Gerace, Christopher P. 733
Geraci, Greg 170
Geraci, Gavin 680
Geraffo, Rich 643
Geraghty, Joanna 483
Geraghty, Timothy J 620
Geraghty, Paul D. 931
Gerard, Jeff 802
Gerardi, Marlene 382
Gerardot, Jennie S 764
Gerber, Craig 117
Gerberding, Julie L. 566
Gerbino, Paul 794
Gerentine, Michael 470
Gerety, John 722
Gericke, Johan 158
Gerjets, Sven 557
German, Scott 344
Germann, Jim 12
Germano, Don 264
Germanson, Christine 722
Germany, Bill 335
Gerrard, Robert 370
Gers, Alison E. 148
Gersch, Nicole 224
Gershenhorn, Alan 875
Gershkowitz, Todd 792
Gerspach, John C. 203
Gerstenberger, Tom 601
Gerster, Brennan 457
Gerstle, Douglas 693
Gervasi, Martha (Marty) 413
Gesell, Peter 105
Gesing, Rick 71
Geske, Jon 162
Gessner, Marilyn 767
Gestle, Mark 248
Geter, Kathi 709
Getman, George J. 228
Getschow, Alec 737
Gettelman, Elisabeth 476
Getz, James F. (Jim) 853
Gevondyan, Hilary 358
Gewirtz, Henry 555
Geyer, Debi 786
Geyzel, David Van 28
Ghai, Rahul 411
Ghanayem, Steve 71
Ghanayem, Darren 911
Ghartey-Tagoe, Kodwo 286
Ghasemi, Seifi 22
Ghazi, Leili 214
Ghia, Filippo 109
GHIRARDINI, DAVID 378
Ghisla, Anthony V 313
Ghisla, Tony 313
Ghorieshi, Reza 599
Ghose, Mohit 582
Ghosh, Anirvan 129
Giacobbe, Scott 7
Giacobbe, Ken 75
Giacomin, Jon 161
Gialamas, John 18
Giambrone, Angelo 582
Giametta, Lauren 131
Giammatteo, Robb 79
Giamouridis, Kostas 671

Giampalmi, Joe 87
Gianarkis, Dean 672
Giancola, Thomas 30
Giangola, Louis 533
Giannantoni, Leslie 109
Giannetta, Mario 754
Giannini, Noreen 18
Giannone, Gregory 888
Gianopulos, James N. (Jim) 896
Giansante, Ruth 929
Giarratano, Bob 936
Gibbons, Thomas P. (Todd) 105
Gibbons, Mike 135
Gibbons, Daniel 550
Gibbons, Peter D. 557
Gibbons, Dale M. 916
Gibbons, Angela F 936
Gibbs, Janice 330
Gibbs, Lisa 558
Gibbs, Robert 562
Gibbs, Jackie 898
Gibbs, David W. 939
Gibney, Ronald 201
Gibson, Eileen 94
Gibson, Wes 181
Gibson, Camille 383
Gibson, Chris 385
Gibson, Kim 406
Gibson, John W. 641
Gibson, Amy 724
Gibson, Blaine 735
Gibson, Lee R. 779
Gick, Dan 355
Gick, Daniel J 355
Gideon, Richard A. (Rick) 263
Gideon, Rick 263
Gido, Jeffrey 395
Giedlin, Tom 582
Gielink, Michael 557
Giesecke, Dan 281
Giess, Tim 18
Giessing, Mark 914
Gifford, William F. (Billy) 36
Gifford, Jenny 99
Gifford, Gerard H (Jerry) 244
Gifford, Bill 393
Gigax, Robert 378
Giglia, Garret 358
Giglio, Gaby 45
Gil, Eduardo 687
Gilberd, Adam 748
Gilbert, Dana 13
Gilbert, James 122
Gilbert, Clay 170
Gilbert, Mike 355
Gilbert, Percy 470
Gilbert, Randy 530
Gilbert, E 550
Gilbert, E. Scott 550
Gilbert, Barry 563
Gilbert, Andrew 707
Gilbert, Irene 557
Gilbert, Samantha 829
Gilbert, Jon 838
Gilbert, William M. (Bill) 869
Gilbert, Steve 890
Gilbertson, Phillip 526
Gilchrist, David 176
Gilchrist, Grant 423
Gilder, Sandy 378
Gileadi, Ido 334
Giles, William T. (Bill) 90
Giles, William 555
Giles, Joseph 895
Giles, David 897
Gilkes, Martin 557
Gilkey, Glenn 365
Gill, Sukhbir 131
Gill, Eric 489
Gill, Bryan K. 680
Gill, G. Andrew (Andy) 754
Gill, Charles D. 879
Gill, David 941
Gillam, Adam 204
Gillan-Myer, Maureen A. 445
Gillani, Aleem 799
Gillaspy, Donna 941

Gillern, Jeffry H. (Jeff) von 888
Gilles, Jean H. 260
Gillespie, Preston 286
Gillespie, Peter K. 449
Gillespie, Michael 497
Gillespie, Phillip S. 791
Gilley, William 101
Gilleylen, Russ 593
Gilliam, Dabney T. P. (Dexter) 48
Gilliam, Kyle 99
Gilliam, Scott 196
Gilligan, Peggy 507
Gilligan, Terrence 932
Gilliland, M. Amy 380
Gilliland, Amy 380
Gilliland, Terry 762
Gillin, Greg 533
Gillis, Kathy 12
Gillis, Michelle A. (Shelly) 47
Gillis, Jim 786
Gillman, Heike 808
Gillmon, Brett 550
Gillmore, Ron 570
Gilmartin, Thomas N. 853
Gilmore, Patty 307
Gilmore, Dennis J. 339
Gilmore, Sally 692
Gilmore, Rob 707
Gilmore, Richard 765
Gilmour, James 863
Gilronan, Kevin 849
Gilstrap, Carol 888
Gim, Mark K. W. 906
Gina, Son 103
Ginaldi, Joel 157
Ginel, Ken 715
Gingerich, Bradley 170
Gingras, France M. 746
Ginn, Porter 754
Ginn, Cheryl 941
Ginsberg, Gary L. 838
Ginsburg, Eric J 378
Ginsburg, Brandon 517
Ginter, Matt 3
Ginty, Mike 770
Gionfriddo, Robert P. (Bob) 420
Giordanella, Kim 557
Giordano, James 117
Giordano, Anthony 632
Giorelli, Michela 270
Giorgianni, Kathryn 37
Giovanetti, Victor E. 526
Giovinazzi, Brian 698
Gipple, Todd A. 706
Gipson, James (Jimmie) 441
Girardin, Jason 927
Giraud, Damien 166
Girion, Sherwood 332
Giromonte, Ron 106
Giroux, Marc 240
Girten, William 585
Girton, Tani 104
Girton, James 336
Gitles, Chuck 559
Gitlin, David L. 879
Giuseppe, Tony 517
Giust, Flavio 498
Givler, Sean 197
Gizaw, Mulu 813
Glacken, Gary 570
Gladden, Brian T. 584
Glade, Doug 254
Gladney, Karen 224
Gladson, Richard 530
Gladu, Robert 863
Glarner, Brian 306
Glasby, Anthony 293
Glascoe, Tracy L 322
Glaser, Nancy 95
Glaser, Daniel S. (Dan) 550
Glaser, Thomas A. 894
Glasgow, Dane 293
Glasgow, Mark 574
Glass, Linda 98
Glass, Karina 101
Glass, Steven 366
Glass, Dennis R. 529

Glass, Shannon 615
Glass, Robert W. 734
Glasscock, Dave 168
Glasscock, James S. 647
Glasscock, Larry C. 940
Glassman, Ed 555
Glatch, Lisa 185
Glatt, Darren 186
Glavin, Patrick 182
Glazer, Victor 131
Glazer, Lesley 204
Glazer, Benjamin (Ben) 687
Glazier, Tony 147
Gleason, George G. 107
Gleason, Nikki 347
Gleason, Patrick 598
Gleason, John J. 743
Gleason, Leona A. 927
Gleiser, Betsy 246
Gleissle, Karin 934
Glendinning, Stewart F. 859
Glenn, Marie 6
Glenn, T. Michael 330
Glenn, Staci 449
Glenn, Stephanie 748
Glenn, Rebecca 849
Glennon, Christopher 476
Gleyzer, Alex 643
Glick, Joe 33
Glick, Patricia 266
Glick, Andrew 620
Glidden, Craig B. 385
Glied, Sherry A. 606
Glispin, Chip 824
Glisson, Britton L. (Britt) 545
Glockner, Jacqueline 53
Glocksen, Jennifer 558
Glorioso, Jeanne 246
Glosenger, Carolyn 811
Glover, Bob 161
Glover, Jeff 181
Glover, Andy 214
Glover, Smokey 376
Glover, William 376
Glover, Tom 484
Glover, Marcus 573
Glover, Jerry 585
Glover, Tamara 672
Glover, Mark 676
Glowacki, John 14
Glowasky, Bob 555
GLUCK, JONATHAN 88
Gluck, Mitch 339
Gluck, Melanie 555
Gluckman, Thomas 101
Gluckman, Laurence 604
Glumm, Natalie 343
Gluski, Andr©s R. 16
Glynn, Richard 45
Gmelich, Justin G. 395
Gmuer, Stefan 791
Gnetz, Patricia 888
Gnodde, Richard J. 395
Goare, Douglas M. (Doug) 562
Goas, Thomas 530
Gobbel, Liz 806
Goben, Randy 189
Gober, James R. 461
Goch, Doreen 249
Gockel, Douglas 844
Godbold, Kristy 548
Godbole, Seemantini 813
Goddard, Gosia 205
Goddard, Steven 330
Goddard, Edward 502
Godfrey, Red 617
Godfrey, Leslie 678
Godfrey, Terry 932
Godin, Barbara (Barb) 721
Godlewski, Daniel 498
Godo, Michael 215
Godridge, Leslie V. 888
Godshaw, Gary 395
Godwin, Jim D. 116
Godwin, Jimmy 116
Godwin, Barrie 274
Godwin, Hank 334

Godwin, Glen N. 461
Godwin, Cristina 536
Godwin, Cliff 643
Goebel, Brian 729
Goeke, George 84
Goel, Vikas 792
Goelkel, Chris 617
Goemaat, Bruce 84
Goetsch, Craig 533
Goetz, William W. (Bill) 807
Goetz, Bill 808
Goff, Corinne Le 57
Goff, Gregory J. (Greg) 63
Goff, Stacey W. 181
Goff, Kevin 413
Goforth, Patricia 139
Goggin, Patrick (Pat) 135
Goggins, Brock 390
Goglia, John 88
Goh, Martin 550
Gohsman, Judy 392
Goins, Randy 382
Goins, Amy 806
Gokhale, Pradeep 53
Golash, Terry 18
Gold, Victor 45
Gold, Stephen J. 252
Gold, Gerri 425
Gold, Richard S. 538
Gold, Scott 548
Goldberg, Scott L. 213
Goldberg, Linda 234
Goldberg, Jillian 297
Goldberg, Daniel 395
Goldberg, Wendy 456
Goldberg, Bruce 489
Goldberg, Gary J. 609
Goldberg, Richard 656
Goldberg, Randy 729
Goldberg, Larry 767
Goldberg, Allison 838
Goldberg, Nancy 881
Goldberg, Howard 888
Goldberger, Mayer 413
Goldblatt, Steve 903
Golden, Andrew 413
Golden, Deanna 507
Golden, Elizabeth 671
Goldenberg, Scott 839
Goldfarb, Amy 131
Goldin, Adam 489
Goldman, Kenneth (Ken) 34
Goldman, Karen 131
Goldman, Nathan D. 245
Goldman, Rachel 720
Goldman, Earl 927
Goldner, Brian D. 415
Goldschmidt, Guy 456
Goldsmith, Tom 109
Goldsmith, Gordon 274
Goldsmith, Denise 656
Goldsmith, Ilyse 888
Goldstein, Jeff 84
Goldstein, Lawrence A. (Larry) 125
Goldstein, Rob L. 131
Goldstein, Marlo 440
Goldstein, Marc 457
Goldstein, Robert G. (Rob) 513
Goldstein, Jeff 838
Goldstone, Steven F. (Steve) 232
Goldwater, John K. 122
Golestani, Clark 566
Golias, Tom 194
Golisano, Courtney 131
Golladay, Catherine 754
Gollihue, Tiffani 114
Gollisz, Gustav 203
Golodryga, Zhanna 423
Golson, Kelly Jo 13
Golub, Bennett W. 131
Golub, Scott 131
Golub, David 332
Golumbeski, George 175
Gomberg, Mark 891
Gomel, Rick 248
Gomer, Jay 450
Gomes, Sandra 273

Gomez, Steve 94
Gomez, Jorge M. 161
Gomez, Cesar 203
Gomez, Ed 313
Gomez, Henry 425
Gomez, Evelyn 615
Gomez, Rick H. 813
Gomez, Miguel 928
Gomi, Hideki 574
Goncalves, Armando F. 664
Gonnella, Thomas 201
Gonos, Caroline 928
Gonsior, Tim 378
Gonzales, Maralessa 246
Gonzales, Yolanda 246
Gonzales, Jesse 808
Gonzalez, Richard A. (Rick) 6
Gonzalez, Ismario 16
Gonzalez, Ellen B 178
Gonzalez, Angel K 178
Gonzalez, Jaime 241
Gonzalez, Melissa 272
Gonzalez, Rafael 395
Gonzalez, Rick 450
Gonzalez, Eliza 468
Gonzalez, Edward A. (Eddie) 756
Gonzalez, Chary 757
Gonzalez, Eva 760
Gonzalez, Hector 860
Gonzalez, Alfonso 888
Gonzalez, Beatrice 890
Gonzalez, Robert 899
Gonzalez-Benedict, Elizabeth 494
Goo, Sook 435
Gooch, Mark A. 230
Gooch, Harold 582
Good, Steven 52
Good, Jim 96
Good, Lynn J. 285
Good, Jack 665
Good, Mary 668
Goodarzi, Sasan K. 476
Goodell, Denise 323
Goodell, Timothy 423
Goodell, Michael 431
Gooden, Tonya 355
Goodfriend, Jim 337
Goodger, Simon 671
Goodman, Sean D. 78
Goodman, Bennett J. 133
Goodman, Scott R. 306
Goodman, Stacey 374
Goodman, Randy 390
Goodman, Laurie 489
Goodman, Richard 537
Goodman, Adam 555
Goodman, Scott 557
Goodman, Gregg M. 770
Goodman, Mark 903
Goodrich, David 18
Goodrich, Donna C. 116
Goodsir, Michelle 201
Goodwin, Eric 539
Goodwin, Mary 881
Goodwin, Brian 942
Goodwyn, Bill 270
Goone, David S. (Dave) 466
Gopalakrishnan, Raja 334
Goracke, Pam 117
Gorantla, Uma 792
Gord, Elvira 528
Gorder, Joseph W. (Joe) 890
Gordineer, Kenneth 668
Gordon, Marc D. 44
Gordon, Murdo 144
Gordon, Lori 161
Gordon, Derek A. 219
Gordon, Tom 244
Gordon, Sandy 262
Gordon, Tanya 320
Gordon, Ilene S. 462
Gordon, Ray 496
Gordon, Gail 536
Gordon, Erin 582
Gordon, Russell L. 742
Gordon, Nikita 786
Gordon, Cima 809

Gore, Brian 30
Gorecki, Teresa 484
Gorelik, Ariel 60
Gorham, Roger B. 28
Gorham, Bo 44
Gorham, James 185
Gorin, Ariane 316
Goris, Patrick 738
Gorka, Diane 927
Gorman, Patty 178
Gorman, Mark 199
Gorman, Christopher M. (Chris) 497
Gorman, James P. 587
Gorman, Jim 664
Gorman, Mark J. 679
Gorman, Robert M. (Rob) 867
Gorman, Piers 929
Gormley, Frank 224
Gorodetzer, Kristen 195
Gorska, Anna 180
Gorski, Mark 635
Gorsky, Alex 484
Gorsuch, Charles 888
Gorton, Scott 876
Gorzak, John 637
Gosebruch, Henry O. 6
Gosling, Brian 94
Gosnell, Monica 431
Goss, Cathy P. 403
Gossner, Harald 465
Goswami, Chitra 258
Goswami, Ranjan 262
Gotelli, Robert 104
Gottesfeld, Stephen P. 609
Gottfied, Jonathon R 808
Gotti, Paul 161
Gottschalk, Adrian 129
Gottschalk, Keith 637
Gottscho, Richard A. (Rick) 512
Gottsegen, Jonathan M 876
Gottuso, Vince 250
Gottwals, Bill 354
Gotwals, Janet W 99
Goudie, Craig 739
Goudreau, Christopher 470
Gough, Mitzy 135
Gough, Lisa 808
Gouin, Kevin 334
Goulart, Steven J. 569
Gould, Anthony 200
Gould, Jason 250
Gould, Dan 610
Gould, Karen O. 856
Goulet, Beverly K. 41
Goulet, Ken 67
Gourlay, Alexander W. (Alex) 901
Gover, Bonnie 84
Govindan, Muthu 625
Gowan, Jim 810
Gowen, James 102
Gowen, Nick 447
Gowen, Kevin P. 806
Graaf, Bill Van de 219
Grabavoy, Steve 558
Grabavoy, Steven 559
Grace, Helen 45
Grace, Bethany 170
Grace, Mark 917
Gracheck, Jack 558
Graddick-Weir, Mirian M. 566
Grade, Joel T. 808
Grady, Gerry 332
Grady, Melissa 570
Grady, Timothy 912
Graf, R. Mark 269
Graf, Alan B. 330
Graff, Tim 299
Graham, Jonathan P. 57
Graham, Robert M. (Bob) 64
Graham, Jon 68
Graham, Jonathan 256
Graham, Dan 282
Graham, Kristin 316
Graham, Mark 325
Graham, Renee 400
Graham, Molly 530
Graham, Heather 643

Graham, John 705
Graham, Kerri 707
Graham, Deeney 750
Graham, Stephen P 788
Graham, Christopher A. (Chris) 794
Graham, James 808
Graham, Ned 876
Grainger, Guy 486
Gramlich, Tom 474
Grammas, Dean 205
Granata, Thomas 49
Granchi, Annie 397
Grand, Hillary 131
Granderson, David W 593
Grandfield, Michael 124
Grandinetti, Russell 37
Graney, Kevin M. 380
Granger, Darron 153
Grannis, Dick 708
Grant, Tim 72
Grant, Bob 87
Grant, Jesse 170
Grant, Michael 171
Grant, Shane 216
Grant, Hugh 585
Grant, Jeffrey 623
Grant, Jasmine 799
Grant-anderson, Belinda 84
Grantham, Bryan 722
Grantham, Connee 775
Graseck, Peter 897
Grasse, Nancy 863
Grasshoff, Michaela 550
Grasso, Sebastian 133
Grasso, Maria A. 366
Grasso, Janine 470
Grasso, Davide 615
Grassy, Richard 18
Grau, Randy 889
Grauer, Scott B. 137
Gravanis, Georges 91
Gravatt, Sherry 867
Gravel, Karine 671
Gravelle, Michael L. (Mike) 332
Graves, William W. 90
Graves, Marcia F 224
Graves, Victoria 261
Graves, Shawn 447
Graves, Christopher 567
Grawe, George 32
Gray, Keisha 106
Gray, Sean A. 124
Gray, Jonathan D. 133
Gray, Harry W 135
Gray, Chris 273
Gray, Paul 298
Gray, Randall 337
Gray, Rebecca 337
Gray, Jonathan D. 427
Gray, William 429
Gray, James D. (Jim) 462
Gray, Anne 470
Gray, Brad 531
Gray, Jeff 537
Gray, Rick 553
Gray, Diedre 683
Gray, James W. 726
Gray, David J. 831
Gray, Ginny 852
Gray, Myron A. 875
Graybill, Greg 297
Grayson, Alan 330
Grayson, Deann 763
Graziano, Thomas 604
Grazioli, John 587
Grealish, Joe 332
Greasheimer, Sharon 161
Greathouse, Thomas 666
Greaves, Stacey 892
Grebenc, Jane 345
Grebstein, Marci 661
Grech, Jim 361
Grech, Joe 628
Grech, Brent 643
Greco, Thomas R. (Tom) 12
Greco, Anneke 487
Greco, Ignazio 570

Greco, Joseph 627
Greco, John R. 654
Greco, Joe 760
Greek, Darby 241
Greeley, Neal 14
Green, Tim 14
Green, Mark 16
Green, Keith 31
Green, Anthony C. 65
Green, Phil 131
Green, Phillip D. 246
Green, Lindsey 273
Green, Allen R. 279
Green, Gregory 310
Green, Guy 385
Green, Andy 451
Green, Terri 470
Green, Michael 488
Green, Matthew 489
Green, Mark A. 495
Green, Shannon 530
Green, Darryl E. 543
Green, Herman 555
Green, Bryan 598
Green, Allyson 606
Green, Peter 672
Green, Roberta 715
Green, Howard 767
Green, Joyce 769
Green, Ryan 780
Green, Michael W 808
Green, Nancy 830
Green, Warren 863
Green, Paul S. 874
Green, Monique 888
Green, Tara 903
Green-Kelley, Taira A 18
Greenberg, Raymond S. 884
Greenberg, Andrew 896
Greenberg, Alan 897
Greenblatt, Robert (Bob) 222
Greene, Mike 52
Greene, Jason K. 125
Greene, Tom 219
Greene, Thomas (Tom) 219
Greene, Jeff 358
Greene, Douglas 749
Greene, George 767
Greene, Aaron 767
Greene, Keith 806
Greene, Ezra 896
Greene, Ryan 941
Greener, Todd 12
Greener, Geoffrey S. 101
Greenfeig, Sid 573
Greenfield, Susan W 109
Greenfield, David B 409
Greengold, Alexander 272
Greengrass, Seth 395
Greenhaw, Mark 107
Greenlaw, David 628
Greenleaf, Lari 497
Greenspan, Peter 656
Greenspon, Tom 139
Greenstein, Scott A. 771
Greenstein, Sara A. 878
Greensweig, Gary 266
Greenwald, Kristin 551
Greenwalt, Rodgers K. 125
Greenwood, Nigel 45
Greenwood, Jon 449
Greenya, Cyril J. 279
Greer, Kevin 80
Greer, K. Gordon 99
Greer, Emily 379
Greer, Greg 799
Greer, Steven K. 844
Greer, Louis E. 855
Greeter, Gerald 652
Greff, Brian 480
Grega, Jocelyn 886
Gregg, Levante 124
Gregg, Paul 273
Gregoire, Kevin P. 361
Gregoire, Daniel N. (Dan) 541
Gregorian, Lisa 838
Gregory, Ramon 161

Gregory, Ryan 176
Gregory, William 197
Gregory, Lentz 355
Gregory, Kevin 378
Gregory, Markeba 380
Gregory, Catherine 413
Gregory, Sherman 707
Gregory, Paul C. 709
Gregory, Audrey 818
Gregory, Jonathan 824
Gregory, Kay 863
Gregory, Suzanne 932
Greindl, Jean-Marie 685
Greiner, Mark 198
Grele, Kathy 558
Grella, Christopher 53
Grensteiner, Ronald J. (Ron) 43
Grenz, Dianne M. 891
Grescovich, Mark J. 110
Grese, Frank 402
Gresham, John 183
Greslick, Richard L 211
Grether, James 942
Gretz, Joe 861
Greuel, Norm 519
Greve, Norman de 252
Grewcock, Bruce E. 670
Grexa, Karen 497
Grey, Robert 686
Grey, Melisse 941
Greyber, Rob 316
Grgg, Walter E 680
Gribbin, Patrick 429
Grice, Bill 486
Grici, Donna 849
Grieco, Anthony 18
Grieder, Daniel 705
Grieshaber, Joe 506
Griesing, Thomas 664
Griffin, Brian T. 66
Griffin, Ronald B. (Ron) 90
Griffin, Corey A. 141
Griffin, Troy 222
Griffin, Gretchen 343
Griffin, Alyson 465
Griffin, Carl 643
Griffin, Ian 650
Griffin, James 750
Griffin, Monty J. 764
Griffin, John 792
Griffin, Ken 816
Griffin, Sean F. 874
Griffin, Darragh 927
Griffis, Eileen 262
Griffith, John B. 1
Griffith, Roger 191
Griffith, Timothy T. 544
Griffith, Jill 668
Griffith, S. Patricia (Tricia) 695
Griffith, Derek 731
Griffith, Joanne 896
Griffith, Kimberly 912
Griffiths, Moira 671
Griffiths, Ed 849
Grigaux, Paul 295
Grigaux, Paul J. 777
Griggs, Stewart 107
Griggs, W. G. (Trey) 153
Griggs, Malcolm D. 205
Griggs, Tanya 620
Grignon, Perianne 759
Grill, Neil 106
Grills, Denise 643
Griman, Emilio 470
Grimes, Jennifer 246
Grimes, Joseph P. (Joe) 821
Grimes, Joe 821
Grimes, Sally 859
Grimminger, Kurt 930
Grimshaw, Matt 168
Grimshaw, Eric 641
Grinberg, Paul J. 137
Grindberg, Guy 881
Griner, Patricia 763
Grippa, Thomas 767
Grippi-Virag, Alicia 395
Grisius, Timothy 548

Grissen, David J. 548
Grissom, Sheri R 371
Grist, Toby 378
Grizzard, Maynard 834
Grob, Matthew S. (Matt) 707
Groba, Kevin 378
Grobbel, Brian 563
Groch, James R. (Jim) 169
Groetken, Doug 919
Groff, Stacey 453
Groff, Jim 834
Groff, Michael R. (Mike) 845
Groff, Mike 863
Grogan, Annie 332
Grogan, Edwin 513
Grogin, Jeffrey P. 662
Groh, Kelly L. 389
Grommesh, Michelle 680
Groner, Mark 172
Gros, Richard R. 557
Gross, Hilly 60
Gross, Jeff 106
Gross, Kevin 107
Gross, Rick 135
Gross, Jeff 440
Gross, Bob 486
Gross, Bruce E. 518
Gross, Linda 533
Gross, Gary 537
Gross, Mark 801
Gross, Rick 849
Gross, Roger 888
Grosshauser, Dan 907
Grossi, Stephen D. 137
Grossi, Therese 161
Grossi, Kevin 737
Grossi, Adriana 792
Grossman, Rick 266
Grossman, Robert I. 606
Grossman, Stephanie F 934
Grosso, Steve 172
Grosvenor, John C. 97
Grosz, Robert 272
Grothues, Arnold 661
Grova, Beverly 266
Grove, Jennifer 217
Grove, Steve 470
Grove, Hannah 791
Grover, Owen 457
Grover, Tom 836
Groves, John 300
Groves, Mary 457
Groves, Tina M. 768
Grow, Erin H 101
Grozier, Paul 115
Grubber, Karen 440
Grubbs, James L. 324
Gruber, Julie 830
Gruber, Scott L. 842
Gruber, Frank 928
Gruca, Damian 6
Grudecki, Mark 504
Gruenberg, Bruce 754
Gruenkemeier, Jens 37
Grunin, Josh 414
Grunwald, Stefan 161
Grusd, Cammy 457
Grygiel, Nancy 57
Gu, Yaobin (Richard) 59
Gu, Yueru 620
Gu, Hanson 705
Guagliardo, Paul (Guyardo) 270
Guardino, Lenny 549
Guarino, John 852
Guay, Martin 786
Guckian, Paul 707
Gude, David 439
Gudibande, Aroon 750
Guedry, John 916
Guemple, James 194
Guenault, Karl 478
Guenther, Chris 610
Guenthner, Kevin J. 354
Guenza, Jill 521
Guenza, Jill 523
Guerin, Cheryl 555
Guerra, Deborah 105

Guerra, Michael 314
Guerra, R. David 468
Guerra, Marquita 604
Guerrazzi, Mark 199
Guerrero, Juan O. 682
Guerrero, Frank 750
Guerrieri, Gary 367
Guerrini, Martino Scabbia 894
Guertin, Shawn M. 17
Guertler, Walter 86
Guess, Brian 497
Guevara, Marcina 593
Guggemos, Michael 463
Guggenheim, Paul A. 657
Gugino, Ann B. 657
Guglielmi, Joseph M 589
Guglielmo, Joseph 857
Gugliuzza, Michael 80
Guhe, Joachim 654
Guidi, Michael 792
Guido, Robert L. 227
Guido, Steve 370
Guidry, Darren 429
Guilfoile, Peter W. 224
Guillaume, Kent 387
Guilleaume, Mike 729
Guillen, Jerome 823
Guillory, Cory 722
Guinan, Tom 103
Guinan, Thomas G. 644
Guinan, Mark J. 709
Guindo, Chirfi 129
Guinn, Max A. 260
Guinn, Max 612
Guio, Laura 470
Guirard, Cal 578
Guise, Jamie 635
Guisinger, Debra L 337
Guisinger, Matt 881
Gula, Allen J. 806
Gulbrandsen, Jaclyn 849
Gullickson, Diane 45
Gulling, Douglas R. (Doug) 915
Gullion, Ann 679
Gullo, Chris 824
Gullucci, Chris 668
Gulmon, Gary 805
Gumba, Rosemarie 185
Gumbar, Gitika 395
Gumbert, Jack 516
Gumerson, John 770
Gunderman, Robert E. (Bob) 926
Gunderson, Gene 806
Gundimeda, Ravi 620
Gunning, Pat 752
Gunnufson, Scott R. 739
Gunsteens, Anne 548
Gunter, Stanley 117
Gunter, Martin 934
Gunther, Shirley 266
Gunther, Conrad J. 268
Gunthner, Richard 555
Gunza, Rich 446
Guo, Peng (Patrick) 820
Gupta, Sanjay 31
Gupta, Suren 31
Gupta, Ashwini (Ash) 44
Gupta, Vineet 131
Gupta, Avinash 181
Gupta, Munish 201
Gupta, Sanjiv 385
Gupta, Rohit 388
Gupta, Pranjal 483
Gupta, Manish 539
Gupta, Deepak 668
Gupta, Vishal 707
Gurgens, Cydney 863
Gurgovits, Stephen J. (Steve) 367
Gurkan, Tarkan 668
Gurmu, Rizvan 395
Gurnani, Roger 893
Gurvitz, Howard 31
Gushie, Steve 12
Gustafson, Dan 608
Gustafson, Joel 613
Gustitus, Nancy 733
Guthery, Christopher 272

Guthrie, Elizabeth 72
Guthrie, Steve 447
Guthrie, Scott 576
Gutierrez, Harvey 246
Gutierrez, Hector 250
Gutierrez, Luz 423
Gutierrez, Becky 582
Gutierrez, Mauricio 625
Gutsch, James L. (Jim) 756
Gutt, David 932
Guttery, John 294
Gutting, Gregory J. (Greg) 310
Guttman, Tim G. 56
Guttman, Robert S. 862
Guy, Rupert 715
Guy, Steven 895
Guyett, Gregory L. 290
Guyot, Pierre 260
Guyse, Clyde 99
Guzik, Bill 9
Guzman, Sandra 202
Guzman, Jennifer 635
Guzy, Edward 550
Guzzi, Anthony J. (Tony) 298
Gwin, Robert G. (Bob) 61
Gwin, Marie 122
Gwizdala, Lori A. 187
Gwynn, Genna 748
Gyftopoulos, Artie 604
Gysbers, Niki 578

H

Ha, Joseph 615
Haag, Natalie 159
Haag, Erin 241
Haag, Donald 652
Haagenson, Deb 168
Haahr, J. Tyler 568
Haan, Taco de 365
Haas, Tracie 6
Haas, Bernard 261
Haase, Bill 222
Haase, Joseph 416
Haasen, Don 749
Haber, Jack 220
Haberern, Andrew 214
Haberfield, Patrick 745
Habern, Jim 697
Habib, Reham 615
Habib, Helen 635
Hablian, Tony 734
Hablitzel, Thomas C. 764
Habr, Dany 6
Hack, Ted 380
Hackemer, Thomas E 84
Hackenberg, Amy L. 349
Hackenson, Elizabeth 16
Hacker, Mark S. 589
Hacker, Howard 818
Hackett, William F. (Bill) 237
Hackett, Jim 370
Hackett, John 765
Hackley, Lloyd 860
Hackney, Dave 722
Hackney, Daniel 881
Hadad, Henry 144
Hadavi, Judith 671
Haddad, Michael 56
Haddad, David 838
Hadican, Brian 306
Hadley, Ralph 220
Hadley, Tim 635
Hadley, Todd 942
Hadrava, Rick 715
Hadsell, Charlie 298
Haeberle, Carol 699
Haefele, Alan 678
Haefner, Larry A. 210
Haefner, Francis J 279
Haes, Jon 379
Haessler, Laura 272
Hafdelin, Mike 800
Hafer, Michael 919
Haffner, Jon E 224
Haffner, Paul 713

Hafner, Steve 689
Haft, Steven 172
Hafter, Jeffrey M. (Jeff) 122
Hagan, Michael 431
Hagan, Kevin 454
Hagan, Benjamin 649
Hagan, David 855
Hageboeck, Charles R. (Skip) 207
Hagedorn, Avery 252
Hagedorn, Michael D. (Mike) 863
Hagelin, Carl 105
Hagelsieb, Marco 750
Hagen, Don 14
Hagen, Jonathan Hirt 310
Hagen, Thomas B. 310
Hagen, Terence D. 481
Hagen, Mary 567
Hagen, Russell S. 922
Hager, David A. (Dave) 263
Hager, Roger 300
Hager, George V. 386
Hager, Cary J 449
Hager, Tim 456
Hager, Michael W 666
Hager, Christopher 754
Hagerman, Douglas M. (Doug) 738
Hagerty, James 906
Haggerty, Kathleen 45
Haggerty, Patrick 803
Haggerty, Paul 858
Haggy, Bret 449
Hagmann, Cheryl 665
Hague, Delbert 905
Hagy, Carole 861
Hahn, Heidi 80
Hahn, Terrence S. 434
Hahn, Josh 863
Haight, Mark A 725
Haight, Sharon 934
Haile, Kempton C. 834
Hailey, V. Ann 95
Hailey, Clint 818
Haines, Ann 537
Haines, Gary 905
Hainey, Chris 637
Haintz, Dion 558
Hair, Brian 449
Hairston, John M. 406
Hairston, Michelle 704
Haise, Olivier 889
Hajdik, Brock 423
Hajzak, Kristina 335
Hakim, Veronique 571
Hakim, Elias 875
Hakimzadeh, Kahilla 457
Halberstadt, Geoffrey L. 148
Halbert, Doug 94
Halbur, Rita 888
Haldeman, Charles E. (Ed) 746
Hale, Karen 6
Hale, Jean R. 230
Haley, Greg 18
Haley, Jeffrey V. 48
Haley, Christopher 249
Haley, Colleen 332
Haley, Crissy 487
Halfin, Simon 269
Halfman, Mark 708
Halit, Bander 115
Halkins, Jim 550
Hall, Tom 31
Hall, William (Bill) 33
Hall, Jason 45
Hall, Rhonda 101
Hall, Jay 117
Hall, Justin 133
Hall, Jill 137
Hall, Adam 143
Hall, Craig 170
Hall, Stephanie 176
Hall, Charles 191
Hall, Walter 201
Hall, Mary Dean 291
Hall, Robert 304
Hall, Kaye 324
Hall, Maryjane 328
Hall, Tammy 355

Hall, Alexandra 358
Hall, Duncan 389
Hall, Charles J. (Chuck) 416
Hall, Jeff 602
Hall, Ladd R. 626
Hall, Tammy 635
Hall, Leslie (Les) 705
Hall, J. Franklin (Frank) 712
Hall, O. B. Grayson 721
Hall, Jerron 722
Hall, Julie 748
Hall, Tom 757
Hall, John 773
Hall, R. Wayne 776
Hall, Bill 813
Hall, Jack 820
Hall, Kerry L. 823
Hall, Cynthia 831
Hall, Keith 852
Hall, Bradley C. 861
Hall, Alan 875
Hall, Jonathan 903
Hall, Denise 908
Hall, Justin M. 937
Halladay, Tim 395
Hallberg, Joe 32
Hallenbeck, Robert L 750
Haller, Christopher 860
Halliday, Jim 121
Halliday, Sarah A. 598
Halligan, Catherine 862
Hallinan, Patrick D. 371
Hallman, Dwayne D. 435
Hallman, Samantha 720
Hallmark, Michael 454
Halloran, Brian 227
Halmy, Christopher A. 33
Halnon, Bill 729
Halper, Julie 122
Halper, John 473
Halperin, Scott 87
Halpin, Edward D. (Ed) 673
Halprin, Joseph 555
Halstead, Mark 172
Halter, Bob 31
Halter, Patrick G. (Pat) 691
Halter, Michael P. (Mike) 818
Halter, John 860
Halupnik, Mark 261
Halvacs, Greg 161
Halverson, Bradley M. (Brad) 166
Halverson, Thomas 214
Halverson, Michelle 813
Halvorsen, Cheryl 856
Haly, Gregg 170
Ham, Ning 488
Hamano, Wayne Y. 102
Hamaoka, Eiji 685
Hamberlin, Mark 256
Hamblin, Vicky 117
Hamburg, Marc D. 123
Hamer, Marc A. 757
Hameren, Dirk-Jan van 615
Hames, Danette R 224
Hamid, Asad 649
Hamid, Sarah J 700
Hamill, Laura 57
Hamill, Tim 487
Hamilton, Craig 88
Hamilton, Julie 216
Hamilton, Anne 274
Hamilton, Henry 332
Hamilton, Bonita 365
Hamilton, Joanne G. 440
Hamilton, John 502
Hamilton, Jeff 530
Hamilton, Andrew 606
Hamilton, Jean 699
Hamilton, Derrick 786
Hamilton, Robin 824
Hamilton, Jason 911
Hamlin, Phil 459
Hamlin, Amanda 465
Hamlisch, Eliot 932
Hammad, Rania 536
Hammer, Bonnie 222
Hammer, Doug 467

Hammergren, John H. 563
Hammerschmidt, John P 119
Hammes, Eric 2
Hammock, Gary 102
Hammock, Brian 245
Hammond, Mike 224
Hammond, Harlan 467
Hammond, Marlene 530
Hammond, Peter 735
Hammond, Matthew 800
Hammond, Jason 809
Hammonds, Kim 135
Hammouri, Monte 458
Hampel, Leslie 787
Hampton, Mark A. 324
Hampton, Jon 533
Hampton, Jerry 677
Hamre, Lasse 457
Hamren, Liz 576
Han, Shufeng 261
Han, Bernard L. (Bernie) 271
Han, Sam 366
Hance, Debbie 117
Hanchey, William 181
Hanco, Carlos 395
Hancock, Wendy 172
Hancock, C. Wayne 230
Hancock, Matthew 276
Hancock, Lain 282
Hancock, Michael 498
Hancock, Brian 923
Hand, Fred 151
Hand, Larry 266
Handanyan, Lynne 671
Handler, Richard B. 520
Handler, Rebecca 713
Handley, Terry W. 164
Handley, Thomas W. (Tom) 294
Handley, Bill W 489
Handley, Teresa 927
Handlon, Carolyn B. 548
Handren, Scott 129
Handt, Scott 519
Handy, Edward O. (Ned) 906
Hanes, Vladimir 57
Haney, Paul R 246
Haney, Joe 748
Hang, Edward 820
Hangen, Charles 310
Hanif, Farina 158
Haniffa, Johara 548
Hanifin, Kristi 710
Hanigan, Kevin J. 515
Haning, Tony 487
Hank, Jeffrey P 476
Hanke-baier, Petra 693
Hankins, Anthony P. 452
Hankins, Robert 726
Hankins, Steven 860
Hankinson, Beverly 246
Hanko, Edward 72
Hanks, W. Bruce 182
Hanky, Donald 834
Hanley, Walter P. 534
Hanley, Colleen 698
Hanley, Joseph R. 817
Hanlon, Crystal 431
Hanna, Wade 343
Hanna, Kathy 507
Hanna, Patti 870
Hannah, D. Jay 98
Hannan, Beth 182
Hannan, Carolyne 222
Hanner, John 72
Hannigan, Andrew 489
Hannigan, Marie 748
Hannon, Mary 106
Hannon, Michael J. 680
Hanrahan, Jack 339
Hansberry, Shameka 107
Hanscom, Morgan 185
Hansel, Elizabeth 628
Hansen, Mike 15
Hansen, John 74
Hansen, Patti 158
Hansen, J. Michael (Mike) 198
Hansen, Russell 201

Hansen, Gary D 273
Hansen, Bruce 609
Hansen, Garrett H 710
Hansen, Tim 715
Hansen, Jeff 794
Hansen, Derek 888
Hansen, Corey 888
Hansen, Craig 911
Hansen, Dennis R. 915
Hanson, Philip 2
Hanson, Harley 14
Hanson, Breck F. 80
Hanson, Maggie 119
Hanson, Jackson 210
Hanson, Rachel 214
Hanson, Jim 226
Hanson, Jay 293
Hanson, Rodney D 297
Hanson, Bryan C. 314
Hanson, Bryan C 316
Hanson, Greg 394
Hanson, Lillian 470
Hanson, Bradley C. (Brad) 568
Hanson, Terri 637
Hanson, Michael 661
Hanson, Ronald 770
Hanson, Milagros 813
Hanson, Karen 863
Hanson, George 866
Hansotia, Eric 20
Hantak, Greg 825
Happel, Charles T. 325
Happer, Dan 838
Happy, Katherine 224
Harada, Craig 201
Haran, Edward 746
Harbaugh, Todd 903
Harbeck, Stephen P. 759
Harber, Nick 643
Harbeson, Roger 109
Harbison, Cecilia 881
Harbour, Shawn 863
Hardecke, Matthew 306
Hardie, James R. 842
Hardig, John J. 936
Hardiman, Nathan 530
Hardin, Frank 94
Hardin, Scott 530
Hardin, Marie 831
Harding, Tom 60
Harding, Bobbi 325
Harding, John D 377
Harding, James A. (Jim) 752
Harding, Debra 875
Harding, Joe 926
Harding, Lori 942
Hardison, Ann 116
Hardman, Renee 754
Hardman, Dan 803
Hardtke, Mark 620
Hardwick, Mark K. 355
Hardy, John D 93
Hardy, Stephen G. 228
Hardy, Karen 454
Hardy, Jon 519
Hardy, James 791
Hardy, Jody 867
Hare, Joshua 201
Hare, Douglas 863
Hargett, Carla 715
Hargis, Jonathan 186
Hargis, Michael 550
Hargis, Jaron 635
Hargrove, Robin S. (Rob) 584
Harik, Mario A. 936
Harika, Michelle 133
Harker, Timothy 754
Harkey, Jean 419
Harkins, Tara 530
Harkness, Gordon 467
Harkness, David C. 933
Harlacher, Donna 539
Harlan, Jim 808
Harlan, Wendy 886
Harlow, David R. 98
Harlow, Terri 800
Harman, David 194

Harman, William 786
Harman, Phil 786
Harmening, Jeffrey L. 383
Harmon, Allen 115
Harmon, David 176
Harmon, Jane 875
Harms, Timothy W 262
Harms, Luke 923
Harnetiaux, Kevin 413
Harnett, James 497
Harney, Michael 200
Harold, Jim 425
Harp, Rickey D. 324
Harp, Sarah 896
Harper, Sean E. 57
Harper, Hamilton 248
Harper, Gant 355
Harper, Craig 447
Harper, Stacey 533
Harper, Nancy 548
Harper, Ryan 607
Harper, Bryan 722
Harper, Bobby 726
Harper, Sandra 903
Harrah, Keith 722
Harralson, Jefferson L. 869
Harrell, John 108
Harrell, Randy 199
Harrell, Evelyn 517
Harrell, James A. 775
Harrington, Ben 99
Harrington, Charles 131
Harrington, Michael W. (Mike) 148
Harrington, Dennis 312
Harrington, Barbara J. 342
Harrington, Michael J. 358
Harrington, Christopher 457
Harrington, Michael J. 528
Harrington, George 570
Harrington, Parker 799
Harris, Scott 31
Harris, Donald 44
Harris, David 45
Harris, Stephen 51
Harris, Angelee J. 97
Harris, Brian 99
Harris, Andrew 101
Harris, Mitchell E. 105
Harris, Timothy 129
Harris, Mark 135
Harris, Michael 135
Harris, Henriette Henriette 158
Harris, Jonathan 185
Harris, Michael 189
Harris, Isaiah (Ike) 195
Harris, Diane 201
Harris, Crystal 220
Harris, John 246
Harris, Richard 248
Harris, David G. 263
Harris, Timothy K. (Tim) 349
Harris, Nigel 370
Harris, Ruth 383
Harris, Daniel 395
Harris, Jeffrey 404
Harris, Stephen 413
Harris, Brian 487
Harris, Paul N. 497
Harris, Brock 516
Harris, Yvette 573
Harris, Stephen 582
Harris, Brenda 631
Harris, James 663
Harris, Mike 697
Harris, Timothy P. 699
Harris, John D. 716
Harris, Todd 722
Harris, Tammy 722
Harris, Randy 726
Harris, Paul V 732
Harris, Henry (Sandy) 762
Harris, Jennifer 770
Harris, Donald 774
Harris, Mark 803
Harris, Donald 869
Harris, Sandra 894
Harris, Raymond 895

Harris, Don 896
Harris, Monica 896
Harris, Phyllis 903
Harris, Rosalyn 903
Harris, Jeff M. 907
Harris, Rafiq 928
Harris, Chad 934
Harris, Todd 942
Harrison, Andrew R. 26
Harrison, Tim 53
Harrison, Thomas 115
Harrison, Miranda 131
Harrison, Gregory 139
Harrison, Suzan F. 219
Harrison, Olga 246
Harrison, Leslie 367
Harrison, Kimberly 450
Harrison, A. Marc 467
Harrison, Joe 517
Harrison, Winifred 536
Harrison, Chris M. 542
Harrison, Deborah 548
Harrison, Nico 615
Harrison, Peter 637
Harrison, Dan 641
Harrison, Dan L 641
Harrison, Katherine 762
Harrison, Bo 865
Harrison, Linda 935
Harrod, Tricia 474
Harrod, Lawrence 882
Harrold, Jason M 176
Harshbarger, Catherine 112
Harshbarger, Karen 590
Harstad, Brian 300
Hart, Christopher 106
Hart, Robert 201
Hart, Gerald 330
Hart, Betty 376
Hart, Kevin 382
Hart, Michael 593
Hart, Kevin 652
Hart, Mark J. 654
Hart, R. Rick 726
Hart, Amy St 757
Hart, Chet 762
Hart, Mark 786
Hart, Sharon E. Donovan 791
Hart, Brent 847
Hart, Craig 860
Hart, Brett 861
Hart, Brett J. 871
Hart, Gregory L. (Greg) 871
Hart, Kirk 932
Hartanov, Creighton 559
Harter, Scott 27
Harti, Mohamed 672
Hartigan, Gregory 170
Hartigan, Matthew D 731
Hartinger, Mark 18
Hartings, Ben 355
Hartings, Benjamin J 355
Hartkemeier, David 196
Hartl, Thomas 587
Hartley, Karen 53
Hartley, Jerry 336
Hartley, Jeff 808
Hartley, Lisa 884
Hartlieb, Jim 343
Hartman, Taymar 6
Hartman, Bret 199
Hartman, Jamie 252
Hartman, Andrew 395
Hartman, Michael 748
Hartman, Art 797
Hartman, Richard T. (Rick) 841
Hartman, Kevin 875
Hartman, Michael 934
Hartmann, Ronald 366
Hartmann, Nancy 429
Hartmann, William L. (Bill) 497
Hartmann, Margot 656
Hartmann, Jocelyn 803
Hartnett, John R. 458
Hartnett, Dan 654
Harton, H. Lynn 869
Hartsell, Kelly 770

Hartsfield, Keith 442
Hartsfield, Russell 823
Hartshorn, Brian 276
Hartshorn, Michael J. 740
Hartwell, Alan 643
Hartwick, Gary 313
Hartwig, Scott 722
Harty, Harriet K. 31
Hartz, Gregory J. 842
Hartzell, Steve 809
Hartzog, Dan 437
Harvell, Glen 548
Harvey, Lauren 124
Harvey, Robert 158
Harvey, David C. 250
Harvey, Thomas H. 559
Harvey, Anna L. 606
Harvey, Gene 620
Harvey, Darrell 668
Harvey, Justin 809
Harwell, David 726
Harwood, Chris 60
Harwood, Randall R. 399
Harwood, Darrell W. 857
Hasaligil, Ahmet 175
Hasan, Ben-Saba 903
Hasenkamp, Michael 306
Hasenzahl, Catherine 488
Haser, H. William 820
Hashim, Faiz 204
Haskell, Mark 273
Haskell, Gabrielle 610
Haskins, Scott 185
Haskins, Eric 487
Hassan, Fred 95
Hassan, Fred 95
Hassell, Gerald L. 105
Hasselman, Jeff 224
Hasserjian, Kirk 71
Hassett, Joseph (John) 62
Hassett, Tom 264
Hassfurther, Thomas A. (Tom) 652
Hassing, Ben 904
Hastings, Scott 107
Hastings, Steven 413
Hatch, Jessica 550
Hatcher, Mel 185
Hatcher, Rochelle 507
Hathaway, Scot C. 278
Hathaway, Robert 645
Hathaway, Jim 668
Hathi, Neesha 754
Hatley, Kim F 416
Hatmaker, Brian 230
Hattey, Steve 224
Hau, Robert W. (Bob) 361
Hauch, Carl 12
Haudrich, John 649
Hauenstein, Glen W. 262
Hauer, Clarence 168
Hauersperger, Joe 390
Haugan, Russell 465
Haugeh, Robert 251
Haugen, Robert W. 251
Haugh, Samantha 97
Haugh, Don 300
Haugh, Dave 311
Haught, Deanna 577
Haught, Jim 916
Haugli, Brian 409
Haupert, Sue 872
Haupt, Axel 528
Haupter, Ralph 576
Hauptman, Mindy 226
Hauptmeier, Wayde 929
Hauser, Betsy 155
Hauser, William 446
Hauser, Susan 576
Haushalter, Todd 573
Hausler, Wendy 245
Hausman, William 720
Hautman, Milla 881
Havard, Robert 484

Havel, James M. 319
Havern, Lindsay 671
Haversang, Ed 687
Haverty-Stacke, Dylan 45
Hawkins, James jay 189
Hawkins, Jay james 189
Hawkins, Tobin 194
Hawkins, Heath 224
Hawkins, Vern 224
Hawkins, Steve J. 353
Hawkins, John 419
Hawkins, Myke 494
Hawkins, Jessica L 555
Hawkins, Jay 574
Hawkins, Eric 603
Hawkins, Mark J. 748
Hawkins, Duane F. 784
Hawkins, J. Michael 898
Hawkins, Rodney 926
Hawkins, Darren D. 937
Hawn, Marcela Manjarrez 176
Haworth, Joanne 415
Hay, Lewis (Lew) 363
Hayden, Bill 161
Hayden, John 724
Haydon, John B. 709
Hayer, Lauren 520
Hayes, John A. 96
Hayes, Bob 153
Hayes, Rejji P. 210
Hayes, Maria Reeves 470
Hayes, Robin 483
Hayes, Joy 489
Hayes, Deborah 530
Hayes, Lisa 582
Hayes, Robert 643
Hayes, Kathleen 664
Hayes, John 705
Hayes, Larry 710
Hayes, Holly 715
Hayes, Kristin 754
Hayes, Terry 811
Hayes, Christina 813
Hayes, Thomas P. (Tom) 859
Hayes, Todd M. 876
Hayes, Gregory J. 879
Hayes, Janet M. 925
Hayes-Giles, Joyce V. 283
Hayhurst, James B. 868
Hayles, Carol 201
Haynes, Stephan 42
Haynes, Holliday 555
Haynes, Joan E. 624
Haynes, Brian 724
Haynes, Angie 769
Haynie, Tammy 201
Hays, Carolyn 207
Hays, Ed 216
Hays, Paul 237
Hays, Steven 766
Haytaian, Peter D. 66
Hayton, Fred 162
Hayward, Jeffery R. 322
Hayward, Lani 864
Haywood, Jerry 748
Hazen, Samuel N. (Sam) 416
Hazime, Inaya 266
Hazlin, John 219
He, Dennis 804
Heacock, David A. 278
Heacock, Mike 935
Head, Greg 273
Head, Chris 489
Headrick, Michael 808
Heady, Christopher (Chris) 133
Heagler, Brian 497
Healton, Cheryl G. 606
Healy, Christopher 224
Healy, Luke 247
Healy, Chris 274
Healy, Denis 366
Healy, Tom 395
Healy, Russell 452
Healy, Michael 470
Healy, John 494
Heaney, Joe 569
Heard, Mike 213

Hearne, David 763
Heater, Nicole 725
Heath, Chad 80
Heath, Kay 99
Heath, William 528
Heath, David 866
Heaton, Gregory L. (Greg) 367
Heavner, Jim 365
Hebden, Jacqui 840
Hebel, Daniel 32
Hebert, Amy 173
Hebert, Thomas 191
Hebert, Karl 788
Hebert, Jason 855
Hebner, Scott 470
Hechtner, Mike 214
Heck, Christopher B. (Chris) 285
Heck, Matthew 754
Heck, John 832
Hecker, Rob 886
Heckler, Mark A. 558
Heckman, Pam 487
Hedayati, Zhian 786
Hedgebeth, Reggie 546
Hedgebeth, Reginald D 546
Hedstrom, Jeff 941
Heebner, David 380
Heenan, Regina 297
Heenan, Palmer T. 362
Heenan, Kregg 680
Hees, Bernardo V. 505
Heeson, Lee 175
Hefel, Victoria 872
Heffernan, Edward J. (Ed) 30
Heffernan, John 788
Heffernan, Rick 849
Heffernan, Daniel 860
Heffler, Mava K. 298
Heffner, Art 39
Heffner, Stephen 170
Heffner, Jacquelyn 205
Heffron, Tom 904
Heflin, Robert 226
Hefter, Marcia Z. 143
Hegarty, Kevin P. 720
Hegedus, Mike 852
Hegele, Steve 336
Heger, Mary P. 40
Hegi, Maria 768
Hegwood, Neil 580
Heidrick, Richard 228
Heidt, Alex 411
Heier, Timothy C. 754
Heijmen, Jos 929
Heikes, Parker 226
Heil, Tim 259
Heilbronn, Charles 862
Heim, Chris 805
Heim, Michael A. 812
Heim, Michael 923
Heiman, Scott 511
Heimburg, Sue Von 738
Heimes, Terry J. 601
Heine, Robert 528
Heinemann, Tom 185
Heinmets, David 511
Heinonen, Cheryl 95
Heintz, Karen 735
Heintzelman, Daniel 261
Heintzman, David P. 796
Heinz, Greg 504
Heinze, Stefan 811
Heinzelmann, Nick 530
Heise, Arthur G. (Art) 80
Heise, John M 345
Heise, Angela L. 516
Heisel, David 827
Heiser, Aaron 615
Heishman, Dennis P. 635
Heiskell, Jay 536
Heist, John 713
Heitke, Ruth 168
Hejka, Marcin 465
Helding, Erik M. 213
Heldke, Gail 343
Heldman, Paul 507
Hele, John C. R. 569

Heleen, Mark L. 595
Heleen, Mark L 595
Helke, Sue 18
Heller, David 96
Heller, Alan 115
Heller, Richard 407
Heller, Paul G. 449
Heller, Marc 610
Heller, Jeffrey S 618
Heller, Gene 752
Heller, Aneen 802
Helling, Larry J. 706
Hellman, Wendy 88
Hellman, Thomas 546
Helm, Robert 380
Helm, Bob 380
Helm, James 550
Helm, Lucy Lee 787
Helm, Larry L. 824
Helmers, David 197
Helmey, Brian 935
Helmick, Ann 666
Helms, Lloyd W. (Bill) 308
Helms, Cory 309
Helsel, Christopher 397
Helt, Peter 105
Helton, Marianna 97
Helton, Cary 245
Helton, Vicky 869
Heltz, George 237
Helvaty, Thomas 722
Hemade, Sagar 820
Hemani, Sul 109
Hemelryck, Tom Van 905
Heminger, Gary R. 544
Hemingway, W David 941
Hemker, David J. (Dave) 512
Hemler, Alan J 671
Hempen, Rande 161
Hempfield, Tom 425
Hemphill, Stuart R. 777
Hempton, Sue 358
Hemsley, Stephen J. 881
Henak, William S. 814
Henderson, Chris 170
Henderson, Rebecca 179
Henderson, Terrance 224
Henderson, Joseph 304
Henderson, Douglas 337
Henderson, Richie 447
Henderson, Reginald 537
Henderson, Scott 717
Henderson, Julie 858
Henderson, Scott 911
Hendley, Shawna 618
Hendren, Bradley 109
Hendren, Mike 677
Hendrick, Bryan 727
Hendricks, Tom 365
Hendricks, Karissa 449
Hendricks, Steve 745
Hendricks, Martin 820
Hendrickson, David 486
Hendrickson, Nancy 840
Hendrikse, Pieter 486
Hendrikse, Danny 671
Hendrix, Ron 335
Hendrix, Ben 855
Hendry, Andrew 220
Heneberry, Richard 31
Heneghan, James M. (Jim) 186
Heneghan, James 620
Hengel, Susan 722
Henigin, Susan 345
Henke, Kim 735
Henkelman, Paula 300
Henkes, Scott 860
Henley, Robert W. 629
Henn, Anthony 196
Henn, Tony 197
Henn, Vicki C. 680
Henneberger, Mark 903
Hennessy, Tara 72
Hennessy, Lisa 693
Hennessy, Ray 705
Hennigan, Mike 544
Hennike, Toni 423

Henning, James P. (Jim) 285
Henning, Brian 635
Henning, Geoffrey 661
Henninger, Tadd J 686
Henrichsen, Kim 467
Henry, Maurice 81
Henry, Janet 168
Henry, Jeff 172
Henry, Martin 261
Henry, Doug 440
Henry, Brian 468
Henry, Maria G. 499
Henry, Christopher 573
Henry, Peter B. 606
Henry, Heather 799
Henry, Furtick 849
Henry, Angelisa 903
Henseler, Glenn D 717
Hensey, Bernard 135
Henshaw, Melissa 769
Hensing, John 111
Henslee, Gregory L. (Greg) 630
Hensler, Ann M 715
Hensley, Robin T 423
Hensley, Pat 453
Hensley, Scott 620
Hensley, Ed 912
Henson, Christopher L. (Chris) 116
Henson, Cliff 425
Henson, Mark 613
Henson, Rob 635
Henson, Erica 903
Henson, Meghan A. 936
Hepburn, Cc 507
Hepler, David 345
Herbel, Vern D. 844
Herbert, Toni 270
Herbert, James H. 358
Herbert, Courtney 539
Herbert, Don 875
Herbst, Jeff 628
Herd, Teresa 465
Herde, Patrick 172
Herder, Karla 463
Herena, Monique R. 105
Herencia, Roberto R. 340
Hererra, Janeen 57
Hergesheimer, Karin 392
Herington, Dave 2
Herington, Charles M. 95
Herlihy, Donagh 95
Herman, Judy 14
Herman, Mark I. 210
Herman, Deborah 459
Herman, Mike 668
Herman, Robert A. (Bob) 675
Hermann, Val©rie 713
Hermans, Jan 94
Hermel, Oren 881
Hermida, Adam 133
Hermon, Christopher J. 837
Hernan, Javier 88
Hernandez, Pedro 14
Hernandez, John 109
Hernandez, Mark 159
Hernandez, Cynthia 202
Hernandez, Abdon 237
Hernandez, Martin 249
Hernandez, Carlos M. 365
Hernandez, Patrice 421
Hernandez, Gregorio 425
Hernandez, Dolores 454
Hernandez, Kelly 517
Hernandez, Patricio 555
Hernandez, Enrique (Rick) 562
Hernandez, Jeff 673
Hernandez, Rene 849
Hernandez, Lucy 890
HERNANDEZ, VICTOR 890
Hernandez, Oscar 892
Hernandez, Victor 903
Herndon, Brad 717
Hernquist, Thomas 422
Hern ndez, Juan G. 365
Herr, David 847
Herranz, Mario 334
Herrema, Gregory J. (Greg) 836

Herrenbruck, David W 337
Herrera, Lisa 558
Herrera, Ailisa 558
Herrero, Jose 365
Herrick, Glen W. 568
Herrin, Tad 33
Herring, Jim 75
Herring, Lloyd 465
Herriott, Penni 106
Herrman, Ernie 839
Herrmann, Gunnar 370
Herrmann, Bernie J. 725
Herron, Wayne 266
Herron, John 286
Herron, John 304
Herron, Steve 313
Herron, Dallas I. 392
Herron, Michael 530
Herron, C. Keith 721
Herron, Yllon 849
Herron, Paul 895
Herschel, Tom 171
Herseth, Steve 559
Hersh, Marc 587
Herskovitz, Rachel 457
Herthel, Kevin 727
Herting, Joshua 786
Hertz, Sally 486
Herzfeld, Michael 204
Heskett, Todd 185
Heskin, John 201
Hess, William H. (Hal) 51
Hess, Rick D. 62
Hess, Susan 146
Hess, John B. 423
Hess, Carol 442
Hess, Ross 692
Hessberger, Tammy 409
Hession, Michael 413
Hest, Daniel 317
Hester, Travis 385
Hester, Kevin D. 430
Hester, David 452
Hester, Randy D. 697
Hesterberg, Earl J. 401
Heston, Mary 748
Hetterich, F. Paul 236
Hettler, Charlie M 799
Hetzer, Ben 550
Hetzler, Dustin 724
Heugly, Jacob 941
Hevner, Dave 799
Hewatt, Russell 107
Hewitt, Robert C. 122
Hewitt, Dan 449
Hewitt, Jill 632
Hewitt, Dennis E. 639
Hewitt, Rod 895
Hey-Hadavi, Judith 672
Heyde, Charles Von Der 676
Heydlauff, Dale E. 42
Heyman, William H. 759
Heyman, William H. (Bill) 849
Heyman, Neal 881
Heymann, Sandra 484
Hiatt, Wendy 453
Hiatt, Ruth 699
Hibbert, Eric 109
Hickerson, Neale 429
Hickerson, Marcus 429
Hickey, Scott S. 80
Hickey, Dennis J. 219
Hickey, Adam 227
Hickey, Michael A. (Mike) 294
Hickey, Brian E. 538
Hickman, Phillip 80
Hickman, Angie 639
Hickman, Elizabeth 722
Hickman, Robert 888
Hickox, Michelle S. 460
Hicks, Weston M. 28
Hicks, Malcolm 107
Hicks, Ann 117
Hicks, George T. 146
Hicks, Ted 179
Hicks, JO 226
Hicks, David 284

Hicks, Flori 429
Hicks, Jenny 502
Hicks, Kirkland L. 529
Hicks, Jeff 564
Hicks, David 643
Hicks, Sherrie 678
Hicks, Phil 749
Hicks, Bridget 813
Hicks, R. Steven (Steve) 884
Hicks, Roland 893
Hicok, Bob 241
Hicok, Gary 628
Hidalgo, Robert 204
Hidalgo, Melissa 530
Hiemstra, David John 720
Higberg, Vern 875
Higginbotham, John 137
Higginbotham, Lesley B 224
Higginbotham, Cole 226
Higginbotham, Robert 809
Higgins, Kevin 3
Higgins, Martha T. 141
Higgins, Thomas 185
Higgins, Thomas (Tom) 348
Higgins, Christopher 395
Higgins, Jeanne 489
Higgins, Sam 539
Higgins, Christine 573
Higgins, Kerri 578
Higgins, Brian S 643
Higgins, Brian 643
Higgins, Kevin 671
Higgins, Chip 677
Higgins, Joseph J 709
Higgins, Amy 759
Higgins, Kevin 834
Higgins, Scott F. 849
Higgins, Lorrie 849
High, Joseph C. 398
Highfield, Karen 333
Higley, Ralph 770
Higson, John P. 95
Hijkoop, Frans 569
Hilbush, Mark 875
Hildebrand, J. Bruce 350
Hildreth, Christopher 735
Hile, Michael 517
Hileman, Donald P. 349
Hiles, Andy 18
Hilfiker, Amy 442
Hilger, Andy 29
Hilger, James K. (Jim) 258
Hilger, Autumn 266
Hill, W. Guy 31
Hill, Eddie 45
Hill, Anne 91
Hill, J. Tomilson 133
Hill, Shawn 135
Hill, Daniel 135
Hill, Jean M 151
Hill, John B. (Thad) 153
Hill, Edwin J. (Ed) 162
Hill, ED 162

Hill, Mara 187
Hill, Colin M 194
Hill, Garrett 224
Hill, Pam 226
Hill, Frank 226
Hill, Craig D. 325
Hill, Kenneth 380
Hill, Gregory P. (Greg) 423
Hill, Tom 439
Hill, Tom 449
Hill, Herbert 456
Hill, Michael 465
Hill, Scott A. 466
Hill, Peter 483
Hill, Keith 483
Hill, Michele Y 528
Hill, Judy 558
Hill, Robert 598
Hill, Brian 609
Hill, Elliott J. 615
Hill, David R. 625
Hill, Peter 643
Hill, Charles H. (Chuck) 671

Hill, Nina 672
Hill, Robert R. 776
Hill, Robert 811
Hill, Jamie 849
Hill, Adam 867
Hill, Allen 875
Hill, Deryl 875
Hill, Stephanie 882
Hill, Mike 886
Hill, Becky 888
Hill, John 890
Hill, Lee 904
Hill-Edgar, William Keyes 896
Hillard, Teddy 146
Hillard, Lloyd C. 324
Hillebrand, Lana L. 42
Hillebrand, James A. (Ja) 796
Hillemeier, A. Craig 831
Hiller, Sharon 927
Hillhouse, Alison 896
Hilliard, Wes 886
Hillier, Scott A. 531
Hillman, Kristin 813
Hillman, Alex 934
Hills, John 927
Hilton, Calvin 30
Hilzinger, Kurt J. 446
Himelfarb, Richard J. 795
Hinaga, Reid 103
Hinckle, Veronica 162
Hinde, Jason 313
Hindel, Joanne 337
Hinderstein, Chase 735
Hinds, Jim 72
Hinds, Donald 722
Hinds, Tom 935
Hinds, David 942
Hinduja, Anil 374
Hiner, Patrick 2
Hiner, Troy 750
Hines, Michael 170
Hines, Brenda 370
Hines, Eric 493
Hines, Russell 808
Hing, Rebecca 929
Hingsbergen, Michael 197
Hingston, Alex 620
Hingtgen, Tim L. 230
Hinkley, Brian 15
Hinkley, Richard 199
Hinman, Jacqueline C. (Jacque) 185
Hinnenkamp, Paul D. 304
Hinrichs, Joseph R. (Joe) 370
Hinrichs, Kenneth 425
Hinsdale, Mark 245
Hinsdale, Bill 911
Hinshaw, Ken 172
Hinshaw, Janice 518
Hinson, W. Ron 389
Hinson, Donald J. 421
Hinson, Jeffrey T. 926
Hinton, Matthew 142
Hinton, Michelle 244
Hintz, Brian 342
Hintze, Scott 197
Hintzen, Daniel 620
Hiotelis, Peter 792
Hippen, Lyle 181
Hipskind, Jennifer 661
Hiraki, Justin 808
Hirata, Vernon 822
Hirji, Ali 204
Hirko, Andrew 272
Hirose, Don 170
Hirsch, Roderick 680
Hirschberg, Alan 570
Hirsh, Peter 131
Hirsh, Brent 557
Hirshberg, Eric 10
Hirst, Ben 262
Hirst, Alistair D. 493
Hishikawa, Maki 19
Hitchings, Stephen 743
Hitchner, Kenneth W. 395
Hite, Amanda 101
Hitt, David 682
Hitt, Charles 936

Hitz, David 601
Hitz, Phil 784
Hixson, Richard 488
Hjelm, Christopher T. (Chris) 506
Hjelm, Chris 507
Hnat, James G. (Jim) 483
HO, Duong 7
Ho, Ivan 94
Ho, Peter S. 102
Ho, Rikki 103
Ho, David 170
Ho, Karen 395
Ho, Stephen 548
Ho-Schnell, Wendy 593
Hoaglund, Eric 146
Hobart, Lauren R. 264
Hobart, Brian E. 460
Hobbs, Franklin W. (Fritz) 33
Hobbs, Mitch 245
Hobbs, Michael B. 403
Hobbs, Nicholas (Nick) 447
Hobbs, Rodney 786
Hobbs, David A 876
Hoberg, Troy 15
Hobert, Christine 335
Hobin, Peggy L. 905
Hobson, Christopher K. (Chris) 239
Hobson, Derry L. 282
Hobson, Chris 895
Hocevar, Christopher 194
Hoch, Erich 480
Hochgesang, Mark 105
Hochman, Debra 60
Hochschild, Roger C. 269
Hocken, Natalie L. 651
Hockenson, Tod 453
Hocking, Nona 735
Hodes, Jack 382
Hodes, Sanford 743
Hodge, Ronald 139
Hodge, Terry 841
Hodge, Nancy 942
Hodges, James R. 99
Hodges, Arthur 214
Hodges, Julie 274
Hodges, Jeff 370
Hodges, Eloy 558
Hodges, James 563
Hodges, Timothy B 665
Hodges, Gary 800
Hodges, Milton 806
Hodges, Jonathan 923
Hodgin, Chris 800
Hodgins, Thomas 217
Hodgson, Robert 715
Hodiwalla, Zubin 754
Hodnett, Tim 107
Hodos, Richard 170
Hodous, Brian 10
Hoebener, Pam 14
Hoeckh, Rich 194
Hoefling, Kenneth J. (Ken) 166
Hoeksema, Renze 284
Hoekstra, Frank 463
Hoelscher, Kylene 577
Hoen, Corey 888
Hoene, William A. (Bill) Von 314
Hoerbelt, Greg 722
Hoerig, Patricia 735
Hoersch, Lori 861
Hoerth, Scott 80
Hoesch, Josh 343
Hoey, Bob 470
Hof, Thomas 863
Hofelich, Kurt 762
Hofeling, Dustin 357
Hofer, Patricia 330
Hoff, Olga 941
Hoffer, Theresa 197
Hoffman, Roger 74
Hoffman, Peter 135
Hoffman, Rich 135
Hoffman, Nate 158
Hoffman, Mark 222
Hoffman, Rick 256
Hoffman, Francis 332
Hoffman, Kurt 580

Hoffman, David 643
Hoffman, Rachel 654
Hoffman, Mike 671
Hoffman, Stuart G 680
Hoffman, Warren 700
Hoffman, Kathleen 700
Hoffman, James D. 725
Hoffman, Coley 735
Hoffman, Susan 886
Hoffman, James E. (Jim) 938
Hoffmann, Daryl 246
Hoffmann, K?roly 750
Hoffmeister, Bruce 548
Hofmann, Kevin 431
Hofmann, Herbert 536
Hofmann, Herb E. 536
Hofmann, Richard 566
Hofmeister, Brian 684
Hogan, Mark D. 118
Hogan, Wendy 171
Hogan, Thomas 196
Hogan, James D. 249
Hogan, Ed 370
Hogan, Michael P. (Mike) 379
Hogan, John 456
Hogan, Sean 470
Hogan, Kathleen T. 575
Hogan, David P. 640
Hogan, Mike 643
Hogan, Janet L. 645
Hogan, Peter 683
Hogan, Pete 684
Hogan, Jim 813
Hogenmiller, Mike 431
Hogg, Charlotte M. 898
Hoggatt, Melissa 328
Hoggatt, Candace 454
Hoghaug, Paul 52
Hoglund, Robert N. 234
Hoglund, Robert N. 235
Hogue, Penny 620
Hohenadel, Jim 140
Hoisman, Danny 857
Hoke, Fran 104
Hoke, Margaret 355
Holani, Kimberly 103
Holappa, Bruce 805
Holbrook, Frank 45
Holbrook, Jenni 430
Holbrook, Harry 895
Holcomb, Michele 161
Holcomb, John 813
Holcombe, Robert E 330
Holden, Rochelle 273
Holder, Jim 194
Holder, Mark 245
Holder, Theresa 516
Holder, Todd 863
Holding, Frank B. 344
Holdorf, Diane 493
Holdren, Larry 666
Hole, Joseph 105
Holiday, Al 923
Holifield, Mark Q. 431
Holladay, Evon 168
Holladay, Mark G. 806
Holland, Peter 105
Holland, Tom 330
Holland, Ricky T. 344
Holland, Leslie 355
Holland, Clifford 484
Holland, James 500
Holland, Leslie 533
Holland, Ralph 580
Holland, Rebecca 607
Holland, Edison 778
Holland, Brenda 786
Hollander, Jeffrey 570
Hollaway, David 697
Hollek, Darrell E. 61
Hollenbeck, Martin F. 196
Holler, Keith 849
Holleran, Kevin P. 826
Holley, Rick R. 922
Holliday, Bob 84
Holliday, Brian 434
Holliday, Carl 641

Hollingsworth, Pamela 472
Hollingsworth, Audrey 806
Hollis, Curtis 498
Hollister, Patric 446
Holloman, J. Phillip 198
Holloway, David 39
Holloway, Duane D. 79
Holloway, Anita 446
Hollub, Vicki A. 631
Holly, Michelle 101
Holm, Karen 274
Holman, Gene 107
Holman, Bob 170
Holman, Rolf 425
Holman, Russell L. (Rusty) 526
Holme, Troy 170
Holmer, Hans 903
Holmes, Christopher D 2
Holmes, John 15
Holmes, Clifford 115
Holmes, Mark 117
Holmes, Don 185
Holmes, Neil 191
Holmes, Tom 245
Holmes, Bill 257
Holmes, Phil 273
Holmes, Bradley 302
Holmes, David 415
Holmes, Charlie 504
Holmes, William 548
Holmes, James 705
Holmes, Terraca 818
Holmes, Stephen P. 931
Holmgren, Thor 52
Holness, Russell 654
Holodak, Stephen 253
Holschbach, Leon J. 577
Holscher, Russ 115
Holsclaw, Janet 735
Holshouser, Susan 456
Holst-Andersen, Vibeke 256
Holsten, Joseph M. 534
Holston, Michael J. 566
Holt, Tim 17
Holt, Susan 117
Holt, Jarrod 489
Holthouser, James E. (Jim) 427
Holton, Adam 193
Holton, Alex 487
Holton, Terry J. 756
Holtz, Curt 894
Holub, Kenneth 558
Holwill, Richard 35
Holzen, John 808
Holzer, Damon 84
Holzer, Brian 502
Holzer, Sunita 718
Holzshu, Christopher (Chris) 531
Hom, John 700
Homan, Richard P. 856
Hombach, Robert J 115
Home, Baxter 115
Homer, David P. (Dave) 383
Honda, Amy 103
Honeycutt, John 270
Honeycutt, Janet 353
Honeycutt, Michael 365
Honeyman, Eric 890
Hong, Eleanor E 504
Hong, John 707
Honig, Peter 671
Honma, Clesio 733
Honovic, Johnathan 896
Honovic, Jonny 897
Honovic, John 897
Hood, John 117
Hood, Rob 185
Hood, Chris 493
Hood, Amy E. 576
Hood, Carlton 792
Hoogenboom, Paul G. P. 742
Hook, Rich 663
Hook, Richard 663
Hooley, Joseph L. (Jay) 791
Hooper, Anthony C. (Tony) 57
Hooper, Tony 57
Hooper, Ana 257

Hooper, Valencia 416
Hoos, Tony 57
Hoover, Jessica 161
Hoover, Craig 533
Hoover, Deborah 842
Hoover, Stephen (Steve) 934
Hope, Ken 192
Hope, Jim 808
Hopfer, Rick 582
Hopfinger, Mark M 724
Hopkins, Christopher 102
Hopkins, William C 346
Hopkins, Lynn M. 653
Hopkins, Thomas 764
Hopmans, John 533
Hopp, Melissa 117
Hopp, Daniel 923
Hoppe, Mark A. 558
HOPSON, TIM 453
Hopson, Jeff 724
Horan, Terry 742
Horen, Jolie A 928
Horgan, Joan 668
Horgan, Kathryn M. (Kathy) 791
Horger, Robert R. 776
Horn, Charles L. 30
Horn, Daniel Van 175
Horn, Alan F. 273
Horn, Justin 564
Horn, Jack 727
Horn, Joe Van 890
Hornbuckle, Mertroe 261
Hornbuckle, William J. 572
Hornby, William P. 180
Horne, Lewis 170
Horner, Shawn 654
Horner, Shannan 808
Horner, Matt 930
Horng, Susanna 700
Hornuckle, Mertroe 261
Hornung, Bill 931
Horowitz, Paul 131
Horseman, Neil 899
Horst, Leonard F 621
Horstman, Gregory 158
Horstman, Douglas 923
Horstmann, Douglas J. 419
Horstmann, David L. 419
Hortman, Edwin W. (Ed) 54
Horton, Gilbert 263
Horton, Chris 355
Horton, Rick 439
Horton, Donald R. 439
Horton, Rachel 446
Horton, Michael 685
Horton, Kelly 693
Horton, William E. (Bill) 721
Horton, Jon 762
Horton, Robbie 808
Horton, Andrean 938
Hortum, Debbie 332
Horvac, Paul 654
Horvath, Karen 122
Horvath, Anthony 413
Horvath, Roger 596
Horvath, Rosemarie 632
Horvath, Michael 770
Horwood, Gail 493
Hoskins, Walter 157
Hoskins, Jack 170
Hoskins, Michelle 356
Hoskinson, James W 135
Hoss, Michael 18
Hossein, Abby 567
Host, Gerard R. (Jerry) 855
Hostetler, Kurt 765
Hostetter, David 376
Hostutler, Michael 618
Hosty, Pam 306
Hosty, Neil J. 538
Hotaling, Michael 320
Hotchkiss, James P. 356
Hotop, Jeffrey 226
Hotsuki, Keishi 587
Hottman, Greg 215
Houde, Edward 415
Houdeshell, David D. 756

Houfek, Andrea 195
Houfek, Ryan D 245
Hough, Lynn M 224
Hough, Edana 799
Houghtby, John 294
Houghton, Andrew 548
Houlihan, Robert 567
Hounsel, Brad 888
Hourigan, Tim 431
Hourihan, Michael 551
House, James L. (Jim) 68
House, Dave 691
House, Barbara 840
Householder, Mark 691
Householder, Joseph A. (Joe) 761
Houser, Denise 886
Houser, Catherine 896
Houssaye, Brian de la 928
Houston, Christine 319
Houston, Monica 350
Houston, Randy 370
Houston, Lamont 390
Houston, Helga S. 449
Houston, Paul 534
Houston, Daniel J. (Dan) 691
Houston, Stacy W 715
Houstoun, Travis 403
Houten, Scott Van 57
Houweling, Tara Van 159
Hovde, Rob 261
Hovick, Kevin J. 297
Howard, Linda 10
Howard, Christine 80
Howard, Ida 102
Howard, Olivia 107
Howard, Cheryl 148
Howard, Gale 161
Howard, Kevin D. 186
Howard, Phil 196
Howard, Gary 382
Howard, John L. 398
Howard, Jeff 457
Howard, Kevin 500
Howard, Dima 573
Howard, David 576
Howard, Connie 746
Howard, Dennis 754
Howard, Kevin J. 806
Howard, Terence 810
Howard, Amy 840
Howard, Claude 849
Howard, Steve 849
Howard, W. Relle 852
Howard, J. Kyle 898
Howard, Ken 936
Howard, Doug 941
Howarth, Anne 668
Howat, Dan 489
Howcroft, Jeff 651
Howe, Stewart 457
Howe, Mike 489
Howe, Diane 691
Howell, Keith 24
Howell, Peyton R. 56
Howell, Matthew 133
Howell, Lloyd W. 139
Howell, John 176
Howell, Douglas K. (Doug) 378
Howell, James A. 617
Howell, Gelston 750
Howell, Eric 767
Howell, Robert 807
Howell, Paul 824
Howell, Mark 852
Howes, Jason 12
Howes, Joshua 158
Howland, Bill 749
Howze, Marc A. 260
Hoy, Thomas L. 77
Hoye, Mike 12
Hoyt, Rebecca 68
Hoyt, Hubertus 615
Hoyt, Janet 680
Hpenterprise, Synnex 805
Hricik, Kandy 497
Hrycenko, Mike 680
Hsieh, John 470

Hsiung, Susette 273
Hsiung, Ken 604
Hsu, Christopher P. (Chris) 425
Hsu, Michael D. 499
Hsu, Ted 688
Hsu, Johnny 688
Hsu, Clark 688
Hu, Bradford 203
Hu, Soomin 395
Hu, Eddie 615
Hu, S. Jack 720
Hu, Alex 748
Hua, Daniel 490
Huaco, Michael 563
Huang, Yu 158
Huang, Joseph 313
Huang, Victor 383
Huang, Efen 484
Huang, Gene 489
Huang, Jen-Hsun 627
Huang, Jay 628
Huang, Christopher 749
Hubbard, Wade 402
Hubbard, Mike 609
Hubbs, Justin 313
Huber, Gary E 128
Huber, Edgar O. 242
Huber, Marie Oh 293
Huber, John 337
Huber, J. Kendall 409
Huber, Thomas 732
Huber, Don 932
Hubinger, Jim 187
Hubler, David 920
Hubner, Robert 856
Huck, Deron 185
Huckabay, David 533
Huckle, Amanda 131
Hudak, James L. (Jim) 201
Hudak, John 356
Huddleston, Ron 576
Hudgens, John D. 823
Hudgions, Annette W. 635
Hudnell, Rosalind 465
Hudson, David W. 179
Hudson, Jennifer 232
Hudson, James 330
Hudson, Scott R. 378
Hudson, Dennis S. (Denny) 756
Hudson, Roz 882
Hudson, Sarah 897
Hudson, David T. 933
Hudson-Martin, Gerry 548
Huelskamp, Amy 489
Huelskoetter, Pat 226
Huempfner, Jim 84
Huerta, Miguel 834
Huestis, Tim 677
Huey, Cindy 115
Huff, Christine 332
Huff, Jerry 901
Huff, Scott 903
Huffaker, Renee 137
Huffer, Linda R. 762
Huffman, Ted 87
Huffman, Janet 928
Hufford, Bob 81
Hufman, Chris 809
Hughes, Tom 84
Hughes, Robert 118
Hughes, Tony 151
Hughes, Gregg 185
Hughes, Sean 194
Hughes, Kevin 200
Hughes, Catherine 204
Hughes, Sharon 207
Hughes, Brian D. 269
Hughes, Rick 358
Hughes, Frederick P 365
Hughes, Jim 451
Hughes, Erik 553
Hughes, Jeffrey A. (Jeff) 729
Hughes, Susaan 750
Hughes, Mark 800
Hughes, Kate 839
Hughes, David 909
Hughes, Cheryl 931

Hughson, Stephanie 722
Hugin, Robert J. (Bob) 175
Hugvik, Kjell 793
Hui, Carmen 440
Huie, Stephanie Bond 884
Huiskens, Terry 157
Hulaton, Pat 103
Hulick, Bob 852
Hulihee, John 103
Hull, Leigh 18
Hull, George 481
Hull, Jeane 659
Hull, Anthony E. (Tony) 718
Hulse, Walter S. 641
Hulseberg, Eric 204
Hult, David W. 78
Hultman, Jeff 419
Hultquist, Douglas M. (Doug) 706
Hume, Christopher 573
Hume, Sophie 787
Hume, Richard T. (Rich) 816
Humler, Herve 548
Hummel, Robert 109
Hummel, William 337
Hummel, John M. 874
Hummel, Chris 876
Humphrey, Jason 204
Humphrey, John J. 876
Humphreys, Donna 330
Humphreys, Wayne 722
Humphreys, Adam 799
Humphries, Malcolm 901
Humphris, Ian 659
Hunckler, Stephen P. 788
Hund, Lawrence G. 410
Hund-Mejean, Martina 554
Hundzinski, Ronald T. (Ron) 140
Hunegs, Craig 838
Hung, Jaime 927
Hungerberg, Arnd 576
Hunkin, Andrew 935
Hunniford, Michael 620
Hunsberger, Scott 692
Hunt, Brian 355
Hunt, Wallace 517
Hunt, Neil 603
Hunt, Richard 717
Hunt, Lisa Kidd 754
Hunt, N. Craig 768
Hunt, Sandy 865
Hunter, Kelli A. 52
Hunter, Renee 67
Hunter, Erica 157
Hunter, Jesse N. 176
Hunter, Charles 226
Hunter, Alisa 336
Hunter, Jeaneen 389
Hunter, Paul 425
Hunter, Christopher H. (Chris) 446
Hunter, Sarah 558
Hunter, Kelli 731
Hunter, Lisa W. 768
Hunter, Mark 770
Hunter, Julie 779
Hunter, Jessica 831
Hunter, Rhonda C. 921
Huntington, Bradford 701
Huntley, David S. 84
Huntsman, Peter R. 452
Huntsman, Jon M. 452
Hunziker, Sharie 555
Hurchalla, Chuck 861
Hurd, Jarrod 178
Hurd, Mark V. 642
Hurlbut, Tom 618
Hurlbut, Angela 720
Hurley, Bryne 489
Hurley, Joseph F 511
Hurley, Gail 831
Hurley-Wales, Ed 88
Hurn, Patricia D. 720
Hursh, Kristy 137
Hurst, Robin 25
Hurst, Trent 242
Hurst, David 259
Hurst, Peter 389
Hurst, George 411

Hurst, Tony 661
Hurst, Ron 678
Hurst, Gene 722
Hurst, Chuck 743
Hurt, Lorraine 26
Hurtado, Cesar 199
Hurtuk, David 853
Hurvitz, Elizabeth 899
Hurwick, William J 176
Hurwitz, Jerome V 119
Hurwitz, Phil 676
Hurwitz, Brad 929
Hurzeler, Robert A. 640
Huse, Mark 500
Huska, Patricia 45
Huskins, Keith 407
Husovsky, James 194
Hussain, Aamir 181
Hussey, Lynn 502
Husson, David 14
Husted-Sherman, John 45
Huston, Aurora 267
Huston, Michael 354
Hutcheson, Finbarr 467
Hutcheson, Jennifer 744
Hutcheson, David 841
Hutchins, Michael 374
Hutchinson, William R. 81
Hutchinson, Robert 248
Hutchinson, Randy 304
Hutchinson, Danny 304
Hutchinson, Mark 382
Hutchison, John 672
Hutchison, Larry M. 843
Hutmacher, Dustin 901
Hutson, Larry 61
Hutson, Andy 736
Hutt, Kevin 195
Hutten, Bill 896
Hutter, Dustin 735
Hutto, Richard 25
Hutto, Rick 25
Hutton, Nick 131
Hutton, Peter 270
Hutton, Rob 518
Hutton, Don 643
Hutton, William L. 723
Huval, Timothy S. (Tim) 446
Huval, Tim 757
Huver, Edmund 672
Huxta, Joseph 668
Huydic, Chris 699
Huynh, Tien G 224
Hvizd, Jim 717
Hwang, Gwo J Ching 185
Hwang, Angela 671
Hwang, Julie 799
Hyde, Jeff 187
Hyde, Steve 749
Hyde, Andrew 888
Hyland, Thomas J 135
Hyland, Jason P. 573
Hyland, Michael 704
Hyland, Rosemary 842
Hylton, Tracy 207
Hyman, Shana 330
Hynes, Timothy (Tim) 595
Hyslop, Gregory L. (Greg) 135
Hytinen, Barry A. 407
Hyun-Ko, You 705
Hüttges, Timotheus (Tim) 811

I

Iaconi, Thomas Di 770
Iacono, George 596
Iacono, Greg 840
Iadanza, Jesse 60
Iadanza, John 222
Iampietro, Steve 56
Iannelli, Josephine 112
Iannetta, Mario 273
Ianniello, Joseph R. 171
Iannone, Jamie 903
Iannotti, Thomas J. (Tom) 71
Iantosca, Joseph R. 632

Iasonides, John 905
Ibach, Jason D 377
Ibarra, Erick 754
Ibbotson, Stephen 95
Ibbotson, Mark 903
Ibrahim, Marko 633
Icahn, Carl C. 251
Icahn, Carl C. 455
Ice, Carl R. 150
Ichinaga, Stephen 805
Ichinaga, Steve 805
Ichiuji, Doug 888
Ierulli, Laura 358
Iger, Robert A. (Bob) 273
Iglesias, Lisa G. 886
Iglesias, Javier Iglesias Javier 888
Ihlendorf, Bill 757
Ihm, Steve 31
Iijima, Junichi 643
Iino-Harvey, Jennifer 95
Ikeda, Miki 103
Ilan, Haviv 825
Illig, Clifford W. (Cliff) 183
Im, Audrey 530
Imber, Barry A. 195
Imburgia, Dawn 13
Imholz, Donald G 176
Immaneni, Aravind 336
Imperato, Thomas 610
Imundi, Christine 713
Infeld, Allan 896
Ingerslev, Christian Ingerslev Christian 101
Ingersoll, Denise 735
Ingersoll, Don 936
Ingle, Abhi 84
Inglis, Martin 113
Ingold, Edward 131
Ingram, Bill 11
Ingram, Mitchell W. (Mitch) 61
Ingram, Robert C. (Bob) 310
Inlander, Patricia 131
Inlander, Todd L. 295
Inlander, Todd L. 777
Inman, Larry 246
Insalaco, Sue 760
Insall, Gerard 93
Inscho, Bill 357
Inserra, Andrea 139
Insignares, Valerie 257
Inskeep, Lauren 810
Intemann, Chris 337
Intermaggio, Peter 222
Ioannidis, Sharon 715
Iooss, Sarah 896
Iorio, Tony 550
Ippolito, Peter J. 764
Ipsen, Denise 770
Iqbal, Farhan 80
Irby, Nicole 117
Iredell, Craig 195
Ireland, Gareth 240
Ireland, Jay W. 382
Ireland, Steve 489
Ireland, Frieda 817
Ireton, John 489
Irish, Stephen J. 305
Irish, Erik 735
Irizarry, Laurens 235
Irizarry, Ricardo 890
Irussi, Bruce G. 764
Irvin, Vernon L. 181
Irvin, David 207
Irvine, Jon 97
Irwin, John 449
Irwin, Michael 749
Irwin, Larry (Don) 876
Isaac, Angela 806
Isaacson, Karen 300
Isaman, Tanya 178
Isbell, Ken 226
Iseman, Jay C. 432
Iseman, Andrew J. (Andy) 863
Iseri, Janie 185
Iserman, Lance 89
Ishak, Waguih 240
Isham, Mary 677

Ishaq, Sameera 328
Ishikawa, Brian 103
Ishikawa, Hiroshi 663
Iskalis, Thomas 620
Ismat, Fraz 144
Isom, Robert D. 41
Isom, Kevin 88
Isono, Denis 102
Isono, Denis K. 179
Ispass, Alan 185
Israel, Jill 304
Israel, Leonard (Len) 362
Israel, Lex 705
Israr, Shannon 942
Istas, Frederic 166
Isturiz, Raul 672
Italiano, Lou 332
Ito, Craig 103
Ito, Val 103
Iturrey, Albert 553
Iunghuhn, Cathy 770
Iuorio, Alex 94
Iuppenlatz, Mark 402
IV, William H. W. Crawford 872
Ivanis, Milena 849
Ivannikov, Alexander 676
Ivanov, Stanislav (Stan) 466
Ive, Jonathan 69
Iverson, Mary 199
Ivester, Lyn 599
Ivey, Craig S. 234
Ivey, Brian 389
Iwashchenko, Cynthia 800
Iwegbue, Jennifer 901
Iyer, Chandresh 105
Izaguirre, Luis-Angel Gomez 936
Izmee, Haris 576
Izurieta, Laura 803
Izzo, Ralph 701

J

Jabanoski, James 260
Jabbar, Omar 293
Jabbonsky, Larry 668
Jabbour, Anthony M. 334
Jablon, Mike 932
Jablonski, Dale 497
Jack, Glen 831
Jack, Angela 875
Jackiewicz, Annmarie 700
Jackman, Linda 643
Jackowski, Julia L. (Julie) 164
Jacks, Joann L 332
Jackson, Anthony 3
Jackson, James 67
Jackson, Dean 69
Jackson, Michael J. (Mike) 89
Jackson, Peter 149
Jackson, Lydia 158
Jackson, Rick C. 159
Jackson, Mark 204
Jackson, Brett 224
Jackson, Donald 248
Jackson, Paul 332
Jackson, Brian 430
Jackson, Judy 454
Jackson, Benjamin R. (Ben) 466
Jackson, Stephanie 497
Jackson, Rick 516
Jackson, Robert 553
Jackson, Beverly 573
Jackson, Don 676
Jackson, Joanne B. 677
Jackson, Marla 699
Jackson, Bill 731
Jackson, Ronald B. (Ron) 768
Jackson, Mel 779
Jackson, Sherita 813
Jackson, Philip C. (Phil) 884
Jackson, Charlene 886
Jackson, Michelle 886
Jackson, Neal 912
Jacob, April 88
Jacob, Daniel 115
Jacob, Bobby 246

Jacob, Gregg 263
JACOB, PAUL 295
Jacob, Ravi 465
Jacob, Bernard 699
Jacob, Clay 800
Jacob, Lanika 890
Jacobi, Jacqueline 582
Jacobo, Keyanus 615
Jacobs, Kerry J. 28
Jacobs, Scott 241
Jacobs, Robert 246
Jacobs, Donna 304
Jacobs, Stephen D. (Jake) 368
Jacobs, Kevin J. 427
Jacobs, Lawrence A. (Lon) 513
Jacobs, Todd 615
Jacobs, Glen 635
JAcobs, Leonore 672
Jacobs, Paul E. 708
Jacobs, Kristine 855
Jacobs, Bradley S. 936
Jacobs, Dereck 941
Jacobsen, Rene 7
Jacobsen, Craig 467
Jacobson, Craig A. 186
Jacobson, Paul A. 262
Jacobson, Steve 276
Jacobson, Sue 332
Jacobson, Shalene 404
Jacobson, Jeff A. 486
Jacobson, Karen 590
Jacobson, Scott 731
Jacobson, Jack 905
Jacobson, Karin 928
Jacobson, Jeffrey (Jeff) 934
Jacoby, Rebecca J. 199
Jacoby, Christy A 668
Jacovatos, James 366
Jacques, Daniel 497
Jacques, Dale 735
Jacques, Karen 935
Jadin, Ronald L. 398
Jaeger, Tom 119
Jaeggin, Thomas 620
Jaffe, David R. 79
Jaffe, Elise 79
Jaffe, Jonathan M. (Jon) 518
Jaffe, Eric D. 759
Jaffess, Judith 699
Jaffray, Dawn M. 872
Jafry, Syed A. 836
Jager, Sandy 564
Jager, Bertus de 659
Jagger, Hal 766
Jaglall, Andy 587
Jahn, Gregory S 313
Jaime, Alex 633
Jain, Deepti 67
Jain, Dipika 101
Jain, Ajit 123
Jain, Nitin 176
Jain, Jinesh 182
Jain, Vishal 378
Jain, Ruchira 668
Jain, Sujit 733
Jakeman, Kelly 56
Jakeman, Brad 667
Jakobsen, Henning 219
Jakoby, Jean 668
Jakubik, Ed 935
Jakubowski, Michael S 465
Jalali, Ahmad 707
Jambor, Joan 84
James, Susan (Sue) 34
James, Karen 98
James, Hamilton E. (Tony) 133
James, Jonathan 185
James, Charles 191
James, Jeff 273
James, Kalea 335
James, Schlosser 450
James, Galeota 566
James, Phyllis A. 572
James, Mary 800
James, Kathy 800
James, Bradley G. 842
James, Dianne R. 941

Jameson, Steven E. (Steve) 230
Jameson, Jeremy 306
Jamieson, John 750
Jamieson, Arch 834
Jamil, Dhiaa M. 285
Jamison, Andrew 45
Jamison, Cynthia T. 846
Jamrog, Stephanie Jamrog Stephanie 540
Jan, Couturier 449
Jan, Ng 810
Janaczek, Greg 748
Janakiraman, Ram 87
Janastch, Adam 276
Janatsch, Adam 276
Jandoc, John 805
Janiga, Kathy 257
Janis, Eve 306
Janke, Kenneth S. (Ken) 19
Janke, Ken 19
Janke, Kenneth S 19
Jankovich, Richard 226
Jankowski, John 425
Jankowski, Edward 914
Jannah, Shekar G. 495
Jansen, Kathrin U 671
Jansen, Jacqueline 813
Janson, Julie S. 285
Janson, Steven 559
Janssen, Gwendolyn 5
Janssen, Julie 928
Janus, Michael 113
Janutolo, Kristin 449
Japlon, Howard 9
Jaramillo, Adriana 273
Jardon, Carmen 917
Jaros, Janet 497
Jaroszewski, J Rosow 246
Jarrell, Tammy 116
Jarrell, Paul 649
Jarrett, Mary 80
Jarrold, Tom 713
Jarvis, Glenn 45
Jarvis, Sam 226
Jarvis, Tory 555
Jarvis, Herb 668
Jarvis, Cathy 726
Jasien, William S. (Bill) 759
Jasinowski, Mike 128
Jaskaniec, Andy 503
Jaskowiak, Sheila M 18
Jasnoff, Jeffrey M 502
Jaspal, Puja 899
Jasper, Philip J. (Phil) 739
Jasper, Thomas F. (Tom) 814
Jassy, Andrew R. (Andy) 37
Jastrem, Thomas 249
Jauch, Mike 422
Jaw, Carolyn 328
Jaworski, Peter W. 912
Jay, Ed 44
Jay, Dennis 470
Jay, Colleen E. 693
Jay, Carrick 923
Jayant, Monika 101
Jayaram, Ganesh 260
Jayavant, Rajeev 628
Jazayeri, Nasi 748
Jean, Ronald W. 297
Jeansonne, Kevin 15
Jeantet, Russann 882
Jeff, Galagher 904
Jeffcoat, Stuart 185
Jefferies, Nicole 12
Jefferson, Phelecia 380
Jefferson, Kirby 465
Jeffery, Daniel 45
Jeffrey, Brad Jeffrey Brad 530
Jeffrey, David 748
Jeffreys, Scott 131
Jeffries, Telvin 504
Jefts, Alan 15
Jehle, Kent L. 578
Jejurikar, Shailesh G. 693
Jelenchick, Erin 735
Jelinek, Rick M. 17
Jelinek, W. Craig 241

Jemison, Latrisha 722
Jenckes, Marcien 222
Jenkins, Loren 17
Jenkins, Karen 409
JENKINS, WORTH 519
Jenkins, Brian 530
Jenkins, Steve 649
Jenkins, Jeremy 722
Jenkins, Steve 799
Jenkins, Dustee T 813
Jenkins, William 821
Jenkins, Jeff 834
Jennifer, Lofgren 792
Jennings, Lisa 32
Jennings, Gary 81
Jennings, Cynthia 367
Jennings, Michael C. 429
Jennings, Steve 470
Jennings, Justin 665
Jennings, Richard 743
Jennings, Dick 743
Jennings, Shawn 754
Jennings, Dick 935
Jenny, Kim 678
Jensen, Claus 18
Jensen, Christopher W. (Chris) 173
Jensen, Barry 459
Jensen, Donald 613
Jensen, Derrick A. 709
Jensen, Brian 754
Jensen, Eric 787
Jensen, Chris 800
Jensen, Allen 941
Jensen, Elliot 942
Jenson, Conrad 429
Jenson, James 507
Jenson, Kelly 934
Jeppesen, Jon A 68
Jeppesen, Karl 135
Jepsen, Alan 224
Jepson, Helene 358
Jergenson, Dana 888
Jerger, Mark 707
Jernigan, Janet 102
Jernigan, Wyatt 251
Jernstedt, Tiffin 705
Jerome, Christopher J. (Chris) 886
Jessen, David 273
Jessup, Dan 486
Jester, Diane 107
Jeter, Daniel B. 54
Jett, Robert 723
Jetter, Martin 470
Jewell, Marcus 490
Jewett, Joshua R. (Josh) 276
Jewkes, Roger S. 332
Jex, Jeffrey 355
Jez, Karen 322
Jha, Manoj 88
Jha, Rajesh 575
Jhaveri, Rupal 159
Jia, Keith 489
Jiang, Ming-Fang 146
Jiang, Richard 395
Jicka, Joyce 97
Jiganti, Jeanine M. 258
Jimenez, Josie 101
Jimenez, Esteban 102
Jimenez, Marilu 682
Jimenez, Frank R. 716
Jin, Jeoung (A. J.) 366
Jin, Julie 533
Jin, Wei 699
Jingnan, Liu 287
Jinian, Ani 101
Joachim, Kathy 808
Jobanputra, Rakesh 610
Jobanputra, Rakesh 858
Joergenrud, Odd 733
Joerres, Jeffrey A. 919
Joffrion, Barry 678
Jogaib, Julio 109
Jogrenson, Robert 745
Johansen, Kurt 52
John, Michelle 101
John, Maureen St 155
John, Dotson 191

John, Hundt 194
John, Stan St 434
John, Ashmine 571
John, Gregory St 719
John, Stan St 786
John, Todd St 875
Johns, Natalie 449
Johns, Jeff 489
Johns, John D. 697
Johnsen, Erin 688
Johnson, Collister (Coddy) 10
Johnson, Farrell 18
Johnson, Jimmy 26
Johnson, Craig A. 36
Johnson, Stephen L. (Steve) 41
Johnson, Ted M. 43
Johnson, Matt 56
Johnson, Deron 57
Johnson, Tim 88
Johnson, Brad 94
Johnson, Carol 108
Johnson, Robert J. 116
Johnson, Ken 117
Johnson, Kathleen 117
Johnson, Jennifer 123
Johnson, Timothy A. (Tim) 128
Johnson, Lynn 135
Johnson, Thomas A. 154
Johnson, Mary 161
Johnson, Denise C. 166
Johnson, Nancy 170
Johnson, Monte 181
Johnson, Mark 185
Johnson, James W. (Jay) 190
Johnson, Lynden E. 193
Johnson, Rob 194
Johnson, Beth 205
Johnson, Eric R. 213
Johnson, Bert 214
Johnson, Jay 252
Johnson, Chris B. 267
Johnson, Don 271
Johnson, Richard 291
Johnson, Adam 294
Johnson, Michael 299
Johnson, Kimberly H. 322
Johnson, Margie 337
Johnson, Karen 342
Johnson, Tami 356
Johnson, Richard A. (Dick) 368
Johnson, Rex 370
Johnson, Gregory E. 372
Johnson, Jennifer M. 372
Johnson, Rupert H. 373
Johnson, James J 374
Johnson, Daniel 378
Johnson, S. Daniel (Dan) 380
Johnson, Jill 382
Johnson, Bryant 383
Johnson, James 409
Johnson, Brion 413
Johnson, Michael 413
Johnson, Renee 413
Johnson, David 413
Johnson, Dolph 415
Johnson, R. Milton 416
Johnson, Kelly J. 419
Johnson, Brian 437
Johnson, Wes 446
Johnson, Kelli 454
Johnson, Kathryn 456
Johnson, Bruce 476
Johnson, David A. 486
Johnson, Guy 493
Johnson, Dora 497
Johnson, Monique 498
Johnson, Tami 502
Johnson, Dean 502
Johnson, Kelli 504
Johnson, Gina 508
Johnson, Ginger 515
Johnson, Romaine 539
Johnson, Emily 543
Johnson, Melonie 573
Johnson, Margaret L. (Peggy) 576
Johnson, Peggy 576
Johnson, James 615

Johnson, Patti 615
Johnson, Gregory D. (Greg) 630
Johnson, Linda 636
Johnson, James W. (Jim) 645
Johnson, Dave 649
Johnson, Ann 651
Johnson, Jodie 661
Johnson, Dennis 661
Johnson, Jam 668
Johnson, Rady A. 671
Johnson, Paula A. 675
Johnson, Peggy L 707
Johnson, Dale 722
Johnson, Stuart R. 726
Johnson, Sarah 727
Johnson, Jerry L 733
Johnson, Lisa 749
Johnson, Steve 754
Johnson, Orlan M. 759
Johnson, Amy W. 768
Johnson, Kevin R. 787
Johnson, Julie H 798
Johnson, Susan S. 799
Johnson, Matthew 810
Johnson, Patti 813
Johnson, William D. (Bill) 821
Johnson, Mark M. 823
Johnson, Cheryl H. 826
Johnson, Mike 849
Johnson, Steve 856
Johnson, Shannon A. 863
Johnson, Debbie 863
Johnson, Patrick 863
Johnson, Reginald 863
Johnson, Kelly 864
Johnson, Derrick 875
Johnson, Steven 886
Johnson, Trina 889
Johnson, Clay 903
Johnson, Tracy 935
Johnson, Darrin 935
Johnson, Adam R. 940
Johnson, Jeremy 941
Johnston, Gary 88
Johnston, Linda A. 124
Johnston, Daniel 162
Johnston, Lori A. 173
Johnston, Steven J. 196
Johnston, Charlie 200
Johnston, Bryan L 224
Johnston, Andy 232
Johnston, Michael F. (Mike) 281
Johnston, James J. (Jim) 282
Johnston, Dave 335
Johnston, Kelly 358
Johnston, Thomas 451
Johnston, Rebecka 497
Johnston, Stephen 643
Johnston, Hugh F. 667
Johnston, Mac 677
Johnston, Lynn 722
Johnston, Maryann 746
Johnston, Amy 792
Johnston, Ricky 818
Johnston, Brent 824
Johnston, Brad 860
Johnston, Richard 890
Johnston, Greg 903
Johnstone, William O. 98
Johnstone, Jeff 182
Johnstone, Debbie 872
Johnstun, Paul 419
Johri, Akhil 879
Joiner, Sue 157
Jois, Sunitha 563
Jojo, Linda P. 871
Jolley, Jennifer R 941
Jolley, Jennifer 942
Joly, Hubert 126
Jonas, David 467
Joner, Sue 365
Jones, David 12
Jones, Greg 15
Jones, Grant 18
Jones, Gannon 32
Jones, Philip 53
Jones, Wesley 56

JONES, BOB 69
Jones, Heather 101
Jones, Alicia 101
Jones, Cary 105
Jones, Bradley 105
Jones, Jeremy 131
Jones, Randy 153
Jones, Anthony 168
Jones, Cory 168
Jones, Richard M. 171
Jones, Belinda 172
Jones, Nicole S. 194
Jones, Robert 199
Jones, Rosalyn 201
Jones, Jay 202
Jones, Thomas 224
Jones, Larry W. 230
Jones, D. Andrew 230
Jones, Bill 241
Jones, Clay 246
Jones, Colin 246
Jones, Tim 259
Jones, Keri 264
Jones, Clark 273
Jones, Wendy 293
Jones, Linda 325
Jones, Jan 353
Jones, Charles E. (Chuck) 360
Jones, Bob 395
Jones, Paul J. 410
Jones, Bruce 425
Jones, Kevin 449
Jones, Carolyn 449
Jones, Kristine 453
Jones, Blane 453
Jones, Earl 456
Jones, Marilyn 476
Jones, Kris 492
Jones, Steve 507
Jones, Stephen 507
Jones, Michael 537
Jones, Ren©© F. 538
Jones, Linda 538
Jones, Deanna L. 546
Jones, Beth 548
Jones, Erica 550
Jones, Ingrid R 555
Jones, Paul 578
Jones, Kim 584
Jones, Rachel 590
Jones, Lisa 593
Jones, Dan 615
Jones, Mae 620
Jones, Christopher T. 623
Jones, Neil 623
Jones, Robert G. (Bob) 635
Jones, Chuck 643
Jones, Wilson R. 645
Jones, Douglas E. (Doug) 662
Jones, Kathleen 664
Jones, Laura 668
Jones, Robin 668
Jones, Thomas 672
Jones, Bill 677
Jones, Rex 677
Jones, Diane 678
Jones, Barbara 680
Jones, Catherine 680
Jones, Ingrid 693
Jones, Randall T. (Todd) 702
Jones, Randall T. (Todd) 702
Jones, Bob 715
Jones, Ellen 721
Jones, Karen M. 743
Jones, Tom 743
Jones, Amy 750
Jones, Michael 751
Jones, Danny 754
Jones, Hilliary 799
Jones, Andrea 803
Jones, Tracy 808
Jones, Jeff 813
Jones, Michael S. 814
Jones, Nicholas P. 831
Jones, Bruce R. 849
Jones, Kristopher 858
Jones, Wally 888

Jones, Cornell 890
Jones, Tony 890
Jones, Peggi 895
Jones, Kevin 903
Jones, Jane 915
Jones, Sherry 935
Jonske, James W 32
Jonsson, Thomas 86
Jordan, Fred 45
Jordan, Kevin 80
Jordan, Deborah A. 155
Jordan, Michelle 158
Jordan, Teresa 195
Jordan, Cynthia 224
Jordan, Cedric 224
Jordan, Brenna 252
Jordan, D. Bryan 353
Jordan, Shawn 454
Jordan, Anita 454
Jordan, Amy 461
Jordan, Gregory B. 680
Jordan, Greg 754
Jordan, Robert E. (Bob) 780
Jordan, Ron 875
Jordan, Henry 904
Jordan-smith, Gavin 935
Jorgensen, David S. 206
Jorgensen, Blake J. 296
Jorgensen, Jay T. 903
Jorgenson, Robert 576
Jorgenson, Rob 745
Joseph, Robert 14
Joseph, Loretta 57
Joseph, Tommy S. 472
Joseph, George 567
Joseph, Isaac A. 593
Joseph, Philip 899
Josephs, Scott 194
Joshi, Sachin 45
Joshi, Alok 101
Joshua, Wilcox 387
Jost, Paul 919
Joy, Jennifer 195
Joyce, Deborah 178
Joyce, Thomas P. 256
Joyce, David L. 382
Joyce, Robert J. (Bob) 496
Joyce, Joe 500
Joyce, Brian 511
Joyner, Dee 226
Joyner, J. David 252
Joysizemore, Dian 99
JR, Joseph 248
Jubie, Nicole 317
Juchno, Stacy M. 680
Juday, Ryan 837
Judd, Levi 942
Jude, Peggy 88
Jude, Justin L. 534
Judge, Ann 144
Judge, James J. (Jim) 312
Judge, Kenan 453
Judge, Barb 507
Judge, Will 555
Juelich, Dick 593
Juergensen, Colleen 506
Jugo, Rita C 103
Julian, Paul C. 563
Julian, Steve 762
Julian, Kenneth D. 837
Juliano, Mark 513
Julie, Nosser Crc 158
Julien, Jeffrey P. (Jeff) 715
Juneau, Jeff 787
Juneja, Neeraj 849
Jung, Andrea 95
Jung, May 881
Juniper, Brooke 131
Junk, Luke 735
Junkins, Lowell L. 327
Juppenlatz, Stuart 377
Jurch, Gina 117
Jurco, Tim 613
Jurgens, Deanna 668
Jurgens, Neil 866
Juricev, Alex 204
Jurs, Peter 337

Juster, Andrew A. (Andy) 770
Justiss, Donna 12
Justus, Barry 117
Justus, Henry 705
Juvara, Paolo 643

K

Kaalund, Sekou H 489
Kaatman, Nancy J 135
Kabat, Kevin T. 886
Kablawi, Hani 105
Kacena, Neil 717
Kachel, Vic 370
Kaczmarek, Walter T. (Walt) 420
Kaczmarek, David 912
Kaczmarek, Dave 912
Kaczor, James 14
Kaden, Ellen O 156
Kadien, Thomas G. (Tom) 472
Kadir, Djelal 831
Kadnar, Julie 47
Kadow, Tara 813
Kadre, Manuel 729
Kadri, Ilham 757
Kadyrova, Tatiana 888
Kaempffer, Karen 700
Kaercher, Walter 664
Kaestner, H. Todd 146
Kaestner, H Todd 146
Kafel, Jeff 530
Kafka, Donald L. 340
Kahl, Andrew 602
Kahn, Cheryl 161
Kahn, Alan 676
Kahn, Benjamin 886
Kahne, Michael 355
Kahny, Nicole 897
Kaider, Michael 170
Kain, Peter 598
Kain, Larry 677
Kainer, Darrell 307
Kaiser, George B. 137
Kaiser, Anne 389
Kaiser, Laura S. 467
Kaiser, Frances 604
Kaiser, Gregory 754
Kaiserman, David J. 518
Kajander, Gary 585
Kakuda, Kevin 168
Kalakoti, Vijay 395
Kalamaras, Paul 477
Kalaria, Brij 133
Kalathur, Rajesh (Raj) 260
Kalchik, Mona 107
Kalchuri, Shantanu 628
Kalendjian, Meline 141
Kali, Thomas 133
Kalisek, Brian 574
Kallal, Roger 356
Kallio, Jerry 558
Kallio, Jim 643
Kallsen, Tony E 745
Kallsen, Terri R. 754
Kalman, Betsy 511
Kalmey, Peter K. 502
Kamal, Mostafa M. 541
Kamal, Ashfaq 555
Kamalbatcha, Shajahan 210
Kamara, Abdul 161
Kamen, Seth 252
Kamensky, Allan E. 806
Kametz, William (Bill) 745
Kamford, Peter 122
Kamil, Mohammed O 767
Kamin, Cynthia 170
Kamin, John R. 635
Kaminski, Ken 200
Kaminski, Robert B. 564
Kaminski, Mark V. 725
Kaminsky, Tom 494
Kamman, Sarah 651
Kammholz, Ulrich 650
Kampmeyer, Dan 7
Kamsickas, James K. (Jim) 254
Kanas, John A. 109

Kandarian, Steven A. (Steve) 569
Kane, Chris 15
Kane, Thomas M. (Tom) 237
Kane, Steven 320
Kane, Brian 409
Kane, Brian A. 446
Kane, Terri 467
Kane, John 595
Kane, Martha 656
Kane, Tim 739
Kane, Patrick P 872
Kang, SungWon 313
Kang, Katelyn 435
Kangas, Chris 555
Kanjian, Karen 516
Kannally, Kevin 161
Kansler, Michael R 304
Kant, Nitin 476
Kantamneni, Raje 620
Kantaros, Andrea 664
KANTER, NANCY 273
Kantola, Kevin 881
Kantor, Michael 60
Kantor, Jonathan D. (Jon) 210
Kantor, Steven (Steve) 509
Kantor, Lesley 896
Kantro, Gayle 487
Kanyadan, Jana 580
Kaohi, Cheryl 103
Kapani, Mayur V. 466
Kapfer, Joan E 122
Kapito, Robert S. (Rob) 131
Kapki, Nick Kapki Nick 888
Kaplan, Bob 172
Kaplan, Richard 470
Kaplan, Christine 541
Kaplan, Ryan 754
Kaplan, Robert 791
Kaplan, David 840
Kaplicer, Brett 45
Kaplin, Leo 101
Kapnick, Stewart 558
Kapoor, Kishore 643
Kapoor, Sanjay 784
Kapusinski, Victor 888
Karachiwala, Mufaddal 131
Karafilis, Michael 273
Karakos, Mary 511
Karam, Danny 139
Karamarkovich, Kim 800
Karanam, Raj 256
Karanga, Ruth 615
Karas, James 337
Karas, Frances 483
Karatha, Padmanabhan 224
Karee, Paul 472
Karen, Friedman 935
Kareth, Paul 14
Karhan, Dean 325
Karickhoff, Brenda C 838
Karkhanis, Ketan 748
Karkowsky, Adam 60
Karl, James 15
Karl, Steven 504
Karlen, Chris 170
Karlovich, Robert W. (Trey) 613
Karlson, Doug 88
Karlson, Jennifer 897
Karmazin, Kira 895
Karna, Ajoy 808
Karnes, Merle 697
Karnik, Nihar 620
Karns, Joe 895
Karolis, George C. 78
Karpik, Mike 792
Karr, Kathi 435
Karras, Athanasios 434
Karros, Kirt 425
Karsh, Bruce A. 186
Karst, Darren W. 731
Karter, Laura 497
Karwacki, John 705
Kasbar, Michael J. 929
Kasendorf, Leonard 570
Kashyap, Nagraj 707
Kaska, Tony 453
Kasper, Michael 32

Kass, Jordan T. 736
Kassab, Leanne D. 211
Kassatly, Fady 139
Kassem, Amin 446
Kastanis, Maria 665
Kastberg, Crystal 695
Kasthurirangan, Mala 117
Kastner, Christopher D. 451
Kastner, Christopher K. 552
Kastner, Janeen B. 742
Kaszuba, Marek 923
Katakura, Janet 103
Katanick, Ron 504
Katapodis, Anastasia 870
Katek, James 489
Kath, Sean 700
Kathiresan, Bala 117
Katibian, Benny 707
Katie, Cave 749
Katits, Brian 18
Katsamanis, Evangelia 901
Katsikas, Cindy 558
Katsuyama, Kimberly 582
Katt, Faye 115
Kattner, Steve 224
Kattos, Andrew N. (Andy) 763
Katz, Marc D. 151
Katz, Douglas 161
Katz, Glenn 222
Katz, Robert L. (Bobby) 480
Katz, Todd 570
Katz, Jonathan 656
Kauffman, Holly C 360
Kauffman, Andy 548
Kauffman, Sean 632
Kauffman, Eileen 849
Kaufman, Israel 201
Kaufman, Jules P. 242
Kaufman, Victor A. 317
Kaufman, Neil 395
Kaufman, Jeff 440
Kaufman, Richard 656
Kaufman, Harvey 709
Kaufman, Steven 897
Kaufmann, Michael C. (Mike) 160
Kaul, Shankar 115
Kauth, Wayne 496
Kavanagh, Ben 246
Kavanaugh, Patrick 337
Kavanaugh, James J. 470
Kavanaugh, James P. (Jim) 930
Kavassalis, Tom 935
Kawa, Mark 799
Kawachi, Michael 37
Kawanami, Debora 484
Kawano, Kie 881
Kawiecki, Michele 355
Kay, Gregory S 124
Kay, Katharine 158
Kay, Linda Sloane 180
Kay, Julie 183
Kay, Robert 754
Kay, David 786
Kaye, David J. 141
Kayeum, Thor 195
Kayl, Kelly 170
Kayser, C. Dallas 207
Kayzerman, Alex 488
Kaz, Bob 528
Kazakevich, Vadim 106
Kazazian, Haig 483
Kazianis, Arthur 415
Kean, Steven J. (Steve) 500
Keane, Denise F. 36
Keane, Stella 128
Kearney, Dan 172
Kearney, Daniel P. 361
Kearney, Tim 840
Kearney, Thomas W. 931
Kearns, Richard 81
Kearns, Jack 261
Kearns, James M 274
Kearns, John 310
Kearny, Ric 158
Keating, Leslie 12
Keating, Kim 85
Keating, Johnathan 131

Keating, Tim 135
Keating, Michael 300
Keating, Leslie 470
Keating, Mark R. 792
Keating, Mike 910
Keays, Lynn 808
Kebler, Les 914
Keckler, Marcy 52
Kedia, Seema 720
Kedia, Gunjan 792
Kedia, Gunjan 888
Kee, Rob 462
Kee, Timothy 923
Keefe, Denise M. 13
Keefe, Timothy 559
Keefe, Brenda 770
Keefer, Joseph G. (Joe) 148
Keefer-Hugill, J 148
Keegan, Margaret 478
KEEL, GINA 457
Keeley, Karen 941
Keen, Sandy 635
Keena, Debra 18
Keenan, Steven J. 68
Keenan, Vince 94
Keenan, David R. (Dave) 721
Keenan, Karen D. 792
Keene, Patrick 765
Keener, David 593
Keeney, Clarissa 722
Kees, Jan 912
Keesee, Don 107
Kehl, Eric 390
Kehlbeck, Keith 700
Kehoe, James 584
Kehoe, Stephen 899
Kehring, Douglas 643
Keiffer, Mark 84
Keil, Kristen 665
Keim, Mike 87
Keim, Mark L. 409
Keim, Michael S 884
Keirsey, Amy 497
Keiser, Kenneth A. 249
Keisling, Jeffrey 671
Keitel, William E 707
Keith, Shane 259
Keith, Elizabeth 266
Keith, Roxanne 502
Keith, R. Alexandra 693
Keith, Rob 722
Kekoolani, Kaleo 103
Kelej, Rasha 566
Keliher, Lester 824
Kell, Sarra 935
Kellam, Richard 397
Kellan, Jeff 503
Kellar, Brian 112
Kelleher, Tim 181
Kelleher, Ann B. 465
Kelleher, Colm 587
Kelleher, Brian 627
Kelleher, Kevin J. 718
Keller, Ken 57
Keller, Andy 161
Keller, Anna 161
Keller, Dick 170
Keller, Shawn 237
Keller, Sara Lee 457
Keller, Robert 598
Keller, Kurt A. 654
Keller, Brett 689
Keller, Stacey L 706
Keller, Erika 713
Keller, Gregory S 808
Keller, Greg 808
Keller-Carnap, Torsten 300
Kellett, Darin 677
Kellett, James 724
Kelley, Neisha 98
Kelley, Deborah 128
Kelley, Jack Douglas 196
Kelley, Amey 202
Kelley, Daniel T. (Dan) 214
Kelley, Jessie 226
Kelley, Trevor 273
Kelley, Richard 279

Kelley, Bruce G. 297
KELLEY, BILL 453
Kelley, Stanton 461
Kelley, Thomas M. (Tom) 544
Kelley, Barry 580
Kelley, John 643
Kelley, Cindy 731
Kelley, Tim 749
Kelley, Scott C. 884
Kellick, Andrea 813
Kelligrew, James B. 888
Kellner, Bob 888
Kellogg, Peter N. 175
Kellogg, James 636
Kellow, Glenn L. 659
Kelly, Brian G. 10
Kelly, Thomas B. (Tom) 15
Kelly, Shannon 39
Kelly, Kendra 49
Kelly, Michael A. 57
Kelly, Shawn 82
Kelly, William 101
Kelly, Rochelle Kelly Rochelle 102
Kelly, Pat 109
Kelly, Stephen E. 113
Kelly, Davitt 133
Kelly, Shannon 161
Kelly, Joy 201
Kelly, Keith 205
Kelly, John 207
Kelly, Robert 242
Kelly, Thomas A. 244
Kelly, Edward J. (Ned) 245
Kelly, James 248
Kelly, Cargile 294
Kelly, John 295
Kelly, Eric 297
Kelly, Theresa 366
Kelly, Kathy 404
Kelly, Catherine T. (Kate) 419
Kelly, Steve 454
Kelly, Nicolette 456
Kelly, Joel 457
Kelly, John E. 470
Kelly, Christie B. 486
Kelly, Patrick E. 502
Kelly, Marcella 570
Kelly, Tom 570
Kelly, Laura 665
Kelly, Michael (Mike) 705
Kelly, John 777
Kelly, Gary C. 780
Kelly, Matthew 792
Kelly, Pat 840
Kelly, Alfred F. (Al) 898
Kelmar, Steven B. 17
Kelso, J. Pete 19
Kelson, Richard B. (Rick) 227
Kely, Jim 470
Kemer, Dan 533
Kemp, Kristian 467
Kemp, Stephen J. 681
Kempczinski, Chris (Chris K) 562
Kemper, David W. 226
Kemper, John W. 226
Kemper, Jonathan M. 226
Kemper, J. Mariner 863
Kemps, Steven J. (Steve) 746
Kempton, David D 378
Kendall, Leah 161
Kendall, Dale 914
Kendrick, Robin 140
Kendrick, Lynn 677
Kendricks, Samuel B. 406
Kenefick, Jeffrey P. 338
Kennedy, Brad 15
Kennedy, Bryan J. 30
Kennedy, Colin 45
Kennedy, Maggie 101
Kennedy, Terry 101
Kennedy, Ryan 117
Kennedy, Al 171
Kennedy, Peter 224
Kennedy, James J. 233
Kennedy, John 252
Kennedy, Greg 262
Kennedy, Barbara 311

Kennedy, Cathy 332
Kennedy, Michael 339
Kennedy, Parker S. 339
Kennedy, Kellie 502
Kennedy, Will 576
Kennedy, James E. (Jim) 610
Kennedy, Douglas L. 660
Kennedy, Stacey 674
Kennedy, Thomas A. (Tom) 716
Kennedy, Scott 813
Kennedy, Trina 813
Kennedy, Shaun 823
Kennedy, Beverly 839
Kennedy-Gillette, Kim 849
Kennedy-nichols, Tammy 101
Kennemer, Derek 447
Kenner, Andrew 920
Kennett, Carrie 813
Kenney, Jeanne 304
Kenney, Anthony R. (Tony) 544
Kenney, David 738
Kenney, Eric 782
Kenney, Tom 905
Kennon, S. Gary 281
Kenny, David W. 34
Kenny, Katharine 162
Kenny, David W. 470
Kenny, Natalie 550
Kenny, John 891
Kensington, Sharon 45
Kent, John 131
Kent, Muhtar 216
Kent, Howard 233
Kent, Cory 336
Kent-Sheehan, Kate 358
Kenwood, James 259
Kenyon, John 109
Kenyon, Matt 195
Kenyon, Simone 332
Kenyon, Bill 876
Keogh, Tracy S. 442
Keogh, Tim 749
Keogh, Dawn 892
Keough, Richard 413
Keown, James 84
Keown, Karen 881
Kephart, Marla 869
Keplar, Jeff 643
Kepp, Kevin 128
Keppner, Judy L. 872
Kerber, Lynn M. 187
Kerby, Kevin 914
Kereere, Suzan 45
Kerins, Sean J. 76
Kerkar, Prasad 643
Kerley, Jay 71
Kern, David 609
Kern, Howard P. 762
Kerns, Mike 34
Kerollis, Gillian 705
Kerr, Derek J. 41
Kerr, William 106
Kerr, Connor 170
Kerr, Debbie 516
Kerschbaum, Manfred 71
Kershisnik, Kauleen 929
Kerstetter, Russ 299
Kervin, Karen 888
Kesavan, Sudhakar 7
Keshavarz, Ebrahim 84
Keskar, Dinesh A. 135
Kesler, Shawn 80
Kess, Avrohom J. 849
Kessel, Steve 37
Kessel, Cindy 320
Kesseler, Brian 820
Kesselman, Marc 259
Kesselman, Marc L. 939
Kessler, Angela 12
Kessler, Ben 97
Kessler, Bethmara 156
Kessler, Christy 355
Kessler, Donald 454
Kessler, Marla 478
Kessler-Sanders, Michelle 705
Kester, Paige 429
Ketcham, Jerry 273

Ketchum, John 533
Ketchum, John 612
Kettner, Miles 170
Keulen, Chris van 170
Kewalramani, Rajiv 489
Key, Daniel 214
Key, George 402
Keyes, Kevin G. 65
Keyes, Gregory S 808
Keyes, Gregory 808
Keyes, J. Patrick 909
Keyes, Jim 919
Keyler, Joseph 355
Keys, Thomas C. 810
Khafizova, Ariadna 414
Khalaf, Michel 569
Khan, Nadeem G. 19
Khan, Saeed 185
Khan, Sohail 201
Khan, Raheel 465
Khan, Fareed A. 493
Khan, Salisha 634
Khan, Mehmood 667
Khan, Kanwar Nasir 672
Khan, Atif 713
Khan, Adeel 730
Khandpur, Ashish K. 2
Khang, Chris 382
Khanna, Ajit 117
Khanna, Joe 555
Khavarani, Anthony 754
Khelghatian, Raffi 224
Khemka, Vivek 272
Khera, Neha 142
Khesin, Eugene 327
Khetan, Sharad 465
Khodos, Jane 555
Khourie, Matt 170
Khoury, Raymond 139
Khreich, Gilbert 87
Khu, Elaine 664
Kiam, Raphael 133
Kick, Richard 357
Kidd, Herbert 337
Kidd, Natalie 404
Kidd, Jay 602
Kidd, John 602
Kidder, Paul 754
Kidwell, Bruce 875
Kiefer, Steven 385
Kiehn, Erik 31
Kiehne, Matt 487
Kieli, Kasia 270
Kiernan, Jeff 172
Kiernan, Ryan 429
Kiernan, Michael 602
Kiffer, Tracy 596
Kiger, Mary 526
Kight, Rob 262
Kiida, Mike 509
Kiker, William A. (Bill) 876
Kiker, Bill 876
Kikuchi, Kenji 332
Kilbane, Kevin 715
Kilbane, Catherine 764
Kilberg, James A. (Jim) 921
Kilborn, Robert 106
Kilburn, Garth 226
KILE, JESSE 507
Kilgore, Tom D 821
Kilicyan, Haig 158
Killalea, Tom 37
Killeen, Greg 395
Killeen, Jay 516
Killian, Cathi 273
Killian, Shanna 811
Killinger, Elizabeth 625
Killinger, Clay 890
Killingsworth, Mark 267
Killman, John 117
Kilman, Ginger 869
Kilmer, Raymond J. (Ray) 75
Kilpatrick, David B 14
Kilpatrick, Carole 247
Kilpatrick, Adam 306
Kilpin, Timothy J. (Tim) 10
Kilpin, Tim 557

Kilroy, Jill 435
Kilroy, Thomas M 464
Kim, Christina 3
Kim, Kyo Yung (K Y) 22
Kim, Edward 103
Kim, Daniel 103
Kim, Jim 131
Kim, Anna 161
Kim, Charles 203
Kim, Keith 224
Kim, Charles G. (Chuck) 226
Kim, Doug 295
Kim, John 316
Kim, Claudia 327
Kim, Choung 391
Kim, Claira 395
Kim, Greg D. 408
Kim, Anthony 408
Kim, Jason K 435
Kim, Threnn 496
Kim, Patti 533
Kim, Sarah 570
Kim, Thomas 620
Kim, Annie 652
Kim, Ann 803
Kimball, Stefanie 459
Kimball, Kenny 506
Kimball, Patty 521
Kimball, Patty 523
Kimball, Kevin 548
Kimball, John 578
Kimble, Jim 68
Kimble, Brandy 306
Kimble, Lewis P. 368
Kimble, Chandra 450
Kimble, Donald R. 497
Kimbro-Moore, Vicki 806
Kime, Jeffery L. (Jeff) 837
Kimm, Christopher 893
Kimmel, Robert 190
Kimmel, Jon 530
Kimmet, Pamela O. (Pam) 160
Kimmich, Jeff A 808
Kimmitt, Joseph H. (Jay) 645
Kimpton, Jay 713
Kinak, Melissa 809
Kinasewich, Rob 141
Kinate, Pat 3
Kincheloe, Terry 863
Kinden, Sven 602
Kinder, Richard D. (Rich) 500
Kinder, Lauren 705
Kindig, Karl 213
Kindig, Susan 528
King, Kathryn R 6
King, Steve 31
King, Kathleen 44
King, Janice 45
King, Andrew D. (Andy) 76
King, Gayle 81
King, Dan 88
King, Steve 115
King, Kelly S. 116
King, Carter 158
King, Cathy 161
King, Dan 182
King, Peter 240
King, Stephen 249
King, Timothy B. 268
King, Sam 301
King, Jason 350
King, Laurie 507
King, David P. (Dave) 510
King, Darren J. 538
King, Dale 570
King, Jeffrey 582
King, Martin G. 674
King, Sam 678
King, Thomas 706
King, Susan 712
King, Robert 735
King, Bruce M. 739
King, Jake 754
King, Elizabeth 787
King, Gary A. 810
King, Terry 824
King, Ron 869

King, Sue 896
King, Jeremy 903
King, Kristin 926
King, Jim 942
Kingham, Jennifer 613
Kinghorn, Nichole 355
Kingsbury, Thomas A. (Tom) 151
Kingsbury, Grace-Lynn 414
Kingsbury, Tom 504
Kingsley, Scott A. 228
Kingsley, Stephen 770
Kinkade, Jennifer 221
Kinlin, Clark S. 240
Kinnaird, Jeff 431
Kinner, Michael 272
Kinney, Bryant 286
Kinney, John 413
Kinney, Ross 677
Kinney, Patrick J. 849
Kinra, Vivek 620
Kinser, Tammy 350
Kinsley, Bryce 743
Kinslow, Craig 912
Kintzle, Jeff 729
Kinz, Robert 808
Kip, Pinar 792
Kipnis, Aaron 131
Kipp, Melana C 886
Kipp, Stephen 896
Kipperman, Bruce 181
Kiraly, Robert G. (Bob) 366
Kirby, Jeff 28
Kirby, Jefferson W. 28
Kirby, Brent G. 537
Kirby, J. Scott 871
Kirch, Bob 781
Kirchenbauer, Ronald W 739
Kirchhoefer, Eric 7
Kirchhoefer, Kari 868
Kirchhoff, Micha 733
Kirchner, Mike 52
Kirchner, Tim 121
Kirgan, Danielle 256
Kirihara, Wayne H. 179
Kirk, Richard 249
Kirk, Joan 355
Kirk, Mathew 413
Kirk, Bob 732
Kirk, Melvin (Mel) 743
Kirk, Mel 743
Kirk, Warren J. 818
Kirkeeng, Erin 389
Kirkendall, Eric 805
Kirkham, Ryan 666
Kirkhofer, Eric 504
Kirkland, George L 191
Kirkwood, John 470
Kirsch, Eric M. 19
Kirschner, Randy 14
Kirshner, Alan I. 547
Kirtley, Timothy H. 666
Kirwan, Jeff 830
Kisber, Michael E. 353
Kiscaden, Bradley J. 545
Kisch, Horst 214
Kischell, Jennifer 570
Kiser, Carly 804
Kishore, Ganesh 585
Kishore, Ashok 847
Kiskorna, Mark 680
Kissane, Jonathan (Jon) 602
Kissel, Joe 54
Kissel, Janet 487
Kissling, Lou 247
Kist, Jonathan 474
Kisucky, Michael 191
Kitagawa, Allan S. 822
Kitamura, Jeremy 53
Kitamura, Ryan 103
Kitamura, Sam 332
Kitchen, Ronda 530
Kitchin, Brad 643
Kite, David 273
Kittle, Lori 787
Kittleson, Terry 170
Kittner, Lisa 587
Kittredge, Teri 671

Kitts, Stephen 863
Kitzmann, Jessica 158
Kitzmiller, Kenneth G. 567
Kiyono, Jolene 179
Kjellberg, Henrik V. 316
Kladt, Gilberto 273
Klaeser, Dennis L. 187
Klahre, Robert 570
Klaif, Mitchell (Mitch) 838
Klammer, Thoma P 446
Klappa, Gale E. 909
Klaus, Jeffrey A. (Jeff) 908
Klavsons, David 423
Klebba, Philip 748
Klee, Brian 671
Kleeman, Ray 585
Kleespies, Kurt 895
Kleffel, Julie 757
Kleiman, Mitch 87
Kleiman, Mark 808
Klein, Dorothea 175
Klein, Stacy 202
Klein, John E. 218
Klein, David 222
Klein, Phyllis S. 233
Klein, David 237
Klein, Steven A 246
Klein, Mark 266
Klein, Christopher J. (Chris) 371
Klein, Mike 382
Klein, Cynthia 395
Klein, Jeff 434
Klein, Robert N. 526
Klein, Robert 651
Klein, Richard 665
Klein, Susan 810
Klein, Gerald J. 842
Klein, Michael F. 849
Klein, Bart 863
Klein, Matthew 882
Klein, David 923
Klein, Russ 935
Kleinberg, Joshua 170
Kleiner, Rasiel 511
Kleinhomer, Kevin 101
Kleinman, Robert 14
Klenk, Rick 530
Klenk, Jeffrey P. (Jeff) 849
Klepchick, Andrew 806
Kletter, David 139
Klevorn, Marcy 370
Klick, Dave 912
Kliethermes, Craig W. 732
Klimczak, Bob 564
Klimkowski, Ronald 196
Kline, Betsy 72
Kline, Thomas 115
Kline, Gary J 196
Kline, Clayton 486
Kline, Terry S. 597
Kline, Stephanie 745
Kline, Keith 799
Kline, David 896
Klinger, Gil 717
Klinger, John 840
Klingspor, Jonas 15
Klink, Jeff 892
Klinkner, Kim 80
Klippel, Charles 18
Klis, Janette 681
Klobnak, Jennifer L. 732
Klodd, Annie 831
Klotz, Jim 760
Klotzbach, Kevin B. 338
Kluck, Sior P 170
Klug, Loren C. 445
Klug, Sue 729
Klyce, Harvey 489
Klym, Nick 489
Kman, Ed 300
Kmietek, Kathy 413
Knapik, Will 927
Knapke, Murph 350
Knapp, Raymond 338
Knapp, Tracy W. 492
Knapp, Michael 574
Knapp, Ken Knapp Ken 722

Knauer, Ron 425
Knauer, Brian 876
Knauss, Bob 861
Knauss, Robert 861
Knavish, Timothy M. 685
Kneeland, Michael J. 876
Kneidinger, Michael (Mike) 256
Knickerbocker, Rick 582
Knies, Theresa 664
Kniffin, Ogden 715
Knight, Barbara 25
Knight, Michael 159
Knight, Angela 224
Knight, August 224
Knight, Michael 304
Knight, Michelle 336
Knight, Jeffrey W. 400
Knight, Jeff 400
Knight, Michael 489
Knight, Jeffrey L. (Jeff) 635
Knight, Christine 700
Knight, Phil 834
Knight, Robert M. 868
Knightly, Kevin C. 478
Knighton, Frankie 146
Knirsch, Charles 671
Kniss, Kam 928
Knoblauch, Paul 492
Knoller, Karen 814
Knollmaier, Sherry 3
Knollmeyer, Pete 365
Knopf, Matthew 262
Knopf, David 505
Knorr, Molly 881
Knott, Timothy 492
Knott, Greg 743
Knott, Irene 834
Knotts, Daniel L. (Dan) 280
Knowles, Debie 49
Knowles, Leo 232
Knowles, Dennis 537
Knowling, Doug 723
Knoy, Shane 504
Knuckles, Beth 508
Knudson, Jeffrey 252
Knupp, Catherine A. (Cathy) 943
Knutilla, Tom 743
Knutsson, Jesper 199
Ko, Al 476
Kobashigawa, Scot 754
Kobayashi, Edison 103
Koble, Keith 105
Kobus, David 18
Koch, Dan 81
Koch, Pam 158
Koch, Matt 226
Koch, Paul C 246
Koch, Phillip 413
Koch, Robert 502
Koch, Stephen P. (Steve) 725
Koch, Kim 884
Koch, Kimberly 884
Kochanov, Oleg 109
Kocher, Eric 45
Kocherlakota, Swamy 746
Kochvar, Mark 745
Kocim, Jeffrey A 852
Kocoris, Steven 767
Kocur, John 68
Kodl, Amy 748
Koebler, Ellen 288
Koehler, Mike 314
Koehler, Hans 502
Koehler, Mary 927
Koehnen, Michael W. 851
Koel, Mike 861
Koellner, Meliss A 446
Koellner, Jackie 498
Koen, Kenneth 171
Koenig, Jim 170
Koenig, Ron 226
Koenig, Benjamin 901
Koenig, Joseph G. (Joe) 930
Koening, John 411
Koenn, James 754
Koepsell, Karen 97
Koeperich, Marie 419

Koffer, Danielle 220
Koh, Peter 435
Kohen, Ian 248
Kohlbeck, Don 12
Kohler, Kayleen 110
Kohler, Pete 140
Kohler, Tim 811
Kohler, Lori 863
Kohler, Paul 911
Kohler, David 942
Kohls, Scott 888
Kohn, Thomas W. 187
Kohr, Jeff 80
Kohring, Darlene 497
Kokate, Santosh 806
Kokenge, Nancy 378
Koki, Donovan 103
Kokke, Jorgen 462
Kokkoris, Rita 794
Kolakowski, Chrissy 889
Kolander, Geoffrey M. 206
Kolar, Mark 498
Kolatkar, Neil 170
Kolb, Amy 80
Kolbe, Chris 504
Kolkman, Arjan 300
Kollatz, Christoph 75
Kollen, Ron 273
Kolodzieski, Ed 903
Koltookian, Aram 837
Kolytiris, Valerie 339
Komanowski, Chris 170
Komidar, John 849
Komorowski, Raymond 550
Kondal, Jaspreet 334
Kondrotis, Krisstie 784
Kong, Oliver 175
Kong, Michelle 273
Konik, David 450
Konings, Frank 484
Konkolics, Charles 834
Konort, Phil 45
Konrad, Jocelyn 731
Konstantinovsky, Irina 115
Kontopanos, Kostas 219
Konz, Jim 832
Koo, Weilin 487
Kooda-Chizek, Kristi 52
Koogler, Rob 449
Koon, Lachelle 722
Koonce, Paul D. 278
Koons, Michael 199
Koosmann, Willie 941
Kopelman, Donna 489
Kopera, Donna 115
Kopfensteiner, Thomas R. 168
Kopischkie, Mike 735
Kopnisky, Joe 804
Kopp, Katharina 45
Kopp, Greg 754
Koppel, Paul 365
Koptyra, Kristin 97
Kopycinski, Gloria 247
Korchek, Jeff 557
Kordahi, Rony C. 647
Korecki, Joseph 665
Korenberg, Matthew 395
Korhonen, Katie 607
Koricanac, Nick 928
Korins, Danielle 705
Koritko, Martin 530
Kornbluth, Sally 287
Korneffel, Laurie 181
Korner, Barbara O. 831
Korowitz, Alan 457
Korsapati, Venka 39
Korsh, Les B. 657
Korsmeyer, Mark 254
Korten, Patrick 502
Korzekwinski, Francis W. (Frank) 366
Kosharek, Jamie 715
Koski, Susan 356
Koski, Philip 888
Koslow, John 45
Koss, Bill 800
Kossar, Robert 486
Koster, Steven 151

Koster, Teresa 378
Koster, Barbara G. 699
Koster, James 787
Kostroski, Pete 486
Kotas, Paul 37
Koth, Dan 735
Kotick, Robert A. (Bobby) 10
Kotler, Kristin 808
Kotlowski, Mike 545
Kotnik, Sue 94
Kotsol, Carolyn 113
Kottapalli, Kishore 792
Kottayil, Divya 173
Kottler, Robert M. (Bob) 454
Kotwal, Shailesh M. 888
Kotylo, Kenneth 817
Kotzin, Brian 57
Kouchoukos, John 15
Koulouris, Richard R. 683
Koumouris, Rick 365
Kouri, Stephen 773
Koury, Emile 406
Koury, Jeffrey (Jeff) 818
Kousemaeker, Laurent de 549
Koushik, Srinivas (Srini) 541
Kovacevich, Richard 200
Kovach, Gary 350
Kovacs, Clark C 286
Kovacs, James A 465
Koval, Kathy 760
Kovalan, Deann 928
Kovalchik, Richard 131
Koviak, Jeff 820
Kovich, Jana 287
Kovoor, George 668
Kowalchuk, Edward 365
Kowaleski, Tim 210
Kowalski, Christine 484
Kowkabany, Rob 54
Kowlzan, Mark W. 652
Kowolenko, Dave 222
Kozak, Dave 453
Kozak, Colleen 759
Kozakov, Alex 170
Kozar, Paul Kozar Paul 888
Kozel, David F. (Dave) 705
Kozen, Raymond 380
Koziner, Pablo M. 166
Koziol, Patrick 106
Koziol, Tracey 935
Kozlow, Steve 53
Kozlowski, Damian 827
Kozsurek, Joe 517
Krackenberger, Melissa 454
Kracov, Eric 604
Kraemer, Theodore 139
Kraft, Robert O. (Rocky) 252
Kraft, Kevin 287
Kraft, Ted 419
Kraft, Christopher 759
Krajicek, Catherine 546
Krakaur, Ken 762
Krakowsky, Philippe 473
Kral, Jon 722
Kralingen, Bridget A. van 470
Krall, Donna M. 362
Krallman, Amy B 932
Kramer, Bill 84
Kramer, Kelly A. 199
Kramer, Richard J. (Rich) 397
Kramer, Lewis 509
Kramer, Kevin 578
Kramer, Phillip D. (Phil) 679
Kramer, Mark 731
Kramer, Julie 808
Kramer, Karl 808
Krane, Hilary K. 615
Krantz, Missy S 454
Kranzel, Jerome 170
Krasnoff, Jeffrey P. (Jeff) 518
Krasowski, Janet D. 698
Kratz, Denise 749
Kratzert, Niki 502
Kraus, Marie 158
Kraus, Frederick 513
Kraus, John 842
Krause, Douglas P. 290

Krause, Frank 334
KRAUSE, ROBERT 794
Krause, Kim 799
Krause, Robert 876
Krauss, Soheir 201
Krauss, Jim 762
Kravetz, Lisse 87
Krawczyk, Brian 395
Krawczyk, Michael 809
Krawiec, Dan 240
Kreatsoulas, John 465
Krebs, Donald E. (Don) 492
Krebs, Don 492
Krebs, Marty 585
Krebs, James 896
Krehbiel, Bruce 474
Kremer, Donald 192
Kremer, Lisa 550
Kremer, Wesley D. 716
Kremin, Donald H. (Don) 437
Krempl, Stephen 787
Krenkel, David S. 279
Kresl, Michael 49
Kress, Jean 391
Kress, Colette M. 627
Kress, Kathy 904
Kreuzer, Barry 248
Krevans, Sarah 802
Krey, Julie 543
Krick, Brian 760
Krieger, Laurel 442
Krieger, Sarah 660
Krieger, Noah 699
Kriel, Aileen 395
Kriens, Scott G. 490
Krietsch, Judith 101
Krimbill, H. Michael 613
Kring, Steven C. 436
Krippner, Brian 863
Krish, Bharani 582
Krishnamurthy, Karthik 199
Krishnamurthy, Nikki 316
Krishnamurthy, Ram 379
Krishnamurthy, Srini 413
Krishnan, Sai 300
Kristo, Joni 615
Kritemeyer, Ellen 664
Krmpotic, Deb 111
Kroboth, Michael 686
Krocheski, Joseph 18
Kroeker, Harrald F. 72
Krohn, Shannon 80
Kroiss, Valerie 863
Krol, Wojciech 219
Kroll, Brannon 246
Kroll, Sue 838
Krom, Stephen 222
Kromm, Elizabeth 483
Krone, Stacey 332
Krone, Roger A. 516
Krone, Roger A 517
Kronour, Randall 53
Kropf, Jonathan 358
Kroungold, Danielle 536
Krueger, Pam 84
Krueger, Glenn 383
Kruesi, Susan 559
Kruger, Mike 84
Kruger, James D. (Jim) 601
Kruger, Jill 697
Kruger, Bob 816
Kruger, Bill 875
Krulewitch, Jerry 562
Krumbock, Monika 757
Krummen, William 337
Krupa, David E. 746
Krupetsky, Greta 599
Krupp, Jeff 718
Kruse, Karen 353
Kruse, Cory 371
Kruse, Shelly 402
Kruse, Karl 453
Krusinski, Laura 497
Kruszewski, Ronald J. (Ron) 795
Kruthaupt, Bob 693
Krutsch, Alanna 161
Krygoski, Haide 760

Krynauw, Pieter 434
Krzanich, Brian M. 465
Krzeminski, Robert E 912
Ksenak, Stephen M. 39
Kubacki, Michael L. 512
Kubar, Susan 106
Kuberski, Craig 370
Kuchny, Allison 479
Kuczek, Sara F 113
Kuczora, Deb 504
Kueber, Ken 213
Kuehl, Kevin 128
Kuehn, Gina 2
Kuelbs, Brian P. 97
Kuether, Bret 80
Kugel, Irene 106
Kugler, Mitch 717
Kuhl, Lisa 715
Kuhlow, John 447
Kuhn, Rebecca (Becky) 111
Kuhn, Laura 273
Kuhns, Dewey 207
Kuiper, Jeremy L. 827
Kularski, Patty 409
Kulaszewicz, Frank C. 738
Kulchitskaya, Yanina 204
Kulkarni, Manmath 643
Kulkin, Harvey 764
Kullman, Wayne 31
Kum, Chong Guk (C. G.) 408
Kumar, Vipin 72
Kumar, Vijay 185
Kumar, Sunil 483
Kumar, Rashmi 563
Kumar, Rajesh 731
Kumar, Subramaniam 849
Kumbalek, Doug 517
Kumbier, Michelle A. 410
Kumler, Alan 869
Kumm, Wendy 80
Kumnick, Phillip 899
Kunde, Gerald 808
Kunde, Chip 808
Kundrat, Nikki 107
Kundurthy, Praveen 465
Kuney, Terry 449
Kunk, James E. 449
Kunkel, Jay K. 514
Kunkel, Thomas M. (Tom) 849
Kunst, Jeff 240
Kuntz, John F. 698
Kuntz, Ned 799
Kuntz, Michael J. (Mike) 856
Kunze, Shane 702
Kunze, Shane 703
Kuper, Debra 20
Kupfer, Lawrence J. (Larry) 529
Kupper, Randy 52
Kurali, Andreas 674
Kurani, Maheboob 408
Kurapati, Raja 131
Kurapka, David 131
Kurek, Robert 497
Kurey, Tammy 80
Kurian, George 199
Kurian, George 601
Kurian, Thomas 602
Kurian, Thomas 643
Kuritzkes, Andrew 791
Kurkowski, Susan J 528
Kurland, Stanford L. 662
Kurlander, Ronnie 810
Kurlapski, Matthew 919
Kurmas, Steven E. 283
Kurnick, Robert H. 663
Kuropas, Stephen M 620
Kurosaka, Angie 176
Kurth, Keith 915
Kurtov, Ines 604
Kurtz, Kevin 840
Kurumunda, Phil 570
Kuryan, Jacob 94
Kurzendoerfer, Mike 507
Kurzius, Lawrence E. 560
Kus, Julie 692
Kuselias, Jason 413
Kush, Henry 310

Kushel, J. Richard (Rich) 131
Kushner, Jay 896
Kuslits, Thomas R. 362
Kusnadi, Ann 831
Kustell, Melissa 557
Kustenbauter, Jim 831
Kutchera, Kris 26
Kuykendall, Ronald E. 749
Kuzbel, Jeffrey 158
Kuzemkan, Cynthia 643
Kuzniasz, Stacey 249
Kvamme, John 80
Kvech, Joe 852
Kvernland, Hege 593
Kwan, Irene E B 103
Kwan, Sarah 804
Kwapong, Opokua 668
Kwasnica, Christina 266
Kwiatkowski, Larry 224
Kwok, Alex 34
Kyff, Emilia 570
Kyle, Rex 107
Kymes, Stacy C. 137
Kyre, Erik 449
Kyriakidis, Alex 548
KYRILLOS, J 708
Kyse, Julie 316

L

Laan, Ron Van Der 106
LaBarge, Kathleen 332
Labat, Misty 454
Labelle, Larry 330
LaBelle, Jeanne 339
Laben, Nancy J. 139
Labib, Joseph 698
LaBonte, David 875
Labovich, Gary D. 139
Labrique, Steve 67
Labrosse, Derek 107
Lacaille, Rick 791
Lacassagne, Gtraudmarie 243
Lacasse, Janet 101
Lacerda, Ana 6
Lacerda, Carolina 487
Lacey, Jeff 726
Lachance, Margaret P. (Meg) 705
Lacher, Thomas 359
Lacher, Joseph P. (Joe) 495
Lack, Andrew R. (Andy) 222
Lack, John 247
Lackhouse, Gary 84
Lacobie, William 191
Lacombel, Phillip 380
Lacour, Raymond 715
LaCrosse, Lisa 494
Lacy, James 84
Lacy, Jamie 677
Lacy, Nicholas 715
Lacy-Wilson, Kat 378
Ladd, Emma 530
Laderman, Gerald (Gerry) 871
Ladesich, Linda 18
Laemmle, Mark 502
Laenger, William 722
Lafaive, Brad 140
Lafferty, Kevin 263
Lafiandra, Craig 881
Lafitte, Michael J. (Mike) 169
Lafleur, Danielle 705
Lafond, Dan 84
LaFreniere, Kevin 413
Laga, Michael 918
Lagacy, Julie A. 166
Lagano, Roxanne 943
LaGatta, Loreen A. 867
Lagioia, Andrea 219
Lagnado, Silvia 562
Lago, Virginia Del 550
Lagomasino, Maria Elena (Mel) 95
Laguardia, Brian 764
Laguarta, Ramon 667
Laguerre, Monique 507
LaHaise, James A. 54
LaHatte, Bernard 834

Lahoud, Sami 555
Lahr, Troy 135
Lai, Suet 274
Lai, John 573
Laine, Jim 353
Laing, Sheila 453
Laipple, Chad 888
Laird, Bruce 199
Laisch, Frank 60
Lake, Charles D. 19
Lake, Marianne 488
Lake, Stephen 641
Lakkis, Miguel El 610
Lakshman, Girish 759
Lalama, Kristen 327
Lalikos, Ben 454
Lalithakumar, Ananth 176
Lall, Vishal 425
Lally, Helen 47
Lally, James B. 306
Lalor, Angela S. 256
Lalor, Angie 256
Lalwani, Ellen 511
Lam, Michael 105
Lam, Samsonz 290
Lam, Alvin 488
Lam, Josiah 489
Lam, Winnie W 792
Lamanna, John 729
Lamanno, Lori 863
Lamar, Paula 266
Lamar, William (Bibb) 763
Lamarche, Michael Lamarche Michael 888
Lamay, Troy 87
Lamb, Chris 45
Lamb, Todd 161
Lamb, Phil 300
Lamb, Brian 336
Lamb, John 390
Lamb, Emily 392
Lamb, Rob 470
Lamb, Robert 752
Lamba, Lavlesh 114
Lamberger, Dave 457
Lamberies, Mark 781
Lambert, Karen A. 13
Lambert, Jeff 131
Lambert, Richard F. 699
Lambert, Cameron 713
Lambertson, Stephen 834
Lambeth, Tracy 580
Lamboy, Benjamin 488
Laming, Michael S. 389
Lamkin, Bryan 11
Lamm, Kim 117
Lammers, Rene 668
Lamneck, Kenneth T. (Ken) 463
LaMontagna, Peter 889
Lamotte, Joseph 399
Lamparski, Jerry 31
Lampe, Gregory 377
Lampert, Edward S. (Eddie) 759
Lamphear, Sue 171
Lamphere, Ralph 599
Lampier, Carol 246
Lampley, Barry 350
Lampo, Craig A. 58
Lamus, Fernando 94
Lanasa, Sam 204
Lancaster, Christopher 414
Lancaster, Olin 713
Land, Jeff 266
Land, Jeffrey 266
Landa, Jon 533
Landau, Glenn R. 472
Lande, Kris 748
Landeche, Dean M 300
Landenwich, Joseph L. 501
Lander, Mike 912
Landgraf, John 858
Landmark, Greg 849
Landon, Jim 24
Landre, Jay 628
Landrith, Jody 155
Landry, David 247
Landry, Robert E. 719

Landry, Steve 769
Landry, Chris 863
Landry, Lenee 912
Landschulz, Mark 362
Landsman, Liza K. 903
Landy, Sarah 897
Lane, Andrew H. 4
Lane, Danny 81
Lane, Randy 201
Lane, Janet 247
Lane, Larry 386
Lane, Eric S. 395
Lane, Jamie 423
Lane, Jeffrey H. 572
Lane, Brian 654
Lane, J. Bret 761
Lane, Richard 806
Lane, Rick 858
Lane, Anne 941
Lanesey, Rob 476
Laney, G. Timothy (Tim) 591
Lang, Robert 258
Lang, Michael (Mike) 270
Lang, J Brad 693
Lang, Edward A 729
Lang, Lenore 748
Lang, William 754
Lang, Rebecca A 863
Lang, Rebecca 863
Langan, Chris 875
Langdon, Lynn M 772
Lange, Bob De 166
Lange, Barbara 273
Lange, Jeffrey 413
Lange, James 620
Lange, Peter 664
Langenbahn, Paul 599
Langeness, Troy 637
Langenfeld, Camilla 400
Langenfeld, Jon A. 735
Langenohl, Michael 935
Langenus, John 67
Langer, Robert 273
Langfitt, Gary B. 164
Langley, Judi 504
Langley, Michael 668
Langley-Hawthorne, Tim 919
Langone, Elizabeth 569
Langston, Lewis 926
Lanham, Christian 146
Laniado, Linda 440
Lanier, Lawrence 330
Lanigan, Susan 275
Lanis, Nancy 752
Lankler, Douglas M. (Doug) 671
Lankton, Madelyn 849
Lannen, Angela 55
Lannie, P. Anthony 68
Lannie, Anthony P 68
Lannie, P 68
Lanning, Al 540
Lanning, Justin 934
Lansbury, Stephen 374
Lansing, Jane 299
Lantrip, Reese T. 308
Lantzsch, Thomas P. (Tom) 465
Lanza, Michael H. 760
Lanzino, Becky 377
Lapadula, Mike 708
Lapczynski, Susan 131
Lapierre, Monique 799
Lapinski, Maura 511
Laplant, Michael 863
LaPlante, Joe 3
Lapolice, Matt 737
Laponzina, Richard 750
LaPorta, Cosimo 787
LaPorta, Cos 787
Lappala, Kris 670
LaPrade, Frank G. 158
Laprade, Ken 411
Lapriore, Ellen 643
Laraway, Dennis L. 111
Larbalestier, Laura 672
Larchevesque, Lee Lee Larchevesque 896
Lardinois, Tim 782

Lardy, Dave 657
Larence, Robert 413
Largay, Keith 487
Larkin, Deanna 445
Larkin, Gary 457
Larkin, Terrence B. (Terry) 514
Larkin, Heidi 656
Larkin, Amy 866
Larkins, Thomas F. 71
Larmour, Grant 170
LaRocca, Andrew 604
LaRocco, Michael E. (Mike) 788
LaRoche, Mark 502
Larochelle, Steven R. 305
Larocque, Peter 805
LaRose, Jason 866
LaRossa, Ralph A. 701
Laroyia, Varun 534
Larrimer, Karen L. 680
Larsen, Kenneth A. (Ken) 110
Larsen, Christine E. 348
Larsen, Michael M. 458
Larsen, Ron 767
Larsen, Shild 793
Larson, Steven 94
Larson, Erik 107
Larson, Luke 168
Larson, David 172
Larson, Tyla 355
Larson, Gregory J. (Greg) 440
Larson, Connie 454
Larson, Keith 465
Larson, Julie 541
Larson, Timothy M. 681
Larson, Don 684
Larson, Todd C. 723
Larson, Michael 770
Larson, Eric 792
Larson, Steve 809
Larson, David L. 927
Larson, Kent T. 933
Larson, Laura 942
Larsson, Greg 413
Larsson, Naya 555
Lasaracino, David 18
Lasaracino, Dave 18
Lash, James H. (Jim) 360
Lashbrook, Bill G 680
Lasher, Daniel 816
Lashier, Mark E. 192
Lashmet, Craig 748
Lasky, Charles 360
Laso, Karolina 881
Lasorsa, Maria 790
Laspisa, Jerry 539
Laspisa, Esther 935
Lass, John J. 376
Lassar, Alex 486
Lasser, Cathy 470
Lassiter, Lynn 677
Last, Daniel 498
Lastovica, Thomas 447
Lastrap, Karla 158
Latawiec, Michal 927
Latchford, Bob 875
Latella, Robert N. 338
Latimer, Elise 454
Latovin, Alex 620
Latreille, Steve 462
Lattmann, Susan E. 121
Latuga, Tina 875
Laturette, Deborah 805
Latypova, Alisa 693
Latz, Wade 422
Lau, Timothy J. 80
Lau, Malcom 103
Lau, Cindy 159
Lau, Stephen 219
Lau, Jacky 480
Lau, Andy 496
Lau, Michele 563
Lau, Elisa 573
Lau, Pam 688
Lau, Colin 748
Lauber, Scott J. 909
Lauderdale, Dawn 558
Lauer, Nicholas 74

Lauer, Trevor F. 283
Lauer, Trevor F. 284
Laufer, Eyal 465
Laughlin, Robert 94
Laughlin, Terence P. (Terry) 101
Laughlin, Kyle 273
Laughlin, John P. 723
Launer, Justin 358
Lauren, Jerry 713
Lauren, Ralph 714
Lauren, David 714
Laurence, Scott 483
Laurenzi, Benjamin 550
Lauria, Kristen 470
Lauria, Lynette 770
Laurie, Bob 94
Laurie, David 668
Laurin, Sean 367
Lauro, Jeff 630
Lauro, Neil 715
Laursen, Thomas E. 941
Lauterbach, Robert 96
Lautmann, Max 804
Laux, Nancy 911
Lavallee, Kristen 665
Lavallee, Paul 886
LaValley, Steve 149
Lavender, Shelley K. 135
Laver, Michael 606
Laverty, David 470
Laverty, John 849
Lavery, Anna 570
Lavey, Richard W. (Dick) 409
Lavigne, Joe 141
Lavin, Connie 356
Lavin, John 728
Lavin, Marty 927
Lavric, Daniela 240
Law, Phil 84
Law, Christina 383
Law, Kirk 602
Law, Scott 941
Lawal, Lekan J 582
Lawhead, Casey 454
Lawhon, Pres 733
Lawhorn, Andy 841
Lawicki, Pat 595
Lawit, Jason A 620
Lawler, Robert D. (Doug) 189
Lawler, Chris 222
Lawler, Keith 413
Lawlor, Mike 413
Lawlor, Richard 423
Lawlor, Daniel 928
Lawrance, Paul 484
Lawrence, Kevin 98
Lawrence, Timothy 115
Lawrence, Ralph 139
Lawrence, Tim 139
Lawrence, Charlotte 204
Lawrence, Sidwell 261
Lawrence, Jared 286
Lawrence, Larry 300
Lawrence, Gerry R 300
Lawrence, Dugan 395
Lawrence, Guy 570
Lawrence, Pamela 587
Lawrence, Edward P. 656
Lawrence, Art 667
Lawrence, Taylor W. 716
Lawrence, Allison 786
Lawrence, Ronald 895
Laws, Matt 196
Laws, John 382
Lawshe, Pam 769
Lawson, Linda 81
Lawson, Kenneth 170
Lawson, David C. (Dave) 221
Lawson, Johnathan 261
Lawson, Rodger A. 288
Lawson, Jeremy 533
Lawson, Scott P. 609
Lawson, Andrew 748
Lawter, Kim 692
Lawton, Harry A. (Hal) 293
Lawton, Douglas 623
Lawton, Patrick S. (Pat) 735

Lawton, Chuck 890
Lax, Robert 204
Laxer, Richard A. (Rich) 382
Laxton, Gregory 135
Lay, Tony 573
Layden, David 886
Layne, Beverly 697
Layton, Kert 243
Layton, Donald H. (Don) 373
Lazaridis, Nick 442
Lazarus, Larry S. 112
Lazarus, Mark H. 222
Lazarus, Franz E. 241
Lazas, Ronald 501
Lazoritz, Stephen 911
Lazzaris, Diane E. 914
Le, Viet 94
LE, Michelle 117
Le, Janice 425
Le, David 507
LE, Tuyen 664
Lea, Doretha F. (DeDe) 896
Leach, Mark 266
Leackfeldt, Stephen M. 112
Leadbeater, Seth M. 226
Leager, Mary 539
Leal, Danny 246
Leal, Cynthia 754
Leaman, Andrew 885
Lean, Brenda 117
Leary, Alison 606
Leavell, Kristin 102
Leavell, Christopher M. 339
Leavell, Bill E. 844
Leavengood, Marty 182
Leavenworth, Elaine R. 4
Leaverton, Lindsey 117
Leavitt, Shawn 222
Leavitt, Bruce 467
Leavy, David C. 270
Leavy, Jack 691
Lebeau, Christina 390
Lebeck, Shelley 161
Lebel, Joseph J. 632
LeBlanc, Claude L. 39
Leblanc, Roch 297
LeBlanc, Robert J. 470
Lebo, Charles 502
Lebowitz, Michael 131
Lebrun, Robert 128
LeBrun, Bob 128
Lecator, Priscilla 896
Lech, Micheal 801
Lechleiter, John C. 528
Lechner, Kim 259
Leckey, Kathy 530
Leckman, Linda C. 467
LeClair, Stephen O. (Steve) 418
LeClaire, Brian P. 446
Lecuyer, Andrew 272
Ledbetter, Barry K. 768
Leddy, Kim 304
Lederer, James 707
Lederer, Kim 882
Lederman, Ira S. 122
Ledet, Don 454
LEDET, CARLOS 488
Ledford, Randall D. 299
Ledford, Laurie 550
Ledford, Andrea L. 599
Ledford, Doug 799
Leduc, Robert F. 879
Lee, Cindy 6
Lee, Anderson 45
Lee, Lori M. 84
Lee, Charles 135
Lee, Jeff 158
Lee, Trina Hoppin 162
Lee, Ellen 168
Lee, James 170
Lee, Edgar 186
Lee, Gam 204
Lee, Eugene I. (Gene) 256
Lee, Shreve 262
Lee, John M. 290
Lee, Jay 293

Lee, Bruce 322
Lee, Ken 389
Lee, William A. 391
Lee, Bonita I. (Bonnie) 408
Lee, Bruce K. 419
Lee, Brandon 435
Lee, Lisa 435
Lee, James 488
Lee, Jason 489
Lee, Charlotte 492
Lee, Yong 497
Lee, Al 518
Lee, Melanie 536
Lee, Lara L. 537
Lee, David 539
Lee, Nancy 548
Lee, Natasha 550
Lee, Yohan 557
Lee, Esther 569
Lee, Todd 593
Lee, Sungwoo 593
Lee, Jeff 604
Lee, Ming-Ju 628
Lee, Thomas H. 656
Lee, Sean 661
Lee, Julien 665
Lee, Felitia 668
Lee, Chewah 671
Lee, Chip 715
Lee, Jeffery (Jeff) 756
Lee, Schavrien 762
Lee, Thai 766
Lee, Henry 768
Lee, Peter 792
Lee, Peter 799
Lee, Jennifer 849
Lee, Michael 866
Lee, David 875
Lee, Debra L. 896
Lee, Sang 899
Lee, James 903
Lee, Ian 923
Lee, Don 931
Lee, Victor 935
Leebron, Jack 146
Leece, Lynne 337
Leech, Kim 454
Leech, Wilson 620
Leedom, David W. 568
Leekha, Sameer 102
Leemhuis, Bill 449
Leer, Julie 770
Lees, Susan L. 31
Leets, Karen 499
Leeuwen, Jay Van 650
Lefferson, C. Douglas (Doug) 349
Lefko, Cindy 228
Lefkowitz, Steve 838
LeFort, Alan 465
Lefton, Alan 39
Lefurge, Raymond H. 872
Leger, Tamela 454
Legere, John J. 810
Legg, Matt 726
Legge, Jeffrey D. (Jeff) 207
Legge, Jeff 207
Leggette, Sharon 530
Leggio, John 628
Leggio, Joseph S 896
Legrand, Joseph 813
Legters, Robert 334
Lehan, Felicia 604
Lehman, Jeff 205
Lehman, Vicci 507
Lehman, Jeffrey S. 606
Lehmann, Mary 57
Lehn, Chuck 111
Lehner, Jon 792
Lehrer, Ronald 604
Leibel, Stephen 196
Leibman, Maya 41
Leidahl, Todd 383
Leiding, Robert 487
Leidwinger, Kevin 211
Leigh, Justin 383
Leigh, Howard 548
Leigh, Stacey 735

Leinenbach, Keith A. 390
Leininger, Scott 184
Leinroth, Peter 473
Leipzig, Inna 840
Leira, Renee 105
Leissring, Kevin 449
Leitch, Nick 204
Leitch, Glenn R. 437
Leite, Adriana 219
Leiter, Michael 516
Leithauser, Jeffrey 336
Leitner, Roger 678
Leiva, John 607
Lekich, Teresa 101
Leland, Todd 395
Lele, Prashant 643
Leleux, Denise 293
Lell, Brian 754
Lella, Louise 185
Lelonek, Susan 449
Lem, Marivi 563
Lembo, Philip J. (Phil) 312
Lemchak, Joseph J. 228
Lemchak, Joe 228
Lemelin, Tracey 530
Lemert, Jennifer 332
Lemery, Becky 146
Lemkau, Gregg R. 395
Lemke, James P. (Jim) 736
Lemke, Tom 739
Lemke, Heather 881
Lemly, Chris 149
Lemmerman, Bryan 189
Lemmon, Jody 31
Lemmon, David J. 773
Lemoine, Kevin 158
Lemoine, Colleen 454
Lemon, Anita 390
Lemon, Paulette 432
Lemon, Matt 508
Lemson, Steve 45
Lenckos, John 101
Lenfert, Natalie 507
Lenger, Scot 248
Lenhoff, Timothy K. 268
Lennaman, Lara 101
Lennie, William G. (Bill) 431
Lens, Simonne 6
Lenseth, Patti 32
Lents, Thad 667
Lentz, Mike E. 440
Lentz, Rick 618
Lenz, Mike 330
Leo, Alan 72
Leo, Bruno V. Di 470
Leo, Koguan 766
Leo, James (Jim) 910
Leo, Jim 910
Leon, Sonny 81
Leon, Cynthia 168
Leon, Josefina 273
Leon, Richard 274
Leon, Lori De 804
Leonard, David E. (Dave) 28
Leonard, James C. 336
Leonard, Dennis 382
Leonard, Harris 451
Leonard, Randal 735
Leonard, Robert M. 854
Leonardi, Evaristo 16
Leonardi, Mark 665
Leonardis, Jim 122
Leonardo, Rochelle 511
Leone, Roger E. 803
Leong, Robyn 39
Leonti, Joseph R. 654
Leopold, Diane G. 278
Leopold, Anthony 876
Lepak, Kathleen 664
Lepard, Bruce 49
Lepera, Bob 593
Lepiane, Gary 915
Lepin, Julie 566
Lepore, Matthew 672
Lerman, Jason 643
Lerner, Arnold S. 305
Lerner, Mark 555

Lerner, Jack 699
Lerner, Mark 882
Lesar, David J. (Dave) 405
LeSchack, Michael 60
Lescure, John 664
Leshe, Lynn 105
Lesikar, John 224
Lesjak, Catherine A. (Cathie) 442
Lesko, Dirk 380
Lesko, Johnathan 504
Lesko, J 504
Lesko, James 935
Leskow, Robert E. (Bob) 509
Lesley, Chad 170
Leslie, Claudia 105
Leslie, Martin 299
Leslie, Sam 895
Lesser, Brian 84
Lester, Kelly 526
Lesueur, Lohr 383
Leszun, Ryan 912
Letchworth, Kenneth 507
Lete, Laura 518
Leto, Francis J. 148
Lettig, William 497
Leuenberger, Jeffrey 932
Leuenberger, Jeff 932
Leuhmann, John 450
Leung, Alan 39
Leung, Sandra 144
Levar, Mary E 735
Levatich, Matthew S. (Matt) 410
Levchets, Regina 635
LeVecchio, Anthony J. 515
Leveille, Tim D. 192
Leveille, Mark 224
Levenson, Susan 548
Levenson, Rodger 931
Lever, Brian K. 529
Leverett, Allen L. 909
Levi, David F. 287
Levier, Jack 650
Levin, Matt 395
Levin, Bob 570
Levin, Gerson 700
Levine, Jonathan M. 122
Levine, Alan 191
Levine, Jeff 395
Levine, Britt 457
Levine, Jay N. 640
Levine, Alec 715
Levine, Todd 749
Levine, Jay N 784
Levine, Judy 870
Levine, Layne L. 926
Levings, Stuart 389
Levingston, Charles D. 289
Levinson, Arthur D. (Art) 69
Levinson, Andrew 468
Levinson, Eric 882
Levitt, Mallory 171
Levitt, Evan J. 418
Levitts, Larry 908
Levy, Dan 15
Levy, Paul S. 150
Levy, Adam 172
Levy, Deb 289
Levy, Judd 328
Levy, Lance 334
Levy, Jeffrey 528
Levy, Rich 533
Levy, Jeffrey M. 598
Levy, Susan C. 620
Levy, Dana 713
Levy, Stuart 729
Levy, Patricia 800
Levy, David 838
Levy, Andrew C. 871
Levy, Robert 935
Lewin, Pablo 493
Lewis, Shiro 10
Lewis, Lisa 52
Lewis, Cindi H. 54
Lewis, Jeff 84
Lewis, Kimberly 101
Lewis, Stephen G 117
Lewis, Wayne 226

Lewis, Rodney 240
Lewis, Michael A. 285
Lewis, John D. 362
Lewis, Kenneth A. 372
Lewis, Michael 409
Lewis, Scott 413
Lewis, Daniel J 414
Lewis, Ric 425
Lewis, Cathy 470
Lewis, Jenae 472
Lewis, Thomas 483
Lewis, John 539
Lewis, Cecilia 548
Lewis, Neil 573
Lewis, William (Will) 610
Lewis, Jessica E 623
Lewis, Mark 643
Lewis, Haston 667
Lewis, Sarae J 678
Lewis, Karla R. 725
Lewis, Gary 770
Lewis, Stacey 770
Lewis, Randal D. 782
Lewis, Greg 824
Lewis, Bryant H 849
Lewis, Mark 855
Lewis, Steve 857
Lewis, Kim 881
Lewis, David 907
Lewis, Marcie 915
Lewis, Linda 925
Lewis, Clinton A. (Clint) 943
Lewis-Hall, Freda C. 671
Lewnes, Ann 11
Lex, Nancy R 204
Ley, A. Lily 650
Leyden, Bob 413
Leyden, Shawn 701
Leyendecker, Ernest A. 61
Leyendecker, Ernie 61
Leyendecker, R. Greg 419
Leygraaf, Greg 841
Leyland, Ben 849
Lezon, Stanley 700
Lhota, Joseph J. 571
LI, Yuliang 39
Li, Daniel 103
Li, Ying 131
Li, Xuemei 144
Li, GE 248
Li, Patrick 440
Li, Rennis 555
Li, Zhenqin 587
LI, Isabella 688
Li, Bo 805
Liang, Kai 201
Liang, George C. 531
Liang, Lilly 615
Liao, Aaron 39
Liao, Samuel 256
Liao, James 457
Libbra, Todd 903
Libby, Tom 456
Libby, Russell T. 808
Liberatore, Lynne 570
Liberty, Tiffanie De 237
Liberty, Daniel 539
Liberty, Lory 799
Librandi, Nancy 604
Libstag, Gwen R. 395
Licata, Charlie 336
Lich, Brad A. 291
Lichacz, Shawn 849
Lichtenstein, Jodee 289
Lichtman, David B. 358
Liddiad, Imelda 536
Liddle, Daniel 750
Liding, Lawrence (Larry) 171
Lie, Penelope 643
Liebel, Hartmut 480
Lieberherr, Werner 739
Liebermann, Nancy 322
Liebler, William Bill 470
Liebler, Bill 470
Liechty, Jon 787
Liedl, Duane 131
Lienert, James 631

Lienhard, Jerome T. 799
LIFFENGREN, PAUL 754
Lifford, Pam 838
Light, Steve 161
Lighty, Josh 121
Ligons, Douglas 273
Liguori, Peter 34
Liguori, Thomas (Tom) 94
Liguori, Debbie 799
Likes, Robert 497
Likins, Steven 834
Lilja, Mathias 555
Lill, Thorsten 512
Lillis, Terrance 691
Lilly, Brian 204
Lilly, Jeff 207
Lilly, E. Stephen (Steve) 346
Lilly, Brian F. 591
Lilly, Randy 635
Lilly, Catherine 720
Lim, James 119
Lim, Cecilia 258
Lim, Jean 408
Lim, Rachel 435
Lim, Aerin 804
Lim-Johnson, Hannah 494
Lima, Giovanni 553
Lima, Candido 553
Limbaugh, Corey 489
Limerick, Thomas S. (Stan) 350
Limjoco, Adrianne 735
Limjoco, Michael 927
Lin, Tong 87
Lin, Sandy 173
Lin, Steve 792
Lin, Sarah 805
Linares, Tony 67
Lincevski, Tanya 106
Lincoln, Robert 113
Lincoln, Daniel 170
Lind, Sharon 111
Lind, Roger 246
Lind, Dennis 274
Lind, H 337
Linda, Doherty 656
Lindblom, Kristin M 735
Lindbloom, Chad M. 736
Lindboe, Laura 813
Linde, Tamara L. 701
Linde, Brian 715
Lindekugel, Jon T. 2
Lindell, Andrew 754
Lindemann, Michael 87
Lindemann, James J. (Jim) 299
Linden, Andrew 834
Linden, Tomas 923
Linderman, Jerome 361
Linderman, Tricia 824
Linderman, LeeAnne B. 941
Lindley, Dan 620
Lindner, S. Craig 47
Lindner, Carl H. 47
Lindner, Richard 84
Lindsay, Phillip 502
Lindsay, Steven 512
Lindsay, Kristin 808
Lindsay, Jeff 838
Lindseth, Michael G 677
Lindseth, Alfred A. (Al) 679
Lindseth, Al 679
Lindsey, Steven 102
Lindsey, Jeff 182
Lindsey, Scott 678
Lindstrom, Johan 555
Lindstrom, Scott 610
Lindstrom, Merl R. 675
Linebarge, Thomas 248
Linebarger, N. Thomas (Tom) 248
Lineberger, Terry 735
Linford, D 14
Ling, Christopher 139
Ling, Sam 161
Ling, Hai 554
Lingsch, Bob 12
Link, Doug 440
Link, Mike 530
Linnartz, Stephanie C. 548

Linnemann, Andrew 787
Linnen, Edward P. (Ned) 93
Linnen, Ned 93
Linnenbrink, John 204
Lintag, Ronald 133
Linton, Phillip 170
Linton, Tim 839
Linville, Jud 203
Linzner, Joel 296
Liollio, Dean 679
Lionello, Gemma 617
Liotine, Joseph T. 923
Liotta, Gary P. 366
Lipe, John B 735
Lipinski, John J. (Jack) 251
Lipka, Michael 413
Lipke, Kenneth 109
Lipker, Stephen 31
Lipkin, Gerald H. 891
Lipper, Philip 486
Lippert, Martin J. (Marty) 569
Lippert, Cheryl 880
Lippmann, Patrick A 98
Lippmann, Jordan 813
Lips, Rob 476
Lipscomb, Mark 823
Lipton, Andrew 587
Lisboa, Persio V. 597
Lisenby, Jeffrey P. 692
Liska, Matt 149
Lisman, Michael 911
Liss, Kurt 487
Lissalde, Fr ©d ©ric B. 140
List-Stoll, Teri L. 830
Lister, Chip 274
Liston-kraft, Edward 656
Litchfield, David 286
Litchfield, Caroline 566
Litchford, Mike 267
Litschgi, Dave 470
Litster, Kelly 573
Littel, John 541
Littell, Noah 644
Litteral, Malesa 114
Litteral, Dave 457
Little, Frank R. 2
Little, Jay 87
Little, Mark 135
Little, Kimani 328
Little, Patricia A. 422
Little, Charles 477
Little, T. Mitchell (Mitch) 546
Little, Daniel F. (Dan) 616
Little, Daniel 720
Little, Chuck 788
Little, Chase 804
Little, James 880
Little, Melissa 923
Littler, Greg 876
Littrell, John 559
Littzi, John 122
Litwin, Barry 888
Litzinger, Ronald L. 295
Liu, Chang 97
Liu, Yanfang 144
Liu, Stanley 159
Liu, Katy 329
Liu, Grace 792
Liu, Don H. 813
Liu, John 923
Liutkus, Tom 847
Liverett, Deborah 620
Livesay, Bruce A. 353
Livesay, Cheryl 882
LIVEZEY, BEV 168
Livingston, John T. 14
Livingston, Robert A. (Bob) 281
Livne, Omer 465
Lizardi, Rafael R. 825
Lizarraga, Michelle 573
Lizhong, Yu 606
Llewellyn, Steve 668
Llinas, Javier 220
Lloyd, Michael 170
Lloyd, Scott 258
Lloyd, Robert A. (Rob) 379
Lloyd, Don 392

Lloyd, Jack 419
Lloyd, Carole 602
Lo, Alice 489
Loar, Theresa 185
Lobel, Heidi 274
Lobo, Kevin A. 797
Lochen, Richard S. 667
Locher, Duane 226
Locher, Vince 853
Lochner, David 449
Lochner, James 860
Lochowicz, Julie 665
Lock, Jim 593
Locker, David 463
Lockery, Michael 158
Lockett, Mark 907
Lockhart, Darci 101
Lockhart, David 203
Lockhart, Carri 793
Lockwood, Kenneth 365
Lodder, Alan 467
Lodder, Dan 563
Loder, Greg 699
Lodes, Terry 919
Loeb, Daniel S. 34
Loeber, Gary 252
Loeffler, Martin H. 59
Loeffler, Kelly 466
Loeger, Julie A. 269
Loewald, Thomas W. (Tom) 836
Loewengart, Victoria 113
Loffredo, Rosemarie 607
Lofrumento, Michael 854
Loftin, Shelly 119
Loftin, Paul J. 725
Lofton, Kevin E. 168
Logan, Jonathan B. 214
Logan, Erik 270
Logan, Stephen 413
Logan, Stephen 465
Logan, James 503
Logan, Lyle L 620
Logan, Brendan 643
Logan, John 799
Logeman, Scott 456
Loghman-Adham, Mahmoud 115
Logothetis, Peter 31
Logue, Joseph (Joe) 139
Logue, Andrew 728
Loh, William 573
Loh, Evan 671
Lohec, Wes 191
Lohmeier, Michelle J. 784
Lohse, Harry 579
Loiacono, Nicholas 563
Loiacono, Jim 752
Loignon, Lynn 504
Lokay, Jon 748
Lokkesmoe, Keith 294
Lollar, Wes 836
Lomas, Alisa 890
Lombardi, Laura 10
Lombardi, Leonard V. 345
Lombardi, Bill 413
Lombardi, Rita 699
Lombardi, Michael J. 847
Lombardo, Joseph T 380
Lombardo, Kevin 411
Lombardo, Greg 415
Lombardo, Edward 607
Lombardo, Lauren 770
Lombra, Sherri 274
Lommel, Ryan D 530
Lon, Lyons 226
Lonardo, Anthony 528
Lonczak, Mary 665
London, Adam 172
Londono, Carlos 649
Lonegro, Frank A. 245
Lonergan, Robert A. 82
Long, Ann 4
Long, Christopher 52
Long, Michael J. (Mike) 76
Long, Jodi 108
Long, Suzanne 131
Long, Tom 153
Long, Suzette M. 166

Long, Tony 170
Long, Rodney 176
Long, Jeffrey R. 241
Long, Thomas E. (Tom) 302
Long, Deborah J. 697
Long, Michelle 722
Long, Mike 727
Long, Rebeckah 782
Long, Andy 836
Long, Mike 890
Long, Susan 903
Long, Mark P. 917
Long-Knize, Michelle 273
Longhofer, T. Luke 350
Longhurst, John 131
Longo, Christopher M. 60
Longo, Jeffrey 849
Longobardi, Sara M. 664
Longshore, Rob 87
Longwater, Lance 800
Longwell, Sharon 563
Longworth, Ann 892
Look, Christian 103
Loomis, Thomas 15
Loomis, Nate 935
Looney, Patricia 191
Loosmore, Susan 811
Lootens, Ken 224
Loparco, Michael J. 480
Loper, D. Shane 406
Lopes, Diane 18
Lopes, Dina 665
Lopez, Rachel 37
Lopez, Emilia 158
Lopez, Albert 159
Lopez, Samuel 247
Lopez, Tracy 486
Lopez, Randolph 489
Lopez, Tom 505
Lopez, Andres A. 649
Lopez, Virgilio 665
Lopez, Jesus 903
Lopez-Lay, Ginoris 340
Lopreto, Vincent 768
Loranger, Michelle 792
Loranger, Tom 875
Lorber, Jason 748
Lorberbaum, Jeffrey S. 580
Lord, Pat 512
Lord, Mike 811
Lord, Ellen 826
Lore, Marc 903
Loree, James M. (Jim) 786
Loren, Singletary 593
Lorenson, Katie A. 578
Lorent, Patrick 664
Lorentson, Jeff 355
Lorentson, Jeffery B. 355
Lorenz, Jonathan C. 215
Lorenz, Renee 302
Lorenzen, Jeffrey D. (Jeff) 43
Lorenzen, Shauna 313
Lorenzi, David 222
Lorenzo, Alejandro R. 584
Lorenzo, Ron 672
Lores, Enrique 442
Lorge, Timothy J. (Tim) 244
Lori, William E. 502
Lorsson, Devin 510
Losch, William C. (BJ) 353
Loscher, Pam 555
Losenegger, Michael J. 343
Losh, J. Michael (Mike) 552
Losik, Dennis 94
Loth, Melissa 813
Lothary, Jim 735
Lothrop, Dave 256
Lott, Yolanda 108
Loucks, Andrew 493
Loughlin, Anne 587
Loughman, Tim 930
Loughridge, Charles 941
Loughry, Ed C. 678
Loui, Rae 14

Louie, Joe 102
Louis, Lynette 103
Louissaint, Obed 470
Loukotka, Jonathan 722
Louvet, Jacques 222
Louvet, Patrice J. L. 713
Louwagie, Ben 299
Love, Lisa 32
Love, Talvis 161
Love, Kelli 161
Love, Marcella 191
Love, Judith S. 223
Love, David 337
Love, Valerie 484
Love, David 521
Love, David 523
Love, Peggy 713
Love, Michelle 738
Love, John 901
Love, George 934
Loveless, Kris 863
Lovell, Kim 799
Lovely, Dave 875
Loveman, Gary W. 17
Lovering, Larry 908
Lovett, Michael 334
Lovett, Robert 847
Lovett, Melendy E. 852
Lovik, Kenneth 353
Lovins, Gregory S. (Greg) 91
Low, Julianne 159
Low, Tom 170
Low, Jim 462
Low, Steffen 602
Low, Mark 639
Lowden, Simon 667
Lowe, John E. 68
Lowe, Karen 214
Lowe, Meg 270
Lowe, Rich 416
Lowe, Chad 449
Lowe, Bill 533
Lowe, Wendy 587
Lowe, Edward A. (Sandy) 631
Lowe, Jacki 778
Lowe, Charlotte 824
Lowe, Albert 903
Lowe, Patricia 912
Lowe, Patty 912
Lower, Joseph T. (Joe) 633
Lowery, Richard M. 122
Lowery, Norman D. 351
Lowery, Dee 360
Lowery, Peter 757
Lowery, Frederick M. (Fred) 836

Lowery, Kelli 881
Lowery-Biggers, LoriAnn V. 596
Lowery-Yilmaz, Barbara 423
Lowman, David B. (Dave) 374
Lown, Christian 595
Lowney, Peter 343
Lowrey, Mark 370
Lowrey, Charles F. (Charlie) 699
Lowrie, Dan 450
Lowrimore, Bonnie 158
Lowry, Bard 350
Lowson, James 102
Lowther, Rob 700
Lowthers, Bruce 334
Lowy, Laura 109
Loya, Rene 185
Loyd, Heath 676
Loyd, Robert 929
Lozano, Rebecca 109
Lozano, Nativido 468
Lozano, Philip 530
Lrimore, Larry 400
Lu, Eugene Y. C. 22
LU, Laura 135
Lu, Chris 167
Lu, Hong 671
Lubelczyk, Stephen 598
Lubert, Ira M. 831
Lubian, Patricia 109
Lubinskas, Amy 146
Lubitz, Kevin 335

Lubitz, Allan 567
Lubow, Stuart H. 268
Luc, Phuong 901
Luca, Guerrino 69
Lucarelli, Jason 912
Lucas, Allison 395
Lucas, John T. 397
Lucas, David 533
Lucas, Randy 593
Lucas, Kyle 643
Lucas, Alessandra 668
Lucas, Thomas J. (Tom) 764
Lucchi, Anthony 266
Lucero, Tina 332
Lucey, Matthew C. 658
Luchinsky, Michael 555
Luchtel, Pat 197
Luciano, Juan R. 74
Luciano, Louis 839
Lucie, Alexandra 267
Lucien, Kent T. 103
Luckoff, Jeff 457
Lucy, William P. (Bill) 664
Ludeman, Christopher R. 169
Ludford, Brad 168
Ludington, Bob 832
Ludwick, Brent 680
Ludwig, Logan 503
Ludwig, Jeffrey G. 577
Ludwig, Dan 684
Lueth, Allen 161
Luetkenhaus, Brandy 555
Lugo, Dennis 204
Luh, Bing 644
Luisa, Jennifer F 409
Luiz, Gerald 628
Lujan, Arthur 220
Luk, Rebecca 672
Lukasheva, Oksana 409
Lukasko, Donna 87
Luke, David Luke David 722
Luke, Brick F 806
Luken, Lauren 507
Lukens, John J. 233
Luksik, Roger 337
Lulla, Pankaj 199
Lumpkins, Robert L. 588
Lumsden, Evin 722
Lumsden, Chris A. 762
Luna, Antonio 809
Lunak, Leslie N. 109
Lunceford, Erika 105
Lund, John T. 872
Lund-Jurgensen, Kirsten 671
Lundgren, David J. 406
Lundin, Deana 942
Lundquist, Jane L. 459
Lundquist, Stephanie A. 813
Lundquist, Curt 890
Lungu, Daniel 200
Luo, Jason 370
Luo, Susan 792
Luong, Roger 717
Luongo, Grace 88
Lupetini, Elizabeth 495
Lupo, Kimberly 615
Lupone, E. Robert 826
Luque, Santiago 6
Lusco, C. Matthew 721
Luse, Bill 470
Lusk, John M. 373
Lutek, Ben W. 844
Lutes, Kevin 332
Luther, Lisa C. 617
Luthi, Francesca 82
Luton, Shan 259
Luttig, J. Michael (Mike) 135
Luty, Thomas 550
Lutz, John 1
Lutz, Robert S 255
Lutz, Ron 537
Lutz, Laurent C. 772
Lutzel, Geraldine 105
Luxton, Sam 893
Luz, Eduardo 505
Luzar, Jay 497
Luzzi, Joan 242

Luzzi, Thomas 320
Ly, Eddie 573
Lyall, Kathy 582
Lybarger, Ray 261
Lydon, Katy 907
Lyer, Ramiya 521
Lyer, Ramiya 523
Lyga, Joseph 118
Lykins, Chris 115
Lykins, Gregory B. (Greg) 342
Lyle, Tommy 855
Lynam, Ben 582
Lynaugh, Johnny 722
Lynch, Karen S. 17
Lynch, Art 18
LYNCH, KEVIN 69
Lynch, Brian E. 79
Lynch, Peter 87
Lynch, Ann 105
Lynch, Thomas J. 144
Lynch, Anne 185
Lynch, Charles 318
Lynch, R. Dale 327
Lynch, Kevin 353
Lynch, Christopher S. 374
Lynch, Thomas 395
Lynch, Richard 423
Lynch, Michael 558
Lynch, Kevin J. 644
Lynch, Jennifer 664
Lynch, Tom 714
Lynch, Timothy G. 720
Lynch, Tom 729
Lynch, Thomas 778
Lynch, Ryan 863
Lynch, Bill 895
Lynham, Lisa 615
Lynn, Patricia 195
Lynn, Richard 261
Lynn, Scott J. 744
Lynn, David 896
Lynskey, Peter 199
Lyon, Matt 413
Lyon, Nancy 620
Lyons, Martin J. 40
Lyons, Cathy 117
Lyons, Terrence 337
Lyons, Sarah 378
Lyons, Robert C. 399
Lyons, John 409
Lyons, Garry 554
Lyons, Michael P. 680
Lyons, Thomas M. 698
Lyons, Brenda 791
Lyons, Francine 792
Lyons, Marlo 896
Lyski, James (Jim) 162
Lyublanovits, Robert 715
Lyubomirsky, Robert 935
L'archenesque, Lee 896
L'archevesque, Lee 896
L⌐fvenholm, Johan 86
L⌐thi, Pierre 687

M

Ma, Kenny 131
Ma, Kader 158
MA, Harry 705
Maanicus, Ton 45
Maas, Kevin 754
Maass, Brian W. 814
Maass, Paul T. 832
Maaty, Yehia 934
Mabe, Katherine (Kathy) 31
Maberry, Matt 224
Mabie, Patrice 865
Mabry, Steven 284
Mac, Bruce 875
Macadaeg, Reyne 105
Macak, Jeffrey 121
Macak, Jeff 121
Macchiaverna, Frank 618
Macchio, Ralph 242
Macciocchi, Vince F. 74
Macculley, Diana 158

MacDonald, Stuart 18
MacDonald, W. Timothy 141
MacDonald, Carolyn 197
Macdonald, Isabel 273
MacDonald, Vivian 297
MacDonald, Kenneth 628
Macdonald, James 664
Macdonald, Paul 749
Macdonald, David 839
MacDonald, Michael 862
MacDonald, Gregg 911
Macdougall, Lynn 934
Macduff, Michael 935
Mace, Andrew 450
Macek, Paul 809
MacEwen, Matthew 881
MacFarlane, Taylor 409
MacGowan, William N. (Bill) 609
MacGregor, Alastair 15
Mach, Gary P 224
Machado, Colleen 224
Machan, Gary 860
Machen, J. Matthew (Matt) 119
Maciak, Jeannine 579
Macias, Ruben 101
Maciel, Roxanna 137
Maciel, Andre 505
Macieunas, Joe 686
Macina, Anthony 274
Macina, Tom 715
MacInnes, Glenn I. 908
Macintyre, David 338
Mack, Carolyn 483
Mack, Stephen 492
Mack, Steve 492
Mack, Susan 536
Mack, Richard L. (Rich) 588
Mack, Robert P. (Bob) 681
Macke, Kevin M. 863
MacKeen, Ray 834
Mackenzie, Bill 147
MacKenzie, Alexander R. (Rod) 671
Mackenzie, Celia 799
Mackenzie, Marie 942
Mackey, Rick 94
Mackey, Edward F. 142
Mackey, John 313
Mackey, James 365
Mackey, James G. 374
Mackey, Shelby 722
Mackie, Heather 18
Mackie, H. Spurgeon 454
Mackin, Ginny 286
Macky, Edward 18
MacLauchlan, Jeffrey 739
Maclean, Cynthia 204
MacLean, Brian W. 848
MacLellan, Kevin 222
Macleod, Mark 191
MacLeod, Genofiir 836
Macleod, Simantha 839
MacMahon, John P 240
MacMillan, John 224
MacMillan, Michael 839
Macnamara, Brian 440
Macnary, Shelley 304
Macnee, Walt W. 554
MacPhaul, Pam 328
Macpherson, Donald G. (D.G.) 398
MacQuillan, Sandra J. 499
MacRae, Kristine 582
Macri, Rocco 105
Macrie, Sari 31
Macrillo, Sam 202
Macura, Paul 643
Macy, Mike 124
Macyauski, Michael 330
Madalin, Diane 246
Madarieta, Bernadette 652
Madden, John F. 97
Madden, Donald 847
Maddock, Dennis 480
Maddock, Ernest E. (Ernie) 574
Maddox, Willie A 377
Maddux, Susan 881
Maddy, Chrissy 117
Madeira, Harry R. 148

Madison, Benjamin 202
Madison, Thomas 717
Madison, Brian D. 852
Madkins, Eric 722
Madsen, Kathy 104
Madsen, C. Fred 122
Madsen, C 122
Madsen, Mark 462
Madsen, Eric 905
Madsen, Mark 907
Madson, Tomas R 380
Maduri, John 376
Maeder, Jeff 834
Maercklein, Andy 840
Maes, Betty 226
Maestri, Luca 69
Maestri, Bruno 618
Maffei, Gregory B. (Greg) 524
Maffei, Gregory B. (Greg) 533
Maffei, Gregory B. (Greg) 771
Maffei, Vincent A. (Vince) 516
Maffeo, Vincent 517
Magan, Rahul 570
Magdefrau, Stuart E. 872
Magee, Karen 838
Maggio, Michael 484
Maggs, Thomas O. 854
Magill, R H 620
Maglaque, Neal 52
Maglio, Rafelina 104
Magner, Alvin 487
Magness, James 869
Magnusson, Peter S. 643
Mago, Angela G. 497
Magrini, Joyce Manning 151
Magro, Mario 282
Maguire, Kenny 107
Maguire, William 304
Maguire, Elizabeth 705
Magyar, Adam 620
Mahaffee, Joseph W. (Joe) 139
Mahaffee, Joe 139
Mahaffy, Denise 267
Mahan, Jessalyn 511
Mahar, Matt 770
Mahe, Luke 34
Mahendra-Rajah, Prashanth 62
Maher, Mark 172
Maher, Lee A. 387
Maher, Leslie 425
Maher, Christopher D. 632
Maher, Jeff 659
Maher, Joshua 731
Maher, Steve 860
Maher, Kathy 932
Maher, Lisa 932
Maheux, Amy 665
Mahler, Simon 133
Mahler, William W. (Bill) 735
Mahlke, Thomas 737
Mahmoud, Nadia 799
Mahmud, Shahzad 917
Mahon, Kenneth J. 268
Mahon, Jean 550
Mahoney, Patrick 47
Mahoney, Michael F. (Mike) 142
Mahoney, Robert M. (Bob) 149
Mahoney, Katherine 201
Mahoney, Timothy O. (Tim) 434
Mahoney, Karen 497
Mahoney, Eileen 705
Mahoney, Colin 739
Mahoney, Kathleen M. (Kathy) 781
Mahony, Susan (Sue) 528
Mahramzadeh, Kamran 57
Mahtab, Ajoy 119
Maiella, Rick 282
Maier, Henry J. 330
Maier, Markus 587
Maiers, Joan 79
Maiers, Wayne 380
Mailloux, Robert 374
Maimaron, Christine 304
Main, Richard W. (Dick) 305
Main, Timothy L. (Tim) 480
Maingot, Christian 146
Maio, Mike 106

Maio, Keith D. 941
Mairs, Debra 757
Maiuri, Lou 791
Majak, Alan 117
Majeski, Carl 31
Majka, Don 907
Majon, Judy 927
Major, Paul 52
Major, Kristin 425
Majors, Charles H. (Charlie) 48
Majors, Michael C. 844
Majumdar, Anurita 528
Mak, Derek 199
Mak, Anna 604
Makara, Doreen 539
Makhlin, Leo 930
Maki, Thomas 52
Makris, George A. 768
Malaga, Jim 896
Malandrino, Rocco 596
Malaszenko, Natalie 633
Malat, Scott B. 936
Malcolm, Andrew 808
Maldonado, Elba 6
Maldonado, Liliana 185
Maldonado, R. Danny 826
Male, Timothy 245
Maley, David 504
Malhotra, Saket 57
Malhotra, Anisha 395
Malhotra, Raghu 554
Malik, Kaiser 153
Malik, Sarah 813
Malik, Abinta 830
Malina, Dan 383
Malinowski, Joe 1
Malizia, Vince 382
Mall, Leonard 743
Mallah, Adam 599
Mallahan, Joseph 811
Mallard, Ben 447
Mallard, Dan 715
Mallett, Leonard 307
Mallik, David 834
Malliwal, Mahendra 465
Mallon, ED 131
Mallon, Betsy 538
Mallory, Daniel 903
Mallott, Philip E. 128
Malloy, John P. (Jack) 589
Malmgren, Bob 171
Malone, Daniel J. (Dan) 210
Malone, Daniel J. (Dan) 238
Malone, Kevin 270
Malone, Jessica 377
Malone, John C. 524
Malone, Robert W. 654
Malone, Rob 654
Malone, Robert A. (Bob) 659
Malone, Mike 735
Malone, David 810
Maloney, Robert 101
Maloney, Chris 468
Maloney, Tina 656
Malouf, Michael 570
Maltsbarger, Richard D. 537
Maltz, Richard B. 112
Malugen, William C 849
Maly, Mark 620
Malys, Judy 842
Malzahn, Fred 454
Malzahn, Daniel D. 629
Mamilli, Wafaa 528
Mammadov, Emin 505
Manahan, Thomas J. (Tom) 856
Manahan-smith, Suzanne 320
Manchester, Micheal 671
Mancini, Robert 336
Mancini, Joseph 935
Mancl, Dave 470
Mancuso, David 335
Mancuso, Alfred 337
Mandala, Rocco 170
Mandel, James 378
Mandel, Joseph G. 481
Mandel, Carol A. 606
Mandel, Henry R 664

Mandel, Gail 931
Mandelli, Maela 705
Manderino, Louis 644
Mandil, Daniel 896
Maness, Yolanda 246
Manfredonia, Donald L. 357
Mang, Bill 179
Mangalick, Rita 133
Mangan, Kathy 935
Manganaro, Lynn 701
Mangiacotti, Joseph 170
Mangiaracina, Brian 56
Mangini, Debbie 300
Mango, John 345
Mangold, Ken 447
Mangum, Jamey 713
Mani, Nat 750
Maniates, Zenaida 888
Manis, Jonathan (Jon) 802
Manivannan, Naveen 799
Manjarrez-Williams, Marcela 176
Manlapaz, Nicolo 53
Manley, Duncan 692
Mann, Bill 32
Mann, Laurie 34
Mann, Susan 367
Mann, Bob 597
Mannan, Sabra 45
Mannarino, Gwen 30
Mannarino, Frank A. 786
Mannel, Bill 425
Mannello, Louis J. 400
Manning, Joseph (Joe) 4
Manning, Martin F. (Marty) 13
Manning, Charles 14
Manning, Jack 380
Manning, Fred 449
Manning, Maura 713
Manning, Anna 723
Manos, John G. 108
Manos, Roseann 767
Manos-Mchenry, Debbie 449
Manotti, Kenneth 607
Manseau, James J. 143
Mansell, Kevin B. 503
Mansfield, Bob 69
Mansfield, Jeff 394
Mansfield, William P. 399
Mansuetti, Mike 733
Mantel, Constance 161
Manthey, Mark 654
Mantooth, David 860
Mantua, Philip J. 749
Mantua, Mitch 754
Mantz, Jay 518
Manuel, Paul 226
Manzella, Jaci 355
Manzo, Mark 33
Maples, Tracy 195
Mara, Thomas 520
Marafioti, Michael 713
Marasigan, Darby 201
Marasigan, Glenn 804
Marathe, Manoj 899
Marbach, Kenneth D. 308
Marcano, Hector 457
MarcAurele, Joseph J. (Joe) 906
Marcell, Frederick A 728
Marcellin, Michael (Mike) 490
Marchetto, Eric 852
Marchick, Jill 72
Marchioni, John J. 760
Marchozzi, Thomas 882
Marchozzi, Tom 882
Marciel, Susan 103
Marco, Lori 437
Marco, Maria Di 884
Marconi, Luis G. 437
Marcotte, James A. (Jim) 305
Marcovitz, James 610
Marcum, R. Alan 263
Marcum, Lanette 392
Marcus, Deborah 32
Marcus, Jeffrey A. (Jeff) 186
Marcus, Avi A 636
Marcus, Catherine 700

Marcus, Stuart 875
Marcy, Henry 923
Marcy, Hank 923
Marden, Paul 881
Marelli, Mike 295
Margetts, Dane 942
Margolin, Eric M. 162
Margolis, Karyn 95
Mariani, John 121
Marie, Scott 743
Marien, Scott 615
Marin, Gustavo C. 348
Marina, Eka 423
Marinakis, Eric 240
Marine, Jon 557
Marini, Dick 687
Marino, Madelyn 45
Marino, Anthony S. (Tony) 348
Marino, William J. (Bill) 757
Marino, Shannon 770
Marins, Rubia 337
Marinsik, Daniel 750
Marion, Diane 155
Marion, Marty 732
Mariotti, Marco 674
Maripuri, Latha 610
Maris, George 620
Maritato, Christopher (Chris) 774
Mark, Richard J. 40
Mark, Bryan 222
Mark, Joe 785
Markantonis, George M. 513
Markel, Anthony F. 547
Markel, Steven A. 547
Markell, Peter K. 656
Markevich, Natalie 632
Markey, Jeff 453
Markezich, Ron 576
Markley, John D. 186
Markley, Stephen 377
Markley, Stephen 497
Markling, Jerry 513
Markos, Aaron 356
Markovich, Nick 449
Markovitz, Mike 558
Markowski, Steve 109
Marks, Judy F. 879
Markus, Nika 121
Markwardt, Lynda 691
Marlatt, Geoff T. 647
Marlborough, Kristine 748
Marlett, Michelle 934
Marlette, Tim G. 230
Marlin, Chris 518
Marlow, Annabelle 274
Marmor, Bob 53
Marnick, Cliff 487
Marnick, Samantha (Sam) 784
Marolis, Jessie 870
Maroni, Bradley 129
Marotta, Richard M. 124
Marotta, Michael 416
Marotto, Stephen 358
Maroulis, George 249
Maroulis, George 767
Maroun, Nabih 139
Marpe, Joel 904
Marquardt, Frederick J. (Rick) 599
Marques, Roberto 584
Marquez, Antonio F. 289
Marquez, Michael 882
Marr, Richard R 262
Marra, Peter 767
Marrache, Gilles 57
Marrapodi, Michelle 515
Marrese, Cecelia 470
Marriott, Richard E. 440
Marriott, John 497
Marriott, David 548
Marriott, J. W. (Bill) 549
Marriott, John W 549
Marrone, Nicholas 109
Marrs, Douglas W. (Doug) 400
Marrs, Sally 735
Marschall, Patrick 115
Marsh, Yolanda 176
Marsh, Lisa 252

Marsh, Laurie M. 294
Marsh, Andrew S. (Drew) 304
Marsh, Darcy 332
Marsh, Allison 395
Marsh, John T. 407
Marsh, Celeste 468
Marsh, Leslie 824
Marshal, Jerami A 751
Marshall, Steven C. 51
Marshall, Kimberly L 107
Marshall, Chad 158
Marshall, Stephen 158
Marshall, Jay 453
Marshall, Jim 558
Marshall, Michelle 665
Marshall, Lance 691
Marshall, Russell 697
Marshall, Ryan R. 704
Marshall, John 722
Marsico, Stephen 749
Martchek, Jeffrey D. 629
Martel, Nancy 109
Martel, Roland M. 458
Martell, Rita 830
Marti, Keren 339
Martin, Gordon 25
Martin, Flavius 57
Martin, Pamela 67
Martin, Ruffalo 96
Martin, John 96
Martin, Joan 103
Martin, Kirsten 106
Martin, Jeffery 107
Martin, Paul E. 115
Martin, Mike 115
Martin, Philip 124
Martin, Steve 146
Martin, Sharon 157
Martin, Fabian 158
Martin, Rodney 159
Martin, Grace 178
Martin, R. Brad 189
Martin, Julia 191
Martin, Peter 191
Martin, Kim 224
Martin, John 257
Martin, Christine 332
Martin, Angie 337
Martin, John J. 355
Martin, Rene 355
Martin, John C. 391
Martin, Bradley 435
Martin, Kristin 446
Martin, Sabrena 457
Martin, Lynn 467
Martin, Jeff 483
Martin, Phil 489
Martin, Greg 489
Martin, Thomas A. (Tom) 500
Martin, Maureen 511
Martin, Gail 511
Martin, Elizabeth 511
Martin, Michael J 528
Martin, Roger 530
Martin, Bob 540
Martin, Ron 553
Martin, Jack 576
Martin, Kenny 630
Martin, Andrew 632
Martin, Paul 643
Martin, Cheryl 643
Martin, Joseph 691
Martin, Christopher P. 698
Martin, Carlos 698
Martin, Roger 707
Martin, Katy 708
Martin, Sandy 715
Martin, Andrew D. 720
Martin, Bud 749
Martin, Jeffrey W. 761
Martin, Jim 770
Martin, Jeff 780
Martin, Douglas L. (Doug) 782
Martin, Ian 792
Martin, Mitchell P. 805
Martin, Robert W. 837
Martin, John 838

Martin, Matt 839
Martin, Wendy 870
Martin, Brian 896
Martin, James 904
Martin, Susan H. 909
Martin-Flickinger, Gerri 787
Martin-Fuller, Regis 449
Martindale, Steven L. (Steve) 458
Martinelli, Carol 332
Martines, Arnold D. 179
Martines, Dean 754
Martinez, Joel 158
Martinez, Lesbia 161
Martinez, Jill 214
Martinez, Alvaro 468
Martinez, Dalia 468
Martinez, Brandon 533
Martinez, Robert 618
Martinez, Gemma 643
Martinez, Peter 664
Martinez, Ed 699
Martinez, Maria 748
Martinez, Scott 754
Martinez, Jorge 777
Martinez, John 855
Martinez, Carlos 896
Martinez-Quiroga, Jorge 95
Martini, James (Jim) 834
Martino, Steve 199
Martino, Leandro 204
Martino, Tony 356
Martino, Stephen 573
Martino, Liberino 836
Martino-Valdes, Emilio 340
Martinovich, Robert F. (Rob) 641
Martins, Izzy 93
Martinson, Chris 834
Martiny, Larry 715
Martire, Frank R. 334
Martisus, Derek 550
Martocci, Gino A. 538
Martorana, Chuck 875
Martore-Baker, Susan 154
Martynenko, Vladimir 713
Martz, Stephen 367
Martinez, Enrique R. (Henry) 270
Maruna, Karen 450
Maruszewski, Steve 831
Marventano, David Dave 286
Marventano, David 365
Marvik, Anders 793
Marvin, Kristine 895
Marx, Michael 506
Marx, Gene 715
Mary, Michele St 411
Mary, Howard 454
Maryoto, Erwin 320
Marzec, Brian 539
Marzilli, Christopher (Chris) 380
Marzouk, Shaden 161
Mas, Alberto 119
Mas, Jos© R. 553
Mas, Jorge 553
Mascali, Rich 555
Mascaro, Dan 695
Mase, Dawn 928
Masi, Maria 366
Masiello, Daniel 53
Mason, Heather L. 4
Mason, Gene 60
Mason, Thomas 113
Mason, Jeanne K. 115
Mason, Jeannie K 115
Mason, Steve 161
Mason, Mary V 176
Mason, Mike-Mtown 300
Mason, Thomas P. 302
Mason, Louise 313
Mason, Richard J 377
Mason, Mark K. 432
Mason, Craig A 440
Mason, Margaret 498
Mason, Bob 517
Mason, Tiffany 537
Mason, Brian 665
Mason, Andrew 754
Mason, John 754

Mason, David G. 759
Masone, Tony 37
Masone, Cassie 760
Masoudi, Gerald F. 175
Massa, Tim 507
Massad, Marc 454
Massanelli, Stephen C. 768
Massaro, Anthony A. (Tony) 227
Massengill, Scott R 144
Massengill, Matthew E. (Matt) 917
Masser, Keith E. 831
Masser, Todd 880
Massery, Joe 722
Massey, Edward 97
Massey, Richard N. 119
Massey, Jack 666
Massey, David 799
Massheder, Alfred 340
Massino, Bob 842
Mast, Nicholas 272
Mast, Jorg 487
Mast, Maria 712
Masteller, Dan 754
Masters, Randy 460
Masters, Laurie 497
Masterson, Sarah 503
Masterson, David J. (Dave) 762
Masterson, Mike 927
Mastoris, Bill 909
Mastrarrigo, Julie 713
Mastro, John 799
Mastrocola, Anthony 106
Mastromattei, Mario 199
Mastromihalis, Eleni 901
Mastropaolo, Joan 194
Mastropietro, Vince 917
Masumoto, Kimie 573
Matacunas, Michael (Mike) 276
Matagi, Iosefa 185
Matarese, Andrew 665
MATECKI, PAUL 714
Mateos, Beatriz C 175
Mater, Derek De La 232
Mathai, John 489
Matheis, Lisa 390
Matheny, Drue 267
Mather, Dale 109
Mathern, Mary 699
Matheson, Kathryn 668
Mathew, Sobin 133
Mathew, Julie 175
Mathew, Arun 204
Mathews, Betsy 131
Mathews, Steven 185
Mathews, Rich 196
Mathews, Jane 502
Mathews, Michelle 799
Mathewson, Mark 158
Mathias, Robert J. 164
Mathis, Vincent 16
Mathis, Sam 335
Mathis, Archard 337
Mathis, David 942
Mathisen, Robert 105
Mathison, Doug 895
Mathur, Nikhil 131
Mathur, Ash 181
Mathur, Arun 201
Mathur, Sanjeev 866
Mathur, Tushar 928
Matley, Robert P. 228
Matlock, Mark 74
Matocha, Garry 286
Matos, Patricia 201
Matos, Lourenco de 700
Matousek, James 449
Matovina, John M. 43
Matschullat, Robert W. 899
Matson, Shane 182
Matson, Richard 196
Matson, Timothy (Tim) 723
Matson, Kenneth J. (Ken) 844
Matson, Ralph 941
Matsumoto, Toshiya 103
Matsumoto, Dayna 179
Matsumoto, Patrick 179
Matsuoka, Kelly 888

Mattai, Nan 739
Mattea, Andrea 463
Mattei, Tony 668
Mattei, Andrea 932
Matter, Donald (Chad) 876
Matter, Chad 876
Mattern, Paul 570
Matteson, Timothy J. 511
Matteucci, Peter 620
Matthes, Todd 847
Matthews, Tim 18
Matthews, Shelly 99
Matthews, Jason 117
Matthews, John 241
Matthews, Dwayne E. 254
Matthews, Earl 425
Matthews, Terrence D. (Terry) 447
Matthews, Ryan 486
Matthews, Jerry 607
Matthews, Valerie 668
Matthews, Clay 676
Matthews, William 754
Matthews, Gregory 754
Matthews, Marcia 863
Matthews, Douglas R. 878
Matthews, Charles R. 909
Matti, Louis 366
Mattice, Alicia 337
Mattics, Steven C. 617
Mattina, Mike 920
Mattke, Timothy 572
Mattox, Michael 52
Mattox, David 754
Matturri, Alexander J. (Alex) 746
Matuga, Ed 792
Matviak, Ivan 792
Matz, Glen 187
Matz, R. Kevin 298
Matz, Joe 576
Matzat, James 214
Mauch, Robert P. 56
Mauch, Chris 392
Mauer, Vanessa 578
Maughan, James 185
Maul, Glenn 146
Mauler, Michael K. (Mike) 379
Maunder, Jill 470
Maung, Aung San 576
Maura, David M. 782
Mauradian, Marguerite 881
Mauran, Pascale 672
Maurer, Mark 474
Maurer, Doug 772
Mauricio, Maxine 298
Maurits, Lycia 912
Maurno, Frank 715
Maury, Kent 548
Mavis, Alan 115
Mavra, Joanne 131
Maw, Scott H. 787
MAWSON, ROBERT 477
Max, Sarachaga 57
Maxfield, Casey 246
Maxfield, Richard 932
Maxson, Patricia (Trish) 486
Maxwell, Gary A. 276
Maxwell, David G. 399
Maxwell, Marisa 446
Maxwell, Kenneth 483
Maxwell, Ken 483
Maxwell, Jai 570
Maxwell, M. Craig 654
Maxwell, Terrance P. (Terry) 735
May, Stephen 248
May, Dan 252
May, John C. 260
May, Ron 284
May, Phillip R. 304
May, Thomas J. (Tom) 312
May, Alan 425
May, Karen J. 584
May, Amy 587
May, Ed 604
May, J. Phillip (Phill) 641
May, Warren 691

May, Jerry A. 720
May, Greg 842
May, Thomas J. (Tom) 897
Maybee, Robert 910
Mayberry, Michael C. (Mike) 465
Maybury, Mark T 786
Maye, Joseph R 735
Mayer, Marissa 34
Mayer, Marissa 34
Mayer, Gregory 39
Mayer, Jessica L. 161
Mayer, Kevin A. 273
Mayer, Michael G. 341
Mayer, Lori 386
Mayer, Sandra 701
Mayer, John 773
Mayers, Lela 18
Mayerson, Matthew 643
Mayfield, Jeff 677
Mayfield, Richard 903
Mayhall, Kelly 431
Mayhew, William 286
Maynard, Justin 45
Maynard, Ghen 172
Mayo, Kathleen 186
Mayo, Diane 191
Mayo, Marc 334
Mayo, Mike 378
Mayo, Robert 799
Mayopoulos, Timothy J. (Tim) 322
Mayor, Randy E. 430
Mayor-Mora, Enrique 162
Mays, Cheryl 313
Maza, Kim 286
Mazanec, Mark 765
Mazarakis, S. James (Jim) 931
Mazarakis, James 931
Mazhar, Mir 122
Mazile, Yolette 204
Mazman, Mark 715
Mazur, Bryan 282
Mazur-Hofsaess, Katarzyna 940
Mazza, Valerie 483
Mazza, Daniel J 792
Mazzarella, Kathleen M. 399
Mazzarella, Michael 760
Mazzei, Robert 842
Mazzeo, Anthony 155
Mazzotta, Brian 768
McAbee, Phillip 926
McAdam, Lowell C. 893
McAdoo, Bob 654
McAfee, Jason 279
McAfee, Travis 715
McAleenan, Donald F. 149
McAleenan, Don 149
McAlister, Jeremy 107
Mcalister, Kay 677
McAllister, Kevin G. 135
McAllister, Gene 707
McAlpine, Cheree 94
McAnally, James 425
McAneny, Joe 365
McArdle, Billy 158
McArthur, Gary L. 185
McArthur, John 286
McAtee, David R. 84
McAuley, Greg 153
McAuley, Patty 757
McAuslan, Robert R. (Bob) 916
McAvoy, John T. 234
McAvoy, John T. 235
Mcbeath, Michael 573
McBrayer, Max 711
McBride, Mary E. 214
McBride, R. Perley 376
McBride, Dennis 870
Mcbride, Karla 903
McBroom, Mark 425
Mccabe, Brian 53
McCabe, Natalie 246
McCabe, Pete 382
McCabe, Robert A. (Rob) 678
McCabe, Mary 699
McCabe, Kari 731
McCabe, Brian K. 779
McCabe, Susie 866

Mccaddon, Joe 226
McCafferty, Donna 204
McCafferty, Marty 237
McCafferty, Denise 560
McCaffrey, Jacqueline 18
McCaffrey, Sean 161
McCahon, Jim 487
McCall, Michael W. 408
McCallion, Anne D. 662
McCallister, Michael B. 943
Mccann, Shelly 101
McCann, Andy 453
McCann, Michael V 489
Mccann, Joshua 799
McCann, Peter 857
Mccann, Ellen 886
McCart, Donna 881
McCarter, Kathy 886
McCarthy, Margaret M. (Meg) 17
Mccarthy, Frank 52
McCarthy, Gloria M. 66
McCarthy, J. Kevin 105
McCarthy, Jeff 105
McCarthy, Marie 131
Mccarthy, Vince 172
McCarthy, Cristina 172
McCarthy, Christine M. 273
McCarthy, Barry C. 348
McCarthy, Daniel J. 376
Mccarthy, Donald 392
McCarthy, Brian 420
McCarthy, Eileen 483
McCarthy, Jason 517
Mccarthy, Shaun Mccarthy Shaun 576
Mccarthy, Ayse 751
McCarthy, Peter 752
McCarthy, Bill 768
Mccarthy, Chris 792
McCarthy, Richard 888
McCarthy, Deborah 918
McCartney, David 12
McCartney, Tom 94
McCartney, Thomas 94
McCarty, Patrick 104
McCarty, Mary 393
McCarty, Mollie 813
Mccarty, Jan 935
Mccaslin, Barbara 226
McCaughan, James P. (Jim) 691
McCaughey, Ryan 203
Mccauley, Frank 17
McCauley, Cliff 246
Mccauley, Michael 700
McCauley, Laurie 720
McCaw, Sue 550
McCellon-Allen, Venita 42
McChesney, Lee B. 786
McClain, Steve 128
McClain, Mary 226
McClain, Paula D. 287
McClain, Ronald G. (Ron) 500
Mcclain, Wayne 530
Mcclain, Kenny 715
McClaren, Troy 18
Mcclarnon, Cynthia 811
McClaughlin, Don 199
McClean, Murray R. 227
McClellan, John W. 230
McClellan, Stephen R. (Steve) 397
McClellan, Michael R 618
McClellan, Michelle 806
Mcclelland, James 184
McClelland, David 370
Mcclelland, Hal 692
McClimans, Jason 726
McClincy, Christopher J. 318
Mcclintock, William 71
Mcclintock, Wendy 422
McCloud, Ron 207
McClure, Kathy 240
Mcclure, James 700
McClure, Marc 816
McClurg, Tim 53
McCollum, Chris 12
Mccollum, Thomas 78
McComb, Rebecca 661
McCombe, Mark S. 131

McconkeY, Linda 888
McConnell, Scott 3
McConnell, Niall 175
McConnell, Kelly 224
McConnell, Kelly 332
McConnell, Rob 463
McConnell, Pamela 615
Mcconnell, Rebecca 679
McConnell, Sarah Hlavinka 934
McConville, Cliff 49
McCool, James D. 754
McCool, Todd 860
McCord, Trey 247
Mccormac, Paul 101
McCormack, John 329
McCormack, Steven 539
Mccormick, Patrick 39
Mccormick, Pat 39
McCormick, Jane 119
McCormick, Stanley 247
McCormick, Michael C. 294
McCormick, Terry 715
McCormick, Kevin 792
McCormick, John 821
McCormick, Robert J. 854
McCormick, Ron 903
McCourt, Kiera 665
Mccoy, Michael 94
McCoy, Sherilyn S. (Sheri) 95
McCoy, Sherilyn S. (Sheri) 95
Mccoy, Danny 101
Mccoy, John 115
McCoy, Thomas M. (Tom) 185
Mccoy, Michael 437
McCoy, Mark 511
Mccracken, Kathy 513
MCCRAW, DEBBIE 855
McCrea, Marshall S. (Mackie) 302
McCready, Deirdre 533
Mccready, Jeanne 602
McCreary, Lynn S. 361
McCreary, Ashley 390
McCree, Donald H. (Don) 205
McCrimmond, Ron 462
McCrobie, Mike 150
McCrossen, Ed 199
McCulloch, Michael 635
Mcculloch, Greg 808
McCullough, Ted 25
McCullough, Mark C. 42
McCullough, Ryan 224
McCullough, Theodore J. (Ted) 389
McCullough, Mark A 446
McCullough, Howell D. (Mac) 449
McCullough, Bruce A. 546
Mccullough, Kevin 796
Mccullough, Ross 875
McCully, Ginger 332
Mccully, Maureen 511
McCurdy, Michael W. 147
McCurdy, Lisa 806
Mccurrie, Brad 71
McCurry, Matt 715
McCusker, Jenna 69
McCutcheon, S. Craig 259
McCutcheon, Stewart H. 294
Mcdaniel, Dennis E 197
McDaniel, Cathy 446
McDaniel, Ron 566
McDaniel, Marvin E. 933
McDavid, William H. (Bill) 373
McDermott, Christopher 14
McDermott, Ronald 261
McDermott, Michael P. 537
Mcdermott, Christopher 587
McDermott, John P. 738
McDevitt, Charles B. 400
McDevitt, Sean 668
McDevitt, Kelly 881
McDonagh, Brian 735
McDonald, Robert 3
McDonald, Andrew L. (Andy) 221
McDonald, Michael 340
McDonald, David W. 360
McDonald, Robert 395
McDonald, Bryan D. 421
McDonald, Shawn 486

McDonald, Scott 550
McDonald, Tammy 563
McDonald, Gwendolyn (Gwen) 601
McDonald, Kimberly 722
McDonald, Tim 754
Mcdonald, Caron 839
McDonald, Richard 839
McDonell, Jason 668
McDonie, Patrick J. (Pat) 812
McDonnell, Elaine 45
McDonnell, Tom 247
McDonnell, Michael R. (Mike) 478
McDonnell, Nancy 489
Mcdonough, Tiffany 302
McDonough, Jeanette 545
McDonough, Kevin 593
McDonough, Karissa 665
McDonough, Robert J. (Bob) 879
McDougald, Gene 929
McDowell, Tom 300
McDowell, Pat 487
McDowell, George 566
McDowell, Ronda M. 749
McDowell, Steve 852
McDuffie, John 101
McDunn, David 530
McElhinney, Paul A. 382
McElligott, Kathleen D. (Kathy) 563
McElroy, David 414
Mcelveen, Edward 337
McElwee, Dave 304
McEnaney, John 84
McEniry, James 49
McEvoy, Ashley A. 484
McEvoy, John R. 706
Mcewen, Sean 6
McFall, Thomas G. (Tom) 630
McFarland, Keith 337
McFarland, Sandra 551
McFarland, Joseph M. (Joe) 661
Mcfarlin, Willie 834
McField, Theodore 158
McGarry, Michael H. 685
McGarry, Steven J. 772
McGarry, John F. (Jack) 886
McGary, Skip 847
McGaw, Steve 84
McGaw, Michael 533
McGee, Jeninne 52
McGee, Eric 447
McGee, Richard K. 679
McGee, Callery 713
McGee, Karen 727
McGee, Genemarie 762
McGettrick, Mark F. 278
McGill, Tom 140
McGill, Scott 222
McGill, Donald 337
McGill, John M 528
McGill, Daniel K. (Dan) 666
McGill, James 754
Mcgillivray, Mark 31
McGillivray, Doug 383
McGinley, Joseph 222
McGinley, Paula 413
McGinley, Michael 885
McGinnis, Brian 299
McGinnis, John T. (Jack) 543
McGinnis, Tim 750
McGinnis, David 834
McGinnis, Jeffrey S. (Jeff) 876
McGinty, Mark 613
McGivney, Mark C. 550
McGlenon, Andrew 888
McGlynn, Lorelei 752
McGlynn, Mike 930
Mcgoldrick, Cindy 116
Mcgonigal, Matthew 728
McGough, Thomas M. (Tom) 232
McGovern, Lawrence D. 420
McGovern, Shawn 631
McGowan, Tim 87
McGowan, Patrick 148
McGowan, David 345
McGowan, Veronica 558
McGowan, Chris 647
McGowan, John 722

McGranahan, Devin B. 361
McGrane, Brian J 731
McGrath, Helen 84
McGrath, Garth 175
Mcgrath, Julie 356
McGrath, Robert L. (Bob) 363
McGrath, Kathy 563
McGrath, Elizabeth 656
McGrath, Ted 732
McGrath, Mike 840
McGrath, Bruce 863
McGrath, David 941
McGraw, Deirdre D. 52
McGraw, Ryan 161
McGraw, E. Robinson (Robin) 726
McGraw, Donald F. (Don) 827
McGregor, Thomas 109
McGregor, Gaylyn 226
McGregor, Chris 332
Mcgregor, Mark E 409
McGregor, Sharon 633
McGregor, Kristen 643
McGuckin, Matthew 665
McGuff, Greg 518
McGuffie, Dennis 818
McGuffin, Colleen 161
McGuigan, Gary 74
McGuigan, Charles C. (Charlie) 508
McGuigan, Peter S 671
McGuinness, Steve 425
McGuire, Jim 84
McGuire, Toretha 131
McGuire, Patricia 204
McGuire, Lake 224
McGuire, Michael 252
McGuire, John 550
McGuire, Jim 754
McGuire, Tom 809
McGuire, Thomas 881
Mcguire, Paul 893
McGurk, Monica 859
McGurk, William J. (Bill) 872
McGurn, David 378
McHaffie, Sherry 678
Mchenry, Yvonne 875
McHoul, Kary 273
McHugh, Tracy 69
McHugh, Rob 249
McHugh, Philip R. 336
McHugh, Joe 385
McHugh, Lynne 752
Mchugh, Fred 882
McHutchison, John G. 391
Mcilvried, Mac 759
Mcilwain, Jessica 88
McIlwain, Eric 555
McInerney, Thomas E. 34
McInerney, Thomas J. (Tom) 388
McInerney, Ryan 899
McInnes, James 700
McIntosh, John L. 638
Mcintyre, Dan 3
McIntyre, Gregory T. (Greg) 185
McKay, John D. 241
McKay, Jennifer 249
McKay, Molly 306
McKay, Scott J. 389
Mckay, David 423
Mckay, John 571
McKay, Susan 725
McKeag, Bryan R. 419
McKean, David 597
McKeand, Kevin 85
McKee, Lynn B. 72
McKee, Chris 213
McKee, Michael 378
McKee, Michael 429
McKee, Bob 626
McKeever, Mike 487
Mckeighan, Jim 643
McKemie, Gordon 133
McKenna, Meg 115
McKenna, Wendy 146
McKenna, Judith 903
McKenney, Josh 355
McKenney, Richard P. (Rick) 886
McKennon, Michael 101

McKenzie, Paul 129
McKenzie, Craig 204
McKenzie, Barbara A. (Barb) 691
McKeon, Brian M. 139
McKeon, Rich 563
McKeown, Ann M. 746
Mckewen, Robert 818
McKibben, Sheryl 518
McKibbin, Karen S. 617
McKiernan, Anthony 559
McKim, Anoopa 337
McKim, Tony C. 341
McKinley, Gordon 224
McKinley, David C. (Dave) 752
McKinney, Stewart 72
McKinney, Greg 107
McKinney, Michael 176
McKinney, David E 196
Mckinney, Randy 262
McKinney, Michael 282
Mckinney, George 406
McKinney, James J. 495
McKinney, Rex D. 763
McKinney, Sue 849
McKinney, Ivy 934
McKinnon, Lee 763
McKintosh, Ian 515
McKnight, Joel 153
Mcknight, Gary 246
McKnight, Jodi 912
Mckuin, John 447
McLaren, Christopher 536
Mclarty, Tim 504
McLaughlin, Robert 148
McLaughlin, Linda 148
McLaughlin, Mary 222
McLaughlin, Lynn 226
Mclaughlin, Carl A 246
McLaughlin, Sean J. 310
McLaughlin, R 338
McLaughlin, Edward (Ed) 554
McLaughlin, David W. 606
McLaughlin, Michael 679
McLaughlin, Betsy 732
McLaughlin, Randall 735
McLaughlin, John J. 742
McLaughlin, Meredith 763
McLaughlin, Rosemary 767
McLaughlin, Neal T. 864
McLaughlin, Kathleen 903
McLean, Paul 700
McLean, James 715
McLean, Graham A. 797
McLean, Scott J. 941
McLeland, Allan H. 775
Mclelland, Alistair 21
Mclemore, Carol 507
McLemore, Thomas 623
McLemore, Heidi M 735
McLendon, John 483
Mcleod, Martha 55
McLeod, David G. 400
Mcleod, Bret 440
McLeod, Ben 722
McLester, Scott G. 931
McIntyre, Craig 201
McLoone, Brian 792
McLoughlin, Karen 218
Mcmahan, Dale 101
McMahon, Andrea 332
McMahon, Gerry 493
McMahon, Shamus 497
McMahon, Brian 671
McMahon, Scott 834
McMahon, Molly 888
McManmon, Katherine 394
Mcmanus, Laura 304
McManus, Erin 459
McManus, Jeannie 558
McManus, John M. 572
Mcmartin, Bill 457
McMenamin, William V. 597
McMichael, David 282
McMillan, Dave 117
McMillan, Putnam D 383
McMillan, Marilyn A. 606
McMillan, Steve 643

MCMILLIN, JULIE 453
McMillon, C. Douglas (Doug) 903
McMonigle, Andrew 162
McMonigle, Andy 162
McMullen, Brad 135
McMullen, W. Rodney 506
McMullen, Rodney 507
McMullen, Brad 786
Mcmurray, Dan 241
Mcmurray, Kurston 613
McMurray, Michael C. 648
McMurray, Bill 715
Mcmurtry, Sev 330
McNab, Paul 199
McNabb, Alan 799
McNair, Lakendra 539
McNamara, Stephen 84
McNamara, Bob 194
McNamara, Daniel R. (Dan) 465
McNamara, Marvin 717
McNamara, Michael E. (Mike) 813
McNamee, Brian M. 57
McNamee, Sean 330
Mcnana, John 124
Mcnaughton, James 800
McNeal, Ruth 344
Mcnealis, Anne 491
McNeel, Warren 811
McNeil, Steve 450
McNeill, Jon 823
McNellis, John C. 509
McNett, Malcolm 93
McNiff, Mike 267
McNinch, Scott 425
McNulty, Gregg 252
McNulty, Michael 397
McParland, Jeffrey J. (Jeff) 812
McPartland, James E. (Bo) 844
McPhail, Lora 194
McPhail, Richard 431
McPhail, Alastair 440
McPhaill, Kevin J. 767
McPheeters, Skip 454
Mcpherson, Julie 139
McPherson, Scott E. 239
McPherson, Amy C. 548
McPherson, Heather 809
McQuade, Daniel P. 14
mcQuade, Brian F 875
McQuade, Deb 881
McQueen, Jason 98
McQueen, Todd 832
McRae, Jeff 32
McRae, Lawrence D. (Larry) 240
McRaith, William (Bill) 705
McReynolds, John W. 302
McShepard, Randy 742
McSherry, Bill 135
McSteen, Jeffrey 105
McSweeney, Dianne 907
McTague, Teresa Q. 19
McTernan, Bernita 266
McTiernan, James 106
McTigue, Peggy 170
McTpavish, Julie 623
McVeigh, Scott 765
McWane, Paul 735
McWatters, Denise C. 429
McWherter, Ron 170
McWhinney, Robert 481
McWhirter, William A. (Bill) 852
McWilliams, Jelena 336
McWilliams, Vicki D. 925
Mead, John 52
Mead, David L. 666
Mead, Bruce 880
Meade, Morgan 507
Meade, Michael 572
Meade, William 729
Meador, David E. 283
Meador, David E. 283
Meador, David E. (Dave) 284
Meadows, Angela 101
Meadows, Karen C 157
Meadows, Darryl 870
Meagher, Kevin 537
Meahl, Pierre 886

Meakes, Linda 720
Means, Brian J 486
Mearns, Ian 224
Measel, Kevin 537
Meche, Monique 37
Meden, Scott A. 617
Medenis, Jim 85
Medford, Jeffrey S. 577
Medich, John 6
Medina, Mark 942
Medovic, Tom 912
Medrano, Randolph 105
Mee, David G. 447
Mee, Laurie 708
Meehan, Sean 413
Meehan, Connie 511
Meehan, Sharon 787
Meek, Victor 248
Meek-Wohl, Leslie 555
Meelberg, Andrew 540
Meerendonk, Edwin van der 274
Meers, Trey 927
Mees, Matt 78
Mees, Matthew 78
Meeteren, Jedd Van 942
Meetre, Steve 932
Mefford, Jeffrey 577
Mega, John S. 509
Megargee, Scott R. 827
Megdadi, Janet 748
Meglio, Ron 896
Megowan, Tammy 743
Megregian, Donna 724
Mehdizadeh, Naz 97
Mehdizadeh, Ryan 750
Mehelas, Rosanne 470
Mehler, Mark 875
Mehmood, Rashid 668
Mehnert, Dana A. 411
Mehra, Asit 639
Mehra, Pankaj 917
Mehrain, Yasmin 548
Mehringer, Melinda 557
Mehrotra, Sanjay 574
Mehta, Rajeev (Raj) 218
Mehta, Manan 620
Mehta, Sanjay 708
Mehta, Chintan 901
Mei, Betty 3
Meibar, Graciela 557
Meidt, Greg 187
Meier, Penny 52
Meier, Roland 144
Meier, Richard A. (Randy) 647
Meighan, Shelly 691
Meihoefer, Maria 366
Meijers, Neville 707
Meikle, Will 470
Meiklejohn, Mark J. 147
Meinerding, James A 355
Meinhardt, Erika 332
Meininger, Steve 185
Meintjes, Charles F. 659
Meisinger, Joseph 849
Meislahn, John 313
Meisner, Chad 53
Meister, Todd 199
Meister, Doris P. 538
Meitz, Ann 2
Mejia, Maria F. 493
Mejzak, Richard 131
Mekesa, Kathleen 337
Mekler, Mark K 715
Melchione, Anthony 700
Mele, Jasmine 69
Melendez, Maria 101
Melendi, Robert J. 227
Melfi, Mitch H. 168
Melgar, Joel 609
Melhorn, Les 185
Melim, Marylene 700
Melina, Tom 896
Meline, Dave 3
Meline, David W. 57
Melkote, Keerti 425
Mella, Chas 247
Mella, Joe 395

Melleky, Neil 570
Mellevold, Gene 172
Mello, Joseph 750
Melloh, Heather Klaas 52
Mellon, Jon 602
Melnick, Chad 504
Meloy, Elizabeth 311
Meloy, Mark J. 343
Meloy, Mattthew J. (Matt) 812
Melter, Scott 222
Melton, Stephen A. 54
Melton, Steve A 189
Melton, Carol A. 838
Melton, Jonathon 935
Meltzer, Stephanie 671
Meltzer, Larry 705
Melville, Traci 820
Melvin, Vincent P. (Vin) 76
Melzer, Heather C 735
Men, Simon 615
Menard, Didier 185
Menchaca, Ricardo 446
Mendelsohn, Karen R. 580
Mendelsohn, Andrew 643
Mendenhall, Tom 713
Mendenhall, Dave 912
Mendes, Mark S 72
Mendes, Roberto 836
Mendez, Roberto D. (Bobby) 294
Mendez, Greg 454
Mendez, Carlos 570
Mendicino, Anthony 861
Mendis, Nancy 840
Mendonca, Hubert 860
Mendoza, Edy 172
Mendoza, Mary 332
Mendoza, Tom 602
Menear, Craig A. 431
Menegaz, Denis L 365
Menelly, Denise M. 201
Menendez, Oscar 202
Menezes, Eduardo F. 687
Meng, Francis L Boon 929
Mengebier, David G. 210
Menichini, Ralph 244
Menjou, Emily 313
Menken, Dennis 691
Menneto, Steven D. 681
Mennihan, Peter 863
Menon, Anil 199
Menon, Geeta 606
Mens, Cees 566
Mense, D. Craig 210
Mensing, Stan J 389
Mento, Andrew 587
Menzel, Susan L. (Sue) 213
Menzies, D. Stephen (Steve) 852
Meoli, Marc 749
Mercadel, Demetric 304
Mercado, Kenneth M. 177
Mercado, Fred 553
Mercedes, Amaurys 131
Mercer, Michelle 558
Mercer, Megan 863
Merchant, Richard 12
Merchant, Manisha K. 97
Mercier, Dianne M. 664
Mercurio, Mario 668
Meredith, Ian 142
Meredith, Robert 587
Meredith, Michael 863
Mergelmeyer, Gene E. 82
Mergenthaler, Frank 473
Merilli, Philip 618
Merino, John 330
Merino, Eduardo 748
Meriwether, Kevin 446
Merkel, Matt 635
Merkle, Thomas 336
Merle, Denise M. 922
Merli, Frank 808
Merling, Laura 84
Merlino, John 519
Merlo, Larry J. 252
Merlo, Michael 767
Merrell, Kathryn 855
Merrifield, Lane 273

Merrifield, Gary 896
Merrill, Susan 803
Merriman, Tom 580
Merritt, David C. 186
Merritt, Lynn 615
Merritt, Chip 746
Merritt, Norman 941
Merriweather, Donna 119
Merten, Joseph (J.) 211
Mertens, George 254
Mervis, Loretta 800
Merwe, Martin Van Der 237
Meserole, Richard C 365
Meshechek, Gene 131
Meskiewicz, Paul 105
Mesquita, Jorge S. 484
Messemer, Thomas 768
Messer, Angela M. (Angie) 139
Messerich, John 832
Messina, Debbie 604
Messler, Amy 660
Messler, Michael 754
Messmer, Harold M. 734
Mestas, Terri 14
Meston, Michael 917
Metcalf, Kim 172
Metcalf, Sue 294
Metcalf, Kendra 722
Metcalfe, Gavin 897
Metcalfe, Tom 909
Metheny, Mike 151
METHENY, MARK 519
Metsger, Gary E. 769
Mettel, Kenneth 876
Metz, John 148
Metz, Randy 376
Metz, Karen 574
Metzgar, Mike 793
Metzger, Thomas M. (Tom) 591
Metzger, Doug 881
Metzinger, Adam 106
Metzler, Thomas 569
Metzler, George 620
Metzloff, Kurt 248
Meudt, Mark 380
Meves, Scott C. 908
Mevs, Osei 526
Meyer, Janis 129
Meyer, John 226
Meyer, David 254
Meyer, Kevin 299
Meyer, Michele S. 383
Meyer, David 399
Meyer, Dan 732
Meyer, James E. (Jim) 771
Meyer, Jesse 804
Meyer, Micha 870
Meyer, John 892
Meyer, Vanesa 899
Meyer-Shipp, Michele C 700
Meyercord, F. Duffield (Duff) 660
Meyerhoefer, Patricia 201
Meyers, Leanne 261
Meyers, Randy 676
Meyers, David 834
Meyerson, Bernard 470
Meynard, Craig 262
Meyrowitz, Carol M. 840
Mezeul, Patricia 366
Mhatre, Nitin J. 908
Mialaret, David 158
Miano, John 161
Michael, Marroy 158
Michael, Jonathan E. 732
Michael, Gary 891
Michaels, Rich 620
Michalak, Michael H. 223
Michales, Kevin 705
Michaleski, Katie 728
Michalik, Christian P. 911
Michas, Alexis P. 140
Michaud, Thomas B. (Tom) 795
Michel, Jonathan 517
Michele, Barnett 195
Michele, Daniel De 555
Micheletti, Andrew J. 136
Michener, Cynthia 18

Mick, Darla Mick Darla 224
Mickelson, Sharon 262
Micun, Inez 620
Middlebrooks, Dan C. 812
Middleman, Frances 713
Middleton, Gareth 15
Midler, Laurence H. 170
Miebach, Michael 554
Mielcuszny, Alan 300
Miele, Laura 296
Mieszczanski, Chris 840
Migliocco, Fran 87
Migliori, Richard 880
Migliozzi, Joseph 446
Migliozzi, John 567
Mignini, Luca 156
Mignone, Anthony 518
Mihalek, Jean 457
Mijuskovic, Srdjan 95
Mike, Monahan 201
Mikels, Lawrence 503
MIKESELL, JASON 453
Mikesell, Kelly 770
Mikhail, Karim 566
Mikkelsen, Dorthe 566
Mikkilineni, Krishna 434
Miklich, Jeffrey 764
Miklinski, Mark 528
Miks, Wai 700
Miksch, Ronnie 246
Mikstas, Michael 728
Milam, Billy 711
Milburn, Michael 748
Milby, Ron 402
Milefchik, Edward F. 558
Milem, Anne 772
Miles, Mark W. 125
Miles, Carla 324
Miles, Everett 700
Miles, Elizabeth 808
Miles, Christopher 860
Miley, Kevin 792
Milford, Gregory 109
Mill, Robert 16
Mill, Jim 745
Millane, Martin B. 154
Millard, Robert B. 509
Miller, Frank 12
Miller, Paul 13
Miller, Brian A. 16
Miller, Virgil R 19
Miller, Melisa A. 30
Miller, Steve 31
Miller, Matthew 52
Miller, Jason 53
Miller, Barbara 56
Miller, Judy 84
Miller, Cheryl 89
Miller, MaryAnn G. 94
Miller, Craig 110
Miller, John 133
Miller, Grace 135
Miller, Dean 137
Miller, W. Thaddeus (Thad) 153
Miller, W 153
Miller, John 161
Miller, Sherry 161
Miller, Jacqueline 172
Miller, Joseph 179
Miller, Lisa 181
Miller, Todd 182
Miller, Ken 185
Miller, John R. 186
Miller, Kip 187
Miller, Edward G 194
Miller, Brent 226
Miller, Christopher M. (Chris) 239
Miller, Russ 241
Miller, Barry 243
Miller, Ashlie 253
Miller, Michael 259
Miller, Jeffrey D. 279
Miller, Deb 300
Miller, Mike 311
Miller, Steven (Steve) 319
Miller, Kenneth 329
Miller, Phyllis 332

Miller, James B. 335
Miller, David W. 353
Miller, Megan 356
Miller, Ty 374
Miller, Clint 377
Miller, Jamie S. 382
Miller, Herman 383
Miller, Scot A 400
Miller, Jeffrey A. (Jeff) 405
Miller, Scott 441
Miller, Archie 442
Miller, Scott 456
Miller, Gena 461
Miller, Timothy 479
Miller, Ken 490
Miller, Neal 491
Miller, Brian 503
Miller, Julianne 517
Miller, Stuart A. 518
Miller, Gary 529
Miller, Zach 537
Miller, Linda 548
Miller, Greg 551
Miller, Jane 559
Miller, Eddie 563
Miller, Scott 563
Miller, Dave 564
Miller, Stephanie 570
Miller, Lorraine 578
Miller, Philip 585
Miller, Ernest 599
Miller, Wayne 599
Miller, Bill 602
Miller, Michael 610
Miller, Sara L. 635
Miller, Robert 639
Miller, Brett 649
Miller, Dennis P 661
Miller, Kevin 676
Miller, Linda 686
Miller, James 686
Miller, Craig 688
Miller, Richard 699
Miller, Brian 715
Miller, Scott 754
Miller, Lorraine 760
Miller, Dan 786
Miller, Ashley 800
Miller, Janice 808
Miller, David A. (Dave) 810
Miller, Annette 813
Miller, Jeremy 813
Miller, Alan L. 824
Miller, Carl 849
Miller, Cory 863
Miller, Brad 869
Miller, Bradley J. (Brad) 869
Miller, Alan B. 882
Miller, Marc D. 882
Miller, Katherine M. (Kate) 886
Miller, Scott 888
Miller, Kevin 889
Miller, Terri J 895
Miller, Steve 895
Miller, Julie 899
Miller, Dean A. 925
Miller, Martin 929
Miller, Tonya 930
Miller, Travis 932
Miller, Rena 942
Miller, Michael 942
Millett, Mark D. 794
Milligan, Jim 18
Milligan, John F. 391
Milligan, David R. 915
Milligan, Stephen D. (Steve) 917
Millis, Matt 941
Millones, Peter J. 689
Mills, Martin 21
Mills, Amy 31
Mills, William J. (Bill) 203
Mills, Joe D 248
Mills, Derck 304
Mills, Lucy 334
Mills, Gary R. 346
Mills, Chris 441
Mills, Steve 456

Mills, Lisa 511
Mills, Jennifer 715
Mills, Gary M 807
Mills, Tracey 808
Mills, Robert D. 846
Mills, Scott M. 896
Millsap, Brian 213
Millsap, Mark 453
Millspaugh, Marc 415
Millstone, Sacha 715
Millum, Deborah A 413
Millwala, Adila 502
Milne, Tim 813
Milne, Don L 941
Milner, Mary 105
Milner, Patrick J. 596
Milner, John 628
Milner, Jessica 861
Milone-Nuzzo, Paula 831
Milosevic, Milos 159
Milovich, Steven 273
Milovich, Steve 274
Milroy, James 187
Milspaugh, Glenn 109
Miltenis, John 875
Milton, Aaron 142
Milton, Patricia 159
Milton, David 224
Milton, B. W. 320
Milton, Mark A. 492
Milton, Robert A. 871
Mimicopoulos, Louise 713
Mims, Ricky 33
Mims, Verett 135
Mims, Jessica 720
Mims, Rhonda 911
Mimura, Laura 498
Min, David 273
Min, Sharon 408
Minaai, Cheryl 103
Minard, Timothy 691
Minda, Sherry 489
Minden, Michael 897
Miner, Emily B 596
Minetti, Carlos M. 269
Minicozzi, Rob 914
Minicucci, Benito (Ben) 26
Minicucci, Robert A. 30
Minkel, Scott A. 872
Minnich, Brandt N. 567
Minnick, Ben 826
Mino, Paul 272
Mino, Warren K. 908
Minoia, Nicholas 233
Minopoli, Anthony 502
Minor, Brad 45
Minor, Kirt 805
Minor, Mary 849
Minott, Darrell 101
Minowitz, Robert (Bob) 752
Minsk, Helayna 901
Minter, Doris 304
Minter, Gordon 441
Minton, Stacia 618
Mintz, Antonella 178
Mintz, Antonella 178
Minutoli, Robert 834
Miocevich, Mark 175
Mione, Kelly L 224
Mirabelli, Mary 425
Mirabile, Mark 555
Miracle, Phil 304
Miralles, Albert J. (Al) 211
Miranda, Julio 365
Miranda, Oscar 415
Miranda, Flavia 570
Miranda, Steve 643
Miree, David D. 908
Mireles, Oscar 361
Mirkov, Hristo 203
Mirock, Chad 413
Miron, Robert J. (Bob) 271
Mirts, Julie 335
Mirviss, Jeff 142
Misch, Gary 773
Mishler, Isaac 226
Mishra, Paritosh 16
Mishra, Rakesh 813

Misiak, Dave 657
Misich, Michael T 912
Misko, John John 710
Miskovic, Milanka 224
Miskowiec, Anthony D 87
Mistovich, Michael 912
Mistry, Dinyar B. 673
Mistysyn, Allen J. 764
Mitacek, Don 262
Mitalas, Paul 425
Mitcham, Alvin C 800
Mitchell, Steve 84
Mitchell, Brenda 103
Mitchell, Anthony (Tony) 139
Mitchell, David 161
Mitchell, Robert W 162
Mitchell, Jeff 181
Mitchell, Beth 181
Mitchell, Duncan 200
Mitchell, Howard 201
Mitchell, Thomas 276
Mitchell, David 294
Mitchell, Janelda R. 324
Mitchell, Joey 333
Mitchell, Donald 337
Mitchell, Dave 390
Mitchell, Carolyn 439
Mitchell, Terri 470
Mitchell, P J 470
Mitchell, Charles 507
Mitchell, Joe 530
Mitchell, Edward 550
Mitchell, Nichole 582
Mitchell, Jackie 641
Mitchell, Robert 654
Mitchell, Kevin J. 675
Mitchell, Dennis 678
Mitchell, Robbin 713
Mitchell, Jennifer 735
Mitchell, Kevin 737
Mitchell, Robert 760
Mitchell, Adam 769
Mitchell, Doug 798
Mitchell, Melanie 799
Mitchell, Robert (Rob) 834
Mitchell, R. Brian 844
Mitchell, Betty 935
Mitchell, Cecilia 942
Mitchem, Steven G. 400
Mithipati, Kumar 101
Mitra, Robin 808
Mitsui, Shaun 179
Mittal, Gaurav 555
Mittmann, Paul 135
Mitzenmacher, Steve 602
Mitzner, Nathan 378
Miura, Koji 184
Mixon, Shawna 339
Mizell, Steven C. 585
Mizelle, C 454
Mizener, Kathy 497
Mizuno, Tony 103
Mizusaki, Flavio 75
Mlotek, Mark E. 752
Mlynek, Chris 6
Moag, Tony 834
Moats, Simeon 320
Moats, Andy 678
Mobley, Kelley 191
Mobley, Brian 202
Mobley, Shawn 880
Mochida, Masanori 395
Mock, Jeff 553
Mockus, Steve 875
Modoff, Brian T. 707
Moe, Ronald 517
Moehlenbrock, Todd 263
Moehn, Michael L. 40
Moeller, Kyle 204
Moeller, Jon R. 693
Moenaert, Patricia 175
Moench, Pam 585
Moffat, Bob 470
Moffat, Bob 750
Moffett, Todd 699
Moffett, James 863
Moffitt, Kevin L. 356

Moffitt, Kevin 633
Mogck, Timothy 3
Mogen, Emily 497
Mohammad, Shamim 162
Mohammed, Khundnir 202
Mohammed, Hafeza 511
Mohammedshah, Juzer 699
Mohan, R. Michael (Mike) 126
Mohan, Raj 204
Mohan, Vamsi 216
Mohan, John 906
Mohiuddin, Ashfaq 748
Mohr, Todd M. 15
Mohr, John R 106
Mohr, Rick 743
Mohr, David 762
Mohs, Brad 84
Moison, Franck J. 220
Mojares, Dennis 754
Moje, Elizabeth Birr 720
Mok, Wilbur W. 22
Mokma, William 450
Molaro, Don 204
Molek, Marcie 31
Molina, Elena 57
Molina, Oscar 246
Molina, Hope S 246
Molina, Jose 737
Molinar, Gilbert 470
Molinaro, Vince 490
Molinaro, Frank 818
Molinini, Louis 486
Molino, Michael 517
Moll, Julie 548
Mollenauer, Sean 743
Mollenkopf, Steven M. (Steve) 707
Mollica, Jim 62
Mollica, Anthony 146
Mollica, Paul F. 908
Mollins, Gregg J. 725
Mollins, Sean 725
Molnar, Mike 12
Molnar, Larry 405
Molnar, David A. 853
Molnar, Jacqueline 919
Molster, John A 931
Monacelli, Fred 84
Monaco, Deborah 682
Monaco, Janet 713
Monaghan, Craig T. 78
Monago, Tony 449
Monahan, Jay 293
Moncau, Ursula 927
Moncayo, Erick 605
Moncher, Mark 45
Moncla, Jean 158
Moncrief, Jimmy 678
Moncur, Dave 668
Mondello, Mark T. 480
Mondor, Lori 101
Monfeli, Mike 735
Mongrain, Joe 61
Monhart, James 620
Monin, Jean 57
Moniz, Henry 896
Monk, David H. 831
Monocchio, Joe 356
Monroe, David 7
Monroe, Michael 159
Monroe, Marvin 259
Monroe, Pamela 668
Monroe, Terry 735
Monroe, Courteney 858
Monsen, Brian 582
Monser, Edward L. 299
Monserrate, Grace 654
Monson, Jon 142
Monson, Sally 414
Monson, Kim 497
Monson, Brian 558
Monson, Kevin W. 578
Montag, Thomas K. (Tom) 101
Montalbano, Anthony 366
Montalvo, Michele 161
Montalvo, Jose 185
Montana, Gregory G. (Greg) 334
Montana, Peter 805

Montani, Dominic J 528
Montani, Patrick 735
Montano, Peter 101
Monteferrante, Chris 85
Monteforte, Jason 550
Monteiro, Ken 829
Monteith, Stewart 452
Montelaro, Jody 304
Montelaro, Charles 454
Montenegro, Gerson 484
Monterosso, Becky 357
Montes, John 573
Montes, Myrtho 699
Montesano, Todd 866
Montesino, Orlando C 735
Monteverde, Bryan 106
Montgomery, Norman J. 345
Montgomery, John 446
Montgomery, Sheila 454
Montgomery, Jay 500
Montgomery, Michael 889
Montiel, Marc 602
Montini, Enio A. (Tony) 731
Montoya, Isabel 350
Montoya, Luis 667
Montz, Renee D. 43
Montz, Lawrence 159
Monusky, Gerard 93
Monzon, Gilberto 682
Monz⬚n, Gilberto F. 682
Moo, Jason 395
Moodey, J. Tucker 316
Moodie, Alasdair 836
Moody, Sue 187
Moody, Michael 502
Moody, Mark 715
Moody, Jenny 803
Moon, John 115
Moon, David 722
Moon, Glenn 932
Moon-Eilers, Nancy 507
Mooney, Randy 254
Mooney, Bill 297
Mooney, Howard F. 342
Mooney, Kathleen 353
Mooney, Ryan 355
Mooney, David E 355
Mooney, Kevin 380
Mooney, Beth E. 497
Mooney, David 602
Mooney, Stephen M. (Steve) 818
Moonves, Leslie (Les) 171
Moor, Bill 157
Mooradian, Anne 644
Moore, Karen 13
Moore, Bridgette 31
Moore, Colin 52
Moore, Alison 57
Moore, Kevin 84
Moore, Ann S. 95
Moore, John 105
Moore, Beth 131
Moore, Stephen 139
Moore, Stephen L 168
Moore, Nathan 176
Moore, Kevin 204
Moore, Christine 224
Moore, Richard 224
Moore, Elizabeth D. 235
Moore, Everett 252
Moore, Jessica 273
Moore, Richard H. 341
Moore, Steve 355
Moore, A. Bruce 416
Moore, Elizabeth Berner 449
Moore, Thomas 474
Moore, Mary 539
Moore, Bryan 548
Moore, Andrew 563
Moore, Troy 568
Moore, Frederick V. (Fred) 568
Moore, BJ 576
Moore, Kelly 580
Moore, Daryl D. 635
Moore, Gary L 650
Moore, Greg 668
Moore, Edward W. 742

Moore, Linda 796
Moore, Scott 816
Moore, Christine 823
Moore, Bob 834
Moore, Jason 842
Moore, Heather 842
Moore, Declan 858
Moore, Jason 869
Moore, Michael S. (Mike) 903
Moore, Katie 928
Moore, Karen 935
Moorehead, Alexander A. (Alex) 529
Moorhead, Tim 446
Moorhouse, Scott 15
Moorjani, Shail 158
Moorman, Tom 139
Moorstein, Tim 367
Mora, Elfa 179
Mora, Hugo 615
Moraci, Philip J 882
Morais, Diane 33
Moral-Niles, Christopher J. Del 80
Morales, Raquel 178
Morales, Vincent J. 685
Morales-jaffe, Marcia 929
Moran, Patrick 3
Moran, Patrick 16
Moran, Karen 18
Moran, Rob 19
Moran, John 32
Moran, Edward 53
Moran, Mickey 80
Moran, Michael 395
Moran, Tim 533
Moran, Manuel 533
Moran, Brian 555
Moran, Thomas 558
Moran, Anita 875
Morani, Antonio 836
Morante, Chris 15
Morawski, Mark 45
Morazzani, Christina 693
Morche, Ed 181
More, Debrah 116
Moreau, Maxine L. 181
Moreland, Kenneth V. 809
Moreland, David 935
Morelli, Tony 200
Morelli, John 266
Morelli, Salvatore 413
Morena, Mike 620
Moreno, Maria M 620
Moreno, Marie 768
Moret, Blake D. 738
Morfin, Lindsey 395
Morfit, Debbie 867
Morford, Craig S. 160
Morgan, Bob 45
Morgan, Patrick 72
Morgan, David 93
Morgan, David 192
Morgan, Cindy 224
Morgan, Kip 297
Morgan, Charlie 300
Morgan, Lisa 413
Morgan, Mary 454
Morgan, Paige 486
Morgan, Jeff 488
Morgan, Mary 500
Morgan, James 567
Morgan, Rose 664
Morgan, Jason 796
Morgan, Daniel 806
Morgan, Sherri 806
Morgan, Hugh G 808
Morgan, Michael 810
Morgan, Steven 907
Morganthall, Frederick J. (Fred) 506
Morge, Kenneth 262
Morgenlender, Mark 204
Morgenstern, Mitch 558
Morgenstern, Kara 720
Morgillo, Albert 488
Morgison, Kevin 159
Morgo, Joseph 204
Morhaime, Michael (Mike) 10
Moriarty, Linda 52

Moriarty, Thomas M. 252
Moriarty, Michael 330
Moriarty, Brad 453
Morikis, John G. 764
Morimoto, David S. 179
Morin, Jennifer 155
Morissette, Daniel J. 266
Moriwaki, Lee Y. 179
Morken, CeCe 476
Morley, Jeffrey 729
Morlock, Sonya 768
Moro, Sonya 109
Moro, Gisele 517
Morosov, Anatoly 489
Morovich, Nancy 304
Morrell, Kelley 201
Morrell, Dan 282
Morrell, Jim 818
Morrell, Dan 901
Morrey, Dana 808
Morris, Donna 11
Morris, Jared A. 55
Morris, Gregory A. (Greg) 74
Morris, M. Catherine (Cathy) 76
Morris, Uri 131
Morris, Jim 135
Morris, David 142
Morris, Joe 226
Morris, Craig 300
Morris, Rodney 355
Morris, Gerald 383
Morris, Ken 385
Morris, Robert 389
Morris, Richard 548
Morris, Chris 555
Morris, Maria R. 569
Morris, Pamela 607
Morris, Sandra 665
Morris, Brian J 700
Morris, Jesse E. 709
Morris, Brad 722
Morris, B. Harrison 763
Morris, Pete 786
Morris, John 794
Morris, John 863
Morris, Fran 893
Morris, John J. 907
Morris, Dawn C. 908
Morris, Michael J. 941
Morris-Hipkins, Stuart 647
Morrison, Michael J. 63
Morrison, Christina 72
Morrison, Scott C. 96
Morrison, Denise M. 156
Morrison, Patricia B. (Patty) 160
Morrison, Jim 171
Morrison, Richard 312
Morrison, Millard 454
Morrison, Mark 498
Morrison, Deb 555
Morrison, Jim 563
Morrison, Trevor 606
Morrison, Jeffrey 664
Morrison, Kevin 720
Morrison, Joe 796
Morrison, Dave 804
Morrison, Andrew 811
Morrison, Bill 818
Morriss, Steve 14
Morrissey, Art 96
Morrow, Georgette 172
Morrow, Martha 195
Morrow, Duncan 246
Morrow, Bradley 550
Morrow, Jerry 563
Morrow, Bryan 668
Morrow, Brian R. 740
Mors, Bernhard 555
Morse, Sherry 84
Morse, David L. 240
Morse, Cheryl 304
Morse, Loren 651
Morse, Diane 888
Morstadt, Mary 356
Morsy, Hany 928
Mortensen, Pam 661
Mortenson, Dave 450

Morthland, Lee 715
Mortimer, Patrick 332
Morton, David 55
Morton, Robert 170
Morton, ED 188
Morton, Joe 470
Morton, Susan 550
Morton, Michael J. 558
Morton, Dan 590
Morton, Steve 895
Morton-rowe, Laura 533
Mosa, Dirk 810
Moscaritolo, Daniel 398
Mosele, Joseph 84
Moseler, Cecilia 18
Moseley, Duncan 117
Moseley, Mark 316
Moser, Chris 625
Moses, James M. (Jamie) 124
Moses, Sharon 457
Moses, Christopher 495
Moseska, Spencer 273
Mosher, Allison 228
Mosher, Jason 457
Mosich, Nicholas A. 137
Mosier, Preston 813
Moskowitz, Rick 497
Moskowitz, Paul T. 808
Mosley, Gerald 593
Moss, Kaylene 94
Moss, Kristin 274
Moss, Aaron 295
Moss, Kenneth (Ken) 296
Moss, Linda L. 360
Moss, Judith 483
Moss, Susan 502
Mosshamer, Steven 328
Motamedi, Angela 770
Mote, Jeff 926
Motl, Christopher J. (Chris) 908
Mott, Linda 87
Mott, Randall D. (Randy) 385
Mott, Joe 467
Motta, Jose 259
Motta, Stephen 382
Motte, Anne-Marie 219
Motyleski, Sandy 37
Mouadeb, Daniel 159
Mougalian, Linda 87
Moukaddem, Souheil 139
Moullemaaz, Karim 332
Moullet, Barry 257
Moulton, Paul G. 241
Mound, Missy 383
Mounger, Bridget 678
Mount, Denise 881
Mountjoy, Michelle 863
Mouren-Laurens, Nicole 487
Moutenot, Michael 555
Mouthaan, Frank 643
Mouzon, Stefanie 330
Movassaghi, Eric 454
Movens, Daniel 161
Mowder, David 632
Mowery, Andy 208
Mowery, Geoffrey 449
Moy, Raymond 161
Moy, Mary 172
Moy, Chancellor 290
Moy, Maria 533
Moyad, Andrew 131
Moyano, Grace 497
Moyer, Priscilla 373
Moyer, Eileen 377
Moyer, Steve 574
Moyer, David 580
Moyer, Sandra 587
Moyer, Rob 805
Moylan, James 750
Moynihan, Brian T. 101
Moysen, Demetrio 904
Mozaffar, Hus 713
Mozinski, Cheryl 333
Mrowczynski, Jeff 241
Ms, Julie 13
Mucci, Lisa 273
Mucci, Ron 641

Mucciolo, Brenda 262
Mucera, Adele 886
Mucha, Zenia 273
Mucha, Joseph 383
Mudd, John 441
Mudrick, Christopher 314
Muegge, Tracy 323
Muehl, Mark 222
Muehlen, Constance Von 26
Mueller, David 12
Mueller, Mark 79
Mueller, Roni 172
Mueller, Meg R. 376
Mueller, George 402
Mueller, Paul 409
Mueller, Karl W. 636
Mueller, Manfred 733
Mueller, Bernadette M. 891
Mueller, Michael 932
Muenchau, Jeanne 617
Muhammad, Marfiza 423
Muhammad, Timika 892
Muilenburg, Dennis A. 135
Muir, Thomas 452
Muir, William D. (Bill) 480
Muir, Nick 932
Mukherjee, Arindam 199
Mulcahey, Terri 663
Mulford, Michael D. 349
Mulhere, Timothy P. 294
Mulherin, Matthew J. (Matt) 451
Mulhern, Kevin 170
Mulholland, Mike 875
Mulia, Caroline 585
Mulitz, Barbara 749
Mull, Matthew 107
Mull, Kevin 337
Mull, Lanier 507
Mull, Rohit 760
Mull, Betsy 869
Mullany, Joseph 88
Mullarkey, Pat 878
Mullen, Robert 517
Mullen, Charles 607
Mullen, Frank 743
Mullen, Gregory J 792
Mullen, Frederick L 839
Muller, Jordan 135
Muller, John 293
Muller, Chris 395
Muller, Bart 786
Muller, Chris 908
Mullery, Stephen P. 327
Mulligan, Paul 216
Mulligan, Donal L. (Don) 383
Mulligan, Gene 530
Mulligan, Thomas 570
Mulligan, Mike 797
Mulligan, John J. 813
Mullin, Thomas J. (Tom) 236
Mullin, Tom 237
Mullin, Terence 332
Mullin, Lauren 839
Mullinax, Kenneth 821
Mullins, Brenda 19
Mullins, Kevin 468
Mullins, Bob 712
Mullins, John 799
Mulroy, Thomas P. 795
Mulroy, Molly 909
Mulwee, Crosby 799
Muminovic, Alem 672
Munce, Currie 574
Mundt-Blum, Walter 628
Mundy, Robert P. (Bob) 652
Muney, Alan M. 194
Mungai, Sheri 668
Munger, Charles T. (Charlie) 123
Mungovan, Patrick 643
Muniga, Douglas 224
Muniz, Michelle 222
Muniz, Sean M. 657
Munjal, Leena 759
Munn, Irving 195
Munn, Chuck 808
Munneke, Rich 754
Munnelly, Joseph M. (Joe) 72

Munofo, Jim 385
Munoz, Van 442
Munoz, Oscar 871
Munro, Tiffany 487
Munsch, Dona 602
Munsell, Terri 863
Munsinger, Mary 404
Munson, Paul 849
Munson, Kelly A. 911
Munson, James 935
Munteanu, Rebecca 869
Munton, Owen 406
Muntoni, Roby 746
Murabito, John M. 194
Murai, Kevin M. 805
Murakami, Jon 103
Muraro, Robert 812
Muratore, Magali 617
Muratore, Magali 787
Murchie, Catherine 555
Murchie, Stewart 849
Murdoch, Britton H. 148
Murdoch, Lachlan K. 610
Murdoch, K. Rupert 610
Murdoch, Tim 748
Murdoch, James R. 858
Murdoch, Lachlan K. 858
Murdoch, K. Rupert 858
Murdock, Dana 865
Mureddu, Adriano 923
Murelli, David 39
Murillo, Jessica 470
Murkowski, Michael 330
Murlless, Craig 102
Muro, David 84
Murphy, Christopher J. (Chris) 1
Murphy, Mark D 60
Murphy, John M 67
Murphy, Siobhan 69
Murphy, Thomas J. (Tom) 77
Murphy, Ron 80
Murphy, Sean 84
Murphy, Chris 87
Murphy, Miriam 94
Murphy, William 133
Murphy, John 216
Murphy, James P. (Jim) 241
Murphy, Drew 295
Murphy, Patrick 320
Murphy, Stephen 350
Murphy, Steve 350
Murphy, Gwenn 358
Murphy, Shawn 370
Murphy, Bob 378
Murphy, James H. (Jim) 383
Murphy, Christopher 392
Murphy, Edmund F. 400
Murphy, Tara 449
Murphy, Erica 454
Murphy, Michael T 472
Murphy, John 474
Murphy, Gerry 489
Murphy, Peggy C 489
Murphy, Tony 528
Murphy, Lauren 541
Murphy, Michael 550
Murphy, Timothy H. (Tim) 554
Murphy, Brenda 570
Murphy, R. Madison 590
Murphy, Sharon 604
Murphy, Gregory 626
Murphy, Ryan 678
Murphy, John 695
Murphy, Katie 713
Murphy, Diane 716
Murphy, Cathy 717
Murphy, Chris 724
Murphy, George M. 746
Murphy, Gregory E. 760
Murphy, Tracy 802
Murphy, Courtney 809
Murphy, Neil 861
Murphy, Jack 874
Murphy, Sean 890
Murphy, John 891
Murphy, Yulia 892
Murphy, Luke 896

Murphy, Ken 901
Murphy, Julie 903
Murphy, David 907
Murphy, Richard B. 927
Murphy, Robert 927
Murphy, CJ 931
Murphy, Michael 935
Murphy-harris, Rosemary 88
Murrain, Marie 117
Murray, James 31
Murray, Patricia 176
Murray, Michelle 204
Murray, Scott 293
Murray, Barbara 378
Murray, Michael 439
Murray, Cathleen 559
Murray, Brian 610
Murray, Greg 754
Murray, Dane H 776
Murray, Donna 882
Murray, Oliver 886
Murray, Sue 908
Murrell, Matthew 886
Murren, James J. 572
Murrin, Helena 935
Murtagh, Nigel J. 754
Murter, Jeffrey 516
Murtha, Mark G. 419
Murthy, Ramesh 415
Musa, Jun 672
Musca, Robert 875
Muschong, Lisa 283
Musen, Robert M. 723
Musen, Bob 724
Musgrave, Kendra 449
Musgrove, Craig 668
Music, Julie 666
Musk, Elon 823
Mussenden, Felix 533
Musser, Eric S. 240
Musser, Jeffrey S. 317
Musso, Chris 681
Mustafa, Aman 935
Musynske, Gavin 539
Mutch, Marcy D. 354
Muthler, Craig 367
Muto, Gary P. 79
Muto, Daneen 935
Muzaffar, Farooq 934
Muzumdar, Maha 643
Muzzy, Doug 414
Mwangi, Doreen 507
Myers, Tim D. 75
Myers, Timothy D. (Tim) 104
Myers, Shante 117
Myers, Timothy 135
Myers, Robert J. (Bob) 164
Myers, Christopher D. (Chris) 250
Myers, Carol 351
Myers, Cynthia M. 362
Myers, Curtis J. 376
Myers, Phillip 425
Myers, Thomas D. 495
Myers, Rita 511
Myers, Jodi 573
Myers, Daniel 584
Myers, Fred 606
Myers, Lynn 699
Myers, Landon 715
Myers, Larry L. 810
Myers, William E. 847
Myers, Daniel P. (Dan) 916
Myerson, Terry 576
Myhre, Dan 735
Myron, Thomas R 128
Myszewski, Kurt 735

N

Naageswaran, Rama 199
Naasz, Scott 881
Nabavian, Paige 378
Nabel, Elizabeth G. (Betsy) 656
Nabhan, Chadi 161
Nace, Bernadette 88
Nachajska, Ania 199

Nachmann, Marc 395
Nacpil, Catherine 558
Nadarajan, Gunalan 720
Naddeo, Eric 861
Nadeau, Gerard F. 459
Nadella, Satya 575
Nader, Alfred 919
Nadkarni, Pranay 39
Nadler, Laura 899
Nagarajan, Rajesh 173
Nagarajan, Sundaram (Naga) 458
Nagata, Ron 416
Nageer, Tarique 550
Nagel, Paul J 261
Nagel, Brian 876
Nager, Thomas 47
Nager, Jeff 827
Naggar, David 37
Naggar, Lela 824
Naggiar, Ingrid 750
Nagji, Bansi 563
Nagler, Lorna E. 862
Nagrath, Stephanie 550
Nagy, Kate 337
Nagy, Jane 793
Nahlovsky, Kathy 257
Nahrup, Steve 299
Naik, Piyush 131
Naik, Harshad 452
Nail, Rodney 32
Nair, Vas 75
Nair, Hari 316
Nair, Raj 370
Nair, Roopa 705
Najimi, Parnaz 901
Najjar, Fred 266
Najjar, Ted 395
Nakahara, Tina 103
Nakahara, Steven 103
Nakano, Tom 624
Nakasato, Davin 103
Nakasone, Norman 180
Nakatsuka, Ralph Y. 822
Nakis, Dominic J. 13
Nalamasu, Omkaram (Om) 71
Nallen, John P. 858
Nallin, John 875
Nalluri, Prathima 131
Nalluri, Lakshmi 487
Nam, Keith 366
Nambiar, Vinod 219
Namie, Macario 200
Nanavaty, Maulik 142
Nanberg, Joshua 128
Nance, Ann 487
Nandakumar, Anita 395
Napier, Dale 517
Naples, Richard J. 119
Napol, Marcello 3
Napoli, Gus 440
Napoli, Joe 808
Napoli, Elizabeth 849
Napolitan, Raymond S. 626
Napolitano, Glen 337
Nappi, David 935
Naquin, Michael 454
Naqvi, Asim 379
Narain, Duraiswami 585
Narang, Manu 45
Narang, Steve 111
Narasimhan, Laxman 667
Narayanan, Lakshmi 218
Narayanan, Krishnan 395
Narayanan, Gowri 555
Narayen, Shantanu 11
Narciso, Paul J. 746
Nardecchia, Chris 738
Nardo, Tom Di 910
Nardone, Mary Kaye 511
Nardone, Michael 570
Nardone, Robert 892
Narduzzo, Paul 214
Narosky, Mary 188
Nasby, Thomas 18
Nash, William D. (Bill) 162
Nash, Bill 162
Nash, Bill 530

Nash, Joseph 567
Nash, Michael 863
Nash, Bob 935
Nason, Charlie 559
Nassetta, Christopher J. (Chris) 427
Natale, J 119
Natale, Richard 195
Natale, Joe 910
Natali, Sara 884
Natarajan, Kamal 32
Natarajan, Venkata 699
Natarajan, Murali 732
Natarajan, Shekar 813
Nath, Deepak 4
Nath, Munindra 202
Nathan, Scott 109
Natkow, Jay 715
Naughten, Christopher 332
Naughton, Marc G. 183
Naughton, Duncan C. Mac 276
Naughton, Mary 550
Naughton, W Terrance 912
Naughton, Terry 912
Naughton-Gerdes, Joan 32
Naumann, Peter 881
Navarro, Andy 244
Navarro, Gloria 246
Navarro, Mary W. 449
Navarro, Imelda 468
Navarro, David 813
Navo, Chris 799
Navy, David 497
Nayeri, Juanita 735
Nazzaro, Stephen F. (Steve) 791
Neal, Michelle M. 105
Neal, Krista 201
Neal, Stephen C. 521
Neal, Stephen C. 523
Neal, Gary F. 865
Neal, Joel 901
Neale, George A. 760
Nealon, Gerald 88
Nealon, Thomas M. (Tom) 780
Nearhood, William 337
Nearpass, Troy 354
Neary, David M 153
Neary, Robert D. 227
Nebel, Mary Beth 732
Neborak, Michael K. (Mike) 348
Nebosky, Patricia 124
Nebreda, Julian 16
Necastro, Butch 31
Necastro, Daniel Butch 31
NeCastro, Timothy G. 310
Necessary, Chad 17
Neckorcuk, Richard D 717
Nedder, Michael 366
Neely, Stephanie 32
Neely, Eric 496
Neely, Scott 699
Neely, David 722
Neff, Clay 190
Neff, Lorraine 246
Nefkens, Mike 425
Negrⓘn, Eduardo J. 682
Neher, Terry 888
Neice, Joel 699
Neidorff, Michael F. 176
Neier, Greg 115
Neifert, Kevin T. 716
Neill, James R. (Jim) 387
Neilon, Jay 728
Nell, Steven E. 137
Nelms, David W. 269
Nelsen, Keith J. 126
Nelsen, Kathy 332
Nelsen, Denise 787
Nelsen, Mark 899
Nelson, Cara M 21
Nelson, Ronald L. (Ron) 93
Nelson, Robert 106
Nelson, Shelby 111
Nelson, Dennis 113
Nelson, Kevin 159
Nelson, Scott 161
Nelson, Rosemary 220
Nelson, Brent 248

Nelson, David 261
Nelson, Laura 273
Nelson, Elaine 282
Nelson, Faye A. 284
Nelson, Ann W. 301
Nelson, John P. 301
Nelson, Rolf 313
Nelson, Zac 350
Nelson, Paul 378
Nelson, Kimberly A. (Kim) 383
Nelson, Rick 403
Nelson, Brad 503
Nelson, Anthony 536
Nelson, Philip B 545
Nelson, Sean 563
Nelson, Linda 578
Nelson, Jonathan B. 639
Nelson, Mike 641
Nelson, Bradley M. (Brad) 645
Nelson, Rick 678
Nelson, Carla 735
Nelson, Wendy 768
Nelson, Deanna 770
Nelson, Scott 813
Nelson, Diane 838
Nelson, Jon 839
Nelson, Robert 849
Nelson, Michael S. 882
Nelson, Laura 896
Nelson, George 896
Nelson, David D. (Dave) 915
Nelson, Mary 935
Nemec, Stevie 241
Nemecek, Donna 105
Nemer, Marti 486
Nemerov, Jacki 713
Nemeth, Jeffery 370
Nemeth, Julio 693
Nemphos, Ann 413
Nendza, Adam 892
Nentchev, Nentcho 133
Nentwig, Robert J. 141
Nerbonne, Daniel 679
Nerenhausen, Frank R. 645
Neri, Antonio 425
Neri, Marc 804
NESBIT, JONATHAN 792
Nesbit, Kirk 805
Nesbitt, Stephen R. 445
Nesbitt, Douglas 725
Nesci, James D. 698
Nesi, Victor J. 795
Ness, Steve 907
Nestlerod, John 590
Nestor, Adrienne 53
Nestor, Brian 715
Netherton, Linda 334
Nettesheim, Susan 484
Netzley, Maureen 300
Neu, Laurel 620
Neu, Stacey L. 782
Neubert, Hanswerner 199
Neugarten, Lisa 457
Neugent, Christopher J. 683
Neuman, Jennifer 607
Neumann, Spencer 10
Neumann, Eli 200
Neumann, Karl-Thomas 385
Neumann, Dan 678
Neumeyer, Daniel J. 449
Neuts, Amanda 155
Nevens, T. Michael (Mike) 602
Neville, Robert M. 98
Neville, Everett 319
Nevins, Sheila 838
New, Ryan 726
Newan, Karla 454
Newberg, William 904
Newbern, Thomas B. 90
Newberry, Stephen G. (Steve) 512
Newberry, Neil 800
Newbery, Michelle M. 537
Newborn, Linda 261
Newcomb, Jorey 237
Newcomer, Reagan 101
Newcomer, John 390
Newell, Scott 754

Newell, Michele 907
Newfield, Richard U. 591
Newhouse, Joseph 18
Newhouse, Greg 497
Newkirk, Christopher T. 158
Newlands, William A. (Bill) 236
Newlun, Craig 202
Newman, Randy 27
Newman, Tracy 101
Newman, Kenneth Kenneth Newman 105
Newman, Rebecca 105
Newman, Ken 179
Newman, Drew 204
Newman, David 246
Newman, Sallie 247
Newman, Andrea F 262
Newman, Dennis 272
Newman, Harry 320
Newman, Chris 332
Newman, John 361
Newman, Michael 457
Newman, Fred 483
Newman, Rainer 484
Newman, Dan 504
Newman, Gerald 562
Newman, Brian 667
Newman, Robert 677
Newman, Darran 748
Newman, Gary 858
Newman, Jeff 941
Newmark, Lee 378
Newport, Roger K. 24
Newsom, Richard W. (Rick) 230
Newsome, Earl 687
Newsome, Denise 722
Newsome, Alfred 799
Newton, Lisa 252
Newton, Lloyd 509
Newton, Todd 595
Newton, Carl 757
Newton, Chris 928
Neylon, Brian V. 272
Neylon, Tom 356
Ng, John 39
Ng, Alex 204
Ng, Dominic 290
Ng, Stella 489
NG, Regina 555
Ng, Fiona 604
Ng, Chaki 896
Ngo, A. Catherine 179
Nguyen, Thong M. 101
Nguyen, Quynh 159
Nguyen, Thuy 252
Nguyen, Michael 413
Nguyen, Xuong 474
Nguyen, Tony 570
Nguyen, Tracy 620
Nguyen, David 699
NI, Lisong 720
Niblock, Robert A. 537
Niccol, Brian R. 939
Niccolls, Phil 300
Niccolucci, Dani 834
Nicdao, Nicole 746
Niceberg, Michael 172
Nichol, Janett 615
Nicholas, Georgette C. 389
Nicholas, Jim 488
Nicholas, Brad 704
Nicholls, Timothy S. (Tim) 472
Nichols, Ryan 32
Nichols, Carrie 107
Nichols, Bruce 124
Nichols, Todd 129
Nichols, Lee 157
Nichols, Janet 161
Nichols, Ronald O. 295
Nichols, Jim 351
Nichols, Rodney P. 544
Nichols, John 578
Nichols, Dana L. 706
Nichols, Ronald O. (R.O.) 777
Nichols, Donald 849
Nichols, Todd 888
Nicholson, Glenn 196

Nicholson, E. Allen 250
Nicholson, Daniel 385
Nicholson, George C. 443
Nicholson, Darryl 484
Nicholson, Marla 550
Nicholson, Kelly 699
Nicholson, Sara 811
Nicholson, Lyle 859
Nickel, David 620
Nickel, Kenneth 892
Nickele, Christopher J. (Chris) 213
Nickele, Chris 213
Nickels, Jeff 351
Nickerson, Floyd 42
Nickerson, Richard 155
Nickerson, Barry 503
Nickerson, Cheryl 664
Nickles, Jenny 449
Nickolson, Tracey 799
Nicks, Darlene 454
Nicol, Peter G. 185
Nicolaidis, Tony 786
Nicoletti, Ralph J. 608
Nides, Thomas R. (Tom) 587
Niedbalski, Dave 533
Niederer, Jed 593
Niehaus, James 47
Niehaus, Celie 158
Niekrash, Maggie 449
Nielsen, Chris 109
Nielsen, Joel 370
Nielsen, Mark D. 376
Nielsen, Rob 487
Nielsen, Jane H. 713
Nielsen, Mark D 716
Niem, Eddie 220
Nieman, Maurice 170
Niemann, Richard 108
Niemann, Angela 316
Niemeyer, Bruce 191
Niemoeller, John Arthur 353
Nienaber, Lisa 511
Nierenberg, Andrew 656
Niermann, Mark 259
Nieser, Daniel 276
Nieto, Alejandra 671
Nieuwenhuys, Gerard 663
Nieuwsma, David J. (Dave) 739
Nieves, Roberto 800
Nigam, Naresh 750
Nightingale, Timothy P. 155
Nigon, Thomas 912
Nigro, Joseph (Joe) 314
Nigro, Stephen (Steve) 442
Nigro, James M. 511
Nigro, Rich 735
Niimura, Ken 103
Nijenhuis, Wouter 140
Nikolaus, Donald H. 279
Nikolov, Anita 620
Nikolova, Kalina 896
Niles, Thomas 587
Nill, Michael R. (Mike) 183
Nimbley, Thomas J. 658
Nimer, Richard 3
Ning, Wilson 513
Niper, Chrissy 749
Nisbett, Mark 908
Nishi, Masao 808
Nissenson, Allen R. 258
Niswander, Kathy 88
Nito, Daniel 587
Nittolo, Kathy 668
Niver, Clair 668
Nix, Rudy 307
Nix, Craig L. 344
Nix, Joey 888
Nixon, Randy 87
Nixon, Dennis E. 468
Njonjo, Peter 216
Nkongho, Andrew 713
Nley, Fred 429
Nober, Roger 150
Noble, Quintin 5
Noble, Robert 135
Noble, Jeff 346
Noble, Jen 470

Noble, Craig 664
Noble, Siba 799
Noble, Anthony 896
Noblett, Monique 620
Nocella, Andrew P. 871
Nocero, Michael 800
Nochowitz, Matthew 923
Nodianos, Bridget 116
Noeker, Jeffrey 337
Noel, Brett 45
Noel, Tom 306
Noel, Molaine 548
Noelle, Boudler 794
Noethiger, Robert 171
Noga, James W. (Jim) 656
Nohaile, Mike 57
Nohara, Todd 102
Nohra, Jude J. 870
Nolan, Rebecca 15
Nolan, Joe 71
Nolan, Steve 88
Nolan, Tracy 227
Nolan, Joseph R. (Joe) 312
Nolan, Michael J. (Mike) 332
Nolan, Linda M 620
Nolan, Stefanie 632
Nolan, Dana 722
Nolan, Pat 737
Nolan, Elizabeth 792
Nolan, David A. 940
Noland, Thomas 446
Noland, Matt 855
Nolasco, Teresa 224
Noll, Kelly 31
Noll, Richard A. (Rich) 407
Nollett, Jessica 306
Nolte, Jo 661
Nolte, Reed 858
Noonan, James R. 511
Noordhoek, Jeffrey R. (Jeff) 601
Nooyi, Indra K. 667
Noppenberger, Louis 205
Norcia, Gerardo (Jerry) 284
Norcross, Gary A. 334
Norcross, Jeanne 781
Nord, Mary 289
Nord, Glenn 337
Nord, Jeff 710
Norden, Lisa 710
Nordenson, Victor 555
Nordlie, Elizabeth M. 383
Nordling, Christopher 573
Nordmeyer, Greg 52
Nordmeyer, Jim 649
Nordquist, Jeffery 115
Nordstrom, Mike 383
Nordstrom, Blake W. 616
Nordstrom, Peter E. (Pete) 616
Nordstrom, Erik B. 616
Nordstrom, James F. (Jamie) 617
Norenberg, Nick 299
Noriega, Arnold 365
Norman, Gail 98
Norman, Todd 320
Norman, Paul T. 493
Normandin, Donna 246
Normandin, Michael 935
Normile, Robert (Bob) 557
Normington, Debbie 199
Norquist, William 14
Norris, Derek J. 102
Norris, Naomi 117
Norris, Josephine 488
Norsworthy, Tony 328
North, Paul 411
North, John F. 531
North, Randall 735
Northam, Thadd 550
Northcutt, Scott 276
Northcutt, Carla 409
Northcutt, Martha 446
Northcutt, Kendria 678
Northup, Jim 267
Norton, William Bill 261
Norton, Ted 261
Norton, Susan A. 341
Norton, Ellen 546

Norton, Mike 555
Norton, Robert G. (Bob) 656
Norton, David K. 664
Norton, John 717
Norton, W.D. (Joe) 779
Norton, Noah 942
Norwitt, Richard A. (Adam) 58
Norwood, David 320
Nosca-lay, Paula 135
Noseda, Aldo 585
Noseworthy, Darren 672
Nosler, John S. 725
Nott, Andy 170
Notte, Jerry J 185
Nottingham, Jim 442
Nottingham, Melissa 651
Nourse, Bruce 720
Nova, Janet 858
Novaes, Djalma 244
Novak, Adam 559
Novakovic, Phebe N. 380
Novielli, Jack 698
Noviello, Nicholas 602
Novinger, Tiffany 668
Novo, Guillermo 22
Nowak, Pat 735
Nowbar, Hossein 576
Nowlin, Donna 332
Nowlin, Bill 715
Noyes, Mark 235
Nuchims, Fran 158
Nuckols, Jeff 425
Nudi, Jonathon J. (Jon) 383
Nugent, Anne 242
Nugent, Russell 860
Nunn, Richard 244
Nuon, Leslie 942
Nuss, Joe 60
Nussbaum, Samuel 66
Nussbaum, Rob 449
Nusterer, Norbert 248
Nutheti, Guru 628
Nuti, William R. (Bill) 599
Nuti, Olga 668
Nutt, Wendy 573
Nutter, Gary 164
Nutter, Michael 246
Nuvel, Hubert Van 521
Nuvel, Hubert Van 523
Nuzzolo, Marc 892
Nye, Rodney 447
Nye, Catherine 457
Nygaard, Kristina 185
Nylund, Arne 793
Nyman, Anjuman 548
Nyman, Adrian 615
Nyquist, Christina 17
Nysschen, Carel Johannes de 385
Nystuen, Bob 392
N©emeh, Alain P. 723

O

Oagrady, Becky 383
Oak, Pin 320
Oakes, John 57
Oakland, Steven T. 773
Oakley, Kent 161
Oates, J 195
Oates, Joseph P. 235
Oates, David 266
Oates, Michael P. 334
Oatsvall, Brian 158
Obando, Glenn 105
Obear, Kyle 539
Oberg, Kathleen K. (Leeny) 548
Oberg, Leeny 549
Oberholzer, Bill 688
Obering, Henry A. (Trey) 139
Oberle, Mark 173
Obermeyer, Frank 196
Obermeyer, Paul R. 223
Oberosler, Bob 731
Oberrender, Robert 881
Obleton, Carolynn 806
Obrien, James J 53

OBrien, Laura 170
OBrien, Kevin M. 876
Obryan, Tim 732
Obsitnik, Paul 490
Obzud, John 333
Ocasio-Velez, Anabel 672
Ochalek, Gloria 45
Ochlak, Alfred 818
Oconnell, Dan 94
Oconnor, Debra 13
OConnor, Jim 121
OConnor, Kevin 143
Oconnor, Kimberly 809
Odak, Dina 456
Oddleifson, Christopher (Chris) 459
Odell, Lawrence 340
Odell, David 498
Odinet, Bertrand (Bert) 375
Odonnell, Kevin 269
Odonnell, Jim 488
Odonnell, Michelle 705
Odonnell, Peter 781
Odriozola, Jose Maria (Chema) 875
Odriozola, Jose Maria 875
Oehen, Jurg 175
Oehms, Kristy 406
Oelerich, Molly 558
Oelke, Dawn 419
Oelke, Les 419
Oexmann, Gaven 390
Offenberger, Eric J. 725
Offereins, Diane E. 269
Oganes, Luis 489
Ogata, Hal 200
Ogburn, Robert 635
Ogden, Loralie 170
Ogilvie, Paula 731
Ogle, Mark 625
Ognall, Andrew H. 865
Ogrosky, Kori L. 653
Oh, Irene H. 290
Oh, Davidx 465
Oh, Christopher 573
Ohara, Michele 656
Ohare, Mike 800
Ohlander, Scott 487
Ohler, Andy 450
Ohrenberger, Danielle 607
Oi, Terence 935
Oie, Karen 528
Oja, Henrik 750
Ojukwu, Alfred 576
Okada, Terri 103
Okada, Dave 557
Okamoto, Janis 103
Okamoto, David 103
Okamura, Cindy 103
Okamura, Van 643
Okelley, Paige 626
Okerson, Ted 57
Okerstrom, Mark D. 316
Okland, Jens 793
Okle, Debbie L. 227
Okoye, Kimberly 927
Okray, Thomas B. (Tom) 12
Okubanjo, Abimbola 558
Oladapo, Dele 699
Olafson, Harlee N. 915
Olafsson, Olaf J. 838
Olajide, Temitayo 395
Olczak, Jacek 674
Oldfield, Cheryl 840
Oldham, Rachel 32
Oldham, Jon 158
Oldre, Chris 274
Oldroyd, Robert 942
Olds, Jennifer 598
Olear, Kathleen 545
Oleary, Christophe 383
OLeary, Tim 602
Olech, Bob 224
Oleck, Larry 440
Olejer, Leigh 246
Oleksiak, Peter 283
Oleksiak, Peter B. 284
Oleksiuk, Mary A. 859
Olenskyj, Paula 700

Oleon, John 334
Oler, Carol 196
Olfen, Elizabeth Van 507
Olin, John A. 410
Oliva, Joanna 365
Oliva, Cynthia 677
Oliva, Cindy 678
Olivares, David 395
Olive, Stephen R. 647
Oliveira, Rafael 505
Oliver, Bryan 307
Oliver, John 698
Oliver, Kirk R. 861
Oliver, Kerry 929
Olivera, Michelle 457
Olivier, Leon J. (Lee) 312
Olivier, Darla 652
Olivieri, Nicole 699
Olivo, Maria 849
Oller, Michael 808
Olmstead, Traci 300
Olmstead, Roger 708
Olmstead, Cpcu 788
Olsavsky, Brian T. 37
Olsen, John 37
Olsen, John 931
Olson, Lisa 6
Olson, Christine 45
Olson, W. Kregg 68
Olson, Knute A 84
Olson, Amy 108
Olson, Tiffany P. 160
Olson, Andy 182
Olson, Don 185
Olson, Robert 262
Olson, Eric 378
Olson, Anton 447
Olson, Arik 582
Olson, Maria 602
Olson, Laurie J. 671
Olson, Jim 729
Olson, Thomas 735
Olson, Aaron 754
Olson, Scott 888
Olsson, Jimmy 904
Olszewski, Paul 497
Olurin, Omo 18
Oluwole, Opeyemi 45
Omalley, Peter 115
Omara, Bill 808
Omobono, Karen D 717
Omoss, Mario 241
Ondecker, Marilyn 530
Onders, Mike 497
Onderwater, Leo 365
ONeal, Patrick 398
Oneale, Robert 537
Oneill, Thomas 321
Oneill, Myles 528
ONeill, Heidi 615
Oner, Jake 935
Ong, Bernard 530
Onimo, Alfreda 720
Onofrey, Debbie 882
Onorato, Andrea 891
Onstad, Robert 400
Onumonu, Ngozi 731
Onzuka, Chris 102
Oonnoonny, Abel 754
Oostendorp, Kellie 927
Opedal, Tor 555
Openshaw, Brian 754
Ophaug, Courtney 112
Opp, Susan D. 509
Oppenheim, David 269
Oppenheimer, Richard 840
Oppenhuis, Liz 32
Opstedahl, Deeanna 168
Oravec, Jon 483
Oravitz, Jeffrey J. 685
Orban, Paul W 272
Orbe, John 490
Orbuch, Liz Sorota 220
Orchard, Lisa 787
Orchard, Kenneth R. 853
Ordemann, William (Bill) 307
Orduna, Arthur 93

ORear, Alan 635
OReilly, Catherine 806
Orel, Paula 334
Orenstein, Fern 172
Orie, James G. 367
Oriti, Anthony 865
Orkis, Katherine 449
Orlando, John 171
Orlando, Dave 175
Orlando, Francesco 672
Orlando, David 809
Orleans, Andrea 582
Orloff, Harvey 202
Orlowski, Courtney 88
Orme, James 467
Ormond, Gia 356
Ormsby, Lenard T. 301
Ornato, Gail 713
Ornauer, Christina 175
Orndorff, Robert L. 749
Orona, Ed 431
Orourke, Kevin M 355
Orourke, Evelyn 792
Orourke, Melanie 818
Orourke, Claudia 891
Orozco, Tomas 66
Orozco, Jean-Marc 750
Orr, Mark 402
Orr, Shenjin 901
Orr, Lydia 903
Orsborn, Paul 224
Orsenigo, Carlo 185
Orsini, Mike 494
Orsini, Frank C. 514
Ort, Gary 824
Ortbals, Brian 930
Ortberg, Robert` K. (Kelly) 739
Ortberg, Kelly 739
Ortega, Tina 18
Ortega, Nadine 250
Ortega, David 355
Ortega, Cindy 573
Orth, Linda 604
Orth, Douglas 604
Orthwein, Peter B. 837
Ortiz, Reynaldo 6
Ortiz, Yolanda 39
Ortiz, Mauricio 224
Ortiz-Landazabal, Marie-Dominique 861
Ortkiese, Nancy 117
Orton, Todd 52
Orton, Bryan 559
Osakwe, Franklyn 901
Osbach, William 224
Osberg, Carl 353
Osborn, Ryan 196
Osborn, Brian 722
Osborn, Jo 850
Osborne, Roberta 133
Osborne, William 597
Osborne, Roger 677
Osbourn, Kay E. 206
Osbourn, William F. (Bill) 934
Oscar, Dr 365
Ose, Uriel 191
Oshima, Yuko 723
Oshman, Michele 528
Osmon, Jim 350
Ospina, Reynolds 358
Ossowski, James 704
Ostal☐©, Enrique 903
Ostapovicz, Christopher 440
Osteen, Jamie 763
Osteen, Debra K. 882
Ostendorf, George 558
Osterman, Vincent J. 613
Ostop, Christopher 487
Ostro, Dina 659
Ostrosky, John 671
Ostrowski, Richard 697
Oswalt, David 756
Otero, Arnold 306
Otis, Steve 808
Otjen, Renee 33
OToole, Kevin 176
Ott, Hartmut 39

Ott, Jennifer 80
Ott, Carol 182
Ott, Susan 551
Ott, Jeri 637
Ott, Amy 767
Otte, Chad 80
Ottenjohn, David 486
Ottinger, Eric H. 512
Otto, Christopher 103
Otto, Noreen 453
Otto, Jeff 882
Ouartarone, Jim 810
Ouellette, Douglas 564
Outwater, John 250
Overcash, Julie Ann 787
Overcast, Judy 392
Overgard, Todd 929
Overmyer, David 489
Overson, Chris 516
Overton, Pam 31
Ovokaitys, Daniel S. 343
Owen, John F. 95
Owen, Douglas 106
Owen, Jeffrey C. (Jeff) 276
Owen, Jeffrey 313
Owen, John B. 721
Owen, Jennifer 749
Owenby, Marcus 84
Owens, Dan 117
Owens, Leonard 389
Owens, Charlie 486
Owens, Bruce 555
Owens, Tiffany 563
Owens, Tom 715
Owens, Don G. 763
Owens, Patty 798
Owens, Amanda 811
Oyadomari, David 103
Oyster, Bryan 487
Ozan, Kevin M. 562
Ozbutun, Cetin 643
Ozer, Lynn 376
Ozimek, Michael M. 854
Oztan, Omer 203
O'Brien, Shane 31
O'Brien, Deirdre 69
O'Brien, Tim 84
O'Brien, Gregory 109
O'Brien, Ken 280
O'Brien, Richard E. 445
O'Brien, Gregory P. (Greg) 486
O'Brien, Cristina E 502
O'Brien, Beth 530
O'brien, Michael 570
O'Brien, Lawrence 582
O'Brien, Greg 599
O'Brien, Michael J. 639
O'Brien, William 643
O'Brien, Christopher J. (Chris) 736
O'Brien, Joseph 749
O'Brien, Michael 788
O'Brien, Karen 919
O'Bryant, Allan 723
O'Connell, Pat 52
O'Connell, Patrick 53
O'Connell, Bill 87
O'connell, Tom 224
O'Connell, Alfred 327
O'Connell, Maureen 378
O'Connell, Barbara A 620
O'Connor, Mark 106
O'Connor, Stephen 133
O'Connor, Kevin M. 143
O'Connor, Mary 170
O'Connor, Daniel 246
O'Connor, Nancy 413
O'Connor, Sean M. 474
O'Connor, Michael J. (Mike) 502
O'Connor, Christopher 530
O'Connor, Lane 570
O'Connor, Thomas L. 658
O'Connor, Michael L. (Mike) 908
O'Connor, Timothy (Tim) 933
O'Connor, Thomas J. (T.J.) 937
O'Conor, Raymond F. (Ray) 77
O'Day, Terence L. 422
O'Dell, Ed 526

O'Donnell, Susan 148
O'Donnell, William 195
O'Donnell, Peter G. 886
O'Donohoe, Karen 106
O'Dowd, Sarah A. 512
O'Dwyer, Philip 587
O'Dwyer, Michael 932
O'Flaherty, Lori L. 214
O'Flynn, Thomas M. (Tom) 16
O'Grady, Shawn P. 383
O'Grady, Michael G. 620
O'Hanley, Ronald P. (Ron) 791
O'Hara, Joseph J 649
O'Haver, Cort 864
O'Herlihy, Christopher (Chris) 458
O'Hern, Jim 548
O'Keefe, Pat 170
O'Keefe, Patrick 185
O'Laughlin, Matt 705
O'Leary, Jerry 185
O'Leary, Christopher D. (Chris) 383
O'Leary, Glenn 454
O'Malley, Michael 928
O'Mara, Kellyann 539
O'Meara, Robert P. (Bob) 356
O'Meara, Aidan 894
O'Neal, Clu Jon 49
O'Neil, Daniel 754
O'Neill, Michael 44
O'Neill, Marie 52
O'neill, Angela 80
O'Neill, Timothy J. 395
O'Neill, Lisa M. 511
O'Neill, Liz 521
O'Neill, Liz 523
O'Neill, Myles 528
O'Neill, Jerry 596
O'Neill, Tom 700
O'Neill, Thomas E. 850
O'quinn, Travis 117
O'Quinn, Marvin 266
O'Reagan, Richard 552
O'Reilly, Lawrence P. (Larry) 630
O'Reilly, Charles H. 630
O'Reilly, David E. 630
O'reilly, Sarah 713
O'Reilly, Frank 750
O'Rourke, Joan 252
O'Rourke, James (Joc) 588
O'Rourke, Michael G. 767
O'Rourke, Claudia 891
O'Shaughnessy, Robert T. (Bob) 704
O'Shea, Daniel 413
O'Shea, John 816
O'Sullivan, Juliann 133
O'Sullivan, Michael B. 740
O'Sullivan, Brian 792
O'Sullivan, Richard B. 851
OÂ'Brien, Raymond V. 250
OÂ'Brien, Denis P. 314
OÂ'Brien, Anthony F. 716
OÂ'Connell, Brian 205
OÂ'Hara, Ryan 610
OÂ'Keefe, Thomas J. 638
OÂ'Leary, David 389
OÂ'Neill, Michael J. 44
OÂ'Neill, Heidi 615
OÂ'Sullivan, James P. 786

P

Paanakker, Roland 521
Paanakker, Roland 523
Paanakker, Roland 615
Pabst, Adrienne 456
Paccione, Christina 511
Paccioretti, Steven 413
Pace, Timothy 336
Pace, Rob 425
Pace, Paul 497
Pace, Ericka 518
Pace, Cindy 570
Pace, Tyler 735
Pace-Burke, Susan 604
Pachalska, Carl 246
Pacheco, Diana 115

Pacheco, Josie 356
Pacheco, Maximo 472
Pacheco, Domonic 507
Pacilio, Michael J. 314
Pack, Mike 12
Pack, Phillip 599
Packer, Ginny 584
Padbury, Guy 57
Padden, Brian 764
Padgett, Pamela 374
Padgitt, Laura 161
Padierna, Pedro 667
Padilla, Sara 146
Padilla, Victor 158
Padmanabhan, Srikanth 248
Padmanabhan, Sridhar 643
Paellmann, Nils 811
Pagano, Christopher J. 82
Pagano, Dawn 252
Pagano, John 644
Page, Scott E. 215
Page, Ed 447
Page, Miriah 713
Page, Sandra 870
Page, Monty 881
Page, Dennis 942
Paglia, John 767
Pagnanelli, Jodi 912
Pagni, Marco 901
Paich, Keith 377
Paige, Michele 195
Paik, Elaine 220
Paine, Andrew J. (Randy) 497
Painter, Corning F. 22
Paisley, James A. (Andy) 12
Pak, Chong 179
Pak, Nancy 219
Palace, Mike 810
Paladino, Steven 752
Palafox, Jose 468
Palagiano, Vincent F. 268
Palazzo, Frank 181
Palenbaum, Gary 805
Palencia, Melissa 770
Palenik, Rudy 788
Paleos, Mike 570
Palermo, Tom 337
Paletta, Nilton 478
Paley, Liz 713
Palios, Mark 715
Paliouras, Christina 934
Palis, Jack 550
Palkhiwala, Akash 707
Pall, Christine 53
Palla, Wayne 254
Pallasch, John 550
Pallier, Patricia 175
Pallone, Philip 395
Palm, Erik 245
Palm, Gregory K. 395
Palma, Bryan 199
Palmatier, Jonathan 222
Palmer, Alicia 18
Palmer, John G 84
Palmer, Johnathan 129
Palmer, Paul 155
Palmer, Eric P. 194
Palmer, Denise 313
Palmer, April 332
Palmer, Sheryl 449
Palmer, Anthony J. (Tony) 499
Palmer, Scott 507
Palmer, C. Michael 544
Palmer, Todd 602
Palmer, Thomas (Tom) 609
Palmer, Brian 684
Palmer, Mark 807
Palmer, Frank 834
Palmer, Bryan 881
Palmer, Marcia 888
Palmer, Michael 893
Palmer, Roy 933
Palmerino, Debbie 483
Palmieri, John 194
Palmieri, Tonia 262
Palmietto, Gary 220
Palmisano, Thomas J. (Tom) 777

Palmisano, Tom 777
Palmore, Roderick 383
Palus, Martha 182
Pamiljans, Janis G. 623
Pan, Gordon G. 735
Panagos, Costa 478
Pancham, Cassan 340
Pande, Siddharth 555
Pandey, Nitish 45
Pandey, Sharad 131
Pandey, Sangeeta 131
Pandey, Sanjay 279
Pandey, Ashok 628
Pandian, Vinciya 483
Pandiscio, Paul 484
Pandita, Sunil 425
Pane, Camillo 242
Panetta, Nancy 489
Pang, Laurinda Y. 181
Pang, Turen 507
Pangborn, Robert N. 831
Paniccia, Dominic 45
Panikar, John M. 687
Pann, Stuart C. 442
Panno, Enrico 158
Pantel, Lori 557
Panuccio, Susan 610
Panyard, William 530
Panzarino, James V. 269
Pao, Sun 185
Papa, William 422
Papa, John 484
Papa, Rosemarie Novello 872
Papadopoulos, Stelios 129
Papageorge, Lisa 282
Papasavas, Frank 700
Papathomas, Georgia 484
Papay, Michael 623
Papazis, Petros 191
Pape, Giovanna 489
Paper, Roxanne 261
Papier, Jennifer M 191
Papillo, Carol 15
Papoutsis, Steve 297
Pappas, Nick 170
Paquette, Michael S. 301
Parada, Cristian 935
Paradise, Janice 502
Parahus, Rob 841
Parameswaran, Prabha 219
Parasnis, Abhay 11
Parcell, Jordan 804
Parcella, Mike 71
Parchisanu, Georgeta 693
Parcot, Christophe 34
Pardee, Charles G. (Chip) 821
Pardo, Carletto 57
Pardo, Tara 395
Pardo, Marcella 497
Pardo, Ron 545
Pardue, Wendel 722
Pare, Roger 409
Paredes, Alfredo 713
Pareigat, Thomas G. 827
Pareigat, Tom 827
Pareja, Alvena 806
Parekh, Lisa 643
Parent, June B. 155
Parfait-cooley, Sheila 454
Parimbelli, Alessandro 480
Paris, Marty 158
Paris, Jonathan 530
Parish, Timothy 470
Parisi, Mike 458
Park, Ernie 3
Park, Sun 56
Park, David 97
Park, Cynthia 97
Park, Anthony J. (Tony) 332
Park, Dave 395
Park, Yong 408
Park, Daniel 408
Park, Jaehwa 593
Park, Matt 615
Park, Peter 671
Parke, Richard 700
Parker, W. Douglas (Doug) 41

Parker, Karen 72
Parker, Donald T. 137
Parker, Robert 153
Parker, Ian 170
Parker, Stan 186
Parker, Phil 237
Parker, Greg 246
Parker, Mary Jayne 273
Parker, Jayne 273
Parker, Steven 332
Parker, Mickey 335
Parker, Michael 413
Parker, Brandon 447
Parker, Jefferson G. (Jeff) 454
Parker, Randy P 500
Parker, Karen 550
Parker, Allen 580
Parker, Mark G. 615
Parker, Kurt 615
Parker, Scott T. 640
Parker, Dorothy 656
Parker, John 722
Parker, Bruce 863
Parker, Michael 886
Parker, P. William (Bill) 888
Parker, Rob 893
Parker, Todd 941
Parkinson, Paul 404
Parks, Scott 117
Parks, Creg 266
Parks, Kathaleen 454
Parks, Nick 573
Parks, John 708
Parlapiano, Donna 89
Parmar, Amit 45
Parmelee, Cheryl 18
Parmenter, Barry 201
Parmenter, Sara 933
Parmentier, Jennifer A. 654
Parmeswar, Rajana 18
Paroubek, Yurik 119
Parr, Gregory L 409
Parr, Marla 770
Parra, Jose 191
Parra, Aaron 507
Parrett, Alan 385
Parris, Jacquie 757
Parrish, Jeff 161
Parrish, Michael 395
Parrish, Craig 486
Parrish, ED 528
Parrish, Scott 726
Parrish, Benjamin F. (Ben) 845
Parrott, Mike 735
Parrott, William 754
Parrott, Jennifer 799
Parrott, Keith 818
Parry, Michael J. (Mike) 298
Parry, Heather 533
Parsadaian, Christine 700
Parsley, Billy 99
Parsley, Todd 107
Parsley, E. William (Bill) 680
Parson, Susan 705
Parsonage, Dave 72
Parsonnet, Abby 908
Parsons, Joe 19
Parsons, Joe 84
Parsons, Charlene 194
Parsons, Carla D 449
Parsons-Danisovszky, Linda 891
Partrea, Robert 346
Partyka, Debbie 161
Parvor, Mike 743
Pasch, Coni 888
Pascual, Francisco 340
Pascual, Sarah 849
Pasek, Ron 602
Pasiechnik, Alexander 118
Paskell, Thad 489
Paskiewicz, Sandra 18
Paskoff, Alan 857
Paslar, Cristina 555
Paslick, P. Martin (Marty) 416
Pasma, Diane 720
Pasos, Michelle 899
Pasquale, Victoria 72

Pasquale, Maria E 175
Pasqualicchio, Roderick 570
Pasquarelli, Amy 664
Pasquier, Paul 135
Pasquini, Anna 713
Pasquino, Jennifer 149
Pass, Sherry 637
Passafiume, Ralph 891
Passaro, David 808
Passey, BO 693
Passey, Bret 941
Passwater, Keith 67
Pastapur, Eshwar 435
Pastorek, Greg 555
Pataki, David 861
Patchett, Mary Sue 146
Patchke, Carl 551
Pate, Joanne 84
Pate, R. Hewitt (Hew) 190
Pate, Robert 516
Patel, Siddharth 117
Patel, Ketul J. 168
Patel, Sunit S. 181
Patel, Pankaj S. 199
Patel, Harsh 252
Patel, Yagnesh 266
Patel, Himanshu A. 348
Patel, Raj 440
Patel, Naimish 495
Patel, Barry 628
Patel, Naimesh 680
Patel, Maya 710
Patel, Kirt 731
Patel, Manesh 750
Patel, Anit 799
Patel, Shefali 799
Patel, Jigar 803
Patel, Manish 813
Patel, Ben 820
Patel, Dhiren Patel Dhiren 888
Paterno, Andrew J. 449
Patience, Bob 699
Patil, Sandeep 759
Patino, Josephine 112
Patnala, Sai 131
Patnaude, Jude 187
Patrick, Stacy 17
Patrick, Erin 86
Patrick, Scott 337
Patrick, John J. 347
Patrick, Denit 400
Patrick, Tony 635
Patridge, Denise 754
Patrissi, Peter 555
Pattee, Steve 374
Patten, Charlene 693
Pattermann, Sarah 88
Patterson, Mark 12
Patterson, Ronald 25
Patterson, Lee S 117
Patterson, Lisa 161
Patterson, Frank J. 189
Patterson, Mark 199
Patterson, Steve 334
Patterson, Ryan 397
Patterson, Dave 465
Patterson, Lyle 487
Patterson, Vernon L 497
Patterson, Debra 502
Patterson, George 599
Patterson, Laura 739
Patterson, Rick L 778
Patterson, Jan 814
Patterson, Tracy 855
Patterson, Clinton 863
Patti, Tony 580
Pattis, Lisa J. 927
Patton, Charles R. 42
Patton, Pat 168
Patton, Janet 454
Patton, Gary 470
Patton, Rick 886
Patullo, Rita 550
Patwa, Kishore 895
Paugh, Cathleen 700
Paul, Dev 14
Paul, Ashok 45

Paul, Christopher 201
Paul, Ronald D. 289
Paul, Shannon 337
Paul, Santa 504
Paul, Andrew 550
Paul, Kevin 564
Paul, Cynthia 754
Paul, John 781
Paul, Nick 805
Paul, Deepika 869
Paulett, Adele 818
Paulette, Janet 107
Pauley, Lisa A. 96
Pauley, Matthew 382
Pauley, Brian 494
Pauley, Lisa 548
Paulson, Richard 57
Paulson, Donavon 915
Pauzer, Stanley 610
Pauzer, Stan 858
Pavan, Michael 668
Pavia, Rick 847
Pavkov, Aden 587
Pavlakis, Peter 754
Pavley, John 897
Pavuluri, Manjusha 102
Pawar, Manoj 168
Pawlak, Renard 161
Payne, Jon 81
Payne, David 207
Payne, Kevin M. 295
Payne, Kevin M. 777
Payne, Hubie 825
Payne, Cynthia 862
Payne, Jennifer M. 863
Payne, David L. 915
Paysse, Stephanie 768
Paz, Harold L. 17
Paz, George 319
Paz, Gustavo Calvo 499
Paz, Jeffery 664
Paziora, Debra 760
Pazol, Steve 707
Peabody, Eric 550
Peacock, Philip 61
Peacock, Jonathan 299
Peacock, Donnette 332
Peacock, Danielle 881
Peak, Craig 454
Pearce, Joseph 244
Pearce, David 337
Pearce, Lois K 419
Pearce, Bill 732
Pearce, Ed 823
Pearlstein, Max 87
Pears, Michael 365
Pearsall, Ron 18
Pearson, Bryan A. 30
Pearson, Sharna 117
Pearson, Mark 262
Pearson, Todd 293
Pearson, James F. (Jim) 360
Pearson, Gregory R. (Greg) 465
Pearson, Kevin J. 538
Pearson, Robert 582
Pearson, John 888
Pease, Christopher 550
Peay, D. Anthony (Tony) 867
Pecaric, John P. 280
Pechan, Lisa 849
Pechulis, Gerald 658
Peck, Patrick F. 139
Peck, Nancy 799
Peck, John 804
Peck, Will 813
Peck, Arthur (Art) 830
Peck, Richard 840
Peck, Raphael 866
Peck, Chad 941
Peck, Kristin C. 943
Peckham, John P. 916
Pecora, Anthony P 81
Pecyna, Jim 620
Peden, Michael 799
Pedersen, Brandon S. 26
Pedersen, Chris E. 219
Pedersen, Jeff 735

Pedley, Matthew 133
Pedowitz, Mark 838
Pedraza, Hector 219
Pedrick, Christine 715
Pedro, Max 903
Peeling, Jeffrey 376
Peeples, Trip 176
Pefanis, Harry N. 679
Peffer, Mike 935
Peffly, Chris 350
Peglar, Robert 574
Pehrson, Timothy T. 467
Pehrson, Eric 942
Peigh, Terry D. 473
Peitz, Chelsea 332
Pelc, Cari 882
Pelch, Steve J. 299
Pelcher, Richard 767
Peled, Ori 555
Pelekanos, George 18
Pelham, Peter 104
Pelkey, Diane 866
Pell, Martyn A. 346
Pellakuru, Gurunatham 413
Pellegrinelli, Steven 632
Pellegrini, Elisabeth 313
Pellegrini, Beth 313
Pelleissone, Eduardo 505
Pellerito, Paul 378
Pelletier, MIke 454
Pelletier, Stephen (Steve) 699
Pellette, Thomas (Tom) 166
Pelliccia, Joe 908
Pellon, Brian 452
Pelner, Dave 881
Peloquin, Thomas 413
Pelshaw, Suzy 332
Pelt, Megan Van 759
Peltier, Dwayne 715
Peltomaa, Christer 222
Peluso, Sarah 804
Pember, Marvin G. 882
Pemberton, Shannon 454
Pembleton, S. Gillian 620
Pena, Ric 413
Pena, Amparo De La 528
Pena, Lisa 840
Penberthy, Shannon 252
Pence, Beth 246
Pence, Ed 248
Pence, Stephanie 272
Pendergast, Geoff 170
Pendergrass, Mike 245
Pendergrass, John 324
Penders, Kevin 888
Pendery, Todd 196
Penfield, Susan L. 139
Pengeroth, Phil 792
Peniket, David J. 466
Penley, Jack 365
Penn, Ronda 48
Penn, Steven 413
Penn, Jayson 676
Penn, Brian 735
Penn, Douglas 872
Pennacchio, Stephen 671
Pennacchio, Steve 672
Pennebaker, Lori 519
Pennella, Thomas L. 185
Penning, Bruce 300
Pennington, Trey 170
Pennington, Randy 178
Pennington, Kevin P. 361
Pennington, Becky 799
Pennington, Bob 852
Penrose, Chris 84
Penry, Chuck 860
Pense, Ed 248
Penshorn, John 880
Penske, Roger S. 663
Pentz, Mark von 260
Penvillo, Jim 398
Pepinski, Tom 3
Pepito, Christine 146
Pepper, Randy 330
Pepper, Nancy 688
Peraino, Vito C. 47

Peraza, Rebecca 698
Percarpio, Michael F 701
Percy, Keith 413
Perdue, David 246
Perdue, Richard 454
Perego, Robert 105
Pereira, Dave 45
Pereira, Sam 257
Pereira, Reinaldo 385
Pereira, Timothy 665
Peretz, Richard N. 875
Pereyra, Gerardo 3
Perez, Ventura 101
Perez, Vincent 103
Perez, Cliff 246
Perez, Patricio 246
Perez, Cyndi 313
Perez, Carlos 322
Perez, Rafael 340
Perez, Jerry 415
Perez, Steven 454
Perez, Javier 554
Perez, Mario 555
Perez, Jackie 559
Perez, Jorge 573
Perez, Joao 599
Perez, Jose M 701
Perez, Juan R. 875
Perez, Karla 882
Perez-Ayala, Patricia 95
Perez-coira, Fernando 935
Peria, Yolanda 191
Perikly, Jaime 582
Perillo, Joe 570
Perini, Joe 857
Periquet, Pepper 550
Perisee, Donn 446
Perkins, Sid 15
Perkins, Raymond 84
Perkins, Thomas B. 239
Perkins, Joe Bob 812
Perkins, Kenneth 876
Perkins, Michael L. 912
Perkins, Tabitha 941
Perlin, Jonathan B. (Jon) 416
Perlin, Jill 700
Perlmutter, Robert J. 71
Perlmutter, Roger M. 566
Perlmutter, Colleen 849
Perno, Joseph 483
Peron, Laurent 748
Peronto, Robert 222
Perotti, Daniel S. 662
Perr, Julius 248
Perrault, Paul A. 147
Perrault, Ryan 888
Perreault, Roger 861
Perrett, Margie 720
Perrette, Jean-Briac (JB) 270
Perretti, Leslie 707
Perricone, Jennifer 809
Perrigue, Matt 486
Perrilliat, Javara D. 647
Perriraz, Benny 890
Perrone, Lauren 539
Perrotti, Tom 87
Perry, Bridget 11
Perry, Opal 31
Perry, Harvey P. 182
Perry, Lance 199
Perry, Neil 201
Perry, Jim 270
Perry, Glynn 280
Perry, Samantha 289
Perry, Egbert L. J. 322
Perry, Kenneth 380
Perry, Ken 380
Perry, Kristin 507
Perry, Linda L 577
Perry, Sean 734
Perry, Scott 743
Perry, Lawrence 800
Perry, Curtis J. 806
Perry, James E. 852
Perry, Jim 896
Perryman, Drew 735
Persa, Daniel 686

Pershad, Andre 204
Pershing, John 79
Persiani, Mark 131
Persich, Julie 504
Persons, Robert 806
Persutti, Suzy 222
Peru, Debbie 220
Perugini, Larry 580
Pesano, Rick 709
Pesce, David 596
Pessina, Stefano 901
Pester, Marc 700
Pestikas, Jennifer 5
Pete, Justin 300
Petee, Sandra 720
Peter, Toomey 286
Peterman, Patrick 770
Peters, Charles 299
Peters, Chris 304
Peters, Lauren B. 368
Peters, William E. (Bill) 480
Peters, Greg 603
Peters, Gregory 603
Peters, Leonard 607
Peters, John 715
Peters, Scott M. 721
Peters, Juergen 733
Peters, Harld 875
Peters, James W. (Jim) 923
Petersdorf, John 266
Petersen, Eric 24
Petersen, Christopher 52
Petersen, Frances 99
Petersen, Andy Kramer 111
Petersen, Jim 519
Petersen, Glenn 570
Peterson, Sean 45
Peterson, Brian 94
Peterson, James N. 96
Peterson, Jim 96
Peterson, Chuck 226
Peterson, Jeffrey 261
Peterson, Terry D. 279
Peterson, Bruce D. 283
Peterson, Bruce D. 283
Peterson, Erika 297
Peterson, John 299
Peterson, Gordon 333
Peterson, Stacia 342
Peterson, Lloyd 398
Peterson, Mary B 416
Peterson, Dean 456
Peterson, Joel C. 483
Peterson, Sandra E. 484
Peterson, Robert L. 631
Peterson, Doug 699
Peterson, Douglas L. (Doug) 746
Peterson, Jeff 754
Peterson, Erik 784
Peterson, Bjorn 814
Petit, Elaine 511
Petitgas, Franck 587
Petito, John 838
Petkun, William 144
Petkus, Ed 135
Petmecky, William (Tres) 777
Petno, Douglas B. (Doug) 488
Petraia, Garrett 787
Petrarca, Nick 715
Petrassi, Fiore 489
Petrasso, Mark 942
Petrie, Michael J. 226
Petrillo, Linda 849
Petro, Jeff 191
Petro, Phyllis 194
Petro, Joe 838
Petrocco, Loretta 632
Petrolino, Michael 518
Petrone, Andrew 3
Petrossian, John 808
Petruccelli, Jennifer 530
Petrucci, John M 788
Petruleas, Harry 559
Petrungaro, Debbie 558
Petry, Paul 149
Petters, C. Michael (Mike) 451
Petterson, Tonia 453

Pettigrew, Glenn 88
Pettit, Mark 374
Pettit, Tom 743
Pettit, Richard 806
Petty, Clara 330
Petty, Randy 821
Petty, Tim 888
Petzold, Kevin 124
Peyton, John 718
Pfingsten, Randy 735
Pflederer, Kent A. 652
Pfleger, Carl 668
Pflueger, Amy 462
Phadnis, Amit S 200
Phalen, Michael P. (Mike) 142
Phayre, Nancy 842
Phebus, Linnie 246
Phelan, Dan 117
Phelan, Jean 337
Phelan, David C. 791
Phelps, Jeff 88
Phelps, Ronald 587
Philbert, Martin 720
Philbin, Gary M. 276
Philip, Eric 699
Philipoom, Bruce 714
Philippin, Charles J. 862
Philippopoulos, Evan 19
Philips, Peggy 162
Philips, Gail 489
Philips, Alex 593
Phillipi, John 889
Phillippi, Fred 117
Phillips, Kara 49
Phillips, Judy 84
Phillips, Jane 117
Phillips, Jim 135
Phillips, Eric 270
Phillips, Ted 282
Phillips, Richard D. (Ric) 311
Phillips, Pamela 334
Phillips, Jeanne 386
Phillips, Eric 452
Phillips, Mike 460
Phillips, Mackenzie 486
Phillips, Susan 499
Phillips, Adriana 555
Phillips, Jeremy 610
Phillips, David P. 702
Phillips, David P. 702
Phillips, Wendy 750
Phillips, John 805
Phillips, Don 809
Phillips, Clay 863
Phillips, Thomas 912
Phipps, Cody 311
Phipps, Derek 589
Phipps, P. Cody 647
Phipps, Chad F. 940
Phyfer, Cheri M. 764
Piani, Carlos 505
Pianka, Stephanie 606
Piascik, Robert 699
Piatt, Greg 98
Piazza, Chris 596
Piazza, Patsy 880
Picchione, Nicholas 713
Picciano, Robert J. (Bob) 470
Picco, Gary 298
Piccolomini, Flavio 550
Piccone, Dennis 205
Pichai, Sundar 34
Pichla, Joseph 489
Picinich, Robert 194
Pick, Ted 587
Pick, Jeff 888
Pickard, Mark 282
Pickens, Randi 4
Pickens, Bob 729
Pickering, Sammy G. 308
Pickett, Donald 776
Pickle, Trevor O 262
Picone, Frank 751
Piechoski, Michael J. 670
Piechotta, Craig 282
Pieczynski, James J. (Jim) 653
Piepho, Lindsay 859

Pieragowski, Steve 727
Pierce, Christopher 139
Pierce, Chris 139
Pierce, David A. (Dave) 142
Pierce, Cathy 147
Pierce, Steve 334
Pierce, Sandra E. 449
Pierce, Jeff 453
Pierce, Charles E. 693
Pierce, Susan 705
Pierce, Todd 748
Pierce, Larry 781
Pierce, Gerald 910
Piercy, Kerry 269
Piergallini, Lisa L 148
Pieri, Melody 392
Pierog, Michael 133
Pierpont, Richard 879
Pierre, Lisa 881
Pierre-Louis, Stanley 896
Pierron, Chip 52
Pierson, Brian 99
Pierson, Michael 335
Pierson, Mark 446
Pierson, Christine 863
Pierz, Brian 413
Pierzchalski, Lawrence J. 572
Piestrack, Nancy 110
Pietranton, Anthony F. 912
Pietranton, Tony 912
Pietrantoni, Carlos Power 340
Pietro, Roberto Di 707
Pietropaolo, Sue 910
Pifani, Nick 555
Piggery, Normajo 204
Piggott, Julie A. 150
Pignuolo, Chuck 99
Pigott, M. Jason 189
Pigott, Jason 189
Pigott, Mark C. 650
Pike, Bryon 497
Pilcher, Donna 107
Pilecky, Lidia 185
Pileggi, Lucia 497
Pilgrim, Trip 818
Pilkington, Kevin 631
Pilla, John 784
Pilla, Rocco 919
Pillai, Gopal 901
Pilnick, Gary H. 493
Pilotte, Niki 108
Pimentel, Armando 612
Pina, Angelica 11
Pinchera, Matt 237
Pinckney, Nancy 336
Pinczuk, Ana 425
Pineda, Karen 563
Pinedo, Steve 643
Pingel, Spencer 220
Pingor, Michelle 550
Pinheiro, Jose 385
Piniella, Anthony 599
Pinkes, Andrew J. 210
Pinkham, Elizabeth 748
Pinkham, Stan 891
Pinkston, Ray 526
Pinner, Ian 74
Pinner, Ernest S. (Ernie) 179
Pinninti, Sri 731
Pinson, Brad 337
Pinson, Jody 903
Pinter, John 144
Pinter, Gregory 927
Pinto, Daniel E. 488
Pinto, Drew 548
Pinto, John J. 604
Pintoff, Craig A. 876
Pinyate, Nadia 243
Pinyerd, Alan 591
Piper, Patrick E. 137
Piper, Steve 849
Pippen, Bret 722
Pippett, Kelly 530
Pires, Art 910
Pirkl, Bernhard 86
Piromalli, Dave 88
Piroth, Ingo 218

Pirrung, Nicholas 87
Pisa, Anthony 787
Pisarczyk, Karen 445
Piscioniere, John 88
Pisciotta, Pauline 682
Pisciotti, Marty 810
Pisieczko, Alex 334
Pita, George L. 553
Pitaro, James A. (Jimmy) 273
Pitasky, Scott 787
Pitcher, Terri 125
Pitcher, Daniel D. 325
Pitchford, Chris 370
Piterans, Marianne 827
Pitesa, John W. (Bill) 285
Pitofsky, David B. 610
Pitrone, Scott C. 461
Pitt, Douglas 400
Pittel, Kimberly 370
Pittillo, Chad 769
Pittillo, Joe 805
Pittman, Myrna 25
Pittman, Raymond J. (R.J.) 293
Pittman, Roland 406
Pittman, Robert W. (Bob) 456
Pitton, Kathy 224
Pitts, Jack 133
Pitzer, Dave 282
Pitzer, Cheryl 450
Pivowar, Mike 743
Piwowar, Pawel 643
Pizarro, Pedro J. 295
Pizarro, Pedro J 777
Pizzano, David 380
Pizzarello, Annalisa 57
Pizzi, Michael A. 288
Pizzi, Vince 857
Pizzuti, Linda 105
Pizzuti, Candice 497
Pizzuto, Frank 882
Pla, Angela 371
Place, Amy 13
Placido, Michael 643
Plager, Debbie 266
Plainfield, Vidya 72
Plank, Kevin A. 866
Plank, J S 866
Planos, Robert 550
Plansky, John 792
Plant, John C. 75
Plante, Robert A. (Bob) 660
Plantillas, Will 94
Plass, Debbie 266
Plata, Esteban 6
Plate, William 121
Plate, Bill 121
Platek, Stan 96
Plath, Thomas 472
Platt, Marianne 332
Platt, Jim 610
Platt, Daniel B. 652
Platt, L 881
Plaza, Robert 498
Plebanski, Jenny 80
Plecki, Robert F. (Bob) 342
Pledger, Joe 876
Pleiss, David 390
Plepler, Richard L. 838
Plessis, Esme 383
Pletcher, Brett 391
Plett, Katie 432
Pleuhs, Gerhard (Gerd) 584
Plevritis, Peter 204
Plew, Daniel P. Van 719
Plimpton, Tom 650
Plodzeen, Tom 337
Ploeger, Becky 503
Plotkin, Steve 273
Plotkin, Ben A. 795
Plourde, Robert 881
Ploutz-Snyder, Lori 720
Plowman, Greg 528
Plugge, Rhett 692
Plum, Jay 449
Plumeri, Joseph J. (Joe) 348
Plummer, Ken 97
Plummer, Charles 246

Plummer, Tammy L. 341
Plummer, William B. 876
Plutino, Heather 79
Poch, Andi 172
Pocica, Robert 563
Pocock, Fred 602
Pocrnich, Christina 207
Pocsi, Charles 698
Poczekaj, Ken 300
Poczobut, Skip 665
Poddo, Michael 84
Podesta, Victoria 74
Podgorski, Mark 517
Podsadecki, Thomas 4
Pofahl, Quinn 713
Poferl, Jeff 248
Pohlman, Kevin 657
Pohlman, Steve 820
Poindexter, Philip S. 796
Poinsatte, Richard 794
Pokoj, Rhonda 927
Pol, Sanjay 199
Polanco, Rebecca 842
Polechronis, Stephen 14
Polen, Thomas E. 119
Polen, Michael R. (Mike) 911
Poleon, Annette 94
Poli, Massimo 219
Poli, Kent 342
Politi, Douglas W. (Doug) 87
Politte, Keith 724
Polizzotto, Lawrence 434
Polk, Jim 103
Polk, James C. (Jim) 103
Polk, Michael B. (Mike) 608
Polk, Dennis 805
Pollack, Gary 45
Pollack, Michael 171
Pollack, Beth 615
Pollard, Jeff 555
Polley, Mike 628
Polley, Malcolm E. 745
Pollidore, Diana 800
Pollock, Chris 87
Pollock, Carolyn 99
Pollok, John C. 776
Polly, John 470
Poll□'s, Jeanne 674
Poloni, Lara 14
Polvoriza, Melanie 272
Pomaranski, Joseph A. (Joe) 820
Pomeroy, John 831
Pompa, Mark A. 298
Pomplon, Carl 158
Pomranke, Daryl 355
Ponczoch, John 847
Pons, Jaume 671
Pontarelli, Thomas 210
Pontier, Jim 109
Pontious, Jane 187
Poole, Thomas 221
Poole-Yaeger, Amy 176
Pope, Gene 37
Pope, Julie 44
Pope, John C. (Jack) 280
Pope, Lawrence J. 405
Pope, Jeffrey 748
Pope, David 823
Popeck, Charles 809
Popeck, Cheryl 881
Popham, Matthew 516
Popieski, Tom 757
Popovici, Silviu 667
Popp, Jack 415
Poppe, Patricia K. (Patti) 210
Poppe, Patricia K. (Patti) 238
Popper, Susan 425
Popper, Jozsi 715
Popwell, David T. 353
Porat, Ruth M. 34
Porcini, Mauro 667
Pordon, Anthony R. (Tony) 663
Porru, Martina 671
Port, Alastair 452
Port, Nancy 811
Portacci, Michael T. 230
Portalatin, Julio A. 550

Portalatin, Frances 757
Portantino, Philip 660
Portela, Marvio 643
Porter, John 170
Porter, Cynthia 224
Porter, Pamela G 224
Porter, Tracy L. 227
Porter, Catherine 261
Porter, Biggs C. 365
Porter, Dewitt 365
Porter, David E. 420
Porter, Todd 423
Porter, Katherine 533
Porter, David 576
Porter, Jonathan 723
Porter, Kerrick 732
Porter, Stephen D. 762
Porter, Brian 809
Porter, Jim 811
Porter, Ann 863
Porter-Ward, Michelle 810
Portera, Joseph P. (Joe) 241
Portillo, Marilyn 573
Portnoy, Justin 395
Portnoy, Adam 570
Portnoy, Barry M. 847
Porvaznik, George 184
Posa, Nicola 935
Posada, Barbara 257
Posada, Juan F. 693
Post, Vincent 109
Post, Glen F. 181
Post, Steven M. (Steve) 509
Postema, Bradley G. 310
Postrozny, Hank 185
Potgieter, Dirk 672
Pothier, Robert 101
Potluri, Jalaja 6
Potochar, Christopher 530
Potter, Steve 245
Potter, Stephen N. 620
Potts, Don 158
Potts, David L. 725
Potts, Janna A. 813
Potuzak, Joe 117
Poulakos, Greg 66
Poulley, Sean 470
Poulos, Ray 805
Pouncey, Clarence C. 763
Pound, Greg 613
Povenmire, Rex 272
Powderly, Thomas 105
Powell, Cindy 116
Powell, Heather 263
Powell, Allun 309
Powell, Bradley S. (Brad) 317
Powell, Kendall J. (Ken) 383
Powell, Teresa 420
Powell, Ty 454
Powell, Trey 507
Powell, Tyane 677
Powell, Deana 769
Powell, Cynthia A. 788
Powell, Terry 834
Powell, Vincent 855
Powell, Wayne 875
Powell, David 881
Powell, Timothy 882
Powell, Wm. Eugene (Gene) 884
Power, Nancy 570
Power, Gary 923
Powers, Robert P. (Bob) 42
Powers, James W 135
Powers, John J. 342
Powers, Lance 715
Powers, Dan 748
Powers, Amber 811
Powers, Marsha 818
Powlus, Lee C. 664
Poynter, Charles 935
Poznanski, Greg 799
Pozotrigo, Albert 481
Pozzi, James E. 49
Prabakaran, Sateesh 715
Prabhu, Arjun 628
Prabhu, Vasant M. 898
Prado, Mary 620

Pragada, Robert V. (Bob) 481
Prager, Richard L. (Richie) 131
Prager, Jeff 735
Prahlad, Sheela 356
Prakasam, Haripriya 465
Prakash, Ravi 576
Pramaggiore, Anne R. 314
Prange, Brian 570
Prange, Karen 752
Prasodjo, Bambang 423
Prather, Craig 115
Prather, David 405
Pratico, Lisa 839
Pratico, Joseph 886
Prato, Patrick 449
Pratt, Timothy A. (Tim) 142
Pratt, Amy 201
Pratt, Valerie 715
Pratt, William C. (Bill) 771
Pravlik, Mari 623
Prawer, Noah 45
Pray, Kevin D 409
Prazecky, Jean 346
Preacher, Michael 457
Prechter, Suzette 158
Precourt, Walter F. (Walt) 588
Predmore, Blaine 504
Preete, Kerry J. 585
Preimesberger, Steve 97
Preisinger, Bradley 749
Prejean, Joshua 159
Prejean, Jerry 454
Prekelezaj, Drana 896
Prendergast, David 31
Prener, Anne 115
Prentice, Jodi 487
Prentice, F. Sheldon 598
Prescott, Richard 45
Prescott, Leonard 339
Present, Randall C. (Randy) 439
Preske, Mark 635
Preskenis, Donald 344
Preskenis, Ashley 678
Presnell, Nancy 727
Pressler, Paul S. 95
Pressley, W. Michael 844
Presson, Jeff 175
Preston, Stephanie 205
Preston, James 224
Preston, Susan 313
Preston, Bryan 337
Preston, Mark 446
Preston, Trish 555
Preston, Carolyn 770
Pretorius, Alwyn 609
Pretzer, Pam 840
Previn, Fletcher 470
Price, Kent 44
Price, Zoila 97
Price, Tom 185
Price, Deb 237
Price, Glyn 248
Price, Thomas Michael (Mike) 345
Price, Keri 404
Price, Greg 447
Price, Michael 450
Price, Michael 550
Price, Michael H. 564
Price, Lisa V 617
Price, Chris 620
Price, Shawn 642
Price, Matthew S. 693
Price, Lisa 700
Price, Scott 903
Prida, Aaron 757
Priddle, Justin 124
Pride, Gene 170
Pride, Jason 453
Pridgen, Tracy 39
Priegnitz, Kelly 502
Prieshoff, Matt 533
Priest, Stephen J. (Steve) 483
Priester, William 337
Prieto, Robert 365
Prill, Gina 246
Primmer, Jan 570
Prince, William 31

Prince, Leanne 811
Principato, Patricia 156
Principe, Guy 700
Prinz, Corey 109
Prior, Richard 849
Prising, Jonas 543
Pritchard, Peter 395
Pritchett, Wanda 530
Pritchett, Scott 627
Prizio, Mario 759
Probst, Lawrence F. (Larry) 297
Probst, Marc 467
Prochazka, Scott M. 177
Procida, Thomas 133
Proctor, H. Palmer 335
Proffitt, Julie 453
Progar, Tom 115
Proia, Gina M. 201
Promo, Joe 566
Prophater, Kristen B 886
Prophet, Tony 576
Propst, Beverly L. 399
Proudman, Susi 615
Prough, Allen 923
Proulx, Peter 304
Proulx, Kevin 808
Prouser, Jennifer 497
Provolo, Dann 782
Provost, Stephanie 72
Provost, David T. 187
Pruden, Gary 484
PrudÂ'homme, Sylvain 537
Pruitt, Cassie 117
Pruitt, Kristin L. 511
Pruitt, Tracy 580
Prusaczyk, Mike 555
Pruski, Kristen 483
Pruss-Jones, Catherine J 135
Pruzan, Jonathan 587
Pryor, Jay 190
Pryor, Tom 489
Pryor, James 722
Pryor, D. Scott 812
Pszybylski, Michael 53
Pucci, David 863
Puccio, Frank 109
Pucel, Kenneth J. (Ken) 681
Puckett, Cameron 678
Puddy, Mike 251
Pudlo, Joe 115
Puechl, Robert L. 775
Pugliese, Nate 53
Puglisi, Jeanmarie 374
Pukin, Carl 344
Pukylo, Brian 345
Pulakanti, Abhishek 735
Pulatie, Dave 750
Pulis, Francesca 570
Pullan, Rowena 671
Pullen, Donna 776
Pulliam, Ryan 332
Pulliam, Sammy 634
Pullin, Ericka 246
Pullman, Roger 135
Pullman, Adam 456
Pulmano, Ben 179
Pundarika, Vasanta 715
Pungitore, Dennis 553
Puntney, Jeff 131
Punyamurthula, Sujan 15
Punzina, Carol La 122
Puraleski, Susan 928
Purcell, Cynthia D. (Cindy) 110
Purcell, William 224
Purcell, Beth 266
Purcell, Kathleen 422
Purdum, Mike 507
Purdy, Kimberly 31
Purdy, Rick 499
Purgason, Robert S. (Bob) 924
Puri, Ajay K. (Jay) 627
Purington, Matthew 886
Pursch, Jonathan 246
Purtell, Tim 668
Purtilar, Mark 397
Purugganan, Michael D. 606
Purvis, Craig 261

Purvis, Shawn N. 623
Pushis, Glenn A. 794
Pustay, Jeffrey 550
Put, Dirk Van de 584
Puthussery, Joseph 200
Putkonen, Kurt 680
Putnam, Chris 447
Putnam, Harold 722
Putnam, Natalie 743
Putnam, Eric 863
Putney, Betty 117
Putney, Jennifer 700
Putta, Neeraja 836
Puvvada, Sudhakar 895
Pye, Donna 454
Pyke, Robert 804
Pyle, Robert (Bob) 254
Pyle, Kim 457
Pyne, David 705
P☐©cresse, J☐©r☐me 382

Q

Qadir, Moinuddin 395
Qi, Lu 575
Qiang, Vivian 207
Qka, Richard 799
Quackenbush, Scott 378
Quaglia, Joseph H. 816
Quagliana, Steve 861
Quagliata, Joseph 45
Quagliata, Crystal 604
Quaid, Ann 884
Quale, Matthew 570
Qualls, Bruce 457
Quam, Bethany C. 383
Quandt, Fred 903
Quaranta, Francesco 20
Quarles, Patrick D. (Pat) 173
Quarles, Christa 689
Quartarone, Lisa 754
Quattrochi, Denise 533
Qudah, Mohammad Al 16
Quddus, Sheikh 158
Quebe, Lydie 935
Queenan, Daniel (Danny) 170
Queener, Hugh M. 677
Quehl, Richard W 732
Queiroz, Mario 34
Quenell, Eileen 550
Quennessen, Bernard 242
Quereau, Lindsay 395
Querrey, Dale L. 709
Quesenberry, Jeff 779
Quick, Janet M. 419
Quick, Frank 707
Quicksilver, Robert E. 186
Quigley, Brian W. 36
Quigley, James H. (Jim) 423
Quigley, Peter W. 494
Quigley, Tom 645
Quigley, Janet 656
Quillin, M. Kirk 110
Quillin, Sue 859
Quincey, James R. 216
Quinlan, Michael 207
Quinlan, Tim 207
Quinlan, Thomas 220
Quinlan, Ruth 715
Quinlan, Raymond J. 772
Quinn, Kevin 12
Quinn, Mike 53
Quinn, Robert W. (Bob) 84
Quinn, Rebecca 131
Quinn, Stephen D. 402
Quinn, Jane 511
Quinn, John S. 534
Quinn, William 570
Quinn, R. Patrick 604
Quinn, R 604
Quinn, T. Kyle 650
Quinn, Becky 705
Quinn, Amy 727
Quinn, Barney 770
Quinn, Christopher 886
Quinn, Katherine B. 888

Quinn, Christopher 890
Quinn, Cody 890
Quint, Jason 121
Quintal, Carla De 668
Quintanilla, Abel Coello 244
Quintanilla, Omar 246
Quintero, Gilberto 161
Quinto, Marcos de 216
Quinton, Scott 64
Quirk, Raymond R. (Randy) 332
Quirk, Kathleen L. 375
Quirk, Peter 425
Quirk, Sherry A. 821
Quiroz, Carlos 16
Quiroz, Lisa 838
QUIROZ, ALEJANDRO 923
Quish, Susan 195
Quito, Remy 105

R

Raack, Brian 799
Raaf, Dave 320
Raba, Beth 204
Rabe, Ron 784
Rabiela, Guillermo 45
Rabiller, Olivier 434
Rabinowitz, Marc 483
Rabinsky, Lisa 178
Rabkin, David 45
Rabushka, Anton 57
Raby, Kaye 941
Racanelli, Joe 875
Rachmeler, Kim 37
Racioppi, Michael 752
Rack, Sarah 242
Rack, Karen 632
Racky, William 15
Raco, Katie 497
Ractliffe, Scott 677
Radcliffe, Charles 447
Radcliffe, David 516
Radcliffe, David 517
Radde, Donald E. (Don) 436
Radek, Matthew 185
Radelfinger, Cody 313
Radeloff, Brent 413
Rader, David C 668
Radhakrishnan, Rupkumar 131
Radhakrishnan, Narayanan 395
Radick, James 376
Radinieri, Stephanie 413
Radis, Kathbara J. 870
Radloff, Sue 355
Radney, Theresa 806
Radtke, Drew 923
Radu, Michael R. (Mike) 911
Radziwill, John 474
Rafferty, Steven 631
Rafferty, Noreen 896
Rafferty, Dan 903
Raftery, Michael 567
Rager, Tom 248
Rager, R. Scott 636
Raggi, James 767
Raghavan, Vis 488
Raghavan, Rangesh 512
Raghumandala, Harikrishna 760
Rahaman, Mahin 607
Rahill, Michael 550
Rahim, Rami 490
Rahl, Gary 139
Rahm, Anne 170
Rahman, Khan 15
Rahman, Jinat 60
Raimonde, Michael A. 698
Raimondi, Peter J. 141
Raina, Sunita 249
Rainbolt, David E. 99
Rainbolt, Rocky 108
Rainer, Sallie 304
Raines, John 263
Raines, J. Paul 379
Raines, Kerri 722
Rainey, Kim 135
Rainey, Joseph D. (Joe) 405

Rainey, J 754
Rainone, Andrew 811
Raiss, Sarah E. 227
Raiti, Brian 204
Raja, Prabu G. 71
Rajagopalan, Sri 484
Rajsingh, Peter 607
Rakas, Daniel 256
Rakowitz, Genny 246
Rakowski, Andrew 620
Rales, Steven M. 256
Raley, Zachary W. 59
Raley, Anthony R 803
Ralhan, Dushyant 792
Rallo, Diane 511
Ralston, Patrick R 351
Ralston, Michael 447
Ramalho, Sean 849
Ramamurthy, Sundar 71
Raman, Jeff 252
Ramanathan, Kalyan 700
Ramawy, Dennis 488
Rambo, Jimmy 870
Ramesh, Ram 757
Ramey, Ray 94
Ramey, Eric 237
Ramirez, Joe 11
Ramirez, Francisco Munoz 219
Ramirez, Cindy 246
Ramirez, Terrie 246
Ramirez, Rene 246
Ramirez, Renato 468
Ramirez, Ricardo 468
Ramirez, Patricia 550
Ramirez, Andrew 582
Ramirez, Bonita 590
Ramirez, German 754
Ramirez, Jaime A. 786
Ramlo, Randy A. 872
Ramonat, R. Whitfield 663
Ramonet, Alfonso J. 380
Ramos, Clarissa C 52
Ramos, Carlos X 109
Ramos, Xavier 170
Ramos, Ricardo (Ricky) 219
Ramos, Mario 252
Ramos, Pilar S 555
Ramoutar, Roxanne 258
Ramsay, Omar 449
Ramsay, Paul D. 537
Ramsbacher, Valerie 722
Ramsbottom, Scott 64
Ramsburg, Kevin S. 645
Ramsey, Dean 84
Ramsey, Terry 576
Ramsey, Hank 700
Ramsey, Doug 859
Ramundo, Kate 75
Ranck, Bruce E. 709
Rancour, Joseph 901
Rand, Edward L. (Ned) 692
Randall, Rick 15
Randall, Anne L. 141
Randall, Bruce 366
Randall, Michelle 383
Randall, Markis 447
Randall, Sarah 550
Randall, Chris 732
Randall, David 857
Randello, Jim 550
Randich, David M. 371
Randlett, Brad 204
Randolph, Marjorie 273
Randt, Thomas 808
Raney, Steven M. (Steve) 715
Rangel, Rosa 330
Ranger, Michael 929
Rangoonwala, Munawar 792
Ranicar, Jamie 530
Rankin, Deanna 247
Rankin, David 756
Rankin, Cindy 808
Rankin, Devina A. 907
Ranney, Mark 715
Ranque, Cyril 316
Ransfer, Terrance 72
Ransom, Mark 337

Ransom, Buffy 643
Ranta, Curtis 413
Rantanen, Cindy 507
Rantz, Regina 671
Rao, Sunil 39
Rao, Gowthami 200
Rao, Naveen G. 465
Rao, Anita 465
Rao, Anil 465
Rao, Anu 487
Rao, Jyothi 830
Rao, Mrutyunjaya 923
Rapino, Michael (Mike) 532
Raplee, R. Scott 526
Rapoport, David 313
Rapp, Kris 115
Rapp, Lance 449
Rapp, J D 923
Rapp, Jd 923
Rappa, Victor 896
Rappe, Kristine 909
Rapport, Nicole C 201
Rasell, Alan 437
Rasilainen, Jan 849
Rasmussen, Bart 3
Rasmussen, Kathy 328
Rasmussen, Marc A 905
Rasmussen, Tim 928
Rasmusson, Paul 557
Rastogi, Sharad 199
Rasula, Jay 52
Ratay, Andrea 105
Rath, Karen 449
Rath, John 511
Rath, Brian 550
Rath, Charla 893
Rathbun, Robert S. 187
Ratkevich, Kari 813
Ratliff, Barbara 72
Ratliff, John D. 510
Ratliff, Kurt 901
Ratnaparkhi, Radha 470
Ratner, Richard 170
Ratzan, Scott 484
Ratzi, Robert 168
Rau, Jason 370
Rau, John P. 929
Rauch, Scott L. 656
Rauenzahn, Jason 249
Rauf, Zamir 153
Raus, Gregg 487
Rausch, Nicholas 161
Rauscher, Robert J. 226
Rauscher, Eric 226
Rauschl, Christopher 383
Rauschmayer, Joe 750
Rautenstrauch, J¶rg 826
Rauzi, Petrina 597
Ravaioli, Kevin 566
Ravaschiere, Robert 511
Raven, Gary 149
Raven, David 598
Ravenberg, Chris 50
Ravener, Robert D. (Bob) 275
Ravindra, Shathabi 272
Ravita, John 332
Ravitz, Shawn 900
Ravlich, Nick 750
Rawlings, Rick 439
Rawlins, Rylan 161
Rawls, Brett 178
Ray, Erika 158
Ray, Brenda 676
Ray, Harold 777
Ray, Sheila E. 789
Ray, Neville R. 810
Ray, Michael C. 917
Ray-kuczynski, Stephanie 735
Raychaudhuri, Sarthak 923
Rayeski, Jamie 811
Raykis, Alex 587
Raymon, David 754
Raymond, Philip 25
Raymond, Christopher 135
Raymond, Philip 390
Raymoure, Sue 161
Rayner, Robert 224

Rayner, Craig 834
Rayson, Angela 882
Rayvis, Jason 87
Razek, Dean 367
Razo, Heather 550
Read, Kip 559
Read, Harold T 606
Read, Ian C. 671
Read, Kristen 715
Reagan, James C. (Jim) 516
Reagan, Jeff 900
Real, Peter 62
Reale, John 415
Reali, Joseph 570
Ream, John 486
Reardon, Timothy J. 516
Reasoner, Rod 818
Rebber, Kristine 615
Rebele, John 658
Rebholz, Andrew J. 847
Rec, Bank 317
ReCasino, Maria 201
Recer, James D. (Jim) 823
Rechin, Michael C. (Mike) 355
Rechkemmer, Ben 498
Rechtin, James 258
Reck, Peter 455
Recker, Chris 518
Recktenwald, Lara 727
Rector, Glen 15
Rector, Christopher 219
Rector, Tim 932
Reda, Guy 839
Redahan, Patrick 262
Redden, Robert L 760
Reddick, Sheila 157
Redding, Ron 416
Reddish, Thomas J. (Tom) 851
Reddivari, Darshini 810
Reddy, Sriram 131
Reddy, Neena 395
Redfield, Bob 450
Redfield, Charles 903
Redman, Bill 512
Redman, Jessica 558
Redman, Debbie 935
Redmond, Richard L. 284
Redondo, Ritche 201
Redoutey, Joseph M. 362
Redpath, J. Douglas 786
Redpath, Tammy 813
Redstone, Shari E. 172
Redstone, Shari E. 897
Reeber, Carianne 511
Reece, Aaron 613
Reece, Maurice A. 24
Reed, LaDonna 81
Reed, Holly 84
Reed, James T. (Jim) 110
Reed, Mitzi 181
Reed, Jeff 200
Reed, Keri 204
Reed, Angela 224
Reed, Cory J. 260
Reed, Rachel 320
Reed, Jane 358
Reed, Lee 468
Reed, Chris 530
Reed, Kitty 599
Reed, Colin V. 744
Reed, Debra L. (Debbie) 761
Reed, Robert D. (Bob) 802
Reed, Sam K. 850
Reed, Bart 880
Reed, Stephen 886
Reed, Marc C. 893
Reed, Candice 901
Reed, Matt 912
Reed, Richard 942
Reedy, Thomas W. (Tom) 162
Reedy, Tom 162
Reedy, Bob 181
Reedyk, Amy 813
Reel, Stephanie L. 483
Reens, Jon 533
Reese, Jay 2
Reese, David 57

Reese, Kristin 148
Reese, Mark E. 297
Reese, Bruce T. 468
Reese, Ron 513
Reese, Glenn 570
Reese, Denyse 620
Reese, Bertram S. (Bert) 762
Reese, Brad D 812
Reese, Ken 904
Reeter, Steven 643
Reeve, Michael 350
Reeve, Pamela D. A. 376
Reeves, Robert K. (Bobby) 61
Reeves, Connie 117
Reeves, Jesse 204
Reeves, Chip 337
Reeves, David 370
Reeves, Tom 470
Reeves, Mark 620
Reeves, Roger 666
Reeves, Scott Reeves Scott 863
Reffner, Robert 360
Regan, Marla 735
Regan, Timothy J. 834
Regan, Tim 834
Regan, Michael 858
Reggiardo, Vanessa 95
Regier, Joel 559
Register, Mark 470
Register, Mike 800
Register, Sam 838
Rego, Carlos 929
Regoni, Paul 449
Rehkemper, Virgil 860
Rehm, Doug 763
Rehmke, Bruce C. 419
Reibling, Stephanie 903
Reice, Richard 376
Reich, Kirk W. 24
Reich, Marti 112
Reich, Andrew 453
Reich, Thomas 573
Reich, Joel 601
Reich, Bret 651
Reich, Daniel 896
Reichelt, Karl 15
Reichmann, Randall (Randy) 635
Reid, Eric 15
Reid, Linda 18
Reid, John 50
Reid, Cherylon 107
Reid, Bill 298
Reid, Jeff 446
Reid, Bruce 454
Reid, John 533
Reid, Tony 548
Reid, Jack 551
Reid, Chris 555
Reid, Mark 558
Reid, Michele 604
Reid, Jim 710
Reid, Alan M. 750
Reidy, Christopher R. (Chris) 119
Reidy, M. Bridget 314
Reierson, Jason 678
Reif, David P. 742
Reifke, Pam 479
Reifschneider, Eric 707
Reifsnyder, JoAnne 386
Reifsteck, John 402
Reilley, Dennis H. 546
Reilly, Lee 18
Reilly, Michael 39
Reilly, Michele 158
Reilly, Daniel J 260
Reilly, Dan 261
Reilly, Mary 489
Reilly, Nicole 530
Reilly, Kathleen 555
Reilly, Kevin 580
Reilly, John 618
Reilly, Karen 656
Reilly, Daniel 664
Reilly, Robert Q. (Rob) 680
Reilly, Patti 710
Reilly, Paul C. 715
Reilly, Cathy 806

Reilly, Lisa 813
Reilly, Sally 840
Reilly, Tom 856
Reilly, Joe 941
Reily, Patrick 14
Reiman, Eric (Bill) 111
Reimer, Ashley 513
Rein, Brad 756
Reina, Kevin 332
Reinartz, Ronald 550
Reiners, Derek S. 641
Reingardt, John 454
Reinhard, Colette 530
Reinhardt, Jerry 276
Reinhardt, Stephen 767
Reinhart, Hank 121
Reinholz, Kristi 672
Reinke, Jeff 563
Reinstein, Ava 18
Reinwand, Cole 222
Reis, Mario 242
Reisenauer, Brian 888
Reiser, Jason S. 275
Reiser, Trista 610
Reisinger, Brad 519
Reisner, John R. 349
Reissman, Lynda 159
Reiten, R. Patrick (Pat) 651
Reitnauer, David 903
Reitz, Regina 625
Reitz, Jon 875
Reizman, Elizabeth 104
Rejcek, Leonard J. 857
Relyea, Craig 274
Rembert-Neason, Deena 282
Remiker, Richard (Rich) 449
Remington, Mark 570
Remley, Dylan 394
Remmel, Brian 748
Remmers, Rick 446
Remondi, John F. (Jack) 595
Rempe, Melanie 104
Rempe, Thomas 555
Rempel, Steve 731
Ren, Yi 820
Renard, Steve 220
Renaud, Melanie 415
Rencher, Bradley (Brad) 11
Rende, Tiffany 273
Rendeiro, Martha 470
Rendle, Steven E. (Steve) 895
Rendleman, Linda 816
Renduchintala, Venkata M. (Murthy) 465
Renetzky, Lisa 724
Renfro, Sean 863
Renfro, Larry C. 880
Renfroe, Debbie 406
Renjifo, Boris 6
Renkas, Daniel 934
Renner, Joann 222
Renner, Denise 735
Renner, Troy A 737
Renspie, William 237
Rentch, Sean 809
Rentler, Barbara 740
Renwick, Scott 496
Renwick, Glenn M. 695
Renz, Trish 84
Renz, Brian 99
Renz, Caren 367
Reo, Joseph 570
Repik, Jennifer 201
Repine, Scott 345
Repo, Susan J 823
Reses, Jacqueline D 34
Resinger, James E 429
Reske, James R. 345
Resnick, Jon 478
Resseguie, Dick 620
Restel, Anthony J. 454
Resten, Paul 470
Restiano, Larry 45
Restrepo, Robert P. (Bob) 788
Retail, Scott 276
Rettig, Jeff 149

Retton, Allen 912
Retz, Jocelyn 637
Retzlaff, Doralyn 735
Reuss, Mark L. 385
Reusswig, Michael 923
Reuter, Deborah K. (Debbie) 420
Reuter, John 715
Reuter, Joe 875
Reuterskiold, Christina 606
Revelle, George 57
Revilla, Lisa 103
Rex, John 880
Rexing, Denise 635
Reyes, Laura 224
Reyes, Tisha 460
Reyes, Carlos 808
Reyes, Pedro 884
Reynolds, Stephen R. (Steve) 72
Reynolds, Chuck 72
Reynolds, Mike 99
Reynolds, Lynne 101
Reynolds, James Frank 176
Reynolds, Mark 182
Reynolds, Neil 185
Reynolds, Eric 208
Reynolds, Catherine M. 210
Reynolds, Tamra 214
Reynolds, Donald 226
Reynolds, Wendy 345
Reynolds, Linda 382
Reynolds, Robert L. 400
Reynolds, Alyssa 446
Reynolds, Matthew 489
Reynolds, Emma 563
Reynolds, Deborah 672
Reynolds, Sean 705
Reynolds, Dave 911
Reynolds, Matt 942
Reynoso, Jamie 168
Reznikova, Irina 792
Rhea, Casey 813
Rheaume, Lindsey S. 289
Rhee, Paul 408
Rhein, Francisco 266
Rhinehart, Craig 470
Rho, Joseph K. 408
Rhoads, John 14
Rhoads, Rebecca B. 716
Rhode, Bryan 245
Rhodebeck, Lyle D. 788
Rhodes, William C. (Bill) 90
Rhodes, Ashley 507
Rhodes, Michelle 580
Rhodes, Jeff 677
Rhodin, Michael D. (Mike) 470
Rhone, Denise 901
Rhymer, John 837
Rhynalds, Christian 232
Rhyne, Tommy 117
Rial, Francis 587
Ribe, Raquel 450
Ribeiro, Eduardo 6
Ribeiro, Monica 109
Ribera, Mario 317
Ribieras, Jean-Michel 472
Ribi©ras, Jean-Michel 472
Riccardi, John 3
Ricchetti, Ginger 722
Ricchezza, John 767
Ricchio, Wesley 343
Ricciardi, Robert 148
Ricciardi, John 639
Riccio, Daniel (Dan) 69
Riccio, Dan 69
Riccio, Louis 604
Riccio, Janet 639
Ricciuti, James 18
Rice, Laurn 88
Rice, Peter 124
Rice, Melanie 224
Rice, Kristin K 262
Rice, Charles 304
Rice, Jason 431
Rice, Mary 454
Rice, James 486
Rice, Brian S. 493
Rice, Richard 564

Rice, Ronald A. 742
Rice, Jacqueline Hourigan 813
Rice, Peter 858
Rice, James 860
Rice, Andrea 897
Rice, Jeffrey 912
Rich, Brian F. 210
Rich, Brian F. 238
Rich, Robert 435
Rich, Valia 722
Rich, Blair 838
Richard, Laino 3
Richard, Roger 587
Richard, Henri 601
Richards, Todd 271
Richards, Ticole 273
Richards, Ramon 322
Richards, Christine P. 330
Richards, Patricia R. 467
Richards, Jeff 578
Richards, Stephanie 636
Richards, Jason 668
Richards, Stacey 678
Richards, Lisa 693
Richards, David 745
Richards, Jeff 749
Richards, Rachel M. 774
Richards, Michael 792
Richards, Matt 836
Richards, Barry A. 847
Richards, Mikell 870
Richardson, George 122
Richardson, Bryan D. 146
Richardson, Cindy 157
Richardson, Michael R. (Mike) 164
Richardson, John 185
Richardson, Jannie 262
Richardson, Kristi 330
Richardson, Lee 365
Richardson, Cara 378
Richardson, Dana 385
Richardson, Matt 427
Richardson, Sean P. 449
Richardson, Lauren 508
Richardson, Tricia 550
Richardson, Tonya 570
Richardson, Ed 580
Richardson, Elizabeth 582
Richardson, Beth 582
Richardson, Levi 604
Richardson, Marty 635
Richardson, Fiona 731
Richardson, Philip 748
Richardson, Michael 752
Richburg, Joseph 171
Richels, John 263
Richenhagen, Martin H. 20
Riches, Greg 573
Richey, Ellen 898
Richins, Micah 573
Richman, David 382
Richmond, Stirling 170
Richmond, Michael 446
Richmond, Shaun 852
Richmond, Brent E. 912
Richter, Friedrich 6
Richter, Brian 888
Richter, John 911
Ricia, Catherine 550
Rick, Frederick 201
Rickard, Candice J. 635
Rickel, John C. 402
Ricker, David 818
Rickert, Luann K 261
Ricketts, Carlton A 159
Ricketts, Carl 159
Ricketts, Dave 731
Ricks, David A. 528
Ricks, Ron 780
Riczo, John 808
Riddle, Pam 185
Riddle, Lynn 333
Riddle, Doug 336
Riddleberger, Matt 808
Ridenour, Dean 429
Rider, James 484
Ridgeway, Alan 532

Ridout, Chris 923
Ridzon, Paul 497
Rieck, Lewis 489
Rieck, Alan 831
Riecker, Robert A. 759
Riedel, Norbert 115
Rief, Lisa 555
Riegel, Mike 200
Riegel, Matthew 620
Riel, Pierre 241
Riel, Susan G. 289
Riel, Kevin 624
Rielly, John P. 423
Riepe, James S. (Jim) 389
Riesterer, Terry 738
Rieves, JT 431
Rife, John A. 872
Riffle, Randy 497
Rifkin, Christine 332
Rigatti, Maria 295
Rigby, Mike 570
Rigg, Timothy 158
Riggan, Debbie 304
Riggan, Gisela 697
Riggieri, Rose 839
Riggin, William 201
Riggins, Quentin 25
Riggle, Carrie 345
Riggs, Nancy 507
Riggs, Lane 890
Rights, Nancy 376
Rigney, Patrick 109
Riker, Rick 185
Riley, Claudia 94
Riley, Adam 131
Riley, Steve 151
Riley, Donna 185
Riley, Rick D. 206
Riley, Karla 247
Riley, Rick 304
Riley, Josh 350
Riley, Kevin P. 354
Riley, Brian 358
Riley, Eric 395
Riley, Shawn 498
Riley, Mike 537
Riley, Mark 615
Riley, Paul 674
Riley, Anne 724
Riley, Wesley 760
Riley, Karen 763
Riley, Lori 813
Riley, Allison 942
Rim, Heather 14
Rimel, Brian 715
Rimkus, Michael 811
Rinehart, Mike 550
Rinehart, Charles R. 559
Riney, Stephen J. 68
Ringels, Jared 159
Ringgenberg, Jason T. 937
Ringle, Guy 80
Ringler, Steven 849
Ringold, Kim 935
Ringsdorf, Michele 342
Ringwald, Richard 226
Ringwald, Brad 349
Rini, Anthony 497
Rinker, Jackie 456
Rinn, Russell B. (Russ) 794
Rintoul, David J. 878
Riordan-Pacheco, Ella 767
Rios, Gerardo 693
Rios, Raymond 851
Ripley, Brian 668
Rippey, Loryssa L 43
Rippon, Jeffrey 53
Risch, Therace M. 661
Rischall, Richard 356
Rischar, Kent 56
Rish, Nick 297
Risio, Derek M. Di 701
Risk, Jim 378
Risk, Robert 530
Risley, Hank B 459
Risoleo, James F. 440
Rispoli, Michael 665

Risse, Wendy 53
Risser, Bill 332
Rissman, Michael 729
Ristich, Regan 881
Ritchie, Kevin 195
Ritchie, Michael T. 224
Ritchie, Robert 240
Ritchie, Keely 678
Ritchie, Mike 722
Ritchie, Kevin J. 825
Ritchie, Chris 881
Ritenour, Jeff L. 263
Ritenour, Brent 794
Rittenmeyer, Ronald A. (Ron) 818
Ritter, Mark 246
Ritter, William D. (Bill) 721
Ritti, Frank 274
Rittler, Bob 222
Ritzdorf, Gernot 91
Rivard, Heather 284
Rivas, Hiram 340
Rivenbark, Eric 870
Rivera, Jessica 32
Rivera, Dora 103
Rivera, Alfredo 216
Rivera, Chris 344
Rivera, N©stor O. 682
Rivera, Carlos 707
Rivera-Batista, Nayda 340
Rivero, Mario 899
Rivers, Lori 161
Rivers, Hugh 425
Rivers, Rita 664
Rivet, Jeannine M. 880
Rivetts, Debbie 497
Rizvi, Ali 550
Rizzardi, Russell 915
Rizzo, Lauren 18
Rizzo, Mario 31
Rizzo, John 213
Rizzo, James L. 268
Rizzuto, Katherine 643
Rnian-bivona, Gail 105
Roach, Michael 449
Roach, George 784
Roach, John 890
Roaldsen, Liz 792
Robatel, Nicolas 754
Robb, Stephen M. (Steve) 208
Robb, John 246
Robb, Jennifer 313
Robb, Gregory 367
Robben, John 663
Robbins, Spencer 118
Robbins, Deborah 176
Robbins, Charles H. (Chuck) 199
Robbins, Hadley S. 221
Robbins, Paige K. 398
Robbins, Michael (Mike) 661
Robbins, Cindy 748
Robbins, Ira 891
Robbins, Mike 912
Robbins, Cordon 942
Roberson, Wilborn 117
Roberson, Brian 131
Roberson, Peter 467
Roberson, Danny 722
Roberto, Joseph (Joe) 109
Roberto, Pesaro 713
Roberts, Bob 31
Roberts, Matt 88
Roberts, Matthew 131
Roberts, Vera Rand 155
Roberts, Brian L. 222
Roberts, Jonathan C. 252
Roberts, Meredith 274
Roberts, Terry 304
Roberts, Jorita 333
Roberts, Susan 404
Roberts, John N. 447
Roberts, Bart 483
Roberts, Ned 486
Roberts, Brian 617
Roberts, Dave 654
Roberts, Timothy D. (Tim) 675
Roberts, Cathy 757
Roberts, Leslie 768

Roberts, Patricia 778
Roberts, Alistair 792
Roberts, Mark 825
Roberts, Lori 850
Roberts, Brian 860
Roberts, Chad 863
Roberts, Karen 903
Robertson, Jenifer 84
Robertson, Laura 111
Robertson, Cliff A. 168
Robertson, Rick 185
Robertson, William 355
Robertson, Bill 355
Robertson, John 385
Robertson, Mark 395
Robertson, C 446
Robertson, Scott 484
Robertson, Dawn 548
Robertson, Matthew 558
Robertson, Timothy 705
Robertson, Elizabeth Aulick 715
Robertson, Bruce 762
Robertson, Glenn 931
Robeson, Clark 54
Robi, Tim 115
Robichaud, Michael 555
Robinette, Ken 161
Robino, Diana 555
Robins, Greg 425
Robinson, Harvey G. 98
Robinson, Bill 105
Robinson, Ken 115
Robinson, Charles 197
Robinson, James 205
Robinson, Darryl L. 266
Robinson, Jennifer 328
Robinson, Tori 339
Robinson, Kiersten 370
Robinson, David 382
Robinson, David C. 413
Robinson, Kevin 454
Robinson, Joe 457
Robinson, Patricia 550
Robinson, Leo 587
Robinson, Don 613
Robinson, Rod 668
Robinson, Guilford 705
Robinson, Mary 722
Robinson, Jack 735
Robinson, Robert L. 768
Robinson, Sonal 773
Robinson, Barry 808
Robinson, Larry 810
Robinson, Timothy 875
Robinson, Carole 896
Robinson, David L. 915
Robinson, Rebecca K. 941
Robinton, Charles 715
Roble, John 194
Roble, Mark A. 735
Robles, Alma 555
Robo, James L. (Jim) 612
Robson, Ted 810
Robusto, Dino E. 210
Roby, Anne K. 687
Robyn, Lewis 570
Rocco, Michael Del 109
Rocco, James 158
Rocha, Charles P. 772
Roche, Vincent T. 62
Roche, Dan 84
Roche, Angie 224
Roche, Joan 366
Roche, John C. (Jack) 409
Rocheleau, Duane 620
Rock, Jesse 382
Rock, Bernard 847
Rockey, Joseph E. 680
Rockholt, Tracy 813
Rocklein, Nathan 158
Rockwell, Joshua 224
Roco, Ninna 570
Roda, Craig A. 376
Roddey, Kevin 678
Roddie-Crews, Allison 799
Rodean, Jennifer 93

Rodeghiero, Kelly 530
Roden, Matthew 144
Roden, Michael 170
Rodeo, Karen 792
Roder, Gordon 604
Roderigue, John 808
Rodgers, Karen 330
Rodgers, Steven R. (Steve) 465
Rodgers, Kerri 764
Rodie, Robert 356
Rodkin, Gary M. 95
Rodoni, Tony 748
Rodrigue, Perry 304
Rodrigues, Edison F 465
Rodriguez, Richard 60
Rodriguez, Michael 84
Rodriguez, Carlos A. 87
Rodriguez, Aida 97
Rodriguez, Kathy 103
Rodriguez, Lou 105
Rodriguez, Ellie 109
Rodriguez, Carlos 115
Rodriguez, Sarah 117
Rodriguez, Carlos 128
Rodriguez, Russell 180
Rodriguez, Andres 204
Rodriguez, Maro 246
Rodriguez, Carmen 252
Rodriguez, Javier J. 258
Rodriguez, Abe 266
Rodriguez, Alfredo 272
Rodriguez, Juan 320
Rodriguez, Linda 454
Rodriguez, Gerry 519
Rodriguez, David A. 548
Rodriguez, Priscilla 558
Rodriguez, Jaime 596
Rodriguez, Rita E. 639
Rodriguez, John A. 706
Rodriguez, Abigail 712
Rodriguez, Armando G. 756
Rodriguez, Enrique 771
Rodriguez, Damarie 803
Rodriguez, Tomas 896
Rodriguez, Ana Concepcion 903
Rodriguez-Borjas, Carlos 725
Roe, Scott 60
Roe, Jeffrey 105
Roe, Jonathan 337
Roe, John E. 366
Roe, Mathew 784
Roe, Scott A. 894
Roederer, Nick 715
Roegner, Eric V. 75
Roehm, John 497
Roeloffs, David 750
Roesch, Richard 735
Roesel, Larry M. 90
Roeske, Richard 495
Roesner, Daniel 224
Roesslein, Dennis 558
Roessner, Karl A. 288
Roetzel, Michael 860
Roewe, Gordon 226
Roewe, Randy 350
Roffler, Michael J. (Mike) 358
Rogel, Estrella 191
Rogers, Patrick 31
Rogers, Laura 79
Rogers, Mike 98
Rogers, J. Michael 98
Rogers, Carol 101
Rogers, Jody 161
Rogers, William D. (Bill) 177
Rogers, Sean 203
Rogers, Jason 207
Rogers, Lawrence S. (Larry) 301
Rogers, Gregory S 320
Rogers, John F.W. 395
Rogers, R. Scott 397
Rogers, Brian 408
Rogers, Jay 468
Rogers, Mary Sue 470
Rogers, E 470
Rogers, Nancy 530
Rogers, John C. 666
Rogers, Alexander H. (Alex) 707

Rogers, Alex 708
Rogers, Brian 754
Rogers, William H. (Bill) 799
Rogers, Brian C. 810
Rogers, Michael 860
Rogers, Cregg 889
Rogers, Tony 903
Rogers-McCoy, Alison 18
Roggekamp, Ruud 135
Rogness, Jonathan 888
Rogstad, W. David 857
Rogus, Mark 240
Rohan, Mary 141
Rohan, Russell 665
Rohane, Patricia 175
Rohde, William M. 122
Rohde, Joe 273
Rohde, Bemina 539
Rohlander, Robert 900
Rohr, Mark C. 173
Rohrbaugh, Philmer H. (Phil) 376
Rohrer, Daniel 628
Roig, Ismael 74
Roig, Jorge 682
Rojas, Jose 437
Rojas, Randall 454
Rojas, Daysi 899
Rokas, Georgia 852
Roland, Thierry 445
Rolfes, Francis 157
Rolfes, Francis M 157
Rolheiser, Eric J. 239
Rollauer, Thomas 204
Roller, Dean 467
Rollin, Kelly 576
Rollins, James D. (Dan) 99
Rollins, Rich 222
Rollins, Lisa 664
Rolon, Gil 117
Romaine, Mark A. 393
Romaine, Stephen S. 842
Roman, Michael F. 2
Roman, Juan 39
Roman, James 226
Roman, Edwin 249
Roman, Oraida 258
Roman, Brian 559
Roman, Lawrence (Larry) 857
Roman-Grimaldi, Angela 409
Romaneiro, Marcos 505
Romanelli, Christopher 204
Romano, Frank 567
Romano, Annie 707
Romanoff, Steve 715
Romanowski, Mike 214
Romanowski, Paul 439
Rome, Kelly 700
Romer, Paul 606
Romero, David 72
Romero, Pedro 631
Romero, Kimberly 863
Romero, Tram 903
Rometty, Virginia M. (Ginni) 470
Romig, Timothy D. 249
Romine, Jeremy 109
Romine, Bill 731
Romm, Elisa 555
Rommeney, Chris 182
Romo, Tammy 780
Romstad, Michael 770
Ron, Klimkowski 197
Rona, Michael 171
Ronan, Alicia 157
Roncaglione, Tammy 178
Ronchi, Roberto 923
Ronen, Assaf 37
Ronning, Bruce 820
Roof, John Todd 792
Roof, Don 876
Rooke, Brian 786
Rooks, John 78
Rooks, Marsha 762
Rooney, Timothy 300
Rooney, Mary 332
Rooney, Jim 530
Rooney, Jack 570
Rooney, David 570

Rooney, Robert 587
Rooney, Jerome 725
Roop, Tim 663
Roop, Albert 931
Roos, Jeff 518
Root, Jason 203
Rooy, Mike La 45
Roper, Margie 266
Roper, Craig 307
Roper, Jay 869
Ropp, Stephen E (Steve) 492
Ropp, Richard 492
Ropp, Holly 492
Roques, Guillaume 748
Rorabaugh, David 377
Rosa, Yvette 109
Rosa, Dan De La 506
Rosa, Dan D 507
Rosa, Luis 607
Rosado, Louis 158
Rosado, Robert 790
Rosalsky, Mark 811
Rosamilia, Thomas W. (Tom) 470
Rosanova, Don 506
Rosario, Christie 367
Rosati, Bob 573
Rosato, R. David 664
Rosborough, Mark N. 341
Rose, Matthew K. (Matt) 123
Rose, M. Robert 147
Rose, Matthew K. (Matt) 150
Rose, Timothy L. 241
Rose, Marya M. 248
Rose, Anthony J. 268
Rose, Scott 299
Rose, Jim 336
Rose, Dennis E. 349
Rose, David G. 436
Rose, Elizabeth 459
Rose, Les 509
Rose, Christopher 548
Rose, Cindy 575
Rose, Teryl C 641
Rose, Greg 707
Rose, Carol 738
Rose, Paul 752
Roseborough, Teresa W. 431
Roseborough, Doug 643
Rosebrook, Dana 420
Rosello, Mike 30
Rosemore, Lance B. 195
Rosen, Mickie 34
Rosen, Elaine D. 82
Rosen, Sheri 246
Rosen, Mitch 389
Rosen, Gary 517
Rosen, Marc 521
Rosen, Marc 523
Rosenbach, Lynn 112
Rosenbaum, Eileen 752
Rosenberg, Adam 395
Rosenberg, Paul 488
Rosenberg, Brian 490
Rosenberg, Richard 582
Rosenberg, Donald J. 707
Rosenberger, Angie 453
Rosenblum, Robin 67
Rosenblum, Heather 901
Rosencrans, Dean 80
Rosenfeld, Manny 227
Rosenfeld, Irene B. 584
Rosenfeld, Phyllis 767
Rosenfield, Eliot M. 151
Rosenstein, Jeff 15
Rosenstein, Robert 689
Rosenthal, David 320
Rosenthal, Gary 548
Rosenthaler, Albert E. 524
Rosenzweig, Christina 849
Rosetta, Gladys 570
Roshardt, Christoph 548
Roshek, Sonya 553
Rosics, Don 824
Rosini, Eduardo 576
Roskind, Jim 37
Roslin, Eddie 104
Rosman, Adam L. 348

Rosner, Eli 599
Rosner, Judy 728
Rospond, Nicole 767
Ross, Alisa 88
Ross, Kimberly A. 95
Ross, Wayne 106
Ross, Sherry 117
Ross, Don 146
Ross, Joyce M. 168
Ross, Cheyenne 176
Ross, Roshanie 204
Ross, Rich 270
Ross, Evelyn 368
Ross, Renee 450
Ross, John 483
Ross, Lana D 504
Ross, Richard 570
Ross, Duncan 605
Ross, Andrew D. 654
Ross, Thomas J. 660
Ross, Tom 715
Ross, Stephen M. 720
Ross, Jason 722
Ross, Bridget A. 752
Ross, Dennis E. 791
Ross, James E. (Jim) 792
Ross, Mike 810
Ross, Sara 813
Ross, Gary 849
Rossano, Joann 767
Rossetta, Melanie 888
Rossette, Kathleen 2
Rossetti, Nick 272
Rossetto, Ronald B. 764
Rosshirt, Mark 804
Rossi, Robert 84
Rossi, Mark A. 102
Rossi, Todd 731
Rossi, Hugo 756
Rossi, Jack 798
Rossi, Vince 841
Rossiter, Jay 34
Rossiter, Peter 620
Rossitto, Lynn 194
Rossman, Scott 726
Rossotti, Charles O. 16
Rostan, Richard H. 318
Rostron, Sean 103
Roszczewski, Loretta 504
Roth, Jay 272
Roth, Michael I. 473
Roth, Renee S. 806
Roth, Peter 838
Rothenberg, Craig 484
Rothenberg, Mace 671
Rothenbush, Scott 912
Rother, Joe 507
Rothfuss, Andre 140
Rothman, Natalie 12
Rothman, Craig 161
Rothman, Fred 518
Rothrock, Michael 18
Rothrock, Sandy 831
Rothstein, Diahann 327
Rothstein, Sharon 787
Rothweiler, Robert 84
Rotolo, Jill 103
Rotsztein, Linda 800
Rotter, Matt 181
Rottman, Monica 140
Rottmuller, Lori 558
Roualet, Mark C. 380
Rouly, Chris 332
Roundhill, John 135
Rouse, Michael 550
Rouse, Anthony 890
Rouser, Kirby 643
Roush, Phil 199
Roush, Robin S 392
Roush, Richard 831
Rousse, Troy A 307
Rousseau, Michael T. (Mike) 4
Rousseau, Thomas 109
Rousseau, Paul 305
Routin, Gregory 574
Rouv©, Andreas 782
Roux, Bob 533

Roux, Sommer 813
Rovig, Joseph W. (Joe) 593
Row, Maggie 112
Rowan, Kathryn 55
Rowan, Tim 547
Rowden, Kyle 330
Rowe, Chris 12
Rowe, Greg 87
Rowe, Robert C. 201
Rowe, Alison 735
Rowell, Jim 654
Rowland, Mark 316
Rowland, G. Joyce 761
Rowland, Rick 869
Rowles, Michael G. 532
Roxas, Fred 757
Roy, Abir 53
Roy, Dawn 492
Roy, Sudeepto 707
Royer, Patricia 376
Rozanski, Horacio D. 139
Rozario, Datuk Mark 382
Rozboril, Martin 55
Rozich, Bill 161
Rozwat, Charles A. (Chuck) 642
Rubackin, Lon 170
Rubanenko, Yoram 241
Rubenstein, David M. 287
Ruberg, Tony 450
Rubin, Ann 470
Rubin, Jonathan N. (Jon) 541
Rubin, Patricia Lee 606
Rubin, Roz 664
Rubin, Carl (Chuck) 862
Rubinfeld, Arthur 787
Rubinstein, Rhonda 425
Rubinstein, David 748
Rubio, Carlos 555
Rubocki, Cheri 356
Rubritz, Timothy G. 367
Ruby, Douglas 587
Ruby, Dave 769
Rucas, Gilbert 713
Ruccolo, Domenic 260
Ruchti, Laurie 817
Rucker, Kim K. W. 63
Rucker, Nitra 497
Rucker, Andrew 811
Rudd, W. Troy 14
Rudd, Henry 553
Ruddock, David P. 745
Rude, Tom 343
Rudecki, Walter 49
Rudeen, Christian 3
Ruder, Anna 672
Ruderman, Judith 287
Rudinsky, Charles A. (Chuck) 393
Rudisill, Pamela T. 230
Rudloff, Robert 573
Rudman, Robert H. (Bob) 276
Rudnay, D'Arcy F. 222
Rudolph, Greg 350
Rudolph, John 728
Rudoy, Gregory 394
Rudy, John 15
Rudzik, Chad 337
Ruehle, Corey J. 872
Ruello, Warren 548
Ruese, John 300
Ruff, Jon 404
RUFF, BOB 738
Ruffenach, Joan 710
Ruffer, Kevin 654
Ruffing, Robert H 47
Ruffing, David 503
Rufolo, Rick 875
Rugel, John 32
Ruger, Michael 222
Rugg, Kim 332
Ruggieri, Thomas 328
Ruggiero, David 200
Ruh, William (Bill) 382
Ruhe, Mark 810
Ruhl, Terry A. 185
Ruhullah, Khalid 750
Ruiz, Eidamarie 6
Ruiz, Victor 161

Ruiz, Joseph 295
Ruiz, Odalys 899
Ruiz, Gisel 903
Rulin, Randy 261
Rulli, John 770
Rumbolz, Michael D. (Mike) 301
Rumfola, Annlea 161
Rumple, Belinda 537
Rumrey, Laura 888
Rumsey, Jennifer 248
Rundell, Jason 810
Runge, Marschall S. 720
Runice, Paul 881
Runkel, Mark G. 888
Runkle, Paul 170
Runner, Scott 707
Runyon, Mark 468
Runyon, Kevin B. 660
Ruos, Brian 356
Rupert, Teresa 564
Rupp, Robert R. 413
Ruppert, Paul F. 278
Ruppert, James 313
Ruppert, Mark 580
Rusch, Leon K. 227
Ruscowski, Stephen H. (Steve) 709
Rush, Chris 87
Rush, Dave 149
Rush, David G 713
Rush, Tim 805
Rushing, Matt 20
Rushing, Janet M 378
Rushing, Rodney E. 763
Rushmore, John 105
Rushnak, Jeff 201
Rusnak, Jason 87
Rusnak, Patrick J. (Pat) 652
Rusnak, John A 659
Rusnak, Scott C 708
Rusnak, Dave 836
Russ, Ioana 672
Russ, Mark 725
Russeau, Chris 516
Russell, Darrel 107
Russell, Scott E 117
Russell, John G. 210
Russell, Saira 221
Russell, Nicholas S. (Nick) 228
Russell, John G. 238
Russell, David 243
Russell, Monya 342
Russell, Steven 517
Russell, Sandy 715
Russell, Keith 778
Russell, Craig 787
Russell, Suzann 803
Russell, Jennifer M 863
Russell, David E. 939
Russell, David 941
Russi, Timothy M. (Tim) 33
Russo, John 18
Russo, Tricia 87
Russo, Paul M. 395
Russo, Patricia F. (Pat) 425
Russo, Vincent Null 508
Russo, Eric 668
Russo, Tony 811
Russo, Thomas 892
Russo, Alejandra 901
Russo, Greg 936
Rust, Steven W. (Steve) 110
Rust, John 178
Rust, Bradley M. 390
Rustad, Stephanie 52
Rustand, Kay 725
Ruterman, Derek 487
Ruth, Michael J. 725
Rutherford, William B. (Bill) 416
Rutherford, John R. 679
Rutherford, Linda B. 780
Rutledge, Deann 2
Rutledge, Thomas M. (Tom) 186
Rutledge, Thomas M. (Tom) 186
Rutledge, Justin 870
Rutschman, Cody 457
Rutstein, Mark 57
Ruud, David 284

Ruvolo, Susan 378
Ruzicka, Lawrence J 84
Ryan, Christopher 87
Ryan, William J. (Bill) 124
Ryan, Robert 191
Ryan, John 224
Ryan, Jim 237
Ryan, James 261
Ryan, Marc 376
Ryan, Tom 446
Ryan, Kevin 457
Ryan, Collin 463
Ryan, Linda 470
Ryan, Courtney J. 480
Ryan, Stacey 537
Ryan, Edward A. (Ed) 548
Ryan, Joseph 548
Ryan, Lawrence G. 558
Ryan, Robert 596
Ryan, D 626
Ryan, James C. 635
Ryan, Michael 641
Ryan, Paula 656
Ryan, Dan 736
Ryan, Matthew 787
Ryan, Stephen 799
Ryan, Laura 855
Ryan, Lynn 908
Ryan-Macie, Sheila 772
Rydin, Fredrik 793
Ryge, Svend 802
Rynaski, Theresa 735
Ryno, Marrianne 453
Rytil, Tuula 576
Ryu, Hyungon 628
Ryu, Jeff 787
Rzonca, Peter 94
R'bibo, Daniel 378

S

S.Gragg, Gary 350
Sa, Francisco 505
Saad, Doris 800
Saad, Amina 901
Saag, John 270
Saar, Janet 123
Saari, Dale 559
Saavedra, Ruben 16
Saavedra, Norma 104
Sabatino, Thomas J. (Tom) 17
Sabatowski, Karen A. 362
Sabella, Joe 519
Sabharwal, Vipul 923
Sabio, Robert 122
Sabnani, Janisha 358
Sabnis, Shona 75
Sabo, John 836
Saborio, Bernal 219
Sabry, Ismail 668
Saccaro, James K. 115
Sacco, Joseph 15
Sachdev, Arvind 219
Sacher, Dan 896
Sachs, Howard 715
Sachs, Alan 808
Sachtjen, Karl 635
Sackman, Stuart 87
Sacks, Lee B. 13
Sacks, Denis 668
SacristⅢn, Carlos Ruiz 761
Sadasivan, Pari 470
Sadeghi, Fred 787
Sadek, Hossam 478
Sadi, Eric 770
Sadigh, Mandana 557
Sadler, Jason D. 194
Sadler, David 213
Sadowski, Peter T. 332
Sadowski, John D. 749
Safady, Edward Z. (Eddie) 697
Safarian, Lisa 585
Saffian, Lisa 896
Safranek, Scott 570
Sagar, Bijoy 797
Sagara, Kevin 761

Sage, Deborah 88
Sagehorn, David M. 645
Sagers, David 489
Sagheer, Omer 832
Sagun, Paul 770
Saha, Saurabh 144
Saha, Kunal 890
Saha, Tamal 923
Sahn, Nate 170
Sahoo, Surya 907
Saik, Barry 476
Sain, Jeff 537
Sakamoto, Lynette 103
Sakhrani, Monesh 929
Sako, Gary 620
Saks, David H. 60
Saks, Xan 170
Salah, Joseph 243
Salama, Michael 273
Salama, Maged 731
Salame, Pablo J. 395
Salamone, Carl 910
Salata, Nicole 901
Salazar, Hector 460
Salceda-Wycoco, Anika 370
Salcedo, Mirta 468
Salcito, Tom 668
Saldarelli, John 455
Saldivar, Ricardo E. 431
Sale, Geoffrey 449
Saleem, Amer 118
Saleh, Randa 787
Salehpour, Ali 71
Salek, Mohsen 512
Saleki-Gerhardt, Azita 6
Salerno, Kendra 178
Sales, William K. 725
Saletnik, Laurie 483
Salinas, Jerry 246
Salinas, Dan 720
Saline, Chris 668
Salisbury, Julian 395
Salit, Jan F. 195
Salkic, Edin 863
Sall, Morgan 204
Salla, Francis J. (Frank) La 105
Salle, Andrew Bon 322
Salman, Fatima 720
Salmirs, Scott 7
Salmon, Thomas E. (Tom) 125
Salmon, Rob 602
Salop, Michael A 919
Saloutos, Steve 889
Saltarelli, Theresa 875
Saltiel, Albert (Al) 90
Saltzman, Robert 37
Salupo, Sarah 604
Salvador, Scot R. 854
Salvadori, Daniel 4
Salvato, Dominick 668
Salvatore, Bryan J. 409
Salvatore, Sara 932
Salway, Roberta 355
Salzburger, Karl Heinz 894
Samama, Pascale 57
Samant, Rahul 262
Sambar, Christopher 84
Sameth, David 273
Samir, Mohamed 693
Samitt, Craig E. 66
Sammon, Alison 497
Samoskevich, Steven 122
Sample, Phillip 170
Sample, Neal 319
Samples, Jeff 468
Sampson, Terri 88
Sampson, Kristin M 378
Sampson, Bryan 735
Samra, Dave 224
Sams, James 53
Sams, Thomas 168
Samson, Edward 327
Samson, Denise 715
Samson, Jaime 813
Samuel, Tonya 376
Samuels, Tanesha 178
Samuels, Rob 333

Samuels, John 550
Samuels, Ellen 599
Samuels, Cooper 678
Samuelson, Jeremy 88
Samworth, Martin 170
Sanabria, Magaly 204
Sanandres, Jim 87
Sanchack, Erich 181
Sanchez, Anna 247
Sanchez, Lou 293
Sanchez, Ruben 374
Sanchez, Donny 431
Sanchez, Pablo 445
Sanchez, Reuben 533
Sanchez, Maria 656
Sanchez, Beatriz 672
Sanchez, Tammi 722
Sanchez, Robert E. 742
Sanchez, Brian 754
Sanchez, Cynthia 760
Sand, Duke 756
Sandall, Laura 661
Sandberg, Ellen Y 185
Sandberg, Jon 194
Sandberg, Christopher 256
Sandberg, Sheryl K. 321
Sandberg, Louise T. 664
Sandborn, Cindy 245
Sander, Mark G. 356
Sanders, Todd 12
Sanders, Leslie 25
Sanders, Jay D. 97
Sanders, Sarah 159
Sanders, Michael 204
Sanders, Jeff 246
Sanders, Wayne R. 282
Sanders, Kole 376
Sanders, Ashley 449
Sanders, Marshall 453
Sanders, Dax 500
Sanders, Stacy 519
Sanders, Corey I. 572
Sanders, Henry 576
Sanders, M. Jack 775
Sanders, Ronald J. 838
Sanderson, Kelly 131
Sanderson, Scott 550
Sanderson, Randal 563
Sandfort, Gregory A. (Greg) 845
Sandgren, James 635
Sandgren, Jim 635
Sandh, David 911
Sandilla, Jill 436
Sandor, Chris 447
Sandoval, Lisa A 18
Sandoval, Patricia 135
Sandoval, Andres 483
Sandri, Fabio 676
Sandrin, Joseph 185
Sandrock, Alfred W. 129
Sands, Robert S. (Rob) 236
Sands, Richard 237
Sands, John 246
Sandstead, David 691
Sandstrom, Brad 203
Sandt, James 153
Sandusky, Robert 377
Sanford, Marcus 10
Sanford, Kathleen D. 168
Sanford, Tom 484
Sangalli, John 470
Sanger, Stephen 383
Sangiorgi, Giovanna 643
Sani, Shawn 572
Sanislo, Steve 202
Sankaran, Vivek 667
Sanna, Albert 664
Sanner, Lisa 131
SanPhillip, Cynthia 511
Sans, Maggie 903
Sansalone, Giovanni 395
Sansone, Thomas A. 480
Sant, Gursharan 550
Santacroce, Kevin L. 143
Santangelo, Vicky 84
Santangelo, Janine 202
Santangelo, Lillian 394

Santarosa, Romolo C 408
Santelli, Jonathan N. 715
Santi, E. Scott 458
Santiago, Michael 408
Santillana, Alex 713
Santirocco, Matthew S 606
Santo, Ronald D. 558
Santolucito, Anna 88
Santomassimo, Michael P. 105
Santoro, Antonio 15
Santos, Bernerd Da 16
Santos, Esteban 57
Santos, Lindsay 60
Santos, Fernando 468
Santos, Rossy 722
Santoso, Hendro 190
Santoyo, Raul 201
Santy, Steve 300
Sanz, Oscar 204
Sanz, Erick 411
Saoud, Abdallah 899
Sapenter, Tyrone A 668
Saperstein, Andy 587
Saple, Gaurav 200
Sapnar, Michael C. (Mike) 28
Sapollnik, Adrian 639
Sapozhnikov, Galina 754
Sappenfield, Joel 859
Sappington, Jim 562
Sapra, Puja 671
Sapre, Milind 395
Sarah, Lora 262
Saraiva, Ana 664
Sarandos, Ted 603
Sarangapani, Prakash 465
Sarathy, Kanchana 122
Saravi, Maximo 570
Saravia, Sam 332
Sarazen, Stefan 88
Sardinha, Jeffrey 792
Sargent, Angela M. 376
Sargent, Wes 403
Sargent, Matthew 888
Sari, Robert B. 616
Sarker, Ari 555
Sarma, Karthik 521
Sarma, Karthik 523
Sarmad, Abbas 14
Sarner, David 107
Sarra, Martha 507
Sarre, Pierre 300
Sarre, Tim 857
Sarro, Gary 767
Sarsfield, Luke 395
Sarstedt, Armin 465
Sartain, Paul 896
Sartorius, John 14
Sarvadi, John C. 823
Sarver, Robert G. 916
Sashegyi, Mary J 528
Sass, Delana 735
Sasser, Bob 276
Sastri, Jon 717
Satchell, Chris 222
Satchell, Steve 735
Sato, Sharon 180
Sato, Michael 617
Sato, Margaret 888
Satterthwaite, Tony 248
Satterthwaite, Livingston L. (Tony) 248
Satterwhite, Matthew J. 42
Saucedo, Rosie 825
Sauer, Brad T 2
Sauer, Jon 68
Sauerland, John P. 695
Sauers, Ken 311
Sauerwalt, Craig 809
Sauls, Larry 15
Saun, Bruce Van 205
Saunders, Blair 131
Saunders, James 500
Saunders, Pamela 517
Saunders, Troy 537
Saunders, Jeff L. 596
Saunders, Nancy 602
Saunders, David 767
Saunders, Barry L. 775

Sausen, Ted 620
Sautter, Bruce 449
Sav, Martine 813
Savage, Jean 166
Savage, Josh 335
Savage, Douglas 489
Savage, Joseph J. (Joe) 908
Savage, Stanley D. 941
Savaiano, Helen 409
Savas, Steven 900
Savell, Melanie 454
Savery, Warren 170
Saville, Paul C. 629
Saville, Robert 857
Savitt, Kathy 34
Savko, Brad 727
Savner, David A 380
Saw, Choon Seong 22
Sawatzky, David 470
Sawdey, Mike 49
Sawicki, Michael 806
Sawtell, Herb 450
Sawyer, Scott 162
Sawyer, Chris 356
Sawyer, Connie 467
Sawyer, Guy 735
Sawyer, Stephen 806
Sawyers, Todd 449
Sax, James 3
Sax, Michael E 334
Saxena, Gaurav 45
Saxena, Sorabh 84
Saxon, Michael J. 60
Saxon, Matthew 446
Saxon, Leigh 799
Sayeedi, Nick 272
Sayers, Andrew 886
Saylor, Kurt M. 419
Sayre, Bill 580
Sayre, Rich 615
Sayre, David L. 912
Sazekas, Jacqueline 904
Sbrocco, Julie 178
Scaccia, Tiziana 332
Scaglione, D. Anthony 7
Scala, Luciano 677
Scala, Douglas E. (Doug) 908
Scales, Sam 370
Scallan, Michael 585
Scammahorn, Julie 45
Scammell, George L 932
Scanlan, Patrick 273
Scanlon, Meghan 142
Scanlon, Sharon 530
Scanlon, Suzy 723
Scanlon, Brian 910
Scannell, Timothy J. 797
Scarazzini, Linda 6
Scarborough, Dean A. 91
Scarborough, Mark 269
Scarborough, Thomas 336
Scardina, Michael 32
Scardina, Mike 32
Scardina, Barrie 705
Scarlett, Catherine M. 598
Scarpellini, Paula 705
Scarpone, Frank 632
Scarry, Robert 935
Scarsella, Michael 558
Scavone, April 93
Scerch, Andrea 555
Schaaf, Christopher 888
Schabacker, Marcus 115
Schacht, David 770
Schacter, Adam 201
Schaefer, Rich 5
Schaefer, William 112
Schaefer, Eric 222
Schaefer, Kelly 232
Schaefer, David 370
Schaefer, Steve 585
Schaefer, Milena 705
Schaefer, Robbie 890
Schaeffer, Jim 910
Schaeffler, Kenneth 224
Schaell, Tina 276
Schafer, Todd 181

Schafer, Carol 497
Schafer, John 628
Schaffer, Steve 135
Schaffer, David 715
Schager, Marty 15
Schaible, Jeff 115
Schaidle, Scott 435
Schalk, David 664
Schaller, John 18
Schaller, Janet 809
Schalliol, Charles E. 355
Schallon, Mossie 226
Schamer, David 449
Schamhart, Luc 748
Schantz, Keith 840
Schappert, Rich 164
Schar, Dwight C. 629
Schardijn, Kristina 300
Scharf, David 219
Scharich, Peter 498
Scharmer, Neal R. 872
Scharphorn, Douglas 450
Schatz, John 202
Schatz, Jacob (Jake) 296
Schatzel, Rich 470
Schaum, Debbie 604
Schaupeter, Amy L 332
Schavrien, Lee 762
Schebler, Jeff 578
Schechter, Harold A. 233
Schechter, Lori A. 563
Schechter, Adam H. 566
Schecklman, Dave 645
Scheder, Valerie 84
Schefft, Bob 49
Scheid, Tom 196
Scheitzach, Clay 935
Schelanko, Alex 890
Schell, Brenda 338
Schell, Christoph 442
Schell, Jennifer 749
Scheller, Jay 735
Scheller, Megan 933
Schellinger, Michelle 454
Schembri, Joe 457
Schemm, Todd 45
Schenck, A. William (Bill) 853
Schenk, June 796
Schenkel, Scott F. 293
Schenker, Wendy 928
Scheper, Patrick 804
Schepp, Richard D. (Rick) 503
Scheps, Randall 75
Scheps, Megan 727
Scher, Vince 67
Scherer, Jacob 196
Scherer, Jf 197
Scherer, Laura 493
Scherler, Lynn 214
Schermer, Carol 115
Scherr, Stephen M. 395
Scheschuk, Peter 746
Scheuble, Larry 139
Scheuerman, Paul 863
Scheuermann, Rob 295
Scheuren, Jeffrey J. 376
Schiada, David 295
Schiavone, Drew 344
Schiavone, Patrick 923
Schick, Art 668
Schieber, George 832
Schieffer, Margaret 429
Schiess, Christine 632
Schiffels, Carolyn M 620
Schiffman, David 181
Schiffrin, Peter 548
Schillace, Darren 858
Schiller, Philip W. 69
Schiller, Weldon 214
Schiller, Steven C. 422
Schiller, Bryan 896
Schilling, Jeffrey 87
Schimmenti, Kathleen 550
Schippers, Harrie C.A.M. 650
Schiraldi, Richard J. 870
Schiralli, Nicholas 109
Schireson, Kern 896

Schirling, Kathleen 664
Schirm, Carla 849
Schjetnan, Chris 350
Schlager, Debbie 81
Schlanger, Marvin O. 861
Schlappig, Michael 133
Schlegel, Stephen 67
Schlegel, John 587
Schlehr, Dan 716
Schleifer, Michaela 337
Schleifer, Leonard S. 719
Schleiff, Henry S. 270
Schlemper, Oliver 643
Schleppi, Andrew 14
Schlesinger, Albert 96
Schlesinger, Jeffrey R. 838
Schlichting, Bryant 204
Schlichting, Warren W. 272
Schlissel, Mark S. 720
Schlitz, Lei Zhang 458
Schloeder, Pam 137
Schlonsky, Michael A. (Mike) 128
Schlosser, John W. 500
Schlotman, J. Michael 506
Schlotterback, Ed 834
Schlueter, Rick 300
Schmechel, Daniel J. (Dan) 294
Schmeltz, Andy 671
Schmid, Peter 693
Schmidt, Karen 45
Schmidt, Philip 84
Schmidt, Michael 93
Schmidt, Darryl 98
Schmidt, Dany 219
Schmidt, Barry 402
Schmidt, Derek 468
Schmidt, Jason 486
Schmidt, Greg 489
Schmidt, Dave 504
Schmidt, Steven 633
Schmidt, James 635
Schmidt, John 861
Schmidt, Brian 863
Schmidt, Craig 876
Schmidt, Gregg 878
Schmiedel, Gary W. 645
Schmieder, William 380
Schmiegelow, Brent 860
Schmit, Dave 504
Schmitt, Matthew 735
Schmitt, Paul 834
Schmitz, John 298
Schmitz, Jackie 558
Schmucker, Tim 88
Schmukler, Louis S. (Lou) 144
Schnalzer, Michael 131
Schneeberger, Carol A. 666
Schneer, Randi 767
Schneider, Richard E. (Rick) 58
Schneider, Natalie 213
Schneider, Neal C. 213
Schneider, Chris 214
Schneider, Glenn P. 269
Schneider, Kathy 272
Schneider, Donald R. (Donny) 360
Schneider, Kevin D. 389
Schneider, Robert 470
Schneider, Kristen 487
Schneider, Michael 498
Schneider, Steve 517
Schneider, Christoph 558
Schneider, Allen 578
Schneider, Elise 713
Schneider, Barry T. 794
Schneider, Mike 820
Schneider, Richard P 820
Schneider, Martin 894
Schneider, Robert 923
Schnettler, Gary 336
Schneyer, Mark 671
Schnieders, Kurt J. 264
Schnieders, Kurt 508
Schnitz, Chad 12
Schnitzer, Alan D. 849
Schnoor, Candace 261
Schnorr, Joseph 105
Schnorr, Roger 637

Schnupp, Craig M 890
Schnurr, Russ 337
Schoch, Dave L. (Dave) 370
Schoech, Brett 596
Schoenberger, Anja 185
Schoeneck, Cathy 294
Schoenecker, Melissa 888
Schoener, Douglas 17
Schoenfish, Errol 576
Schoettley, Jim 224
Schoettlin, Kathy A. 635
Schofield, Mary 332
Scholder, Janet 713
Scholefield, Jim 615
Scholes, John 499
Scholl, Jerry 88
Scholl, Jonathan W. 516
Scholten, Gary P. 691
Scholze, Mike 161
Schonacher, Bill 468
Schonberger, Lyle 52
Schoonmaker, Steve 84
Schoonover, Emerson 342
Schoonover, Mark A. 905
Schorn, Jerry 748
Schott, Brian 749
Schrader, Stacey 286
Schrader, William R 313
Schrader, Lesya 558
Schraer, Karl 668
Schrameck, Amy 498
Schramm, Steve 168
Schramm, Bernie 334
Schramm, Jim 356
Schranz, Tom 96
Schreck, Eric W. 854
Schreger, Charles 838
Schreiber, Steve Schreiber Steve 376
Schreiber, Edward P. (Ed) 941
Schreiner, Leslie 328
Schreiner, Jeff 832
Schreitmueller, Dee Dee 570
Schrenker, Jessica 293
Schreuder, Jana R. 620
Schriber, David 615
Schrider, Daniel J. (Dan) 749
Schroeder, Frank 263
Schroeder, Linda 376
Schroeder, Mark A. 390
Schroeder, John 390
Schroeder, John 572
Schroeder, Marc 668
Schroeder, Michael J. (Mike) 735
Schroeder, Lisa 805
Schroeder, Kathy 903
Schroepfer, Michael (Mike) 321
Schroeter, Martin J. 470
Schuba, Doug 635
SCHUBE, JARRETT 395
Schubert, Allen 185
Schueller, Gayle 3
Schuette, Stuart 50
Schuette, Matt 699
Schuh, Michele 357
Schuh, Jeffrey 724
Schuitema, Kurt 383
Schukar, Shawn E. 40
Schuler, Laurence 170
Schuler, Tatum 754
Schull, Thomas E 262
Schull, Todd 750
Schuller, George J. 659
Schulman, Irv 273
Schult, Doug 676
Schulte, Marcus 57
Schultz, Richard 186
Schultz, Steve 259
Schultz, Kent 300
Schultz, Rob 356
Schultz, Kevin J. 361
Schultz, John F. 425
Schultz, Anthony 434
Schultz, James 449
Schultz, Janet 470
Schultz, Katie 538
Schultz, John M. 577
Schultz, Teri 697

Schultz, Howard D. 788
SCHULTZ, CHIP 863
Schultz, David 881
Schulz, Mitch 213
Schulz, Lance 530
Schulz, David S (Dave) 914
Schulze, Trevor 574
Schumacher, Laura J. 6
Schumacher, Michael 81
Schumacher, Larry 168
Schumacher, Susan 289
Schumacher, Kristene 597
Schumacher, Carol 903
Schuman, Scott 172
Schumann, William H. (Bill) 94
Schumann, Daniel 119
Schupp, Rudy E. 891
Schur, Adam 587
Schur, Thomas P 668
Schurman, Juana 643
Schurr, Daniel (Dan) 193
Schuster, Jack 172
Schuster, Paul 722
Schuster, Paul 723
Schutt, Paul 31
Schutt, Douglas W. (Doug) 241
Schutts, William 84
Schutze, Heinrich 131
Schutzer, Michael A. 511
Schuurmans, Niels 896
Schuyler, Matthew W. (Matt) 427
Schuyler, Joe 786
Schwager, Charles 500
Schwalje, Linda 792
Schwallier, Jerry L. 419
Schwan, Cindy 610
Schwandt, Stephanie 249
Schwaneke, Jeffrey A 176
Schwaninger, Jeff 866
Schwartz, Bart R. 82
Schwartz, Michael (Mike) 95
Schwartz, George G. 141
Schwartz, Rachel 161
Schwartz, Gil 171
Schwartz, Eugene 201
Schwartz, Joel 213
Schwartz, Harvey M. 395
Schwartz, David 762
Schwartz, Melinda 800
Schwarz, Jonathan 256
Schwarz, Douglas 488
Schwarz, Ronald F. 502
Schwarz, Ronald E. (Ron) 511
Schwarz, Tony 708
Schwarz, David 735
Schwarz, Diane K. 826
Schwarz, Michael 912
Schwarzbach, Fred 606
Schwarzman, Stephen A. 133
Schwarzman, Randy 336
Schwebel, Gerardo (Gerald) 468
Schwebel, Gerald 468
Schwedler, David 3
Schwei, Russell P. (Russ) 735
Schweiger, Jaclyn 87
Schweiger, Werner J. 312
Schweighoffer, Michael T. 347
Schweinhart, Martin G. (Marty) 230
Schweitzer, Gregory 860
Schweitzer, Jeffrey M 884
Schweller, Leah 45
Schwenker, Adam 707
Schwetz, Amy B. 659
Schwimmer, Ellie 533
Schwimmer, Howard 730
Schwister, Jay 735
Scibienski, Sean 863
Sclafani, Michael 88
Scobell, Heidi 489
Scofield, Melissa 891
Scogin, Gaynor 722
Scogin, David 904
Scolaro, Robert 533
Scolaro, Rob 533
Scotch, Peter 664
Scott, Walter 12
Scott, Walt 12

Scott, William 42
Scott, Sandra 94
Scott, Dina 102
Scott, Samuel 117
Scott, Dwight 133
Scott, Jim 161
Scott, Abigail 207
Scott, Abigal 207
Scott, David A. (Dave) 222
Scott, Christopher 224
Scott, William 314
Scott, Philip 327
Scott, David 332
Scott, Kevin 344
Scott, James R. 354
Scott, David 370
Scott, Louise 389
Scott, Matthew 413
Scott, Stuart L. 447
Scott, Raymond E. (Ray) 514
Scott, Robert 516
Scott, Nathan 533
Scott, Richard W. 536
Scott, William 573
Scott, J. Kevin 576
Scott, Wesley 631
Scott, Dan 672
Scott, Gina 678
Scott, Steve 678
Scott, Mike 722
Scott, Sharon 722
Scott, Dennis 745
Scott, Randy 765
Scott, Vernon 769
Scott, Wes 798
Scott, Laura 803
Scott, Cameron A. 868
Scott, David C. 876
Scott, Diane 919
Scott, Anthony 928
Scott, Derek 929
Scott-Morgan, Peggy 666
Scottberg, Paul 836
Scotti, Laurie 530
Scotto, Vince 88
Scozzafava, Ralph P. 259
Scrase, Michael 161
Scribner, Michael 597
Scribner, Chris 722
Scrimager, Scott 358
Scrimes, Doug 750
Scroggins, Allen 99
Scruggs, Patrick 170
Scudder, Michael L. 356
Scull, William 470
Scullans, Greg 788
Scullin, Elizabeth 45
Scullin, Matt 888
Scully, Matt 222
Scyphers, Mike 545
Seabaugh, Greg 54
Seabold, Jeffrey T. 97
Seabright, Jefferson 216
Seagraves, Rhonda 221
Seal, Jill Lambert 191
Sear, Steve 262
Seargent, Jennifer 99
Searle, Nigel 320
Sears, Steven 358
Sears, James A. 360
Sears, Rachael 618
Sears, Lee 896
Seasock, Scott 667
Seastone, Bj 53
Seat, David M. 98
Seaton, Timothy 204
Seaton, Mark E. 339
Seaton, Charlee 342
Seaton, David T. 365
Seaver, Mark 470
Seaver, Michael L. 664
Seawahl, Nancy 102
Seay, Brent 904
Sebade, Steven 226
Sebade, Steve 226
Sebeck, Jane 722
Seck, Wai Kwong 791

Secor, Mark E. 436
Sedgwick, Alexander 810
Sedgwick, Dale 935
Sedicino, Dominic 660
Sedigh, Massoud 929
Sedlacek, Lanie 863
Sedov, Dmitri 746
Seeberger, Blake 519
Seedorf, Herman 658
Seeger, Laureen E. 44
Seeger, Rick 151
Sefzik, Peter L. 224
Segal, Jack 222
Segal, Daniel 770
Segatti, Anna 95
Segers, Debbie 334
Segman, Tal 94
Segro-nogueira, Dina 18
Seguin, Joseph 262
Seguin, Adrian 808
Seibel, Jason 181
Seibel, Donald J. (Don) 325
Seibert, Robert 14
Seidcheck, Thomas 735
Seidel, Rob 809
Seidman, Lawrence B. 233
Seifert, James J. (Jim) 294
Seiler, David R. 343
Seiler, Dawn 693
Seiler, Scott 931
Seitz, James R. 1
Seitz, Kevin 793
Seitz, Nikki 813
Seitze, David 246
Sekhar, Chandra 115
Sekmakas, Viktoras R. 685
Selander, Lee S 620
Selby, Victoria 266
Seldenrust, John D. 924
Seldon, Eric B. 19
Sele, Tim 135
Selee, Bob 380
Selfridge, Michael D. (Mike) 358
Selian, Paul J. 791
Selich, Amy 88
Seljan, Jacob 888
Sellers, Nick C 25
Sellers, Nicholas 25
Sellers, Mary E. 102
Sells, Jennifer 82
Selsor, Darlene 246
Seltz, Peter 691
Selwood, Robert C. 572
Selwood, Jim 935
Semancik, Frank 191
Semanie, Mark 634
Semet, Gardner 109
Seminara, Paul 748
Semmler, Carl 530
Sence, John 378
Senia, Vincent 760
Senkyr, Kelly 754
Sennott, John L. (Jack) 28
Senroy, Sid 129
Sensibaugh, Barbara A 350
Sensing, J. Steven (Steve) 743
Sensing, Steve 743
Senske, Thomas 97
Sentiff, Gary 934
Seo, Jeannie 840
Sep☐lveda, Eli S. 682
Sequin, Eric 80
Sera, Jean 93
Serafin, Zig 576
Serafini, Hester 466
Serafino, Joseph 423
Serbun, Joseph 228
Sereda, Peter L. 817
Sergesketer, Randy 261
Sergesketter, Randal 260
Sergesketter, Randy 261
Serianni, Charles F. (Chuck) 729
Serino, Joseph 298
Serna, Michelle 927
SERRANO, SHERRY 103
Serrano, Luis Javier 142
Serrano, Jose Fernando 220

Serricchio, Michael 550
Serros, Joanne 892
Serven, Neal 411
Servodidio, Mark J. 93
Serzon, Jeffrey 203
Seshadri, Raj 554
Sessler, Stephen M 155
Seth, Ajay 429
Sethi, Parvesh 200
Sethi, Parvesh 425
Setia, Sharda 159
Setliff, William 504
Setliff, Will 504
Setlock, Brandon 754
Seto, Jim 707
Setteducato, James 734
Settersten, Scott 862
Settle, Tom 453
Settle, Jondra 678
Seuferer, Kevin 43
Seurynck, Michael 820
Severe, Emily 175
Severino, Michael E. 6
Severino, Nicholas 69
Severino, Vittorio M. 445
Severs, Walter 831
Severson, Brett 849
Severson, Gary 903
Severts, Jeffrey 862
Sevey, Stewart 645
Sevilla-Sacasa, Eugenio 743
Seward, Wade 413
Seward, Andrew 754
Sewell, D. Bruce 69
Sewell, Michael J. (Mike) 196
Sewell, Michelle 273
Sewell, David B. 764
Sexton, John 539
Sexton, Jennifer 799
Sexton, Ellen 880
Seyler, David 634
Seymour, Kim 45
Seymour, Tim 88
Seymour, Ron 378
Sferrazza, Bob 158
Sgaglione, Lucille T. 122
Sgammato, Tom 840
Shaadi, Edgar 852
Shabshab, Nabil 119
Shackell, Daniel 244
Shade, Darren 907
Shadid, Sean 99
Shadix, Michelle 715
Shadix, Ross 787
Shae, Kate 320
Shafer, Thomas C. (Tom) 187
Shafer, Mark 273
Shafer, Walter F. 676
Shafer, Michael 836
Shafer, Jimmy 895
Shafer, Joan M. 909
Shaff, Karen E. 691
Shaffer, Richard 353
Shaffer, Elizabeth 385
Shaffer, Michael A. (Mike) 705
Shaffer, Charles M. (Chuck) 757
Shaffner, Christopher 214
Shafnisky, Adam 18
Shagoury, Antoine 791
Shah, Ken 158
Shah, Ratnesh 204
Shah, Manish 230
Shah, Sonal 392
Shah, Sanjiv 465
Shah, Aarti 528
Shah, Sejal 557
Shah, Ashish 672
Shah, Rajen 792
Shaheen, Jeanne 114
Shaheen, Gabriel L. 435
Shahrabani, David 682
Shahrestani, Navid 804
Shamber, Mark E. 781
Shamberger, Rick 888
Shamburger, Julie N. 779
Shamburger, Mike 810
Shamseddine, Adel 901

Shanahan, Patrick M. (Pat) 135
Shanahan, Julie 419
Shand, Janet 604
Shang, Mark 141
Shank, Melissa 810
Shankar, Guru 161
Shankar, Latha R 582
Shankar, Uday 858
Shankar, Ram 863
Shanks, Robert L. (Bob) 369
Shanks, Eric 858
Shanks, Alan 860
Shannon, Jason 50
Shannon, Albert 247
Shannon, Sean C 316
Shannon, Carol 483
Shannon, Scott 736
Shao, Lei 465
Shapazian, Carole 115
Shapiro, Glenn T. 31
Shapiro, Felice 60
Shapiro, Ronald M. 233
Shapiro, Marc 536
Shapiro, Jodi 589
Shaps, Howard 911
Shara, Thomas J. 511
Sharkawi, Mohamed 200
Sharkey, John 240
Sharkey, Michael D. 558
Sharkey, Benjamin 900
Sharma, Amit 51
Sharma, Ashish 131
Sharma, Devesh 227
Sharma, Vivek 273
Sharma, Vishal 294
Sharma, Anurag 497
Sharma, Ganesh 528
Sharma, Neelima 537
Sharma, Ankur 555
Sharp, Belvia 34
Sharp, M. S. (Scott) 192
Sharp, Crystal 226
Sharp, Robert T. (Bob) 299
Sharp, John 337
Sharp, Erin S. 506
Sharp, Ken 516
Sharp, Michael J. 520
Sharp, Garland 754
Sharp, Andrew 886
Sharp, Jeff 895
Sharpe, Stacy 31
Sharpe, Benjamin 117
Sharpe, Jeff 187
Sharpe, Dean 395
Sharpe, Matthew P. 435
Sharpe, Mikel 892
Sharpin, Tom 932
Shasha, Brian 582
Shashoua, Stanley 770
Shattenkirk, Eric 204
Shattuck, Mayo A. 314
Shatzer, Warren 12
Shaukat, Tariq M. 34
Shaum, Claudia 95
Shaw, Edward 18
Shaw, G W 84
Shaw, Paula 107
Shaw, Ken 135
Shaw, John 199
Shaw, Amy 262
Shaw, William 328
Shaw, Robert K. 400
Shaw, William 497
Shaw, Christi 528
Shaw, Alan H. 618
Shaw, Jeff M. 630
Shaw, Clay 692
Shaw, Barbara 814
Shaw, Craig W. 857
Shaw, Geordie 860
Shaw, Marliese 872
Shaw, Amy 881
Shaw-rice, Jud 446
Shay, Troy 371
Shea, Phil 332
Shea, E. Stewart 454
Shea, Brian 664

Shea, James Joseph 699
Shea, Dennis 792
Shea, Dennis 831
Shea, Molly 919
Sheaffer, Paul 133
Sheahan, Denis K. 154
Sheahan, Jim 334
Shealer, Daniel 483
Sheard, Paul 746
Shearer, Janine 216
Shebik, Steven E. (Steve) 31
Shedlin, Gary S. 131
Sheedy, William M. (Bill) 898
Sheehan, Paul 102
Sheehan, Bill 133
Sheehan, Gary 162
Sheehan, Peter 179
Sheehan, Daniel J. (Dan) 389
Sheehan, Dan 389
Sheehan, James N. 437
Sheehan, Greg 486
Sheehy, Helen 831
Sheeley, Michael J. 872
Sheers, Matthew 272
Shefcik, James 172
Sheffield, Cheryl 652
Shehadi, Ramez 139
Sheilds, Kevin 563
Sheinbaum, Gary 705
Sheinheit, Alvin 570
Sheinman, Kenneth 395
Shelby, Bryan 133
Shelby, Thomas S. 670
Sheldon, Steven 385
Sheldon, Tim 548
Sheldon, Todd N. 704
Shell, Jeff 222
Shell, Yvonne 446
Shelley, Bill 885
Shelley, Ryan 941
Shelowitz, Rachel 242
Shelton, Gen. Henry H. (Hugh) 509
Shelton, Roy 580
Shelton, Kirk 593
Shelton, Dion 599
Shelton, Roland 635
Shelton, Mark S. 759
Shelton, Ken 838
Sheneman, Gary 860
Shenk, Robert G. 279
Shenkin, Kerri 105
Shenkman, Dov 901
Shenoy, Navin 465
Shepard, Andy 14
Shepard, Gerald 158
Shepard, Ann 168
Shepard, Andrew 219
Shepard, Robert 287
Shepard, John 787
Shepardson, Christopher 808
Shepherd, Brian 282
Shepherd, Theresa 907
Shepherd, Brenda 936
Shepler, Jody 345
Sheppard, Charlie 309
Sheppard, Louise 700
Sheppard, Jesse 811
Sheppe, Ted 892
Shera, Gina 489
Sherbin, Bob 627
Sheridan, Maria 185
Sheridan, William 202
Sheridan, Jean 620
Sheridan, Jerry E. 861
Sheridan, Philip 927
Sheridan, Michael 935
Sheriff, Jennifer 530
Sheriff, Abrar 856
Sherlock, Kevin 453
Sherman, Jeffrey S. 119
Sherman, Catherine 157
Sherman, Michael (Mike) 386
Sherman, Peter 639
Sherr, Richard 839
Sherrard, Roger S. 654
Sherrard, J. Andrew 810
Sherrer, Kendell 161

Sherrick, Jim 117
Sherrill, Gregg M. 820
Sherrington, Paul 175
Sherrod, David 869
Shertzer, Teresa 279
Sherwood, Ben 273
Sherwood, Brett 731
Shetty, Suraj 199
Shevsky, David 33
Shiah, James 242
Shick, Jennifer S 18
Shieh, Brian 71
Shiel, James G. 122
Shields, Genny 503
Shields, Kathleen M 770
Shields, Kevin 834
Shields, Inara 923
Shiels, David C. 924
Shiffermiller, Roger 332
Shifflett, Porter 548
Shiffman, Steven B. (Steve) 705
Shiflett, Susan 168
Shifrin, Todd 928
Shigemura, Dean Y. 102
Shih, Elizabeth 266
Shiley, Shawn 739
Shilling, Judy 226
Shilling, Allison 699
Shillingford, Iwona 377
Shimabuku, Hope 934
Shimonishi, Yasuhara 820
Shin, Hak Cheol (H.C.) 2
Shin, Hak 3
Shin, Joonhyok 408
Shin, Jin 408
Shin, Joonhyok 435
Shin, Nam 652
Shin, Jung-tak 672
Shine, Jeff 580
Shine, Daniel P. (Dan) 836
Shinn, Nancy 18
Shinn, David 468
Shinohara, Koji 184
Shinsky, Nate 764
Shipe, Andy 729
Shipley, Michael 170
Shipley, Susan (Susie) Baker 449
Shippey, Mike 926
Shirak, Gregory 912
Shirey, Lonnie 84
Shirk, Amber 757
Shirreffs, James 97
Shirvaikar, Ashwin 203
Shishman, Scott 635
Shiveley, Lisa 808
Shiver, Kim 533
Shiver, Joey 726
Shivers, William C. 449
Shoback, Jacqueline S. 141
Shockley, Harold 468
Shockman, Robert 248
Shoemaker, Carey 605
Sholtis, Donna 390
Shon, Larry D. De 93
Shon, Harim 204
Shonka, Steve 300
Shoop, Charlie 498
Shoquist, Debora C. 627
Shoquist, Debbie 628
Shore, Michael 557
Shore, Barbara 715
Shore, Cara 935
Shoro, Amna 72
Shoro, Claudia 605
Short, Andrea G. 1
Short, Edward T 684
Short, Michael J. (Mike) 736
Short, Brian 737
Short, Marianne D. 880
Shorten, Dermot 709
Shortman, Suzanne 932
Shortt, Thomas 431
Shortt, Tom 431
Shotwell, David F. (Dave) 864
Showers, Mark E. 723
Shrader, Ralph W. 139
Shraga, Ronen 3

Shrestha, Sagun 102
Shriber, Ryan 131
Shrimp, James 923
Shrivastava, Manish M. 704
Shrout, Steve 570
Shroyer, Christopher M. (Chris) 342
Shtjefni, Glen 450
Shudtz, Peter 245
Shue, Russell E 135
Shuff, Joseph 796
Shuffield, Teresa 863
Shugrue, Vincent 380
Shulevich, Gary 767
Shull, David 272
Shulman, Doug 105
Shulman, Cindy 320
Shultz, Jeff 172
Shultz, Katherine 325
Shulusky, Richard 226
Shum, Harry 575
Shuma, Douglas D. 817
Shumacker, Jake 715
Shumaker, Dan 15
Shumate, Michael 49
Shumate, John 668
Shumate, Steve 863
Shuminski, Robert 161
Shunck, Marybeth 349
Shupe, Thomas 72
Shurts, Wayne 808
Shutley, David 454
Shuttleworth, Edward L. 360
Siarkowski, Tracey 337
Sias, Evelyn 897
Siberio, John 891
Sibole, Matthew 786
Sica, Norma 257
Sica, Frank V. 483
Sica, Frank 787
Sichak, Stephen (Steve) 119
Sichel, Hobart (Bart) 151
Siciliano, Betsy 172
Sicola, Sam 697
Siddiqui, Alvia 13
Sideris, Harry K. 286
Sidhu, Jay S. 249
Sidiqi, Khalid 707
Sidor, Kathleen 224
Siebenborn, Bill 254
Siebenmorgen, Tom 365
Siebers, Thomas 47
Siedlecki, Sandy 540
Sieg, Andy 101
Siegel, Tim 15
Siegel, Greg 176
Siegel, Richard 266
Siegel, Kenneth I. 536
Siegel, Michael 582
Siegel, Walter 752
Sieger, Michael D. (Mike) 695
Siegler, Steve 431
Siegmund, Jan 87
Siegrist, Robert N. 154
Siena, James 935
Sienkiewicz, Mark 484
Siereveld, Ryan P 693
Sierra, Joseph 106
Sievert, G. Michael (Mike) 810
Sieving, Charles E. 363
Sieving, Charles E. 612
Sifer, Joseph F. (Joe) 139
Sifer, Joe 139
Sigler, Maggie 337
Sigler, Jon 748
Signorio, Mark 513
Siira, Tyler 886
Silagy, Eric E. 363
Silagy, Eric E. 612
Silander, David 888
Silbaugh, Jason 489
Silberman, Michael 173
Silberstein, Karl 266
Silcock, Chris 427
Silfa, Betty 204
Silitch, Nicholas C. (Nick) 699
Silliman, Craig L. 893
Sills, Stephen J. 28

Sills-Memorial, Clay 635
Silos, Richard 14
Silva, Lauren 53
Silva, Nicole 135
Silva, Stephen 199
Silva, Francisco A. Aristeguieta 203
Silva, Michael 224
Silva, Pedro 248
Silva, Paul 350
Silva, Eduardo 582
Silva, Elif 672
Silva, Ulises 814
Silva, Anthony 901
Silver, Kenneth 171
Silverman, George 330
Silverman, Ami 811
Silvers, Gary 3
Silverstein, Martin B. 391
Silverstein, Ray 787
Silwa, Robert 931
Sim, Joseph 668
Simard, Curtis C. 112
Simco, Lori 860
Simeone, Giovanni 101
Simeone, Robert 533
Simermeyer, Elizabeth A. (Beth) 294
Siminski, Mike 564
Simione, Jay 550
Simkins, Debbie 582
Simkowitz, Daniel A. (Dan) 587
Simler, Jordan 892
Simmerman, George 451
Simmons, Terry 6
Simmons, Paul 97
Simmons, Mark A 224
Simmons, Lori 332
Simmons, Harold 454
Simmons, Jodi 468
Simmons, Brad 503
Simmons, Jeffrey N. (Jeff) 528
Simmons, Catherine 748
Simmons, Earle 799
Simmons, Gary 890
Simmons, Harris H. 941
Simms, Janet 201
Simms, Michael 279
Simms, David 470
Simms, Michael 517
Simms, James 668
Simon, Andrea 172
Simon, Lynn T. 230
Simon, Mindy 232
Simon, Laura 249
Simon, Tracie 355
Simon, Marlene 383
Simon, Samuel J. 461
Simon, Daniel 502
Simon, Arthur L. 509
Simon, Grigore 609
Simon, John R. 673
Simon, Steve 725
Simon, David 770
Simon, Shari 770
Simon, Deborah 770
Simon, Herbert 770
Simon, Larry 771
Simon, Rob 794
Simoncini, Matthew J. 514
Simonds, John 540
Simonds, Michael Q. 886
Simonelli, Lorenzo 382
Simonetti, Beth E. 816
Simons, Kayla 737
Simons, Jerry 808
Simons, Brenda 882
Simons, Doyle R. 921
Simowitz, Rebecca 279
Simpkiss, Courtney 88
Simpson, Joshua 50
Simpson, Terry 131
Simpson, Gerald 185
Simpson, Barry N. 216
Simpson, Shelley 447
Simpson, Kelley 489
Simpson, Kristina 497
Simpson, Sue 539
Simpson, Jay 573

Simpson, David L. 725
Simpson, Mary 777
Simpson, Steve 935
Sims, Jeanie 18
Sims, C. Randall (Randy) 430
Sims, John V. 472
Sims, Robert 645
Sims, Scott 749
Sims, Michael S. 789
Sims, Damon 831
Simson, Thomas H. 143
Sinclair, Christopher A. 557
Sinclair, Donald 722
Sindha, Sam 811
Sindhu, Pradeep S. 490
Singelyn, Matthew 720
Singer, Lori 242
Singer, Jeanine 563
Singer, Amy 896
Singh, Amit 34
Singh, Vipul 87
Singh, Rajinder P. (Raj) 109
Singh, Bobby 131
Singh, Vinod 185
Singh, Rahul 195
Singh, Zorawar Biri 199
Singh, Inder 199
Singh, Irvinder 204
Singh, Manjit 208
Singh, Mala 296
Singh, Rajesh 385
Singh, Rakhee 489
Singh, Harmeet 512
Singh, Harmit J. 521
Singh, Harmit J. 523
Singh, Jasraj 548
Singh, Sonny 643
Singh, Inderjeet 643
Singh, Vishal 643
Singh, Manvinder 707
Singh, Santosh 722
Singh, Shiv 899
Singh, Sanchita 939
Singleton, Alan 184
Singleton, J. Barton 806
Sinha, Smriti 45
Sinha, Dharmendra Kumar 218
Sinhabahu, Charuka 435
Sinko, Jim 764
Sinks, Patrick 572
Sinor, Jim 895
Sipe, Barb 686
Sipes, Kevin 727
Sippo, Art 18
Sippo, William 18
Sirgo, Mauricio 72
Sirkin, Clive 493
Sirkin, David 705
Sirlin, Edwin 767
Sirmans, Jay 772
Sirmon, Gary L. 110
Sirosh, Joseph 576
Siry, Marc 222
Sisco, Sandra 707
Sisemore, Diane 99
Sisemore, Martin B. 857
Sissel, Anne 115
Sitter, David 80
Siu, Paul 573
Sivakumar, Anjana 570
Sivaram, Siva 917
Sivertsen, Laura 261
Sivewright, Bob 109
Siwek, Janusz 429
Six, Beth 483
Six, Sidney 876
Sjodin, Cara 881
Sjonell, Peter 713
Sjoqvist, Nikolaj 907
Skabelund, Hoyt 112
Skaggs, Michael D. (Mike) 821
Skaggs, Sean 888
Skala, Cathy 115
Skala, P. Justin 219
Skalinski, Mark 191
Skally, Matt 617
Skalnik, Alicia 251

Skarbek, Tabetha 6
Skare, Todd A. 687
Skeans, Tracy 939
Skeath, Carter 172
Skeats, Lawrence N. 640
Skelley, Sean 759
Skelton, Bryndon 224
Skelton, Cliff 361
Skerker, Lindsey 220
Skidmore, Timothy 193
Skidmore, Richard 395
Skiles, Todd 743
Skinner, James A. (Jim) 901
Skipper, Colin 185
Skipper, John 273
Skiptunis, Lisa 45
Skivington, Stephanie 912
Sklarew, David 668
Sklens, Tod 596
Skoglund, William B. 637
Skokan, Mike 453
Skolnik, Sheryl 60
Skopick, Richard 178
Skordinski, Matt 773
Skorich, Mike 117
Skorik, Katya 45
Skornicki, Eliezer 227
Skory, John E. 360
Skoufalos, Yannis 693
Skovran, Patrick 141
Skovronsky, Daniel (Dan) 528
Skowronski, Robert 80
Skubak, Mark 928
Skulick, Gino 574
Skyler, Edward 203
Slabach, Christopher 355
Slack, Diane 749
Slack, Jeff 849
Slager, Donald W. (Don) 729
Slappey, Kelley 800
Slate, Larry 135
Slate, Jackie 181
Slate, Kathy 716
Slater, Blake 196
Slater, David 284
Slater, Greg 465
Slater, Catherine I. 472
Slater, Catherine I 472
Slater, Todd A. 638
Slater, Garth 941
Slatin, Mark 749
Slatkin, Diane 159
Slaton, Christie 800
Slattery, Keith 563
Slaugh, Linden 610
Slavens, Scott 528
Slavin, Peter L. 656
Slee, Steven 337
Sleight, Barbara 671
Sleiman, Adham 139
Slepecki, Jason 297
Sleyster, Scott G. 699
Slider, Ray 700
Slifka, Eric 393
Slifka, Andrew 393
Slifka, Richard 394
Slifstein, Barry 742
Slipy, Scott D 480
Slivka, John 170
Sloan, Brian 47
Sloan, Robert 304
Sloan, Rodney L. 419
Sloan, Scott 423
Sloan, Matthew 559
Sloan, Garrett 754
Sloane, Barry R. 180
Sloane, Marshall M. 180
Sloane, Edward G. (Ed) 343
Sloat, Julie 42
Slocum, Michael C. 158
Slofkosky, Sharon 224
Slone, Estella 370
Slone, Greg 413
Slone, Reuben 923
Slootskiy, Alex 665
Slotnik, Joseph J. 147
Sluis, Scott 942

Slusher, John F. 615
Sly, Patrick J. (Pat) 299
Slyconish, John 792
Smaglick, Dorothy 888
Smainwaring, Brenda 868
Small, William J. (Bill) 349
Small, Carolyn 413
Small, Gary M. 870
Small, David 893
Small, Jeff 926
Smalley, Gary G. 857
Smalls, Marva 896
Smart, George M. 360
Smarto, Jean 106
Smeal, Joan 643
Smeaton, Allan 548
Smedley, Jesse 722
Smiddy, Craig R. 636
Smidi, Salam 720
Smiley, Josh 528
Smilie, Karen 620
Smit, Neil 222
Smith, AL 7
Smith, Jeffrey C. 12
Smith, Rob 20
Smith, Lucinda 20
Smith, Julian 25
Smith, Elizabeth 31
Smith, Kathy 32
Smith, Brad D. 34
Smith, Homer 52
Smith, Peter 52
Smith, Nicole 52
Smith, Rodney A. 64
Smith, Denise 69
Smith, Donna N. 80
Smith, Jason 80
Smith, David 81
Smith, Michele 84
Smith, Trey 87
Smith, Nick 88
Smith, Martyn R. 93
Smith, Michael 101
Smith, Deborah 104
Smith, Lorie 107
Smith, Joann 107
Smith, Ryan 111
Smith, Brian 114
Smith, Kimberly 116
Smith, Jeffrey A. 131
Smith, Rob 131
Smith, Justin 133
Smith, Gregory D. (Greg) 135
Smith, Scott 137
Smith, Robert 139
Smith, T. Andrew (Andy) 146
Smith, Drew 148
Smith, Nancy 155
Smith, William G. (Bill) 157
Smith, Skip 157
Smith, Doug 172
Smith, Scott A. 175
Smith, Tiffany 176
Smith, Jim 180
Smith, Chuck 185
Smith, Bradley 190
Smith, D. S. (Dave) 192
Smith, Brian 195
Smith, Peter F. 211
Smith, Brian J. 216
Smith, Allan 226
Smith, Barbara R. 227
Smith, J. David 227
Smith, Wayne T. 230
Smith, P. Paul 230
Smith, Allen 240
Smith, Derrick 245
Smith, Susie 247
Smith, Marc 248
Smith, Richard P. (Rick) 254
Smith, Sherry 261
Smith, Joanne 262
Smith, Glen 272
Smith, Wayne 279
Smith, Al 286
Smith, Molly 293
Smith, Bob 304

Smith, Robert C. 308
Smith, Doug 310
Smith, Donna J 313
Smith, Michael 320
Smith, Ken 323
Smith, J. David 324
Smith, Frederick W. (Fred) 330
Smith, Mikki 337
Smith, Leo 337
Smith, Linda 342
Smith, Jerome R. (Jerry) 343
Smith, Dane P 353
Smith, Thomas 353
Smith, Rita K 355
Smith, Dale A. 358
Smith, Lee M. 362
Smith, Robert E. (Rob) 380
Smith, Mark 380
Smith, Donna 385
Smith, Michael 392
Smith, Sarah E. 395
Smith, Bradford 436
Smith, Michael S. 451
Smith, Dan 457
Smith, Stephen 464
Smith, Stacy J. 465
Smith, Kathleen 470
Smith, Philip A. 474
Smith, Ryan 474
Smith, Brad D. 476
Smith, Steven 488
Smith, Gordon A. 488
Smith, Sara 498
Smith, Mark 500
Smith, Bryan S 507
Smith, Val 507
Smith, Larry D 511
Smith, Nancy 530
Smith, Mark 531
Smith, Jared 533
Smith, Jay 536
Smith, Barry M. 541
Smith, Craig S. 548
Smith, Terry 548
Smith, Janet 555
Smith, Michael R. 560
Smith, Paul A 563
Smith, Deborah 563
Smith, Allen 564
Smith, Joshua 573
Smith, Mary 574
Smith, Bradford L. (Brad) 575
Smith, Donnie 590
Smith, Tricia D. 617
Smith, Herbert 618
Smith, Thomas 620
Smith, Nancy 628
Smith, Gerry P. 633
Smith, Rodger 643
Smith, Ian 643
Smith, Daniel T. (Dan) 648
Smith, Linda 654
Smith, Allen L. 656
Smith, Rhonda 677
Smith, Phil 679
Smith, Harmon D. 704
Smith, Beth 715
Smith, Richard A. 718
Smith, Ronald G. (Ronnie) 721
Smith, Greg 722
Smith, Paula 722
Smith, Scott A. 725
Smith, Matthew L. (Matt) 725
Smith, Susan 727
Smith, Carol Rawls 732
Smith, Shawn B 735
Smith, Pamela 740
Smith, Shawn 744
Smith, Darryl 750
Smith, Carter 750
Smith, Susan F. 768
Smith, B. Scott 774
Smith, O. Bruton 774
Smith, David B. 774
Smith, Bonita 777
Smith, David 784
Smith, Bill 787

Smith, Mark 799
Smith, Laurette 806
Smith, Kristin 808
Smith, Catherine R. (Cathy) 813
Smith, Dennis 825
Smith, Tony 836
Smith, Amos 838
Smith, Greg 842
Smith, Roger C. 843
Smith, Kevin C. 849
Smith, Richard 849
Smith, Richard P. 851
Smith, Stephen W. 852
Smith, Bethany L 855
Smith, Chip 858
Smith, Gerry 863
Smith, L. Duane 867
Smith, Craige L. 869
Smith, William 875
Smith, Ryan 888
Smith, Dan 891
Smith, Kurt 893
Smith, Bob 893
Smith, Ryan 895
Smith, Gregory L. (Greg) 903
Smith, Lesley 903
Smith, Eileen 903
Smith, Dacona 903
Smith, Linda S 905
Smith, Don 907
Smith, James C. (Jim) 908
Smith, Drew 926
Smith, Jeff S. 929
Smith, Paul 935
Smith, Paul V. 936
Smith, Jennifer A. 941
Smith, Virginia 941
Smoke, Tony 25
Smoot, Steve 467
Smoot, Raymond D. (Ray) 867
Smucker, Mark T. 773
Smucker, Richard K. 773
Smullen, Richard (Dick) 529
Smullen-Volz, Lynn 182
Smyklo, Mike 172
Smyth, Gerard 52
Smyth, Jennifer 215
Smyth, Cameron 582
Snead, Ron 286
Snead, Lisa 770
Snedaker, Dianne 358
Snee, James P. 437
Snee, Jim 437
Snell, Erik 262
Snelling, Dawn 539
Snevel, Rick 497
Sng, Yih 820
Snider, Maureen 5
Snider, Kim 334
Snider, Stacey 858
Sniezak, Chris 330
Sniffin, Ted 139
Snively, David F. 585
Snodgrass, Chris 166
Snodgrass, Mark 563
Snook, Amy 808
Snow, Bill 88
Snow, Ola 161
Snow, Kristine A. (Kris) 199
Snowberger, Thomas 114
Snowden, John 57
Snowden, Ed 57
Snyder, Mary 105
Snyder, Steve 140
Snyder, Christine 195
Snyder, Barbara 228
Snyder, Bill 437
Snyder, Tim 446
Snyder, Judy 494
Snyder, Keith 539
Snyder, Rob 635
Snyder, Jay 816
Snyder, Mitch 826
Snyder, Ryan 836
Snyder, Bill 882
Sobas, Laurie 161
Sobeck, Ryan 395

Sobel, Brian M. 104
Sobery, Alan 901
Sobic, Dan 650
Socia, Robert E 385
Socotch, Jayne 454
Soden, Kevin J 161
Soden, Richard 598
Soderbery, Robert 199
Soderini, Anna 395
Soderstrom, Jeff 52
Soehl, Robin 431
Soetenga, Deanne 735
Sogan, Lance 42
Sogge, Todd 214
Sohail, Kashif 555
Sohn, Mike K. 468
Soignier, Scott 159
Soistman, Francis S. (Fran) 17
Sokol, Brandon 610
Sokolov, Richard S. (Rick) 770
Sokolowski, Jeffrey 345
Sola, Jure 750
Solanas, Santiago 200
Solanki, Jigna 901
Solari, Ida 141
Solazzo, Steve 470
Solberg, Jeff 402
Solberg, Jeffrey M 403
Soldi, Marinella 270
Solheim, Leif 74
Soliman, Fady 731
Solis, Andrea 635
Solis, Marissa 668
Solk, Steven (Steve) 201
Sollars, Pat 659
Soller, Kelly 337
Solomon, Randy 18
Solomon, J. Stuart 42
Solomon, John 69
Solomon, Jack 121
SOLOMON, JD 185
Solomon, David M. 395
Solomon, Malou 731
Solomon, Michael 754
Solomon, Janet 799
Solon, Kenneth S. 529
Solotar, Joan 133
Solterer, Karl 858
Somasundaram, Sivasankaran (Soma) 281
Somerfeld, Jessica 122
Somers, Will 671
Sommer, Vince 31
Sommer, Clint 449
Sommer, Christina 555
Sommerdyke, Terry 735
Sommers, Andy 936
Sommese, Julie 885
Son, Richard 408
Son, Jamie 935
Sonecha, Sonia 337
Sonego, Michael J. (Mike) 756
Sonego, Mike 757
Song, J. Jonathan 318
Sonnbichler, Jason 743
Sonnemaker, Scott A. 808
Sonnenberg, Steven A. (Steve) 299
Sonsteby, Charles M. (Chuck) 257
Sonsteng, Chimene 851
Sood, Anjla 6
Sood, Manohar Bindi 204
Sood, Jas 425
Soose, Clinton 131
Soper, Martha 892
Sopko, Jeffrey 502
Soraci, Ben 320
Sorel, Carolle 201
Soren, Laurie 187
Sorensen, Rob 162
Sorensen, Jeralyn 550
Sorensen, Bryan 652
Sorensen, Steven P. 31
Sorenson, John B. (Brad) 142
Sorenson, Rob 162
Sorenson, Arne M. 548
Sorey, James 530
Sorg, Louise 337

Sorge, James 233
Sorgi, Vincent (Vince) 686
Soriano, Lidio V. 682
Soroka, Dina 605
Sortino, Jean 539
Sosebee, Jane 84
Soto, Ramon 18
Soto, Myrna 222
Soto, Andrea 555
Soule, David B. 341
Soules, Steve 139
Soupene, John C. (Jay) 164
Sourisseau, Didier 244
Sousa, Joseph (Joe) 738
South, Ronald 752
Southall, Denise 18
Southard, Sean 923
Southworth, Jeff 885
Souza, Shanae 103
Souza, Ricardo 462
Souza, Michael 547
Souza, Michael 587
Sova, Colleen R. 872
Sovereign, Marla 146
Sowers, Josh 87
Sowinski, Jodi 80
Sowinski, Mark 888
Soza, Miriam 87
Space, Jordan 745
Spackman, Scott 563
Spada, Gerald 792
Spadaccino, Franceen 605
Spagnuolo, John C 767
Spagnuolo, John 767
Spahr, Thomas 431
Spahr, Tom 431
Spahr, Brian 454
Spahr, Shannon 770
Spain, Wade 350
Spain, Wade 350
Spain, Timothy 872
Spaletto, Todd 895
Span, Barbara 919
Spangenberg, Stephan 754
Spangler, Mark 350
Spanier, Mike 601
Spanjers, George 378
Spann, Rick 220
Spanos, Maria 559
Spanos, Mike 667
Spanos, George 912
Sparacino, Serena 620
Sparcino, Michael 750
Sparkman, Ricky D. 230
Sparkman, Julie 720
Sparks, David 214
Sparks, Sara 665
Sparks, Kevin P. 880
Spatafore, Nick 170
Spatoulis, Dino 226
Spaude, Mike 378
Spaulding, Dennis 792
Spaulding, Todd 881
Spaw, Randy O 117
Spayde, Melissa 818
Spears, Stephen 246
Spears, Kyle 459
Speas, Dawn 107
Specht, Bill 715
Spector, Eleanor 365
Spector, David A. 662
Speer, Don 88
Speer, Stephen 109
Speer, Terry 663
Speetzen, Michael T. (Mike) 681
Speidell, Paul 762
Speight, J. Daniel (Dan) 789
Speirs, Ryan 941
Spence, Timothy N. 336
Spence, Karis 450
Spence, William H. 686
Spence, Kenneth F. (Ken) 849
Spencer, Steve 25
Spencer, Steven 25
Spencer, James F. 154
Spencer, John 185
Spencer, James 201

Spencer, Terry K. 641
Spencer, Christine 715
Spencer, Terry 834
Spencer, Ipyana 881
Spencer, Dennis 941
Spencer, Ian 942
Spendiff, Craig 87
Spengler, Richard S. 477
Speranza, James 604
Sperber, Loryn 131
Spero, Bryan V 122
Spero, Vincent A. 660
Speyer, Sharon S. 449
Spicer, Marlene 446
Spicer, Randy 881
Spiegel, Joan 550
Spiegel, Steve 623
Spies, Steve 322
Spiess, David 754
Spiewak, Brian 3
Spillane, Michael 615
Spiller, Kevin 248
Spilman, Thomas 497
Spilman, Jeff 548
Spina, Dario 896
Spinner, Steven L. (Steve) 874
Spira, Steven S. 838
Spira, Aaron 923
Spires, Adrian 88
Spirit, Free 897
Spirko, Kate 161
Spitser, Christy 168
Spitzer, Allison 104
Spitzfaden, Thomas 261
Spivey, Mark 117
Splain, Michael E. (Mike) 643
Splain, Mike 643
Splaine, Thomas F. 511
Spoerry, Jon 559
Spong, Karen 117
Spooner, Patty 101
Spooner, David 839
Sposito, Thomas J. 745
Spracher, John 346
Spradley, Scott 859
Spradlin, Shane M. 663
Sprague, Joseph A. (Joe) 26
Sprague, Robert 87
Sprague, Raymond J. (Ray) 413
Sprain, Keith 370
Sprajcar, John 101
Spray, Stephen 197
Sprecher, Steve 117
Sprecher, Jeffrey C. (Jeff) 466
Spreen, Paul 478
Sprengel, Julie 266
Spreter, Grant 454
Sprigg, Steve 707
Spriggs, Ted 897
Springfield, Susan L. 353
Springmeyer, Douglas 582
Sprinkle, Todd 710
Sprunk, Eric D. 615
Spurgeon, William W. (Bill) 280
Spurling, David A. 421
Spurr, Paul 530
Spylka, John 383
Squadere, Bonnie 497
Squeri, Stephen J. (Steve) 44
Squeri, Steve 45
Squier, Jenny 220
Squire, David 338
Squires, James A. (Jim) 618
Squires, Eric 896
Sreenivasan, Katepalli R. (Sreeni) 606
Sridharan, Balaji 811
Srinivasan, Mukund 71
Srinivasan, Veena 203
Sriram, Subhashini 620
Srivastava, Raj 467
Srivastava, Sam K. 541
Srivastava, Shubhra 555
Srivatsan, Nagaraja 218
Sroka, Kenneth P. 122
Srouji, Johny 69
St-Louis, Serge 385
Staalenburg, Leanne 157

Stachowiak, Tomasz 856
Stachowiak, Tom 856
Stack, John 45
Stack, Edward W. (Ed) 264
Stackalis, Jack 834
Stacy, Jill 246
Stacy, Kelly 409
Stacy, Neel 454
Staczek, Eric 558
Staelens, Kurt C. 759
Staffieri, Victor A. 686
Stafford, Gloria 158
Stafford, Connell 216
Stafford, William P. 346
Stafford, Vernon H. 353
Stafford, Richard 666
Staggs, Lynn 161
Stagias, Peter 550
Stagliano, Joseph R. 598
Stagner, Beth 722
Stagnitti, David 389
Stahl, Kurt 15
Stahl, Neil 719
Stahler, David 935
Stahlman, Ed 769
Stair, Richard 940
Stake, James 737
Staley, Nina 620
Staley, Don 808
Stalick, Theodore R. 567
Stalker, Rebecca 105
Stall, Michelle 248
Stallings, Jay 112
Stallings, Tony 142
Stallings, John G. 867
Stallmeyer, Jan 18
Stamatis, Jay 6
Stamey, Russell H 620
Stamm, John 78
Stammen, Brice 497
Stanbrough, John 731
Stanchfield, Jim 941
Stanczyk, Thomas J 739
Standard, Jim 643
Standish, William A. (Bill) 64
Standley, John T. 731
Standridge, Brant J. 116
Staneff, Matt 811
Stanek, Mary Ellen 735
Stanford, Terry 137
Stanford, Linda 325
Stankey, John T. 84
Stanley, George 88
Stanley, Karen W. 155
Stanley, Jenny 226
Stanley, Gina 332
Stanley, Michael 504
Stanley, Susan D 664
Stanley, Graham 752
Stanley, Marc 932
Stansberry, Heather 739
Stansbury, Christopher D. (Chris) 76
Stansbury, H. Tayloe 476
Stansbury, Tayloe 476
Stanski, Bruce A. 365
Stanton, Jill A. 349
Stanton, Mary 487
Stanton, Kevin J. 554
Stanton, Oliver K. 847
Stanush, Dan 890
Stanutz, Nicholas G. (Nick) 449
Stapel, William 559
Staples, David M. (Dave) 781
Stapleton, Jack 226
Stapleton, Ben 487
Stapleton, Rebecca 745
Stapp, Scott 623
Stark, Arthur (Art) 121
Stark, Kim 405
Stark, Sandra 787
Stark, Brent 936
Starke, John A 487
Starke, James 661
Starnes, Clarke R. 116
Starnes, Karen 117
Starnes, Lee 240
Starnes, Will 334

Starnes, Stacey 498
Starnes, W. Stancil (Stan) 692
Starr, Brett 196
Starr, G. Gabrielle 606
Starr, Tammy 836
Stary, Randy 735
Staskowski, Thomas 39
Staskowski, Darryl 494
Stassi, Phillip J. 481
Stata, Ray 62
States, Lauren 470
Stathakopoulos, George 69
Statler, Kent L. 739
Staton, Melissa 446
Staub, Steve 360
Staub, W. Richard 478
Staublin, Valerie 530
Staudt, Donald 701
Stauffer, Tom 274
Staunton, Mark 558
Staupe, Ase 793
Stavropoulos, Nickolas (Nick) 673
Stchelski, Lisa 539
Stearn, David 519
Stearns, Leah C. 51
Stearns, Christopher D 72
Stearns, Scott 241
Stearns, Caitlin 339
Stec, Lisa 101
Stecher, Kenneth W. (Ken) 197
Stecher, Esta E. 395
Stecher, John 395
STECHER, VERA J 672
Steck, David 752
Stecklein, Mark 881
Stedfast, Sarah B. 898
Stedman, Brian 99
Steel, Richard 131
Steele, Sally A. 228
Steele, Audrey 858
Steele, Don 896
Steenbergen, Phil 337
Steenbergen, Ewout L. 746
Steenstra, Jack 707
Steer, Robert L. 756
Steere, William 672
Steers, Paige 486
Stefanac, John 707
Stefansic, Robert J. (Bob) 462
Stefek, Kyle 720
Steffe, Greg 699
Steffensen, Mark 445
Steffensen, Dwight 805
Stefkovich, Nick 729
Stegeman, John A. 418
Stegeman, Jeff 497
Stegen, Andrew 536
Steger, Troy 419
Steger, Pete 558
Stegner, Robert L. (Bob) 805
Stegner, Bob 805
Steigelman, Jeffrey 927
Steigman, Liz 413
Steimer, Richard 337
Stein, Gary 39
Stein, Jeffrey S. 39
Stein, David L. 80
Stein, Derek K. 131
Stein, Laura 208
Stein, Clint E. 221
Stein, William G. 239
Stein, Sophie 332
Stein, Richard 336
Stein, Bob 370
Stein, Trudy 478
Stein, Richard 838
Stein, Anna 886
Steinbach, Justin 247
Steinbeck, Daryl 834
Steinberg, Joseph S. 443
Steinberg, Stephen 487
Steinberg, Matthew 502
Steinberg, Matt 509
Steinberg, Joseph S. 520
Steiner, Judy 110
Steiner, Tim 147
Steiner, Jeffrey 360

Steiner, David 456
Steiner, Melanie 705
Steiner, Curt 888
Steinfeld, Trudy 606
Steingart, Adam 896
Steinhilber, Greg 170
Steinman, Jennifer 13
Steinman, Justin 18
Steinman, Jonathan 53
Steinman, Axel 576
Steinmetz, Bill 842
Steinour, Stephen D. (Steve) 449
Steinwart, Scott 355
Steinwert, Kent A 323
Stella, John 53
Stelling, Kessel D. 806
Stelman, Randee 5
Stelman, Randee 6
Stemmler, Matt 715
Stemper, William R. (Bill) 222
Stencel, Douglas 735
Stender, David 538
Stengel, William P. (Will) 418
Stengele, Isabella M 550
Stenzel, Christopher (Chris) 237
Stepanova, Ekaterina 483
Stepanski, Kim 671
Stephen, Chris 299
Stephen, Jim 593
Stephen, Buschmeyer 857
Stephens, John J. 84
Stephens, Danny 94
Stephens, Jason 106
Stephens, Anita 115
Stephens, Mark 117
Stephens, Garrett 720
Stephens, Steven D. 941
Stephens-Chemelewski, Stacy 355
Stephenson, Randall L. 84
Stephenson, Jacqueli 135
Stephenson, Winn 330
Stephenson, Stephanie 882
Stepp, Elizabeth 117
Sterbenz, Isaac 749
Sterghos, Nick 580
Sterin, Steven M. (Steve) 63
Sterin, Steven 173
Sterling, Christine 334
Sterling, Michelle 707
Sterling, Kira 841
Stern, Paula 95
Stern, Brian 105
Stern, Marty 220
Stern, Jonathan 366
Stern, Michael K. 585
Stern, Judy 767
Stetler, Eric 735
Stettin, Glen D. 319
Stetz, Gary 118
Steuterman, Chris 226
Steve, Harman 181
Steve, Enos 935
Steven, Lanigan 888
Stevens, Jim 2
Stevens, Timothy (Chip) 19
Stevens, Scott 60
Stevens, James P 96
Stevens, Laura 122
Stevens, Mark 178
Stevens, Sharon 201
Stevens, Dominique 334
Stevens, Shannon 356
Stevens, Charles K. (Chuck) 385
Stevens, Meri 484
Stevens, Roy 517
Stevens, Robyn 666
Stevens, John 836
Stevens, W. Arthur 855
Stevens, Kenneth 862
Stevens, Simon 880
Stevens, Shelli 903
Stevenson, Casey 224
Stevenson, Phil 678
Stevenson, Mark P. 836
Stevenson, Tom 931
Stevenson, Ryan 941
Stevison, Mitch 717

Steward, Jeff 115
Steward, Russ 821
Steward, David L. 930
Stewart, Jerry L 25
Stewart, Lisa 68
Stewart, Thad F 108
Stewart, William (Bill) 139
Stewart, Janie 157
Stewart, Alice 176
Stewart, Jennifer 341
Stewart, Michael J. (Mike) 355
Stewart, John F. 366
Stewart, Nate 453
Stewart, Carol 493
Stewart, Barbara 502
Stewart, Marlene 506
Stewart, Tyler 513
Stewart, Heather 607
Stewart, Don 671
Stewart, Crystal 675
Stewart, Melanie 774
Stgeorge, Marty 483
Stibler, Ellen 555
Stice, J. Mike 924
Stickland, Davina 131
Stickles, Kevin 910
Stidham, Cathy 635
Stiefel, Lester 103
Stiegler, James 279
Stiehl, William G. 757
Stiers, Mark W. 284
Stiff, Cory 672
Stiff, Jacqueline 880
Stiffler-claus, Vanessa 261
Stigers, Michael C. (Mike) 801
Stiles, Dean 487
Stiles, Mark W 852
Still, Mark 194
Still, Kevin A. 214
Stilla, John 332
Stillabower, Gabriel 507
Stilts, Kelly 176
Stilwell, Craig G. 207
Stimson, Bob 678
Stingily, Karl 330
Stinnett, Clay 796
Stinnett, Joseph 878
Stinson, Deirdre 654
Stipanov, John C 688
Stiritz, William P. (Bill) 683
Stirling, David 941
Stirratt, Nada 896
Stis, David 259
Stober, Renee L 135
Stockdale, Barry 53
Stockdale, James 486
Stocke, Sandra 938
Stockman, James 267
Stockmeister, Aaron 336
Stockslager, Matthew 266
Stockton, John 18
Stockton, Charles 246
Stockton, Dmitri L. 382
Stockton, Todd 570
Stockton, David J. 759
Stockton, Jocelyn 905
Stoddard, Sharon 57
Stoddard, Lorilee 942
Stodghill, Jeffrey P 502
Stoecker, Chris 804
Stoeckert, Michael 692
Stoehr, David L. 927
Stoering, Mark E. 933
Stoffel, Dawn 754
Stoffels, Paulus (Paul) 484
Stoffers, Brian F. 169
Stoffregen, Ken 470
Stogner, Thomas 661
Stogner, Joan 895
Stohlmann, Oliver 484
Stoian, Tina 220
Stok, Leon 470
Stokes, Will 153
Stokes, Russell 382
Stokes, Bobby 416
Stokes, Kristen 550
Stokes, Allen 821

Stokke, Doug 287
Stokluska, Rich 378
Stolarsky, Daniel 927
Stolasz, Jeff 593
Stolfi, Carl 394
Stoll, Scott 643
Stollings, Anthony M. (Tony) 349
Stolp, Michael 754
Stoltmann, Gary 503
Stoltz, Don 178
Stone, Peg 13
Stone, Tim 37
Stone, Christina 60
Stone, Brenda 105
Stone, Greg 116
Stone, Robert D. 122
Stone, Nathan 204
Stone, Natalie 243
Stone, Jeffrey 286
Stone, Paul 306
Stone, Carolyn 307
Stone, John 358
Stone, Mitch 365
Stone, Neil 395
Stone, Anita 483
Stone, Marianne 504
Stone, Steven M. 508
Stone, Michael 528
Stone, Samuel G. 564
Stone, Claire 668
Stone, E William 680
Stone, Scott 723
Stone, Mike 870
Stone, Kent V. 888
Stone, Nancy 890
Stone, Bob 937
Stoneburner, Charles 196
Stonehill, Robyn Price 82
Stonesifer, Timothy C. (Tim) 425
Stoness, Scott 500
Stookey, Paula 427
Stooksbury, Spencer 47
Stoops, Elizabeth 332
Storch, Gerald L. 801
Storer, Carrie 270
Storey, Jeffrey K. (Jeff) 181
Storey, Marie 334
Stork, Ryan D. 131
Storto, David E. 656
Story, Jeryl 779
Story, Mark 810
Stoss, Douglas 446
Stotler, Tracy 425
Stotts, Teresa 6
Stoudt, Marilyn J 17
Stouffer, Stephen 770
Stout, Neil 220
Stover, Jeremy 506
Stowe, Jay C. 821
Stowell, John A 273
Stowell, John 286
Strable-Soethout, Deanna D. 691
Strader, H. Gregg 48
Strader, Gregg 48
Straffi, Glenn R. 660
Strafford, Katrina 297
Strah, Steven E. (Steve) 360
Strahan, William 222
Strahlman, Ellen R. 119
Strain, Robert D. (Rob) 96
Strain, Larry 394
Strain, Charles 875
Strain, John F. 925
Stram, Randy 570
Strang, Bill 389
Strang, Carol E 632
Strange, Nicholas (Nick) 705
Strangfeld, John R. 699
Stranghoener, V. Raymond (Ray) 226
Stranghoener, V 226
Strapp, Jennifer 507
Strasburger, John 894
Strasser, Robert H 935
Stratan, Miruna 395
Stratman, R. Joseph 626
Stratton, Ed 125
Stratton, Sarah 224

Stratton, John G. 893
Straub, Maximiliane 733
Straube, Andrew 224
Straubel, Jeffrey B. (JB) 823
Straus, David H. 432
Strauss, Sarah 158
Strauss, Allan H. 233
Strauss, Katrina 274
Strauss, Christianne 383
Strauss, John L 487
Strauss, Richard 555
Stravitz, Mitchell 170
Straw, Mona 345
Stream, Kevin 519
Stredwick, William 45
Strianese, Michael T. 509
Stribley, Lucy 139
Stribling, Heath 726
Strickholm, Glenn 860
Strickland, Hoyt J. 49
Strickland, Samuel R 139
Strickland, Mark 157
Strickland, Robert G 168
Strickland, Tamara 332
Strickland, Eric 620
Strickland, Robert 810
Strickland, Shawn 893
Strimmenos, Sarah 635
Stringer, David 357
Stringer, Sjaloom 548
Stringer, Peter 824
Stringfellow, Tom 247
Stringham, Brian 942
Strittmatter, Kirk 201
Stritzinger, Gina 454
Strode, Nick 241
Stroeh, Brad 350
Stroh, Rosa 422
Stromberg, Stephanie 468
Stromberg, William J. (Bil) 809
Strongin, Steven H. 395
Stroud, Denise 247
Strozzi, Gianluca 671
Strubell, Taylor 232
Struble, Rich 494
Struck, Richard 888
Strunk, Thomas W. (Tom) 930
Struth, Werner 733
Stryker, David M. 452
Stuart, Nicholas 497
Stuart, Jack 726
Stuart, Tim 729
Stubbins, Val 88
Stubbs, Michael 281
Stuccio, Nina 566
Stuhr, Kim 413
Stukenborg, John 837
Stumbo, Kevin J. 230
Stump, James M. 429
Sturdivant, Lisa 131
Sturgell, Robert A. (Bobby) 739
Sturges, Rick 16
Sturycz, Robert 805
Stutts, Garry 346
Stutts, William 886
Stutz, Robert 576
Stuver, Douglas K. (Doug) 651
Styles, Maurice 84
Suarez, Jennifer 171
Suarez, Jaime 674
Suarez, JP 903
Subilia, Sam 803
Sublett, Clay 497
Sublette, Derek J 618
Subramaniam, Venkatachalam 87
Sucher, Steve 557
Suchomel, Joel 269
Suddath, Deena 99
Sudhakar, Ranganathan 200
Sudnick, Steve 337
Suetens, David 791
Suever, Catherine A. (Cathy) 654
Sugar, Robert J. 725
Sugrue, Brian 400
Suh, Willie 643
Suhar, Richard 503
Suhoza, Chris 330

Sukola, Joe 566
Sukumar, Gautam 88
Sukys, Dan 497
Sulentic, Robert E. (Bob) 169
Sulerzyski, Charles W. 666
Sulkes, Carol 269
Sullivan, Christine 31
Sullivan, Steven R 40
Sullivan, Shannon 57
Sullivan, Timothy J. 68
Sullivan, T 68
Sullivan, Gene 109
Sullivan, Bryan 133
Sullivan, Michael 153
Sullivan, Andrew 195
Sullivan, Peter 204
Sullivan, Chip 222
Sullivan, Kathleen 266
Sullivan, William P. (Bill) 295
Sullivan, Bill 313
Sullivan, Robert 336
Sullivan, Briana 415
Sullivan, Rick 425
Sullivan, TJ 457
Sullivan, Gary 457
Sullivan, Jason 463
Sullivan, Adam 604
Sullivan, David 620
Sullivan, John 663
Sullivan, Linda 668
Sullivan, Kevin 671
Sullivan, Jamey 715
Sullivan, Teresa 720
Sullivan, Frank C. 742
Sullivan, Lynne 750
Sullivan, George E. 791
Sullivan, Steve 809
Sullivan, Karen 811
Sullivan, John 827
Sullivan, Mark L. 853
Sullivan, Joanne 881
Sullivan, Brendan 895
Sullivan, Jackie 895
Sullivan, Julie 919
Sullivan-Marx, Eileen 606
Sullivan-Yelko, Teri 700
Sulston, Patrick 555
Summerfelt, William 13
Summerford, R. Michael 855
Summers, James 6
Summers, Kevin V. 94
Summers, Diane M. 97
Summers, Tina 550
Summers, Michael 729
Summers, Dan 806
Summers, Ryan 888
Summerwill, Kelly 620
Summitt, Nicole 576
Sumner, Christopher 533
Sumner, Randee 638
Sumoski, David A. 626
Sumpter, Tammy 668
Sun, Albert 290
Sunada, Masako 133
Sundal, Deborah 881
Sundaram, Eash 483
Sunday, Mark E. 643
Sundell, Daniel 888
Sunderwirth, David 105
Sung, Devin 548
Sunn, Nikki 334
Sunstrom, Torrie 107
Sunu, Virginia 735
Sunywcc, Instructor 484
Suozzi, Christopher 60
Supancich, Kristin 494
Suraci, Armond 84
Suranjan, Magesvaran 693
Surapaneni, Srinivas 919
Suratos, Arnold 628
Sureda, Rob 201
Surette, Jahn 413
Suri, Tanuj 45
Surovich, Robert 511
Surowiec, Yvonne 88
Surplus, Scott 429
Susarla, Manoj 395

Susca, Vito 767
Susi, Scott 602
Susik, Daniel 743
Suske, Lori 550
Suskind, Dennis A. 143
Susman, Sally 671
Susor, Mark 875
Sussan, Georgina 440
Sussman, Andrew J. (Andy) 252
Sustana, Mark 518
Sutaris, Joseph E. 228
Sutcliffe, Marianne 6
Suter, Liz 836
Sutherland, Kenneth 818
Sutherland, David S. (Dave) 878
Sutherland, Jeff 888
Sutter, Victor 533
Sutton, Mark 3
Sutton, Dave 81
Sutton, Scott M. 173
Sutton, Matthew 185
Sutton, Mark S. 472
Sutton, Simon 838
Suyash, Ashu 746
Svanstrom, Johan 316
Svihus, Jennifer 802
Svinte, Mike 470
Svoboda, Michael 170
Svoboda, Rose 356
Svoboda, Frank M. 844
Svoboda, Dan B. 930
Svp, Bernard 49
Swaby, S 941
Swain, Kathleen 31
Swain, Steven E. (Steve) 272
Swain, Skip 869
Swais, Ala 356
Swan, Bob 293
Swan, Robert H. (Bob) 465
Swan, Laura 503
Swan, Michael 517
Swan, Mara E. 543
Swan, Kyle 804
Swango, Gary 402
Swann, Paul 466
Swann, Don 904
Swanner, Angela 661
Swanson, Brian 101
Swanson, Brian 136
Swanson, Duane 196
Swanson, Roxann 199
Swanson, Jordan 446
Swanson, Erika 476
Swanson, Brett 497
Swanson, Cynthia 668
Swanson, Al 679
Swanson, Scott 699
Swanson, Wendy 724
Swanson, Leslie 770
Swanson, Jon 927
Swartley, Richard 884
Swartz, Jeffrey 364
Swartz, Russell 777
Swearengin, Mike 630
Swearingen, John S. 544
Swearingen, Jeffery 668
Sweat, Marcia 796
Swedberg, Joe 437
Swedberg, Greg 457
Swedish, Joseph R. 67
Sweedler, Jonathan 628
Sweeney, Jean 3
Sweeney, Joseph E. (Joe) 52
Sweeney, Gerald 194
Sweeney, Sean 196
Sweeney, Yvonne 273
Sweeney, Richard S. 360
Sweeney, John 517
Sweeney, Karen 735
Sweeney, Tim 743
Sweet, Joy 32
Sweet, Lindsay S 355
Sweetall, Pat 379
Sweney, Elizabeth 661
Swensen, Karl 218
Swensen, Mark 890
Swenson, Lynn 141

Swenson, Ann 665
Swenson, Rod 888
Swerdlow, Steven A. (Steve) 169
Swestka, Jason 578
Swett, Christian R. (Chris) 863
Swiader, Josten 839
Swiecicki, Peter 639
Swieringa, John W. 272
Swift, James 269
Swift, Christopher J. 413
Swift, Malcolm 560
Swift, Thomas 735
Swift, Bob 750
Swift, Robert 750
Swift, Mickey 803
Swiftney, Steven 224
Swiger, Andrew P. (Andy) 320
Swiley, Thomas S. 515
Swindle, J. Dean 168
Swindlehurst, Mary 814
Swinkey, Linda 454
Switalla, Amy 361
Switalski, Pamela 4
Switz, Robert E. (Bob) 574
Switzer, Stephen 191
Switzer, Gary 750
Switzer, John 863
Swoboda, Eric 539
Swoffer, Dale 161
Swofford, Stephen 273
Swords, Sheridan C. 641
Syal, Rajeev (Raj) 449
Sybert, Steve 643
Syed, Hammad 241
Syed, Salman 555
Syhre, Danny 15
Sykes, John 456
Sylstra, Michael 382
Sylvester, Scott 54
Sylvester, Brad 189
Sylvester, Maryrose T. 382
Symeonides, Kara 356
Symonds, Chris 314
Symons, Robert A. 686
Syms, Martha 882
Synek, Christopher R. 936
Syngal, Sonia 830
Synnamon, Bill 905
Syper, John 101
Syrinek, Jason 224
Szablak, Chester J. (Chet) 305
Szallar, Lori 905
Szambelan, Jill 691
Szczepanski, Chet 279
Szczepanski, Chester J. 279
Szczesniak, Stephen 204
Szczupak, David T. (Dave) 923
Szemborski, Anne 623
Szerlong, Timothy J. (Tim) 210
Szeto, Yva 582
Szeto, Ringo 593
Szima, Joseph 847
Szlinis, Bill 337
Szlosek, Thomas A. (Tom) 434
Sznewajs, Robert D. 97
Sznewajs, John G. 552
Szuba, Philip S. (Phil) 782
Szuldman, Diego 204
Szwankowski, Anthony 195
Szymanowski, Joe 337
S¶derlund, Patrick 296

T

Taaffe, Dan 246
Taake, Janet 862
Taback, Jason 273
Tabaczuk, Andrew 53
Tabaka, William 445
Taber, Gerry 672
Tabert, Julius 170
Tabler, Jeff 337
Taborda, Marcelo 474
Taborda, Ruben 484
Tabraham, Dan 420
Tachna, Jeremiah 273

Tacka, David 422
Tackett, Willie 449
Tackitt, Susan 141
Tackoor, Gary 97
Tadlock, Harper 454
Tady, Deborah 175
Taets, Joseph D. (Joe) 74
Tagaras, Neil 715
Taggart, Richard G. 791
Tai, Pin 167
Taiclet, James D. (Jim) 51
Taira, John 179
Tait, Steven (Steve) 361
Takac, Kevin 498
Takahashi, Lance 179
Takashima, Denise 822
Takis, Josh 799
Takushi, Dana 103
Talaga, Dana 355
Talamo, John 838
Talaulicar, Anant 248
Talavera, Judith 42
Talbot, Jeff 507
Talbot, Brian 564
Talbot, Chris 707
Talbott, Jeff 810
Talcott, Christine 87
Talcott, Patrick 664
Talhouet, Patrice de 242
Talla, Deepu 628
Tallent, Jimmy C. 869
Talley, Cyndi 416
Talley, Doug 809
Tallman, Brad 490
Talpey, Greg 700
Tam, Cherry 204
Tam, Jamie 395
Tammy, Miller 389
Tan, Alex 22
Tan, Irving 200
Tan, Yak 201
Tan, Phillip 356
Tan, Lee 425
Tan, Jacqueline 465
Tan, Jenny 693
Tanaka, Robyn 102
Tanasijevich, George 513
Tancrati, Juliana 109
Tandon, Saurabh 67
Tandon, Ashish 158
Tandy, Sonya 226
Taneja, Rajat 898
Tanen, Lauren 705
Tang, Jesse 253
Tang, George 570
Tang, Pengbo 792
Tangen, Melissa 18
Tangney, Eugene 743
Taniguchi, Arthur K 103
Tanimoto, Dale 103
Tanis, Justin 456
Tank, Cindy P 517
Tankesley, Mark 226
Tanksley, Rob 859
Tannehill, Martha 392
Tanner, Teresa J. 336
Tanner, Kirk 667
Tanoue, Donna A. 103
Tans, Gillian 689
Tansey, Douglas 395
Tant, Greg 580
Tanwar, Ankit 102
Tanz, Larry 603
Taparausky, Kevin 839
Tappan, Skip 156
Tappeiner, Max 513
Tarafa, Jose 553
Tarantino, George 484
Taranto, Tony 172
Taraporevala, Cyrus 791
Tarasova, Natasha 551
Tarbell, Mike 615
Tarbet, Linda 754
Tarbox, Ned 486
Tarby, Todd 380
Tarchetti, Mark S. 608
Tareen, Irfan 45

Tarkinton, Timothy 643
Tarnowski, Dennis 870
Tarr, Jeffrey 246
Tartaglione, Paul 139
Tarter, Jeff 53
Tarvin, Julie 468
Tashjian, Lee 365
Tasser, Linda 345
Tastad, Carolyn 693
Tasy, Mark 632
Tatachar, Gopinath 105
Tate, Greg 748
Tate, Cornelius 772
Tate, Howard M 812
Tateosian, David 358
Tatera, Robert 220
Tatterson, W. Mark 869
Tatum, Greg 676
Taubert, Jennifer 484
Taubman, Ross E. 692
Taugher, Tom 504
Taunton, Michael 76
Tavakoli, Nader 39
Tavalsky, Gregory 470
Tavares, Chris 135
Tavlarides, Toula 105
Tawasha, Nelson 446
Tawney, Jeff 840
Tay, Talal 246
Taychakhoonavudh, Neeracha 748
Taylor, J 49
Taylor, Ryan 80
Taylor, Shawna 101
Taylor, Daniel 113
Taylor, Steven W 122
Taylor, Kandice 135
Taylor, Ashley 158
Taylor, Jacque 159
Taylor, Linda 176
Taylor, Eric 196
Taylor, Clinton 204
Taylor, Brock 214
Taylor, Warren 249
Taylor, Lyndon C. 263
Taylor, Judy 274
Taylor, Rhonda M. 275
Taylor, Emily 276
Taylor, Stephen M. (Steve) 294
Taylor, Karen 307
Taylor, Kenneth 313
Taylor, Ken 313
Taylor, Robert C. 365
Taylor, Bernadette 377
Taylor, Cynthia 378
Taylor, Robert 392
Taylor, Paul W. 403
Taylor, Pamela J. (Pam) 432
Taylor, Erin 447
Taylor, Brandon 447
Taylor, Jim 451
Taylor, Anna 454
Taylor, Ben 457
Taylor, Kevin 470
Taylor, Tom 487
Taylor, Michael 489
Taylor, Patti L 507
Taylor, Bruce 559
Taylor, Scott 590
Taylor, Howard 625
Taylor, Roger 661
Taylor, Tim G. 675
Taylor, David S. 693
Taylor, Julie 693
Taylor, Sharon C. 699
Taylor, Sue 699
Taylor, Bob 715
Taylor, Hinton 722
Taylor, Sarah 731
Taylor, Angela Pittman 735
Taylor, Bret 748
Taylor, Shirley 752
Taylor, Carter 754
Taylor, Kenneth R. (Ken) 766
Taylor, Darnessa 769
Taylor, Shelli 787
Taylor, Malcolm 831
Taylor, Steve 860

Taylor, Renee 863
Taylor, Fritz 866
Taylor, Kelly 875
Taylor, Ashley 903
Taylor, Nick 912
Taylor, Patricia A. 916
Taylor, Mike P. 930
Taylor, Michael 930
Taylor, Rebecca 935
Taylor, Russ 942
Tchobanova, Boriana 44
Teagle, Walter C. 358
Teague, A. James (Jim) 307
Teague, Jim 307
Teague, Sarah 677
Teal, Pam 333
Teare, Alan 185
Tebon, Dennis 60
Tech, Eric 597
Tedeschi, Anthony 818
Tedjarati, Shane 434
Teed, Ellie 722
Teel, Jordan 569
Teel, Lawrence E. (Skip) 920
Teerdhala, Partha 182
Teitelbaum, Mark 170
Tejeda, Ray 457
Telesmanic, Robert 218
Telesz, Todd E. 214
Telesz, Scott E. 687
Telfer, Pamela 530
Telles, Mark 337
Tellez, George 332
Tellkamp, Scott 246
Temares, Steven H. (Steve) 121
Temelkov, Emil 366
Tempel, Trent 609
Temple, Mike 378
Temple, Michael G. (Mike) 697
Templeton, Richard K. (Rich) 825
Templin, Donald C. (Don) 544
Templin, Roy W 923
Tendler, Craig 484
Tenenbaum, Brian M. 725
Teng, Frank 486
Tengel, Jeffrey J. (Jeff) 664
Tengelin, Michael 382
Tengler, Nancy 419
Tennant, Nancy 923
Tennessen, Jeffrey 722
Tennet, Nancy 923
Tenney, Dan 2
Tennison, Lynden L. 868
Tennity, Jennifer Villa 201
Tennyson, Jeff 712
Tennyson, Crystal 763
Tenorio, Orlando 219
Tenpas, Kevin S. 419
Teo, Gary 290
Teplinsky, Nellie 768
Tepper, Beth 457
Terbush, Randy 87
Terekhova, Victoria 497
Teresi, Todd 69
Terifay, Robert J. 719
Terkelsen, Franklin 894
Terlescki, Cathy 882
Terpsma, Daniel W. 187
Terrell, Karenann 115
Terrell, Mike 196
Terribile, Jennifer 202
Terris, Maria 708
Terry, Sara 146
Terry, Rick O. 419
Terry, Cheryl 454
Terry, Thomas S. (Tom) 863
Tervort, Nathan 941
Terzolo, Dave 170
Tesker, Steve 875
Teslik, Sarah B 68
Tessler, Herv © 934
Testa, Christopher P. 874
Testor, Joseph 31
Tetreault, Kristin 413
Tewes, Timothy A. (Tim) 601
Thacker, Dan 796
Thackray, Brian 131

Thaden, Terry 668
Thaker, Ashish 37
Tham, Russell 71
Thaman, Michael H. (Mike) 648
Thames, Andria 760
Thames, Thomas B. 762
Thanh, Mai Trang 434
Tharby, Linda M. 119
Tharmaratnam, Anand 478
Tharp, Morris A. 767
Tharp, Randall 863
Thaus, Kurt B. 817
Thayer, Jonathan W. (Jack) 314
Theiler, Kris 273
Theiller, George J. 233
Thein, Timothy 204
Theis, Chris 109
Theisen, Linda 557
Theisen, Jen 737
Theisen, Randall S. 916
Theiss, Paul 620
Theiss, Dave 895
Theissing, Jennifer 53
Thelan, John 241
Theleman, David 598
Thengvall, Kelly 84
Theobald, Chris 3
Theodorou, Tasos 774
Theriault, Ryan 942
Thermos, Elli 489
Theuerkauf, Mark 261
Thevenet, Richard 124
Thezan, Alexander 158
Thiara, Tara 37
Thibeault, Anne 700
Thibodeau, Johnathan 668
Thibodeaux, Faron J. 68
Thibodeaux, Shelia 454
Thiel, John 101
Thielen, Bruce J 590
Thieneman, Timothy 680
Thiers, Bernard P. 580
Thiesing, James 481
Thiessen, Eric 760
Thigpen, Carl S. 697
Thirakoune, Kham 792
Thirot, Olivier G. 494
Thirumurugan, Appou 374
Thiry, Kent J. 258
Thissen, Karen Wilson 52
Thole, Karen 831
Thom, Matt 383
Thoma, Ronald 244
Thoma, Jane 390
Thoma, Joy 555
Thomaes, Marc 604
Thomas, Toby L. 42
Thomas, LeAnn M 52
Thomas, Dan 107
Thomas, Michael M. (Mike) 139
Thomas, Carolyn 176
Thomas, Julie 185
Thomas, Christopher 185
Thomas, Howard 185
Thomas, Anthony 204
Thomas, Steve 222
Thomas, Greg 248
Thomas, Brandi 262
Thomas, David J. 282
Thomas, Amy 300
Thomas, Bridgett 304
Thomas, William R. 308
Thomas, Gary L. 308
Thomas, Stephanie 332
Thomas, Ian 365
Thomas, David M. 371
Thomas, Jim 390
Thomas, Suzanne C. 406
Thomas, Deborah M. (Deb) 415
Thomas, Clay 454
Thomas, Bradley 497
Thomas, Michael 497
Thomas, Steve 504
Thomas, Rob 516
Thomas, Joseph 537
Thomas, Roni 539
Thomas, Nixon 550

Thomas, Jill 557
Thomas, Christy 580
Thomas, Betty 582
Thomas, David 605
Thomas, Geevy S.K. 616
Thomas, Paige L. 617
Thomas, Shundrawn 620
Thomas, Stephen 670
Thomas, Brande 677
Thomas, Laurita 720
Thomas, Paul 733
Thomas, Martin (Marty) 738
Thomas, Randy 750
Thomas, John M. 821
Thomas, Timothy 842
Thomas, Karen 888
Thomas, Cheryl 890
Thomas, Anne 903
Thomas, Denise 908
Thomas, Anthony W. (Tony) 926
Thomasjr, William 863
Thomason, Troy 135
Thomason, Linton J. (Lin) 400
Thomason, David S. 673
Thomason, Chad 763
Thomason, Amy 818
Thomasson, Jim 300
Thome, James 875
Thomison, Phil 875
Thompson, Matthew A. (Matt) 11
Thompson, Matt 11
Thompson, Cheryl 25
Thompson, Jeffrey D. (Jeff) 125
Thompson, Elizabeth M. (Betty) 139
Thompson, Terry 139
Thompson, Dale A. 157
Thompson, Dana 159
Thompson, Michael 170
Thompson, Gregg 185
Thompson, Bruce 191
Thompson, Mike 198
Thompson, Brandon 222
Thompson, Lisa 224
Thompson, William A. 233
Thompson, Lori 248
Thompson, Christopher 295
Thompson, Patrick 317
Thompson, Craig 330
Thompson, Kent T. 349
Thompson, Michael 377
Thompson, Leslie 392
Thompson, Laura K. 397
Thompson, Steve 411
Thompson, Kirk 447
Thompson, Mark E. 449
Thompson, Angel 470
Thompson, Rich 487
Thompson, Brenda 504
Thompson, Matt 507
Thompson, Rebecca 507
Thompson, Brian 517
Thompson, James 530
Thompson, Matthew 550
Thompson, Robert 559
Thompson, John W. 576
Thompson, Kevin L. 577
Thompson, Jim 634
Thompson, Geoff 635
Thompson, Lewis 643
Thompson, Deanna 651
Thompson, Amy 665
Thompson, Julian 671
Thompson, Maria 680
Thompson, Peter 680
Thompson, Paul W. 686
Thompson, James H. (Jim) 707
Thompson, Scott 715
Thompson, Mike 743
Thompson, Marcy J. 775
Thompson, Kathy C. 796
Thompson, Sean 804
Thompson, Mike 811
Thompson, Crystal 855
Thompson, Beryl 893
Thompson, John D. (David) 918
Thompson, Kenny D 923
Thompson, Robert 923

Thompson, Joseph F. 927
Thompson, Brian 937
Thomson, James A. 24
Thomson, Wayne 45
Thomson, Brooke 84
Thomson, Glenn 294
Thomson, Robert 610
Thomson, Ross 767
Thomson, Michael R 805
Thomson, Andrew J. (Andy) 836
Thornberry, Richard G. (Rick) 712
Thorne, James 506
Thorneburg, Amber 101
Thorner, Ben 566
Thornton, Larry 207
Thornton, Randolph I. 239
Thornton, Bob 358
Thornton, Janis 550
Thornton, Daniel P. (Dan) 664
Thornton, Piper 668
Thornton, Robin 769
Thorpe, Linda 111
Thorpe, Debra (Deb) 494
Thorpe, Brad 665
Thorson, Daniel 713
Thorson, Robert A. 915
Thottikamath, Sethu 334
Thrane, Cara 813
Thrash, Trent 935
Threlkeld, Linda 453
Thresher, Brad 769
Thrush, Bryan 440
Thulin, Inge G. 2
Thull, Todd 241
thumbnail, Richard Stevenson 942
Thuning, Elizabeth 888
Thurber, Robert 808
Thurber, Robert C 808
Thurm, Patrick 752
Thurman, Charles 115
Thurman, William 336
Thurston, Stephen 190
Thurston, Charlie 222
Thwing, Rob 385
Thygesen, Mikael 770
Th©paut, Eric 142
Tibke, Kathy 530
Tichenor, Jim 659
Tidwell, Todd 101
Tidwell, Rishma 191
Tidwell, Kristopher 813
Tiede, Robert C. (Rob) 775
Tiedemann, Ed 707
Tiegs, Randy 824
Tierney, Brian X. 42
Tierney, Kathleen M. 122
Tierney, Thomas J. (Tom) 293
Tierney, James 530
Tierney, Kevin 715
Tierney, Timothy 891
Tiffany, Toby 849
Tigani, Greg 162
Tighe, Vince 563
Tighe, Steve 645
Tigre, Margaret 16
Tilchin, Mike 185
Tilden, Bradley D. (Brad) 26
Tilghman, Richard G 808
Till, Mark 332
Tillemans, Todd W. 422
Tillinghast, Liza 555
Tillman, Audrey Boone 19
Tillman, Tonia 400
Tillman, Lee M. 546
Tillman, Joseph 875
Tilton, Glenn F 191
Timanus, H. E. (Tim) 697
Timchak, Gary 202
Timko, Michael 555
Timm, Bryan L. 865
Timmel, Timothy 196
Timmer, Kristin 540
Timmerman, Douglas 33
Timmerman, Gail 489
Timmins, Lawrence 106
Timmons, Brian 157
Timmons, James T. (Jimmy) 518

Timmons, Tom 912
Timol, Tarek 551
Tindal, Carrie 808
Tindall, Todd 715
Tinga, Wiebe 415
Tinkey, James 590
Tinsley, James 153
Tinson, Jim 893
Tippit, John 456
Tippl, Thomas 10
Tipton, John (Stephen) 430
Tirador, Gabriel 567
Tisbert, Brian 487
Tisch, Jonathan M. 536
Tisch, James S. 536
Tisch, Andrew H. 536
Tischler, Mary 172
Tishman, Daniel R. (Dan) 15
Tisone, Bob 935
Tistinic, Wendy 262
Tithof, Scott 87
Titova, Zornitsa 928
Titus, James 754
Titzman, Donna 890
Tizzio, Vincent C. 596
Tkacz, Richard M. 872
Tobias, Hugh 901
TOBIN, JIM 45
Tobison, Gary 371
Tocher, Catherine S. 400
Toczydlowski, Greg C 849
Todaro, Susie 497
Todaro, Michael J. 538
Todd, Pam 179
Todd, Paul 293
Todd, Michael 385
Todd, Terry 404
Todd, Colin 425
Todd, Ron 745
Todd, Brian R 808
Todeschini, Diego J 899
Todhunter, Jeff 432
Toffey, Bryan 15
Tognoli, John 530
Toh, Ryugo 699
Tokar, Jeff 576
Tokuda, Jason 700
Tokuda, Lisa 700
Tolan, Matthew 93
Tolar, Miranda 7
Tolbert, Rita 881
Toledano, Udi 28
Toledo, Aimara 700
Toler, Chandara 582
Toll, Robert I. 841
Tolle, Jessica 668
Tollison, Eddie 259
Tolliver, Michael 7
Tolliver, Paula 465
Tolly, Morris 149
Tolson, Glenda 769
Tom, Chester 195
Tom, Teresa 770
Tomak, Scott 497
Tomas, Jose 67
Tomasevic, Josip 20
Tomasi, Peter 891
Tomassetti, Michele 88
Tomasso, Joseph 242
Tomb, Matthew C. (Matt) 345
Tomczyk, James E. 187
Tomei, Joseph 784
Tomek, Michael 159
Tomek, Bob 176
Tomic, Brano 350
Tomich, Walt 449
Tomkiewicz, Tracy 72
Tomko, Carole 311
Tomlen, Melissa 938
Tomlin, Randy 84
Tomlinson, Scott 495
Tomlinson, Marc 530
Tomlinson, Robert 834
Tomoda, Scott 587
Tompkins, Cathlyn L. (Cathy) 189
Tompkins, Cathy 189
Tompkins, Richard 582

Tompkins, Richard 668
Tom©, Carol B. 431
Tonelli, John 332
Toner, Richard 699
Toner, John 699
Toney, Frederiek 370
Toney, Charles 567
Tong, Ming 213
Tong, Christine 486
Tong, Winifer 875
Tonnison, John 816
Tonno, Jim 699
Tonyan, Peter 929
Toohey, Sean 294
Tooker, A. Morris (Mo) 413
Toolen, Linda 194
Tooley, Mark 593
Tooley, Russell 859
Toomajian, Marty 113
Toomey, John 817
Toporek, Dan 904
Topalian, Noha 668
Topkins, Alex 395
Topp, Jonathan 158
Torchiana, David F. 656
Torchiana, David 656
Torette, Debra 805
Toretti, Christine J. 745
Torgow, Gary H. 187
Torma, Frank J 593
Tornga, Mark 133
Torno, Vitaliano 649
Tornquist, Alice 707
Toro, Reinaldo 18
Torocsik, Andras 528
Torok, Ken 135
Torok, Ken 875
TORRANCE, JEFFERY 708
Torreano, Gail 85
Torrence, Joseph 187
Torres, Carole 498
Torres, Mark 518
Torres, Russ 608
Torres, Debra 668
Torres, Laura 682
Torres, Hector 895
Tosi-Renna, Barbara Ann 604
Toso, Greg 905
Tostengard, Scott 889
Tostevin, Christy 509
Tostevin, Peter 875
Toth, Scott 259
Toulon, Rik 172
Toussaint, Donald R. 250
Touza, Carlos 356
Tovin, Hal R. 149
Towe, Nancy 904
Tower, Erika 840
Towle, Terry 365
Towler, Fred 472
Towne, Kyle 266
Townes, Chad 84
Towns, Cheryl 497
Towns, Fred 805
Townsend, Ronald D. (Ron) 113
Townsend, Kent G. 159
Townsend, Tally 161
Townsend, Adam 171
Townsend, Jay 173
Townsend, Jeffrey A. (Jeff) 183
Townsend, Richard 261
Townsend, Alan 287
Townsend, Bruce A 330
Townsend, Drew 419
Townsend, Gayle 507
Townsend, Jason 720
Toy, Brian 504
Toy, David 505
Tozzi, Vincent 233
Tozzi, Andre 293
Tracey, Scott 125
Trach, Andrei 553
Trachimowicz, Richard J. 872
Trachtman, Clare 115
Traci, Dana 269
Tracy, Angela 507
Tracy, Thomas (Tom) 624

Tracy, William 722
Tracy, Jennifer 896
Traficanti, Joseph J. (Joe) 874
Trafton, Eric 18
Trafton, Dale 503
Trager, A. Scott 727
Trager, Steven E. (Steve) 727
Trager, Bernard M. 727
Tragianopoulos, Victoria 897
Tragl, Karl 75
Trahan, Claude 234
Trahan, Claude 235
Trahan, Jeff 261
Trahan, Scott 840
Traicoff, Andy 397
Train, Michael H. 299
Trakimas, Ann 214
Tramack, Michael 804
Trammell, Kenneth R. (Ken) 820
Tramontin, Shannon 564
Trampas, Mike 661
Tran, Long 131
Tran, Henry 224
Tran, Courtney 507
Tran, Hung 901
Tranchita, Daniel 735
Trandai, Tim S 750
Trani, Cara 486
Transon, Robert 31
Transue, Bill 787
Trant, Greg 811
Trapani, Carol 170
Trasatt, Andrew 356
Trask, Tallman 286
Traub, Michael 733
Trauberman, Jeff 135
Traut, Stephanie 787
Trautfetter, Henry 201
Trautman, David L. 653
Trautman, Robert E. 664
Travaille, Tim 376
Travis, Joy 404
Travis, Amanda 504
Travis, Mary 507
Trawick, John G. 778
Trawicki, Roman 943
Traynham, William W. 48
Traynis, Arnold 266
Treadway, Jeff 224
Treadway, Terry 300
Treadway, Todd 635
Treadway, Brandy 661
Treanor, John 59
Trease, Richard 863
Trebilcock, James R. (Jim) 282
Trebilcock, Jim 282
Treece, Christopher G. 403
Treese, Brad 811
Tregaskis, Gay 467
Treibic, Adam 355
Treichel, Gus 892
Trelease, Mark 615
Trella, Ronald 218
Trella, Chris 380
Tremblay, Stephan 875
Trembley, Mike 383
Trenary, Ty 810
Trend, Jonathan 570
Trenski, Gregory 182
Trent, Robert 103
Trentsch, Brian 754
Treon, Todd 161
Tressler, Charles 671
Trevathan, James E. 907
Trezise, Scott A. 181
Triano, Anthony R 298
Tribble, Agnes 855
Trice, Michael 117
Trice, David W. 308
Trick, David 39
Trigg, Donald D. 183
Trigg, Shane 748
Trigo, David 570
Trillo, Manny 899
Trimble, Andrea 122
Trimmer, Kim 511
Trinh, Roger 5

Trinh, Roger 6
Tripathi, Sushma 87
Tripeny, R. Tony 240
Triplett, Michael W. 194
Triplett, Michael 260
Triplett, Neal 287
Triplett, Robin 449
Triplett, Rob 635
Tripoli, Domenic 470
Tripp, Mark 81
Tripp, Ann K. 409
Tritschler, David J 934
Tritsis, Mary 108
Tritt, Gary 259
Tritton, Mark J. 813
Troan, Ole 199
Troberman, Gayle 456
Troccoli, Alejandro 627
Trocin, Jeffrey E. (Jeff) 714
Trodden, Timothy 911
Trofino, Ed 919
Troia, Maria 901
Trolli, Michele D. 538
Trollope, Rowan M. 199
Tropf, Peter 772
Tropp, Tom 378
Trost, Greg 53
Trosvig, Kelli 720
Trotman, Kwame 893
Trotter, Beth 454
Trout, Christopher 447
Trovato, Joseph 570
Trovillion, Raleigh 863
Troxell, Tami 494
Troy, Thomas M. 31
Troyan, John 454
Troyer, Todd 157
Trozinski, Steve 484
Trubiano, Steve 457
Truckermiller, Debbie 377
Trudell, Cynthia M. 667
Truelove, Brian D. 423
Truesdale, Kellyanne 598
Truitt, Jim 772
Trump, Christine 607
Trunko, Tiffany 671
Truschke, Donald J 224
Truscott, William F. (Ted) 52
Truskey, George 287
Truso, Stephen 888
Trusty, Mick 404
Trusty, Steven W. (Steve) 768
Tryba, Martha 370
Tryniski, Mark E. 228
Tsacalis, Norman 896
Tsafaridis, George 52
Tsang, Florence 570
Tsao, Andy 804
Tse, Kenneth 446
Tse, Cindy 713
Tsen, Irene 350
Tsen, Lisa 350
Tseng, Peter 297
Tsentas, Michael 159
Tshudy, Doug 376
Tsiakals, Joseph 115
Tsien, Matthew (Matt) 385
Tsigaras, Jennifer 713
Tsimbinos, Steven J. 632
Tsokova, Olga 358
Tsou, Rose 34
Tsourapas, Panagiotis 219
Tsourapas, George 693
Tsourmas, John 849
Tsuchitani, Yuri 465
Tsujihara, Kevin 838
Tu, Lawrence P. (Larry) 171
Tubb, William 807
Tubb, Bill 808
Tucciarone, Louis 15
Tuchschmidt, Tom C 573
Tucker, Mark 18
Tucker, Michael K. 93
Tucker, Mike 115
Tucker, Jay 116
Tucker, Chris 300
Tucker, David 307

Tucker, Jason 355
Tucker, Jason 489
Tucker, Amy 665
Tucker, Jeff 678
Tucker, Sam 895
Tucker, Adam 896
Tucky, Kelley 573
Tudor, Sorin 131
Tudor, Charlotte 273
Tueckes, Amy 332
Tuffaha, Sam 84
Tuffin, Mark 507
Tuftee, Debbie 224
Tuggle, Anthony 84
Tuggle, Charles T. 353
Tuley, Sean 526
Tulimieri, Jay 852
Tullier, Kelly M. 898
Tullo, John 555
Tulloss, John 117
Tulsi, Japjit 293
Tummala, Gopi 643
Tummillo, Michael 537
Tunanidas, Amy 911
Tunez, Roland 84
Tung, Teik 555
Tunnicliff, Dan 777
Tuohy, Matthew 88
Turato, John 93
Turecek, Claudia 57
Turetsky, Larisa 105
Turi, Carol 106
Turits, Michael 715
Turley, Bob 15
Turley, Cassidy 176
Turnage, Sue 246
Turnbach, Thomas 827
Turnbull, Robert 246
Turnbull, Jenifer 802
Turnbull, John R 881
Turner, Brian 6
Turner, Dustin J 122
Turner, Jill 181
Turner, Amanda 197
Turner, Julie 204
Turner, Gregory 213
Turner, Jeffrey 226
Turner, Jim L. 259
Turner, Keene S. 306
Turner, Kerry 333
Turner, Mark 370
Turner, Joseph W. (Joe) 400
Turner, William V. 400
Turner, Michael R. (Mike) 423
Turner, Simon 452
Turner, John C. 580
Turner, M. Terry 677
Turner, John M. 721
Turner, David J. 721
Turner, Michele 731
Turner, Mike 808
Turner, Jonathan 808
Turner, Steve 901
Turner, Mark A. 931
Turney, Patricia 57
Turnini, Jimmy 263
Turowski, Steven 827
Turton, Daniel 304
Tusinski, Matt 409
Tuthill, Allen 82
Tuthill, Debra 800
Tutkovics, Julie C. 449
Tutor, Ronald N. (Ron) 857
Tutt, James 635
Tutt, Eddie 903
Tuttle, Russ 770
Tuttle, Douglas 942
Tuzun, Tayfun 336
Tveretinova, Vera 84
Twachtman, Erich 18
Twardowski, Kirk 628
Twitchell, Elaine 792
Twohig, Paul 787
Twombly, Dillon 570
Tyacke, Gene 69
Tydings, Tom 810

Tye, Chris 365
Tyle, Craig S. 373
Tylee, Faye 932
Tyler, Tina M 813
Tyler, Breck W. 855
Tyler, Nick 860
Tymms, Jason 555
Tyndall, William 286
Tyndall, Robert 700
Tynes, Tommy 722
Tyree, Sarah 214
Tyree, Nancy 563
Tyree, Laurie 799
Tyrholm, Laura 131
Tyros, John 425
Tyrrell, Robert 39
Tyrrell, Nathan S. 440
Tyrrell, Pat 882
Tyson, John H. 860
Tysseland, Bernt 793

U

Ubell, Elizabeth 398
Uchida, Kathryn 56
Udhwan, Robin 849
Uebelhor, Steve 677
Uehara, Daizo 415
Ufland, Bob 770
Ugarte, Alfonso J 224
Ugas, Jonathan 665
Ugron, Blake 936
Uhlir, Beth 356
Ulbrich, Christian 486
Ulibarri, Connie 882
Uliyar, Suhas 643
Ullman, Greg 666
Ullmann, Michael H. 484
Ullsperger, Dewayne 881
Ulrich, Beth 378
Umanoff, Adam S. 295
Umek, Tony 365
Umpleby, D. James (Jim) 166
Underberg, Scott 722
Underhill, Kim 499
Underhill, Mike 508
Underwood, Jennifer 705
Unger, Sharon 479
Unger, David 932
Unkraut, Scott 337
Unninayar, Kam 836
Unowsky, Keri Goldstein 353
Unthank, Ryan 735
Upadek, Kristen 891
Upchurch, Jim 12
Upchurch, Eric 191
Upchurch, John 286
Upchurch, W. Howard 407
Updyke, Howard 667
Urbain, Donna 479
Urban, Tony 164
Urban, Greg 558
Urban, Kevin J. 705
Urban, Adrienne 929
Urdapilleta, Eduardo 137
Urech, Greg 519
Urias, John M. 645
Uribe, Elias 202
Uribe-Granja, Manuel 6
Uricoli, Dave 714
Urland, Taisha 548
Urrabazo, Ignacio 468
Urtin, Charles G. 745
Utermark, D. Chad 626
Utermark, Chad 626
Utley, Tana L. 166
Utrup, Brian 497
Utter, Matthew 178
Utter, Carl 332
Utz, John A. 80
Utz, Jennifer K 548
Utzschneider, Peter 643
Uyeda, Dean 103
Uzzell, Lonny 779

V

VACCARO, SPHR 596
Vaccha, Kenneth 665
Vacha, Chad 860
Vacheron, Terry 799
Vachon, Dave 530
Vadlamannati, Ramaparasad (Ram) 685
Vagelos, P. Roy 719
Vahedian, Tony 161
Vail, Bob 382
Vail, Angela 656
Vaillancourt, Jane 602
Vainisi, William 31
Vairavamurthy, Vidy 131
Vakacherla, Ravi 664
Vakil, Joyen 573
Valderrama, Ernesto 12
Valdez, James 246
Valdron, Mike 668
Valdés, Luis 691
Vale, Michael G. 2
Valek, Carrie 355
Valenca, Alan 809
Valencia, Antonio 254
Valenti, Franco 243
Valenti, Brian 754
Valenti, Susan M. 842
Valenti, Joe 935
Valentine, Melinda 105
Valentine, Ken 336
Valentine, Mark 602
Valentine, Raymond 774
Valentine, Veronica 891
Valentino, Carl 15
Valenzuela, Brittna 494
Valerio, Chuck 869
Valiao, Janis 563
Valicevic, Joe 564
Valin, Jim Van 446
Valine, Yousef A. 353
Valiveti, Srihari 792
Valkenburg, Tina Van 564
Valle, Mauricio Del 153
Vallejo, Anthony 246
Vallely, Art 663
Valles, Montserrat 175
Valls, Juan 458
Valon, Raina 808
Valovcin, David 470
Valseschini, Monica 895
Valverde, Fernando 446
Vamvalis, Laura 77
Van, Neil 18
Van, Don 18
Van, David 477
Van-praag, Mary 243
Vanalebeek, Hans 615
Vanallen, Linda 818
Vanaria, Raymond 233
Vanbebber, David 860
Vance, Tyler 107
Vance, Brian L. 421
Vance, Quonta 431
Vance, Jim 441
Vance, Jennifer 808
VanCleaf, Dannette 634
VanCleef, Alan 390
VanCuren, William T. (Bill) 599
Vande, Sarah 226
Vandenberg, Jeff 282
Vandenberg, Veronika Kwan 838
Vandenbergh, Robert A. 511
VanDenburgh, Diane 793
Vanderhorst, Richard 910
Vanderhyde, Robert 273
Vandervinne, Jeri 706
VanderVoort, Bret 378
Vanderzee, Tracy 842
VanDeVelde, Doug 493
VandeVenter, Debra 886
Vanek, Kate 614
Vanella, Gerard 488
Vangrevenhof, Heather 31
VanLammeren, Patty 31
Vanlandingham, Martel 635

VanLeuven, Megan 197
Vann, David 752
Vann, Brian 935
Vannan, E. Bradley (Brad) 466
Vanneste, Jeffrey H. 514
Vanni, Rob 240
Vanni, Mark 555
Vanommen, Mike 540
Vanstraelen, Bob 748
Vantrieste, Martin 57
Vanweelden, Jim 729
Vanzo, Kendra L. 635
Varadhan, Ashok 395
Varcados, Thomas 204
Vardas, Michael A 620
Vardeleon, Christian 133
Varela, Javier 489
Varga, Stephen A. 747
Vargas, Jennifer Dwyer 95
Vargas, Mirta 161
Vargas, Jorge L 224
Vargas, David 708
Varilek, James A. 638
Varkanis, George 175
Varley, Elizabeth 53
Varley, Victoria 765
Varma, Ravi 45
Varma, Vivek 787
Varma, Prasad 824
Varner, Marc 939
Varney, Cary 720
Varney, Al 934
Varnhagen, Karen 587
Varones, George 53
Varzaly, Brent 137
Vasami, Michael 767
Vascocu, Norman 454
Vasconcellos, Fábio 705
Vashist, Naveen 738
Vasilatos-Younken, Regina 831
Vasos, Todd J. 275
Vasquez, Jaime 24
Vasquez, Janice 57
Vasquez, Bertha 890
Vass, Brooke 919
Vassalluzzo, Joseph S. (Joe) 633
Vatistas, Robert 244
Vatter, Alissa 332
Vaughan, Charles 16
Vaughan, Pegg 446
Vaughan, Peggy 470
Vaughan, Ken 808
Vaughn, Tony D. 263
Vaughn, Greg 500
Vaughn, Jack 771
Vaught, Jamey 454
Vaughters, Charlie 867
Vaupel, Mark D. 437
Vayda, Joseph 497
Vazquez, Joe 220
Vazquez, John 569
Vazquez, Jose 682
Vazquez, John 893
Vazquez, Javier 899
Veach, Steve 449
Veale, Chris 754
Vealey, Anne 185
Vecchio, Jennifer 151
Vedagarbha, Hemanth 643
Vedrenne, Vincent 273
Veeder, Mark 431
Veeraghavachary, Srinivasan 218
Veeramani, Venkat 928
Vega, Olga De La 84
Vega, David 213
Vega, Venus 226
Vega, Omar 541
Vega, Alma 808
Vegher, Michael 137
Vehec, Philip 395
Veiel, Eric L. 809
Veksler, Galina 558
Veksler, Angela D. 905
Vela, Manuel R. (Manny) 818
Velardi, Angela 494
Velasquez, Margaret 247

Velazquez, David M. (Dave) 314
Velazquez, Carlos 929
Velde, Tamara Vande 159
Veldhuizen, Norbert Van 131
Vella, James G. (Jim) 369
Vella, Sal 470
Vellinga, David H. 168
Velotta, Michael 32
Veltmaat, Hans-Bernd 20
Vemana, Prat 431
Ven, Michael G. (Mike) Van de 780
Venhuizen, John S. 9
Venkata, Prasad 929
Venkatachalam, Ps 220
Venkatachalam, Ramu 536
Venkatesh, Kim 216
Ventresca, Dino 934
Ventsam, Steve 516
Ventura, Tom 938
Verbos-Ford, Shelly 454
Verburg, Ken 672
Verderano, Steve 87
Verdesca, Justin 105
Verdi, Joseph G 735
Verdin, Michael 849
Verduin, Patricia 219
Vergara, Yanira 39
Vergine, Stephen 84
Verhoff, Gary 349
Verich, John 645
Verity, John R. 320
Verity, Susannah 896
Verlinghieri, Ray 72
Verma, Vic 45
Verma, Amit 204
Verma, Pawan 368
Verma, Anuraag 395
Vernasco, John 836
Verney, Jeffery 881
Vernon, Zana 538
Vernon, Amy 942
Verret, Stephanie 454
Verrier, James R. 140
Verrill, Scott 792
Verruso, Janis 881
Verst, Cynthia L. 478
Versteegh, Jerry 328
Vervlied, Michele 249
Verwers, Joel 226
Verwers, Kaz 226
Verwers, George 226
Verzera-Fair, Staci 457
Vescera, Dean 570
Vespoli, Leila L. 360
Vespoli, James 680
Vessa, Michael 511
Vessey, S.J. Rupert 175
Vestberg, Hans 893
Vester, Thomas 678
Vester, Bryan 739
Vetrano, Frank 409
Vetrano, Maria 767
Vetta, David J. (Dave) 343
Vetter, David R. (Dave) 816
Vian, Kathy 339
Viands, Larry 661
Viator, Elizabeth 454
Vibert, Paul 115
Vice, resi
Vice, Charles A. (Chuck) 466
Vice, resi
Vice, resi
Vichare, Anjali 740
Vicicondi, Lisa 563
Vick, Teresa 722
Victoria, Ana 300
Victorino, Chris 550
Videka, Lynn 606
Videka, Lynn 720
Vido, Eileen 882
Vidovich, Chad 754
Vielehr, Byron C. 361
Viergutz, Jason 786
Vieten, Kevin 760
Vifquain, Scott 504
Vigar, Andy 570
Vigilante, Kevin 139

Vignola, Nancy 713
Vigoroso, Mark 599
Vihn, Daniel 548
Vikara, Jerry 693
Vikram, Ashish 539
Vilandai, Anantha 204
Villa, David 314
Villa, Melisa 875
Villaman, Jonathan 204
Villaneda, Robert 97
Villanueva, Kelly 409
Villanyi, Stephen 483
Villaraos, Adrian 45
Villareal, Al 468
Villaronga, Diane 117
Villars, Curtis 555
Viltz, Simon 422
Vinall, David 99
Vincent, Sandra 106
Vincent, Curtis 158
Vincent, Lucie Claire 219
Vincent, Anton 383
Vincent, Simon 427
Vincent, Deb 489
Vinci, Don 304
Vinczeller, Shiela P 472
Vines, Michael 882
Vinett, Scott 486
Vining, Alexis 749
Vinkler, David 582
Vinnai, Lynn 383
Vinney, Les C. 156
Vinson, Andrew 116
Vinson, Lisa 330
Viohl, Evelyn 557
Viola, Victor 222
Viola, John 449
Viola, Carol 698
Viola, Mark 752
Viotty, Michelle 550
Viozzi, V. Anthony 279
Viozzi, Tony 279
Virag, Sharon 18
Viris, Jim 700
Virta, Ronald F 903
Virta, Ron 904
Viselli, Michael 754
Vishwanathan, Vish 182
Visweswariah, Deepak 602
Vita, Janet 664
Vitale, Domenick 377
Vitale, Joseph 558
Vitale, Robert V. 683
Vitale, Steven 891
Vitale, Gail 905
Vitelli, Tom 467
Vittorio, Michael N. 357
Vivas, Francisco J 754
Viviano, Jeffery 420
Vizza, Mark 680
Vlastelica, Pete 10
Vnenchak, David 724
Vnuck, Steve 570
Vo, Phillip 68
Voda, Cindy 558
Vogel, Jerry 628
Vogel, Becky 705
Vogel, Richard L. 834
Vogelpohl, Joe 810
Voges, Henry 487
Voglewede, Tiffany 923
Vogt, Mark 700
Vohs, Laurie 865
Voirand, Pascal 748
Volino, Robert S. 268
Voliva, Richard L. 429
Volk, Christopher H. (Chris) 112
Volk, Octaviana 665
Volker, Dan 294
Volkert, Michael 513
Volkmer, Mark 863
Vollmer, Greg 336
Vollmer, Richard 504
Volpetti, Stefano 693
vonBechmann, Dawn 904
Vonderhaar, Jennifer 886
Vonk, John 222

Vopni, Scott K. 259
Vora, Sonia 620
Vora, Raj 620
Vorel, Mark 80
Vorpahl, Larry L. 437
Vortherms, Joseph J. (Joe) 177
Vortman, Kolina 700
Voruz, Natalia 585
Vosburg, Craig 554
Vosper, Donna 770
Voss, David 557
Voss, Susan 722
Votek, Glenn A. 65
Votek, Glenn Alan 201
Vounatsos, Michel 129
Voyles, Robb L. 405
Voyles, Brent A. 834
Voytovich, Thomas 68
Vrecenak, Thomas 799
Vu, John 582
Vu, Bonnie 901
Vucelik, Ann 912
Vuich, Richard 705
Vukelich, Ty 301
Vuppala, Kiran 131
Vyskocil, Bill 869
V□zquez, Carlos J. 682

W

Waccard, John 101
Wachel-Florczyk, Magda 664
Wachira, Grace 185
Wachs, Gary 754
Waclawski, Michael 135
Wada, Julia 845
Waddell, Michael K. 353
Waddell, M. Keith 734
Waddey, Melissa O. 526
Waddle, Rick 796
Wade, Ralph 139
Wade, Betsy 168
Wade, Travis 282
Wade, Heather 454
Wade, James 717
Wade, Donna 726
Wade, Anne 870
Wadhera, Shilpa 269
Wadsworth, Jeffrey (Jeff) 113
Wadsworth, Ron 161
Wadsworth, Jeff 668
Waeltz, Brian 161
Waerum, Jesper 705
Wagers, Gary W. 110
Waghray, Ajay 82
Wagler, Theresa E. 794
Wagner, Lee 84
Wagner, Elizabeth 105
Wagner, Matt 117
Wagner, Janette 157
Wagner, Greg 192
Wagner, Scott 230
Wagner, Cindy 332
Wagner, Kevin 355
Wagner, Chris 487
Wagner, Robert F 537
Wagner, Carol 548
Wagner, Matthew P. (Matt) 652
Wagner, Patricia K. (Patti) 761
Wagstaff, Craig C. 278
Wahl, Jeffrey 715
Wahlig, Michael 813
Wainscott, Thomas 497
Waite, Jonathan 557
Waite, Stacey 570
Waits, Christopher 431
Wajner, Matthew F. 339
Wajnrajch, Michael 671
Wajsgras, David C. 716
Wakamura, Keith 179
Wake, Art 72
Wake, Caryn 228
Walby, Dave 743
Walchirk, Mark S. 657
Waldbillig, Sharon 101
Waldburger, Daniel 707

Waldeck, Phil 699
Walden, Theodore 377
Walden, Joshua M. (Josh) 465
Walden, Deborah 489
Walden, Dana 858
Walden, Marni M. 893
Waldman, Richard 449
Waldman, Mitchell B. (Mitch) 451
Waldman, Mitch 451
Waldman, David 570
Waldron, John 395
Waldron, John 434
Waldrop, Gabe 447
Waleski, Anne G. 545
Walker, Joan 31
Walker, Mike 34
Walker, Mark 49
Walker, R. A. (Al) 61
Walker, Nancy 69
Walker, Sara 80
Walker, Marvonia 84
Walker, Clay 101
Walker, Eric 115
Walker, Kristin 117
Walker, Trish 126
Walker, John 158
Walker, Chad 161
Walker, Karen 199
Walker, David 224
Walker, Sean N. 383
Walker, Kathryn 429
Walker, Kellye L. 451
Walker, Cody 454
Walker, Chris 465
Walker, Gregg 487
Walker, Gregory 489
Walker, Jack 517
Walker, Frank 518
Walker, Myron 548
Walker, William 550
Walker, Geoffrey H. 557
Walker, Geoff 557
Walker, Donald 563
Walker, Trent 573
Walker, Mark 576
Walker, Thomas 615
Walker, Cynthia L. 631
Walker, Dan 641
Walker, David M. (Dave) 662
Walker, Ron 668
Walker, Roberto 691
Walker, Steven G. 697
Walker, Jimmy 722
Walker, Jim 739
Walker, John 749
Walker, Rob 804
Walker, Todd 860
Walker, Bryan 863
Walker, Ben 870
Walker, Stephen William 886
Walker, Carol 941
Walkup, Kevin 750
Wall, David 14
Wall, George 191
Wall, Daniel R. 317
Wall, Shane D. 442
Wall, Robert 602
Wallace, Molly 3
Wallace, Robert 14
WALLACE, STEVE 135
Wallace, Jeff 158
Wallace, Noel R. 219
Wallace, Mark K. 245
Wallace, Mark E. 254
Wallace, John 336
Wallace, Dave 420
Wallace, Brent E. 467
Wallace, Kent H. 502
Wallace, Henry D. G. 514
Wallace, Jeff 533
Wallace, Leslie 539
Wallace, Tricia Primrose 548
Wallace, Jennifer 625
Wallace, Jonna 722
Wallace, Bruce E. 803
Wallace, Antoinette 840
Wallace, Rich 846

Wallace, Timothy R. 852
Wallace, Madelyn 863
Wallace, Melissa 866
Wallace, Mark R. 875
Wallach, Russell 533
Wallander, Barbara 330
Walle, Kristin 87
Waller, Rayne 57
Waller, Jerilynn 81
Waller, Kathy N. 216
Waller, Tom 728
Wallis, Jason 107
Walljasper, William J. (Bill) 164
Walls, Robert H. 456
Walls, Janet 903
Walno, Vicki 197
Walsh, Jim 3
Walsh, Denise 10
Walsh, Lambert 11
Walsh, Brian 32
Walsh, Timothy A. 49
Walsh, Tim 84
Walsh, Sara 101
Walsh, Steven 122
Walsh, Joseph 122
Walsh, Derrick 137
Walsh, Karen 170
Walsh, Ian 201
Walsh, Catherine 242
Walsh, Tim 287
Walsh, Melissa 378
Walsh, Caitlin 395
Walsh, Elia 413
Walsh, Michael 467
Walsh, Joe 467
Walsh, Timothy J. 656
Walsh, Amanda 749
Walsh, Marguerite 752
Walsh, Martin 774
Walsh, Ian K. 826
Walsh, Joe 839
Walsh, John L. 861
Walstrom, Dean 872
Walter, Luc 58
Walter, Michael 117
Walter, Kenneth 118
Walter, Tim 204
Walter, Frank E. 419
Walter, Aimee 446
Walter, Glen 584
Walter, Richard 692
Walter, Rob 899
Walter, Robert D. (Bob) 939
Walters, Cynthia 224
Walters, Thomas 320
Walters, Howard 449
Walters, Leigh 453
Walters, John 486
Walters, Kirk W. 664
Walters, Jay 861
Walters, David 863
Walther, Leanna 4
Walther, Leanna 6
Waltman, Naomi 172
Walton, David T. (Dave) 166
Walton, Peter 423
Walton, Lynell 635
Walton, Thomas W. H. (Tom) 652
Walton, Paul 668
Waltz, Mike 81
Waltz, Catherine 502
Walz, Andy 191
Walz, Charles 587
Wambeke, Carol 374
Wambold, Richard 820
Wamboldt, John 109
Wampler, Kevin S. 276
Wampler, Dan 453
Wampler, Terrance 643
Wan, Penny 57
Wand, Jordan 866
Wandeler, Roland 57
Wandell, Keith E. 254
Wandelt, Andreas 672
Wander, John 133
Wandling, Janet 635
Wandschneider, Robin 226

Waner, Leo 820
Wang, Liya 105
Wang, Xiaoman 201
Wang, Jason 204
Wang, Dan 222
Wang, Andy 299
Wang, Jack P 332
Wang, Jiahong 382
Wang, Dan 489
Wang, Li 528
Wang, Ed 555
Wang, Emily 573
Wang, Rex 643
Wang, Jing 707
Wang, Andy 736
Wang, Min 899
Wangsmo, Doug 573
Wanjara, Bernard 517
Wanless, Ben 226
Wann, Robert 604
Wanta, Gregory T. 472
WAPNER, BETH 707
Wappel, Paul 435
Warbinton, Craig 84
Ward, David 94
Ward, Carletha 117
Ward, Anita 161
Ward, Paul J. 228
Ward, Patrick J. (Pat) 248
Ward, Maria 248
Ward, F. Stephen 341
Ward, David 353
Ward, Bill 358
Ward, Steven E. 419
Ward, Mary 477
Ward, Richard 489
Ward, Cherie 489
Ward, Michael 490
Ward, Paul 587
Ward, Brant 767
Ward, John 792
Ward, Ron 806
Ward, Jacquelyn M. (Jackie) 808
Ward, Laysha L. 813
Ward, Peter P. 847
Ward, Will 870
Ward, Susan 875
Ward, Karl 941
Warden, Kathy J. 623
Wardlaw, Van M. 821
Wardlow, Howard 59
Wardlow, Mark 865
Wardwell, Myra 101
Wardynski, Paula 610
Ware, Stacey 101
Ware, Andrew 313
Ware, Hilary 603
Ware, Scott D. 937
Waren, Darris 454
Warfel, Eric 217
Wargo, Eileen 729
Waring, Michael 179
Warkenthien, Jeff 691
Warman, D. Scott N. 538
Warmbier, Kimberly (Kim) 259
Warne, Jen 530
Warner, Cynthia (CJ) 63
Warner, Jane 458
Warner, Jason 563
Warner, Mark 620
Warner, Ryan 942
Warnick, Chad 563
Warnock, Greg 496
Warren, Armida 101
Warren, Jody 112
Warren, Kathleen 115
Warren, Kathy 115
Warren, Karmon 129
Warren, Cindy 484
Warren, Tiffany R 639
Warren, Ken 677
Warren, Alice 888
Warren, Kevin M. 934
Warrington, Michael 502
Warrington, Jacquelyn 886
Wartenbergh, Marcela 705
Warthen, Ruth 808

Waschull, Matthew 148
Wascom, D. G. 320
Waser, Eric H. 660
Washburne, Tom 635
Washeleski, Janice C 17
Washienko, Robin 449
Washington, Mike 170
Washington, Roderick 246
Washington, A. Eugene 287
Washington, Robin L. 391
Washington, Bill 875
Washkau, Bill 87
Washkowitz, Alan H. 509
Wasielewski, Larry 717
Wasilewski, Raymond W. 325
Wassef, Wael 731
Wasser, Marilyn J. 718
Wasserstein, M-Laurie 881
Wassmer, Michael J. 158
Watase, Brian 103
Waterfall, Marcy 550
Waterman, Josh 53
Waterman, Richard 517
Waters, Terry 25
Waters, Laura 45
Waters, Stephen M. 141
Waters, Tom 185
Waters, Andy D. 230
Waters, Jim 580
Waters, Ron 749
Waters, Kristy 818
Waters, Robin 863
Watkin, Jared L. 4
Watkins, Ron 441
Watkins, Scott 647
Watkins, Bradford L. 789
Watkins, Jeremy 936
Watson, Esther 18
Watson, William 49
Watson, Jimmy 49
Watson, Tim 81
Watson, Amanda 178
Watson, Ryan 204
Watson, David N. (Dave) 222
Watson, David 240
Watson, Lois 332
Watson, John 332
Watson, Randi 378
Watson, John 379
Watson, Katie L. 391
Watson, William 454
Watson, Lucas 476
Watson, Greg 562
Watson, Rob 643
Watson, Tony 808
Watson, Angela 875
Watt, Graeme A. 94
Watt, John H. 598
Watters, Lyle 370
Watterson, Andrew 780
Wattley, Mark 901
Watts, Phillip R. 267
Watts, Myles J. 327
Watts, Gary 334
Watts, Alan 427
Watts, Brian 792
Waugh, Harry 722
Waugh, Alasdair 750
Waun, Tom 470
Waxman, William 170
Way, Pam 282
Waycaster, C. Mitchell (Mitch) 726
Wayles, Doug 787
Wayling, Brian 468
Waynick, Pat 903
Wayton, Kathleen 780
Weadick, Chris 935
Weagley, Anthony C. (Tony) 233
Weagley, Anthony C. (Tony) 233
Wear, Ralph 713
Wear, Diane 821
Weast, Jennifer 98
Weathers, Michael 334
Weaver, Bob 25
Weaver, Jason 49
Weaver, Dawn 102
Weaver, David H. 116

Weaver, Troy 117
Weaver, Emily 256
Weaver, Murry 389
Weaver, Casey 558
Weaver, Jeff 580
Weaver, Susan 604
Weaver, Janine M 617
Weaver, Scott 618
Weaver, Pamela 722
Weaver, Amy E. 748
Weaver, Paul 911
Weaver, Keith 936
Webb, Maynard G. 34
Webb, Maynard G. 34
Webb, Randy 71
Webb, Timothy 101
Webb, Brad 107
Webb, Patricia G. (Pat) 168
Webb, Sonny 185
Webb, James R. 189
Webb, Thomas J. (Tom) 210
Webb, Thomas J. (Tom) 238
Webb, Jeffrey 273
Webb, Mark O. 278
Webb, Byron 313
Webb, James 330
Webb, Brian 447
Webb, Jan C. 460
Webb, Charles 519
Webb, Jan 530
Webb, Ian 555
Webb, Carl 597
Webb, Campbell 643
Webb, Chad 722
Webb, Scott 756
Webb, Rick 903
Webb, Martin 935
Webber, Jerome 84
Webber, Lisa 101
Webber, Patrick 440
Webber, Diane 792
Weber, Susan 155
Weber, Jesse 170
Weber, Scott 186
Weber, Todd 246
Weber, Daniel 261
Weber, Pat 261
Weber, Dave 342
Weber, Robert 355
Weber, Christopher T. (Chris) 405
Weber, Randy 431
Weber, Robert 470
Weber, John 530
Weber, Cathi 578
Weber, Hubert 584
Weber, Henry 718
Weberling, Matt 559
Webster, Nancy 378
Webster, Douglas 454
Webster, Michele 786
Wechsler, Joel 170
Wechsler, Ron 827
Weddington, Brian 105
Wede, Thomas 69
Wedepohl, Eric 383
Weeks, Wendell P. 240
Weeks, Felicia 454
Weeks, David 494
Weeks, Andrew M. 654
Weeks, Laura 912
Weems, Alonzo 528
Wegman, Colleen 910
Wegman, Nicole 910
Wegman, Daniel R. (Danny) 910
Wegrzyn, Daniel 786
Wehber, Wayne 300
Wehmer, Edward J. 927
Wehner, David M. (Dave) 321
Wehrly, Donald W. 544
Wehrwein, Kelli 489
Weibel, Kurt 112
Weidenheimer, James 801
Weidenkopf, Thomas W. (Tom) 17
Weidick, Tania 643
Weidlein, Sean 170
Weigand, Jennifer 176
Weigand, Krista 782

Weigman, Mark 809
Weil, Robert J. 168
Weil, Meredith S 827
Weiland, Bob 115
Weiland, John 942
Weiler, Robert K. (Bob) 642
Weilinghoff, Andreas 294
Weimer, Aaron 222
Weimer, Robert 248
Weimer, Gail 570
Weinandt, Tom 866
Weinbach, Lawrence A. (Larry) 95
Weinberger, Brian 748
Weiner, Charles 273
Weiner, Edward G. 847
Weiner, Brian 899
Weinkle, Brian 587
Weinseiss, Karen 18
Weinstein, Laura 242
Weinstock, Craig L. 593
Weinstock, Randall 881
Weir, Cecile A 1
Weis, Don 170
Weise, Kurt 578
Weise, Stuart 726
Weisel, Thomas W. (Thom) 795
Weisenberger, Brian 507
Weisenborn, Dennis 40
Weisenhorn, John 105
Weishan, Dennis 735
Weiske, Martie 813
Weisler, Dion J. 442
Weiss, Mark A 47
Weiss, Karl E. 166
Weiss, Justin 176
Weiss, Kyle 224
Weiss, Mary 224
Weiss, Jerry 374
Weiss, Barry 425
Weiss, David J 473
Weiss, Mark 536
Weiss, Gregory 555
Weissel, Andy 563
Weissert, J 715
Weisz, Karen 615
WEITGENANT, DAVID 358
Weitz, Melanie C 731
Weitzel, Jennifer 576
Weitzman, Debbie 161
Weitzner, Michael 881
Welbaum, Bryan 587
Welborn, Jamie 580
Welch, Marty 72
Welch, John K. 114
Welch, Glenn S. 124
Welch, Meghan 158
Welch, Thomas 176
Welch, Daniel 708
Welch, Susan 831
Welch, Jerry 836
Welch, James L. 937
Weldon, Mary 337
Weldon, Michael 935
Weliver, Adam 541
Welke, Tom 20
Welkie, Katherine A. (Katy) 467
Welkomer, Dalena 735
Wellborn, W. Christopher (Chris) 580
Welleck, Andrew 470
Welles, Scott 139
Welling, Brandon 224
Wellman, Arnold 875
Wellman, Michael 911
Wells, Brooks 15
Wells, Chris 117
Wells, Stephen G 224
Wells, Scott R. 456
Wells, Charles 483
Wells, David 603
Wells, Brent 692
Wells, Scott 722
Wells, Gregory D. (Greg) 780
Wells, Jim 787
Wells, Tim 907
Welsh, Lori 237
Welsh, Kelly R 620
Welsh, Bob 786

Welsh, Bill 860
Welt, Philip S. 122
Weltman, Matthew 767
Weltz, Frank 194
Welzen, James van 628
Welzenbach, Mark 409
Wen, Pauline 896
Wendel, Jon S. 453
Wendelboe, Steven 539
Wender, Herbert 712
Wendler, Kenneth 201
Wendler, John 845
Wendling, Adam 435
Wenerstrom, Stewart 128
Wenger, E. Philip (Phil) 376
Wenger, Philip 376
Wenig, Devin N. 293
Wenkoff, Carman 276
Wenner, Ken 349
Wennlund, Lloyd A 620
Wentworth, Brian 4
Wentworth, Peter 224
Wentworth, Harold M. (Harry) 228
Wentworth, Hal 228
Wentworth, Steven D. 308
Wentworth, Timothy (Tim) 319
Wenzel, Gregory G. (Greg) 139
Wenzel, Brian 675
Wenzky, Holger 476
Wepman, Josh 517
Werbeckes, Jim 301
Werber, Rick 440
Werle, Haley 201
Werneck, Melissa 505
Werner, Frederick W. (Fred) 14
Werner, Gene 101
Werner, Todd S. 111
Werner, Tony G. 222
Werner, Tom 232
Werner, Melissa 497
Werner, Mary 800
Werner, Joe 803
Werner, Kenneth (Ken) 838
Wernhoff, Stephanie 665
Wernikoff, Daniel A. (Dan) 476
Werpy, Todd A. 74
Werra, Greg 620
Wersch, Wouter Van 382
Wertheim, Ram D. 559
Wesen, Darcel 135
Weslock, Kathleen 199
Weslock, Kathleen 376
Wesolowski, Tom 449
Wessel, Aulene 45
Wessel, Thomas 62
Wessel, Daniel 176
West, Ed 157
West, Robert F. (Rob) 214
West, Wayne G. (Gil) 262
West, Roderick K. (Rod) 304
West, Shawn 365
West, Cliff 487
West, Diann 577
West, Mindy K. 590
West, Lori 590
West, Richard 652
West, Colleen 656
West, Tony 667
West, Mark D. 720
West, Robert 731
West, Terri 825
West, Melissa 855
West, Eric 935
Westad, Erik 793
Westbay, James 754
Westbrook, Woodie 201
Westbrook, Larry 389
Westbrook, Bennett D. 744
Westbrooks, Wes 98
Westenberg, Rick 385
Westerdahl, Joyce 642
Westerfield, Rick 457
Westerlund, David A 96
Western, Keith A. 110
Westfall, Sean 604
Westfield, Mike 536
Westlin, William 175

Westlund, M. Randolph (Rand) 706
Westman, David 98
Westman, Shelley 470
Westmoreland, Rick 135
Weston, Kathleen 371
Weston, Karl 725
Wetmore, Edward 59
Wetstein, Daniel 185
Wetta, Jim 507
Wetter, Phil 497
Wettstein, Mary 80
Wetzel, Kurt 106
Wever, Karen 194
Wexner, Leslie H. 508
Weyerhaeuser, William T. 221
Whalen, Ellie 105
Whalen, Douglas 148
Whalen, Kim 344
Whalen, James W. 812
Whalen, Julie P. 925
Whaley, Kristi 159
Wham, Terry 248
Wharry, Sarah 860
Wharton, Delphine 109
Wharton, Charles 912
Wheat, William W. (Bill) 439
Wheatlake, Franklin C. 187
Wheatley, Tim 727
Wheaton, Guy 610
Wheeler, Al 12
Wheeler, BO 103
Wheeler, John 248
Wheeler, Hanley 252
Wheeler, Peter 497
Wheeler, Deborah 558
Wheeler, Jason 595
Wheeler, Michael J. 618
Wheeler, David 724
Wheeler, Robert H. 837
Wheeler, David 893
Whelan, Kellie 497
Whetsell, Paul W 536
Whetstone, Chesney 99
Whippo, Jeffrey 302
Whisenand, Casey 101
Whisenhunt, Dan 69
Whistle, Kristi 551
Whitaker, Randy 107
Whitaker, Maureen 713
Whitcher, Angela 530
White, Miles D. 4
White, Brad 15
White, Teresa L. 19
White, John 49
White, John 71
White, John O 124
White, Keith P 135
White, Janice 157
White, Sylvia 157
White, Becky 158
White, Steve 222
White, Patricia 242
White, Anthony 247
White, J T 248
White, Robert A. 249
White, Bill 251
White, Jim 256
White, John 259
White, Kevin 287
White, Lance 333
White, Marcus 344
White, Gregory A. 347
White, David D 378
White, Blayne 379
White, Steve 409
White, James C. (Jim) 460
White, John 470
White, Ray 486
White, Ed 488
White, Barbara 507
White, John P. 509
White, Jeff 555
White, Joseph W. 581
White, Lynn 593
White, Joe 599
White, Mark 603
White, Robert 607

White, Elizabeth V 620
White, Jeff 620
White, Scott 623
White, Michael 672
White, J. Edward (Ed) 677
White, J. Harvey 677
White, Edward 678
White, Matthew J. (Matt) 687
White, Stuart 722
White, Gary 722
White, Andrew 729
White, Megan 745
White, Brett 765
White, Clifton 769
White, Paul 786
White, John M 792
White, Stephanie 800
White, Lynn 806
White, Clark 812
White, William 813
White, Laverne 813
White, Noel 859
White, Paul 875
White, Wayne 881
White, Tim 923
White, Jeff 929
White, Patrick 935
Whited, Gary L. 380
Whited, Elizabeth F. (Beth) 868
Whitefield, Adam 941
Whitehead, Mark 447
Whitehead, Dane E. 546
Whitehead, Craig 672
Whitehead, Roy M. 905
Whitehouse, Edward 517
Whitehouse, Kirk 855
Whitehurst, Bradford D. (Brad) 302
Whiteley, Sherry 476
Whiteman, Keith 606
Whiteman, Charles H. 831
Whitemyer, Jennifer 101
Whitenack, Kimberly 327
Whitener, Michelle 176
Whitener, Matt 300
Whitesell, Nancy 813
Whiteside, Hayes V. 692
Whiteside, Cathie 706
Whiting, Carol 57
Whiting, Ted 573
Whitley, Tammy 107
Whitley, Scott 299
Whitley, Keva 863
Whitman, Reed H 147
Whitman, Margaret C. (Meg) 425
Whitman, Terri 450
Whitman, Michael 665
Whitmer, Jeff 628
Whitmer, Tom 705
Whitmer, Thomas 705
Whitmore, Martin 840
Whitney, Robert 226
Whitney, Matt 808
Whitney, Lisa 895
Whitsel, Joe 938
Whitt, Richard R. 545
Whitt, Mark 912
Whitteaker, Jennifer 284
Whittemore, John 149
Whittet, Jim 735
Whittington, John 810
Whittle, Suzanne 621
Whitton, R 759
Whitton, James 842
Whittow, Richard 735
Whitwell, Rodney C 794
Whitwer, Derek 289
Whorley, John F. (Jeff) 595
Whyte, Mike 890
Wichmann, David S. 880
Wicinski, Tom 330
Wick, Steven 3
Wick, Tom 294
Wickens, Kim 162
Wicker, Kirstin 454
Wicker, Cary 824
Wickham, Gregory I. (Greg) 254
Wicklund, Tom 881

Wickman, Paul 713
Wickwar, Dean 786
Widdel, John 818
Widdicombe, Mark 577
Widdows, Katherine C 406
Wie, Andy Van 782
Wiebe, Robert L. 266
Wiedenfels, Gunnar 270
Wiedman, Mark K. 131
Wiegand, Aaron 676
Wiegert, Joel 140
Wiegert, Cory 470
Wiehoff, John P. 736
Wiele, Dana 724
Wieneke, Michelle 722
Wiener, James S. (Jim) 105
Wiener, David 536
Wiener, Mike 901
Wiens, Aaron 306
Wier, Jeff A 149
Wiersma, Marc 194
Wiertel, Edward 371
Wiese, Stefanie 739
Wiese, Edward A. 809
Wiese, Cary 860
Wiesner, Paula 159
Wiessing, Theodore E. 817
Wiethers, Asha 380
Wietmarschen, Mark 196
Wiggin, Pete 185
Wiggin, Jeff 811
Wight-Tally, Nancy 731
Wiglesworth, Janet 898
Wik, Kate 573
Wiker, Neil 376
Wikert, Lisa 333
Wikinson, Martin 261
Wilbanks, Cynthia H. 720
Wilbert, Smith 262
Wilborn, Susan 226
Wilbur, Sara 665
Wilcher, Patti 178
Wilcox, Greg 224
Wilcox, Lee F. 279
Wilcox, James 395
Wilcox, Jim 492
Wilcox, Mark A. 760
Wilcox, William H. (Bill) 818
Wilde, Dominic 425
Wilde, Malcolm 474
Wilde, Frederic de 674
Wildman, Brian J. 558
Wiles, Rob 454
Wiley, Deborah 69
Wiley, J. Thomas 789
Wilgar, Jackie 533
Wilhelm, Curt 297
Wilhelm, Melissa 355
Wilhelm, Julia 487
Wilk, Brian 415
Wilk, Rob 576
Wilke, Jeffrey A. (Jeff) 37
Wilke, Brent 420
Wilken, Shane 350
Wilkes, Kathy 226
Wilkin, Charles 613
Wilkin, Laura 903
Wilkins, Michael T. 872
Wilkins, Charles L. (Chad) 908
Wilkinson, Charles 207
Wilkinson, Martin L 260
Wilkinson, Brian 454
Wilkinson, Vince 901
Wilkinson, Mark 942
Wilks, Jeff 836
Will, Kristin 550
Willard, Howard A. 36
Willard, Veronika 47
Willard, Kathy 532
Willard, Lauren 656
Willcoxon, Jennifer 697
Willden, Stephen 941
Willeat, Susan 724
Willemsen, Eugene 667
Willen, Sandy 796
Willensky, Scott M. 933
Willets, Jason 101

Willey, Stan 760
William, Aston 57
Williams, Matt J 6
Williams, Ardine 37
Williams, Ann© 44
Williams, Brandy 45
Williams, Tim 45
Williams, Dan 49
Williams, Bill 52
Williams, Jason 52
Williams, David 53
Williams, Dawn 53
Williams, Jeffrey E. (Jeff) 69
Williams, Xavier 84
Williams, Steve 84
Williams, Thomas 86
Williams, Eric 94
Williams, Leroy 96
Williams, Jack 101
Williams, Leilani 103
Williams, Bill 109
Williams, John 112
Williams, J Mel 117
Williams, Tom 137
Williams, Shawn 148
Williams, Richard 175
Williams, Marian 176
Williams, Lexie 178
Williams, Glynn 181
Williams, Donna L 198
Williams, Carol 203
Williams, Jeremy 213
Williams, Craig 216
Williams, Malcolm 219
Williams, Thomas L. (Tom) 222
Williams, Michael 246
Williams, Ben 263
Williams, Benjamin 263
Williams, Janice L. 289
Williams, Weston 295
Williams, Randa D. 307
Williams, Jerry 311
Williams, James 332
Williams, Pamela 332
Williams, Jacque 335
Williams, Maurice 337
Williams, Jason 341
Williams, James R. 349
Williams, Karen 366
Williams, John C. 367
Williams, Barbara 395
Williams, Gary 446
Williams, Tom 447
Williams, Kristin 453
Williams, Sadie 470
Williams, Travis 484
Williams, Jeff 489
Williams, Phil 492
Williams, Alan 497
Williams, Carol 504
Williams, R 506
Williams, Dave 519
Williams, Vivian 539
Williams, Christine 551
Williams, Jerry 553
Williams, Holly 564
Williams, Clay C. 593
Williams, Jeffrey 604
Williams, Chris 618
Williams, Peter 620
Williams, Jeffery L 620
Williams, Carol A. 649
Williams, Thomas L. (Tom) 654
Williams, Michael 664
Williams, Geisha J. 673
Williams, Michele 673
Williams, Kelly 700
Williams, Donna 705
Williams, W. Mark 726
Williams, Tim 733
Williams, Jason 736
Williams, Ken 754
Williams, Rossann 787
Williams, Michael 792
Williams, Sabrina 799
Williams, Renee 811
Williams, David 824

Williams, Tim G 825
Williams, Kim 838
Williams, Darren K. 869
Williams, Debbie 869
Williams, Dyfan 890
Williams, Susan 894
Williams, Daniel 903
Williams, Charles 907
Williams, Richard L. 918
Williams-Roll, Jacqueline 383
Williamson, Graeme 142
Williamson, Angela 157
Williamson, Keith H. 176
Williamson, Rich 196
Williamson, Brenda 495
Williamson, Tracey 610
Williamson, Paul 643
Williamson, David 643
Williamson, Kemal 659
Williamson, Scott H. 817
Williamson, Stephen 836
Williamson, Daniel E. (Dan) 940
Williman, Glenn 84
Willingham, Edward L. (Ed) 344
Willingham, Phil 734
Willis, Shareron 84
Willis, Jonathan 141
Willis, Lee 320
Willis, John 726
Willis, John 794
Willman, Claire 502
Willman, Richard 799
Willoughby, Dawn 208
Willoughby, Michele B. 264
Wills, Michele 929
Wilmot, Edward 47
Wilmoth, Floyd 891
Wilshaw, Robert K 663
Wilson, Thomas J. 31
Wilson, Harry J. 34
Wilson, Phil 45
Wilson, Dont□□ L. 116
Wilson, Ron 126
Wilson, Michelle 148
Wilson, David J. 161
Wilson, Joseph 162
Wilson, Julia M. (Julie) 183
Wilson, J. Michael 228
Wilson, James 228
Wilson, James D. (Jim) 244
Wilson, Clay 252
Wilson, Tracy 273
Wilson, Carolyn 273
Wilson, Suzanne V 273
Wilson, Jenene 295
Wilson, Andrew 296
Wilson, Mike 304
Wilson, Linda 313
Wilson, Cindy 328
Wilson, Jan 332
Wilson, Chris 342
Wilson, Rebekkah 361
Wilson, Anthony 389
Wilson, Jay 423
Wilson, Ralph Martin 446
Wilson, Michael 453
Wilson, Timothy 454
Wilson, Kevin 462
Wilson, Samuel 511
Wilson, Melissa 513
Wilson, Brian 530
Wilson, Debbie 548
Wilson, Huey 557
Wilson, Thomas 559
Wilson, Mark 576
Wilson, Tom 585
Wilson, Judith 620
Wilson, Sharon 635
Wilson, Christine 749
Wilson, Ted 750
Wilson, Wayne 769
Wilson, Bill 823
Wilson, Christopher 858
Wilson, Uma 863
Wilson, D. Ellen 880
Wilson, Glenda 886
Wilson, Ward 888

Wilson, Robert 911
Wilson, Malcolm 936
Wilson-Scott, Dalila 222
Wilson-Thompson, Kathleen 901
Wilten, Mark 686
Wilton, Keith A. 420
Wilton, Tricia 573
Wiltsie, Todd 818
Wiltz, Dianne 890
Wimberly, Todd 855
Wimmer, Kelly 39
Wimmer, John 84
Winchar, Brian 620
Winchester, Katie 345
Winchip, D. Scott 733
Winders, Matt 67
Windley, John F. 776
Windrow, Kimberly G. 914
Wine, Scott W. 681
Winek, Chris 323
Wineman, Matthew 518
Winfield, Donna 604
Winfrey, Christopher L. (Chris) 186
Wing, Scott 831
Wingard, Brian W. 211
Wingate, Angel 287
Wingender, Lynn 632
Wingenroth, Sharon 377
Winiecki, David 80
Winkel, Mike 27
Winkel, Alma 489
Winkeler, Jay 516
Winker, Mark 863
Winkle, Claudia 839
Winkler, Barry 85
Winkler, Judy 85
Winkler, Beth 839
Winlove-smith, Shannon 382
Winn, Cathy 31
Winn, Kenneth V. 338
Winslow, Alisa 680
Winsor, Elizabeth 18
Winter, Matthew E. (Matt) 31
Winter, Kurt 31
Winter, Kevin 139
Winter, Amy 226
Winter, Shaun 643
Winterbottom, Brad L. 915
Winters, Tom 668
Wipf, Todd V. 764
Wipfler, Gary 69
Wireman, Rich 691
Wirth, Michael K. (Mike) 190
Wirtz, Monika 32
Wisadkosin, Yukontorn (Vickie) 370
Wisbar, Beverly 810
Wise, Jarrod 98
Wise, Deanna L. 266
Wise, Sherrill 267
Wise, Brad 355
Wise, Steve 429
Wise, Dena 808
Wise, Jackie 863
Wiseman, Mark 131
Wisenbaker, Randall C. 709
Wisnoski, Kenneth (Ken) 75
Wisnoski, Mark 808
Wiswell, Sherri 731
Wit, Leigh 897
Witcher, Lisa 489
Witcombe, David 672
Witek, David 258
Witham, John 37
Withers, Lisa 935
Witherspoon, Jay 185
Withrow, Lynn 194
Withrow, Randy 677
Witko, Jason 693
Witt, Judith 108
Witt, Karen Y 117
Witt, Mary J. 726
Witt, Kelly 735
Witt, Marshall 805
Wittbecke, Steven 214
Witte, Ryan 927
Witten, Darryl 727
Witter, Jonathan W. 158

Witter, Gene 246
Witter, Marcia 366
Witterschein, Robert 306
Wituszynski, Theresa 124
Witwicki, Witold 3
Witynski, Michael 276
Wixson, Chris 563
Wobma, Paul 185
Woelfer, W. Todd 837
Woerner, John R. 52
Wofford, Martha 258
Wofford, Susanne L. 606
Wohl, Richard H. 250
Wohland, William 242
Wohlberg, Christopher 671
Wohlgemuth, Jay G. 709
Wojcik, Paul 809
Wojnar, T. J. 320
Wojnar, Bradley 345
Wolbach, Cindy 454
Wolcott, Tom 664
Woldt, Sheldon 620
Wolf, Michael J. 34
Wolf, Zachary 60
Wolf, Warren 266
Wolf, Christine 322
Wolf, Michael 365
Wolf, Frank 416
Wolf, Brian 537
Wolf, Tom 570
Wolf, Matt 582
Wolf, Dale B. 582
Wolf, Christopher G. 681
Wolf, Joseph B. 725
Wolf, Joseph P. 725
Wolfe, Blake 71
Wolfe, Kate 453
Wolfe, Nancy 585
Wolfe, Bernie 663
Wolfe, Bobby 715
Wolfe, Joanne 839
Wolfe, Harriet M. 908
Wolff, Adam 274
Wolff, Jeffrey 332
Wolff, Drew 788
Wolff-Bye, Charlotte 793
Wolfram, Katie 506
Wolgemuth, Elizabeth 555
Wolitzer, Joel 201
Wolking, Christopher A. (Chris) 635
Wollberg, Johnny 793
Wolloff, Michelle 376
Wolochuk, Lee 15
Wolsfeld, Joseph 559
Wolters, Janice 342
Woltman, Andy 800
Womack, Robert R. 227
Womack, Christopher 389
Womble, Hill 763
Wonderlich, Jessica 453
Wong, John Q 15
Wong, Gordon 105
Wong, Melanie 105
Wong, Danny 105
Wong, Irwin 166
Wong, Rebecca 202
Wong, Wilfred 513
Wong, Cindy 573
Wong, Richard 587
Wong, Philip 688
Wong, John 688
Wong, Annie 705
Wong, Joe 750
Wong, Francis 781
Wong, Belinda 787
Wong, Stephanie 903
Woo, Elizabeth 836
Woo, Joni 934
Wood, Christine 87
Wood, James M. (Jim) 153
Wood, William C. (Cliff) 162
Wood, Peery 170
Wood, John J 185
Wood, Delfina 204
Wood, Stephen 271
Wood, Hugh 273
Wood, Stan 282

Wood, Chris 380
Wood, Tommie 447
Wood, Lauren 456
Wood, Brian 550
Wood, Lee 569
Wood, Brad R 593
Wood, Bob 602
Wood, Carolyn 607
Wood, Sarah 610
Wood, Michael 717
Wood, Mike 722
Wood, Grant 748
Wood, Michael 763
Wood, Adam 775
Wood, Ken 895
Wood, Brian 899
Woodall, James W. (Woody) 334
Woodard, Denise 668
Woodard, R. Bryan 792
Woodbury, Eileen 456
Woodbury, Chip 891
Woodbury, Thomas 908
Woodcock, Tim 356
Woodford, Brent A. 273
Woodlin, Kenneth 903
Woodman, Doug 454
Woodman, Clare 587
Woodruff, Steve 107
Woodruff, Bob 615
Woodruff, Seth 671
Woods, Don 81
Woods, Terrell 201
Woods, John F. 205
Woods, J. Pat 308
Woods, Darren W. 320
Woods, Mike 402
Woods, Anne 502
Woods, Jennifer L 585
Woods, Abbott 717
Woods, Marie 752
Woods, Chris 834
Woods, Carla T 860
Woodside, David B. 112
Woodson, Cheryl 18
Woodward, Keith 383
Woodward, Brett 754
Woodward, Joan Kois 849
Woodward, Dixon 870
Woodworth, Leigh 809
Woolard, Randy 135
Wooldridge, Christy 350
Woolley, Ian 45
Woolley, Hunter 555
Woollums, Cathy 651
Woolschlager, Ted 119
Woolsey, Danielle 413
Woolverton, Paul 580
Woolway, Paul V. 754
Woolwine, Steve 15
Woonton, David B. 180
Wooten, Nancy H 454
Wooten, James H 458
Wootton, Charles A. 341
Wootton, Ken 929
Workley, Keila 262
Workman, Vince 207
Workman, Mike 773
Worley, Robert B. 454
Worman, Douglas M. (Doug) 210
Worner, John R 731
Wornson, Bryon 672
Worrall, Judy 378
Worrall, Robert (Bob) 490
Worrell, Sally 148
Worrell, Robert G 868
Worth, Denny 402
Worth, Read 713
Worth, David 899
Worthen, John 486
Worthington, Alice 137
Worthington, John 337
Worthington, John 503
Worthington, Joel 528
Worthy, Steve 813
Worzel, Kenneth J. (Ken) 617
Woseth, Rob N. 801
Wotring, Randall A. (Randy) 14

Woytowich, Justin 122
Wozniak, David 530
Wrang, William E. 908
Wranovix, Tim 715
Wrassman, Owen 735
Wray, Lucian 68
Wrazej, John 713
Wren, John D. 639
Wright, Bruce 7
Wright, Will 14
Wright, Winston 72
Wright, Cooper 133
Wright, Frank H. 159
Wright, Chris 178
Wright, Jack 194
Wright, Lance 226
Wright, Jordan 266
Wright, Roy 282
Wright, Alan 304
Wright, Robert R. 318
Wright, James 389
Wright, Christopher 395
Wright, Pat 413
Wright, Scott J. 452
Wright, Howard 465
Wright, James 550
Wright, Greg 559
Wright, Robert 570
Wright, David 668
Wright, Dennis 722
Wright, Stacy 810
Wright, Mark 849
Wright, Robert 852
Wright, Dennis 863
Wright, Deborah 869
Wright, Tom 923
Wright, Larry 928
Wright, Richard M. (Rick) 931
Wright-Jones, Angela 226
Wrigley, Clark 658
Wrocklage, Laura 224
Wu, Ben 131
WU, Iris 465
Wu, Ed 596
Wu, Alice 840
Wu, Shengpo (Samuel) 923
Wulf, Deandra 328
Wulf, Clark 497
Wulf, Jon 599
Wunder, Lori A. 233
Wurm, Greg 67
Wurm, David 383
Wurth, Nancy 124
Wurtz, Steven 664
Wustefeld, Ed 570
Wuthrich, Jim 838
Wyant, Michael 161
Wyant, Jill S. 294
Wyant, Ashley 337
Wyatt, Natalie 162
Wyatt, E. Lee 371
Wyatt, Will 707
Wyatt, Markel 722
Wyatt, John H. A. 786
Wyckoff, Kristin 332
Wyffels, Michael J. 706
Wygal, Justin 722
Wyk, Steven C. (Steve) Van 680
Wyks, Philip 644
Wyles, Jessica K 717
Wylie, Lydia 191
Wylie, Sean 896
Wyman, Scott R 360
Wyne, Laura 107
Wynn, Jason 45
Wyrick, Cynthia 103
Wyrsch, Martha B. 761
Wyse, Kenneth L. (Ken) 705

X

Xavier, Sonia 748
Xiao, Harry 570
Xie, Bing 825
Xing, Julie 528
Xu, Jack 199

Xu, Ling 366
Xun, H 191

Y

Yabuki, Jeffery W. 361
Yacob, Ezra Y. 308
Yadley, Sloan 715
Yagi, Sakurako 550
Yajnik, Sanjiv 158
Yako, Osamu 184
Yale, Phyllis R. 502
Yalof, Stephen J. 770
Yamamoto, Cassandra 103
Yamanaka, Mary 939
Yamynn, Angelis 250
Yan, Scott 570
Yan, Yingli (Christine) 786
Yanagihara, Jason 131
Yanagisawa, David S. 511
Yancey, Carol B. 387
Yancopoulos, George D. 719
Yanehiro, Jan 104
Yang, Ying 202
Yang, Irene 202
Yang, Taiyin 391
Yang, Peter 408
Yang, Ian 465
Yang, Kristie 688
Yang, Phillip 699
Yanik, Sahin 266
Yanke, Peg 80
Yankiv, Elvira 282
Yankowski, Daniel H. (Dan) 687
Yano, James A. (Jay) 788
Yantis, Debbie 183
Yap, Stella 131
Yaple, Glenna 313
Yapp, Kevin 94
Yarbrough, Kevin 117
Yarbrough, Jenny 590
Yarbrough, Mary 893
Yarkoni, Charlotte 576
Yaros, Joseph 211
Yarrington, Patricia E. (Pat) 190
Yasgur, Howard 735
Yates, Gregory 14
Yates, W. Rufus 116
Yates, Catherine 187
Yates, Lloyd M. 285
Yates, Pat 454
Yates, Steve 498
Yates, Beth 498
Yates, Matthew 528
Yates, Michael 564
Yates, Kim 895
Yau, Benjamin 423
Yau, Mike 620
Yaudes, Jason T. 50
Yauger, Theresa 356
Yavorsky, Robert 705
Ybarra, Paco 203
Yeager, Fair 185
Yeager, David 567
Yeager, Rande K. 636
Yeager, Tom 801
Yeap, Geoffrey 707
Yearley, Douglas C. (Doug) 841
YEE, TAMMY 45
Yee, James 80
Yee, Victoria 332
Yee, Darryl 748
Yee, Michael 830
Yellin, Todd 603
Yellock, Dorothy 722
Yelverton, Greg 457
Yen, Kitty 109
Yen, David 199
Yen, Andy 290
Yen, David 490
Yen, George 643
Yennie, Heather 453
Yerby, Phil 185
Yerigan, Marna 350
Yerneni, Siva 792
Yesho, LaDawn D. 745

Yetto, Kristin 293
Yeung, Ivan 102
Yeung, Rebecca 330
Yi, Steve 170
Yi, Won 570
Yi, Sang 940
Yih, Thomas 537
Yingling, Nathaniel 332
Yingling, Jenny 757
Yip, Karen 643
Yitbarek, Anbessie 135
Ylonen, Paul 888
Yoder, Lamont 112
Yoder, Lisa M 248
Yoho, Franklin H. 285
Yon, Roberto 101
Yon, Linda 912
Yoney, Dennis 731
Yoo, Alicia 47
Yoo, Charles 435
Yoon, Steve 150
Yoor, Brian B. 4
Yordy, Matt 563
York, Max 382
York, Jill E. 558
York, Amy 664
York, Traci 787
Yorks, Andrew 530
Yosafat, Walter A. 931
Yoshizawa, Dirk 103
Yost, Jerry 247
Yosufzai, Shariq 191
Youdeem, Gilda 97
Youel, Lisa 316
Younessi, Ramin 166
Young, Dennis 43
Young, Ray G. 74
Young, Diane 84
Young, Robin 85
Young, Michael 101
Young, Teri 103
Young, Chad 103
Young, Keith 153
Young, Melody 161
Young, Stephen 178
Young, Mary 178
Young, Brenda 191
Young, Karen 204
Young, Ruben 219
Young, Dave 226
Young, Larry D. 282
Young, Steven K. 285
Young, Bob 302
Young, Byron 304
Young, Kevin 391
Young, Daniel 395
Young, Christopher D. (Chris) 411
Young, Marlon 445
Young, Lesli C 446
Young, Jeremy 454
Young, Kathy 454
Young, Mark 454
Young, Pete 481
Young, Cathy 548
Young, Catherine 548
Young, Cynthia 582
Young, Trish 615
Young, C. Erik 658
Young, John D. 671
Young, Marty 735
Young, Dennis R. 750
Young, Richard 792
Young, Mark R. 847
Young, Charlie 860
Young, Douglas 870
Young, Mark 881
Young, Guy 890
Young, Joby 903
Young, Robert H. 912
Young, Mark 932
Young, Mark R. 941
Younger, Rob 158
Younggren, Craig 497
Youngman, Jason 336
Youngs, June 252
Yount, Michael C. 911
Yousef, Cynthia 60

Youssef, Tarek 671
Youtsey, Mark 307
Yovich, Mark 533
Yrena, Friedmann 18
Yu, Lori 224
Yu, Li 688
Yu, Nick 707
Yu, Angel 787
Yu, Daniel 888
Yun, William Y. 373
Yuse, Richard R. (Rick) 716
Yusuf, Kareem 470
Yuza, Chad 232

Z

Zabinska, Anna 792
Zacconi, Riccardo 10
Zachariah, Jason 502
Zachem, Kathy 222
Zachensky, Michele 570
Zack, Linda 450
Zackery, Vickie 332
Zadoks, Jeff A. 683
Zaeske, Mark A. 445
Zagar, Frank 507
Zagari, Martin 57
Zagzebski, Ken 16
Zahn, Stephen 604
Zajicek, Randall C. (Randy) 725
Zakhary, Sherif 569
Zakhour, Lutfi 139
Zakian, Aram 107
Zakrzewski, Mike 518
Zakrzewski, Lorrie 530
Zaleski, Ronald J. 760
Zalewski, Mark 735
Zalich, David 108
Zalisk, Jonathan R 470
Zallaps, Jeff 919
Zallie, James P. 462
Zalman, David 697
Zaluzney, Michelle 161
Zaluzney, Joseph B. 647
Zamansky, Steve 504
Zambuto, Mike 910
Zammit, Patrick 94
Zammit, Patrick 816
Zamorano, Juan Pablo 219
Zamudio, Jennifer 803
Zamudio, Jaime 892
Zanayed, Juwana 637
Zandvliet, Vincent 470
Zanetos, John 170
Zanetton, Fausto 587
Zanganeh, Marty 805
Zanghellini, Luigi 555
Zank, Dennis W. 715
Zankman, Dan 425
Zanolli, Michael 330
Zanten, Walter van 679
Zapalac, Richard A. (Rick) 177
Zapata, Ray 247
Zapletal, Laurie 116
Zapletal, Robert 573
Zappa, James (Jim) 193
Zara, Antonio 385
Zarate, Christina 32
Zarcone, Dominick P. (Nick) 534
Zarcone, Michael 570
Zaremskas, Michelle 195
Zargar, Ehsan 443
Zarghami, Cyma 896
Zarhoun, Jalal 693
Zaslav, David M. 270
Zaslavsky, Leah 242
Zatta, Jayson M. 912
Zavada, Michael 135
Zavala, Elsa I. 250
Zavala, Ken 713
Zavala, Veronica 901
Zaveduk, Mitchell 558
Zavery, Amit 643
Zawacki, Mark 463
Zayas, Ricardo 144
Zazo, Lisa 842

Zazon, Sue E. 449
Zbell, Jennifer 908
Zdunek, Zenon 484
Zebula, Charles E. (Chuck) 42
Zechmeister, Michael P. 874
Zegdi, Malik 896
Zegler, Curt 856
Zeiger, Richard 497
Zeigler, Shelly 71
Zeigler, Michael 574
Zeiler, Thomas 557
Zeiler, Karen 582
Zeiler, Gerhard 838
Zekhout, Samy 693
Zekoski, Joseph (Joe) 397
Zeldenthuis, Ray 553
Zeldin, Marian 570
Zelenka, Janet 311
Zeleszko, Tony 891
Zelinske, John 570
Zell, Samuel 64
Zell, Lisa 193
Zell, Kristin 637
Zellner, Jon 457
Zelter, Andrew 105
Zemaitis, Greg 929
Zember, Dennis J. 54
Zemering, Christo 173
Zemkoski, Alex 246
Zemlyak, James M. 795
Zemore, Pamela 720
Zeng, Lawrence 395
Zepeda, Curt 724
Zeringue, Theresa 722
Zeske, Terry 80
Zettinger, Daniel 80
Zettler, Casey 330
Zetwick, James (Jim) 609
Zevola, Andrew 117
Zgonc, Kevin 336
Zhang, Dan 34
Zhang, Mingqiang 57
Zhang, Gene 122
Zhang, Frank 204
Zhang, Stella 204
Zhang, Jizhi 628
Zhang, Caroline 700
Zhang, Rocky 826
Zhao, Peng 14
Zhao, Shaoling 14
Zhao, Dorothy 290
Zheng, Ru 142
Zhou, James 45
Zidar, Thomas P. (Tom) 927
Ziebell, William F. 378
Ziegler, Richard 158
Ziegler, Gregg 841
ZIELINSKI, MIKE 3
Zielinski, Thomas C. 66
Zielinski, Richard 503
Zielinski, Miroslaw 674
Ziemba, Lawrence M. (Larry) 675
Zillwood, Trevor 299
Ziman, Richard S. 730
Zimmerli, Bert R. 467
Zimmerman, Angel 3
Zimmerman, Matt 328
Zimmerman, Michael R. 458
Zimmerman, Stanley 550
Zimmerman, Andrew 587
Zimmerman, Steven 678
Zimmerman, Kent 724
Zimmerman, Christine 733
Zimmerman, Conrad 735
Zimmerman, Matthew T. 837
Zimmerman, Robert 860
Zimmermann, Robert 748
Zimmermann, Nicole 919
Zimpfer, Troy 161
Zimpfer, Matthew J. (Matt) 213
Zimpfer, Matt 213
Zink, Mark 336
Zino, Jillian 705
Zinselmeier, Kristie 115
Zinterhofer, Eric L. 186
Ziolo, Mykel 423
Zipf, Bruce G. 718

Zirkle, Matthew 693
Zisa, David 566
Zito, Judy 488
Zito, Joseph 875
Zivelonghi, G. Larry 250
Zizzi, Michele 382
Zizzo, Larry 24
Zkri, Adel 260
Zlotsky, Tatyana 45
Zock, George J 435
Zoe, Benjamin 701
Zoeller, Kathrin 610
Zoellner, Hanns 227
Zogg, Jack 378
Zoiss, Edward J. (Ed) 411
Zoller, Jeff 809
Zollotuchen, Mandi 636
Zolper, Andy 715
Zoltick, Steve 415
Zook, Dennis R. 241
Zorn, Russ 53
Zorn, Cassandra 313
Zotter, Nina 712
Zou, Cathy 185
Zuanich, Mark 12
Zuazo, Tony 276
Zuazo, Anthony 276
Zuberi, Faheem 446
Zubretsky, Joseph M. 582
Zucaro, Aldo C. (Al) 636
Zuccas, Marcelo 599
Zucker, Jeff 838
Zuckerberg, Mark 321
Zuckerman, Lisa 266
Zuckerman, Jason 705
Zuehlke, Vonnie 813
Zuelow, Guenter 115
Zuengler, Hugh 901
Zufall, David 272
Zuhl, Colleen A. 837
Zuhlke, Dan 467
Zukis, Katy 452
Zulueta, Alfonso G. (Chito) 528
Zumwalt, LeAnne M. 258
Zuniga, Jennifer J 224
Zuniga, Gaspar 484
Zuraitis, Marita 435
Zuro, Matthew 345
Zwang, Jonathan 713
Zwany, Abe 139
Zweifach, Gerson A. 858
Zweig, Jeremy 896
Zwerman, Evan 559
Zwiebel, Rob 735
Zwinger, Susan 643
Zydel, Brian 20
Zygiel, Kenneth 413
Zyskind, Barry D. 60
Zyworonek, Anna 558